KS & VANS

& TRUCKS

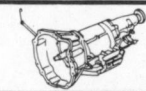

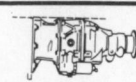
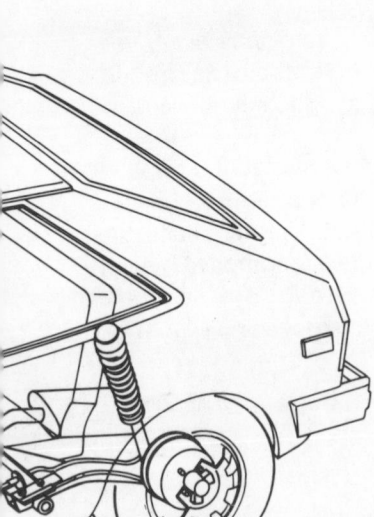

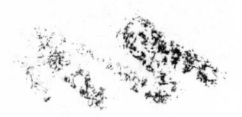

PREFACE

This is the 1985 edition of Mitchell Information Services
Transmission Service and Repair Manual.
This book, like the many Mitchell publications which have preceded it,
represents our commitment to professionalism.
in the automotive service market.

The automotive industry advances every year,
and Mitchell Information Services pledges to advance and improve its products
as we maintain the quality and usefulness of all Mitchell publications.

We cordially acknowledge the good will
and mutual goals that exist in the automotive business,
and it is in this spirit that we thank the automotive manufacturers,
distributors, dealers and the entire automotive industry
for their fine cooperation and assistance
which have made this publication possible.

MITCHELL ™

1985 EDITION
TRANSMISSION
SERVICE & REPAIR
DOMESTIC CARS,
LIGHT TRUCKS
& VANS
IMPORTED CARS
& TRUCKS

MANUALS FOR THE AUTOMOTIVE PROFESSIONAL

Published By:
MITCHELL INFORMATION SERVICES, INC.
A Cordura Company
P.O. BOX 26260
SAN DIEGO, CA 92126

ISBN 0-8470-1202-6

MITCHELL™
information services inc.
a Cordura Company

PUBLISHER
Barry A. Norton, President

SALES
James E. Lown, Vice President

EDITORIAL
Vice President
Editor-in-Chief
Kenneth A. Young

Managing Editor
Daniel M. Kelley

Ass't. Managing Editor
Terry L. Blomquist

Art Director
Eloise S. Stiverson

Detroit Editors
Lynn D. Meeker
Andy Henry

Coordinating Editors
Daryl F. Visser
Philip G. Wallan
Thomas L. Landis
Daniel D. Fleming

ACKNOWLEDGEMENT

Mitchell Information Services, Inc. thanks the domestic and import automobile and light truck manufacturers, distributors, and dealers for their generous cooperation and assistance which makes this manual possible.

Technical Editors
Eddie Santangelo
Patrick T. Rice
David L. Skora
Thomas G. Meyer
Richard Langley
Chuck Ackerman
David R. Koontz
David R. Costantino
Ramiro Gutierrez
John von Euen
James Anas
Chuck Vedra
Randy S. Russell
Paul Nutt
Leonard A. St. Amand
Roger Leftridge
William B. Disch

PUBLISHED BY

MITCHELL INFORMATION SERVICES, INC.
9889 Willow Creek Road
P.O. Box 26260
San Diego, California 92126-0260

a subsidiary of
CORDURA PUBLICATIONS, INC.
George C. Evanoff, President
John Opelt, Senior Vice President of Finance & Administration
Peter B. Jones, Vice President of Business Development
Robert W. Ladd, Vice President of Manufacturing

For Subscription Information:
CALL TOLL FREE 800–854-7030. In California CALL TOLL FREE 800–421-0159. Or WRITE: P.O. Box 26260, San Diego, CA 92126-0260

ISBN 0-8470-1202-6

Tool Applications

ALL MANUFACTURERS

DESCRIPTION

Tool applications used in this manual are noted in the text of all articles where applicable. These tools are usually specific tools that must be used to perform a specific function in Removal, Installation, Overhaul or Testing of a component.

For example; "Using Spline Adapter (J-28513) and Holding Wrench (J-28514), tighten pinion nut until end play is taken up." Although other tools could possibly be substituted, the tool references in text are those that are recommended by the vehicle manufacturer. These tools should be used whenever possible. In cases where a non-specific tool is called for, no tool number will be given.

For example; "Place bearing insert in rod and install guides on rod bolts. Compress piston rings using ring compressor." Since just about any ring compressor that works and does not damage the components can be used, no specific tool number will be called out.

The following descriptions show an example of the reference in text, the maker of the tools recommended by the manufacturer and the tool maker address. Further information on tools and local suppliers of the tools can be obtained from the tool maker. It is also possible, for example, that a Kent-Moore tool may be cross-referenced to another tool maker. In this case it is imperative that the tools be exactly the same in design, or the specific function of the tool may not be able to be performed.

CHRYSLER CORP.

Chrysler Corp. tool applications called out in this manual will appear as follows: "Assemble pinion locating spacer (SP-6030) over body of main tool (SP-5385). Install shaft locating sleeve (L-4507), washer (C-4656) and compression nut (SP-533)."

The prefixes "C," "L" and "SP" mean that the tools are manufactured by Miller Special Tools. The number after the letter prefix is the basic tool part number. Any letters or numbers after the basic part number designate either a revised tool number or that the tool is part of a set.

CHRYSLER CORP.
TOOL MANUFACTURER

Miller Special Tools
Division of Utica Tool Co., Inc.
32615 Park Lane
Garden City, Mich. 48135
Telephone (313) 522-6717

FORD MOTOR CO.

Ford Motor Co. tool applications called out in this manual will appear as follows: "Remove pinion bearing with slide hammer (T50T-100A with attachment T58L-101-A). Remove bearing with puller (T81P-3504-S, T58L-101-A and T81P-3504-T)."

Ford Motor Co. tools are manufactured by Owatonna Tools. The prefix used with Ford tool numbers means that the tools are essential tools. The number after the prefix is the basic tool part number. Any letters or numbers after the basic part number designate either a revised tool number or that the tool is part of a set.

FORD MOTOR CO.
TOOL MANUFACTURER

Owatonna Tool Co. Inc.
Owatonna, Minn. 55060
Telephone (507) 455-2626
Telex 29-0876

GENERAL MOTORS

General Motors tool applications called out in this manual will appear as follows; "Install pivot pin remover (J-21854-1) and remove pins. Using pin punch (J-22635), drive out lever pin."

The "J" in front of the first set of numbers means that it is a Kent-Moore tool. The second set of numbers is the basic tool part number. Part numbers with no additional characters after the basic part number means that the tool listed is a complete tool. The last number means that it is either part of a set (-2,-3 etc.), or a revised tool number (-02,-03, or -B,-C etc,).

GENERAL MOTORS
TOOL MANUFACTURER

Kent-Moore Tool Division
29784 Little Mack
Roseville, Mich., 48066-2298
Telephone (313) 774-9500
Telex 23-5377

JEEP

Jeep tool applications called out in this manual will appear as follows: "Use bearing remover (J-21473-1) and extension (J-21054-1) to drive out bearing." The "J" in front of the first set of numbers means that it is a Kent-Moore tool. The second set of numbers is the basic tool part number. Part numbers with no additional characters after the basic part number means that the tool listed is a complete tool. The last number means that it is either part of a set (-2,-3 etc.), or a revised tool number (-02,-03, or -B,-C etc,).

JEEP TOOL MANUFACTURER

Kent-Moore Tool Division
29784 Little Mack
Roseville, Mich., 48066-2298
Telephone (313) 774-9500
Telex 23-5377

1985 Light Truck Model Identification

In this manual, Light Truck models will be referred to by the manufacturer's model and/or series designation. When a specific model does not have a designated model or series designation, it will be referred to by model name.

NOTE: When General Motors is referred to within this manual (rather than Chevrolet or GMC), the Chevrolet numerical vehicle series designations will be abbreviated for common reference to both Chevrolet and GMC models. The GMC counterpart models will be identified as follows: 10 = 1500 (except S15); 20 = 2500; 30 = 3500.

CHEVROLET

MODEL IDENTIFICATION

Model	Description
C10	[1] 1/2 Ton Conventional Cab 2WD
C20	[1] 3/4 Ton Conventional Cab 2WD
C30	1 Ton Conventional Cab 2WD
K10	[1] 1/2 Ton Conventional Cab 4WD & Blazer
K20	[1] 3/4 Ton Conventional Cab 4WD
K30	1 Ton Conventional Cab 4WD
G10	1/2 Ton Van
G20	3/4 Ton Van
G30	[2] 1 Ton Van
M	Astro Panel & Passenger Van
P20	3/4 Ton Parcel Delivery Van
P30 (42)	1 Ton Parcel Delivery Van
S10	1/2 Ton Conventional Cab 2WD & Blazer
T10	1/2 Ton Conventional Cab 4WD & Blazer

[1] – Includes Suburban models.
[2] – Includes Front Section and Hi-Cube models.

DODGE

MODEL IDENTIFICATION

Model	Description
AD150	Ramcharger 2WD
AW150	Ramcharger 4WD
B150	1/2 Ton Van/Wagon
B250	3/4 Ton Van/Wagon
B350	1 Ton Van/Wagon
D100	Light Duty 1/2 Ton Conventional Cab 2WD
D150	Heavy Duty 1/2 Ton Conventional Cab 2WD
D250	3/4 Ton Conventional Cab 2WD
D350	1 Ton Conventional Cab 2WD
K	Caravan & Mini Ram Van
W100	Light Duty 1/2 Ton Conventional Cab 4WD
W150	Heavy Duty 1/2 Ton Conventional Cab 4WD
W250	3/4 Ton Conventional Cab 4WD
W350	1 Ton Conventional Cab 4WD

FORD

MODEL IDENTIFICATION

Model	Description
Aerostar	Trim-Sized Panel & Passenger Van
Bronco	Full-Sized Family 4WD Wagon
Bronco II	Trim-Sized Family 4WD Wagon
E150	1/2 Ton Van
E250	3/4 Ton Van

FORD (Cont.)

MODEL IDENTIFICATION

Model	Description
E350	[1] 1 Ton Van
F150	1/2 Ton Conventional Cab 2WD & 4WD
F250	3/4 Ton Conventional Cab 2WD & 4WD
F350	1 Ton Conventional Cab 2WD & 4WD
Ranger	1/2 Ton Conventional Cab 2WD & 4WD

[1] – Includes Front Section models.

GMC

MODEL IDENTIFICATION

Model	Description
C1500	[1] 1/2 Ton Conventional Cab 2WD
C2500	[1] 3/4 Ton Conventional Cab 2WD
C3500	1 Ton Conventional Cab 2WD
K1500	[1] 1/2 Ton Conventional Cab 4WD & Blazer
K2500	[1] 3/4 Ton Conventional Cab 4WD
K3500	1 Ton Conventional Cab 4WD
G1500	1/2 Ton Van
G2500	3/4 Ton Van
G3500	[2] 1 Ton Van
M	Safari Panel & Passenger Van
P2500	3/4 Ton Parcel Delivery Van
P3500 (42)	1 Ton Parcel Delivery Van
S15	1/2 Ton Conventional Cab 2WD & Blazer
T15	1/2 Ton Conventional Cab 4WD & Blazer

[1] – Includes Suburban models.
[2] – Includes Front Section and Hi-Cube models.

JEEP

MODEL IDENTIFICATION

Model	Description
Cherokee (77)	Cherokee 4WD (2-Door)
Cherokee (78)	Cherokee 4WD (4-Door)
CJ7 (87)	94" Wheelbase Utility Vehicle 4WD
Grand Wagoneer (15)	Heavy Duty Fam. Wagon 4WD
J10 (25)	119" Wheelbase 1/2 Ton Conv. Cab 4WD
J10 (26)	131" Wheelbase 1/2 Ton Conv. Cab 4WD
J20 (27)	3/4 Ton Conventional Cab 4WD
Scrambler (88)	104" Wheelbase Utility Vehicle 4WD
Wagoneer (75)	Wagoneer 4WD (4-Door)

PLYMOUTH

MODEL IDENTIFICATION

Model	Description
H	Voyager

1985 DOMESTIC
GENERAL INDEX

The first step in using these pages
is to locate the listed components that you require
information on. Go down the list under the specific component heading
to the model or transmission type of the vehicle you are working on. On the
right-hand side of the column is the number of the article you require.

1985 Domestic General Index

SECTION 1

DOMESTIC GENERAL SERVICING

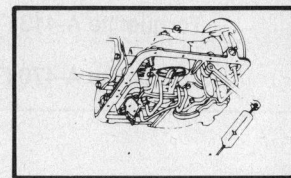

NOTE: ALSO SEE GENERAL INDEX.

Transmission Application

AUTOMATIC TRANSMISSIONS — DOMESTIC CARS

MANUFACTURER & MODEL	TRANSMISSION MODEL
AMERICAN MOTORS Alliance & Encore 1.4L & 1.7L Eagle 4.2L	Renault MB1 (Transaxle) Torque-Command 998
CHRYSLER CORP. Diplomat, Fifth Avenue, Gran Fury & Newport	Torqueflite A-904-LA
Aries, Caravelle, Charger, Chrysler, Daytona, Horizon, Lancer, Laser, LeBaron, LeBaron GTS, Omni, Reliant, Turismo & 600 – 2.2L	Torqueflite A-413 (Transaxle)
Aries, Caravelle, Chrysler, Le Baron, New Yorker, Reliant & 600 – 2.6L	Torqueflite A-470 (Transaxle)
FORD MOTOR CO. Escort, EXP & Lynx 1.6L Tempo & Topaz 2.3L	Ford Motor Co. ATX (Transaxle)
Capri, Cougar, LTD, Marquis, Mustang & Thunderbird – 2.3L	Ford Motor Co. C-3
Capri, Cougar, LTD, Marquis, Mustang & Thunderbird – 3.8L	Ford Motor Co. C-5
Cougar, LTD, Marquis & Thunderbird – 3.8L	
Capri, Crown Victoria, Continental, Cougar, Grand Marquis, Lincoln, LTD, Marquis, Mark VII, Mustang & Thunderbird – 5.0L	Ford Motor Co. Automatic Overdrive
Continental & Mark VII – 2.4L Turbo Diesel	ZF 4 HP-22
GENERAL MOTORS BUICK – Century 2.5L, 2.8L & 3.0L, Somerset Regal, Skyhawk & Skylark CADILLAC – Cimarron CHEVROLET – Cavalier, Celebrity & Citation II OLDSMOBILE – Calais, Ciera 2.5L, 2.8L & 3.0L, Firenza PONTIAC – Fiero, Grand Am, Sunbird & 6000	Turbo Hydra-Matic 125C (Transaxle)
CHEVROLET – Chevette 1.6L PONTIAC – 1000 1.6L	Turbo Hydra-Matic 180C
BUICK – LeSabre & Estate Wagon 3.8L, Regal 3.8L, 4.3L, 4.3L Diesel & 5.0L (VIN H) CHEVROLET – Caballero & El Camino 3.8L, 4.3L & 5.0L (VIN H), Caprice & Impala 3.8L, 4.3L, 5.0L (VIN H) & 5.7L Diesel, Malibu & Monte Carlo 3.8L, 4.3L & 5.0L (VIN H) OLDSMOBILE – Cutlass 3.8L, 4.3L Diesel, 5.0L (VIN H & Y) & 5.7L Diesel, 88 3.8L, 5.0L (VIN Y) & 5.7L Diesel PONTIAC – Bonneville & Grand Prix 3.8L, 5.0L (VIN H) & 5.7L Diesel, Parisienne 3.8L, 4.3L, 5.0L (VIN H) & 5.7L Diesel	Turbo Hydra-Matic 200C
BUICK – LeSabre & Estate Wagon 5.0L (VIN Y) & 5.7L Diesel, Regal 3.8L, 4.3L & 5.0L (VIN H) CADILLAC – Fleetwood Brougham CHEVROLET – Caballero & El Camino 4.3L & 5.0L (VIN G & H), Caprice & Impala 4.3L, 5.0L (VIN H) & 5.7L Diesel, Malibu & Monte Carlo 4.3L & 5.0L (VIN G & H) OLDSMOBILE – Cutlass 3.8L, 5.0L (VIN H, Y & 9) & 5.7L Diesel, 88 3.8L, 5.0L (VIN Y) & 5.7L Diesel PONTIAC – Bonneville, Grand Prix & Parisienne 5.0L (VIN H) & 5.7L Diesel	Turbo Hydra-Matic 200-4R
BUICK – Riviera 3.8L, 5.0L (VIN Y) & 5.7L Diesel CADILLAC – Eldorado & Seville OLDSMOBILE – Toronado	Turbo Hydra-Matic 325-4L

AUTOMATIC TRANSMISSIONS – DOMESTIC CARS (Cont.)

MANUFACTURER & MODEL	TRANSMISSION MODEL
GENERAL MOTORS (Cont.) BUICK – Century 2.8L, 3.0L, 3.8L & 4.3L Diesel, Electra CADILLAC – DeVille & Fleetwood CHEVROLET – Celebrity 2.8L & 4.3L Diesel OLDSMOBILE – Ciera 2.8L, 3.8L & 4.3L Diesel, 98 PONTIAC – 6000 2.8L & 4.3L Diesel	Turbo Hydra-Matic 440-T4 (Transaxle)

CHEVROLET – Caballero & El Camino 4.3L & 5.0L (VIN H),
  Camaro 2.5L, 2.8L & 5.0L (VIN F & H),
  Caprice & Impala 4.3L, 5.0L (VIN H) & 5.7L (VIN 6),
  Corvette, Malibu & Monte Carlo 4.3L & 5.0L (VIN H)
PONTIAC – Bonneville & Grand Prix 5.0L (VIN H),
  Firebird 2.5L, 2.8L & 5.0L (VIN F & H),
  Parisienne 4.3L & 5.0L (VIN H)
	Turbo Hydra-Matic 700-R4

MANUAL TRANSMISSIONS – DOMESTIC CARS

MANUFACTURER & MODEL	TRANSMISSION MODEL
AMERICAN MOTORS Alliance & Encore Eagle	Renault JB0, JB1 Or JB3 Transaxle Borg-Warner T5 5-Speed
CHRYSLER CORP. Aries, Daytona, Horizon, Lancer, Laser, LeBaron, LeBaron GTS, Omni, Rampage, Reliant & 600	A-460 4-Speed or A-525 5-Speed
FORD MOTOR CO. Escort, EXP, Lynx, Tempo & Topaz Capri & Mustang – 2.3L OHC Capri, Cougar, Mustang & Thunderbird	Ford MTX 4 or 5-Spd. (Transaxle) 85 ET 4-Speed T5-OD (5-Speed Overdrive)
GENERAL MOTORS BUICK – Skyhawk, Skylark & Somerset Regal CHEVROLET – Cavalier, Celebrity, Citation II OLDSMOBILE – Calais & Firenza PONTIAC – Fiero, Grand Am & Sunbird	GM 4 or 5-Speed (Transaxle)
CHEVROLET – Chevette Diesel PONTIAC – 1000 Diesel	Isuzu 69.5 MM 5-Speed
CHEVROLET – Chevette Gasoline PONTIAC – 1000 Gasoline	GM 70 MM 4-Speed
CHEVROLET – Camaro PONTIAC – Firebird	GM 76 MM 4-Speed
CHEVROLET – Camaro & Chevette Gasoline PONTIAC – Firebird & 1000 Gasoline	GM 77 MM 5-Speed
CHEVROLET – Corvette	GM 83 MM 4-Speed w/Overdrive

Transmission Application
AUTOMATIC TRANSMISSIONS – LIGHT TRUCKS

MANUFACTURER & MODEL	TRANSMISSION MODEL
CHRYSLER CORP. Ram Van/Wagon, 2WD/4WD Pickup, 4WD Ramcharger	Chrysler Corp. Loadflite A-727
Ram Van/Wagon, 2WD/4WD Pickup	Chrysler Corp. Loadflite A904T
Ram Van/Wagon, 2WD/4WD Pickup, 2WD/4WD Ramcharger	Chrysler Corp. Loadflite A999
Caravan, Mini Ram Van, Voyager	Chrysler Corp. Torqueflite A-413
Caravan, Mini Ram Van, Voyager	Chrysler Corp. Torqueflite A-470
FORD Aerostar, 2WD/4WD Ranger, Bronco II	Ford A4LD Automatic Overdrive
F-150 Pickup (4.9L & 5.0L)	Ford C-5
Bronco, E-150/350 Van, 2WD/4WD F-150/350 Pickup	Ford C-5
Bronco, E-150/250 Van, 2WD/4WD F-150/250 Pickup	Ford C-6
GENERAL MOTORS "C" Series, "G" Series, "K" Series	Turbo Hydra-Matic 400
Astro/Safari Van, "C" Series, "G" Series, "K" Series, "P" Series, "S" Series	Turbo Hydra-Matic 700-4R
"C" Series, "G" Series, "K" Series, "S" Series	Turbo Hydra-Matic 200C
JEEP CJ7, J10 Pickup, Scrambler, Grand Wagoneer	Chrysler Corp. Loadflite 999
J10/20 Pickup, Grand Wagoneer	Chrysler Corp. Loadflite 727
Cherokee, Wagoneer	Chrysler Corp. Loadflite 904

MANUAL TRANSMISSIONS – LIGHT TRUCKS

MANUFACTURER & MODEL	TRANSMISSION MODEL
CHRYSLER CORP. 2WD/4WD Pickups, Ramcharger	New Process 435 4-Speed
Ram Van/Wagon, 1/2 Ton 2WD Pickup	Overdrive-4
Caravan, Voyager, Mini Ram Van	Chrysler A-460 4-Speed
Caravan, Voyager, Mini Ram Van	Chrysler A-525 5-Speed (Close Ratio)

FORD
Bronco II, Ranger
  Gas
  Diesel
	
	Ford 5-Speed Overdrive
	Ford 4-Speed / FM 145 5-Speed

F-150 Pickup	Ford 3.03 3-Speed
Bronco, F-150/350 Pickup	New Process 435 4-Speed
Bronco, F-150/350 Pickup	Warner T-18 4-Speed
Bronco, F-150/250 2WD Pickup, F-150 4WD Pickup	Ford Top Shifter (TOD) 4-Speed Overdrive Ford 3.03 3-Speed
F-250/350 Pickup (6.9L Diesel & 7.5L Gas)	Warner T-19B/19D 4-Speed
E-150/350 Van	Ford 4-Speed R.U.G. Overdrive Ford 3.03 3-Speed
GENERAL MOTORS Astro/Safari Van	GM 76 MM 4-Speed
"S" Series	GM 77.5 MM 4-Speed
Astro/Safari Van, "S" Series	GM 77 MM 5-Speed
"C" Series, "G" Series, "K" Series, "P" Series	Muncie 76 MM 3-Speed
"C" Series, "G" Series, "K" Series, "P" Series	New Process 89 MM 4-Speed Overdrive
"C" Series, "G" Series, "K" Series, "P" Series	GM 117 MM 4-Speed
JEEP CJ7, Scrambler	Borg-Warner T4 4-Speed
CJ7, Scrambler	Borg-Warner T5 5-Speed Overdrive
J10 Pickup, Grand Wagoneer (Fleet)	Borg-Warner T176 4-Speed
Cherokee, Wagoneer	Aisin AX4 4-Speed
Cherokee, Wagoneer	Aisin AX5 5-Speed Overdrive

Automatic Transmissions

OIL PAN GASKET IDENTIFICATION

Fig. 1: AMC (Renault) MB1

Fig. 2: AMC/Jeep 904 & 998
and Chrysler Corp. A-904 & A-999

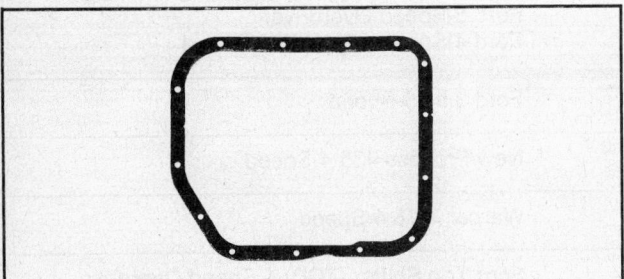

Fig. 3: Chrysler Corp. A-413 & A-470

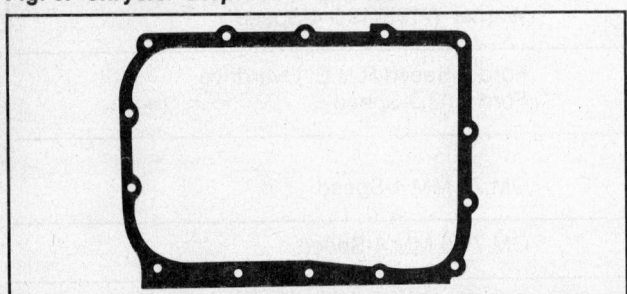

Fig. 4: Chrysler Corp. & Jeep A-727

Fig. 5: Ford Motor Co. A4LD

Fig. 6: Ford Motor Co. AOT

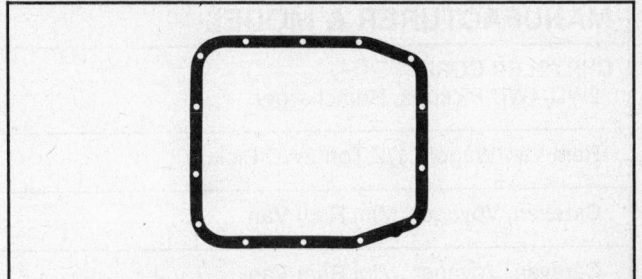

Fig. 7: Ford Motor Co. ATX

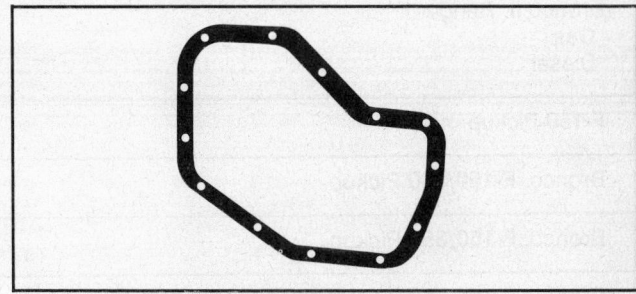

Fig. 8: Ford Motor Co. C3

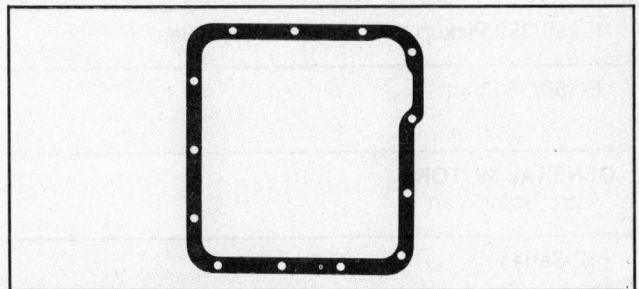

Fig. 9: Ford Motor Co. C5

Fig. 10: Ford Motor Co. C6

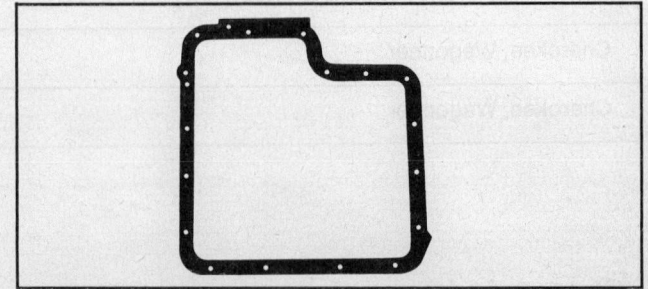

OIL PAN GASKET IDENTIFICATION (Cont.)

Fig. 11: Ford Motor Co. ZF HP-22

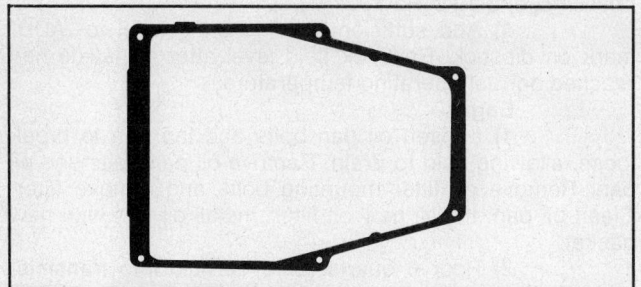

Fig. 12: General Motors THM 125C

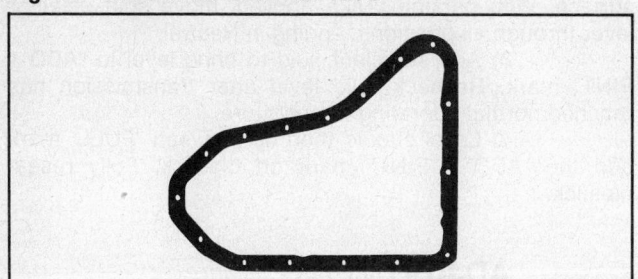

Fig. 13: General Motors THM 180C

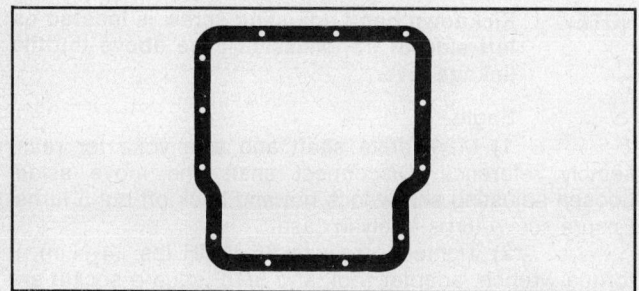

Fig. 14: General Motors THM 200C

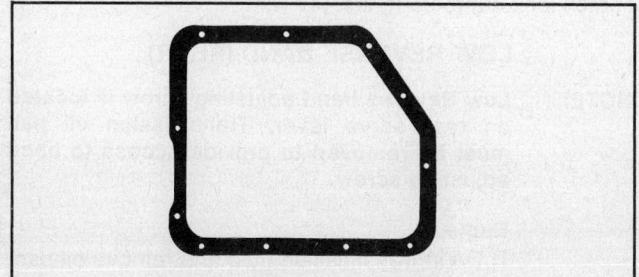

Fig. 15: General Motors THM 200-4R

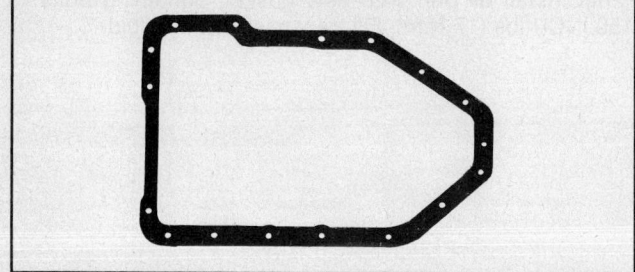

Fig. 16: General Motors THM 325-4L

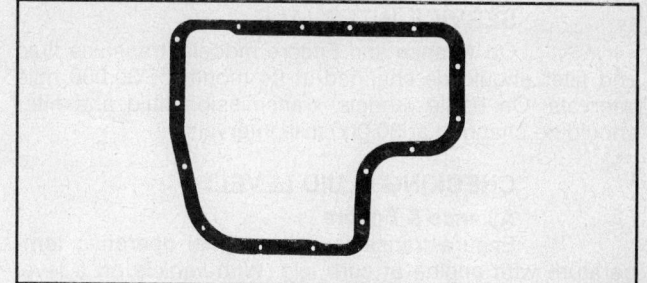

Fig. 17: General Motors THM 350C

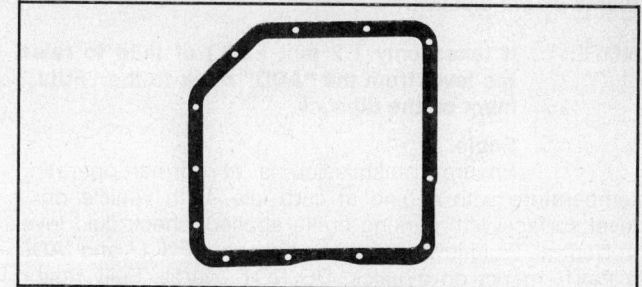

Fig. 18: General Motors THM 400

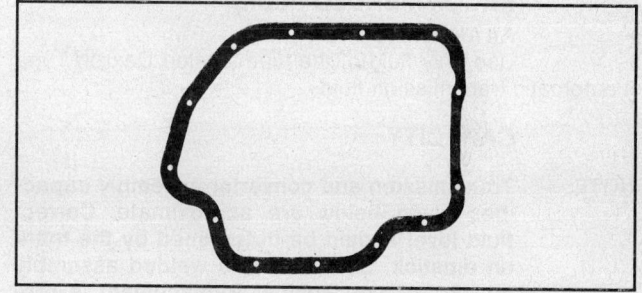

Fig. 19: General Motors THM 440-T4

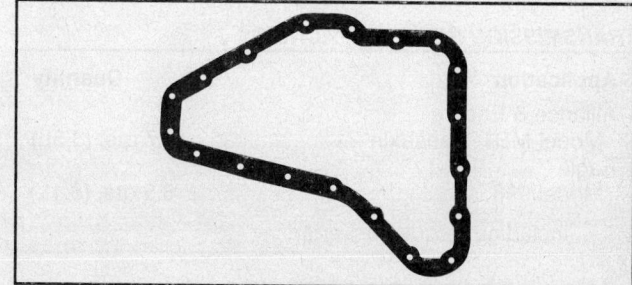

Fig. 20: General Motors THM 700-R4

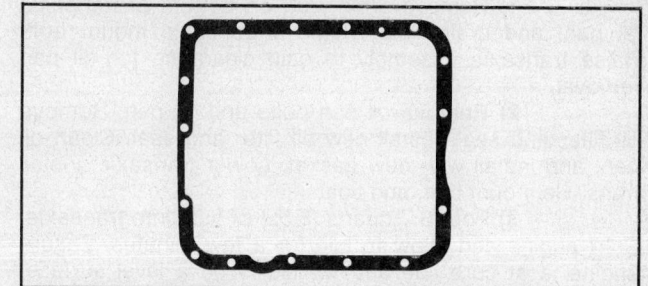

AMERICAN MOTORS

LUBRICATION

SERVICE INTERVALS

On Alliance and Encore models, transaxle fluid and filter should be changed at 24 month or 30,000 mile intervals. On Eagle models, transmission fluid and filter should be changed at 30,000 mile intervals.

CHECKING FLUID LEVEL

Alliance & Encore

Ensure transaxle is at normal operating temperature with engine at curb idle. With vehicle on a level surface and parking brake applied, check fluid level in Park. Fluid level should be between the "FULL" and "ADD" marks on the dipstick.

NOTE: **It takes only 1/2 pint (.25L) of fluid to raise the level from the "ADD" mark to the "FULL" mark on the dipstick.**

Eagle

Ensure transmission is at normal operating temperature with engine at curb idle. With vehicle on a level surface with parking brake applied, check fluid level in Neutral. Fluid level should be between "FULL" and "ADD 1 PINT" marks on dipstick. DO NOT overfill. Fully reseat dipstick.

RECOMMENDED FLUID

All Models

Use only fluid of the type labeled Dexron Type II automatic transmission fluid.

CAPACITY

NOTE: **Transmission and converter assembly capacities given below are approximate. Correct fluid level should be determined by the mark on dipstick. Converter is a welded assembly and is not serviceable. Replacement is recommended if contaminated.**

TRANSMISSION REFILL CAPACITIES

Application	Quantity
Alliance & Encore	
Model MB1 Transaxle	3.7 qts. (3.5L)
Eagle	
Model 998	¹ 8.5 qts. (8.1L)

¹ – Including torque converter.

DRAINING & REFILLING

Alliance & Encore

1) Remove drain plug on bottom of transaxle oil pan, and drain fluid. Remove transaxle mount bolt. Raise transaxle assembly to gain clearance for oil pan removal.

2) Remove oil pan bolts and oil pan. Remove oil filter and seal. Install new oil filter and seal. Clean oil pan, and install with new gasket. Lower transaxle, install transaxle mount bolt, and tighten.

3) Pour 3.7 quarts (3.5L) of fluid into transaxle. Start engine and allow to idle for a few minutes. Ensure engine is at curb idle and vehicle is on a level surface.

With parking brake applied, move shift selector through all positions, ending in Park.

4) Add sufficient fluid to bring level to "ADD" mark on dipstick. Recheck fluid level after transaxle has reached normal operating temperature.

Eagle

1) Loosen oil pan bolts and tap pan to break loose, allowing fluid to drain. Remove oil pan bolts and oil pan. Remove oil filter mounting bolts and remove filter. Clean oil pan. Install new oil filter. Install oil pan with new gasket.

2) Pour 6 quarts (5.7L) of fluid into transmission. Start engine and allow to idle for at least 2 minutes. Ensure engine is at curb idle, and vehicle is on a level surface. With parking brake applied, move shift selector lever through all positions, ending in Neutral.

3) Add sufficient fluid to bring level to "ADD 1 PINT" mark. Recheck fluid level after transmission has reached normal operating temperature.

4) Level should then be between "FULL" mark and the "ADD 1 PINT" mark on dipstick. Fully reseat dipstick.

ADJUSTMENT

KICKDOWN BAND (FRONT)

NOTE: **Kickdown band adjusting screw is located on left side of transmission case above throttle linkage lever.**

Eagle

1) Mark drive shaft and axle yoke for reassembly reference. Disconnect shaft and move aside. Loosen adjusting screw lock nut and back off nut 5 turns. Ensure screw turns freely in case.

2) Tighten screw to 36 INCH lbs. (4 N.m), if torque wrench, adapter tool, and 5/16" square socket are used. If not, tighten screw to 72 INCH lbs. (8 N.m). Back off adjusting screw 3 turns. Hold screw in this position and tighten lock nut to 35 ft. lbs. (47 N.m).

LOW-REVERSE BAND (REAR)

NOTE: **Low-Reverse band adjusting screw is located on rear servo lever. Transmission oil pan must be removed to provide access to band adjusting screw.**

Eagle

1) Drain transmission fluid and remove oil pan. Remove band adjusting screw lock nut. Tighten screw to 72 INCH lbs. (8 N.m). Back off screw 4 turns.

2) Install and tighten lock nut to 35 ft. lbs. (47 N.m). Install oil pan with new gasket, tightening bolts to 150 INCH lbs (17 N.m). Fill transmission with fluid.

AMERICAN MOTORS (Cont.)

Fig. 1: View of Transmission Showing Location of Low-Reverse Band (REAR) Adjusting Screw

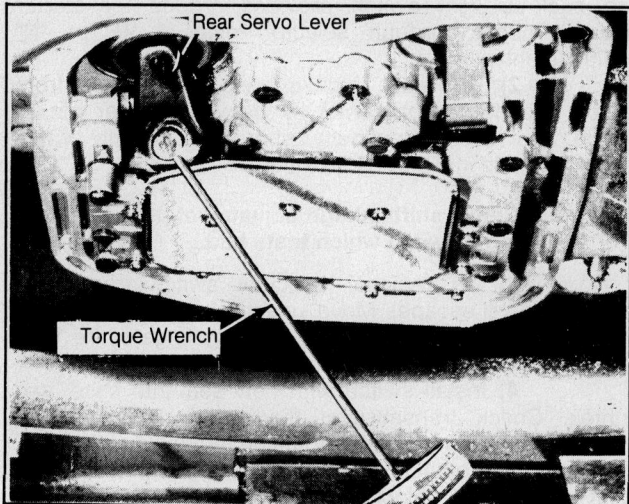

Rear Servo Lever

Torque Wrench

Oil pan must be removed to provide access to adjusting screw.

THROTTLE POSITION POTENTIOMETER
Alliance & Encore

1) Remove air filter assembly. Turn ignition on. Using a digital volt-ohmmeter, insert negative lead into terminal "C" of potentiometer. *See Fig. 2.*

2) DO NOT disconnect connector. Insert voltmeter lead in rear of connector, and push-in to contact terminal. Insert positive lead into terminal "B" of throttle position sensor.

3) Move throttle plate to wide open throttle position. Be sure throttle contacts stop. Note the exact voltmeter reading. It should be about 4.3 volts. This is the input voltage.

4) Remove positive lead from terminal "B", and insert in terminal "A" of throttle position sensor. Open throttle plate to wide open throttle position. Note the exact voltmeter reading. This is the output voltage.

5) Adjust potentiometer so that output voltage is 4% ± 0.5% of input voltage. For rough adjustment, loosen bottom potentiometer "C" retaining screw and pivot potentiometer on adjustment slot. For fine adjustment, loosen top "D" retaining screw and pivot potentiometer.

Fig. 2: View of Throttle Position Potentiometer Showing Testing and Adjustment Locations

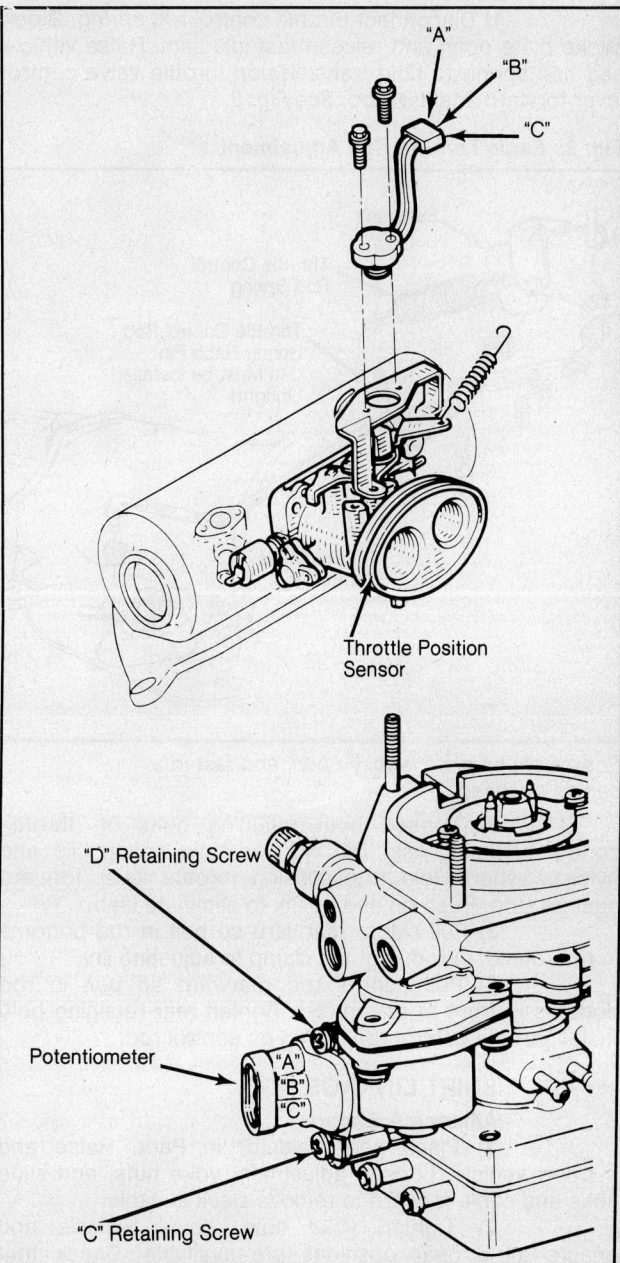

"A"
"B"
"C"

Throttle Position Sensor

"D" Retaining Screw

Potentiometer
"A"
"B"
"C"

"C" Retaining Screw

Rough adjustment done by "C" retaining screw, and fine adjustment done by "D" retaining screw.

AMERICAN MOTORS (Cont.)

TRANSMISSION THROTTLE ROD
Eagle

1) Disconnect throttle control rod spring. Block choke plate open and release fast idle cam. Raise vehicle and use spring to hold transmission throttle valve control lever forward against stop. *See Fig. 3.*

Fig. 3: Eagle Throttle Rod Adjustment

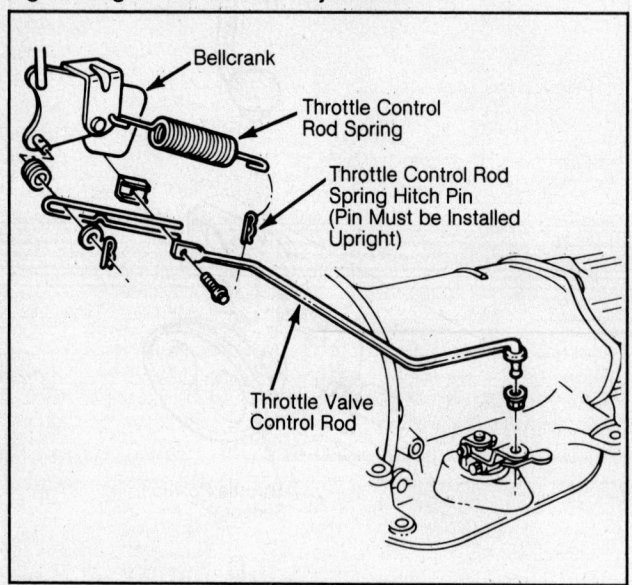

Ensure choke plate is fully open, and fast idle cam is released.

2) Loosen both retaining bolts on throttle control adjusting link. DO NOT remove spring clip and nylon washer. Hold transmission throttle lever forward against stop. Push on end of link to eliminate lash.

3) Pull clamp rearward so bolt in rod bottoms in rear of slot in rod. Tighten clamp to adjusting link.

4) Pull control rod rearward so bolt in rod bottoms in front of slot in rod. Tighten rear retaining bolt. Install throttle control rod spring on control rod.

SHIFT LINKAGE
Alliance & Encore

1) Place gear selector in Park. Raise and support vehicle. Loosen adjustment yoke nuts, and slide yoke and cable forward to remove slack in cable.

2) Tighten yoke nuts. Lower vehicle and ensure all 6 gear positions are available. Check that vehicle starts in Park position.

Eagle

1) Loosen rod trunnion setscrews. Place gearshift lever in Park position. Move valve body lever rearward into park detent.

2) Check for positive engagement by attempting to rotate driveshaft. Adjust shift rod trunnion to eliminate lash, and to obtain free pin fit in bellcrank arm. Tighten trunnion setscrews.

NEUTRAL START & BACK-UP LIGHT SWITCH
Alliance & Encore

The neutral start and back-up light switch is not adjustable and is incorporated in a multifunction switch. The multifunction switch is located on transaxle.

Eagle

1) Center terminal of 3-terminal neutral start and back-up light switch provides ground for starter solenoid circuit through selector lever in "P" or "N" positions only.

2) To test, remove wiring connector from switch and check for continuity between center pin of switch and case. Continuity should exist only when transmission is in "P" or "N" position.

NOTE: **Check shift linkage adjustment before replacing a switch which tests bad.**

3) To replace, unscrew switch from case (some fluid will escape). Move selector lever to "P" and "N" positions. Check that switch operating fingers are centered in switch opening in case.

4) Install switch with new seal into case, and tighten. Check transmission fluid level. Back-up light switch circuit is through the 2 outside terminals of switch.

5) Continuity between the 2 terminals should exist only when selector lever is in "R" position. No continuity should exist from either terminal to case.

Fig. 4: Installed View of Neutral Start and Back-Up Light Switch

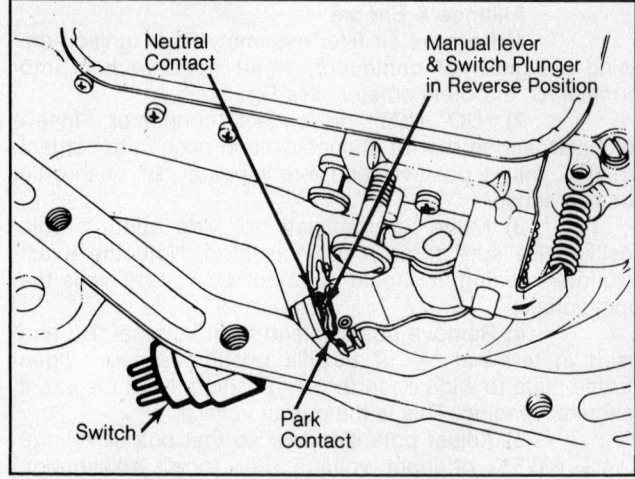

Check shift linkage adjustment before replacing a switch which tests bad.

CHRYSLER CORP. DOMESTIC CARS

LUBRICATION

SERVICE INTERVALS

Check fluid level every 6 months. Draining, refilling and band adjustments are not required under normal driving conditions. Under heavy duty (severe service) conditions, change fluid, replace filter, and adjust bands every 15,000 miles.

CHECKING FLUID LEVEL

Rear Wheel Drive Models

1) With vehicle on level ground, apply parking brake, and run engine at curb idle. Shift selector through all positions, ending in Neutral.

2) Fluid level should be between "ADD" and "FULL" marks on dipstick. Check condition of fluid for contamination or burned smell. Fully reseat dipstick.

Front Wheel Drive Models

1) With vehicle on level ground, apply parking brake, and run engine at curb idle for at least 60 seconds. Shift selector through all positions, ending in Park.

2) Fluid level should check between lower hole of dipstick (fluid warm), and upper hole of dipstick (fluid hot). Check condition of fluid for contamination or burned smell. Do not overfill. Fully seat dipstick.

RECOMMENDED FLUID

Use only fluids of the type labeled Dexron II Automatic Transmission Fluid.

CAPACITY

NOTE: **Transmission and converter assembly capacities given below are approximate. Correct fluid level should be determined by mark on dipstick. Converter is a welded assembly and is not serviceable, replacement is recommended if contaminated.**

TRANSMISSION REFILL CAPACITIES

Application	Quantity
A-904-LA (Lock-Up)	[1] 17.1 pts. (8.1L)
A-413 & A-470	[2] 17.8 pts. (8.4L)

[1] – Add .5 pts. (.2L) for non-lock-up converter.
[2] – Add 1.4 pts. (.7L) for fleet models.

DRAINING AND REFILLING

1) Loosen oil pan bolts at one corner. Tap pan to break it loose, allowing fluid to drain. Remove pan bolts and remove pan. Adjust rear band on rear wheel drive models, if required.

2) Install a new filter and gasket (if equipped) on bottom of valve body and tighten screws. Clean pan.

3) On rear wheel drive models, install pan with new gasket. Make sure round magnet is over boss in right front corner of oil pan. On front wheel drive models, install new pan, using RTV to form gasket.

4) On all models, add 4 quarts (3.8L) of transmission fluid. Start engine and allow to idle for at least 2 minutes (1 minute on front wheel drive models).

5) With engine at curb idle and parking brake applied, move shift selector lever through all positions, ending in "N" position ("P" on front wheel drive models).

Add enough fluid to bring level to "ADD" mark on dipstick (1/8" below ADD on front wheel drive models).

6) Recheck fluid level after transmission has reached normal operating temperature. On rear wheel drive models, fluid level should be between "FULL" and "ADD" marks on dipstick. On front wheel drive models, fluid level should check between lower hole of dipstick (fluid warm), and upper hole of dipstick (fluid hot). Do not overfill. Ensure dipstick is fully seated.

ADJUSTMENT

KICKDOWN BAND (FRONT)

NOTE: **Kickdown band adjusting screw is located on left side of transmission case above throttle linkage lever on rear wheel drive models, and on left side (top front) of transaxle case on front wheel drive models.**

All Models

1) Loosen adjusting screw lock nut, and back off 5 turns. After making sure adjusting screw turns freely in case, tighten screw to 72 INCH Lbs. (8 N.m).

2) Back off screw 2 1/2 turns. Hold adjusting screw in this position and tighten lock nut.

KICKDOWN BAND ADJUSTMENT

Application	Back Off Screw
All Models	2 1/2 Turns

LOW–REVERSE BAND (REAR)

NOTE: **Low-Reverse band adjusting screw is located on rear servo lever. Transmission oil pan must be removed to provide access to band adjusting screw.**

Fig. 1: Low-Reverse Band Adjustment (Rear) Screw Location

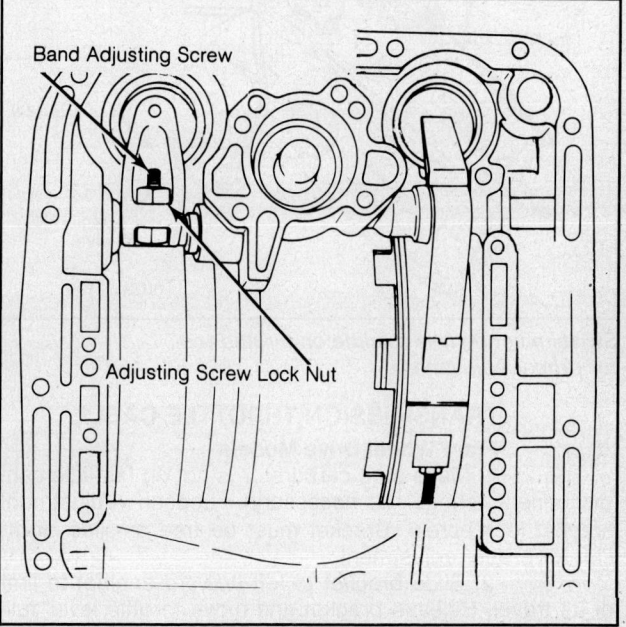

Automatic Transmission Servicing

CHRYSLER CORP. DOMESTIC CARS (Cont.)

All Models

1) Drain transmission and remove oil pan. Loosen band adjusting screw lock nut about 5 turns. Ensure adjusting screw turns freely in case. On rear wheel drive models, tighten screw to 72 INCH Lbs. (8 N.m). On front wheel drive models, tighten adjusting screw to 41 INCH lbs. (4.6 N.m).

2) On all models, back off adjusting screw specified number of turns given in Low-Reverse Band Adjustment table. Hold in this position and tighten lock nut. Install oil pan and fill transmission with fluid.

LOW-REVERSE BAND ADJUSTMENT

Application	Back Off Screw
A-904-LA	4 Turns
A-413 & A-470	3 1/2 Turns

TRANSMISSION THROTTLE ROD

Rear Wheel Drive Models

1) Make sure carburetor is not on fast idle cam (disconnect choke if necessary). Raise vehicle on hoist to make adjustment at transmission throttle lever. Loosen adjustment swivel lock screw. Swivel must be free to slide along flat end of throttle rod so that preload spring action is not restricted.

2) Hold transmission lever firmly forward against its internal stop, and tighten swivel lock screw. This completes throttle rod adjustment, as linkage backlash was automatically removed by the preload spring.

3) To check linkage freedom of operation, move throttle rod rearward, and release slowly. Ensure it returns to full forward position.

Fig. 2: Throttle Rod Adjustment Diagram on Rear Wheel Drive Models

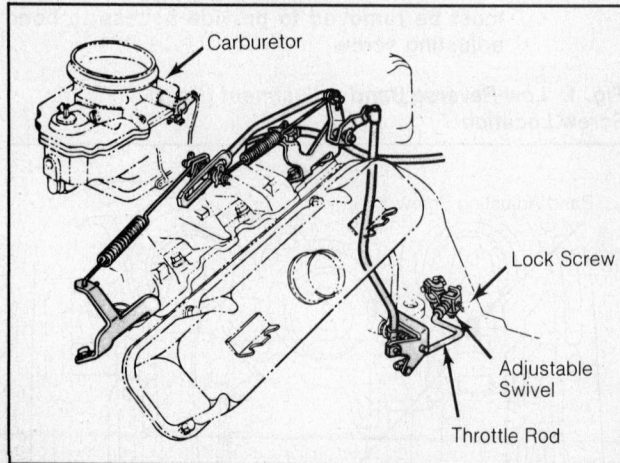

Swivel must be free to slide on throttle rod for proper adjustment.

TRANSMISSION THROTTLE CABLE

Front Wheel Drive Models

1) Make sure carburetor is not on fast idle cam (disconnect choke if necessary). Loosen adjustment bracket lock screw. Bracket must be free to slide on its slot for proper adjustment.

2) Slide bracket to left (toward engine) to limit of its travel. Release bracket and move throttle lever fully to right, against its internal stop. Tighten adjusting bracket

Fig. 3: Throttle Cable Adjustment Diagram on Front Wheel Drive Models

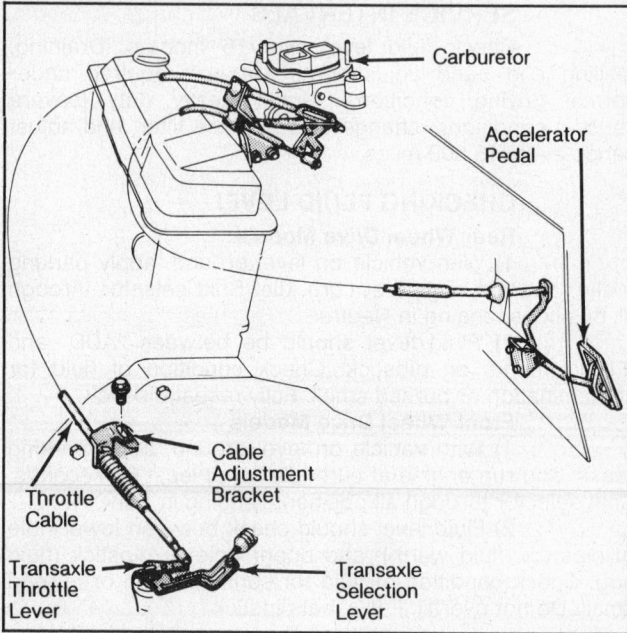

Adjustment bracket must be free to slide for correct adjustment.

lock screw. This completes adjustment, as backlash was automatically removed.

3) To check linkage freedom of operation, move transaxle throttle lever forward and slowly release. Ensure it returns to full rear position.

SHIFT LINKAGE

Column Shift (Rear Wheel Drive Models)

1) Place shift selector in "P" position. Loosen adjustable swivel lock screw, making sure swivel block is free to turn on shift rod. Move shift lever on transmission

Fig. 4: Column Shift Linkage Adjustment on Rear Wheel Drive Models

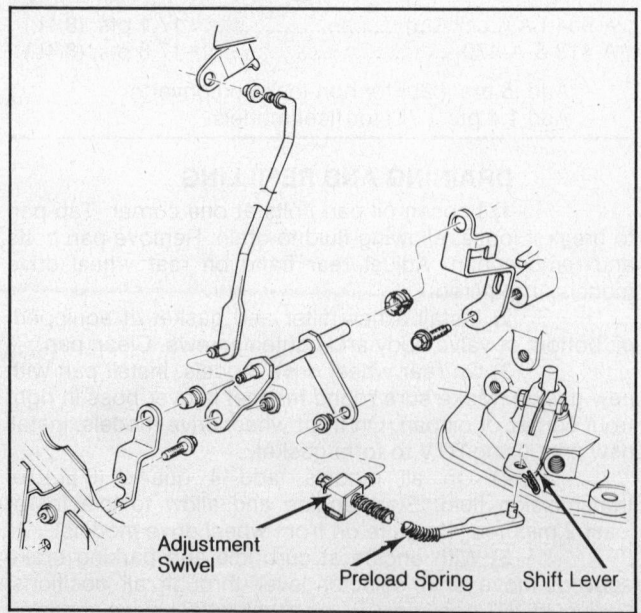

Adjustment made with shift lever in "P" Position.

all the way to rear detent position (Park). Tighten swivel lock screw.

2) Check adjustment by moving shift selector. Detents for Drive and Neutral should be within limits of selector gate stops. Starter should operate only with selector in Park or Neutral.

NOTE: **If it is necessary to disassemble linkage cable from lever, replace old plastic grommets with new ones. Use pliers to snap new grommet into lever and rod into grommet.**

Fig. 5: Floor Shift Linkage Adjustment on Front Wheel Drive Models

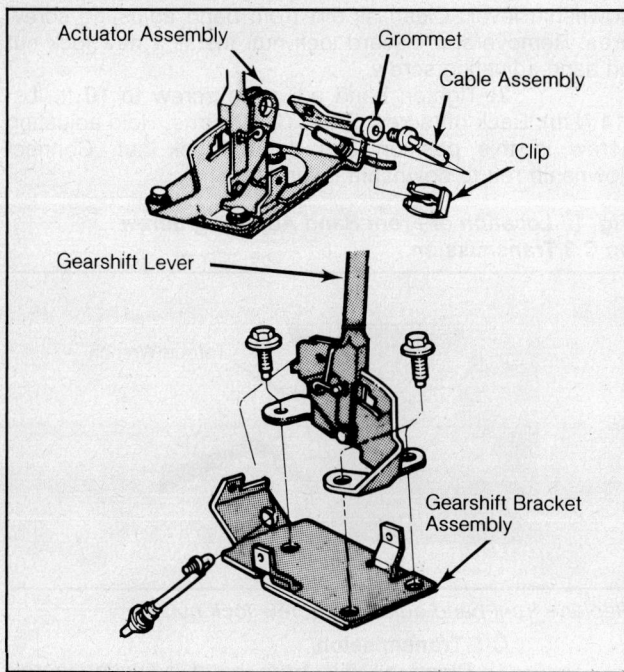

Replace grommet if linkage is disconnected.

Fig. 6: Transmission Shift Lever Adjustment on Front Wheel Drive Models

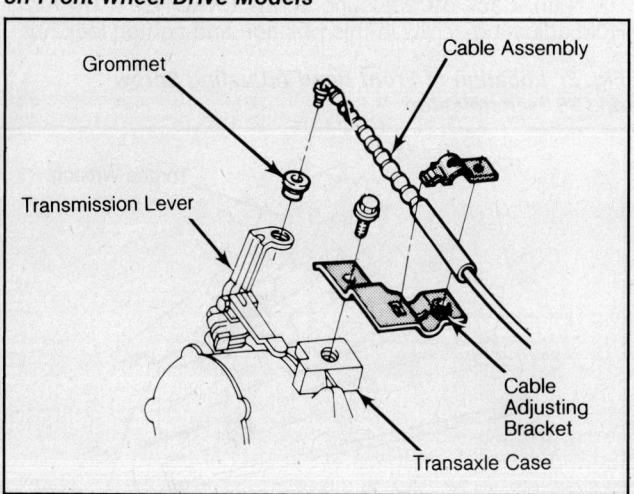

Adjusting bracket located on transaxle case.

Console or Column Shift
(Front Wheel Drive Models)
Place shift selector in "P" position. Loosen lock bolt on cable adjusting bracket on transaxle. Move shift lever on transaxle all the way to rear detent (Park) and hold. Tighten lock bolt.

NOTE: **If it is necessary to disassemble linkage cable from lever, replace old plastic grommets with new ones. Use pliers to snap new grommet into lever and rod into grommet.**

NEUTRAL SAFETY SWITCH
All Models
1) Center terminal of the 3 terminal neutral starting and back-up light switch provides ground for starter solenoid circuit through shift selector lever in Park or Neutral positions only.

2) To test, remove wiring connector from switch and check for continuity between center pin of switch and case. Continuity should exist only when transmission is in Park or Neutral.

NOTE: **Check shift linkage adjustment before replacing a switch that tests bad.**

3) To replace, unscrew switch from case (some fluid will escape). Move shift selector lever to Park, and then to Neutral position. Check to see that switch operating fingers are centered in switch opening in case.

4) Install switch with new seal into case and tighten. Check transmission fluid level. The back-up light switch circuit is through the 2 outside terminals of the switch.

5) Continuity should exist between the two terminals only when transmission is in reverse. No continuity should exist from either terminal to case.

Automatic Transmission Servicing

FORD MOTOR CO. DOMESTIC CARS

LUBRICATION

SERVICE INTERVALS

Check fluid level at every engine oil change. Fluid, filter changes and band adjustments are not required under normal operation. Under heavy duty (severe service), change fluid every 30 months or 30,000 miles. Adjust bands when fluid is changed.

NOTE: **The ZF 4 HP-22 transmission requires that fluid be drained and new fluid added every 30,000 miles.**

CHECKING FLUID LEVEL

1) With transmission at normal operating temperature, place vehicle on level ground. Apply parking brake, and run engine at curb idle. Shift selector through all positions, ending in Park.

2) With transmission at normal operating temperature, fluid level should be between "ADD" and "DON'T ADD" marks on dipstick. If transmission is at room temperature, fluid level should be between middle and top holes on dipstick.

3) If fluid level is correct at room temperature, it will be between "ADD" and "DON'T ADD" marks on dipstick when normal operating temperature is reached. Do not overfill. Check condition of fluid for contamination or burned smell. Fully reseat dipstick.

RECOMMENDED FLUID

All transmissions except C-5 use Dexron II type automatic transmission fluid (Ford XT-2-QDX). C-5 transmission uses Motorcraft Automatic Transmission Fluid Type H (or equivalent meeting Ford specification ESP-M2C166-H).

CAPACITY

NOTE: **Transmission and converter assembly capacities given below are approximate, and correct fluid level should be determined by mark on dipstick, rather than by amount added.**

TRANSMISSION REFILL CAPACITIES

Application	[1] Quantity
AOT	12.3 qts. (11.6L)
ATX	8.3 qts. (7.9L)
C-3	8.0 qts. (7.6L)
C-5	11.0 qts. (10.4L)
ZF 4 HP-22	7.5 qts. (7.1L)

[1] – Includes oil cooler (if equipped).

DRAINING & REFILLING

1) To drain torque converter on AOT transmission, remove lower engine dust cover. Rotate torque converter until drain plug is accessible. Remove plug and allow to drain. Flush cooler lines completely. This procedure must be done before any other operation.

2) On "pan-filled" C-5 transmissions, disconnect fluid filler tube from transmission pan to drain fluid. Remove oil pan. On ZF 4 HP-22 transmissions, remove drain plug to drain fluid. Remove oil pan.

3) On all other models, loosen oil pan attaching bolts to drain fluid. Remove oil pan. On all except AOT transmissions, remove and clean filter screen. Reinstall filter screen using a new gasket. On AOT transmissions, discard used filter and gasket. Install new filter and gasket. On all models, clean oil pan, and install pan with new gasket.

4) On "pan-filled" C-5 transmissions, connect fluid filler tube to oil pan and tighten fitting. On all models, pour 3 quarts (2.8L) of fluid through filler tube. Check fluid level.

ADJUSTMENT

INTERMEDIATE BAND (FRONT)

C3 Transmission

1) Remove downshift rod from transmission downshift lever. Clean all dirt from band adjusting screw area. Remove and discard lock nut. Install a new lock nut on band adjusting screw.

2) Tighten band adjusting screw to 10 ft. lbs. (14 N.m). Back off screw EXACTLY 2 turns. Hold adjusting screw in this position and tighten lock nut. Connect downshift rod to downshift lever.

Fig. 1: Location of Front Band Adjusting Screw on C-3 Transmission

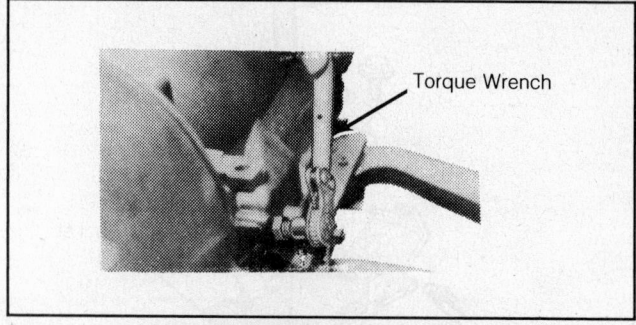
Torque Wrench

Replace front band adjusting screw lock nut.

C-5 Transmission

1) Clean all dirt from band adjusting screw area. Remove and discard adjusting screw lock nut. Install a new lock nut on adjusting screw, leaving lock nut loose.

2) Tighten band adjusting screw to 10 ft. lbs. (14 N.m). Back off adjusting screw EXACTLY 4 1/4 turns. Hold adjusting screw in this position and tighten lock nut.

Fig. 2: Location of Front Band Adjusting Screw on C-5 Transmission

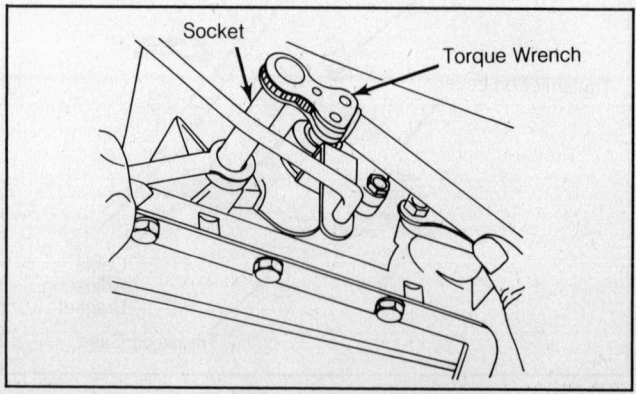
Socket
Torque Wrench

Replace front band adjusting screw lock nut.

FORD MOTOR CO. DOMESTIC CARS (Cont.)

LOW REVERSE BAND (REAR)
C-5 Transmission
1) Clean all dirt from band adjusting screw area. Remove and discard adjusting screw lock nut. Install a new adjusting screw lock nut, leaving nut loose.

2) Tighten band adjusting screw to 10 ft. lbs. (14 N.m). Back off screw EXACTLY 3 turns. Hold adjusting screw in this position and tighten lock nut.

Fig. 3: Location of Rear Band Adjusting Screw on C-5 Transmission

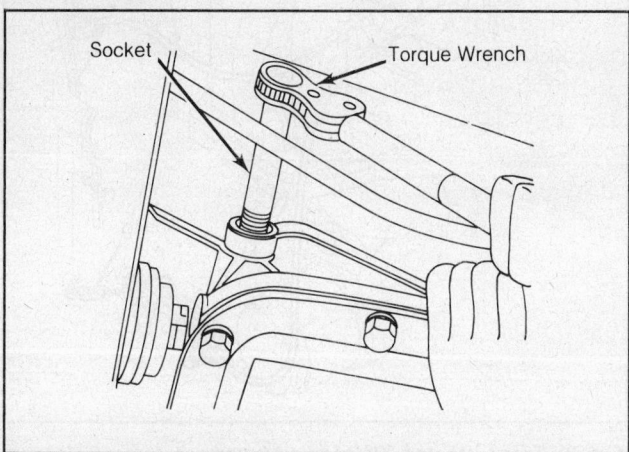

Replace rear band adjusting screw lock nut.

KICKDOWN CONTROL
ATX (FWD) Transaxle
1) On 2.3L CFI engine, hold throttle open to maintain engine speed at 1000 RPM and, at the same

Fig. 4: Kickdown Linkage Adjustment ATX Transaxle for FWD vehicles

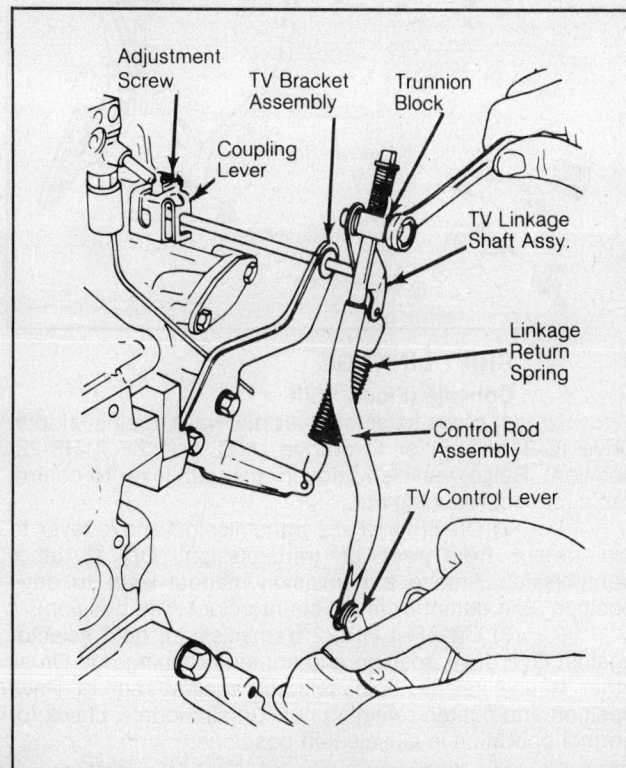

time, lightly press on idle speed control (ISC) motor shaft. After ISC shaft fully retracts, release throttle and quickly unplug ISC motor connector.

2) On all other engines, engine must be at normal operating temperature (choke fully open). Curb idle speed must be set to specification.

3) On all engines, loosen bolt on sliding trunnion block at least 1 turn. Make sure that block can slide freely on rod. *See Fig. 4.*

4) Rotate transaxle TV control lever upward with finger, using a force of about 1 pound to ensure that it is against internal idle stop. Hold this pressure and tighten trunnion block bolt.

Automatic Overdrive Transmission (AOT)
1) Engine must be at normal operating temperature. On models without idle speed control (ISC), throttle lever must be resting on idle stop or throttle solenoid positioner stop. On all models, place transmission selector lever in Neutral and set parking brake.

2) On vehicles with ISC, locate the self test connector and self test input connector in engine compartment. *See Fig. 5.* Connect a jumper wire between the self test input connector and the signal return ground terminal.

Fig. 5: Location of Self Test Connectors

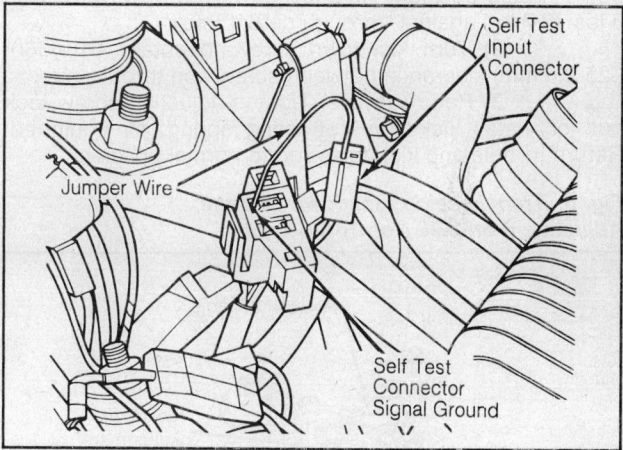

Use jumper wire to return ISC to idle position.

3) Turn ignition key to "RUN" position. DO NOT start engine. Wait 10 seconds to allow ISC plunger to fully retract. Turn ignition key off. Remove jumper wire and air cleaner.

4) On all vehicles, back out linkage adjusting screw counterclockwise until screw end is flush with lever face. Turn adjusting screw clockwise to obtain .005" (.12 mm) clearance between end of screw and throttle lever.

5) Open and close throttle to eliminate friction and recheck clearance. DO NOT apply any load on levers while checking. Turn adjusting screw clockwise 3 full turns.

6) If screw travel is limited, 1 turn minimum is permitted, however 3 turns are preferred. If idle speed requires adjustment of more than 50 RPM, turn adjustment screw on linkage lever.

NOTE: If adjustment of linkage lever screw is not possible, adjustment of the TV control rod at transmission is required. This adjustment is also required when a new TV control rod is installed.

Automatic Transmission Servicing

FORD MOTOR CO. DOMESTIC CARS (Cont.)

AOT Throttle Valve (TV) Control Rod

1) Engine must be at normal operating temperature. On models without idle speed control (ISC), throttle lever must be resting on idle stop or throttle solenoid positioner stop. On vehicles equipped with ISC, retract the ISC plunger as previously described. On all models, place transmission selector lever in Neutral and set parking brake.

2) Set linkage lever adjustment screw about mid-range. Raise vehicle and allow exhaust system to cool. Loosen bolt on TV control rod trunnion block at transmission lever. Ensure that trunnion block is free to slide on rod.

3) Push upward on lower end of TV rod (at transmission) to ensure that carburetor linkage is held firmly against throttle lever. Control rod should stay in position when released.

4) Firmly hold TV control lever on transmission upward against internal stop and tighten trunnion block bolt in position. Lower vehicle. On models without ISC, check that throttle lever resting on idle stop or throttle solenoid positioner stop. On models with ISC, reconnect ISC motor electrical connector.

C-3 & C-5 Transmission

1) Hold carburetor or throttle body at wide open throttle position. Hold kickdown rod downward with 6 lbs. (2.7 kg) against "through detent" stop.

2) Turn kickdown screw to obtain .010-.080" (.25-2.0 mm) clearance between screw and throttle arm.

3) Return to idle. Tighten adjusting screw lock nut, or install kickdown retracting spring, as equipped. Return throttle and kickdown rod to normal position.

Fig. 6: Transmission Kickdown Linkage Adjustment on 2.3L Non-Turbo Engine

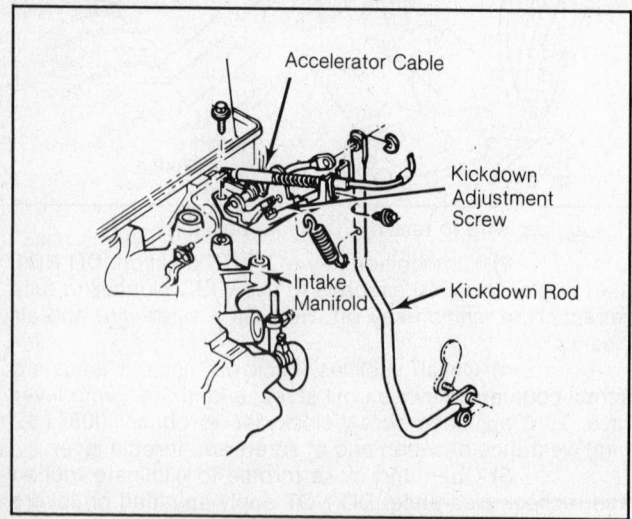

ZF 4 HP-22 Transmission

1) Place injection pump top lever to full throttle position. Tighten adjusting nut on threaded barrel to obtain 1.54-1.57" (39-40 mm) clearance between edge of crimped bead on barrel and end of threaded barrel. See Fig. 9.

2) Tighten lock nut to 80-106 INCH lbs. (9-12 N.m) to lock cable assembly to bracket. Recheck gap and repeat adjustment if necessary.

Fig. 7: Transmission Kickdown Linkage Adjustment on 2.3L Turbo Engine

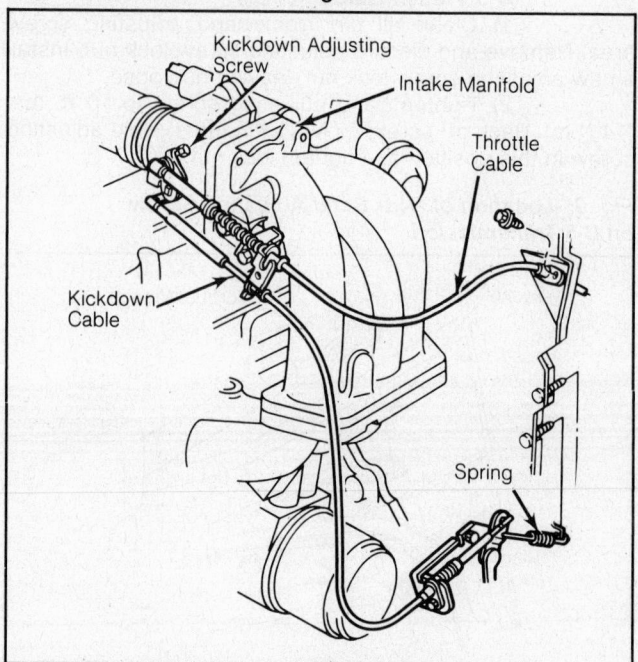

Fig. 8: Transmission Kickdown Linkage Adjustment on 3.8L Engine

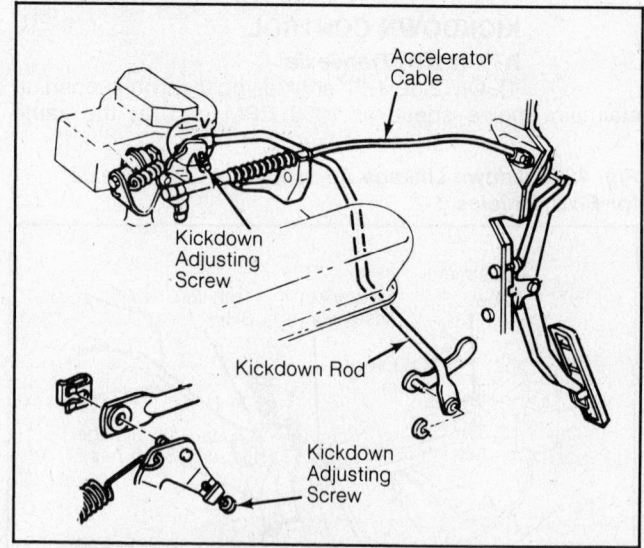

SHIFT LINKAGE

Console (Floor) Shift

1) Move selector lever rearward against stop in Drive (C-3 or C-5) or Overdrive (AOT and ZF 4 HP-22) position. Raise vehicle. Loosen manual lever-to-control cable (or rod) retaining nut.

2) On ZF 4 HP-22 transmission, move lever to 3rd detent from rear of transmission. On all other transmissions, move transmission manual lever to drive position (2nd detent from full counterclockwise position).

3) On ZF 4 HP-22 transmission, hold selector against Overdrive position and tighten retaining nut. On all other transmissions, hold selector against rear of Drive position and tighten retaining nut. On all models, check for normal operation in all selected positions.

FORD MOTOR CO. DOMESTIC CARS (Cont.)

Fig. 9: Kickdown Linkage Adjustment on ZF 4 HP-22 Transmission

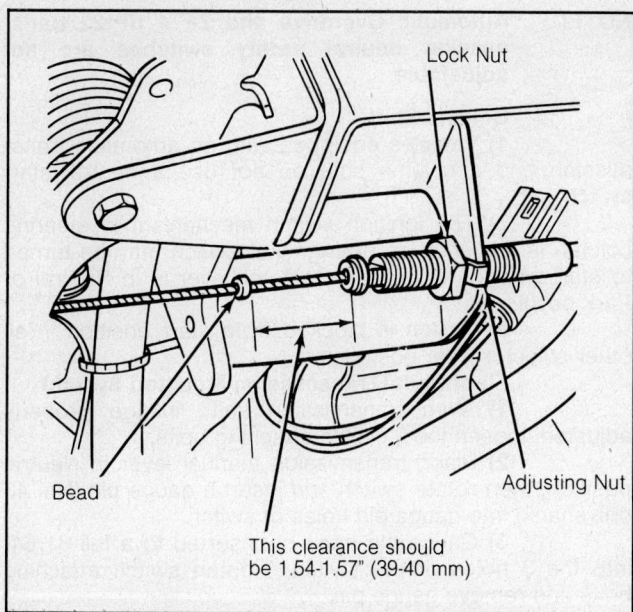

This adjustment must be done at fuel injection pump.

Fig. 10: Console (Floor) Shift Linkage Adjustment

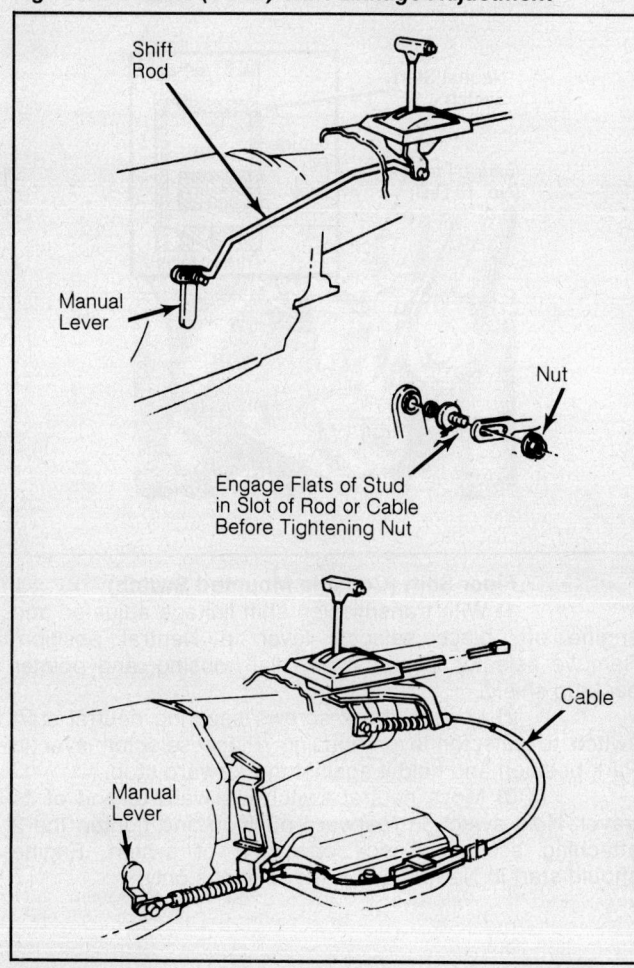

Shift rod or cable must be held against detent for proper adjustment.

Column Shift

1) Place selector in Drive (Overdrive on AOD and ZF 4 HP-22) position. Make sure selector lever remains against stop by hanging an 8 lb. (3.6 kg) weight on selector lever.

2) Loosen shift rod adjusting bolt (or nut). Push manual transmission lever downward to lowest position (2nd detent from full counterclockwise position). On ZF 4 HP-22 transmission, move manual lever to 3rd detent position from rear of transmission.

3) Ensure the slotted rod end has flats aligned with flats on mounting stud, if equipped. Ensure selector lever has not moved from Drive (C-3 and C-5) or Overdrive (AOD and ZF 4 HP-22) position. Tighten bolt (or nut) and check operation in all selector detent positions.

Fig. 11: Column Shift Linkage Adjustment

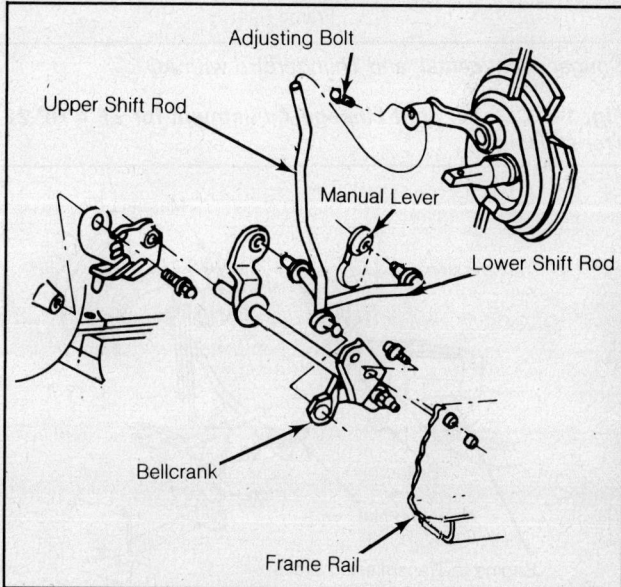

Crown Victoria, Grand Marquis & Lincoln with AOT.

Fig. 12: Column Shift Linkage Adjustment

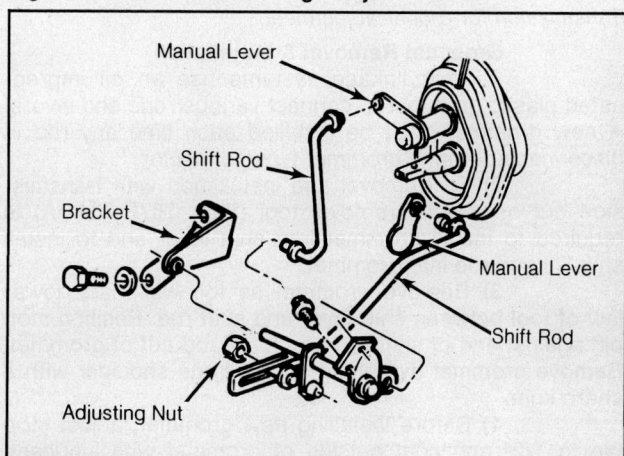

Cougar, LTD, Marquis, & Thunder with C-3 & C-5 Transmission.

Automatic Transmission Servicing

FORD MOTOR CO. DOMESTIC CARS (Cont.)

Fig. 13: Column Shift Linkage Adjustment

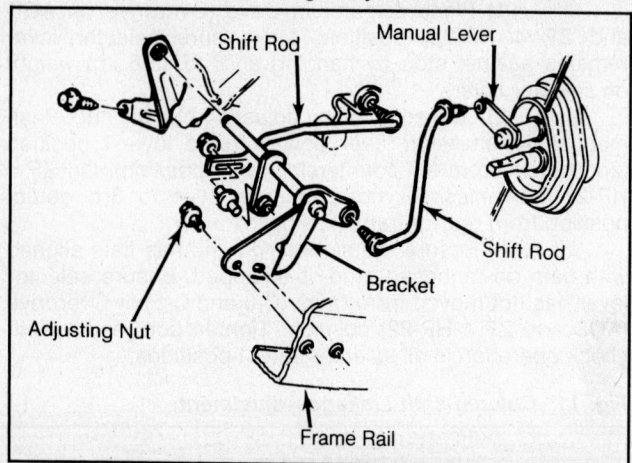

Cougar, Continental, and Thunderbird with AOT.

Fig. 14: Column Shift Linkage Adjustment for ZF 4 HP-22 Transmission

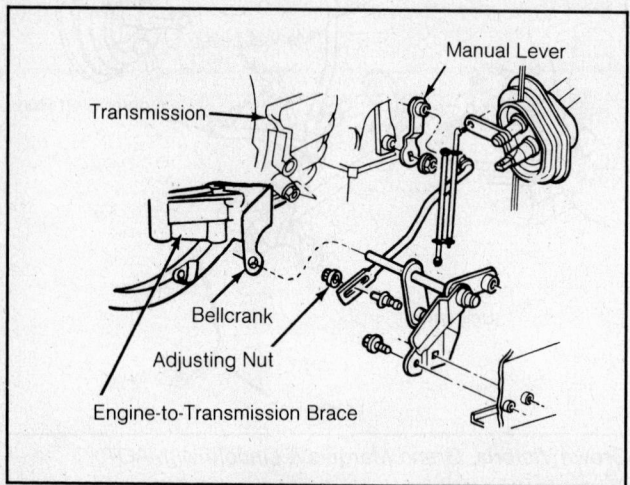

Lever must be held against 3rd detent from rear of transmission for proper adjustment.

Grommet Removal & Installation

1) Shift linkage systems use an oil impregnated plastic grommet to connect various rods and levers. A new grommet must be installed each time any rod is disconnected from a grommet-type connector.

2) For removal and installation with transmission out of vehicle, removal tool (Ford T67P-7341-A) is required to install grommet into shift lever and to install shift linkage rod into grommet.

3) Remove grommet as follows: Place lower jaw of tool between shift lever and shift rod. Position stop pin against end of shift rod and force rod out of grommet. Remove grommet by cutting off the large shoulder with a sharp knife.

4) Before installing new grommet, adjust stop pin to 1/2" and coat outside of grommet with lubricant. Place grommet on stop pin and force into lever hole.

5) Turn grommet several times to ensure proper seating. Squeeze rod into bushing until stop washer seats against grommet.

NEUTRAL SAFETY SWITCH

NOTE: Automatic Overdrive and ZF 4 HP-22 transmission neutral safety switches are not adjustable.

Column Shift

1) Vehicles equipped with an automatic transmission and a column shift do not use a neutral start switch.

2) The ignition switch mechanism in steering column is designed so that ignition switch may be turned to start position only when selector lever is in Neutral or Park positions.

3) Switch is blocked from start position in all other selector lever positions.

Floor Shift (Transmission Mounted Switch)

1) With transmission shift linkage properly adjusted, loosen the 2 switch attaching bolts.

2) Place transmission manual lever in Neutral position, then rotate switch and insert a gauge pin (No. 43 drill shank) into gauge pin holes of switch.

3) Gauge pin must be inserted to a full 31/64" into the 3 holes of the switch. Tighten switch attaching bolts and remove gauge pin.

4) Check operation of switch. Engine should start in Neutral and Park positions only.

Fig. 15: Transmission Mounted Neutral Safety Switch

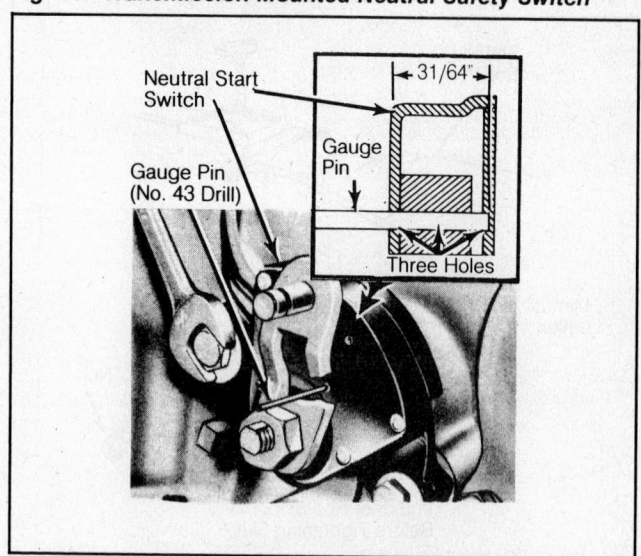

Floor Shift (Console Mounted Switch)

1) With transmission shift linkage adjusted and engine off, place selector lever in Neutral position. Remove selector lever handle, dial housing, and pointer back-up shield.

2) Loosen the 2 screws securing neutral start switch to selector lever housing. Place selector lever in Park position and hold it against the forward stop.

3) Move neutral switch rearward to end of its travel. Hold switch in rearward position and tighten the 2 attaching screws. Check operation of switch. Engine should start in Neutral and Park positions only.

GENERAL MOTORS – CADILLAC

LUBRICATION

SERVICE INTERVALS

Check fluid level at every oil change. Transmission fluid should be changed and filter replaced every 100,000 miles under normal operating conditions.

Under continuous extreme operating conditions (trailer towing, heavy city traffic with ambient temperature over 90°F/32°C or delivery service), fluid and filter should be changed every 15,000 miles.

CHECKING FLUID LEVEL

CAUTION: **Do not overfill. One pint of fluid will raise level from "ADD 1 PT. OR .5L" to "FULL HOT" mark on dipstick with a hot transmission.**

1) Warm transmission to normal operating temperature by at least 15 miles of highway driving. With engine at curb idle, move selector lever through all ranges, ending in Park.

2) Remove dipstick. Wipe dipstick clean and reinstall. Remove again and inspect level. Fluid level should check between "ADD 1 PT. OR .5L" and "FULL HOT" marks on dipstick.

CAUTION: **If vehicle has been operated for an extended period of time at high speed, in city traffic in hot weather, or if vehicle has been pulling a trailer, an accurate fluid level cannot be determined until fluid has cooled down (about 30 minutes after vehicle has been parked).**

RECOMMENDED FLUID

Use only Dexron II or equivalent automatic transmission fluid.

CAPACITY

NOTE: **Quantities listed are approximate. Correct fluid level should be determined by mark on dipstick rather than by amount added.**

TRANSMISSION REFILL CAPACITIES

Application	Refill Quantity	Total Quantity
THM 125C	10.5 pts. (3.8L)	20 pts. (9.5L)
THM 200-4R	10.6 pts. (5.0L)	22 pts. (10.4L)
THM 325-4L	10.6 (5.0L)	26.0 (12.3L)
THM 440-T4	13.0 pts. (6.2L)	20 pts. (9.5L)

DRAINING & REFILLING

Oil Pans Installed With RTV Sealant

1) If oil pan is installed with RTV sealant, a modified oil pan bolt must be used to remove pan. Modify an old pan bolt by grinding down a section of the shank, just below head of bolt, to 3/16" diameter. *See Fig. 1.*

2) With vehicle raised and drain pan placed under transmission, remove all oil pan bolts, except "A" and "B". Remove bolt "A" and install modified oil pan bolt. Loosen bolt "B" 4 turns. *See Fig. 1.*

Fig. 1: Removal of Oil Pan Bolts on Transmissions Using RTV Sealant Instead of A Gasket

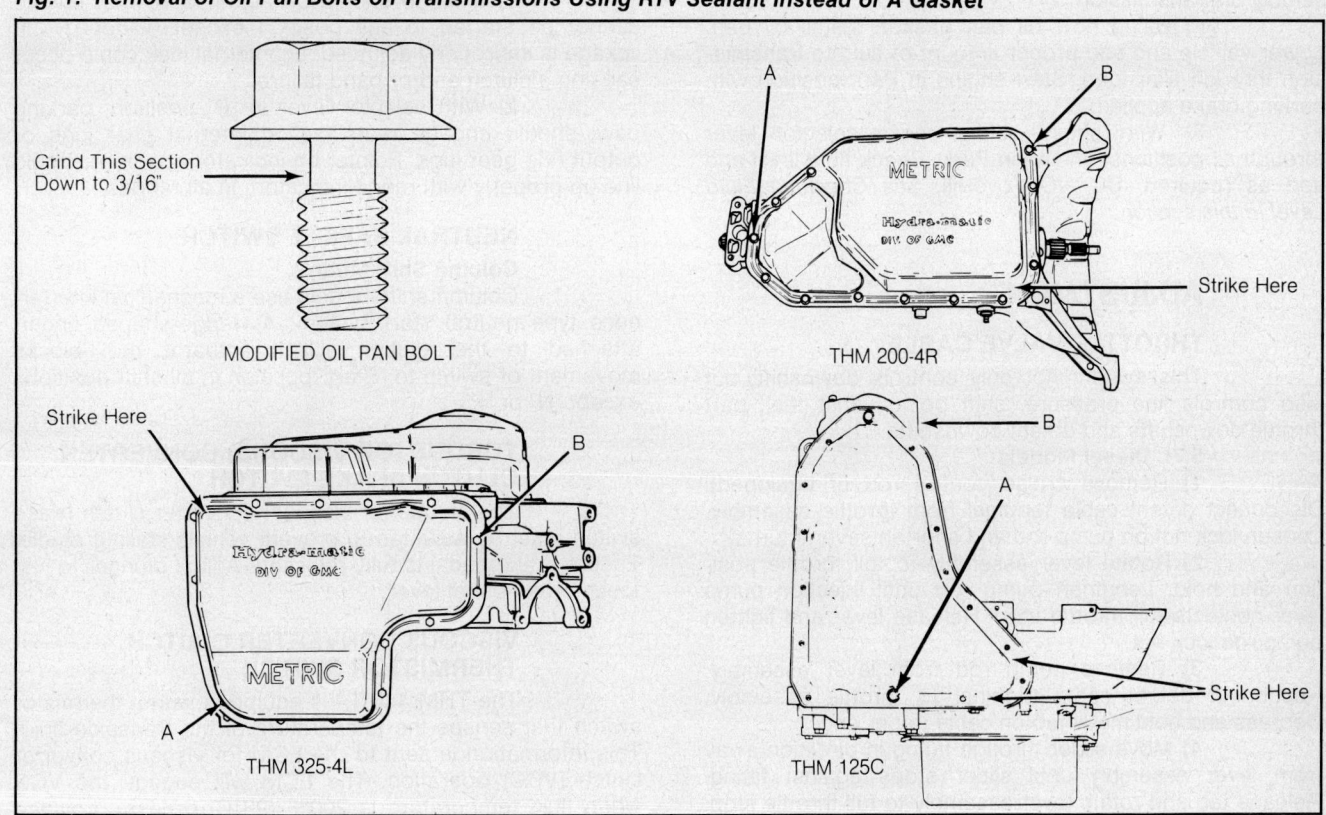

Modified oil pan bolt must be used to remove oil pan.

Automatic Transmission Servicing

GENERAL MOTORS – CADILLAC (Cont.)

3) DO NOT pry pan loose, as damage to pan flange or case will occur. Using a rubber mallet, strike oil pan corner. *See Fig. 1.* Remove modified oil pan bolt and allow fluid to drain. Remove screen/filter-to-valve body bolts and remove screen/filter with gasket.

4) Thoroughly clean pan and remove excess RTV sealant. Install new gasket or "O" rings lubricated with clean oil into new screen/filter assembly and install screen/filter assembly to transmission.

5) Apply 1/16" bead of RTV sealant on oil pan flange, and install pan while RTV is still wet. Lower vehicle and add proper amount of fluid to transmission through filler tube. Start engine in Park position with parking brake set.

6) With engine idling, move selector lever through all positions, ending in Park. Check fluid level and add as required. DO NOT overfill. *See Checking Fluid Level in this section.*

Oil Pans Installed With Gasket

1) With vehicle raised and drain pan placed under transmission, remove front and side oil pan bolts. On THM 440-T4, loosen rear oil pan bolts about 4 turns and carefully pry oil pan loose with screwdriver. Allow fluid to drain. Remove remaining oil pan bolts and pan with gasket attached.

2) On all other models, strike oil pan corner opposite remaining bolt with a rubber mallet. Remove remaining bolt and allow fluid to drain.

3) On all models, remove screen/filter-to-valve body bolts and remove screen/filter with gasket. Thoroughly clean pan with solvent and dry with compressed air. Install new gasket or "O" rings lubricated with clean oil into new screen/filter assembly. Install screen/filter assembly on transmission.

4) Using new oil pan gasket, install oil pan. Lower vehicle and add proper amount of fluid to transmission through filler tube. Start engine in Park position with parking brake applied.

5) With engine idling, move selector lever through all positions, ending in Park. Check fluid level and add as required. DO NOT overfill. *See Checking Fluid Level in this section.*

ADJUSTMENT

THROTTLE VALVE CABLE

This system not only controls downshift, but also controls line pressure, shift points, shift feel, part throttle downshifts and detent downshifts.

5.7L Diesel Models

1) Remove cruise control rod (if equipped). Disconnect detent cable terminal from throttle assembly. Loosen lock nut on pump rod and shorten several turns.

2) Rotate lever assembly to full throttle position and hold. Lengthen pump rod until injection pump lever contacts full throttle stop. Release lever and tighten pump rod lock nut.

3) Remove pump rod from lever assembly. Reconnect detent cable terminal to throttle assembly. Depress and hold metal tab on cable upper end.

4) Move slider through fitting in direction away from lever assembly until slider stops against fitting. Release tab and rotate lever assembly to full throttle stop. Release lever. Reconnect pump rod.

5) If equipped with cruise control, reconnect rod and adjust servo rod to minimum slack, then install

clip in first free hole closest to bellcrank, but within servo bail.

Self-Adjusting Type TV Cable

1) Depress lock tab and move slider back through fitting away from throttle body or pump lever until slider stops against fitting.

2) Release lock tab and open throttle to full throttle stop position to automatically adjust TV cable. Release throttle.

Fig. 2: Self-Adjusting Throttle Valve Cable

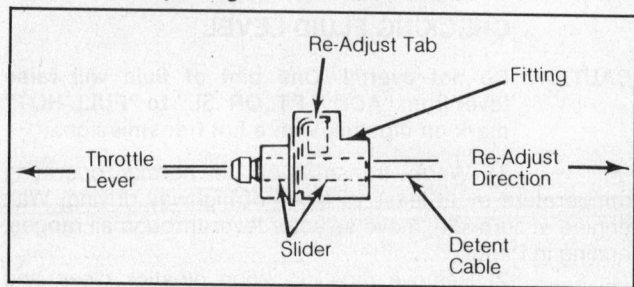

Press tab to move slider in correct direction.

VACUUM REGULATOR VALVE (DIESEL MODELS)

A vacuum regulator valve (VRV) is used on vehicles with diesel engines, only. *Refer to Automatic Transmission Servicing GENERAL MOTORS BUICK, CHEVROLET, OLDSMOBILE & PONTIAC in this section for applicable adjustment procedure.*

SHIFT LINKAGE

1) Linkage should be adjusted so that engine cannot be started in any position except "P" or "N". If linkage is improperly adjusted, an internal leak could occur causing a clutch and/or band failure.

2) With selector lever in "P" position, parking pawl should engage rear/reaction internal gear lugs or output ring gear lugs. Pointer on indicator quadrant should line up properly with range indicators in all ranges.

NEUTRAL SAFETY SWITCH

Column Shift Models

Column shift models use a mechanical interference type neutral start system. A wedge-shaped finger, attached to the ignition switch actuator rod, blocks movement of switch to "Start" position in all shift positions except "N" or "P".

TORQUE (OR VISCOUS) CONVERTER CLUTCH BRAKE SWITCH

The torque (or viscous) converter clutch brake switch must be adjusted to prevent vehicle stalling at idle. Ensure brake pedal is fully released. Adjust plunger to just touch brake pedal lever.

VISCOUS CONVERTER CLUTCH THERMISTOR SWITCH

The THM 440-T4 is equipped with a thermistor switch that senses the temperature of the transaxle fluid. This information is sent to the ECM for viscous converter clutch (VCC) operation. The ECM will engage the VCC when fluid temperature is 200°F (93°C) or less, provided all other conditions have been met. If fluid temperature is higher than this, ECM will not allow VCC engagement until vehicle speed is about 36 MPH.

GENERAL MOTORS
BUICK, CHEVROLET, OLDSMOBILE & PONTIAC

LUBRICATION

SERVICE INTERVALS

Check fluid level at every oil change. Transmission fluid should be changed and filter replaced every 100,000 miles under normal operating conditions.

Under continuous extreme operating conditions (trailer towing, heavy city traffic with ambient temperature over 90°F/32°C or delivery service), fluid and filter should be changed every 15,000 miles.

CHECKING FLUID LEVEL

CAUTION: **Do not overfill. One pint of fluid will raise level from "ADD 1 PT. OR .5L" to "FULL HOT" mark on dipstick with a hot transmission.**

1) Warm transmission to normal operating temperature by at least 15 miles of highway driving. With engine at curb idle, move selector lever through all ranges, ending in Park.

2) Remove dipstick. Wipe dipstick clean and reinstall. Remove again and inspect level. Fluid level should check between "ADD 1 PT. OR .5L" and "FULL HOT" marks on dipstick.

CAUTION: **If vehicle has been operated for an extended period of time at high speed, in city traffic in hot weather, or if vehicle has been pulling a trailer, an accurate fluid level cannot be determined until fluid has cooled down (about 30 minutes after vehicle has been parked).**

RECOMMENDED FLUID

Use only Dexron II or equivalent automatic transmission fluid.

CAPACITY

NOTE: **Quantities listed are approximate. Correct fluid level should be determined by mark on dipstick rather than by amount added.**

TRANSMISSION REFILL CAPACITIES

Application	Refill Quantity	Total Quantity
THM 125C	8 pts. (3.8L)	12 pts. (5.7L)
THM 180C	6 pts. (2.8L)	10 pts. (4.7L)
THM 200C	7 pts. (3.3L)	19 pts. (9.0L)
THM 200-4R	7 pts. (3.3L)	22 pts. (10.4L)
THM 325-4L	10 pts. (4.7L)	24 pts. (11.4L)
THM 440-T4	6 pts. (2.8L)	10 pts. (4.7L)
THM 700-R4	10 pts. (4.7L)	23 pts. (10.9L)

DRAINING & REFILLING
All Models

1) With vehicle raised and drain pan placed under transmission, remove front and side transmission oil pan bolts. Loosen rear pan bolts about 4 turns each.

2) Carefully pry pan loose with screwdriver, allowing fluid to drain. Remove remaining bolts and oil pan with gasket. Remove screen/filter-to-valve body bolts and remove screen/filter with gasket.

3) Thoroughly clean pan and screen with solvent and dry with compressed air. Paper type filters should be replaced. Install new gasket or "O" rings, lubricated with clean oil, into screen/filter assembly.

4) Install screen/filter assembly to transmission. Use new pan gasket and install pan. Add proper amount of fluid to transmission through filler tube.

5) Start engine with shift selector lever in Park position and with parking brake set. Check fluid level and add as required. DO NOT overfill.

ADJUSTMENT

THROTTLE VALVE (TV) CABLE
Gasoline Models

1) Depress metal lock tab on adjuster and hold it in depressed position. Move slider back through fitting, away from carburetor lever, until slider stops at fitting.

2) Release lock tab and open throttle lever to full throttle stop to automatically adjust slider to correct setting. Release throttle lever.

Diesel Models (Exc. Celebrity, Century, Ciera & 6000)

1) Remove cruise control rod (if equipped). Disconnect detent cable terminal from throttle assembly. Loosen lock nut on pump rod and shorten several turns. Rotate lever assembly to full throttle position and hold.

2) Lengthen pump rod until injection pump lever contacts full throttle stop. Release lever and tighten pump rod lock nut.

3) Remove pump rod from lever assembly. Reconnect detent cable terminal to throttle assembly. Depress and hold metal tab on cable upper end. Move slider through fitting in direction away from lever assembly until slider stops against fitting.

4) Release tab and rotate lever assembly to full throttle stop. Release lever. Reconnect pump rod. If equipped with cruise control, reconnect rod and adjust servo rod to minimum slack. Install clip in first free hole closest to bellcrank, but within servo bail.

Fig. 1: Throttle Valve (TV) Cable Adjustment

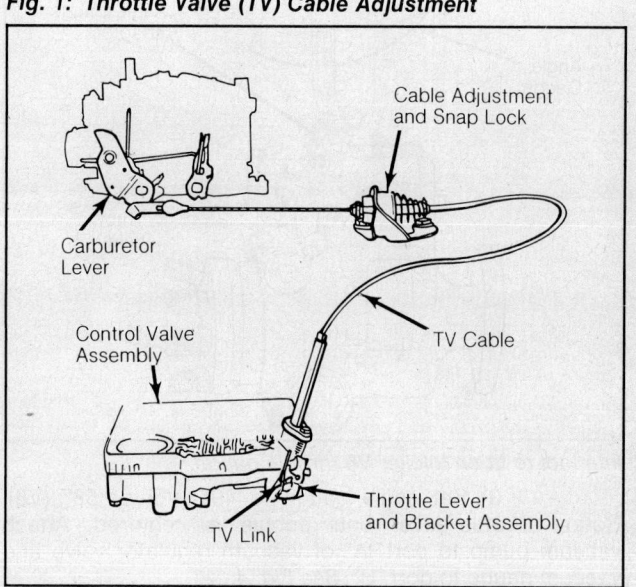

Automatic Transmission Servicing
GENERAL MOTORS
BUICK, CHEVROLET, OLDSMOBILE & PONTIAC (Cont.)

Diesel Models (Celebrity, Century, Ciera & 6000)

1) Remove pump rod from lever assembly and depress metal lock tab. Hold tab and move slider through fitting away from lever assembly until slider stops against fitting.

2) Release lock tab and rotate lever assembly to full throttle position to automatically adjust slider to correct setting. Release the lever and reconnect pump rod to lever assembly.

Fig. 2: Self-Adjusting Throttle Valve Cable

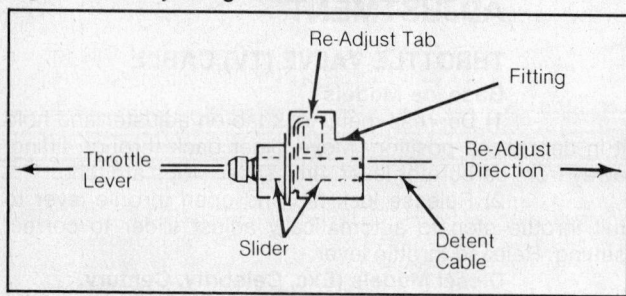

Press tab to move slider in correct direction.

VACUUM REGULATOR VALVE (DIESEL MODELS)

1) Remove air crossover and install screen covers over openings. On V6 models, disconnect throttle and T.V./detent cables from pump throttle lever. On V8 models, disconnect throttle rod from pump.

2) Loosen vacuum regulator valve-to-pump bolts. Install carburetor angle gauge to injection pump throttle lever. Rotate throttle lever to wide-open throttle position and set angle gauge to zero degrees, then center bubble.

Fig. 3: Angle Gauge & Adapter Installation

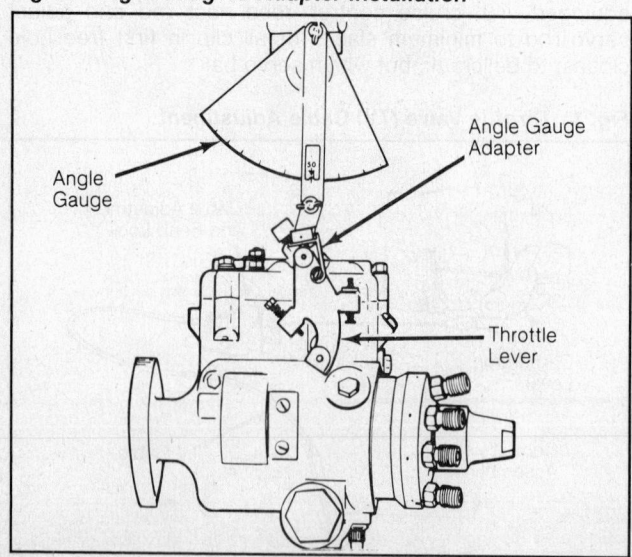

File tool to fit on thicker V6 throttle gauge.

3) Set angle gauge to 49° (V6) or 58° (V8). Rotate throttle lever until bubble is centered. Attach vacuum pump to port "A" of vacuum regulator valve and vacuum gauge to port "B". *See Fig. 4.*

4) Apply 18-24 in. Hg vacuum to port "A", then rotate vacuum valve clockwise to obtain 10.6 in. Hg.

Tighten bolts and remove vacuum gauge, pump and angle gauge.

5) Connect throttle and T.V./detent cables (V6) or throttle rod to pump lever (V8). Remove screen covers on intake manifold. Install air crossover.

Fig. 4: Vacuum Regulator Valve Port Locations

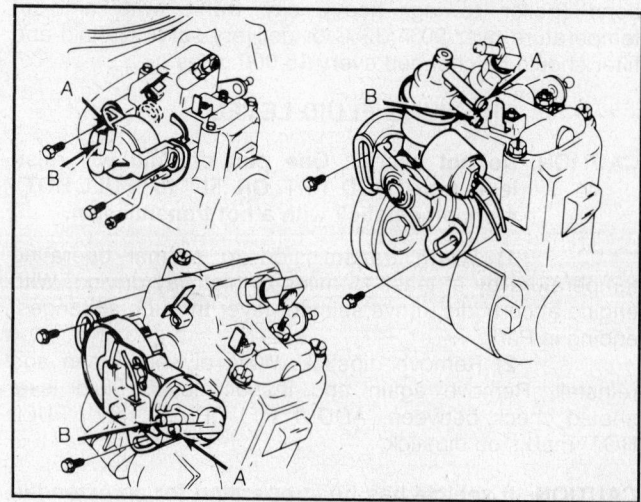

Attach pump to port "A", gauge to port "B".

SHIFT LINKAGE

1) Linkage should be adjusted so that engine cannot be started in any position except "P" or "N". If linkage is improperly adjusted, an internal leak could occur causing a clutch and/or band failure.

2) With selector lever in "P" position, parking pawl should engage rear/reaction internal gear lugs or output ring gear lugs. Pointer on indicator quadrant should line up properly with range indicators in all ranges.

Fig. 5: Rod Type Column Shift Linkage

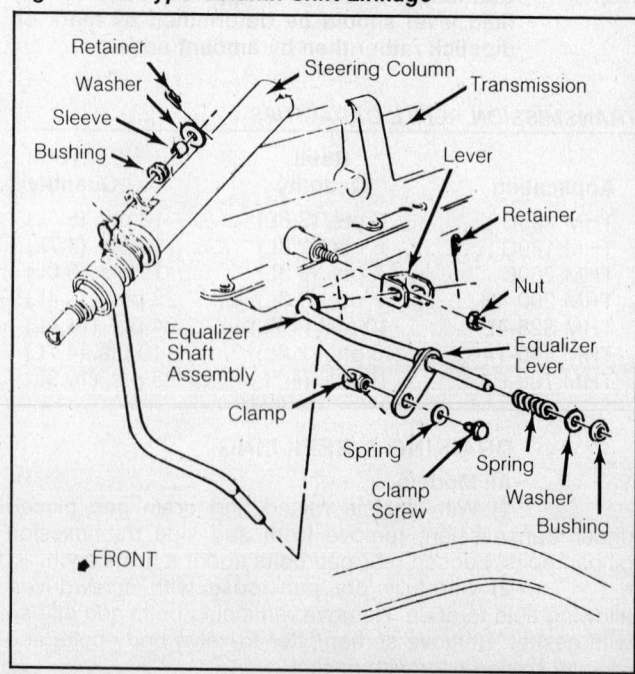

Ensure there is no tension on either equalizer lever or selector rod.

GENERAL MOTORS
BUICK, CHEVROLET, OLDSMOBILE & PONTIAC (Cont.)

Column Shift (Rod Type)
Rear Wheel Drive Models

1) Position steering column shift lever in Neutral gate notch. Loosen swivel clamp lock screw and place transmission lever in Neutral.

2) Hold swivel clamp against equalizer lever. Tighten clamp screw without applying tension on either equalizer lever or selector rod.

Floor Shift (Rear Wheel Drive)

1) Disconnect shifter link from shifter assembly and place shifter assembly in Neutral notch of detent plate.

2) Place transmission lever in Neutral position by moving clockwise to maximum detent position, then back (counterclockwise) 2 detents to Neutral. Adjust link until hole and pin line up. Install shim and retainer.

Fig. 6: Floor Shift Linkage (Chevette & 1000)

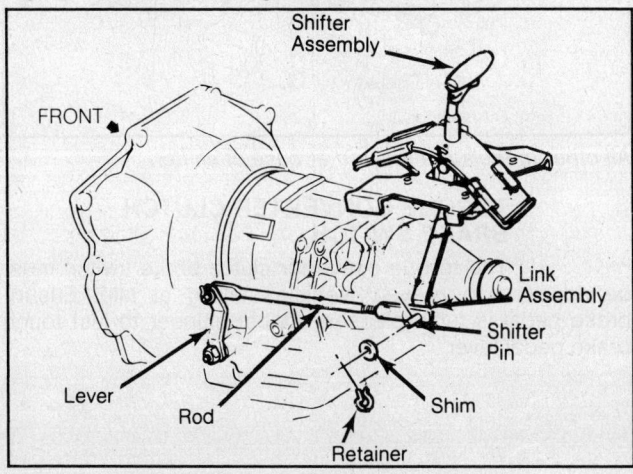

Chevette & 1000 shown; others similar.

Floor Shift (Front Wheel Drive)

1) Place shift lever in Neutral position. Place transaxle lever in Neutral notch. Loosely assemble nut to pin through transaxle lever with transaxle cable assembled to pin.

2) Assemble steering column shift lever pin and transaxle control cable bracket. Tighten nut. Lever must be held out of Park when tightening nut.

Fig. 7: Floor Shift Column Lock (Corvette)

Fig. 8: Floor Shift Linkage (Front Wheel Drive)

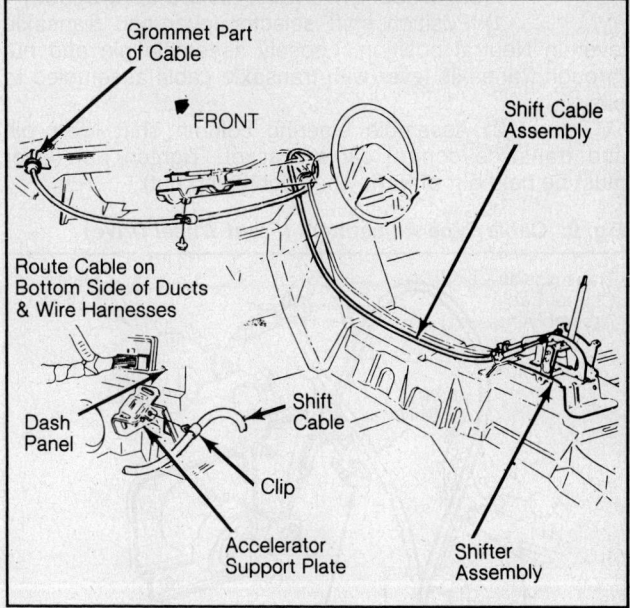

Cable Type (Riviera & Toronado)

1) Position shift selector lever in Neutral gate notch. Loosen nut on pin at attachment point of cable to steering column.

2) Move transaxle lever to Neutral position and ensure that pin is free to move in slot. Tighten pin without applying tension on cable or lever.

Floor Shift Column Lock
(Corvette)

1) Place steering column lock lever in locked position. Place selector lever in Park position. Release cable retainer at column lock pin.

2) Apply tension to the shifter rearward on the park stop. Pull cable adjustment tab up. Reinstall cable retainer at column lock pin. Push cable adjustment tab down.

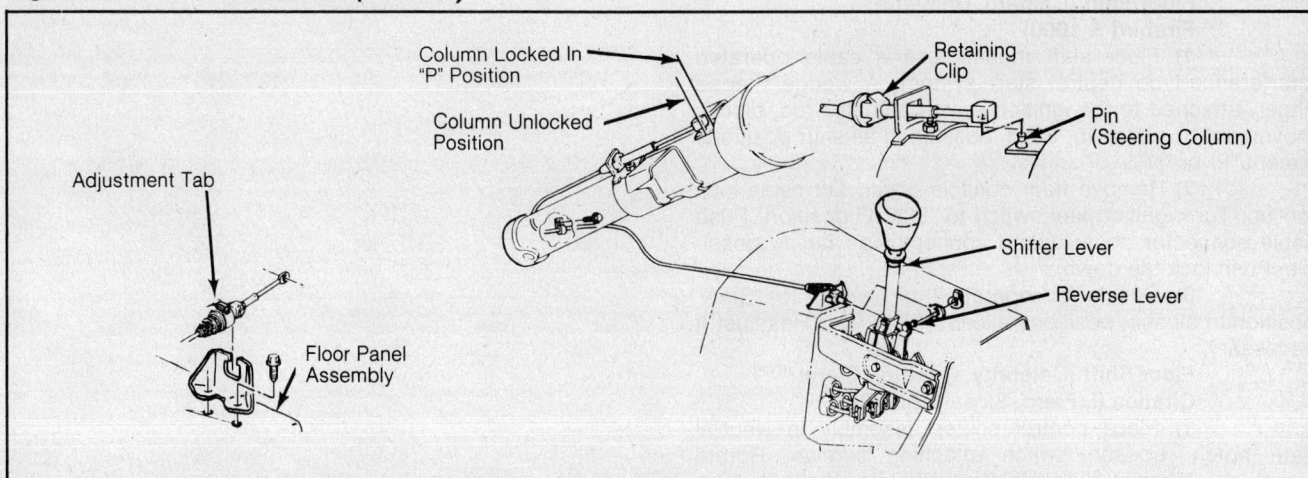

Shifter must be in Park for adjustment.

1-24

Automatic Transmission Servicing
GENERAL MOTORS
BUICK, CHEVROLET, OLDSMOBILE & PONTIAC (Cont.)

Cable Type
Front Wheel Drive (Exc. Riviera & Toronado)

1) Position shift selector lever and transaxle lever in Neutral position. Loosely assemble pin and nut through transaxle lever with transaxle cable assembled to pin.

2) Assemble steering column shift lever pin and transaxle control cable bracket. Tighten nut (lever must be held out of Park when tightening nut).

Fig. 9: Cable Type Adjustment (Front Wheel Drive)

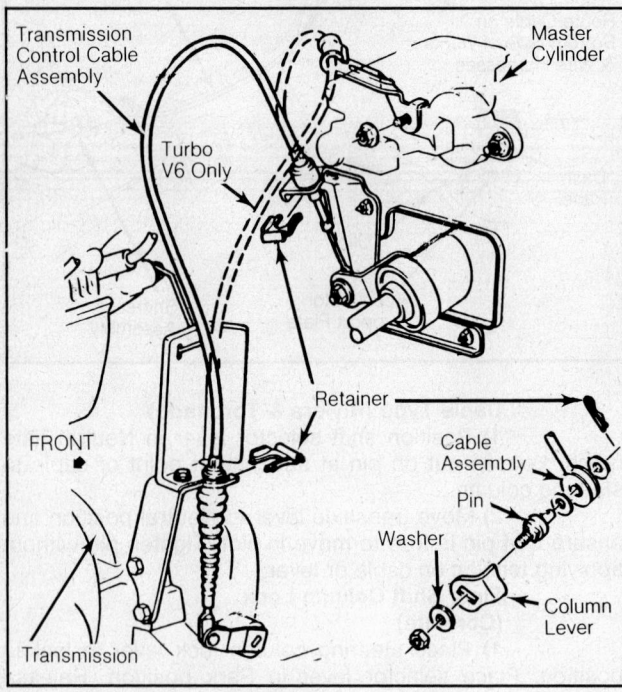

Ensure pin is free to move in slot.

NEUTRAL SAFETY SWITCH
Column Shift Models
Column shift models use a mechanical interference-type neutral start system. A wedge-shaped finger, attached to the ignition switch actuator rod, blocks movement of switch to "Start" position in all shift positions except "P" or "N".

Floor Shift (Camaro, Chevette, Firebird & 1000)
1) Floor shift models use a cable operated interference-type neutral start system. A wedge-shaped finger, attached to the ignition switch actuator rod, blocks movement of switch to "Start" position in all shift positions except "P" or "N".

2) Remove floor console cover. Lift cable lock tab up. Turn ignition key switch to "LOCK" position. Push cable connector nose toward connector as far as possible. Push lock tab down.

3) Check for operation of switch to "Start" position in all shift positions except "P" or "N". Readjust if necessary.

Floor Shift (Celebrity, Century, Ciera, Citation II, Fiero, Skylark & 6000)
1) Place control shifter assembly in Neutral gate notch. Loosen switch attaching screws. Rotate switch on shifter to align adjustment hole with carrier tang hole.

2) Insert a 3/32" gauge pin into the hole to a depth of .60" (15 mm). Tighten switch attaching screws. Remove gauge pin.

Fig. 10: Floor Shift Column Lock (Corvette)

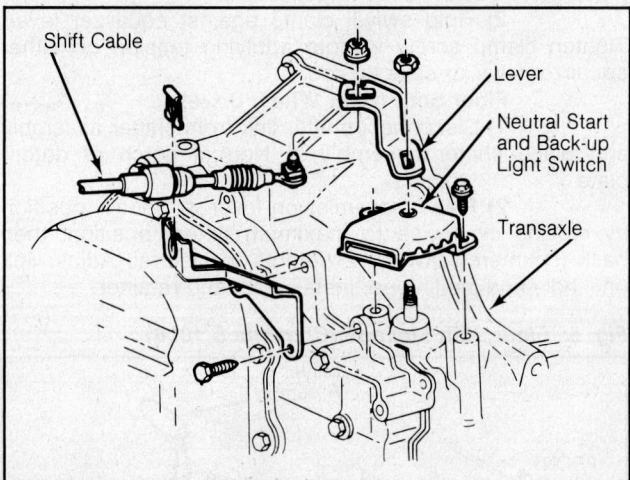

All other models are located at base of shifter.

TORQUE CONVERTER CLUTCH
BRAKE SWITCH
The torque converter clutch brake switch must be adjusted to prevent vehicle stalling at idle. Ensure brake pedal is fully released. Adjust plunger to just touch brake pedal lever.

LUBRICATION

SERVICE INTERVALS
Check fluid level at each engine oil change. When operated under normal conditions, passenger car transmissions do not require periodic service. However, under heavy duty conditions, transmission should be drained, refilled and bands adjusted every 15,000 miles.

Trucks and Vans used in normal, light duty service require transmission servicing (fluid drained and refilled, bands adjusted) every 37,500 miles. Under normal heavy duty conditions, service transmission every 24,000 miles. Vehicles subjected to severe heavy duty conditions should have transmission serviced every 12,000 miles.

CHECKING FLUID LEVEL
All Models

1) Check fluid level with vehicle parked on level surface, engine idling at normal operating temperature and parking brake applied. Move selector lever through all gear ranges, ending in "P" (FWD models) or "N" (RWD models).

2) Fluid level should be between "FULL" and "ADD" marks on dipstick. Check condition of fluid for contamination or burned smell. Seat dipstick carefully to seal out water and dirt. NEVER overfill transmission.

RECOMMENDED FLUID
Use only Dexron II type automatic transmission fluid when topping off or refilling transmission.

CAPACITY
When filling transmission, use capacities listed in table as a guideline, only. Correct fluid level should always be determined by marks on dipstick, rather than by amount of fluid added. Capacities listed include torque converter.

TRANSMISSION REFILL CAPACITIES [1]

Application	Capacity Pints (Liters)
A-413 & A-470	
Fleet	18.4 (8.7)
Except Fleet	17.8 (8.4)
A-727	
Lock-Up	16.7 (7.9)
Non Lock-Up	17.1 (8.1)
A-904 Series	
Lock-Up & All Trucks	17.1 (8.1)
Non Lock-Up	17.6 (8.3)
A-999	17.1 (8.1)

[1] – Includes torque converter.

DRAINING & REFILLING
All Models

1) Loosen oil pan bolts. Tap lightly at one corner to break loose and allow fluid to drain. Remove pan. Install new filter on bottom of valve body and tighten retaining screws. Clean oil pan. Ensure that magnet (if used) is over boss in right front corner of pan. Install pan with new gasket.

2) Pour 4 quarts (3.8L) of transmission fluid through filler tube. Start engine and allow to run at idle for at least 2 minutes. With engine at curb idle and parking brake applied, move shift selector lever through all ranges, ending in "P" (FWD vehicles) or "N" (RWD vehicles). Add fluid up to "ADD" mark on dipstick. Do not overfill.

3) Reseat dipstick fully to seal out water and dirt. Recheck fluid level when transmission reaches normal operating temperature.

ADJUSTMENT

KICKDOWN (FRONT) BAND
All Models

1) Locate kickdown band adjusting screw at left side of transmission case, near throttle lever shaft. Loosen adjusting screw lock nut and back off 5 turns. Ensure adjusting screw turns freely in case.

2) Using Wrench (C-3380-A) with Adapter (C-3705), tighten adjusting screw to 48 INCH lbs. (5 N.m). If adapter is not used, tighten adjusting screw to 72 INCH lbs. (8 N.m), which is the true torque.

3) Back off front adjusting screw specified number of turns. See KICKDOWN BAND ADJUSTMENT table. Hold adjusting screw in position and tighten lock nut to 35 ft. lbs. (47 N.m).

KICKDOWN BAND ADJUSTMENT

Application	Back Off Screw
A-413 & A-470	2 1/2 Turns
A-904	
Fleet	2 Turns
All Others	2 1/2 Turns
A-727 & A-999	2 1/2 Turns

Fig. 1: Adjusting Kickdown Band

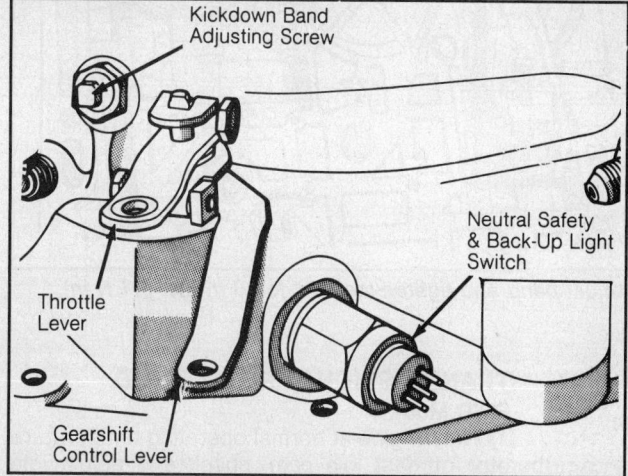

Kickdown Band Adjusting Screw

Neutral Safety & Back-Up Light Switch

Throttle Lever

Gearshift Control Lever

With band properly adjusted, tighten lock nut to 30 ft. lbs. (41 N.m).

LOW-REVERSE (REAR) BAND
RWD Models

1) Drain transmission and remove oil pan. Locate low-reverse band adjusting screw on rear servo lever. On passenger cars with A-904 transmission and 6-cylinder engine, remove band adjusting screw lock nut and tighten Allen screw at servo end of lever to 41 INCH lbs. (4.6 N.m).

CHRYSLER CORP. LIGHT TRUCKS (Cont.)

2) On all other models, loosen adjusting screw lock nut and back off about 5 turns. Ensure that screw turns freely in lever. Using Wrench (C3380-A), tighten adjusting screw to 72 INCH lbs. (8 N.m).

3) On all models, back off rear adjusting screw specified number of turns. See LOW-REVERSE BAND ADJUSTMENT table. Hold adjusting screw in position and tighten lock nut to 30 ft. lbs. (41 N.m). Clean oil pan, install new gasket with pan and fill transmission with fluid.

FWD Models

1) Drain transaxle fluid and remove oil pan. Apply 30 psi (2.1 kg/cm^2) air pressure to low-reverse servo and measure gap between band ends. If less than .080" (2.0 mm), band is excessively worn and should be replaced.

2) To adjust band on A-413 and A-470 models, loosen lock nut approximately 5 turns and tighten adjusting screw to 41 INCH lbs. (4.6 N.m). Back off adjusting screw specified number of turns as given in table, hold screw in position and tighten lock nut.

LOW-REVERSE BAND ADJUSTMENT

Application	Back Off Screw
A-413 & A-470	3 1/2 Turns
A-904LA, A-904T & A-999	4 Turns
A-727	2 Turns

Fig. 2: Low-Reverse (Rear) Band Adjustment Location

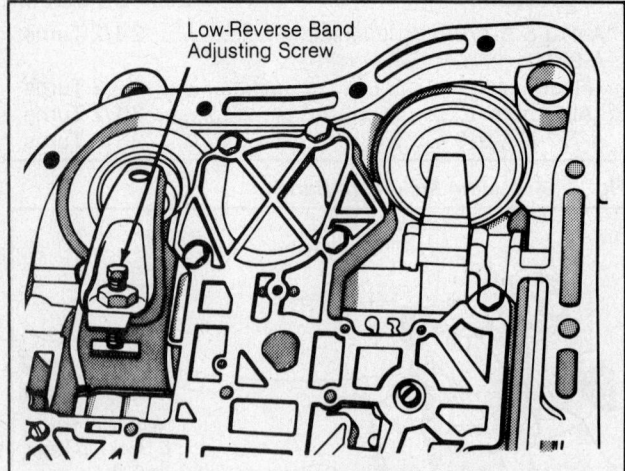

Adjust band and tighten lock nut to 30 ft. lbs. (41 N.m).

TRANSMISSION THROTTLE ROD
RWD Models

1) With engine at normal operating temperature and carburetor off fast idle cam, check and adjust idle speed as needed. Turn off engine and disconnect choke at carburetor or block choke valve in full open position. Open throttle slightly to release fast idle cam and return throttle to curb idle position.

2) Raise vehicle on hoist. Loosen swivel lock screw. Ensure swivel is free to slide along flat end of throttle rod so that preload spring action is not restricted. If necessary, disassemble and clean parts to assure free action.

3) Hold transmission lever firmly forward against internal stop and tighten swivel lock screw. Adjust-

Fig. 3: Throttle Rod Adjustment

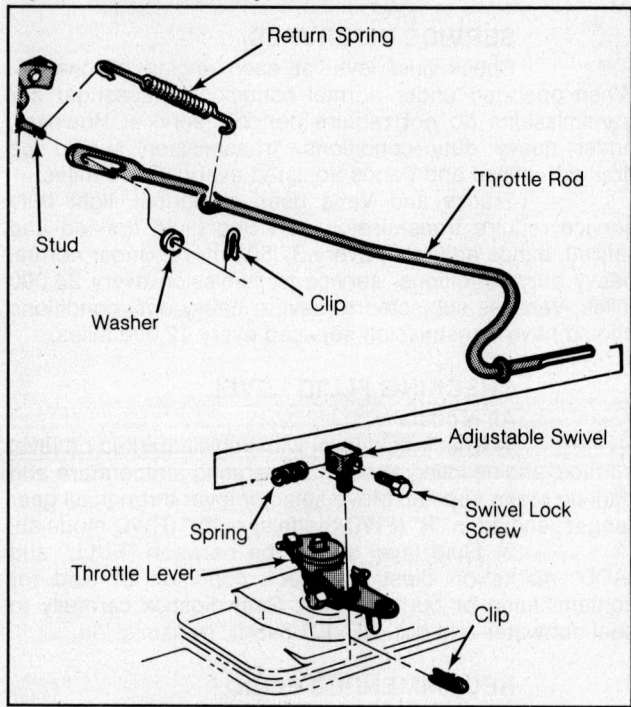

Linkage for vehicles equipped with 6-cylinder engine.

ment is complete. Linkage backlash is automatically removed by preload spring.

4) Lower vehicle and reconnect choke. To test linkage, move throttle rod rearward and slowly release it to confirm full forward return.

Fig. 4: Throttle Rod Adjustment

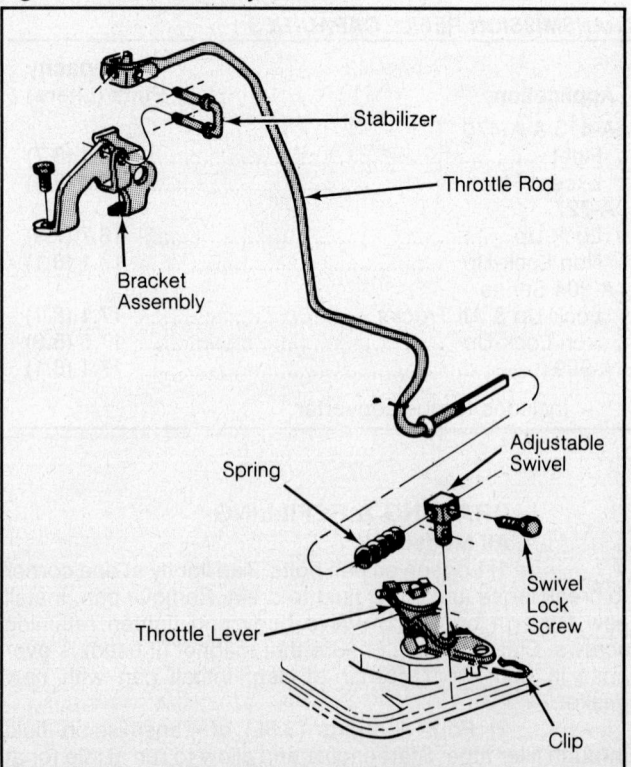

Linkage for vehicles equipped with V8 engines.

CHRYSLER CORP. LIGHT TRUCKS (Cont.)

FWD Models

1) Ensure carburetor is not on fast idle cam (disconnect choke if necessary). Loosen adjustment bracket lock screw. Ensure bracket slides freely along full length of adjustment.

2) Slide bracket to the left (toward engine) to the limit of its travel. Release bracket and move throttle lever fully to the right against its internal stop and tighten lock screw. This completes adjustment. Cable backlash is automatically removed.

3) To check cable freedom of operation, move transaxle throttle lever forward and slowly release, making sure it returns to full rear position.

Fig. 5: Throttle Cable Adjustment

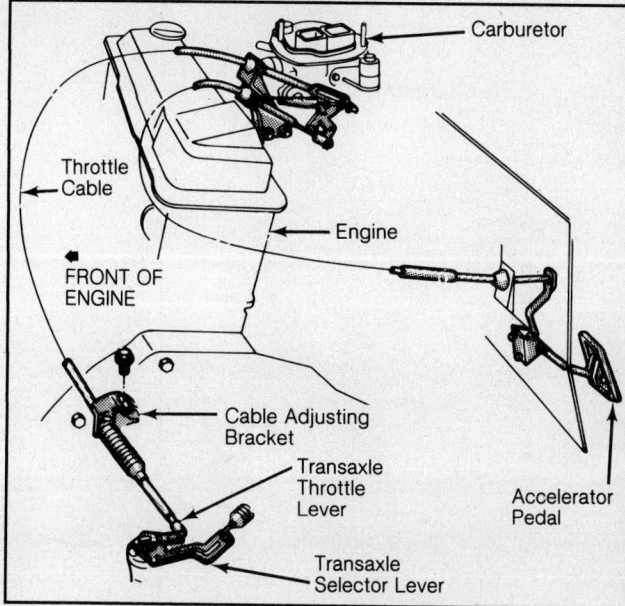

This applies to front wheel drive models only.

SHIFT LINKAGE
Column Shift (RWD Models)

1) With column shift lever in "P" position, loosen adjustable swivel lock screw and ensure that swivel is free to move on shift rod. Disassemble and clean components if required.

2) Move shift lever on transmission to full rear detent (Park) position and tighten swivel lock screw. When linkage is properly adjusted, detent positions for Neutral and Drive will be within limits of shift lever gate stops and engine will start only in "P" or "N".

Floor Shift (RWD Models)

1) Loosen adjustable rod swivel lock screw, place selector in "P" and move shift lever on transmission all the way to rear detent (Park) position.

2) Adjust swivel so no load is placed on linkage in either direction, then tighten swivel lock screw. Check adjustment so shift effort is free, detents are solid, and all gate stops are positive.

3) Detent position should be close enough to gate stops in "N" and "D" so shift selector lever will not remain out of detent position when placed against gate and released. Starter should operate only in "N" or "P" positions.

Fig. 6: Column Shift Linkage Adjustment

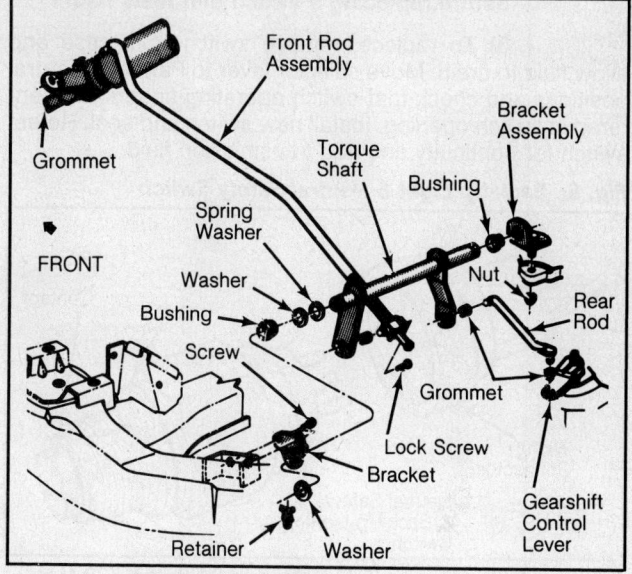

Floor Shift (FWD Models)

Place shift selector in "P" position. Loosen lock bolt on cable adjusting bracket on transaxle. Move shift lever on transaxle all the way to rear detent (Park) position and hold. Tighten lock bolt.

NOTE: If linkage cable is disconnected from transmission lever for any reason, always use a new plastic grommet when reassembling linkage.

Fig. 7: Shift Linkage Adjustment on FWD Models

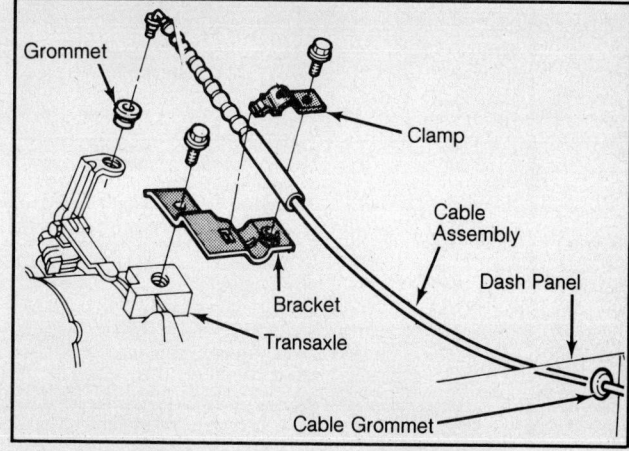

Adjusting bracket is located on transaxle case.

NEUTRAL SAFETY SWITCH
All Models

1) With transmission linkage properly adjusted, switch should allow starter operation in Park and Neutral only. To test switch, remove wire connector and test for continuity between center pin of switch and case. Continuity should exist only when transmission is in Park or Neutral.

2) Check for continuity between 2 outer pins. Continuity should exist with transmission in Reverse, only. There should be no continuity between either outside pin and the transmission case.

CHRYSLER CORP. LIGHT TRUCKS (Cont.)

NOTE: **Ensure gearshift linkage is properly adjusted before replacing a switch that tests bad.**

   3) To replace, remove switch from case and allow fluid to drain. Move selector lever to Park and Neutral positions and check that switch operating fingers are centered in switch opening. Install new switch and seal. Retest switch for continuity and add transmission fluid.

Fig. 8: Back-Up Light & Neutral Safety Switch

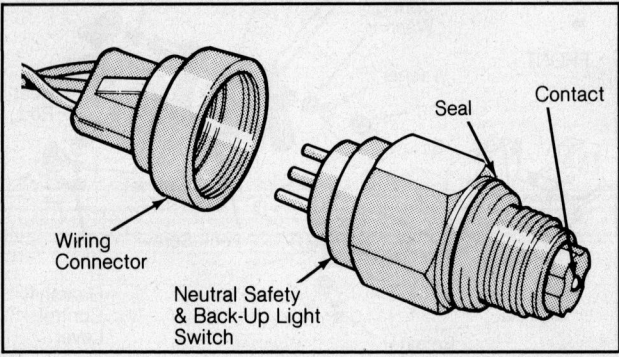

When installing new switch, tighten to 24 ft. lbs. (33 N.m).

FORD LIGHT TRUCKS

LUBRICATION

SERVICE INTERVALS

Vehicles used in normal service do not require regularly scheduled maintenance. Fluid level should be checked whenever underhood maintenance is performed, or if leakage is detected. Clutch bands on C-5 and C-6 transmissions should be adjusted when the quality of shifts deteriorates or otherwise indicates improper band adjustment.

On vehicles used for fleet service, or those operated under severe conditions, drain and refill transmission at 30,000 mile intervals.

CHECKING FLUID LEVEL

1) With transmission at normal operating temperature, place vehicle on level ground. Apply parking brake, and run engine at curb idle. Shift selector through all positions, ending in Park.

2) With transmission at normal operating temperature, fluid level should be between "ADD" and "DON'T ADD" marks on dipstick. If transmission is at room temperature, fluid level should be between middle and top holes on dipstick.

3) If fluid level is correct at room temperature, it will be between "ADD" and "DON'T ADD" marks on dipstick when normal operating temperature is reached. Do not overfill. Check condition of fluid for contamination or burned smell. Fully reseat dipstick.

RECOMMENDED FLUID

The C-6, AOD and A4LD transmissions require "Dexron II" type transmission fluid. The C-5 requires Ford "Type H" (Ford Specification ESP-M2C166-H).

CAPACITY

NOTE: **Transmission and converter assembly capacities listed are approximate. Determine correct fluid level by mark on dipstick rather than by amount of fluid added.**

TRANSMISSION REFILL CAPACITIES

Application	Quantity
AOD Transmission	12.3 qts. (11.6L)
A4LD Transmission	9.0 qts. (8.5L)
C-5 Transmission	11.0 qts. (10.4L)
C-6 Transmission	
2WD Models	12.0 qts. (11.4L)
4WD Models	13.5 qts. (12.7L)

DRAINING & REFILLING

1) On C-5 models, disconnect fluid filler tube from oil pan to drain fluid, then remove pan. On all other models, loosen oil pan bolts and tap pan to break gasket seal. Allow fluid to drain, then remove oil pan bolts and oil pan. On all models, clean pan and reinstall with new filter, gasket and pan gasket. On C-5 models, install filler tube.

2) Add 3 quarts (2.8L) transmission fluid through filler tube. Check fluid level as described. When filling a dry transmission and converter, refer to *Transmission Refill Capacity chart.* Recheck fluid level when transmission is at normal operating temperature. Do not overfill.

ADJUSTMENT

INTERMEDIATE (FRONT) BAND
C-5 & C-6 Only

Clean dirt from band adjusting screw area. Remove and discard band adjusting screw lock nut. Install new lock nut. Tighten adjusting screw to 120 INCH lbs. (14 N.m). Back off screw exact number of turns as indicated in *Intermediate (Front) Band Adjustment* table. Hold adjusting screw in position and tighten new lock nut to 40 ft. lbs. (54 N.m).

INTERMEDIATE (FRONT) BAND ADJUSTMENT

Application	Back Off (Turns)
C-5	4 1/4
C-6	1 1/2

Fig. 1: Adjusting Intermediate Band

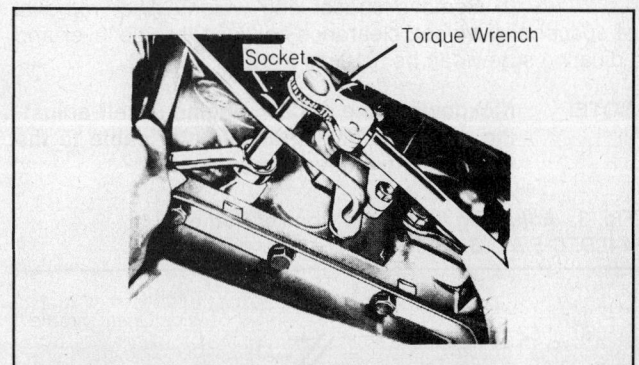

Ford C-5 models shown; C-6 similar.

LOW-REVERSE (REAR) BAND
C-5 Only

Clean all dirt from band adjusting screw area, then remove and discard band adjusting screw lock nut. Install new lock nut on adjusting screw. Tighten screw tighten adjusting screw to 120 INCH lbs. (14 N.m), then back off 3 full turns. Hold screw in position and tighten lock nut to 40 ft. lbs. (54 N.m).

Fig. 2: Adjusting Low-Reverse Band (C-5 Only)

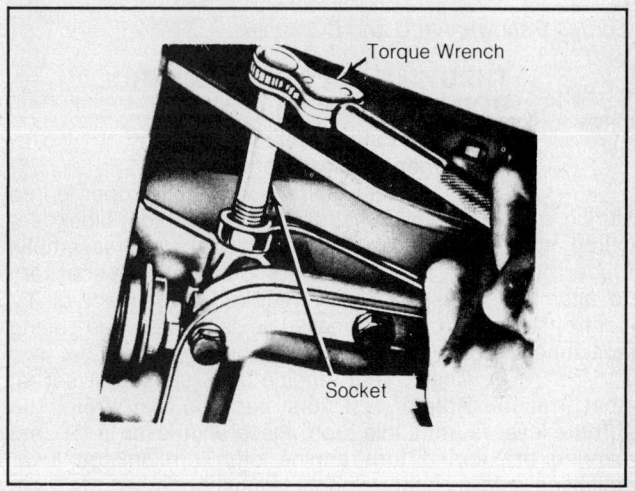

FORD LIGHT TRUCKS (Cont.)

KICKDOWN CONTROL

NOTE: Linkage must be free and must return to idle when released. Throttle linkage must be properly adjusted before attempting to make kickdown control adjustment.

A4LD, C-5 & C-6

1) Check for wide-open carburetor and linkage travel at full throttle. Carburetor full-throttle stop must be contacted by throttle linkage and there must be a slight amount of movement left in downshift linkage. Be sure downshift linkage return spring is connected and downshift lever returns to closed position.

2) Apply 6 lb. (2.7 kg) to transmission kickdown lever. Rotate throttle to wide open throttle position. Insert a .060" (1.52 mm) spacer between throttle lever and adjusting screw. *See Fig. 3.* Loosen lock nut and rotate adjusting screw until contact is made between screw and spacer.

3) Remove spacer and weight. After removal of spacer and weight, clearance between throttle lever and adjusting screw can be .010-.070" (.25-1.78 mm).

NOTE: Kickdown cable on 2.3L engine is self-adjusting after depressing accelerator cable to the floor. No adjustment is required.

Fig. 3: Adjusting Kickdown Control Rod on A4LD, C-5 & C-6 Models

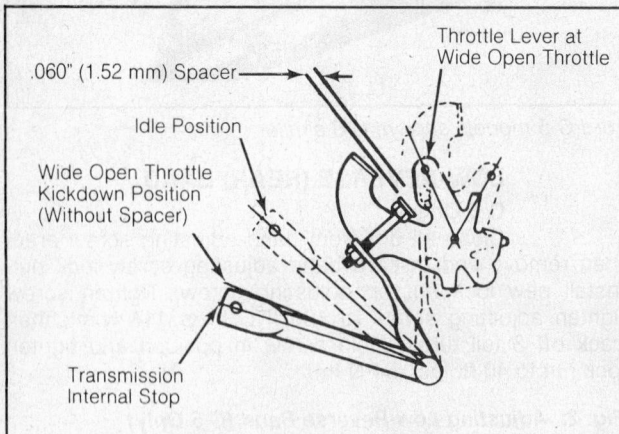

Ford C-5 shown, A4LD and C-6 similar.

THROTTLE VALVE (TV) CONTROL ROD LINKAGE

AOD Only (5.0L 2-Bbl.)
Adjustment at Carburetor

1) TV control linkage is set to its proper length during initial assembly using sliding trunnion block secured at transmission end of TV control rod assembly. Under normal circumstances, it should not be necessary to alter this adjustment. Any required adjustment of TV control linkage can normally be accomplished using adjustment screw on linkage lever at carburetor.

2) Check that engine idle speed is set at specification. Rotate fast idle cam on carburetor so throttle lever is at its idle stop. Place shift lever in "N", set parking brake and turn engine off. Turn linkage lever adjusting screw counterclockwise until screw end is flush with lever face. *See Fig. 4.*

3) Turn adjusting screw clockwise to obtain .005" (.12 mm) clearance between end of screw and throttle lever. Open and close throttle to eliminate friction and recheck clearance. DO NOT apply any load on levers while checking. Turn adjusting screw clockwise 4 full turns.

4) If screw travel is limited, 2 turns minimum are permitted, however 4 turns are preferred. If idle speed requires adjustment of more than 50 RPM, turn adjustment screw on linkage lever.

NOTE: If adjustment of linkage lever screw is not possible, adjustment of the TV control rod at transmission is required. This adjustment is also required when a new TV control rod is installed.

Fig. 4: Adjusting TV Linkage at Carburetor

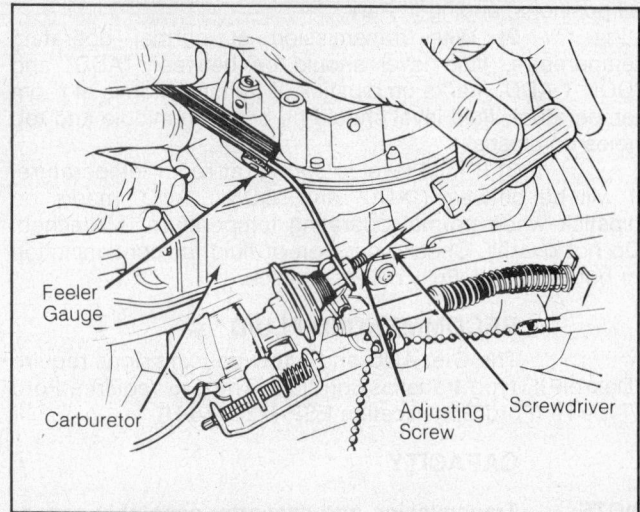

Adjustment at Transmission

1) Ensure engine idle speed is properly set. Rotate fast idle cam on carburetor so throttle lever is at its idle stop. Place transmission selector lever in Neutral and set parking brake.

2) Set linkage lever adjustment screw about mid-range. Raise vehicle and allow exhaust system to cool. Loosen bolt on TV control rod trunnion block at transmission lever. Ensure that trunnion block is free to slide on rod.

3) Push upward on lower end of TV rod (at transmission) to ensure that carburetor linkage is held firmly against throttle lever. Control rod should stay in position when released.

4) Firmly hold TV control lever on transmission upward against internal stop and tighten trunnion block bolt in position. Lower vehicle. Check that throttle lever is against idle stop.

THROTTLE VALVE (TV) CONTROL CABLE SYSTEM

AOD Only (4.9L & 5.0L EFI)
Adjustment at Carburetor/Throttle Body

1) TV control cable is set and locked to its proper length during initial assembly by pushing in locking tab at carburetor/throttle body end of cable assembly. When tab is unlocked, cable is released for adjustment.

FORD LIGHT TRUCKS (Cont.)

Under normal circumstances, it should not be necessary to alter or readjust initial setting of TV control cable.

    2) On 4.9L enigne, Idle Speed Control (ISC) plunger automatically extends when engine is shut off and moves throttle lever to fast idle in preparation for next time engine is started. The ISC plunger must be retracted as follows:

    3) In engine compartment, near right fender well, locate Self Test connector and self test input (STI) connector. These 2 connectors are located next to each other. *See Fig. 5.* Connect a jumper wire between STI connector and Signal Return (ground) of Self Test connector. *See Fig. 6.*

Fig. 5: Location of Self Test Connectors

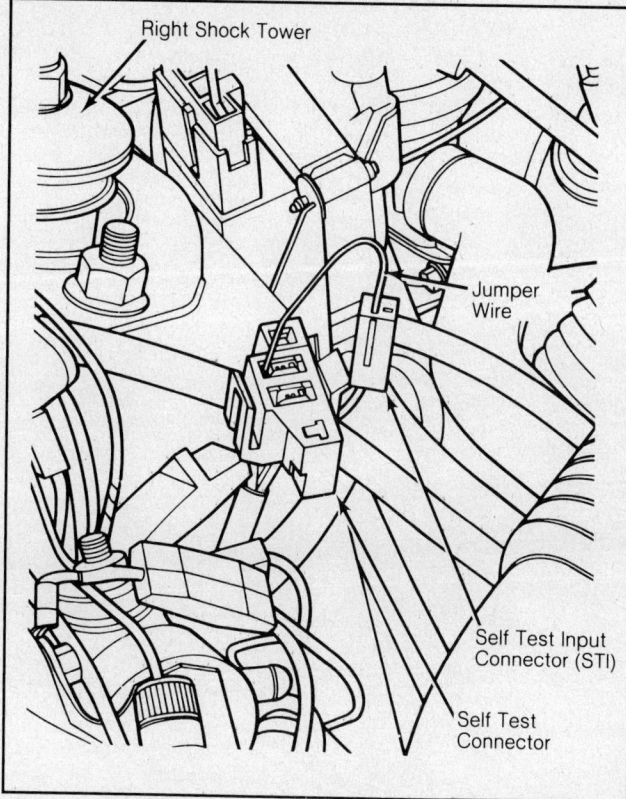

Note location of jumper wire.

Fig. 6: Connecting Ground on Self Test Connectors

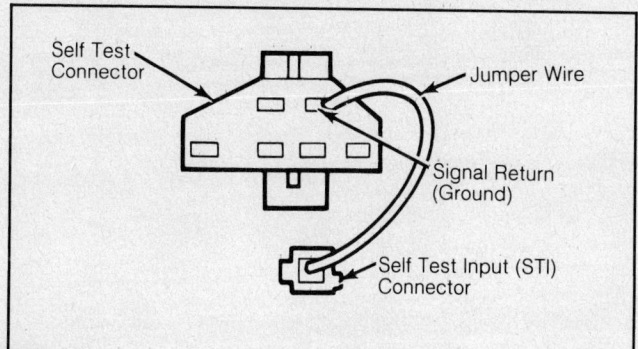

    4) Turn ignition to "Run" position but DO NOT start engine. ISC plunger will retract. Wait until plunger is fully retracted (about 10 seconds). Turn key off. Remove jumper wire and air cleaner.

    5) On 4.9L and 5.0L EFI engines, set parking brake and put selector in "N". Ensure that throttle lever is resting against idle stop. Verify cable routing is free of sharp bends or pressure points and cable operates freely. Unlock locking tab at carburetor/throttle body end by pushing up from below, and prying up rest of way to free cable.

    6) A retention spring must be installed on TV control lever to hold it in idle position (as far to rear as lever will travel) with about 10 lbs. (4.5 kg) of force. If a suitable single spring is not available, 2 throttle return springs may be used. Attach retention spring(s) to transmission TV lever and hook rear end of spring to transmission case.

    7) On 4.9L engines, rotate fast idle cam on carburetor so throttle lever is at its idle stop. Carburetor throttle lever must be in anti-diesel idle position.

    8) Verify take-up spring (carburetor/throttle body end of cable) properly tensions cable. If spring is loose or bottomed out, check for bent cable brackets. Push down on locking key until flush. Remove retention spring(s) from transmission TV lever. On 4.9L engines, reconnect ISC motor.

SHIFT LINKAGE
All Models (Exc. Aerostar)
    1) With engine off and parking brake applied, place shift lever in "D" (Overdrive on AOD). On models with column-mounted shift levers, hold against stop by hanging an 8 lb. (3.6 kg) weight from selector lever.

    2) Loosen nut on slotted shift rod at transmission. Move shift lever at transmission all the way to the rear, then forward 2 steps (4 steps on Bronco II and Ranger). This places lever in "D" position.

    3) On Bronco II and Ranger, apply light forward pressure on shifter control lever. On all models, tighten nut at slotted lever to 144-216 INCH lbs. (16-24 N.m). Remove weight from shift lever. Move lever through all positions, making sure transmission is at full detent in each position.

Aerostar A4LD
    1) From inside vehicle, place shift lever in "D" (Overdrive) position. From below vehicle, loosen adjustment screw on shift cable and remove end fitting from manual lever ball stud.

    2) Position manual lever at transmission in "D" (Overdrive) position by moving lever all the way rearward, and then moving it 3 detents forward. Connect cable end fitting to manual lever.

NOTE: **Too much pressure on shift control lever lower arm can move shifter to "D" (Drive) position. Apply pressure only until resistance of detent notch is felt.**

    3) Tighten adjustment screw to 45-60 INCH lbs. (5-7 N.m). After adjustment, be sure selector lever positively engages in "P" (Park) position. Control lever must move to right when engaged in "P" (Park) detent. Check transmission control lever in all detent positions with engine running to ensure correct detent/transmission action. Readjust if required.

NEUTRAL START SWITCH

NOTE: **Automatic Overdrive and A4DL switches are not adjustable.**

1) With transmission shift linkage properly adjusted, loosen the 2 switch attaching bolts.

2) Place transmission manual lever in Neutral position, then rotate switch and insert a gauge pin (No. 43 drill shank) into gauge pin holes of switch.

3) Gauge pin must be inserted to a full 31/64" into the 3 holes of the switch. Tighten switch attaching bolts and remove gauge pin.

4) Check operation of switch. Engine should start in Neutral and Park positions only.

Fig. 7: Location of Neutral Start Switch

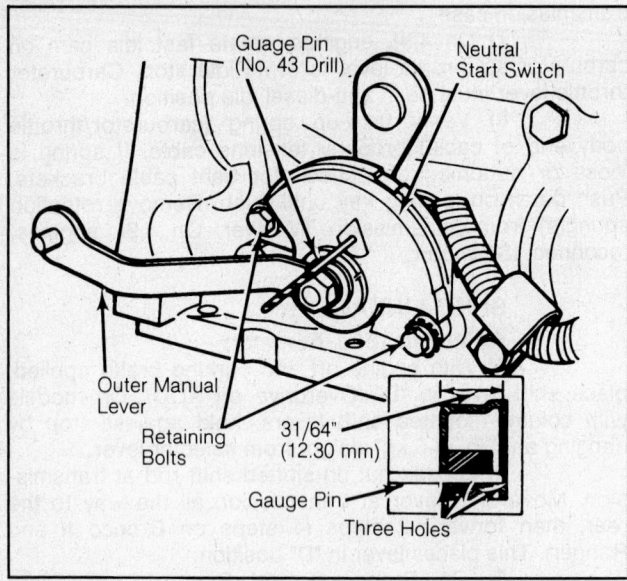

Note the location of the No. 43 Drill.

GENERAL MOTORS LIGHT TRUCKS

LUBRICATION

SERVICE INTERVALS

Check transmission fluid level at each engine oil change. Change transmission fluid and filter at 100,000 mile intervals on vehicles in normal use. If used in severe service conditions (commercial use, trailer pulling, constant stop and go city traffic), change fluid and filter every 15,000 miles.

CHECKING FLUID LEVEL

NOTE: **One pint of fluid will raise level from "ADD" mark to "FULL" mark on dipstick in a hot transmission. Do not overfill.**

With engine at curb idle, move selector lever through all positions, ending in "P". Remove dipstick and touch end cautiously to find out if fluid is cool, warm or hot. Wipe dipstick clean and check level, by temperature, as follows:

COOL (65-85°F)
Fluid level should check between the 2 dimples below "ADD" mark on dipstick.

WARM
Fluid level should check close to the "ADD" mark (either above or below) on dipstick.

HOT
Fluid is hot when it cannot be touched comfortably. Fluid level should check between "ADD" and "FULL" marks on dipstick. If vehicle has been operated for an extended period of time at high speed, in city traffic, or pulling a trailer, an accurate fluid level cannot be immediately determined. Transmission must cool for about 30 minutes, after vehicle is parked, before fluid level is checked.

RECOMMENDED FLUID

Use only DEXRON II automatic transmission fluid, or equivalent.

CAPACITY

NOTE: **Transmission refill capacities given below are approximations. Correct fluid level should always be determined by marks on dipstick, rather than by amount added. DO NOT overfill transmission.**

TRANSMISSION REFILL CAPACITIES

Application	Refill Quantity	Dry Fill Quantity
THM 200C	3.5 qts. (3.3L)	9.5 qts. (9.0L)
THM 350C	3.2 qts. (3.0L)	10.0 qts. (9.5L)
THM 400	4.5 qts. (4.3L)	11.0 qts. (10.4L)
THM 700-R4	5.0 qts. (4.7L)	11.5 qts. (10.9L)

DRAINING & REFILLING

With engine at normal operating temperature, loosen transmission oil pan bolts. Pry pan loose with a large screwdriver and allow fluid to drain. Remove oil pan and gasket. Replace old filter. Install oil pan with new gasket. Add fluid to proper mark on dipstick.

ADJUSTMENT

DETENT (DOWNSHIFT) OR THROTTLE VALVE (TV) CABLE

Diesel Engines

1) Remove cruise control rod (if equipped). Disconnect cable terminal at throttle assembly. Loosen lock nut on pump rod and back off several turns.

2) Rotate throttle lever assembly (at valve body) to full open position and hold. Lengthen pump rod until injection pump lever contacts full throttle stop. Release throttle lever and tighten pump rod lock nut.

Fig. 1: Detent/TV Cable Adjustment Components

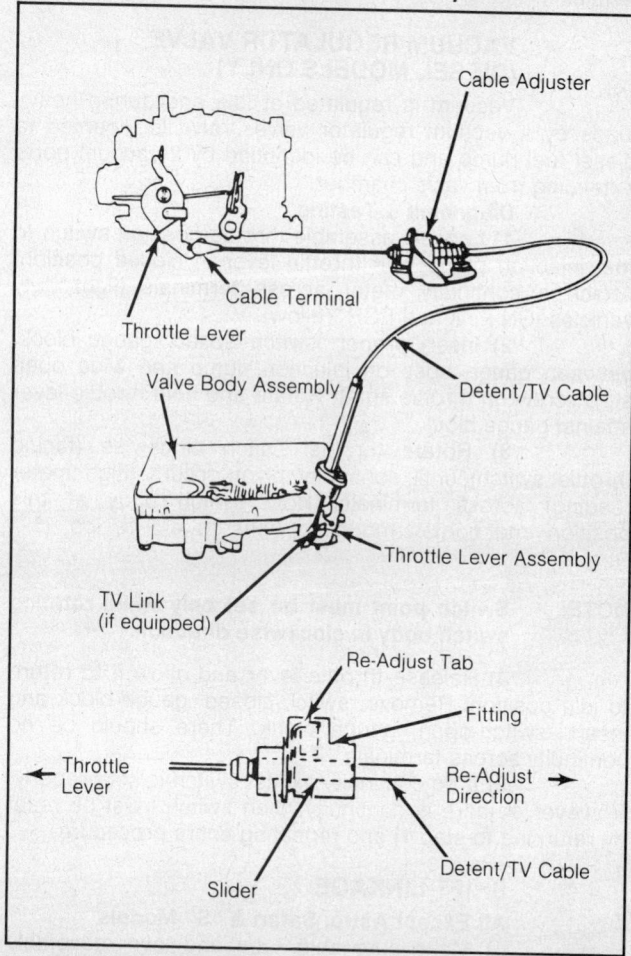

TV cable is used on 200C and 700-R4 transmissions, only. All other models use detent cable.

3) Remove pump rod from lever assembly. Reconnect cable terminal at throttle lever. Depress and hold metal adjusting tab on cable adjuster. Move slider through fitting, away from throttle lever, until slider stops against fitting. Release tab.

4) Rotate lever assembly to full throttle position and release. Reconnect pump rod. If equipped with cruise control, reconnect rod and adjust servo throttle rod to minimum slack with engine off. Put clip in free hole nearest to bellcrank, within servo bail.

Gas Engines

1) Gasoline engine equipped vehicles use "self-adjusting" cables. A brief procedure is required, however, to allow cable to adjust.

GENERAL MOTORS LIGHT TRUCKS (Cont.)

2) Press tab in cable re-adjuster and move slider back through fitting, away from throttle lever, until slider stops against fitting. Release tab. Move throttle lever to full open position. This automatically adjusts cable. Release lever.

DETENT (DOWNSHIFT) SWITCH
THM 400 Only

With engine off, push detent switch plunger as far forward as possible. This presets switch for adjustment. Depress accelerator pedal to wide open position; switch will self adjust. Operation of detent switch circuit can be checked by connecting a test lamp across switch terminals.

VACUUM REGULATOR VALVE (DIESEL MODELS ONLY)

Vacuum is regulated at idle and during heavy loads by a vacuum regulator valve. Valve is mounted to diesel fuel pump and can be identified by 2 vacuum ports extending from valve chamber.

Diagnosis & Testing

1) Loosely assemble throttle position switch to fuel injection pump with throttle lever in closed position. Attach a continuity meter across terminals (light duty vehicles IGN Pink and EGR Yellow).

2) Insert proper "switch-closed" gauge block, between gauge boss on injection pump and wide open stop screw on throttle shaft. Rotate and hold throttle lever against gauge block.

3) Rotate throttle switch clockwise (facing throttle switch) until continuity pivot occurs (high meter reading) across terminals. Hold switch body at this position and tighten mounting bolts to 4-5 ft. lbs. (5-7 N.m).

NOTE: **Switch point must be set only while rotating switch body in clockwise direction.**

4) Release throttle lever and allow it to return to idle position. Remove "switch-closed" gauge block and insert "switch-open" gauge block. There should be no continuity across terminals.

5) If no continuity exists, switch is set properly. However, if there is continuity, then switch must be reset by returning to step 1) and repeating entire procedure.

SHIFT LINKAGE
All Except Astro, Safari & "S" Models

1) Make sure shift tube and lever assembly are free in steering column. Disconnect shift lever rod from swivel at lower column lever. Move transmission lever clockwise to stop, then counterclockwise 2 detents. This is Neutral position. Place selector lever in Neutral. Locate position using mechanical stops, NOT indicator pointer.

2) Slide swivel and clamp onto shift lever rod. Install grommets, washers and nut (as needed) but do not tighten nut. Hold lower column lever against Neutral stop on Park side. Tighten swivel nut to 20 ft. lbs. (27 N.m).

Astro, Safari & "S" Models

1) Make sure shift tube and lever are free in steering column. To adjust linkage, remove screw and spring washer from swivel. Turn transmission lever clockwise to stop, then counterclockwise 2 detents. This is Neutral position.

2) Place selector lever in Neutral. Locate proper position using mechanical stops, NOT indicator pointer. Hold swivel against shift lever, install spring washer and screw and tighten finger tight. Avoid applying force in either direction (along shift rod or lever) while tightening screw to 20 ft. lbs. (27 N.m).

NEUTRAL SAFETY SWITCH
All Models With Column Mounted Switch

Place gearshift selector lever in neutral position and loosen switch attaching screws. Rotate switch on column until a .095" (2.5 mm) gauge pin can be inserted into switch gauge hole to a depth of 3/8" (10 mm). Tighten switch attaching screws and remove gauge pin. Check for engine starting in Neutral and Park only.

All Models With Trans. Mounted Switch

Raise and support vehicle and loosen switch mounting bolts. Align hole in switch lever with hole in switch assembly. Insert a .095" (2.5 mm) gauge pin through switch holes to hold switch in neutral position. With selector lever on transmission in neutral detent position, tighten switch mounting bolts and remove gauge pin. Lower vehicle and check operation of switch.

JEEP

LUBRICATION

SERVICE INTERVALS

Check fluid level and condition of fluid at each engine oil change. Under light duty service conditions, change fluid, replace filter and adjust bands every 28 months or 27,500 miles. Under heavy duty service conditions, change fluid, replace filter and adjust bands every 12 months or 12,500 miles.

CHECKING FLUID LEVEL

1) Park vehicle on level surface and apply parking brake. With engine at normal operating temperature and idling, move transmission selector lever through all gear ranges, ending in Neutral. Check fluid level.

2) Fluid level should be between "FULL" and "ADD ONE PINT" marks on dipstick. Fluid level should never be above "FULL" mark. Make sure dipstick seats properly to seal out water and dirt.

RECOMMENDED FLUID

Use only Dexron II type automatic transmission fluid.

CAPACITY

NOTE: Transmission and converter capacities are approximate only. Fluid level should always be determined by reading on dipstick, rather than amount of fluid added.

TRANSMISSION REFILL CAPACITIES

Application	Quantity
All Models	
Including Converter	8.5 qts. (8.0L)
Without Converter	4.3 qts. (4.0L)

DRAINING & REFILLING

1) Loosen oil pan bolts, tap pan to break it loose and allow fluid to drain. Remove pan. Install new filter on bottom of valve body and tighten retaining screws. Install new "O" ring on fluid pickup pipe (if needed). Clean oil pan and install with a new gasket.

2) Pour 4 quarts of transmission fluid through filler tube. Start engine and allow to run at curb idle for a few minutes. With engine idling and parking brake applied, move shift selector lever through all ranges, ending in neutral. Add fluid up to "ADD ONE PINT" mark on dipstick.

3) With transmission at normal operating temperature, check fluid level. Fluid should be between "ADD" and "FULL" marks on dipstick. Transmission must NOT be overfilled. Seat dipstick fully to seal out water and dirt.

ADJUSTMENT

KICKDOWN (FRONT) BAND

1) Locate kickdown band adjusting screw on left side of case, near throttle lever shaft. Loosen adjusting screw lock nut and back off approximately 5 turns. Make sure adjusting screw turns freely in case.

2) Using adapter tool (J-24063) and 5/16" square socket, tighten screw to 36 INCH lbs. (4 N.m). If adapter is not used, tighten screw to 72 INCH lbs. (8 N.m).

Back off screw 2 1/2 turns. Hold adjusting screw in position and tighten lock nut to 35 ft. lbs. (48 N.m).

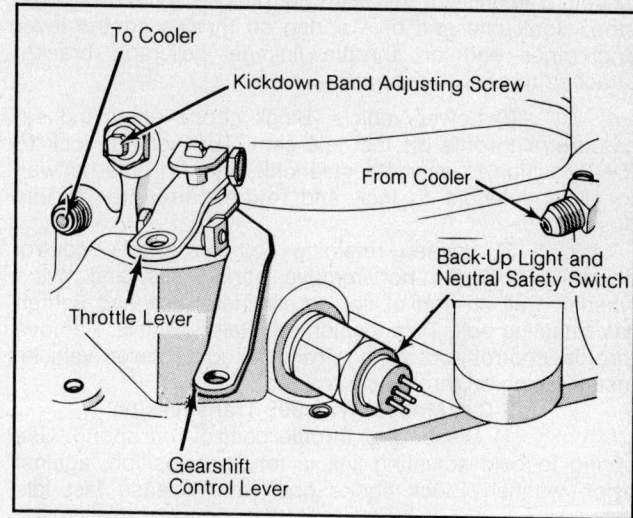

Fig 1: *Kickdown Band Adjusting Screw Location*

Adjust band every 27,500 miles in light duty service, every 12,500 miles for heavy duty service.

LOW REVERSE (REAR) BAND

1) Raise vehicle, drain transmission fluid and remove oil pan. Locate adjusting screw on rear servo lever. Loosen adjusting screw lock nut and back off about 5 turns. Tighten screw to 41 INCH lbs. (4.6 N.m).

2) Back off screw specified number of turns. *See Low-Reverse Band Adjustment Table.* Hold adjusting screw in position and tighten lock nut to 35 ft. lbs. (48 N.m). Install oil pan and fill transmission with fluid.

LOW-REVERSE BAND ADJUSTMENT TABLE

Application	Back Off Screw
Model 727	2 Turns
Model 904	7 Turns
Model 999	4 Turns

Fig. 2: *Adjusting Low-Reverse Band*

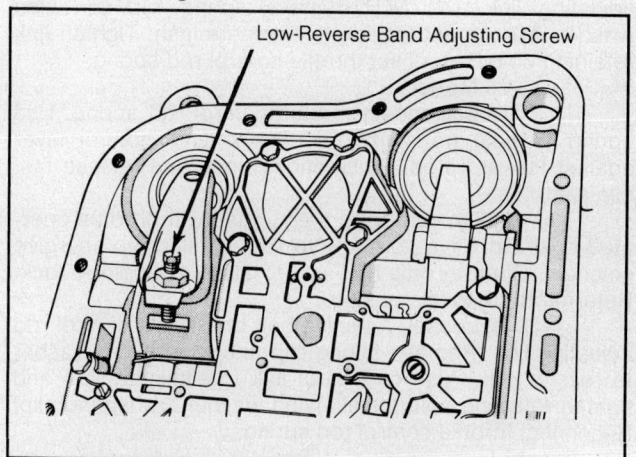

Band should be adjusted whenever oil pan is removed.

JEEP (Cont.)

TRANSMISSION THROTTLE LINKAGE

4-Cyl. Models With 904 Transmission

1) Disconnect throttle control rod spring at carburetor. Raise vehicle. Use throttle control rod spring to hold transmission throttle control lever forward against stop. Hook one end of a spring on throttle control lever and other end on throttle linkage bellcrank bracket attached to converter housing.

2) Lower vehicle. Block choke open and set carburetor throttle off fast idle cam. Turn ignition lock to "ON" position to energize solenoid. Open throttle halfway to allow solenoid to lock and return carburetor to idle position.

3) Loosen retaining bolt on throttle control adjusting link. Do not remove spring clip and nylon washer. Pull on end of link to eliminate lash and tighten link retaining bolt. Turn ignition off. Raise vehicle. Remove throttle control rod spring from linkage. Lower vehicle. Install spring on throttle control rod.

6-Cyl. Models With 999 Transmission

1) Disconnect throttle control rod spring. Use spring to hold adjusting link in forward position, against nylon washer. Block choke open and release fast idle cam.

2) Raise vehicle. Loosen both retaining bolts on adjusting link clamp. DO NOT remove spring clip or nylon washer.

3) Use a spare spring to hold transmission throttle lever against forward stop.

4) Push adjusting link to eliminate lash and pull clamp to rear so bolt in rod bottoms in rear of slot in rod. Tighten forward clamp retaining bolt.

5) Pull throttle control rod to rear so bolt in rod bottoms in front of slot and tighten rear retaining bolt. Remove spare spring. Lower vehicle and reconnect throttle control rod spring.

6-Cyl. Models With 727 Transmission

1) Disconnect throttle control rod spring. Use spring to hold transmission throttle control lever forward, against stop. Block choke open and release fast idle cam.

2) On carburetors equipped wih throttle operated solenoid valve, turn key to "ON" position to energize solenoid. Open throttle half-way to allow solenoid to lock. Return throttle to idle position.

3) Loosen retaining bolt on throttle control adjusting link. DO NOT remove spring clip or nylon washer. Pull on end of link to eliminate lash. Tighten link retaining bolt. Reconnect throttle control rod spring.

V8 Models

1) Disconnect throttle control rod spring. Use spring to hold transmission throttle valve control lever against forward stop. Block choke open and release fast idle cam.

2) On carburetors equipped with throttle operated solenoid valve, turn key to "ON" position to energize solenoid. Open throttle half-way to allow solenoid to lock. Return throttle to idle position.

3) Loosen retaining bolt on throttle control rod adjusting link. Remove spring clip and slide nylon washer to rear of link. Push on end of link to eliminate lash and tighten retaining bolt. Install nylon washer and spring clip. Reconnect throttle control rod spring.

NEUTRAL SAFETY SWITCH

1) Switch combines functions of neutral safety switch and back-up light switch. With transmission linkage properly adjusted, switch should allow starter operation in "P" and "N" only.

2) To test switch, remove wire connector and test for continuity between center pin of switch and case. Continuity should only exist when transmission is in "P" or "N". Check for continuity between 2 outer pins. Continuity should exist with transmission in "R" only. There should be no continuity between either outer pin and transmission case. If these conditions are not met, the switch should be replaced.

3) Remove switch from case and allow fluid to drain into a container. Move selector lever to "P" and "N" positions and check that switch operating fingers are centered in switch opening. Install switch and new seal and tighten. See Fig. 3.

Fig. 3: Back-Up Light/Neutral Safety Switch Location

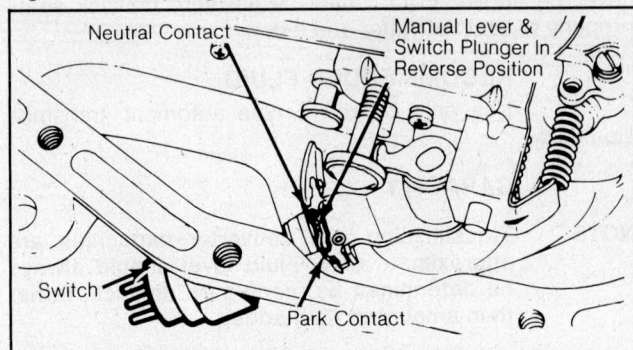

When installing switch, tighten to 24 ft. lbs. (33 N.m).

SHIFT LINKAGE

1) Loosen shift rod trunnion jam nuts at transmission lever. Remove lock pin retaining shift rod to bellcrank. Disengage trunnion and shift rod. Place selector lever in "P" position and lock steering column. Move transmission shift lever to full rear (Park) position.

2) Adjust shift rod trunnion to obtain free pin fit in bellcrank arm. Tighten jam nuts. Make sure gearshift linkage lash is eliminated by pulling downward on shift rod and pushing upward on outer bellcrank when tightening jam nuts.

3) Check steering column lock for ease of operation. Check that engine starts in "N" or "P", only. If starter engages in any drive gear, or does not work in "N" or "P", check for proper shift linkage adjustment or faulty neutral safety switch.

AMERICAN MOTORS

REMOVAL & INSTALLATION

TORQUE-COMMAND 998
Removal

NOTE: **Transmission and converter must be removed as an assembly to prevent damage to drive plate, pump bushing, and oil seal.**

1) Open hood. Disconnect fan shroud (if equipped). Disconnect transmission filler tube at upper bracket. Place transmission in Neutral. Raise vehicle on a hoist.

NOTE: **Hood must remain open during tranmission removal to prevent damage to hood and air cleaner when rear crossmember is removed.**

2) Mark propeller shafts and yokes for installation reference. Remove propeller shafts and skid plate. Disconnect exhaust pipe from manifold and move it aside to provide working clearance.

3) Remove converter housing inspection cover. Remove tranmission filler tube. Remove starter and sfiffening braces.

4) Remove speedometer adapter and cable assembly. Plug adapter bore in case. Disconnect gearshift and throttle linkage. If equipped with column shift, remove linkage, and bellcrank bracket-to-converter housing bolt. Disconnect neutral safety switch wires.

5) Mark converter drive plate and converter for installation reference. Remove converter-to-drive plate attaching bolts.

NOTE: **Use a ratchet and socket on crankshaft front pulley bolt to rotate crankshaft and drive plate for access to converter attaching bolts.**

6) Support transmission and transfer case with a transmission jack. Retain tranmission on jack with safety chain. Lower transmission slightly and disconnect oil cooler lines at transmission.

7) Remove rear support cushion-to-transmission attaching bolts. Remove crossmember. Remove engine-to-transmission attaching bolts.

8) Move transmission, transfer case and converter rearward to clear crankshaft. Hold converter in place and lower tranmission assembly until converter housing clears engine.

Installation
1) If torque converter was removed, insert Pump Aligner (J-24033) into pump. Engage pump rotor, rotate tool until drilled hole is vertical, then remove tool. Rotate converter until pump drive slots are vertical and carefully install converter into pump.

2) Using a transmission jack, raise assembly and align converter with drive plate (aligning marks made during removal). Move transmission forward, carefully aligning bellhousing pilot holes with dowels in engine.

3) Install 2 lower bellhousing attaching bolts and pull housing up snug. Install remaining bolts and tighten all bellhousing bolts. To complete installation, reverse removal procedures.

MB 1 TRANSAXLE
Removal

NOTE: **Engine and transaxle must be removed as an assembly.**

1) Disconnect negative battery cable. Drain transaxle oil and engine oil. Drain cooling system from bottom of radiator and from cylinder block.

2) Remove air cleaner assembly. Remove radiator. Disconnect wire harness connectors attached to engine assembly. Disconnect vacuum hoses that would interfere with engine removal. Disconnect ground cable from transaxle.

3) Disconnect accelerator cable. Remove exhaust pipe clamp from exhaust manifold. Remove heater hoses, and set aside. Disconnect power brake booster vacuum hose.

4) Remove the 2 selector lever bracket retaining bolts and spacers, and remove gearshift selector lever assembly. Disconnect the automatic transaxle booster vacuum hoses.

5) Remove front wheels. Using Extractor (T.Av. 476), remove tie rod end ball joints. Remove brake calipers and suspend from vehicle body using wire.

6) Remove axle shaft on left side by removing 3 bolts attaching boot plate, and remove shock absorber bottom mounting bolts. Tilt stub axle assembly to release axle shaft. Use care to avoid damaging boot at wheel end.

7) Remove axle shaft on right side by removing roll pins holding axle shaft to sun wheel. Remove shock absorber bottom mounting bolts and withdraw axle shaft. Do not damage boot at wheel end.

8) Using an engine hoist, support engine/transaxle assembly. Remove front and rear engine and transaxle mounting nuts, then carefully lift engine/transaxle assembly from vehicle.

Installation
To install, reverse removal procedure and note the following: Fill enigne and transaxle oil sumps to correct fluid level. See AUTOMATIC TRANSMISSION SERVICING in this section. Fill and purge cooling system. Use new bolts when installing exhaust pipe clamp.

TIGHTENING SPECIFICATIONS

Application	Ft. Lbs. (N.m)
Torque Command 998	
Converter-to-Flywheel	22 (30)
Rear Mount-to-Transmission	30 (41)
Transmission-to-Engine	30 (41)
MB 1 Transaxle	
Engine Mount	25 (35)
Exhaust Flange Bolts	20-26 (29-35)
Tie Rod End	25 (35)
Transaxle-to-Engine	31 (42)

Automatic Transmission Removal

CHRYSLER CORP. DOMESTIC CARS

REMOVAL & INSTALLATION

TORQUEFLITE (RWD MODELS)

Removal

1) Disconnect negative battery cable. Remove engine to transmission struts (if equipped). Remove cooler lines at transmission. Remove cooler line bracket, starter motor and torque converter cover. Loosen oil pan bolts, tap pan to break it loose allowing fluid to drain. Reinstall pan.

NOTE: Some models require that exhaust system be dropped for clearance.

2) Mark converter and drive plate for installation reference. Using a socket wrench on crankshaft vibration damper bolt, rotate engine clockwise to position converter attaching bolts for removal. Mark propeller shaft and yoke for installation reference. Remove propeller shaft.

3) Disconnect electrical leads. Disconnect gearshift rod, torque shaft assembly, and throttle rod lever from left side of transmission. Remove linkage at bellcrank (if so equipped) from transmission.

4) Remove oil filler tube and speedometer cable. Support rear of engine with safety stand. Raise transmission slightly to relieve load on mounts. Remove bolts securing transmission mount-to-crossmember and crossmember-to-frame. Remove crossmember.

5) Remove converter housing-to-engine attaching bolts. Carefully work transmission and converter assembly rearward off engine block dowels, and disengage converter hub from end of crankshaft.

NOTE: Attach a small "C" clamp to edge of converter housing to hold torque converter in place during transmission removal.

6) Lower transmission and remove from under vehicle. To remove converter assembly, remove "C" clamp from edge of converter housing, and carefully slide assembly out of transmission.

Installation

CAUTION: If transmission was removed to correct a malfunction that generated sludge or heavy accumulations of metal or friction material particles, the oil cooler and and cooler lines must be thoroughly flushed and torque converter replaced.

1) To install, reverse removal procedures and note the following: To install the converter, rotate pump rotors with pump tool C-3756 for A-904-LA until 2 small holes in handle are vertical.

2) Carefully slide converter over input shaft and reaction shaft. Make sure converter hub slots are also vertical and fully engage pump inner rotor lugs. Test for full engagement by placing a straightedge on face of case. Surface of converter front cover lug should be at least 1/2" to rear of straightedge when converter is pushed all the way into transmission.

3) Attach a small "C" clamp to converter housing to hold converter in place during transmission installation. Inspect converter drive plate for distortion or cracks and replace if necessary. Coat converter hub hole in crankshaft with multi-purpose grease.

NOTE: When drive plate replacement is necessary, make sure both transmission dowel pins are

in engine block and that they are protruding far enough to hold transmission in alignment.

4) Place transmission and converter assembly on a transmission jack and position under vehicle for installation. Raise or tilt as necessary to align transmission to engine. Rotate converter so mark on converter (made during removal) will align with mark on drive plate.

5) Offset holes in drive plate are located next to 1/8" hole in inner circle of plate. A stamped "O" identifies offset hole in converter.

6) Carefully work transmission assembly forward over engine block dowels with converter hub entering crankshaft opening. Place transmission in position rear of engine. Install and tighten all bolts. Adjust shift and throttle linkage. Refill transmission with DEXRON II automatic transmission fluid.

7) To complete installation, reverse removal procedures. Tighten bolts holding strut-to-transmission before tightening strut-to-engine bolts (on models equipped with engine-to-transmission struts).

REMOVAL & INSTALLATION

All FWD MODELS (A-413 & A-470 Transaxle)

Removal

1) Disconnect negative battery cable. Disconnect throuttle linkage and shift linkage from transaxle. Remove upper and lower oil cooling lines. Install engine support fixture. Remove hub cotter pin and castle nut. Raise vehicle on a hoist.

2) Remove front wheels. Remove left splash shield. Remove speedomater cable from housing. Disconnect sway bar and remove pinch bolts at lower control arm ball joint. Pry control arm down to remove ball joint. Remove drive axles frm hub.

3) Remove drive axles from transaxle and from vehicle. Remove torque converter dust cover. Mark torque converter and flex-plate and remove flex-plate bolts. Remove access plug (in right shield) to rotate engine. Remove neutral safety switch connector.

4) Remove engine mount bracket from front crossmember. Remove front mount through-bolt and bell housing bolts. Position a jack under transaxle. Remove left engine mount. Lower transaxle on jack. Pry engine for clearance and remove transaxle from vehicle.

Installation

To install, reverse removal procedures. Adjust throttle and shift linkage as necessary. Fill transaxle and differential sumps to correct level when installation is completed. Road test vehicle. *See AUTOMATIC TRANSMISSION SERVICING in this section.*

TIGHTENING SPECIFICATIONS

Application	Ft. Lbs. (N.m)
Torqueflite	
Converter-to-Flywheel	22 (30)
Rear Mount-to-Transmission	30 (41)
Transmission-to-Engine	30 (41)
A-413 & A-470 Torqueflite	
Ball Joint Bolt	50 (68)
Converter-to-Flywheel	40 (54)
Mount-to-Transaxle	40 (54)
Transaxle-to-Engine	70 (95)

FORD MOTOR CO. DOMESTIC CARS

REMOVAL & INSTALLATION

ZF (Diesel Engines)
Removal

1) Remove T.V. cable from injection pump side lever and cable bracket. Place gear selector into "N". Raise vehicle and drain transmission. Remove shifter linkage. Remove positon sensor from converter housing. Remove stiffener brace to engine.

2) Support transmission with a jack. Mark position of torque converter to flex-plate and remove flex-plate bolts. Mark position of yokes and remove drive shaft. Disconnect electrical harnesses. Remove extension housing damper. Remove bolts and rear crossmember.

3) Remove rear exhaust support. On Continental with column shift, remove 2 bolts securing bellcrank bracket. Using push connector service tool (T82L-9500-AH), disconnect oil cooling lines. Disconnect speedometer wiring harness. Remove starter motor.

4) Secure transmission to jack with a chain and lower jack sightly. Remove 4 bellhousing bolts. Remove filler tube and dipstick. Remove transmission from engine. Mount transmission in a holding fixture.

Installation

To install transmission, reverse the removal procedures. Ensure flex-plate bolts are secure and fluid levels are correct. Road test vehicle. *See AUTOMATIC TRANSMISSION SERVICING in this section.*

AUTOMATIC OVERDRIVE & C-3 (Gasoline Engines)
Removal

1) Raise and support vehicle. Place drain pan under transmission oil pan, then loosen pan bolts and allow transmission fluid to drain. Remove converter drain plug access cover and adapter plate bolts from lower end of converter housing.

2) Remove the 4 flex-plate nuts. Using a wrench on crankshaft pulley bolt, turn engine to gain access to nuts.

CAUTION: On belt driven overhead camshaft engines, NEVER turn engine backwards.

3) Place a drain pan under converter, then remove converter drain plug and allow fluid in converter to drain. After all fluid has drained, reinstall drain plug and tighten.

4) Mark position of yokes and remove propeller shaft and install a seal remover tool in extension housing to prevent fluid leakage. Disconnect speedometer cable from extension housing. Disconnect shift rod and downshift rod from transmission levers.

5) Remove starter bolts and place starter out of the way. Disconnect neutral safety switch wires from switch and vacuum line from transmission vacuum unit. Position jack under transmission and raise it slightly.

6) Remove crossmember bolts from engine rear support and frame side support, then remove crossmember. Remove inlet pipe steady rest from inlet pipe and rear engine support, then disconnect muffler inlet pipe at exhaust manifold and secure it out of way.

7) Lower transmission jack and place a screw jack under front of engine to gain access to the 2 upper converter housing-to-engine attaching bolts.

8) Disconnect oil cooling lines at transmission and plug all openings to prevent entry of dirt. Remove lower converter housing-to-engine attaching bolts.

9) Remove transmission filler tube. Secure transmission to jack with a safety chain. Remove the 2 upper converter housing-to-engine attaching bolts. Slide transmission to the rear and down to remove it from vehicle.

Installation

1) If not previously done, tighten torque converter drain plug. Position converter to transmission making sure the converter hub is fully engaged in pump gear.

2) With converter correctly installed, place transmission on a jack and secure with safety chain. Rotate converter so that drive studs and drain plug are in alignment with holes in flywheel.

3) With transmission mounted on jack, move converter and transmission assembly forward into position being careful not to damage flywheel and converter pilot. Install the 2 upper converter housing-to-engine attaching bolts and tighten.

CAUTION: Do not allow transmission to get into a nosed down position as this will cause converter to move forward and disengage from pump gear. Converter must rest squarely against flywheel.

4) To complete installation, reverse removal procedure and note the following: Fill transmission with fluid to proper level. *See AUTOMATIC TRANSMISSION SERVICING in this section.* Adjust manual and downshift linkage as required.

C-5
Removal

1) Disconnect negative battery cable. If equipped with a 3.8L engine, remove air cleaner and disconnect thermactor air tube to catalytic converter check valve. Remove fan shroud. On 3.8L engines, remove 2 bolts from top of bellhousing.

2) Raise vehicle on a hoist and drain transmission. Mark postion of yokes and remove drive shaft. Remove muffler inlet pipe from catalytic converter outlet. Remove header pipe from exhaust manifold. Remove catalytic converter. Remove speedometer cable from housing. Remove electrical wiring harnesses and kick down rod.

3) Disconnect shifter linkage. Remove torque converter cover and remove flex-plate bolts. Remove starter motor. Loosen nuts on rear crossmember. Support transmission with a jack and remove bolts from rear crossmember. Lower transmission and remove oil cooling lines.

4) Remove converter housing to engine bolts. Disengage transmission from engine and lower transmission from vehicle.

Installation

To install reverse removal procedure, and note the following: Adjust manual and downshift linkage. Fill transmission with fluid to proper level. *See AUTOMATIC TRANSMISSION SERVICING in this section.*

CAUTION: The converter must rest squarely against flywheel. This indicates that converter pilot is not binding in engine crankshaft.

Automatic Transmission Removal

FORD MOTOR CO. DOMESTIC CARS (Cont.)

ATX TRANSAXLE

Removal (Escort, EXP & Lynx)

1) Disconnect negative battery cable. Remove bolts attaching managed air valve-to-valve body cover. Disconnect wiring from neutral safety switch. Disconnect throttle valve linkage and manual lever cable at respective levers.

2) Remove the 2 upper transaxle-to-engine attaching bolts. Raise and support vehicle. Remove control arm-to-steering knuckle attaching bolt and nut (at ball joint). Repeat this step on remaining side. Use a pry bar to separate control arms from steering knuckles.

CAUTION: **Use care not to damage ball joint boot with pry bar when separating control arms from steering knuckles. Pry bar must not contact lower arm.**

3) Remove bolts attaching stablizer bar brackets to frame. Remove stabilizer bar-to-control arm attaching nut and washer. Pull bar out of control arms.

4) Remove bolts attaching brake hose routing clips to suspension strut brackets. Disconnect tie rod ends from steering knuckles. Pry axle shaft out of right side of transaxle and position shaft on transaxle housing.

5) Using a driver, inserted through right side differential side gear, drive left axle shaft from differential side gear. Pull axle shaft from transaxle and support out of way. Install plugs (T81P-1177-B) into differential seals to prevent spline misalignment.

6) Remove starter support bracket and disconnect starter cable. Remove starter. Remove transaxle support bracket. Remove dust cover from torque converter housing, then remove flex-plate nuts.

7) Remove nuts attaching left front insulator to body bracket, bracket-to-body bolts and remove bracket. Remove left rear insulator bracket attaching nut.

8) Disconnect oil cooling lines at transaxle. Remove bolts attaching manual lever bracket to transaxle case. Position transmission jack under transaxle and remove the 4 remaining transaxle-to-engine attaching bolts.

9) Insert a screwdriver between flex-plate and torque converter, and carefully move transaxle and converter away from engine. When converter studs are clear of flywheel, lower transaxle slightly (2-3"). Disconnect speedometer cable and lower transaxle from vehicle.

NOTE: **If transaxle contacts body before converter studs clear flex-plate, remove left front insulator.**

Installation

1) To install, reverse removal procedure, and note the following: Prior to installing axle shaft, replace snap ring on CV joint stub shaft.

2) To install axle shaft, carefully align splines on shaft with differential splines. Push CV joint until snap ring is felt to seat in groove in side gear.

3) Attach lower ball joint to steering knuckle, taking care not to damage or cut ball joint boot. Install new service pinch bolt, and install new nut.

4) Fill transaxle with fluid to proper level. See *AUTOMATIC TRANSMISSION SERVICING* in this Section.

Removal (Tempo & Topaz)

NOTE: **Engine/Transaxle are removed as assembly.**

1) Mark hinges for reinstallation. Remove hood. Disconnect negative battery cable. Remove air cleaner assembly. Drain cooling system. Remove upper and lower radiator hoses. If equipped, disconnect transmission oil cooling lines at hoses below radiator.

2) Remove coil assembly. Disconnect cooling fan. Remove radiator shroud and fan as assembly. Remove radiator. Discharge A/C system and disconnect hoses at compressor. Disconnect all electrical and vacuum lines.

3) Disconnect T.V. linkage. Disconnect accelerator linkage, fuel lines at engine, and thermactor discharge hose at pump.

4) If equipped, disconnect power steering hoses at pump. Remove hose bracket at cylinder head. Attach engine support tool to lifting eye. Raise vehicle.

5) Remove starter cable, hose from catalytic converter, exhaust pipe bracket bolt at oil pan, and exhaust pipe-to-manifold nuts. Remove exhaust system from grommets and set aside. Disconnect speedometer cable at transaxle.

6) Disconnect heater hoses at engine. Remove water pump inlet tube and clamps. Disconnect control arms at body. Remove stabilizer bar brackets. Remove axle shaft assemblies and install alignment plugs in differential side gears. See *AXLE SHAFT Removal and Installation* in DRIVE AXLE Section.

7) Disconnect manual shift cable clip and remove manual shift linkage bracket. Remove left-hand rear insulator mount bracket. Remove left-hand front insulator-to-transaxle mount bolts. Lower vehicle. Attach engine hoist to lifting eyes. Remove engine support tool.

CAUTION: **Do not allow front wheels to touch floor.**

8) Remove right-hand insulator intermediate bracket from engine bracket and insulator. Lower engine/transaxle assembly to floor.

Installation

1) To install, reverse removal procedure, and note the following: Prior to installing axle shaft, replace snap ring on CV joint stub shaft.

2) To install axle shaft, carefully align splines on shaft with differential splines. Push CV joint until snap ring is felt to seat in groove in side gear.

3) Attach lower ball joint to steering knuckle, taking care not to damage or cut ball joint boot. Install new service pinch bolt, and install new nut.

4) Fill transaxle with fluid to proper level. See *AUTOMATIC TRANSMISSION SERVICING* in this Section.

TIGHTENING SPECIFICATIONS

Application	Ft. Lbs. (N.m)
C-3, C-5 & AOT	
Bell Housing-to-Engine	
3.8L & 5.0L	28-38 (38-52)
2.3L & AOT	40-50 (54-68)
Converter Drain Plug	8-23 (11-31)
Converter-to-Flywheel	
C-3	27-49 (37-67)
AOT & C-5	20-34 (27-46)
Oil Cooler Line	7-10 (10-14)
Escort, EXP, Lynx, Tempo & Topaz	
Ball Joint Bolt	36-44 (50-60)
Converter-to-Flywheel	23-39 (31-53)
Oil Pan-to-Transaxle	30-39 (41-53)
Transaxle-to-Engine	25-33 (34-45)

GENERAL MOTORS DOMESTIC CARS

REMOVAL & INSTALLATION
THM 180C, THM 200C, THM 200-4R
& THM 700-R4 (RWD MODELS)
Removal

1) Disconnect negative battery cable. Remove air cleaner, T.V. cable at its upper end, and oil dipstick and tube. Raise vehicle on a hoist. Mark position of yokes and remove drive shaft.

NOTE: **On Corvette models, remove complete exhaust system and driveline beam. On Camaro and Firebird, remove torque arm from rear suspension. On Cadillac, remove header pipe at exhaust manifold, catalytic converter, and fuel line to transmission bracket.**

2) Remove floor reinforcement (if used). Remove speedometer cable at transmission. Remove shifter linkage and electrical connectors. Remove flexplate cover. Mark flexplate and torque converter and remove bolts.

3) On gasoline engines, remove catalytic converter support bracket. Remove transmission support to transmission mount bolts and transmission support to frame bolts (and insulators, if used). Support and raise transmission slightly.

4) Slide transmission support rearward to remove. Lower transmission to gain access to oil cooling lines and T.V. cable attachments. Support engine with a screw jack and remove transmission to engine bolts. Remove transmission being careful not to damage cables, lines or linkage. Install holding torque converter holding tool (J-21366) and lower transmission from vehicle.

Installation

1) To install transmission, reverse removal procedures noting the following: Observe marks made during disassembly and line-up in original positions.

2) Make sure weld nuts on torque converter are flush with flexplate.

3) Test torque converter for freedom of rotation.

4) Tighten flexplate bolts finger tight, then tighten to specifications.

THM 325-4L (TRANSAXLE)
Removal

(Riviera, Eldorado & Seville, Toronado)

1) Remove negative battery cable, air cleaner and speedometer cable at transaxle. Remove turbo, if equipped. On diesel models, install cover (J-26996-1) and remove T.V. cable from bellcrank. On gasoline engines, remove T.V. cable from actuating lever.

2) Remove top left final drive to transaxle bolt and 5 accessible transaxle to engine bolts. Disconnect air line to catalytic converter and remove bolt on back of engine to air tube from catalytic converter.

3) Raise vehicle on a hoist and drain transmission. Remove shift cable, starter motor, wiring connectors and oil cooling lines. Plug cooling line openings. Remove 3 bolts and lower torque converter cover. Mark flexplate and torque converter to aid in reassembly. Remove 3 flexplate bolts.

4) Disconnect header pipe at exhaust manifold. Remove catalytic converter. Remove 4 bolts and crossmember. Support transaxle with a jack and remove right side transaxle mount through-bolt. Remove 3 bolts and right side mount bracket. Remove right side bottom transaxle to engine bolt.

5) Remove remaining final drive to transmission bolts. Remove light side mount through-bolt. Remove 6 bolts and left side mount bracket. Move transmission back 1" (25 mm) away from frame to gain access. Lower transmission and seperate from final drive.

Installation

1) Reverse removal procedure and note the following: Install new transaxle-to-final drive gasket. To assist in the engagement of final drive to transmission splines, ensure all mounting faces are in alignment with each other.

2) After splines are engaged, loosely install 2 final drive-to-transaxle lower attaching bolts. After final drive and transaxle are mated, align transaxle bell housing with engine and install remaining attaching bolts.

3) Before installing flexplate bolts, make sure that the weld nuts on converter are flush with flexplate and the converter rotates freely by hand in this position. Hand start all 3 bolts and then tighten. This will ensure proper converter alignment.

4) Adjust shift linkage and T.V. cable as necessary. Fill transaxle to proper level with fluid. *See AUTOMATIC TRANSMISSION SERVICING in this section.*

THM 125C & 440-T4 (TRANSAXLE)
Removal (Celebrity, 6000, Ciera, Century, Citation II & Skylark)

NOTE: **Anytime the cradle assembly is removed or lowered from vehicle, the rack and pinion steering assembly must be properly disconnected from the cradle. The rack and pinion steering assembly must then be supported in a manner in which it is not allowed to "hang" by the intermediate shaft. Failure to do so will result in damage to the intermediate shaft.**

1) Disconnect negative battery cable. Remove air cleaner, wiring and cable routing clips and straps. Remove bolt securing T.V. cable to transaxle. Install engine support (J-28467). Raise vehicle on a hoist. Drain transaxle fluid. Remove strut shock bracket bolts and oil cooling lines from transaxle.

2) Remove transaxle to engine bolts leaving bolt near starter loosely installed. Remove speedometer cable at upper and lower couplings. Remove shifter linkage retaining clip, washer and bracket from transaxle.

3) Remove front and left sections of cradle. Position axle shaft removal tool (J-33008) and slide hammer (J-2619-01) behind axle shaft cones and pull cones away from transaxle. Pull left axle shaft out of transaxle and plug bore to minimize fluid leakage.

4) Rotate strut so axle shaft is out of way. Remove starter motor and converter shields. Mark torque converter and remove flex-plate bolts. Remove 2 transaxle extension bolts from engine to transaxle. Remove rear transaxle mount bracket. (It may be necessary to raise transaxle).

5) Support transaxle with a jack. Remove 2 braces to right end of transaxle boots. Remove remaining transaxle to engine bolt (located near starter). Slide transaxle from engine, toward driver's side. Lower transaxle from vehicle.

Automatic Transmission Removal

GENERAL MOTORS DOMESTIC CARS (Cont.)

Removal (Cavalier, Sundbird, Firenza, Skyhawk, Cimarron, Grand Am, Calais & Somerset Regal)

1) Disconnect negative battery cable. Remove air cleaner and T.V. cables from carburetor and transaxle. On 3.0L engines, remove mass air flow air intake duct. Remove shift linkage and wiring routing clips and straps.

2) Remove dipstick tube and install engine holding fixture (J-28467). On Cavalier, Sunbird, Firenza, Skyhawk and Cimarron, insert a 1/4" x 2" bolt in hole at front right motor mount to maintain driveline alignment. Remove nut securing wiring harness to transaxle.

3) Remove wiring connectors from transaxle. Disconnect shifter linkage. Remove top 2 transaxle to engine bolts and left upper transaxle bracket and mount. Remove rubber hose from transaxle to vent pipe. Remove remaining upper engine to transaxle bolts.

4) Raise vehicle on a hoist. Remove front wheels. Drain transaxle. Remove shift linkage bracket from transaxle. Remove lower ball joints from control arms. Remove and support axles. Remove transaxle mounting strut. Remove left stabilizer bar link pin bolt and left stabilizer bar frame bushing clamp nuts.

5) Remove left frame support assembly. Remove header pipe at exhaust manifold (if equipped with 1.8L). Remove speedometer cable and starter motor. Remove torque converter cover. Mark position of flex-plate and torque converter. Remove flexplate bolts. Remove oil cooling lines. Remove transaxle to engine support bracket. Position jack under transaxle. Remove remaining engine to transaxle bolts. Slide transaxle from engine and lower from vehicle.

Installation (All Models)

To install, reverse removal procedure and note the following: As transaxle is being installed, guide right axle shaft into transaxle. Adjust T.V. and shift cables. Refill transaxle to proper fluid level. *See AUTOMATIC TRANSMISSION SERVICING in this section.*

THM 125C (TRANSAXLE)
Removal (Fiero)

1) Remove air cleaner and negative battery cable. Remove ground strap, shift cable and T.V. cable at transaxle. Remove electrical connectors. Remove upper transaxle-to-engine bolts. Install engine support fixture (J-28467).

NOTE: **Remove neutral start switch connector in a straight horizontal movement. DO NOT rock or tip connector when removing. Contacts may bend, preventing proper operation when reconnected.**

2) Raise vehicle. Remove rear wheels. Remove both axle shafts. *See DRIVE AXLE removal and installation*

procedures in *DRIVE AXLES* section. Remove catalytic converter heat shield. Remove header pipe at manifold. Remove cradle nuts-to-engine and transaxle. Support cradle. Remove remaining cradle nuts and lower cradle out of way.

3) Remove oil cooling lines. Remove starter shield and starter. Mark position of flex-plate and torque converter. Remove flexplate nuts. Position jack under transaxle. Remove lower transaxle-to-engine bolts. Lower transaxle from vehicle.

Installation

Reverse removal procedure and note the following: Adjust T.V. and shift cables. Refill transaxle to proper level with fluid. *See AUTOMATIC TRANSMISSION SERVICING in this section.*

NOTE: **In the following table the letter "A" refers to Celebrity, 6000, Ciera and Century. The letter "X" refers to Citation II and Skylark. The letter "J" refers to Cavalier, Sunbird, Firenza, Skyhawk & Cimarron.**

TIGHTENING SPECIFICATION

Application	Ft. Lbs. (N.m)
THM 180C, 200C, 200-4R & 700-R4	
Converter Housing-to-Engine	35 (47)
Transmission-to-Mount	35 (47)
Torque Converter-to-Flexplate	35 (47)
THM 125C (Fiero)	
Engine Mount-to-Cradle	40 (54)
Torque Converter-to-Flexplate	35 (47)
Front Cradle-to-Body	67 (90)
Rear Cradle-to-Body	76 (103)
Transaxle-to-Engine	55 (75)
Transaxle Mount-to-Cradle	
Front	36 (48)
Rear	18 (24)
THM 125C & 440-T4 (Except Fiero)	
Converter Housing-to-Engine	55 (75)
Cooler Lines	16 (22)
Front Cradle Assembly	
"J" Body Models	65 (88)
Torque Converter-to-Flexplate	
"A" & "X" Body Models with 4.3L Diesel	35 (47)
All Others	35 (47)
Transaxle-to-Mount Nuts	40 (54)
THM 325-4L	
Converter Housing-to-Engine	35 (47)
Cooler Lines	16 (22)
Final Drive-to-Transaxle	30 (41)
Transaxle-to-Frame Mount	40 (54)
Torque Converter-to-Flexplate	35 (47)

CHRYSLER CORP. RWD LIGHT TRUCKS

TRANSFER CASE
MODEL NP-205
Removal

1) Raise vehicle, remove plug and drain transfer case. Replace plug. Disconnect speedometer cable. Remove skid plate, crossmember and strut rods as needed. Disconnect propeller shafts and wire out of way. Do not allow propeller shafts to hang free, as damage to universal joints may result.

2) Disconnect shift lever rod from shift rail link. Support transfer case and remove transfer case-to-transmission adapter bolts. Move transfer case to rear until input shaft clears adapter. Lower transfer case from vehicle.

Installation

Reverse removal procedures to install transfer case. Ensure that all attaching bolts are tight. Fill transfer case with lubricant.

MODEL NP-208
Removal

1) Raise vehicle, remove plug and drain transfer case. Mark front and rear output shaft yokes and propeller shafts for reassembly reference. Disconnect speedometer cable and indicator switch wires. Disconnect shift lever link from operating lever.

2) Support transfer case with transmission jack and remove crossmember. Disconnect front and rear propeller shafts at yokes and wire to frame.

3) If necessary, disconnect parking brake cable guide from pivot on right frame rail. Remove bolts attaching exhaust pipe support bracket to transfer case. Remove transfer case-to-transmission bolts. Move assembly to the rear until clear of output shaft. Lower transfer case from vehicle.

4) Remove all gasket material from rear of transmission adapter housing.

Installation

Install new transmission-to-transfer case gasket with sealer on both sides. Align transfer case with transmission. Rotate transfer case output shaft until transmission output shaft engages transfer case input shaft. Move transfer case until case seats flush against transmission. Install transfer case attaching bolts. Reverse removal procedures to complete installation.

TRANSMISSION

ALL MODELS

NOTE: **Transmission and converter must be removed and installed as an assembly to prevent damage to converter drive plate, front pump bushing, and oil seal. DO NOT allow weight of transmission to rest on plate during removal or installation.**

Removal

1) Remove transfer case from 4WD vehicles. Disconnect negative battery cable. Disconnect lower exhaust system as needed for removal clearance. Remove engine-to-transmission struts (if equipped). Disconnect cooler lines at transmission. Remove starter, cooler line bracket and converter access cover.

2) Loosen oil pan bolts, tap pan to break loose and allow fluid to drain. Reinstall pan. Rotate crankshaft clockwise with socket on vibration damper bolt to gain access to converter-to-drive plate bolts. Remove bolts. Mark propeller shaft for reassembly reference and remove from vehicle.

NOTE: **Crankshaft flange bolt circle, inner and outer circle of holes in drive plate and tapped holes in converter all have 1 hole offset so parts can only be installed in original position.**

3) Disconnect wiring connector from back-up light/neutral safety switch. Disconnect gearshift rod and torque shaft assembly from transmission. Disconnect transmission throttle rod from lever. Remove linkage bellcrank assembly, if equipped. Remove oil filler tube. Disconnect speedometer cable.

4) Install an engine support fixture under rear of engine. Raise transmission with service jack to relieve load on suports. Remove bolts securing crossmember to transmission and frame, then remove crossmember. Remove all converter housing-to-engine attaching bolts.

5) Carefully work transmission and converter assembly rearward off engine block dowel pins, disengaging converter hub from end of crankshaft. Attach a small "C" clamp on edge of converter housing to hold converter in place while transmission is being removed. Lower transmission and remove from vehicle.

Installation

1) Before installing converter, rotate front pump rotors with alignment tool (C3881) until 2 small holes in tool handle are vertical. Slide torque converter over input and reaction shafts, making sure converter hub slots are vertical, and fully engage pump inner rotor lugs.

2) Test for full engagement by placing a straightedge across face of transmission case. Surface of converter front cover lug should be at least 1/2" to rear of straightedge when converter is fully engaged. Attach a small "C" clamp to edge of converter housing to hold converter in place while installing transmission.

3) Inspect converter drive plate for distortion or cracks and replace if necessary. Install drive plate and tighten bolts to 55 ft. lbs. (75 N.m).

4) Coat converter hub hole in crankshaft with multi-purpose grease. Place transmission assembly on jack and position under vehicle. Make sure marks on converter and drive plate (made during removal) are aligned. Carefully work transmission assembly into position over dowels. Install all converter housing-to-engine retaining bolts. Tighten bolts to 30 ft. lbs. (41 N.m).

5) To install reverse removal procedure. Adjust shift and throttle linkages and fill transmission with fluid. On 4WD models, install transfer case.

TIGHTENING SPECIFICATIONS

Application	Ft. Lbs. (N.m)
Converter Housing-to-Engine	30 (41)
Cooler Line Fitting	15 (20)
Drain & Fill Plugs	
NP-205 Transfer Case	30 (41)
NP-208 Transfer Case	18 (24)
Oil Pan Bolts	13 (18)
Torque Converter-to-Drive Plate Bolts	22 (30)
Transfer Case-to-Transmission	40 (54)

Automatic Transmission Removal

CHRYSLER CORP. FWD LIGHT TRUCKS

TRANSAXLE

ALL MODELS

NOTE: Transaxle removal does not require engine removal.

CAUTION: Transaxle and torque converter must be removed as an assembly; other wise, the torque converter drive plate, pump bushing or oil seal may be damaged. The drive plate will not support a load; therefore, none of the weight of the transaxle should be allowed to rest on the plate during removal.

Removal

1) Disconnect battery negative cable. Disconnect throttle linkage and shift linkage from transaxle. Remove upper and lower oil cooler hoses. Support engine using an engine support fixture. Remove bell housing upper bolts. Remove hub castle lock, nut and cotter pin.

2) Raise vehicle and remove front wheels. Remove wheel hub nut and driveshafts. Remove left splash shield. Remove speedometer adapter, cable and pinion as an assembly. Disconnect sway bar. Remove both lower ball joint-to-steering knuckle bolts.

3) Pry lower ball joint from steering knuckle. Remove driveshaft from hub. Remove both driveshafts. Remove dust cover, mark torque converter and drive plate, and remove torque converter mounting bolts. Remove access plug in right splash shield to rotate engine crankshaft.

4) Remove neutral safety switch connector. Remove engine mount bracket from front crossmember. Remove front mount insulator through-bolt and bell housing bolts. Position transmission jack under transaxle. Remove left engine mount. Remove starter and lower bell housing bolts.

5) Slowly lower transaxle. It may be necessary to pry at engine to provide for clearance.

Installation

To install, reverse removal procedure. Be sure to adjust gearshift and throttle cables. Refill transaxle with Dexron II type automatic transmission fluid.

TIGHTENING SPECIFICATIONS

Application	Ft. Lbs. (N.m)
Bell Housing Cover	9 (12)
Flex Plate-to-Crankshaft	
A-413	65 (88)
A-470	100 (136)
Flex Plate-to-Torque Converter	40 (54)
Transaxle-to-Cylinder Block	70 (95)
Lower Bell Housing Cover	9 (12)
Manual Control Lever	9 (12)
Speedometer-to-Extension	5 (7)
Starter-to-Transaxle Bell Housing	40 (54)
Throttle Cable-to-Transaxle Case	9 (12)
Throttle Lever-to-Transaxle Shaft	9 (12)
Manual Cable-to-Transaxle Case	21 (28)
Front Motor Mount	40 (54)
Left Motor Mount	40 (54)

FORD LIGHT TRUCKS

TRANSFER CASE

NP-208 (BRONCO, F-150 & F-250)
Removal

1) Raise and support vehicle. Remove drain plug and drain fluid from transfer case. Replace plug. Disconnect 4WD indicator switch connector at transfer case. Disconnect speedometer driven gear from transfer case rear bearing retainer.

2) Remove transmission shift lever-to-transfer case retaining nut. Remove skid plate from frame. Support transfer case with transmission jack. Disconnect front and rear propeller shafts from transfer case output shaft yokes and wire out of way. Do not allow shafts to hang free as damage to universal joints may result.

3) Remove transfer case-to-transmission adapter bolts. Remove gasket between transfer case and adapter and lower transfer case out of vehicle.

Installation

To install transfer case, reverse removal procedures. Fill case with 7 pints (3.3 liters) of Dexron II type automatic transmission fluid.

BORG-WARNER 1345 (F-150–F350)
Removal

1) Raise vehicle. Remove drain plug and drain fluid from transfer case. Replace plug. Disconnect 4WD indicator switch connector at transfer case. If equipped, remove skid plate.

2) Disconnect front and rear propeller shafts from transfer case output shaft yokes, and wire out of way. Do not allow shafts to hang free as damage to universal joints may result.

3) Disconnect speedometer driven gear from rear bearing retainer. Remove retaining clips and shift rod from transfer case control and transfer case shift levers. Disconnect vent hose from case.

4) Remove heat shield. Support transfer case with transmission jack, remove transfer case-to-transmission adapter bolts and slide transfer case off of transmission output shaft (towards rear). Lower transfer case out of vehicle and remove gasket from between transfer case and adapter.

Installation

Reverse removal procedures to install transfer case. Fill case with 6.5 pints (3.1 liters) of Dexron II type automatic transmission fluid.

BORG-WARNER 1350
(BRONCO II & RANGER)
Removal

1) Raise vehicle. Remove skid plate (if equipped). Remove drain plug and drain fluid from case. Replace plug. Disconnect 4WD indicator switch connector at transfer case. Disconnect front propeller shaft from front axle. Loosen front shaft boot clamp and slide out propeller shaft and boot as an assembly.

2) Disconnect rear propeller shaft from transfer case. Disconnect speedometer driven gear from transfer case rear cover. Disconnect vent hose from control lever.

3) Loosen or remove large and small bolts (1 each) retaining shifter to extension housing. Pull on control lever until bushing slides off transfer case shift lever pin. Unscrew shift lever from control lever, as needed.

4) Remove heat shield from transfer case. Support transfer case with jack and remove transfer case-to-transmission extension housing bolts (5). Slide transfer case to the rear and off of transmission output shaft. Lower case from vehicle. Remove gasket from between transfer case and extension housing.

Installation
Reverse removal procedures to install transfer case, noting the following:

1) When installing shift lever assembly, tighten large bolt first, then small bolt.

2) When installing vent assembly, White marking on hose should be positioned in notch in shifter with upper end of hose 2 inches above top of shifter, inside of shift lever boot.

3) Before installing front propeller shaft into transfer case, lubricate female splines of transfer case input shaft with multi-purpose grease.

4) Fill transfer case to bottom of fill plug hole with Dexron-II automatic transmission fluid.

TRANSMISSION

A4LD (BRONCO II & RANGER)
Removal
1) Raise vehicle on hoist. Place drain pan under transmission fluid pan. Starting at rear of pan and working toward front, loosen attaching bolts and allow fluid to drain.

2) Remove all pan attaching bolts except 2 at front, to allow fluid to further drain. After all fluid has drained, install 2 bolts on rear side of pan to temporarily hold it in place.

3) Remove converter access cover and adapter plate bolts from lower end of converter housing. Remove 4 flywheel to converter attaching nuts. Crank engine to turn converter to gain access to nuts, using a wrench on crankshaft pulley attaching bolt.

NOTE: On belt driven overhead camshaft engines, never turn engine backwards.

4) Remove driveshaft and install extension housing seal replacer tool in extension housing. Remove speedometer cable from extension housing. Disconnect shift rod at manual lever and downshift rod at dowshift lever.

5) Remove starter-to-converter housing attaching bolts and position starter out of way. Disconnect neutral start switch wires from switch. Remove vacuum line from vacuum modulator.

6) Position a jack under transmission and raise slightly. Remove engine rear support-to-crossmember bolts. Remove crossmember-to-frame side support attaching bolts and remove crossmember insulator and support and damper,

7) Lower jack and allow transmission to hang. Position jack at front of engine and raise engine to gain access to 2 upper converter housing-to-engine attaching bolts. Disconnect oil cooler lines at transmission

8) Plug all openings to keep out dirt. Remove lower converter housing-to-engine attaching bolts. Remove transmission filler tube. Secure transmission to jack with a safety chain.

9) Remove 2 upper converter housing-to-engine attaching bolts. Move transmission to rear and down to remove it from under vehicle.

Installation
To install, reverse removal procedure. Ensure full converter engagement in transmission before installing it. During installation, keep transmission in a "nose-up" position at all times to prevent disengagement of the torque converter and pump gear.

A4LD (AEROSTAR)
Removal
1) Raise vehicle on hoist. Place drain pan under transmission. Starting at rear of pan and working toward front, loosen attaching bolts and allow fluid to drain.

2) Remove all bolts except the 2 at front to allow further draining. After all fluid has been drained, install 2 bolts on rear side of pan also to temporarily retain pan.

3) Remove converter access cover and adapter plate bolts from lower end of converter housing. Remove 4 flywheel-to-converter nuts by placing a 22 mm socket and breaker bar on crankshaft pulley attaching bolt. Rotate pulley clockwise to gain access to each of the nuts.

CAUTION: On belt driven overhead cam engines, never rotate pulley in a counterclockwise direction.

4) Scribe a mark indexing driveshaft to rear axle pinion flange. Remove "U" bolts and nuts retaining driveshaft to flange. Remove driveshaft. Install an extension housing seal replacer tool in housing to prevent fuel spillage.

5) Remove speedometer cable from extension housing. Disconnect neutral start switch wires and converter clutch solenoid. Remove kickdown cable from upper selector lever. Remove retaining clip from selector cable bracket.

6) Remove selector cable from ball stud on lower selector lever. Depress tab on retainer and remove kickdown cable from bracket. Disconnect vacuum hose from transmission vacuum modulator.

7) Disconnect relay-to-starter cable at starter terminal. Remove starter mounting bolts and ground cable. Remove starter. Remove filler tube from transmission. Position transmission jack under transmission. Place a safety chain around transmission. Slightly raise transmission.

8) Remove insulator crossmember retaining nuts. Remove crossmember-to-frame side support attaching nuts nad bolts. Remove crossmember. If required, remove bolts retaining insulator to transmission and remove insulator.

9) Remove converter housing-to-engine fasteners. Slightly lower jack to gain access to oil cooler lines. Disconnect oil cooler lines at transmission. Plug all openings to keep dirt and contamination out.

Automatic Transmission Removal

FORD LIGHT TRUCKS (Cont.)

10) Move transmission to rear so it disengages from dowel pins and converter is disengaged from flywheel. Lower transmission from vehicle.

NOTE: If transmission is to be removed for a period of time, support engine with a safety stand and wood block.

Installation

To install, reverse removal procedure. Make sure torque converter rotates freely and is not bound up. Replace fluid and check for leaks.

C-5 (F-150)

Removal

1) Disconnect battery negative cable. On 4WD vehicles, remove filler tube bracket bolt from valve cover bracket. On all models, raise and support vehicle. Drain transmission fluid and replace pan. Remove converter drain plug access cover. On 2WD models, remove adapter plate bolts from lower end of converter housing.

2) On all models, remove converter-to-flex plate attaching nuts and converter drain plug. Allow fluid to drain from converter, then reinstall and tighten drain plug. On 2WD models, mark propeller shaft for reassembly. Disconnect shaft at rear axle and slide out of transmission.

3) On all models, disconnect battery cable from starter motor and remove starter. Disconnect neutral start switch wires at connector. Remove rear mount-to-crossmember nuts and 2 crossmember-to-frame bolts. Remove right and left gussets. On 4WD vehicles, remove rear insulator-to-extension housing bolts (2).

4) On all models, disconnect throttle valve (TV) linkage rod from transmission TV lever. Disconnect manual rod from manual lever at transmission. On 4WD models, disconnect downshift and manual linkage rods from levers on transmission. Remove vacuum hose from diaphragm unit. Remove vacuum line from retaining clip.

5) On all models, remove bellcrank housing-to-converter housing bolts (2). Remove transfer case (4WD models). Raise transmission enough to allow removal of crossmember. Remove rear mount from crossmember, then remove crossmember.

6) Lower transmission as needed to disconnect oil cooler lines. Disconnect cooler lines. Disconnect speedometer cable from extension housing. On 2WD models, remove transmission filler tube-to-engine bolt and lift filler tube out of transmission.

7) On all models, secure transmission to jack with safety chain. Remove converter housing-to-engine bolts. Carefully remove transmission and converter assembly from vehicle.

Installation

To install transmission, reverse removal procedures, noting the following:

1) Ensure that converter is fully engaged with pump gear before installation.

2) When installing filler tube, install a new "O" ring on bottom of tube.

3) On 2WD models, when installing damper assembly over engine rear support studs, make sure that the painted surface of the damper is facing forward when installed in vehicle.

4) Before installing rear propeller traft, apply a small amount of multi-purpose grease to splines of yoke.

C-6 ("E" SERIES)

Removal

1) Working inside vehicle, remove engine compartment cover and disconnnect electrical leads at plug connector. Remove flex hose from air cleaner heat tube (V8 models only), then remove upper converter housing-to-engine attaching bolts. Remove fluid filler tube-to-engine bolt.

2) Raise vehicle, drain transmission pan and remove converter drain plug access cover. Remove converter-to-flex plate attaching nuts and converter drain plug. Drain fluid and replace drain plug.

3) Disconnect propeller shaft. Remove filler tube. Disconnect starter cable and remove starter. Position an engine support bar to side rail and oil pan flanges. Disconnect oil cooler lines and vacuum lines from transmission.

4) Remove speedometer driven gear from extension housing and manual and downshift linkage rods from transmission control levers. Support transmission with transmission jack and secure with safety chain.

5) Remove bolts and nuts securing rear mount to crossmember and bolts retaining crossmember to side rails. Remove 2 support inserts, raise transmission with jack and remove crossmember. Remove remaining converter housing-to-engine bolts and lower assembly out of vehicle.

Installation

Reverse removal procedures to install, noting the following: Be sure that converter is fully engaged with pump gear during installation. Always use a new "O" ring on the end of the fluid filler tube. When installation is complete, fill transmission with Dexron II type automatic transmission fluid.

C-6 (BRONCO & "F" SERIES)

Removal

1) Disconnect negative cable from battery. Remove 2 upper converter housing-to-engine bolts. Raise vehicle, drain transmission pan and remove converter drain plug access cover.

2) Remove converter-to-flex plate attaching nuts and converter drain plug. Allow fluid to drain, then reinstall and tighten converter drain plug. On 2WD models, disconnect propeller shaft at rear axle and slide shaft out of transmission.

3) On all models, disconnect speedometer cable from extension housing. Disconnect downshift and manual linkage rods from levers at transmission. Disconnect oil cooler lines from transmission.

4) Remove vacuum line from vacuum unit. Remove vacuum line retaining clip. Disconnect starter cable from starter and remove starter. On 4WD models, remove transfer case.

5) On all models, remove 2 rear crossmember-to-frame attaching bolts. Remove 2 rear support-to-extension housing attaching bolts and 6 bolts securing second crossmember to frame side rails.

6) Raise transmission with a transmission jack and remove both crossmembers. Secure transmission to the jack with safety chain. Remove remaining converter housing-to-engine attaching bolts. Move transmission away from engine, lower the jack and remove converter and transmission assembly from vehicle.

FORD LIGHT TRUCKS (Cont.)

Installation

Reverse removal procedure to install, noting the following: Make sure that torque converter is fully engaged in transmission before and during installation. When installing fluid filler tube, always use a new "O" ring on end of tube. When installation is complete, fill transmission with Dexron II type automatic transmission fluid.

AUTOMATIC OVERDRIVE
(E-150/250, F-150/250 & BRONCO)
Removal

1) Disconnect negative battery cable. Raise vehicle and drain transmission fluid. Remove converter drain plug access cover. Remove converter-to-flex plate attaching nuts and torque converter drain plug. Drain converter, then reinstall and tighten converter drain plug.

2) Disconnect propeller shaft from rear axle and remove shaft from transmission. Disconnect starter cable and remove starter. Disconnect neutral start switch wires at connector.

3) Remove rear mount-to-crossmember bolts and crossmember-to-frame bolts. Remove bolts securing engine rear support to extension housing. Disconnect TV linkage rod and manual rod from transmission levers.

4) Remove bellcrank bracket-to-converter housing bolts (2). Raise transmission with jack and remove crossmember. Lower transmission enough to remove oil cooler lines.

5) Disconnect speedometer cable from extension housing. Remove bolt securing filler tube to engine and remove filler tube. Secure transmission to jack with safety chain. Remove converter housing-to-engine bolts. Move transmission to rear and down to remove from vehicle.

Installation

Reverse removal procedures to install transmission, noting the following: Ensure that converter is fully seated in transmission before and during installation procedure. Install new "O" ring on end of fluid filler tube before installing tube. When installation is complete, fill transmission with Dexron II type automatic transmission fluid.

TIGHTENING SPECIFICATIONS

Application	Ft. Lbs. (N.m)
Converter Housing-to-Engine	
C-5	40-50 (55-67)
C-6	
Gas Engine	40-50 (55-67)
Diesel Engine	50-65 (67-87)
AOT	40-50 (55-67)
A4LD	28-38 (38-51)
Converter-to-Flex Plate	
A4LD	20-34 (27-46)
All Others	20-30 (28-40)

GENERAL MOTORS LIGHT TRUCKS

TRANSFER CASE

NP-205 (30 SERIES)
Removal

1) Raise and support vehicle on hoist. Drain transfer case. Disconnect speedometer cable. Remove skid plate and crossmember supports as necessary. Disconnect rear drive shaft from transfer case and tie up away from work area.

2) Disconnect front drive shaft from transfer case and tie up shaft away from work area. Disconnect shift lever rod from shift rail link. Support transfer case and remove bolts attaching transfer case to transmission adapter.

3) Move transfer case to rear until input shaft clears adapter and lower assembly from vehicle.
Installation
To install, reverse removal procedure.

NP-207 ("S" SERIES)
Removal

1) With transfer case shift lever in "4 Hi" position, disconnect negative battery cable. Raise vehicle and remove skid plate. Drain transfer case. Mark front and rear output shaft yokes and propeller shafts for reassembly reference and remove shafts.

2) Disconnect speedometer cable and vacuum harness from transfer case. Remove shift lever from case. Remove catalytic converter hanger bolts at converter. Raise transmission and transfer case assembly with jack and remove transmission mount bolts. Remove mount.

3) Lower complete assembly. Support transfer case alone and remove transmission-to-transfer case bolts. Remove shift lever bracket from transfer case adapter in order to reach upper left attaching bolt.

4) Separate transfer case from transmission adapter and remove from vehicle.
Installation
Reverse removal procedures to install. Always use a new gasket between the transfer case and adapter.

NP-208 (10 & 20 SERIES)
Removal

1) Place transfer case in "4H". Raise vehicle. Drain lubricant from transfer case. Remove cotter pin from shift lever swivel. Mark transfer case front and rear output shaft yokes and propeller shafts for assembly alignment reference.

2) Disconnect speedometer cable and indicator switch wires. Disconnect front drive shaft at transfer case yoke. Disconnect parking brake cable guide from pivot located on right frame rail, if necessary. Remove engine strut rod from transfer case.

3) Place support under transfer case and remove transfer case-to-transmission adapter bolts. Move transfer case assembly rearward until free of transmission output shaft and remove assembly. Remove all gasket material from rear of transmission adapter housing.
Installation
To install, reverse removal procedure.

GENERAL MOTORS LIGHT TRUCKS (Cont.)

TRANSMISSIONS

ALL MODELS EXCEPT ASTRO/SAFARI VAN, "S" & "K" SERIES

Removal

1) Disconnect negative battery cable. Remove air cleaner and disconnect TV or detent cable at carburetor. Remove dipstick and filler tube support bracket bolt. Raise and support vehicle. Mark propeller shaft for reassembly reference and remove from vehicle.

2) Disconnect speedometer cable and shift linkage and all electrical leads from transmission. Remove transmission support brackets (if present) and flywheel inspection cover.

3) Mark flex plate and torque converter for reassembly in same position and remove torque converter-to-flex plate bolts. Disconnect catalytic converter support bracket (if equipped).

4) Remove transmission rear mount bolts. Support transmission with jack and raise slightly. Remove transmission support-to-frame bolts and insulators. Remove support.

5) Lower transmission enough to remove oil cooler lines and TV or detent cable from transmission. Disconnect lines and cable. Support engine with jack and remove transmission-to-engine bolts.

6) Disconnect transmission assembly from engine. Install torque converter retaining tool (J-21366) and remove transmission from vehicle.

Installation

To install, reverse removal procedure and note the following: Before installing flex plate-to-converter bolts, make certain that the weld nuts on converter are flush with the flex plate and the converter rotates freely by hand in this position. Install converter-to-flex plate bolts (3) and tighten finger tight before tightening to proper specification.

ASTRO/SAFARI VAN

Removal

1) Open hood and disconnect negative cable at battery. Remove engine cover. Disconnect T.V. cable at its upper end. Raise vehicle. Remove propeller shaft. Disconnect speedometer cable at transmission. Disconnect shift linkage at transmission.

2) Disconnect all electrical leads at transmission and any clips that retain leads to transmission case. Remove transmission support brace attaching bolts at converter. Disconnect exhaust crossover pipe from exhaust manifolds.

3) Remove converter cover and mark flywheel and torque converter to maintain original balance. Remove torque converter to flywheel bolts and/or nuts. Position a transmission jack under transmission and raise it slightly.

4) Remove transmission crossmember to mount bolts and crossmember to frame bolts (and insulator if used). Slide crossmember rearward and remove from vehicle. Lower transmission to gain access to oil cooler lines and T.V. Cable attachments. Disconnect oil cooler lines and T.V. cable. Cap all openings.

5) Support engine with a suitable tool and remove transmission to engine bolts. Disconnect transmission assembly, being careful not to damage any cables, lines or linkage. Install torque converter holding tool J-21366 and remove transmission assembly from vehicle.

Installation

To install, reverse removal procedure.

"K" SERIES

Removal

1) Disconnect negative battery cable. Remove air cleaner and disconnect TV or detent cable at carburetor. Remove transfer case shift lever knob and boot. Raise and support vehicle.

2) Mark propeller shafts for reassembly reference and remove from vehicle. Disconnect speedometer cable, shift linkage and all electrical leads from transmission and transfer case. Disconnect transfer case shift linkage.

3) Remove transmission support strut rods and flywheel inspection cover. Mark flex plate and converter for reassembly reference. Remove torque converter-to-flex plate retaining bolts.

4) Disconnect transmission oil cooler lines from transmission. Support transmission and transfer case assembly with a jack and remove transfer case-to-frame bracket bolts. Remove mount bolts and crossmember.

5) Remove transmission/transfer case assembly mounting bolts and remove assembly from vehicle. Separate transmission from transfer case.

Installation

Reverse removal procedures to install, noting the following: Before installing flex plate-to-converter bolts, make certain that the weld nuts on converter are flush with the flex plate and the converter rotates freely by hand in this position. Then, hand start all 3 bolts and tighten finger tight before tightening to specifications.

"S" SERIES

NOTE: On 4WD models, refer to Transfer Case removal procedures to remove transfer case.

Removal

1) Disconnect negative battery cable. Remove air cleaner and disconnect TV cable at carburetor. On models with 1.9L 4-cylinder engine, remove upper starter retaining nut. On all models, raise and support vehicle.

2) Mark propeller shaft for reassembly reference and remove shaft. Disconnect speedometer cable, shift linkage and all electrical leads from transmission. Remove brake line to crossmember clips and remove crossmember (4WD only).

3) Remove transmission support brace bolts and converter cover (if equipped). Remove exhaust crossover pipe and converter attaching bolts. Remove crossover and converter as an assembly.

4) Remove flywheel inspection plate and mark flex plate and torque converter for reassembly reference. Remove torque converter-to-flex plate bolts. Disconnect catalytic converter support bracket.

5) Place a jack under transmission and raise slightly. Remove transmission support-to-mount bolt and support-to-frame bolts and insulators. Remove left body mounting bolts and loosen radiator support mount bolt.

6) Raise cab on left side as needed to remove upper transmission-to-engine bolts. Support cab with wood block between body and frame. Slide transmission support towards rear and lower transmission enough to remove oil cooler lines and TV cable. Disconnect lines and cable.

GENERAL MOTORS LIGHT TRUCKS (Cont.)

7) Support engine with jack and remove remaining transmission-to-engine bolts. Slide transmission away from engine and install torque converter retaining tool (J-21366) to prevent converter damage as transmission is removed from vehicle. Remove transmission.

Installation

Reverse removal procedures to install, noting the following: Before installing flex plate-to-converter bolts, make certain that the weld nuts on converter are flush with the flex plate and the converter rotates freely by hand in this position. Then, hand start all 3 bolts and tighten finger tight before tightening to specifications.

TIGHTENING SPECIFICATIONS

Application	Ft. Lbs. (N.m)
Transmission-to-Engine	
"S" Series	25 (34)
All Others	35 (47)

TIGHTENING SPECIFICATIONS

Application	Ft. Lbs. (N.m)
Converter-to-Flex Plate	
"S" Series	35 (47)
All Others	35 (47)
Transmission Mount-to-Crossmember	
"S" Series	25 (34)
All Others	35 (47)
Transmission-to-Mount	
"S" Series	35 (47)
All Others	35 (47)
Crossmember-to-Frame	
"S" Series	25 (34)
All Others	35 (47)
Transfer Case-to-Adapter	
"S" Series	20-25 (27-34)
All Others	25 (34)
Transmission-to-Adapter	25 (34)

JEEP

TRANSFER CASE

MODEL NP-207

Removal

1) Shift transfer case into "4H" position. Raise and support vehicle. Drain lubricant from transfer case. Mark rear axle yoke and drive shaft for installation reference. Remove rear drive shaft. Disconnect speedometer cable, vacuum hoses and vent hose from transfer case.

2) Raise transmission and transfer case and remove transmission crossmember attaching bolts. Remove crossmember and lower transmission and transfer case. Mark transfer case front output shaft flange and drive shaft for installation reference.

3) Disconnect front drive shaft from transfer case. Disconnect shift lever linkage rod at transfer case. Remove shift lever bracket bolts. Support transfer case and remove transfer case attaching bolts. Remove tranfer case assembly.

Installation

To intall, reverse removal procedure.

MODEL NP-208

Removal

1) Raise vehicle. Drain lubricant from transfer case. Disconnect speedometer cable and indicator switch wires and disconnect transfer case shift lever link at operating lever. Place a safety stand under transmission and remove the rear crossmember.

2) Mark transfer case front and rear output shaft yokes and drive shafts for assembly alignment reference. Disconnect front and rear drive shafts at transfer case yokes. Secure shafts to frame rails with wire. Disconnect parking brake cable guide from pivot located on right frame rail, if necessary.

3) Remove bolts attaching exhaust pipe support bracket-to-transfer case, if necessary. Remove transfer case-to-transmission bolts. Move transfer case assembly rearward until free of transmission output shaft and remove assembly. Remove all gasket material from rear of transmission adapter housing.

Installation

To install, reverse removal procedure.

MODEL NP-229

Removal

1) Raise and support vehicle. Drain lubricant from transfer case. Disconnect speedometer cable and vent hose. Disconnect transfer case shift lever link at operating lever. Place a safety stand under transmission and remove rear crossmmember.

2) Mark transfer case front and rear output shafts at transfer case yokes and drive shafts for installation alignment reference. Disconnect front and rear drive shafts at transfer case yokes. Secure Shafts. Disconnect shift motor vacuum hoses.

3) Disconnect transfer case shift linkage. Remove transfer case-to-transmission bolts. Move transfer case assembly rearward until clear of transmission oupput shaft and remove assembly. Remove all gasket material from rear of transmission adapter housing.

Installation

To install, reverse removal procedure.

MODEL NP-300

Removal

1) Remove floor covering, if equipped and remove transmission access cover from floorpan. Raise vehicle and drain lubricant from transfer case. Position support stand under clutch housing to support engine and transmission and remove rear crossmember.

2) Disconnect front and rear drive shafts at transfer case. Mark drive shaft yokes for assembly reference. Disconnect speedometer cable at transfer case. If necessary, disconnect parking brake cable at equalizer. Disconnect exhaust pipe support bracket at transfer case, if equipped. Remove bolts attaching transfer case to transmission and remove tranfer case.

Installation

To install, reverse removal procedure.

TRANSMISSION

ALL MODELS

Removal

1) Disconnect fan shroud and transmission fill tube upper bracket. Raise vehicle. Remove converter inspection cover and fill tube. Remove starter.

2) Mark drive shafts for reassembly. Disconnect shafts at transfer case and wire to frame rails. DO NOT allow shafts to hang free as damage to universal joints may result. On V8 models, disconnect exhaust pipes from exhaust manifolds. Drain transfer case lubricant. Disconnect speedometer cable from transmission.

3) Disconnect all shift and throttle linkages and wiring from transmission and transfer case. Mark converter drive plate and converter for reassembly and remove torque converter-to-drive plate bolts. Rotate crankshaft to gain access to bolts.

4) Suport transmission/transfer case assembly with jack and secure with chain. Remove bolts and rear crossmember. Lower transmission enough to disconnect cooler lines at transmission. Remove transmission-to-engine retaining bolts and slowly slide transmission assembly away from engine.

5) Hold converter in position while lowering transmission assembly from vehicle. Separate transmission from transfer case.

Installation

Reverse removal procedures to install, noting the following: Do not tighten exhaust pipe attaching bolts until crossmember has been installed and transmission jack has been removed. Make sure all index marks made at removal are aligned. Tighten all bolts to specification and fill transmission and transfer case with fluid.

TIGHTENING SPECIFICATIONS

Application	Ft. Lbs. (N.m)
Cooler Line Nuts	25 (34)
Torque Converter-to-Drive Plate	22 (30)
Transfer Case-to-Transmission	40 (54)
Transmission-to-Engine	30 (41)

Automatic Transmissions

AMC EAGLE & JEEP TROUBLE SHOOTING

Every diagnosis of automatic transmission problems should begin with a check of the transmission fluid and linkage. Most of the following conditions can be caused by one or more of the following factors: (1) Incorrect fluid level, (2) Contaminated fluid, (3) Improperly adjusted linkage, or (4) Damaged or worn linkage.

CONDITION	POSSIBLE CAUSE	CORRECTION
Harsh Engagement of "R", "D", "2", "1"	Engine idle speed	Check setting and adjust
	Throttle linkage	Check for smooth travel; clean linkage pivot points as required, but do not lubricate them and then adjust
	Hydraulic pressure	Perform hydraulic pressure test; Repair hydraulic components as required; Check and correct throttle and line pressure settings
	Rear band	Check and adjust rear band
	Accumulator	Clean and inspect for broken seal rings, scratched bore or broken/collapsed spring; Check piston for cracks or evidence of it cocking in bore
	Valve body	Remove, disassemble, clean thoroughly and inspect valves and plugs for nicks, scratches, burrs and rounded edges on valve lands; Check bores for scratches, springs for collapsed coils, and all mating surfaces for nicks, burrs or warpage; Reassemble and install, tightening all screws to specification
	Front clutch	Clean and inspect all parts; Examine retainer and piston for scores and scratches; discs and plates for wear; return springs for collapsed coils; and seal rings for damage; vent check ball in retainer must operate freely
	Rear clutch	Inspect all rear clutch parts as outlined for front clutch
Slow to Engage "N", "R", "D", "2", "1"	Fluid level and condition	Fluid should be at "FULL" mark with engine at idle; replace fluid if "milky" and full of bubbles, or dark and smells burned
	Gearshift linkage	Check and adjust linkage
	Engine idle speed	Check setting and adjust
	Hydraulic pressure	Perform hydraulic pressure test; Repair hydraulic components as required; Check and correct throttle and line pressure settings
	Clogged oil filter	Inspect and replace filter
	Rear band	Check and adjust rear band
	Clutch and band operation	Remove valve body and perform air pressure test to apply clutches and bands to check operation
	Accumulator	Clean and inspect for broken seal rings, scratched bore or broken/collapsed spring; Check piston for cracks or evidence of it cocking in bore
	Valve body	Remove, disassemble, clean thoroughly and inspect valves and plugs for nicks, scratches, burrs and rounded edges on valve lands; Check bores for scratches, springs for collapsed coils, and all mating surfaces for nicks, burrs or warpage; Reassemble and install, tightening all screws to specification

CONDITION	POSSIBLE CAUSE	CORRECTION
Slow to Engage "N", "R", "D", "2", "1" (Cont.)	Oil pump	Clean pump and check all clearances; Inspect rotors for scoring and seal and bushings for wear; Inspect pump housing and reaction shaft support mating surfaces for flatness
	Front clutch	Clean and inspect all parts; Examine retainer and piston for scores and scratches; discs and plates for wear; return springs for collapsed coils; and seal rings for damage; vent check ball in retainer must operate freely
	Rear clutch	Inspect all rear clutch parts as outlined for front clutch
	Seal Rings	Inspect seal rings on reaction shaft support and governor support for wear, cracks or breakage; Inspect ring grooves on both support assemblies for nicks, burrs or distortion; Inspect bores in front clutch retainer and output shaft support for nicks, grooves, wear, cracks, or scratches
No Upshift, Stuck in Low Gear	Fluid level and condition	Fluid should be at "FULL" mark with engine at idle; replace fluid if "milky" and full of bubbles, or dark and smells burned
	Throttle linkage	Check for smooth travel; clean linkage pivot points as required, but do not lubricate them and then adjust
	Gearshift linkage	Check and adjust linkage
	Hydraulic pressure	Perform hydraulic pressure test; Repair hydraulic components as required; Check and correct throttle and line pressure settings
	Governor valve	Clean and inspect all parts; Check weights, shaft and valve for burrs, nicks, scores or binding; Check spring for collapsed or distorted coils and snap rings for distortion; Check filter for dirt and debris; Inspect body for cracks or warpage; Check torque on governor and output shaft support bolts
	Valve body	Remove, disassemble, clean thoroughly and inspect valves and plugs for nicks, scratches, burrs and rounded edges on valve lands; Check bores for scratches, springs for collapsed coils, and all mating surfaces for nicks, burrs or warpage; Reassemble and install, tightening all screws to specification
	Front band	Check and adjust front band
	Front servo and linkage	Inspect piston for wear, cracks and worn or broken seal rings; Check springs for collapsed or broken coils; Check servo bore for scratches, nicks or wear; Check lever, strut and band for damage; Check lever shaft for wear, looseness in case, or for leaking "O" ring
	Clutch and band operation	Remove valve body and perform air pressure test to apply clutches and bands to check operation

AMC EAGLE & JEEP TROUBLE SHOOTING (Cont.)

CONDITION	POSSIBLE CAUSE	CORRECTION
No Upshift, Stuck in Low Gear (Cont.)	Oil pump	Clean and check all clearances; Inspect rotors for scoring and seal and bushings for wear; Inspect housing and reaction shaft support mating surfaces for flatness
	Front clutch	Clean and inspect all parts; Examine retainer and piston for scores and scratches; discs and plates for wear; return springs for collapsed coils; and seal rings for damage; vent check ball in retainer must operate freely
No Low Gear, Moves in 2nd or 3rd Gear	Governor valve	Clean and inspect all parts; Check weights, shaft and valve for burrs, nicks, scores or binding; Check spring for collapsed or distorted coils and snap rings for distortion; Check filter for dirt and debris; Inspect body for cracks or warpage; Check torque on governor and output shaft support bolts
	Valve body	Remove, disassemble, clean thoroughly and inspect valves and plugs for nicks, scratches, burrs and rounded edges on valve lands; Check bores for scratches, springs for collapsed coils, and all mating surfaces for nicks, burrs or warpage; Reassemble and install, tightening all screws to specification
No Kickdown or Normal Downshift	Fluid level and condition	Fluid should be at "FULL" mark with engine at idle; replace fluid if "milky" and full of bubbles, or dark and smells burned
	Throttle linkage	Check for smooth travel; clean linkage pivot points as required, but do not lubricate them and then adjust
	Gearshift linkage	Check and adjust linkage
	Front band	Check and adjust front band
	Hydraulic pressure	Perform hydraulic pressure test; Repair hydraulic components as required; Check and correct throttle and line pressure settings
	Governor valve	Clean and inspect all parts; Check weights, shaft and valve for burrs, nicks, scores or binding; Check spring for collapsed or distorted coils and snap rings for distortion; Check filter for dirt and debris; Inspect body for cracks or warpage; Check torque on governor and output shaft support bolts
	Valve body	Remove, disassemble, clean thoroughly and inspect valves and plugs for nicks, scratches, burrs and rounded edges on valve lands; Check bores for scratches, springs for collapsed coils, and all mating surfaces for nicks, burrs or warpage; Reassemble and install, tightening all screws to specification
	Front servo and linkage	Inspect piston for wear, cracks and worn or broken seal rings; Check springs for collapsed or broken coils; Check servo bore for scratches, nicks or wear; Check lever, strut and band for damage; Check lever shaft for wear, looseness in case, or for leaking "O" ring
	Clutch and band operation	Remove valve body and perform air pressure test to apply clutches and bands to check operation

Automatic Transmissions

AMC EAGLE & JEEP TROUBLE SHOOTING (Cont.)

CONDITION	POSSIBLE CAUSE	CORRECTION
Delayed Erratic Shifts – Harsh at Times	Fluid level and condition	Fluid should be at "FULL" mark with engine at idle; replace fluid if "milky" and full of bubbles, or dark and smells burned
	Throttle linkage	Check for smooth travel; clean linkage pivot points as required, but do not lubricate them and then adjust
	Gearshift linkage	Check and adjust linkage
	Hydraulic pressure	Perform hydraulic pressure test; Repair hydraulic components as required; Check and correct throttle and line pressure settings
	Front band	Check and adjust front band
	Governor valve	Clean and inspect all parts; Check weights, shaft and valve for burrs, nicks, scores or binding; Check spring for collapsed or distorted coils and snap rings for distortion; Check filter for dirt and debris; Inspect body for cracks or warpage; Check torque on governor and output shaft support bolts
	Clogged oil filter	Inspect and replace filter
	Valve body	Remove, disassemble, clean thoroughly and inspect valves and plugs for nicks, scratches, burrs and rounded edges on valve lands; Check bores for scratches, springs for collapsed coils, and all mating surfaces for nicks, burrs or warpage; Reassemble and install, tightening all screws to specification
	Front servo and linkage	Inspect piston for wear, cracks and worn or broken seal rings; Check springs for collapsed or broken coils; Check servo bore for scratches, nicks or wear; Check lever, strut and band for damage; Check lever shaft for wear, looseness in case, or for leaking "O" ring
	Rear servo and linkage	Inspect piston for wear, cracks, worn or broken seal ring, or damaged seal; Check springs for collapsed or broken coils; Check servo bore for scratches, nicks or wear; Check lever and band for damage; Check lever shaft for wear or looseness in case
	Oil pump	Clean pump and check all clearances; Inspect rotors for scoring and seal and bushings for wear; Inspect pump housing and reaction shaft support mating surfaces for flatness
Slips in Forward Drive Ranges	Fluid level and condition	Fluid should be at "FULL" mark with engine at idle; replace fluid if "milky" and full of bubbles, or dark and smells burned
	Throttle linkage	Check for smooth travel; clean linkage pivot points as required, but do not lubricate them and then adjust
	Gearshift linkage	Check and adjust linkage
	Hydraulic pressure	Perform hydraulic pressure test; Repair hydraulic components as required; Check and correct throttle and line pressure settings
	Front band	Check and adjust front band

AMC EAGLE & JEEP TROUBLE SHOOTING (Cont.)

CONDITION	POSSIBLE CAUSE	CORRECTION
Slips in Forward Drive Ranges (Cont.)	Valve body	Remove, disassemble, clean thoroughly and inspect valves and plugs for nicks, scratches, burrs and rounded edges on valve lands; Check bores for scratches, springs for collapsed coils, and all mating surfaces for nicks, burrs or warpage; Reassemble and install, tightening all screws to specification
	Front servo and linkage	Inspect piston for wear, cracks and worn or broken seal rings; Check springs for collapsed or broken coils; Check servo bore for scratches, nicks or wear; Check lever, strut and band for damage; Check lever shaft for wear, looseness in case, or for leaking "O" ring
	Rear servo and linkage	Inspect piston for wear, cracks, worn or broken seal ring, or damaged seal; Check springs for collapsed or broken coils; Check servo bore for scratches, nicks or wear; Check lever and band for damage; Check lever shaft for wear or looseness in case
	Accumulator	Clean and inspect for broken seal rings, scratched bore or broken/collapsed spring; Check piston for cracks or evidence of it cocking in bore
	Clutch and band operation	Remove valve body and perform air pressure test to apply clutches and bands to check operation
	Oil pump	Clean pump and check all clearances; Inspect rotors for scoring and seal and bushings for wear; Inspect pump housing and reaction shaft support mating surfaces for flatness
	Front clutch	Clean and inspect all parts; Examine retainer and piston for scores and scratches; discs and plates for wear; return springs for collapsed coils; and seal rings for damage; vent check ball in retainer must operate freely
	Rear clutch	Inspect all rear clutch parts as outlined for front clutch
	Rear band	Inspect band for wear and for good bonding of lining to band; Inspect lining for burn marks, glazing, uneven wear patterns, flaking or if band grooves are worn away at any portion of band; Replace band if any of these conditions are present
	Seal Rings	Inspect seal rings on reaction shaft support and governor support for wear, cracks or breakage; Inspect ring grooves on both support assemblies for nicks, burrs or distortion; Inspect bores in front clutch retainer and output shaft support for nicks, grooves, wear, cracks, or scratches
Slips in Reverse Only	Fluid level and condition	Fluid should be at "FULL" mark with engine at idle; replace fluid if "milky" and full of bubbles, or dark and smells burned
	Gearshift linkage	Check and adjust linkage

CONDITION	POSSIBLE CAUSE	CORRECTION
Slips in Reverse Only (Cont.)	Hydraulic pressure	Perform hydraulic pressure test; Repair hydraulic components as required; Check and correct throttle and line pressure settings
	Front band	Check and adjust front band
	Valve body	Remove, disassemble, clean thoroughly and inspect valves and plugs for nicks, scratches, burrs and rounded edges on valve lands; Check bores for scratches, springs for collapsed coils, and all mating surfaces for nicks, burrs or warpage; Reassemble and install, tightening all screws to specification
	Rear servo and linkage	Inspect piston for wear, cracks, worn or broken seal ring, or damaged seal; Check springs for collapsed or broken coils; Check servo bore for scratches, nicks or wear; Check lever and band for damage; Check lever shaft for wear or looseness in case
	Clutch and band operation	Remove valve body and perform air pressure test to apply clutches and bands to check operation
	Oil pump	Clean pump and check all clearances; Inspect rotors for scoring and seal and bushings for wear; Inspect pump housing and reaction shaft support mating surfaces for flatness
	Front clutch	Clean and inspect all parts; Examine retainer and piston for scores and scratches; discs and plates for wear; return springs for collapsed coils; and seal rings for damage; vent check ball in retainer must operate freely
	Rear band	Inspect band for wear and for good bonding of lining to band; Inspect lining for burn marks, glazing, uneven wear patterns, flaking or if band grooves are worn away at any portion of band; Replace band if any of these conditions are present
Will Not Move in Forward or Reverse	Fluid level and condition	Fluid should be at "FULL" mark with engine at idle; replace fluid if "milky" and full of bubbles, or dark and smells burned
	Gearshift linkage	Check and adjust linkage
	Hydraulic pressure	Perform hydraulic pressure test; Repair hydraulic components as required; Check and correct throttle and line pressure settings
	Clogged oil filter	Inspect and replace filter
	Valve body	Remove, disassemble, clean thoroughly and inspect valves and plugs for nicks, scratches, burrs and rounded edges on valve lands; Check bores for scratches, springs for collapsed coils, and all mating surfaces for nicks, burrs or warpage; Reassemble and install, tightening all screws to specification
	Clutch and band operation	Remove valve body and perform air pressure test to apply clutches and bands to check operation

AMC EAGLE & JEEP TROUBLE SHOOTING (Cont.)

CONDITION	POSSIBLE CAUSE	CORRECTION
Will Not Move in Forward or Reverse (Cont.)	Converter drive plate	Check plate for flatness, cracks at mounting bolt holes, loose attaching bolts or damaged ring gear teeth; A broken drive plate may indicate engine-to-transmission misalignment caused by loose, missing or misaligned dowels
	Oil pump	Clean pump and check all clearances; Inspect rotors for scoring and seal and bushings for wear; Inspect pump housing and reaction shaft support mating surfaces for flatness
	Planetary gear set	Clean and inspect annulus gear, planet pinion carrier assembly and sun gear for worn thrust washers, damaged gear teeth and excessive pinion end clearance; Examine bushings in sun gear for excessive wear
Slips in Low Gear "D" Only, But Not in "1"	Overrunning clutch	Clean and inspect clutch parts for brinelled clutch rollers or cam, or improperly assembled rollers or springs; Check for collapsed springs and bent spring retainer tabs
Reverse Okay, Will Not Move Forward in "D", "2", "1"	Gearshift linkage	Check and adjust linkage
	Hydraulic pressure	Perform hydraulic pressure test; Repair hydraulic components as required; Check and correct throttle and line pressure settings
	Valve body	Remove, disassemble, clean thoroughly and inspect valves and plugs for nicks, scratches, burrs and rounded edges on valve lands; Check bores for scratches, springs for collapsed coils, and all mating surfaces for nicks, burrs or warpage; Reassemble and install, tightening all screws to specification
	Clutch and band operation	Remove valve body and perform air pressure test to apply clutches and bands to check operation
	Rear clutch	Inspect all rear clutch parts as outlined for front clutch
No Reverse	Gearshift linkage	Check and adjust linkage
	Hydraulic pressure	Perform hydraulic pressure test; Repair hydraulic components as required; Check and correct throttle and line pressure settings
	Front band	Check and adjust front band
	Rear servo and linkage	Inspect piston for wear, cracks, worn or broken seal ring, or damaged seal; Check springs for collapsed or broken coils; Check servo bore for scratches, nicks or wear; Check lever and band for damage; Check lever shaft for wear or looseness in case
	Clutch and band operation	Remove valve body and perform air pressure test to apply clutches and bands to check operation
	Front clutch	Clean and inspect all parts; Examine retainer and piston for scores and scratches; discs and plates for wear; return springs for collapsed coils; and seal rings for damage; vent check ball in retainer must operate freely

Automatic Transmissions

AMC EAGLE & JEEP TROUBLE SHOOTING (Cont.)

CONDITION	POSSIBLE CAUSE	CORRECTION
No Reverse (Cont.)	Rear band	Inspect band for wear and for good bonding of lining to band; Inspect lining for burn marks, glazing, uneven wear patterns, flaking or if band grooves are worn away at any portion of band; Replace band if any of these conditions are present
Moves in Neutral Position (Creeps)	Gearshift linkage	Check and adjust linkage
	Valve body	Remove, disassemble, clean thoroughly and inspect valves and plugs for nicks, scratches, burrs and rounded edges on valve lands; Check bores for scratches, springs for collapsed coils, and all mating surfaces for nicks, burrs or warpage; Reassemble and install, tightening all screws to specification
	Rear clutch	Inspect all rear clutch parts as outlined for front clutch
Drags or Locks Up	Hydraulic pressure	Perform hydraulic pressure test; Repair hydraulic components as required; Check and correct throttle and line pressure settings
	Front band	Check and adjust front band
	Front band	Check and adjust front band
	Park lock	Check condition of lock rod, lock rod ball, sprag reaction plug, governor support, and sprag shaft; Replace parts as required
	Valve body	Remove, disassemble, clean thoroughly and inspect valves and plugs for nicks, scratches, burrs and rounded edges on valve lands; Check bores for scratches, springs for collapsed coils, and all mating surfaces for nicks, burrs or warpage; Reassemble and install, tightening all screws to specification
	Front servo and linkage	Inspect piston for wear, cracks and worn or broken seal rings; Check springs for collapsed or broken coils; Check servo bore for scratches, nicks or wear; Check lever, strut and band for damage; Check lever shaft for wear, looseness in case, or for leaking "O" ring
	Rear servo and linkage	Inspect piston for wear, cracks, worn or broken seal ring, or damaged seal; Check springs for collapsed or broken coils; Check servo bore for scratches, nicks or wear; Check lever and band for damage; Check lever shaft for wear or looseness in case
	Accumulator	Clean and inspect for broken seal rings, scratched bore or broken/collapsed spring; Check piston for cracks or evidence of it cocking in bore
	Front clutch	Clean and inspect all parts; Examine retainer and piston for scores and scratches; discs and plates for wear; return springs for collapsed coils; and seal rings for damage; vent check ball in retainer must operate freely
	Rear clutch	Inspect all rear clutch parts as outlined for front clutch

CONDITION	POSSIBLE CAUSE	CORRECTION
Drags or Locks Up (Cont.)	Planetary gear set	Clean and inspect annulus gear, planet pinion carrier assembly and sun gear for worn thrust washers, damaged gear teeth and excessive pinion end clearance; Examine bushings in sun gear for excessive wear
	Rear band	Inspect band for wear and for good bonding of lining to band; Inspect lining for burn marks, glazing, uneven wear patterns, flaking or if band grooves are worn away at any portion of band; Replace band if any of these conditions are present
	Overrunning clutch	Clean and inspect clutch parts for brinelled clutch rollers or cam, or improperly assembled rollers or springs; Check for collapsed springs and bent spring retainer tabs

TRANSMISSION NOISY

CONDITION	POSSIBLE CAUSE	CORRECTION
Grating, Growling or Scraping Noise	Fluid level and condition	Fluid should be at "FULL" mark with engine at idle; replace fluid if "milky" and full of bubbles, or dark and smells burned
	Park lock	Check condition of lock rod, lock rod ball, sprag reaction plug, governor support, and sprag shaft; Replace parts as required
	Output shaft bearing, bushing, or seal	Remove extension housing, inspect parts, and replace parts as required
	Clogged oil filter	Inspect and replace filter
	Converter drive plate	Check plate for flatness, cracks at mounting bolt holes, loose attaching bolts or damaged ring gear teeth; A broken drive plate may indicate engine-to-transmission misalignment caused by loose, missing or misaligned dowels
	Oil pump	Clean pump and check all clearances; Inspect rotors for scoring and seal and bushings for wear; Inspect pump housing and reaction shaft support mating surfaces for flatness
	Front clutch	Clean and inspect all parts; Examine retainer and piston for scores and scratches; discs and plates for wear; return springs for collapsed coils; and seal rings for damage; vent check ball in retainer must operate freely
	Planetary gear set	Clean and inspect annulus gear, planet pinion carrier assembly and sun gear for worn thrust washers, damaged gear teeth and excessive pinion end clearance; Examine bushings in sun gear for excessive wear
	Overrunning clutch	Clean and inspect clutch parts for brinelled clutch rollers or cam, or improperly assembled rollers or springs; Check for collapsed springs and bent spring retainer tabs
	Torque Converter	If converter hub seal surface or drive slots are damaged or if converter contains foreign material, burned-oxidized fluid or debris, replace converter; Do not attempt to clean or flush converter
Buzzing Noise	Fluid level and condition	Fluid should be at "FULL" mark with engine at idle; replace fluid if "milky" and full of bubbles, or dark and smells burned

CONDITION	POSSIBLE CAUSE	CORRECTION
TRANSMISSION NOISY (Cont.)		
Buzzing Noise (Cont.)	Governor valve	Clean and inspect all parts; Check weights, shaft and valve for burrs, nicks, scores or binding; Check spring for collapsed or distorted coils and snap rings for distortion; Check filter for dirt and debris; Inspect body for cracks or warpage; Check torque on governor and output shaft support bolts
	Valve body	Remove, disassemble, clean thoroughly and inspect valves and plugs for nicks, scratches, burrs and rounded edges on valve lands; Check bores for scratches, springs for collapsed coils, and all mating surfaces for nicks, burrs or warpage; Reassemble and install, tightening all screws to specification
	Clutch and band operation	Remove valve body and perform air pressure test to apply clutches and bands to check operation
	Oil pump	Clean pump and check all clearances; Inspect rotors for scoring and seal and bushings for wear; Inspect pump housing and reaction shaft support mating surfaces for flatness
	Torque Converter	If converter hub seal surface or drive slots are damaged or if converter contains foreign material, burned-oxidized fluid or debris, replace converter; Do not attempt to clean or flush converter
Oil Blows Out Filler Tube	Fluid level and condition	Fluid should be at "FULL" mark with engine at idle; replace fluid if "milky" and full of bubbles, or dark and smells burned
	Transmission Oil Cooler	Check lines and cooler for obstructions, or leaks (look for transmission fluid in radiator coolant, or milky-colored transmission fluid which indicates coolant in fluid)
	Clogged oil filter	Inspect and replace filter
	Valve body	Remove, disassemble, clean thoroughly and inspect valves and plugs for nicks, scratches, burrs and rounded edges on valve lands; Check bores for scratches, springs for collapsed coils, and all mating surfaces for nicks, burrs or warpage; Reassemble and install, tightening all screws to specification
	Oil pump	Clean pump and check all clearances; Inspect rotors for scoring and seal and bushings for wear; Inspect pump housing and reaction shaft support mating surfaces for flatness
	Transmission vent	Make sure vent is open and not obstructed
Transmission Overheats	Fluid level and condition	Fluid should be at "FULL" mark with engine at idle; replace fluid if "milky" and full of bubbles, or dark and smells burned
	Engine idle speed	Check setting and adjust
	Transmission Oil Cooler	Check lines and cooler for obstructions, or leaks (look for transmission fluid in radiator coolant, or milky-colored transmission fluid which indicates coolant in fluid)
	Front band	Check and adjust front band

CONDITION	POSSIBLE CAUSE	CORRECTION
	TRANSMISSION NOISY (Cont.)	
Transmission Overheats (Cont.)	Hydraulic pressure	Perform hydraulic pressure test; Repair hydraulic components as required; Check and correct throttle and line pressure settings
	Clogged oil filter	Inspect and replace filter
	Front band	Check and adjust front band
	Valve body	Remove, disassemble, clean thoroughly and inspect valves and plugs for nicks, scratches, burrs and rounded edges on valve lands; Check bores for scratches, springs for collapsed coils, and all mating surfaces for nicks, burrs or warpage; Reassemble and install, tightening all screws to specification
	Converter drive plate	Check plate for flatness, cracks at mounting bolt holes, loose attaching bolts or damaged ring gear teeth; A broken drive plate may indicate engine-to-transmission misalignment caused by loose, missing or misaligned dowels
Starter Will Not Operate in Neutral or Park	Gearshift linkage	Check and adjust linkage
	Neutral start switch	Check wires and connections; Test switch; See if valve body manual lever grounds switch in "P" and "N" positions; If not okay, check ground strip at valve body manual lever; If okay, check starting circuit
	Engine performance	Verify proper engine operation; Be sure compression meets specifications and that fuel and ignition systems are functioning properly
	Valve body	Remove, disassemble, clean thoroughly and inspect valves and plugs for nicks, scratches, burrs and rounded edges on valve lands; Check bores for scratches, springs for collapsed coils, and all mating surfaces for nicks, burrs or warpage; Reassemble and install, tightening all screws to specification
Sluggish Acceleration, Excessive Throttle Needed to Maintain Speed	Fluid level and condition	Fluid should be at "FULL" mark with engine at idle; replace fluid if "milky" and full of bubbles, or dark and smells burned
	Engine performance	Verify proper engine operation; Be sure compression meets specifications and that fuel and ignition systems are functioning properly
	Throttle linkage	Check for smooth travel; clean linkage pivot points as required, but do not lubricate them and then adjust
	Stall test	Perform stall test to check holding ability of converter and transmission clutches
	Hydraulic pressure	Perform hydraulic pressure test; Repair hydraulic components as required; Check and correct throttle and line pressure settings
	Torque Converter	If converter hub seal surface or drive slots are damaged or if converter contains foreign material, burned-oxidized fluid or debris, replace converter; Do not attempt to clean or flush converter

Automatic Transmissions
AMC EAGLE & JEEP TROUBLE SHOOTING (Cont.)

CONDITION	POSSIBLE CAUSE	CORRECTION
TRANSMISSION NOISY (Cont.)		
Sluggish Acceleration, Excessive Throttle Needed to Maintain Speed (Cont.)	Rear clutch	Inspect all rear clutch parts as outlined for front clutch
LOCK-UP CONVERTER DIAGNOSIS		
No Lock-Up	Faulty oil pump	Replace oil pump
	Sticking governor valve	Repair or replace as required

	Valve body malfunction
	  Stuck switch valve
	  Stuck lock-up valve
	  Stuck fail-safe valve
		Repair or replace valve body or its internal components as required

	Failed locking clutch	Replace torque converter
	Leaking turbine hub seal	Replace torque converter
	Faulty input shaft or seal ring	Repair or replace as required
Will Not Unlock	Sticking governor valve	Repair or replace as required

	Valve body malfunction
	  Stuck switch valve
	  Stuck lock-up valve
	  Stuck fail-safe valve
		Repair or replace valve body or its internal components as required

Stays Locked Up at Too Low a Speed in Direct	Sticking governor valve	Repair or replace as required

	Valve body malfunction
	  Stuck switch valve
	  Stuck lock-up valve
	  Stuck fail-safe valve
		Repair or replace valve body or its internal components as required

Locks Up or Drags in Low or Second	Faulty oil pump	Replace oil pump

	Valve body malfunction
	  Stuck switch valve
	  Stuck fail-safe valve
		Repair or replace valve body or its internal components as required

Sluggish or Stalls in Reverse	Faulty oil pump	Replace oil pump
	Plugged cooler, cooler lines or fittings	Flush or replace cooler and flush lines and fittings

	Valve body malfunction
	  Stuck switch valve
	  Faulty input shaft or seal ring
		Repair or replace valve body or its internal components as required

Loud Chatter During Lock-Up Engagement (Cold)	Faulty torque converter	Replace torque converter
	Failed locking clutch	Replace torque converter
	Leaking turbine hub seal	Replace torque converter
Vibration or Shudder During Lock-Up Engagement	Faulty oil pump	Repair or replace oil pump
	Valve body malfunction	Repair or replace valve body or its internal components as required
	Faulty torque converter	Replace torque converter
	Engine performance	Diagnose and tune engine
Vibration After Lock-Up Engagement	Faulty torque converter	Replace torque converter
	Exhaust system vibration	Align exhaust system
	Engine performance	Diagnose and tune engine

CONDITION	POSSIBLE CAUSE	CORRECTION
LOCK-UP CONVERTER DIAGNOSIS (Cont.)		
Vibration After Lock-Up Engagement (Cont.)	Throttle linkage misadjusted	Check and adjust throttle linkage
Vibration When "Reved" in Neutral	Torque converter out of balance	Replace torque converter
Overheating: Oil Blows Out of Dipstick Tube or Pump Seal	Plugged cooler, cooler lines or fittings	Flush or replace cooler and flush lines and fittings
	Stuck switch valve	Repair switch valve in valve body or replace valve body
Shudder After Lock-Up Engagement	Faulty oil pump	Repair or replace oil pump
	Plugged cooler, cooler lines or fittings	Flush or replace cooler and flush lines and fittings
	Valve body malfunction	Repair or replace valve body or its internal components as required
	Faulty torque converter	Replace torque converter
	Faulty locking clutch	Replace torque converter
	Exhaust system vibration	Align exhaust system
	Engine performance	Diagnose and tune engine
	Throttle linkage misadjusted	Check and adjust throttle linkage

Automatic Transmissions

CHRYSLER CORP. TROUBLE SHOOTING

Every diagnosis of automatic transmission problems should begin with a check of the transmission fluid and linkage. Most of the following conditions can be caused by one or more of the following factors: (1) Incorrect fluid level, (2) Contaminated fluid, (3) Improperly adjusted linkage, or (4) Damaged or worn linkage.

CONDITION	POSSIBLE CAUSE	CORRECTION
Harsh Engagement From Neutral to "D"	Engine idle speed too high	Check setting and adjust
	Valve body malfunction or leakage	Check valve body operation and perform HYDRAULIC PRESSURE tests
	Hydraulic pressure too high	Check and adjust hydraulic pressure
	Worn or faulty rear clutch	Check and replace clutch
	Faulty lock-up clutch (except A413 & A470)	Check and replace lock-up clutch
	Engine performance (A413 & A470)	Perform engine diagnosis and tune-up
Harsh Engagement From Neutral to "R"	Engine idle speed too high	Check setting and adjust
	Valve body malfunction or leakage (except A413 & A470)	Check valve body operation and perform HYDRAULIC PRESSURE tests
	Hydraulic pressure too high	Check and adjust hydraulic pressure
	Worn or faulty front clutch	Check and replace front clutch
	Faulty lock-up clutch (except A413 & A470)	Check and replace lock-up clutch
	Low-Reverse band worn or misadjusted (A413 & A470)	Check and replace, or adjust Low-Reverse band
	Low-Reverse servo, band or linkage malfunction (A413 & A470)	Check servo, band and linkage for damage
	Engine performance (A413 & A470)	Perform engine diagnosis and tune-up
Delayed Engagement From Neutral to "D"	Hydraulic pressure too low	Check and adjust hydraulic pressure
	Valve body malfunction or leakage	Check valve body operation and perform HYDRAULIC PRESSURE tests
	Low fluid level	Check and replenish as required
	Incorrect gearshift linkage control adjustment	Check and adjust linkage, see GENERAL SERVICING
	Oil filter clogged	Clean and replace filter
	Faulty oil pump	Check and replace oil pump
	Worn or broken input shaft seal rings	Check and replace seal rings
	Air in transmission fluid	Check and replace fluid
	Engine idle speed too low	Check setting and adjust
	Worn or broken reaction shaft support seal rings (except A413 & A470)	Check and replace seal rings
	Worn or faulty rear clutch	Check and replace clutch
Delayed Engagement From Neutral to "R"	Low-Reverse servo, band or linkage malfunction	Check servo, band and linkage for damage
	Low-Reverse band misadjusted or worn out (A413 & A470)	Check and adjust, or replace, Low-Reverse band
	Hydraulic pressure too low	Check and adjust hydraulic pressure
	Valve body malfunction or leakage	Check valve body operation and perform HYDRAULIC PRESSURE tests
	Low fluid level	Check and replenish as required

CHRYSLER CORP. TROUBLE SHOOTING (Cont.)

CONDITION	POSSIBLE CAUSE	CORRECTION
Delayed Engagement From Neutral to "R" (Cont.)	Incorrect gearshift linkage control adjustment	Check and adjust linkage, see GENERAL SERVICING
	Oil filter clogged	Clean and replace filter
	Faulty oil pump	Check and replace oil pump
	Worn or broken input shaft seal rings	Check and replace seal rings
	Air in transmission fluid	Check and replace fluid
	Engine idle speed too low	Check setting and adjust
	Worn or broken reaction shaft support seal rings	Check and replace seal rings
	Worn or faulty front clutch	Check and replace clutch
Runaway Upshift	Hydraulic pressure too low	Check and adjust hydraulic pressure
	Valve body malfunction or leakage	Check valve body operation and perform HYDRAULIC PRESSURE tests
	Low fluid level	Check and replenish as required
	Oil filter clogged	Clean and replace filter
	Air in transmission fluid	Check and replace fluid
	Incorrect throttle linkage adjustment	Check and adjust linkage, see GENERAL SERVICING
	Kickdown servo band or linkage malfunction	Check and adjust band and/or linkage
	Worn or faulty front clutch	Check and replace clutch
	Worn or broken reaction shaft support seal rings	Check and replace seal rings
No Upshift	Hydraulic pressure too low	Check and adjust hydraulic pressure
	Valve body malfunction or leakage	Check valve body operation and perform HYDRAULIC PRESSURE tests
	Low fluid level	Check and replenish as required
	Incorrect gearshift linkage control adjustment	Check and adjust linkage, see GENERAL SERVICING
	Incorrect throttle linkage adjustment	Check and adjust linkage, see GENERAL SERVICING
	Governor support seal rings broken or worn (A413 & A470)	Check and replace support seal rings
	Worn or broken reaction shaft support seal rings	Check and replace seal rings
	Governor malfunction	Check and repair or replace governor
	Kickdown servo band or linkage malfunction	Check and adjust band and/or linkage
	Worn or faulty front clutch	Check and replace clutch
	Engine performance (A413 & A470)	Perform engine diagnosis and tune-up
3-2 Kickdown Runaway	Hydraulic pressure too low	Check and adjust hydraulic pressure
	Valve body malfunction or leakage	Check valve body operation and perform HYDRAULIC PRESSURE tests
	Low fluid level	Check and replenish as required
	Air in transmission fluid	Check and replace fluid
	Incorrect throttle linkage adjustment	Check and adjust linkage, see GENERAL SERVICING

Automatic Transmissions

CHRYSLER CORP. TROUBLE SHOOTING (Cont.)

CONDITION	POSSIBLE CAUSE	CORRECTION
3-2 Kickdown Runaway (Cont.)	Kickdown band out of adjustment	Check and adjust kickdown band
	Governor support seal rings broken or worn (A413 & A470)	Check and replace support seal rings
	Worn or broken reaction shaft support seal rings (except A413 & A470)	Check and replace seal rings
	Kickdown servo band or linkage malfunction	Check and adjust band and/or linkage
	Worn or faulty front clutch	Check and replace clutch
No Kickdown or Normal Downshift	Valve body malfunction or leakage	Check valve body operation and perform HYDRAULIC PRESSURE tests
	Incorrect throttle linkage adjustment	Check and adjust linkage, see GENERAL SERVICING
	Governor malfunction	Check and repair or replace governor
	Kickdown servo band or linkage malfunction	Check and adjust band and/or linkage
Shifts Erratic	Hydraulic pressure too low	Check and adjust hydraulic pressure
	Valve body malfunction or leakage	Check valve body operation and perform HYDRAULIC PRESSURE tests
	Low fluid level	Check and replenish as required
	Incorrect gearshift linkage control adjustment	Check and adjust linkage, see GENERAL SERVICING
	Oil filter clogged	Clean and replace filter
	Faulty oil pump	Check and replace oil pump
	Air in transmission fluid	Check and replace fluid
	Incorrect throttle linkage adjustment	Check and adjust linkage, see GENERAL SERVICING
	Governor support seal rings broken or worn	Check and replace support seal rings
	Worn or broken reaction shaft support seal rings	Check and replace seal rings
	Governor malfunction	Check and repair or replace governor
	Kickdown servo band or linkage malfunction	Check and adjust band and/or linkage
	Worn or faulty front clutch	Check and replace clutch
	Engine performance (A413 & A470)	Perform engine diagnosis and tune-up
Slips in Forward Drive Positions	Hydraulic pressure too low	Check and adjust hydraulic pressure
	Valve body malfunction or leakage	Check valve body operation and perform HYDRAULIC PRESSURE tests
	Low fluid level	Check and replenish as required
	Incorrect gearshift linkage control adjustment	Check and adjust linkage, see GENERAL SERVICING
	Oil filter clogged	Clean and replace filter
	Faulty oil pump	Check and replace oil pump
	Worn or broken input shaft seal rings	Check and replace seal rings
	Air in transmission fluid	Check and replace fluid

CHRYSLER CORP. TROUBLE SHOOTING (Cont.)

CONDITION	POSSIBLE CAUSE	CORRECTION
Slips in Forward Drive Positions (Cont.)	Incorrect throttle linkage adjustment	Check and adjust linkage, see GENERAL SERVICING
	Overrunning clutch not holding, or clutch is worn, broken, or seized	Check and replace overrunning clutch
	Worn or faulty rear clutch	Check and replace clutch
Slips in Reverse Only	Low-Reverse band worn or misadjusted	Check and replace, or adjust Low-Reverse band
	Hydraulic pressure too low	Check and adjust hydraulic pressure
	Valve body malfunction or leakage	Check valve body operation and perform HYDRAULIC PRESSURE tests
	Low-Reverse servo, band or linkage malfunction	Check servo, band and linkage for damage
	Low fluid level	Check and replenish as required
	Incorrect gearshift linkage control adjustment	Check and adjust linkage, see GENERAL SERVICING
	Faulty oil pump	Check and replace oil pump
	Air in transmission fluid	Check and replace fluid
	Worn or broken reaction shaft support seal rings	Check and replace seal rings
	Worn or faulty front clutch	Check and replace clutch
Slips in All Positions	Hydraulic pressure too low	Check and adjust hydraulic pressure
	Valve body malfunction or leakage	Check valve body operation and perform HYDRAULIC PRESSURE tests
	Low fluid level	Check and replenish as required
	Oil filter clogged	Clean and replace filter
	Faulty oil pump	Check and replace oil pump
	Worn or broken input shaft seal rings	Check and replace seal rings
	Air in transmission fluid	Check and replace fluid
No Drive in Any Position	Hydraulic pressure too low	Check and adjust hydraulic pressure
	Valve body malfunction or leakage	Check valve body operation and perform HYDRAULIC PRESSURE tests
	Low fluid level	Check and replenish as required
	Oil filter clogged	Clean and replace filter
	Faulty oil pump	Check and replace oil pump
	Planetary gear sets broken or seized	Check and replace gear sets
No Drive in Forward Drive Positions	Hydraulic pressure too low	Check and adjust hydraulic pressure
	Valve body malfunction or leakage	Check valve body operation and perform HYDRAULIC PRESSURE tests
	Low fluid level	Check and replenish as required
	Worn or broken input shaft seal rings	Check and replace seal rings
	Overrunning clutch not holding, or clutch is worn, broken, or seized	Check and replace overrunning clutch
	Worn or faulty rear clutch	Check and replace clutch
	Planetary gear sets broken or seized	Check and replace gear sets
No Drive in Reverse	Low-Reverse band worn or misadjusted	Check and replace, or adjust Low-Reverse band
	Hydraulic pressure too low	Check and adjust hydraulic pressure
	Valve body malfunction or leakage	Check valve body operation and perform HYDRAULIC PRESSURE tests

CONDITION	POSSIBLE CAUSE	CORRECTION
No Drive in Reverse (Cont.)	Low-Reverse servo, band or linkage malfunction	Check servo, band and linkage for damage
	Incorrect gearshift linkage control adjustment	Check and adjust linkage, see GENERAL SERVICING
	Worn or broken reaction shaft support seal rings	Check and replace seal rings
	Worn or faulty front or rear clutch	Check and replace defective clutch
	Planetary gear sets broken or seized	Check and replace gear sets
Drives in Neutral (Creeps)	Valve body malfunction or leakage	Check valve body operation and perform HYDRAULIC PRESSURE tests
	Incorrect gearshift linkage control adjustment	Check and adjust linkage, see GENERAL SERVICING
	Insufficient clutch plate clearance	Check and adjust clutch plate clearance
	Dragging, faulty, or worn rear clutch	Check and replace rear clutch
Drags or Locks-Up	Low-Reverse band worn or misadjusted	Check and replace, or adjust Low-Reverse band
	Kickdown band adjustment too tight	Check and adjust kickdown band adjustment
	Planetary gear sets broken or seized	Check and replace gear sets
	Overrunning clutch worn, broken, or seized	Check and replace overrunning clutch
	Stuck lock-up valve (except A413 & A470)	Check, clean and/or replace valve
	Faulty oil pump (except A413 & A470)	Check and replace oil pump
Slips in Reverse or Manual Low (except A413 & A470)	Low-Reverse band misadjusted	Check and adjust Low-Reverse band
	Oil filter clogged	Clean and replace filter
Harsh Upshift	Hydraulic pressure too high or too low	Check and adjust hydraulic pressure
	Incorrect throttle linkage adjustment	Check and adjust linkage, see GENERAL SERVICING
	Kickdown band out of adjustment	Check and adjust kickdown band
	Faulty lock-up clutch (except A413 & A470)	Check and replace lock-up clutch
	Engine performance (A413 & A470)	Perform engine diagnosis and tune-up
Delayed Upshift	Incorrect throttle linkage adjustment	Check and adjust linkage, see GENERAL SERVICING
	Kickdown band out of adjustment	Check and adjust kickdown band
	Governor support seal rings broken or worn	Check and replace support seal rings
	Worn or broken reaction shaft support seal rings	Check and replace seal rings
	Governor malfunction	Check and repair or replace governor
	Kickdown servo band or linkage malfunction	Check and adjust band and/or linkage
	Worn or faulty front clutch	Check and replace clutch
	Engine performance (A413 & A470)	Perform engine diagnosis and tune-up
TRANSMISSION NOISY		
Grating, Growling or Scraping Noise	Low-Reverse band worn or misadjusted	Check and replace, or adjust Low-Reverse band
	Kickdown band adjustment too tight	Check and adjust kickdown band adjustment

CONDITION	POSSIBLE CAUSE	CORRECTION
TRANSMISSION NOISY (Cont.)		
Grating, Growling or Scraping Noise (Cont.)	Drive shafts(s) bushing(s) damaged (A413 & A470)	Replace bushings
	Planetary gear sets broken or seized	Check and replace gear sets
	Overrunning clutch worn, broken, or seized	Check and replace overrunning clutch
	Output shaft bearing and/or bushing damaged (except A413 & A470)	Replace bearing and/or bushing
Buzzing Noise	Valve body malfunction or leakage	Check valve body operation and perform HYDRAULIC PRESSURE tests
	Low fluid level	Check and replenish as required
	Faulty oil pump	Check and replace oil pump
	Air in transmission fluid	Check and replace fluid
	Overrunning clutch inner race damaged	Check and replace overrunning clutch
Hard to Fill, Oil Blows Out Filler Tube	Oil filter clogged	Clean and replace filter
	Air in transmission fluid	Check and replace fluid
	Fluid level too high	Correct fluid level
	Transmission breather clogged (except A413 & A470)	Clean breather
Transmission Overheats	Stuck switch valve	Clean and replace valve
	Engine idle speed too high	Check setting and adjust
	Hydraulic pressure too low	Check and adjust hydraulic pressure
	Low fluid level	Check and replenish as required
	Incorrect gearshift linkage control adjustment	Check and adjust linkage, see GENERAL SERVICING
	Faulty oil pump	Check and replace oil pump
	Kickdown band adjustment too tight	Check and adjust kickdown band adjustment
	Insufficient clutch plate clearance	Check and adjust clutch plate clearance
	Faulty cooling system	Check for damaged or restricted cooling lines
LOCK-UP CONVERTER DIAGNOSIS – EXCEPT A413 & A470		
No Lock-Up	Faulty oil pump	Check and replace oil pump
	Sticking governor valve	Clean and replace governor valve
	Valve body malfunction	Check valve body operation and perform HYDRAULIC PRESSURE tests
	Stuck switch valve	Clean and replace switch valve
	Stuck lock-up valve	Clean and replace lock-up valve
	Stuck fail-safe valve	Clean and replace fail-safe valve
	Faulty torque converter	
	Possible failed locking clutch	Replace torque converter
	Possible leaking turbine hub seal	Replace hub seal
	Faulty input shaft or seal ring	Check and replace input shaft or seal ring
Will Not Unlock	Sticking governor valve	Clean and replace governor valve
	Valve body malfunction	Check valve body operation and perform HYDRAULIC PRESSURE tests
	Stuck switch valve	Clean and replace switch valve

Automatic Transmissions

CHRYSLER CORP. TROUBLE SHOOTING (Cont.)

CONDITION	POSSIBLE CAUSE	CORRECTION
LOCK-UP CONVERTER DIAGNOSIS – EXCEPT A413 & A470 (Cont.)		
Will Not Unlock (Cont.)	Stuck lock-up valve	Clean and replace lock-up valve
	Stuck fail-safe valve	Clean and replace fail-safe valve
Stays Locked Up At Too Low a Speed in Direct	Sticking governor valve	Clean and replace governor valve
	Valve body malfunction	Check valve body operation and perform HYDRAULIC PRESSURE tests
	Stuck switch valve	Clean and replace switch valve
	Stuck lock-up valve	Clean and replace lock-up valve
	Stuck fail-safe valve	Clean and replace fail-safe valve
Locks-Up or Drags in Low or Second	Faulty oil pump	Check and replace oil pump
	Valve body malfunction	Check valve body operation and perform HYDRAULIC PRESSURE tests
	Stuck switch valve	Clean and replace switch valve
	Stuck fail-safe valve	Clean and replace fail-safe valve
Stalls or is Sluggish in Reverse	Faulty oil pump	Check and replace oil pump
	Plugged cooler, lines, or fittings	Check cooler, lines, and fittings for obstruction
	Valve body malfunction	Check valve body operation and perform HYDRAULIC PRESSURE tests
	Stuck switch valve	Clean and replace switch valve
	Faulty input shaft or seal ring	Check and replace input shaft or seal ring
Loud Chatter During Lock-Up Engagement (Cold)	Faulty torque converter	
	Possible failed locking clutch	Replace torque converter
	Possible leaking turbine hub seal	Replace hub seal
Vibration or Shudder During Lock-Up Engagement	Faulty oil pump	Check and replace oil pump
	Valve body malfunction	Check valve body operation and perform HYDRAULIC PRESSURE tests
	Faulty torque converter	Replace torque converter
	Engine performance	Diagnose and perform engine tune-up
Vibrations After Lock-Up Engagement	Faulty torque converter	Replace torque converter
	Misaligned exhaust system	Check and align exhaust system
	Engine performance	Diagnose and perform engine tune-up
	Throttle linkage misadjusted	Check and adjust throttle linkage, see GENERAL SERVICING
Shudder After Lock-Up Engagement	Faulty oil pump	Check and replace oil pump
	Plugged cooler, lines, or fittings	Check cooler, lines, and fittings for obstruction
	Valve body malfunction	Check valve body operation and perform HYDRAULIC PRESSURE tests
	Faulty torque converter	
	Possible failed locking clutch	Replace torque converter
	Engine performance	Diagnose and perform engine tune-up
	Misaligned exhaust system	Check and align exhaust system
	Throttle linkage misadjusted	Check and adjust throttle linkage, see GENERAL SERVICING

CHRYSLER CORP. TROUBLE SHOOTING (Cont.)

CONDITION	POSSIBLE CAUSE	CORRECTION
LOCK-UP CONVERTER DIAGNOSIS – EXCEPT A413 & A470 (Cont.)		
Vibration When "Reved" in Neutral	Faulty torque converter	
	Converter out of balance	Replace torque converter
Overheating; Blowing Oil Out Dipstick or Pump Seal	Plugged cooler, lines, or fittings	Check cooler, lines, and fittings for obstruction
	Stuck switch valve	Clean and replace switch valve

Automatic Transmissions

FORD MOTOR CO. (EXC. ATX & ZF 4 HP-22) TROUBLE SHOOTING

Every diagnosis of automatic transmission problems should begin with a check of the transmission fluid and linkage. Most of the following conditions can be caused by one or more of the following factors: (1) Incorrect fluid level, (2) Contaminated fluid, (3) Improperly adjusted linkage, or (4) Damaged or worn linkage.

CONDITION	POSSIBLE CAUSE	CORRECTION
Slow Initial Engagement	Improper fluid level	Check fluid level; See GENERAL SERVICING
	Damaged or improperly adjusted linkage	Service or adjust linkage; See GENERAL SERVICING
	Contaminated fluid	Check fluid condition
	Improper clutch and band application, or low main control pressure	Perform CONTROL PRESSURE test
Rough Initial Engagement	Improper fluid level	Check fluid level; See GENERAL SERVICING
	Engine idle speed too high	Check and adjust idle speed
	Automatic choke on (warm temperatures)	Disengage choke
	Looseness in propeller shaft, "U" joints, or engine mounts	Service and repair, or replace components as required
	Improper clutch or band operation, or oil control pressure	Perform CONTROL PRESSURE test
	Sticking or dirty valve body	Clean, service or replace valve body
	Converter clutch not disengaging (A4LD)	Check converter clutch engagement and disengagement
Harsh Engagements – Warm Engine	Improper fluid level	Check fluid level; See GENERAL SERVICING
	T.V. linkage misadjusted (long), disconnected, sticking or damaged; disconnected return spring (A.O.T.)	Check and adjust, or repair T.V. linkage
	Curb idle speed too high	Check and adjust idle speed
	Valve body bolts loose or too tight	Tighten valve body bolts to specification
	Valve body dirty or contains sticking valves	Clean, inspect and repair, or replace valve body
No or Delayed Forward Engagement – Reverse OK	Improper fluid level	Check fluid level; See GENERAL SERVICING
	Manual linkage misadjusted or damaged	Check and adjust linkage or service as required
	Low main control pressure (leakage)	Perform CONTROL PRESSURE test and note results
	Forward clutch stator support seal rings leaking – No. 3 & No. 4 on A.O.T. (except A4LD)	Perform AIR PRESSURE test or visually inspect if forward clutch plates are burnt
	Forward clutch assembly burnt or damaged	Perform AIR PRESSURE test or visually inspect if forward clutch plates are burnt
	Forward clutch cylinder check ball leaking; leaking piston seal rings	Perform AIR PRESSURE test or visually inspect if forward clutch plates are burnt
	Valve body bolts loose or too tight	Tighten valve body bolts to specification
	Valve body dirty or contains sticking valves	Clean, inspect and repair or replace valve body
	Transmission filter plugged	Replace filter
	Pump damaged or leaking	Inspect pump gears; replace pump if required
No or Delayed Reverse Engagement – Forward OK	Improper fluid level	Check fluid level; See GENERAL SERVICING
	Manual linkage misadjusted or damaged	Check and adjust linkage, or service as required

Automatic Transmissions

FORD MOTOR CO. (EXC. ATX & ZF 4 HP-22) TROUBLE SHOOTING (Cont.)

CONDITION	POSSIBLE CAUSE	CORRECTION
No or Delayed Reverse Engagement – Forward OK (Cont.)	Low main control pressure in Reverse	Perform CONTROL PRESSURE test
	High reverse clutch or reverse clutch stator support seal rings leaking (No. 1 & No. 2 on A.O.T.)	Perform AIR PRESSURE test or visually inspect if reverse clutch plates are burnt
	Reverse clutch assembly burnt or worn	Perform AIR PRESSURE test or visually inspect if reverse clutch plates are burnt
	Reverse clutch piston check ball leaking; leaking piston seal rings	Perform AIR PRESSURE test or visually inspect if reverse clutch plates are burnt
	Valve body bolts loose or too tight	Tighten valve body bolts to specification
	Valve body dirty or contains sticking valves	Clean, inspect and repair or replace valve body
	Transmission filter plugged	Replace filter
	Pump damaged or leaking	Inspect pump gears; replace pump if required
	Intermediate servo piston seal cut or leaking (C5)	Check and replace piston seal
	Low-reverse servo piston seal cut or leaking (A4LD)	Perform AIR PRESSURE test; Check and replace piston seal; Check and replace low-reverse band
No or Delayed Reverse Engagement and/or No Engine Braking in Manual Low (1)	Improper fluid level	Check fluid level; See GENERAL SERVICING
	Manual linkage (T.V. linkage on A.O.T.) misadjusted or damaged	Check and adjust linkage or service as required
	Low-reverse band burnt or worn	Perform AIR PRESSURE test
	Low-reverse servo piston seal leaking	Perform AIR PRESSURE test or visually inspect if low-reverse band is burnt
	Band out of adjustment (C5)	Adjust reverse band
	Polished, glazed low-reverse band or drum (A4LD & C5)	Service or replace as required
	Planetary low one-way clutch damaged (except A4LD)	Replace low one-way clutch
	End play clearance too tight	Check and adjust transmission end play clearance
	Overdrive clutch, overdrive one-way clutch damaged (A4LD)	Check and replace if necessary
	Rear one-way clutch damaged (A4LD)	Replace rear one-way clutch
No Engine Braking in Manual 2nd	Intermediate band out of adjustment	Adjust intermediate band
	Improper clutch or band operation, or oil control pressure	Perform CONTROL PRESSURE test
	Intermediate servo leaking	Perform AIR PRESSURE test of intermediate servo to check for leakage; Service as required
	Intermediate one-way clutch damaged (except A4LD)	Replace clutch
	Polished or glazed band or drum	Service or replace as required
No Engine Braking in Manual 2nd (Cont.)	Overdrive clutch or overdrive one-way clutch damaged (A4LD)	Replace as required

Automatic Transmissions

FORD MOTOR CO. (EXC. ATX & ZF 4 HP-22) TROUBLE SHOOTING (Cont.)

CONDITION	POSSIBLE CAUSE	CORRECTION
Slips, Shudders or Chatters Upon Forward Engagement	Improper fluid level	Check fluid level; See GENERAL SERVICING
	T.V. linkage misadjusted or short (A.O.T.)	Adjust T.V. linkage
	Manual linkage misadjusted or damaged (except A.O.T.)	Check and adjust, or service as required
	Low main control pressure	Perform CONTROL PRESSURE test
	Valve body bolts loose or too tight	Tighten valve body bolts to specification
	Valve body dirty or contains sticking valves	Clean, inspect and repair or replace valve body
	Forward clutch piston check ball not seating or leaking	Replace forward clutch cylinder; Service transmission as required
	Forward clutch piston seal(s) cut or worn	Replace seal and service clutch as required
	Forward clutch stator support seal rings leaking – No. 3 & No. 4 on A.O.T. (except A4LD)	Perform AIR PRESSURE test or visually inspect if forward clutch plates are burnt
	Planetary low one-way clutch damaged (except A4LD)	Replace low one-way clutch
	Overdrive one-way clutch damaged (A4LD)	Repair or replace clutch
	Rear one-way clutch damaged (A4LD)	Determine cause of condition and service as required
Slips, Shudders or Chatters Upon Reverse Engagement	Improper fluid level	Check fluid level; See GENERAL SERVICING
	Low main control pressure in Reverse	Perform CONTROL PRESSURE test
	Low-reverse servo leaking	Perform AIR PRESSURE test; Visually inspect seal rings and piston bore
	Planetary low one-way clutch damaged (except A4LD)	Replace low one-way clutch
	Reverse clutch drum bushing damaged (except A4LD)	Determine cause of condition and service as required
	Reverse clutch stator support seal rings or ring grooves worn or damaged (except A4LD)	Determine cause of condition and service as required
	Reverse clutch piston seal cut or worn (except A4LD)	Determine cause of condition and service as required
	Overdrive and/or rear one-way clutch damaged (A4LD)	Determine cause of condition and service as required
	Overdrive and/or rear reverse-high clutch drum bushing damaged (A4LD)	Determine cause of condition and service as required
	Overdrive and/or rear reverse-high clutch center support seal rings or ring grooves worn or damaged (A4LD)	Determine cause of condition and service as required
	Overdrive and/or rear reverse-high clutch piston seals cut or worn	Determine cause of condition and service as required

Automatic Transmissions

FORD MOTOR CO. (EXC. ATX & ZF 4 HP-22) TROUBLE SHOOTING (Cont.)

CONDITION	POSSIBLE CAUSE	CORRECTION
Slips, Shudders or Chatters Upon Reverse Engagement (Cont.)	Low-reverse servo piston damaged or worn (A4LD)	Service as required
	Low-reverse band out of adjustment	Inspect and adjust low-reverse band on C5 and A4LD; Nonadjustable on all others, service as required
	Low-reverse servo piston, seals, or bores damaged (A4LD)	Perform AIR PRESSURE test
	Looseness in propeller shaft, "U" joints, or engine mounts	Service and repair or replace components as required
No Drive, Slips or Chatters in 1st Gear – All Other Gears OK (1st Gear in "D" or "OD" – A.O.T. & A4LD)	Worn or damaged planetary one-way clutch (rear one-way clutch on A4LD)	Service or replace clutch as required
No Drive, Slips or Chatters in 2nd Gear	Intermediate band out of adjustment (except A.O.T.)	Check and adjust intermediate band
	Intermediate friction clutch or one-way clutch worn or damaged (A.O.T.)	Service as required
	Intermediate clutch piston bleed hole blocked or not positioned at 12 o'clock (A.O.T.)	Clean and install bleed hole at 12 o'clock position
	Improper band or clutch application, or control pressure	Perform CONTROL PRESSURE test
	Damaged or worn intermediate servo piston seals and/or internal leaks (C3, C5 & C6)	Perform AIR PRESSURE test
	Damaged or worn intermediate servo piston and/or internal leaks (A4LD)	Perform AIR PRESSURE test
	Dirty or sticky valve body	Clean, service or replace valve body
	Polished, glazed intermediate band or drum (except A.O.T.)	Replace or service as required
Starts Up in 2nd or 3rd	Improper band or clutch application, or control pressure	Perform CONTROL PRESSURE test
	Intermediate clutch pack clearance too tight (A.O.T.)	Check and adjust clearance
	Damaged, worn, or sticking governor	Check governor and clean screen, or replace and service governor as required
	Valve body loose	Tighten valve body
	Dirty or sticky valve body	Clean, service or replace valve body
	Cross leaks between valve body and case mating surface	Service or replace valve body and/or case as required
Incorrect Shift Points	Improper fluid level	Check fluid level; See GENERAL SERVICING
	Vacuum line damaged, clogged, or leaks (except A.O.T.)	Perform VACUUM SUPPLY test
	Improper operation of EGR system (except A.O.T.)	Check and repair as required
	T.V. linkage out of adjustment (A.O.T.)	Check and adjust T.V. linkage
	Improper speedometer gear installed	Check and replace gear
	Improper band or clutch application, or control pressure	Perform CONTROL PRESSURE test

Automatic Transmissions

FORD MOTOR CO. (EXC. ATX & ZF 4 HP-22) TROUBLE SHOOTING (Cont.)

CONDITION	POSSIBLE CAUSE	CORRECTION
Incorrect Shift Points (Cont.)	Damaged or worn governor	Clean screen; Service or replace governor
	T.V. control rod or vacuum diaphragm bent, sticking, or leaks (C3, C5 & C6)	Replace as required
	Vacuum diaphragm bent, sticking or leaks (A4LD)	Service or replace as required
	Dirty or sticky valve body	Clean, service or replace valve body
	Vacuum regulator valve misadjusted or damaged (C6 with 6.9L Diesel engine)	Check adjustment and function; Adjust or replace
All Upshifts Harsh or Delayed, or No Upshifts	Improper fluid level	Check fluid level; See GENERAL SERVICING
	Throttle linkage disconnected, sticking, damaged or misadjusted (too long) or return spring disconnected (A.O.T.)	Check and adjust throttle linkage; Service as required
	Manual linkage misadjusted or damaged	Check and adjust linkage; Service as required
	Governor valve sticking	Perform GOVERNOR TEST; Service as required
	Main control pressure too high	Perform CONTROL PRESSURE test; Service as required
	T.V. control rod incorrect (C5)	Check and replace T.V. control rod
	Valve body bolts loose or too tight	Tighten valve body bolts to specification
	Valve body dirty or contains sticking valves	Clean, inspect and repair or replace valve body
	Vacuum leak to diaphragm unit (C3, C5 & A4LD)	Check and service vacuum lines to diaphragm unit; Perform VACUUM SUPPLY and DIAPHRAGM tests
	Vacuum diaphragm bent, sticking or leaks (C3, C5 & A4LD)	Check diaphragm unit and service as required
	Vacuum regulator valve misadjusted or damaged (C6 with 6.9L Diesel engine)	Check adjustment and function; Adjust or replace
All Upshifts Early or Mushy	Improper fluid level	Check fluid level; See GENERAL SERVICING
	T.V. throttle linkage sticking, damaged or misadjusted – too short (A.O.T.)	Check and adjust throttle linkage; Service as required
	Low main control pressure	Perform CONTROL PRESSURE test and note results
	Valve body bolts loose or too tight	Tighten valve body bolts to specification
	Valve body or throttle control valve sticking	Clean, inspect and repair or replace as required
	Governor valve sticking	Perform GOVERNOR TEST; Service as required
	T.V. control rod too short	Install correct T.V. control rod (except A4LD)
	Vacuum regulator valve misadjusted or damaged (C6 with 6.9L Diesel engine)	Check adjustment and function; Adjust or replace
	Kickdown linkage misadjusted, sticking, or damaged (A4LD)	Adjust linkage; Service as required
No 1-2 Upshift	Improper fluid level	Check fluid level; See GENERAL SERVICING
	T.V. throttle linkage disconnected, sticking, or misadjusted – too long (A.O.T.)	Check and adjust throttle linkage; Service as required

FORD MOTOR CO. (EXC. ATX & ZF 4 HP-22) TROUBLE SHOOTING (Cont.)

CONDITION	POSSIBLE CAUSE	CORRECTION
No 1-2 Upshift (Cont.)	Kickdown system damaged (A4LD)	Replace damaged parts
	Manual linkage misadjusted or damaged	Check and adjust, or service as required
	Low main control pressure to intermediate intermediate friction clutch (A.O.T.)	Perform CONTROL PRESSURE test and note results
	Governor valve sticking	Perform GOVERNOR TEST; Service as required
	Intermediate band out of adjustment (except A.O.T.)	Adjust intermediate band
	Vacuum leak to diaphragm unit (C3, C5 & A4LD)	Check and service vacuum lines to diaphragm unit
	Vacuum diaphragm bent, sticking or leaks (C3, C5 & A4LD)	Check diaphragm unit and service as required
	Valve body bolts loose or too tight	Tighten valve body bolts to specification
	Valve body dirty or contains sticking valves	Clean, inspect and repair or replace valve body
	Intermediate clutch band and/or servo assembly burnt	Perform AIR PRESSURE test
Rough, Harsh or Delayed 1-2 Upshift	Improper fluid level	Check fluid level; See GENERAL SERVICING
	Poor engine performance	Diagnose and tune engine
	T.V. linkage misadjusted (long) or damaged (A.O.T.)	Adjust linkage; Service as required
	Intermediate band out of adjustment (except A.O.T.)	Adjust intermediate band
	Main control pressure too high	Perform CONTROL PRESSURE test; Note results
	Governor valve sticking	Perform GOVERNOR TEST; Service as required
	Kickdown linkage misadjusted (A4LD)	Adjust linkage
	Damaged intermediate servo (C3, C5 & A4LD)	Perform AIR PRESSURE check of intermediate servo
	Engine vacuum leak (except A.O.T.)	Check engine vacuum lines and service as required; Check vacuum diaphragm unit and service as required; Perform VACUUM SUPPLY and DIAPHRAGM tests
	Valve body bolts loose or too tight	Tighten valve body bolts to specification
	Valve body dirty or contains sticking valves	Clean, inspect and repair or replace valve body
	Vacuum leak to diaphragm unit (C3, C5 & A4LD)	Check and service vacuum lines to diaphragm unit
	Vacuum diaphragm bent, sticking or leaks (C3, C5 & A4LD)	Check diaphragm unit and service as required
	Vacuum regulator valve misadjusted or damaged (C6 with 6.9L Diesel engine)	Check adjustment and function; Adjust or replace
Early, Mushy, Soft or Slipping 1-2 Upshift	Improper fluid level	Check fluid level; See GENERAL SERVICING
	Main regulator or throttle valve stuck (A4LD)	Service as required
	Incorrect engine performance	Diagnose and tune engine
	T.V. throttle linkage misadjusted (short), sticking, or damaged (A.O.T.)	Adjust linkage; Service as required

Automatic Transmissions

FORD MOTOR CO. (EXC. ATX & ZF 4 HP-22) TROUBLE SHOOTING (Cont.)

CONDITION	POSSIBLE CAUSE	CORRECTION
Early, Mushy, Soft or Slipping 1-2 Upshift (Cont.)	Intermediate band out of adjustment (except A.O.T.)	Adjust intermediate band
	Low main control pressure	Perform CONTROL PRESSURE test; Note results
	Valve body bolts loose or too tight	Tighten valve body bolts to specification
	Valve body dirty or contains sticking valves	Clean, inspect and repair or replace valve body
	Intermediate friction clutch burnt or worn (A.O.T.)	Determine cause of condition and service as required
	Governor valve sticking	Perform GOVERNOR TEST; Service as required
	Damaged intermediate servo or band	Perform AIR PRESSURE check; Service as required
	Polished, glazed intermediate band or drum (except A.O.T.)	Service or replace as required
	Vacuum regulator valve misadjusted or damaged (C6 with 6.9L Diesel engine)	Check adjustment and function; Adjust or replace
No 2-3 Upshift	Improper fluid level	Check fluid level; See GENERAL SERVICING
	T.V. throttle linkage misadjusted (long), sticking, or damaged (except A4LD)	Adjust linkage; Service as required
	Kickdown system damaged (A4LD)	Replace damaged parts
	Low main control pressure to direct clutch (except A4LD)	Perform CONTROL PRESSURE test; Note results
	Low main control pressure to reverse-high clutch (A4LD)	Perform CONTROL PRESSURE test; Note results
	Valve body bolts loose or too tight	Tighten valve body bolts to specification
	Valve body dirty or contains sticking valves	Clean, inspect and repair or replace valve body
	Direct clutch or reverse-high clutch assembly burnt or worn	Perform STALL test (except A4LD); Determine cause of condition and service as required
	Converter damper hub weld broken (A.O.T.)	Check converter damper hub weld; Replace torque converter if required
Harsh or Delayed 2-3 Upshift	Incorrect engine performance	Diagnose and tune engine
	Engine vacuum leak (except A.O.T.)	Check engine vacuum lines and service as required; Check vacuum diaphragm unit and service as required; Perform VACUUM SUPPLY and DIAPHRAGM tests
	T.V. throttle linkage misadjusted (long), sticking, or damaged (except A4LD)	Adjust linkage; Service as required
	2-3 accumulator piston apply passage plugged or omitted (A.O.T.)	Remove 2-3 accumulator piston and visually inspect, or AIR test to detect plugging or omission
	2-3 accumulator piston seals cut or worn (A.O.T.)	Determine cause of condition and replace seals; Service as required
	Damaged 2-3 accumulator (A.O.T.)	Service as required

FORD MOTOR CO. (EXC. ATX & ZF 4 HP-22) TROUBLE SHOOTING (Cont.)

CONDITION	POSSIBLE CAUSE	CORRECTION
Harsh or Delayed 2-3 Upshift (Cont.)	Damaged or worn intermediate servo release and high clutch piston check ball (C3, C5 & C6)	Perform AIR PRESSURE test of intermediate servo; Apply and release high clutch piston check ball; Service as required
	Valve body bolts loose or too tight	Tighten valve body bolts to specification
	Valve body dirty or contains sticking valves (2-3 capacity modulator valve on A.O.T.)	Clean, inspect and repair or replace valve body
	Vacuum diaphragm or T.V. control rod bent, sticking or leaking	Check diaphragm and rod; Service or replace as required
	Damaged or worn intermediate servo release and reverse-high clutch piston check ball (A4LD)	Perform AIR PRESSURE test of intermediate servo; Apply and release reverse-high clutch piston check ball; Service as required
	Throttle valve stuck (A4LD)	Service as required
	Vacuum regulator valve misadjusted or damaged (C6 with 6.9L Diesel engine)	Check adjustment and function; Adjust or replace
Soft, Early or Mushy 2-3 Upshift	T.V. throttle linkage misadjusted (short), sticking, or damaged (A.O.T.)	Adjust linkage; Service as required
	Kickdown system damaged (A4LD)	Replace damaged parts
	Valve body bolts loose or too tight	Tighten valve body bolts to specification
	Valve body dirty or contains sticking valves	Clean, inspect and repair or replace valve body
	Direct clutch or reverse-high clutch assembly burnt or worn (A.O.T.)	Perform STALL test; Determine cause of condition and service as required
	Vacuum diaphragm or T.V. control rod bent, sticking or leaking	Check diaphragm and rod; Service as required
	Vacuum regulator valve misadjusted or damaged (C6 with 6.9L Diesel engine)	Check adjustment and function; Adjust or replace
	Throttle valve stuck (A4LD)	Service as required
Erratic Shifts	Improper fluid level	Check fluid level; See GENERAL SERVICING
	Poor engine performance	Diagnose and tune engine
	T.V. linkage binding or sticking (A.O.T.)	Check linkage; Service as required
	Vacuum line damaged (A4LD)	Check engine vacuum lines and service as required
	Valve body bolts loose or too tight	Tighten valve body bolts to specification
	Valve body dirty or contains sticking valves	Clean, inspect and repair or replace valve body
	Governor valve sticking	Perform GOVERNOR TEST; Service as required
	Output shaft collector body seal rings damaged	Service as required
Shifts 1-3 in Drive or "OD" – A.O.T. & A4LD	Intermediate band out of adjustment (except A.O.T.)	Check and adjust intermediate band
	Intermediate friction clutch burnt or damaged (A.O.T.)	Determine cause of condition and service as required

Automatic Transmissions

FORD MOTOR CO. (EXC. ATX & ZF 4 HP-22) TROUBLE SHOOTING (Cont.)

CONDITION	POSSIBLE CAUSE	CORRECTION
Shifts 1-3 in Drive or "OD" – A.O.T. & A4LD (Cont.)	Intermediate one-way clutch damaged (A.O.T.)	Determine cause of condition and service as required
	Damaged intermediate servo and/or internal leaks (except A.O.T.)	Perform AIR PRESSURE test; Service front servo and/or internal leaks
	Improper band or clutch application, or control pressure	Perform CONTROL PRESSURE test
	Polished, glazed intermediate band or drum (except A.O.T.)	Replace or service as required
	Dirty or sticky valve body	Clean, service or replace valve body
	Governor valve sticking	Perform GOVERNOR TEST; Service as required
	Kickdown system damaged (A4LD)	Replace damaged parts
Engine Overspeeds on 2-3 Upshift	Linkage out of adjustment (except A4LD)	Service or adjust linkage
	Throttle linkage binding, damaged, misadjusted, or sticking (A.O.T.)	Check and adjust linkage; Service as required; Check vacuum regulator valve on C6 with 6.9L diesel engine
	Kickdown system damaged (A4LD)	Replace damaged parts
	Improper band or clutch application, or control pressure	Perform CONTROL PRESSURE test
	Damaged or worn high clutch (reverse-high clutch on A4LD) and/or intermediate servo	Perform AIR PRESSURE test; Service as required
	Intermediate servo piston seals cut or worn	Replace seal; Check for leaking
	Dirty or sticky valve body	Clean, service or replace valve body
	Throttle valve stuck (A4LD)	Service as required
	Vacuum diaphragm damaged (A4LD)	Replace vacuum diaphragm
	Torque converter damper or hub broken (A.O.T.)	Check converter damper hub weld; Replace torque converter if required
Engine Overspeeds on 3-2 Downshift (C3, C5 & A4LD)	Linkage out of adjustment	Service or adjust linkage
	Intermediate band out of adjustment	Check and adjust intermediate band
	Improper band or clutch application, and one-way clutch, or control pressure	Perform CONTROL PRESSURE test; Service clutch
	Damaged or worn intermediate servo	Perform AIR PRESSURE test; Service servo and/or seals
	Polished, glazed intermediate band or drum	Replace or service as required
	Dirty or sticky valve body	Clean, service or replace valve body
No 3-4 Upshift, Stays in 3rd – A.O.T. Only	T.V. throttle linkage misadjusted (long), bent or sticking	Adjust throttle linkage; Service as required; Bent, sticking or misadjusted T.V. throttle linkage will not properly synchronize with carburetor lever at time 3-4 shift should occur

FORD MOTOR CO. (EXC. ATX & ZF 4 HP-22) TROUBLE SHOOTING (Cont.)

CONDITION	POSSIBLE CAUSE	CORRECTION
No 3-4 Upshift, Stays in 3rd – A.O.T. Only (Cont.)	Direct clutch circuit leakage – Burnt plates will help confirm leakage in direct clutch circuit; Replacing plates without finding cause of problem will result in repeat occurrence	Perform DIRECT CLUTCH PRESSURE test; Check and tighten valve body bolts to specification to prevent leaks; Replace case if nicks or porosity are found in case passages or valve body-to-case mating surfaces; Perform CHECK BALL leak test to test direct clutch piston check ball for leaking, and replace piston if leakage is confirmed; Check and replace clutch piston inner and outer seal rings if leaking; Check No. 5 and No. 6 direct clutch output shaft seal rings for free movement on shaft and for metal shavings or burrs between seal and shaft, and replace as required; Check large seal rings (Nos. 7, 8, 9, 10) on output shaft for freedom of movement on shaft and for metal shavings, and replace as required; Inspect output shaft feed passages and cup plug for leakage and replace as required
	Dirty or sticky valve body	Clean valve body; Check for following sticking valves: Overdrive servo regulator valve, 3-4 shift valve, 3-4 T.V. modulator valve, orifice control valve and replace valve body if sticking valve cannot be freed
	Main control gasket distorted	Ensure gasket is not blocking an orifice; Replace if required
	Case warpage causing sticking valve	Reduce valve body bolt torque to minimum side of specification
	Governor leaking	Check last 2 large seal rings (Nos. 9, 10) for freedom of movement and metal shavings or burrs between seal and output shaft, and replace as required; Check seal ring bore at rear of case for scoring (light scoring is OK) and deep grooving, and replace case if required; Check governor-to-output shaft retaining ring for proper seating on output shaft, and service as required; Check fit of governor counterweight on output shaft, and replace counterweight if fit is loose
No 3-4 Upshift (A4LD Only)	Kickdown system damaged	Replace damaged parts
	Vacuum line damaged	Repair or replace as required
	Vacuum diaphragm damaged	Repair or replace as required
	Throttle valve stuck	Service as required
	Overdrive servo damaged or leaking	Check and replace overdrive piston seal if required
	Polished, glazed overdrive band or drum	Replace or service as required
	Dirty or sticky valve body	Clean, service or replace valve body
Harsh or Delayed 3-4 Upshift – A.O.T. Only	T.V. linkage misadjusted (long), bent or sticking	Check and adjust, or repair T.V. linkage
	T.V. return spring at carburetor (throttle body) not on T.V. lever	Replace spring
	Valve body bolts loose or too tight	Tighten valve body bolts to specification

1-82

Automatic Transmissions

FORD MOTOR CO. (EXC. ATX & ZF 4 HP-22) TROUBLE SHOOTING (Cont.)

CONDITION	POSSIBLE CAUSE	CORRECTION
Harsh or Delayed 3-4 Upshift – A.O.T. Only (Cont.)	Valve body dirty or contains sticking valves	Clean, inspect and repair, or replace valve body
	Incorrect engine performance	Diagnose and tune engine
	3-4 accumulator piston seals worn or cut	Determine cause of condition and service as required
	3-4 accumulator piston drain passage blocked	Determine cause of condition and service as required
Slips in 4th Gear (A.O.T. Only)	Overdrive circuit leaking or blocked passage – Burnt overdrive band will help confirm leakage in overdrive circuit; Replacing overdrive band without finding cause of problem will result in repeat occurrence	Check and tighten valve body bolts to specification; Check and replace servo cover "O" rings as required; Check and replace overdrive servo piston seal if found leaking; Check overdrive servo cover for cracks and porosity by covering with fluid and apply air to overdrive servo apply passage with Adapter (T80L-77030-B), replace cover if bubbles appear on overdrive servo cover
	Overdrive servo piston not applying overdrive band and/or band not applying	Overdrive servo case apply passage blocked; Perform AIR PRESSURE test and replace case if required
	Overdrive band mislocated	Service overdrive servo piston if not seated to band-end seat; Service overdrive band if not seated to anchor pin
	Converter damper plate and hub fracturing, weld or rivet fatigue, or damper springs broken	Using Adapter (T83L-7902-A), check converter damper and hub assembly weld, and replace converter if shaft turns more than 2° or if grinding noise is heard while applying 50 ft. lbs. (78 N.m) torque
	Direct drive shaft splines distorted	Check and replace direct drive shaft if splines on ends of shaft or spines in direct clutch cylinder are distorted
Slips in 4th Gear (A4LD Only)	Overdrive servo damaged or leaking	Check and replace overdrive piston seal if required
	Polished, glazed overdrive band or drum	Replace or service as required
Shift Hunting 3-4 and 4-3 (A.O.T. Only)	Poor engine performance, or EGR solenoid worn or damaged	Diagnose and tune engine; Replace EGR solenoid
	Throttle linkage misadjusted	Inspect and adjust throttle linkage
	Manual linkage misadjusted	Check and adjust or service as required
Rough Shudder 3-1 Shift at Closed Throttle in "D" – "OD" for A.O.T. & A4LD	Incorrect engine idle or engine performance	Diagnose and tune engine; Adjust idle speed
	Improper kickdown linkage adjustment (A4LD)	Service or adjust kickdown linkage

FORD MOTOR CO. (EXC. ATX & ZF 4 HP-22) TROUBLE SHOOTING (Cont.)

CONDITION	POSSIBLE CAUSE	CORRECTION
Rough Shudder 3-1 Shift at Closed Throttle in "D" – "OD" for A.O.T. & A4LD (Cont.)	Improper linkage adjustment (except A4LD)	Service or adjust linkage; Check vacuum regulator valve on C6 with 6.9L diesel engine
	Improper band or clutch application or control pressure	Perform CONTROL PRESSURE test
	Improper governor operation	Perform GOVERNOR test and service as required
	Dirty or sticky valve body	Clean, service or replace valve body
Rough or Mushy 4-2 or 3-1 Downshift (A.O.T.)	Incorrect engine performance	Diagnose and tune engine
	Improper throttle or manual linkage adjustment	Service or adjust linkage
	Improper application of intermediate friction and one-way clutch	Service as required
	Dirty or sticky valve body	Clean, service or replace valve body
No Forced Downshifts	Kickdown linkage (cable) out of adjustment (except A.O.T.)	Service or adjust linkage
	Damaged internal kickdown linkage (except A.O.T.)	Service internal linkage
	Damaged or misadjusted (short) throttle linkage (A.O.T.)	Inspect and adjust throttle linkage; Service as required
	Improper band or clutch application or control pressure	Perform CONTROL PRESSURE test
	Dirty or sticking governor	Check governor and clean screen, or replace and service governor as required
	Dirty or sticky valve body	Clean, service or replace valve body
High Shift Effort	Manual shift linkage misadjusted or damaged	Check and adjust, or service as required
	Inner manual lever nut loose	Tighten nut to specification
	Manual lever retainer pin damaged	Adjust linkage and install new pin
Transmission Overheats	Improper fluid level	Check fluid level; See GENERAL SERVICING
	Incorrect engine performance	Diagnose and tune engine
	Improper band or clutch application, or control pressure	Perform CONTROL PRESSURE test
	Restriction in cooler or lines	Check cooler and lines for obstruction and service as required
	Seized converter one-way clutch	Replace one-way clutch
	Dirty or sticky valve body	Clean, service or replace valve body
Transmission Leaks	Damaged or obstructed case breather vent	Check and service as required
	Leakage at gasket, seals, etc.	Remove all traces of lubricant on exposed surfaces; Check vent for obstruction and damage; Operate transmission at normal temperatures and perform FLUID LEAKAGE test; Service as required
Poor Vehicle Acceleration	Poor engine performance	Diagnose and tune engine
	Torque converter one-way clutch locked up	Replace torque converter

Automatic Transmissions

FORD MOTOR CO. (EXC. ATX & ZF 4 HP-22) TROUBLE SHOOTING (Cont.)

CONDITION	POSSIBLE CAUSE	CORRECTION
TRANSMISSION NOISY		
Valve Resonance	Improper fluid level	Check fluid level; See GENERAL SERVICING
	Linkage out of adjustment	Adjust or service linkage
	Improper band or clutch application or control pressure	Perform CONTROL PRESSURE test
	Cooler lines grounding	Free cooler lines
	Dirty or sticky valve body	Clean, service or replace valve body
	Internal leakage or pump cavitation	Service pump as required
Other Than Valve Resonance	Linkage adjustment	Check and adjust, or replace linkage
	Improper fluid level	Check fluid level; See GENERAL SERVICING
	Contaminated fluid	Disassemble, clean and service transmission; Flush torque converter and cooler
	Faulty torque converter	Service or replace torque converter
	Faulty oil pump	Service or replace oil pump
	Faulty speedometer driven gear	Replace speedometer driven gear
	Worn or damaged extension housing bushing or seal	Service as required
	Faulty propeller shaft	Service as required
	Faulty planetary gear set	Service gear set as required
	Faulty one-way clutch	Service one-way clutch as required
	Loose converter-to-flywheel mounting bolts	Tighten bolts to specification
TORQUE CONVERTER DIAGNOSIS – A4LD ONLY		
Converter Clutch Does Not Engage	Converter clutch solenoid not being energized electrically	Perform EEC-IV KEY ON-ENGINE OFF test
	Wires to solenoid shorted or open	Perform EEC-IV KEY ON-ENGINE OFF test
	Transmission case connector not seated	Perform EEC-IV KEY ON-ENGINE OFF test
	Open or short inside solenoid	Perform EEC-IV KEY ON-ENGINE OFF test
	Faulty engine coolant temperature sensor (CTS)	Perform EEC-IV KEY ON-ENGINE OFF test
	Faulty throttle position sensor (TPS)	Perform EEC-IV KEY ON-ENGINE OFF test
	Faulty manifold absolute pressure (MAP) sensor	Perform EEC-IV KEY ON-ENGINE OFF test
	Vacuum line disconnected from MAP sensor	Perform EEC-IV KEY ON-ENGINE OFF test
	Brake switch faulty	Perform EEC-IV ENGINE RUNNING test
	Faulty EEC-IV processor	Run diagnostic check on processor
	Converter clutch solenoid being energized electronically, but foreign material on solenoid valve preventing valve closure	Remove oil pan and valve body; Remove solenoid and check operation; Service as required
	Converter clutch shuttle valve stuck in unlocked position (against plug) or spring load too high	Remove valve body and check operation of shuttle valve; Remove any contamination; Spring load should be about 4 lbs. at .512" (1.8 kg at 13 mm)

FORD MOTOR CO. (EXC. ATX & ZF 4 HP-22) TROUBLE SHOOTING (Cont.)

CONDITION	POSSIBLE CAUSE	CORRECTION
TORQUE CONVERTER DIAGNOSIS – A4LD ONLY (Cont.)		
Converter Clutch Does Not Engage (Cont.)	Converter clutch shift valve stuck in downshift position	Remove valve body and check operation of shift valve; Remove any contamination; Make sure valve moves freely
	Torque converter internal malfunction preventing lock-up piston application	Replace torque converter
Converter Clutch Always Engaged (Vehicle Moves Only With Engine at High RPM in "OD")	Converter clutch shift valve stuck in locked position	Remove valve body and check to ensure shift valve moves freely
	Converter clutch shuttle valve stuck in locked position	Remove valve body and check to ensure shuttle valve moves freely
	Lock-up piston in torque converter will not disengage	Replace torque converter
Converter Clutch Will Not Disengage on Coastdown	Faulty throttle position sensor (should unlock at closed throttle)	Perform EEC-IV KEY ON-ENGINE OFF test
	Converter clutch solenoid sticking	Remove valve body and check operation of solenoid; Replace if required

Automatic Transmissions

FORD MOTOR CO. ZF 4 HP-22 TROUBLE SHOOTING

Every diagnosis of automatic transmission problems should begin with a check of the transmission fluid and linkage. Most of the following conditions can be caused by one or more of the following factors: (1) Incorrect fluid level, (2) Contaminated fluid, (3) Improperly adjusted linkage, or (4) Damaged or worn linkage.

CONDITION	POSSIBLE CAUSE	CORRECTION
Transmission Does Not Engage Park	Improperly adjusted linkage	Check and adjust linkage
	Excessive friction in Park mechanism	Check cam, connection rod and pawl; Service as required
Transmission Does Not Hold Park	Improperly adjusted linkage	Check and adjust linkage
Engine Cannot Be Started	Improperly adjusted linkage	Check and adjust linkage
	Neutral safety switch faulty	Replace switch
No or Delayed Reverse Gear Engagement	Improperly adjusted linkage	Check and adjust linkage
	Transmission filter plugged	Replace filter
	Valve body dirty or contains sticking valves	Replace valve body
	Clutch burnt or worn (no 3rd gear)	Replace transmission
	Clutch burnt or worn (no engine braking in "1")	Replace transmission
	Clutch burnt or worn (no engine braking in "1", "2" or "3")	Replace transmission
Slipping or Chatter at Start in Reverse Gear	Clutches damaged, burnt or worn	Replace transmission
Harsh Engagement from Park or Neutral to Reverse or Distinct Double-Jerk for Same Engagement (Below 1500 RPM)	Valve body malfunction (same symptoms when changing 2nd to 3rd gear	Replace valve body
Vehicle Moves in Neutral (Creeps)	Improperly adjusted linkage	Check and adjust linkage
	Clutch seized	Replace transmission
No Drive in "OD"	Improperly adjusted linkage	Check and adjust linkage
	Transmission filter plugged	Replace filter
	Clutch burnt or worn	Replace transmission
	1st gear one-way clutch slips	Replace transmission
Slipping or Chatter at Driveaway in "OD"	Clutch burnt or worn	Replace transmission
Jerk During Neutral to Drive Shift Below 1500 RPM (in "OD")	Clutch damper malfunction	Replace valve body
	Clutch burnt or worn	Replace transmission
No 1-2 or 2-1 Shift in "OD"	Governor valve sticking	Replace governor
	1-2 shift valve sticking	Replace valve body
No 1-2 Shift in "OD"	Clutches burnt or worn	Replace transmission
No 2-3 or 3-2 Shift in "OD"	Governor valve sticking	Replace governor
	2-3 shift valve sticking	Replace valve body
No 2-3 Shift in "OD"	Clutch burnt or worn	Replace transmission
No 3-4 or 4-3 Shift in "OD"	Governor valve sticking	Replace governor
	3-4 shift valve sticking	Replace valve body
No 3-4 Shift in "OD"	Clutch burnt or worn	Replace transmission

FORD MOTOR CO. ZF 4 HP-22 TROUBLE SHOOTING (Cont.)

CONDITION	POSSIBLE CAUSE	CORRECTION
Vehicle Starts in 2nd Gear in "OD"	Sticking governor	Replace governor
	1-2 shift valve sticking	Replace valve body
Vehicle Starts in 3rd Gear in "OD"	Sticking governor	Replace governor
	1-2 and 2-3 shift valves sticking	Replace valve body
Shits 1-3 in Drive and "OD"	2-3 shift valve sticking	Replace valve body
No Upshifts in "OD"	Stuck governor	Replace governor
	Shift valves sticking	Replave valve body
Shift Points Incorrect at Full Throttle in "OD"	Throttle cable misadjusted	Check and adjust throttle cable; See GENERAL SERVICING
No 1-2 or 2-1 Shift at Kickdown in "OD"	Throttle cable misadjusted	Check and adjust throttle cable; See GENERAL SERVICING
No 2-3 or 3-2 Shift at Kickdown in "OD"	Throttle cable misadjusted	Check and adjust throttle cable; See GENERAL SERVICING
No 4-3 Shift at Kickdown in "OD"	4-3 kickdown valve sticking	Replace valve body
Harsh Shifts at Light Throttle in "OD"	Valve body malfunction	Replace valve body
Harsh Shifts at Full Throttle and Kickdown in "OD"	Valve body malfunction	Replace valve body
Soft Shifts at Full Throttle and Kickdown in "OD"	Clutch plates burnt or worn	Replace transmission
	Valve body malfunction	Replace valve body
No 3rd Gear Engine Braking in "D"	Clutch plates burnt or worn	Replace transmission
No Manual 2-1 Downshift in "L"	Dirty or sticking valve body	Replace valve body
	Governor sticking	Replace governor
No Engine Braking in "L"	Clutch plates burnt or worn	Replace transmission
Throttle Cable Sticking	Too much friction in sleeve of throttle cable	Replace throttle cable
	Throttle pressure valve sticking	Replace valve body
Noisy and No Drive After Long Journey	Dirty oil filter on valve body	If no burnt clutch plate lining in oil sump, replace filter; Otherwise replace transmission
Very Noisy and No Drive	Damaged flex plate	Replace flex plate or transmission
	Worn pump drive	Replace transmission
Oil Dripping From Converter Housing	Damaged seal ring in pump housing	Replace seal ring
	Pump housing porous	Replace transmission
	Converter leaking from welded seam	Replace transmission
Leakage Between Transmission and Oil Pan	Incorrect torque on bolts	Tighten bolts to specification
	Pan gasket damaged	Replace gasket
Leakage Between Intermediate Plate and Main Housing (Especially at Pump Pressure Point)	Converter housing bolts worked loose	Tighten bolts to specification

Automatic Transmissions

FORD MOTOR CO. ZF 4 HP-22 TROUBLE SHOOTING (Cont.)

CONDITION	POSSIBLE CAUSE	CORRECTION
Oil Loss at Speedometer Gear	Damage speedometer gear "O" ring	Replace "O" ring
Oil Leak at Throttle Connection Cable	Damaged "O" ring connection	Replace "O" ring or complete cable
Oil Leak at Extension Housing	Output oil seal damaged	Replace seal
Loss of Oil Through Breather	Oil level too high	Check and correct oil level; See GENERAL SERVICING
	No breather cap	Replace cap or change breather
	Breather "O" ring damaged	Remove extension housing and replace "O" ring
	Securing clip broken or damaged	Replace clip
Leak in Cooler Lines	Loose connections	Check connections and tighten
Oil Leak at Intermediate Plate	Plugs loose	Tighten plugs; Replace washers
Leakage Between Main Case and Extension Housing	Loose bolts	Tighten bolts to specification
	Gasket damaged	Replace gasket

TRANSMISSION NOISY

CONDITION	POSSIBLE CAUSE	CORRECTION
High Pitched Noise in All Positions (Especially With Cold Oil)	Improper fluid level	Check fluid level; See GENERAL SERVICING
	Leaking valve body	Replace valve body
High Pitched Squeaking Noise (Dependent on Engine Speed) in All Gears When Oil is Warm, Combined With No Drive After Long Journey	Dirty filter	If no debris found in sump, replace filter; Otherwise replace transmission
Loud Noise During Converter Lock-Up	Torsional damper malfunction	Replace transmission
Torsional Vibrations From Engine During Converter Lock-Up	Engine speed too low or lock-up shift point incorrect	Replace valve body
Other Than Valve Resonance	Linkage adjustment	Check and adjust, or replace linkage
	Improper fluid level	Check fluid level; See GENERAL SERVICING
	Contaminated fluid	Disassemble, clean and service transmission; Flush torque converter and cooler
	Faulty torque converter	Service or replace torque converter
	Faulty oil pump	Service or replace oil pump
	Faulty speedometer driven gear	Replace speedometer driven gear
	Worn or damaged extension housing bushing or seal	Service as required
	Faulty propeller shaft	Service as required
	Faulty planetary gear set	Service gear set as required
	Faulty one-way clutch	Service one-way clutch as required
	Loose converter-to-flywheel mounting bolts	Tighten bolts to specification

FORD MOTOR CO. ZF 4 HP-22 TROUBLE SHOOTING (Cont.)

CONDITION	POSSIBLE CAUSE	CORRECTION
TORQUE CONVERTER DIAGNOSIS		
Lock-Up Points Incorrect	Valve body malfunction	Replace valve body
	Governor pressure incorrect	Replace governor
Shift Too Harsh	Damper malfunction	Replace valve body
	Torque converter malfunction	Replace transmission
No Lock-Up	Valve body malfunction	Replace valve body
	Torque converter malfunction	Replace transmission

FORD MOTOR CO. ATX TROUBLE SHOOTING

Every diagnosis of automatic transaxle problems should begin with a check of the transmission fluid and linkage. Most of the following conditions can be caused by one or more of the following factors: (1) Incorrect fluid level, (2) Contaminated fluid, (3) Improperly adjusted linkage, or (4) Damaged or worn linkage.

CONDITION	POSSIBLE CAUSE	CORRECTION
Slow Initial Engagement	Improper fluid level	Check fluid level; See GENERAL SERVICING
	Damaged or improperly adjusted linkage	Service or adjust linkage; See GENERAL SERVICING
	Contaminated fluid	Check fluid condition
	Improper clutch and band application, or low main control pressure	Perform CONTROL PRESSURE test
	Dirty valve body	Clean, service or replace valve body
Rough Initial Engagement (Forward or Reverse)	Improper fluid level	Check fluid level; See GENERAL SERVICING
	Engine idle speed too high	Check and adjust idle speed
	Automatic choke on (warm temperatures)	Disengage choke
	Looseness in half-shafts, "CV" joints, or engine mounts	Service and repair, or replace components as required
	Improper clutch or band operation, or oil control pressure	Perform CONTROL PRESSURE test
	Sticking or dirty valve body	Clean, service or replace valve body
No Drive in Any Gear	Improper fluid level	Check fluid level; See GENERAL SERVICING
	Damaged or improperly adjusted manual linkage	Check and adjust; See GENERAL SERVICING
	Improper clutch or band operation, or oil control pressure	Perform CONTROL PRESSURE test
	Internal leakage	Check and service as required
	Valve body bolts loose or too tight	Tighten valve body bolts to specification
	Damaged or worn clutches or band	Perform AIR PRESSURE test; Service as required
	Valve body dirty or contains sticking valves	Clean, inspect and repair, or replace valve body
	Broken pump or turbine shaft	Service as required
No Forward Engagement – Reverse OK	Improper fluid level	Check fluid level; See GENERAL SERVICING
	Manual linkage misadjusted or damaged	Check and adjust linkage or service as required
	Improper one-way clutch, band application, or oil control pressure	Perform CONTROL PRESSURE test; Service as required

Automatic Transmissions

FORD MOTOR CO. ATX TROUBLE SHOOTING (Cont.)

CONDITION	POSSIBLE CAUSE	CORRECTION
No Forward Engagement – Reverse OK (Cont.)	Valve body bolts loose or too tight	Tighten valve body bolts to specification
	Valve body dirty or contains sticking valves	Clean, inspect and repair or replace valve body
	Damaged or worn band or servo	Perform AIR PRESSURE test; Service as required
Slips, Shudders or Chatters In Reverse – Forward OK	Improper fluid level	Check fluid level; See GENERAL SERVICING
	Manual linkage misadjusted or damaged	Check and adjust linkage or service as required
	Improper control pressure	Perform CONTROL PRESSURE test
	Valve body bolts loose or too tight	Tighten valve body bolts to specification
	Valve body dirty or contains sticking valves	Clean, inspect and repair or replace valve body
	Damaged or worn Reverse clutch	Perform AIR PRESSURE test; Service as required
Will Not Start in "N" or "P"	Neutral safety switch improperly adjusted	Check and adjust switch
	Neutral safety switch wire disconnected or damaged	Service as required
	Manual linkage misadjusted or damaged	Check and adjust linkage or service as required
Slips or Chatters in 1st	Improper fluid level	Check fluid level; See GENERAL SERVICING
	Damaged or worn band	Service or replace band
Slips or Chatters in 2nd	Improper fluid level	Check fluid level; See GENERAL SERVICING
	Internal leakage	Check and service as required
	Valve body dirty or contains sticking valves	Clean, inspect and repair, or replace valve body
	Improper clutch application	Perform CONTROL PRESSURE test; Service as required
	Intermediate friction clutch faulty	Service clutch
	Polished, glazed band or drum	Replace or service as required
Starts Up in 2nd or 3rd	Improper fluid level	Check fluid level; See GENERAL SERVICING
	Manual linkage misadjusted or damaged	Check and adjust linkage or service as required
	Governor valve stuck	Perform GOVERNOR CHECK; Service or replace governor
	Improper clutch or band operation, or oil control pressure	Perform CONTROL PRESSURE test
	Valve body bolts loose or too tight	Tighten valve body bolts to specification
	Valve body dirty or contains sticking valves	Clean, inspect and repair, or replace valve body
	Cross leaks between valve body and case mating surface	Replace valve body and/or case as required
Incorrect Shift Points	Improper fluid level	Check fluid level; See GENERAL SERVICING
	Damaged or worn governor	Clean screen; Service or replace governor
	Improper band or clutch application, or control pressure	Perform CONTROL PRESSURE test
	Dirty or sticky valve body	Clean, service or replace valve body
No Upshift in Any Speed in "D"	Improper fluid level	Check fluid level; See GENERAL SERVICING
	Damaged or worn governor	Service or replace governor; Clean screen
	Valve body dirty or contains tricking valves	Clean, inspect and repair or replace valve body

CONDITION	POSSIBLE CAUSE	CORRECTION
No Upshift at Any Speed in "D" (Cont.)	Improper clutch or band operation, or oil control pressure	Perform CONTROL PRESSURE test
Shifts 1-3 in Drive	Dirty or sticking valve body	Clean, service or replace valve body
	Intermediate friction clutch burnt or damaged	Service as required
	Improper clutch application, or control pressure	Perform CONTROL PRESSURE test
Engine Overspeeds on 2-3 Upshift	Improper fluid level	Check fluid level; See GENERAL SERVICING
	Improper band or clutch application, or control pressure	Perform CONTROL PRESSURE test
	Damaged or worn direct clutch and/or servo	Perform AIR PRESSURE test; Service as required
	Dirty or sticking valve body	Clean, service or replace valve body
Early, Mushy, Soft or Slipping 1-2 Upshift	Improper fluid level	Check fluid level; See GENERAL SERVICING
	Improper intermediate clutch application, or oil control pressure	Perform CONTROL PRESSURE test
	Damaged intermediate clutch	Perform AIR PRESSURE test
	Valve body dirty or contains sticking valves	Clean, inspect and repair or replace valve body
Rough, Harsh or Delayed 1-2 Upshift	Improper fluid level	Check fluid level; See GENERAL SERVICING
	Incorrect engine performance	Diagnose and tune engine
	Improper intermediate clutch application, or oil control pressure	Perform CONTROL PRESSURE test
	Valve body dirty or contains sticking valves	Clean, inspect and repair or replace valve body
Rough 2-3 Shift (1-2 Shift OK)	Improper fluid level	Check fluid level; See GENERAL SERVICING
	Incorrect engine performance	Diagnose and tune engine
	Improper band release or direct clutch application, or oil control pressure	Perform CONTROL PRESSURE test
	Damaged or worn servo release and direct clutch piston check ball	Perform AIR PRESSURE test on servo apply and release, and direct clutch piston check ball; Service as required
	Dirty or sticking valve body	Clean, service or replace valve body
	Internal leakage or pump cavitation	Service pump as required
Rough 3-2 Shift at Closed Throttle in "D"	Improper fluid level	Check fluid level; See GENERAL SERVICING
	Incorrect engine idle or performance	Diagnose and tune engine
	Improper band or clutch application, or oil control pressure	Perform CONTROL PRESSURE test
	Improper governor operation	Perform GOVERNOR test; Service as required
	Dirty or sticking valve body	Clean, service or replace valve body

Automatic Transmissions

FORD MOTOR CO. ATX TROUBLE SHOOTING (Cont.)

CONDITION	POSSIBLE CAUSE	CORRECTION
No Forced Downshifts	Improper fluid level	Check fluid level; See GENERAL SERVICING
	Improper band or clutch application, or control pressure	Perform CONTROL PRESSURE test
	Damaged internal T.V. lever	Service internal lever
	Dirty or sticky valve body	Clean, service or replace valve body
	Dirty or sticking governor	Clean or replace governor
Engine Overspeeds on 3-2 or 3-1 Downshift (1-2 Shift OK)	Improper fluid level	Check fluid level; See GENERAL SERVICING
	Dirty or sticking valve body	Clean, service or replace valve body
	Band or clutch out of adjustment	Check and adjust servo rod travel
	Improper band or clutch application, or control pressure	Perform CONTROL PRESSURE test
	Damaged or worn servo	Perform AIR PRESSURE test; Service servo and/or seals
	Polished, glazed band or drum	Replace or service as required
No Engine Braking in Manual 1st	Improper fluid level	Check fluid level; See GENERAL SERVICING
	Manual linkage misadjusted or damaged	Check and adjust linkage or service as required
	Band or clutch out of adjustment	Check direct clutch and service as required; Check and adjust servo rod travel
	Improper control pressure	Perform CONTROL PRESSURE test
	Polished, glazed band or drum	Replace or service as required
	Dirty or sticking valve body	Clean, service or replace valve body
No Engine Braking in Manual 2nd	Improper fluid level	Check fluid level; See GENERAL SERVICING
	Manual linkage misadjusted or damaged	Check and adjust linkage or service as required
	Improper band or clutch application, or control pressure	Perform CONTROL PRESSURE test
	Leaking servo	Perform AIR PRESSURE test on servo to detect leaks; Service as required
	Polished, glazed band or drum	Replace or service as required
Transaxle Overheats	Excessive tow loads	Check owner's manual for restrictions
	Improper fluid level	Check fluid level; See GENERAL SERVICING
	Incorrect engine idle or performance	Diagnose and tune engine
	Improper band or clutch application, or control pressure	Perform CONTROL PRESSURE test
	Restriction in cooler or lines	Check cooler and lines for obstruction and service as required
	Seized converter one-way clutch	Replace torque converter
	Dirty or sticky valve body	Clean, service or replace valve body
Transaxle Leaks	Improper fluid level	Check fluid level; See GENERAL SERVICING
	Leakage at gasket, seals, etc.	Remove all traces of lubricant on exposed surfaces; Check vent for obstruction and damage; Operate transaxle at normal temperatures and perform FLUID LEAKAGE test; Service as required

FORD MOTOR CO. ATX TROUBLE SHOOTING (Cont.)

CONDITION	POSSIBLE CAUSE	CORRECTION
	TRANSAXLE NOISY	
Valve Resonance	Improper fluid level	Check fluid level; See GENERAL SERVICING
	Improper band or clutch application or control pressure	Perform CONTROL PRESSURE test
	Cooler lines grounding	Free cooler lines
	Dirty or sticking valve body	Clean, service or replace valve body
	Internal leakage or pump cavitation	Service pump as required
Other Than Valve Resonance	Linkage adjustment	Check and adjust, or replace linkage
	Improper fluid level	Check fluid level; See GENERAL SERVICING
	Contaminated fluid	Disassemble, clean and service transaxle; Flush torque converter and cooler
	Faulty speedometer driven gear	Replace speedometer driven gear
	Faulty half-shafts or "CV" joints	Service as required
	Faulty planetary gear set	Service gear set as required
	Faulty final drive gear set	Service gear set as required
	Loose converter-to-flywheel mounting bolts	Tighten bolts to specification

Automatic Transmissions

GENERAL MOTORS CONVERTER CLUTCH TROUBLE SHOOTING

Every diagnosis of automatic transmission problems should begin with a check of the transmission fluid and linkage. Most of the following conditions can be caused by one or more of the following factors: (1) Incorrect fluid level, (2) Contaminated fluid, (3) Improperly adjusted linkage, or (4) Damaged or worn linkage. When diagnosing Converter Clutch problems, ensure engine and vacuum systems are in perfect operating order.

CONDITION	POSSIBLE CAUSE	CORRECTION
No Converter Clutch Apply	Problem in Electronic Control Module (if equipped with Computer Command Control)	Verify Electronic Control Module operation
	Electrical Problem	
	Voltage not reaching transmission	Ensure 12 volts reach transmission to engage solenoid
	Ground inside transmission	Ensure solenoid is not grounded inside case
	Defective connector, wiring harness, or solenoid	Check and repair or replace as required
	Defective pressure switch (if equipped)	Check and replace pressure switch as required
	3rd clutch switch inoperative (THM 440-T4)	Check and replace switch as required
	4th clutch switch inoperative (THM 440-T4)	Check and replace switch as required
	Valve Body Assembly	
	Sticking converter clutch apply valve	Clean, service and/or replace valve body as required
	Sticking converter clutch shift valve	Clean, service and/or replace valve body as required
	Sticking throttle valve	Clean, service and/or replace valve body as required
	No. 10 check ball missing (THM 440-T4)	Inspect valve body and service as required
	Oil Pump Assembly	
	Orifice plugged for converter signal oil in pump	Clean and inspect orifice for blockage
	Solenoid "O" ring damaged or missing	Check and replace "O" ring
	Oil pump wear plate or gasket mispositioned or damaged	Check and replace wear plate or gasket
	Improper torque on oil pump-to-converter housing bolts	Tighten bolts to specifications
	Turbine shaft seals damaged	Check and replace seals
	Orifice cup plug omitted from cooler in passage	Check and install plug
	Channel Plate (THM 440-T4)	Check and replace converter clutch blow-off check ball if not seated or if damaged; Check and replace torque converter clutch accumulator piston or seal if damaged
Converter Clutch Apply Rough, Slipping, or Shudders	Converter clutch pressure plate faulty	Check plate for damage and service as required
	Damaged or missing check ball in end of turbine shaft	Check and replace turbine shaft, if required
	Converter clutch regulator valve stuck	Clean, service and/or replace valve body as required
	Converter clutch accumulator piston or seal damaged	Check and service as required
	Channel plate spring damaged (THM 440-T4)	Replace channel plate
	Incorrect converter clutch blow-off spring installed (THM 440-T4)	Check and install correct spring

GENERAL MOTORS CONVERTER CLUTCH TROUBLE SHOOTING (Cont.)

CONDITION	POSSIBLE CAUSE	CORRECTION
Converter Clutch Apply Rough, Slipping, or Shudders (Cont.)	Channel plate seals damaged or missing	Check and service as required
	Turbine shaft seals damaged or missing (THM 440-T4)	Check and replace turbine shaft seals or shaft
Converter Clutch Does Not Release	Solenoid does not exhaust	Verify Electronic Control Module operation (vehicles with Computer Command Control)
	Converter clutch apply valve stuck	Clean, service and/or replace valve body as required
	Check damaged converter	Replace torque converter
	Cup plug missing from pump release passage	Check and replace plug or pump assembly
	Turbine shaft end seal damaged or missing	Check and replace end seal or turbine shaft as required
	Hole not drilled through turbine shaft	Replace turbine shaft

GENERAL MOTORS THM 125C TROUBLE SHOOTING

Every diagnosis of automatic transmission problems should begin with a check of the transmission fluid and linkage. Most of the following conditions can be caused by one or more of the following factors: (1) Incorrect fluid level, (2) Contaminated fluid, (3) Improperly adjusted linkage, or (4) Damaged or worn linkage.

CONDITION	POSSIBLE CAUSE	CORRECTION
Delayed, Full Throttle, or No Upshifts	Improper fluid level	Check fluid level; See GENERAL SERVICING
	Manual linkage out of adjustment	Check and adjust linkage; see GENERAL SERVICING
	T.V. cable out of adjustment, damaged or sticking	Check and adjust or service as required; see GENERAL SERVICING
	Governor	
	Cover worn	Replace cover or governor as required
	Thrust washer omitted	Check and install thrust washer
	Governor seal worn or cut	Check and replace seal or governor assembly
	Spring not seated	Service as required
	Weights binding	Service as required
	Check ball missing	Install check ball
	Intermediate Servo	
	Wrong apply pin installed	Check and replace apply pin
	Seals cut, damaged, or leaking	Replace seals as required
	Piston damaged	Replace piston or intermediate servo as required
	Porosity in case bore area	Check and replace case
	Piston or apply pin sticking	Clean and service as required

CONDITION	POSSIBLE CAUSE	CORRECTION
Delayed, Full Throttle, or No Upshifts (Cont.)	Valve Body	
	Contains sticking valves	Clean, inspect and replace valve body as required
	Spacer plate gaskets leaking or incorrectly installed	Check and replace gaskets
	Valve body-to-case spacer plate clearance misadjusted	Check and adjust clearance as required
	Restricted feed orifice to 1-2 and 2-3 valves, and Drive to governor	Clean and clear obstruction; Service as required
	Intermediate band burnt or worn	Replace transmission
	Porous case cover, undrilled holes or missing plugs	Check and replace as required
	Leaks in governor passages and/or pipe in case cover	Perform pressure test and replace as required
	Case or case cover 2nd oil passage leaking	Check and service as required
	Driven gear stripped	Replace driven gear
1-2 Shift Complaint	Improper fluid level	Check fluid level; See GENERAL SERVICING
	T.V. cable out of adjustment, damaged or sticking	Check and adjust or service as required; see GENERAL SERVICING
	Oil pressure too high or too low	Perform OIL PRESSURE test and service as required
	Intermediate Servo	
	Seals cut, damaged, or leaking	Replace seals as required
	Piston damaged	Replace piston or intermediate servo as required
	Porosity in case bore	Check and replace case
	Servo orifice bleed cup plug missing	Check and install plug
	Leak between servo apply pin and case	Clean and service as required
	Wrong intermediate apply pin installed	Check and replace apply pin
	Band apply pin binds in case	Clean and service as required
	Valve Body	
	Contains sticking valves	Clean, inspect and replace valve body as required
	T.V. plunger, shift T.V. valve, or 1-2 accumulator valve binding	Service and replace as required
	1-2 accumulator piston binding, spring broken or missing, piston seal damaged, or piston bore damaged	Service as required
	Spacer plate gaskets leaking or incorrectly installed	Check and replace gaskets
	Case or case cover 2nd or servo apply oil passages leaking	Check and service as required
	Case or case cover 1-2 accumulator oil passage leaking	Check and service as required
	Intermediate band burnt	Check cause of condition; Service transmission
	Case cover bolts improperly tightened	Tighten bolts to specification
2-3 Shift Complaint	Improper fluid level	Check fluid level; See GENERAL SERVICING
	T.V. cable out of adjustment, damaged or sticking	Check and adjust or service as required; see GENERAL SERVICING

GENERAL MOTORS THM 125C TROUBLE SHOOTING (Cont.)

CONDITION	POSSIBLE CAUSE	CORRECTION
2-3 Shift Complaint (Cont.)	Manual linkage out of adjustment	Check and adjust linkage; see GENERAL SERVICING
	Oil pressure too high or too low	Perform OIL PRESSURE test and service as required
	Direct Clutch	
	Feed orifice in spacer plate restricted	Clear obstruction; Service as required
	Direct clutch check ball or capsule leaking	Service as required
	Accumulator exhaust hole plugged or not drilled	Clear obstruction; Service as required
	Exhaust valve check ball No. 1 missing, out of place, or leaking	Check position and seal of check ball; Service as required
	Accumulator exhaust check valve not seating in case	Check cause of condition; Service as required
	Piston seals missing or damaged	Service as required
	Direct clutch piston or housing cracked or damaged	Service as required
	Direct clutch apply ring missing or incorrect	Service direct clutch assembly
	Incorrect number of clutch plates	Install correct number of clutch plates
	Porosity in direct clutch case cover passages or incorrect case cover gaskets	Check porosity and gasket installation; Service as required
	Intermediate Servo	
	Piston-to-case oil seal ring missing or damaged	Replace seal as required
	Piston or case servo bore damaged	Service and repair or replace as required
	Orifice plug missing from case in servo bore area	Check and install plug
	Valve Body	
	Throttle valve and plunger, or shift T.V. valve binding	Clean and service as required
	Spacer plate gaskets leaking or incorrectly installed	Check and replace gaskets
	Valve body-to-case spacer plate clearance misadjusted	Check and adjust clearance as required
	Case cover check ball No. 5 not seating	Clean and clear obstruction; Service as required
	Driven Sprocket	
	Support passages interconnected, leaking, or restricted	Check passages; Service as required
	Support oil seal rings damaged or missing	Check seal rings; Service as required
	Sleeve loose or out of position	Check and correctly install sleeve
No or Delayed 2-3 Upshift – 1-2 OK	Improper fluid level	Check fluid level; See GENERAL SERVICING
	T.V. cable out of adjustment, damaged or sticking	Check and adjust or service as required; see GENERAL SERVICING
	Manual linkage out of adjustment	Check and adjust linkage; see GENERAL SERVICING

Automatic Transmissions

GENERAL MOTORS THM 125C TROUBLE SHOOTING (Cont.)

CONDITION	POSSIBLE CAUSE	CORRECTION
No or Delayed 2-3 Upshift – 1-2 OK (Cont.)	Case cover bolts loose, or center gasket leaking	Tighten bolts to specification; Replace gasket
	Case no. 5 case check ball missing or improperly seated	Service as required
	Governor	
	Cover worn	Replace governor assembly
	Thrust washer missing	Install thrust washer
	Seal worn or cut	Replace seal or governor assembly
	Spring not seated	Clean and properly seat or replace spring
	Weights binding	Correct cause of condition; Service as required
	Driven gear stripped or loose	Service as required
	Intermediate Servo	
	Piston-to-case oil seal ring missing or damaged	Replace seal as required
	Piston or case servo bore damaged	Service and repair or replace as required
	Orifice bleed plug missing from case	Check and install plug
	Direct clutch accumulator cup plug (in case) leaking or missing	Check or replace cup plug
	Porosity in case bore area	Check and replace case
	Accumulator exhaust check valve not seating in case	Check cause of condition; Service as required
	Valve Body	
	Valve body and spacer plate 2-3 shift, 2-3 T.V., or shift T.V. valves sticking	Clean and service as required
	Governor feed to 2-3 valve or direct clutch feed orifices restricted	Clean and clear obstruction; Service as required
	Spacer plate or gaskets leaking or incorrectly installed	Check and replace gaskets or spacer plate
	Case cover check ball No. 5 not seating	Clean and clear obstruction; Service as required
	Case-to-governor shaft sleeve damaged or missing	Service sleeve as required
	Direct Clutch	
	Piston seals missing or damaged	Service as required
	Piston or housing cracked	Service as required
	Clutch plates damaged or missing	Replace clutch plates
	Backing plate snap ring not seated in groove	Install snap ring properly
	Check ball capsule damaged or leaking	Service as required
	Driven Sprocket	
	Support passages interconnected, leaking, or restricted	Check passages; Service as required
	Support oil seal rings damaged or missing	Check seal rings; Service as required
	Sleeve loose or out of position	Check and correctly install sleeve
Delay in Drive & Reverse	Improper line pressures	Perform LINE PRESSURE tests; Service as required
	Converter drainback (noted by 3-5 second delay in "D" and "R" with engine off for 1 hour or longer)	Check and replace converter
	Turbine shaft Teflon seals damaged	Replace turbine shaft or seals; Replace scarf-cut seals with solid seals

GENERAL MOTORS THM 125C TROUBLE SHOOTING (Cont.)

CONDITION	POSSIBLE CAUSE	CORRECTION
No Drive in "D" or Intermediate Range (Lo & Reverse OK)	Lo roller clutch not holding	Service as required
No Drive in Forward Gears (Reverse Ties Up)	Sleeve turned in driven sprocket support	Service as required
No Drive Forward or Reverse in Any Gear	**Pulls Engine Down**	
	Internal mechanical damage	Disassemble and inspect components; Service as required
	Differential broken up	Disassemble and inspect components; Service as required
	Link and/or sprocket faulty	Check link and sprocket assembly for obstruction and alignment; Service as required
	Acts Like Neutral	
	Improper fluid level	Check fluid level; See GENERAL SERVICING
	Converter-to-flex plate bolts	Ensure all bolts are present and properly tightened
	Improper line pressures	Perform LINE PRESSURE tests; Service as required
	Manual linkage not moving manual valve	Service internal and external linkage as required
	Input shaft broken away from forward clutch drum	Inspect and service as required
	Reaction carrier broken at lo roller clutch cam	Inspect and service as required
	Chain assembly broken	Inspect and replace chain assembly
	Pressure regulator valve sticking	Clean and inspect regulator valve
	Worn pump seals	Replace seals
	Clutch plates burnt or worn	Check and replace clutch plates
	Broken oil pump shaft	Inspect and replace oil pump
No Drive in "D" (Reverse, Lo & Intermediate OK)	Improper fluid level	Check fluid level; See GENERAL SERVICING
	Forward clutch feed in input shaft restricted (if problem occurs only with cold engine or at fast engine idle)	Inspect and service as required
	Leak between case cover and driven sprocket support passages (if problem acts like Neutral or slips)	Replace gaskets
No Drive in Any Forward Gear (Reverse OK)	Improper line pressures	Perform LINE PRESSURE tests; Service as required
	Manual linkage not moving manual valve	Service internal and external linkage as required
	Drive oil passage in driven sprocket support or driven sprocket support-to-case cover gasket restricted	Check and replace gasket
	Drive oil passage leak in case cover	Check and replace case cover
	Sleeve in driven sprocket support loose or mislocated	Replace sleeve or sprocket support
	Forward clutch burnt	Determine cause and replace clutch
	Valve body pipe in control valve pump assembly leaking or missing	Replace pump assembly

Automatic Transmissions

GENERAL MOTORS THM 125C TROUBLE SHOOTING (Cont.)

CONDITION	POSSIBLE CAUSE	CORRECTION
No Reverse (All Forward Gears OK)	Forward clutch will not release	Replace clutch plates if burnt; Replace piston seal ring; Clean exhaust check ball
	Improper line pressures	Perform LINE PRESSURE tests; Service as required
	Case-to-lo and reverse clutch housing cup plug assembly restricted or not fully seated	Replace plug assembly
	Lo and reverse clutch seals or piston leaks	Perform AIR PRESSURE test; Service as required
	Lo and reverse pipe "O" ring or washer damaged or missing	Replace "O" ring, washer of pipe as required
	Incorrect gasket for driven sprocket support height	Replace gasket
	Case cover leaking or damaged	Replace gasket or cover
	Plugged or missing lo 1st orifice in spacer plate	Clear obstruction or replace spacer plate
	Direct clutch or lo and reverse clutch burnt	Determine cause and replace clutch
Starts Up in 2nd, Misses 1st at Times	Governor springs distorted or out of place	Replace governor assembly
	Governor weights binding	Determine cause of condition and service as required
	1-2 shift valve or 1-2 throttle valve sticking in upshift position	Clean and inspect valve body; Service as required
Shifts 3-1 at High Speeds for Passing Gear (Detent Downshifts)	Governor faulty	Check and replace governor assembly
	Intermediate servo sticking	Clean and inspect servo; Service as required
	Direct clutch orifice controlled by No. 2 check ball restricted	Clear obstruction; Service as required
	1-2 accumulator piston missing, or seal leaking	Inspect and replace piston assembly
Slips, Chatters in 1st Gear	Improper fluid level	Check fluid level; See GENERAL SERVICING
	Improper line pressures	Perform LINE PRESSURE tests; Service as required
	T.V. cable out of adjustment, damaged or sticking	Check and adjust or service as required; see GENERAL SERVICING
	Restricted feed to forward clutch	Clear obstruction and service as required
	Forward clutch burnt	Determine cause of condition; Service as required
	Rough machine surface on driven sprocket support	Service as required
	Incorrect case cover gaskets	Install correct gaskets
Shifts 1-3	Intermediate servo sticking, leaking, or damaged	Service intermediate servo as required
	Accumulator exhaust check valve sticking, or not seating	Service check valve as required
	1-2 valve sticking in control valve pump assembly	Clean and service as required
	Spacer plate gaskets incorrectly installed	Replace gaskets

CONDITION	POSSIBLE CAUSE	CORRECTION
Shifts 1-3 (Cont.)	Governor feed to 1-2 valve in spacer plate blocked	Clean and clear obstruction; Replace spacer plate
	Spacer plate intermediate band apply feed orifice blocked	Clean and clear obstruction; Replace spacer plate
	Wrong spacer installed	Check and replace spacer plate
	Intermediate servo apply passage (2nd oil passage) in case or case cover blocked	Clean and clear obstruction; Replace case or case cover
	Intermediate band improperly installed, burnt or broken	Service intermediate band as required
No Full Throttle (Detent) Downshift 3-2	T.V. cable out of adjustment, damaged or sticking	Check and adjust or service as required; see GENERAL SERVICING
	Accelerator pedal and/or linkage will not open carburetor to wide open throttle	Service control linkage as required
	Control valve pump assembly shift T.V. valve or throttle valve binding	Clean and service as required
	Spacer plate holes plugged (gaskets mispositioned or damaged)	Check and replace gasket or spacer plate
No 2nd Gear	Servo oil seal ring missing or damage	Replace servo oil seal ring
	Intermediate band out of position, broken or burnt	Determine cause of condition; Service as required
	1-2 accumulator piston or pin damaged or missing	Replace accumulator piston assembly
No Overrun Braking in Lo (Reverse OK)	Manual linkage out of adjustment	Check and adjust manual linkage; See GENERAL SERVICING
	Lo-Reverse pipe or Lo-Reverse piston seals leaking	Service as required
	Lo blow-off valve assembly damaged	Service as required
TRANSAXLE NOISY		
Park, Neutral & All Drive Ranges	Pump Cavitation Improper fluid level	Check fluid level; See GENERAL SERVICING
	Damaged "O" ring seal	Replace seal
	Porosity in case intake area	Check for porosity; Service as required
	Water in oil	Determine cause; Service as required
	Drive Link Assembly Rubbing on case	Inspect and service as required
	Pump or driven sprocket needle bearing improperly installed	Check installation; Service as required
	Converter Loose converter-to-flex plate bolts	Tighten bolts to specification
	Cracked or broken flex plate	Check and replace flex plate
	Converter damaged	Replace converter

Automatic Transmissions

GENERAL MOTORS THM 125C TROUBLE SHOOTING (Cont.)

CONDITION	POSSIBLE CAUSE	CORRECTION
	TRANSAXLE NOISY (Cont.)	
During Acceleration – Any Gear	Transmission cooler lines grounded to underbody	Service as required
	Sprocket support needle bearings worn or damaged	Check installation; Service as required
	Drive link assembly worn or damaged	Replace drive link assembly
Squeal at Low Vehicle Speeds (Hot)	Speedometer driven gear shaft seal faulty or needs lubrication	Lubricate or replace shaft seal
	Speedometer adapter too long	Replace speedometer adapter
1st & Reverse Gears Only	Worn or damaged input gear set	Inspect and replace gear set
	Worn or damaged reaction gear set	Inspect and replace gear set
	Worn or damaged final drive gear set	Inspect and replace gear set
	Worn or damaged differential gear set	Inspect and replace gear set
	Worn or damaged planetary gear set	Inspect and replace gear set
2nd Gear Only	Worn or damaged input gear set	Inspect and replace gear set
	Worn or damaged final drive gear set	Inspect and replace gear set
	Worn or damaged differential gear set	Inspect and replace gear set
	Worn or damaged planetary gear set	Inspect and replace gear set
3rd Gear Only and/or on Turns	Worn or damaged final drive gear set	Inspect and replace gear set
	Worn or damaged differential gear set	Inspect and replace gear set
	Worn or damaged planetary gear set	Inspect and replace gear set

GENERAL MOTORS THM 180C TROUBLE SHOOTING

Every diagnosis of automatic transmission problems should begin with a check of the transmission fluid and linkage. Most of the following conditions can be caused by one or more of the following factors: (1) Incorrect fluid level, (2) Contaminated fluid, (3) Improperly adjusted linkage, or (4) Damaged or worn linkage.

CONDITION	POSSIBLE CAUSE	CORRECTION
No Drive in Any Drive Range	Improper fluid level	Check fluid level; See GENERAL SERVICING
	Blocked suction screen	Clean screen
	Manual valve linkage or inner transmission selector lever disconnected	Service as required
	Input shaft broken	Replace input shaft assembly
	Pressure regulator valve stuck open	Clean and service as required
	Oil pump faulty	Replace oil pump
Delayed Drive in Any Drive Range (Possible After Repeat Selector Movement)	Manual Valve Position Does Not Coincide With Valve Body Channels	
	Selector shaft retaining pin missing	Replace retaining pin
	Connecting rod to manual valve loose	Repair or replace rod
	Selector lever shaft nut loose	Tighten nut

GENERAL MOTORS THM 180C TROUBLE SHOOTING (Cont.)

CONDITION	POSSIBLE CAUSE	CORRECTION
No Drive After Shifting from "P" to "D", "L₂" or "L₁" (Inadequate Engine Acceleration	Parking Pawl Does Not Disengage	Service as required
Sudden Drive Only After Increase of Engine RPM	Band servo piston jamming	Determine cause and service as required
	Improper fluid level	Check fluid level; See GENERAL SERVICING
	Oil pump faulty	Replace oil pump
	Oil screen missing	Replace screen
	Sealing ball in valve body missing	Replace ball
Heavy Jerking When Starting	Incorrect oil pressure	Perform PRESSURE test; Service as required
	Wrong modulator valve	Inspect and install correct valve
	Pressure regulator valve stuck	Determine cause; Service as required
	Sealing ball in valve body missing	Replace ball
No Drive in "D" or "L₂" ("L₁" & "R" OK)	Input sprag faulty or installed backward	Check and properly install or replace sprag
No Drive in "D" or "L₂" & "L₁" ("R" OK)	Band worn, does not grip	Replace band
	Band servo piston jamming	Determine cause; Service as required
	Excessive leak in band servo	Service as required
	Parking pawl does not disengage	Service as required
No Drive in "R" (All Others OK)	Reverse clutch failure	Replace clutch assembly
Drives in Neutral	Inadequate selector lever linkage	Replace linkage
	Planetary gear set broken	Replace planetary gear set
	Improper band adjustment	Adjust band; See GENERAL SERVICING
No 1-2 Upshift in "D" and "L₂" (Transmission Remains in 1st)	Governor valves stuck	Clean and free valves; Service as required
	1-2 shift valve stuck in 1st gear position	Clean and free valve; Service as required
	Oil pump hub seal rings leaking	Replace seal rings or oil pump hub
	Leak in governor pressure circuit	Perform PRESSURE test; Service as required
	Governor screen blocked	Clear blockage
No 2-3 Upshift in "D" (Transmission Remains in 2nd)	2-3 shift valve stuck	Clean and free valve; Service as required
	Leak in governor pressure circuit	Perform PRESSURE test; Service as required
Upshifts in "D" & "L₂" Only at Full Throttle	Faulty vacuum modulator	Replace vacuum modulator
	Leak or block in modulator vacuum line	Determine cause and service as required
	Engine vacuum leaks	Service as required
	Detent valve or cable stuck	Service as required
Upshifts in "D" & "L₂" Only at Part Throttle (No Detent Position)	Detent pressure regulator valve stuck	Clean and free valve; Service as required
	Detent cable broken or misadjusted	Check and adjust, or replace cable
Drive Only in 1st Gear of "D" & "L₂" (Blocks in 2nd & "R")	"L₁" and "R" control valve stuck in "L₁" or "R"	Clean and free valves; Service as required

Automatic Transmissions

GENERAL MOTORS THM 180C TROUBLE SHOOTING (Cont.)

CONDITION	POSSIBLE CAUSE	CORRECTION
No Part Throttle 3-2 Downshift at Low Speeds	3-2 downshift control valve stuck	Clean and free valve; Service as required
No Forced Downshift	Detent cable broken or misadjusted	Check and adjust, or replace cable
	Detent pressure regulator valve stuck	Clean and free valve; Service as required
After Full Throttle Upshift, Transmission Shifts to Lower Gear When Foot Eases Off Accelerator Pedal		
	Detent valve stuck in open position	Clean and free valve; Service as required
	Detent cable stuck	Service as required
	Leak or block in modulator vacuum line	Determine cause and service as required
At Higher Speed, Transmission Shifts to Lower Gear		
	Selector lever shaft retaining pin in transmission dropped out	Replace pin
	Loose selector lever linkage to manual valve	Tighten or replace linkage
	Pressure loss at governor	Perform PRESSURE test; Service as required
Hard Disengagement of Lever From "P"		
	Steel guide bushing of parking pawl actuating rod missing	Check and replace guide bushing
	Manual selector valve stuck	Clean and free valve; Service as required
Slipping 1-2 Upshift (Engine Flares)		
	Improper fluid level	Check fluid level; See GENERAL SERVICING
	Valve body sealing ball dropped out	Replace sealing ball
	Second clutch piston seals leaking	Service as required
	Second clutch centrifugal ball stuck open	Clean and free ball; Service as required
	Second clutch piston cracked or broken	Replace piston assembly
	Second clutch plates worn	Replace plates
	Oil pump hub seal rings leaking	Replace seal rings or oil pump hub
Slipping 2-3 Upshift (Engine Flares)		
	Improper fluid level	Check fluid level; See GENERAL SERVICING
	Band adjustment loose	Adjust band
	Third clutch piston seals leaking	Service as required
	Third clutch centrifugal ball stuck open	Clean and free ball; Service as required
	Third clutch piston cracked or broken	Replace piston assembly
	Input shaft bearing worn	Replace input shaft bearing
	Valve body sealing ball dropped out	Replace sealing ball
Abrupt 1-2 Upshift	High oil pressure	Perform PRESSURE test; Service as required
	1-2 accumulator valve stuck	Clean and free valve; Service as required
	Broke second clutch spring cushion	Service as required
	Second gear ball valve missing	Replace valve
Abrupt 2-3 Upshift	High oil pressure	Perform PRESSURE test; Service as required
	Incorrect band adjustment	Check and adjust band
Abrupt 3-2 Detent Downshift at High Speed	High speed downshift valve stuck open	Clean and free valve; Service as required
	Incorrect band adjustment	Check and adjust band
Abrupt 3-2 Coast Downshift	Low speed downshift timing valve stuck open	Clean and free valve; Service as required

CONDITION	POSSIBLE CAUSE	CORRECTION
Flare on High Speed Forced Downshift	Low oil pressure	Perform PRESSURE test; Service as required
	Incorrect band adjustment	Check and adjust band
Flare on Low Speed Forced Downshift	Low oil pressure	Perform PRESSURE test; Service as required
	Incorrect band adjustment	Check and adjust band
	High speed downshift timing valve stuck closed	Clean and free valve; Service as required
	Sprag race does not grip on 3-1 downshifting	Determine cause of condition; Service as required
No Engine Braking in "L₁"	Selector lever linkage improperly adjusted	Adjust linkage
	Manual low control valve stuck	Clean and free valve; Service as required
No Engine Braking in "L₂"	Selector lever linkage improperly adjusted	Adjust linkage
No Park	Selector lever linkage improperly adjusted	Adjust linkage
	Parking lock actuator spring	Check and replace spring
	Parking pawl	Check and replace pawl
	Governor hub	Check and replace governor assembly
TRANSMISSION NOISY		
Excessive Noise in All Drive Ranges	Too much backlash between sun gear and planetary gear	Check backlash; Service as required
	Lock plate on planetary carrier loose	Tighten or replace plate or planetary gear set
	Defective thrust bearing	Replace thrust bearing
	Bearing bushings worn	Replace bearing assembly
	Excessive transmission axial play	Determine cause of condition; Service as required
	Unhooked parking pawl spring contacts governor hub	Service as required
	Converter balancing weights loose	Replace converter
	Converter housing attaching bolt loose and contacting converter	Check for damage; Service as required
Screeching Noise When Starting	Converter failure	Determine cause of condition; Replace converter
Short Vibrating, Hissing Noise Shortly Before 1-2 Upshift	Dampening cushion of reverse clutch wearing into transmission case	Determine cause of condition; Service as required
Buzzing Noise	Clogged oil filter	Replace oil filter and gasket

Automatic Transmissions

GENERAL MOTORS THM 200C TROUBLE SHOOTING

Every diagnosis of automatic transmission problems should begin with a check of the transmission fluid and linkage. Most of the following conditions can be caused by one or more of the following factors: (1) Incorrect fluid level, (2) Contaminated fluid, (3) Improperly adjusted linkage, or (4) Damaged or worn linkage.

CONDITION	POSSIBLE CAUSE	CORRECTION
No Drive in "D"	Improper fluid level	Check fluid level; See GENERAL SERVICING
	Manual linkage misadjusted	Adjust linkage; See GENERAL SERVICING
	Low oil pressure	Perform PRESSURE test; Service as required
	Forward clutch Does not apply	Check piston for cracks and/or damaged or missing seals
	Burnt clutch plates	Determine cause of condition; Service as required
	Snap ring out of groove	Check and correctly install
	Oil seal rings missing or damaged on turbine shaft	Check and replace seal rings or turbine shaft
	Leak in feed circuits	Clean and check circuits; Service as required
	Pump-to-case gasket mispositioned or damaged	Replace gasket
	Clutch housing check ball stuck or missing	Clean and free ball; Service as required
	Cup plug leaking or missing in rear of turbine shaft in clutch apply passage	Check and replace cup plug
	Wrong forward clutch piston assembly	Check and replace piston assembly
	Wrong number of clutch plates	Verify number of plates; Service as required
	Turbine shaft feed orifice plugged	Clean and clear obstruction; Service as required
	Roller Clutch Springs missing	Replace roller clutch
	Rollers galled or missing	Service as required
1-2 Shift at Full Throttle Only	Throttle valve cable binding, unhooked, broken or misadjusted	Service as required
	Throttle lever and bracket assembly binding or unhooked	Service as required
	T.V. exhaust ball lifter or No. 5 ball binding, mispositioned, or unhooked (Allowing No. 5 ball to seat causes full T.V. pressure regardless of throttle valve position)	Service as required
	Throttle valve and plunger binding	Clean and free valve and plunger; Service as required
	Valve body assembly gaskets leaking, damaged, incorrectly installed	Service as required
1st Only, No 1-2 Upshift	Governor and Governor Feed Passages Plugged governor oil feed orifice in spacer plate	Clear obstruction; Service as required
	Plugged governor oil-to-shift valve passage in spacer plate	Clear obstruction; Service as required
	Governor ball(s) missing	Replace governor assembly
	Inner governor cover "O" ring seal missing or leaking	Replace seal (If outer "O" ring seal leaks, leak will be present with no upshifts)
	Governor shaft seal missing or damaged	Replace seal
	Governor weights binding on pin	Replace governor

GENERAL MOTORS THM 200C TROUBLE SHOOTING (Cont.)

CONDITION	POSSIBLE CAUSE	CORRECTION
1st Only, No 1-2 Upshift (Cont.)	Case	
	Porosity in channels or undrilled 2nd speed feed holes	Service as required
	Excessive leakage between case bore and intermediate band apply ring	Service as required
	Intermediate band anchor pin missing or unhooked from band	Replace anchor pin
	Broken or missing band	Service as required
	Intermediate Servo Assembly	
	Servo-to-cover oil seal ring missing or damaged	Replace oil seal
	Porosity in cover or piston	Service as required
	Wrong intermediate band apply pin	Replace pin
	Incorrect usage of cover and pin	Service as required
	1-2 shift valve or 1-2 throttle valve in valve body stuck in downshift position	Clean and free valve; Service as required
1st & 2nd Only, No 2-3 Shift	Valve Body and Spacer Plate	
	2-3 shift valve or 2-3 throttle valve stuck in downshift position	Clean and free valve; Service as required
	Direct clutch feed orifice in spacer plate plugged	Clean and clear obstruction; Service as required
	Valve body gaskets leaking, damaged or incorrectly installed	Replace gasket
	Pump	
	Channels plugged or leaking	Clean and clear obstruction; Service as required
	Pump-to-case gasket mislocated	Replace gasket
	Rear oil seal ring leaking or missing	Replace oil seal ring
	Direct Clutch	
	Oil seals missing or damaged on piston	Replace oil seals
	Piston or housing cracked	Service as required
	Plates damaged or missing	Replace plates
	Backing plate snap ring out of groove	Install or replace snap ring
	Intermediate Servo Assembly	
	Servo-to-case oil seal ring broken or missing on piston	Replace intermediate servo piston
	Exhaust hole in case between piston seal rings plugged or undrilled	Service as required
	Porosity in case channels	Service as required

Automatic Transmissions

GENERAL MOTORS THM 200C TROUBLE SHOOTING (Cont.)

CONDITION	POSSIBLE CAUSE	CORRECTION
Drive in Neutral (Creeps)	Manual linkage misadjusted or disconnected	Adjust or service as required; See GENERAL SERVICING
	Forward clutch does not release	Determine cause of condition; Service as required
	Cross leakage in pump passages	Determine cause of condition; Service as required
	Cross leakage to forward clutch passages in case	Determine cause of condition; Service as required
No Drive or Slips in Reverse	Throttle valve cable binding or misadjusted	Adjust or service as required; See GENERAL SERVICING
	Manual linkage misadjusted	Adjust linkage; See GENERAL SERVICING
	Throttle valve binding	Clean and service as required
	Shift T.V. valve binding in valve body bore	Clean and service as required
	Reverse boost valve binding in valve body bore	Clean and service as required
	Low overrun clutch valve binding in valve body bore (Line pressure readings normal)	Clean and service as required
	Reverse clutch piston cracked, broken, or seals missing	Service as required
	Reverse clutch plates burnt	Determine cause of condition; Service as required
	Reverse clutch has wrong selective spacer ring	Inspect and determine correct spacer ring; Service as required
	Direct Clutch Passages	
	Porosity in case passages	Service as required
	Pump case-to-pump gasket faulty	Check gasket for correct positioning and damage; Replace gasket
	Pump channels leaking or restricted	Determine condition and service as required
	Pump cover oil seal rings faulty	Check for presence of rings and condition; Replace oil seal rings
	Piston or housing cracked	Replace piston or housing
	Piston seals cut or missing	Replace piston seals
	Housing check ball faulty	Inspect check ball for sticking, leaking, or missing; Service as required
	Plates burnt	Determine cause of condition; Service as required
	Incorrect piston	Inspect and replace piston, if required
	Spacer plate orifices plugged	Clean and clear obstruction; Service as required
	Intermediate servo-to-case oil seal ring cut or missing	Check and replace oil seal ring
Slipping 1-2 Shift	Improper fluid level	Check fluid level; See GENERAL SERVICING
	Spacer plate 2nd speed feed orifice partially blocked	Clean and clear obstruction; Service as required
	Spacer plate gaskets damaged or mispositioned	Replace spacer plate gaskets

GENERAL MOTORS THM 200C TROUBLE SHOOTING (Cont.)

CONDITION	POSSIBLE CAUSE	CORRECTION
Slipping 1-2 Shift (Cont.)	1-2 accumulator valve sticking in valve body	Clean valve; Service as required
	Weak or missing 1-2 accumulator valve spring	Replace valve and spring assembly
	1-2 accumulator piston seal leaking, spring broken or missing	Service as required
	Leak between 1-2 accumulator piston and pin	Determine cause and service as required
	Wrong intermediate band apply pin	Check and determine correct apply pin; Service as required
	Excessive leakage between intermediate band apply pin and case	Determine cause and service as required
	Porosity in intermediate servo piston	Service as required
	Intermediate servo assembly cover-to-servo oil seal ring damaged or missing	Replace oil seal ring
	Incorrect intermediate servo assembly cover and piston	Check and determine correct cover and piston; Service as required
	Throttle valve cable misadjusted	Adjust or service as required; See GENERAL SERVICING
	Throttle valve binding	Clean and service as required
	Shift T.V. valve binding in valve body bore	Clean and service as required
	Intermediate band worn or burnt	Determine cause of condition; Service as required
	Case porosity in 2nd clutch passages	Service as required
Rough 1-2 Shift	Throttle valve cable misadjusted or binding	Adjust or service as required; See GENERAL SERVICING
	Throttle valve binding	Clean and service as required
	Throttle valve plunger binding	Clean and service as required
	Shift T.V. valve binding	Clean and service as required
	1-2 accumulator valve binding	Clean valve; Service as required
	Wrong intermediate servo band apply pin	Check and determine correct apply pin; Service as required
	Intermediate servo piston-to-case oil seal ring damaged or missing	Replace oil seal ring
	1-2 accumulator oil ring damaged	Replace oil ring
	1-2 accumulator piston stuck	Clean and clear piston; Service as required
	1-2 accumulator spring broken or missing	Replace 1-2 accumulator
	1-2 accumulator bore damaged	Service as required
Slipping 2-3 Shift	Improper fluid level	Check fluid level; See GENERAL SERVICING
	Throttle valve cable misadjusted	Adjust as required; See GENERAL SERVICING
	Throttle valve binding	Clean and service as required
	Direct clutch orifice partially blocked in spacer plate	Clean and clear obstruction; Service as required
	Spacer plate gaskets damaged or mispositioned	Replace gaskets
	Intermediate servo-to-case oil seal ring damaged	Determine cause and service as required

Automatic Transmissions

GENERAL MOTORS THM 200C TROUBLE SHOOTING (Cont.)

CONDITION	POSSIBLE CAUSE	CORRECTION
Slipping 2-3 Shift (Cont.)	Direct Clutch Feed	
	Porosity in feed channels in case	Service as required
	Pump case-to-pump gasket faulty	Check gasket for correct positioning and damage; Replace gasket
	Pump channels leaking or restricted	Determine condition and service as required
	Pump cover oil seal rings faulty	Check for presence of rings and condition; Replace oil seal rings
	Piston or housing cracked	Replace piston or housing
	Piston seals cut or missing	Replace piston seals
	Plates burnt	Determine cause of condition; Service as required
Rough 2-3 Shift	Throttle valve cable misadjusted or binding	Adjust or service as required; See GENERAL SERVICING
	Throttle valve binding	Clean and service as required
	Throttle valve plunger binding	Clean and service as required
	Shift T.V. valve binding	Clean and service as required
	Exhaust hole undrilled or plugged between intermediate servo piston seals, not allowing piston to complete stroke	Service as required
	Direct clutch exhaust valve check ball No. 4 missing or mispositioned	Replace No. 4 check ball
No Engine Braking in "L2"	Intermediate boost valve binding in valve body	Clean and service as required
	Intermediate reverse check ball (No. 3 check ball) mispositioned or missing	Replace No. 3 check ball
	Shift T.V. check ball (No. 1 check ball) mispositioned or missing	Replace No. 1 check ball
	Intermediate servo assembly cover-to-servo oil seal ring damaged or missing	Replace oil seal ring
	Intermediate band off anchor pin	Service as required
	Intermediate band broken or burnt	Determine cause of condition; Service as required
No Engine Braking in "L1"	Low overrun clutch valve binding in valve body	Clean and service as required
	Low-Reverse clutch assembly worn or damaged	Service as required
No Engine Braking in "L1" With No Reverse	Piston seals broken or missing	Replace seals
	Porosity in piston or housing	Service as required
	Clutch housing snap ring out of case	Replace snap ring
	Cup plug or rubber seal missing or damaged between case and Low-Reverse clutch housing	Service as required
No Part Throttle Downshift	Throttle plunger bushing passages not open	Determine cause of condition; Service as required
	2-3 throttle valve bushing passages not open	Determine cause of condition; Service as required
	Valve body gaskets mispositioned or damaged	Replace valve body gaskets

GENERAL MOTORS THM 200C TROUBLE SHOOTING (Cont.)

CONDITION	POSSIBLE CAUSE	CORRECTION
No Part Throttle Downshift (Cont.)	Spacer plate hole plugged or undrilled	Service as required
	Throttle valve cable improperly set	Adjust or replace; See GENERAL SERVICING
	Shift T.V. valve binding	Clean and free valve; Service as required
	Throttle valve binding	Clean and free valve; Service as required
No Park	Manual linkage misadjusted	Adjust linkage; See GENERAL SERVICING
	Internal linkage parking pawl binding in case or broken	Service as required
	Internal linkage actuator rod or plunger damaged	Service as required
	Internal linkage parking bracket loose or damaged	Service as required
	Inside detent lever and pin assembly nut loose, or lever hole worn or damaged	Service as required
	Manual detent roller and spring assembly bolt loose holding roller assembly to valve body, or pin or roller damaged, mispositioned or missing	Service as required

GENERAL MOTORS THM 200-4R TROUBLE SHOOTING

Every diagnosis of automatic transmission problems should begin with a check of the transmission fluid and linkage. Most of the following conditions can be caused by one or more of the following factors: (1) Incorrect fluid level, (2) Contaminated fluid, (3) Improperly adjusted linkage, or (4) Damaged or worn linkage.

CONDITION	POSSIBLE CAUSE	CORRECTION
No Drive in "D"	Improper fluid level	Check fluid level; See GENERAL SERVICING
	Manual linkage out of adjustment	Check and adjust linkage; see GENERAL SERVICING
	Low oil pressure	
	Plugged or restricted oil filter	Replace oil filter
	Cut or missing oil filter "O" rings	Replace "O" rings or filter
	Pump pressure regulator stuck	Clean and free regulator; Service as required
	Pump rotor tangs damaged by converter	Determine cause of condition; Service as required
	Porosity in filter-to-pump intake bore	Service as required
	Overdrive unit springs missing in roller clutch	Replace roller clutch
	Overdrive unit rollers galled or missing	Replace roller clutch
	Forward Clutch	
	Does not apply – piston cracked; piston seals damaged or missing; clutch plates burnt; snap ring out of groove	Service as required
	Oil seal rings missing or damaged on turbine shaft; leak in feed circuits; pump-to-case gasket mispositioned or damaged	Service as required
	Clutch housing check ball stuck or missing	Replace check ball
	Cup plug leaking or missing in rear of forward clutch shaft in clutch apply passage	Replace cup plug

Automatic Transmissions

GENERAL MOTORS THM 200-4R TROUBLE SHOOTING (Cont.)

CONDITION	POSSIBLE CAUSE	CORRECTION
No Drive in "D" (Cont.)	Lo and Reverse roller clutch springs missing in roller clutch	Replace roller clutch
	Lo and Reverse roller clutch rollers galled or missing	Replace roller clutch
1-2 Shift at Full Throttle Only	Throttle valve cable binding, unhooked, broken, or misadjusted	Service as required; See GENERAL SERVICING
	Throttle lever and bracket assembly binding or unhooked	Service as required
	T.V. exhaust ball lifter binding, mispositioned, or unhooked (No. 5 check ball sealing causes full T.V. pressure regardless of throttle valve position)	Service as required
	Throttle valve and plunger binding	Clean and free valve and plunger; Service as required
	Valve body gaskets leaking, damaged, or mispositioned	Replace valve body gaskets
	Porosity in case assembly	Service as required
1st Only – No 1-2 Shift	Governor and Governor Feed Passages Plugged governor oil feed orifice in spacer plate	Clean orifice of blockage
	Governor ball(s) missing	Replace governor assembly
	Governor shaft seal missing or damaged	Replace governor shaft seal
	Governor driven gear stripped	Replace governor assembly
	Governor weights binding on pin	Determine cause of condition; Service as required
	Governor driven gear not engaged with governor shaft	Service as required
	1-2 shift, Lo-1st/Detent, or 1-2 throttle valves stuck in downshift position in valve body	Service as required
	Spacer plate gaskets mispositioned	Replace spacer plate gaskets
	Porosity in case channels or undrilled 2nd oil feed hole in case	Service as required
	Excessive leakage between case bore and intermediate band apply rings	Service as required
	Intermediate band anchor pin missing or unhooked from band	Replace band anchor pin
	Broken or missing intermediate band	Replace intermediate band
	Intermediate servo cover oil seal ring missing	Replace oil seal ring
	Porosity in intermediate servo, cover, inner piston, or outer piston	Service as required
	Wrong intermediate band apply pin	Check and determine correct band apply pin; Service as required
	Incorrect usage of intermediate cover and piston	Check and determine correct cover and piston; Service as required
	1-2 accumulator housing bolts loose, housing face damaged, or damaged or missing accumulator plate	Service as required

GENERAL MOTORS THM 200-4R TROUBLE SHOOTING (Cont.)

CONDITION	POSSIBLE CAUSE	CORRECTION
1st & 2nd Only – No 2-3 Shift	Valve Body and Spacer Plate Assembly 2-3 shift or 2-3 throttle valves stuck in downshift position	Clean and free valves; Service as required
	Gaskets leaking, damaged or mispositioned	Replace gaskets
	Reverse/3rd check ball not seating, damaged or missing	Replace Reverse/3rd check ball
	Porosity in case channels	Service as required
	Center support direct clutch feed passage plugged or not drilled	Service as required
	Center support steel oil rings damaged	Replace center support
	Direct Clutch Inner oil seal ring missing or damaged on piston	Replace oil seal or piston
	Center oil seal ring missing or damaged on direct clutch hub	Replace oil seal or clutch
	Check ball and/or retainer damaged or missing from piston	Replace direct clutch piston
	Piston or housing damaged or missing	Service as required
	Plates damaged or missing	Replace plates
	Backing plate snap ring out of groove	Install or replace snap ring
	Release spring guide mislocated	Replace release spring guide
	Intermediate Servo Assembly (3rd Clutch Accumulator Oil Passages) Servo-to-case oil seal ring broken or missing on piston	Replace intermediate servo piston
	Intermediate servo and/or capsule missing or damaged	Replace intermediate servo assembly
	Exhaust hole in case between piston seal rings plugged or undrilled	Service as required
	Bleed orifice cup plug missing from intermediate servo pocket in case	Replace bleed orifice cup plug
No Drive or Slips in "R"	Throttle valve cable binding or misadjusted	Adjust or replace cable; See GENERAL SERVICING
	Manual linkage misadjusted	Adjust manual linkage; See GENERAL SERVICING
	Throttle valve binding	Clean and free valve; Service as required
	T.V. limit valve binding	Clean and free valve; Service as required
	Line bias valve binding	Clean and free valve; Service as required
	Reverse boost valve bind in pressure regulator bore	Clean and free valve; Service as required
	Reverse/3rd or Lo/Reverse check ball missing or spacer plate seat damaged	Replace check ball or spacer plate
	Reverse clutch piston cracked, or missing inner or outer seals	Replace Reverse clutch piston assembly
	Reverse clutch plates burnt	Determine cause of condition; Service as required
	Reverse clutch oil seal in case missing or damaged	Replace oil seal
	Reverse clutch missing clutch or wave plate	Service as required

Automatic Transmissions

GENERAL MOTORS THM 200-4R TROUBLE SHOOTING (Cont.)

CONDITION	POSSIBLE CAUSE	CORRECTION
No Drive or Slips in "R" (Cont.)	Center support attaching bolts loose or missing	Tighten or replace bolts
	Center support passages blocked or holes not drilled	Service as required
	Center support porosity	Replace center support
	Direct clutch piston or housing cracked	Replace piston or housing
	Direct clutch check ball in housing or piston missing or damaged	Replace check ball
	Direct clutch plates burnt	Determine cause of condition; Service as required
	Lo/Reverse overrun clutch orifice in spacer plate plugged	Clean and clear obstruction; Service as required
Drives in Neutral (Creeps)	Manual linkage misadjusted or disconnected	Service or adjust manual linkage; See GENERAL SERVICING
	Forward clutch does not release	Determine cause of condition; Service as required
	Foward clutch exhaust check ball sticking	Clean and free check ball; Service as required
	Forward clutch plates burnt	Determine cause of condition; Service as required
	Cross leakage in case to forward clutch passage	Determine cause of condition; Service as required
Slipping 1-2 Shift	Improper fluid level	Check fluid level; See GENERAL SERVICING
	Spacer plate gaskets damaged or mispositioned	Replace spacer plate gaskets
	Accumulator valve sticking in valve body, or weak or missing spring	Service as required
	1-2 accumulator piston seal leaking	Replace 1-2 accumulator piston assembly
	1-2 accumulator piston spring broken or missing	Replace accumulator piston assembly
	Leak between 1-2 accumulator piston and pin	Determine cause and service as required
	1-2 accumulator piston binding or piston bore damaged	Service as required
	Wrong intermediate band apply pin	Check and determine correct band apply pin; Service as required
	Excessive leakage between intermediate band apply pin and case	Determine cause and service as required
	Intermediate band apply pin feed hole not completely drilled	Service as required
	Porosity in intermediate servo piston	Service as required
	Leak between intermediate servo apply pin and case	Determine cause and service as required
	Throttle valve cable misadjusted	Adjust throttle valve cable; See GENERAL SERVICING
	Throttle valve binding	Clean and free valve; Service as required
	T.V. limit valve sticking	Clean and free valve; Service as required
	Line bias valve binding	Clean and free valve; Service as required
	Intermediate band worn or burnt	Determine cause of condition; Service as required
	Case porosity in 2nd clutch passage	Service as required

GENERAL MOTORS THM 200-4R TROUBLE SHOOTING (Cont.)

CONDITION	POSSIBLE CAUSE	CORRECTION
Rough 1-2 Shift	Throttle valve cable misadjusted or binding	Adjust or service throttle valve cable; See GENERAL SERVICING
	Throttle valve or T.V. plunger binding	Clean and free valve or plunger; Service as required
	T.V. limit valve binding	Clean and free valve; Service as required
	Accumulator valve binding	Clean and free valve; Service as required
	Line bias valve binding	Clean and free valve; Service as required
	Wrong intermediate servo apply pin	Check and determine correct apply pin; Service as required
	Intermediate servo-to-case oil seal ring damaged or missing	Replace oil seal ring
	Bleed orifice cup plug missing from intermediate servo pocket in case	Replace bleed orifice cup plug
	1-2 accumulator piston oil ring damaged	Replace 1-2 accumulator piston assembly
	1-2 accumulator piston spring broken or missing	Replace accumulator piston assembly
	1-2 accumulator piston bore damaged	Service as required
	1-2 shift check ball No. 8 missing or sticking	Service as required
Slipping 2-3 Shift	Improper fluid level	Check fluid level; See GENERAL SERVICING
	Throttle valve cable misadjusted	Adjust throttle valve cable; See GENERAL SERVICING
	Throttle valve binding	Clean and free valve; Service as required
	Spacer plate direct clutch orifice partially blocked	Clean and clear obstruction; Service as required
	Spacer plate gaskets damaged or mispositioned	Replace spacer plate gaskets
	Intermediate servo-to-case oil seal ring damaged or missing	Replace oil seal ring
	Intermediate servo piston or servo bore damaged	Service as required
	Bleed orifice cup plug missing from intermediate servo pocket in case	Replace bleed orifice cup plug
	Porosity in case in servo bore area	Service as required
	Direct Clutch Feed	
	Porosity in feed channels in case	Service as required
	Case-to-support bolts not tight	Tighten bolts to specifications
	Piston or housing cracked	Replace piston or housing
	Piston seals cut or missing	Replace piston seals
	Plates burnt	Determine cause of condition; Service as required
	Check ball in piston and/or housing missing, damaged or leaking	Replace check ball
	Check ball capsule damaged	Replace check ball capsule
	Release spring guide mislocated preventing check ball from seating	Replace release spring guide
	Center support channels cross feeding, leaking or restricted	Determine cause and service as required
	Center support oil seal rings damaged or missing	Replace support oil seal rings

Automatic Transmissions

GENERAL MOTORS THM 200-4R TROUBLE SHOOTING (Cont.)

CONDITION	POSSIBLE CAUSE	CORRECTION
Rough 2-3 Shift	Improper fluid level	Check fluid level; See GENERAL SERVICING
	Throttle valve cable misadjusted or binding	Adjust or service throttle valve cable; See GENERAL SERVICING
	Throttle valve or T.V. plunger binding	Clean and free valve or plunger; Service as required
	T.V. limit valve binding	Clean and free valve; Service as required
	Intermediate servo exhaust hole undrilled or plugged between servo piston seals, not allowing piston to complete stroke	Service as required
	3-2 exhaust check ball No. 4 missing or mispositioned	Replace No. 4 check ball
	3rd accumulator check ball No. 2 missing or mispositioned	Replace No. 2 check ball
Slipping 3-4 Shift	Improper fluid level	Check fluid level; See GENERAL SERVICING
	Spacer plate gaskets or spacer plate damaged or mispositioned	Replace spacer plate gaskets
	Valve body accumulator valve sticking	Clean and free valve; Service as required
	Weak or missing accumulator valve spring in valve body	Replace accumulator valve assembly
	3-4 accumulator piston stuck, bore damaged, or oil ring damaged	Service as required
	Center support porosity	Service as required
	Center support attaching bolts loose	Tighten bolts to specification
	4th clutch piston surface damaged	Determine cause of condition; Service as required
	4th clutch piston seals damaged	Determine cause of condition; Service as required
	Improper 4th clutch plate usage	Replace 4th clutch plates
	4th clutch plates burnt	Determine cause of condition; Service as required
	Case porosity	Service as required
	1-2 accumulator housing bolts loose	Tighten bolts to specification
	3-4 accumulator piston seal damaged	Determine cause of condition; Service as required
	3-4 accumulator leaking between piston and pin	Determine cause of condition; Service as required
	3-4 accumulator bore damaged	Determine cause of condition; Service as required
Rough 3-4 Shift	Throttle valve cable mispositioned or missing	Service or replace throttle valve cable
	Throttle valve plunger or valve binding	Clean and free valve; Service as required
	T.V. limit valve binding	Clean and free valve; Service as required
	3-4 accumulator piston stuck or bore damaged	Service as required
	4th clutch piston binding	Clean and free piston; Service as required
1st, 2nd & 3rd Only – No 3-4 Shift	3-4 shift valve or 3-4 throttle valve stuck in valve body	Clean and free valve; Service as required
	Orifice in spacer plate plugged	Clean and clear obstruction; Service as required

CONDITION	POSSIBLE CAUSE	CORRECTION
1st, 2nd & 3rd Only – No 3-4 Shift (Cont.)	Center support oil passages plugged or not drilled; attaching bolts loose or missing	Service as required
	Center support 4th clutch piston cracked or damaged, or piston seals damaged, missing or improperly assembled	Replace piston or piston seals
	Improper center support plate usage	Check and install proper support plate
	Overrun clutch plates or 4th clutch plates burnt	Determine cause of condition; Service as required
	Case porosity	Replace case
	Orifice cup plug missing in case 3-4 accumulator passage	Replace orifice cup plug
	Leakage between accumulator piston and pin in case	Determine cause and service as required
	3-4 accumulator bore damaged in case	Service as required
No Engine Braking in "L₁"	Valve Body and Spacer Plate Manual linkage out of adjustment	Adjust linkage; See GENERAL SERVICING
	Spacer plate orifice D3 plugged	Clean and clear obstruction; Service as required
	Gaskets leaking, damaged or improperly installed	Replace gaskets
	D2 oil pipe leaking or out of position	Replace D2 oil pipe
	Lo overrun clutch valve binding	Clean and free valve; Service as required
	Lo-Reverse check ball (No. 10) or Lo-Detent check ball (No. 9) mispositioned or missing	Replace No. 9 or No. 10 check ball
	Lo-Reverse overrun clutch orifice in spacer plate plugged	Clean and clear obstruction; Service as required
	Part throttle D3 check ball (No. 3) mispositioned or missing	Replace No. 3 check ball
	Turbine Shaft and Overrun Clutch (Also Cause No "L₃" or "L₂") D3 oil passage not drilled in turbine shaft or overrun clutch hub, or plugged in turbine shaft	Service as required
	Oil seals missing or damaged in clutch piston	Replace oil seals
	Clutch plates burnt	Determine cause of condition; Service as required
	Clutch backing plate snap ring out of groove	Replace snap ring
	Case porosity	Replace case
	Lo-Reverse Clutch Assembly (Also Cause No "R") Piston seals broken or missing	Replace piston seals
	Clutch housing snap ring out of case	Replace snap ring
	Piston or housing cracked or porous	Replace piston or housing
	Cup plug or rubber seal missing or damaged between case and clutch housing	Replace cup plug or rubber seal
No Engine Braking in "L₂"	Valve Body and Spacer Plate Manual linkage out of adjustment	Adjust linkage; See GENERAL SERVICING
	Gaskets leaking, damaged or improperly installed	Replace gaskets

Automatic Transmissions

GENERAL MOTORS THM 200-4R TROUBLE SHOOTING (Cont.)

CONDITION	POSSIBLE CAUSE	CORRECTION
No Engine Braking in "L₂" (Cont.)	Valve Body and Spacer Plate (Cont.) D2 oil pipe leaking or out of position	Replace D2 oil pipe
	Spacer plate orifice D3 plugged	Clean and clear obstruction; Service as required
	Part throttle D3 check ball (No. 3) mispositioned or missing	Replace No. 3 check ball
	Case porosity	Replace case
	Intermediate servo cover-to-case oil seal ring missing or damaged	Replace cover-to-case oil seal ring
	Intermediate band off anchor pin, broken, or burnt	Determine cause of condition; Service as required
	Turbine Shaft and Overrun Clutch D3 oil passage not drilled in turbine shaft or overrun clutch hub, or plugged in turbine shaft	Service as required
	Oil seals missing or damaged in clutch piston	Replace oil seals
	Clutch plates burnt	Determine cause of condition; Service as required
	Clutch backing plate snap ring out of groove	Replace snap ring
No Engine Braking in "L₃"	Valve Body and Spacer Plate Manual linkage out of adjustment	Adjust linkage; See GENERAL SERVICING
	Spacer plate orifice D3 plugged	Clean and clear obstruction; Service as required
	Gaskets leaking, damaged or improperly installed	Replace gaskets
	Part throttle D3 check ball (No. 3) mispositioned or missing	Replace No. 3 check ball
	Turbine Shaft and Overrun Clutch D3 oil passage not drilled in turbine shaft or overrun clutch hub, or plugged in turbine shaft	Service as required
	Oil seals missing or damaged in clutch piston	Replace oil seals
	Clutch plates burnt	Determine cause of condition; Service as required
	Clutch backing plate snap ring out of groove	Replace snap ring
No Park	Manual linkage out of adjustment	Adjust linkage; See GENERAL SERVICING
	Internal linkage binding, mispositioned, loose, or missing	Replace components as required
	Inside detent lever and pin assembly nut loose, or hole in lever worn or damaged	Tighten nut or replace lever
	Manual detent roller and spring assembly bolt loose holding roller assembly to valve body, or pin or roller damaged, mispositioned, or missing	Service as required
No Part Throttle Downshifts	Throttle valve or T.V. limit valve binding	Clean and free valve; Service as required
	Spacer plate hole plugged or undrilled	Service as required
	Valve body gaskets mispositioned or damaged	Replace valve body gaskets
	T.V. modulator downshift valve stuck	Clean and free valve; Service as required
	Throttle valve cable improperly set	Adjust cable; See GENERAL SERVICING

Automatic Transmissions

GENERAL MOTORS THM 200-4R TROUBLE SHOOTING (Cont.)

CONDITION	POSSIBLE CAUSE	CORRECTION
No Part Throttle 4-3 Downshift (Only Models With P.T. Passage in Throttle Plunger Bushing)	Throttle plunger bushing or 3-4 throttle valve bushing passages not open	Clean and clear obstruction; Service as required
	Part throttle D3 check ball (No. 3) mispositioned or missing	Replace No. 3 check ball
	Valve body gaskets mispositioned or damaged	Replace valve body gaskets
	Throttle valve cable improperly set	Adjust cable; See GENERAL SERVICING
	T.V. limit valve binding	Clean and free valve; Service as required

GENERAL MOTORS THM 325-4L TROUBLE SHOOTING

Every diagnosis of automatic transaxle problems should begin with a check of the transaxle fluid and linkage. Most of the following conditions can be caused by one or more of the following factors: (1) Incorrect fluid level, (2) Contaminated fluid, (3) Improperly adjusted linkage, or (4) Damaged or worn linkage.

CONDITION	POSSIBLE CAUSE	CORRECTION
No Drive in "D"	Improper fluid level	Check fluid level; See GENERAL SERVICING
	Low oil pressure	Perform OIL PRESSURE test
	Manual linkage out of adjustment	Adjust linkage; See GENERAL SERVICING
	Torque converter stator roller clutch broken (moves but very sluggish)	Replace torque converter
	Overdrive roller clutch springs or rollers damaged	Replace overdrive roller clutch
	Overdrive carrier pinions, sun gear or internal gear damaged	Replace overdrive carrier assembly
	Oil pump gears damaged	Replace oil pump
	Drive link broken, or sprockets/bearings damaged	Service as required
	Forward Clutch Assembly	
	Piston seals damaged	Determine cause and service as required
	Piston cracked	Replace piston
	Clutch misassembled	Replace forward clutch
	Input shaft seals damaged	Replace input shaft seals
	Clutch plate damaged	Determine cause and service as required
	Release springs and/or retainer damaged	Service as required
	Input or reaction carrier pinions, sun gear or internal gear damaged	Service as required
	Lo roller clutch springs or rollers damaged	Replace roller clutch
	Forward clutch input shaft broken	Replace forward clutch input shaft
1st Only, No 1-2 Shift	Governor Assembly	
	Weights binding on pin	Clean and free weights; Service as required
	Springs bent or distorted	Replace governor assembly

Automatic Transmissions

GENERAL MOTORS THM 325-4L TROUBLE SHOOTING (Cont.)

CONDITION	POSSIBLE CAUSE	CORRECTION
1st Only, No 1-2 Shift (Cont.)	Governor Assembly (Cont.)	
	Valve body spacer plate or gaskets blocked	Clear obstruction; Service as required
	Drive or driven gear broken or damaged	Service as required
	Seal damaged	Replace seal
	Case passages blocked	Clear obstruction; Service as required
	Oil seal damaged	Replace oil seal
	Valve body contains sticking 1-2 shift, Lo/1st detent, or 1-2 throttle valves	Clean and free valve; Service as required
	Intermediate band burnt, damaged, misassembled or anchor missing	Service as required
	Intermediate servo band apply pin too short	Replace servo apply pin
	Wrong intermediate servo piston and cover combination	Service as required
1-2 Shift, Full Throttle Only	T.V. cable misadjusted, disconnected or T.V. link bent	Adjust or service as required; See GENERAL SERVICING
	T.V. lever and bracket assembly misassembled or roll pin wedged against valve body casting	Service as required
	No. 5 check ball seated – T.V. link broken or missing	Replace T.V. link
	Throttle valve or plunger stuck or binding	Clean and free valve or plunger; Service as required
	Spacer plate and gaskets mispositioned or blocked	Service as required
1st & 2nd Only (No 2-3 Shift)	Valve body contains sticking or binding 2-3 shift or throttle valve	Clean and free valve; Service as required
	Spacer plate and gaskets mispositioned or blocked	Service as required
	Interconnected case passages or case porosity	Replace case
	Case Cover	
	No. 7 check ball and spring not seating	Determine cause and service as required
	3rd/Reverse cup plug leaking	Replace cup plug
	Porosity or interconnected passages	Replace case cover
	Gasket damaged	Replace case cover gasket
	Attaching bolts loose	Tighten bolts to specifications
	Driven sprocket support attaching bolts loose, oil seal rings faulty, or damaged support gasket	Service as required
	No. 6 check ball missing or leaking	Replace No. 6 check ball
	Direct clutch misassembled, piston or oil seals damaged, or ball capsule damaged	Service as required
	Governor Assembly	
	Drive gear worn	Replace governor assembly
	Check ball not seating	Determine cause of condition; Service as required
	Weights binding	Clear and free weights; Service as required
	Springs damaged	Replace governor assembly

GENERAL MOTORS THM 325-4L TROUBLE SHOOTING (Cont.)

CONDITION	POSSIBLE CAUSE	CORRECTION
No or Slips in "R"	Manual linkage out of adjustment	Adjust linkage; See GENERAL SERVICING
	Lo-Reverse clutch piston or seals, or cup plug/seal assembly damaged	Service as required
	Direct clutch misassembled, piston or seals damaged, or ball capsule damaged	Service as required
	Reverse boost valve binding or stuck	Clean and free valve; Service as required
	Reverse oil pipe leaking	Replace oil pipe No. 10
	No. 6 or No. 10 check ball missing or leaking	Replace No. 6 or No. 10 check ball
	Spacer plate mispositioned or damaged	Replace spacer plate
	Reverse passage leak in case cover, case or valve body	Service as required
Drives in Neutral (Creeps)	Manual linkage out of adjustment	Adjust linkage; See GENERAL SERVICING
	Leak in "D4" oil passage in case or case cover	Service as required
	Forward clutch plates fused, or ball capsule will not release	Service as required
Slipping 1-2 Shift	Improper fluid level	Check fluid level; See GENERAL SERVICING
	Spacer plate and/or roller gaskets mispositioned or blocked	Service as required
	Accumulator housing bolts loose or housing porosity	Service as required
	1-2 accumulator piston or seal damaged, binding or stuck	Service as required
	Intermediate band damaged or burnt	Determine cause of condition; Service as required
	Wrong intermediate servo apply pin	Replace apply pin
	Porosity in intermediate servo assembly, or damaged piston or seal	Service as required
	Pressure regulator valve sticking or binding	Clean and free valve; Service as required
	Line bias valve, throttle valve or plunger binding or stuck	Clean and free valve; Service as required
	T.V. cable misadjusted	Adjust T.V. cable; See GENERAL SERVICING
	Leak in 2nd oil passage in case or case cover	Determine cause and service as required
Rough 1-2 Shift	T.V. cable misadjusted or binding	Adjust or free T.V. cable; See GENERAL SERVICING
	Throttle valve or plunger binding or stuck	Clean and free valve; Service as required
	T.V. limit valve, line bias valve or accumulator binding or stuck	Clean and free valve or accumulator; Service as required
	Wrong intermediate servo apply pin, or piston bleed orifice missing	Service as required
	1-2 accumulator piston or seal damaged, binding or stuck	Service as required
	No. 8 check valve missing or leaking	Replace No. 8 check ball
	Servo bleed orifice cup plug in case cover missing or blocked	Service as required
Slipping 2-3 Shift	Improper fluid level	Check fluid level; See GENERAL SERVICING
	T.V. cable misadjusted	Adjust T.V. cable; See GENERAL SERVICING
	Spacer plate and/or gaskets mispositioned or blocked	Service as required

Automatic Transmissions

GENERAL MOTORS THM 325-4L TROUBLE SHOOTING (Cont.)

CONDITION	POSSIBLE CAUSE	CORRECTION
Slipping 2-3 Shift (Cont.)	No. 7 chack ball and spring leaking	Replace No. 7 check ball and spring
	Servo piston seal rings damaged	Replace seal rings
	Servo bleed orifice cup plug in case cover missing or blocked	Service as required
	Leak in 3rd clutch passage of driven sprocket support, case, or case cover	Determine cause and service as required
	Direct Clutch Damaged ball capsule, piston and housing	Determine cause and service as required
	Piston and seal damaged	Replace direct clutch piston
	Misassembled or burnt plates	Service as required
Rough 2-3 Shift	T.V. cable misadjusted	Adjust T.V. cable; See GENERAL SERVICING
	Throttle valve or plunger, T.V. limit or line bias valve, or M.T.V. up valve stuck or binding	Clean and free valve or plunger; Service as required
No 3-4 Shift	Shift valve or 3-4 throttle valve stuck or binding	Clean and free valve; Service as required
	4th clutch assembly piston or seals damaged, or feed "O" ring seal missing or leaking	Service as required
	Accumulator housing leaking in 3-4 accumulator circuit (missing cup plug)	Determine cause and service as required
	Spacer plate and/or gaskets mispositioned or blocked	Service as required
Slipping 3-4 Shift	Accumulator housing bolts loose, or accumulator piston or seal damaged	Service as required
	Accumulator valve binding or stuck (leaking cup plug)	Service as required
	4th clutch assembly leaking internally, damaged piston seal, feed "O" ring damaged or housing bolts loose	Service as required
Rough 3-4 Shift	T.V. cable misadjusted	Adjust T.V. cable; See GENERAL SERVICING
	Throttle valve or plunger binding or stuck	Clean and free valve or plunger; Service as required
	3-4 accumulator piston and seal damaged or stuck, or spring missing or weak	Service as required
No Engine Braking in Manual Ranges	Manual linkage out of adjustment	Adjust linkage; See GENERAL SERVICING
	Spacer plate and/or gaskets mispositioned, damaged or plugged	Service as required
	4-3 control valve binding or stuck (manual 3rd only)	Clean and free valve; Service as required
	"D2" signal pipe leaking (manual 2nd only)	Replace "D2" signal pipe
	No. 3, No. 9 or No. 10 check ball leaking or missing	Replace No. 3, No. 9 or No. 10 chack ball
	Lo overrun clutch valve binding or stuck (manual Lo only)	Clean and free valve; Service as required
	Overrun clutch piston or seals damaged, or burnt clutch plates	Service as required
	Blocked turbine shaft oil passage	Clean and free obstructions; Service as required

Automatic Transmissions

GENERAL MOTORS THM 325-4L TROUBLE SHOOTING (Cont.)

CONDITION	POSSIBLE CAUSE	CORRECTION
No Part Throttle Downshift	T.V. valve or plunger stuck or binding	Clean and free valve or plunger; Service as required
	Spacer plate and/or gaskets mispositioned or blocked	Service as required
	T.V. cable misadjusted	Adjust T.V. cable; See GENERAL SERVICING
	T.V. modulator downshift valve binding or stuck	Clean and free valve; Service as required
No Park	Manual linkage out of adjustment	Adjust linkage; See GENERAL SERVICING
	Internal linkage damaged, mispositioned or misassembled	Check and replace internal linkage components as required

GENERAL MOTORS THM 350C TROUBLE SHOOTING

Every diagnosis of automatic transmission problems should begin with a check of the transmission fluid and linkage. Most of the following conditions can be caused by one or more of the following factors: (1) Incorrect fluid level, (2) Contaminated fluid, (3) Improperly adjusted linkage, or (4) Damaged or worn linkage.

CONDITION	POSSIBLE CAUSE	CORRECTION
No Drive in "D"	Improper fluid level	Check fluid level; See GENERAL SERVICING
	Manual linkage out of adjustment	Adjust linkage; See GENERAL SERVICING
	Low oil pressure	Perform OIL PRESSURE test
	Manual lever disconnected from inner lever in valve body	Service as required
	Forward Clutch Does not apply – piston cracked; piston seals damaged or missing; clutch plates burnt; snap ring out of groove	Service as required
	Clutch Plates Pump feed circuit to forward clutch oil seal rings missing or broken on pump cover, leak in feed circuits, pump-to-case gasket mispositioned or damaged, clutch drum check ball missing or stuck	Service as required
	Broken roller clutch assembly spring or damaged case	Replace roller clutch assembly
1-2 Shift, Full Throttle Only	Detent valve misadjusted, sticking or binding linkage	Service as required
	Vacuum leak	Repair engine vacuum lines or fittings
	Valve body gaskets leaking, damaged, or improperly positioned	Replace gaskets
	Detent valve train or 1-2 shift valve stuck in valve body	Clean and free valve; Service as required
	Case porosity	Replace case
1st Gear Only, No 1-2 Upshift	Governor Assembly Valve sticking	Clean and free valve; Service as required
	Drive gear loose damaged or worn (check for pin in case and length of pin showing; if gear is damaged, check output shaft drive gear for nicks or rough finish)	Service as required

CONDITION	POSSIBLE CAUSE	CORRECTION
1st Gear Only, No 1-2 Upshift (Cont.)	Valve Body	
	1-2 shift valve train stuck closed	Clean and free valve; Service as required
	Governor feed channels blocked	Clean and clear obstruction; Service as required
	Gaskets leaking, damaged or improperly positioned	Replace gaskets
	Case porosity between channels	Replace case
	Case governor feed channels blocked or cross pressure leak (due to scored or worn governor bore)	Service as required
	Intermediate clutch piston seals missing, improperly sealed or cut	Replace piston seals
	Intermediate roller clutch spring broken or cage damaged	Replace intermediate roller clutch
1st & 2nd Only (No 2-3 Shift)	2-3 shift valve train stuck in valve body	Clean and free valve; Service as required
	Valve body gaskets leaking, damaged, or incorrectly positioned	Replace gaskets
	Direct clutch pump hub oil seal rings broken or missing	Replace oil seal rings
	Direct clutch piston seals missing, improperly assembled or cut, or piston check ball stuck or missing	Service as required
No "R", Or Slips In "R"	Improper fluid level	Check fluid level; See GENERAL SERVICING
	Manual linkage out of adjustment	Adjust linkage; See GENERAL SERVICING
	Incorrect oil pressure	
	Modulator valve stuck	Clean and free valve; Service as required
	Modulator and reverse boost valve stuck	Clean and free valve; Service as required
	Direct clutch pump hub oil seal rings broken or missing	Replace oil seal rings
	Direct clutch piston seals cut or missing	Replace piston seals
	Low/Reverse clutch piston seal cut or missing	Replace piston seal
	Valve body gaskets leaking, damaged, or incorrectly positioned	Replace gaskets
	2-3 shift valve stuck in upshift position in valve body (can also cause 1-3 upshift in "D")	Clean and free valve; Service as required
	1-2 shift valve stuck in upshift position in valve body (can also cause 1-3 upshift in "D")	Clean and free valve; Service as required
	Intermediate servo piston or pin stuck (applies intermediate overrun band)	Service as required
	Low/Reverse clutch piston out, or seal damaged or missing	Replace piston or seal
	Direct clutch outer seal damaged or missing, or plates burnt	Determine cause and service as required
	Forward clutch not releasing (also causes creeping in "N")	Determine cause and service as required
Drives In Neutral (Creeps)	Manual linkage out of adjustment	Adjust linkage; See GENERAL SERVICING
	Forward clutch not releasing (also causes no "R")	Determine cause and service as required

GENERAL MOTORS THM 350C TROUBLE SHOOTING (Cont.)

CONDITION	POSSIBLE CAUSE	CORRECTION
Slips in All Gears	Improper fluid level	Check fluid level; See GENERAL SERVICING
	Improper oil pressure	
	Inoperative vacuum modulator	Tighten fittings and clear obstructions in line
	Modulator valve stuck	Clean and free valve; Service as required
	Oil filter plugged or leaking	Replace filter
	Pressure regulator valve stuck	Clean and free valve; Service as required
	Pump-to case gasket damaged or improperly installed	Replace pump-to case gasket
	Forward clutch slipping due to cross leaks or porosity	Determine cause and service as required
Slipping 1-2 Shift	Improper fluid level	Check fluid level; See GENERAL SERVICING
	Improper oil pressure	
	Inoperative vacuum modulator	Tighten fittings and clear obstructions in line
	Modulator valve stuck	Clean and free valve; Service as required
	Pump pressure regulator valve faulty	Replace pressure regulator
	2-3 accumulator oil ring is damaged or missing	Replace oil ring
	1-2 accumulator oil ring is damaged or missing, or case bore damaged	Service as required
	Pump-to-case gasket damaged or mispositioned	Replace pump-to-case gasket
	Case porosity between channels	Replace case
	Intermediate clutch piston seals missing, improperly sealed or cut, or clutch plates burnt	Service as required
Rough 1-2 Shift	Improper oil pressure	
	Inoperative vacuum modulator	Tighten fittings and clear obstructions in line
	Modulator valve stuck	Clean and free valve; Service as required
	Regulator or boost valve stuck in valve body	Clean and free valve; Service as required
	Pump-to-case gasket damaged or mispositioned	Replace pump-to-case gasket
	Case porosity between channels	Replace case
	1-2 Accumulator Assembly	
	Oil rings damaged	Replace oil rings
	Piston stuck	Clean and free piston; Service as required
	Broken or missing spring	Replace spring
	Bore damaged	Service as required
	Restricted accumulator feed hole in valve body plate	Clear obstruction; Service as required
Slipping 2-3 Shift	Improper fluid level	Check fluid level; See GENERAL SERVICING
	Improper oil pressure	
	Inoperative vacuum modulator	Tighten fittings and clear obstructions in line
	Modulator valve stuck	Clean and free valve; Service as required
	Regulator or boost valve stuck in valve body	Clean and free valve; Service as required
	Pump-to-case gasket damaged or mispositioned	Replace pump-to-case gasket
	Case porosity between channels	Replace case
	Direct clutch piston seals or check ball leaking	Service as required

Automatic Transmissions

GENERAL MOTORS THM 350C TROUBLE SHOOTING (Cont.)

CONDITION	POSSIBLE CAUSE	CORRECTION
Rough 2-3 Shift	Improper Oil Pressure Vacuum leak	Clean and service vacuum line
	Inoperative vacuum modulator	Tighten fittings and clear obstructions in line
	Modulator valve stuck	Clean and free valve; Service as required
	Regulator or boost valve stuck in valve body	Clean and free valve; Service as required
	2nd accumulator spring broken or missing	Replace spring
No Engine Braking In "L2"	Intermediate servo and/or 2-3 accumulator oil rings or bores leaking, or servo piston stuck	Service as required
	Intermediate overrun band broken or burnt	Determine cause and service as required
	Pressure regulator and/or boost valve stuck	Clean and free valve; Service as required
No Engine Braking In "L1"	Manual low control valve stuck	Clean and free valve; Service as required
	Intermediate overrun band broken or burnt	Determine cause and service as required
	Pressure regulator and/or boost valve stuck	Clean and free valve; Service as required
	Pressure regulator and/or boost valve stuck	Clean and free valve; Service as required
	Low/Reverse clutch piston inner seal damaged or missing	Replace piston inner seal
No Kickdown Shift	Vacuum modulator assembly, modulator valve or pressure regulator valve stuck or binding	Perform PRESSURE TEST; Service as required
	Detent valve and linkage sticking, disconnedted or broken	Service as required
	2-3 shift valve stuck	Clean and free valve; Service as required
No Detent Downshifts	2-3 shift valve stuck	Clean and free valve; Service as required
	Detent valve and linkage sticking, disconnedted or broken	Service as required
No "Park"	Manual linkage out of adjustment	Adjust linkage; See GENERAL SERVICING
	Internal linkage damaged, mispositioned, or misassembled	Clean or replace internal linkage as required
Locks Up in "L" (Usually When Hot)	Convertor pressure leaking into direct clutch through stator shaft	Check stator shaft postion; Service as required
	Direct clutch bore undersized, piston oversize, or feed hole missing small chamber	Service as required
2nd Only, or Slips in 2nd Only	Incorrect number of intermediate clutch plates or wrong intermediate clutch piston	Service as required
Locks Up in "R" (Usually When Hot)	Forward clutch bore undersized or piston oversize	Service as required
	Direct clutch feeding forward clutch through stator shaft	Check stator shaft postion; Service as required
Locks When Moving From "P" to "R"	Burrs on leading edge of parking pawl	Service parking pawl
"R" But No "D" When Cold	Pressure regulator bore or sleeve to tight	Service as required

GENERAL MOTORS THM 350C TROUBLE SHOOTING (Cont.)

CONDITION	POSSIBLE CAUSE	CORRECTION
Shifts Cold But Not Warm	Governor roll pin too short or missing	Replace roll pin
No "D" ("L1" OK)	Low/Reverse roller clutch installed backward	Install roller clutch correctly
No 1-2 Shift (1-3 Shift Normal, All Manual Shifts Normal)	Intermediate roller clutch not locking	Determine cause and service as required
Slow "R" Actuation When Cold	Improper fluid level	Check fluid level; See GENERAL SERVICING
Harsh 1-2 Shift	1-2 accumulator piston or spring faulty, or feed hole restricted in valve plate	Service as required
Slow "R" Actuation When Hot	Leaking valva body support plate	Determine cause and service as required
	Shift selector damaged or improperly assembled	Inspect shift selector components and service as required

GENERAL MOTORS THM 400 TROUBLE SHOOTING

Every diagnosis of automatic transmission problems should begin with a check of the transmission fluid and linkage. Most of the following conditions can be caused by one or more of the following factors: (1) Incorrect fluid level, (2) Contaminated fluid, (3) Improperly adjusted linkage, or (4) Damaged or worn linkage.

CONDITION	POSSIBLE CAUSE	CORRECTION
No or Delayed 1-2 Shift	Improper fluid level	Check fluid level; See GENERAL SERVICING
	Disconnect Electrical Plug From Transmission	
	Normal upshift	Check for short circuit and correct detent switch or wiring
	No upshift	Perform LINE PRESSURE test; Service as required
1-2 Shift Complaints	Improper fluid level	Check fluid level; See GENERAL SERVICING
	Poor engine performance	Check and tune engine
	Improper line pressure	Perform LINE PRESSURE test; Service as required
	Vacuum system leaking	Check vacuum lines and modulator; Service as required
2-3 Shift Complaints	Improper fluid level	Check fluid level; See GENERAL SERVICING
	Poor engine performance	Check and tune engine
Drives In Neutral (Creeps)	Manual linkage binding or out of adjustment	Adjust or service linkage; See GENERAL SERVICING
	Manual valve disconnected or end broken	Service as required
	Pressure leak into forward clutch apply passage	Check pump assembly and service as required
	Wrong forward clutch plate usage or burnt plates	Determine cause of condition; Service as required

Automatic Transmissions

GENERAL MOTORS THM 400 TROUBLE SHOOTING (Cont.)

CONDITION	POSSIBLE CAUSE	CORRECTION
Will Not Hold or Release Park	Manual linkage binding or out of adjustment	Adjust or service linkage; See GENERAL SERVICING
	Internal linkage damaged, mispositioned, or misassembled	Check and replace internal linkage components as required
No Engine Braking in "L1"	Lo-Reverse check ball mispositioned or missing, or case damaged at Lo-Reverse check ball area	Replace check ball or case
	Rear servo oil seal ring, bore or piston damaged	Service as required
	Rear Servo band apply pin too short or improperly assembled	Service as required
	Rear band broken, burnt, not engaged on anchor pins and/or servo pin	Determine cause of condition; Service as required
No Engine Braking in "L2"	Front servo and accumulator oil rings and/or bores leaking, or front servo piston cocked or stuck	Service as required
	Front band broken, burnt, not engaged on anchor pin and/or servo pin	Service as required
No or Slips in "R"	Improper fluid level	Check fluid level; See GENERAL SERVICING
	Manual linkage binding or out of adjustment	Adjust or service linkage; See GENERAL SERVICING
	Low Line Pressure (in "R")	Determine cause of condition; Service as required
	Normal Line Pressure (in "R") 2-3 valve train stuck open (also cause 1-3 shift in "D")	Clean and free valve; Service as required
	Cross channel leak or porosity in reverse feed passage in case or valve body	Determine cause and service as required
	Valve body gaskets leaking	Replace gaskets
	Rear servo piston seal ring damaged or missing	Replace servo piston seal ring
	Short rear servo band apply pin	Replace rear servo band apply pin
	Damaged rear servo piston or bore	Service as required
	Forward clutch does not release (also cause drive in "N")	Determine cause of condition; Service as required
	Direct clutch plate burnt	Determine cause of condition; Service as required
	Rear band broken, burnt, or apply pin or anchor pins not engaged	Determine cause of condition; Service as required
	Center support oil seal rings or grooves damaged or worn	Replace center support oil seal rings
1st & 2nd Only (No 2-3 Upshift)	Valve body gasket mispositioned or leaking, or 2-3 valve stuck	Service as required
	Direct clutch plates burnt	Determine cause of condition; Service as required
	Improper vacuum	Check engine vacuum lines and modulator; Service as required

GENERAL MOTORS THM 400 TROUBLE SHOOTING (Cont.)

CONDITION	POSSIBLE CAUSE	CORRECTION
No Drive in "D"	Improper fluid level	Check fluid level; See GENERAL SERVICING
	Manual linkage binding or out of adjustment	Adjust or service linkage; See GENERAL SERVICING
	Low Line Pressure (in "D")	Determine cause of condition; Service as required
	Normal Line Pressure (in "D") Forward clutch feed passage not drilled or restricted in pump assembly	Service as required
	Forward clutch plates burnt	Determine cause of condition; Service as required
	Lo roller clutch damaged or installed backward	Service as required
No Detent Downshift	Place vehicle on lift. Turn ignition on (engine off). Disconnect electrical plug from transmission. Connect test light to "detent" terminal of disonnected wiring harness. Fully depress accelerator. Light On Detent solenoid inoperative, poor connections, shorted wire, open wire, valve stuck, or orifice plugged	Service as required
	Detent valve train stuck or binding in valve body	Clean and free valve; Service as required
	Light Off Detent solenoid switch inproperly adjusted	Adjust detent solenoid switch; See GENERAL SERVICING
	Faulty switch, connections, fuse, or shorted wire	Service as required

TRANSMISSION NOISY

CONDITION	POSSIBLE CAUSE	CORRECTION
Park, Neutral & All Driving Ranges	Improper fluid level	Check fluid level; See GENERAL SERVICING
	Wrong, plugged, or restricted oil filter	Replace oil filter
	Pump intake pipe split, "O" ring damaged, or porosity in case intake pipe hose	Service as required
	Water in fluid	Determine cause of condition; service as required and replace fluid
	Porosity or voids at transmission case (pump face) intake port	Service as required
	Pump-to-case gasket mispositioned	Replace gasket
	Pump gears damaged, faulty, driving gear installed backward; cresent interference; pressure regulator cup plug damaged or missing; seal rings damaged or worn	Service as required
	Loose converter-to-flywheel bolts	Tighten bolts and check for damage; Service as required
1st, 3rd & "R" Only	Planetary gears or thrust bearings damaged	Thoroughly clean bearings and races; Inspect needle bearings and surfaces for pitting and roughness; Replace planetary gear set
	Planetary gear set front internal gear ring damaged	Replace planetary gear set

GENERAL MOTORS THM 400 TROUBLE SHOOTING (Cont.)

CONDITION	POSSIBLE CAUSE	CORRECTION
During Acceleration in Any Gear	Transmission cooling lines grounded to underbody	Service as required
	Broken or loose motor mounts	Replace motor mounts
Squeak at Low Speeds	Speedometer driven gear shaft seal faulty or needs lubrication	Service as required
	Extension housing oil seal faulty or needs lubrication	Service as required

GENERAL MOTORS THM 440-T4 TROUBLE SHOOTING

Every diagnosis of automatic transaxle problems should begin with a check of the transaxle fluid and linkage. Most of the following conditions can be caused by one or more of the following factors: (1) Incorrect fluid level, (2) Contaminated fluid, (3) Improperly adjusted linkage, or (4) Damaged or worn linkage.

CONDITION	POSSIBLE CAUSE	CORRECTION
No Drive in "D"	Improper fluid level	Check fluid level; See GENERAL SERVICING
	Manual linkage out of adjustment or disconnected	Adjust linkage; See GENERAL SERVICING
	Low oil pressure	Perform OIL PRESSURE test
	Torque converter stator roller clutch sluggish, or converter not bolted to flex plate	Service as required
	Oil pump drive shaft or pump damaged	Replace oil pump
	Input clutch/reverse check ball (No. 8 check ball) missing	Replace check ball
	Damaged drive link, sprocket or bearings	Service as required
	Input Clutch Assembly	
	Burnt or missing plates	Determine cause and service as required
	Damaged piston or seals	Replace piston assembly
	Housing check ball assembly worn or damaged	Replace check ball or assembly as necesssary
	Input shaft seals damaged or fluid passages blocked	Service as required
	Input sprag and sun gear assembly improperly assembled or sprag damaged	Service as required
	Input and reaction carrier pinions, internal gear, or sun gear damaged	Replace component(s) as necessary
	1-2 band assembly burnt	Determine cause and service as required
	1-2 servo piston or seal damaged or incorrect apply pin installed	Replace piston, seal and/or apply pin as required
	Leaking 1-2 servo oil pipes	Service as required
	Final drive assembly internally damaged	Replace component(s) as necessary
	Final drive sun gear shaft sides, gears, or pinion are internally damaged	Replace component(s) as necessary
	Parking pawl spring broken	Replace spring
	Output shaft damaged or improperly installed to axle	Service or repair as required

GENERAL MOTORS THM 440-T4 TROUBLE SHOOTING (Cont.)

CONDITION	POSSIBLE CAUSE	CORRECTION
1st Gear Only, No 1-2 Upshift	Governor weights binding, springs or gear damaged	Replace governor
	Accumulator & Pipes Exhaust check balls missing or damaged	Replace check balls
	Cover or pipes leaking	Service as required
	No. 14 check ball missing	Replace check ball
	1-2 shift valve stuck in valve body	Clean and free valve; Service as required
	2nd clutch plates, piston or seals damaged or misassembled	Service as required
	Driven sprocket support oil seal rings damaged	Replace oil seal rings
	Reverse reaction drum splines damaged, or drum plates missing	Replace reaction drum assembly
Harsh Or Soft 1-2 Shift	Improper oil pressure	Perform PRESSURE test
	Accumulator cover bolts loose, or pistons, seals or springs damaged	Service as required
	Accumulator valve stuck in valve body	Clean and free valve; Service as required
	2nd clutch check ball (check ball No. 4) missing	Replace check ball
High Or Low 1-2 Shift Speed	T.V. cable disconnected or misadjusted	Service or adjust cable; See GENERAL SERVICING
	T.V. link or lever assembly bent or damaged	Replace link or lever assembly
	T.V. valve or plunger stuck or binding	Clean and free valve or plunger; Service as required
	Incorrect governor pressure	Determine cause and service as required
1st & 2nd Only (No 2-3 Shift)	Incorrect 1-2 servo apply pin	Replace apply pin
	Check ball missing from capsule in case	Replace check ball
	1-2 servo bore orifice cup plug missing	Replace cup plug
	2-3 shift valve train stuck in valve body	Clean and free valve; Service as required
	No. 6 check ball not seating	Determine cause and service as required
	Valve body bolts improperly tightened	Tighten bolts to specification
	Input seals damaged or oil passages blocked	Service as required
	3rd clutch plates burnt or piston seals or check ball assembly damaged	Service as required
	Damaged 3rd roller clutch cage, rollers out of cage, springs damaged, or roller clutch improperly assembled on input sun gear shaft	Service as required
	2-3 accumulator exhaust valve check ball (check ball No. 3) damaged or 2-3 accumulator feed check ball (check ball No. 3) damaged or not seating, or 2-3 accumulator valve stuck in valve body	Replace check ball; Clean and free valve; Service as required
Harsh Or Soft 2-3 Shift	Improper Oil Pressure	Perform PRESSURE test
	1-2 servo feed check ball (No. 7 check ball) mislocated	Replace check ball

Automatic Transmissions

GENERAL MOTORS THM 440-T4 TROUBLE SHOOTING (Cont.)

CONDITION	POSSIBLE CAUSE	CORRECTION
High Or Low 2-3 Shift Speed	T.V. cable disconnected or misadjusted	Service or adjust cable; See GENERAL SERVICING
	T.V. link or lever assembly bent or damaged	Replace link or lever assembly
	T.V. valve or plunger stuck or binding	Clean and free valve or plunger; Service as required
	Incorrect governor pressure	Determine cause and service as required
No 3-4 Shift	Governor weights binding, springs or gear damaged	Replace governor
	3-4 shift valve stuck in valve body	Clean and free valve; Service as required
	Burnt 4th clutch plates, piston or seals damaged, or plates or pistom mislocated	Service as required
	4th clutch shaft spline damaged	Replace 4th clutch shaft
Harsh Or Soft 3-4 Shift	Improper Oil Pressure	Perform PRESSURE test
	Accumulator cover bolts loose, or pistons, seals or springs damaged	Service as required
	4th clutch check ball (No. 1 check ball) mislocated	Replace check ball
High Or Low 3-4 Shift Speed	T.V. cable disconnected or misadjusted	Service or adjust cable; See GENERAL SERVICING
	T.V. link or lever assembly bent or damaged	Replace link or lever assembly
	T.V. valve or plunger stuck or binding	Clean and free valve or plunger; Service as required
	Incorrect governor pressure	Determine cause and service as required
Harsh 4-3 Downshift	4th clutch check ball (No. 1 check ball) missing	Replace check ball
Harsh 3-2 Downshift	1-2 servo control valve, 3-2 control valve or 3-2 coast valve stuck in valve body, or 1-2 servo feed check ball (No. 7 check ball) or 3rd clutch check ball (No. 2 check ball) missing	Clean and free valve; Service as required; Replace missing check ball(s)
	Damaged input clutch accumulator piston or seal in channel plate	Replace piston or seal
Harsh 2-1 Downshift	Reverse servo feed check ball (No. 4 check ball) missing	Replace check ball
No Drive In "R"	Low oil pressure	Perform OIL PRESSURE test
	Oil pump drive shaft or pump damaged	Replace oil pump
	Damaged drive link, sprocket or bearings	Service as required
	Reverse band burnt or damaged	Determine cause and service as required
	Input Clutch Assembly Burnt or missing plates	Determine cause and service as required
	Damaged piston or seals	Replace piston assembly
	Housing check ball assembly worn or damaged	Replace check ball or assembly as necesssary
	Input shaft seals damaged or fluid passages blocked	Service as required
	Input sprag and sun gear assembly improperly assembled or sprag damaged	Service as required

GENERAL MOTORS THM 440-T4 TROUBLE SHOOTING (Cont.)

CONDITION	POSSIBLE CAUSE	CORRECTION
No Drive In "R" (Cont.)	Reverse servo piston or seal damaged, or wrong apply pin	Replace piston or pin as required
	Input and reaction carrier pinions, internal gear, or sun gear damaged	Replace component(s) as necessary
No Park	Final drive park pawl, spring or gear damaged	Replace component(s) as necessary
Harsh "N" To "R" (Or "N" To "D")	Reverse servo feed check ball (No. 4 check ball) missing (harsh "R")	Replace check ball
	1-2 servo feed check ball missing (harsh "D")	Replace check ball
	Spacer plate thermal elements do not close when warm	Determine cause and service as required
No Viscous Clutch Apply (If Equipped)	Verify proper computer command control operation; check for damaged thermistor or temperature switch	Service as required

GENERAL MOTORS THM 700-R4 TROUBLE SHOOTING

Every diagnosis of automatic transmission problems should begin with a check of the transmission fluid and linkage. Most of the following conditions can be caused by one or more of the following factors: (1) Incorrect fluid level, (2) Contaminated fluid, (3) Improperly adjusted linkage, or (4) Damaged or worn linkage.

CONDITION	POSSIBLE CAUSE	CORRECTION
1st Only, No Upshift	Governor Assembly Valve sticking	Clean and free valve; Service as required
	Driven gear loose or damaged	Replace governor assembly
	Drive gear retaining pin missing	Replace retaining pin
	Nicks or burrs on output shaft, governor sleeve, or case bore	Service as required
	Improper support pin length	Replace support pin
	Governor weights or springs missing, damaged, or binding	Service as required
	1-2 shift valve sticking in valve body, or spacer plate or gaskets mispositioned or damaged	Service as required
	Case-to-valve body face not flat or damaged, or governor screen restricted or damaged	Service as required
	2-4 Servo Assembly Restricted or blocked case passages	Clean and clear obstructions
	Nicks or burrs on servo pin or case pin bore	Service as required
	Missing or damaged piston or pin seals	Replace piston or seals
	4th servo piston installed backward	Replace servo piston
	2-4 band worn or damaged, or band anchor pin not engaged	Service as required

CONDITION	POSSIBLE CAUSE	CORRECTION
Slips in 1st	Forward Clutch Assembly	
	Clutch plates worn	Replace clutch plates
	Piston porosity or damaged	Replace piston
	Piston seals missing or damaged	Replace piston seals
	Input housing-to-forward clutch housing "O" ring seal missing or damaged	Replace "O" ring seal
	Damaged housing	Replace housing
	Housing retainer and ball assembly not seating or damaged	Replace retainer and ball assembly
	Input housing and shaft assembly turbine shaft seals missing or damaged	Replace turbine shaft seals
	Accumulator valve stuck in valve body	Clean and free valve; Service as required
	Valve body face not flat, damaged lands, or interconnected passages	Replace valve body
	Spacer plate or gaskets incorrect, mispositioned, or damaged	Replace spacer plate or gaskets
	T.V. cable binding or broken	Service or replace as required
	1-2 Accumulator Piston Assembly	
	Porosity in piston or cover and pin assembly	Replace piston or cover and pin assembly
	Damaged piston ring grooves	Replace piston
	Piston seal missing or damaged	Replace piston seal
	Cover gasket missing or damaged	Replace cover gasket
	Broken accumulator spring	Replace spring
	Improper oil presure	Perform PRESSURE test; Service as required
High or Low 1-2 Shift Speeds	T.V. cable improperly adjusted, binding or broken	Adjust or service cable; See GENERAL SERVICING
	Governor Assembly	
	Valve sticking	Clean and free valve; Service as required
	Driven gear loose or damaged	Replace governor assembly
	Drive gear retaining pin missing	Replace retaining pin
	Nicks or burrs on output shaft, governor sleeve, or case bore	Service as required
	Improper support pin length	Replace support pin
	Governor weights or springs missing, damaged, or binding	Service as required
	Throttle lever and bracket assembly misassembled, binding or damaged, or T.V. link missing, binding or damaged	Service as required
	Valve body face not flat, T.V. exhaust check ball stuck, or T.V. plunger sticking	Service as required
	Oil pump assembly or case face not flat	Replace oil pump assembly or case
Slipping or Rough 1-2 Shift	Throttle lever and bracket assembly incorrectly installed or damaged, or T.V. cable broken or binding	Replace throttle lever and bracket assembly or T.V. cable
	Valve Body Assembly	
	Throttle valve sticking	Clean and free valve; Service as required
	T.V. bushing turned in bore	Replace bushing

GENERAL MOTORS THM 700-R4 TROUBLE SHOOTING (Cont.)

CONDITION	POSSIBLE CAUSE	CORRECTION
Slipping or Rough 1-2 Shift (Cont.)	Valve Body Assembly (Cont.) 1-2 shift valve train, line bias valve, accumulator valve or T.V. limit valve stuck	Clean and free valve; Service as required
	Gaskets or spacer plate incorrect, mispositioned or damaged	Replace gaskets or spacer plate
	Body face not flat	Replace valve body
	2-4 Servo Assembly Apply pin too long or too short	Replace apply pin
	Servo seals or "O" ring seals missing or damaged	Replace servo seals or "O" ring seals
	Restricted or missing oil passages	Service as required
	Case servo bore damaged	Service as required
	2nd Accumulator Porosity in 1-2 accumulator housing or piston	Replace piston or housing
	Piston seal or groove damaged	Replace piston
	Nicks or burrs in 1-2 accumulator housing	Service as required
	Missing or restricted oil passages	Replace accumulator
	Worn or mispositioned 2-4 band	Replace 2-4 band
	Oil pump assembly or case faces not flat	Replace oil pump or case
Slipping, Rough or No 2-3 Shift	Internal converter damage	Replace converter
	Governor Assembly Valve stuck	Clean and free valve; Service as required
	Drive gear retaining pin missing or loose	Replace retaining pin
	Weights binding	Service as required
	Governor drive gear damaged	Replace drive gear
	Support pin in case too long or too short	Replace support pin
	Oil pump stator shaft sleeve scored or mislocated	Replace shaft sleeve
	Valve Body 2-3 valve train or accumulator valve stuck	Clean and free valve train; Service as required
	Spacer plate or gaskets incorrect, mispositioned or damaged	Replace spacer plate or gaskets
	Throttle valve or T.V. limit valve stuck	Clean and free valve; Service as required
	Input Housing Assembly Forward or 3-4 clutch plates worn	Determine cause of condition; Service as required
	Excessive clutch plate travel	Determine cause and service as required
	Forward or 3-4 piston seals damaged	Replace piston seals
	Porosity in 3-4 clutch housing or piston, or 3-4 piston check ball stuck, damaged or not sealing	Replace 3-4 clutch housing, piston or piston check ball
	Restricted apply passages	Clean and clear obstructions; Service as required

Automatic Transmissions

GENERAL MOTORS THM 700-R4 TROUBLE SHOOTING (Cont.)

CONDITION	POSSIBLE CAUSE	CORRECTION
Slipping, Rough or No 2-3 Shift (Cont.)	Input Housing Assembly (Cont.) Forward clutch piston or 3rd accumulator retainer and ball assembly not seating	Replace retainer and ball assembly
	Sealing balls loose or missing	Replace sealing balls
	2-4 servo pin seals or 2nd apply piston seals missing or damaged	Replace pin seals
Rough, Slipping or No 3-4 Shift	Governor	
	Weights binding	Service as required
	Valve sticking	Clean and free valve; Service as required
	Drive gear damaged, or retaining pin missing or loose	Replace drive gear or retaining pin
	Improper support pin length	Replace support pin
	Oil pump assembly faces not flat, or pump cover retainer and ball assembly omitted or damaged	Replace pump or cover retainer and ball assembly
	Valve Body Assembly 2-3 valve train, accumulator valve, throttle valve, T.V. limit valve, 1-2 shift valve or 3-2 control valve stuck	Clean and free valve; Service as required
	Manual valve link bent or damaged	Replace manual valve link
	Spacer plates or gaskets incorrect, mispositioned or damaged	Replace spacer plates or gaskets
	2-4 Servo Assembly	
	Incorrect band apply pin	Replace band apply pin
	Missing or damaged servo seals	Replace seals
	Porosity in pistons, cover or case	Service as required
	Plugged or missing orifice cup plug	Clean and clear obstruction or replace cup plug
	Case	
	3rd accumulator retainer and ball assembly leaking	Determine cause and service as required
	Porosity in 3-4 accumulator piston or bore	Replace piston or case
	3-4 accumulator piston seal or seal grooves damaged	Replace piston seal or piston
	Plugged or missing orifice cup plug	Clean and clear obstruction or replace cup plug
	Restricted oil passage	Clear obstruction; Service as required
	Input Housing Assembly Forward or 3-4 clutch plates worn, or excessive plate travel	Determine cause of condition; Service as required
	Forward or 3-4 piston seals damaged	Replace piston seals
	Porosity in 3-4 clutch housing or piston	Replace 3-4 clutch housing or piston
	3-4 piston check ball or sealing balls stuck, damaged or not sealing	Replace check ball or sealing balls
	Restricted apply passages	Clean and clear obstructions; Service as required
	Forward clutch piston retainer and ball assembly not seating	Replace retainer and ball assembly
	2-4 band assembly worn or misassembled	Replace band assembly

GENERAL MOTORS THM 700-R4 TROUBLE SHOOTING (Cont.)

CONDITION	POSSIBLE CAUSE	CORRECTION
No or Slips in "R"	**Input Housing Assembly**	
	3-4 apply ring stuck in applied position	Clean and free ring; Service as required
	Forward clutch not releasing	Determine cause of condition; Service as required
	Turbine shaft seals missing or damaged	Replace turbine shaft seals
	Manual linkage out of adjustment	Adjust linkage; See GENERAL SERVICING
	Oil Pump Assembly	
	Retainer and ball assembly missing or damaged	Replace retainer and ball assembly
	Stator shaft seal rings or ring grooves damaged	Replace shaft or seal rings
	Stator shaft sleeve scored or damaged	Replace shaft sleeve
	Reverse boost valve stuck, damaged or misassembled	Clean and free, or replace valve
	Cup plug missing	Replace cup plug
	Restricted oil passage	Clean and clear obstructions; Service as required
	Faces not flat	Replace pump assembly
	Converter clutch apply valve stuck	Clean and free valve; Service as required
	Valve Body Assembly	
	2-3 shift valve stuck	Clean and free valve; Service as required
	Manual linkage out of adjustment	Adjust linkage; See GENERAL SERVICING
	Spacer plate and gaskets incorrect, mispositioned or damaged	Replace spacer plate or gaskets
	Reverse Input Clutch	
	Clutch plate worn	Determine cause of condition; Service as required
	Housing and drum assembly cracked at weld	Replace housing and drum assembly
	Clutch plate or return spring assembly retaining ring out of groove	Replace retaining ring
	Piston deformed or dished	Replace piston
	Seals damaged or missing	Replace seals
	Retainer and ball assembly not sealing	Replace retainer and ball assembly
	Restricted apply passage	Clean and clear obstructions; Service as required
	Lo-Reverse Clutch	
	Clutch plates worn or retaining ring mispositioned	Determine cause of worn plates; Replace retaining ring
	Porosity in piston	Replace piston
	Seals damaged	Replace seals
	Return spring assembly retaining ring mispositioned	Replace retaining ring
	Restricted apply passage	Clean and clear obstructions; Service as required
	Case porosity	Replace case
	Case cover plate improperly tightened, or gasket missing or damaged	Tighten bolts; Replace gasket

Automatic Transmissions

GENERAL MOTORS THM 700-R4 TROUBLE SHOOTING (Cont.)

CONDITION	POSSIBLE CAUSE	CORRECTION
No Part Throttle or Delayed Downshifts	External linkage not adjusted	Adjust linkage; See GENERAL SERVICING
	2-4 Servo Assembly Apply pin seal damaged or missing	Replace apply pin seal
	Servo cover retaining ring missing or misassembled	Replace retaining ring
	4th apply piston damaged or misassembled	Replace 4th apply piston
	Inner housing damaged or misassembled	Replace inner housing
	Governor weights binding, or valve stuck	Service as required
	Valve Body Assembly Throttle valve, 3-2 control valve or T.V. modulated downshift valve stuck	Clean and free valve; Service as required
	T.V. sleeve turned in bore	Replace T.V. sleeve
	4-3 sequence valve body channel blocked	Clean and clear channel of obstruction; Service as required
	No. 5 check ball missing	Replace No. 5 check ball
No Overrun Braking in "L_1", "L_2" or "L_3"	External linkage out of adjustment	Adjust linkage; Service as required
	Valve Body Assembly 4-3 sequence valve or throttle valve stuck	Clean and free valve; Service as required
	No. 3 check ball mispositioned	Replace No. 3 check ball
	Spacer plate and gaskets incorrect, damaged or mispositioned	Replace spacer plate or gaskets
	Input Clutch Assembly Turbine shaft oil passages plugged or not drilled	Service as required
	Turbine shaft seal rings damaged	Replace shaft seal rings
	Turbine shaft sealing balls loose or missing	Replace sealing balls
	Porosity in forward or overrun clutch piston	Replace forward or overrun clutch piston
	Overrun piston seals damaged or missing	Replace piston seals
	Overrun piston check ball not sealing	Replace check ball
Drives in Neutral (Creeps)	Forward clutch not releasing	Determine cause of condition; Service as required
	Internal converter damage	Replace converter
	Converter clutch apply valve stuck in oil pump	Clean and free valve; Service as required
	Internal leakage in case, or face not flat	Replace case
Starts in 2nd in "D"	Governor support pin too long or missing, or valve stuck in governor assembly	Service as required
	Forward sprag clutch assembly installed backward	Replace sprag clutch assembly
No Park	Parking linkage binding, mispositioned, loose, or missing	Replace components as required

Manual Transmission Servicing

AMERICAN MOTORS

LUBRICATION

SERVICE INTERVALS
Check fluid level every 7500 miles. Drain and refill at every 30,000 mile service.

CHECKING FLUID LEVEL
Check lubricant level at filler plug hole on side of transmission. Lubricant should be level with bottom of filler plug hole. Add lubricant as necessary to bring to correct level.

RECOMMENDED FLUID
Use AMC SAE 80 W, or SAE 90 W multipurpose gear lubricant.

CAUTION: **DO NOT use gear lubricants containing lead, sulfur or chlorine compounds.**

CAPACITY

TRANSMISSION REFILL CAPACITIES

Application	Quantity
4-Speed	
JB 0 Transaxle	6.8 pts. (3.2L)
5-Speed	
T5	4.5 pts. (2.1L)
JB 1 Transaxle	7.0 pts. (3.4L)

ADJUSTMENT

SHIFT ROD LINKAGE
Alliance & Encore
1) Shift transaxle into second gear. Raise vehicle. Wedge transaxle shift lever to prevent movement during adjustment. Loosen shift rod clamp bolt below shifter lever.

2) Lower vehicle. Remove shift lever boot. Place a .020" (.5 mm) feeler gauge between the reverse stop release holder and the left side gearshift lever housing.

3) Have an assistant hold shift lever against feeler gauge. Raise vehicle. Tighten shift rod clamp bolt. Rear edge of clamp should be positioned about .313" (8 mm) from end of shift rod. Check transaxle for proper gear engagement.

Fig. 1: Location of Transaxle Shift Lever

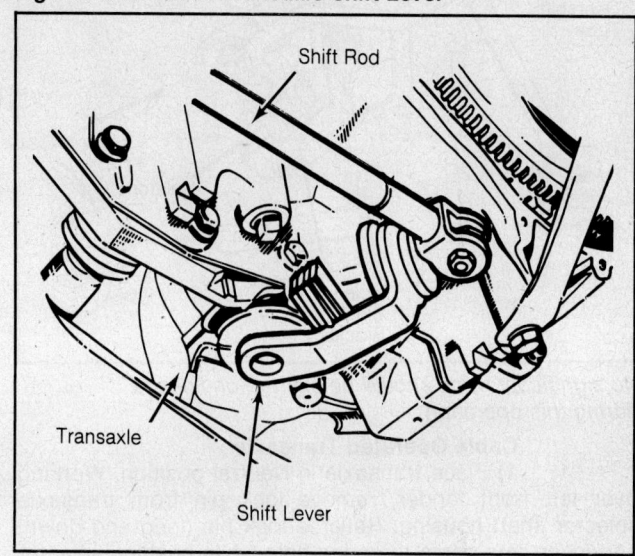

CHRYSLER CORP. DOMESTIC CARS

LUBRICATION

SERVICE INTERVALS
Check fluid level every 6 months. Draining and refilling are not required, except at time of overhaul or service.

CHECKING FLUID LEVEL
Check lubricant level at filler plug hole on top of transaxle. Lubricant should be level with bottom of filler plug hole. Add lubricant as necessary to bring to correct level.

CAPACITY

TRANSAXLE REFILL CAPACITIES

Application	Quantity
4-Speed	
A-460	4.0 pts. (1.8L)
5-Speed	
A-525	4.6 pts. (2.1L)

RECOMMENDED FLUID
A-460 & A-525 Transaxles
Use Dexron II automatic transmission fluid.

ADJUSTMENT

SHIFT LINKAGE
Rod Operated Transaxles
1) Place transaxle in Neutral position. Working over left front fender, remove lock pin from transaxle selector shaft housing. Reverse lock pin (long end down) and insert into same threaded hole while pushing selector shaft into selector housing.

2) Raise vehicle on hoist. Loosen clamp bolt that secures gearshift tube to gear shift connector. Check to see that gearshift connector slides and turns freely in gearshift tube. *See Fig. 1.*

3) Position shifter mechanism connector assembly so isolator is contacting the upstanding flange, and rib on isolator is aligned fore and aft with the hole in the block-out bracket. Hold in this position while tightening

CHRYSLER CORP. DOMESTIC CARS (Cont.)

clamp bolt on gearshift tube to 14 ft. lbs. (19 N.m). No significant force should be exerted on linkage during this operation.

    4) Lower vehicle. Remove lock pin from selector shaft housing and reinstall lock pin upside down in selector shaft housing. Tighten lock pin. Check for shift into 1st and Reverse. Check for block-out into Reverse.

Fig. 1: Rod Operated Gearshift Linkage Adjustment

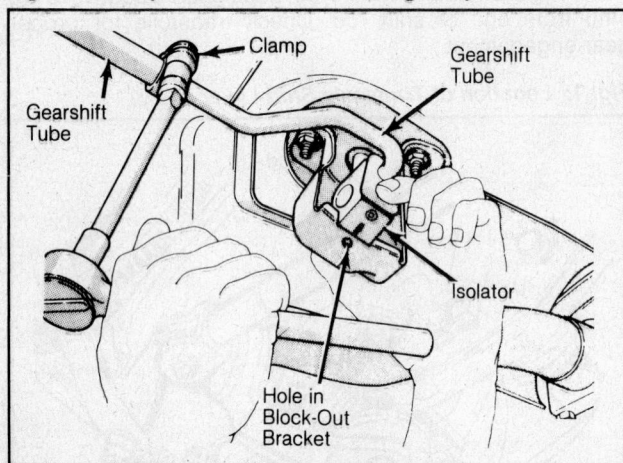

No significant force should be exerted on linkage during this operation.

Cable Operated Transaxle
    1) Place transaxle in Neutral position. Working over left front fender, remove lock pin from transaxle selector shaft housing. Reverse lock pin (long end down) and insert into same threaded hole while pushing selector shaft into selector housing.

    2) Remove gear shift knob, retaining nut and pull-up ring. Remove screws attaching center console and

remove console. Fabricate 2 adjustment pins from 3/16" diameter rod. *See Fig. 2.* Install adjustment pins in gear shifter mechanism.

    3) Loosen crossover and selector cable adjustment screws. Allow both cables to center themselves in the adjustment slot. Retighten cable adjustment set screws to 55 INCH. lbs. (6 N.m).

CAUTION: Proper torque on crossover and selector cable set screws is very important.

Fig. 2: Cable Operated Gearshift Linkage Adjustments

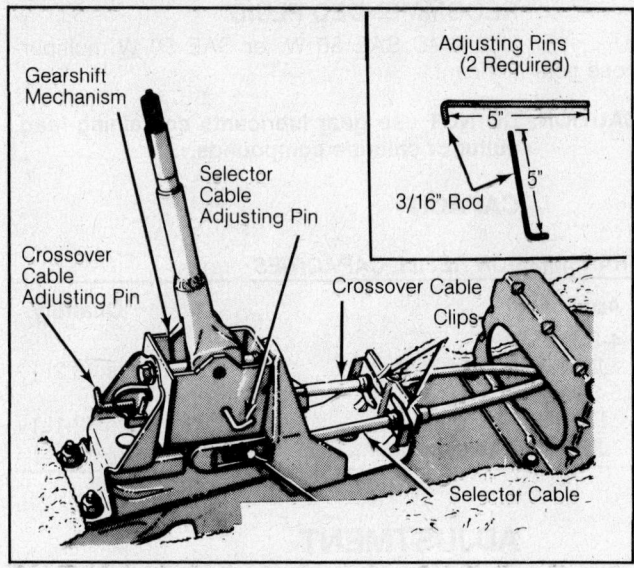

Inset shows adjustment pin fabrication.

FORD MOTOR CO. DOMESTIC CARS

LUBRICATION

SERVICE INTERVALS
    Check fluid level at 15 month/15,000 mile intervals. Draining and refilling are not required, except at time of overhaul or service.

CHECKING FLUID LEVEL
    Check lubricant level at filler plug hole on side of transmission. Lubricant should be level with bottom of filler plug hole. Add lubricant as necessary to bring to correct level.

RECOMMENDED FLUID
85 ET Transmission
Use SAE 80 W, or SAE 90 W multipurpose gear lubricant of API GL-5 quality.
MTX Transaxle & T5-OD
5-Speed Transmission
Use Dexron II automatic transmission fluid.

CAPACITY

TRANSMISSION REFILL CAPACITIES

Application	Quantity
4-Speed	
MTX Transaxle	5.0 pts. (2.5L)
85 ET	2.8 pts. (1.3L)
5-Speed	
MTX Transaxle	6.1 pts. (2.9L)
T5-OD 5-Speed Overdrive	5.6 pts. (2.6L)

ADJUSTMENT

SHIFT LINKAGE
    No in-service adjustment of shift linkage is necessary.

GENERAL MOTORS DOMESTIC CARS

LUBRICATION

SERVICE INTERVALS

Check fluid level at 3 month/3000 mile intervals. Draining and refilling is not required, except at time of overhaul or service.

CHECKING FLUID LEVEL

Check lubricant level at filler plug hole on side of transmission. Lubricant should be level with bottom of filler plug hole. Add lubricant as necessary to bring to correct level.

NOTE: **Check fluid level when transmission/transaxle is cold. If hot, fluid may flow from filler hole when plug is removed. This could result in burned hands or incorrect level readings.**

RECOMMENDED FLUID

**Manual Transmission
(Except 69.5 MM, 70 MM
& Camaro & Firebird 76 MM)**
Use SAE 80 W, or SAE 90 W multipurpose gear lubricant of API GL-5 quality.
**Manual Transaxle (Including 69.5 MM
& 70 MM Transmission)**
Use SAE 5 W-30 W engine oil SF, SF/CC or SF/CD.

**Manual Transmission
(Corvette Overdrive Unit
& Camaro & Firebird 76 MM)**
Use Dexron II automatic transmission fluid.

CAPACITY
TRANSMISSION REFILL CAPACITIES

Application	Quantity
4-Speed	
70 MM	3.4 pts. (1.6L)
76 MM	3.5 pts. (1.7L)
83 MM	2.0 pts. (1.0L)
76 MM Transaxle	6.0 pts. (2.8L)
5-Speed	
69.5 MM	3.3 pts. (1.5L)
77 MM	3.5 pts. (1.7L)
76 MM Transaxle	6.0 pts. (2.8L)
Overdrive	4.0 pts. (2.0L)

ADJUSTMENT

SHIFT LINKAGE
69.5 MM, 70 MM 4-Speed & 77 MM 5-Speed

NOTE: **Integral type shift linkage is used, therefore, no adjustment is necessary.**

76 MM 4-Speed
1) Raise and support vehicle. Loosen lock nuts at swivel on shift rods. Place transmission shift levers in Neutral. Place shift control lever in Neutral. *See Fig. 1.*
2) Align control assembly levers and insert gauge pin into levers and assembly to hold levers in Neutral position.
3) Tighten lock nuts at shift rod swivels and remove gauge pin. Check transmission shift operation. Readjust as necessary.

76 MM 4-Speed (Transaxle)
1) Place transaxle into 1st gear before making adjustments. Remove shifter boot and retainer. Install 2 pins (No. 22 drill bits or 5/32" pins) into alignment holes in shifter control assembly. This will secure assembly in 1st position. *See Fig. 2.*
2) Attach 2 shift cables to control assembly, using studs with pin retainers. Be sure cables are properly routed and operate freely.
3) Manually place transaxle into 1st gear by pushing rail selector shaft inward (down) until inhibitor spring resistance is first felt. Rotate shift lever fully clockwise.
4) Install stud of cable (1) into slotted area in shift lever (2). Install stud of cable (3) into slotted hole of select lever (4) to remove lash. *See Fig. 2.* Tighten nuts on studs.
5) Remove 2 drill bits or pins from control assembly and road test vehicle. Check for proper shifting. Adjust cable position as necessary after road testing.

77 MM 5-Speed (Transaxle)
1) Disconnect negative battery cable and place transaxle in 3rd gear position. Remove locking pin at transaxle and reinstall tapered end down, locking transaxle in 3rd gear. *See Fig. 3.* Loosen shift cable attaching nuts at transaxle shift levers.
2) From inside vehicle, remove console trim plate, slide shifter boot up and remove console. Install a

Fig. 1: View of 76 MM 4-Speed Floor Mounted Shift Linkage

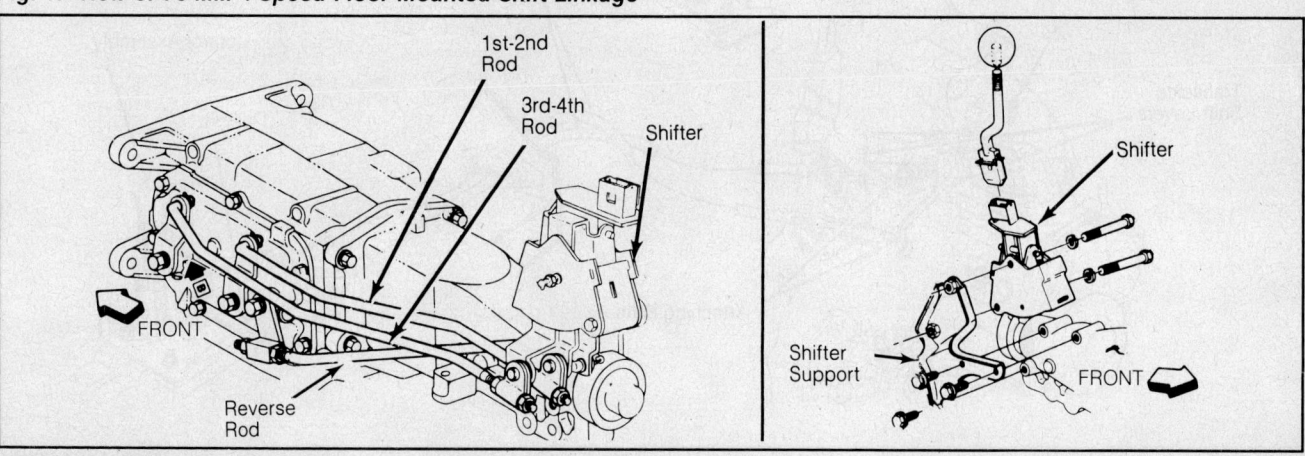

Shift rods should pass freely through swivels.

Manual Transmission Servicing
GENERAL MOTORS DOMESTIC CARS (Cont.)

Fig. 2: *Adjusting Transaxle Shift Cables*

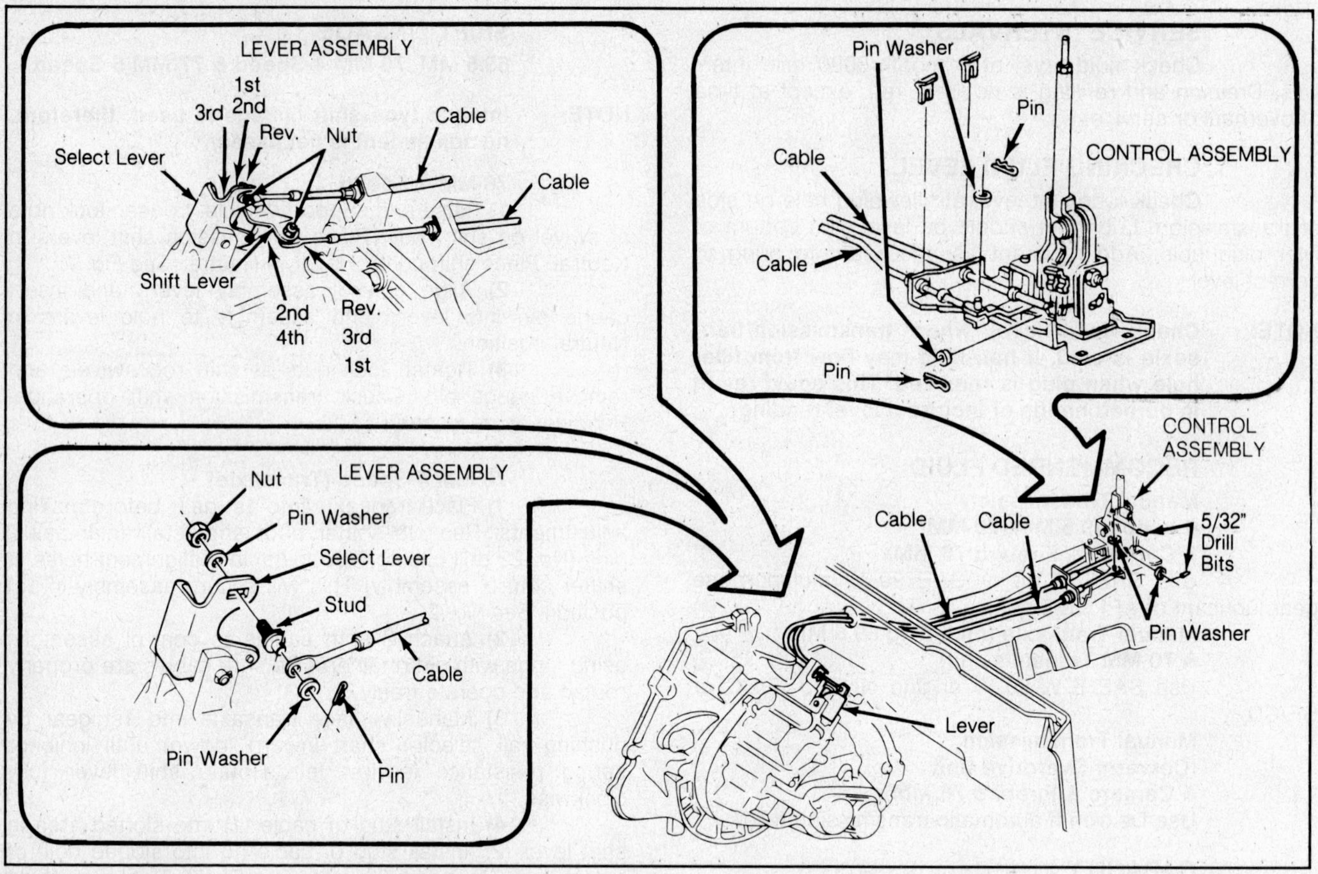

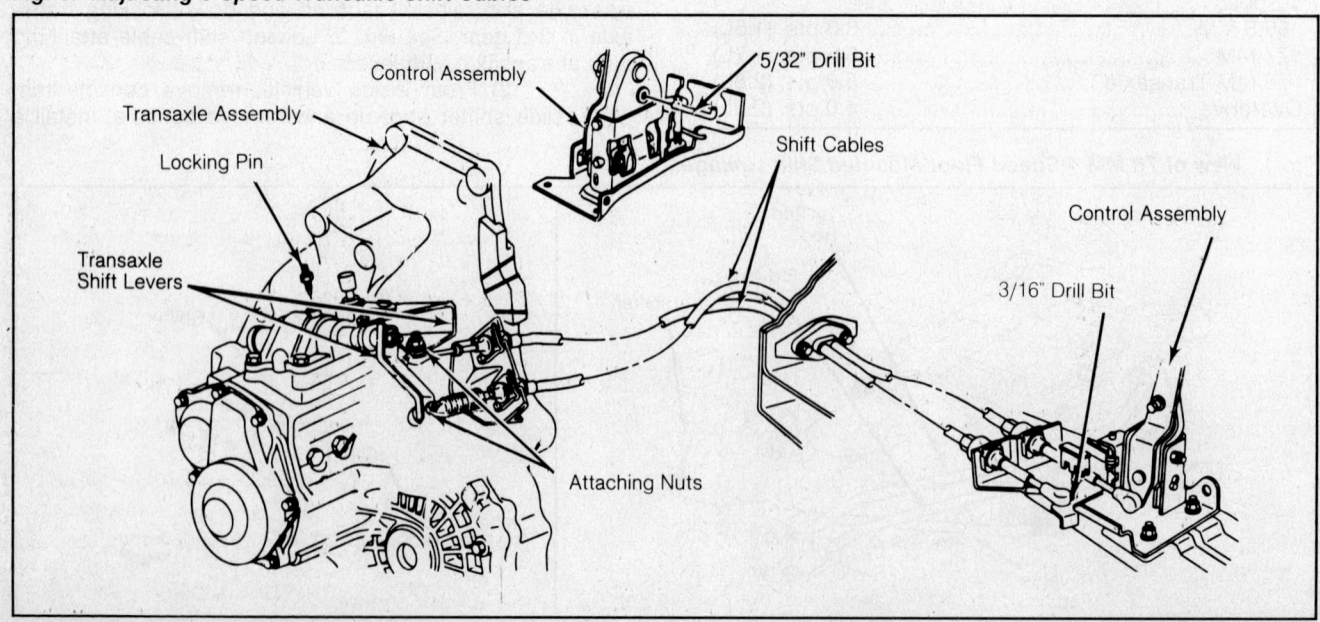

Place transaxle in 1st gear before making adjustment.

5/32" drill bit (No. 22) in alignment hole in shifter assembly. Align slot in shifter lever with shifter plate and install 3/16" drill bit.

    3) Tighten attaching nuts loosened in step **1).** Remove both drill bits. Remove locking pin at transaxle

and reinstall, tapered end up. Install console, shifter boot and trim plate. Reconnect negative ground cable.

    4) Road test vehicle to ensure proper linkage adjustment. Readjust if necessary.

Fig. 3: *Adjusting 5-Speed Transaxle Shift Cables*

Adjustment is performed with transaxle in 3rd gear position.

GENERAL MOTORS DOMESTIC CARS (Cont.)

83 MM 4-Speed Overdrive (Corvette)

1) Disconnect negative battery cable. Remove left seat. If equipped with power seats, remove electrical leads. Remove shift knob, console cover and shifter cover. Loosen lock nuts at shift rod swivels. Place shift levers in Neutral at transmission. Rods should pass freely through swivels. *See Fig. 4.*

2) Move shift control lever into neutral detent and align control assembly levers. Insert alignment gauge pin into lever adjustment slot. Tighten lock nuts at shift rod swivels and remove locating gauge pin.

Fig. 4: View of 83 MM 4-Speed Overdrive Gearshift Linkage Showing Adjustment Points

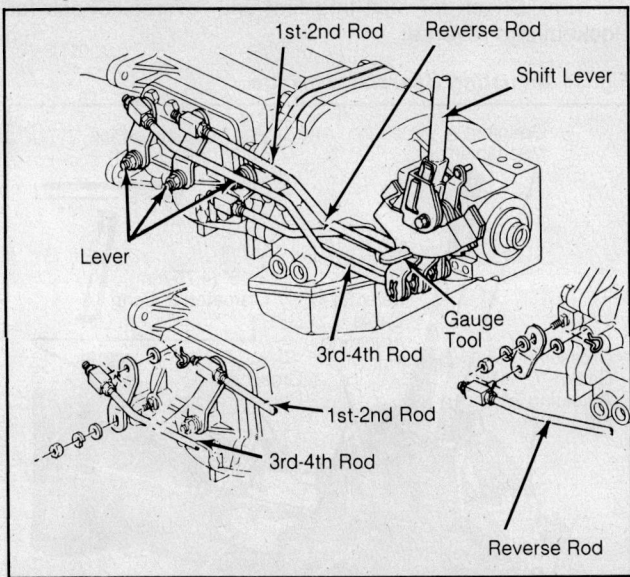

Shift rods should pass freely through swivels.

3) After adjustments have been made, the centerlines of shift levers must be aligned to each other to provide free crossover motion. Check transmission shift operation. Readjust as necessary. Reinstall interior in vehicle.

PARK LOCK CABLE

83 MM 4-Speed Overdrive (Corvette)

1) Disconnect negative battery cable. Remove left seat. If equipped with power seats, remove electrical leads. Remove shift knob, console cover and shifter cover.

2) Lift up adjuster locking tab on top of transmission tunnel to release cable. Position steering column lock lever in lock position. Shift transmission into reverse gear.

3) Insert a .060" (1.5 mm) gauge against the lever stop and pull reverse lever until reverse pawl contacts gauge. Push down on adjusting tab to set cable. Remove gauge and pull back on shifter lever. Check that reverse pawl hits stop and locks shifter in reverse.

THROTTLE VALVE CABLE

83 MM 4-Speed Overdrive (Corvette)

1) Depress and hold metal lock tab. Move slider back through fitting in direction away from throttle lever until slider stops against fitting. Release lock tab. *See Fig. 5.*

2) Rotate throttle lever to full open stop position to obtain a minimum of 1 click adjustment at the cable fitting. Repeat step **1)** if necessary.

Fig. 5: 83 MM 4-Speed Overdrive Throttle Cable Adjustment

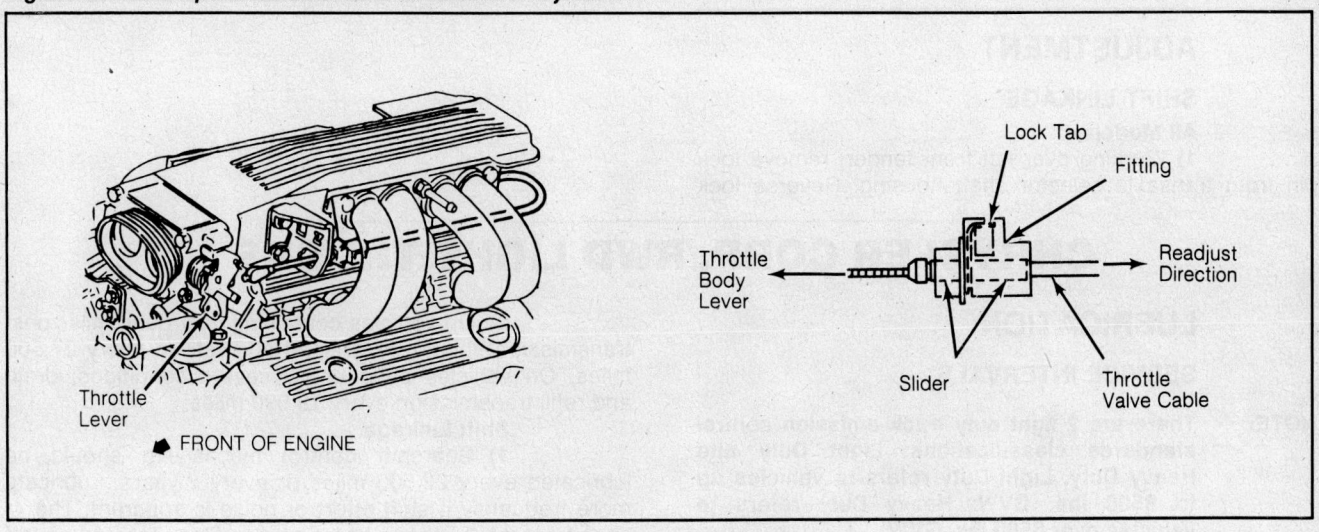

Manual Transmission Servicing

CHRYSLER CORP. FWD LIGHT TRUCKS

LUBRICATION

SERVICE INTERVALS

All Models

1) Under normal operating conditions, fluid installed at factory will give satisfactory lubrication for life of vehicle. Fluid changes are not necessary unless lubricant has become contaminated with water.

2) If vehicle is operated at sustained high speed during hot weather, above 90°F (32°C), transmission fluid should be changed and magnet, attached to inside of differential pan, cleaned every 15,000 miles.

Shift & Clutch Linkage

1) If linkage begins to squeak or grunt, pivot hole in adjuster and teeth of adjusting positioner should be lubricated with a thin film of multipurpose grease.

2) Gearshift control mechanism should be lubricated whenever high shift effort or noise (mechanism rattling) is apparent. A multipurpose grease is suitable for this application.

CHECKING FLUID LEVEL

Check lubricant level at filler plug hole on side of transmission. Lubricant should be level with bottom of filler plug hole. Add lubricant as needed to bring to correct level.

RECOMMENDED FLUID

FWD vehicles may be equipped with the A-460 or A-525 manual transaxles. If it becomes necessary to add fluid, use only fluids of the type labeled Dexron II automatic transmission fluid.

CAPACITY

TRANSMISSION REFILL CAPACITIES

Application	Quantity
All Models [1]	2.1 qts. (2.0L)

[1] – Measure given is approximate.

ADJUSTMENT

SHIFT LINKAGE

All Models

1) Working over left front fender, remove lock pin from transaxle selector shaft housing. Reverse lock pin, long end down, and insert lock pin into same threaded hole while pushing selector shaft into selector housing. A hole in selector shaft will align with lock pin, allowing lock pin to be screwed into housing. This operation locks selector shaft in 1-2 neutral position.

2) Remove gearshift knob, retaining nut, and pull-up ring. Remove boot from console and remove console. Install 2 cable adjusting pins. Torque selector cable adjusting screw to 55 INCH lbs. (6 N.m). Torque crossover cable adjusting screw to 55 INCH lbs. (6 N.m). See Fig. 1.

3) Install console, boot, pull-up ring, retaining nut and gearshift knob. Remove lock pin from selector shaft housing and reinstall lock pin (so long end is up) in selector shaft housing. Tighten lock pin to 106 INCH lbs. (12 N.m). Check for shift into first and reverse. Check for blockout into reverse.

Fig. 1: Adjusting Gearshift Linkage

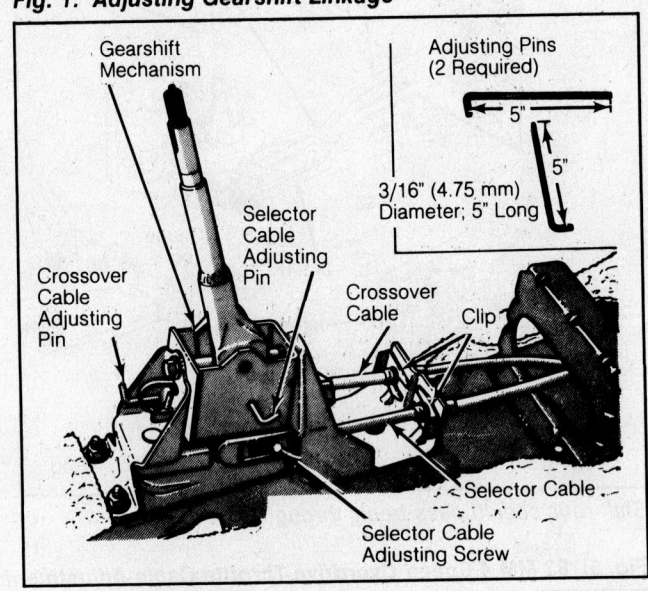

CHRYSLER CORP. RWD LIGHT TRUCKS

LUBRICATION

SERVICE INTERVALS

NOTE: There are 2 light duty truck emission control standards classifications: Light Duty and Heavy Duty. Light Duty refers to vehicles up to 8500 lbs. GVW; Heavy Duty refers to vehicles over 8500 lbs. GVW.

All Models

1) Check fluid level whenever vehicle is serviced. On vehicles used in normal service with heavy duty emissions, transmission should be drained and refilled every 36,000 miles.

2) On vehicles containing light duty emissions, transmission should be drained and refilled every 37,500 miles. On vehicles used under severe conditions, drain and refill transmission every 18,000 miles.

Shift Linkage

1) Gearshift control mechanism should be lubricated every 22,500 miles or every 2 years. Lubricate more frequently if shift effort or noise is apparent. The 4-speed gearshift linkage has a grease fitting located on left side of mechanism. Lubricate linkage from under vehicle.

2) Use a high pressure grease gun to lubricate linkage with multipurpose grease. Lubricate until grease is visible on operating levers.

CHRYSLER CORP. RWD LIGHT TRUCKS (Cont.)

NOTE: Vehicle must be in reverse gear position, engine OFF, when lubricating gearshift control mechanism.

CHECKING FLUID LEVEL

Check lubricant level at filler plug hole on side of transmission. Lubricant should be level with bottom of filler plug hole. Add lubricant as needed to bring to correct level.

RECOMMENDED FLUID

New Process 435 4-Speed

Either multipurpose gear lubricants meeting API specification GL-5 or engine oils labeled for API Service "SF" may be used.

If multipurpose gear lubricant is used and the minimum anticipated atmospheric temperature is:

- Above 90°F (32°C), use SAE 140.
- As low as -10°F (-23°C), use SAE 90.
- Below -10°F (-23°C), use SAE 80.

If engine oil is used, and the minimum anticipated atmospheric temperature is:

- Above 32°F (0°C), use SAE 50.
- Below 32°F (0°C), use SAE 30.

Overdrive 4-Speed

Use Dexron II Automatic Transmission Fluid. If gear rattle is apparent during idle or acceleration, multipurpose gear lubricant SAE 90, SAE 75W, 75W-80, SAE 80W-90 or SAE 85W-90 may be used.

CAPACITY

TRANSMISSION REFILL CAPACITIES

Application	Quantity
All Models	3.5 qts. (3.3L)

ADJUSTMENT

SHIFT LINKAGE

Overdrive 4-Speed

1) Install floor shift lever aligning tool to hold levers in neutral crossover position. *See Fig. 1.* Remove all rods from transmission shift levers and place levers in neutral detent positions.

2) Rotate shift rods until they are centered in transmission lever mounting holes, starting with 1st-2nd shift rod. Replace all washers and clips. Remove aligning tool and test shifting action.

Fig. 1: Overdrive 4-Speed Gearshift Linkage Adjustment

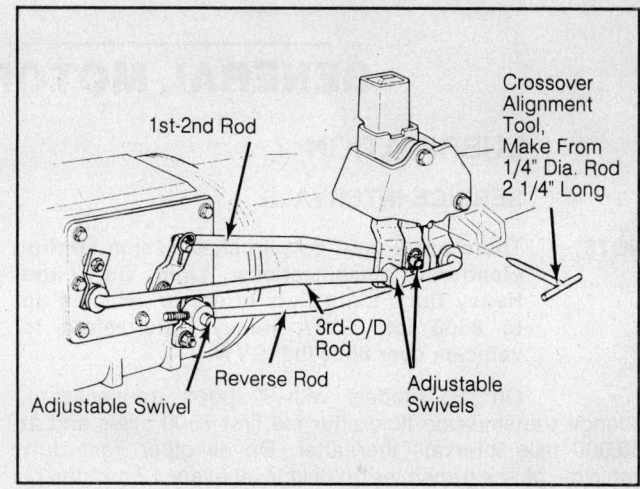

FORD LIGHT TRUCKS

LUBRICATION

SERVICE INTERVALS

Check fluid level whenever malfunction is suspected, leakage is observed, or after vehicle operation in water. Periodic draining and refilling is not required.

CHECKING FLUID LEVEL

Check lubricant level at transmission filler plug hole. It should be level with bottom of filler hole. Add lubricant as needed.

RECOMMENDED FLUID

All transmissions except Warner T19B should use 80W multi-purpose gear lubricant meeting Ford specification ESP-M2C83-C, or equivalent. Warner T19B transmissions use SAE 30 or SAE 50 engine oil, depending upon ambient air temperatures. If vehicle will be operated at temperatures below 0°F (-18°C), SAE 30 should be used. SAE 50 should be used if temperatures are consistently above 0°F (-18°C).

CAPACITY

NOTE: Capacities given below are approximate. Correct fluid level should be determined by level at filler plug hole, rather than by amount added.

TRANSMISSION REFILL CAPACITIES

Application	Quantity
Pickup, Van, Bronco	
Ford 3.03 3-Speed	3.5 pts. (1.6L)
Warner T-18 4-Speed	7.0 pts. (3.3L)
Warner T-19B 4-Speed	7.0 pts. (3.3L)
New Process 435 4-Speed	
With Extension	7.0 pts. (3.3L)
Without Extension	6.5 pts. (3.0L)
Ford Top Shifter (TOD)	
4-Speed Overdrive	4.5 pts. (2.1L)
Ford 4-Speed Overdrive	4.5 pts. (2.1L)
Bronco II & Ranger	
Mitsubishi 5-Speed	4.9 pts. (2.3L)
Toyo Kogyo 5-Speed Overdrive	3.0 pts. (1.4L)
Aerostar	
Mazda 5-Speed Overdrive	3.0 pts. (1.4L)

Manual Transmission Servicing

FORD LIGHT TRUCKS (Cont.)

ADJUSTMENT

SHIFT LINKAGE

Shift linkage may be adjusted on the 3-Speed and 4-Speed Overdrive transmissions, only. All other models use internal shift linkage which cannot be adjusted.

3-Speed

1) Insert a 3/16" gauge pin through steering column shift levers and plastic spacer.

2) Loosen shift rod lock nuts at transmission shift levers. Place both shift levers in Neutral position. Tighten lock nuts and remove gauge pin. Check shift linkage operation for smoothness.

4-Speed Overdrive

1) Disconnect all 3 shift rods and insert a 1/4" diameter pin in alignment hole in shifter assembly. Align 1-2 (rear) and 3-4 (front) shift levers in Neutral position. Turn Reverse (middle) lever counterclockwise to Neutral position.

2) Rotate transmission output shaft to be sure all levers are in Neutral. Then turn reverse lever fully clockwise to reverse position. This causes the interlock system to align 1-2 and 3-4 rails in precise neutral positions. Install 1-2 and 3-4 shift rods on shift levers and tighten lock nuts.

3) Rotate reverse lever back to Neutral position. Install reverse shift rod and lock nut. Remove alignment pin and check for proper linkage operation.

GENERAL MOTORS LIGHT TRUCKS

LUBRICATION

SERVICE INTERVALS

NOTE: There are 2 light duty truck emission control standards classifications: Light Duty and Heavy Duty. Light Duty refers to vehicles up to 8500 lbs. GVW; Heavy Duty refers to vehicles over 8500 lbs. GVW.

On "S" models with 4-speed transmission, change transmission fluid after the first 7500 miles and at 30,000 mile intervals thereafter. On all other light duty vehicles, check transmission fluid level every 12 months or 7500 miles. On heavy duty vehicles, check fluid level every 12 months or 6000 miles. Periodic draining and refilling is not required.

CHECKING FLUID LEVEL

Check lubricant level at transmission filler plug hole. Lubricant should be level with bottom of hole. Add as needed.

RECOMMENDED FLUID

All manual transmissions except 4-Speed Overdrive, Astro/Safari 5-Speed and those in the "S" Series, use SAE 80W, GL-5 or SAE 80W-90 GL-5 multipurpose gear lubricant. The 4-Speed Overdrive, Astro/Safari 5-Speed and "S" Series manual transmissions use Dexron II automatic transmission fluid.

CAPACITY

NOTE: Capacities listed in the following chart are approximations only. Correct fluid level should be determined by level at filler plug hole, rather than by amount added.

TRANSMISSION REFILL CAPACITIES

Application	Quantity
3-Speed (76 MM)	3.0 pts. (1.4L)
4-Speed (76 MM)	4.0 pts. (1.9L)
4-Speed (117 MM)	8.0 pts. (3.7L)
4-Speed w/Overdrive (89 MM)	4.5 pts. (2.1L)
Astro/Safari & "S" Models	[1]

[1] – Add fluid to bottom of filler plug hole.

ADJUSTMENT

SHIFT LINKAGE

All With Shifter on Column

1) Place gear selector lever in reverse position. Turn transmission shift lever fully clockwise to forward stop. Turn ignition switch to "LOCK" position. Attach primary shift rod to column shift lever with retainer.

2) Slide swivel on to end of shift rod and insert swivel into transmission shift lever. Loosely assemble with bolt and washer. Turn column shift lever down as far as possible and tighten bolt.

3) Turn ignition switch to "UNLOCK" position and move gear selector lever to neutral. Turn transmission shift lever and cross shaft lever clockwise to full forward positions, then back 1 detent to Neutral.

4) Align gauge holes in column shift levers (3) and insert 1/4" gauge pin through holes. Repeat adjustment procedure with secondary shift rod. Remove gauge pin and check for proper linkage operation. Ignition switch should turn to "LOCK" position with shifter in reverse position, only.

All With Floor-Mounted Shifter

1) Disconnect all shift rods from transmission shift levers. With shift selector lever in neutral position, insert a 1/4" diameter pin through alignment holes in shifter assembly.

2) Align all shift levers at transmission in Neutral position. Rotate transmission output shaft to be sure all levers are in neutral. Loosen lock nuts on shift rod ends and align rod ends with shift lever holes. Install shift rods in levers, tighten lock nuts and install lock pins.

3) Remove alignment pin and check for proper linkage operation.

Astro/Safari 5-Speed & "S" Series

On Astro/Safari 5-Speed and "S" Series vehicles, the shift control lever mounts directly to the transmission. Therefore no adjustment is necessary.

JEEP

LUBRICATION

SERVICE INTERVALS

Under normal driving conditions, check fluid level every 5000 miles or when serviced. Under severe driving conditions, check fluid level every 3000 miles. Transmission lubricant should be changed at 27,500 mile intervals.

CHECKING FLUID LEVEL

Check lubricant level at transmission filler plug hole. Lubricant should be level with bottom of hole. Add lubricant as needed.

RECOMMENDED FLUID

The only recommended lubricant for Jeep with manual transmission is AMC/Jeep Manual Transmission Fluid, Part No. 89 83 000 000.

CAPACITY

NOTE: Capacities given below are approximate. Correct fluid level should be determined by level at filler plug hole.

TRANSMISSION REFILL CAPACITIES

Application	Quantity
4-Speed	
AX4	7.4 pts. (3.5L)
T4	3.5 pts. (1.7L)
T-176	3.5 pts. (1.7L)
5-Speed	
AX5	7.0 pts. (3.3L)
T5	4.0 pts. (1.9L)

SHIFT LINKAGE

NOTE: All Jeep models use transmission shift linkage which does not require external adjustment.

Manual Transmission Removal

AMERICAN MOTORS

REMOVAL & INSTALLATION

EAGLE

Removal

1) Shift transmision into neutral. Remove console (if equipped). Remove gearshift lever, bezel and boot from floor pan. Slide boot upward on lever to remove bolts attaching gearshift lever to lever mounting cover.

2) Remove gearshift lever. Raise vehicle and support on jack stands. Remove skid pan and mark position of speedometer adapter for installation reference. Remove speedometer retainer, adapter and cable. Plug adapter hole to prevent oil spillage.

3) Disconnect drive shafts and mark for installation reference. Disconnect exhaust (if necessary). Disconnect back-up light switch wire. Place a jack stand under engine. Support transmission and transfer case with a transmission jack.

4) Remove rear crossmember. Remove catalytic converter bracket from transfer case. Remove bolts attaching transmission to clutch housing. Remove transmission and transfer case as an assembly.

ALLIANCE & ENCORE

Removal

1) Raise vehicle and support on jack stands. Remove wheel assemblies and disconnect axle shafts. Disconnect gearshift lever linkage and engine-to-transaxle rod. Remove clutch shield and all mounting pad nuts.

2) Remove air filter. Disconnect back-up light switch wire connector and remove sensor. Disconnect clutch cable, speedometer cable and ground wire. Re-move radiator and lay it on engine without disconnecting hoses.

3) Raise engine enough to free rear mounts. Remove starter motor. Remove transaxle retaining bolts, separate transaxle from engine and lift it free of chassis. On models with JB 1 transaxle, slide 5th gear casing between side members.

Installation

To install, reverse removal procedure and note the following: Fill Transmission/Transaxle with fluid to proper level. See MANUAL TRANSMISSION SERVICING in this section.

Raise vehicle and support on jack stands. Remove wheel assemblies and disconnect axle shafts. Disconnect gearshift lever linkage and engine-to-transaxle rod. Remove clutch shield and all mounting pad nuts.

TIGHTENING SPECIFICATIONS

Application	Ft. Lbs. (N.m)
Alliance & Encore	
Transaxle-to-Engine Bolts	32 (42)
Starter Motor Bolts	32 (42)
Eagle	
Bell Housing-to-Engine	
6-Cylinder	
Top Bolts	27 (37)
Bottom Bolts	43 (58)
Transmission-to-Bell Housing	55 (75)
Rear Crossmember Studs	30 (41)
Support-to-Crossmember	18 (24)

CHRYSLER CORP. DOMESTIC CARS

REMOVAL & INSTALLATION

FWD MODELS

Removal

1) Disconnect negative battery cable. Support engine with engine support fixture. Disconnect shift linkage from transaxle selector shaft. Disconnect back-up light switch wire. Remove starter.

2) Disconnect clutch cable. Remove bolt securing speedometer adapter to transaxle. Carefully work adapter and pinion out of transaxle.

3) Loosen wheel hub nuts with vehicle on floor. Raise and support vehicle. Remove wheel assemblies. Disconnect right drive axle shaft and tie out of the way. Remove left drive axle shaft and set aside. See FRONT WHEEL DRIVE AXLE SHAFTS in DRIVE AXLE section.

4) Remove left splash shield. Remove small dust cover at bell housing. Remove large dust cover bolts at bell housing.

5) Drain fluid from transaxle. Place jack under transaxle and chain in place. Remove bolts from left engine mount. Remove bolt attaching transaxle-to-engine. Slide transaxle assembly to the left and rear of vehicle.

Installation

To install, reverse removal procedure and note the following: Adjust clutch cable and fill transaxle with fluid to proper level. See MANUAL TRANSMISSION SERVICING in this section.

TIGHTENING SPECIFICATIONS

Application	Ft. Lbs. (N.m)
Ball Joint Clamp Bolt	50 (68)
Strut-to-Block & Case	70 (95)
Transaxle Case-to-Engine Block	70 (95)

FORD MOTOR CO. DOMESTIC CARS

REMOVAL & INSTALLATION

EXC. ESCORT, EXP, LYNX
TEMPO & TOPAZ
Removal (85 ET 4-Speed)

1) Remove shift lever. From under vehicle, remove upper bolts from clutch housing. Raise vehicle on a hoist. Mark position of and remove drive shaft. Remove clutch release cover and cable.

2) Remove starter motor and speedometer cable. Support rear of engine and remove crossmember bolts. Remove bolts that attach crossmember to extension housing of transmission. Lower engine to permit removal of clutch housing bolts. Slide transmission from engine and lower from vehicle.

Removal (T50D)

1) Raise vehicle on hoist. Mark position of and remove drive shaft. Remove 4 bolts and catalytic converter. Remove 2 nut attaching rear transmission support to crossmember. On Thunderbird Coupe 2.3L Turbo models, remove header pipe from exhaust manifold.

2) Support engine and transmission with a jack. Remove 2 nuts from crossmember bolts. Remove bolts and crossmember. Lower transmission to expose 2 bolts securing shift handle to shift tower. Remove 2 nuts and bolts and shift handle.

3) Disconnect wiring harness from back-up light switch. On 5.0L engine, disconnect top gear sensing switch. Remove speedometer cable from housing. Remove 4 bolts securing transmission to clutch housing. Slide transmission from engine and lower from vehicle.

Installation

Reverse removal procedure and note the following: Fill transmission with fluid to proper level. See *MANUAL TRANSMISSION SERVICING in this section.*

TEMPO & TOPAZ
Removal (MTX 5-speed)

1) Wedge a wood block (7" long) under clutch pedal. Disconnect clutch cable clutch release lever. Remove 2 top transaxle-to-engine bolts. Remove air cleaner. Raise vehicle on a hoist.

2) Remove front stabilizer bar. Remove pinch bolts and nuts from lower control arm ball joints. Pry control arms away from knuckle. Using Tool (D83P-4026-A), pry inboard CV joint from transaxle. Install shipping plugs (T81P-1177-B).

3) Remove inboard CV joint from transaxle by grasping left hand steering knuckle and swinging knuckle and halfshaft outward from transaxle. Tie halfshaft in a near level position. Remove back-up light switch connector.

4) Remove engine roll restrictor and starter motor. Remove shift mechanism stabilizer bar-to-transaxle attaching bolt. Remove sheet metal screw and control select indicator switch and bracket. Remove speedometer cable.

5) Remove 2 bolts from oil pan to clutch housing. Position jack under transaxle. Remove 2 nuts securing left hand front insulator to body bracket. Lower jack until transaxle clears rear insulator.

6) Support engine with a screw jack stand under oil pan. Use a 2x4 block on top of jack stand. Remove 4 engine-to-transaxle attaching bolts. Remove ground strap and wiring harness bracket.

Installation

Reverse removal procedure and note the following: Fill the transmission with fluid to proper level. *See MANUAL TRANSMISSION SERVICING in this section.*

ESCORT, EXP & LNYX
Removal (MTX 5-Speed)

1) Wedge a block of wood (7" long) under clutch pedal. Remove clutch cable from clutch release lever and from rib on top surface of transaxle case. Remove 2 top transaxle-to-engine mounting bolts.

2) On 1.6L engines, remove top bolt that secures air management valve bracket. Raise vehicle on a hoist. Remove pinch bolt and nut from left lower control arm ball joint. Pry lower control from steering knuckle.

3) Pry left inboard CV joint from transaxle. Install shipping plug (T81P-1177-B) to prevent lubricant from leaking from transaxle. Tie halfshaft up, in a near level position. Remove pinch bolt and nut from right lower control arm ball joint. Pry lower control from steering knuckle.

4) Remove back-up light switch connector. On EFI vehicles, remove neutral sensing switch. Remove starter motor. Remove shift mechanism-to-shift shaft attaching bolt and nut and selector indicator switch arm.

5) Remove shift shaft. Remove shift mechanism stabilizer bar-to-transaxle attaching bolt, switch and bracket. Remove speedometer cable from housing. Remove stiffener brace bolts. Remove 2 bolts securing rear mount to floor pan brace.

6) Loosen nut in bottom of front mount. Remove 3 bolts securing front mount. Lower transaxle jack until transaxle clears rear mount. Support engine with screw jack (use a 2x4 piece of wood) under oil pan. Remove 4 engine to transaxle attaching bolts. Slide transaxle from engine and lower from vehicle.

Installation

Reverse removal procedure and note the following: Fill the transmission with fluid to proper level. *See MANUAL TRANSMISSION SERVICING in this section.*

TIGHTENING SPECIFICATIONS

Application	Ft. Lbs. (N.m)
Escort, EXP, Lynx, Tempo & Topaz	
Front Mounting Bolts	25-35 (34-47)
Lower Ball Joint	37-44 (50-60)
Rear Mounting Bolts	35-50 (47-68)
Transaxle-to-Engine	25-35 (34-47)
All Others	
Bell Housing-to-Engine	38-55 (52-75)
Transmission-to-Support	36-50 (48-68)

Manual Transmission Removal
GENERAL MOTORS DOMESTIC CARS

REMOVAL & INSTALLATION

CHEVETTE, 1000, CAMARO & FIREBIRD
(70 MM 4-SPEED & 77 MM 5-SPEED)
Removal

1) Disconnect negative battery cable. Remove screws from transmission shift lever boot retainer and slide boot up lever. Remove shift lever attaching bolts at transmission and remove lever. Raise vehicle on a hoist. On Camaro and Firebird models, remove torque arm on rear suspension.

2) Mark position and remove drive shaft. Disconnect speedometer cable from housing. Remove back-up light switch connector and clutch cable from clutch release lever. Remove crossmember-to-transmission mount bolts.

3) Remove header pipe and catalytic converter. Remove crossmember-to-frame bolts. Remove dust cover and clutch housing retaining bolts. Slide transmission from engine and lower from vehicle.

CORVETTE
(83 MM 4-SPEED W/OVERDRIVE)
Removal

1) Disconnect negative battery cable. Remove air cleaner and disconnect TV cable at throttle lever. Remove distributor cap and lay aside. Raise vehicle on a hoist. Remove entire exhaust system. Be sure to disconnect oxygen sensor lead before removing exhaust system.

2) Support transsmission with a jack. Remove bolts attaching drive line beam at axle and transmission. Remove drive line beam from vehicle. Mark position of and remove drive shaft. Disconnect overdrive cooling lines. Disconnect TV cable at overdrive lever.

3) Disconnect shift linkage and electrical connectors from transmission switches. Lower transmission and support engine. Remove 4 attaching bolt from transmission to clutch housing. Slide transmission from engine and lower from vehicle.

FIERO
Removal

1) Remove air cleaner and negative battery cable. Remove ground strap and shifter cables from transaxle. Remove upper transaxle-to-engine bolts. Install engine support fixture (J-28467).

2) Raise vehicle on a hoist. Remove both rear wheels and drive axles. *Refer to Drive Axles Section for removal procedures.* Remove catalytic converter heat shield. Remove header pipe from exhaust manifold.

3) Remove cradle-to-engine nuts. Support cradle with a screw jack and remove remaining cradle nuts. Lower cradle from vehicle. Remove starter shield and starter motor. Support transaxle with a jack and remove lower transaxle to engine bolts. Slide transaxle from engine and lower from vehicle.

ALL MODELS
Installation

To install transmission (transaxle), reverse installation procedures. Adjust TV cable and clutch cable. Fill transmission (transaxle) with lubricant to proper level. *See MANUAL TRANSMISSION SERVICING in this section.*

REMOVAL & INSTALLATION

FRONT WHEEL DRIVE MODELS
Removal

1) Disconnect negative battery cable. Install engine holding fixture (J-28467) and raise engine just enough to take pressure off motor mounts. On models equipped with hydraulic clutch, remove lower bezel from under steering column. Remove clutch master cylinder actuating rod and remove slave cylinder from transaxle.

2) On all other models, remove heater hose clamp from mount bracket. Disconnect and remove horns and air cleaner. Disconnect clutch cable from clutch shift lever. If V6 equipped, remove fuel lines and clamps at clutch cable bracket and remove exhaust crossover pipe.

3) On all models, remove transaxle mount and bracket. Disconnect shift cables, retaining clamps and ground strap from transaxle. Remove upper transaxle-to-engine bolts.

4) Raise vehicle on hoist and drain transaxle. Remove air managemet valve attaching bolts (if equipped). Remove front wheels and remove drive axles. *Refer to DRIVE AXLES Section for removal procedures.* Disconnect speedometer cable from housing.

5) Support transaxle with a jack and remove lower transaxle-to-engine bolts. Slide transaxle from engine and lower from vehicle.

Installation

To install transaxle, reverse removal procedure and note the following: When installing transaxle, guide right axle shaft into bore as transaxle is being raised. Fill transaxle with fluid to proper level. *See MANUAL TRANSMISSION SERVICING in this section.*

TIGHTENING SPECIFICATION

Application	Ft. Lbs. (N.m)
Front Wheel Drive Models	
Bell Housing-to-Engine	55 (75)
Support-to-Body	75 (100)
Transaxle-to-Support	40 (50)
Fiero	
Engine Mount-to-Cradle	40 (55)
Front Cradle-to-Body	67 (90)
Rear Cradle-to-Body	76 (103)
Transaxle-to-Engine	55 (75)
Transaxle Mount-to-Cradle	
Front	36 (48)
Rear	18 (24)
All Other Models	
Bell Housing-to-Engine	
70 MM 4-Speed	25 (34)
77 MM 5-Speed	30 (40)
Propeller Shaft Support Beam-to-Transmission	
83 MM 4-Speed Overdrive	50 (60)
Support-to-Transmission	
70 MM 4-Speed	32 (43)
77 MM 5-Speed	30 (40)
Transmission Filler Plug	
70 MM 4-Speed	25 (34)
77 MM 5-Speed	20 (27)
83 MM 4-Speed Overdrive	30 (38)
Transmission-to-Bell housing	
83 MM 4-Speed Overdrive	52 (70)

CHRYSLER CORP. RWD LIGHT TRUCKS

TRANSFER CASE

MODEL NP-205
Removal

1) Raise and support vehicle. Remove plug and drain transfer case. Replace plug. Disconnect speedometer cable. Remove skid plate, crossmember and strut rods as needed. Disconnect propeller shafts and wire out of way. Do not allow propeller shafts to hang free, as damage to universal joints may result.

2) Disconnect shift lever rod from shift rail link. Support transfer case and remove transfer case-to-transmission adapter bolts. Move transfer case to rear until input shaft clears adapter. Lower transfer case from vehicle.

Installation

Reverse removal procedures to install transfer case. Ensure that all attaching bolts are tight. Fill transfer case with lubricant.

MODEL NP-208
Removal

1) Raise vehicle, remove plug and drain transfer case. Mark front and rear output shaft yokes and propeller shafts for reassembly reference. Disconnect speedometer cable and indicator switch wires. Disconnect shift lever link from operating lever.

2) Support transfer case with transmission jack and remove crossmember. Disconnect front and rear propeller shafts at yokes and wire to frame.

3) If necessary, disconnect parking brake cable guide from pivot on right frame rail. Remove bolts attaching exhaust pipe support bracket to transfer case. Remove transfer case-to-transmission bolts. Move assembly to the rear until clear of output shaft. Lower transfer case from vehicle.

4) Remove all gasket material from rear of transmission adapter housing.

Installation

1) Install new transmission-to-transfer case gasket with sealer on both sides. Align transfer case with transmission. Rotate transfer case output shaft until transmission output shaft engages transfer case input shaft.

2) Move transfer case until case seats flush against transmission. Install transfer case attaching bolts. Reverse removal procedures to complete installation.

TRANSMISSION

ALL MODELS
Removal

1) Disconnect negative battery cable. Remove retaining screws from floor pan and slide boot up and off shift lever.

2) On models equipped with New Process 435 transmission, remove shift lever retainer by pressing down, rotating retainer clockwise and releasing.

3) On models equipped with Overdrive 4-Speed transmission, remove shift lever by inserting a .010" (.25 mm) feeler gauge between floor shift assembly and shift lever, and disengaging internal spring clip. *See Fig. 1.*

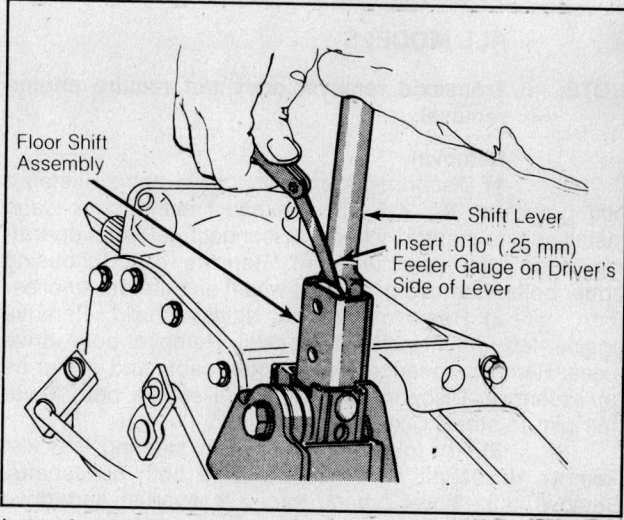

Fig. 1: Removing Overdrive 4-Speed Shift Lever

Floor Shift Assembly

Shift Lever

Insert .010" (.25 mm) Feeler Gauge on Driver's Side of Lever

Insert feeler gauge to remove spring clip.

4) Remove bolts and washers securing shift lever to mounting plate on extension housing and remove.

5) On all models, drain fluid from transmission. On 4WD models, remove transfer case. On all vehicles, remove propeller shaft from transmission at rear universal joint. Disconnect speedometer cable and back-up light switch. Install engine support fixture (C-3487-A).

6) On models equipped with New Process 435 transmission, place adapters (DD-1279) firmly over frame rails. On all models, make sure support ends of engine fixture tool are up against underside of oil pan flange.

7) Raise engine slightly with support fixture. On models with Overdrive 4-Speed transmission, disconnect extension housing from removable center crossmember.

8) On all models, support transmission with a jack and remove crossmember. Remove transmission-to-clutch housing bolts. Slide transmission rearward until drive pinion shaft clears clutch disc, then lower and remove transmission.

Installation

1) To install reverse removal procedure. Apply a small amount of high-temperature grease to the pilot shaft bushing in the flywheel and on pinion bearing retainer release bearing sleeve area before installing transmission.

2) As transmission is installed, engage pinion shaft with clutch disc by slowly turning shaft to engage teeth. DO NOT allow transmission to hang free once clutch disc has been engaged.

TIGHTENING SPECIFICATIONS

Application	Ft. Lbs. (N.m)
Transfer Case-to-Transmission	40 (54)
Crossmember-to-Frame	30 (41)
Ext. Housing-to-Rear Mount Bolt	50 (68)
Transmission Case-to-Clutch Housing	
Overdrive 4-Speed	50 (68)
NP-435	105 (142)

Manual Transmission Removal

CHRYSLER CORP. FWD LIGHT TRUCKS

TRANSAXLE

ALL MODELS

NOTE: **Transaxle removal does not require engine removal.**

Removal

1) Disconnect battery negative cable. Install a "lifting eye" on No. 4 Cylinder exhaust manifold bolt and install engine support fixture. Disconnect gearshift operating lever from selector shaft. Remove clutch housing upper bolts. Remove both front wheel and tire assemblies.

2) Remove left front splash shield. Remove engine left mount from transaxle. Remove both drive axles. Remove speedometer adapter, cable and pinion as an assembly. Disconnect sway bar. Remove both lower ball joint-to-steering knuckle bolts.

3) Pry lower ball joint from steering knuckle. Remove driveshaft from hub. Remove both driveshafts. Remove dust cover, mark torque converter and drive plate, and remove torque converter mounting bolts. Remove access plug in right splash shield to rotate engine crankshaft.

4) Remove neutral safety switch connector. Remove engine mount bracket from front crossmember. Remove front mount insulator through-bolt and bell housing bolts. Position transmission jack under transaxle. Remove left engine mount. Remove starter and lower bell housing bolts.

5) Slowly lower transaxle. It may be necessary to pry at engine to provide for clearance.

Installation

To install, reverse removal procedure. Be sure to adjust gearshift and throttle cables. Refill transaxle with Dexron II type automatic transmission fluid. When installing transaxle, it may be helpful to use two locating pins in place of the top two transaxle to engine block bolts. After transaxle is in place, install bolts and remove locating pins before removing jack.

TIGHTENING SPECIFICATIONS

Application	Ft. Lbs. (N.m)
Bell Housing Cover	9 (12)
Flex Plate-to-Crank	
A-413	65 (88)
A-470	100 (136)
Flex Plate-to-Torque Converter	40 (54)
Transaxle-to-Cylinder Block	70 (95)
Lower Bell Housing Cover	9 (12)
Manual Control Lever	9 (12)
Speedometer-to-Extension	5 (7)
Starter-to-Transaxle Bell Housing	40 (54)
Throttle Cable-to-Transaxle Case	9 (12)
Throttle Lever-to Transaxle Shaft	9 (12)
Manual Cable-to-Transaxle Case	21 (28)
Front Motor Mount	40 (54)
Left Motor Mount	40 (54)

FORD LIGHT TRUCKS

TRANSFER CASE

NP-208 (BRONCO, F-150 & F-250)
Removal

1) Raise and support vehicle. Remove drain plug and drain fluid from transfer case. Replace plug. Disconnect 4WD indicator switch connector at transfer case. Disconnect speedometer driven gear from transfer case rear bearing retainer.

2) Remove transmission shift lever-to-transfer case retaining nut. Remove skid plate from frame. Support transfer case with transmission jack. Disconnect front and rear propeller shafts from transfer case output shaft yokes and wire out of way. Do not allow shafts to hang free as damage to universal joints may result.

3) Remove transfer case-to-transmission adapter bolts. Remove gasket between transfer case and adapter and lower transfer case out of vehicle.

Installation

To install transfer case, reverse removal procedures. Fill case with 7 pints (3.3 liters) of Dexron II type automatic transmission fluid.

BORG-WARNER 1345 (F-150 & F-350)
Removal

1) Raise vehicle. Remove drain plug and drain fluid from transfer case. Replace plug. Disconnect 4WD indicator switch connector at transfer case. If equipped, remove skid plate.

2) Disconnect front and rear propeller shafts from transfer case output shaft yokes, and wire out of way. Do not allow shafts to hang free as damage to universal joints may result.

3) Disconnect speedometer driven gear from rear bearing retainer. Remove retaining clips and shift rod from transfer case control and transfer case shift levers. Disconnect vent hose from case.

4) Remove heat shield. Support transfer case with transmission jack, remove transfer case-to-transmission adapter bolts and slide transfer case off of transmission output shaft (towards rear). Lower transfer case out of vehicle and remove gasket from between transfer case and adapter.

Installation

Reverse removal procedures to install transfer case. Fill case with 6.5 pints (3.1 liters) of Dexron II type automatic transmission fluid.

BORG-WARNER 1350 (BRONCO II & RANGER)
Removal

1) Raise vehicle. Remove skid plate (if equipped). Remove drain plug and drain fluid from case. Replace plug. Disconnect 4WD indicator switch connector at transfer case. Disconnect front propeller shaft from front axle. Loosen front shaft boot clamp and slide out propeller shaft and boot as an assembly.

FORD LIGHT TRUCKS (Cont.)

2) Disconnect rear propeller shaft from transfer case. Disconnect speedometer driven gear from transfer case rear cover. Disconnect vent hose from control lever.

3) Loosen or remove large and small bolts (1 each) retaining shifter to extension housing. Pull on control lever until bushing slides off transfer case shift lever pin. Unscrew shift lever from control lever, as needed.

4) Remove heat shield from transfer case. Support transfer case with jack and remove transfer case-to-transmission extension housing bolts (5). Slide transfer case to the rear and off of transmission output shaft. Lower case from vehicle. Remove gasket from between transfer case and extension housing.

Installation
Reverse removal procedures to install transfer case, noting the following:

1) When installing shift lever assembly, tighten large bolt first, then small bolt.

2) When installing vent assembly, White marking on hose should be positioned in notch in shifter with upper end of hose 2 inches above top of shifter, inside of shift lever boot.

3) Before installing front propeller shaft into transfer case, lubricate female splines of transfer case input shaft with multi-purpose grease.

4) Fill transfer case to bottom of fill plug hole with Dexron-II automatic transmission fluid.

TRANSMISSION

5-SPEED TOYO KOGYO (BRONCO II & RANGER)
Removal

1) Place shift lever in neutral position. Remove boot retainer screws and bolts attaching retainer cover to gearshift lever retainer. Disconnect clutch master cylinder push rod from clutch pedal.

2) Pull gearshift lever assembly, shim and bushing straight up and away from lever retainer. Cover shift tower in extension housing with a cloth to avoid dropping dirt into transmission.

3) Disconnect clutch hydraulic system master cylinder push rod from clutch pedal. Open hood and disconnect battery negative cable from battery terminal. Raise vehicle. Disconnect drive shaft at rear axle drive flange.

4) Pull drive shaft rearward and disconnect from transmission. Install a suitable plug in extension housing to prevent lubricant leakage. Remove clutch housing dust shield and slave cylinder and secure it at one side.

5) Remove speedometer cable from extension housing. Disconnect starter motor and back-up lamp switch wires. Place jack under engine, protecting oil pan with a wood block.

6) On 4WD vehicles, remove transfer case. Remove starter motor. Position a transmission jack under transmission. Remove bolts, lock washers and flat washers attaching transmission to engine rear plate.

7) Remove nuts and bolts attaching transmission mount and damper to crossmember. Remove nuts attaching crossmember to frame side rails and remove crossmember.

8) Lower engine jack. Work clutch housing off locating dowels and slide transmission rearward until input shaft spline clears clutch disc. Remove transmission from vehicle.

Installation
To install, reverse removal procedure.

5-SPEED MITSUBISHI (BRONCO II & RANGER)
Removal

1) Place gearshift selector in neutral. Remove boot retainer bolts. Remove bolts attaching retainer cover to gearshift lever retainer. Pull gearshift lever assembly out of transfer case adapter. Cover opening in transfer case adapter with a cloth to prevent dirt from falling into adapter.

2) Open hood and disconnect battery negative cable from battery terminal. Raise vehicle. Index rear drive shaft to front axle flange and transfer case. Disconnect drive shaft at rear axle flange. Pull rear drive shaft rearward and disconnect drive shaft from transmission.

3) Install a suitable plug in transfer case adapter to prevent lubricant leakage. Remove clutch housing dust shield. Disconnect hydraulic fluid line from clutch slave cylinder. Plug line to prevent fluid leakage. Disconnect speedometer from transfer case adapter.

4) Disconnect starter motor cable, back-up lamp switch wire and shift indicator switch wire. Disconnect neutral position switch (2.3L EFI engine). Place jack under engine block, protecting oil pan with wood block. Remove transfer case from vehicle.

5) Remove starter. Place a transmission jack under transmission. Remove bolts, lock washers and flat washers attaching transmission to engine and plate. Remove nuts and bolts attaching transmission mount and damper to crossmember.

6) Remove nuts attaching crossmember to frame side rails and remove crossmember. Lower engine jack. Work clutch housing off locating dowels and slide transmission rearward until input shaft clears clutch disc. Remove transmission from vehicle.

Installation
To install, reverse removal procedure.

3.03 3-SPEED ("E" SERIES)
Removal

1) Raise and support vehicle. Remove lower extension housing-to-transmission bolt to drain lubricant. Disconnect propeller shaft from flange at transmission and wire out of way. Do not allow shaft to hang free as damage to universal joint may result.

2) Disconnect speedometer cable and shift control rods from transmission shift levers. Place jack under transmission and secure transmission to jack with safety chain.

3) Raise transmission slightly and remove 4 bolts retaining transmission extension housing to insulator and retainer assembly. Remove transmission-to-clutch housing bolts. Install engine support bar on frame, under engine, and lower transmission out of vehicle.

Installation
Reverse removal procedures to install. Fill transmission with lubricant. Adjust clutch and shift linkages.

Manual Transmission Removal

FORD LIGHT TRUCKS (Cont.)

3.03 3-SPEED ("F" SERIES)

Removal

1) Raise vehicle and support on safety stands. Support engine with jack and wood block under oil pan. To drain fluid from transmission, remove lower extension housing-to-transmission bolt.

2) Place jack under transmission and secure transmission to jack with safety chain. Disconnect shift linkage at transmission. Disconnect speedometer cable and back-up switch wires.

3) Disconnect propeller shaft and wire out of way. Do not allow shaft to hang free as damage to universal joint may result. Raise transmission and remove rear support, insulator and retainer.

4) Remove transmission-to-clutch housing attaching bolts. Move transmission rearward until input shaft clears clutch housing. Lower transmission out of vehicle. Do not depress clutch pedal at any time while transmission is out of vehicle.

Installation

Reverse removal procedures to install, noting the following: Apply a thin film of multi-purpose grease to the release bearing inner hub surfaces, release lever fulcrum and fork, and the transmission front bearing retainer. With installation complete, fill transmission with lubricant. Adjust clutch and shift linkage.

4-SPEED OVERDRIVE ("E" SERIES)

Removal

1) Raise and support vehicle. Mark propeller shaft position for reassembly reference. Disconnect propeller shaft from rear axle and slide shaft out of transmission. Disconnect speedometer cable and shift rods. Remove bolts connecting shift control to transmission case.

2) Remove rear transmission support-to-crossmember bolts. Support engine with transmission jack and raise transmission enough to take weight off number 3 crossmember. Remove bolts holding crossmember to frame side supports. Remove crossmember.

3) Place jack under rear of engine and raise high enough to remove weight from forward crossmember. Remove crossmember. With transmission supported by and secured to transmission jack, remove clutch housing-to-transmission bolts.

4) Move transmission to the rear until input shaft clears clutch housing and remove transmission. Do not depress clutch pedal while transmission is out of vehicle.

Installation

Reverse removal procedures to install.

(T.O.D.) 4-SPEED OVERDRIVE ("F" SERIES 2WD)

Removal

1) Raise vehicle on hoist. Mark drive shaft to aid as reference at reassembly. Disconnect drive shaft from rear flange. Slide drive shaft off transmission output shaft and intall extension housing seal installation tool into extension housing to prevent lubrication leakage.

2) Disconnect speedometer cable from extension housing. Disconnect back-up lamp switch and high gear switch wires. Remove shift lever from transmission. Support engine with a transmission jack tand remove extension housing-to-engine rear support attaching bolts.

3) Raise rear of engine high enough to remove weight from crossmember. Remove bolts retaining crossmember to frame side supports and remove crossmember. Support transmission on a jack and remove bolts attaching transmission to flywheel housing.

4) Move transmission and jack rearward until transmission input shaft clears flywheel housing. If necessary, lower engine enough to obtain clearance for transmission removal. DO NOT depress clutch pedal while transmission is removed.

Installation

To install, reverse removal procedure.

(T.O.D.) 4-SPEED OVERDRIVE (BRONCO & F-150 4WD)

Removal

1) Raise vehicle on a hoist. Drain transmission and transfer case. Disconnect 4WD indicator switch wire connector at transfer case. Disconnect back-up lamp switch wire connector at transmission. Remove skid plate, if equipped, from frame. Mark front and rear drive shafts for reference at reassembly.

2) Disconnect rear drive shaft from transfer case and wire it out of way. Disconnect front drive shaft from transfer case and wire out of way. Remove speedometer cable from transfer case. Remove retaining clips and shift rod from transfer case control lever and transfer case shift lever.

3) Disconnect vent hose from transfer case. Remove shift lever from transmission. Support transmission with a transmission jack and remove transmission housing-to-engine rear support bracket. Raise rear of transmission high enough to remove weight from crossmember.

4) Remove 2 nuts connecting upper gusset to frame on both sides of frame. Remove nut and bolt assembly connecting gusset to support. Remove gusset on left side. Remove bolts holding transmission to transmission support plate on crossmember. Raise transmission with a transmission jack.

5) Remove nut and bolt assemblies connecting support plate to crossmember. Remove support plate and right gusset. Remove nut and bolt assemblies connecting crossmember to frame. Remove crossmember. Remove heat shield from transfer case. Support transfer case with a transmission jack.

6) Remove 6 bolts retaining transfer case to transmission adapter. Slide transfer case rearward off of transmission output shaft and lower transfer case from vehicle and remove gasket between transfer case and adapter. Support transmission on a jack and remove bolts attaching transmission to flywheel housing.

7) Move transmission and jack rearward until transmission input shaft clears flywheel housing. If necessary, lower engine enough to obtain clearance for transmission removal. DO NOT depress clutch pedal while transmission is removed.

Installation

To install, reverse removal procedure.

NP 435 4-SPEED (BRONCO & "F" SERIES)

Removal

1) Remove floor mat. Remove shift lever, shift ball and boot as an assembly. On 4WD models, remove transfer case shift lever, shift ball and boot as an

FORD LIGHT TRUCKS (Cont.)

assembly. Remove floor pan transmission cover or weather pad on F150-350 models. Remove seat if necessary.

2) To remove gearshift lever and knob, first remove inner cap with puller (T73T 7220 A or equivalent). Remove seat and spring. Remove gearshift lever. Disconnect back-up light.

3) Raise vehicle. Disconnect speedometer cable and rear propeller shaft. Wire shaft out of way. On 4WD models, drain transfer case, remove front propeller shaft from case and wire out of way.

4) Remove cotter pin holding shift link and remove link. Remove bolts holding bracket to transfer case. Position transmission jack under transfer case.

5) Remove transfer case-to-transmission bolts and remove transfer case. On all models, place transmission jack under transmission and lift slightly. Remove transmission-to-insulator, insulator-to-crossmember and crossmember-to-frame bolts. Remove insulator and crossmember.

6) Remove transmission-to-clutch housing bolts and lower transmission out of vehicle.

Installation
To install transmission, reverse removal procedures.

WARNER T-18 ("F" SERIES 2WD)
Removal

1) Working from inside vehicle, remove floor mat and body floor pan cover. Remove gearshift lever, shift ball and boot as an assembly. Remove weather pad. Raise and support vehicle. Disconnect speedometer cable.

2) Disconnect back-up light switch from rear of gear shift housing cover. Disconnect propeller shaft from transmission and wire out of way. Do not allow shaft to hang free as damage to universal joint may result. Disconnect clutch linkage.

3) Remove skid plate (if equipped) and heat shield. Support transmission with jack. Remove crossmember gusset-to-frame bolts and gusset-to-crossmember bolts. Remove transmission-to-insulator bolts. Raise transmission and remove insulator-to-crossmember bolts. Remove insulator

4) Remove right gusset, crossmember-to-frame bolts and crossmember. Remove transmission-to-clutch housing bolts. Move transmission away from clutch housing until input shaft clears housing. Lower transmission out of vehicle.

Installation
Reverse removal procedures to install, noting the following: When installing shift lever, shift ball and boot assembly, lubricate the spherical ball seat with multi-purpose grease.

WARNER T-18 (BRONCO & "F" SERIES 4WD)
Removal

1) Working from inside vehicle, remove floor mat and access cover to floor pan. Place shift lever in reverse position and remove cover, insulator and dust cover. Remove transfer case shift lever, shift ball and boot as an assembly.

2) Remove transmission shift lever, shift ball and boot as an assembly. Raise vehicle. Remove drain plug and allow transmission to drain. Replace plug. Disconnect front and rear propeller shafts from transfer case and wire out of way. Do not allow shafts to hang free

as damage to universal joint may result.

3) Remove shift link retainer ring and remove shift link from transfer case. Disconnect speedometer cable. Place transmission jack under transfer case. Remove transfer case-to-transmission bolts and lower transfer case out of vehicle.

4) Remove rear support bracket-to-transmission bolts (8), position transmission jack under transmission and remove rear support bracket and brace. Remove transmission-to-clutch housing bolts (4) and remove transmission.

Installation
Reverse removal procedures to install transmission.

WARNER T19B ("F" SERIES 2WD)
Removal

1) Working from inside vehicle, remove floor mat and body floor pan cover. Remove gearshift lever, shift ball and boot as an assembly. Remove weather pad.

2) Raise vehicle. Place transmission jack under transmission and disconnect speedometer cable. Disconnect back-up light switch from rear of gear shift housing cover. Disconnect propeller shaft and clutch linkage. Wire out of way.

3) Remove transmission rear insulator and lower retainer. Remove skid plate (if equipped) and heat shield. Remove upper gusset bolts and gusset-to-crossmember bolts. Remove left side gusset.

4) Remove transmission-to-support plate bolts, raise transmission slightly and remove support plate-to-crossmember bolts. Remove support plate and right gusset. Remove crossmember-to-frame bolts and remove crossmember.

5) Remove transmission-to-clutch housing bolts. Move transmission to the rear until input shaft clears housing and remove transmission.

Installation
Reverse removal procedures to install transmission, noting the following: When installing the shift lever, shift ball and boot assembly, lubricate spherical ball seat with multipurpose grease.

WARNER T19B & T19D ("F" SERIES 4WD)
Removal

1) Working from inside vehicle, remove floor mat and access cover to floor pan (shift lever in reverse when removing cover). Remove insulator and dust cover. Remove transfer case shift lever, shift ball and boot as an assembly.

2) Remove transmission shift lever, shift ball and boot as an assembly. Raise vehicle. Drain transmission and replace drain plug. Disconnect front and rear drive shafts from transfer case and wire out of way.

3) Remove shift link retainer ring and remove link from transfer case. Disconnect speedometer cable. Place transmission jack under transfer case and remove transfer case-to-transmission bolts (6). Lower transfer case out of vehicle.

4) Remove rear support bracket-to-transmission bolts (8). Place transmission jack under transmission and remove rear support bracket and brace. Remove transmission-to-clutch housing bolts (4) and remove transmission.

Installation
To install transmission, reverse removal procedures.

Manual Transmission Removal
FORD LIGHT TRUCKS (Cont.)

5-SPEED MAZDA OVERDRIVE (AEROSTAR)
Removal

1) Disconnect negative battery cable from battery terminal. Place transmission in neutral. Remove 4 bolts attaching boot assembly to floor. Pull boot up shift lever. Remove 4 bolts retaining shift lever assembly to transmission remote shift rail adapter. Remove lever, knob and boot assembly.

2) Raise vehicle on hoist. Disconnect starter cable and wires. Remove starter retaining bolts and remove starter. Remove clip retaining tube to hydraulic clutch slave cylinder. Remove tube and fittng from slave cylinder to prevent entry of contaminants.

3) Disconnect back-up lamp switch and shift indicator and neutral position wires from senders on transmission. Remove cable (conventional speedometer) or disconnect wire (electronic speedometer) from fitting.

4) Scribe a mark on driveshaft and rear axle flange to index driveline position for installation and balance purposes. Remove "U" bolts and nuts from rear axle flange. Remove driveshaft. Cap transmission extension housing to prevent lubricant spillage.

5) Remove nuts retaining insulator to crossmember. Loosen nut and washer assemblies attaching front insulators to crossmember brackets. Position a transmission jack under transmission. Place jack safety chain around transmission. Slightly raise transmission.

6) Remove nuts and bolts retaining crossmember to frame and remove crossmember. Remove bolts retaining clutch housing to engine. Bring transmission rearward to separate clutch housing from dowel pins in rear of engine block. Slowly lower transmission from vehicle.

NOTE: If transmission is to be removed from vehicle for an extended period, support rear of engine with safety stand and wood block.

7) If required, remove nuts retaining clutch housing to transmission and remove housing and clutch slave cylinder.

Installation
To install, reverse removal procedure.

TIGHTENING SPECIFICATIONS

Application	Ft. Lbs. (N.m)
Transmission-to-Clutch Housing	
Bronco II & Ranger	30-40 (42-56)
All Others	
3-Speed	42-50 (59-70)
4-Speed	35-50 (49-70)
Transfer Case-to-Transmission	
NP-208	20-25 (28-35)
Borg-Warner 1345	25-43 (35-60)
Borg-Warner 1350	25-35 (35-49)
Insulator-to-Crossmember	
3-Speed	50-70 (70-98)
4-Speed Overdrive	50-70 (70-98)
Bronco II & Ranger	71-94 (98-132)
All Others	
2WD	50-70 (70-98)
4WD	35-45 (49-63)
Insulator-to-Transmission	
3-Speed ("E" Models)	50-70 (70-98)
4-Speed Overdrive	50-70 (70-98)
T19B 4-Speed	45-60 (63-84)
All Others	60-80 (84-112)

GENERAL MOTORS LIGHT TRUCKS

TRANSFER CASE

NP-205 (30 SERIES)
Removal

1) Raise and support vehicle on hoist. Drain transfer case. Disconnect speedometer cable. Remove skid plate and crossmember supports as necessary. Disconnect rear drive shaft from transfer case and tie up away from work area.

2) Disconnect front drive shaft from transfer case and tie up shaft away from work area. Disconnect shift lever rod from shift rail link. Support transfer case and remove bolts attaching transfer case to transmission adapter.

3) Move transfer case to rear until input shaft clears adapter and lower assembly from vehicle.

Installation
To install, reverse removal procedure.

NP-207 ("S" SERIES)
Removal

1) With transfer case shift lever in "4 Hi" position, disconnect negative battery cable. Raise vehicle and remove skid plate. Drain transfer case. Mark front and rear output shaft yokes and propeller shafts for reassembly reference and remove shafts.

2) Disconnect speedometer cable and vacuum harness from transfer case. Remove shift lever from case. Remove catalytic converter hanger bolts at converter. Raise transmission and transfer case assembly with jack and remove transmission mount bolts. Remove mount.

3) Lower complete assembly. Support transfer case alone and remove transmission-to-transfer case bolts. Remove shift lever bracket from transfer case adapter in order to reach upper left attaching bolt.

4) Separate transfer case from transmission adapter and remove from vehicle.

Installation
Reverse removal procedures to install. Always use a new gasket between the transfer case and adapter.

NP-208 (10 & 20 SERIES)
Removal

1) Place transfer case in "4H". Raise vehicle. Drain lubricant from transfer case. Remove cotter pin from shift lever swivel. Mark transfer case front and rear output shaft yokes and propeller shafts for assembly alignment reference.

2) Disconnect speedometer cable and indicator switch wires. Disconnect front drive shaft at transfer case yoke. Disconnect parking brake cable guide from pivot located on right frame rail, if necessary. Remove engine strut rod from transfer case.

3) Place support under transfer case and remove transfer case-to-transmission adapter bolts. Move transfer case assembly rearward until free of transmission output shaft and remove assembly. Remove all gasket material from rear of transmission adapter housing.

Installation
To install, reverse removal procedure.

TRANSMISSION

ASTRO/SAFARI VAN
Removal

1) Raise vehicle and drain lubricant from transmission. Remove drive shaft. Disconnect speedometer cable. Disconnect electrical connectors at transmission. Disconnect shift linkage at shifter. Remove shifter support attaching bolts at transmission.

2) Remove transmission mount attaching bolts. Support transmission and remove crossmember attaching bolts and crossmember from vehicle. Remove transmission attaching bolts and remove transmission from vehicle.

Installation
To install, reverse removal procedure. Apply a light coating of high temperature grease to main drive gear bearing retainer and splined portion of transmission drive gear shaft to assure free movement of clutch and transmission components during assembly.

ALL EXCEPT "K" & "S" SERIES
Removal

1) On models with 117 MM 4-speed, remove attaching screws from shift lever boot retainer. Slide boot assembly up shift lever and remove lever. To remove shift lever, push down on collar and turn counterclockwise.

2) On all models, raise and support vehicle under frame. Drain fluid from transmission. Disconnect speedometer cable at transmission. Remove shift controls from transmission (if not already removed). Remove parking brake lever, controls, and back-up switch wire as needed.

3) Disconnect propeller shaft at transmission and position support under transmission assembly. Disconnect exhaust pipes from exhaust manifolds as needed. Remove frame crossmember and flywheel inspection plate.

4) On 117 MM 4-speed, remove top 2 transmission-to-clutch housing bolts and install guide pins. On all models, remove all transmission-to-clutch housing attaching bolts, slide transmission rearward until input shaft is clear of clutch hub and remove assembly from vehicle. Remove guide pins if used.

NOTE: **Support clutch release bearing and support assembly when removing transmission main drive gear from flywheel housing. This will prevent release bearing from falling out of flywheel housing.**

Installation
Apply a light coating of high temperature grease to main drive gear bearing retainer and splined portion of transmission main drive gear shaft. Reverse removal procedures to complete installation.

ALL "K" SERIES
Removal

1) On models with 117 MM 4-speed, remove attaching screws from shift lever boot retainer. Slide boot assembly up shift lever and remove lever. To remove shift lever, push down on collar and turn counterclockwise.

2) On all models, raise and support vehicle under frame. Drain fluid from transmission and transfer case. Disconnect speedometer cable. Disconnect front and rear propeller shafts at transfer case and wire out of way. Disconnect transfer case shift lever.

3) Position support under transfer case. Remove transfer case-to-adapter bolts and remove transfer case. Disconnect shift control rods from shifter levers if not already removed. Separate exhaust pipes from exhaust manifolds as needed.

4) Support rear part of engine and remove 2 adapter bolts. Remove crossmember. Remove 2 top transmission-to-clutch housing cap screws. Insert 2 guide pins (J-1126 on 117 MM, J-2216 all others) in holes. Remove 2 lower transmission-to-clutch housing cap screws.

5) Slide transmission and adapter assembly rearward until clutch gear is free of splines in clutch disc. Guide pins will support transmission and prevent damage to clutch disc. Remove transmission and adapter as an assembly. Remove adapter from transmission.

Installation
Apply a light coating of high temperature grease to main drive gear bearing retainer and splined portion of transmission main drive gear shaft. Reverse removal procedures to complete installation.

ALL "S" SERIES

NOTE: **If vehicle is a 4WD model, refer to Transfer Case removal procedures and remove case.**

Removal

1) Disconnect negative battery cable. On 77.5 MM 4-speed, remove upper starter motor nut. On all models, remove shift lever boot screws and slide boot up shift lever. Shift transmission into neutral and remove shift lever bolts at transmission. Remove shift lever.

2) Disconnect electrical connector and clip at transmission, if present. Raise vehicle and remove propeller shaft. Disconnect exhaust pipe at manifold, if needed.

3) Disconnect speedometer cable, electrical connector and clutch cable at transmission. Support transmission on jack and remove mount attaching bolts. Remove catalytic converter hanger. Remove crossmember attaching bolts and crossmember. Remove flywheel inspection cover.

4) On 77.5 MM 4-speed, remove lower starter motor attaching bolt. Remove body mounting bolts on left side of body and loosen radiator support bolt. Raise cab on left side as needed to remove upper bell housing attaching bolts. Support cab with wood block between frame and cab.

Manual Transmission Removal

GENERAL MOTORS LIGHT TRUCKS

5) Remove transmission-to-engine bolts on all models. Remove transmission.

Installation

Reverse removal procedures to install transmission, noting the following: On 77 MM 4-speed, coat main drive gear bearing retainer and splined portion of transmission main drive gear with high temperature grease before installation.

TIGHTENING SPECIFICATIONS

Application	Ft. Lbs. (N.m)
Transmission-to-Clutch Housing	
All Except "S" Series	75 (102)
"S" Series	
1.9L 4-Cylinder	25 (35)
2.8L V6	55 (75)

TIGHTENING SPECIFICATIONS (Cont.)

Application	Ft. Lbs. (N.m)
Crossmember-to-Frame	
"S" Series	25 (30)
All Others	55-65 (75-88)
Crossmember-to-Mount	
"S" Series	25 (30)
All Others	40-45 (54-61)
Mount-to-Transmission Bolt	35 (50)
Radiator Support Mounting Bolt	45-60 (60-80)
Cab Mounting Bolts	45-60 (60-80)
Transfer Case-to-Extension Housing	
"S" Series	19-29 (26-40)
All Others	26-40 (36-56)
Adapter-to-Transmission	
"S" Series	
All Others	26-40 (36-56)

JEEP

TRANSFER CASE

MODEL NP-207

Removal

1) Shift transfer case into "4H" position. Raise and support vehicle. Drain lubricant from transfer case. Mark rear axle yoke and drive shaft for installation reference. Remove rear drive shaft. Disconnect speedometer cable, vacuum hoses and vent hose from transfer case.

2) Raise transmission and transfer case and remove transmission crossmember attaching bolts. Remove crossmember and lower transmission and transfer case. Mark transfer case front output shaft flange and drive shaft for installation reference.

3) Disconnect front drive shaft from transfer case. Disconnect shift lever linkage rod at transfer case. Remove shift lever bracket bolts. Support transfer case and remove transfer case attaching bolts. Remove transfer case assembly.

Installation

To install, reverse removal procedure.

MODEL NP-208

Removal

1) Raise vehicle. Drain lubricant from transfer case. Disconnect speedometer cable and indicator switch wires and disconnect transfer case shift lever link at operating lever. Place a safety stand under transmission and remove the rear crossmember.

2) Mark transfer case front and rear output shaft yokes and drive shafts for assembly alignment reference. Disconnect front and rear drive shafts at transfer case yokes. Secure shafts to frame rails with wire. Disconnect parking brake cable guide from pivot located on right frame rail, if necessary.

3) Remove bolts attaching exhaust pipe support bracket-to-transfer case, if necessary. Remove transfer case-to-transmission bolts. Move transfer case assembly rearward until free of transmission output shaft and remove assembly. Remove all gasket material from rear of transmission adapter housing.

Installation

To install, reverse removal procedure.

MODEL NP-229

Removal

1) Raise and support vehicle. Drain lubricant from transfer case. Disconnect speedometer cable and vent hose. Disconnect transfer case shift lever link at operating lever. Place a safety stand under transmission and remove rear crossmember.

2) Mark transfer case front and rear output shafts at transfer case yokes and drive shafts for installation alignment reference. Disconnect front and rear drive shafts at transfer case yokes. Secure shafts. Disconnect shift motor vacuum hoses.

3) Disconnect transfer case shift linkage. Remove transfer case-to-transmission bolts. Move transfer case assembly rearward until clear of transmission ouput shaft and remove assembly. Remove all gasket material from rear of transmission adapter housing.

Installation

To install, reverse removal procedure.

MODEL NP-300

Removal

1) Remove floor covering, if equipped and remove transmission access cover from floorpan. Raise vehicle and drain lubricant from transfer case. Position support stand under clutch housing to support engine and transmission and remove rear crossmember.

2) Disconnect front and rear drive shafts at transfer case. Mark drive shaft yokes for assembly reference. Disconnect speedometer cable at transfer case. If necessary, disconnect parking brake cable at equalizer. Disconnect exhaust pipe support bracket at transfer case, if equipped. Remove bolts attaching transfer case to transmission and remove tranfer case.

Installation

To install, reverse removal procedure.

TRANSMISSION

ALL MODELS
Removal

1) Remove screws attaching shift lever boot to floorpan. Slide boot over lever. On models with T4 or T5 transmission, remove shift lever and lever housing from transmission.

2) On models with T-176 transmission, press and turn shift lever retainer counterclockwise to release lever. Remove lever, boot, spring and seat as an assembly.

3) On all models, raise vehicle and support with safety stands. Disconnect rear drive shaft from transfer case and wire out of way. DO NOT allow shaft to hang free, as damage to universal joint may result.

4) Disconnect front parking brake cable at equalizer. Remove rear cable clip from crossmember. Place a jack under clutch housing to support engine. Remove rear crossmember from frame.

5) Disconnect speedometer cable, back-up light switch wire and 4WD indicator switch wire. Disconnect transfer case vent hose. Disconnect front drive shaft and wire out of way.

6) On "CJ" and Scrambler models, remove transfer case shift lever by removing shifter shaft retaining nut. Remove cotter pins retaining shift control link pins in shift rods and remove pins. Remove shifter shaft and disengage shift lever from shift control links. Move lever out of the way.

NOTE: **On some models, shifter shaft must be unthreaded from shift lever in order to be removed. On other models, shaft can be removed by sliding it out of lever.**

7) Remove cotter pin and washers connecting link to shift lever. Separate link from lever. Support transmission and transfer case with jack.

8) Remove bolts securing transmission to clutch housing and remove transmission and transfer case. Separate transfer case and transmission.

Installation
Reverse removal procedures to install transmission. Adjust clutch and shift linkage.

TIGHTENING SPECIFICATIONS

Application	Ft. Lbs. (N.m)
Transmission-to-Clutch Housing	55 (75)
Transmission Cover Bolts	55-65 (75-88)
Housing-to-Transmission Case	40-45 (54-61)
Crossmember Attaching Bolts	34-40 (47-54)
Filler Plug	13-15 (18-20)

Manual Transmissions

GENERAL MANUAL TRANSMISSION/TRANSAXLE TROUBLE SHOOTING

It is essential that thorough trouble shooting and diagnostic procedures be followed prior to disassembly of any transmission/transaxle components for repair. Shift difficulties are frequently caused by conditions outside the transmission-/transaxle; such as linkage, cable, alignment of assemblies, or clutch problems.

Drive train noises may come from many sources; such as tires, road surfaces, wheel bearings, drive axles, engine, or exhaust system, etc. Adjustment or replacement of transmission/transaxle parts will not correct these problems. Gear "roll-over" noise is inherent in most constant-mest transmissions and will disappear when clutch is disengaged or transmission is in gear. Clutch release bearing noise will disappear when clutch release mechanism is moved enough to slide release bearing away from contact with pressure plate. DO NOT attempt transmission/transaxle repairs to correct gear "roll-over" or clutch release bearing noise.

If noise persists, drive vehicle on a smooth asphalt road to reduce tire and body noises. With vehicle fully warmed up, note speed and in which gear noise appears, whether noise occurs on pull, coast, or steady drive conditions. Refer to following conditions, possible cause, and correction for appropriate action.

CONDITION	POSSIBLE CAUSE	CORRECTION
Noisy in Forward Gears	Improper fluid level or type	Check fluid level and type; See GENERAL SERVICING
	Contaminated fluid	Check fluid condition; See GENERAL SERVICING
	Road or tire noise	Determine cause and service as required
	Drive axle/shaft noise telescoped to transmission	Determine cause and service as required
	Vehicle body components or exhaust system grounding on chassis	Determine cause and service as required
	Transmission or clutch housing bolts loose	Tighten bolts to specification
	Clutch housing misaligned with crankshaft	Check and align clutch housing
	Worn bearings or gears	Replace bearings or gears
	Brake noise telescoped through drive train	Determine cause and service as required
	Loose or worn engine mounts	Tighten or replace engine mounts
	Speedometer gear or teeth worn	Replace speedometer gear
Gear Clash When Shifting Forward Gears	Engine idle speed too high	Adjust engine idle speed
	Clutch out of adjustment	Adjust clutch
	Shift linkage damaged or out of adjustment	Adjust or replace linkage; See GENERAL SERVICING
	Pilot bushing or bearing damaged	Replace bushing or bearing
	Gears or synchronizers damaged	Service as required
	Insufficient or improper fluid	Check fluid level and type; See GENERAL SERVICING
Transmission Shifts Hard	Clutch out of adjustment	Adjust clutch
	Insufficient or improper fluid	Check fluid level and type; See GENERAL SERVICING
	Clutch disc warped or deformed	Replace clutch disc
	Shift lever or rail binding or deformed	Determine cause of condition and service as required
	Sliding gears or synchronizers binding	Determine cause of condition and service as required
	Pilot bushing or bearing binding	Determine cause of condition and service as required
	Housing and/or shafts out of alignment	Check and adjustment alignment
	Shift linkage binding or requires lubricant	Service or lubricate linkage

GENERAL MANUAL TRANSMISSION/TRANSAXLE TROUBLE SHOOTING (Cont.)

CONDITION	POSSIBLE CAUSE	CORRECTION
Will Not Shift into One Gear – Shifts into All Others	Shift linkage out of adjustment or damaged or worn	Adjust or replace linkage; See GENERAL SERVICING
	Back-up switch ball frozen or damaged	Replace switch ball
	Damaged or worn synchronizer sleeves or hubs	Replace sleeves or hubs
	Internal gearshift mechanism worn, damaged or improperly adjusted	Adjust or replace internal gearshift mechanism
Locked in One Gear – Cannot be Shifted Out	Shift linkage out of adjustment or damaged or worn	Adjust or replace linkage; See GENERAL SERVICING
	Internal gearshift mechanism worn, damaged or improperly adjusted	Adjust or replace internal gearshift mechanism
	Broken gear teeth on clutch shaft, countershaft gear or reverse idler gear	Replace clutch shaft, countershaft gear or reverse idler gear
	Shift fork loose on shift rail	Tighten or replace shift fork or rail
Transmission Jumps Out of Gear	Shift linkage damaged or out of adjustment	Adjust or service linkage; See GENERAL SERVICING
	Engine mounts loose or broken	Tighten or replace mounts
	Engine, transmission, or shift lever bolts loose	Tighten bolts to specification
	Clutch shaft or roller bearings worn	Replace shaft or bearings
	Pilot bushing or bearing worn	Replace bushing or bearing
	Gear teeth worn or tapered	Replace gear
	Internal shift mechanism worn, damaged or misadjusted	Adjust or service interal shift mechanism
	Shift lever seal binding	Determine cause and service as required
Shift Linkage Binds, Sticks or Rattles	Shift rods or cables out of adjustment	Adjust shift rods or cables; See GENERAL SERVICING
	Steering column shift tube out of alignment	Align shift tube
	Console shift assembly damaged or worn	Service as required
	Engine and/or transmission/transaxle mounts worn or broken	Replace mounts
	Shift lever pivot balls worn or loose	Replace shift lever pivot assembly
	Control assembly body weld bolts missing or loose	Tighten or replace bolts
	Shift linkage bushings worn, broken or missing	Replace bushings
Transmission Leaks	Improper fluid level or type	Check fluid; See GENERAL SERVICING
	Worn or damaged shift lever seal	Replace seal
	Propeller shaft yoke worn	Replace yoke
	Extension housing oil seal worn or damaged	Replace housing oil seal
	Components other than tranmission/transaxle leaking	Check and service other components

General Servicing

DRIVE AXLE GEAR TOOTH PATTERNS

INSPECTION

Wipe lubricant from internal parts. Rotate gears and inspect for wear or damage. Mount a dial indicator to housing and check backlash at several points around ring gear. Backlash must be within specifications at all points. If no defects are found, check gear tooth contact patterns.

GEAR TOOTH CONTACT PATTERN

NOTE: **Drive pattern should be well centered on ring gear teeth. Coast pattern should be centered but may be slightly toward toe of ring gear teeth.**

1) Paint ring gear teeth with gear marking compound. Apply some form of load to differential case to resist rotation. Rotate pinion gear until ring gear has made 1 full revolution.

2) Turn pinion gear in opposite direction to complete 1 full revolution of ring gear. Examine ring gear teeth for contact pattern. Correct as necessary by moving appropriate shims.

ADJUSTMENTS

GEAR BACKLASH & PINION SHIM CHANGES

NOTE: **Change in tooth pattern is directly related to change in shim and/or backlash adjustment.**

1) With no change in backlash, moving pinion further from ring gear moves drive pattern toward heel and top of tooth, and moves coast pattern toward toe and top of tooth.

2) With no change in backlash, moving pinion closer to ring gear moves drive pattern toward toe and bottom of tooth, and moves coast pattern toward heel and bottom of tooth.

3) With no change in pinion shim thickness, an increase in backlash moves ring gear further from pinion. Drive pattern moves toward heel and top of tooth, and coast pattern moves toward heel and top of tooth.

4) With no change in pinion shim thickness, a decrease in backlash moves ring gear closer to pinion gear. Drive pattern moves toward toe and bottom of tooth, and coast pattern moves toward toe and bottom of tooth.

Fig. 1: Drive Axle Gear Tooth Patterns Showing Necessary Corrections

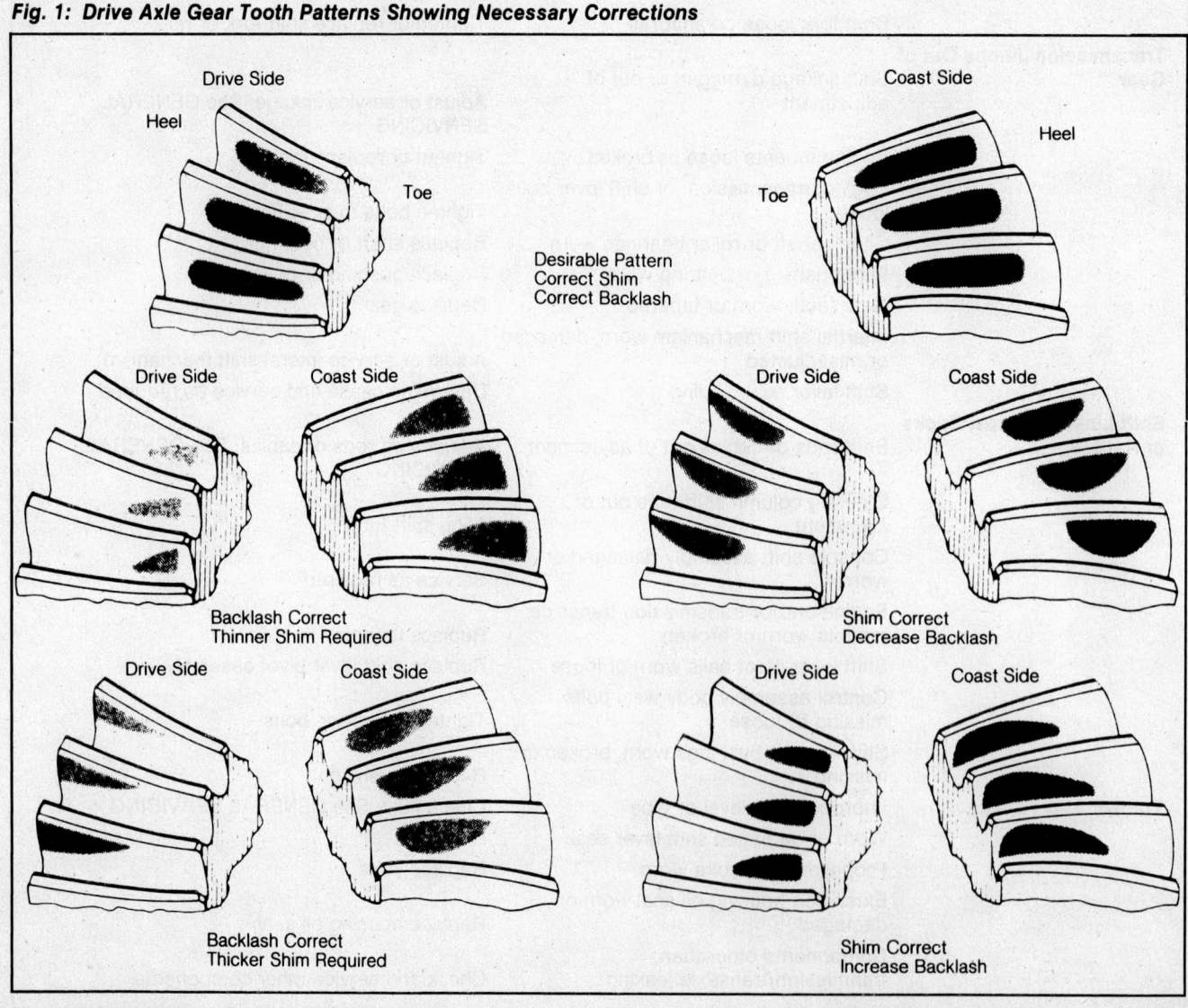

SECTION 2

DOMESTIC AUTOMATIC TRANSMISSIONS

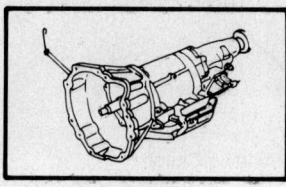

NOTE: ALSO SEE GENERAL INDEX.

Automatic Transmissions

AMERICAN MOTORS, CHRYSLER CORP. & JEEP 727, 904, 998 & 999

APPLICATIONS

CHRYSLER CORP.

Chrysler Corp. passenger cars use A-904LA Torqueflite transmissions. All models (except some fleet engines) use lock-up type torque converter. Dodge and Plymouth trucks and vans use Loadflite A-727, A-904T or A-999 transmissions. Those with A-904T and A-999 transmissions use lock-up converter, while A-727 equipped models may use either lock-up or conventional type torque converter, depending on GVWR and application.

AMC/JEEP

AMC Eagle uses 998 model. Jeep CJ7 and Scrambler use 999 model. Cherokee and Wagoneer use 904 model. Grand Wagoneer and J-10/20 trucks use 999 model in 6-cylinder models and 727 model in 8-cylinder models. The 727 is also used in 6-cylinder models with 3.31 axle ratio. Lock-up torque converter may be used with any of these applications.

NOTE: **All future references to transmission will be by number only (i.e. 727, 904, 999). Unless otherwise specified, model reference will include all models of that series. For example, reference to 904 will include 904, A-904, A-904LA and A-904T models.**

IDENTIFICATION

Transmission identification number is stamped on pad on left side of transmission case oil pan flange. Identification number is decoded as shown in *Fig. 1*.

Fig. 2: Transmission Identification Number

PK 3681063
4436 0001
Plant Code
Part Number
Serial Number
Date Code

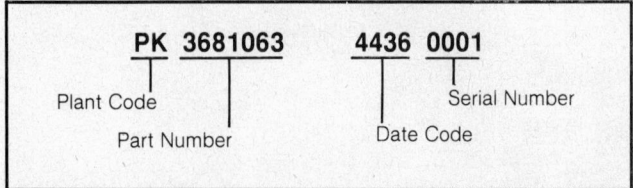

CAUTION: **Transmission operation requirements are different for each vehicle and engine combination, and some internal parts will differ between models. Always refer to 7-digit part number for positive transmission identification when replacing parts.**

DESCRIPTION

Transmission combines torque converter and fully automatic 3-speed gear system. Converter housing and transmission case are integral aluminum casting. Transmission consists of 2 multiple disc clutches, overrun-

Fig. 1: Cross-Sectional View Of Chrysler Corp. Model 727 Automatic Transmission

Lock-Up Clutch
Stator
Oil Pump
Front Planetary Gear Set
Rear Planetary Gear Set
Impeller
Turbine
Rear Clutch
Low & Reverse Band
Front
Clutch
Overrunning Clutch
Seal
Governor
Bearing
Output Shaft
Bushing
Extension Housing
Parking Lock Assy.
Valve Body
Sun Gear Driving Shell
Input Shaft
Oil Filter
Drive Plate
Kickdown (Front) Band

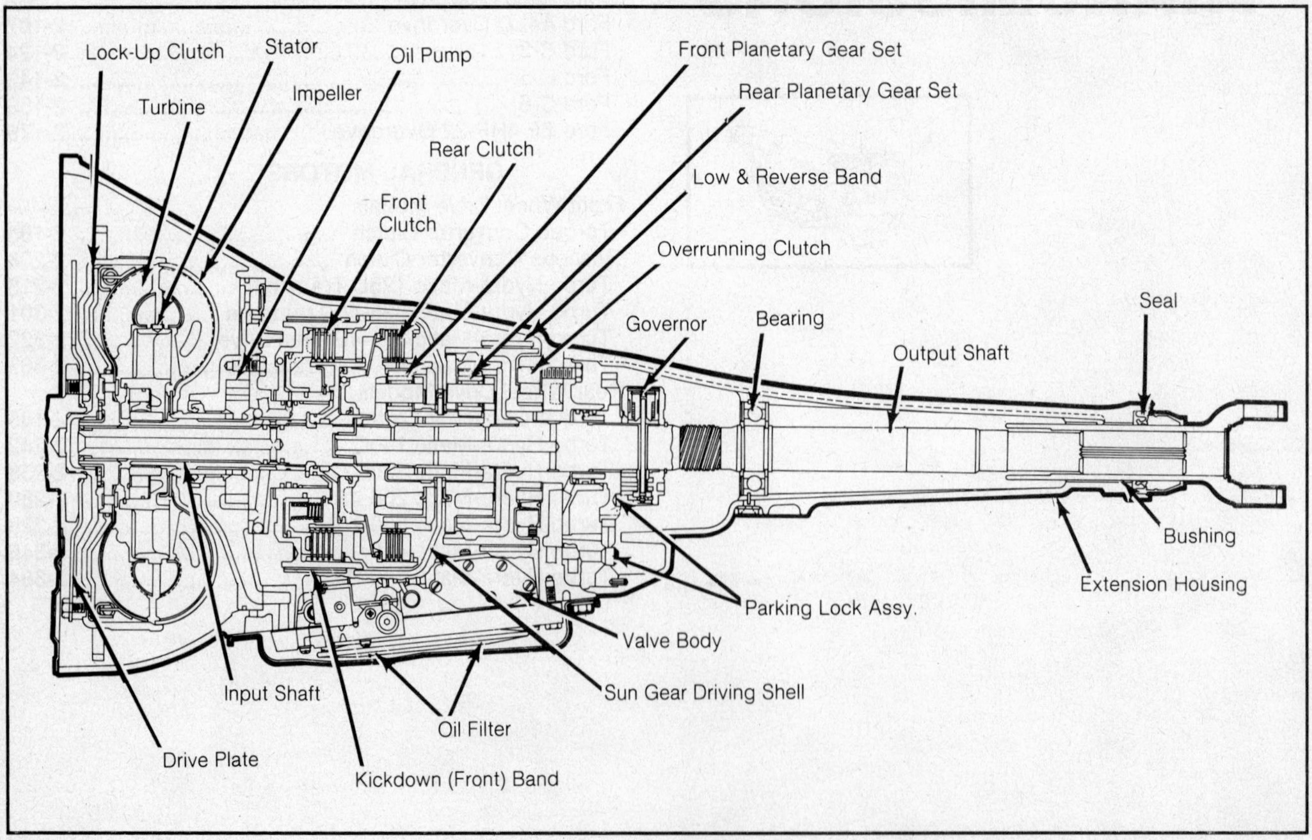

AMERICAN MOTORS, CHRYSLER CORP. & JEEP
727, 904, 998 & 999 (Cont.)

ning clutch, 2 servos and bands, and 2 planetary gear sets to provide 3 forward ratios and reverse ratio. Common sun gear of planetary gear sets is connected to front clutch by driving shell which is splined to sun gear and to front clutch retainer. Hydraulic system consists of oil pump and control valve body in which all valves except governor valve are found.

Torque converter is attached to crankshaft through flexible driving plate. Cooling of converter is accomplished by circulating transmission fluid through fluid-to-fluid type cooler, which is located in radiator lower tank. Torque converter assembly is sealed unit which cannot be disassembled.

Lock-up clutch is located inside most torque converters. Lock-up mode is activated only in direct drive and above minimum preset vehicle speed. At wider throttle openings, where 2-3 upshift occurs above minimum lock-up speed, lock-up shift will occur immediately after 2-3 upshift. Lock-up and conventional converters and transmissions are NOT interchangeable.

LUBRICATION & ADJUSTMENTS

See appropriate AUTOMATIC TRANSMISSION SERVICING article in DOMESTIC GENERAL SERVICING section.

TROUBLE SHOOTING

See appropriate AUTOMATIC TRANSMISSION TROUBLE SHOOTING article in DOMESTIC GENERAL SERVICING section.

TESTING

ROAD TEST

1) Before road testing, be certain that fluid level and control linkage adjustments have been checked

AUTOMATIC SHIFT SPEEDS & GOVERNOR PRESSURES – CHRYSLER CORP. TRUCKS & VANS

Engine	3.7L		5.2L & 5.9L			
Model Axle Ratio Tire Size	150 3.21 P195/75R15	250 3.54 8.00 X 16.5-D	150 2.71 P195/75R15	150 2.94 P195/75R15	250 4.10 8.00 X 16.5-D	350 4.56 8.00 X 16.5-E
Throttle Closed 1-2 Upshift 2-3 Upshift 3-1 Downshift	8-11 11-14 8-11	8-11 11-14 8-11	9-12 13-17 9-12	9-11 12-15 9-11	7-9 9-12 7-9	6-8 8-11 6-8
Throttle Wide Open 1-2 Upshift 2-3 Upshift	30-40 55-60	30-40 55-60	36-48 65-77	33-44 60-71	26-35 47-56	23-31 42-50
Kickdown Range 3-2 Downshift 3-1 Downshift	51-61 24-33	51-61 24-33	60-72 29-39	55-67 26-36	44-53 21-29	39-47 19-26
Governor Pressure [1] 15 psi 50 psi 75 psi	16-18 39-45 59-62	16-18 39-45 59-62	19-21 46-53 67-74	17-19 43-49 62-68	14-15 34-39 48-54	12-14 30-35 43-48

[1] – Governor pressure should be from zero to 1.5 psi at stand-still or downshift may not occur.

CLUTCH & BAND APPLICATION CHART (ELEMENTS IN USE)

Selector Lever Position	Front Clutch	Rear Clutch	Over-running Clutch	Converter Lock-up Clutch	Front (Kickdown) Band	Rear (Low-reverse) Band
D – DRIVE						
First		X	X			
Second		X			X	
Third	X	X		X		
2 – SECOND						
First		X	X			
Second		X			X	
1 – LOW (First)		X				X
R – REVERSE	X					X

NEUTRAL or PARK – All clutches and bands released and/or ineffective.

Automatic Transmissions

AMERICAN MOTORS, CHRYSLER CORP. & JEEP
727, 904, 998 & 999 (Cont.)

Fig. 3: Cross-Sectional View Of Chrysler Corp. Model 904/999 & AMC/Jeep Model 904 Automatic Transmission

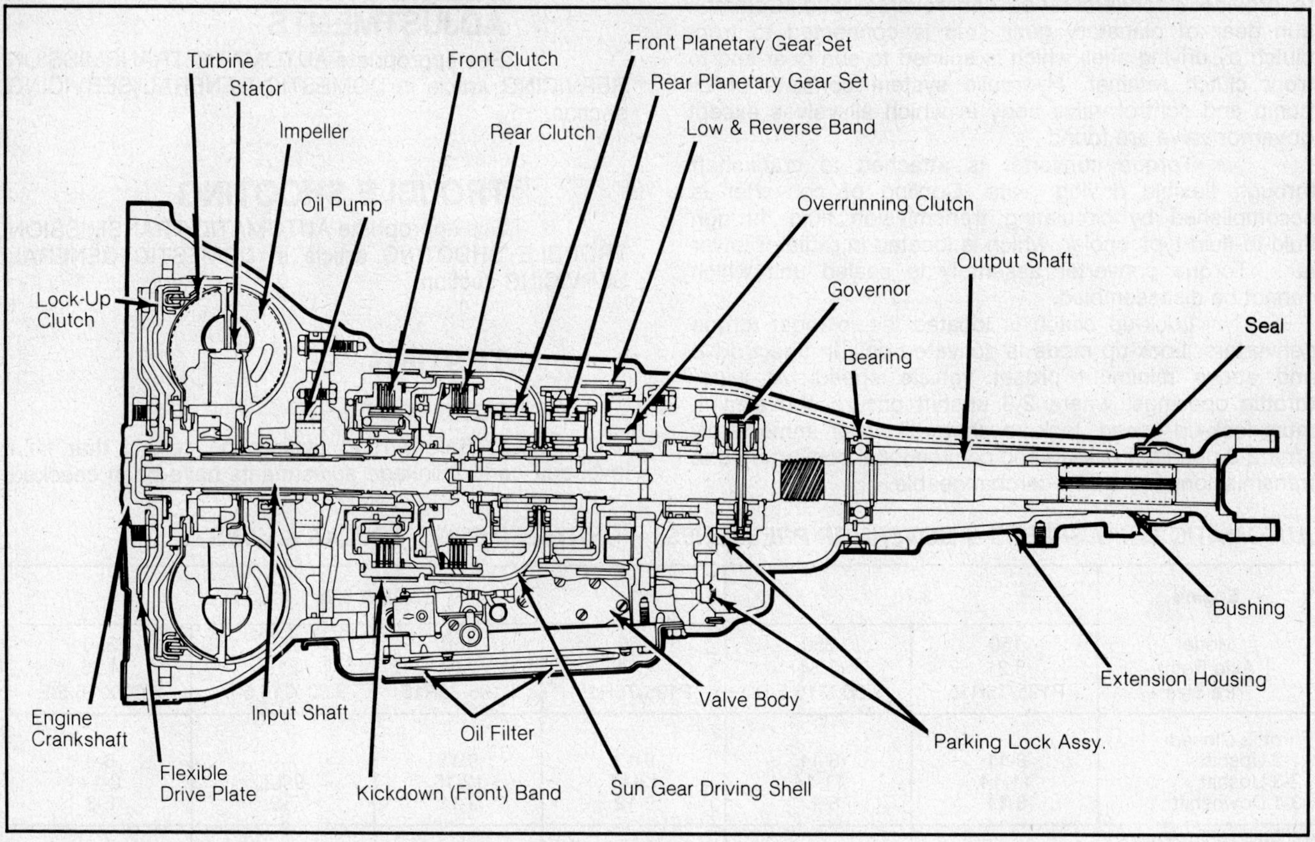

Fig. 4: Cross-Sectional View Of AMC/Jeep Model 727 Automatic Transmission

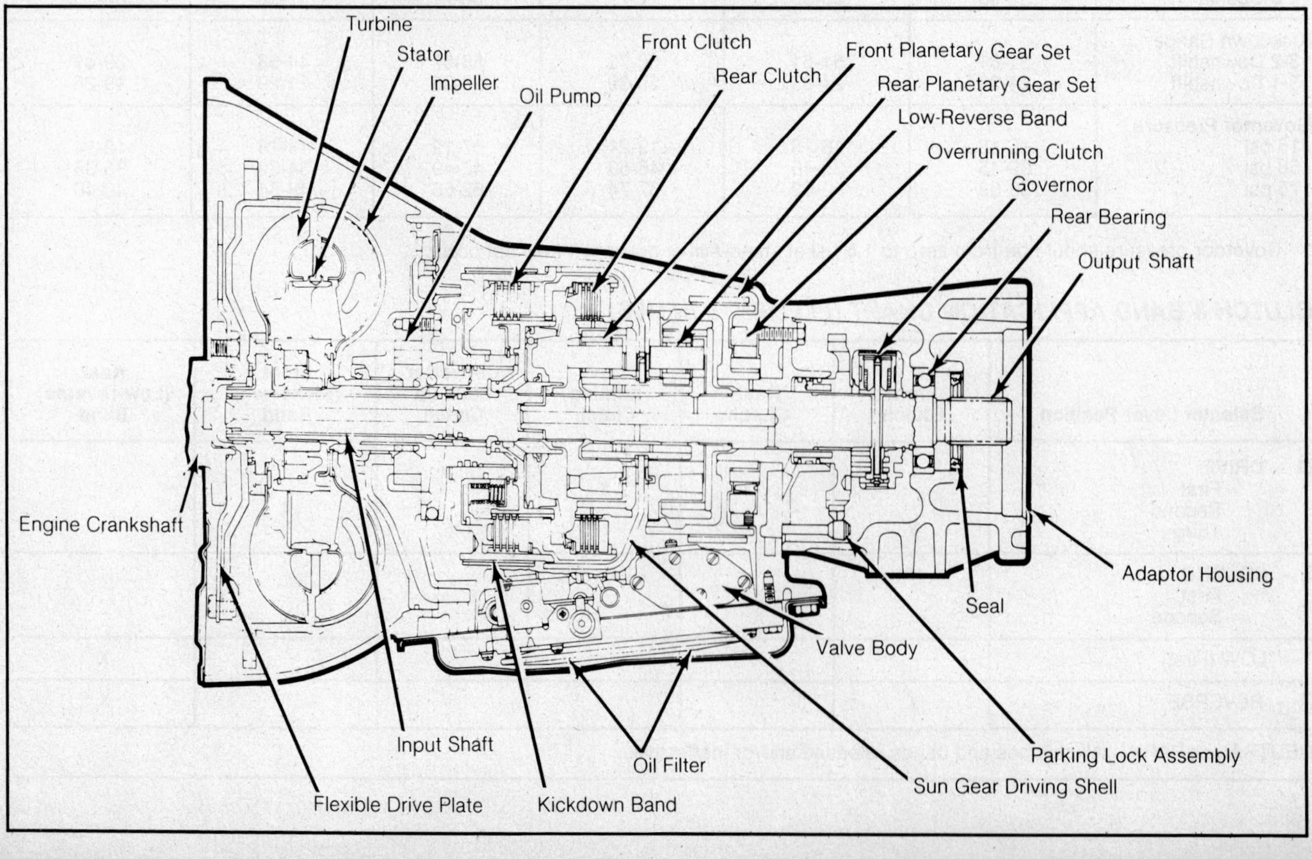

AMERICAN MOTORS, CHRYSLER CORP. & JEEP
727, 904, 998 & 999 (Cont.)

Fig. 5: Cross-Sectional View Of AMC/Jeep Model 998/999 Automatic Transmission

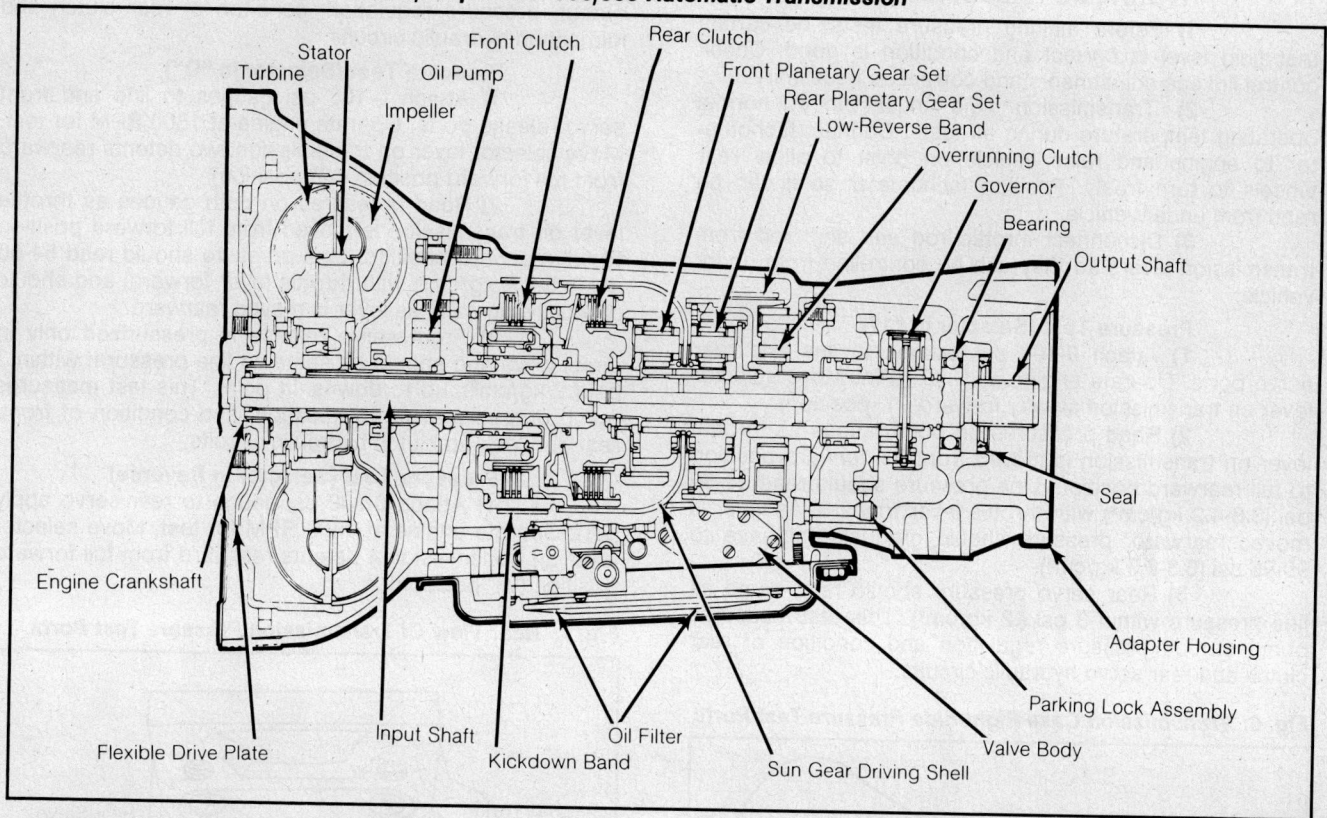

AUTOMATIC SHIFT SPEEDS & GOVERNOR PRESSURES – CHRYSLER CORP. PASSENGER CARS

Application	2.26 Axle Ratio [1] (MPH)	2.94 Axle Ratio [1] (MPH)
Throttle Closed		
1-2 Upshift	12-15	9-11
2-3 Upshift	16-20	13-16
Lock-Up	38-53	30-41
Throttle Wide Open		
1-2 Upshift	37-56	31-43
2-3 Upshift	75-93	58-72
Kickdown Range		
3-2 Downshift	69-87	54-67
3-1 Downshift	35-40	27-31
Governor Pressure [2]		
15 psi	23-25	17-20
50 psi	51-59	39-45
75 psi	78-85	60-66

[1] – With standard tire size P205/75R15.

[2] – Governor pressure should be from zero to 1.5 psi at stand-still or downshift may not occur.

and corrected as needed. During testing, transmission should upshift and downshift automatically at approximate speeds shown in AUTOMATIC SHIFT SPEEDS & GOVERNOR PRESSURES chart.

2) Exact speeds will vary somewhat from 1 vehicle to another. This is due to differences in production tolerances, rear axle ratio and tire size. Of greater importance than shift speed is quality of shifts. All shifts should be smooth and responsive with no slipping or engine speed flare-up.

3) Slipping or flare-up in any gear usually indicates clutch, band or overrunning clutch problems. Clutch or band which is slipping can be determined by noting transmission operation in all selector positions and by comparing which internal units are applied in those positions.

4) For example, if transmission slips in high gear with selector lever in "D", either front or rear clutch is slipping. By selecting another gear which uses 1 but not both of these assemblies, unit which is slipping can be identified. If transmission also slips in Reverse, front clutch is slipping. If transmission does not also slip in Reverse, rear clutch is slipping.

5) Although this process of elimination can be used to detect any unit which slips and to confirm proper operation of good units, actual cause of malfunction usually cannot be determined. Practically any condition can be caused by leaking hydraulic circuits or sticking valves.

6) Unless obvious condition exists, transmission should never be disassembled until hydraulic and air pressure tests have been performed. Engine tachometer can be used to determine if lock-up clutch in converter is functioning.

7) Instantaneous rise in engine speed of more than 150 RPM at 45 MPH when throttle is opened just short of kickdown, indicates lock-up clutch is slipping more than normal. Slippage less than 150 RPM is normal.

Automatic Transmissions

AMERICAN MOTORS, CHRYSLER CORP. & JEEP
727, 904, 998 & 999 (Cont.)

HYDRAULIC PRESSURE TESTS

1) Before making pressure tests, be certain that fluid level is correct and condition is good. Check control linkage adjustments and correct as necessary.

2) Transmission fluid must be at normal operating temperature during all tests. Connect tachometer to engine and raise vehicle on hoist to allow rear wheels to turn freely. Position tachometer so it can be read from under vehicle.

3) Disconnect throttle rod and shift rod from transmission levers so they can be controlled from under vehicle.

Pressure Test (Selector in "1")

1) Attach 0-100 psi gauges to line and rear servo ports. Operate engine at 1000 RPM. Move selector lever on transmission all way forward ("1" position).

2) Read pressures on both gauges as throttle lever on transmission is moved from full forward position to full rearward position. Line pressure should read 54-60 psi (3.8-4.2 kg/cm²) with throttle lever forward. As lever is moved rearward, pressure should gradually increase to 90-96 psi (6.3-6.7 kg/cm²).

3) Rear servo pressure should read same as line pressure within 3 psi (.2 kg/cm²). This test measures pump output, pressure regulation and condition of rear clutch and rear servo hydraulic circuits.

Fig. 6: Transmission Case Right Side Pressure Test Ports

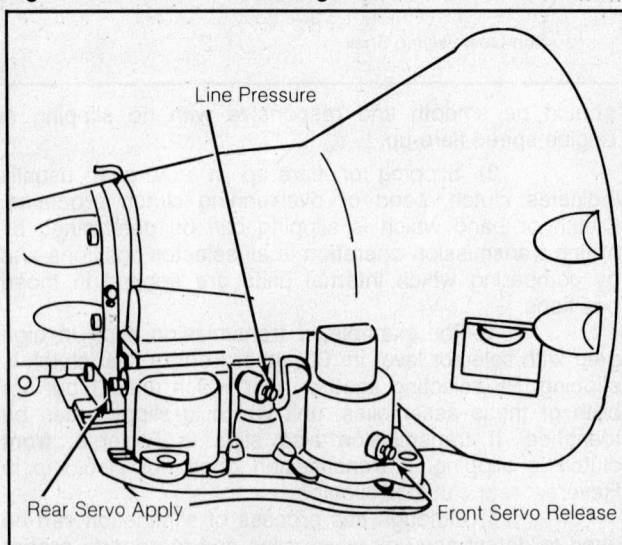

Fluid level, condition and control linkage adjustments must be correct before performing hydraulic tests.

Pressure Test (Selector in "2")

1) Install "T" fitting at rear cooler line fitting. Attach 0-100 psi gauges to "T" connection and line pressure port. Operate engine at 1000 RPM for test. Move selector lever on transmission 1 detent rearward from full forward position ("2" position).

2) Read pressures on both gauges as throttle lever on transmission is moved from full forward position to full rearward position. Line pressure should read 54-60 psi (3.8-4.2 kg/cm²) with throttle lever forward. As lever is moved rearward, pressure should gradually increase to 90-96 psi (6.3-6.7 kg/cm²).

3) Lubrication pressure should be 5-15 psi (.35-1.05 kg/cm²) with lever forward, and 10-30 psi (.7-2.1 kg/cm²) with lever rearward. This test measures pump output, pressure regulation, conditon of rear clutch and lubrication hydraulic circuits.

Pressure Test (Selector in "D")

1) Attach 0-100 psi gauges to line and front servo release ports. Operate engine at 1600 RPM for test. Move selector lever on transmission two detents rearward from full forward position ("D" position).

2) Read pressures on both gauges as throttle lever on transmission is moved from full forward position to full rearward position. Line pressure should read 54-60 psi (3.8-4.2 kg/cm²) with throttle lever forward, and should gradually increase as lever is moved rearward.

3) Front servo release is pressurized only in direct drive and should be same as line pressure, within 3 psi (.2 kg/cm²), up to downshift point. This test measures pump output, pressure regulation, and condition of front, rear and lock-up clutch hydraulic circuits.

Pressure Test (Selector in Reverse)

1) Attach 0-300 psi gauge to rear servo apply port. Operate engine at 1600 RPM for test. Move selector lever on transmission 4 detents rearward from full forward position ("R" position).

Fig. 7: Rear View Of Transmission Pressure Test Ports

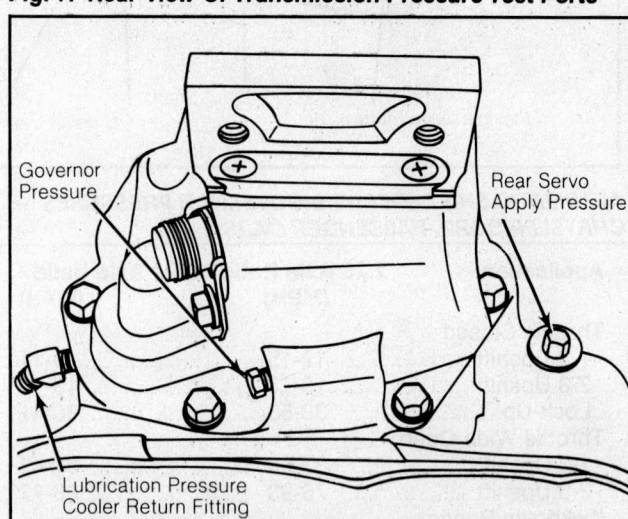

Gauge used to check pressure at rear servo apply port (shift lever in "R") MUST read to 300 psi (21 kg/cm²).

2) Rear servo pressure should read 145-175 psi (10.2-12.3 kg/cm²) with throttle lever forward and should gradually increase, as lever is moved rearward, to 230-280 psi (16.2-19.7 kg/cm²). This tests pump output, pressure regulation, condition of front clutch and rear servo hydraulic circuits.

3) Move selector lever on transmission to "D" position and check that rear servo pressure drops to zero. This test checks for leakage into rear servo due to case porosity, which can cause reverse band to burn out.

Governor Pressure

1) Connect 0-100 psi gauge to governor pressure port. Operate transmission in 3rd gear and read pressures. Compare readings with those shown in AUTOMATIC SHIFT SPEEDS & GOVERNOR PRESSURES chart.

AMERICAN MOTORS, CHRYSLER CORP. & JEEP
727, 904, 998 & 999 (Cont.)

NOTE: This test should only be performed if transmission shifts at wrong vehicle speeds when throttle rod is correctly adjusted.

2) If governor pressures are incorrect at given speeds, governor valve and/or weights are sticking. Governor pressure should return to 0-1.5 psi (0-.11 kg/cm²) when vehicle is stopped.

NOTE: High governor pressure (above 2 psi) at stand-still will prevent transmission from downshifting.

Throttle Pressure

No gauge port is provided for testing throttle pressure. Incorrect throttle pressure should only be suspected if part throttle upshift speeds are either delayed or occur too soon in relation to vehicle speeds. Engine runaway on either upshifts or downshifts can also be indicator of incorrect (low) throttle pressure.

Pressure Test Diagnosis

1) If line pressure is normal (minimum to maximum) in any one test, pump and pressure regulator are working properly.

2) If line pressure is normal in "R" but low in all forward gears ("D", "2" and "1"), rear clutch circuit leakage is indicated (servo, clutch seals or governor support seal rings).

3) Normal line pressure in "1" with low pressure in "D" and "R" indicates leakage in front clutch area (servo, clutch seals, retainer bore or pump seal rings).

4) Normal line pressure in "2" with low pressure in "R" and "1" indicates leakage in rear servo circuit.

5) Low line pressure in all positions indicates defective pump, clogged filter or stuck pressure regulator valve.

HYDRAULIC PRESSURE ADJUSTMENTS

NOTE: Throttle rod should always be checked and adjusted before checking or adjusting throttle pressure.

Throttle Pressure

1) Throttle pressures cannot be tested accurately. Adjustment should be measured if malfunction is evident.

2) Remove valve body assembly from transmission. Loosen throttle lever stop screw lock nut and back off screw approximately 5 turns.

3) Insert gauge pin of Gauge (C-3763 on Chrysler Corp. models; J-24031 on AMC/Jeep models) between throttle lever cam and kickdown valve. Push in on gauge and compress kickdown valve against spring so valve is completely bottomed inside valve body.

4) As force is being exerted to compress spring, turn throttle lever stop screw with Allen wrench. Adjustment is correct when head of screw touches throttle lever tang, with throttle lever cam touching gauge and throttle valve bottomed.

CAUTION: Be sure adjustment is made with spring fully compressed and valve bottomed in valve body.

Fig. 8: Adjusting Throttle Pressure

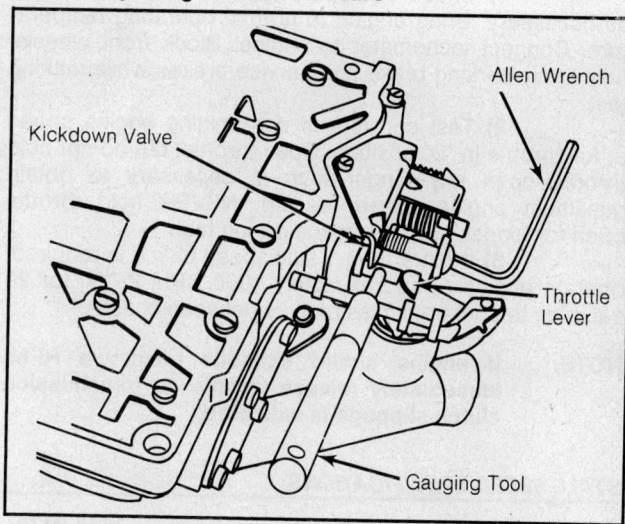

Gauge must be used to obtain proper adjustment.

Line Pressure

1) Incorrect throttle pressure setting will cause incorrect line pressure readings even though line pressure adjustment is correct. Always inspect and correct throttle pressure adjustment before adjusting line pressure.

2) Turn Allen screw in end of pressure regulator spring bracket so measurement between valve body and inner edge of adjusting nut is 1 5/16" (33.34 mm). Due to manufacturing tolerances, adjustment can be varied to obtain specified line pressure.

Fig. 9: Measuring Line Pressure Adjustment

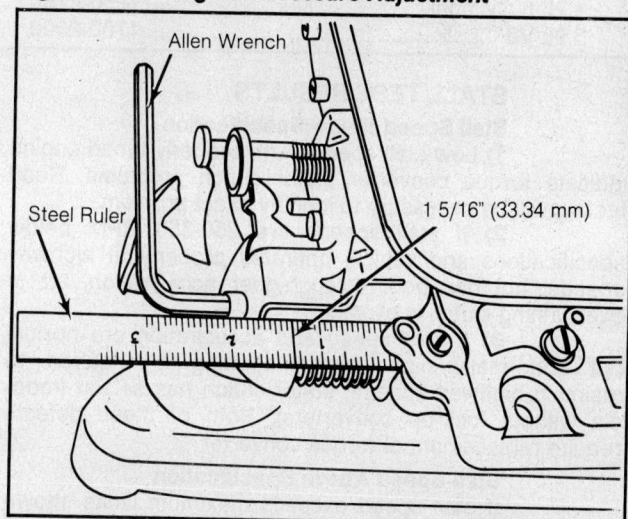

Exact adjustment may be varied slightly to obtain correct pressure reading.

3) One complete turn of adjusting screw changes closed throttle line pressure approximately 1.7 psi (.12 kg/cm²). Turning adjusting screw counterclockwise increases pressure; clockwise decreases pressure.

STALL TEST

CAUTION: Do NOT allow anyone to stand in front of vehicle during this test.

Automatic Transmissions

AMERICAN MOTORS, CHRYSLER CORP. & JEEP
727, 904, 998 & 999 (Cont.)

1) Check transmission fluid level and correct as necessary. Bring engine to normal operating temperature. Connect tachometer to engine. Block front wheels, fully apply parking brake and service brakes while making test.

2) Test consists of determining engine speed at full throttle in "D" position. Open throttle, but do not hold throttle open any longer than is necessary to obtain maximum engine speed reading. NEVER hold throttle open for longer than 5 seconds during test.

3) If more than 1 stall speed check is required, operate engine at approximately 1000 RPM in "N" for 20 seconds to cool transmission fluid between checks.

NOTE: **If engine speed exceeds maximum RPM, immediately release throttle as transmission clutch slippage is indicated.**

STALL SPEED SPECIFICATIONS

Application	Stall RPM
AMC	
4.2L 6-Cylinder	1850-2150
Chrysler Corp.	
3.7L 6-Cylinder	1800-2100
5.2L V8	1700-2000
5.9L V8 2-Bbl	1775-2075
5.9L V8 4-Bbl	1700-2000
Jeep	
Model 904	
2.5L 4-Cylinder	2350-2550
2.8L V6	2100-2300
All Other Models	
4.2L 6-Cylinder	1850-2150
5.9L V8	1700-2000

STALL TEST RESULTS

Stall Speed Below Specification

1) Low stall speeds with properly tuned engine indicate torque converter stator clutch problems. Road testing will be necessary to identify exact problem.

2) If stall speeds are 250-350 RPM below specifications and vehicle operates properly at highway speeds, but has poor through-gear acceleration, stator overrunning clutch is slipping.

3) If stall speed and acceleration are normal but abnormally high throttle opening is required to maintain highway speeds, stator clutch has seized (models without lock-up converters). Both of these defects require replacement of torque converter.

Stall Speed Above Specification

If stall speed exceeds maximum limits shown by more than 200 RPM, transmission clutch slippage is indicated. Make hydraulic pressure and air pressure checks to determine cause of slippage.

Noise During Stall Test

1) Whining or siren-like noise due to fluid flow is normal during stall test with some converters. However, loud metallic noises from loose parts or interference within assembly indicates defective converter.

2) To be sure noise originates in converter, raise vehicle on hoist and operate at light throttle in "D" and "N" while listening under transmission bellhousing.

AIR PRESSURE TESTS

"No Drive" condition can exist even with correct fluid pressure because of inoperative clutches and/or bands. Cause can be located by applying compressed air to appropriate case passages after valve body has been removed. If clutches and servos operate correctly, no upshift and/or erratic shift condition indicates malfunction in valve body.

NOTE: **Compressed air must be free of any dirt or moisture. Use air pressure of 30 psi (2.1 kg/cm²) for tests.**

Front Clutch

Direct air pressure into front clutch apply passage. Operation of clutch is indicated by dull thud which may be heard or felt. Hold air pressure for few seconds to check system for excessive air leaks.

Fig. 10: Air Pressure Test Points In Bottom Of Transmission Case

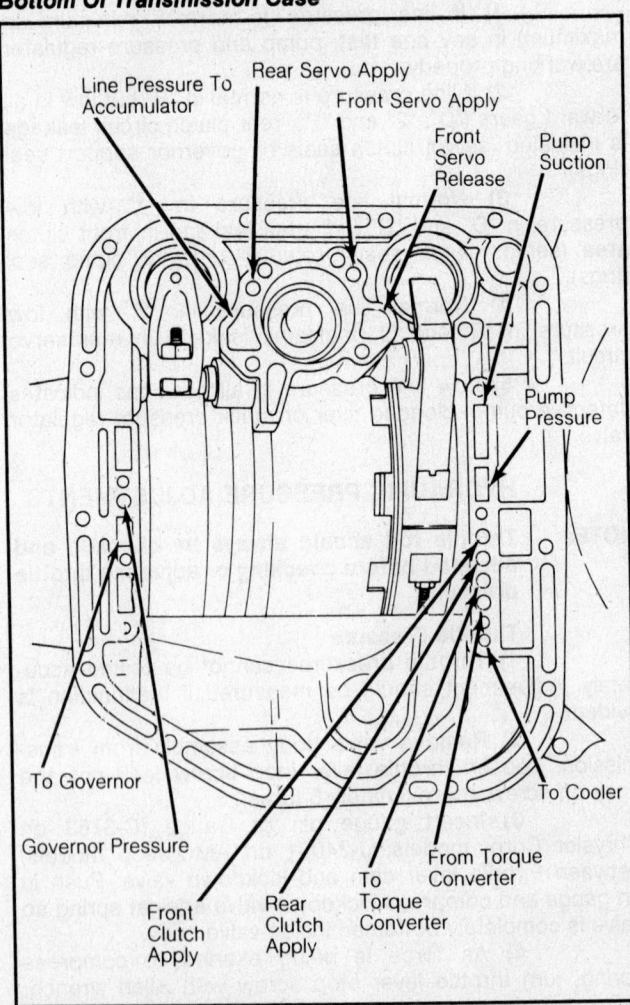

Use only filtered, compressed air to check system.

Rear Clutch

1) Direct air pressure into rear clutch apply passage. Operation of clutch is indicated by dull thud which may be heard or felt.

AMERICAN MOTORS, CHRYSLER CORP. & JEEP
727, 904, 998 & 999 (Cont.)

2) If clutch operation is not detected, place finger tips on clutch housing and again apply air pressure. Movement of piston can be felt as air is applied. Also check for excessive air leaks.

Front (Kickdown) Servo

Direct air pressure into front servo apply passage. Operation of servo is indicated by tightening of front band. Spring tension on servo piston should release band.

Rear (Low-Reverse) Servo

Direct air pressure into rear servo apply passage. Operation of servo is indicated by tightening of rear band. Spring tension of servo piston should release band.

SERVICE (IN VEHICLE)

SPEEDOMETER PINION

Removal

Remove bolt and clamp securing speedometer pinion adapter in extension housing. With cable housing connected, carefully work adapter and pinion out of extension housing.

Fig. 11: Exploded View Of Speedometer Drive Assembly

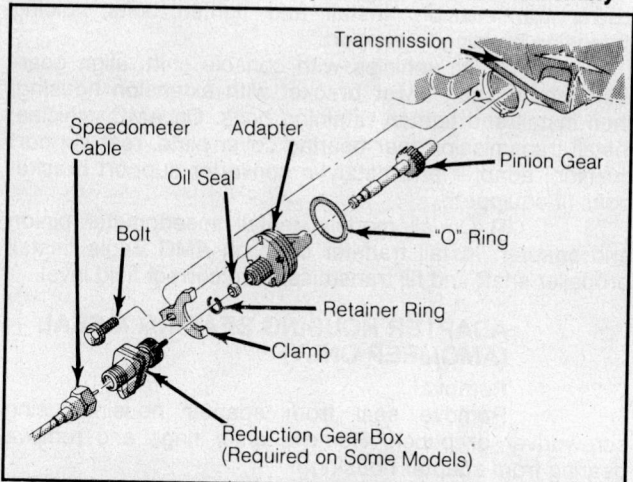

Chrysler Loadflite model is shown; other models are similar.

Seal Replacement

If transmission fluid is found inside cable housing, replace seal in adapter (if used) or speedometer pinion and seal assembly (Torqueflite models). Start seal and retainer ring in adapter. Push into adapter using Seal Installer (C-4004) until tool bottoms.

Fig. 12: Installing Speedometer Cable Adapter Oil Seal

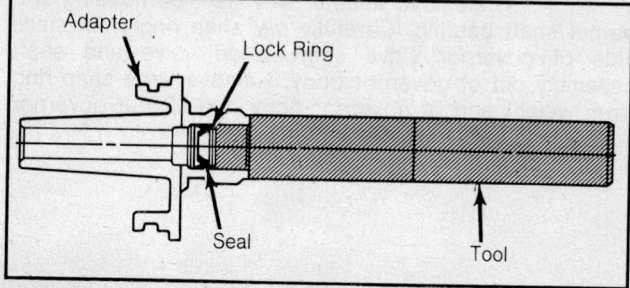

Installation

1) Note number on adapter, which corresponds to number of teeth on gear. Install correct speedometer pinion gear into adapter. Rotate pinion gear and adapter assembly so number on adapter is in 6 o'clock position.

NOTE: **To avoid misalignment and possible damage to speedometer pinion gear, make sure adapter flange and mating surfaces are clean before installation.**

2) Install pinion gear and adapter assembly. Install clamp and bolt with clamp tangs in adapter positioning slots. Tap adapter firmly into extension housing and tighten bolt.

Fig. 13: Speedometer Pinion & Adapter Installation

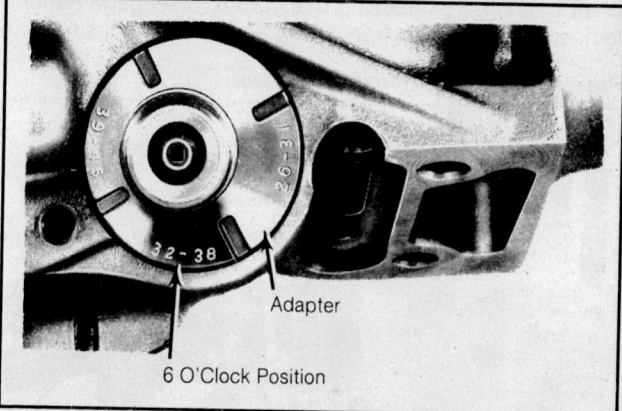

Adapter and mounting surface must be clean.

NEUTRAL SAFETY SWITCH

Refer to appropriate AUTOMATIC TRANSMISSION SERVICING article in DOMESTIC GENERAL SERVICING section.

OUTPUT SHAFT OIL SEAL
Removal

Mark propeller shaft and rear axle flange for reassembly and remove propeller shaft, being careful not to nick or scratch splined yoke. Using removal tool or large screwdriver, remove seal from extension housing.

Installation

Position new seal in opening of extension housing and drive seal into housing. Install propeller shaft, aligning marks made during disassembly.

EXTENSION HOUSING, BEARING & BUSHING
Removal

1) On 4WD models, remove transfer case. On all models, disconnect propeller shaft at rear axle and slide shaft assembly out of extension housing. Remove extension housing oil seal, speedometer pinion and adapter assembly. Drain about 2 quarts of transmission fluid.

2) Remove bolts holding extension housing to crossmember and support. Raise transmission slightly with jack and remove crossmember and support. On AMC passenger cars, remove catalytic converter support bracket bolts, rear support cushion with adapter and

AMERICAN MOTORS, CHRYSLER CORP. & JEEP
727, 904, 998 & 999 (Cont.)

transmission rear bearing cover plate from extension housing.

3) On models equipped with console shift mechanism, remove 2 bolts securing gearshift torque shaft lower bracket to housing, then swing bracket out of way for extension housing removal.

NOTE: When removing or installing extension housing, gearshift lever must be in "1" (Low) position. This positions parking lock control rod rearward so it can be disengaged or engaged with parking lock sprag.

4) Remove bolts holding extension housing to transmission. Remove 2 retaining screws, plate and gasket from bottom of housing mounting pad. With large snap ring pliers, spread snap ring on output shaft bearing as far as possible and tap extension housing off output shaft bearing. Pull housing rearward to disengage parking lock control rod knob from sprag and remove housing.

Fig. 14: Extension Housing Removal

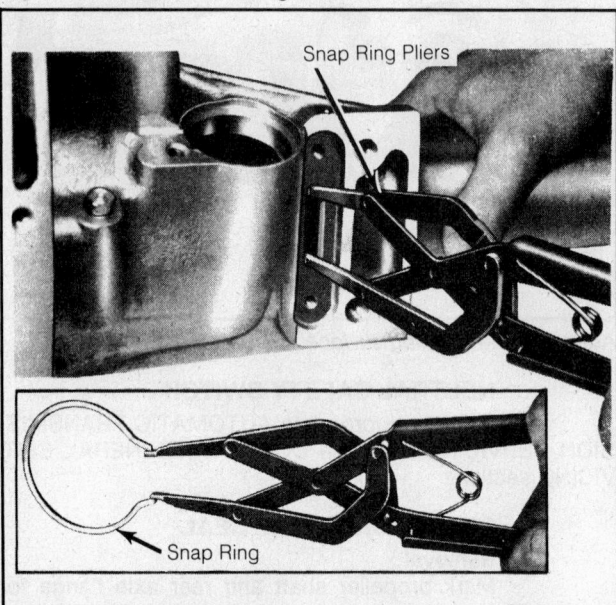

Spread snap ring as far as possible and remove extension housing.

Fig. 15: Output Shaft Rear Bearing Installation

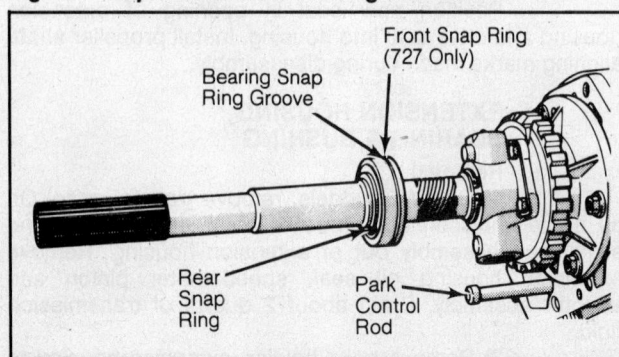

Snap ring groove on outer race must face toward front.

Bushing Replacement
Remove bushing from extension housing with bushing driver. Align hole in new bushing with oil slot in extension housing. Drive or press bushing into housing and install new oil seal.

Bearing Replacement
Remove output shaft bearing rear snap ring and bearing from output shaft. Replace snap ring in front groove on output shaft (if removed). Install new bearing on output shaft with ring groove on outer race toward front. Install rear snap ring.

Installation
1) Install new gasket on transmission case. Position output shaft bearing retaining snap ring in extension housing. Slide extension housing on output shaft, guiding parking lock control rod knob past parking sprag. While spreading large snap ring in housing, carefully tap housing into place and release snap ring.

NOTE: Ensure snap ring is fully seated in bearing outer race ring groove.

2) Install and tighten bolts holding extension housing to transmission case. Install gasket, plate and screws on bottom of extension housing mounting pad. Install center crossmember and rear mount assembly. Lower transmission. Install and tighten bolts holding extension housing to support.

3) On vehicles with console shift, align gearshift torque shaft lower bracket with extension housing, then install and tighten retaining bolts. On AMC vehicles, install transmission rear bearing cover plate, rear support cushion, adapter and catalytic converter support bracket bolts (if equipped).

4) On all models, install speedometer pinion and adapter. Install transfer case on AMC Eagle. Install propeller shaft and fill transmission to correct fluid level.

ADAPTER HOUSING BEARING & SEAL (AMC/JEEP ONLY)
Removal
Remove seal from adapter housing using screwdriver or punch. Remove snap rings and remove bearing from adapter housing.

Installation
Install new bearing in housing and install snap rings. Install new seal in housing. Seal should be seated flush with edge of seal bore.

GOVERNOR & PARKING GEAR
Removal
NOTE: To remove governor and parking gear from 4WD models, transfer case must be removed.

1) Remove adapter or extension housing and output shaft bearing. Carefully pry snap ring from small side of governor valve shaft. Slide valve and shaft assembly out of governor body. Remove large snap ring from weight end of governor body and lift out governor weight assembly.

AMERICAN MOTORS, CHRYSLER CORP. & JEEP
727, 904, 998 & 999 (Cont.)

Fig. 16: Governor, Support & Parking Gear Assembly

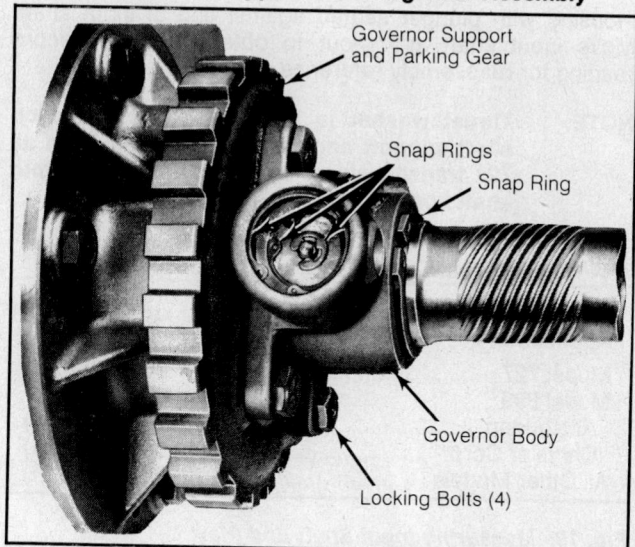

Governor Support and Parking Gear

Snap Rings

Snap Ring

Governor Body

Locking Bolts (4)

2) Remove snap ring from inside governor weight. Remove inner weight and spring from outer weight. Remove snap ring from behind governor body. Slide body and support assembly off output shaft. Remove bolts and separate governor body from support and parking gear.

Inspection
Inspect all parts for wear or damage. Check spring for distortion. Weights and valves should fall freely in bores when clean and dry. Remove any roughness with crocus cloth.

Installation
1) Assemble governor body to support and tighten bolts finger tight, making sure oil passage in governor body aligns with passage in support. Position support and governor assembly on output shaft. Align assembly so valve shaft hole in body mates with hole in output shaft.

2) Slide assembly into place, install snap ring behind governor body and tighten bolts holding body to support. Assemble governor weights and spring. Secure with snap ring inside large governor weight.

3) Place assembly in governor body and install snap ring. Place governor valve on valve shaft. Insert assembly into body and through governor weights. Install valve shaft retaining snap ring.

Fig. 17: Exploded View Of Governor Assembly

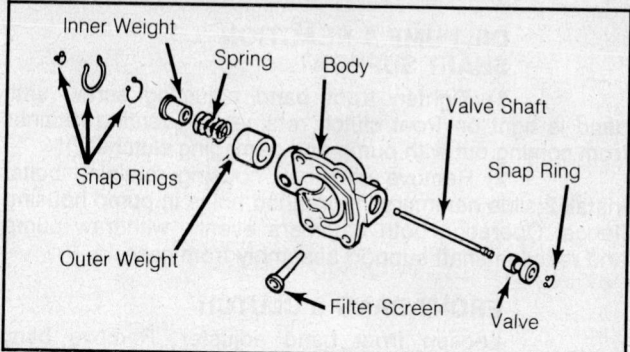

Inner Weight

Spring

Body

Valve Shaft

Snap Ring

Snap Rings

Outer Weight

Filter Screen

Valve

4) Inspect valve and weight assembly for free movement. Install output shaft bearing and extension housing or adapter housing.

PARKING LOCK
Removal
With extension or adapter housing removed, slide shaft out of housing to remove parking sprag and spring. Remove snap ring and slide reaction plug and pin assembly out of housing.

Inspection
Check sprag shaft for scores and free movement in housing and sprag. Check springs for loss of tension or distortion. Check square lug on sprag and lugs on governor support (park gear) for broken edges. Check knob on end of control rod for nicks, burrs and free movement.

Fig. 18: Parking Lock Component Installation

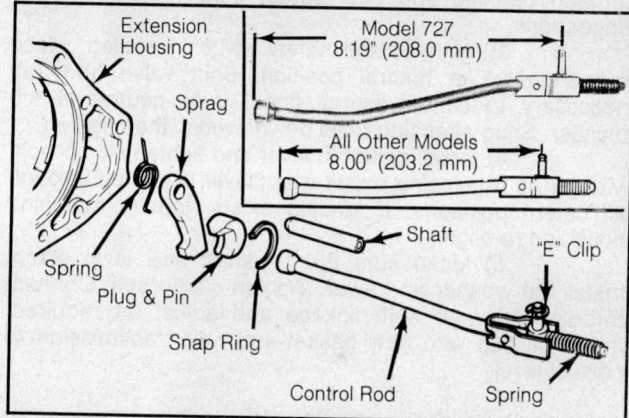

Extension Housing

Sprag

Model 727
8.19" (208.0 mm)

All Other Models
8.00" (203.2 mm)

Shaft

"E" Clip

Spring

Plug & Pin

Snap Ring

Control Rod

Spring

Adjust control rod to length as shown.

Installation
Install reaction plug and pin assembly in housing and secure with snap ring. Position sprag and spring in housing and insert shaft, making sure square lug on sprag is toward parking gear and spring is positioned so it moves sprag away from gear. Control rod length should be adjusted to 8.19" (208.0 mm) on 727 transmissions and 8.00" (203.2 mm) on all others. Install extension or adapter housing.

VALVE BODY ASSEMBLY & ACCUMULATOR PISTON
Removal
1) Loosen oil pan bolts, tap on pan to break it loose and allow fluid to drain. Remove oil pan. Loosen clamp bolts and remove transmission levers. Remove neutral safety switch.

2) While holding valve body in position, remove bolts holding valve body to transmission case. Move valve body down and forward to remove. Rotate propeller shaft as needed to align parking gear and sprag to allow knob on end of control rod to pass sprag.

3) Remove accumulator piston and spring from case. Inspect all parts for wear or damage and replace as needed.

AMERICAN MOTORS, CHRYSLER CORP. & JEEP
727, 904, 998 & 999 (Cont.)

Manual Lever Shaft Seal Replacement

If shaft seal requires replacement, drive seal from case with punch. Drive new seal into case using 15/16" socket and hammer.

NOTE: Seal may be replaced without removing valve body from case by using small screwdriver to pry seal out of case. Take care not to damage shaft or seal bore in case.

Installation

1) Place valve body manual lever in "1" position. Using screwdriver, push park sprag into engagement with parking gear, turning output shaft to verify engagement. This allows knob on end of control rod to move past sprag as valve body is installed.

2) Install accumulator piston in transmission case and accumulator spring between piston and valve body. Lift valve body into position, working park rod through opening and past sprag. Install retaining bolts finger tight.

3) With neutral safety switch installed, place manual valve in neutral position. Shift valve body as necessary to center neutral finger over neutral switch plunger. Snug attaching bolts down evenly, then tighten.

4) Install gearshift lever and tighten clamp bolt. Make sure no binding exists when lever is moved through all detent positions. If binding exists, loosen attaching bolts and re-align.

5) Make sure throttle shaft seal is in place. Install flat washer and lever. Tighten clamp bolt. Connect throttle and gear shift linkage and adjust as required. Install oil pan with new gasket and refill transmission to correct level.

REMOVAL & INSTALLATION

See appropriate AUTOMATIC TRANSMISSION REMOVAL article in DOMESTIC GENERAL SERVICING section.

TORQUE CONVERTER

1) Torque converter is welded assembly and is not serviceable. If malfunction occurs or if converter becomes contaminated with foreign material, it must be replaced. It cannot be flushed or repaired.

2) Input shaft and valve body used with lock-up converter are significantly different from those used in transmissions utilizing conventional converter. Two different types of converters are NOT INTERCHANGEABLE.

3) If starter ring gear on lock-up type torque converter requires replacement, complete converter must be replaced. Welding new ring gear onto lock-up converter will damage friction material used in converter.

TRANSMISSION DISASSEMBLY

INPUT SHAFT END PLAY

1) Measuring end play before disassembly will usually indicate whether change in thrust washer is required to properly adjust end play during reassembly (except when major parts are replaced).

2) Attach dial indicator to transmission bellhousing with plunger seated against end of input shaft. Move input shaft in-and-out to obtain reading. Record reading for reassembly reference.

NOTE: Thrust washer is located between reaction shaft support and front clutch retainer on all 727 transmissions; between input and output shafts on all other models.

TRANSMISSION END PLAY SPECIFICATIONS

Application	End Play In. (mm)
Model 727	.035-.084 (.89-2.13)
Model 999	
AMC/Jeep	.016-.059 (.41-1.50)
Chrysler Corp.	.022-.091 (.56-2.31)
All Other Models	.022-.091 (.56-2.31)

Fig. 19: Measuring Input Shaft End Play

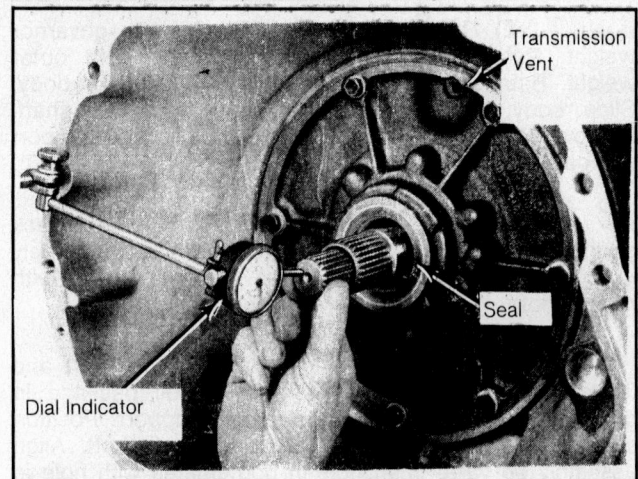

Transmission Vent

Seal

Dial Indicator

Measure end play before disassembly.

VALVE BODY & ACCUMULATOR PISTON
See SERVICE (IN VEHICLE).

EXTENSION/ADAPTER HOUSING
See SERVICE (IN VEHICLE).

GOVERNOR
See SERVICE (IN VEHICLE).

OIL PUMP & REACTION SHAFT SUPPORT

1) Tighten front band adjusting screw until band is tight on front clutch retainer, preventing retainer from coming out with pump and damaging clutches.

2) Remove oil pump housing retaining bolts. Install 2 slide hammers in threaded holes in pump housing flange. Operating both hammers evenly, withdraw pump and reaction shaft support assembly from case.

FRONT BAND & CLUTCH

Loosen front band adjuster. Remove band strut (and anchor on Model 727). Slide band out of case. Slide front clutch out of case.

AMERICAN MOTORS, CHRYSLER CORP. & JEEP
727, 904, 998 & 999 (Cont.)

INPUT SHAFT & REAR CLUTCH

Grasp input shaft by hand. Slide input shaft and rear clutch assembly out of case.

CAUTION: Do not lose thrust washer located between rear end of input shaft and forward end of output shaft.

PLANETARY GEAR ASSEMBLIES, SUN GEAR & DRIVING SHELL

While supporting output shaft and driving shell, carefully slide assembly forward and out through case.

CAUTION: Do not damage machined surfaces on output shaft during removal.

REAR BAND & LOW-REVERSE DRUM
AMC/Jeep

Remove low-reverse drum. Loosen rear band adjusting screw and thread 1/4" bolt into actuating lever pivot pin. Remove pin from case. Remove lever, linkage and rear band from case.

Chrysler Corp.

Remove drum, loosen rear band adjuster and remove band strut and link. Remove band from case. On models with double-wrap band, loosen band adjusting screw. Remove band and low-reverse drum.

OVERRUNNING CLUTCH

Note relative positions of overrunning clutch rollers and springs for reassembly reference. Carefully slide out clutch hub, then remove rollers and springs.

FRONT (KICKDOWN) SERVO

Compress kickdown servo and remove snap ring. Remove rod guide, springs and piston rod from case. Take care not to damage piston rod or guide. Remove piston from transmission case.

REAR (LOW-REVERSE) SERVO

Compress low-reverse servo piston spring and remove snap ring. Remove spring retainer, spring, servo piston and plug assembly from case. Tag spring for reassembly reference.

COMPONENT DISASSEMBLY & REASSEMBLY

VALVE BODY DISASSEMBLY

NOTE: Tag all valves and springs for reassembly reference as they are removed.

Filter, Transfer Plate & Pressure Regulators

1) Place valve body assembly on stand, remove filter retaining screws and filter. Remove top and bottom screws from spring retainer/adjustment screw bracket. Holding spring retainer firmly against spring pressure, remove last screw from side of valve body.

2) Remove spring retainer with line and throttle pressure adjusting screws (do not disturb settings). Remove line pressure and switch valve regulator springs.

3) Slide switch valve and line pressure valve from bores. Remove screws from lock-up module (stiffen-

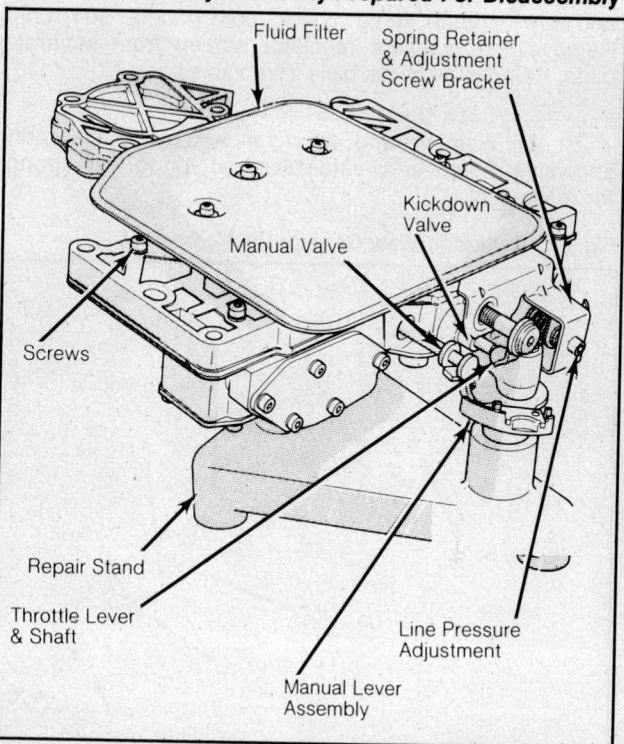

Fig. 20: Valve Body Assembly Prepared For Disassembly

Fluid Filter — Spring Retainer & Adjustment Screw Bracket — Kickdown Valve — Manual Valve — Screws — Repair Stand — Throttle Lever & Shaft — Manual Lever Assembly — Line Pressure Adjustment

Support valve body in stand during disassembly procedure.

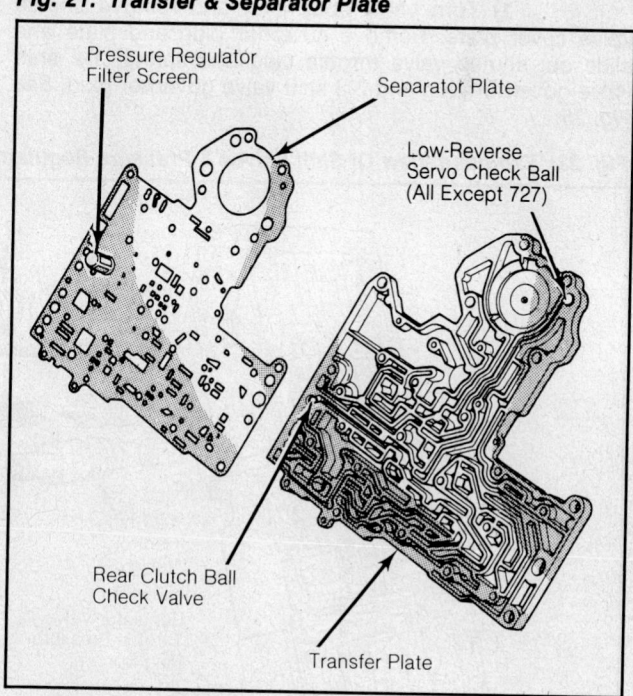

Fig. 21: Transfer & Separator Plate

Pressure Regulator Filter Screen — Separator Plate — Low-Reverse Servo Check Ball (All Except 727) — Rear Clutch Ball Check Valve — Transfer Plate

er plate on models with conventional converter) and carefully remove tube and lock-up module (or stiffener plate). Disassemble lock-up module, tagging springs for reassembly reference.

4) Remove transfer plate retaining screws and lift off transfer plate and separator plate assembly. Remove screws from stiffener and separator plate and

Automatic Transmissions

AMERICAN MOTORS, CHRYSLER CORP. & JEEP
727, 904, 998 & 999 (Cont.)

separate parts for cleaning. Remove rear clutch check ball and low-reverse servo check ball (Model 904 only). Remove line pressure regulator screen from separator plate. Remove all check balls from valve body.

Lock-Up Module
Remove end cover, slide out lock-up spring and valve. Remove fail-safe valve and spring. Tag springs for reassembly.

Fig. 22: Exploded View Of Lock-Up Module

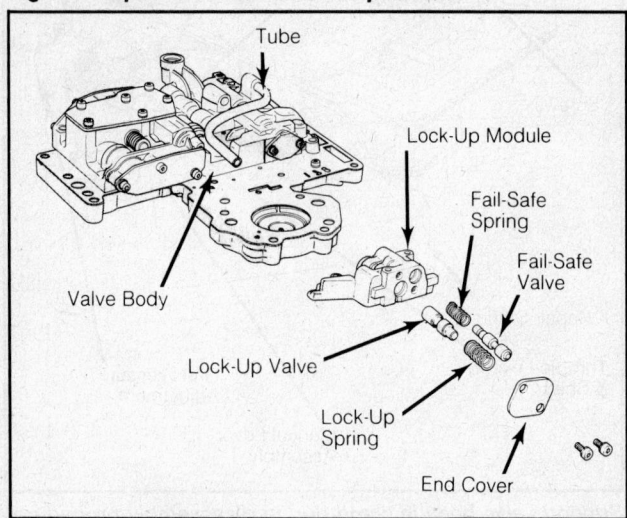

Shuttle Valve & Governor Plugs
1) Turn valve body over and remove shuttle valve cover plate. Remove governor plug end plate and slide out shuttle valve throttle plug and spring, 1-2 shift valve governor plug and 2-3 shift valve governor plug. *See Fig. 25.*

2) Remove shuttle valve "E" clip and slide shuttle valve from bore. Also remove secondary spring and guides retained by "E" clip. Remove "E" clip and park control rod from manual lever.

Pressure Regulators & Manual Control
1) Remove "E" clip and washer from throttle lever shaft. Remove any burrs from shaft. While holding manual lever detent ball and spring in bore, slide manual lever off throttle shaft. *See Fig. 24.*

2) Remove detent ball and spring. Slide manual valve from bore and remove kickdown detent, kickdown valve, throttle valve spring and throttle valve.

Shift Valves & Regulator Valve
Pressure Sensing Plugs
1) Remove line pressure regulator valve end plate. *See Fig. 23.* Slide out regulator valve sleeve, line pressure plug, throttle pressure plug and spring.

2) Remove end plate. On models with downshift valve housing, remove housing assembly. Remove throttle plug, slide out retainer and remove spring and limit valve from housing. On all models, remove shift valves and springs (3) from valve body.

VALVE BODY INSPECTION
1) Wash all parts in solvent and dry with compressed air. Inspect all parts for nicks, burrs, scratches or distortion. Small nicks and burrs can be removed with crocus cloth. Use extreme care not to round off any machined sharp edges. These edges are necessary to prevent foreign matter from lodging between valve and bore, which could cause valve to stick or drag.

2) Make sure all passages are clean and free of obstructions. All metering holes in steel plate and valve body must be open. Insert 1/32" drill through orifice into 1-

Fig. 23: Exploded View Of Shift Valves & Pressure Regulator Valve Plugs

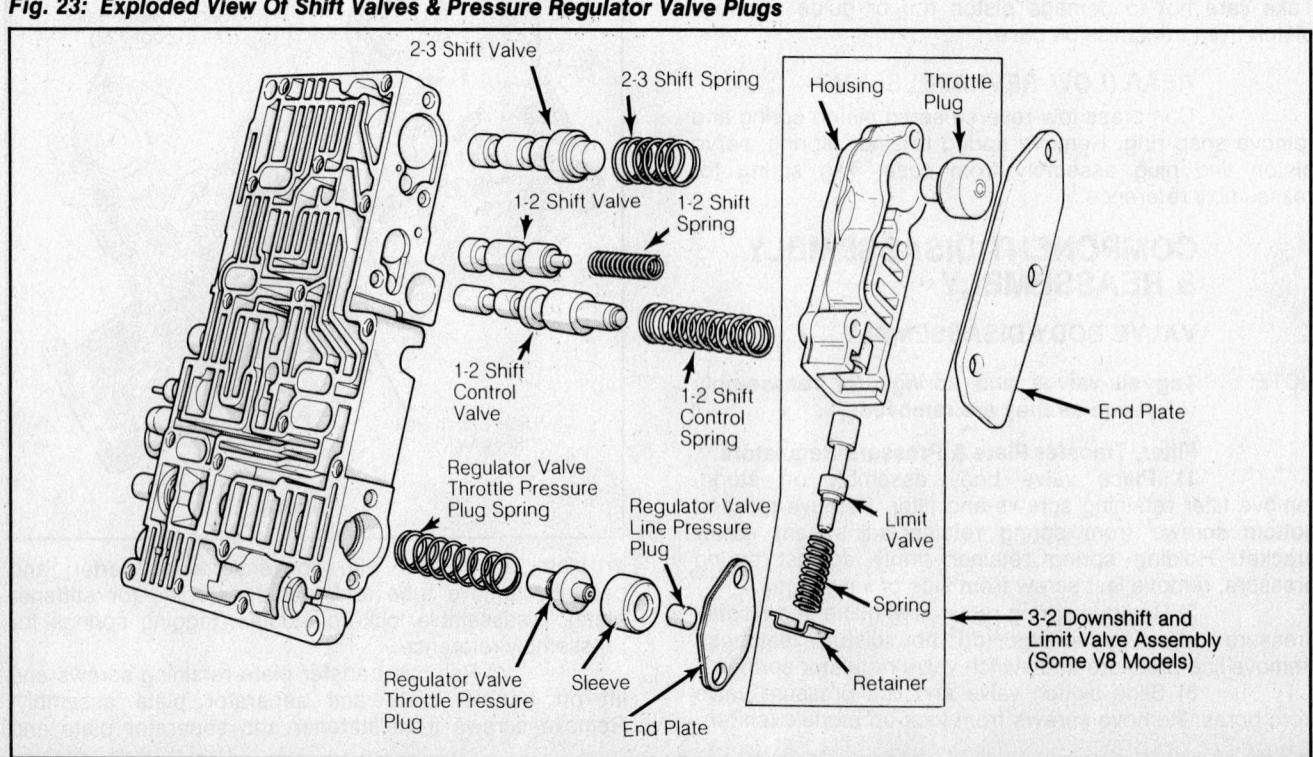

AMERICAN MOTORS, CHRYSLER CORP. & JEEP
727, 904, 998 & 999 (Cont.)

2 shift control bore to make sure it is open. Inspect all springs for distortion and/or collapsed coils.

3) Inspect manual and throttle valve operating levers and shafts. If bent, worn or loose on shaft, assembly should be replaced. DO NOT attempt to straighten bent levers.

4) When bores, valves and plugs are clean and dry, valves and plugs should fall freely into bores.

VALVE BODY REASSEMBLY
Shift Valves & Regulator Valve
Pressure Sensing Plugs
1) Slide shift valves and springs into proper valve body bores. On models with downshift housing assembly, insert limit valve and spring into housing and slide spring retainer into groove. Install throttle plug in housing bore. Position assembly against shift valve springs.

2) On all models, install end plate and tighten retaining screws. Install throttle pressure spring, plug, sleeve and regulator valve plug. Install end plate and tighten retaining screws.

Shuttle Valve & Governor Plugs
1) Place 1-2 and 2-3 shift valve governor plugs in bores. Install shuttle valve into bore. Install spring guides, secondary spring and "E" clip on opposite end of valve.

2) Install primary shuttle valve spring and throttle plug into bore. Install governor plug end plate. Install and tighten retaining screws. Install shuttle valve cover plate and tighten retaining screws.

Pressure Regulators & Manual Control
1) Install throttle valve, valve spring, kickdown valve and detent into bore. Slide manual valve into its bore. Install throttle lever and shaft on valve body. Insert detent ball and spring into bore.

Fig. 25: Exploded View Of Shuttle Valve & Governor Plugs

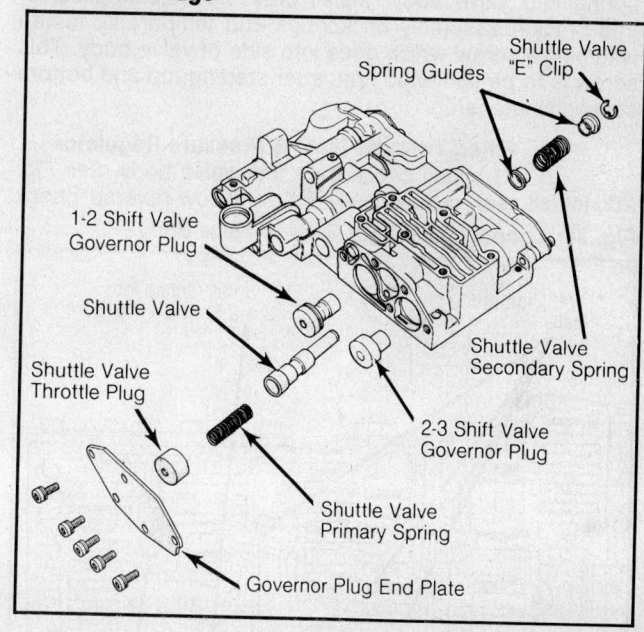

Fig. 24: Exploded View Of Pressure Regulators & Manual Controls

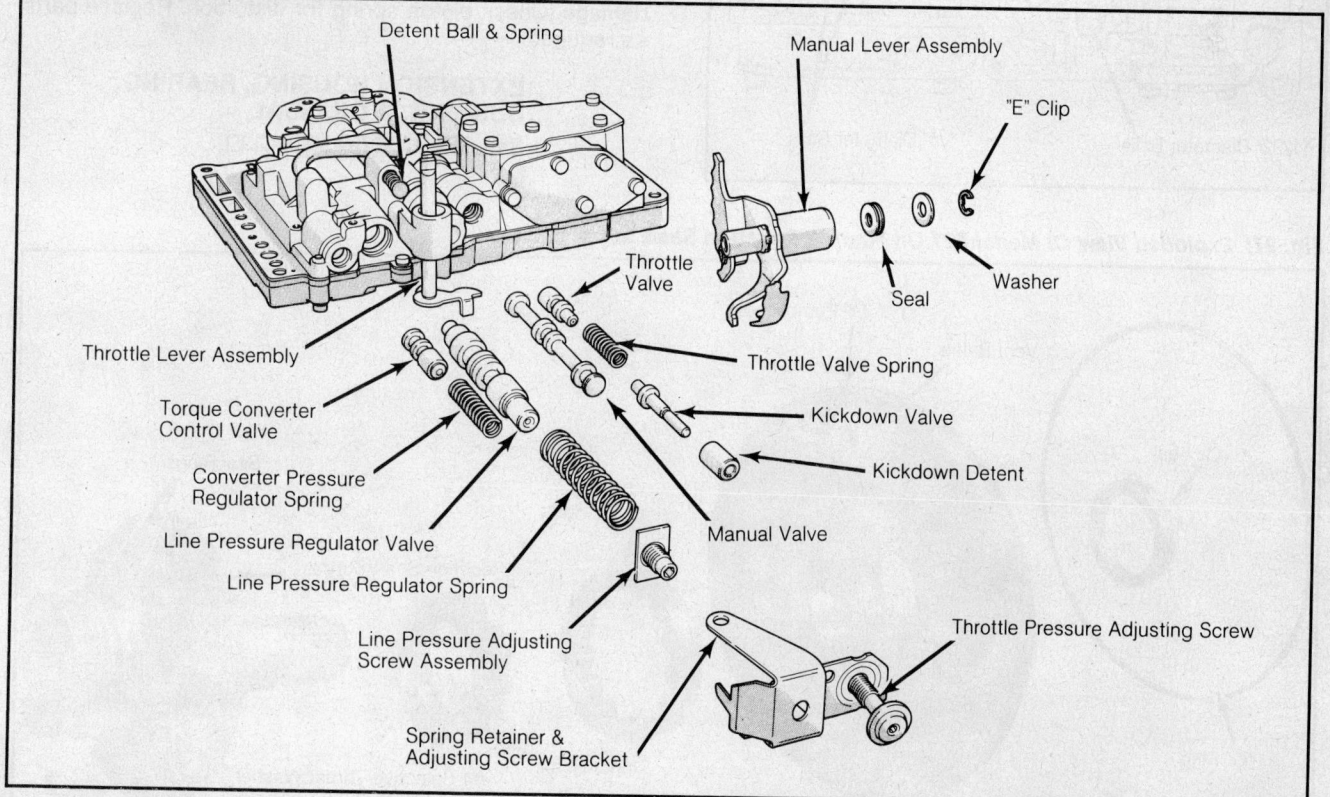

Automatic Transmissions

AMERICAN MOTORS, CHRYSLER CORP. & JEEP
727, 904, 998 & 999 (Cont.)

2) Depress ball and spring in bore. Slide manual lever over throttle shaft so it engages manual valve and detent ball. Install seal, retaining washer and "E" clip on throttle shaft. Insert switch valve and spring into valve body.

3) Insert line pressure regulator valve and spring into valve body. Install pressure adjusting screw and bracket assembly on springs and temporarily fasten with single screw which goes into side of valve body. This screw is to be tightened first, after starting top and bottom screws in later step.

Filter, Transfer Plate & Pressure Regulator

1) Install check balls into valve body. *See Fig. 26.* Install rear clutch check ball and low-reverse check

Fig. 26: Location Of Check Balls In Valve Body

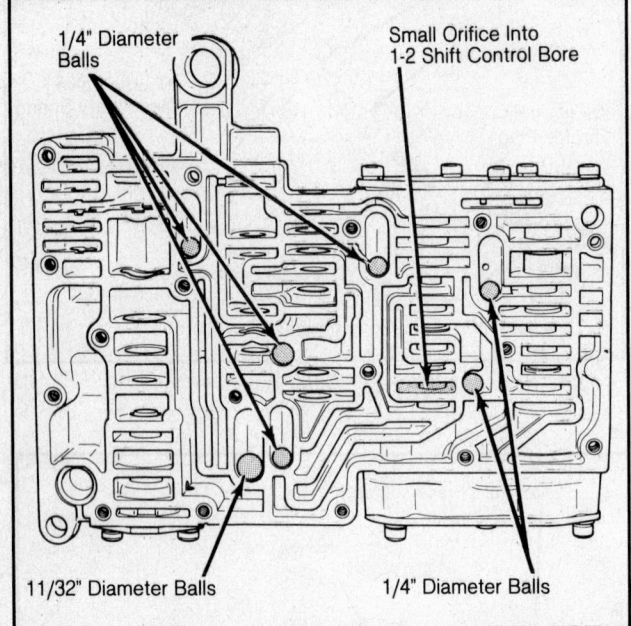

1/4" Diameter Balls

Small Orifice Into 1-2 Shift Control Bore

11/32" Diameter Balls

1/4" Diameter Balls

ball (Model 904 only) in transfer plate. Install regulator valve screen in separator plate. Install 3 screws in separator plate.

2) Place transfer plate assembly on valve body. Install 17 short screws into assembly finger tight (3 long screws are for oil filter), aligning holes for filter screen at same time. Tighten screws starting from center and working outward.

3) Slide switch valve, line pressure valves and springs into respective bores. Install pressure adjusting screw and bracket assembly on springs and temporarily fasten single screw which goes into side of valve body. This screw will be tightened first, after starting top and bottom screws in later step.

4) Install oil filter and tighten screws. Install lock-up valve and spring. Install fail-safe spring and valve into lock-up module. Install lock-up module to transfer and separator plate assembly with 3 screws (install stiffener plate on models with conventional converter).

5) After valve body has been reassembled, check throttle and line pressure adjustments. Make adjustments as required. Do not disturb settings if adjustments were correct prior to valve body disassembly. Install parking lock rod and "E" clip retainer to manual lever.

ACCUMULATOR PISTON & SPRING
Inspection
1) Inspect seal rings for wear or damage and ensure they turn freely in grooves. Do not remove seal rings unless replacement is required.

2) Inspect piston for nicks, burrs, scores or wear. Check piston bore in case for scores or other damage. Check piston spring for distortion. Replace parts as required.

EXTENSION HOUSING, BEARING, BUSHING, & OIL SEAL
See SERVICE (IN VEHICLE).

Fig. 27: Exploded View Of Model 727 Oil Pump & Reaction Shaft Support

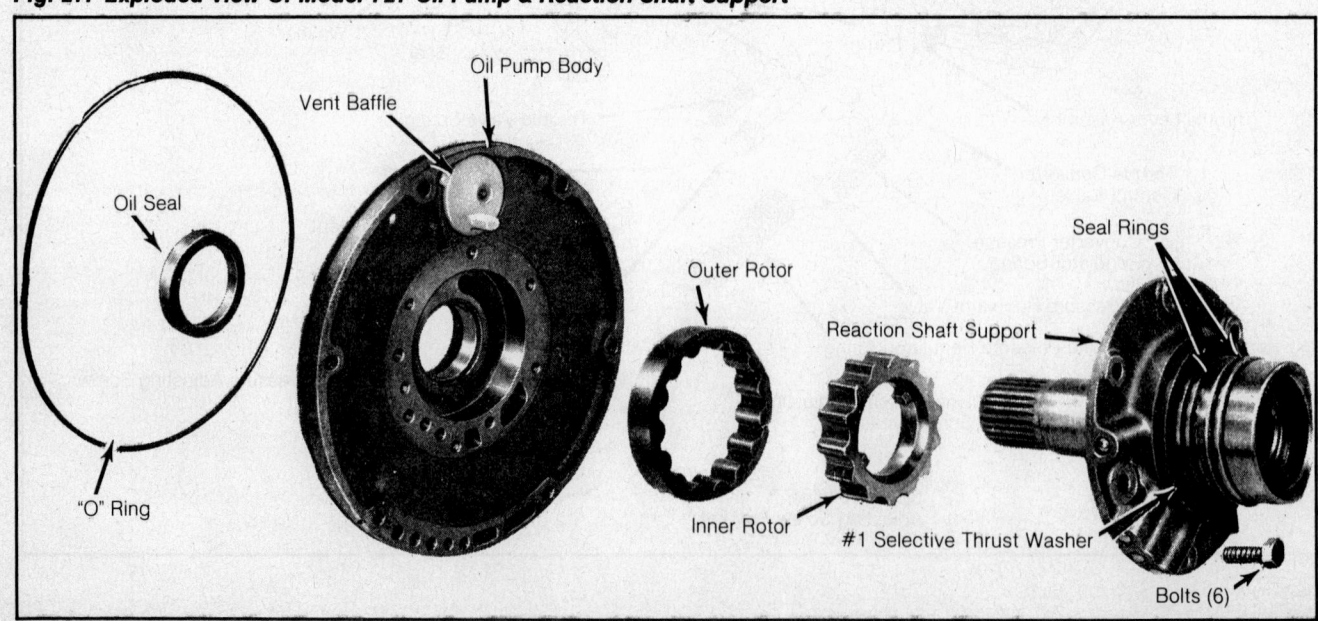

Oil Pump Body

Vent Baffle

Oil Seal

Seal Rings

Outer Rotor

Reaction Shaft Support

"O" Ring

Inner Rotor

#1 Selective Thrust Washer

Bolts (6)

AMERICAN MOTORS, CHRYSLER CORP. & JEEP
727, 904, 998 & 999 (Cont.)

PARKING SPRAG & LEVER
See SERVICE (IN VEHICLE).

GOVERNOR
See SERVICE (IN VEHICLE).

OIL PUMP/REACTION SHAFT SUPPORT
Disassembly
Remove bolts from rear side of reaction shaft support and lift support off pump. Remove rubber seal ring from pump body flange. Drive out oil seal with blunt punch. Mark top of pump rotors with chalk to ensure proper installation during reassembly.

Fig. 28: Exploded View Of Oil Pump & Reaction Shaft Support

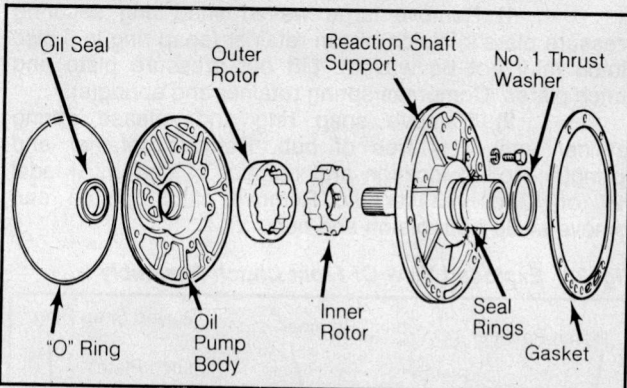

This covers all versions except Model 727.

Inspection
1) Inspect interlocking seal rings on support for wear or damage. Make sure rings turn freely in grooves. Do not remove rings unless replacement is required. Inspect pump body and support bushings for wear or scores.

2) Check machined surfaces of pump body and support for nicks or burrs. Check pump rotors for scoring or pitting. With rotors cleaned and installed in pump body, place straightedge across face of rotors and pump body. Using feeler gauge, measure clearance between straightedge and rotor faces. Clearance should be .001-.0025" (.03-.06 mm).

3) Measure rotor tip clearance between inner and outer rotor teeth. Clearance should be .005-.010" (.13-.25 mm). Clearance between outer rotor and oil pump body bore should be .004-.008" (.10-.20 mm).

NOTE: On all models except 727, remove seal rings so that thrust washer between front clutch retainer and reaction shaft can be removed. If washer thickness is not .061-.063" (1.55-1.60 mm), it should be replaced.

Pump Bushing Replacement
1) Place pump housing (rotor cavity down) on clean smooth surface. Drive bushing straight down and out of bore, being careful not to cock tool in bore.

2) With hub end of pump housing down, drive new bushing into place in pump cavity. Stake bushing in place using blunt punch.

3) Using narrow blade knife, remove high points or burrs around staked area. Do not use file or any tool that would remove more metal than necessary.

Fig. 29: Installing New Oil Pump Bushing

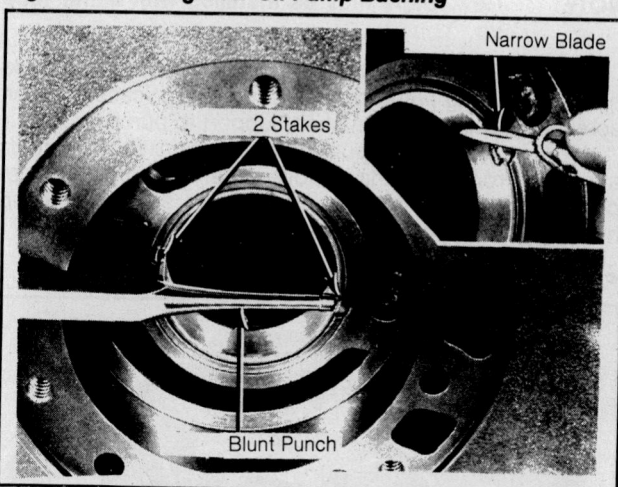

Stake bushing in place with blunt punch.

Reaction Shaft Bushing Replacement
1) Thread bushing remover into bushing. Remove bushing from reaction shaft. Support reaction shaft upright on clean smooth surface.

2) Using bushing installer, drive new bushing (chamfered end up) into place in reaction shaft.

NOTE: Do not clamp any part of reaction shaft or support in vise.

Fig. 30: Replacing Reaction Shaft Bushing

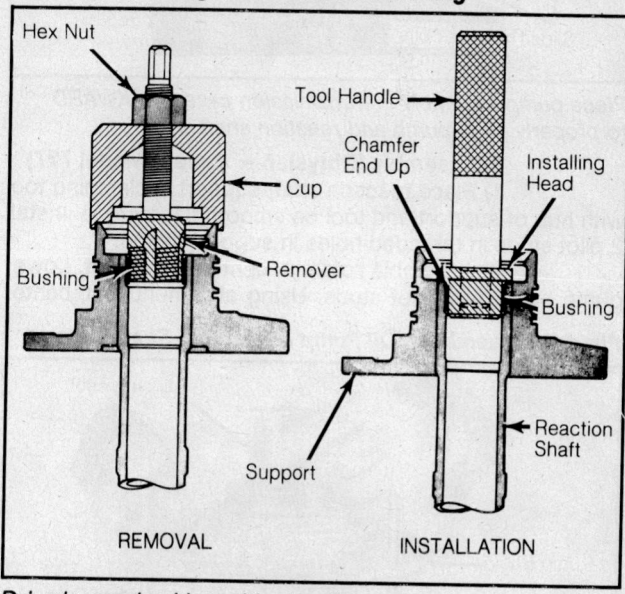

Drive in new bushing with chamfered end up.

Reassembly (AMC/Jeep)
1) Install rotors in pump housing (marks made at disassembly facing up). Align and loosely assemble reaction shaft support to pump housing. Do not tighten bolts at this time.

2) Thread 2 slide hammer bolts (from back-to-front) into threaded reaction shaft support holes, until bolt ends are recessed 1/16" below front machined surface of pump housing. Install 1 pilot stud into case pump opening.

AMERICAN MOTORS, CHRYSLER CORP. & JEEP
727, 904, 998 & 999 (Cont.)

NOTE: New rotors may be installed with either face up.

3) Insert pump assembly backward into case opening, tapping pump as needed to seat in case. Tighten screws attaching reaction shaft support to pump housing.

4) Remove pump and reaction shaft support assembly from case and remove slide hammer bolts from pump. Using seal installer, drive new seal into pump housing (seal lip facing inward).

Fig. 31: Aligning AMC Oil Pump

Place pump assembly in transmission case BACKWARD to properly align pump and reaction shaft.

Reassembly (Chrysler – Except Model 727)
1) Place reaction shaft support in clamping tool with hub of support and tool on smooth flat surface. Install 2 pilot studs in threaded holes in support flange.

2) Assemble rotors in center of support. Lower pump body over pilot studs. Using alignment tool, center

Fig. 32: Assembling Oil Pump & Reaction Shaft Support

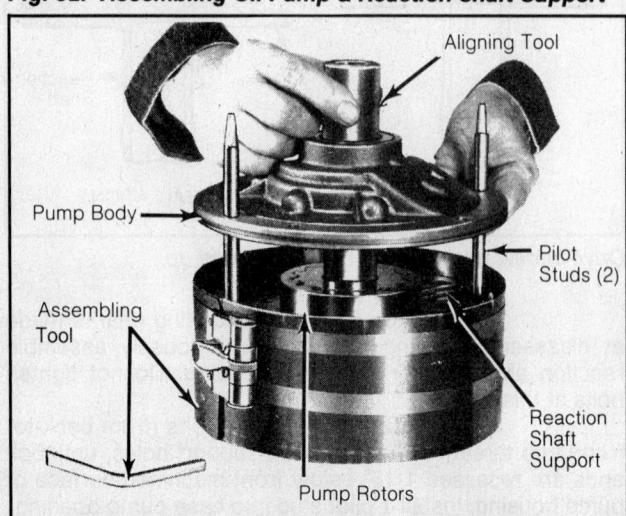

All Chrysler Corp. models except 727.

rotors in pump body. With pump body firmly against reaction shaft support, tighten clamping tool securely. *See Fig. 32.*

3) Invert pump and tool assembly. Install and evenly tighten bolts holding support to pump bolts. Remove clamping tool, pilot studs and aligning tool. Drive new pump oil seal into housing with lip of seal facing in.

Reassembly (Chrysler – 727)
Install pump rotors and "O" ring in pump housing. Install reaction shaft support and retaining bolts. Place new seal in opening of pump housing with lip of seal facing inward and press into place with driver.

FRONT CLUTCH
Disassembly
1) Remove large waved snap ring securing pressure plate in clutch piston retainer (snap ring in 5 disc clutch may not be waved). Lift out pressure plate and clutch plates. Compress spring retainer and spring(s).

2) Remove snap ring and release spring retainer until it is free of hub. Remove retainer and spring(s), noting location and number of springs (Model 727 only) for reassembly. Remove clutch piston and remove seals from piston and hub.

Fig. 33: Exploded View Of Front Clutch Assembly

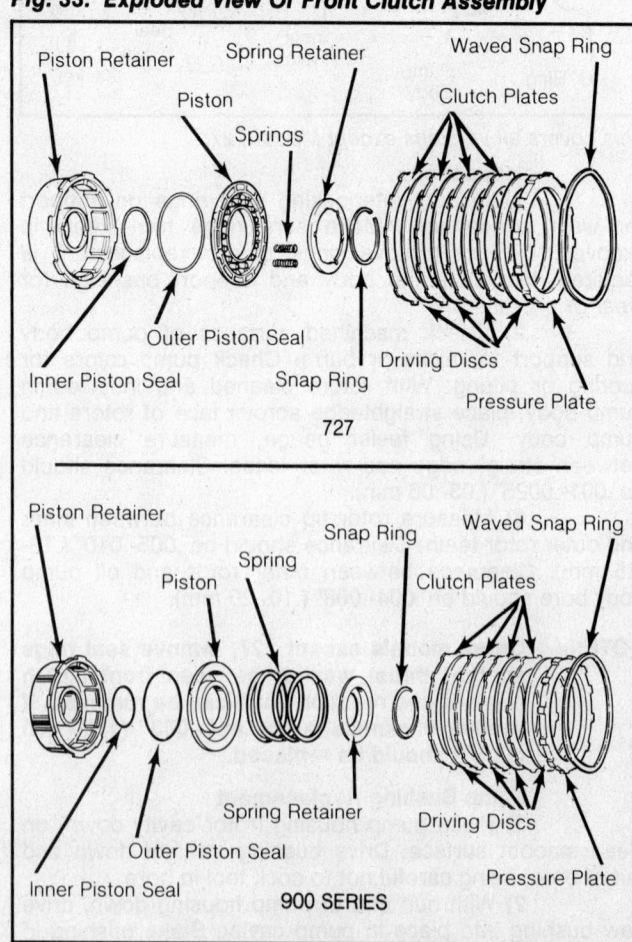

AMERICAN MOTORS, CHRYSLER CORP. & JEEP
727, 904, 998 & 999 (Cont.)

Inspection

1) Inspect plates and discs for flatness. They must not be warped or cone-shaped. Inspect facing material on all driving discs. Replace discs as needed.

2) Inspect discs and plates for wear on splines or lugs. Check clutch retainer for damaged lug grooves or band contacting surface. Make sure check ball in clutch retainer moves freely.

3) Check neoprene seals for wear, hardness or deterioration. Inspect piston spring(s), retainer and snap ring for distortion.

Front Clutch Retainer Bushing Replacement

1) Lay clutch retainer (open end down) on clean smooth surface. Drive bushing straight down and out of bore, taking care not to cock tool in bore.

2) To install, lay clutch retainer (open end up) on clean smooth surface. Drive bushing into place in clutch retainer bore with bushing installer.

Reassembly

1) Lubricate and install inner seal on hub of clutch retainer. Make sure lip of seal faces down and is properly seated in groove. Install outer seal on clutch piston with lip of seal toward bottom of clutch retainer.

2) Lubricate seals to ease installation. Install and carefully seat piston in bottom of retainer. Install return spring on piston hub. On Model 727, install same number of springs as were removed. See *Fig. 34* for spring location.

3) Position spring retainer and snap ring over hub. Compress and install snap ring in hub groove. Remove compressor tool. Lubricate all clutch plates. Install 1 steel plate followed by 1 faced disc until all clutch plates are installed. See FRONT CLUTCH PLATE USAGE chart.

4) Install pressure plate and snap ring. Make sure snap ring is properly seated. With front clutch completely assembled, measure maximum clearance where snap ring is waved away from pressure plate. Refer to FRONT CLUTCH PLATE CLEARANCES chart for specified clearance.

Fig. 35: *Measuring Front Clutch Plate Clearance*

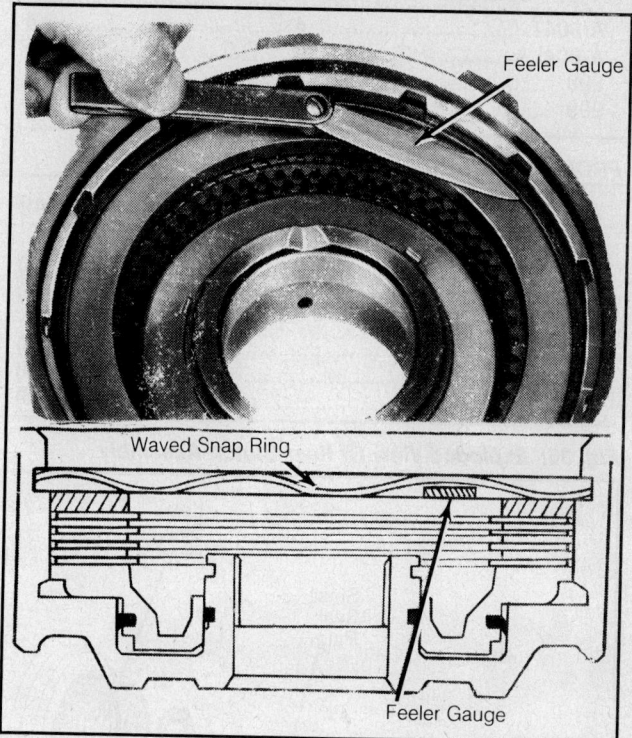

Use feeler gauge to measure gap.

Fig. 34: *Model 727 Front Clutch Spring Installation*

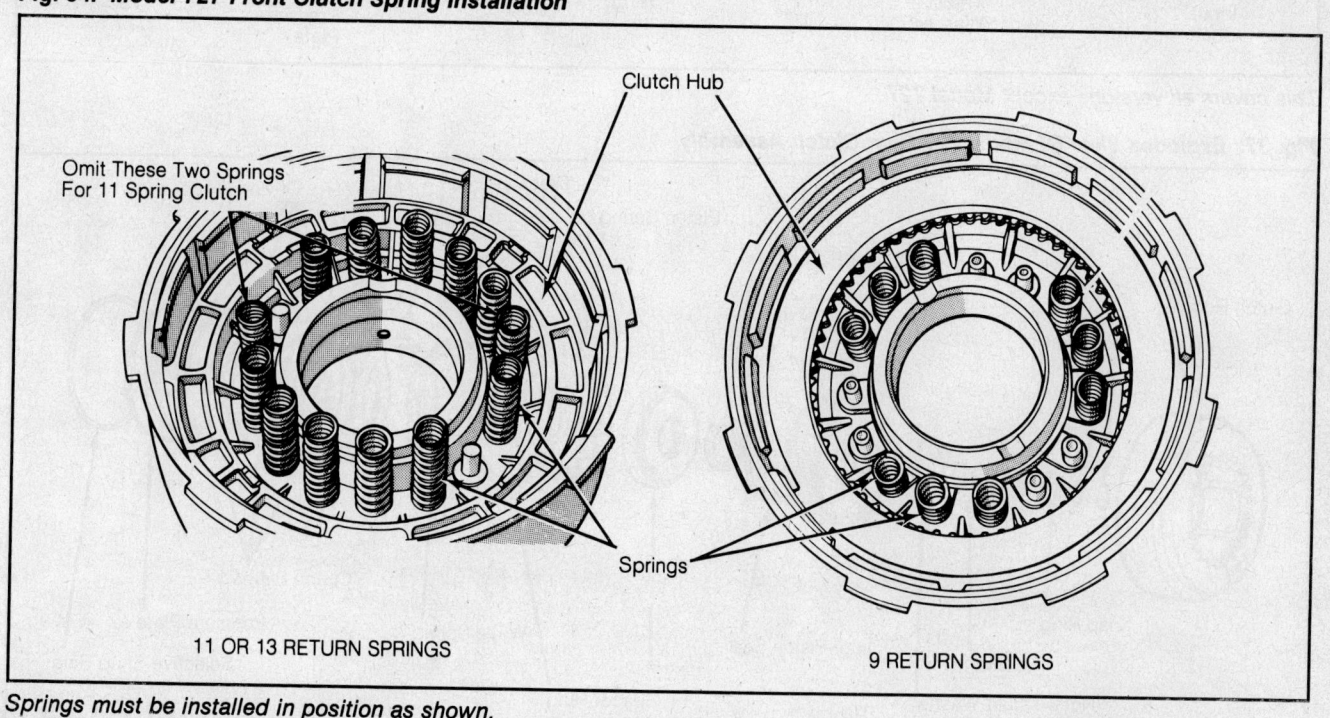

Springs must be installed in position as shown.

Automatic Transmissions

AMERICAN MOTORS, CHRYSLER CORP. & JEEP
727, 904, 998 & 999 (Cont.)

FRONT CLUTCH PLATE USAGE

Application	Steel Plates	Composition Plates
727	4	4
A-904T	4	4
A-904LA	5	5
998	4	4
999	5	5

FRONT CLUTCH PLATE CLEARANCES

Application	Specification In. (mm)
Model 727	
AMC/Jeep	.070-.129 (1.78-3.28)
Chrysler Corp.	.082-.151 (2.08-3.84)
All Other Models	
3 Disc	.074-.125 (1.88-3.18)
4 Disc	.067-.134 (1.70-3.40)
5 Disc	.075-.152 (1.91-3.86)

REAR CLUTCH

Disassembly

1) Remove large selective snap ring securing pressure plate in clutch retainer. Lift pressure plate, clutch plates and inner pressure plate out of retainer. Pry one end of wave spring out of groove in clutch retainer. Remove wave spring, spacer ring (Model 727) and clutch piston spring.

2) Invert clutch piston retainer assembly and bump on wood block to remove piston. Remove seals from piston. If necessary, remove snap ring and press input shaft from clutch piston retainer.

Inspection

1) Inspect plates and discs for flatness. Replace any that are warped or cone-shaped. Inspect facing material on all drive discs; replace if damaged. Inspect disc and plates for wear on splines or lugs and check lug grooves in clutch retainer for damage.

Fig. 36: Exploded View Of Rear Clutch Assembly

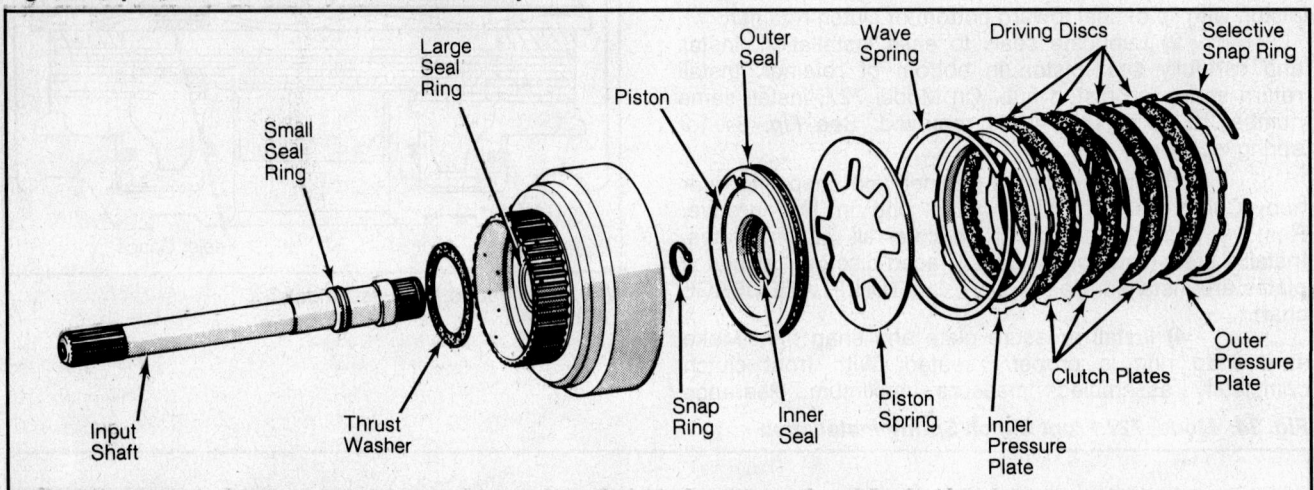

This covers all versions except Model 727

Fig. 37: Exploded View Of Model 727 Rear Clutch Assembly

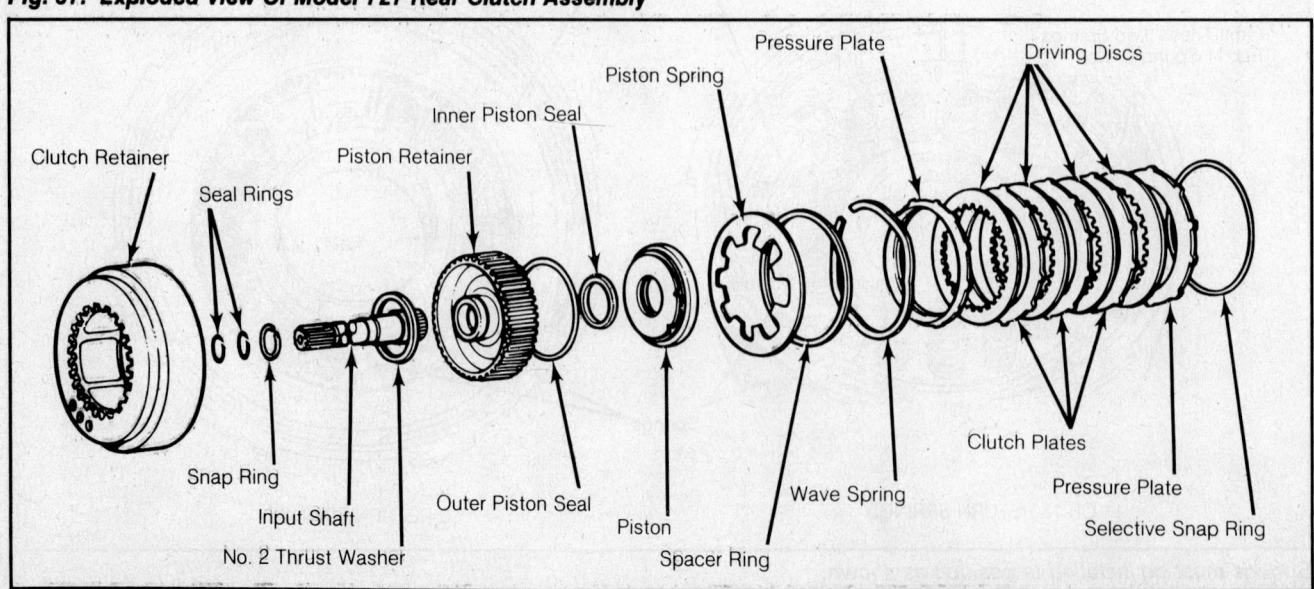

AMERICAN MOTORS, CHRYSLER CORP. & JEEP
727, 904, 998 & 999 (Cont.)

2) Make sure check ball in piston moves freely. Check seal ring surfaces in clutch retainer for nicks and scratches. Check neoprene seals for wear, hardness or deterioration.

3) Inspect interlocking seal rings on input shaft for wear or broken locks. Make sure rings turn freely in grooves. Do not remove rings unless replacement is required.

4) Check bushing in input shaft for wear or scores. Measure thrust washer between rear clutch and front clutch for wear. If washer is not .061-.063" (1.55-1.60 mm) thick, it should be replaced.

Input Shaft Bushing Replacement (727)

1) Clamp input shaft in soft-jawed vise, taking care not to clamp seal ring lands or journals. Thread bushing remover into bushing and withdraw bushing from shaft.

2) Thoroughly clean input shaft to remove any metal chips made by tool. Drive new bushing into place.

Fig. 38: Replacing Input Shaft Bushing

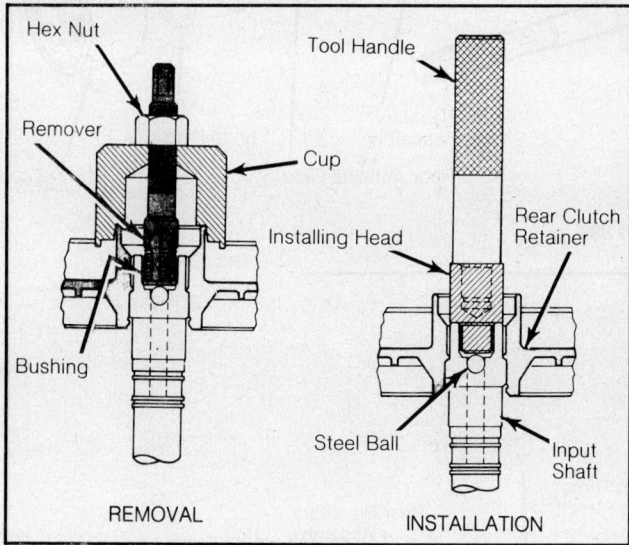

Clean input shaft to remove any metal chips made by tool.

Reassembly

1) If removed, press input shaft into clutch piston retainer and install snap ring. Lubricate and install inner and outer seal rings on clutch piston. Make sure lips of seals face toward head of clutch retainer and are properly seated in grooves.

2) Place piston assembly in retainer. Seat piston in bottom of retainer with twisting motion. On Model 727, position clutch retainer over piston retainer splines and support assembly so clutch retainer remains in place.

3) On all models, place piston spring and spacer ring (Model 727) on top of piston. Make sure they are positioned in retainer recess. Start one end of wave spring in retainer groove. Progressively push or tap spring into place. Make sure spring is fully seated in groove.

4) Install inner pressure plate in retainer with raised portion of plate against spring. Lubricate all clutch plates with ATF. Install 1 faced disc followed by 1 steel plate until all clutch plates are installed. See REAR CLUTCH PLATE USAGE chart. Install outer pressure plate and selective snap ring.

REAR CLUTCH PLATE USAGE

Application	Steel Plates	Composition Plates
All Models	3	4

5) Compress clutch pack by pressing down firmly on outer pressure plate. Maintain steady pressure with "C" clamp or press. Measure rear clutch plate clearance by inserting feeler gauge between plate and snap ring. See REAR CLUTCH PLATE CLEARANCES table for correct clearance range. If possible, lower limit is preferred setting.

REAR CLUTCH PLATE CLEARANCES

Application	[1] Clearance In. (mm)
727	.025-.045 (.64-1.14)
All Others	.032-.055 (.81-1.40)

[1] – Lower limit of range is preferred.

6) If clearance is incorrect, adjust it by installing different size snap ring. Selective snap rings are available in thicknesses of .060", .074", .088" and .106" (1.52, 1.88, 2.24, 2.69 mm) for Model 727, .060", .068" and .076" (1.52, 1.73, 1.93 mm) for all other Chrysler models and .060", .074 and .098" (1.52, 1.88, 2.49 mm) for all other AMC/Jeep models.

PLANETARY GEAR TRAIN

End Play Check

1) Measure end play of planetary gear assemblies, sun gear and driving shell before removing from output shaft. Stand assembly upright with forward end of output shaft supported on wood block so all parts will move forward against snap ring at front of shaft.

2) Insert feeler gauge between rear annulus gear support hub and shoulder on output shaft. Clearance should be .009-.044" (.23-1.12 mm) for Model 727, and .001-.047" (.025-1.20 mm) for all other models. If not, replace thrust washer and/or necessary parts.

Fig. 39: Checking Planetary Gear Train End Play

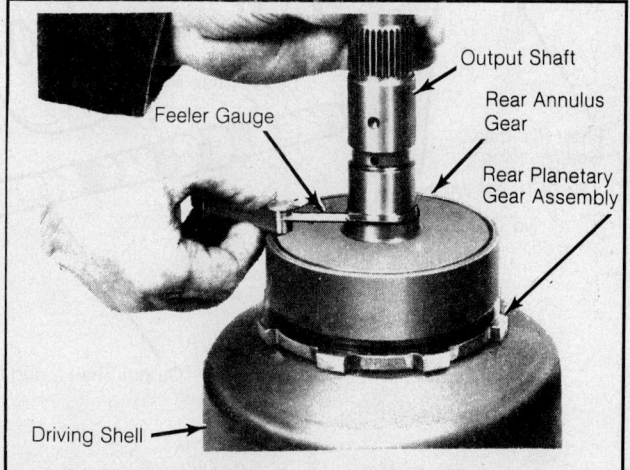

Measure end play of planetary gear before disassembly.

Automatic Transmissions

AMERICAN MOTORS, CHRYSLER CORP. & JEEP
727, 904, 998 & 999 (Cont.)

Fig. 40: Exploded View Of Planetary Gear Train & Output Shaft

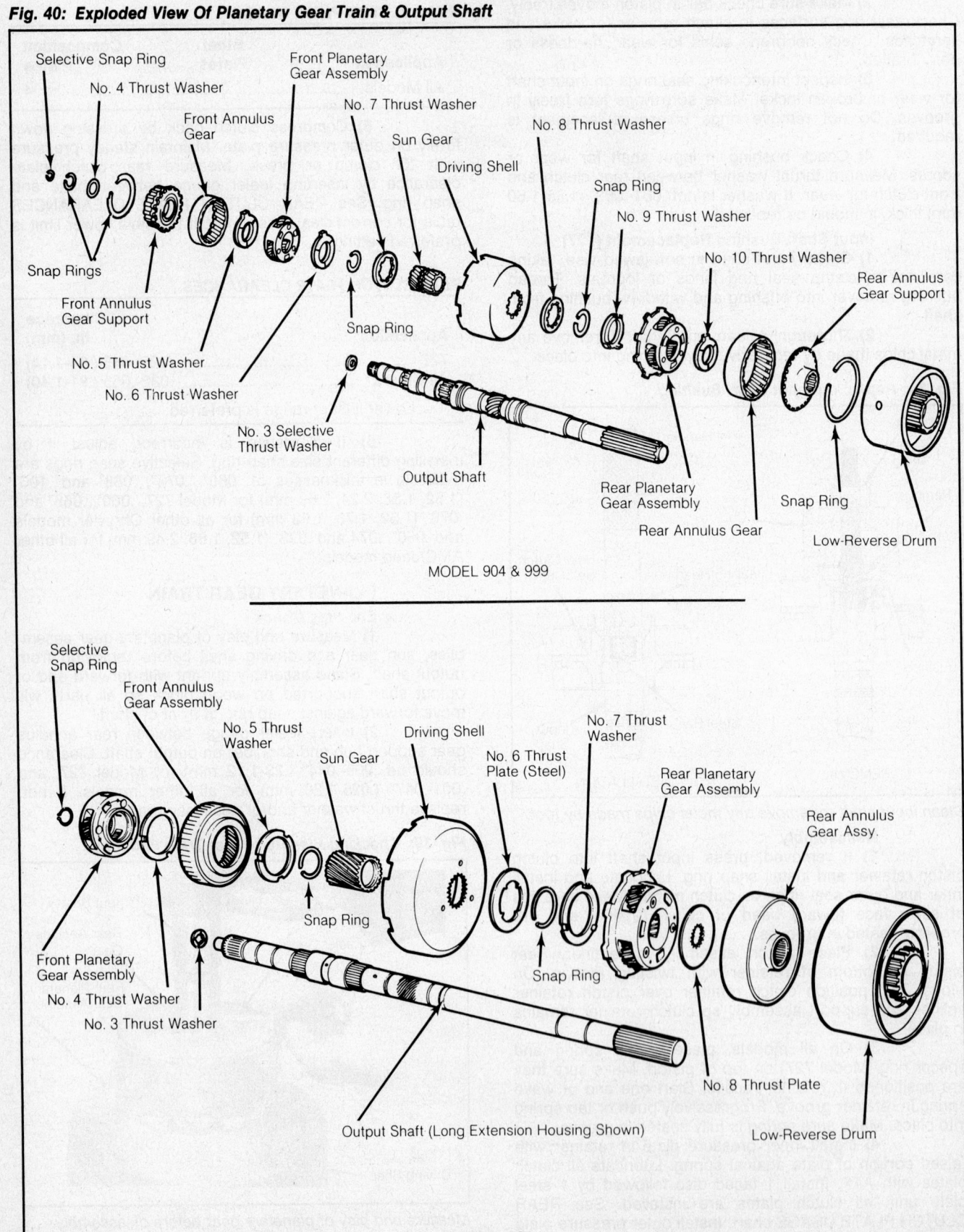

MODEL 904 & 999

MODEL 727

AMERICAN MOTORS, CHRYSLER CORP. & JEEP
727, 904, 998 & 999 (Cont.)

Disassembly (Model 727)

1) Remove thrust washer and selective snap ring from forward end of output shaft. Slide front planetary assembly off shaft. Slide front annulus gear off planetary gear set. Remove thrust washer from rear side of gear set.

2) Slide sun gear, driving shell and rear planetary assembly off output shaft. Lift sun gear and driving shell off rear planetary assembly. Remove thrust washer from inside driving shell.

3) Remove snap ring and steel washer from sun gear (rear side of driving shell) and slide gear out of shell, removing front snap ring from sun gear if necessary. Note that front end of sun gear is longer than rear.

4) Remove thrust washer from forward side of rear planetary assembly. Remove planetary gear set and thrust plate from annulus gear.

Disassembly (All Other Models)

1) Remove thrust washer and selective snap ring from forward end of output shaft. Slide front planetary assembly off of shaft. Remove snap ring and thrust washer from forward hub of front planetary gear assembly. Slide front annulus gear and support off planetary gear set.

2) Remove thrust washer from front side of planetary gear set, then remove thrust washer from rear side of planetary gear assembly. Separate support from annulus gear, removing snap ring from front of annulus gear if necessary. Slide sun gear, driving shell and rear planetary assembly off output shaft.

3) Lift sun gear and driving shell off rear planetary assembly. Remove snap ring and thrust plate from sun gear at rear side of driving shell. Slide sun gear out of shell.

4) Remove snap ring (or spacer on wide ratio model) and thrust plate from opposite end of sun gear. Remove thrust washer from forward side of rear planetary assembly and remove planetary gear set from assembly. Remove thrust washer from rear of gear set. If necessary, remove snap ring from rear of annulus gear to separate support from gear.

Inspection

1) Inspect all parts for nicks, burrs, scores or other damage. Light scratches, small nicks or burrs may be removed with crocus cloth or fine stone. Inspect bushings in sun gear for wear or scores. Replace assembly if bushings are damaged.

2) Inspect all thrust washers for wear and scores. Replace if damaged or worn below specifications. Make sure oil passages in shaft are open and clean. Replace distorted lock rings.

Reassembly (Model 727)

1) Install rear annulus gear on output shaft. Lightly grease thrust plate and place it on shaft, in annulus gear. Make sure teeth are over shaft splines. Position rear planetary gear assembly in rear annulus gear and install thrust washer on front side of gear assembly.

2) Install snap ring in front groove of sun gear (long end of gear). Insert sun gear through front side of driving shell. Install rear steel washer and snap ring. Slide driving shell and sun gear assembly on output shaft. Engage sun gear teeth with rear planetary pinion teeth.

3) Place thrust washer inside front of driving shell. Place thrust washer on rear hub of planetary gear set. Slide assembly into front annulus gear. Work front planetary and annulus gear assembly onto output shaft. Mesh planetary pinions with sun gear teeth.

4) With all components installed, place selective snap ring on front end of output shaft. Measure end play of assembly. Replace snap ring to obtain correct end play as needed. Snap rings are available in thicknesses of .048", .055" and .062" (1.22, 1.40, 1.57 mm).

Reassembly (All Other Models)

1) Install rear annulus gear support in annulus gear and install snap ring. Install thrust washer on rear side of rear planetary gear assembly and install in annulus gear. Install thrust washer on front of rear planetary gear assembly.

2) Insert output shaft in rear opening of rear annulus gear. Carefully work shaft through annulus gear support and planetary gear assembly, making sure shaft splines are fully engaged in splines of annulus gear support.

3) Install thrust plate and snap ring (or spacer on wide-ratio models) on end of sun gear. Insert sun gear through front side of driving shell. Install thrust plate and snap ring on opposite end.

4) Carefully slide driving shell and sun gear assembly onto output shaft, engaging sun gear teeth with rear planetary pinion teeth. Place front annulus gear support in annulus gear and install snap ring.

5) Place thrust washer on front of front planetary gear assembly and position assembly in front annulus gear. Place thrust washer over planetary gear assembly hub and install snap ring.

6) Position thrust washer on rear of planetary gear assembly. Carefully work front planetary and annulus gear assembly onto output shaft, meshing planetary pinions with sun gear teeth.

7) With all components properly positioned, install selective snap ring on front end of output shaft. Remeasure end play of assembly. Clearance may be adjusted with various thicknesses of selective snap rings. Snap rings are available in thicknesses of .042, .064 and .084" (1.02, 1.63, 2.13 mm).

OVERRUNNING CLUTCH

Inspection

Check clutch rollers for smooth round edges. Inspect roller contacting surfaces in cam and race for wear. Check roller springs for distortion, wear or other damage. Inspect cam set screw for tightness (Model 727). Tighten and restake case around screw if loose.

Overrunning Clutch Cam
Replacement (Model 727)

1) Remove set screw from case (below clutch cam) and remove bolts securing output shaft support to rear of case. Insert punch through bolt holes and drive cam from case. Alternate punch from one hole to another so cam will be driven evenly from case.

2) If support requires replacement, tap support rearward with soft-faced hammer. To install, screw 2 pilot studs into case and position support over studs. Tap firmly into place using soft-faced hammer.

CAUTION: Output shaft support must be in case to install overrunning clutch cam.

Automatic Transmissions

AMERICAN MOTORS, CHRYSLER CORP. & JEEP
727, 904, 998 & 999 (Cont.)

3) Clean all burrs and chips from case. Place spring retainer on cam and make sure retainer lugs snap firmly into notches on cam. Position cam in case, aligning cam serrations with case grooves.

4) Tap cam evenly into case as far as possible with soft mallet. Using Cam Aligner and Adapter (C-3863-A and SP-5124) tighten nut on aligner to seat cam in case.

5) Make sure cam is firmly bottomed in case. Install cam retaining set screw. Stake case around set screw to prevent it from coming loose. Remove aligner and pilot studs. Install and tighten support retaining bolts. Stake case around cam in 12 places with blunt chisel.

Fig. 41: Installing Model 727 Overrunning Clutch Cam

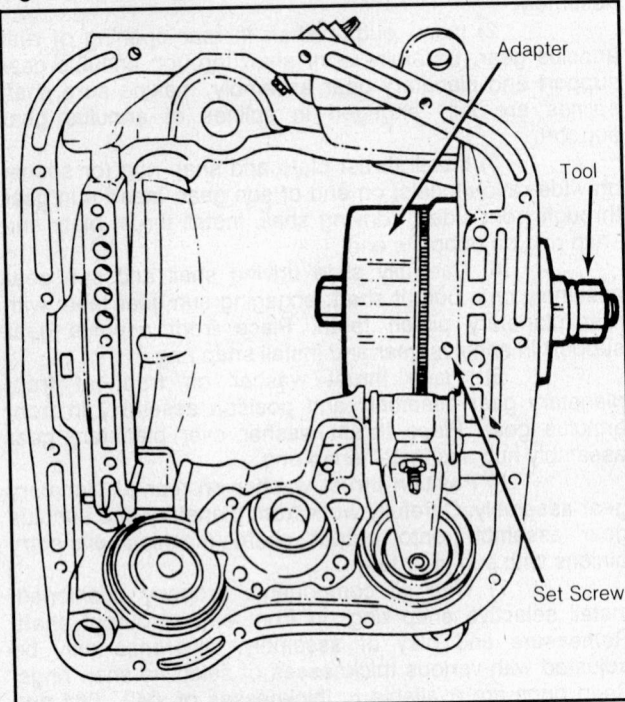

Tighten nut on tool to seat cam in case.

Overrunning Clutch Cam
Replacement (All Except Model 727)

1) Replacement parts are retained in case with bolts instead of rivets. To install, remove 4 bolts securing output shaft support to rear of transmission case. Tap support rearward out of case with soft-faced hammer.

2) Center punch rivets in center of each rivet head. Drill out rivet with 3/8" drill, being careful not to drill into transmission case. Remove rivet heads with small chisel.

3) Drive rivets and cam from case with blunt punch. Carefully enlarge rivet holes in case with 17/64" drill. Remove any metal chips, burrs and/or foreign material from case.

NOTE: Alternate punch from one hole to another so cam will be driven evenly from case.

4) Install replacement cam and spring retainer into case with bolt holes in cam and retainer aligned with holes in case. Thread retaining screws and washers into cam and install cam in case using soft-faced hammer.

5) Alternately and evenly tighten retaining screws to 100 INCH lbs. (11 N.m). Thread 2 pilot studs

into case. Position support over studs. Tap support firmly into place using soft-faced hammer. Remove pilot studs and install and tighten retaining bolts.

KICKDOWN SERVO & BAND (FRONT)
Disassembly

Disassemble controlled load servo piston by removing small snap ring from servo piston. Remove washer, spring and piston rod from servo piston.

Fig. 42: Exploded View Of Kickdown Servo

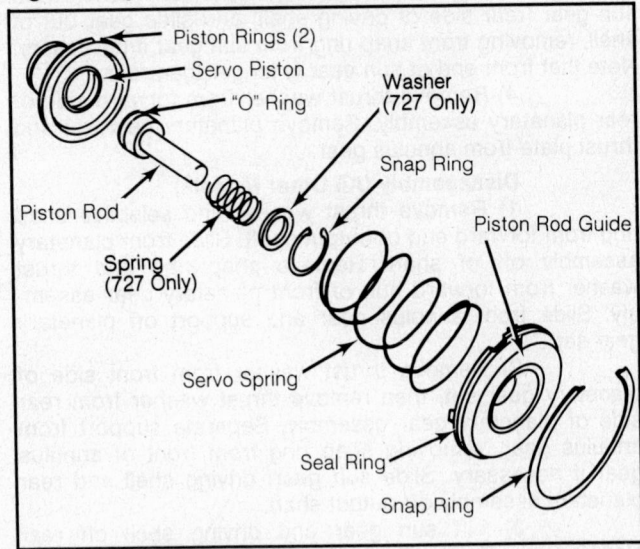

This is controlled load type.

Inspection

1) Inspect all parts for wear or damage. Be sure piston and guide seal rings turn freely in grooves. Do not remove seal rings unless replacement is required. Inspect piston bore in case for scoring or other damage. Inspect fit of guide on piston rod. Check position spring for distortion.

Fig. 43: Exploded View Of Kickdown Servo

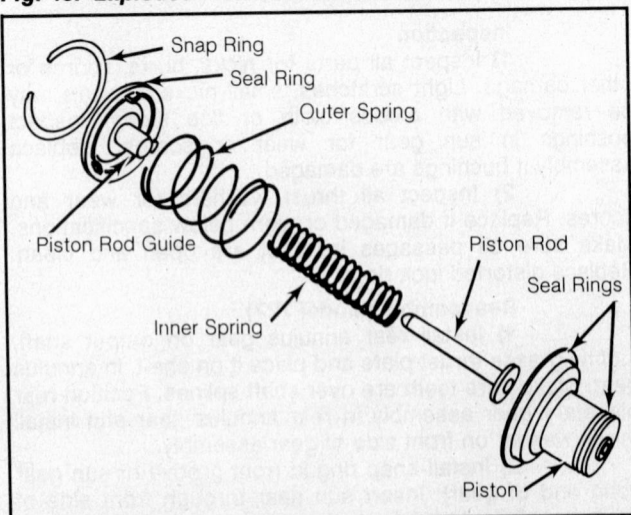

This is non-controlled load type.

2) If equipped with controlled load servo piston, inspect bore in piston and "O" ring on piston rod. Inspect band lining for wear or damage; if lining is worn so

AMERICAN MOTORS, CHRYSLER CORP. & JEEP
727, 904, 998 & 999 (Cont.)

grooves are not visible at ends, or at any portion of band, replace band.

Reassembly

Assemble controlled load servo piston as follows: Grease "O" ring and install on piston rod. Install piston rod into servo piston. Install spring, flat washer and snap ring.

LOW-REVERSE SERVO & BAND (REAR)
Disassembly

Remove snap ring from piston and remove piston plug and spring.

Fig. 44: Exploded View Of Low-Reverse Servo

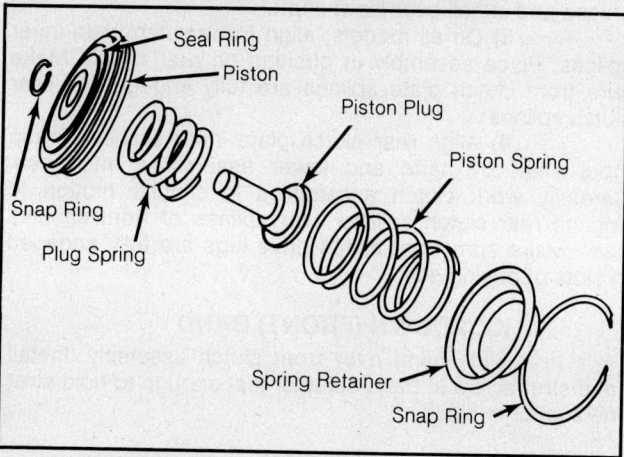

Inspection

1) Inspect seal for wear, deterioration and hardness. Inspect piston and plug for cracks, burrs, scores and wear. Piston plug must operate freely in piston. Inspect piston bore for scores or damage.

2) Check springs for distortion. Inspect band lining for wear and bond of lining to band. If lining is worn so grooves are not visible at end or any portion of band, replace band.

Reassembly

Lubricate and insert piston plug and spring in piston. Secure with snap ring.

TRANSMISSION REASSEMBLY

NOTE: Use only Dexron ATF to lubricate transmission parts during reassembly.

OVERRUNNING CLUTCH

With transmission case in upright position, insert clutch hub inside cam. Install overrunning clutch rollers and springs. See Fig. 45.

LOW-REVERSE SERVO & BAND (REAR)

1) Carefully work servo piston into case with twisting motion. Place spring, retainer and snap ring over piston. Compress low-reverse servo piston and install snap ring.

2) On models with double-wrap band, install replacement "O" ring on reaction pin. Insert pin into case until flush with gasket surface. Position band in case so both lugs rest against reaction pin. Install low-reverse drum into rear band. Install operating lever and pivot pin.

3) On all other models, position rear band in case and install short strut. Connect long link and anchor to band. Screw in band adjuster enough to hold strut in place. Install low-reverse drum.

Fig. 45: Installed View Of Overrunning Clutch

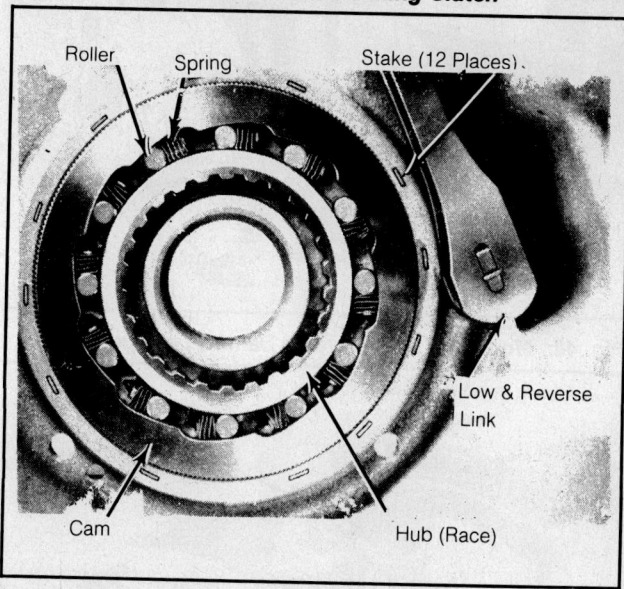

Install parts as shown.

Fig. 46: Double-Wrap Low-Reverse Band & Linkage

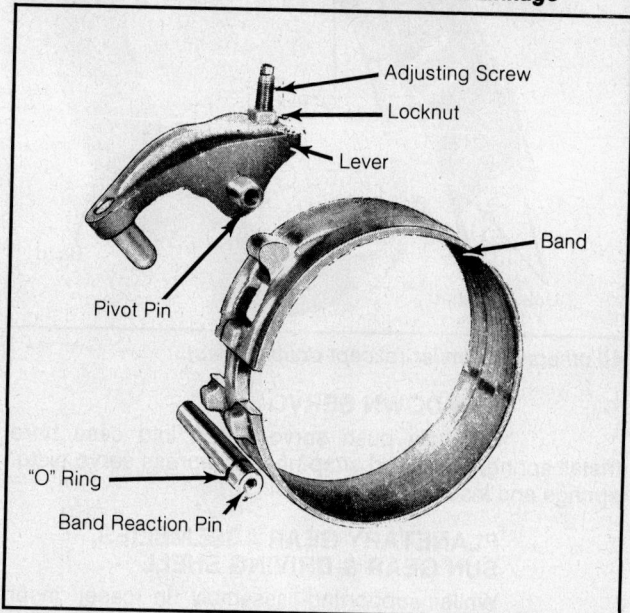

Automatic Transmissions

AMERICAN MOTORS, CHRYSLER CORP. & JEEP
727, 904, 998 & 999 (Cont.)

Fig. 47: Double-Wrap Band Linkage Installation

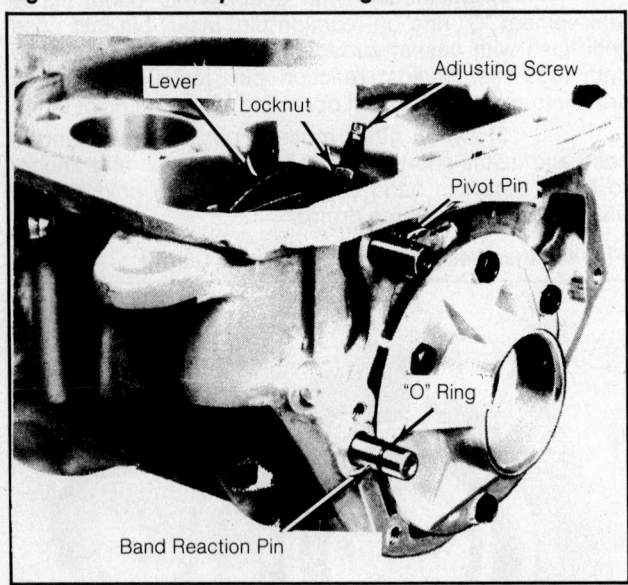

Lever
Locknut
Adjusting Screw
Pivot Pin
"O" Ring
Band Reaction Pin

Fig. 48: Model 727 Low-Reverse Band & Linkage

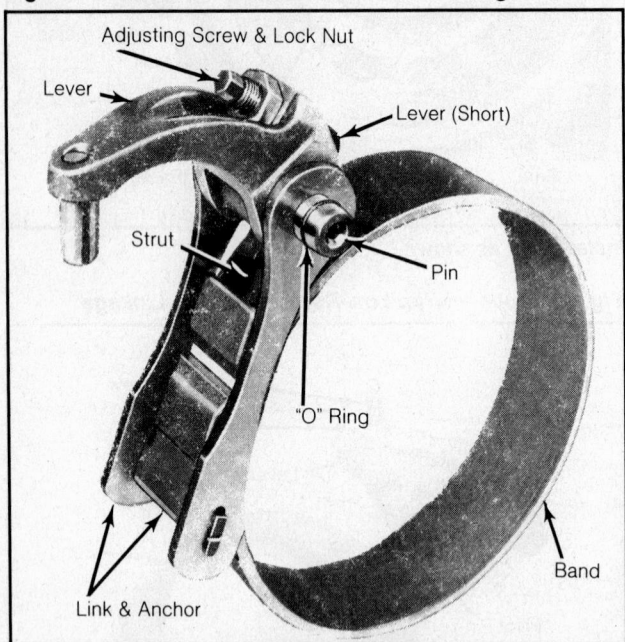

Adjusting Screw & Lock Nut
Lever
Lever (Short)
Strut
Pin
"O" Ring
Link & Anchor
Band

All others are similar (except double-wrap).

KICKDOWN SERVO
Carefully push servo piston into case bore. Install spring, guide and snap ring. Compress servo piston springs and install snap ring.

PLANETARY GEAR ASSEMBLIES, SUN GEAR & DRIVING SHELL
While supporting assembly in case, insert output shaft through rear support. Carefully work assembly rearward, engaging rear planetary carrier lugs into low-reverse drum slots.

CAUTION: Do not damage machined surfaces on output shaft during installation.

FRONT & REAR CLUTCH ASSEMBLIES

NOTE: **Front and rear clutches, front band, oil pump and reaction shaft support are easier to install with transmission in upright position.**

1) Apply thin coat of grease on thrust washer that goes between input shaft and output shaft. Install washer on front end of output shaft. If end play was incorrect when checked during disassembly (all except Model 727), replace washer with one of correct thickness. See THRUST WASHER chart.

2) On Model 727, apply thin coating of grease to thrust washer and install in rear clutch piston retainer. On all other models, coat input shaft thrust washer with grease and install over input shaft.

3) On all models, align front clutch plate inner splines. Place assembly in position on rear clutch. Make sure front clutch plate splines are fully engaged on rear clutch splines.

4) Align rear clutch plate inner splines. Grasp input shaft by hand and lower assemblies into case. Carefully work clutch assemblies in circular motion to engage rear clutch splines over splines of front annulus gear. Make sure front clutch drive lugs are fully engaged in slots of driving shell.

KICKDOWN (FRONT) BAND
Slide band over front clutch assembly. Install band strut screw in band adjuster just enough to hold strut and anchor in place.

Fig. 49: Kickdown Band & Linkage

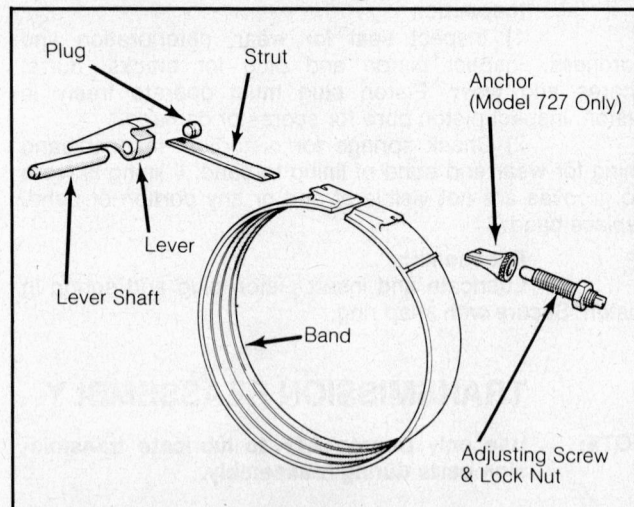

Plug
Strut
Anchor (Model 727 Only)
Lever
Lever Shaft
Band
Adjusting Screw & Lock Nut

Anchor is used on Model 727 only.

OIL PUMP & REACTION SHAFT SUPPORT

NOTE: **If difficulty was encounterd in removing pump assembly due to an exceptionally tight fit, it may be necessary to expand case in pump area with heat lamp prior to installation.**

1) Install thrust washer on reaction shaft support hub. If input shaft end play was incorrect when checked during disassembly (Model 727), replace thrust

AMERICAN MOTORS, CHRYSLER CORP. & JEEP
727, 904, 998 & 999 (Cont.)

THRUST WASHER CHART

Thrust Washer	A-727		ALL OTHERS	
	Washer No.	Thickness Inches (mm)	Washer No.	Thickness Inches (mm)
Reaction Shaft Support Thrust Washer	1	Selective Natural: .061-.063 (1.55-1.60) Red: .084-.086 (2.13-2.18) Yellow: .102-.104 (2.59-2.64)	1	.061-.063 (1.55-1.60)
Rear Clutch Retainer	2	Natural: .061-.063 (1.55-1.60)	2	.061-.063 (1.55-1.60)
Input Shaft Thrust Plate		....		.024-.026 (.61-.66)
Output Shaft Thrust Washer	3	.062-.064 (1.57-1.63)	3	Selective Tin: .052-.054 (1.32-1.37) Red: .068-.070 (1.73-1.78) Green: .083-.086 (2.11-2.18)
Output Shaft Thrust Plate		.030-.032 (.76-.81)		....
Front Annulus Thrust Washer		....	4	.121-.125 (3.07-3.18)
Front Carrier (To Annulus) Thrust Washer	4	.059-.062 (1.50-1.57)	5	.048-.050 (1.22-1.27)
Drive Shell (To Front Annulus) Thrust Washer	5	.059-.062 (1.50-1.57)		....
Front Carrier (To Drive Shell) Thrust Washer		....	6	.048-.050 (1.22-1.27)
Sun Gear Drive Shell Thrust Plate	6	.034-.036 (.86-.91)	7 8	.050-.052 (1.27-1.32) .050-.052 (1.27-1.32)
Rear Carrier (To Drive Shell) Thrust Washer	7	.059-.062 (1.50-1.57)	9	.048-.050 (1.22-1.27)
Rear Carrier (To Annulus) Thrust Plate	8	.034-.036 (.86-.91)		....
Rear Carrier (To Annulus) Thrust Washer		....	10	.048-.050 (1.22-1.27)

washer with one of proper thickness. Refer to THRUST WASHER chart.

2) Screw 2 pilot studs into pump opening in case. Install new gasket over studs. Place new rubber seal ring in groove on outer flange of pump housing, make sure seal is not twisted.

3) Coat seal ring with grease. Install pump assembly into case, tapping lightly with soft mallet if necessary. Remove pilot studs. Install bolts and snug down evenly.

4) Rotate input and output shafts to see that no binding exists. Tighten pump attaching bolts. Check shafts again for free rotation. Adjust both bands.

GOVERNOR
See SERVICE (IN VEHICLE).

EXTENSION/ADAPTER HOUSING
See SERVICE (IN VEHICLE).

VALVE BODY ASSEMBLY & ACCUMULATOR PISTON
See SERVICE (IN VEHICLE).

Automatic Transmissions

AMERICAN MOTORS, CHRYSLER CORP. & JEEP
727, 904, 998 & 999 (Cont.)

TIGHTENING SPECIFICATIONS

Application	Ft. Lbs. (N.m)
Band Adjusting Screw Lock Nut	30 (41)
Flex Plate-to-Crankshaft Bolt	55 (75)
Flex Plate-to-Torque Converter Bolt	
AMC/Jeep	40 (54)
Chrysler Corp.	23 (31)
Neutral Safety Switch	25 (34)
Output Shaft Housing-to-Insulator Bolt	50 (68)
Output Shaft Housing-to-Transmission Bolt	
Chrysler Corp	32 (43)
AMC/Jeep	24 (33)
Transmission-to-Engine Bolts	
Jeep Turbo Diesel	55 (75)
All Other Models	30 (41)

	INCH Lbs. (N.m)
Cooler Line Fitting	110 (12)
Cooler Line Nut	
AMC/Jeep	175 (20)
Chrysler Corp.	85 (10)
Governor Body-to-Support Bolts	100 (11)
Kickdown Lever Shaft Plug	150 (17)
Oil Pan Bolts	130 (15)
Output Shaft Support Bolt	150 (17)
Overrunning Clutch Cam Set Screw	40 (5)
Pressure Test Port Plug	110 (12)
Pump Hsg.-to-Transmission Case	175 (20)
Reaction Shaft Support-to-Oil Pump Bolt	148 (17)
Valve Body Screws	35 (4)
Valve Body-to-Transmission Case Bolt	100 (11)

Automatic Transmissions

AMC/RENAULT ALLIANCE & ENCORE MB1/3

APPLICATION

All Alliance/Encore 1.4L models with automatic transaxle use the Renault model MB1. When equipped with 1.7L engine, an MB3 transaxle is used.

IDENTIFICATION

Transmission identification number is stamped on metal tag attached to transaxle case under a rear case-to-intermediate case attaching bolt. Models are identified by "TYPE MB1 or MB3" stamped on tag.

Fig. 1: Transaxle Identification Tag

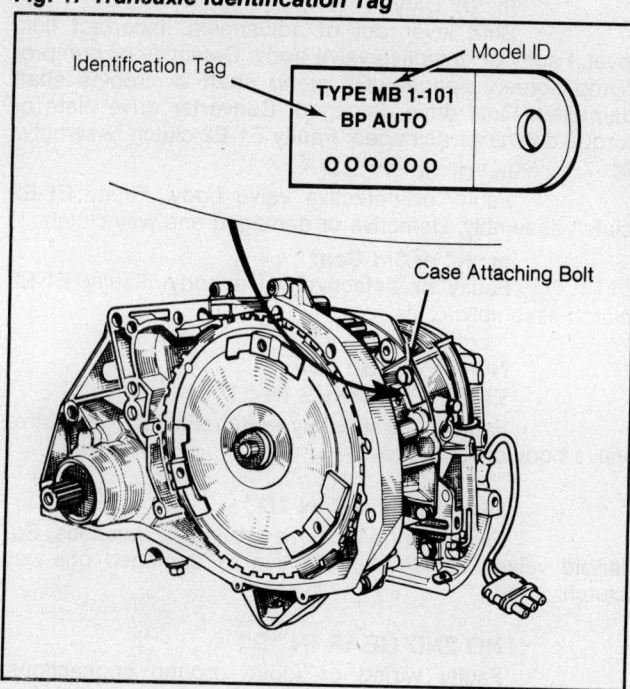

Always replace tag when reassembling transaxle case.

DESCRIPTION

The Renault MB1 and MB3 automatic transaxles are computer controlled, 3-speed unit consisting of the torque converter, differential assembly and transmissions. The differential assembly consists primarily of the differential case and 2 planetary gears. Step down gears are used to change direction of the drive centerline.

The transmission assembly consists of 2 planetary gear sets, a clutch assembly (containing 2 clutches), 2 brakes, a one-way clutch and the transmission control systems. Control systems are of 3 types: mechanical, hydraulic and electrical.

NOTE: Clutch packs on MB3 models are serviced as an assembly and cannot be disassembled and repaired.

ELECTRICAL COMPONENTS
Control Module

The control module is a microprocessor which recieves information from the vehicle speed sensor, throttle position sensor, neutral/safety switch, and kickdown switch. It converts this information into electrical signals which are sent to the solenoid valves to control gear shifts.

Solenoid Valves

Located on the valve body, the solenoid valves directly control pilot valve position in the valve body.

Neutral/Safety Switch

Switch is mounted on the rear of the transaxle and actuated by selector lever position. Depending on lever position, switch controls starting circuit, back-up lights and shift solenoid valves.

Throttle Position & Vehicle Speed Sensors

The throttle position sensor is a potentiometer which provides variable voltage to the control module depending on throttle position. The vehicle speed sensor is fitted opposite the park ring which senses vehicle speed.

LUBRICATION & ADJUSTMENTS

See appropriate AUTOMATIC TRANSMISSION SERVICING article in DOMESTIC GENERAL SERVICING section.

VACUUM MODULATOR VALVE
Adjustment

1) Remove lower plug on side of transaxle case. *See Fig. 3.* Install Pressure Gauge (B.Vi 466-04) at port and position gauge so that it may be seen from inside vehicle.

2) Test drive vehicle at full throttle and note pressure on gauge just before full-throttle 2-3 upshift. Pressure reading should be 75 psi (5.3 kg/cm^2). If fluid pressure is incorrect it may be adjusted by turning the vacuum capsule.

3) To increase fluid pressure, turn capsule clockwise. Counterclockwise rotation of capsule will reduce pressure. Turning capsule 2 notches changes pressure by about 1.5 psi (.11 kg/cm^2).

THROTTLE POSITION SENSOR
Adjustment

1) With engine off, turn ignition switch to "ON" position. With electrical connector attached, insert negative probe of digital volt-ohmmeter through back of connector at terminal "C", until probe contacts terminal. Insert positive lead of meter into terminal "B".

2) Hold throttle at wide open position, ensuring that throttle contacts stop. Note exact voltage reading on meter. Reading should be about 4.3 volts. This is input voltage.

3) Remove positive probe from terminal "B" and insert in terminal "A" of connector. With throttle still held in wide open position, check voltage reading. This is output voltage.

4) Output voltage should be within 3.5-4.5% of input voltage. For example, if input voltage is 5.0 volts, output voltage should be within .03 (.5% of 5) of .20 volts (4% of 5), or .17-.23 volts.

5) If voltage relationship is incorrect, loosen bottom mounting screw and pivot sensor to make coarse adjustment. Tighten screw. Loosen upper mounting screw and pivot sensor to make fine adjustment.

AMC/RENAULT ALLIANCE & ENCORE MB1/3 (Cont.)

**Fig. 2: Throttle Position Sensor
Location and Adjustment**

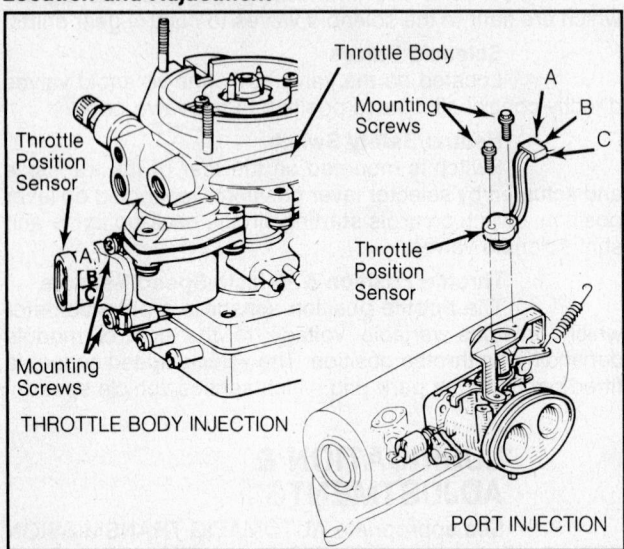

Loosen lower mounting screw to make coarse sensor adjustment, upper screw for fine adjustment.

TROUBLE SHOOTING

After each vehicle condition, several possible causes of that condition are listed. See COMPONENT TESTING when specific components are called out.

ENGINE IDLES ROUGH OR STALLS

Idle speed incorrect. Check ignition timing and spark plug condition. Check throttle cable adjustment. Check vacuum modulator valve and line for leak in vacuum circuit.

VEHICLE CREEPS IN "N"

Shift lever out of adjustment. E1-E2 clutch defective or damaged.

EXCESSIVE CREEPING IN "D"

Idle speed incorrect. Check throttle cable adjustment. Torque converter damaged.

SLIPS WHEN STARTING IN "D" OR "R"

Incorrect fluid level. Vacuum modulator valve adjustment (oil pressure) incorrect. Faulty or defective valve body. Torque converter damaged.

SLIPS WHEN STARTING IN "D", ONLY

Defective E1-E2 clutch. Defective or damaged one-way clutch.

SLIPS DURING SHIFTS

Vacuum modulator valve adjustment (oil pressure) incorrect. Faulty or defective valve body. Oil pump screen clogged. Faulty E1-E2 clutch assembly or F2 brake.

SURGES WHEN MOVING OFF

Idle speed incorrect. Check throttle cable adjustment and fluid level.

SURGES DURING SHIFTS

Vacuum modulator valve adjustment (oil pressure) incorrect. Leak in vacuum circuit. Faulty or defective valve body.

SHIFT SPEEDS INCORRECT

Check throttle cable and throttle position sensor adjustment. Faulty wiring or loose ground connections. Kickdown switch or control computer faulty. Defective vehicle speed sensor.

NO MOVEMENT

In "D" Only

Shift lever out of adjustment. Incorrect fluid level. Faulty or defective valve body. Defective oil pump or pump screen clogged. Oil pump shaft or turbine shaft damaged. Final drive damaged. Converter drive plate or torque converter damaged. Faulty E1-E2 clutch assembly.

In "D" or "1"

Faulty or defective valve body. Faulty E1-E2 clutch assembly. Defective or damaged one-way clutch.

In "R" or 3rd Gear

Faulty or defective valve body. Faulty E1-E2 clutch assembly.

NO REVERSE, OR, ENGINE BRAKES IN "1"

Faulty neutral/safety switch. Faulty or defective valve body or F1 brake.

NO 1ST GEAR IN "D"

Faulty wiring or loose ground connections. Solenoid valves damaged. Defective or damaged one-way clutch.

NO 2ND GEAR IN "D"

Faulty wiring or loose ground connections. Faulty or defective valve body or F2 brake.

NO 3RD GEAR IN "D"

Faulty wiring or loose ground connections. Control computer faulty. Solenoid valves damaged. Faulty neutral/safety switch. Faulty or defective valve body.

NO 1ST GEAR HOLD

Shift lever out of adjustment. Faulty wiring or loose ground connections. Control computer faulty. Faulty neutral/safety switch or valve body.

NO 2ND GEAR HOLD

Shift lever out of adjustment. Faulty wiring or loose ground connections. Control computer faulty. Faulty neutral/safety switch.

REMAINS IN 1ST IN "D"

Faulty wiring or loose ground connections. Control computer faulty. Solenoid valves damaged. Vehicle speed sensor defective. Faulty or defective valve body.

REMAINS IN 3RD GEAR

Check fuses. Check for damaged wiring or loose ground connections. Control computer faulty. Defective oil pump. Faulty or defective valve body.

AMC/RENAULT ALLIANCE & ENCORE MB1/3 (Cont.)

SKIPS SOME GEARS, SHIFT LEVER ABNORMAL

Shift lever or selector control out of adjustment. Faulty manual valve control.

IMPROPER OPERATION IN "P"

Shift lever out of adjustment. Faulty manual valve control.

STARTER NOT WORKING

Shift lever or selector control incorrectly adjusted. Faulty wiring or loose ground connections. Control computer faulty. Faulty neutral/safety switch.

NO BACK-UP LIGHTS

Shift lever or selector control incorrectly adjusted. Faulty wiring or loose ground connections. Control computer faulty. Faulty neutral/safety switch.

TESTING

TESTING EQUIPMENT

Diagnosis of the electrical control system of the MB1 transaxle is possible with a volt-ohmmeter. However, use of Renault test box B. Vi. 958 will both reduce diagnosis time and give more accurate test results. Instructions for use are included with the test box. Procedures given here are for testing with volt-ohmmeter.

CONTROL PRESSURE TEST

1) Bring engine to normal operating temperature. Check fluid level and control linkage (cable) adjustment. Connect a pressure gauge to plug orifice on side of transaxle. There should be enough connecting hose so that gauge may held inside of vehicle. *See Fig. 3.*

2) Drive a few miles to ensure fluid is at operating temperature. Place selector lever in 2nd gear. Press accelerator pedal to floor. Apply brakes and stabilize speed to 50 MPH (80 km/h). Pressure should be 64 psi (4.5 kg/cm^2).

ROAD TEST

1) Before road testing, check fluid level and control linkage (cable) adjustments have been checked and corrected as needed. Also check fluid condition. During test, transaxle should upshift and downshift at approximately the specified speeds. See SHIFT SPEED SPECIFICATIONS chart.

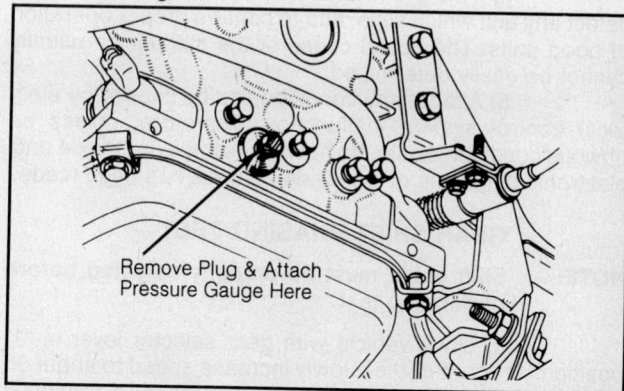

Fig. 3: Testing Control Pressure

Remove Plug & Attach Pressure Gauge Here

2) All shifts may vary somewhat due to production tolerances or tire size. What is important is the quality of the shifts. All shifts should be smooth, responsive, and with no slippage or engine speed runaway.

SHIFT SPEED SPECIFICATIONS

Application	Shift Speed (MPH)
Closed Throttle	
1-2 Upshift	16
2-3 Upshift	28
3-2 Downshift	16
2-1 Downshift	9
Full Throttle [1]	
1-2 Upshift	37
2-3 Upshift	62
3-2 Downshift	40
2-1 Downshift	25
Kickdown [1]	
1-2 Upshift	43
2-3 Upshift	68
3-2 Downshift	59
2-1 Downshift	34

[1] – Full throttle test is with kickdown switch disconnected. Connect switch for kickdown test.

3) Slippage or engine speed runaway in any gear usually indicates clutch or brake problems. The slipping unit in a particular gear can usually be identified by noting transaxle operation in other selector positions and comparing which internal units are applied in those positions. See TRANSAXLE COMPONENT APPLICATION Chart.

TRANSAXLE COMPONENT APPLICATION CHART (ELEMENTS IN USE)

Selector Lever Position	E1 Clutch	E2 Clutch	F1 Brake	F2 Brake	One-Way Clutch	Solenoid Valve 1	Solenoid Valve 2
D — DRIVE							
First	X				X		X
Second	X			X			X
Third	X	X		X		X	X
2 — SECOND HOLD	X			X		X	X
1 — FIRST HOLD	X		X				X
R — REVERSE		X	X				X
NEUTRAL OR PARK							X

AMC/RENAULT ALLIANCE & ENCORE MB1/3 (Cont.)

4) This process of elimination can be used to detect any unit which slips, and to confirm proper operation of good units. The actual cause of the malfuncion usually cannot be easily determined.

5) Almost any condition can be caused by electrical control system malfunction. Therefore, unless an obvious condition exists, do not disassemble transaxle until electronic diagnosis of transaxle controls has been made.

GEAR SHIFT PHASING TEST

NOTE: **Shift cable must be properly adjusted before performing test.**

1) Drive vehicle with gear selector lever in "1" position. At light throttle, slowly increase speed to about 35 MPH. Transaxle should remain in low range. If transaxle shifts to 2nd gear, replace neutral/safety switch.

2) Move selector lever to "2" position and maintain sustained speed of 35 MPH. Transaxle should shift automatically from low range to 2nd gear. If not, neutral/safety switch should be replaced.

3) With gear selector lever still in "2" position, increase vehicle speed to 50 MPH. Transaxle should remain in 2nd gear. If shift to 3rd occurs, replace neutral/safety switch. If all tests are satisfactory, shift operation is correct.

4) In any test, if neutral/safety switch is replaced and problem remains, check control module electrical connections. If connections are good, replace control module.

Fig. 4: 6-Way Connector Terminal Identification

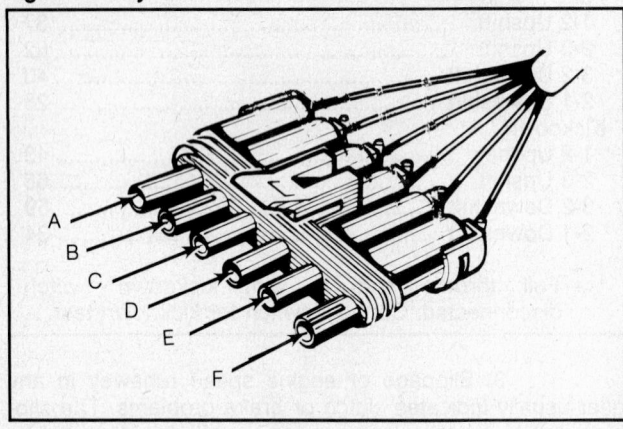

ELECTRONIC CONTROL COMPONENT TESTING

6-Way Connector

1) Turn ignition off. Unplug connector from control module. Using an ohmmeter, check resistance between pin "B" and ground. If resistance is not 1-7 ohms, check back-up light bulbs and wiring circuit. Repair as needed.

2) Connect voltmeter between terminal "A" and ground. With ignition off, voltage should be 10-14 volts. If not, check back-up light fuse and accessory plate wiring. Repair as needed.

3) Turn ignition switch on. Using an ohmmeter, check resistance from terminal "E" to ground. If resistance is not zero, check chassis ground circuit and repair as needed.

4) Connect voltmeter between terminal "F" and ground with ignition switch on. Voltage reading should be 10-14 volts. If not, check power supply circuit to control module. Repair wiring as needed.

5) Connect voltmeter between terminal "C" and ground. Check voltage reading while operating starter. If reading is not 10-14 volts, check starter, starter relay and wiring circuit. Repair or replace as needed.

3-Way Connector

Turn ignition off. Unplug 3-way connector. Turn ignition on and connect voltmeter between terminal "B" (center terminal) and ground. Reading should be 3.8-4.8 volts. If not, perform 6-way connector test. If 6-way connector check reveals no problems, control module is defective and should be replaced.

Solenoid Valves & Harness

1) Turn ignition off. Unplug solenoid valve connector at control module. Using an ohmmeter, check resistance between terminals "A" and "C" of connector. *See Fig. 5.* Reading on ohmmeter should be 20-40 ohms. If resistance is zero, closely inspect wiring harness from connector to solenoid valves and repair or replace as needed. If harness is okay, replace solenoid valves.

Fig. 5: 3-Way Connector Terminal Identification

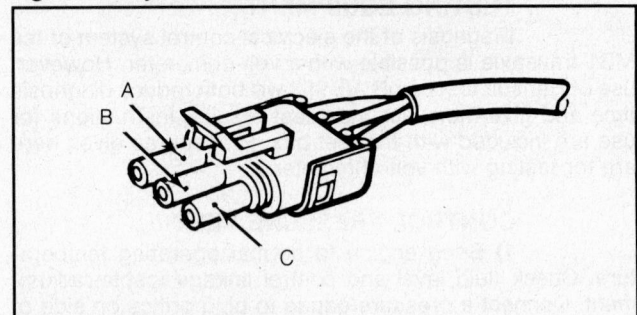

Terminal identification is the same for both 3-way connectors.

2) If resistance value in step 1) is between 40 and 80 ohms, connection is loose or dirty. Inspect and repair.

3) Check resistance between terminals "B" and "C". If resistance value is not 20-40 ohms, inspect wiring and replace if damaged. If wiring harness is OK, replace solenoid valves.

4) Connect ohmmeter between terminal "C" and ground. Resistance value should be infinite. If not, solenoid valves are shorted to ground. Check wiring harness for short and repair or replace as needed. If harness is OK, replace solenoid valves.

Solenoid Valves

1) Disconnect wiring harness connector at solenoid valves. Check resistance value between terminals "A" and "C" of solenoid connector. *See Fig. 6.* Check value between terminals "B" and "C". Resistance value should be 20-40 ohms in both cases.

2) If either reading is zero, replace the solenoid valves. If resistance value obtained is greater than 40 ohms, but less than 80 ohms, check wiring and connections to solenoid valves. Clean or repair as needed.

3) If resistance between either set of terminals is infinite, replace solenoid valves. Finally, check resistance from terminal "C" to ground. Reading should be infinite. If it is not, there is a short between solenoid valve windings and ground. Replace valves.

AMC/RENAULT ALLIANCE & ENCORE MB1/3 (Cont.)

Fig. 6: Solenoid Valve Connector Terminal Identification

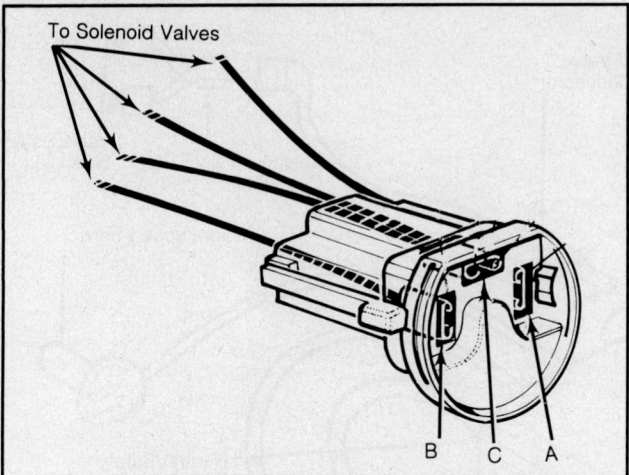

To Solenoid Valves

B   C   A

Throttle Position Sensor

1) Unplug throttle position sensor connector. With throttle closed, check resistance between connector sockets "C" and "B". See Fig. 7. Value should be 3000-5000 ohms. Check resistance between sockets "A" and "B". Value should be 1500-3500 ohms.

Fig. 7: Throttle Position Sensor Socket Identification

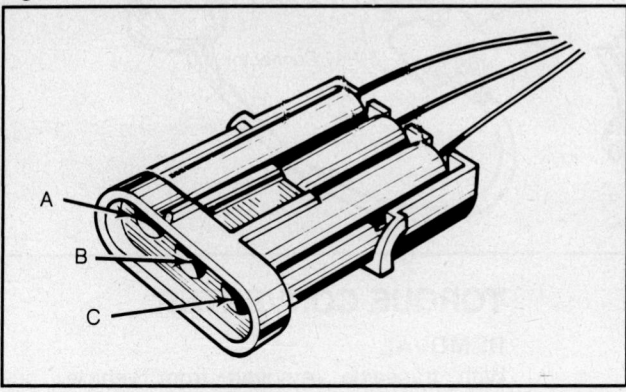

A
B
C

2) If either reading in step **1)** is incorrect, sensor is either faulty or incorrectly adjusted.

3) With ohmmeter connected between terminals "A" and "B", slowly open throttle from closed to full open position. Resistance should change with respect to throttle valve position, but never go to infinity. If so, TPS is faulty or out of adjustment.

Fig. 8: Neutral/Safety Switch Socket Identification

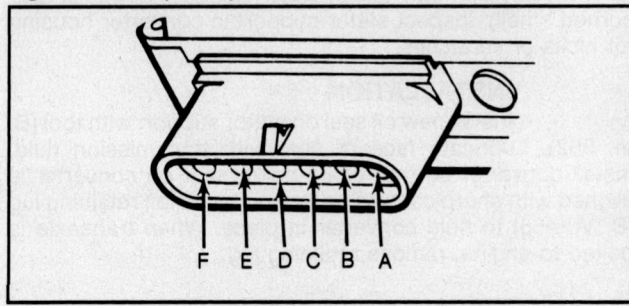

F   E   D   C   B   A

Neutral/Safety Switch

1) Turn ignition off. Unplug 6-way connector from control module. With gear selector lever in "R", check resistance value between sockets "A" and "B" in control module connection. Value should be zero.

2) With gear selector lever in "P" or "N", check resistance between sockets "E" and "C". As in step **1)**, value should be zero. If either resistance is incorrect (not zero), ensure proper electrical connections. If connections are good, replace neutral/safety switch.

NOTE: Renault tester (B. Vi. 958) is required for complete testing of switch.

SERVICE (IN VEHICLE)

DRIVE AXLE SHAFTS

See AMC/Renault Alliance & Encore article in MANUAL TRANSMISSIONS section.

VACUUM MODULATOR VALVE
Removal & Installation

Drain about 2 qts. (1.9L) of fluid from transaxle. Remove vacuum hose from modulator valve. Remove retaining bolt and retainer. Remove valve. Reverse removal procedure to install valve. Add fluid to proper level. Adjust vacuum modulator valve. See LUBRICATION and ADJUSTMENTS in this article.

VALVE BODY
Removal

1) Raise and support vehicle. Drain transaxle fluid. Remove front transaxle mount bolt and raise transaxle enough to gain clearance for oil pan removal. Remove pan, filter and "O" ring.

2) Remove valve body retaining bolts (8) and carefully remove valve body and seals (2). Remove regulator valve. Remove vacuum modulator valve from pressure regulator valve, then remove manual valve from manual lever assembly. See Fig. 10.

3) Locate electrical connector in corner of case, remove retaining clip and disconnect connector.

Installation

1) Assemble electrical connector and install in case. Retain with clip. Place valve body and seals in position and install center valve body bolt finger tight.

2) Install manual valve and connect to manual lever. Install vacuum modulator valve and position it against regulator valve. Install remaining valve body bolts finger tight.

3) Tighten 2 locating bolts. See Fig. 10. Tighten remaining bolts, center bolt first. Install oil filter and seal. Install oil pan. Lower transaxle and install transaxle mount bolt. Lower vehicle and fill transaxle with fluid.

THROTTLE POSITION SWITCH

Throttle position information is supplied to the computer by the throttle position sensor. This information is used, in part, to determine optimum gear selection under any given set of operating conditions. Proper sensor adjustment is essential to smooth transaxle operation.

Removal & Installation

Remove air cleaner assembly. Disconnect electrical connector from throttle position sensor. Remove attaching screws (2) and remove sensor. Reverse removal procedure to install sensor. Whenever sensor is removed,

Fig. 9: Electronic Control Module With Electrical Components & Connectors

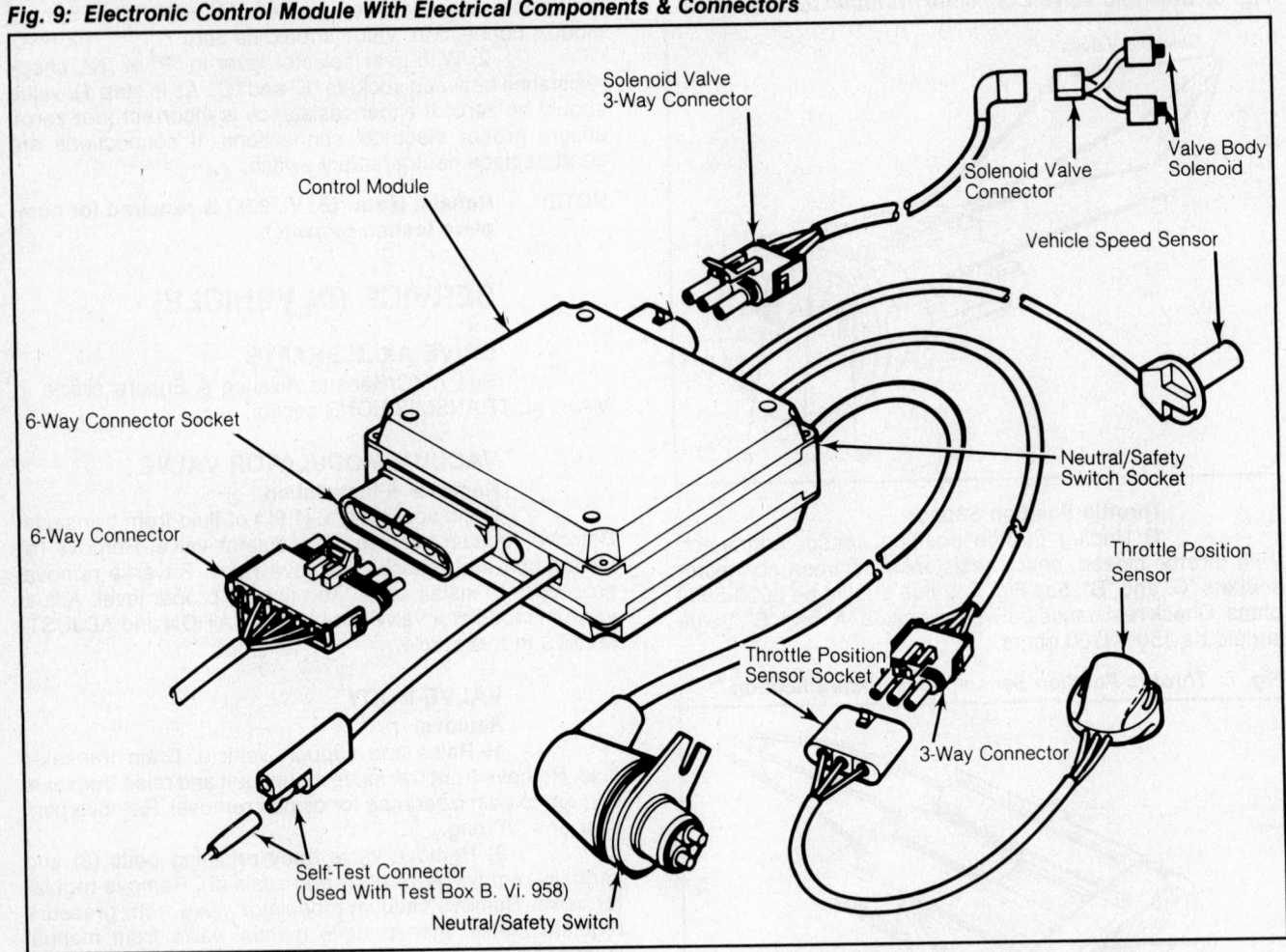

or if a new sensor is installed, it must be adjusted. See THROTTLE POSITION SENSOR in LUBRICATION & ADJUSTMENTS in this article.

SPEEDOMETER PINION OIL SEAL
Removal

NOTE: Special Puller (B. Vi. 905) should be used to remove seal. It includes an extractor, nut, 2 spacers and an inserting tool.

1) Disconnect speedometer cable at transaxle. With nut and thin spacer installed on extractor, screw extractor into case until it contacts seal.

2) Turn extractor in an additional 3 turns to engage seal. Tighten nut while holding extractor in position. As nut is tightened, seal will be pulled from case.

Installation
To install new seal, install seal on inserting tool, lip first. Lubricate seal with transmission fluid and push into case.

REMOVAL & INSTALLATION

TRANSAXLE
See appropriate AUTOMATIC TRANSMISSION REMOVAL article in DOMESTIC GENERAL SERVICING section.

TORQUE CONVERTER

REMOVAL
With transaxle removed from vehicle, pull torque converter straight out of converter housing. Pry oil seal off of stator support.

INSPECTION
1) Check general condition of the following converter components: Center boss on flywheel side, seal bearing surface, bushings on 3 mounting points, and timing target.

2) Replace converter if damaged or oil is contaminated by burned brake or clutch linings (black oil and/or burned smell). Inspect stator support in converter housing for nicks or scratches.

INSTALLATION
Install new oil seal on stator support with tool (B. Vi. 962). Lubricate face of seal with transmission fluid. Install converter so that White paint mark on converter is aligned with sharp corners on flex plate. Install retaining lug (B. Vi. 465) to hold converter in place. When transaxle is bolted to engine, remove retaining lug.

TRANSAXLE DISASSEMBLY

NOTE: All components must be kept clean and free of dust, dirt, or lint during the following proce-

AMC/RENAULT ALLIANCE & ENCORE MB1/3 (Cont.)

dures. Disassembly and assembly procedures should be carried out on a shock resistant bench (rubber or thick plastic).

Fig. 10: Removing Valve Body From Transaxle Case

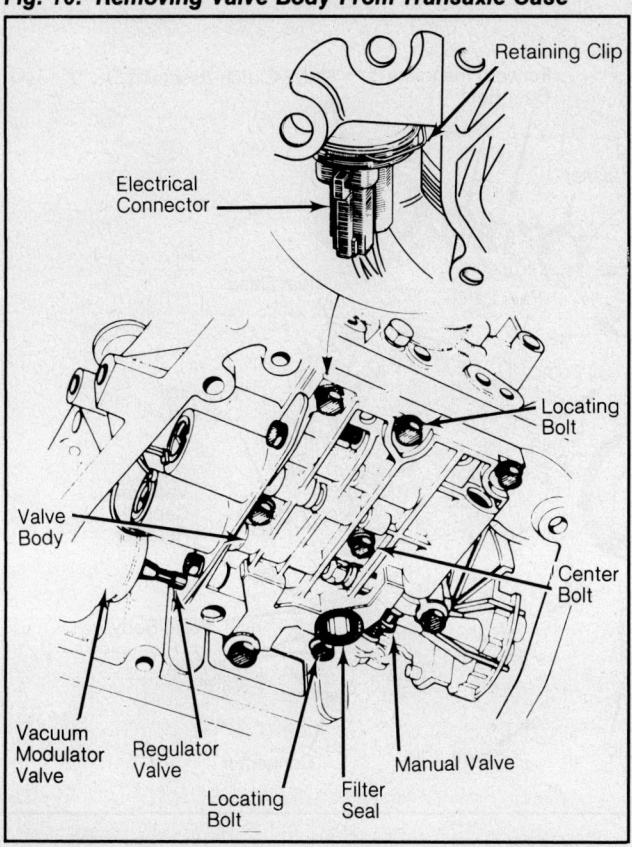

Use center bolt to support valve body during installation. Tighten locating bolts first. Then tighten remaining bolts.

Fig. 11: Replacing Speedometer Pinion Oil Seal

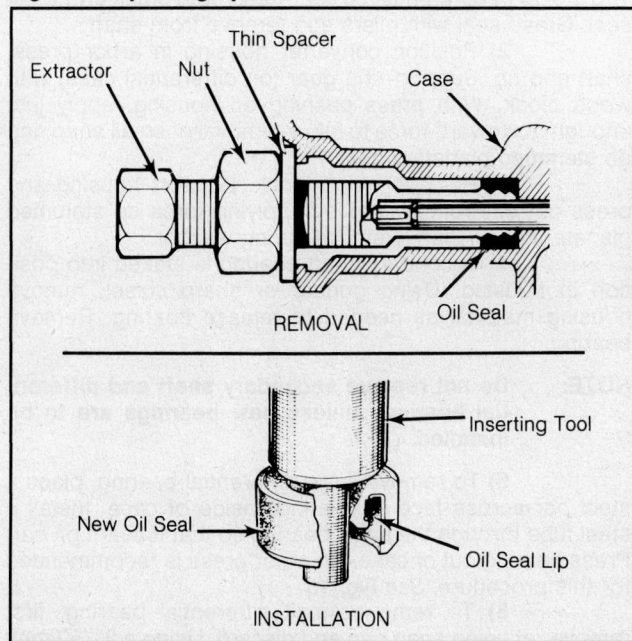

Place seal on inserting tool as shown and push into case.

VACUUM MODULATOR VALVE
See SERVICE (IN VEHICLE).

VALVE BODY
See SERVICE (IN VEHICLE)

Fig. 12: Removing F1 Piston

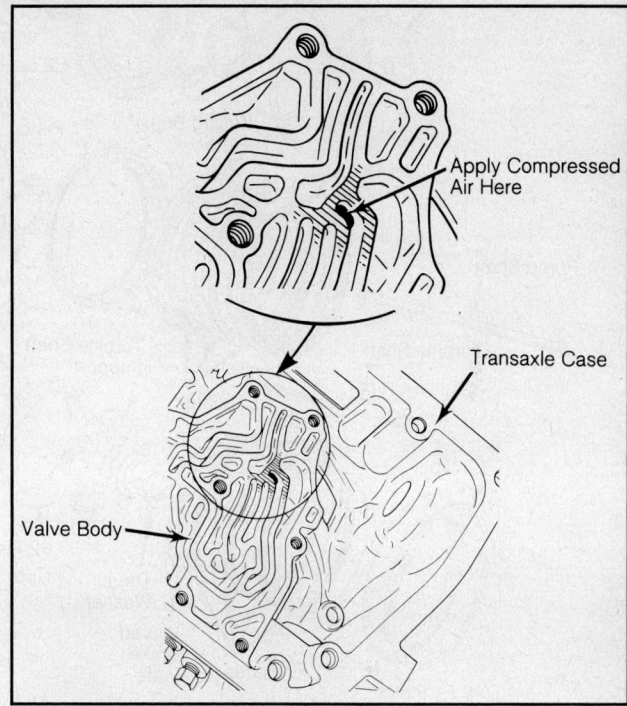

To remove piston, apply compressed air at valve body passage indicated.

REAR CASE
1) Remove torque converter from transaxle assembly. With transaxle on work bench, remove case attaching bolts indicated in *Fig. 23*. Remove "O" ring from locator bolt.

2) When separating cases, leave end play adjusting shim and spacer in position on output shaft. *See Fig. 17.* Lift park wheel and nylon washer from rear case. Remove park latch linkage and safety clip.

3) Remove large circlip. Lift out one-way clutch and reverse planetary gear set. Remove F1 plates and discs. To remove F1 piston, apply compressed air to valve body passage indicated in *Fig. 12*. Note position of springs on piston for reassembly reference and remove springs.

4) Lift out washer, E2 bellhousing, washer, forward planetery gear set, bearing, and E1-E2 clutch assembly.

5) Remove circlip and lift out F1 piston carrier, F2 plates and discs, thrust bearing, and turbine shaft support. Remove F2 piston cup and springs. Lift out F2 piston with Remover (B.Vi. 952). *See Fig. 14.*

INTERMEDIATE CASE
1) Remove remaining attaching bolts and separate intermediate case from differential and converter housing. Remove secondary shaft and output shaft snap rings. Remove output shaft assembly, secondary shaft, and step down driven gear.

Automatic Transmissions

AMC/RENAULT ALLIANCE & ENCORE MB1/3 (Cont.)

Fig. 13: *Exploded View of MB1 Automatic Transaxle Rear Case Assembly*

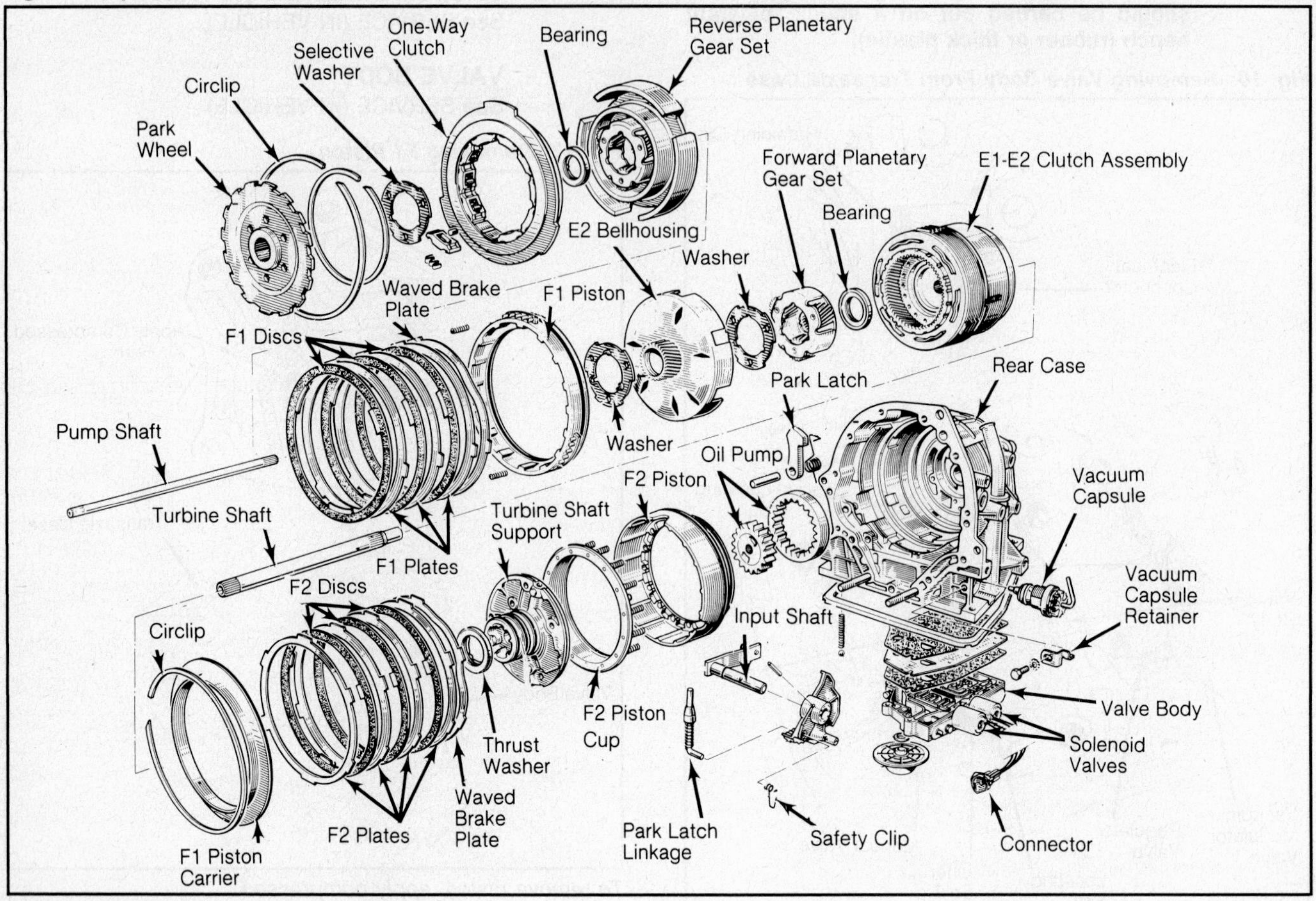

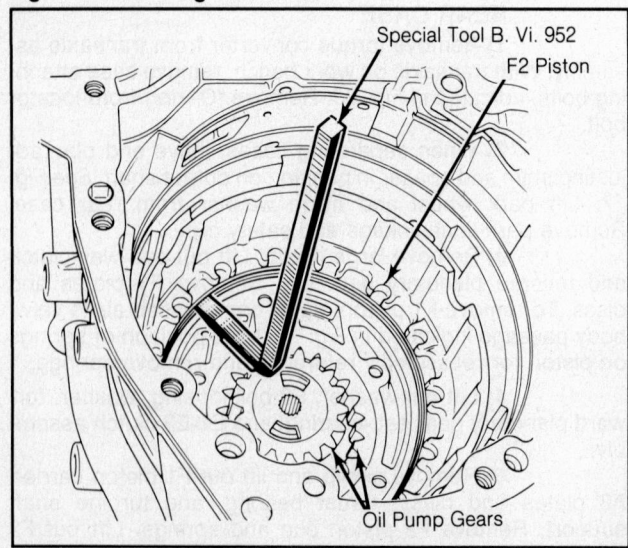

Park Wheel · Circlip · Selective Washer · One-Way Clutch · Bearing · Reverse Planetary Gear Set · Forward Planetary Gear Set · E1-E2 Clutch Assembly · Bearing · E2 Bellhousing · Washer · Waved Brake Plate · F1 Piston · Rear Case · Park Latch · Pump Shaft · F1 Discs · Washer · Oil Pump · Vacuum Capsule · Turbine Shaft · F2 Piston · Vacuum Capsule Retainer · F1 Plates · Turbine Shaft Support · Input Shaft · F2 Discs · Circlip · Thrust Washer · F2 Piston Cup · Valve Body · Solenoid Valves · F1 Piston Carrier · F2 Plates · Waved Brake Plate · Park Latch Linkage · Safety Clip · Connector

MB3 is similar.

Fig. 14: *Removing F2 Piston*

Special Tool B. Vi. 952 · F2 Piston · Oil Pump Gears

Lift out piston with Remover (B.Vi. 952).

2) If bearings are to be replaced, remove bearing retaining snap rings and, using a bearing puller, remove bearings from case. It is not necessary to remove bearings unless new bearings are to be installed.

DIFFERENTIAL & CONVERTER HOUSING

1) Remove "O" ring from planetary gear shaft. Tap 1 side of differential oil seal lightly with small drift to tilt seal. Grasp seal with pliers and remove from shaft.

2) Position converter housing in arbor press, shaft end up. Support ring gear (on differential case) with wood block. With press pushing on housing, apply just enough downward force to allow removal of small snap ring on stemmed planetary gear.

3) Remove wood block. Support housing and press out differential case by applying force on stemmed planetary gear shaft. Remove spring washer.

4) Secondary shaft bearing is staked into position in housing. Using grinder or sharp chisel, remove housing material as needed to release bearing. Remove bearing.

NOTE: Do not remove secondary shaft and differential bearings unless new bearings are to be installed.

5) To remove large differential bearing, place a steel bar across face of bearing, inside of case. Install a steel tube through the small bearing so that it bears on bar. Press bearing out of case. An arbor press is recommended for this procedure. *See Fig. 15.*

6) To remove small differential bearing, first remove retaining snap ring and discard. Using a 2" (50 mm) tube and arbor press, remove bearing by pressing it INTO

Fig. 15: Removing Large Differential Bearing

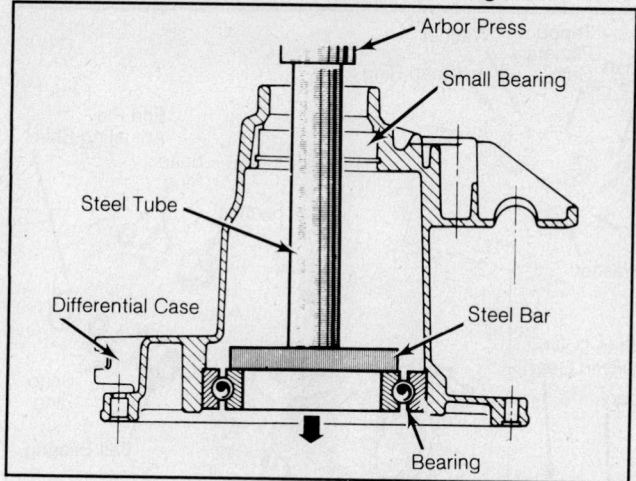

Pass steel tube through small bearing to bear against bar on large bearing.

tube and arbor press, remove bearing by pressing it INTO the case. Remove bearing through large bearing opening. *See Fig. 16.*

Fig. 16: Removing Small Differential Bearing

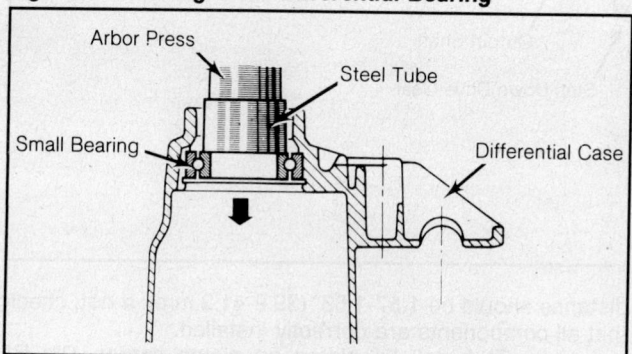

COMPONENT DISASSEMBLY & REASSEMBLY

VALVE BODY
Disassembly
1) Remove manual valve. Carefully remove cover plate retaining bolts (2) while holding plate in position. Slowly release plate to ensure that springs and valves remain in position.

2) While removing components, be sure to note position in valve body for reassembly reference. Withdraw pressure regulating valve, spring and plunger. Remove pilot valves and plungers.

3) Remove sequence valves and spring. Remove pressure limiting valve seal. Remove pressure limiting valve, spring and check ball.

Cleaning & Inspection
1) Check all valves for scratches or excessive wear. If any valve or valves is damaged, entire valve body must be replaced. All valves should slide freely in their bores without sticking or binding.

2) Check springs for damage or collapsed coils. Inspect check ball closely for scratches or other signs of unusual wear. Clean valve body with mineral spirits and lint

free rags. Blow out passages and dry valve body with compressed air.

Reassembly
Reverse disassembly procedure to assemble valve body, noting the following: Install sequence valve with larger head towards spring. Solenoid valve marked with arrow must be installed on pressure regulating valve side. *See Fig. 18.*

DIFFERENTIAL
Disassembly
Remove speedometer drive gear from stemmed planetary gear shaft. With case held in soft-jawed vise, remove snap ring and washer. Lift out planetary gears, shaft, and side gears (with washers). Tie side gear washers to their respective side gears to ensure that washers are installed with correct gears during transaxle reassembly.

Inspection
Check all components for signs of scoring or excessive wear. Differential case components are designed as matched sets. If any differential component is damaged (planetary gear, differential case, side gears, washers or shaft), entire assembly must be replaced.

Reassembly
To assemble differential, reverse disassembly procedures. Dip all components in automatic transmission fluid before assembly. Ensure tab on speedometer drive gear is aligned with notch in differential case when parts are assembled.

TRANSAXLE INSPECTION, REASSEMBLY & ADJUSTMENT

INSPECTION
1) Clean case and housings thoroughly with solvent and lint free rags. DO NOT use solvents containing trichloroethylene as it may damage seals. Dry components with compressed air. Direct air stream into all holes, oil feed passages and lubrication channels.

2) Check condition of F1 and F2 brake plates and discs. Any plates which show signs of overheating (discoloration) should be replaced. Check for damage to plate surfaces, excessive runout or taper. Replace as needed.

3) Inspect discs for excessive wear and burned or torn linings. In most cases, if either or both brakes show signs of having been severely overheated, E1-E2 clutch assembly as well as all F1 and F2 plates and discs should be replaced.

4) Check sealing ring lands on turbine shaft support. If excessively worn, or if bottom of lands is not square, support should be replaced. Ensure that seal ring ends are square and hooked together properly.

5) Inspect all snap ring and circlip grooves. Worn or damaged grooves will prevent proper seating of retainers. Therefore, any component with worn grooves should be replaced. Check condition of machined surfaces and sleeves on all components. Replace as needed.

6) Check condition of teeth on all geared components. Ensure that forward and reverse planetary gear sets rotate freely on shafts.

7) Inspect secondary shaft bearing seat area in converter housing. Remove any burrs or scratches with emery cloth. Wipe bore clean with dry cloth and blow out with compressed air.

AMC/RENAULT ALLIANCE & ENCORE MB1/3 (Cont.)

Fig. 17: Exploded View of Intermediate Case, Differential & Converter Housing Assemblies

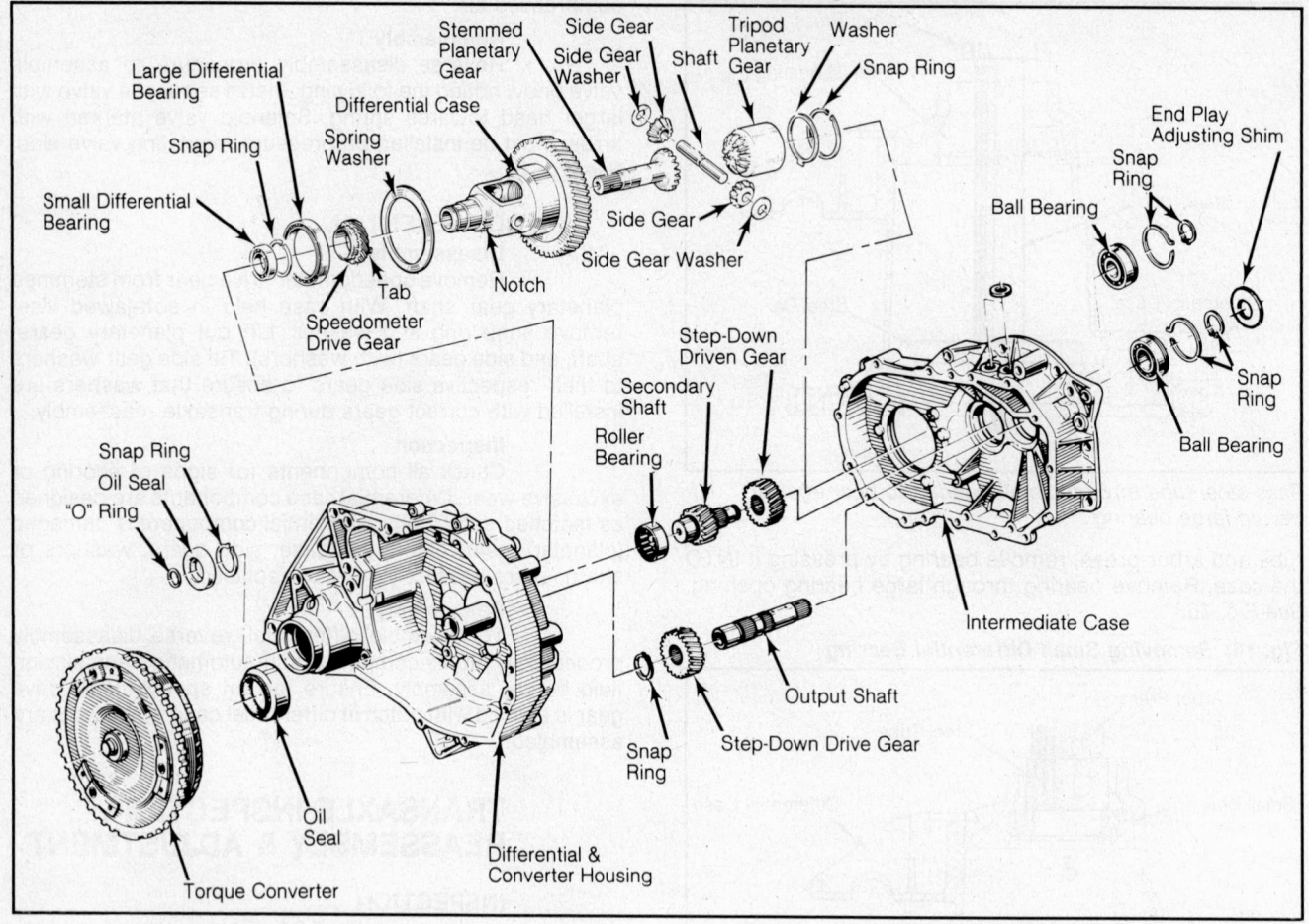

REASSEMBLY

Rear Case

1) Install oil pump gears in case. Ensure that gears rotate freely. Replace seals on F2 piston and install piston and piston cup in case. Make sure that piston springs are seated correctly in piston.

2) Install Guide Pins (B. Vi. 952) in case and install turbine shaft support, using pins to guide support into position. *See Fig. 19.* Remove pins, install retaining bolts and tighten alternately and evenly. Install thrust bearing. Install F2 brake steel clips.

3) Install waved brake plate. Dip F2 plates and discs in transmission fluid. Install 1 disc, then 1 plate in case. Continue alternating discs and plates until all have been installed. Install F1 piston carrier and large circlip.

4) Check clearance between discs and plates. Clearance should be .05-.13" (1.3-3.2 mm). If clearance is incorrect, check that all plates and discs are in correct position and re-check plate and disc condition. Ensure that circlip is fully seated in its groove.

5) Assemble E1-E2 clutch, roller bearing, forward planetary gear set, .06" (1.5 mm) washer, E2 bellhousing and turbine shaft. Ensure that tabs of clutch assembly fit into notches of E2 bellhousing. Install complete assembly in case so that tabs of F2 plates and discs are located in notches of E2 bellhousing.

6) Measure distance from face of F1 piston carrier to outside face of E1-E2 clutch assembly. Total

distance should be 1.57-1.63" (39.9-41.3 mm). If not, check that all components are correctly installed.

7) Install F1 piston on piston carrier. Dip F1 plates and discs in transmission fluid. Install 1 plate, then 1 disc in case. Continue alternating plates and discs until all have been installed.

8) Check clearance between plates and discs. Operating clearance should be .03-.10" (.8-2.7 mm). If clearance is incorrect, check that all plates and discs are in correct position and re-check plate and disc condition.

9) Install one-way clutch in reverse planetary gear set. Install .06" (1.5 mm) washer on E2 bellhousing. Install reverse planetary gear set/one-way clutch assembly in case. Make sure that tabs on washer engage slots in planetary gear set. Install large circlip.

10) If any component in rear case was removed or replaced during transaxle overhaul, reverse planetary gear set adjustment and total end play adjustment must be checked. These adjustments must be made before final assembly of transaxle cases. See Reverse Planetary Gear Set Adjustment in ADJUSTMENT section in this article. Install valve body, filter and pan.

Differential/Converter Housing & Intermediate Case

1) Install large bearing retaining snap rings in intermediate case. Install bearings with Driver (B. Vi. 947). Assemble step down drive gear on output shaft and retain with snap ring. Install assembly in intermediate case and install snap ring.

AMC/RENAULT ALLIANCE & ENCORE MB1/3 (Cont.)

Fig. 18: Exploded View of Renault Models MB1/3 Valve Body Assembly

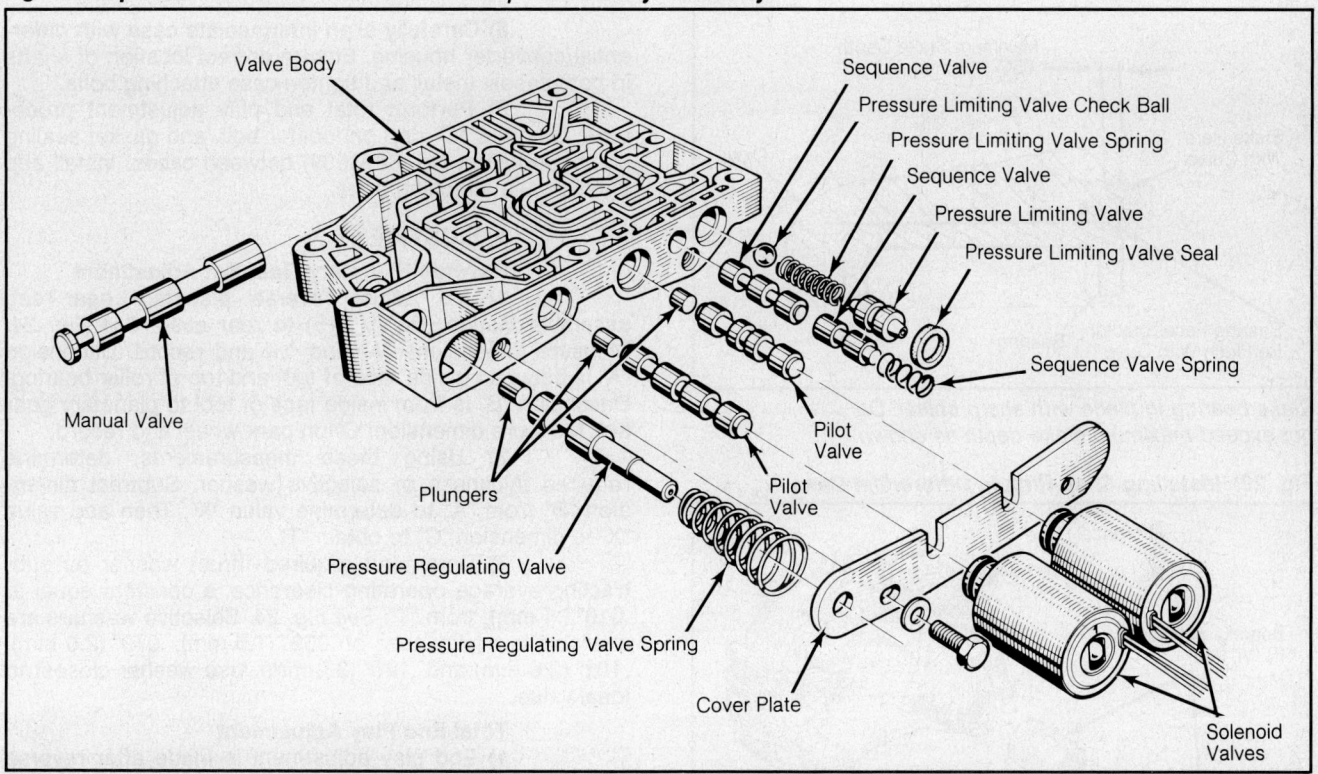

Labels: Valve Body, Manual Valve, Plungers, Pressure Regulating Valve, Pressure Regulating Valve Spring, Cover Plate, Pilot Valve, Pilot Valve, Sequence Valve, Pressure Limiting Valve Check Ball, Pressure Limiting Valve Spring, Sequence Valve, Pressure Limiting Valve, Pressure Limiting Valve Seal, Sequence Valve Spring, Solenoid Valves

Fig. 19: Installing Turbine Shaft Support in Rear Case

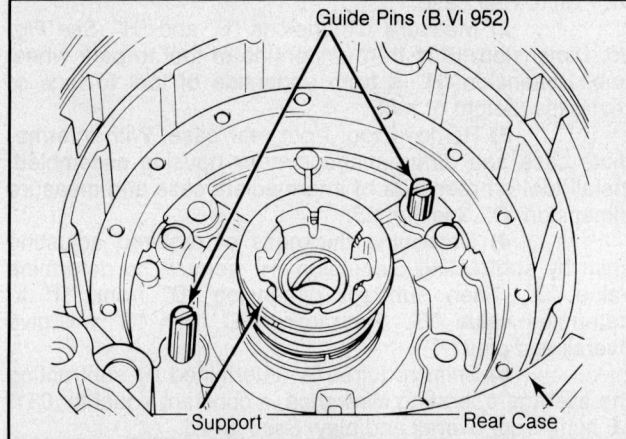

Labels: Guide Pins (B.Vi 952), Support, Rear Case

Install guide pins in case to align support.

2) Install step down driven gear and secondary shaft in intermediate case and retain with snap ring.

3) Position small differential bearing in housing and press into place with arbor press and 2.5" (65 mm) pipe. Install new snap ring. Place large differential bearing in position. Place a slightly shouldered bar or 5.0" (127 mm) steel pipe on bearing and press bearing into case.

4) Install secondary shaft bearing in converter housing. Press bearing in until it is flush with face of case. Stake in place with chisel. *See Fig. 21.*

5) Using Seal Installer (B. Vi. 962), install new converter oil seal over stator shaft support. Tap new seal onto shaft until outer face of tool is flush with end of support.

Fig. 20: E1-E2 Clutch Assembly

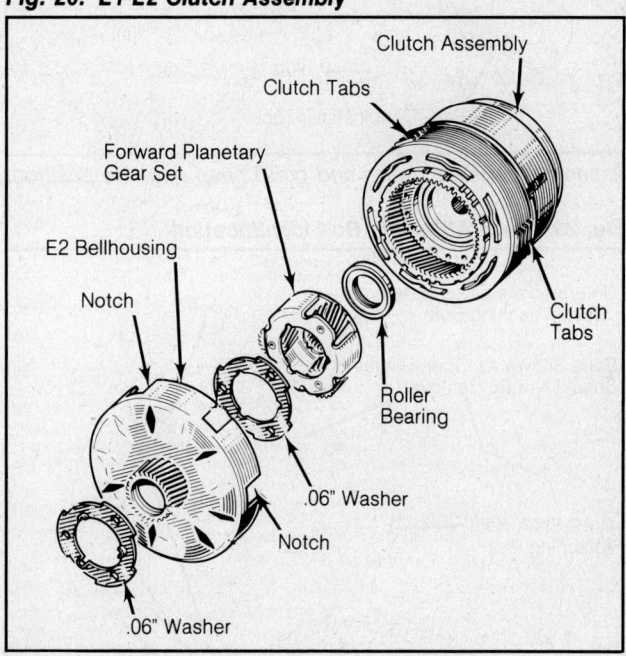

Labels: Clutch Assembly, Clutch Tabs, Forward Planetary Gear Set, E2 Bellhousing, Notch, .06" Washer, Notch, .06" Washer, Roller Bearing, Clutch Tabs

Tabs of clutch must align with slots in bellhousing.

6) Install spring washer on base of differential case with outside edge of washer against gear. Install differential in housing.

7) Support differential case with wood block. Install part C of Tool Set (B. Vi. 946) on planetary gear stem and install snap ring on part C. *See Fig. 22.* Position part D of Tool Set (B. Vi. 946) on part C and press snap ring into groove. Install oil seal on planetary gear shaft.

AMC/RENAULT ALLIANCE & ENCORE MB1/3 (Cont.)

Fig. 21: Secondary Shaft Bearing Installation

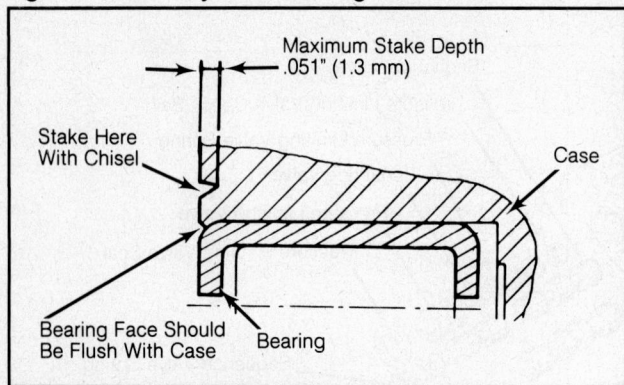

Stake bearing in place with sharp chisel. Do not exceed maximum stake depth as shown.

Fig. 22: Installing Snap Ring in Differential Case

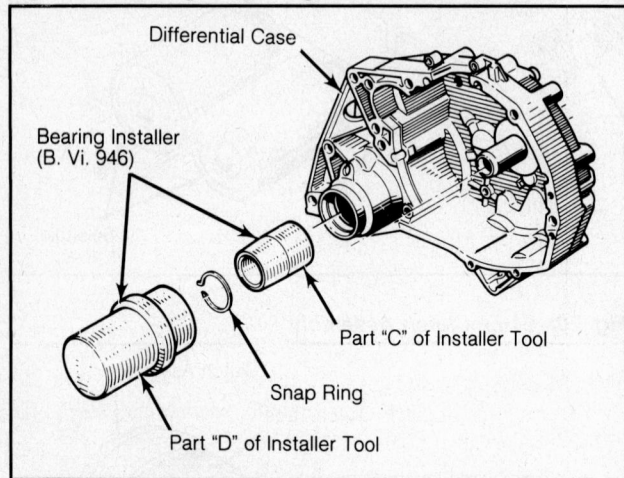

Assemble tools as shown and press snap ring into position.

Fig. 23: Case Attaching Bolt Identification

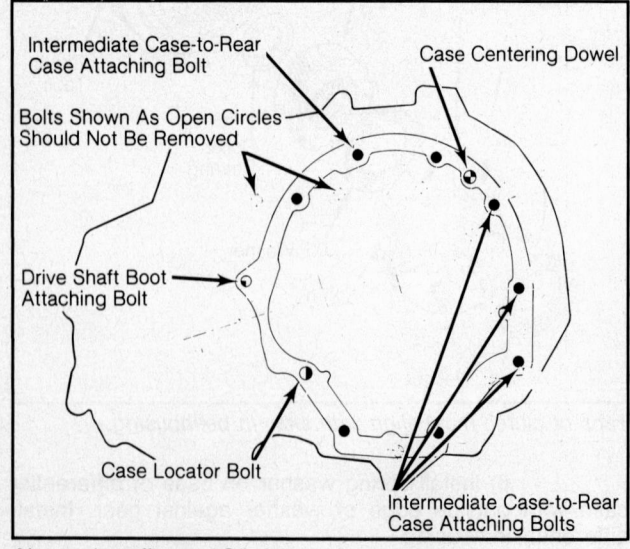

Always install new "O" ring on locator bolt.

NOTE: Use arbor press when installing snap ring.

8) Carefully align intermediate case with differential/converter housing. Ensure correct location of shafts in both cases. Install and tighten case attaching bolts.

9) Perform total end play adjustment procedure. Use new "O" ring on locator bolt, and gasket sealing compound (Part No. 8993539) between cases. Install and tighten case attaching bolts.

ADJUSTMENT

Reverse Planetary Gear Set Adjustment

1) To adjust reverse planetary gear set, assemble Gauge (B. Vi. 715) to rear case. *See Fig. 24.* Measure dimensions "A" and "B" and record. Dimension "A" is between inside face of tool and top of roller bearing. Dimension "B" is from inside face of tool to planetary gear set. Measure dimension "C" on park wheel and record.

2) Using these measurements, determine required thickness of selective washer. Subtract dimension "B" from "A" to determine value "X". Then add value "X" to dimension "C" to obtain "T".

3) Determine required thrust washer by subtracting average operating clearance, a constant equal to .016" (.4 mm), from "T". *See Fig. 24.* Selective washers are available in thicknesses of .059" (1.5 mm), .079" (2.0 mm), .102" (2.6 mm) and .126" (3.2 mm). Use washer closest to ideal value.

Total End Play Adjustment

1) End play adjustment is made after reverse planetary gear set adjustment. With gear set selective washer in place, install park gear and assemble Gauge (B. Vi. 715) to rear case.

2) Measure dimensions "F" and "H". *See Fig. 25.* Dimension "F" is from underside of tool to park wheel hub. Dimension "H" is from underside of tool to face of rear case (height of tool).

3) Remove tool from rear case. With intermediate case and differential/converter housing assembled, install tool on rear side of intermediate case and measure dimension "D". *See Fig. 25.*

4) Determine thickness of required adjusting shim by subtracting dimension "H" from "F" to determine value "G". Then subtract dimension "D" from "H" to determine value "E". Subtracting "E" from "G" will give overall end play ("T").

5) Shim required is determined by subtracting the average operating clearance, a constant equal to .031" (.8 mm), from overall end play. *See Fig. 25.*

6) End play adjusting shims are available in thicknesses of .010" (.25 mm), .028" (.70 mm), .043" (1.1 mm), .067" (1.7 mm) and .090" (2.3 mm). Use washer which is closest to ideal value.

TIGHTENING SPECIFICATIONS

Application	Ft. Lbs. (N.m)
Differential & Converter Housing-to-Intermediate Case	18 (25)
Rear Case-to-Intermediate Case	18 (25)
Transaxle-to-Engine Block	31 (42)
Turbine Shaft Retaining Bolts	11 (15)
	INCH Lbs. (N.m)
Transaxle Oil Pan Bolts	54 (6)
Valve Body Attaching Bolts	90 (10)

AMC/RENAULT ALLIANCE & ENCORE MB1/3 (Cont.)

Fig. 24: Measuring Reverse Planetary Gear Set Adjustment

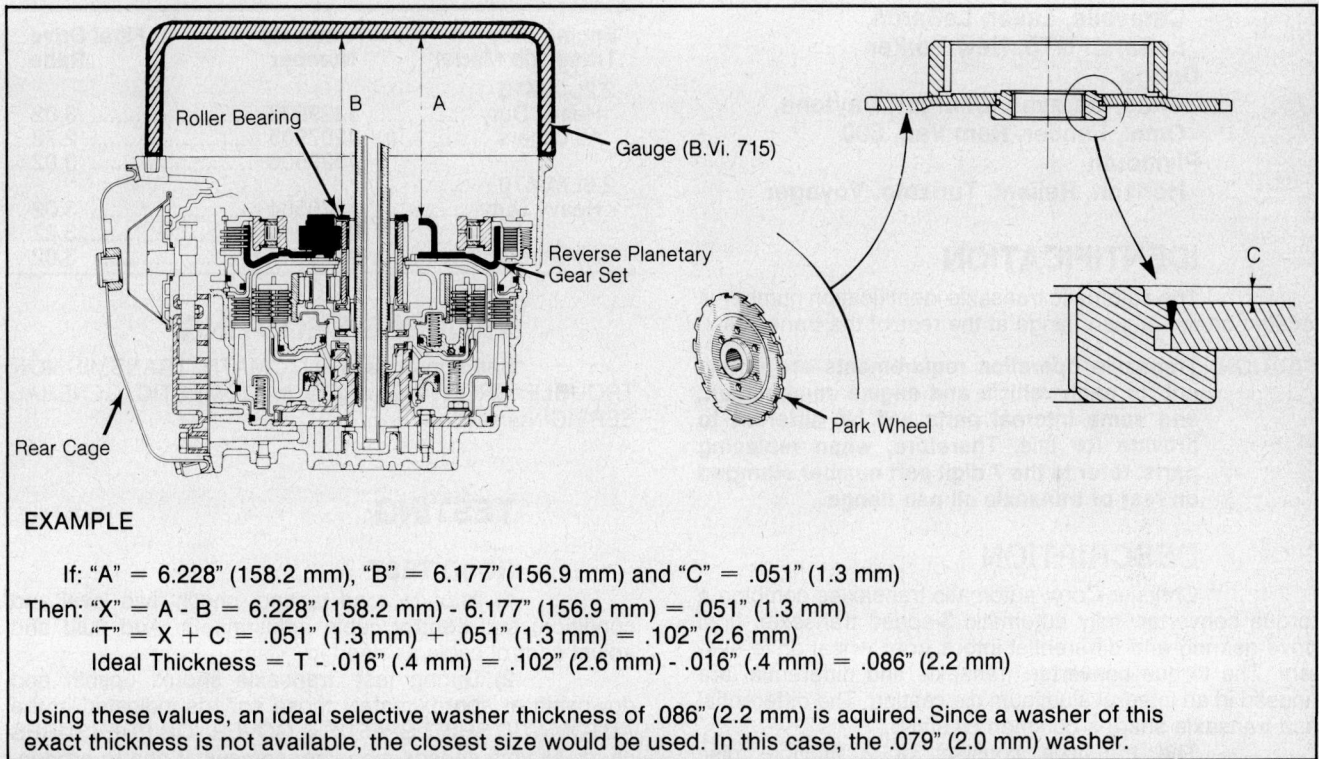

EXAMPLE

If: "A" = 6.228" (158.2 mm), "B" = 6.177" (156.9 mm) and "C" = .051" (1.3 mm)

Then: "X" = A - B = 6.228" (158.2 mm) - 6.177" (156.9 mm) = .051" (1.3 mm)
"T" = X + C = .051" (1.3 mm) + .051" (1.3 mm) = .102" (2.6 mm)
Ideal Thickness = T - .016" (.4 mm) = .102" (2.6 mm) - .016" (.4 mm) = .086" (2.2 mm)

Using these values, an ideal selective washer thickness of .086" (2.2 mm) is aquired. Since a washer of this exact thickness is not available, the closest size would be used. In this case, the .079" (2.0 mm) washer.

Measure dimensions shown and use values to determine required selective washer thickness.

Fig. 25: Measurements Required for Total End Play Adjustment

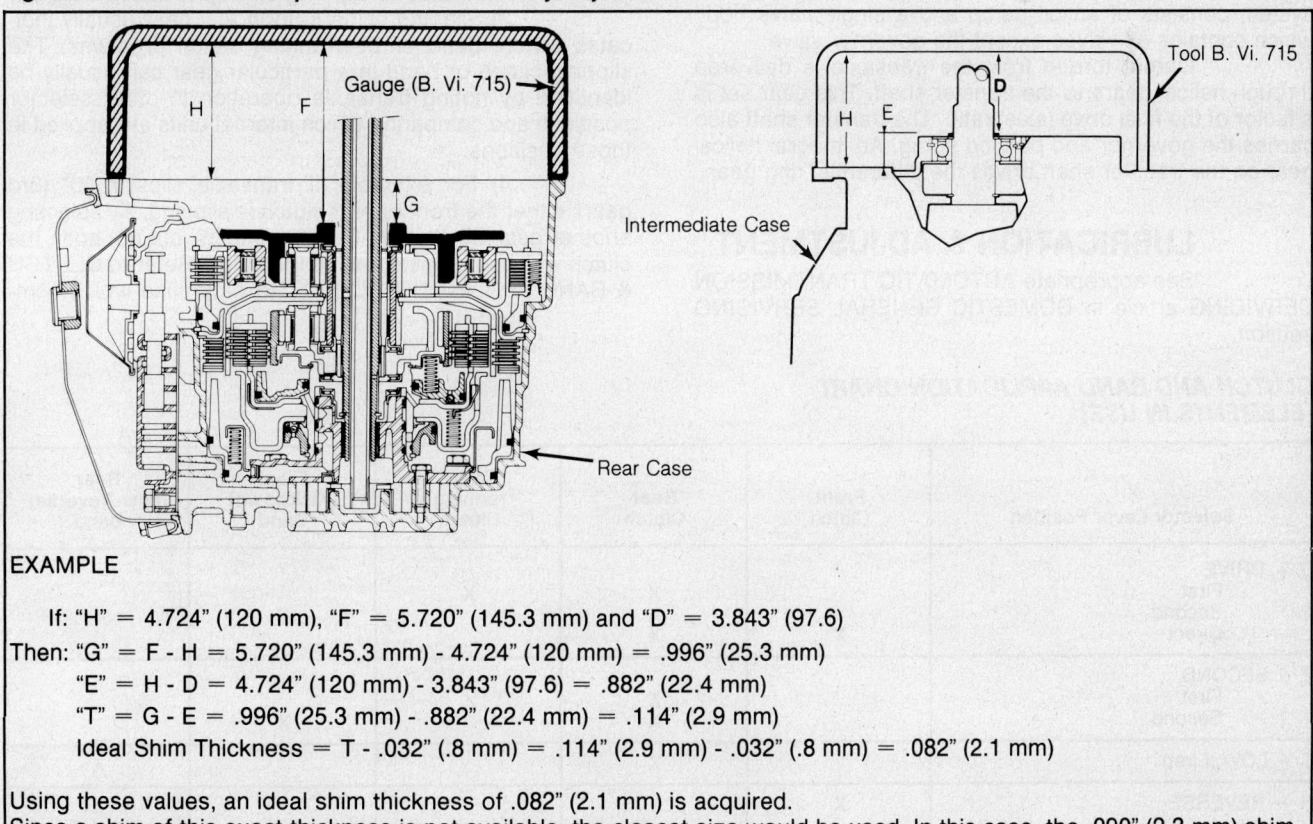

EXAMPLE

If: "H" = 4.724" (120 mm), "F" = 5.720" (145.3 mm) and "D" = 3.843" (97.6 mm)

Then: "G" = F - H = 5.720" (145.3 mm) - 4.724" (120 mm) = .996" (25.3 mm)
"E" = H - D = 4.724" (120 mm) - 3.843" (97.6 mm) = .882" (22.4 mm)
"T" = G - E = .996" (25.3 mm) - .882" (22.4 mm) = .114" (2.9 mm)
Ideal Shim Thickness = T - .032" (.8 mm) = .114" (2.9 mm) - .032" (.8 mm) = .082" (2.1 mm)

Using these values, an ideal shim thickness of .082" (2.1 mm) is acquired.
Since a shim of this exact thickness is not available, the closest sraze would be used. In this case, the .090" (2.3 mm) shim.

Measure dimensions shown and use values to determine required shim thickness.

Automatic Transmissions
CHRYSLER CORP. A-413 & A-470

Chrysler
  Caravelle, Laser, LeBaron,
  LeBaron GTS, New Yorker
Dodge
  Aries, Caravan, Charger, Daytona,
  Omni, Lancer, Ram Van, 600
Plymouth
  Horizon, Reliant, Turismo, Voyager

IDENTIFICATION

The automatic transaxle identification number is located on the oil pan flange at the rear of the transaxle.

CAUTION: Transaxle operation requirements are different for each vehicle and engine combination, and some internal parts will be different to provide for this. Therefore, when replacing parts, refer to the 7 digit part number stamped on rear of transaxle oil pan flange.

DESCRIPTION

Chrysler Corp. automatic transaxles combine a torque converter, fully automatic 3-speed transaxle, final drive gearing and differential into a front wheel drive system. The torque converter, transaxle and differential are housed in an integral aluminum die casting. The differential and transaxle share a common oil sump.

The transaxle consists of 2 multiple disc clutches, an overrunning clutch, 2 servos, a hydraulic accumulator, 2 bands and 2 planetary gear sets to provide 3 forward gear ratios and a reverse ratio. The hydraulic system consists of an oil pump and a single valve body which contains all valves except the governor valve.

Output torque from the transaxle is delivered through helical gears to the transfer shaft. This gear set is a factor of the final drive (axle) ratio. The transfer shaft also carries the governor and parking sprag. An integral helical gear on the transfer shaft drives the differential ring gear.

LUBRICATION & ADJUSTMENT

See appropriate AUTOMATIC TRANSMISSION SERVICING article in DOMESTIC GENERAL SERVICING section.

TRANSAXLE APPLICATION

Engine Size/ Transaxle Model	Transaxle Number	Final Drive Ratio
2.2L/A-413		
Heavy Duty	4329538	3.02
All Others	4207905	2.78
	4329506	3.02
2.6L/A-470		
Heavy Duty	4329564	3.02
	4329565	3.22
All Others	4329547	3.02

TROUBLE SHOOTING

See appropriate AUTOMATIC TRANSMISSION TROUBLE SHOOTING article in DOMESTIC GENERAL SERVICING section.

TESTING

ROAD TEST

1) Prior to road testing, check fluid level and condition, and control cable adjustments. Add fluid and adjust control cable as needed.

2) During test, transaxle should upshift and downshift at approximately those speeds indicated in the AUTOMATIC SHIFT SPEEDS & GOVERNOR PRESSURES chart. All shift speeds may vary somewhat due to production tolerances, rear axle ratio, or tire size. The important factor is the quality of the shifts. All shifts should be smooth, responsive, and with no slipping or engine speed flare-up.

3) Slipping or flare-up in any gear usually indicates clutch, band or overrunning clutch problems. The slipping clutch or band in a particular gear can usually be identified by noting transaxle operation in other selector positions and comparing which internal units are applied in those positions.

4) For example, if transaxle slips in "D" (3rd gear), either the front or rear clutch is slipping. By selecting another gear which uses 1 of those units, but not both, the clutch which is slipping can be identified. Refer to CLUTCH & BAND APPLICATION CHART to determine which com-

CLUTCH AND BAND APPLICATION CHART (ELEMENTS IN USE)

Selector Lever Position	Front Clutch	Rear Clutch	Over-running Clutch	Front (Kickdown) Band	Rear (Low-Reverse) Band
D – DRIVE					
First		X	X		
Second		X		X	
Direct	X	X			
2 – SECOND					
First		X	X		
Second		X		X	
1 – LOW (First)		X			X
R – REVERSE	X				X

NEUTRAL OR PARK – All clutches and bands released and/or ineffective.

Fig. 1: Cutaway View of Chrysler Corp. Automatic Transaxle

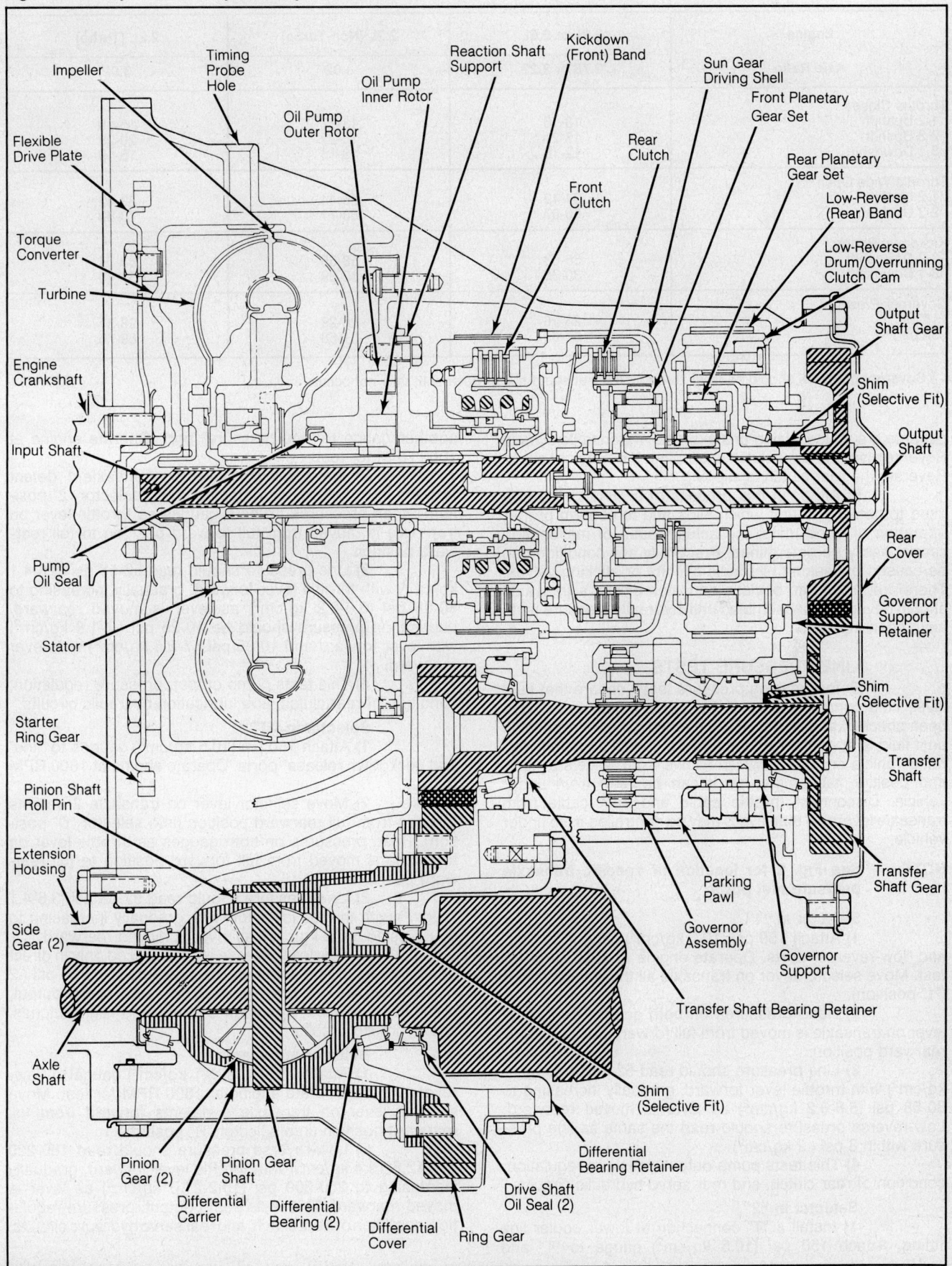

AUTOMATIC SHIFT SPEEDS & GOVERNOR PRESSURES

Engine	2.2L or 2.6L	2.2L (Non-Turbo)	2.2L (Turbo)
Axle Ratio	2.78 or 3.22	3.02	3.02
Throttle Closed			
1-2 Upshift	13-16	13-17	15-19
2-3 Upshift	17-21	18-22	20-25
3-1 Downshift	12-15	13-16	15-19
Throttle Wide Open			
1-2 Upshift	34-42	36-44	38-42
2-3 Upshift	60-67	63-71	70-80
Kickdown Range			
3-2 Downshift	55-63	58-66	64-74
3-1 Downshift	30-38	32-39	37-40
Governor Pressure [1]			
15 psi	23-26	26-29	28-31
50 psi	57-65	61-68	69-76

[1] – Governor pressure should be from zero to 3.0 psi at stand-still or downshift may not occur.

ponents are in use. Using this example, if transaxle slips in Reverse also, the front clutch is slipping. If it does not slip in Reverse, the rear clutch is slipping.

5) Although this process of elimination can be used to detect any unit which slips and to confirm proper operation of good units, the actual cause of malfunction cannot easily be determined. Practically any condition can be caused by leaking hydraulic circuits or sticking valves. Therefore, unless an obvious condition exists, a transaxle should never be disassembled until hydraulic pressure tests have been made.

LINE PRESSURE TESTS

Before making pressure tests, ensure that fluid level, fluid condition, and control cable adjustments have been checked and corrected as needed. Operate transaxle until fluid is at operating temperature. Install a tachometer, raise vehicle on a hoist which allows front wheels to turn, and position tachometer so it can be read from under vehicle. Disconnect throttle cable and shift cable from transaxle levers so that levers may be controlled from under vehicle.

NOTE: See Fig. 2 for location of specific transaxle pressure test ports.

Selector in "1"

1) Attach 150 psi (10.5 kg/cm^2) gauges to "line" and "low-reverse" ports. Operate engine at 1000 RPM for test. Move selector lever on transaxle all the way rearward ("1" position).

2) Read pressures on both gauges as throttle lever on transaxle is moved from full forward position to full rearward position.

3) Line pressure should read 52-58 psi (3.6-4.1 kg/cm^2) with throttle lever forward, gradually increasing to 80-88 psi (5.6-6.2 kg/cm^2) as lever is moved rearward. Low-reverse pressure should read the same as line pressure within 3 psi (.2 kg/cm^2).

4) This tests pump output, pressure regulation, condition of rear clutch, and rear servo hydraulic circuits.

Selector in "2"

1) Install a "T" connection at lower cooler line fitting. Attach 150 psi (10.5 kg/cm^2) gauge to "T" and

another gauge to "line pressure" port. Operate engine at 1000 RPM for test.

2) Move selector lever on transaxle 1 detent forward from full rearward position (into selector "2" position). Read pressures on both gauges as throttle lever on transaxle is moved from full forward position to full rearward position.

3) Line pressure should read 52-58 psi (3.6-4.1 kg/cm^2) with throttle lever forward, gradually increasing to 80-88 psi (5.6-6.2 kg/cm^2) as lever is moved rearward. Lubrication pressure should be 10-25 psi (.7-1.8 kg/cm^2) with lever forward and 10-35 psi (.7-2.5 kg/cm^2) with lever rearward.

4) This tests pump output, pressure regulation, condition of rear clutch, and lubrication hydraulic circuits.

Selector in "D"

1) Attach 150 psi (10.5 kg/cm^2) gauges to "line" and "kickdown release" ports. Operate engine at 1600 RPM for test.

2) Move selector lever on transaxle 2 detents forward from full rearward position (into selector "D" position). Read pressures on both gauges as throttle lever on transaxle is moved from full forward position to full rearward position.

3) Line pressure should read 52-58 psi (3.6-4.1 kg/cm^2) with throttle lever forward, gradually increasing to 80-88 psi (5.6-6.2 kg/cm^2) as lever is moved rearward.

4) Kickdown release is pressurized only in direct drive and should be same as line pressure within 3 psi (.2 kg/cm^2), up to kickdown point. This tests pump output, pressure regulation, condition of front and rear clutches, and hydraulic circuits.

Selector in Reverse

1) Attach a 300 psi (21 kg/cm^2) gauge to "low-reverse" port. Operate engine at 1600 RPM for test. Move selector lever on transaxle 4 detents forward from full rearward position (into selector "R" position).

2) Low-reverse pressure should read 180-220 psi (12.6-15.4 kg/cm^2) with throttle lever forward, gradually increasing to 260-300 psi (18.2-21.0 kg/cm^2) as lever is moved rearward. This tests pump output, pressure regulation, condition of front clutch, and rear servo hydraulic circuits.

Fig. 2: View of Left Side of Transaxle Case Showing Pressure Test Port Locations

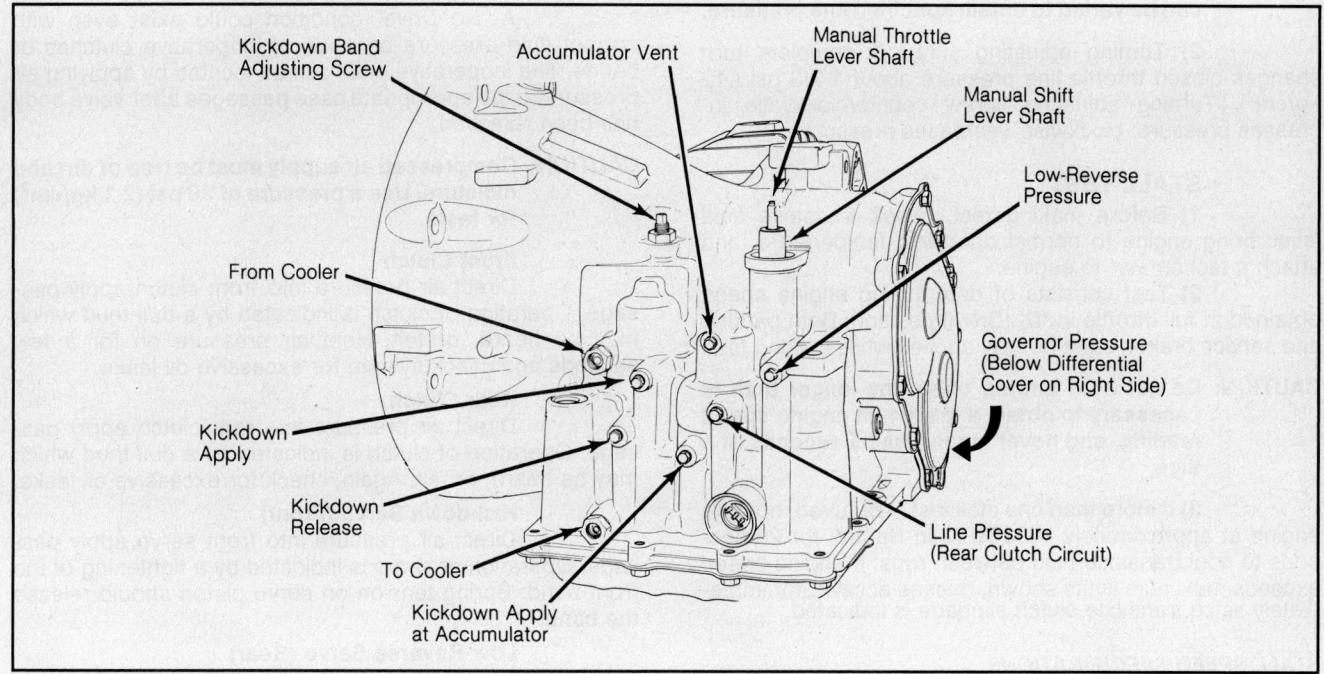

3) Move selector lever on transaxle to "D" position to check that rear servo pressure drops to zero. This tests for leakage into rear servo, due to case porosity, which can cause reverse band burn out.

PRESSURE TEST INDICATIONS

1) If proper minimum-to-maximum line pressure is found in any test, pump and pressure regulator are working properly.

2) Low pressure in "D", "1", and "2", but correct pressure in "R", indicates rear clutch circuit leakage.

3) Low pressure in "D" and "R", but correct pressure in "1", indicates front clutch circuit leakage.

4) Low pressure in "R" and "1", but correct pressure in "2", indicates rear servo circuit leakage.

5) Low line pressure in all positions indicates a defective pump, clogged filter, or stuck pressure regulator valve.

NOTE: The following GOVERNOR PRESSURE TEST need only be performed if transaxle shifts at wrong vehicle speed with throttle cable correctly adjusted.

GOVERNOR PRESSURE TEST

1) Connect a 150 psi (10.5 kg/cm²) pressure gauge to governor pressure take-off point, located below differential cover at lower right side of case.

2) Operate transaxle in 3rd gear to read pressures. Compare pressure readings obtained with governor pressure specifications given in AUTOMATIC SHIFT SPEEDS & GOVERNOR PRESSURES chart.

3) If governor pressures are incorrect at given vehicle speed, governor valves are probably sticking.

4) Governor pressure should respond smoothly to changes in MPH and should return to 0-3 psi (0-.2 kg/cm²) when vehicle is stopped. Pressure above 3 psi (.2 kg/cm²) at standstill will prevent the transaxle from downshifting.

THROTTLE PRESSURES

No gauge port is provided for testing throttle pressure. Incorrect throttle pressure should only be suspected if part throttle upshift speeds are either delayed or occur too early in relation to vehicle speeds. Engine runaway on either upshifts or downshifts can also be an indication of incorrect (low) throttle pressure setting.

CAUTION: In no case should throttle pressure be adjusted until transaxle throttle cable adjustment has been checked and corrected as needed.

HYDRAULIC PRESSURE ADJUSTMENTS

NOTE: An incorrect throttle pressure setting will cause incorrect line pressure readings even though line pressure adjustment is correct. Therefore, always inspect and correct throttle pressure adjustment before adjusting line pressure.

Throttle Pressure

1) Remove valve body from transaxle. Back off throttle lever stop screw approximately 5 turns. Insert gauge pin of Gauge (C-3763) between throttle lever cam and kickdown valve.

2) By pushing in on tool, compress kickdown valve against spring so that valve is completely bottomed.

3) Turn throttle lever stop screw until head of screw touches throttle lever tang with throttle lever cam touching tool and throttle valve bottomed.

CAUTION: Ensure adjustment is made with spring fully compressed and valve bottomed in valve body bore.

Line Pressure

1) Turn Allen screw in end of pressure regulator spring bracket so measurement between valve body and inner edge of adjusting nut is 1 5/16".

NOTE: **Due to manufacturing tolerances, adjustment can be varied to obtain specified line pressure.**

2) Turning adjusting screw 1 complete turn changes closed throttle line pressure about 1 2/3 psi (.12 kg/cm²). Turning adjusting screw counterclockwise increases pressure; clockwise decreases pressure.

STALL TEST

1) Before making test, check transaxle fluid level, bring engine to normal operating temperature, and attach a tachometer to engine.

2) Test consists of determining engine speed obtained at full throttle in "D" (Drive) position. Both parking and service brakes must be fully applied while making test.

CAUTION: **Do not hold throttle open any longer than is necessary to obtain a maximum engine speed reading, and never longer than 5 seconds at a time.**

3) If more than one stall test is required, operate engine at approximately 1000 RPM in Neutral for 20 seconds to cool transaxle fluid between runs. If engine speed exceeds maximum limits shown, release accelerator immediately since transaxle clutch slippage is indicated.

STALL SPEED SPECIFICATIONS

Engine	Transaxle Model	Stall RPM
2.2L		
Non-EFI	A-413	2650-2850
EFI	A-413	[1] 2280-2480
Turbo	A-413	3020-3220
2.6L	A-470	[2] 2400-2600

[1] – 2650-2850 on Lazer and Daytona.
[2] – 2450-2650 on Caravan, Ram Van and Voyager.

STALL TEST RESULTS

Stall Speed Above Specification

If stall speed exceeds maximum limits shown by more than 200 RPM, transaxle clutch slippage is indicated. Make hydraulic pressure and air pressure checks to determine cause of slippage.

Stall Speed Below Specification

1) Low stall speeds (with a properly tuned engine) indicate torque converter stator clutch problems. A road test will be necessary to identify exact problem.

2) If stall speeds are 250-350 RPM below specifications, and vehicle operates properly at highway speeds, but has poor through-gear acceleration, stator overrunning clutch is slipping.

3) If stall speed and acceleration are normal, but abnormally high throttle opening is required to maintain highway speeds, stator clutch has seized.

4) Both of the preceding stator defects require replacement of the torque converter.

Noise During Stall Test

1) A whining or siren-like noise due to fluid flow is normal during stall operation with some converters; however, loud metallic noises from loose parts or interference within the assembly indicate a defective torque converter.

2) To be sure that noise originates within the converter, raise vehicle on hoist and operate at light throttle in "D" and "N" while listening under transaxle bellhousing.

AIR PRESSURE TESTS

A "No Drive" condition could exist even with correct fluid pressure because of inoperative clutches or bands. The inoperative units can be located by applying air pressure to the appropriate case passages after valve body has been removed.

CAUTION: **Compressed air supply must be free of dirt and moisture. Use a pressure of 30 psi (2.1 kg/cm²) for tests.**

Front Clutch

Direct air pressure into front clutch apply passage. Operation of clutch is indicated by a dull thud which may be heard, or felt. Hold air pressure on for a few seconds and check system for excessive oil leaks.

Rear Clutch

Direct air pressure into rear clutch apply passage. Operation of clutch is indicated by a dull thud which may be heard, or felt. Again, check for excessive oil leaks.

Kickdown Servo (Front)

Direct air pressure into front servo apply passage. Operation of servo is indicated by a tightening of the front band. Spring tension on servo piston should release the band.

Low-Reverse Servo (Rear)

Direct air pressure into rear servo apply passage. Operation of servo is indicated by a tightening of the rear band. Spring tension of servo piston should release the band.

NOTE: **If clutches and servos operate properly, no upshift or erratic shift conditions indicate malfunctions in valve body assembly**

SERVICE (IN VEHICLE)

NOTE: **The valve body, extension housing oil seal, parking sprag, and governor assembly may be removed with transaxle still installed in vehicle. See procedures given in TRANSAXLE DISASSEMBLY and TRANSAXLE REASSEMBLY & ADJUSTMENT.**

SPEEDOMETER PINION GEAR

NOTE: **Any time that speedometer pinion adapter is removed, a new "O" ring must be installed on outside diameter of adapter. Speedometer pinion must be removed before removing right drive axle shaft.**

Removal

Remove bolt and washer securing speedometer pinion adapter in extension housing. With cable housing connected, carefully work adapter and pinion out of extension housing. Remove retainer and remove pinion from adapter.

Seal Replacement

If transaxle fluid is found in cable housing, install a new speedometer pinion and seal assembly. If fluid is found between cable and adapter, replace small "O" ring on cable.

Fig. 3: Bottom View of Transmission Case (With Valve Body Removed) Showing Air Pressure Test Points

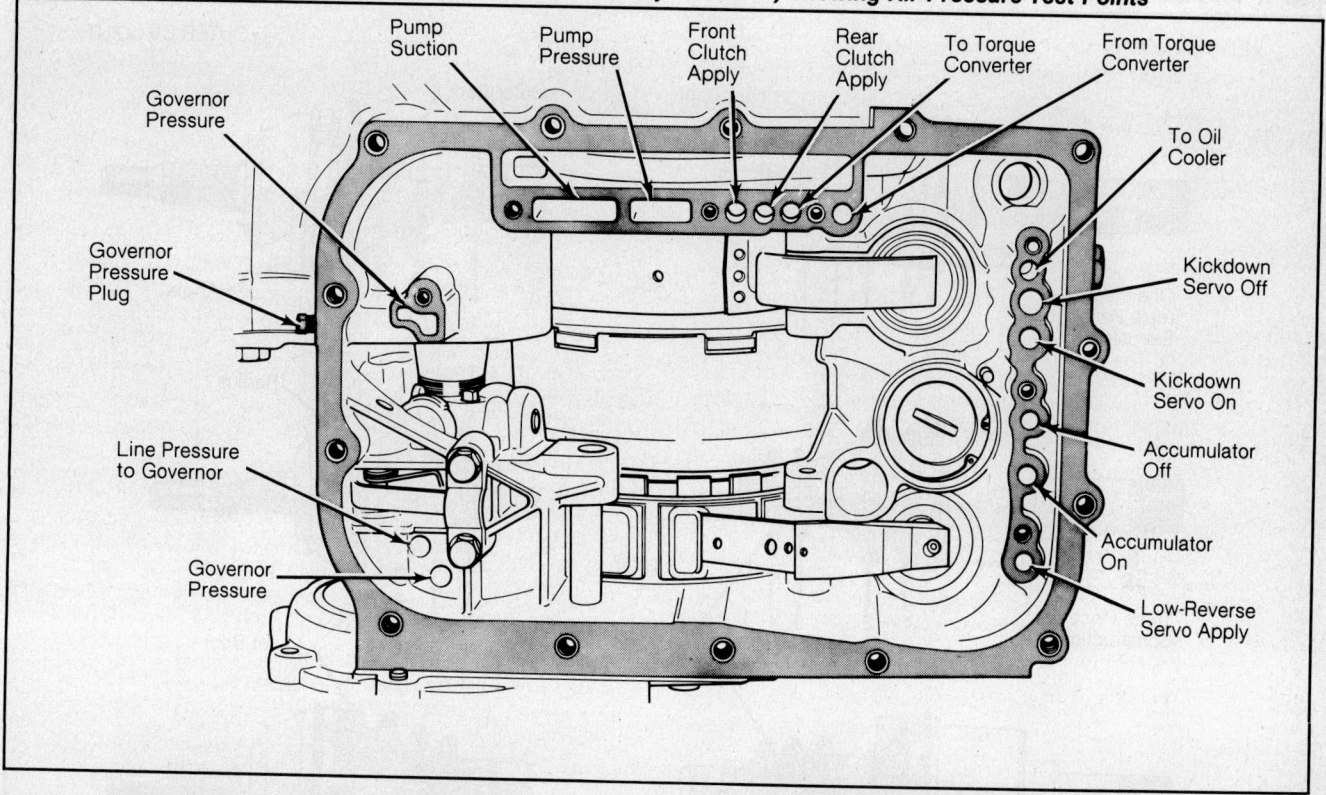

Installation

Before installing pinion, adapter and cable assembly ensure adapter flange and its mating areas on extension housing are clean. Dirt or sand will cause misalignment resulting in speedometer pinion gear damage. Install and tighten bolt.

NEUTRAL SAFETY SWITCH

See appropriate AUTOMATIC TRANSMISSION SERVICING article in DOMESTIC GENERAL SERVICING section.

WHEEL BEARINGS

Removal

1) Remove drive axle shafts. See DRIVE AXLE SHAFTS in this article. Remove disc brake rotor. Separate ball joint stud from knuckle. Loosen 3 bearing retainer bolts. Install Bearing Remover (C-4811). Position thrust button inside hub bore.

2) Tighten remover to remove hub from bearing. Remove bearing remover and 3 bearing retainer bolts. Pry seal from knuckle. Press bearing from knuckle using Bearing Remover (C-4811).

NOTE: Replace bearing whenever hub is removed.

Installation

1) Press new bearing into knuckle. Install new outer seal and bearing retainer. Press hub onto bearing. Install new inner seal. Lubricate wear sleeve. Install wear sleeve and drive shaft.

2) Install knuckle assembly on lower control arm. Install tie rod end and disc brake rotor. Install caliper assembly and brake hose retainer. Install washer and hub

nut. Tighten to specification. Install spring washer, lock nut and cotter pin

DRIVE AXLE SHAFTS

All models (except turbo) have unequal length axle shafts. Turbo models have 2 short, equal length axle shafts. The right axle shaft (turbo only) has an intermediate shaft with support assembly mounted to engine block. Different make axle shafts (ACI, GKN or Citroen) may be used. Service replacement parts ARE NOT interchangeable. To avoid problems, the make of shaft must be determined prior to ordering parts. See Fig. 4.

CAUTION: The axle shaft (when installed) acts as a bolt and secures the hub/bearing assembly. If vehicle is to be supported or moved on its wheels, install a bolt through the hub to ensure that hub/bearing assembly cannot loosen.

Removal

1) Remove hub retaining nuts at wheel assemblies. Drive shafts are retained in differential side gears by constant force of spring in inboard CV joint. To remove right-side drive shaft, first remove speedometer pinion.

2) Remove clamp bolt securing ball joint stud on steering knuckle. Separate ball joint stud from steering knuckle by prying against knuckle leg and control arm without damaging ball joint or CV joint boots. Separate outer CV joint splined shaft from hub by holding CV housing while moving knuckle (hub) assembly away.

NOTE: Do not pry on or otherwise damage wear sleeve on CV joint.

Fig. 4: Chrysler Corp. Axle Shaft Identification

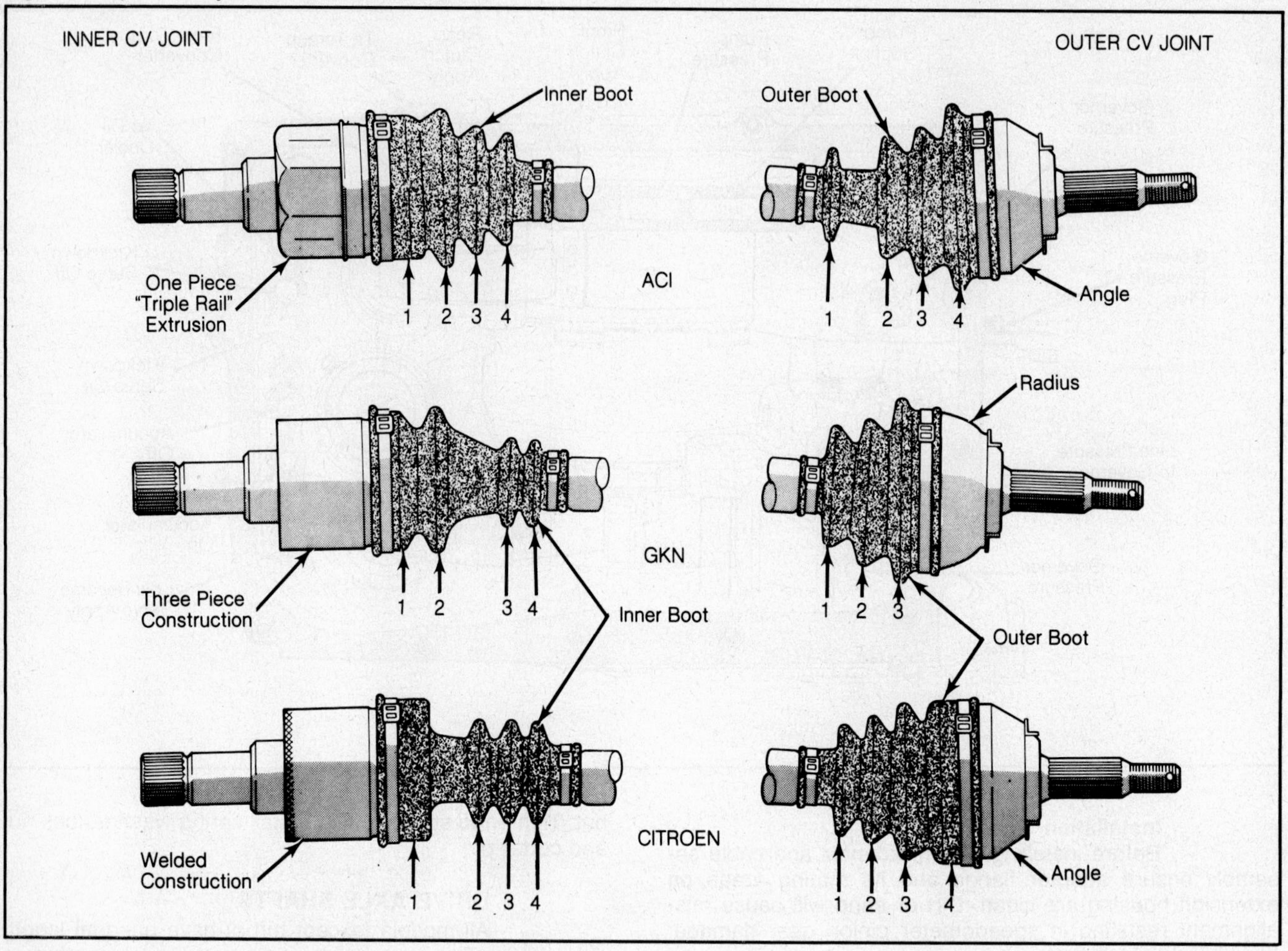

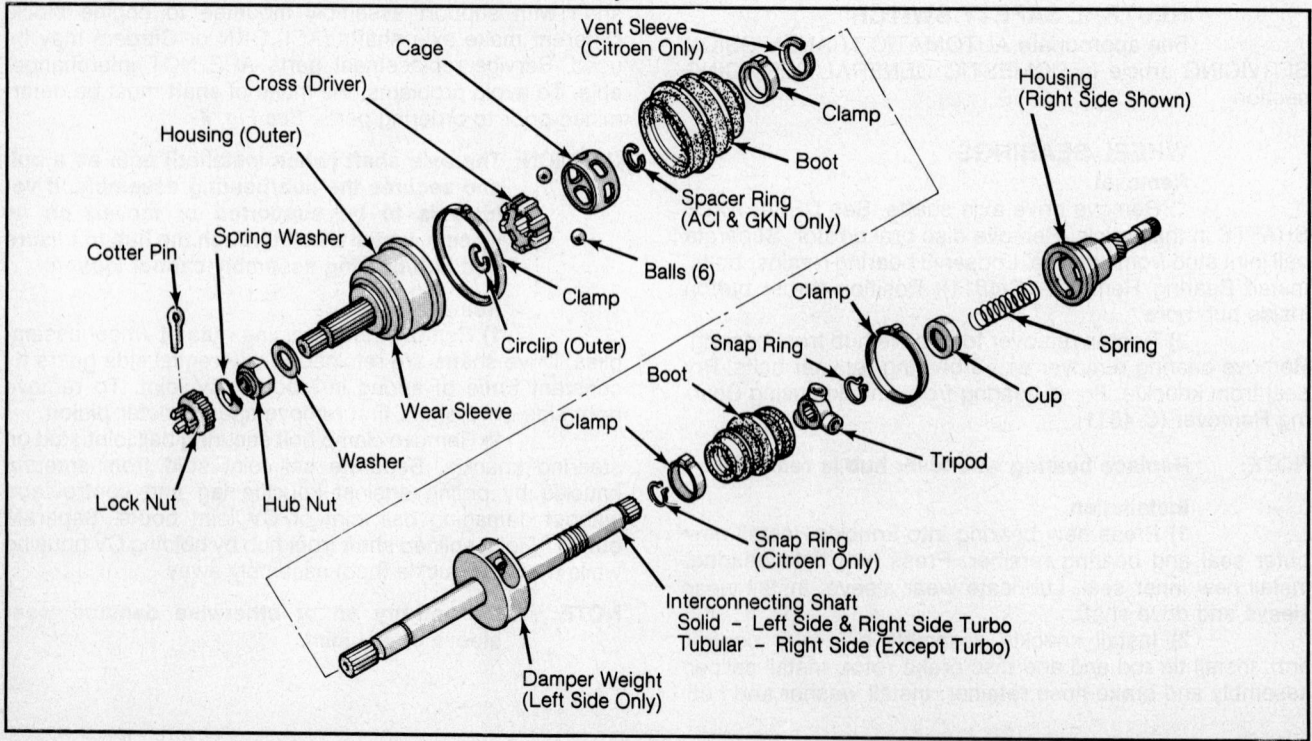

INNER CV JOINT

OUTER CV JOINT

Inner Boot

Outer Boot

One Piece "Triple Rail" Extrusion

ACI

Angle

Radius

Three Piece Construction

GKN

Inner Boot

Outer Boot

Welded Construction

CITROEN

Angle

Fig. 5: Exploded View of Front Drive Axle Shaft Assembly

Cage

Cross (Driver)

Housing (Outer)

Spring Washer

Cotter Pin

Lock Nut

Hub Nut

Washer

Wear Sleeve

Circlip (Outer)

Clamp

Balls (6)

Vent Sleeve (Citroen Only)

Clamp

Boot

Spacer Ring (ACI & GKN Only)

Housing (Right Side Shown)

Spring

Cup

Clamp

Snap Ring

Boot

Clamp

Tripod

Snap Ring (Citroen Only)

Interconnecting Shaft
Solid – Left Side & Right Side Turbo
Tubular – Right Side (Except Turbo)

Damper Weight (Left Side Only)

CHRYSLER CORP. A-413 & A-470 (Cont.)

3) Support assembly at CV joint housings. Remove by pulling outward on inner joint housing. DO NOT pull on shaft.

Installation

1) Lubricate wear sleeve and steering knuckle grease seal. These components MUST be lubricated any time knuckle and drive shaft are separated.

2) Hold inner joint assembly at housing while aligning and guiding inner joint spline into transaxle (or intermediate shaft assembly on Turbo models). If equipped with ACI CV joint, ensure that tripod is engaged in housing and boot is not twisted.

3) To install outer CV joint, push knuckle (hub) assembly out and install splined outer CV joint shaft in hub. Reinstall knuckle assembly on ball joint stud. Install and tighten clamp bolt.

4) Install speedometer pinion gear. Install and tighten hub retaining nut. Check transaxle fluid level and add as needed.

5) If inboard boot is collapsed or deformed, boot must be vented. Remove boot clamp (if rubber clamp is used, venting may be accomplished without removing clamp) and insert a blunt, small diameter rod between boot and axle shaft.

6) Squeeze boot to remove air pockets, ensuring that no dirt enters, or grease escapes from boot. Install new clamp.

INNER CV JOINT
Disassembly

1) With axle shaft assembly removed from vehicle, remove clamps and pull back boots to provide access to tripod retention system. On ACI and GKN joints, bend retaining tabs away from rollers. On Citroen joints, slightly deform retaining ring at each roller.

2) Support housing as retention spring pushes it off of tripod. Hold rollers in position when removing housing to prevent rollers from falling off of studs. Secure rollers to studs by wrapping with tape. If a new retainer ring is to be used on Citroen joints, carefully cut away old retainer ring.

3) Remove snap ring from end of shaft and remove tripod. Tap tripod with brass punch and small hammer as needed to remove. Remove as much grease as possible from assembly. Inspect joint housing, ball raceway, tripod components, spring, spring cup and rounded end of shaft for excessive wear. Replace components as needed.

Reassembly

1) Slide new rubber seal onto stub shaft, past splines, and seat in groove (Turbo models, only). Slide small rubber clamp onto shaft (some ACI or GKN joints), or install small metal clamp or buckle. Slide end of boot over shaft.

2) On tubular shafts (right-side except Turbo), position boot lip even with locating mark on shaft. On solid shafts (left-side and right-side Turbo), position small boot end in machined groove in shaft.

3) Clamp boot in place by positioning rubber clamp over boot, or by tightening metal clamp. If using a bridge-type clamp, position clamp over boot. Ensure that it is properly located over boot and shaft, and is not twisted. Locate clamp tangs in slot, making clamp as tight as possible by hand. Complete tightening by clamping bridge with Clamp Pliers (C-4124).

4) If using Citroen-type binding clamp, wrap binding strap around boot twice, plus an additional 2 1/2",

then remove strap. Pass one end of strap through buckle and fold back about 1 1/8" over inside of buckle. Place strap over boot with eye toward you and wrap strap around boot twice, passing end of strap through eye each time.

5) Fold strap back slightly to prevent it from slipping backwards. Open Clamp Pliers (C-4653) and place strap in narrow slot about 1/2" away from buckle. Hold strap with left hand and push clamp pliers forward and slightly upward, then fit hook of clamp pliers into eye of buckle.

6) Tighten strap by closing plier handles. Rotate plier (handles) downward while slowly releasing pressure on handles. Allow handles to open progressively. Fully open pliers and remove sideways from strap.

7) If strap is not tight enough, repeat procedure, always with pliers about 1/2" away from buckle. When strap is tight enough, remove pliers and cut strap off about 1/8" away from buckle. Complete by folding strap back neatly (end of strap must not extend beyond eye).

8) Slide tripod on shaft with non-chamfered end (ACI and GKN) facing retainer groove at end of shaft (both ends of Citroen tripod are the same). Install snap ring in groove at end of shaft. Lubricating grease is provided in Boot Joint Kit. Distribute 1 packet (ACI), 2 packets (GKN) or 2/3 packet (Citroen) of grease in boot. Distribute remaining grease in CV joint housing.

9) Position spring in housing spring pocket. Place a small amount of grease on concave side of spring cup and place cup over end of spring. Remove tape from tripod and install housing assembly over tripod. On GKN joints, bend retaining tabs down to original position and check for positive retention of tripod. DO NOT bend tabs on ACI joints. Boot will hold housing on shaft.

10) On Citroen joints, hold rollers in place on tripod while installing housing. Reform retainer ring with hammer and a dull punch. If a new ring is required, "roll" edge into housing groove with punch and hammer. While performing this operation, hold retaining collar in place with 2 "C" clamps. Check for positive retention of tripod.

11) On all models, position boot over housing, placing boot lip in housing groove. Install boot clamp as described in steps **3)** through **7)**.

OUTER CV JOINT
Disassembly

1) Cut boot clamp on boot and discard. Wipe grease away to expose joint. Support shaft in soft-jawed vise. Support outer joint. Using a hammer, tap top of joint body sharply to dislodge joint from internal circlip. Circlip is installed in groove at outer end of shaft.

NOTE: **DO NOT remove wear sleeve from housing unless damaged.**

2) Remove circlip from shaft groove and discard. Do not remove heavy spacer ring from shaft unless shaft is damaged and requires replacement. With joint separated, proceed as follows:

3) If outer CV joint was operating properly and grease does not appear to be contaminated, replace boot. Further disassembly is not required. If outer joint is noisy or badly worn, replace entire unit.

4) Wipe off surplus grease and mark relative position of inner cross, cage and housing with a dab of paint. Hold joint vertically in soft-jawed vise by clamping on splined shaft.

5) Press down on one side of inner race to tilt cage and remove ball from opposite side. If joint is tight, use hammer and brass drift to tap inner race. DO NOT HIT CAGE. Repeat until all 6 balls are removed. A screwdriver may be used to pry out balls, as needed.

6) Tilt cage and inner race assembly vertically and position 2 opposing cage windows in area between ball grooves. *See Fig. 6.* Remove cage and inner race assembly by pulling upward, away from housing.

7) Turn inner cross (driver) 90° to cage and align 1 spherical land of race with cage window. Raise land into cage window and remove inner race by swinging out.

Fig. 6: Removing Cage & Cross from Outer CV Joint

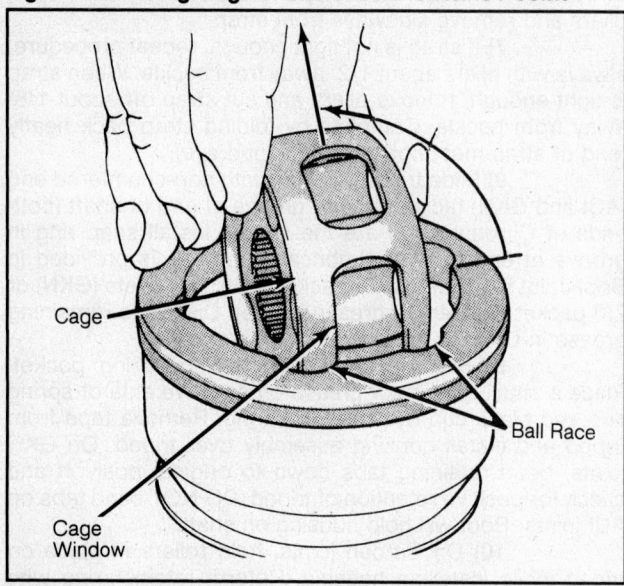

Turn cage 90° to position openings between ball races, then rotate cage out.

Inspection

1) Wash all parts in solvent and dry with compressed air. Inspect housing ball races for excessive wear and scoring. Check splined shaft and nut threads for damage. During any service procedure where steering knuckle and axle shaft are separated, thoroughly clean seal and wear sleeve with solvent.

2) Inspect all 6 balls for pitting, cracks, scoring and wear. Dulling of surface is normal. Inspect cage for excessive wear on inside and outside spherical surfaces, surface ripples on cage window, cracks and chipping.

3) Inspect inner race (cross) for excessive wear or scoring of ball races. If any of the preceding is found, complete CV joint should be replaced.

NOTE: **Polished areas in races (cross and housing) and on cage spheres are normal and do not indicate need for joint replacement unless they are suspected of causing noise and/or vibration.**

Reassembly

1) If wear sleeve was removed, position new sleeve on housing and install with Installer (C-4698). Lightly oil all components before reassembling outer joint. Align parts according to paint markings made at disassembly.

2) Insert 1 inner race (cross) land into a cage window and feed race into cage. Pivot cross 90° to complete cage assembly.

3) Align opposing cage window with housing land and feed race assembly into housing. Pivot cage 90° to complete installation. When properly assembled, large cross counterbore (ACI and GKN) or cross and cage chamfers (Citroen) will be facing outward from joint. *See Fig. 7.*

Fig. 7: Cutaway View of Outer CV Joint Showing Correct Cage & Cross Installation

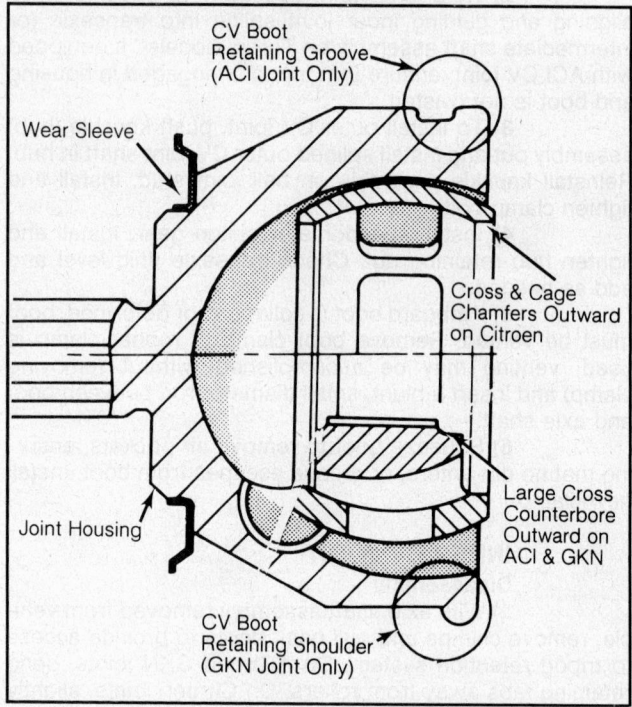

4) Apply lubricant to ball races from packet provided in kit and distribute equally between all sides of ball grooves. One packet is sufficient to lubricate joint. Insert balls into races by tilting cage and inner race assembly.

5) Install boot on shaft as described in steps 3) through 7) of INNER CV JOINT REASSEMBLY procedure. On Citroen joints, install vent sleeve under small end of outer boot. Install new circlip (provided with kit) on shaft, using care not to expand or twist clip during installation. Lubricate wear sleeve and steering knuckle grease seal. *See Fig. 8.*

6) Install hub nut on end of stub shaft to protect threads. Position outer joint on splined end of shaft, engage splines and tap hub nut sharply with a mallet. Check that circlip is properly seated by attempting to pull joint from shaft.

7) Locate large end of boot over joint housing, checking that boot is not twisted. Install boot clamp as described in steps 3) through 7) of INNER CV JOINT REASSEMBLY procedure.

INTERMEDIATE SHAFT ASSEMBLY (TURBO ONLY)
Removal

Remove right axle shaft and speedometer drive pinion as previously described. Remove screws from bearing support-to-engine bracket. Pull intermediate shaft assembly from transaxle.

Fig. 8: Lubricating Wear Sleeve & Grease Seal

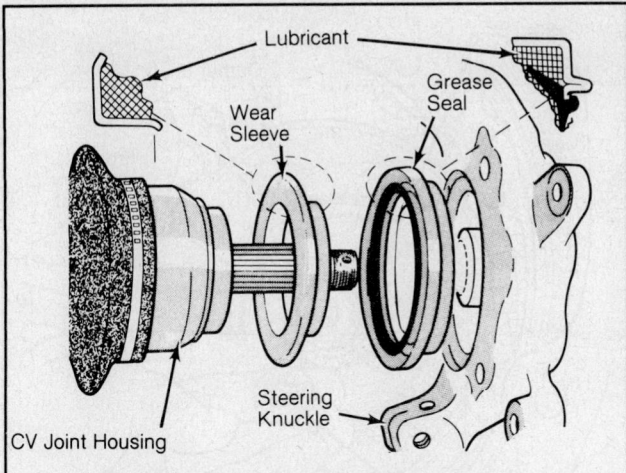

Clean and lubricate sleeve and seal any time knuckle and drive shaft are separated.

Disassembly (Universal Joint)

Mark axle shafts for correct reassembly. Remove universal joint retaining clips from inner edge of bearing caps. Use 1 1/8" socket and hammer to remove caps from yoke.

Reassembly

Place universal joint cross between yokes. Position caps and drive into position with hammer, guiding cross into caps. Install new retaining clips.

Disassembly (Bearing Assembly)

Remove 2 bearing assembly-to-bracket screws. Press stub shaft from bearing assembly. Do not damage inner slinger, rubber seal or end of stub shaft. Remove slinger if damaged.

Reassembly

To install slinger, use a 2" (51 mm) diameter by 3" (76 mm) long pipe. Press bearing assembly onto shaft until there is a minimum 1/32" (1 mm) clearance between bearing and slinger. Press outer slinger into position until it bottoms on shoulder of shaft.

Installation

1) Loosely attach support bracket to bearing. Guide axle shaft into transaxle. Attach support bracket assembly to engine and tighten bracket-to-engine bolts to 40 ft. lbs. (54 N.m).

2) Push shaft into transaxle as far as possible. Hold shaft in position and tighten support bracket-to-bearing bolts to 21 ft. lbs. (28 N.m). Apply a liberal amount of grease to inner splines and pilot bore on bearing end of shaft. Install speedometer pinion and right axle shaft.

AXLE SHAFT POSITIONING

1) Place vehicle on alignment rack or platform hoist, so all 4 wheels are supporting vehicle. Ensure vehicle is completely assembled. Front wheels must be aligned and straight ahead.

2) Measure distance from bottom inner edge of outboard CV boot (small end) to bottom inner edge of inboard CV boot (large end). Compare measurement to specifications given in AXLE SHAFT POSITIONING SPECIFICATIONS chart.

3) If either axle shaft is not positioned correctly, engine may be moved to adjust. To adjust, support engine with floor jack to remove load on motor mounts. Loosen vertical bolts on right motor mount. Loosen front engine mount bracket-to-front crossmember bolts.

4) Pry engine right or left to position axle shafts. Tighten right engine vertical bolts to 21 ft. lbs. (28 N.m). Tighten front engine mount bolts to 40 ft. lbs. (54 N.m). Lower floor jack and recheck axle shaft positioning.

5) If axle shafts cannot be positioned, check for bent or damaged side rails. After axle shafts are properly positioned, transaxle shift linkage must be adjusted. See appropriate AUTOMATIC TRANSMISSION SERVICING article in DOMESTIC GENERAL SERVICING section.

AXLE SHAFT POSITIONING SPECIFICATIONS

Application	Side/Tape Color	Measurement In. (mm)
Caravan, Ram Van & Voyager	Rt./Blue	20.5-20.9 (520-532)
	Lt./Blue	10.0-10.6 (255-270)
	Rt./Green	21.3-21.6 (542-549)
	Lt./Green	10.6-11.2 (270-285)
Charger, Horizon Omni, Turismo (Exc. Turbo)	Rt./Yellow	19.6-20.0 (498-509)
	Lt./Yellow	9.5-10.0 (240-253)
	Rt./Red	18.5-19.0 (469-478)
	Lt./Red	8.2-8.6 (208-218)
	Rt./Green	18.3-18.8 (465-477)
	Lt./Green	8.3-8.7 (211-220)
	Rt./Blue	18.2-18.6 (463-472)
	Lt./Blue	8.0-8.4 (204-213)
All Models With 2.2L Turbo	Rt./Tan	10.1-10.4 (257-265)
	Lt./Silver	10.0-10.6 (254-269)
	Rt./Red	9.5-9.9 (241-252)
	Lt./Yellow	9.4-10.0 (238-255)
	Rt./Org.	8.3-8.7 (211-220)
	Lt./Org.	8.3-8.7 (211-220)
All Others 2.2L	Rt./Blue	19.9-20.3 (498-515)
	Lt./Blue	10.2-10.9 (259-277)
	Rt./Green	18.8-19.1 (477-485)
	Lt./Green	9.0-9.6 (229-244)
	Rt./Org.	19.4-19.7 (492-500)
	Lt./Org.	9.6-10.2 (243-258)
	Rt./White	18.9-19.4 (480-492)
	Lt./White	9.4-10.0 (238-255)
2.6L	Rt./Silver	19.7-20.1 (501-510)
	Lt./Silver	10.0-10.6 (254-269)
	Rt./Yellow	18.9-19.4 (480-492)
	Lt./Yellow	9.4-10.0 (238-255)

REMOVAL & INSTALLATION

See appropriate AUTOMATIC TRANSMISSION REMOVAL article in DOMESTIC GENERAL SERVICING section.

TORQUE CONVERTER

The torque converter is a welded assembly and is not serviceable. Therefore, if a malfunction occurs or if the converter becomes contaminated with foreign material, it must be replaced. It cannot be flushed or repaired.

Automatic Transmissions
CHRYSLER CORP. A-413 & A-470 (Cont.)

TRANSAXLE DISASSEMBLY

INPUT SHAFT END PLAY

To check end play, attach a dial indicator to transaxle bellhousing with its plunger seated against end of input shaft. Move input shaft in and out to obtain end play reading. End play should be .007-.073" (.18-1.85 mm). Record end play reading for reassembly reference.

DISASSEMBLY

1) Place transaxle in a holding fixture. Remove attaching bolts and lift off transaxle oil pan. Remove screws and lift off oil filter and gasket. Remove neutral safety/back-up light switch.

2) Remove parking rod retaining "E" clip and remove parking rod. Remove valve body attaching bolts (7). Lift valve body assembly from transaxle using care not to damage governor tubes.

Fig. 9: *Removing Valve Body Assembly*

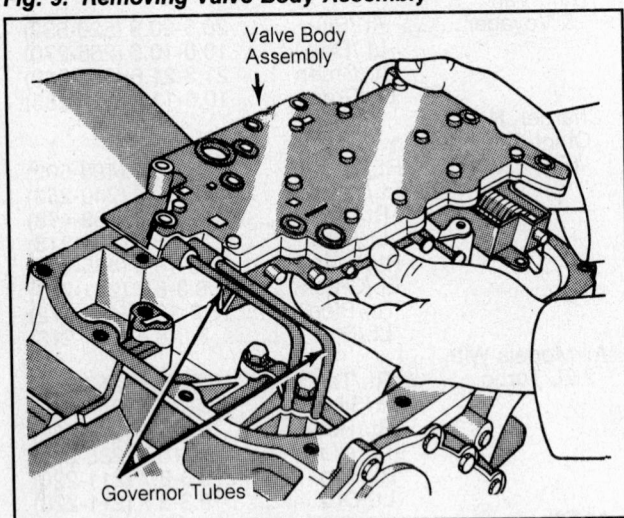

Use care when removing valve body to avoid damage to governor tubes.

3) Tighten kickdown band adjusting screw to retain parts when oil pump is removed. Remove oil pump attaching bolts. Using 2 slide hammer pullers installed opposite each other, pull oil pump and No. 1 thrust washer from case. Remove pump-to-case gasket. Loosen kickdown band adjusting screw.

4) Slide kickdown band and strut from case. Remove front clutch assembly. Slide rear clutch assembly out of case by pulling input shaft. Remove thrust washer No. 2 from input shaft and clutch drum.

5) Remove No. 3 thrust washer from end of output shaft. *See Fig. 10.* Remove snap ring retaining front planetary gear assembly in case. Slide out gear assembly.

6) Remove thrust washer No. 6 from sun gear driving shell, then slide out driving shell. Remove thrust washer No. 9 from rear planetary gear set. Remove gear set from case.

NOTE: **Thrust washers No. 7 and 8 are assembled with sun gear driving shell assembly.**

7) Remove thrust washer No. 10. Withdraw overrunning clutch cam assembly. Remove overrunning clutch rollers and springs (8). Loosen low-reverse band

Fig. 10: *Removing No. 3 Thrust Washer*

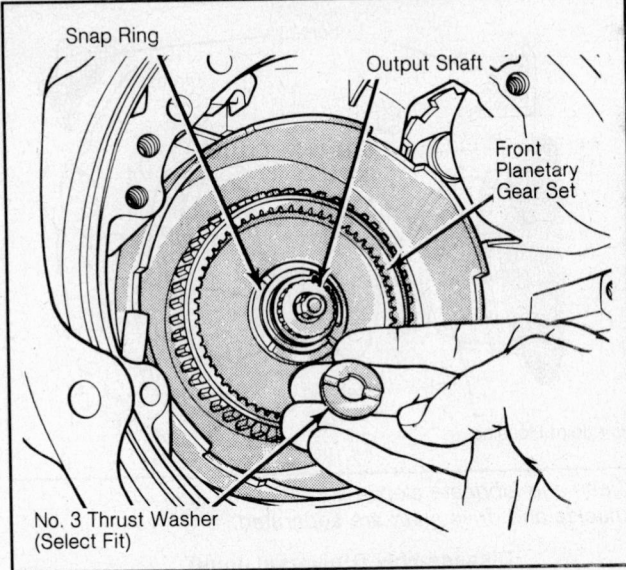

Fig. 11: *Removing Overrunning Clutch Rollers & Springs*

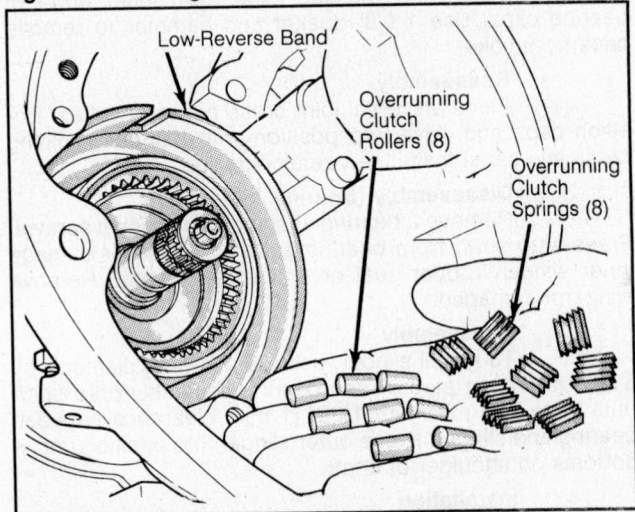

adjusting screw. Remove band and strut from case. Withdraw thrust washer No. 11 from case.

8) Remove attaching bolts and lift off rear cover. Install Special Holder (L-4434) to hold transfer shaft stationary. Remove transfer shaft gear retaining nut and washer.

9) Using gear puller, remove transfer shaft gear and selective fit shim installed behind gear. Remove governor support retainer. Remove low-reverse band anchor pin. Slide governor assembly from transfer shaft.

10) Remove transfer shaft retaining snap ring. Using a slide hammer and Adapter (L-4437), pull transfer shaft and bearing retainer assembly from case.

11) Remove attaching bolts and lift off parking pawl retainer. Slide pivot shaft out. Remove parking pawl and return spring.

12) Hold output shaft stationary with Holder (L-4434). Remove output shaft retaining nut and washer. Remove output shaft gear with puller. Slide out selective fit shim installed behind gear. From front of case slide out output shaft and annulus gear.

Fig. 12: Removing Parking Pawl & Pivot Shaft

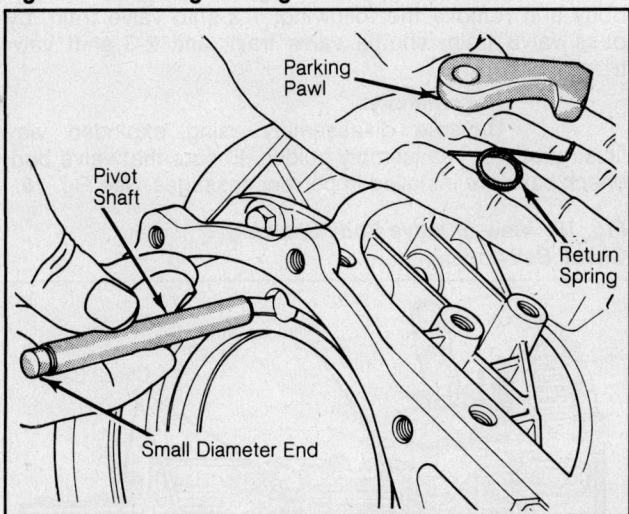

Pivot shaft is installed with small diameter to rear.

Fig. 13: Removing Differential Bearing Retainer

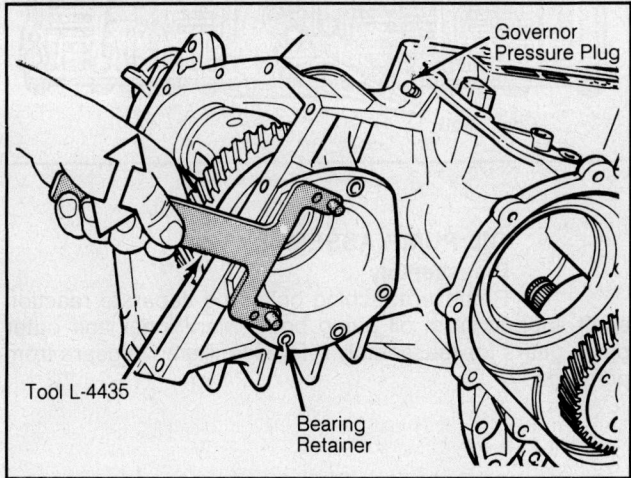

Rock wrench back and forth to remove retainer.

13) Using a screwdriver, pry oil seal out of extension housing. Remove attaching bolts and lift off differential cover.

14) Remove differential bearing retainer bolts. Rotate retainer back and forth with Wrench (L-4435) to remove.

15) Remove extension housing attaching bolts. Rotate housing back and forth to remove. Lift differential assembly out of transaxle case.

CAUTION: Hold on to differential assembly to prevent it from falling out of case when removing extension housing.

COMPONENT DISASSEMBLY & REASSEMBLY

VALVE BODY ASSEMBLY

NOTE: As valve trains are removed from each valve body bore, place individual parts in correct order in relative position to valve body to simplify reassembly.

Disassembly

1) Remove attaching screw and lift detent spring assembly from valve body. With Socket (L-4553), remove valve body screws (16). Lift separator plate and transfer plate off valve body, noting position of screen.

2) Note installation position of valve body check balls (8) in valve body passages. Remove balls from valve body.

3) Remove "E" clip and washer from end of throttle valve lever assembly. Slide manual valve lever assembly off throttle valve lever. Slide throttle valve lever assembly from valve body.

4) Remove manual valve from valve body. Remove pressure regulator and adjusting screw bracket attaching screws. Lift off bracket and adjusting screws. Slide out pressure regulator and manual control valve trains. *See Fig. 14.*

Fig. 14: Exploded View of Pressure Regulators & Manual Controls

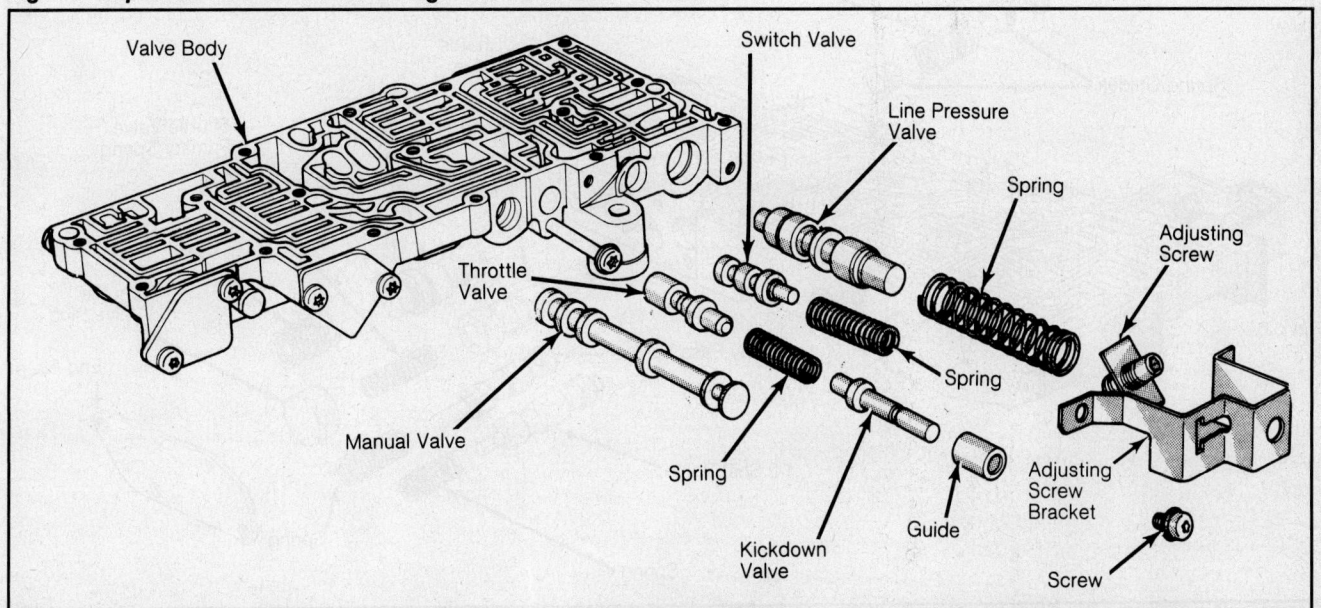

5) Remove end plate and slide out 2-3 shift valve governor plug. Remove next end plate and slide out 1-2 shift valve governor plug. *See Fig. 15.*

Fig. 15: Exploded View of Governor Plugs

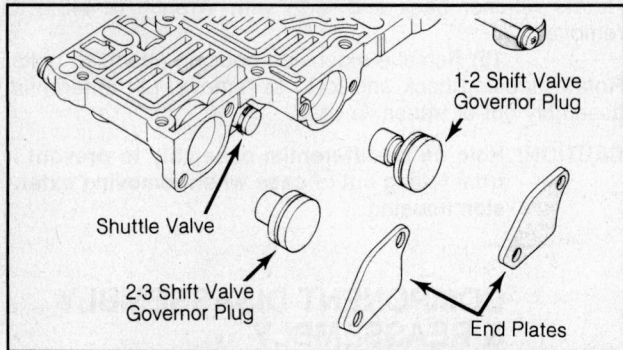

6) Remove end plate screws and carefully remove end plate. Remove regulator valve throttle pressure plug spring and regulator valve throttle pressure plug. *See Fig. 16.*

Fig. 16: Exploded View of Regulator Valve Throttle Pressure Plug Assembly

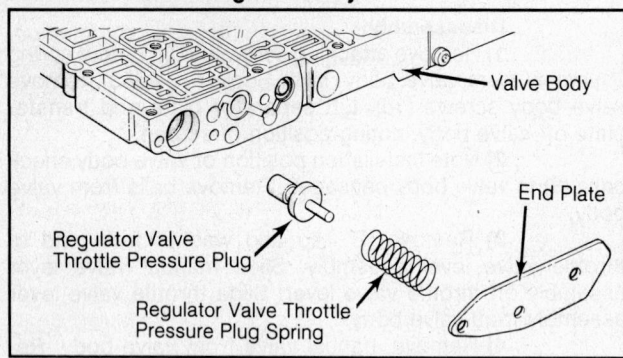

Remove end plate carefully to prevent losing spring.

7) Remove remaining end plate from valve body and remove the following: 1-2 shift valve train, by-pass valve train, shuttle valve train, and 2-3 shift valve train. *See Fig. 17.*

Reassembly

Reverse disassembly using exploded view illustrations as reassembly guides. Ensure that valve body check balls are installed in correct passages. *See Fig. 18.*

Fig. 18: View of Valve Body Showing Check Ball Locations

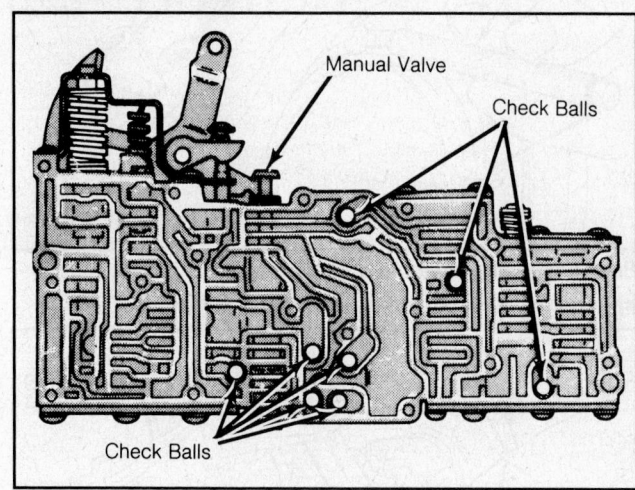

OIL PUMP ASSEMBLY
Disassembly

Remove attaching bolts and separate reaction shaft support from oil pump body. Mark inner and outer pump gears for reassembly reference. Remove gears from pump body.

Fig. 17: Exploded View of Shuttle Valve & Shift Valve Trains

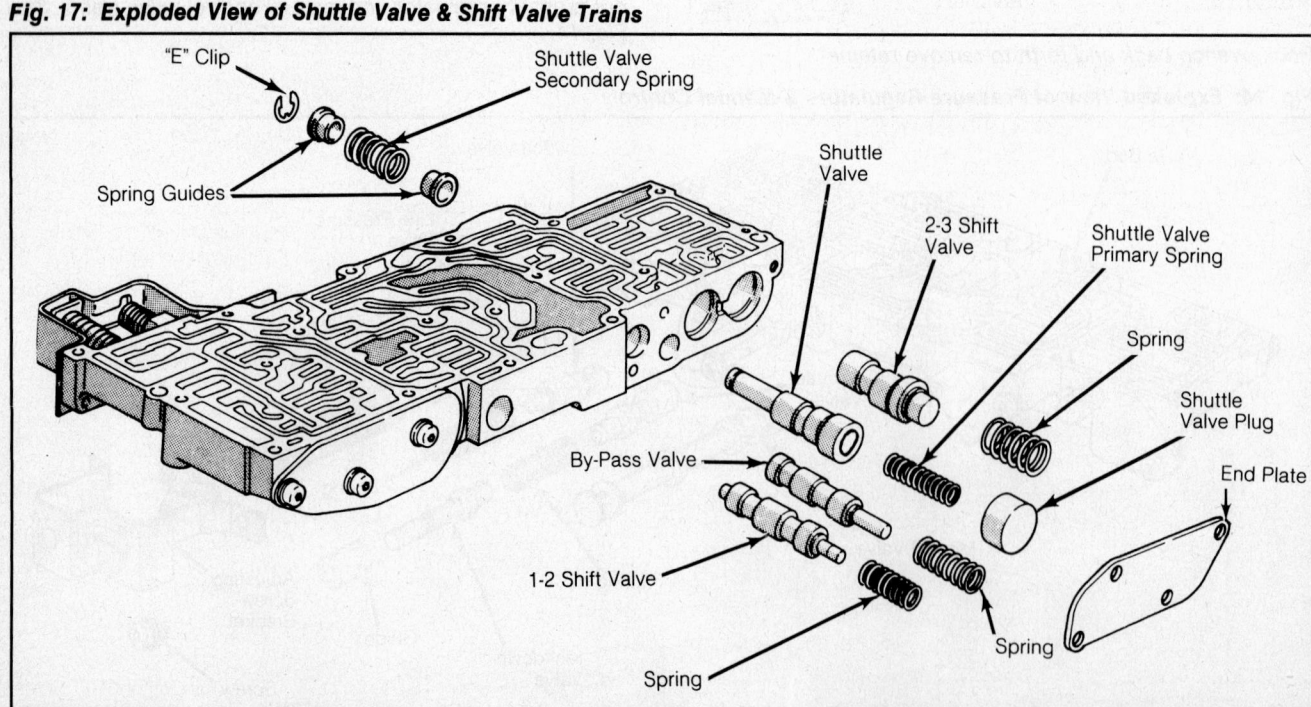

CHRYSLER CORP. A-413 & A-470 (Cont.)

OIL PUMP SPECIFICATIONS

Measurement	Clearance In. (mm)
Outer Gear-to-Pocket	.002-.006 (.045-.141)
Outer Gear I.D.-to-Crescent	.006-.012 (.150-.306)
Outer Gear Side Clearance	.001-.002 (.025-.050)
Inner Gear O.D.-to-Crescent	.006-.012 (.160-.316)
Inner Gear Side Clearance	.001-.002 (.025-.050)

Reassembly

1) Install inner and outer gears into pump body. Using feeler gauge, measure oil pump clearances indicated in OIL PUMP SPECIFICATIONS table.

2) If oil pump clearances are not within specifications, oil pump assembly should be replaced. After clearances have been measured, install reaction shaft support-to-pump body and install attaching bolts.

FRONT CLUTCH ASSEMBLY
Disassembly

1) Using a screwdriver, pry waved snap ring from clutch drum. Lift out reaction plate along with clutch plates and driving discs.

Fig. 19: Removing Front Clutch Return Spring Snap Ring

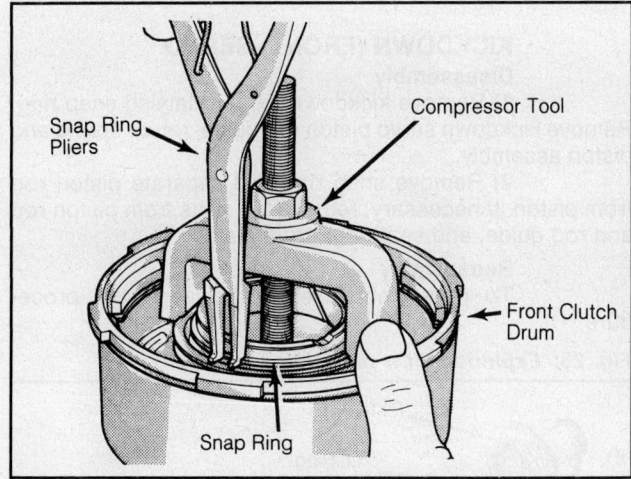

Fig. 20: Installing Front Clutch Plates & Driving Discs into Clutch Drum

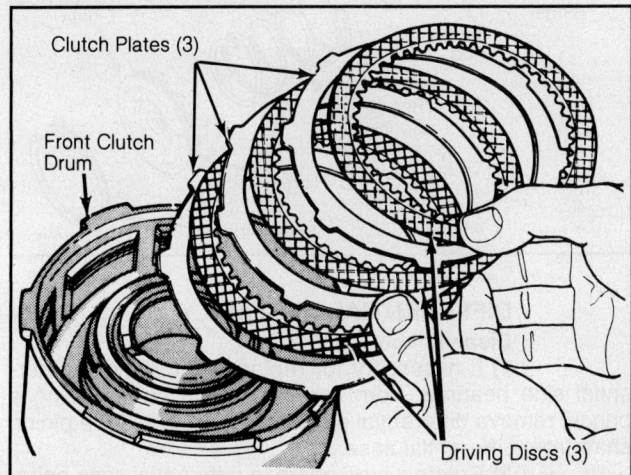

2) Compress clutch return spring and remove retaining snap ring. Remove compressor and lift out return spring retainer, return spring and clutch piston.

3) If necessary for replacement, remove lip seals from clutch piston and from inside of clutch drum.

Reassembly

1) Reverse disassembly procedure to assemble clutch, noting the following:

2) Install clutch plates (3) and driving discs (3) into clutch drum. With clutch plates and discs correctly installed, install reaction plate and retaining snap ring.

3) With front clutch assembly reassembled, use a feeler gauge to measure clearance from reaction plate to farthest wave on waved snap ring. Clearance should be .087-.133" (2.2-3.4 mm) on all models.

REAR CLUTCH ASSEMBLY
Disassembly

1) Pry selective snap ring from rear clutch drum. Lift out reaction plate, clutch plates, driving discs and pressure plate. Record number of clutch plates and driving discs for reassembly reference.

2) Pry piston spring waved snap ring from clutch drum. Remove piston spring and piston. If necessary, remove seals from piston. If necessary, remove input shaft snap ring from inside clutch drum. Press input shaft out of drum.

Fig. 21: Removing Rear Clutch Piston & Spring

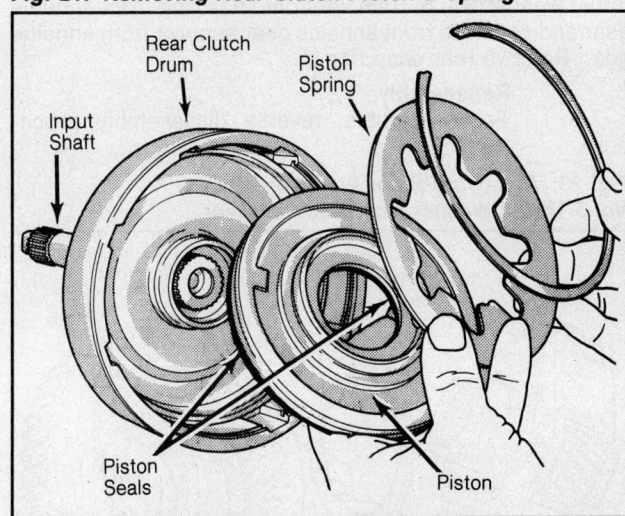

Reassembly

1) To reassemble, reverse disassembly procedure. Install clutch plates and driving discs into rear clutch drum. *See Fig. 22.*

2) With rear clutch reassembled, measure clearance between waved snap ring and reaction plate using a feeler gauge. Clearance should be .026-.043" (.67-1.10 mm), regardless of number of discs used.

3) If clearance is not within correct limits, install selective snap ring as required to obtain correct clearance. Snap rings are available in thicknesses of .048-.050" (1.22-1.27 mm), .060-.062" (1.52-1.57 mm), .068-.070" (1.73-1.78 mm), .074-.076" (1.88-1.93 mm) and .087-.089" (2.21-2.26 mm).

Fig. 22: Installing Clutch Plates & Driving Discs

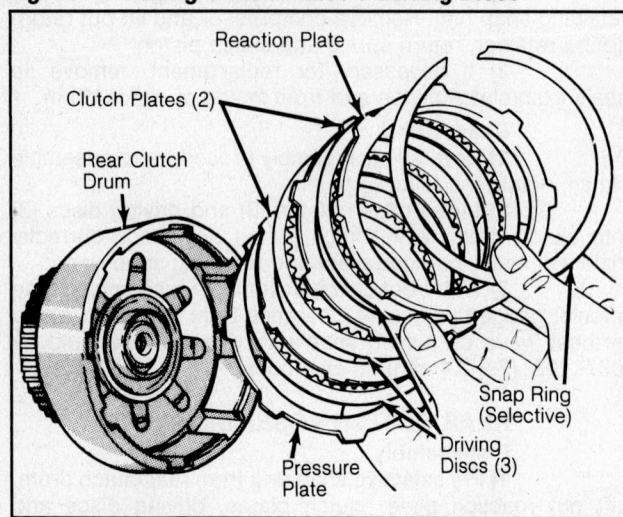

FRONT PLANETARY & ANNULUS GEAR
Disassembly

1) Remove snap ring retaining front planetary gear set in annulus gear. Remove thrust washer No. 4 which is located under snap ring.

2) Lift planetary gear from annulus gear. Lift out thrust washer No. 5. Remove front snap ring from annulus gear and separate front annulus gear support from annulus gear. Remove rear snap ring.

Reassembly

To reassemble, reverse disassembly procedure.

Fig. 23: Removing Front Planetary Gear & No. 5 Thrust Washer from Annulus Gear

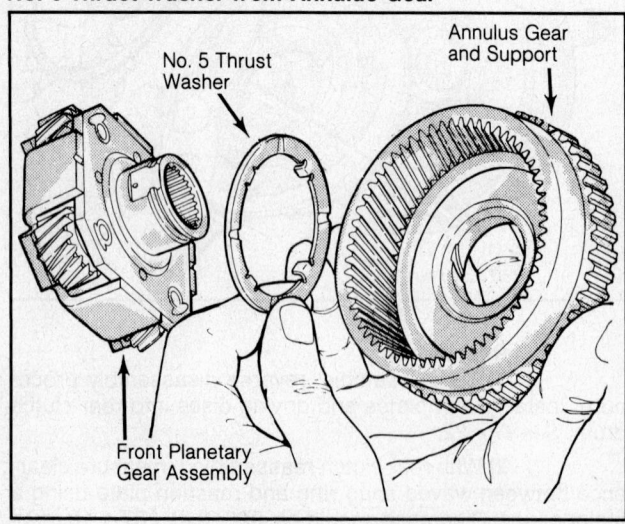

LOW-REVERSE SERVO
Disassembly & Reassembly

Remove servo retainer snap ring from servo bore in case. Lift out servo retainer, return spring and low-reverse servo assembly. Reverse disassembly procedure. Replace servo assembly lip seal if necessary.

ACCUMULATOR ASSEMBLY
Disassembly & Reassembly

Remove accumulator retaining snap ring. Lift accumulator plate from case bore. Withdraw accumulator spring and piston. If necessary, remove seal rings from piston. To reassemble, reverse disassembly procedure.

Fig. 24: Removing Accumulator Piston & Spring

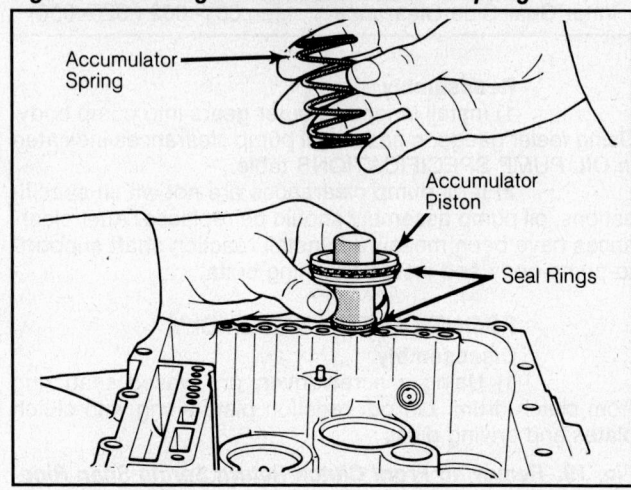

KICKDOWN (FRONT) SERVO
Disassembly

1) Remove kickdown servo retaining snap ring. Remove kickdown servo piston rod guide, return spring and piston assembly.

2) Remove snap ring and separate piston rod from piston. If necessary, remove "O" rings from piston rod and rod guide, and seal rings from piston.

Reassembly

To reassemble, reverse disassembly procedure.

Fig. 25: Exploded View of Kickdown Servo

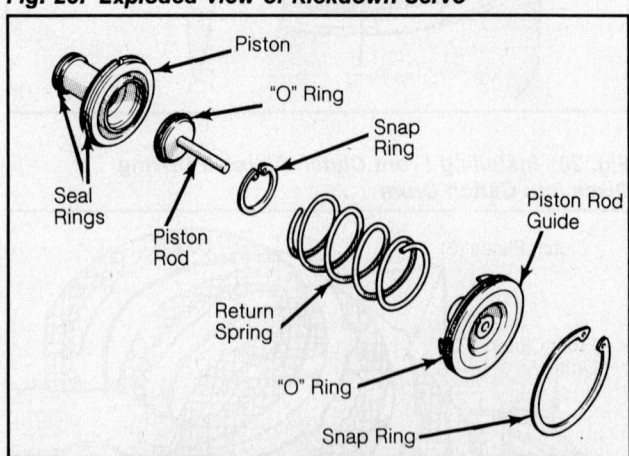

DIFFERENTIAL ASSEMBLY
Disassembly

1) If necessary for replacement, remove differential side bearings from carrier using a puller. Using a punch, remove differential pinion shaft roll pin. Drive pinion shaft from differential case.

2) Rotate pinion gears to differential case opening, then remove pinion gears, side gears and the 4 thrust

washers. If necessary for replacement, remove ring gear attaching bolts. Press ring gear off differential case.

Reassembly

To reassemble, reverse disassembly procedure. Immerse ring gear in boiling water for 15 minutes before installing on differential case.

Fig. 26: Exploded View of Differential Gears, Thrust Washers & Pinion Shaft

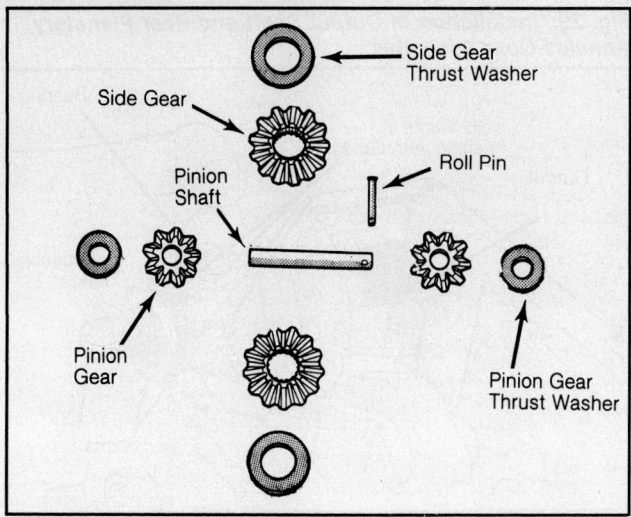

TRANSAXLE REASSEMBLY & ADJUSTMENT

DIFFERENTIAL ASSEMBLY

Differential bearing preload must be adjusted if any of the following components have been replaced:
- Transaxle Case
- Differential Carrier
- Differential Bearing Retainer
- Extension Housing
- Differential Bearings

If none of these parts are replaced, differential may be reassembled using the original adjusting shims.

1) Remove differential bearing outer race and preload adjusting shim from differential bearing retainer. If differential bearings have been replaced, also replace outer race in extension housing.

2) Install .020" (.50 mm) gauging shim in differential bearing retainer and reinstall bearing outer race. Install a new outer race in extension housing (if removed).

3) Position differential assembly in transaxle case. Install extension housing on case and tighten attaching bolts. Install differential bearing retainer and tighten attaching bolts.

4) Position transaxle assembly vertically in support stand and install Adapter (L-4436) into extension housing. Rotate differential at least 1 full turn to ensure tapered roller bearings are fully seated.

NOTE: Adapter (L-4436) fits through extension housing and rests on pinion shaft.

5) Attach dial indicator to case. See Fig. 27. Zero dial indicator and position indicator tip on end of adapter.

Fig. 27: Measuring Differential End Play

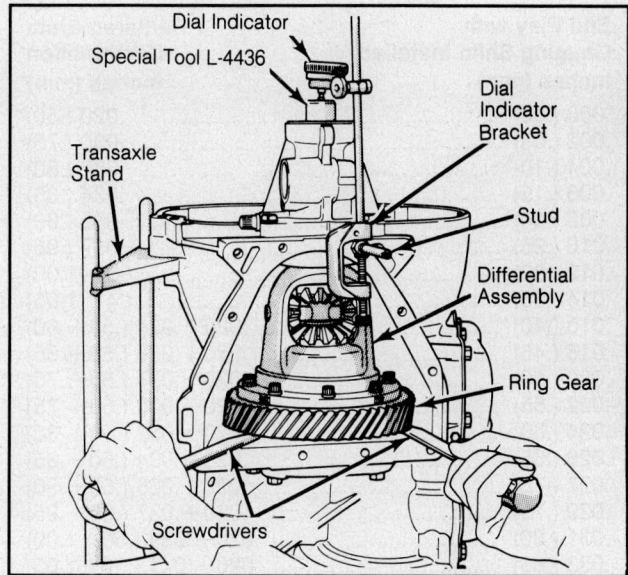

Lift ring gear with 2 large screwdrivers.

6) Place a large screwdriver under each side of ring gear and lift. Check dial indicator for amount of end play.

CAUTION: Do not damage transaxle case or differential cover sealing surface when lifting ring gear.

7) To determine shim combination required to obtain correct differential bearing preload, refer to DIFFERENTIAL BEARING SHIM CHART.

8) Remove differential bearing retainer. Remove differential bearing outer race and gauging shim from retainer. Install proper shim combination, as determined in step 7), under bearing race. Ensure oil baffle is installed properly in retainer, below bearing shims and race. Reinstall bearing retainer in case. Use RTV sealant between retainer and case.

9) To check adjustment, oil differential bearings. Insert Adapter (L-4436) through extension housing to engage differential assembly.

Fig. 28: Using Adapter (L-4436) to Measure Differential Turning Torque

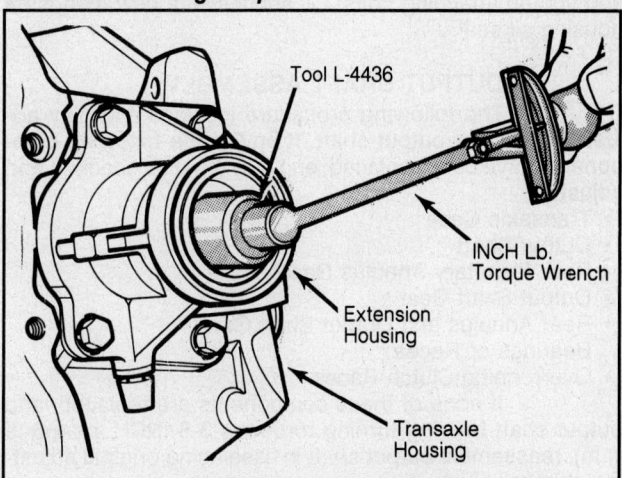

DIFFERENTIAL BEARING SHIM CHART

End Play with Gauging Shim Installed Inches (mm)	Required Shim Combination Inches (mm)
.000 (.00)	[1] .020 (.50)
.002 (.05)	.030 (.75)
.004 (.10)	.032 (.80)
.006 (.15)	.034 (.85)
.008 (.20)	.035 (.90)
.010 (.25)	.037 (.95)
.012 (.30)	.039 (1.00)
.014 (.35)	.041 (1.05)
.016 (.40)	.020+.024 (.50+.60)
.018 (.45)	.020+.026 (.50+.65)
.020 (.50)	.020+.027 (.50+.70)
.022 (.55)	.020+.030 (.50+.75)
.024 (.60)	.020+.032 (.50+.80)
.026 (.65)	.020+.034 (.50+.85)
.027 (.70)	.020+.035 (.50+.90)
.029 (.75)	.020+.037 (.50+.95)
.031 (.80)	.020+.039 (.50+1.00)
.033 (.85)	.020+.041 (.50+1.05)
.035 (.90)	.039+.024 (1.00+.60)
.037 (.95)	.039+.026 (1.00+.65)
.039 (1.00)	.039+.027 (1.00+.70)
.041 (1.05)	.039+.030 (1.00+.75)
.043 (1.10)	.039+.032 (1.00+.80)
.045 (1.15)	.039+.034 (1.00+.85)
.047 (1.20)	.039+.035 (1.00+.90)
.049 (1.25)	.039+.037 (1.00+.95)
.051 (1.30)	.039+.039 (1.00+1.00)
.053 (1.35)	.039+.041 (1.00+1.05)
.055 (1.40)	.041+.041 (1.05+1.05)

[1] – Gauging shim.

10) Using an INCH lb. torque wrench, check differential turning torque. Turning torque with differential bearing preload correctly adjusted should be 5-18 INCH lbs. (.55-2.0 N.m.). If not, install a .002" (.05 mm) thinner shim to decrease torque or a .002" (.05 mm) thicker shim to increase torque.

11) When correct torque has been obtained, remove torque wrench, apply 1/8" bead of RTV sealant around differential cover and install cover on case. Install and tighten attaching bolts. Oil and install a new extension housing oil seal.

OUTPUT SHAFT ASSEMBLY
The following procedure includes end play adjustment for the output shaft. If any of the following components have been replaced, end play must be checked and adjusted.
- Transaxle Case
- Output Shaft
- Rear Planetary Annulus Gear
- Output Shaft Gear
- Rear Annulus and Output Shaft Gear Bearings or Races
- Overrunning Clutch Races

If none of these components are replaced, and output shaft bearing turning torque is 3-8 INCH lbs. (.3-.9 N.m), reassemble output shaft in case using original adjusting shim (spacer).

1) Install output shaft into transaxle case. Install .537" (13.65 mm) and .053" (1.34 mm) gauging shims on planetary rear annulus gear hub using grease to hold shims in place.

NOTE: The .537" (13.65 mm) gauging shim has a larger inside diameter and must be installed over output shaft first. The .053" (1.34 mm) shim pilots on the output shaft.

Fig. 29: Installation of Output Shaft and Rear Planetary Annulus Gear Assembly

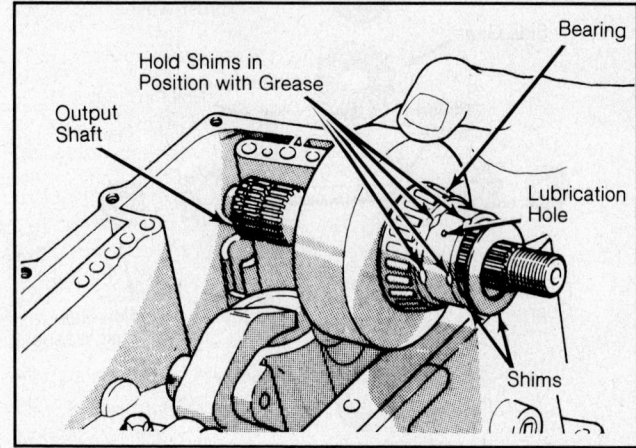

OUTPUT SHAFT BEARING SHIM CHART

End Play with Gauging Shims Installed Inches (mm)	Required Shim Combination Inches (mm)
.000 (.00)	[1] .537+.053 (13.65+1.34)
.002 (.05)	.537+.049 (13.65+1.24)
.004 (.10)	.537+.047 (13.65+1.19)
.006 (.15)	.537+.045 (13.65+1.14)
.008 (.20)	.537+.043 (13.65+1.09)
.010 (.25)	.537+.041 (13.65+1.04)
.012 (.30)	.537+.039 (13.65+.99)
.014 (.35)	.537+.037 (13.65+.94)
.016 (.40)	.518+.055 (13.15+1.39)
.018 (.45)	.518+.053 (13.15+1.34)
.020 (.50)	.518+.051 (13.15+1.29)
.022 (.55)	.518+.049 (13.15+1.24)
.024 (.60)	.518+.047 (13.15+1.19)
.026 (.65)	.518+.045 (13.15+1.14)
.028 (.70)	.518+.043 (13.15+1.09)
.030 (.75)	.518+.041 (13.15+1.04)
.032 (.80)	.518+.039 (13.15+.99)
.034 (.85)	.518+.037 (13.15+.94)
.036 (.90)	.498+.055 (12.65+1.39)
.038 (.95)	.498+.053 (12.65+1.34)
.040 (1.00)	.498+.051 (12.65+1.29)
.042 (1.05)	.498+.049 (12.65+1.24)
.044 (1.10)	.498+.047 (12.65+1.19)
.046 (1.15)	.498+.045 (12.65+1.14)
.048 (1.20)	.498+.043 (12.65+1.09)
.049 (1.25)	.498+.041 (12.65+1.04)
.051 (1.30)	.498+.039 (12.65+.99)
.053 (1.35)	.498+.037 (12.65+.94)

[1] – Gauging shims.

2) Place output shaft gear in position on output shaft. Install washer and retaining nut. Hold output shaft stationary and tighten retaining nut to 200 ft. lbs. (271 N.m).

3) Attach Holder (L-4432) to output shaft gear. Mount a steel ball into end of output shaft and retain in place with grease. Push and pull gear while rotating back and forth to ensure seating of roller bearings. Attach a dial indicator to case and position plunger against steel ball.

4) Move output shaft in and out and measure end play. Refer to OUTPUT SHAFT BEARING SHIM CHART to determine required shim combination.

NOTE: **The .537" (13.65 mm), .518" (13.15 mm) and .498" (12.65 mm) shims are always installed first. These shims have lubrication slots which are necessary for proper bearing lubrication.**

5) With proper shim combination determined, remove output shaft gear from case. Remove gauging shims from annulus gear hub and install correct shims. Hold shims in place with grease. Reinstall output shaft gear and tighten retaining nut.

6) Using an INCH lb. torque wrench, check output shaft bearing turning torque. Turning torque should be 3-8 INCH lbs. (.3-.9 N.m). If torque is not within limits, correct by changing shim thickness in increments of .002" (.05 mm). To reduce torque, increase total shim thickness. To increase torque, decrease shim thickness.

TRANSFER SHAFT, GOVERNOR & PARKING PAWL ASSEMBLIES

1) Position parking pawl and return spring in place in transaxle case. Slide parking pawl pivot shaft (small diameter to rear) through case bore and into parking pawl and spring. Install parking pawl retainer and tighten attaching bolts.

2) If necessary for replacement, install new oil seal and "O" rings on transfer shaft bearing retainer. Slide retainer onto transfer shaft.

3) Using Installer (L-4512), install transfer shaft into transaxle case. Install transfer shaft bearing retainer snap ring. Snap ring must be fully seated in groove in case.

Fig. 30: Using Installer (L-4512) to Install Transfer Shaft into Case

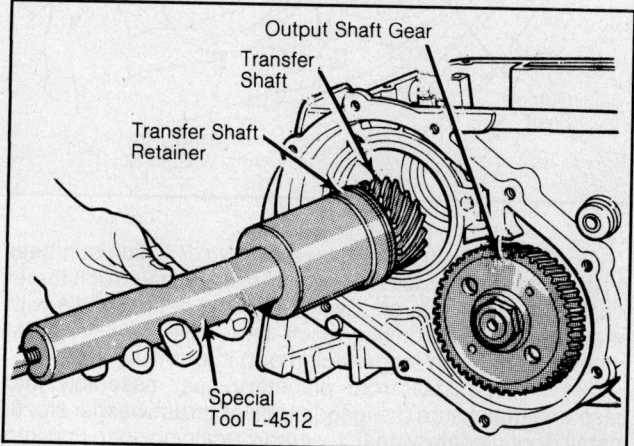

4) Slide governor assembly onto transfer shaft. Install low-reverse band anchor pin into bore in transaxle case. Install governor support retainer.

Fig. 31: Governor Support Retainer Installation

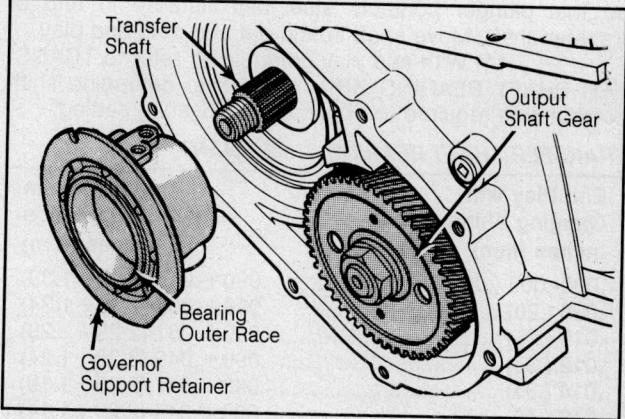

5) If 1 or more of the following components have been replaced, transfer shaft end play must be measured and adjusted.

- Transaxle Case
- Transfer Shaft
- Transfer Shaft Gear
- Transfer Shaft Bearings
- Governor Support Retainer
- Transfer Shaft Bearing Retainer
- Retainer Snap Ring
- Governor Support

6) If none of these components are replaced, skip steps **7)** through **12)** and reassemble transfer shaft assembly using original adjusting shims. See *Fig. 32* for location of shim.

7) Install .090" (2.29 mm) and .055" (1.39 mm) gauging shims on transfer shaft, behind governor support. Install transfer shaft gear and bearing assembly.

8) Hold transfer shaft stationary with holder. Install gear retaining nut and washer and tighten to 200 ft. lbs. (271 N.m).

9) With holder installed, mount a steel ball into end of transfer shaft and hold in place with grease. Push and pull transfer shaft gear while rotating back and forth to ensure seating of bearings.

Fig. 32: View of Transfer Shaft with Gear Removed Showing Location of Adjusting Shim

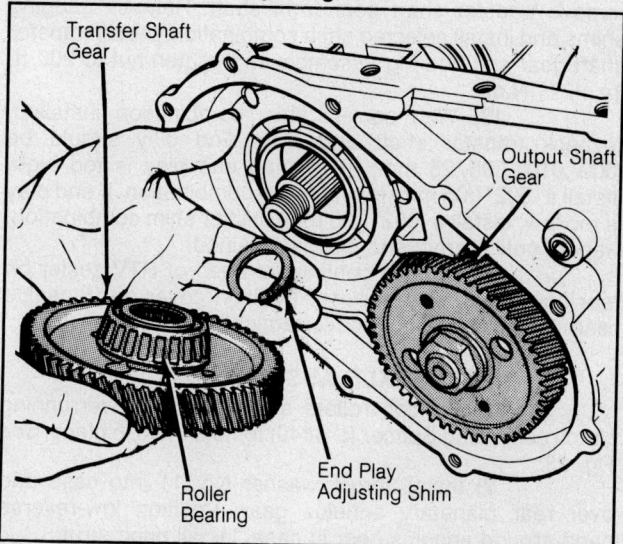

10) Attach a dial indicator to case and position so that plunger contacts steel ball installed in end of transfer shaft. Move shaft in and out and read end play.

11) With end play determined, refer to TRANSFER SHAFT BEARING SHIM CHART to determine shim combination required to obtain proper bearing setting.

TRANSFER SHAFT BEARING SHIM CHART

End Play with Gauging Shims Installed Inches (mm)	Required Shim Combination Inches (mm)
.000-.006 (.00-.15)	[1] .090+.055 (2.29+1.39)
.008 (.20)	.090+.053 (2.29+1.34)
.010 (.25)	.090+.051 (2.29+1.29)
.012 (.30)	.090+.049 (2.29+1.24)
.014 (.35)	.090+.047 (2.29+1.19)
.016 (.40)	.090+.045 (2.29+1.14)
.018 (.45)	.090+.043 (2.29+1.09)
.020 (.50)	.090+.041 (2.29+1.04)
.022 (.55)	.090+.039 (2.29+.99)
.024 (.60)	.072+.055 (1.84+1.39)
.026 (.65)	.072+.053 (1.84+1.34)
.028 (.70)	.072+.051 (1.84+1.29)
.030 (.75)	.072+.049 (1.84+1.24)
.032 (.80)	.072+.047 (1.84+1.19)
.034 (.85)	.072+.045 (1.84+1.14)
.036 (.90)	.072+.043 (1.84+1.09)
.038 (.95)	.072+.041 (1.84+1.04)
.040 (1.00)	.072+.039 (1.84+.99)
.042 (1.05)	.055+.055 (1.39+1.39)
.044 (1.10)	.055+.053 (1.39+1.34)
.046 (1.15)	.055+.051 (1.39+1.29)
.048 (1.20)	.055+.049 (1.39+1.24)
.049 (1.25)	.055+.047 (1.39+1.19)
.050 (1.30)	.055+.045 (1.39+1.14)
.052 (1.35)	.055+.043 (1.39+1.09)
.055 (1.40)	.055+.041 (1.39+1.04)
.057 (1.45)	.055+.039 (1.39+.99)
.059 (1.50)	.037+.055 (.94+1.39)
.061 (1.55)	.037+.053 (.94+1.34)
.063 (1.60)	.037+.051 (.94+1.29)

[1] – Gauging shims.

12) With correct shim combination determined, remove transfer shaft gear from shaft. Remove gauging shims and install selected shim combination. Install transfer shaft gear and bearing assembly and tighten nut to 200 ft. lbs. (271 N.m).

13) With correct shim combination installed, recheck transfer shaft end play. End play should be .002-.010" (.05-.25 mm). If bearing end play is too high, install a .002" (.05 mm) thinner shim combination. If end play is too low, install a .002" (.05 mm) thicker shim combination. Repeat until correct end play is obtained.

14) Apply a continuous bead of RTV sealer on rear cover mounting surface. Position cover on transaxle case. Install and tighten cover attaching bolts.

TRANSAXLE ASSEMBLY
1) Position rollers and springs in overrunning clutch cam using Spacer (L-4440) to hold them in place. *See Fig. 33.*

2) Install thrust washer No. 11 into case and over rear planetary annulus gear. Position low-reverse band around annulus gear in case. Install band strut.

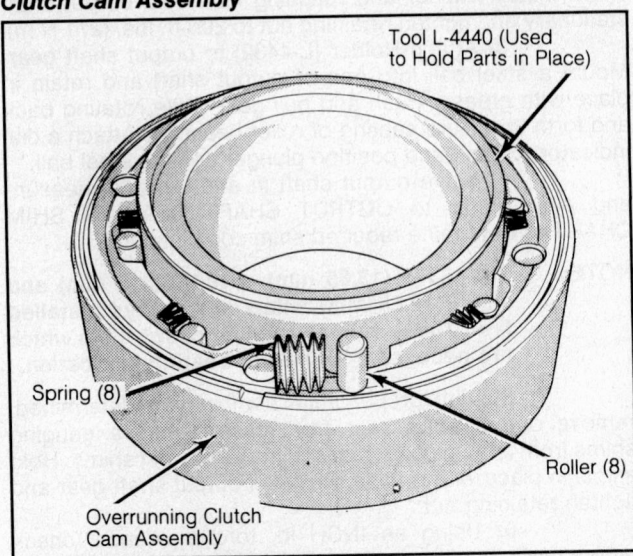

Fig. 33: *Installing Rollers and Springs in Overrunning Clutch Cam Assembly*

3) Install overrunning clutch cam assembly (Spacer L-4440 installed) into case and remove spacer. Install thrust washer No. 10 (with tangs facing out) into position in rear planetary annulus gear.

4) Install rear planetary gear assembly into rear annulus gear. Install thrust washer No. 9 into case and ensure tabs on washer engage slots in planetary assembly.

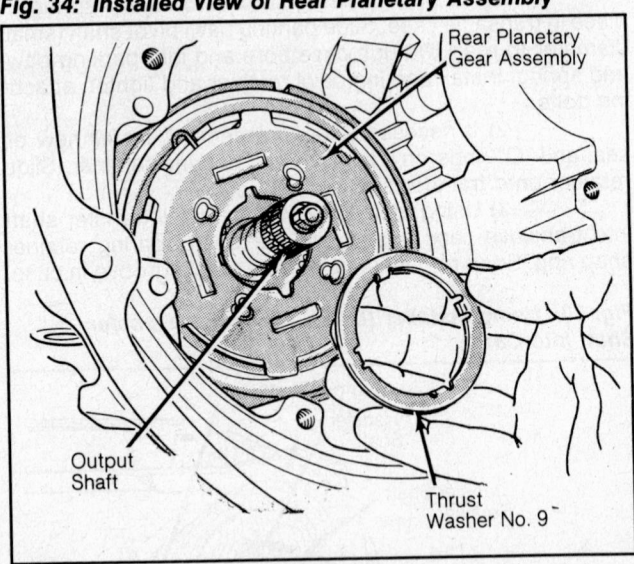

Fig. 34: *Installed View of Rear Planetary Assembly*

5) Position thrust washer No. 7 inside sun gear driving shell and install sun gear in shell. Install No. 8 thrust washer on back side of driving shell and hold in place with snap ring. Install driving shell into case. Install thrust washer No. 6 (with tangs facing out) into driving shell.

6) Install front planetary gear assembly into case and make sure it engages tabs of thrust washer No. 6. Install front planetary gear assembly retaining snap ring into groove in output shaft.

7) Slide thrust washer No. 3 onto end of output shaft. Position thrust washer No. 2 in rear clutch drum. Install rear clutch/input shaft assembly in case.

Automatic Transmissions

CHRYSLER CORP. A-413 & A-470 (Cont.)

Fig. 35: Installation of Front Planetary Gear Assembly Retaining Snap Ring

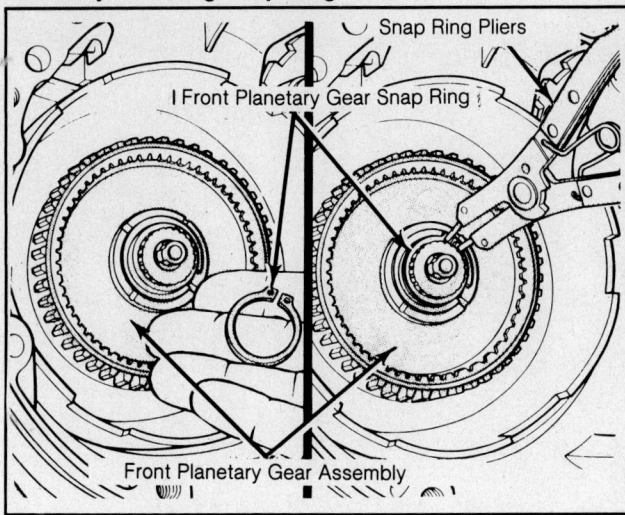

CAUTION: Thrust washer No. 3 controls input shaft end play. Refer to INPUT SHAFT END PLAY in this article. If necessary, install a new thrust washer of correct thickness.

8) Install front clutch assembly in case. Ensure tabs on front clutch drum engage slots in rear clutch drum.

9) Position kickdown (front) band in place on front clutch drum. Install band strut. Tighten kickdown band adjusting screw just enough to hold parts in place.

10) Install oil pump gasket in case. Ensure oil holes in gasket align with holes in case. Install oil pump assembly and thrust washer No. 1 in case. Use NEW bolts when installing pump.

NOTE: Input shaft end play should be rechecked to ensure correct thrust washer No. 3 has been installed.

11) If necessary, remove oil pump oil seal using Seal Remover (C-3981). See Fig. 36. Drive new seal (lip seal facing inward) into oil pump until it is fully seated.

Fig. 36: Oil Pump Seal Removal

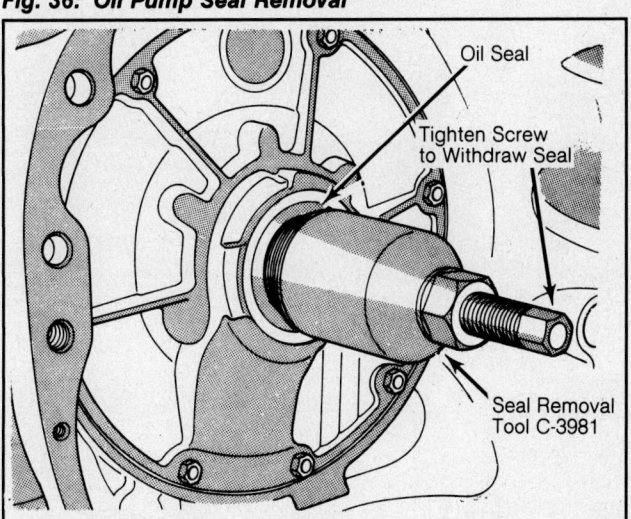

12) Carefully install valve body assembly in case while guiding governor tubes into position. Install valve body attaching bolts and tighten alternately and evenly.

Fig. 37: Parking Rod Installation

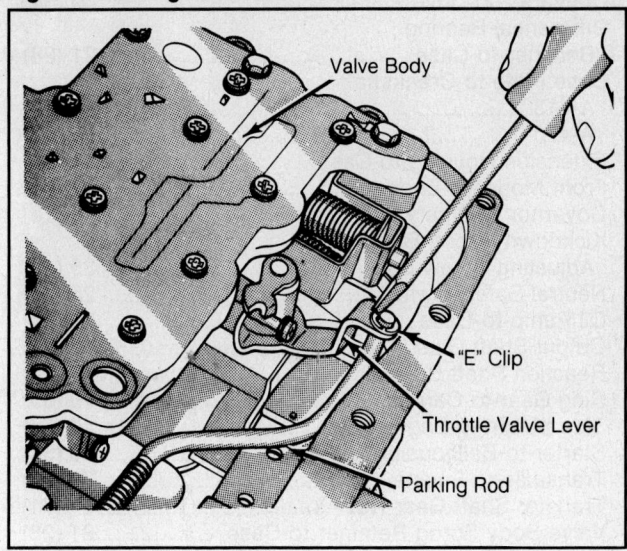

13) Install parking rod into case and secure to throttle valve lever with retaining "E" clip. Install neutral safety/back-up light switch. Install oil filter on valve body and tighten attaching screws. Install oil pan on case using only RTV sealer.

THRUST WASHER CHART

Thrust Washer (No.)	Thickness In. (mm)
Reaction Shaft Support (1)	.061-.063 (1.55-1.60)
Rear Clutch Retainer (2)	.061-.063 (1.55-1.60)
Output Shaft – Selective (3)	.077-.080 (1.98-2.03)
	.085-.087 (2.15-2.22)
	.092-.095 (2.34-2.41)
Front Annulus (4)	.116-.120 (2.95-3.05)
Front Carrier (5 & 6)	.048-.050 (1.22-1.28)
Sun Gear (7 & 8)	.033-.036 (.85-.91)
Rear Carrier (9 & 10)	.048-.050 (1.22-1.28)
Reverse Drum (11)	.061-.063 (1.55-1.60)

TIGHTENING SPECIFICATIONS

Application	Ft. Lbs. (N.m)
Ball Joint Clamp Bolt	70 (95)
Converter-to-Drive Plate	40 (54)
Differential Bearing Retainer-to-Case	21 (28)
Drive Plate-to-Crankshaft	
A-413	65 (88)
A-470	100 (136)
Extension Housing-to-Case	21 (28)
Front Mount-to-Engine	40 (54)
Governor Counterweight Screw	21 (28)
Kickdown (Front) Band Adjusting Screw Lock Nut	35 (47)
Neutral Safety Switch	25 (34)
Oil Pump-to-Case	23 (31)
Output Shaft Gear Nut	200 (271)
Reaction Shaft Bolt	21 (28)
Ring Gear-to-Carrier	70 (95)
Side Mount-to-Engine	40 (54)
Starter-to-Bellhousing	40 (54)
Transaxle-to-Engine	70 (95)
Transfer Shaft Gear Nut	200 (271)
Valve Body Sprag Retainer-to-Case	21 (28)

	INCH Lbs. (N.m)
Bellhousing Cover	105 (12)
Differential Cover-to-Case	165 (19)
Governor-to-Support	60 (7)
Oil Pan-to-Case	165 (19)
Rear Cover-to-Case	165 (19)
Reverse Band Shaft Plug	60 (7)
Speedometer Pinion Retaining Bolt	60 (7)
Valve Body	
Attaching Bolts	40 (5)
Oil Filter Screws	40 (5)
Transfer Plate Screws	40 (5)
Transfer Plate-to-Case	105 (12)

FORD MOTOR CO. ATX — AUTOMATIC TRANSAXLE

Escort, EXP, Lynx, Tempo, Topaz

IDENTIFICATION

Transaxle can be identified by the letter "B" or "O" on the lower line of the Vehicle Certification Label under "TR". The gear ratio is determined by the letter code under "AX" of the Vehicle Certification Label. The label is attached to the left side door lock panel.

Transaxle can be identified by a metal tag attached to the ATX case. First line on tag shows the build date code and model number. Bottom line on tag shows the serial and assembly part number prefix and suffix.

TRANSAXLE INDENTIFICATION CODES

Application All Models	Axle Ratio	Code
Auto. Trans.	2.31:1	1
Auto. Trans.	3.23:1	2

DESCRIPTION

The ATX combines an automatic transmission and differential into a single unit designed for front wheel drive vehicles. Transmission and differential are housed in a light-alloy housing. The transmission uses 3 friction clutches, 1 band, and a single one-way clutch. These components are applied as necessary to transmit engine torque through a compound planetary gear set.

The planetary provides 3 forward gear ratios and 1 reverse. The planetary transmits engine torque to the input gear, which meshes with the differential idler gear. The idler gear meshes with the differential ring gear, which is riveted to the differential case. Engine torque flows outward to the wheels through the differential gears.

To minimize torque converter inefficiency, the ATX contains a splitter gear to provide a mechanical connection between the engine and transaxle. The splitter gear is similiar to a planetary gear set. In 1st and reverse, engine torque is hydraulically transmitted. In 2nd gear, 62% of engine torque is transmitted mechanically through the splitter gear. Converter slip is less than 7% when ATX is in 3rd gear.

LUBRICATION & ADJUSTMENTS

See appropriate AUTOMATIC TRANSMISSION SERVICING article in DOMESTIC GENERAL SERVICING section.

TROUBLE SHOOTING

See appropriate AUTOMATIC TRANSMISSION TROUBLE SHOOTING article in DOMESTIC GENERAL SERVICING section.

LINKAGE CHECK

Throttle Linkage

Check for wide open carburetor and linkage travel at full throttle. Carburetor full throttle stop must be contacted by the carburetor throttle linkage and there must be a slight amount of movement left in transaxle throttle linkage. Ensure throttle return spring is connected and carburetor throttle lever returns to a closed position.

Manual Linkage

This is a CRITICAL adjustment. Ensure the "D" detent in transaxle corresponds exactly with stop in console. Hydraulic leakage at manual valve can cause delay in engagements and/or slipping while operating if linkage is not correctly adjusted.

Transaxle Shifting Troubles Related to Throttle Linkage Adjustments

1) If shifts are excessively early and/or soft upshifts with or without slip-bump feel. Or, no forced downshift (kickdown) function at appropriate speeds, T.V. control linkage is set too short. Adjust linkage. See appropriate AUTOMATIC TRANSMISSION SERVICING article in DOMESTIC GENERAL SERVICING section.

2) If shifts are extremely delayed and harsh upshifts and harsh idle engagement are experienced, T.V. control linkage is set too long. Adjust linkage. See appropriate AUTOMATIC TRANSMISSION SERVICING article in DOMESTIC GENERAL SERVICING section.

3) If harsh idle engagements after engine has warmed-up; or, shift-clunk when throttle is backed off after full or heavy throttle acceleration; or, harsh coasting downshifts are experienced; or, there are delayed upshifts at light acceleration, 1 possibility is there is interference due to hoses or wires which is preventing return of T.V. control rod or T.V. linkage shaft.

4) Another possibility is there is excessive friction due to binding of grommets preventing return of T.V. contol linkage. Check for bent or twisted rods or levers causing misalignment of grommets. Replace defective components, if damaged, and readjust T.V. control linkage.

5) If there are erratic/delayed upshifts, possibly no kickdown, or harsh engagements, clamping bolt on trunnion at upper end of T.V. control rod is loose. Reset and readjust T.V. control linkage.

6) If there is no upshifts and harsh engagements, reconnect T.V. control rod. Replace grommets if rod disconnected was due to defective grommets. Also check return spring and replace or reconnect as necessary.

TRANSAXLE FLUID CONDITION CHECK

1) Make normal fluid checks as outlined in AUTOMATIC TRANSMISSION GENERAL SERVICING section. Observe color and odor of fluid. If should be Red; not Brown or Black. Odor can sometimes indicate an overheating condition or clutch disc or band failure.

2) Use an absorbent White facial tissue to wipe dipstick. Examine stain for evidence of solids (specks) and for coolant signs (gum or varnish on dipstick).

3) If specks are present or if there is evidence of coolant, transaxle oil pan must be removed for further inspection. If fluid contaminates or transaxle failure is confirmed by further evidence of coolant or excessive solids in the oil pan, transaxle must be disassembled and completely cleaned and serviced.

Automatic Transmissions
FORD MOTOR CO. ATX – AUTOMATIC TRANSAXLE (Cont.)

CLUTCH AND BAND APPLICATION CHART (ELEMENTS IN USE)

Selector Lever Position	Band	Direct Clutch	Intermed. Clutch	Reverse Clutch	Intermed. One-Way Clutch
D — DRIVE					
First Gear	X				X
Second Gear	X		X		
Third Gear		X	X		
2 — INTERMEDIATE					
Second Gear	X		X		
1 — LOW					
First Gear	X	X			X
R — REVERSE		X		X	X
P — Park					X
N — Neutral					X

4) This includes cleaning the torque converter and transaxle cooling system. During disassembly and assembly, all overhaul checks and adjustments must be performed.

5) After transaxle hase been serviced, all diagnosis tests and adjustments must be completed to ensure that the problem has been corrected.

ENGINE IDLE SPEED CHECK

If idle speed is too low, engine will run roughly. An idle speed that is too high will cause vehicle to creep, have harsh engagements, and harsh closed throttle downshifts. Whenever it is required to adjust engine idle speed by more than 50 RPM, readjust throttle linkage.

TESTING

ROAD TEST

1) Check minimum throttle upshifts in Drive. Transaxle should start in 1st gear, shift to 2nd, and then shift to 3rd at approximately the speeds shown in ATX SHIFT SPEEDS table.

2) With transaxle in 3rd, depress accelerator pedal to the floor. Transaxle should shift from 3rd to 2nd or 1st, depending on vehicle speed. See ATX SHIFT SPEEDS table.

3) Check closed throttle downshifts from 3rd to 1st by coasting down from approximately 30 MPH in 3rd gear. Shift should occur at approximate speed shown in ATX SHIFT SPEEDS table.

NOTE: When selector lever is at "2", transaxle will operate in 1st and 2nd gears.

4) With transaxle in 3rd and road speed above 30 MPH, transaxle should shift to 2nd gear when selector lever is moved from Drive to "2", to "1". This check will determine if governor pressure and shift control valves are functioning properly.

NOTE: The following is for checking vehicle in the shop. This test will check shift valve operation, governor circuits, shift delay pressures, throttle boost and downshift valve action.

CAUTION: Never exceed 60 MPH speedometer speed when performing the following test.

5) Place transaxle in Drive and make a minimum throttle 1-2, 2-3 shift test. At this point of shift, the speedometer needle will make a momentary surge and a driveline bump will be felt.

6) If shift points are within specifications, 1-2 and 2-3 shift valves, and governor are okay. If shift points are incorrect, perform GOVERNOR CHECK to isolate the problem.

GOVERNOR CHECK

Accelerate vehicle to 30-40 MPH, then back off throttle completely. If governor is functioning properly, transaxle will shift to 3rd gear.

LINE PRESSURE TEST

1) Connect a 0-300 psi pressure gauge to line pressure test port on transaxle case. See Fig. 1. Run engine until normal operating temperature is reached.

2) Apply service and parking brakes. Check line pressure in all selector lever positions with engine at idle and then with engine at wide open throttle. Pressures should be as specified. See LINE PRESSURE SPECIFICATIONS table.

LINE PRESSURE TEST RESULTS
Low at Idle in All Ranges

Check engine EGR system. Check for low fluid level, restricted intake screen or filter, loose valve body or regulator-to-case bolts, loose oil tubes, excessive leakage in oil pump, case, valve body or sticking control pressure regulator valve.

High at Idle in All Ranges

Check throttle valve or control rod adjustment, and T.V. linkage return spring, or sticking regulator boost valve(s).

FORD MOTOR CO. ATX – AUTOMATIC TRANSAXLE (Cont.)

ATX SHIFT SPEEDS

Drive Range	MPH
ATX Models PMA-V4, Z5 PMB-C4; R1 & PMA-U3, PMB-D1	
At Idle In Drive	
1-2 Upshift	12-19
2-3 Upshift	16-31
3-2 Downshift	17-24
2-1 Downshift	9-15
In Manual/Low	
2-1 Downshift	25-43
At Part Throttle [1]	
1-2 Upshift	11-27
2-3 Upshift	27-45
3-2 Downshift	20-39
2-1 Downshift	11-19
At Wide Open Throttle	
1-2 Upshift	31-49
2-3 Upshift	59-77
3-2 Downshift	53-71
2-1 Downshift	22-39
Models PMA-N4, AA3	
At Idle	
1-2 Upshift	11-18
2-3 Upshift	16-32
3-2 Downshift	17-25
2-1 Downshift	9-15
Manual/Low	
2-1 Downshift	20-38
At Part Throttle [2]	
1-2 Upshift	12-28
2-3 Upshift	27-44
3-2 Downshift	18-37
2-1 Downshift	13-20
At Wide Open Throttle	
1-2 Upshift	25-43
2-3 Upshift	53-70
3-2 Downshift	48-65
2-1 Downshift	15-31

[1] – On PMA-V4, Z5 and PMB-C4; R1 models, partial throttle shift speeds are made with line pressure at 90-108 psi (6.3-7.5 kg/cm²). On PMA-U3 and PMB-D1 models, partial throttle shift speeds are made with line pressure at 97-115 psi (6.8-8.0 kg/cm²).

[2] – Partial throttle shift speeds are made with line pressure at 85-103 psi (5.9-7.2 kg/cm²).

Low in "P" or "N"
Faulty valve body.

Low in "D"
Faulty servo or valve body.

Low in "2"
Faulty valve body and/or intermediate servo.

Low in "1"
Faulty direct clutch and/or valve body.

Low in "R"
Faulty direct clutch and/or reverse clutch. Faulty valve body.

STALL TEST

1) Start engine and allow it to reach normal operating temperature. Apply both parking and service brakes. Stall test is made in all Drive ranges and Reverse at full throttle.

Fig. 1: Line Pressure Test Port

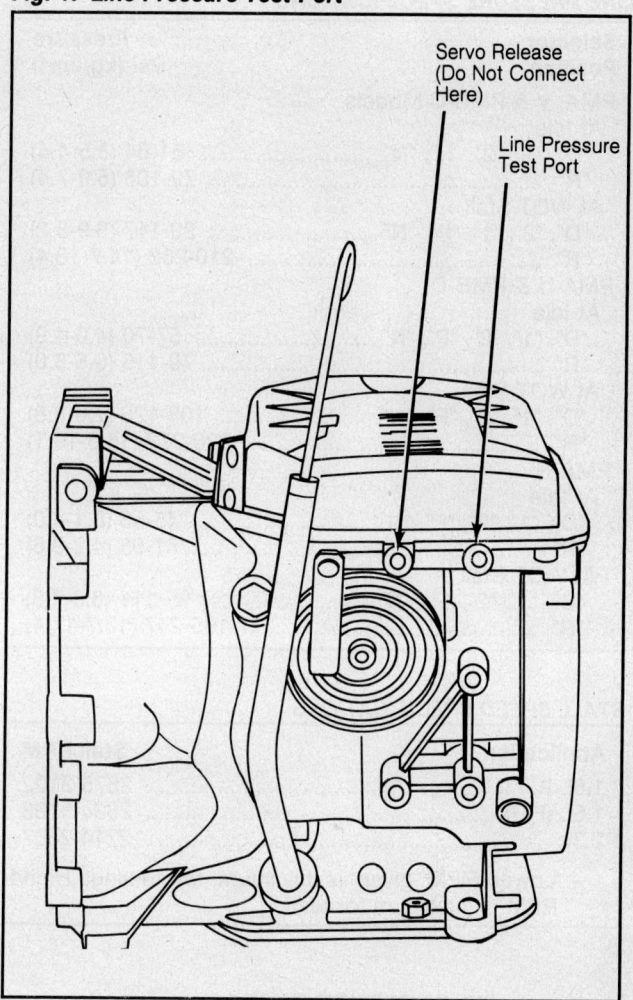

2) Stall testing is to check engine performance, converter operation or installation and holding ability of the direct clutch, reverse clutch and low-intermediate band brake and gear train one-way clutch.

NOTE: While performing this test, DO NOT hold throttle open for more than 5 seconds at a time.

3) After test, move gear selector lever to "N" and run engine at 1000 RPM for about 15 seconds to cool the converter before making next test. If engine speed recorded by tachometer exceeds maximum limits given in specifications, RELEASE ACCELERATOR IMMEDIATELY because clutch or band brake slippage is indicated.

STALL TEST RESULTS

1) If stall speed(s) are high (slip) in "D" or "2", check turbine shaft one-way clutch. If condition exists in "D", "2" and "1", check low-intermediate band or servo. If condition exists in "R", check reverse clutch. If condition exists in all driving ranges, check T.V. control adjustment and perform line pressure test.

2) If stall speeds are low, check engine for tune-up. If tune is okay, remove torque converter and bench test for reactor one-way clutch slippage.

FORD MOTOR CO. ATX — AUTOMATIC TRANSAXLE (Cont.)

LINE PRESSURE SPECIFICATIONS

Selector Position	Pressure Psi (kg/cm²)
PMA, V & PMB-C Models	
At Idle	
"D", "1", "2", "P", "N"	51-64 (3.5-4.4)
"R"	72-106 (5.0-7.4)
At WOT Stall	
"D", "2", "1", "P", "N"	99-117 (6.9-8.2)
"R"	210-262 (14.7-18.4)
PMA-U & PMB-D	
At Idle	
"D", "1", "2", "P", "N"	57-70 (4.0-4.9)
"R"	79-115 (5.5-8.0)
At WOT Stall	
"D", "1", "2", "P", "N"	108-126 (7.6-8.8)
"R"	220-272 (15.5-19.1)
PMA-N	
At Idle	
"D", "1", "2", "P", "N"	45-58 (3.1-4.0)
"R"	61-95 (4.2-6.6)
At WOT Stall	
"D", "1", "2", "P", "N"	95-111 (6.6-7.8)
"R"	195-247 (13.7-17.4)

STALL SPEED SPECIFICATIONS

Application	[1] Stall RPM
1.6L E.F.I.	2675-3102
1.6L (HO)	2634-3103
2.3L	2214-2607

[1] – Lower RPM given is minimum for testing. Higher RPM is maximum for testing.

AIR PRESSURE TESTS

A "No Drive" condition can exist even with correct transaxle fluid pressure, because of inoperative clutches or band. Erratic shifts could be caused by a stuck governor valve. The inoperative units can be located through a series of checks by substituting air pressure for the fluid pressure to determine location of malfunction.

Fig. 2: Air Pressure Test Apply Ports on Adapter Plate

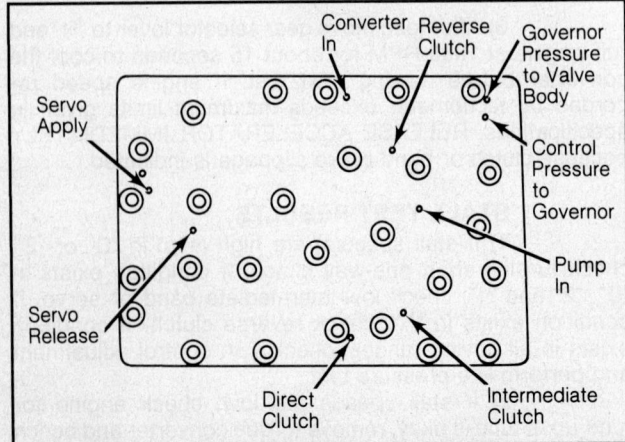

To make air pressure checks, loosen valve body cover bolts, then remove cover and valve body assembly.

Install the Special Adapter Plate (P/N T82P-7006-B) in place of valve body. *See Fig. 2.* The inoperative units can be located by applying air pressure in transaxle case passages, through adapter plate, leading to the clutches, servo, and governor. *See Fig. 2.*

NOTE: Air pressure test adapter plate should be installed with a new valve body gasket. Tighten attaching bolts to 80-100 INCH lbs. (9-11 N.m).

Band Apply Servo
Apply air pressure to servo apply passage. The band should apply. A dull thud should be heard when air pressure is removed, allowing servo piston to return to release position.

Direct Clutch
Apply air pressure to direct clutch apply passage. A dull thud can be heard or movement of piston can be felt as piston is applied. If direct clutch seals are leaking, a hissing noise will be heard.

Intermediate Clutch
Apply air pressure to intermediate clutch apply passage. A dull thud can be heard or movement of piston can be felt on case as piston is applied. If intermediate clutch seals are leaking, a hissing noise will be heard.

Reverse Clutch
Apply air pressure to reverse clutch apply passage. A dull thud can be heard or movement of piston can be felt on case as piston is applied. If reverse clutch seals are leaking, a hissing noise will be heard.

Converter In
This passage can only be checked for blockage. If passage holds air pressure, remove adapter plate and check for an obstruction or damage.

Control Pressure-to-Governor
Remove governor cover. Apply air pressure to control pressure-to-governor apply passage. Watch for movement of governor valve.

Governor Pressure-to-Valve Body
This passage can only be checked for blockage. If passage holds air pressure, remove adapter plate and check for an obstruction or damage.

Pump In (Bench Test)
With transaxle removed from vehicle and converter removed, apply air pressure to pump in apply passage. Rotation of pump gears should be heard when air pressure is applied.

NOTE: "Pump In" check is normally performed during the assembly of an overhauled transaxle.

SERVICE (IN VEHICLE)

VALVE BODY
Removal
1) Apply parking brake. Open hood and remove battery and battery tray. Remove ignition coil and transaxle dipstick. Disconnect supply hoses and vacuum lines from managed air valve, then remove valve from valve body cover.

2) Remove remote air cleaner (if equipped). Remove managed air valve from valve body cover.

3) Remove attaching bolts, then lift off valve body cover and gasket. Remove valve body-to-case attach-

FORD MOTOR CO. ATX — AUTOMATIC TRANSAXLE (Cont.)

Fig. 3: ATX Automatic Transaxle Hydraulic Circuits Diagram

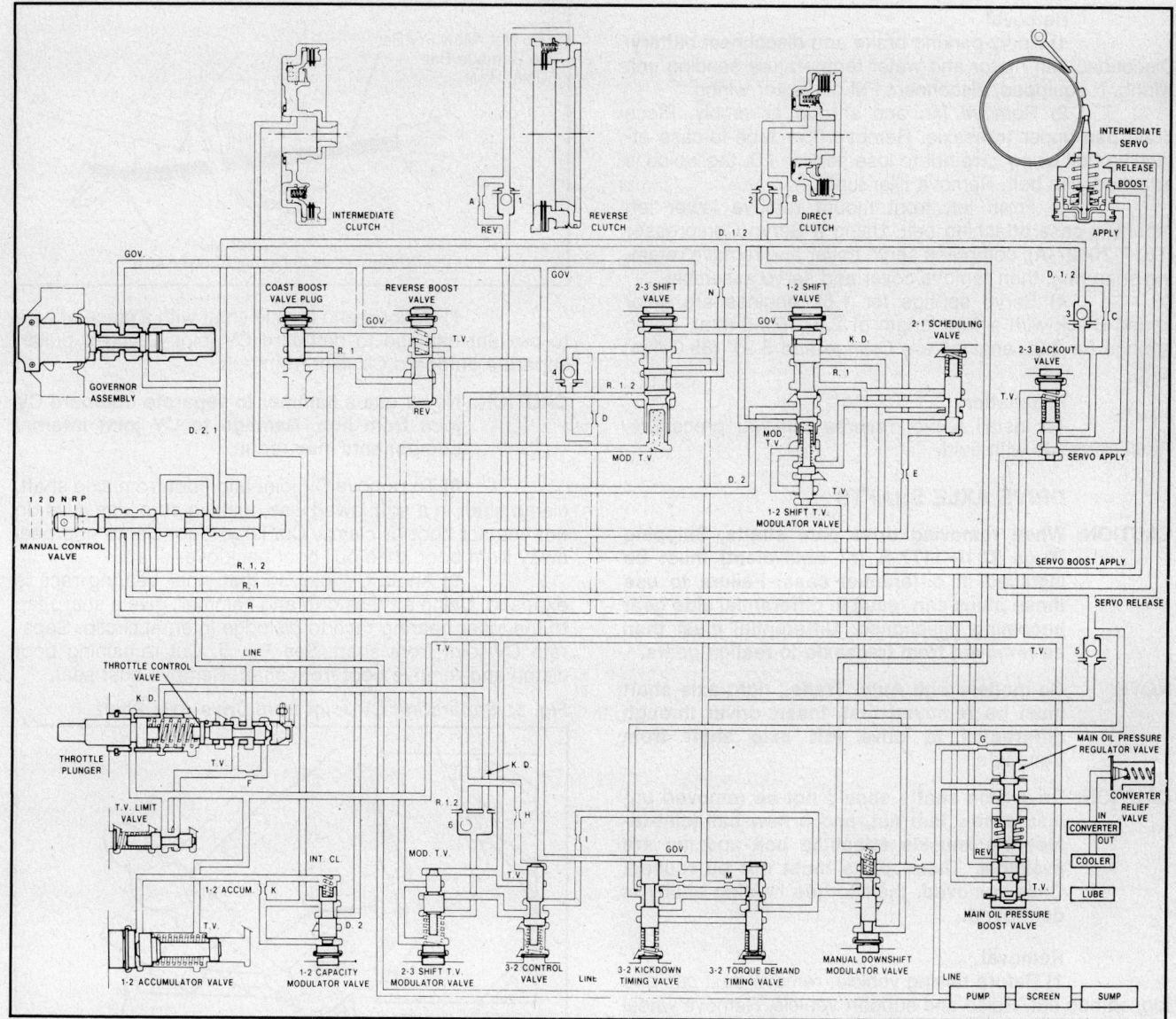

ing bolts, then remove valve body and gasket from transaxle case.

Installation

1) Install 2 Alignment Pins (T80L-77100-A) into opposing valve body attaching bolt holes, then install valve body-to-case gasket. Install valve body assembly into case, removing 1 alignment pin to allow attachment of manual valve to "Z" link. Reinstall alignment pin.

NOTE: Ensure roller on end of throttle valve plunger has engaged cam on end of throttle lever shaft.

2) Connect throttle valve control spring. Remove alignment pins. Install the 27 valve body attaching bolts, detent spring and oil pressure regulator exhaust plate (baffle plate). Tighten valve body attaching bolts.

3) Install new valve body cover gasket on case, then install and tighten cover attaching bolts, making sure transaxle I.D. tag is installed in its original position.

4) To complete installation, reverse removal procedure. Check and adjust transaxle fluid level.

GOVERNOR
Removal

1) Apply parking brake and disconnect battery. On 1.6L HO equipped models, remove the 2 managed air valve supply rear hoses and all vacuum lines from managed air valve. Remove managed air valve supply hose band-to-intermediate shift control bracket attaching bolt.

2) On all models, remove air cleaner. Using a long screwdriver, remove governor retaining clip. Remove governor cover and pull out governor.

Installation

To install governor, reverse removal procedure. Install a new "O" ring seal on governor cover. Check transaxle fluid level and add fluid if necessary.

LOW-INTERMEDIATE SERVO

Removal

1) Apply parking brake and disconnect battery. Disconnect fan motor and water temperature sending unit wiring. If equipped, disconnect FM capacitor wiring.

2) Remove fan and shroud assembly. Place drain pan under transaxle. Remove filler tube-to-case attaching bolt using care not to lose service I.D. tag which is attached with bolt. Remove filler tube.

3) From left front mount remove lower left mount-to-case attaching bolt. Using a Servo Compressor (T81P-70027-A), compress servo cover and remove retaining snap ring, then remove cover and servo assembly.

4) Servo springs for 1.6L engines are color coded Black with a free length of 2.97" (75.5 mm). Servo springs for 2.3L engines are Orange and 3.35" (85.0 mm) long.

Installation

To install servo, reverse removal procedure. Refill transaxle with fluid.

DRIVE AXLE SHAFTS

CAUTION: **When removing drive axle shafts, Shipping Plugs T81P-1177-B (or equivalent) must be installed in differential case. Failure to use these plugs can result in differential side gear becoming misaligned. Differential must then be removed from transaxle to realign gears.**

NOTE: **On models with Auto. Trans., right axle shaft must be removed first. Insert driver through differential to drive left axle shaft from transaxle.**

CAUTION: **Drive axle shafts should not be removed unless a new hub nut, and a new ball joint-to-steering knuckle attaching bolt and nut are available. These parts must not be reused. Once removed, their torque holding ability is destroyed.**

Removal

1) Before raising vehicle, remove dust cap and loosen hub nut. Raise and support vehicle. Remove wheel assembly.

2) Remove hub nut and washer. The hub nut must be loosened without unstaking. Use of a chisel may damage spindle threads. Discard hub nut when removed, it must not be reused.

3) Remove bolt attaching brake hose retaining clip to suspension strut. Remove ball joint-to-steering knuckle bolt, then drive bolt out of knuckle using a punch and hammer.

4) Discard ball joint-to-steering knuckle bolt and nut. They are of a torque prevailing design and cannot be reused.

5) Separate ball joint from steering knuckle using a pry bar positioned with the end outside the bushing pocket to prevent damage to bushing. *See Fig. 4.* The plastic disc brake shield must be bent back away from ball joint while prying ball joint from steering knuckle.

6) Using a pry bar, separate drive axle shaft from differential housing. Position bar between housing and shaft and use care not to damage dust deflector, differential oil seal, joint boot, or CV joint dust deflector.

Fig. 4: Separating Ball Joint from Steering Knuckle

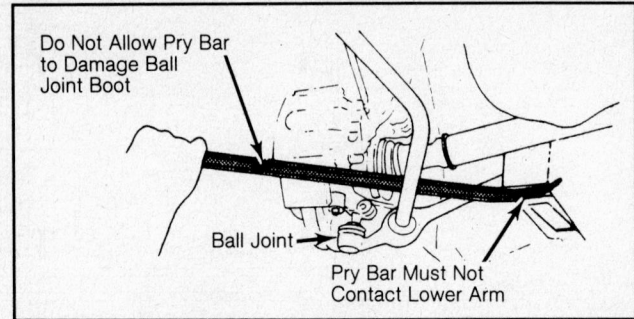

7) Support end of axle shaft with a piece of wire to prevent damage to outboard CV joint. Using a puller, separate outboard CV joint from hub.

CAUTION: **Never use a hammer to separate outboard CV joint from hub. Damage to CV joint internal components may result.**

8) To remove CV joint and boot from axle shaft, clamp shaft in a soft-jawed vise, making sure vise jaws do not contact boot or clamp. Cut large boot clamp and peel away from boot, then pull boot back over shaft.

9) Angle CV joint so that inner bearing race is exposed. Using a brass drift and hammer, give a sharp tap to the inner bearing race to dislodge internal circlip. Separate CV joint from shaft. *See Fig. 5.* Cut remaining boot clamp and remove boot from shaft. Remove dust seal.

Fig. 5: Separating CV Joint from Drive Axle Shaft

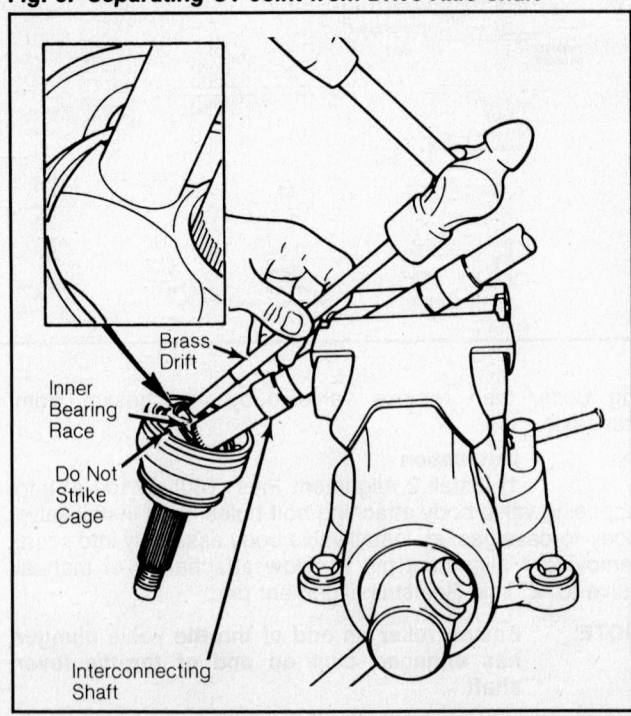

10) Remove snap ring from end of shaft and discard. The stop ring, located just below snap ring, should be removed only if inspection shows it to be damaged or worn.

FORD MOTOR CO. ATX – AUTOMATIC TRANSAXLE (Cont.)

Disassembly (Outboard CV Joint)

1) Clamp CV joint stub shaft in a vise with bearing facing up. Press down on inner race until it tilts enough to remove ball bearing. With cage tilted, remove ball from cage. Repeat this step until all 6 balls are removed. Remove boot and dust seal.

2) A tight bearing cage can be tilted by tapping the inner race with a wooden dowel or hammer. Do not hit the cage. If balls are tight, use a blunt screwdriver to pry them from cage. Do not scratch or damage cage.

3) Pivot bearing cage and inner race assembly until it is straight up and down in outer race. Align cage windows with outer race lands while pivoting bearing cage. Lift assembly from outer race.

4) To separate inner race from cage, align 1 of the inner race bands with 1 of the elongated windows and position race through window, then rotate race up and out of cage.

Reassembly (Outboard CV Joint)

1) Apply a light coating of grease on inner and outer races. Install inner race into cage, then install race and cage into outer race by installing assembly vertically and pivoting 90° into position.

NOTE: When correctly installed, shallow counterbore cut into inner race will be facing up.

2) Align bearing cage and inner race with outer race, then tilt race and cage and install ball bearing. Repeat this step until all 6 ball bearings are installed.

3) After installing bearings, pack CV joint with 1 packet of specified grease (supplied in service kit). Pack grease into joint by forcing it through splined hole in inner race.

Disassembly (Inboard CV Joint)

1) Remove snap ring from end of CV joint stub shaft. Using a pair of side cutters, cut and remove ball retainer. Discard ball retainer when removed. A new retainer is not required for reassembly.

2) Gently tap CV joint on bench until cage and inner race assembly can be removed by hand. Remove ball bearings by prying from cage with a blunt screwdriver. Do not scratch or otherwise damage race and cage spheres.

3) Rotate inner race to align lands with cage windows. Lift inner race from bearing cage through wider end of cage.

Reassembly (Inboard CV Joint)

1) Install snap ring on stub shaft by starting one end of ring in groove of shaft and then working snap ring over shaft end and into groove. This will avoid over expanding snap ring.

2) Install inner race through large end of cage with inner race circlip counterbore facing large end of cage.

Fig. 6: Exploded View of Drive Axle Shaft and CV Joint Assembly (Right Side Assembly Shown; Left Side Similar)

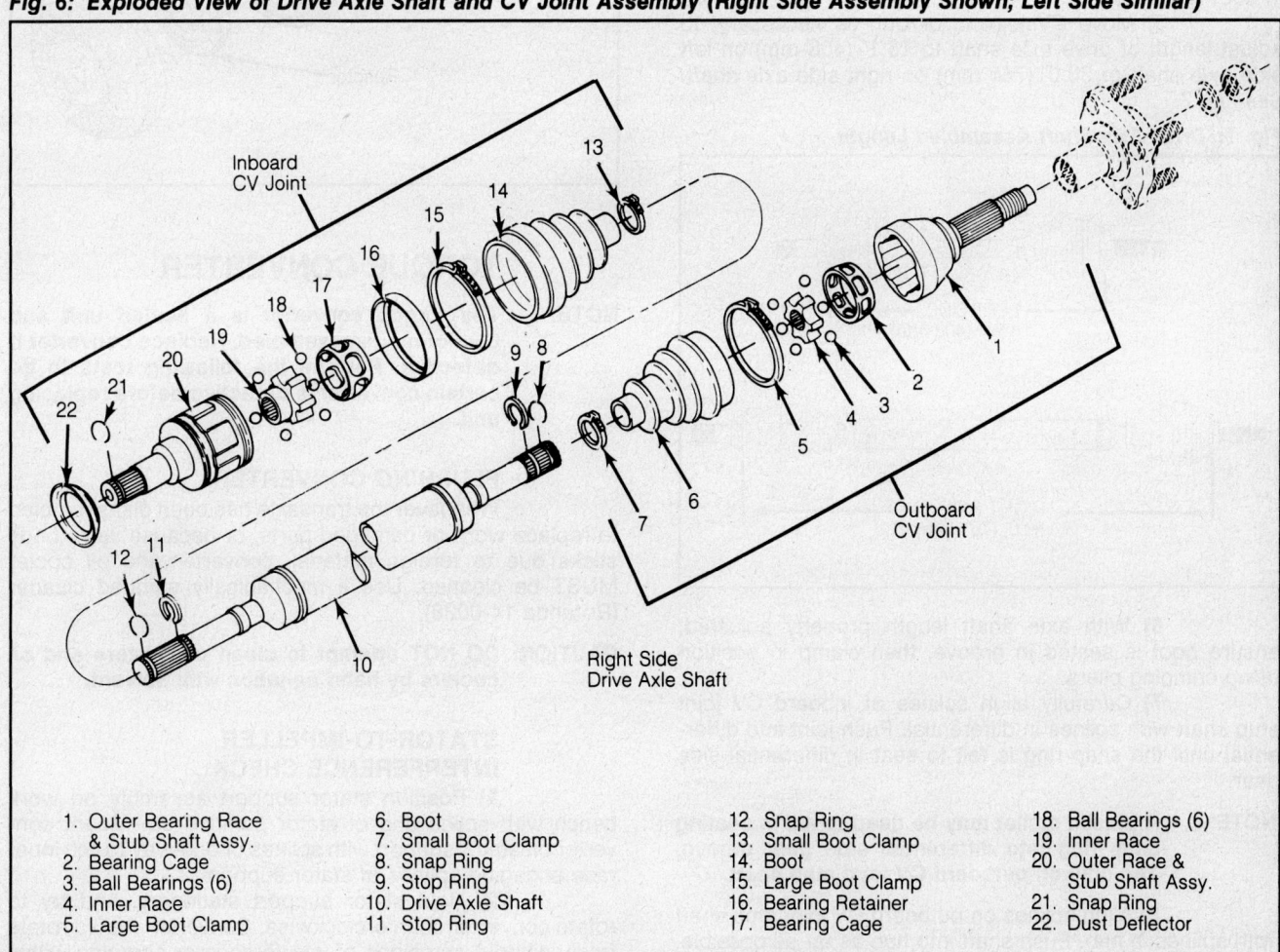

1. Outer Bearing Race & Stub Shaft Assy.	6. Boot	12. Snap Ring	18. Ball Bearings (6)
2. Bearing Cage	7. Small Boot Clamp	13. Small Boot Clamp	19. Inner Race
3. Ball Bearings (6)	8. Snap Ring	14. Boot	20. Outer Race & Stub Shaft Assy.
4. Inner Race	9. Stop Ring	15. Large Boot Clamp	21. Snap Ring
5. Large Boot Clamp	10. Drive Axle Shaft	16. Bearing Retainer	22. Dust Deflector
	11. Stop Ring	17. Bearing Cage	

With inner race and cage properly aligned, press ball bearings through cage with hand.

3) Pack outer race with 2 packets of grease (supplied with service kit). Position inner race and bearing assembly in outer race. When properly assembled, inner race circlip counterbore will face into outer race.

NOTE: CV joint shaft outboard end is approximately 1/4" longer (from end of shaft to end of boot groove) than inboard end.

Installation

1) If removed, install a new stop ring into groove on drive axle shaft. Install a new snap ring in groove nearest end of inboard CV joint. Use care not to over expand it. If removed, install CV joint boot on axle shaft. Make sure boot is seated in groove and clamp in position using crimping pliers.

2) With joint boot peeled back, position CV joint on shaft and tap into position using a plastic mallet. When fully seated, the snap ring locks in groove cut into CV joint inner race.

3) Before positioning boot over CV joint, pack joint and boot with lubricant supplied in service kit. Fill boots of CV joints with 1 packet each. Fill inboard CV joint with 2 packets and outboard CV joint with 1 packet.

4) Remove excess grease from CV joint external surfaces, then position boot over joint. Before installing boot, make sure any air pressure which might have built-up in boot is relieved.

5) Move CV joint in or out, as necessary, to adjust length of drive axle shaft to 16.1" (408 mm) on left side axle shaft or 30.0" (763 mm) on right side axle shaft. *See Fig. 7.*

Fig. 7: Drive Axle Shaft Assembled Length

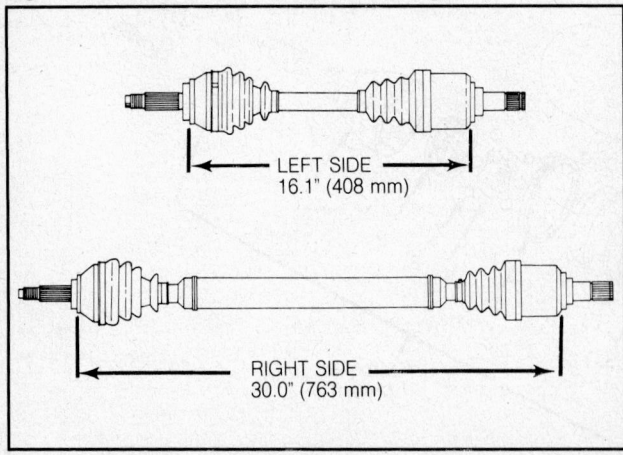

LEFT SIDE
16.1" (408 mm)

RIGHT SIDE
30.0" (763 mm)

6) With axle shaft length properly adjusted, ensure boot is seated in groove, then clamp in position using crimping pliers.

7) Carefully align splines of inboard CV joint stub shaft with splines in differential. Push joint into differential until the snap ring is felt to seat in differential side gear.

NOTE: A plastic mallet may be used to aid in seating snap ring into differential side gear groove. Tap only on outboard CV joint stub shaft.

8) Align splines on outboard CV joint stub shaft with splines in hub. Push shaft into hub as far as possible. Use a puller to pull shaft fully into hub.

9) Connect control arm to steering knuckle and install a NEW bolt and nut. Position brake hose routing clip in position on suspension strut and install attaching bolt.

10) Install hub nut washer and a NEW hub nut. Tighten hub nut to specification. Install wheel and tire assembly.

REMOVAL & INSTALLATION

TRANSAXLE

See appropriate AUTOMATIC TRANSMISSION REMOVAL article in DOMESTIC GENERAL SERVICING section.

Fig. 8: Exploded View of ATX Torque Converter

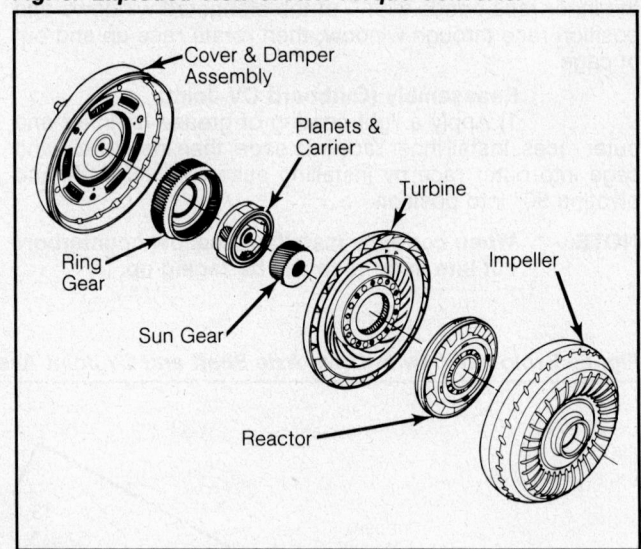

Cover & Damper Assembly

Planets & Carrier

Turbine

Impeller

Ring Gear

Sun Gear

Reactor

TORQUE CONVERTER

NOTE: The torque converter is a sealed unit and cannot be disassembled. Replace converter if defective. Perform the following tests to be certain converter is defective before replacing unit.

FLUSHING CONVERTER

Whenever the transaxle has been disassembled to replace worn or damaged parts, or because valve body sticks due to foreign material, converter and oil cooler MUST be cleaned. Use a mechanically agitated cleaner (Rotunda 14-0028).

CAUTION: DO NOT attempt to clean converters and oil coolers by hand agitation with solvent.

STATOR-TO-IMPELLER INTERFERENCE CHECK

1) Position stator support assembly on work bench with spline end of stator pointing up. Mount converter on stator support with splines of one-way clutch inner race engaging splines of stator support.

2) Hold stator support stationary, and try to rotate converter counterclockwise. Converter should rotate freely without any signs of interference or scraping within converter assembly.

FORD MOTOR CO. ATX – AUTOMATIC TRANSAXLE (Cont.)

3) If scraping is heard or felt, trailing edges of stator blades may be interfering with leading edges of impeller blades. In such cases, converter must be replaced.

STATOR-TO-TURBINE INTERFERENCE CHECK

1) Position converter on bench with front side down. Install stator support assembly to engage mating splines of stator support and stator, and pump drive gear lugs. Install turbine shaft, engaging splines with turbine hub.

2) Hold stator support stationary and attempt to rotate turbine with turbine shaft. Turbine should rotate freely in each direction without interference or noise. If interference exists, stator front washer may be worn. In such cases, converter must be replaced.

REACTOR ONE-WAY CLUTCH CHECK

1) Align slot in converter front thrust washer with holding lug. Insert One-Way Clutch Holder (T81P-7902-A) into holding lug. While holding tool in position, install One-Way Clutch Torque Adapter (T81P-7902-B) in reactor spline.

2) Continue holding tool and turn torquing tool counterclockwise with a torque wrench. If torquing tool begins to turn before torque wrench reads 10 ft. lbs. (14 N.m), replace converter.

CONVERTER END PLAY CHECK

1) Position End Play Checker (T81P-7902-D) in torque converter hub. Tighten nut on tool to secure tool in converter. Mount a dial indicator on end play checking tool.

2) With indicator stylus contacting converter shell and with indicator zeroed, lift on checking tool handles. If indicator reading is above .010-.040" (.254-1.016 mm), replace torque converter.

TRANSAXLE DISASSEMBLY

1) Mount transaxle in a holding stand. Pull torque converter from case, then remove oil pump drive shaft. Remove filler tube from case. Remove governor cover. Remove oil pan attaching bolts, then remove oil pan. Remove attaching bolts and lift out oil filter and seal.

2) Remove differential bearing retainer-to-case attaching bolts, then pry retainer from case. Remove differential bearing preload and tapered shims located under bearing retainer. Remove differential assembly from transaxle case.

3) Remove valve body cover. Disconnect and remove throttle valve control spring. Remove valve body attaching bolts and remove baffle plate and detent/roller assembly. Disengage "Z" link from manual valve and remove valve body assembly. Lift governor screen from bore in case (located under valve body).

NOTE: **The 7 baffle plate attaching bolts are longer than the other valve body attaching bolts.**

4) Remove cover and pull governor from case. Pry speedometer driven gear retaining pin partially out of case, then remove pin using side cutters. Tap driven gear from case using a hammer handle.

5) Remove oil pump attaching bolts and washers. Remove pump from case using a slide hammer puller. Remove and discard pump gasket. Remove thrust bearing

(needle) from top of intermediate clutch, then remove clutch assembly from case.

6) Remove thrust bearing (needle) from direct clutch, then remove direct clutch from case. Remove intermediate clutch hub and ring gear assembly. Remove thrust bearing (needle) from planetary assembly.

7) Remove large snap ring securing reverse clutch in case, then pull reverse clutch pack from case. Remove planetary assembly and thrust washer from case. Remove reverse clutch return springs and holder assembly. Pull reverse clutch piston from case. Pry reverse clutch drum up to loosen and remove from case.

8) Using a compressor tool, compress servo and remove retaining snap ring. Slowly release spring pressure, then remove compressor tool and servo assembly. Remove low-intermediate band from inside case.

9) Remove sun gear and drum assembly from case, then remove thrust washer from final drive housing at rear of case. Remove final drive housing-to-case attaching bolts. Use a screwdriver and pry housing from idler gear shaft and remove from case.

NOTE: **Discard final drive gear housing bolts. Replace with new bolts with high strength thread adhesive.**

10) Remove thrust bearing (needle) from input gear and remove input gear from case. Remove input gear caged needle bearing, and thrust bearing, located under it from case.

11) Position a 12 mm Allen wrench in idler gear shaft and allow wrench to catch on band strut. With wrench holding idler gear shaft, remove nut from rear of shaft. Tap idler gear shaft with a hammer handle to loosen "O" ring, then remove shaft from case.

12) Remove reactor support from case if damaged or unservicable. Reactor support is pressed in case. Remove with Puller (T81P-70363-A).

COMPONENT DISASSEMBLY & REASSEMBLY

OIL PUMP
Disassembly

1) Remove selective fit thrust washer and oil seal rings from clutch support. Remove pump-to-case oil seal ring from outside diameter of clutch support.

Fig. 9: Exploded View of Oil Pump

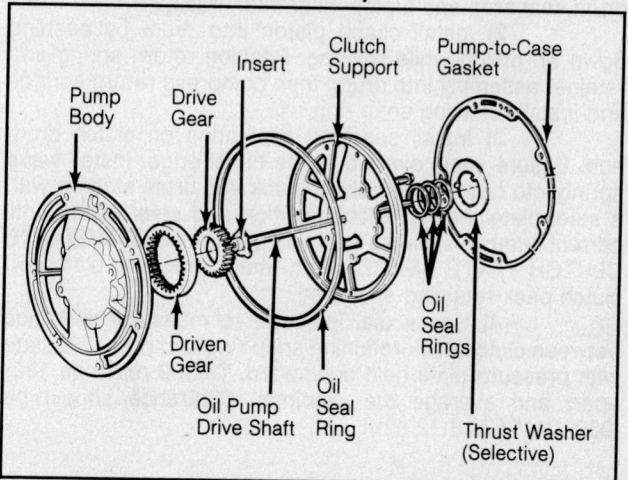

2) Remove clutch support-to-pump body attaching bolts, then separate support from pump body. Remove insert from pump drive gear. Remove driven gear and drive gear from pump body.

Reassembly

Reverse disassembly procedure making sure ends of scarf-cut oil seal rings are correctly positioned. Tighten support-to-pump bolts to specifications.

INTERMEDIATE CLUTCH
Disassembly

1) Remove intermediate shaft snap ring, then pull shaft from intermediate clutch drum. If damaged, remove stop ring from intermediate shaft.

2) Remove clutch pack retaining snap ring and withdraw pressure plate, wave spring, and clutch pack. Remove seal rings from clutch drum hub.

3) Using a Clutch Spring Compressor (T81P-70222-A), compress clutch return springs and remove retaining snap ring. Remove tool and lift return spring retainer and spring assembly from clutch drum.

4) Using pliers, remove clutch piston from drum. Remove inner piston seal from clutch drum and outer piston seal from clutch piston.

Cleaning & Inspection

1) Inspect clutch drum thrust surfaces, piston bore, and clutch plate serrations for scores or burrs. Minor scores or burrs may be removed with crocus cloth. Replace drum if it is badly scored or damaged.

2) Check fluid passage in clutch drum for obstructions. Clean out all passages. Inspect clutch piston for scores and replace if necessary. Inspect piston check ball for freedom of movement and proper seating.

3) Inspect clutch return springs for distortion and cracks. Inspect composition plates, steel plates and pressure plate for worn or scored bearing surfaces. Replace all parts that are deeply scored.

4) Check clutch plates for flatness and fit on clutch drum hub serrations. Replace any plate that does not slide freely on serrations or that is not flat.

5) Check clutch hub thrust surfaces for scores and clutch hub splines for wear. Inspect shaft bearing surfaces for scores. Check shaft splines for wear.

Reassembly

1) Inspect piston check ball and ensure ball is present and free. Install outer piston seal on piston with lip facing up and inner piston seal in clutch drum with lip facing down. Apply a light film of petroleum jelly to piston seals, drum seal area and piston inner seal area.

2) Install clutch piston into drum by pushing down on piston while rotating. Position return spring and retainer assembly into drum, then compress return springs and install retaining snap ring.

3) Install scarf-cut seal rings on clutch drum hub. Ensure seals overlap at the bevel edge. Install wave spring into drum. Install clutch pack into drum starting with a steel plate. Alternate composition and steel plates until correct number of plates are installed. See INTERMEDIATE CLUTCH PLATE USAGE chart. Install pressure plate and clutch pack retaining snap ring.

4) Use a dial indicator to measure clearance between clutch pack retaining snap ring and pressure plate with pressure plate held downward. Take 2 readings 180° apart and average the readings. Clearance should be .030-.044" (.75-1.12 mm).

INTERMEDIATE CLUTCH PLATE USAGE CHART

Application	Composition Plates	Steel Plates
All Models	3	3

5) On all models, if clearance is not within specifications, selective snap rings are available in the following thicknesses: .049-.053" (1.245-1.346 mm), .059-.063" (1.499-1.600 mm), and .070-.074" (1.778-1.880 mm). Install correct size snap ring and recheck clearance.

6) If removed, install stop ring on intermediate shaft. Install shaft into clutch drum, then install intermediate shaft retaining snap ring.

DIRECT CLUTCH
Disassembly

1) Remove sun gear/one-way clutch race assembly. Remove thrust washer, then withdraw one-way clutch.

2) Remove clutch pack retaining snap ring. Remove pressure plate, clutch pack, and wave spring from clutch drum. Remove thrust bearing. Using Compressor (T81P-70235), compress piston return spring retainer and remove retaining snap ring. Remove tool and piston return spring retainer.

3) Remove piston from clutch drum using pliers. Remove inner piston seal from clutch drum and outer piston seal from piston.

Inspection

See INTERMEDIATE CLUTCH inspection.

Reassembly

1) Inspect clutch drum check ball and ensure it is present and free. Install inner seal on clutch drum with seal lip facing down. Install outer piston seal on piston with seal lip facing up. Apply a light film of petroleum jelly to piston seals, then install piston into drum using a rotating motion while applying downward pressure.

2) Position return springs, retainer and retaining snap ring in clutch drum, then compress retainer and install snap ring in groove. Install thrust bearing on top of return spring retainer.

3) Install wave spring. Install clutch pack into drum starting with a steel clutch plate and alternating composition clutch plates and steel plates until correct number of clutch plates have been installed. See DIRECT CLUTCH PLATE USAGE chart. Install pressure plate and clutch pack snap ring.

DIRECT CLUTCH PLATE USAGE CHART

Application	Composition Plates	Steel Plates
1.6L	3	3
2.3L	4	4

4) Install one-way clutch over turbine shaft and into clutch drum. Install thrust washer into drum and ensure that tabs of washer are facing down against shoulder of one-way clutch inner race.

5) Using a feeler gauge or dial indicator, measure clearance between clutch pack retaining snap ring and pressure plate with pressure plate held down. Take 2 measurements 180° apart from each other. Direct clutch clearance should be .031-.047" (.78-1.20 mm) on 3 plates or .040-.056" (1.01-1.43 mm) on 4 plates.

FORD MOTOR CO. ATX — AUTOMATIC TRANSAXLE (Cont.)

Fig. 10: Exploded View of Intermediate Clutch Assembly

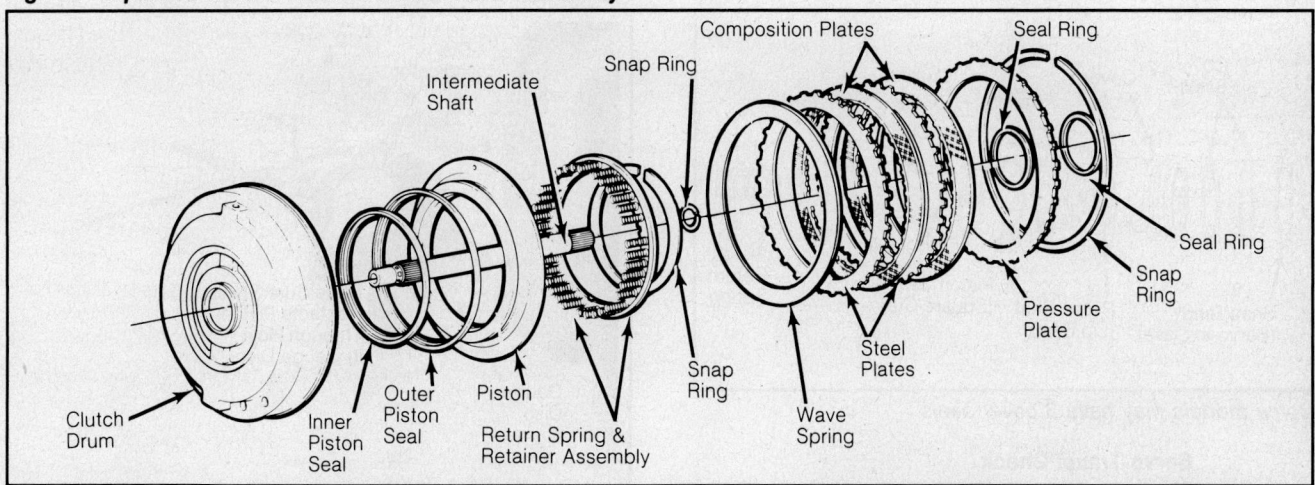

6) If clearance is not within specified limits, selective fit snap rings are available in the following thicknesses: .050-.054" (1.26-1.36 mm), .062-.066" (1.58-1.68 mm) and .075-.079" (1.90-2.00 mm). Install correct size snap ring and recheck clearance.

7) Install sun gear/one-way clutch outer race assembly over turbine shaft and into clutch drum. Check operation of one-way clutch. When properly assembled the one-way clutch allows sun gear/outer race assembly to rotate in one direction only.

REVERSE CLUTCH

NOTE: **Reverse clutch was disassembled under Transaxle Disassembly and will be reassembled during Transaxle Reassembly. The following procedure is for replacing piston seals.**

Piston Seal Replacement
Remove seals from clutch cylinder and clutch piston. Install new seal (large) on clutch cylinder with seal lips facing up. Install new inner seal (small) on piston with seal lip facing down, then install new outer seal on piston.

NOTE: **The outer piston seal is square-cut, making direction of installation unimportant.**

Inspection
1) Inspect clutch piston bore and piston inner and outer bearing surfaces for scores. Check air bleed ball valve in piston for free movement. Check orifice for obstructions.

2) Check fluid passages for obstructions. All passages must be clean and free of obstructions. Inspect clutch plates for wear, scoring and fit on clutch hub serrations. Replace all plates that are badly scored, worn, or do not fit freely in hub serrations.

3) Inspect clutch pressure plate for scores on clutch plate bearing surface. Check clutch return springs for distortion or collapsed coils.

BAND APPLY SERVO
Disassembly
Remove piston return spring, then separate servo piston from cover. Remove piston rod circlip, then slide piston rod, cushion spring and spring retaining washer from piston. Remove seals from servo cover and piston.

Inspection
1) Inspect servo body for cracks and piston bore for scores. Check fluid passages for obstructions. Inspect band and struts for distortion. Inspect band ends for cracks.

2) Inspect servo spring for distortion. Inspect band lining for excessive wear and bonding to metal band. Replace damaged seals.

NOTE: **The following Servo Travel Check needs to be performed only if one of the following components has been replaced:**
- **Transaxle Case**
- **Band Assembly**
- **Drum and Sun Gear Assembly**
- **Servo Piston Rod**
- **Servo Piston**
- **Band Anchor Strut**

Fig. 11: Exploded View of Direct Clutch Assembly

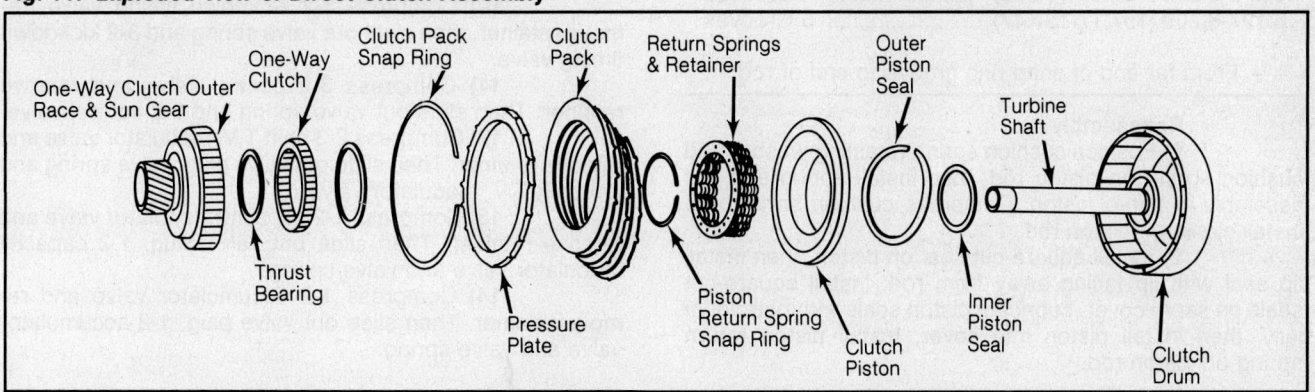

Fig. 12: Exploded View of Band Apply Servo

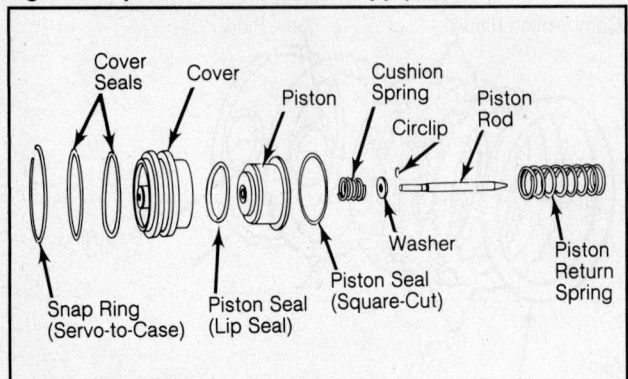

Some models may have 3 cover seals.

Fig. 13: Measuring Servo Piston Travel

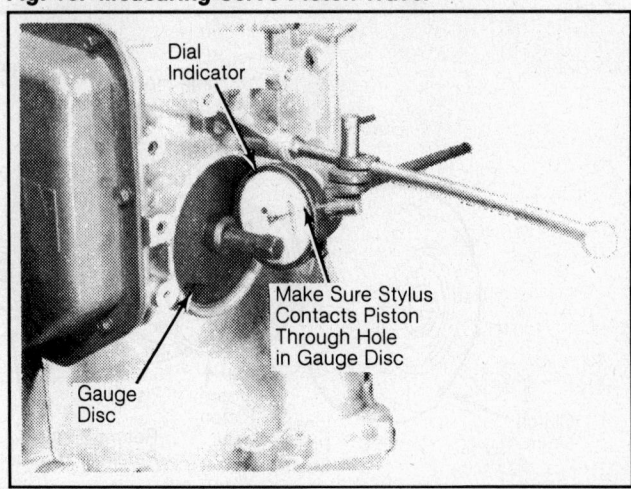

Servo Travel Check

1) Clean and assemble servo piston without piston seals. Install Return Spring (T81P-70027-A) on piston rod and position piston in case.

2) Install Servo Piston Selector (T81P-70023-A) and secure in case using servo cover retaining snap ring. Tighten gauge disc screw to 10 ft. lbs. (14 N.m). *See Fig. 13.*

3) Mount a dial indicator and position indicator stylus through hole in gauge disc, making sure stylus contacts servo piston. Zero dial indicator.

4) Back-off gauge disc screw until piston movement stops and read dial indicator. The amount of piston travel shown on indicator will determine piston rod length to install.

5) If piston travel is .203-.247" (5.15-6.27 mm), correct piston rod is installed and no change is required. If travel is less than specifications, piston rod is too long and a shorter rod (more grooves) will have to be installed. If travel is more than specified, rod is too short and a longer rod (less grooves) will have to be installed.

6) Select a new piston rod if necessary. See SERVO PISTON ROD SELECTION table. Install selected rod and recheck servo travel.

SERVO PISTON ROD SELECTION

Rod Length [1] In. (mm)	Rod I.D.
6.313-6.324 (160.22-160.52)	No Grooves
6.289-6.300 (159.61-159.90)	1 Groove
6.265-6.276 (159.00-159.30)	2 Grooves
6.240-6.252 (158.39-158.69)	3 Grooves
6.216-6.223 (157.88-158.08)	4 Grooves
6.197-6.209 (157.17-157.47)	5 Grooves

[1] – From far end of snap ring groove to end of rod.

Reassembly

1) Position cushion spring retaining washer and cushion spring on piston rod, then install spring and rod assembly in servo piston. Compress cushion spring and install circlip on piston rod.

2) Install square-cut seal on piston, then install lip seal with lip facing away from rod. Install square-cut seals on servo cover. Lubricate piston seals with petroleum jelly, then install piston into cover. Install piston return spring on piston rod.

VALVE BODY ASSEMBLY
Disassembly

1) Remove the 2 separator plate attaching screws and remove separator plate from valve body, then remove check balls and relief valve from valve body cored passages. *See Fig. 14.*

2) Compress reverse boost valve plug. Using tweezers, remove retainer and slide out valve plug, spring and reverse boost valve.

3) Compress 2-3 shift valve plug, remove retainer and slide out valve plug, 2-3 shift valve and valve spring.

4) Compress 1-2 shift valve, remove retainer, then slide out valve plug, 1-2 shift valve, modulator valve spring and 1-2 T.V. modulator valve.

5) Compress 2-1 scheduling valve, remove retainer, then slide out valve spring and 2-1 scheduling valve.

6) Compress 2-3 backout valve, remove retainer, then slide out valve plug, valve spring and 2-3 backout valve.

7) Compress main oil pressure regulator and remove retainer. Then slide out main oil pressure booster sleeve, main oil regulator boost valve, regulator valve spring, spring retainer and main oil regulator valve.

8) Compress manual low downshift modulating valve, remove retainer. Then slide out valve plug, manual low downshift valve and valve spring.

9) Compress 3-2 torque demand timing valve, remove retainer, then slide out valve spring and 3-2 torque demand timing control valve.

10) Compress 3-2 kickdown timing valve, remove retainer, then slide out valve spring and 3-2 kickdown timing valve.

11) Compress 3-2 control valve and remove retainer. Then slide out valve spring and 3-2 control valve.

12) Compress 2-3 shift T.V. modulator valve and remove retainer. Then slide out valve plug, valve spring and 2-3 shift T.V. modulator valve.

13) Compress 1-2 capacity modulator valve and remove retainer. Then slide out valve plug, 1-2 capacity modulator valve and valve spring.

14) Compress 1-2 accumulator valve and remove retainer. Then slide out valve plug, 1-2 accumulator valve and valve spring.

FORD MOTOR CO. ATX — AUTOMATIC TRANSAXLE (Cont.)

Fig. 14: Exploded View of Valve Body Valve Trains

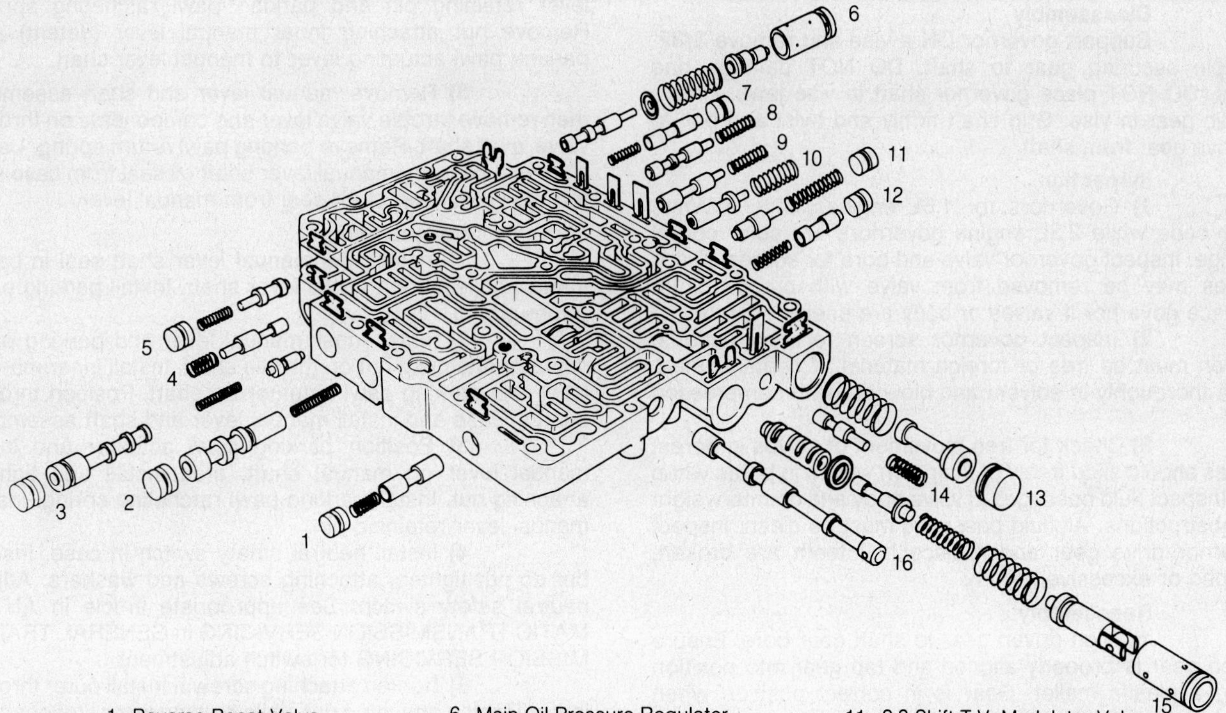

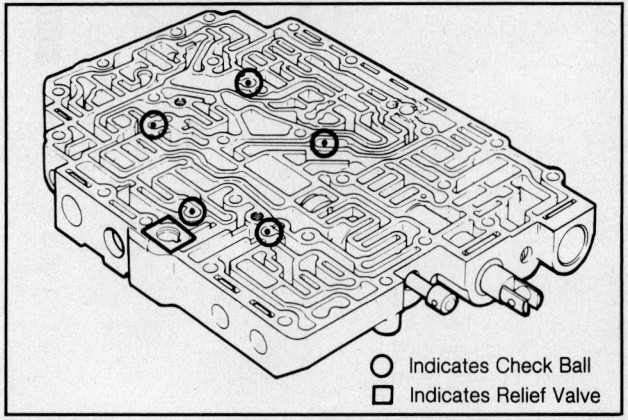

1. Reverse Boost Valve	6. Main Oil Pressure Regulator	11. 2-3 Shift T.V. Modulator Valve
2. 2-3 Shift Valve	7. Manual Low Downshift	12. 1-2 Capacity Modulator Valve
3. 1-2 Shift Valve	Modulating Valve	13. 1-2 Accumulator Valve
4. 1-2 Scheduling Valve	8. 3-2 Torque Demand Timing Valve	14. T.V. Limit Valve
5. 2-3 Backout Valve	9. 3-2 Kickdown Timing Valve	15. Throttle Pressure Control Valve
	10. 3-2 Control Valve	16. Manual Control Valve

NOTE: See numbered step under Valve Body Disassembly which corresponds to valve train reference number for identification of individual valve train components.

---

15) Compress T.V. limit valve and remove retainer. Then slide out valve spring and T.V. limit valve.

16) Compress throttle pressure valve and remove retainer. Then slide out throttle valve plunger sleeve, throttle pressure valve, plunger return spring (large), throttle valve spring (small) and small throttle pressure valve and washer.

CAUTION: DO NOT turn throttle valve adjusting screw and lock nut. Adjustment screw is set during manufacture and must not be altered.

17) Using a drift, drive out retaining pin and remove throttle pressure adjusting sleeve. Slide the manual control valve from the valve body bore.

Cleaning & Inspection

1) Clean all parts thoroughly in clean solvent, and blow dry with moisture-free compressed air.

2) Inspect all valve and plug bores for scores. Check all fluid passages for obstructions. Inspect all mating surfaces for burrs or distortion. Inspect all plugs and valves for burrs and scores.

NOTE: If necessary, use crocus cloth to polish valve and plugs. Avoid rounding off sharp edges of valves and plugs with cloth.

3) Inspect all springs for distortion. Check all valves and plugs for free movement in their bores. Valves and plugs, when dry, must fall from their own weight in their

respective bores. Roll manual control valve on a flat surface to check for bent condition.

Reassembly

1) Reverse disassembly procedure and note the following: Install 5 check balls and relief valve into valve body passages. *See Fig. 15.*

2) Use Alignment Pins (T80L-77100-A) when installing separator plate and gasket to ensure that they are properly aligned with valve body. Tighten separator plate bolts to specification.

Fig. 15: View of Valve Body Showing Location of Check Balls and Relief Valve

○ Indicates Check Ball
□ Indicates Relief Valve

FORD MOTOR CO. ATX – AUTOMATIC TRANSAXLE (Cont.)

GOVERNOR
Disassembly

Support governor ON a vise and remove 3/32" roll pin securing gear to shaft. DO NOT damage ring lands. DO NOT place governor shaft in vise jaws. Clamp plastic gear in vise. Grip shaft firmly and twist and pull to remove gear from shaft.

Inspection

1) Governors for 1.6L engines have a White color code while 2.3L engine governors are color coded Orange. Inspect governor valve and bore for scores. Minor scores may be removed from valve with crocus cloth. Replace governor if valves or body are deeply scored.

2) Inspect governor screen for obstructions. Screen must be free of foreign material. If contaminated, clean thoroughly in solvent and blow dry with compressed air.

3) Check for free movement of valves in bores. Valves should slide freely of their own weight in bores when dry. Inspect fluid passages in valve body and counterweight for obstructions. All fluid passages must be clean. Inspect governor drive gear and replace it if teeth are broken, chipped or excessively worn.

Reassembly

1) Align driven gear to shaft gear bore. Ensure driven gear is properly aligned and tap gear into position using a plastic mallet. Gear is in correct position when shoulder is seated against governor shaft.

2) Support governor on a non-machined surface. Using a drill press, align drill bit to prevent damaging governor shaft and drill a 1/8" hole through driven gear. Install NEW roll pin.

MANUAL & THROTTLE LINKAGE
Disassembly

1) Hold outer throttle lever stationary to prevent damage to throttle shaft cam and remove throttle valve outer lever. Remove attaching screws and washers, then slide neutral safety switch from shaft.

2) Using needle nose pliers, remove manual lever retaining pin and parking pawl ratcheting spring. Remove nut attaching inner manual lever (detent) and parking pawl actuating lever to manual lever shaft.

3) Remove manual lever and shaft assembly, then remove throttle valve lever and components on throttle valve lever shaft. Remove parking pawl return spring. Using a screwdriver, pry manual lever shaft oil seal from case and throttle valve lever shaft seal from manual lever.

Reassembly

1) Install new manual lever shaft seal in case. Install new seal on throttle lever shaft. Install parking pawl return spring.

2) Install inner manual lever and parking pawl actuator attaching nut on throttle shaft. Install inner manual lever and parking pawl actuator on shaft. Position throttle shaft in case and install manual lever and shaft assembly.

3) Position parking pawl actuator and inner manual lever on manual shaft, then install and tighten attaching nut. Install parking pawl ratcheting spring. Install manual lever retaining pin.

4) Install neutral safety switch in case. Install, but do not tighten, attaching screws and washers. Adjust neutral safety switch. See appropriate article in AUTOMATIC TRANSMISSION SERVICING in GENERAL TRANSMISSION SERVICING for switch adjustment.

5) Tighten attaching screws. Install outer throttle lever. Tighten attaching nut while holding lever stationary to prevent damage to throttle shaft cam.

DIFFERENTIAL ASSEMBLY
Disassembly

1) Remove bolts attaching differential bearing retainer to case. Using 2 screwdrivers, remove retainer. Remove bearing spacer shims. Remove differential from case. Using Puller (T77F-4220-B1), remove differential carrier bearings. Pull speedometer drive gear from case.

2) Remove side gears and thrust washers from differential case by rotating the gears toward case win-

Fig. 16: Exploded View of Manual and Throttle Linkage Components

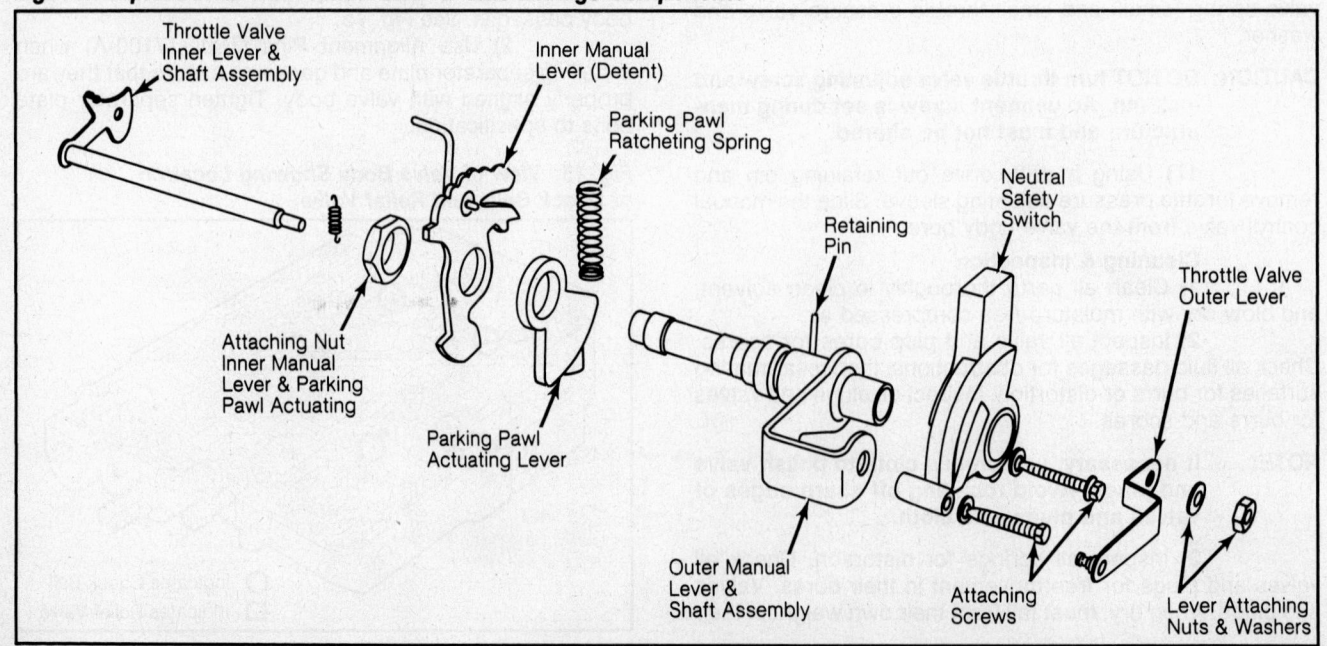

Throttle Valve Inner Lever & Shaft Assembly

Inner Manual Lever (Detent)

Parking Pawl Ratcheting Spring

Attaching Nut Inner Manual Lever & Parking Pawl Actuating

Parking Pawl Actuating Lever

Retaining Pin

Neutral Safety Switch

Throttle Valve Outer Lever

Outer Manual Lever & Shaft Assembly

Attaching Screws

Lever Attaching Nuts & Washers

FORD MOTOR CO. ATX – AUTOMATIC TRANSAXLE (Cont.)

dows. Using a punch, drive out differential pinion gear shaft retaining pin, then remove gears and thrust washers from case.

3) If necessary, remove ring gear from differential case as follows: Using a 5/16" drill, drill formed side of attaching rivets, then remove heads of rivets with a chisel. Using a punch, drive remaining rivet shank from case and remove ring gear.

Cleaning & Inspection

1) Thoroughly clean all parts in new solvent. Do not spin dry bearings using compressed air. Oil side bearings immediately after cleaning to prevent corrosion. Inspect parts for any major defect.

NOTE: When a scored or chipped gear is replaced, transaxle case must be cleaned thoroughly to insure all chips are removed.

2) Examine pinion and side gears for scoring, excessive wear, nicks and chips. Worn, scored and damaged gears must be replaced.

3) Make sure differential case bearing journals are smooth. Inspect case bearing shoulders for damage caused by bearing removal. Check fit (free rotation) of side gears in their cavities.

4) Check bearing races for deep scores, galling or chipping. If races are not damaged, do not remove from transaxle case or differential retainer. If races must be replaced, remove and install with appropriate tools.

Fig. 17: Exploded View of Differential Assembly

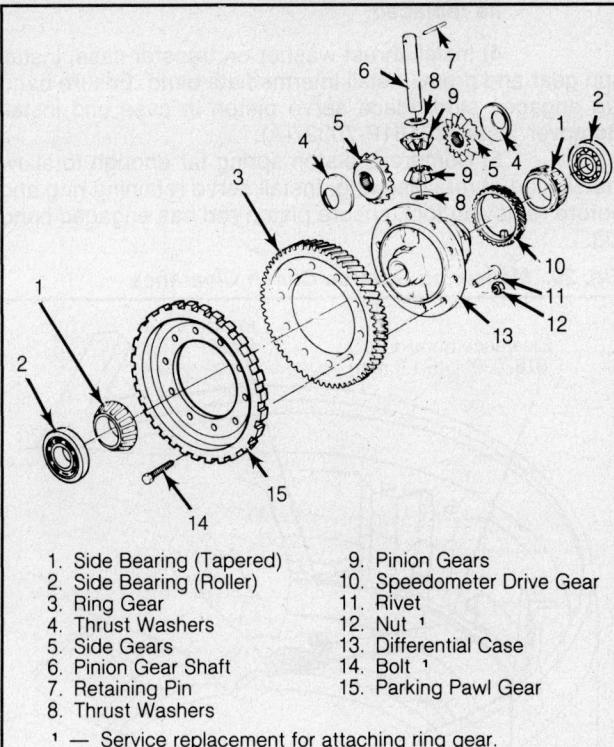

1. Side Bearing (Tapered)	9. Pinion Gears
2. Side Bearing (Roller)	10. Speedometer Drive Gear
3. Ring Gear	11. Rivet
4. Thrust Washers	12. Nut ¹
5. Side Gears	13. Differential Case
6. Pinion Gear Shaft	14. Bolt ¹
7. Retaining Pin	15. Parking Pawl Gear
8. Thrust Washers	

¹ — Service replacement for attaching ring gear.

5) Check side bearings for smooth rotation in races. Examine bearing roller ends for step wear. If inspection reveals either a damaged race or bearing, both parts must be replaced as they are a matched set.

Reassembly

1) To reassemble differential assembly, reverse disassembly procedure. Lubricate all thrust washers and thrust surfaces on gears and in case with automatic transmission fluid.

2) If removed, press ring gear onto differential case and attach to case with service replacement nuts and bolts. Install bolts with heads on parking pawl gear side of ring gear.

NOTE: Differential side gears must be aligned in case. This alignment must be held while installing differential assembly in case. Failure to maintain alignment will make it impossible to install axle drive shafts through side gears.

Differential Bearing Preload Adjustment

1) Differential bearing preload is set at the factory and need not be checked or adjusted unless one of the following parts is replaced:
• Transaxle Case
• Differential Case
• Differential Bearings
• Differential Bearing Retainer

2) To adjust preload, install differential assembly into transaxle case. Place Shim Spacer (T83P-4451-BA) on differential ball bearing outer race. Thickness of spacer tool should be .054-.055" (1.39-1.41 mm).

3) Remove bearing retainer "O" ring and oil seal. Install bearing retainer in case. Install Differential Bearing Preload Shim Selector (T81P-4451-A) in differential retainer.

4) Ensure tool is centered in differential seal bore. Position gauge bar of selector tool across bearing retainer and install 2 attaching bolts. See Fig. 18.

5) Tighten center screw of gauge bar to 10 INCH lbs. (1 N.m), then rotate differential assembly several times to seat bearings. Retighten screw to 10 INCH lbs. (1 N.m).

Fig. 18: Differential Bearing Preload Tool Installation

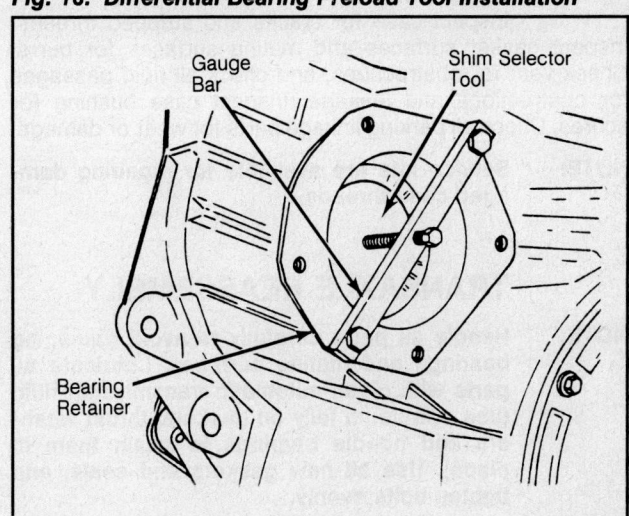

Gauge Bar

Shim Selector Tool

Bearing Retainer

6) Using a feeler gauge, measure clearance between bearing retainer and transaxle case at 3 positions around retainer. Add the 3 measurements together and divide by 3 to obtain the average of all measurements.

7) To determine the shim needed for correct bearing preload, subtract the average measurement ob-

tained in step **6**) from 1.35 mm (1.35 mm is a constant based on spacer tool). Result is the thickness of preload shim to install.

NOTE: **Bearing preload shims are available in thicknesses of .012"-.051" (.305-1.29 mm) in various increments. If calculations result in shim thickness which falls between 2 available thicknesses, always use the thinner shim.**

8) Remove gauge bar, selector tool and bearing retainer. Install new differential oil seal in retainer and new "O" ring on retainer. Position shim in position on ball bearing outer race. Install bearing retainer by tapping evenly around outside edge of retainer face.

9) Apply sealer to bolt threads, then install differential bearing retainer-to-case attaching bolts. Tighten bolts to specifications.

PINION CARRIERS

NOTE: **Individual parts of the planet carrier are not serviceable. If any part is worn or damaged, complete planet carrier must be replaced.**

Inspection

Inspect pins and shafts for loose fit and/or complete disengagement. Check shaft welds. Inspect pinion gears for damage or excessively worn teeth. Check for free rotation of pinion gears.

INPUT, IDLER & FINAL DRIVE GEARS
Inspection

Inspect gear teeth; they should be smooth with a uniform contact pattern without signs of excessive wear. Replace any gear which is cracked, chipped, broken or excessively worn.

TRANSAXLE CASE
Inspection

Inspect case for cracks and stripped threads. Inspect gasket surfaces and mating surfaces for burrs. Check vent for obstructions, and check all fluid passages for obstructions and leakage. Inspect case bushing for scores. Check all parking linkage parts for wear or damage.

NOTE: **Service kits are available for repairing damaged case threads.**

TRANSAXLE REASSEMBLY

NOTE: **Handle all parts carefully to avoid damaging bearings and mating surfaces. Lubricate all parts with clean automatic transmission fluid (use petroleum jelly on gaskets, thrust washers and needle bearings to retain them in place). Use all new gaskets and seals, and tighten bolts evenly.**

1) Clean up threads of idler gear shaft and install a new "O" ring. Place idler gear and shaft in case. Insert a 12 mm Allen wrench in idler gear shaft and position it to catch on the band anchor strut.

2) Apply thread locking sealant (E0AZ-19554-A) to attaching nut. Install and tighten nut to specification using a 32 mm 12-point socket. Install thrust bearing and input gear caged needle bearing. See Fig. 19.

Fig. 19: Installing Thrust Bearing and Caged Needle Bearing

3) Install input gear over reactor support, then install needle bearing on input gear. Position transfer housing in case and ensure it is firmly seated on alignment dowels. Install NEW transfer housing attaching bolts and tighten to specifications.

NOTE: **Before installing transfer housing, ensure that band strut is rotated into its operating position. Also, transmission case and housing are matched parts. If one is damaged, both must be replaced.**

4) Install thrust washer on transfer case. Install sun gear and drum. Install intermediate band. Ensure band lug engages stud. Place servo piston in case and install Remover/Installer (T81P-70027-A).

5) Compress piston spring far enough to allow installation of retaining ring. Install servo retaining ring and before removing tool, ensure piston rod has engaged band lug.

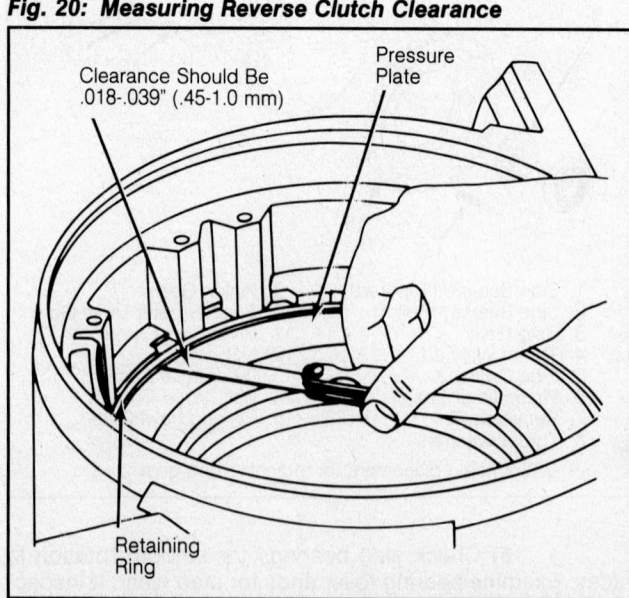

Fig. 20: Measuring Reverse Clutch Clearance

6) Place reverse clutch cylinder in case and tap cylinder using a hammer handle. Using Seal Protector (T81P-70402-A), apply even pressure and install reverse

FORD MOTOR CO. ATX – AUTOMATIC TRANSAXLE (Cont.)

clutch piston in clutch cylinder. Remove seal protector. Install thrust washer on planetary gear set, then install assembly on sun gear.

NOTE: **Before installing reverse clutch piston return spring and holder assembly, reverse clutch clearance must be checked as follows:**

7) Install clutch pack wave spring, clutch pack and pressure plate, then install clutch pack retaining ring. Using a feeler gauge, measure clearance between retaining ring and pressure plate at 2 places 180 degrees apart.

8) If average clearance is .030-.053" (.76-1.35 mm), clutch clearance is correct. If clearance is less than .030" (.76 mm), install a thinner retaining ring. If clearance is greater than .053" (1.35 mm), install a thicker retaining ring.

NOTE: **Whenever a new retaining ring is installed, repeat clearance check. Reverse clutch retaining rings are available in the following thicknesses: .074-.078" (1.89-1.99 mm), .092-.096" (2.33-2.43 mm), .109-.113" (2.77-2.87 mm), and .126-.130" (3.21-3.31 mm).**

REVERSE CLUTCH PLATE USAGE CHART

Application	Composition Plates	Steel Plates
All Models	3	3

9) Remove reverse clutch pack retaining ring, pressure plate, clutch pack and wave spring. Install reverse clutch return spring and holder assembly, then reinstall wave spring, clutch pack, pressure plate and retaining ring.

10) Install thrust bearing (needle) on planetary assembly. Install intermediate clutch hub and ring gear assembly into case. Install direct clutch assembly into case, then position thrust bearing (needle) on direct clutch.

11) Install intermediate clutch assembly into case and check for proper clutch engagement as follows: Position thrust bearing on one of the machined tabs and push it up against the case. If bearing is flush with, or slightly below machined pump housing surface in case, clutch is fully engaged. *See Fig. 21.* Position thrust bearing on clutch drum.

12) Install oil pump Alignment Pins (T81P-77100-A) and pump housing gasket. Position transaxle End Play Checking Tools (T81P-77389-A and T80L-77003-A) in intermediate clutch as shown in *Fig. 22.*

13) Using a micrometer, measure distance from top of gauge bar to top of thrust bearing installed on intermediate clutch. Make measurement at 2 places 180 degrees apart and use the average. From micrometer reading, choose correct end play thrust washer to install. See END PLAY THRUST WASHER SELECTION CHART.

14) Install selected transaxle end play thrust washer on oil pump, then position pump in case and tap into place using a hammer handle. Remove pump alignment pins and install pump attaching bolts and washers.

CAUTION: **Attaching bolt washers provide the bolt seal and must not be substituted. Failure to use sealing washers may result in a fluid leak.**

15) Position differential assembly in transaxle case. Install differential bearing spacer shim. Install new "O"

Fig. 21: *Checking Intermediate Clutch for Proper Engagement*

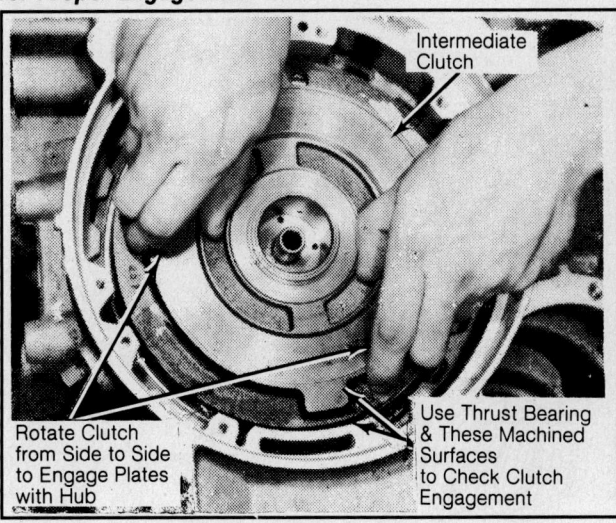

Intermediate Clutch

Rotate Clutch from Side to Side to Engage Plates with Hub

Use Thrust Bearing & These Machined Surfaces to Check Clutch Engagement

Fig. 22: *Assembling Transaxle End Play Measuring Tools*

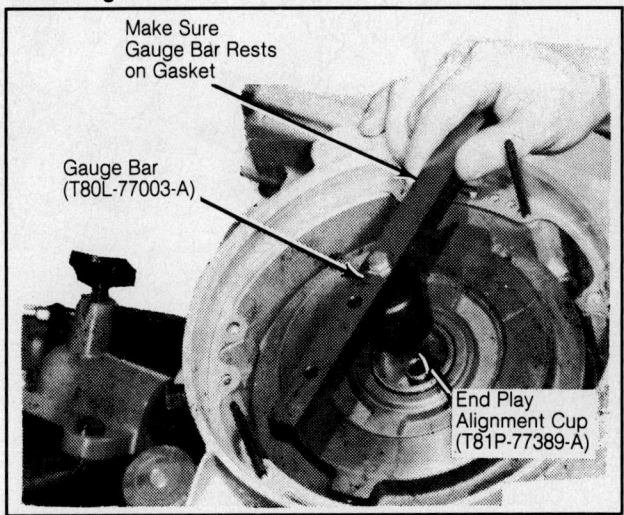

Make Sure Gauge Bar Rests on Gasket

Gauge Bar (T80L-77003-A)

End Play Alignment Cup (T81P-77389-A)

END PLAY THRUST WASHER SELECTION CHART

End Play Measurement	[1] Thrust Washer Part I.D.
.070-.079" (1.77-2.00 mm)	AA
.079-.087" (2.00-2.20 mm)	BA
.087-.095" (2.20-2.41 mm)	CA
.057-.070" (1.46-1.77 mm)	EA

[1] – If washer thickness is not known, measure its thickness using a micrometer. Washer "AA" is .055-.057" (1.40-1.45 mm); washer "BA" is .063-.065" (1.60-1.65 mm); washer "CA" is .071-.073" (1.80-1.85 mm); washer "EA" is .045-.047" (1.15-1.20 mm).

ring seal on differential retainer and position retainer in case (tap into place if necessary). Apply sealer to bolt threads, then install and tighten retainer attaching bolt.

Fig. 23: Exploded View of ATX Automatic Transaxle Assembly

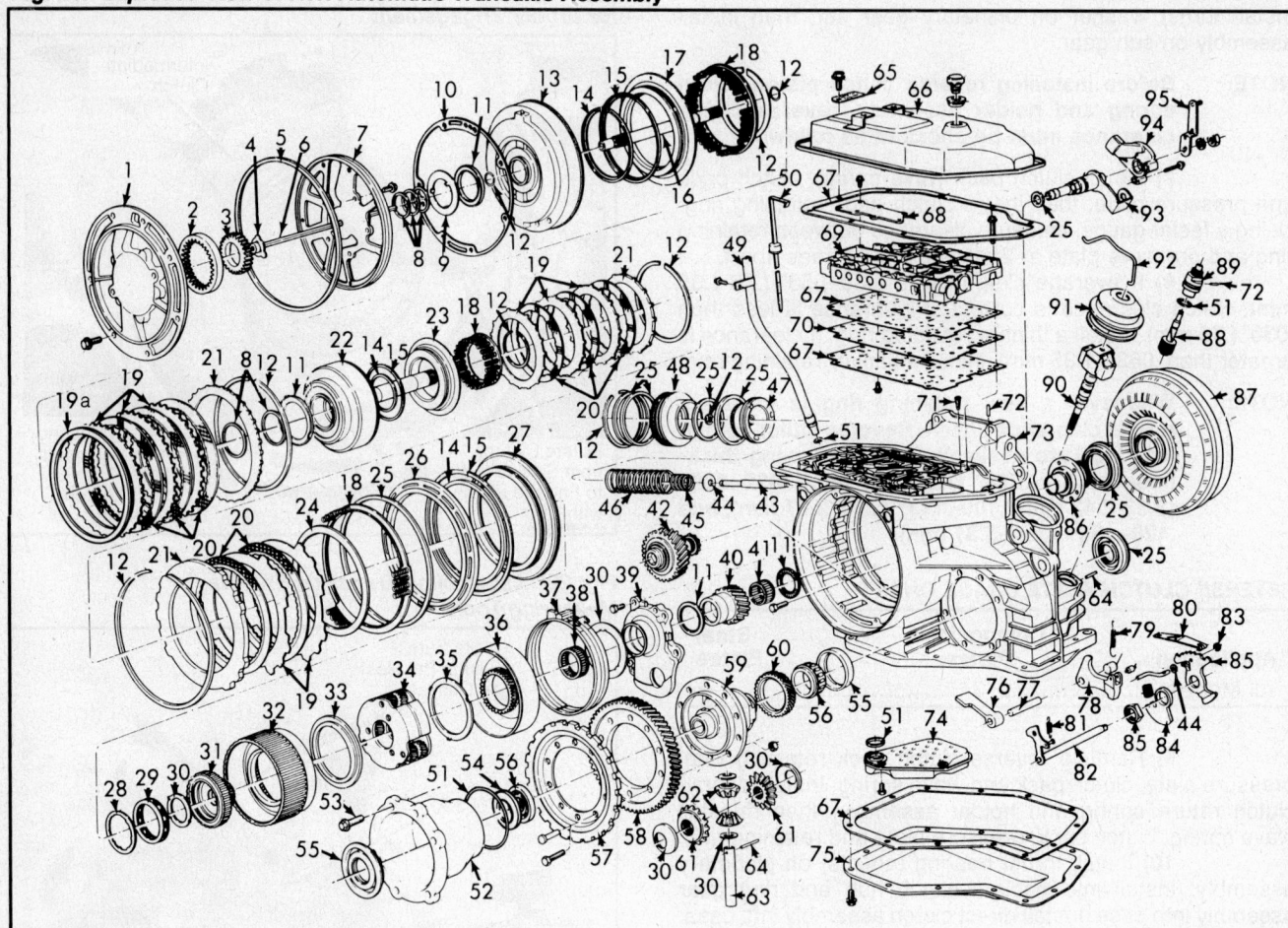

1. Oil Pump Body	25. Seal	50. Dipstick	75. Oil Pan
2. Pump Driven Gear	26. Reverse Clutch Piston	51. "O" Ring	76. Band Anchor Strut
3. Pump Drive Gear	27. Reverse Clutch Drum	52. Differential Retainer	77. Park Pawl Shaft
4. Pump Gear Insert	28. One-Way Clutch Bearing	53. Retainer Bolt	78. Park Pawl Assembly
5. Oil Pump Seal	29. Spring & Roller Assy.	54. Side Bearing Preload Shim	79. Park Pawl Return Spring
6. Oil Pump Shaft	30. Thrust Washer	55. Oil Seal	80. Manual Valve Detent Spring
7. Clutch Support	31. 1st/3rd, Reverse Gear	56. Differential Side Bearing	81. TV Lever Control Spring
8. Teflon Oil Seals	32. Interm. Clutch Hub & Ring Gear	57. Parking Pawl Gear	82. TV Lever Actuating Shaft
9. End Play Thrust Washer	33. Planet Rear Thrust Bearing	58. Ring Gear	83. Nut
10. Pump Gasket	34. Planetary Assy.	59. Differential Case	84. Park Pawl Actuating Lever
11. Thrust Bearing	35. Planet Front Thrust Washer	60. Speedometer Drive Gear	85. Manual Valve Inner Lever
12. Snap Ring	36. Sun Gear & Drum Assy.	61. Side Gears	86. Reactor Support
13. Interm. Clutch Drum	37. Band	62. Pinion Gears	87. Torque Converter
14. Inner Piston Seal	38. Transfer Hsg. Bearing	63. Pinion Gear Shaft	88. Speedometer Driven Gear
15. Outer Piston Seal	39. Final Drive Gear Housing	64. Retaining Pin	89. Speedometer Gear Retainer
16. Interm. Clutch Shaft	40. Input Gear, Final Drive	65. Transaxle I.D. Tag	90. Governor
17. Interm. Clutch Piston	41. Input Gear Bearing	66. Valve Body Cover	91. Governor Cover
18. Return Spring Assy.	42. Idler Gear	67. Gasket	92. Retainer Wire
19. Steel Clutch Plates	43. Servo Rod	68. Baffle Plate	93. Manual Lever
19a. Wave Spring	44. Washer	69. Valve Body Assy.	94. Neutral Safety Switch
20. Composition Clutch Plates	45. Cushion Spring	70. Separator Plate	95. TV Outer Lever
21. Pressure Plate	46. Piston Spring	71. Governor Screen	
22. Direct Clutch Drum	47. Servo Piston	72. Dowel Pin	
23. Direct Clutch Piston	48. Servo Cover	73. Transaxle Case	
24. Wave Spring	49. Oil Filler Tube	74. Oil Filter	

FORD MOTOR CO. ATX – AUTOMATIC TRANSAXLE (Cont.)

Fig. 24: Installing Governor Screen

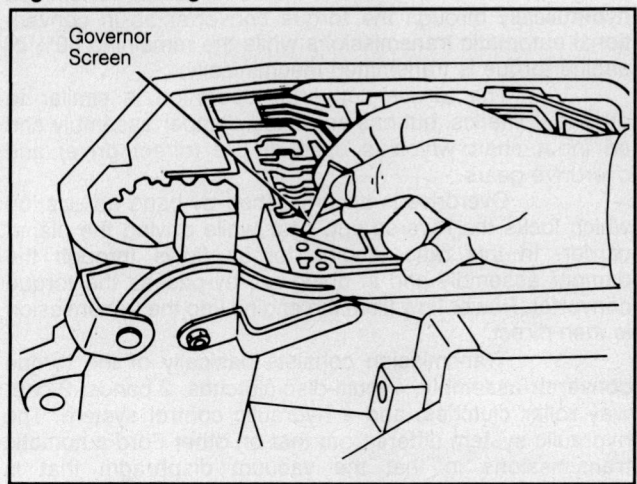

Fig. 25: Tightening Sequence for Valve Body Attaching Bolts

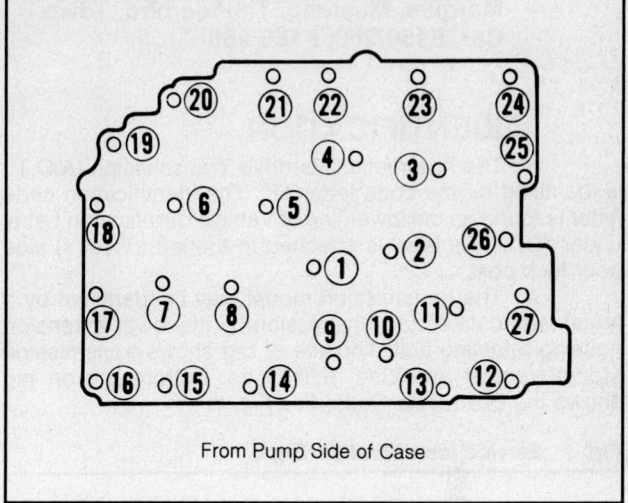

From Pump Side of Case

16) Position new seal on oil filter and install filter in case. Install oil pan using a new gasket. Install new seal on speedometer driven gear retainer and position retainer in case. Tap retainer into position using a plastic tipped hammer. With retainer properly positioned, tap retaining pin into case.

17) Install governor into case, then install new seal on governor cover and position cover on case. Tap cover into place using a plastic tipped hammer and install cover retaining wire.

18) Position governor screen into case bore. *See Fig. 24.* Position valve body gasket on case and install alignment pins to hold gasket in place. Place valve body in position in case and at the same time connect "Z" link to manual valve.

19) Connect throttle valve control spring to inner lever cam and to separator plate. With valve body correctly positioned, make sure roller on end of throttle valve plunger has engaged cam on end of throttle lever shaft.

20) Install detent roller assembly, baffle plate and the remaining valve body attaching bolts. Tighten valve body attaching bolts in sequence. *Fig. 25.* Position a new valve body cover gasket on case, then install cover and tighten attaching bolts.

21) Install oil pump shaft. Install torque converter into transaxle case.

TIGHTENING SPECIFICATIONS

Application	Ft. Lbs. (N.m)
Control Arm-to-Knuckle	37-44 (50-60)
Cooler Tube Fitting-to-Case	18-23 (24-31)
Differential Retainer-to-Case	15-19 (20-26)
Final Drive Housing-to-Case	18-23 (24-31)
Front Wheel Hub Nut	80-105 (108-144)
Idler Shaft Attaching Nut	80-100 (108-136)
Inner Manual Lever-to-Shaft Nut	32-48 (43-65)
Oil Pan-to-Case	15-19 (20-26)
	INCH Lbs. (N.m)
Filter-to-Case	84-108 (9-12)
Outer Throttle Lever-to-Shaft Nut	90-114 (10-13)
Pressure Test Port Plug-to-Case	84-132 (9-15)
Pump Support-to-Pump Body	72-96 (8-11)
Reaction Support-to-Case	72-96 (8-11)
Separator Plate-to-Valve Body	72-96 (8-11)
Valve Body-to-Case	72-96 (8-11)
Valve Body Cover-to-Case	84-108 (9-12)

Automatic Transmissions
FORD MOTOR CO. A.O.T.

Capri, Continental, Cougar, Crown Victoria, Grand Marquis, LTD, Mark VII, Marquis, Mustang, Thunderbird, Town Car, E150/250, F150/250

IDENTIFICATION

The Automatic Overdrive Transmission (A.O.T.) is identified by the code letter "T". The identification code letter is found on the lower line of Vehicle Certification Label under "TR". This label is attached to the left (driver's) side door lock post.

The transmission model may be identified by a metal tag attached to transmission by the lower extension housing retaining bolt. Top line of tag shows transmission Model Number and Line Shift Code. Bottom line on tag shows the Build Date Code. *See Fig. 1.*

Fig. 1: Service Identification Tag

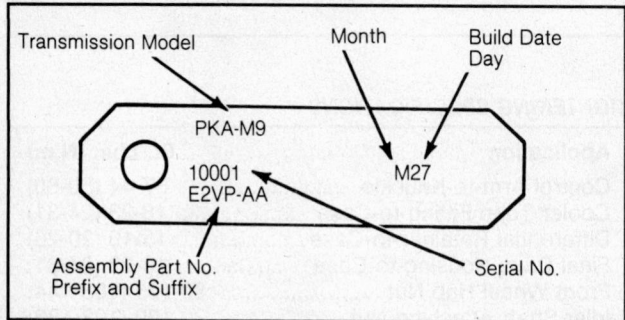

DESCRIPTION

The Automatic Overdrive Transmission (A.O.T.) is a 4-speed, fully automatic transmission which combines automatic shifting with two fuel saving features: An overdrive gear ratio and mechanical lock-out split torque path in 3rd gear. In this range, 40% of the torque is transmitted hydraulically through the torque converter as in conventional automatic transmissions while the remaining 60% of engine torque is transmitted mechanically.

The torque converter operation is similar to other automatics, but has an added damper assembly and an input shaft which is used in 3rd (direct drive) and overdrive gears.

Overdrive is accomplished by band application which locks the reverse sun gear while driving the planet carrier. In this ratio, engine torque flows through the damper assembly and in doing so, by-passes the torque converter. Power flow from the engine into the transmission is then direct.

Transmission consists basically of the torque converter assembly, 4 multi-disc clutches, 2 bands, 2 one-way roller clutches, and a hydraulic control system. The hydraulic system differs from that on other Ford automatic transmissions in that the vacuum diaphragm that is normally used for the "engine load" input has been eliminated. In place of this vacuum device, mechanical linkage is employed from the carburetor to the transmission. As a result, throttle (T.V.) fluid pressure is controlled mechanically rather than by vacuum.

LUBRICATION & ADJUSTMENTS

See appropriate AUTOMATIC TRANSMISSION SERVICING article in DOMESTIC GENERAL SERVICING section.

TROUBLE SHOOTING

See appropriate AUTOMATIC TRANSMISSION TROUBLE SHOOTING article in DOMESTIC GENERAL SERVICING section.

Fig. 2: Cross-Sectional View of Automatic Overdrive Transmission

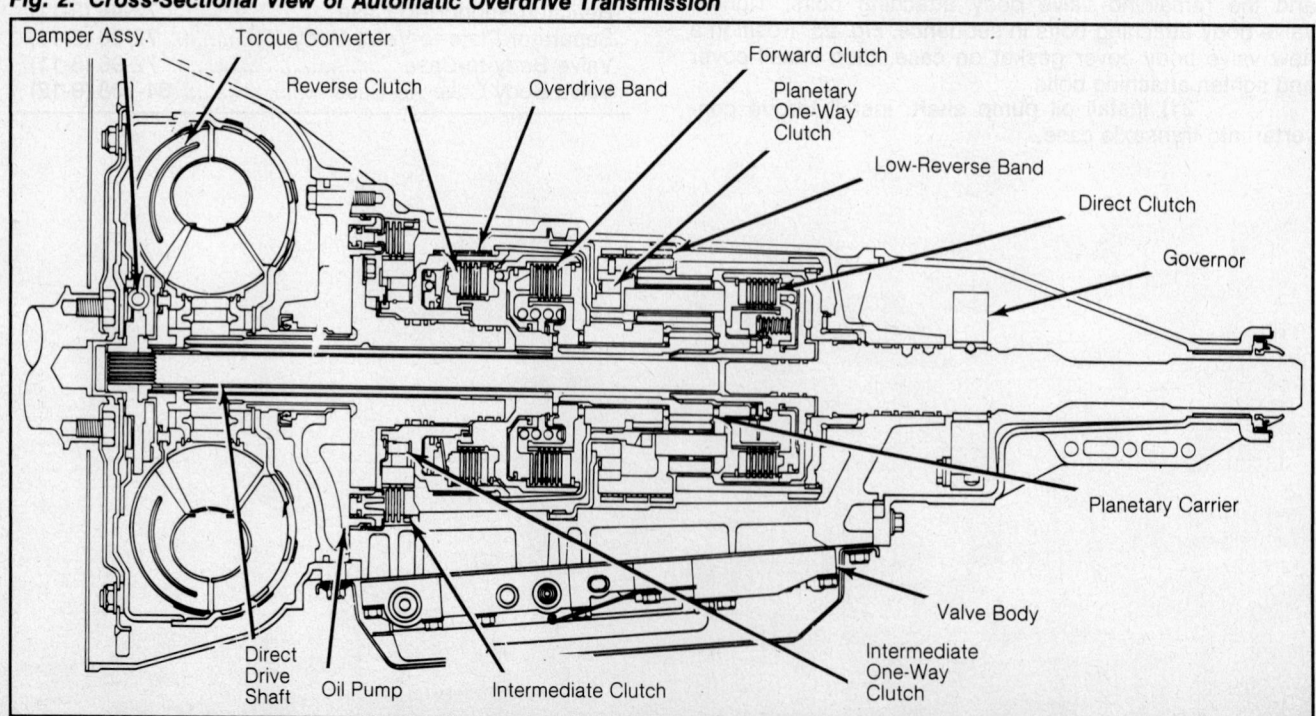

FORD MOTOR CO. A.O.T. (Cont.)

CLUTCH AND BAND APPLICATION CHART (ELEMENTS IN USE)

Selector Lever Position	Intermed. Clutch	Intermed. One-Way Clutch	Overdrive Band	Reverse Clutch	Forward Clutch	Planetary One-Way Clutch	Low-Reverse Band	Direct Clutch
O/D — OVERDRIVE								
First Gear					X	X		
Second Gear	X	X			X			
Third Gear	X				X			X
Fourth Gear	X		X					X
3 — OVERDRIVE LOCKOUT								
First Gear					X	X		
Second Gear	X	X			X			
Third Gear	X				X			X
1 — LOW								
First Gear					X	X	X	
Second Gear	X	X	X		X			
R — REVERSE				X			X	
P — PARK							X	

NEUTRAL — All clutches and bands released and/or ineffective.

TESTING

ROAD TEST

1) Check minimum throttle upshifts in "O/D". Transmission should start in 1st gear, shift to 2nd, then shift to 3rd, and finally shift to 4th gear at approximately the speeds shown in SHIFT SPEED table.

NOTE: Choke must be "OFF" when checking minimum throttle upshifts. If not, shift points will be affected.

2) Check partial throttle upshifts in "O/D". Transmission should start in 1st gear, shift to 2nd, then shift to 3rd, and finally shift to 4th gear. See SHIFT SPEED table.

3) With transmission in 4th gear (overdrive), depress accelerator pedal to the floor. Transmission should downshift to 3rd or to 2nd gear, depending on vehicle speed. See SHIFT SPEED table.

4) Since closed throttle downshifts are extremely difficult to detect, it will be necessary to attach pressure gauges to forward and direct clutch pressure taps in order to detect OD to 3rd gear and 3rd to 2nd gear coast downshifts.

5) With gauges attached, a 4th to 3rd gear coast (closed throttle) downshift is signified by the application of the forward clutch, and 3rd to 2nd gear coast downshift is signified by the release of the direct clutch. See SHIFT SPEED table. A 2nd to 1st gear downshift should not be felt.

6) With transmission selector lever in "1" (manual low), transmission should operate only in 1st gear.

7) When selector lever is moved from either overdrive or direct drive ranges to "1" position, transmission should downshift into 2nd gear if vehicle speed is above 25 MPH, and into 1st gear if speed is less than 25 MPH.

NOTE: The A.O.T. will not shift into overdrive at wide open throttle. Also, this transmission will not make a 4th to 1st gear downshift.

CONTROL PRESSURE TEST

NOTE: When testing line pressure on the Automatic Overdrive Transmission, two readings must be taken; one at idle position (zero T.V.) and the other at wide open, full throttle (full T.V.).

Line Pressure

1) With engine at normal operating temperature, connect a 0-300 psi pressure gauge to line pressure port tap on left side of transmission case just above control levers.

2) With throttle off fast idle cam, check line pressure in all ranges with engine at idle. Pressures should be approximately as specified. See CONTROL PRESSURE SPECIFICATIONS table.

NOTE: T.V. linkage must be properly adjusted when performing line pressure test.

3) Next, apply parking and service brakes. Check line pressure in all ranges with throttle in wide open position. Pressures should be approximately as specified. See CONTROL PRESSURE SPECIFICATIONS table.

CAUTION: Pressure test at wide open throttle position should be taken at Full Stall conditions. Also, this test must be made as quickly as possible to prevent overheating transmission. Run engine at a fast idle in Neutral for cooling between tests.

Throttle Valve Pressure (All Except 4.9L)

1) Connect a 0-100 psi pressure gauge to T.V. pressure tap at right side of the transmission case. See Fig. 3. Gauge hose must be long enough so that gauge can be read from under the hood.

2) Ensure throttle lever is at idle stop position (fast idle cam off). Adjust curb idle to specification. Set parking brake. Start engine and let idle in Neutral. Remove

Automatic Transmissions
FORD MOTOR CO. A.O.T. (Cont.)

SHIFT SPEED SPECIFICATIONS (MPH)

NOTE: On all models, all part throttle speeds except 3-4 are for a T.V. pressure of 60 PSI. The 4-3 and 3-4 part throttle shift speeds are quoted at a different throttle setting, 40 PSI, to keep them within a reasonable speed range.

NOTE: Shift speeds shown are approximate. All shift speeds may vary somewhat due to production tolerances and emission control equipment. In the following charts, "O.P.S." refers to output shaft speed (RPM).

MODEL PKA-CH
5.0L MARK VII, 50 STATE

Throttle	Range	Shift	OPS—R.P.M.	Column Number 1	Column Number 2
Closed Throttle See Note	Ⓓ ,D	1-2	310-460	9-13	8-13
	Ⓓ ,D	2-3	660-820	18-23	18-22
	Ⓓ	3-4	1180-1580	33-45	32-43
	Ⓓ	4-3	1330-900	37-26	36-25
	Ⓓ ,D	3-2	800-640	22-18	21-18
	Ⓓ ,D	2-1	410-240	11-7	11-7
	1	3-1, 2-1	1100-730	31-21	30-20
Part Throttle See Note	Ⓓ ,D	1-2	600-920	17-26	16-25
	Ⓓ ,D	2-3	1200-1620	34-46	33-44
	Ⓓ	3-4	1500-2140	42-61	41-59
	Ⓓ	4-3	1500-1060	42-30	41-29
	Ⓓ ,D	3-2	1250-780	35-22	34-21
	Ⓓ ,D	2-1	670-440	19-12	18-12
Wide Open See Note	Ⓓ ,D	1-2	1250-1760	35-50	34-48
	Ⓓ ,D	2-3	2410-2760	68-78	66-75
	Ⓓ ,D	3-2	2310-1950	65-55	63-53
	Ⓓ ,D	2-1	1420-920	40-26	38-25

Tire Size	Axle Ratio 2.73
	Use Column No.
P215/70R15	1
P215/65R15	2

MODEL PKA-BD & PKA-BV
5.0L CONTINENTAL & MARK VII
50 STATE & HIGH ALTITUDE

Throttle	Range	Shift	OPS—R.P.M.	Column Number 1	Column Number 2
Closed Throttle See Note	Ⓓ ,D	1-2	310-460	8-12	7-11
	Ⓓ ,D	2-3	680-830	17-21	16-20
	Ⓓ	3-4	1300-1680	32-42	32-41
	Ⓓ	4-3	1440-1060	36-27	35-26
	Ⓓ	3-2	800-600	20-15	19-15
	Ⓓ ,D	2-1	410-240	10-6	10-6
	1	3-1, 2-1	1110-730	28-18	27-18
Part Throttle See Note	Ⓓ ,D	1-2	670-1020	17-26	16-25
	Ⓓ ,D	2-3	1330-1710	33-43	32-42
	Ⓓ	3-4	1600-2210	40-56	39-54
	Ⓓ	4-3	1600-1200	40-30	39-29
	Ⓓ ,D	3-2	1440-1020	36-26	35-25
	Ⓓ ,D	2-1	690-480	17-12	17-12
Wide Open See Note	Ⓓ ,D	1-2	1370-1800	34-45	33-44
	Ⓓ ,D	2-3	2470-2810	62-71	60-68
	Ⓓ ,D	3-2	2420-2080	61-52	59-51
	Ⓓ ,D	2-1	1450-1020	36-26	35-25

Tire Size	Axle Ratio 3.08
	Use Column No.
P215/70R15	1
P215/65R15	2

MODEL PKA-M
5.0L LINCOLN TOWN CAR
50 STATE

Throttle	Range	Shift	OPS—R.P.M.	Column Number 1
Closed Throttle See Note	Ⓓ ,D	1-2	310-460	8-12
	Ⓓ ,D	2-3	660-820	17-21
	Ⓓ	3-4	1330-1680	33-42
	Ⓓ	4-3	1440-1060	36-27
	Ⓓ ,D	3-2	800-640	20-16
	Ⓓ ,D	2-1	410-240	10-6
	1	3-1, 2-1	1100-730	28-18
Part Throttle See Note	Ⓓ ,D	1-2	600-920	15-23
	Ⓓ ,D	2-3	1200-1620	30-41
	Ⓓ	3-4	1600-2210	40-56
	Ⓓ	4-3	1600-1200	40-30
	Ⓓ ,D	3-2	1250-780	31-20
	Ⓓ ,D	2-1	670-440	17-11
Wide Open See Note	Ⓓ ,D	1-2	1250-1760	31-44
	Ⓓ ,D	2-3	2410-2760	61-69
	Ⓓ ,D	3-2	2310-1950	58-49
	Ⓓ ,D	2-1	1420-920	36-23

Tire Size	Axle Ratio 3.08
	Use Column No.
P215/70R15	1

SHIFT SPEED SPECIFICATIONS MPH (Cont.)

MODEL PKA-BC
5.0L LINCOLN TOWN CAR
50 STATE & HIGH ALTITUDE

Throttle	Range	Shift	OPS—R.P.M.	Column Number 1	Column Number 2
Closed Throttle See Note	Ⓓ,D	1-2	310-460	7-10	
	Ⓓ,D	2-3	680-830	15-18	
	Ⓓ	3-4	1420-1780	31-39	
	Ⓓ	4-3	1560-1200	34-26	
	Ⓓ,D	3-2	800-650	17-14	
	Ⓓ,D	2-1	410-240	9-5	
	1	3-1, 2-1	1100-730	24-16	
Part Throttle See Note	Ⓓ,D	1-2	700-1100	15-24	
	Ⓓ,D	2-3	1400-1770	30-38	
	Ⓓ	3-4	1700-2290	37-50	
	Ⓓ	4-3	1720-1320	37-29	
	Ⓓ,D	3-2	1500-1120	33-24	
	Ⓓ,D	2-1	710-510	15-11	
Wide Open See Note	Ⓓ,D	1-2	1440-1850	31-40	
	Ⓓ,D	2-3	2510-2850	55-62	
	Ⓓ,D	3-2	2460-2130	54-46	
	Ⓓ,D	2-1	1480-1080	32-33	

Tire Size	Axle Ratio 3.55
	Use Column No.
P215/70R15	1

MODEL PKA-AG
5.0L FORD/MERCURY, 50 STATE
FORD POLICE W/LOW GEAR LOCKOUT

Throttle	Range	Shift	OPS—R.P.M.	Column Number 1	2	3	4
Closed Throttle See Note	Ⓓ,D	1-2	310-460	8-11	8-12	8-11	8-12
	Ⓓ,D	2-3	660-820	16-20	17-21	17-21	17-21
	Ⓓ	3-4	1300-1680	32-42	33-43	33-42	33-43
	Ⓓ	4-3	1440-1060	36-26	36-27	36-27	37-27
	Ⓓ,D	3-2	800-640	20-16	20-16	20-16	20-16
	Ⓓ,D	2-1	410-240	10-6	10-6	10-6	10-6
	1	3-1, 2-1	1100-730	27-18	28-18	28-18	28-19
Part Throttle See Note	Ⓓ,D	1-2	600-920	15-26	15-23	15-23	15-23
	Ⓓ,D	2-3	1200-1620	30-40	30-40	30-41	31-41
	Ⓓ	3-4	1600-2210	40-55	40-56	40-56	41-56
	Ⓓ	4-3	1600-1200	40-30	40-30	40-30	41-31
	Ⓓ,D	3-2	1250-780	31-19	32-20	31-20	32-20
	Ⓓ,D	2-1	670-440	17-11	17-11	17-11	17-11
Wide Open See Note	Ⓓ,D	1-2	1250-1760	31-44	32-45	31-44	32-45
	Ⓓ,D	2-3	2410-2760	60-69	61-70	61-69	62-70
	Ⓓ,D	3-2	2310-1950	58-49	58-49	58-49	59-50
	Ⓓ,D	2-1	1420-920	36-23	36-23	36-23	36-23

Tire Size	Axle Ratio 3.08
	Use Column No.
P215/75R14	1
P205/75R15	2
P205/70R15	3
P225/70R15	4

PKA-AU
5.0L FORD POLICE, 50 STATE

Throttle	Range	Shift	OPS—R.P.M.	Column Number 1
Closed Throttle See Note	Ⓓ,D	1-2	310-460	8-12
	Ⓓ,D	2-3	660-820	17-21
	Ⓓ	3-4	1300-1680	33-43
	Ⓓ	4-3	1440-1060	37-27
	Ⓓ,D	3-2	800-640	20-16
	Ⓓ,D	2-1	410-240	10-6
	1	3-1, 2-1	1100-730	28-19
Part Throttle See Note	Ⓓ,D	1-2	600-920	15-23
	Ⓓ,D	2-3	1200-1620	31-41
	Ⓓ	3-4	1600-2210	41-56
	Ⓓ	4-3	1600-1200	41-31
	Ⓓ	3-2	1250-780	32-20
	Ⓓ	2-1	670-440	17-11
Wide Open See Note	Ⓓ,D	1-2	1250-1760	32-45
	Ⓓ,D	2-3	2410-2760	61-70
	Ⓓ,D	3-2	2310-1950	59-50
	Ⓓ,D	2-1	1420-920	36-23

Tire Size	Axle Ratio 3.08
	Use Column No.
P225/70R15	1

PKA-AY
FORD/MERCURY &
POLICE W/LOW GEAR LOCKOUT

Throttle	Range	Shift	OPS—R.P.M.	Column Number 1	2	3	4
Closed Throttle See Note	Ⓓ,D	1-2	310-460	7-10	7-10	7-10	7-10
	Ⓓ,D	2-3	680-830	15-18	15-18	15-18	15-18
	Ⓓ	3-4	1420-1780	31-39	31-39	31-39	31-39
	Ⓓ	4-3	1560-1200	34-26	34-26	34-26	35-27
	Ⓓ,D	3-2	800-650	17-14	18-14	17-14	18-14
	Ⓓ,D	2-1	410-240	9-5	9-5	9-5	9-5
	1	3-1, 2-1	1100-730	24-16	24-16	24-16	24-16
Part Throttle See Note	Ⓓ,D	1-2	700-1100	15-24	15-24	15-24	15-24
	Ⓓ,D	2-3	1400-1770	30-38	31-39	30-39	31-39
	Ⓓ	3-4	1700-2290	37-50	37-50	37-50	38-51
	Ⓓ	4-3	1720-1320	37-29	38-29	37-29	38-29
	Ⓓ,D	3-2	1500-780	32-24	33-25	33-24	33-24
	Ⓓ,D	2-1	710-510	15-11	16-11	15-11	16-11
Wide Open See Note	Ⓓ,D	1-2	1440-1850	31-40	32-41	31-40	32-41
	Ⓓ,D	2-3	2510-2850	54-62	55-63	55-62	56-63
	Ⓓ,D	3-2	2460-2130	53-46	54-47	54-46	55-47
	Ⓓ,D	2-1	1480-1080	32-23	32-24	32-24	33-24

Tire Size	Axle Ratio 3.55
	Use Column No.
P215/75R14	1
P205/75R15	2
P215/70R15	3
P225/70R15	4

Automatic Transmissions
FORD MOTOR CO. A.O.T. (Cont.)

SHIFT SPEED SPECIFICATIONS MPH (Cont.)

PKA-BB
5.0L FORD POLICE
50 STATE & HIGH ALTITUDE

Throttle	Range	Shift	OPS—R.P.M.	Column Number 1
Closed Throttle See Note	(D) ,D	1-2	310-460	7-10
	(D) ,D	2-3	680-830	15-18
	(D)	3-4	1420-1780	31-39
	(D)	4-3	1560-1200	34-26
	(D) ,D	3-2	800-650	18-14
	(D) ,D	2-1	410-240	9-5
	1	3-1, 2-1	1100-730	24-16
Part Throttle See Note	(D) ,D	1-2	700-1100	15-24
	(D) ,D	2-3	1400-1770	31-39
	(D)	3-4	1700-2290	38-51
	(D)	4-3	1720-1320	38-29
	(D)	3-2	1500-1120	33-25
	(D) ,D	2-1	710-510	16-11
Wide Open See Note	(D) ,D	1-2	1440-1850	32-41
	(D) ,D	2-3	2510-2850	55-63
	(D) ,D	3-2	2460-2130	54-47
	(D) ,D	2-1	1480-1080	32-23

Tire Size	Axle Ratio 3.55
	Use Column No.
P225/70R15	1

PKA-CE, CF
5.0L HO LTD POLICE
50 STATE & HIGH ATITUDE
W/ & W/O LOW GEAR LOCKOUT

Throttle	Range	Shift	OPS—R.P.M.	Column Number 1
Closed Throttle See Note	(D) ,D	1-2	310-410	7-10
	(D) ,D	2-3	680-830	16-20
	(D)	3-4	1420-1780	34-42
	(D)	4-3	1560-1200	37-28
	(D)	3-2	800-650	19-15
	(D) ,D	2-1	410-240	10-6
	1	3-1, 2-1	1100-730	26-17
Part Throttle See Note	(D) ,D	1-2	700-1100	16-26
	(D) ,D	2-3	1400-1770	33-42
	(D)	3-4	1700-2290	40-54
	(D)	4-3	1720-1320	41-31
	(D)	3-2	1500-1120	35-26
	(D) ,D	2-1	710-510	17-12
Wide Open See Note	(D) ,D	1-2	1440-1850	34-44
	(D) ,D	2-3	2510-2850	59-67
	(D) ,D	3-2	2460-2130	58-50
	(D) ,D	2-1	1480-1080	35-25

Tire Size	Axle Ratio 3.08
	Use Column No.
P205/70R14	1

PKB-BW
5.0L HO CAPRI, LTD
MARQUIS TOURING SEDAN &
MUSTANG, 50 STATE & HIGH ATITUDE

Throttle	Range	Shift	OPS—R.P.M.	Column Number 1	2	3
Closed Throttle See Note	(D) ,D	1-2	310-460	7-10	7-10	7-10
	(D) ,D	2-3	680-830	15-19	15-18	15-19
	(D)	3-4	1420-1780	32-40	32-40	32-40
	(D)	4-3	1560-1200	35-27	35-27	35-27
	(D)	3-2	800-650	18-15	18-14	18-15
	(D) ,D	2-1	410-240	9-5	9-5	9-5
	1	3-1, 2-1	1100-730	25-16	24-16	25-16
Part Throttle See Note	(D) ,D	1-2	700-1100	16-25	16-24	16-25
	(D) ,D	2-3	1400-1770	31-40	31-39	32-40
	(D)	3-4	1700-2290	38-51	38-51	38-52
	(D)	4-3	1720-1320	39-30	38-29	39-30
	(D)	3-2	1500-120	34-25	33-25	34-25
	(D)	2-1	710-510	16-11	16-11	16-11
Wide Open See Note	(D) ,D	1-2	1440-1850	32-41	32-41	32-42
	(D) ,D	2-3	2510-2850	56-64	56-63	57-64
	(D) ,D	3-2	2460-2130	55-48	55-47	56-48
	(D) ,D	2-1	1480-1080	33-24	33-24	33-24

Tire Size	Axle Ratio 3.27
	Use Column No.
P195/75R14	1
P205/70R14	1
P205/70VR14	2
P225/60VR15	3
P220/55R390	3
P205/70HR14	2

PKA-CG
5.0L HO MARK LSC
50 STATE & HIGH ALTITUDE

Throttle	Range	Shift	OPS—R.P.M.	Column Number 1	2
Closed Throttle See Note	(D) ,D	1-2	310-460	7-11	7-10
	(D) ,D	2-3	680-830	15-19	15-19
	(D)	3-4	1420-1780	34-42	32-41
	(D)	4-3	1560-1200	37-28	36-27
	(D) ,D	3-2	800-650	19-15	18-15
	(D) ,D	2-1	410-240	10-6	9-5
	1	3-1, 2-1	1100-730	26-17	25-17
Part Throttle See Note	(D) ,D	1-2	700-1100	16-26	16-25
	(D) ,D	2-3	1400-1770	33-42	32-40
	(D)	3-4	1700-2290	40-54	39-52
	(D)	4-3	1720-1320	41-31	39-30
	(D)	3-2	1500-1120	35-29	34-26
	(D) ,D	2-1	710-510	17-12	16-12
Wide Open See Note	(D) ,D	1-2	1440-1850	34-44	33-42
	(D) ,D	2-3	2510-2850	59-67	57-65
	(D) ,D	3-2	2460-2130	58-50	56-49
	(D) ,D	2-1	1480-1080	35-25	34-25

Tire Size	Axle Ratio 3.27
	Use Column No.
P215/70R15	1
P215/65R15	2

FORD MOTOR CO. A.O.T. (Cont.)

SHIFT SPEED SPECIFICATIONS MPH (Cont.)

PKB-A
5.0L CARBURETED E-150/250
50 STATE

Throttle	Range	Shift	OPS—R.P.M.	Column Number 1	2	3	4	5
Closed Throttle See Note	Ⓓ ,D	1-2	290-420	6-9	6-10	6-10	7-10	6-10
	Ⓓ ,D	2-3	650-810	14-18	15-19	15-19	16-20	15-19
	Ⓓ	3-4	1470-1820	32-40	34-42	35-43	36-45	34-43
	Ⓓ	4-3	1620-1270	35-28	37-30	38-30	40-31	38-30
	Ⓓ ,D	3-2	780-630	17-14	18-15	18-15	19-16	18-15
	Ⓓ ,D	2-1	370-230	8-5	8-5	8-5	9-6	8-5
	1	3-1, 2-1	1100-730	24-16	25-17	26-17	27-18	25-17
Part Throttle See Note	Ⓓ ,D	1-2	590-860	13-19	13-20	14-20	14-21	13-20
	Ⓓ ,D	2-3	1180-1570	26-35	27-36	28-37	29-39	27-27
	Ⓓ	3-4	1730-2300	38-51	40-53	41-55	42-57	40-54
	Ⓓ	4-3	1750-1380	38-31	40-32	41-33	43-34	41-32
	Ⓓ ,D	3-2	1210-760	26-17	28-18	28-18	29-19	28-18
	Ⓓ ,D	2-1	640-420	14-9	14-10	15-10	15-10	15-10
Wide Open See Note	Ⓓ ,D	1-2	1220-1710	27-38	28-40	29-41	30-42	28-40
	Ⓓ ,D	2-3	2340-2690	51-60	54-63	55-64	57-66	55-63
	Ⓓ ,D	3-2	2250-1900	49-42	52-44	53-45	55-47	52-44
	Ⓓ ,D	2-1	1360-900	30-20	31-21	32-21	33-22	31-21

Tire Size	Axle Ratio 3.50	3.55	3.73
	Use Column No.		
P205/75R15SL	1		
P225/75R15SL	2		
P235/75R15XL	3		
LT215/85R16D		4	5
8.00 x 16.5D		2	1
8.75 x 16.5E		3	2

PKB-A
5.0L CARBURETED F-150/250
50 STATE

Throttle	Range	Shift	OPS—R.P.M.	Column Number 1	2	3	4	5	6
Closed Throttle See Note	Ⓓ ,D	1-2	290-420	6-9	6-10	6-9	7-11	7-10	7-11
	Ⓓ ,D	2-3	650-810	14-18	15-19	14-18	16-21	16-20	16-21
	Ⓓ	3-4	1470-1820	32-41	34-42	31-39	38-47	36-45	38-47
	Ⓓ	4-3	1620-1270	36-28	38-30	35-28	42-33	40-31	41-33
	Ⓓ ,D	3-2	780-630	17-14	18-14	16-14	20-16	19-16	20-16
	Ⓓ ,D	2-1	370-230	8-5	8-5	8-5	9-6	9-6	9-6
	1	3-1, 2-1	1100-730	24-16	25-17	23-16	28-19	27-18	28-19
Part Throttle See Note	Ⓓ ,D	1-2	590-860	13-19	13-20	12-19	15-22	14-21	15-22
	Ⓓ ,D	2-3	1180-1570	26-35	27-37	35-34	30-41	29-39	30-41
	Ⓓ	3-4	1730-2300	38-51	40-54	37-50	44-60	42-57	44-59
	Ⓓ	4-3	1750-1380	39-30	41-32	37-30	45-36	43-34	45-36
	Ⓓ ,D	3-2	1210-760	27-17	28-18	26-16	31-20	29-19	31-20
	Ⓓ ,D	2-1	640-420	14-9	15-10	13-9	16-11	15-10	16-11
Wide Open See Note	Ⓓ ,D	1-2	1220-1710	27-38	28-40	26-37	31-44	30-42	31-44
	Ⓓ ,D	2-3	2340-2690	52-60	55-83	50-58	60-70	57-66	60-69
	Ⓓ ,D	3-2	2250-1900	50-42	52-45	48-41	58-49	55-47	58-49
	Ⓓ ,D	2-1	1360-900	30-20	31-21	29-19	35-23	33-22	35-23

Tire Size	Axle Ratio 3.55
	Use Column No.
P215/75R15SL	1
P235/75R15XL	2
P195/75R15SL	3
7.50R x 16D	4
LT215/85R16C	5
LT215/85R16D	5
LT235/85R16E	6
LT235/85R16D	6

PKB-E
4.9L F-150
50 STATE & HIGH ALTITUDE

Throttle	Range	Shift	OPS—R.P.M.	Column Number 1	2	3
Closed Throttle See Note	Ⓓ ,D	1-2	290-420	7-11	7-11	7-10
	Ⓓ ,D	2-3	650-810	16-21	17-22	16-20
	Ⓓ	3-4	1470-1820	37-47	39-49	36-45
	Ⓓ	4-3	1620-1270	41-33	43-34	40-32
	Ⓓ ,D	3-2	780-630	20-16	21-17	19-16
	Ⓓ ,D	2-1	370-230	9-6	10-6	9-6
	1	3-1, 2-1	1100-730	28-19	29-20	27-18
Part Throttle See Note	Ⓓ ,D	1-2	590-860	15-22	16-23	14-21
	Ⓓ ,D	2-3	1180-1570	30-41	32-42	29-39
	Ⓓ	3-4	1730-2300	44-59	46-62	43-57
	Ⓓ	4-3	1750-1380	45-36	47-37	43-34
	Ⓓ ,D	3-2	1210-760	31-20	32-20	30-19
	Ⓓ ,D	2-1	640-420	16-11	17-11	16-10
Wide Open See Note	Ⓓ ,D	1-2	1130-1640	29-42	30-44	28-41
	Ⓓ ,D	2-3	2260-2620	58-68	61-71	56-65
	Ⓓ ,D	3-2	2180-1820	56-47	59-49	54-45
	Ⓓ ,D	2-1	1300-770	33-20	35-21	32-19

Tire Size	Axle Ratio 3.08
	Use Column No.
P215/75R15	1
P235/75R15	2
P195/75R15	3

PKB-F
4.9L E-250
50 STATE & HIGH ALTITUDE

Throttle	Range	Shift	OPS—R.P.M.	Column Number 1	2	3	4	5
Closed Throttle See Note	Ⓓ ,D	1-2	290-420	7-10	6-10	6-10	6-9	6-10
	Ⓓ ,D	2-3	650-810	16-20	15-19	14-19	14-18	15-19
	Ⓓ	3-4	1590-1890	39-47	37-44	36-43	34-41	38-45
	Ⓓ	4-3	1700-1410	42-35	39-33	38-32	37-31	40-34
	Ⓓ ,D	3-2	780-630	19-16	18-15	17-14	17-14	18-15
	Ⓓ ,D	2-1	370-230	9-6	8-5	8-5	8-5	8-5
	1	3-1, 2-1	1100-730	27-18	25-17	25-17	24-16	26-17
Part Throttle See Note	Ⓓ ,D	1-2	590-860	14-21	13-20	13-20	12-19	14-21
	Ⓓ ,D	2-3	1180-1570	29-39	27-37	27-36	25-34	28-38
	Ⓓ	3-4	1830-2360	45-58	43-55	41-54	39-51	43-56
	Ⓓ	4-3	1830-1500	45-37	43-35	41-34	39-33	43-36
	Ⓓ ,D	3-2	1210-760	29-19	28-18	27-17	26-17	28-18
	Ⓓ ,D	2-1	640-420	15-10	15-10	14-9	13-9	15-10
Wide Open See Note	Ⓓ ,D	1-2	1130-1640	27-40	26-39	25-38	24-36	27-39
	Ⓓ ,D	2-3	2260-2620	55-65	53-61	51-60	49-57	54-63
	Ⓓ ,D	3-2	2180-1820	53-45	51-43	49-42	47-40	52-43
	Ⓓ ,D	2-1	1300-770	32-19	30-18	29-18	28-17	31-18

Tire Size	Axle Ratio 3.55	3.73
	Use Column No.	
LT215/85R16D	1	2
8.0 x 16.5D	3	4
8.75 x 16.5E	5	3

Automatic Transmissions

FORD MOTOR CO. A.O.T. (Cont.)

SHIFT SPEED SPECIFICATIONS MPH (Cont.)

PKB-F
4.9L E-150 & F-150
50 STATE & HIGH ALTITUDE

Throttle	Range	Shift	OPS—R.P.M.	Column Number 1	2	3	4
Closed Throttle See Note	Ⓓ ,D	1-2	290-420	6-9	6-9	6-10	6-9
	Ⓓ ,D	2-3	650-810	14-18	15-19	15-19	14-18
	Ⓓ	3-4	1590-1890	35-42	36-44	37-45	34-41
	Ⓓ	4-3	1700-1410	37-31	39-33	40-34	36-31
	Ⓓ ,D	3-2	780-630	17-14	18-15	18-15	16-14
	Ⓓ ,D	2-1	370-230	8-5	8-5	8-5	8-5
	1	3-1, 2-1	1100-730	24-16	25-17	26-17	23-16
Part Throttle See Note	Ⓓ ,D	1-2	590-860	13-19	14-20	14-20	12-19
	Ⓓ ,D	2-3	1180-1570	26-35	27-36	28-37	25-34
	Ⓓ	3-4	1830-2360	40-52	42-55	43-56	40-51
	Ⓓ	4-3	1830-1500	40-33	42-35	43-36	39-32
	Ⓓ	3-2	1210-760	26-17	28-18	28-18	26-16
	Ⓓ ,D	2-1	640-420	14-9	14-9	15-10	13-9
Wide Open See Note	Ⓓ ,D	1-2	1130-1640	25-36	26-38	26-39	24-36
	Ⓓ ,D	2-3	2260-2620	50-58	52-61	53-62	48-57
	Ⓓ ,D	3-2	2180-1820	48-40	50-42	51-43	47-39
	Ⓓ ,D	2-1	1300-770	28-17	30-18	30-18	28-17

Tire Size	Axle Ratio 3.50	3.55
	Use Column No.	
P205/75R15SL	1	
P225/75R15SL	2	
P235/75R15XL	3	
P215/75R15SL		1
P235/75R15XL		3
P195/75R15SL		4

PKB-J
5.0L E.F.I F-150/250
50 STATE & HIGH ALTITUDE

Throttle	Range	Shift	OPS—R.P.M.	Column Number 1	2	3	4
Closed Throttle See Note	Ⓓ ,D	1-2	370-530	8-12	8-12	8-11	9-13
	Ⓓ ,D	2-3	720-890	16-20	17-21	15-19	18-22
	Ⓓ	3-4	1460-1850	32-41	34-43	31-40	36-46
	Ⓓ	4-3	1580-1200	35-27	37-28	34-26	39-30
	Ⓓ	3-2	870-700	19-16	20-16	18-15	21-17
	Ⓓ ,D	2-1	470-320	10-7	11-7	10-7	11-8
	1	3-1, 2-1	1230-810	27-18	29-19	26-18	30-20
Part Throttle See Note	Ⓓ ,D	1-2	670-1050	15-24	15-25	14-23	16-26
	Ⓓ ,D	2-3	1350-1780	30-40	31-42	29-39	33-44
	Ⓓ	3-4	1790-2420	40-54	42-57	38-52	44-60
	Ⓓ	4-3	1760-1340	39-30	41-32	38-29	43-33
	Ⓓ ,D	3-2	1390-830	31-19	32-20	30-18	34-20
	Ⓓ ,D	2-1	750-500	16-11	17-12	16-11	18-12
Wide Open See Note	Ⓓ ,D	1-2	1400-1940	31-43	32-45	30-42	34-48
	Ⓓ ,D	2-3	2650-3020	59-68	62-71	57-65	65-75
	Ⓓ ,D	3-2	2530-2170	56-49	59-51	54-47	65-54
	Ⓓ ,D	2-1	1560-1060	34-24	23-25	33-23	38-26

Tire Size	Axle Ratio 3.55	3.73
	Use Column No.	
P215/75R15SL	1	
P235/75R15XL	2	
P195/75R15SL	3	
7.5R x 16D		4
LT215/85R16D		2
LT235/85R16E		4

PKB-K
5.0L E.F.I. BRONCO &
F-150/250 (4 x 4)

Throttle	Range	Shift	OPS—R.P.M.	Column Number 1	2	3
Closed Throttle See Note	Ⓓ ,D	1-2	370-530	8-12	9-13	9-14
	Ⓓ ,D	2-3	720-890	16-21	17-22	18-23
	Ⓓ	3-4	1460-1850	34-43	36-46	37-48
	Ⓓ	4-3	1580-1200	37-28	39-30	41-31
	Ⓓ ,D	3-2	870-700	20-16	21-17	22-18
	Ⓓ ,D	2-1	470-320	11-7	11-8	12-8
	1	3-1, 2-1	1230-810	28-19	30-20	32-21
Part Throttle See Note	Ⓓ ,D	1-2	670-1050	15-25	16-26	17-27
	Ⓓ ,D	2-3	1350-1780	31-42	33-44	35-46
	Ⓓ	3-4	1790-2420	42-57	44-60	46-63
	Ⓓ	4-3	1760-1340	41-31	43-33	45-34
	Ⓓ	3-2	1390-830	32-20	34-21	36-22
	Ⓓ ,D	2-1	750-500	17-11	18-12	19-13
Wide Open See Note	Ⓓ ,D	1-2	1400-1940	32-46	34-48	36-50
	Ⓓ ,D	2-3	2650-3020	62-71	66-75	68-78
	Ⓓ ,D	3-2	2530-2170	59-51	63-54	65-56
	Ⓓ ,D	2-1	1560-1060	36-25	38-26	40-28

Tire Size	Axle Ratio 3.55	3.54
	Use Column No.	
P235/75R15XL	1	
10 x 15C	2	
7.50 x 16D		3
LT215/85R16D	2	
LT235/85R16D		3
LT235/85R16E		3

PKB-L
5.0L E.F.I. F-250
50 STATE & HIGH ALTITUDE

Throttle	Range	Shift	OPS—R.P.M.	Column Number 1	2	3
Closed Throttle See Note	Ⓓ ,D	1-2	370-530	8-12	7-11	8-12
	Ⓓ ,D	2-3	740-900	16-20	15-19	16-20
	Ⓓ	3-4	1600-1960	35-44	34-42	35-44
	Ⓓ	4-3	1720-1350	38-30	36-29	38-30
	Ⓓ ,D	3-2	870-720	19-16	18-15	19-16
	Ⓓ ,D	2-1	470-320	10-7	10-7	10-7
	1	3-1, 2-1	1230-810	27-18	26-17	27-18
Part Throttle See Note	Ⓓ ,D	1-2	770-1220	17-27	16-26	17-27
	Ⓓ ,D	2-3	1570-1940	35-43	33-41	35-43
	Ⓓ	3-4	1890-2510	42-56	40-54	42-56
	Ⓓ	4-3	1810-1480	42-33	40-32	42-33
	Ⓓ ,D	3-2	1670-1270	37-29	35-27	37-28
	Ⓓ ,D	2-1	790-580	17-13	16-12	17-13
Wide Open See Note	Ⓓ ,D	1-2	1610-2030	36-46	34-43	36-45
	Ⓓ ,D	2-3	2760-3110	62-70	59-67	61-70
	Ⓓ ,D	3-2	2690-2360	60-53	57-50	60-53
	Ⓓ ,D	2-1	1630-1220	36-27	34-26	36-27

Tire Size	Axle Ratio 4.10
	Use Column No.
7.5R x 16D	1
LT215/85R16D	2
LT235/85R16E	3

FORD MOTOR CO. A.O.T. (Cont.)

SHIFT SPEED SPECIFICATIONS MPH (Cont.)

PKB-M
5.0L E.F.I. BRONCO &
F-150/250 (4 x 4)
50 STATE & HIGH ALTITUDE

Throttle	Range	Shift	OPS—R.P.M.	Column Number		
				1	2	3
Closed Throttle See Note	Ⓓ ,D	1-2	370-530	8-12	8-11	7-11
	Ⓓ ,D	2-3	740-900	16-20	16-19	15-18
	Ⓓ	3-4	1600-1960	35-44	34-42	33-40
	Ⓓ	4-3	1720-1350	38-30	37-29	35-28
	Ⓓ	3-2	870-720	19-16	18-15	17-15
	Ⓓ ,D	2-1	470-320	10-7	10-7	9-6
	1	3-1, 2-1	1230-810	27-18	26-17	25-16
Part Throttle See Note	Ⓓ ,D	1-2	770-1220	17-27	16-26	15-25
	Ⓓ ,D	2-3	1570-1940	35-43	33-42	32-40
	Ⓓ	3-4	1890-2510	42-56	40-54	39-51
	Ⓓ	4-3	1890-1480	42-33	40-32	38-30
	Ⓓ	3-2	1670-1270	37-28	36-27	34-26
	Ⓓ ,D	2-1	790-580	17-13	17-12	16-12
Wide Open See Note	Ⓓ ,D	1-2	1610-2030	36-46	34-44	33-42
	Ⓓ ,D	2-3	2760-3110	62-70	59-67	56-64
	Ⓓ ,D	3-2	2690-2360	60-53	58-51	55-48
	Ⓓ ,D	2-1	1630-1220	37-27	35-26	33-25

Tire Size	Axle Ratio	
	4.10	4.11
	Use Column No.	
7.50 x 16D	1	
LT215/85R16D	2	
LT235/85R16D	1	
LT235/85R16E	1	
P235/75RXL		3
10 x 15C		2

PKA-CB, CD
3.8L CAPRI, COUGAR, LTD,
MARQUIS, MUSTANG & THUNDERBIRD

Throttle	Range	Shift	OPS—R.P.M.	Column Number			
				1	2	3	4
Closed Throttle See Note	Ⓓ ,D	1-2	370-530	8-12	8-12	8-11	8-11
	Ⓓ ,D	2-3	740-910	16-20	17-21	15-19	16-20
	Ⓓ	3-4	1680-2060	37-45	38-47	35-43	36-45
	Ⓓ	4-3	1840-1460	41-32	42-33	38-30	40-31
	Ⓓ	3-2	870-720	19-16	20-16	18-15	19-16
	Ⓓ	2-1	470-320	10-7	11-7	9-6	10-7
	1	3-1, 2-1	1230-810	27-18	28-18	25-17	27-17
Part Throttle See Note	Ⓓ ,D	1-2	730-1140	16-25	17-26	15-23	16-25
	Ⓓ ,D	2-3	1500-1890	33-42	34-43	31-39	32-41
	Ⓓ	3-4	1970-2590	43-57	45-59	41-54	42-56
	Ⓓ	4-3	1990-1780	44-39	45-40	41-37	43-38
	Ⓓ	3-2	1580-1170	35-26	36-27	33-24	34-25
	Ⓓ	2-1	770-540	17-12	17-12	16-11	16-11
Wide Open See Note	Ⓓ ,D	1-2	1430-1900	32-42	32-43	30-40	31-41
	Ⓓ ,D	2-3	2630-3000	58-66	60-68	55-63	57-65
	Ⓓ ,D	3-2	2570-2220	57-49	58-50	53-46	56-48
	Ⓓ ,D	2-1	1520-1060	33-23	35-24	31-22	33-23

Tire Size	Axle Ratio	
	3.27	3.45
	Use Column No.	
P205/70R14	1	3
P215/70R14	2	4
P215/70HR14	2	4
P220/55R390	1	3

PKA-CJ
5.0L COUGAR & THUNDERBIRD
CALIF. ONLY

Throttle	Range	Shift	OPS—R.P.M.	Column Number			
				1	2	3	4
Closed Throttle See Note	Ⓓ ,D	1-2	310-460	8-12	8-13	8-12	8-12
	Ⓓ ,D	2-3	660-820	18-22	18-22	17-22	17-22
	Ⓓ	3-4	1300-1680	35-45	35-46	35-46	34-44
	Ⓓ	4-3	1440-1060	38-28	39-29	39-29	38-28
	Ⓓ	3-2	800-640	21-17	22-17	22-17	21-17
	Ⓓ ,D	2-1	410-240	10-6	11-6	11-7	10-6
	1	3-1, 2-1	1100-730	29-20	30-20	29-20	29-19
Part Throttle See Note	Ⓓ ,D	1-2	600-920	16-25	16-25	16-25	15-24
	Ⓓ ,D	2-3	1200-1620	32-43	33-44	32-44	31-43
	Ⓓ	3-4	1600-2210	42-59	43-60	43-60	42-58
	Ⓓ	4-3	1600-1200	42-32	43-33	43-33	42-32
	Ⓓ	3-2	1250-780	33-21	34-21	34-21	33-21
	Ⓓ	2-1	670-440	17-12	18-12	18-12	17-12
Wide Open See Note	Ⓓ ,D	1-2	1250-1760	33-47	34-48	34-48	33-47
	Ⓓ ,D	2-3	2410-2760	64-74	65-75	65-75	63-73
	Ⓓ ,D	3-2	2310-1950	61-52	63-53	62-53	61-51
	Ⓓ ,D	2-1	1420-920	37-25	38-25	38-25	37-24

Tire Size	Axle Ratio
	2.73
	Use Column No.
P205/70R14	1
P215/70R14	2
P215/70HR14	3
P220/55R390	4

PKA-K
5.0L COUGAR & THUNDERBIRD
50 STATE & HIGH ALTITUDE

Throttle	Range	Shift	OPS—R.P.M.	Column Number			
				1	2	3	4
Closed Throttle See Note	Ⓓ ,D	1-2	310-460	7-11	7-11	7-11	7-11
	Ⓓ ,D	2-3	680-830	16-19	16-20	16-20	16-19
	Ⓓ	3-4	1420-1780	33-42	34-43	34-43	33-41
	Ⓓ	4-3	1560-1160	37-28	38-29	38-29	36-28
	Ⓓ ,D	3-2	800-650	19-15	19-16	19-16	19-15
	Ⓓ ,D	2-1	410-240	10-6	10-6	10-6	9-6
	1	3-1, 2-1	1100-730	26-17	27-18	26-18	26-17
Part Throttle See Note	Ⓓ ,D	1-2	700-1100	16-26	17-27	17-26	16-26
	Ⓓ ,D	2-3	1400-1770	33-42	34-43	34-43	32-41
	Ⓓ	3-4	1700-2290	40-54	41-56	41-55	40-54
	Ⓓ	4-3	1720-1320	41-31	41-32	41-32	40-31
	Ⓓ ,D	3-2	1500-1120	35-26	36-27	36-27	35-26
	Ⓓ ,D	2-1	710-510	17-12	17-12	17-12	16-12
Wide Open See Note	Ⓓ ,D	1-2	1440-1850	34-44	35-45	35-45	33-43
	Ⓓ ,D	2-3	2510-2580	59-67	61-69	60-69	59-67
	Ⓓ ,D	3-2	2460-2130	58-50	60-52	59-51	57-50
	Ⓓ ,D	2-1	1480-1080	35-26	36-26	36-26	35-25

Tire Size	Axle Ratio
	3.08
	Use Column No.
P205/70R14	1
P215/70R14	2
P215/70JR14	3
P220/55R390	4

CONTROL PRESSURE SPECIFICATIONS [1]

Throttle Position	Line Pressure psi (kg/cm²)	T.V. Limit Pressure psi (kg/cm²)
At Idle		
In "R"	75-90 (5.3-6.3)	0
All Other Ranges	55-65 (3.9-4.6)	0
At W.O.T. Stall		
In "R"		
3.8L & 4.9L	241-279 (16.9-19.6)	74-86 (5.2-6.0)
All Others	250-290 (17.5-20.3)	79-91 (5.5-6.4)
All Other Ranges		
3.8L & 4.9L	176-204 (12.4-14.3)	74-86 (5.2-6.0)
All Others	180-215 (12.6-15.1)	79-91 (5.5-6.4)

[1] – With governor pressure at zero.

air cleaner and shut off air conditioner. Disconnect and plug vacuum throttle modulator (if equipped).

3) Place a .397" (10 mm) drill bit or gauge block between linkage lever adjustment screw and throttle lever. T.V. limit pressure should be 30-40 psi (2.1-2.8 kg/cm²). If not, turn adjustment screw.

4) Remove gauge block, allowing T.V. lever to return to idle. T.V. pressure should be less than 5 psi (.35 kg/cm²). If above 5 psi (.35 kg/cm²), back out adjusting screw until pressure drops below 5 psi (.35 kg/cm²).

5) Install gauge block and check T.V. pressure again. If pressures can not be adjusted correctly, adjust linkage rod at transmission.

CONTROL PRESSURE TEST RESULTS
Low in "P"
Faulty valve body or low-reverse servo.

Fig. 3: Right Side of Transmission Case Showing T.V. Limit Pressure Tap

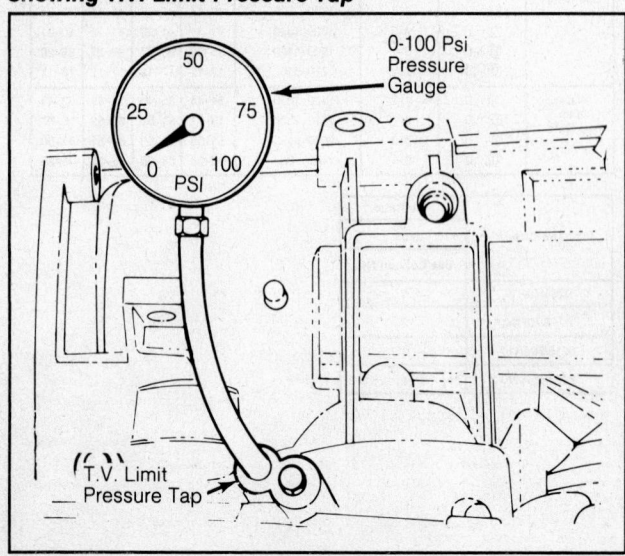

Low in "R"
Faulty reverse clutch or low-reverse servo.

Low in "N"
Faulty valve body.

Low in "O/D"
Check for faulty forward clutch, overdrive servo, or for faulty valve body.

Low in "3"
Faulty forward clutch or intermediate servo.

Low in "1"
Faulty forward clutch or low-reverse servo.

Low at Idle in All Ranges
Check for low fluid level, restricted intake screen or filter, loose valve body bolts, pump leakage, case leakage, faulty valve body, excessively low engine idle, fluid too hot.

High at Idle in All Ranges
Check throttle valve linkage adjustment and condition and for faulty valve body.

Pressure Okay at Idle but Low at W.O.T.
Check for internal leakage, pump leakage, restricted intake screen of filter, damaged or out of adjustment T.V. valve linkage. Also check for sticking T.V. or T.V. limit valve in valve body.

DIRECT CLUTCH PRESSURE TEST
1) Attach accurate 0-300 psi pressure gauges to the forward and direct clutch pressure taps on right side of transmission. Forward clutch pressure tap is closest to torque converter while direct clutch tap is farthest from torque converter. Have sufficient hose so gauges may be read in vehicle.

2) Drive the vehicle. When pressure is applied to direct clutch, note the difference between the line pressure on forward clutch gauge and direct clutch gauge. If difference is less than 15 psi (1.1 kg/cm²), direct clutch circuit is good.

3) If difference is greater than 15 psi (1.1 kg/cm²), there could be a leak in the direct clutch pressure circuit.

GOVERNOR CHECK
Accelerate vehicle to 25 MPH and back off throttle completely. If governor is operating properly, transmission will shift to 3rd gear.

STALL TEST
Testing Precautions
When performing stall test, do not hold throttle open longer than 5 seconds. Allow a cooling period of 15 seconds with transmission in Neutral and engine speed at 1000 RPM between each test. If engine speed exceeds maximum limits shown, release accelerator immediately as this is an indication of clutch or band slippage.

Testing Procedure
Bring engine to normal operating temperature. Apply parking and service brakes. Stall test transmission in each driving range at full throttle. Note maximum RPM obtained. Engine speed should be within limits. See STALL SPEED SPECIFICATIONS table.

Fig. 4: *Automatic Overdrive Transmission Hydraulic Circuits Diagram*

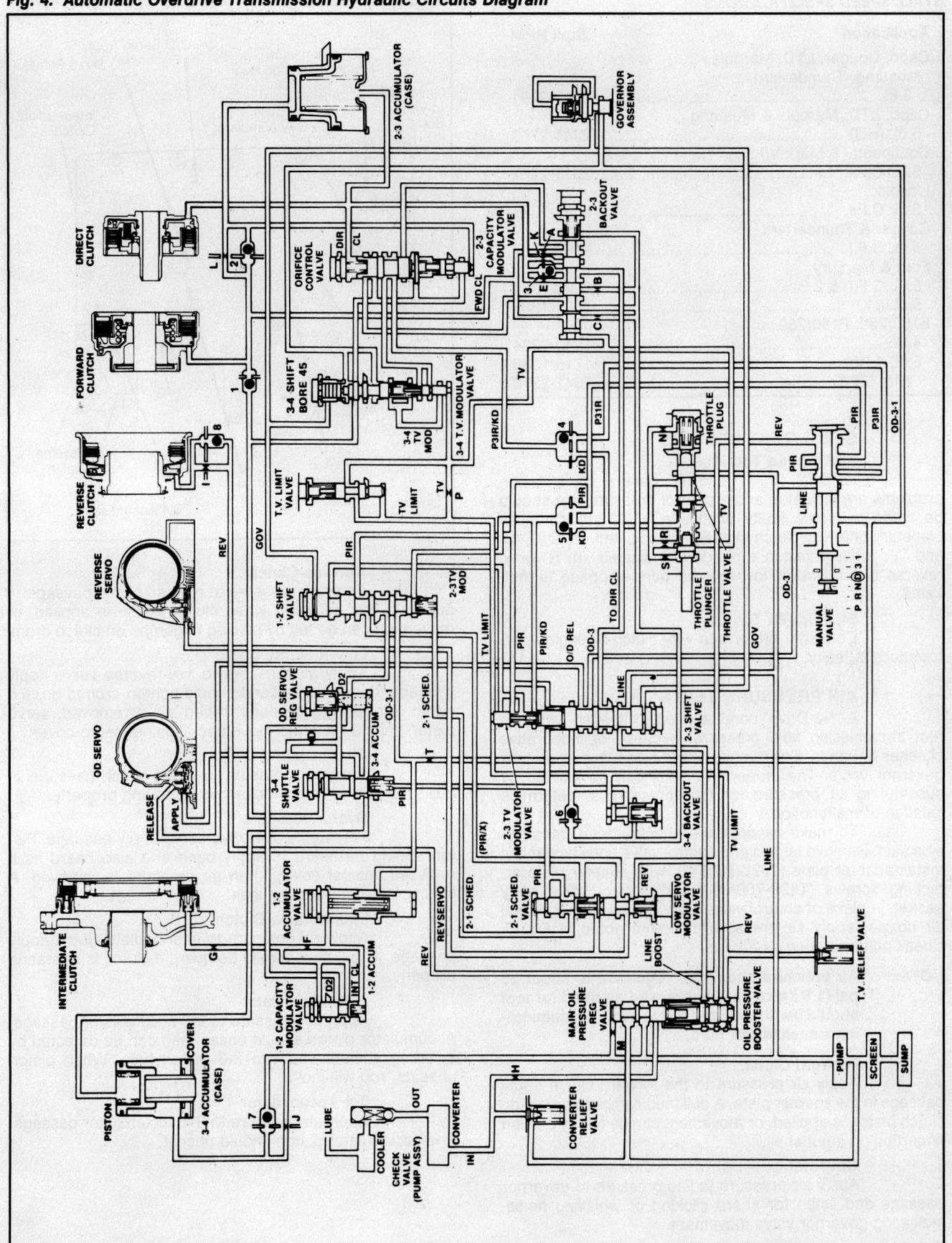

STALL SPEED SPECIFICATIONS

Application	Stall RPM
Capri, Cougar, LTD, Marquis, Mustang, Thunderbird	
3.8L	2067-2391
Capri, LTD, Marquis & Mustang	
5.0L (HO)	2344-2753
Continental & Mark VII	
5.0L C.F.I.	2013-2307
Lincoln	
5.0L C.F.I.	2009-2327
Cougar & Thunderbird	
5.0L C.F.I.	1989-2287
Ford & Mercury	
5.0L C.F.I. & 2 Bbl.	2020-2336
5.0L (HO)	1523-1838
E150/250, F150/250	
4.9L	1940-2234
5.0L 4 Bbl.	1715-1966
With E.F.I	2041-2378

STALL TEST RESULTS
Stall Speed Too High
In "O/D", "3", "1" and "R"; general transmission problems are indicated and a control pressure test should be made to locate faulty unit(s). In "O/D" and "3" only; planetary one-way clutch slippage is indicated. In "O/D" "3" and "1"; forward clutch slippage is indicated. In "R" only; reverse clutch and/or low-reverse band slippage is indicated.

Stall Speed Too Low
Converter stator one-way clutch or engine performance is faulty.

AIR PRESSURE TESTS
A "No Drive" condition can exist even with correct transmission fluid pressure, because of inoperative clutches or bands. Erratic shifts could be caused by a stuck governor valve. The inoperative units can be located by substituting air pressure for fluid pressure to determine location of malfunction.

To make air pressure checks, drain transmission fluid. Remove oil pan and control valve body assembly. Install adapter plate (T82L-7006-A), with adapter plate attaching screws (T82P-7006-C), and control valve body gasket, in place of control valve body. With a rubber tipped air nozzle, apply air pressure at points noted in *Fig. 5*. Check unit operation as follows:

NOTE: **Air pressure should be regulated to about 25 psi (1.8 kg/cm^2). Compressed air used for test should be filtered and dry to avoid contaminating transmission fluid.**

Forward Clutch
Apply air pressure to the forward clutch apply passage in the adapter plate. A dull thud can be heard when clutch piston is applied, or movement can be felt by placing fingertips on input shell.

Governor
Apply air pressure to line pressure-to-governor passage and listen for sharp clicking or whistling noise, indicating governor valve movement.

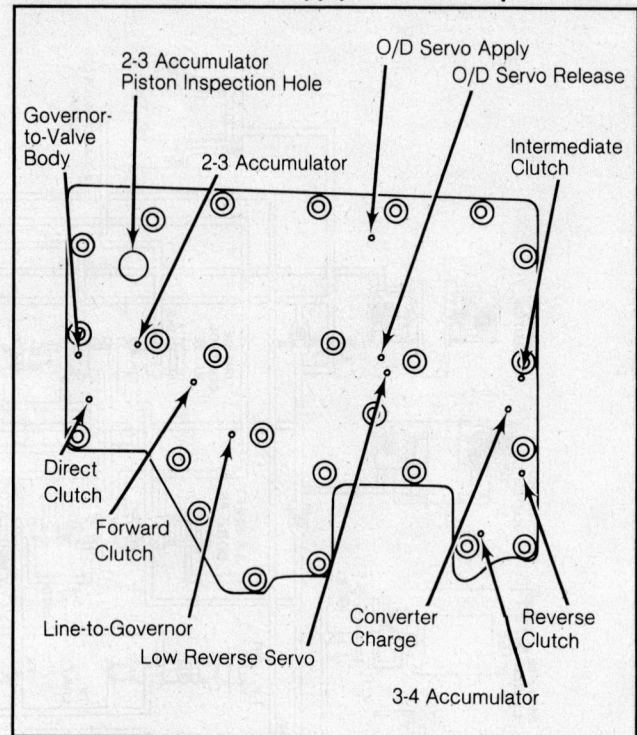

Fig. 5: Air Pressure Test Apply Ports on Adapter Plate

Reverse Clutch
Apply air pressure to reverse clutch passage. A dull thud can be heard when clutch piston is applied, or movement can be felt by placing fingertips on clutch drum.

Low-Reverse Servo
Apply air pressure to low-reverse servo apply passage. Low-reverse band should tighten around drum if servo is operating properly. When air is removed, servo piston should be felt to move back against servo cover.

Direct Clutch
Apply air pressure to direct clutch passage. A dull thud can be heard if clutch is operating properly.

Overdrive Servo
Pressurize overdrive servo apply passage. Piston should be heard to apply band and also heard as it releases against cover when air pressure is removed. A hissing noise indicates a leak.

Intermediate Clutch
Apply air pressure to intermediate clutch apply passage. A dull thud should be heard if clutch is operating properly.

2-3 Accumulator
Apply air pressure to 2-3 accumulator passage. Accumulator piston should unseat and can be detected by inserting a metal rod into 2-3 piston hole. When piston unseats, rod will move.

3-4 Accumulator
Apply air pressure to 3-4 accumulator passage. The accumulator piston should unseat.

SERVICE (IN VEHICLE)

VALVE BODY ASSEMBLY
Removal

1) Raise vehicle on a hoist. Loosen oil pan retaining bolts and allow transmission fluid to drain. Remove oil pan and gasket.

2) Remove filter-to-valve body retaining bolts and remove filter, grommet and gasket. Remove detent spring retaining bolt and spring. Remove retaining bolts (24). Remove valve body from transmission.

Installation

1) Using guide pins, position valve body (with new gasket) in case, making sure that inner manual lever and inner T.V. lever are engaged. Install and tighten valve body retaining bolts.

2) Install and tighten detent spring and retaining bolts. Remove guide pins and install remaining 2 valve body retaining bolts. Load throttle lever torsion spring against separator plate. Install oil pan and refill with fluid.

OVERDRIVE SERVO ASSEMBLY
Removal

1) Remove valve body as previously described. Depress overdrive servo piston cover and remove retaining snap ring.

2) Apply air pressure to servo piston release passage to remove piston, cover, and spring. Separate piston from cover and remove rubber seals from piston and cover.

Installation

1) Install new seals on piston and cover. Lubricate piston seals with automatic transmission fluid or petroleum jelly, then install piston into cover.

2) Lubricate cover seals and overdrive servo pocket in transmission case. Assemble spring to piston. Install assembly into case pocket.

3) Depress servo cover and install retaining snap ring. To complete installation, reverse removal procedures.

LOW-REVERSE SERVO ASSEMBLY
Removal

1) Remove valve body assembly as previously described. Depress low-reverse servo piston cover and remove retaining snap ring and cover.

2) Remove piston and spring from case by applying compressed air to low-reverse servo release passage in case.

CAUTION: Low-reverse servo piston may spring free from case when cover is removed.

Installation

To install, reverse removal procedure. Make sure servo piston is installed with the same length rod as was removed.

3-4 ACCUMULATOR PISTON
Removal

1) Remove valve body assembly as previously described. Depress 3-4 accumulator cover and remove retaining snap ring.

2) Slowly release pressure on cover and remove cover, piston, and (if equipped) return spring. Remove seals from piston and cover.

NOTE: If necessary, 3-4 accumulator piston can be removed by applying compressed air to hydraulic apply passage.

Installation

To install, reverse removal procedures. Lubricate rubber seals and accumulator pocket in case prior to accumulator installation. Make sure that accumulator cover is seated snug against retaining snap ring.

2-3 ACCUMULATOR PISTON
Removal

Remove valve body assembly as previously described. Depress 2-3 accumulator piston cover. Remove retaining snap ring, cover, and spring. Remove accumulator piston and seals from piston.

Installation

To install, reverse removal procedure. Lubricate piston seals and piston pocket in case prior to installation.

EXTENSION HOUSING BUSHING & REAR OIL SEAL
Removal

1) Raise vehicle on a hoist and disconnect propeller shaft from transmission. Remove oil seal using puller (T74P-77248-A).

2) Remove bushing using puller (T77L-7697-A), using care not to damage output shaft splines.

Installation

Install new bushing into extension housing using driver (T80L-77034-A). Install new seal into housing using driver (T61L-7657-A). Coat inside diameter of rubber portion of seal with a lubricant. Install propeller shaft.

EXTENSION HOUSING
Removal

1) Raise and support vehicle. Disconnect parking brake cable from equalizer, (if so equipped). Remove propeller shaft and disconnect speedometer cable from extension housing.

2) Remove engine rear support-to-extension housing retaining bolts. Raise transmission just enough to remove weight from rear support. Remove rear support-to-crossmember retaining bolt and remove rear support.

3) Lower transmission and remove extension housing retaining bolts. Slide housing off output shaft and allow fluid to drain. Remove and discard extension housing-to-case gasket.

Installation

1) Clean mating surface on transmission and extension housing. Position new gasket on transmission. Slide extension housing into place.

2) Clean the bolts and case holes for the 2 bottom bolts and the lower right hand corner bolt (as viewed from the rear of the extension housing). Coat the bolts with Teflon tape and install. Install remaining bolts and tighten all to specification. To complete installation, reverse removal procedures.

GOVERNOR ASSEMBLY
Removal

1) Remove extension housing as previously described. Remove governor-to-output shaft retaining snap ring. Using a mallet, tap governor assembly off output shaft.

2) Remove governor drive ball. Remove governor-to-counterweight retaining screws and lift governor from counterweight.

Installation
1) Lubricate governor parts with clean transmission fluid and make sure valve moves freely in bore. Position governor body on counterweight with cover facing toward front of vehicle. Install and tighten 2 retaining screws.

2) Position governor drive ball into pocket on output shaft. Align keyway in counter weight with drive ball and drive assembly onto output shaft with mallet. Install governor-to-output shaft retaining snap ring. To complete installation, reverse removal procedures.

INTERNAL & EXTERNAL SHIFT LINKAGE

NOTE: **On some vehicles it may be necessary to remove the fan shroud and lower the transmission to remove linkage.**

Removal
1) Raise vehicle on a hoist. Apply penetrating oil to outer throttle lever retaining nut to prevent breaking inner throttle lever. Disconnect any interfering exhaust system components.

2) Loosen oil pan retaining bolts and allow fluid to drain. Remove oil pan. Disconnect shift rod and throttle valve linkage at transmission.

3) Disconnect inner throttle lever spring. Remove detent spring. Hold outer throttle lever stationary and remove throttle lever retaining nut and lock washer. Using a small screwdriver, remove outer throttle lever seal.

4) Grasp manual lever roll pin with vise grip pliers and remove pin. Hold manual lever firmly in position and remove manual lever retaining nut using a box wrench. Remove outer manual lever from case.

5) Remove inner throttle lever and spring. Remove inner manual lever and park pawl actuating rod. Disconnect park pawl actuating rod from inner manual lever. Remove manual lever oil seal using a screwdriver.

Installation
1) Install new manual lever oil seal into case using a driver. With manual lever nut on inner throttle lever, slide inner throttle lever through inner manual lever.

2) Install outer manual lever in case ensuring lever is in proper position (either up or down). Install inner throttle lever and shaft into outer manual lever.

3) Tighten manual lever attaching nut to specifications. Install T.V. lever torsion spring. Push manual lever into case. Ensure inner manual lever pin is engaged on manual valve and inner throttle lever is acting on T.V. valve.

4) Install new manual lever retaining pin in case. Pin must be flush or below pan gasket surface. Install throttle lever seal .030-.060" (.76-1.52 mm) below surface of case.

5) Install detent spring. Install throttle valve outer lever, lockwasher, and nut. Tighten retaining nut to specification. Check operation of T.V. and manual levers. Connect shift linkage. Adjust linkage as necessary. See appropriate AUTOMATIC TRANSMISSION SERVICING article in DOMESTIC GENERAL SERVICING section.

REMOVAL & INSTALLATION

TRANSMISSION
See appropriate AUTOMATIC TRANSMISSION REMOVAL article in DOMESTIC GENERAL SERVICING section.

TORQUE CONVERTER

LEAKAGE CHECK
See procedures given in FORD MOTOR CO. C-6 article.

FLUSHING CONVERTER
See procedures given in FORD MOTOR CO. C-6 article.

TURBINE & STATOR END PLAY CHECK
See procedures given in FORD MOTOR CO. C-6 article.

TRANSMISSION DISASSEMBLY

1) Mount transmission in a holding fixture. Remove torque converter. Remove retaining bolts and lift off oil pan and gasket. Remove oil filter, grommet, and gasket.

2) Remove detent spring and roller assembly. Remove valve body retaining bolts and lift off valve body and gasket. Note length of bolts for reassembly. Push down on 3-4 accumulator cover and remove retaining snap ring. Remove cover, piston, and spring.

3) If necessary, accumulator cover and piston can also be removed by applying compressed air to accumulator hydraulic apply passage. Also, some models do not use a spring on the 3-4 accumulator piston.

Fig. 6: Bottom View of Transmission Case

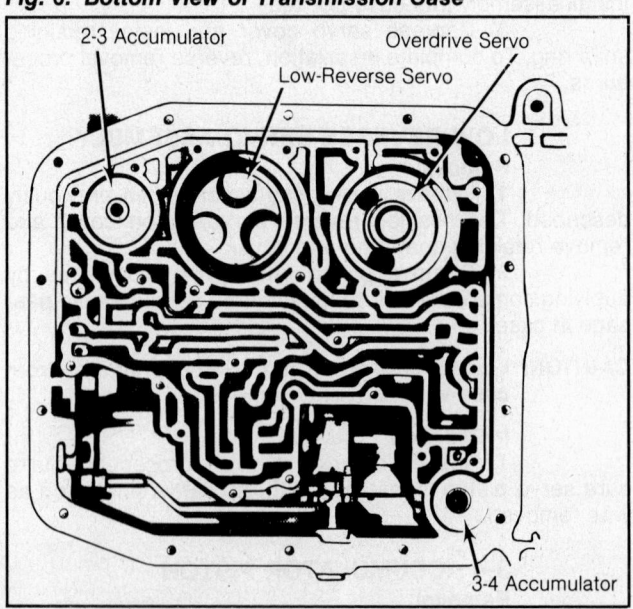

4) Remove 2-3 accumulator assembly, low-reverse servo assembly, and overdrive servo assembly. Note length of low-reverse servo piston rod for reassembly purposes.

NOTE: **Length of low-reverse piston rod may vary. Three possible rod lengths are available.**

Fig. 7: Exploded View of Automatic Overdrive Transmission

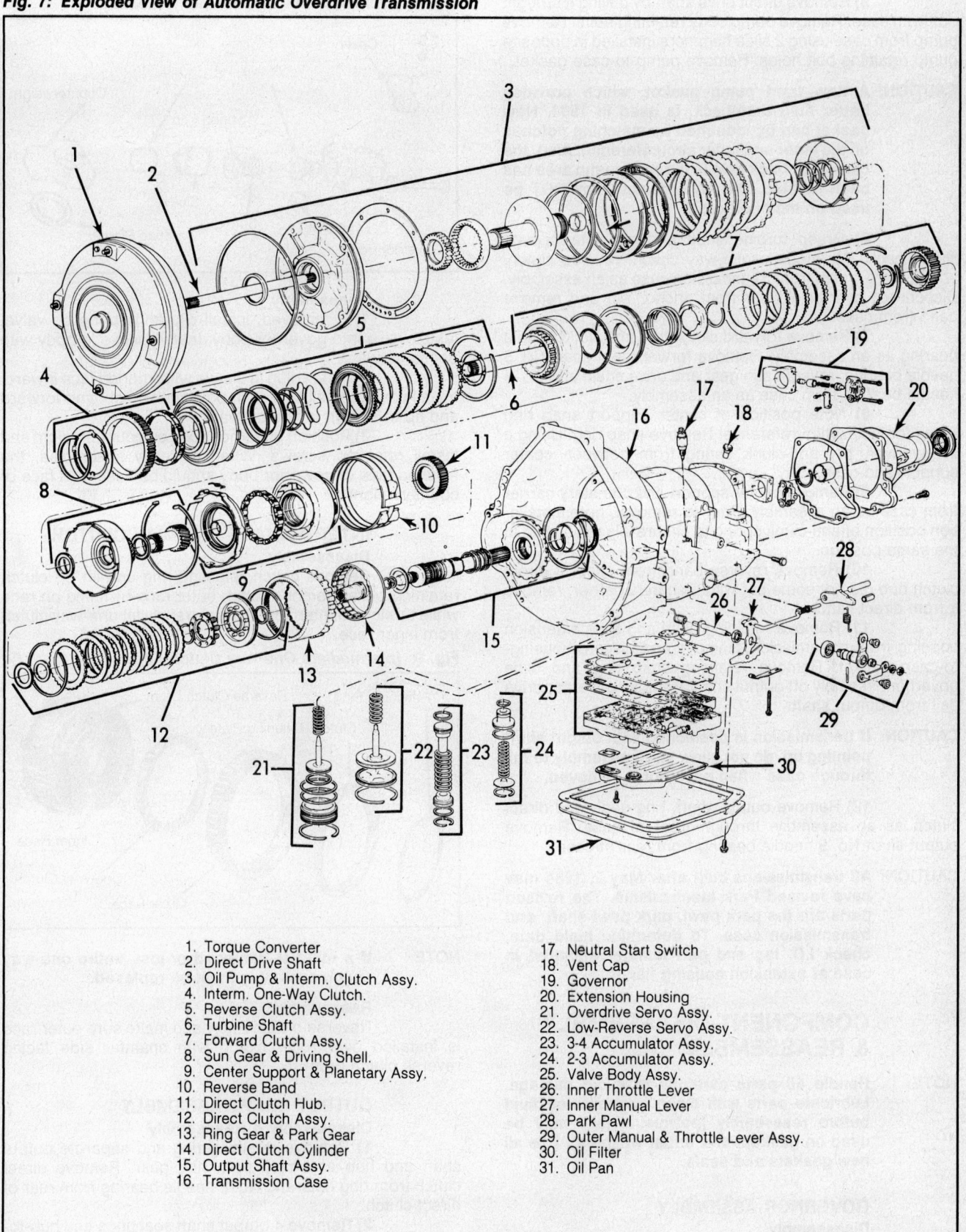

1. Torque Converter
2. Direct Drive Shaft
3. Oil Pump & Interm. Clutch Assy.
4. Interm. One-Way Clutch.
5. Reverse Clutch Assy.
6. Turbine Shaft
7. Forward Clutch Assy.
8. Sun Gear & Driving Shell.
9. Center Support & Planetary Assy.
10. Reverse Band
11. Direct Clutch Hub.
12. Direct Clutch Assy.
13. Ring Gear & Park Gear
14. Direct Clutch Cylinder
15. Output Shaft Assy.
16. Transmission Case

17. Neutral Start Switch
18. Vent Cap
19. Governor
20. Extension Housing
21. Overdrive Servo Assy.
22. Low-Reverse Servo Assy.
23. 3-4 Accumulator Assy.
24. 2-3 Accumulator Assy.
25. Valve Body Assy.
26. Inner Throttle Lever
27. Inner Manual Lever
28. Park Pawl
29. Outer Manual & Throttle Lever Assy.
30. Oil Filter
31. Oil Pan

5) Remove direct drive shaft by pulling it straight out from case. Remove pump body retaining bolts. Remove pump from case using 2 slide hammers installed in opposite pump retaining bolt holes. Remove pump-to-case gasket.

CAUTION: **A new front pump gasket, which provides better fluid drainback, is used in 1984. New gasket can be identified by matching notches on the inner and outer circumference. Also, the case drainback hole in the front pump area has been deleted. Old style gasket may NOT be used on modified case.**

6) Grasp turbine shaft and pull intermediate clutch pack, intermediate one-way clutch, reverse clutch, and forward clutch from transmission case as an assembly. Disconnect overdrive band from anchor pin and remove band from case.

7) Remove forward clutch hub and No. 3 needle bearing as an assembly. Remove forward sun gear, No. 5 needle bearing, reverse sun gear and drive shell, and No. 4 needle bearing from case as an assembly.

8) Note position of center support snap ring tangs for installation reference. Remove snap ring. Using a screwdriver, pry anti-clunk spring from between center support and case.

9) Remove center support and planetary carrier from case as an assembly. Prior to removal, note installation position of anti-clunk spring to ensure it is reinstalled in the same position.

10) Remove reverse band from case. If direct clutch hub did not come out with planetary carrier, remove it from direct clutch.

11) Remove retaining bolts and slide extension housing from transmission. Remove and discard housing-to-case gasket. Remove retaining snap ring and slide governor assembly off output shaft. Remove governor drive ball from output shaft.

CAUTION: **If transmission is positioned with output shaft pointing up, do not allow shaft assembly to fall through case when governor is removed.**

12) Remove output shaft, ring gear, and direct clutch as an assembly, through front of case. Remove output shaft No. 9 needle bearing from rear of case.

CAUTION: **All transmissions built after May 2, 1984 may have revised Park mechanisms. The revised parts are the park pawl, park pawl shaft, and transmission case. To determine build date, check I.D. tag and part number stamped in case at extension housing flange.**

COMPONENT DISASSEMBLY & REASSEMBLY

NOTE: **Handle all parts carefully to avoid damage. Lubricate parts with clean transmission fluid before reassembly (petroleum jelly may be used on gaskets and thrust washers). Use all new gaskets and seals.**

GOVERNOR ASSEMBLY
Disassembly
Remove retaining screws and separate counterweight from governor body. Remove cover screws and cover. Remove plug, sleeve, and valve from governor body.

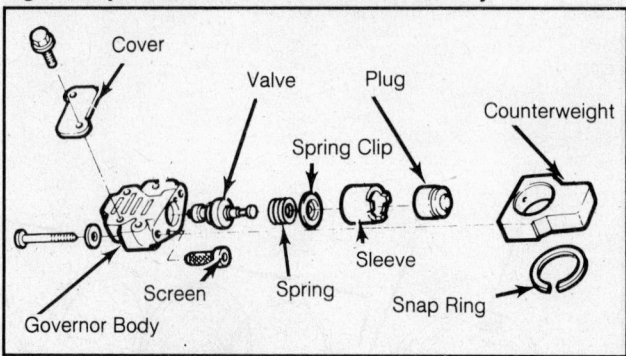

Fig. 8: Exploded View of Governor Assembly

Reassembly
1) If removed, install clip and spring on valve. Install valve into governor body. Install sleeve in body with points outward.

2) Install plug in sleeve with knurled face inward. Install cover. Install screen in body with steel band forward and tip of screen facing outward.

3) Position governor body on counterweight and install retaining screws. When correctly assembled, the finished face of governor body should be flush with face of counterweight.

INTERMEDIATE ONE-WAY CLUTCH
Disassembly
Remove clutch retaining ring and lift off clutch retaining plate. Remove clutch outer race by lifting on race while turning counterclockwise. Carefully lift one-way clutch from inner race.

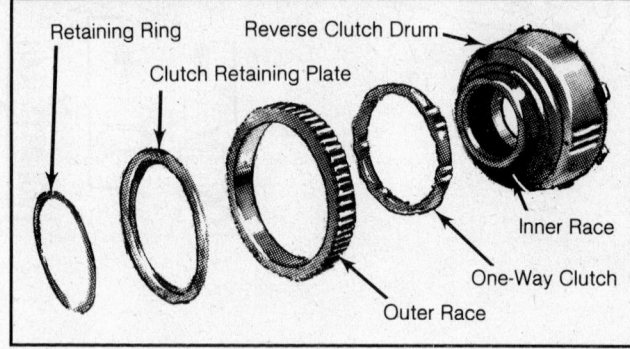

Fig. 9: Intermediate One-Way Clutch Assembly

NOTE: If a roller is damaged or lost, entire one-way clutch assembly must be replaced.

Reassembly
Reverse disassembly and make sure outer race is installed over roller clutch with chamfer side facing reverse clutch drum.

OUTPUT SHAFT ASSEMBLY
Disassembly & Reassembly
1) Remove retaining ring and separate output shaft and hub assembly from ring gear. Remove direct clutch from ring gear and No. 8 needle bearing from rear of direct clutch.

2) Remove 4 output shaft seal rings and hub-to-shaft retaining ring. Separate hub from output shaft. Remove the 2 direct clutch seal rings from end of output shaft. To assemble, reverse disassembly procedures.

Fig. 10: Exploded View of Output Shaft Assembly

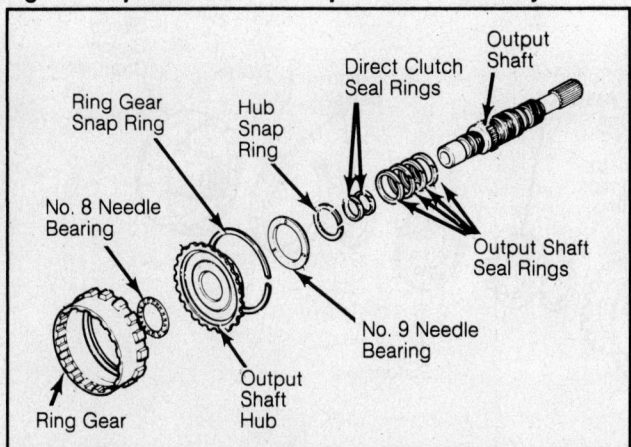

Fig. 11: Bottom View of Transmission Case

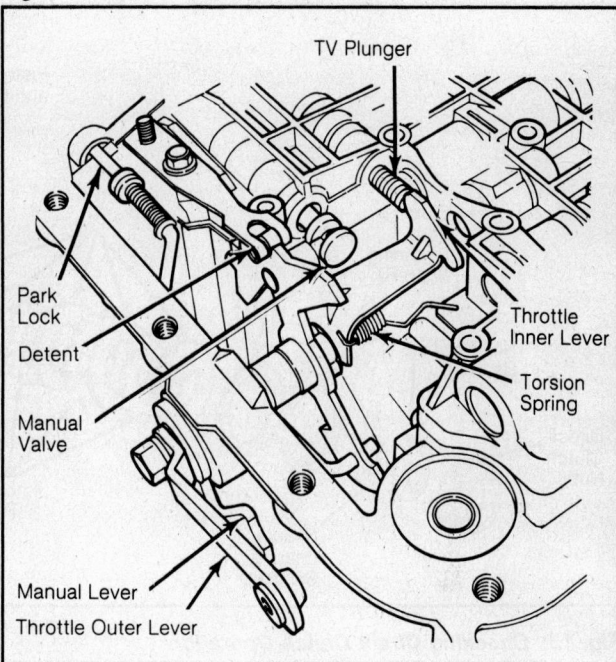

Illustration shows manual and throttle linkage locations.

MANUAL & THROTTLE LINKAGE
Disassembly

1) Hold outer throttle lever stationary and remove retaining nut, lock washer, and throttle lever. Using a small screwdriver, remove oil seal from outer manual lever counterbore.

CAUTION: Failure to hold outer throttle lever stationary when removing retaining nut will allow inner throttle lever to rotate against valve body surface, which could result in damage to surface.

2) Using a pair of diagonal cutters, remove manual shaft retaining pin from case. Hold inner manual lever stationary and remove retaining nut. Remove throttle lever. Remove inner throttle lever and torsion spring.

3) Remove inner manual lever and parking pawl actuating rod as an assembly. Separate rod from lever if necessary. Remove manual lever shaft seal from case using a seal puller.

Reassembly

Reverse disassembly procedures. Install new manual lever seal using seal installer (T74P-77498-A). Before installing outer throttle lever, install new seal in outer manual lever using a 13 mm socket. Install seal with identification number facing outward.

DIRECT CLUTCH ASSEMBLY
Disassembly

1) Remove No. 7 direct clutch hub inner needle bearing and bearing support. Using a screwdriver, remove clutch pack selective retaining snap ring and lift out clutch pack.

2) Using a compressor tool, compress piston return springs and remove retaining snap ring. Remove tool and lift spring retainer assembly and piston from clutch drum. If necessary, piston can be removed by applying compressed air to lubrication hole in clutch drum.

3) Note position and direction of lip seals. Remove seals from drum and piston.

Inspection

1) Check piston check ball for freedom of movement. Check for leakage by turning piston upside down (flat side up), allowing check ball to seat in piston.

2) Pour small quantity of solvent over check ball. If solvent drips past check ball, replace piston.

Reassembly

1) Using a Seal Protector (T80L-77234-A), install inner seal on clutch drum hub with sealing lip facing down into drum. Lubricate seals and seal protector with petroleum jelly prior to installation. Install outer seal on piston with lip pointing away from spring posts.

2) Coat piston seals, clutch drum sealing area, and piston inner seal area with petroleum jelly. Install piston into clutch drum using Seal Protector (T80L-77254-A) to prevent damaging seals.

3) Position piston spring and retainer assembly in clutch drum. Compress assembly and install retaining snap ring. Install clutch pack into drum. Install pressure plate on top of clutch pack. Install clutch pack selective retaining ring.

DIRECT CLUTCH PLATE USAGE CHART

Application	Steel Plates	Friction Plates
3.8L	4	4
All Others	5	5

4) Using a feeler gauge, measure clearance between clutch pack retaining ring and pressure plate with pressure plate held down. Clearance should be .040-.058" (1.02-1.47 mm) if equipped with 3.8L engine and .050-.070" (1.27-1.80 mm) for all others.

5) If clearance is not within limits, selective snap rings are available in the following thicknesses: .050-.054", .064-.068", .078-.082" and .092-.096". Install correct size snap ring and recheck clearance.

6) To check clutch for proper operation use compressed air 30 psi (2.1 kg/cm^2). *See Fig. 13.* Clutch should be heard and felt to apply smoothly and without leakage.

Fig. 12: Exploded View of Direct Clutch Assembly

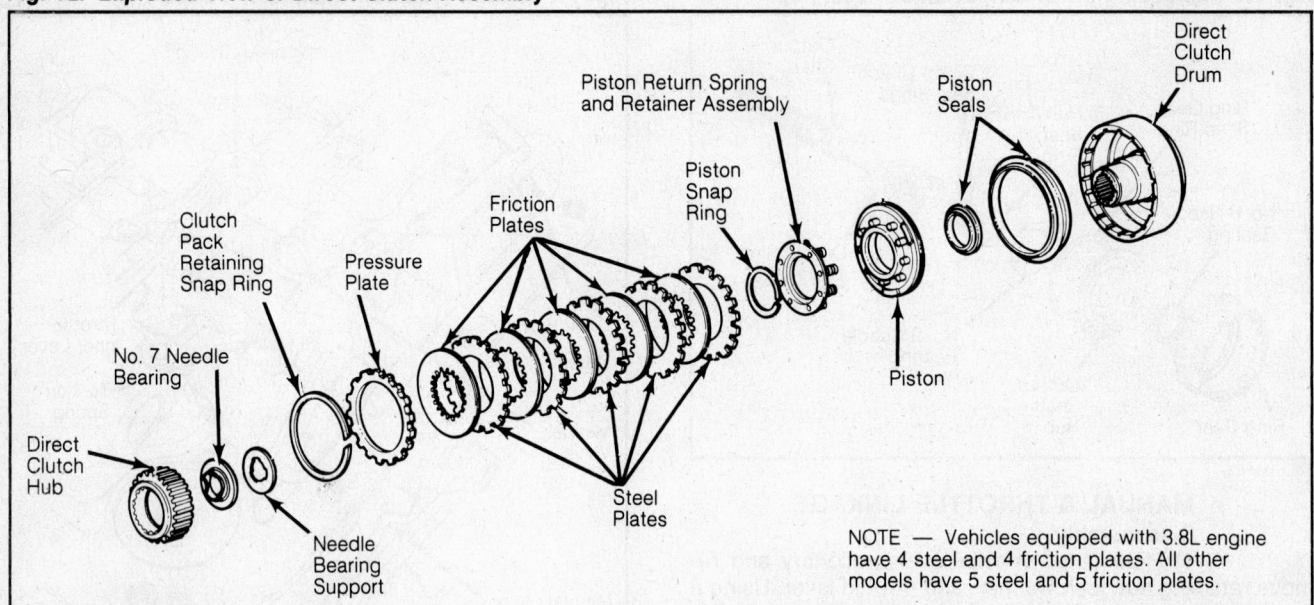

NOTE — Vehicles equipped with 3.8L engine have 4 steel and 4 friction plates. All other models have 5 steel and 5 friction plates.

Fig. 13: Checking Direct Clutch Operation

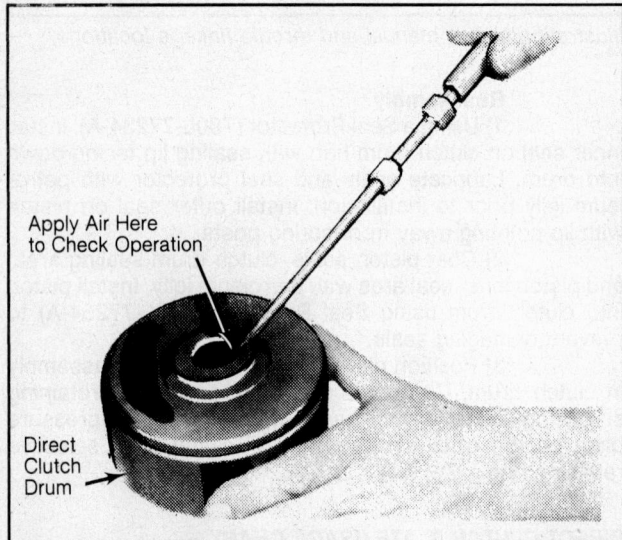

Apply no more than 30 psi (2.1 kg/cm²) to check operation.

FORWARD CLUTCH
Disassembly

1) Lift clutch hub and No. 3 needle bearing from forward clutch assembly. Using a screwdriver, pry clutch pack retaining snap ring from drum. Remove clutch pack.

FORWARD CLUTCH PLATE USAGE CHART

Application	Steel Plates	Friction Plates
5.8L Engine	5 [1]	5
All Others	4 [1]	4

[1] – Plus 1 waved plate installed next to piston.

2) Using a compressor tool, compress piston return spring and remove retaining snap ring. Lift out retainer and return spring.

3) Remove clutch piston from drum. Note position of inner and outer piston seals, then remove seals. Ensure check balls in piston are free.

NOTE: **If transmission is equipped with revised forward clutch drum (1/32" chamfer), a No. 7F278 pressure plate must be used on reassembly.**

Reassembly

1) Lubricate and install inner and outer seals on piston with seal lips facing into clutch drum. Lubricate piston seals and drum sealing area with petroleum jelly. Install piston into drum using a Seal Protector (T80L-77140-A) to prevent damaging seals.

2) Position return spring and retainer on piston. Compress return spring and install retaining snap ring. Install clutch pack into clutch drum starting with waved plate. Install clutch pack retaining snap ring.

3) Using a feeler gauge, measure clearance between retaining snap ring and pressure plate with pressure plate held downward. Clearance should be .050-.089" (1.27-2.26 mm) if equipped with 5.8L engine, and .040-.071" (1.02-1.80 mm) for all others.

4) If forward clutch clearance is not within limits, selective snap rings are available in the following thicknesses: .060-.064", .074-.078", .088-.092" and .102-.106". Install correct size snap ring and recheck clearance.

5) With reassembly completed, use compressed air and check forward clutch operation. Clutch should be heard and felt to apply smoothly and without leakage.

REVERSE CLUTCH
Disassembly

1) Remove No. 2 thrust washer. Using a screwdriver, pry clutch pack retaining snap ring from clutch drum. Lift out clutch pack.

2) Compress return spring and remove waved snap ring. Remove return spring and thrust ring. Remove piston from drum. Remove seals from piston.

Fig. 14: Exploded View of Forward Clutch Assembly

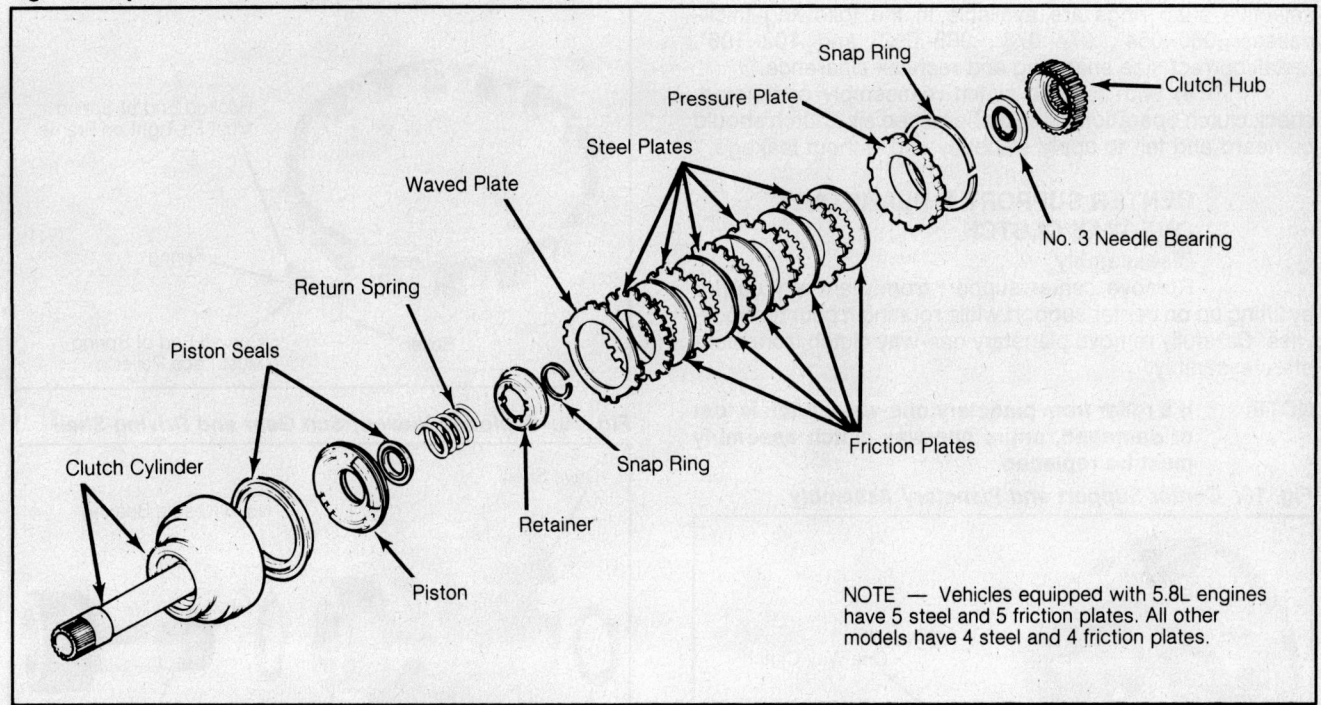

NOTE — Vehicles equipped with 5.8L engines have 5 steel and 5 friction plates. All other models have 4 steel and 4 friction plates.

3) It may be necessary to apply compressed air to clutch drum lubrication hole to remove piston. Block remaining hole with finger.

4) Reverse clutch drums for 1984 have been changed. Modified clutch drum has an extra internal identification groove next to the snap ring groove. If modified drum is used, new intermediate one-way clutch snap ring and Part No. 7E311 friction plates must be used.

Reassembly

1) Prior to reassembly, make sure that check ball in inner piston seal is free. Install new oil seal on piston. Coat seals and sealing surface in clutch drum with petroleum jelly.

2) Install piston into clutch drum using Inner and Outer Seal Protectors (T80L-77403-B and A) to prevent damaging seals. Seals used on reverse clutch piston are square cut, therefore direction of installation is not important.

3) Install thrust ring and return spring. Compress return spring and install waved snap ring. Install apply plate into clutch drum with dished side facing piston. Install clutch pack and retaining snap ring.

REVERSE CLUTCH PLATE USAGE CHART

Engine Application	Steel Plates	Friction Plates
5.8L	3	4
All Others	2	3

4) Using a feeler gauge, measure clearance between clutch pack snap ring and pressure plate while pushing down on pressure plate. Clearance should be .040-.075" (1.02-1.91 mm) for 5.8L engine, and .030-.056" (.76-1.42 mm) for all other models.

Fig. 15: Exploded View of Reverse Clutch Assembly

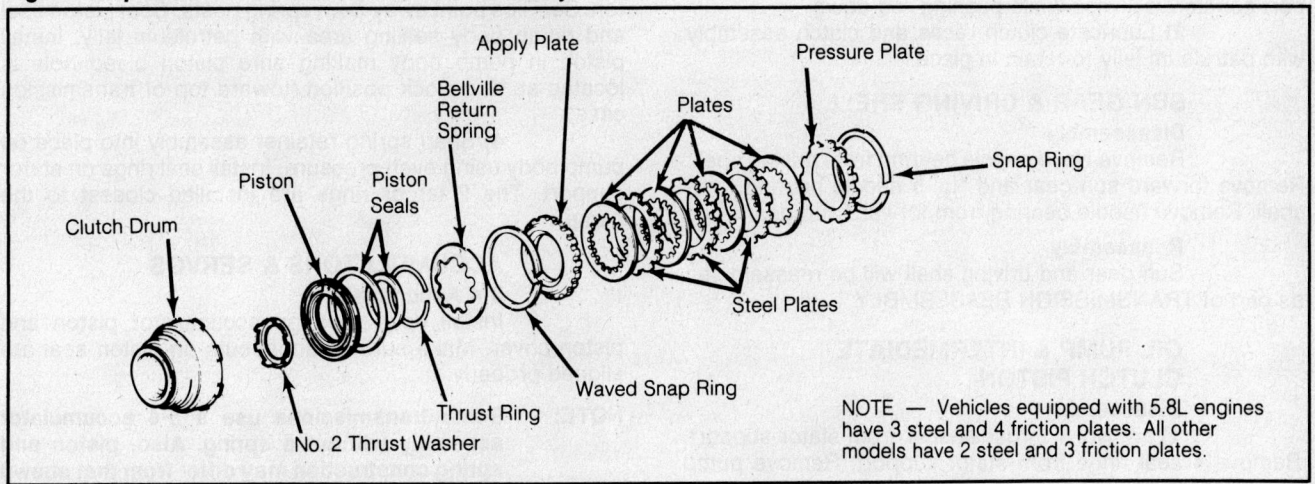

NOTE — Vehicles equipped with 5.8L engines have 3 steel and 4 friction plates. All other models have 2 steel and 3 friction plates.

5) If reverse clutch clearance is not within limits, selective snap rings are available in the following thicknesses: .060-.064", .074-.078", .088-.092", and .102-.106". Install correct size snap ring and recheck clearance.

6) With reverse clutch reassembly completed, check clutch operation using compressed air. Clutch should be heard and felt to apply smoothly and without leakage.

CENTER SUPPORT & PLANETARY ONE-WAY CLUTCH
Disassembly

Remove center support from planetary carrier by lifting up on center support while rotating it counterclockwise. Carefully remove planetary one-way clutch from planetary assembly.

NOTE: If a roller from planetary one-way clutch is lost or damaged, entire one-way clutch assembly must be replaced.

Fig. 16: Center Support and Planetary Assembly

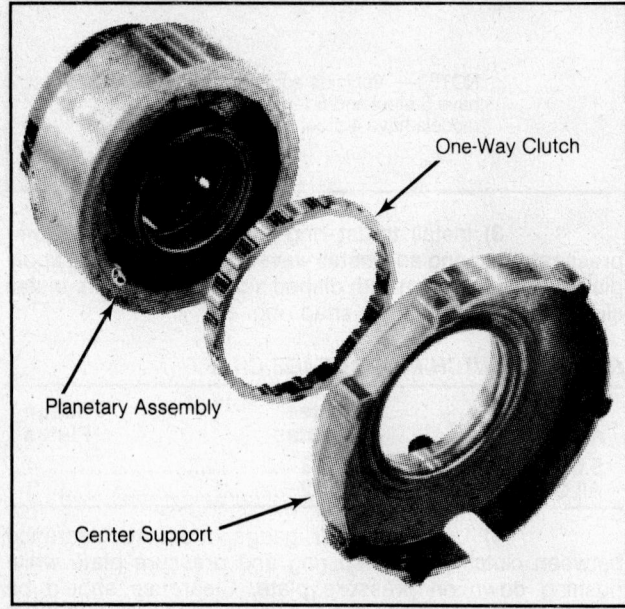

Reassembly

1) If necessary, assemble one-way clutch. See Fig. 17. Install one-way clutch in planetary carrier. Install center support into one-way clutch by rotating center support counterclockwise while pushing rod down.

2) Lubricate clutch races and clutch assembly with petroleum jelly to retain in place.

SUN GEAR & DRIVING SHELL
Disassembly

Remove No. 4 needle bearing from driving shell. Remove forward sun gear and No. 5 needle bearing from shell. Remove needle bearing from forward sun gear.

Reassembly

Sun gear and driving shell will be reassembled as part of TRANSMISSION REASSEMBLY

OIL PUMP & INTERMEDIATE CLUTCH PISTON
Disassembly

1) Lift No. 1 thrust washer from stator support. Remove 4 seal rings from stator support. Remove pump body-to-case seal and discard.

Fig. 17: Assembling Planetary One-Way Clutch

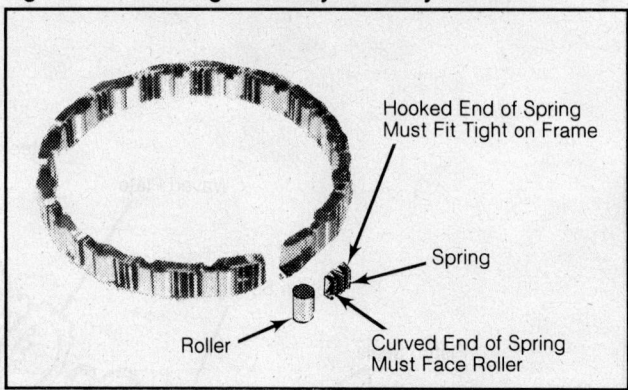

Fig. 18: Exploded View of Sun Gear and Driving Shell

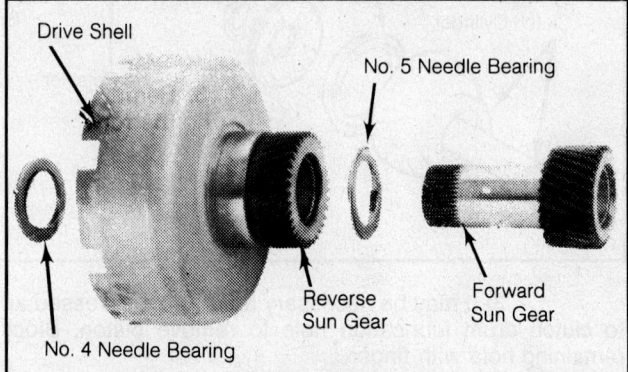

NOTE: Reverse clutch seal rings on stator support are larger than forward clutch seal rings.

2) Remove spring retainer assembly by carefully dislodging the tabs. Lift intermediate clutch piston from pump assembly. Remove retaining bolts and separate stator support from pump body. Remove drive and driven gears from pump body.

Reassembly

1) Install drive gear and driven gear into pump body with chamfers on both gears facing into pump body.

2) Position stator support on pump body. Install and tighten retaining bolts. Install pump-to-case seal around outer diameter of pump body.

3) Install new seals on intermediate clutch piston. Seal lips point away from spring posts. Coat piston seal and pump body sealing area with petroleum jelly. Install piston in pump body making sure piston bleed hole is located at 12 o'clock position (toward top of transmission case).

4) Snap spring retainer assembly into place on pump body using even pressure. Install seal rings on stator support. The 2 larger rings are installed closest to the pump.

ACCUMULATORS & SERVOS
3-4 Accumulator

Install new seals on accumulator piston and piston cover. Make sure diagonal cuts on piston seal are aligned properly.

NOTE: Some transmissions use a 3-4 accumulator assembly without a spring. Also, piston and spring construction may differ from that shown in Fig. 20.

Fig. 19: Exploded View of Oil Pump and Intermediate Clutch Piston

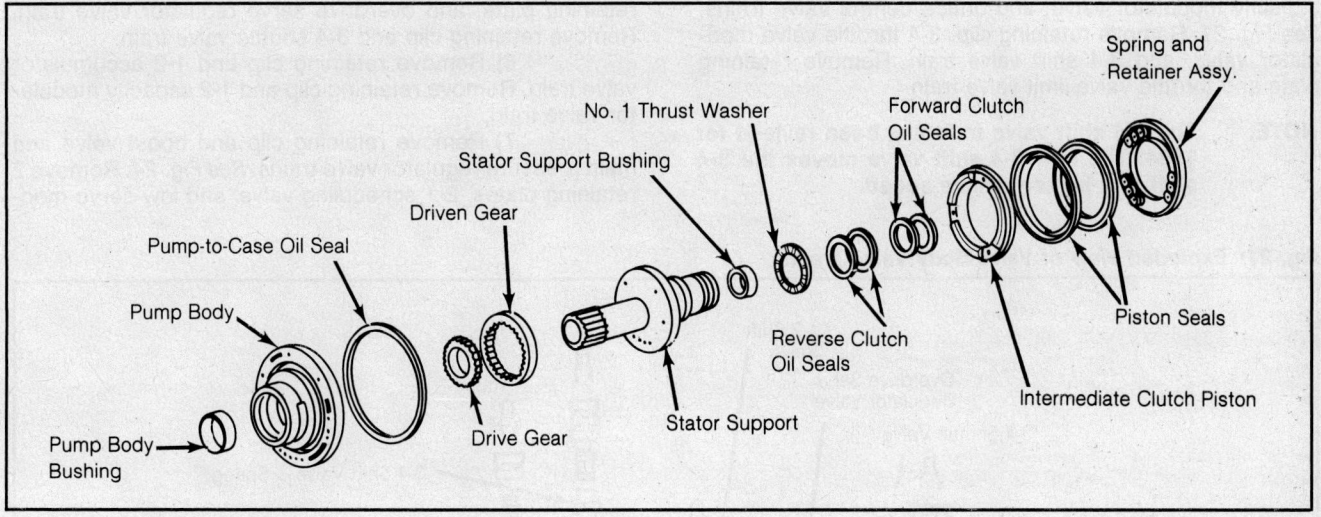

2-3 Accumulator

Install new seals on accumulator piston. Make sure diagonal cuts on seals are properly aligned.

Low-Reverse Servo

Inspect sealing edge on both servo cover and piston. Replace cover or piston, if necessary.

Overdrive Servo

Separate piston from servo cover. Install new seals on piston and cover. Assemble piston to cover.

VALVE BODY ASSEMBLY

NOTE: As valve trains are removed from each valve body bore, place individual parts in correct order and in relative position to valve body to simplify reassembly. Tag all springs as they are removed for reassembly reference.

Disassembly

1) Remove and discard valve body gasket. Remove retaining bolts. Remove separator plate, reinforcement plates, and separator plate gasket. Discard gasket.

2) Remove 2 relief valves and 7 check balls from valve body. Note location of Orange check ball. It is not interchangeable with 6 Black balls. *See Fig. 22.*

3) Remove manual valve. *See Fig. 23.* Remove retaining clip and slide throttle control valve train from valve body. Remove retaining clip and 2-3 backout valve train.

Fig. 20: Exploded View of Accumulator and Servo Assemblies

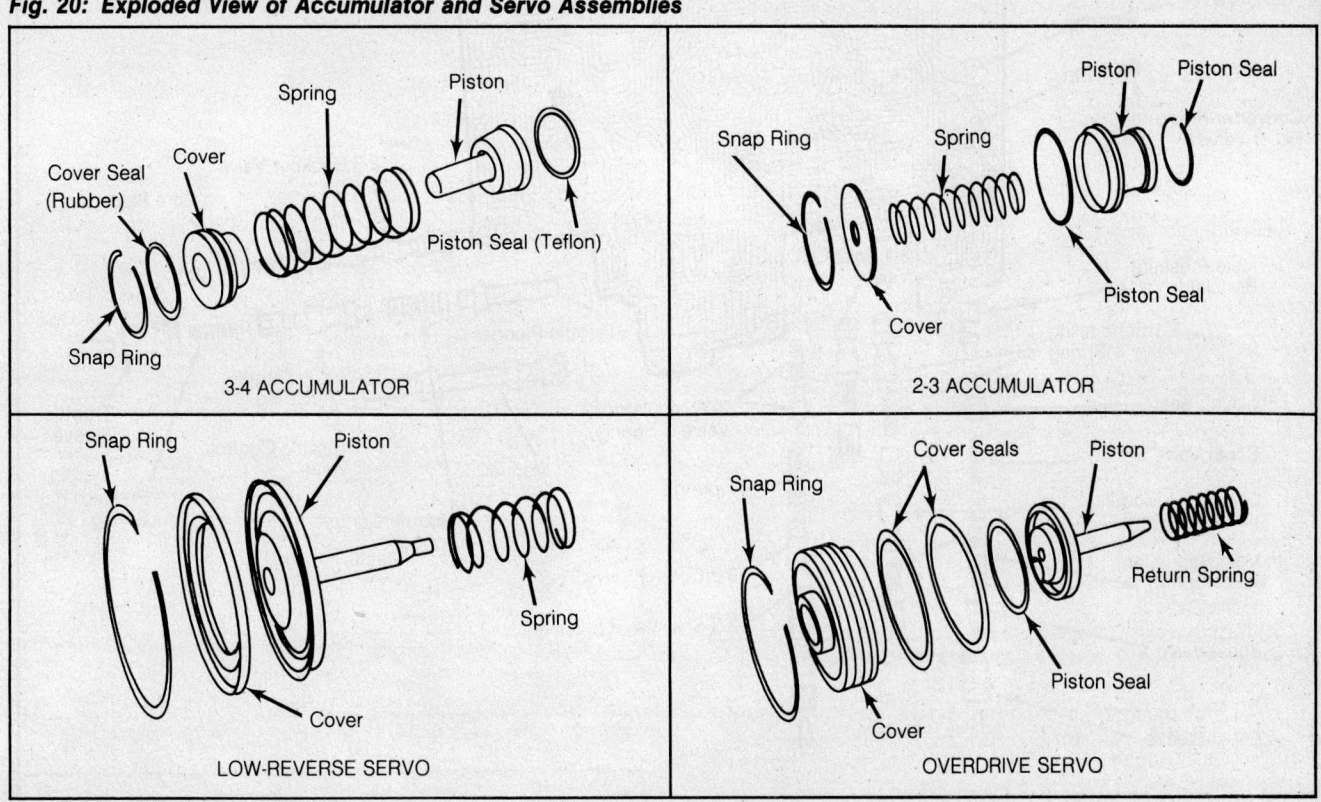

Automatic Transmissions
FORD MOTOR CO. A.O.T. (Cont.)

4) Remove retaining clip, retaining plate, 2-3 capacity modulator valve, and orifice control valve trains. *See Fig. 21.* Remove retaining clip, 3-4 throttle valve modulator valve, and 3-4 shift valve train. Remove retaining plate and throttle valve limit valve train.

NOTE: **The 3-4 shift valve train has been revised for 1984. The new 3-4 shift valve moves the 3-4 shift to a higher vehicle speed.**

5) Remove retaining clip, 1-2 shift valve train, retaining plate, and overdrive servo regulator valve train. Remove retaining clip and 3-4 shuttle valve train.

6) Remove retaining clip and 1-2 accumulator valve train. Remove retaining clip and 1-2 capacity modulator valve train.

7) Remove retaining clip and boost valve and main pressure regulator valve trains. *See Fig. 24.* Remove 2 retaining plates, 2-1 scheduling valve, and low servo mod-

Fig. 21: Exploded View of Valve Body Valve Trains

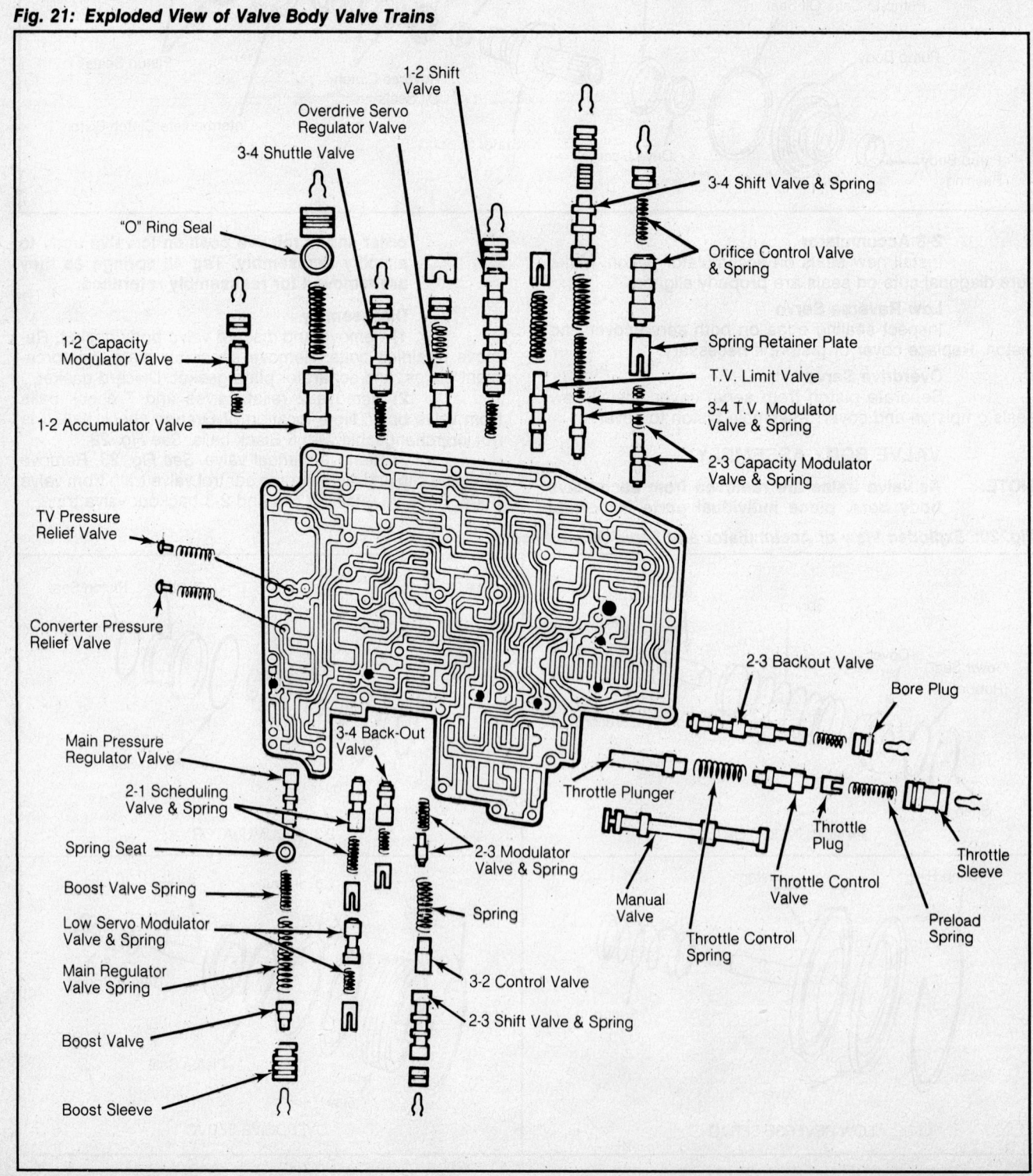

ulator valve trains. Remove retaining plate and 3-4 backout valve train.

8) Remove the retaining clip, 2-3 shift valve, and 2-3 throttle valve modulator valve trains.

Cleaning & Inspection

1) Clean all parts thoroughly in clean solvent, and blow dry with moisture-free compressed air. Inspect all valves and plug bores for scores. Check all fluid passages for obstructions.

2) Inspect all mating surfaces, plugs, and valves for burrs and scores. If necessary, use crocus cloth to polish valves and plugs.

3) Inspect all springs for distortion. Check all valves and plugs for free movement in their respective bores. Valves and plugs, when dry, must fall free from their own weight in their respective bores.

CAUTION: Avoid rounding off the sharp edges of valves and plugs with the crocus cloth. These edges perform a cleaning action.

Reassembly

1) Install all valve trains into their respective bores using illustrations as assembly guides. Note chamfered stem of throttle control valve faces throttle plunger. Retainer plate used for 2-3 capacity modulator valve is thicker and longer than other retainer plates.

2) The 1-2 accumulator valve and valve body diameters are not the same for all models. Install valve body check balls. *See Fig. 21.* Make sure that Orange check ball is correctly installed. This check ball is larger than the others and is not interchangeable. Install pressure relief valves and springs. *See Fig. 25.*

Fig. 22: View of Transmission Valve Body

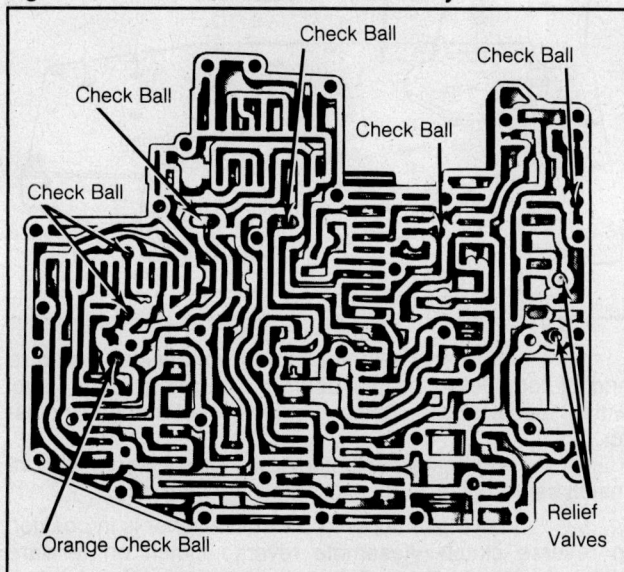

3) Install Alignment Pins (T80L-77100-A) into holes. *See Fig. 26.* These 2 holes are smaller than the other bolt holes to assure proper alignment of gasket and separator plate with valve body. These 2 holes also align valve body gasket and valve body assembly with case.

4) Using a new separator plate gasket, slide plate, and gasket over alignment pins. Position the 3 reinforcement plates and loosely install retaining bolts.

5) Loosely install detent spring guide bolt. Detent spring guide bolt is the same length as short valve body-to-case retaining bolts. Starting at center (large) reinforcement plate and working outward, tighten retaining bolts. Remove alignment pins.

TRANSMISSION REASSEMBLY

NOTE: Handle all parts carefully to avoid damaging bearings and mating surfaces. Lubricate all parts with clean transmission fluid. Use petroleum jelly on gaskets, thrust washers, and needle bearings to retain in place. Use new gaskets and seals.

1) Install No. 9 output shaft needle bearing in transmission case. Install bearing support, No. 7 needle bearing and direct clutch hub in direct clutch assembly. Assemble output shaft hub to output shaft and install retaining snap ring.

2) Place No. 8 needle bearing on rear of direct clutch drum. Slide output shaft into direct clutch drum. Attach output shaft hub to ring gear with retaining ring. Install output shaft, ring gear, and direct clutch assembly into transmission case.

3) Position governor drive ball in pocket on output shaft. Slide governor assembly onto output shaft with cover and attaching screws facing toward front of case. Install governor retaining snap ring.

4) Clean mating surface on transmission and extension housing. Position new gasket on transmission. Slide extension housing into place.

5) Clean the bolts and case holes for the 2 bottom bolts and, the lower right hand corner bolt (as viewed from the rear of the extension housing). Coat the bolts with Teflon tape and install. Install remaining bolts and tighten all to specification.

Fig. 23: Exploded View of Manual Valve, Throttle Control Valve Train and 2-3 Backout Valve Train

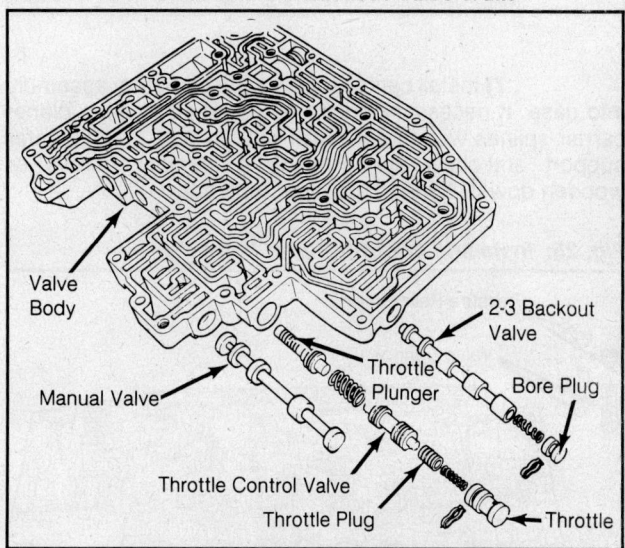

6) Install low-reverse band into transmission case and make sure band is seated on anchor pins. When properly installed, center of band actuating rod seat can be seen through servo piston bore.

Fig. 24: Exploded View of Valve Body Valve Trains

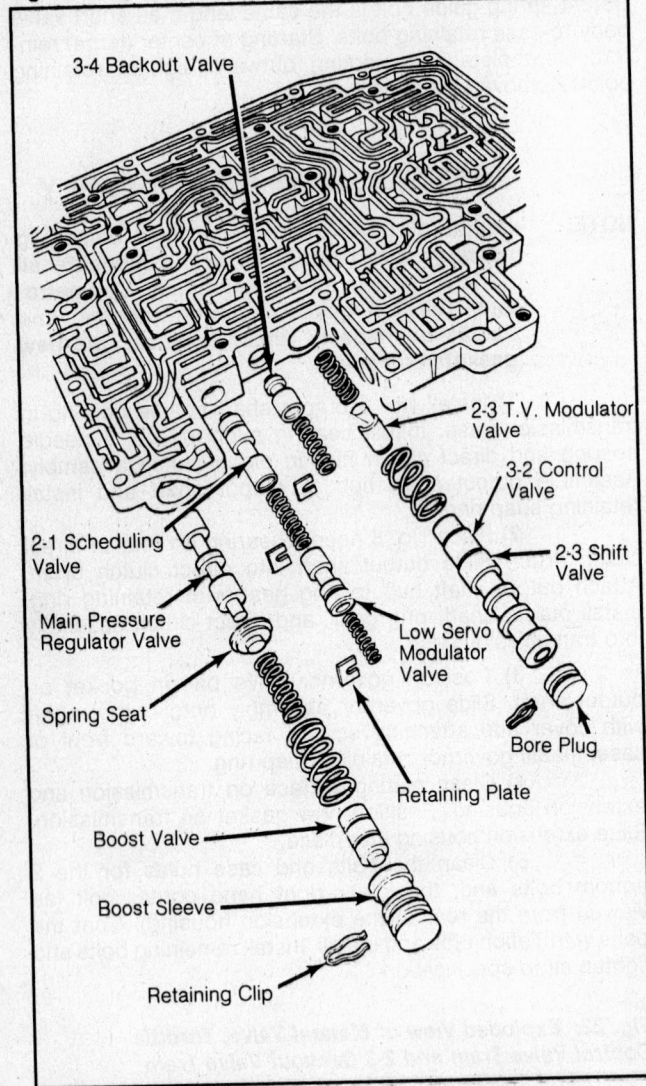

7) Install center support and planetary assembly into case. If necessary, rotate output shaft to align planet carrier splines with direct clutch hub splines. Install center support anti-clunk spring using a hammer handle or wooden dowel. Spring tabs must face out.

Fig. 25: Installing Pressure Relief Valve

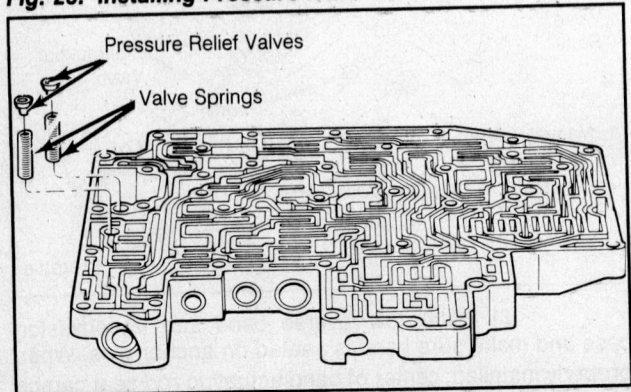

8) Install center support retaining ring. Center support and planet carrier cannot be installed unless notch cut in center support is aligned with overdrive band anchor pin.

9) Determine correct length of low-reverse servo pin to use. Install servo piston and return spring. Do not install cover or retaining ring. Install Servo Selector Gauge (T80L-77030-A) into servo bore.

10) Tighten band apply bolt on tool to 50 INCH lbs. (5.6 N.m). Attach dial indicator. See Fig. 28. Position indicator stem on flat portion of servo piston. Zero dial indicator.

11) Thread bolt out of selector tool until piston stops against bottom of tool. Read amount of piston travel on dial indicator. If travel is 0.112"-.237" (2.845-6.020 mm), correct servo pin is installed. If travel is not within specifications, selective pistons are available in lengths of: 2.936" identified by 1 groove, 2.989" (2 grooves), and 3.043" (3 grooves).

Fig. 26: View of Transmission Valve Body

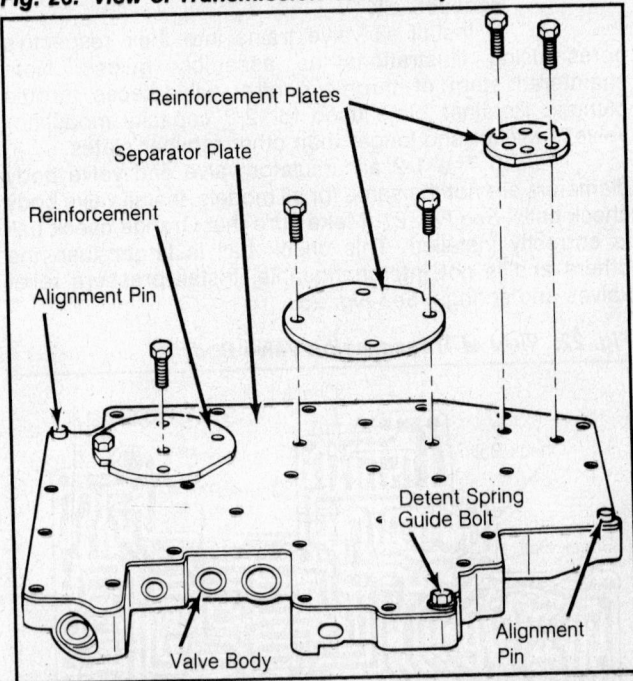

12) Length is measured from base of piston to end of rod. Select proper servo pin to bring servo travel within specifications. Remove selector tool and dial indicator.

13) Install selected low-reverse servo piston. Install servo cover and cover retaining snap ring.

14) Make sure No. 2 thrust washer is in position in reverse clutch. Assemble reverse clutch on forward clutch. Install No. 3 needle bearing and forward clutch hub in forward clutch. Position No. 4 needle bearing on forward clutch hub.

15) Install drive shell over clutch assemblies. Install No. 5 needle bearing and forward sun gear on drive shell. Install complete assembly into case, rotating output to aid in engaging sun gear with planetary gears.

16) Install overdrive band into case and around drive shell assembly. Ensure band anchor is properly positioned on anchor pin. Using a screwdriver to hold overdrive band in position, install overdrive servo.

Fig. 27: Installing Direct Clutch Assembly

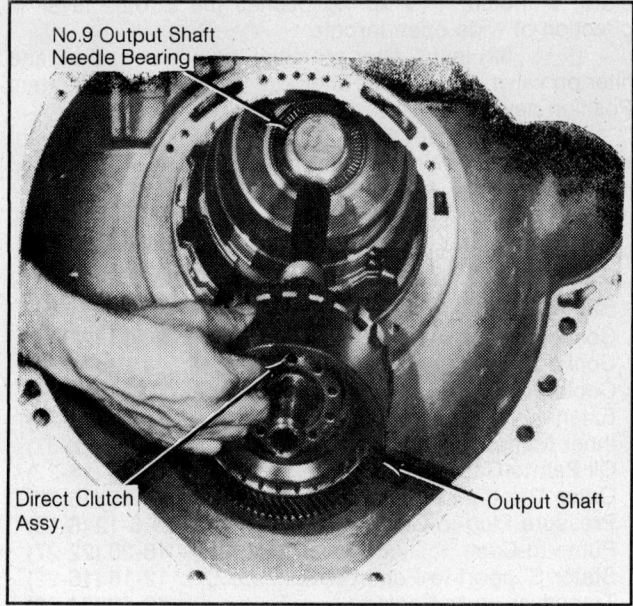

17) With overdrive servo installed, inspect band and apply pin for proper position and engagement. If band anchor and apply pin are not properly engaged, remove servo and reposition band as necessary.

18) Install intermediate clutch pack components into case in the following order: Pressure plate, clutch pack (starting with a friction plate and alternating steel and friction plates) and selective steel plate. Measure intermediate clutch clearance as follows.

19) Intermediate clutch clearance is measured using a depth micrometer and end play checking tool (T80L-77003-A). See Fig. 29. Set end play tool across pump case mounting surface. Locate micrometer end play bar and read depth.

20) Check depth again with micrometer at 180° opposite from previous measurement. Depth at intermediate clutch selective steel plate should be 1.629-1.640" (41.38-41.66 mm) if vehicle is equipped with 3.8L engine,

Fig. 28: Low-Reverse Servo Pin Selection

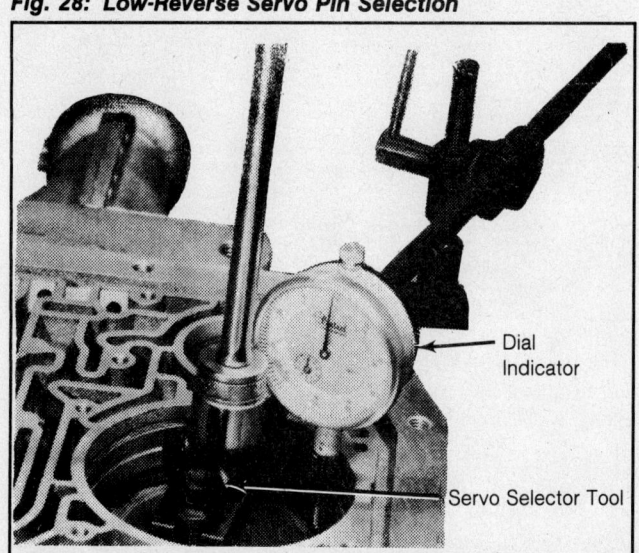

Position indicator stem on flat portion of servo piston.

and 1.634-1.646" (41.50-41.81 mm) for all other models. Average of the 2 measurements should be within this range.

NOTE: A downward pressure must be applied to clutch pack while measuring intermediate clutch clearance.

21) If intermediate clutch clearance is not within tolerance, the following size selective steel plates are available: .067-.071", .077-.081", .087-.091", and .097-.101". Install correct size plate and recheck clearance.

22) Check transmission end play by locating depth micrometer on End Play Check Bar (T80L-77003-A), so that depth is measured at reverse clutch drum thrust face.

23) Check end play 180° opposite to determine average depth. Thrust washer controlling transmission end play is located on stator support which is attached to back of pump housing.

INTERMEDIATE CLUTCH PLATE USAGE

Engine Application	Steel Plates	Friction Plates
3.8L	2	2
All Others	3	3

Fig. 29: Measuring Intermediate Clutch Clearance

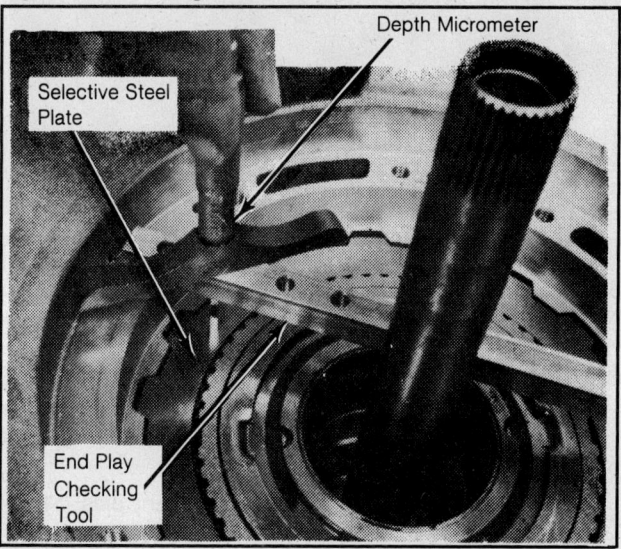

Push down on clutch pack while measuring clearance.

24) Transmission end play can be adjusted using one of the selective thrust washers available for service. After measuring depth, select required thrust washer. See END PLAY THRUST WASHER SELECTION CHART.

25) Install selected transmission end play thrust washer on stator support. Use petroleum jelly to hold it in place. Install pump alignment dowel, made by cutting the head from a M8-1.25 bolt, into pump mounting bolt hole at 6 o'clock position.

26) Install new pump gasket into case. Install pump assembly into case using 2 slide hammers to lower pump into position. Remove alignment dowel.

27) Coat all pump-to-case bolts with Teflon tape and install. Alternately tighten bolts a few turns at a time to draw pump into case.

END PLAY THRUST WASHER SELECTION CHART

Measured Depth	Washer Thickness	Color Code
1.483-1.500" (37.67-38.10)	.050-.054" (1.27-1.37)	Green
1.501-1.517" (38.13-38.53)	.068-.072" (1.73-1.83)	Yellow
1.518-1.534" (38.56-38.96)	.085-.089" (2.16-2.26)	Natural
1.535-1.551" (38.99-39.40)	.102-.106" (2.59-2.69)	Red
1.552-1.568" (39.42-39.83)	.119-.123" (3.02-3.12)	Blue

Fig. 30: Measuring Transmission End Play

Depth Micrometer

End Play Checking Tool

Reverse Clutch Drum Thrust Face

After measuring depth, select thrust washer from table.

28) Assemble 3-4 accumulator. Install piston (and spring, if so equipped) into case. Lubricate rubber seal on accumulator cover and top of bore to help cover installation. Install cover and retaining ring. Install 2-3 accumulator assembly.

CAUTION: After installation, 3-4 accumulator cover must be seated firmly against retaining ring. Use air pressure if necessary to seat cover against ring.

29) Install 2 valve body alignment pins (T80L-77100-A) into valve body. Install valve body gasket and valve body assembly over pins, making sure manual and throttle levers are properly positioned before installing valve body retaining bolts.

30) Loosely install valve body retaining bolts. Starting at center and working outward, tighten bolts. Remove alignment pins and install bolts. Install detent spring and roller assembly and tighten bolts.

NOTE: Two different length valve body retaining bolts are used. Shorter bolts are used at the 4 front, 1 center and 3 rear locations.

31) Position torsion spring against separator plate "V" notch. This spring pushes the throttle lever in direction of wide open throttle.

32) Install filter grommet, new filter gasket, and filter on valve body. Install filter attaching bolts and tighten. Position new pan gasket on case and install oil pan.

33) Slide direct drive shaft into turbine input shaft. Install torque converter, making sure it is fully seated in pump

TIGHTENING SPECIFICATIONS

Application	Ft. Lbs. (N.m)
Converter-to-Flywheel	20-34 (27-46)
Converter Plug-to-Converter	8-23 (11-38)
Cooler Line-to-Case	10-14 (14-19)
Extension-to-Case	16-20 (22-27)
Inner Manual Lever-to-Shaft	19-27 (26-37)
Oil Pan-to-Case	12-16 (16-22)
Outer Throttle Lever-to-Shaft	12-16 (16-22)
Pressure Plug-to-Case	6-12 (8-16)
Pump-to-Case	16-20 (22-27)
Stator Support-to-Pump	12-16 (16-22)
Transmission-to-Engine	40-50 (54-68)

Application	INCH Lbs. (N.m)
Cover-to-Governor Body	20-30 (2.3-3.4)
Filter-to-Valve Body	80-100 (9-11)
Governor Body-to-Counterweight	50-60 (6-7)
Reinforcing Plate-to-Valve Body	80-100 (9-11)
Separator Plate-to-Valve Body	80-100 (9-11)
Valve Body-to-Case	80-100 (9-11)

FORD MOTOR CO. A4LD

Aerostar, 2WD/4WD Bronco II, Ranger

IDENTIFICATION

The A4LD automatic transmission is identified by code letter "T", which is shown on lower line of Vehicle Certification Label under "TRANS". Label is attached to driver's front door lock panel or pillar.

Transmission model may be identified by metal tag attached to transmission at lower extension housing retaining bolt. Top line of tag shows transmission model number and line shift code. Bottom line on tag shows build date code. *See Fig. 1.*

Fig. 1: Service Identification Tag

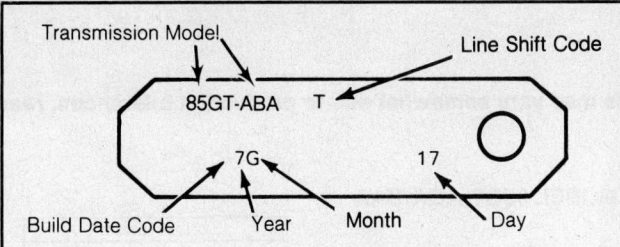

Tag is on lower left extension housing bolt.

DESCRIPTION

The A4LD is a 4-speed automatic overdrive derivative of the C3 3-speed automatic transmission. Manual selection of all gears is provided.

It is the first Ford Motor Company production automatic transmission to use electronic controls intergrated in the on-board EEC-VI system. These controls operate a piston/plate clucth in the torque converter that eliminates torque converter slip when applied.

Transmission consists of torque converter, planetary gear train, 3 multiple disc clutch packs, one-way clutch and hydraulic control system.

LUBRICATION & ADJUSTMENT

See appropriate AUTOMATIC TRANSMISSION SERVICING article in DOMESTIC GENERAL SERVICING section.

TROUBLE SHOOTING

See appropriate AUTOMATIC TRANSMISSION TROUBLE SHOOTING article in DOMESTIC GENERAL SERVICING section.

TESTING

Check fluid level and correct if necessary. Use initial road test to verify malfunction of transmission. Make sure that engine appears to be running properly. If transmission problems occur on initial road test, check adjustments and fluid levels.

ROAD TEST

1) Check minimum throttle upshifts in "O/D". Transmission should start in 1st gear, shift to 2nd, then shift to 3rd, and finally shift to 4th gear at approximately the speeds shown in SHIFT SPEED table.

NOTE: **Choke must be "OFF" when checking minimum throttle upshifts. If not, shift points will be affected.**

2) Check partial throttle upshifts in "O/D". Transmission should start in 1st gear, shift to 2nd, then shift to 3rd, and finally shift to 4th gear. See SHIFT SPEED table.

3) With transmission in 4th gear (overdrive), depress accelerator pedal to the floor. Transmission should downshift to 3rd or 2nd gear, depending on vehicle speed. See SHIFT SPEED table.

4) Since closed throttle downshifts are extremely difficult to detect, it will be necessary to attach pressure gauges to forward and direct clutch pressure taps in order to detect OD to 3rd gear and 3rd to 2nd gear coast downshifts.

5) With gauges attached, a 4th to 3rd gear coast (closed throttle) downshift is signified by the application of the forward clutch, and 3rd to 2nd gear coast downshift is signified by the release of the direct clutch. See SHIFT SPEED table. A 2nd to 1st gear downshift should not be felt.

6) With transmission selector lever in "1" (manual low), transmission should operate only in 1st gear.

7) When selector lever is moved from either overdrive or direct drive ranges to "1" position, transmission should downshift into 2nd gear if vehicle speed is above 25 MPH, and into 1st gear if speed is less than 25 MPH.

VACUUM MODULATOR

1) Remove hose from vacuum modulator unit. If transmission fluid is evident on vacuum side of diaphragm or in vacuum hose, replace modulator unit. Fluid indicates that diaphragm is broken.

2) Hookup vacuum pump to fitting on modulator. Operate pump until gauge shows 18 in. Hg. If gauge reading holds steady, modulator unit is good. If gauge reading drops, modulator unit is bad and must be replaced.

3) With modulator removed from transmission, draw 18 in. Hg. on vacuum pump attached to vacuum port of unit. Hold finger over end of control rod of modulator unit. When hose is removed, good modulator unit will push out on control rod due to internal spring pressure.

ENGINE VACUUM PRESSURE

1) If vacuum modulator is working properly and downshift linkage is adjusted correctly, all shifts should occur within certain road speed limits. See SHIFT SPEEDS tables. If shifts do not occur at proper points or slipping occurs during shifts, check engine vacuum, vacuum supply, and vacuum units for possible cause of problem.

2) Connect tachometer to engine. Connect vacuum gauge to manifold vacuum line, using "T" fitting at modulator hookup. Attach pressure gauge to control pressure outlet on transmission case. See Fig. 3. Plug for pressure take-off is located on left side of case just behind manual shift linkage.

CAUTION: **Pressure gauge affects quality of transmission shifting. When gauge is installed in transmission port, DO NOT accelerate or decelerate rapidly as transmission failure could occur.**

Automatic Transmissions
FORD MOTOR CO. A4LD (Cont.)

3) Apply parking brake firmly. Start engine. Adjust engine idle speed to correct RPM. If engine idle cannot be brought within limits, check throttle and downshift linkages for binding. Check for vacuum leaks in hoses and tubes if linkage is correctly in place. Check vacuum units such as power brake booster for leaks.

4) Vacuum reading at gauge should be steady with engine idling. Reading must be acceptable for altitude where test is being done. If vacuum reading is correct at idle, accelerate engine rapidly and release throttle immediately. Vacuum reading must drop rapidly during acceleration.

5) Vacuum should return as soon as throttle is released. If vacuum reading does not respond correctly, check lines for restriction or plugging. Also make sure that vacuum line is not hooked up to reservoir.

SHIFT SPEEDS (MPH)

NOTE: Figures given below are approximate. All shift speeds may vary somewhat due to production tolerances, rear axle ratio, or emission control equipment.

CONTROL PRESSURE TEST

NOTE: Governor can be checked at same time control pressure test is performed and in same manner.

1) Disconnect engine vacuum line from modulator unit. Hookup vacuum pump to unit. Apply parking and service brakes. Start engine and apply 15 in. Hg. vacuum to modulator. Select all ranges of transmission. Read and record control pressures.

2) Run engine up to 1000 RPM and set vacumm pump at 10 in. Hg. Read and record control pressures in 4 forward ranges. Keeping engine speed at 1000 RPM, reduce vacuum to 1 in. Hg. Read and record control pressures in 4 forward ranges and in Reverse range.

MODEL 85GT-ABA/ACA

Throttle	Range	Shift	OPS — R.P.M.	1	2	3	4	5
	Ⓓ, D	1-2	509-764	9-15	10-16	8-14	9-14	
	Ⓓ, D	2-3	713-1069	13-21	14-22	12-19	13-20	
Closed	Ⓓ	3-4	1832-2240	35-43	37-45	32-39	33-41	
Throttle	Ⓓ, D	CL	2036-2494	39-48	41-50	35-44	37-46	
10-15in.	Ⓓ, D	CU	See Note 1					
hg.	Ⓓ, D	4-3	814-1120	15-22	16-23	14-20	15-21	
Vacuum	Ⓓ, D	3-2	509-814	9-16	10-16	8-14	9-15	
	Ⓓ, D	2-1	356-560	6-11	7-11	6-10	6-11	
	1	2-1	1476-1781	28-34	29-36	25-31	27-33	
	Ⓓ, D	1-2	1425-1731	27-33	28-35	25-30	26-32	
	Ⓓ, D	2-3	2036-2341	39-45	41-47	35-41	37-43	
To Detent	Ⓓ, D	3-4*	2499-2804	48-54	50-56	43-49	45-52	
1.5in. hg.	Ⓓ, D	CL*	2433-2738	46-53	49-55	42-48	44-50	
Vacuum	Ⓓ, D	CU	See Note 1					
	Ⓓ	4-3	2647-2952	50-57	53-60	46-52	48-54	
	Ⓓ, D	3-2	1629-1934	31-37	32-39	28-34	29-36	
Through	Ⓓ, D	1-2	1832-2138	35-41	37-43	32-38	33-39	
Detent	Ⓓ, D	2-3	3156-3461	60-67	63-70	55-61	58-64	
WOT	Ⓓ, D	CL	See Note 1					
1.0in. hg.	Ⓓ, D	CU	See Note 1					
Vacuum	Ⓓ, D	3-2	2952-3258	56-63	59-66	51-57	54-60	
	Ⓓ, D	3-1	1527-1832	29-35	30-37	26-32	28-34	

* Check 3-4 upshift and converter clutch lock up at 7.0 in hg vacuum.
CL — Converter Clutch Lock Up
CU — Converter Clutch Unlock

MODEL 85GT-AGA/BAA

Throttle	Range	Shift	OPS — R.P.M.	1	2	3	4	5
	Ⓓ, D	1-2	458-712	8-14	9-14	8-13		
	Ⓓ, D	2-3	814-1221	15-24	16-25	15-23		
Closed	Ⓓ	3-4	1781-2290	34-44	36-46	33-43		
Throttle	Ⓓ, D	CL	1578-1985	30-38	31-40	29-37		
10-15in.	Ⓓ, D	CU	See Note 1					
hg.	Ⓓ, D	4-3	865-1170	16-23	17-24	16-22		
Vacuum	Ⓓ, D	3-2	458-763	8-15	9-15	8-14		
	Ⓓ, D	2-1	356-560	6-11	7-11	6-11		
	1	2-1	1527-1832	29-35	30-37	28-34		
	Ⓓ, D	1-2	1476-1781	28-34	30-36	27-33		
	Ⓓ, D	2-3	2087-2392	40-46	42-48	38-44		
To Detent	Ⓓ, D	3-4*	2372-2677	46-51	48-54	44-50		
2.0in. hg.	Ⓓ, D	CL*	1990-2296	38-44	40-47	36-43		
Vacuum	Ⓓ, D	CU	See Note 1					
	Ⓓ	4-3	2698-3003	51-58	54-60	50-56		
	Ⓓ, D	3-2	1680-1985	32-38	34-40	31-37		
Through	Ⓓ, D	1-2	1781-2087	34-40	36-42	33-39		
Detent	Ⓓ, D	2-3	3003-3308	57-64	61-67	56-61		
WOT	Ⓓ, D	CL	See Note 1					
2.0in. hg.	Ⓓ, D	CU	See Note 1					
Vacuum	Ⓓ, D	3-2	2850-3156	54-61	58-64	53-59		
	Ⓓ, D	3-1	1578-1883	30-36	32-38	29-35		

* Check 3-4 upshift and converter clutch lock up at 7.0 in hg vacuum.
CL — Converter Clutch Lock Up
CU — Converter Clutch Unlock

MODEL 85GT-AEA/ALA/AMA/BCA

Throttle	Range	Shift	OPS — R.P.M.	1	2	3	4	5
	Ⓓ, D	1-2	458-712	9-15	10-16	8-14	9-14	8-13
	Ⓓ, D	2-3	814-1221	16-26	17-27	15-24	16-25	15-23
Closed	Ⓓ	3-4	1781-2290	37-48	38-50	34-44	36-46	33-43
Throttle	Ⓓ, D	CL	1578-1985	32-41	34-43	30-38	31-40	29-37
10-15in.	Ⓓ, D	CU	See Note 1					
hg.	Ⓓ, D	4-3	865-1170	18-24	18-26	16-23	17-24	16-22
Vacuum	Ⓓ, D	3-2	458-763	9-16	10-17	8-15	9-15	8-14
	Ⓓ, D	2-1	356-560	7-12	7-12	6-11	7-11	6-11
	1	2-1	1527-1832	31-38	33-40	29-35	30-37	28-34
	Ⓓ, D	1-2	1476-1871	30-37	32-39	28-34	30-36	27-33
	Ⓓ, D	2-3	2087-2392	43-50	45-52	40-46	42-48	38-44
To Detent	Ⓓ	3-4*	2372-2677	49-56	51-58	46-51	48-54	44-50
2.0in.	Ⓓ, D	CL*	1990-2296	41-48	43-50	38-44	40-47	36-43
Vacuum	Ⓓ	CU	See Note 1					
	Ⓓ	4-3	2698-3003	56-63	59-66	51-58	54-60	50-56
	Ⓓ, D	3-2	1680-1985	34-41	36-43	32-38	34-40	31-37
Through	Ⓓ, D	1-2	1781-2087	37-44	38-46	34-40	36-42	33-39
Detent	Ⓓ, D	2-3	3003-3308	62-69	65-73	57-64	61-67	56-61
WOT	Ⓓ, D	CL	See Note 1					
2.0in. hg.	Ⓓ, D	CU	See Note 1					
Vacuum	Ⓓ, D	3-2	2850-3156	59-66	62-69	54-61	58-64	53-59
	Ⓓ, D	3-1	1578-1883	32-39	34-41	30-36	32-38	29-35

* Check 3-4 upshift and converter clutch lock up at 7.0 in hg vacuum.
CL — Converter Clutch Lock Up
CU — Converter Clutch Unlock

NOTE:

1 The converter clutch upshift/downshift is scheduled hydraulically but can be overridden electronically. The converter clutch is prevented from engaging or is disengaged during the following driving modes:

- engine coolant below 128°F or above 240°F
- application of brakes
- closed throttle
- heavy or W.O.T. throttle accelerations
- quick tip-ins
- quick tip-outs

- when the actual engine speed is below a certain value at lower vacuums (this ensures all 4-3 torque demands will be made on an unlocked converter).

Fig. 2: Gauge Hookup for Pressure Testing

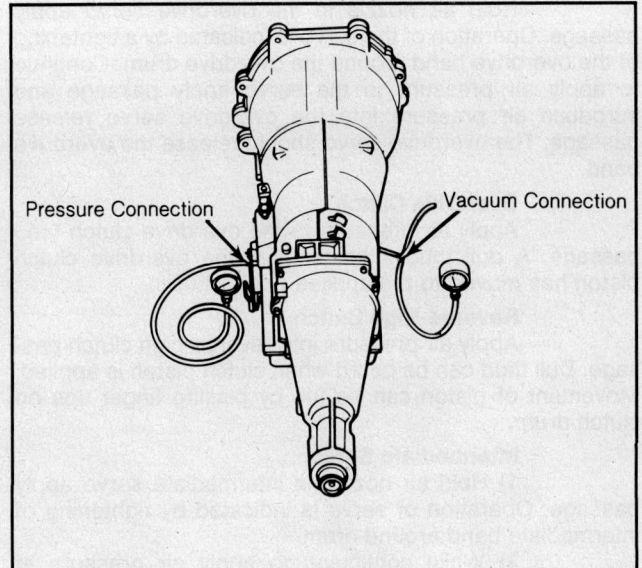

Pressure Connection

Vacuum Connection

CONTROL PRESSURE SPECIFICATIONS (psi)

Transmission Type	Transmission Model	Range	15" & Above	Idle 10"	WOT Stall Thru Detent
A4LD	85GT-ABA/ACA/ AEA/AGA/ALA/ AMA/BAA/BCA	OD*,D,2,1 R P,N	50-70 75-109 50-70	92-113 158-178	167-195 282-316
A4LD (Altitude)	85GT-ALA/AMA/BAA	OD,D,2,1 R P,N	50-60 66-78 50-60	70-93 122-145	144-177 247-282

*Absolute barometric pressure (ABP) 29.0-30.0
@Absolute barometric pressure (ABP) 24.0-25.0

CONTROL PRESSURE RESULTS

Compare recorded control pressures to control pressures listed in table. See CONTROL PRESSURE SPECIFICATIONS (psi) table. If control pressures are outside of specified ranges, use following list to determine cause of trouble:

High at Idle in All Ranges

Check engine EGR system, vacuum diaphragm unit and manifold vacuum line. Check throttle valve, control rod and regulator boost valves for sticking.

Low at Idle in All Ranges

Check engine EGR system. Check fluid level. Check for restricted intake screen or filter. Check for loose oil tubes. Check if valve body-to-case or regulator-to-case bolts are loose. Check for excessive leakage in oil pump, control valve body and case. Check control pressure regulator valve for sticking.

Normal at Idle; Low at 10 in. Hg

Check vacuum diaphragm unit. Control rod or throttle valve stuck.

Normal at Idle and 10 in. Hg; Low at 1 in. Hg

Check for excessive leakage, low pump capacity or restricted oil pan screen.

Low in "P" or "N"

Check valve body.

Low in "O/D"

Check forward clutch and/or overdrive servo.

Low in "D"

Check forward clutch and/or overdrive clutch.

Low in "2"

Check forward clutch or overdrive clutch and/or intermediate servo.

Low in "1"

Check forward clutch or overdeive clutch and/or reverse clutch and servo.

Low in "R"

Check reverse-high clutch or overdrive clutch and/or low and reverse servo.

CONVERTER CLUTCH TEST

NOTE: Engine coolant temperature must be above 128°F (53°C) and below 240°F (116°C). This temperature can be obtained after approximately 15 minutes of highway driving. Since most converter clutch shifts are difficult to feel a tachometer and/or vacuum gauge must be connected to the engine.

1) To check the converter for engagement to disengagement, drive the vehicle at approximately 50 MPH. While maintaining this speed tap the brake pedal with the left foot.

2) Engine RPM and vacuum should increase when the clutch disengages, with light brake pedal application. RPM will decrease when the pedal is released and the clutch engages.

3) If converter clutch does not engage, see appropriate AUTOMATIC TRANSMISSION TROUBLE SHOOTING article in DOMESTIC GENERAL SERVICING section.

GOVERNOR PRESSURE TEST

CAUTION: Never exceed 60 MPH speedometer reading during governor pressure test. After each test, move selector lever to Neutral and run engine at 1000 RPM to cool transmission.

1) Raise vehicle until rear wheels are clear of ground. Disconnect and plug vacuum line to vacuum diaphragm unit. Connect hand-held vacuum pump to diaphragm unit.

2) Place transmission in "D2". Apply 10 in. Hg to diaphragm unit with no load on engine. Increase speed slowly and watch speedometer. Note speed at which control pressure cut-back occurs. It should occur between 8-11 MPH.

3) Decrease vacuum to 0-2 in. Hg and repeat test. Control pressure cut-back should occur at 9-13 MPH. Governor is okay if cut-back occurs as specified. If not, check shift speeds to verify that problem is in governor and not due to stuck cut-back valve. Repair or replace governor.

STALL TEST

Testing Precautions

1) Engine coolant and transmission fluid must be at proper levels and operating temperatures. T.V. linkage must be set properly. Hold accelerator down just long enough to get stable tachometer reading. Do not floor accelerator for more than 5 seconds.

2) Do not exceed maximum specified RPM for vehicle. Before shifting into each selector position, run engine in "N" at 1000 RPM for 15 to 20 seconds to cool

transmission. If engine speed exceeds upper specification, release accelerator immediately as this is an indication of clutch or band slippage.

Testing Procedure

1) Connect tachometer to engine. Apply parking and service brakes firmly. Place selector lever in "O/D" position, and push accelerator completely to floor. Record tachometer reading.

2) Engine speed should be within specifications given in STALL SPEEDS table. Repeat procedure in "D", "2", "1", and "R" positions.

STALL SPEEDS

Application	Stall RPM
2.3L	2331-2704
2.8L	2497-2943

STALL TEST RESULTS

Low in All Ranges

Poor engine performance. Faulty torque converter stator one-way clutch.

High in All Ranges

General transmission problems are indicated. Perform control pressure tests.

High in "O/D" Only

Forward clutch faulty.

High in "O/D", "D" & "1"

Overdrive one-way clutch and/or rear one-way clutch faulty.

High in "D", "2" & "1"

Forward clutch and/or overdrive clutch faulty.

High in "2" Only

Overdrive one-way clutch or intermediate band or servo faulty.

High in "1" Only

Low/Reverse band or servo faulty.

High in "R" Only

Overdrive clutch, overdrive one-way clutch, reverse and high clutch, low/reverse band or servo faulty.

AIR PRESSURE CHECKS

1) Condition of "No Drive" (no movement of output shaft) can exist, even with correct transmission fluid pressure. Inoperative clutches or bands may cause this problem.

2) Inoperative units can be located through series of checks by substituting air pressure for fluid pressure to determine location of malfunction.

3) Loosen oil pan bolts and allow transmission fluid to drain. Remove oil pan and control valve body. Apply air at points noted in *Fig. 3*. Check unit operation as follows:

Forward Clutch

Apply air pressure into forward clutch passage. Dull thud can be heard when clutch piston is applied. Movement of piston can be felt by placing finger tips on input shell if no thud heard.

Governor

Apply air pressure into control pressure-to-governor passage. Listen for sharp clicking or whistling noise indicating governor valve movement.

Overdrive Servo

Hold air nozzle in the overdrive servo apply passage. Operation of the servo is indicated by a tightening of the overdrive band around the overdrive drum. Continue to apply air pressure to the servo apply passage and introduce air pressure into the overdrive servo release passage. The overdrive servo should release the overdrive band.

Overdrive Clutch

Apply air pressure to the overdrive clutch feed passage. A dull thud indicates that the overdrive clutch piston has moved to the applied position.

Reverse-High Clutch

Apply air pressure into reverse-high clutch passage. Dull thud can be heard when clutch piston is applied. Movement of piston can be felt by placing finger tips on clutch drum.

Intermediate Servo

1) Hold air nozzle in intermediate servo apply passage. Operation of servo is indicated by tightening of intermediate band around drum.

2) While continuing to apply air pressure at servo apply passage, apply air pressure to intermediate servo release passage. Intermediate servo should then release band against pressure in apply passage.

Low-Reverse Servo

Apply air pressure to low-reverse servo apply passage. Low-reverse band should tighten around drum if servo is operating properly.

NOTE: If air pressure applied to either clutch passages fails to operate clutch, or operates both clutches at once, remove and check fluid passages in case and oil pump. Use air pressure to detect obstructions.

SERVICE (IN VEHICLE)

CONTROL VALVE BODY

Removal

Remove oil pan, filter screen and gasket. Remove rear servo cover and gasket. Remove valve body retaining bolts. Carefully ease valve body from case while unlocking and detaching selector lever connecting rod.

NOTE: Note size and location of valve body retaining bolts. Bolts are of different sizes and must be replaced in proper position at reassembly.

Installation

1) Attach and lock selector lever connecting rod ("Z" link) to manual valve. Ease control valve body to case. Install and tighten valve body retaining bolts. Install detent spring, hooking it to valve body bolt at upper right in *Fig. 5*.

2) Install rear servo cover with new gasket. Clean filter screen. Install filter screen and gasket. Install oil pan using new gasket. Tighten pan bolts evenly. Lower vehicle and fill transmission with 3 quarts of fluid. Start engine and add fluid as necessary. Check for leaks.

REAR SERVO

Removal

With oil pan and filter screen removed, remove rear servo cover retaining bolts, cover, gasket, servo piston, and spring.

Fig. 3: Bottom View of Transmission Case

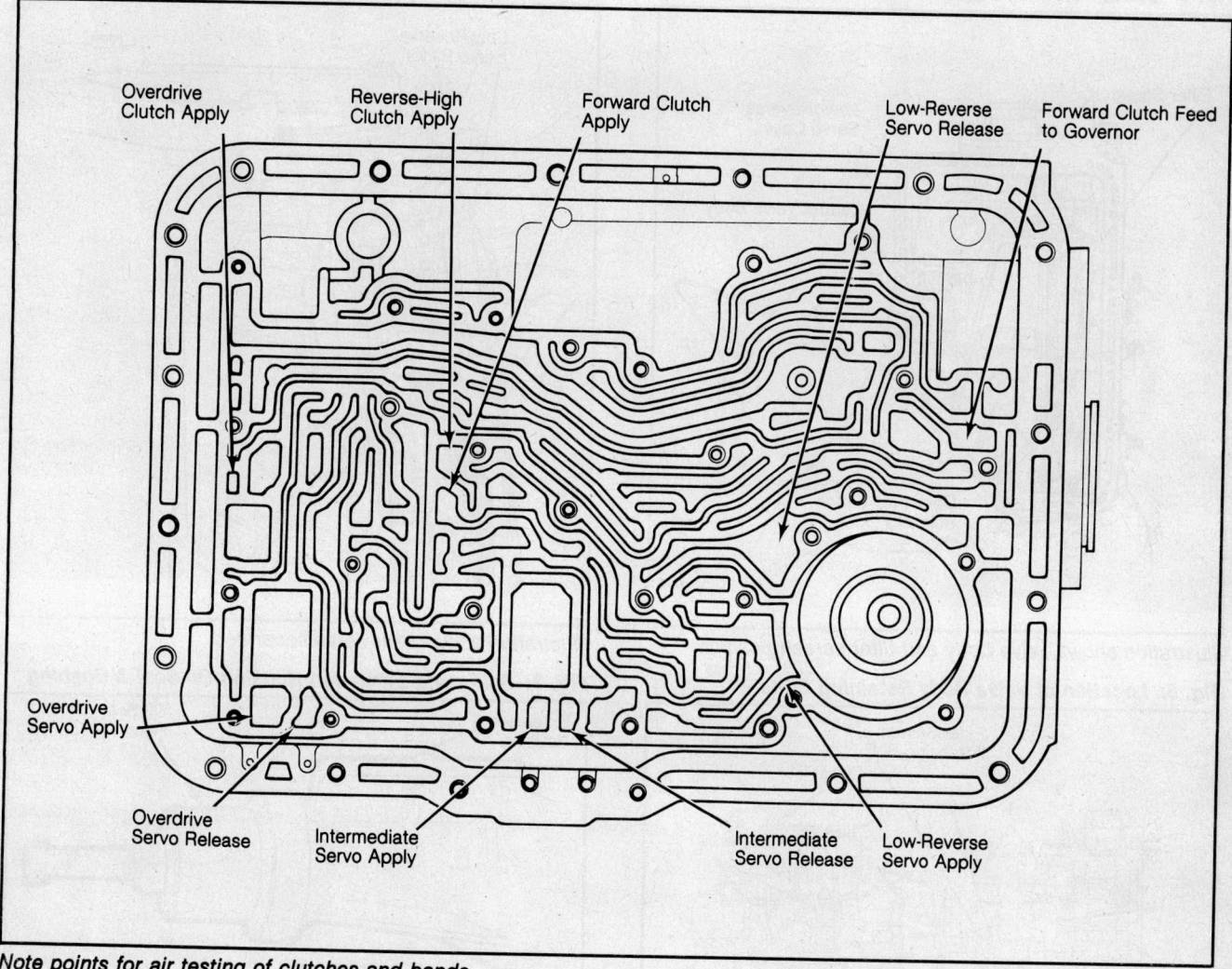

Note points for air testing of clutches and bands.

NOTE: Force of servo spring will push cover off.

Installation
Reverse removal procedure.

EXTENSION HOUSING REAR SEAL & BUSHING
Removal

1) Raise and support vehicle. Mark propeller shaft end yoke and rear axle companion flange for reassembly reference. Remove propeller shaft.

2) Remove extension housing rear oil seal and bushing using Pullers (T71P-7657-A for seal and T77L-7697-E for bushing). See Fig. 7.

Installation

Check sealing surface of yoke for scoring. Replace if scoring found. Check housing counterbore for burrs and remove with crocus cloth if necessary. Drive new bushing and oil seal into extension housing using Drivers (T77L-7697-F for bushing and T74P-77052-A for oil seal). Install propeller shaft, aligning reference marks made at removal.

EXTENSION HOUSING
Removal

1) Raise and support vehicle. Mark propeller shaft for installation reference. Remove shaft. Disconnect speedometer cable from extension housing. Support transmission with jack.

2) Remove rear support-to-crossmember bolts. Raise transmission slightly and remove rear support from extension housing.

3) Loosen extension housing retaining bolts and allow transmission fluid to drain. Remove bolts and slide extension housing off output shaft.

Installation

Use new gasket. Position extension housing on case. Pay special attention to correctly seating operating rod parking notch. Install and tighten bolts. To complete installation, reverse removal procedure.

GOVERNOR
Removal

Remove extension housing as previously described. Remove governor body-to-oil collector body retaining bolts. Remove governor body, valve, spring, and weight from collector body. See Fig. 8.

Automatic Transmissions
FORD MOTOR CO. A4LD (Cont.)

Fig. 4: Bottom View of Case

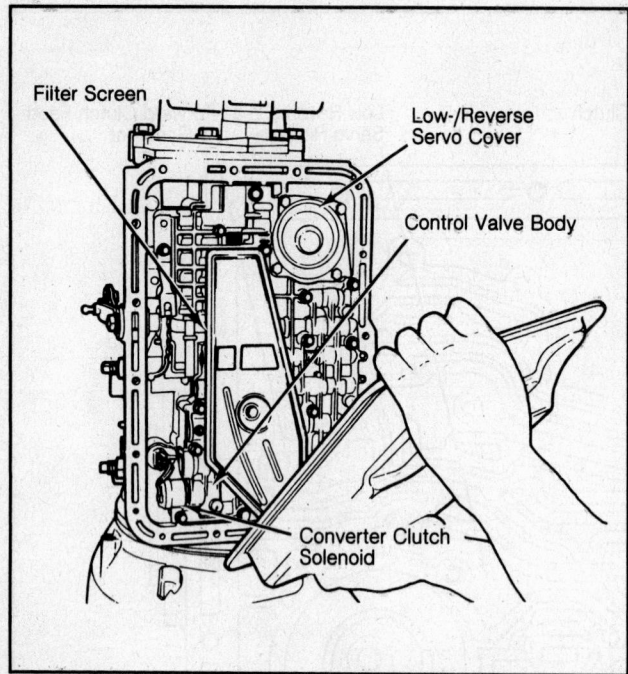

Illustration shows valve body and filter screen position

Fig. 5: Location of Valve Body Retaining Bolts

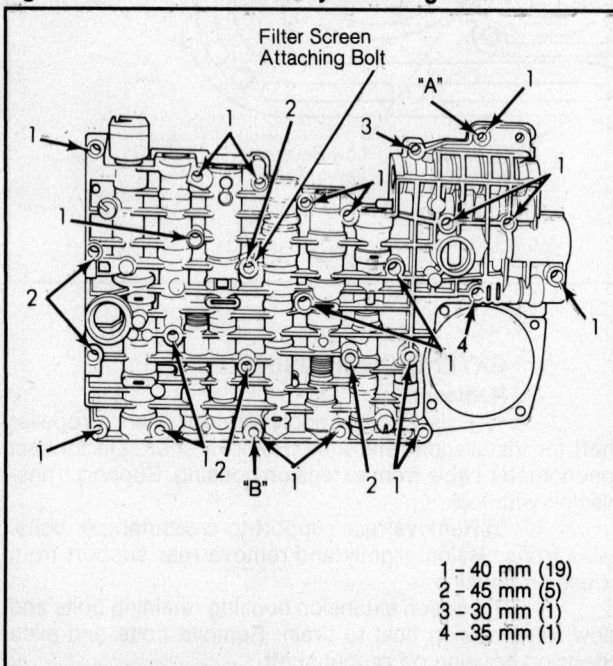

1 – 40 mm (19)	
2 – 45 mm (5)	
3 – 30 mm (1)	
4 – 35 mm (1)	

Use "A" and "B" bolts for locating valve body. Bolts must go into original locations.

NOTE: Components are not retained once governor body bolts have been removed. It is necessary to hold body and components while removing and installing governor.

Installation
Assemble governor body and components. Position body over oil feed holes of oil collector body. Install retaining bolts. Install extension housing.

Fig. 6: Bottom View of Transmission Case

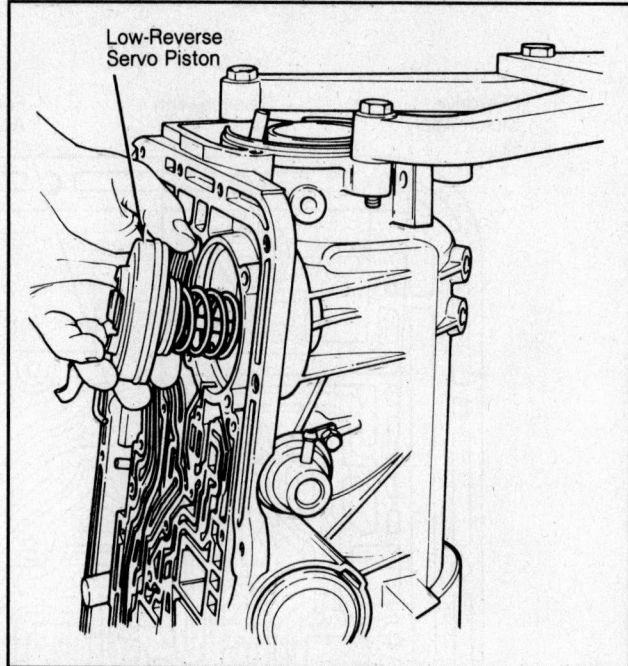

Illustration shows rear servo separated.

Fig. 7: Removing Extension Housing Oil Seal & Bushing

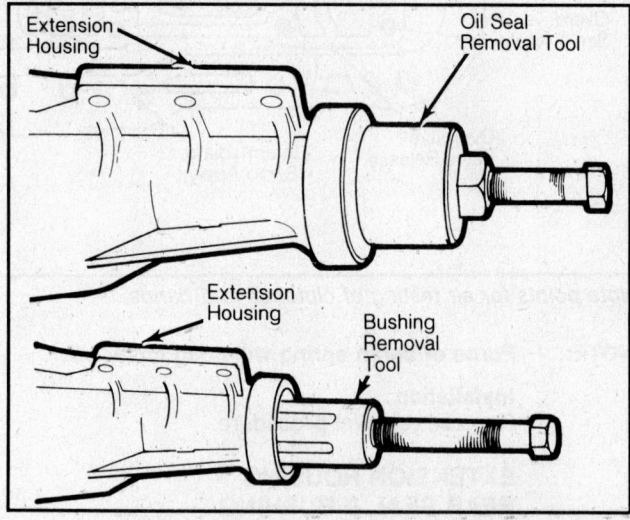

VACUUM DIAPHRAGM ASSEMBLY
Removal
Disconnect hoses from unit. Remove retaining bracket (do not pry or bend bracket). Remove vacuum diaphragm, actuating pin and throttle valve from case. Remove "O" ring from assembly. See Fig. 10.

Installation
Install new "O" ring. Install throttle valve, actuating pin and vacuum diaphragm (with tube pointing rearward). Install retaining bracket and tighten bolt.

REMOVAL & INSTALLATION

TRANSMISSION
See appropriate AUTOMATIC TRANSMISSION REMOVAL article in DOMESTIC GENERAL SERVICING section.

Fig. 8: Removing Governor Assembly

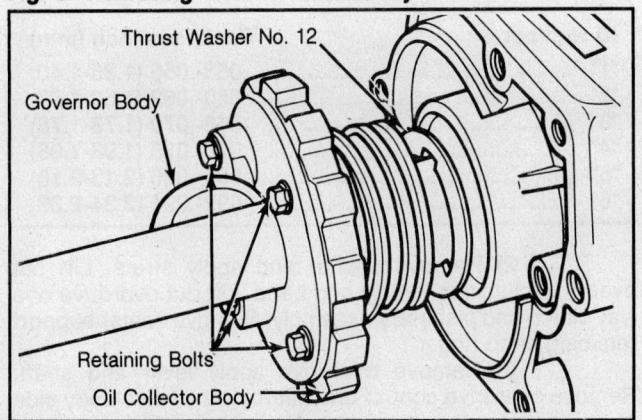

Fig. 10: Side View of Transmission Case

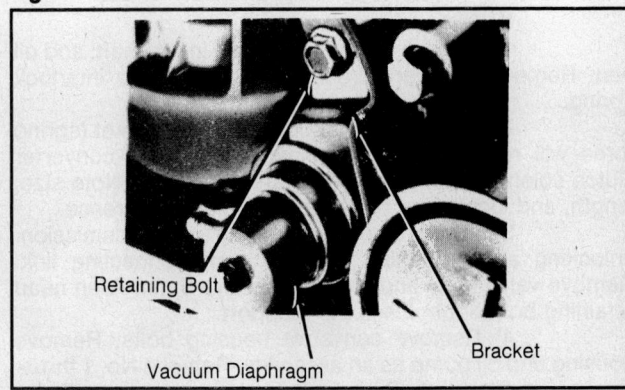

Illustration shows vacuum diaphragm installed.

TORQUE CONVERTER

LEAKAGE CHECK
See procedure given in FORD C-6 article.

FLUSHING CONVERTER
See procedure given in FORD C-6 article.

TURBINE & STATOR END PLAY CHECK
See procedure given in FORD C-6 article.

STATOR ONE-WAY CLUTCH CHECK
See procedure given in FORD C-6 article.

STATOR INTERFERENCE CHECKS
See procedure given in FORD C-6 article.

TRANSMISSION DISASSEMBLY

NOTE: There are 10 thrust washers and 2 thrust bearing being used in this transmission, with No. 1 at front pump and No. 12 at governor. Note that No. 2 and No. 8 are needle roller bearings performing thrust function. Refer to Fig. 12 for identification and location of thrust washers.

Fig. 9: Cutaway View of Transmission Showing Thrust Washer Identification and Location

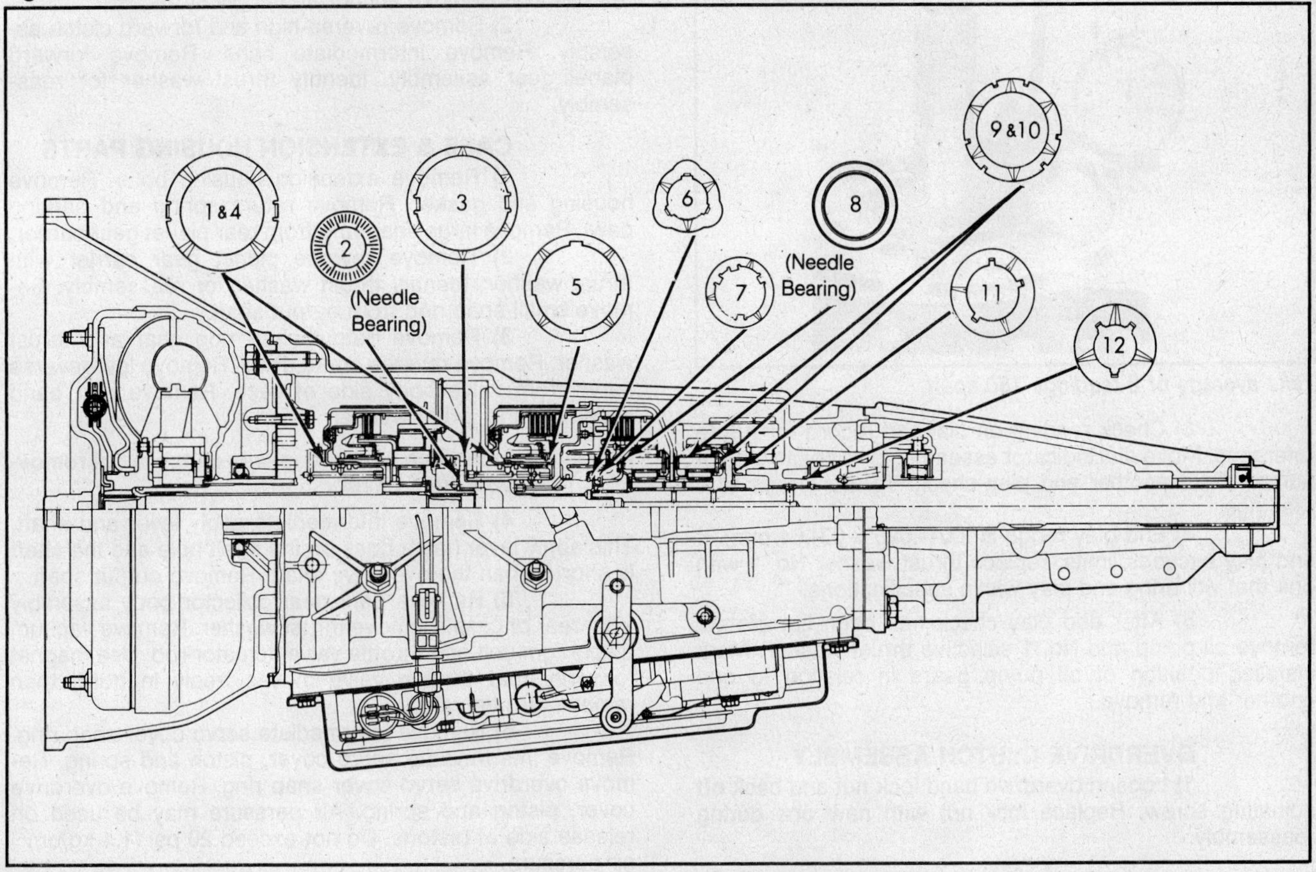

REAR SERVO, VALVE BODY & OIL PUMP

1) Remove torque converter, input shaft, and oil pan. Remove oil filter screen, gasket. Remove interlock spring.

2) Remove rear servo cover and gasket (spring force will raise cover). Disconnect 2 wires at converter clutch solenoid. Remove bolts from valve body. Note size, length, and location of bolts for reassembly reference.

3) Slowly remove valve body from transmission, unlocking and detaching selector lever connecting link. Remove valve body and gasket. Remove 5 mm Allen head retaining bolt that holds center support.

4) Remove converter housing bolts. Remove housing and oil pump as an assembly. Remove No. 1 thrust washer and gasket. Remove oil pump seal with Puller (T74P-77248-A). Remove oil pump from converter housing. Remove steel plate (behind oil seal) with "O" ring.

NOTE: Before continuing with disassembly, transmission end play should be measured.

TRANSMISSION END PLAY CHECK

1) Install oil pump (without gasket) and existing No. 1 thrust washer into transmission case. Make sure pump body is below case gasket surface.

2) Mount dial indicator on oil pump with plunger resting on transmission housing. *See Fig. 11.* Zero dial indicator, then swing indicator around so plunger contacts oil pump.

Fig. 11: Tool Set-Up for Transmission End Play Check

Take average of 2 readings 180 apart.

3) Check reading on dial and record for future reference. Move dial indicator assembly to opposite side of pump. Make another end play check. Take average of 2 readings.

4) End play range is .001-.025" (.03-.64 mm). If end play exceeds limits, replace thrust washer No. 1 with one that will bring end play within specifications.

5) After end play check has been completed, remove oil pump and No. 1 selective thrust washer. Mark installed position of oil pump gears in relation to one another and remove.

OVERDRIVE CLUTCH ASSEMBLY

1) Loosen overdrive band lock nut and back off adjusting screw. Replace lock nut with new one during reassembly.

SELECTIVE THRUST WASHER NO. 1

ID Number	Thickness Inch (mm)
"1"	.053-.055 (1.35-1.40)
"2"	.060-.062 (1.52-1.57)
"3"	.068-.070 (1.73-1.78)
"4"	.076-.078 (1.93-1.98)
"5"	.084-.086 (2.13-2.18)
"6"	.092-.094 (2.34-2.39)

2) Remove anchor and apply struts. Lift out overdrive clutch assembly and band. Lift out overdrive one way clutch and planetary assembly. Remove center support retaining snap ring.

3) Remove overdrive apply lever and shaft. Remove overdrive control bracket from the valve body side of case.

NOTE: The overdrive apply lever does not have a boss on the shaft hole as compared to the intermediate apply lever. The overdrive apply lever shaft is longer as compared to the intermediate apply lever shaft.

4) Remove thrust washer on top of center support. Identify thrust washer for reassembly.

5) Remove center support being careful to pry upward evenly. Remove thrust washer below center support. Identify thrust washer for reassembly.

REVERSE-HIGH & FORWARD CLUTCH ASSEMBLY

1) Loosen intermediate band lock nut and back off adjusting screw. Replace lock nut with new one during reassembly. Remove anchor and apply struts.

2) Remove reverse-high and forward clutch assembly. Remove intermediate band. Remove forward planet gear assembly. Identify thrust washer for reassembly.

CASE & EXTENSION HOUSING PARTS

1) Remove extension housing bolts. Remove housing and gasket. Remove return spring and parking pawl. Remove large snap ring from rear planet gear carrier.

2) Remove reverse planet gear carrier with thrust washer. Identify thrust washer for reassembly. Remove small snap ring from output shaft.

3) Remove output shaft ring gear and thrust washer. Remove reverse brake drum. Remove low-reverse servo from valve body side of case. Remove rear band assembly and thrust washer.

NOTE: Inner race of rear one-way clutch is not removable from case.

4) Remove intermediate apply lever and shaft. This apply lever has a boss on the shaft hole and the shaft is shorter than the overdrive shaft. Remove output shaft.

5) Remove park gear/collector body assembly from rear of case. Remove thrust washer. Remove vacuum diaphragm unit and throttle valve actuator rod. Use magnet to verify that throttle valve moves freely in bore, then remove throttle valve.

6) Remove intermediate servo cover snap ring. Remove intermediate servo cover, piston and spring. Remove overdrive servo cover snap ring. Remove overdrive cover, piston and spring. Air perssure may be used on release side of pistons. Do not exceed 20 psi (1.4 kg/cm²) air perssure.

Fig. 12: Exploded View of Forward Gear Train

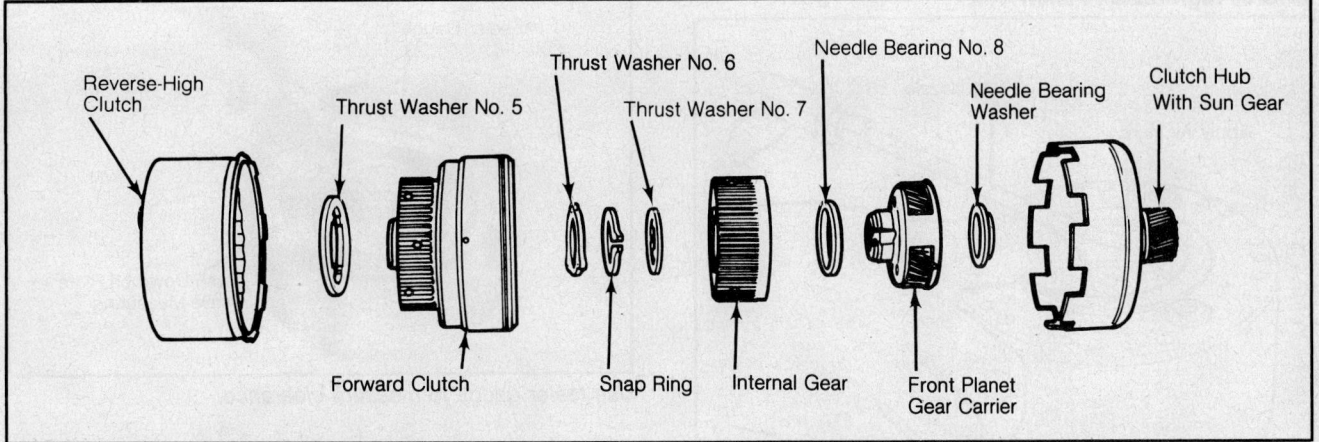

(Labels: Reverse-High Clutch, Thrust Washer No. 5, Thrust Washer No. 6, Thrust Washer No. 7, Needle Bearing No. 8, Needle Bearing Washer, Clutch Hub With Sun Gear, Forward Clutch, Snap Ring, Internal Gear, Front Planet Gear Carrier)

7) Remove neutral safety switch. Use thin-walled socket to remove neutral safety switch. Open-end wrench will crush switch. Remove kickdown lever nut, lever and "O" ring seal.

8) Remove linkage centering pin. Remove manual lever, internal kickdown lever and park pawl rod and detent plate assembly. Remove lever shaft oil seal.

9) Remove torque converter clutch solenoid connector. A tab on the outside of the case on backside of connector must be depressed while pulling with pliers. The tab is depressed with a small pair of locking pliers.

NOTE: The clutch solenoid connector does not need to be removed unless it is to be replaced and/or if the case is immersed in degreaser.

COMPONENT DISASSEMBLY & REASSEMBLY

OVERDRIVE CLUTCH
Disassembly
Disassembly of the overdrive clutch is the same as the reverse-high clutch except for removing the clutch piston. The piston is removed by air pressure. Use finger to close off air leak.

Reassembly
1) Reassembly of the overdrive clutch is the same as the reverse-high clutch with the exception of the following.

2) Install clutch plates beginning with a steel plate, then alternate friction, steel, friction the pressure plate and retaining clip. Use feeler gauge to check the clearance between the retaining ring and pressure plate.

3) Clearance should be between .026"-.053". Selective snap rings are available in following thicknesses: .054", .068", .082", and .096" (1.37, 1.73, 2.08, and 2.44 mm).

FORWARD GEAR TRAIN ASSEMBLY
Remove clutch hub and sun gear. Remove front planet gear carrier with internal gear and needle bearing No. 8. If necessary, remove sun gear from input shell after removing retainer. Replace thrust washer No. 9 if damaged. Remove forward drive clutch and thrust washer No. 5

NOTE: Reassembly of forward gear train assembly is covered at end of COMPONENT DISASSEMBLY and REASSEMBLY.

REVERSE-HIGH CLUTCH
Disassembly
1) Remove large pressure plate retaining ring. Remove pressure plate and clutch pack. Using Spring Compressor (T65L-77515-A), compress piston return springs and remove small retaining ring. *See Fig. 13.* Carefully release pressure on springs.

Fig. 13: Compressing Piston Return Springs and Retainer

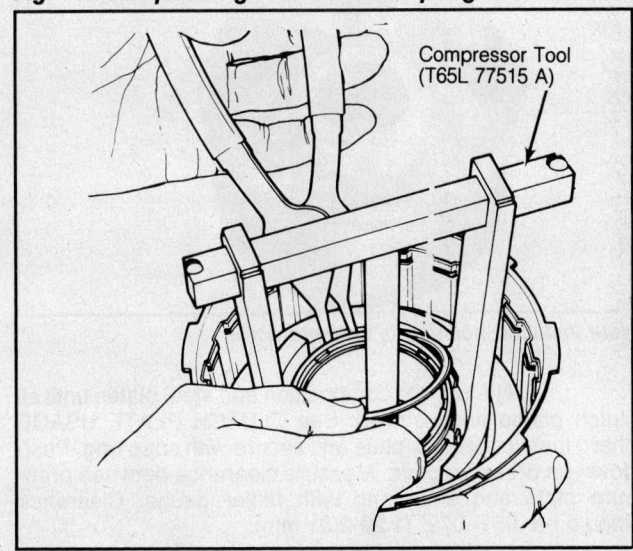

(Label: Compressor Tool (T65L 77515 A))

2) Remove spring retainer and return springs. Turn clutch body over and carefully force out piston with compressed air. *See Fig. 14.* Remove "O" rings from piston and clutch body.

Reassembly
1) Inspect all parts for wear, damage, or effects of overheating. If new composition clutch plates are to be used, soak in transmission fluid for 30 minutes before installing.

2) Install new "O" rings on piston and clutch body. Carefully install clutch piston, using Seal Protectors (T74P-77404-A and B) to protect inner and outer seals. *See Fig. 17.*

3) Install 20 piston return springs and spring retainer. Compress springs with tool used at disassembly. Install snap ring and remove compressing tool. Install clutch plates, starting with steel plate.

Fig. 14: Using Compressed Air to Remove Reverse-High Clutch Piston

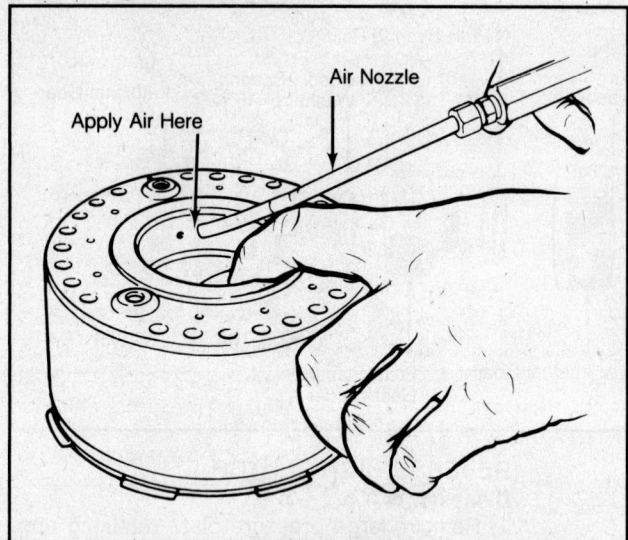

Fig. 15: Reverse-High Clutch Piston Installation

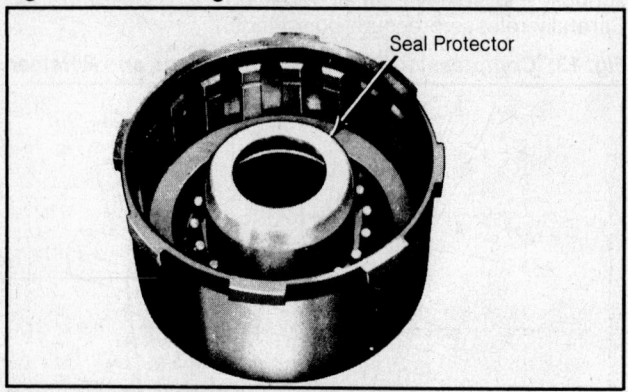

Note installed position of seal protector.

4) Alternate composition and steel plates until all clutch plates are installed. See CLUTCH PLATE USAGE chart. Install pressure plate and secure with snap ring. Push down on pressure plate. Measure clearance between pressure plate and snap ring with feeler gauge. Clearance should be .051-.079" (1.29-2.01 mm).

5) If clearance is not within specifications, install correct thickness selective snap ring. Reverse-High clutch selective snap rings are available in following thicknesses: .054", .068", .082" and .096" (1.37, 1.73, 2.08 and 2.44 mm).

FORWARD CLUTCH
Disassembly
1) Remove large retaining ring. Lift out pressure plate, clutch pack, and rubber cushion spring. Using Spring Compressor (T65L-77515-A), compress piston return springs. Remove small retaining ring. *See Fig. 18.*

2) Carefully release pressure on springs. Remove spring retainer and springs. Using compressed air, carefully force clutch piston from clutch body. Remove "O" rings from piston and clutch body.

Reassembly
1) Inspect all parts for wear, damage, or effects of overheating. If new composition clutch plates are to be

Fig. 16: Clutch Pressure Plate Clearance

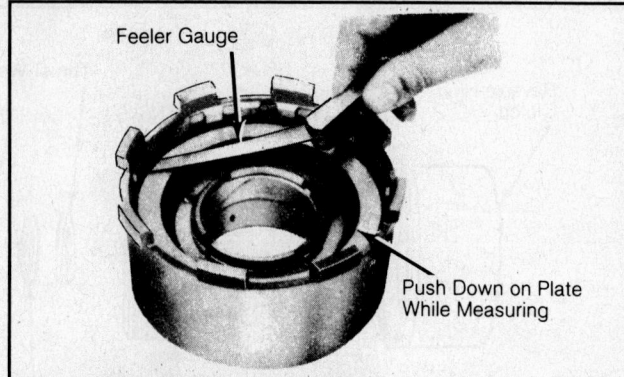

Use feeler gauge to measure clearance.

CLUTCH PLATE USAGE

Application	Composition Plates	Steel Plates
2.3L & 2.8L Forward Clutch	5	5
2.3L Reverse-High Clutch	4	4
2.8L Reverse-High Clutch	5	5
2.3L & 2.8L Overdrive Clutch	2	2

used, soak in transmission fluid for 30 minutes before installing.

2) Use Protective Tool (T74P-77548-A and B) to prevent damage to inner and outer seals. Install new "O" rings. Apply petroleum jelly to rings and to shoulder at clutch stub. Carefully install piston.

3) Install 15 piston return springs and spring retainer. Compress springs with tool used at disassembly. Install snap ring and remove tool.

4) Install rubber cushion in groove on outer face of hydraulic piston. Install clutch plates. Start with steel plate. Alternate composition and steel plates until all clutch plates are installed. See CLUTCH PLATE USAGE chart.

5) Install pressure plate and large retainer ring. Measure clearance between retainer ring and pressure plate following procedures given for Reverse-High clutch. Clearance for forward clutch is .055-.083" (1.39-2.11 mm).

6) Install new steel seals on clutch hub. Forward clutch selective snap rings are available in following thicknesses: .054", .068", .082" and .096" (1.37, 1.73, 2.08 and 2.44 mm).

INTERNAL GEAR & PLANET GEAR ASSEMBLY
Disassembly
Remove snap ring, planet gear carrier internal gear, and thrust washer No. 7. Separate planet gear carrier from internal gear. Remove needle bearing No. 8.

Reassembly
Insert planet gear carrier with needle bearing No. 8 into internal gear. Position thrust washer No. 7 in place and secure with new snap ring. Make sure internal gear is free from planet gear carrier.

Fig. 17: Exploded View of Reverse-High Clutch Assembly

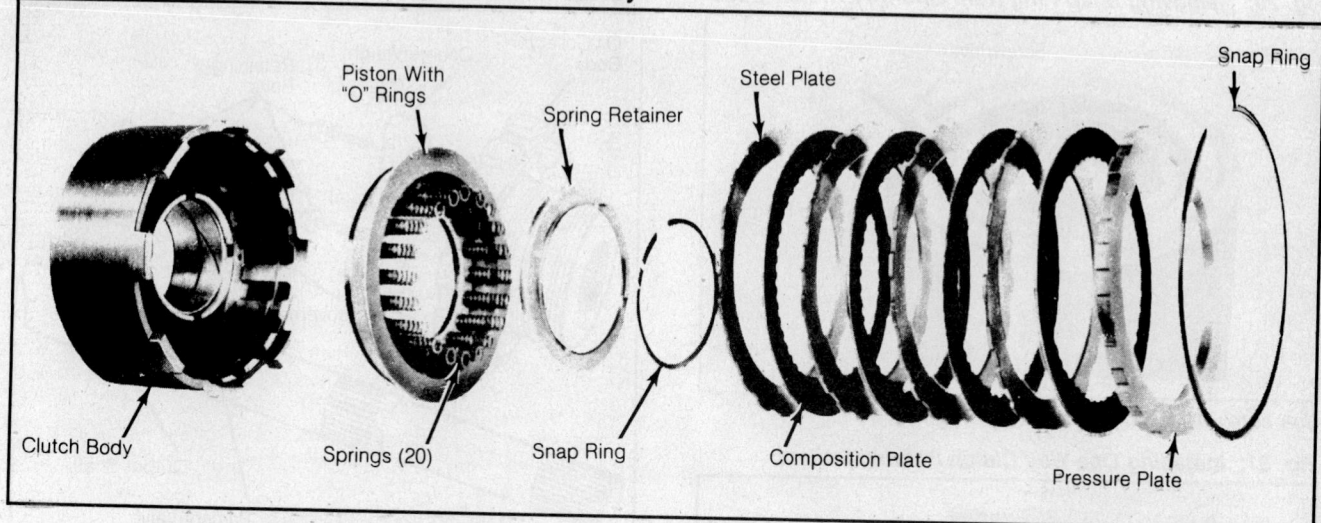

Snap Ring

Piston With "O" Rings

Spring Retainer

Steel Plate

Clutch Body

Springs (20)

Snap Ring

Composition Plate

Pressure Plate

FORWARD GEAR TRAIN ASSEMBLY
Reassembly

1) Place reverse-high clutch assembly on bench in vertical position. Install thrust washer No. 5 and forward gear clutch assembly. Position thrust washer No. 6 on planet gear carrier and retain with petroleum jelly. See Fig. 12.

2) Install internal gears and planet gear assembly. Assemble input shell with sun gear to planet gear carrier. Install assembled unit to reverse-direct clutch body.

ONE-WAY CLUTCH
Disassembly

Using screwdriver, remove snap ring. See Fig. 20. Lift out cage with springs and bearing rollers as unit.

Reassembly

Inspect all parts for wear or damage. Install cage with springs. Insert bearing rollers one by one. Use screwdriver to compress springs. Install snap ring. See Fig. 21.

GOVERNOR
Disassembly

Remove governor body-to-oil collector body retaining bolts. When these bolts are removed, governor

Fig. 19: Positioning of Seal Protectors for Forward Clutch Piston Installation

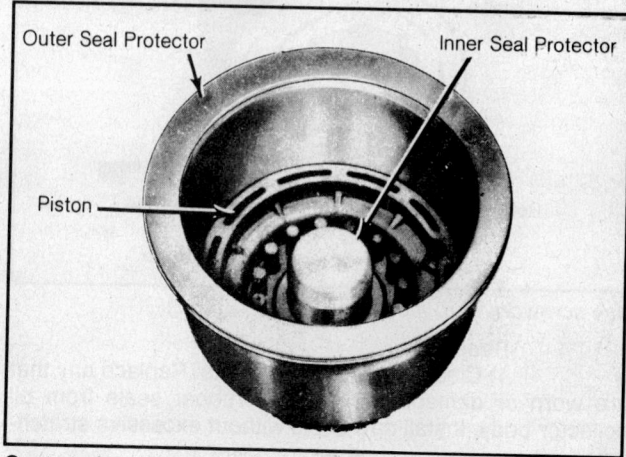

Outer Seal Protector

Inner Seal Protector

Piston

Coat seals with petroleum jelly before installing.

components are no longer retained in position in body. Care must be taken not to drop governor body and components when bolts are removed. Remove components from governor body. Remove counterweight.

Fig. 18: Exploded View of Forward Clutch Assembly

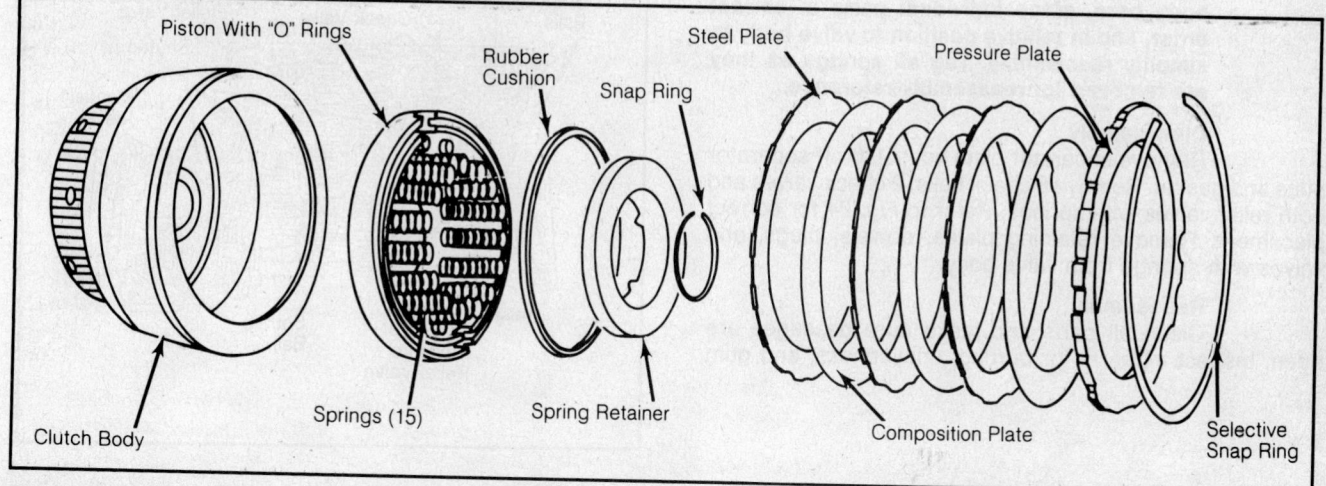

Piston With "O" Rings

Rubber Cushion

Snap Ring

Steel Plate

Pressure Plate

Clutch Body

Springs (15)

Spring Retainer

Composition Plate

Selective Snap Ring

Automatic Transmissions
FORD MOTOR CO. A4LD (Cont.)

Fig. 20: Removing Snap Ring from One-Way Clutch Cage

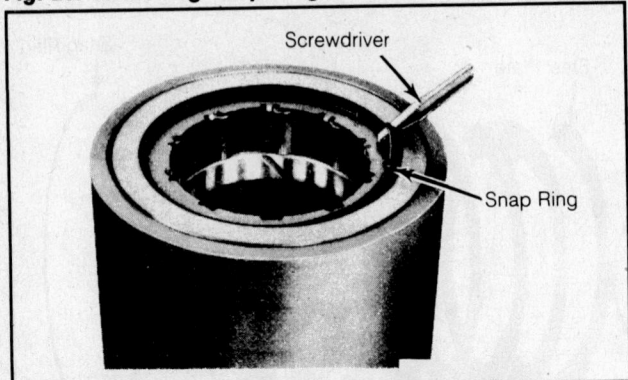

Use screwdriver to remove snap ring.

Fig. 21: Installing One-Way Clutch Bearing Rollers

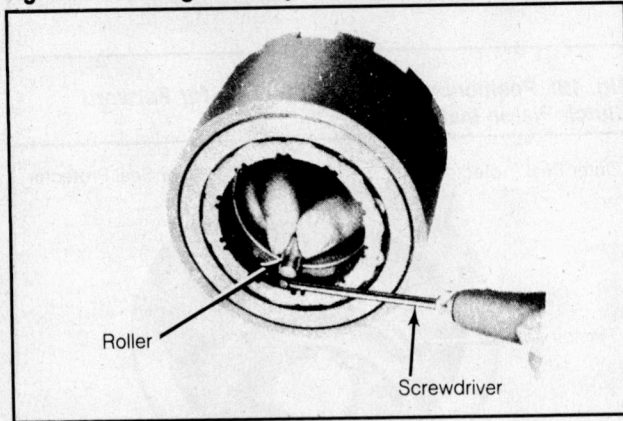

Use screwdriver to install rollers.

Reassembly

1) Clean and inspect all parts. Replace any that are worn or damaged. Remove 3 rubber seals from oil collector body. Install new seals without excessive stretching.

2) Assemble counterweight spring and primary valve in governor body. Assemble governor body and counterweight to oil collector body. *See Fig. 22.*

CONTROL VALVE BODY

NOTE: As valve trains are removed from each valve body bore, place individual parts in correct order, and in relative position to valve body to simplify reassembly. Tag all springs as they are removed for reassembly reference.

Disassembly

Remove separator plate bolts. Lift off separator plate and gasket. Remove 6 check balls, 2 check valves and both relief valves with springs. Refer to *Fig. 24* for correct placement. Remove retaining plates, dowels, plugs, and valves with springs from valve body.

Reassembly

Clean all parts and make sure passages are open. Inspect all parts for burring, unevenness, and gum

Fig. 22: Exploded View of Governor Assembly

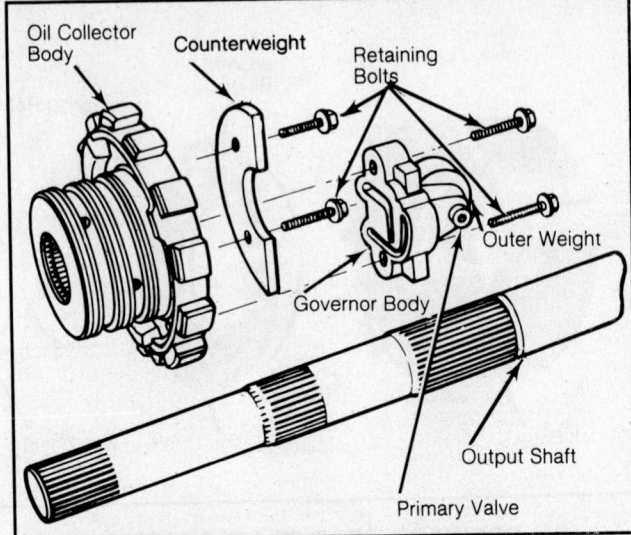

Attaching bolts also hold governor components together.

Fig. 23: Valve Body Separator Plate and Bolt Locations

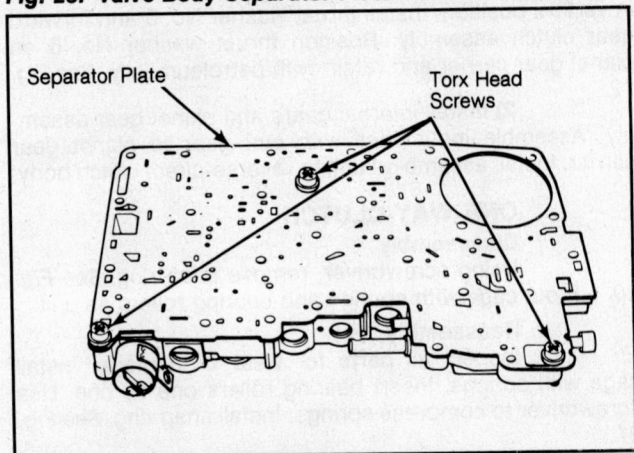

Fig. 24: Locations of Check Balls, Check Valves and Pressure Relief Valves in Valve Body

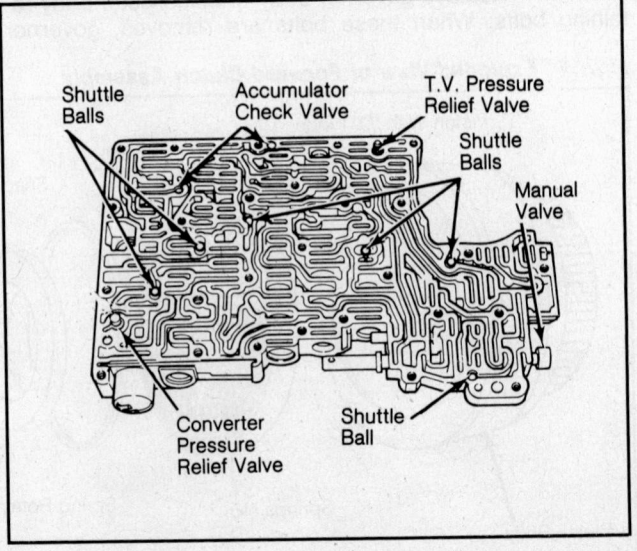

Fig. 25: Valve Body Assembly

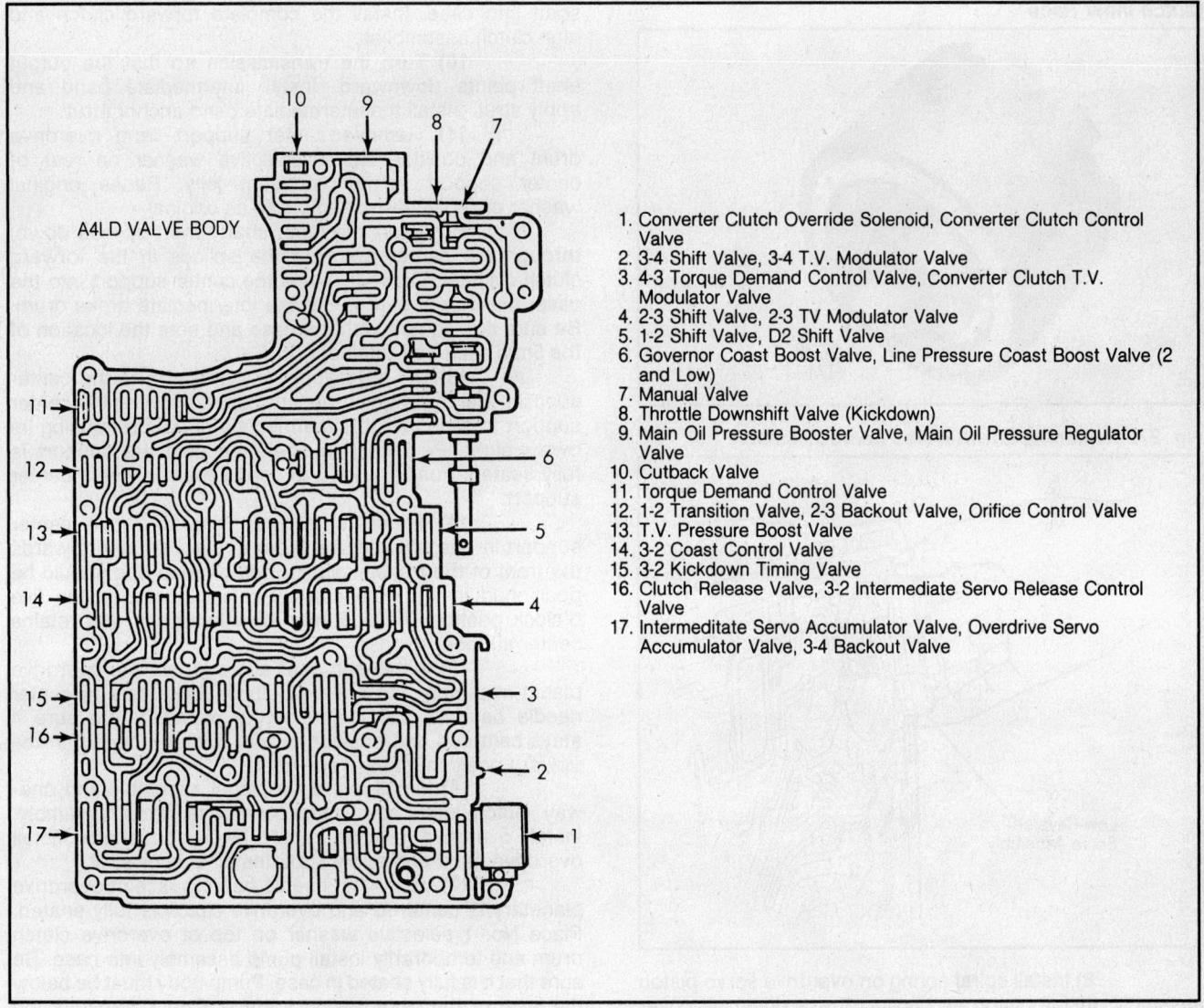

A4LD VALVE BODY

1. Converter Clutch Override Solenoid, Converter Clutch Control Valve
2. 3-4 Shift Valve, 3-4 T.V. Modulator Valve
3. 4-3 Torque Demand Control Valve, Converter Clutch T.V. Modulator Valve
4. 2-3 Shift Valve, 2-3 TV Modulator Valve
5. 1-2 Shift Valve, D2 Shift Valve
6. Governor Coast Boost Valve, Line Pressure Coast Boost Valve (2 and Low)
7. Manual Valve
8. Throttle Downshift Valve (Kickdown)
9. Main Oil Pressure Booster Valve, Main Oil Pressure Regulator Valve
10. Cutback Valve
11. Torque Demand Control Valve
12. 1-2 Transition Valve, 2-3 Backout Valve, Orifice Control Valve
13. T.V. Pressure Boost Valve
14. 3-2 Coast Control Valve
15. 3-2 Kickdown Timing Valve
16. Clutch Release Valve, 3-2 Intermediate Servo Release Control Valve
17. Intermeditate Servo Accumulator Valve, Overdrive Servo Accumulator Valve, 3-4 Backout Valve

deposits. Lubricate all parts with transmission fluid. Install valves, springs, plugs, and pins. *See Fig. 25.* Using new gasket, install separator plate.

TRANSMISSION REASSEMBLY

NOTE: **Lubricate all parts with transmission fluid before reassembly. Thrust washers and gaskets should be held in place with petroleum jelly. See Fig. 10 for identification and location of thrust washers.**

1) Before installing center support into case, install new high clutch seals on the support hub. It is also necessary to size these seals. Apply a liberal amount of petroleum jelly to the center support hub and seals.

NOTE: **If sizing is not done, the seals will be cut or rolled over when entering the intermediate brake drum cavity.**

2) Use the overdrive brake drum as a sizing tool. Calefully rotate the center support while inserting it into drum housing. Observe the seals as they enter the cavity to see that they do not roll over or get cut.

3) Be sure the center support is seated fully into the overdrive drum. Allow to stand for several minutes so that the seals seat in the grooves. Set aside until required for reassembly.

4) Position thrust washer No. 12 in case. Install collector body in rear of case. Install output shaft and governor assembly, taking care to avoid damaging rubber oil seal rings.

5) Position thrust washer No. 11 in case. Install low-reverse brake drum. Install internal gear and attach with snap ring. Position thrust washer No. 10 to back of planet carrier. Install carrier and attach to rear brake drum with snap ring.

6) Install low-reverse band. Replace low-reverse servo piston or "O" ring if necessary. Install low-reverse servo piston to hold band in position. *See Fig. 27.*

7) Install spiral spring on intermediate servo piston assembly. Install piston and cover. Press down on cover with Compressor (T74P-77028-A). Install snap ring.

Fig. 26: Clutch Replacing Guide Used to Install One-Way Clutch Inner Race

Guide
(T74P-77193-A)

Fig. 27: Replacing Low-Reverse Servo Assembly

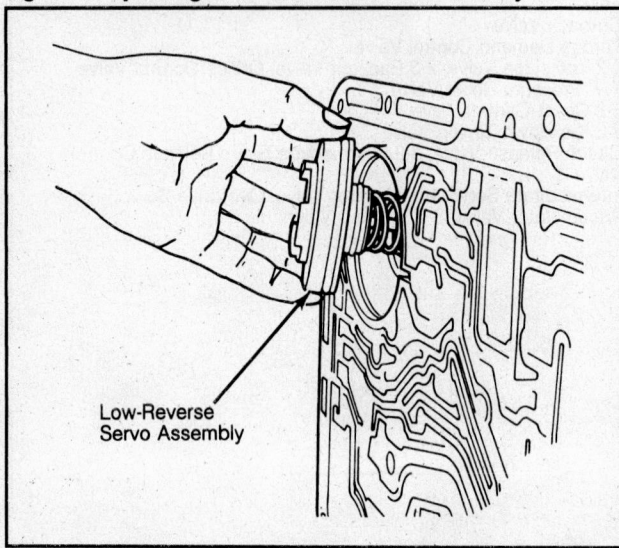

Low-Reverse
Servo Assembly

8) Install spiral spring on overdrive servo piston assembly. Install piston and cover. Press down on cover with Compressor (T74P-77028-A). Install snap ring. *See Fig. 28.*

Fig. 28: Tool Set-Up for Servo Snap Ring Installation

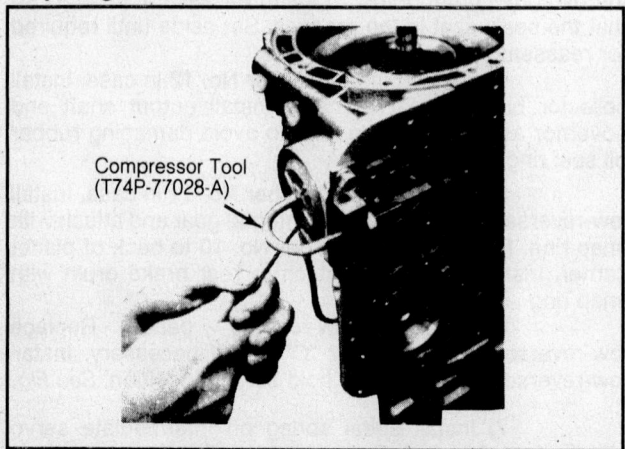

Compressor Tool
(T74P-77028-A)

9) Install intermediate servo apply lever and shaft into case. Install the complete forward clutch and high clutch assemblies.

10) Turn the transmission so that the output shaft points downward. Install intermediate band and apply strut. Install the intermediate band anchor strut.

11) Remove center support from overdrive drum and position No. 4 selective washer on rear of center support using petroleum jelly. Reuse original washer or replace with same size as original.

12) Insert the input shaft (short splines down) through the center and into the splines in the forward clutch cylinder. Carefully place the center support into the case, but do not seat it into the intermediate brake drum. Be sure it is square with the case and note the location of the 5mm allen bolt retainer nut.

13) DO NOT apply any pressure to the center support. Gently "wiggle" the input shaft allowing the center support to slide into the intermediate brake drum using its own weight. Perform this operation until the support is fully seated. Position No. 3 thrust washer on top of center support.

14) Install large snap ring to retain center support in position with the taper of the snap ring towards the front of the transmission. Ends of snap ring should be positioned in the wide shallow cavity located in the five o'clock postion. Install 5 mm Allen head bolt that retains center suppoer to case.

15) Install sun gear and support into overdrive planet assembly and one-way clutch. Take care to center needle bearing race inside of the planetary. Be sure it stays centered and positioned with the extruded lip in the upward position (toward sun gear).

16) Install overdrive planet assembly and one-way clutch into case. Install overdrive drum assembly. Install overdrive bracket, apply lever and shaft. Install overdrive band and apply strut. Install anchor strut.

17) Verify that needle bearing race in overdrive planetary is centered and overdrive clutch is fully seated. Place No. 1 selective washer on top of overdrive clutch drum and temporarily install pump assembly into case. Be sure that it is fully seated in case. Pump body must be below the level of the case gasket surface. Check transmission end play. See TRANSMISSION END PLAY CHECK in TRANSMISSION DISASSEMBLY section.

Fig. 29: Installing Pump Into Case

Thrust Washer

NOTE: Check for damaged or missing front pump support seal. Replace if necessary.

18) Position separator plate on the coverter housing. Place the 2 pump gears into the pump housing.

The inside edge of the small gear has a chamfer on one side. This chamfer must be positioned toward the front of the transmission. The larger gear has a dimple on one side which must be positioned towards the rear of the transmission. Position pump assembly onto the separator plate and converter housing. Install bolts finger tight.

NOTE: **The rough appearance of the pump stator casting is intentional and is not a flaw. Function of the pump is not affected, and it should not be replaced due to this appearance.**

Fig. 30: Correct Positioning of Adapter Plate on Housing

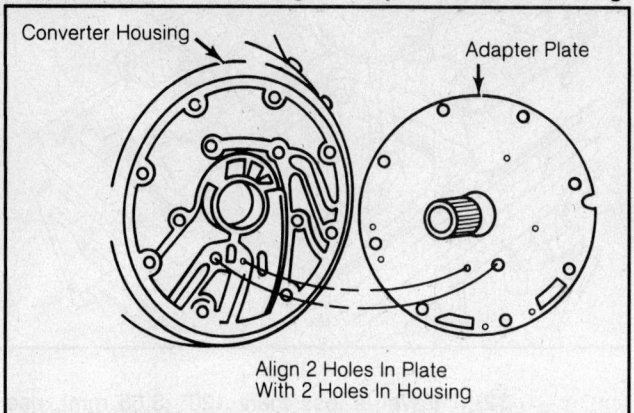

19) Front pump alignment requires special Pump Aligner (T74P-77103-X). Aligner consists of 4 special sleeves and handle. Each sleeve has same O.D. but different I.D.

CAUTION: **As this measurement is critical, make sure that sleeve gauging surfaces are in good condition. Damage to sleeve gauging surfaces may result in incorrect pump-to-converter housing alignment. Pump seal leakage, pump gear breakage, or bushing failure will occur.**

20) Select smallest I.D. sleeve which will fit completely over support shaft. Assemble selected sleeve to handle. Slide tool down over shaft until it bottoms against pump.

21) Outside diameter of sleeve centers pump in converter housing. Tighten retaining bolts and remove centering tool. Install input shaft into pump. Install converter into pump gears. Rotate converter to check for free movement.

22) Remove converter and input shaft. Position selected No. 1 thrust washer to pump housing. Install new "O" ring. Carefully install converter housing with pump using new gasket. Use care to avoid damaging steel oil seals.

23) Install bolts and tighten. Be sure to use new aluminum washers. Adjust overdrive and intermediate bands. Perform air pressure tests to ensure proper transmission operation as described under AIR PRESSURE CHECKS in this article.

24) Install shift lever oil seal using Shift Lever Seal Replacer (74P-77498-A). Install internal shift linkage and centering pin. Install "O" ring, kickdown lever and 13 mm nut. Install converter clutch solenoid connector.

25) Intall throttle valve, vacuum diaphragm, retaining clamp and bolt. Be sure the throttle valve moves freely in its bore. Use a pencil magnet to check movement.

Fig. 31: Special Front Pump Alignment Tool

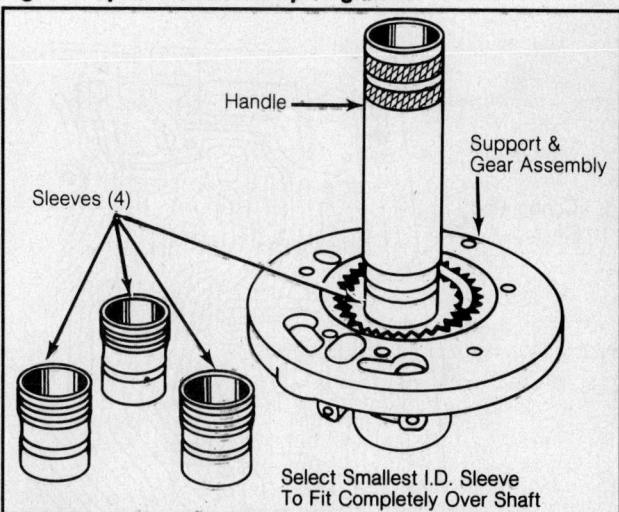

T74P-77103-X consists of 4 sleeves and handle.

Fig. 32: Front View of Converter Housing.

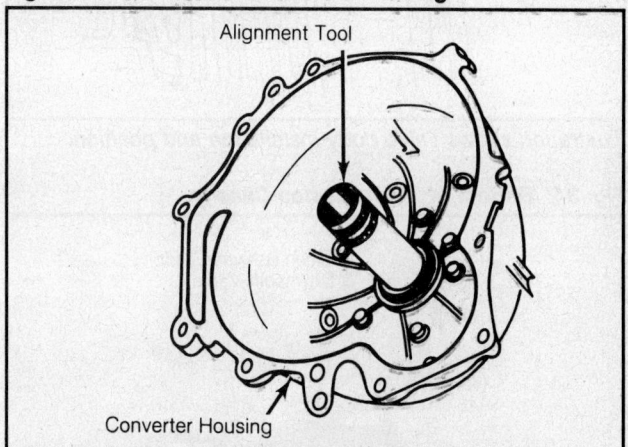

Illustration shows position of pump alignment tools.

26) Align valve body to separator plate and gasket using tapered punches. Install 2 10 mm and tighten to 84-107 INCH lbs. (10-12 N.m). Place control valve body in position. Attach and lock connecting rod to manual valve. Be careful not to bend connecting rod ("Z" link). Install and finger tighten retaining bolts "A" and "B" to locate control valve body. *See Fig. 5* for bolt locations.

27) Install and tighten all remaining bolts except filter screen bolts. Remove bolt "A" and attach detent spring to bolt. Reinstall bolt "A" and tighten bolts "A" and "B" completely. Make sure inner downshift lever is seated between stop and downshift valve.

CAUTION: **Because valve body retaining bolts are of different lengths, make sure each bolt head bottoms on valve body housing.**

28) Assemble servo piston rod, servo piston, and spring. Install additional reverse servo Piston Spring (D4ZZ-7D031-A) to check piston travel. Install piston assembly into rear servo bore. Make sure piston rod is correctly seated in reverse band apply end.

29) Install servo rod Selecting Guide (T74P-77190-A) using new servo cover gasket. Install and tighten 3 retaining bolts (servo cover bolts are not long enough to attach tool to case; use three valve body retaining bolts).

Fig. 33: Interior View of Transmission Case

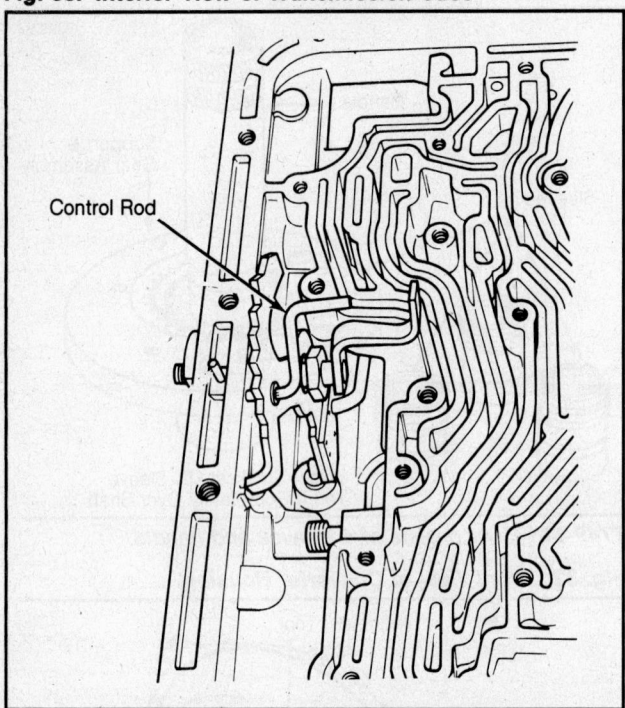

Illustration shows valve body installation and position.

Fig. 34: Bottom of Transmission Case

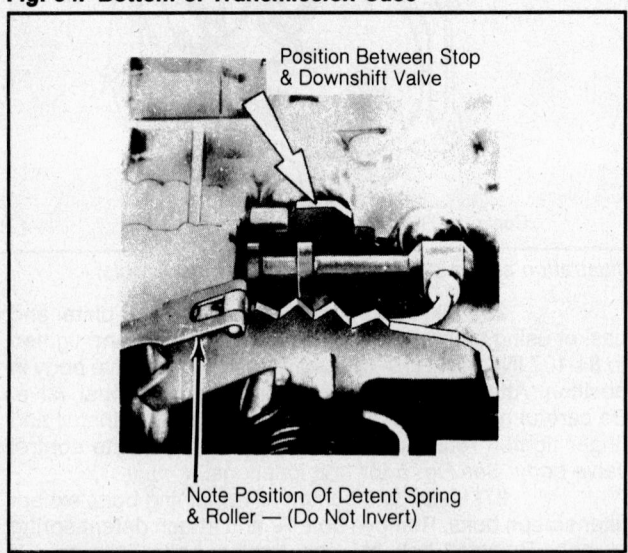

Illustration shows inner downshift lever position.

30) Tighten servo tool adjusting screw to 36 INCH lbs. (4 N.m). Install dial indicator on case. Position indicator tip on one of 3 servo piston pads accessible through cut-out of tool. Zero dial indicator. *See Fig. 35.*

31) Back out tool adjusting screw until servo piston bottoms out on tool. Record distance servo piston moved. If servo piston travel is .120-.220" (3.05-5.59 mm), servo piston rod is acceptable. If piston travel is greater than .220" (5.59 mm), use next longer servo piston and rod.

NOTE: Servo piston rods are available in 3 sizes and identified by grooves on rod. Rod sizes and

I.D. are as follows: 2.085-2.112" (1 groove), 1.986-2.014" (no groove), and 1.888-1.915" (2 grooves).

Fig. 35: Tool Set-Up for Rear Servo Pin Selection

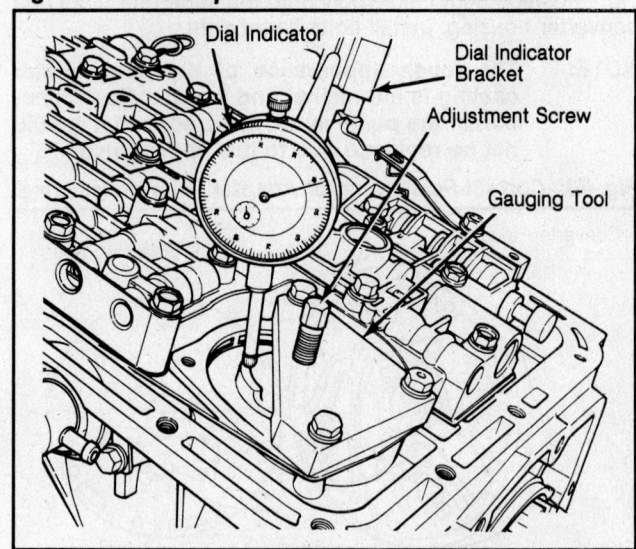

32) If travel is less than .120" (3.05 mm), use next shorter piston and rod. Install correct servo piston and rod. Recheck piston travel. Remove servo adjusting tool and additional reverse servo spring (only used for checking piston travel).

33) Reinstall servo assembly. Install servo cover and bolts. Install oil pan, using new gasket. Tighten pan bolts to specifications in 2 steps. Install neutral start switch. Install input shaft and torque converter.

Fig. 36: Rear Servo Piston Travel Measurement

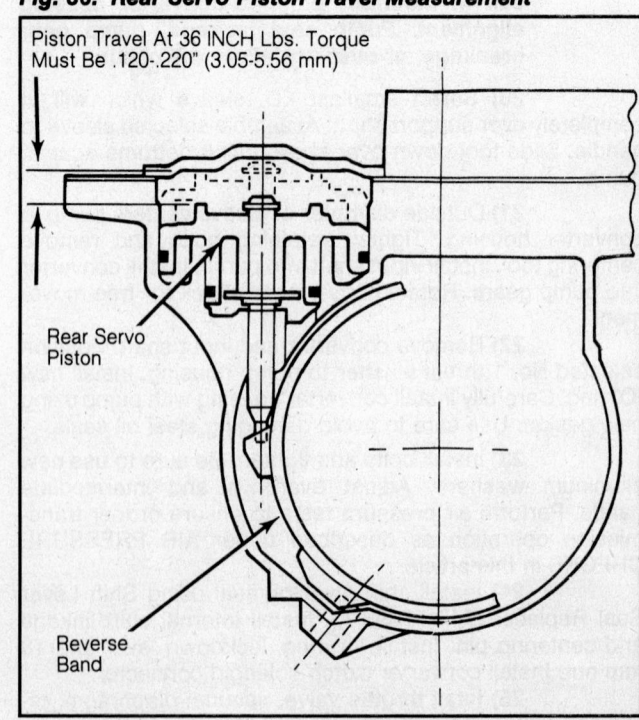

FORD MOTOR CO. A4LD (Cont.)

34) Install parking pawl and its return spring in extension housing and preload. Using new gasket, install extension housing. Make sure to correctly seat operating parking rod in extension guide cup. Install and tighten bolts. Replace extension housing oil seal and bushing.

Fig. 37: Rear of Transmission Housing

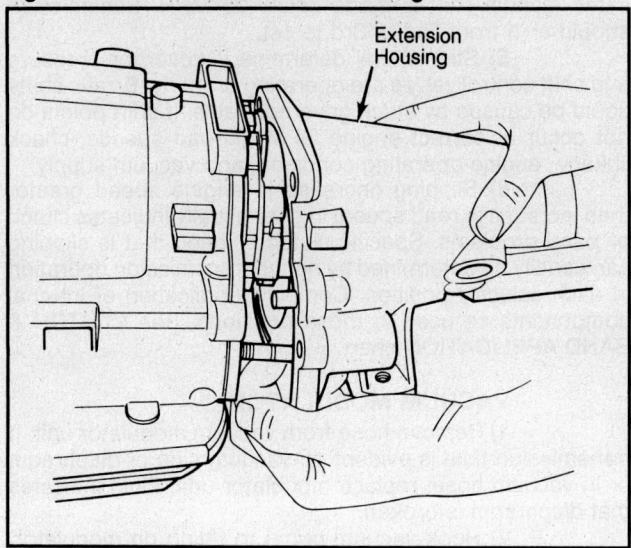

Note proper installation of extension housing.

TIGHTENING SPECIFICATIONS

Application	Ft. Lbs. (N.m)
Converter Housing-to-Case	27-39 (37-53)
Converter Housing-to-Engine	28-38 (38-52)
Connector-to-Case	10-15 (14-20)
Converter-to-Flywheel	27-49 (37-67)
Extension Housing-to-Case	27-39 (37-53)
Filler Tube to Engine Clip	28-38 (38-52)
Flywheel-to-Crankshaft	48-53 (65-72)
Intermediate Band Adjusting Screw Lock Nut	35-45 (47-61)
Oil Pan-to-Case	12-17 (16-23)
Overdrive Band Adjusting Screw Lock Nut	35-45 (47-61)
Manual Lever Inner Nut	30-40 (41-54)
Transmission-to-Engine	28-38 (38-52)

	INCH lbs.
Center Support-to-Case	71-97 (8-11)
Downshift Lever Outer Nut	84-11 (10-15)
Main Control-to-Case	71-97 (8-11)
Separator Plate-to-Valve Body	84-107 (10-12)
Governor-to-Collector Body	84-120 (10-14)
Oil Cooler Line or By-Pass Tube-to Connector	84-120 (10-14)
One Way Clutch Inner Race-to-Case	84-120 (10-14)
Neutral Switch-to-Case	84-120 (10-14)
Pump-to-Converter Housing	84-120 (10-14)
Rear Servo Cover-to-Case	84-120 (10-14)
Valve Body-to-Case	71-97 (8-11)
Vaccum Diaphragm Retaining Clip to Case	84-120 (10-14)

Automatic Transmissions

FORD MOTOR CO. C-3

Capri, Cougar, LTD, Marquis,
Mustang, Thunderbird

IDENTIFICATION

The C-3 automatic transmission is identified by code letter "V", which is shown on lower line of Vehicle Certification Label under "TR" or "TRANS". Label is attached to driver's front door lock panel or pillar.

Transmission model may be identified by metal tag attached to transmission by lower extension housing retaining bolt. Top line of tag shows transmission model number and line shift code. Bottom line on tag shows build date code. *See Fig. 1.*

The C-3 transmission may be visually identified by location of vacuum diaphragm (modulator). Diaphragm unit is located at right center of case, just to rear of intermediate (front) servo. The C-3 transmission is used on passenger car models with 2.3L engines.

Fig. 1: Service Identification Tag

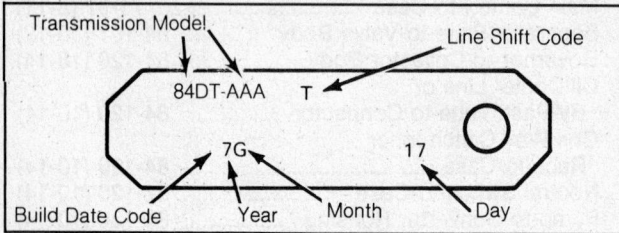

Tag is on lower left extension housing bolt.

DESCRIPTION

Transmission has 3 forward speeds. Manual selection of 1st and 2nd gears is provided. Transmission consists of torque converter, planetary gear train, 2 multiple disc clutches, one-way clutch, and hydraulic control system. Only front band adjustment is required.

LUBRICATION & ADJUSTMENT

See appropriate AUTOMATIC TRANSMISSION SERVICING article in DOMESTIC GENERAL SERVICING Section.

TESTING

Check fluid level and correct if necessary. Use initial road test to verify malfunction of transmission. Make sure that engine appears to be running properly. If transmission problems occur on initial road test, check adjustments and fluid levels.

ROAD TEST

1) If vehicle is not so equipped, attach tachometer to engine. Check minimum throttle upshifts in "D" position. See SHIFT SPEEDS tables. Transmission should start in 1st gear, shift to 2nd, and then shift to 3rd gear as speed increases.

2) With transmission in 3rd gear, depress accelerator through detent (to floor). Transmission should shift from 3rd to 2nd, or 3rd to 1st, depending on vehicle speed.

3) Check closed throttle downshift from 3rd to 1st by coasting down from about 30 MPH in 3rd gear. Shift

should occur at correct vehicle speed. With transmission selector lever in "2" position, transmission should operate only in 2nd gear.

4) With transmission in 3rd gear and road speed over 30 MPH, transmission should downshift to 2nd gear when selector lever is moved from "D" to "2" or "1". When same manual shift is made below 25 MPH, transmission should shift from 2nd or 3rd to 1st.

5) Step 4) will determine if governor pressure and shift control valves are operating properly. Erratic shifts could be caused by stuck governor valve. If shift points do not occur at correct engine RPM or road speeds, check linkage, engine operating condition, and vacuum supply.

6) Slipping (increase in engine speed greater than increase in road speed) in gear usually indicates clutch or band problems. Specific clutch or band that is slipping can usually be determined by noting transmission operation in each selector position. Compare application of internal components as used in those positions. See CLUTCH & BAND APPLICATION chart.

VACUUM MODULATOR

1) Remove hose from vacuum modulator unit. If transmission fluid is evident on vacuum side of diaphragm or in vacuum hose, replace modulator unit. Fluid indicates that diaphragm is broken.

2) Hook vacuum pump to fitting on modulator. Operate pump until gauge shows 18 in. Hg. If gauge reading holds steady, modulator unit is good. If gauge reading drops, modulator unit is bad and must be replaced.

3) With modulator removed from transmission, draw 18 in. Hg on vacuum pump attached to vacuum port of unit. Hold finger over end of control rod of modulator unit. When hose is removed, good modulator unit will push out on control rod due to internal spring pressure.

ENGINE VACUUM PRESSURE

1) If vacuum modulator is working properly and downshift linkage is adjusted correctly, all shifts should occur within certain road speed limits. See SHIFT SPEEDS tables. If shifts do not occur at proper points or slipping occurs during shifts, check engine vacuum, vacuum supply, and vacuum units for possible cause of problem.

2) Connect tachometer to engine. Connect vacuum gauge to manifold vacuum line, using "T" fitting at modulator hookup. Attach pressure gauge to control pressure outlet on transmission case. *See Fig. 3.* Plug for pressure take-off is located on left side of case just behind manual shift linkage.

CAUTION: **Pressure gauge affects quality of transmission shifting. When gauge is installed in transmission port, DO NOT accelerate or decelerate rapidly as transmission failure could occur.**

3) Apply parking brake firmly. Start engine. Adjust engine idle speed to correct RPM. If engine idle cannot be brought within limits, check throttle and downshift linkages for binding. Check for vacuum leaks in hoses and tubes if linkage is correctly in place. Check vacuum units such as power brake booster for leaks.

4) Vacuum reading at gauge should be steady with engine idling. Reading must be acceptable for altitude where test is being done. If vacuum reading is correct at idle, accelerate engine rapidly and release throttle immediately. Vacuum reading must drop rapidly during acceleration.

Fig. 2: Cutaway View of C-3 Automatic Transmission Assembly

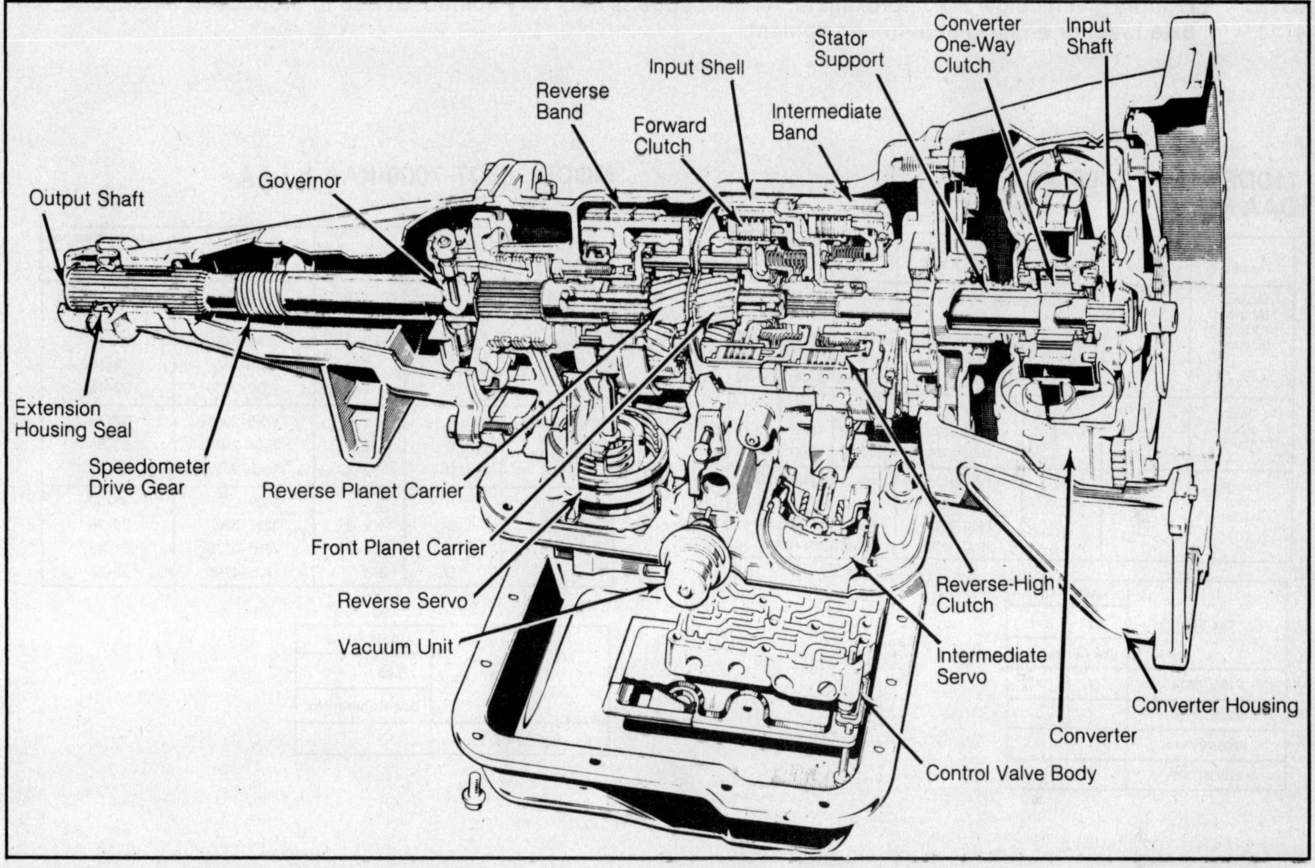

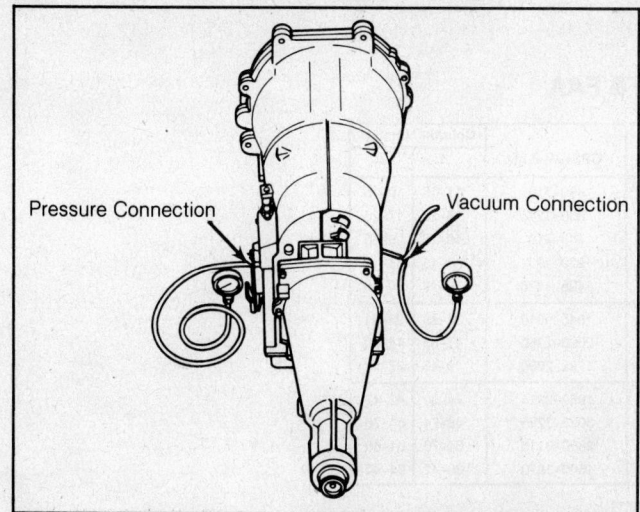

Fig. 3: Gauge Hook-Up for Pressure Testing

1) Disconnect engine vacuum line from modulator unit. Hook up vacuum pump to unit. Apply parking and service brakes. Start engine and apply 15 in. Hg vacuum to modulator. Select all ranges of transmission. Read and record control pressures.

2) Run engine up to 1000 RPM and set vacumm pump at 10 in. Hg. Read and record control pressures in 3 forward ranges. Keeping engine speed at 1000 RPM, reduce vacuum to 1 in. Hg. Read and record control pressures in 3 forward ranges and in Reverse range.

CONTROL PRESSURE RESULTS

Compare recorded control pressures to control pressures listed in table. See CONTROL PRESSURE SPECIFICATIONS (psi) table. If control pressures are outside of specified ranges, use following list to determine cause of trouble:

High at Idle in All Ranges

Check engine EGR system, vacuum diaphragm unit, and manifold vacuum line. Check throttle valve, control rod, and regulator boost valves for sticking.

Low at Idle in All Ranges

Check engine EGR system. Check fluid level. Check for restricted intake screen or filter. Check for loose oil tubes. Check if valve body-to-case or regulator-to-case bolts are loose. Check for excessive leakage in oil pump, control valve body, and case. Check control pressure regulator valve for sticking.

Normal at Idle; Low at 10 in. Hg

Check vacuum diaphragm unit. Control rod or throttle valve stuck.

5) Vacuum should return as soon as throttle is released. If vacuum reading does not respond correctly, check lines for restriction or plugging. Also make sure that vacuum line is not hooked up to reservoir.

CONTROL PRESSURE TEST

NOTE: Governor can be checked at same time control pressure test is performed and in same manner.

Automatic Transmissions
FORD MOTOR CO. C-3 (Cont.)

SHIFT SPEEDS (MPH)

NOTE: Figures given below are approximate. All shift speeds may vary somewhat due to production tolerances, rear axle ratio, or emission control equipment.

MODEL 85DT-7000-AAA, BAA, DAA & JAA

Throttle	Range	Shift	OPS—R.P.M.	Column Number 1	2	3
Closed (Above 17" Vacuum)	D	1-2	445-670	10-15	10-15	9-14
	D	2-3	750-1070	17-24	16-23	16-22
	D	3-2	490-760	11-17	11-17	10-16
	D	2-1	220-490	5-11	5-11	4-10
	1	2-1	1425-1870	32-42	31-41	30-39
To Detent (Torque Demand)	D	1-2	1460-1735	32-39	32-38	31-37
	D	2-3	1960-2225	44-50	43-49	41-47
	D	3-2	1600-1870	36-42	35-41	34-39
Through Detent (WOT)	D	1-2	1915-2180	43-49	42-48	40-46
	D	2-3	2980-3250	66-73	66-72	63-69
	D	3-2	2800-3070	63-69	62-68	59-65
	D	3-1, 2-1	1600-1870	36-42	35-41	34-39

Tire Size	Axle Ratio 3.27	3.45
	Use Column No.	
P195/75R14	1	3
P205/70R14	1	3
P205/70VR14	1	3
220/55R390	2	3

MODEL 85DT-7000-KAA & LAA

Throttle	Range	Shift	OPS—R.P.M.	Column Number 1
Closed (Above 17" Vacuum)	D	1-2	580-790	12-17
	D	2-3	845-1215	18-26
	D	3-2	530-845	11-18
	D	2-1	425-740	9-16
	1	2-1	1530-2060	32-44
To Detent (Torque Demand)	D	1-2	1740-2060	37-44
	D	2-3	2480-2800	53-60
	D	3-2	1640-1955	35-42
Through Detent (WOT)	D	1-2	2038-2325	43-50
	D	2-3	3257-3560	70-76
	D	3-2	2850-3170	61-68
	D	3-1, 2-1	1425-1795	30-38

Tire Size	Axle Ratio 3.45
	Use Column No.
225/60VR15	1

MODEL 85DT-7000-EAA & FAA

Throttle	Range	Shift	OPS—R.P.M.	Column Number 1	2
Closed (Above 17" Vacuum)	D	1-2	490-710	11-16	10-15
	D	2-3	800-1245	18-28	17-26
	D	3-2	445-710	10-16	9-15
	D	2-1	220-490	5-11	4-10
	1	2-1	1425-1870	32-42	30-40
To Detent (Torque Demand)	D	1-2	1645-1910	37-43	35-41
	D	2-3	2090-2360	47-53	44-50
	D	3-2	1735-2000	39-45	37-42
Through Detent (WOT)	D	1-2	1960-2225	44-50	42-47
	D	2-3	3025-3295	68-74	64-70
	D	3-2	2850-3115	64-70	61-66
	D	3-1, 2-1	1600-1870	36-42	34-40

Tire Size	Axle Ratio 3.27	3.45
	Use Column No.	
P195/75R14	1	2
P205/70R14	1	2

CONTROL PRESSURE SPECIFICATIONS (psi)

Transmission Model	Range	16" & Above	15" & Above	10"	WOT Stall Thru Detent
85DT-AAA/BAA/DAA/JAA	*D,2,1		50-60	74-94	165-195
	R		66-78	129-148	278-316
	P,N		50-60		
85DT-DAA/JAA	%D,2,1		50-60	53-75	144-177
	R		66-78	94-116	244-282
	P,N		50-60		
85DT-KAA/LAA	*D,2,1	51-61		70-90	180-222
	R	67-82		123-143	302-330
	P,N	51-61			
85DT-LAA	%D,2,1	51-61		62-82	171-195
	R	67-82		109-129	292-311
	P,N	51-61			

* Barometric pressure 29.0-30.0 in. Hg.
% Barometric pressure 24.0-25.0 in. Hg.

Normal at Idle and 10 in. Hg.; Low at 1 in. Hg
Check for excessive leakage, low pump capacity, or restricted oil pan screen.

Low in "P" or "N"
Check valve body.

Low in "D"
Check forward clutch.

Low in "2"
Check forward clutch and/or intermediate servo or clutch.

Low in "1"
Check forward clutch and/or reverse clutch and servo.

Low in "R"
Check reverse-direct clutch and/or reverse servo.

GOVERNOR PRESSURE TEST

CAUTION: **Never exceed 60 MPH speedometer reading during governor pressure test. After each test, move selector lever to Neutral and run engine at 1000 RPM to cool transmission.**

1) Raise vehicle until rear wheels are clear of ground. Disconnect and plug vacuum line to vacuum diaphragm unit. Connect hand-held vacuum pump to diaphragm unit.

2) Place transmission in "D". Apply 10 in. Hg to diaphragm unit with no load on engine. Increase speed slowly and watch speedometer. Note speed at which control pressure cut-back occurs. It should occur between 6-20 MPH.

3) Decrease vacuum to 0-2 in. Hg and repeat test. Governor is okay if cut-back occurs as specified. If not, check shift speeds to verify that problem is in governor and not due to stuck cut-back valve. Repair or replace governor.

STALL TEST
Testing Precautions
1) Engine coolant and transmission fluid must be at proper levels and operating temperatures. TV linkage must be set properly. Hold accelerator down just long enough to get stable tachometer reading. Do not floor accelerator for more than 5 seconds.

2) Do not exceed maximum specified RPM for vehicle. Before shifting into each selector position, run engine in "N" at 1000 RPM for 15 to 20 seconds to cool transmission. If engine speed exceeds upper specification,

release accelerator immediately as this is an indication of clutch or band slippage.

Testing Procedure
1) Connect tachometer to engine. Apply parking and service brakes firmly. Place selector lever in "D" position, and push accelerator completely to floor. Record tachometer reading.

2) Engine speed should be within specifications given in STALL SPEEDS table. Repeat procedure in "2", "1", and "R" positions.

STALL SPEEDS

Application	Stall RPM
2.3L	
Capri, LTD, Marquis, Mustang	2442-2827
2.3L Turbo	
Cougar, Thunderbird	2963-3439

STALL TEST RESULTS
Low in All Ranges
Poor engine performance. Faulty torque converter stator one-way clutch.

High in All Ranges
General transmission problems are indicated. Perform control pressure tests.

High in "D" Only
Planetary one-way clutch faulty.

High in "D", "2" & "1"
Forward clutch faulty.

High in "2" Only
Intermediate band or servo faulty.

High in "1" Only
Low/Reverse band or servo faulty.

High in "R" Only
Reverse-Direct clutch faulty. Low/Reverse band faulty.

AIR PRESSURE CHECKS
1) Condition of "No Drive" (no movement of output shaft) can exist, even with correct transmission fluid pressure. Inoperative clutches or bands may cause this problem.

2) Inoperative units can be located through series of checks by substituting air pressure for fluid pressure to determine location of malfunction.

3) Loosen oil pan bolts and allow transmission fluid to drain. Remove oil pan and control valve body. Apply air at points noted in *Fig. 5*. Check unit operation as follows:

Forward Clutch
Apply air pressure into forward clutch passage. Dull thud can be heard when clutch piston is applied. Movement of piston can be felt by placing finger tips on input shell if no thud heard.

Governor
Apply air pressure into control pressure-to-governor passage. Listen for sharp clicking or whistling noise indicating governor valve movement.

Reverse-Direct Clutch
Apply air pressure into reverse-direct clutch passage. Dull thud can be heard when clutch piston is applied. Movement of piston can be felt by placing finger tips on clutch drum.

Automatic Transmissions
FORD MOTOR CO. C-3 (Cont.)

Fig. 4: C-3 Automatic Transmission Hydraulic Circuits Diagram

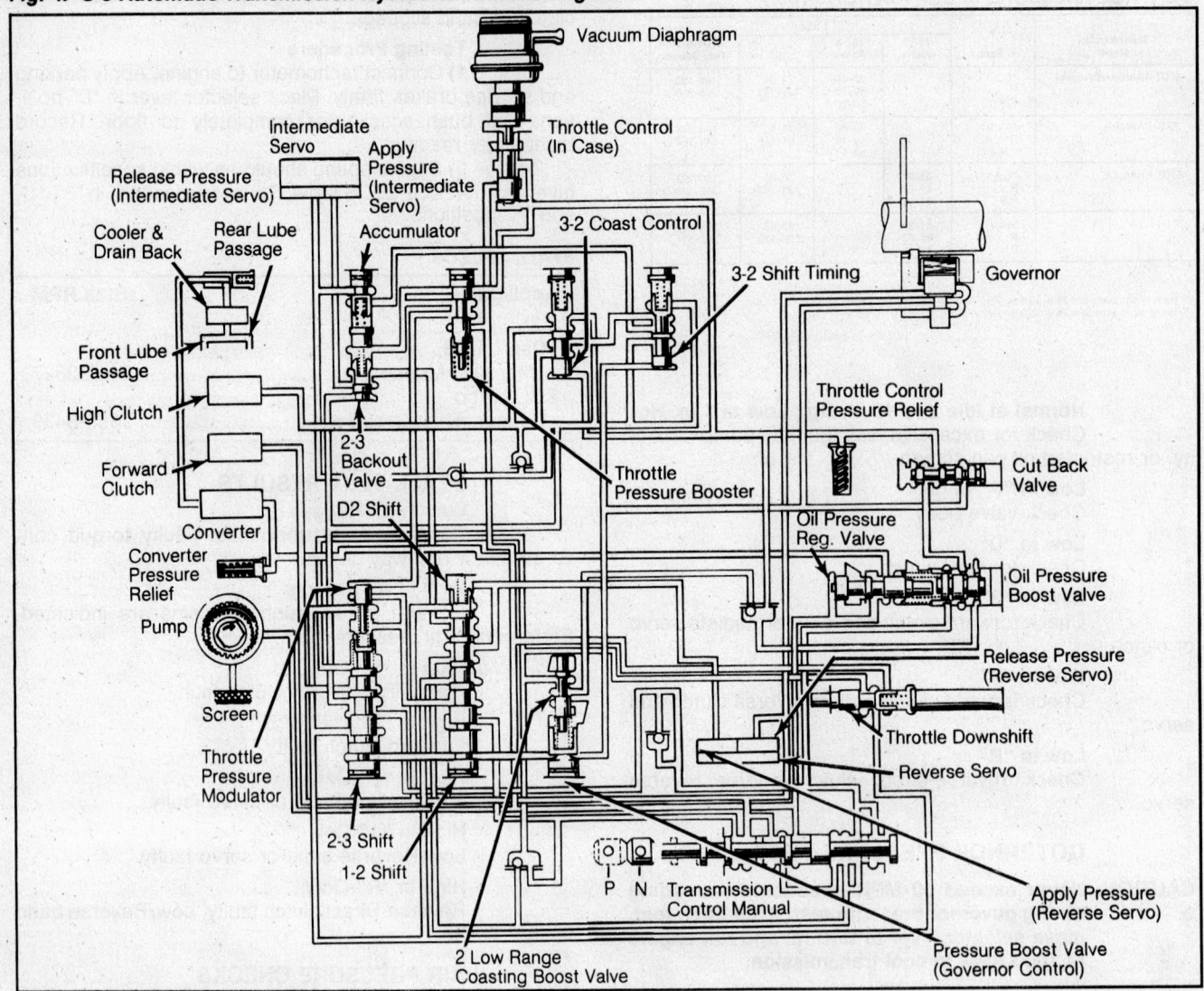

CLUTCH AND BAND APPLICATION (ELEMENTS IN USE)

Selector Lever Position	Intermediate Band	Low-Reverse Band	Forward Clutch	Reverse-Direct Clutch	One-Way Clutch
D – DRIVE First Second Third	 Applied Applied		 Applied Applied Applied	 Applied	 Applied
2 – INTERMEDIATE Second	 Applied		 Applied		
1 – LOW First		 Applied	 Applied		
R – REVERSE		Applied		Applied	
N – NEUTRAL					
P – PARK					

Fig. 5: *Bottom View of Transmission Case*

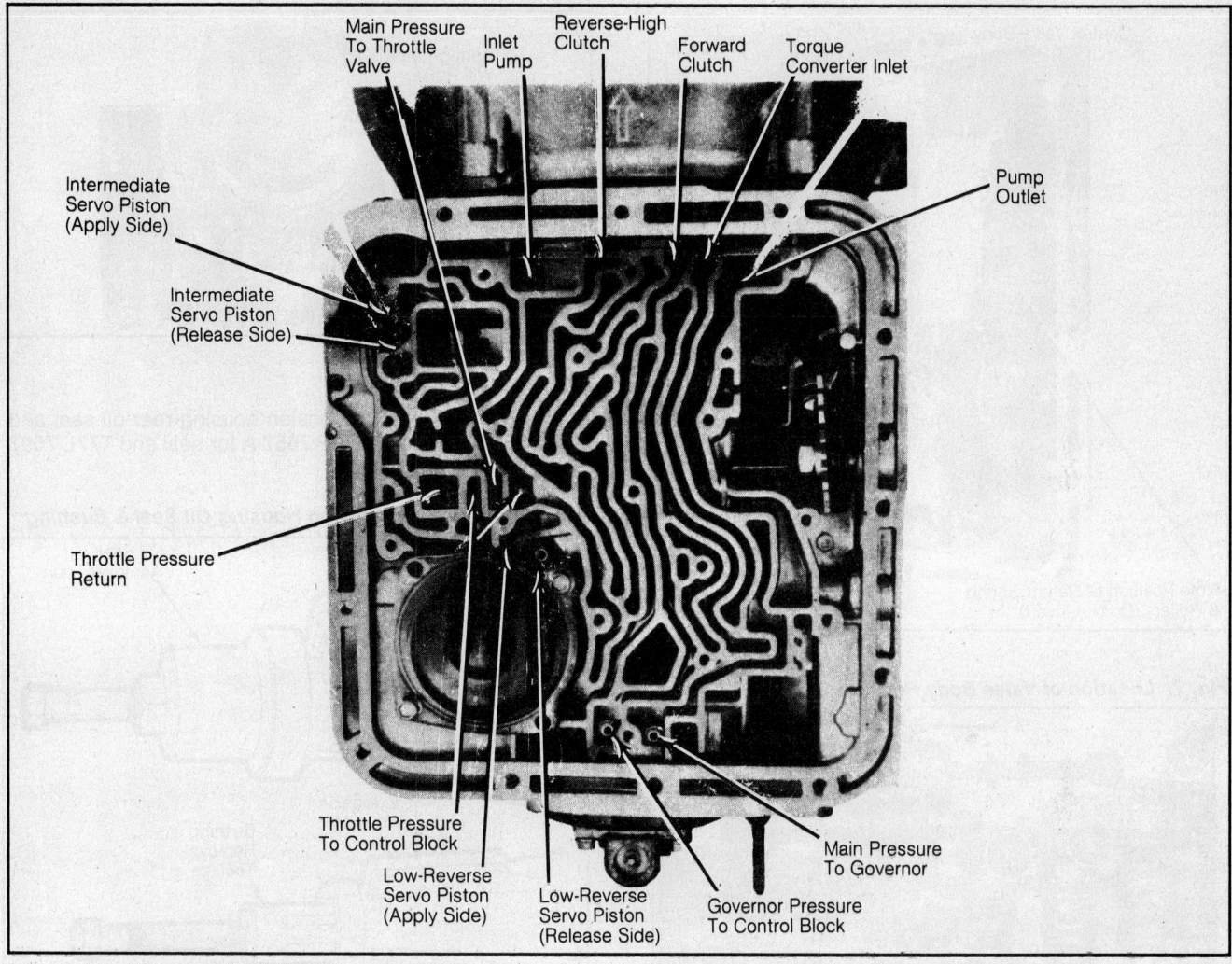

Intermediate Servo Piston (Apply Side)

Intermediate Servo Piston (Release Side)

Main Pressure To Throttle Valve

Inlet Pump

Reverse-High Clutch

Forward Clutch

Torque Converter Inlet

Pump Outlet

Throttle Pressure Return

Throttle Pressure To Control Block

Low-Reverse Servo Piston (Apply Side)

Low-Reverse Servo Piston (Release Side)

Governor Pressure To Control Block

Main Pressure To Governor

Note points for air testing of clutches and bands.

Intermediate Servo

1) Hold air nozzle in intermediate servo apply passage. Operation of servo is indicated by tightening of intermediate band around drum.

2) While continuing to apply air pressure at servo apply passage, apply air pressure to intermediate servo release passage. Intermediate servo should then release band against pressure in apply passage.

Low-Reverse Servo

Apply air pressure to low-reverse servo apply passage. Low-reverse band should tighten around drum if servo is operating properly.

NOTE: **If air pressure applied to either clutch passages fails to operate clutch, or operates both clutches at once, remove and check fluid passages in case and oil pump. Use air pressure to detect obstructions.**

SERVICE (IN VEHICLE)

CONTROL VALVE BODY
Removal

Remove oil pan, filter screen, and gasket. Remove rear servo cover and gasket. Remove valve body retaining bolts. Carefully ease valve body from case while unlocking and detaching selector lever connecting rod.

NOTE: **Note size and location of valve body retaining bolts. Bolts are of different sizes and must be replaced in proper position at reassembly.**

Installation

1) Attach and lock selector lever connecting rod ("Z" link) to manual valve. Ease control valve body to case. Install and tighten valve body retaining bolts. Install detent spring, hooking it to valve body bolt at upper right in *Fig. 7.*

2) Install rear servo cover with new gasket. Clean filter screen. Install filter screen and gasket. Install oil pan using new gasket. Tighten pan bolts evenly. Lower vehicle and fill transmission with 3 quarts of fluid. Start engine and add fluid as necessary. Check for leaks.

REAR SERVO
Removal

With oil pan and filter screen removed, remove rear servo cover retaining bolts, cover, gasket, servo piston, and spring.

NOTE: **Force of servo spring will push cover off.**

Fig. 6: Bottom View of Case

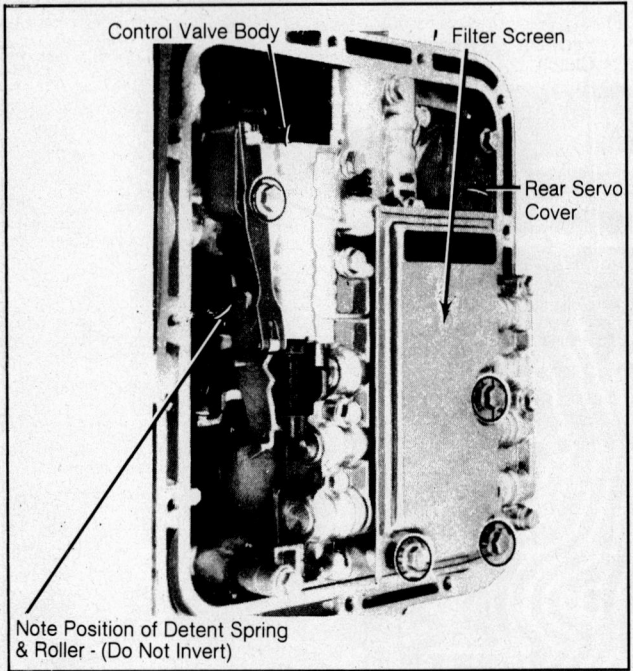

Fig. 7: Location of Valve Body Retaining Bolts

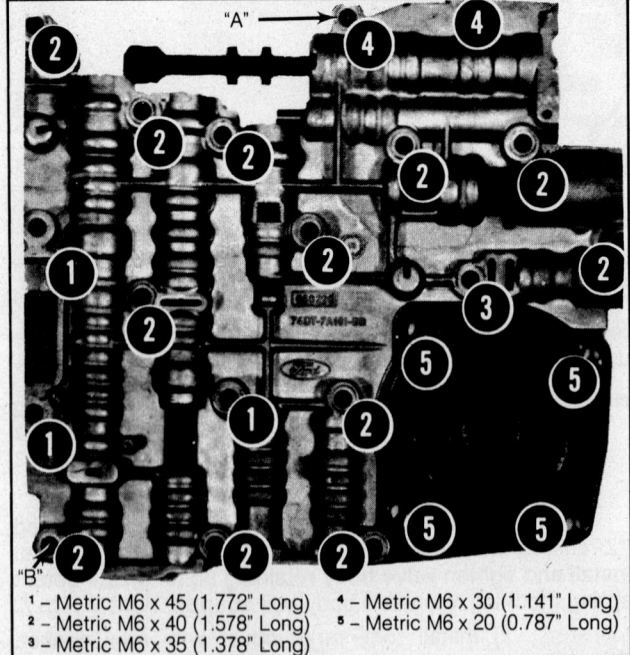

¹ – Metric M6 x 45 (1.772" Long) ⁴ – Metric M6 x 30 (1.141" Long)
² – Metric M6 x 40 (1.578" Long) ⁵ – Metric M6 x 20 (0.787" Long)
³ – Metric M6 x 35 (1.378" Long)

Use "A" and "B" bolts for locating valve body. Bolts must go into original locations.

Installation
Reverse removal procedures.

EXTENSION HOUSING
REAR SEAL & BUSHING
Removal
1) Raise and support vehicle. Mark propeller shaft end yoke and rear axle companion flange for reassembly reference. Remove propeller shaft.

Fig. 8: Bottom View of Transmission Case

2) Remove extension housing rear oil seal and bushing using Pullers (T71P 7657 A for seal and T77L 7697 E for bushing). *See Fig. 9.*

Fig. 9: Removing Extension Housing Oil Seal & Bushing

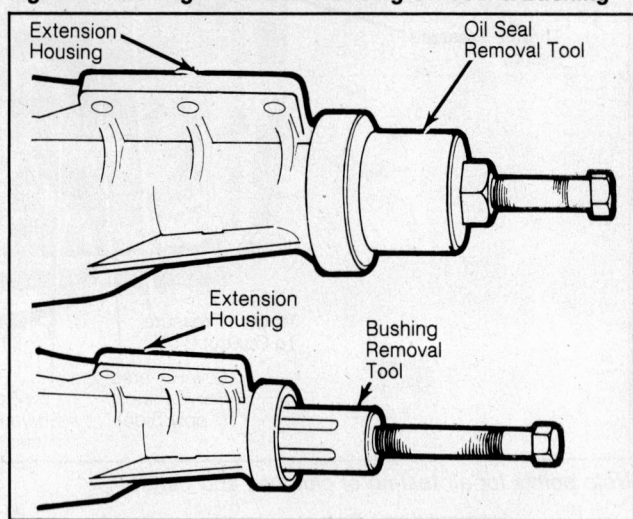

Installation
Check sealing surface of yoke for scoring. Replace if scoring found. Check housing counterbore for burrs and remove with crocus cloth if necessary. Drive new bushing and oil seal into extension housing using Drivers (T77L 7697 F for bushing and T74P 77052 A for oil seal). Install propeller shaft, aligning reference marks made at removal.

EXTENSION HOUSING
Removal
1) Raise and support vehicle. Mark propeller shaft for installation reference. Remove shaft. Disconnect speedometer cable from extension housing. Support transmission with jack.
2) Remove rear support-to-crossmember bolts. Raise transmission slightly and remove rear support from extension housing.
3) Loosen extension housing retaining bolts and allow transmission fluid to drain. Remove bolts and slide extension housing off output shaft.

FORD MOTOR CO. C-3 (Cont.)

Installation

Use new gasket. Position extension housing on case. Pay special attention to correctly seating operating rod parking notch. Install and tighten bolts. To complete installation, reverse removal procedures.

GOVERNOR
Removal

Remove extension housing as previously described. Remove governor body-to-oil collector body retaining bolts. Remove governor body, valve, spring, and weight from collector body. *See Fig. 10.*

NOTE: Components are not retained once governor body bolts have been removed. It is necessary to hold body and components while removing and installing governor.

Fig. 10: Removing Governor Assembly

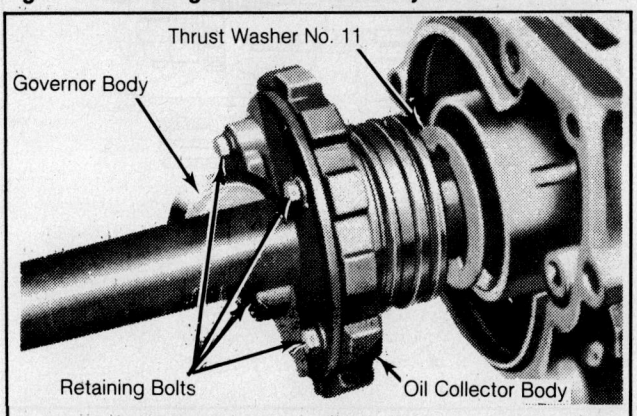

Installation

Assemble governor body and components. Position body over oil feed holes of oil collector body. Install retaining bolts. Install extension housing.

VACUUM DIAPHRAGM ASSEMBLY
Removal

Disconnect hoses from unit. Remove retaining bracket (do not pry or bend bracket). Remove vacuum diaphragm, actuating pin and throttle valve from case. Remove "O" ring from assembly. *See Fig. 11.*

Fig. 11: Side View of Transmission Case

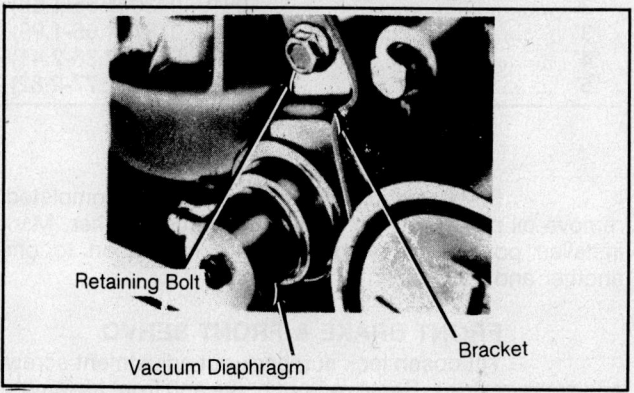

Installation

Install new "O" ring. Install throttle valve, actuating pin and vacuum diaphragm (with tube pointing rearward). Install retaining bracket and tighten bolt.

REMOVAL & INSTALLATION

See FORD MOTOR CO. articles in AUTOMATIC TRANSMISSION REMOVAL section.

TORQUE CONVERTER

LEAKAGE CHECK

See procedures given in FORD MOTOR CO. C-6 article.

FLUSHING CONVERTER

See procedures given in FORD MOTOR CO. C-6 article.

TURBINE & STATOR END PLAY CHECK

See procedures given in FORD MOTOR CO. C-6 article.

STATOR ONE-WAY CLUTCH CHECK

See procedures given in FORD MOTOR CO. C-6 article.

STATOR INTERFERENCE CHECKS

See procedures given in FORD MOTOR CO. C-6 article.

TRANSMISSION DISASSEMBLY

NOTE: Ten thrust washers and one thrust bearing are used in this transmission, with No. 1 at front pump and No. 11 at governor. Note that No. 6 is needle roller bearing performing thrust function. This adds one to thrust washer count. Because this bearing is part of staked portion of planet assembly, it is not removable. Refer to Fig. 12 for identification and location of thrust washers.

REAR SERVO, VALVE BODY & OIL PUMP

1) Remove torque converter, input shaft, and oil pan. Remove oil filter screen, gasket, and 3 spacers (if equipped). Remove interlock spring.

2) Remove rear servo cover and gasket (spring force will raise cover). Remove bolts from valve body. Note size, length, and location of bolts for reassembly reference.

3) Slowly remove valve body from transmission, unlocking and detaching selector lever connecting link. Remove valve body and gasket. Remove converter housing bolts. Remove housing and oil pump as an assembly.

4) Remove No. 1 thrust washer and gasket. Remove oil pump seal with Puller (T74P 77248 A). Remove oil pump from converter housing. Remove steel plate (behind oil seal) with "O" ring.

Fig. 12: Cutaway View of Transmission Showing Thrust Washer Identification and Location

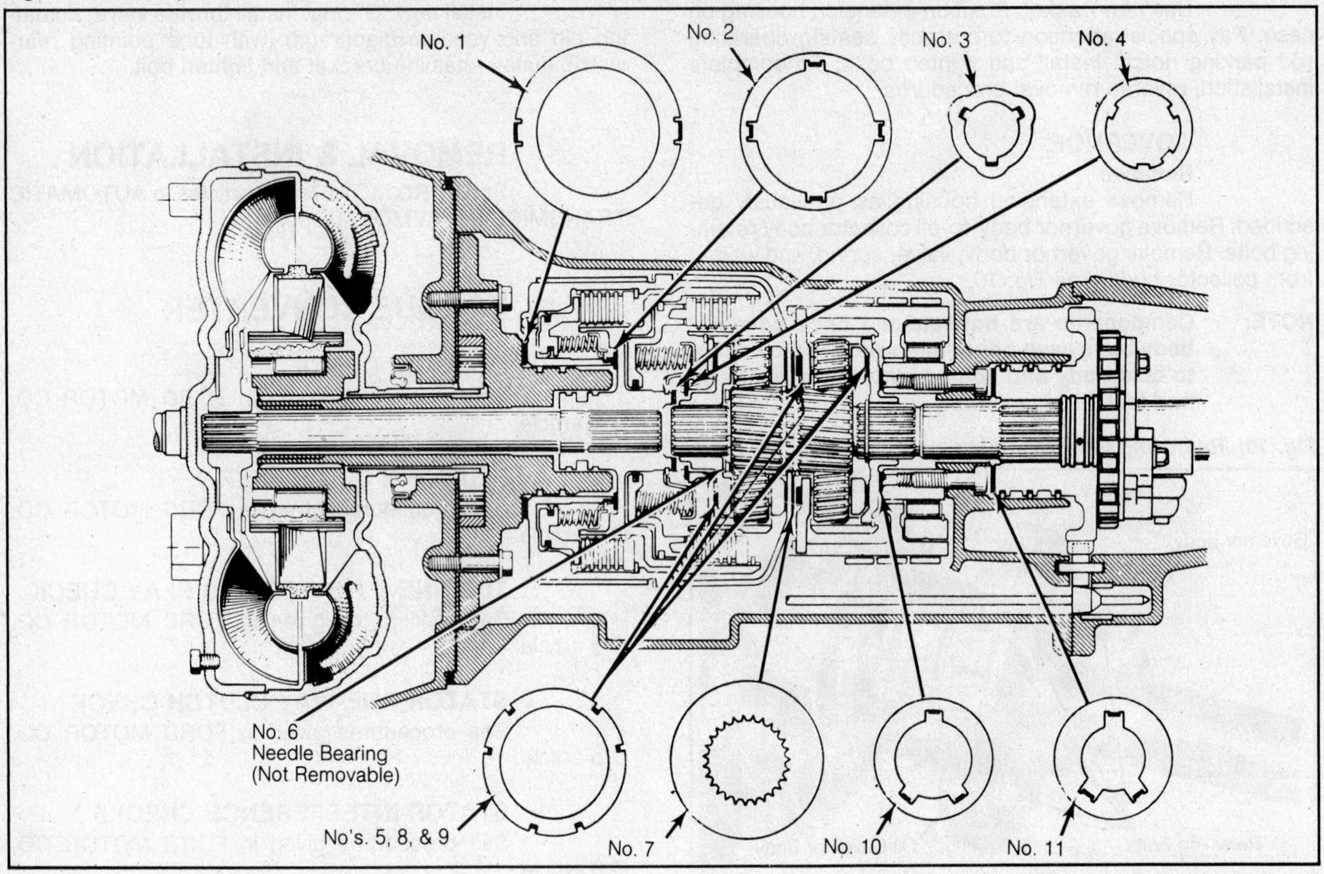

No. 1   No. 2   No. 3   No. 4

No. 6
Needle Bearing
(Not Removable)

No's. 5, 8, & 9   No. 7   No. 10   No. 11

NOTE: Before continuing with disassembly, transmission end play should be measured.

TRANSMISSION END PLAY CHECK

1) Install oil pump (without gasket) and existing No. 1 thrust washer into transmission case. Make sure pump body is below case gasket surface.

2) Mount dial indicator on oil pump with plunger resting on transmission housing. *See Fig. 13.* Zero dial indicator, then swing indicator around so plunger contacts oil pump.

Fig. 13: Tool Set-Up for Transmission End Play Check

Dial Indicator

Take average of 2 readings 180 apart.

3) Check reading on dial and record for future reference. Move dial indicator assembly to opposite side of pump. Make another end play check. Take average of 2 readings.

4) End play range is .001-.025" (.03-.64 mm). If end play exceeds limits, replace thrust washer No. 1 with one that will bring end play within specifications.

SELECTIVE THRUST WASHER NO. 1

ID Number	Thickness In. (mm)
"1"	.0488-.0508 (1.24-1.29)
"2"	.0610-.0630 (1.55-1.60)
"3"	.0768-.0787 (1.95-1.99)
"4"	.0929-.0949 (2.36-2.41)
"5"	.1091-.1110 (2.77-2.82)

5) After end play check has been completed, remove oil pump and No. 1 selective thrust washer. Mark installed position of oil pump gears in relation to one another and remove.

FRONT BRAKE & FRONT SERVO

1) Loosen lock nut, back out adjustment screw, and remove struts. Remove front brake and front assembly, including thrust washer No. 8. *See Fig. 14.*

FORD MOTOR CO. C-3 (Cont.)

Fig. 14: Front Band Removal

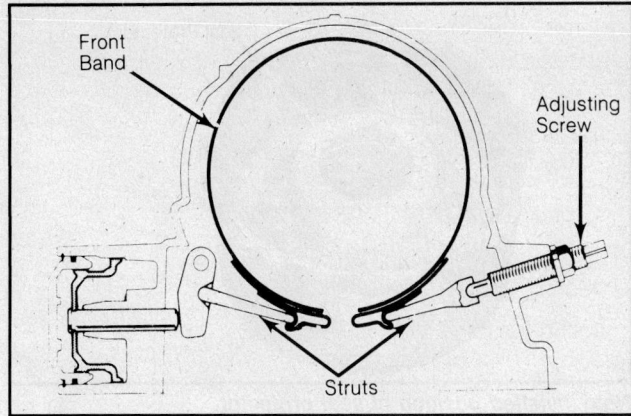

2) Press inward slightly on front servo cover and remove snap ring. Carefully force out servo piston assembly using compressed air through bottom of transmission case. *See Fig. 15.*

Fig. 15: Bottom View of Transmission Case

CASE & EXTENSION HOUSING PARTS

1) Remove extension housing bolts. Remove housing and gasket. Remove return spring and parking pawl. Remove large snap ring from rear planet gear carrier.

2) Remove planet gear carrier with thrust washer No. 5 from case. Remove small snap ring from output shaft. Remove output shaft and governor with thrust washer No. 11. *See Fig. 16.*

Fig. 16: Locations of Planet Gear Carrier Snap Rings

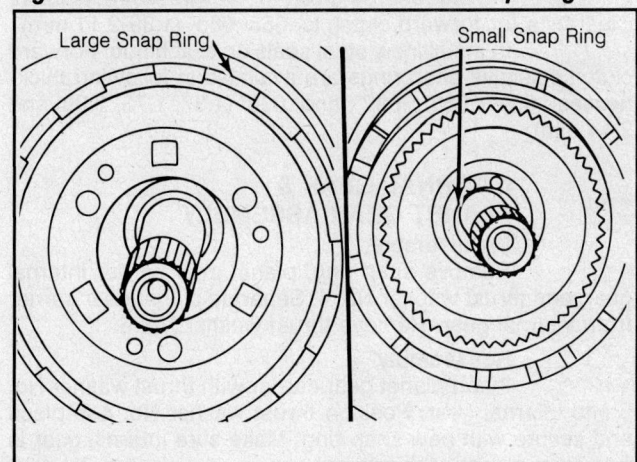

3) Remove internal gear, No. 10 thrust washer, and reverse brake drum. Remove rear band assembly. Remove one-way clutch inner race if worn or damaged. *See Fig. 17.* Remove vacuum diaphragm unit. Remove neutral safety switch.

CAUTION: Use thin-walled socket to remove neutral safety switch. Open-end wrench will crush switch.

Fig. 17: Interior View of Transmission Case

Illustration shows one-way clutch inner race

4) If replacing shift lever oil seal, press inward on downshift lever and remove "O" ring. Remove shift lever roll pin from case. Remove shift lever nut (outside). Remove parking pawl actuating rod.

5) Remove selector lever from outside case. Remove downshift lever shaft from inside case. Pry out shift lever oil seal with screwdriver. Install new oil seal using Seal Driver (T74P 77498 A).

6) Install downshift lever inside case and shift lever outside. Install nuts and parking pawl actuating rod. Install roll pin, new "O" ring, and downshift lever.

COMPONENT DISASSEMBLY & REASSEMBLY

FRONT ASSEMBLY
Disassembly

Remove clutch hub and sun gear. Remove front planet gear carrier with internal gear and thrust washer No. 5. If necessary, remove sun gear from input shell after removing retainer. Replace thrust washer No. 7, if damaged. Remove forward drive clutch and thrust washer No. 2.

NOTE: Reassembly of front assembly is covered at end of COMPONENT DISASSEMBLY and REASSEMBLY.

REVERSE-DIRECT CLUTCH
Disassembly

1) Remove large pressure plate retaining ring. Remove pressure plate and clutch pack. Using Spring Compressor (T65L 77515 A), compress piston return springs and remove small retaining ring. *See Fig. 18.* Carefully release pressure on springs.

Fig. 18: Compressing Piston Return Springs and Retainer

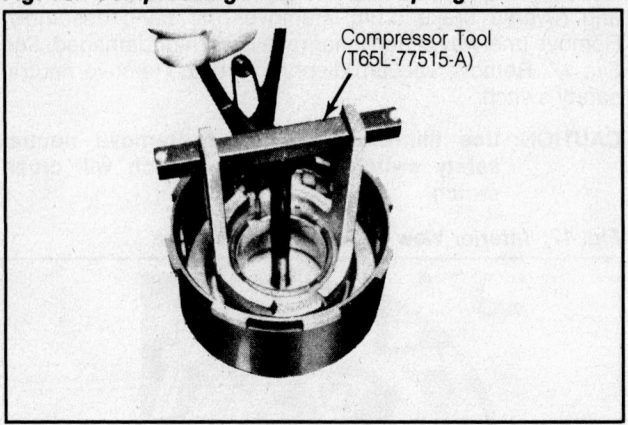

Fig. 20: Reverse-Direct Clutch Piston Installation

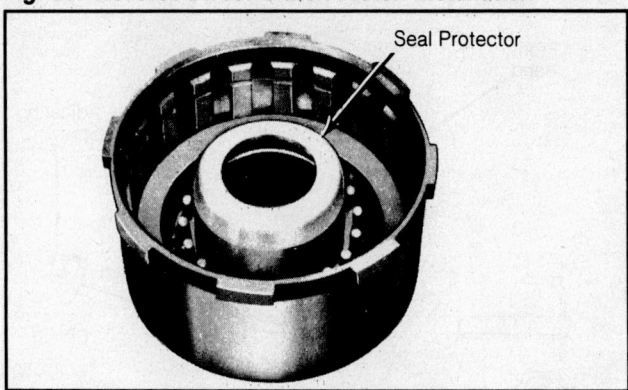

Note installed position of seal protector.

2) Remove spring retainer and return springs. Turn clutch body over and carefully force out piston with compressed air. See Fig. 19. Remove "O" rings from piston and clutch body.

Fig. 19: Using Compressed Air to Remove Reverse-Direct Clutch Piston

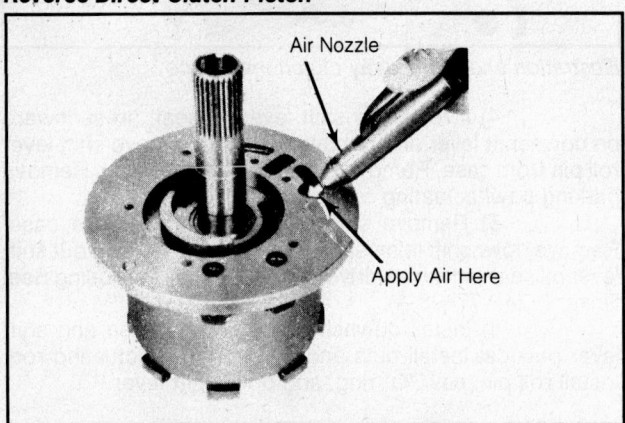

Reassembly

1) Inspect all parts for wear, damage, or effects of overheating. If new composition clutch plates are to be used, soak in transmission fluid for 30 minutes before installing.

2) Install new "O" rings on piston and clutch body. Carefully install clutch piston, using Seal Protectors (T74P 77404 A and B) to protect inner and outer seals. See Fig. 23.

3) Install 20 piston return springs and spring retainer. Compress springs with tool used at disassembly. Install snap ring and remove compressing tool. Install clutch plates, starting with steel plate.

4) Alternate composition and steel plates until all clutch plates are installed. See CLUTCH PLATE USAGE chart. Install pressure plate and secure with snap ring. Push down on pressure plate. Measure clearance between pressure plate and snap ring with feeler gauge. Clearance should be .051-.079" (1.29-2.01 mm).

5) If clearance is not within specifications, install correct thickness selective snap ring. Reverse-Direct clutch selective snap rings are available in following thicknesses: .054", .068", .082", and .096" (1.37, 1.73, 2.08, and 2.44 mm).

FORWARD CLUTCH
Disassembly

1) Remove large retaining ring. Lift out pressure plate, clutch pack, and rubber cushion spring. Using Spring Compressor (T65L 77515 A), compress piston return springs. Remove small retaining ring. See Fig. 25.

2) Carefully release pressure on springs. Remove spring retainer and springs. Using compressed air, carefully force clutch piston from clutch body. Remove "O" rings from piston and clutch body.

Reassembly

1) Inspect all parts for wear, damage, or effects of overheating. If new composition clutch plates are to be used, soak in transmission fluid for 30 minutes before installing.

2) Use Protective Tool (T74P 77548 A & B) to prevent damage to inner and outer seals. Install new "O" rings. Apply petroleum jelly to rings and to shoulder at clutch stub. Carefully install piston.

3) Install 15 piston return springs and spring retainer. Compress springs with tool used at disassembly. Install snap ring and remove tool.

4) Install rubber cushion in groove on outer face of hydraulic piston. Install clutch plates. Start with steel plate. Alternate composition and steel plates until all clutch plates are installed. See CLUTCH PLATE USAGE chart.

5) Install pressure plate and large retainer ring. Measure clearance between retainer ring and pressure plate following procedures given for Reverse-Direct clutch. Clearance for forward clutch is .055-.083" (1.39-2.11 mm).

6) Install new steel seals on clutch hub. Forward clutch selective snap rings are available in following thicknesses: .054", .068", .082", and .096" (1.37, 1.73, 2.08, and 2.44 mm).

INTERNAL GEAR & PLANET GEAR ASSEMBLY
Disassembly

Remove snap ring, planet gear carrier internal gear, and thrust washer No. 4. Separate planet gear carrier from internal gear. Remove thrust washer No. 5.

Reassembly

Insert planet gear carrier with thrust washer No. 5 into internal gear. Position thrust washer No. 4 in place and secure with new snap ring. Make sure internal gear is free from planet gear carrier.

Fig. 21: Exploded View of C-3 Automatic Transmission Assembly

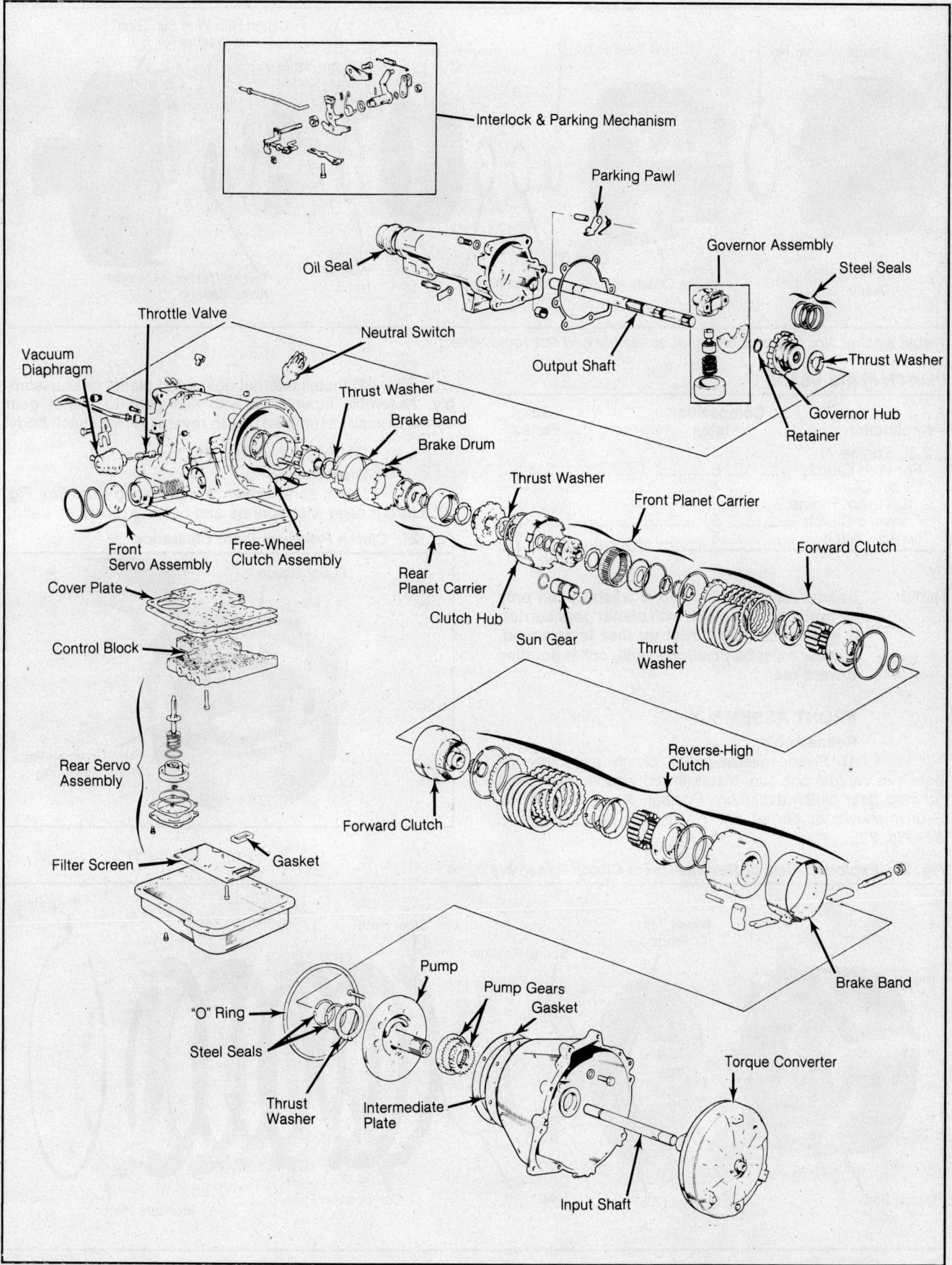

Automatic Transmissions
FORD MOTOR CO. C-3 (Cont.)

Fig. 22: Exploded View of Forward Part of Transmission Gear Train

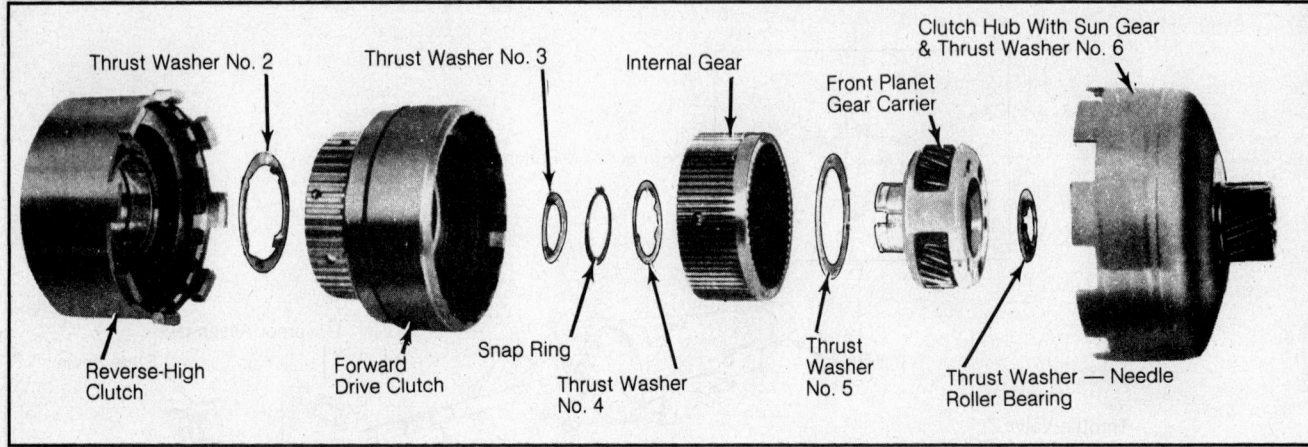

Thrust washer No. 6 is part of planet assembly and not removable.

CLUTCH PLATE USAGE

Application	Composition Plates	Steel Plates
2.3L Engine		
Forward Clutch	5	5
Direct Clutch	4	4
2.3L Turbo Engine		
Forward Clutch	5	5
Direct Clutch	5	5

NOTE: Needle roller bearing (No. 6 washer) can only be replaced complete, with planet gear carrier. If needle bearing thrust washer is removed, washer must be positioned with collar pointing toward rear.

FRONT ASSEMBLY
Reassembly

1) Place reverse-direct clutch assembly on bench in vertical position. Install thrust washer No. 2 and forward gear clutch assembly. Position thrust washer No. 3 on planet gear carrier and retain with petroleum jelly. *See Fig. 22.*

2) Install internal gears and planet gear assembly. Assemble input shell with sun gear to planet gear carrier. Install assembled unit to reverse-direct clutch body.

ONE-WAY CLUTCH
Disassembly

Using screwdriver, remove snap ring. *See Fig. 27.* Lift out cage with springs and bearing rollers as unit.

Fig. 24: Clutch Pressure Plate Clearance

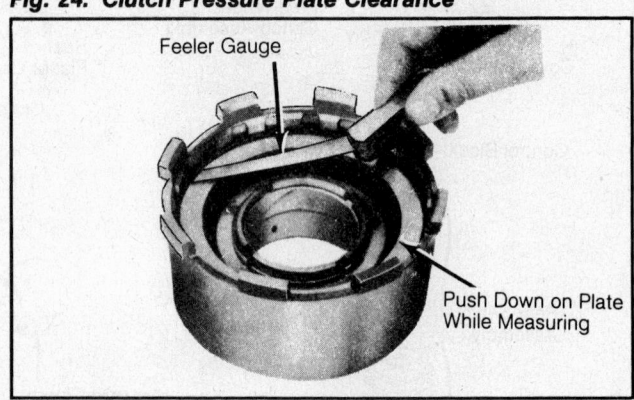

Fig. 23: Exploded View of Reverse-Direct Clutch Assembly

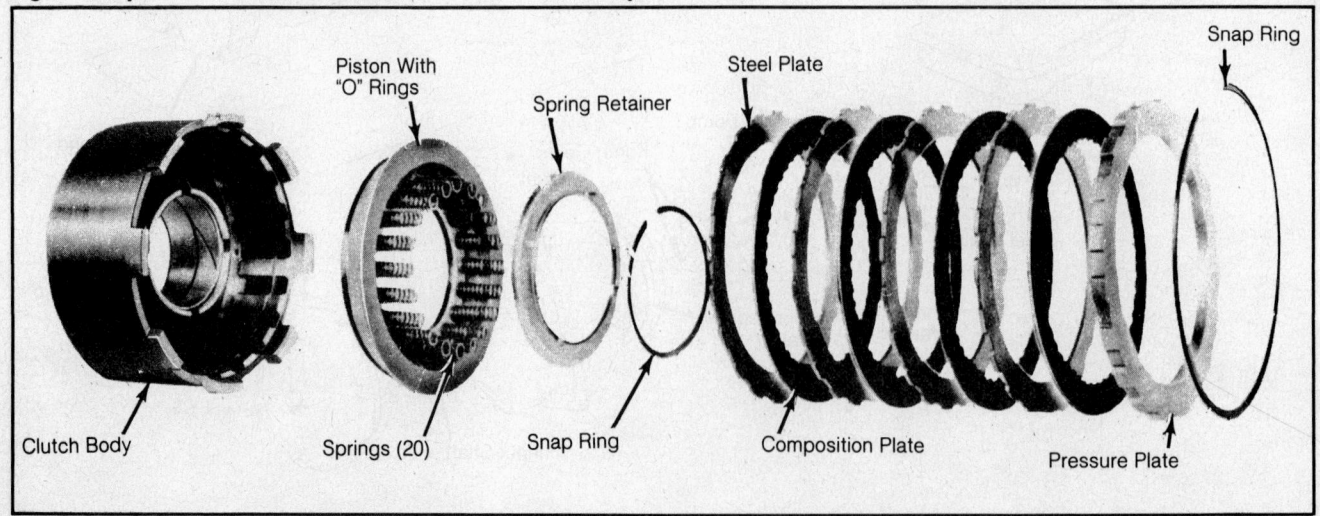

FORD MOTOR CO. C-3 (Cont.)

Fig. 25: Exploded View of Forward Clutch Assembly

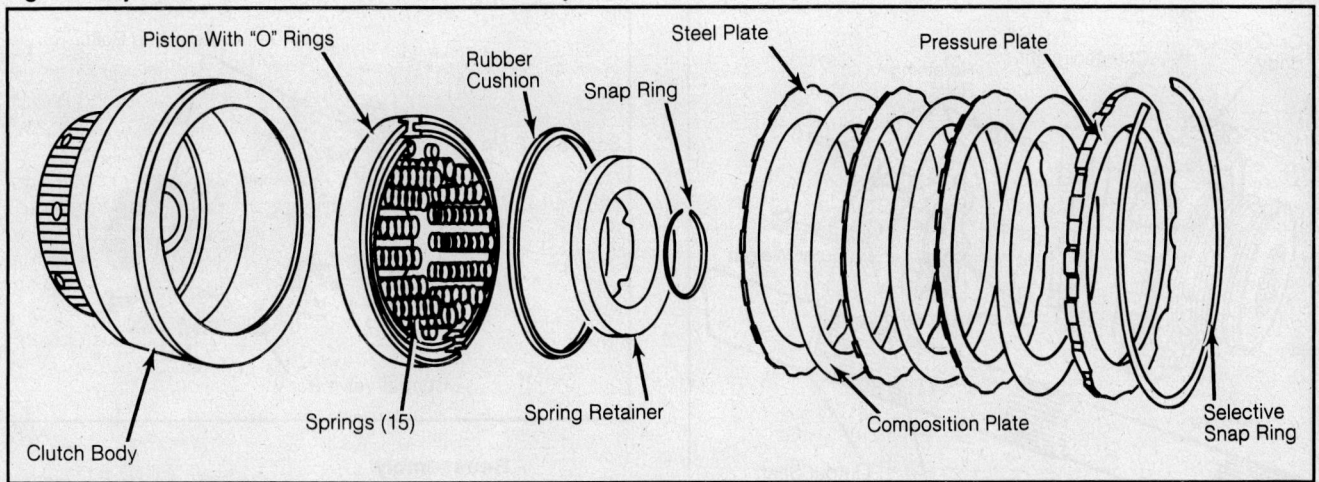

Fig. 26: Positioning of Seal Protectors for Forward Clutch Piston Installation

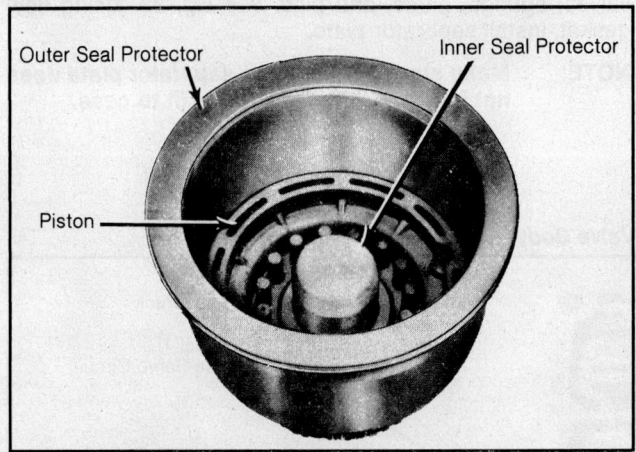

Coat seals with petroleum jelly before installing.

Fig. 27: Removing Snap Ring from One-Way Clutch Cage

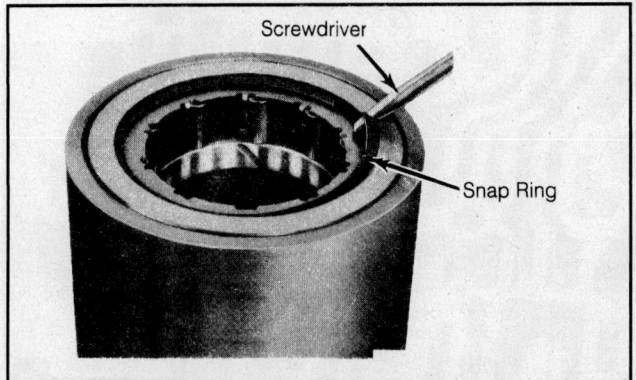

Use screwdriver to remove snap ring.

Reassembly

Inspect all parts for wear or damage. Install cage with springs. Insert bearing rollers one by one. Use screwdriver to compress springs. Install snap ring. *See Fig. 28.*

Fig. 28: Installing One-Way Clutch Bearing Rollers

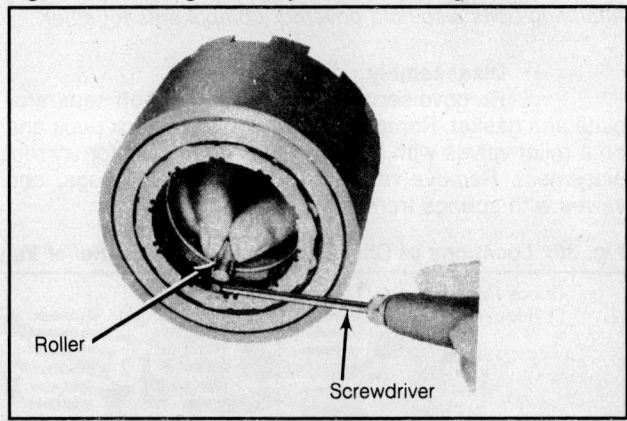

Use screwdriver to install rollers.

GOVERNOR

Disassembly

Remove governor body-to-oil collector body retaining bolts. When these bolts are removed, governor components are no longer retained in position in body. Care must be taken not to drop governor body and components when bolts are removed. Remove components from governor body. Remove counterweight.

Reassembly

1) Clean and inspect all parts. Replace any that are worn or damaged. Remove 3 rubber seals from oil collector body. Install new seals without excessive stretching.

2) Assemble counterweight spring and primary valve in governor body. Assemble governor body and counterweight to oil collector body. *See Fig. 29.*

CONTROL VALVE BODY

NOTE: As valve trains are removed from each valve body bore, place individual parts in correct order, and in relative position to valve body to simplify reassembly. Tag all springs as they are removed for reassembly reference.

Automatic Transmissions

FORD MOTOR CO. C-3 (Cont.)

Fig. 29: Exploded View of Governor Assembly

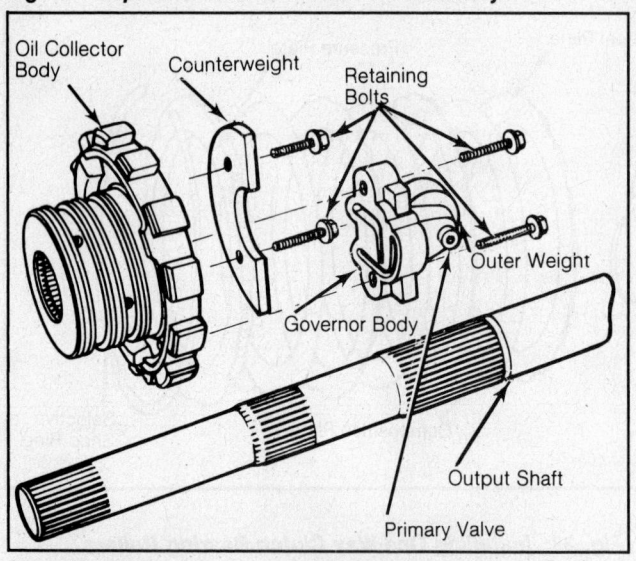

Attaching bolts also hold governor components together.

Fig. 31: Valve Body Separator Plate and Bolt Locations

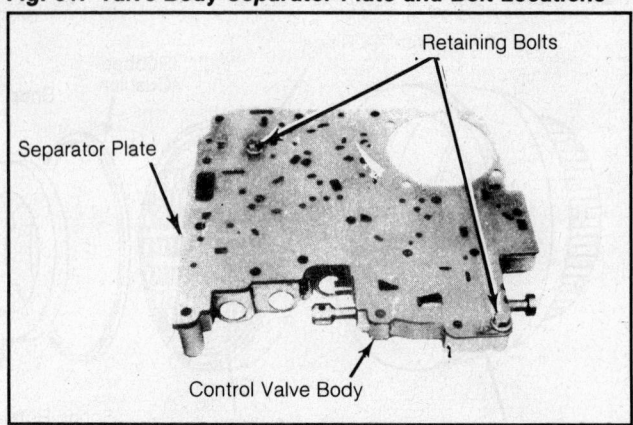

Disassembly

Remove separator plate bolts. Lift off separator plate and gasket. Remove 4 check balls, 1 check puck and both relief valves with springs. Refer to *Fig. 30* for correct placement. Remove retaining plates, dowels, plugs, and valves with springs from valve body.

Reassembly

Clean all parts and make sure passages are open. Inspect all parts for burring, unevenness, and gum deposits. Lubricate all parts with transmission fluid. Install valves, springs, plugs, and pins. *See Fig. 32.* Using new gasket, install separator plate.

NOTE: Make sure that ID tag on separator plate does not interfere with valve body fit to case.

Fig. 30: Locations of Check Balls and Pressure Relief Valve in Valve Body

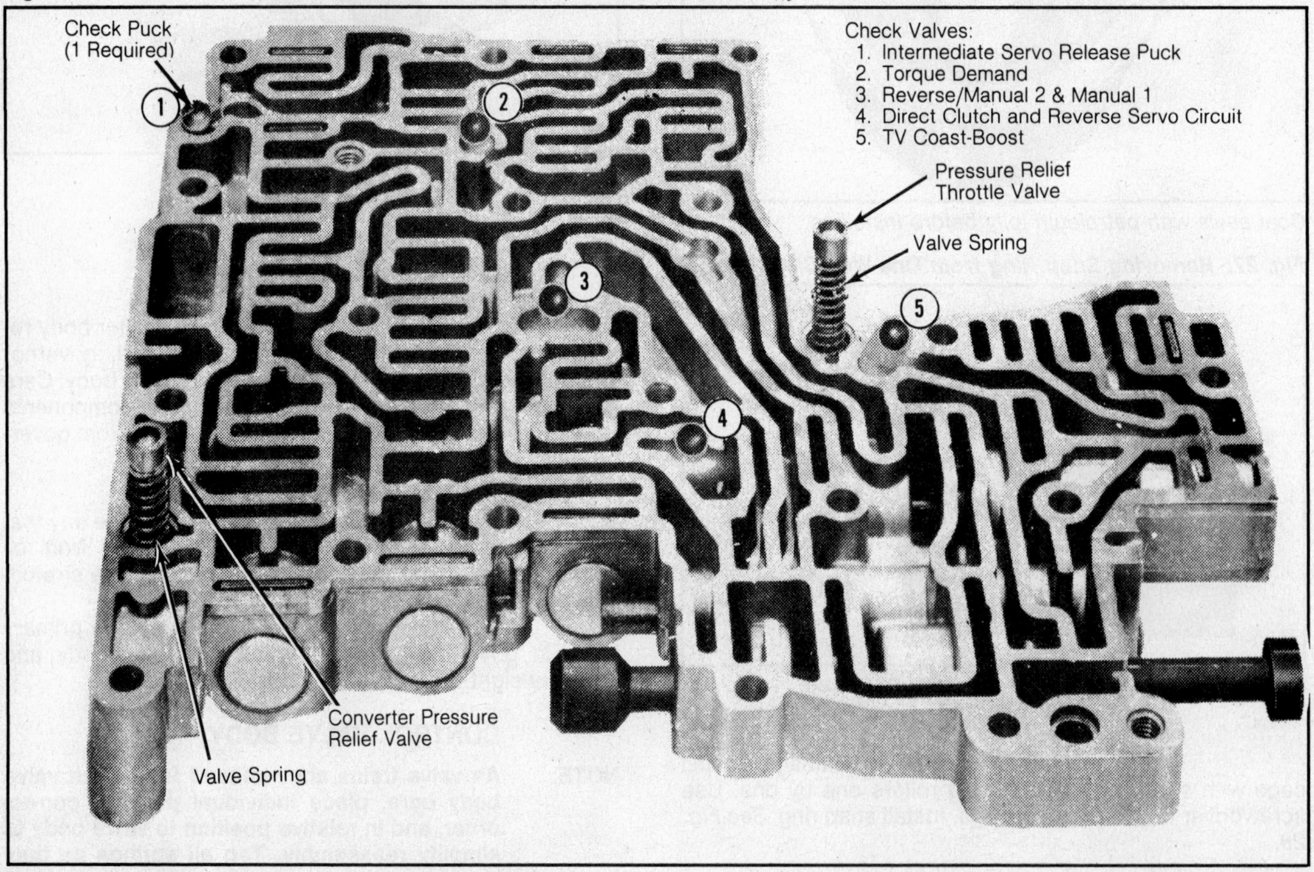

Check Valves:
1. Intermediate Servo Release Puck
2. Torque Demand
3. Reverse/Manual 2 & Manual 1
4. Direct Clutch and Reverse Servo Circuit
5. TV Coast-Boost

Note that 4 check balls and 1 check puck are used.

Fig. 32: Exploded View of Valve Body Assembly

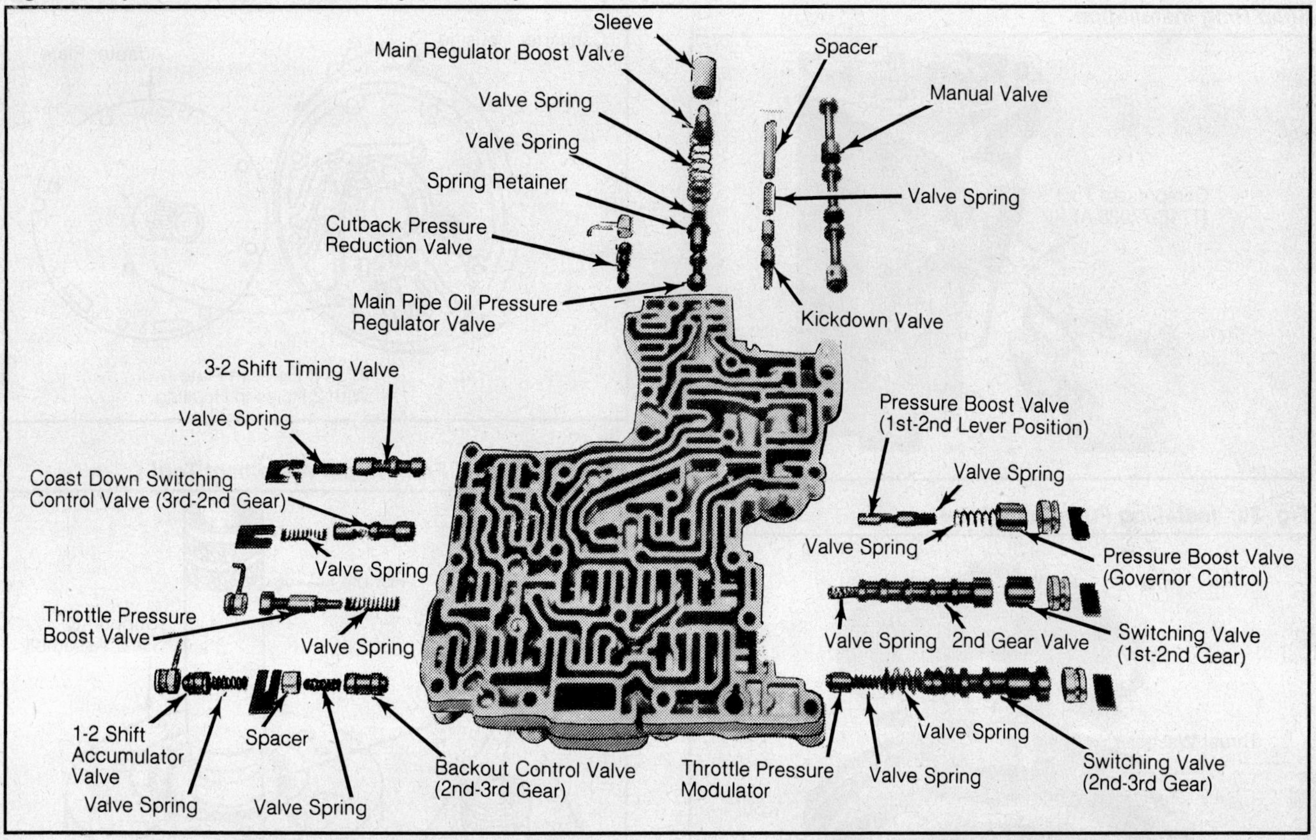

Sleeve
Main Regulator Boost Valve
Spacer
Valve Spring
Manual Valve
Valve Spring
Spring Retainer
Valve Spring
Cutback Pressure Reduction Valve
Main Pipe Oil Pressure Regulator Valve
Kickdown Valve
3-2 Shift Timing Valve
Valve Spring
Pressure Boost Valve (1st-2nd Lever Position)
Coast Down Switching Control Valve (3rd-2nd Gear)
Valve Spring
Valve Spring
Valve Spring
Pressure Boost Valve (Governor Control)
Throttle Pressure Boost Valve
Valve Spring
Valve Spring   2nd Gear Valve
Switching Valve (1st-2nd Gear)
1-2 Shift Accumulator Valve
Spacer
Backout Control Valve (2nd-3rd Gear)
Throttle Pressure Modulator
Valve Spring
Valve Spring
Switching Valve (2nd-3rd Gear)
Valve Spring
Valve Spring
Valve Spring

TRANSMISSION REASSEMBLY

NOTE: **Lubricate all parts with transmission fluid before reassembly. Thrust washers and gaskets should be held in place with petroleum jelly. See Fig. 12 for identification and location of thrust washers.**

1) Install new pump oil seal, using Installer Head with Handle (T74P 77248 B). Install new "O" ring on vacuum diaphragm unit. Install throttle valve, actuating pin and vacuum diaphragm (tubes pointing to rear).

2) Install retaining bracket and tighten bolt. Install one-way clutch inner race (if removed), using Clutch Replacing Guide (T74P 77193 A). See Fig. 34.

3) Position thrust washer No. 11 in case. Install output shaft and governor assembly, taking care to avoid damaging rubber oil seal rings.

4) Position rear band in housing. Make sure it is aligned with guide pilots. Position thrust washer No. 10 in case. Install rear brake drum using Clutch Replacing Guide (T74P 77193 A).

Fig. 33: Exploded View of Front Servo Assembly

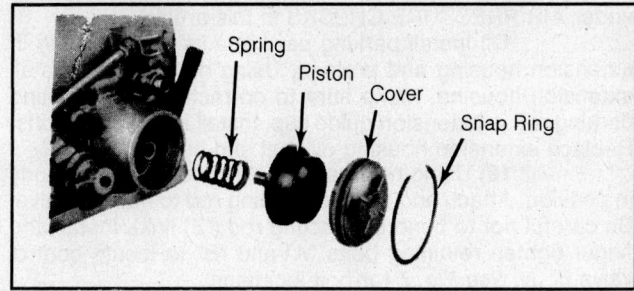

Spring
Piston
Cover
Snap Ring

5) Remove guide. Install internal gear and attach with snap ring. Position thrust washer No. 9 to back of planet carrier. Install carrier and attach to rear brake drum with snap ring.

6) Position thrust washer No. 8 on planet gear carrier and install front assembly. Replace front servo piston or "O" rings at this time, if necessary. See Fig. 33.

7) Install spiral spring on front servo piston assembly. Install piston and cover. Press down on cover with Compressor (T74P 77028 A). Install snap ring.

8) Install brake band and struts, starting with strut at servo piston lever. Being careful not to damage oil seals, turn transmission so output shaft points downward. See Fig. 35.

Fig. 34: Clutch Replacing Guide Used to Install One-Way Clutch Inner Race

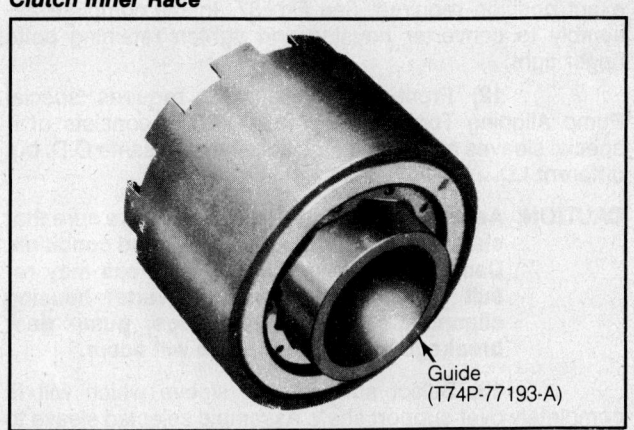

Guide (T74P-77193-A)

Fig. 35: Tool Set-Up for Front Servo Snap Ring Installation

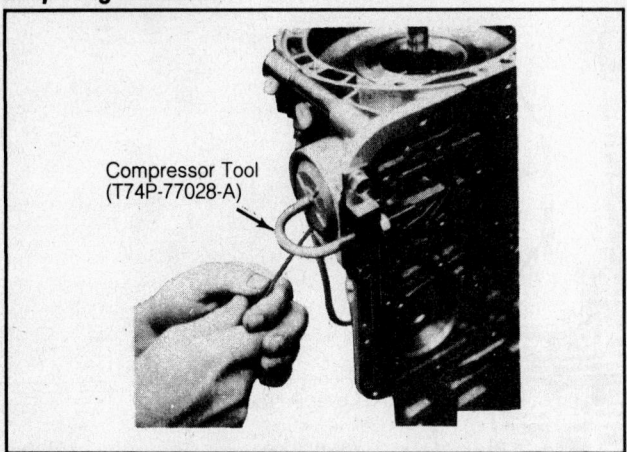

Compressor Tool (T74P-77028-A)

Fig. 36: Installing Pump Into Case

Thrust Washer

Fig. 37: Correct Positioning of Adapter Plate on Housing

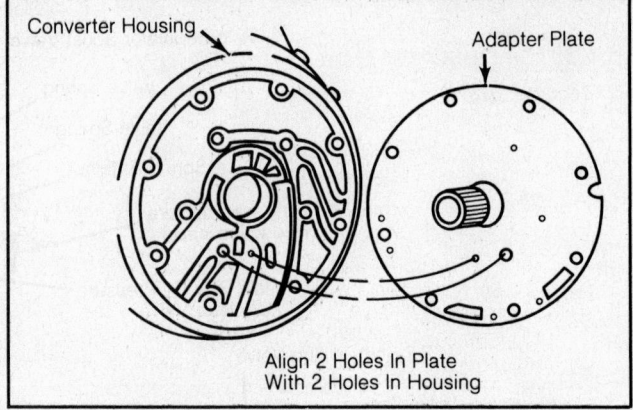

Converter Housing

Adapter Plate

Align 2 Holes In Plate With 2 Holes In Housing

Fig. 38: Special Front Pump Alignment Tool

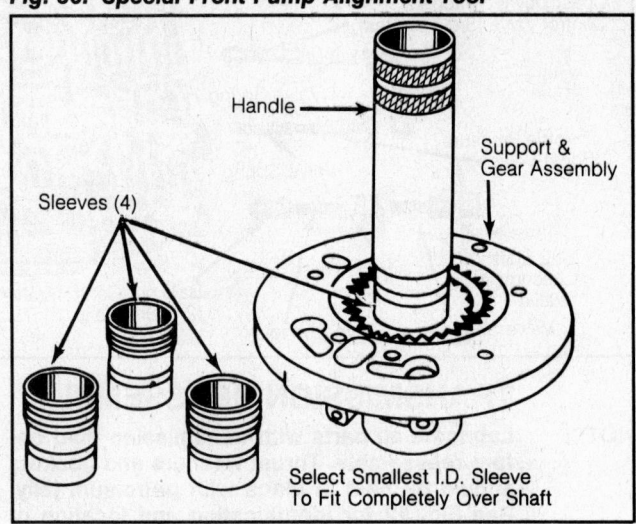

Handle

Support & Gear Assembly

Sleeves (4)

Select Smallest I.D. Sleeve To Fit Completely Over Shaft

Tool T74P 77103 X consists of 4 sleeves and handle.

9) Install oil pump and thrust washer No. 1. Recheck transmission end play as described this article under TRANSMISSION DISASSEMBLY. Replace thrust washer if end play is not within range.

CAUTION: End play setting is critical. Be sure to check end play during reassembly procedure.

10) Remove oil pump and thrust washer again. Install inside and outside pump gears. Make sure small gear has I.D. pump drive flat recess facing upward, and large gear has chamfer facing downward.

11) Position steel adapter plate on oil pump in exact position required. See Fig. 37. Install complete assembly to converter housing and tighten retaining bolts finger tight.

12) Front pump alignment requires special Pump Aligning Tool (T74P 77103 X). Tool consists of 4 special sleeves and handle. Each sleeve has same O.D. but different I.D.

CAUTION: As this measurement is critical, make sure that sleeve gauging surfaces are in good condition. Damage to sleeve gauging surfaces may result in incorrect pump-to-converter housing alignment. Pump seal leakage, pump gear breakage, or bushing failure will occur.

13) Select smallest I.D. sleeve which will fit completely over support shaft. Assemble selected sleeve to

handle. Slide tool down over shaft until it bottoms against pump.

14) Outside diameter of sleeve centers pump in converter housing. Tighten retaining bolts and remove centering tool. Install input shaft into pump. Install converter into pump gears. Rotate converter to check for free movement.

15) Remove converter and input shaft. Position selected No. 1 thrust washer to pump housing. Install new "O" ring. Carefully install converter housing with pump using new gasket. Use care to avoid damaging steel oil seals.

16) Install bolts and tighten. Be sure to use new aluminum washers. Adjust front band. Perform air pressure tests to ensure proper transmission operation as described under AIR PRESSURE CHECKS in this article.

17) Install parking pawl and its return spring in extension housing and preload. Using new gasket, install extension housing. Make sure to correctly seat operating parking rod in extension guide cup. Install and tighten bolts. Replace extension housing oil seal and bushing.

18) Using new gasket, place control valve body in position. Attach and lock connecting rod to manual valve. Be careful not to bend connecting rod ("Z" link). Install and finger tighten retaining bolts "A" and "B" to locate control valve body. See Fig. 7 for bolt locations.

Automatic Transmissions

FORD MOTOR CO. C-3 (Cont.)

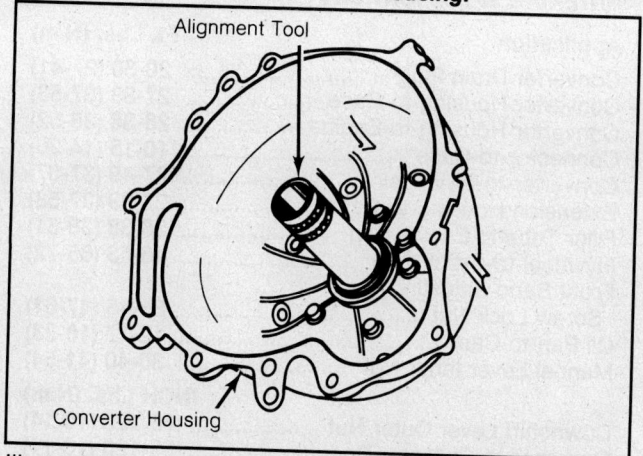

Fig. 39: Front View of Converter Housing.

Illustration shows position of pump alignment tools.

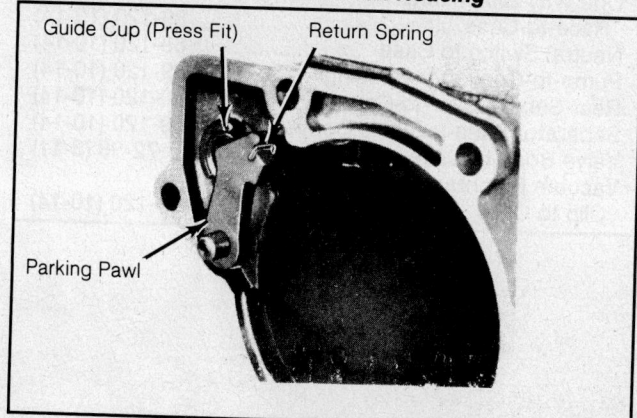

Fig. 40: Interior View of Extension Housing

Note correct installation of parking pawl.

Fig. 41: Rear of Transmission Housing

Note proper installation of extension housing.

19) Install and tighten all remaining bolts except filter screen bolts. Remove bolt "A" and attach detent spring to bolt. Reinstall bolt "A" and tighten bolts "A" and "B" completely. Make sure inner downshift lever is seated between stop and downshift valve as shown in *Fig. 43*.

CAUTION: Because valve body retaining bolts are of different lengths, make sure each bolt head bottoms on valve body housing.

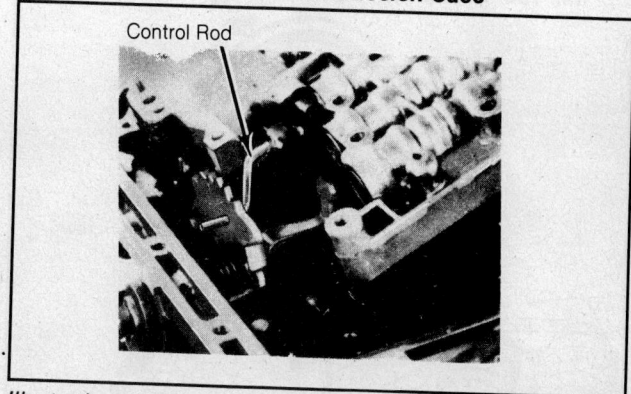

Fig. 42: Interior View of Transmission Case

Illustration shows valve body installation and position.

Fig. 43: Bottom of Transmission Case

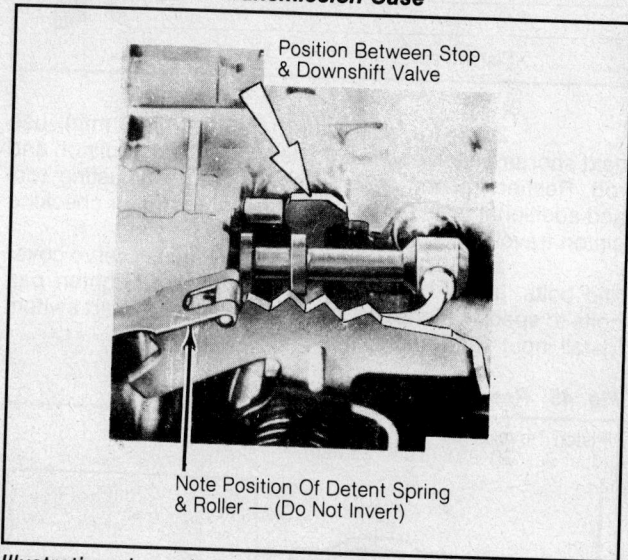

Illustration shows inner downshift lever position.

20) Assemble servo piston rod, servo piston, and spring. Install additional reverse servo Piston Spring (D4ZZ 7D031 A) to check piston travel. Install piston assembly into rear servo bore. Make sure piston rod is correctly seated in reverse band apply end.

21) Install servo rod Selecting Guide (T74P 77190 A) using new servo cover gasket. Install and tighten 3 retaining bolts (servo cover bolts are not long enough to attach tool to case; use three M6x30 valve body retaining bolts).

22) Tighten servo tool adjusting screw to 36 INCH lbs. (4 N.m). Install dial indicator on case. Position indicator tip on one of 3 servo piston pads accessible through cut-out of tool. Zero dial indicator. *See Fig. 44.*

23) Back out tool adjusting screw until servo bottoms out on tool. Record distance servo piston moved. If servo piston travel is .120-.220" (3.05-5.59 mm), servo piston rod is acceptable. If piston travel is greater than .220" (5.59 mm), use next longer servo piston and rod.

NOTE: Servo piston rods are available in 3 sizes and identified by grooves on rod. Rod sizes and I.D. are as follows: 2.085-2.112" (1 groove), 1.986-2.014" (no groove), and 1.888-1.915" (2 grooves).

Automatic Transmissions
FORD MOTOR CO. C-3 (Cont.)

Fig. 44: Tool Set-Up for Rear Servo Pin Selection

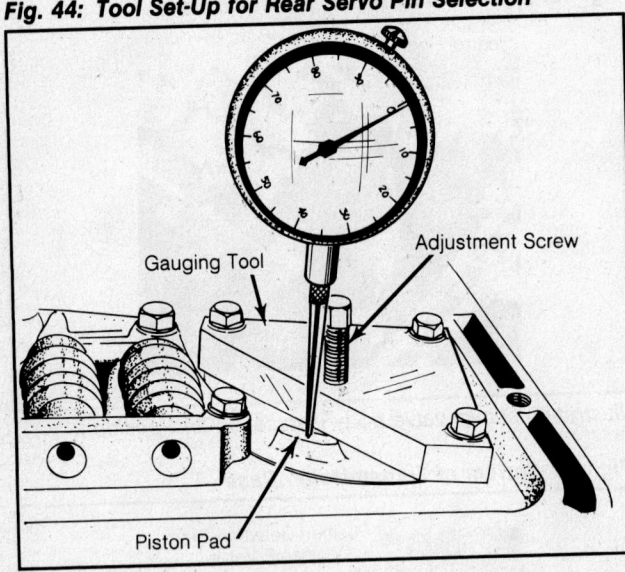

Gauging Tool

Adjustment Screw

Piston Pad

24) If travel is less than .120" (3.05 mm), use next shorter piston and rod. Install correct servo piston and rod. Recheck piston travel. Remove servo adjusting tool and additional reverse servo spring (only used for checking piston travel).

25) Reinstall servo assembly. Install servo cover and bolts. Install oil pan, using new gasket. Tighten pan bolts to specifications in 2 steps. Install neutral start switch. Install input shaft and torque converter.

Fig. 45: Rear Servo Piston Travel Measurement

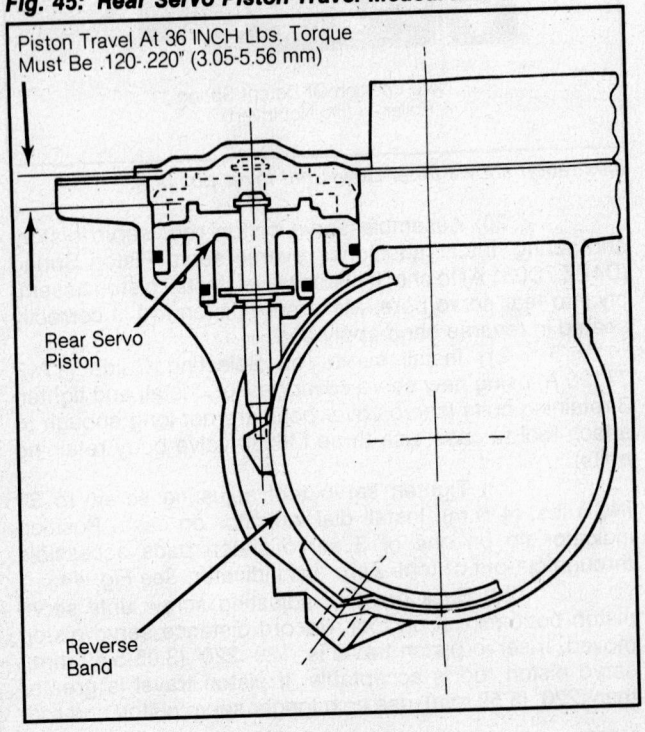

Piston Travel At 36 INCH Lbs. Torque Must Be .120-.220" (3.05-5.56 mm)

Rear Servo Piston

Reverse Band

TIGHTENING SPECIFICATIONS

Application	Ft. Lbs. (N.m)
Converter Drain Plug	20-30 (27-41)
Converter Housing-to-Case	27-39 (37-53)
Converter Housing-to-Engine	28-38 (38-52)
Connector-to-Case	10-15 (14-20)
Converter-to-Flywheel	27-49 (37-67)
Extension Housing-to-Case	27-39 (37-53)
Filler Tube to Engine Clip	28-38 (38-51)
Flywheel-to-Crankshaft	48-53 (65-72)
Front Band Adjusting Screw Lock Nut	35-45 (47-61)
Oil Pan-to-Case	12-17 (16-23)
Manual Lever Inner Nut	30-40 (41-54)

Application	INCH Lbs. (N.m)
Downshift Lever Outer Nut	89-120 (10-14)
Governor-to-Collector Body	89-120 (10-14)
Oil Cooler Line or By-Pass Tube-to Connector	89-120 (10-14)
One Way Clutch Inner Race-to-Case	89-120 (10-14)
Neutral Switch to Case	89-120 (10-14)
Pump-to-Converter Housing	89-120 (10-14)
Rear Servo Cover-to-Case	89-120 (10-14)
Separator Plate-to-Valve Body	89-120 (10-14)
Valve Body-to-Case	72-96 (8-11)
Vacuum Diaphragm Retaining Clip to Case	89-120 (10-14)

FORD MOTOR CO. C-5

Capri, Cougar, LTD, Marquis,
Mustang, Thunderbird, F150 Pickups

IDENTIFICATION

The C-5 automatic transmission is identifed by code letter C (passenger cars) or W (truck models), which is shown on lower line of Vehicle Certification Label under "TR" or "TRANS". Label is located on driver's door lock panel of pillar.

Transmission may also be identified by a metal tag which is attached under lower front intermediate servo cover bolt. The first line on tag shows transmission model prefix and suffix. A number appearing after the suffix indicates that internal parts have been changed after initial production start up.

TRANSMISSION IDENTIFICATION CODES

Application	Code
F150 Pickups	"W"
Passenger Cars	"C"

DESCRIPTION

The C-5 transmission is a fully automatic 3-speed unit capable of providing automatic upshifts and downshifts through 3 forward gear ratios and also capable of providing manual selection of 1st and 2nd gears.

The unit consists essentially of a converter clutch torque converter, a compound planetary gear train controlled by 2 bands, 2 disc clutches, a one-way clutch and a hydraulic control system.

LUBRICATION & ADJUSTMENTS

See appropriate AUTOMATIC TRANSMISSION SERVICING article in DOMESTIC GENERAL SERVICING section.

TROUBLE SHOOTING

See appropriate AUTOMATIC TRANSMISSION TROUBLE SHOOTING article in DOMESTIC GENERAL SERVICING section.

TESTING

STALL TEST
Testing Precautions

1) When making test, DO NOT hold throttle open longer than 5 seconds. Allow a cooling period of I5 seconds with transmission in Neutral and engine speed at 1000 RPM between each test.

2) If engine speed exceeds maximum limits shown, release accelerator immediately as this is an indication of clutch or band slippage.

Testing Procedure

1) Install tachometer and fully apply parking and service brakes. Start engine and run at curb idle and at normal operating temperature.

2) Stall test transmission in each driving range at full throttle. Note maximum RPM obtained. Engine speed should be within limits shown in STALL SPEED SPECIFICATIONS table.

STALL SPEED SPECIFICATIONS

Engine Size	Converter Size	Stall Speed RPM
3.8L 2 Bbl.	12"	1688-1966
3.8L C.F.I.	12"	1760-2050
4.9 & 5.0L [1]	12"	1597-1851

[1] – F150 pickup only.

STALL TEST RESULTS
Stall Speed Too High

In "D", "2", "1" and "R"; general transmission problems are indicated and a control pressure test should be made to locate faulty unit(s). In "D" only; planetary one-way clutch slippage is indicated. In "D", "2" and "1"; forward clutch slippage is indicated. In "R" only, high clutch or reverse band slippage is indicated.

Stall Speed Too Low

Converter stator one-way clutch or engine performance is faulty.

ROAD TEST

1) Check minimum throttle upshifts in "D". Transmission should start off in 1st gear, shift to 2nd, and then shift to 3rd as speed increases.

2) With transmission in 3rd gear, depress accelerator pedal through detent (to floor). Transmission should shift from 3rd to 2nd, or 3rd to 1st, depending on vehicle speed. See SHIFT SPEEDS chart.

3) Check closed throttle downshift from 3rd to 1st by coasting down from about 30 MPH in 3rd gear. Shift should occur as shown in table.

4) With transmission in "2" position, transmission should operate only in 2nd gear.

5) With transmission in 3rd gear and road speed above 30 MPH, transmission should shift to 2nd gear when selector lever is moved from "D", to "2" or "1". When same manual shift is made below 25 MPH, transmission will shift from 2nd or 3rd to 1st.

NOTE: **Preceding check will determine if governor pressure and shift control valves are operating properly.**

6) Slipping or engine speed flare-up in any gear usually indicates clutch or band problems. In most cases, the clutch or band that is slipping can be determined by noting transmission operation in all selector lever positions, and comparing which internal units are applied in those positions. See CLUTCH and BAND APPLICATION chart.

CONTROL PRESSURE TEST

1) Attach a tachometer to engine. Attach a hand vacuum pump to transmission vacuum diaphragm unit. Attach a hydraulic pressure gauge to control pressure outlet on transmission. See Figs. 2 and 4.

2) Apply parking brake. If equipped with a vacuum brake release, apply service brake. Start engine and allow it to reach normal operating temperature. Set idle speed to specifications.

Automatic Transmissions

FORD MOTOR CO. C-5 (Cont.)

Fig. 1: Cutaway View of Ford Motor Co. C-5 Automatic Transmission Assembly

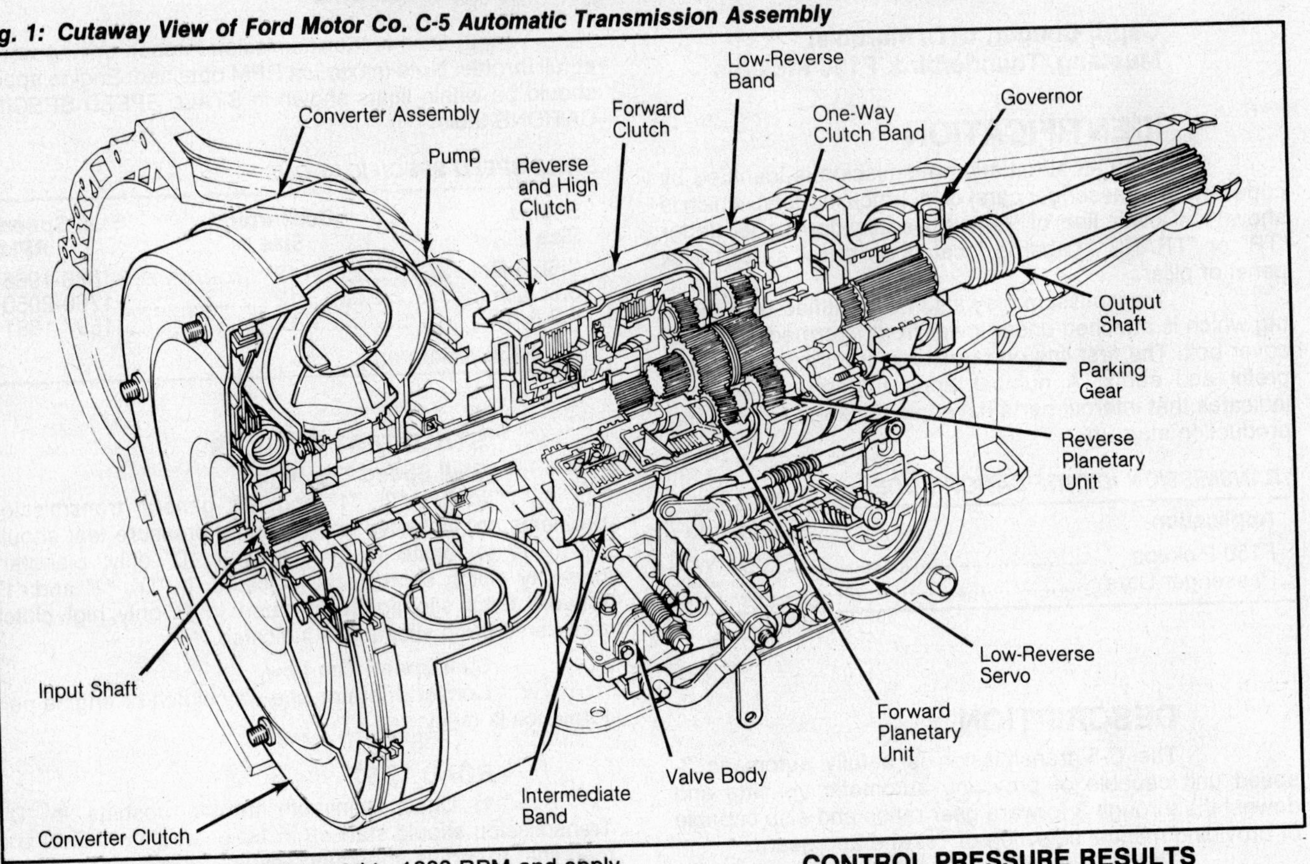

Converter Assembly
Pump
Reverse and High Clutch
Forward Clutch
Low-Reverse Band
One-Way Clutch Band
Governor
Output Shaft
Parking Gear
Reverse Planetary Unit
Low-Reverse Servo
Forward Planetary Unit
Valve Body
Intermediate Band
Converter Clutch
Input Shaft

3) Adjust engine speed to 1000 RPM and apply 10 in. Hg. to vacuum diaphragm unit. Read and record control pressure in all selector positions. Compare obtained pressure readings with readings in CONTROL PRESSURE table.

CONTROL PRESSURES

Color Code	Rod Length Inches (mm)
Green	1.5875-1.5925 (40.3-40.4)
Blue	1.6025-1.6075 (40.7-40.8)
Orange	1.6175-1.6225 (41.1-41.2)
Black	1.6325-1.6375 (41.5-41.6)
Pink & White	1.6535-1.6585 (42.0-42.1)

4) If recorded pressure is within specifications, no change is required. If recorded pressure is below specifications, use next longest rod. If recorded pressure is above specifications, use next shortest rod.

Fig. 2: Vacuum Gauge Installation

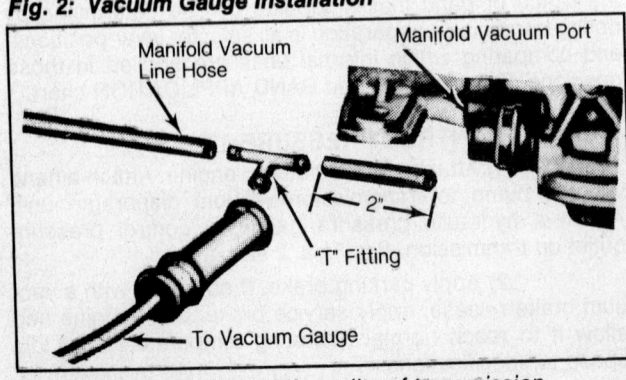

Manifold Vacuum Line Hose
Manifold Vacuum Port
"T" Fitting
2"
To Vacuum Gauge

Pressure gauges affect shift quality of transmission.

CONTROL PRESSURE RESULTS

If control pressures are not within specification, use the following to determine cause of trouble:

Control Pressure Low at Idle in All Ranges
Check for low fluid level, restricted oil filter, loose valve body to case bolts, low engine idle, pump leakage, case leakage, valve body leakage, fluid is too hot, or main oil regulator valve sticking.

Control Pressure High at Idle in All Ranges
Check engine EGR system. Check vacuum diaphragm unit, manifold vacuum line, throttle valve linkage, and control rod. Check for sticking regulator boost valve(s).

Control Pressure OK at Idle in All Ranges, But Low at 10 in. Hg
Check vacuum diaphragm unit. Control rod or throttle valve are stuck.

Control Pressure OK at Idle in All Ranges, OK at 10 in. Hg, But Low at 1 in. Hg
Check for excessive leakage, low pump capacity, or restricted oil pan screen.

Fig. 3: View of Left Side of Transmission Case

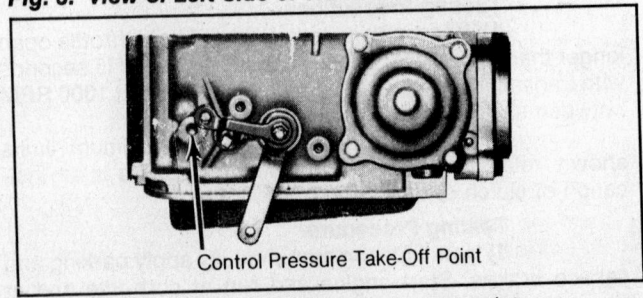

Control Pressure Take-Off Point

Illustration shows location of pressure test point.

FORD MOTOR CO. C-5 (Cont.)

CLUTCH & BAND APPLICATION (ELEMENTS IN USE)

Gear	Rev. & High Clutch	Forward Clutch	One-Way Clutch	Intermediate Band	Low-Reverse Band
1st (D Range)		Applied	Applied		
1st (1 Range)		Applied			Applied
2nd		Applied		Applied	
3rd	Applied	Applied			
Reverse	Applied				Applied

SHIFT SPEEDS (MPH)

MODELS PEP-AF
3.8L CAPRI/MUSTANG

Throttle	Range	Shift	OPS—R.P.M.	Column Number 1
Closed (Above 17" Vacuum)	D	1-2	409-444	10-12
	D	2-3	580-761	15-21
	D	3-1, 2-1	331-366	8-10
	1	2-1	1074-1273	28-34
To Detent (Torque Demand)	D	1-2	588-1035	15-28
	D	2-3	1226-1638	32-44
	D	3-2	1242-1491	33-40
Through Detent (WOT)	D	1-2	1489-1726	39-46
	D	2-3	2633-2912	69-78
	D	3-2	2381-2539	63-68
	D	3-1, 2-1	1076-1306	28-35

Tire Size	Axle Ratio 2.73 — Use Column No.
P195/75R14	1
P205/70R14	1
205/70VR14	1
220/55R390	1

MODEL PEP-AM, AN, AL
3.8L LTD/MARQUIS &
COUGAR/THUNDERBIRD

Throttle	Range	Shift	OPS—R.P.M.	Column Number 1	Column Number 2
Closed (Above 17" Vacuum)	D	1-2	399-446	9-11	9-11
	D	2-3	500-744	11-18	12-18
	D	3-1, 2-1	331-366	7-9	8-9
	1	2-1	1091-1317	26-31	26-32
To Detent (Torque Demand)	D	1-2	723-1135	17-27	17-28
	D	2-3	1366-1762	32-42	33-43
	D	3-2	1354-1564	32-37	32-38
Through Detent (WOT)	D	1-2	1514-1775	36-42	36-43
	D	2-3	2666-2981	63-71	64-72
	D	3-2	2407-2602	57-62	58-63
	D	3-1, 2-1	1094-1344	26-32	26-33

Tire Size	Axle Ratio 2.73 — Use Column No.
P195/75R14	1
P205/70R14	1
P215/70R14	2
P215/70HR14	2
P220/55R390	1

MODEL PEA-CW
5.0L F150

Throttle	Range	Shift	OPS—R.P.M.	Column Number 1	Column Number 2	Column Number 3
Closed (Above 17" Vacuum)	D	1-2	413-456	10-11	11-12	10-12
	D	2-3	580-761	14-19	15-21	14-20
	D	3-1, 2-1	331-366	8-9	8-10	8-9
	1	2-1	1122-1320	28-33	30-36	28-34
To Detent (Torque Demand)	D	1-2	964-1240	24-31	26-34	24-32
	D	2-3	1600-1852	40-42	43-50	41-18
	D	3-2	1459-1614	36-40	39-43	37-42
Through Detent (WOT)	D	1-2	1516-1755	37-44	41-48	39-45
	D	2-3	2621-2901	65-72	71-79	67-75
	D	3-2	2359-2516	58-63	63-68	60-65
	D	3-1, 2-1	1110-1341	27-33	30-36	28-35

Tire Size	Axle Ratio 3.08 — Use Column No.
P195/75R15SL	1
P215/75R15SL	2
P235/75R15XL	3

MODEL PEJ-CU
4.9L F150

Throttle	Range	Shift	OPS—R.P.M.	Column Number 1	Column Number 2	Column Number 3	Column Number 4
Closed (Above 17" Vacuum)	D	1-2	405-449	10-11	10-12	10-12	
	D	2-3	574-776	14-19	15-21	14-20	
	D	3-1, 2-1	331-366	8-9	8-10	8-10	
	1	2-1	1004-1192	25-30	27-32	25-31	
To Detent (Torque Demand)	D	1-2	724-995	18-25	19-27	18-26	
	D	2-3	1341-1536	36-38	36-41	34-40	
	D	3-2	1070-1259	26-31	29-34	27-33	
Through Detent (WOT)	D	1-2	1373-1598	34-40	37-43	35-41	
	D	2-3	2413-2681	60-67	65-73	62-69	
	D	3-2	2170-2324	54-58	58-63	56-60	
	D	3-1, 2-1	998-1218	24-30	27-33	25-32	

Tire Size	Axle Ratio 3.08 — Use Column No.
P195/75R15SL	1
P215/75R15SL	2
P235/75R15XL	3

Automatic Transmissions

FORD MOTOR CO. C-5 (Cont.)

SHIFT SPEEDS (MPH) (Cont.)

MODEL PEP-AC, AD, AE, AP, Z 3.8L LTD/MARQUIS

Throttle	Range	Shift	OPS—R.P.M.	Column Number			
				1	2	3	4
Closed (Above 17" Vacuum)	D	1-2	399-446	10-12	10-12	9-11	9-11
	D	2-3	500-744	13-20	13-20	11-18	12-18
	D	3-1, 2-1	331-366	9-10	9-10	7-9	8-9
	1	2-1	1091-1317	29-35	29-36	25-31	26-32
To Detent (Torque Demand)	D	1-2	609-1061	16-28	16-29	14-25	15-26
	D	2-3	1237-1656	33-44	33-45	29-39	30-40
	D	3-2	1242-1564	32-42	32-43	29-37	30-38
Through Detent (WOT)	D	1-2	1514-1775	40-48	41-49	35-42	36-43
	D	2-3	2666-2981	70-80	72-82	62-71	64-72
	D	3-2	2407-2602	63-70	65-71	56-62	58-63
	D	3-1, 2-1	1094-1344	28-36	29-37	25-32	26-33

Tire Size	Axle Ratio	
	2.73	3.08
	Use Column No.	
P195/75R14	1	3
P205/70R14	1	3
P215/70R14	2	4
215/70HR14	2	4
220/55R390	1	3

Control Pressure Low In "2"
Check forward clutch and/or intermediate servo.

Control Pressure Low In "D"
Check for faulty forward clutch.

Control Pressure Low In "1"
Check forward clutch and/or reverse/high servo.

Control Pressure Low In "R"
Check reverse-high clutch and/or rear servo.

GOVERNOR CHECK

1) Raise and support vehicle so that rear wheels are clear of floor. Disconnect and plug vacuum line to vacuum diaphragm unit. Connect hose from a remote vacuum pump to vacuum diaphragm unit.

2) Attach tachometer to engine. Attach a 0-400 psi pressure gauge to control pressure take-off point at transmission.

CAUTION: Do not exceed 60 MPH speedometer speed during governor pressure test.

3) Place transmission in manual "2", no load on engine, and apply 10 in. Hg to vacuum diaphragm unit. Increase speed slowly and watch speedometer. Check MPH at which control pressure cutback occurs. It should occur between 10-14 MPH on F150, an 10-20 MPH on all other models.

NOTE: After each test, shift into Neutral and run engine at 1000 RPM to cool transmission.

4) On all models, if cutback does not occur within specifications, check shift speeds to verify that it is the governor and not a stuck cutback valve, then repair or replace governor.

VACUUM DIAPHRAGM CHECK
Vacuum Supply to Diaphragm Unit

1) Check supply by disconnecting vacuum line at vacuum unit and connect it to a vacuum gauge. With engine idling, gauge must show steady acceptable vacuum.

2) If reading is low, check for vacuum leak or poor engine vacuum. If reading is OK, rapidly accelerate engine momentarily. Reading must drop rapidly at acceleration and return immediately upon release of accelerator.

3) If reading does not change or changes slowly, transmission vacuum line is plugged, restricted, or connected to a reservoir supply. Correct as necessary.

Vacuum Diaphragm Unit

1) Remove unit from transmission. Use a distributor tester equipped with a vacuum pump. Start pump and set regulator knob so that vacuum gauge reads 18 in. Hg, with end of hose blocked off.

2) Connect vacuum hose to manifold vacuum port. If gauge still reads 18 in. Hg, vacuum unit diaphragm is not leaking. If reading does not hold at 18 in. Hg, but drops, diaphragm is leaking and unit must be replaced.

3) As hose is removed from vacuum unit, hold a finger over end of control rod. When hose is removed, the internal spring of vacuum unit should push control rod outward.

4) Check also for presence of transmission fluid in vacuum side of diaphragm or in vacuum hose. If fluid is present, diaphragm is leaking and must be replaced.

AIR PRESSURE CHECKS

1) A "No Drive" condition can exist, even with correct transmission fluid pressure, because of inoperative clutches or bands. Erratic shifts could be caused by a stuck governor valve.

2) The inoperative units can be located through a series of checks by substituting air pressure for the fluid pressure to determine location of malfunction.

3) To make air pressure checks, loosen oil pan bolts and allow transmission to drain. Remove oil pan and control valve body. Apply air to fluid passages to ensure that unit operation is as follows:

Forward Clutch

Apply air pressure to forward clutch passage. A dull thud can be heard when clutch piston is applied, or movement of the piston can be felt by placing finger tips on input shell.

Governor

Apply air pressure to control pressure-to-governor passage and listen for a sharp clicking or whistling noise indicating governor valve movement.

Reverse-High Clutch

Apply air pressure to reverse-high clutch passage. A dull thud can be heard when clutch piston is applied, or movement of piston can be felt by placing finger tips on clutch drum.

Intermediate Servo

1) Hold air nozzle in intermediate servo apply passage. Operation of servo is indicated by tightening of intermediate band around drum.

2) While continuing to apply air pressure at servo apply passage, apply air pressure to intermediate servo release passage or front release tube. Front or intermediate servo should release band against the applied pressure.

Fig. 4: C-5 Automatic Transmission Hydraulic Circuits Diagram

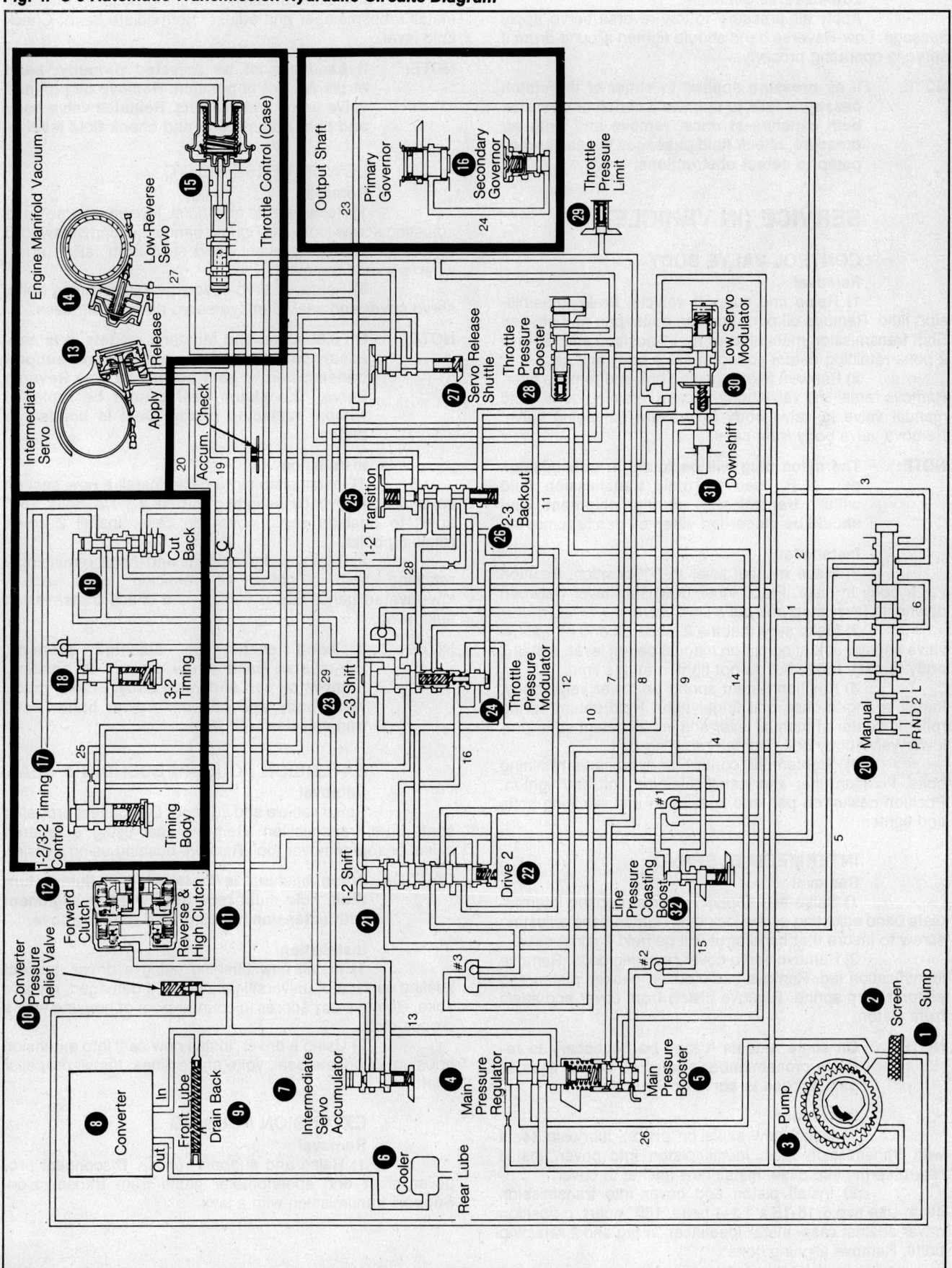

Low-Reverse Servo

Apply air pressure to low-reverse servo apply passage. Low-Reverse band should tighten around drum if servo is operating properly.

NOTE: **If air pressure applied to either of the clutch passages fails to operate a clutch or operates both clutches at once, remove and, with air pressure, check fluid passages in case and oil pump to detect obstructions.**

SERVICE (IN VEHICLE)

CONTROL VALVE BODY
Removal

1) Raise and support vehicle. Drain transmission fluid. Remove oil pan retaining bolts, pan and gasket. Shift transmission manual lever to "P" position and remove 2 bolts retaining detent spring to valve body and case.

2) Remove filter retaining bolt and remove filter. Remove remaining valve body-to-case retaining bolts. Hold manual valve in valve body to prevent damaging valve. Remove valve body from case.

NOTE: **The nylon plug will be found in transmission pan. It is used to retain transmission fluid within transmission during shipment and should be discarded when oil pan is removed.**

Installation

1) Place manual lever in "P" position. Position valve body in case. Place inner downshift lever between downshift lever stop and downshift valve.

2) Make sure that the 2 lands on end of manual valve engage actuating pin on manual detent lever. Install 7 body-to-case bolts, but do not tighten at this time.

3) Position detent spring on lower valve body. Install spring-to-case bolt finger tight. Hold detent spring roller in center of manual lever and install detent spring-to-lower valve body bolt. Tighten retaining bolt.

4) Tighten all control body-to-case retaining bolts. Position filter and install retaining bolt and tighten. Position gasket on pan and install pan and retaining bolts and tighten.

INTERMEDIATE SERVO
Removal

1) Raise and support vehicle. Loosen intermediate band adjusting screw lock nut. Tighten band adjusting screw to insure that band strut will be held against case.

2) Remove servo cover retaining bolts. Remove identification tag. Remove servo cover, gasket, piston and piston return spring. Remove piston from cover and seals from piston.

NOTE: **On some models it may be necessary to remove crossmember and/or oil cooler lines to gain access to servo cover bolts.**

Installation

1) Install new seals on piston, lubricate seals with transmission fluid. Install piston into cover. Install return spring into case. Install new gasket to cover.

2) Install piston and cover into transmission case. Use two 5/16-18 x 1 1/4 bolts, 180° apart to position cover against case. Install identification tag and 2 retaining bolts. Remove aligning bolts.

3) Install remaining retaining bolts and tighten. Install crossmember and adjust intermediate band. Check fluid level.

NOTE: **If band cannot be adjusted properly, band struts are not in position. Remove oil pan and valve body, install struts. Reinstall valve body and pan. Adjust band and check fluid level.**

LOW-REVERSE SERVO
Removal

1) Raise vehicle on a hoist, loosen reverse band adjusting screw lock nut. Tighten band adjusting screw to l0 ft. lbs. (14 N.m) to prevent band strut from falling down when servo is removed.

2) Remove servo cover-to-case retaining bolts, servo cover and seal. Remove servo piston from case.

NOTE: **On 3.8L Capri and Mustang models, it is necessary to remove crossmember and support transmission to gain access to Low Reverse Servo. The piston seal cannot be replaced without replacing piston. Seal is bonded to piston.**

Installation

1) Install piston into case. Install a new seal on cover. Install cover by using two 5/16-18 x 1 1/4" bolts, 180° apart to position servo cover on case. Install 2 cover retaining bolts.

2) Remove aligning bolts and install remaining 2 retaining bolts. Tighten all retaining bolts. Adjust low-reverse band. Lower vehicle and check transmission fluid level.

NOTE: **If band cannot be adjusted properly, low-reverse band struts are not in position. Remove oil pan and valve body. Install struts, valve body and oil pan. Adjust band. Refill transmission with fluid.**

EXTENSION HOUSING BUSHING & SEAL
Removal

Raise vehicle and support. Disconnect propeller shaft from transmission. Remove seal using a tapered chisel or seal remover tool. Remove bushing using a puller.

CAUTION: When bushing is installed, the fluid return drain hole must face downward in alignment with extension housing fluid return groove.

Installation

1) Install new bushing using a driver. Inspect sealing surface of universal joint yoke. If damaged, replace yoke. Remove any scores in counter bore of housing with a crocus cloth.

2) Using a driver, install new seal into extension housing. Lubricate seal, yoke and splines. Install propeller shaft.

EXTENSION HOUSING
Removal

1) Raise and support vehicle. Disconnect propeller shaft and speedometer cable from transmission. Support transmission with a jack.

2) Remove rear support-to-crossmember retaining bolts and nuts. Raise transmission and remove rear support from extension housing.

3) Remove extension housing-to-case retaining bolts and vacuum tube clip. On "cable" floor shift models, remove retainer from extension housing. On all models, remove extension housing.

Installation
To install, reverse removal procedures. Tighten all bolts and adjust fluid level.

GOVERNOR
Removal
With extension housing removed, remove governor housing-to-governor distributor retaining bolts. Remove housing from distributor.

Installation
To install, reverse removal procedures. Tighten all bolts, and adjust fluid level.

REMOVAL & INSTALLATION

TRANSMISSION
See appropriate AUTOMATIC TRANSMISSION REMOVAL article in DOMESTIC GENERAL SERVICING section.

TORQUE CONVERTER

LEAKAGE CHECK
See procedures given in FORD MOTOR CO. C-6 article.

FLUSHING CONVERTER
See procedures given in FORD MOTOR CO. C-6 article.

TURBINE & STATOR END PLAY CHECK
See procedures given in FORD MOTOR CO. C-6 article.

STATOR ONE-WAY CHECK
See procedures given in FORD MOTOR CO. C-6 article.

STATOR INTERFERENCE CHECKS
See procedures given in FORD MOTOR CO.C-6 article.

TRANSMISSION END PLAY CHECK
See procedures given in FORD MOTOR CO. C-6 article.

TRANSMISSION DISASSEMBLY

NOTE: Ten thrust washers are used in this transmission, with No. 1 located at the front pump and No. 10 located at the parking pawl ring gear. It is important that each thrust washer be installed in the correct position during reassembly.

1) Remove converter assembly. Remove input shaft. Mount transmission to holding fixture. Loosen transmission oil pan retaining bolts and allow fluid to drain. Remove oil pan bolts, pan and gasket.

2) Locate oil filler tube shipping plug in case. Remove and discard plug. Remove filter screen retaining bolt and filter screen. Remove 9 valve body retaining bolts and lift valve body out of transmission case. Remove filter screen from pick-up passage.

3) Remove converter housing retaining bolts and detach housing from case. Insert a large screwdriver between input shell and reverse planet carrier, and pry input shell forward until pump can be removed from case.

NOTE: Check stator support for No. 1 and No. 2 thrust washers. If washers are not present, remove them from top of reverse-high clutch.

4) Loosen intermediate band adjusting screw lock nut, thread adjusting screw out of case, and remove band struts. Turn intermediate band counterclockwise until band lugs are aligned with clearance relief provided in case.

5) Remove band, clutch packs, front planetary, and input shell as an assembly. Remove reverse planetary assembly. Loosen low-reverse band adjusting screw lock nut, thread adjusting screw out of case, and remove band struts.

6) Remove lock nut from adjusting screw and discard lock nut. Rotate low-reverse band until lugs are aligned with clearance relief provided in case. Remove band. Remove extension housing retaining bolts, vacuum diaphragm and throttle valve.

7) Remove extension housing and gasket. Remove and discard rubber shipping plug from output shaft. Remove governor retaining bolts and slide governor off output shaft.

8) Using a magnet, lift governor filter out of governor distributor body. Using snap ring pliers, remove snap ring retaining reverse ring gear and hub assembly to output shaft.

9) Remove reverse ring gear hub and assembly. To gain access to snap ring, it may be necessary to push the output shaft forward.

10) Remove low-reverse drum and detach No. 8 thrust washer from drum. Lift governor distributor and output shaft out of case as an assembly.

11) Remove distributor sleeve retaining bolts and lift sleeve from case taking care not to bend oil tubes. Remove parking gear and No. 10 thrust washer.

12) Remove parking pawl, pivot pin, and return spring from case as an assembly. Using socket (T65P-7B456-B or equivalent) remove one-way clutch outer race retaining bolts, positioning one hand in case to catch clutch assembly before last bolt is removed.

COMPONENT DISASSEMBLY & REASSEMBLY

NOTE: Handle all parts carefully to avoid damaging bearing or mating surfaces. Lubricate all internal parts with clean automatic transmission fluid only (gaskets and thrust washers may be held in place with petroleum jelly). Use all new gaskets, and tighten all bolts evenly.

Automatic Transmissions
FORD MOTOR CO. C-5 (Cont.)

Fig. 5: Exploded View of C-5 Valve Body Assembly

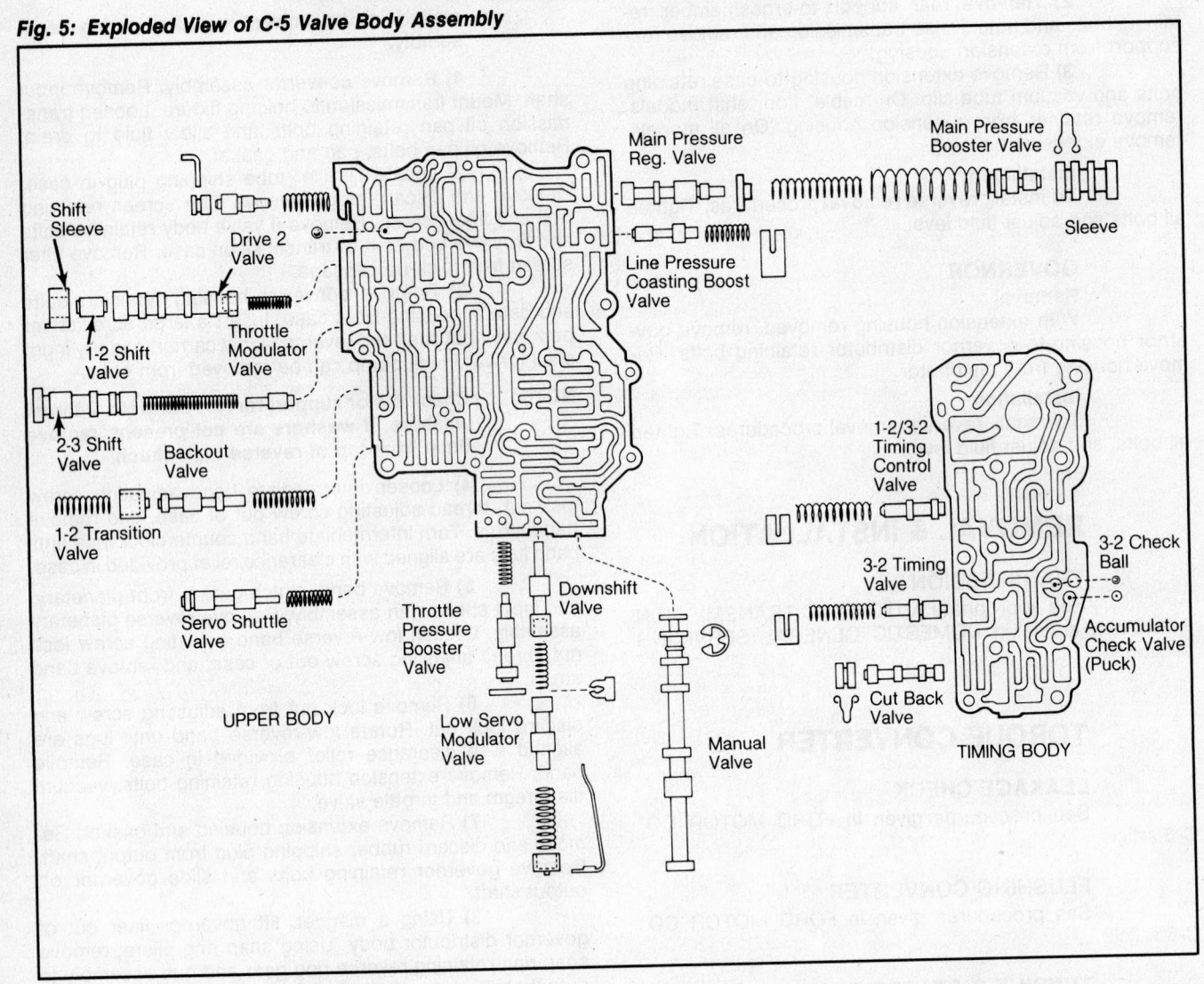

CONTROL VALVE BODY
Disassembly

1) Remove timing body retaining bolts. Remove timing body and relief valve from lower body. Remove timing body separator plate retaining screw, separator plate, check valve, and check ball from timing body.

2) Remove upper body to lower body retaining bolts, turn valve body over and remove lower body to upper body retaining bolts. Hold separator plate against lower body and lift lower body half away from upper body half.

3) Turn lower body over and place it on a bench with separator plate facing up. Remove separator plate and gasket from body and discard gasket.

4) Remove check balls and pressure limit valve from lower body half. Remove the check ball from upper body half.

Reassembly

1) Install check valve and check ball in timing body. Position separator and gasket with plate on timing body. Install retaining bolts and tighten using alignment pins to prevent plate from turning.

2) Install check balls and pressure limit valve in lower half of valve body. The steel ball is larger than other check balls and must be positioned as shown in *Fig. 6*.

3) Install gasket and separator plate on lower body half. Install check ball in upper body half. Hold separator plate firmly against lower body half while turning it over.

4) Position lower body half on upper body half. Install retaining bolts and tighten. Turn valve body over and install upper to lower body retaining bolts and tighten.

5) Install detent spring and roller assembly on lower body half. Position a drift punch in valve body to hold assembly in alignment. Install retaining bolt and tighten.

6) Install check valve in lower body half and position timing body on lower body half. Install timing body retaining bolts and tighten.

INTERMEDIATE SERVO
Disassembly

Remove servo cover, gasket, piston, and return spring. Remove seal rings from piston and servo piston cover. Using snap ring pliers, remove snap ring and remove piston rod from piston.

Reassembly

Reverse disassembly procedures.

FORD MOTOR CO. C-5 (Cont.)

Fig. 6: Check Ball Location in Valve Body Components

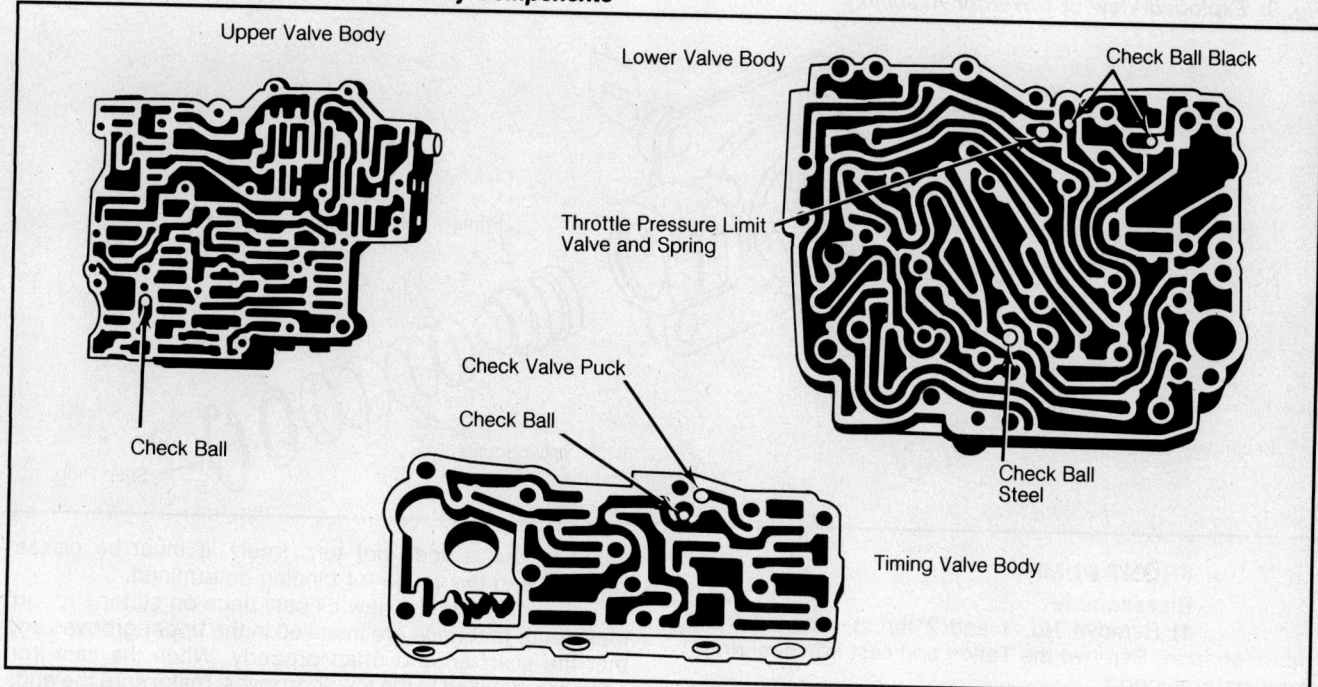

Fig. 7: Exploded View of Intermediate Servo

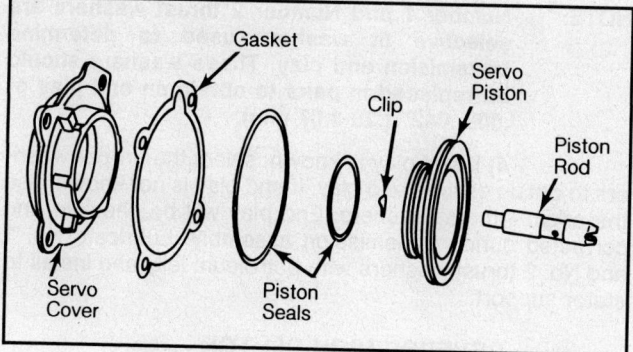

Fig. 8: Exploded View of Low-Reverse Servo

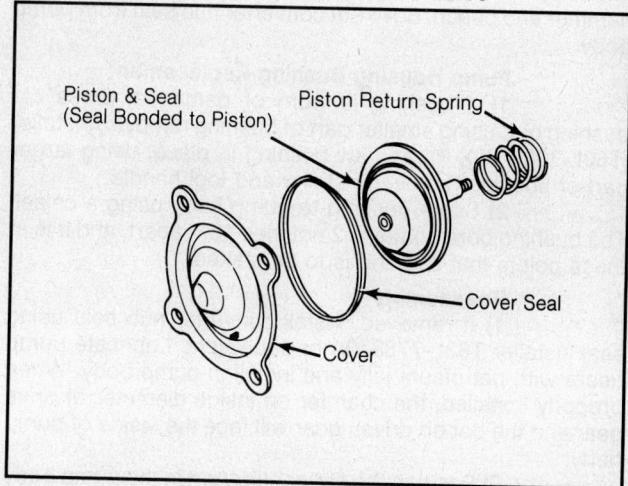

LOW-REVERSE SERVO

Disassembly

Remove servo cover, cover seal, piston, and piston return spring from transmission case.

NOTE: Servo piston seal is bonded to piston and can not be replaced without replacing piston.

Reassembly

Reverse disassembly procedure.

GOVERNOR

Disassembly

Remove snap ring from governor bore. Remove primary valve spring, spring seat washer, and primary valve. Remove secondary valve spring retaining plate. Remove secondary valve and spring from governor bore.

Reassembly

Reverse disassembly procedures.

MANUAL & THROTTLE LINKAGE

Disassembly

1) Remove outer throttle lever retaining nut and lock washer. Remove lever from shaft. Remove inner lever and shaft assembly.

NOTE: Shaft seal is located in the neutral safety switch and will be removed when shaft is pulled out of case.

2) Remove retaining bolts and slide neutral safety switch off outer manual lever. Remove inner manual lever retaining nut and lever. Remove outer manual lever and shaft assembly.

3) Using large screwdriver, pry out manual lever shaft seal from case. Remove front parking pawl linkage retaining clip. Remove rear parking pawl linkage retaining clip, flat washer and linkage.

Reassembly

Install manual lever shaft seal using seal installer (T74P-77498-A or equivalent). If tool is not available, a socket can also be used. Reverse disassembly procedures to complete reassembly.

Automatic Transmissions

FORD MOTOR CO. C-5 (Cont.)

Fig. 9: Exploded View of Governor Assembly

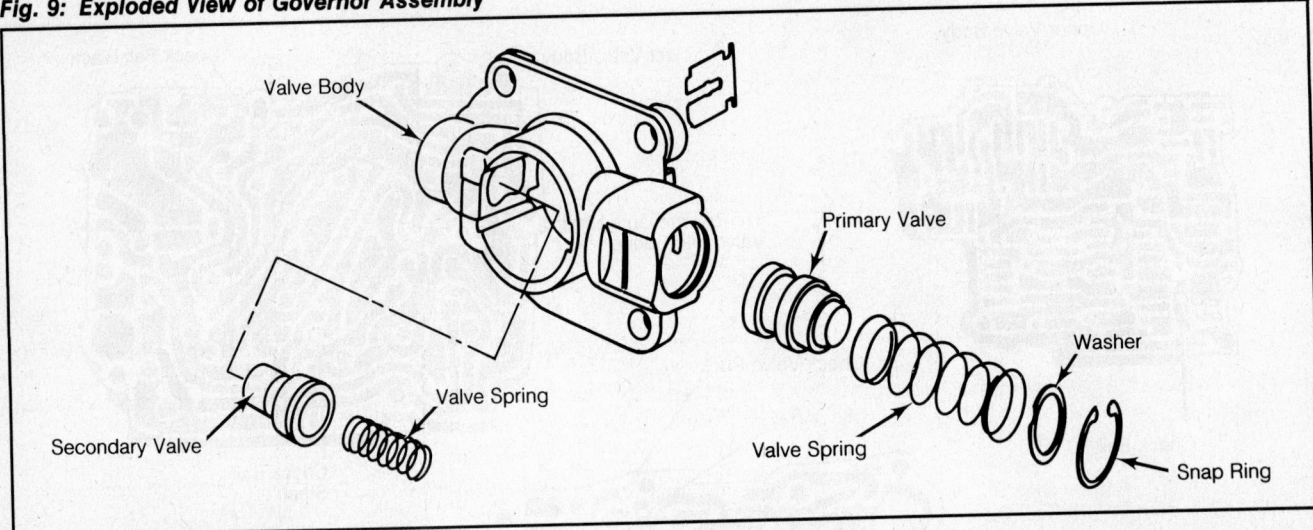

FRONT PUMP
Disassembly
1) Remove No. 1 and 2 thrust washers from stator support. Remove the Teflon and cast iron seal rings from stator support.

2) Remove retaining bolts and lift stator support out of pump body. Remove gears from pump body. Using hammer and punch, drive out converter hub seal from pump body.

Pump Housing Bushing Replacement
1) If bushing is worn or damaged, press old bushing out, using smaller part of bushing remover/installer (T66L-7003-C2). Press new bushing in place, using larger part of bushing remover/installer and tool handle.

2) Stake bushing to pump body using a chisel. The bushing bore contains 2 notches 180° apart, and it is at these points that bushing is to be staked.

Reassembly
1) If removed, install converter hub seal using seal installer T63L-778370A or equivalent. Lubricate pump gears with petroleum jelly and install in pump body. When properly installed, the chamfer on inside diameter of drive gear and the dot on driven gear will face the inside of pump body.

2) Position the stator suppport in the pump body and install 5 attaching bolts. Position assembled pump on the torque converter making sure that the converter hub engages the pump drive gear. Hold converter and turn the

pump. If pump does not turn freely, it must be disassembled and the cause for binding determined.

3) Install 4 new oil seal rings on stator support. Make sure that rings are installed in the upper grooves and that the scarf ends overlap properly. When the cast iron rings are installed in the lower grooves, make sure the ends are securely interlocked.

NOTE: Number 1 and Number 2 thrust washers are selective fit washers used to determine transmission end play. These washers should be replaced in pairs to obtain an end play of .008-.042" (.20-1.07 mm).

4) If end play is known, select the proper washers to obtain desired end play. If end play is not known, use the original thrust washers. End play will be checked and corrected during transmission assembly. Lubricate No. 1 and No. 2 thrust washers with petroleum jelly and install to stator support.

REVERSE-HIGH CLUTCH
Disassembly
1) Remove clutch pack retaining ring and clutch pack from drum. Using clutch spring compressor (T65L-77515-A or equivalent), compress piston return spring. Remove spring retaining ring using external snap ring pliers.

2) Remove clutch piston. If piston is difficult to remove, air pressure can be used to help remove piston.

Fig. 10: Exploded View of Oil Pump Assembly

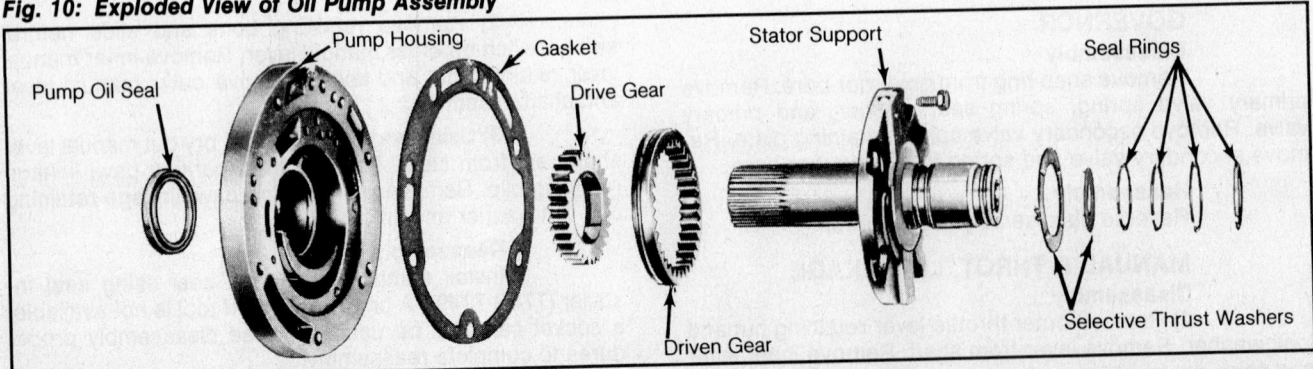

FORD MOTOR CO. C-5 (Cont.)

Fig. 11: Exploded View of Manual and Throttle Linkage

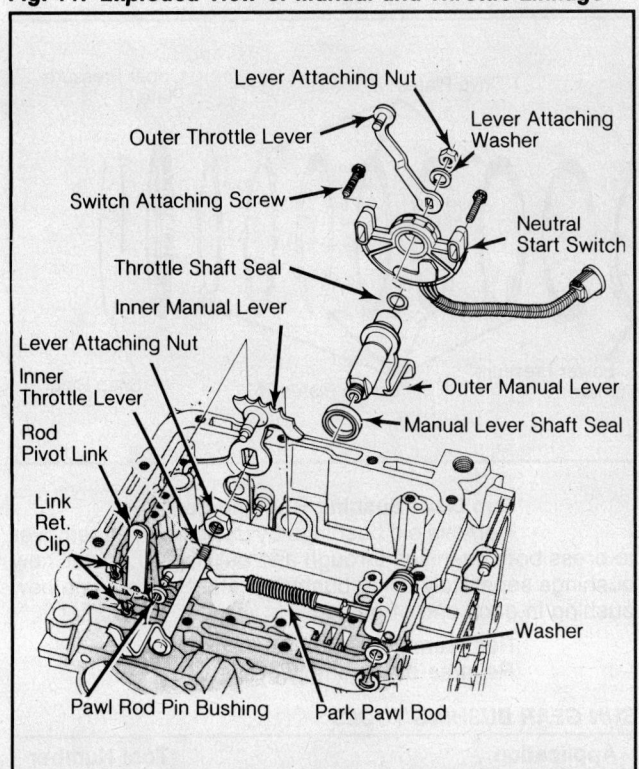

- Lever Attaching Nut
- Outer Throttle Lever
- Lever Attaching Washer
- Switch Attaching Screw
- Neutral Start Switch
- Throttle Shaft Seal
- Inner Manual Lever
- Lever Attaching Nut
- Inner Throttle Lever
- Rod Pivot Link
- Outer Manual Lever
- Manual Lever Shaft Seal
- Link Ret. Clip
- Washer
- Pawl Rod Pin Bushing
- Park Pawl Rod

Remove clutch piston seal and inner seal from clutch drum hub.

Reassembly

1) To complete reassembly, reverse disassembly procedures. If old composition plates are to be used, clean by wiping with a lint-free cloth.

2) If new composition plates are to be installed, soak in transmission fluid for 15 minutes before installing.

3) To check clutch pack clearance, install steel plate in clutch drum. Install composition and steel plates alternately until 2 composition plates remain.

4) Install remaining 2 composition plates, disc spring and pressure plate (thicker steel plate). Install retaining ring.

NOTE: This is not correct plate installation sequence. This sequence is only used to check clutch pack clearance.

5) Using a feeler gauge, check the clearance between pressure plate and retaining ring. If clearance exceeds .025-.050" (.64-1.35 mm), install a snap ring of required thickness. Snap rings are available in .050-.054", .064-.068", .078-.082" and .092-.096" thicknesses.

6) After clearance has been checked and proper snap ring selected, remove clutch plates from clutch drum and reinstall as follows: install a steel plate, then alternately install composition and steel plates. Install pressure plate and disc spring with splines facing snap ring. Install retaining ring.

NOTE: Using air pressure, check clutch for proper operation. Clutch should be heard and felt to assure smooth operation, without leakage. Piston should return to released position when air pressure is removed.

FORWARD CLUTCH

Disassembly

1) Remove clutch pack retaining ring and remove clutch plates from drum. Using a screwdriver, disengage piston retaining ring from clutch drum ring groove.

2) Remove piston retaining ring, piston return spring, and thrust ring. Remove clutch piston outer seal from piston and inner seal from clutch drum hub.

Reassembly

1) Install a new seal on clutch drum hub. Install a new seal on the clutch piston, making sure the seal lip faces into the cylinder. Lubricate the piston seals with petroleum jelly. Install clutch piston in the clutch drum.

2) Seat the piston by rotating and pushing down. Install thrust ring in the groove on the piston. Install piston return spring with disk side down. Install piston retaining ring. Make sure ring is fully seated in the clutch drum groove. Install the forward pressure plate.

3) Dished side of plate should face piston. Install clutch pack. If new clutch plates are installed, they must be soaked in transmission fluid for 15 minutes before clutch pack is assembled. Starting with a composition plate, alternately install composition and steel plates. The last plate to be installed is the rear pressure plate.

4) Install clutch pack retaining ring. Using a feeler gauge, check clearance between pressure plate and retaining ring. Hold pressure plate down when making measurement.

5) Clearance should be .025-.050" (.64-1.35 mm). If clearance is not within limits, install a snap ring of

Fig. 12: Exploded View of Reverse-High Clutch Assembly

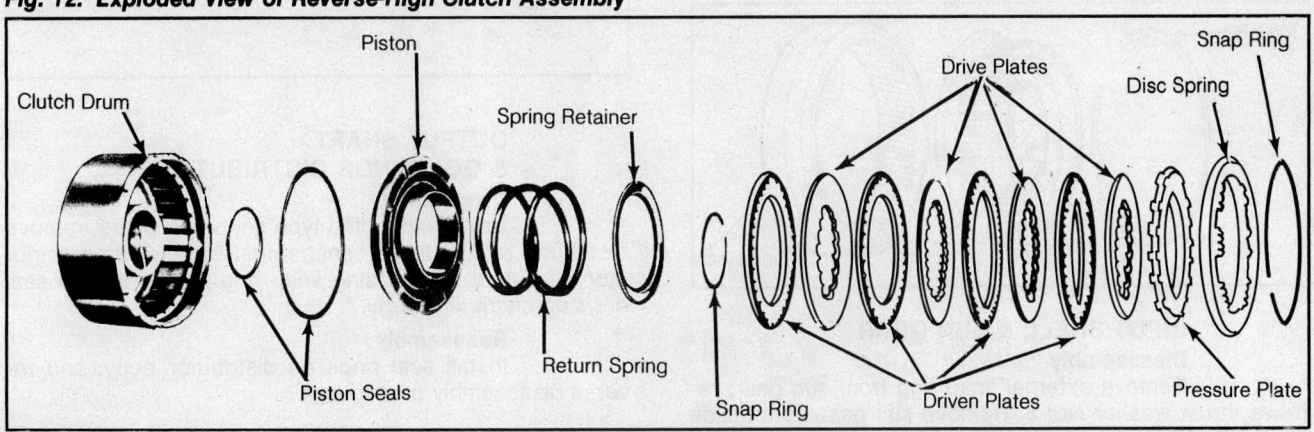

- Piston
- Snap Ring
- Clutch Drum
- Spring Retainer
- Drive Plates
- Disc Spring
- Snap Ring
- Pressure Plate
- Piston Seals
- Return Spring
- Snap Ring
- Driven Plates

Fig. 13: Exploded View of Forward Clutch Assembly

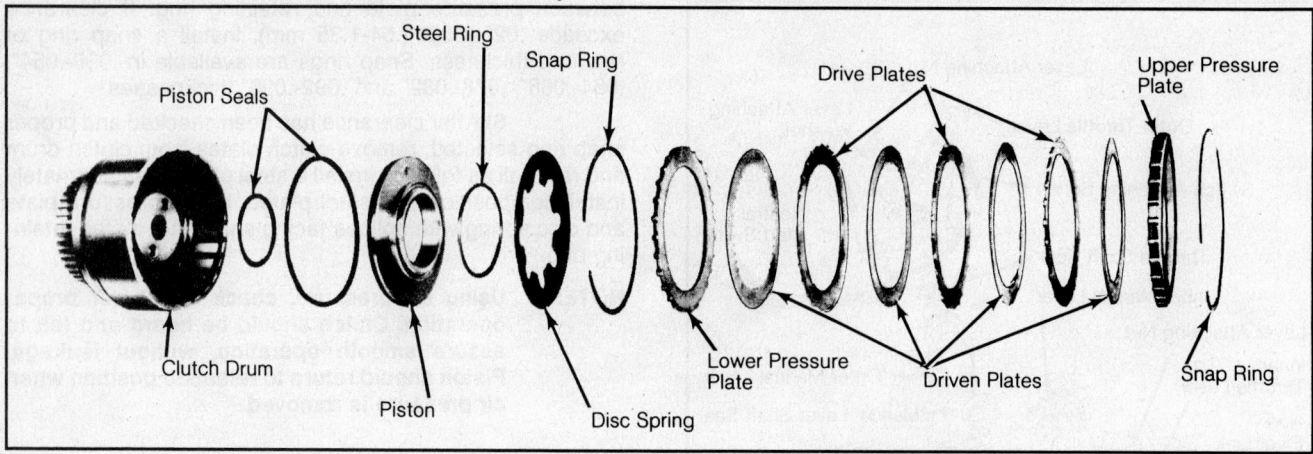

required thickness. Snap rings are available in .050-.054", .064-.068", .078-.082", .092-.096", and .104-.108" thicknesses.

6) Apply air pressure to clutch and check operation. Clutch should be heard and felt to assure smooth operation, without leakage. Piston should return to released position when air pressure is removed.

CLUTCH PLATE USAGE CHART

Application	Steel Plates	Composition Plates
Reverse-High Clutch		
F150	4	4
All Others	3	3
Forward Clutch		
All Models	4	5

FORWARD CLUTCH HUB & RING GEAR
Disassembly

Remove forward clutch hub snap ring and withdraw hub from ring gear. If necessary, remove and install clutch hub bushing using bushing drivers.

Reassembly

Install forward clutch hub in ring gear, make sure hub is bottomed in groove of gear. Install clutch hub snap ring, being sure snap ring is fully seated in groove of ring gear.

Fig. 14: View of Forward Clutch Hub and Ring Gear

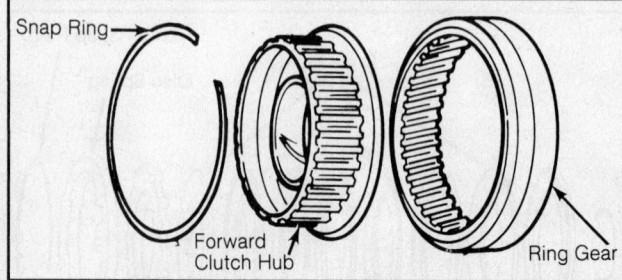

INPUT SHELL & SUN GEAR
Disassembly

Remove external snap ring from sun gear, remove thrust washer No. 5. Remove sun gear from inside input shell. Remove internal snap ring from sun gear.

Sun Gear Bushing Replacement

Remove old bushings by using bushing remover to press both bushings through and out of gear. Install new bushings separately using bushing installer to press a new bushing in each end of gear.

Reassembly

Reverse disassembly procedures.

SUN GEAR BUSHING TOOLS

Application	Tool Number
Bushing Remover	
F150	T66L-7003-B6
All Others	T66L-7003-C5
Bushing Installer (All Models)	T66L-7003-C3

Fig. 15: Input Shell and Sun Gear Assembly

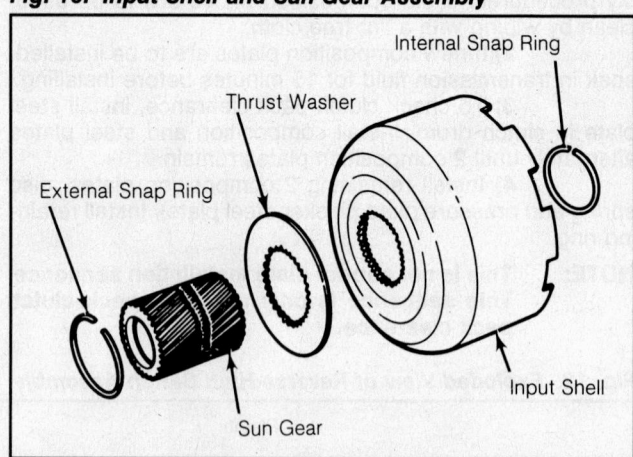

OUTPUT SHAFT & GOVERNOR DISTRIBUTOR
Disassembly

Using expanding type snap ring pliers, remove distributor to output shaft snap ring. Slide governor distributor off output shaft. Using snap ring pliers, remove seal rings on distributor body.

Reassembly

Install seal rings on distributor body, and reverse disassembly procedures.

FORD MOTOR CO. C-5 (Cont.)

REVERSE RING GEAR & HUB

Disassembly

Remove hub snap ring from reverse ring gear and withdraw hub from ring gear.

Reassembly

Install hub in reverse ring gear, make sure hub is fully seated in groove. Install snap ring in reverse ring gear, making sure snap ring is fully seated in snap ring groove of ring gear.

LOW-REVERSE BRAKE DRUM BUSHING REPLACEMENT

To remove bushing, use a cape chisel and cut along bushing seam until chisel breaks through bushing wall. Pry loose ends of bushing up with an awl and remove bushing. Use bushing driver (T66L-7003-B6) to install new bushing.

TRANSMISSION REASSEMBLY

NOTE: Handle all parts carefully to avoid damaging bearing and mating surfaces. Lubricate all parts with clean automatic transmission fluid only (gaskets and thrust washers may be held in place with petroleum jelly). Use all new gaskets and seals. Tighten all bolts evenly.

1) Install low-reverse servo piston and return spring in transmission case. Place a new seal on servo cover and position cover on case, install bolts and tighten. Route the neutral start switch through the clip. Bend the clip over slightly to hold harness in position.

2) Position new gasket on intermediate servo cover, making sure that notch in gasket will align with fluid port in case. Install servo cover, piston, and return spring as an assembly. Install cover bolts and tighten.

3) Lightly coat No. 9 thrust washer with petroleum jelly and position washer in case. Position one-way clutch in case. Install bolts and tighten. Position No. 10 thrust washer and parking gear in case.

4) Install parking pawl, pivot pin, and return spring in case as an assembly. Install pawl spring by looping the bend in spring over spring seat provided in case.

5) Install distributor sleeve on case, make sure oil tubes are properly seated in case fluid passages. Install distributor sleeve retaining bolts and tighten. Install governor oil collector body on the transmission case.

6) Install output shaft through oil collector body and into case. Operate the manual lever to check the operation of the park lock. Lightly coat No. 8 thrust washer with petroleum jelly, and position it on low-reverse drum. Install low-reverse drum in case.

NOTE: Check one-way clutch for proper operation by turning low-reverse drum both counterclockwise and clockwise. Drum should turn when rotated clockwise and lock-up when turned counterclockwise.

7) Install reverse ring gear and hub assembly. Using external snap ring pliers, install reverse ring gear and hub assembly retaining ring. If necessary, push output shaft forward to gain access to snap ring groove.

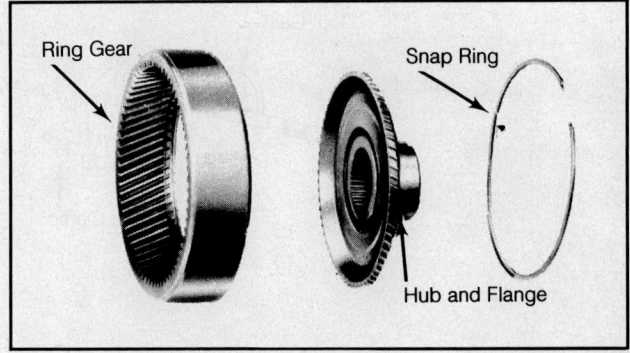

Fig. 16: Reverse Ring Gear and Hub

Ring Gear   Snap Ring   Hub and Flange

SELECTIVE THRUST WASHER CHART

Washer No. & Color	Thickness In. (mm)	Combined Thickness In. (mm)
1 Red	.053-.058 (1.35-1.46)	
1 Red & #2		.110-.115 (2.79-2.92)
1 Green	.070-.075 (1.78-1.90)	
1 Green & #3		.144-.149 (3.66-3.78)
1 Natural (White) [1]	.087-.092 (2.21-2.32)	
1 Natural & #2 [1]		.177-.182 (4.50-4.62)
1 Natural [1]	.087-.092 (2.21-2.32)	
1 Natural & #3 [1]		.194-.199 (4.93-5.01)

[1] – Spacer must be used and installed next to stator support to obtain correct end play. Spacer thickness is .033" (.84 mm)

8) Align band lugs with clearance provided in case. Install low-reverse band, making sure the double lug faces adjuster screw.

9) Install band struts, using a new lock nut on adjuster screw, and thread screw into case tightening it enough to hold band in place. Install governor screen in governor distributor body.

10) Position governor on the governor collector body and install and tighten retaining bolts in a cross pattern. Install new gasket to extension housing. Position extension housing on case with a new seal. Install throttle valve.

11) Install reverse planetary assembly in case, making sure that lugs are fully engaged in low-reverse drum slots. Install forward clutch in reverse-high clutch drum. Lightly coat No. 3 thrust washer with petroleum jelly. Position washer on forward clutch hub.

12) Lightly coat No. 4 thrust washer with petroleum jelly. Position washer on front planetary assembly. Install planetary assembly in forward clutch hub.

13) Install forward clutch hub and ring gear in forward clutch. Install input shell and sun-gear assembly on

Automatic Transmissions

FORD MOTOR CO. C-5 (Cont.)

Fig. 17: Exploded View of Transmission Showing Main Components

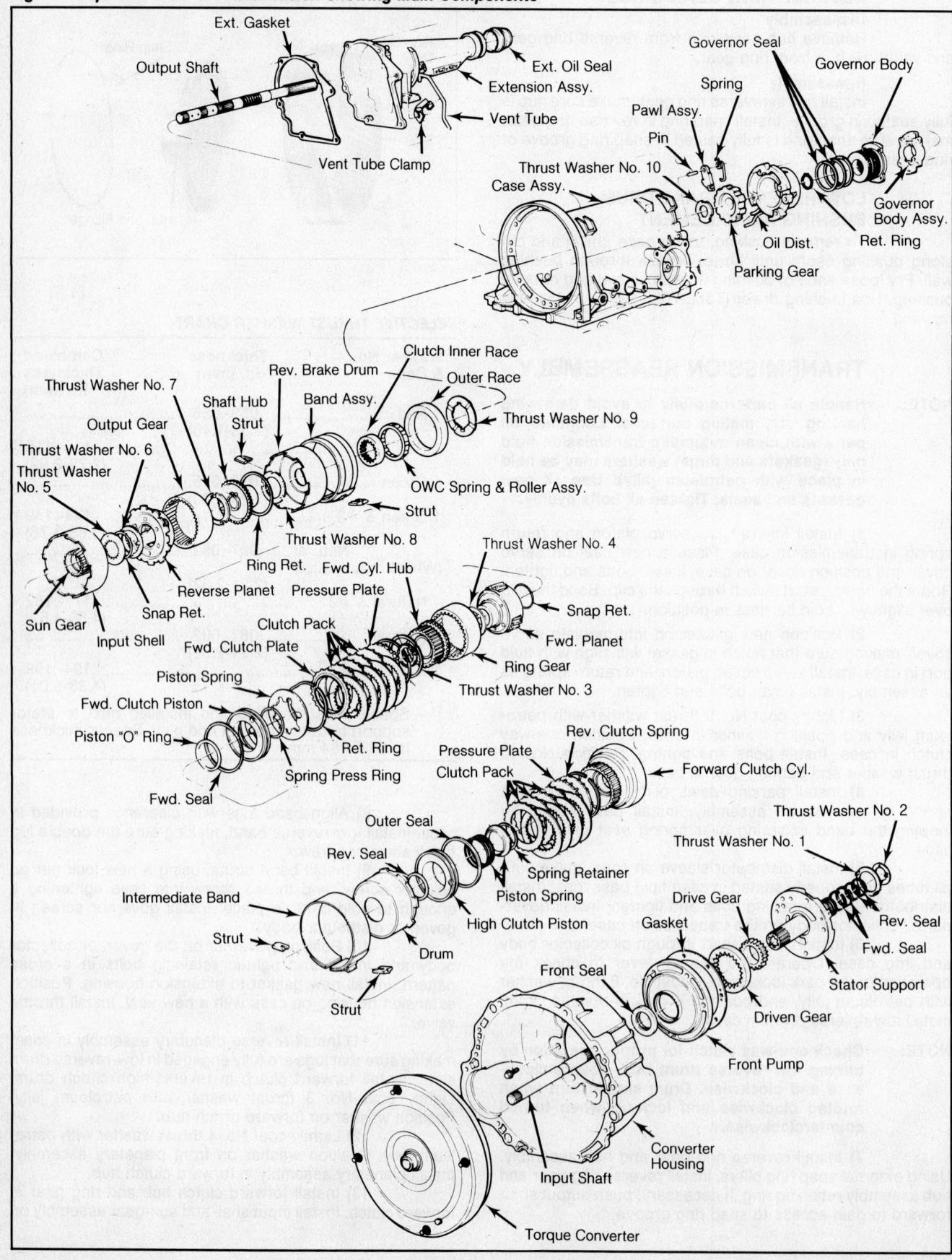

FORD MOTOR CO. C-5 (Cont.)

reverse-high clutch. Rotate input shaft to ensure proper assembly of clutch packs.

14) Position clutch packs, front planetary, and input shell as an assembly in case. Align intermediate band lugs with relief clearance provided in case. Install band and struts.

15) Install new lock nut on adjuster screw and thread into case, tightening enough to hold band in position. Position new gasket on front pump assembly.

16) Place pump assembly in case. Install and tighten converter housing-to-pump retaining bolts. Install input shaft. Mount a dial indicator on case and position indicator stylus against end of input shaft.

17) Position a screwdriver against lug on reverse-high clutch and push gear train rearward by tapping on screwdriver handle. Make sure that input shaft is fully seated, then zero indicator.

18) Position a screwdriver blade between input shell and reverse planetary assembly. Pry input shell forward and observe dial indicator.

Fig. 18: Measuring Transmission End Play

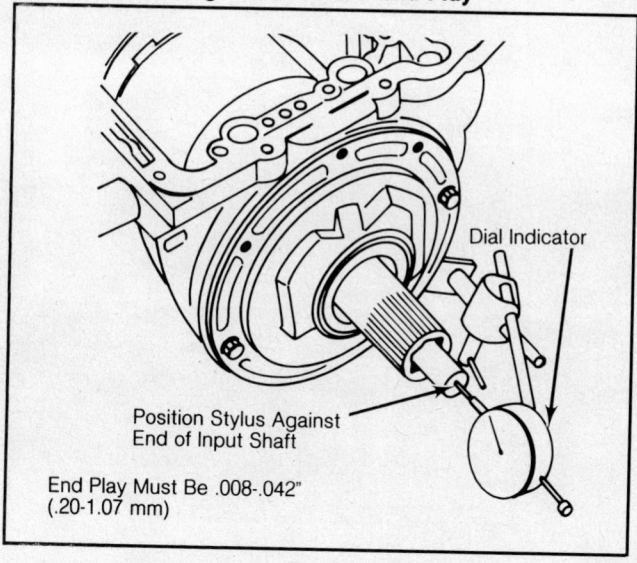

Dial Indicator

Position Stylus Against
End of Input Shaft

End Play Must Be .008-.042"
(.20-1.07 mm)

19) If end play is greater than .008-.042" (.20-1.07 mm), No. 1 and No. 2 thrust washers must be changed. Thrust washers should be replaced in pairs to obtain proper clearance.

20) If end play was within specifications, remove dial indicator and bolts holding front pump assembly in case. Position converter housing on case. Install housing-to-pump retaining bolts and tighten.

NOTE: If end play measurement was not within specifications, it will be necessary to remove front pump assembly and install proper thrust washers to obtain proper clearance. Install dial indicator and recheck end play measurement.

21) Adjust intermediate and low-reverse bands. See appropriate AUTOMATIC TRANSMISSION SERVICING article in DOMESTIC GENERAL SERVICING section. Check transmission for proper assembly by turning output shaft using a slip yoke.

22) Output shaft should turn in both directions. Using shift linkage, place transmission in "P" position, grasp yoke and attempt to turn output shaft. Output shaft should not turn in either direction.

23) Using air pressure regulated at 25 psi, apply air to proper hydraulic circuit to ensure proper assembly of clutch packs and band servos. Clutches should be heard and felt, and should operate smoothly.

Fig. 19: Air Pressure Test Locations on Case

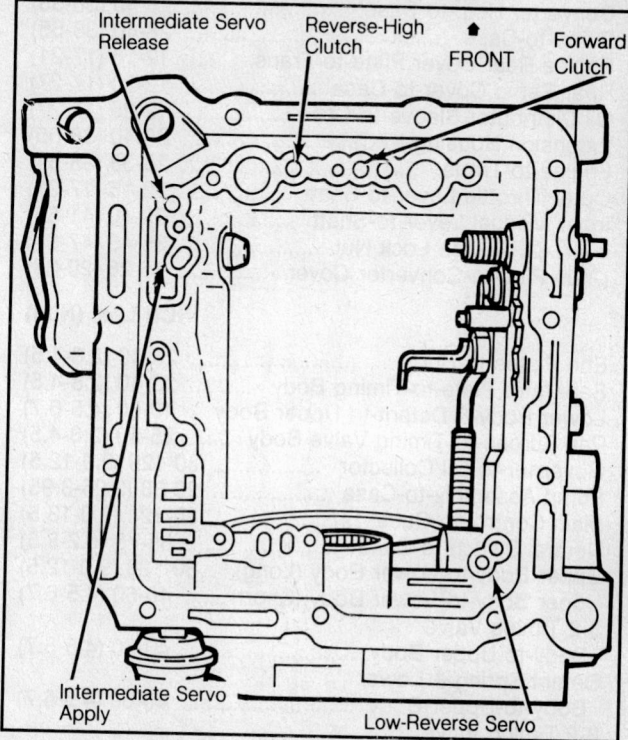

Intermediate Servo Release

Reverse-High Clutch

FRONT

Forward Clutch

Intermediate Servo Apply

Low-Reverse Servo

24) Check for leakage and ensure that clutch returns to released position when air pressure is removed. When air pressure is applied, it is possible to see servos in operation, and to see them release when air is removed.

25) Install inlet pump filter in case. Install valve body in case, make sure manual valve engages the manual lever. Make sure that the throttle lever is positioned to engage the throttle valve.

26) Note location of the 2 longer valve body retaining bolts, install all bolts, and tighten. Make sure filter seal is properly positioned on filter. Place filter on valve body. Install retaining bolts and tighten.

27) Position a new gasket on oil pan. Install pan on transmission housing. Install oil pan bolts and tighten. Install input shaft with oil groove end first.

28) Position torque converter on shaft making sure that it is fully seated. Make sure input shaft, stator support, and pump drive gear engage.

Automatic Transmissions

FORD MOTOR CO. C-5 (Cont.)

TIGHTENING SPECIFICATIONS

Application	Ft. Lbs. (N.m)
Oil Line-to-Transmission	18-23 (24-31)
Overrunning Clutch Race-to-Case	13-20 (18-27)
Oil Pan-to-Case	12-16 (17-21)
Reactor Support-to-Pump Converter Hsg.	12-20 (17-27)
Cover-to-Converter Hsg.	12-16 (17-21)
Converter Hsg.-to-Case	28-40 (38-55)
Pump-to-Case	28-40 (38-55)
Engine Rear Cover Plate-to-Trans.	12-16 (17-21)
Rear Servo Cover-to-Case	12-20 (17-27)
Oil Distributor Sleeve-to-Case	12-20 (17-27)
Extension Housing-to-Case	28-40 (38-55)
Engine-to-Trans.	28-38 (38-51)
Outer Throttle Lever-to-Shaft	12-16 (17-21)
Inner Manual Lever-to-Shaft	30-40 (41-55)
Inter. & Reverse Lock Nut	35-45 (47-61)
Drain Plug-to-Converter Cover	15-28 (20-38)

	INCH Lbs. (N.m)
End Plates-to-Body	25-40 (2.8-4.5)
Separator Plate-to-Timing Body	25-40 (2.8-4.5)
Lower Body & Detent-to-Upper Body	40-60 (4.5-6.7)
Pan Screen-to-Timing Valve Body	25-40 (2.8-4.5)
Governor-to-Oil Collector	80-120 (9.0-12.5)
Pump Assembly-to-Case	20-38 (2.25-3.95)
Main Control-to-Case	80-120 (9.0-13.5)
Neutral Switch-to-Case	55-75 (6.2-8.5)
Upper Body-to-Lower Body (Long)	80-120 (9.0-12.5)
Upper Body-to-Lower Body (Short)	40-60 (4.5-6.7)
3-2 Timing Valve Body-to-Upper Body	40-60 (4.5-6.7)
Detent Spring & Lower Body-to-Upper Body	40-60 (4.5 6.7)
3-2 Timing Valve Body-to-Lower Body	
5/16" Bolts	40-60 (4.5-6.7)
3/8" Bolts	75 (8.5)
1/4-20 Bolts	52-72 (5.9-8.1)
10-24 Screws	40-60 (4.51-6.77)

E150, 250 & 350,
F150, 250 & 350,
Bronco, F350 4WD

IDENTIFICATION

An identification tag is located under lower front intermediate servo cover bolt. A number appearing after the suffix indicates internal parts in transmission have been changed after initial production start-up.

For example, a PJA-AL 15 model transmission that has been changed internally would read PJA-AL 16. *See Fig. 1.*

Fig. 1: C-6 Transmission Identification Tag

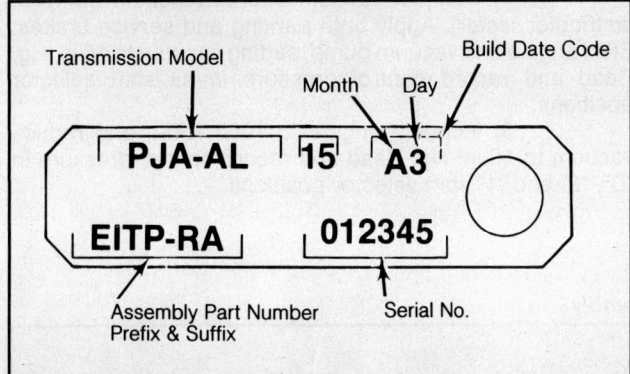

Tag is located under lower front intermediate servo cover bolt.

TRANSMISSION IDENTIFICATION CODES

Application	Models
Bronco, F150-350	K
E150-350	G

DESCRIPTION

Transmission is a 3-speed unit capable of providing automatic upshifts and downshifts through 3 forward gear ratios and also providing manual selection of 1st and 2nd gears.

Transmission consists basically of a torque converter, compound planetary gear train controlled by a single band, 3 multiple disc clutches, a one-way clutch and hydraulic control system.

LUBRICATION & ADJUSTMENTS

See appropriate AUTOMATIC TRANSMISSION SERVICING article in DOMESTIC GENERAL SERVICING section.

TROUBLE SHOOTING

See appropriate AUTOMATIC TRANSMISSION TROUBLE SHOOTING article in DOMESTIC GENERAL SERVICING section.

TESTING

ROAD TEST

1) Check minimum throttle upshift in "D". Transmission should start in 1st gear, shift to 2nd, and then shift to 3rd as speed increases. See SHIFT SPEEDS table.

2) With transmission in 3rd gear depress accelerator through detent (to floor). Transmission should shift from 3rd to 2nd or 3rd to 1st, depending on vehicle speed. See SHIFT SPEEDS table.

3) Check closed throttle downshift from 3rd to 1st by coasting down from about 30 MPH in 3rd gear. Shift should occur as shown in table.

4) With transmission selector lever in "2" position, transmission should operate only in 2nd gear.

5) With transmission in 3rd gear and road speed above 30 MPH, transmission should shift to 2nd gear when selector lever is moved from "D" into "2" or "1". When manual shift is made below 30 MPH, transmission should shift from 2nd or 3rd to 1st.

NOTE: **This check will determine if governor pressure and shift control valve are operating properly.**

6) Slipping or engine speed flare-up in any gear usually indicates clutch or band problems. In most cases, the clutch or band that is slipping can be determined by noting transmission operation in all selector positions and comparing which internal units are applied in those positions. See CLUTCH and BAND APPLICATION CHART.

CLUTCH AND BAND APPLICATION CHART (ELEMENTS IN USE)

Selector Lever Position	Intermediate Band	Reverse Clutch	Forward Clutch	High Clutch	One-Way Clutch
D – DRIVE					
First Gear			X		X
Second Gear	X		X		
Third Gear			X	X	
L2 – INTERMEDIATE					
Second Gear	X		X		
L1 – LOW		X	X		
R – REVERSE		X		X	

NEUTRAL OR PARK – All clutches, brakes, and bands released and/or ineffective.

Automatic Transmissions

FORD MOTOR CO. C-6 (Cont.)

CONTROL PRESSURE TEST
Engine Vacuum Method
1) Attach tachometer to engine. Install vacuum gauge (using "T") into manifold vacuum line at vacuum diaphragm unit. Attach a 0-400 psi gauge to control pressure take-off point at transmission. *See Figs. 2 and 5.*

Fig. 2: Side View of Transmission Case

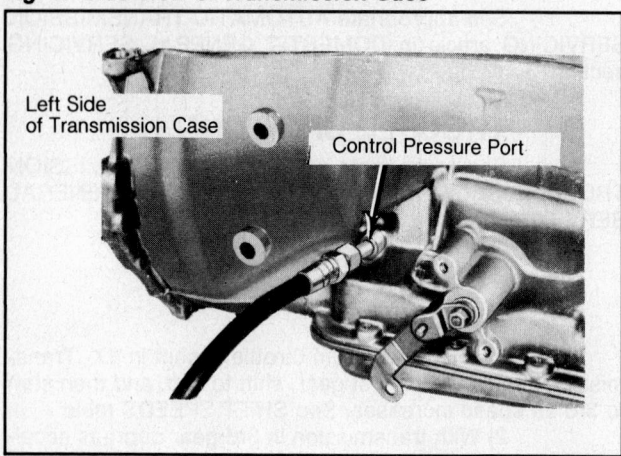

Left Side of Transmission Case

Control Pressure Port

Pressure gauges affect shift quality of transmission.

2) Apply both parking and service brakes. With engine at curb idle speed and normal operating temperature. Read and record control pressure in all selector positions at specified manifold vacuum. Compare control pressures obtained in tests with pressures given in CONTROL PRESSURE table.

CAUTION: **Release throttle immediately if slippage is indicated. Also shift transmission to Neutral and run engine at 1000 RPM to cool transmission fluid between tests.**

Vacuum Pump Method
1) Attach tachometer to engine and a 0-400 psi gauge to pressure take-off point at transmission. Disconnect and plug manifold vacuum line at diaphragm unit.

2) Connect vacuum source (vacuum pump in distributor tester). Apply both parking and service brakes. Start engine and vacuum pump, setting vacuum to 15 in. Hg. Read and record control pressure in all shift selector positions.

3) Increase engine to 1000 RPM, and reduce vacuum to 10 in. Hg. Read and record control pressure in "D", "2" and "1" shift selector positions.

Fig. 3: Sectional View of Ford C-6 Automatic Transmission Assembly

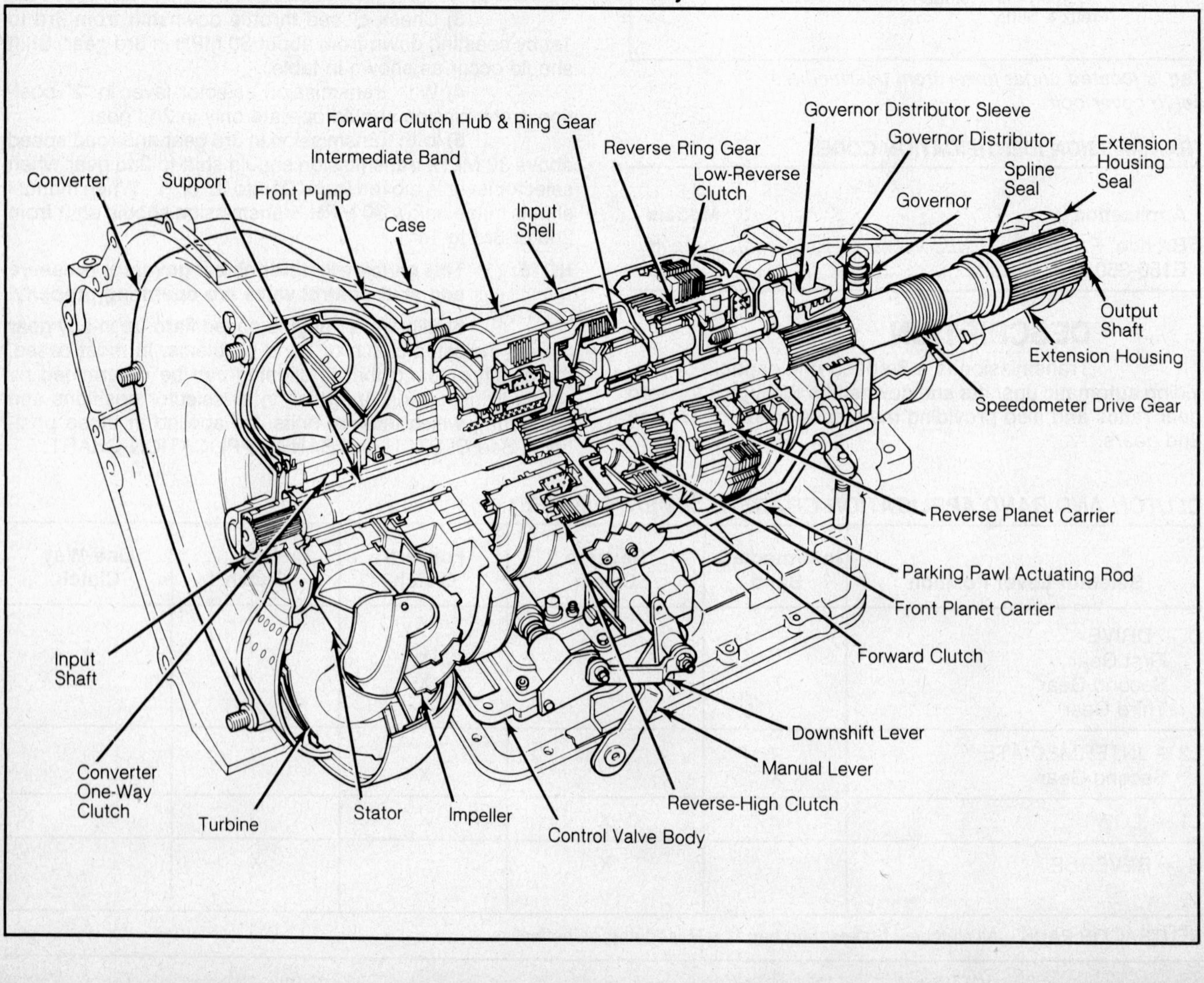

Forward Clutch Hub & Ring Gear

Intermediate Band

Front Pump

Case

Input Shell

Reverse Ring Gear

Low-Reverse Clutch

Governor Distributor Sleeve

Governor Distributor

Governor

Spline Seal

Extension Housing Seal

Converter

Support

Output Shaft

Extension Housing

Speedometer Drive Gear

Reverse Planet Carrier

Parking Pawl Actuating Rod

Front Planet Carrier

Forward Clutch

Input Shaft

Downshift Lever

Manual Lever

Reverse-High Clutch

Converter One-Way Clutch

Turbine

Stator

Impeller

Control Valve Body

Automatic Transmissions

FORD MOTOR CO. C-6 (Cont.)

Fig. 4: Ford C-6 Automatic Transmission Hydraulic Circuits Diagram

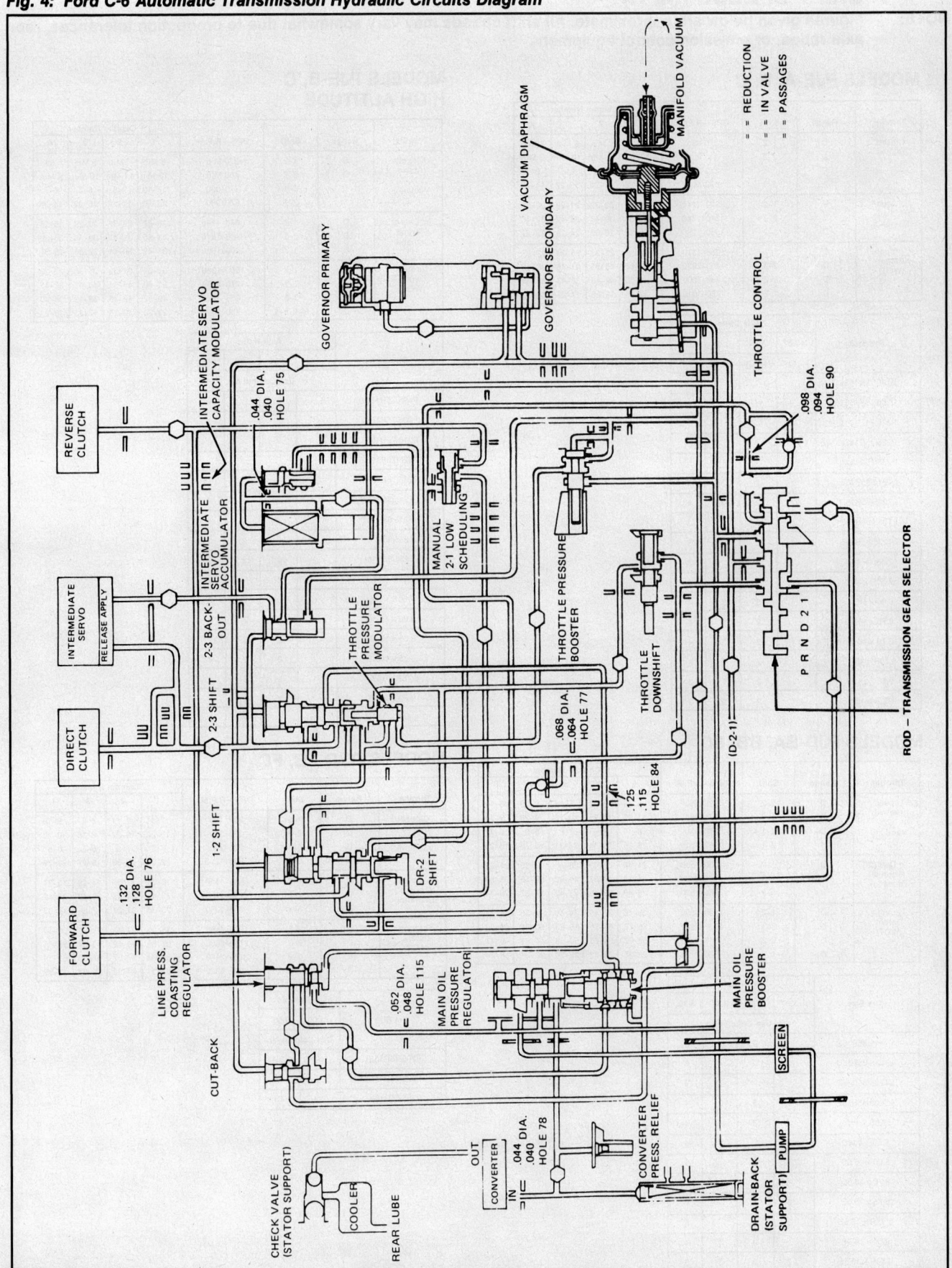

Automatic Transmissions
FORD MOTOR CO. C-6 (Cont.)

SHIFT SPEEDS (MPH)

NOTE: Figures given below are approximate. All shift speeds may vary somewhat due to production tolerances, rear axle ratios, or emission control equipment.

MODELS PJE-A, B, C

Throttle	Range	Shift	OPS—R.P.M.	Column Number 1	2	3	4
Closed (Above 17" Vacuum)	D	1-2	270 Min	8 Min	7 Min	6 Min	6 Min
	D	2-3	450 Min	13 Min	11 Min	10 Min	9 Min
	D	3-1	270-330	8-10	7-8	6-8	6-7
	1	2-1	670-960	20-28	17-24	15-22	14-20
To Detent (Torque Demand)	D	1-2	940-1240	28-33	23-32	21-29	20-27
	D	2-3	1540-1840	45-54	39-46	35-42	32-40
	D	3-2	1050-1280	31-38	26-32	24-29	22-27
Through Detent (WOT)	D	1-2	1080-1310	32-39	27-33	25-30	23-27
	D	2-3	1800-2030	53-60	45-51	41-46	38-42
	D	3-2	1680-1900	49-56	42-48	38-43	35-40
	D	3-1, 2-1	750-1010	22-30	19-25	17-23	16-21

Tire Size	Axle Ratio 3.07	3.54	3.73	4.10
	Use Column No.			
P195/75R15SL				
P205/75R15SL				
P215/75R15SL				
P225/75R15SL				
P235/75R15XL				
LT215/85R16C		2	3	4
LT215/85R16D		2	3	4
LT235/85R16D		2	2	3
LT235/85R16E	1	2	2	3
7.50D × 16D		2		3
7.50R × 16D			2	3
8.00 × 16.5D		3	3	4
8.75 × 16.5D		2	3	4
8.75 × 16.5E	1	2	3	4
8.75R × 16.5E	1	2	3	4
9.50 × 16.5E		2	2	3
9.50R × 16.5E	1	2	2	3

MODELS PJE-B, C HIGH ALTITUDE

Throttle	Range	Shift	OPS—R.P.M.	Column Number 1	2	3	4
Closed (Above 17" Vacuum)	D	1-2	270 Min	8 Min	7 Min	6 Min	6 Min
	D	2-3	450 Min	13 Min	11 Min	10 Min	9 Min
	D	3-1	270-330	8-10	7-8	6-8	6-7
	1	2-1	670-960	20-28	17-24	15-22	14-20
To Detent (Torque Demand)	D	1-2	870-1260	26-37	22-32	20-29	18-26
	D	2-3	1440-1870	43-55	36-47	33-43	30-39
	D	3-2	1200-1650	35-49	30-41	27-38	25-34
Through Detent (WOT)	D	1-2	1060-1330	31-39	27-33	24-30	22-28
	D	2-3	1770-2050	52-60	44-51	40-47	37-43
	D	3-2	1650-1920	49-52	42-48	38-43	35-40
	D	3-1, 2-1	730-1020	22-30	19-25	17-23	16-21

Tire Size	Axle Ratio 3.07	3.54	3.73	4.10
	Use Column No.			
P195/75R15SL				
P205/75R15SL				
P215/75R15SL				
P225/75R15SL				
P235/75R15XL				
LT215/85R16C		2	3	4
LT215/85R16D		2	3	4
LT235/85R16D		2	2	3
LT235/85R16E	1	2	2	3
7.50D × 16D		2		3
7.50R × 16D			2	3
8.00 × 16.5D		3	3	4
8.75 × 16.5D		2	3	4
8.75 × 16.5E	1	2	3	4
8.75R × 16.5E	1	2	3	4
9.50 × 16.5E		2	2	3
9.50R × 16.5E	1	2	2	3

MODELS PJD-BA, BB, BC

Throttle	Range	Shift	OPS—R.P.M.	Column Number 1	2	3	4	5
Closed (Above 17" Vacuum)	D	1-2	270-660	8-19	8-18	7-16	6-15	6-14
	D	2-3	375-880	11-26	10-25	10-23	9-20	8-18
	D	3-1	270-330	8-10	8-9	7-8	6-8	6-7
	1	2-1	880-1210	26-36	25-34	23-31	20-28	18-25
To Detent (Torque Demand)	D	1-2	1030-1550	31-46	29-43	26-40	23-35	21-32
	D	2-3	1700-2400	51-72	47-67	44-62	39-55	35-50
	D	3-2	960-1620	29-48	27-45	25-42	22-37	20-34
Through Detent (WOT)	D	1-2	1320-1600	39-48	37-45	34-41	30-36	28-33
	D	2-3	2230-2560	65-76	61-71	56-66	50-58	46-53
	D	3-2	1940-2260	58-67	54-63	50-58	44-51	40-47
	D	3-1, 2-1	870-1170	26-35	24-33	22-30	20-27	18-24

Tire Size	Axle Ratio 3.07	3.54	3.73	4.10
	Use Column No.			
LT215/85R16C		3	4	5
LT215/85R16D		3	4	5
LT235/85R16D			3	4
LT235/85R16E	1	3	3	4
7.50 × 16D		3		4
7.50R × 16D			3	4
8.00 × 16.5D		4		5
8.75 × 16.5D		3		5
8.75 × 16.5E	2	3		5
8.75R × 16.5E	2	3		5
9.50 × 16.5E		3	3	4
9.50R × 16.5E	2	3	3	5

MODELS PGD-FB, FC

Throttle	Range	Shift	OPS—R.P.M.	Column Number 1	2	3	4
Closed (Above 17" Vacuum)	D	1-2	270-420	7-11	7-11	6-9	6-10
	D	2-3	375-830	10-22	10-22	8-18	9-20
	D	3-1	270-330	7-9	7-9	6-7	6-8
	1	2-1	860-1200	22-31	23-33	19-27	21-29
To Detent (Torque Demand)	D	1-2	620-1310	16-34	17-36	14-29	15-31
	D	2-3	890-1780	23-46	24-48	20-40	21-42
	D	3-2	770-1380	20-36	21-37	17-31	18-33
Through Detent (WOT)	D	1-2	1270-1590	33-41	34-43	28-35	30-38
	D	2-3	2190-2560	57-66	59-69	49-57	52-61
	D	3-2	2120-2470	55-64	57-67	47-55	51-59
	D	3-1, 2-1	900-1220	23-31	24-33	20-27	21-29

Tire Size	Axle Ratio 3.00	3.50
	Use Column No.	
P205/75R15SL	1	3
P225/75R15SL	2	4
P235/75R15XL	2	4

SHIFT SPEEDS (MPH) (Cont.)

MODELS PGD-EV, EY
HIGH ALTITUDE

Throttle	Range	Shift	OPS—R.P.M.	Column Number			
				1	2	3	4
Closed (Above 17" Vacuum)	D	1-2	270-610	7-16	6-15	6-13	6-13
	D	2-3	400-980	11-26	10-24	9-21	8-21
	D	3-1	270-330	7-9	6-8	6-7	6-7
	1	2-1	990-1380	26-36	24-33	21-30	21-29
To Detent (Torque Demand)	D	1-2	1040-1820	27-48	25-43	22-39	22-38
	D	2-3	1780-2870	47-76	42-68	38-62	37-60
	D	3-2	1200-2450	32-64	29-58	26-53	25-51
Through Detent (WOT)	D	1-2	1480-1890	39-50	35-45	32-41	31-39
	D	2-3	2560-3060	67-81	61-73	56-67	53-63
	D	3-2	2240-2700	59-71	53-64	49-59	47-56
	D	3-1, 2-1	940-1360	25-36	22-32	20-30	20-28

Tire Size	Axle Ratio				
	3.50	3.54	3.55	3.73	4.10
	Use Column No.				
P195/75R15SL			3		
P205/75R15SL	3				
P215/75R15SL			3		
P225/75R15SL	2				
P235/75R15XL	2		2		
LT215/85R16C		1	1	2	3
LT215/85R16D		1	1	2	3
LT235/85R16D			1	1	3
LT235/85R16E		1	1	1	3
7.50D × 16D		1			3
7.50R × 16D			1	1	3
8.00 × 16.5D		2	3	3	4
8.75 × 16.5D		2	2	3	4
8.75 × 16.5E		2	2	3	4
8.75R × 16.5E		2	2	3	4
9.50 × 16.5E		1		2	3
9.50R × 16.5E		1		2	3

MODELS PGD-EV, EY

Throttle	Range	Shift	OPS—R.P.M.	Column Number			
				1	2	3	4
Closed (Above 17" Vacuum)	D	1-2	270-620	7-16	6-15	6-13	6-13
	D	2-3	400-990	11-26	10-24	9-21	8-21
	D	3-1	270-330	7-9	6-8	6-7	6-7
	1	2-1	990-1380	26-36	24-33	21-30	21-29
To Detent (Torque Demand)	D	1-2	1130-1790	30-47	27-43	25-39	24-37
	D	2-3	1920-2820	51-74	46-67	42-63	40-59
	D	3-2	1380-2390	36-63	33-57	30-52	29-50
Through Detent (WOT)	D	1-2	1510-1860	40-49	36-44	33-40	31-39
	D	2-3	2600-3020	68-79	62-72	57-66	54-63
	D	3-2	2270-2660	60-70	54-63	49-58	47-55
	D	3-1, 2-1	970-1340	26-35	23-32	21-29	20-28

Tire Size	Axle Ratio				
	3.50	3.54	3.55	3.73	4.10
	Use Column No.				
P195/75R15SL			3		
P205/75R15SL	3				
P215/75R15SL			3		
P225/75R15SL	2				
P235/75R15XL	2		2		
LT215/85R16C		1	1	2	3
LT215/85R16D		1	1	2	3
LT235/85R16D			1	1	3
LT235/85R16E		1	1	1	3
7.50D × 16D		1			3
7.50R × 16D			1	1	3
8.00 × 16.5D		2	3	3	4
8.75 × 16.5D		2	2	3	4
8.75 × 16.5E		2	2	3	4
8.75R × 16.5E		2	2	3	4
9.50 × 16.5E		1		2	3
9.50R × 16.5E		1		2	3

MODELS PGD-AW, EG
HIGH ALTITUDE

Throttle	Range	Shift	OPS—R.P.M.	Column Number			
				1	2	3	4
Closed (Above 17" Vacuum)	D	1-2	270-640	7-17	7-16	6-15	6-14
	D	2-3	375-930	10-25	9-3	9-21	8-19
	D	3-1	270-330	7-9	7-8	6-8	6-8
	1	2-1	890-1260	24-34	22-32	20-29	19-26
To Detent (Torque Demand)	D	1-2	770-1520	22-40	21-37	19-35	18-32
	D	2-3	1330-2330	35-63	33-59	30-53	27-50
	D	3-2	730-1640	21-45	20-42	18-38	18-35
Through Detent (WOT)	D	1-2	1250-1630	34-45	31-42	28-38	26-35
	D	2-3	2200-2630	59-70	55-65	50-59	46-55
	D	3-2	1980-2380	54-64	50-60	45-54	41-50
	D	3-1, 2-1	830-1230	23-32	21-30	19-27	18-25

Tire Size	Axle Ratio				
	3.50	3.54	3.55	3.73	4.10
	Use Column No.				
P195/75R15SL			3		
P205/75R15SL	3				
P215/75R15SL			3		
P225/75R15SL	3				
P235/75R15XL	2		2	2	4
LT215/85R16C		2	2	2	4
LT215/85R16D		2	2	2	3
LT235/85R16D			2	2	3
LT235/85R16E		1	2		
7.50D × 16D		2			3
7.50R × 16D			2	2	3
8.00 × 16.5D		3	3	3	4
8.75 × 16.5D		2	2	3	4
8.75 × 16.5E		2	2	3	4
8.75R × 16.5E		2	2	3	4
9.50 × 16.5E		2		2	3
9.50R × 16.5E		2		2	4

SHIFT SPEEDS (MPH) (Cont.)

MODELS PGD-AW, EG, EK

Throttle	Range	Shift	OPS—R.P.M.	Column Number 1	2	3	4
Closed (Above 17" Vacuum)	D	1-2	270-560	7-15	7-14	6-13	6-12
	D	2-3	375-870	10-24	9-22	9-20	8-18
	D	3-1	270-330	7-9	7-8	6-8	6-8
	1	2-1	890-1260	24-34	22-32	20-29	19-26
To Detent (Torque Demand)	D	1-2	710-1310	19-35	18-33	16-30	15-27
	D	2-3	1260-1940	34-52	32-49	29-44	26-40
	D	3-2	600-1510	16-41	15-38	14-34	13-31
Through Detent (WOT)	D	1-2	1250-1590	34-43	31-40	28-36	26-33
	D	2-3	2190-2570	59-69	55-64	50-58	46-54
	D	3-2	1990-2340	54-63	50-59	45-53	41-49
	D	3-1, 2-1	840-1200	23-32	21-30	19-27	18-25

Tire Size	Axle Ratio 3.50	3.54	3.55	3.73	4.10
	Use Column No.				
P195/75R15SL			3		
P205/75R15SL	3				
P215/75R15SL			3		
P225/75R15SL	3				
P235/75R15XL	2		2	2	4
LT215/85R16C		2	2	2	4
LT215/85R16D		2	2	2	3
LT235/85R16D			2	2	3
LT235/85R16E		1	2		
7.50D × 16D		2			3
7.50R × 16D			2	2	3
8.00 × 16.5D		3	3	3	4
8.75 × 16.5D		2	2	2	4
8.75 × 16.5E		2	2	2	3
8.75R × 16.5E		2	2	3	4
9.50 × 16.5E		2	2	2	3
9.50R × 16.5E		2		2	4

Fig. 5: Connecting Vacuum Gauge for Pressure Test

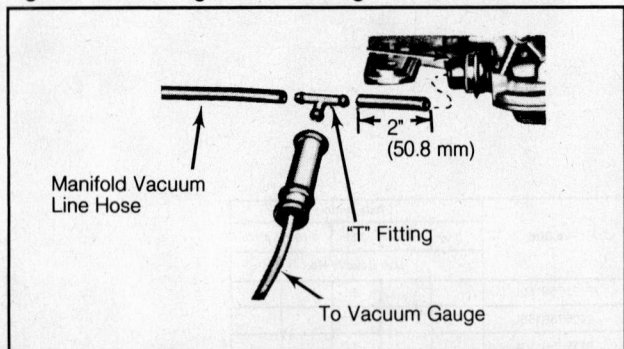

Manifold Vacuum Line Hose

"T" Fitting

2" (50.8 mm)

To Vacuum Gauge

This is for the engine vacuum test method

4) With engine still at 1000 RPM, reduce vacuum to 1 in. Hg. Read and record control pressure in "D", "2", "1" and "R". Compare control pressures obtained in tests with pressures given in CONTROL PRESSURE table.

NOTE: Governor can be checked at same time Control Pressure Test is performed.

5) With vehicle raised, place selector lever in "2", no load on engine and apply 10 in. Hg. Increase speed slowly while watching speedometer, check speed at which control pressure cutback occurs. It should occur between 10-20 MPH.

6) Decrease vacuum to 0.2 in. Hg and repeat test. Control pressure cutback should occur between 30-50 MPH. If cutback does not occur within specifications, check shift speeds to make sure that it is the governor and not a stuck cutback valve.

CAUTION: Do not exceed 60 MPH speedometer speed during test. If control pressures are not within specifications, proceed to Control Pressure Test Results to determine problems.

CONTROL PRESSURE TEST RESULTS

Low at Idle in All Ranges

Check for low fluid level, restricted intake screen or filter, and loose oil tubes. Check for loose valve body or regulator-to-case bolts. Check for excessive leakage in front pump, case or control valve body. Check for sticking control pressure regulator valve.

OK at Idle in All Ranges, But Low at 10 in. Hg

Check vacuum diaphragm unit. Check if control rod or throttle valve is stuck.

High at Idle in All Ranges

Check vacuum diaphragm unit, manifold vacuum line, throttle rod, and control rod. Check for sticking regulator boost valve(s).

OK at Idle in All Ranges, OK at 10 in. Hg, But Low at 1 in. Hg

Check for excessive leakage, low pump capacity or restricted oil pan screen.

Low In "P"
Check valve body pressure regulator.

Low in "R"
Check high clutch and/or reverse clutch.

Low in "N"
Check valve body for correct operation.

Low in "D"
Check for faulty forward clutch operation.

Low in "2"
Check forward clutch and servo.

Low in "1"
Check forward clutch and/or reverse clutch.

CONTROL PRESSURE SPECIFICATIONS

Trans. Type	Transmission Model	Idle 15" & Above Altitude	Non Altitude	10" Vacuum Altitude	Non Altitude	WOT Stall Altitude	Non Altitude
C6	PGD-EV-EY-FD-DW-DL						
	D,2,1	42-61# 53-81@	52-76	68-95# 86-113@	88-111	134-159# 150-185@	150-185
	R	66-95# 81-126@	81-119	106-148# 135-177@	137-173	209-249# 235-285@	245-275
	P,N	42-61# 53-81 @	52-76				
C6	PGD-AW-EG-FE-FF PJE-B-C						
	D,2,1	42-61# 53-81@	42-63	68-95# 86-113@	75-110	134-159# 150-185@	155-180
	R	66-95# 81-126@	66-99	106-148# 135-177@	117-157	209-249# 235-285@	245-275
	P,N	42-61# 53-81@	42-63				
C6	PGD-EK-FB-FC PJE-A						
	D,2,1	42-63		75-110		155-180	
	R	66-99		117-157		245-275	
	P,N	42-63					
C6	PJD-BA-BB-BC						
	D,2,1	67-91		99-119		155-180	
	R	94-142		155-186		245-275	
	P,N	67-91					

\# At 5000 ft   @ At sea level
Bar = 24.5   Bar = 29.5

VACUUM DIAPHRAGM UNIT

Vacuum Supply Check

1) Disconnect vacuum line at vacuum unit and connect vacuum gauge. With engine idling, gauge must show a steady acceptable vacuum. If reading is low, check for vacuum leak or poor engine vacuum.

2) If reading is acceptable, rapidly accelerate engine momentarily, vacuum must drop rapidly at acceleration and return immediately upon deceleration. If vacuum reading does not change or changes slowly, vacuum line is plugged, restricted or connected to reservoir supply. Repair as required.

Vacuum Diaphragm Unit Check

1) Remove unit from transmission. Use tester equipped with vacuum pump. Start pump and set regulator knob so vacuum gauge reads 18 in. Hg with end of hose blocked off.

2) Connect vacuum hose to port on unit. If gauge still reads 18 in. Hg, unit is not leaking. If vacuum does not hold at 18 in. Hg, unit is leaking and must be replaced.

3) When hose is removed from unit, hold finger over end of control rod. Internal spring in unit should push control rod outward. Also, check for presence of transmission fluid in vacuum side of diaphragm or in vacuum hose. If fluid is present, unit is leaking and must be replaced.

VACUUM REGULATOR VALVE (VRV)

Operational Check & Adjustment

6.9L Diesel Only

1) Shut engine off. Disconnect 2 port vacuum connector from VRV which is located on left side of fuel injection pump. Remove throttle cable from lever on right side of pump.

2) Remove throttle return spring. Install 1 end of spring over throttle lever ball stud and other end over throttle cable support bracket. Insert Gauge Block (T83T-7B200-AH), or 0.515" gauge block, between pump boss and throttle wide open stop. Ensure lever stop is against block.

3) Attach a vacuum pump to upper port of VRV (vacuum supply side). Attach a vacuum gauge to lower port of VRV, (labeled TRANS on VRV). Apply and maintain 20 in. Hg to VRV.

4) It will be necessary to pump vacuum up as it bleeds off. Gauge attached to lower port should indicate 6.5-7.5 in. Hg if reading is incorrect, adjust VRV.

5) To adjust, loosen 2 adjustment screws that attach VRV to fuel injection pump. Rotate VRV until proper vacuum is obtained. Tighten adjusting screws after correct vacuum is obtained. If VRV cannot be adjusted to proper specifications, replace VRV and repeat procedure in step **2)**.

6) Remove gauge block. Reattach throttle return spring and throttle cable. Again apply and maintain 20 in. Hg to VRV. Vacuum gauge MUST indicate at least 13 in. Hg with throttle at idle position.

7) If vacuum gauge indicates less than 13 in. Hg, VRV must be replaced and procedure for adjustment must be repeated. After final adjustment, remove vacuum pump and gauge from VRV and reattach vacuum connector.

8) Start engine and check throttle operation and check transmission shifts.

STALL SPEED TEST

CAUTION: Do not hold throttle open longer than 5 seconds at a time during testing. If engine speed exceeds maximum limit of stall speed, release throttle immediately as clutches or bands are slipping.

Testing Procedure

Install tachometer and fully apply parking and service brakes. Start engine and run at curb idle and at normal operating temperature. Stall test transmission in each driving range at full throttle. Note maximum RPM obtained. Engine speed should be within limits shown in STALL SPEEDS table.

NOTE: Allow a cooling period of 15 seconds with transmission in Neutral and engine speed at 1000 RPM between each test.

STALL TEST RESULTS

Stall Speed Too High

In "D", "2", "1", and "R"; general transmission problems are indicated and a control pressure test should be made to locate faulty unit(s). In "D" only; planetary one-way clutch slippage is indicated. In "D", "2", and "1"; forward clutch slippage is indicated. In "R" only; high and/or reverse clutch slippage indicated.

Stall Speed Too Low

Converter stator one-way clutch faulty.

CAUTION: Make sure engine performance is satisfactory before condemning converter assembly. Converter cannot be overhauled and must be replaced if defective.

STALL SPEEDS

Application	Stall RPM
F150	
4.9L & 5.0L	1597-1851
F150 (4x2/4x4), E-150	
4.9L	1616-1871
F250 (4x2/4x4)	
4.9L	1583-1838
F350 (4x2/4x4)	
4.9L	1521-1764
E150	
4.9L	1603-1848
Bronco & E250/350	
4.9L	1534-1779
F150/250/350	
Bronco & E150/250/350	
5.8L 4 Bbl.	2125-2488
E250/350	
7.5L	1822-2136
F250/350	
6.9L Diesel	1744-2021

AIR PRESSURE CHECKS

1) A "No Drive" condition can exist, even with correct transmission fluid pressure, because of inoperative clutches or bands. Erratic shifts could be caused by stuck governor valve.

2) The inoperative units can be located through a series of checks by substituting air pressure for the fluid pressure to determine location of malfunction.

3) To make air pressure checks, loosen oil pan bolts and allow transmission to drain. Remove oil pan and control valve body. Apply air at points noted. *See Fig. 6.* Check unit operations as follows:

Forward Clutch
Apply air pressure to transmission case forward clutch passage. A dull thud can be heard when clutch piston is applied, or movement of piston can be felt by placing a finger on input shell.

Governor
Apply air pressure to governor control pressure passage and listen for sharp clicking or whistling noise, indicating governor valve movement.

Reverse-High Clutch
Apply air pressure to reverse-high clutch passage, dull thud should be heard when clutch piston is applied. If not, place finger tips on clutch drum, movement should be felt.

Fig. 6: Bottom View of Transmission Case

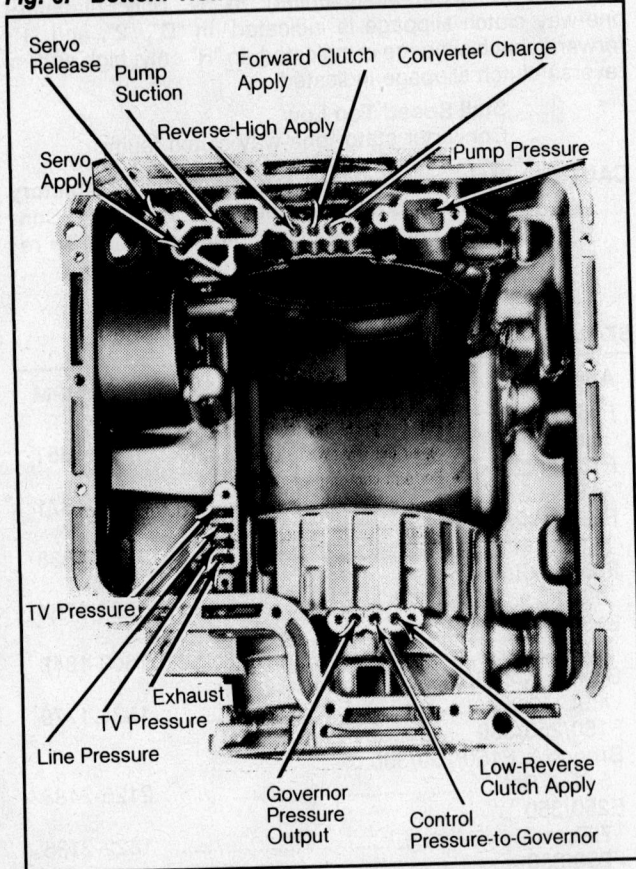

Illustration shows fluid passages for air pressure checks

Intermediate Servo
Hold air nozzle in intermediate servo apply passages. Operation of servo will be indicated by tightening of intermediate band around drum. With air still applied at apply passage, use 2nd air nozzle to apply air at the servo release passage. Band should now release (combination of air pressure and spring on release side of piston should overcome apply pressure).

Low-Reverse Clutch
Apply air pressure to reverse clutch apply passage. A dull thud should be heard if clutch is operating properly.

SERVICE (IN VEHICLE)

VALVE BODY
Removal
1) Loosen oil pan retaining bolts, tap pan to break it loose allowing fluid to drain. Remove oil pan and gasket. Remove and discard nylon shipping plug from filler tube hole.

NOTE: This plug is used to retain fluid in transmission during shipment and should be discarded when oil pan is removed.

2) Remove valve body retaining bolts and lower valve body from transmission case.

Installation
Position valve body to case, ensure selector and downshift levers are engaged. Install and tighten retaining bolts evenly. Install oil pan with new gasket, and tighten retaining bolts evenly.

INTERMEDIATE SERVO
Removal
Remove engine rear support-to-crossmember bolt. Remove crossmember-to-frame retaining bolts and remove crossmember. Disconnect muffler inlet pipe from exhaust manifolds and allow pipe to hang. Place a drain pan under servo and remove cover retaining bolts. Remove cover, piston, spring and gasket.

NOTE: As piston is being removed, screw in band adjusting screw. This keeps tension on band, keeping struts properly engaged in band end notches as piston is removed.

Fig. 7: Disassembled View of Intermediate Servo

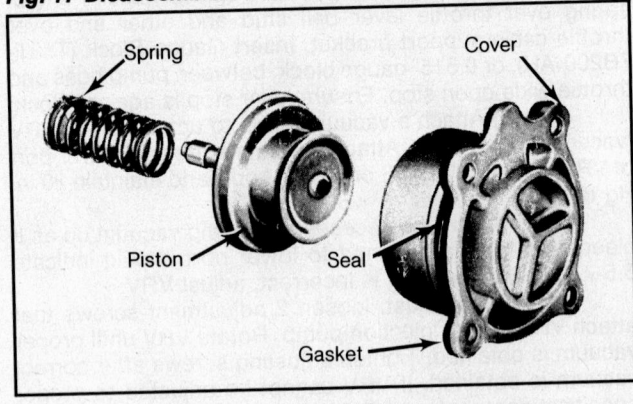

Seal Replacement
1) Apply air pressure to port in servo cover and remove piston and rod. Remove seal from cover. Replace complete piston and rod assembly if piston or piston sealing lips are damaged.

2) Dip new seal in transmission fluid and install on cover. Coat 2 new gaskets with petrolatum and install on cover. Dip piston in transmission fluid and install in cover.

Installation
To install, reverse removal procedure. Install service identification tag and back off band adjusting screw as servo cover bolts are being tightened. Adjust intermediate band and refill transmission to correct fluid level.

EXTENSION HOUSING SEAL & BUSHING

Removal

Disconnect propeller shaft at transmission. Using a tapered chisel, carefully remove rear seal. Using a bushing remover tool, remove bushing from extension housing.

NOTE: Use tool carefully so that spline seal is not damaged.

Installation

1) Install bushing into extension housing using a bushing driver. Before installing a new seal, inspect sealing surface of propeller shaft yoke for wear or damage. If scores are found, replace yoke.

2) Using a seal driver, install seal in extension housing, ensure that it is fully seated in bore. Coat inside of seal and yoke spline with wheel bearing grease and install propeller shaft.

EXTENSION HOUSING & GOVERNOR

Removal

1) Remove propeller shaft. Remove transfer case (if equipped) and speedometer cable. Remove engine rear support-to-extension housing bolts. Raise transmission with jack to take weight off support and remove support from crossmember.

2) Place drain pan under rear of transmission and remove extension housing-to-case bolts. Slide housing off output shaft. Remove governor housing-to-flange bolts and separate governor from flange.

Installation

To install, reverse removal procedure. Tighten all nuts and bolts. Make sure all mating surfaces are kept clean and refill transmission to correct fluid level.

REMOVAL & INSTALLATION

TRANSMISSION

See appropriate AUTOMATIC TRANSMISSION REMOVAL article in DOMESTIC GENERAL SERVICING section.

TORQUE CONVERTER

NOTE: Converter is a sealed unit and cannot be disassembled for service. Replace if found to be defective. Make the following tests to be certain converter is defective before replacing unit.

FLUSHING CONVERTER

Whenever transmission has been disassembled to replace worn or damaged parts or because valve body sticks due to foreign material, converter and oil cooler must be cleaned using a mechanically agitated cleaner (Rotunda 140028). Under no conditions should converter or oil cooler be cleaned by hand agitation using solvent.

LEAK TEST

NOTE: If torque converter welds indicate leakage, attach Torque Converter Leak Detector (Rotunda 720004) to converter and follow detector kit instructions.

TURBINE & STATOR END PLAY CHECK

1) Insert test tool (T80L-7902-D) into converter pump drive hub until it bottoms. Expand sleeve in turbine spline by tightening threaded inner post of test tool until tool is securely locked into spine.

Fig. 8: Checking Torque Converter Turbine and Stator End Play

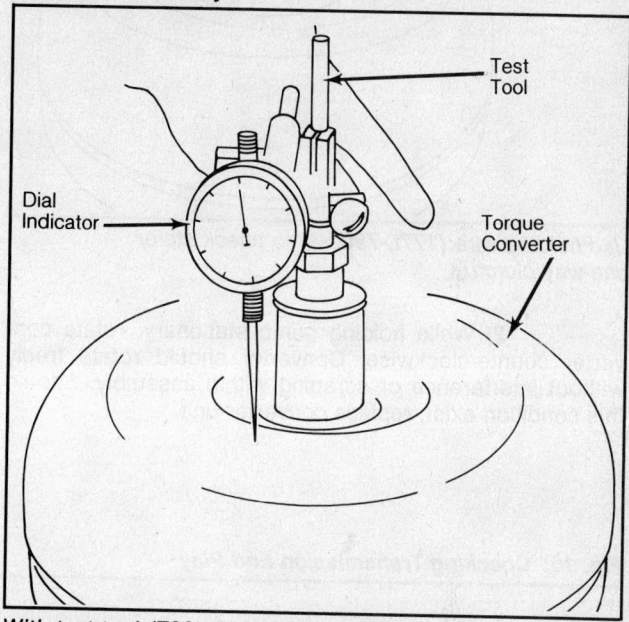

With test tool (T80L-7902-D) inserted and secured in hub check end play.

2) Attach a dial indicator to tool with button on indicator on converter pump drive hub. Zero dial face. Lift tool upward as far as it will go and note indicator reading.

3) Reading is total end play of turbine and stator. If end play exceeds .021" (.53 mm) new or rebuilt converter, or .040" (1.02 mm) used converter, replace torque converter assembly.

STATOR ONE-WAY CLUTCH CHECK

1) Insert one-way clutch holding tool into one of the grooves in the stator thrust washer. Insert torque adapter (T83L-7902-A1) into converter pump drive hub so as to engage one-way clutch inner race.

2) Attach a torque wrench to torque adapter. With clutch holding wire held stationary, turn torque wrench counterclockwise. The converter one-way clutch should lock-up and hold a 10 ft. lb. (14 N.m) force. One-way clutch should rotate freely in a clockwise direction.

3) Repeat lock-up test in at least 5 different locations around torque converter. If clutch fails to lock-up and hold, replace torque converter.

STATOR INTERFERENCE CHECK

Stator-to-Impeller Interference Check

1) Position front pump assembly on bench with spline end of stator shaft pointing up. Mount converter on pump so splines of one-way clutch inner race engage splines of stator support and converter hub engages pump drive gear.

Automatic Transmissions
FORD MOTOR CO. C-6 (Cont.)

Fig. 9: Stator One-Way Clutch Check

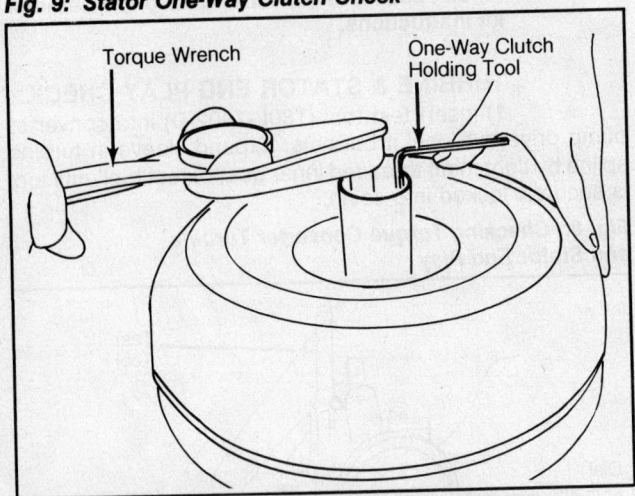

Torque Wrench

One-Way Clutch Holding Tool

Use holding wire (T77L-7902-A) to check stator one-way clutch.

2) While holding pump stationary, rotate converter counterclockwise. Converter should rotate freely without interference or scraping within assembly. Should this condition exist, replace converter unit.

Stator-To-Turbine Interference Check

1) Place converter on bench, front side down. Install front pump assembly to engage mating splines of stator support, stator and pump drive gear lugs.

2) Install input shaft, engaging the splines with turbine hub. While holding pump stationary, rotate turbine with input shaft.

3) Turbine should rotate freely in both directions without interference or noise. If interference or noise exists, stator front thrust washer may be worn; the converter should be replaced.

TRANSMISSION DISASSEMBLY

1) With transmission in a holding fixture, remove oil pan and gasket. Remove retaining bolts and lift valve body assembly from transmission case.

2) Attach a dial indicator to front pump with indicator contact against input shaft. Install oil seal replacing tool (T61L-7657-B) in extension housing to center output shaft.

3) Check transmission end play as follows: Push gear train to rear of case. Press input shaft inward until bottomed. Zero dial indicator.

4) Push gear train forward. Read and record end play for reference at reassembly. Remove checking tools from transmission. *See Fig. 10.*

5) Remove vacuum diaphragm, rod and primary throttle valve from case. Slide input shaft from front pump.

Fig. 10: Checking Transmission End Play

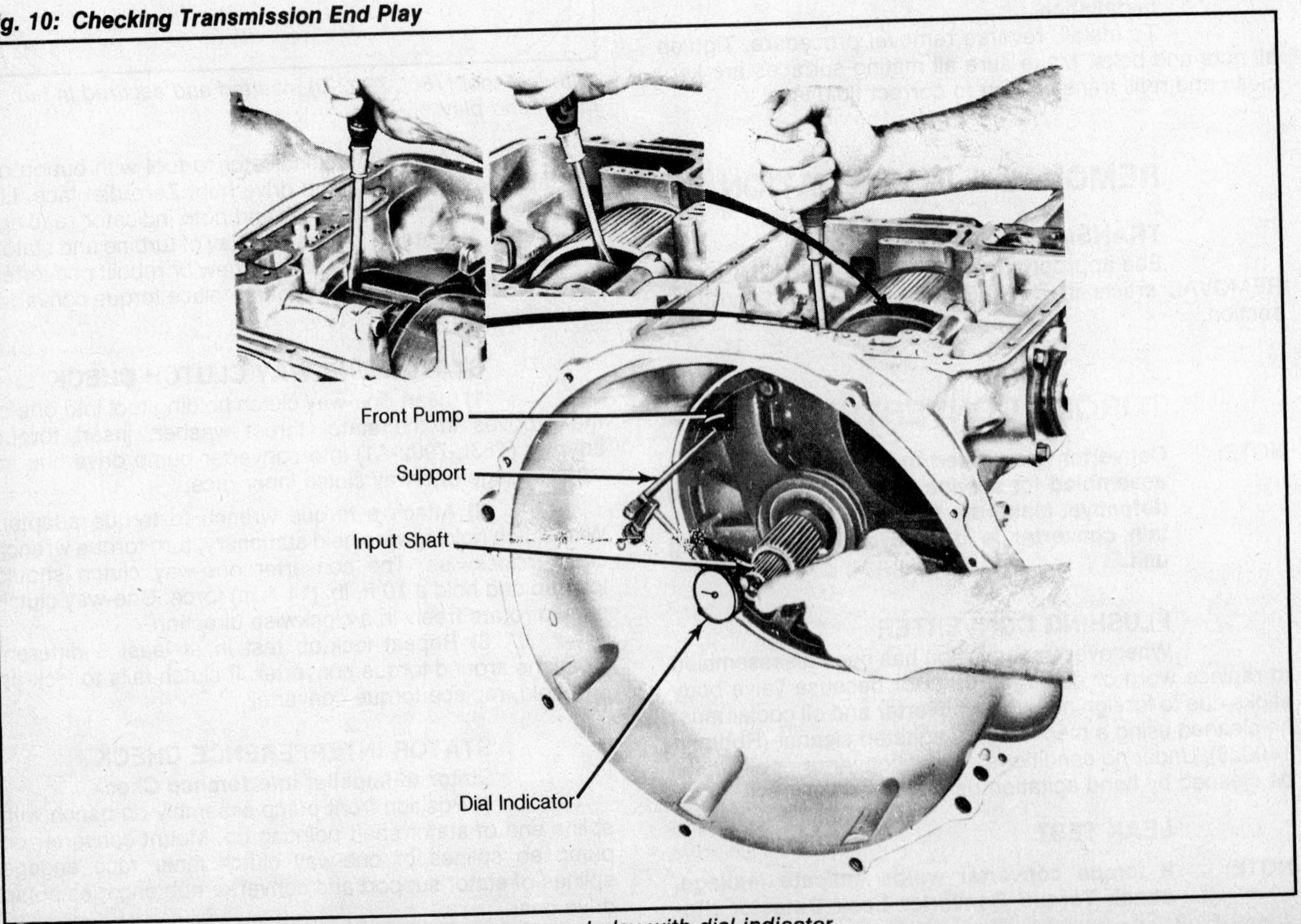

Front Pump

Support

Input Shaft

Dial Indicator

Push gear train forward and backward, and measure end play with dial indicator.

TRANSMISSION END PLAY

Application	In. (mm)
C-5	.008-.042 (.21-1.07)
C-6	.008-.044 (.21-1.12)

Remove front pump retaining bolts, pry gear train forward and remove pump.

6) Loosen band adjusting screw and remove 2 band struts. Rotate band 90° counterclockwise to align band ends with slot in case. Remove band from reverse-high clutch drum.

7) Remove forward part of gear train from transmission as an assembly. Remove servo cover retaining bolts, servo cover, piston, spring and gasket from case. Remove large snap ring securing reverse planet carrier in low-reverse clutch hub.

Fig. 11: Removing Reverse-High Clutch Drum

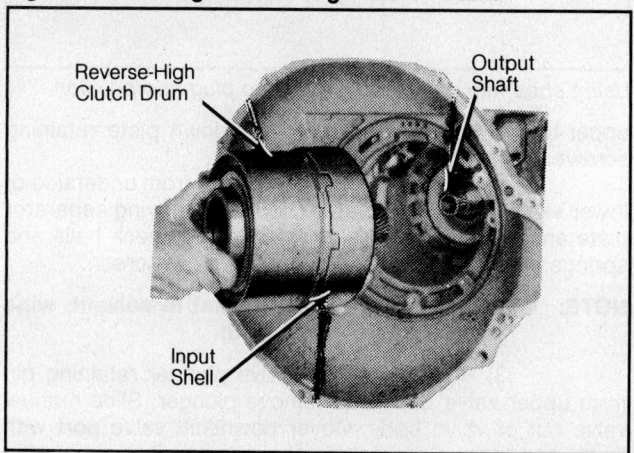

8) Lift carrier from drum. Remove snap ring securing reverse ring gear and hub on output shaft and slide assembly from shaft. Rotate low-reverse hub in clockwise direction and remove from case.

9) Remove reverse clutch snap ring and withdraw clutch discs, plates and pressure plate from case. Remove extension housing retaining bolts and vent tube from case.

10) Remove extension housing and gasket. Slide output shaft asssembly from case. Remove distributor sleeve retaining bolts. Remove sleeve, parking pawl gear and thrust washer.

NOTE: If thrust washer is staked in place, use a sharp chisel and cut off metal from behind thrust washer. Remove any metal particles from case.

11) Compress reverse clutch piston release spring. Remove snap ring and lift out springs and retainer assembly.

12) Remove one-way clutch inner race retaining bolts from rear of case and remove inner race. Remove reverse clutch piston by applying air pressure to low-reverse apply passage in case.

NOTE: See Fig. 6 for location of low-reverse apply passage.

COMPONENT DISASSEMBLY & REASSEMBLY

DOWNSHIFT & MANUAL LINKAGE
Disassembly

1) Remove nut and lock washer securing outer downshift lever to transmission and remove lever. Slide downshift lever out from inside case and remove seal from recess in manual lever shaft.

2) Remove neutral safety switch bolts and remove switch. Remove "C" clip securing parking pawl actuating rod to manual lever. Remove rod from case.

3) Remove nut retaining inner manual lever to shaft. Remove inner lever from shaft. Slide outer lever and shaft from case. Remove seal from case using a puller and slide hammer.

Fig. 12: Installed View of Downshift and Manual Linkage Components

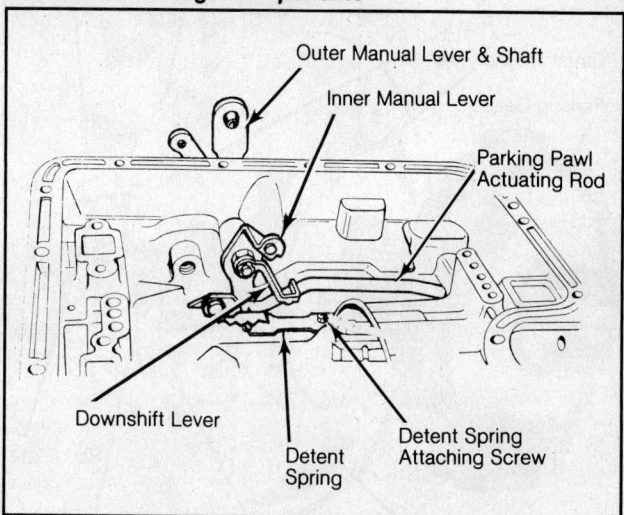

Reassembly

1) Dip new seal in transmission fluid and install into case using installing tools. Slide outer manual lever and shaft into case. Position inner lever on shaft, making sure leaf spring roller is positioned in inner manual lever detent.

2) Install retaining nut and tighten. Install parking pawl actuating rod and secure to inner manual lever with "C" clip. Slide neutral safety switch onto outer shaft lever.

3) Install retaining bolt. With manual lever in neutral, rotate switch and install gauge pin (No. 43 drill) into gauge pin hole. Tighten switch retaining bolt.

4) Install a new downshift lever seal in outer lever shaft recess. Slide downshift lever and shaft into position. Place outer downshift lever on shaft. Install and tighten lock washer and nut.

PARKING PAWL LINKAGE
Disassembly

1) Remove bolts retaining parking pawl guide plate to case. Remove plate. Remove spring, parking pawl and shaft from case.

2) Working from pan mounting surface, drill a 1/8" hole through center of cupped plug. Pull plug from case with a wire hook.

3) Unhook end of spring from park plate slot. Thread a 1/4-20 x 1 1/4" screw into park plate shaft. Pull shaft from case with screw. Remove spring and park plate.

Automatic Transmissions

FORD MOTOR CO. C-6 (Cont.)

Reassembly

1) Position spring and park plate in case and install shaft. Place end of spring into slot of park plate. Install a new cupped plug to retain shaft. Install parking pawl shaft in case.

2) Slip parking pawl and spring into place on shaft. Position guide plate on case, making sure actuating rod is seated in slot of plate. Secure plate with 2 bolts and lock washers.

Fig. 13: Installed View of Parking Pawl Linkage Assembly

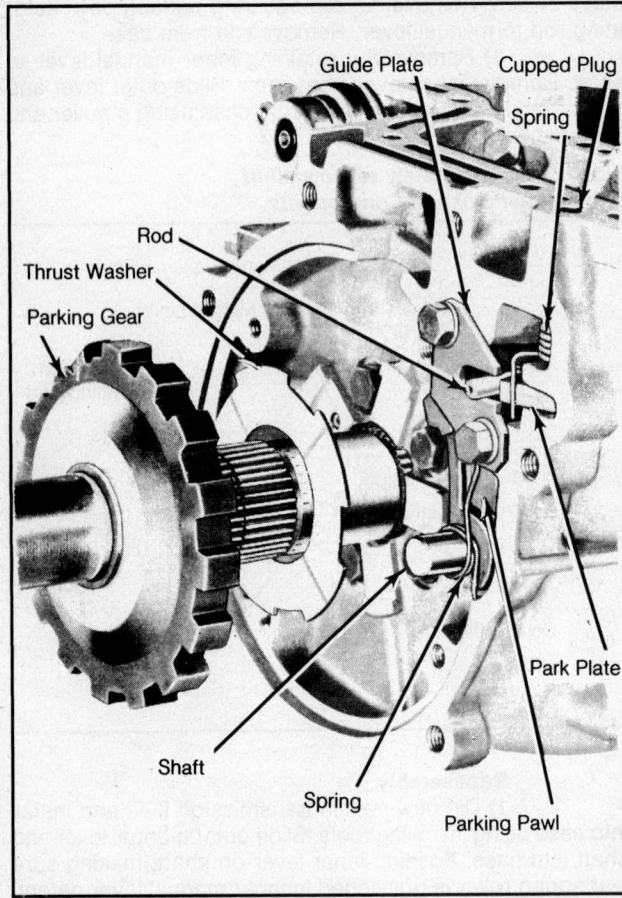

Note location of springs and guide pins.

SERVO APPLY LEVER

Disassembly

Working from inside case, carefully tap on servo apply lever shaft to remove the cup plug; shaft can be withdrawn by hand.

Reassembly

Hold servo apply lever in position and install shaft. Using fabricated shop tool shown in *Fig. 14*, drive cup plug into positon in case. Make sure plug is flush with shoulder of counterbore.

NOTE: **Cup plug should be coated with Loctite to prevent leakage.**

CONTROL VALVE BODY

Disassembly

1) Remove 9 screws retaining screen-to-lower valve body and remove screen and gasket. Remove 5

Fig. 14: Installing Servo Apply Lever Cup Plug

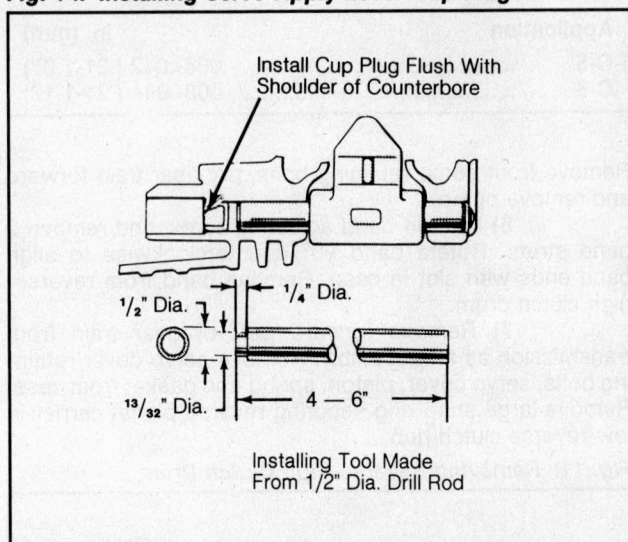

Using shop fabricated tool, drive cup plug into position.

upper-to-lower valve body and hold down plate retaining screws.

2) Remove 7 retaining screws from underside of lower valve body and separate bodies, removing separator plate and gasket. Be sure to avoid losing check balls and springs. Remove and clean separator plate screen.

NOTE: **Do not clean screen gasket in solvent; wipe clean with a lint-free cloth.**

3) Remove manual valve plunger retaining pin from upper valve body and remove plunger. Slide manual valve out of valve body. Cover downshift valve port with finger and remove downshift valve retainer. Remove spring and downshift valve.

4) Apply pressure to pressure boost valve sleeve and remove retaining clip from underside of valve body. Slowly release pressure and remove sleeve and pressure boost valve. Remove 2 springs, retainer and main regulator valve from bore.

5) Apply pressure to throttle boost valve plate and remove 2 retaining screws. Release pressure and remove plate, throttle boost valve, spring and manual low 2-1 scheduling valve and spring from bore.

6) Apply hand pressure on remaining valve body plate and remove 8 retaining screws. Hold valve body so plate faces upward.

7) Release hand pressure on plate and remove. Remove spring and intermediate servo modulator valve from body. Remove intermediate servo accumulator valve and springs.

8) Remove 2-3 back-out valve, spring and 3-2 shift timing valve plug (if not peened on end). Remove 2-3 shift valve, spring and throttle modulator valve.

9) Remove 1-2 shift valve, DR-2 shift valve and spring. Remove coasting regulator valve and cutback valve from body.

NOTE: **Do not attempt to remove 3-2 shift timing plug if end is peened over. Condition will not affect transmission operation.**

Reassembly

To reassemble, reverse disassembly procedure. Coat check balls with petrolatum to hold in place

FORD MOTOR CO. C-6 (Cont.)

Fig. 15: Exploded View of Control Valve Body Assembly

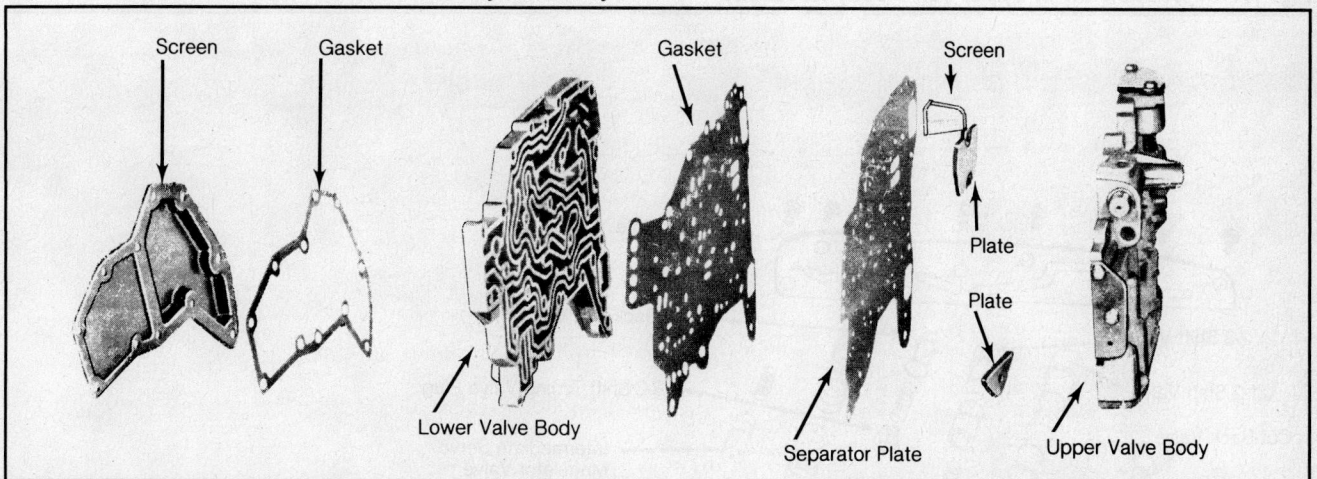

during reassembly. When installing screen in separator plate, make sure tabs are flush with separator plate surface. Tighten all bolts and screws evenly.

FRONT PUMP

NOTE: Front seal can be replaced with pump installed in transmission.

Disassembly

1) Remove 2 seal rings and selective thrust washer. Remove large square cut seal from outside diameter of pump housing.

2) Remove 5 bolts securing stator support to pump housing. Lift support from housing. Remove drive and driven gears from housing.

Pump Housing Bushing Replacement

Remove bushing from pump housing using a driver and hammer. Place new bushing into position. Make sure half moon slot in bushing is on top and in line with oil lube hole near seal bore. Press bushing in .060-.080" (15.24-2.03 mm) below front face of bushing bore.

NOTE: After assembly, half moon slot must be below lube hole to provide proper lubrication.

Reassembly

1) Install drive and driven gear into pump housing with identification mark or chamfered surface of each gear installed toward front of pump housing. Position stator support in pump housing. Install and tighten retaining bolts.

Fig. 16: View of Valve Body Showing Location of Check Valves and Balls

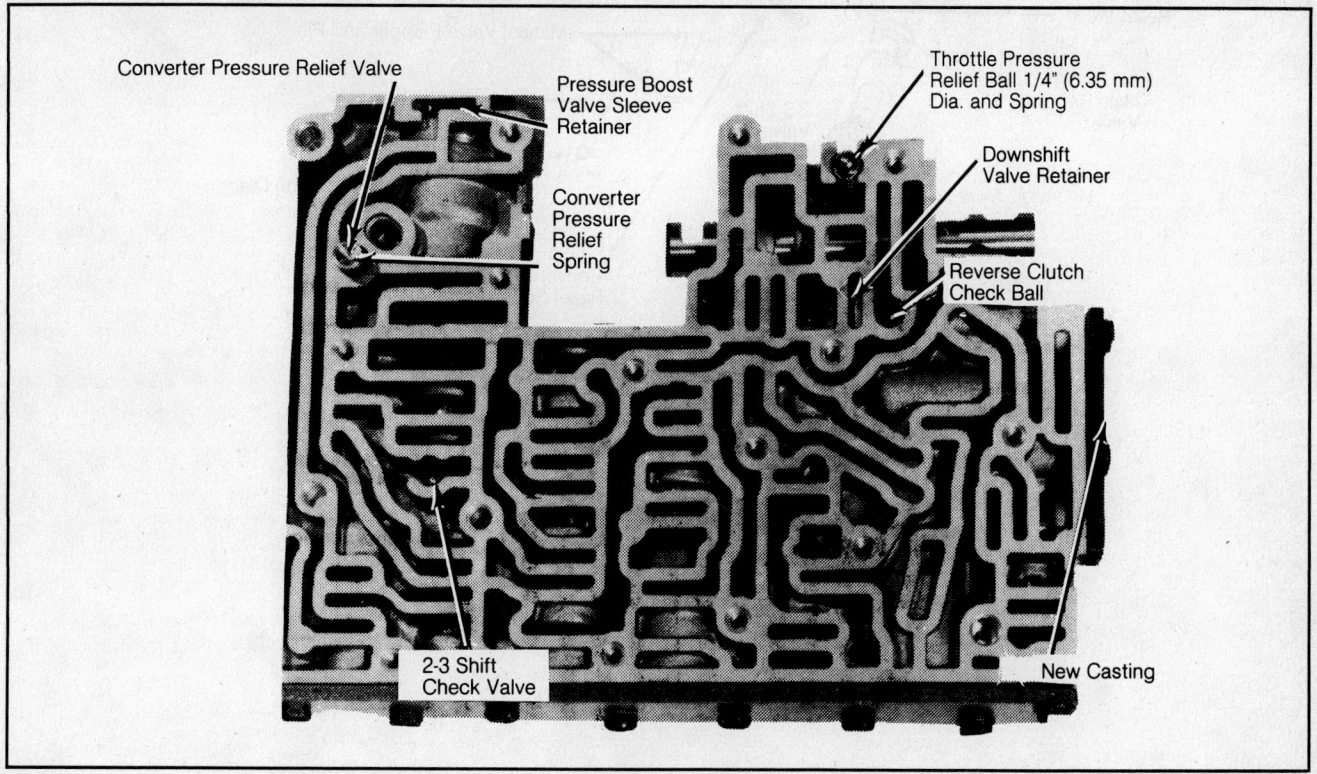

Automatic Transmissions
FORD MOTOR CO. C-6 (Cont.)

Fig. 17: *Exploded View of Upper Valve Body Assembly*

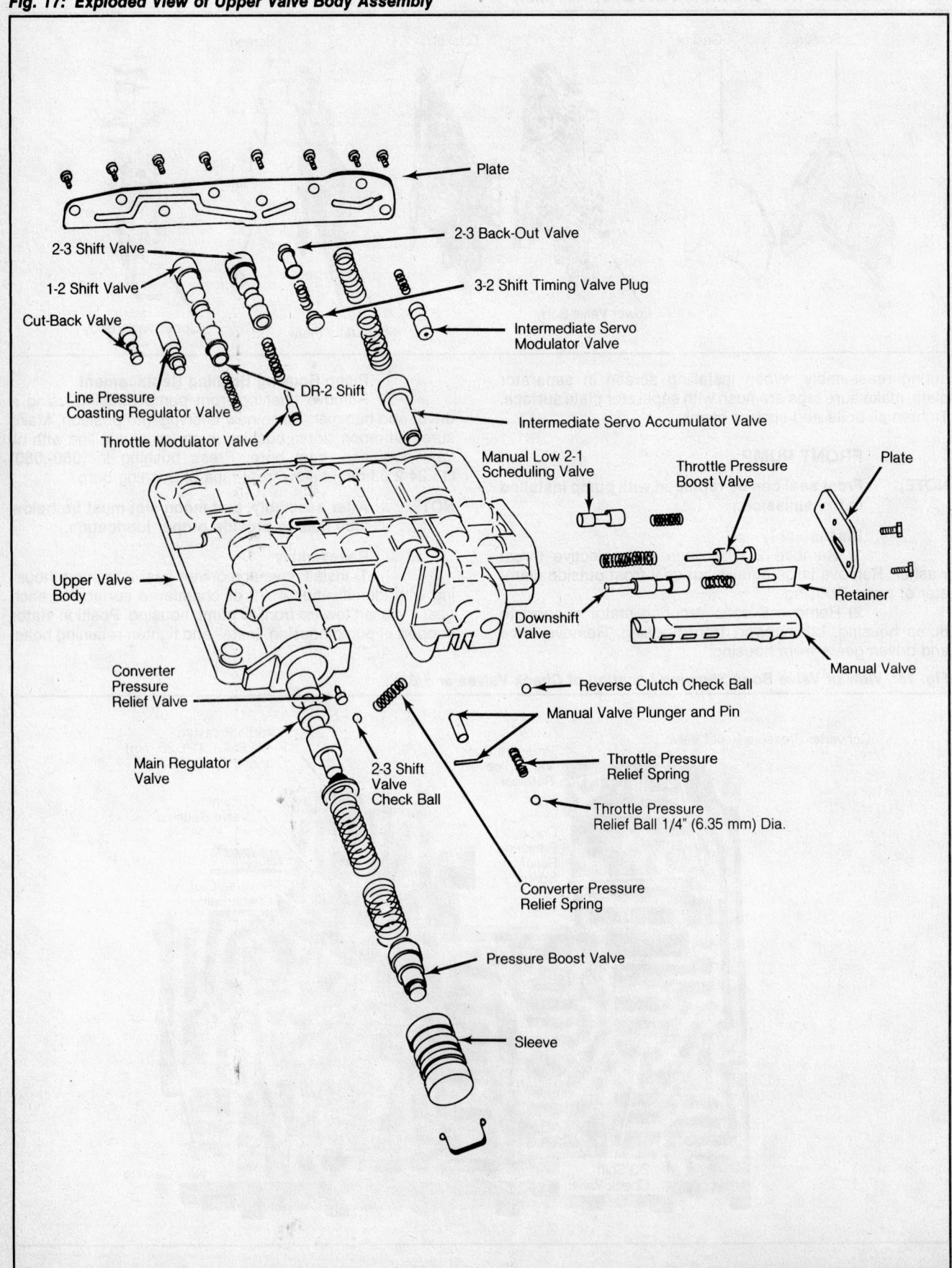

Plate

2-3 Back-Out Valve

2-3 Shift Valve

1-2 Shift Valve

3-2 Shift Timing Valve Plug

Cut-Back Valve

Intermediate Servo Modulator Valve

Line Pressure Coasting Regulator Valve

DR-2 Shift

Throttle Modulator Valve

Intermediate Servo Accumulator Valve

Manual Low 2-1 Scheduling Valve

Throttle Pressure Boost Valve

Plate

Upper Valve Body

Downshift Valve

Retainer

Manual Valve

Converter Pressure Relief Valve

Reverse Clutch Check Ball

Main Regulator Valve

Manual Valve Plunger and Pin

2-3 Shift Valve Check Ball

Throttle Pressure Relief Spring

Throttle Pressure Relief Ball 1/4" (6.35 mm) Dia.

Converter Pressure Relief Spring

Pressure Boost Valve

Sleeve

Fig. 18: Exploded View of Front Pump Assembly

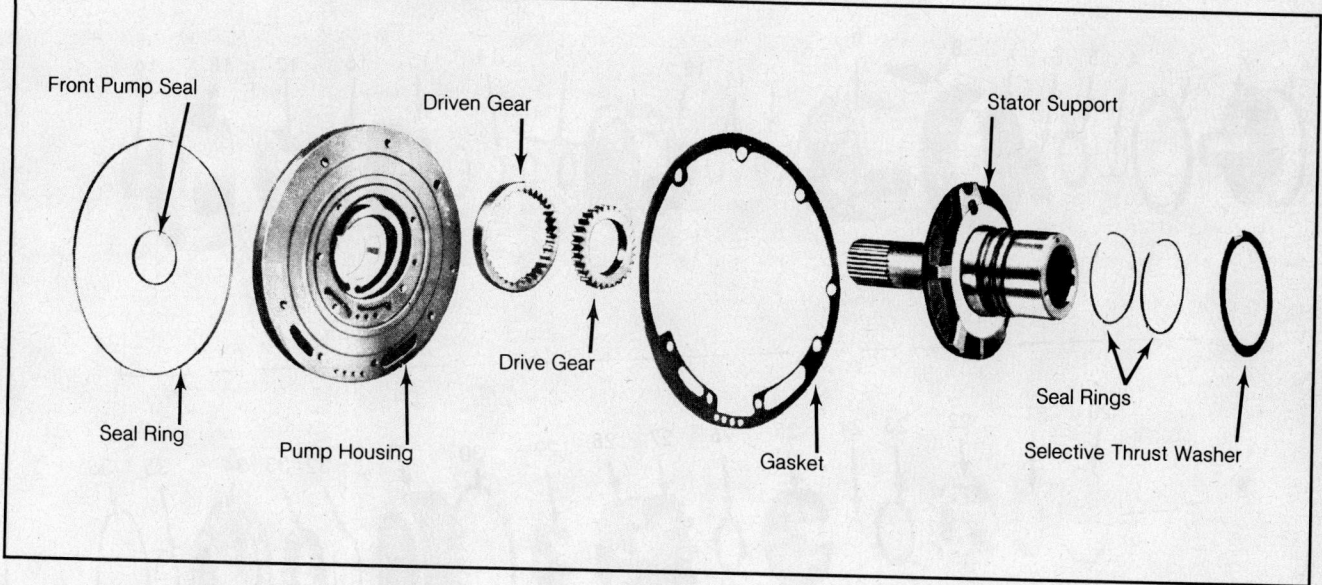

2) Carefully install 2 new seal rings on stator support. Make sure ends of rings are engaged to lock them in place. Install a new square cut seal on outside diameter of pump housing.

3) Install selective thrust washer. Place pump on torque converter. Make sure drive gear engages converter hub. Rotate pump to ensure that gears rotate freely.

NOTE: Different clutch assemblies are used in various models. When disassembling clutches, note number and location of plates used for reassembly reference

FRONT PUMP SELECTIVE THRUST WASHERS

Color Code	Thickness In. (mm)
Blue	.056-.060 (1.42-1.52)
Natural (White)	.073-.077 (1.85-1.96)
Red	.088-.092 (2.24-2.34)

REVERSE-HIGH CLUTCH
Disassembly

1) Remove pressure plate snap ring by prying up with screwdriver. Remove pressure plate, drive and driven plates. Using Clutch Spring Compressor (T65L-77515-A) compress piston return springs.

2) Remove snap ring, spring retainer and springs. Apply air pressure to piston apply hole in drum and remove piston. Remove piston outer seal from piston and inner seal from clutch drum.

Bushing Replacement

To remove front bushing, use a cape chisel and cut along bushing seam until chisel breaks through bushing wall. Pry loose ends of bushing up to remove. Remove rear bushing using a press ram and bushing adapter. Install bushings using bushing drivers.

Fig. 19: Exploded View of Reverse-High Clutch Assembly

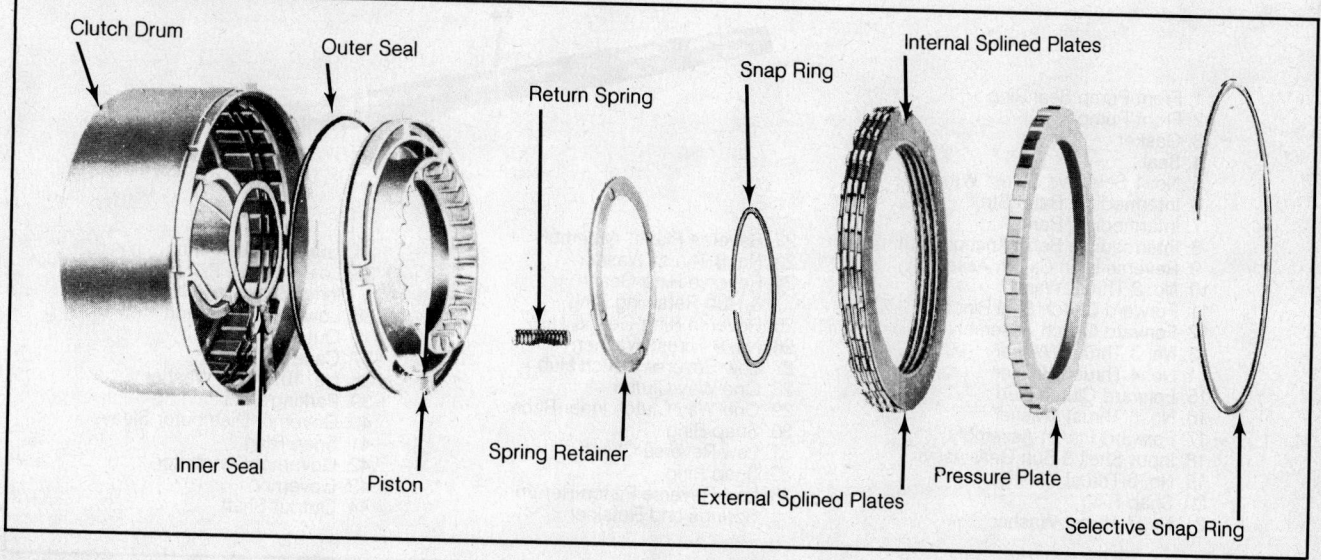

Automatic Transmissions
FORD MOTOR CO. C-6 (Cont.)

Fig. 20: Exploded View of Transmission Case and Drive Train Assembly

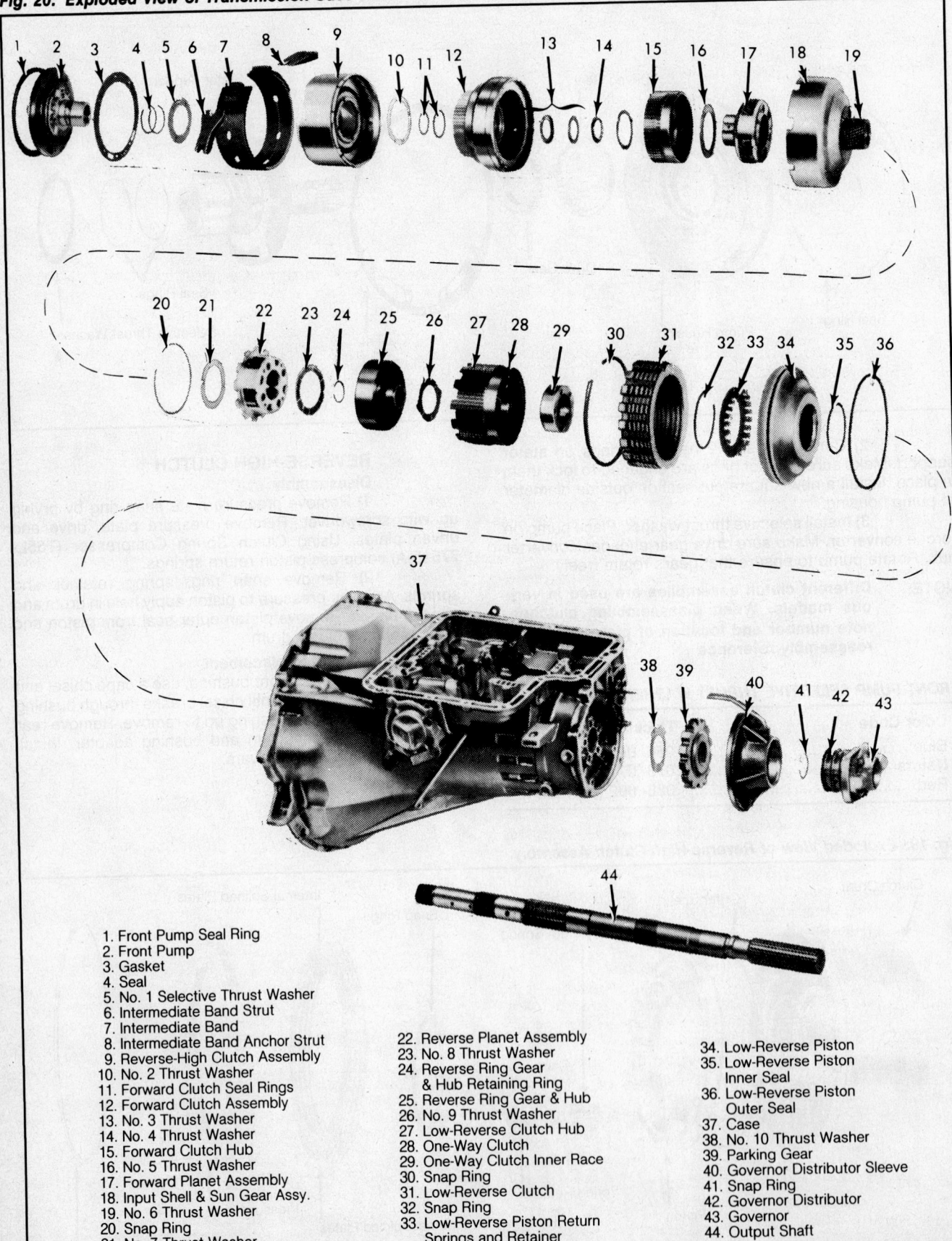

1. Front Pump Seal Ring
2. Front Pump
3. Gasket
4. Seal
5. No. 1 Selective Thrust Washer
6. Intermediate Band Strut
7. Intermediate Band
8. Intermediate Band Anchor Strut
9. Reverse-High Clutch Assembly
10. No. 2 Thrust Washer
11. Forward Clutch Seal Rings
12. Forward Clutch Assembly
13. No. 3 Thrust Washer
14. No. 4 Thrust Washer
15. Forward Clutch Hub
16. No. 5 Thrust Washer
17. Forward Planet Assembly
18. Input Shell & Sun Gear Assy.
19. No. 6 Thrust Washer
20. Snap Ring
21. No. 7 Thrust Washer

22. Reverse Planet Assembly
23. No. 8 Thrust Washer
24. Reverse Ring Gear
    & Hub Retaining Ring
25. Reverse Ring Gear & Hub
26. No. 9 Thrust Washer
27. Low-Reverse Clutch Hub
28. One-Way Clutch
29. One-Way Clutch Inner Race
30. Snap Ring
31. Low-Reverse Clutch
32. Snap Ring
33. Low-Reverse Piston Return
    Springs and Retainer

34. Low-Reverse Piston
35. Low-Reverse Piston
    Inner Seal
36. Low-Reverse Piston
    Outer Seal
37. Case
38. No. 10 Thrust Washer
39. Parking Gear
40. Governor Distributor Sleeve
41. Snap Ring
42. Governor Distributor
43. Governor
44. Output Shaft

FORD MOTOR CO. C-6 (Cont.)

Reassembly

1) Dip new seals in transmission fluid and install one seal on piston and one in drum. Install piston into clutch drum. Position return springs in pockets as shown. Place spring retainer over springs. Using compressor tool, compress springs and install snap ring. *See Fig. 21.*

Fig. 21: View of Reverse-High Clutch Piston Return Springs

Springs Must Be Installed In Pockets Marked X Only

NOTE: **Before releasing tool, make sure snap ring is seated inside 4 snap ring guides on spring retainer.**

2) Install clutch plates alternately starting with a steel drive plate. If new clutch plates are being installed, composition plates must be soaked in transmission fluid for 15 minutes before installation.

3) Install pressure plate and retaining snap ring. See CLUTCH PLATE CHART for the number of clutch plates required.

4) Using a feeler gauge, check clearance between pressure plate and snap ring. Hold pressure plate downward while measuring. Clearance should be .022-.036" (.56-.91 mm).

5) If clearance is not within specifications, selective snap rings are available in the following thickness:
.056-.060" (1.42-1.52 mm)
.065-.069" (1.65-1.75 mm)
.074-.078" (1.88-1.98 mm)

.083-.087" (2.11-2.21 mm)
.092-.096" (2.34-2.44 mm)
.110-.114" (2.79-2.90 mm)
.128-.132" (3.25-3.35 mm)
Install correct thickness snap ring and recheck clearance.

CLUTCH PLATE CHART

Application	Flat Steel Plates	Composition Plates
Forward Clutch		
PGD, PJD	[1] 4	4
High Clutch		
PGD, PJD	3	3
Reverse Clutch		
PJD	[2] 5	5
PGD	[2] 4	4

[1] - Plus one WAVED plate installed next to inner pressure plate.
[2] - Plus one WAVED plate installed next to piston.

FORWARD CLUTCH

Disassembly

1) Remove clutch pressure plate retaining snap ring. Remove rear pressure plate, drive and driven plates and forward pressure plate from clutch drum.

2) Remove snap ring securing disc spring in drum and remove disc spring. Apply air pressure to clutch apply passage in drum and remove piston. Remove seals from piston and drum.

Reassembly

1) Dip 2 new seals in transmission fluid. Install smaller seal on clutch hub and other seal on piston. Install clutch piston in cylinder.

2) Make sure steel pressure ring is in groove on piston. Place disc spring in clutch drum with dished face downward. Secure in place with retaining snap ring.

NOTE: **If new composition plates are being installed, soak them in transmission fluid for 15 minutes prior to installation.**

3) Install forward pressure plate with flat side up and beveled side downward. Dip clutch plates in transmission fluid.

Fig. 22: Exploded View of Forward Clutch Assembly

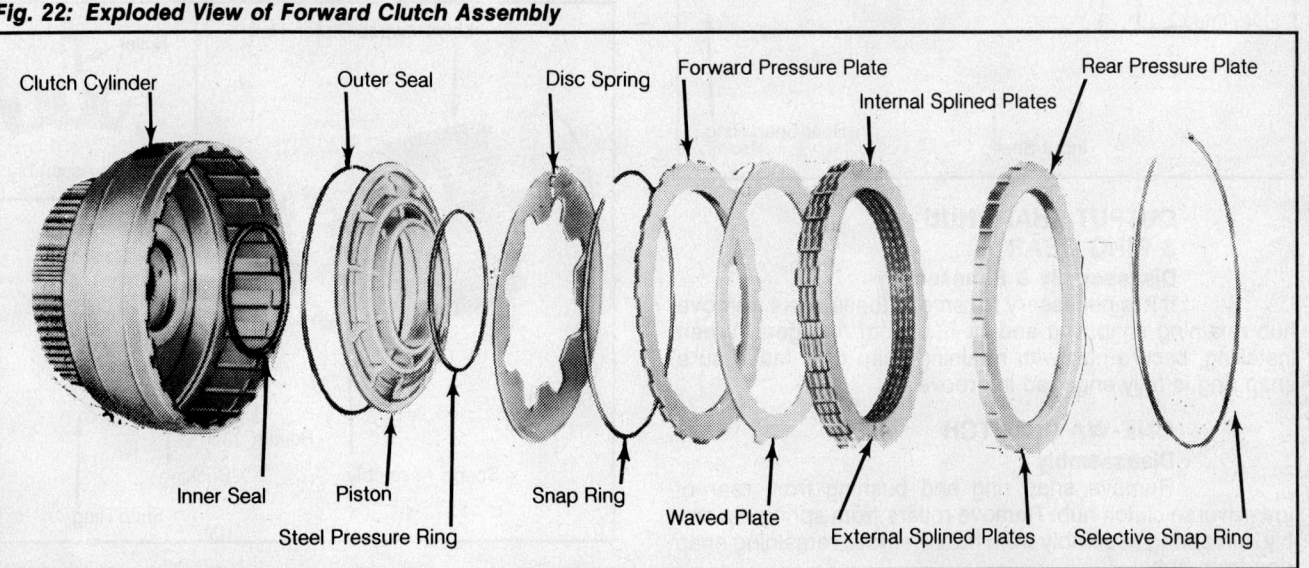

Clutch Cylinder — Outer Seal — Disc Spring — Forward Pressure Plate — Internal Splined Plates — Rear Pressure Plate

Inner Seal — Piston — Steel Pressure Ring — Snap Ring — Waved Plate — External Splined Plates — Selective Snap Ring

4) Install clutch plates starting with the waved plate, then a steel plate and a composition plate. Install remaining plates in this sequence.

NOTE: See CLUTCH PLATE CHART for the number of clutch plates required.

5) Using a feeler gauge, check clearance between snap ring and pressure plate. Hold pressure plate down while measuring.

6) Clearance should be .021-.046" (.53-1.17 mm). If clearance is not within specifications, selective snap rings are available in following thicknesses:

.056-.060" (1.42-1.52 mm)
.065-.069" (1.65-1.75 mm)
.074-.078" (1.88-1.98 mm)
.083-.087" (2.11-2.21 mm)
.092-.096" (2.34-2.44 mm)
.110-.114" (2.79-2.90 mm)
.128-.132" (3.25-3.35 mm).

Install correct thickness snap ring and recheck clearance.

INPUT SHELL & SUN GEAR
Disassembly

Remove rear (external) snap ring from sun gear and remove thrust washer from sun gear and input shell. Working inside input shell, remove sun gear. Remove forward (internal) snap ring from gear.

Reassembly

Install forward snap ring on short end of sun gear. Working inside input shell, slide sun gear and snap ring into place. Making sure longer end of gear is at rear. Place thrust washer on rear side of input shell. Install rear snap ring. See Fig. 23.

Fig. 23: Exploded View of Input Shell & Sun Gear

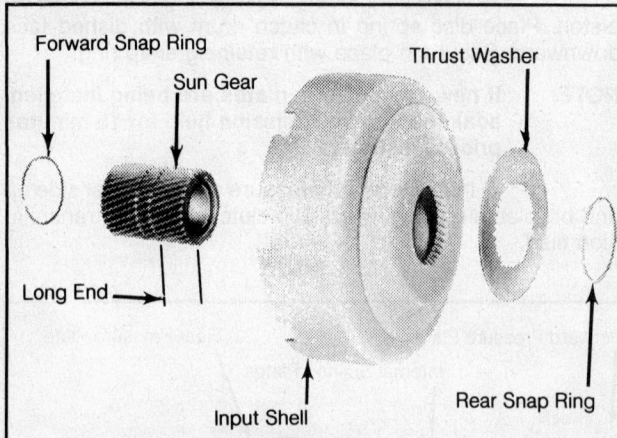

OUTPUT SHAFT HUB & RING GEAR
Disassembly & Reassembly

If it is necessary to remove these parts, remove hub retaining snap ring and lift hub from ring gear. When installing, secure hub with retaining snap ring. Make sure snap ring is fully engaged in groove.

ONE-WAY CLUTCH
Disassembly

Remove snap ring and bushing from rear of low-reverse clutch hub. Remove rollers from spring assembly. Lift spring assembly from hub. Remove remaining snap ring from hub.

Fig. 24: Output Shaft Hub and Ring Gear Assembly

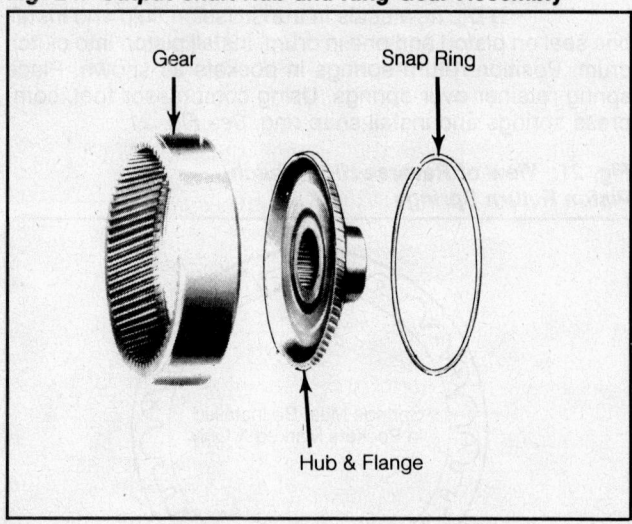

Reassembly

1) Install snap ring in forward groove of low-reverse clutch hub. Place hub on bench with forward end down. Install spring assembly on top of snap ring.

2) Install a roller into each spring assembly compartment. Install bushing on top of spring assembly. Install remaining snap ring at rear of clutch hub to secure assembly.

INTERMEDIATE SERVO
Disassembly

Apply air pressure to port in servo cover and remove piston assembly. Remove seal from cover.

NOTE: Piston and rod are serviced as an assembly. Replace if piston or sealing lips are damaged.

Reassembly

Dip new seal in transmission fluid and install on cover. Dip piston assembly in transmission fluid and install in cover.

Fig. 25: Exploded View of One-Way Clutch Assembly

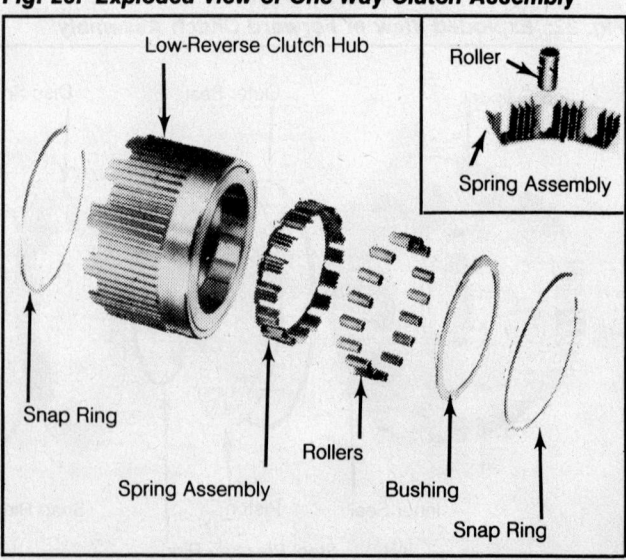

Automatic Transmissions

FORD MOTOR CO. C-6 (Cont.)

LOW-REVERSE CLUTCH PISTON

NOTE: **Clutch is assembled as part of transmission reassembly; replace seals as follows:**

Remove inner and outer seals from clutch piston. Dip new seals in transmission fluid and install on piston.

GOVERNOR
Disassembly
Remove governor retaining bolts and governor. Remove snap ring securing governor distributor to output shaft. Slide distributor off front of shaft. Remove seal rings from governor distributor.

Reassembly
1) Carefully install new seal rings on distributor. Working from front end of output shaft, slide governor distributor into place on shaft.

2) Secure in place with snap ring. Make sure snap ring is fully seated in groove. Position governor on distributor. Install and tighten retaining screws.

TRANSMISSION REASSEMBLY

1) With transmission mounted in fixture, tap low-reverse clutch piston into case with soft mallet. Hold one-way clutch inner race in position, then install and tighten retaining bolts.

2) Install low-reverse clutch return spring and retainer assembly in clutch piston. Position snap ring on one-way clutch inner race. Compress return spring and retainer and seat snap ring in groove.

3) Place transmission case on bench with front end facing downward. Position parking gear thrust washer and gear on case. It is not necessary to restake thrust washer. Position oil distributor and tubes on rear of case.

4) Install and tighten retaining bolts. Install output shaft and governor as an assembly. Place a new gasket on rear of case. Install extension housing and retaining bolts. Tighten bolts to specifications. Install vent tube.

5) Coat 2 new servo cover gaskets with petroleum jelly and position them on servo cover. Place servo spring on piston rod and install in case.

6) Install retaining bolts. Make sure identification tag is under one of the cover bolts and tighten. Align low-reverse clutch hub and one-way clutch with inner race at rear of case.

7) Rotate low-reverse clutch hub clockwise while applying pressure to seat it on inner race. Install low-reverse clutch plates, starting with the waved plate next to piston and follow with a steel, then a composition plate until all plates are installed.

8) Retain plates with petroleum jelly. Install pressure plate and snap ring. Test operation of low-reverse clutch assembly by applying air pressure to clutch pressure apply hole in case.

9) Install reverse planet ring gear thrust washer, ring gear and hub assembly. Install snap ring in groove of output shaft. Install front and rear thrust washers onto reverse planet assembly. Retain with petroleum jelly.

10) Install assembly into ring gear and install snap ring. Place reverse-high clutch on bench with front end facing downward. Install thrust washer on rear end of assembly and retain with petrolatum.

11) Install splined end of forward clutch into open end of reverse-high clutch with splines engaging direct clutch plates. Install thrust washer on front end of forward planet ring gear and hub. Retain with petroleum jelly.

12) Install ring gear into forward clutch and install thrust washer on front end of forward planet assembly and retain with petroleum jelly.

13) Install assembly into ring gear. Install input shell and sun assembly. Install reverse-high clutch, forward clutch, forward planet assembly, input shell and sun gear as an assembly into case.

14) Install intermediate band around direct clutch drum. Install band struts and tighten band adjusting screw enough to retain band.

15) Place selective bronze thrust washer on rear shoulder of stator support and retain with petroleum jelly.

16) If end play was not within specifications when disassembled, replace washer at this time with one of proper thickness. See TRANSMISSION END PLAY table in TRANSMISSION DISASSEMBLY.

17) Using 5/16 x 3" bolts, make 2 alignment studs by cutting the heads off and grinding a taper on the cut end. Install the studs opposite each other in case mounting holes.

18) Slide a new gasket onto studs. Position pump on case, being careful not to damage seal on pump housing, and remove studs. Install 6 of the mounting bolts and tighten.

Fig. 26: Exploded View of Output Shaft and Governor Assembly

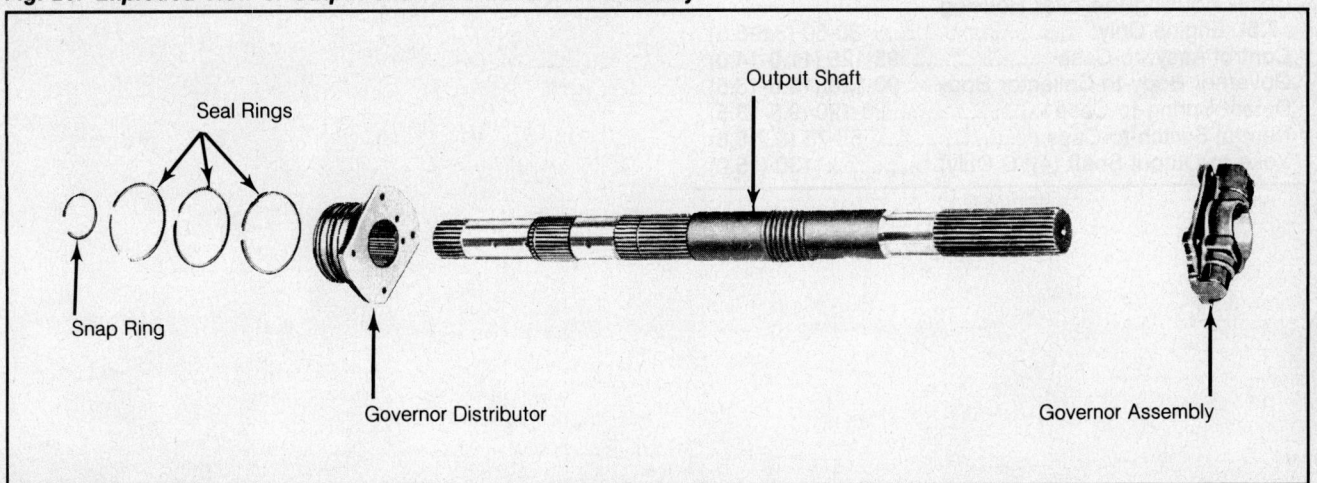

Automatic Transmissions
FORD MOTOR CO. C-6 (Cont.)

19) Tighten intermediate band adjusting screw to 10 ft. lbs. (14 N.m). Back off screw exactly 1 1/2 turns. Hold adjusting screw in this position and tighten lock nut to specifications.

20) Install input shaft with long splined end inserted into forward clutch assembly. Check end play again to ensure correct assembly. Install control valve body into case, making sure levers engage valves properly.

21) Install primary throttle valve, rod and vacuum diaphragm in case. Install oil pan with new gasket. Install retaining bolts and tighten. Install torque converter.

TIGHTENING SPECIFICATIONS

Application	Ft. Lbs. (N.m)
Converter-to-Flywheel	20-34 (27-46)
Front Pump-to-Case	16-30 (22-41)
Overrunning Clutch Race-to-Case	18-25 (24-34)
Stator Support-to-Pump	12-16 (16-22)
Converter Cover-to-Housing	12-16 (16-22)
Guide Plate-to-Case	12-16 (16-22)
Intermediate Servo Cover-to-Case	14-20 (19-27)
Diaphragm Assembly-to-Case	12-16 (16-22)
Distributor Sleeve-to-Case	12-16 (16-22)
Extension Housing-to-Case	25-35 (34-48)
Band Adjusting Screw Lock Nut	35-45 (48-61)
Cooler Tube Connector Lock	20-35 (27-48)
Converter Drain Plug	8-28 (11-38)
Manual Valve Inner Lever-to-Shaft	30-40 (41-54)
Downshift Lever-to-Shaft	12-16 (16-22)
Filler Tube-to-Engine	
Econoline - 5.0L, 5.8L, 7.5L	40-50 (54-68)
Econoline - 4.9L	33-42 (45-57)
Econoline - 6.9L	24-35 (33-48)
Transmission-to-Engine (Diesel)	50-65 (68-88)
Transmission-to-Engine (Gasoline)	40-50 (54-68)
Rear Engine Support-to-Trans.	60-80 (82-109)
Ext. Hsg.-to-Bearing Ret. Stud	35-50 (48-68)
Bearing Ret.-to-Ext. Housing	35-45 (48-61)
	INCH Lbs. (N.m)
End Plates-to-Valve Body	20-40 (2.5-4.5)
Inner Downshift Lever Stop	20-45 (2.5-5.0)
Reinforcement Plate-to-Valve Body	20-45 (2.5-5.0)
Screen & Lower-to-Upper Valve Body	40-55 (4.5-6.2)
Shift Valve Plate-to-Upper Body	20-45 (2.5-5.0)
Upper-to-Lower Body	40-55 (4.5-6.2)
Cover Housing-to-Cover Housing	
7.5L Engine Only	30-60 (3.5-6.5)
Control Assy.-to-Case	95-125 (11.0-14.0)
Governor Body-to-Collector Body	90-120 (10.5-13.5)
Detent Spring-to-Case	80-120 (9.5-13.5)
Neutral Switch-to-Case	55-75 (6.2-8.0)
Yoke-to-Output Shaft (4WD Only)	130 (15.0)

FORD MOTOR CO. ZF 4HP-22 AUTOMATIC OVERDRIVE

**Continental & Mark VII
With 2.4L Diesel Engine**

IDENTIFICATION

The ZF automatic overdrive transmission can be identified by code letter "T", which is shown on lower line of Vehcile Certification Label under "TR". Label is attached on driver's door lock panel or pillar.

Also transmission may be identified by a stamped metal plate which is located adjacent tu manual lever. *See Fig. 1.*

Fig. 1: Service Identification Tag

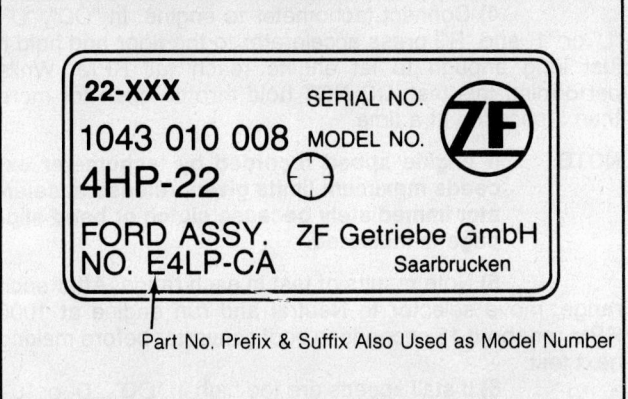

Identification tag is located adjacent to manual lever.

DESCRIPTION

Transmission is a 4-speed transmission that provides automatic upshifts through 4 forward gear ratios. Selector positions are the same as Ford AOD transmission, but with an entirely different gear train and torque converter lock-up feature.

OPERATION

TORQUE CONVERTER

Torque converter operates as a conventional torque multiplier and fluid coupling in all gears except overdrive. In overdrive, a specific combination of road speed and accelerator position signals call for a lock-up to mechanical drive. When this occurs, valve body applies pressure to a hydraulic clutch in converter which locks the impeller to turbine.

DRIVE TRAIN

Drive train is controlled by 7 disc clutches and 3 one-way clutches. It has a front compound planetary gear train that operates in 1st, 2nd, 3rd and reverse. A separate overdrive gear set provides 4th gear and is locked for direct (through) drive in all other gears. The output shaft is housed in a conventional Ford extension housing, with a C-3 bushing and slip yoke seal. A pawl and gear are used for park lock.

HYDRAULIC SYSTEM

The valve body is controlled by the manual selector, a centrifugal govervor on the output shaft, and a manual TV (kickdown) cable to signal throttle position. The cable is attached to cable bracket and injection pump side lever.

SHIFT SELECTOR POSITIONS & OPERATIONS

The ZF transmission is fully automatic in either "OD" (overdrive) or "D" (overdrive lock-out) positions. Manual upshifting and downshifting is available through the forward drive positions "OD", "D", "L" (Continental), or "1" (Mark VII).

"OD" (Overdrive)

This is the normal position for a automatic overdrive transmission. In this position the transmission starts in 1st gear and as the vehicle accelerates, automatically upshifts to 2nd, 3rd and 4th gears. The transmission will automatically downshift as vehicle speed decreases. Transmission will not shift into or remain in overdrive when accelerator is pushed to the floor.

"D" (Overdrive Lock-out)

In this position the transmission operates as in "OD" except there will be no shift to into the overdrive gear and no converter clutch lock-up. This position may be used when driving up or down mountainous roads to provide better performance and greater engine braking than the "OD" position. Transmission may be shifted from "OD" to "D" or "D" to "OD" at any vehicle speed.

"L" or "1" (Low)

This position can be used when maximum engine braking is desired. To help brake the vehicle on hilly roads where "D" (overdrive lock-out) does not provide enough braking, shift selector to "L" or "1" (low). At vehicle speeds above approximately 20 MPH (32 km/h) the transmission will shift to 2nd gear, and remain in 2nd gear. When vehicle speed drops below approximately 20 MPH (32 km/h) transmission will downshift to 1st gear, and remain in 1st gear. Upshifts from "L" or "1" can be made by manually shifting to "OD" or "D". When "L" or "1" position is selected for initial driveaway, transmission will remain in the selected gear range until selector is moved into another gear position.

"P", "R" or "N"

These positions operate the same as other automatic transmissions.

Reverse Inhibitor

If selector is moved to "R" with vehicle still moving forward at 19 MPH (30 km/h) or more, the transmission will not shift to reverse gear.

Forced Downshifts

1) At vehicle speeds from approximately 50-20 MPH (80-32 km/h) with transmission in "OD" or "D", transmission will downshift to 2nd gear when the accelerator is pushed to the floor.

2) At vehicle speeds above appoximately 50 MPH (80 km/h) the transmission will not downshift to 2nd gear.

3) At vehicle speeds below approximately 20 MPH (32 km/h) the transmission will downshift to 1st gear when accelerator is pushed to the floor.

4) At most vehicle speeds, when the transmission is in "OD" the transmission will downshift from 4th gear to 3rd gear when accelerator is pushed for moderate to heavy acceleration.

FORD MOTOR CO. ZF 4HP-22 AUTOMATIC OVERDRIVE (Cont.)

LUBRICATION & ADJUSTMENT

LUBRICATION
See appropriate AUTOMATIC TRANSMISSION SERVICING article in DOMESTIC GENERAL SERVICING section.

ADJUSTMENT
TV (Kickdown) Cable
1) No internal adjustments are possible on this transmission. The only adjustment possible is for the TV (kickdown) cable. When installing a new TV cable, the reference bead will be loose on the cable.

2) Set injection pump top lever to the full throttle position. Tighten rear adjusting nut on the threaded barrel until a gap of 1.54-1.57" (39-40 mm) exists between the edge of the crimped bead on the cable closest to the barrel and the end of the threaded barrel. Use Gauge (D84P-70332-B) to gauge this dimension.

3) Tighten the forward adjusting nut to 80-106 INCH lbs. (9-12 N.m) to lock the cable assembly to the bracket. Recheck gap and readjust if necessary. *See Fig. 2.*

Fig. 2: Kickdown (TV) Cable Adjustment

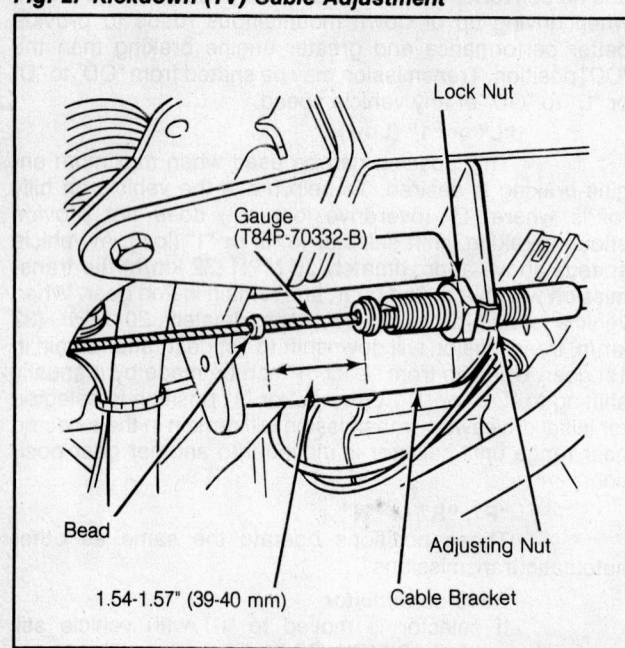

Lock Nut
Gauge (T84P-70332-B)
Bead
Adjusting Nut
Cable Bracket
1.54-1.57" (39-40 mm)

NOTE: Kickdown on this transmission is controlled by the injection pump linkage adjustments. Ensure injection pump linkage is properly adjusted.

TESTING

CONTROL PRESSURE TEST
There is no control pressure test for ZF transmission.

STALL TEST
1) Stall test check converter clutch operation and installation, the holding ability of the forward clutch, reverse clutch, the low-reverse bands, the planetary one-way clutch and engine performance.

2) Test should be performed only with engine coolant and transmission fluid at proper levels and at operating temperature, and with TV linkage adjusted properly.

3) Apply service and parking brakes firmly for each stall test. Determine specified speed stall RPM for vehicle. See STALL SPEEDS table. Use a grease pencil to mark RPM on dial of tachometer.

STALL SPEEDS

Application	RPM
ZF	
Minimum Speed	2600
Maximum Speed	2900

4) Connect tachometer to engine. In "OD", "D", "L" or "1" and "R", press accelerator to the floor and hold it just long enough to let engine reach full RPM. While performing this test, DO NOT hold throttle open for more than 5 seconds at a time.

NOTE: If engine speed recorded by tachometer exceeds maximum limits given, release accelerator immediately because clutch or band slippage is indicated.

5) Note results of test in each range. After each range, move selector to Neutral and run engine at 1000 RPM for about 15 seconds to cool converter before making next test.

6) If stall speeds are too high in "OD", "D" or "L", this is an indication of clutch slippage. Replace transmission. If speeds are too high in all ranges, check TV adjustment; if okay, replace transmission. If speeds are too high in "R" only, this indicates clutch slippage. Replace transmission.

7) If stall speeds are too low in "OD", "D", "R" or "L", check engine tune and injector pump linkage for proper adjustment. If tune and linkage adjustments are okay, replace transmission due to torque converter one-way clutch slip.

GOVERNOR CHECK
Perform a shift point check while on a road test or in the shop. If shift points are not within specifications, proceed with the following:
Accelerate vehicle to 30 MPH (48 km/h), then completely back off the throttle. Transmission should shift to 3rd gear.

SHIFT POINT CHECKS (ROAD TEST)
1) This check will determine if governor pressure and shift control valves are operating properly. During shift point check operation, if transmission does not shift within specifications or certain gear ratios cannot be obtained, refer to TROUBLESHOOTING in this article.

2) Check shift points with engine at normal operating temperature so choke operation does not effect shift point spacing. Operate vehicle with gear selector in "OD" detent (lock-up). Transmission should accomplish 1st to 2nd, 2nd to 3rd and 3rd to 4th upshifts within shift speed specifications.

Improper Shift Timing
(4th to 3rd Backout Shift)
Improper shift timing: 4th to 3rd backout shift (4th to 3rd on full backout of accelerator pedal, accompa-

FORD MOTOR CO. ZF 4HP-22 AUTOMATIC OVERDRIVE (Cont.)

nied by 3rd to 4th shift when accelerator depressed) may by diagnosed/serviced by the verification of the following:
- Loose governor: Output shaft snap ring not seated or missing locator ball.
- Worn or broken output shaft seal rings: Large diameter.
- Worn seal ring grooves.
- Worn collector bore.
- Output shaft holes blocked.

Refer to ROAD TEST CHART and check for proper engagement, correct upshift and downshift speeds, or any signs of slip, harshness, mushiness or other shift feel condition.

ROAD TEST CHART

Range	Check For:
"L"	Engagement
	No 1st to 2nd Upshift
	Engine Braking in 1st & 2nd Gear
	Slipping
"D"	Engagement & Shift Feel
	1st, 2nd, 3rd Upshifts at Spec. Speeds
	4th Gear Lockout
	Torque Demand 3rd to 2nd Only
	W.O.T. Kickdown to 2nd or 1st
	Smooth Coastdown
	Slipping
"OD"	Engagement & Shift Feel
	1st, 2nd, 3rd, 4th Upshifts at Spec. Speeds
	Torque Demand to 3rd Gear from OD
	W.O.T. Kickdown to 2nd or 1st
	No 4th Gear at W.O.T.
	Smooth Coastdown
	Slipping
"R"	Engagement
	Back-up Without Slip
	Slipping

SHIFT POINT CHECKS (IN SHOP)

1) A shift test can be performed in shop to check shift valve operation, governor circuits, shift delay pressures, throttle boost and downshift valve action. Raise vehicle with an axle or frame hoist so that rear wheels are clear of floor.

CAUTION: NEVER exceed 60 MPH (97 km/h) speedometer speed.

2) To determine if automatic upshifts occur, place transmission selector lever in "OD" and make a minimum throttle 1st to 2nd, 2nd to 3rd and 3rd to 4th upshift.

3) When shift occurs, you will see speedometer needle make a momentary surge and feel a driveline bump. If shift points are within specifications, the 1st to 2nd, 2nd to 3rd and 3rd to 4th shift valves and governor are okay.

CAUTION: Gradually apply brakes to stop rear wheels.

4) If shift points are not within specifications, perform a governor check to isolate the problem. ALWAYS after each test move selector lever to Neutral and run engine at 1000 RPM to cool transmission.

SHIFT SPEED CHART:

THROTTLE	RANGE	SHIFT	SHIFT SPEEDS ACTUAL MPH
Part Throttle	Ⓓ , D	1-2	14-15
	Ⓓ , D	2-3	22-23
	Ⓓ	3-4	31-34
	Ⓓ	CL	41-44
	Ⓓ	CU	40-43
	Ⓓ	4-3	26-30
	Ⓓ , D	3-2	20-21
	Ⓓ , D	2-1	10-11
To Detent	Ⓓ , D	1-2	25-26
	Ⓓ , D	2-3	49-54
	Ⓓ	3-4	71-75
	Ⓓ	4-3	58-63
	Ⓓ , D	3-2	35-40
	Ⓓ , D	2-1	22-24
Throttle Detent	Ⓓ , D	1-2	32-36
	Ⓓ , D	2-3	56-60
WOT	Ⓓ , D	3-2	53-57
	Ⓓ , D	2-1	26-31

Axle Ratio — 3.73:1
CL = Converter Clutch Lockup CU = Converter Clutch Unlock
Tire Sizes P205/75R15 — P215/70R15 — P215/65R15

TROUBLE SHOOTING

See appropriate MANUAL TRANSMISSION TROUBLE SHOOTING article in DOMESTIC GENERAL SERVICING section.

SERVICE (IN VEHICLE)

VALVE BODY

Removal

1) Raise vehicle on a hoist so transmission and oil pan are accessible. Drain transmission fluid. Disconnect filler stub tube from oil pan. Using a 10 mm socket, remove bolts and clamps attaching oil pan to case. Remove oil pan.

2) Remove 3 TORX head bolts retaining oil pan screen. Remove 13 attaching bolts to remove valve body from transmission. Clean case and valve body mating surfaces. Inspect for burrs or distortion of surfaces.

NOTE: Remove only large head bolts with Torx Drive Bit (D79P-2100-T27).

Installation

1) Position valve body under case to engage inner manual lever pin in manual valve. Pull on kickdown cable to position accelerator cam so that roller on throttle valve clears the cam.

2) Position valve body against case. Note length and location and install 13 valve body bolts fingertight to hold valve body in alignment to case. Align valve body by inserting Valve Body Gauge (T84P-77003-A) between throttle valve pin and valve body housing.

FORD MOTOR CO. ZF 4HP-22 AUTOMATIC OVERDRIVE (Cont.)

3) If valve pin interferes with the gauge and does not allow it to pass through, use the notch in gauge handle to grip pin and draw the throttle valve further out of its bore.

4) Push valve body forward (toward converter) until gauge is held snug. (Light pressure is required to move the gauge up or down). Tighten Bolt "B-1" firmly, to hold valve body is position. *See Fig. 3.*

Fig. 3: Valve Body Attaching Bolt Location

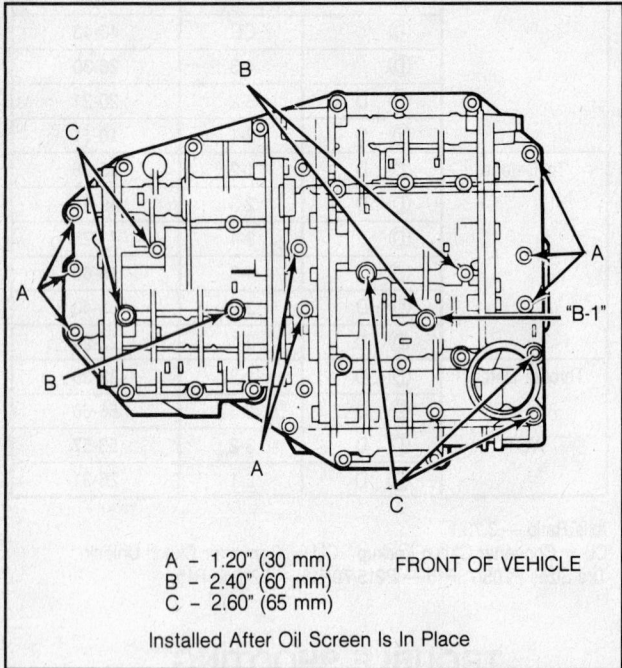

A – 1.20" (30 mm)
B – 2.40" (60 mm)
C – 2.60" (65 mm)

FRONT OF VEHICLE

Installed After Oil Screen Is In Place

5) Clean filter screen with solvent. If required, install a NEW "O" ring onto inlet of oil screen. Install oil screen using 3 TORX head bolts. Tighten bolts to specifications.

6) If required, place a magnet into indentations in oil pan. Install oil pan gasket onto oil pan. Install long clamps with radius on all 4 corners and short clamps on both sides of oil pan. Install and tighten six 10 mm bolts.

7) Lower vehicle and fill transmission with proper grade (Dexron II) and quantity of fluid. Operate vehicle and verify proper operation.

EXTENSION HOUSING
Removal
1) Raise vehicle on a hoist or stands. Disconnect driveshaft from rear axle flange and remove it from transmission. To maintain driveline balance, mark rear driveshaft yoke and axle companion flange so driveshaft can be installed in its original position.

2) Disconnect speedometer wiring harness from extension housing. Remove position sensor from converter housing. Remove engine rear support-to-extension housing attaching bolts.

3) Place a jack under transmission and raise it just enough to remove weight from engine rear support. Remove nuts that secure engine rear support to cross-member and remove support.

4) Place a drain pan under rear of transmission case. Lower transmission and remove 9 extension housing attaching bolts. Slide extension housing off input shaft and allow fluid to drain. Remove and discard gasket.

Installation
1) Clean and inspect extension housing. Install a NEW extension housing gasket on case. Install guide pins into extension housing and position extension housing to case. Install 9 bolts and tighten to specifications.

2) Install rear support and lower transmission. Install attaching bolts and tighten to specifications. Remove transmission jack. Install attaching nuts and tighten to specifications.

3) Install position sensor to converter housing. Install speedometer wiring harness. Install driveshaft using scribe marks as a guide to assure correct balance. Lower vehicle and fill transmission with fluid. Check for leaks.

EXTENSION HOUSING BUSHING & REAR SEAL
Removal
1) Raise vehicle and disconnect driveshaft at transmission. To maintain balance, mark rear driveshaft yoke and axle companion flange so driveshaft can be installed in its original position.

2) Remove seal with Extension Housing Seal Remover (T71P-7657-A). Carefully remove bushing using Extension Housing Bushing Remover (T77L-7697-E). DO NOT damage splines.

Installation
To install, reverse removal procedure. If replacing bushing, install new bushing using Bushing Replacer (T77L-7697-F). Before installing new seal, inspect sealing surface of universal joint yoke for scores. If necessary, replace yoke.

BREATHER ASSEMBLY
Removal
Remove extension housing as previously outlined. Remove breather cap from breather. With pliers, remove lock washer retaining breather assembly to extension housing. Remove breather assembly from inside of extension housing.

Installation
Install breather assembly with a NEW "O" ring into extension housing. Install NEW lock washer to retain breather to extension housing. Snap breather cap onto breather. Install extension housing.

PARKING PAWL, SHAFT & SPRING
Removal
Remove extension housing as previously outlined. Remove bolt attaching guide plates to transmission case and remove plates. Remove parking pawl, shaft and leg spring from transmission case.

NOTE: Leg spring load is reduced when shaft and pawl are removed.

Installation
Install parking pawl shaft and leg spring into case. Install pawl onto shaft and place the 90° leg of spring into hole in pawl. Then, rotate pawl clockwise to set spring load. Install guide plates with 1 bolt and tighten to specification. Install extension housing.

SELECTOR LINKAGE, ACCELERATOR CAM & PARKING PAWL ROD
Removal
1) Put selector in Neutral before raising vehicle. Disconnect and remove outer manual lever. Remove oil

FORD MOTOR CO. ZF 4HP-22 AUTOMATIC OVERDRIVE (Cont.)

pan, screen and valve body as previously outlined. Disconnect "T" bar end of kickdown cable fron its seat in accelerator cam.

2) Punch out roll pin from inner manual lever and manual lever shaft. Pull out shaft to remove leg spring, cam and inner manual lever. Unhook parking pawl rod and pull it out of case. Remove and discard shaft seal.

Installation

1) Install a NEW manual lever shaft seal. Drive it flush with case. Connect park rod to inner manual lever. Install rod and lever. Ensure that rod protudes through guide plates in rear of case.

2) Install manual lever shaft through case and into inner manual lever bore. Fit leg spring into cam. Install cam and spring in case, with leg of spring on case support. Push shaft in until it stops.

3) Align holes in shaft and inner manual lever. Install a NEW roll pin, with slot to rear of transmission. Rotate accelerator cam once to set load of leg spring; then seat "T" bar end of cable in cam. Install valve body, screen and oil pan.

CONVERTER HOUSING INTERMEDIATE PLATE GASKET & PUMP SEAL
Removal

1) Remove transmission and converter assembly from vehicle. Remove converter assembly from housing using Handles (T81P-7902-C).

NOTE: **Oil will be running out of converter. Handle carefully to avoid damage to pump bushing and oil seal lip.**

2) Mount transmission in holding fixture. Remove 12 long bolts closest to pump shaft. Pull converter housing and intermediate plate assembly away as a unit. DO NOT disturb input shaft and clutch cylinder.

3) Remove pump seal with an appropriate tool. Remove 6 short bolts farthest from pump shaft and remove converter housing from intermediate plate.

Installation

1) Position intermediate plate to converter housng and install 6 bolts. Tighten bolts to specifications. Install pump seal flush with pump surface using a block of wood to tap seal into place.

2) Install converter housing and intermediate plate onto pump shaft. Ensure thrust washer and thrust bearings are properly positioned. See Fig. 4.

Fig. 4: Thrust Washer & Bearing Position

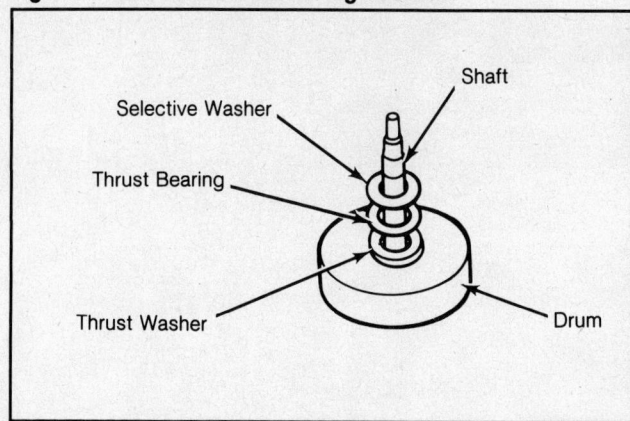

3) Use petroleum jelly to hold in place while plate is assembled. Install 12 bolts and tighten to specifications. Guide converter carefully onto pump shaft using Handles (T81P-7902-C) until it seats. Install transmission and converter.

KICKDOWN CABLE
Removal

In engine compartment, remove cable and insert from injection pump side lever and cable bracket. Raise vehicle on a hoist. Remove transmission oil pan, sump screen and valve body. Pry cable out of case with 2 screwdrivers. Unhook "T" bar end of cable from accelerator cam and remove cable.

Installation

Push cable cover into transmission case. Rotate accelerator cam once to set load of leg spring. Then, seat "T" bar end of cable in cam. Install valve body, screen and oil pan.

New Cable

1) If a NEW cable is installed, spin the rear adjusting nut back to the end of the threaded barrel and place threaded barrel through slot in cable bracket. Pull threaded barrel into hole in bracket.

2) Set adjusting nut approximately in the center of threaded barrel. Pull "T" head until you feel detent step, about .25" (6.4 mm) before maximum cable travel. DO NOT PULL ANY FURTHER.

3) Slide bead along cable until there is a gap of 1.54-1.57" (39-40 mm) between the end of threaded barrel and end of bead closest to barrel. Crimp bead to braided cable core using wire terminal crimpers.

4) Be careful not to distort bead. Remove threaded barrel from cable bracket and proceed to Used Cable Installation.

Used Cable

1) Place braided cable core wire on split in White plastic lever insert with "T" head on trunnion side and pull it through. Snap "T" head into insert trunnions.

2) Snap insert into lower rectangular hole of injection pump side lever after threading braided cable core through slot. Spin rear adjusting nut back to end of threaded barrel and place threaded barrel through slot in cable bracket.

3) Pull threaded barrel into hole in bracket. Adjust cable as previously outlined.

DISASSEMBLY & ASSEMBLY

GOVERNOR
Disassembly

Remove interlocking snap ring from output shaft. Remove parking gear, governor and split drive rings which are splined to output shaft. Remove 2 bolts retaining governor housing to governor hub. Remove counterweight and clamp. Remove "O" ring, snap ring and seal rings.

Assembly

1) Install seal rings, snap ring and "O" ring. Insert couterweight into governor hub and secure with clamp. Install governor housing to governor hub with 2 bolts. Tighten bolts to specifications.

2) Install parking gear onto governor hub with 2 bolts. Tighten bolts to specifications. Lubricate "O" ring on output shaft and slide parking gear with split drive ring, and

FORD MOTOR CO. ZF 4HP-22 AUTOMATIC OVERDRIVE (Cont.)

governor assebly onto output shaft until it reaches the stop. Install interlocking snap ring to output shaft.

TIGHTENING SPECIFICATIONS

Application	Ft. Lbs. (N.m)
Converter Housing-to-Oil Pump	
Attaching Bolts	34 (46)
Extension Housing Attaching Bolts	17 (23)
Intermediate Plate-to-Converter	
Attaching Bolts	34 (46)
	INCH Lbs.
Governor Hub Attaching Bolts	89 (10)
Guide Plate Attaching Bolts	89 (10)
Kickdown Cable Barrel Nut	80-106 (9-12)
Oil Strainer Attaching Bolts	71 (8)
Parking Gear-to-Governor Hub	
Attaching Bolts	89 (10)
Valve Body Attaching Bolts	71 (8)

GENERAL MOTORS TORQUE CONVERTER CLUTCH

All GM Automatic Transmissions and Transaxles Exc. THM 400

DESCRIPTION

The Torque Converter Clutch (TCC) assembly consists of a 3-element torque converter with the addition of a converter clutch. The converter clutch is an internal mechanism with friction material attached to the front face. It is splined to the turbine assembly in the converter. When in operation, the clutch applies against the converter cover, providing a mechanical direct drive coupling of the engine to the transmission planetary gears. Applying the TCC eliminates converter slippage, resulting in improved fuel economy and reduced fluid operating temperatures. When the converter clutch is released, the assembly operates as a conventional torque converter.

TCC apply and release is controlled by several factors. On 4WD vehicles, a relay allows TCC in 2WD drive only. When transfer case is shifted from 2H to 4L or 4H, circuit to TCC system is opened. In this position (4L or 4H) TCC will not apply. When transfer case is shifted back to 2H, TCC system operates in normal manner. If vehicle does not shift out of 4L or 4H, TCC will not apply.

TCC apply and release is controlled by the position of the TCC apply valve, located in oil pump on THM 180C, 200C and 440-T4, valve body on THM 200-4R, 325-4L and 700-R4, and in auxiliary valve body on THM 125C, 250C and 350C. Apply valve operation is controlled by a solenoid.

In order for the TCC to engage, the transmission must be operating in 3rd gear (3rd or 4th on 4-speed models) and vehicle speed must be over a specific level (typically 30-35 MPH). In addition, several other controls may be incorporated in the vacuum/electrical system to aid in the apply and release of the TCC. Specific additional component use is determined by whether or not the TCC is controlled by the Computer Command Control (CCC) system, and some other factors. On vehicles with the CCC control system, operation of the apply solenoid is controlled by the Electronic Control Module (ECM). On systems without CCC control, the solenoid control signal is routed through whatever additional controls are used, any of which may break the circuit if specific operating conditions are not met. These controls are external to the transmission and operate as described.

TCC CONTROL COMPONENTS

The following components supply engine condition information to the ECM on CCC equipped vehicles:

Barometric Pressure Sensor
Used on Cadillac models with DFI, this sensor provides ECM with altitude information. When vehicle is operated at high altitude, the TCC is disengaged.

Brake Release Switch
Used on all engines, switch releases converter clutch when brakes are applied to prevent engine stalling.

Diesel Controls
Some Diesel models with CCC use a Cold Inhibit Switch (CIS) and a Vacuum Regulator Valve (VRV). These switches provide the same information to the ECM as a non-CCC controlled TCC.

Engine Coolant Temperature Sensor
Used on some models, this sensor provides the ECM with engine coolant temperature information. The ECM will not allow TCC operation until the signal from this sensor indicates a coolant temperature higher than 130°-150°F (55°-65°C).

Throttle Position Sensor (TPS)
Provides the ECM with throttle position information. TCC operation is prevented below a specific signal level.

Third and/or Fourth Gear Switches
Used on some models, these switches prevents TCC operation until direct drive (3rd and/or 4th gear) is obtained.

Vacuum Sensor
Used on models which do not use the Engine Coolant Temperature Sensor, this sensor provides the ECM with engine vacuum (load) information.

Vehicle Speed Sensor (VSS)
Used on some models, this component relates vehicle speed to ECM. It is located behind speedometer gauge.

NOTE: **On systems using the ECM of the CCC system for solenoid control, the emission control systems of the vehicle must be in perfect operating condition to guarantee proper TCC function.**

The following components are used on vehicles without the CCC control system. Not all components will be present on all vehicles.

A/C High Pressure Switch
Switch closes when A/C high side pressure reaches or exceeds 370 psi (26 kg/cm²). This increases fan speed and bypasses delay feature in TCC Delay Module. Does not prevent TCC operation when Governor Pressure Switch is closed.

Brake Release Switch
Used on all engines, switch releases converter clutch when brakes are applied to prevent engine stalling.

Fig. 1: View of General Motors Torque Converter With TCC

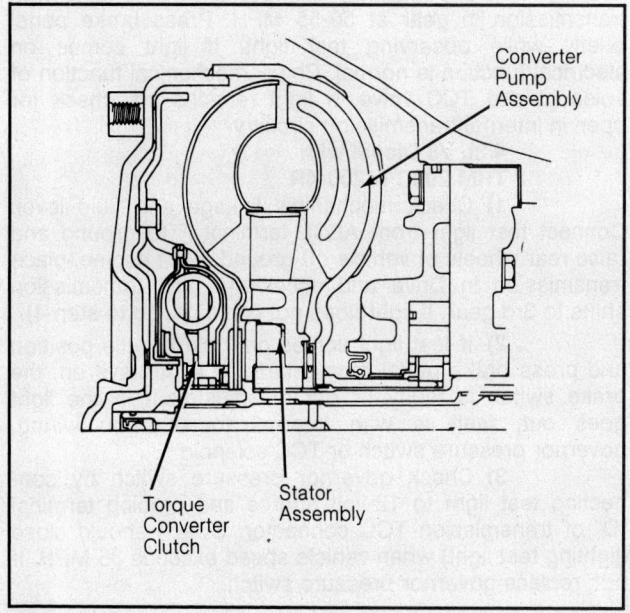

Converter Pump Assembly

Torque Converter Clutch

Stator Assembly

THM 700-R4 shown; other models are similar.

Automatic Transmissions

GENERAL MOTORS TORQUE CONVERTER CLUTCH (Cont.)

Cold Inhibit Switch

This switch is used to prevent TCC engagement until the engine is at operating temperature.

Diesel Electronic Controller

Used on some models with diesel engines. This component receives information from the VSS and TPS. Under certain conditions, the controller applies voltage to the TCC through the brake release switch.

Engine Coolant Fan Temperature Switch

A 2-position switch which closes when coolant temperature exceeds about 250°F (120°C). This increases fan speed and bypasses delay feature in TCC Delay Module. Does not prevent TCC operation when Governor Pressure Switch is closed.

Governor Pressure Switch

Completes ground circuit for TCC and EGR solenoids at or above specific vehicle speed, typically about 35 MPH.

High Vacuum Switch

Used on vehicles with diesel engines, switch releases TCC during closed throttle deceleration.

Low Vacuum Switch

Releases TCC when vacuum signal drops below about 1.5-3.0 in. Hg during moderate acceleration and prior to a part throttle or detent downshift.

Pulse Relay

Used on some models with diesel engines. This relay opens and closes the TCC electrical circuit during gear shift changes.

Thermal Vacuum Valve

Used with most gasoline engines to prevent TCC operation below a specific engine coolant temperature, typically 130°F (55°C).

Third and/or Fourth Gear Switch

Signals TCC Delay Module that transaxle is operating in direct drive (3rd and/or 4th gear). Prevents TCC operation in 1st and 2nd gear.

TCC Delay Module

Delays TCC engagement to prevent TCC and direct clutch application at the same time, causing an audible "thump".

Vacuum Delay Valve

Used with some gasoline engines to slow vacuum switch response to sudden changes in engine vacuum.

Vacuum Regulator Valve (VRV)

Used on some models with diesel engines. Opens at about 3/4 or more throttle to disengage TCC during heavy acceleration.

VSS Tripper Module

Used on some models with diesel engines. This module allows TCC operation when vacuum regulator valve is closed, vehicle speed is 40-46 MPH and transmission is in 3rd or 4th gear.

TROUBLE SHOOTING

See GENERAL MOTORS TORQUE CONVERTER CLUTCH TROUBLE SHOOTING TABLE in AUTOMATIC TRANSMISSION TROUBLE SHOOTING.

TESTING

NOTE: Use TCC TEST TABLES for all 4.3L (remote EGR) and 5.7L diesel engines and all gas engines with CCC controlled TCC. Also see appropriate VSS TEST CHART.

ELECTRICAL DIAGNOSIS (WITHOUT CCC)

CAUTION: **Transmission selector must be in 2WD mode on 4WD vehicles for TCC test.**

All Exc. 4.3L V6 Diesel

1) Ensure mechanical linkage and fluid level are correct. Attach test light from TCC test point in ALDL connector or fuse block to ground. Run engine at 1500 RPM with transmission in "P". Note light. If test light is off, check for blown fuse, brake switch operation, VRV, low vacuum switch or opens in wiring harness.

2) Low vacuum switch should be open with engine off and at full throttle or closed at idle and part throttle. VRV should be closed at idle and part throttle or open at full throttle. On Cadillac diesels, check operation of cold inhibit switch.

Fig. 2: Torque Converter Clutch System Schematic

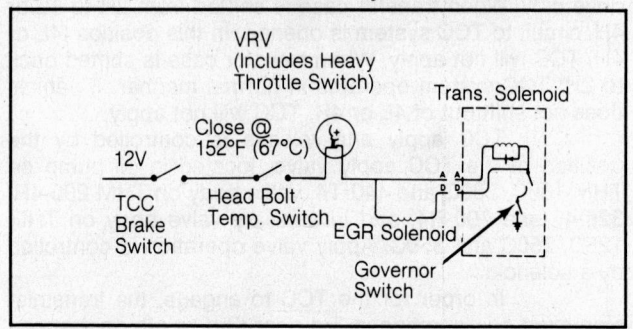

Typical for all without CCC system (except 200C & 350C Diesel).

3) If test light illuminates, press brake pedal. Light should go out. If not, adjust or replace brake switch. If light goes out, disconnect light from ground and connect to 12-volt source at fuse block. If light comes on, internal transmission wiring, switches and/or solenoid may be grounded.

4) If light stays off when attached to power source, raise drive wheels off floor and run engine with transmission in gear at 50-55 MPH. Press brake pedal briefly while observing test light. If light comes on electrical function is normal. Check mechanical function of solenoid and TCC valve. If light remains off, check for open in internal transmission circuitry.

4.3L V6 Diesel with THM 200C & 200-4R

1) Check mechanical linkage and fluid level. Connect test light from ALCL terminal F to ground and raise rear wheels of vehicle off ground. Start engine, place transmission in Drive and accelerate until transmission shifts to 3rd gear. If light does not come on, go to step 4).

2) If test light comes on, hold throttle position and press brake pedal momentarily. If light stays on, the brake switch is faulty or out of adjustment. If the light goes out, fault is with internal transmission wiring, governor pressure switch or TCC solenoid.

3) Check governor pressure switch by connecting test light to 12-volt source and probing terminal "D" of transmission TCC connector. Switch should close (lighting test light) when vehicle speed exceeds 35 MPH. If not, replace governor pressure switch.

GENERAL MOTORS TORQUE CONVERTER CLUTCH (Cont.)

Fig. 3: Torque Converter Clutch System Schematic

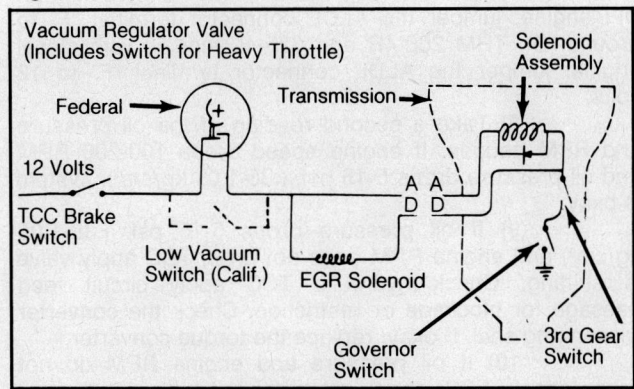

All 200C & 350C Diesel, transmission in 3rd gear.

Fig. 4: Transmission Connector Terminal Identification

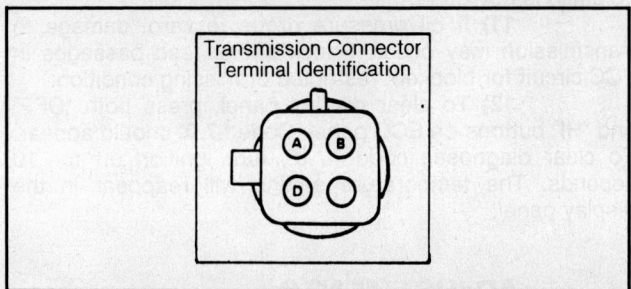

4) If test light does not come on in step **1)**, check for blown fuse and repair as needed. Check operation of brake switch and for opens in wiring harness. Check for proper 3rd gear switch operation. Switch should be open with transmission in 3rd gear.

5) Check continuity of VRV switch with test light. There should be continuity up to 3/4 throttle. Check ground to VRV. If all checks in this step and step **4)** are OK, replace delay module assembly.

6) If TCC operates in 2nd gear, perform the following test. With ignition key "ON" and engine off, attach test light from ALCL terminal "F" to ground. If the test light does not come on, TCC solenoid, TCC control valve or the torque converter itself is faulty. If the test light comes on, check for engine overheating and/or excessive A/C high pressure. Repair as needed and check TCC operation.

7) If TCC still engages in 2nd gear, check operation of 3rd gear switch. Connect test light to 12-volt source and remove harness connector at transmission. Probe terminal "B" of connector. If test light comes on, replace delay module assembly. If not, replace 3rd gear switch or repair faulty wiring to switch.

4.3L V6 Diesel with THM 125C

1) Check for proper linkage adjustment and fluid level. Check gauge fuse. Connect test light between ALCL terminals "F" and "A" (ground). Turn ignition key on, engine not running. Raise driving wheels off ground. If test light is off, go to step **7)**.

2) If test light is on, lightly press brake pedal. If test light stays on, adjust or replace brake release switch. Check for short between Pink/Black and Light Blue wires.

3) If test light is off, move throttle pedal to wide open position. Test light should be off when throttle is open from 3/4 to wide open throttle positions. If test light is on, adjust or replace VRV.

4) If VRV is okay, connect test light between 12-volt source and pin "D" of transaxle connector. Start engine and accelerate vehicle to over 35 MPH in 3rd gear. If test light if off, repair open wiring in transaxle or replace governor pressure switch.

5) If test light is on, reconnect test light to ALCL terminal "F" and ground. Turn engine off. Position throttle wide open. Connect a jumper wire between terminal "F" of diesel diode module and ground. If test light is on, check A/C head pressure and 2-speed coolant fan switches.

6) If test light is off, check for open wire between diesel diode module and TCC delay module. If wire is okay, replace diesel diode module or TCC delay module.

7) Connect test light to pin "A" of TCC delay module. If test light is off, adjust or replace brake release switch. If test light is on, reconnect test light to ALCL terminal "F" and ground.

8) Connect a jumper wire between Light Green wire of either A/C head pressure or 2-speed coolant fan switch to ground. If test light is on, check VRV and third gear switch.

9) If test light is off, ground the A/C head pressure switch. Using a high-impedance voltmeter, check voltage at the Light Green/Black wire of the TCC delay module. If less than 2 volts, replace the TCC delay module. If more than 2 volts, check for open circuit in diesel diode module wiring.

4.3L V6 Diesel with THM 440-T4

1) Check for proper linkage adjustment and fluid level. Check gauge fuse. Connect test light between ALCL terminals "F" and "A" (ground). Turn ignition key on, engine not running. Raise driving wheels off ground. If test light is off, check brake release switch adjustment or open wire in brake release switch circuit.

2) If test light is on, connect test light ground to Purple/White wire of TCC controller. Connect a jumper wire between Light Green/Black wire of either A/C head pressure or 2-speed coolant fan switch to ground. If test light is off, go to step **5)**.

3) If test light is on, disconnect EGR solenoid. Connect test light to Light Blue/Black wire on VRV. Test light should be on when throttle is closed or open to 3/4 throttle positions. If test light is off, check VRV circuit wiring, adjust or replace VRV, or check diesel diode module.

4) If VRV is okay, reconnect the EGR solenoid. Connect test light to 12 volt source. Connect test probe to Light Blue/Black wire of VSS tripper module or VRV. Accelerate vehicle. If test light goes on after vehicle speed is 40-46 MPH, VSS tripper module is okay. If not, check VSS tripper module. See the appropriate VSS TEST CHART in this article.

ELECTRICAL DIAGNOSIS (WITH CCC; EXC. 4.3L DIESEL WITH REMOTE EGR)

CAUTION: Transmission selector must be in 2WD mode on 4WD vehicles for TCC test.

1) Ensure TPS and brake release switches are adjusted. See ADJUSTMENTS. Connect test light to terminal "F" of ALDL connector and ground. Turn ignition on. Place transmission in "P" or "N". If test light is off, go to step **5)**.

Automatic Transmissions

GENERAL MOTORS TORQUE CONVERTER CLUTCH (Cont.)

2) If test light is on, turn engine off, turn ignition key on. Move throttle pedal to about 1/4 open. If test light is off, electrical system is okay.

3) If test light is on, check voltage at ECM terminal "A-10". Voltage should be 1 volt at closed throttle and about 5 volts at wide open throttle. If not, check TPS system and adjustment.

4) If voltage at ECM is okay, check for good contact between terminal "A-2" and ECM. If connection is good, replace ECM.

5) Turn engine off, turn ignition key on. Check for blown fuse. If okay, disconnect electrical connector at transmission. Connect a test light between terminals "A" and "D". If test light is on, check for ground between terminal "D" and ECM. If no wires are grounded, replace ECM.

6) If test light is off, connect test light from terminal "A" to ground. If test light is off, repair open in brake release switch or adjust switch.

7) If test light is on, reconnect test light between terminals "A" and "D". Ground TCC test terminal. If test light is on, check for faulty connection at transmission solenoid or solenoid circuit. If test light if off, repair open wire from transmission to test terminal.

NOTE: Use TCC TEST TABLES FOR DIESEL ENGINES with remote EGR and CCC Controlled TCC. If VSS testing is required, see the appropriate VSS TEST CHART.

HYDRAULIC DIAGNOSIS

Cavalier, Cimarron, Firenza, Skyhawk & Sunbird with THM 125C; Eldorado, Fleetwood & Seville with THM 200-R4 or 325-4L

1) Check ATF level. Install 0-50 psi (0-3.5 kg/cm²) pressure gauge to oil cooler outlet line. Connect tachometer to engine. Raise driving wheels off floor.

2) Disconnect TCC electrical connector at brake switch (THM 125C) or disconnect cold inhibit switch connector (all with diesel engine). Place transmission in Drive range.

3) On Eldorado, Fleetwood and Seville with DFI, enter diagnostics mode on the Electronic Climate Control (ECC) panel. Turn ignition on. Depress both "OFF" and "WARMER" buttons on the ECC panel and hold until code ".." appears on display panel. Release buttons and ensure code "-1.8.8" appears as a check of all display segments.

4) Code "-1.8.8" should remain on display panel for a period of time and change to ".7.0". Press "RESET" button on Fuel Data Panel. Code ".9.0" will be displayed.

NOTE: If code "-1.8.8" does not appear or any other code appears, do not proceed with TCC diagnosis. The DFI system may have a problem and must be corrected.

5) Press "INSTANT/AVERAGE" button on Fuel Data Panel until ".1.1" appears on display panel. After one second, engine RPM (divided by 10) will be displayed. To clear display panel, go to step 12).

6) Accelerate and hold throttle steady at 35 MPH (gasoline) or 40 MPH (diesel). Note tachometer and oil pressure gauges. On THM 125C models, jumper the TCC brake switch connector.

7) On THM 200-4R and 325-4L models with DFI engine, jumper the ALDL connector terminal "F" to ground. On THM 200-4R and 325-4L models with diesel engine, jumper the ALDL connector terminal "F" to 12 volts.

8) Take a second reading of the oil pressure and RPM gauges. If engine speed drops 100-200 RPM and oil pressure drops 5-15 psi. (.35-1.05 kg/cm²), system is okay.

9) If oil pressure drops 5-15 psi. (.35-1.05 kg/cm²) and engine RPM does not drop, TCC apply valve is shifting. Check hydraulic TCC apply circuit feed passage for blockage or restriction. Check the converter friction ring seal. If okay, replace the torque converter.

10) If oil pressure and engine RPM do not drop, check TCC apply valve for sticking, binding or damage condition. Check TCC solenoid for missing or damaged check ball, seat, or "O" ring. Ensure TCC solenoid is not loose.

11) If oil pressure drops to zero, damage to transmission may occur. Check cooler feed passages in TCC circuit for blocked, restricted or missing condition.

12) To clear display panel, press both "OFF" and "HI" buttons on ECC panel. Code ".7.0" should appear. To clear diagnostic code ".7.0", turn ignition off for 10 seconds. The temperature setting will reappear in the display panel.

ADJUSTMENTS

TCC BRAKE SWITCH

The TCC brake switch must be adjusted to prevent vehicle stalling at idle. Ensure brake pedal is fully released. Adjust plunger to just touch brake pedal lever.

NOTE: The following adjustments are to vehicles with gasoline engines, only.

THROTTLE POSITION SENSOR (TPS)
Carburetted Models

1) DO NOT remove the TPS adjustment screw plug unless the TPS is not adjusted correctly. Using a 5/64" drill bit, carefully drill a hole in the steel cup plug covering the TPS adjustment screw.

2) Plug is located next to the TPS plunger bore. Remove steel plug using a small slide hammer. Disconnect the TPS connector and jumper all three

THROTTLE POSITION SENSOR SPECIFICATIONS

Application	Volts@Idle Throttle Position
Light Duty Trucks	
2.8L V6	.26V
4.3L V6	.25V
Calif. 5.0L & 5.7L V8	.41V
Passenger Vehicles	
2.8L V6	.30V
3.0L V6	.60V
3.8L V6 (VIN A)	.30V
5.0L V8 (VIN G & H)	.48V
5.0L V8 (VIN Y & 9)	.40V
5.7L (VIN 6)	.48V

GENERAL MOTORS TORQUE CONVERTER CLUTCH (Cont.)

terminals. Connect a digital voltmeter from TPS connector center terminal (B) to bottom terminal (C).

3) With ignition on, engine stopped, turn the TPS screw with flat bladed screwdriver to obtain specified volts at curb idle position. A/C must be off and Idle Speed Control fully retracted.

4) After adjustment, a new cup plug or silicone sealant rubber RTV must be inserted in the air horn.

Fuel Injected Models

1) On 4-cylinder models, disconnect the TPS connector and jumper all 3 wires. Connect a digital voltmeter to terminals "B" and "C" of TPS. With ignition switch on and engine off, turn TPS assembly to adjust TPS voltage.

2) On V6 MFI, SFI and 5.7L V8 dual TBI engines, disconnect the TPS connector and jumper all 3 wires. Connect a digital voltmeter to the middle and bottom terminals of TPS. See Fig. 5. With ignition on and engine off, turn TPS assembly to adjust TPS voltage.

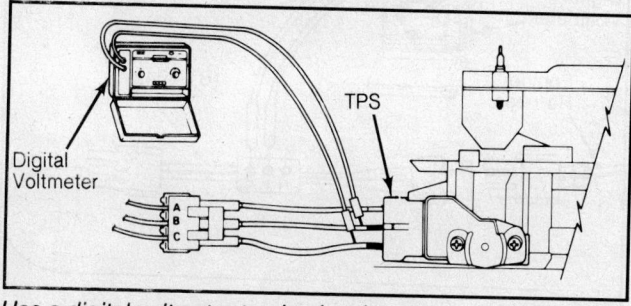

Fig. 5: Checking TPS on Typical TBI

Use a digital voltmeter to check voltage.

3) On 4.1L and 6.0L DFI engines, disconnect the TPS connector and jumper all 3 wires. Connect a digital voltmeter to terminals "B" and "A" of TPS. With ignition switch on and engine off, turn TPS assembly to adjust TPS voltage.

THROTTLE POSITION SENSOR SPECIFICATIONS

Application	Volts@Idle Throttle Position
1.8L & 2.5L 4-Cyl.	[1] .45-1.25V
2.0L 4-Cyl.	[1] .45-.60V
2.8L V6 (VIN S & W)	[2] .55V
2.8L V6 (VIN 9)	[1]
3.0L MFI V6	[2] .55V
3.8L MFI V6	[2] .40V
3.8L SFI V6	[2] .40V
4.3L TBI V6	[2] .53V
4.1L & 6.0L V8	.45-.55V
5.0L & 5.7L V8	.54V

[1] – TPS is not adjustable.
[2] – Set with IAC extended and with base idle at 550 RPM in Drive.

NOTE: The following adjustment procedures apply to vehicles with diesel engines, only.

TRANSMISSION VACUUM REGULATOR VALVE
4.3L V6 & 5.7L V8 Passenger Vehicles (Includes Caballero and El Camino)

1) Remove air crossover. Install screened covers on intake manifold. Remove throttle rod from throttle lever on V8 engines; throttle cable and detent/TV cable from throttle lever on V6 engines. Loosen vacuum regulator valve-to-injection pump bolts.

2) Install carburetor angle gauge adapter (J-26701-15) on injection pump throttle lever and place angle gauge on adapter. Rotate throttle lever to wide open position. Center bubble in level with gauge set at 0°.

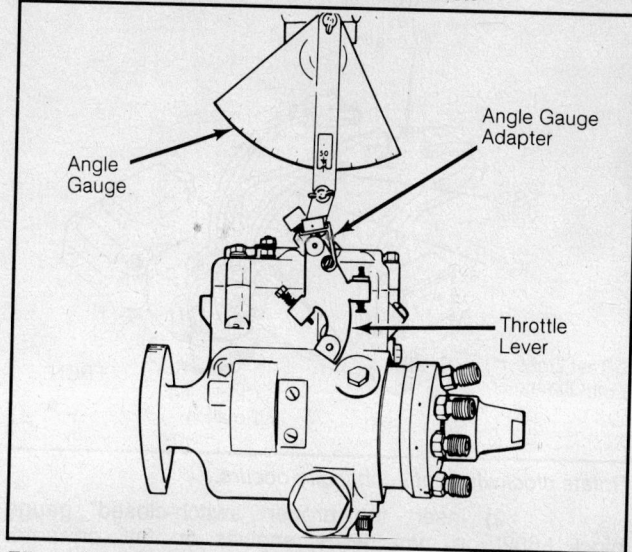

Fig. 6: Angle Gauge & Adapter Installation

Angle Gauge

Angle Gauge Adapter

Throttle Lever

File tool as needed to fit on thicker V6 throttle lever.

3) Set gauge to 58° (V8) or 49° (V6) and rotate throttle lever until bubble is centered. Attach vacuum pump to regulator port "A" and a vacuum gauge to port "B". Apply 18-24 in. Hg of vacuum at port "A".

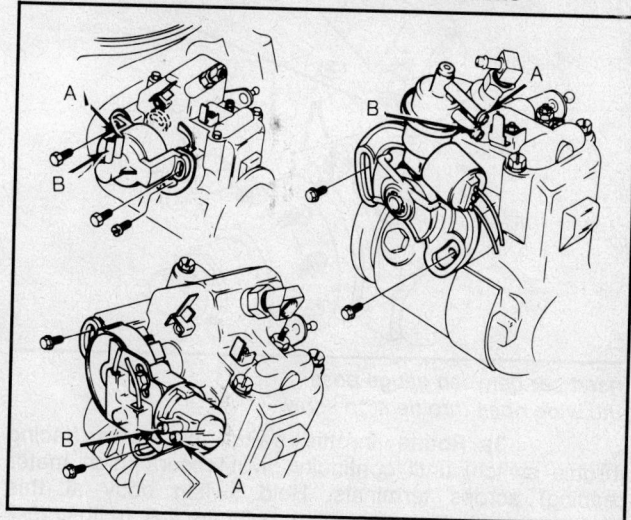

Fig. 7: Vacuum Regulator Valve Port Locations

Attach vacuum pump to port "A", gauge to port "B".

4) Rotate vacuum valve clockwise until vacuum gauge reads 10.6 in. Hg and tighten valve mounting bolts. Remove vacuum source and gauge. Install throttle rod or throttle cable and detent/TV cable to pump throttle lever. Remove screened covers and install air crossover.

GENERAL MOTORS TORQUE CONVERTER CLUTCH (Cont.)

THROTTLE POSITION SENSOR (TPS)

6.2L V8 Federal Light Truck Only

1) Loosely assemble TPS to fuel injection pump with throttle in the closed position. Attach a continuity meter across terminals (IGN Pink and EGR Yellow on light duty engines). See Fig. 8.

Fig. 8: Adjusting Throttle Position Switch

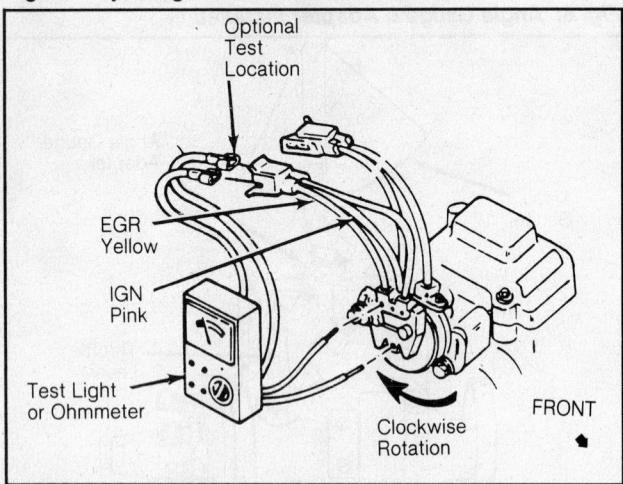

Rotate clockwise until continuity occurs.

2) Insert the proper "switch-closed" gauge block (.602" on man. trans. engines or .646 on auto. trans.), between gauge boss on injection pump and wide open stop screw on throttle shaft. Rotate and hold throttle lever against gauge block. See Fig. 9.

Fig. 9: Installing Gauging Block

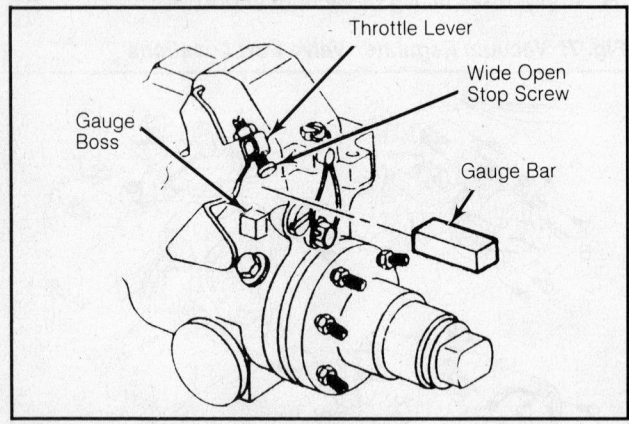

*Insert bar between gauge boss
and wide open throttle stop screw.*

3) Rotate throttle switch clockwise (facing throttle switch) until continuity pivot occurs (high meter reading) across terminals. Hold switch body at this position and tighten mounting bolts to 4-5 ft. lbs. (5-7 N.m).

NOTE: **Switch point must be set only while rotating switch body in clockwise direction.**

4) Release throttle lever and allow it to return to idle position. Remove "switch-closed" gauge block and insert "switch-open" gauge block (.624" on man. trans. or .668" on auto. trans.). Rotate throttle lever against "switch-open" gauge block. There should be no continuity across terminals.

5) If no continuity exists, switch is set properly. However, if there is continuity, then switch must be reset by returning to step 1) and repeating the entire procedure. See Fig. 8 and Fig. 9.

METERING VALVE SENSOR (MVS)

4.3L V6 (Calif. Only)

1) Warm engine to operating temperature. Apply the parking brake. Remove the air cleaner. Remove the air crossover and install screens (J-34678) to air intake openings.

2) Disconnect the MVS wiring harness. Install a test harness (BT-8342) to MVS. Connect a tachometer to engine. Ensure MVS assembly is mounted solid to pump. See Fig. 10.

Fig. 10: Installing MVS Test Harness

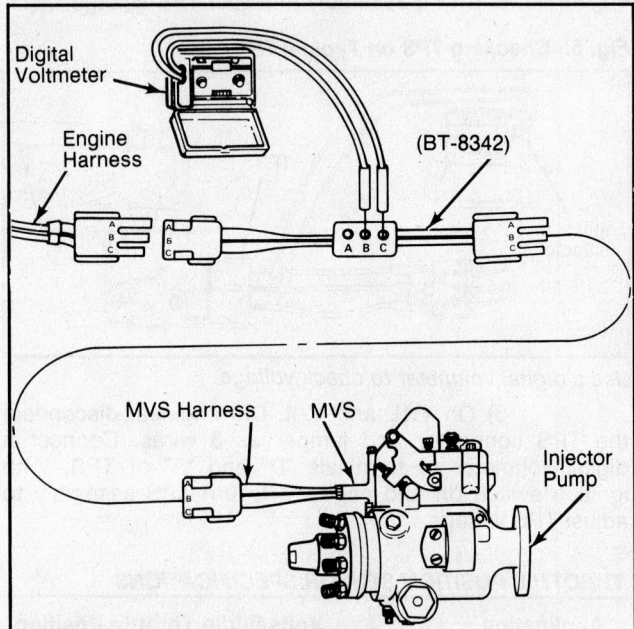

Use a digital voltmeter to check MVS.

3) Start engine in Park and accelerate to 1500 RPM for 10-20 seconds. Return engine to idle speed. Place transmission in Drive. Set engine speed to 650 RPM with alternator connected.

4) Connect a digital voltmeter leads to terminals "A" and "C" of the test harness. This voltage is the "V-REF" voltage. Record this voltage. Measure the "MVS VOLTAGE" by connecting voltmeter leads to terminals "B" and "C" of the test harness. Note this voltage reading.

5) Compare the "V-REF" voltage to the "MVS Voltage" specification. See the MVS VOLTAGE SPECIFICATIONS Table. To adjust the MVS, turn off the engine. Hold the MVS assembly and remove the adjustment hole plug. See Fig. 11.

6) Use tool (J-34829) to adjust MVS voltage. Turn screw clockwise to increase voltage. Turn screw counter-clockwise to decrease voltage. Install the MVS adjustment plug finger tight.

7) Recheck the "V-REF" and "MVS Voltage" as in steps 3) and 4). Install a new adjustment plug "O" seal and tighten to 30 INCH lbs. (3.5 N.m). Check for leaks. Reinstall components to complete procedure.

GENERAL MOTORS TORQUE CONVERTER CLUTCH (Cont.)

Fig. 11: Rear View of MVS & Adjustment Plug

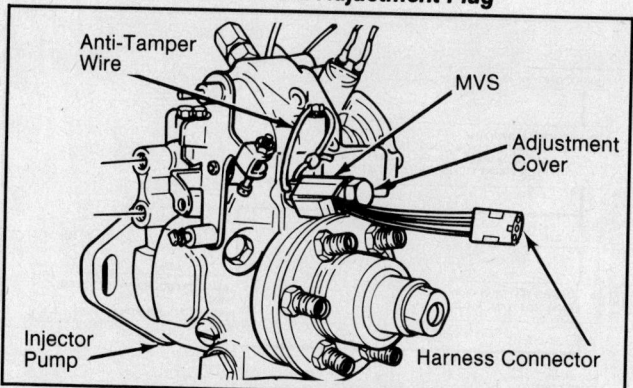

Turn adjustment screw in 1/8 increments.

MVS VOLTAGE SPECIFICATIONS

V-REF	650 RPM in Drive MVS Voltage
4.5V	.53-.55V
4.6V	.54-.56V
4.7V	.55-.57V
4.8V	.57-.59V
4.9V	.58-.60V
5.0V	.59-.61V
5.1V	.60-.62V
5.2V	.61-.63V
5.3V	.63-.65V
5.4V	.64-.66V
5.5V	.65-.67V

TCC TEST CHARTS FOR DIESEL ENGINES WITH CCC

4.3L (With Remote EGR) & 5.7L Diesel TCC Test Chart

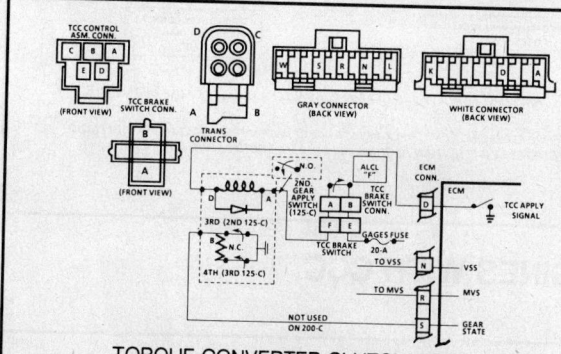

TORQUE CONVERTER CLUTCH (TCC) ELECTRICAL DIAGNOSIS (Chart One)

1) Checks voltage from ignition switch through brake switch, 2nd gear apply switch (if equipped), and TCC switch. Light should have turned on by 35 MPH. Due to variations in specific TCC calibrations, it is possible to have a narrow margin between 3rd gear apply switch closing (if equipped) and ECM grounding of TCC circuit from ECM terminal "P". Test light may turn on just momentarily within this margin.

2) Checks ECM ground for TCC solenoid. Light should go off.

3) This increases throttle opening to increase MVS output. If MVS output is too low, clutch will not apply. On some applications, running free does not require enough throttle opening to allow transmission to shift.

4) Checks for low voltage at MVS input at ECM. At wide open throttle, voltage should be approximately 5 volts. Too low a MVS output should prevent TCC from applying.

5) Checks for VSS signal at ECM. VSS signal is necessary to engage TCC.

6) Checks for open in circuits to terminal "S". ECM supplies 12 volts to this terminal through a resistor. Normally both circuits should have low voltage readings since circuits are normally closed with vehicle stopped. An open circuit will read about 12 volts.

7) Switch(es) open when transmission up shifts. Check that transmission circuit functions normally by voltage going high (near battery voltage) as switches open.

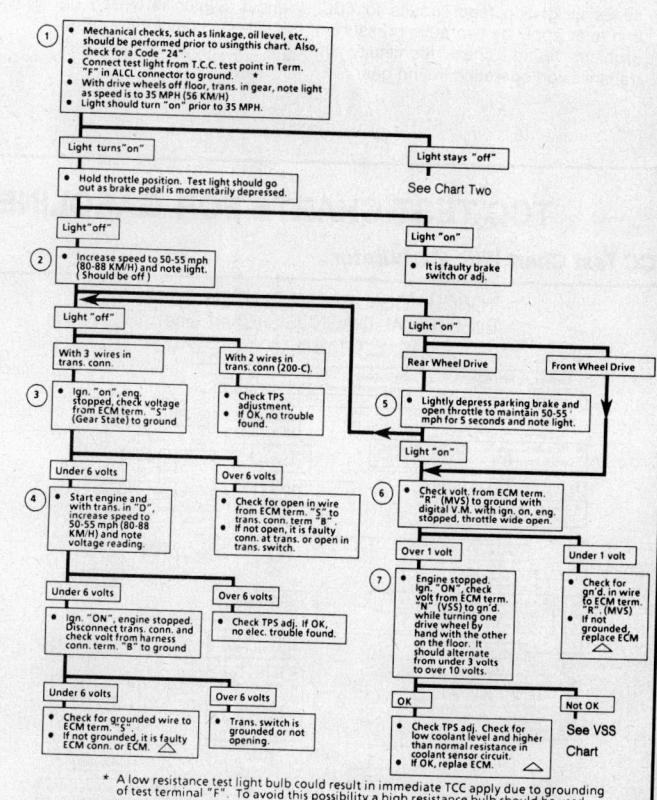

* A low resistance test light bulb could result in immediate TCC apply due to grounding of test terminal "F". To avoid this possibility a high resistance bulb should be used.

△ BEFORE REPLACING ECM, CHECK RESISTANCE BETWEEN TERMINALS OF TCC SOLENOID. IF RESISTANCE IS LESS THAN 20 OHMS, REPLACE SOLENOID ALONG WITH ECM.

GENERAL MOTORS TORQUE CONVERTER CLUTCH (Cont.)

4.3L (With Remote EGR) & 5.7L Diesel TCC Test Chart (Cont.)

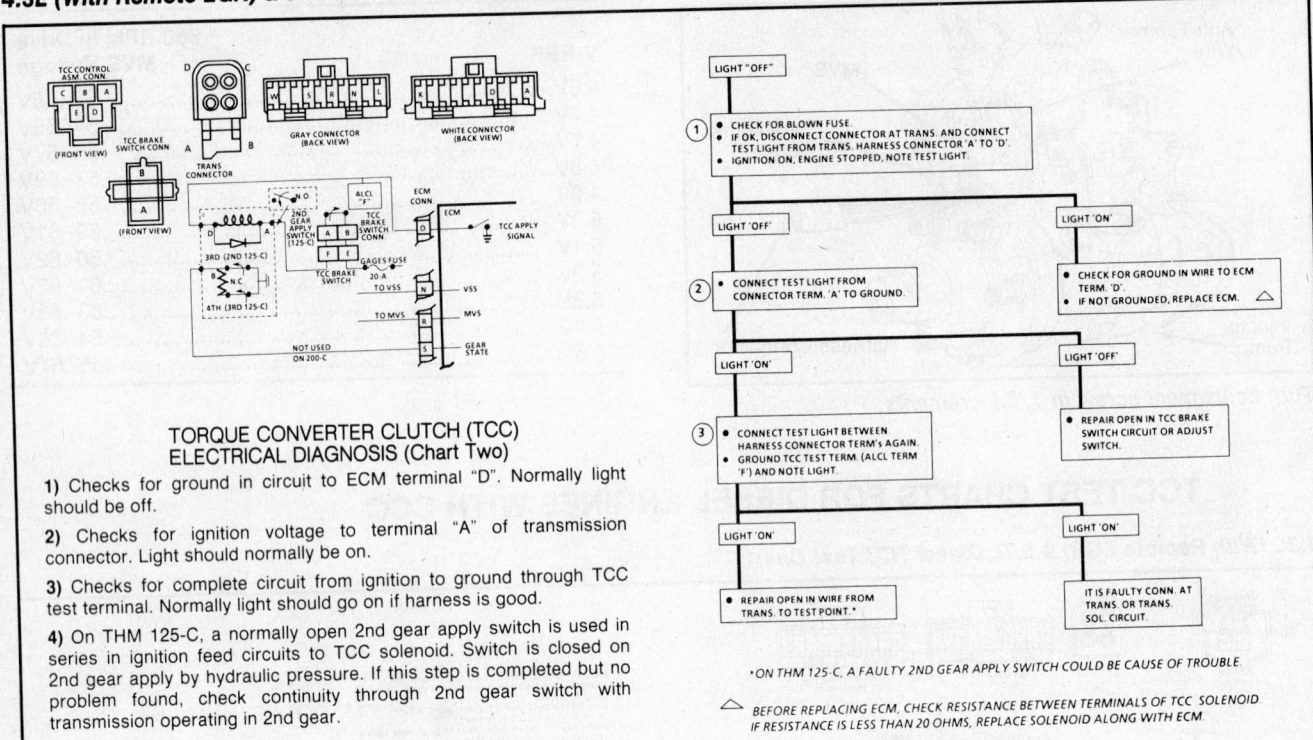

TORQUE CONVERTER CLUTCH (TCC) ELECTRICAL DIAGNOSIS (Chart Two)

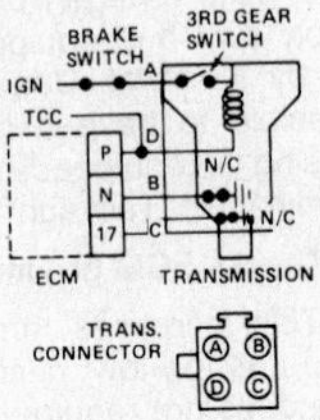

1) Checks for ground in circuit to ECM terminal "D". Normally light should be off.

2) Checks for ignition voltage to terminal "A" of transmission connector. Light should normally be on.

3) Checks for complete circuit from ignition to ground through TCC test terminal. Normally light should go on if harness is good.

4) On THM 125-C, a normally open 2nd gear apply switch is used in series in ignition feed circuits to TCC solenoid. Switch is closed on 2nd gear apply by hydraulic pressure. If this step is completed but no problem found, check continuity through 2nd gear switch with transmission operating in 2nd gear.

*ON THM 125-C, A FAULTY 2ND GEAR APPLY SWITCH COULD BE CAUSE OF TROUBLE.

△ BEFORE REPLACING ECM, CHECK RESISTANCE BETWEEN TERMINALS OF TCC SOLENOID. IF RESISTANCE IS LESS THAN 20 OHMS, REPLACE SOLENOID ALONG WITH ECM.

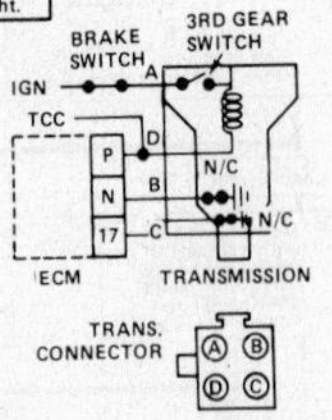

TCC TEST CHARTS FOR GASOLINE ENGINES WITH CCC

TCC Test Chart With Carburetor

GENERAL MOTORS TORQUE CONVERTER CLUTCH (Cont.)

TCC Test Chart With TBI & Port Fuel Injection (Except 3.8L & 4.3L Turbo)

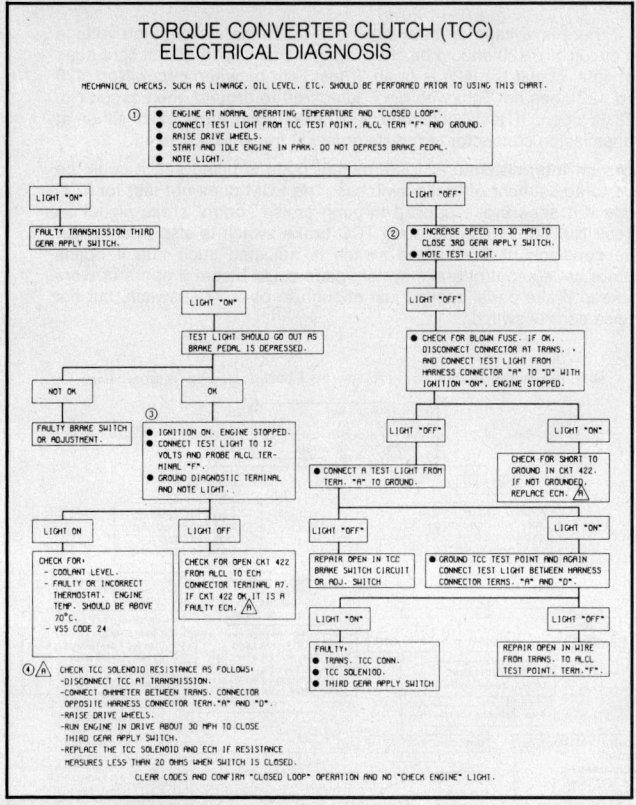

TCC Test Chart With 3.8L & 4.3L Turbo MFI & SFI Fuel Injection

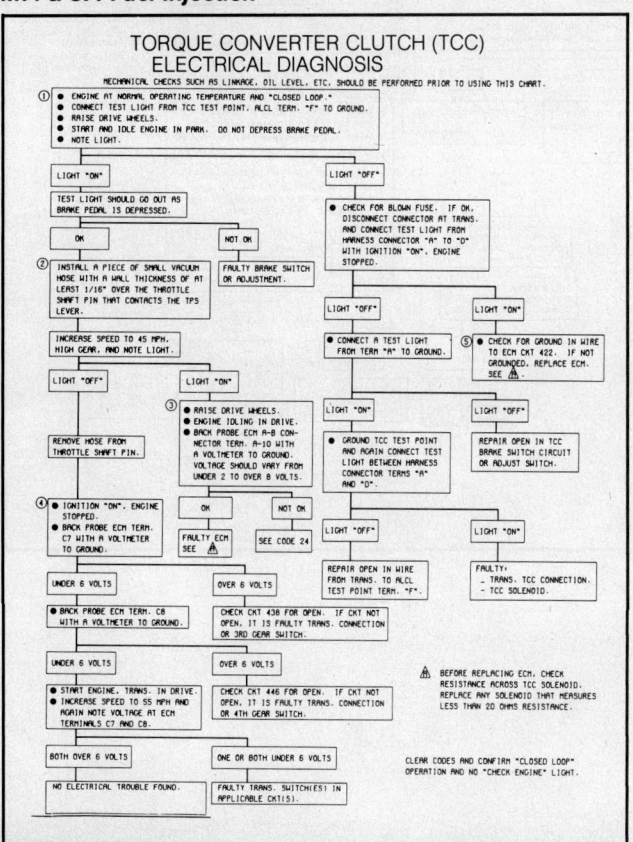

TCC Test Chart With Fuel Injection and 700-4R Transmission

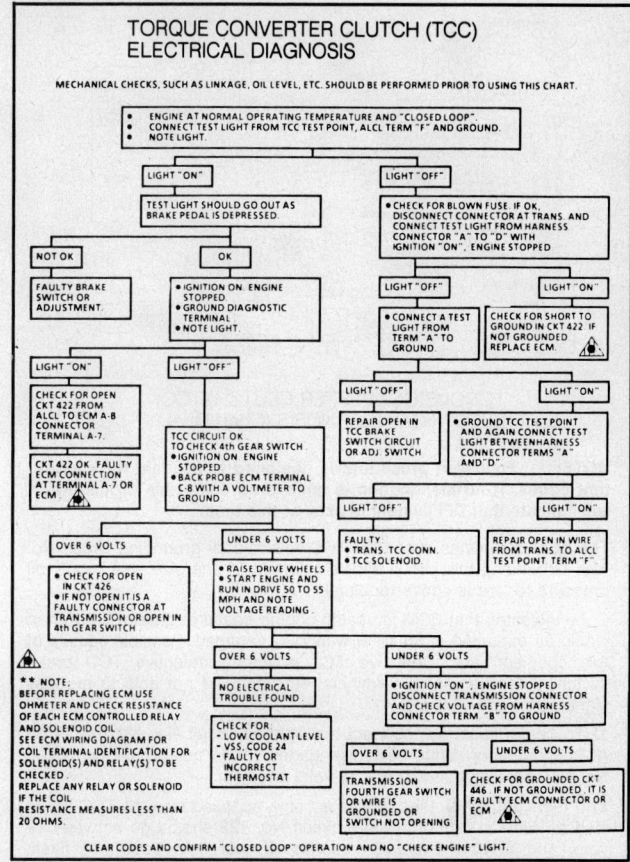

GENERAL MOTORS TORQUE CONVERTER CLUTCH (Cont.)

TCC Test Chart With DFI Fuel Injection

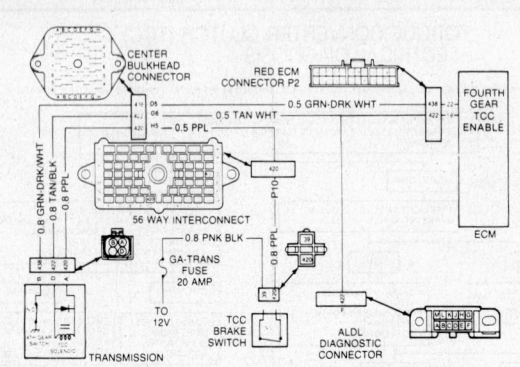

TORQUE CONVERTER CLUTCH (TCC)
ELECTRICAL DIAGNOSIS (Chart One)

NOTE: Following procedure is designed to account for intermittent codes. If no malfunction is uncovered using this procedure, it will indicate that DFI system is okay at this time.

The ECM completes circuit for TCC solenoid by grounding circuit No. 422. Grounding this circuit allows solenoid to energize and supply oil pressure to torque converter clutch.

Code indicates that ECM is seeing engine speed at greater RPM than would be expected at 55 MPH with TCC engaged. Possible causes of this condition are: Defective TCC solenoid, defective TCC brake switch, defective wiring, terminals, etc., or ECM not able to process signals properly.

1) To begin diagnosis, connect test light to circuit No. 422 (pin F) on ALDL connector. With TCC disengaged (ECM not grounding circuit No. 422), test light should see 12 volts and light.

2) If test light lights, then power is being supplied through TCC brake switch. While in output cycling, circuit No. 422 should go between 12 volts and 0 volts every 3 seconds. If test light does not flash, transmission should be checked for short circuit. If resistance between pins A and D is less than 15 ohms, solenoid or wires are shorted and should be repaired. This low resistance through transmission may have damaged ECM, therefore, after repairs have been made, check output of ECM in output cycling.

If resistance is greater than 15 ohms, then circuit No. 422 should be checked for open to ECM. If wire is okay, check for faulty ECM connector or faulty ECM.

3) If test light goes on and off every 3 seconds, then ECM and wiring are okay. Fault could be mechanical problem in transmission, therefore, road test should be performed. When the 4th gear status light comes on, shift from Drive to manual 3rd. If no downshift occurs, verify that parameter ".1.2" is within 2 MPH of that shown on speedometer before continuing. Drive at 55 MPH with TCC solenoid energized (test light off), engine RPM is factor of driveline gear ratio if TCC is working properly. At 55 MPH, engine data parameter ".1.1" should be as shown in chart.

If RPM reading is greater than this limit, TCC has failed to engage and should be diagnosed.

4) If test light does not light on circuit No. 422, then there must be an open between ALDL connector and battery. First use switch tests to check TCC brake switch for proper operation. If there is no voltage on both sides of connector, either switch or circuit feeding switch is open.

5) If there is voltage on both sides of TCC brake switch, then voltage on circuit No. 420 should be checked at transmission. If test light does not light, circuit No. 420 is open. If test light between circuit Nos. 420 and 422 does not light with pin F jumpered to ground, then circuit No. 422 is open. If test light does light, then open must exist either at transmission connector terminals or inside transmission itself.

Note on Intermittents – If intermittent code is being set, it could be due to adjustment of brake switches. The ECM does not test for TCC code if it sees brake applied through cruise control brake signal on circuit No. 86. This is because TCC brake switch is also open under this condition. If TCC brake switch is adjusted such that it opens before cruise control brake switch, code could be set if operator were to keep brake pedal applied just enough to open TCC switch, but not cruise control switch.

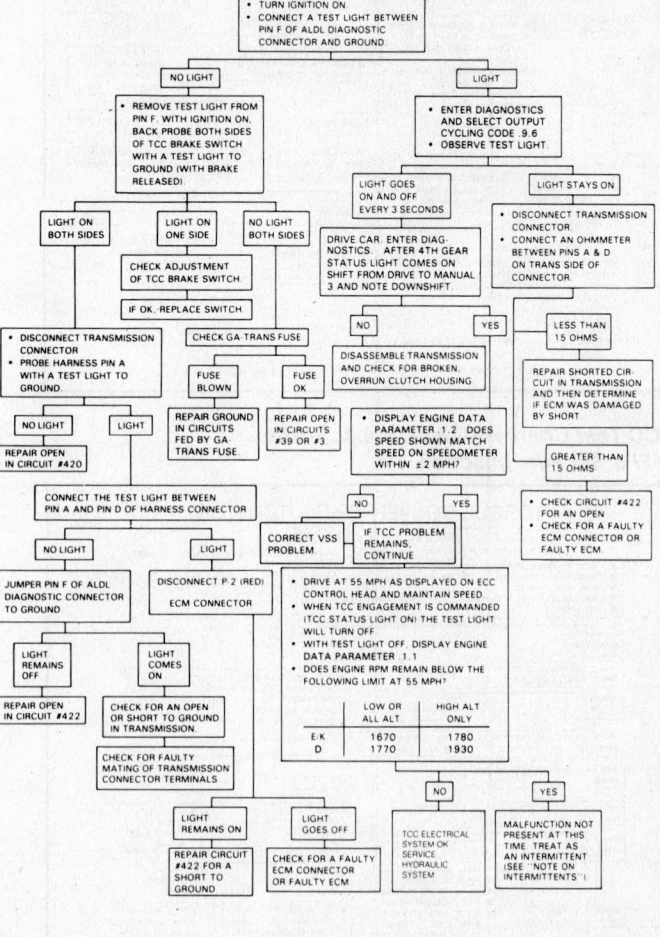

GENERAL MOTORS TORQUE CONVERTER CLUTCH (Cont.)

All Models With Seperate Buffer VSS Test Charts

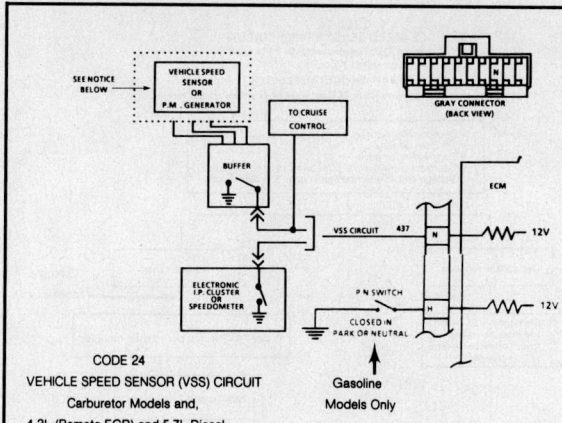

CODE 24
VEHICLE SPEED SENSOR (VSS) CIRCUIT
Carburetor Models and,
4.3L (Remote EGR) and 5.7L Diesel

The ECM applies and monitors 12 volts on circuit 437. Circuit 437 connects to the vehicle speed sensor which alternately grounds circuit 437 when the drive wheels are turning. This pulsing action takes place about 2000 times per mile and the ECM calculates vehicle speed based on the time between pulses.

1) This test monitors the ECM voltage on circuit 437. With the wheels turning, the pulsing action varies the voltage. This variation is greater at low speeds to an average of 4-6 volts at about 20 mph (32 km/h).

2) This test checks for a grounded circuit. A voltage of less than 1 volt indicates that circuit 437 is shorted to ground. Disconnect circuit 437 at the VSS, the VSS is faulty if the voltage now reads above 10 volts. If the voltage remains less than 10 volts, then circuit 437 wire is grounded. If the wire is not grounded, check for a faulty ECM connector or ECM.

3) A steady 8-12 volts at the ECM connector indicates circuit 437 is open or a faulty VSS.

4) Normal voltage is 1-6 volts and varing. This may indicate an intermittent problem if code 24 is shown.

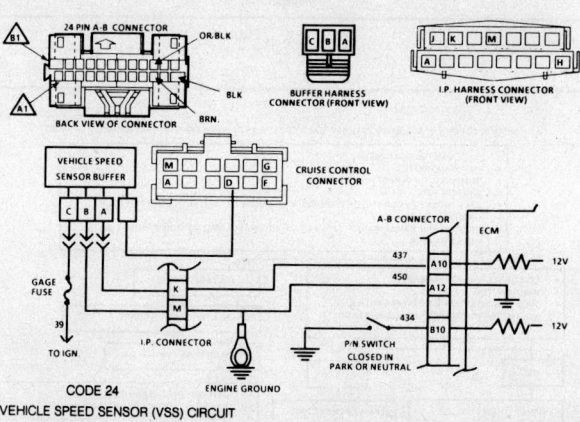

CODE 24
VEHICLE SPEED SENSOR (VSS) CIRCUIT
TBI Models

The ECM supplies and limits current to 12 volts on circuit 437. The Vehicle Speed Sensor (VSS) located near the intrument panel will sense speedometer rotating element and furnish this information to buffer as a "pulsed" signal (2 cable revolutions of 2002 pulses per mile). The buffer assembly will switch circuit 437 to ground for each pulse received. The ECM uses the time between pulses to determine vehicle speed.

Code 24 is set by the following: Circuit 437 voltage is constant. Engine spped between 1500 and 4400 RPM. Park/Neutral switch indicates transmission is in Drive range. Low MAP (high vacuum) indicating engine deceleration. Loss of VSS will affect TCC and IAC

1) This step checks to see if there is a VSS signal to ECM while turning a drive wheel. Normal voltage will vary from less than 3 volts to over 6 volts as wheel is turned slowly. The faster the wheel is turned, the less the variation.

2) This step checks for proper voltage from ECM to buffer connection. If voltage output from ECM to buffer is in normal 10-12 volt range, the fault is in buffer connections or buffer. Low voltage indicates a ground or open to, or in the ECM.

DISREGARD CODE 24 SET WHEN DRIVE WHEELS ARE NOT TURNING.

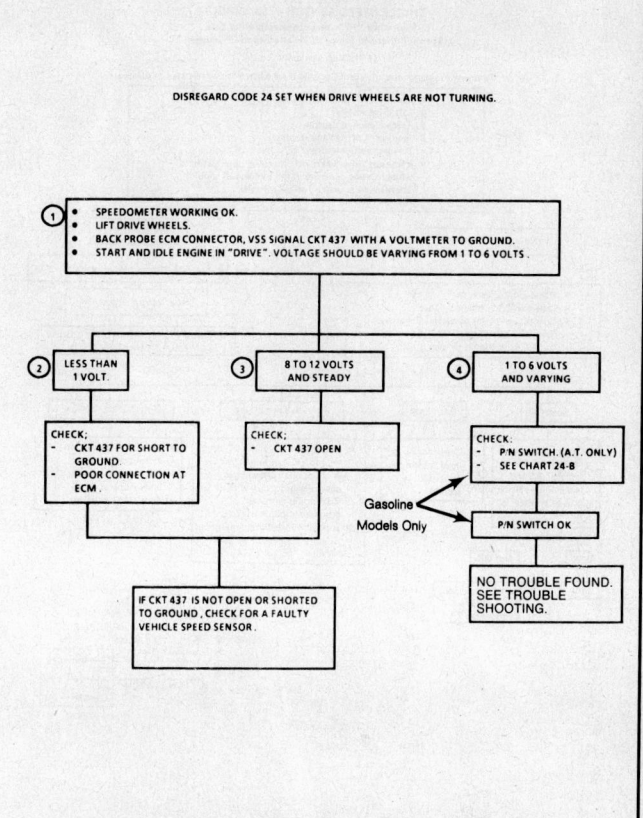

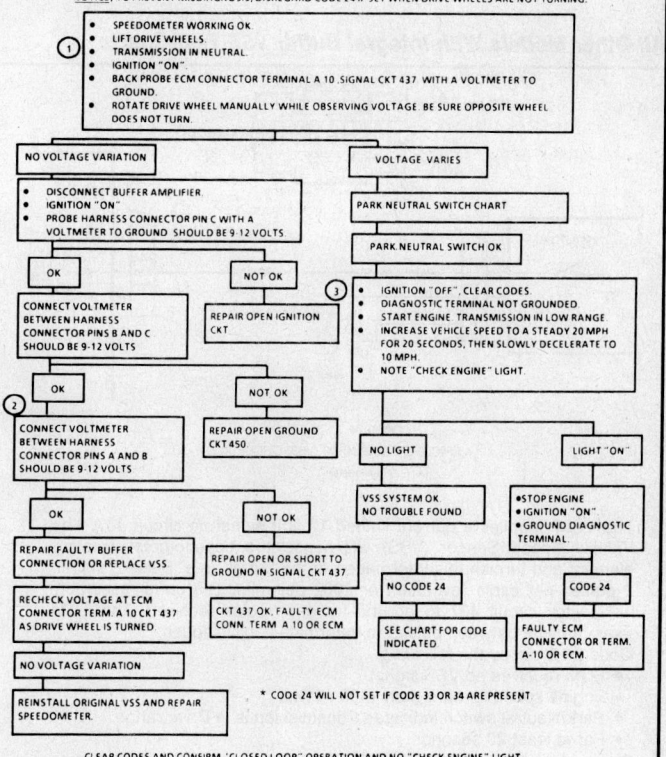

GENERAL MOTORS TORQUE CONVERTER CLUTCH (Cont.)

All TBI Models With Integral Buffer VSS Test Charts

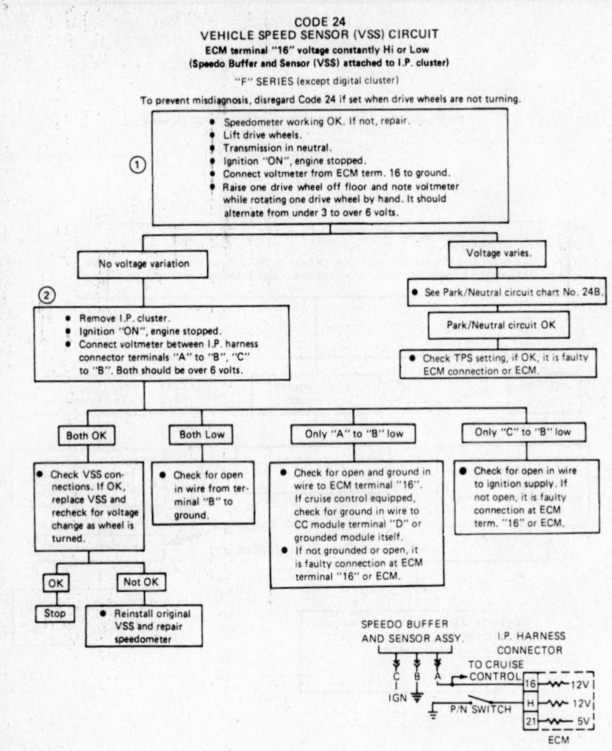

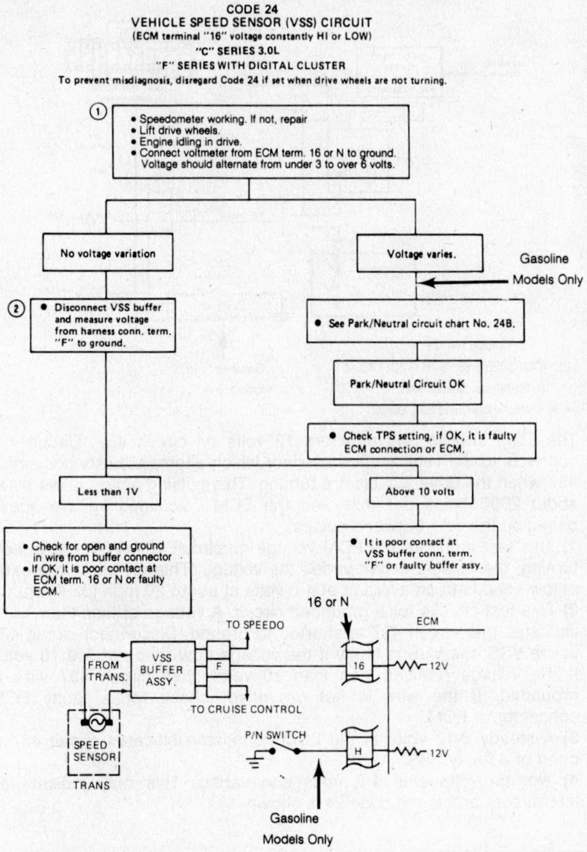

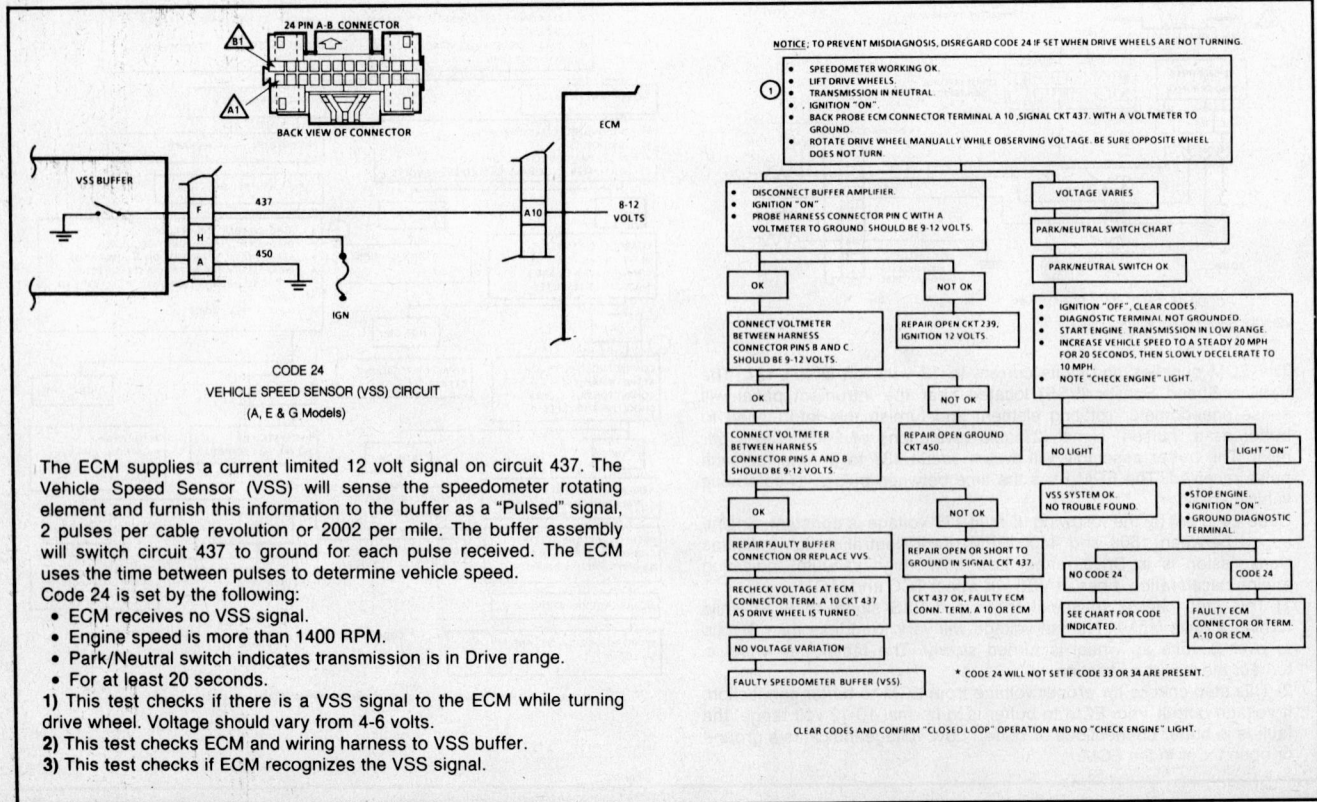

All Other Models With Integral Buffer VSS Test Charts

CODE 24
VEHICLE SPEED SENSOR (VSS) CIRCUIT
(A, E & G Models)

The ECM supplies a current limited 12 volt signal on circuit 437. The Vehicle Speed Sensor (VSS) will sense the speedometer rotating element and furnish this information to the buffer as a "Pulsed" signal, 2 pulses per cable revolution or 2002 per mile. The buffer assembly will switch circuit 437 to ground for each pulse received. The ECM uses the time between pulses to determine vehicle speed.

Code 24 is set by the following:

- ECM receives no VSS signal.
- Engine speed is more than 1400 RPM.
- Park/Neutral switch indicates transmission is in Drive range.
- For at least 20 seconds.

1) This test checks if there is a VSS signal to the ECM while turning drive wheel. Voltage should vary from 4-6 volts.
2) This test checks ECM and wiring harness to VSS buffer.
3) This test checks if ECM recognizes the VSS signal.

GENERAL MOTORS TORQUE CONVERTER CLUTCH (Cont.)

All TBI Models With Integral Buffer VSS Test Charts (Cont)

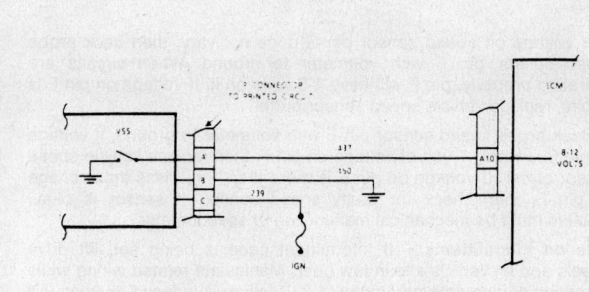

CODE 24
VEHICLE SPEED SENSOR (VSS) CIRCUIT
(A,C & N Models) With Digital Dash

The ECM supplies a current limited 12 volt signal on circuit 437. The Vehicle Speed Sensor (VSS) will sense the speedometer rotating element and furnish this information to the buffer as a "Pulsed" signal, 2 pulses per cable revolution or 2002 per mile. The buffer assembly will switch circuit 437 to ground for each pulse received. The ECM uses the time between pulses to determine vehicle speed.

Code 24 is set by the following:
- ECM receives no VSS signal.
- Engine speed is more than 1800 RPM.
- Park/Neutral switch indicates transmission is in Drive range.
- For at least 25 seconds.

1) This test checks for a VSS signal to the ECM while turning drive wheel. Voltage should vary from 4-6 volts.

2) This test checks ECM and wiring harness to VSS buffer.

3) This test checks if ECM recognizes the VSS signal.

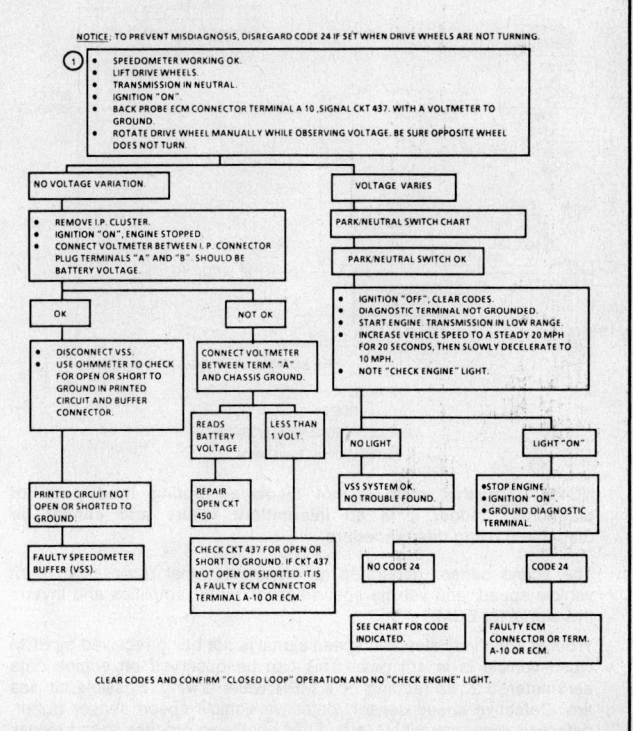

NOTICE: TO PREVENT MISDIAGNOSIS, DISREGARD CODE 24 IF SET WHEN DRIVE WHEELS ARE NOT TURNING.

(1)
- SPEEDOMETER WORKING OK.
- LIFT DRIVE WHEELS.
- TRANSMISSION IN NEUTRAL.
- IGNITION "ON".
- BACK PROBE ECM CONNECTOR TERMINAL A 10 ,SIGNAL CKT 437, WITH A VOLTMETER TO GROUND.
- ROTATE DRIVE WHEEL MANUALLY WHILE OBSERVING VOLTAGE. BE SURE OPPOSITE WHEEL DOES NOT TURN.

NO VOLTAGE VARIATION.

VOLTAGE VARIES

- REMOVE I.P. CLUSTER.
- IGNITION "ON", ENGINE STOPPED.
- CONNECT VOLTMETER BETWEEN I. P. CONNECTOR PLUG TERMINALS "A" AND "B". SHOULD BE BATTERY VOLTAGE.

PARK/NEUTRAL SWITCH CHART

PARK/NEUTRAL SWITCH OK

OK

NOT OK

- IGNITION "OFF", CLEAR CODES.
- DIAGNOSTIC TERMINAL NOT GROUNDED.
- START ENGINE. TRANSMISSION IN LOW RANGE.
- INCREASE VEHICLE SPEED TO A STEADY 20 MPH FOR 20 SECONDS, THEN SLOWLY DECELERATE TO 10 MPH.
- NOTE "CHECK ENGINE" LIGHT.

- DISCONNECT VSS.
- USE OHMMETER TO CHECK FOR OPEN OR SHORT TO GROUND IN PRINTED CIRCUIT AND BUFFER CONNECTOR.

CONNECT VOLTMETER BETWEEN TERM. "A" AND CHASSIS GROUND.

READS BATTERY VOLTAGE

LESS THAN 1 VOLT.

NO LIGHT

LIGHT "ON"

PRINTED CIRCUIT NOT OPEN OR SHORTED TO GROUND.

REPAIR OPEN CKT 450.

VSS SYSTEM OK. NO TROUBLE FOUND.

- STOP ENGINE.
- IGNITION "ON".
- GROUND DIAGNOSTIC TERMINAL.

FAULTY SPEEDOMETER BUFFER (VSS).

CHECK CKT 437 FOR OPEN OR SHORT TO GROUND. IF CKT 437 NOT OPEN OR SHORTED. IT IS A FAULTY ECM CONNECTOR TERMINAL A-10 OR ECM.

NO CODE 24

CODE 24

SEE CHART FOR CODE INDICATED.

FAULTY ECM CONNECTOR OR TERM. A-10 OR ECM.

CLEAR CODES AND CONFIRM "CLOSED LOOP" OPERATION AND NO "CHECK ENGINE" LIGHT.

GENERAL MOTORS TORQUE CONVERTER CLUTCH (Cont.)

All Cadillac DFI VSS Test Charts

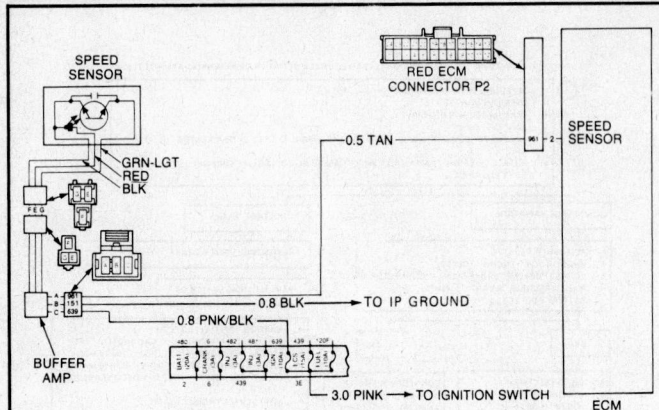

CODE 24
VEHICLE SPEED SENSOR (VSS) CIRCUIT
Models Without Digital Dash

NOTE: If this code is not displayed during third pass of diagnostic codes, it is an intermittent failure and cannot be diagnosed using this procedure.

The speed sensor generates an electrical signal representative of vehicle speed, and vehicle speed sensor buffer amplifies and inverts this signal for ECM.

Trouble code indicates that speed signal is not being received by ECM when vehicle is in 4th gear. This can be observed on engine data parameter .1.2. as reading of 0 MPH while driving. Possible causes are: Defective speed sensor, defective vehicle speed sensor buffer, defective wiring, terminals, etc., ECM unable to process speed signal, or speedometer that does not function properly.

1) To begin diagnosis, lift a drive wheel on vehicle, and measure voltage on circuit No. 961 at ECM. If voltage varies between 0.6 and 11 volts when drive wheel is rotated, then vehicle must be test driven to determine whether malfunction was intermittent or if ECM is not processing this speed signal properly.

2) If there is no voltage variation, next step is to determine if voltage signal from ECM is reaching vehicle speed sensor buffer. If voltage on circuit No. 961 is 0 volts on ECM side of vehicle speed sensor (buffer amplifier), check circuit for open or short to ground. If circuit No. 961 is okay, check for faulty ECM connector or faulty ECM.

3) If there is between 10 and 12 volts on circuit No. 961, then determine if circuit No. 639 is supplying power to vehicle speed sensor buffer. Circuit No. 639 should be at 12 volts when system is operating properly. If there is no voltage, the 10 amp ignition fuse should be checked and circuit No. 639 should be repaired as necessary.

4) If 12 volts is present on circuit No. 639, measure voltage between it and circuit No. 450. If voltage is 0, then circuit No. 450 is open and not supplying ground to vehicle speed sensor buffer.

5) If there is a reading of 12 volts between circuit Nos. 639 and 450, reconnect vehicle speed sensor buffer. Back probe speed sensor pin G with voltmeter to ground while manually turning speedometer drive mechanism. If voltage varies between 0 and 5 volts, replace vehicle speed sensor buffer.

6) If voltage on speed sensor pin G does not vary, then back probe speed sensor pin F with voltmeter to ground. When circuits are operating properly, pin F will have 4-6 volts on it. If voltage on pin F is 0 volts, replace vehicle speed sensor buffer.

7) Back probe speed sensor pin E with voltmeter to ground. If voltage on pin E is within 1 volt of voltage on pin F, then replace vehicle speed sensor buffer. If voltage on pin E is more than 1 volt less than voltage on pin F, then check for faulty speed sensor. If sensor is okay, problem must be mechanical malfunction of speedometer.

Note on Intermittents – If intermittent code is being set, lift drive wheels and let vehicle idle in low gear. Manipulate related wiring while observing engine data parameter .1.2. If failure is induced, reading will drop from normal reading to a reading of 0 MPH. This will help to isolate location of malfunction.

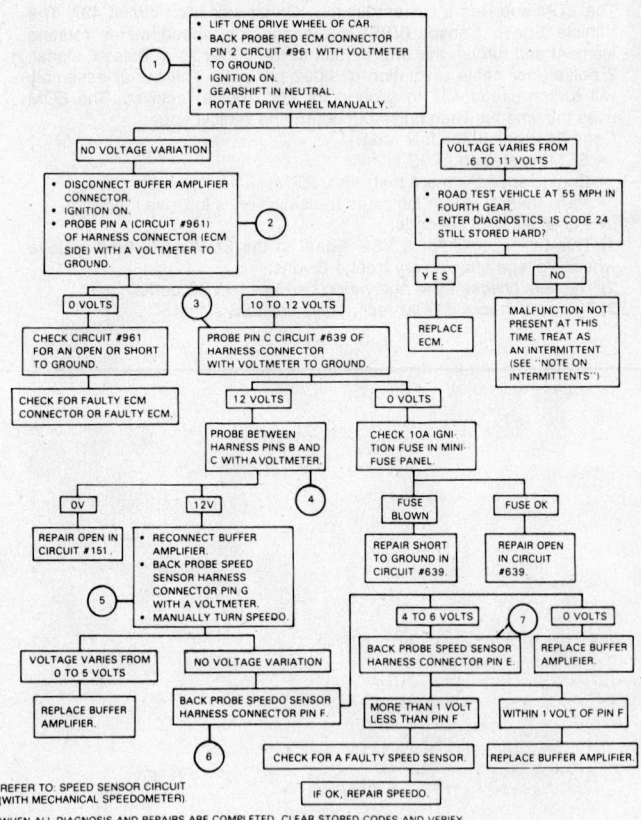

GENERAL MOTORS TORQUE CONVERTER CLUTCH (Cont.)

All Cadillac DFI VSS Test Charts (Cont.)

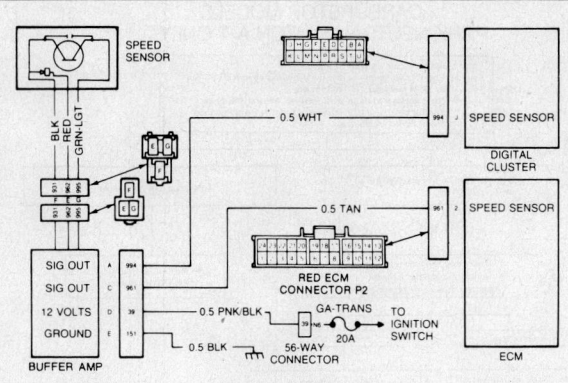

CODE 24
VEHICLE SPEED SENSOR (VSS) CIRCUIT
Models With Digital Dash

NOTE: If this code is not displayed during third pass of diagnostic codes, it is an intermittent failure and cannot be diagnosed using this procedure.

The speed sensor generates an electrical signal representative of vehicle speed, and vehicle speed sensor buffer (buffer amplifier) amplifies and inverts this signal for ECM.

Trouble code indicates that speed signal is not being received by ECM when vehicle is in 4th gear. This can be observed on engine data parameter .1.2. as reading of 0 MPH while driving. Possible causes are: Defective speed sensor, defective vehicle speed sensor buffer, defective wiring, terminals, etc., ECM unable to process speed signal, or speedometer that does not function properly.

1) If digital cluster displays vehicle speed properly, then problem must be in circuits used only by the ECM. Lift a drive wheel on vehicle, and measure voltage on circuit No. 961 at ECM. If voltage varies between 0.6 and 11 volts when drive wheel is rotated, then vehicle must be test driven to determine whether malfunction was intermittent or if ECM is not processing this speed signal properly.

2) If there is no voltage variation, next step is to determine if voltage signal from ECM is reaching vehicle speed sensor buffer. If voltage on circuit No. 961 is 0 volts on ECM side of vehicle speed sensor buffer connector, check circuit for open or short to ground. If circuit No. 961 is okay, check for faulty ECM connector or faulty ECM. If voltage is between 10 and 12 volts on circuit No. 961, replace vehicle speed sensor buffer.

3) If digital cluster displays 0 MPH all the time, then problem must be in those circuits shared between digital cluster and ECM. First step is to verify that speedometer cable is installed properly. If cable is properly turning speedometer, then determine if circuit No. 39 is supplying power to vehicle speed sensor buffer. Circuit No. 39 should be at 12 volts when system is operating properly. If there is no voltage, the 20 amp "GA-TRANS" fuse should be checked and circuit No. 39 should be repaired as necessary.

4) If 12 volts is present on circuit No. 39, measure voltage between it and circuit No. 151. If voltage is 0, then circuit No. 151 is open and not supplying ground to vehicle speed sensor buffer.

5) If there is a reading of 12 volts between circuit Nos. 39 and 151, reconnect vehicle speed sensor buffer. Back probe speed sensor pin G with voltmeter to ground while manually turning speedometer drive mechanism. If voltage varies between 0 and 5 volts, replace vehicle speed sensor buffer.

6) If voltage on speed sensor pin G does not vary, then back probe speed sensor pin F with voltmeter to ground. When circuits are operating properly, pin F will have 4-6 volts on it. If voltage on pin F is 0 volts, replace vehicle speed sensor buffer.

7) Back probe speed sensor pin E with voltmeter to ground. If voltage on pin E is within 1 volt of voltage on pin F, then replace vehicle speed sensor buffer. If voltage on pin E is more than 1 volt less than voltage on pin F, then check for faulty speed sensor. If sensor is okay, problem must be mechanical malfunction of speedometer.

Note on Intermittents – If intermittent code is being set, lift drive wheels and let vehicle idle in low gear. Manipulate related wiring while observing engine data parameter .1.2. If failure is induced, reading will drop from normal reading to a reading of 0 MPH. This will help to isolate location of malfunction.

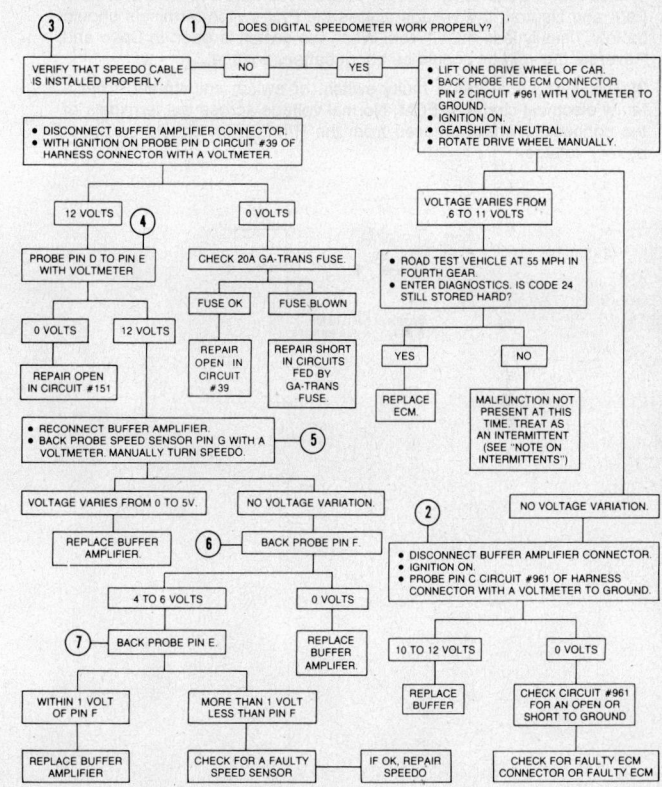

REFER TO: SPEED SENSOR CIRCUIT (WITH DIGITAL SPEEDOMETER)
WHEN ALL DIAGNOSIS AND REPAIRS ARE COMPLETED, CLEAR CODES AND VERIFY PROPER OPERATION.

Automatic Transmissions

GENERAL MOTORS TORQUE CONVERTER CLUTCH (Cont.)

Park/Neutral Test Charts

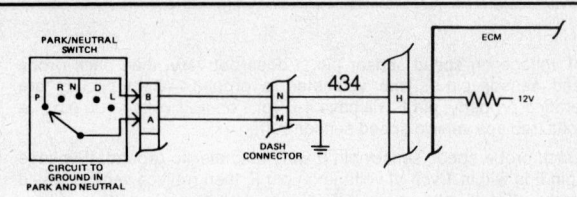

Park/Neutral Chart

The P/N switch is closed when the gear selector is in Park or Neutral. One side of the switch is connected to the ECM which supplies a buffered 12 volts, the other side is grounded. The P/N switch is an input to the ECM. When the voltage at ECM term. "H" is high (12 volts), the ECM allows activation, at the proper time, of other controls such as TCC, EST, VSS and others.

1) This test checks for good P/N circuit. When the switch is closed in Park and Neutral, the voltage across the P/N switch terminals should be low, usually less than 1 volt. When the switch is open in Drive and Reverse, the voltage should be about battery voltage.

2) This step separates a faulty switch, or switch adjustment, from a faulty electrical circuit or ECM. Normal voltage across the terminals of the connector, when removed from the P/N switch, should be about battery voltage.

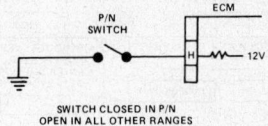

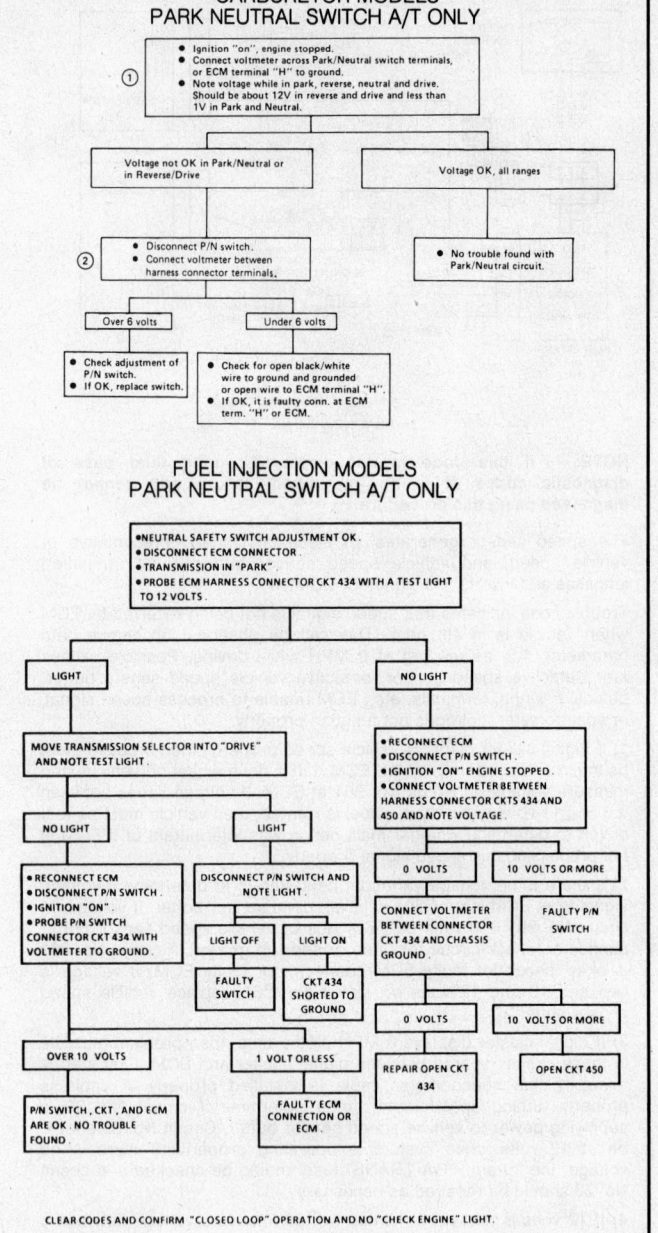

GENERAL MOTORS TORQUE CONVERTER CLUTCH (Cont.)

NOTE: For TCC wiring and control switch locations on the THM 325-4L and THM 350C automatic transmissions, see the appropriate transmission article.

Fig. 12: THM 125C TCC Wiring & Controls

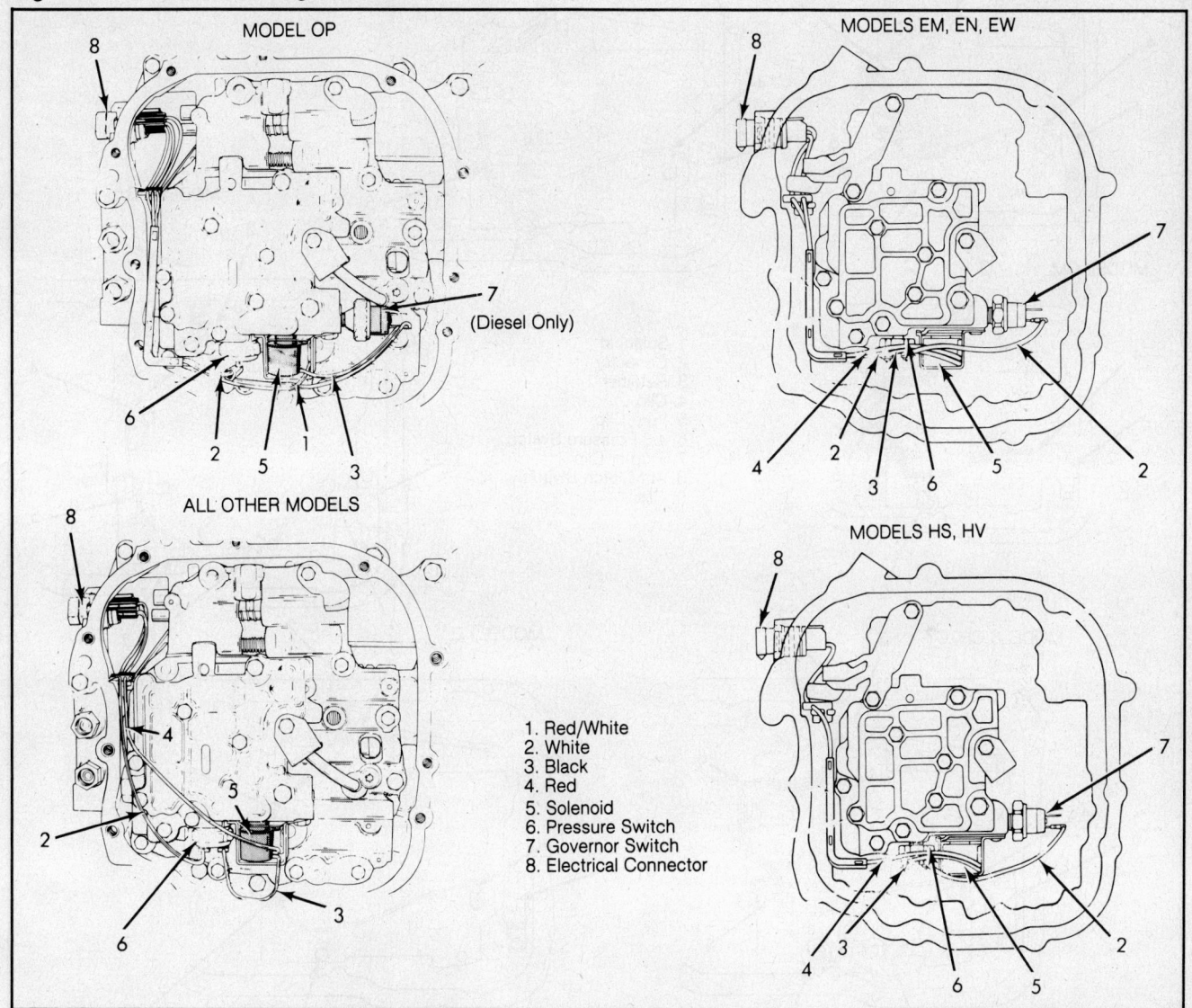

MODEL OP

(Diesel Only)

MODELS EM, EN, EW

ALL OTHER MODELS

MODELS HS, HV

1. Red/White
2. White
3. Black
4. Red
5. Solenoid
6. Pressure Switch
7. Governor Switch
8. Electrical Connector

GENERAL MOTORS TORQUE CONVERTER CLUTCH (Cont.)

Fig. 13: THM 200-4R TCC Wiring & Controls

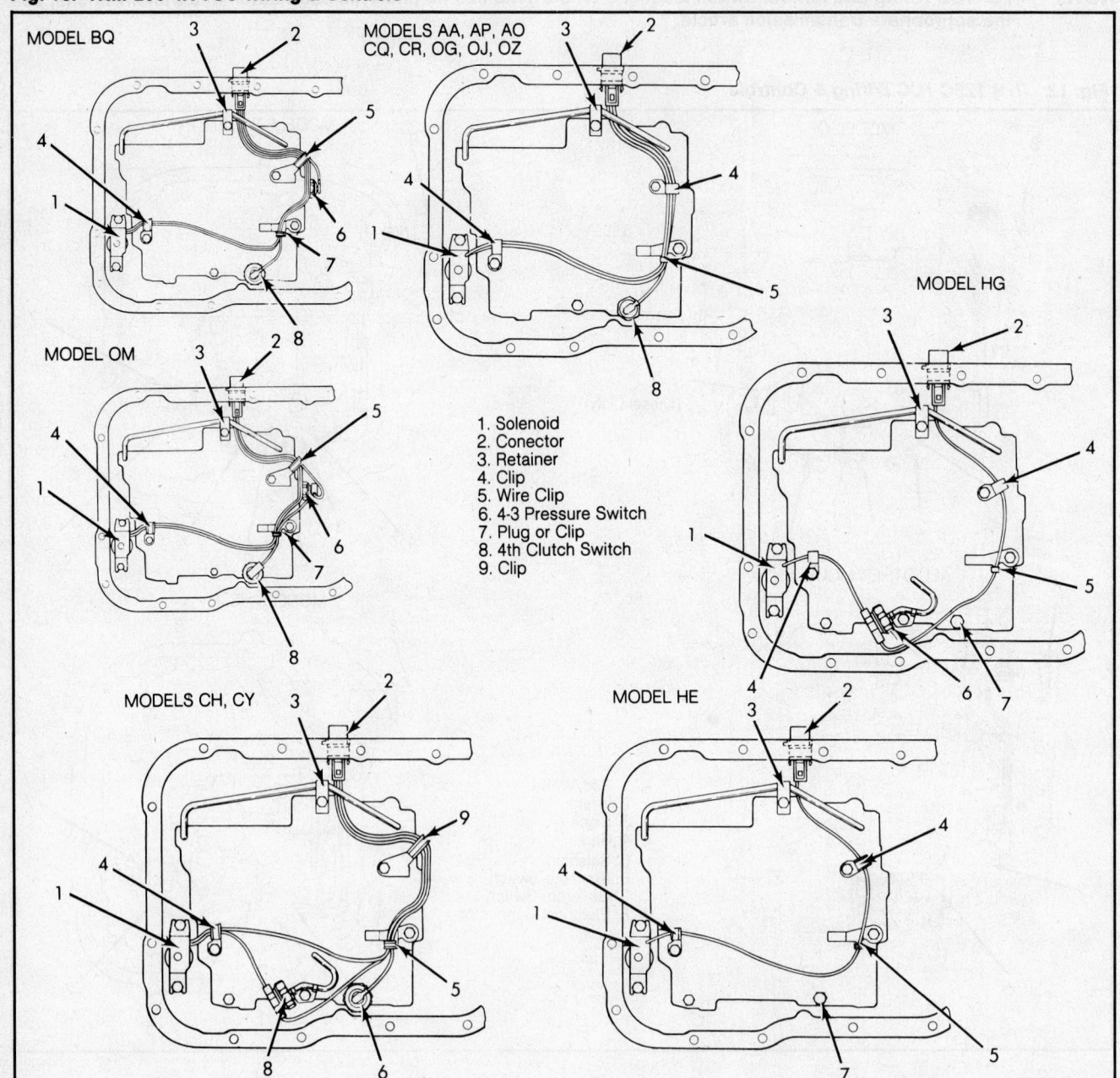

1. Solenoid
2. Conector
3. Retainer
4. Clip
5. Wire Clip
6. 4-3 Pressure Switch
7. Plug or Clip
8. 4th Clutch Switch
9. Clip

GENERAL MOTORS TORQUE CONVERTER CLUTCH (Cont.)

Fig. 14: *THM 700-R4 TCC Wiring & Controls*

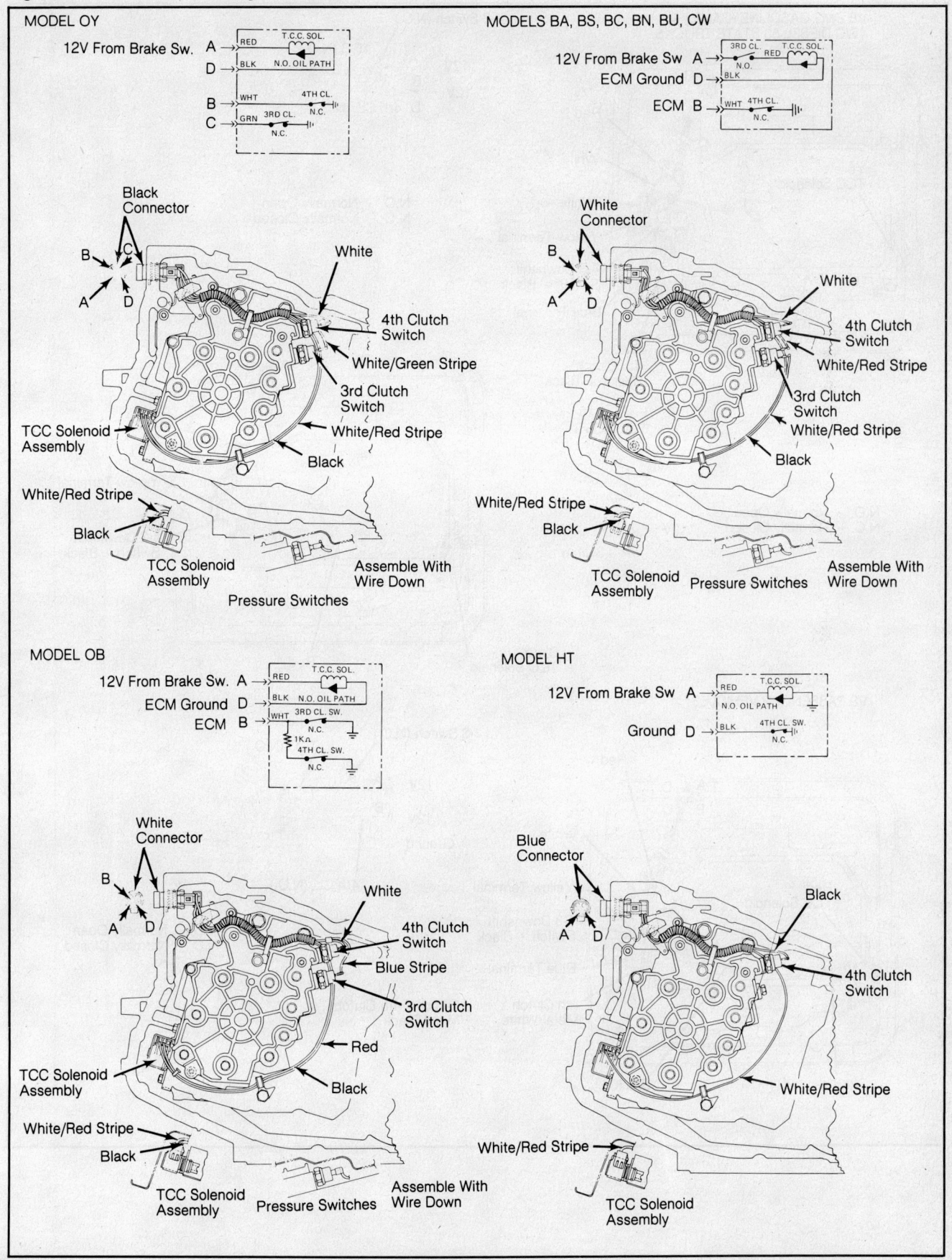

GENERAL MOTORS TORQUE CONVERTER CLUTCH (Cont.)

Fig. 15: THM 700-R4 TCC Wiring & Controls (Cont.)

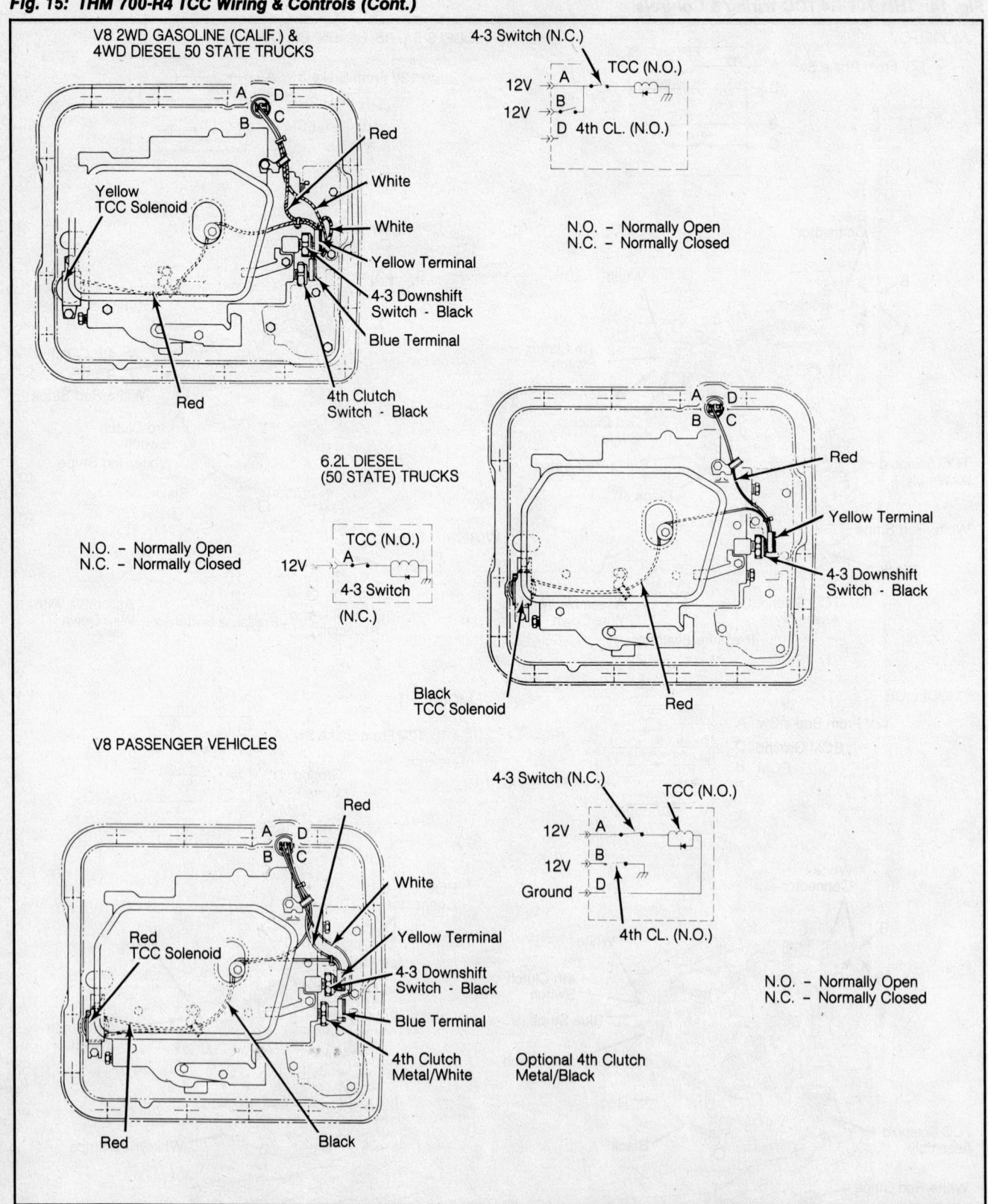

Fig. 16: THM 700-R4 TCC Wiring & Controls (Cont.)

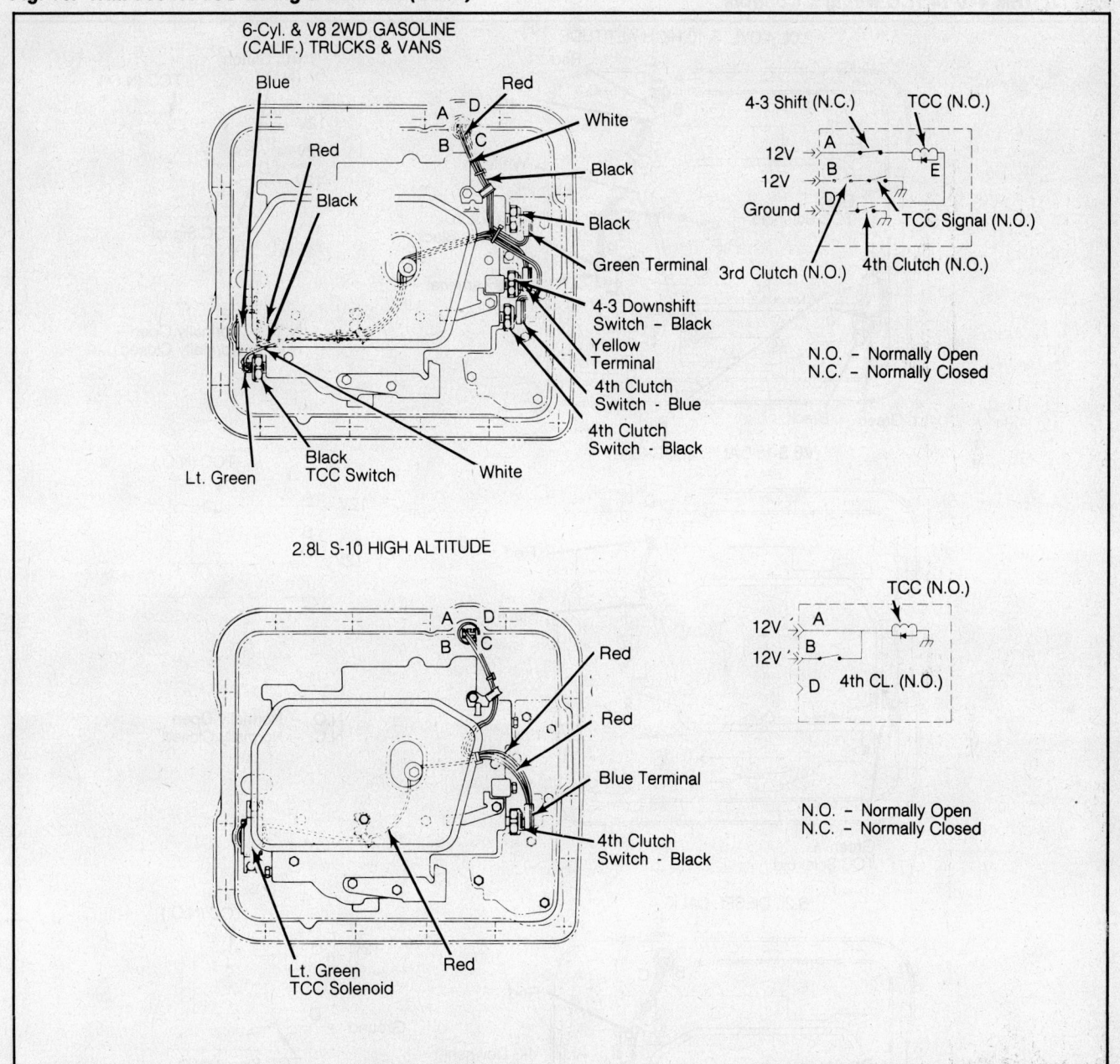

Automatic Transmissions

GENERAL MOTORS TORQUE CONVERTER CLUTCH (Cont.)

Fig. 17: THM 440-T4 TCC Wiring & Controls

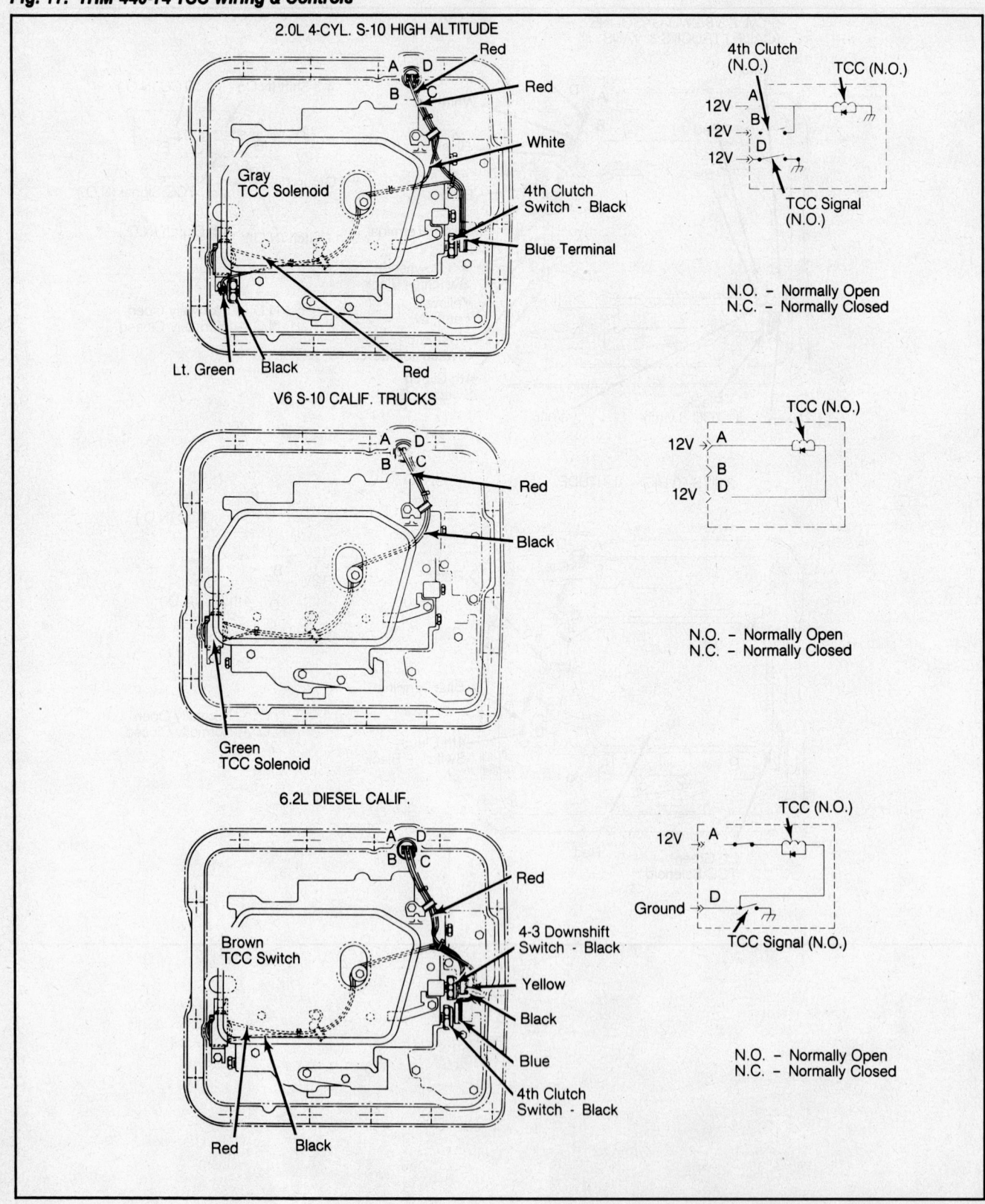

GENERAL MOTORS TORQUE CONVERTER CLUTCH (Cont.)

Fig. 18: TCC System Schematic

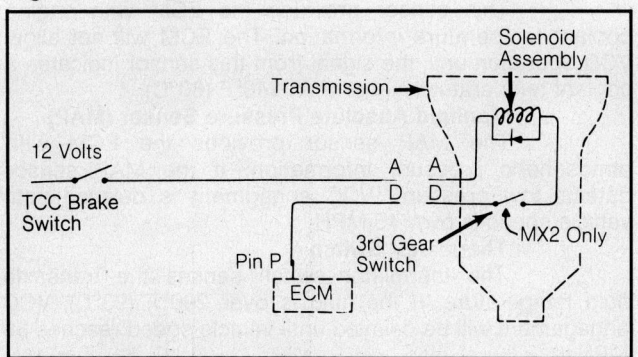

Typical 3-speed with TCC in 3rd gear only.

Fig. 19: TCC System Schematic

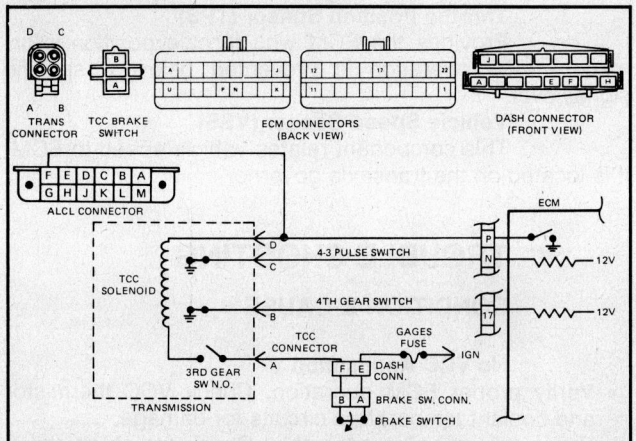

Typical 4-speed with TCC in all forward gears and carburetor.

Fig. 20: TCC System Schematic

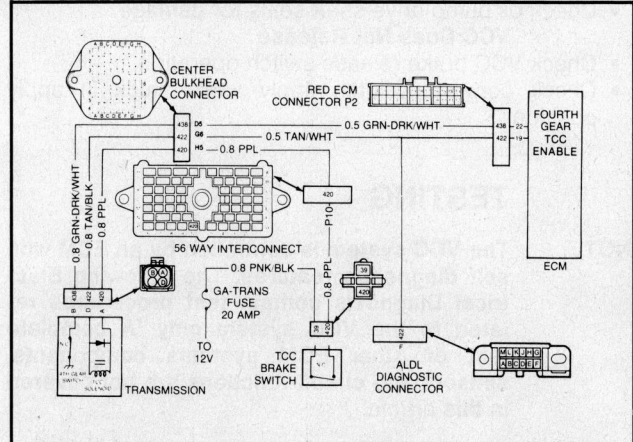

All THM 200-4R and 325-4L Cadillac with DFI.

Fig. 21: TCC System Schematic

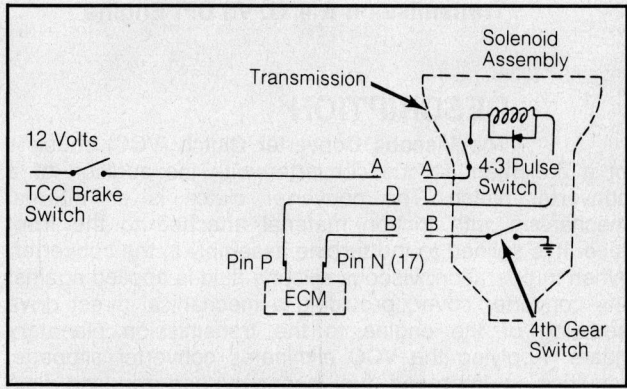

Typical 4-speed with TCC in 3rd or 4th gear only.

Fig. 22: TCC System Schematic

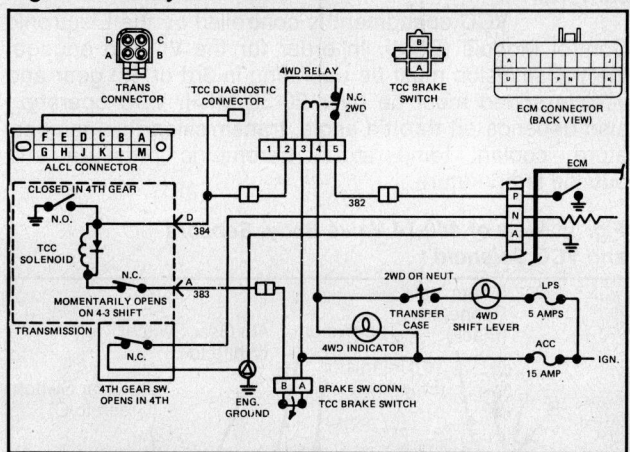

All light duty and S-10 trucks with 4WD.

Fig. 23: TCC System Schematic

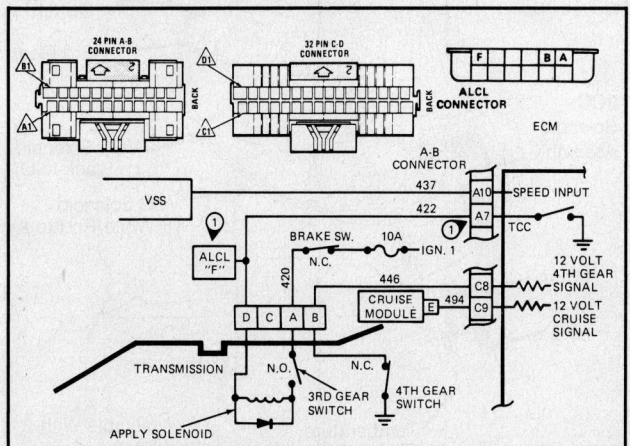

Typical 4-speed with fuel injection.

Automatic Transmissions

GENERAL MOTORS VISCOUS CONVERTER CLUTCH

**DeVille & Fleetwood with 440-T4
Transmission & 4.1L V8 DFI Engine**

DESCRIPTION

The Viscous Converter Clutch (VCC) consists of a 3-element torque converter with the addition of a converter clutch. The converter clutch is an internal mechanism with friction material attached to the front face. It is splined to the turbine assembly in the converter. When in operation, viscous silicone fluid is applied against the converter cover, providing a mechanical direct drive coupling of the engine to the transmission planetary gears. Applying the VCC eliminates converter slippage, resulting in improved fuel economy and reduced fluid operating temperatures. When the converter clutch is released, the assembly operates as a conventional torque converter.

VCC engagment is controlled by the Electronic Control Module (ECM). In order for the VCC to engage, the transmission must be operating in 3rd or 4th gear and vehicle speed must be over 20-30 MPH. VCC operation also depends on throttle angle, transmission fluid temperature, coolant temperature, barometric pressure and outside temperature.

Fig. 1: View of 440-T4 Valve Body, Sensors and VCC Solenoid

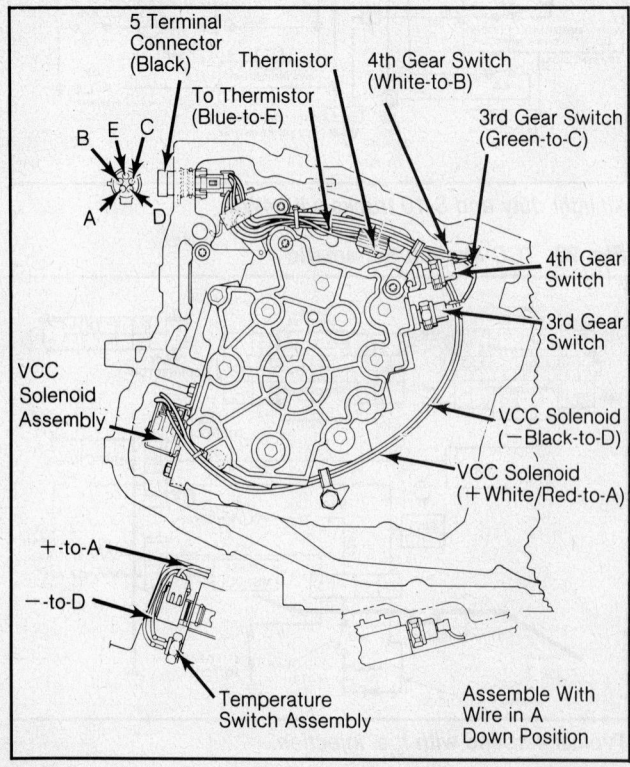

Ensure wiring is not damaged during inspection or reassembly.

VCC CONTROL COMPONENTS

The following components supply engine condition information to the ECM:

Brake Release Switch

This switch releases VCC when brakes are applied to prevent engine stalling.

Coolant Temperature Sensor

This sensor provides the ECM with engine coolant temperature information. The ECM will not allow VCC operation until the signal from this sensor indicates a coolant temperature higher than 140°F (60°C).

Manifold Absolute Pressure Sensor (MAP)

The MAP sensor provides the ECM with atmospheric pressure information. If the MAP sensor detects low pressure, VCC engagment is delayed until vehicle speed is over 45 MPH.

Thermistor Switch

The thermistor switch senses the transaxle fluid temperature. If the fluid is over 200°F (93°C), VCC engagement will be delayed until vehicle speed reaches 36 MPH.

Third and/or Fourth Gear Switches

These switches prevents VCC operation until direct drive (3rd and/or 4th gear) is obtained.

Throttle Position Sensor (TPS)

Provides the ECM with throttle position information. VCC operation is prevented below a specific signal level.

Vehicle Speed Sensor (VSS)

This component relates vehicle speed to ECM. It is located on the transaxle governor cover.

TROUBLE SHOOTING

CONDITION & CAUSE

No VCC Application
- Verify proper ECM operation. Check VCC thermistor and coolant temperature circuits for damage.
- Verify control valve assembly. Check for stuck clutch apply valve. Check for missing number 10 check ball.
- Check converter clutch blow off check ball in channel plate not seating or damaged.
- Check turbine shaft seals for damage.
- Check oil pump drive shaft seals for damage.

VCC Does Not Release
- Check VCC brake release switch operation.
- Check converter clutch apply valve stuck in apply position.

TESTING

NOTE: **The VCC system is controlled by an ECM with self diagnostic features. The following Electrical Diagnosis contain test procedures related to the VCC system only. A complete test of other ECM systems components, sensors and circuit functions are not covered in this article.**

ELECTRICAL DIAGNOSIS

NOTE: **DO NOT preform this test if ECM hard codes E21, E22 or E24 are present.**

1) Check mechnical linkage and fluid level. Turn ignition on. Connect test light from the ALDL connector terminal "F" to ground. If test light is off, go to step 13).

2) If test light is on, start the engine. Turn engine off and within 2 seconds turn ignition on. Depress

GENERAL MOTORS VISCOUS CONVERTER CLUTCH (Cont.)

both "Off" and "Warmer" buttons on the Climate Control Panel (CCP). Hold down both buttons until all display panel segments illuminate.

Fig. 2: VCC System Schematic

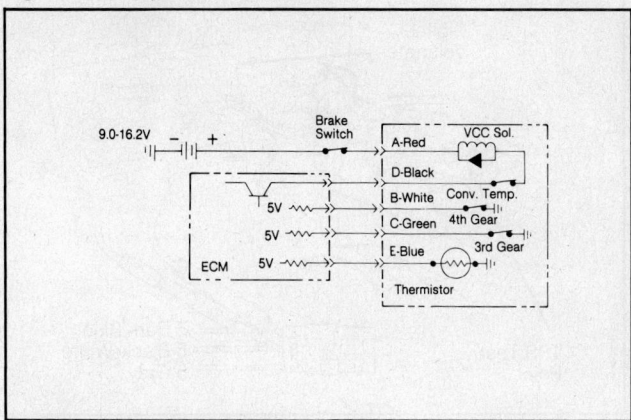

Transaxle connector has 5 terminals.

3) If any ECM trouble codes are present, the CCP "Data Center" panel will display a "8.8.8" for 1 second. If any SOFT trouble codes are stored, a "..E" will be displayed for 2 seconds. All stored trouble codes will be displayed for 2 seconds in numerical order.

4) If any HARD trouble codes are stored, a ".E.E" will be displayed. All stored trouble codes will be displayed for 2 seconds in numerical order. After all trouble codes or if no codes are displayed, a ".7.0" will appear on the "Data Center" panel.

NOTE: **Record any SOFT and HARD trouble codes stored in the ECM.**

5) When code ".7.0" is displayed in the "Data Center" panel, depress the "Hi" button. Code "E.9.5" will appear on the "Data Center" panel. Depress the throttle pedal and release it (to open and close the TPS). Code "E.9.6" will appear on the "Data Center" panel.

6) If code ".E.9.6" does not appear on the "Data Center" panel, refer to ECM Switch Test code "E.7.2". If test light flashes, go to step **9)**. If test light is on, disconnect connector at transaxle. Connect an ohmmeter between transaxle pins "A" and "D".

7) If ohmmeter reads greater than 15 ohms, check and repair open in wiring between transaxle connector terminal "D" to Red ECM connector terminal "19". Check for a faulty ECM connector or faulty ECM.

8) If ohmmeter reads less than 15 ohms, repair short in transaxle circuit. Ensure ECM was not damaged by short. After 2 minutes code "E.9.6" will automatically return to code "E.9.5". Return to code ".7.0" by clearing the ECM trouble codes.

9) If test light flashes on and off every 3 seconds. Raise driving wheels off ground. With code ".7.0" displayed, press and release the "Lo" button on the CCP.

10) The "Data Center" panel will change to code "E.9.0". This diagnostic parameter contains engine data information. The parameters number from "P.0.1" to "P.1.3".

11) Advance to parameter "P.1.1" (engine RPM ÷ 10). To advance parameter number, depress the "Hi" button. To return to a lower parameter number, depress the "Lo" button. Accelerate and maintain a vehicle speed of 55 MPH.

12) Note engine RPM. Gently tap the brake pedal. Watch for a drop in engine speed of at least 100 RPM. If engine speed drops, VCC system is okay. If not, problem is not electrical. *See Trouble Shooting section of this article.* Return to code ".7.0" by clearing ECM trouble codes.

13) If test light is off, perform ECM Switch Tests and repair as necessary. If test light is on, disconnect the transaxle connector. Connect a test light between wire harness terminal "A" to ground.

14) If test light is off, repair open wire in circuit number 420 (harness terminal "A" to brake light switch). If test light is on, connect test light between wire harness terminals "A" and "D".

15) Jumper terminal "P" in the ALDL connector to ground. If test light is off, repair open wire in circuit number 422 (harness terminal "D" to Red ECM connector terminal "19").

16) If test light is on, check for faulty connector at transaxle or an open wire in the transaxle.

ECM SWITCH TESTS

1) Engine must be running and diagnostic code ".7.0" must be displayed. To enter diagnostic code ".7.0", turn ignition on and start engine. Depress both "Off" and "Warmer" buttons on the Climate Control Panel (CCP). Hold down both buttons until all display panel segments illuminate.

2) Code ".7.0" should appear. Depress and release brake pedal. This will start the switch test procedure and code "E.7.1" will be displayed. If code "E.7.1" is NOT displayed, refer to diagnostic charts. *See "Trouble Code .7.1".*

NOTE: **Each test must action must be performed within 10 seconds after codes appear on "Data Center" panel or ECM will store code as a failure and proceed to next code.**

3) Ensure "E.7.1." is displayed, depress and release brake pedal again. Code "E.7.2" should appear. With code "E.7.2" displayed, depress throttle to an open throttle position and slowly release. This checks throttle switch for proper operation.

4) Code "E.7.7" should appear. With code "E.7.4" displayed, shift transaxle to Reverse and back to Neutral. This checks operation of the Park/Neutral switch. Code "E.7.6" should appear.

NOTE: **To pass codes "E.7.5", "E.7.6" and "E.7.7" on vehicles without cruise control, allow codes to appear for 10 seconds each, to time out diagnostic test. Proceed to step 7). Codes will cycle through ECM and are stored as failures.**

5) With code "E.7.5" displayed, switch cruise control on and off once. This checks operation of the cruise control switch. Code "E.7.6" should appear. With code "E.7.6" displayed, switch cruise control on. Depress and release "Set/Coast" button. This checks operation of the "Set/Coast" switch. Code "E.7.7" should appear.

6) With code "E.7.7" displayed, switch cruise control on. Depress and release "Resume/Acceleration" switch. This checks operation of the "Resume/Acceleration" switch. Code "E.7.8" should appear.

Automatic Transmissions

GENERAL MOTORS VISCOUS CONVERTER CLUTCH (Cont.)

7) With code "E.7.8" displayed, turn wheels from straight ahead to either full right or left and return to straight ahead position. This checks operation of the power steering pressure switch.

8) When the switch tests are complete, the ECM will cycle back and display the switch codes that did not test properly. Each code that did not pass will be displayed in numerical order. The codes will not disappear until the affected circuit has been repaired and retested. *See the Diagnostic Charts at end of this article.*

9) After switch tests are completed and all circuits pass, the "Data Center" panel will display "E.0.0". After "E.0.0" is displayed the "Data Center" will display ".7.0". A display of "E.0.0" indicates that all circuits are working properly.

10) On vehicles without cruise control, codes "E.7.5", "E.7.6" and "E.7.7" will be displayed as faults. "E.0.0" will not be displayed until the ECM trouble codes are cleared.

CLEARING ECM TROUBLE CODES

Depress both "Off" and "HI" buttons on the CCP. Hold buttons until "F.0.0" or "E.0.0" appears. The "Data Center" panel will change from "F.0.0" or "E.0.0" to ".7.0". With ".7.0" displayed, turn ignition off for at least 10 seconds before re-entering the diagnostic mode.

To exit the ECM diagnostic mode without clearing the trouble codes, depress the "Auto" button. Turning the ignition switch off for 10 seconds will also exit from the ECM diagnostic mode.

ADJUSTMENTS

BRAKE RELEASE SWITCH

1) Remove wiring connector. Depress brake pedal. Push brake switch into retainer until body seats on the retainer.

2) Pull brake switch rearward until audible clicking of switch can no longer be heard.

3) Release brake pedal and repeat step **2)** to ensure proper adjustment. Reconnect wiring connector.

TPS POSITION

1) Open throttle valve and close it against the throttle stop screw. Turn the ignition on. Back probe the TPS connector terminals "B" and "C". This is the Reference Voltage. Record this voltage.

2) Connect a digital voltmeter set on the 2-volt scale to the TPS connector. Connect the positive test lead to the TPS connector terminal "A". Connect the negative test lead to the TPS connector terminal "B". *See Fig. 3.*

3) Ensure the throttle is against the throttle stop screw. Check the TPS voltage. If the voltage is within .05-volts of specification, TPS position is okay.

TPS VOLTAGE SPECIFICATIONS

Reference Voltage	TPS Voltage
4.9V or less	.48V
4.9V-5.1V	.50V
5.1V-5.3V	.52V
5.3V or more	.54V

4) If voltage is not within specification, loosen TPS mounting screws. Position TPS until TPS voltage is in

specification. DO NOT use excessive force to adjust the TPS. Tighten mounting screws. Repeat steps **2)** and **3)**.

Fig. 3: Checking TPS Adjustment

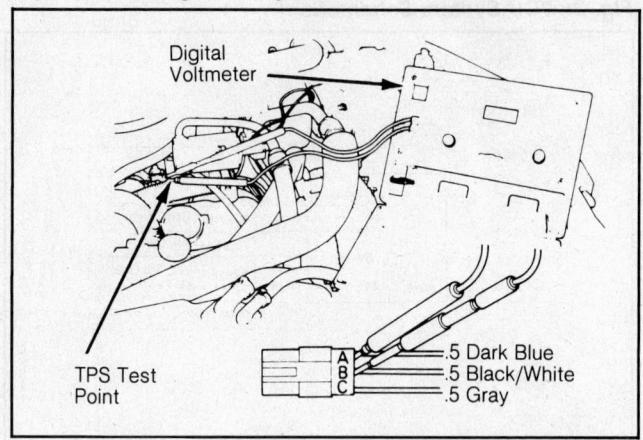

VCC DIAGNOSTIC CHARTS

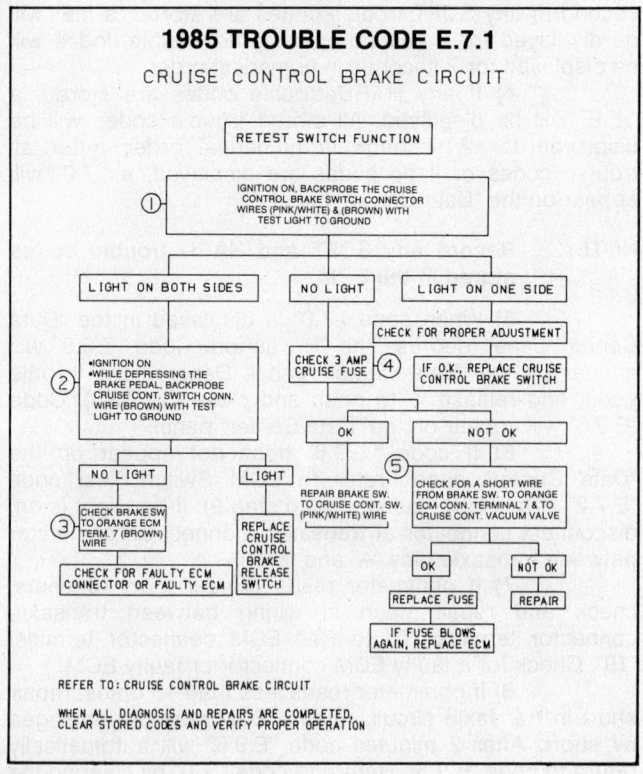

GENERAL MOTORS VISCOUS CONVERTER CLUTCH (Cont.)

1985 TROUBLE CODE E.7.2

THROTTLE SWITCH CIRCUIT

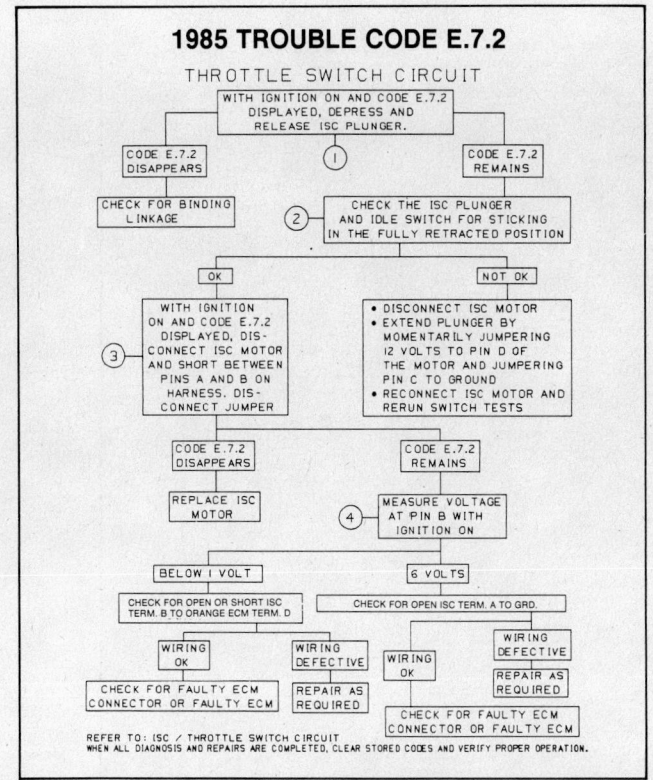

REFER TO: ISC / THROTTLE SWITCH CIRCUIT
WHEN ALL DIAGNOSIS AND REPAIRS ARE COMPLETED, CLEAR STORED CODES AND VERIFY PROPER OPERATION.

1985 TROUBLE CODE E.7.4

PARK/NEUTRAL SWITCH CIRCUIT

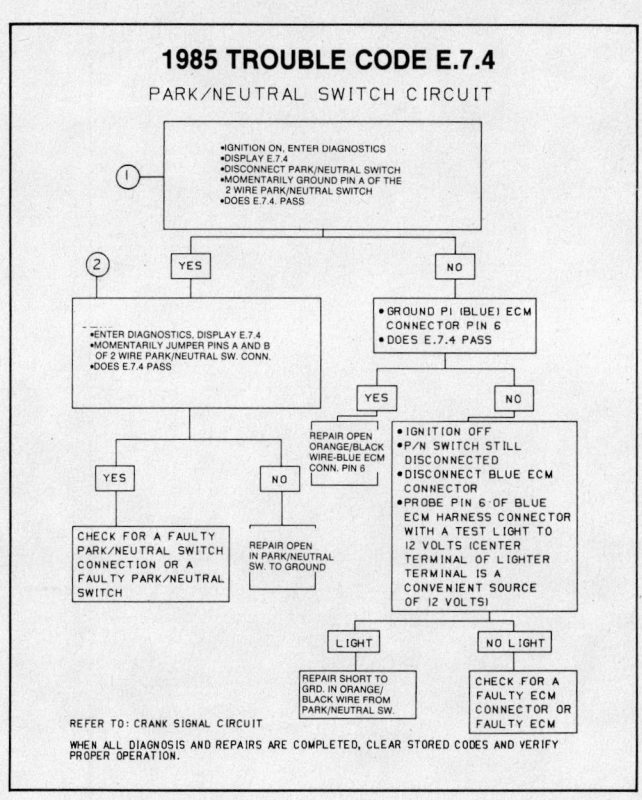

REFER TO: CRANK SIGNAL CIRCUIT
WHEN ALL DIAGNOSIS AND REPAIRS ARE COMPLETED, CLEAR STORED CODES AND VERIFY PROPER OPERATION.

1985 TROUBLE CODE E24

SPEED SENSOR CIRCUIT PROBLEM

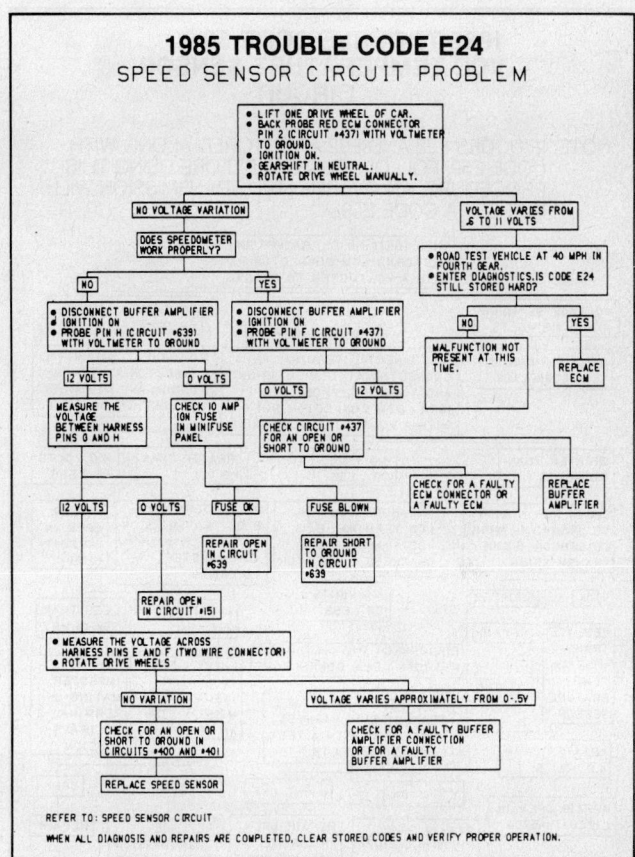

REFER TO: SPEED SENSOR CIRCUIT

WHEN ALL DIAGNOSIS AND REPAIRS ARE COMPLETED, CLEAR STORED CODES AND VERIFY PROPER OPERATION.

1985 TROUBLE CODE E28

OPEN 3RD OR 4TH GEAR CIRCUIT

NOTE: BEFORE FOLLOWING THIS PROCEDURE, REPAIR ANY OTHER HARD CODES.

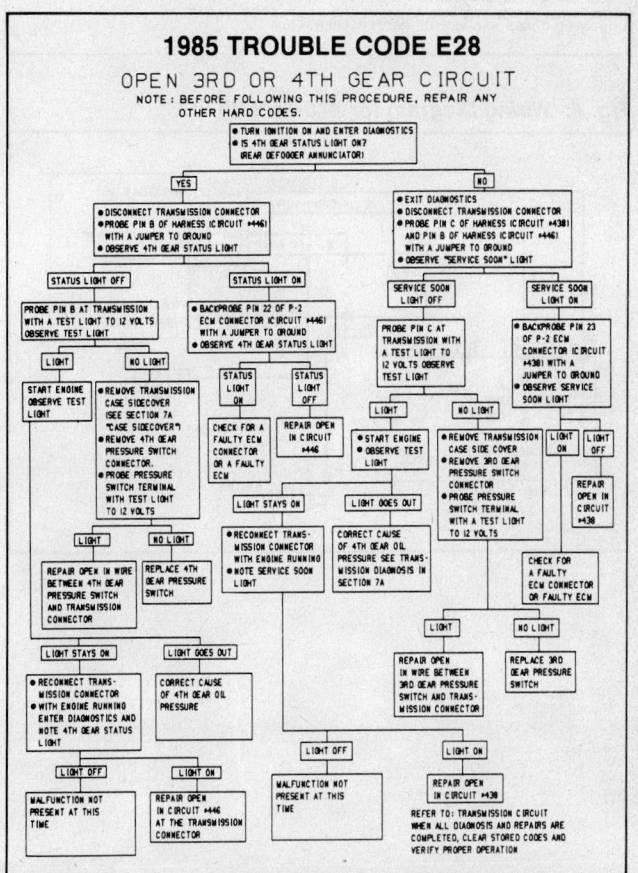

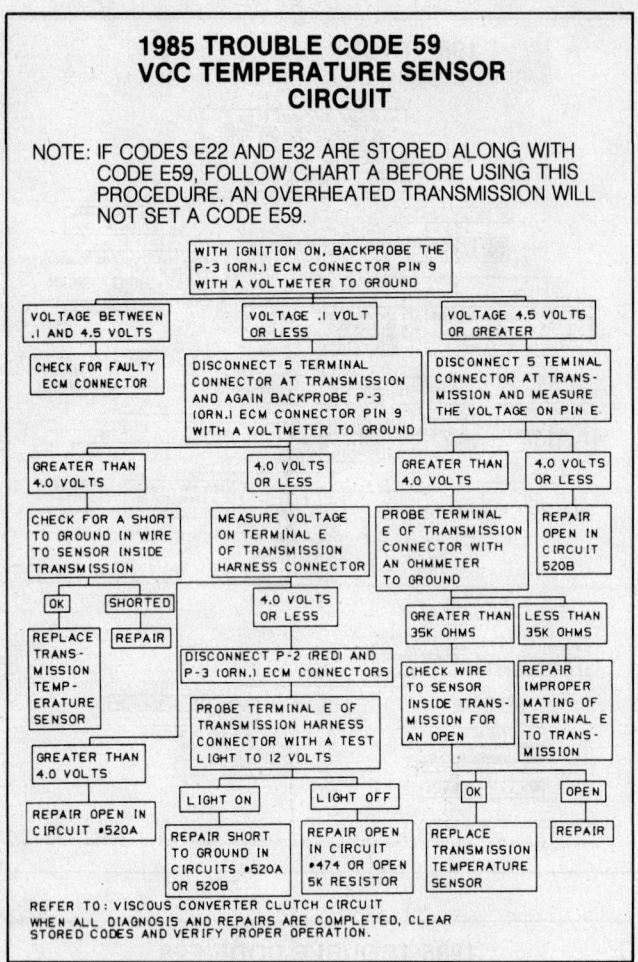

1985 TROUBLE CODE 59 VCC TEMPERATURE SENSOR CIRCUIT

NOTE: IF CODES E22 AND E32 ARE STORED ALONG WITH CODE E59, FOLLOW CHART A BEFORE USING THIS PROCEDURE. AN OVERHEATED TRANSMISSION WILL NOT SET A CODE E59.

Fig. 4: Wiring Diagram for 440-T4 With VCC

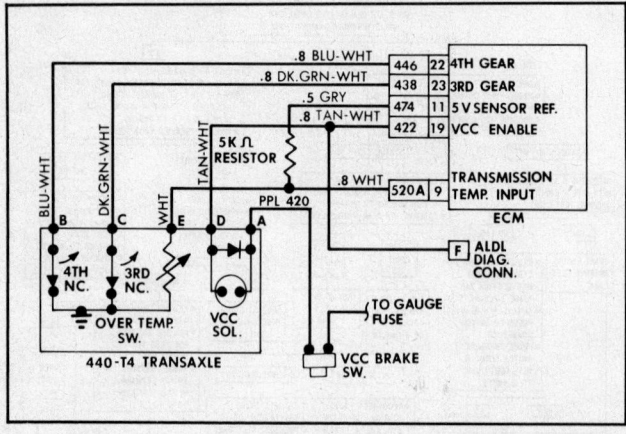

GENERAL MOTORS TURBO HYDRA-MATIC 125C TRANSAXLE

Buick
  Century, Skyhawk, Skylark
    Somerset Regal
Cadillac
  Cimmaron
Chevrolet
  Cavalier, Celebrity, Citation II
Oldsmobile
  Calais, Cutlass Ciera, Firenza
Pontiac
  Fiero, Grand Am, Sunbird, 6000

IDENTIFICATION

MODEL IDENTIFICATION

Models	Body Code
Celebrity, Century Cutlass Ciera, 6000	A
Cavalier, Cimarron Firenza, Skyhawk, Sunbird	J
Calais, Grand Am, Somerset Regal	N
Citation II, Skylark	X
Fiero	P

The transaxle Vehicle Identification Number (VIN) code is stamped on a machined pad located to the rear of the valve body cover and to the right of the dipstick tube. The transaxle model code is stamped on a machined pad located on the top center of the transaxle case.

TRANSAXLE CODES

Application	Code Letters
Buick	BF, BL, BP, CA, CB, CE CL, CT, CX, HS, OP, PD PE, PG, PJ, PN, PW,
Cadillac	CA, CB, CC, CI, CJ
Chevrolet	CA, CB, CC, CE, CI, CJ, CK CL, CT, CX, HS, HV, OP, PD PW, HW, H6, OP, PL, PW
Oldsmobile	BL, BF, BP, CA, CB, CJ, HS OP, PD, PE, PG, PN, PW, 5HJ
Pontiac	BP, CA, CB, CD, CL, CT, CU, HS OP, PD, PE, PF, PJ, PN, PW, 5PS

DESCRIPTION

The THM-125C transaxle combines a torque converter, fully automatic 3-speed transmission, final drive gearing and differential into a front wheel drive system (except RWD Fiero). The 4-element torque converter couples the engine crankshaft to the planetary gear set through a dual sprocket and drive link assembly.

The 4-element torque converter consists of a pump, a turbine, a pressure plate splined to the turbine and a stator assembly. The pressure plate, when applied, provides a mechanical direct drive coupling between the engine and the planetary gear set.

Three multi-disc clutches, a roller clutch and a single band provide the friction elements required to obtain the desired function of the planetary gear sets. The hydraulic system is pressurized by a vane-type pump which provides the working pressure required to operate the friction elements and automatic controls.

The differential is integral with the transmission. Power transfer to the differential is by direct mesh of final drive sun gear to final drive sun gear pinions, located in the differential housing. An internal gear, held stationary by the case, provides the pinion track that forces rotation of final drive assembly.

LUBRICATION & ADJUSTMENT

See appropriate AUTOMATIC TRANSMISSION SERVICING article in DOMESTIC GENERAL SERVICING section.

TROUBLE SHOOTING

See appropriate AUTOMATIC TRANSMISSION TROUBLE SHOOTING article in DOMESTIC GENERAL SERVICING section.

TESTING

ROAD TEST

"D" Range

1) With selector lever in "D" range, accelerate from a standstill. A 1-2 and 2-3 shift should occur at all throttle openings (shift points will vary depending upon throttle opening).

2) Check part throttle 3-2 downshift at 30 MPH by quickly opening throttle approximately 3/4. At 50 MPH, transmission should downshift 3-2 by depressing accelerator fully.

"2" Range

1) With selector lever in "2", accelerate vehicle from a standstill. A 1-2 shift should occur at all throttle openings (no 2-3 shift can be obtained in this range). The 1-2 shift point will vary with throttle opening.

2) At approximately 20 MPH move selector from "2" to "1", a 2-1 downshift should occur. The 1-2 shift in "2" range is normally somewhat firmer than in "D" range.

3) With selector lever in "D" range and vehicle speed at approximately 50 MPH, release accelerator and move selector lever to "2" range. A 3-2 downshift should occur accompanied by an increase in engine speed and an engine braking effect.

"1" Range

1) With selector lever in "1" range, accelerate vehicle from a standstill. No upshift should occur in this range. At 40 MPH in "2" range, with throttle closed, move selector lever to "1".

2) A 2-1 downshift should occur between approximately 25 to 45 MPH, depending on valve body calibration. A 2-1 downshift at closed throttle should be accompanied by increased engine speed and an engine braking effect.

Converter Clutch

Install a tachometer and bring engine to normal operating temperature. With vehicle speed between 40-45 MPH, in 3rd gear, converter clutch should apply. Observing tachometer, a drop of 200 RPM's will occur when clutch is applied.

Automatic Transmissions
GENERAL MOTORS TURBO HYDRA-MATIC 125C TRANSAXLE (Cont.)

Fig. 1: Exploded View of Transaxle Case and Related Components

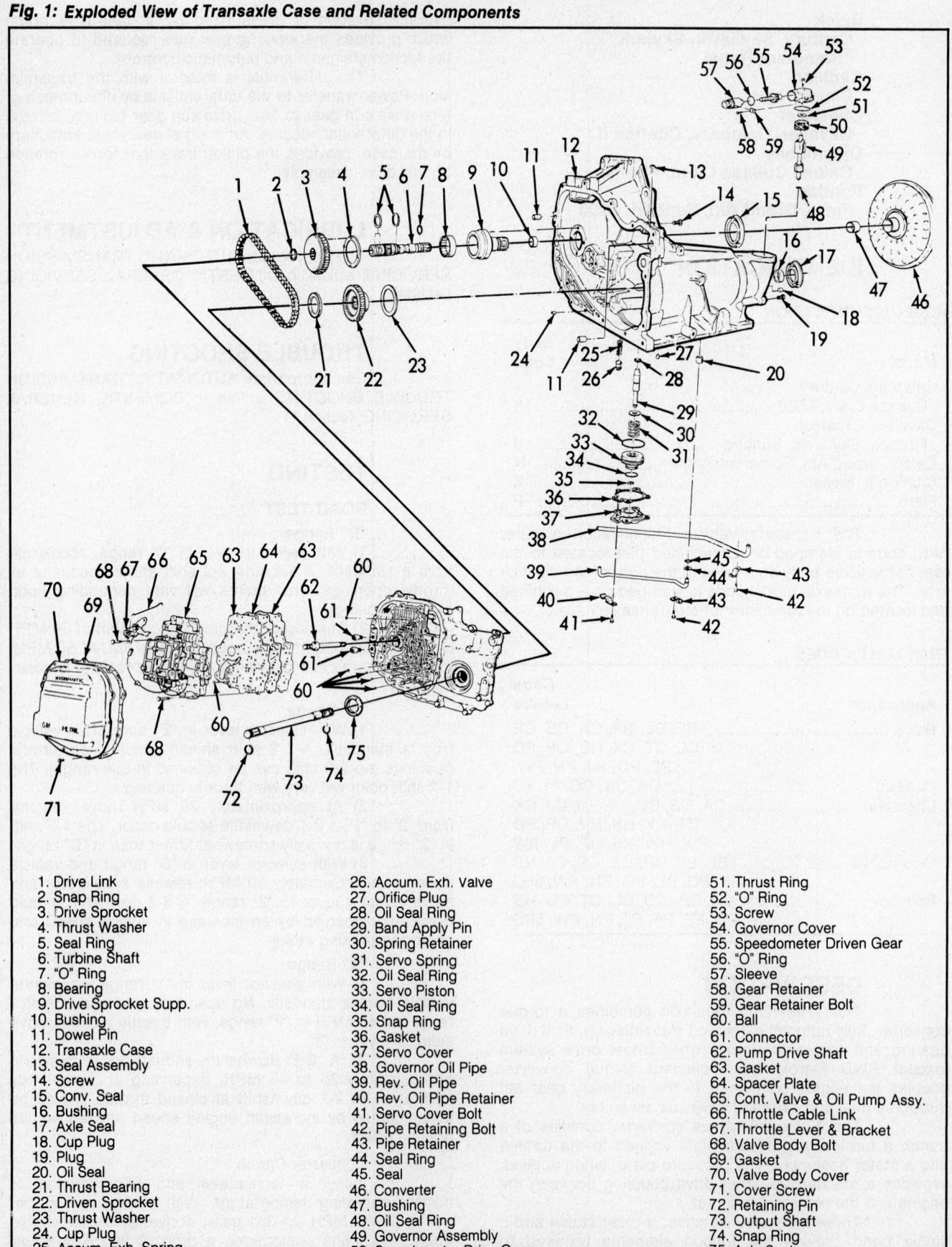

1. Drive Link	26. Accum. Exh. Valve	51. Thrust Ring
2. Snap Ring	27. Orifice Plug	52. "O" Ring
3. Drive Sprocket	28. Oil Seal Ring	53. Screw
4. Thrust Washer	29. Band Apply Pin	54. Governor Cover
5. Seal Ring	30. Spring Retainer	55. Speedometer Driven Gear
6. Turbine Shaft	31. Servo Spring	56. "O" Ring
7. "O" Ring	32. Oil Seal Ring	57. Sleeve
8. Bearing	33. Servo Piston	58. Gear Retainer
9. Drive Sprocket Supp.	34. Oil Seal Ring	59. Gear Retainer Bolt
10. Bushing	35. Snap Ring	60. Ball
11. Dowel Pin	36. Gasket	61. Connector
12. Transaxle Case	37. Servo Cover	62. Pump Drive Shaft
13. Seal Assembly	38. Governor Oil Pipe	63. Gasket
14. Screw	39. Rev. Oil Pipe	64. Spacer Plate
15. Conv. Seal	40. Rev. Oil Pipe Retainer	65. Cont. Valve & Oil Pump Assy.
16. Bushing	41. Servo Cover Bolt	66. Throttle Cable Link
17. Axle Seal	42. Pipe Retaining Bolt	67. Throttle Lever & Bracket
18. Cup Plug	43. Pipe Retainer	68. Valve Body Bolt
19. Plug	44. Seal Ring	69. Gasket
20. Oil Seal	45. Seal	70. Valve Body Cover
21. Thrust Bearing	46. Converter	71. Cover Screw
22. Driven Sprocket	47. Bushing	72. Retaining Pin
23. Thrust Washer	48. Oil Seal Ring	73. Output Shaft
24. Cup Plug	49. Governor Assembly	74. Snap Ring
25. Accum. Exh. Spring	50. Speedometer Drive Gear	75. Axle Seal

GENERAL MOTORS TURBO HYDRA-MATIC 125C TRANSAXLE (Cont.)

Fig. 2: Inside View of Case Cover Showing Oil Passages

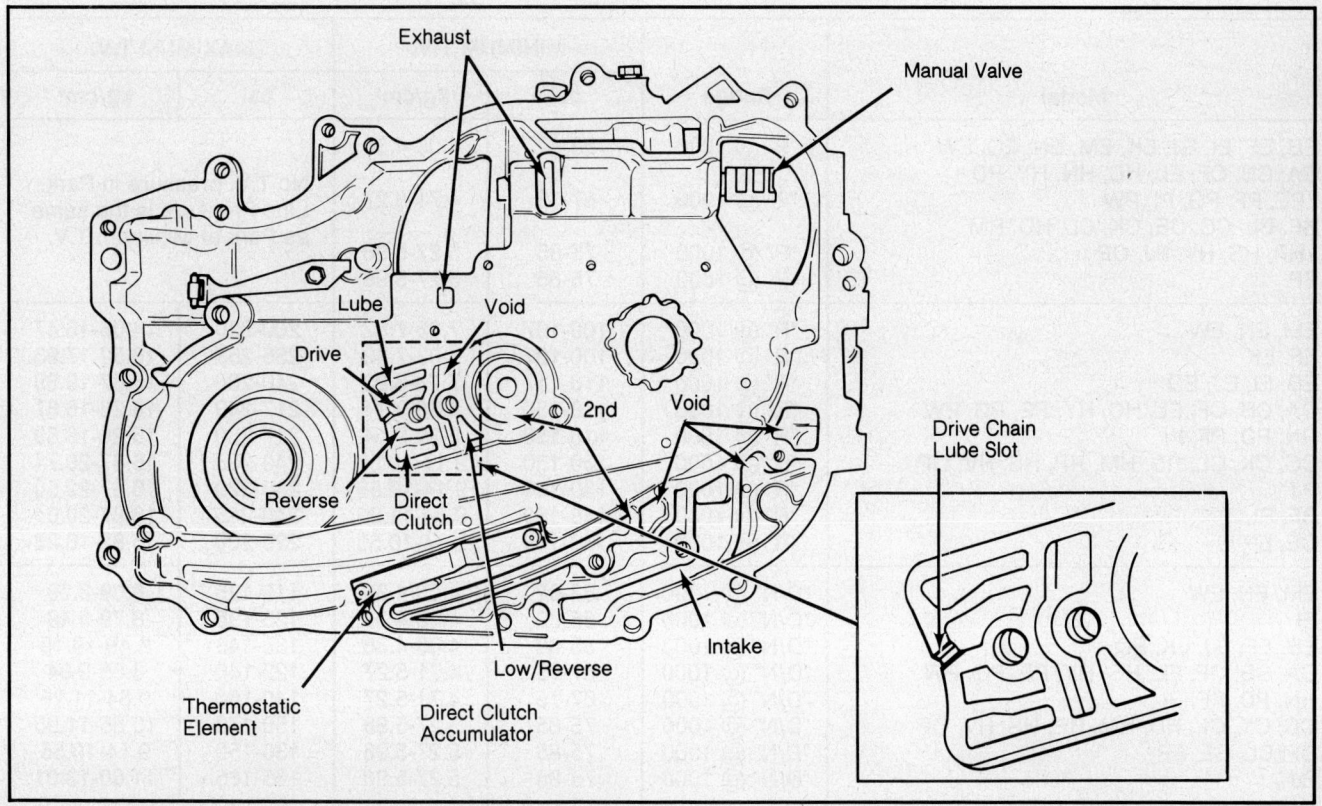

Fig. 3: Outside View of Case Cover Showing Oil Passages

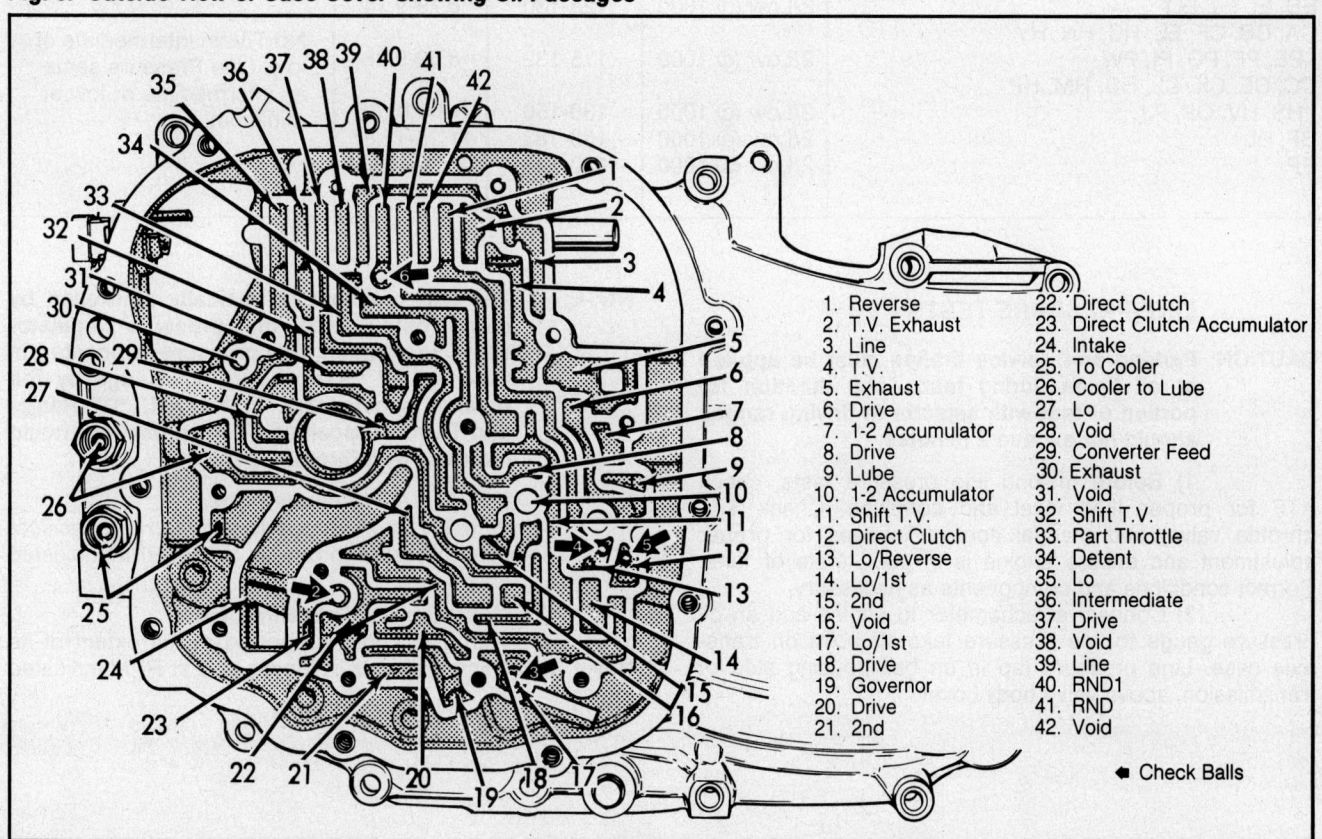

1. Reverse	22. Direct Clutch
2. T.V. Exhaust	23. Direct Clutch Accumulator
3. Line	24. Intake
4. T.V.	25. To Cooler
5. Exhaust	26. Cooler to Lube
6. Drive	27. Lo
7. 1-2 Accumulator	28. Void
8. Drive	29. Converter Feed
9. Lube	30. Exhaust
10. 1-2 Accumulator	31. Void
11. Shift T.V.	32. Shift T.V.
12. Direct Clutch	33. Part Throttle
13. Lo/Reverse	34. Detent
14. Lo/1st	35. Lo
15. 2nd	36. Intermediate
16. Void	37. Drive
17. Lo/1st	38. Void
18. Drive	39. Line
19. Governor	40. RND1
20. Drive	41. RND
21. 2nd	42. Void

◆ Check Balls

Automatic Transmissions
GENERAL MOTORS TURBO HYDRA-MATIC 125C TRANSAXLE (Cont.)

THROTTLE VALVE LINE PRESSURE CHECK

Model	Range	MINIMUM T.V.		MAXIMUM T.V.	
		psi	kg/cm²	psi	kg/cm²
EB, EF, EI, EJ, EK, EM, EN, EQ, EW	"P" @ 1000	58-62	4.08-4.36	No T.V. pressure in Park. Line Pressure is the same as Park at Minimum T.V.	
CA, CB, CF, EL, HC, HN, HY, PD PE, PF, PG, PI, PW	"P" @ 1000	67-75	4.71-5.27		
BF, BL, CC, CE, CK, CL, HD, HM HP, HS, HV, PJ, OP	"P" @ 1000	75-85	5.27-5.98		
EP	"P" @ 1000	75-85	5.27-5.98		
EM, EN, EW	"R" @ 1000	100-107	7.03-7.52	200-220	14.06-15.47
EF, EK	"R" @ 1000	100-107	7.03-7.52	235-255	16.52-17.93
EB, EI, EJ, EQ	"R" @ 1000	110-117	7.73-8.23	240-280	16.87-19.69
CA, CB, CF, EL, HC, HY, PE, PG, PW	"R" @ 1000	118-130	8.30-9.14	217-240	15.26-16.87
HN, PD, PF, PI	"R" @ 1000	118-130	8.30-9.14	217-280	15.26-19.69
CC, CK, CL, HD, HM, HP, HS, HV, OP	"R" @ 1000	130-150	9.14-10.55	240-295	16.87-20.74
PJ	"R" @ 1000	130-150	9.14-10.55	240-320	16.87-22.50
BF, BL	"R" @ 1000	140-160	9.84-11.25	240-285	16.87-20.04
CE, EP	"R" @ 1000	130-150	9.14-10.55	225-260	15.82-18.28
EM, EN, EW	"D/N" @ 1000	58-62	4.08-4.36	115-125	8.09-8.79
EI	"D/N" @ 1000	58-62	4.08-4.36	125-135	8.79-9.49
EB, EF, EJ, EK, EQ	"D/N" @ 1000	58-62	4.08-4.36	135-145	9.49-10.19
CA, CB, CF, EL, HC, HY, PE, PG, PW	"D/N" @ 1000	67-75	4.71-5.27	123-140	8.65-9.84
HN, PD, PF, PI	"D/N" @ 1000	67-75	4.71-5.27	140-160	9.84-11.25
CC, CK, CL, HD, HM, HP, HS, HV, OP	"D/N" @ 1000	75-85	5.27-5.98	150-170	10.55-11.95
BF, CL, CE, EP	"D/N" @ 1000	75-85	5.27-5.98	130-150	9.14-10.55
PJ	"D/N" @ 1000	75-85	5.27-5.98	165-185	11.60-13.01
EF, EK, EM, EN, EW	2/Low @ 1000	105-110	7.38-7.73	No T.V. in intermediate or low. Line Pressure same as intermediate or low at minimum.	
EB, EI, EJ, EQ	2/Low @ 1000	125-130	8.79-9.14		
CA, CB, CF, EL, HC, HN, HY PE, PF, PG, PI, PW	2/Low @ 1000	115-132	8.09-9.28		
CC, CE, CK, CL, HD, HM, HP HS, HV, OP, PJ	2/Low @ 1000	130-150	9.14-10.55		
BF, BL	2/Low @ 1000	160-183	11.25-12.87		
EP	2/Low @ 1000	130-150	9.14-10.55		

LINE PRESSURE TESTS

CAUTION: Parking and service brakes must be applied at all times during test. Total duration for portion of test with selector in driving ranges should not exceed 2 minutes.

1) Before making line pressure tests, check ATF for proper fluid level and condition. Check T.V. (throttle valve) and manual control linkages for proper adjustment and ensure engine is in good state of tune. Correct conditions and components as necessary.

2) Connect a tachometer to engine and an oil pressure gauge to line pressure take-off point on transaxle case. Line pressure tap is on bell housing side of transmission, above valve body cover.

NOTE: The line pressure is basically controlled by pump output and the pressure regulator valve. In addition, line pressure is boosted in Reverse, "2" Range and "1" Range by the reverse boost valve. In Neutral, "D" Range and Reverse positions, line pressure should increase with throttle opening.

Minimum T.V. Pressure Check
With T.V. cable properly adjusted to specifications, check line pressure in ranges and at RPM indicated on chart.

Maximum T.V. Pressure Check
With T.V. cable supported at full extent of its travel, check line pressure in ranges and at RPM indicated in chart.

GENERAL MOTORS TURBO HYDRA-MATIC 125C
TRANSAXLE (Cont.)

LINE PRESSURE TEST RESULTS

Line Pressure Too Low

1) Check for low fluid level. Check oil strainer "O" ring seal for leakage or damage and plugged oil strainer. If pressure is low in Neutral and Drive and low to normal in "2" and Reverse, the T.V. cable may be incorrect or out of adjustment. Inspect T.V. linkage for binding.

2) Inspect control valve and pump assembly for loose bolts or internal leaks. Check T.V. valve and plunger, shift T.V. valve, pressure regulator valve, T.V. boost valve and pressure relief valve for sticking in bore or damaged valves. Check for missing or off location No. 5 or 6 check ball.

3) Check 1-2 accumulator piston and/or seal for leaking or missing. For Low range only, check for damaged low blow-off valve and missing or off location No. 4 check ball. For Reverse only, inspect Low-Reverse clutch housing-to-case cup plug assembly for leaking.

4) Inspect oil pump for loose bolts and damaged or missing pump valve seals. Check intermediate oil passages to pressure regulator for blockage. Check driven sprocket support-to-case cover for leaks.

Line Pressure Too High

1) With pressure high in Neutral and Drive and normal to high in "2" and Reverse, check for broken, sticking or out of adjustment T.V. cable.

2) Inspect T.V. linkage for binding or incorrect cable. Check throttle valve or shift T.V. valve for sticking. Inspect T.V. lifter for bend, damage or too short condition.

3) Inspect components of control valve and pump assembly for sticking or damaged T.V. valve and plunger, shift T.V. valve, pressure regulator valve, T.V. boost valve and/or pump slide.

4) Check for worn or missing pressure regulator valve retaining pin. For Low only, check Low blow-off valve for sticking closed. Inspect internal pump or case cover for leaks.

SERVICE (IN VEHICLE)

The following components may be removed from transaxle without removing transaxle from vehicle: Throttle valve control cable with "O" ring, governor assembly, filler pipe with "O" ring, intermediate servo assembly with direct clutch accumulator check valve, Low-Reverse oil pipe/seal assembly and speedometer drive gear assembly.

The following may also be removed without removing transaxle: Oil pan with gasket/strainer assembly, control valve body assembly with cover, throttle lever with bracket, oil pump drive shaft, parking pawl and axle shafts.

For removal and installation procedures of components other than drive axles, see TRANSAXLE DISASSEMBLY and TRANSAXLE REASSEMBLY procedures in this article.

DRIVE AXLE SHAFTS

NOTE: Removal, Inspection and Installation procedures apply to either side drive axle assembly.

CAUTION: When either or both drive shaft ends are detached, DO NOT over-extend assembly or separation of internal components will result.

Description

There are two types of drive axle designs. The two designs both use the same type outer Constant Velocity (CV) joint. One design, for "X" model vehicles, uses a Double Offset inner joint. The other design, for "A", "J" and "P" models, uses a Tripod inner joint.

The drive axles are completely flexible assemblies consisting of an inner and outer joints connected by an axle shaft. The inner joint is completely flexible and has the capability of in and out movement. The outer joint is also flexible but cannot move in or out.

The right-hand inboard joint of the automatic transaxle incorporate a male spline and interlocks with the transaxle gear through the use of a barrel type snap ring. The left-hand inboard shaft attachment utilizes a female spline which installs over a stub shaft protruding from the transaxle. The drive shaft spline end which mates with the steering knuckle/hub assembly incorporates a slight helical spline to assure a tight press-type fit.

Removal (Except Fiero)

1) Remove hub nut with washer. Raise and support front of vehicle. Remove wheels and tires. Install Boot Seal Protectors (J-28712) for all outer CV joints, Boot

CLUTCH AND BAND APPLICATION CHART (ELEMENTS IN USE)

Selector Lever Position	Direct Clutch	Forward Clutch	Low & Reverse Clutch	Intermediate Band	Low Roller Clutch
D – Drive					
First Gear		X			X
Second Gear		X		X	
Third Gear	X	X			
2 – Intermediate					
First Gear		X			X
Second Gear		X		X	
1 – Low					
First Gear		X	X		X
R – Reverse	X		X		

NEUTRAL OR PARK – All clutches and bands released and/or ineffective.

Automatic Transmissions
GENERAL MOTORS TURBO HYDRA-MATIC 125C TRANSAXLE (Cont.)

Protectors (J-33162) for all Tripod inner joints and Boot Protectors (J-28712) for all Double Offset joints. *See Fig. 4.*

2) Remove brake caliper and rotor. Support caliper out of way. If necessary, mark strut-to-steering knuckle relation to insure proper camber alignment on reassembly. Remove strut-to-steering knuckle mount bolts/nuts. Separate strut from knuckle. If necessary, detach stabilizer bar/tie rod from steering knuckle/lower control arm.

3) Using slide hammer type puller with Adapter (J-28468 or J-33008 with J-29749), as shown in *Fig. 4*, pull drive axle from transaxle. Support drive axle end with wire. Using Puller (J-28733), separate axle shaft from spindle hub/bearing assembly. Remove drive axle for vehicle.

Fig. 4: Removing Drive Axles From Transaxle Assembly

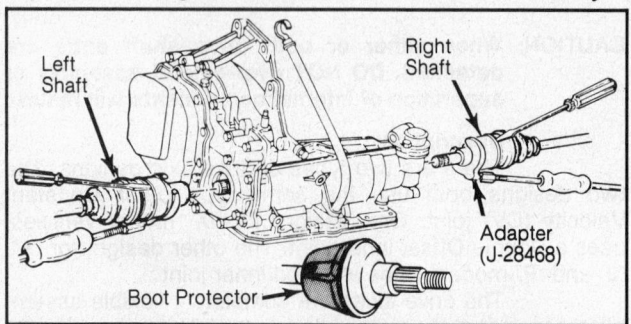

Do not damage drive axle boot seals during removal.

Disassembly (Except Fiero)

1) Procedure is similar for outer CV joints and inner Double Offset joints. *See Figs. 5 and 7.* For Tripod Joint disassembly, *See Fig. 6 and 8.* If equipped with rubber deflector ring, remove by pulling from groove of outer race and discard.

2) If equipped with steel deflector ring, remove by tapping off with brass drift. Using side cutters, cut seal retainer clamp on small end of seal and discard. Using brass drift, tap lightly around edge of seal retainer to remove retainer from CV joint assembly. Spread snap ring and pull shaft from joint assembly.

3) For outer CV joint, use brass drift to tap lightly on bearing cage until it tilts enough to remove one

ball bearing. Rotate cage and repeat procedure to remove remaining balls from cage.

4) To remove inner cage and race, pivot components until 90° to normal installed position is obtained (cage windows will align with lands of outer race). *See Fig. 7, No. 5.* Lift cage and inner race from outer race. Rotate inner race upward and out of cage.

5) On inner Double Offset joint, remove components as previously described. Remove ball race retaining ring. Balls will come out when cage and inner race are removed from outer race.

Inspection (Except Fiero)

1) Wash all parts in solvent and dry with compressed air. Inspect outer ball races for excessive wear and scoring. Inspect splined stub shaft for wear, cracks and twisted splines.

2) Inspect all 6 balls for pitting, cracking or scoring. Dulling of surface is normal. Inspect cage for excessive wear on inside and outside spherical surfaces. Look for heavy brinelling of cage windows. Check components for cracks or chips.

3) Inspect inner race for excessive wear or scoring. If any damage is found, replace entire CV or Double Offset joint assembly. Polished areas in races and on cage spheres are normal and do not require joint replacement.

Reassembly (Except Fiero)

1) Apply a light coat of grease on ball grooves of inner and outer races. Install inner race into cage using a rotating action opposite of removal. Inner race snap ring should face axle side.

2) On inner Double Offset joints, be sure ball bearing retaining ring is installed on inner race side facing small end of cage. Align windows of cage with outer race lands. Pivot cage with inner race into tilted position (opposite of removal).

3) Install ball bearings, one at a time, into outer CV joint as cage is tilted and rotated. On inner Double Offset joint, insert ball bearings through cage windows. After balls are installed into cage of outer joint, pivot cage and inner race into installed position.

4) Slide new seal clamp (for small end of boot seal), boot seal and seal retainer onto axle shaft. Coat inside lip (large diameter end) of seal with grease. Slide seal retainer on end of seal. Spread ears of bearing race

Fig. 5: Exploded View of Constant Velocity/Double Offset Joints For Drive Axle Assembly

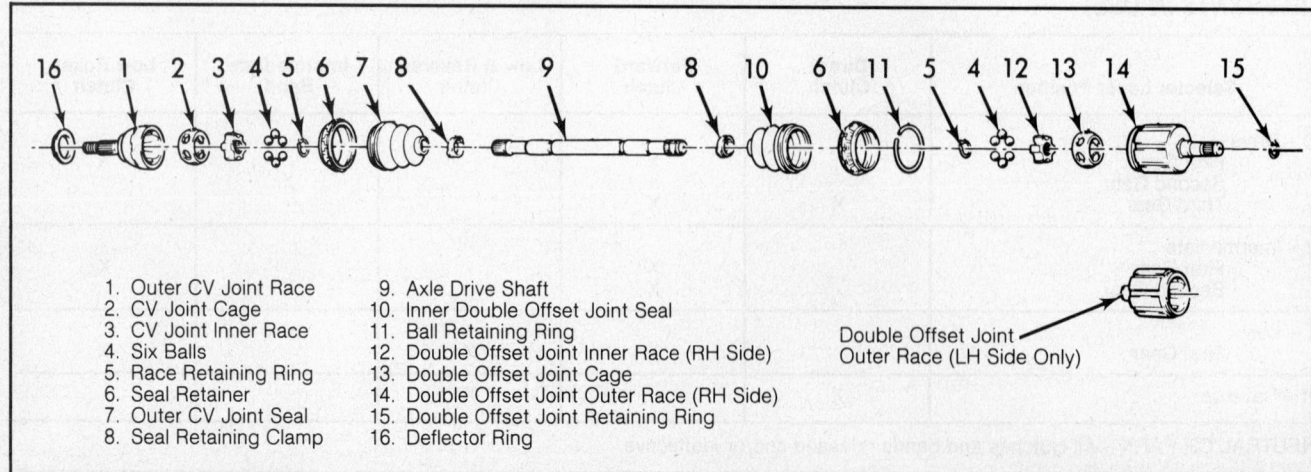

1. Outer CV Joint Race
2. CV Joint Cage
3. CV Joint Inner Race
4. Six Balls
5. Race Retaining Ring
6. Seal Retainer
7. Outer CV Joint Seal
8. Seal Retaining Clamp
9. Axle Drive Shaft
10. Inner Double Offset Joint Seal
11. Ball Retaining Ring
12. Double Offset Joint Inner Race (RH Side)
13. Double Offset Joint Cage
14. Double Offset Joint Outer Race (RH Side)
15. Double Offset Joint Retaining Ring
16. Deflector Ring

Double Offset Joint
Outer Race (LH Side Only)

GENERAL MOTORS TURBO HYDRA-MATIC 125C TRANSAXLE (Cont.)

Fig. 6: Exploded View of Constant Velocity/Tripod Joints For Drive Axle Assembly

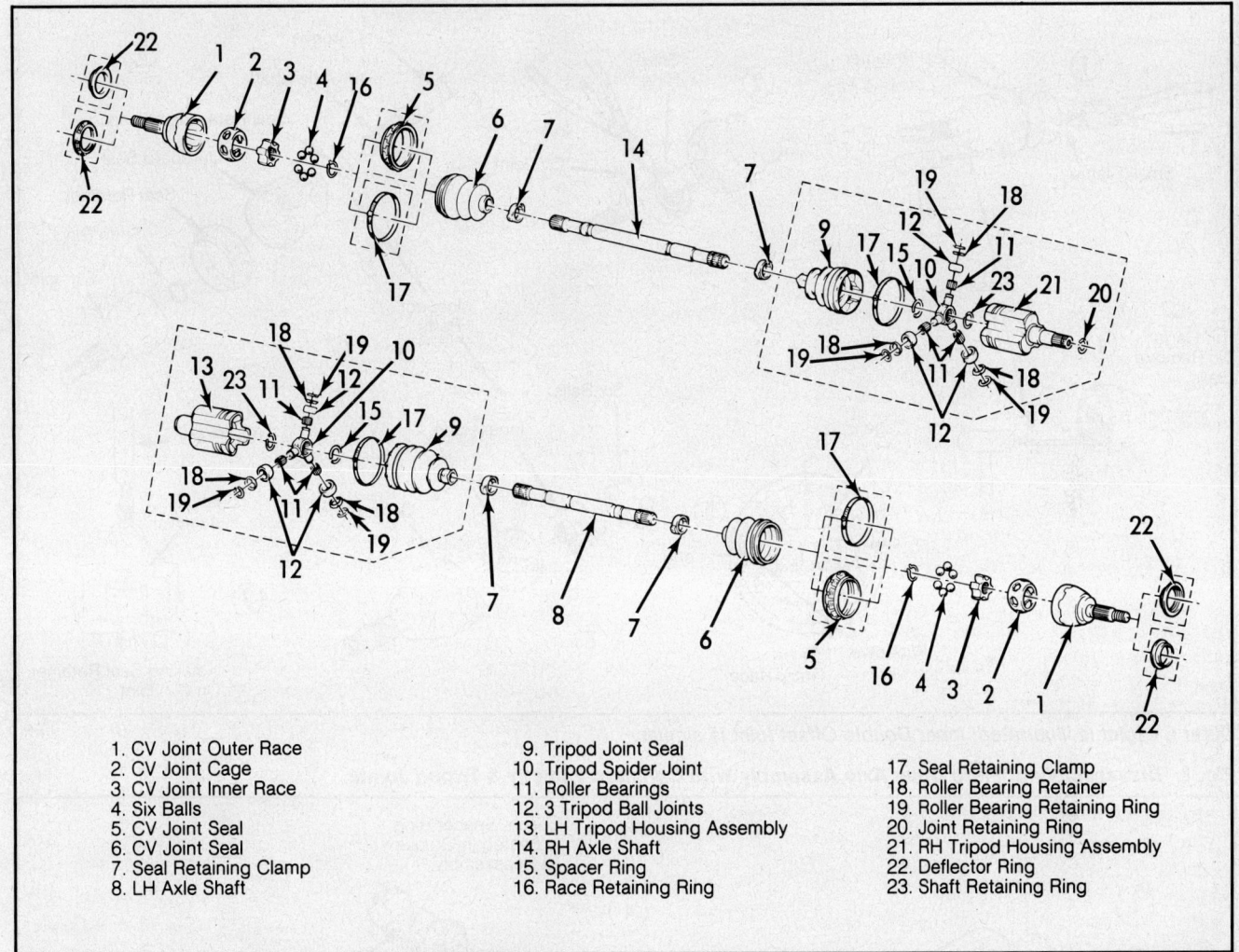

1. CV Joint Outer Race
2. CV Joint Cage
3. CV Joint Inner Race
4. Six Balls
5. CV Joint Seal
6. CV Joint Seal
7. Seal Retaining Clamp
8. LH Axle Shaft
9. Tripod Joint Seal
10. Tripod Spider Joint
11. Roller Bearings
12. 3 Tripod Ball Joints
13. LH Tripod Housing Assembly
14. RH Axle Shaft
15. Spacer Ring
16. Race Retaining Ring
17. Seal Retaining Clamp
18. Roller Bearing Retainer
19. Roller Bearing Retaining Ring
20. Joint Retaining Ring
21. RH Tripod Housing Assembly
22. Deflector Ring
23. Shaft Retaining Ring

snap ring and slide CV joint onto axle shaft until snap ring seats in groove.

5) Pack joint with approximately one-half grease provided in seal kit. Apply remaining grease inside seal. Slide seal toward joint until small end of seal is in groove in axle shaft. Position small clamp over small end of seal and into groove and tighten.

6) Place assembly vertically into an arbor press, with joint up so seal retainer is supported. *See Fig. 7, No. 7.* Press joint down onto retainer. Ensure seal stays on retainer during reassembly. If equipped, stretch rubber deflector ring and set in groove.

7) Install steel deflector ring using 2 1/2" pipe coupling over ring. Install a .118" (3 mm) sheet steel plate with .945" (24 mm) drilled hole (in center) over drive shaft end. Install nut on drive shaft end and tighten until ring seats in position.

Installation (Except Fiero)

1) Position drive axle loosely into steering knuckle and transaxle. Install steering knuckle onto strut bracket. Tighten strut bracket bolts finger tight only. Assemble stabilizer bar/tie rod as necessary.

2) Install rotor and brake caliper. Tighten mount bolts. Install drive axle through steering knuckle. Insert a drift in rotor slot to prevent hub from turning. Install new hub nut and tighten to 70 ft. lbs. (100 N.m).

3) Seat drive axle at transaxle using a screwdriver in groove provided on inner retainer. *See Fig. 4.* Tap screwdriver until shaft is seated. Install wheels and tires. Lower vehicle. Final tighten hub nut to 185-225 ft. lbs. (250-305 N.m).

Removal (Fiero)

1) Remove hub nut and discard. Raise and support vehicle. Remove rear wheels and tires. Install Drive Boot Seal Protectors (J-28712 and/or J-33162) on outer seal as necessary.

2) Remove tie link rod at knuckle assembly and parking brake cables at cradle. Detach brake line bracket at underbody (in inner wheel house opening). Using Hub Spindle Remover (J-28733), separate axle shaft from hub/bearing assembly.

NOTE: Support Tripod joint in up position when handling drive axle. If allowed to hang, weight of housing can separate it from spider bearing assembly.

3) With axle shaft supported, remove clamp bolt from lower control arm ball stud. Separate knuckle from lower control arm. Pull strut, knuckle and caliper assembly away from body and secure in this position.

Automatic Transmissions
GENERAL MOTORS TURBO HYDRA-MATIC 125C TRANSAXLE (Cont.)

Fig. 7: Disassembly of Drive Shaft Assembly With Double Offset & CV Joints

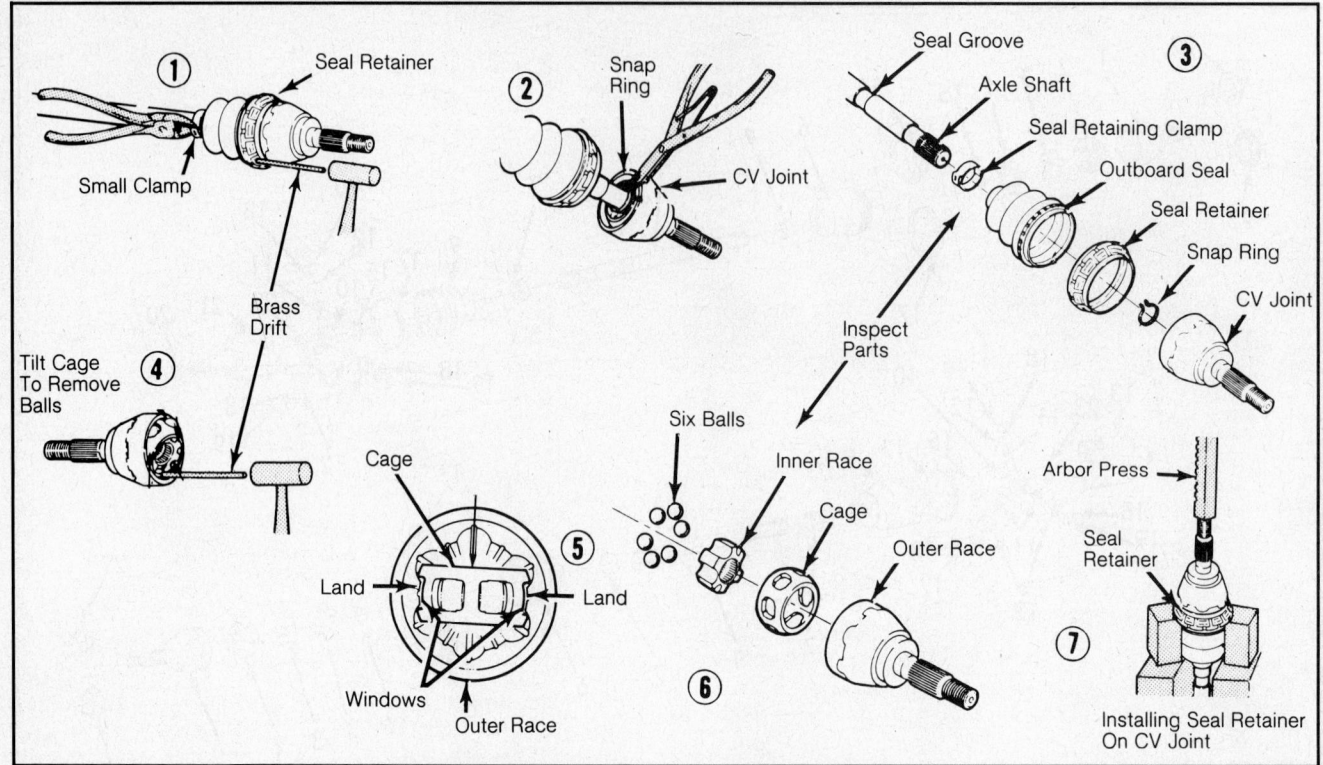

Outer CV joint is illustrated; inner Double Offset joint is similar.

Fig. 8: Disassembly of Fiero Drive Axle Assembly With Constant Velocity & Tripod Joints

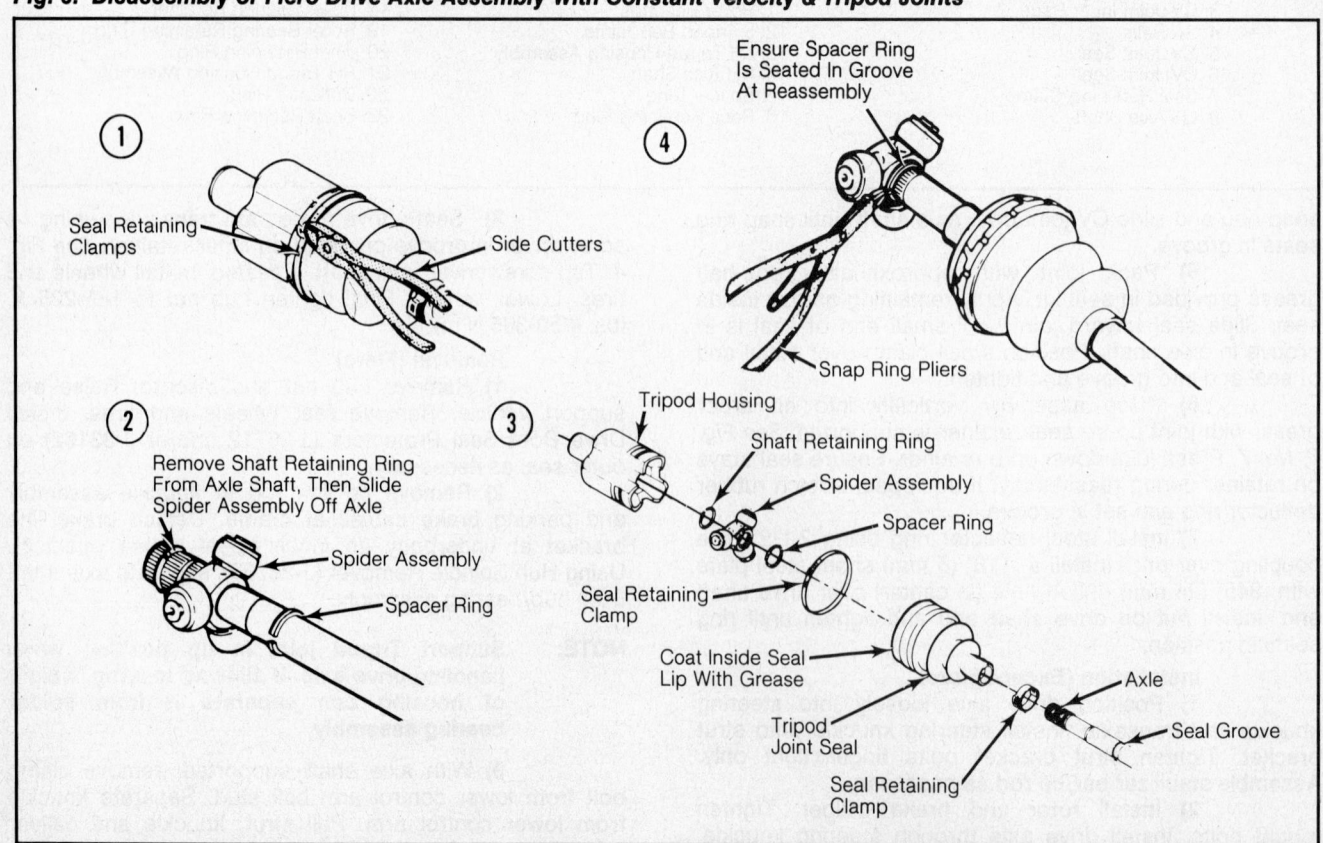

Slide the spider gear onto the drive axle with counter bore facing inner (transaxle) end of shaft.

4) Disengage snap ring retaining drive axle at transaxle. Using slide hammer and Adapter (J-33008), remove drive axle from transaxle assembly. DO NOT hold drive axle assembly vertically or joints will separate.

Disassembly (Fiero & All Tripod Joint Models)

1) Remove and disassemble outer CV joint as previously described. To remove inner Tripod joint, first detach seal retainer clamp by cutting it off of boot.

2) Using brass drift, tap lightly and evenly around seal retainer until loose. Remove retainer. Detach drive shaft retaining snap ring and slide spider assembly off drive axle. Remove spacer ring.

Inspection (Fiero & All Tripod Joint Models)

Inspect drive axle boot for tears or excessive wear. Check spider assembly for worn or damaged needle bearings. Inspect snap rings, spacer ring and drive shaft grooves for excessive wear. Replace components as necessary. If drive axle is replaced, install new knuckle seal.

Reassembly (Fiero & All Tripod Joint Models)

1) Flush grease from housing and repack with half of grease furnished with new seal. Apply remainder of grease to seal. Slide spacer ring on end of drive shaft. Ensure ring is seated in groove.

2) Slide spider gear onto axle with counter bore facing inner (transaxle) end of shaft. Install shaft retaining ring. Install inner and outer boot seal protectors.

Installation (Fiero)

1) Drive axle assembly into transaxle. Seat axle using screwdriver and groove provided on inner retainer. Install axle through hub at knuckle. Install seal boot clamps and tighten using Keystone Clamp Pliers (J-22610).

2) Remove boot protectors. Install and tighten lower control arm ball stud bolt to 33 ft. lbs. (45 N.m). Install toe link rod-to-knuckle assembly and tighten mount bolt to 35 ft. lbs. (47 N.m).

3) Install remaining components in reverse of disassembly procedure. Install and tighten new hub nut to 70 ft. lbs. (100 N.m). Install wheels and tires. Lower vehicle. Retighten hub nut to 185-225 ft. lbs. (250-305 N.m).

REMOVAL & INSTALLATION

TRANSAXLE

See appropriate AUTOMATIC TRANSMISSION REMOVAL article in DOMESTIC GENERAL SERVICING section.

TORQUE CONVERTER

NOTE: Torque converter is a sealed unit and cannot be disassembled for service or repair.

LEAKAGE CHECK

1) Install Pressure Tester (J-21369-B) into converter hub. Tighten hex nut on tool to expand it. Ensure safety strap is installed to prevent tool from blowing out when air pressure is applied. See Fig. 9. Apply 80 psi (5.6 kg/cm²) air pressure to air valve in tool. Submerge converter in water and check for air bubbles in water indicating leaks.

Fig. 9: Installing Torque Converter Leakage Tester

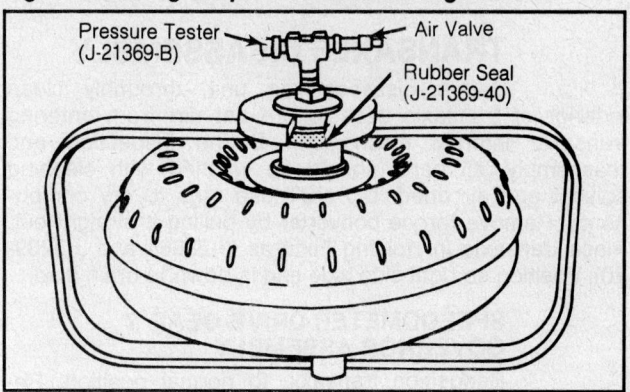

Pressure Tester (J-21369-B)
Air Valve
Rubber Seal (J-21369-40)

Apply 80 psi (5.6 kg/cm²) air pressure to air valve.

CAUTION: After leak checking converter, bleed air pressure from test tool before removing tool from converter hub.

2) With leakage tester removed, inspect converter hub surfaces for signs of scoring or wear. Check converter bushing for damage, cracks or scoring. If any components are excessively worn or damaged, replace torque converter assembly.

END CLEARANCE CHECK

1) Install collet end of End Clearance Checker (J-28538) into converter hub and hand tighten counterclockwise. Mount dial indicator onto hub of tool collet so dial indicator plunger rests on converter.

2) Zero dial indicator. Lift up on tool and read clearance at dial indicator. Converter end clearance should be 0-.050" (0-1.27 mm). If clearance is greater than .050" (1.27 mm), replace torque converter assembly.

Fig. 10: Measuring Torque Converter End Play

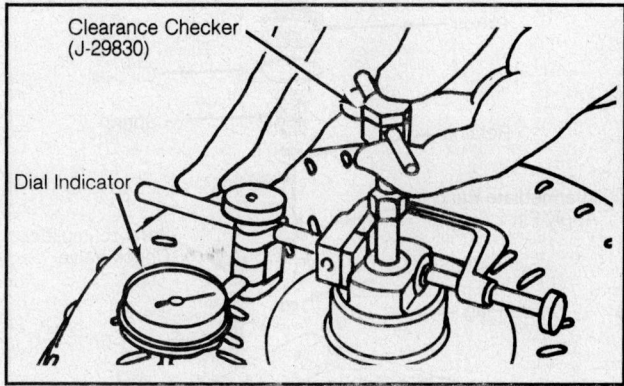

Clearance Checker (J-29830)
Dial Indicator

The converter end play must not exceed .050" (1.27 mm).

3) When replacing torque converter, ensure converter is installed fully toward rear of transaxle. Ensure converter is installed so that there is at least .50" (13 mm) between engine mounting face of case and front face of converter cover lugs.

GENERAL MOTORS TURBO HYDRA-MATIC 125C TRANSAXLE (Cont.)

NOTE: After end play and leakage tests, check torque converter stator assembly for freewheeling in both directions or assembly remains locked up at all times. Replace converter assembly if either condition exists.

TRANSAXLE DISASSEMBLY

Before disassembling unit, throughly clean exterior of transaxle case to prevent dirt from entering transaxle internal mechanism. During inspection and reassembly, all parts should be washed with cleaning solvent and air dried. DO NOT use rags to dry components. Remove torque converter by pulling it straight out. Place transaxle in Holding Fixtures (J-28664 and J-3289-20). Position so right side axle end is down to drain fluid.

SPEEDOMETER DRIVE GEAR & GOVERNOR ASSEMBLY

Reposition transaxle to normal position. Remove speedometer driven gear mount bolt with retainer. Withdraw driven gear assembly from governor cover. Remove governor cover bolts and lift off cover with "O" ring. Lift out governor and speedometer drive gear as an assembly.

INTERMEDIATE SERVO ASSEMBLY

1) Position transaxle so oil pan is up. Remove oil pan, gasket and oil strainer assembly from lower case assembly. Remove and discard oil strainer "O" ring.

2) Remove bolt holding reverse oil pipe retaining bracket to servo cover. Remove remaining servo cover bolts. Lift off servo cover and gasket. Withdraw intermediate servo assembly. *See Fig. 11.*

Fig. 11: Removing Intermediate Servo Assembly

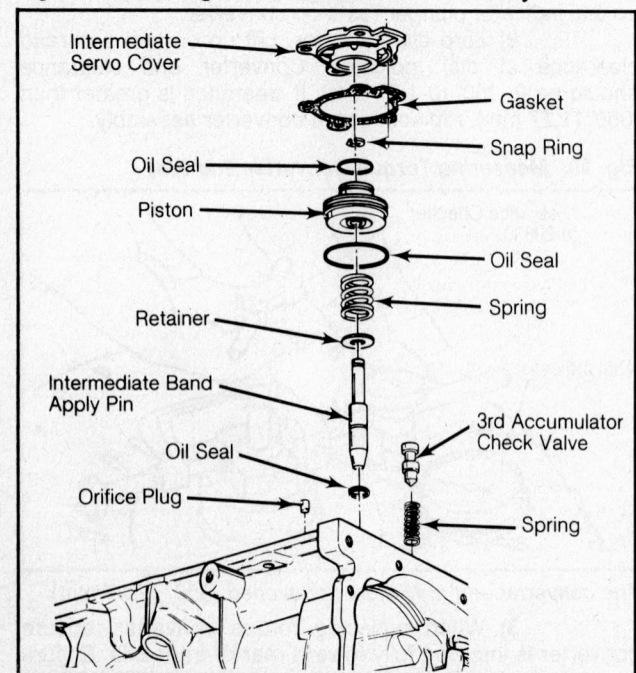

Do not remove the servo piston "O" ring seals unless replacement is necessary.

3) If necessary, detach "E" clip and remove intermediate band apply pin from intermediate servo piston. Discard "O" ring seals. Remove 3rd accumulator check valve and spring. *See Fig. 12.*

Fig. 12: Removing 3rd Accumulator Check Valve & Spring

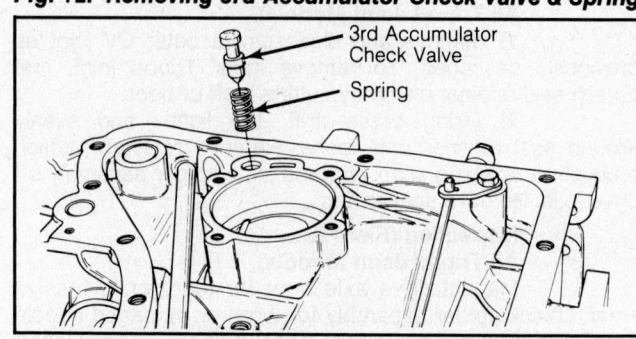

Inspect spring and check valve for wear or damage.

NOTE: Make intermediate band apply pin selection check at this time to determine correct pin to use during reassembly.

Band Apply Pin Selection Check

1) Install Intermediate Band Apply Pin Gauge (J-28535) over intermediate servo bore. Retain with 2 servo cover bolts. Remove band apply pin from intermediate servo assembly.

2) Install Band Apply Ain Gauge Extension (J-28535-4) onto servo piston end of band apply pin. Install band apply pin and gauge extension into gauge on servo bore. *See Fig. 13.*

Fig. 13: Checking for Proper Band Apply Pin

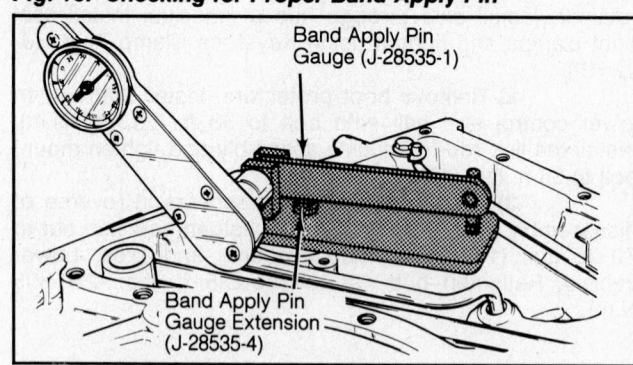

Ensure the White line on gauge extension appears in the window of gauge or different length pin will be needed.

3) Apply 100 INCH lbs. (11.2 N.m) of torque to hex nut on selection gauge to compress band. White line, on gauge extension, should appear in window on selection gauge to indicate proper pin installed.

4) If White line cannot be seen, change band apply pin (longer or shorter as necessary) and recheck. See INTERMEDIATE BAND APPLY PIN table. With proper apply pin selected, remove gauge. Install new seals, assemble and install components in reverse of removal procedure.

GENERAL MOTORS TURBO HYDRA-MATIC 125C TRANSAXLE (Cont.)

INTERMEDIATE BAND APPLY PIN

Length	Identification
Short	2 Grooves
Medium	1 Groove
Long	No Grooves

OUTPUT SHAFT & LOW-REVERSE SEAL

1) With oil pan, gasket, strainer assembly, reverse oil pipe bracket, intermediate servo assembly and 3rd accumulator check valve (with spring) removed, detach Low-Reverse oil pipe, oil pipe seal back-up washer and "O" ring seal.

2) Grind approximately .75" (20 mm) from end of a No. 4 screw extractor. Insert ground end into Low-Reverse cup plug. DO NOT hammer or force screw extractor into cup plug. Carefully twist screw extractor to remove cup plug. See Fig. 14.

Fig. 14: Removing Low-Reverse Cup Plug Assembly

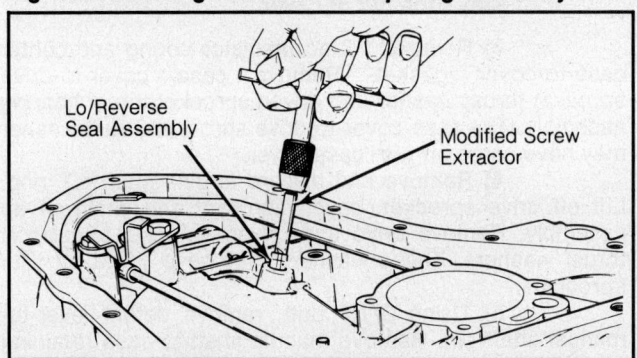

Lo/Reverse Seal Assembly

Modified Screw Extractor

DO NOT hammer or force screw extractor into cup plug.

3) Remove dipstick stop and parking lock bracket from above parking pawl and parking pawl actuator rod. Rotate final drive unit until open ends of output shaft retaining "C" ring are visible through access window of differential carrier.

4) Using output shaft "C" Ring Remover (J-28583), push both ends of retaining "C" ring down to partially dislodge from output shaft. Rotate output shaft/final drive until retaining "C" ring is visible through access window.

5) Carefully remove retaining "C" ring by pulling it up and out using needle nose pliers, then discard retaining ring. Remove output shaft.

CONTROL VALVE BODY & OIL PUMP ASSEMBLY

1) Rotate transaxle so that control valve body oil pan is up. Detach mount bolts. Tap pan edge with rubber mallet to loosen control valve cover and gasket. DO NOT pry on cover during removal, damage to pan flange or case will occur.

2) Remove 2 bolts securing throttle lever and bracket assembly to control valve. Lift off throttle lever and bracket assembly with throttle valve cable link. Use care not to bend link.

3) Remove the auxiliary valve body screws EXCEPT for the lower left screw. See Fig. 15. Remove remaining control valve assembly bolts. Carefully lift off control valve and pump assembly. Place on bench with machined surface up.

Fig. 15: Removing Control Valve & Pump Assembly Bolts

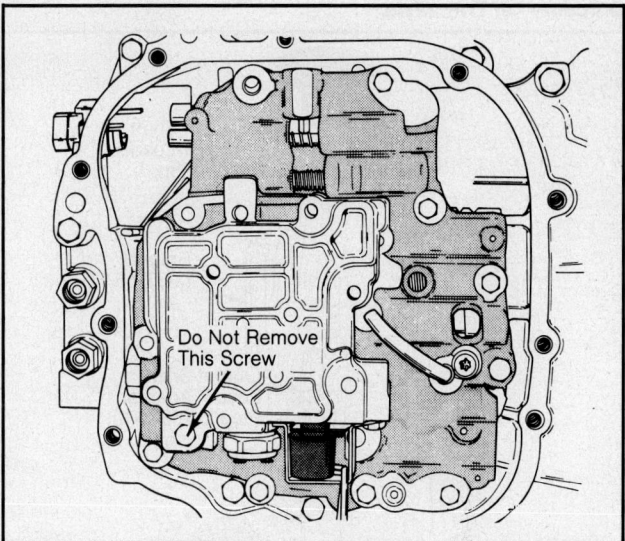

Do Not Remove This Screw

DO NOT remove lower left bolt from control valve and pump assembly unless auxiliary valve body removal is necessary.

4) Remove No. 1 check ball from direct clutch passage on spacer plate. Lift out oil pump drive shaft. Carefully remove spacer plate and spacer plate gaskets. Remove the 5 check balls from case cover. See Fig. 16.

Fig. 16: Check Ball Locations in Case Cover

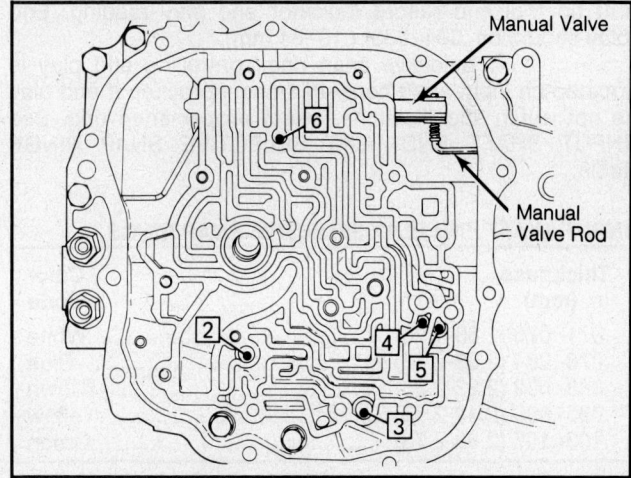

Manual Valve

Manual Valve Rod

The No. 1 check ball is located in the direct clutch passage on the spacer plate.

NOTE: Before proceeding with transaxle disassembly, input shaft-to-case cover end play must be checked to determine proper selective snap ring to install during reassembly.

Input Shaft-to-Case Cover End Play

1) Rotate transaxle assembly until right axle end is up. Install Output Shaft Loader Adapter Plug (J-26958-10) into right side axle end. Mount Output Shaft Aligner/Loader (J-26958) and Bracket (J-26958-11) to right side axle end of case as shown in Fig. 17.

Fig. 17: Positioning Output Shaft Aligner & Loader on Transaxle.

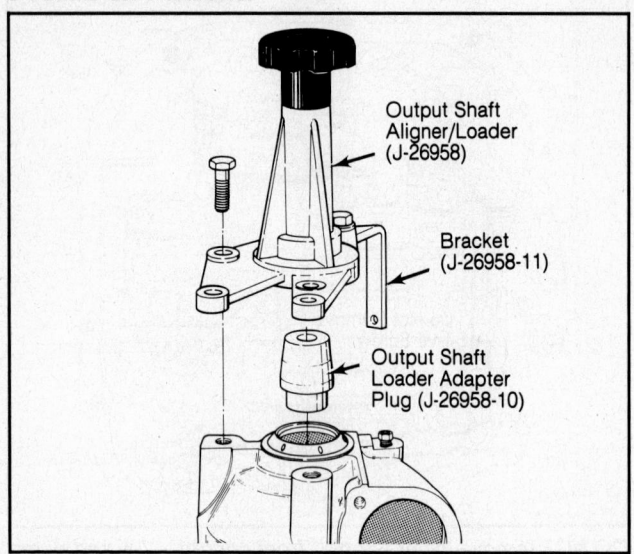

Adjust the loader to the correct load by turning the handle until the knob bottoms.

2) Install Input Shaft Lifter (J-28544) into input shaft bore and tighten by turning handle clockwise. Install dial indicator with Extension Post (J-25025-7), placing indicator plunger on end of lifter.

3) Press down on lifter and zero dial indicator. Lift up tool and record indicator end play reading. End play should be .004-.033" (.10-.84 mm).

4) Selective snap ring controlling end play is located on input shaft beneath driven sprocket. If end play is not within specifications, select proper snap ring. See INPUT SHAFT END PLAY SELECTIVE SNAP RINGS table.

INPUT SHAFT END PLAY SELECTIVE SNAP RINGS

Thickness In. (mm)	Color Code
.071-.076 (1.83-1.93)	White
.078-.084 (2.03-2.13)	Blue
.088-.092 (2.23-2.33)	Brown
.095-.099 (2.43-2.53)	Yellow
.103-.107 (2.63-2.73)	Green

CAUTION: Oil soaked snap rings may tend to discolor. Measure snap ring for its actual thickness and replace as necessary.

TRANSMISSION CASE COVER & INPUT UNIT ASSEMBLY

1) Disconnect manual valve rod from manual valve. *See Fig. 16.* Remove remaining transmission case cover mount bolts. Install two M12 X 1.75 X 50 bolts into case cover dowel pin holes. *See Fig. 18.*

2) The bolts will self-tap, bottom out on dowel pins and separate case cover from case. DO NOT pry cover from case or damage to machined surfaces will result. Remove case cover.

Fig. 18: Removing Transmission Case Cover from Case

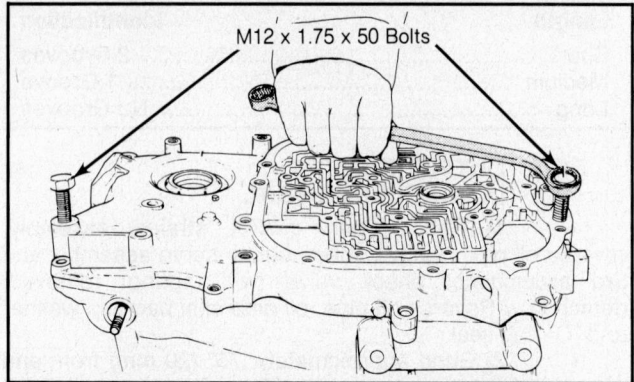

Bolts installed in cover dowel pin holes will self tap, bottom out on dowel pins and separate cover from case.

NOTE: When removed, lay case cover with 1-2 accumulator side up or 1-2 accumulator pin may drop out of cover.

3) Remove 1-2 accumulator spring and center case-to-cover gasket. Remove case cover-to-drive sprocket thrust washer and driven sprocket thrust bearing assembly. The case cover-to-drive sprocket thrust washer may have come off with case cover.

4) Remove and discard turbine shaft "O" ring. Lift off drive sprocket, driven sprocket and chain as an assembly. Remove drive and driven sprocket-to-support thrust washers. These washers may have come off with sprockets.

5) Using 3/16" drift, remove detent lever-to-manual shaft pin. Remove manual shaft-to-case retaining pin. Withdraw manual shaft from case and lift out manual valve rod and detent lever assembly. Remove park lock actuator rod.

6) Remove driven sprocket support and thrust washer. *See Fig. 19.* Thrust washer may come out with driven sprocket support. Remove intermediate band anchor hole plug and intermediate band assembly.

Fig. 19: Removing Manual Shaft & Driven Sprocket Support Assembly

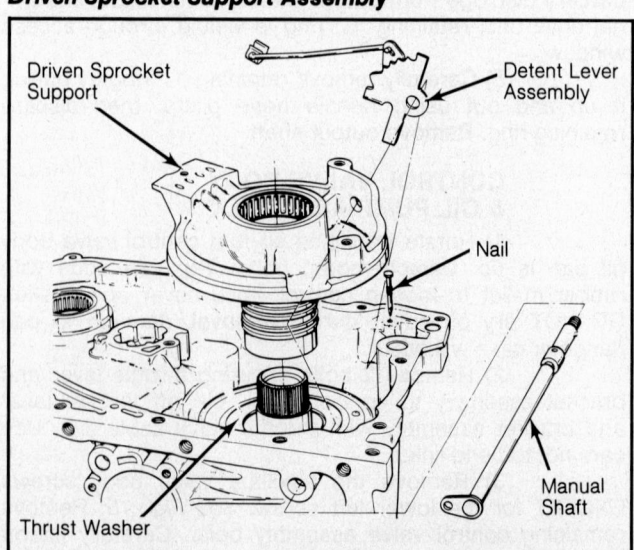

GENERAL MOTORS TURBO HYDRA-MATIC 125C TRANSAXLE (Cont.)

7) While lifting up on input shaft, remove direct and forward clutch assemblies. Separate direct and forward clutch assemblies. Remove input internal gear-to-input shaft thrust washer. Remove input internal gear.

8) Remove input carrier assembly, input carrier-to-input internal gear thrust washer and input carrier-to-input sun gear thrust washer. Remove input sun gear and input drum.

REACTION UNIT

NOTE: Before proceeding with disassembly of reaction unit parts, reaction sun gear-to-input drum selective snap ring and Reverse clutch housing-to-Low race selective thrust washer end play measurements should be taken to determine correct snap ring and thrust washer to install during reassembly.

Reaction Sun Gear-to-Input Drum End Play

1) Install Output Shaft Aligner/Loader (J-26958) in fully loaded position. Install Reaction Sun Gear Snap Ring Gauge (J-28588) to case using 2 case cover bolts. Position gauge extension between open ends of selective snap ring.

2) Press reaction sun gear down to make sure it is seated. Install a dial indicator onto Extension Post (J-25025-7). Position feeler gauge beneath shoulder of gauge extension. Zero dial indicator.

3) Rotate selective snap ring under gauge extension. Swing feeler gauge from beneath extension while checking full range of indicator needle movement. Reading should be +.013 to -.005" (+.33 to -.13 mm) when measured from zero reference point.

4) The selective snap ring controlling this end play is located on reaction sun gear shaft. Measure thickness of snap ring for proper identification. To select proper snap ring to be installed, see REACTION SUN GEAR-TO-INPUT DRUM SNAP RING SELECTION table.

REACTION SUN GEAR-TO-INPUT DRUM SNAP RING SELECTION

Thickness In. (mm)	Color Code
.089-.093 (2.27-2.36)	Pink
.096-.100 (2.44-2.54)	Brown
.103-.107 (2.61-2.71)	Lt. Blue
.109-.113 (2.78-2.88)	White
.116-.120 (2.95-3.05)	Yellow
.123-.127 (3.12-3.22)	Lt. Green
.129-.133 (3.29-3.39)	Orange
.136-.140 (3.46-3.56)	No Color

Low-Reverse Clutch Housing-to-Low Roller Clutch Race Thrust Washer End Play

1) With dial indicator and output shaft aligner-/loader installed as it was for measurement of reaction sun gear-to-input drum snap ring, press down reaction sun gear to ensure it is seated. Zero dial indicator.

2) Insert screwdriver through parking pawl case opening next to parking pawl. Lift reaction internal gear to check Low-Reverse clutch selective end play. Read resulting end play. DO NOT rest screwdriver on spacer in parking pawl case opening when prying reaction internal gear. Spacer damage will result. See Fig. 20.

Fig. 20: Checking Low-Reverse Clutch Housing-to-Low Roller Clutch Race Thrust Washer End Play

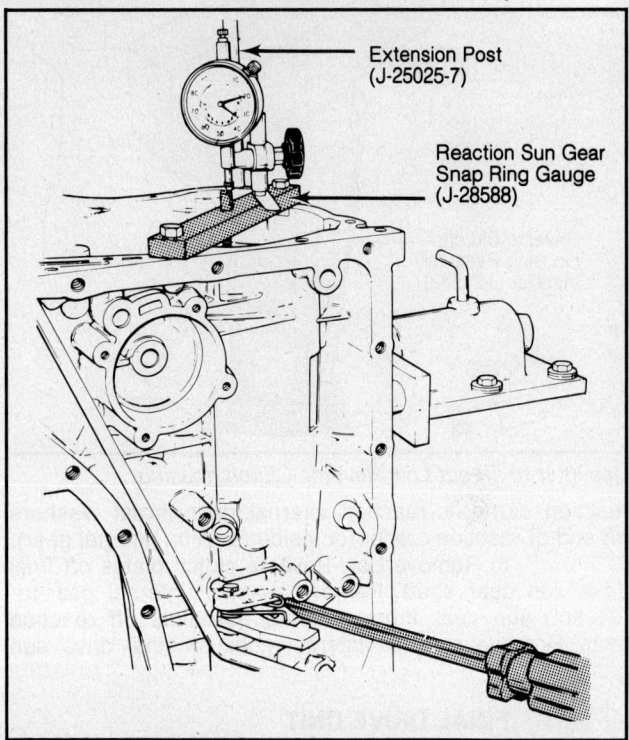

DO NOT rest screwdriver on spacer in parking pawl case opening when prying reaction internal gear.

3) End play should be .003-.046" (.08-1.17 mm). The selective washer controlling this end play is located between Low-Reverse clutch housing and low roller clutch assembly. Select proper thrust washer. See REVERSE CLUTCH HOUSING-TO-LOW RACE WASHER table.

REVERSE CLUTCH HOUSING-TO-LOW RACE WASHER

Thickness In. (mm)	Identification Code
.039-.043 (1.00-2.20)	1
.056-.060 (1.42-1.52)	2
.072-.076 (1.84-1.94)	3
.089-.093 (2.26-2.36)	4
.105-.109 (2.68-2.78)	5
.122-.126 (3.10-3.20)	6

4) Remove dial indicator, gauge and output shaft loading/aligning tool. Leave output shaft loader adapter in place for use when final drive-to-case end play is measured.

5) Remove reaction sun gear. Sun gear will lift straight out. Remove Low-Reverse clutch housing-to-case snap ring. Snap ring is .092" (2.36 mm) thick. Using Low-Reverse Clutch Housing Remover/Installer (J-28542), lift out Low-Reverse Clutch housing. See Fig. 21.

6) Remove Low-Reverse clutch housing-to-case spacer ring from groove in case. Spacer ring is .042" (1.07 mm) thick. Lift out final drive sun gear shaft and reaction gear set as an assembly.

7) Remove roller clutch and reaction carrier assembly off final drive sun gear shaft. Remove 4 tanged

Automatic Transmissions
GENERAL MOTORS TURBO HYDRA-MATIC 125C TRANSAXLE (Cont.)

Fig. 21: Removing Low-Reverse Clutch Housing

Reverse Clutch Housing Remover/ Installer (J-28542)

Use lifter to lift out Low-Reverse Clutch housing.

reaction carrier-to-reaction internal gear thrust washers off end of reaction carrier (or inside reaction internal gear).

8) Remove Low-Reverse clutch plates off final drive sun gear shaft. Remove reaction internal gear-to-reaction sun gear thrust bearing assembly off reaction gear. Remove reaction internal gear off final drive sun gear shaft.

FINAL DRIVE UNIT

NOTE: Before proceeding with transaxle disassembly, final drive-to-case end play should be checked to determine proper final drive differential-to-case selective thrust washer for install during reassembly. Also, case bushing should be inspected for wear and replaced if necessary.

Final Drive-to-Case End Play

1) Rotate transaxle so right hand axle end is up. With Output Shaft Aligner/Loader Adapter Plug (J-26958-10) in place, press down on adapter to fully seat final drive onto final drive internal gear-to-case snap ring.

2) Install dial indicator onto post and install post into one of the motor mount bolt holes. Ensure indicator plunger rests on top of adapter. Zero dial indicator while pressing down on adapter.

3) Insert large screwdriver into transaxle governor bore. Lift final drive by prying up on governor drive gear. Read end play at dial indicator. End play should be .005-.032" (.12-.82 mm).

4) Selective washer controlling end play is located between differential carrier and differential carrier case thrust bearing assembly. Select correct thrust washer. See FINAL DRIVE-TO-CASE END PLAY table.

5) Remove dial indicator, indicator post and loader/aligner adapter. Remove final drive internal gear spacer-to-case snap ring. The snap ring is .092" (2.36 mm) thick. Remove final drive internal gear spacer. DO NOT deform or bend spacer when removing.

6) Using Final Drive Unit Remover/Installer (J-28545), lift final drive unit from case. Remove final drive differential-to-case selective thrust washer. Remove differential carrier-to-case thrust roller bearing assembly from final drive assembly. The thrust washer and thrust bearing may be located in case.

FINAL DRIVE-TO-CASE END PLAY

Thickness In. (mm)	Identification Code
.055-.059 (1.40-1.50)	0
.059-.062 (1.50-1.60)	1
.062-.066 (1.60-1.70)	2
.066-.070 (1.70-1.80)	3
.070-.074 (1.80-1.90)	4
.074-.078 (1.90-2.00)	5
.078-.082 (2.00-2.10)	6
.082-.086 (2.10-2.20)	7
.086-.091 (2.20-2.30)	8
.091-.095 (2.30-2.40)	9

COMPONENT DISASSEMBLY & REASSEMBLY

NOTE: During disassembly, note component locations for reassembly reference. When reassembling transaxle unit, lubricate all bushings, seals, thrust bearings and internal mating surfaces with transmission fluid. Use petroleum jelly to lubricate and retain all thrust washers.

TRANSAXLE CASE

NOTE: Disassembly procedures include drive sprocket support, drive sprocket roller bearing, third oil cup plug, parking pawl and governor oil pipe removal. It is not necessary to remove and service these components unless they are damaged or worn.

Disassembly

1) Rotate transaxle case until case cover side is up. Using slide hammer and Adapter (J-26941), remove drive sprocket support roller bearing assembly. Inspect bearing bore and roller bearing race on drive sprocket for wear or damage. Replace components as needed.

2) Inspect drive sprocket support for damaged journals or splines. If removal is needed, turn transaxle case so right axle side is up. Remove converter oil seal. From inside torque converter housing, unbolt and remove drive sprocket support.

3) Inspect parking pawl shaft cup plug for damage. If replacement is needed, turn transaxle case so oil pan side is up. Using a 3/8" drift, remove parking pawl shaft cup plug from oil pan side of case. Inspect parking pawl for damage.

4) If replacement is needed, remove parking pawl shaft retainer, parking pawl shaft, parking pawl and return spring from case. Check governor pipe for damage, cracks or possible leak points. If replacement is necessary, remove governor oil pipe clamp screw and clamp.

CAUTION: If governor pipe needs replacement, remove right hand axle end first. The pipe is sealed strongly in place and may require a high effort to break loose. DO NOT damage machined case surface if pipe must be pryed out.

GENERAL MOTORS TURBO HYDRA-MATIC 125C
TRANSAXLE (Cont.)

5) Pry right side end up first, then pry left side end of pipe from case. Remove pipe. Inspect third oil cup plug for wear or damage. If removal is needed, grind .50" (13 mm) from end of No. 3 easy out and install into third oil cup plug. Twist screw extractor out counterclockwise and remove cup plug.

6) Check manual shaft oil seal for damage. If removal is needed, rotate transaxle case so oil pan side is down. Remove manual shaft seal. Inspect axle oil seal and guard for damage. If seal guard is damaged, seal will need replacement also. Pry axle seal from case.

NOTE: If final drive case bushing is worn or scored, bushing must be replaced to prevent damage to right axle shaft or seal.

7) With final drive assembly and right axle shaft removed from case, inspect final drive case bushing for wear or scoring. If bushing removal is needed, remove right axle seal assembly from case. Using Bushing Remover (J-28537-6) with Driver (J-8092), remove bushing.

Inspection

1) Inspect case assembly for damage, cracks, porosity or interconnected oil passages. Inspect exhaust vent holes and ensure they are open. Inspect for damaged or stripped bolt holes.

2) Check case lugs, intermediate servo bore and snap ring grooves for damage. Inspect case bushings for wear or scoring. Inspect drive sprocket support bearing assembly for pitting and scoring to carrier and rollers. Check rollers for excessive clearance.

3) Inspect drive sprocket support for damage to journal splines. Check for heat discoloration and cracks on support assembly. Inspect governor pipe for damage, cracks and possible point of leakage. Check parking pawl shaft cup plug, parking pawl shaft and parking pawl for damage and excessive wear.

4) Inspect third oil cup plug for tightness in bore or damage. Use a straightedge to check all sealing and mating surfaces for straightness. If final drive case bushing was removed, inspect case and new bushing for loose aluminum or burrs. remove all loose material.

Reassembly

1) If final drive case bushing was removed, install new bushing using Bushing Installer (J-28537-2) with Driver Handle (J-8092). Press or drive bushing into position until tool bottoms.

2) Using Seal Driver (J-26938 or J-29130) and Handle (J-8092), install new right hand axle seal assembly. DO NOT damage seal guard during installation. If manual shaft oil seal needs replacement, install seal with lip up, using a 9/16" socket.

3) Install new third cup plug using a 1/4" drift. Cup plug should seat fully in bore when installed. Before installing, coat ends of governor oil pipe with sealing compound (Loctite), to seal against leakage. Install governor pipe and retaining clamp. Lightly tap pipe into place to secure against leakage.

4) Install parking pawl and spring, parking pawl shaft and retainer. Ensure large loop of pawl spring is positioned on right side of pawl. Coat parking pawl shaft cup plug with sealant and install plug using a 3/8" drift.

5) Install drive sprocket support roller bearing assembly with bearing identification facing up. Lightly tap drive sprocket support bearing in place using Bearing Installer (J-28677). Install new converter oil seal using seal Driver (J-28540).

DIFFERENTIAL & FINAL DRIVE
Disassembly & Inspection

1) Remove final drive internal gear and roller thrust bearing. Lift out final drive sun gear and sun gear roller thrust bearing. Inspect final drive internal gear and final drive sun gear for cracks, damage, heat discoloration and worn or missing teeth.

Fig. 22: Exploded View of Differential & Final Drive Unit

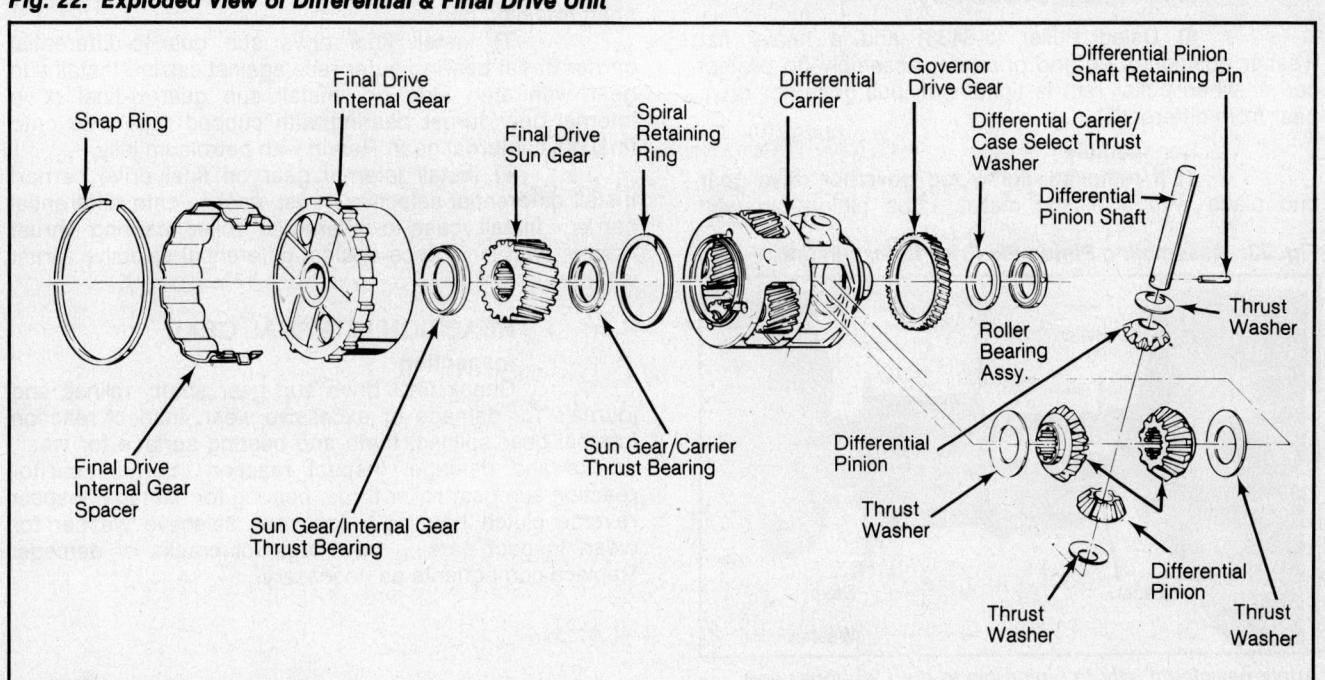

Automatic Transmissions

GENERAL MOTORS TURBO HYDRA-MATIC 125C TRANSAXLE (Cont.)

2) Inspect differential side gears and pinions for damage or excessive wear and replace as needed. Using a 3/16" pin punch, drive out differential pinion shaft retaining pin from final drive side. Withdraw differential pinion shaft.

NOTE: **Pinion shaft retaining pin can be removed and installed from one end of retaining pin bore only. The pin MUST exit carrier assembly toward governor drive gear and MUST be installed from governor drive gear end toward final drive end of carrier.**

3) Remove differential pinion gears and thrust washers by rotating 1 differential side gear (until gear is in differential carrier window) while holding the other in place. Push pinion gears from differential. Ensure dished pinion thrust washers are removed with pinion gears.

4) Slide 1 differential side gear toward center of carrier and remove, then remove other gear in same manner. Remove side gear thrust washers, making sure they are kept with gear from which they were removed.

5) Inspect side gear and pinion thrust washers for scoring, elongated inside diameter, heat discoloration and flattened outer edges. Check final drive pinion end play by inserting feeler gauge between carrier and final drive pinion.

6) End play is .009-.025" (.24-.63 mm). Inspect final drive pinions for excessive wear or damage. If pinions must be removed, detach spiral pinion pin snap ring. Withdraw pinion pins.

7) Carefully remove pinion gears and thrust washers together to prevent dropping needle roller bearings. Remove 36 upper and lower needle bearings from each pinion gear. Inspect all parts for damage.

NOTE: **It is not necessary to remove governor drive gear for inspection or repair of differential and final drive unit. Remove gear only if replacement is necessary.**

8) Using Puller (J-8433) and a heavy flat washer positioned on end of carrier assembly (to protect carrier when puller ram is tightened), pull governor drive gear from differential.

Reassembly
1) If removed, lightly tap governor drive gear into place with a plastic mallet. Lube pinion pin with petroleum jelly and slide 1 steel thrust washer onto end of pin. Install 18 needle bearings around diameter of pin, against steel thrust washer.

2) Install needle bearing spacer onto pin and install remaining 18 needle bearings to pin on opposite side of spacer. *See Fig. 23*. Push needle bearing and pinion pin assembly into pinion gear.

3) Install steel pinion thrust washer onto end of pin (side opposite first thrust washer). Install 1 bronze pinion thrust washer to each end of pin. Slide pinion pin from assembly (keeping bearings intact in gear).

4) Install pinion gear assembly into final drive carrier. Install pinion pin (stepped end last) into carrier through pinion gear assembly. Repeat this procedure for remaining final drive pinion gears. Install spiral pinion pin snap ring.

NOTE: **Install pinion pin so step is outside. Ensure that there is a bronze thrust washer between carrier and steel thrust washer on each end of final drive pinion.**

5) Install differential side gear thrust washers and side gears. Retain in place with petroleum jelly. Coat side gear pinion dished thrust washers with petroleum jelly and install onto side gear pinions. Install pinion gears in differential carrier windows.

NOTE: **The side gear clearance on left side of differential is greater than on right side. Do not replace carrier due to looseness on left side. Left side gear-to-carrier clearance is .023-.032" (.58-.81 mm). Right side gear-to-carrier clearance is .0020-.0050" (.051-.127 mm).**

6) Slide differential pinion shaft through both pinion gears to align. Remove shaft, without disturbing pinion location. Rotate pinions into place. Install pinion shaft into carrier through both pinion gears. Install pinion shaft retaining pin.

7) Install final drive sun gear-to-differential carrier thrust bearing outer race against carrier. Install sun gear with step side up. Install sun gear-to-final drive internal gear thrust bearing with cupped race side onto final drive internal gear. Retain with petroleum jelly.

8) Install internal gear on final drive carrier. Install differential selective thrust washer onto differential carrier. Install case-to-differential roller bearing thrust washer with inner race against differential selective thrust washer.

REACTION INTERNAL GEAR
Inspection
Check final drive sun gear shaft, splines and journals for damage or excessive wear. Inspect reaction internal gear splines, teeth and bearing surface for wear, cracks and damage. Inspect reaction internal gear-to-reaction sun gear roller thrust bearing for damage. Inspect reverse clutch housing-to-low race selective washer for wear. Inspect parking pawl lugs for cracks or damage. Replace components as necessary.

Fig. 23: Assembling Pinion Pin Prior to Installation

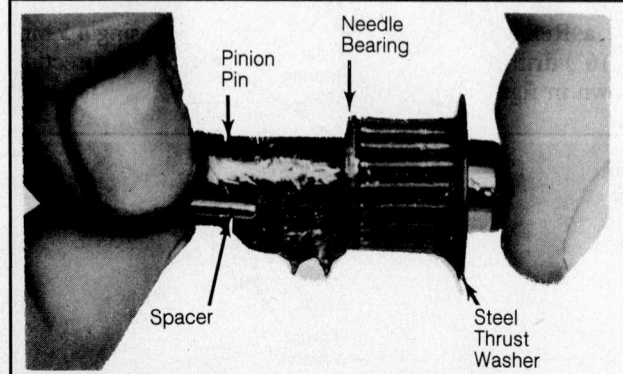

Apply petroleum jelly to pinion pin to hold 36 upper and lower needle bearings during installation.

GENERAL MOTORS TURBO HYDRA-MATIC 125C TRANSAXLE (Cont.)

LOW ROLLER CLUTCH & REACTION CARRIER ASSEMBLY

Disassembly

With transaxle rotated so case cover side is up, remove spacer and low roller clutch race. Pull low roller clutch from reaction carrier assembly. Lift reaction carrier-to-low roller clutch thrust washer from carrier. Pull final drive sun gear shaft from reaction internal gear.

Inspection

1) Inspect low roller clutch race and splines for scoring or wear. With low roller clutch assembly removed, inspect roller clutch bearings, cage and springs for wear, heat discoloration and damage.

2) Inspect the 4 tanged thrust washers for scoring, excessive wear and distorted tangs. Inspect reaction carrier, roller clutch cam ramps and bushing for damage or scoring.

3) Inspect reaction pinions for damage, rough bearings or tilt. Check pinion pins for tightness. Ensure pinion pins do not rotate. Using a feeler gauge, check pinion end play. Pinion end play should be .009-.027" (.24-.69 mm).

Reassembly

1) Install thrust washer into reaction carrier. Install all rollers that may have come out of roller clutch cage by compressing energizing spring with finger and inserting roller from outer edge.

2) Install roller clutch into carrier, then install clutch race, (splined side out) and rotate race clockwise until it drops into position. Install 4 tanged thrust washers onto reaction carrier assembly.

3) Align washer tangs into slot on pinion side of carrier and retain with petroleum jelly. Install reaction internal gear onto final drive sun gear shaft. Install reaction internal gear-to-reaction sun gear roller thrust bearing onto shaft.

4) Install reaction carrier and roller clutch assembly into reaction internal gear. Install Low-Reverse clutch housing-to-Low roller clutch race selective washer. Install reaction gear set into transaxle.

LOW-REVERSE CLUTCH HOUSING

Disassembly

Compress Low-Reverse clutch spring retainer, remove snap ring, then lift out retainer. Remove waved release spring and clutch piston from housing. Remove inner and outer piston seals and clutch apply ring (if equipped).

Inspection

1) Inspect clutch housing for damage or plugged feel hole. Check backing plate for cracks, damage or warpage. Inspect clutch splines and snap ring groove for damage or burrs. Remove any burrs on splines or snap ring groove.

2) Inspect clutch piston for distortion, cracks or damage. Inspect piston seals for nicks, cuts or hardening. Check apply ring for distortion, cracks or damage.

3) Inspect composite and steel clutch plates for signs of wear or burning. Inspect all other parts for damage or wear and replace components as necessary.

Fig. 24: Exploded View of Reaction Carrier & Low-Reverse Clutch Assembly

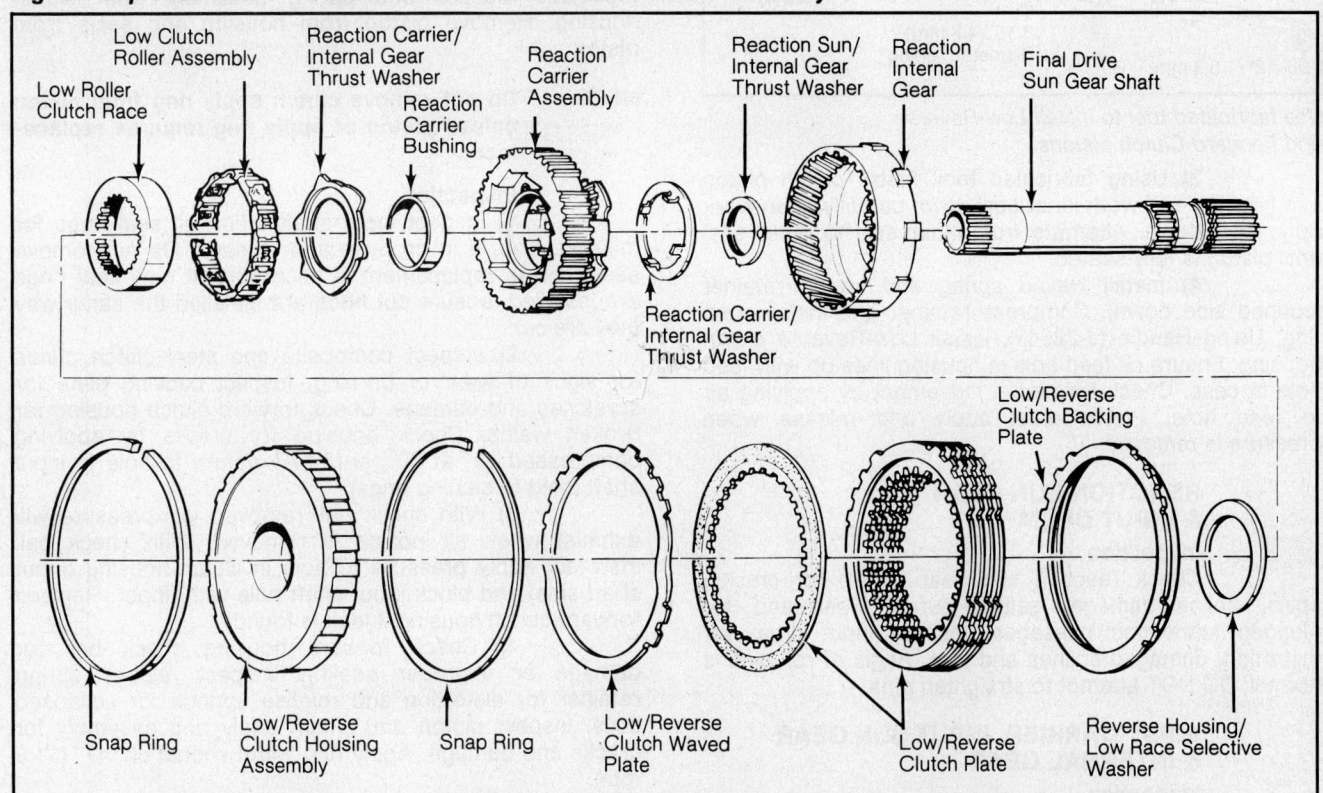

When low-reverse clutch assembly uses an apply ring, the adjoining steel clutch plate will be flat.

Automatic Transmissions
GENERAL MOTORS TURBO HYDRA-MATIC 125C TRANSAXLE (Cont.)

NOTE: When using old design Low-Reverse clutch assembly, the clutch housing oil feed orifice will be .157" (4 mm) in diameter. New design housing feed hole is .079" (2 mm) in diameter. Use only new design components together and vice versa.

Reassembly

1) Install Low-Reverse backing plate with stepped side down. When installing composite clutch plates, lubricate with ATF and install plates alternately, starting with one composite plate. Install waved steel plate last.

2) Install Low-Reverse clutch housing-to-case spacer ring. Spacer ring is .0042" (1.07 mm) thick. Install new inner and outer seals onto piston with lips facing Low-Reverse housing. Lubricate seal lips with transmission fluid.

NOTE: It will be necessary to fabricate a piston installing tool to aid in proper installation and positioning of clutch seals. Using a 6" length of 3/16" diameter tubing and two 2 3/4" sections of .015" diameter wire, fabricate tool to dimensions in Fig. 25.

Fig. 25: Piston Seal Installer

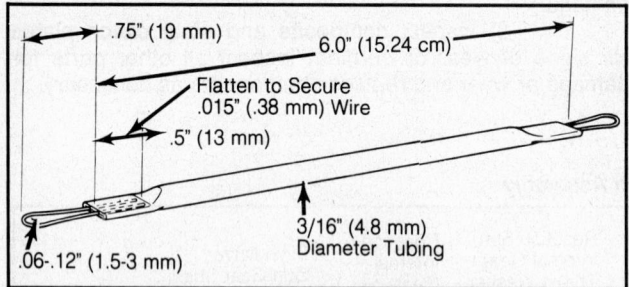

Use fabricated tool to install Low-Reverse and Forward Clutch pistons.

3) Using fabricated tool, install clutch piston into housing and work inner seal down partially, then work outer seal down. Alternate from inner seal to outer seal until piston is fully seated.

4) Install waved spring and spring retainer (cupped side down). Compress retainer and install snap ring. Using Handle (J-28542), install Low-Reverse clutch housing. Ensure oil feed hole in housing lines up with feed hole in case. Check for piston movement by applying air to feed hole. Piston must apply and release when pressure is removed.

REACTION SUN GEAR & INPUT DRUM
Inspection

Check reaction sun gear (shaft) for cracks, splits, spline damage, gear-to-journal wear and for plugged lubrication passages. Inspect input drum for distortion, damaged splines and pins. Angle of roll pins is normal. DO NOT attempt to straighten pins.

INPUT CARRIER, INPUT SUN GEAR & INTERNAL GEAR
Inspection

1) Check all parts for pitting, scoring, damaged gear teeth and cracks. Ensure all lubrication holes are open. Check input carrier thrust washers for wear and distortion of tangs.

2) Check carrier pinion pins for tightness. Pin should not rotate. Using a feeler gauge, check input carrier pinion end play. End play should be .009-.027" (.24-.69 mm).

Fig. 26: Exploded View of Input Unit

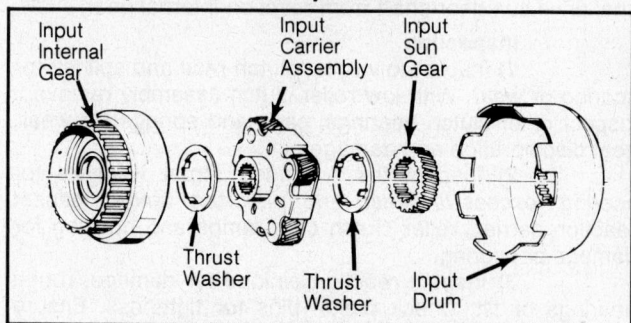

FORWARD CLUTCH ASSEMBLY

NOTE: Some models may not be equipped with an apply ring.

Disassembly

1) Place forward clutch housing in a holding fixture, clutch pack facing up. Remove clutch pack retaining snap ring. Remove backing plate, composite and steel clutch plates from housing.

2) Using an arbor press and/or Clutch Pack Compressor (J-23456) and Adapter (J-23327-1), compress retainer and spring assembly. Remove snap ring. Remove tool. Lift retainer and spring assembly from clutch housing. Remove piston from housing and seals from piston.

NOTE: Do not remove clutch apply ring from piston unless piston or apply ring requires replacement.

Inspection

1) Inspect input shaft teflon oil seal rings for missing, free fit in grooves and damage. Do not remove seals unless replacement is necessary. If new seal rings are installed, ensure cut ends are installed the same way they are cut.

2) Inspect composite and steel clutch plates for signs of wear or burning. Inspect backing plate for scratches and damage. Check forward clutch housing for broken welds. Check housing for cracks by applying compressed air, at 30 psi (2.11 kg/cm²), to hole in input shaft (next to sealing rings).

3) With check ball removed, air pressure will exhaust when air nozzle is removed. With check ball installed, apply pressure to hole in clutch housing (input shaft side) and block input shaft hole with finger. Replace forward clutch housing if leak is found.

4) Check forward housing check ball for damage or improper sealing. Inspect release spring retainer for distortion and release springs for collapsed coils. Inspect piston and clutch apply ring assembly for cracks and damage. Apply ring width should be .47" (11.9 mm).

5) Check snap ring groove in clutch housing for damage or burrs. Inspect input shaft splines and

GENERAL MOTORS TURBO HYDRA-MATIC 125C TRANSAXLE (Cont.)

Fig. 27: Exploded View of Forward Clutch Assembly

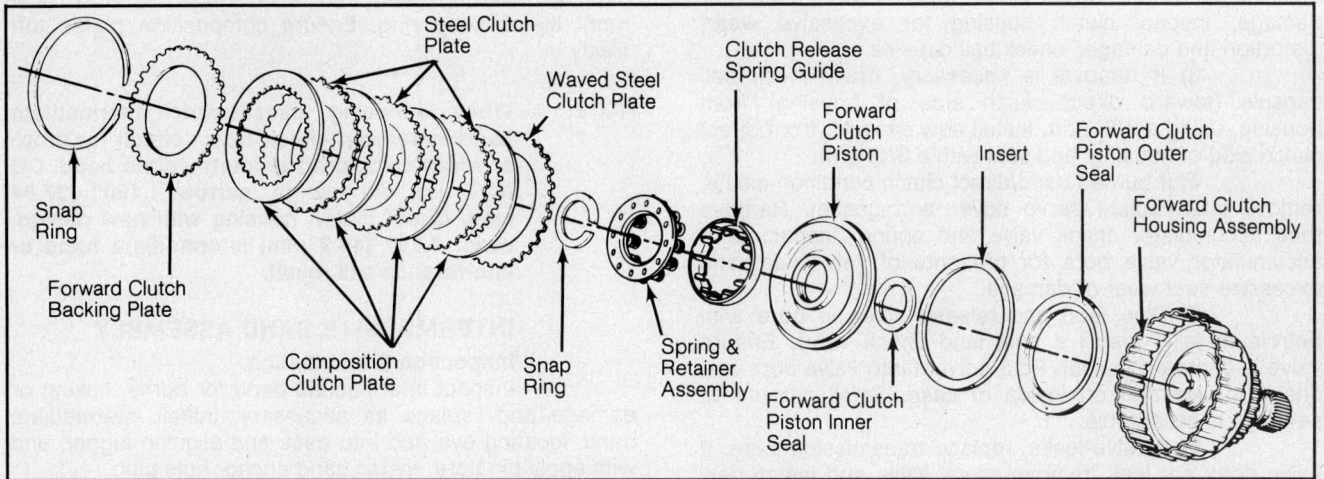

Use care when installing forward clutch piston past large forward clutch snap ring groove or seal could be cut.

journals for distortion or damage. Input shaft sleeve must not turn. The slot in sleeve must align with hole in input shaft. Replace components as necessary.

Reassembly

1) If removed, install apply ring on piston. Install new inner and outer seals on piston with lips facing away from apply ring side. Lubricate seals and install piston into clutch housing using tool fabricated for Low-Reverse clutch piston installation.

2) Position spring guide, retainer and spring assembly into clutch housing. Compress retainer and spring assembly past snap ring groove and install snap ring. Remove compressor.

3) Lubricate and install forward clutch plates into housing. Start with waved steel plate then install a composition plate. Waved steel plate should be .06" (1.6 mm) thick. Alternate until 4 composition and 3 flat steel plates are installed. See FORWARD CLUTCH PLATE USAGE table.

FORWARD CLUTCH PLATE USAGE

Application	Flat Steel	Composition
All Models	¹ 3	4

¹ – Plate thickness is .08" (1.9 mm)

4) Install clutch backing plate into housing with identification side up. Install snap ring. Ensure composition clutch plates turn freely. Measure clearance between backing plate and snap ring with a feeler gauge. DO NOT compress waved clutch plate.

5) If clearance is not within .04-.07" (1.0-1.5 mm), choose a selective thickness backing plate to correct clearance. Backing plates are available in the following sizes: .18-.19" (4.6-4.8 mm), .20-.2I" (5.1-5.3 mm) and .23-.24" (5.8-6.1 mm).

6) If removed, install new input shaft seal rings, making sure cut ends are assembled in same relationship as cut. Rings must be seated in groove. Retain with petroleum jelly. See Fig. 28.

Fig. 28: Installing Input Shaft Seal Ring

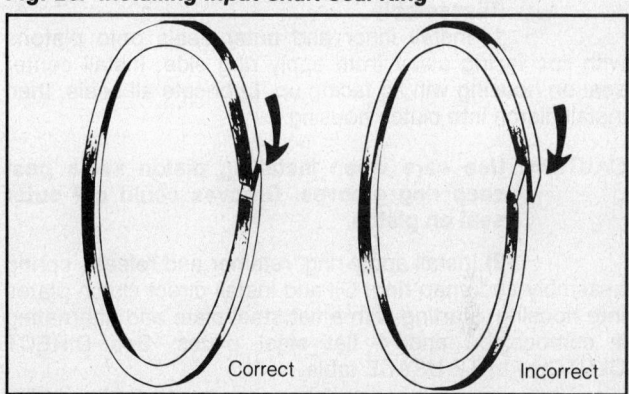

Correct   Incorrect

When new seal rings are installed, ensure the cut ends are installed the same way that they are cut.

DIRECT CLUTCH ASSEMBLY

NOTE: All THM 125C transmissions being serviced for a burnt band and direct clutch condition must have a new dual land third accumulator check valve and conical spring installed.

Disassembly

1) Remove clutch pack snap ring. Withdraw backing plate, composite and steel clutch plates from clutch housing. Ensure direct clutch plates are kept separated from forward clutch plates (if forward clutch is disassembled).

2) Remove snap ring holding apply ring and release spring assembly. Withdraw ring and spring assembly from housing. Remove direct clutch piston from clutch housing. Remove inner and outer seals from piston. Remove center seal from clutch housing.

Inspection

1) Inspect direct clutch housing bushings for damage, cracks or scoring. Inspect composition plates, steel plates and backing plate for wear, burning or scoring. Inspect apply ring, retainer and release spring assembly for damage, collapsed springs and proper apply ring width.

2) The apply ring width should be .750" (19.05 mm). Inspect direct clutch piston for distortion, cracks or damage. Inspect clutch housing for excessive wear, distortion and damaged check ball capsule.

3) If removal is necessary, drive check ball capsule (toward direct clutch side of housing) from housing, using a 3/8" drift. Install new capsule, from direct clutch side of housing, and seat with a 3/8" drift.

4) If burned band/direct clutch condition exists, remove intermediate servo cover and gasket. Remove third accumulator check valve and spring. Inspect third accumulator valve bore for presents of valve seat and excessive seat wear or damage.

5) Plug feed and release holes in bore with petroleum jelly. Install a dual land check valve. Ensure valve is centered in seat. Pour solvent into valve bore and check for leakage on inside of case. Small amount of seepage is acceptable.

6) If valve leaks, replace transmission case. If valve does not leak, remove check valve and install new conical spring onto the valve (small end first). Install valve with spring into bore. Replace servo gasket and cover.

Reassembly

1) Install inner and outer seals onto pistons with lips facing away from apply ring side. Install center seal on housing wih lip facing up. Lubricate all seals, then install piston into clutch housing.

CAUTION: **Use care when installing piston seals past snap ring grooves. Grooves could cut outer seal on piston.**

2) Install apply ring, retainer and release spring assembly and snap ring. Oil and install direct clutch plates into housing, starting with a flat steel plate and alternating 4 composition and 4 flat steel plates. See DIRECT CLUTCH PLATE USAGE table.

DIRECT CLUTCH PLATE USAGE

Application	Flat Steel	Composition
All Models	[1] 4	4

[1] – Plate thickness is .09" (2.3 mm).

3) Install backing plate into housing with flat side up. Backing plate thickness should be .190" (4.92 mm). Install snap ring. Ensure composition plates turn freely.

NOTE: **When servicing direct clutch/intermediate band assembly, check direct clutch for proper width compaired to intermediate band. DO NOT use old design, narrow 1.490" (37.84 mm), direct clutch housing with new design, wider 1.74" (44.2 mm) intermediate band or interference will result.**

INTERMEDIATE BAND ASSEMBLY
Inspection & Installation

Inspect intermediate band for burns, flaking or damage and replace as necessary. Install intermediate band, locating eye end into case and aligning lugged end with apply pin bore. Install band anchor hole plug.

CAUTION: **When installing, ensure lugged end of intermediate band is properly located or band will be inoperative.**

DRIVEN SPROCKET SUPPORT
Inspection

1) Inspect driven sprocket support and sleeve for cracks, burrs or damage. Sleeve must be tight in its bore and align with holes in support. Inspect driven sprocket support bushing and bearing assembly for damage and wear.

2) If necessary to replace bearing assembly, pull out using slide hammer and Bearing Remover (J-26941). Using Bearing Installers (J-28677 and J-8092), install bearing with manufacturing identification facing up.

3) Check bearing race on driven sprocket. If race requires replacement, driven sprocket support must be replaced. Inspect seal rings for nicks or cuts. Replace worn or damaged components as needed.

Fig. 29: Exploded View of Direct Clutch Assembly

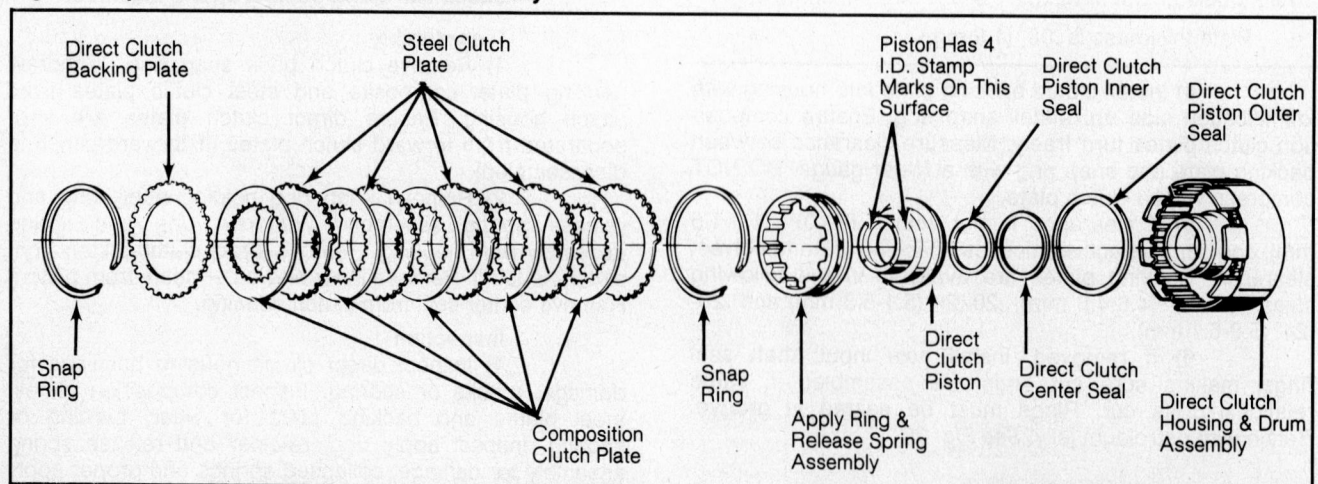

GENERAL MOTORS TURBO HYDRA-MATIC 125C TRANSAXLE (Cont.)

MANUAL SHAFT
Inspection
1) Inspect manual valve rod, rod retainer and detent lever for damage. Check threads of manual shaft for damage and check flats for any raised edges. File down any raised edges.

2) Inspect parking lock actuator rod for damage or broken retainer lugs. If removed, install parking lock actuator rod into manual shaft lever. The manual shaft and detent lever assembly are made as a matched set. Replace as an assembly only.

DRIVE LINK ASSEMBLY (CHAIN, DRIVE & DRIVEN SPROCKETS)
Inspection
1) Inspect drive chain for damage, stretching or loose links. With drive link assembly installed, check chain slack at each extreme and mark case for reference. If chain slack is more than 1.063" (27 mm), replace drive chain.

2) Inspect driven gear thrust bearing race. If damaged, replace driven gear, drive gear (flat side up) and drive support bearing assembly. Inspect drive sprocket teeth for nicks, burrs, scoring or wear.

3) Check internal splines for nicks, burrs and excessive wear. Inspect turbine shaft for excessive wear or damage. Inspect turbine shaft seal ring grooves and seal ring for damage. Do not remove seal ring unless replacing.

4) If turbine shaft oil seal removal is necessary, proceed as follows:

Turbine Shaft Oil Seal Replacement
1) Carefully remove old seals from turbine shaft. Place seal installer tool over the turbine shaft. Lubricate the installer with petroleum jelly.

2) Use Seal Installer (J-29569-1) on the 2 seals on valve body side of sprocket. Use Seal Installer (J-29829-1) on the seal on case side of sprocket.

3) Place solid oil seal ring over seal installer and carefully, but quickly, slide seal down over seal ring groove. Remove installer. Lubricate inside of sizer with petroleum jelly.

4) Use Sizer (J-29569-2) on 2 seals on valve body side of sprocket and Sizer (J-29829-2) on the seal on case side of sprocket. Push sizer down over seal and turn. Remove tool and inspect seal to be sure it is properly seated in the groove. Repeat procedure as needed.

CASE COVER
Disassembly
1) Remove detent spring/roller assembly retaining screw and spring/roller assembly. Remove 2 thermostatic roll pin washers. Remove thermostatic element and plate. Remove axle oil seal and guard if necessary.

2) Using a drift, drive out manual valve cup plug. Carefully withdraw manual valve. DO NOT use manual valve to drive out cup plug.

Inspection
1) Inspect case cover for damage, cracks, porosity or interconnected oil passages. Check for damaged threads in any threaded hole and repair with Heli-coil kit. Inspect vent assembly for damage and clogging. Check manual valve for damage and freedom of movement.

2) Check manual valve electrical connector for damage and replace as needed. Inspect manual detent spring and roller assembly for damage. Check case cover sleeve. Ensure hole in sleeve aligns with case cover passages that intersect case cover (pump shaft) bore.

3) Inspect 1-2 accumulator piston seals for damage and for free fit in grooves. Inspect thermostatic element for damage or distortion. Inspect vent assembly and cooler line connectors for damage. Replace components as necessary.

NOTE: Do not disassemble case cover unless repair or replacement of cover and/or components is necessary.

Reassembly
1) Using Seal Installer (J-26938 or J-29130), install new axle oil seal. Install seal guard if removed. Install detent spring and roller assembly. If 1-2 accumulator piston seal was removed, install new seal ring as shown in *Fig. 28*. Install 1-2 accumulator piston (flat side down).

2) Install 1-2 accumulator piston pin. Install manual valve assembly with small diameter first. Using a 3/8" drift, replace manual valve cup plug. Coat cup plug with sealant before installing. With new "O" ring on electrical connector, install connector with tab located at case slot.

3) If removed, install thermostatic element roll pins into case. Using Roll Pin Height Checker (J-29023), adjust installed height of capped roll pin to .24" (6 mm). *See Fig. 30*. Install thermostatic element plate.

Fig. 30: Measuring Thermostatic Element Capped Roll Pin Installed Height

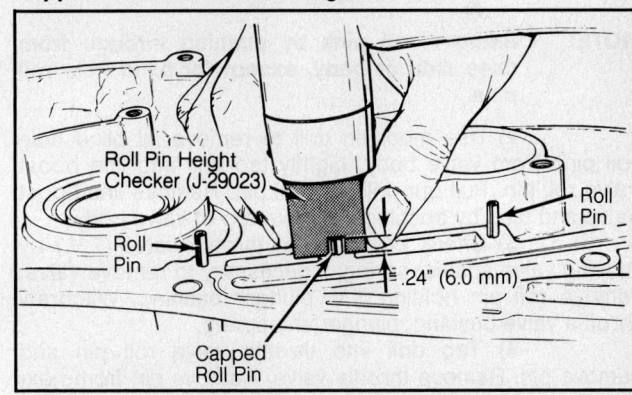

Always use measuring tool to check thermostatic element roll pin for proper installed height.

4) Install thermostatic element onto roll pins. Place Roll Pin Height Checker (J-29023) against roll pin, between case surface and thermostatic element. Install roll pin washers and tap them down onto roll pins until element contacts gauge. Set roller pin washer height to .21" (5.4 mm). *See Fig. 31*.

NOTE: This adjustment is important for thermostatic element operation. Thermostatic element controls fluid level in control valve cover oil sump.

2-234

Automatic Transmissions
GENERAL MOTORS TURBO HYDRA-MATIC 125C TRANSAXLE (Cont.)

Fig. 31: Adjusting Thermostatic Element Roll Pin Washer Height

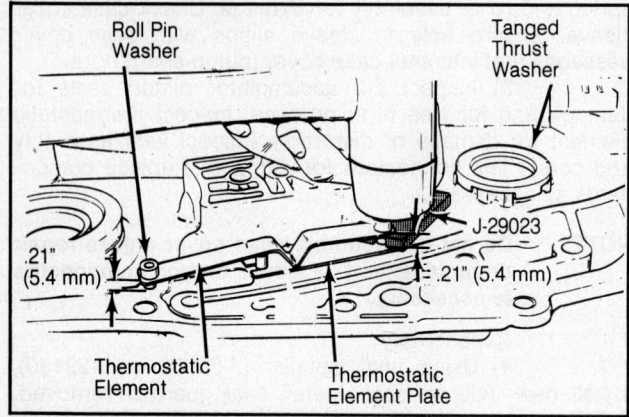

Set roll pin washer height after installing and setting capped roll pin height.

CONTROL VALVE BODY & OIL PUMP ASSEMBLIES

NOTE: As valve train assemblies are removed from their bore, place individual parts, in correct order, in relative position to valve body. Valves, bushings and springs are not interchangeable.

Disassembly

1) Position control valve body with cored face up and line boost valve at top. Check operation of line boost valve. If replacement is needed, grind a taper on one end of a No. 49 (.073") drill.

NOTE: Remove roll pins by pushing through from case side of body, except for blind hole roll pins.

2) Use modified drill to remove all blind hole roll pins from valve body. Lightly tap drill into line boost valve roll pin. Pull out drill and roll pin. Remove line boost valve and plug by pushing valve out top of valve body.

3) Check operation of throttle valve (T.V.) by moving valve against spring. If necessary to remove valve, remove roll pin holding T.V. plunger bushing. Withdraw throttle valve bushing, plunger and spring.

4) Tap drill into throttle valve roll pin and remove pin. Remove throttle valve. Remove pin from next bore down (same side). Withdraw T.V. boost valve assembly with bushing, reverse boost valve with bushing, pressure regulator valve and spring.

CAUTION: Remaining roll pins in valve body have pressure against them. Use caution when removing to prevent personal injury, loss or damage to parts.

5) Remove roll pin from next bore down, left side of valve body assembly. Slide out 3-2 shift T.V. valve and spring. Turn valve body over and remove roll pin, valve bore plug, shift T.V. valve and spring.

6) Remove spring retaining sleeve. Withdraw pressure relief spring and check ball. Remove roll pin from next bore down and withdraw 1-2 accumulator valve bore plug, valve, bushing and spring.

7) Remove roll pin from next bore down and remove 2-3 throttle valve bushing, spring, throttle valve and shift valve. Remove roll pin from next bore down and remove 1-2 throttle valve bushing, spring, valve and 1-2 shift valve.

8) Remove spring retaining sleeve from 3-2 control valve bore in the lower right hand corner. Remove 3-2 control valve and spring. Using a 1/4" punch, remove low-blowoff spring, plug assembly and ball.

NOTE: The low-blowoff assembly must be removed and replaced if valve body is washed in solvent.

9) Turn control valve body so oil pump side is facing up. If pump assembly must be serviced, remove roll pin from oil pump priming spring bore. Remove priming spring cup plug and priming spring.

10) Remove auxiliary valve body cover screw, auxiliary valve body, gasket and cover. Remove pump slide, rotor, 7 vanes and 2 vane rings.

CAUTION: DO NOT service oil pump rotor if pump pocket or auxiliary valve body/pump cover surfaces are scored. Service oil pump rotor and slide ONLY if selective pump rotor, pump drive shaft or pump slide is worn.

Inspection

1) Using solvent, wash control valve body, valves, springs, other valve train components, pump cover, pump slide, pump rotor, vanes and vane rings. DO NOT wash pump seals in solvent.

2) Inspect control valve body/oil pump body for cracks, damage or scoring of valve bores, pump pocket and pump cover. Inspect pump shaft seal and bearing for smooth operation and damage. If seal is damaged, pry out with screwdriver.

3) If necessary, replace bearing assembly using Bearing Remover/Installers (J-28698 and J-7092-2). Drive bearing out toward case cover side. Using bearing installers, install new bearing from pump pocket side. Install bearing until race is .040-.048" (1.00-1.20 mm) ABOVE pump pocket face.

4) After installation, check bearing installed height with feeler gauge. Using installer tools, install new oil seal (with steel side up) from case cover side. Ensure seal is .02" (.5 mm) to flush above case surface. DO NOT drive seal below case surface.

5) Recheck bearing race height once seal is installed. Inspect valve bushings for cracks and scored bores. Inspect bore plugs, pump slide, pump rotor, pump vanes and pump vane rings for damage, cracks or wear. Inspect springs for distortion or collapsed coils.

Oil Pump Rotor & Slide Replacement

1) If pump rotor and/or slides are defective, the replacement parts must provide the same end play originally built into the transaxle. Use the following procedure to obtain an end clearance of .0026-.0036" (.066-.092 mm).

2) Use a micrometer to measure the pump/rotor or slide thickness. Measure on flat, undamaged surface. Using the original measurement, order replacement part using SELECTIVE PUMP ROTOR and SELECTIVE PUMP SLIDE tables.

GENERAL MOTORS TURBO HYDRA-MATIC 125C
TRANSAXLE (Cont.)

Fig. 32: Exploded View of Control Valve Body & Oil Pump Assembly

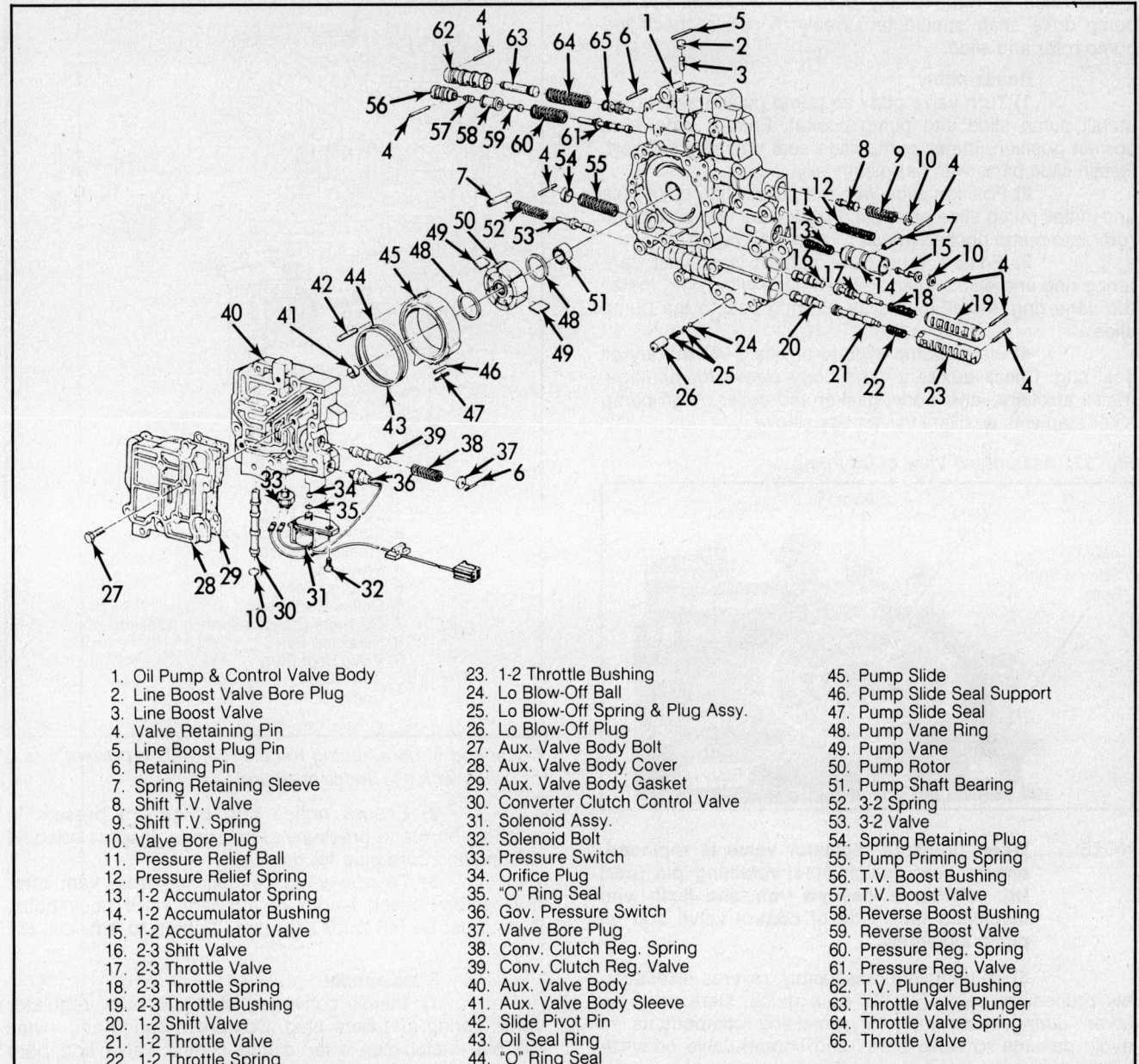

1. Oil Pump & Control Valve Body	23. 1-2 Throttle Bushing	45. Pump Slide
2. Line Boost Valve Bore Plug	24. Lo Blow-Off Ball	46. Pump Slide Seal Support
3. Line Boost Valve	25. Lo Blow-Off Spring & Plug Assy.	47. Pump Slide Seal
4. Valve Retaining Pin	26. Lo Blow-Off Plug	48. Pump Vane Ring
5. Line Boost Plug Pin	27. Aux. Valve Body Bolt	49. Pump Vane
6. Retaining Pin	28. Aux. Valve Body Cover	50. Pump Rotor
7. Spring Retaining Sleeve	29. Aux. Valve Body Gasket	51. Pump Shaft Bearing
8. Shift T.V. Valve	30. Converter Clutch Control Valve	52. 3-2 Spring
9. Shift T.V. Spring	31. Solenoid Assy.	53. 3-2 Valve
10. Valve Bore Plug	32. Solenoid Bolt	54. Spring Retaining Plug
11. Pressure Relief Ball	33. Pressure Switch	55. Pump Priming Spring
12. Pressure Relief Spring	34. Orifice Plug	56. T.V. Boost Bushing
13. 1-2 Accumulator Spring	35. "O" Ring Seal	57. T.V. Boost Valve
14. 1-2 Accumulator Bushing	36. Gov. Pressure Switch	58. Reverse Boost Bushing
15. 1-2 Accumulator Valve	37. Valve Bore Plug	59. Reverse Boost Valve
16. 2-3 Shift Valve	38. Conv. Clutch Reg. Spring	60. Pressure Reg. Spring
17. 2-3 Throttle Valve	39. Conv. Clutch Reg. Valve	61. Pressure Reg. Valve
18. 2-3 Throttle Spring	40. Aux. Valve Body	62. T.V. Plunger Bushing
19. 2-3 Throttle Bushing	41. Aux. Valve Body Sleeve	63. Throttle Valve Plunger
20. 1-2 Shift Valve	42. Slide Pivot Pin	64. Throttle Valve Spring
21. 1-2 Throttle Valve	43. Oil Seal Ring	65. Throttle Valve
22. 1-2 Throttle Spring	44. "O" Ring Seal	

SELECTIVE PUMP ROTOR REPLACEMENT

Part No.	Thickness In. (mm)
8637768	.7055-.7059 (17.920-17.930)
8637769	.7060-.7064 (17.932-17.943)
8637178	.7065-.7069 (17.945-17.955)
8637179	.7070-.7074 (17.958-17.968)
8637180	.7075-.7079 (17.971-17.981)

SELECTIVE PUMP SLIDE REPLACEMENT

Part No.	Thickness In. (mm)
8631800	.7070-.7074 (17.958-17.968)
8631801	.7075-.7079 (17.971-17.981)
8631802	.7080-.7084 (17.983-17.993)
8631803	.7085-.7089 (17.996-18.006)
8631804	.7090-.7094 (18.009-18.019)

Automatic Transmissions

GENERAL MOTORS TURBO HYDRA-MATIC 125C TRANSAXLE (Cont.)

3) Hone both sides of the replacement rotor and/or slide to remove any burrs. After assembly, the pump drive shaft should turn freely. If not, recheck the pump rotor and slide.

Reassembly

1) Turn valve body so pump pocket side is up. Install pump slide into pump pocket. Ensure slide is in correct position. Install pump slide seal and seal support. Retain slide parts with petroleum jelly.

2) Position slide with the pump slide pivot hole and install pump slide pivot pin. Install vane ring and pump rotor into pump pocket. Install 7 vanes into pump.

3) Ensure vane wear pattern is against centering ring and each vane is seated flush with rotor. Install top vane ring. Install new slide "O" ring seal in the pump slide.

4) Install pump slide-to-auxiliary valve body oil seal ring. Check auxiliary valve body sleeve for damage. Install auxiliary valve body, gasket and cover. Align pump rotor step with auxiliary valve body sleeve.

Fig. 33: Assembled View of Oil Pump

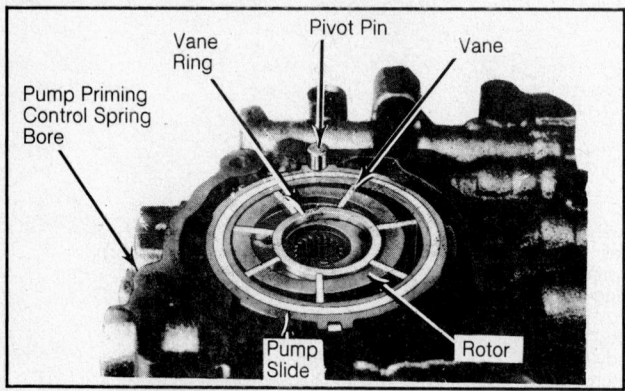

NOTE: When pressure regulator valve is replaced, ensure new design steel retaining pin (part No. 112496) is inserted from and flush with machined face side of control valve and oil pump assembly.

5) To complete reassembly, reverse disassembly procedure, using *Fig. 32* as a guide. Care must be taken during reassembly of remaining components to avoid damage to valve bores and control valve body-to-case cover mating surfaces.

AUXILIARY VALVE BODY

Disassembly

1) Remove solenoid screw and solenoid. Using 24 mm socket, remove pressure switch and, if equipped, governor pressure switch. Remove auxiliary valve body cover, gasket and screw.

2) Remove converter clutch control valve and bore plug. With end of bore covered, remove roll pin (under pressure) from converter clutch control regulator valve. Remove bore plug, valve and spring. *See Fig. 34.*

Inspection

1) Wash all auxiliary valve body parts, except solenoid, in solvent. Inspect valves and valve body for cracks, scoring valve bores or pump face and other damage. Inspect spring for distortion or collapsed coils.

Fig. 34: Exploded View of Auxiliary Valve Body

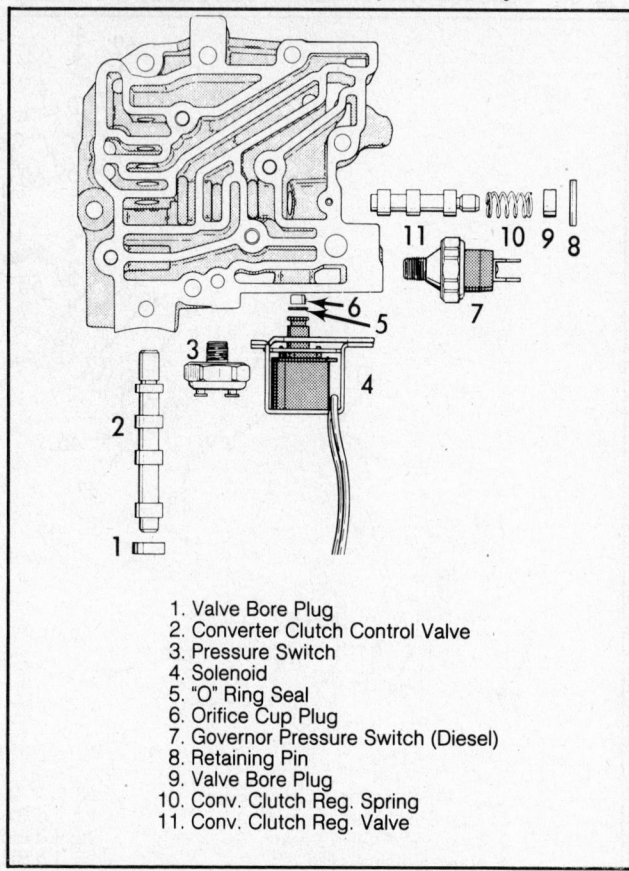

1. Valve Bore Plug
2. Converter Clutch Control Valve
3. Pressure Switch
4. Solenoid
5. "O" Ring Seal
6. Orifice Cup Plug
7. Governor Pressure Switch (Diesel)
8. Retaining Pin
9. Valve Bore Plug
10. Conv. Clutch Reg. Spring
11. Conv. Clutch Reg. Valve

Cover end of bore, during roll pin removal, to prevent loss of spring which is under pressure.

2) Ensure orifice cup plugs are present in solenoid bore and pressure switch parts. Inspect solenoid "O" ring and bore plug for damage.

3) To prevent oil exhausting from vent after reassembly, check length of auxiliary valve body bolts. Bolts must be M6 X 1.0 X 20 mm. Tighten to 8 ft. lbs. (11 N.m).

Reassembly

1) Install converter clutch control regulator valve, spring and bore plug. Compress spring and install roll pin. Install converter clutch control valve and bore plug.

2) Install auxiliary valve body, gasket and screws. Ensure auxiliary valve body sleeve is aligned with step in pump rotor. Tighten mount screw to 8 ft. lbs. (11 N.m). Install pressure switches and tighten to 8 ft. lbs. (11 N.m).

3) Before installing solenoid, check for metal clip attached to valve body and discard if found. Install new design solenoid with new "O" ring and plastic wire routing clip. Install cover gasket and screw.

INTERMEDIATE SERVO

NOTE: Ensure proper apply ring size is determined before final reassembly and installation.

Disassembly & Inspection

1) Remove "E" clip from apply pin. Separate intermediate servo piston, cushion spring, spring retainer and apply pin. Remove and discard all "O" ring seals. *See Fig. 35.*

Fig. 35: Exploded View of Intermediate Servo Assembly

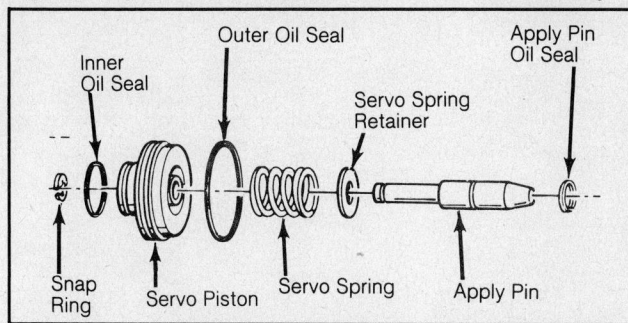

Remove and discard all of the intermediate servo assembly "O" ring seals whenever assembly is removed.

NOTE: If THM 125C transaxle (code BL, CE, CT or OP) is being serviced for 3-2 coast-down clunk condition, check for broken, cracked or damaged intermediate servo spring. If spring (White) needes replacement, be sure to use spring (Violet) with part No. 8652057.

2) Inspect all parts for damage, cracks, scoring and distortion. Check apply pin for free fit in bore. Check servo cover and piston assembly for porosity.

3) Reassemble servo using new inner and outer oil seals on piston and new seal on apply pin (proper apply pin size determined during disassembly).

GOVERNOR/SPEEDOMETER GEAR ASSEMBLY

Inspection

1) Check for plugged oil passage, wash in solvent and blow out oil passage. If necessary, remove speedometer drive gear from governor shaft and inspect gear for nicks or damage. Check governor cover for damage or distortion of mating surface. Remove and discard cover "O" ring.

2) Inspect governor driven gear for nicks or damage. Check governor shaft seal rings for cuts, damage and free fit in groove. Check for free operation of governor weights. The weights must operate freely and independent of each other. Check for damaged, mispositioned or tilted springs. *See Fig. 36.*

3) Inspect for presence of 2 check balls. Inspect governor shaft and thrust washer for damage. If seal ring is being replaced, ensure cut ends of seal are assembled in the same relationship as cut. *See Fig. 28.*

4) Install speedometer drive gear and thrust bearing assembly onto governor assembly. Install governor assembly into transaxle. Install governor cover with new "O" ring. Ensure governor shaft is piloted in cover before tightening retaining bolts. Install speedometer drive gear and retainer.

TRANSAXLE REASSEMBLY

NOTE: All selective snap ring and thrust washer measurements taken during disassembly should be rechecked at appropriate stage of reassembly. Follow procedures given in TRANSAXLE DISASSEMBLY.

Fig. 36: Sectional View of Governor Assembly

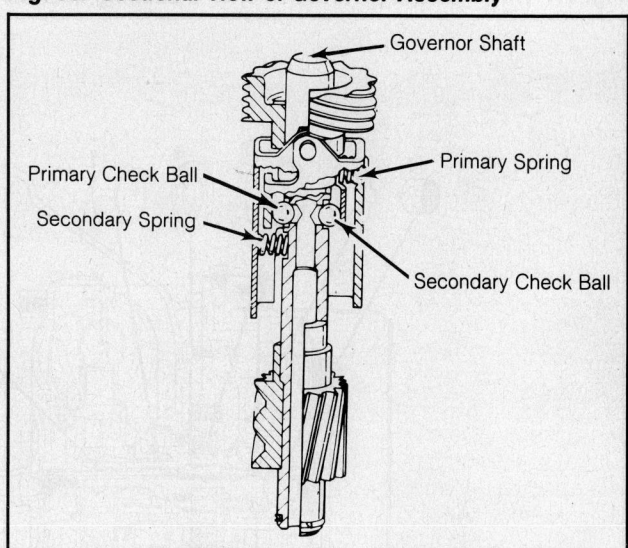

Ensure that the governor weights operate freely and are independent of each other.

1) Turn transaxle so case cover end is up. Install proper final drive-to-case thrust washer and thrust bearing assembly to final drive unit (inner race of bearing against selective washer). Install differential and final drive assembly into case.

2) Install final drive internal gear spacer (cupped side against final drive internal gear). Ensure opening in spacer aligns with parking pawl opening in case. Check to see that parking pawl passes through spacer freely.

3) Install final drive spacer-to-case snap ring with ring gap away from parking pawl opening in case. Install reaction sun gear set into case.

4) Install Low-Reverse clutch backing plate (stepped side down) into case, then install clutch plates, starting with a composition plate and alternating steel and composition plates until all plates are installed. See LOW-REVERSE CLUTCH PLATE USAGE table.

LOW-REVERSE CLUTCH PLATE USAGE

Application	Flat Steel	Composition
All Models	4	5

5) Install Low-Reverse clutch housing-to-case spacer ring. This case spacer ring is .042" (1.07 mm) thick. Install Low-Reverse clutch housing into transaxle case. Ensure clutch feed hole in housing lines up with clutch feed hole in case.

6) Install proper selective snap ring onto reaction sun gear. Install reaction sun gear onto final drive sun gear shaft in transaxle. Rotate reaction sun gear while pushing down on the Low-Reverse clutch housing until clutch housing drops below snap ring groove in case.

7) Install Low-Reverse clutch housing-to-case snap ring. This snap ring is .092" (2.36 mm) thick. Install input drum onto reaction sun gear. Install input sun gear into input drum. Install input carrier-to-input sun gear tanged thrust washer to pinion side of carrier.

8) Install input carrier-to-input internal gear tanged thrust washer to internal gear side of carrier (input

Automatic Transmissions
GENERAL MOTORS TURBO HYDRA-MATIC 125C
TRANSAXLE (Cont.)

Fig. 37: Thrust Bearing, Thrust Washer & Bushing Locations

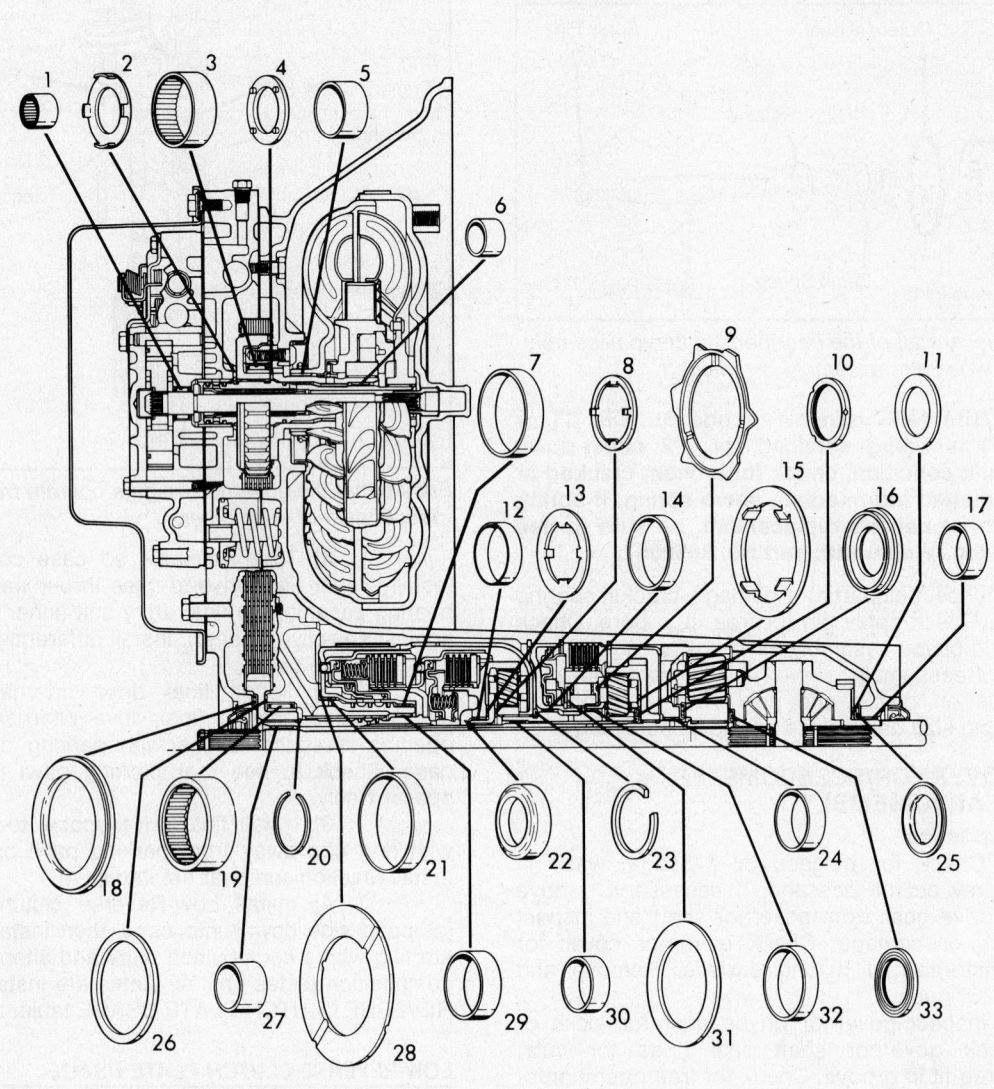

1. Pump Shaft Bearing Assy.
2. Case Cover-to-Driven Sprocket Thrust Washer
3. Bearing Assy.
4. Case Cover-to-Drive Sprocket Thrust Washer
5. Converter Bushing
6. Drive Sprocket Support Bushing
7. Direct Clutch Drum Bushing
8. Input Carrier-to-Input Sun Gear Thrust Washer
9. Reaction Carrier-to-Lo Race Thrust Washer
10. Reaction Sun Gear-to-Internal Gear Thrust Bearing
11. Differential Carrier-to-Case Selective Thrust Washer
12. Input Internal Gear Bushing
13. Input Carrier-to-Input Internal Gear Thrust Washer
14. Lo and Reverse Clutch Housing Bushing
15. Reaction Carrier-to-Internal Gear Thrust Washer
16. Sun Gear-to-Internal Gear Thrust Bearing
17. Case Bushing

18. Driven Sprocket Thrust Bearing Assy.
19. Bearing Assy.
20. Selective Snap Ring
21. Direct Clutch Bushing
22. Input Shaft Thrust Washer
23. Selective Snap Ring
24. Final Drive Internal Gear Bushing
25. Differential Case Thrust Bearing Assy.
26. Driven Sprocket Support Thrust Washer
27. Input Shaft Bushing
28. Thrust Washer
29. Driven Sprocket Support Bushing
30. Reaction Sun Gear Bushing
31. Reverse Housing-to-Lo Race Selective Thrust Washer
32. Reaction Carrier Bushing
33. Sun Gear-to-Carrier Thrust Bearing

GENERAL MOTORS TURBO HYDRA-MATIC 125C
TRANSAXLE (Cont.)

carrier-to-input internal gear thrust washer is larger of 2). Install input pinion carrier onto input sun gear.

9) Install input internal gear over input carrier. Place forward clutch assembly on bench with input shaft up. Install direct clutch assembly over input shaft onto the forward clutch housing.

10) When clutch housings are fully seated together, it should be about 1 7/32" (31 mm) from tang end of direct clutch housing to end of forward clutch housing drum. *See Fig. 38.*

Fig. 38: Measuring Forward Clutch-to-Direct Clutch Assembled Height

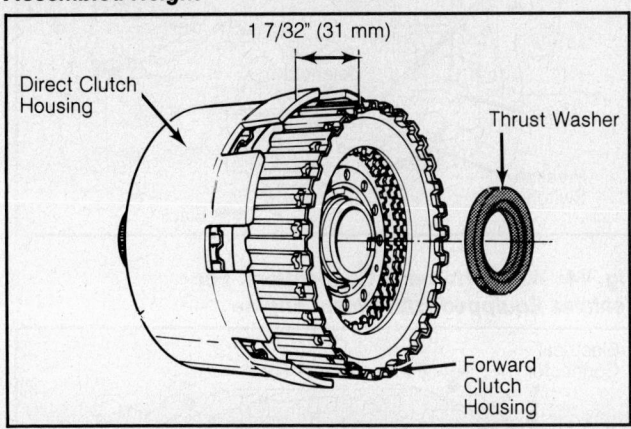

11) Install input shaft-to-input internal gear thrust washer, with rounded side against input shaft and stepped side facing outward, onto forward and direct clutch assembly.

12) Install direct and forward clutch assemblies into case. Rotate clutch assemblies, without pushing down, until they drop into fully seated position in case. When correctly installed, case face-to-direct clutch housing measurement should be 1.688" (42 mm). *See Fig. 39.*

Fig. 39: Checking Installed Position of Direct & Forward Clutch Assemblies

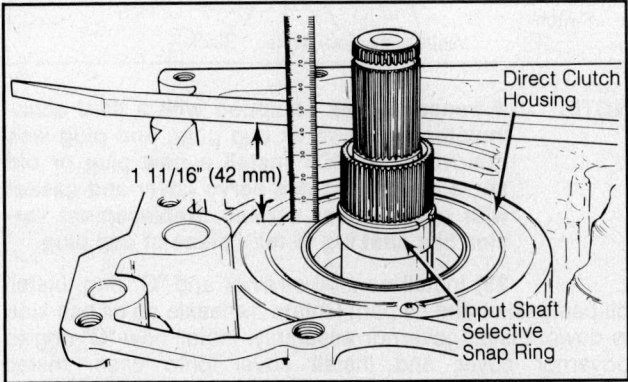

13) Install intermediate band, locating eye of band into case and aligning lugged end with apply pin bore. Install band anchor hole plug (use new design hole plug with securing tab attached).

14) Install driven sprocket support-to-direct clutch housing thrust washer. Install driven sprocket support. *See Fig. 19.*

NOTE: Manual shaft and detent lever assemblies are made as a matched set. Replacement of complete set is required if either part is damaged.

15) Install manual shaft and parking lock actuator rod into case through driven sprocket support. Install detent lever on manual shaft (hub side away from driven sprocket support) and push manual shaft in place.

16) Install detent lever-to-manual shaft retaining nail. Install manual shaft-to-case retaining pin. *See Fig. 19.*

Fig. 40: Case Cover Bolt Locations

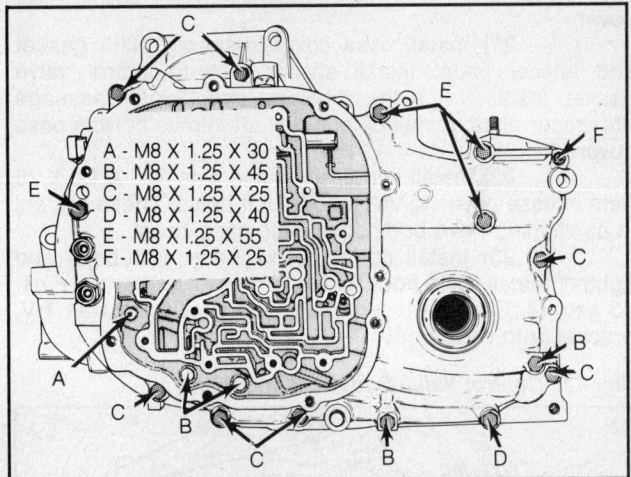

A - M8 X 1.25 X 30
B - M8 X 1.25 X 45
C - M8 X 1.25 X 25
D - M8 X 1.25 X 40
E - M8 X I.25 X 55
F - M8 X 1.25 X 25

Fig. 41: View of Spacer Plate Showing Passage Location

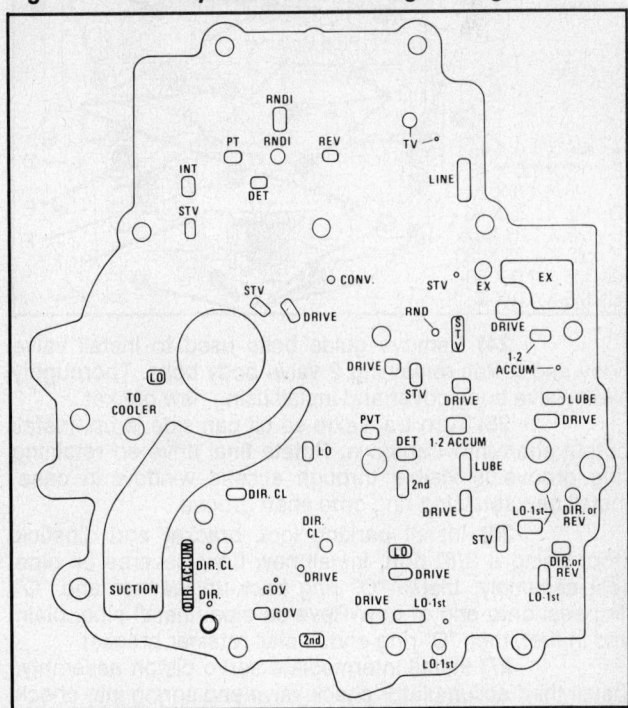

17) Assemble drive and driven sprockets with link assembly and install drive and driven thrust washers to sprockets. Install drive link assembly onto transaxle. The colored guide link, which has numerals, must face the case cover.

Automatic Transmissions
GENERAL MOTORS TURBO HYDRA-MATIC 125C TRANSAXLE (Cont.)

18) Install case cover-to-driven sprocket roller bearing thrust washer (outer race against sprocket). Install 1-2 accumulator piston. Install thermostatic spring if removed.

19) Install 1-2 accumulator spring in its bore in case. Install inner and outer case-to-cover gaskets and case cover. Install 2 case cover bolts from inside torque converter housing (M8 X 1.25 X 14 mm). Install remaining case cover bolts using *Fig. 40* as a guide.

20) Connect manual valve rod to manual valve. Using *Fig 16* as a guide, install No. 2 check ball into direct clutch accumulator passage, No. 3 check ball in circular Low-First passage, No. 4 check ball in Low-Reverse slot and No. 5 check ball in direct clutch passage in case cover.

21) Install case cover-to-spacer plate gasket and spacer plate. Install spacer plate-to-control valve gasket. Install No. 1 check ball on direct clutch passage on spacer plate. Install oil pump shaft into its bore in case cover.

22) Install two 6 mm guide pins (M6 X 1.0 X 75 mm) in case cover-to-valve body bolt holes. These will aid in positioning valve body down onto case cover.

23) Install control valve body with bolts and tighten. Install valve body wiring harness as shown in *Figs. 43 and 44*. Connect lever link to T.V. bracket. Install T.V. bracket onto valve body.

Fig. 42: Control Valve Body Bolt Locations

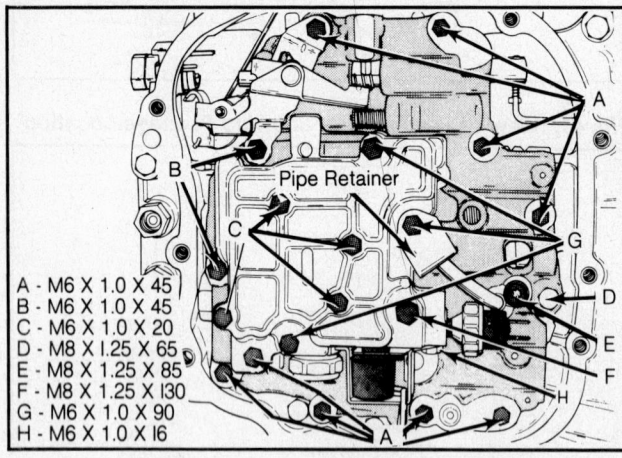

A - M6 X 1.0 X 45
B - M6 X 1.0 X 45
C - M6 X 1.0 X 20
D - M8 X 1.25 X 65
E - M8 X 1.25 X 85
F - M8 X 1.25 X I30
G - M6 X 1.0 X 90
H - M6 X 1.0 X I6

24) Remove guide bolts used to install valve body and install remaining 2 valve body bolts. Thoroughly clean valve body cover and install using new gasket.

25) Turn transaxle so oil pan side is up. Install output shaft into transaxle. Rotate final drive so retaining ring groove is visible through access window in case. Install new retaining ring onto shaft groove.

26) Install parking lock bracket and dipstick stop. Using a 3/8" drift, install new Low-Reverse oil pipe seal assembly. Install "O" ring back-up washer and "O" ring seal onto end of Low-Reverse pipe. Install pipe, plain end in first, then "O" ring end. Install retainer bracket.

27) Install intermediate servo piston assembly. Install third accumulator check valve and spring into check valve bore next to servo piston. Install intermediate servo cover and 3 bolts.

28) Install reverse oil pipe bracket to oil pipe and servo cover. Install remaining servo cover bolt through bracket and cover. Tighten servo cover bolts.

Fig. 43: Wiring Harness Connections For Vehicles Equipped With Gasoline Engine

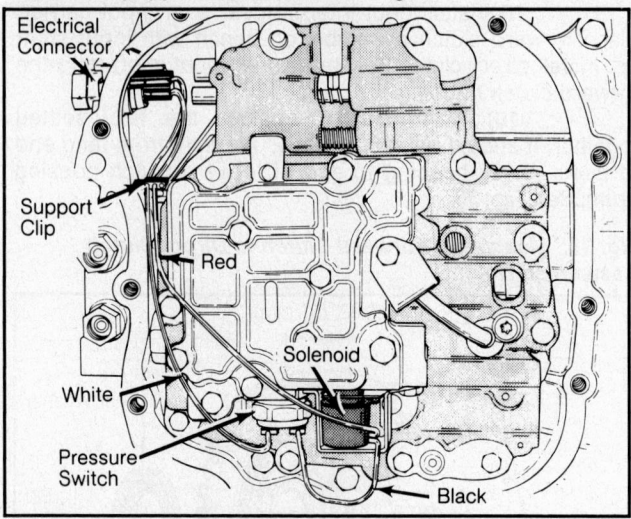

Fig. 44: Wiring Harness Connections For Vehicles Equipped With Diesel Engine

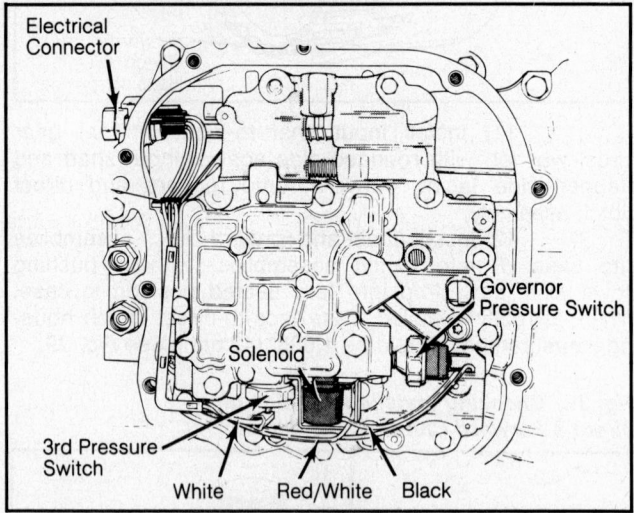

NOTE: If transaxle was equipped with a third accumulator check valve cup plug, and plug was removed, DO NOT install a new plug or old servo cover. Replace servo cover and gasket with replacement version. Replacement version has cast lug to take place of cup plug.

29) Install new oil strainer and "O" ring. Install oil pan gasket and oil pan. Rotate transaxle so oil pan side is down. Install governor assembly. Install new "O" ring to governor cover and install cover onto case. Install speedometer driven gear assembly into governor cover.

NOTE: Ensure governor shaft is piloted in governor cover before tightening cover bolts.

30) Install torque converter. Converter is properly installed if the distance is .50" (13 mm) minimum between engine mount face of case and front face of converter cover lugs.

GENERAL MOTORS TURBO HYDRA-MATIC 125C TRANSAXLE (Cont.)

TIGHTENING SPECIFICATIONS

Application	Ft. Lbs. (N.m.)
Case Cover-to-Case	18 (24)
Case-to-Drive Sprocket Support	18 (24)
Drive Axle Hub Nut [1]	
Initial Tightening Torque	70 (100)
Final Tightening Torque	185-225 (250-305)
Fltwheel-to-Torque Converter Bolt	41-52 (55-70)
Oil Pan & Valve Body Cover	12 (16)
Parking Lock Bracket-to-Case	18 (24)
Pipe Retainer-to-Case	18 (24)
Pump Cover-to-Case Cover	18 (24)
Valve Body-to-Case	18 (24)
Valve Body-to-Driven	
Sprocket Support	18 (24)

	INCH Lbs.
Auxiliary Valve Body	96 (11)
Cooler Connector	96 (11)
Governor Cover-to-Case	96 (11)
Intermediate Servo Cover	96 (11)
Line Pressure Take-Off	96 (11)
Manual Detent	
Spring-to-Case	96 (11)
Pressure Switch	96 (11)
Pump Cover-to-Valve Body	96 (11)
Solenoid-to-Valve Body	96 (11)
T.V. Cable-to-Case	72 (9)
Valve Body-to-Case Cover	96 (11)

[1] – Discard hub nut whenever it is removed and use only a new hub nut during installation.

Automatic Transmissions
GENERAL MOTORS TURBO HYDRA-MATIC 180C

Chevrolet Chevette
Pontiac 1000

TRANSMISSION IDENTIFICATION

The transmission identification code is stamped on a tag located on left side of transmission case near rear edge of torque converter housing.

DESCRIPTION

The 180C transmission is a fully automatic unit consisting primarily of a 4-element hydraulic torque converter and a compound planetary gear set. Three multiple-disc clutches, a roller clutch and a band provide the friction elements required to obtain the desired function of the compound planetary gear set. A hydraulic system pressurized by a gear-type pump provides the working pressure required to operate the friction elements and automatic controls.

LUBRICATION & ADJUSTMENTS

See appropriate AUTOMATIC TRANSMISSION SERVICING article in DOMESTIC GENERAL SERVICING section.

TROUBLE SHOOTING

See appropriate AUTOMATIC TRANSMISSION TROUBLE SHOOTING article in DOMESTIC GENERAL SERVICING section.

TESTING

ROAD TEST
Drive Range ("D")
With selector lever in "D" range, accelerate vehicle from a standstill. A 1-2 and 2-3 shift should occur at all throttle openings (shift points will vary with throttle openings). As vehicle speed decreases to zero MPH, a 3-2 and 2-1 downshift should occur.

Intermediate Range ("L2")
Place selector lever in "L2" and accelerate vehicle from a standstill. A 1-2 shift should occur at all throttle openings. No 2-3 shift can be obtained in this range. The 1-2 shift point will vary with throttle opening. As vehicle speed decreases to zero MPH, a 2-1 downshift should occur.

Low Range ("L1")
Place selector lever in "L1" and accelerate vehicle from a standstill. No upshift should occur in this range.

2nd Gear ("L2") Overrun Braking
With selector lever in "D" range and vehicle moving in high gear, lift foot off accelerator and move selector lever to intermediate range ("L2"). An increase in engine RPM and an engine braking effect should be noted.

1st Gear ("L1") Overrun Braking
With selector lever in "L2" range, and vehicle speed approximately 30 MPH at constant throttle, move selector lever to "L1" range. An increase in engine RPM and an engine braking effect should be noted.

CONTROL PRESSURE TEST
Remove transmission crossmember side bolts and lower transmission slightly to gain access to line pressure take-off point. Connect a tachometer to engine and a pressure gauge to line pressure take-off point on left side of transmission case. With transmission fluid at correct level and operating temperature, pressure can be checked by road testing or by running engine with vehicle on a hoist as follows:

CLUTCH AND BAND APPLICATION CHART (ELEMENTS IN USE)

Selector Lever Position	Reverse Clutch	2nd Clutch	3rd Clutch	Sprag Clutch	Low Band
D – Drive					
1st Gear				X	X
2nd Gear		X			X
3rd Gear		X	X	X	
L2 – Intermediate					
2nd Gear		X			X
L1 – Low			X	X	X
R – Reverse	X		X	X	

NEUTRAL OR PARK – All clutches and bands released and/or ineffective.

GENERAL MOTORS TURBO HYDRA-MATIC 180C (Cont.)

Stationary Test (Modulator Disconnected)

Make test with vehicle stationary, service brakes applied, engine speed set at 1500 RPM, vacuum modulator line disconnected, and pressure gauge installed. Transmission line pressure should be approximately as shown in CONTROL PRESSURES table.

CONTROL PRESSURES

Shift Lever Position	[1] psi (kg/cm²)
Drive ("D")	118 (8.3)
Intermediate ("L2")	118 (8.3)
Low ("L1")	160 (11.2)

[1] – Maximum pressure.

Coasting Check (Modulator Connected)

With vehicle coasting at 30 MPH (foot off throttle), pressure gauge installed and vacuum modulator line connected, transmission line pressure should be approximately as shown in CONTROL PRESSURES table.

CONTROL PRESSURES

Shifter Position	[1] psi (kg/cm²)
Drive ("D")	65 (4.6)
Intermediate ("L2")	65 (4.6)
Low ("L1")	95 (6.7)

[1] – Minimum pressure.

CONTROL PRESSURE TEST RESULTS

Control Pressure Too Low
- Low oil level.
- Clogged suction screen.
- Leak in oil pump suction circuit.
- Leak in oil pressure circuit.
- Pressure regulator valve mulfunction.
- Sealing ball in valve body dropped out.

Control Pressure Too High
- Modulator vacuum line leaking or interrupted.
- Failed vacuum modulator.
- Vacuum leak in engine or accessory vacuum system.
- Pressure regulator valve malfunction.

SERVICE (IN VEHICLE)

The following components may be removed from transmission for inspection or repair, without removing transmission from vehicle:
- Governor Cover, Seals & Assembly
- Governor Pressure Switch (Diesel Only)
- Intermediate Servo Cover, Seal & Assembly
- Oil Pan & Screen Assembly
- Control Valve Assembly
- Check Balls & Valve Body Space Plates & Gaskets
- Inside Detent Range Lever
- Manual Detent Roller & Spring Assembly
- Throttle Lever & Bracket Assembly
- TV Detent Cable & "O" Ring
- Parking Pawl Actuator Rod
- Parking Pawl & Bracket
- Manual Shift & Seal
- Manual Valve
- Manual Valve Link
- Extension Housing, Gasket & Rear Seal
- 1-2 Accumulator Assembly
- Vacuum Modulator
- Cooler Fittings
- Oil Filter Pipe & "O" Ring
- Speedometer Driven Gear & Assembly
- Converter Clutch Solenoid
- Solenoid Wire Clips
- Electrical Connectors
- Governor Feed Screen
- Modulator Valve
- Low Band Adjustment

NOTE: For removal and installation procedures on these components, see TRANSMISSION DISASSEMBLY and TRANSMISSION REASSEMBLY in this article.

REMOVAL & INSTALLATION

TRANSMISSION

See appropriate AUTOMATIC TRANSMISSION REMOVAL article in DOMESTIC GENERAL SERVICING section.

TORQUE CONVERTER

NOTE: Torque converter is a sealed unit and cannot be disassembled for service.

LEAKAGE CHECK

See procedure given in G.M. Turbo Hydra-Matic 400 article in this section.

NOTE: For additional information on the Torque Converter Clutch (TCC) system used with this transmission see GENERAL MOTORS TORQUE CONVERTER CLUTCH (TCC) SYSTEM article in this section.

TRANSMISSION DISASSEMBLY

TORQUE CONVERTER & CONVERTER HOUSING OIL SEAL

1) Remove oil filter tube. Remove converter by pulling straight out. Install transmission in a holding fixture with oil pan up.

2) If converter housing oil seal replacement is necessary, remove oil seal using puller and slide hammer.

INPUT SHAFT END PLAY

See SELECTING TRANSMISSION END PLAY SELECTIVE THRUST WASHER section in this article.

Automatic Transmissions

GENERAL MOTORS TURBO HYDRA-MATIC 180C (Cont.)

Fig. 1: Exploded View of 180C Automatic Transmission THM 180C

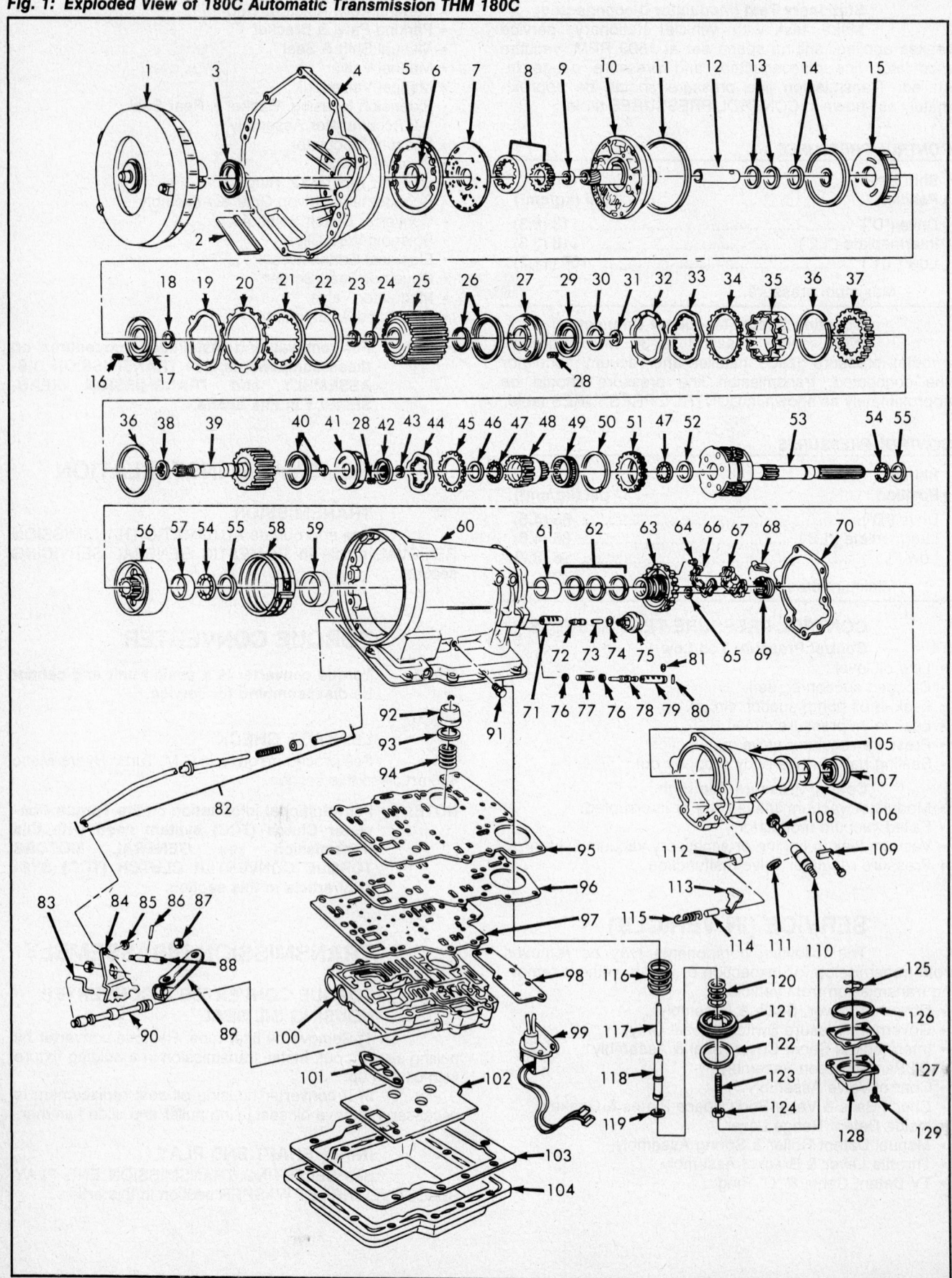

GENERAL MOTORS TURBO HYDRA-MATIC 180C (Cont.)

Automatic Transmission Components (Use With Fig. 1)

1. Converter
2. Inspection Plate
3. Hub Seal
4. Converter Housing
5. Seal Kit
6. Bushing
7. Oil Pump Wear Plate
8. Oil Pump Gear
9. Oil Pump Bushing
10. Oil Pump w/Gasket & Wear Plate
11. Seal Kit
12. Bushing
13. Seal
14. Seal Kit
15. Reverse Clutch Piston
16. Reverse Clutch Piston Return Springs (24)
17. Spring Seat
18. Return Spring Seat Ring
19. 3 Pong Cushion Spring
20. Driven Plate
21. Drive Plate
22. Reverse Clutch Pressure
23. Thrust Washer
24. Clutch Drum Second Speed Bushing
25. Outer Clutch Drum
26. Inner & Outer Seal Ring Set
27. Piston
28. Piston Return Springs (24)
29. Spring Seat
30. Snap Ring
31. Bronze Thrust Washer
32. Cushion Spring Plate
33. Drive Plate
34. Driven Plate
35. Second Speed Clutch Plate Spacer
36. Retaining Ring
37. Ring Gear
38. Steel Thrust Washer
39. Third Speed Clutch Drum w/Shaft
40. Inner & Outer Seal Set
41. Piston
42. Return Spring Seat
43. Return Spring Seat Ring
44. Drive Plate
45. Third Speed Driven Plate
46. Input Sun Gear Race
47. Sun Gear Bearing
48. Input Sun Gear
49. Input Sprag
50. Sprag Race Retaining Ring
51. Race & Retainer
52. Input Sun Gear to Planetary Carrier Race
53. Planetary Carrier
54. Sun Gear Reaction Bearing
55. Sun Gear Reaction Race
56. Rection Sun w/Drum Gear
57. Input Sun Gear Bushing
58. Low Brake Band
59. Reaction Sun Gear Drum Bearing Sleeve
60. Transmission Case w/Bushing
61. Transmission Case Bushing
62. Governor Hub Seal Ring
63. Governor Hub
64. Oil Pump Governor Screen
65. Snap Ring
66. Governor Gasket
67. Governor Body
68. Speedometer Drive Gear Clip
69. Speedometer Drive Gear
70. Gasket
71. Vacuum Modulator Valve Sleeve
72. Vacuum Modulator Valve
73. Sleeve
74. Gasket
75. Vacuum Modulator
76. Spring Seat
77. Spring
78. Oil Pump Pressure Regulator Boost Valve
79. Valve Sleeve
80. Retainer Pin
81. "O" Ring Seal
82. Parking Lock Actuator
83. Transmission Manual Valve Lever Link
84. Parking Lock Lever Nut
85. Snap Ring
86. Case Side Pin
87. Parking Lock Lever Nut
88. Parking Lock & Range Selector Shaft
89. Detent w/Roller Spring
90. Transmission Manual Valve
91. Pressure Tap Plug
92. Accumulator Piston
93. Accumulator Piston Ring
94. Thrust Ring
95. Transfer Plate to Transmission Case Gasket
96. Valve Body Transfer Plate
97. Valve Body Gasket
98. Oil Pump Suction Transfer Plate
99. Solenoid
100. Transmission Valve Body
101. Oil Pump Suction Screen Gasket
102. Screen
103. Oil Pan Gasket
104. Oil Pan
105. Extension
106. Extension Bushing
107. Seal
108. Speedometer Driven Gear
109. Speedometer Bracket
110. Speedometer Guide
111. Seal Ring
112. Actuator Sleeve
113. Parking Lock Pawl
114. Parking Pawl Shaft
115. Parking Pawl Disengaging Spring
116. Low Servo Piston Return Spring
117. Piston Apply Rod
118. Piston Adjusting Sleeve
119. Spring Seat
120. Piston Cushion Spring
121. Low Servo Piston
122. Piston Oil Seal Ring
123. Piston Adjusting Stud
124. Piston Adjusting Nut
125. Piston Retaining Inner Ring
126. Piston Retaining Outer Ring
127. Gasket
128. Low Servo Cover
129. Cover Bolt

OIL PAN, VALVE BODY & SERVO PISTON

1) Remove attaching bolts and lift off oil pan. Remove oil pan gasket. Remove manual detent roller and spring assembly. Remove oil strainer assembly and discard gasket.

2) Disconnect governor pressure switch electrical connector and solenoid wiring harness. Remove governor pressure switch, converter clutch solenoid and solenoid pipes. DO NOT bend solenoid pipes when removing.

3) Remove transfer plate reinforcement attaching bolts and remove reinforcement. Remove servo cover attaching bolts and remove cover and gasket. Remove remaining bolts attaching valve body to case. Carefully remove valve body with gasket and transfer plate. *See Fig. 2.*

Fig. 2: Removing Valve Body from Transmission

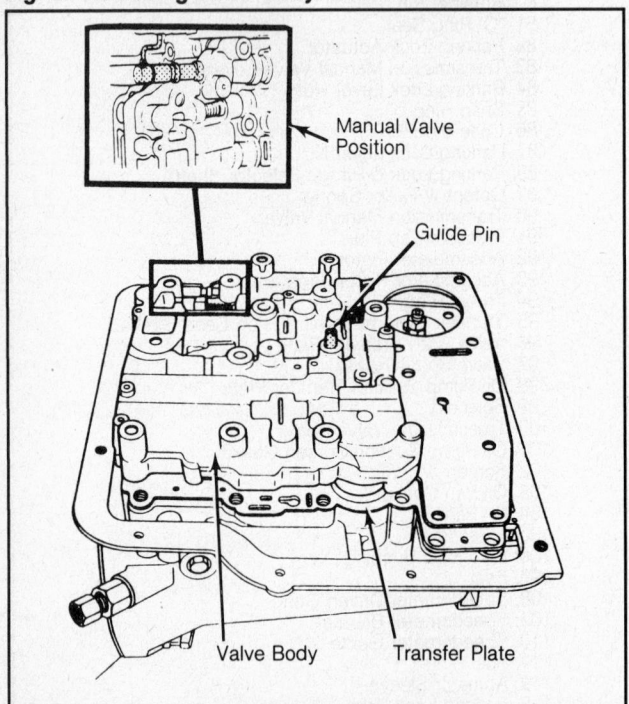

Care must be taken so that manual valve and link are not damaged or lost during valve body removal.

4) Remove 2 bolts holding transfer plate to valve body, then remove plate and gasket. Remove 2 check balls located in oil passages in transmission case.

NOTE: Location of these 2 check balls must be noted to ensure that they are reinstalled correctly.

5) Using Compressor (J-23075), compress servo piston and remove retaining snap ring. Remove compressor and servo piston assembly.

MODULATOR ASSEMBLY

Remove vacuum modulator from transmission case. Use care not to lose the modulator plunger. Remove modulator valve and sleeve from case. Remove "O" ring seal, by using internal snap ring pliers.

Fig. 3: Location of Check Balls in Case Oil Passages

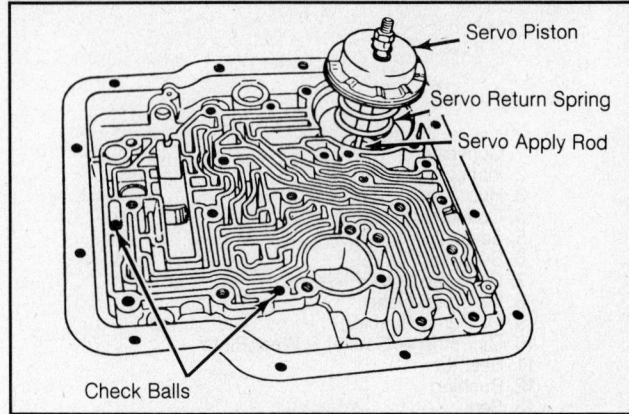

Arrows indicate check ball location.

Fig. 4: Compressing Servo Piston to Remove Snap Ring

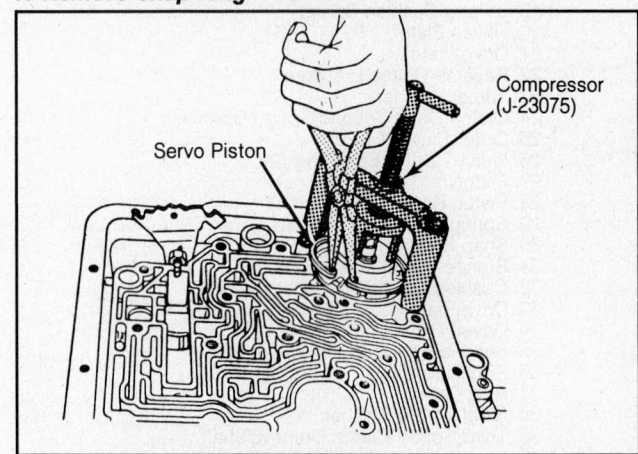

Servo is under high spring tension.

SELECTOR LEVER, SHAFT & DETENT VALVE ASSEMBLY

1) Remove lock nut securing inner lever to selector shaft, then remove inner lever. Remove selector lever shaft spring pin by pulling upwards with pliers. *See Fig. 5.*

Fig. 5: Removing Selector Lever Shaft Spring Pin

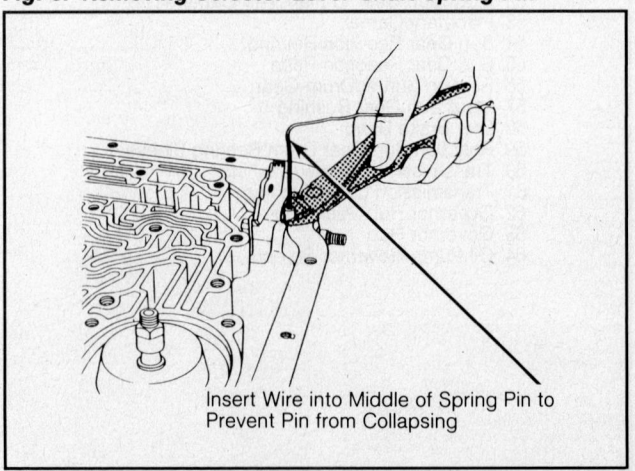

Insert Wire into Middle of Spring Pin to Prevent Pin from Collapsing

GENERAL MOTORS TURBO HYDRA-MATIC 180C (Cont.)

2) Remove selector lever shaft. Remove selector lever shaft oil seal. Discard oil seal. Remove electrical connector from transmission case. Remove vacuum modulator as previously described.

3) Remove detent valve spring pin using pliers. Push on spring seat of detent valve assembly from front of case and remove detent valve, sleeve, spring, and spring seat from rear of case.

EXTENSION HOUSING & SPEEDOMETER DRIVEN GEAR

1) Remove bolt holding speedometer driven gear housing retainer. Carefully remove retainer and pull driven gear assembly from extension housing bore.

2) Remove extension housing attaching bolts. Slide extension housing and gasket from case, while noting position of parking pawl in housing. Remove parking pawl actuator lever and actuator rod from transmission case. *See Fig. 6.*

Fig. 6: Removing Parking Pawl Actuator Rod

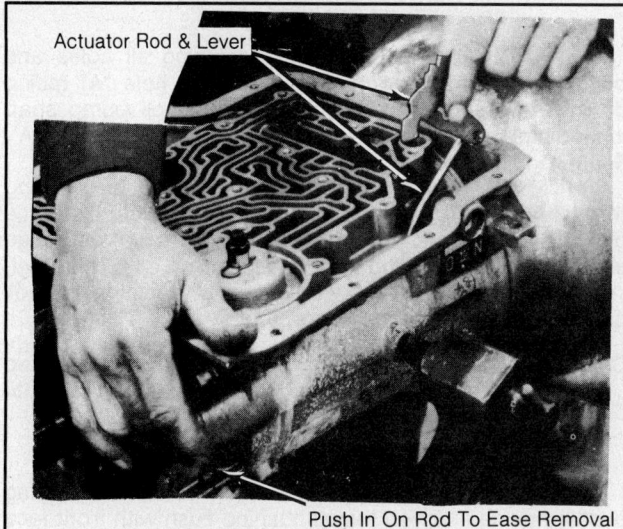

Actuator Rod & Lever

Push In On Rod To Ease Removal

SPEEDOMETER DRIVE GEAR, GOVERNOR BODY & HUB

1) Depress speedometer drive gear retaining clip and slide gear off output shaft.

2) Remove 4 attaching bolts from governor body, slide governor body off output shaft. Remove governor hub retaining snap ring, and slide hub from output shaft.

CONVERTER HOUSING, OIL PUMP, REVERSE CLUTCH & 2ND CLUTCH ASSEMBLY

1) Turn transmission in holding fixture so that converter housing is facing up. Remove the 7 converter housing attaching bolts. Loosen, but do not remove, the 5 oil pump attaching bolts. *See Fig. 7.*

2) Remove "O" ring seal from input shaft. Remove converter housing with oil pump, oil pump flange gasket and reverse clutch assemblies. Do not lose selective thrust washer, located between oil pump hub and 2nd clutch drum.

3) Remove 2nd clutch and 3rd clutch assemblies by lifting up on input shaft. Separate 2nd clutch and 3rd

Fig. 7: View of Converter Housing Showing Housing & Oil Pump Attaching Bolts

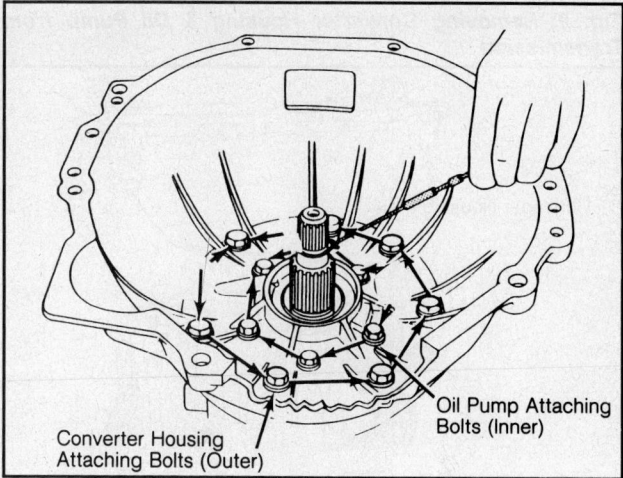

Converter Housing Attaching Bolts (Outer)

Oil Pump Attaching Bolts (Inner)

Outer bolts are converter housing bolts. Inner bolts are oil pump attaching bolts.

clutch assemblies. Remove reverse clutch plates and aluminum pressure plate from transmission case.

3RD CLUTCH, PLANETARY CARRIER, REACTION SUN GEAR & LOW BAND

1) Remove inside selector lever and parking lock actuator rod from transmission case. Lift out 3rd clutch assembly and input shaft. Remove planetary carrier and output shaft by sliding out.

NOTE: Care should be taken not to lose the 2 thrust bearings and 1 thrust washer from planetary carrier assembly.

2) Pull reaction sun gear and drum straight out of case. Remove thrust bearing from rear of transmission case. Remove low band by slightly compressing band and pulling straight out. If necessary, remove transmission case vent.

NOTE: If transmission case vent is removed, a new vent must be installed. DO NOT attempt to reinstall old vent.

COMPONENT DISASSEMBLY & REASSEMBLY

CONVERTER HOUSING, OIL PUMP & REVERSE CLUTCH

Disassembly

1) Remove 2nd clutch assembly from oil pump shaft. Remove selective washer from oil pump shaft.

2) Remove oil pump outer seal. Remove oil pump bolts from converter housing. Separate oil pump from housing. Remove oil pump wear plate. *See Fig. 8.*

3) Remove converter housing oil seal, and if necessary, remove housing bushing using a bushing driver. Mark relative location of oil pump gears and remove gears from oil pump body.

4) Using compressor, compress reverse clutch return springs and remove snap ring. Remove reverse clutch retaining ring and 24 return springs. Remove reverse clutch piston.

Fig. 8: Removing Converter Housing & Oil Pump from Transmission

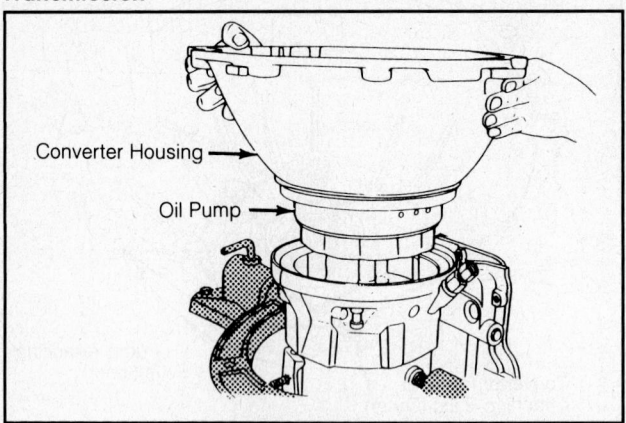

Converter Housing

Oil Pump

NOTE: **Pressure regulator valve and boost valve should not be removed unless it was determined by oil pressure checks to have been malfunctioning.**

Inspection

1) Clean converter housing thoroughly. Check converter pump hub for nicks, burrs or other damage. Remove nicks and burrs. Inspect the pressure regulator boost valve, the pressure regulator valve and the converter clutch actuator valve for nicks or damage.

2) Thoroughly clean the pressure regulator boost valve, pressure regulator valve and converter clutch actuator valve. Immerse valves in transmission fluid before installing in their bores. Inspect oil pump hub oil seal rings. Replace if damage or side wear is found.

3) Inspect reverse clutch piston for damage and replace if necessary. Inspect reverse clutch piston springs for wear or distortion and replace as necessary.

Fig. 9: Exploded View of Valves in Oil Pump

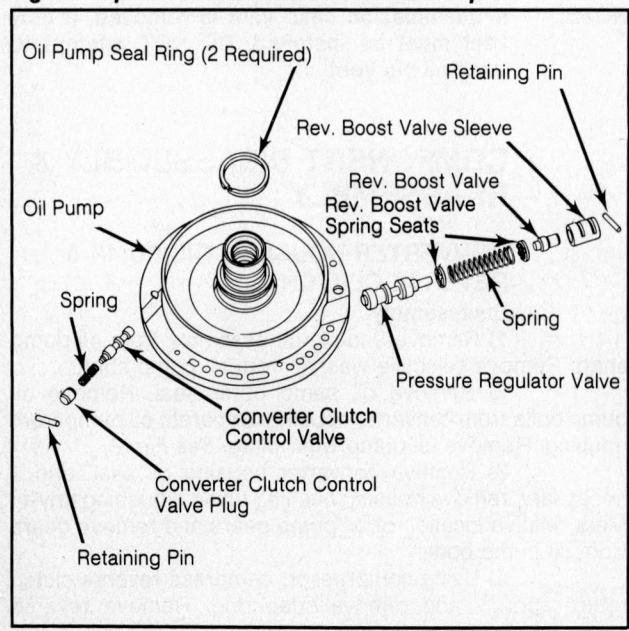

Oil Pump Seal Ring (2 Required)

Retaining Pin

Rev. Boost Valve Sleeve

Rev. Boost Valve
Rev. Boost Valve
Spring Seats

Oil Pump

Spring

Spring

Pressure Regulator Valve

Converter Clutch
Control Valve

Converter Clutch Control
Valve Plug

Retaining Pin

4) Inspect oil pump and gears for any signs of wear or damage, and replace as necessary. Install gears into oil pump and check end clearance of both gears.

5) Use a straightedge and feeler gauge and measure clearance between face of gears and pump face. Clearance should be .0005-.0035" (.013-.089 mm).

6) Next, measure clearance between drive gear and crescent while rotating gears one complete revolution. Clearance should be .005-.009" (.127-.229 mm).

7) Measure clearance between outside of driven gear and housing. Clearance here should be .003-.007" (.076-.178 mm). Finally, measure between inside of driven gear and crescent segment. Rotate gear one revolution. Clearance should be a minimum of .005" (.127 mm).

Oil Pump Hub Bushing Replacement

1) Inspect oil pump hub bushing for wear or damage and replace as necessary. If replacement is needed, thread a 3/4" standard pipe tap into bushing. Using a drift on tap, press oil pump bushing out with arbor press.

NOTE: **Use rag or cloth to protect oil pump face when pressing out bushing.**

2) Clean pump body, including all holes and pockets thoroughly. With oil pump shaft hole "A" facing downward, scribe an alignment mark on oil pump shaft inner diameter at the center of oil groove to right of hole "A". *See Fig. 10.*

3) Scribe mark on outer edge of bushing through centers of small and large drilled holes "B". Place bushing into oil pump shaft with small hole up, and align scribe marks on bushing with those made in oil pump shaft.

4) Use arbor press to drive bushing into oil pump shaft until seated in bore.

CAUTION: **Care must be taken so that bushing is pressed in straight, using scribe marks as a guide until firmly seated.**

Reassembly

1) If removed, install a new converter housing bushing using a driver. Install bushing flush with front face of housing. Install new converter housing oil seal.

2) Immerse pressure regulator valve in transmission fluid, install valve in oil pump body bore. Install pressure regulator spring, 2 spring seats, boost valve and sleeve into pump bore. Depress regulator boost valve sleeve until back end lines up with pin holes. Install retaining spring pin.

3) Install 2 new oil seals on reverse clutch piston. Install reverse clutch piston onto rear face of oil pump using a liberal amount of transmission fluid.

4) Install 24 reverse clutch piston return springs, then install retaining seat. Compress return springs and seat and install retaining snap ring.

CAUTION: **DO NOT air check reverse clutch as the clutch is not complete and damage to return spring retaining seat may occur.**

5) Turn oil pump and reverse clutch assembly so that oil pump face is up. Install oil pump gears using location marks made at disassembly. Install oil pump wear plate onto oil pump.

6) Insert guide pin into oil pump for alignment of converter housing and lower housing onto pump. Loosely install bolts into converter housing.

Fig. 10: Installing Oil Pump Hub Bushing

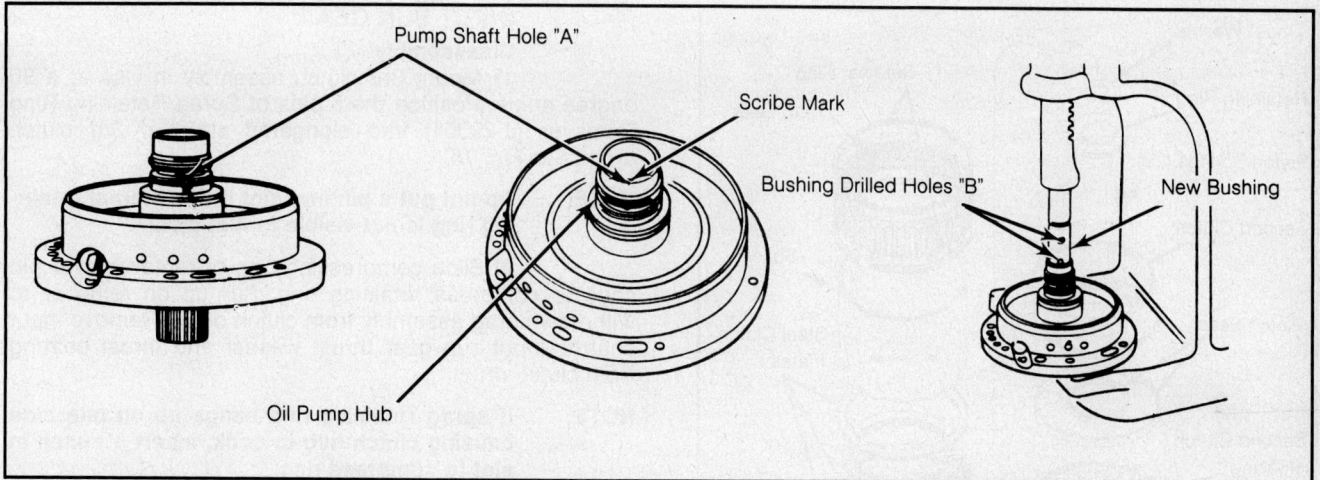

Scribe alignment marks on pump hub and bushing.

7) Use Aligner (J-23082-01) to align converter housing to pump. *See Fig. 11.* Aligner should bottom on oil pump gear.

Fig. 11: Using Aligner to Align Converter Housing to Oil Pump

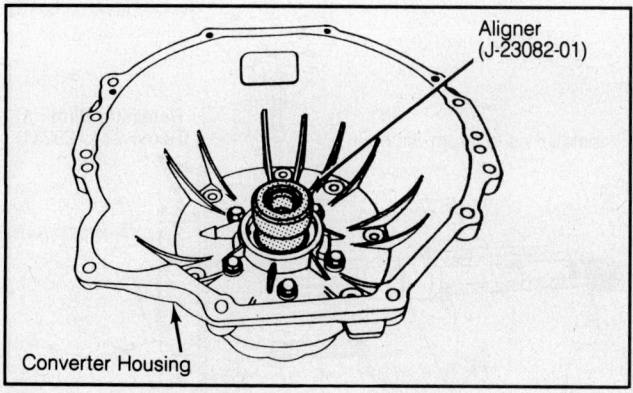

When correctly installed aligner should bottom on oil pump gear.

8) Tighten oil pump attaching bolts in two stages to specified torque. Remove aligner. Install new converter housing-to-case rubber oil seal.

2ND CLUTCH ASSEMBLY
Disassembly
1) Remove ring gear retaining ring from 2nd clutch drum, then pull ring gear from drum. Remove 2nd clutch spacer plate retaining ring, then remove spacer plate, steel and composition clutch plates from clutch drum.

NOTE: Keep clutch plates in same sequence as they were installed in clutch drum.

2) Remove 2nd clutch-to-3rd clutch thrust washer. Using compressor, compress 2nd clutch return springs and remove retaining snap ring. Remove compressor and withdraw spring retaining seat and return springs. Remove clutch piston from drum.

Inspection
1) Inspect clutch piston. If piston is damaged or if check ball falls out upon inspection, replace piston. Also, inspect piston lip seals and replace if worn or damaged.

2) Inspect piston return springs for wear and distortion and replace as necessary. Inspect clutch hub bushing, and if necessary use a driver to remove and install bushing.

3) Inspect clutch plates for wear, damage or signs of burning or glazing. Replace as necessary.

NOTE: If the surface of steel clutch plate; is smooth and an even color smear is indicated, plate should be reused. If severe heat spot discoloration or surface scuffing is indicated, plate should be replaced.

Fig. 12: Installing 2nd Clutch Piston

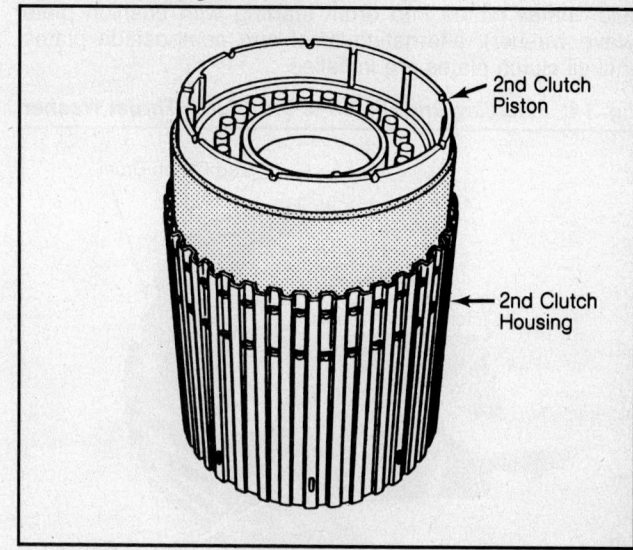

Reassembly
1) Lubricate piston seals with transmission fluid, then install piston into drum using Seal Protector (J-23080) to keep from damaging lip seals.

2) Install 22 piston return springs and spring seat on piston. Compress return springs and seat and install retaining snap ring.

NOTE: Care should be taken so that spring seat does not catch in snap ring groove.

Fig. 13: Exploded View of 2nd Clutch Assembly

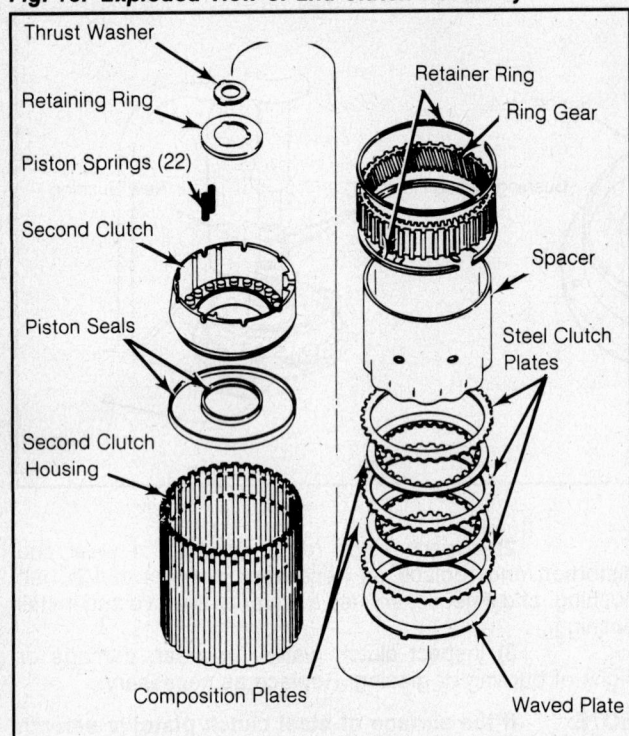

3) Install 2nd clutch-to-3rd clutch thrust washer so that tang seats in slot of 2nd clutch hub. Retain washer with petrolatum. *See Fig. 14.*

4) Lubricate clutch plates with transmission fluid. Install plates into drum starting with cushion plate (wave washer), alternating steel and composition plates until all clutch plates are installed.

Fig. 14: Installing 2nd Clutch-to-3rd Clutch Thrust Washer

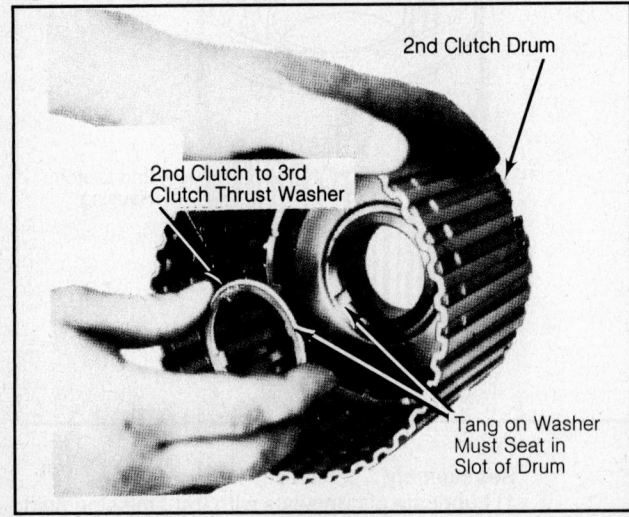

5) Install 2nd clutch spacer plate into drum. If necessary, expand spacer plate with screwdriver until ends are evenly butted together seating tightly into drum. Install spacer plate retaining snap ring. Install ring gear into drum with grooved edge facing up, then install retaining snap ring.

3RD CLUTCH ASSEMBLY, SPRAG & INPUT SUN GEAR

Disassembly

1) Mount 3rd clutch assembly in vise at a 90 degree angle. Position the 5 pins of Sprag Retaining Ring Remover (J-29351) into elongated slots of 3rd clutch drum. *See Fig. 15.*

NOTE: Do not put a pin into slot if the internal retaining ring is not visible in that slot.

2) Slide compressing ring of remover over pin cage to compress retaining ring. Pull up on remover to withdraw sprag assembly from clutch drum. Remove input shaft-to-input sun gear thrust washer and thrust bearing from clutch drum.

NOTE: If sprag retaining ring hangs up on one side causing clutch hub to cock, insert a punch in slot to compress ring.

3) Lift clutch plates from drum, noting the number and installation sequence for reassembly reference.

Fig. 15: Installing Retaining Ring Remover on 3rd Clutch Assembly

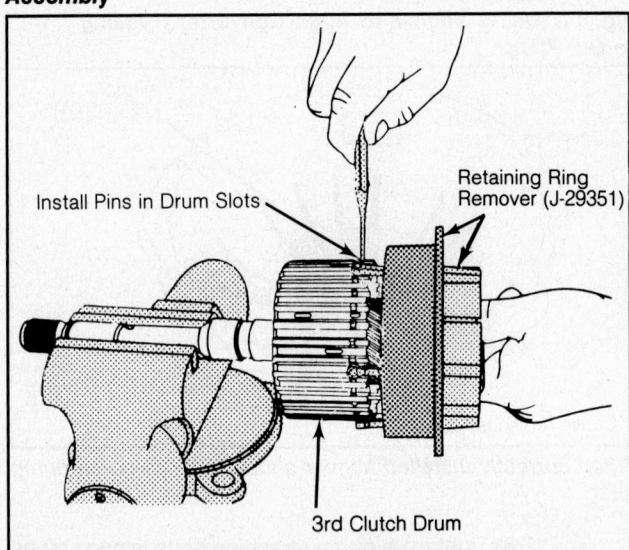

Insert punch in slot only if ring is visible.

4) Remove input sprag race and retainer assembly from clutch hub and input sun gear assembly. Push sprag assembly and retaining rings from sprag race and retainer.

5) Using compressor, compress 3rd clutch piston return springs and remove snap ring. Remove retaining seat and 12 piston return springs. Remove piston from drum.

Inspection

1) Inspect piston return springs for wear and distortion. Replace as necessary. Inspect clutch piston for wear, damage and condition of check ball. If check ball is missing or falls out upon inspection, replace piston.

2) Inspect steel thrust washer on front face of 3rd clutch drum. Replace if scored or damaged. Inspect all other thrust washers and thrust bearing for wear or damage and replace as necessary.

3) Inspect condition of composition and steel clutch plates. Replace as necessary. Inspect sprag assembly for wear, damage or sprags that fall freely out of cage.

GENERAL MOTORS TURBO HYDRA-MATIC 180C (Cont.)

Fig. 16: Sprag Assembly

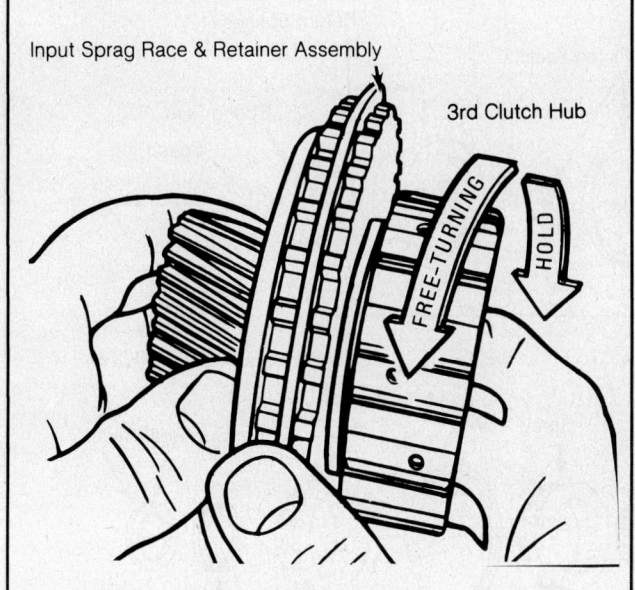

Input Sprag Race & Retainer Assembly

3rd Clutch Hub

FREE-TURNING

HOLD

Check sprag for correct operation.

Inspect input sun gear for chipped or nicked teeth or abnormal wear. Replace as necessary.

Reassembly

1) Lubricate and install new lip seals on clutch piston. Carefully install new oil seal on input shaft inside 3rd clutch drum, with lip pointing downward.

2) Install piston into drum using care not to damage lip seals. Install 12 piston return springs onto piston, then install spring seat over springs. Using compressor, compress return springs and seat. Install retaining snap ring.

NOTE: Care must be taken so that spring seat does not catch in snap ring groove when compressing springs.

3) Install 3rd clutch plates on hub in following order: steel plate, compostion plate, steel plate, composition plate, steel plate, and conical steel plate. When installed correctly, the I.D. of conical plate will touch steel plate below it but, O.D. will not.

NOTE: Install the same number of clutch plates as were removed. Also, lubricate plates with transmission fluid before installing.

4) Install thrust washer and thrust bearing onto input shaft, with inner lips of bearing toward washer. Retain in place with petrolatum.

5) Install sprag onto clutch hub with flare shoulder on cage outer diameter toward input sun gear. Install sprag race and retainer assembly over sprag assembly.

NOTE: When correctly assembled, sprag should rotate when turned counterclockwise and lock up when turned clockwise.

6) Slightly turn clutch hub and sprag assembly to engage it to clutch plate splines until sprag race rests on clutch drum.

7) Align teeth of sprag race with splines of clutch drum. Using a small screwdriver, press retaining ring all around into ring groove, at the same time applying pressure on sprag race. Slide sprag into clutch drum until retaining ring snaps into clutch drum groove.

REACTION SUN GEAR & DRUM
Inspection

1) Inspect reaction sun gear for chipped or nicked teeth and inspect sun gear for scoring. If necessary, replace complete assembly.

2) Inspect reaction sun gear drum bushing for wear or damage. If bushing requires replacement, use a chisel and remove bushing at bushing joint from sun gear.

Fig. 17: Installing 3rd Clutch Drum Retaining Ring

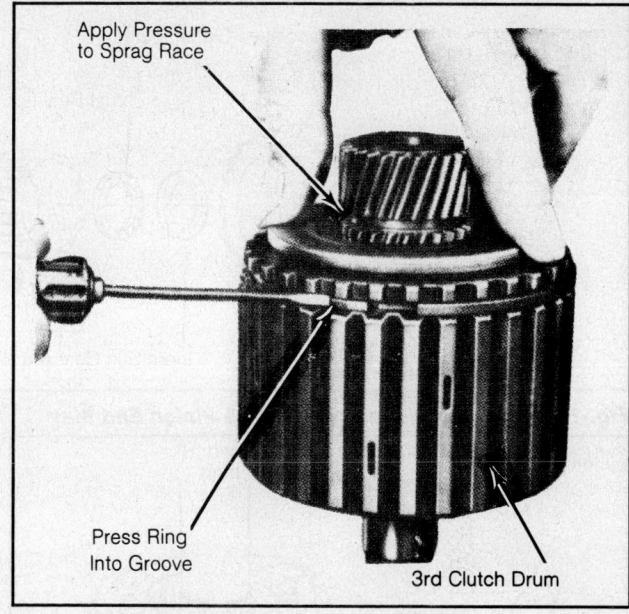

Apply Pressure to Sprag Race

Press Ring Into Groove

3rd Clutch Drum

3) Thoroughly clean drum. Install new bushing using a driver. Bushing should be installed flush with rear face of sun gear drum hub.

PLANETARY CARRIER
Inspection

1) Inspect planetary carrier and output shaft for distortion or damage. Inspect planetary pinions for excessive wear or damage, such as chipped teeth.

2) Check end play of all planetary pinions using a feeler gauge at points "A" and "B". See Fig. 19. End play should be .005-.035" (.127-.89 mm). If end play is not as specified, replace complete planetary carrier.

3) Tighten planetary carrier lock plate retaining screws to 20-35 ft. lbs. (27-48 N.m.)

GOVERNOR BODY
Disassembly

Depress secondary valve spring with small screwdriver and remove secondary valve spring retainer. Remove secondary valve spring, secondary valve and primary valve from governor body.

Inspection

1) Inspect primary and secondary valves for nicks, burrs and other damage. If necessary, use crocus cloth to remove small burrs.

NOTE: Do not remove the sharp edges of the valve since these edges perform a cleaning action within the valve bore.

Fig. 18: Exploded View of 3rd Clutch Assembly, Sprag & Input Sun Gear Assembly

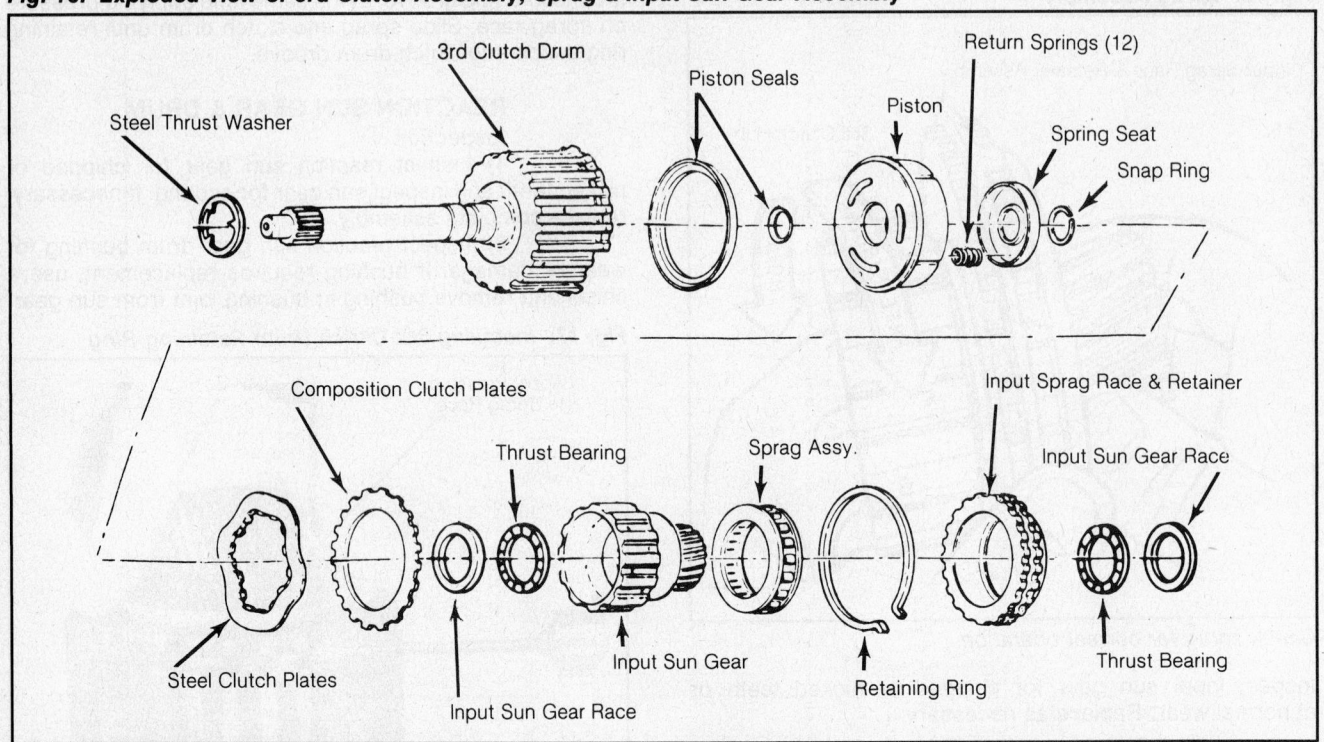

Fig. 19: Checking Planetary Carrier & Pinion End Play

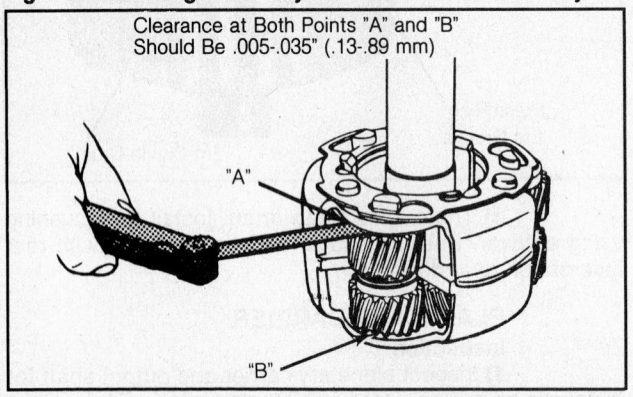

Clearance at Both Points "A" and "B" Should Be .005-.035" (.13-.89 mm)

Fig. 20: Exploded View of Governor Body

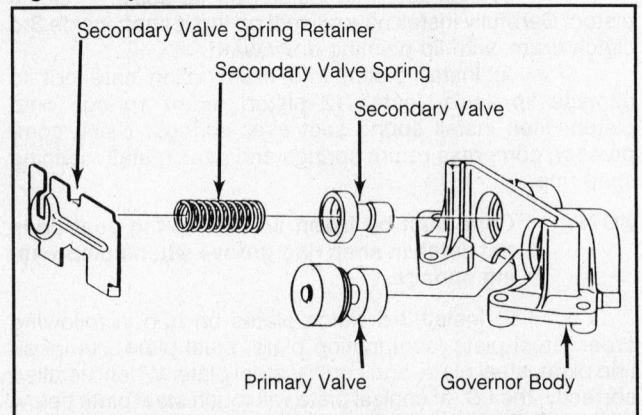

2) Inspect secondary valve spring for distortion or breakage. Clean governor body in solvent and below out all passages with compressed air. Replace governor body if damaged or worn.

NOTE: **Lubricate governor valves with transmission fluid before installation.**

Reassembly
Install primary valve in governor, small end first. Install secondary valve (small end first) into governor body. Install secondary valve spring, then depress spring and install retainer.

GOVERNOR HUB
Inspection
1) Inspect governor hub oil seal rings for wear or damage, and if necessary replace. Remove governor hub oil screen, using care not to lose or damage screen.

2) Inspect screen and clean with solvent and air dry. Install governor screen flush with hub. Inspect governor hub splines for cracks or chipped teeth in splines. Replace governor hub if required.

Fig. 21: Exploded View of Servo Piston Assembly

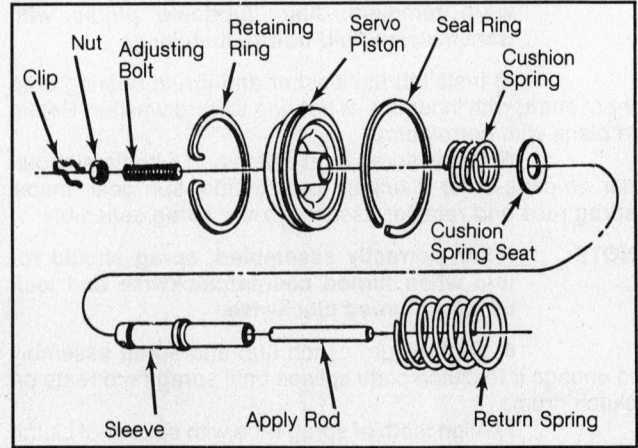

EXTENSION HOUSING
Inspection
1) Inspect extension housing for damage and replace housing if necessary. Check parking pawl and spring for damage and replace as necessary.

2) If extension housing rear seal requires replacement, use a screwdriver and pry seal from housing. If bushing requires replacement, use a driver and drive bushing from housing.

3) Clean housing of dirt and foreign matter. Install new housing bushing into housing using a bushing driver until bushing is flush with shoulder of extension housing. Install new oil seal into rear of housing.

SERVO PISTON
Disassembly
1) Remove servo piston apply rod. Holding servo piston sleeve at flat portion of sleeve with wrench, loosen adjusting bolt lock nut and remove.

2) Depress servo piston sleeve and remove piston sleeve retaining ring. Push sleeve through piston and remove cushion spring and spring retainer. Remove servo piston ring.

Inspection
Inspect cushion spring, adjusting bolt, and piston sleeve for damage. Inspect piston for damage and piston ring for side wear. Replace if necessary. Reverse disassembly procedure to reassemble.

VALVE BODY ASSEMBLY

NOTE: As valve trains are removed from each valve body bore, place individual parts in correct order and in relative postion to valve body to simplify reassembly. Valves and springs are not interchangeable, all parts must be reinstalled in correct order in proper valve body bore. Use valve body exploded view illustration as a disassembly and reassembly guide.

Disassembly
1) Remove manual valve and link from valve body. Turn valve body so that transfer plate is facing upward and remove the two bolts attaching plate to valve body. Remove transfer plate and gasket.

2) Using a small "C" clamp, compress accumulator piston and remove retaining ring. *See Fig. 22.* Carefully loosen "C" clamp as accumulator is under spring tension, then remove accumulator piston, oil ring and spring.

3) Remove retaining pin then slide out 1-2 shift control valve sleeve, control valve, 1-2 shift valve spring and valve.

NOTE: It may be necessary to remove burrs in valve body bores made by retaining pin prior to removal of sleeves and valves.

4) Remove 2-3 shift control valve retaining pin and sleeve, then slide out 2-3 shift control valve, spring seat, spring and 2-3 shift valve.

5) Remove 3-2 control valve retaining pin and plug. Remove 3-2 control valve spring and control valve.

6) Remove detent pressure regulator valve retaining pin, then remove spring and detent pressure regulator valve.

Fig. 22: Removing Accumulator Piston Retaining Ring with "C" Clamp

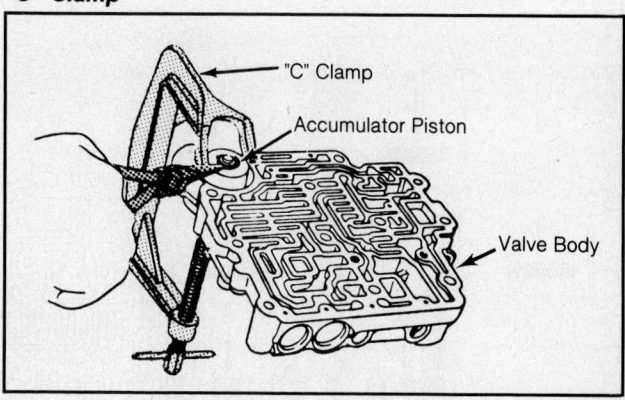

7) Remove high speed downshift timing valve retaining pin, then remove spring and valve.

8) Remove downshift timing valve plug retaining pin, then remove plug. Remove low speed downshift timing valve and spring.

9) Remove manual low and reverse control valve retaining pin, then remove spring and manual low control valve and reverse control valve.

10) Remove the 1-2 accumulator valve retaining pin and remove 1-2 accumulator valve plug, accumulator valve and spring.

Inspection
1) Inspect each valve for free movement in its respective bore. If necessary, use crocus cloth to remove small burrs on valves.

CAUTION: Do not remove the sharp edges of the valves as these edges perform a cleaning action within the bore.

2) Inspect valve springs for distortion or collapsed coils. Replace complete valve body assembly if any part is damaged. Inspect transfer plate for dents or distortion. Replace transfer plate if necessary.

Reassembly
Reverse disassembly procedure using a liberal amount of transmission fluid on all valves, plugs and springs.

TRANSMISSION CASE
Inspection
1) Inspect case for damage. Clean oil passages with cleaning solvent and air. Check for good retention of band anchor pins. Inspect all threaded holes for thread damage.

2) Inspect detent valve and modulator valve bores for scratches or scoring. Inspect case bushing inside case at rear. If damaged, remove and install bushing using a driver. Install bushing flush with rear of case.

3) Inspect reaction sun gear drum bushing sleeve inside case at rear for scoring. If necessary, replace sleeve before installing new case bushing.

CAUTION: Care must be used when removing sleeve in order that aluminum case is not damaged.

Fig. 23: Exploded View of Valve Body Assembly

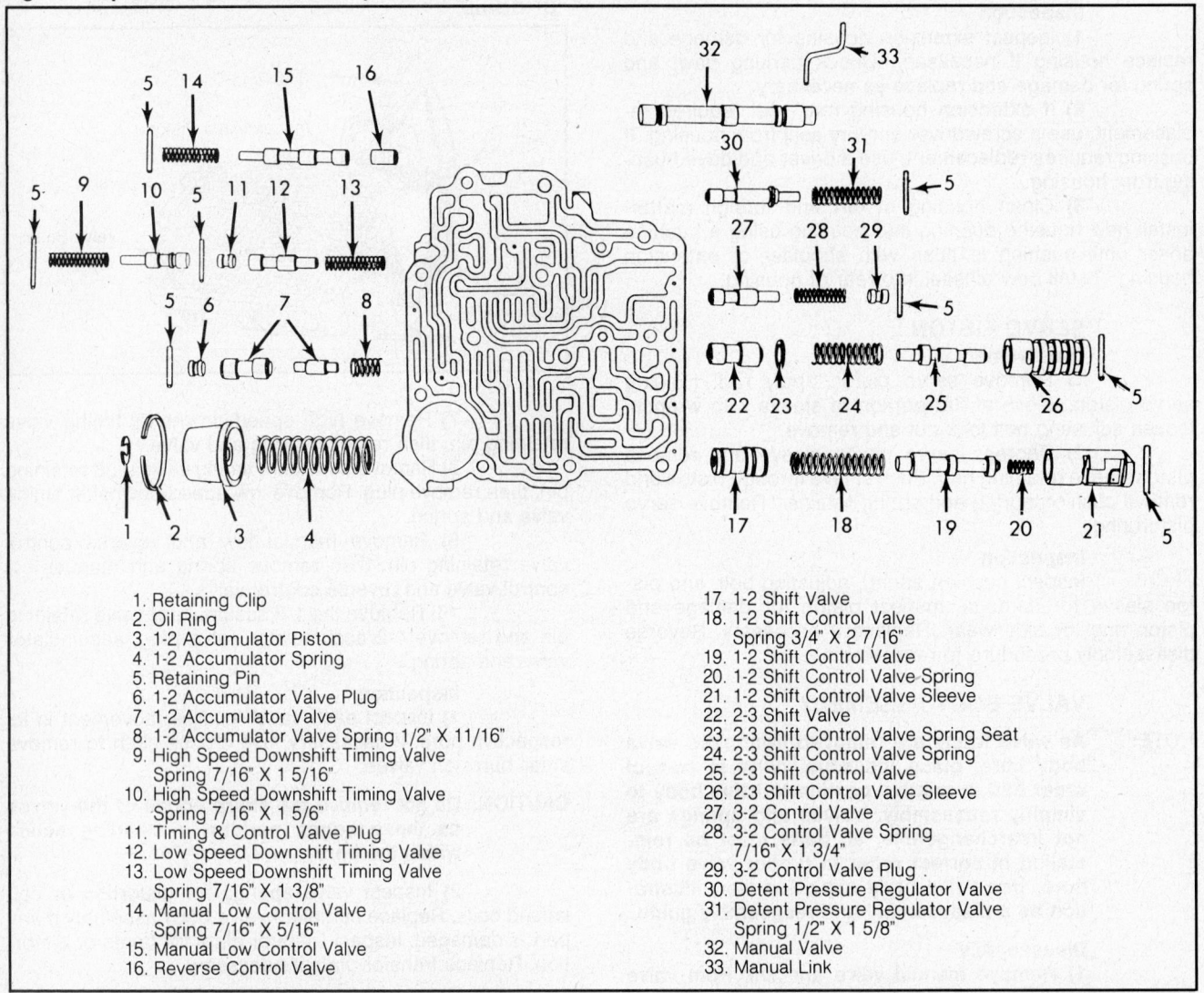

1. Retaining Clip
2. Oil Ring
3. 1-2 Accumulator Piston
4. 1-2 Accumulator Spring
5. Retaining Pin
6. 1-2 Accumulator Valve Plug
7. 1-2 Accumulator Valve
8. 1-2 Accumulator Valve Spring 1/2" X 11/16"
9. High Speed Downshift Timing Valve Spring 7/16" X 1 5/16"
10. High Speed Downshift Timing Valve Spring 7/16" X 1 5/6"
11. Timing & Control Valve Plug
12. Low Speed Downshift Timing Valve
13. Low Speed Downshift Timing Valve Spring 7/16" X 1 3/8"
14. Manual Low Control Valve Spring 7/16" X 5/16"
15. Manual Low Control Valve
16. Reverse Control Valve
17. 1-2 Shift Valve
18. 1-2 Shift Control Valve Spring 3/4" X 2 7/16"
19. 1-2 Shift Control Valve
20. 1-2 Shift Control Valve Spring
21. 1-2 Shift Control Valve Sleeve
22. 2-3 Shift Valve
23. 2-3 Shift Control Valve Spring Seat
24. 2-3 Shift Control Valve Spring
25. 2-3 Shift Control Valve
26. 2-3 Shift Control Valve Sleeve
27. 3-2 Control Valve
28. 3-2 Control Valve Spring 7/16" X 1 3/4"
29. 3-2 Control Valve Plug
30. Detent Pressure Regulator Valve
31. Detent Pressure Regulator Valve Spring 1/2" X 1 5/8"
32. Manual Valve
33. Manual Link

TRANSMISSION REASSEMBLY

SELECTOR LEVER & SHAFT

1) Install new selector lever shaft oil seal in case, with grooved end (with metric threads) outside of case. Insert selector shaft through case from outside.

NOTE: Use care not to damage oil seal when installing shaft.

2) Insert spring pin in case to secure selector lever shaft. Guide selector lever over shaft and secure with lock nut. Insert parking pawl actuator rod from front of case and through hole in rear of case, then install retaining ring.

LOW BAND & REACTION SUN GEAR & DRUM

1) Turn transmission case so that front of case is upward. Place band in case and locate onto anchor pins in case.

2) Place thrust bearing into case and retain with petrolatum. The case bushing acts as a guide to center bearing.

3) Insert reaction sun gear and drum into low band with reaction sun gear facing upward. Install thrust bearing onto sun gear and hold in place with petrolatum.

OUTPUT SHAFT & PLANETARY CARRIER

1) Install thrust washer and Torrington bearing into planetary carrier. Retain in place with petrolatum.

2) Insert output shaft and planetary carrier from front of case. Ensure that planetary carrier engages reaction sun gear.

2ND & 3RD CLUTCH ASSEMBLIES

1) With 2nd clutch assembly on bench, align drive plates in drum. Insert 3rd clutch drum and input shaft through top of 2nd clutch drum, seating 3rd clutch drum splines with 2nd clutch plate splines.

2) Holding clutch assemblies by input shaft, lower into transmission case, indexing 2nd clutch drum ring gear with long planetary pinion gear teeth.

GENERAL MOTORS TURBO HYDRA-MATIC 180C (Cont.)

Fig. 24: Cutaway View of Transmission Case Showing Location of Washers & Bushings

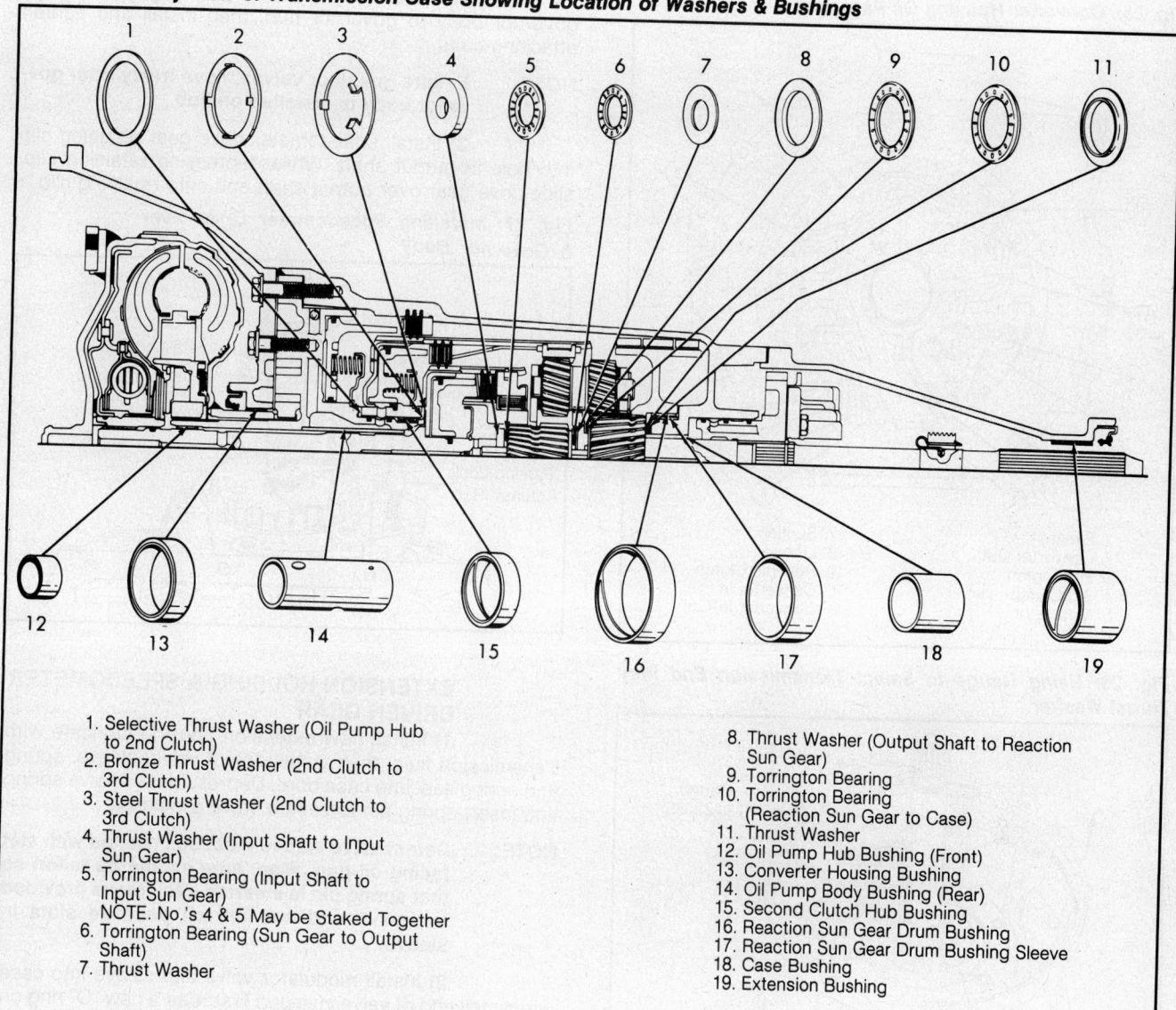

1. Selective Thrust Washer (Oil Pump Hub to 2nd Clutch)
2. Bronze Thrust Washer (2nd Clutch to 3rd Clutch)
3. Steel Thrust Washer (2nd Clutch to 3rd Clutch)
4. Thrust Washer (Input Shaft to Input Sun Gear)
5. Torrington Bearing (Input Shaft to Input Sun Gear)
   NOTE. No.'s 4 & 5 May be Staked Together
6. Torrington Bearing (Sun Gear to Output Shaft)
7. Thrust Washer

8. Thrust Washer (Output Shaft to Reaction Sun Gear)
9. Torrington Bearing
10. Torrington Bearing (Reaction Sun Gear to Case)
11. Thrust Washer
12. Oil Pump Hub Bushing (Front)
13. Converter Housing Bushing
14. Oil Pump Body Bushing (Rear)
15. Second Clutch Hub Bushing
16. Reaction Sun Gear Drum Bushing
17. Reaction Sun Gear Drum Bushing Sleeve
18. Case Bushing
19. Extension Bushing

REVERSE CLUTCH PLATES

1) Install aluminum pressure plate into transmission case with flat side up. Ensure lug on pressure plate engages with one of the narrow notches in case.

2) Lubricate steel and composition reverse clutch plates with transmission fluid. Install clutch plates into transmission case starting with a steel plate and alternating composition and steel clutch plates until all plates are installed.

3) Install reverse clutch cushion plate (wave washer) into case, so that all three of its lugs are engaged into narrow notches in case.

SELECTING TRANSMISSION END PLAY SELECTIVE THRUST WASHER

1) Place Gauge (J-23085) on case flange and against input shaft. See Fig. 26. Loosen thumb screw to allow inner shaft of gauge to drop onto 2nd clutch drum hub.

2) Tighten thumb screw and remove gauge. Compare thickness of selective thrust washer No. "1" removed during transmission disassembly with protruding portion of gauge inner shaft.

3) Selective thrust washer used in reassembly should be the thickest washer available without exceeding the dimension of shaft protruding from gauge.

NOTE: **The dimension of thrust washer selected should be equal to or slightly less than inner shaft dimension for correct transmission end play. Selective thrust washers for end play are available in the following thicknesses: .069-.074", .075-.079", .080-.084", .085-.089", .090-.094", and .095-.100" (1.7-1.8 mm, 1.9-2.0 mm, 2.0-2.1 mm, 2.2-2.3 mm, 2.3-2.4 mm, and 2.4-2.5 mm).**

4) If correct thickness thrust washer has been installed, transmission end play should be .014-.031" (.36-.79 mm).

Fig. 25: *Converter Housing Oil Passages*

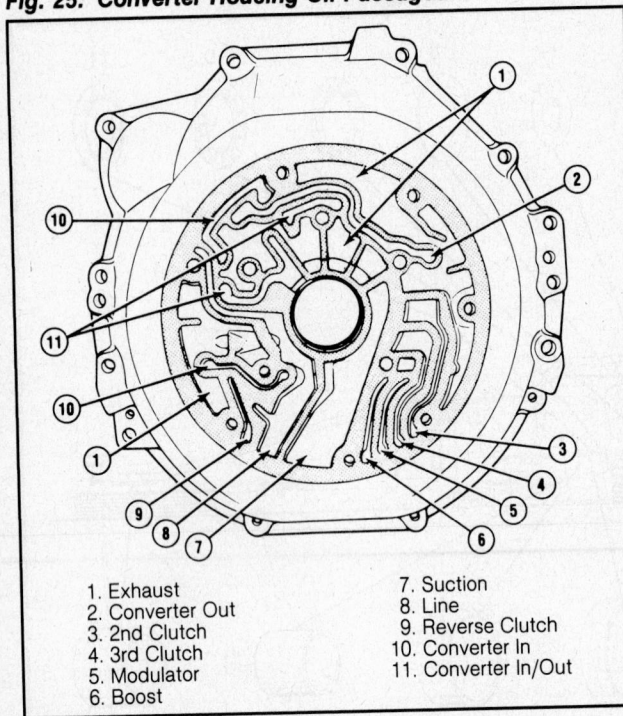

1. Exhaust
2. Converter Out
3. 2nd Clutch
4. 3rd Clutch
5. Modulator
6. Boost
7. Suction
8. Line
9. Reverse Clutch
10. Converter In
11. Converter In/Out

Fig. 26: *Using Gauge to Select Transmission End Play Thrust Washer*

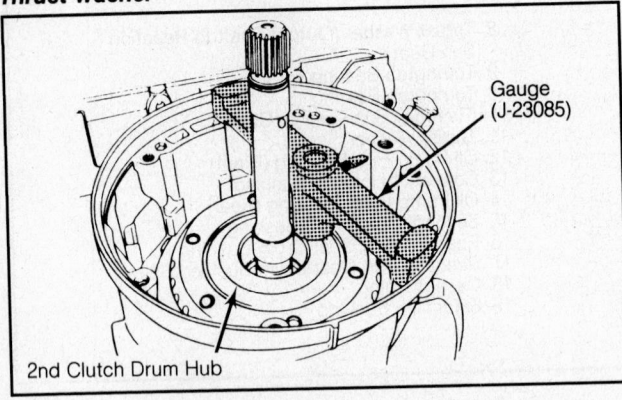

Gauge (J-23085)

2nd Clutch Drum Hub

CONVERTER HOUSING, OIL PUMP & REVERSE CLUTCH ASSEMBLY

1) Install new oil pump flange gasket. Place transmission end play thrust washer, as previously determined, onto oil pump shaft and retain with petroleum jelly.

2) Install guide pin in case and lower converter housing and oil pump into case. Use Oil Pump Aligner (K-23082) to align converter housing with oil pump and case, then install and tighten converter housing attaching bolts.

3) Check for correct assembly by turning input shaft by hand. Shaft should rotate freely without binding.

GOVERNOR ASSEMBLY & SPEEDOMETER DRIVE GEAR

1) Turn transmission so that bottom face is upward. Lubricate governor hub seal rings with transmission fluid, then slide hub onto output shaft until it seats in case. Install snap ring into output shaft groove to lock hub in place.

2) Install new governor body gasket. Install governor body to governor hub, then install and tighten attaching bolts.

NOTE: **Ensure governor valves move freely after governor body is installed on hub.**

3) Install speedometer drive gear retaining clip into hole in output shaft. While depressing retaining clip, slide drive gear over output shaft and onto retaining clip.

Fig. 27: *Installing Speedometer Drive Gear & Governor Body*

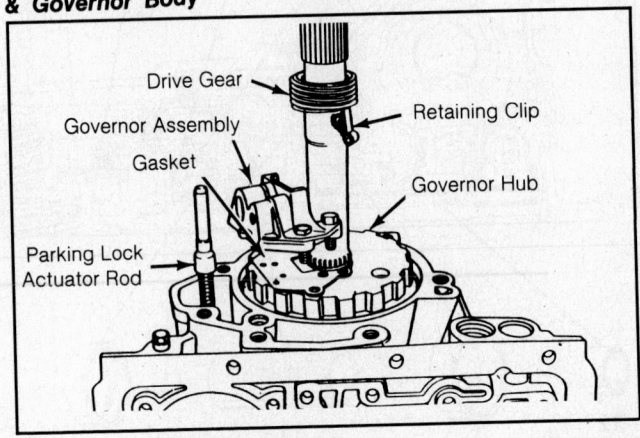

Drive Gear
Governor Assembly
Gasket
Retaining Clip
Governor Hub
Parking Lock Actuator Rod

EXTENSION HOUSING & SPEEDOMETER DRIVEN GEAR

1) Install new extension housing lubricate with transmission fluid, then install detent valve, sleeve, spring and spring seat into case bore. Depress detent valve spring and insert spring pin to secure valve assembly.

NOTE: **Detent valve sleeve must be installed with slot facing oil pan. Also, care should be taken so that spring pin is inserted into groove provided in sleeve and not into oil passage slots in sleeve.**

2) Install modulator valve and sleeve into case with small end of valve installed first. Use a new "O" ring on modulator, then install plunger and thread modulator into case and tighten.

SERVO ASSEMBLY

1) Install servo apply rod, spring and piston into case using a liberal amount of transmission fluid. Compress servo piston spring and install retaining ring while lightly tapping piston until piston is seated.

2) To adjust servo, use a 3/16" hex head wrench on servo adjusting bolt and tighten bolt to 40 INCH lbs. Back off bolt EXACTLY 5 turns. Hold adjusting bolt stationary and tighten lock nut.

VALVE BODY ASSEMBLY

1) Position steel check balls into case oil passages. *See Fig. 3.* Locate guide pin in case. *See Fig. 2.* Install new transfer plate-to-case gasket. Install bolts holding transfer plate to valve body.

2) Install manual valve into valve body bore using liberal amount of transmission fluid. Install long side of manual valve link into valve, then install short end of link into selector lever as valve body and transfer plate are installed over guide pins.

GENERAL MOTORS TURBO HYDRA-MATIC 180C (Cont.)

3) Install selector lever roller spring and retainer. Tighten valve body attaching bolts by starting at the center and working outward. Install reinforcement plate bolts to case and tighten.

EXTERNAL PARTS
Installation

1) Install governor pressure switch. Install solenoid valve and piping. Connect electrical wires. Negative wire connects to governor pressure switch and positive wire connects to case electrical connector.

2) Install oil strainer assembly using new gasket. Install servo cover using new gasket. Bolt oil pan to transmission using new gasket.

3) Slide torque converter over stator shaft and input shaft. Be sure that converter pump hub keyway is seated into oil pump drive lugs. With converter properly seated, distance between engine mounting face of case and the front face of converter cover straps should be 1".

TIGHTENING SPECIFICATIONS

Application	Ft. Lbs. (N.m.)
Extension Housing-to-Case	23 (31)
Converter Housing-to-Engine	25 (34)
Support-to-Extension Housing	33 (45)
Shift Lever-to-Extension Housing	20 (27)
Converter-to-Drive Plate	35 (48)
Reinforcement Plate-to-Case	14 (19)
Servo Cover-to-Case	18 (24)
Converter Housing-to-Oil Pump	14 (19)
Converter Housing-to-Case	25 (34)
Servo Adjusting Bolt Lock Nut	14 (19)
	INCH Lbs.
Converter Inspection Cover	84 (10)
Transfer Plate-to-Valve Body	84 (10)
Oil Pan-to-Case	96 (11)
Oil Pressure Tap	72 (8)
Selector Lever Lock Nut	108 (12)
Governor Body-to-Hub	72 (8)

Automatic Transmissions
GENERAL MOTORS TURBO HYDRA-MATIC 200C

Buick
  LeSabre, Regal
Chevrolet
  Caprice, El Camino, Impala,
  Monte Carlo
GMC
  Caballero,
Oldsmobile
  Cutlass Supreme, Delta 88
Pontiac
  Bonneville, Grand Prix, Parisienne

TRANSMISSION IDENTIFICATION

Transmission model may be identified by the production code number, located on an identification plate attached to right side of transmission case, near modulator. Number consists of a year code, 2 letter model code, and a build date code. Transmission model codes are listed in the following table.

TRANSMISSION MODEL CODES

Application	¹ Code
Buick	BH, HH & HL
Chevrolet	CV, HH, HL, OS, OU, 5C0, 5C5 & 5C6
GMC	CS, CV, HH, HL & OU
Oldsmobile	BH, HH, HL, OI & OU
Pontiac	CS, CV, BH, HH, HL & OU

¹ – Model CO, CZ and JY transmissions may also be used. Application not specified by manufacturer.

DESCRIPTION

The Turbo Hydra-Matic 200C automatic transmission is a fully automatic unit consisting primarily of a 3-element hydraulic torque converter with the addition of a converter clutch and a compound planetary gear set. Three multiple-disc clutches, a roller clutch and a band provide friction elements required to obtain the desired function of the compound planetary gear set. A hydraulic system pressurized by a gear type pump provides the working pressure required to operate the friction elements and automatic controls.

The 3-element torque converter consists of a pump or driving member, a turbine or driven member, and a stator assembly. The stator assembly is mounted on a one-way roller clutch which will allow stator to turn clockwise but not counterclockwise. The converter clutch is splined to the turbine assembly, and when operated, applies against the converter cover, providing mechanical direct drive coupling of the engine to the transmission planetary gears. When converter clutch is released, the assembly operates as a normal torque converter.

NOTE: See GENERAL MOTORS TORQUE CONVERTER CLUTCH article in this section for information on the Torque Converter Clutch (TCC) system used in the THM 200C.

LUBRICATION & ADJUSTMENTS

See appropriate AUTOMATIC TRANSMISSION SERVICING article in DOMESTIC GENERAL SERVICING section.

TROUBLE SHOOTING

See appropriate AUTOMATIC TRANSMISSION TROUBLE SHOOTING article in DOMESTIC GENERAL SERVICING section.

TESTING

ROAD TEST
Drive Range
Position selector lever in Drive range and accelerate vehicle. A 1-2 and 2-3 shift should occur at all throttle openings (shift points will vary with throttle opening). Check part throttle 3-2 downshift at 30 MPH by quickly opening throttle approximately three-fourths, transmission should downshift 3-2. Check for 3-2 downshifts at 50 MPH, by depressing accelerator fully.

Intermediate Range
Position selector lever in Intermediate range and accelerate vehicle. A 1-2 shift should occur at all throttle openings (shift point will vary with throttle opening). No 2-3 shift can be obtained in this range. Check detent 2-1 downshift at 20 MPH. Transmission should downshift 2-1.

Low Range
Position selector lever in Low range and accelerate vehicle. No upshift should occur in this range.

Intermediate Range Overrun Braking
Position selector lever in Drive range and with vehicle speed at approximately 50 MPH, with closed throttle, move selector lever to Intermediate range. Transmission should downshift to 2nd. An increase in engine RPM and an engine braking effect should be noticed.

Low Range Overrun Braking
At 40 MPH, with throttle closed, move selector lever to Low. A 2-1 downshift should occur in speed range of approximately 40-25 MPH, depending on axle ratio and control valve assembly calibration. The 2-1 downshift at closed throttle will be accompanied by increasing engine RPM and an engine braking effect should be noticed.

Reverse Range
Position selector lever in Reverse range and check for reverse operation.

CONTROL PRESSURE TEST
Preliminary Checking Procedure
Perform the following prior to making control pressure test:
- Check transmission fluid level.
- Check and adjust T.V. cable.
- Check and adjust outside manual linkage.
- Check engine tune-up.
- Install oil pressure gauge. *See Fig. 2.*
- Connect tachometer to engine

Minimum T.V. Pressure Check
With T.V. cable adjusted to specifications and brake applied, check line pressure in ranges and at engine RPM indicated in CONTROL PRESSURE SPECIFICATIONS chart.

Fig. 1: Sectional View of Turbo Hydra-Matic 200C Automatic Transmission

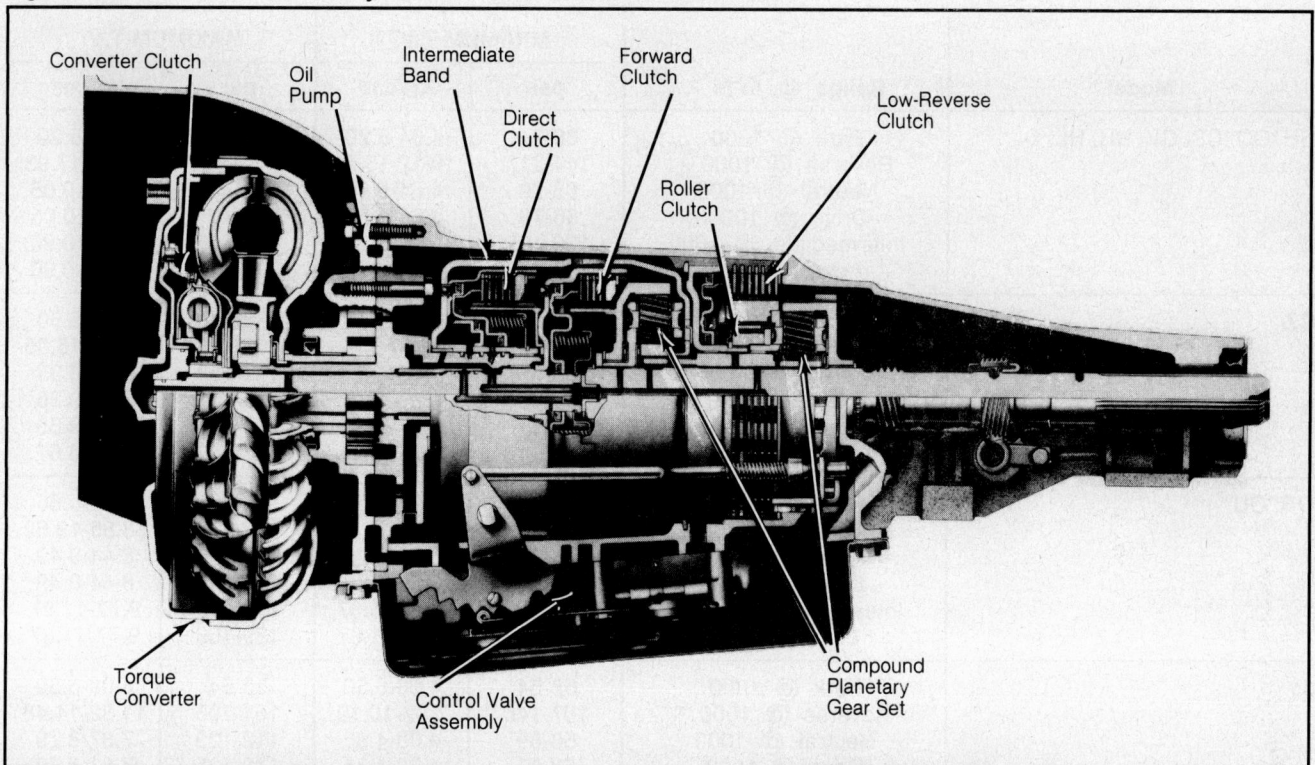

Fig. 2: View of Transmission Showing Location of Control Pressure Test Take-Off Point

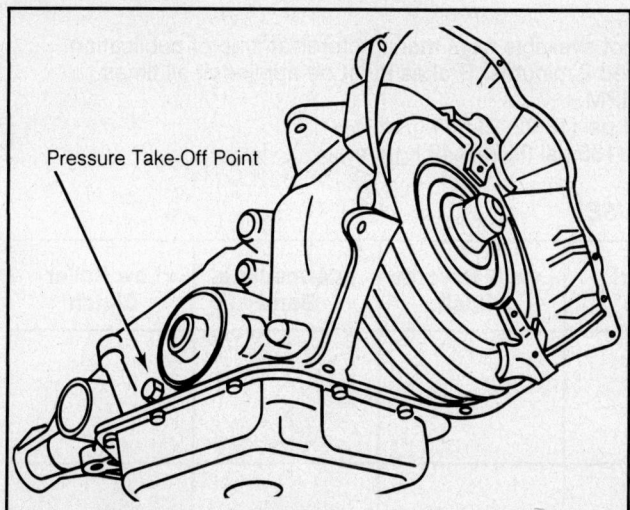

Check line pressure in ranges and at engine RPM indicated.

Full T.V. Pressure Check
With T.V. cable at full extent of its travel and brakes applied, check line pressure in ranges and at engine RPM indicated in CONTROL PRESSURE SPECIFICATIONS chart.

CONTROL PRESSURE RESULTS
High Or Low Oil Pressures
- T.V. cable misadjusted, binding, unhooked or broken.
- Throttle lever and bracket assembly binding, unhooked or mispositioned.
- Throttle valve or plunger binding.
- Shift T.V. valve binding.

- No. 1 check ball missing or leaking.
- Pressure regulator valve binding.
- Wrong pressure regulator valve spring installed.
- Oil pressure control orifice in pump cover plugged (causes high oil pressure).
- Pressure regulator bore plug leaking.
- Manual valve not connected.
- Intermediate boost valve binding (pressure will be incorrect in intermediate and low ranges only).
- Orifice in spacer plate at end of intermediate boost valve plugged.
- Reverse boost valve binding (pressures will be incorrect in reverse only).
- Orifice in spacer plate at end of reverse boost valve plugged.

SERVICE (IN VEHICLE)
The following components may be removed from transmission without removing transmission from vehicle.
- Governor Assembly.
- Governor Pressure Switch (Diesel Only).
- Intermediate Servo Assembly.
- Oil Pan and Oil Screen (Intake Pipe) Assembly.
- 3rd Accumulator Check Valve Assembly.
- Control Valve Body Assembly.
- Check Balls and Valve Body Spacer Plate and Gaskets.
- Pressure Regulator Parts.
- Inside Detent/Range Lever.
- Manual Detent and Roller Assembly.
- Throttle Lever and Bracket Assembly.
- T.V. Cable and "O" Ring.
- Parking Pawl Actuator Rod, Bracket, and Parking Pawl.

Automatic Transmissions
GENERAL MOTORS TURBO HYDRA-MATIC 200C (Cont.)

CONTROL PRESSURE SPECIFICATIONS

Model [1]	Range @ RPM [2]	MINIMUM T.V.		MAXIMUM T.V.	
		psi	kg/cm²	psi	kg/cm²
BH, CO, CS, CV, HH, HL, OI	Park @ 1000	66-74	4.64-5.20	66-74	4.64-5.20
	Reverse @ 1000 [3]	144-217	10.12-15.26	205-264 [4]	14.55-17.93
	Neutral @ 1000	66-79	4.64-5.55	127-143 [5]	8.93-10.05
	Drive @ 1000	66-79	4.64-5.55	127-143 [5]	8.93-10.05
	Intermediate @ 1000	130-155	9.14-10.90	130-155	9.14-10.90
	Low @ 1000	130-155	9.14-10.90	130-155	9.14-10.90
CZ	Park @ 1000	58-64	4.08-5.50	58-64	4.08-5.50
	Reverse @ 1000 [3]	107-145	7.52-10.19	168-214	11.81-15.05
	Neutral @ 1000	58-69	4.08-4.85	119-133	8.37-9.35
	Drive @ 1000	58-69	4.08-4.85	119-133	8.37-9.35
	Intermediate @ 1000	82-94	5.77-6.61	119-133	8.37-9.35
	Low @ 1000	82-94	5.77-6.61	82-94	7.77-6.61
OR, OU	Park @ 1000	76-85	5.34-5.60	76-85	5.34-5.60
	Reverse @ 1000 [3]	153-229	10.76-16.10	197-279	13.85-19.62
	Neutral @ 1000	76-90	5.34-6.33	120-135	8.44-9.49
	Drive @ 1000	76-90	5.34-6.33	120-135	8.44-9.49
	Intermediate @ 1000	139-166	9.77-11.67	139-166	9.77-11.67
	Low @ 1000	139-166	9.77-11.67	139-166	9.77-11.67
JY	Park @ 1000	58-64	4.08-5.50	58-64	4.08-5.50
	Reverse @ 1000 [3]	107-145	7.52-10.19	161-206	11.32-14.48
	Neutral @ 1000	58-69	4.08-4.85	112-125	7.87-8.79
	Drive @ 1000	58-69	4.08-4.85	112-125	7.87-8.79
	Intermediate @ 1000	95-112	6.68-7.87	112-125	7.87-8.79
	Low @ 1000	95-112	6.68-7.87	95-112	6.68-8.78

[1] – Information on OS, 5C0, 5C5 and 5C6 model transmissions not available from manufacturer at time of publication.
[2] – Total running time for this combination of tests is not to exceed 2 minutes. Brakes must be applied at all times.
[3] – Maximum T.V. reverse line pressure to be checked at 2000 RPM.
[4] – Maximum T.V. pressure on model OI transmission is 198-264 psi (13.92-18.56 kg/cm²).
[5] – Maximum T.V. line pressure on model OI transmission is 121-135 psi (8.51-9.49 kg/cm²).

CLUTCH AND BAND APPLICATION CHART (ELEMENTS IN USE)

Selector Lever Position	Direct Clutch	Forward Clutch	Low & Reverse Clutch	Intermediate Band	Low Roller Clutch
D – DRIVE					
First Gear		X			X
Second Gear		X		X	
Third Gear	X	X			
S or L2 – INTERMEDIATE					
First Gear		X			X
Second Gear		X		X	
L or L1 – LOW					
First Gear		X	X		
R – REVERSE	X		X		

NEUTRAL OR PARK – Band and clutches released and/or ineffective.

GENERAL MOTORS TURBO HYDRA-MATIC 200C (Cont.)

- Manual Shaft and Seal.
- Manual Valve.
- Rear Seal.
- 1-2 Accumulator and Spring.
- Low-Reverse Clutch Cup Plug.
- Cooler Fittings.
- Oil Filter Pipe & "O" Ring.
- Speedometer Driven Gear Assembly.
- Solenoid Wire Clips.
- Electrical Connector

For removal and installation of these components, see TRANSMISSION DISASSEMBLY and TRANSMISSION REASSEMBLY.

REMOVAL & INSTALLATION

TRANSMISSION

See appropriate AUTOMATIC TRANSMISSION REMOVAL article in DOMESTIC GENERAL SERVICING section.

TORQUE CONVERTER

NOTE: Torque converter is a sealed unit and cannot be disassembled for service.

LEAKAGE CHECK

See procedure given in GENERAL MOTORS TURBO HYDRA-MATIC 400 article in this section.

END CLEARANCE CHECK

See procedure given in GENERAL MOTORS TURBO HYDRA-MATIC 400 article in this section.

CONVERTER FLUSHING

See procedure given in GENERAL MOTORS TURBO HYDRA-MATIC 400 article in this section.

NOTE: For additional information on the Torque Converter Clutch (TCC) system used on the THM 200C transmission, see GENERAL MOTORS TORQUE CONVERTER CLUTCH article in this section.

TRANSMISSION DISASSEMBLY

EXTERNAL PARTS

1) Mount transmission in a holding fixture and remove torque converter by pulling straight out. Remove oil pan and discard gasket. Remove oil screen and discard gasket.

NOTE: The two oil screen attaching bolts are about 3/8" (10 mm) longer than valve body attaching bolts, and they are not interchangeable.

2) On diesel models, remove governor pressure switch lead wire from switch and wire clips. Remove pressure switch using a 1 1/16" oil sending unit socket.

3) On all models, remove throttle lever and bracket assembly, using care not to bend throttle lever link. T.V. exhaust valve lifter and spring may separate from lever and bracket assembly.

Fig. 3: Removing Throttle Valve and Bracket Assembly

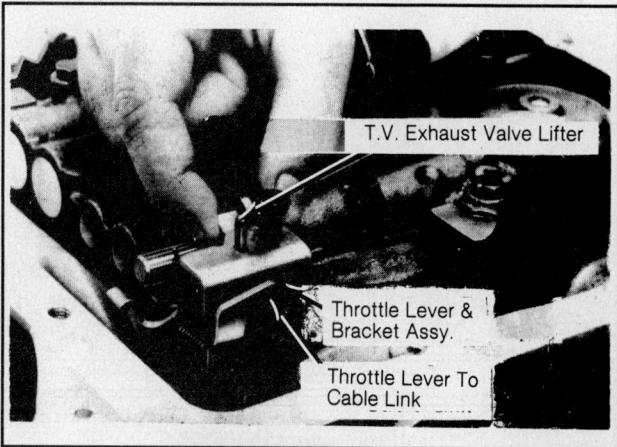

T.V. Exhaust Valve Lifter

Throttle Lever & Bracket Assy.

Throttle Lever To Cable Link

Do not bend throttle linkage.

4) Remove manual detent roller and spring assembly and remaining valve body attaching bolts. Holding manual valve with finger, remove valve body assembly, spacer plate, and gaskets together, to prevent dropping the 4 check balls located in valve body.

5) Remove 1-2 accumulator spring. Remove fifth check ball from bore in transmission case. See Fig. 4. Using a small screwdriver, remove governor cover retaining ring, then remove cover using pliers and discard cover seal rings. Remove governor assembly and governor-to-case washer.

NOTE: It may be necessary to rotate output shaft counterclockwise while removing governor. Do not use any type of pliers to ren.ove governor.

6) Remove lead wire from case electrical connector and solenoid wire clip, then compress fingers on connector sleeve and withdraw connector.

7) Depress intermediate servo cover and remove retaining ring. Using pliers, pull servo cover from case and discard cover seal ring. Remove intermediate servo piston and band apply pin assembly.

Fig. 4: Removing Fifth Check Ball From Transmission Case

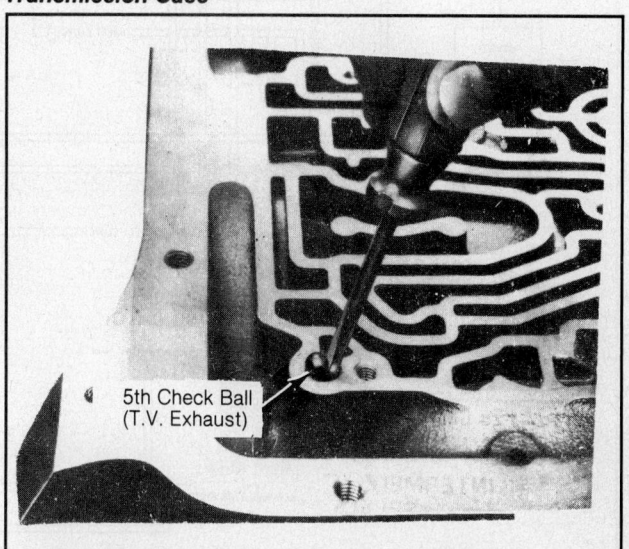

5th Check Ball (T.V. Exhaust)

Automatic Transmissions
GENERAL MOTORS TURBO HYDRA-MATIC 200C (Cont.)

Fig. 5: Turbo Hydra-Matic 200C Hydraulic Circuits Diagram (All Except Diesel Models)

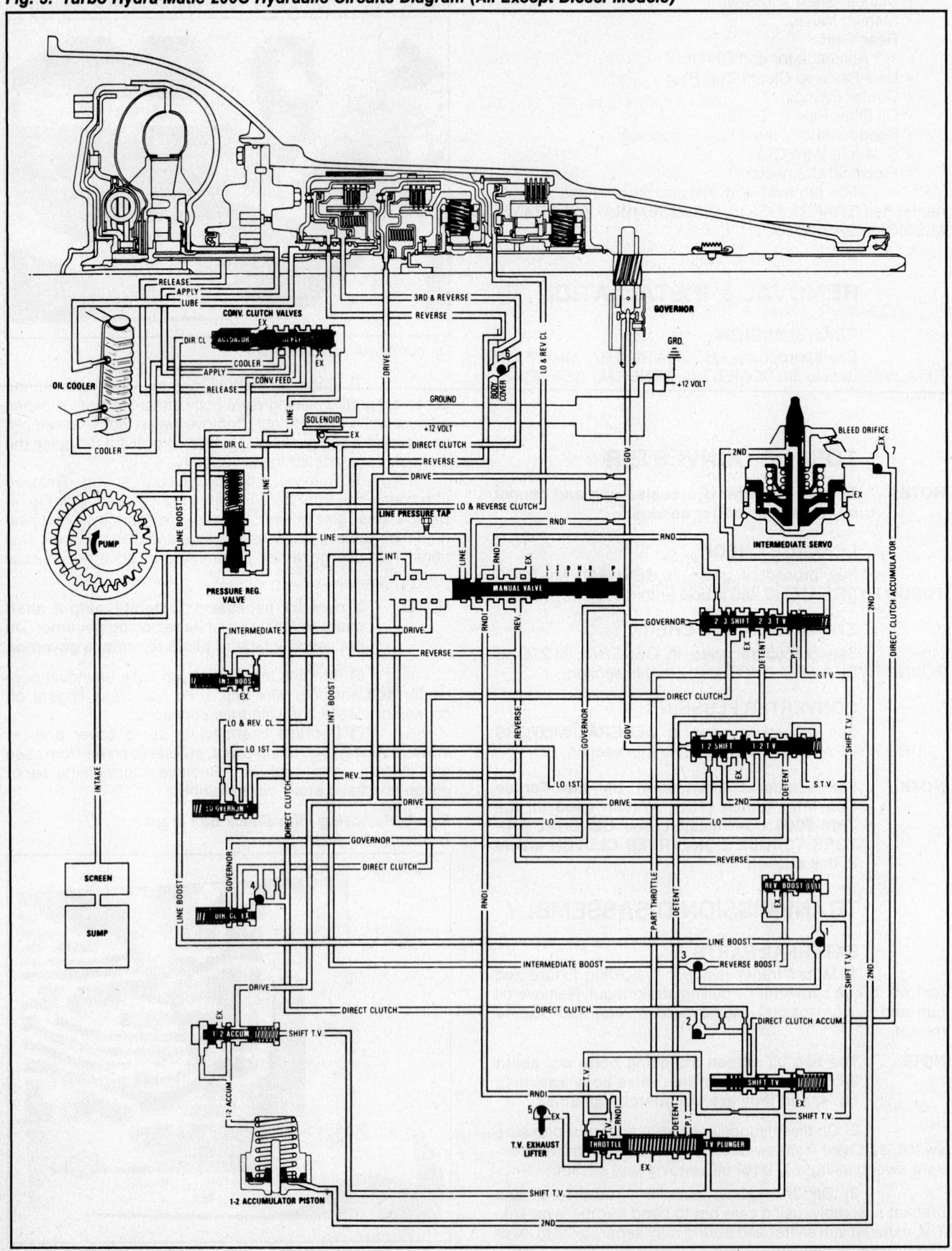

Fig. 6: Turbo Hydra-Matic 200C Hydraulic Circuits Diagram (Models With Diesel Engines)

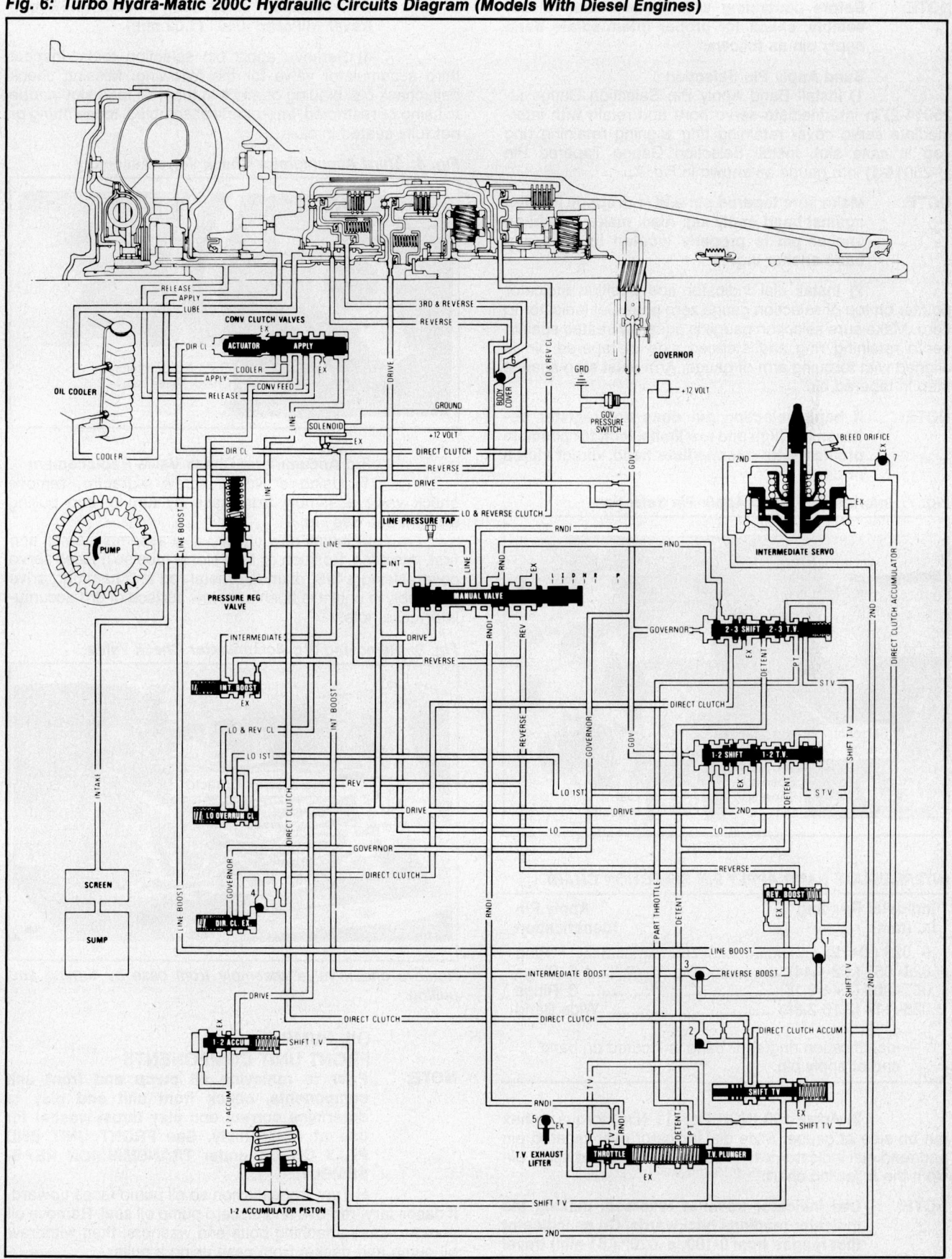

Automatic Transmissions
GENERAL MOTORS TURBO HYDRA-MATIC 200C (Cont.)

NOTE: Before continuing with Transmission Disassembly, check for proper intermediate band apply pin as follows:

Band Apply Pin Selection

1) Install Band Apply Pin Selection Gauge (J-25014-2) in intermediate servo bore and retain with intermediate servo cover retaining ring aligning retaining ring gap in case slot. Install Selection Gauge Tapered Pin (J-25014-1) into gauge as shown in *Fig. 7.*

NOTE: Make sure tapered pin end is properly located against band apply lug. Also, make sure band anchor pin is properly located in case and band anchor lug.

2) Install dial indicator and position indicator pointer on top of selection gauge zero post. Set indicator to zero. Make sure selection gauge is squarely seated against servo retaining ring and stepped side of tapered pin is aligned with torquing arm of gauge. Arm must stop against step in tapered pin.

NOTE: If band selection pin does not register between the high and low limits, look for possible problem with intermediate band, direct clutch or case.

Fig. 7: Intermediate Band Apply Pin Selection

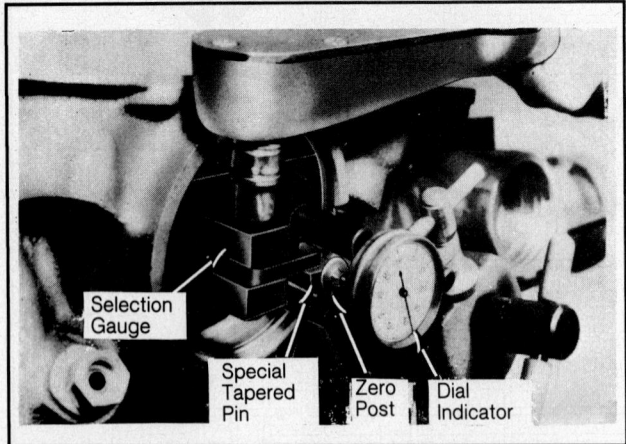

INTERMEDIATE BAND APPLY PIN SELECTION CHART

Indicator Reading In. (mm)	[1] Apply Pin Identification
.0-.029 (.0-.72)	1 Ring
.029-.057 (.72-1.44)	2 Rings
.057-.086 (1.44-2.16)	3 Rings
.086-.114 (2.16-2.88)	Wide Band

[1] – Identification ring(s) or band is located on band end of apply pin.

3) Apply 100 INCH lbs. (11 N.m) torque to hex nut on side of gauge. Slide dial indicator over tapered pin and read dial indicator travel. Select correct band apply pin from the following chart:

NOTE: Dial indicator travel is reversed, making the indicator readings backwards. On an indicator that ranges from 0-100, a .020" (.51 mm) travel

will read .080" (2.03 mm), a .060" (1.52 mm) travel will read .040" (1.02 mm).

4) Remove apply pin selection tools. Inspect third accumulator valve for the following: Missing check ball, check ball binding or stuck in tube, oil feed slot in tube missing or restricted, improperly assembled, loose fitting or not fully seated in case.

Fig. 8: Third Accumulator Check Valve Assembly

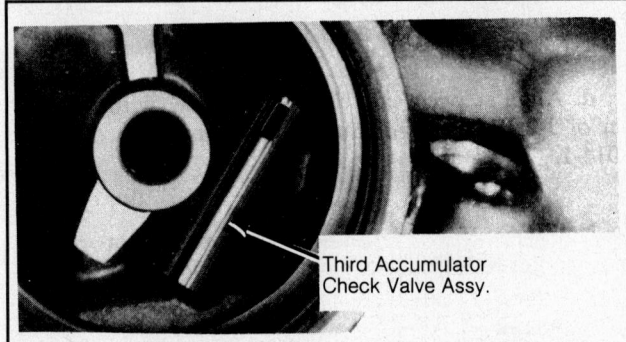

Third Accumulator Check Valve Assy.

3rd Accumulator Check Valve Replacement

1) Using a No. 4 screw extractor, remove check valve assembly from case by turning and pulling straight out. *See Fig. 9.*

2) Install new check valve assembly, small end first, into case. Position oil feed slot in tube so it faces servo cover. Using a 3/8" diameter metal rod and hammer, drive assembly in until it is flush or below surface of 3rd accumulator case hole.

Fig. 9: Removing 3rd Accumulator Check Valve

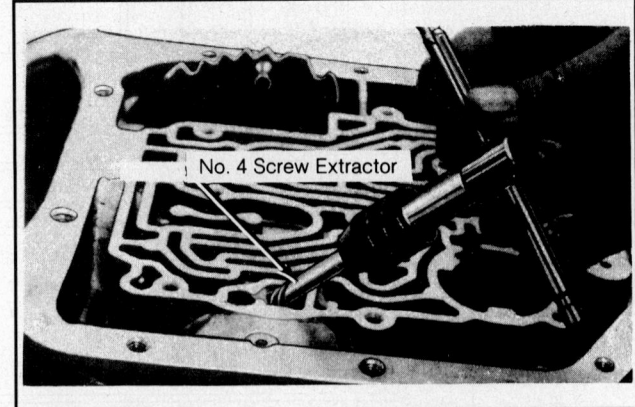

No. 4 Screw Extractor

Remove check valve assembly from case by turning and pulling.

OIL PUMP & FRONT UNIT COMPONENTS

NOTE: Prior to removing oil pump and front unit components, check front unit end play to determine correct end play thrust washer for use at reassembly. See FRONT UNIT END PLAY CHECK under TRANSMISSION REASSEMBLY.

1) Turn transmission so oil pump faces upward. If necessary, remove and discard pump oil seal. Remove oil pump-to-case attaching bolts and washers, then withdraw oil pump and gasket from case using a puller.

2) Grasp turbine shaft and pull direct and forward clutch assemblies from transmission case. Pull direct clutch assembly off forward clutch assembly.

NOTE: **Direct-to-forward clutch thrust washer may stick to end of direct clutch housing.**

3) Remove intermediate band assembly and anchor pin from case. Withdraw output shaft-to-turbine shaft front selective thrust washer.

NOTE: **Output shaft-to-turbine shaft selective thrust washer may be stuck to end of turbine shaft.**

FRONT INTERNAL GEAR

NOTE: **At this time, check rear unit end play to determine correct end play thrust washer for use at reassembly. See REAR UNIT END PLAY CHECK under TRANSMISSION REASSEMBLY.**

Using snap ring pliers, remove output shaft-to-selective washer snap ring, then withdraw front internal gear, rear selective thrust washer, and thrust washer. Remove front carrier assembly and front internal gear-to-front carrier roller bearing assembly. Remove front sun gear, and front sun gear-to-front carrier thrust bearing assembly.

Fig. 10: Removing Front Internal Gear

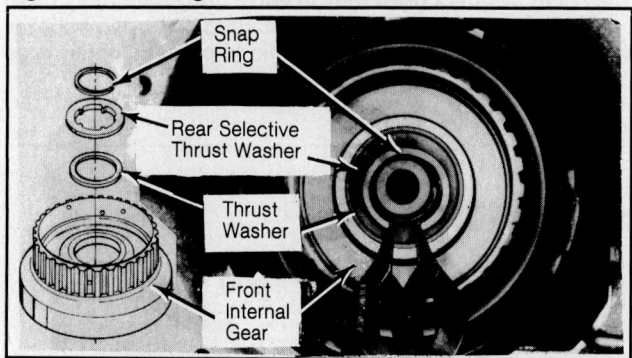

The front sun gear-to-front carrier thrust bearing may come out with front carrier.

Fig. 11: Removing Low-Reverse Clutch Housing To Case Cup Plug

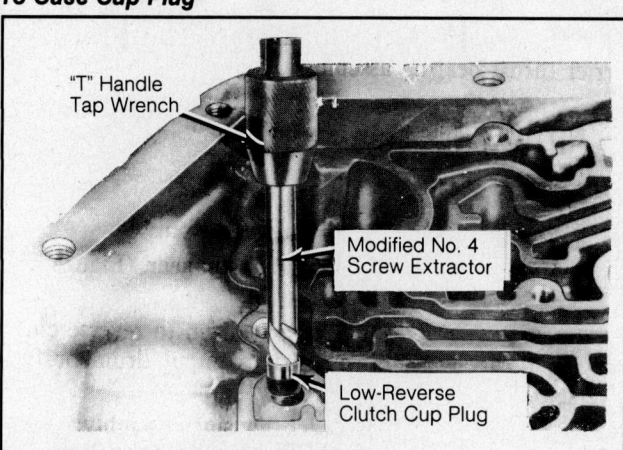

INPUT DRUM, REAR SUN GEAR & LOW-REVERSE CLUTCH HOUSING

1) Remove input drum and rear sun gear from case. Remove the 4-tanged input drum-to-reverse clutch housing thrust washer from rear of input drum or from reverse clutch housing.

2) Grind approximately 3/4" from end of a No. 4 screw extractor to remove housing-to-case cup plug. Remove cup plug assembly by turning easy-out 2 or 3 turns and pulling straight out. See Fig. 11.

3) Remove low-reverse clutch housing-to-case beveled snap ring. Flat side of snap ring should have been against housing with beveled side up. Withdraw low-reverse clutch housing assembly from case. Remove clutch housing-to-case spacer ring.

REAR GEAR COMPONENTS

NOTE: **Make sure governor has been removed before removing rear gear components.**

1) Grasp output shaft and lift out rear unit parts and lay them down in a horizontal position. Slide roller clutch and rear carrier assembly off output shaft. Remove 4-tanged rear carrier-to-rear internal gear thrust washer off end of rear carrier or inside rear internal gear.

2) Remove low-reverse clutch plates from output shaft. Remove rear internal gear-to-rear sun gear thrust bearing assembly from rear internal gear. Remove rear internal gear from output shaft.

Fig. 12: Removing Rear Internal Gear Components

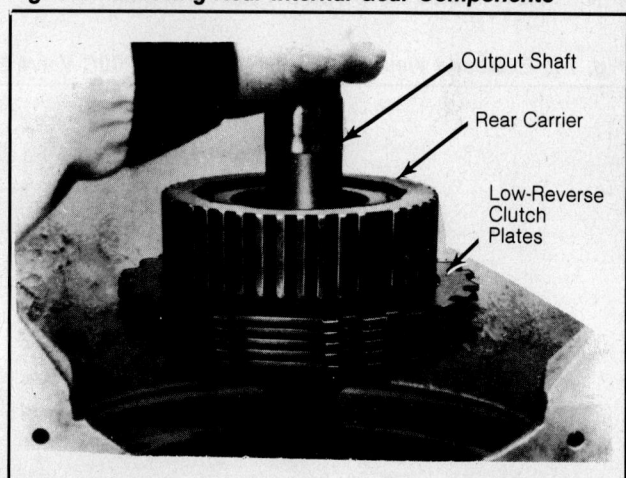

MANUAL SHAFT & PARKING LINKAGE

1) Remove hex nut holding inside detent lever to manual shaft, then remove parking actuator rod and detent lever. Remove manual shaft retaining pin from case and slide manual shaft out. If necessary, pry manual shaft seal from case.

2) Remove parking lock bracket. Remove parking pawl shaft retaining pin. Grind approximately 3/4" from end of a No. 4 screw extractor. Remove parking pawl cup plug and discard. See Fig. 13.

3) Using sheet metal screw or No. 3 screw extractor, remove parking pawl shaft. Remove parking pawl and return spring.

Automatic Transmissions

GENERAL MOTORS TURBO HYDRA-MATIC 200C (Cont.)

Fig. 13: *Removing Parking Pawl Shaft Cup Plug*

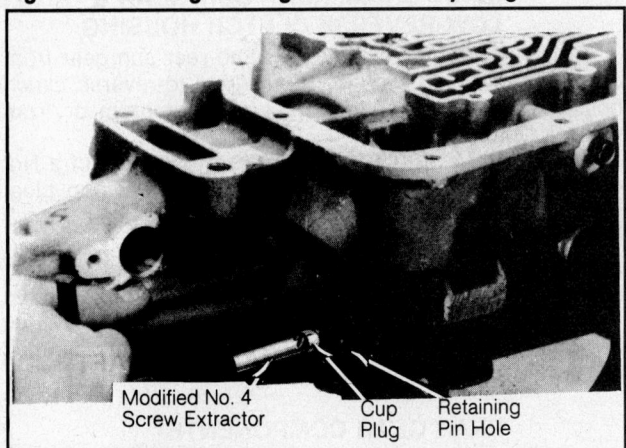

Modified No. 4 Screw Extractor   Cup Plug   Retaining Pin Hole

Fig. 15: *Removing Shift T.V. Valve Train*

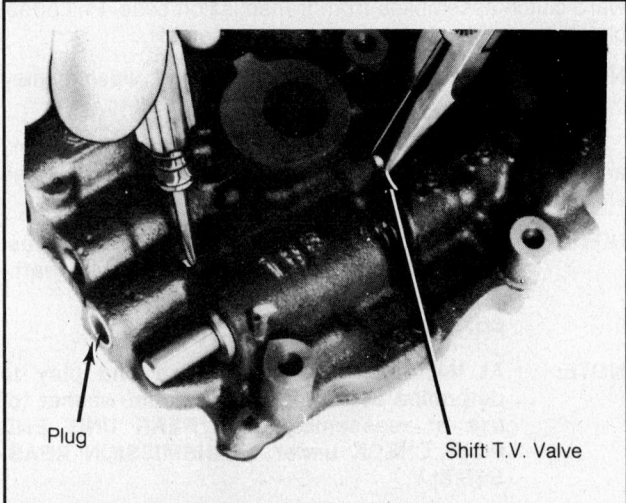

Plug   Shift T.V. Valve

Valves and valve springs are not interchangeable.

COMPONENT DISASSEMBLY & REASSEMBLY

VALVE BODY

As valve trains are removed from each valve body bore, place individual parts in correct order in relative position to valve body to simplify reassembly.

Valves and springs are not interchangeable, and all parts must be installed in correct order in proper valve body bore. *See Fig. 14.* Remove all coiled pins by pushing through from rough case surface of body, except the 2 pins which retain throttle valve and throttle valve plunger.

Disassembly

1) Position valve body with cored face upward and 1-2 accumulator pocket at lower left. *See Fig. 14.* Remove four check balls from cored passages of valve body (5th check ball is in case), then remove 1-2 accumulator piston. From upper bore, remove manual valve.

CAUTION: Some coiled pins in valve body assembly have pressure against them. Hold a shop towel over bore while removing pin to prevent losing bore plug or spring.

Fig. 14: *Exploded View of Turbo Hydra-Matic 200C Valve Body Assembly*

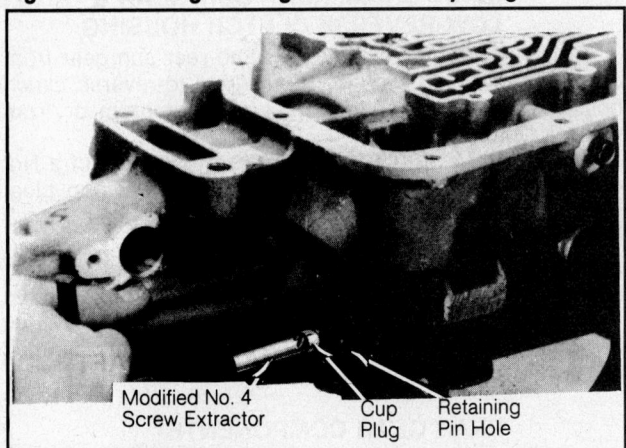

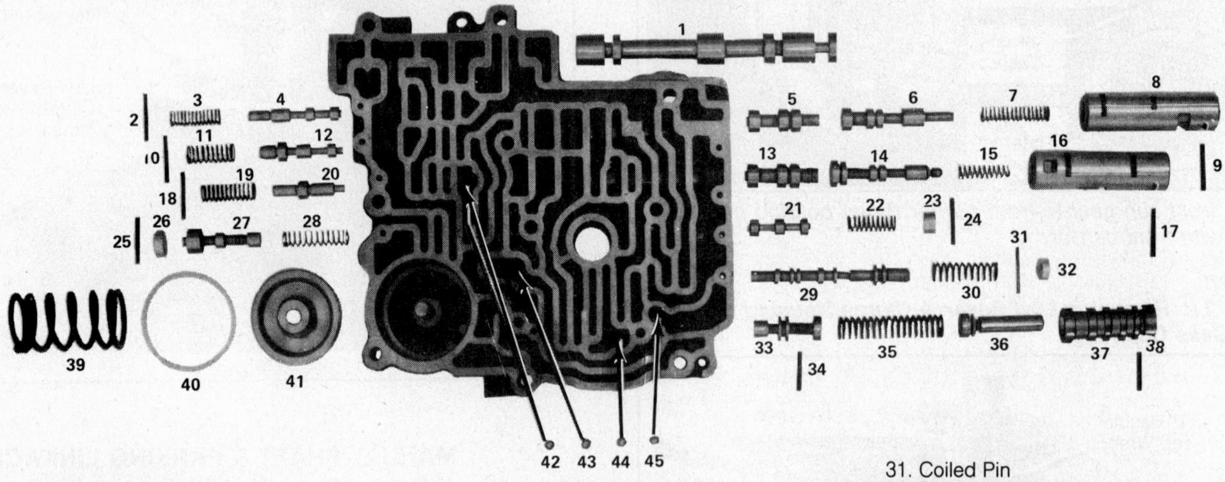

1. Manual Valve
2. Coiled Pin
3. Intermediate Boost Spring
4. Intermediate Boost Valve
5. 2-3 Shift Valve
6. 2-3 Throttle Valve
7. 2-3 Throttle Spring
8. 2-3 Throttle Bushing
9. Coiled Pin
10. Coiled Pin
11. Low Overrun Clutch Spring
12. Low Overrun Clutch Valve
13. 1-2 Shift Valve
14. 1-2 Throttle Valve
15. 1-2 Throttle Spring
16. 1-2 Throttle Bushing
17. Coiled Pin
18. Coiled Pin
19. Direct Clutch Exhaust Spring
20. Direct Clutch Exhaust Valve
21. Reverse Boost Valve
22. Reverse Boost Spring
23. Reverse Boost Bore Plug
24. Coiled Pin
25. Coiled Pin
26. 1-2 Accumulator Bore Plug
27. 1-2 Accumulator Valve
28. 1-2 Accumulator Spring
29. Shift T.V. Tralve
30. Shift T.V. Spring
31. Coiled Pin
32. Shift T.V. Bore Plug
33. Throttle Valve
34. Coiled Pin
35. Throttle Valve Spring
36. Throttle Valve Plunger
37. Throttle Valve Plunger Bushing
38. Coiled Pin
39. 1-2 Accumulator Spring
40. 1-2 Accumulator Piston Seal
41. 1-2 Accumulator Piston
42. Check Ball No. 4
43. Check Ball No. 3
44. Check Ball No. 2
45. Check Ball No. 1
   (NOTE: 5th Check Ball in Case)

GENERAL MOTORS TURBO HYDRA-MATIC 200C (Cont.)

Fig. 16: Removing Throttle Valve Inner Pin

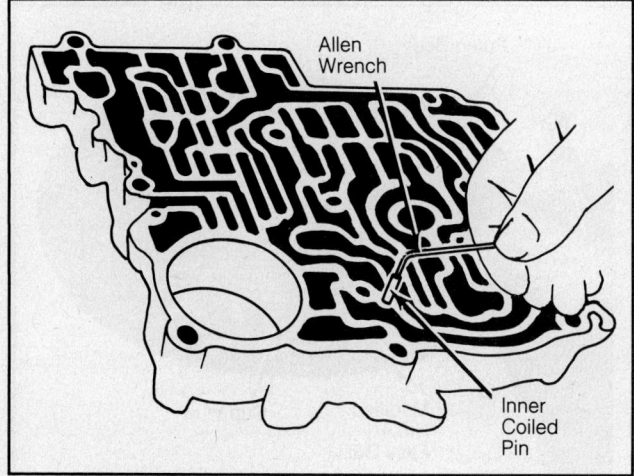

Use modified Allen Wrench.

2) From upper right side bore, remove the 2-3 valve train. From next bore down, remove the 1-2 valve train. From next bore down, remove the reverse boost valve train.

NOTE: Some valves and springs may be inside valve bushings.

3) If necessary to remove shift T.V. valve train, remove coiled pin and place valve body with rough casting surface up. Use needle nose pliers and push in on valve, then hold in place with a small screwdriver.

4) Position a 1/4" diameter rod, 3/8" long against end of valve, pry on rod with a screwdriver, remove small screwdriver, and remove plug, spring, and valve.

5) From lower right side bore, remove outer coiled pin and withdraw throttle valve bushing, plunger and spring. Remove throttle valve detent pin. Using a 1/16" Allen wrench, with sides ground to fit inside pin, remove inner coiled pin, and then withdraw throttle valve. *See Fig. 16.*

6) From upper left side bore, remove intermediate boost valve train. From next bore down, remove low overrun clutch valve train. From next bore down, remove direct clutch exhaust valve train. From lower left side bore, remove 1-2 accumulator valve train.

Inspection

Wash all parts in solvent and air dry. Inspect 1-2 accumulator piston and seal for damage; do not remove seal unless replacement is required. Check valve body for cracks, damage, or scored bores. Inspect valves and plugs for scores, cracks, and free movement in valve body bores. Inspect springs for distortion and collapsed coils.

Reassembly

Reverse disassembly procedure using *Fig. 17* as a guide and note the following:
- Install all flared coiled pins (zinc coated) flare end out, and away from machined surface of valve body.
- Install the two tapered coiled pins (black finish) that retain throttle valve and throttle valve bushing, tapered end first.
- Coiled pins do not fit flush on rough casting face. Make sure pins are flush at machined face.
- When installing 1-2 throttle bushing and 2-3 throttle bushing, align in bores, so that coiled pins can be

installed in pin slot. *See Fig. 16.*
- Install manual valve with inside detent lever pin groove to the right.

Fig. 17: Installing Throttle Valve Bushings

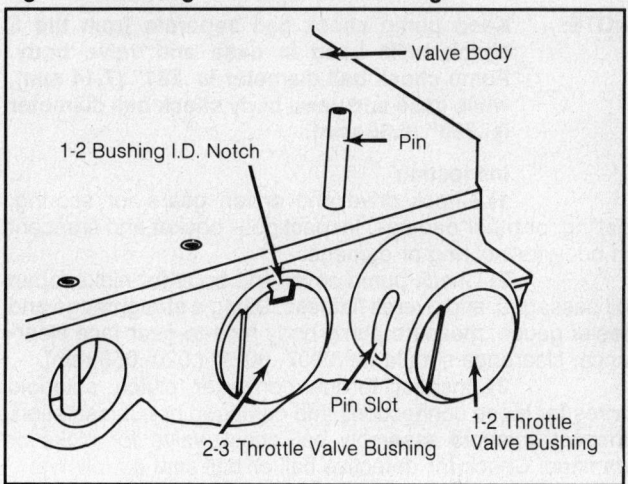

OIL PUMP

Disassembly

1) Remove pump-to-case seal ring. Position pump on bench with cover side facing up. Remove pump-to-direct clutch thrust washer, and if replacement is necessary, remove 3 Teflon oil seal rings.

2) Remove solenoid wires from wire clips, then remove attaching bolts and lift torque converter clutch solenoid assembly from pump cover. Remove "O" ring from solenoid and discard.

3) Remove converter clutch valve bushing retaining pin and remove bushing, apply valve and actuator valve from pump cover bore. *See Fig. 18.*

4) Using a small screwdriver, push in on pressure regulator bore plug and remove retaining ring. Release spring tension slowly and remove pressure regulator valve train.

Fig. 18: Removing Converter Clutch Valve Assembly

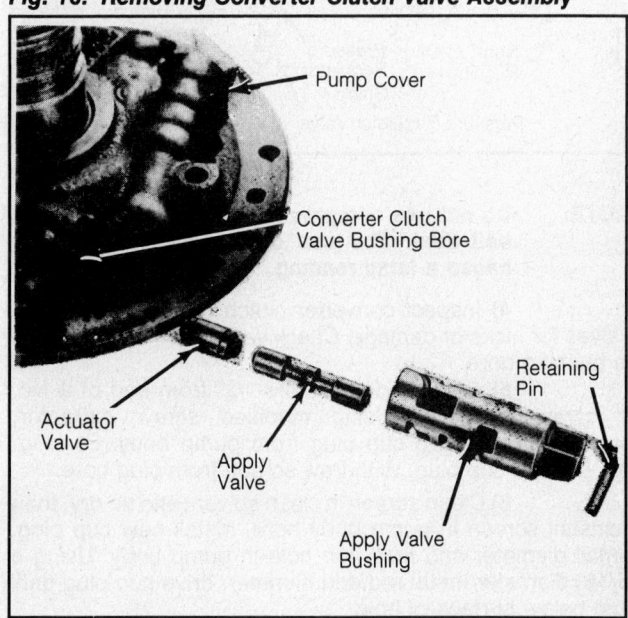

Automatic Transmissions

GENERAL MOTORS TURBO HYDRA-MATIC 200C (Cont.)

5) Remove attaching bolts and separate pump cover from body using care not to drop check ball from body. Remove check ball. Remove pump gears, marking them for reassembly in same position.

NOTE: Keep pump check ball separate from the 5 check balls used in case and valve body. Pump check ball diameter is .281" (7.14 mm), while case and valve body check ball diameter is .250" (6.35 mm).

Inspection

1) Check drive and driven gears for scoring, galling, or other damage. Inspect gear pocket and crescent in body for scoring or damage.

2) Check pump cover and body for nicks, open oil passages, and overall flatness. Using a straightedge and feeler gauge, measure pump body face-to-gear face clearance; clearance should be .0007-.0021" (.020-.055 mm).

3) Inspect torque converter clutch solenoid wires for loose connections and damaged or cut insulation. Inspect solenoid assembly ball check valve for nicks or damage. Check for defective ball or ball seat as follows:
- Blow air into ball seat with solenoid de-energized; air should pass through ball seat.
- Noting polarity, energize solenoid with +12 volts D.C. and again blow air into ball seat; air should not pass through ball seat.

Fig. 19: Exploded View of Oil Pump Assembly

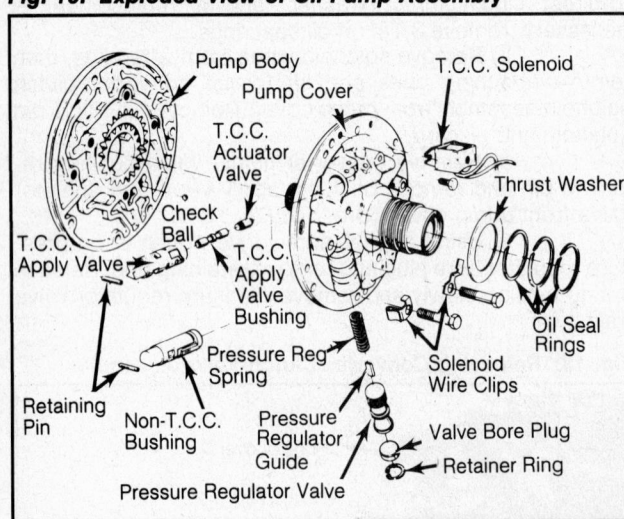

NOTE: Do not use compressed air to check ball and ball seat. The use of compressed air may cause a false reading.

4) Inspect converter clutch apply and actuator valves for nicks or damage. Check valves for free operation in bushing bore.

5) Grind approximately 1/2" from end of a No. 4 screw extractor. Using modified screw extractor, remove and discard cup plug from pump body. See Fig. 20. Discard cup plug. Withdraw screen from plug bore.

6) Clean screen in clean solvent and air dry, then reinstall screen in pump body bore. Install new cup plug, small diameter end first, into hole in pump body. Using a 5/16" diameter metal rod and hammer, drive cup plug until just below surface of hole.

Fig. 20: Removing Cup Plug From Pump Body

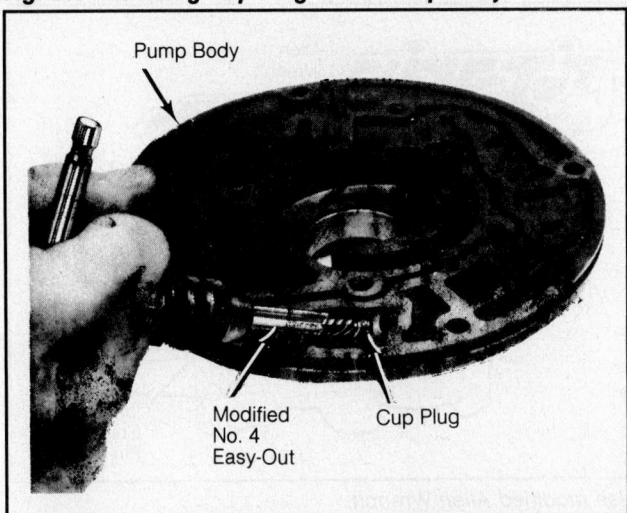

7) Inspect pressure regulator valve bore in pump cover and pressure regulator valve assembly for wear or damage and make sure parts operate freely in bore. Inspect the 6 cup plugs in pump cover for damage or leaks. If necessary, replace cup plug.

Pump Cover Cup Plug Replacement
Remove old cup plugs using care not to damage pump cover. Drive new cup plugs to 1/32" below top of hole, using a 1/4" diameter rod on smaller plug and a 5/16" rod on the 5 larger plugs. Stake top of hole in 2 places, directly opposite each other, to retain plugs.

Fig. 21: Pump Body Oil Passages

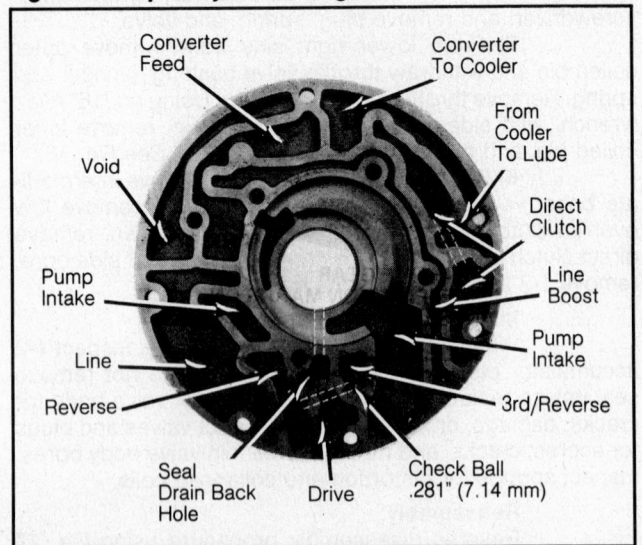

Make sure all castings are clean and true.

Reassembly

1) Install driven gear into pump body with identification mark down against gear pocket. See Fig. 22. Install drive gear into pump body with identification marks on tangs up. See Fig. 23. Place check ball into pocket in pump body as shown in Fig. 21. Retain with petroleum jelly.

2) Assemble pump cover and body using Alignment Strap (J-25015) and lace bolt or screwdriver through

pump-to-case bolt hole. Install and tighten pump cover attaching bolts and remove strap.

Fig. 22: Pump Driven Gear Identification Marks

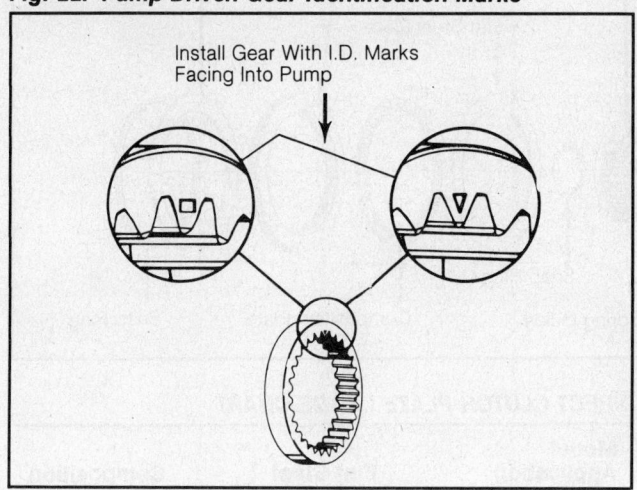

Install Gear With I.D. Marks Facing Into Pump

3) Install pressure regulator spring, spring guide, valve (stem end out), and bore plug (hole end out) into pump cover bore. Compress pressure regulator valve assembly and install retaining ring.

4) Install actuator valve into bushing bore of pump cover. Install apply valve into bushing, then install bushing into cover. Install apply valve bushing retaining pin and pin clip and bolt. See Fig. 18.

5) Install new pump-to-case gasket on pump and retain with petroleum jelly. Lubricate with petroleum jelly and install new "O" ring on solenoid assembly, then install solenoid on pump and tighten attaching bolts. Install solenoid wires into wire clip.

6) If removed, install 3 new oil seal rings on pump cover stator shaft, making sure cut ends are assembled in the same relationship as cut. Also, make sure rings are seated in grooves to prevent damage during transmission reassembly. Retain rings with petroleum jelly.

Fig. 23: Pump Drive Gear Identification Marks

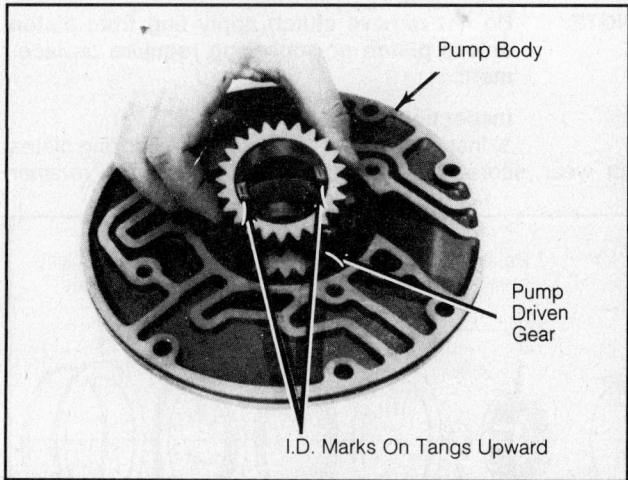

Pump Body

Pump Driven Gear

I.D. Marks On Tangs Upward

Install drive gear into pump body with I.D. marks on tangs facing up.

7) Install pump-to-case seal ring (chamfered side out), making sure ring is not twisted. Install pump-to-direct clutch thrust washer and retain with petroleum jelly.

Fig. 24: Pump Cover Oil Passages

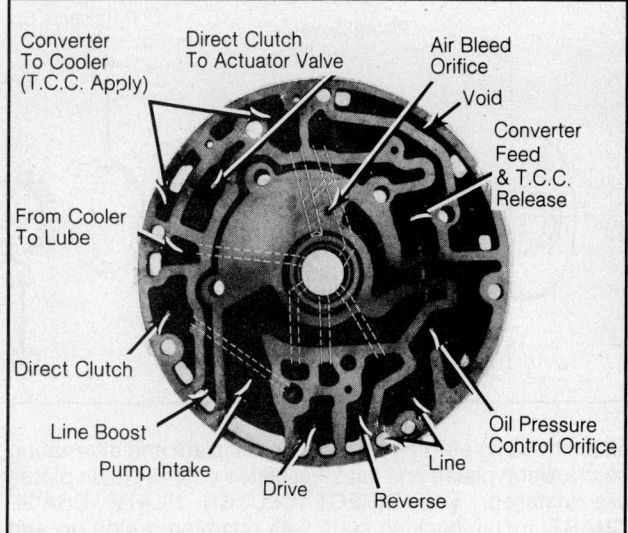

Converter To Cooler (T.C.C. Apply)
Direct Clutch To Actuator Valve
Air Bleed Orifice
Void
Converter Feed & T.C.C. Release
From Cooler To Lube
Direct Clutch
Oil Pressure Control Orifice
Line Boost
Pump Intake
Drive
Reverse
Line

Make sure castings are clean.

DIRECT CLUTCH
Disassembly

1) Remove clutch pack snap ring. Remove backing plate from clutch housing. Remove clutch plates from housing and keep them separate from the forward clutch plates.

2) Using a compressor tool, compress retainer and spring assembly and removed snap ring. Remove tool and lift retainer and spring assembly from clutch housing.

3) Remove release spring guide from clutch housing. Remove clutch piston from housing. Remove inner and outer seals from piston and center seal from housing.

NOTE: Do not separate apply ring from clutch piston unless ring or piston requires replacement.

Inspection

1) Inspect composition plates, steel plates, and backing plate for wear, burning, or scoring. Check release springs and retainer for damage or a collapsed condition. Inspect clutch piston for distortion, cracks and free operation of check ball.

2) Check clutch housing for cracks, wear, and open passages, and for free operation of check ball. Inspect snap ring grooves and bushing in housing for wear or damage.

Reassembly

1) Install apply ring on clutch piston, then install new inner and outer seals on piston, with seal lips facing away from clutch apply ring side. Install a new center seal into direct clutch housing, with seal lip facing upward. Install Seal Protector (J-25010) over oil seals, lubricate seals with transmission fluid, and install clutch piston.

CAUTION: Use care when installing piston past larger snap ring groove in clutch housing as groove could cut outer seal on piston.

2) Install release spring guide with omitted rib over check ball in piston as shown in Fig. 26. Install retainer and spring assembly into housing, making sure all parts are positioned correctly.

3) Using tool used at disassembly, compress release springs and install retaining snap ring. Lubricate clutch plates with transmission fluid, then install them into

Automatic Transmissions
GENERAL MOTORS TURBO HYDRA-MATIC 200C (Cont.)

Fig. 25: Exploded View of Direct Clutch Assembly

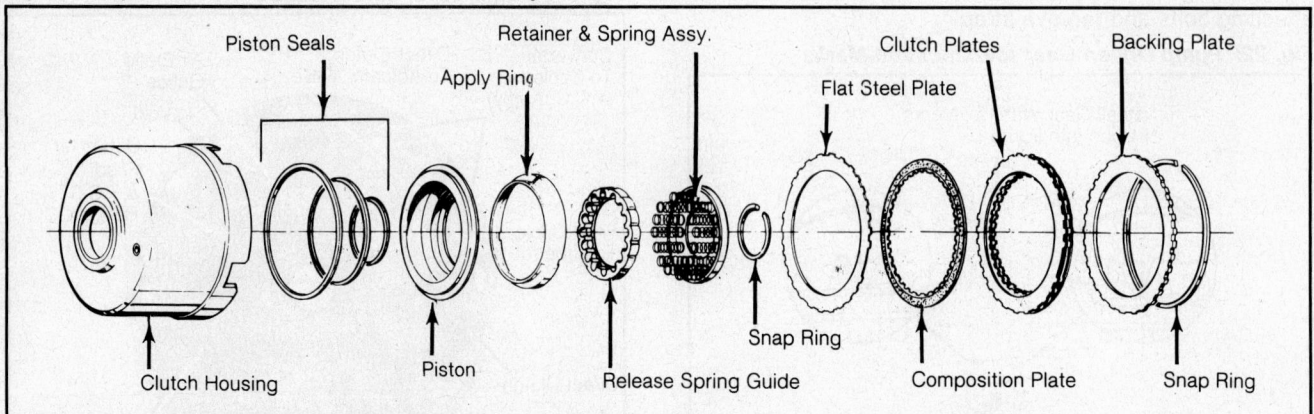

clutch housing starting with a flat steel plate and alternating composition plates and flat steel plates until all clutch plates are installed. See DIRECT CLUTCH PLATE USAGE CHART. Install backing plate with chamfered side up and clutch pack retaining snap ring.

NOTE: After reassembly is completed, ensure that composition faced clutch plates turn freely.

Fig. 26: Assembling Release Spring Guide to Piston

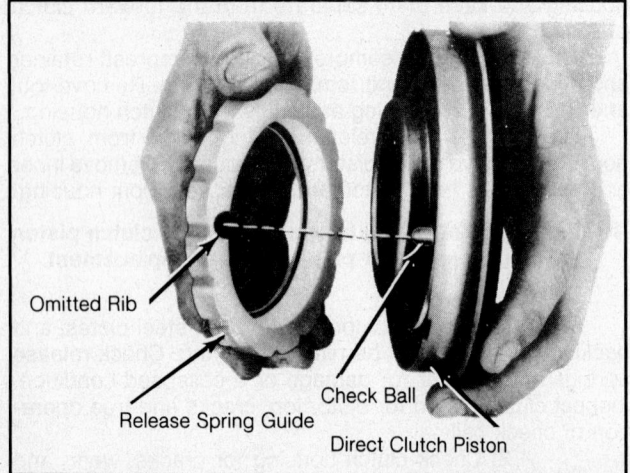

Install release spring guide with omitted rib over check ball in piston.

Fig. 27: Exploded View of Forward Clutch Assembly

DIRECT CLUTCH PLATE USAGE CHART

Model Application	Flat Steel [1]	Composition
CS, CZ & JY	4	4
BH, CO, CV, HH, HL, OI, OR & OU	5	5

[1] – Plate thickness is 0.091" (2.31 mm).

FORWARD CLUTCH
Disassembly
1) Remove forward clutch-to-direct clutch thrust washer. If replacement is required, remove teflon oil seal rings from turbine shaft. Remove clutch pack snap ring and lift out backing plate and clutch plates.

NOTE: Keep forward clutch plates separate from direct clutch plates.

2) Using an arbor press, compress retainer and spring assembly and remove retaining snap ring. Release arbor press slowly, then remove retainer and spring assembly. Remove piston from clutch housing, then remove inner and outer seals from piston.

NOTE: Do not remove clutch apply ring from piston unless piston or apply ring requires replacement.

Inspection
1) Inspect composition, steel and backing plates for wear, scores or other damage. Check spring retainer

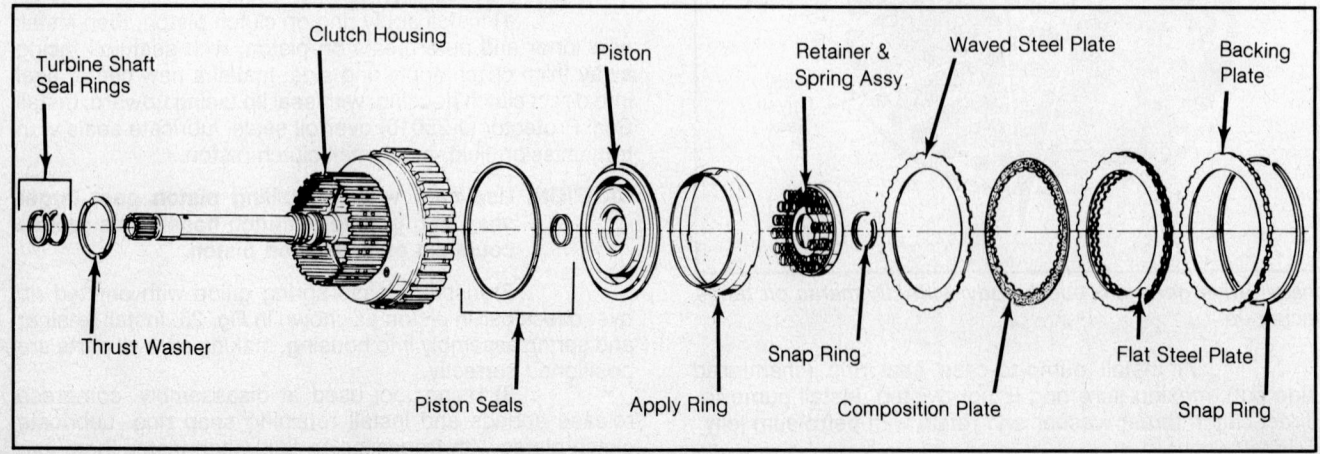

and release springs for distortion or collapse. Inspect piston and housing for cracks, distortion, open oil passages, or other damage. Inspect snap ring grooves for wear or damage, and make sure ball check in housing operates freely.

2) Check turbine shaft for open passages on both ends of shaft, and check journals for damage. Inspect clutch housing cup plug and if damaged, remove using a No. 3 screw extractor (grind to fit). Install new cup plug to .039" (1.0 mm) below surface (grind to fit). Install new cup plug to .039" (1.0 mm) below surface.

Reassembly
1) Install clutch apply ring on piston, then install new inner and outer seals on piston, with seal lips facing away from apply ring side. Lubricate seals with transmission fluid, then install piston into housing. Install retainer and spring assembly into housing, compress retainer and springs, and install retaining snap ring.

CAUTION: Use care when installing piston past large snap ring groove as groove could cut outer piston seal.

2) Lubricate with transmission fluid then install forward clutch plates into housing starting with the waved steel plate then alternating composition plates and flat steel plates until all clutch plates are installed. See FORWARD CLUTCH PLATE USAGE CHART. Install backing plate (chamfered side up) and clutch pack snap ring. If removed, install new turbine shaft seal rings and forward clutch-to-direct clutch thrust washer.

NOTE: After reassembly is completed, ensure that composition faced clutch plates turn freely.

FORWARD CLUTCH PLATE USAGE CHART

Model Application	Flat Steel [1]	Composition
CS, CZ & JY	2 [2]	3
BH, CO, CV, HH, HL, OI, OR & OU	3 [2]	4

[1] – Plate thickness is 0.077" (1.96 mm).
[2] – Plus 1 WAVED steel plate 0.062" (1.57 mm) thick, installed first.

FRONT CARRIER, SUN GEAR & INTERNAL GEAR
Inspection
Check all parts for pitting, scoring, damaged gear teeth and cracks. Make sure all lubrication holes are open. Check front internal gear thrust washers for wear or other damage and front carrier roller thrust bearing for roughness and pitting. Check pinion end play of front carrier. End play should be .009-.027" (.23-.69 mm).

REAR SUN GEAR & INPUT DRUM
Inspection
Check rear sun gear for cracks, splits, spline damage, gear or journal wear, and for plugged lubrication holes. If necessary, remove snap ring and separate sun gear from input drum and inspect drum splines for damage. Check input drum-to-low-reverse clutch housing thrust washer for scoring or distorted tangs.

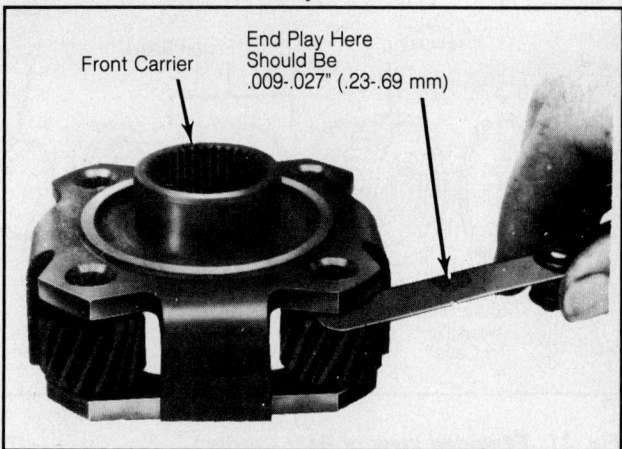

Fig. 28: Using Feeler Gauge to Measure Front Carrier Pinion End Play

Front Carrier

End Play Here Should Be .009-.027" (.23-.69 mm)

If not within specifications, replace.

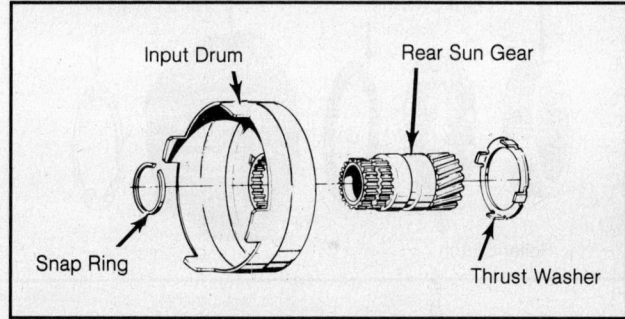

Fig. 29: Exploded View of Rear Sun Gear and Input Drum Assembly

Input Drum

Rear Sun Gear

Snap Ring

Thrust Washer

LOW-REVERSE CLUTCH
Disassembly
Compress low-reverse clutch spring retainer, remove snap ring and retainer. Check for damage and distortion. Withdraw waved spring and clutch piston. Remove inner and outer seals and clutch apply ring.

Inspection
Check clutch housing for scoring or wear, damaged bushing, and plugged oil feed hole. Inspect splines and snap ring groove for damage or burrs. Check piston assembly for distortion, cracks, or damage. Inspect clutch plates for signs of scoring or burning. Check retainers and spring for damage or distortion.

Reassembly
1) Install clutch apply ring and new inner and outer seals on clutch piston (seal lips facing away from apply ring side). Lubricate clutch seal with transmission fluid and place a seal protector into clutch housing.
2) Using a flat tip screwdriver to start seal into housing, install clutch piston, rotating while pushing down into bore. Remove seal protector, then install waved spring, retainer (cupped side down) and snap ring.

REAR CARRIER, ROLLER CLUTCH & INTERNAL GEAR
Inspection
Check rear internal gear splines, teeth, bearing surface and parking pawl lugs for wear, cracks or other damage. Inspect roller clutch race and spline for scoring or wear, and roller bearings, cage and springs for wear,

Fig. 30: Exploded View of Low-Reverse Clutch Assembly

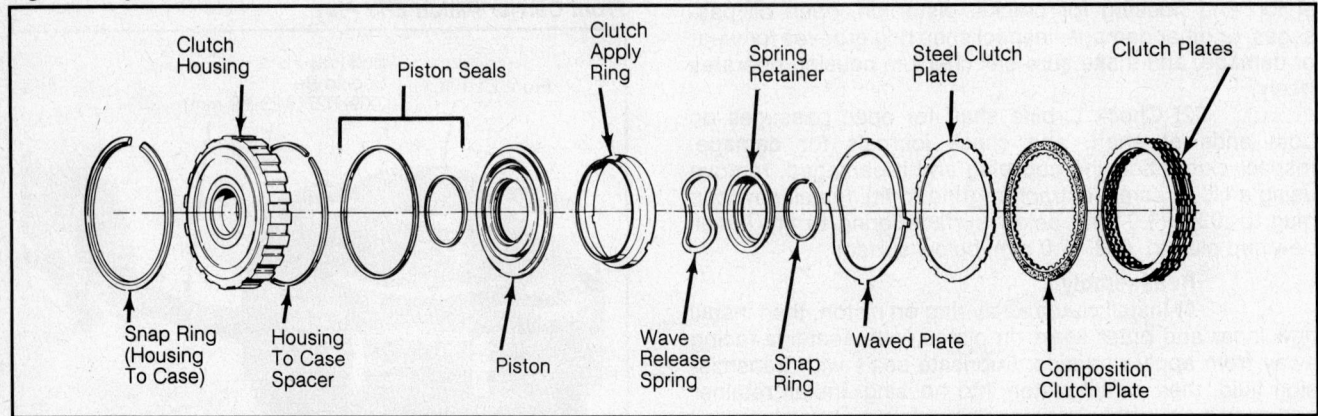

Fig. 31: Exploded View of Rear Carrier and Roller Clutch Assembly

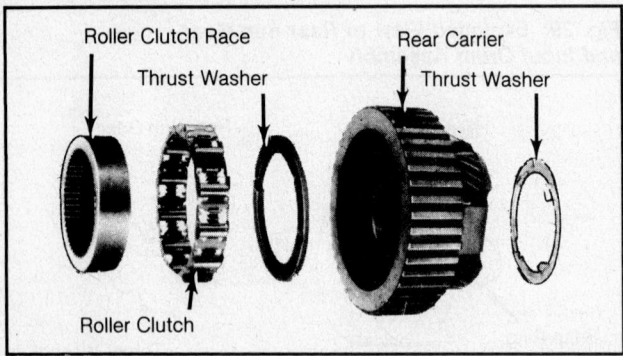

rear end of output shaft. Using a driver, drive gear onto shaft until distance from rear end of shaft to rear face of gear is 6 5/32" (156.37 mm).

Fig. 32: Output Shaft and Speedometer Drive Gear

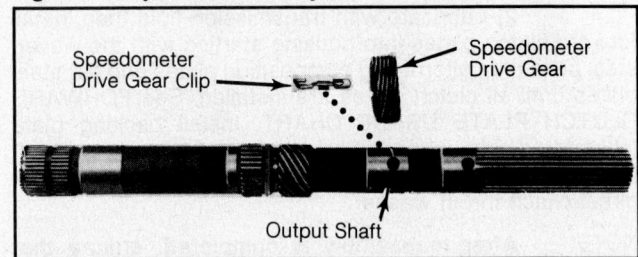

Align slot of gear with clip and install gear.

scoring, distortion or collapse. Inspect thrust washers for excessive wear or damaged tangs. Check rear carrier roller clutch cam ramps and bushing for scoring or other damage. Inspect planet pinions for damage, rough bearings, tilt and correct end play. End play should be .009-.027" (.23-.69 mm).

OUTPUT SHAFT
Inspection
Inspect journals and snap ring grooves for wear or damage. Check for plugged or damaged lubrication holes. Inspect shaft splines and governor drive gear for rough or damaged surfaces. Check speedometer drive gear and retaining clip for wear or damage.

NOTE: The service replacement output shaft has one speedometer drive gear clip hole at the front speedometer gear location which is about 1/4" diameter and opposite this hole is another clip hole which is about 5/32". The shaft also has the same size holes at the rear speedometer gear location.

Speedometer Drive Gear Replacement
1) If equipped with a nylon gear, depress gear clip and slide drive gear and clip off output shaft. To install, place gear clip with tanged end in correct hole in shaft, then align slot of gear with slip and install gear.
2) If equipped with a steel gear, remove gear using puller. To install, position front end of shaft on a block of wood to prevent damaging shaft during installation. Position gear (large chamfered inside diameter first) over

INTERMEDIATE SERVO
Disassembly
Compress intermediate servo piston spring. Using small flat blade screwdriver, remove servo pin-to-piston snap ring. Separate band apply pin, spring and washer from servo piston.

Inspection
1) Check intermediate servo pin for wear, damage and proper fit in case bore. Inspect inner and outer seal rings for damage and proper fit in seal ring grooves of piston.

CAUTION: Do not remove seal rings from piston unless replacement is required.

2) Check servo piston and cover for cracks or other damage. Inspect servo spring for collapsed coils or distortion. Check intermediate servo cover and piston assembly for proper combination and usage. See INTERMEDIATE SERVO COVER & PISTON USAGE chart.

INTERMEDIATE SERVO COVER & PISTON USAGE

Application Model	Cover I.D. No.	Piston Casting No.	Piston I.D.
BH, CV & HH [1]	8635692	8633563	3 Steps
CS [1]	8630569	8633564	Band
CO, CZ, HL, OI & OU	8635692	8633563	3 Steps
JY & OR	8630569	8633564	Band

[1] – Use orificed cup plug with piston.

Reassembly

1) Install retainer on band apply pin and install snap ring. Install band apply pin (retainer end first) through servo pistons. If removed, install new inner and outer seal rings on piston, making sure seal ring ends are assembled in the same relationship as cut and seal rings are seated in grooves.

2) Lubricate with petroleum jelly and install new seal ring on intermediate servo cover. Install servo piston assembly into servo cover.

Fig. 33: Exploded View of Intermediate Servo Assembly

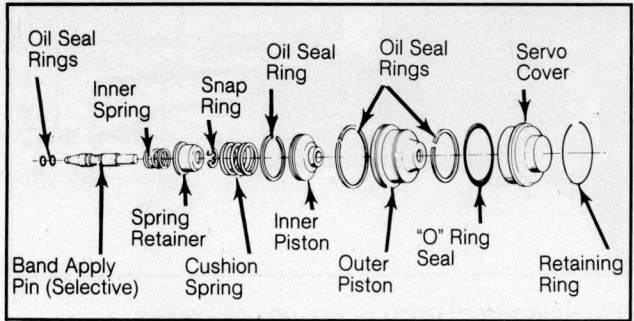

GOVERNOR ASSEMBLY
Inspection

1) Inspect governor cover for damage, scored or worn bore and plugged oil passage. Wash governor assembly in cleaning solvent and blow out oil passage. Inspect governor driven gear, weights, springs, shaft and washer for wear or damage.

2) Check governor shaft seal ring for cuts, damage and free fit in groove. If damaged, cut ring off shaft and install new seal ring. Lubricate seal with petroleum jelly. Inspect for presence of two check balls.

TRANSMISSION CASE
Inspection

1) Check case assembly for cracks, porosity and interconnected oil passages. Inspect reverse clutch lugs, governor bore, intermediate servo bore, speedometer bore and snap ring grooves for wear and other damage. Make sure all vents and passages are open and clear.

2) Inspect vent assembly in case for damage. DO NOT remove unless replacement is required. Check cooler line connectors for damage. DO NOT remove unless replacement is required.

TRANSMISSION REASSEMBLY

MANUAL SHAFT & PARKING LINKAGE

1) Place transmission in a horizontal position, oil pan side up. Install a new manual shaft seal into case with seal lip facing inward. Place parking pawl and return spring into case, making sure pawl tooth faces inside of case. Be sure spring is positioned under pawl tooth and spring ends locate against case pad.

2) Align pawl and spring with shaft bore in case and install pawl shaft (tapered end first). Using a 3/8" diameter rod, install a new shaft cup plug (open end out) into shaft bore, past retaining pin hole. Install parking pawl shaft retaining pin.

Fig. 34: Installing Parking Actuator Rod

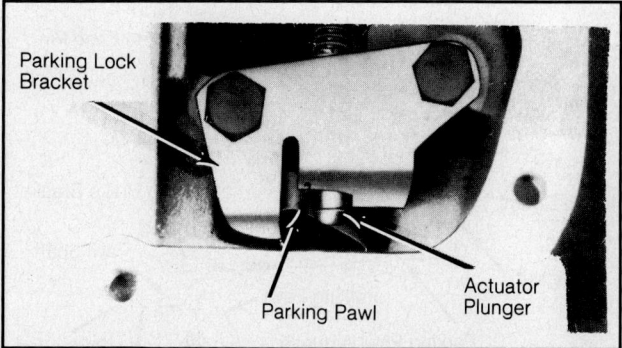

Be careful not to bend rod during installation.

3) Install parking lock bracket into case, with parking pawl positioned between guides of bracket. Then install and tighten 2 attaching bolts. Install parking lock actuator rod into inside detent lever (on pin side) locating lever between actuator rod tangs. Install rod and lever assembly into case with lever pin toward center of transmission and actuator plunger between parking pawl and parking lock bracket.

NOTE: File off any burrs or raised edges on manual shaft that could damage seal during installation of shaft.

4) Install manual shaft (small I.D. ring groove first) through case. Install manual shaft-to-case retaining pin, indexing with larger groove on manual shaft. Align inside detent lever with flats on manual shaft, position lever on shaft, then install and tighten nut on manual shaft.

OUTPUT SHAFT & REAR INTERNAL GEAR

If removed, install a new rear internal gear-to-output shaft snap ring into groove on output shaft, then install rear internal gear (hub end first) onto shaft. Position rear internal gear-to-rear sun gear roller thrust bearing assembly over shaft by placing small diameter race against rear internal gear.

ROLLER CLUTCH & REAR CARRIER

1) Install rear internal gear, hub end first, on output shaft. Install internal gear-to-rear sun gear roller thrust bearing assembly into internal gear by placing small diameter race over output shaft.

2) Install roller clutch-to-rear carrier thrust washer into rear carrier. Install rollers that may have come out of roller clutch cage, by compressing energizing spring with forefinger and inserting roller from outer edge. Install roller clutch assembly into roller clutch cam.

3) Install roller clutch race, spline side out and rotate clutch race counterclockwise into position. Install 4 tanged rear carrier-to-rear internal gear thrust washer onto carrier and align tangs into slots of carrier. Retain washer with petroleum jelly. Install roller clutch and carrier assembly into rear internal gear on output shaft.

4) Install Output Shaft Support (J-25013) on rear of transmission as follows: Place Support Sleeve (J-25013-1) into rear of case, open end first. Then bolt Bracket (J-25013-5) into rear mount bolt holes on extension housing. *See Fig. 37.*

5) Turn case to a vertical position, with pump end upward. Install rear unit parts (output shaft, rear inter-

Fig. 35: Exploded View of Manual and Parking Linkage

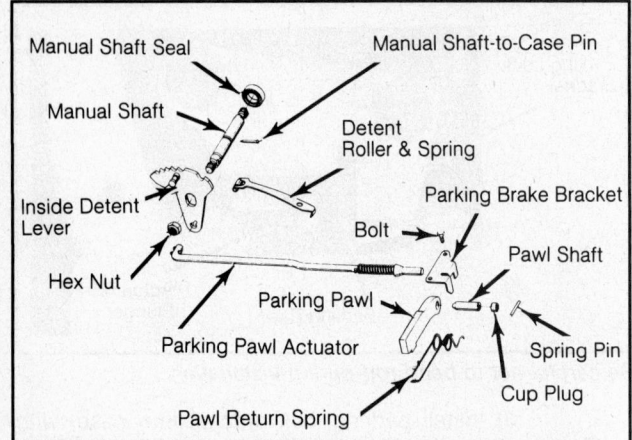

LOW-REVERSE CLUTCH

1) Lubricate with transmission fluid then install low-reverse clutch plates, starting with a flat steel plate, and alternating composition and flat steel plates until all clutch plates are installed. See LOW-REVERSE CLUTCH PLATE USAGE CHART. Install waved steel clutch plate on top of last flat steel plate.

Fig. 37: Installing Output Shaft Support

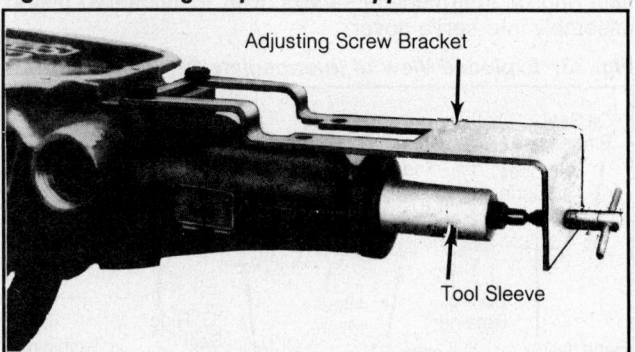

nal gear, and rear carrier previously assembled) into transmission case and into support sleeve, indexing rear internal gear parking pawl lugs to pass by parking pawl tooth.

6) Using adjusting screw on bracket and looking through parking pawl case slot, adjust height of the rear internal gear parking pawl lugs to align flush with the parking pawl tooth.

CAUTION: With rear internal gear parking pawl lugs correctly aligned, make sure speedometer drive gear is visible through speedometer gear bore of case. If gear is not visible, it may be located on wrong journal of output shaft.

LOW-REVERSE CLUTCH PLATE USAGE CHART

Model Application	Flat Steel [1]	Composition
CS, CZ & JY	5 [2]	4
BH, CO, CV, HH, HL, OI, OR & OU	7 [2]	6

[1] – Plate thickness is 0.077" (1.96 mm).
[2] – Plus 1 WAVED steel plate 0.077" (1.96 mm) thick, installed last.

Fig. 36: Bottom of Transmission Case Showing Oil Passages

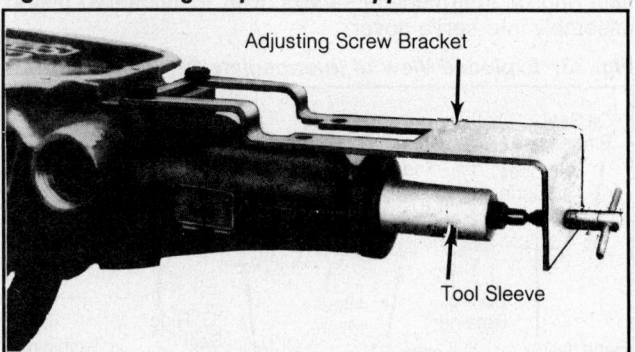

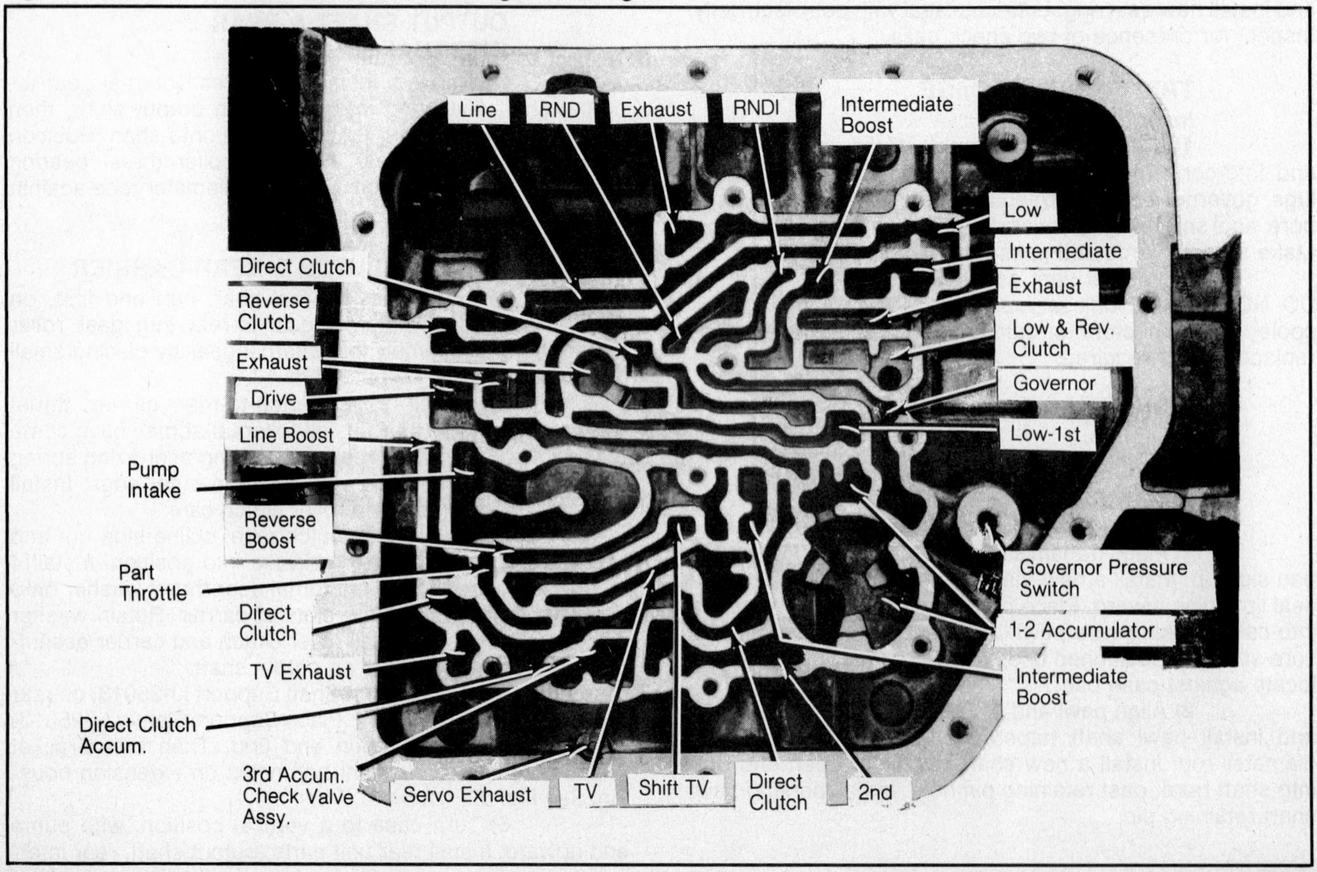

2) Install low-reverse clutch housing-to-case spacer ring into case, then install low-reverse clutch housing assembly, aligning housing oil feed hole with case oil feed passage.

3) If housing does not seat past snap ring groove, proceed as follows: Install input drum and rear sun gear assembly into case and rotate back and forth to align roller clutch race and low-reverse clutch hub splines, then remove input drum and sun gear.

Fig. 38: Installing Low-Reverse Clutch Housing To Case Snap Ring

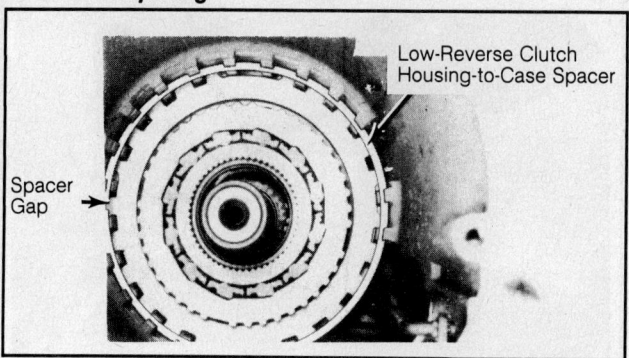

Align housing oil feed hole with case oil feed passage.

4) Repeat preceding step if low-reverse clutch housing still is not seated past case snap ring groove. With parts properly seated, install low-reverse clutch housing-to-case snap ring, with flat side of ring against housing (beveled side upward). Locate snap ring gap opposite parking pawl rod.

NOTE: It may be necessary to loosen adjusting screw on output shaft support tool to install low-reverse clutch housing-to-case snap ring.

REAR SUN GEAR, INPUT DRUM & FRONT SUN GEAR

Position thrust washer (four tangs) on input drum over sun gear end, align washer tangs with slots in drum, and retain with petroleum jelly. Install rear sun gear and input drum assembly into case. Install front sun gear, with drill spot or groove on face against input drum-to-rear sun gear snap ring. Install front sun gear-to-front carrier thrust bearing and race assembly with roller thrust bearing against front sun gear.

NOTE: The front sun gear-to-front carrier thrust bearing requires only 1 thrust race.

Fig. 39: Front Sun Gear Identification Marks

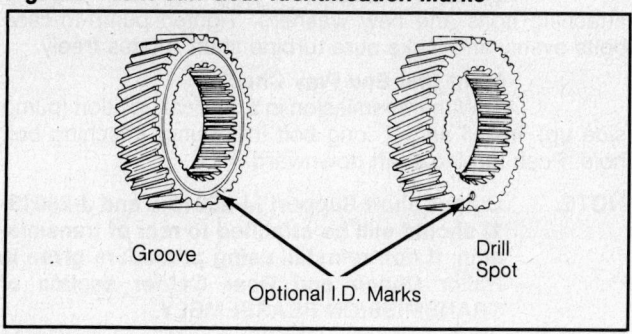

FRONT CARRIER

Position front carrier-to-front internal ring gear thrust bearing assembly on front carrier, with small diameter race against carrier and retain in place with petroleum jelly. Install front carrier and thrust bearing assembly into case, engaging front sun gear.

FRONT INTERNAL GEAR

Install thrust washer on front internal gear and retain with petroleum jelly, then install front internal gear into case. Install rear unit selective thrust washer on top of internal gear thrust washer, then install output shaft-to-thrust washer snap ring and make sure snap ring is fully seated in output shaft groove.

NOTE: At this time, measure rear unit end play to ensure correct selective thrust washer has been installed.

Rear Unit End Play Check

1) Loosen adjusting screw on Output Shaft Support (J-25013-5) and push output shaft fully downward. Mount a dial indicator on transmission case as shown in *Fig. 40* and position indicator button on output shaft. Do not clamp indicator to any machined surface.

2) Zero dial indicator. Move output shaft upward by turning adjusting screw on output shaft support tool, until white or scribed line on tool sleeve begins to disappear. Read resulting end play on indicator.

3) Rear unit end play should be .004-.025" (.10-.64 mm). If not, the selective thrust washer located between front internal gear thrust washer and output shaft snap ring must be changed. See REAR UNIT SELECTIVE THRUST WASHER CHART. Install correct thickness thrust washer (with I.D. number toward front of case), then reinstall output shaft snap ring making sure it is fully seated in groove.

REAR UNIT SELECTIVE THRUST WASHER CHART

Washer Thickness In. (mm)	I.D. Number	I.D. Color
.114-.119 (2.90-3.01)	1	Orange
.121-.126 (3.08-3.19)	2	White
.128-.133 (3.26-3.37)	3	Yellow
.135-.140 (3.44-3.55)	4	Blue
.143-.147 (3.62-3.37)	5	Red
.150-.154 (3.80-3.91)	6	Brown
.157-.161 (3.98-4.09)	7	Green
.164-.168 (4.16-4.27)	8	Black
1.71-.175 (4.34-4.45)	9	Purple

4) Remove dial indicator assembly and loosen adjusting screw on output shaft support tool. Install output shaft-to-turbine shaft front selective thrust washer, locating it on output shaft and retain with petroleum jelly.

Fig. 40: Checking Rear Unit End Play

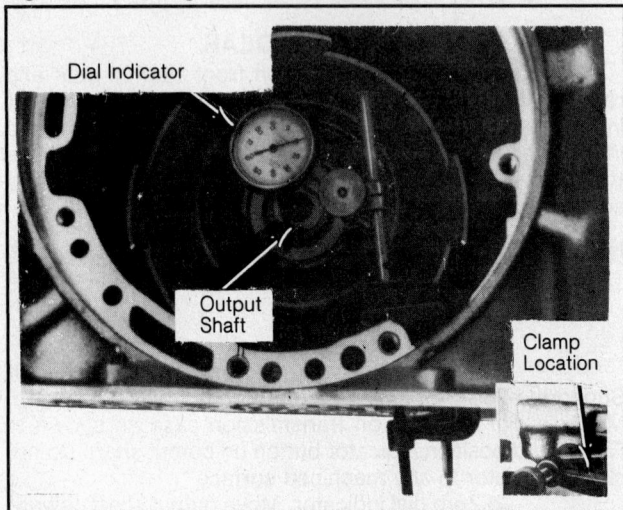

Dial indicator is located on output shaft.

DIRECT CLUTCH, FORWARD CLUTCH & INTERMEDIATE BAND

NOTE: Align direct clutch composition clutch plate teeth one above the other to make forward clutch assembly easier to install.

1) Position direct clutch over hole in bench with clutch plate end upward. Make sure forward clutch-to-direct clutch thrust washer is still in place on forward clutch, then install forward clutch (turbine shaft first) into direct clutch. Hold direct clutch housing and rotate forward clutch back and forth until forward clutch is seated.

Fig. 41: Checking Forward Clutch Engagement

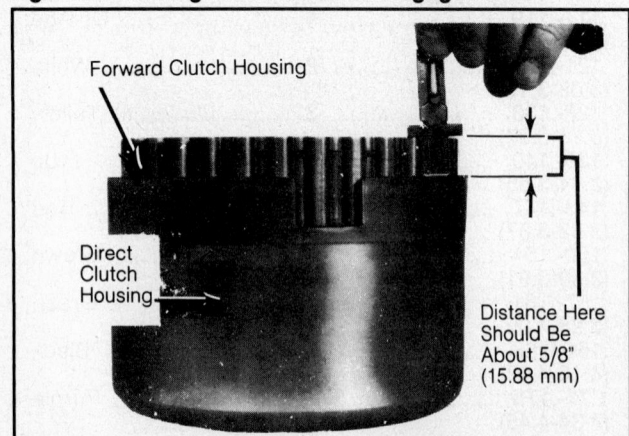

NOTE: When properly seated, end of forward clutch drum will be approximately 5/8" (15.88 mm) from tang end of direct clutch housing.

2) Position intermediate band into case, locating band apply lug and anchor pin lug in case slots. Install direct and forward clutch assemblies into case as a unit, rotating into position.

NOTE: When correctly seated, the direct clutch housing will be approximately 1 5/16" (33.34 mm) from pump face in case.

Fig. 42: Checking for Proper Installation of Direct and Forward Clutch Assemblies

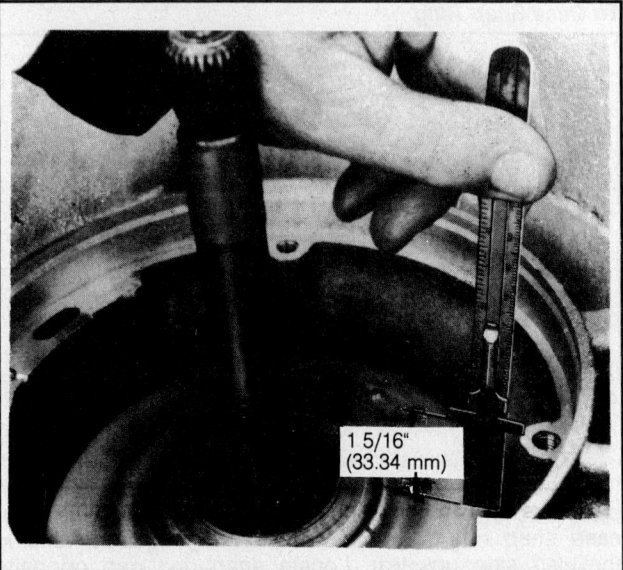

Assembly must be completely seated before measuring.

OIL PUMP

1) Install new pump-to-case gasket on pump and retain with petroleum jelly. Install 2 pump-to-case alignment pins in case, opposite each other.

NOTE: Before installing pump, ensure intermediate band anchor pin lug is aligned with band anchor pin hole in case.

2) Install pump assembly and finger start pump-to-case bolts and new washers, except 1 bolt which will be used to make front unit end play check.

CAUTION: If turbine shaft cannot be rotated as pump is pulled into place, forward or direct clutch housings are not properly indexed with all clutch plates. This condition must be corrected before pump is pulled fully into place.

3) Remove alignment pins and install 2 pump attaching bolts and new washers. Tighten pump-to-case bolts evenly and make sure turbine shaft rotates freely.

Front Unit End Play Check
1) With transmission in a vertical position (pump side up), install an 11" long bolt into pump attaching bolt hole. Push turbine shaft downward.

NOTE: Output Shaft Support (J-25013-5 and J-25013-1) should still be attached to rear of transmission; if not, reinstall using procedure given in Roller Clutch and Rear Carrier section of **TRANSMISSION REASSEMBLY.**

2) Install End Play Gauging Fixture and Adapter (J-24773 and J-25022) on end of turbine shaft. *See Fig. 43.*

GENERAL MOTORS TURBO HYDRA-MATIC 200C (Cont.)

Mount dial indicator on bolt and position indicator button against cap nut of gauging fixture.

Fig. 43: Checking Front Unit End Play

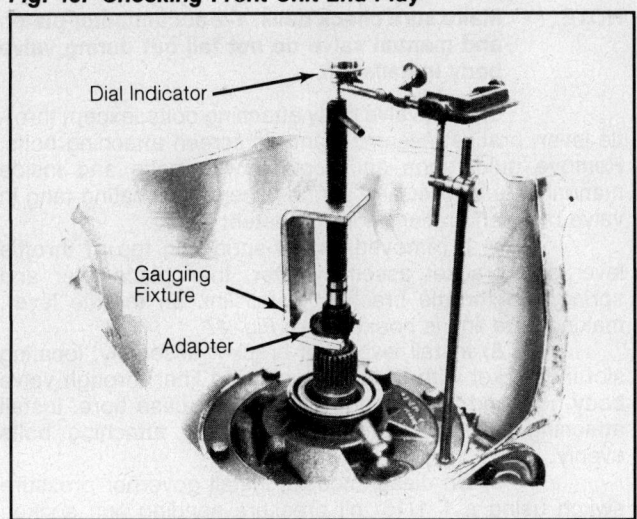

3) Move output shaft upward by turning adjusting screw on output shaft support tool until white or scribed line on sleeve begins to disappear, then zero dial indicator. Pull turbine shaft upward and read end play on indicator. Front unit end play should be .022-.051" (.56-1.30 mm).

4) Selective thrust washer controlling front unit end play is located between output shaft and turbine shaft.

FRONT UNIT SELECTIVE THRUST WASHER CHART

Washer Thickness In. (mm)	I.D. Number	I.D. Color
.065-.070 (1.66-1.77)	1	....
.070-.075 (1.79-1.90)	2	....
.076-.080 (1.92-2.03)	3	Black
.081-.085 (2.05-2.16)	4	Light Green
.086-.090 (2.18-2.29)	5	Scarlet
.091-.095 (2.31-2.42)	6	Purple
.096-.100 (2.44-2.55)	7	Cocoa Brown
.101-.106 (2.57-2.68)	8	Orange
.106-.111 (2.72-2.81)	9	Yellow
.111-.116 (2.83-2.94)	10	Light Blue
.117-.121 (2.96-3.07)	11	Blue
.122-.126 (3.09-3.20)	12	....
.127-.131 (3.22-3.33)	13	Pink
.132-.136 (3.35-3.46)	14	Green
.137-.141 (3.48-3.59)	15	Gray

If more or less washer thickness is required to bring end play within specifications, remove oil pump and forward and direct clutch assemblies, and install correct thickness washer on end of output shaft. See FRONT UNIT SELECTIVE THRUST WASHER CHART.

5) Remove front unit end play checking tools. Install remaining pump-to-case bolt and tighten. Remove output shaft support.

GOVERNOR

1) If removed, install new seal ring on governor shaft and place seal ring end into governor cover to size seal. Lubricate seal with petroleum jelly. Lubricate and install 2 new seal rings on governor cover.

NOTE: Make sure 2 check balls are in governor before installation.

2) Install governor assembly (seal end first) into cover. Install governor assembly and cover into case, aligning governor shaft with shaft hole in case. Rotate assembly and output shaft slightly to ease installation. Install governor retaining ring and align ring gap with an end showing in case slot.

NOTE: If retaining ring cannot be installed, governor shaft is not aligned with case hole. Also, governor cover fits tight in case bore the last 1/16" (1.59 mm).

BAND ANCHOR PIN & INTERMEDIATE SERVO

Install anchor pin (stem end first) into case, making sure stem locates in hole of intermediate band lug. Install servo assembly into case and make sure tapered end of band apply pin is properly located against band apply lug. Compress servo cover and install retaining ring. Align ring gap with an end showing in case slot.

Fig. 44: Installing Intermediate Band Anchor Pin

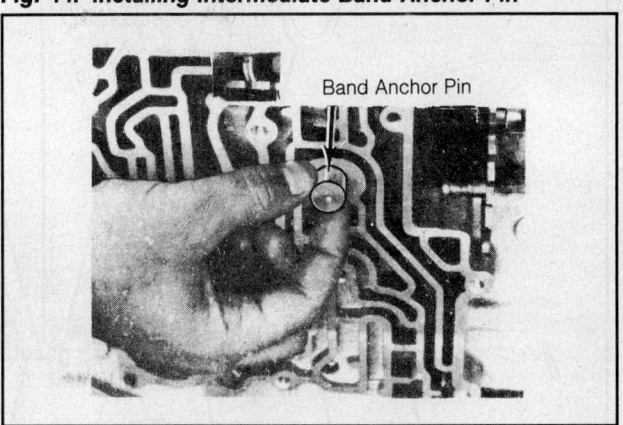

VALVE BODY

1) Install new low-reverse clutch housing-to-case cup plug and seal assembly, with seal end first, into hole in case. See Fig. 45. Using a 3/8" diameter metal rod and hammer, drive plug and seal assembly into case until it seats against low-reverse clutch housing.

2) Lubricate with petroleum jelly and install new "O" ring seal on torque converter clutch electrical connector. Connect solenoid lead wire to electrical connector. Install connector into case with lock tabs facing into case and locator tab in notch on side of case.

Fig. 45: *Installing Low-Reverse Clutch Housing to Case Cup Plug and Seal Assembly*

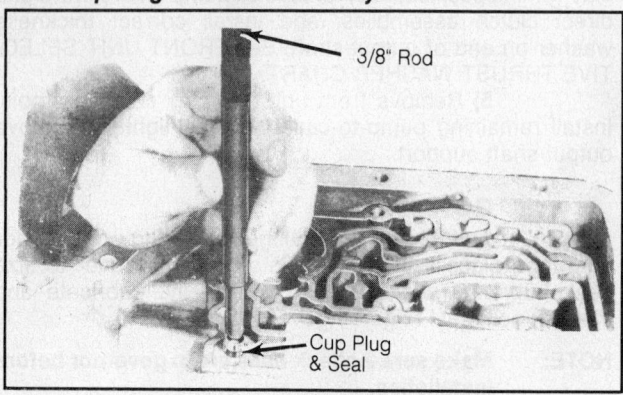

3/8" Rod

Cup Plug & Seal

3) Install 1-2 accumulator spring into case pocket. Install fifth check ball into case. *See Fig. 4.* Install two guide pins into case to align valve body parts. Install remaining four check balls into ball seat pockets in valve body and retain with petroleum jelly. *See Fig. 14.*

4) Position valve body-to-spacer plate gasket (marked "VB") on valve body, then place spacer plate on top of gasket. Place spacer plate-to-case gasket (marked "C") on top of spacer plate.

5) Insert two valve body attaching bolts through valve body, gaskets and spacer plate, then install valve body assembly, aligning manual valve with detent lever pin.

NOTE: Make sure check balls, 1-2 accumulator piston and manual valve do not fall out during valve body installation.

6) Start valve body attaching bolts, except throttle lever, bracket assembly and oil screen attaching bolts. Remove guide pins and replace with bolts and inside manual detent roller and spring assembly, locating tang in valve body and roller on inside detent lever.

7) If removed, install spring on top of throttle lever and bracket assembly lifter, then place lifter and spring into throttle bracket. Install link on throttle lever, making sure link is hooked. *See Fig. 47.*

8) Install lever and bracket assembly, locating slot in bracket with coiled pin, aligning lifter through valve body hole and link through T.V. linkage case bore. Install attaching bolts. Tighten all valve body attaching bolts evenly.

9) On diesel models, install governor pressure switch using a 1 1/16" oil pressure sending unit socket. Connect long solenoid lead wire to governor pressure switch terminal. Press solenoid lead wires into wire clip.

Fig. 46: *Cutaway View of Transmission Showing Location of Thrust Washers, Thrust Bearings and Bushings*

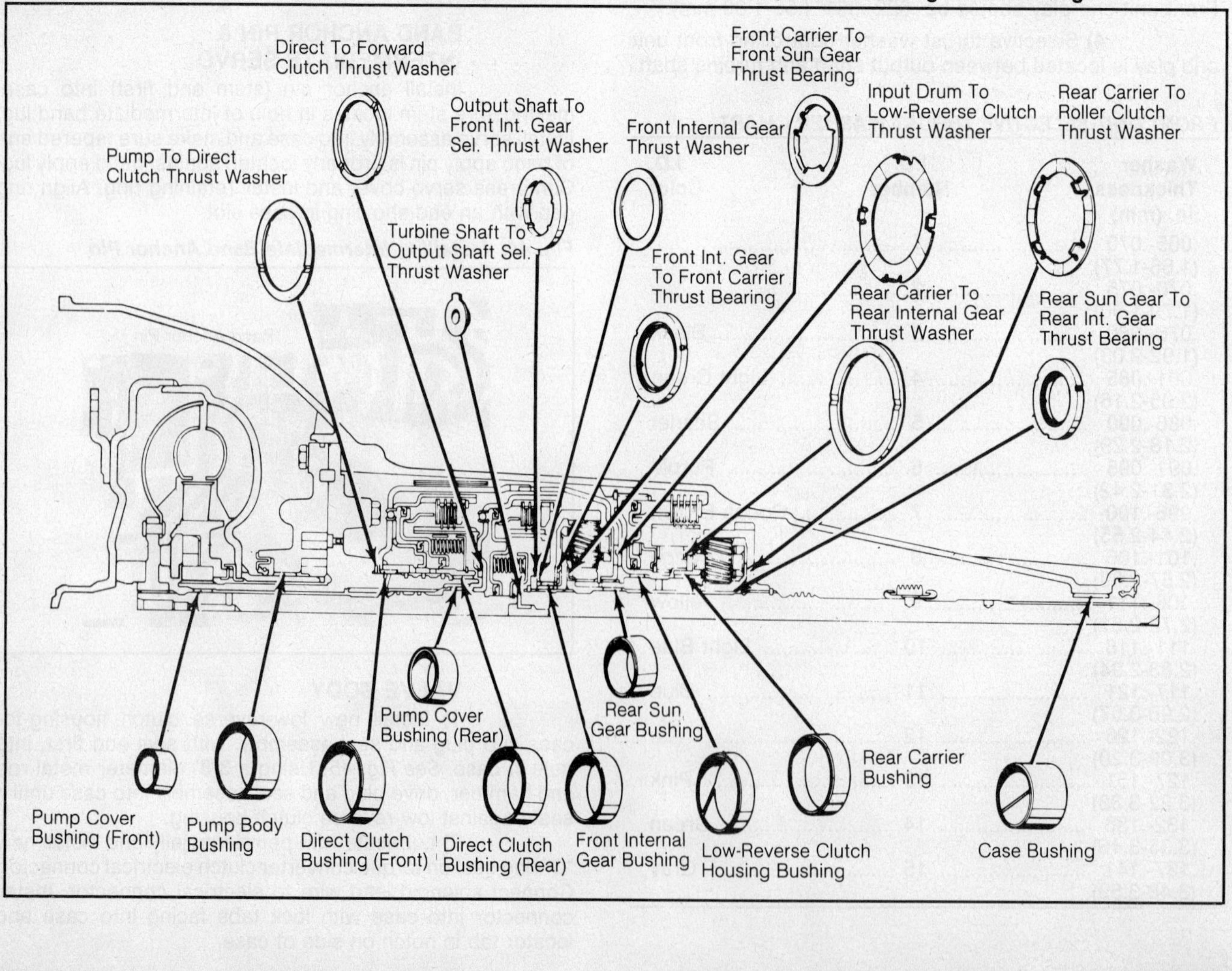

Direct To Forward Clutch Thrust Washer

Output Shaft To Front Int. Gear Sel. Thrust Washer

Front Carrier To Front Sun Gear Thrust Bearing

Front Internal Gear Thrust Washer

Input Drum To Low-Reverse Clutch Thrust Washer

Rear Carrier To Roller Clutch Thrust Washer

Pump To Direct Clutch Thrust Washer

Turbine Shaft To Output Shaft Sel. Thrust Washer

Front Int. Gear To Front Carrier Thrust Bearing

Rear Carrier To Rear Internal Gear Thrust Washer

Rear Sun Gear To Rear Int. Gear Thrust Bearing

Pump Cover Bushing (Rear)

Rear Sun Gear Bushing

Rear Carrier Bushing

Pump Cover Bushing (Front)

Pump Body Bushing

Direct Clutch Bushing (Front)

Direct Clutch Bushing (Rear)

Front Internal Gear Bushing

Low-Reverse Clutch Housing Bushing

Case Bushing

Fig. 47: Throttle Lever and Bracket Assembly

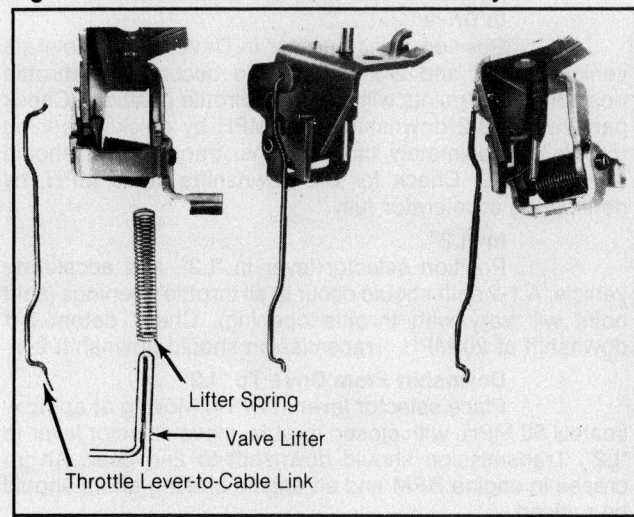

Lifter Spring

Valve Lifter

Throttle Lever-to-Cable Link

OIL SCREEN, OIL PAN & SPEEDOMETER DRIVEN GEAR

Install a new screen gasket on oil screen, retain with petroleum jelly, then install screen on valve body and install and tighten attaching bolts. Position a new pan gasket on case, install oil pan and attaching bolts and tighten. If necessary, install a new "O" ring seal on speedometer driven gear housing, install housing into case, then install retainer and attaching bolt, aligning slot in housing with retainer.

TORQUE CONVERTER

Install torque converter into pump assembly. Ensure converter hub drive slots are fully engaged with pump drive gear tangs. Converter must be fully installed towards rear of transmission.

NOTE: When properly installed, the distance between engine mounting face of transmission case and front face of converter cover drive lugs will be at least 1".

TIGHTENING SPECIFICATIONS

Application	Ft. Lbs. (N.m)
Converter-to Flywheel	41-52 (55-70)
Manual Shaft-to-Detent Lever	20-25 (27-34)
Pump Body-to-Pump Cover	15-20 (20-27)
Pump-to-Case	15-20 (20-27)
Park Lock Bracket-to-Case	15-20 (20-27)
Transmission-to-Engine	
V6 (2.8L)	55 (75)
All Others	35 (47)

	INCH Lbs. (N.m)
Governor Pressure Switch (Diesel)	62-124 (7-14)
Line Pressure Take Off	62-124 (7-14)
Oil Pan-to-Case	124-160 (14-18)
Oil Screen-to-Case	115-151 (13-17)
Speedo Driven Gear Retainer-to-Case	71-124 (8-14)
Throttle Lever Bracket-to-Case	115-151 (13-17)
T.C.C. Solenoid-to-Pump	27-44 (3-5)
Valve Body-to-Case	115-151 (13-17)

Automatic Transmissions

GENERAL MOTORS TURBO HYDRA-MATIC 200-4R

Buick, Cadillac, Chevrolet,
Oldsmobile, Pontiac

IDENTIFICATION

Transmission is identified by the production number, located on an I.D. plate attached to right side (rear) of case, near modulator. Production number consists of a year code, a 2 character model code and a build date code. See TRANSMISSION MODEL CODES table.

TRANSMISSION MODEL CODES

Application	Codes
Buick	BQ,HE,OG,OJ,OM
Cadillac	AA,AO,AP,OM
Chevrolet	CH,CR,CQ,HG,OM,5CY
Oldsmobile	BY,OZ
Pontiac	CR,DM,HG

DESCRIPTION

The Turbo Hydra-Matic 200-4R transmission is a fully automatic unit consisting of 3 major components; a 3-element torque converter (with a torque converter clutch), a compound planetary gear set, and an overdrive unit.

Friction elements used in this transmission include 5 multiple-disc clutches, 2 roller clutches and a band.

A hydraulic system, pressurized by a variable capacity vane-type pump, provides the working pressure required to operate the friction elements and automatic controls.

NOTE: **See GENERAL MOTORS TORQUE CONVERTER CLUTCH article in this section for information on the converter clutch system used in the THM 200-4R.**

LUBRICATION & ADJUSTMENTS

See appropriate AUTOMATIC TRANSMISSION SERVICING article in DOMESTIC GENERAL SERVICING section.

TROUBLE SHOOTING

See appropriate AUTOMATIC TRANSMISSION TROUBLE SHOOTING article in DOMESTIC GENERAL SERVICING section.

TESTING

LEAKAGE

See procedure FOR G.M. TURBO HYDRA-MATIC 400.

ROAD TEST

In Drive

Position selector lever in Drive, and accelerate vehicle. A 1-2 and 2-3 shift should occur at all throttle positions (shift points will vary with throttle position). Check part throttle 3-2 downshift at 30 MPH by quickly opening throttle approximately three-fourths, transmission should downshift 3-2. Check for 3-2 downshifts at 50 MPH, by depressing accelerator fully.

In "L2"

Position selector lever in "L2", and accelerate vehicle. A 1-2 shift should occur at all throttle openings (shift point will vary with throttle opening). Check detent 2-1 downshift at 20 MPH. Transmission should downshift 2-1.

Downshift From Drive To "L2"

Place selector lever in Drive. Moving at approximately 50 MPH, with closed throttle, move selector lever to "L2". Transmission should downshift to 2nd gear. An increase in engine RPM and an engine braking effect should be noticed.

In ("L1")

Place selector lever in Low ("1"), and accelerate vehicle. No upshift should occur.

Downshift From "L2" To "L1"

At 40 MPH, with throttle closed, move selector lever to "1st". A 2-1 downshift should occur at about 40-25 MPH, depending on axle ratio and control valve assembly calibration. The 2-1 downshift at closed throttle will be accompanied by increasing engine RPM and an engine braking effect should be noticed.

In Reverse

Place selector lever in Reverse and check for proper reverse operation.

HYDRAULIC PRESSURE TESTS

Preliminary Checking Procedure

Prior to making control pressure test: check transmission fluid level, check and adjust T.V. cable, check and adjust outside manual linkage, check engine tune, install oil pressure gauge to transmission and connect tachometer to engine.

CAUTION: **When performing T.V. pressure checks, DO NOT sustain engine test speed more than 2 minutes.**

Minimum T.V. Pressure Check

With T.V. cable adjusted to specifications and brakes applied, check line pressure in selector lever positions and at 1000 RPM. See CONTROL PRESSURE SPECIFICATIONS table.

Maximum T.V. Pressure Check

With T.V. cable held at in fully extended position, and brakes applied, check for correct line pressure in selector lever positions and at 1000 RPM. See CONTROL PRESSURE SPECIFICATIONS table.

PRESSURE TEST RESULTS

High or Low Pressures

- T.V. cable out of adjustment, binding, unhooked, broken or wrong link.
- Throttle lever and bracket assembly binding, unhooked or mispositioned.
- Throttle valve or plunger valve binding.

Fig. 1: Cutaway View of Turbo Hydra-Matic 200-4R Transmission

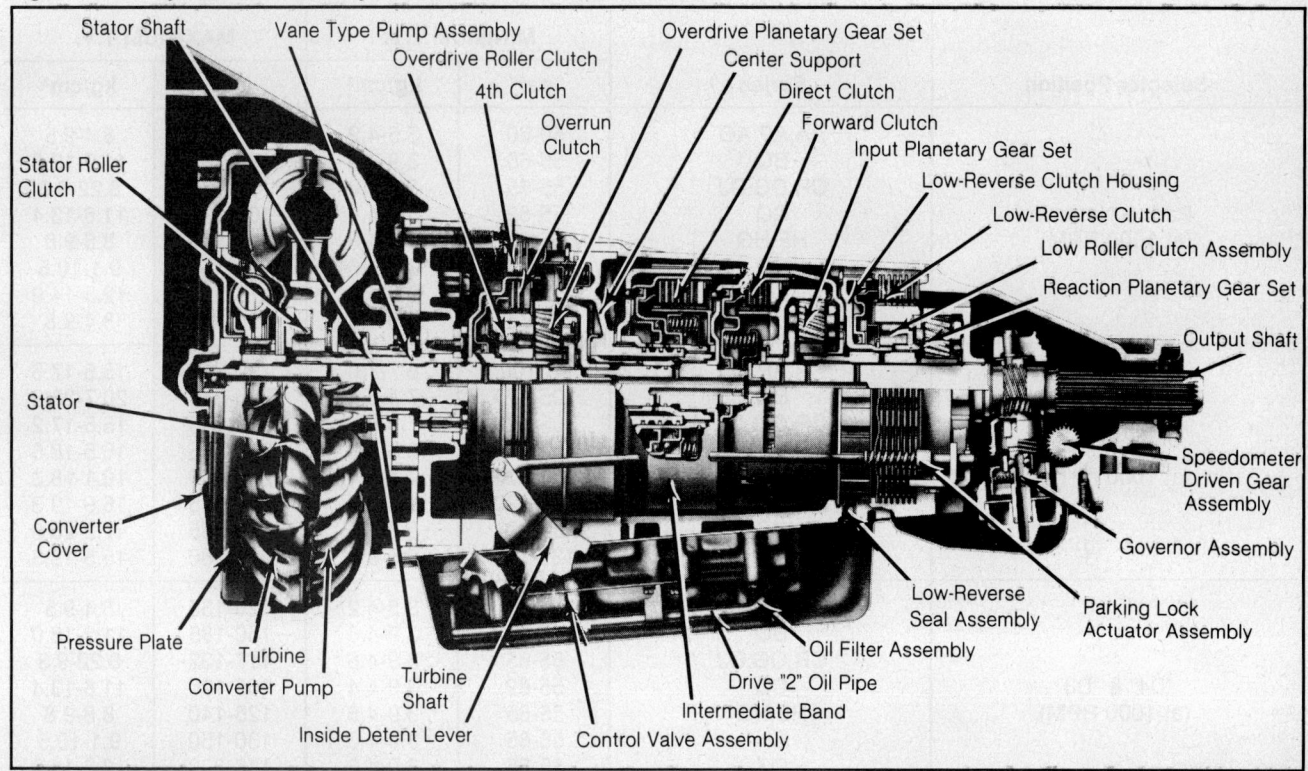

- Pressure regulator valve binding.
- T.V. Boost valve binding or wrong valve installed (causing low oil pressure only).
- Reverse Boost valve binding.
- Manual valve unhooked, or mispositioned.
- Pressure relief valve ball missing or spring damaged.
- Oil pump slide stuck, or slide seal missing or damaged.
- Pump decrease air bleed orifice missing or damaged (causing low oil pressure only).
- Pump decrease air bleed orifice plugged (causing low oil pressure only).
- T.V. Limit valve binding.
- Line Bias valve binding in open position (causing high oil pressure).
- Line Bias valve binding in closed position (causing low oil pressure).

NOTE: Control valve assembly spacer plate and case should be closely inspected for corroded orifices and passages.

CLUTCH AND BAND APPLICATION CHART (ELEMENTS IN USE)

Selector Lever Position	Overrun Clutch	Intermediate Band	Overdrive Roller Clutch	Direct Clutch	Low Roller Clutch	4th Clutch	Forward Clutch	Low-Reverse Clutch
D – DRIVE								
1st Gear			X		X		X	
2nd Gear		X	X				X	
3rd Gear			X	X			X	
Overdrive				X	X	X		
"3" – MANUAL 3rd	X			X			X	
"L2" – MANUAL 2nd	X	X					X	
"L1" – MANUAL LOW	X						X	X
"R" – REVERSE			X	X				X
NEUTRAL or PARK			X					

Automatic Transmissions

GENERAL MOTORS TURBO HYDRA-MATIC 200-4R (Cont.)

CONTROL PRESSURE SPECIFICATIONS

Selector Position	Series [1]	MINIMUM T.V.		MAXIMUM T.V.	
		psi	kg/cm²	psi	kg/cm²
Park & Neutral (at 1000 RPM)	AA,AP,AO	50-60	3.5-4.2	120-135	8.4-9.5
	BQ	55-65	3.9-4.6	160-185	11.2-13.0
	CR,OG,OJ	55-65	3.9-4.6	117-132	8.22-9.3
	CQ	55-62	3.9-4.4	165-190	11.6-13.4
	HE,HG	55-65	3.9-4.6	125-140	8.8-9.8
	CH	55-65	3.9-4.6	130-150	9.1-10.5
	OZ	55-65	3.9-4.6	175-200	12.3-14.0
	OM	65-75	4.6-5.3	120-140	8.4-9.8
Reverse (at 1000 RPM)	AA,AP,AO	95-100	6.7-7.0	220-250	15.5-17.6
	BQ	105-120	7.4-8.4	295-340	20.7-23.9
	CR,OG,OJ	105-120	7.4-8.4	220-245	15.5-17.2
	CQ	80-90	5.6-6.3	235-265	16.5-18.6
	HE,HG	105-120	7.4-8.4	230-260	16.1-18.3
	CH	105-120	7.4-8.4	240-275	16.9-19.3
	OZ	80-90	5.6-6.3	245-285	17.2-20.0
	OM	121-140	8.5-9.8	220-260	15.5-18.3
"D4" & "D3" (at 1000 RPM)	AA,AP,AO	50-60	3.5-4.2	120-135	8.4-9.5
	BQ	55-65	3.9-4.6	160-185	11.2-13.0
	CR,OG,OJ	55-65	3.9-4.6	117-132	8.22-9.3
	CQ	55-62	3.9-4.4	165-190	11.6-13.4
	HE,HG	55-65	3.9-4.6	125-140	8.8-9.8
	CH	55-65	3.9-4.6	130-150	9.1-10.5
	OZ	55-65	3.9-4.6	175-200	12.3-14.0
	OM	65-75	4.6-5.3	120-140	8.4-9.8
"D2" & "D1" (at 1000 RPM)	AA,AP,AO	112-127	7.9-8.9	112-127	7.9-8.9
	BQ,CH,CR,HG,HE,OG,OJ	122-137	8.6-8.9	122-137	8.6-8.9
	CQ,OZ	115-130	8.0-9.1	115-130	8.0-9.1
	OM	140-165	9.8-11.6	140-165	9.8-11.6

[1] – Information on 5CY series transaxle not available from manufacturer at time of publication.

SERVICE (IN VEHICLE)

The following components can be removed from transmission without removing transmission from vehicle. For removal and installation procedures for these components, see TRANSMISSION DISASSEMBLY in this article.

- Extention Housing Seal
- Governor Assembly
- Intermediate Servo Piston Assembly
- Oil Pan and Screen
- Control Valve Assembly
- Check Balls and Valve Body Spacer Plate and Gaskets
- Pressure Regulator Parts
- Inside Detent/Selector Lever
- Manual Detent Roller and Spring Assembly
- Throttle Lever and Bracket Assembly
- T.V. Cable and "O" Ring
- T.V. Boost Valve and Bushing
- Parking Pawl Actuator Rod, Bracket and Pawl
- Manual Shaft and Seal
- Manual Valve and Link
- Rear Seal
- 1-2 Accumulator Assembly
- 3-4 Accumulator Assembly
- Low/Reverse Cup Plug
- Reverse Boost Valve and Bushing
- Stop Valve
- Intermediate Band Anchor Pin
- 4-3 Pressure Switch
- 4th Clutch Pressure Switch
- Speedometer Driven Gear Assembly
- Converter Clutch Valve and Spring
- Converter Clutch Solenoid
- Solenoid Wire Clips
- Electrical Connectors
- Cooler Fittings
- Oil Filter Pipe and "O" Ring

REMOVAL & INSTALLATION

TRANSMISSION

See appropriate AUTOMATIC TRANSMISSION REMOVAL article in DOMESTIC GENERAL SERVICING section.

NOTE: See GENERAL MOTORS TORQUE CONVERTER CLUTCH article in this section for information on the converter clutch system used in the THM 200-4R.

TRANSMISSION DISASSEMBLY

INPUT SHAFT END PLAY

See procedure FOR G.M. TURBO HYDRA-MATIC 400.

EXTERNAL PARTS

1) Mount transmission in a holding fixture and remove torque converter. Rotate transmission so that oil pan is facing up. Remove oil pan and gasket. Remove oil filter intake pipe and "O" rings. "O" rings may be located in pump bore.

2) Disconnect wire leads at electrical connector and pressure switches. *See Fig. 2.* Using a 3/4" box wrench to compress connector tangs, withdraw electrical connector and "O" ring from case. Remove converter clutch solenoid assembly bolts, clips and solenoid.

Fig. 2: Bottom View of Transmission Case

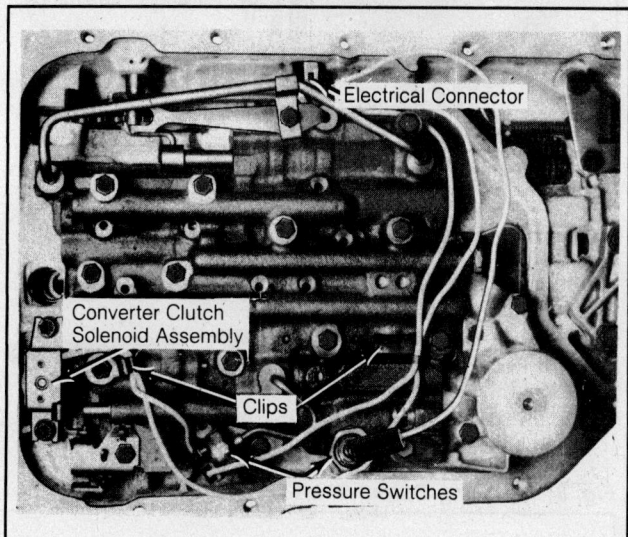

3) Using care not to bend throttle lever link, remove throttle lever and bracket assembly. T.V. exhaust valve lifter and spring may separate from lever and bracket assembly. Remove manual detent roller and spring assembly, signal (Drive "2") oil pipe retaining clip and oil pipe.

4) Remove 4-3 pressure switch and retaining bolt, then remove remaining valve body attaching bolts. Hold manual valve in bore and carefully lift control valve assembly from case. Care must be taken as 3 check balls are located on top of spacer plate-to-valve body gasket. Remove check balls.

5) Remove 1-2 accumulator housing, then withdraw spring, gasket, plate and piston from housing. It may be necessary to apply low air pressure (approximately 3 psi) to orifice in accumulator housing passage to remove piston.

6) Remove control valve assembly gaskets and spacer plate from transmission case. Withdraw 3-4 accumulator spring, piston and pin from bore in case. It may be necessary to apply low air pressure (approximately 3 psi) to orifice in case core passage to remove piston. *See Fig. 3.*

7) Remove 8 check balls from core passages in case. *See Fig. 4.* Remove governor cover and gasket from case, then remove governor assembly while rotating output shaft counterclockwise to ease removal.

Fig. 3: View of Case Core Passage

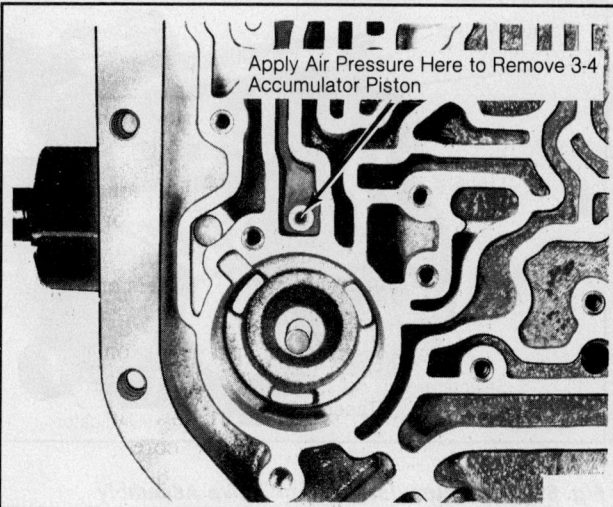

Use approximately 3 psi to remove piston.

Fig. 4: Removing Check Balls From Case

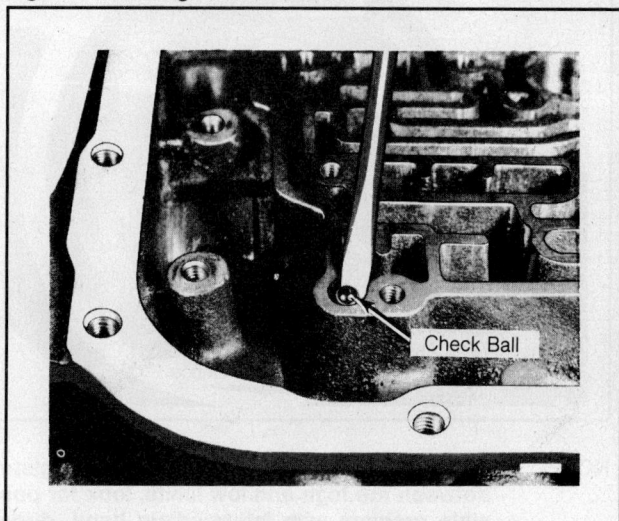

CAUTION: Do not use pliers to remove governor assembly.

8) Pry intermediate servo cover retaining ring from groove in case. Remove servo cover and discard seal ring. Remove servo piston and band apply pin from bore in case.

NOTE: Before continuing with Transmission Disassembly, check for proper intermediate band apply pin as follows.

Intermediate Band Apply Pin Selection

1) Install Band Apply Pin Selection Gauge (J-25014-2) in intermediate servo bore and retain with servo cover retaining ring, aligning ring with gap at case slot. Install Selection Gauge Tapered Pin (J-25014-1) into gauge. *See Fig. 5.*

NOTE: Ensure tapered pin end is properly located against band apply lug. Also, ensure band anchor pin is properly located in case and band anchor lug.

Fig. 5: Intermediate Band Apply Pin Selection

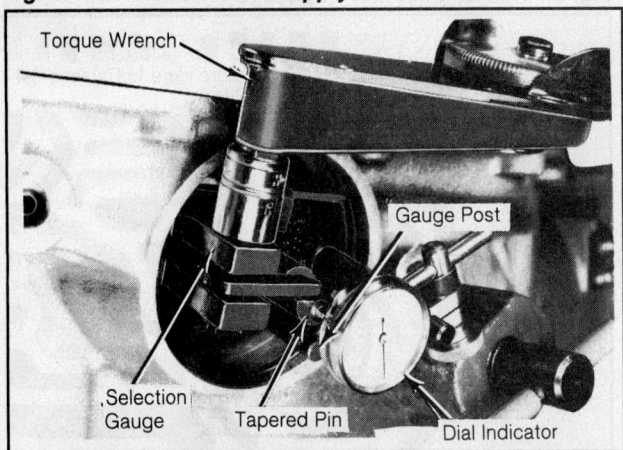

Fig. 6: 3rd Accumulator Check Valve Assembly

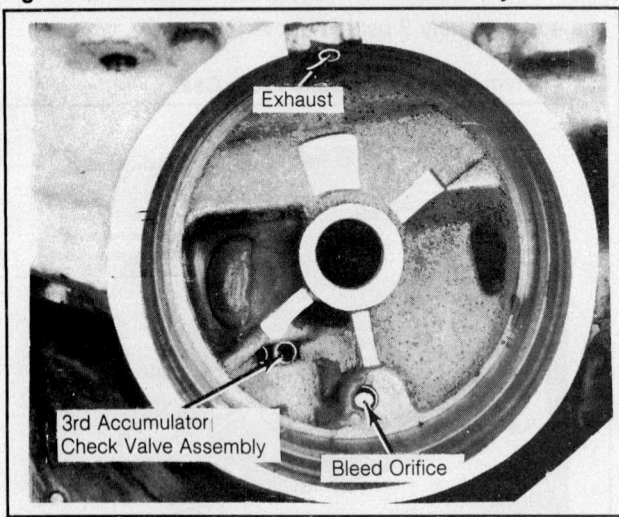

NOTE: If band selection tapered pin does not register between the high and low limits, look for possible problem with intermediate band, direct clutch housing or transmission case.

2) Install dial indicator and position indicator point on top of selection gauge post. Set indicator to zero. Ensure selection gauge is squarely seated against servo retaining ring and stepped side of tapered pin is aligned with torquing arm of gauge.

NOTE: Dial indicator travel is reversed, making the indicator readings backwards. On an indicator that ranges from 0-100, a .020" (.51 mm) travel will read .080" (2.03 mm), a .060" (1.52 mm) travel will read .040" (1.02 mm).

INTERMEDIATE BAND APPLY PIN SELECTION

Indicator Reading Inches (mm)	Apply Pin I.D.
0-.029 (0-.72)	1 Groove
.029-.057 (.72-1.44)	2 Grooves
.057-.086 (1.44-2.16)	3 Grooves
.086-.114 (2.16-2.88)	None

3rd Accumulator Check Valve Replacement

1) Inspect 3rd accumulator check valve for the following conditions: Missing check ball, check ball binding or stuck in tube, oil feed slot in tube missing or restricted, improperly assembled, loose fitting or not fully seated in case. If check valve requires replacement, go to step 2).

2) Using a No. 4 screw extractor, remove check valve assembly from case by turning and pulling straight out. *See Fig. 7.*

3) Install new check valve assembly, small end first, into case. Position oil feed slot in tube so it faces servo. Using a 3/8" diameter metal rod and hammer, drive assembly until it is seated in case hole.

Fig. 7: Removing 3rd Accumulator Check Valve Assembly

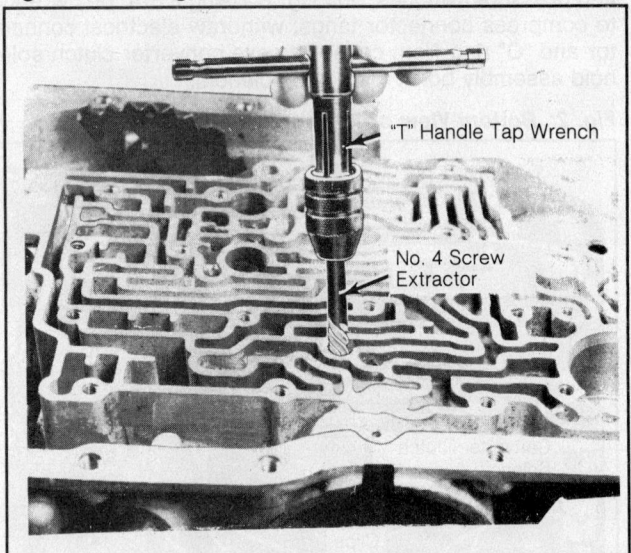

Fig. 8: Installing Output Shaft Loader

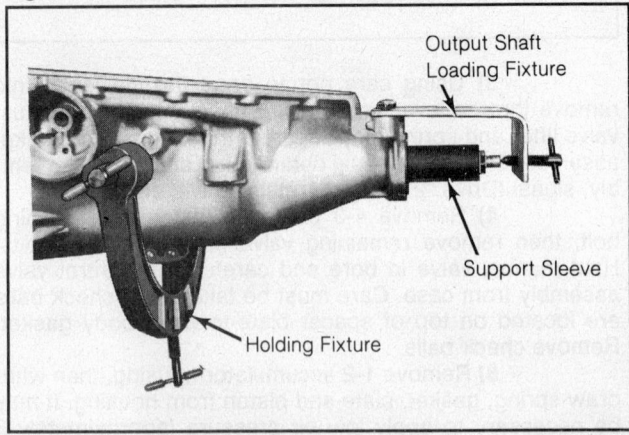

OVERDRIVE UNIT PARTS

NOTE: Prior to removing overdrive unit parts, check overdrive unit end play to determine correct end play thrust washer for use during reassembly.

Overdrive End Play

1) Install Output Shaft Loading Fixture (J-29332) and Support Sleeve (J-25013-1) on output shaft. *See Fig. 8.* Turn transmission to vertical position, pump side up.

GENERAL MOTORS TURBO HYDRA-MATIC 200-4R (Cont.)

2) Remove 1 pump-to-case bolt and washer and install an 11" long bolt into pump bolt hole. Attach Overdrive End Play Checker (J-25022) and Oil Pump Remover (J-24773-5) to turbine shaft. *See Fig. 9.*

Fig. 9: Checking Overdrive Unit End Play

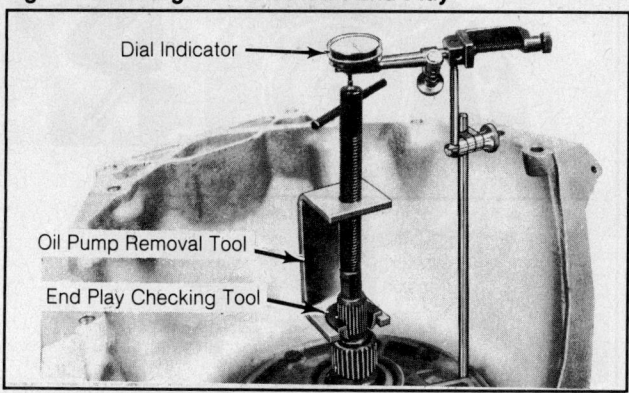

NOTE: The following step must be performed to eliminate the tolerance difference between turbine shaft snap ring and overdrive carrier.

3) Mount a dial indicator and clamp assembly on long bolt, positioning indicator point cap on top of pump remover. Lift upward on remover with approximately 3 lbs. force and zero indicator while maintaining the upward force.

4) With dial indicator zeroed, increase upward force to approximately 20 lbs. (9.1 kg) and read end play on indicator. Overdrive unit end play should be .004-.027" (.10-.69 mm). The selective thrust washer controlling this end play is located between pump cover and overdrive clutch housing. If more or less washer thickness is required to bring end play within specification, select correct washer. See OVERDRIVE UNIT END PLAY WASHER SELECTION chart.

OVERDRIVE UNIT END PLAY WASHER SELECTION

Washer Thickness	I.D. Number	I.D. Color
.167-.171"	0	Scarlet
.172-.176"	1	White
.177-.180"	2	Brown
.181-.185"	3	Grey
.186-.190"	4	Yellow
.191-.195"	5	Lt. Blue
.196-.200"	6	Purple
.201-.204"	7	Orange
.205-.209"	8	Green

Component Removal

1) If necessary, pry oil pump seal from pump. Remove pump-to-case bolts and washers. Install Oil Pump Remover (J-24773-A) on turbine shaft. *See Fig. 9.* Remove oil pump assembly from case. Remove pump-to-case gasket and tanged oil deflector plate located under pump.

2) Remove 4th clutch plate-to-case snap ring, then grasp turbine shaft and lift overdrive assembly and 4th clutch plates from case. Remove clutch plates from overdrive assembly and the remaining steel plate from case.

3) Remove overdrive internal gear-to-carrier thrust washer from inside internal gear. Remove internal gear and internal gear-to-support thrust washer from case.

4) Using a spring compressor, compress 4th clutch spring and retainer assembly. Remove support-to-clutch snap ring, spring and retainer. Remove compressor from retainer assembly. Lift 4th clutch piston from case.

FRONT UNIT PARTS

NOTE: Prior to removing front unit parts, check front unit end play to determine correct thrust washer to install at reassembly.

Front Unit End Play

1) Push forward clutch shaft downward, then install Forward And Direct Clutch Remover (J-29337) in end of shaft. Mount dial indicator and clamp assembly. *See Fig. 10.* Position indicator point on top of clutch remover.

NOTE: Perform this check with output shaft loading fixture and support sleeve in place.

Fig. 10: Checking Front Unit End Play

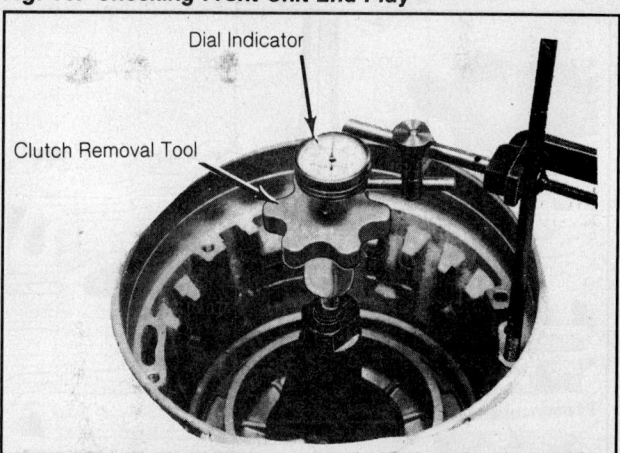

2) Move output shaft upward by turning adjusting screw on output shaft loading fixture. Move shaft upward until White or scribed line on support sleeve begins to disappear. Zero dial indicator.

3) Pull clutch remover upward and read resulting end play on dial indicator. Front unit end play should be .022-.051" (.56-1.30 mm). Selective thrust washer controlling this end play is located between output shaft and forward clutch shaft. If more or less washer thickness is required to bring end play within specification, select proper washer. See FRONT UNIT END PLAY WASHER SELECTION chart.

Component Removal

1) Remove 2 center support bolts. *See Fig. 11.* From inside case, remove center support beveled snap ring. Lift center support from case using Slide Hammer (J-7004) and Puller (J-29334-1). Remove center support/direct clutch thrust washer.

NOTE: Center support/direct clutch thrust washer may be stuck to back of direct clutch.

2) Install Direct And Forward Clutch Remover (J-29337) in end of forward clutch shaft. *See Fig. 10.* Pull direct and forward clutch assemblies from case. Separate direct clutch from forward clutch. Remove intermediate band assembly and band anchor pin from case. Remove output shaft/forward clutch shaft selective thrust washer.

GENERAL MOTORS TURBO HYDRA-MATIC 200-4R (Cont.)

FRONT UNIT END PLAY WASHER SELECTION

Washer Thickness	I.D. Number	I.D. Color
.065-.070"	1	.....
.070-.075"	2	.....
.076-.080"	3	Black
.081-.085"	4	Lt. Green
.086-.090"	5	Scarlet
.091-.095"	6	Purple
.096-.100"	7	Brown
.101-.106"	8	Orange
.106-.111"	9	Yellow
.111-.116"	10	Lt. Blue
.117-.121"	11	.....
.122-.126"	12	.....
.127-.131"	13	Pink
.132-.136"	14	Green
.137-.141"	15	Grey

Fig. 11: Removing Center Support Bolts

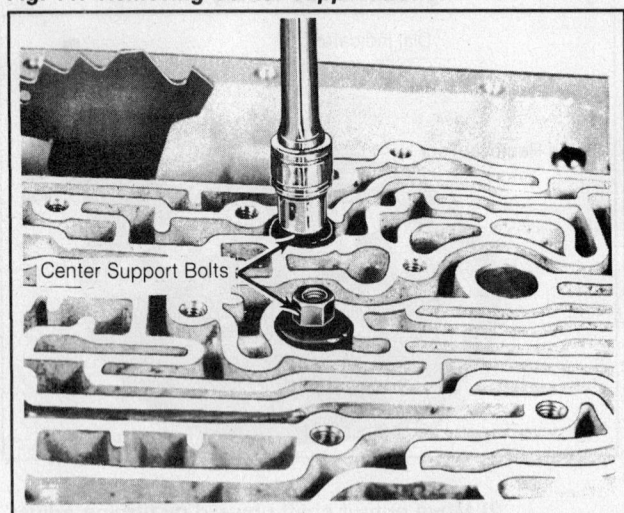

Center Support Bolts

NOTE: The direct-to-forward clutch thrust washer may stick to end of direct clutch housing when separating clutch assemblies.

FRONT GEAR PARTS

NOTE: Prior to removing front gear parts, check rear unit end play to determine correct thrust washer to install at transmission reassembly.

Rear Unit End Play

1) Loosen adjusting screw on output shaft loading fixture (installed at overdrive end play check) and push output shaft downward. Install a "C" clamp on case. See Fig. 12. Mount a dial indicator and extension on "C" clamp.

2) Position dial indicator extension against end of output shaft and set indicator to zero. Move output shaft upward by turning screw on loading fixture until White or scribed line on support sleeve begins to disappear, then read indicator end play.

3) Rear unit end play should be .004-.025" (.10-.64 mm). Selective thrust washer controlling this end play is located between front internal gear thrust washer and output shaft snap ring. If more or less thrust washer thickness is required to bring end play within specification, select proper washer. REAR UNIT END PLAY WASHER SELECTION chart. Remove dial indicator and "C" clamp.

Fig. 12: Checking Rear Unit End Play

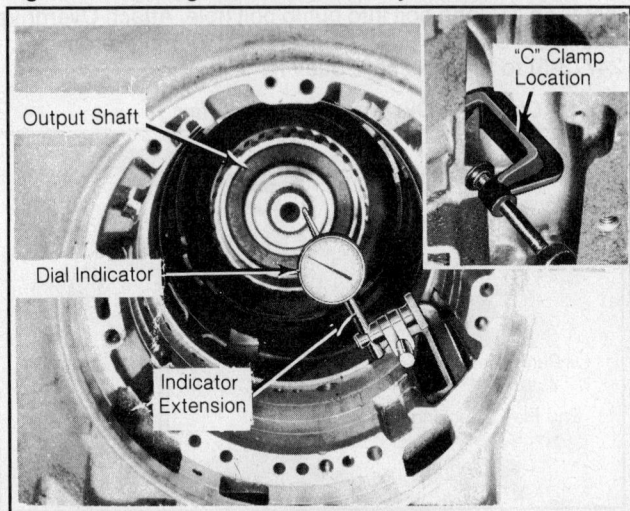

Output Shaft

"C" Clamp Location

Dial Indicator

Indicator Extension

REAR UNIT END PLAY WASHER SELECTION

Washer Thickness	I.D. Number	I.D. Color
.097-.102"	0	.....
.114-.119"	1	Orange
.121-.126"	2	White
.128-.133"	3	Yellow
.135-.140"	4	Blue
.143-.147"	5	Red
.150-.154"	6	Brown
.157-.161"	7	Green
.164-.168"	8	Black
.171-.175"	9	Purple

Component Removal

1) Remove output shaft-to-selective washer snap ring, then lift front internal gear, rear selective washer and thrust washer from case and remove washers from front internal gear.

2) Remove front carrier assembly and front internal gear-to-front carrier thrust bearing assembly. If it did not come out with front carrier, remove front sun gear and sun gear-to-front carrier thrust bearing assembly.

Fig. 13: Removing Output Shaft Snap Ring

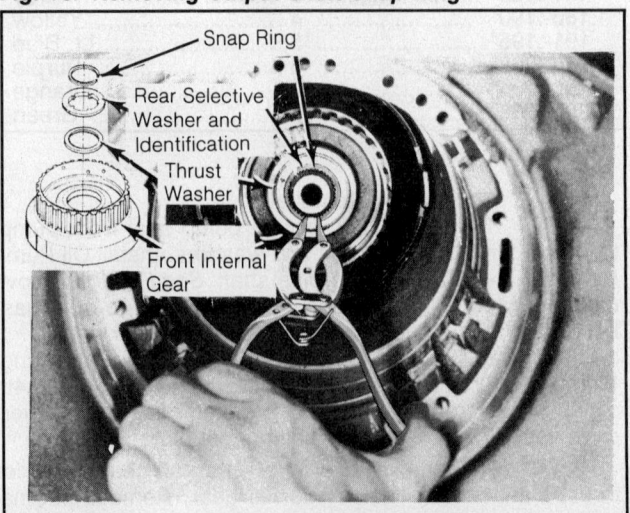

Snap Ring

Rear Selective Washer and Identification

Thrust Washer

Front Internal Gear

NOTE: The front sun gear-to-front carrier thrust bearing requires only 1 race.

3) Remove input drum and rear sun gear. Remove the 4-tanged input drum-to-reverse clutch housing thrust washer from rear of drum or front clutch housing.

4) Grind approximately 3/4" from end of a No. 4 screw extractor, then insert Easy-out into low/reverse clutch housing-to-case cup plug. Turn screw extractor 2 or 3 turns and pull out cup plug. Remove low/reverse clutch-to-case beveled snap ring. Lift clutch assembly from case. Remove low/reverse clutch housing-to-case spacer ring.

NOTE: Do not reuse low/reverse clutch housing cup plug and seal assembly.

Fig. 14: Removing Low/Reverse Clutch Housing Cup Plug

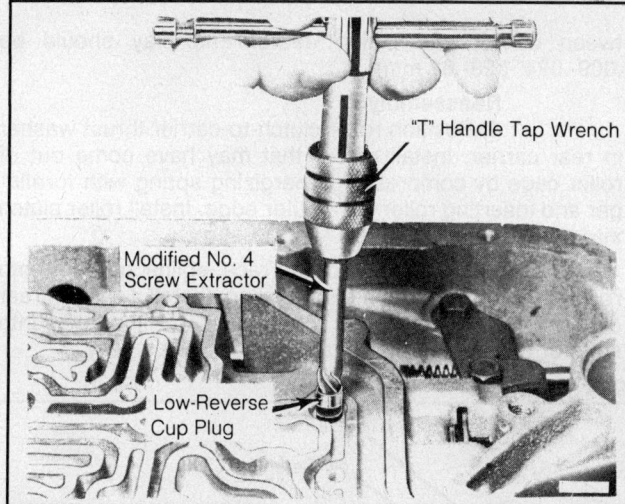

"T" Handle Tap Wrench

Modified No. 4 Screw Extractor

Low-Reverse Cup Plug

REAR GEAR PARTS

NOTE: Governor assembly must be removed before removing rear gear parts.

1) Grasp output shaft and lift out remaining rear unit parts and lay in a horizontal position. Remove roller clutch and rear carrier from output shaft. Remove the 4-tanged rear carrier-to-rear internal gear thrust washer from end of carrier or from inside rear internal gear.

2) Pull low/reverse clutch plates from output shaft. Remove rear internal gear-to-rear sun gear thrust bearing assembly from internal gear, then remove internal gear from output shaft. If necessary, remove rear oil seal from transmission case.

MANUAL SHAFT & PARKING PAWL PARTS

1) Turn transmission to a horizontal position, oil pan side up. If necessary, remove manual shaft and parking pawl linkage.

2) Remove hex nut securing inside detent lever to manual shaft. Remove parking lock actuator rod and inside detent lever. Remove manual shaft retaining pin from case and slide shaft out. If damaged, pry manual shaft oil seal from case.

3) Remove parking lock bracket. Remove parking pawl shaft retaining pin, then remove parking pawl cup plug using a No. 4 screw extractor with 3/4" ground from

end. Using No. 4 screw extractor, remove parking pawl shaft from case. Remove parking pawl and spring.

Fig. 15: Removing Parking Pawl Cup Plug

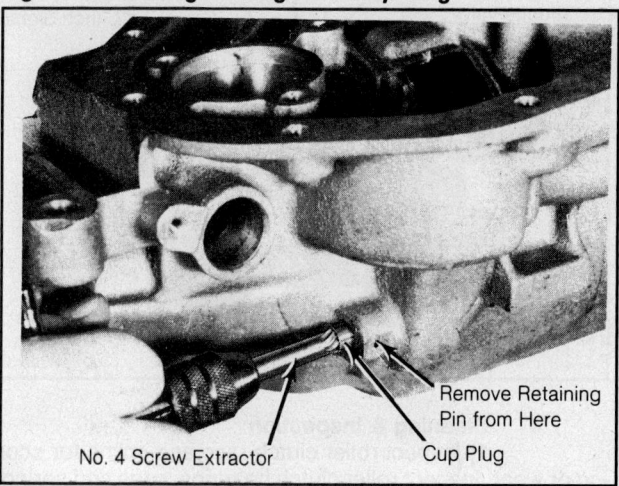

Remove Retaining Pin from Here

No. 4 Screw Extractor — Cup Plug

TORQUE CONVERTER

NOTE: The torque converter is a sealed unit and cannot be disassembled for service.

COMPONENT DISASSEMBLY & REASSEMBLY

TRANSMISSION CASE
Cleaning & Inspection

1) Inspect case assembly for damage, cracks, porosity or interconnected oil passages. Inspect orifice plug in intermediate servo bore. If plug requires replacement, install new plug, orifice end first, flush to slightly below top of plug hole.

2) Inspect case exhaust passages for restrictions. Inspect reverse clutch lugs, governor, intermediate servo bore, speedometer bore, and snap ring grooves for damage. Inspect all bolt holes for damage or stripped holes. Inspect case bushing for damage and scoring.

REAR GEAR PARTS
Cleaning & Inspection

1) Inspect output shaft journals, snap ring groove and splines for wear or damage. Check lubrication passages for damage or obstructions. Check governor drive gear for rough or damaged teeth.

2) Inspect rear internal gear splines, teeth and bearing surface for wear, cracks or damage. Inspect parking pawl lugs for cracks or damage. Thoroughly clean, air dry and inspect rear internal gear-to-rear sun gear thrust bearing assembly for pitted or rough conditions.

ROLLER CLUTCH & REAR CARRIER ASSEMBLY
Disassembly

Remove roller clutch inner race and lift roller clutch assembly from rear carrier. Remove rear carrier-to-clutch thrust washer (4 tangs) from rear of carrier and roller clutch-to-rear carrier thrust washer from inside carrier.

Automatic Transmissions

GENERAL MOTORS TURBO HYDRA-MATIC 200-4R (Cont.)

Fig. 16: Front View of Transmission Case Showing Oil Passages

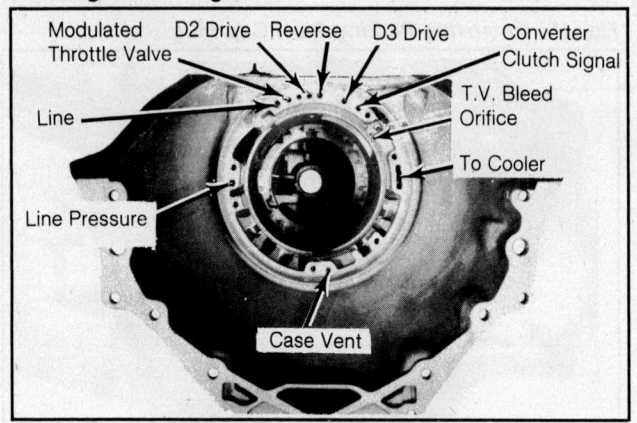

Fig. 18: Exploded View of Roller Clutch and Rear Carrier Assembly

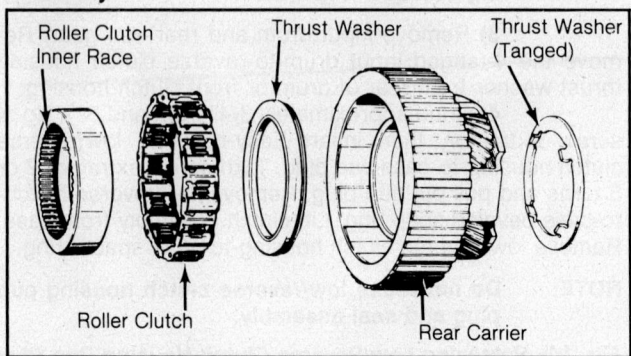

tween carrier and pinion gears. End play should be .009-.024" (.23-.61 mm).

Reassembly

1) Position roller clutch-to-carrier thrust washer in rear carrier. Install rollers that may have come out of roller cage by compressing energizing spring with forefinger and inserting roller from outer edge. Install roller clutch into rear carrier.

2) Install roller clutch race, spline side out, into roller clutch and rotate it into position. Install 4-tanged rear carrier-to-rear internal gear thrust washer. Align tangs into slots of rear carrier and retain with petroleum jelly.

Cleaning & Inspection

1) Inspect roller clutch race and spline for scoring or wear. Inspect roller clutch bearings, cage and springs for damage or wear. Inspect thrust washers for signs of scoring or excessive wear and check tanged thrust washer for bent tangs.

2) Inspect rear carrier for damage to roller clutch cam ramps. Inspect bushing for damage and scoring. Inspect planet pinions for damage, rough bearings or tilt. Check pinion end play using a feeler gauge inserted be-

Fig. 17: Bottom View of Transmission Case Showing Oil Passages

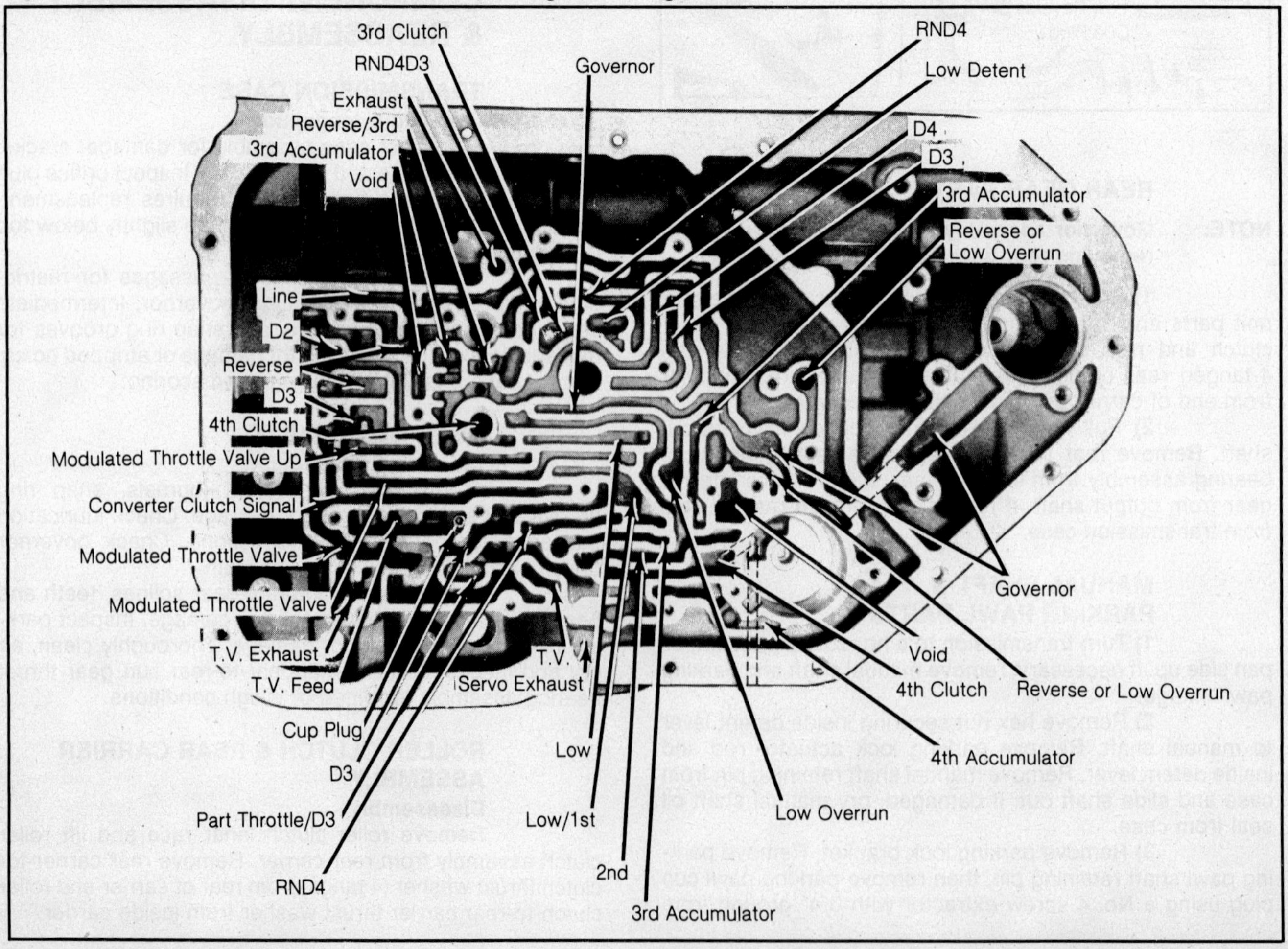

Fig. 19: Exploded View of Low/Reverse Clutch Assembly

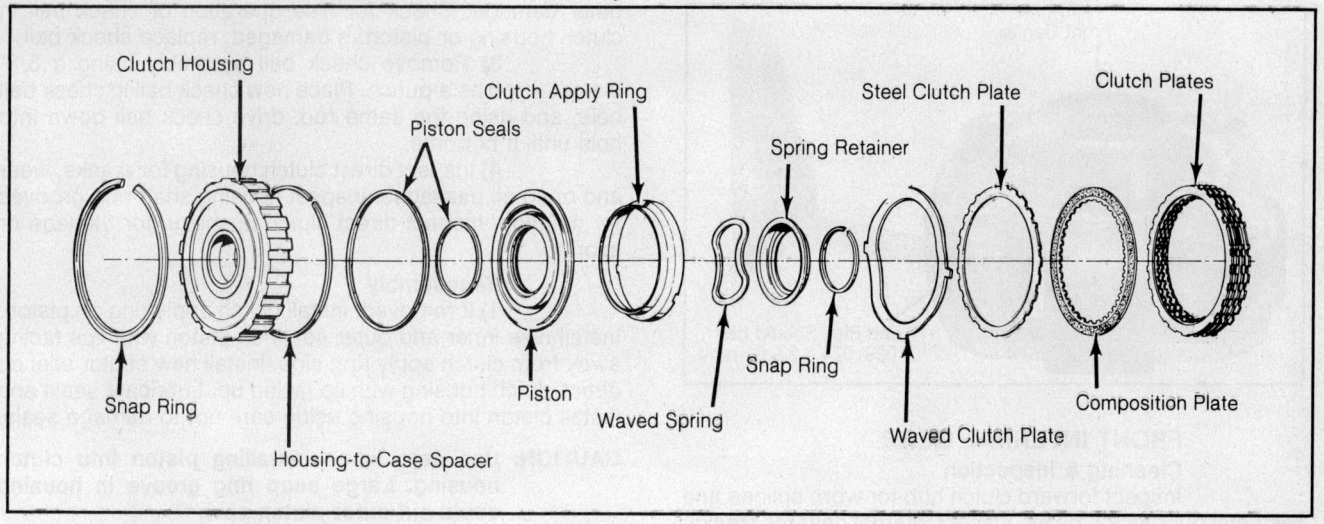

LOW/REVERSE CLUTCH

Disassembly

Compress low/reverse clutch spring retainer and remove snap ring. Remove waved spring from top of piston, then remove piston from housing. Remove inner and outer seals from piston. Remove clutch apply ring.

NOTE: **Low/reverse clutch assembly clutch plates and disc were removed during Transmission Disassembly.**

Cleaning & Inspection

1) Inspect composition, steel and waved clutch plates for signs of wear or burning. Check spring retainer and waved spring for damage or distortion. Inspect clutch housing for damage or plugged feed hole. Inspect clutch housing bushing for damage or scoring.

2) Inspect clutch housing splines and snap ring groove for damage or burrs. Remove burrs with crocus cloth. Inspect clutch piston and apply ring assembly for distortion, cracks or damage. Inspect clutch housing-to-case spacer ring for damage.

Reassembly

1) Position clutch apply ring on piston, then install new inner and outer seals on piston with seal lips facing away from apply ring side. Lubricate seals with automatic transmission fluid, then install piston into housing using care not to damage seals.

2) Install waved release spring on clutch piston. Install spring retainer, cupped face up, on top of piston, then compress retainer and install snap ring.

REAR SUN GEAR & INPUT DRUM

NOTE: **Rear sun gear and input drum need not be disassembled unless inspection shows it to be necessary.**

Disassembly

Remove input drum-to-rear sun gear snap ring. Separate sun gear from input drum. Remove tanged thrust washer from drum.

Cleaning & Inspection

Inspect rear sun gear for cracks, splits, damaged spline, worn gear or journals and plugged lubrication holes. Inspect sun gear bushing for damage tor scoring.

Inspect input drum for damage. Inspect 4-tanged input drum-to-low and reverse clutch housing thrust washer for scoring or distorted tangs. If damaged, replace sun gear-to-input drum snap ring.

Reassembly

Install sun gear into input drum, spline side first, and retain with snap ring. Install 4-tanged thrust washer on drum over sun gear end. Align tangs into drum and retain with petroleum jelly.

Fig. 20: Disassembled View of Rear Sun Gear and Input Drum Assembly

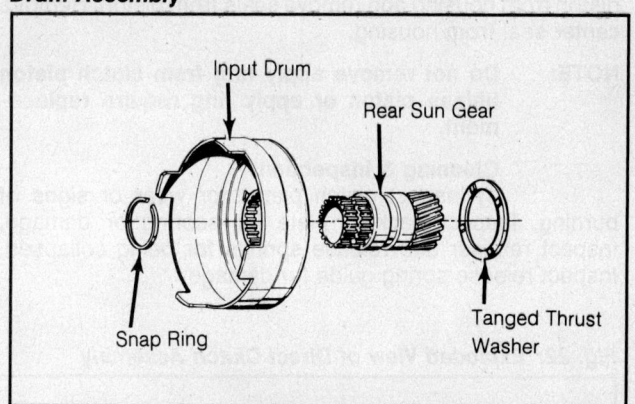

FRONT SUN GEAR

Cleaning & inspection

Inspect front sun gear splines and teeth for damage or wear. Inspect machined face for pitting, scoring or damage.

FRONT CARRIER ASSEMBLY

Cleaning & Inspection

1) Inspect front carrier for damage. Check pinions for damage, rough bearings or tilt. Check pinion end play using a feeler gauge. See Fig. 21. End play should be .009-.024" (.23-.61 mm).

2) Inspect front carrier-to-front internal gear thrust bearing assembly for pitted or rough conditions.

Automatic Transmissions

GENERAL MOTORS TURBO HYDRA-MATIC 200-4R (Cont.)

Fig. 21: Checking Front Carrier Pinion End Play

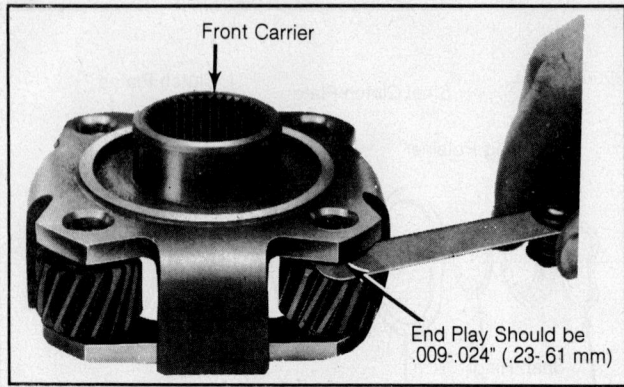

Front Carrier

End Play Should be
.009-.024" (.23-.61 mm)

FRONT INTERNAL GEAR
Cleaning & Inspection

Inspect forward clutch hub for worn splines and restricted lubrication holes. Inspect internal gear for cracks, damage and worn gear teeth. Check bushing for damage or scoring. Inspect front internal gear-to-selective thrust washer for scoring or damage. See Fig. 13.

DIRECT CLUTCH ASSEMBLY
Disassembly

1) Remove snap ring and lift out clutch backing plate, composition clutch plates and steel clutch plates. Keep clutch plates separated from forward clutch plates.

2) Compress retainer and spring assembly and remove snap ring. Withdraw retainer and spring assembly from clutch housing. Remove release spring guide. Remove piston from housing and remove seals from piston. Remove center seal from housing.

NOTE: Do not remove apply ring from clutch piston unless piston or apply ring require replacement.

Cleaning & Inspection

1) Inspect clutch plates for wear or signs of burning. Inspect backing plate for scoring or damage. Inspect retainer and release springs for being collapsed. Inspect release spring guide for damage.

2) Inspect clutch piston for distortion, cracks or other damage. Check for free operation of check ball in clutch housing or piston. If damaged, replace check ball.

3) Remove check ball assembly using a 3/8" diameter rod as a punch. Place new check ball in check ball hole, and using the same rod, drive check ball down into hole until it bottoms.

4) Inspect direct clutch housing for cracks, wear and open oil passages. Inspect housing snap ring grooves for damage. Inspect direct clutch bushings for damage or scoring.

Reassembly

1) If removed, install clutch apply ring on piston. Install new inner and outer seals on piston with lips facing away from clutch apply ring side. Install new center seal on direct clutch housing with lip facing up. Lubricate seals and install piston into housing using care not to damage seals.

CAUTION: Use care when installing piston into clutch housing. Large snap ring groove in housing could cut outer piston seal.

2) Install release spring guide with the omitted rib over check ball in piston. See Fig. 23. Install retainer and spring assembly, compress springs and install snap ring.

Fig. 23: Installing Direct Clutch Release Spring Guide

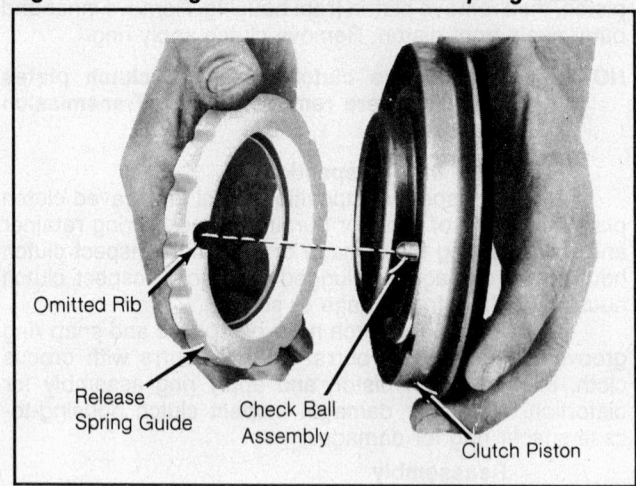

Omitted Rib

Release
Spring Guide

Check Ball
Assembly

Clutch Piston

Fig. 22: Exploded View of Direct Clutch Assembly

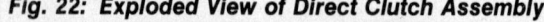
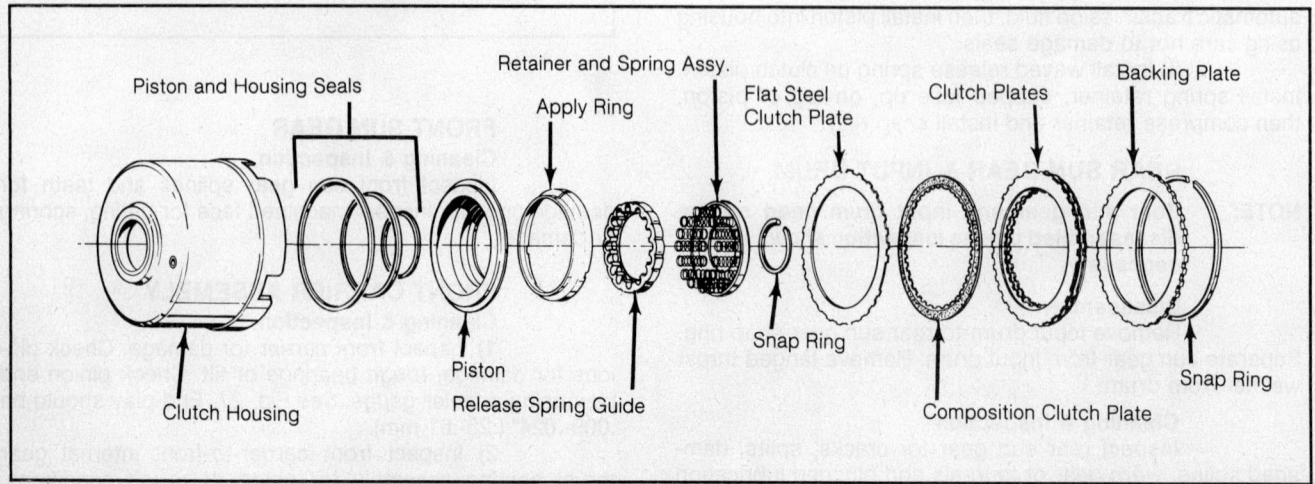

Piston and Housing Seals

Retainer and Spring Assy.

Apply Ring

Flat Steel
Clutch Plate

Clutch Plates

Backing Plate

Clutch Housing

Piston

Release Spring Guide

Snap Ring

Composition Clutch Plate

Snap Ring

GENERAL MOTORS TURBO HYDRA-MATIC 200-4R (Cont.)

3) Oil and install clutch plates into clutch housing. Start with a flat steel and alternate composition and flat steel clutch plates. See DIRECT CLUTCH PLATE USAGE chart. Install backing plate, micro-finish down. Install clutch pack retaining snap ring. Ensure composition clutch plates turn freely.

DIRECT CLUTCH PLATE USAGE

Application	Steel	Composition
All Models	6	 6

FORWARD CLUTCH ASSEMBLY
Disassembly
1) If damaged, remove Teflon oil seal rings from forward clutch shaft. Remove forward clutch-to-direct clutch thrust washer. Remove retaining snap ring and withdraw backing plate, composition plates and steel plates from clutch housing and keep them separated from direct clutch plates.

2) Compress retainer and release spring assembly and remove snap ring. Remove retainer and spring assembly from housing. Remove forward clutch piston from housing, then remove inner and outer oil seals from piston. If necessary, remove clutch apply ring from piston.

NOTE: **Clutch apply ring should not be removed from piston unless apply ring or piston requires replacement.**

Cleaning & Inspection
Forward clutch assembly inspection is identical to direct clutch assembly inspection except for the following differences; Replace forward clutch housing cup plug if damaged or missing. Remove plug using a No. 3 screw extractor (grind to fit). Install new cup plug .039" (1 mm) below surface.

Reassembly
1) If removed, install clutch apply ring on clutch piston. Install new inner and outer seals on clutch piston. Lubricate piston seals and install piston into clutch housing using care to prevent seals from being damaged when installing piston past large snap ring groove in housing.

Fig. 25: Forward Clutch Housing

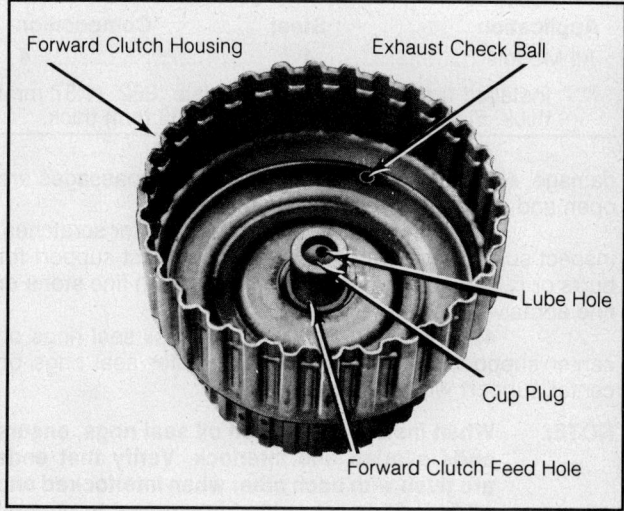

2) Install release springs and retainer assembly on piston. Compress retainer and install snap ring. Lubricate (ATF) and install clutch plates into housing, starting with the waved steel plate and alternating compostion plates and flat steel plates. See FORWARD CLUTCH PLATE USAGE chart.

3) Install backing plate into housing with micro-finish side down. Install clutch pack retaining snap ring and ensure composition clutch plates rotate freely in housing. Install forward-to-direct clutch thrust washer and retain with petrolatum.

4) If removed, install new forward clutch shaft oil seal rings, making sure cut ends are assembled in the same relationship as cut and that rings are seated in their groove. Retain with petrolatum.

CENTER SUPPORT
Cleaning & Inspection
1) Remove 4th clutch inner and outer seal rings from center support. Check condition of cast iron oil rings, and if necessary, remove from center support.

2) Inspect bushings for scoring, wear or galling. Check oil ring grooves and oil rings for nicks or other

Fig. 24: Exploded View of Forward Clutch Assembly

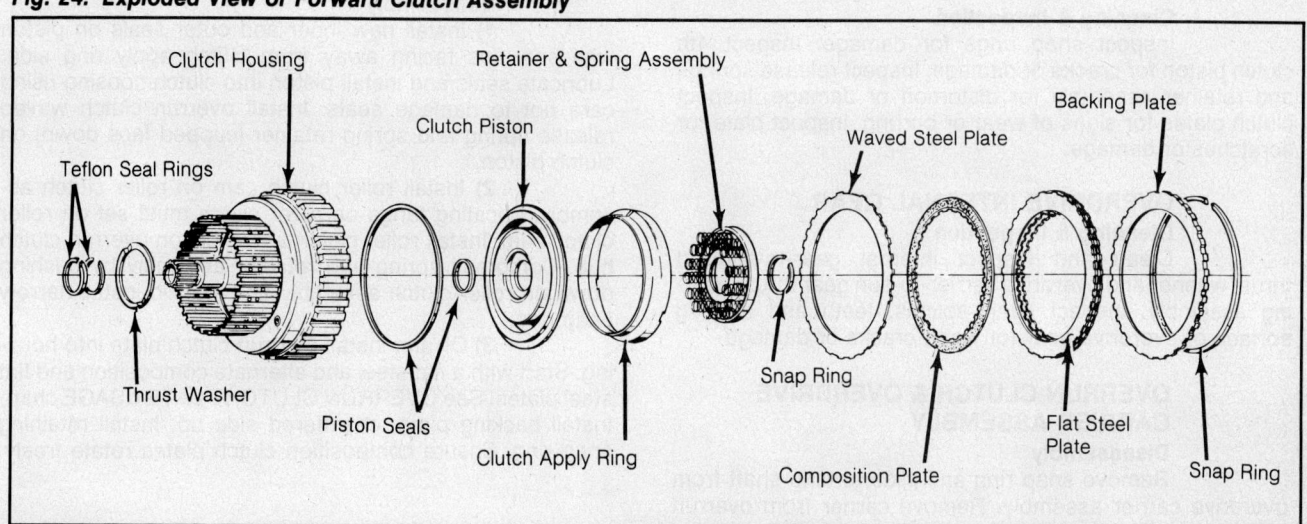

FORWARD CLUTCH PLATE USAGE

Application	Steel	Composition
All Models	4 [1]	4

[1] – Installed first is 1 waved steel plate .062" (1.57 mm) thick. Flat steel plates are .077" (1.96 mm) thick.

damage. Apply air to oil passages to ensure passages are open and are not interconnected.

3) Inspect piston sealing surfaces for scratches. Inspect support for cracks or porosity. Inspect support for burrs or raised edges. If present, remove with fine stone or fine abrasive paper.

4) If removed, install cast iron oil seal rings on center support. Install new inner and outer seal rings on center support with seal lips down.

NOTE: When installing cast iron oil seal rings, ensure ends overlap and interlock. Verify that ends are flush with each other when interlocked and oil seal rings are seated in grooves to prevent damage to ring during assembly of mating parts.

Fig. 26: Location of Cast Iron Seals on Center Support

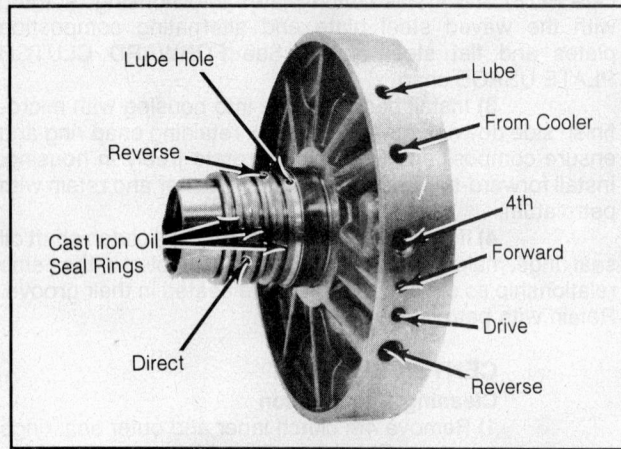

4TH CLUTCH ASSEMBLY

NOTE: The 4th clutch assembly was disassembled during Transmission Disassembly.

Cleaning & Inspection

Inspect snap rings for damage. Inspect 4th clutch piston for cracks or damage. Inspect release springs and retainer assembly for distortion or damage. Inspect clutch plates for signs of wear or burring. Inspect plate for scratches or damage.

OVERDRIVE INTERNAL GEAR
Cleaning & Inspection

Clean and inspect internal gear-to-support thrust washer and overdrive carrier-to-sun gear thrust bearing assembly. Inspect gear, splines, teeth and bearing surface of overdrive gear for wear, cracks or damage.

OVERRUN CLUTCH & OVERDRIVE CARRIER ASSEMBLY
Disassembly

Remove snap ring and slide turbine shaft from overdrive carrier assembly. Remove carrier from overrun clutch assembly. Remove sun gear from clutch assembly.

NOTE: Reassembly of this unit follows the disassembly and reassembly of the individual components.

OVERRUN CLUTCH ASSEMBLY
Disassembly

1) Remove retaining snap ring and lift backing plate, steel clutch plates and composition clutch plates from overrun clutch housing. Keep clutch plates separated from the other plate assemblies.

2) Using snap ring pliers, remove overrun clutch hub snap ring. Lift overdrive roller clutch cam assembly from housing, then separate roller clutch from cam assembly.

3) Remove retainer and wave spring assembly from clutch housing. Remove overrun clutch piston from housing, then remove inner and outer seals from piston.

Fig. 27: Removing Overdrive Roller Clutch Cam Assembly

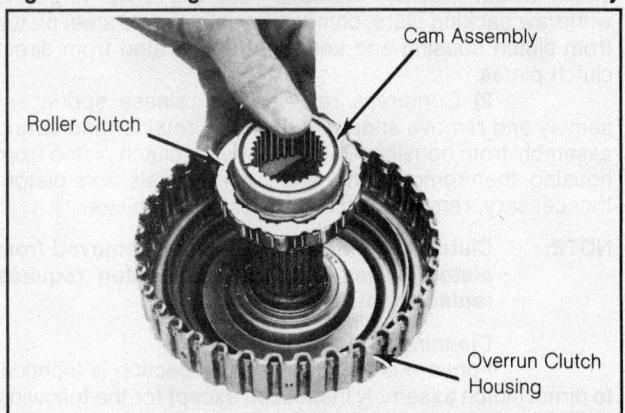

Cleaning & Inspection

1) Inspect clutch plates for signs of wear or burning. Inspect roller clutch cam ramps for damage. Check roller bearings, cage and springs of roller clutch for wear or damage.

2) Inspect retainer and wave spring for damage. Inspect clutch piston for distortion, cracks and damage. Inspect housing for cracks, wear and open oil passages. Check clutch housing snap ring groove and bushing for damage or scoring.

Reassembly

1) Install new inner and outer seals on piston with seal lips facing away from clutch apply ring side. Lubricate seals and install piston into clutch housing using care not to damage seals. Install overrun clutch waved release spring and spring retainer (cupped face down) on clutch piston.

2) Install roller clutch cam on roller clutch assembly. Locating tangs on roller clutch must set on roller clutch cam. Install roller clutch assembly on overrun clutch hub. Compress spring and retainer assembly by pushing down on roller clutch assembly and installd install narrow snap ring.

3) Oil and install overrun clutch plate into housing. Start with a flat steel and alternate composition and flat steel plates. See OVERRUN CLUTCH PLATE USAGE chart. Install backing plate, chamfered side up. Install retaining snap ring. Ensure composition clutch plates rotate freely.

GENERAL MOTORS TURBO HYDRA-MATIC 200-4R (Cont.)

OVERRUN CLUTCH PLATE USAGE

Application	Flat Steel	Composition
All Models	2 [1]	2

[1] – Plate thickness is .077" (1.96 mm).

OVERDRIVE CARRIER
Disassembly
1) Remove overdrive carrier snap ring. Using pliers, remove pinion pins. Remove pinions, thrust washers and roller bearings. Inspect pinion pocket thrust faces for burrs, and remove if present.

2) Remove overdrive sun gear-to-overdrive carrier thrust bearing assembly. Thoroughly clean, air dry and closely inspect thrust bearing assembly for pitting or rough condition.

Cleaning & Inspection
1) Inspect locating splines for damage and roller clutch race for scratches and wear. Inspect carrier housing for cracks and wear.

2) Inspect pinions for damage, rough bearings or tilt. Using a feeler gauge, measure pinion end play between pinion and carrier. End play should be .009-.024" (.23-.61 mm). If necessary to disassemble carrier, go to disassembly procedure.

Fig. 28: Assembling Overdrive Carrier Pinions

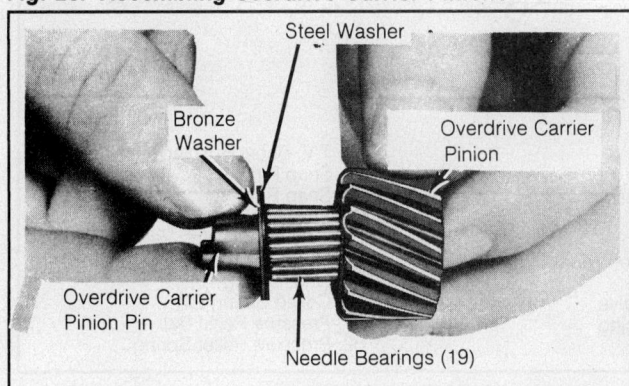

Reassembly
1) Install thrust bearing into carrier housing with small diameter race down. Retain bearing in place with petroleum jelly. Install 19 needle bearings into each pinion and hold them in place. Place a bronze and steel thrust washer on each side of pinion so that steel washer is against pinion. Hold washers in place with petroleum jelly.

2) Install a pinion assembly in place in housing and use a pilot shaft to align parts. Push pinion pin into place while rotating pinions from the side. Repeat procedure for remaining pinions. Install overdrive carrier snap ring to retain pinion pins.

TURBINE SHAFT
Cleaning & Inspection
1) Inspect Teflon oil seals on turbine shaft for damage and free fit in grooves. Do not remove seal unless replacement is necessary. Inspect snap ring for damage. Check journals and snap ring grooves for wear or damage.

2) Inspect both ends of turbine shaft for open oil passages. Inspect journals aor damage. Check for free operation of check ball in end of shaft. If check ball is damaged, go to step 3).

3) Straighten tangs of retainer and check valve assembly capsule in end of shaft. Remove check ball. Using a No. 4 screw extractor, and remove check valve retainer from turbine shaft by turning and pulling straight out.

4) Install new check valve assembly, check valve seat first, into turbine shaft. Using a 3/8" diameter rod, drive retainer and check valve assembly until it is 1/8" below top surface of turbine shaft.

Fig. 29: Turbine Shaft Assembly

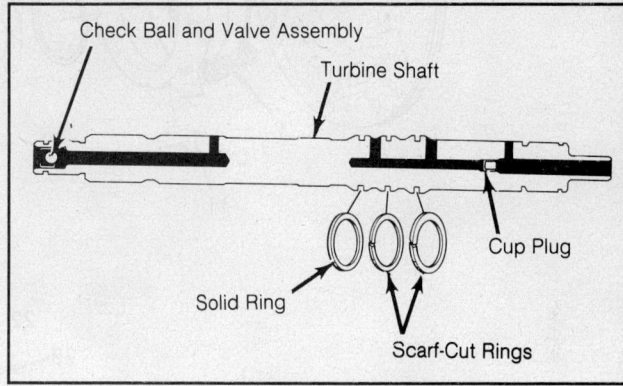

OVERRUN CLUTCH & OVERDRIVE CARRIER ASSEMBLY
Reassembly
1) Install overdrive sun gear on overrun clutch hub with groove up. Center clutches in overrun clutch housing. Position overdrive carrier in overrun clutch with pinion side of carrier facing up. It may be necessary to rotate carrier counterclockwise to seat it.

2) Position clutch and carrier assembly (clutch up) over hole in work bench. Install turbine shaft, ring grooved spline first, into carrier assembly. Turn assembly sideways and install NEW turbine shaft snap ring.

CAUTION: A new turbine shaft snap ring must be installed as damage to unit may occur if old snap ring is used.

PUMP ASSEMBLY
Disassembly
1) Remove pump-to-case seal ring. Remove pump cover-to-pump body attaching bolts and separate cover from body. Remove stator shaft-to-overrun selective thrust washer.

2) Push in on T.V. boost valve bushing, compressing pressure regulator spring, and remove retaining snap ring. Release spring tension slowly and remove valve train.

3) Push in on converter clutch stop valve, compressing converter clutch valve spring and remove snap ring. Release spring tension slowly and remove stop valve and converter clutch valve. Using a punch, remove pressure relief spring retaining pin. Remove relief spring and ball.

4) If replacement of stator shaft and flange assembly is required, remove attaching screws and press stator shaft until it is removed from pump cover bore.

5) Place shop towel over pump slide spring (spring is under high pressure) and using a screwdriver, remove spring from pump body. Remove pump slide, slide-to-wear plate oil seal and back-up "O" ring seal, rotor, rotor guide, 7 vanes and 2 vane rings, pump slide seal support and seal. Remove pivot slide pin and spring.

Fig. 30: Exploded View of Pump Assembly

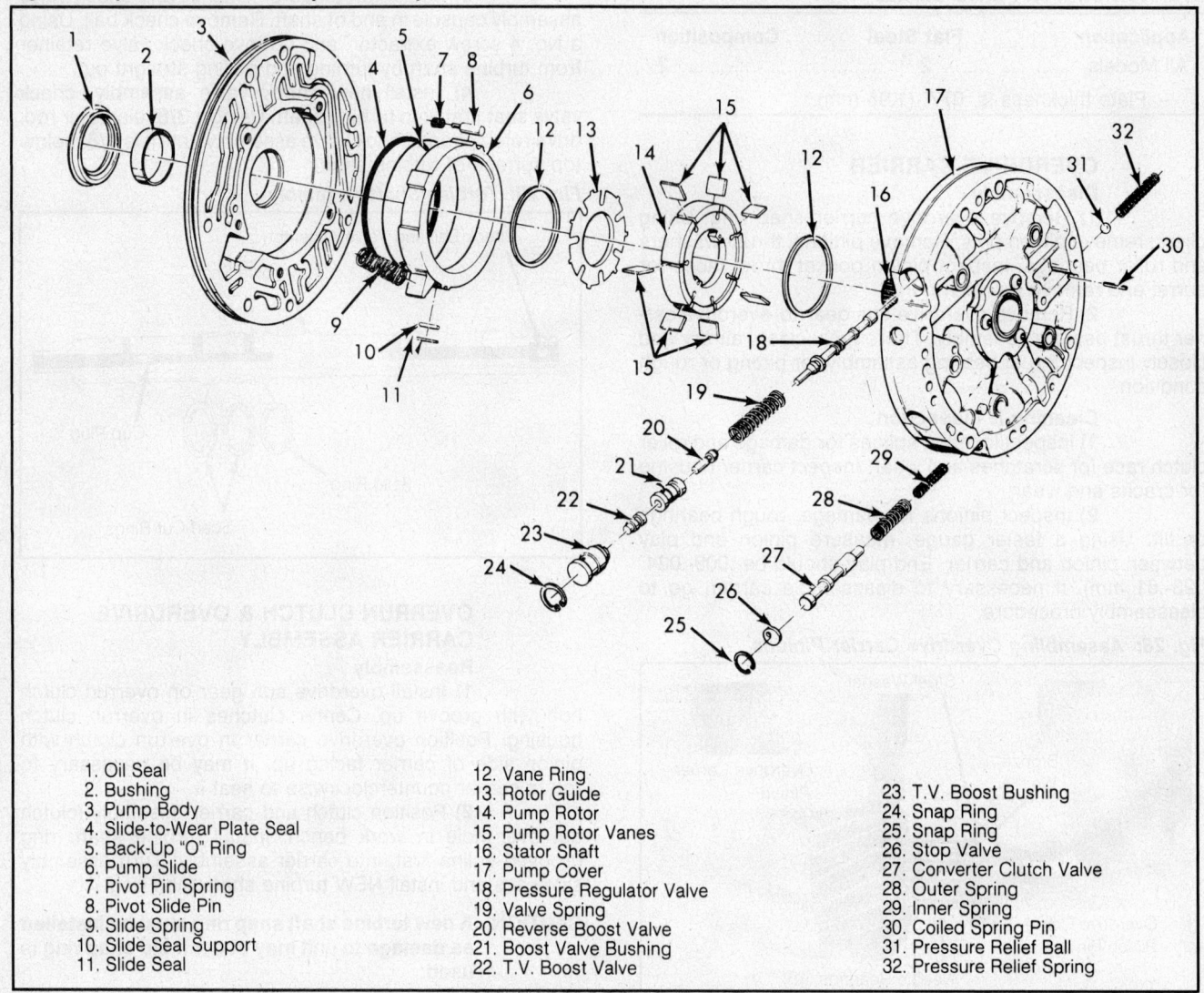

1. Oil Seal	12. Vane Ring	23. T.V. Boost Bushing
2. Bushing	13. Rotor Guide	24. Snap Ring
3. Pump Body	14. Pump Rotor	25. Snap Ring
4. Slide-to-Wear Plate Seal	15. Pump Rotor Vanes	26. Stop Valve
5. Back-Up "O" Ring	16. Stator Shaft	27. Converter Clutch Valve
6. Pump Slide	17. Pump Cover	28. Outer Spring
7. Pivot Pin Spring	18. Pressure Regulator Valve	29. Inner Spring
8. Pivot Slide Pin	19. Valve Spring	30. Coiled Spring Pin
9. Slide Spring	20. Reverse Boost Valve	31. Pressure Relief Ball
10. Slide Seal Support	21. Boost Valve Bushing	32. Pressure Relief Spring
11. Slide Seal	22. T.V. Boost Valve	

Cleaning & Inspection

1) Inspect pump-to-case seal ring groove in pump body for damage. Inspect stator shaft-to-overrun selective washer for wear and damage. Wash pump body, springs, pump slide, rotor, vanes, vane rings and rotor guide. Do not put pump seals in solvent.

2) Inspect pump pocket and pump body for damage or scoring. Check pump body bushing for wear or scoring. Inspect springs for damage or distortion and pump slide for damage, cracks or wear. Check rotor for damage, cracks or wear. Inspect vanes and vane rings for damage, cracks or wear. Inspect pump body face for nicks and overall flatness and open oil passages.

3) Inspect T.V. boost valve, reverse boost valve, stop valve and converter clutch valve for nicks or damage. Check valves for free operation in bushing or cover bore. Inspect all springs for damage or distortion. Inspect stator shaft and flange assembly for damaged splines or bushing. Check stator shaft for damaged or missing orifice cup plug in dowel pin. Do not remove cup plug unless damaged.

4) Inspect pump cover for open oil passages. Check pump cover face for nicks and overall flatness. Inspect for chips in pressure regulator, pressure relief and converter clutch bores. Inspect cup plugs and orifice plugs in cover and if damaged, replace plugs.

Pump Cover Cup Plug Replacement

If cup plug is missing, drive a new plug to 1/32" below top of hole, using a 9/32" diameter rod on the 2 smaller plugs, a 5/16" rod on the line-to-case cup plug, and a 7/16" rod on the large plug. Stake top of hole in 2 places, directly opposite each other, to retain plug.

Pump Cover Orifice Plug Replacement

If plugs require replacement, place new plug, orifice end first, into plug hole from rough casting side of cover. Drive new plug flush to .100" (2.8 mm) below top of hole, on rough casting side. Stake top of hole in 2 places to retain plug.

Reassembly

1) Turn pump body so that pump pocket side is up. Install slide "O" ring and slide-to-wear plate oil seal in slide and retain with petrolatum. Install slide into pump pocket with seal side down. Install slide seal support and pump slide seal. See Fig. 32. Retain with petrolatum. Install pivot pin and spring into bore in pump body (opposite pivot pin and spring).

GENERAL MOTORS TURBO HYDRA-MATIC 200-4R (Cont.)

Fig. 31: View of Pump Cover and Body Showing Hydraulic Passages

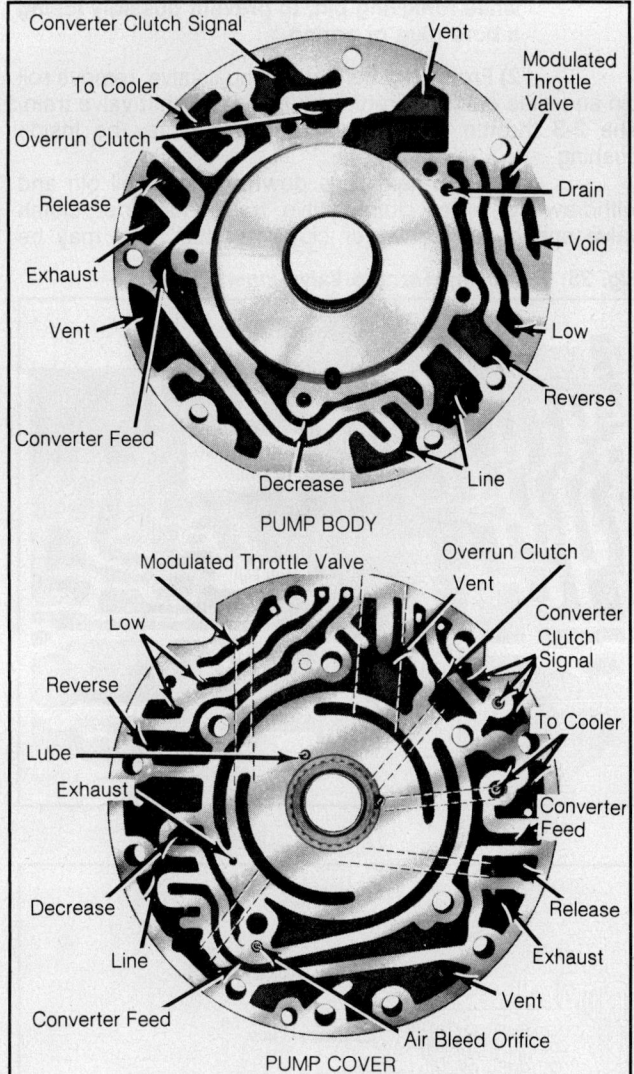

PUMP BODY

PUMP COVER

is installed against vane ring. Install top vane ring. Install pump slide spring.

3) If stator shaft and flange assembly was removed from pump cover, install as follows: Align dowel pin of stator shaft with hole in pump cover. Using a press, press stator shaft into cover until fully seated on cover. Install stator shaft and flange assembly attaching bolts.

4) Install all valve trains in reverse order of removal. *See Fig. 2.* Assemble pump cover to pump body and install attaching bolts finger tight. Align cover to body using Alignment Strap (J-25015), and tighten attaching bolts. Install pump-to-case seal ring, chamfered side out, making sure seal is not twisted. Install stator shaft-to-overrun clutch selective thrust washer and retain with petroleum jelly.

GOVERNOR ASSEMBLY
Cleaning & Inspection

1) Inspect governor cover for damage, plugged oil passage, scored or worn bore. Inspect governor driven gear for nicks or damage. If replacement is necessary, remove retaining ring and slide gear and thrust washer from shaft.

CAUTION: Care must be taken after removing driven gear to keep governor in a vertical position to retain governor weight pin in its holding position.

2) Inspect governor shaft seal ring for cuts, damage and free fit in groove. Inspect for free operation of weights. Weights must operate freely and independently of each other. Check spring for damage and correct installation. Check for presence of 2 check balls. Inspect shaft for damage.

INTERMEDIATE SERVO ASSEMBLY
Disassembly

Using a small screwdriver, remove intermediate pin-to-retainer snap ring. Separate band apply pin, spring and washer from servo pistons.

Cleaning & Inspection

Inspect pin oil seal rings for damage and replace if necessary. Inspect pin for damage and fit in case. Inspect inner and outer piston seal rings for damage and free fit in grooves; do not replace unless damaged. Inspect spring for damage and distortion.

2) Install a vane ring in pump pocket. Install rotor guide in pump rotor, then install rotor into pump pocket. Center and seat rotor on guide so rotor is flush with pump slide. Install 7 vanes into pump. Ensure vane pattern

Fig. 32: Installing Slide Seal and Support

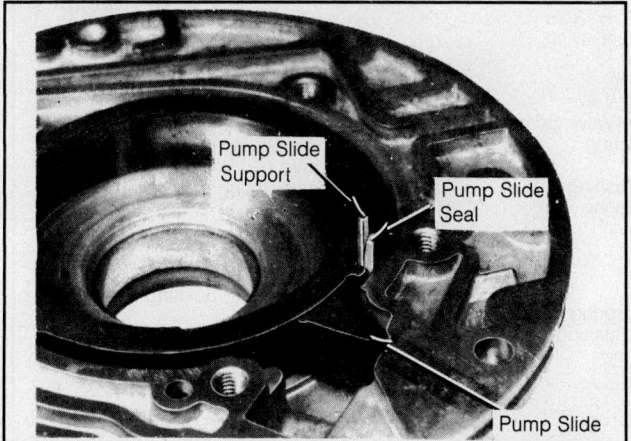

Fig. 33: Exploded View of Intermediate Servo

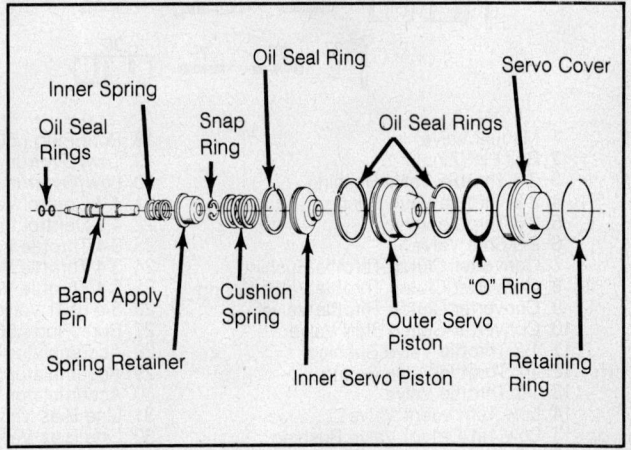

2-296

Automatic Transmissions
GENERAL MOTORS TURBO HYDRA-MATIC 200-4R (Cont.)

Reassembly

1) Install retainer on band apply pin, then install snap ring. Install apply pin, retainer end first, through servo pistons. If removed, install new inner and outer piston seal rings, making sure cut ends are assembled in same relationship as cut, and retain with petrolatum.

2) Lubricate with petrolatum and install new seal ring on intermediate servo cover. Install servo piston into servo cover.

CAUTION: **Intermediate servo cover seal rings must be well lubricated to prevent damage or cutting of ring.**

CONTROL VALVE ASSEMBLY

NOTE: **As valve trains are removed from each valve body bore, place individual parts in correct order in relative position to valve body to ease reassembly. Valves, bushings and springs are not interchangeable, and all parts must be installed in correct order in proper valve body bore. Remove all roll pins and spring retaining sleeves by pushing through from rough case surface side of valve body, except for the blind hole roll pins.**

Disassembly

1) Lay control valve assembly with machined face up and manual valve at upper left corner. If not removed at Transmission Disassembly, remove 3 check balls from cored passages of valve body. From upper left corner bore, remove manual valve.

CAUTION: **Some roll pins in valve body have pressure against them. Hold a shop towel over bore while removing pin, to prevent possibly losing a bore plug or spring.**

2) From bore beneath manual valve, remove roll pin and slide out 2-3 throttle valve and 2-3 shift valve train. The 2-3 throttle valve spring and valve may be inside bushing.

3) From next bore down, remove roll pin and withdraw converter clutch valve train. Converter clutch valve spring and converter clutch throttle valve may be

Fig. 35: Removing Throttle Valve Inner Roll Pin

Fig. 34: Exploded View of Control Valve Assembly

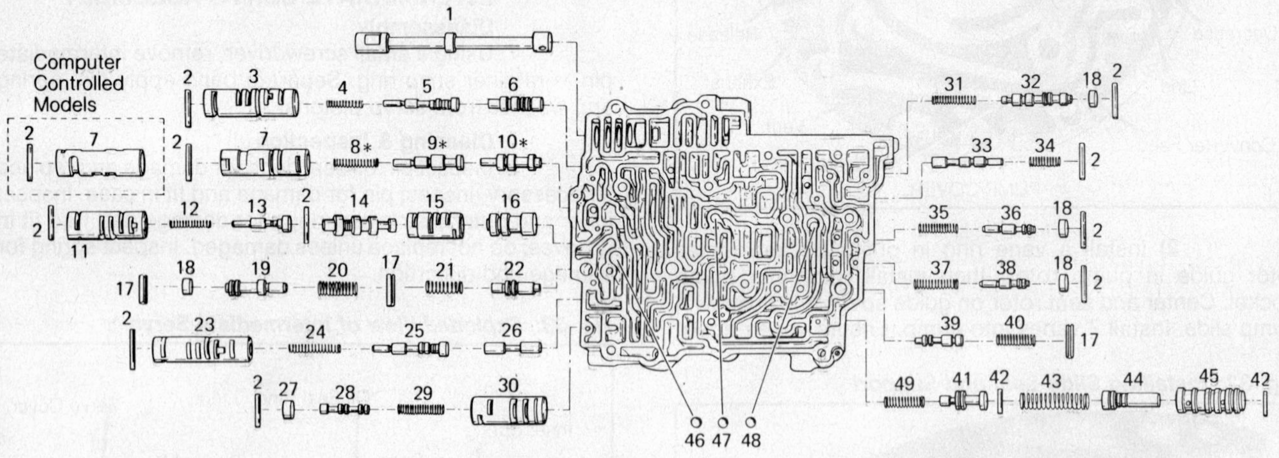

1. Manual Valve
2. Roll Pin (Zinc)
3. 2-3 Throttle Valve Bushing
4. 2-3 Throttle Vave Spring
5. 2-3 Throttle Valve
6. 2-3 Shift Valve
7. Converter Clutch Throttle Bushing
8. Converter Clutch Throttle Valve Spring
9. Converter Clutch Throttle Valve
10. Converter Clutch Shift Valve
11. 1-2 Throttle Valve Bushing
12. 1-2 Throttle Valve Spring
13. 1-2 Throttle Valve
14. Low 1st/Detent Valve
15. Low 1st/Detent Valve Bushing
16. 1-2 Shift Valve
17. Spring Retaining Sleeve
18. Bore Plug (.50")
19. Low/Overrun Clutch Valve
20. Low/Overrun Clutch Valve Spring
21. 4-3 Control Valve Spring
22. 4-3 Control Valve
23. 3-4 Throttle Valve Bushing
24. 3-4 Throttle Valve Spring
25. 3-4 Throttle Valve
26. 3-4 Shift Valve
27. Bore Plug (.560")
28. Accumulator Valve
29. Accumulator Valve Spring
30. Accumulator Valve Bushing
31. Line Bias Valve Trapring
32. Line Bias Valve
33. 3-2 Control Valve
34. 3-2 Control Valve Spring
35. T.V. Modulator Upshift Valve Spring
36. T.V. Modulator Upshift Valve
37. T.V. Modulator Downshift Valve Spring
38. T.V. Modulator Downshift Valve
39. T.V. Limit Valve
40. T.V. Limit Valve Spring
41. Throttle Valve
42. Roll Pin (Black)
43. Throttle Valve Spring
44. Throttle Valve Plunger
45. Throttle Valve Plunger Bushing
46. "D3" Check Ball
47. 1-2 Shift Check Ball
48. Low/1st Check Ball

* Items 8, 9 & 10 are not used on diesel models.

GENERAL MOTORS TURBO HYDRA-MATIC 200-4R (Cont.)

inside bushing. On Computer Command Control models, clutch throttle valve and spring have been eliminated.

4) From next bore down, remove outer roll pin and remove 1-2 throttle valve train and low 1st/detent valve. Remove inner roll pin and slide out low 1st/detent valve bushing and 1-2 shift valve.

5) Cover the next bore down to prevent loss of spring, then remove outer spring retaining sleeve. Remove bore plug and 4-3 control valve and spring. Remove inner spring retaining sleeve and withdraw low/overrun clutch valve spring and valve.

6) From next bore down, remove roll pin and slide out 3-4 throttle valve train. From last bore down, remove roll pin and bore plug and withdraw accumulator valve train.

7) From upper right corner, remove roll pin and remove line bias valve train. From next bore down, remove roll pin and 3-2 control valve train.

8) From next bore down, remove roll pin, then remove T.V. modulator upshift valve train. From next bore down, remove roll pin and T.V. modulator downshift valve train.

9) Cover the next bore down to prevent loss of spring, then remove spring retaining sleeve and withdraw T.V. limit valve train.

10) From last bore, remove outer roll pin, then remove throttle valve bushing, plunger and spring. Remove inner pin as follows: Grind a taper to end of a No. 49 drill. Lightly tap tapered end of drill into roll pin, then pull drill and roll pin out. Remove throttle valve.

Cleaning & Inspection

1) Wash control valve body, springs, valves and other parts in clean solvent and air dry. Inspect valves for scoring, cracks and free movement in their bores.

2) Inspect bushings for cracks and scored bores. Inspect valve body for cracks, damage or scored bores. Inspect springs for distortion or collapsed coils. Inspect bore plugs for damage.

Reassembly

Reassembly is the reverse of disassembly procedure. Reassemble control valve assembly using exploded view as a guide. Note the following:

- Install all flared roll pins (zinc coated) flared end out and from machined face of valve body.
- Install the 2 tapered roll pins (Black finish) that retain throttle valve and throttle valve bushing, tapered end first.
- Roll pins do not fit flush on rough casting face. Ensure all roll pins are flush at machined face or damage to transmission will occur.
- Ensure all spring retaining sleeves are installed from machined face and that they are level with or below machined surface.
- Install all bore plugs with hole out.
- Install all valve sleeves so that slot in sleeve aligns with roll pin hole in valve body.

TRANSMISSION REASSEMBLY

MANUAL SHAFT & PARKING PAWL PARTS

1) Turn transmission to horizontal position with oil pan side up. If removed, install new manual shaft seal with lip facing into case using a 9/16" socket to seat seal.

Install parking pawl and spring into case with tooth toward inside of case and spring under pawl tooth with spring ends toward inside of case. Ensure spring ends locate against case pad.

2) Align parking pawl and spring with case shaft hole, then install parking pawl shaft, tapered end first. Using a 3/8" diameter rod, install new parking pawl cup plug, open end out, past retaining pin hole. Install retaining pin.

Fig. 36: Manual Shaft and Parking Parts

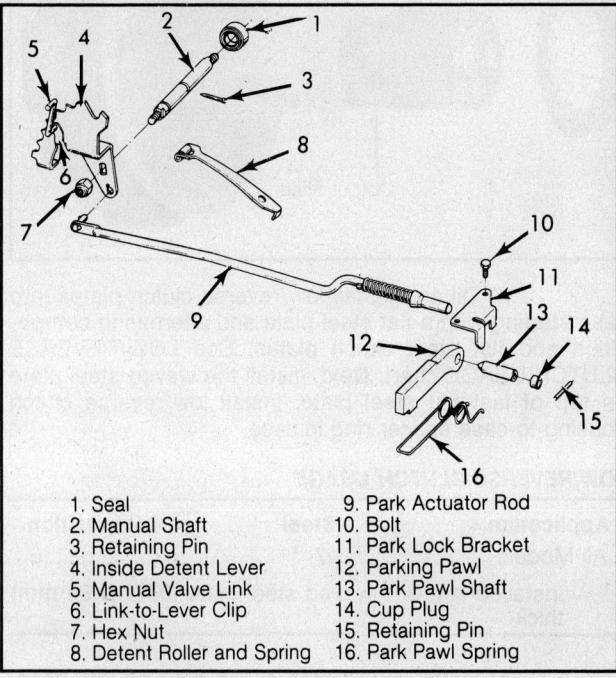

1. Seal	9. Park Actuator Rod
2. Manual Shaft	10. Bolt
3. Retaining Pin	11. Park Lock Bracket
4. Inside Detent Lever	12. Parking Pawl
5. Manual Valve Link	13. Park Pawl Shaft
6. Link-to-Lever Clip	14. Cup Plug
7. Hex Nut	15. Retaining Pin
8. Detent Roller and Spring	16. Park Pawl Spring

3) While holding parking pawl toward center of transmission, install parking lock bracket and tighten attaching bolts. Assemble parking actuator rod on pin side of inside detent lever, locating lever between actuator rod tangs. Install rod and detent lever into case with detent lever pin toward center of transmission and actuator plunger between parking pawl and parking lock bracket.

NOTE: **File any burrs or raised edges off manual shaft that could damage manual shaft seal during installation of shaft.**

4) Install manual shaft, small identification ring groove first, through case. Align inside detent lever with flats on shaft, then install detent lever on manual shaft. Install hex nut on manual shaft and tighten. Install manual shaft retaining pin, indexing with large groove on shaft.

REAR GEAR PARTS

1) Install rear internal gear, hub end first, onto output shaft. Install rear internal gear-to-rear thrust bearing assembly, inside diameter race against gear, over output shaft and into internal gear.

2) Install roller clutch and rear carrier assembly into rear internal gear. Install output shaft loading fixture and support sleeve into rear of case. See Fig. 8. Turn case to vertical position, pump end up. Install rear unit parts into case, indexing internal gear parking pawl lugs to pass by parking pawl tooth.

3) Using adjusting screw on output shaft loading fixture, adjust height of rear internal gear parking pawl lugs to align flush with parking pawl tooth.

Fig. 37: Installing Rear Internal Gear & Thrust Bearing

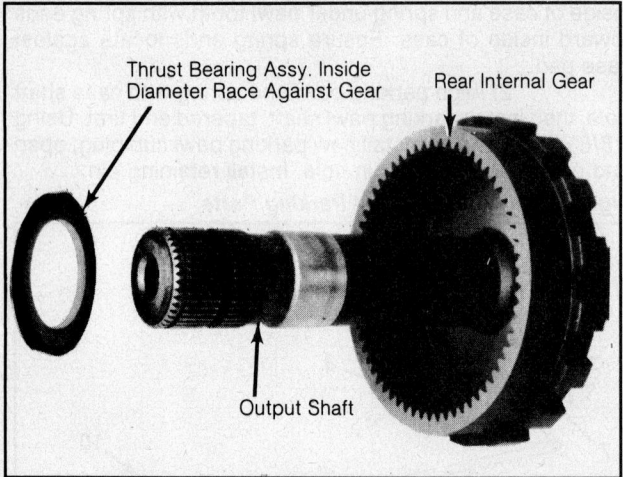

Thrust Bearing Assy. Inside Diameter Race Against Gear

Rear Internal Gear

Output Shaft

4) Oil and install low/reverse clutch plates into case starting with a flat steel plate and alternating composition and flat steel clutch plates. See LOW/REVERSE CLUTCH USAGE chart. Next, install the waved steel plate on top of last flat steel plate. Install low/reverse clutch housing-to-case spacer ring in case.

LOW/REVERSE CLUTCH USAGE

Application	Steel	Composition
All Models	7 [1]	6

[1] – Installed last is 1 waved steel plate .077" (1.96 mm) thick.

5) Install low/reverse clutch housing into case, aligning feed hole in housing with reverse clutch feed passage in case. If clutch housing does not seat past case snap ring groove, install input drum and rear sun gear into case.

6) Rotate sun gear back and forth, tapping lightly with input drum to align roller clutch race with low/reverse clutch hub splines. Remove input drum and rear sun gear assembly.

7) Install low/reverse clutch-to-case snap ring with flat side against clutch (beveled side up). Position snap ring groove on opposite side of parking pawl rod.

Fig. 38: Installing Low/Reverse Clutch Housing Cup Plug and Seal Assembly

3/8" Rod

Cup Plug and Seal Assembly

NOTE: It may be necessary to loosen adjusting screw on output shaft loading fixture to install clutch-to-case snap ring.

8) If removed, install new low/reverse clutch housing-to-case cup plug and seal. Use a 3/8" diameter rod to drive cup plug and seal assembly into case until it seats against clutch housing. See Fig. 38.

FRONT GEAR PARTS

1) Install 4-tanged thrust washer on input drum over sun gear end; align tangs into input drum and retain with petrolatum. Install rear sun gear and input drum assembly into case.

2) Install front sun gear into case and input drum with face of gear having identification groove against input drum. Install front sun gear-to-front carrier thrust bearing and race assembly into case with needle bearings against sun gear.

3) Install front carrier-to-front internal gear thrust bearing assembly on carrier with small diameter race against carrier. Install front carrier and thrust bearing assembly into transmission.

4) Install thrust washer on front internal gear and retain with petrolatum. Install front internal gear and thrust washer into case. Install rear unit end play selective washer into case with identification number on washer toward front of transmission. Install wide retaining snap ring. See Fig. 13.

NOTE: At this point, recheck rear unit end play to verify that correct selective thrust washer has been installed. See REAR UNIT END PLAY.

5) Install output shaft-to-forward clutch shaft selective thrust washer into case and position washer. See Fig. 39.

Fig. 39: Installing Front Selective Washer

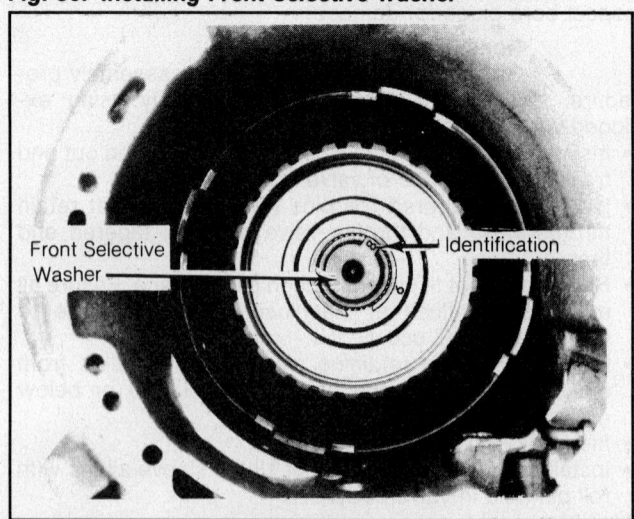

Front Selective Washer

Identification

FRONT UNIT PARTS

1) Install intermediate band into case, locating band apply lug and anchor pin lug in case slot. Install band anchor pin.

2) Position direct clutch assembly, clutch plate end up, over hole in work bench. Align teeth of composition

GENERAL MOTORS TURBO HYDRA-MATIC 200-4R (Cont.)

plates in direct clutch, then install forward clutch assembly, shaft first, into direct clutch assembly. Hold direct clutch and rotate forward clutch back and forth until fully seated.

NOTE: **When forward clutch is fully seated, it will be approximately 5/8" from tang end of direct clutch housing to end of forward clutch drum.**

3) Install direct and forward clutch assemblies into case and rotate into position. When assemblies are correctly installed, it will be approximately 4 1/8" from pump face in case to direct clutch housing.

4) Install center support-to-direct clutch thrust washer on center support. Visually align center support with case bolt holes and install center support into case. Install, but do not tighten, center support attaching bolts. Install center support-to-case snap ring with beveled side up. Tighten center support attaching bolts.

NOTE: **At this point, recheck input shaft end play to verify that correct front selective washer has been installed. See INPUT SHAFT END PLAY.**

OVERDRIVE UNIT PARTS

1) Install 4th clutch outer and inner seals on center support with lips facing down, apply petrolatum to seals. Install 4th clutch piston into case, aligning piston tab with wide case spline. Position return spring and retainer assembly on piston, then compress retainer assembly and install support-to-4th clutch spring snap ring.

NOTE: **The 4th clutch inner seal, installed on center support, is identified by a white stripe.**

2) Install internal gear-to-support thrust washer into case with tangs down. Install overdrive internal gear, hub end first, on forward clutch shaft. Install overdrive carrier-to-sun gear thrust bearing assembly into overdrive internal gear with large diameter race against carrier.

3) Grasp turbine shaft and lower overrun clutch and overdrive carrier assembly into case and rotate into position. Select proper 4th clutch plates. See 4th CLUTCH PLATE USAGE chart. Oil and install 4th clutch plates into case. *See Fig. 40.* Install clutch pack retaining snap ring. Install oil deflector plate into case with tangs facing up.

Fig. 40: Fourth Clutch Plate Installation Sequence

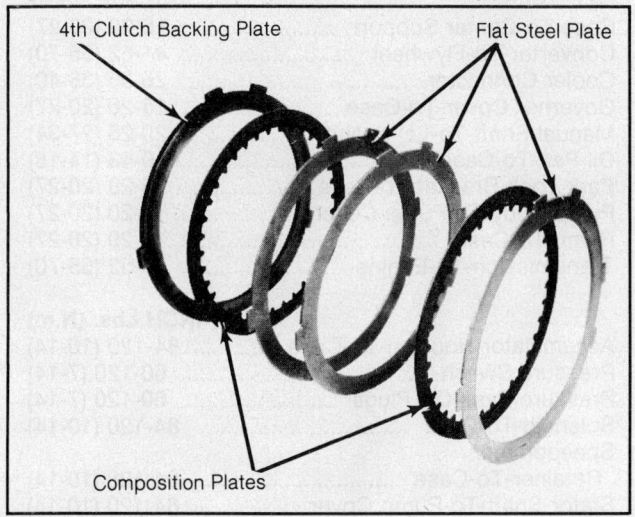

CAUTION: **Note installation order of 4th clutch plates. The center has 2 steel plates together and the thick plate is on top. Incorrect installation sequence will cause damage.**

4) Install a new pump-to-case gasket on pump and retain with petrolatum. Install 2 alignment pins into pump attaching bolt holes opposite each other. Install pump assembly in case. Install pump attaching bolts with NEW washers. Remove alignment pins and install remaining bolts and washers. Tighten oil pump attaching bolts.

NOTE: **At this point, recheck overdrive unit end play to verify that correct overdrive end play thrust washer has been installed. See OVERDRIVE UNIT END PLAY.**

EXTERNAL PARTS

1) Remove output shaft loading fixture and support sleeve from rear of transmission case. Turn transmission to horizontal position with oil pan side up. If removed, install new oil seal ring on governor shaft. Install governor assembly into case, then install governor cover and tighten attaching bolts.

CAUTION: **Ensure governor shaft is piloted in governor cover before tightening cover attaching bolts.**

2) With correct band apply pin installed, as determined during Transmission Disassembly, install intermediate servo assembly into case. Ensure tapered end of apply pin is properly located against band apply lug. Install servo cover retaining ring and align ring gap with end showing in case slot.

NOTE: **Intermediate servo cover seal rings must be well lubricated with petrolatum to prevent damage or cutting of ring.**

Fig. 41: Installing 3/4 Accumulator Assembly

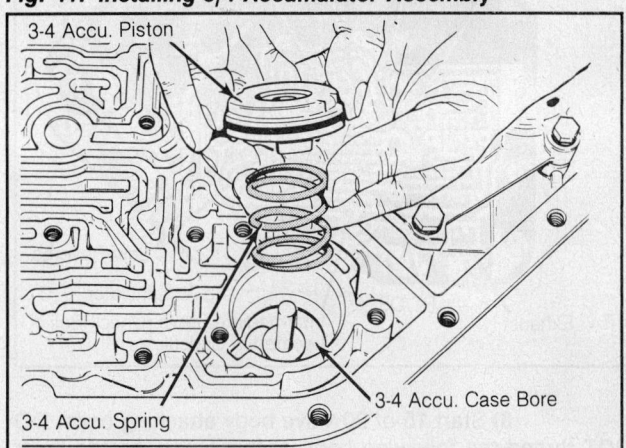

On "OG" & "OJ" models, invert piston, then install piston first and spring second.

4th CLUTCH PLATE USAGE

Application	Steel	Composition
All Models	3	2

3) Lubricate with petrolatum and install new "O" rings on case electrical connector. Install electrical connector with lock tabs facing into case, positioning locator tab in notch on side of case.

4) Install a new Teflon seal on 3-4 accumulator piston. Install accumulator pin in case, then install accumulator piston and spring. *See Fig. 41.*

NOTE: On "OG" & "OJ" model transmissions, invert piston, install piston first, and install spring second. On "OZ" models, spring is not used. On all other models, install as shown. See Fig. 45.

5) Install 9 check balls into locations in case. *See Fig. 42.* Install 2 valve body alignment pins into opposing bolt holes. Install spacer plate-to-case gasket (marked "C") on case, then install spacer plate.

6) Install valve body assembly-to-spacer plate gasket (marked "VB") on spacer plate. Position 1-2 accumulator plate and gasket in place on case, install accumulator spring on plate. Install a new teflon seal on 1-2 accumulator piston, install piston in accumulator housing with dome up. Install 1-2 accumulator assembly, then install and tighten 5 attaching bolts.

7) Position remaining 3 check balls in valve body. *See Fig. 35.* Retain with petrolatum. Remove alignment pins. Install valve body assembly making sure to align manual valve with detent lever.

CAUTION: It is possible during reassembly to position manual valve too far into valve body and still connect the selective lever link to it. This will prevent valve body from fitting properly in case.

Fig. 42: Location of Check Balls in Bottom of Case

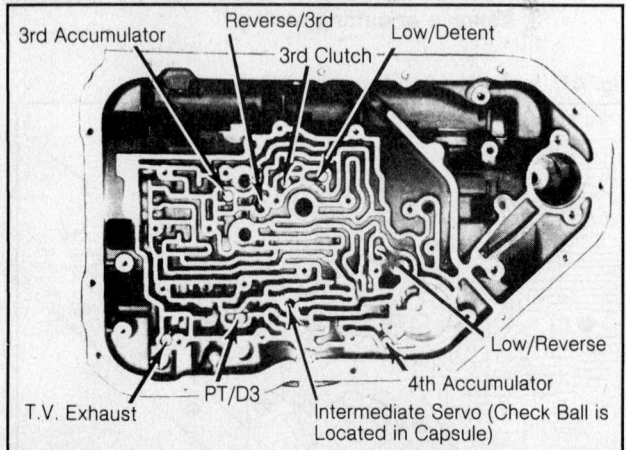

8) Start 15 of 20 valve body attaching bolts. DO NOT thread the following bolts at this time: Throttle lever and bracket assembly, manual detent roller and spring assembly and clip retaining bolts. Install signal oil pipe in valve body assembly.

9) Install manual detent roller and spring assembly, locating tang in valve body and roller on inside detent lever. If removed, install throttle and bracket assembly spring on top of lifter. Install link on throttle. Ensure link is hooked. *See Fig. 44.* Install throttle lever and bracket assembly, locating slot in bracket with roll pin and aligning lifter through valve body hole and link through T.V. linkage case bore. Install retaining bolt.

Fig. 43: Proper Positioning of Manual Valve and Selective Lever Link in Valve Body

10) With locating pipe in hole, install 4-3 pressure switch (on non Computer Command Control models only) and attaching bolt. Install filter intake pipe "O" ring on pipe and coat with petrolatum. Install filter in pump bore. Install oil pan using a new gasket and tighten attaching bolts.

Fig. 44: Throttle Lever and Bracket Installation

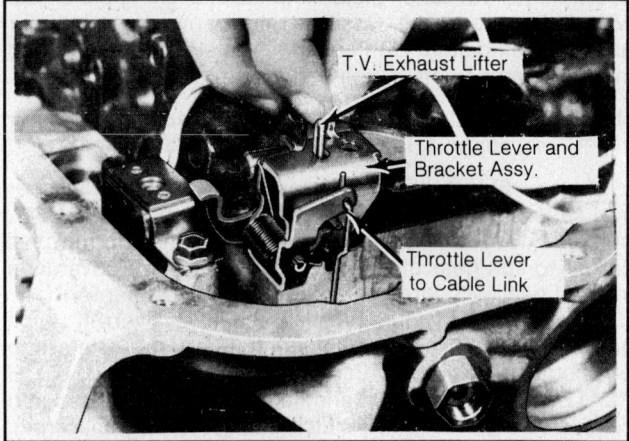

TIGHTENING SPECIFICATIONS

Application	Ft. Lbs. (N.m)
Case-To-Center Support	15-20 (20-27)
Converter-To-Flywheel	41-52 (55-70)
Cooler Connector	26-30 (35-40)
Governor Cover-To-Case	15-20 (20-27)
Manual Shaft-To-Lever Nut	20-25 (27-34)
Oil Pan-To-Case	10-13 (14-18)
Park Lock Bracket-To-Case	15-20 (20-27)
Pump Body-To-Pump Cover	15-20 (20-27)
Pump-To-Case	15-20 (20-27)
Transmission-To-Engine	41-52 (55-70)

	INCH Lbs. (N.m)
Accumulator Housing-To-Case	84-120 (10-14)
Pressure Switch	60-120 (7-14)
Pressure Take Off Plugs	60-120 (7-14)
Solenoid-To-Case	84-120 (10-14)
Speedometer Retainer-To-Case	84-120 (10-14)
Stator Shaft-To-Pump Cover	84-120 (10-14)
Valve Body-To-Case	84-120 (10-14)

Automatic Transmissions

GENERAL MOTORS TURBO HYDRA-MATIC 325-4L

Buick, Cadillac, Oldsmobile

IDENTIFICATION

The Transmission I.D. Number is stamped on a plate attached to left side of torque converter housing. In addition, the word "METRIC" is stamped on bottom of oil pan. Transmission code letters are listed in TRANSMISSION MODEL CODES table.

TRANSMISSION MODEL CODES

Application	Codes
Buick	BJ,OE,OK,OQ
Cadillac	AJ,AL
Oldsmobile	AB,AE,AG, AL,AM,BE, BJ,OJ,OK

DESCRIPTION

The Model 325-4L automatic transaxle is a fully automatic FWD unit consisting primarily of a 4-element hydraulic torque converter with a converter clutch, 3 compound planetary gear sets and an overdrive unit. Five multiple-disc clutches, 2 roller clutches and a band provide friction elements required to obtain desired function of compound planetary gear set and overdrive unit

NOTE: See GENERAL MOTORS TORQUE CONVERTOR CLUTCH article article in this section for information on the converter clutch system used in the THM 325-4L.

LUBRICATION & ADJUSTMENTS

See appropriate AUTOMATIC TRANSMISSION SERVICING article in DOMESTIC GENERAL SERVICING section.

TROUBLE SHOOTING

See appropriate AUTOMATIC TRANSMISSION TROUBLE SHOOTING article in DOMESTIC GENERAL SERVICING section.

TESTING

ROAD TEST
In "D"

With selector lever in Drive, accelerate vehicle from a standstill. A 1-2, 2-3, and 3-4 shift should occur at all throttle openings (shift points will vary with throttle openings). As vehicle speed decreases to zero MPH, 4-3, 3-2 and 2-1 downshifts should occur.

In "L2"

With selector level in "L2", accelerate vehicle from a standstill. A 1-2 shift should occur at all throttle openings (No 2-3 shift can be obtained when selector lever in this position). The 1-2 shift point will vary with throttle opening. As vehicle speed decreases to zero MPH, a 2-1 downshift should occur.

In "L1"

Place selector lever in "L1", and accelerate vehicle from a standstill. No upshift should occur in this range. DO NOT exceed 40 MPH during this test.

Downshift to "L1"

With selector lever in "L2", and vehicle speed approximately 30 MPH at constant throttle, move selector lever to "L1". A downshift, an increase in engine RPM and an engine braking effect should be noted.

Downshift to "L2"

With selector lever in Drive, lift foot from accelerator and move selector lever to "L2". An increase in engine RPM and an engine braking effect should be noted.

HYDRAULIC PRESSURE TESTS

Before making pressure tests, ensure that fluid level, condition and control linkage adjustments have been checked and corrected if necessary. Install a tachometer to engine and an pressure gauge to pressure take-off point on transmission case. *See Fig 1.* Go to MINIMUM T.V. LINE PRESSURE CHECK.

Fig. 1: Pressure Take-Off Point

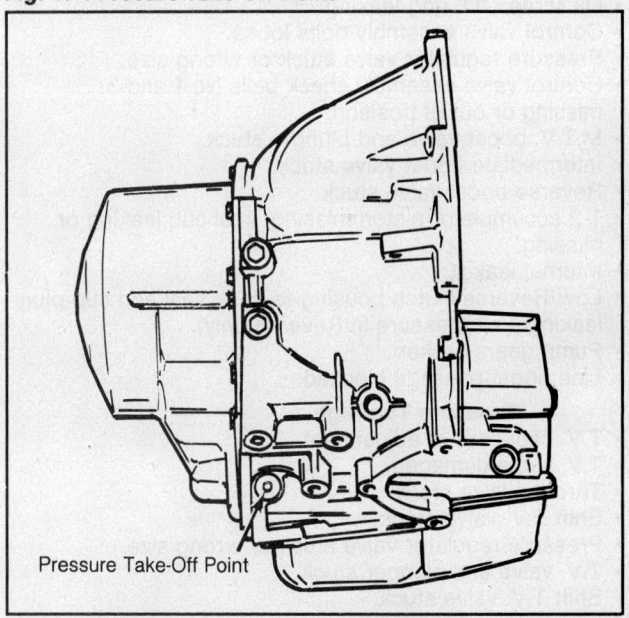

Pressure Take-Off Point

Minimum T.V. Line Pressure Check

With T.V. cable properly adjusted and brakes applied, check line pressure readings in various selector lever positions, at 1000 RPM. See CONTROL PRESSURE SPECIFICATIONS (PSI) table. Go to MAXIMUM T.V. LINE PRESSURE CHECK.

Maximum T.V. Line Pressure Check

With T.V. cable held fully open and brakes applied, check line pressure readings in various selector lever positions, at 1000 RPM. See CONTROL PRESSURE SPECIFICATIONS (PSI) table.

Automatic Transmissions

GENERAL MOTORS TURBO HYDRA-MATIC 325-4L (Cont.)

CONTROL PRESSURE SPECIFICATIONS (PSI)

Selector Lever Position	Minimum T.V. Pressure	Maximum T.V. Pressure
"P","N", "D4", "D3"		
AL,OK	55-65	108-131
OE,OQ	64-77	126-156
AB,AE,AJ	55-65	118-145
BJ	64-77	137-166
"D1","D2"		
AL,OK,AB,AE,AJ	128-152	128-152
OE,OQ	148-179	148-179
BJ	148-179	148-179
Reverse		
AL,OK	109-129	214-259
OE,OQ	126-152	251-311
AB,AE,AJ	109-129	235-287
BJ	126-152	271-329

PRESSURE TEST RESULTS

Pressure Too Low

- Oil level low.
- T.V. cable out of adjustment.
- T.V. linkage damaged.
- Throttle valve stuck.
- Shift T.V. valve stuck.
- Oil screen plugged.
- Oil screen "O" ring leaking.
- Control valve assembly bolts loose.
- Pressure regulator valve stuck or wrong size.
- Control valve assembly check balls No.1 and 3, missing or out of position.
- M.T.V. boost valve and plunger stuck.
- Intermediate boost valve stuck.
- Reverse boost valve stuck.
- 1-2 accumulator piston missing, seal cut, leaking or missing.
- Internal leaks.
- Low/Reverse clutch housing-to-case seal and cup plug leaking (low pressure in Reverse only).
- Pump gears broken.
- Line boost passage blocked.

Pressure Too High

- T.V. cable out of adjustment.
- T.V. cable damaged.
- Throttle valve stuck.
- Shift T.V. valve stuck.
- Pressure regulator valve stuck or wrong size.
- T.V. valve and plunger stuck.
- Shift T.V. valve stuck.
- Intermediate boost valve stuck.
- Reverse boost valve stuck.
- Reverse boost orifice in spacer plate plugged (low pressure in Reverse only).
- Internal pump or case leaks.

SERVICE (IN VEHICLE)

NOTE: For information on removing and installing DRIVE AXLES, OUTPUT SHAFTS AND RIGHT OUTPUT SHAFT SUPPORT, and BEARING SERVICE procedures, see G.M. TURBO HYDRA-MATIC FINAL DRIVE article.

The following components can be removed from transmission without removing transmission from vehicle. For removal and installation procedures for these components, see TRANSMISSION DISASSEMBLY in this article.

- Extention Housing Seal
- Governor Cover, Seals and Assembly
- Governor Pressure Switch (Diesel Only)
- Governor Pipe
- Intermediate Servo Cover and Seal
- Intermediate Servo Piston Assembly
- Oil Pan and Screen, Intake Pipe Assembly
- Control Valve Assembly
- Check Balls
- Valve Body Spacer Plates and Gaskets
- Pressure Regulator Parts
- Manual Detent Roller and Spring Assembly
- Throttle Lever and Bracket Assembly
- T.V./Detent Cable and "O" Ring
- M.T.V. Boost Valve and Bushing
- Manual Valve
- Manual Valve Link
- 1-2 Accumulator Assembly
- 3-4 Accumulator Assembly
- Low and Reverse Clutch Cup Plug
- Reverse Boost Valve and Bushing
- Stop Valve
- 4-3 Pressure Switch
- 4th Clutch Pressure Switch
- Cooler Fittings
- Oil Pipe and "O" Ring
- Speedometer Driven Gear Assembly
- Speedometer Drive Gear
- Converter Clutch Valve and Springs
- Converter Clutch Solenoid
- Solenoid Wire Clips
- Electrical Connectors

PRESSURE REGULATOR, REVERSE BOOST & MODULATOR THROTTLE BOOST VALVE (M.T.V.) ASSEMBLIES

Removal

1) Drain fluid from transmission, then remove oil pan and screen. Using a small screwdriver, push in on valve assembly and compress spring.

2) Remove valve assembly retaining ring, then slowly release tension on spring. Remove M.T.V. boost valve and bushing. Remove reverse boost bushing, valve, spring, pressure regulator and bushing assembly.

Installation

Install all valves in reverse order of disassembly. Push M.T.V. boost assembly into case bore past retaining ring groove by compressing spring. Install retaining ring, screen, gasket and oil pan. Fill transmission with fluid.

CONTROL VALVE ASSEMBLY

Removal

1) Drain transmission fluid from oil pan, then remove pan and screen. Remove screw and washer securing cable to transmission and disconnect T.V. cable. Remove throttle lever and bracket assembly, using care not to bend throttle lever link.

2) Disconnect Torque Converter Control (T.C.C.) wiring connector. Remove oil transfer pipes (4) and hold down brackets. Support valve assembly and remove retaining bolts. Lay control valve assembly down with spacer plate side up and note location of check ball in valve body. Note location of check balls and remove spacer plate. Note location of check balls in accumulator housing.

GENERAL MOTORS TURBO HYDRA-MATIC 325-4L (Cont.)

seal rings with petroleum jelly. Install servo piston into servo cover.

2) Lubricate with petroleum jelly and install new seal ring on servo cover. Install intermediate servo assembly into case, tapping with a plastic hammer if necessary.

NOTE: **Ensure tapered end of band apply pin in properly located against band apply lug.**

3) Compress servo cover. Install retaining ring and align ring end with gap showing in case slot.

REMOVAL & INSTALLATION

TRANSMISSION

See appropriate AUTOMATIC TRANSMISSION REMOVAL article in DOMESTIC GENERAL SERVICING section.

TORQUE CONVERTER

NOTE: **Torque converter is a sealed unit and cannot be disassembled for service.**

LEAKAGE CHECK

See procedure for GENERAL MOTORS TURBO HYDRA-MATIC 400.

END CLEARANCE CHECK

See procedure for GENERAL MOTORS TURBO HYDRA-MATIC 400.

CONVERTER FLUSHING

See procedure for GENERAL MOTORS TURBO HYDRA-MATIC 400.

TRANSMISSION DISASSEMBLY

INPUT SHAFT END PLAY

1) Install Output Shaft Aligning And Loading Tool (J-26958) to output end of transmission. *See Fig 4.*

2) Remove driven sprocket support-to-case bolt and install a dial indicator post. Install Input Shaft Lifter Bar (J-28494). *See Fig 5.* Push input shaft down.

3) Mount a dial indicator on indicator post positioning indicator point against end of input shaft. Move output shaft upwards by tightening adjusting screw on aligning and loading assembly until it stops. Set indicator to zero.

4) Using lifter bar, raise input shaft and read end play recorded on dial indicator. Input unit end play should be .022-.051" (.56-1.29 mm). Selective washer controlling end play is located between output shaft and input shaft. If more or less washer thickness is required to bring end play within specifications, select proper washer. See INPUT UNIT END PLAY WASHER THICKNESS chart.

5) Remove dial indicator, indicator post and input shaft lifter bar.

TRANSMISSION

1) Position transmission in a holding fixture. Remove torque converter by pulling it straight out. Rotate

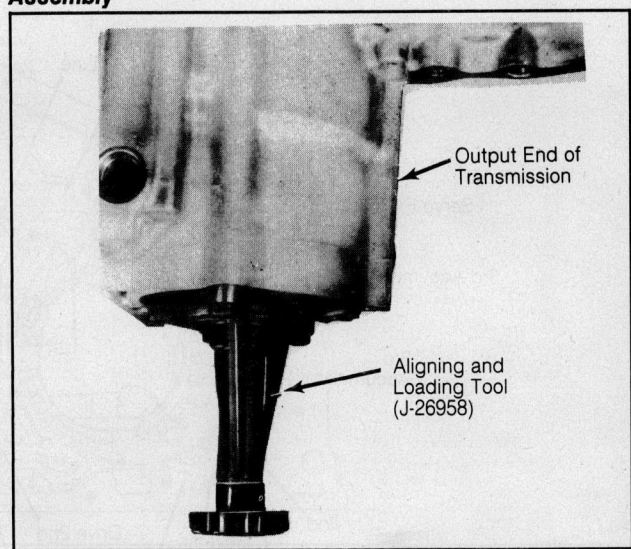

Fig. 4: *Installation of Output Shaft Aligning and Loading Assembly*

Output End of Transmission

Aligning and Loading Tool (J-26958)

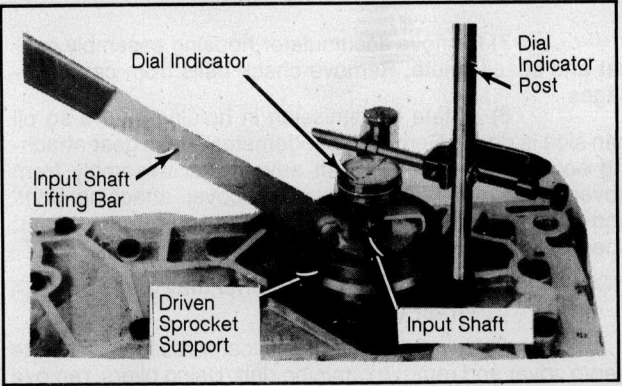

Fig. 5: *Checking Input Unit End Play*

Dial Indicator

Dial Indicator Post

Input Shaft Lifting Bar

Driven Sprocket Support

Input Shaft

transmission so that oil pan is facing up, then remove oil pan, gasket, oil screen assembly and intake pipe "O" ring.

2) Disconnect wire leads at case electrical connector and pressure switches. Remove electrical connector and "O" ring seal from case. Use a small screwdriver to depress connector tangs while pushing out on connector. Remove solenoid assembly attaching bolts, solenoid and "O" ring seal.

3) Remove pressure regulator assembly retaining snap ring. Remove T.V. boost valve bushing and valve, reverse boost valve bushing and valve, pressure regulator spring and pressure regulator bushing and valve.

4) Remove converter clutch apply valve retaining snap ring. Remove converter clutch valve bushing, valve and spring. Remove "D2" signal, reverse signal and overrun pipe retainers. Remove remaining oil pipes and solenoid assembly.

5) Remove throttle lever and bracket assembly. Remove control valve assembly attaching bolts and disconnect manual valve. Do not drop valve. Remove control valve assembly, noting location of check balls on spacer plate. Remove check balls. *See Fig. 8.*

6) Remove 1-2 and 3-4 accumulator housing bolts, accumulator housing and 1-2 spring. One check ball will be exposed on top of spacer plate to valve body gasket. Remove check ball. *See Fig. 8.*

Fig. 6: Front view of Case Showing Oil Passages

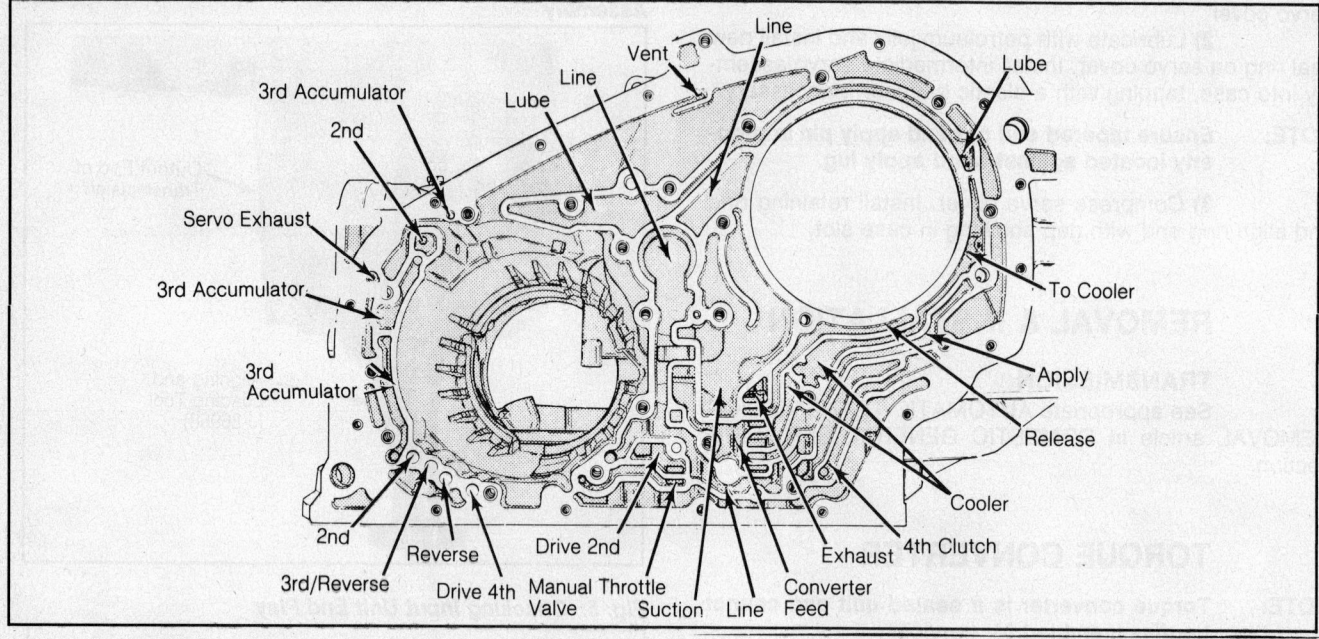

7) Remove accumulator housing assembly gasket and spacer plate. Remove check balls from case passages.

8) Rotate transmission in holding fixture so oil pan side is down. Remove speedometer driven gear attaching bolt and retainer clip. Lift driven gear assembly from governor cover. Remove governor cover attaching bolts and lift off cover. Remove governor, thrust washer and speedometer drive gear from case.

NOTE: The governor thrust washer may come out with governor cover.

9) Using a compressor, compress intermediate servo cover and remove retaining ring. Using pliers, remove servo cover. Remove servo piston and band apply pin assembly.

NOTE: If intermediate servo cover cannot be removed easily, apply air pressure into intermediate servo exhaust port to force assembly from case.

NOTE: Before proceeding with transmission disassembly, band apply pin selection check should be made to determine correct pin for use at reassembly.

10) Install Band Apply Pin Selection Gauge (J-25014-2) in intermediate servo bore and retain with servo cover retaining ring, aligning ring with gap at case slot.

11) Install Gauge Pin (J-25014-1) into selection gauge and ensure tapered end of pin is properly located against band apply lug. Install a dial indicator. See Fig. 10.

Fig. 7: Wiring & Pipe Locations

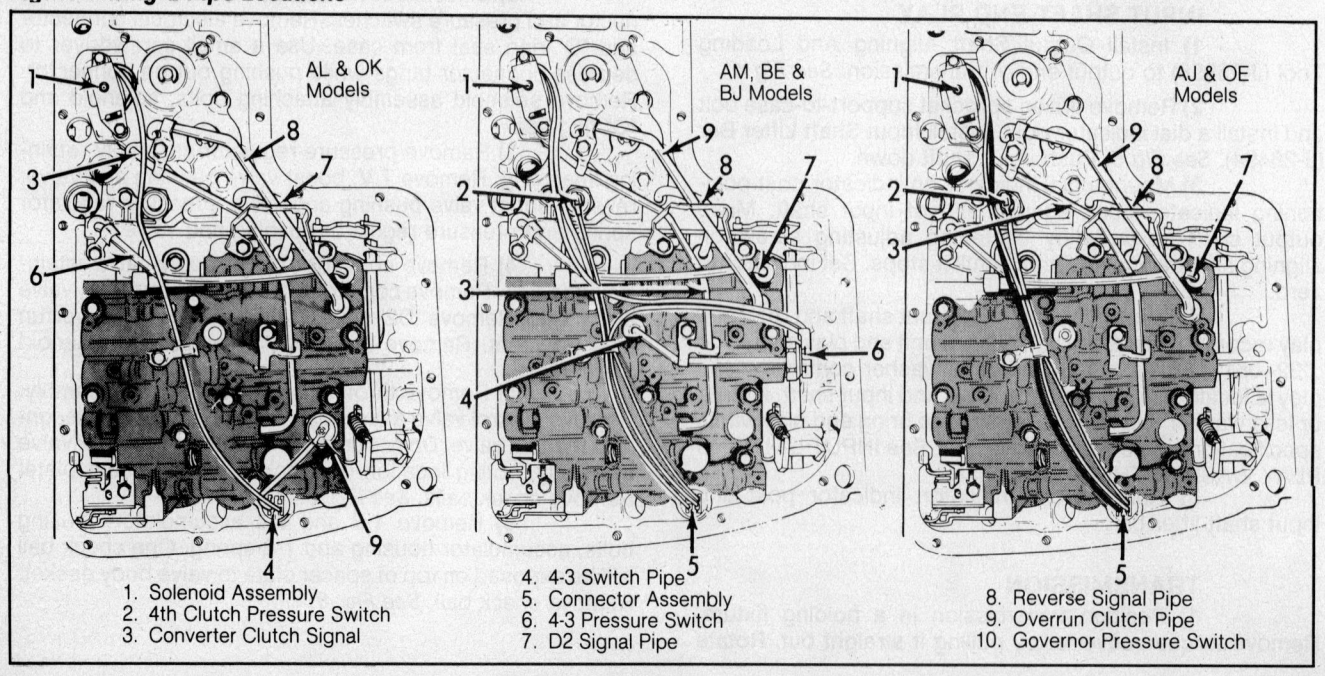

1. Solenoid Assembly
2. 4th Clutch Pressure Switch
3. Converter Clutch Signal
4. 4-3 Switch Pipe
5. Connector Assembly
6. 4-3 Pressure Switch
7. D2 Signal Pipe
8. Reverse Signal Pipe
9. Overrun Clutch Pipe
10. Governor Pressure Switch

Fig. 8: Location of Check Balls

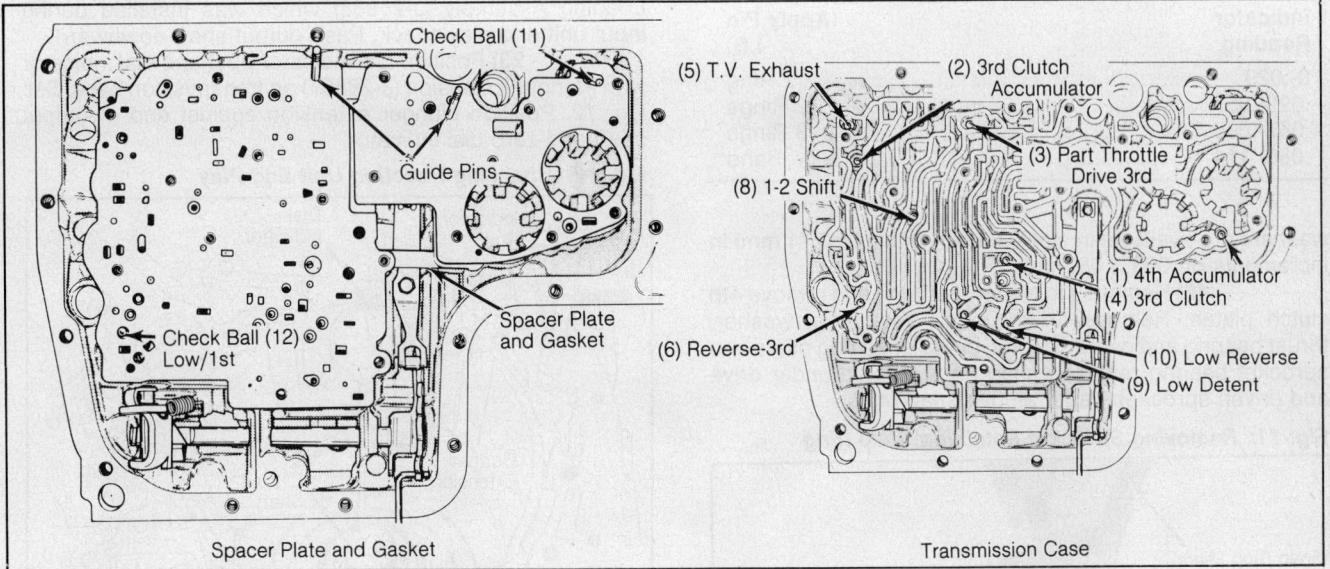

Spacer Plate and Gasket

Transmission Case

INPUT UNIT END PLAY WASHER THICKNESS

Thickness In. (mm)	Identification No. And/Or Color
.065-.070 (1.66-1.77)	1
.070-.075 (1.79-1.90)	2
.076-.080 (1.93-2.03)	3 – Black
.081-.085 (2.05-2.16)	4 – Light Green
.086-.090 (2.18-2.29)	5 – Scarlet
.091-.095 (2.31-2.42)	6 – Purple
.096-.100 (2.44-2.55)	7 – Cocoa Brown
.101-.106 (2.57-2.68)	8 – Orange
.106-.111 (2.70-2.81)	9 – Yellow
.111-.116 (2.83-2.94)	10 – Light Blue
.117-.121 (2.96-3.07)	11
.122-.126 (3.09-3.20)	12
.127-.131 (3.22-3.33)	13 – Pink
.132-.136 (3.35-3.46)	14 – Green
.137-.141 (3.48-3.59)	15 – Grey

Fig. 9: Using Compressed Air To Remove Intermediate Servo Assembly

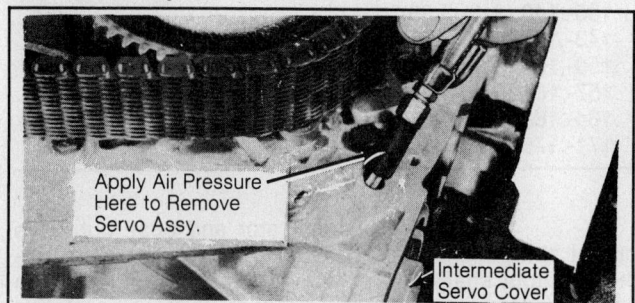

Apply Air Pressure Here to Remove Servo Assy.

Intermediate Servo Cover

Position indicator point on top of selection gauge zero post. Set dial indicator to zero.

    12) Seat selection gauge squarely against servo retaining ring. Align stepped side of gauge pin with torquing arm of selection gauge. Arm must stop against step of gauge pin.

Fig. 10: Intermediate Band Apply Pin Selection

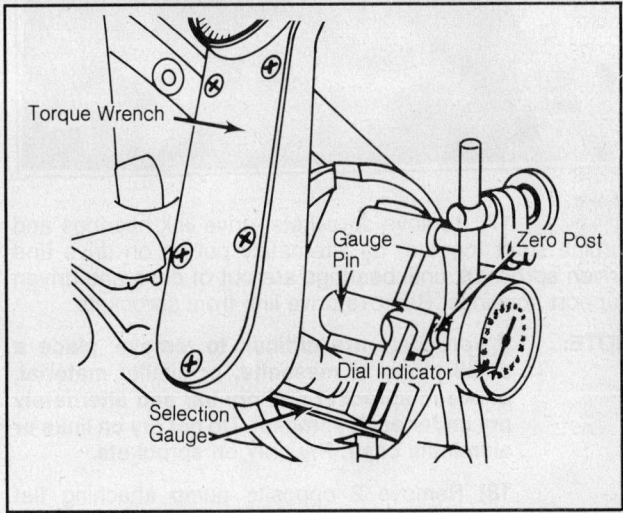

Torque Wrench

Gauge Pin

Zero Post

Dial Indicator

Selection Gauge

NOTE: If band selection pin does not register between high and low limits, look for possible problem with intermediate band, direct clutch or transmission case.

    13) Apply 108 INCH lbs. (11 N.m) of torque to hex nut on side of selection gauge pin. Using indicator reading, select correct band apply pin to use during reassembly. See INTERMEDIATE BAND APPLY PIN SELECTION chart.

NOTE: Dial indicator travel is reversed, making indicator readings backwards. On an indicator that ranges from 0-100, a .020" (.5 mm) travel will read .080" (2.0 mm), a .060" (1.5 mm) travel will read .040" (1.0 mm).

    14) Rotate transmission to sprocket cover side up. Remove sprocket cover. Diesel model transmissions have 5 bolts with mounting studs. Note location of these bolts. Remove cover and clean sealant from cover.

    15) Check and record overdrive unit end play. End play should be .004"-.029" (.10-.74 mm). Overdrive unit

INTERMEDIATE BAND APPLY PIN SELECTION

Indicator Reading	Apply Pin I.D.
0-.029"	1 Ring
.029-.057"	2 Rings
.057-.086	3 Rings
.086-.114	Wide Band

washers are available in sizes .063"-.144" (1.63-3.71 mm) in increments of .003" (.08 mm).

16) Remove 4th clutch snap ring and remove 4th clutch plates. Remove turbine shaft snap ring, washer, thrust bearing and overdrive unit. Install snap ring pliers into sprocket bearing retaining snap rings located under drive and driven sprockets, and remove snap rings.

Fig. 11: Removing Sprocket Retaining Snap Ring

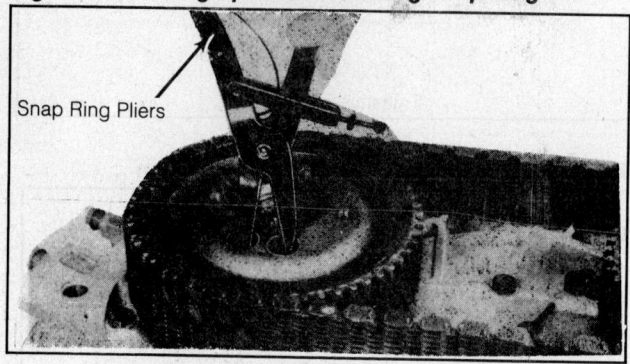

Snap Ring Pliers

17) Remove sprockets, drive link bearings and turbine shaft together by alternately pulling on drive and driven sprockets until bearings are out of drive and driven support housings. Remove drive link from sprockets.

NOTE: If sprockets are difficult to remove, place a small piece of masonite, or similar material, between sprocket and pry bar and alternately pry under each sprocket. Do not pry on links or aluminum case. Pry only on sprockets.

18) Remove 2 opposite pump attaching flat head screws from drive sprocket support and install two 5/16-18x4" guide pins or bolts. Remove remaining pump attaching screws from support. With 1 hand, hold underside of pump, then gently tap guide pins until pump is removed from case.

19) Before proceeding wih disassembly of transmission, check input unit end play. See INPUT UNIT END PLAY. After checking endplay do not remove output shaft aligning and loading assembly. Go to next step.

20) Remove case cover attaching bolts, but do not remove driven sprocket support bolts at this time. Remove case cover and gasket. Remove thrust washer from hub of sprocket support.

21) Pull direct and forward clutch assemblies from transmission case. Lift direct clutch assembly from forward clutch assembly. Lift intermediate band from case.

NOTE: The direct-to-forward clutch thrust washer may stick to end of direct clutch housing when it is removed from forward clutch housing.

22) Remove output shaft-to-input shaft selective thrust washer. Check reaction unit end play as follows:

Loosen adjusting screw on Output Shaft Aligning And Loading Assembly (J-26958) which was installed during input unit end play check. Push output shaft downward.

23) Position dial indicator post and dial indicator with Plunger Extension (J-28667) on transmission case. See Fig. 12. Position plunger extension against end of output shaft and zero dial indicator.

Fig. 12: Checking Reaction Unit End Play

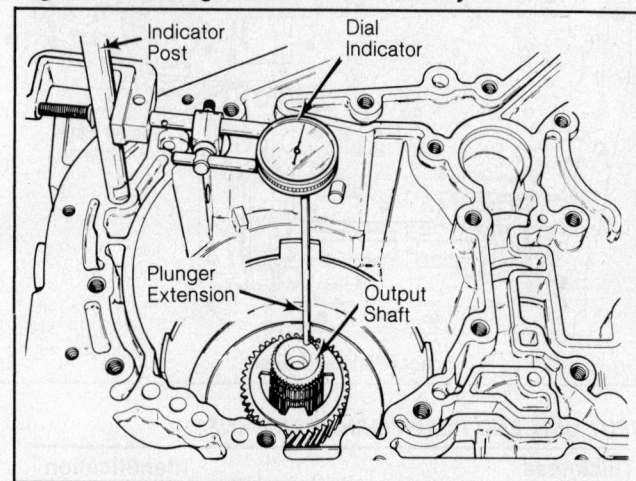

Indicator Post

Dial Indicator

Plunger Extension

Output Shaft

24) Move output shaft upward by turning adjusting screw on aligning assembly until it stops. Read and record end play on dial indicator. Reaction unit end play should be .004-.025" (.10-.64 mm).

25) The selective washer controlling reaction unit end play is located between input internal gear thrust washer and output shaft snap ring. If more or less washer thickness is required to bring end play within specifications, select proper washer from REACTION UNIT END PLAY WASHER SELECTION chart.

REACTION UNIT END PLAY WASHER SELECTION

Thickness In. (mm)	I.D. Number And Color
.114-.119 (2.90-3.01)	1 – Orange
.121-.126 (3.08-3.19)	2 – White
.128-.133 (3.26-3.37)	3 – Yellow
.135-.140 (3.44-3.55)	4 – Blue
.143-.147 (3.62-3.73)	5 – Red
.150-.154 (3.80-3.91)	6 – Brown
.157-.161 (3.98-4.09)	7 – Green
.164-.168 (4.16-4.27)	8 – Black
.171-.175 (4.34-4.45)	9 – Purple

26) Remove dial indicator and post, but leave output shaft aligning and loading assembly installed. Remove output shaft-to-selective washer snap ring. Tighten adjusting screw on loading assembly to remove snap ring.

27) Remove input internal gear, reaction selective thrust washer and tanged thrust washer from end of output shaft. Remove input carrier assembly and input internal gear-to-input carrier thrust bearing assembly.

28) Remove input sun gear-to-input carrier thrust bearing if it did not come out with carrier, remove input sun gear. Remove input drum and reaction sun gear from case. Remove tanged input drum-to-low-reverse clutch housing thrust washer from rear of input drum or from low-reverse clutch housing.

29) Grind approximately 3/4" from end of a No. 4 screw extractor, then use screw extractor to remove low/reverse cup plug. *See Fig. 13.* Remove low/reverse clutch-to-case beveled snap ring. Remove low/reverse clutch housing assembly from case. Remove low/reverse clutch housing-to-case spacer.

Fig. 13: Removing Low/Reverse Clutch Cup Plug

Use modified No. 4 screw extractor to pull cup plug.

30) Ensure governor valve assembly has been removed. Grasp output shaft and pull reaction unit parts from case. Remove roller clutch and reaction carrier assembly from output shaft. Remove tanged thrust washer from end of reaction carrier or inside reaction internal gear.

31) Pull low/reverse clutch plates off output shaft. Remove reaction internal gear-to-sun gear thrust bearing from internal gear, then remove internal gear from output shaft. Remove governor drive gear from output shaft.

Fig. 14: View of Output Shaft Showing Governor Drive Gear Removal

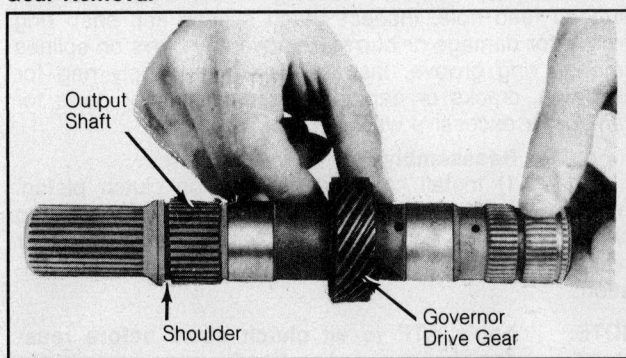

32) Rotate transmission in holding fixture so oil pan side is up, then remove output shaft aligning and loading assembly. If necessary, remove manual shaft and parking linkage from case as follows:

33) Remove manual detent roller and spring assembly. Remove parking strut shaft retaining ring. Grind approximately 3/4" from end of a No. 4 screw extractor, then use screw extractor to remove parking strut shaft cup plug. *See Fig. 15.*

Fig. 15: Removing Parking Strut Shaft Cup Plug

Use modified No. 4 screw extractor to pull cup plug.

34) Using sheet metal screws or No. 3 screw extractor, pull parking strut shaft from case. Remove parking lock spring, strut and lever. Remove parking lock cam.

35) Remove hex nut attaching inside detent lever to manual shaft, then remove shaft and lever assembly. If damaged, pry manual shaft seal from case bore using a screwdriver. Using sheet metal screw or No. 3 screw extractor, pull parking pawl shaft from case. Remove parking pawl and return spring.

Fig. 16: Exploded View of Manual Shaft and Parking Linkage

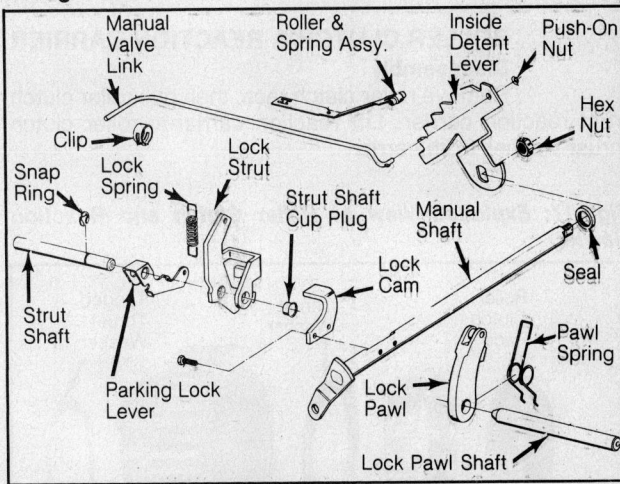

COMPONENT DISASSEMBLY & REASSEMBLY

TRANSMISSION CASE

Cleaning & Inspection

1) Inspect case assembly for damage, cracks, porosity or interconnected oil passages. Inspect orifice plug in case cover face. Inspect exhaust passages for blockage.

2) Inspect reverse clutch lugs, governor bore, intermediate servo bore and snap ring grooves for damage. Inspect low and reverse clutch seal and intermediate band anchor pin for damage.

2-310

Automatic Transmissions
GENERAL MOTORS TURBO HYDRA-MATIC 325-4L (Cont.)

3) Inspect vent assembly in case for damage. Do not remove vent unless replacement is necessary. Inspect cup plugs for damage or leaks.

NOTE: **If vent was removed, apply Loctite "T" to outside diameter of vent that locates in case and Loctite 35 to vent hole in case. Install vent using a rubber or plastic hammer.**

MANUAL SHAFT & PARKING LINKAGE
Cleaning & Inspection
1) Inspect parking pawl for cracks or damage and for free rotation of roller. Inspect return spring for deformed end or coils. Inspect pawl shaft for damage.

2) Check parking lock spring, strut, lever, shaft and shaft snap ring for damage. Inspect manual shaft for damaged threads and flat for raised edges (file down any raised edges).

3) Inspect outside manual lever, parking lock cam and inside detent lever for damage. Check manual detent spring for cracks and properly working roller. Inspect manual valve link for damage, or broken retainer lugs.

OUTPUT SHAFT & REACTION INTERNAL GEAR
Cleaning & Inspection
1) Inspect output shaft journals and snap ring grooves for wear or damage. Inspect shaft lubrication passages for restrictions or damage. Inspect splines for damage and governor drive gear for rough or damaged teeth.

2) Inspect reaction internal gear splines, teeth and bearing surface for wear, cracks or damage. Inspect parking pawl lugs for cracks or damage.

ROLLER CLUTCH & REACTION CARRIER
Disassembly
Remove roller clutch race, then pull roller clutch from reaction carrier. Lift reaction carrier-to-roller clutch thrust washer from carrier.

Fig. 17: Exploded View of Roller Clutch and Reaction Carrier

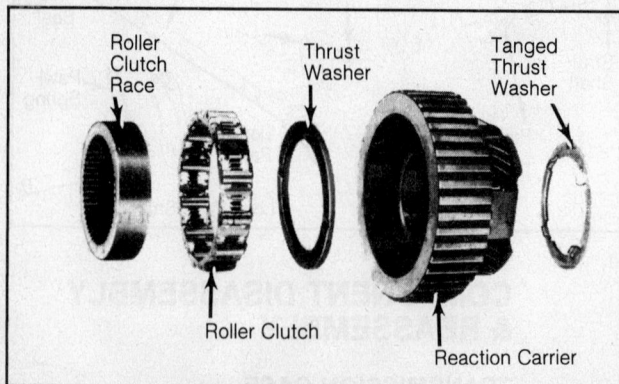

Cleaning & Inspection
1) Inspect roller clutch race and spline for scoring or wear. Inspect roller clutch bearings, cage and springs for damage or wear. Inspect thrust washers for signs of scoring or excessing wear and distorted tangs on tanged thrust washer.

2) Inspect reaction carrier, roller clutch cam ramps and bushing for damage or scoring. Inspect planetary pinions for damage, rough bearings or tilt. Using a feeler gauge, check pinion end play. *See Fig. 18.* Pinion end play should be .009-.027." (.23-.69 mm).

Fig. 18: Measuring Planetary Pinion End Play

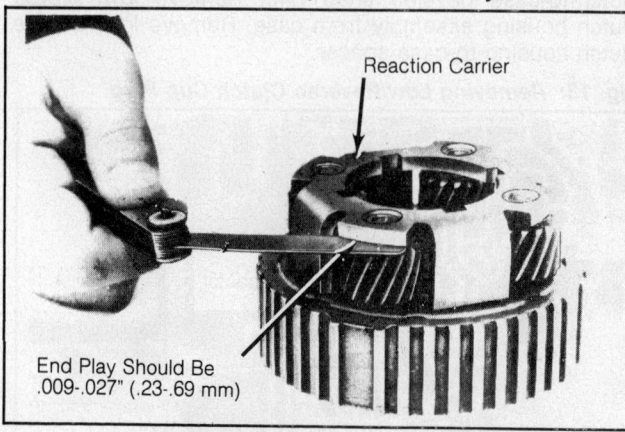

Reassembly
1) Install thrust washer into reaction carrier. Install rollers that may have come out of roller clutch cage, by compressing energizing spring with forefinger and inserting roller from outer edge.

2) Install roller clutch into carrier, then install clutch race (spline side out) and rotate race clockwise into position. Install tanged thrust washer, aligning tangs into slots of reaction carrier and retain with petroleum jelly.

LOW/REVERSE CLUTCH HOUSING
Disassembly
Compress low/reverse clutch spring retainer, remove snap ring and lift out retainer. Remove waved spring and clutch piston from housing. Remove inner and outer piston seals and clutch apply ring.

Cleaning & Inspection
Inspect clutch housing for damage, scoring or plugged feed hole. Inspect clutch splines and snap ring groove for damage or burrs. Remove any burrs on splines or snap ring groove. Inspect piston and apply ring for distortion, cracks or damage. Inspect all other parts for damage or excessive wear.

Reassembly
1) Install clutch apply ring on clutch piston. Install new inner and outer seals on piston with lips facing away from clutch apply ring side. Install a seal protector over seals to prevent damage to seals during piston installation.

NOTE: **Apply ATF to all clutch seals before reassembly.**

2) Using a small, flat blade screwdriver, install low/reverse clutch piston, while rotating and pushing down into place in clutch housing. Remove seal protector. Install waved spring and spring retainer (cupped face down), then compress retainer and install snap ring.

REACTION SUN GEAR & INPUT DRUM
Cleaning & Inspection
1) Check reaction sun gear for cracks, splits, spline damage, gear or journal wear and plugged lubrication holes.

2) If necessary, remove snap ring and separate sun gear from input drum and inspect drum splines for damage. Check input drum-to-low/reverse clutch housing thrust washer for scoring or distorted tangs.

INPUT CARRIER, SUN GEAR & INTERNAL GEAR
Cleaning & Inspection
1) Check all parts for pitting, scoring, damaged gear teeth and cracks. Ensure all lubrication holes are open.

2) Check internal gear thrust washers for wear or other damage. Check input carrier thrust bearing for roughness and pitting. Using a feeler gauge, check input carrier pinion end play. End play should be .009-.027" (.24-.69 mm).

Fig. 19: Exploded View of Reaction Sun Gear and Input Drum Assembly

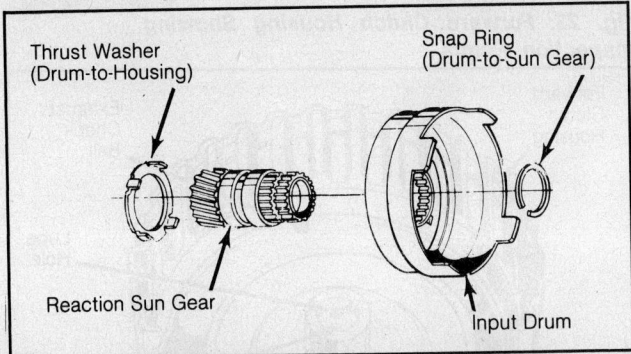

Thrust Washer (Drum-to-Housing)

Snap Ring (Drum-to-Sun Gear)

Reaction Sun Gear

Input Drum

DIRECT CLUTCH ASSEMBLY
Disassembly
1) Remove clutch pack snap ring and withdraw backing plate and clutch plates from clutch housing, keeping clutch plates separated from forward clutch plates.

2) Using a compressor, compress retainer and spring assembly and remove snap ring. Remove compressor. Remove retainer and spring assembly from clutch housing.

3) Remove release spring guide. Remove direct piston from clutch housing, then remove inner and outer seals from piston. Remove center seal from clutch housing.

NOTE: Do not remove clutch apply ring from piston unless piston or apply ring requires replacement.

Fig. 20: Exploded View of Low/Reverse Clutch Assembly

Cleaning & Inspection
1) Inspect composition plates, steel plates and backing plate for wear, burring or scoring. Check retainer and spring assembly for damage, distortion or collapse.

2) Inspect direct clutch piston for distortion, cracks, damage and check ball for free operation. Inspect housing for cracks, wear and open oil passages. Check for free operation of check balls. Closely check for damaged check ball capsule. Inspect snap ring grooves and bushing in housing for wear or damage.

Reassembly
1) If removed, install clutch apply ring on piston. Install new inner and outer seals on piston with seal lips facing away from apply ring side. Install new center seal on clutch housing with lip facing up. Install a seal protector over piston seals.

CAUTION: Use care when installing direct clutch piston past larger clutch snap ring groove. Groove could cut outer seal on piston.

2) Lubricate seals and install piston into clutch housing, then remove seal protector. Install release spring guide with omitted rib over check ball in piston. *See Fig. 22.* Install retainer and spring assembly into clutch housing using care to guide retainer past snap ring groove.

3) Compress retainer and spring assembly and install snap ring. Oil and install clutch plates into direct clutch housing, starting with a flat steel and alternating composition and flat steel clutch plates until correct number of clutch plates are installed. See DIRECT CLUTCH PLATE USAGE chart.

4) Install backing plate into housing with polished side down. Install snap ring and ensure that composition plates turn freely.

FORWARD CLUTCH ASSEMBLY
Disassembly
1) Remove forward clutch-to-direct clutch thrust washer. Remove clutch pack retaining snap ring, then remove backing plate and clutch plates from clutch housing.

2) Using a compressor, compress retainer and spring assembly and remove snap ring. Remove compressor, then lift retainer and spring assembly from housing. Remove piston from housing and seals from piston.

NOTE: Do not remove clutch apply ring from piston unless piston or apply ring requires replacement.

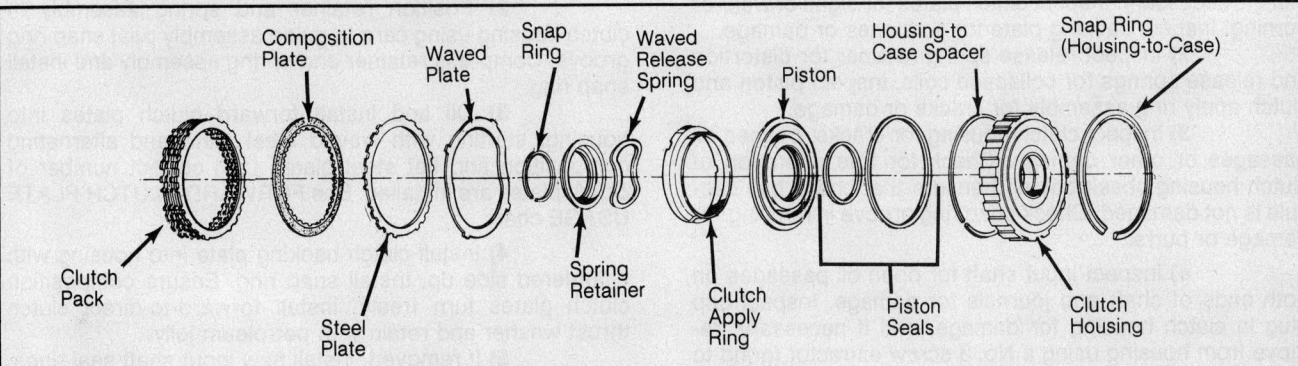

Composition Plate

Waved Plate

Snap Ring

Waved Release Spring

Housing-to-Case Spacer

Snap Ring (Housing-to-Case)

Piston

Clutch Pack

Steel Plate

Spring Retainer

Clutch Apply Ring

Piston Seals

Clutch Housing

Fig. 21: Exploded View of Direct Clutch Assembly

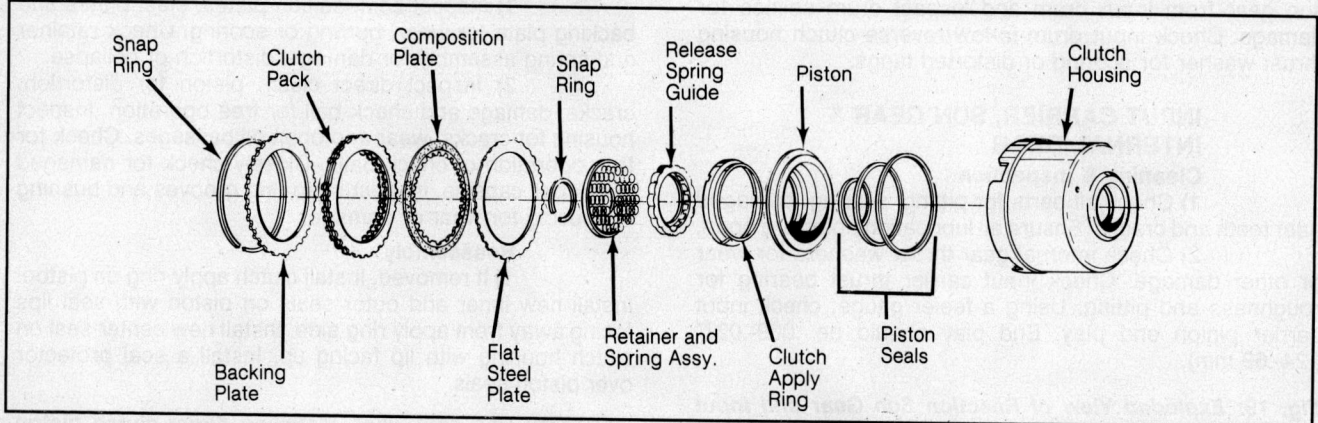

Snap Ring — Clutch Pack — Composition Plate — Snap Ring — Release Spring Guide — Piston — Clutch Housing — Backing Plate — Flat Steel Plate — Retainer and Spring Assy. — Clutch Apply Ring — Piston Seals

Fig. 22: Installing Release Spring Guide

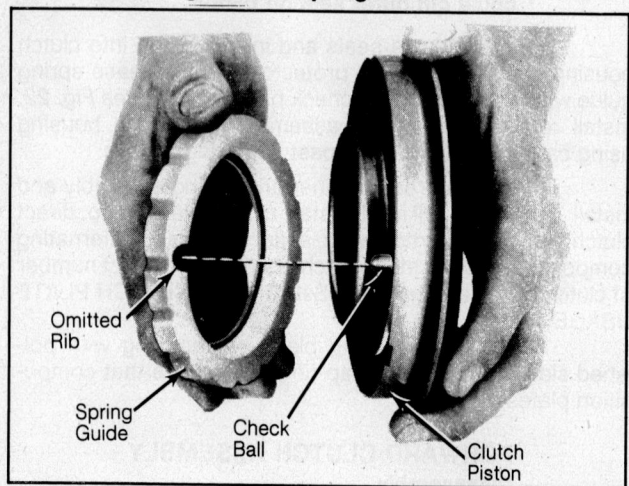

Omitted Rib — Spring Guide — Check Ball — Clutch Piston

Fig. 23: Forward Clutch Housing Showing Inspection Points

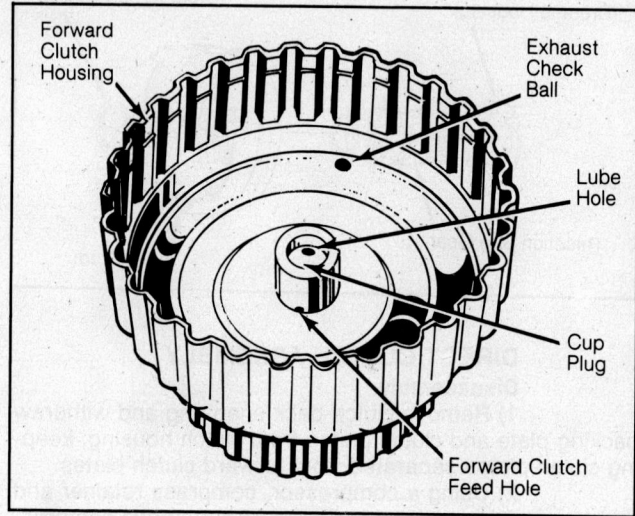

Forward Clutch Housing — Exhaust Check Ball — Lube Hole — Cup Plug — Forward Clutch Feed Hole

DIRECT CLUTCH PLATE USAGE

Application	Flat Steel [1]	Composition
All Models	6	6

[1] – Plate thickness is .091" (2.3 mm).

Cleaning & Inspection

1) Inspect oil seals on input shaft for damage and free fit in grooves. Do not remove seals unless replacement is necessary. Inspect clutch plates for signs of wear or burning. Inspect backing plate for scratches or damage.

2) Inspect release spring retainer for distortion and release springs for collapsed coils. Inspect piston and clutch apply ring assembly for cracks or damage.

3) Inspect clutch housing for cracks, opened oil passages or other damage. Check for free operation of clutch housing check ball and ensure that check ball capsule is not damaged. Check snap ring groove in housing for damage or burrs.

4) Inspect input shaft for open oil passages on both ends of shaft and journals for damage. Inspect cup plug in clutch housing for damage, and if necessary, remove from housing using a No. 3 screw extractor (grind to fit). Install new cup plug to .039" (1.0 mm) below surface.

Reassembly

1) If removed, install apply ring onto piston. Install new inner and outer seals on piston with lips facing away from clutch apply ring side. Lubricate seals and install piston into clutch housing.

CAUTION: Use care when installing piston past large forward clutch snap ring groove in clutch housing. Groove could cut outer seal on piston.

2) Position retainer and spring assembly in clutch housing using care to guide assembly past snap ring groove. Compress retainer and spring assembly and install snap ring.

3) Oil and install forward clutch plates into housing, starting with waved steel plate and alternating composition and flat steel plates until correct number of clutch plates are installed. See FORWARD CLUTCH PLATE USAGE chart.

4) Install clutch backing plate into housing with chamfered side up. Install snap ring. Ensure composition clutch plates turn freely. Install forward-to-direct clutch thrust washer and retain with petroleum jelly.

5) If removed, install new input shaft seal rings, making sure cut ends are assembled in same relationship

GENERAL MOTORS TURBO HYDRA-MATIC 325-4L (Cont.)

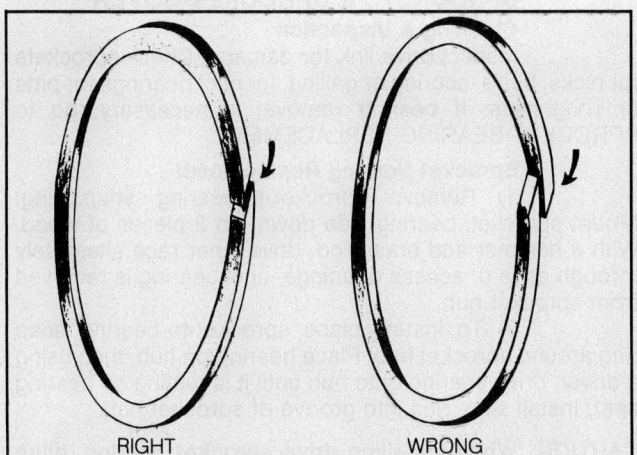

Fig. 24: View of Teflon Oil Seal Rings Showing Correct Installation Position

RIGHT   WRONG

as cut and rings are seated in their groove. Retain with petroleum jelly. See Fig. 24.

FORWARD CLUTCH PLATE USAGE CHART

Application	Flat Steel [1]	Composition
All Models	3 [2]	4

[1] – Plate thickness is .077" (1.96 mm)
[2] – Plus 1 waved steel plate .062" (1.57 mm) thick, installed first.

CASE COVER, DRIVE & DRIVEN SPROCKET SUPPORTS
Cleaning & Inspection

1) Inspect case cover for cracks and damage. Check machined surface of cover for flatness. Check cover for interconnected oil passages. Inspect cup plugs for damage or leaks. Verify that 3rd accumulator exhaust pellet and spring are in place. Be sure pressure relief valve and spring are in place.

2) Inspect drive sprocket support and support stator shaft spline for damage. Inspect driven sprocket support for damage. Check driven sprocket support oil seal rings but do not remove unless damaged.

NOTE: Drive and driven support housing assemblies are pressed into and removed with cover. Do

not remove unless it is necessary. If replacement of case cover or sprocket supports is required, proceed as follows:

3) Remove remaining sprocket support-to-case cover attaching bolts. Using a plastic mallet, strike stator shaft of drive sprocket support and hub of driven sprocket support until they are removed from case cover bores.

NOTE: When driving sprocket supports out of cover, avoid damaging or distorting stator shaft or ring grooves in hub of driven support.

4) Remove and discard sprocket support-to-cover gaskets. Remove and inspect converter out check valve from pump cover and check for interconnected oil passages.

5) To install, position converter out check valve into pump cover (tanged end first) and coil remainder of valve within itself. See Fig. 26. Install drive support-to-case cover gasket, then install support into cover by using a plastic mallet to seat housing. Use flathead screws for guides.

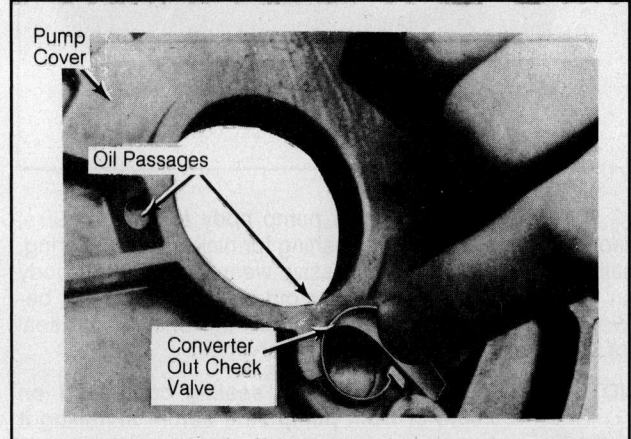

Fig. 26: Installing Converter Out Check Valve

Pump Cover

Oil Passages

Converter Out Check Valve

6) Install driven sprocket support-to-case cover gasket. Install driven sprocket support-to-cover bolts for gasket guides, then drive support into case cover using a plastic mallet. Install driven support-to-cover attaching bolts and tighten evenly.

Fig. 25: Exploded View of Forward Clutch Assembly

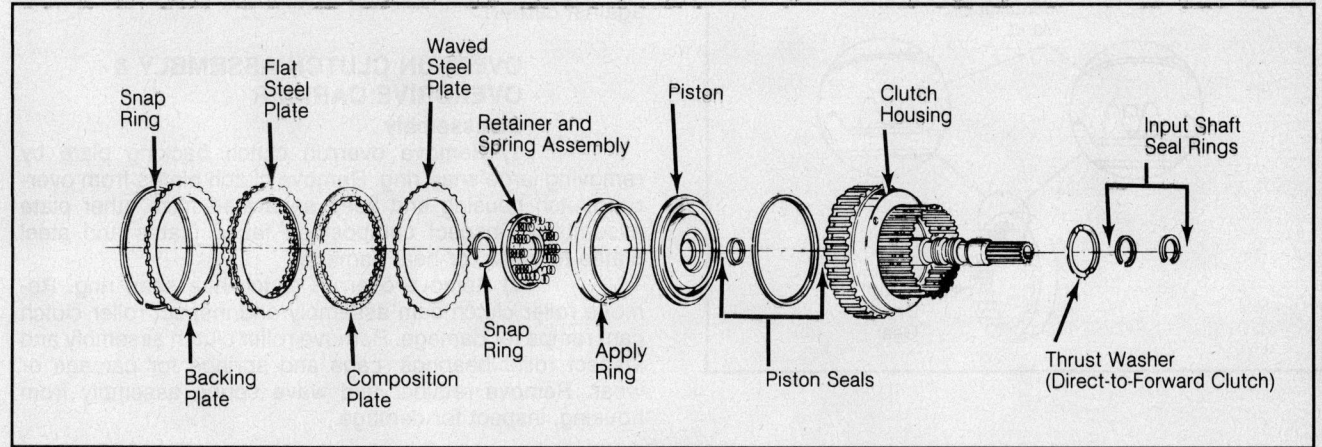

Snap Ring

Flat Steel Plate

Waved Steel Plate

Retainer and Spring Assembly

Piston

Clutch Housing

Input Shaft Seal Rings

Backing Plate

Composition Plate

Snap Ring

Apply Ring

Piston Seals

Thrust Washer (Direct-to-Forward Clutch)

OIL PUMP
Disassembly

Remove drive and driven gears from pump body. Remove and discard pump body-to-case "O" ring seal.

Cleaning & Inspection

1) Inspect gear pocket and crescent for nicks, burrs, scoring or galling. Check pump body-to-gear face clearance. *See Fig. 27.* Clearance should be .0013-.0035" (.033-.089 mm).

Fig. 27: Checking Pump Body-To-Gear Face Clearance

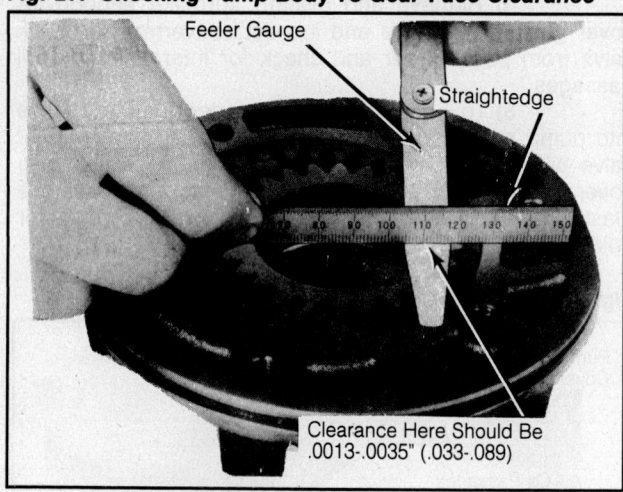

Feeler Gauge

Straightedge

Clearance Here Should Be .0013-.0035" (.033-.089)

2) Check face of pump body for nicks, burrs, scoring or galling. Inspect bushing for nicks, burrs, scoring, galling, out-of-round or excessive wear. Install pump body on converter hub and look for out-of-round condition between pump bushing and converter hub. Check front seal for damage and replace if necessary.

NOTE: Use a non-hardening sealing compound on outside of front pump seal before installing it into pump.

Reassembly

Install driven gear into pump with I.D. mark down against gear pocket. Install drive gear into pump body with I.D. mark on drive tang up. *See. Fig. 28.* Install a new pump-to-case "O" ring seal.

Fig. 28: Pump Driven Gear I.D. Mark

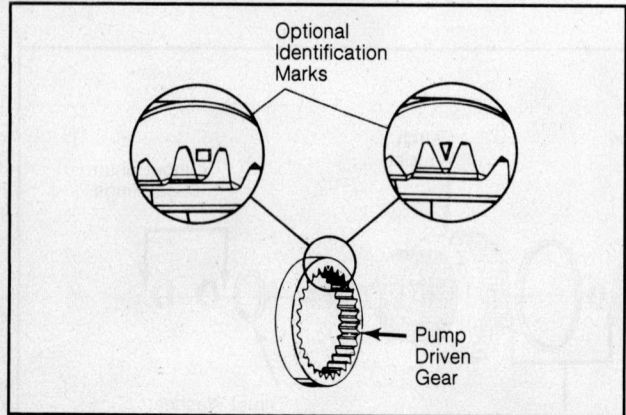

Optional Identification Marks

Pump Driven Gear

DRIVE LINK, DRIVE & DRIVEN SPROCKETS & SPROCKET COVER
Cleaning & Inspection

Inspect drive link for damage. Check sprockets for nicks, burrs, scoring or galling. Inspect bearings for pitts or roughness. If bearing removal is necessary, go to SPROCKET BEARING REPLACEMENT.

Sprocket Bearing Replacement

1) Remove sprocket-to-bearing snap ring. Mount sprocket, bearing side down, on 2 pieces of wood. With a hammer and brass rod, drive inner race alternately through each of access openings, until bearing is removed from sprocket hub.

2) To install, place sprocket-to-bearing snap ring around sprocket hub. Place bearing on hub, then using a driver, drive bearing onto hub until it is resting on bearing seat. Install snap ring into groove of sprocket hub.

CAUTION: When installing drive sprocket bearing, align bearing race groove with locating pin of sprocket hub.

FOURTH CLUTCH ASSEMBLY
Cleaning & Inspection

1) Inspect housing for burrs, raised edges, cracks or porosity. Inspect piston sealing surfaces for scratches. Air check clutch oil passage to be sure it is open and not interconnected. Inspect snap ring, release spring and retainer assembly for distortion or damage.

2) Inspect composition faced and steel plates for signs of wear or burning. Inspect backing plate for scratches or damage.

Reassembly

1) Install 4th clutch outer and inner seals on clutch housing with lips facing down and apply petroleum jelly. Inner seal is identified by a White stripe. Install clutch piston into housing. Install 4th clutch spring and retainer assembly. Using press and 4th clutch spring and retainer compressor, compress spring and retainer assembly and install snap ring.

2) If 4th clutch housing "O" ring seal was removed or is remaining on housing replace with new "O" ring. Install 4th clutch housing and attaching bolts and tighten.

OVERDRIVE INTERNAL GEAR

Thoroughly clean, air dry and inspect overdrive carrier-to-sprocket thrust bearing assembly for pitted or rough conditions. Install overdrive carrier-to-sprocket thrust bearing assembly by placing large diameter race against carrier.

OVERRUN CLUTCH ASSEMBLY & OVERDRIVE CARRIER
Disassembly

1) Remove overrun clutch backing plate by removing large snap ring. Remove clutch plates from overrun clutch housing and keep separated from other plate assemblies. Inspect composition faced plates and steel plates for wear, or heat damage.

2) Remove overrun clutch hub snap ring. Remove roller clutch cam assembly and inspect roller clutch cam ramps for damage. Remove roller clutch assembly and inspect roller bearings, cage and springs for damage or wear. Remove retainer and wave spring assembly from housing, inspect for damage.

3) Remove overrun clutch piston assembly and remove inner and outer seal from overrun clutch piston. Inspect piston assembly for distortion, cracks and damage. Inspect housing for cracks, wear and open oil passages. Check snap ring groove and bushing for damage or scoring.

4) Inspect overdrive carrier for worn or damaged parts. Check pinion end play with a dial indicator. End play should be .009-.024" (.24 .60 mm).

Reassembly

1) Install new inner and outer seals on piston with lips facing away from clutch apply ring side. Install Seal Protector (J-29335). Lubricate seals and install overrun clutch piston. Remove seal protector and install overrun clutch waved release spring retainer with cupped face down.

2) Install roller clutch cam on roller clutch assembly. The locating tangs on roller must set on roller clutch cam. Install roller clutch assembly on overrun clutch hub and push down to install narrow snap ring. Lubricate and install overrun clutch plates into housing, starting with a flat steel and alternating composition faced and flat steel clutch plates. See OVERRUN CLUTCH USAGE chart.

OVERRUN CLUTCH USAGE

Application	Flat Steel [1]	Composition
All Models	2	2

[1] – Plate thickness is .077" (1.97 mm).

3) Install backing plate with micro-finish down. Install snap ring. Ensure composition clutch plates turn freely.

GOVERNOR & SPEEDOMETER DRIVE GEAR
Cleaning & Inspection

1) If necessary, remove speedometer drive gear from governor shaft and inspect gear for damage or nicks. Check governor cover for damage, then wash in cleaning solvent and blow out oil passages.

2) Inspect governor driven gear for nicks or damage. Check governor shaft seal rings for cuts, damage and free fit in groove. Check for free operation of governor weights. Check for damaged, mispositioned, or tilted springs.

3) Inspect for presence of 2 check balls. Inspect governor shaft for damage. Inspect governor thrust washer for damage. If seal is damaged, cut seal ring off governor shaft, using care not to damage seal ring groove.

INTERMEDIATE SERVO
Disassembly

Separate inner and outer pistons, inner spring, spring retainer and cushion spring. If band apply pin requires replacement, separate pin from retainer.

Cleaning & Inspection

1) Check band apply pin for damage and proper fit in case. Check apply pin seal rings for damage. Do not remove seal rings unless replacement is necessary.

2) Inspect inner and outer piston seal rings for damage and free fit in grooves. Do not remove seals from

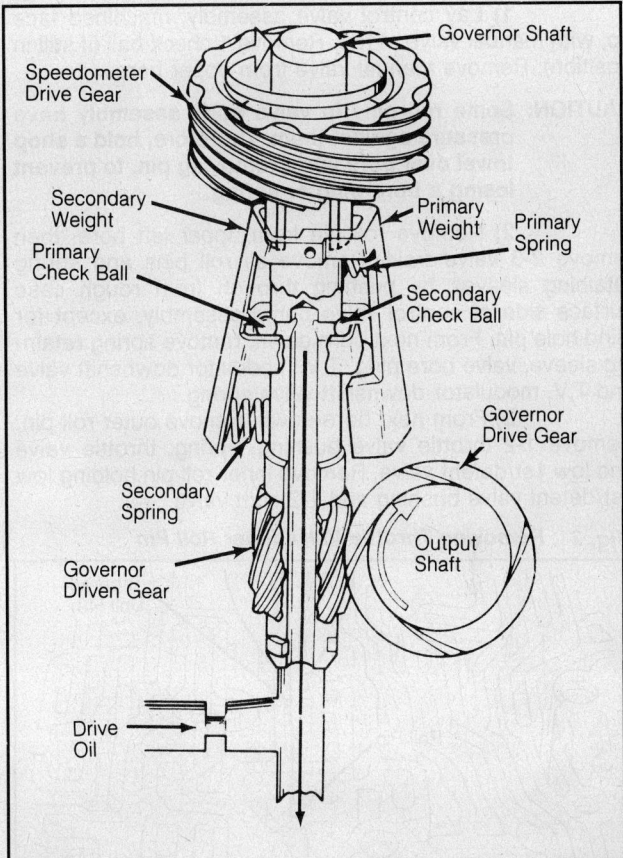

Fig. 29: Cross-Section of Governor Assembly

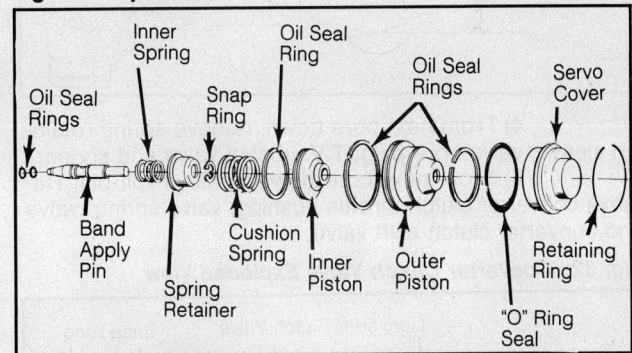

Fig. 30: Exploded View of Intermediate Servo Assembly

piston unless replacement is necessary. Inspect springs and retainer for damage.

Reassembly

Install retainer on band apply pin, then install retaining snap ring. If removed, install new seal rings on pistons and apply pin and ensure cut ends are assembled in same relationship as cut. To complete reassembly, reverse disassembly procedure.

CONTROL VALVE ASSEMBLY

NOTE: As valve trains are removed from each valve body bore, place parts in correct order and in relative position to valve body to simplify reassembly. Valves, bushings and springs are not interchangeable.

2-316

Automatic Transmissions
GENERAL MOTORS TURBO HYDRA-MATIC 325-4L (Cont.)

Disassembly

1) Lay control valve assembly, machined face up, with manual valve at top. Remove 1 check ball (if still in position). Remove manual valve from upper bore.

CAUTION: **Some roll pins in valve body assembly have pressure against them. Therefore, hold a shop towel over bore while removing pin, to prevent losing a bore plug or spring.**

2) Remove roll pin from upper left bore, then remove 2-3 valve train. Remove all roll pins and spring retaining sleeves by pushing through from rough case surface side of control valve pump assembly, except for blind hole pin. From next bore down, remove spring retaining sleeve, valve bore plug, T.V. modulator downshift valve and T.V. modulator downshift valve spring.

3) From next bore down, remove outer roll pin. Remove 1-2 throttle valve bushing, spring, throttle valve and low 1st/detent valve. Remove inner roll pin holding low 1st/detent valve bushing and 1-2 shift valve.

Fig. 31: Removing Throttle Valve Inner Roll Pin

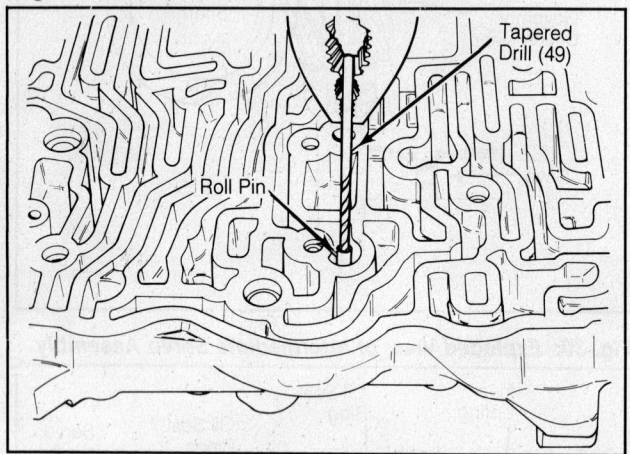

4) From next bore down, remove spring retaining sleeve, valve bore plug, T.V. upshift valve and spring.

5) From next bore down, remove roll pin. Remove converter clutch throttle bushing, valve spring, valve and converter clutch shift valve.

Fig. 32: Converter Clutch Valve Exploded View

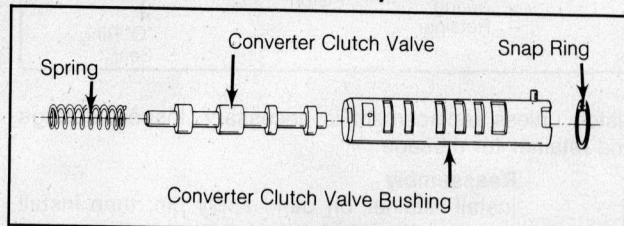

6) From last bore down, remove roll pin, bore plug and low/overrun clutch valve spring. From same bore, remove inner spring retaining sleeve. Remove 3-2 control valve spring and 3-2 control valve.

7) From upper right bore, remove spring retaining sleeve. Remove T.V. limit valve spring and T.V. limit valve.

8) From next bore down, remove roll pin. Remove 3-4 throttle valve bushing, 3-4 valve spring, 3-4 valve and 3-4 shift valve.

9) From next bore down, remove roll pin. Remove 4-3 control valve spring and 4-3 control valve.

10) From next bore down, remove spring retaining sleeve, valve bore plug, line bias valve and valve spring.

11) From next bore down, remove roll pin and bore plug. Remove accumulator valve bushing, valve and accumulator spring.

12) From last bore, remove outer roll pin from rough casting side, throttle valve plunger bushing, plunger and throttle valve spring. Remove inner roll pin as follows: Grind a taper to one end of a No. 49 drill. Insert tapered end into roll pin. Pull drill and coil retaining pin out. Remove throttle valve.

Cleaning & Inspection

Wash control valve body, valves, springs, and other parts in clean solvent and air dry. Inspect valves for scoring, cracks and free movement in their bores. Inspect bushings and valve body for cracks, damage or scored bores. Inspect springs for distortion or collapsed coils. Inspect bore plugs for damage.

NOTE: **Install zinc coated, flared roll pins with flared end out, and away from machined face of control valve assembly. Install 2 tapered roll pins (plain finish) that retain throttle valve and bushing, tapered end first. Roll pins do not fit flush on rough casting face. Ensure all roll pins are flush at machined face.**

Reassembly

To reassemble, reverse disassembly procedure. All parts must be installed in correct order and in proper valve body bore. Ensure check balls are located properly. Lubricate all parts and seals with ATF. When installing 1-2 throttle bushing and 2-3 throttle bushing, align in bores so retaining pin can be installed in pin slot. *See Fig. 33.*

Fig. 33: Installing Throttle Valve Bushing Roll Pin

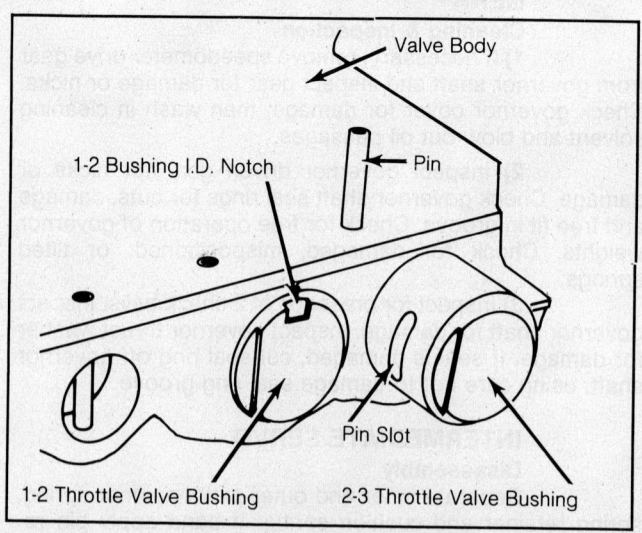

PRESSURE REGULATOR
Disassembly

Compress pressure regulator valve in bushing, and remove inner roll pin. Release pressure regulator valve spring slowly, then remove valve, guide and spring from bushing.

GENERAL MOTORS TURBO HYDRA-MATIC 325-4L (Cont.)

Fig. 34: Exploded View of Pressure Regulator

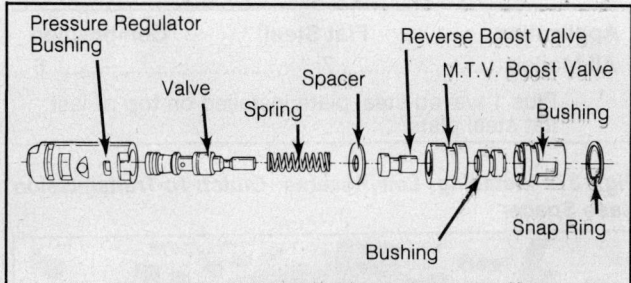

reverse boost valve into reverse boost valve bushing, small end first. Install reverse boost valve and bushing into case. Install M.T.V. boost valve into bushing. Install M.T.V. valve and bushing into case and install snap ring.

CONVERTER CLUTCH VALVE
Cleaning & Inspection
Inspect converter valve and bushing for damage and check for freeness in bushing. Inspect spring for distortion or collapsed coils.

Cleaning & Inspection
Inspect pressure regulator valve for damage and freeness in bushing. Inspect bushing for damage and spring for distortion. Inspect reverse boost valve for damage and freeness in bushing. Check valve bushing for damage. Inspect M.T.V. boost valve and bushing for damage.

Reassembly
Install pressure regulator bushing and regulator spring into case, then install valve bushing spacer. Install

TRANSMISSION REASSEMBLY
1) Turn transmission in holding fixture so oil pan side is up. If removed, install new manual shaft seal with lip facing inward into case using a 9/16" (14 mm) socket to seat seal. Install parking pawl and return spring with tooth toward inside of case and parking pawl return spring under pawl tooth with spring ends toward inside of case and ensure spring ends locate in case slot.
2) Align parking pawl and return spring with case shaft bore, then install parking pawl shaft, tapered end

Fig. 35: Exploded View of 325-4L Control Valve Assembly

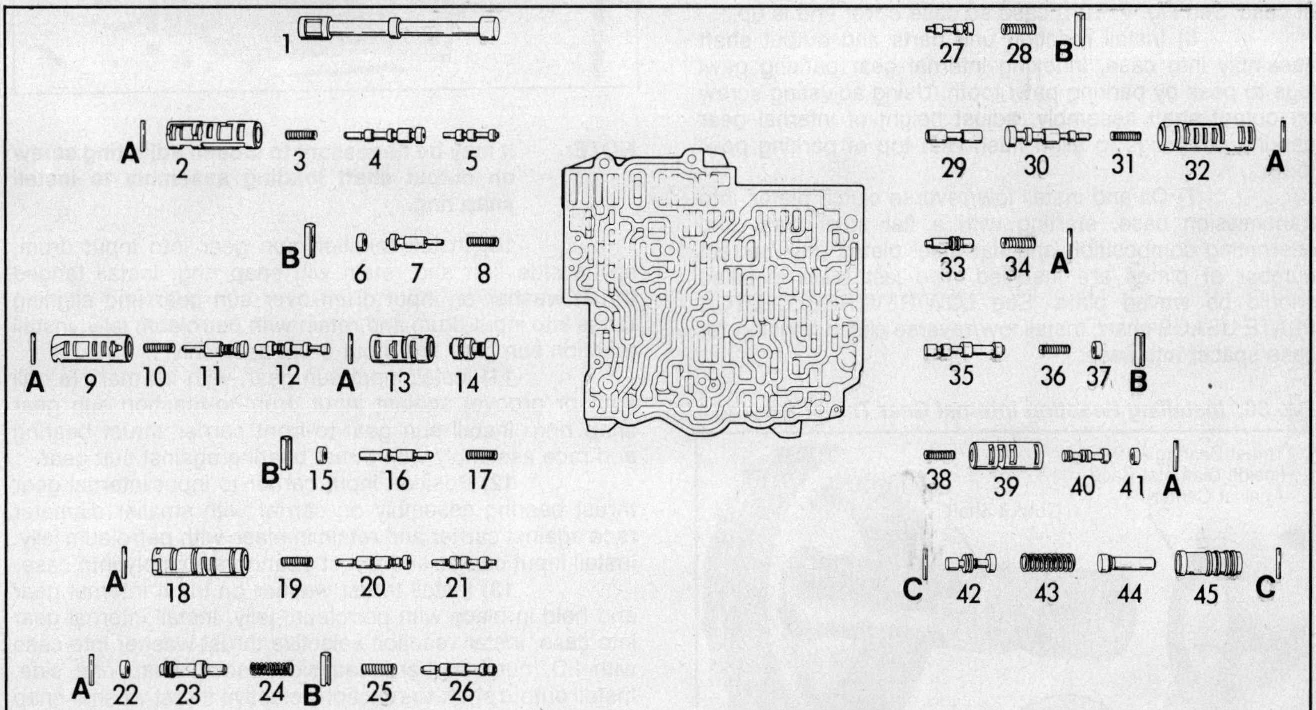

1. Manual Valve	17. M.T.V. Upshift Valve Spring	33. 4-3 Control Valve
2. 2-3 Throttle Valve Bushing	18. Converter Clutch Throttle Valve Bushing	34. 4-3 Control Valve Spring
3. 2-3 Valve Spring	19. Converter Clutch Throttle Valve Spring	35. Line Bias Valve
4. 2-3 Throttle Valve	20. Converter Clutch Throttle Valve	36. Line Bias Valve Spring
5. 2-3 Shift Valve	21. Converter Clutch Shift Valve	37. Bore Plug
6. Bore Plug	22. Bore Plug	38. Accumulator Valve Spring
7. M.T.V. Downshift Valve	23. Low/Overrun Clutch Valve	39. Accumulator Valve Bushing
8. M.T.V. Spring	24. Low/Overrun Clutch Valve Spring	40. Accumulator Bushing
9. 1-2 Throttle Valve Bushing	25. 3-2 Control Valve Spring	41. Bore Plug
10. 1-2 Valve Spring	26. 3-2 Control Valve	42. Throttle Valve
11. 1-2 Throttle Valve	27. T.V. Limit Valve	43. Throttle Valve Spring
12. Low-1st Detent	28. T.V. Limit Valve Spring	44. Throttle Valve Plunger
13. Low-1st Detent Valve Bushing	29. 3-4 Shift Valve	45. Throttle Valve Plunger Bushing
14. 1-2 Shift Valve	30. 3-4 Throttle Valve	A. Coiled Spring Pin/Zinc
15. Bore Plug	31. 3-4 Throttle Valve Tspring	B. Coiled Spring Pin/Plain
16. M.T.V. Upshift Valve	32. 3-4 Throttle Valve Bushing	C. Spring Retaining Sleeve

first. File any burrs or raised edges off manual shaft that could damage seal, then install shaft and inside detent lever assembly into case, making sure that shaft flats align with lever hole. Install hex nut on manual shaft and tighten.

NOTE: **If disassembly of manual valve link from inside detent lever is necessary, reassemble with a new push-on nut.**

3) Install parking lock cam and tighten bolts. Start strut shaft into case. Align parking lock strut and lever with parking shaft bore in case and verify that lower strut arm is positioned between lever tangs. Install strut shaft completely into case and install retaining ring. Install parking lock spring. Using a 3/8" (9.5 mm) rod, install new parking strut shaft cup plug, open end out, flush with face. Install manual detent roller and spring assembly and tighten bolt. Check for proper operation of parking lock assembly.

4) Install reaction internal gear, hub end first, on output shaft. Install internal gear-to-reaction sun gear thrust bearing assembly into internal gear by placing small diameter race over output shaft. See Fig. 36.

5) Install roller clutch and reaction carrier assembly into reaction internal gear. Install Output Shaft Aligning And Loading Assembly (J-26958) onto output end of case. See Fig. 4. Turn case so case cover end is up.

6) Install reaction unit parts and output shaft assembly into case, indexing internal gear parking pawl lugs to pass by parking pawl tooth. Using adjusting screw on output shaft assembly, adjust height of internal gear parking pawl lugs to align flush with top of parking pawl tooth.

7) Oil and install low/reverse clutch plates into transmission case, starting with a flat steel plate and alternating composition and flat steel plates until correct number of plates are installed. The last plate installed should be waved plate. See LOW/REVERSE CLUTCH PLATE USAGE chart. Install low/reverse clutch housing-to-case spacer into case.

Fig. 36: Installing Reaction Internal Gear Thrust Bearing

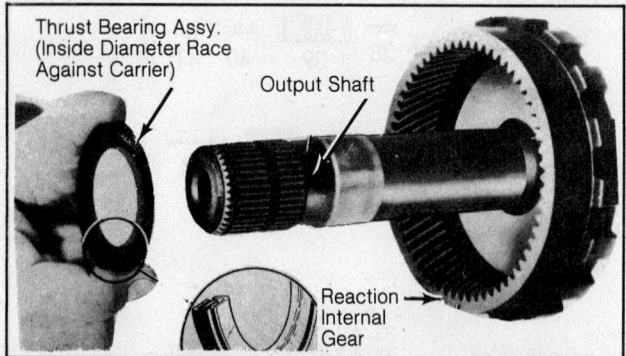

8) Install low/reverse clutch housing into case, aligning reverse clutch housing feed hole to reverse clutch case feed passage. If housing does not seat past case snap ring groove, proceed as follows:

9) Using reaction sun gear and input drum as a tool, install input drum and sun gear in case. Rotate reaction sun gear back and forth, tapping lightly with input drum, to align roller clutch race and low/reverse clutch hub splines. Remove drum and sun gear. If necessary repeat this procedure until clutch housing is fully seated. Install clutch housing-to-case snap ring, flat side against housing.

LOW/REVERSE CLUTCH PLATE USAGE

Application	Flat Steel	Composition
All Models	7 [1]	6

[1] – Plus 1 waved steel plate installed on top of last flat steel plate.

Fig. 37: Installing Low/Reverse Clutch-To-Transmission Case Spacer

Low/Reverse Clutch Housing-to-Case Spacer

NOTE: **It may be necessary to loosen adjusting screw on output shaft loading assembly to install snap ring.**

10) Install reaction sun gear into input drum, spline side first and retain wih snap ring. Install tanged thrust washer on input drum over sun gear end aligning tangs into input drum and retain with petroleum jelly. Install reaction sun gear and input drum assembly.

11) Install input sun gear, with I.D mark (a drill spot or groove) against input drum-to-reaction sun gear snap ring. Install sun gear-to-front carrier thrust bearing and race assembly with thrust bearing against sun gear.

12) Position input carrier-to-input internal gear thrust bearing assembly on carrier with smaller diameter race against carrier and retain in place with petroleum jelly. Install input carrier and thrust bearing assembly into case.

13) Install thrust washer on input internal gear and hold in place with petroleum jelly. Install internal gear into case. Install reaction selective thrust washer into case with I.D. number (hardened side) facing snap ring side. Install output shaft-to-reaction selective thrust washer snap ring on output shaft and ensure that it is fully seated in output shaft groove.

NOTE: **It may be necessary to move output shaft upward by tightening output shaft loading assembly adjusting screw to install snap ring.**

14) Before proceeding with transmission reassembly, recheck reaction unit end play to ensure that correct reaction selective thrust washer has been installed. See REACTION UNIT END PLAY in this article.

15) Install output shaft-to-input shaft selective thrust washer on end of output shaft and retain with petroleum jelly. Install intermediate band into case, locating anchor pin lug on anchor pin and apply lug in case slot.

GENERAL MOTORS TURBO HYDRA-MATIC 325-4L (Cont.)

Fig. 38: Installing Output Shaft-To-Reaction Selective Thrust Washer

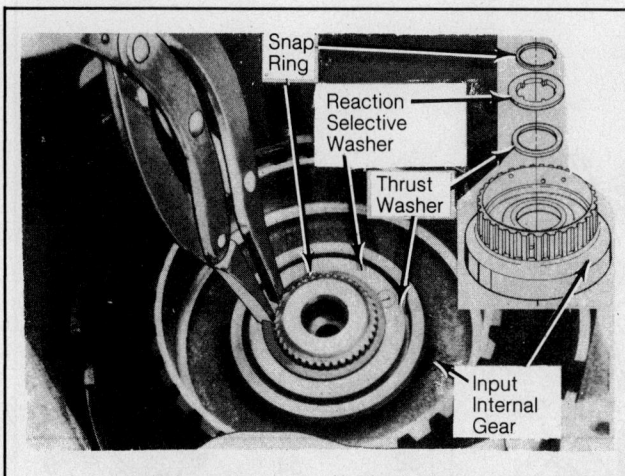

16) Position direct clutch assembly (clutch plate end up) over hole in work bench and align composition plate teeth one above the other. Install forward clutch assembly (input shaft first) into direct clutch. Hold direct clutch and rotate forward clutch back and forth until seated.

NOTE: **When forward clutch is seated, it will be approximately 5/8" (15.8 mm) from tang end of direct clutch housing to end of forward clutch drum.**

17) Install direct and forward clutch assemblies into case and rotate into position. When correctly installed, direct clutch housing will be approximately 7/16" (11 mm) from case cover face.

18) Install thrust washer on hub of driven sprocket support and ensure tabs on washer engage holes in hub. Retain washer in place with petroleum jelly. If removed, install oil seal rings into grooves in hub of driven sprocket support. Install case cover assembly on transmission using a new gasket, then install and tighten attaching bolts.

CAUTION: **If input shaft cannot be rotated as case cover is bolted into place, forward or direct clutch housing has not been installed properly to index with clutch plates. This condition must be corrected before case cover is pulled fully into place.**

19) Recheck input unit end play at this time to ensure correct output shaft-to-input shaft selective thrust washer has been installed. See INPUT SHAFT END PLAY in this article. Remove output shaft aligning and loading assembly from rear of case.

20) Mount 2 guide pins into opposing pump attaching bolt holes. Align guide pins with bolt holes in pump body, then install pump assembly into case. Install and tighten pump attaching bolts.

21) If removed, install new oil seal rings on turbine shaft. Place drive link around drive and driven sprockets so that links engage teeth of sprockets. The colored guide link which has etched numerals, faces sprocket cover.

NOTE: **Turbine shaft may appear not to be pressed fully into sprockets. Do not attempt pressing shaft into sprockets further as a specific**

length dimension is held during initial assembly.

22) Place drive link and sprocket assembly into sprocket support. Using a plastic mallet, gently seat sprocket bearing assemblies into sprocket supports. Install sprockets-to-sprocket support snap ring. Install 4th clutch housing and attaching bolts.

23) Install overdrive internal gear, overrun clutch and overdrive carrier assembly units into 4th clutch housing. Install sprocket cover, thrust washers, snap ring and 4th clutch snap ring. Recheck overdrive unit end play. See OVERRUN CLUTCH & OVERDRIVE CARRIER in this article.

24) Rotate transmission in holding fixture so oil pan side is down. If removed, install new seal ring on governor shaft and place seal ring end into pilot hole in case to size seal, then lubricate seal wih petroleum jelly. Install speedometer drive gear on governor shaft (weight side) and ensure slot in gear aligns with pin in shaft. Install drive gear-to-governor cover thrust washer.

25) Install governor and speedometer drive gear assembly (governor gear end first) into case. Install new "O" ring seal on governor cover, then install cover and ensure governor shaft aligns with hole in cover. Install cover attaching bolts. Install speedometer driven gear assembly, bolt and retaining clip, and tighten bolt.

26) Install intermediate servo piston assembly into servo cover. Lubricate with petroleum jelly and install new seal rings on cover. Install servo assembly into case, tapping lightly with a plastic mallet, if necessary. Using a compressor, compress servo cover and install retaining ring.

NOTE: **When installing servo assembly into case, ensure tapered end of band apply pin is properly located against band apply lug.**

27) Place a new low/reverse clutch housing-to-case cup plug (rubber end first) into hole in case. Ensure cup plug is located properly. *See Fig. 13.* Using a 3/8" (9.5 mm) diameter by 6" metal rod and hammer, drive plug until it seats against low/reverse clutch housing.

28) Install check balls in proper locations, then install 2 guide pins. Position spacer plate to case gasket, on case. Place valve body spacer plate on gasket marked "CB". Place spacer plate to control valve assembly gasket marked "VB" on valve body.

29) Install 1 check ball into ball seat pocket in control valve assembly and retain with petroleum jelly. Install control valve assembly using 2 pins as guides. Start 2 case bolts and remove guide pins. Install 1-2 accumulator piston with new seal on piston. Install 3-4 accumulator piston with new seal on piston. Install manual valve link into manual valve. Install throttle lever and bracket assembly.

30) Install wiring and oil pipes. All pipes must be fully seated. Install electrical connectors with lock tabs facing into case. Install, and tighten remaining control valve assembly retaining bolts.

31) Install pressure regulator, bushing, spring assembly, reverse boost valve, bushing, M.T.V. boost valve and bushing into case. Compress all 3 valve assemblies and install retaining snap ring.

32) Install clutch converter valve, short stem first, into valve bushing. Install spring and valve assembly into case. Retain with snap ring.

33) Install new "O" ring seal on intake pipe of oil screen and lubricate "O" ring with petroleum jelly. Install oil screen assembly into case. Using a new gasket, install oil pan on case and tighten attaching bolts.

Fig. 39: Overdrive & Drive Link Components

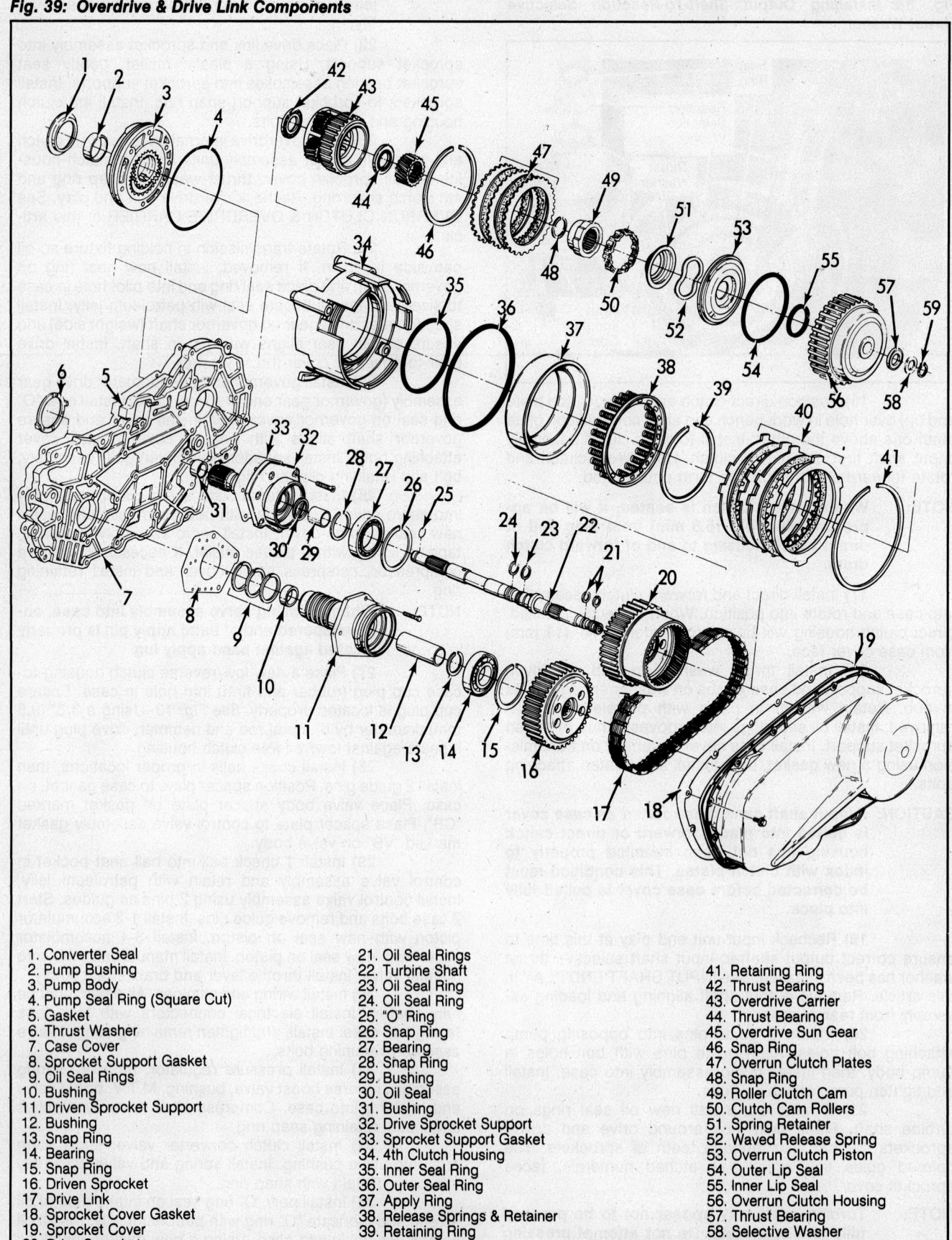

1. Converter Seal
2. Pump Bushing
3. Pump Body
4. Pump Seal Ring (Square Cut)
5. Gasket
6. Thrust Washer
7. Case Cover
8. Sprocket Support Gasket
9. Oil Seal Rings
10. Bushing
11. Driven Sprocket Support
12. Bushing
13. Snap Ring
14. Bearing
15. Snap Ring
16. Driven Sprocket
17. Drive Link
18. Sprocket Cover Gasket
19. Sprocket Cover
20. Drive Sprocket

21. Oil Seal Rings
22. Turbine Shaft
23. Oil Seal Ring
24. Oil Seal Ring
25. "O" Ring
26. Snap Ring
27. Bearing
28. Snap Ring
29. Bushing
30. Oil Seal
31. Bushing
32. Drive Sprocket Support
33. Sprocket Support Gasket
34. 4th Clutch Housing
35. Inner Seal Ring
36. Outer Seal Ring
37. Apply Ring
38. Release Springs & Retainer
39. Retaining Ring
40. 4th Clutch Plates

41. Retaining Ring
42. Thrust Bearing
43. Overdrive Carrier
44. Thrust Bearing
45. Overdrive Sun Gear
46. Snap Ring
47. Overrun Clutch Plates
48. Snap Ring
49. Roller Clutch Cam
50. Clutch Cam Rollers
51. Spring Retainer
52. Waved Release Spring
53. Overrun Clutch Piston
54. Outer Lip Seal
55. Inner Lip Seal
56. Overrun Clutch Housing
57. Thrust Bearing
58. Selective Washer
59. Snap Ring

Fig. 40: Throttle Lever and Bracket Assembly

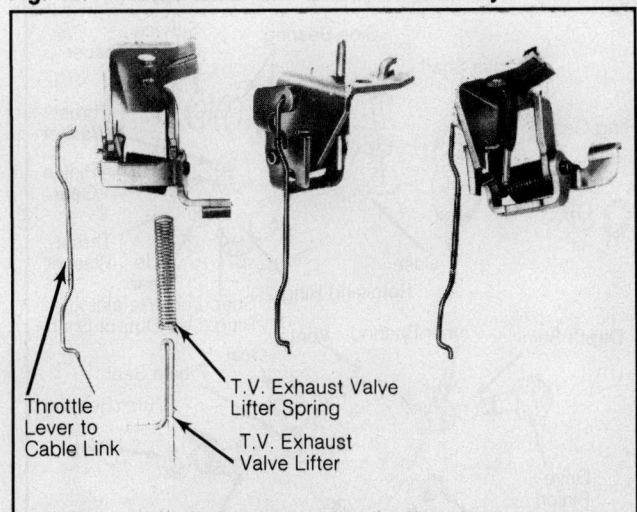

Throttle Lever to Cable Link

T.V. Exhaust Valve Lifter Spring

T.V. Exhaust Valve Lifter

Fig. 41: Installing Throttle Valve and Bracket

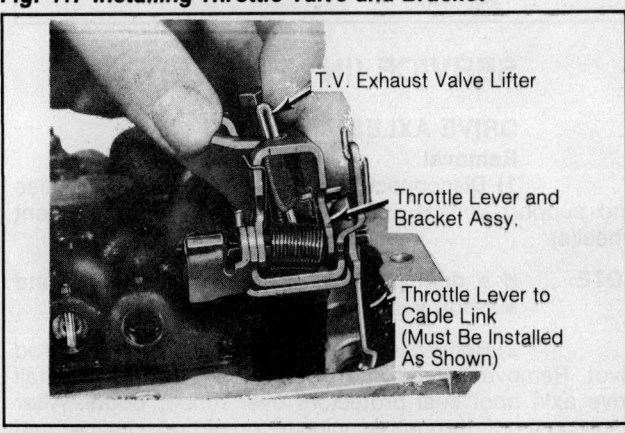

T.V. Exhaust Valve Lifter

Throttle Lever and Bracket Assy.

Throttle Lever to Cable Link (Must Be Installed As Shown)

TIGHTENING SPECIFICATIONS

Application	Ft. Lbs. (N.m)
Case Cover Bolts	18 (24)
Converter-To-Flywheel	41-52 (55-70)
Cooler Connector	28 (38)
Detent Spring Assy.-To-Case	11 (15)
Driven Sprocket-To-Case Cover	18 (24)
Final Drive-To-Transmission	30 (41)
Fourth Clutch Housing-To-Case	18 (24)
Manual Shaft-To-Inside Detent Lever	23 (31)
Oil Pan-To-Case	10 (13)
Transmission-To-Engine	35 (48)
Valve Body-To-Case	11 (15)

Application	INCH Lbs. (N.m)
Cam-To-Manual Shaft	108 (12)
Governor Cover-To-Case	96 (11)
Line Pressure Take-Off	120 (14)
Pressure Switch	120 (14)
Sprocket Cover-To-Case	108 (13)

Automatic Transmission
GENERAL MOTORS TURBO HYDRA-MATIC 325-4L FINAL DRIVE

Buick Riviera
Cadillac Eldorado & Seville
Oldsmobile Toronado

DESCRIPTION

Front wheel final drive assembly is mounted on and splined directly to THM 325-4L automatic transaxle. Unit consists of a pinion drive gear, ring gear and differential case assembly.

Torque from final drive unit is transmitted to output shafts, which are connected to drive axles. Output shafts are splined to final drive side gears. Drive axles are flexible assemblies consisting of axle shafts and inner and outer constant velocity joints.

AXLE RATIO & IDENTIFICATION

Axle ratio code and build date are stamped on left side of housing cover mounting surface. Axle ratio can be identified by last 3 letters in code number. See AXLE RATIO IDENTIFICATION chart.

AXLE RATIO IDENTIFICATION

Axle Ratio	Code	No. of Teeth [1] Pinion/Ring
2.73:1	4ML	15-41
2.93:1	4MK	14-41
3.15:1	4MM	13-41
3.36:1	4MN	14-47

[1] - Ring gear is 8" (204 mm) on all models.

Fig. 1: Axle Ratio Code Location

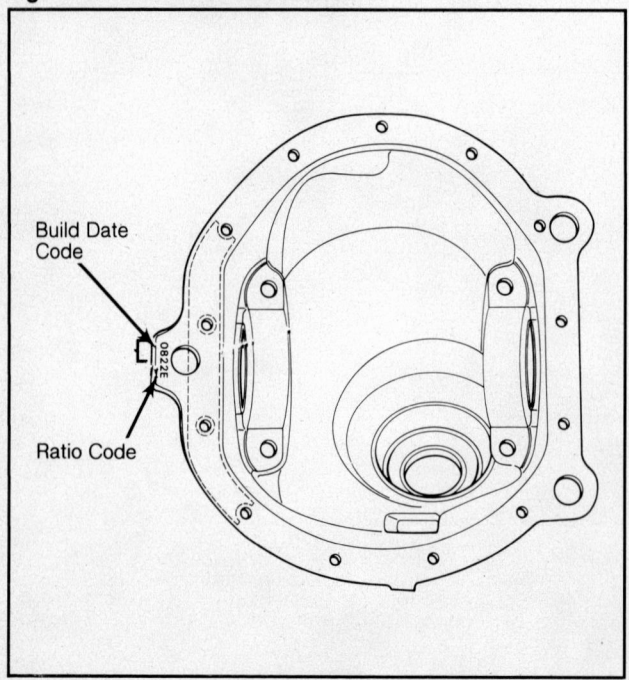

Build Date Code

Ratio Code

Fig. 2: Exploded View of Final Drive Assembly

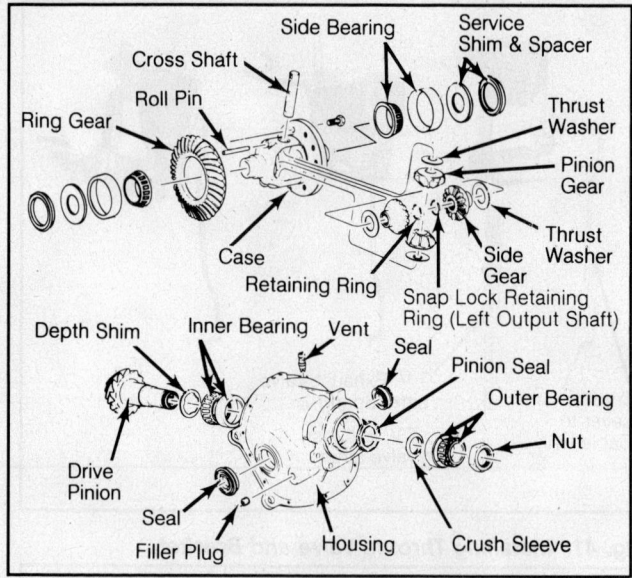

Side Bearing — Service Shim & Spacer — Cross Shaft — Roll Pin — Ring Gear — Thrust Washer — Pinion Gear — Thrust Washer — Side Gear — Snap Lock Retaining Ring (Left Output Shaft) — Case — Retaining Ring — Depth Shim — Inner Bearing — Vent — Seal — Pinion Seal — Outer Bearing — Nut — Drive Pinion — Seal — Filler Plug — Housing — Crush Sleeve

SERVICE (IN VEHICLE)

DRIVE AXLES
Removal

1) Disconnect battery negative cable(s). Raise and support vehicle under frame horns. Remove front wheel(s).

NOTE: If a dual post-type hoist is used, raise and support vehicle, then lower front post.

2) Remove cotter pin, nut and shield from tie rod pivot. Remove tie rod end from steering knuckle. Install drive axle boot seal protectors over rubber boots. After inserting a drift through opening in top of brake caliper and into vane of brake rotor to keep axle from turning, remove cotter pin, retainer, nut and washer from drive axle.

3) Remove drive axle-to-output shaft attaching bolts. Remove cotter pin and nut from upper ball joint, pushing drive axle inward to gain access to nut. Pull brake hose clip off of ball joint stud and loosely reinstall nut.

4) Using hammer and brass drift, pound downward on steering knuckle to unseat ball joint stud. It may be necessary to pry upward on upper control arm. Remove nut and separate upper ball joint from steering knuckle. Guide drive axle out of knuckle and remove from vehicle.

CAUTION: Do not stretch or pull on brake hose.

Installation
To install, reverse removal procedure.

OUTPUT SHAFTS

NOTE: If both right and left output shafts and/or seals are to be removed or replaced, final drive assembly should be removed from vehicle.

Removal

1) Remove drive axle from vehicle. On right output shaft, remove 2 bolts attaching battery cable retainer to support and 2 bolts attaching output shaft support to engine. On both output shafts, remove front nut and bolt from frame brace. Rotate frame brace outward for access.

Automatic Transmission
GENERAL MOTORS TURBO HYDRA-MATIC 325-4L FINAL DRIVE (Cont.)

2-323

2) Use a hammer and a large brass drift to tap on flanged end of output shaft until shaft comes out of retaining ring. Carefully guide shaft from vehicle. Use a small pry bar to remove shaft seal from housing and discard seal.

NOTE: Pry shaft seal at 2 or 3 different locations to avoid cocking seal and damaging housing.

Installation

1) Install new output shaft seal, and apply clean wheel bearing grease between seal lips. Being careful not to damage seal, index output shaft splines with side gear splines and use a soft hammer to tap on center of flanged end of shaft until shaft snaps into place.

NOTE: Check spline fit to ensure that there will be no drive line clunk. Do not let shaft and support assembly hang in final drive unit or align shaft off center in seal, as damage to seal may result.

2) On right output shaft, align shaft support with holes in engine block, loosely install bolts and washers. Move flanged end of shaft up and down and back and forth to find center location, then fully tighten bolts.

3) Install battery cable retainer to support with 2 bolts. On both output shafts, install drive axle and restore frame brace to original position.

RIGHT OUTPUT SHAFT SUPPORT BEARING
Removal

Remove right output shaft and support assembly from vehicle. Remove 3 self-tapping bolts attaching bearing retainer to support. Slide split halves of bearing remover between flanged end of output shaft and flat area of shaft support and tighten bolts. Press shaft support, bearing, retainer and slinger off of output shaft as an assembly.

Fig. 3: Right Output Shaft and Support Bearing Assembly

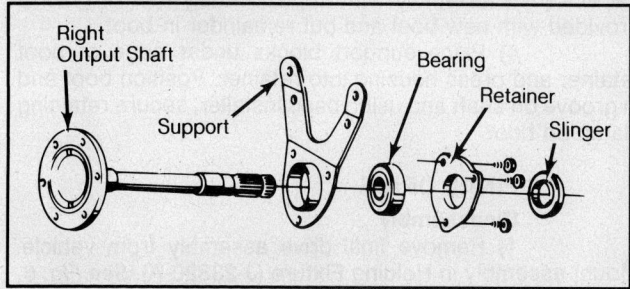

Installation

Pack bearing with wheel bearing grease and install in output shaft support. Install retainer and secure using 3 self-tapping bolts. Place assembled parts and slinger on output shaft. Press bearing and assembled parts on shaft until seated. Check for free bearing rotation and install output shaft and support on vehicle.

FINAL DRIVE ASSEMBLY
Removal

1) Disconnect battery negative cable(s). Raise and support vehicle under frame horns. Remove right and left frame brace front attaching bolts and rotate braces outward to gain access. Loosen final drive cover bolts and

drain lubricant, then remove bolts and cover. Install drive axle boot seal protectors.

NOTE: If a dual post-type hoist is used, raise and support vehicle, then lower front post.

2) Remove drive axle-to-output shaft attaching bolts and separate output shaft and drive axle flanges to provide clearance for final drive removal. Remove 2 bolts attaching battery cable retainer to right output shaft support and 2 bolts attaching support to engine. Rotate support downward for clearance during removal.

3) Remove final drive-to-transmission bolt attaching rear of final drive shield to transmission and loosen final drive support bracket screw attaching front of shield to final drive. Slide shield outward and forward to remove from vehicle.

Fig. 4: Attachment of Final Drive Assembly

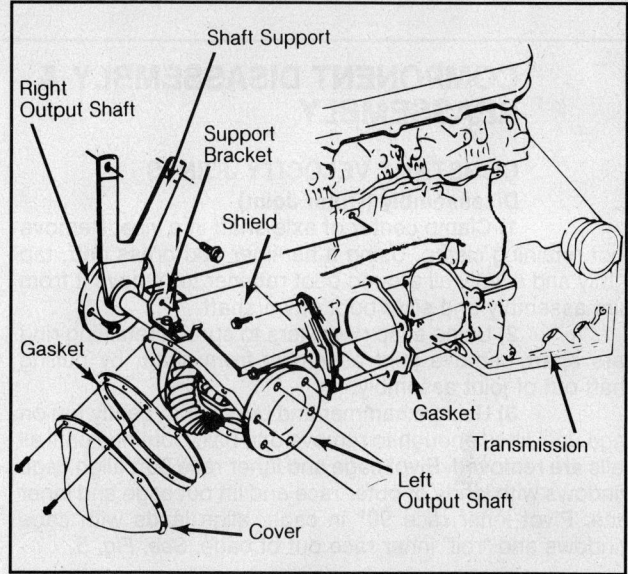

4) Remove final drive support bracket-to-engine block bolt and 5 remaining final drive-to-transmission bolts. Separate steering linkage intermediate shaft from pitman and idler arms and push linkage toward front of vehicle. Using a transmission jack, slide final drive assembly forward, off of transmission splined shaft and remove unit from vehicle with output shafts attached.

CAUTION: Do not use output shafts as "handles" to maneuver or support final drive assembly. Damage to splines or seals may occur.

Installation

Position new final drive-to-transmission gasket on final drive. To complete installation, reverse removal procedure and note the following:

- Tie arm of right hand output shaft support to hole in shaft flange closest to twelve o'clock position.
- To ensure proper alignment of right output shaft, loosely install support bolts, move output shaft flange end up and down and back and forth to find central location, and tighten bolts.

2-324

Automatic Transmission
GENERAL MOTORS TURBO HYDRA-MATIC 325-4L FINAL DRIVE (Cont.)

Fig. 5: Front Drive Axle Assembly

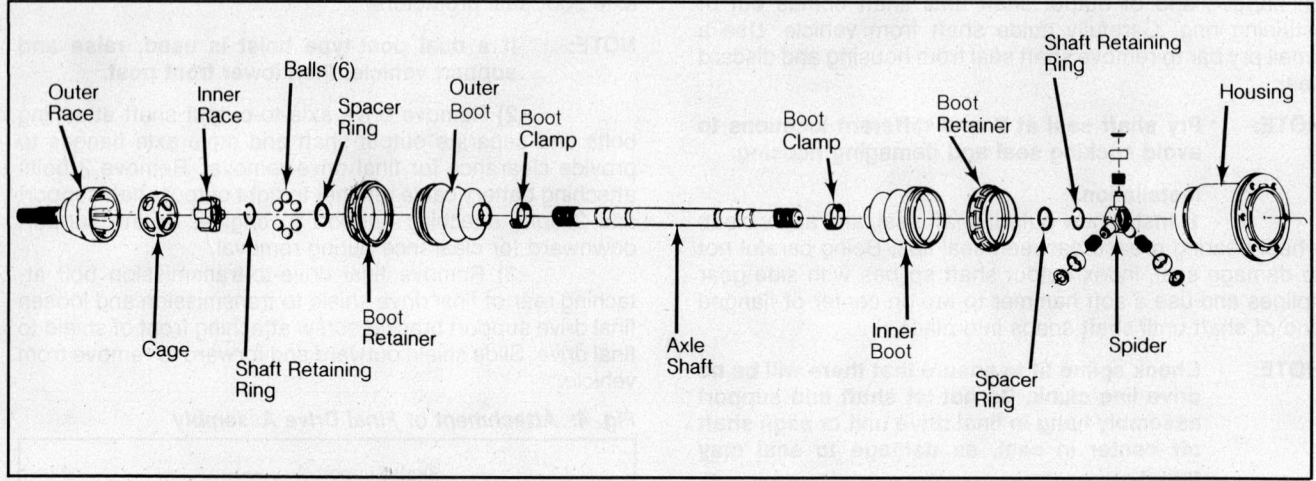

COMPONENT DISASSEMBLY & REASSEMBLY

CONSTANT VELOCITY JOINTS
Disassembly (Outer Joint)
1) Clamp center of axle shaft in a vise. Remove boot retaining clamp. Using a hammer and brass drift, tap lightly and evenly all around boot retainer to remove it from joint assembly and slide boot down shaft.

2) Using snap ring pliers to spread retaining ring ears apart, remove joint assembly from shaft, by pulling shaft out of joint assembly.

3) Using a hammer and brass drift, gently tap on cage until tilted enough to remove one ball. Continue until all balls are removed. Pivot cage and inner race 90°, align cage windows with lands of outer race and lift out cage and inner race. Pivot inner race 90° in cage, align lands with cage windows and "roll" inner race out of cage. See. Fig. 5.

Reassembly
1) Place a light coat of grease on ball grooves of inner and outer races. To complete installation of cage, reverse disassembly procedure. After cage is reassembled, go to step 2).

NOTE: **Retaining ring side of inner race must face axle shaft.**

2) Slide boot retaining clamp, boot and boot retainer onto shaft. Push joint assembly onto shaft until race retaining ring is fully seated in groove.

3) Coat inside of boot lip with grease and slide lip into boot retainer. Repack joint assembly with approximately half of grease provided with new boot and put remainder in boot. Place support blocks under edge of boot retainer and press joint assembly into retainer. Position boot end in groove on shaft and, secure boot retaining clamp on boot.

Disassembly (Inner Joint)
1) Clamp center of axle shaft in a vise. Use side cutters to remove boot retaining clamp. Using a hammer and brass drift, tap lightly and evenly all around boot retainer to remove it from housing and slide boot down shaft. Pull housing off shaft.

2) Using snap ring pliers to slide spacer ring back, remove spider assembly from shaft. Slide spider assembly back to expose shaft retaining ring. Remove ring and pull spider assembly off shaft.

Reassembly
1) Slide boot retaining clamp, boot and boot retainer onto shaft. Repack housing with approximately half of grease provided with new boot and put remainder in boot.

2) Slide spacer ring onto shaft about 4". Hold spider assembly with counterbore facing away from shaft and slide assembly onto shaft beyond shaft retaining ring groove on end of shaft. Install shaft retaining ring in groove. Slide spider assembly back toward end of shaft until it locks in place over retaining ring. Slide spacer ring toward end of shaft until it contacts spider and seat it in groove.

NOTE: **Raised ring on spider assembly must face axle shaft.**

3) Slide housing over spider assembly. Coat inside of boot lip with grease and slide lip into boot retainer. Repack joint assembly with approximately half of grease provided with new boot and put remainder in boot.

4) Place support blocks under edge of boot retainer and press housing into retainer. Position boot end in groove on shaft and using band installer, secure retaining clamp on boot.

FINAL DRIVE
Disassembly
1) Remove final drive assembly from vehicle. Mount assembly in Holding Fixture (J-23320-A). See Fig. 6.

NOTE: **Before disassembling unit, check and record ring gear-to-pinion backlash, total drive pinion preload torque and ring gear runout.**

2) Mark bearing caps for reference at reassembly. Remove cap bolts and bearing caps. Using pry bar, remove differential case by prying against ring gear bolt. Mark shims for reference at reassembly.

3) Remove all but 2 ring gear-to-case bolts, leaving them loosely installed 180° apart. Remove ring gear from case by alternately tapping on these 2 bolts. See Fig. 7.

4) If differential side bearings are to be replaced, remove using a puller or press. Using a punch and hammer, drive pinion cross shaft roll pin out of differential case and

Automatic Transmission
GENERAL MOTORS TURBO HYDRA-MATIC 325-4L FINAL DRIVE (Cont.)

2-325

Fig. 6: Mounting Fixture & Base

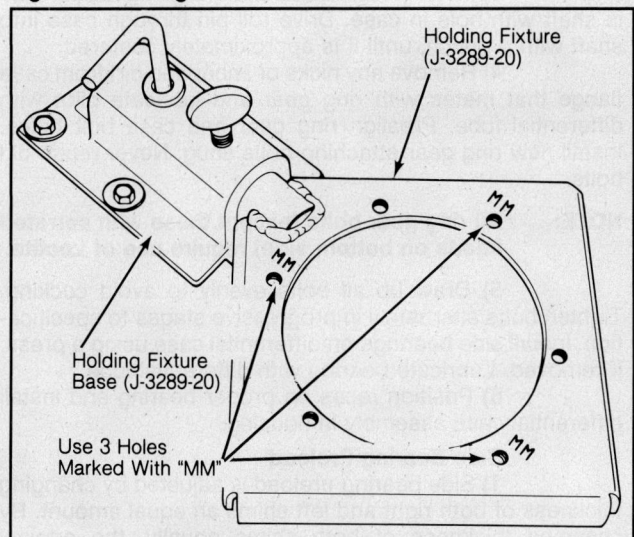

Fig. 7: Removing Ring Gear

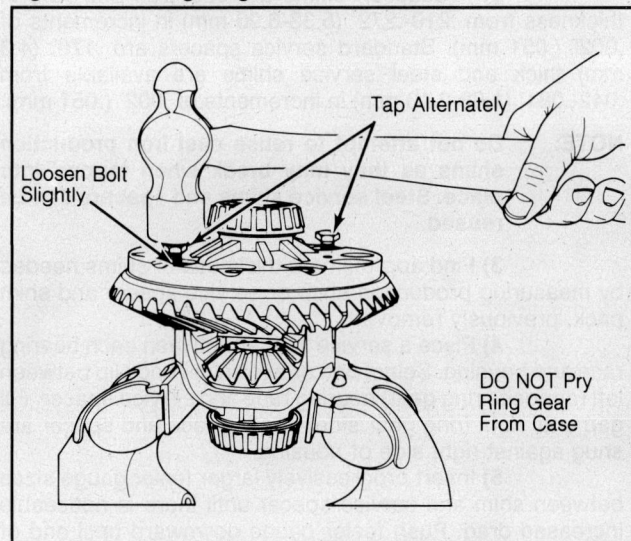

remove pinion cross shaft. Remove pinion gears, side gears and washers by rotating gears to opening in case and removing. Mark pinion gears, side gears and washers for reference at reassembly.

5) Check pinion bearing preload using Spline Adapter (J-28513) and 3/8" drive torque wrench. Record reading. To remove pinion nut, hold nut while turning pinion CLOCKWISE with spline adapter. Remove pinion by threading original nut partially onto pinion to protect threads and tap with hammer to free pinion. *See Fig. 8.*

6) Remove nut, outer bearing, crush sleeve and pinion. Using hammer and drift, drive pinion seal out of housing, toward inside of housing. Drive pinion outer bearing race outward (from inside of housing).

NOTE: Ensure drain hole is not plugged when replacing pinion oil seal.

7) Remove pinion inner bearing race by installing Bearing Race Remover (J-28512) between housing bore and race. Attach bearing race remover to slide hammer and tap race out. Using Bearing Remover (J-9746-02) and a

press, press pinion shaft from inner bearing and note thickness of pinion depth shim.

Fig. 8: Removing or Installing Pinion Nut

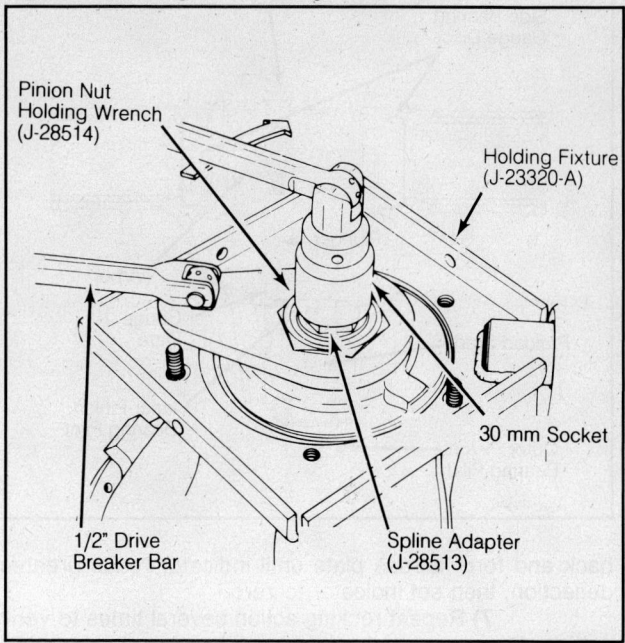

Cleaning & Inspection

Wash all parts in solvent or mineral spirits. Dry thoroughly using dry, compressed air. Using a clean cloth, wipe inside of housing clean. Inspect all parts for chips, nicks and excessive wear. Replace parts as necessary.

Pinion Depth Setting

1) If original ring gear, pinion and inner pinion bearing are to be reinstalled, original shim thickness may be used. If installing new components, go to step **2)**.

CAUTION: Inner pinion bearing race is used as a stop gauge for pinion oil seal installer. Inner race MUST be installed before pinion seal. If race is not correctly seated, seal may leak.

2) Clean housing assembly and all gauge parts to ensure accurate measurements. If removed, install pinion bearing races and install lubricated pinion bearings in their races.

NOTE: Use Pinion Gauge Set (J-21777-75) to obtain proper pinion depth setting.

3) Position inner pinion bearing pilot on short threaded end of preload stud. Thread gauge plate onto stud and tighten against pilot. Insert stud through inner and outer bearings. Install outer pinion bearing pilot and nut. Rotate bearings to ensure proper seating. Tighten nut until 20 INCH lbs. (2.26 N.m) are required to rotate bearings.

4) Mount side bearing gauging discs on ends of arbor with smaller steps facing out. Place assembly in housing, making sure discs are properly seated. Install bearing caps and bolts finger tight to prevent movement.

5) Install dial indicator on mounting post of arbor. The contact button must rest on top surface of plunger. Preload dial indicator 1/2 revolution and tighten in this position.

6) Rotate gauge plate until plunger rests squarely on flat surface of plate. Rock plunger rod slowly

2-326

Automatic Transmission
GENERAL MOTORS TURBO HYDRA-MATIC 325-4L FINAL DRIVE (Cont.)

Fig. 9: Pinion Depth Gauge Installation

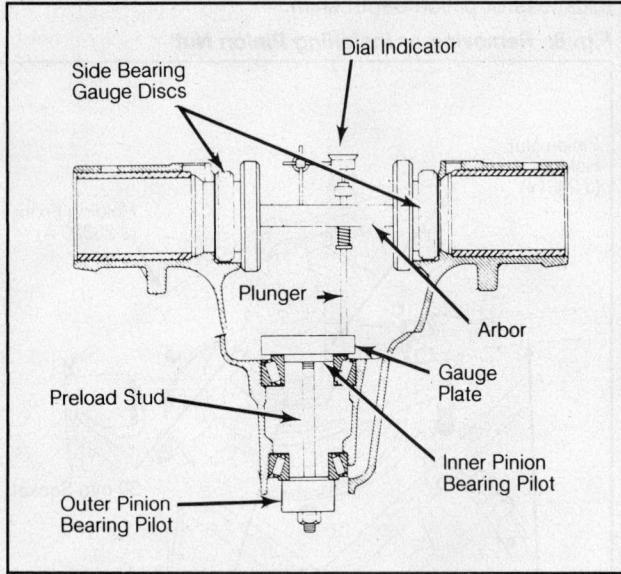

back and forth across plate until indicator reads greatest deflection, then set indicator to zero.

7) Repeat rocking action several times to verify setting. After zero reading is obtained, swing plunger until it is removed from gauge plate. Dial indicator will now read required pinion shim thickness.

8) Remove bearing caps and gauge assembly from housing. Place selected shim pack on pinion and install lubricated bearing onto pinion shaft using a press.

Pinion Installation & Preload Adjustment

1) Install pinion seal in housing and lubricate with transmission fluid. Lubricate inner bearing with differential lube, install seal protector on pinion and position pinion in housing.

2) Lubricate outer pinion bearing with transmission fluid and install new crush sleeve, outer pinion bearing and nut (finger tight) on pinion shaft.

3) Using spline adapter and holding wrench, tighten pinion nut until end play begins to be taken up. (Turning spline adapter COUNTERCLOCKWISE tightens nut). See Fig. 8.

4) When no further end play is felt, use spline adapter and 3/8" drive torque wrench to check preload. Continue tightening nut and checking preload until specified preload is obtained.

CAUTION: If preload is exceeded, a new crush sleeve must be installed and nut retightened to obtain proper preload.

Case Reassembly

1) Install thrust washers and side gears into case. If original parts are being reused, install in original positions. Install output shaft retaining ring in machined groove of left side gear, before installing gears in case.

2) Position pinions and thrust washers through loading hole in case 180° apart so that they engage side gears. Rotate gears until differential pinion bores and case cross shaft bores are aligned.

3) Install pinion cross shaft, aligning roll pin hole in shaft with hole in case. Drive roll pin through case into shaft with a punch, until it is approximately centered.

4) Remove any nicks or imbedded dirt from case flange that mates with ring gear and lubricate pilot with differential lube. Prealign ring gear and case bolt holes. Install new ring gear attaching bolts snug. Never reuse old bolts.

NOTE: All ring gear bolts (except those with serrated heads on bottom side) require use of Loctite.

5) Draw up all bolts evenly to avoid cocking. Tighten bolts alternately in progressive stages to specification. Install side bearings on differential case using a press, if removed. Lubricate bearing with differential lube.

6) Position races on proper bearing and install differential case assembly in housing.

Side Bearing Preload

1) Side bearing preload is adjusted by changing thickness of both right and left shims an equal amount. By changing thickness of both shims equally, the original backlash will be maintained.

2) Production shims are cast iron and vary in thickness from .210-.272" (5.33-6.90 mm) in increments of .002" (.051 mm). Standard service spacers are .170" (4.3 mm) thick and steel service shims are available from .042-.084" (1.08-2.13 mm) in increments of .002" (.051 mm).

NOTE: Do not attempt to reuse cast iron production shims as they may break when tapped into place. Steel service shims and spacers can be reused.

3) Find approximate thickness of shims needed by measuring production shim or service spacer and shim pack, previously removed.

4) Place a service spacer between each bearing race and housing. Select one or two shims and slip between left (opposite ring gear) bearing race and service spacer. Fill gap until right (ring gear side) bearing race and spacer are snug against right side of housing.

5) Insert progressively larger feeler gauge sizes between shim and service spacer until there is noticeable increased drag. Push feeler gauge downward until end of gauge makes contact with housing, to obtain an accurate reading.

6) Light drag is caused by weight of case against housing, while heavy drag is caused by side bearing preload. By starting with a thin feeler gauge, a sense of "feel" is obtained so that beginning of preload can be recognized to obtain zero clearance.

7) The point just before additional drag is felt, is correct feeler gauge thickness. The total shim pack needed (with no preload) is this feeler gauge reading plus thickness of shims used in step 4).

8) Select two shims of about equal size which have a total thickness equal to value obtained in step 7). Install these shims between each side bearing race and service spacer on right and left sides.

Ring Gear & Pinion Backlash

1) Mount dial indicator on axle housing. Check backlash at 4 locations around ring gear. Variation should not exceed .002" (.05 mm). New gear backlash should be as specified. If old gears are reinstalled, reset backlash to reading recorded before disassembly.

GENERAL MOTORS TURBO HYDRA-MATIC 325-4L FINAL DRIVE (Cont.)

Fig. 10: Determining Side Bearing Shim Requirements

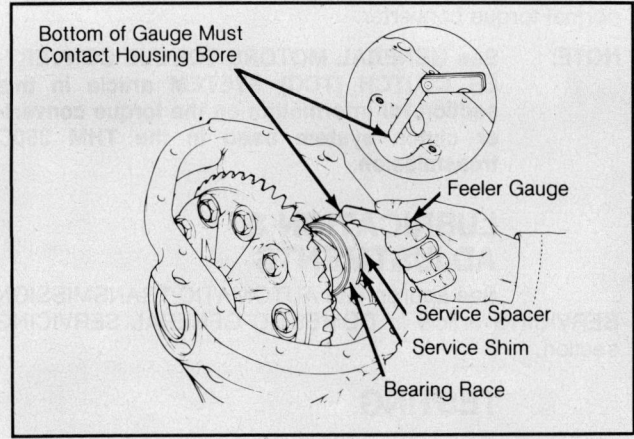

Bottom of Gauge Must Contact Housing Bore

Feeler Gauge

Service Spacer

Service Shim

Bearing Race

2) To adjust backlash, increase thickness of 1 shim and decrease thickness of opposite shim by equal amount until correct reading is obtained. Install bearing caps, recheck backlash and readjust if necessary.

AXLE ASSEMBLY SPECIFICATIONS

Application	Specification
Side Bearing Preload ... [1] Slip Fit Plus .006" (.16 mm)
Pinion Bearing Preload	
Used Bearings	[2]
New Bearings	18-24 INCH lbs. (2-2.7 N.m)
Ring Gear-to-Pinion Backlash	
Used Gears	[3]
New Gears	.005-.009" (.13-.23 mm)
Capacity	3.2 Pts. (1.5L)

[1] – Add .003" (.08 mm) to each side after setting backlash.
[2] – Pre-disassembly reading plus 5 INCH lbs. (.6 N.m)
[3] – Restore to pre-disassembly reading.

TIGHTENING SPECIFICATIONS

Application	Ft. Lbs. (N.m)
Bearing Cap Bolts	52 (70)
Drive Axle-To-Output Shaft Bolts	61 (82)
Drive Axle Nut	176 (238)
Final Drive Shield (Diesel Only)	33 (45)
Final Drive Support Bracket-to-Engine	
All Except 4.1L V8	70 (95)
4.1L V8	35 (47)
Final Drive Support Bracket-to-Housing	33 (45)
Final Drive-To-Transmission Bolts	30 (41)
Housing Cover Bolts	7 (10)
Lower Control Arm Bushing Bolt	86 (120)
Output Shaft Support-to-Engine Bolts	
All Except 4.1L V8	50 (68)
4.1L V8	29 (39)
Ring Gear-to-Case Bolts	96 (130)
Tie Rod-to-Steering Knuckle Nut	40 (54)
Upper Control Arm Bushing Bolt	70 (95)

Automatic Transmissions
GENERAL MOTORS TURBO HYDRA-MATIC 350C

Chevrolet, GMC

IDENTIFICATION

The Turbo Hydra-Matic 350C transmission can be identified by the two letter code stamped near the dipstick tube on the right hand side. See TRANSMISSION MODEL CODES for a list of the two letter codes used.

TRANSMISSION MODEL CODES

Application	Model Code
All Models	XA, XX

DESCRIPTION

The Turbo Hydra-Matic 350C transmission is a fully automatic unit consisting primarily of a 4-element torque converter and 2 planetary gear sets. Four multiple-disc clutches, 2 roller clutches and an intermediate overrun band provide the friction elements required to obtain the desired function of the 2 planetary gear sets.

A hydraulic system pressurized by a gear type pump provides the working pressure required to operate the friction elements and automatic controls. The torque converter clutch assembly consists of a 3-element torque converter with the addition of a converter clutch.

The converter clutch is splined to the turbine assembly, and when operated, applies against the converter cover, providing mechanical direct drive coupling of the engine to the transmission planetary gears. When the converter clutch is released, the assembly operates as a normal torque converter.

NOTE: See GENERAL MOTORS TORQUE CONVERTER CLUTCH (TCC) SYSTEM article in this section for information on the torque converter clutch system used in the THM 350C transmission.

LUBRICATION & ADJUSTMENTS

See appropriate AUTOMATIC TRANSMISSION SERVICING article in DOMESTIC GENERAL SERVICING section.

TESTING

ROAD TEST
Drive Range

With selector lever in "D", accelerate vehicle from zero MPH. A 1-2 and 2-3 shift should occur at all throttle openings. (Shift points will vary with throttle openings.) As vehicle speed decreases to zero MPH, 3-2 and 2-1 shifts should occur.

"2" – Forward Range (L2)

Place selector lever in "2" and accelerate vehicle from zero MPH. A 1-2 shift should occur at all throttle openings. No 2-3 shift can be obtained in this range. The 1-2 shift point will vary with throttle opening. As vehicle speed decreases to zero MPH, a 2-1 shift should occur. The 1-2 shift in intermediate range may be somewhat firmer than in Drive range; this is normal.

Fig. 1: Sectional View of Turbo Hydra-Matic 350C Automatic Transmission

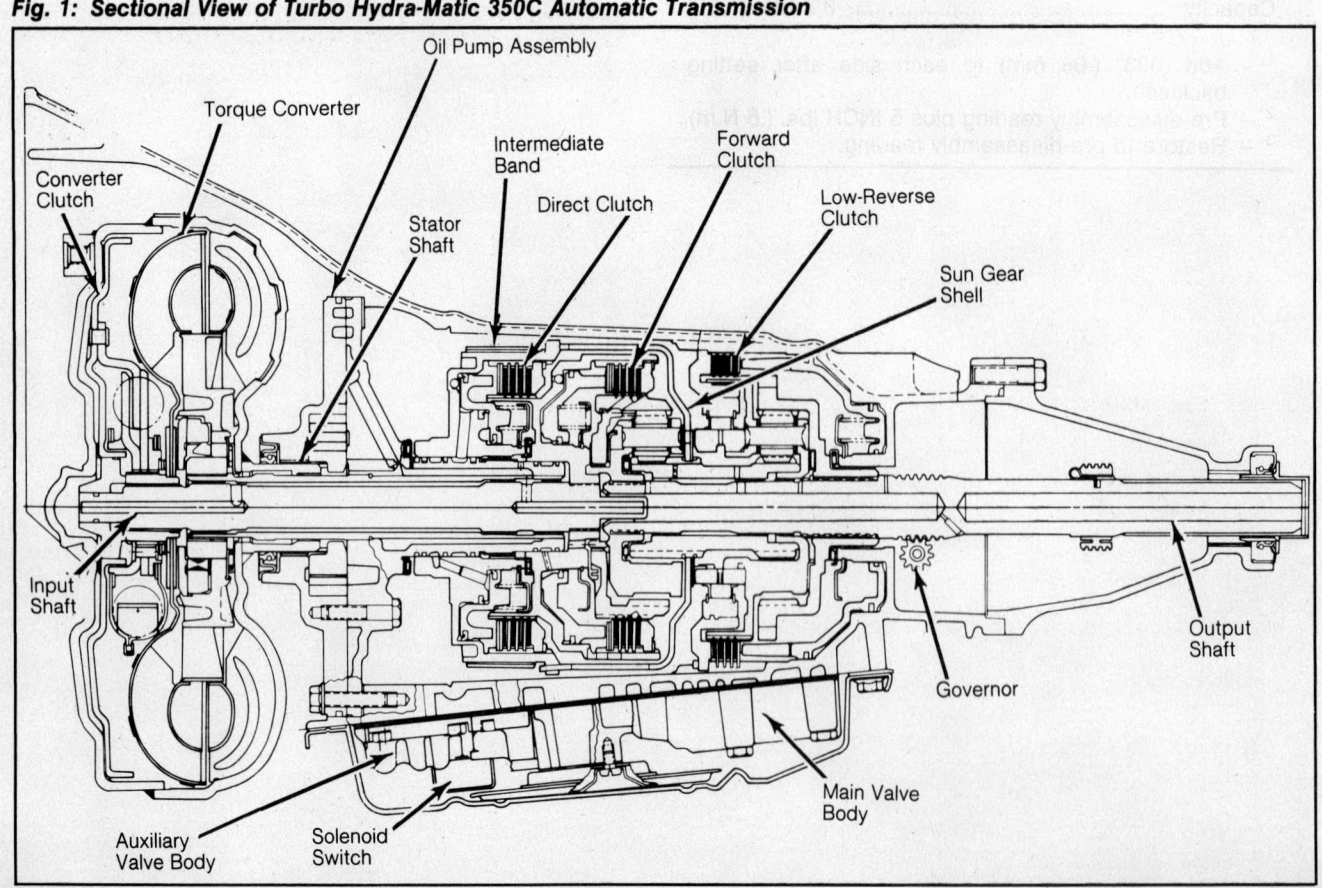

Fig. 2: Exploded View of Turbo Hydra-Matic 350C External Parts

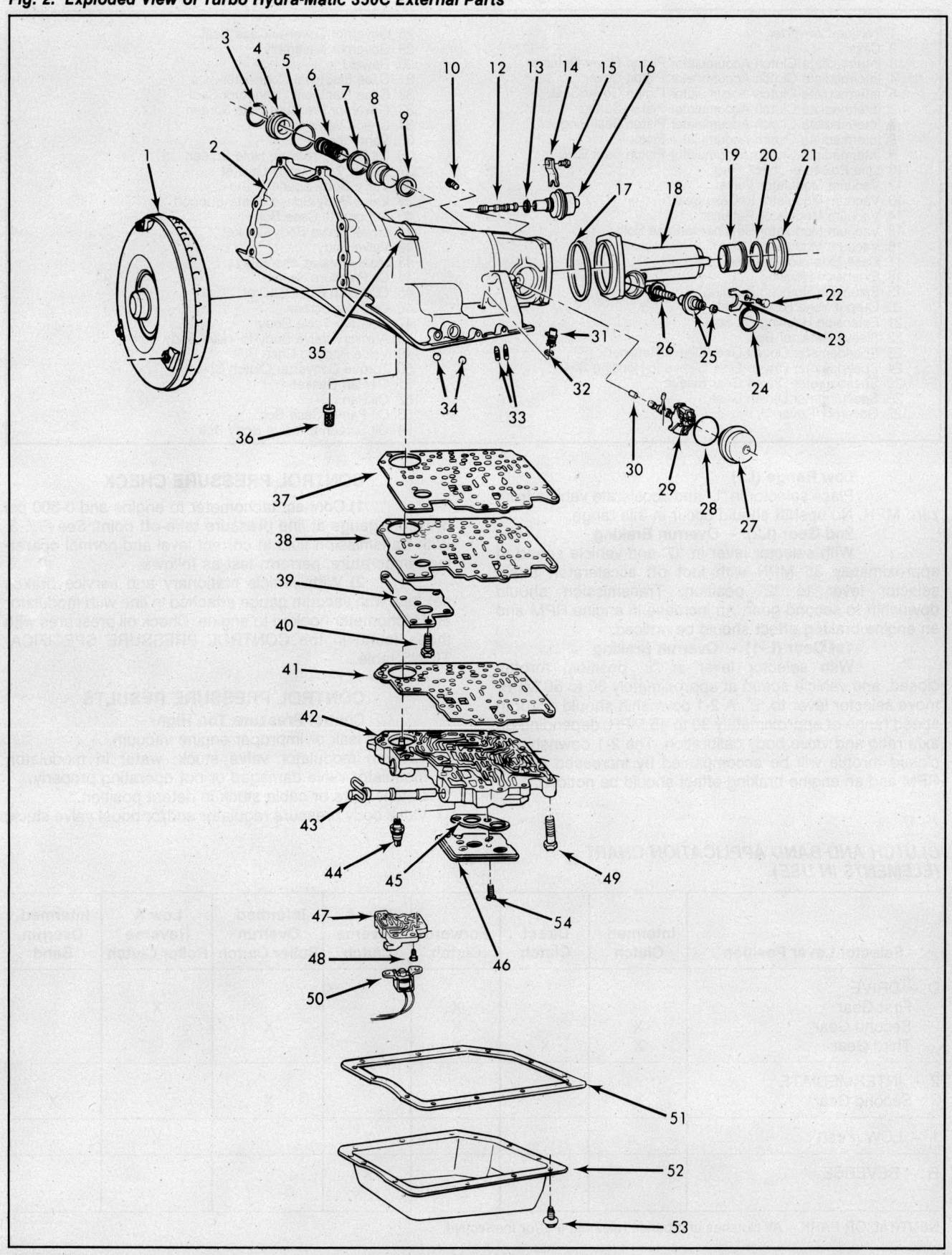

Automatic Transmissions
GENERAL MOTORS TURBO HYDRA-MATIC 350C (Cont.)

Turbo Hydra-Matic 350C External Parts (Use With Fig. 2)

1. Torque Converter
2. Case
3. Intermediate Clutch Accumulator Piston Cover Retainer
4. Intermediate Clutch Accumulator Piston Cover
5. Intermediate Clutch Accumulator Piston Cover Seal
6. Intermediate Clutch Accumulator Piston Spring
7. Intermediate Clutch Accumulator Piston Seal Ring
8. Intermediate Clutch Accumulator Piston
9. Intermediate Clutch Accumulator Piston Seat Ring
10. Line Pressure Check Plug
12. Vacuum Modulator Valve
13. Vacuum Modulator-to-Case Seal
14. Vacuum Modulator Retainer
15. Vacuum Modulator Retainer-to-Case Bolt
16. Vacuum Modulator
17. Case Extension-to-Case Seal
18. Extension Housing
19. Extension Housing Bushing
20. Output Yoke Sleeve Seal
21. Extension Housing Oil Seal
22. Sleeve Retainer Bolt
23. Speedometer Driven Gear Sleeve Retainer
24. Speedometer Driven Gear Sleeve-to-Housing Seal
25. Speedometer Driven Gear Sleeve
26. Speedometer Driven Gear
27. Governor Cover
28. Governor Cover-to-Case Seal
29. Governor Assembly
30. Dowel Pin
31. Case Electrical Connector
32. Case Electrical Connector Seal
33. Governor Pressure Hole Screen
34. Check Valve Ball
35. Vent Pipe
36. Oil Pump Pressure Hole Screen
37. Upper Valve Body Gasket
38. Valve Body Spacer Plate
39. Valve Body Spacer Plate Support
40. Support-to-Case Bolt
41. Lower Valve Body Gasket
42. Valve Body
43. Manual Valve Assembly
44. Oil Pressure Switch
45. Oil Pump Filter Gasket
46. Oil Filter Screen
47. Auxiliary Valve Body
48. Auxiliary Valve Body-to-Valve Body Bolt
49. Valve Body-to-Case Bolt
50. Torque Converter Clutch Solenoid
51. Oil Pan Gasket
52. Oil Pan
53. Oil Pan-to-Case Bolt
54. Oil Screen-to-Valve Body Bolt

Low Range (L1)
Place selector in "L" and accelerate vehicle from zero MPH. No upshift should occur in this range.

2nd Gear (L2) – Overrun Braking
With selector lever in "D" and vehicle speed at approximately 35 MPH with foot off accelerator, move selector lever to "2" position. Transmission should downshift to second gear. An increase in engine RPM and an engine braking effect should be noticed.

1st Gear (L-1) – Overrun Braking
With selector lever in "2" position, throttle closed, and vehicle speed at approximately 30 to 50 MPH, move selector lever to "L". A 2-1 downshift should occur in speed range of approximately 30 to 45 MPH, depending on axle ratio and valve body calibration. The 2-1 downshift at closed throttle will be accompanied by increased engine RPM and an engine braking effect should be noticed.

CONTROL PRESSURE CHECK
1) Connect tachometer to engine and 0-300 psi pressure gauge at line pressure take-off point. *See Fig. 3.* With transmission fluid at correct level and normal operating temperature, perform test as follows:

2) With vehicle stationary and service brakes set, test with vacuum gauge attached in line with modulator and tachometer hooked to engine. Check oil pressures with those found in the CONTROL PRESSURE SPECIFICATIONS table.

CONTROL PRESSURE RESULTS
Control Pressure Too High
- Vacuum leak or improper engine vacuum.
- Vacuum modulator valve stuck; water in modulator; modulator valve damaged or not operating properly.
- Detent valve or cable stuck in detent position.
- Valve body pressure regulator and/or boost valve stuck;

CLUTCH AND BAND APPLICATION CHART (ELEMENTS IN USE)

Selector Lever Position	Intermed. Clutch	Direct Clutch	Forward Clutch	Low & Reverse Clutch	Intermed. Overrun Roller Clutch	Low & Reverse Roller Clutch	Intermed. Overrun Band
D – DRIVE							
First Gear			X			X	
Second Gear	X		X		X		
Third Gear	X	X	X				
2 – INTERMEDIATE							
Second Gear	X		X		X		X
1 – LOW (First)			X	X		X	
R – REVERSE		X		X			

NEUTRAL OR PARK – All clutches and bands released and/or ineffective.

GENERAL MOTORS TURBO HYDRA-MATIC 350C (Cont.)

boost valve sleeve broken or defective; incorrect pressure regulator valve spring; 2-3 shift control valve and sleeve installed in pressure regulator bore; pressure regulator exhaust hole blocked or not drilled.

Control Pressure Too Low
- Low transmission fluid level.
- Defective vacuum modulator assembly.
- Oil screen blocked or restricted; gasket omitted or damaged.
- Incorrect oil pump gear clearance; pump gears damaged, worn or installed backward; pump-to-case gasket out of position; defective pump body and/or cover; bottom seal ring on pump cover hub omitted or damaged; priming valve in pump omitted.
- Valve body pressure regulator or boost valve stuck; pressure regulator valve spring too weak; No. 1 check ball omitted from valve body; loose valve body bolts; valve body spacer plate support omitted; reverse and modulator boost valve stuck.
- Internal leak in forward clutch circuit (pressure low in Drive, normal in Neutral and Reverse); check pump oil seal rings and forward clutch seals.
- Internal leak in direct clutch circuit (pressure low in Reverse, normal in other ranges); direct clutch outer seal and 1-2 and 2-3 accumulator pistons and rings damaged or missing.
- Intermediate servo piston seal ring broken or omitted.
- Check ball missing from cored passage in transmission case face.

No Control Pressure
- Flashing blocking suction cavity in case.
- Priming valve in pump omitted.
- Front pump drive gear lugs sheared off.
- Vacuum modulator valve omitted.
- Pump-to-case gasket incorrectly installed.

GOVERNOR PRESSURE CHECK
1) With vehicle on a hoist (rear wheels off ground), disconnect vacuum line to modulator, then install a tachometer to engine and a pressure gauge to line pressure take-off point on transmission case. See Fig. 3.

2) Start engine. Keeping foot off brake, move shift lever to Drive range and check line pressure with engine speed at 1000 RPM. Slowly increase engine speed to 3000 RPM and determine if a pressure drop occurs (7 psi or more).

3) If no pressure drop takes place, inspect governor for a stuck valve, weight or restricted orifice in governor valve. Check governor feed system for plugged or restricted screen in control valve assembly, restrictions in feed line or scored governor bore.

VACUUM MODULATOR CHECK
See procedure given in GENERAL MOTORS TURBO HYDRA-MATIC 400 article in this section.

TORQUE CONVERTER CLUTCH CHECK
See Testing in GENERAL MOTORS TORQUE CONVERTER CLUTCH (TCC) SYSTEM article in this section.

SERVICE (IN VEHICLE)
The following components can be removed from transmission without removing transmission from vehicle:
- Governor Assembly
- Intermediate Servo Cover and Seals
- Oil Pan and Oil Screen
- Valve Body Assembly
- Auxiliary Valve Body Assembly
- Check Balls and Valve Body Spacer Plates and Gaskets
- Pressure Regulator Parts
- Inside Detent Lever
- Manual Detent Roller and Spring Assembly
- Detent Cable and "O" Ring
- Parking Pawl, Actuator Rod and Bracket
- Manual Shaft and Seal
- Extension Housing, Gasket and Seal
- 1-2 Accumulator Housing, Gasket and Spring
- Vacuum Modulator
- Cooler Fittings
- Oil Filler Pipe and "O" Ring
- Speedometer Driven and Drive Gears
- Converter Clutch Solenoid
- Solenoid Wire Clips
- Electrical Connectors
- Governor Feed and Pump Pressure Screens
- Modulator Valve

For removal and installation of these components, see TRANSMISSION DISASSEMBLY and TRANSMISSION REASSEMBLY procedures.

REMOVAL & INSTALLATION
See appropriate AUTOMATIC TRANSMISSION REMOVAL article in DOMESTIC GENERAL SERVICING Section.

TORQUE CONVERTER
NOTE: Torque converter is a sealed unit and cannot be disassembled for service.

LEAKAGE CHECK
See procedure given in GENERAL MOTORS TURBO HYDRA-MATIC 400 article in this section.

Fig. 3: Pressure Take-Off Points

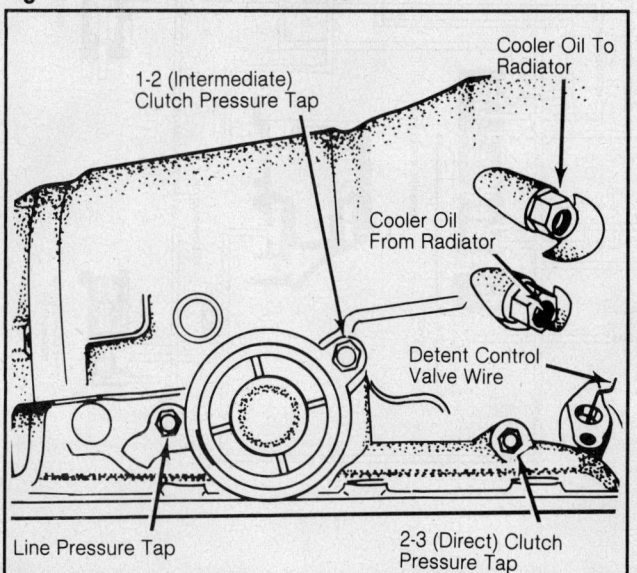

1-2 (Intermediate) Clutch Pressure Tap

Cooler Oil To Radiator

Cooler Oil From Radiator

Detent Control Valve Wire

Line Pressure Tap

2-3 (Direct) Clutch Pressure Tap

Fig. 4: Turbo Hydra-Matic 350C Hydraulic Circuits Diagram

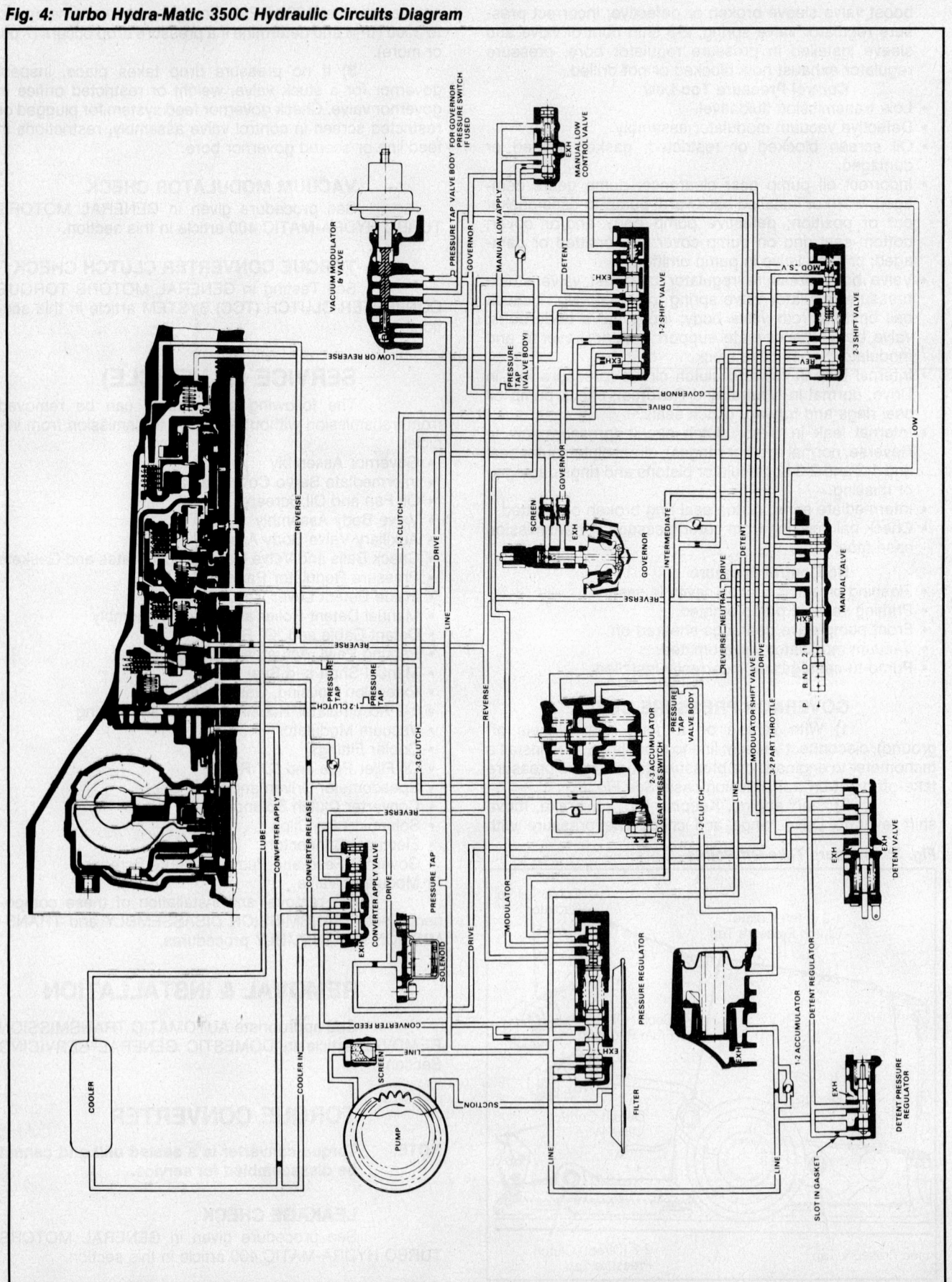

GENERAL MOTORS TURBO HYDRA-MATIC 350C (Cont.)

CONTROL PRESSURE SPECIFICATIONS – psi (kg/cm²)

Range	Models	Modulator [1] Line Connected	Modulator [2] Line Disconnected
DRIVE – BRAKES APPLIED [3]	XA	68-88 (4.8-6.2)	148-171 (10.4-12.0)
	XX	55-64 (3.9-4.5)	148-173 (10.4-12.2)
L2 or L1 – BRAKES APPLIED [3]	XA	89-111 (6.3-7.8)	148-172 (10.4-12.1)
	XX	80-93 (5.6-6.5)	148-173 (10.4-12.2)
REVERSE – BRAKES APPLIED [3]	XA	102-134 (7.2-9.4)	226-259 (15.9-18.2)
	XX	83-97 (5.8-6.8)	237-270 (16.7-19.0)
NEUTRAL – BRAKES APPLIED	XA	68-86 (4.8-6.0)	148-170 (10.4-12.0)
	XX	55-62 (3.9-4.4)	148-173 (10.4-12.2)
DRIVE IDLE SET ENGINE IDLE TO SPECIFICATIONS BRAKES APPLIED	XA	68-88 (4.8-6.2)	.....
	XX	55-64 (3.9-4.5)	.....
DRIVE – 30 MPH CLOSED THROTTLE OR ON HOIST	XA	68-88 (4.8-6.2)	.....
	XX	55-64 (3.9-4.5)	.....

[1] – MODULATOR LINE CONNECTED: Run engine to 1000 RPM, close throttle and check PSI.
[2] – MODULATOR LINE DISCONNECTED: Check PSI at 1000 RPM, throttle open.
[3] – Total elapsed time for DRIVE, LOW and REVERSE tests not to exceed 2 minutes.

END CLEARANCE CHECK

See procedure given in GENERAL MOTORS TURBO HYDRA-MATIC 400 article in this section.

CONVERTER FLUSHING

See procedure given in GENERAL MOTORS TURBO HYDRA-MATIC 400 article in this section.

TRANSMISSION DISASSEMBLY

CONVERTER, MODULATOR ASSEMBLY, & SPEEDOMETER DRIVEN GEAR

1) With transmission in a holding fixture, remove torque converter assembly. It may be necessary to pry converter from transmission with a screwdriver due to a suction condition caused by the input shaft "O" ring.

2) Remove vacuum modulator attaching bolt and retainer, then remove modulator, "O" ring seal and modulator valve from case.

EXTENSION HOUSING

1) Remove retaining bolt and speedometer driven gear from side of extension housing. Remove housing attaching bolts then remove housing from case. Remove speedometer drive gear and retaining clip.

2) Remove square cut oil seal from housing. Remove extension housing lip seal using screwdriver. Remove oil pan and gasket. Remove filter and gasket.

VALVE BODY ASSEMBLY

1) Remove detent roller and spring assembly from valve body. See Fig. 5. Remove actuator pin from detent valve actuator lever assembly. Remove detent con-

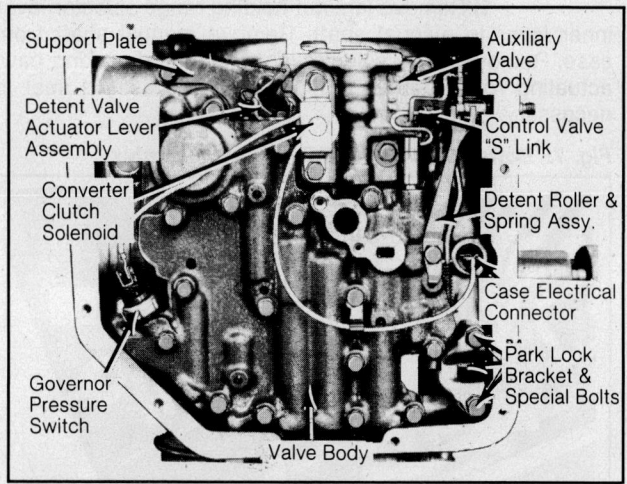

Fig. 5: Locations of Valve Body Components

trol link. Disconnect solenoid wires. If replacement is necessary, remove pressure switch. Remove solenoid attaching bolts and solenoid.

2) Remove manual shaft retaining clip with screwdriver and slide manual shaft outward. Remove control valve "S" link. Remove valve body attaching bolts and valve body. Remove auxiliary valve body attaching bolts and auxiliary valve body. Remove support plate attaching bolts and support plate.

3) Remove spacer plate and gaskets. Spacer plate to valve body gasket has a Yellow ink stripe for identification purposes. Be sure not to confuse it with spacer plate-to-case gasket.

4) Remove 5 check balls, noting locations for reference at reassembly. Remove park lock bracket and special bolts. *See Fig. 6.* Remove oil pump pressure screen from the case. Remove governor screen from case. Remove case electrical connector and "O" ring by depressing tabs.

Fig. 6: Location of Check Balls

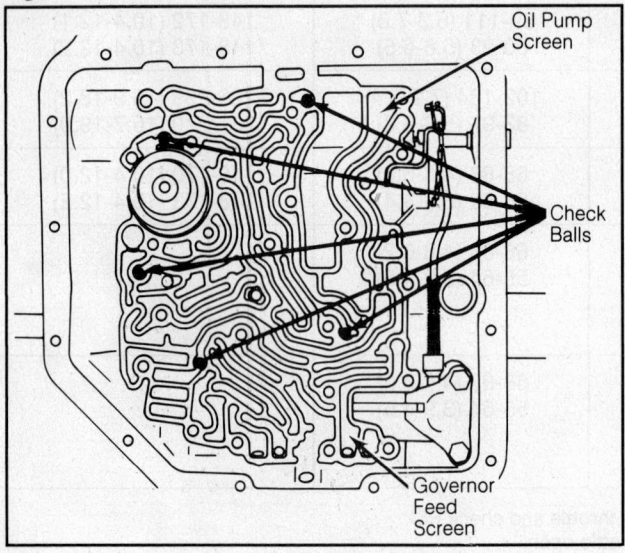

Fig. 8: Intermediate Servo Removal

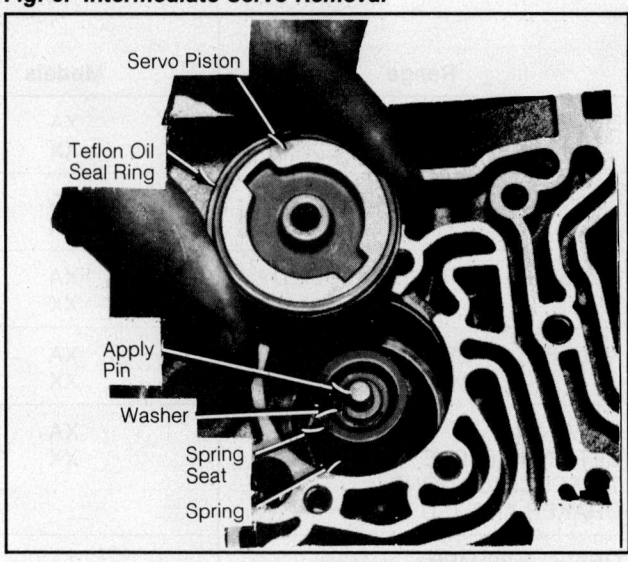

MANUAL SHAFT & PARKING PAWL

1) Remove jam nut holding range selector lever inner lever to manual shaft. Remove manual shaft from case. Remove range selector inner lever and parking pawl actuating rod. Remove manual shaft to case lip seal, if necessary.

Fig. 7: Bottom View of Parking Pawl Assembly

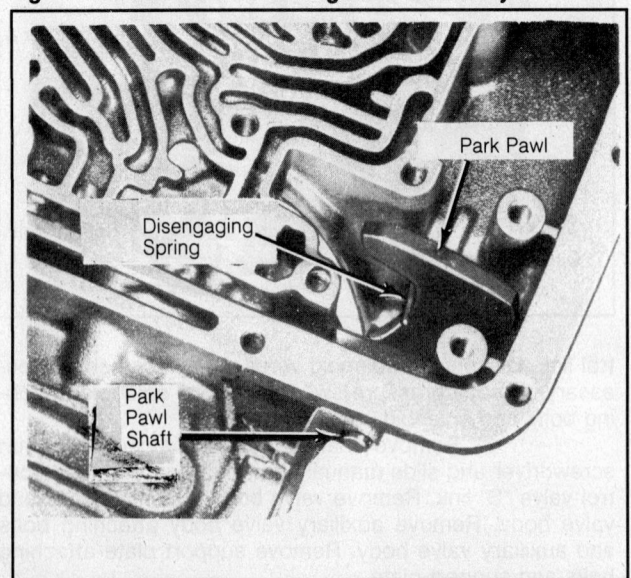

2) Remove parking pawl retaining plug, parking pawl shaft, parking pawl and disengaging spring. *See Fig. 7.* Remove intermediate servo piston, washer, spring seat, and apply pin. *See Fig. 8.* If piston or seal need replacement, both will have to be replaced as an assembly.

OIL PUMP & INTERNAL COMPONENTS

1) Remove oil pump-to-case attaching bolts with washer type seals, then discard seals. Install 2 slide hammers into threaded holes in pump body, tighten jam nuts and remove pump from case. Remove and discard gasket.

2) Remove intermediate clutch cushion spring, faced clutch plates, steel separator plates, wave spring and pressure plate from case. Remove intermediate overrun brake band. Grasp input shaft and pull direct and forward clutches from case as an assembly.

3) Remove forward clutch housing-to-input ring gear front thrust washer. Remove input ring gear and ring gear-to-output carrier needle thrust bearing. Remove output carrier-to-output shaft snap ring and remove output carrier.

4) Remove sun gear driving shell assembly. Remove low and reverse roller clutch support-to-case snap ring. Grasp output shaft and pull up until low and reverse roller clutch and support assembly clear retainer spring. Then remove suport assembly from case. Remove retainer (anti-clunk) spring.

5) Remove low and reverse clutch faced plates and steel separator plates, noting number and position of plates used for reassembly reference. Remove reaction carrier assembly from output ring gear and shaft assembly, then remove output ring gear and shaft assembly from case. Remove reaction carrier-to-output ring gear needle thrust bearing.

6) Remove output ring gear to case needle bearing assembly from output shaft assembly or case. If necessary, remove ring gear to output shaft snap ring, then remove output ring gear from ouput shaft. Using a compressor tool, compress low and reverse clutch piston spring retainer.

7) Remove piston retaining ring, spring retainer and springs. Remove low and reverse clutch piston assembly by applying air pressure to oil passage in case. *See Fig. 9.* Remove seals from low and reverse clutch piston.

8) Using Compressor (J-23069), compress intermediate clutch accumulator piston cover and remove retaining ring. Remove cover, "O" ring seal, accumulator piston spring and piston assembly.

Fig. 9: Removing Low-Reverse Clutch Piston

Apply Air Pressure Here to Remove Low-Reverse Piston

NOTE: Do not remove accumulator piston Teflon oil seal rings. If seal rings are damaged, the piston assembly must be replaced.

Fig. 10: Exploded View of Intermediate Accumulator Assembly

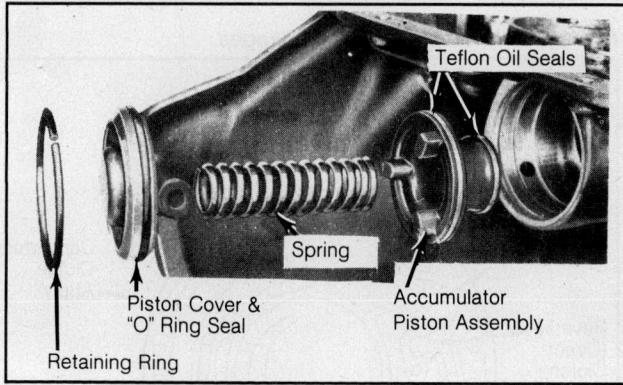

Teflon Oil Seals

Spring

Piston Cover & "O" Ring Seal

Accumulator Piston Assembly

Retaining Ring

COMPONENT DISASSEMBLY & REASSEMBLY

VALVE BODY

NOTE: As valve trains are removed from each valve body bore, place individual parts in correct order and in relative position to valve body to simplify reassembly. Valves and springs are not interchangeable, and all parts must be installed in correct order in proper valve body bore. *See Fig. 11.*

Disassembly

1) Position valve body assembly with cored face up. Position direct clutch accumulator piston pocket at upper left. Remove manual valve from lower left-hand bore (bore J).

2) From lower right-hand bore (bore A) remove retaining pin, then remove pressure regulator valve train.

3) From next bore up (bore B), remove retaining pin, then remove 2-3 shift valve train.

4) From next bore up (bore C), remove retaining pin, then remove 1-2 shift valve train.

5) From the next bore up (bore E), remove retaining pin, plug manual low control valve spring and manual low control valve.

6) From the next bore up (bore F), remove retaining pin, spring seat and detent regulator valve.

7) Install a compressor tool on direct clutch accumulator piston (G), then compress piston only enough to remove retaining "E" clip (piston may be damaged if over compressed). Remove "E" clip, accumulator piston and spring.

NOTE: If direct clutch accumulator piston seal needs replacing, the piston assembly must be replaced.

8) From the next bore down from direct clutch accumulator (bore D), remove detent actuating lever bracket bolt, bracket, actuating lever and retaining pin, then remove detent valve train.

Inspection

Wash all parts in cleaning solvent, air dry and blow out all passages. Inspect all valves for scoring, cracks and free movement in their bores. Inspect sleeves for cracks, scratches or distortion. Inspect valve body for cracks, scored bores, interconnected oil passages and flatness of mounting face. Check all springs for distortion or collapsed coils.

Reassembly

To reassemble, reverse disassembly procedure. Align piston and oil seal ring when installing direct clutch accumulator piston spring and piston with same tool used at disassembly and secure with retaining ring.

CAUTION: When installing direct clutch accumulator piston into valve body, compress piston only enough to install retaining "E" clip. Piston may be damaged if over compressed.

AUXILIARY VALVE BODY

Disassembly

Position auxiliary valve body assembly core face up. From bore, remove retaining pin, seat, spring and converter clutch apply valve.

Inspection

Inspect apply valve for scoring, cracks and free movement in bore. Check valve body for cracks, scored bore, interconnected oil passage and flatness of mounting face. Check spring for distortion.

Reassembly

Install apply valve, spring and spring seat into bore. Install retaining pin.

OIL PUMP

Disassembly

1) Remove pump cover-to-body attaching bolts. Remove intermediate clutch return springs, retainer assembly and clutch piston assembly from pump cover. Remove inner and outer seals from piston.

2) Remove 3 direct clutch-to-pump hub oil rings. If damaged, remove 2 forward clutch-to-pump hub teflon oil seal rings. Remove pump cover-to-direct clutch drum needle thrust bearings and, if equipped, remove input shaft end play adjusting shim.

NOTE: If replacement of forward clutch-to-pump hub Teflon oil seal rings is necessary, use 2 metal hook-type service replacement rings.

Fig. 11: *Exploded View of Valve Body Assembly*

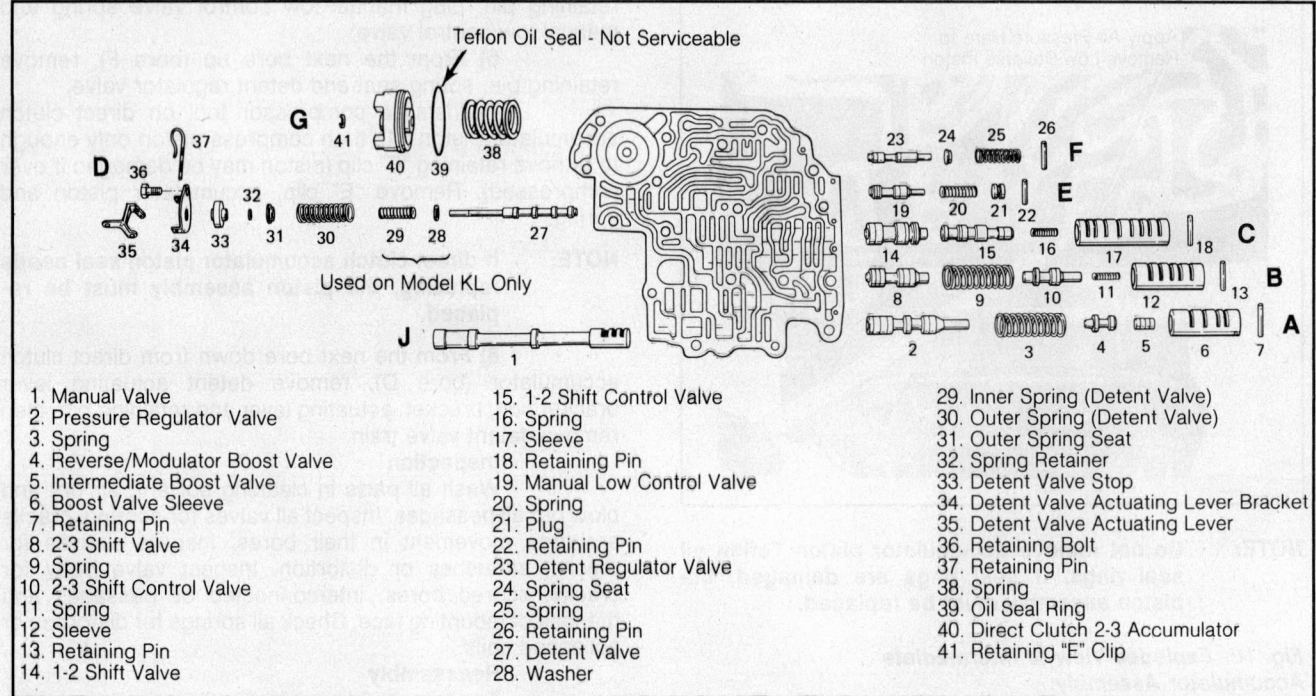

1. Manual Valve
2. Pressure Regulator Valve
3. Spring
4. Reverse/Modulator Boost Valve
5. Intermediate Boost Valve
6. Boost Valve Sleeve
7. Retaining Pin
8. 2-3 Shift Valve
9. Spring
10. 2-3 Shift Control Valve
11. Spring
12. Sleeve
13. Retaining Pin
14. 1-2 Shift Valve

15. 1-2 Shift Control Valve
16. Spring
17. Sleeve
18. Retaining Pin
19. Manual Low Control Valve
20. Spring
21. Plug
22. Retaining Pin
23. Detent Regulator Valve
24. Spring Seat
25. Spring
26. Retaining Pin
27. Detent Valve
28. Washer

29. Inner Spring (Detent Valve)
30. Outer Spring (Detent Valve)
31. Outer Spring Seat
32. Spring Retainer
33. Detent Valve Stop
34. Detent Valve Actuating Lever Bracket
35. Detent Valve Actuating Lever
36. Retaining Bolt
37. Retaining Pin
38. Spring
39. Oil Seal Ring
40. Direct Clutch 2-3 Accumulator
41. Retaining "E" Clip

Fig. 12: *Auxiliary Valve Body Exploded View*

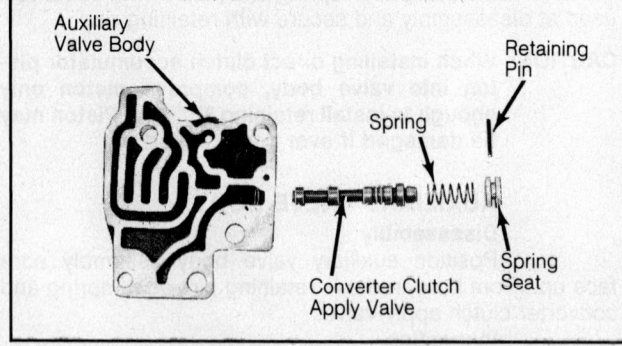

Fig. 13: *Oil Pump Body Oil Passages*

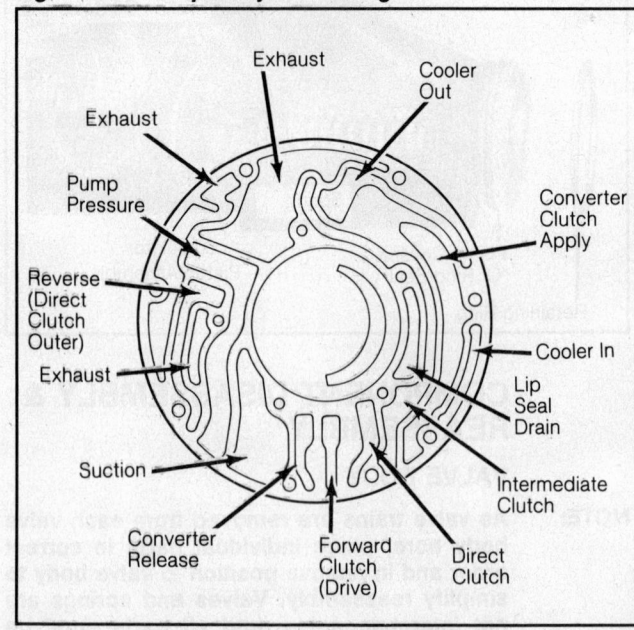

3) Check steady ring. If cut or frozen in groove, remove and replace with a new ring of the same color. The different colors compensate for groove depth. ALWAYS replace this ring with a new ring of the same color.

4) Separate pump cover and stator shaft assembly from pump body. Remove pump drive gear and driven gear from pump body. Remove pump to case square cut "O" ring seal. If required, remove pump body-to-converter hub lip seal.

Inspection

1) Wash all parts in cleaning solvent, blow out all passages and air dry. Do not use rags to dry parts. Inspect pump drive and driven gears, gear packet and crescent for nicks, scoring or other damage. Inspect pump body and cover for nicks or scoring.

2) Inspect pump cover hub outer diameter for nicks or burrs which might damage direct clutch drum bushing. Check pump cover and hub lubrication holes for restrictions. If replacement of forward clutch teflon seal rings is necessary, replace with 2 metal hook-type rings.

Reassembly

1) If pump body oil seal was removed, place pump body on wood blocks, coat outside diameter of new seal with a non-hardening sealer, then install seal fully into its counterbore.

2) Install pump drive and driven gear. Drive gear has offset tangs. Assemble with tang face up to prevent damage to converter. Assemble pump cover to pump body.

3) Install new inner and outer seals on intermediate clutch piston, then install piston assembly into pump cover, using care not to damage seals. Install spring retainer on clutch piston.

4) Install pump cover-to-body attaching bolts finger tight. Place Alignment Strap (J-21368) over cover and body, then tighten attaching bolts. Remove alignment strap. Install pump outside diameter square-cut "O" ring.

GENERAL MOTORS TURBO HYDRA-MATIC 350C (Cont.)

Fig. 14: Pump Cover Oil Passages

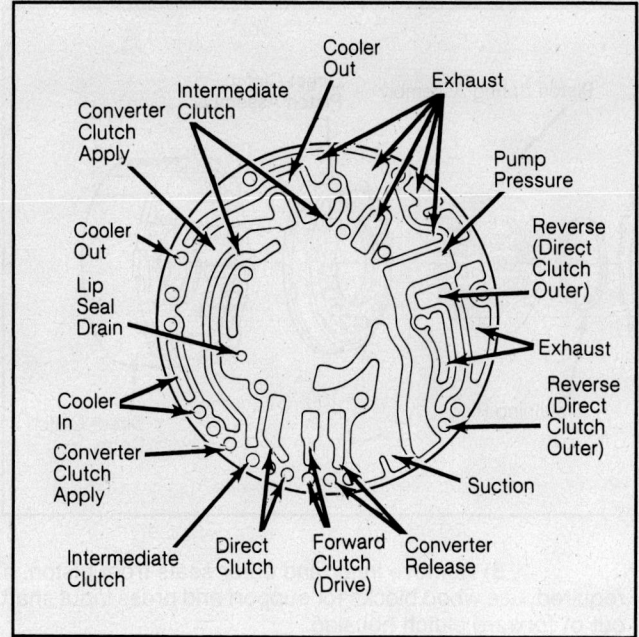

5) Install 3 direct clutch-to-pump hub scarf-cut oil seal rings. If removed, install 2 new forward clutch-to-pump hub hook-type seal rings. Check that 3 pump cover oil holes are not restricted.

DIRECT CLUTCH & INTERMEDIATE OVERRUN ROLLER CLUTCH

Disassembly

1) Remove intermediate overrun clutch front retainer ring and retainer. Remove intermediate overrun clutch outer race, then remove overrun clutch assembly.

NOTE: Overrun clutch inner race is a press fit. Do not remove unless replacement is necessary.

2) Remove direct clutch drum-to-forward clutch housing needle roller bearing. Remove direct clutch pressure plate-to-drum retaining ring and pressure plate. With draw composition plates, steel plates and cushion spring from direct clutch housing.

3) Using a compressor tool, compress direct clutch piston springs and remove retaining ring. Remove compressor tool and lift out spring seat, piston return springs and direct clutch piston. Remove inner and outer seals from piston and center seal from clutch drum.

Inspection

Inspect drive and driven clutch plates for burning, scoring, or wear. Check springs for collapsed coils or signs of distortion. Inspect piston for cracks. Inspect clutch housing for wear, scoring, open oil passages and free operation of ball check.

Reassembly

1) Install inner and outer seals (lips down) on clutch piston. Install center seal (lip up) in clutch drum and install clutch piston into housing using the aid of a .020" (.5 mm) wire crimped into copper tubing. Use a liberal amount of ATF during assembly.

2) Install spring retainer and springs by compressing springs and installing retaining ring. Lubricate with ATF and install composition plates and steel plates starting with steel and alternating with composition plate. Install direct clutch pressure plate and retaining ring.

3) Install intermediate overrun roller clutch assembly. Roller clutch must be installed with 4 holes up (toward front of transmission). Install intermediate clutch overrun outer race. When properly installed, it should free-wheel in the counterclockwise direction only. Install intermediate overrun clutch retainer and retaining ring.

DIRECT & INTERMEDIATE CLUTCH PLATE USAGE

Trans. Code	Faced Plates	Steel Plates
Direct Clutch [1]	4	4
Intermediate Clutch [2]	3	3

[1] – Clutch piston thickness is .833" (21.16 mm).
[2] – Clutch piston thickness is .992" (25.20 mm).

Fig. 15: Exploded View of Oil Pump Assembly

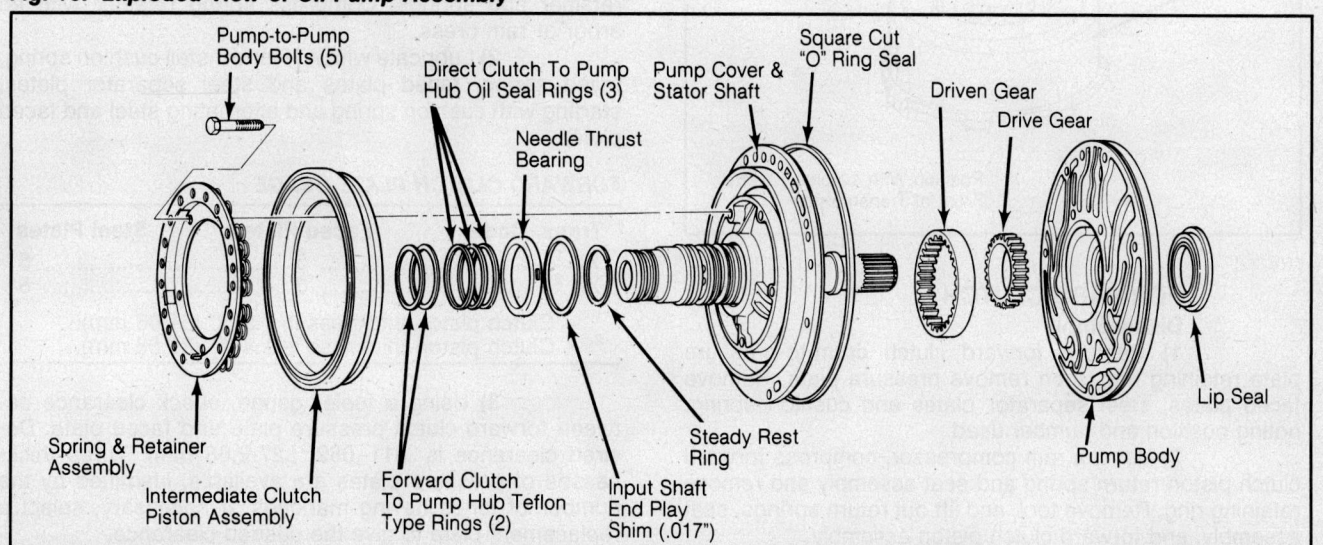

Automatic Transmissions

GENERAL MOTORS TURBO HYDRA-MATIC 350C (Cont.)

Fig. 16: Exploded View of Direct Clutch Assembly

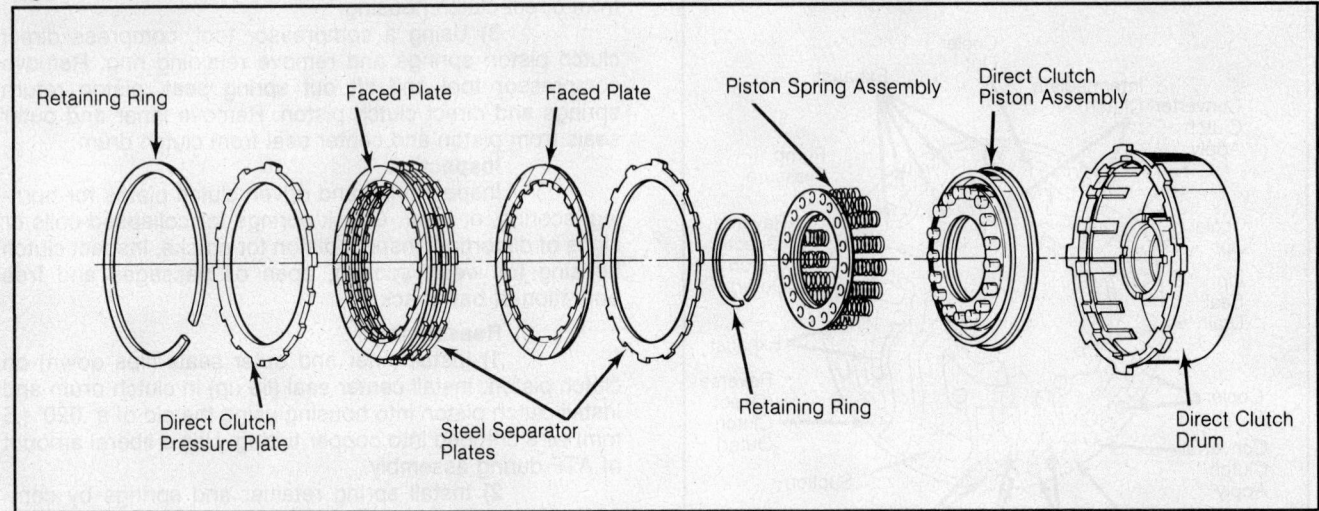

Fig. 17: Exploded View of Intermediate Overrun Roller Clutch Assembly

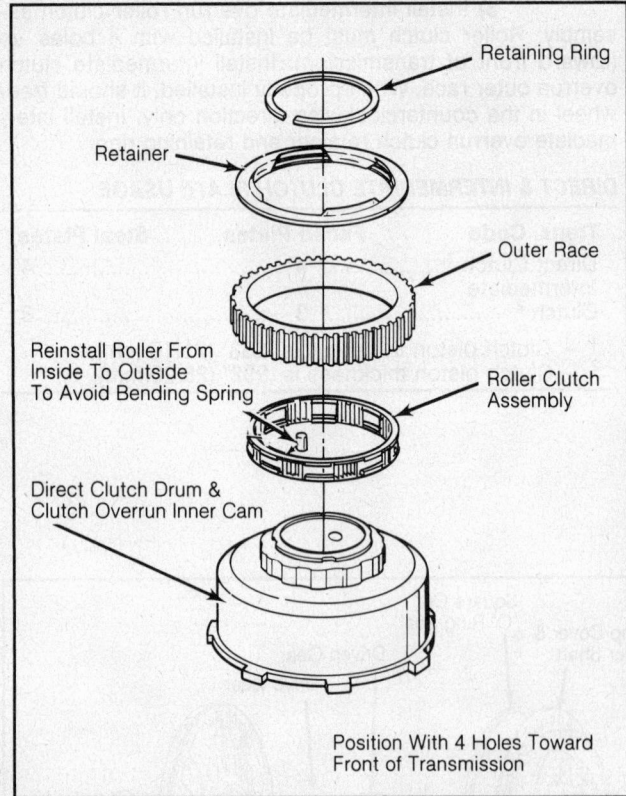

Position With 4 Holes Toward Front of Transmission

FORWARD CLUTCH

Disassembly

1) Remove forward clutch drum-to-pressure plate retaining ring, then remove pressure plate. Remove faced plates, steel separator plates and cushion spring, noting position and number used.

2) Using a ram compressor, compress forward clutch piston return spring and seat assembly and remove retaining ring. Remove tool, and lift out return springs, seat assembly, and forward clutch piston assembly.

3) Remove inner and outer seals from piston. If required, use wood blocks for support and press input shaft out of forward clutch housing.

NOTE: When pressing the input shaft into the forward clutch housing, care must be taken not to place excessive force on the input shaft as damage may result.

Inspection

1) Inspect lined and steel separator plates for signs of burning, scoring or wear. Inspect piston return springs for collapsed coils or signs of distortion or overheating. Inspect piston for cracks. Inspect clutch housing for wear, scoring, open oil passages and free operation of exhaust check ball.

2) Inspect input shaft for open lubrication passages at ends, damaged splines, damaged ground bushing journals and cracks or distortion.

Reassembly

1) Install forward clutch inner piston seal and outer piston seal, (if removed). Install the forward clutch piston assembly using a thin feeler gauge. Install spring retainer and springs. Compress spring retainer with an arbor or ram press.

2) Lubricate with ATF and install cushion spring, faced spring, faced plates and steel separator plates, starting with cushion spring and alternating steel and faced plates.

FORWARD CLUTCH PLATE USAGE

Trans. Code	Faced Plates	Steel Plates
XX [1]	5	5
XA [2]	5	5

[1] – Clutch piston thickness is 1.223" (31.06 mm).
[2] – Clutch piston thickness is 1.405" (35.68 mm).

3) Using a feeler gauge, check clearance between forward clutch pressure plate and faced plate. Desired clearance is .011-.082" (.27-2.08 mm). Three thicknesses of pressure plates are available, identified by the number of tangs having markings. If necessary, select a replacement plate to give the desired clearance.

Fig. 18: Exploded View of Foward Clutch Assembly

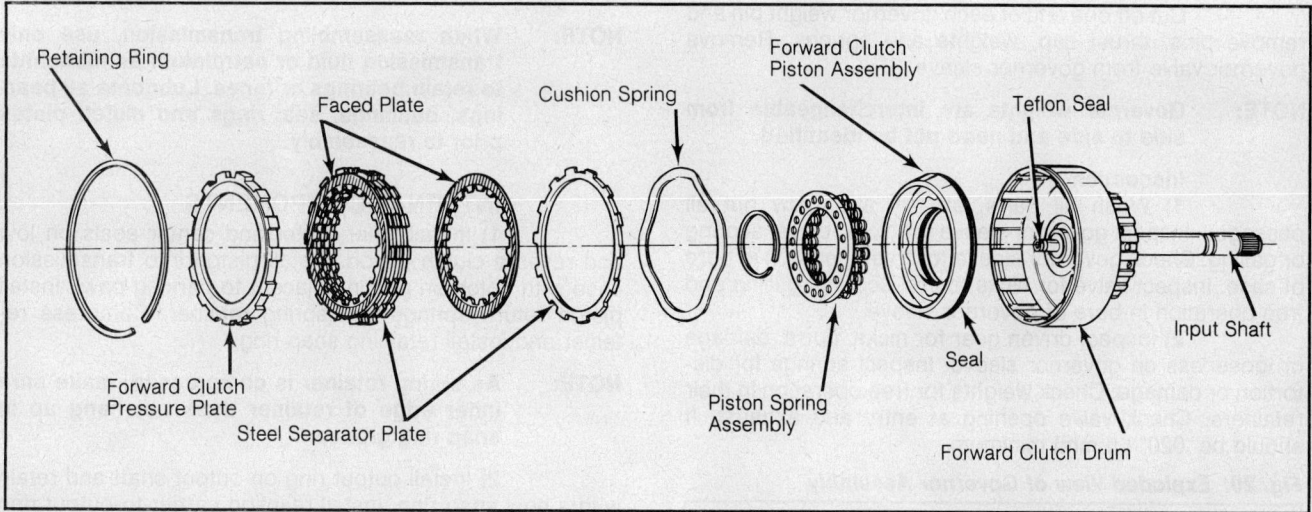

FORWARD CLUTCH PRESSURE PLATE IDENTIFICATION MARK & THICKNESS SPECIFICATIONS

No. of Marks	In. (mm)
None	.245-.255 (6.22-6.47)
1 Mark	.275-.285 (6.98-7.23)
2 Marks	.306-.316 (7.77-8.02)

SUN GEAR & SUN GEAR DRIVE SHELL
Disassembly
Remove and discard sun gear-to-sun gear drive shell rear retaining ring. Remove sun gear-to-drive shell flat rear steel thrust washer. Remove sun gear assembly from drive shell, then remove and discard front retaining ring.

Reassembly
Install new front retaining ring on sun gear. Install sun gear into sun gear shell. Install sun gear-to-drive shell flat steel thrust washer. Install new sun gear-to-sun gear shell drive retaining ring.

NOTE: **Do not overstress front and rear sun gear retaining rings when installing.**

LOW & REVERSE ROLLER CLUTCH ASSEMBLY
Disassembly
Remove low-reverse clutch-to-sun gear shell thrust washer. Remove low-reverse overrun clutch inner race. Remove low-reverse roller clutch retaining ring. Remove low reverse roller clutch assembly.

Reassembly
1) Install low and reverse roller clutch assembly to inner race. Install overrun roller clutch assembly and inner race into low and reverse clutch support with 4 holes down or to rear of transmission. When properly installed, inner race should freewheel in clockwise direction only.

2) Install low and reverse clutch-to-cam retaining ring. Install low and reverse-to-sun gear driving shell thrust washer.

Fig. 19: Exploded View of Low and Reverse Clutch Support and Overrun Roller Clutch Assembly

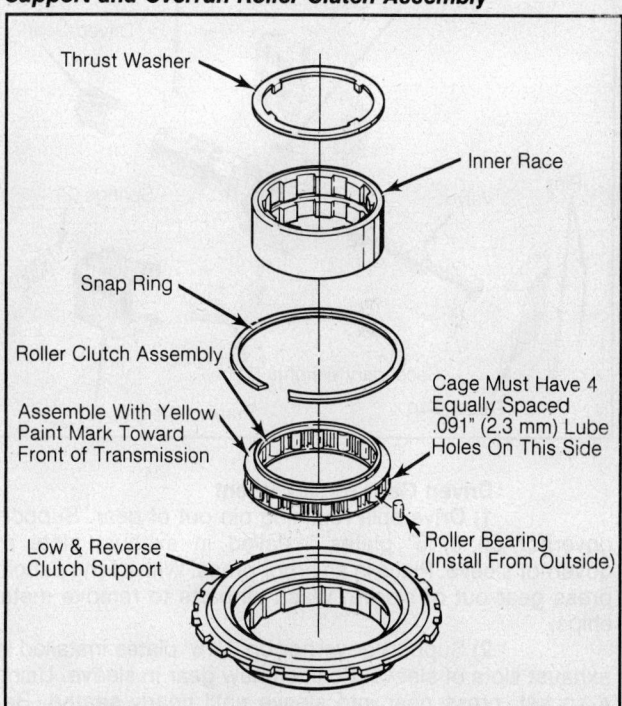

LOW & REVERSE CLUTCH PLATE USAGE

Trans. Code	Faced Plates	Steel Plates
XX [1]	5	5
XA [2]	5	5

[1] – Clutch piston thickness 2.921" (74.19 mm).
[2] – Clutch piston thickness 3.106" (78.89 mm).

GOVERNOR ASSEMBLY
Governor, including driven gear, is serviced as a complete assembly. Driven gear, however, may be serviced separately. Disassembly is necessary to replace a driven gear. Disassembly may also be necessary due to improper operation.

Disassembly

Cut off one end of each governor weight pin and remove pins, thrust cap, weights and springs. Remove governor valve from governor sleeve.

NOTE: Governor weights are interchangeable from side to side and need not be identified.

Inspection

1) Wash all parts, air dry and blow out all passages. Inspect governor sleeve for nicks, burrs, scoring or galling. Check governor sleeve for free operation in bore of case. Inspect valve for nicks, burrs, scoring, galling and free operation in bore of governor sleeve.

2) Inspect driven gear for nicks, burrs, damage or looseness on governor sleeve. Inspect springs for distortion or damage. Check weights for free operation in their retainers. Check valve opening at entry and exhaust. It should be .020" (.5 mm) minimum.

Fig. 20: Exploded View of Governor Assembly

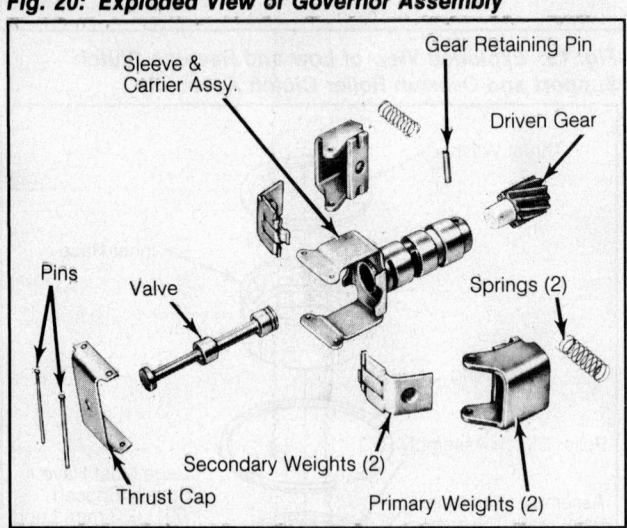

Sleeve & Carrier Assy.
Gear Retaining Pin
Driven Gear
Pins
Valve
Springs (2)
Secondary Weights (2)
Thrust Cap
Primary Weights (2)

Driven Gear Replacement

1) Drive split retaining pin out of gear. Support governor on 3/16" plates installed in exhaust slots of governor sleeve. Place in an arbor press. With a long punch, press gear out of sleeve. Wash all parts to remove metal chips.

2) Support governor on 3/16" plates installed in exhaust slots of sleeve. Position new gear in sleeve. Using a socket, press gear into sleeve until nearly seated. Remove any chips that may have shaved off gear hub, then press gear in until it bottoms on shoulder.

3) Locate a new pin hole position 90° from existing hole. Make hole with center punch and while supporting governor in press, drill a new 1/8" hole through sleeve and gear. Install split retaining pin. Wash governor assembly thoroughly to remove any metal clips.

Reassembly

1) Install governor valve in bore of sleeve (large land end first). Install weights and springs and thrust cap on governor sleeve. Align pin holes in thrust cap, weight assemblies and governor sleeve.

2) Install new pins and crimp both ends of pins to keep them from falling out. Check weight assemblies for free operation on pins. Check governor valve for free movement in governor sleeve.

TRANSMISSION REASSEMBLY

NOTE: When reassembling transmission, use only transmission fluid or petrolatum as lubricants to retain bearings or races. Lubricate all bearings, bushings, seal rings and clutch plates prior to reassembly.

INTERNAL COMPONENTS

1) Install inner, outer and center seals on low and reverse clutch piston. Install piston into transmission case with notch on piston adjacent to parking pawl. Install piston return springs and spring retainer. Compress retainer and install retaining snap ring.

NOTE: As spring retainer is compressed, make sure inner edge of retainer does not hang up in snap ring groove.

2) Install output ring on output shaft and retain with a new snap ring. Install reaction carrier-to-output gear needle thrust bearing with lip side face up. Install output ring gear-to-case needle thrust bearing assembly with lip on inner race pointing toward rear of transmission.

3) Install reaction carrier assembly into output ring gear and shaft assembly. Install output shaft and reaction carrier assembly into case. Oil and install low and reverse clutch plates, starting with a steel plate and alternating with faced plates.

4) Make sure notches in steel plates are placed toward bottom of case. Install low and reverse clutch support retainer (anti-clunk) spring. See Fig. 22. Install low and reverse clutch support assembly into case, pushing firmly until support assembly is seated past top of low and reverse support retainer spring. Install support-to-case retaining ring.

NOTE: Make sure splines on inner race of roller clutch align with splines on reaction carrier.

5) Install low-reverse clutch support inner race-to-sun gear drive shell thrust washer and install drive shell. Install output carrier assembly. Install input ring gear-to-output carrier needle thrust bearing (lip side face down), then install a new output carrier-to-output shaft snap ring.

6) Install input ring gear into case, then install forward clutch-to-input ring gear front thrust washer. Washer has 3 tangs. Install direct clutch drum-to-forward clutch housing needle roller bearing. Install direct clutch assembly to forward clutch assembly.

7) Install assemblies into case making sure forward clutch faced plates are positioned over input ring gear and tangs on direct clutch housing are installed into slots on sun gear drive shell. Install intermediate overrun brake band with anchor lug and apply lug positioned properly. Install intermediate clutch pressure plate.

8) After lubricating with transmission fluid, install intermediate clutch plates, starting with a faced plate, then alternating steel and faced plates. Install intermediate clutch cushion spring.

9) Install .017" (.43 mm) shim and needle thrust bearing face down on pump cover hub. Before installation, coat both sides of shims and bearing with petrolatum. Lubricate oil pump bore in case, then install a new pump-to-case gasket. Install guide pins to case.

10) Install pump into case bore. Remove guide pins and install 4 pump-to-case attaching bolts. Using new washer type seals, tighten bolts. If input shaft cannot be

Fig. 21: Exploded View of Planetary Gear Train

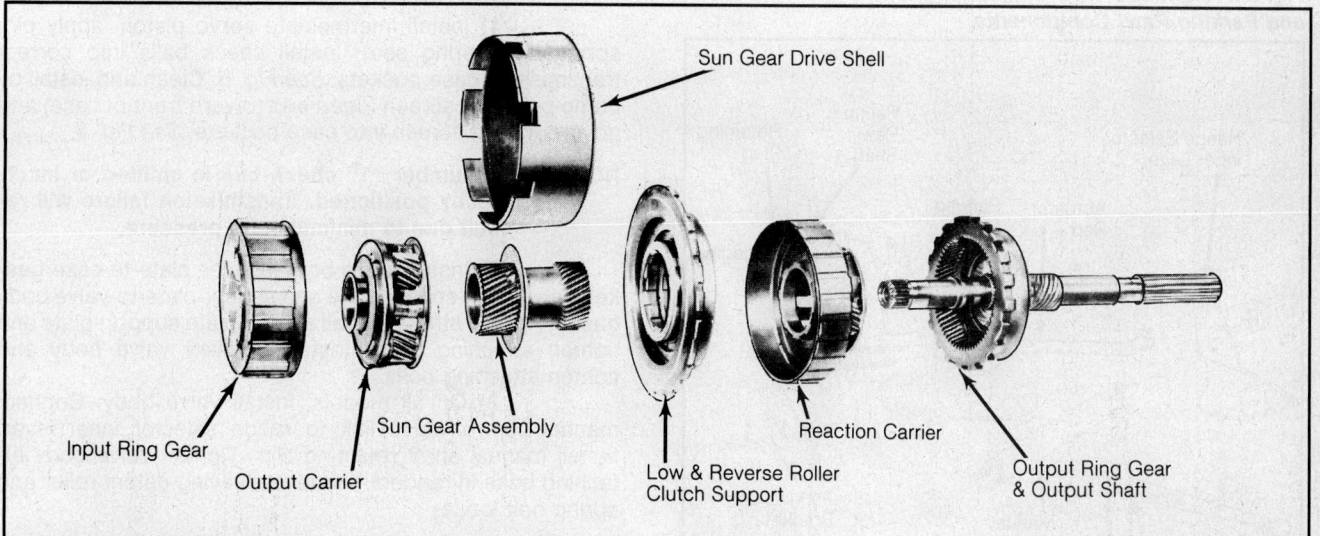

- Sun Gear Drive Shell
- Input Ring Gear
- Output Carrier
- Sun Gear Assembly
- Low & Reverse Roller Clutch Support
- Reaction Carrier
- Output Ring Gear & Output Shaft

Fig. 22: Installing Low and Reverse Clutch Support Retainer (Anti-Clunk) Spring

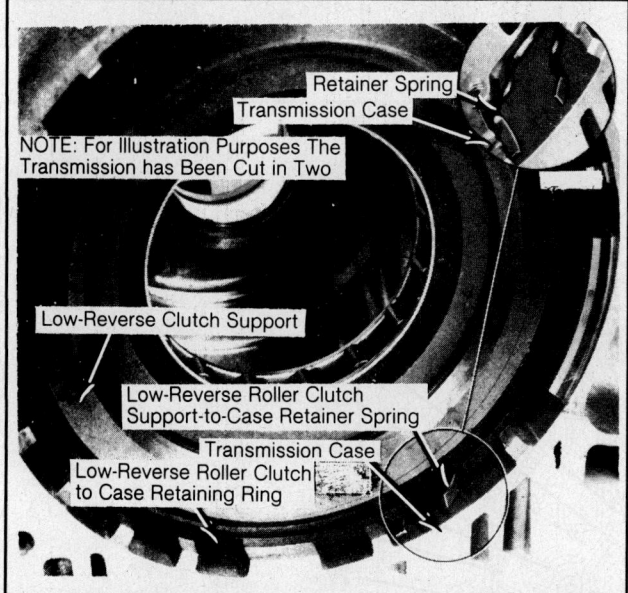

- Retainer Spring
- Transmission Case
- NOTE: For Illustration Purposes The Transmission has Been Cut in Two
- Low-Reverse Clutch Support
- Low-Reverse Roller Clutch Support-to-Case Retainer Spring
- Transmission Case
- Low-Reverse Roller Clutch to Case Retaining Ring

Fig. 23: Measuring Transmission End Play

- Slide Hammer Bolt
- Dial Indicator Assembly

rotated as the pump is being pulled into place, the direct and forward clutch housings have not been properly installed to index the composition plates with their respective parts. Correct this condition before proceeding.

11) Install a slide hammer bolt into threaded hole in pump, then push input shaft rearward. Attach a dial indicator to slide hammer bolt, place indicator pointer on end of input shaft and zero dial indicator. Push on end of output shaft and read resulting end play on indicator.

12) End play should be .010-.044" (.25-1.12 mm). If end play is not within specifications, add or subtract .017" (.43 mm) adjusting shims, located between pump-to-direct clutch needle thrust bearing and oil pump.

13) Remove pump assembly and install correct thickness adjusting shim(s). Install a new square cut "O" ring on oil pump. Install guide pins into case, then install oil pump and tighten attaching bolts.

SPEEDOMETER GEARS & EXTENSION HOUSING

1) Place speedometer drive gear retaining clip into hole in output shaft. Align slot in speedometer drive gear with retaining clip and install.

2) Position square-cut "O" ring seal on extension housing, mount extension housing to case and install and tighten attaching bolts. Install speedometer driven gear and retainer. Install and tighten retainer bolt.

MANUAL LINKAGE

1) Install parking pawl into case with tooth toward inside of case. Install parking pawl shaft into case through disengaging spring. Install spring on parking pawl and slide shaft through parking pawl.

2) Using a 3/8" diameter rod, drive a new shaft retaining plug into case until plug is flush to .010" (.25 mm) below face of case. Stake plug in 3 places to retain in case.

3) Install parking lock bracket and tighten bolts. Install actuator rod under parking lock bracket and parking pawl. If removed, install a new manual shaft-to-case lip seal. Install manual shaft through case and range selector inner lever. Install and tighten manual shaft jam nut. Install manual shaft-to-case spacer clip.

Fig. 24: Exploded View of Manual Shaft and Parking Pawl Components

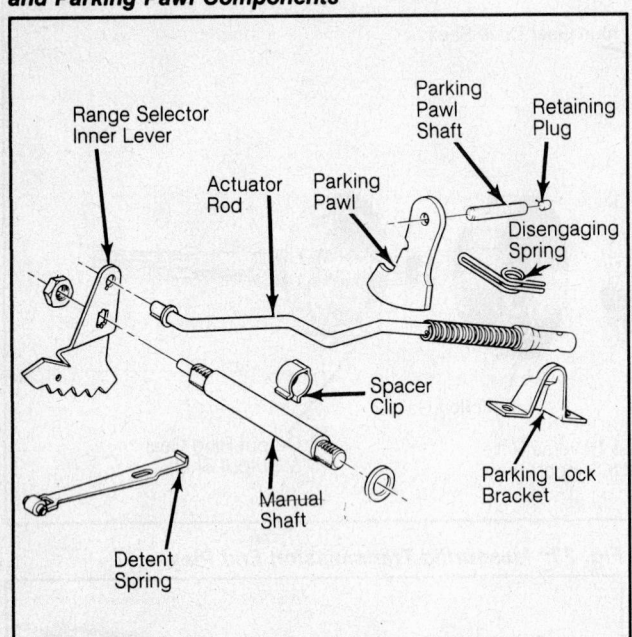

VALVE BODY & OIL PAN

1) Install intermediate servo piston, apply pin, spring and spring seat. Install check balls into correct transmission case pockets. *See Fig. 6.* Clean and install oil pump pressure screen (open end toward front of case) and governor feed screen into case pockets. *See Fig. 6.*

NOTE: If number "1" check ball is omitted or incorrectly positioned, transmission failure will result due to minimum line pressure.

2) Install valve body spacer plate-to-case gasket, valve body spacer plate and spacer plate-to-valve body gasket (Yellow stripe). Install spacer plate support plate and tighten attaching bolts. Install auxiliary valve body and tighten attaching bolts.

3) On all models, install valve body. Connect manual control valve link to range selector inner lever. Install manual shaft retaining clip. Tighten valve body attaching bolts in random sequence leaving detent roller and spring bolt loose.

NOTE: When handling valve body assembly do not touch sleeves as retainer pins may fall into transmission.

Fig. 25: Bottom View of Transmission Case Showing Oil Passages

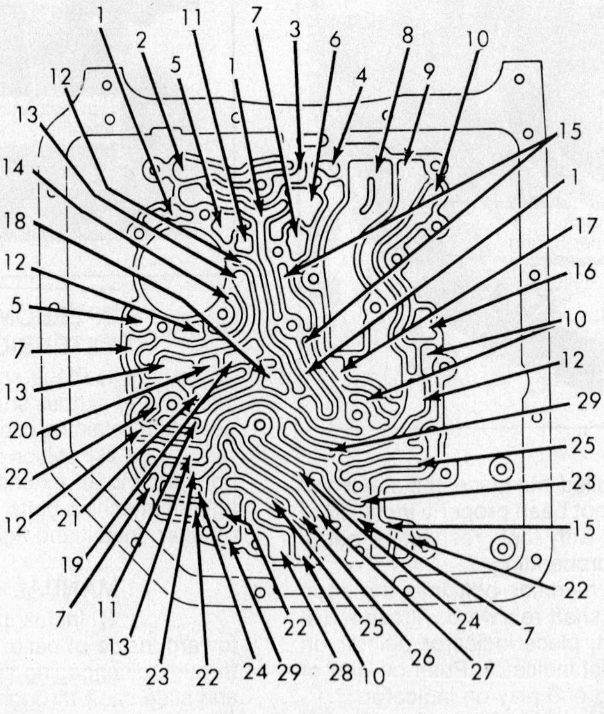

1. Direct Clutch (2-3)
2. Cooler In
3. Converter Apply
4. Converter Release
5. Intermediate Clutch (1-2)
6. Drive Forward Clutch
7. Drain
8. Suction
9. Pump Pressure
10. Reverse
11. Void
12. Intermediate Servo Release (R, N, D)
13. Line
14. 2-3 Clutch
15. Drive
16. Exhaust
17. Converter Feed
18. Exhaust Feed
19. Modulator or Detent Regulator
20. Exhaust Intermediate Clutch
21. Detent Regulator
22. Governor
23. Modulator
24. Detent 2
25. Low
26. Detent Modulator
27. Modulator Thru Detent Valve
28. Low Reverse Clutch
29. Manual Low Control

Fig. 26: Front View of Transmission Case Showing Oil Passages

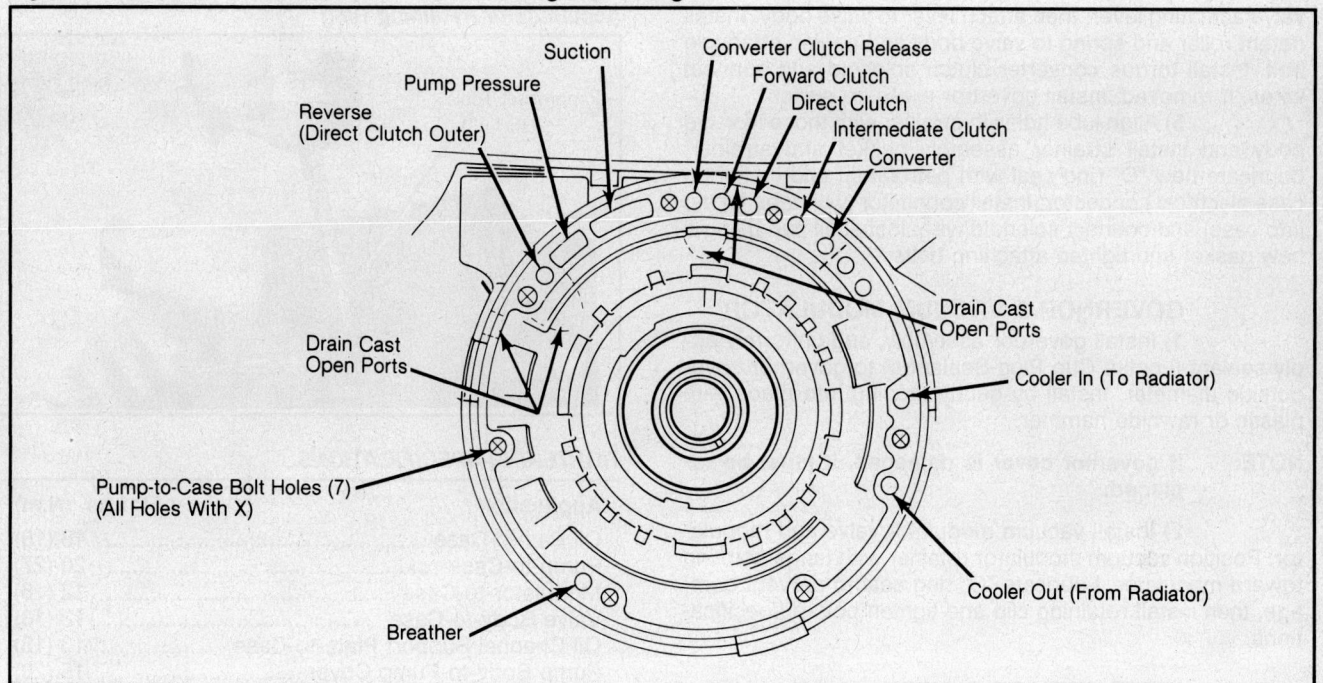

Fig. 27: Valve Body Oil Passages

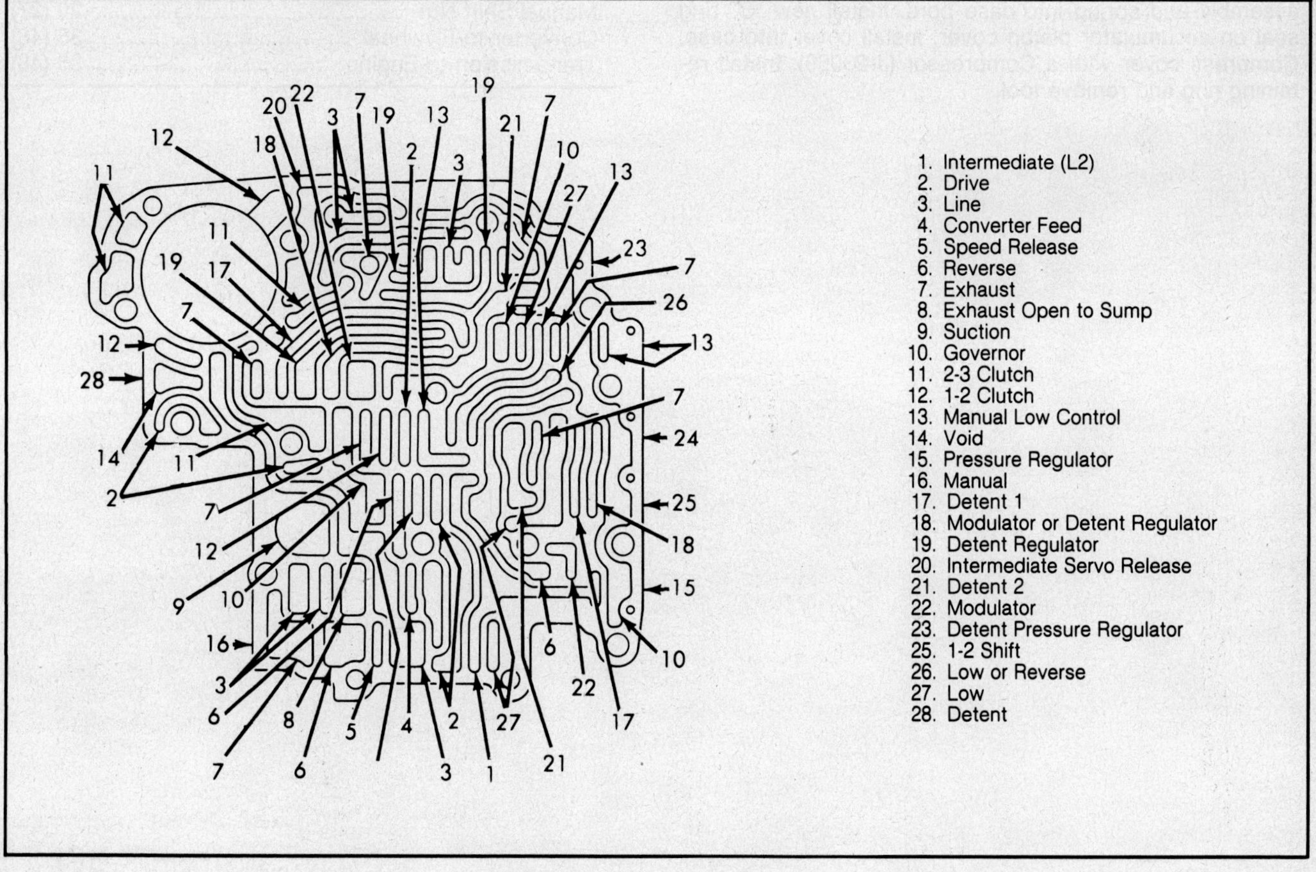

1. Intermediate (L2)
2. Drive
3. Line
4. Converter Feed
5. Speed Release
6. Reverse
7. Exhaust
8. Exhaust Open to Sump
9. Suction
10. Governor
11. 2-3 Clutch
12. 1-2 Clutch
13. Manual Low Control
14. Void
15. Pressure Regulator
16. Manual
17. Detent 1
18. Modulator or Detent Regulator
19. Detent Regulator
20. Intermediate Servo Release
21. Detent 2
22. Modulator
23. Detent Pressure Regulator
25. 1-2 Shift
26. Low or Reverse
27. Low
28. Detent

4) Install detent control valve wire to detent valve actuating lever, then attach lever to valve body. Install detent roller and spring to valve body and tighten attaching bolt. Install torque converter clutch solenoid and connect wires. If removed, install governor pressure switch.

5) Align lube holes in strainer with those in valve body and install strainer assembly gasket and strainer. Lubricate new "O" ring seal with petrolatum and install on case electrical connector. Install connector (with tabs facing into case) and connect solenoid wire. Install oil pan using a new gasket and tighten attaching bolts.

GOVERNOR & VACUUM MODULATOR

1) Install governor assembly, and uniformly apply sealant (Loctite Cup Plug Sealant II) to governor cover outside diameter. Install by gently tapping into place with plastic or rawhide hammer.

NOTE: If governor cover is damaged, it must be replaced.

2) Install vacuum modulator valve and modulator. Position vacuum modulator retainer with tangs pointing toward modulator. Lubricate "O" ring seal to prevent damage, then install retaining clip and tighten bolt to specifications.

INTERMEDIATE CLUTCH ACCUMULATOR

Install intermediate clutch accumulator piston assembly and spring into case bore. Install new "O" ring seal on accumulator piston cover. Install cover into case. Compress cover with a Compressor (J-23069). Install retaining ring and remove tool.

Fig. 28: Installing Intermediate Clutch Accumulator Retaining Ring

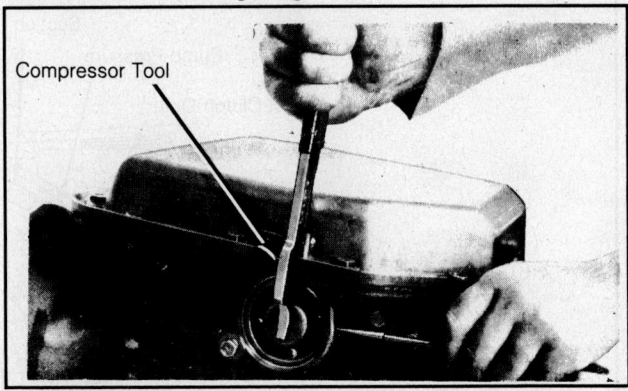

Compressor Tool

TIGHTENING SPECIFICATIONS

Application	Ft. Lbs. (N.m)
Oil Pan-to-Case	13 (18)
Pump-to-Case	20 (27)
Modulator-to-Case	12 (16)
Valve Body-to-Case	13 (18)
Oil Channel Support Plate-to-Case	13 (18)
Pump Body-to-Pump Cover	15 (20)
Extension Housing-to-Case	35 (48)
Inside Shift Nut	30 (41)
External Test Plugs	8 (11)
Manual Shift Nut	20 (27)
Converter-to-Flywheel	35 (48)
Transmission-to-Engine	35 (48)

GENERAL MOTORS TURBO HYDRA-MATIC 400

Chevrolet, GMC

IDENTIFICATION

Transmission serial number is located on Light Blue identification plate attached to right side of transmission case. Number consists of model year, 2 letter model code, and production serial number. Transmission VIN (Vehicle Identification Number) is stamped on left side of transmission case, to rear of manual lever shaft.

DESCRIPTION

Transmission is fully automatic unit consisting of 3-element hydraulic torque converter and compound planetary gear set. Three multiple disc clutches, 2 roller clutches, and 2 bands provide friction elements necessary to control functions of planetary gear set. Hydraulic system pressurized by gear-type pump provides pressure required to operate friction elements and automatic controls.

TESTING

Check fluid level and correct if necessary. Use initial road test to verify malfunction of transmission. Make sure that engine appears to be running properly. If transmission problems occur on initial road test, check adjustments and fluid levels. See AUTOMATIC TRANSMISSION SERVICING article in DOMESTIC GENERAL SERVICING section.

ROAD TEST

1) Connect portable tachometer to engine. Place selector lever in Drive range and accelerate vehicle from standstill at minimum throttle opening. Changes in engine RPM will identify shift points.

2) Upshifts 1-to-2 and 2-to-3 should occur as vehicle reaches correct speed ranges. As vehicle speed decreases, 3-to-2 and 2-to-1 downshifts should occur.

Increase in engine RPM and engine braking effect should be noticed. See SHIFT POINT SPECIFICATIONS table.

SHIFT POINT SPECIFICATIONS

Application	Speed (MPH)
Upshift	Minimum
1-2	15
2-3	30
Detent Downshift	Minimum
3-2	68-73
2-1	28-32
Upshift	Maximum
1-2	44-48
2-3	77-83

3) Stop vehicle and place selector lever in "2" (Intermediate) range. Accelerate from standstill. Upshift 1-to-2 should occur at all throttle openings (shift point will vary with throttle opening). No 2-to-3 upshift should occur. Stop the vehicle and place selector lever in "1" (Low) range. Accelerate from standstill. No upshift should occur regardless of throttle opening.

4) With selector lever in Drive range and vehicle speed at 35 MPH, move selector lever to "2" (Intermediate) range. Transmission should downshift to 2nd gear. Increase in engine RPM and engine braking effect should be noticed.

5) With selector lever in "2" (Intermediate) range and vehicle speed at 25-35 MPH (not over 40 MPH), move selector lever to "1" (Low) range. Throttle must be in closed position for this test. Transmission should downshift to 1st gear. Increase in engine RPM and engine braking effect should be noticed.

6) Stop the vehicle. Place selector lever in Reverse range and check for reverse operation.

CONTROL PRESSURE CHECK

1) Install 0-300 psi (0-21 kg/cm²) oil pressure gauge (J 5907) at pressure take-off point at left side of

CLUTCH AND BAND APPLICATION CHART (ELEMENTS IN USE)

Selector Lever Position	Forward Clutch	Direct Clutch	Front Band	Intermed. Clutch	Intermed. Roller Clutch Or Sprag	Low Roller Clutch	Rear Band
D – DRIVE							
First Gear	X					X	
Second Gear	X			X	X		
Third Gear	X	X		X			
2 – INTERMEDIATE							
First Gear	X					X	
Second Gear	X		X	X	X		
1 – LOW							
First Gear	X					X	X
Second Gear	X		X	X	X		
R – REVERSE		X					X

NEUTRAL OR PARK – All clutches and bands released and/or ineffective.

Automatic Transmissions
GENERAL MOTORS TURBO HYDRA-MATIC 400 (Cont.)

Fig. 1: *Cutaway View of Turbo Hydra-Matic 400 Automatic Transmission*

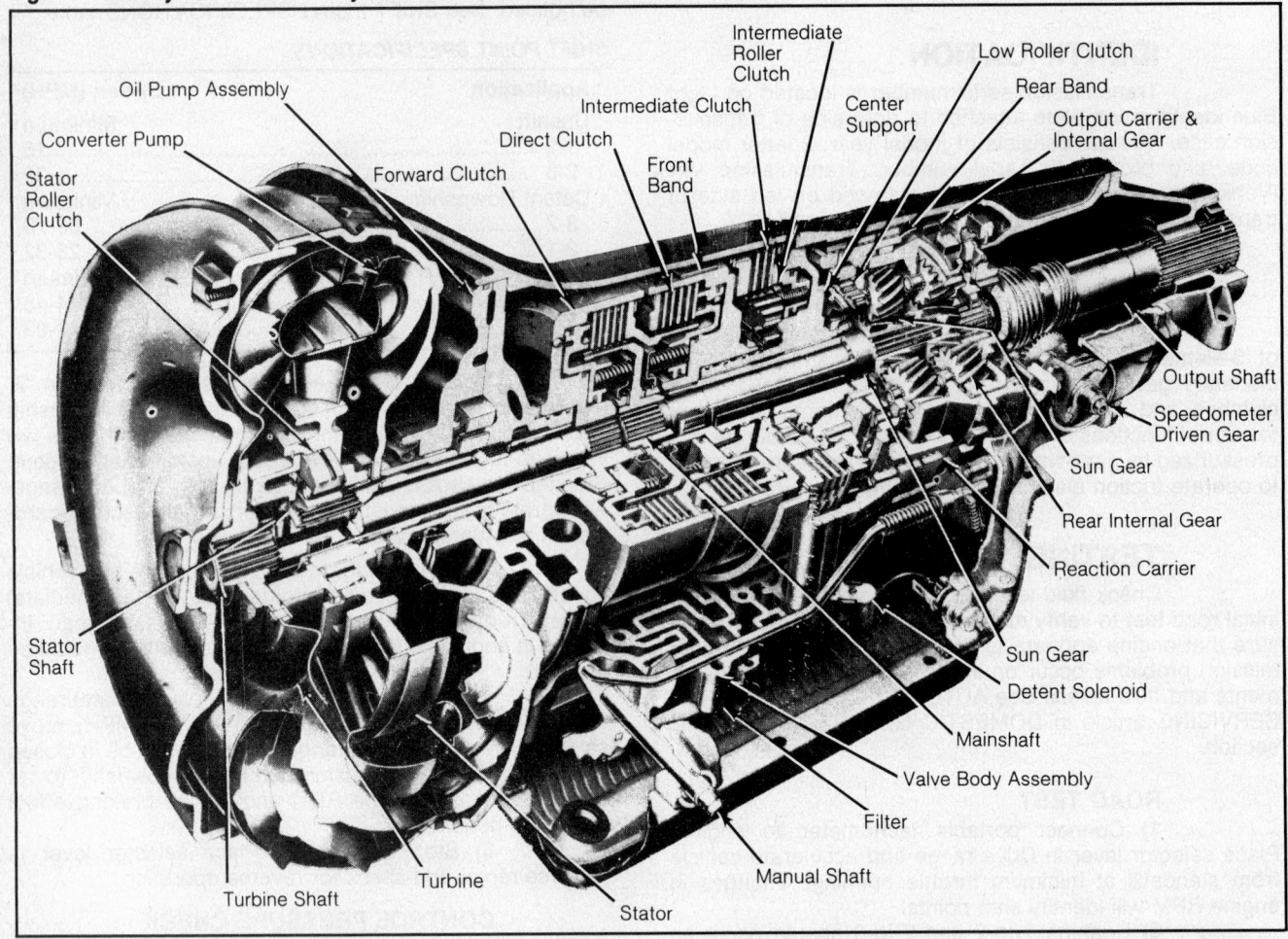

transmission to rear manual lever. Place gauge where it can be seen from driver's seat. Connect tachometer to engine.

　　2) With transmission fluid at correct level and operating temperature, hydraulic pressures can be checked. Check pressures with vehicle stationary and brakes applied as noted. See HYDRAULIC PRESSURES table.

CAUTION: For control pressure tests, total running time in Drive and Reverse ranges with brake applied must not exceed 2 minutes. Damage to transmission may result.

HYDRAULIC PRESSURES

Range @ RPM	psi (kg/cm²)
Neutral [1] @ 1000	55-70 (4-5)
Drive @ Idle	60-85 (4.2-6)
Drive [1] @ 1000	60-90 (4.2-6.3)
Low or "2" [1] @1000	135-160 (9.5-11.2)
Reverse [1] @1000	95-150 (6.7-10.5)
Drive [1] [2] @1000	90-110 (6.3-7.7)

[1] – Brakes applied.
[2] – Downshift switch activated.

　　3) On vehicles equipped with Exhaust Gas Recirculation, throttle is open enough in Drive range at 1000

RPM to cause EGR valve to open. This allows exhaust gas to enter intake manifold and lower manifold vacuum. Transmission line oil pressure rises with lower intake manifold vacuum. Line pressure may go above upper limit.

　　4) If high line pressures are obtained, disconnect and plug vacuum line at EGR valve. Recheck line pressure. If high pressures are still found, check engine vacuum. If low intake vacuum is found, use hand operated vacuum pump and apply 20 in. Hg vacuum to modulator.

　　5) Recheck pressures according to table. If line pressures are normal with external vacuum applied, check engine vacuum and vacuum systems for leaks. If high line pressures are found, refer to CONTROL PRESSURE RESULTS for possible causes.

　　6) When stationary testing is complete, drive vehicle at 30 MPH and allow throttle to close completely. Read pressure on gauge. This test may also be conducted on hoist. Run engine at 3000 RPM with driving wheels off ground, selector in Drive, and brakes released. Close throttle and read pressure between 2000 and 1200 RPM. Pressure should read 55-70 psi (3.8-4.9 kg/cm²).

CONTROL PRESSURE RESULTS
Line Pressure Too Low
- Transmission fluid level low, faulty vacuum modulator assembly. Oil filter blocked or restricted, "O" ring on filter intake pipe omitted or damaged, intake pipe split or leaking, or incorrect filter.

GENERAL MOTORS TURBO HYDRA-MATIC 400 (Cont.)

Fig. 2: Turbo Hydra-Matic 400 Hydraulic Circuits Diagram

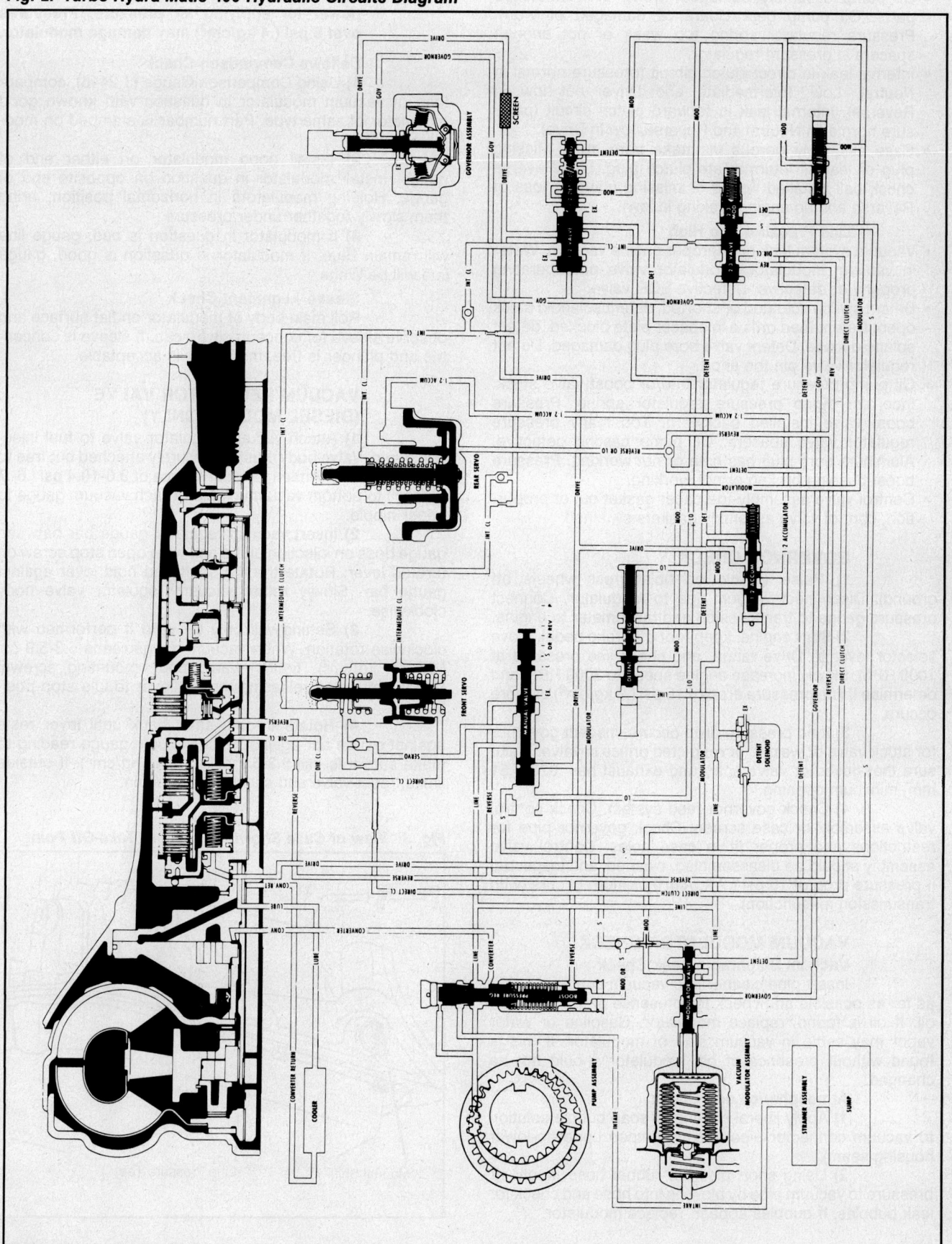

- Oil pump assembly damaged, worn, or mismatched parts. Oil pump gear clearance damaged or worn. Pressure regulator spring too weak or not enough spacers in pressure regulator.
- Internal leak in direct clutch circuit (pressure normal in Neutral, Low, Intermediate and Drive, but low in Reverse). Internal leak in forward clutch circuit (pressure normal in Neutral and Reverse, low in Drive).
- Case assembly porous in intake bore area. Missing plug or leak at intermediate clutch plug. Low-Reverse check ball installed wrong or missing (causing loss of Reverse and no engine braking in low).

Line Pressure Too High

- Vacuum system leak or improper engine vacuum. Water in vacuum modulator. Modulator valve not operating properly or defective. Defective EGR valve.
- Detent switch actuated or shorted, detent solenoid stuck open. Detent feed orifice in spacer plate blocked, detent solenoid loose. Detent valve bore plug damaged. Detent regulator valve pin too short.
- Oil pump pressure regulator and/or boost valve stuck. Incorrect pump pressure regulator spring. Pressure boost valve installed backward. Too many pressure regulator valve spacers. Oil pump casting defective. Aluminum bore plug has hole or not working. Pressure boost bushing broken or not working.
- Control valve assembly-to-spacer gasket out of proportion, control valve assembly gaskets switched.

GOVERNOR CHECK

1) Raise vehicle on hoist (rear wheels off ground). Disconnect vacuum line to modulator. Connect pressure gauge to transmission and tachometer to engine.

2) Start engine, keep foot off brake pedal, move selector lever to Drive range, and check line pressure at 1000 RPM. Slowly increase engine speed to 3000 RPM and determine if line pressure drop of 10 psi (.7 kg/cm^2) or more occurs.

3) If no pressure drop occurs, inspect governor for stuck valve or weight, or restricted orifice in valve. Make sure that governor valve entry and exhaust has .020" (.51 mm) minimum opening.

4) Check governor feed system. Check control valve assembly or case screen. Check governor pipe for restrictions and proper fit in case holes. Control valve assembly should be disassembled, cleaned, and inspected if pressure drop of 10 psi (.7 kg/cm^2) or more occurs (with transmission malfunction).

VACUUM MODULATOR CHECK
Vacuum Diaphragm Leak Check

Insert pipe cleaner into vacuum connector pipe as far as possible and check for presence of transmission oil. If oil is found, replace modulator. Gasoline or water vapor may settle in vacuum side of modulator. If this is found without presence of oil, modulator should not be changed.

Atmospheric Leak Check

1) Apply liberal coating of soap bubble solution to vacuum connector pipe seam (crimped upper-to-lower housing seam).

2) Using short piece of rubber hose, apply air pressure to vacuum pipe by blowing into hose and check for leak bubbles. If bubbles appear, replace modulator.

CAUTION: Do not use any method other than human lung power for applying air pressure. Pressures over 6 psi (.4 kg/cm^2) may damage modulator.

Bellows Comparison Check

1) Using Comparison Gauge (J 2446), compare load of vacuum modulator in question with known good modulator of same type. Part number is stamped on modulator dome.

2) Install good modulator on either end of gauge. Install modulator in question on opposite end of gauge. Holding modulators in horizontal position, bring them slowly together under pressure.

3) If modulator in question is bad, gauge line will remain Blue. If modulator in question is good, gauge line will be White.

Sleeve Alignment Check

Roll main body of modulator on flat surface and observe sleeve for concentricity to can. If sleeve is concentric and plunger is free, modulator is acceptable.

VACUUM REGULATOR VALVE
(DIESEL MODELS ONLY)

1) Attach vacuum regulator valve to fuel injection pump. Valve body must be securely attached but free to rotate on pump. Attach vacuum source of 9.0-10.4 psi (.6-.7 kg/cm^2) to bottom vacuum nipple. Attach vacuum gauge to upper nipple.

2) Insert vacuum regulator gauge bar between gauge boss on injection pump and wide open stop screw on throttle lever. Rotate throttle shaft and hold lever against gauge bar. Slowly rotate vacuum regulator valve body clockwise.

3) Setting will only be valid if performed with clockwise rotation. When vacuum gauge reads 5.3-5.9 psi (.37-.41 kg/cm^2), tighten valve body mounting screws. Check setting by releasing throttle lever to idle stop position.

4) Rotate throttle shaft back until lever rests against gauge bar again. Check vacuum gauge reading to make sure it is still 5.3-5.9 psi (.37-.41 kg/cm^2). If outside limits, reset valve and check setting again.

Fig. 3: View of Case Showing Pressure Take-Off Point

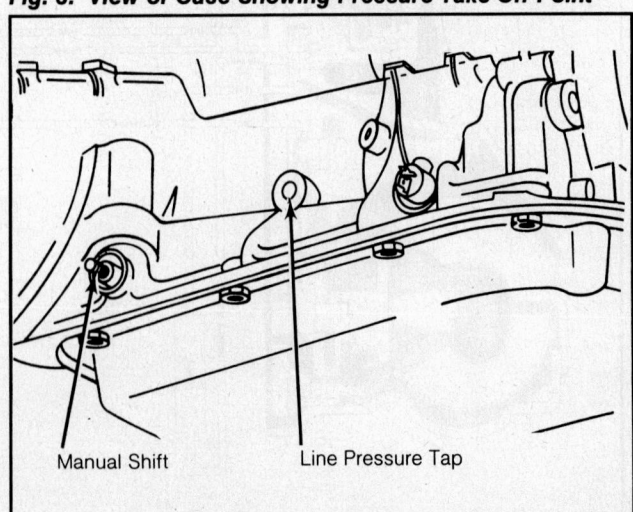

Manual Shift   Line Pressure Tap

GENERAL MOTORS TURBO HYDRA-MATIC 400 (Cont.)

DOWNSHIFT SOLENOID CHECK

1) Place selector lever in "Park". Turn ignition to "ON", but do not start engine. From under hood, slowly move throttle linkage to wide open position. One click should be heard from transmission.

2) Allow throttle to return to closed position. One click should be heard from transmission. If clicks are heard, downshift solenoid is operating properly. If solenoid does not perform as described, go to step **3)**.

3) Use test light to check Brown wire at connector on side of transmission case. Test light should light with throttle wide open and go out when throttle is released.

4) If test light operates as described, but solenoid did not click during tests, replace solenoid after first checking to see that internal wiring is operational.

5) If test light fails to light with throttle open, solenoid circuit is open. If light lights with throttle closed, solenoid circuit is shorted. Check solenoid circuit and repair open or short (Orange wire with Black stripe).

SERVICE (IN VEHICLE)

The following components may be removed from transmission without removing transmission from vehicle.

- Governor Cover and Seals
- Governor Assembly
- Governor Pipes
- Intermediate Servo Piston Assembly
- Rear Servo Assembly
- Front Servo Assembly
- Oil Pan and Oil Screen (Intake Pipe) Assembly
- Valve Body Assembly
- Check Balls and Valve Body Spacer Plates and Gaskets
- Pressure Regulator Parts
- Manual Detent Roller and Spring Assembly
- Parking Pawl Actuator Rod
- Parking Pawl Bracket and Parking Pawl
- Manual Shaft and Seal
- Manual Valve and Valve Link
- Extension Housing and Gasket
- Rear Seal
- 1-2 Accumulator Assembly
- Vacuum Modulator
- Oil Filter Pipe and "O" Ring
- Speedometer Driven Gear Assembly
- Cooler Fittings
- Downshift Solenoid
- Electrical Connectors
- Governor Feed Screen
- Pump Pressure Screen
- Modulator Valve

TRANSMISSION REMOVAL & INSTALLATION

See appropriate AUTOMATIC TRANSMISSION REMOVAL article in DOMESTIC GENERAL SERVICING section.

TORQUE CONVERTER

LEAKAGE CHECK

Install Pressure Test Plug (J 21369 B) into converter hub and tighten tool to expand it. Install safety strap to prevent tool from blowing out when air pressure is applied. Apply 80 psi (5.6 kg/cm^2) air pressure to air valve in tool. Submerge converter in water and check for leaks.

CAUTION: **After leak checking converter, bleed air pressure from test tool before removing tool from converter.**

CLEARANCE CHECK

1) Release collet end of End Play Checker (J 21371). Install end play checking tool into converter hub until collet end of tool bottoms. Expand collet by tightening cap nut to 60 INCH lbs. (6.7 N.m). Install Support Collar (J 21371 3) of checking tool on converter hub.

2) Tighten hex nut to 36 INCH lbs. (4 N.m). Install dial indicator on support collar so that indicator plunger rests against test tool cap nut. Zero dial indicator. *See Fig. 5.* Loosen hex nut while holding cap nut stationary.

3) With hex nut loose and Support (J 21371 3) firmly against converter hub, reading obtained on indicator will be converter end clearance. Converter end clearance should be less than .050" (1.27 mm). If clearance is greater than specified, replace torque converter assembly.

Fig. 4: Assembling Pressure Test Plug to Converter

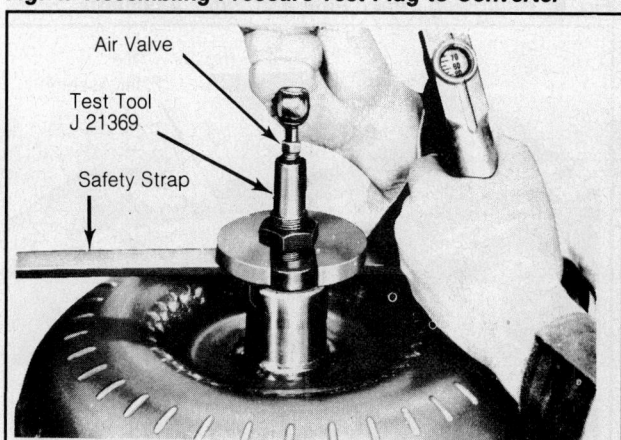

Apply 80 psi (5.6 kg/cm^2) to check for leakage.

Fig. 5: Assembling Measuring Tools to Converter

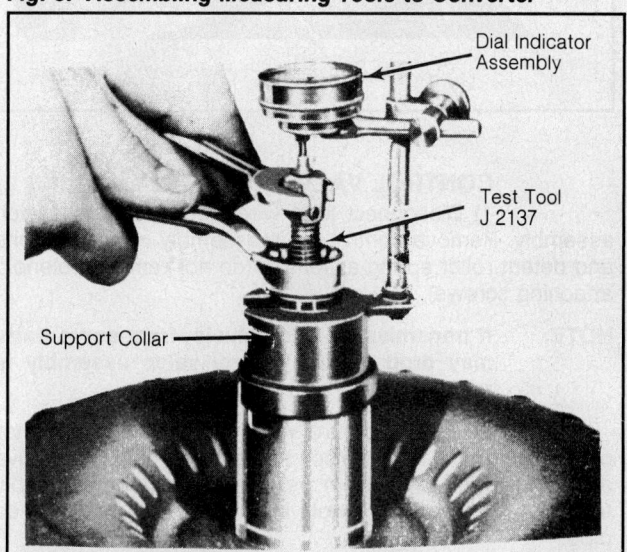

Assembly is used to check converter end clearance.

TRANSMISSION DISASSEMBLY

VACUUM MODULATOR & VALVE

Disconnect vacuum hose from modulator stem. Remove vacuum modulator attaching screw and retainer. Remove modulator and "O" ring seal from case. Discard "O" ring. Remove modulator valve from case bore.

GOVERNOR

Remove attaching screws, cover, and "O" ring, being careful not to distort cover. Remove governor assembly by pulling straight out of case.

SPEEDOMETER DRIVEN GEAR

Disconnect speedometer cable. Remove attaching screw and retainer. Apply slight pressure to remove speedometer driven gear assembly and "O" ring from case.

INTAKE PIPE, FILTER & OIL PAN

Remove pan attaching bolts and remove oil pan. Remove filter retaining bolt, withdraw intake pipe and filter assembly, then discard filter and "O" ring seal from intake pipe.

Fig. 6: Removing Intake Pipe and Filter Assembly

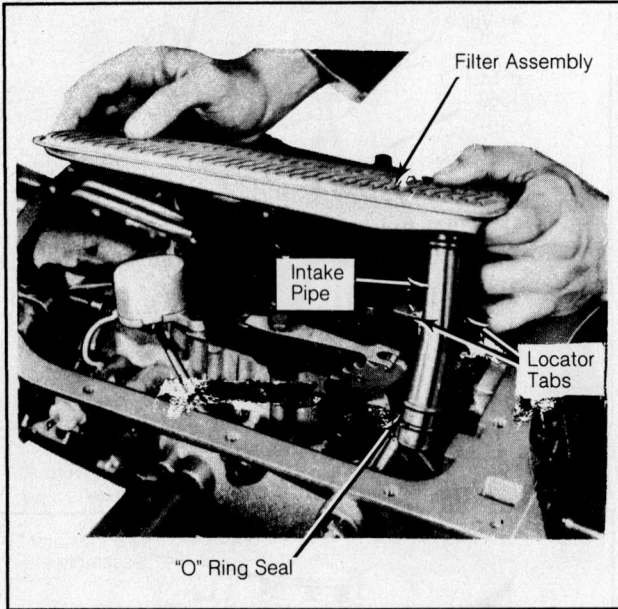

CONTROL VALVE ASSEMBLY

1) Disconnect lead wire from pressure switch assembly. Remove control valve assembly attaching bolts and detent roller spring assembly (do not remove solenoid attaching screws).

NOTE: **If transmission is in vehicle, front servo parts may drop out as control valve assembly is removed.**

2) Remove control valve assembly and governor pipes, using care not to drop manual valve as control valve assembly is removed. Remove governor screen assembly from governor feed pipe hole in case or from end of feed pipe.

3) Remove governor pipes from control valve assembly. Governor pipes are interchangeable and need

not be identified. Disconnect detent solenoid wire from electrical connector.

REAR SERVO

Remove servo cover and gasket and discard gasket. Remove servo assembly and accumulator spring. Make band apply pin selection check at this time to determine correct pin for use at reassembly. This is equivalent to band adjustment.

Band Apply Pin Selection Check

1) Position Band Apply Pin Selection Gauge (J 21370 6) on transmission case over rear servo bore. *See Fig. 7*. Hex nut on side of gauge faces toward parking brake linkage. End of Gauge Pin (J 21370 5) with smaller diameter fits in servo pin bore.

2) Secure gauge with 2 attaching screws. Tighten screws to 18 ft. lbs. (24 N.m). Make sure stepped gauge pin is free to move up and down in both tool and servo pin bore. Stepped side of pin must face front of transmission case.

Fig. 7: Using Gauge to Select Rear Band Apply Pin

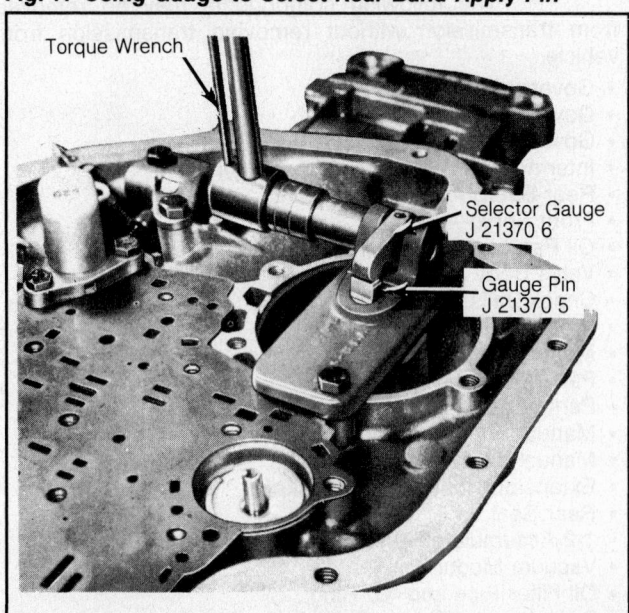

3) Apply 25 ft. lbs. (34 N.m) of force to hex nut on side of gauge. This will cause lever on top of gauge to depress stepped gauge pin into servo pin bore, simulating actual operating conditions. Note relation of steps on gauge pin and machined surface on top of gauge. To determine proper size pin, go to step 4).

4) If machined surface on top of gauge is even with or above upper step on gauge pin, long size (3 rings) pin must be installed. If machined surface is between upper and lower steps on pin, medium size (2 rings) pin must be installed. If machined surface is even with or below bottom step on pin, short size (1 ring) pin must be installed.

5) If new band apply pin is required, make note of pin size for reassembly reference. Remove selection gauge from transmission case.

DETENT SOLENOID, CONTROL VALVE SPACER & FRONT SERVO

Compress connector tabs. Withdraw connector and "O" ring seal. Remove attaching screws and lift off

GENERAL MOTORS TURBO HYDRA-MATIC 400 (Cont.)

detent solenoid assembly and gasket. Remove control valve spacer plate and gasket. Remove 6 check balls from cored passages in case. Remove front servo piston, retainer ring, pin, spring retainer, and spring from case.

CAUTION: If transmission is installed in vehicle, be careful when detent solenoid is removed to prevent spacer plate, gasket, and check balls from dropping out. Make sure to keep control valve spacer plate level when removing so check balls do not fall.

REAR OIL SEAL & EXTENSION HOUSING

If replacement is necessary, pry rear oil seal from extension housing. Remove attaching bolts and remove extension housing and gasket from transmission.

NOTE: Check front unit end play before proceeding with transmission disassembly. Record end play for reassembly procedure.

FRONT UNIT END PLAY CHECK

1) With transmission removed, remove 1 oil pump attaching bolt and bolt sealing washer at either 10 o'clock or 5 o'clock position. Install Slide Hammer Bolt (J 6125 1) and Adapter (J 6125 2) into bolt hole. Mount Dial Indicator (J 8001 02) on bolt. *See Fig. 8.*

2) Set indicator tip to register with end of turbine shaft. Hold output shaft forward and push turbine shaft rearward until it stops. Zero dial indicator, pull turbine shaft forward, and read resulting end play on indicator. End play should be .003-.024" (.08-.61 mm).

FRONT UNIT END PLAY THRUST WASHERS

Washer Thickness	I.D. Number	Color Code [1]
.060-.064"	0	Yellow
.071-.075"	1	Blue
.082-.086"	2	Red
.093-.097"	3	Brown
.104-.108"	4	Green
.115-.119"	5	Black
.126-.130"	6	Purple

[1] – Oil soaked washers may discolor. Measure such washers for actual thickness.

Fig. 8: Measuring Front Unit End Play

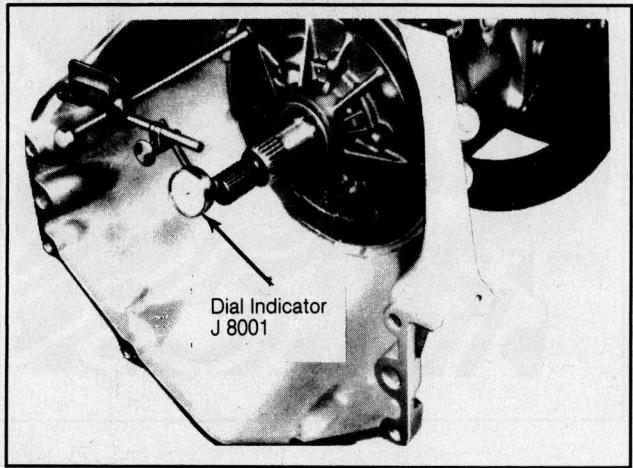

Dial Indicator J 8001

Shown with 3/8" rod in bolt hole.

3) If end play is not within specified limits, select correct thickness washer for use at reassembly. Selective thrust washer controlling end play is located between pump cover and forward clutch housing. Front end play thrust washers are available in varying thicknesses which are color coded. See FRONT UNIT END PLAY THRUST WASHERS table.

OIL PUMP

1) If front seal requires replacement, pry seal out before removing pump assembly. Remove pump attaching bolts. Install 2 Slide Hammers (J 6125 1) and Adapters (J 6125 2), 1 in 10 o'clock bolt hole and 1 in 5 o'clock bolt hole.

2) Operate both hammers at same time to avoid cocking pump assembly. Remove pump assembly from case. Remove slide hammer assemblies from pump. Remove and discard pump-to-case seal ring and gasket.

Fig. 9: Using Slide Hammers to Remove Oil Pump

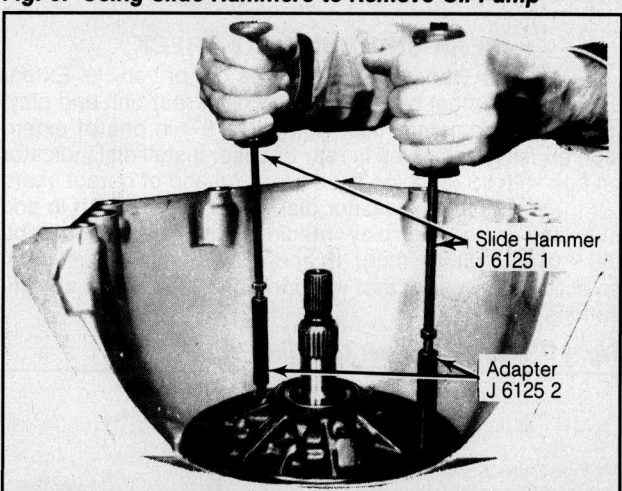

Slide Hammer J 6125 1

Adapter J 6125 2

Operate hammers together with equal force to avoid cocking pump.

DETENT LEVER, MANUAL LEVER, SHAFT & PARKING LINKAGE

1) If necessary for parts replacement, remove manual linkage. Loosen lock nut holding inside detent lever

Fig. 10: Exploded View of Manual Linkage

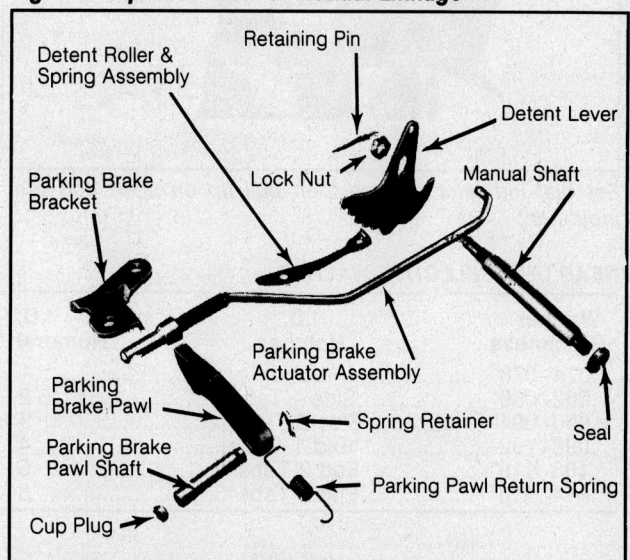

Detent Roller & Spring Assembly

Retaining Pin

Detent Lever

Parking Brake Bracket

Lock Nut

Manual Shaft

Parking Brake Actuator Assembly

Parking Brake Pawl

Spring Retainer

Seal

Parking Brake Pawl Shaft

Parking Pawl Return Spring

Cup Plug

to manual shaft. Remove pin holding manual shaft to case. Remove lock nut and inside detent lever from manual shaft. Remove manual shaft. See Fig. 10.

2) Remove parking actuator rod and detent lever from case. Remove attaching bolts and parking lock bracket. Remove parking pawl return spring. Remove parking pawl shaft spring retainer. Remove parking pawl shaft cup plug. Pry outward to remove plug. Remove parking pawl shaft and parking pawl.

TURBINE SHAFT, FORWARD & DIRECT CLUTCH ASSEMBLIES, SUN GEAR SHAFT & FRONT BAND

Remove forward clutch and turbine shaft assembly from case. Remove forward clutch hub-to-direct clutch housing thrust washer if not removed with forward clutch. Remove direct clutch and intermediate roller assembly. Remove sun gear shaft if it did not come out with direct clutch. Remove front band assembly.

REAR UNIT END PLAY CHECK

1) Transmission must be out of vehicle. Extension housing must be removed to check rear unit end play. Install Speedometer Puller Bolt (J 21797) in one of extension housing bolt holes in rear of case. Install dial indicator on bolt with tip touching flat surface on end of output shaft.

2) Zero indicator dial, move output shaft in and out, and note end play reading. End play should be .007-.019" (.18-.48 mm). If end play needs adjustment, select thrust washer that will bring end play within specifications.

Fig. 11: Measuring Rear Unit End Play

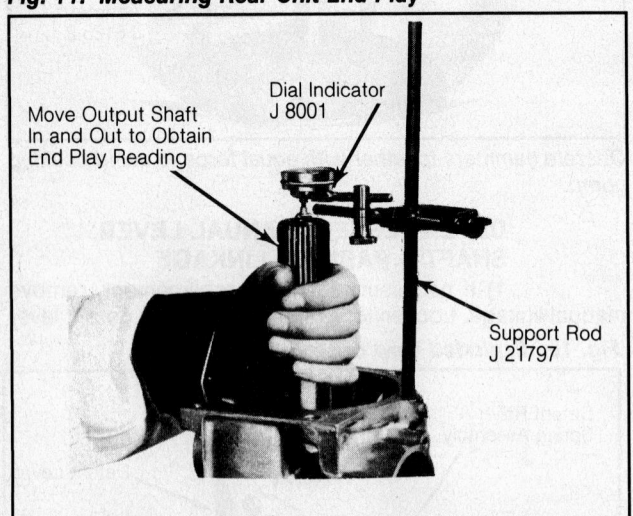

Move Output Shaft In and Out to Obtain End Play Reading

Dial Indicator J 8001

Support Rod J 21797

Set dial indicator at zero then pull up on shaft and read indicator.

REAR UNIT SELECTIVE WASHER

Washer Thickness	I.D. Notches	I.D. Numeral
.074-.078"	None	1
.082-.086"	Side 1 Tab	2
.090-.094"	Side 2 Tabs	3
.098-.102"	End 1 Tab	4
.106-.110"	End 2 Tabs	5
.114-.118"	End 3 Tabs	6

3) Selective washer controlling rear unit end play is steel washer having 3 tabs. It is located between output shaft thrust washer and rear face of transmission case. Notches and/or numerals on tabs of washer identify thickness. See REAR UNIT SELECTIVE WASHER table.

CENTER SUPPORT, REAR BAND, & GEAR UNIT ASSEMBLIES

1) Remove center support bolt from case using 3/8", 12-point thin wall deep socket. Remove intermediate clutch backing plate-to-case snap ring. Withdraw backing plate and 6 clutch plates (3 composition and 3 steel).

2) Remove center support-to-case snap ring. Install Remover (J 21795) on end of mainshaft so that tangs engage groove in shaft. Tighten screw on tool to secure tool on shaft. This will prevent roller clutch movement during gear unit removal.

NOTE: Install piece of pipe over output shaft for use as handle and to prevent spline damage to case bushing when removing gear unit, center support, and reaction carrier.

3) Loosen transmission holding fixture pivot pin slightly so gear unit assembly will not bind during removal from case. With transmission case in horizontal position, shift complete assembly forward and remove from case.

4) Remove output shaft-to-case thrust washer from shaft or case. Place gear unit assembly in Holding Fixture (J 6116 01) using Adapter (J 21364) with mainshaft pointing up. Remove rear unit selective washer from transmission case. Remove center support-to-case spacer.

5) Rotate rear band lugs away from pins and pull band assembly from case. Remove center support assembly from reaction carrier, lifting straight up. Remove center support-to-reaction carrier thrust washer.

6) Washer may be stuck to back of center support. Remove reaction carrier and roller clutch assembly from output carrier. Remove roller clutch assembly from reaction carrier.

Fig. 12: Removing Center Support-to-Case Bolt

Center Support Bolt

COMPONENT DISASSEMBLY & REASSEMBLY

NOTE: When reassembling transmission units, lubricate all bushings, seals, thrust bearings, and mating surfaces with transmission fluid. Use petroleum jelly to lubricate and retain thrust washers.

GOVERNOR

NOTE: Governor, including driven gear, is serviced as complete assembly. Driven gear may be serviced separately and requires disassembly of governor for gear replacement.

Fig. 13: Exploded View of Governor Assembly

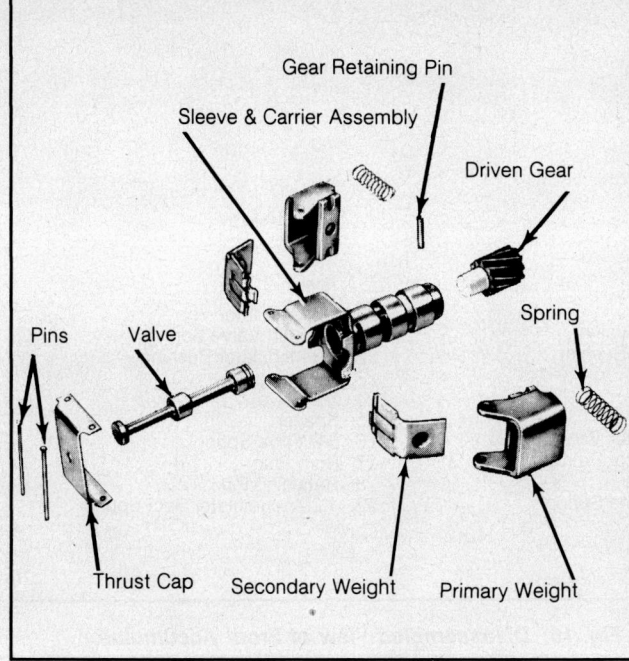

Gear Retaining Pin
Sleeve & Carrier Assembly
Driven Gear
Spring
Pins
Valve
Thrust Cap
Secondary Weight
Primary Weight

Disassembly

Governor weights are interchangeable from side to side and need not be identified for reassembly. Cut off one end of each governor weight pin and remove pins, governor thrust cap, governor weights and springs. Remove governor valve from governor sleeve using care not to damage valve. See Fig. 13.

Inspection

1) Wash all parts in solvent and air dry. Blow out all passages. Inspect sleeve for wear or damage and check for free operation in case bore. Inspect valve for wear or damage and for free operation in sleeve bore. Check driven gear for wear or damage and for looseness on sleeve.

2) Inspect springs for distortion. Make sure weights operate freely in retainers. Make sure valve opening at entry and exhaust is .020" (.51 mm) minimum. Valve opening measurements are made with driven gear up and thrust cap down. Entry measurement is made with weights fully extended while exhaust is measured with weights held completely inward.

Driven Gear Replacement

1) With governor disassembled, drive out gear retaining split pin. Support assembly on 3/16" plates in-

stalled in exhaust slots of sleeve. Place assembly in press. Press gear out of sleeve with long punch. Carefully clean governor sleeve of chips that remain from original gear installation.

2) To install new gear, support governor assembly in same manner as for gear removal. Press gear into sleeve until nearly seated. Remove any chips that may have been shaved off gear. Press gear in until bottomed on shoulder.

3) New pin hole must be drilled through sleeve and gear. Support governor in press. Locate hole position 90° from existing hole. Center punch and drill new hole through sleeve and gear with 1/8" drill. Install retaining split pin.

Reassembly

Install valve in bore of sleeve, then install weights, springs, and thrust cap on sleeve. Align pin holes in thrust cap, weight assemblies, and sleeve. Install new pins. Crimp both ends of pin to prevent them from falling out. Check weight assemblies for free operation in sleeve. Make sure valve is free in sleeve.

CONTROL VALVE ASSEMBLY

NOTE: As each valve is removed, place individual valve in separate location relative to its position in valve body. Place each part from each valve bore in order that it is removed from valve bore. None of valves or springs are interchangeable. Keep them in set with proper valve.

Disassembly

1) Position control valve assembly with gasket surface up and accumulator pocket at bottom. Remove manual valve from upper bore. Install Compressor Tool (J 21885) on accumulator piston. Compress piston and remove "E" retaining ring. Remove piston and spring.

2) Remove all retaining pins (except grooved pin in lower left bore) from bores with pin punch. Drive pins from outer side of valve body. When removing pins, hold hand over bore end in case spring forces components out of bore. See Fig. 14. Pry grooved pin from lower left bore with long nose pliers.

3) Remove 1-2 valve train from upper right bore. Remove 2-3 valve train from center right bore. From lower right bore, remove 3-2 valve train. From upper left bore, remove detent valve train. From lower left bore, remove 1-2 accumulator valve train.

Inspection

1) Wash all parts in clean solvent. Inspect all valves and bushings carefully to make sure they are free from dirt and are not damaged in any way. If burrs are present, remove with fine stone or fine grade crocus cloth and light oil.

CAUTION: When removing burrs from valves, use care not to round off shoulders of valves.

2) Test all valves and bushings in their bores to make sure they slide freely of their own weight. Only manual valve can be serviced separately. If other valves require replacement, complete valve body assembly should be replaced.

3) Inspect valve body for cracks or scored bores. Check all springs for distortion or collapsed coils. Inspect accumulator piston and oil ring for damage.

Fig. 14: Exploded View of Control Valve Assembly

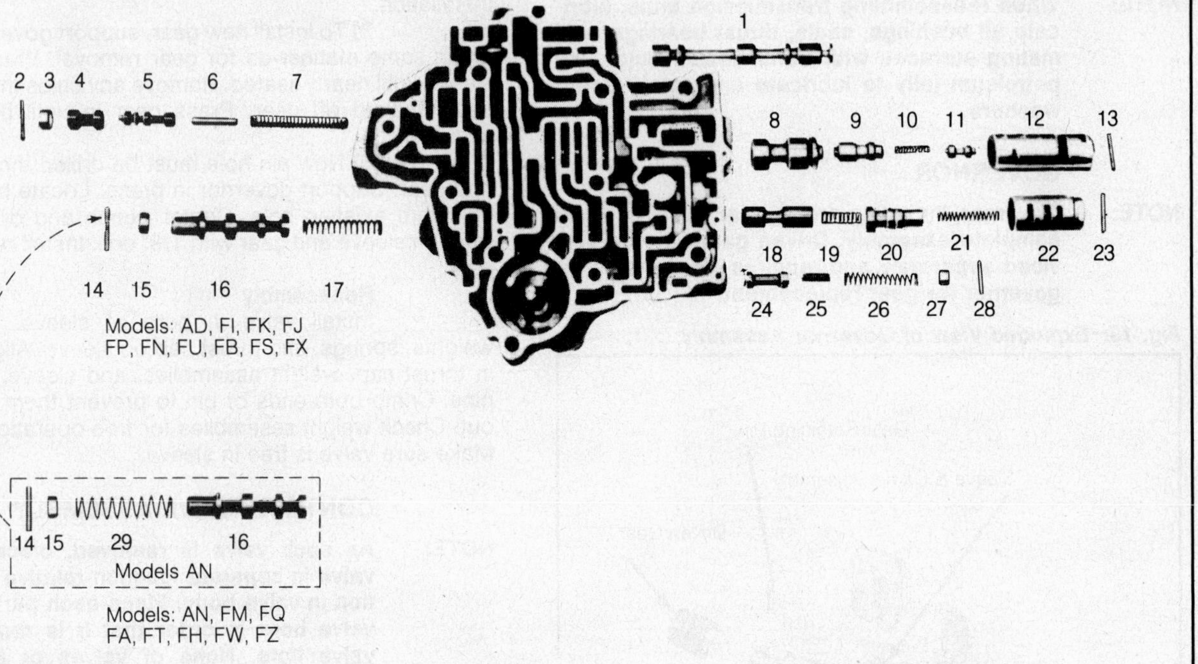

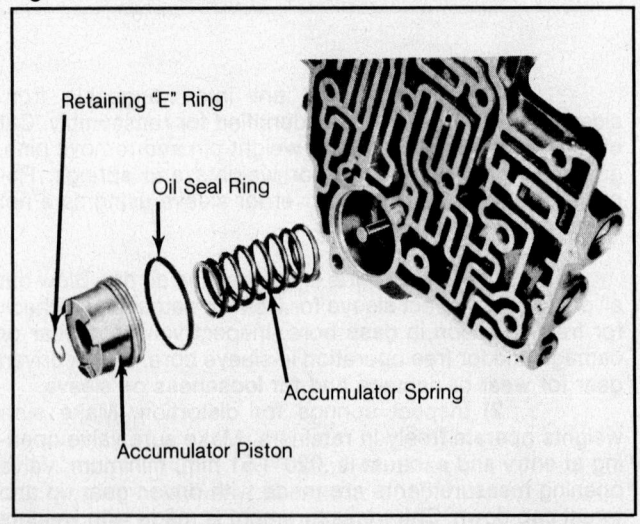

Models: AD, FI, FK, FJ
FP, FN, FU, FB, FS, FX

Models AN

Models: AN, FM, FQ
FA, FT, FH, FW, FZ

1. Manual Valve
2. Retaining Pin
3. Bore Plug
4. Detent Valve
5. Detent Regulator Valve
6. Spacer
7. Detent Regulator Valve Spring
8. 1-2 Shift Valve
9. 1-2 Detent Valve
10. 1-2 Regulator Valve Spring

11. 1-2 Regulator Valve
12. 1-2 Modulator Bushing
13. Retaining Pin
14. Retaining Pin
15. Bore Plug
16. 1-2 Accumulator Valve
17. 1-2 Accumulator Pri. Spring
18. 2-3 Shift Valve
19. 3-2 Intermediate Spring

20. 2-3 Modulator Valve
21. 2-3 Shift Valve Spring
22. 2-3 Modulator Bushing
23. Retaining Pin
24. 3-2 Valve
25. Spacer
26. 3-2 Valve Spring
27. Bore Plug
28. Retaining Pin
29. 1-2 Accumulator Sec. Spring

NOTE: Do not remove Teflon oil seal from front accumulator piston unless seal ring needs replacing. Service oil seal ring is cast iron.

Reassembly

1) Install front accumulator spring and piston into valve body. Compress piston and spring and install retaining "E" clip. In lower left bore, install 1-2 accumulator primary spring and 1-2 accumulator valve, stem end out, then install bore plug. Some control valve assemblies use secondary spring on 1-2 accumulator valve.

2) Secondary spring should be installed between valve and bore plug. It will be necessary to compress secondary spring to install retaining pin. Install retaining pin from cast surface side of valve body, with grooved end of pin installed last. Tap pin in until flush with cast surface of valve body

3) Install spacer inside detent regulator spring. Install spring and spacer in upper left bore, making sure spring seats in bottom of bore. Compress spring and retain in place with small screwdriver. Install detent regulator valve (stem end out) and detent valve (narrow land first).

4) Install bore plug with open end out. Press in plug and remove screwdriver. Install retaining pin from upper side of valve body. Install 3-2 valve in lower right

Fig. 15: Disassembled View of Front Accumulator

Retaining "E" Ring

Oil Seal Ring

Accumulator Spring

Accumulator Piston

bore, then install valve spring with spacer inside. Install bore plug (open end out) and drive in retaining pin from upper side.

5) Install 3-2 intermediate spring into open end of 2-3 valve. Install spring and valve into center right bore, making sure valve seats in bottom of bore. Install 2-3 modulator valve into 2-3 modulator bushing (open end first). Install both parts into center right bore. Install 2-3 shift valve spring into open end of 2-3 modulator valve. Compress spring and install retaining pin from upper side.

6) In upper right bore, install 1-2 shift valve (stem end out). Make sure valve seats in bottom of bore. Install 1-2 regulator valve (large stem first), spring and 1-2 detent valve (hole end first) into 1-2 modulator bushing. Install parts into upper right bore. Compress bushing against spring and install retaining pin. Install manual valve with detent pin groove to right.

REAR SERVO
Disassembly
Remove rear accumulator piston from rear servo piston. Remove "E" ring retaining rear servo piston to band apply pin. Remove seal and rear servo piston from pin. Remove washer, spring and spring retainer. *See Fig. 16.*

CAUTION: Do not remove Teflon oil seal rings from piston unless they require replacement. If small ring requires replacement, use aluminum oil seal ring. If large ring requires replacement, use only Teflon oil seal ring as groove is machined for it.

Inspection
Check freedom of oil seal rings in grooves of piston. Inspect fit of band apply pin in servo piston. Inspect band apply pin for scores or cracks. Make sure band apply pin is proper size as selected during disassembly.

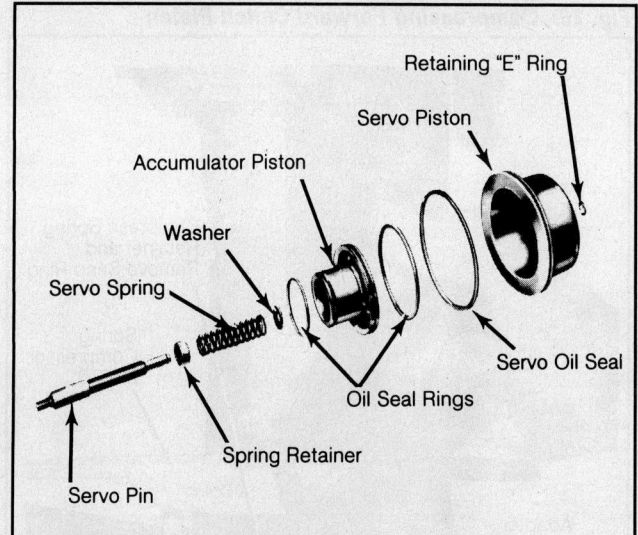

Fig. 16: Exploded View of Rear Servo Assembly

Reassembly
To reassemble, reverse disassembly procedure.

FRONT SERVO
Inspection
Inspect servo pin, piston and oil seal ring for wear or damage. Check fit of servo pin in piston and in case bore.

NOTE: Do not remove Teflon oil seal ring from servo piston unless seal ring requires replacement. Replacement oil seal ring is aluminum.

Fig. 17: Exploded View of Front Servo Assembly

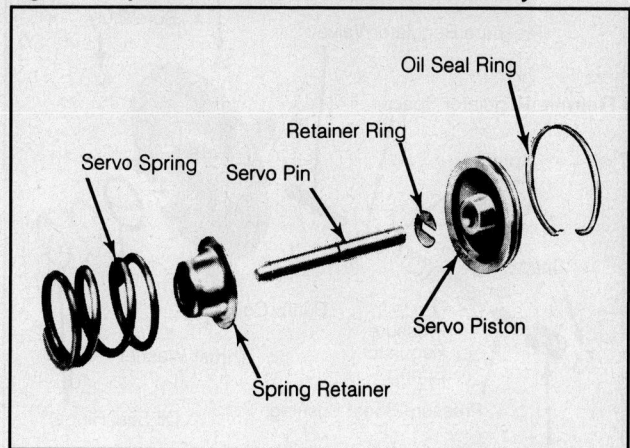

OIL PUMP
Disassembly
1) Place pump assembly in holding fixture (Adapter J 21364 and Rear Unit Holding Fixture J 6116) with stator shaft pointing down. Compress regulator boost valve bushing against pressure regulator spring. Remove snap ring.

CAUTION: Pressure regulator spring is very tightly compressed.

2) Withdraw regulator boost valve bushing and valve, then pressure regulator spring. Remove regulator valve, spring retainer, and spacer(s) if present. Remove 5 pump cover attaching bolts (noting different lengths and relative positions). Separate cover from body. Index mark drive and driven gears for reassembly reference and remove from pump body.

3) Reassembly of pump gears in same position will ensure quietest possible operation of oil pump. Remove retaining pin and bore plug from end of regulator bore. Remove 2 oil seal rings from cover. Remove pump-to-forward clutch housing thrust washer.

Inspection
1) Inspect all parts for scoring, galling, or other damage. Install pump gears in pump body. Check pump body face-to-gear face clearance with feeler gauge and straightedge. Clearance should be .0008-.0035" (.020-.089 mm). Check overall flatness of pump body and cover faces.

2) Check oil ring grooves and stator shaft for damage or wear. Make certain oil passages are clear and nonporous. Make sure pressure regulator and boost valves are free in bore. Install pump cover oil seal rings in counterbore of forward clutch housing and check for proper fit. Make sure 1/8" breather hole in pump cover is open.

NOTE: Several different pump covers are used in service. Current production solid type pressure regulator valve does not contain oil holes or orifice cup plug as did previous models. Solid valve must be used ONLY in pump cover with squared-off pressure regulator boss (at boost bushing end). Previous pressure regulator valve (with oil holes and orifice cup plug) may be used with either type pump cover.

Fig. 18: Exploded View of Oil Pump Cover

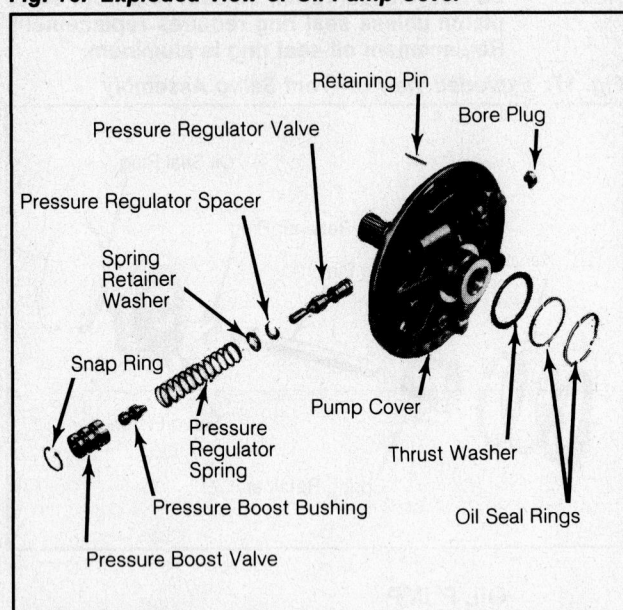

Reassembly

1) Reverse disassembly procedure. When installing front unit thrust washer, make sure it is proper thickness as determined at disassembly. See FRONT UNIT END PLAY CHECK. Install gears in pump body with index marks made at disassembly aligned.

2) If correct, driving tangs on drive gear should face upward. Install pump cover attaching bolts, making sure to install correct length bolts in corresponding holes. Leave bolts one turn loose.

3) Install Alignment Strap (J 21368) to align cover and body. Tighten attaching bolts and remove alignment band. Install new square-cut "O" ring on pump. Install new pump oil seal on front of pump using Installer (J 21359).

Fig. 19: Current Type Pump Cover

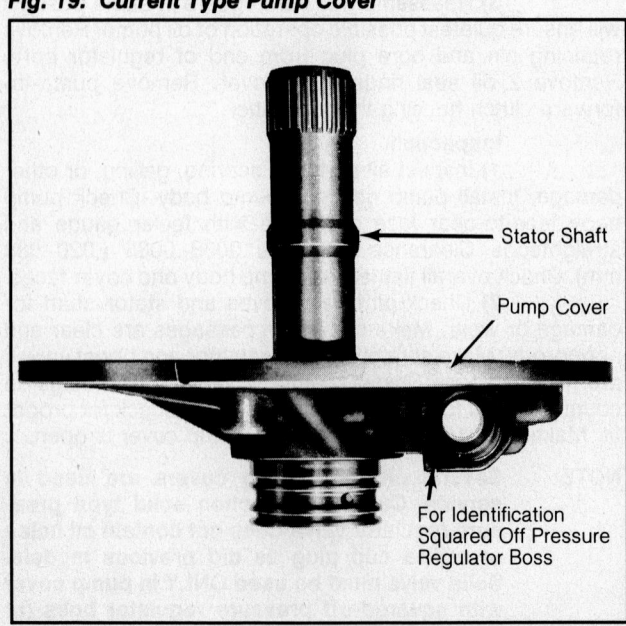

Solid pressure regulator valve must be installed in this type of cover.

Bushing Replacement

1) To replace oil pump body bushing, disassemble pump and remove front seal. Support pump body on wood blocks. Drive bushing from body with Remover/Installer (J 8092 and J 21465 17). Clean pump bushing bore. Drive bushing squarely into bore until flush or .010" (.25 mm) below gear pocket face.

2) To replace stator shaft rear bushing, mount pump cover in vise with stator shaft held in brass jaws. Assemble Remover (J 21465 15) to slide hammer and Adapter (J 2619 and J 2619 4). Thread remover into bushing. Use slide hammer to remove bushing.

3) Clean any shavings from stator bore. Place pump cover in vise with stator shaft resting on block of wood. Place new bushing on shoulder of Installer (J 21465 2). Bushing should be driven squarely into bore to depth of 19/32".

4) To replace stator shaft front bushing, mount pump cover in vise with stator shaft held in brass jaws. Attach bushing Remover (J 21465 15) to Slide Hammer and Adapter (J 2619 and J 2619 4). Thread removal tool into front bushing.

5) Remove bushing with slide hammer. Clean shavings from stator shaft. Assemble Installer with Drive Handle (J 21465 3 and J 8092). Support hub of pump cover on soft material to protect ring lands. Place bushing on installer and drive squarely into bore with lead or brass hammer.

FORWARD CLUTCH
Disassembly

1) Place forward clutch assembly in Adapter and Holding Fixture (J 21364 and J 6116 01) with turbine shaft pointing down. Do not damage turbine shaft. Remove forward clutch housing-to-direct clutch hub snap ring and withdraw hub. Remove forward clutch hub and one thrust washer from each side of hub.

Fig. 20: Compressing Forward Clutch Piston

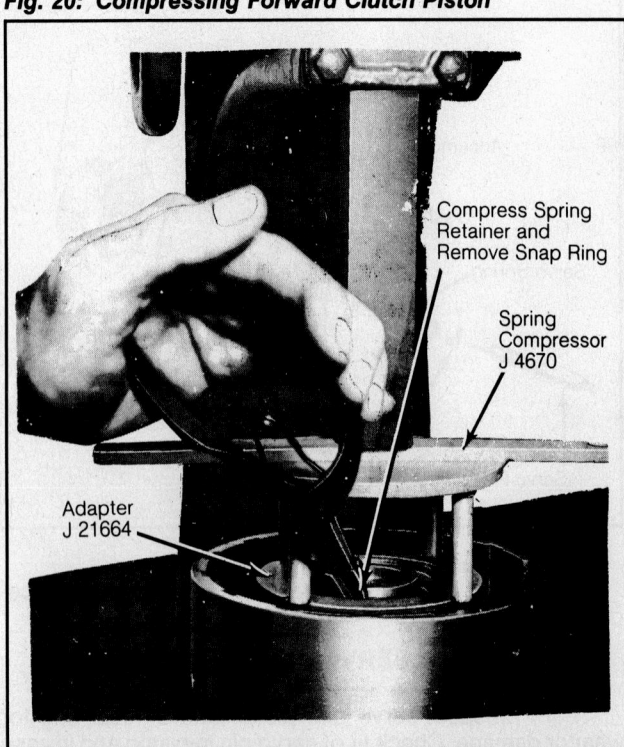

Compress piston to remove snap ring from hub.

GENERAL MOTORS TURBO HYDRA-MATIC 400 (Cont.)

Fig. 21: Exploded View of Forward Clutch Assemby

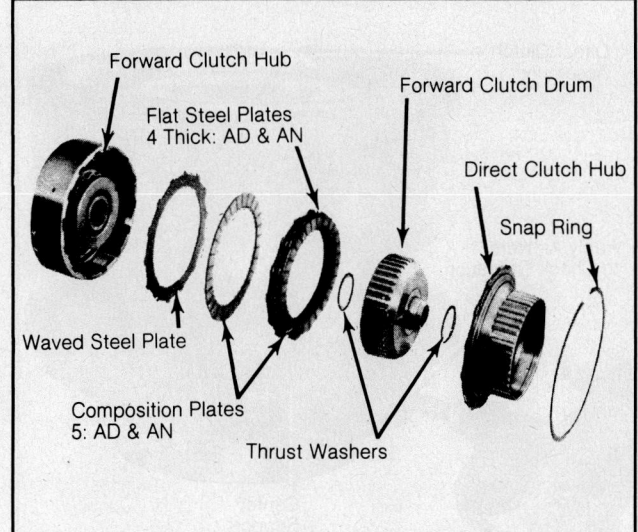

- Forward Clutch Hub
- Flat Steel Plates 4 Thick: AD & AN
- Forward Clutch Drum
- Direct Clutch Hub
- Snap Ring
- Waved Steel Plate
- Composition Plates 5: AD & AN
- Thrust Washers

2) Remove composition and steel clutch plates. Place forward clutch assembly in press with turbine shaft pointing down. Using Clutch Spring Compressor and Adapter (J 4670 01 and J 21664), compress spring retainer and remove snap ring. Remove tools. Lift out spring retainer and 16 clutch release springs.

NOTE: Keep forward clutch release springs separate from direct clutch release springs.

3) Remove forward clutch piston from housing. Remove inner and outer seals from piston. Remove center piston seal from clutch housing. If turbine shaft or housing is damaged, place housing in press with shaft facing down. Using 3" driver, press turbine shaft out of forward clutch housing.

Inspection

Inspect clutch plates for burning, scoring, or wear. Check release springs for distortion or collapsed coils. Inspect clutch hubs for worn splines and thrust faces. Check for clear lubrication passages in housing, hub, and turbine shaft. Check piston for cracks. Check turbine shaft and clutch housing for wear, scoring, or other damage. Make sure ball check in housing moves freely.

Reassembly

1) If turbine shaft was removed, place forward clutch housing in press with flat side up. Align shorter splined end of turbine shaft with splines in forward clutch housing. Carefully press shaft into housing until shaft bottoms out.

NOTE: Start shaft into housing, then back off press so shaft can straighten itself. Repeat this step until shaft is going in straight. Failure to do so can result in damage to shaft or housing splines.

2) Invert forward clutch housing on press with turbine shaft pointing down. Oil and install inner and outer seals on clutch piston with seal lips facing away from spring pockets. Oil and install center seal in clutch housing with seal lips facing upward.

3) Place Inner Seal Protector (J 21362) over clutch hub. Place clutch piston into Installer (J 21409). Install assembly into housing, rotating piston clockwise

slightly until seated. Install 16 clutch release springs into piston pockets.

4) Place spring retainer over springs and compress springs with Compressor and Adapter (J 4670 01 and J 21664). Use care to avoid catching retainer in snap ring groove. Install snap ring. Remove tools and make certain all release springs are standing straight.

NOTE: New type of forward clutch housing center seal is being used. It has beveled edge and is interchangeable with old type seal, which has lip edge. Old type seal cannot be used in later model transmissions. Make sure correct seal is installed.

5) Install forward clutch hub thrust washers. Make sure bronze washer is installed on side of hub facing forward clutch housing. Retain washers in place with petroleum jelly. Place forward clutch hub in clutch housing.

6) Lubricate clutch plates with transmission fluid. Install clutch plates, starting with waved steel plate (plate with "U" notch), then alternating composition and flat steel plates (plate with "V" notch) until all clutch plates are installed. See FORWARD CLUTCH PLATE USAGE chart.

7) Install direct clutch hub and retaining snap ring. Place forward clutch housing on oil pump delivery sleeve. Check operation of forward clutch by applying air through forward clutch passage in pump to actuate piston and move forward clutch. *See Fig. 22.*

FORWARD CLUTCH PLATE USAGE

Steel Plate Thickness	Flat Steel	Composition
.077" (1.96 mm)	3	4
.091" (2.31 mm)	4	5

Fig. 22: Checking Operation of Forward Clutch

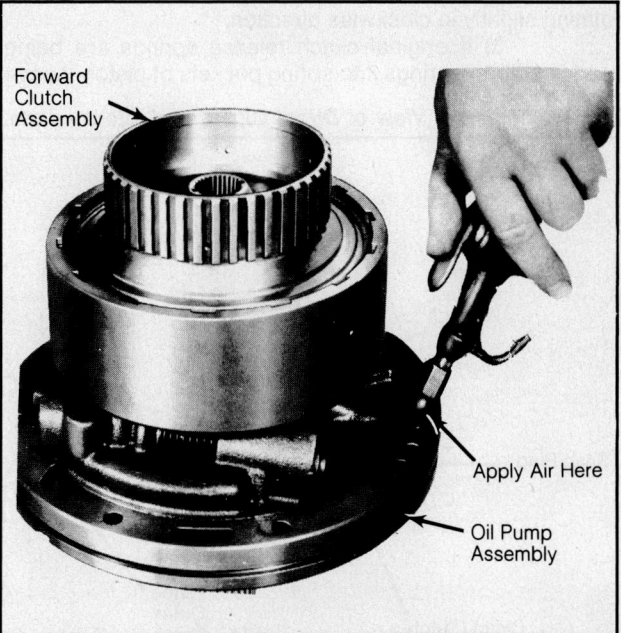

- Forward Clutch Assembly
- Apply Air Here
- Oil Pump Assembly

Compressed air must be clean and dry.

Automatic Transmissions

GENERAL MOTORS TURBO HYDRA-MATIC 400 (Cont.)

DIRECT CLUTCH & INTERMEDIATE ROLLER ASSEMBLY

Disassembly

1) Remove roller retainer snap ring. Remove clutch retainer. Remove roller outer race and roller assembly. Turn unit over and remove direct clutch backing plate-to-clutch housing snap ring. Remove direct clutch backing plate and clutch pack of steel and composition plates.

2) Compress spring retainer and remove snap ring. Use either Clutch Spring Compressor (J 4670), Rear Clutch Spring Compressor (J 6129), or press and Adapter (J 21664) to compress spring retainer. Remove tools, retainer, and 14 clutch release springs.

NOTE: Keep direct clutch release springs separate from forward clutch release springs.

3) Remove direct clutch piston from clutch housing. Remove inner and outer seals from piston. Remove center piston seal from direct clutch housing.

Inspection

1) Inspect roller assembly for damaged rollers, cage, or springs. Inspect cam and outer race for scratches or wear. Inspect clutch housing for cracks, wear, proper opening of oil passages or wear on clutch plate drive lugs.

2) Inspect clutch plates for wear or burning. Inspect backing plate for scratches or damage. Inspect clutch piston for cracks. Ensure free operation of check ball in clutch housing. Check release springs for collapsed coils and distortion.

Reassembly

1) Lubricate piston seals and grooves with transmission fluid. Install new inner and outer seals on clutch piston with seal lips facing away from spring pockets. Install new center seal in clutch housing with seal lip facing upward.

2) Place Seal Protector (J 21362) over clutch hub. Place clutch piston in Installer (J 21409) and insert assembly into clutch housing. Install clutch piston by rotating slightly in clockwise direction.

3) If original clutch release springs are being used, install 14 springs into spring pockets of piston. Leave

Fig. 24: Checking Operation of Direct Clutch Assembly

Compressed air must be clean and dry.

2 opposite pockets with no springs. If replacement springs are used, install 16 springs and use all spring pockets. Place spring retainer on top of springs. Compress springs and retainer with same tool used during disassembly.

4) Install snap ring. Make sure that springs are standing straight. Lubricate clutch plates with transmission fluid. Install plates into clutch housing starting with waved steel plate (if used) or flat steel plate. Alternate composition and flat steel plates until all plates are installed. See DIRECT CLUTCH PLATE USAGE chart. Install backing plate and backing plate snap ring.

NOTE: Do not use radially grooved composition plates in direct clutch. All flat steel plates used in direct clutch are .091" (2.31 mm) thick.

Fig. 23: Exploded View of Direct Clutch and Intermediate Roller Clutch Assembly

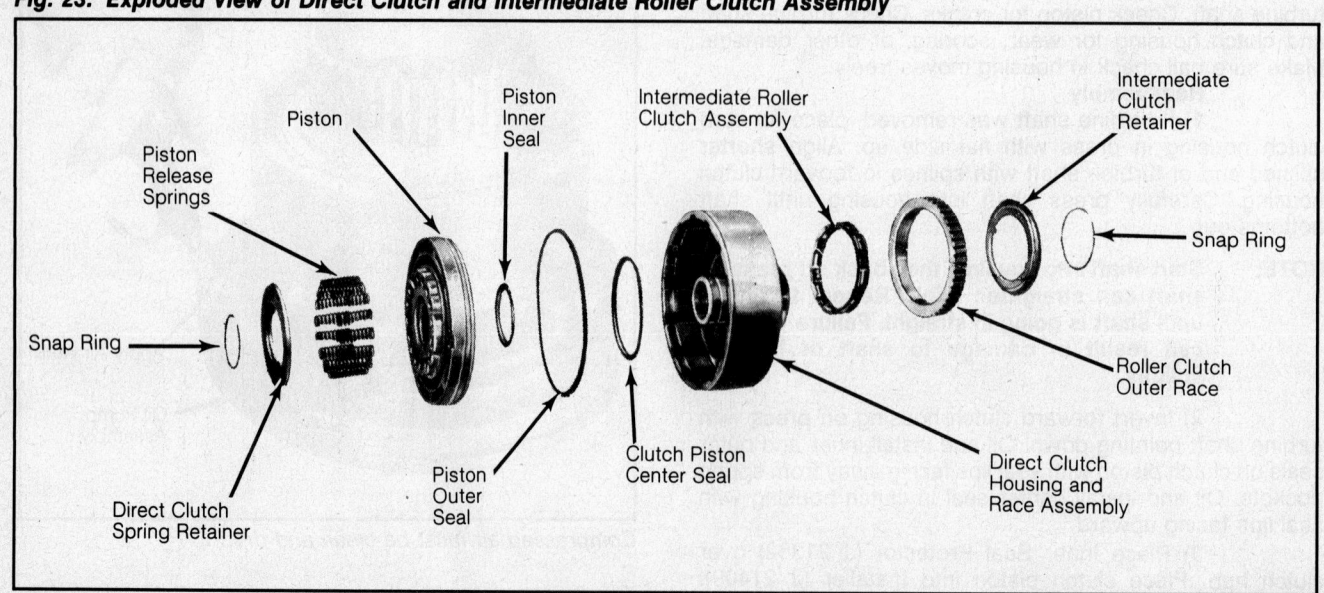

DIRECT CLUTCH PLATE USAGE

Model	Flat Steel Plates	Composition Plates
AA, AB, AC, AE, AH	4	4
AM	6	6
AD [1]	4	5

[1] – Install waved ("U" notch) steel plate first.

5) Install any loose rollers into cage by compressing energizing spring and inserting roller from outer side. Turn unit over and install roller clutch assembly onto intermediate clutch inner cam.

6) Install outer race with clockwise turning motion. Installed outer race should not be able to rotate counterclockwise. Install clutch retainer and snap ring. Place assembly on center support.

7) Check operation of clutch with air. Apply air through left oil feed hole to actuate piston and move clutch plates. Air applied through right oil feed hole (reverse passage) will escape through left oil feed hole. This is normal operation.

CENTER SUPPORT & INTERMEDIATE CLUTCH
Disassembly
Remove 4 center support oil seal rings. Compress spring retainer and remove snap ring. Remove spring retainer and 3 clutch release springs. Remove intermediate clutch spring guide and clutch piston from center support. Remove inner and outer piston seals from piston.

CAUTION: DO NOT remove 3 screws holding roller clutch inner race to center support.

Bushing Replacement
If center support bushing requires replacement, use Driver (J 21465 6) and remove bushing. To install new bushing, align slot in bushing with drilled hole in oil delivery sleeve closest to piston. Drive bushing squarely into bore. Bushing edge should be 0-.010" (0-.25 mm) below top of delivery sleeve.

Inspection
1) Check all parts for wear, scoring or damage. Inspect release springs for distortion or collapsed coils. Check oil ring grooves and oil rings for wear or damage. Rings should fit freely in grooves. Check that lubrication hole of roller clutch inner race is open.

2) Make sure all passages, lubrication grooves and holes are clear of obstructions. Check passages with air to ensure they are not interconnected. Check roller clutch inner race for scratches and indentations. Make sure constant bleed orifice is open .020" (.51 mm).

Reassembly
1) Lubricate and install inner and outer seals on piston with seal lips facing away from spring pockets. Place Seal Protector (J 21363) over center support hub. Install intermediate clutch piston. Make certain that piston fully seats in center support.

2) Install plastic spring guide and evenly space 3 release springs in holes of spring guide. Place spring retainer over springs. Compress springs and install snap ring in groove.

3) Install 4 oil seal rings on center support. Apply air through center oil feed hole to actuate clutch piston. Check operation of clutch piston. See Fig. 25.

Fig. 25: Checking Operation of Intermediate Clutch Piston

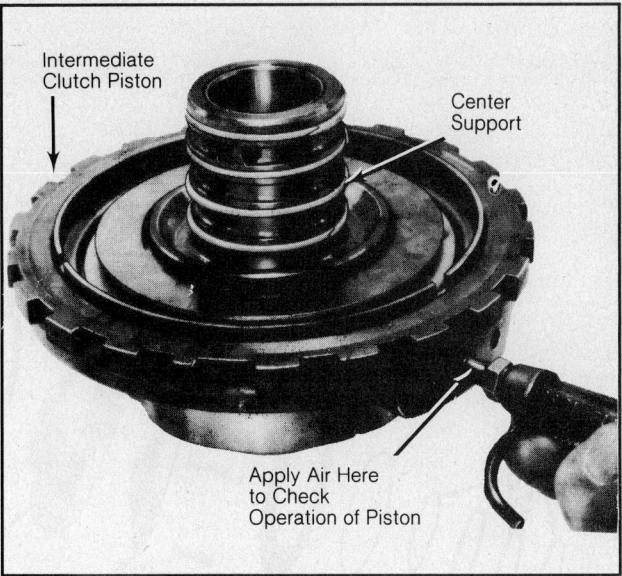

Air must be clean and dry.

NOTE: **All replacement center support oil seal rings are cast iron with overlapping hook ends. Make sure to fit correctly.**

GEAR UNIT
Disassembly
1) Mount gear unit in Holding Fixture (J 6116 01) using Adapter (J 21364). Output shaft must point downward. Remove center support-to-sun gear races and thrust bearing. Outer race may have remained with center support during removal. Remove sun gear from output shaft.

2) Remove reaction carrier-to-output carrier thrust washer. Remove front internal gear ring from output carrier assembly. Turn gear unit over in fixture so main shaft is pointing downward. Remove and discard "O" ring from output shaft. Remove output shaft-to-output carrier snap ring. Remove output shaft.

3) Remove output shaft-to-rear internal gear thrust bearing with both races. Remove rear internal gear and mainshaft from output carrier. Remove rear internal gear-to-sun gear thrust bearing with both races from inner face of rear internal gear. Remove rear internal gear-to-mainshaft snap ring to remove mainshaft.

Inspection
1) Inspect output shaft. Look for galling, damage to lugs or splines, worn thrust washer or bearing surfaces, and rough or damaged teeth on speedometer and governor drive gears.

2) Inspect main shaft. Look for cracks or distortion, damage to splines or snap ring grooves, or ground bushing journal damage. Make sure that lubrication holes are open. Inspect rear internal gear. Check teeth and bearing surfaces for damage or wear. Inspect splines and gear for cracks or damage.

3) Inspect output carrier assembly. Check front internal gear and pinion gears for tooth damage, rough bearings, flaking, cracks, or tilt. Pinion end play range is .009-.024" (.23-.61 mm). Check parking gear lugs for cracks. Check output shaft locating splines for wear.

Automatic Transmissions
GENERAL MOTORS TURBO HYDRA-MATIC 400 (Cont.)

Fig. 26: Exploded View of Center Support Assembly

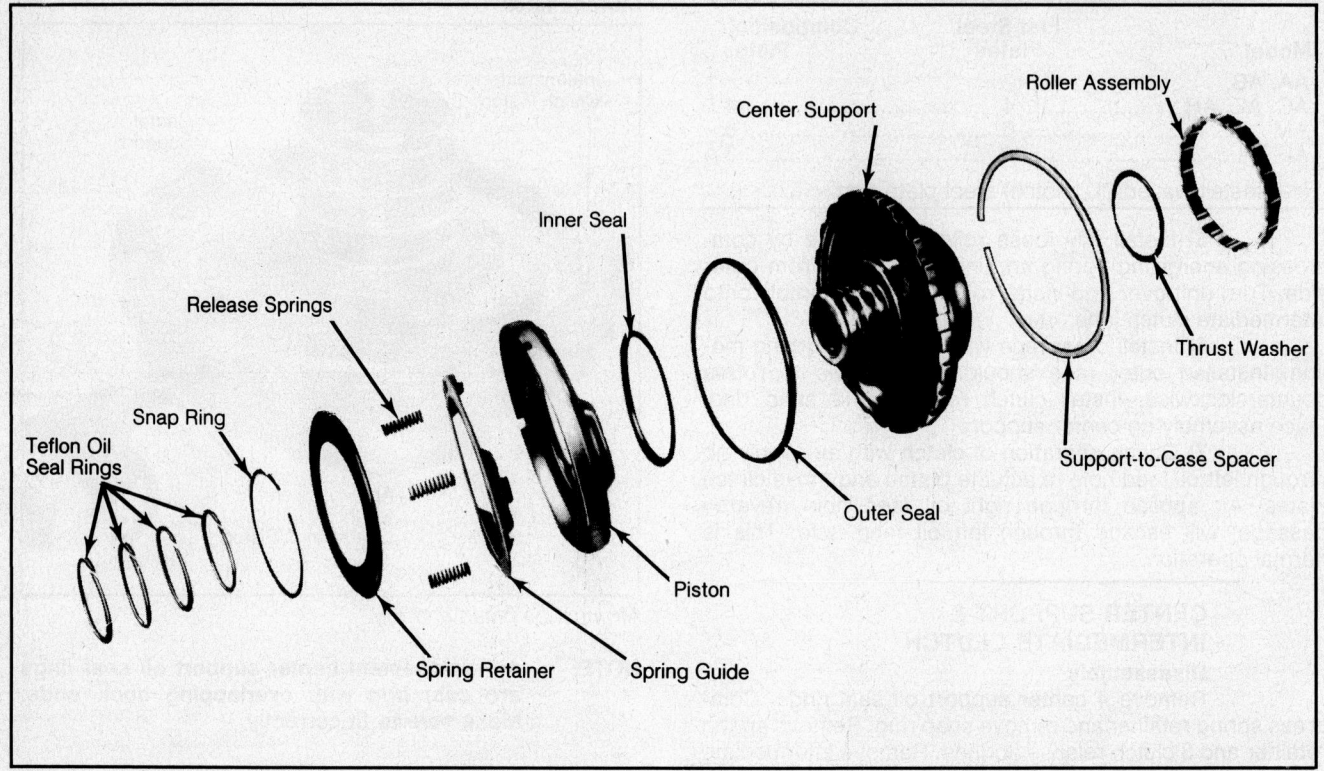

4) Inspect for burning or scoring on reaction carrier band surface, on roller clutch outer cam, and on thrust washer surfaces. If bushing is damaged, carrier must be replaced. Check pinion gears for damage, rough bearings, or excessive tilt. Pinion end play range is .009-.024" (.23-.61 mm).

5) Check roller clutch assembly for damage to rollers, springs, or clutch cage. Inspect sun gear and sun gear shaft for damage or wear to splines, teeth, and bushings. Make sure oil lubrication holes are open on shaft and gear.

Speedometer Drive Gear Replacement
1) Use puller and Gear Remover (J 8433 and J 21427 01) to remove speedometer drive gear. Attach tools on output shaft so puller bolt indexes with end of shaft. Flat face of remover must be under front face of drive gear. Tighten bolt on puller until gear is free on shaft.

2) To install new gear, support output shaft and drive gear on with pipe. Select pipe that does not contact gear teeth, as gear would be damaged during installation. Drive speedometer gear onto shaft until distance from rear face of gear to end of output shaft is 5 21/32" (83.34 mm).

Output Shaft Bushing Replacement
If bushing is worn or galled, thread Bushing Remover (J 21465 16) into bushing. Attach slide hammer and withdraw bushing. Place new bushing on Driver (J 21465 1) and drive into place until tool bottoms. Output flange bushing must be installed so oil hole in flange is aligned with oil hole in hub. Notch in bushing must face outward.

Sun Gear Shaft Bushing Replacement
Support sun gear shaft in soft-jawed vise. Thread Bushing Remover (J 21465 15) into bushing, attach slide hammer, and remove bushing. Place new bushing on Driver (J 21465 5) and drive into place until tool bottoms.

Pinion Gear Replacement
1) Support carrier assembly on front face. Using 1/2" drill, remove stake marks from end of pinion pin(s) to be replaced. This reduces possibility of cracking carrier when pressing out pins. Do not remove any material from carrier as it will be weakened and tend to crack.

2) Using tapered punch, drive or press pinion pins out of carrier. Remove pinion gears, thrust washers and roller needle bearings. Inspect pinion pocket thrust faces for burrs. Remove if present.

3) Install 18 needle bearings into each pinion. Use pinion pin as guide and petroleum jelly to hold bearings in place. Place 1 bronze and 1 steel washer on each side of pinion so steel washer is against pinion. Use petroleum jelly to hold washers in place.

4) Place pinion gear assembly in carrier and install pilot shaft through rear face of assembly to hold parts in place. Drive in new pinion pin from front while rotating pinion gear.

5) Make sure headed end is flush or below face of carrier. Use punch held in bench vise for an anvil. Place carrier over punch and stake pinion pin in 3 places with blunt radius chisel.

NOTE: Both ends of pinion pins must lie below face of carrier or interference may occur.

Reassembly (Complete Gear Assembly)
1) Install rear internal gear on end of mainshaft with snap ring groove. Install snap ring. Install sun gear-to-internal gear thrust races and bearing against inner face of rear internal gear. Retain with petroleum jelly.

2) Place large race against internal gear with flange facing forward or upward. Place thrust bearing in race. Place small race against bearing with inner flange into bearing or downward.

Fig. 27: *Exploded View of Planetary Gear Unit*

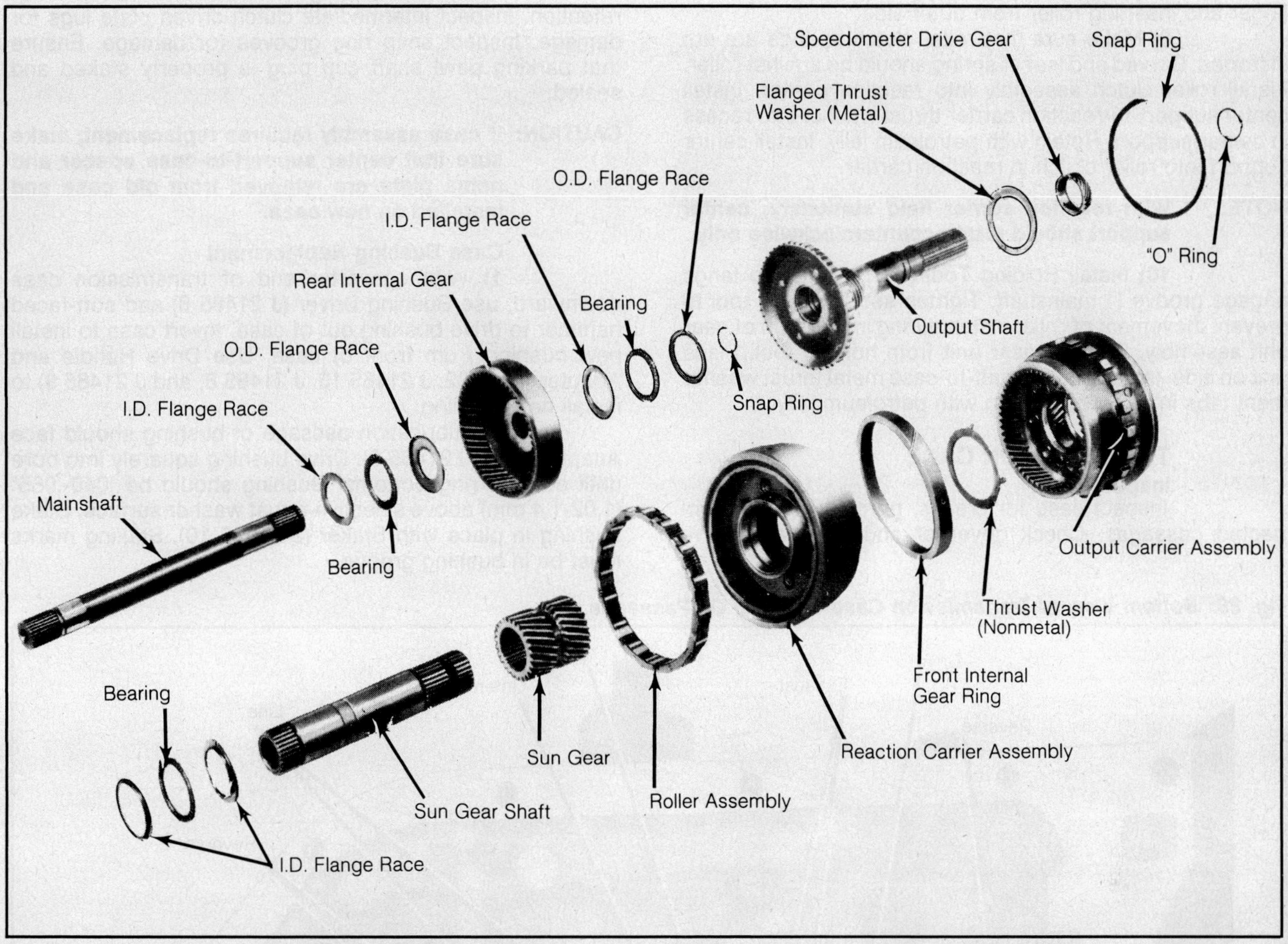

Speedometer Drive Gear — Snap Ring — Flanged Thrust Washer (Metal) — "O" Ring — O.D. Flange Race — I.D. Flange Race — Rear Internal Gear — Bearing — Output Shaft — Snap Ring — Output Carrier Assembly — O.D. Flange Race — I.D. Flange Race — Mainshaft — Bearing — Bearing — Thrust Washer (Nonmetal) — Front Internal Gear Ring — Sun Gear — Sun Gear Shaft — Roller Assembly — Reaction Carrier Assembly — I.D. Flange Race

Fig. 28: *Exploded View of Pinion Assembly*

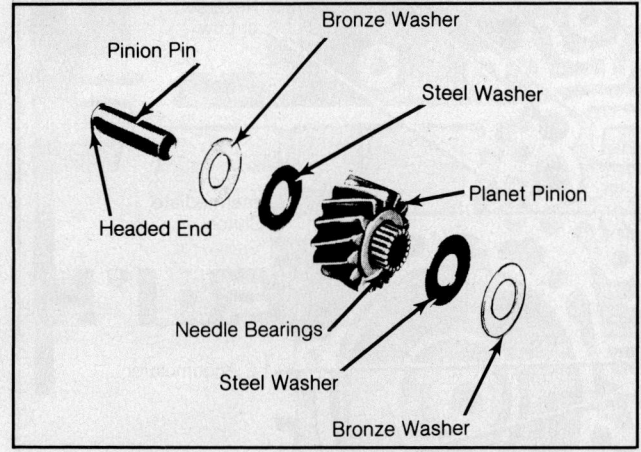

Pinion Pin — Bronze Washer — Steel Washer — Planet Pinion — Headed End — Needle Bearings — Steel Washer — Bronze Washer

3) Oil output carrier pinion gears with transmission fluid. Install output carrier on mainshaft so pinion gears mesh with rear internal gear. Install assembly in Holding Fixture (J 6116 01). Mainshaft must point down. Install rear internal gear-to-output shaft thrust races and bearings. Retain with petroleum jelly.

4) Place small diameter race against internal gear with inner diameter flange facing up. Place thrust bearing in race. Place large diameter race on bearing with outer flange cupped over bearing. Install output shaft into output carrier assembly. Install snap ring holding output shaft into output carrier.

5) Install new output shaft "O" ring. Invert assembly in holding fixture so output shaft faces down. Install reaction carrier-to-output carrier thrust washer with tabs inserted into pockets. Retain with petroleum jelly.

6) Install sun gear so inner chamfer faces down. Install sun gear shaft with longer splined end down. Install gear ring over output carrier. Oil pinion gears in reaction carrier with transmission fluid. Install reaction carrier on output carrier so reaction pinion gears mesh with front internal gear.

NOTE: If front internal gear ring prevents assembly of carrier when new output carrier and/or reaction carrier is being installed, replace front internal gear ring with service gear ring. Front internal gear ring is selective fit at factory but not in service.

7) Install center support-to-sun thrust races and bearing (retain with petroleum jelly). Install large race on sun gear with flange facing up against sun gear shaft. Install thrust bearing on race. Lubricate smaller race with petroleum jelly and install on center support with flange facing toward lower end.

8) Coat reaction carrier-to-center support thrust washer with petroleum jelly. Install thrust washer in recess of center support. Install any rollers that may have come out of roller case by compressing energizing spring with forefinger and inserting roller from outer side.

9) Make sure that roller clutch springs are not distorted. Curved end leaf of spring should be against roller. Install roller clutch assembly into reaction carrier. Install center support-to-reaction carrier thrust washer into recess in center support. Retain with petroleum jelly. Install center support into roller clutch in reaction carrier.

NOTE: With reaction carrier held stationary, center support should rotate counterclockwise only.

10) Install Holding Tool (J 21795 02) so tangs engage groove in mainshaft. Tighten set screw on tool to prevent movement of roller clutch during installation of gear unit assembly. Remove gear unit from holding tool. Place unit on side. Install output shaft-to-case metal thrust washer (bent tabs in pockets). Retain with petroleum jelly.

TRANSMISSION CASE
Inspection
Inspect case for cracks, porosity, or interconnected passages. Check governor and modulator valve bores for scratches or scoring. Check band anchor pins for retention. Inspect intermediate clutch driven plate lugs for damage. Inspect snap ring grooves for damage. Ensure that parking pawl shaft cup plug is properly staked and sealed.

CAUTION: If case assembly requires replacement, make sure that center support-to-case spacer and name plate are removed from old case and installed on new case.

Case Bushing Replacement
1) With converter end of transmission case downward, use Bushing Driver (J 21465 8) and soft-faced hammer to drive bushing out of case. Invert case to install new bushing from front of case. Use Drive Handle and Adapters (J 8092, J 21465 13, J 21465 8, and J 21465 9) to install new bushing.

2) Lubrication passage of bushing should face Adapter Ring (J 21465 9). Drive bushing squarely into bore until adapter ring bottoms. Bushing should be .040-.055" (1.02-1.4 mm) above selective thrust washer surface. Stake bushing in place with Staker (J 21465 10). Staking marks must be in bushing groove.

Fig. 29: Bottom View of Transmission Case Showing Oil Passages

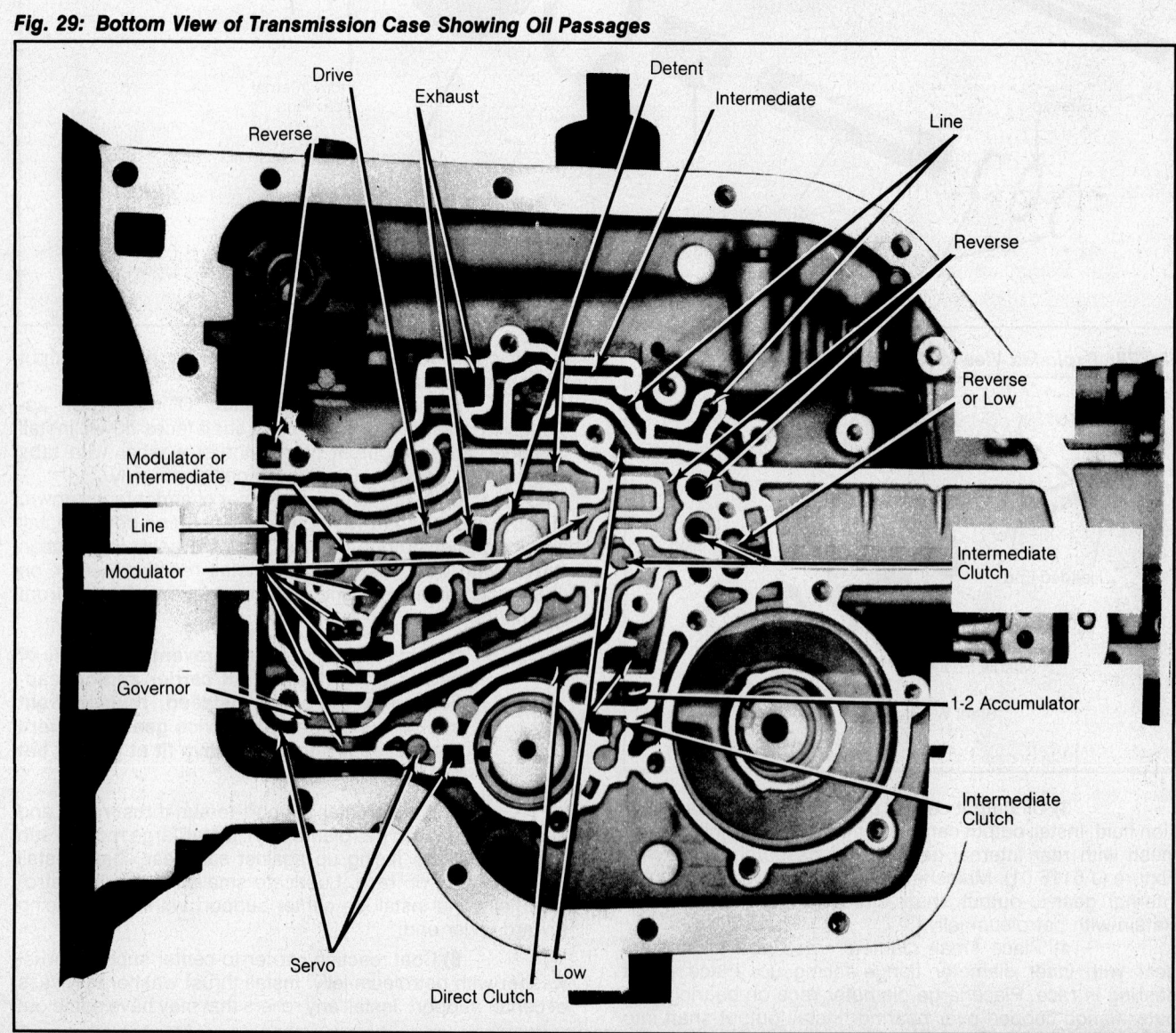

GENERAL MOTORS TURBO HYDRA-MATIC 400 (Cont.)

EXTENSION HOUSING

Inspection

Check housing for cracks or porosity. Inspect gasket mounting face for burrs or other damage. Make sure rear seal drain-back part is not obstructed. Check rear bushing for wear or damage. Replace as necessary.

Bushing Replacement

Remove rear seal and stand extension housing seal end up. Using driver tool, drive or press bushing from extension housing. Use same tool to drive or press bushing into housing. Bushing should be 0-.010" (0-.25 mm) below oil seal counterbore surface. Stake bushing in place using Staker (J 21465 10). Stake marks must be in lube grooves.

NOTE: Staking in production bushings may not be in lubrication groove. Production equipment does not distort bushing surface, making location of stakes optional.

TRANSMISSION REASSEMBLY

PARKING PAWL

Install parking pawl with tooth toward center of transmission. Install parking pawl shaft and shaft retainer clip. Install new shaft cup plug using 3/8" diameter rod. Drive plug into case until shaft bottoms on case rib. Install parking pawl return spring with square end hooked on pawl. Install parking pawl bracket guides over parking pawl.

Fig. 30: Front View of Transmission Case Showing Oil Passages

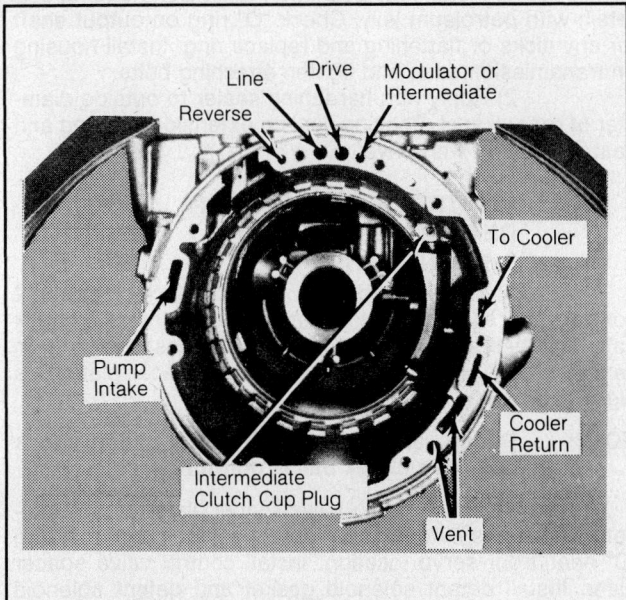

REAR BAND & GEAR UNIT

1) Install rear band assembly so that 2 lugs index with 2 anchor pins. Make sure band is seated on lugs. Install support-to-case spacer against shoulder at bottom of case splines and with gap in spacer adjacent to band anchor pin.

NOTE: Support-to-case spacer is .040" (1.02 mm) thick and both sides are flat. Do not confuse this spacer with either center support-to-case

snap ring, which has one side beveled, or intermediate clutch backing plate-to-case snap ring, which is .093" (2.36 mm) thick and flat on both sides.

2) Install previously selected rear unit end play washer into slots provided inside rear of case. See REAR UNIT END PLAY. Retain washer with petroleum jelly. Place transmission case in horizontal position in holding tool.

3) Install complete gear unit assembly into case by lining up slots. Carefully guide assembly into case. Make sure center support bolt hole is aligned with hole in case.

4) Position transmission vertically with front end of case up. Install center support-to-case snap ring with beveled side up and flat side against center support. Locate gap adjacent to front band anchor pin. Expand snap ring until center support is against shoulder of case.

5) Install case-to-center support bolt by placing locating tool into direct clutch passage of case. See Fig. 31. Handle of tool should be pointing to right (viewed from front of transmission) and parallel to bellhousing mounting face.

6) Apply pressure downward on tool handle. This will rotate center support counterclockwise (viewed from front of transmission). Hold center support firmly counterclockwise against case splines and tighten case-to-center support bolt.

CAUTION: Use care not to burr case valve body mounting surface when using locating tool.

Fig. 31: Using Locating Tool to Install Center Support-to-Case Bolt

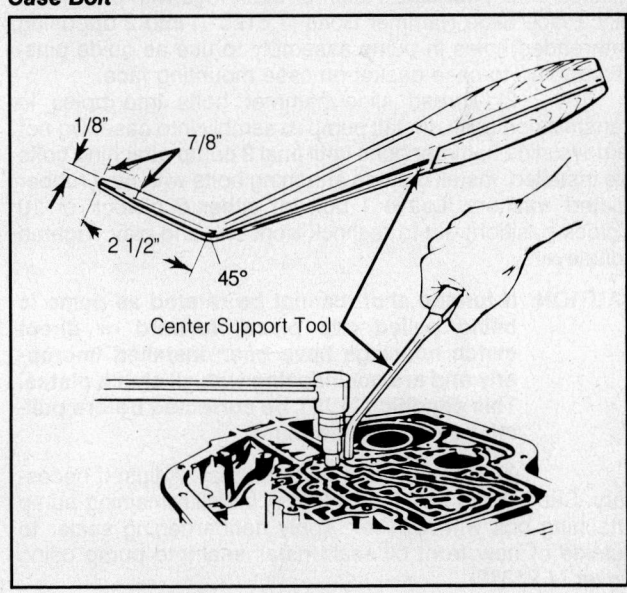

7) Lubricate intermediate clutch plates with transmission fluid. Start with waved steel plate. Alternate composition and flat steel plates until all clutch plates are installed.

8) Install intermediate clutch backing plate with flat machined surface against clutch plates. Install backing plate-to-case snap ring with end gap on side of case opposite front band anchor pin. Before proceeding with transmission reassembly, recheck rear unit end play.

NOTE: Both sides of intermediate backing plate-to-case snap ring are flat. Ring is .093" (2.36 mm) thick.

FRONT BAND & CLUTCH ASSEMBLIES

1) Install front band with band anchor hole over band anchor pin. Apply lug faces servo hole. Install direct clutch housing and intermediate roller assembly. Be certain that clutch housing hub bottoms on sun gear shaft. Splines on forward end of sun gear shaft must be flush with splines in direct clutch housing.

NOTE: It will be necessary to rotate housing to allow roller outer race to index with composition clutch plates.

2) Install forward clutch hub-to-direct clutch housing thrust washer on forward clutch hub. Retain with petroleum jelly. With transmission in horizontal position, install forward clutch and turbine shaft. Be sure that end of mainshaft goes completely into forward clutch hub.

3) Rotate clutch housing so that direct clutch driving hub can index with direct clutch composition plates. When forward clutch is seated, it will be 1 1/4" (32 mm) from pump mounting face in case. Be sure to verify this distance by measuring.

NOTE: Missing internal splines in forward clutch hub are lubrication passages and do not have to be indexed with any particular spline on mainshaft.

OIL PUMP

1) Lubricate turbine shaft journals with transmission fluid. Lubricate Teflon oil seal rings with petroleum jelly. Place Slide Hammer Bolts (J 6125 1) into 2 opposing unthreaded holes in pump assembly to use as guide pins. Align pump-to-case gasket on case mounting face.

2) Thread slide hammer bolts into holes in transmission case. Install pump assembly into case. Do not remove slide hammer bolts until final 2 pump attaching bolts are installed. Install 6 pump attaching bolts with new rubber coated washers. Leave 1 bolt (at either 5 o'clock or 10 o'clock position) out to recheck front unit end play. Tighten bolts evenly.

CAUTION: If turbine shaft cannot be rotated as pump is being pulled into place, forward or direct clutch housings have been installed improperly and are not indexing with all clutch plates. This condition MUST be corrected before pulling pump fully into place.

3) Recheck front unit end play. Adjust if necessary. See FRONT UNIT END PLAY. Install remaining pump attaching bolt with washer. Apply nonhardening sealer to outside of new front oil seal. Install seal into pump using Driver (J 21359).

PARKING LINKAGE, DETENT LEVER & MANUAL SHAFT

Install new manual shaft seal in transmission case using 3/4" diameter rod to seat seal. Install actuator rod into manual detent lever from side opposite pin. Install actuator rod plunger under parking bracket and over parking pawl. Install manual shaft through case and detent lever. Install lock nut on manual shaft and tighten. Install retaining pin, indexing with groove in manual shaft.

NOTE: If work is being done with transmission installed, it may be necessary to bend manual

shaft retaining pin. Straighten pin after installation.

Fig. 32: *View of Oil Pump Cover Passages*

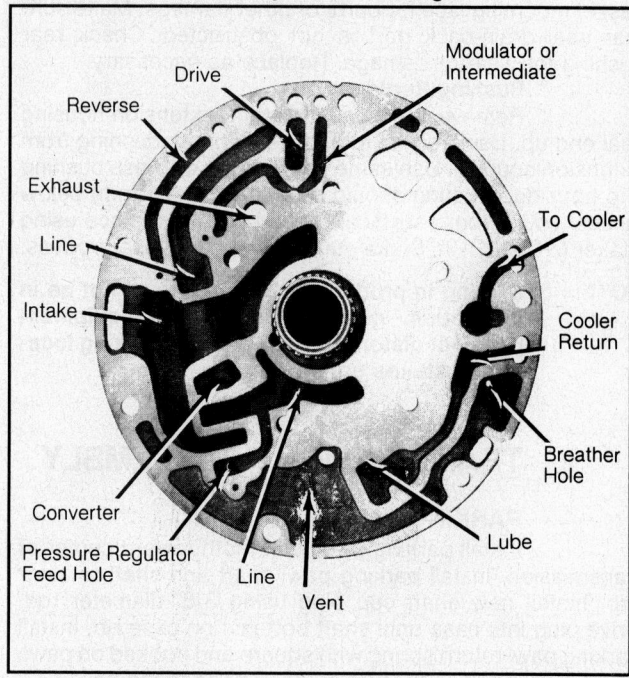

EXTENSION HOUSING

1) Install new gasket on extension housing and retain with petroleum jelly. Check "O" ring on output shaft for any nicks or flattening and replace ring. Install housing on transmission case and tighten attaching bolts.

2) Apply non-hardening sealer to outside diameter of rear oil seal. Position seal on extension housing and seat in housing with driver.

CONTROL VALVE SPACER DETENT SOLENOID, & FRONT SERVO

1) Install 2 guide pins opposite each other into 2 control valve assembly attaching bolt holes. Install 5 check balls into ball seat pockets in case. If transmission is in vehicle, install check balls in pockets of spacer plate. See Figs. 33 and 34.

NOTE: During reassembly, omit direct clutch check ball. This check ball is non-functional.

2) Install control valve spacer plate-to-case gasket. Gasket has extension for detent solenoid and marking "C" near front servo location. Install control valve spacer plate. Install detent solenoid gasket and detent solenoid assembly with connector facing outer edge of case. Do not tighten bolts at this time.

3) Install front servo spring and spring retainer in case. Place retainer ring in groove of front servo pin. Install pin in case with tapered end contacting band. Install Teflon oil seal ring, if removed, on servo piston. Install piston on servo pin with flat side of piston facing bottom pan of transmission.

NOTE: Normal fit of Teflon ring and servo piston is very free. Teflon ring should be replaced only if damaged or if preliminary testing showed evidence of leakage.

Fig. 33: Location of Check Balls in Transmission Case

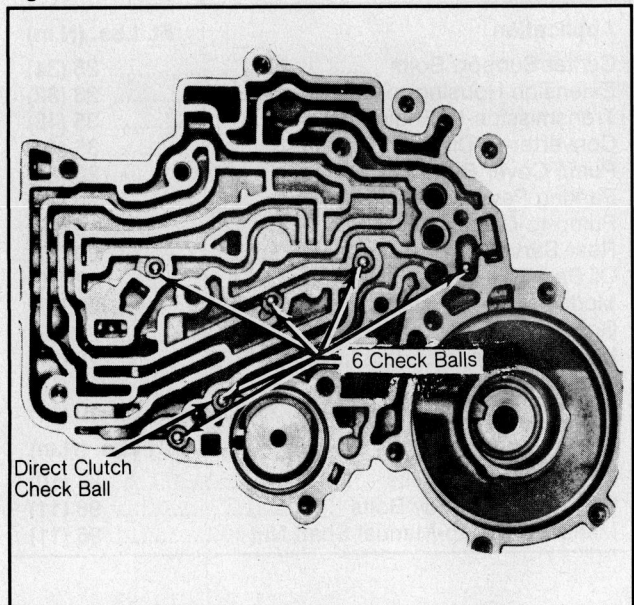

Leave out direct clutch check ball on reassembly.

4) Install new "O" ring on solenoid connector. Install connector with locating tab in notch on side of case. Lock tabs point into case. Connect solenoid lead to terminal on connector.

Fig. 34: Location of Check Balls in Spacer Plate

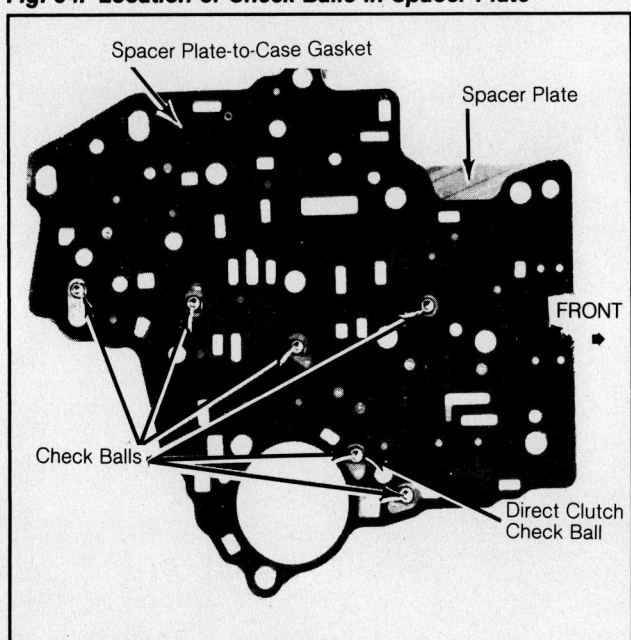

Use this method when transmission is in vehicle.

REAR SERVO

1) Before installing servo, check band apply pin. See BAND APPLY PIN SELECTION CHECK. Make certain that rear band apply lug is aligned with servo pin bore in transmission case.

2) Lubricate inner and outer rear servo bores in case with transmission fluid. Install rear accumulator spring in servo inner bore. Install rear servo assembly. Press down on rear servo assembly and make sure it seats properly in bore. With servo depressed, install gasket and cover. Tighten attaching bolts.

CONTROL VALVE BODY ASSEMBLY

1) Install control valve-to-spacer gasket (gasket marked "VB" near front servo location). Install interchangeable governor pipes on control valve assembly. Install governor screen assembly (open end first) into governor feed pipe hole in case (hole nearest center of transmission).

NOTE: If transmission is installed in vehicle, insert governor screen (closed end first) into governor feed pipe before installing control valve assembly and governor pipes. Feed pipe locates in hole in case nearest center of transmission.

2) Using 2 guide pins, install control valve assembly and governor pipes on transmission. Be careful when aligning governor feed pipe over screen. Make sure gasket and spacer plate are not moved out of position, that manual valve is indexed properly with pin on detent lever, and that governor pipes are properly seated in case holes.

Fig. 35: Installing Detent Roller and Spring

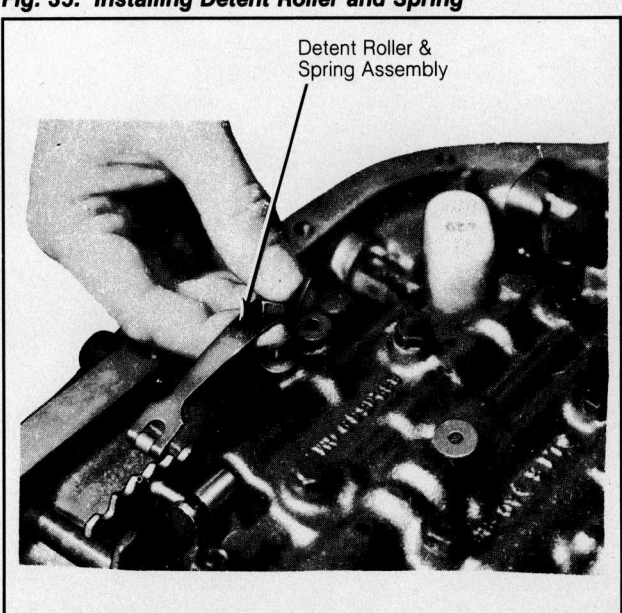

3) Start control valve body-to-case bolts. Remove guide pins. Install detent roller and spring assembly. Install and tighten remaining attaching bolts. Tighten solenoid attaching screws. These screws should be zinc plated to ensure good electrical contact.

GOVERNOR

Install governor assembly into case. Install cover with new gasket and tighten attaching bolts.

SPEEDOMETER DRIVEN GEAR

CAUTION: Speedometer driven gears come in 3 different tooth sizes. Driven gear and matching sleeve must correspond to axle ratio. Never turn sleeve in transmission case as gear damage will result. Shaft center line is eccentric to outside diameter of sleeve.

Install driven gear into sleeve. Install driven gear assembly into case. Install retainer with tangs in sleeve positioning bosses. Install and tighten attaching bolt.

INTAKE PIPE, FILTER & OIL PAN

Install new intake pipe "O" ring seal. Install pipe into new filter assembly. Place filter and intake pipe in case bore. Install filter retaining bolt and tighten. Install oil pan with new gasket. Install and tighten attaching screws.

VACUUM MODULATOR & VALVE

Install modulator valve into case with stem end out. Install new "O" ring seal on vacuum modulator. Install modulator into case with vacuum hose pipe facing front and angled 5° toward top of case. Install modulator retainer with curved side of tangs inboard. Tighten attaching bolt.

CONVERTER ASSEMBLY

Install converter onto turbine shaft. Make sure converter hub drive slots are fully engaged with pump drive gear tangs. Install converter fully toward rear of transmission.

TIGHTENING SPECIFICATIONS

Application	Ft. Lbs. (N.m)
Center Support Bolts	25 (34)
Extension Housing-to-Case Bolts	23 (32)
Transmission-to-Engine Bolts	35 (48)
Converter-to-Drive Plate Bolts	35 (48)
Pump Cover Bolts	20 (27)
Parking Pawl Bracket Bolts	20 (27)
Pump-to-Case Bolts	20 (27)
Rear Servo Cover Bolts	20 (27)
Oil Pan Bolts	12 (16)
Modulator Retainer Bolts	20 (27)
Governor Cover Bolts	20 (27)
Manual Lever-to-Detent Lever	20 (27)
Line Pressure Take-Off Plug	10 (14)
Filter Retainer Bolt	10 (14)
	INCH Lbs. (N.m)
Detent Solenoid Bolts	84 (10)
Control Valve Body Bolts	96 (11)
Manual Lever-to-Manual Shaft Nut	96 (11)

GENERAL MOTORS TURBO HYDRA-MATIC 440-T4
TRANSAXLE

Buick
 Century, Electra
Cadillac
 DeVille, Fleetwood
Chevrolet
 Celebrity, Citation
Oldsmobile
 Cutlass Ciera, Ninety-Eight
Pontiac
 6000

IDENTIFICATION

The transaxle identification code is located on a stamped metal tag on the rear face of transaxle case adjacent to right axle opening.

Fig. 1: THM 440-T4 Transaxle Identification

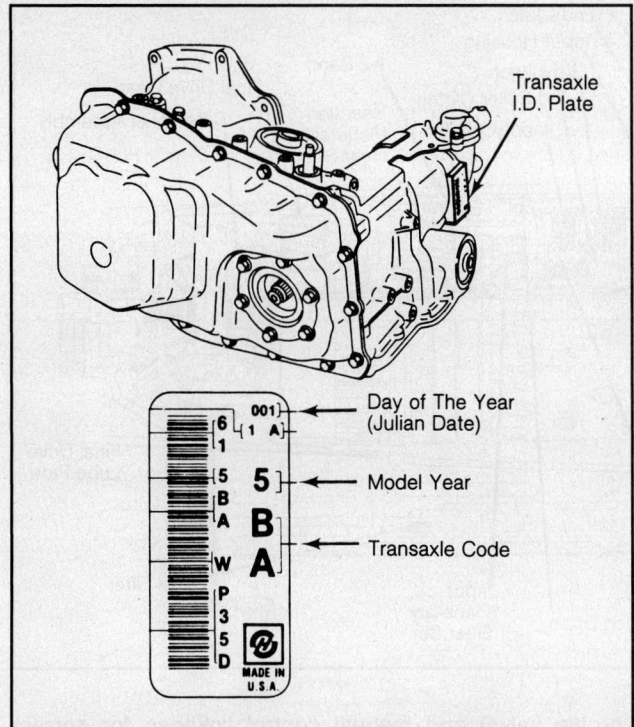

TRANSAXLE IDENTIFICATION CODES

Application	Code
Celebrity & 6000	CW [1], HT [2] & 5CP
Century	BA, BN, BU [3], CW [1] & HT [2]
Ciera	BA & HT [2]
DeVille & Fleetwood	AY [4], OB, OY & 5AM
Electra	BA, BS, BN, BX [5] & OB
Ninety-Eight	BA, BS, BN, BX [5], DY & OB

[1] – Replaced by CN in 1985 1/2 model transaxles.
[2] – Replaced by HJ in 1985 1/2 model transaxles.
[3] – Replaced by BV in 1985 1/2 model transaxles.
[4] – Replaced by AM in 1985 1/2 model transaxles.
[5] – Replaced by BW in 1985 1/2 model transaxles.

DESCRIPTION

The THM 440-T4 transaxle is a 4-speed automatic unit that provides 4 forward speeds, including overdrive. The transaxle assembly consists of a torque converter with clutch, a sprocket and drive link assembly, 1-2 and reverse band assemblies, an input, 2nd, 3rd and 4th multiple-disc clutch assemblies, an input sprag and 3rd roller clutch, a compound planetary gear set, a differential and final drive.

A variable vane type oil pump supplies the transaxle with oil pressure. Oil pressure is regulated by vacuum modulation. Transaxle shift points are controlled by throttle opening through the throttle valve cable.

LUBRICATION & ADJUSTMENTS

See appropriate AUTOMATIC TRANSMISSION SERVICING article in DOMESTIC GENERAL SERVICING section.

TROUBLE SHOOTING

See appropriate AUTOMATIC TRANSMISSION TROUBLE SHOOTING article in DOMESTIC GENERAL SERVICING section.

REMOVAL & INSTALLATION

TRANSAXLE

See appropriate AUTOMATIC TRANSMISSION REMOVAL article in DOMESTIC GENERAL SERVICING section.

TESTING

ROAD TEST
Drive Range
1) From stationary position, accelerate vehicle with selector lever in "D" range. Check 1-2, 2-3 and 3-4 shifts. Shift points will vary depending on throttle opening.
2) Check viscous converter clutch engagement on Cadillac models. Engagement should occur at about 25 MPH at minimum throttle. Engagement speed threshold may increase at high elevation or hot ATF temperature. Viscous converter clutch will not engage if engine coolant temperature is below 140°F (60°C).
3) Check part throttle downshifts by quickly depressing accelerator about 3/4 travel. Check for detent downshifts by fully depressing accelerator at various speeds.

"3" Range
At highway speed in 4th gear, manually shift selector lever in "3". Transmission should shift immediately to 3rd gear. It should not shift back to 4th. Check for detent downshifts by fully depressing accelerator.

"2" Range
While in range "3", shift to range "2". Transmission should shift immediately to "2". Check for 2-1 detent downshift by fully depressing accelerator.

Automatic Transmissions
GENERAL MOTORS TURBO HYDRA-MATIC 440-T4 TRANSAXLE (Cont.)

Fig. 2: Cross Section of Turbo Hydra-Matic 440-T4 Automatic Transaxle

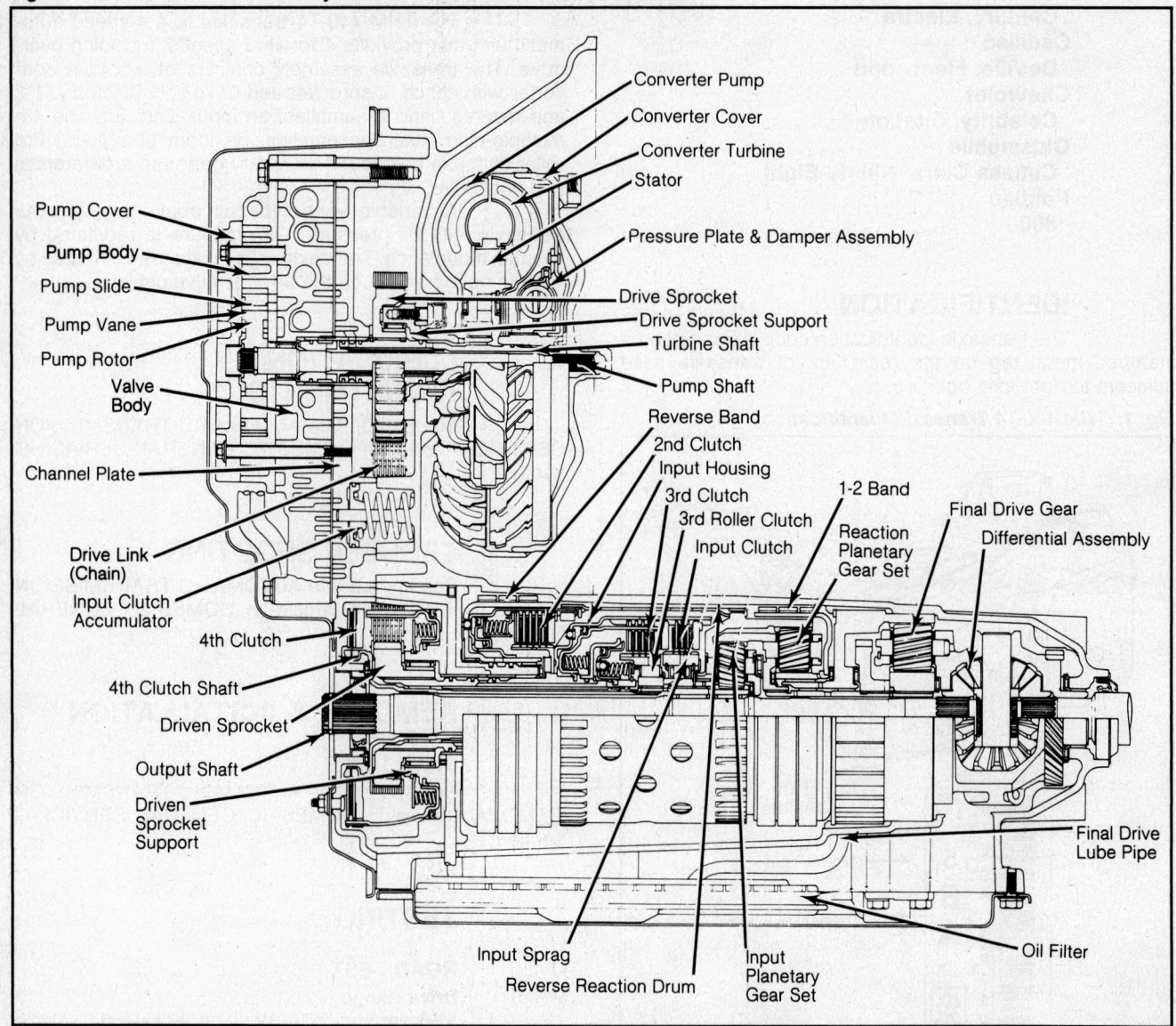

"1" (Low) Range

Position selector lever in "1" and accelerate. A 1-2 upshift should not occur.

Overrun (Engine) Braking

Engine braking can be checked by manually downshifting into next lower range. Engine RPM's should increase and a braking effect should be noticed.

Reverse

Check reverse operation.

HYDRAULIC PRESSURE TESTS

CAUTION: Parking and service brakes must be applied at all times during test. Total time for tests with selector in driving ranges should not exceed 2 minutes.

1) Before making hydraulic pressure tests, check ATF for proper fluid level and condition. Check T.V. (throttle valve) and manual control linkages for correct adjustment. Ensure engine is properly tuned.

2) Check transaxle code *See Fig. 1.* and refer to chart for correct pressure range and engine RPM. Connect a tachometer to engine and an oil pressure gauge to transaxle. *See Fig. 3.*

NOTE: Hydraulic pressure is controlled by pump output and pressure regulator valve. Line pressure is boosted in Reverse, "2" and "1" by reverse boost valve. In Neutral, "D" and Reverse positions, line pressure should increase with throttle opening.

Minimum T.V. Pressure Check

With T.V. cable properly adjusted, check line pressure in ranges and at RPM indicated on chart.

Maximum T.V. Pressure Check

With T.V. cable supported at full extent of its travel, check line pressure in ranges and at RPM indicated in chart.

Automatic Transmissions
GENERAL MOTORS TURBO HYDRA-MATIC 440-T4 TRANSAXLE (Cont.)

2-369

Fig. 3: Hydraulic Pressure Test

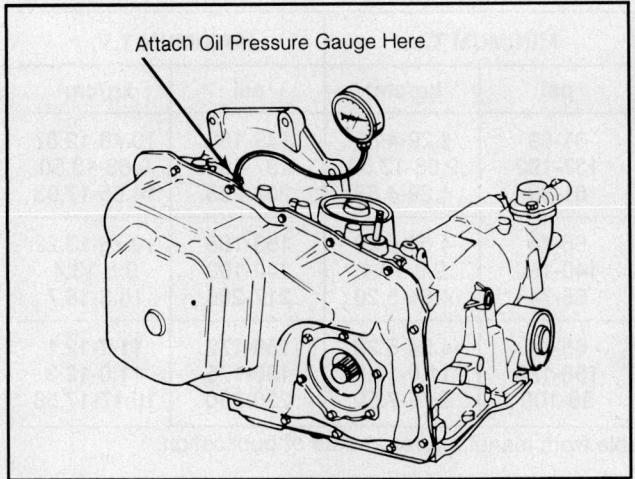

Attach Oil Pressure Gauge Here

Line Pressure Too Low

1) Check for low fluid level, plugged oil strainer or oil strainer "O" ring leaks. Check T.V. cable for incorrect adjustment, binding or breaks.

2) Inspect valve body and pump assembly for loose bolts. Check valve body for missing No. 4, 5 or 6 check balls. Check for stuck or damaged valves.

3) Check 1-2 accumulator piston and seal for damage. Check for damaged low blow-off valve. Check Low-Reverse clutch cup plug for leakage.

4) Check for damaged or missing oil pump vane seals. Check for blocked intermediate oil passages to pressure regulator. Check driven sprocket support-to-case cover for leaks.

Line Pressure Too High

Check T.V. cable for incorrect adjustment, sticking or breaks. Check for sticking throttle valve, pressure regulator valve, T.V. boost valve or shift T.V. valve. Check if low blow-off valve is stuck closed. Inspect pump and case cover for leaks.

SERVICE (IN VEHICLE)

The following components can be serviced without removing transaxle from vehicle: throttle valve control cable, governor assembly, filler pipe, converter-to-flex plate bolts, speedometer driven gear and seal, transaxle pan, transaxle filter, scavenger oil scoop, 1-2 or 3-4 accumulator assemblies and vacuum modulator.

The following components can also be serviced without removing transaxle from vehicle: reverse servo, 1-2 servo, cooler lines, shift control cable, drive axles, case side cover pan, valve body, thermal element, 3rd and 4th pressure switch, solenoid and wiring harness-coverter clutch.

For removal and installation procedures of components other than drive axle shafts, see TRANSAXLE DISASSEMBLY and TRANSAXLE REASSEMBLY procedures in this article.

WHEEL BEARINGS
Removal

1) Losen hub nut. Raise vehicle and remove wheel and tire. Install Boot Protector (J-28712) on drive axle boots. Remove hub nut. Remove brake caliper and rotor. Remove 3 hub and bearing mounting bolts. Remove splash shield.

NOTE: If bearing assembly is to be re-used, mark attaching bolts and corresponding holes for installation in the same position.

2) Install Hub Remover (J-28733) on hub and turn bolt to press hub and bearing assembly off of drive axle. Remove "O" ring. Disconnect stabilizer link bolt at lower control arm. Disconnect ball joint.

3) Remove drive axle from steering knuckle and support out of the way. Remove inner knuckle seal using a brass drift. Hub and bearing are replaced as an assembly.

Installation
To install reverse removal procedure.

DRIVE AXLE SHAFTS

NOTE: Do not overextend joint or internal components could separate, possibly causing joint failure. Use boot seal protectors. Procedures apply to either side drive axle.

Removal

1) Remove hub nut and washer. Raise and support front of vehicle. Remove wheel. Install Boot Protectors (J-29712 for outer boot, J-34754 for inner boot).

2) Remove brake caliper and rotor. Support caliper out of way. Remove stabilizer bar from control arm. Disconnect tie rod end and lower ball joint stud from steering knuckle.

3) Remove drive axle from transaxle with a pry bar, using a wood block fulcrum to protect case cover. Using a Hub Remover (J-28733), remove drive axle from hub and bearing assembly. *See Fig. 4.*

Installation

1) Loosely install drive axle to steering knuckle and transaxle. Connect lower ball joint stud to steering knuckle. Install stabilizer bar to lower control arm. Connect tie rod end to steering knuckle.

2) Install brake caliper and rotor. Install new hub nut and washer. Tighten hub nut to 74 ft. lbs. (100 N.m). Remove boot protectors. Install wheel and tire. Lower vehicle and tighten hub nut to full specification.

CONSTANT VELOCITY (CV) JOINTS
Disassembly

1) Remove rubber deflector ring. Cut off outer joint boot retaining clamps. Spread retaining ring and pull shaft out.

2) To disassemble outer joint, gently tap on cage with a brass drift until cage tilts enough to remove 1 ball bearing. Rotate cage and repeat for each ball bearing.

3) Pivot cage and inner race at 90° to center line of outer race. With cage windows aligned with outer race lands, lift out cage and inner race.

4) To disassemble inner tri-pot joint, cut boot retaining clamps. Remove shaft retaining ring. Slide spider assembly off axle shaft. Remove spacer ring.

Reassembly

1) Coat tri-pot joint boot inside lip with grease and install boot and retaining clamps. Seat spacer ring in axle shaft groove. Slide spider assembly on shaft. Install shaft retaining ring. Install tri-pot housing. Flush grease from housing and repack housing and boot with grease.

2) Assemble outer joint inner race in cage. Apply a light coat of grease on ball bearing grooves of inner and outer races. Install ball bearings.

Automatic Transmissions
GENERAL MOTORS TURBO HYDRA-MATIC 440-T4 TRANSAXLE (Cont.)

HYDRAULIC PRESSURE TESTS

Model [1]	Range @ RPM	MINIMUM T.V.		MAXIMUM T.V.	
		psi	kg/cm²	psi	kg/cm²
AY, BN, BS, BU, CW, HT	"4", "3", "2" @ 1000	61-69	4.29-4.85	149-183	10.48-12.87
	"1" @ 1000	137-192	9.63-13.50	137-192	9.63-13.50
	Reverse @ 1000	61-69	4.29-4.85	207-255	14.55-17.93
BA, BX	"4", "3", "2" @ 1000	66-74	4.64-5.20	153-188	10.76-13.22
	"1" @ 1000	140-190	9.8-13.4	140-190	9.8-13.4
	Reverse @ 1000	66-74	4.64-5.20	217-266	15.3-18.7
OB, OY	"4", "3", "2" @ 1000	66-74	4.64-5.20	158-172	11.1-12.1
	"1" @ 1000	156-175	11.0-12.3	156-175	11.0-12.3
	Reverse @ 1000	96-108	6.75-7.59	230-250	16.17-17.58

[1] – Information on DY, 5AM and 5CP model transaxles not available from manufacturer at time of publication.

CLUTCH AND BAND APPLICATION CHART (ELEMENTS IN USE)

Selector Lever Position	4th Clutch	Reverse Band	2nd Clutch	3rd Clutch	3rd Roller Clutch	Input Clutch	Input Sprag	1-2 Clutch
D – DRIVE								
First Gear						X [2]	[1]	X
Second Gear			X			X [2]	[3]	X
Third Gear			X	X [2]	[1]	X	[1]	
Overdrive	X		X		[3]			
3 – MANUAL THIRD			X	X	[1]	X	[1]	
2 – MANUAL SECOND			X			[2]	[3]	X
1 – MANUAL LOW				X	[1]	X	[1]	X
R – REVERSE		X				X		
NEUTRAL or PARK						[2]	[2]	

[1] – Holding.   [2] – Applied but not effective.   [3] – Overrunning.

Fig. 4: Removing Drive Axle From Hub

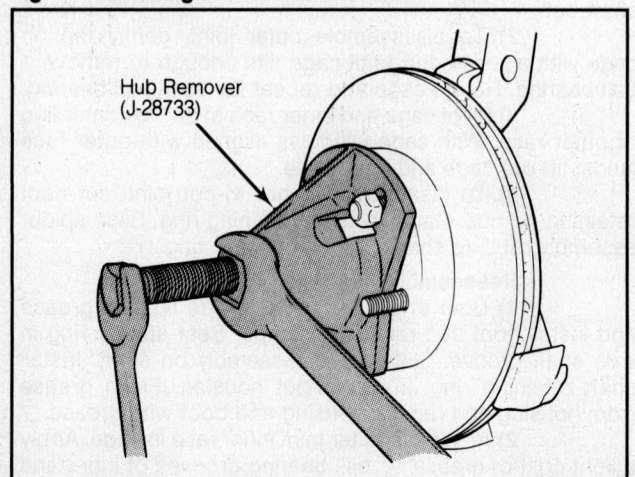

Hub Remover (J-28733)

3) Flush grease from outer joint and repack joint and boot with grease. Push joint assembly onto shaft until retaining ring seats in groove. Install boot retaining clamps. Install rubber deflector ring.

TORQUE CONVERTER

NOTE: **Torque converter is a sealed unit and cannot be disassembled for service or repair. Cadillac models with the 4.3L V6 Diesel engine use a Viscous Converter Clutch. See General Motors Viscous Converter Clutch (VCC) System article in this section.**

LEAKAGE CHECK

Install Pressure Test Plug (J-21369-B) and spacer onto converter hub and tighten. Apply 80 psi (5.6 kg/cm²) air pressure to air valve in tool. Submerge converter in water and check for air bubbles, indicating leaks.

Automatic Transmissions
GENERAL MOTORS TURBO HYDRA-MATIC 440-T4
TRANSAXLE (Cont.)

2-371

Fig. 5: Exploded View of Drive Axle Assembly

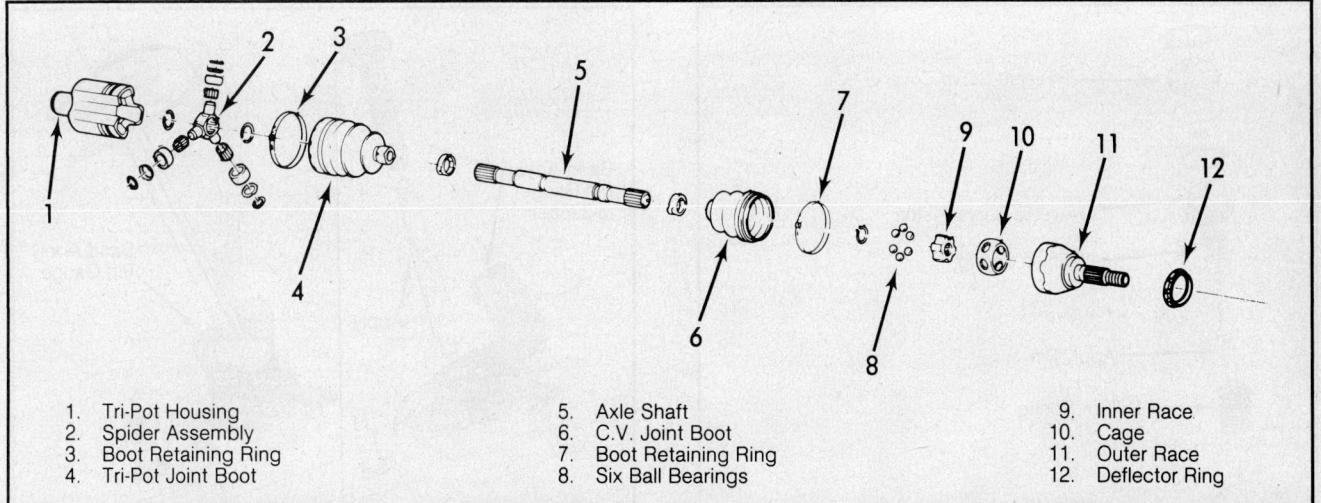

1. Tri-Pot Housing	5. Axle Shaft	9. Inner Race
2. Spider Assembly	6. C.V. Joint Boot	10. Cage
3. Boot Retaining Ring	7. Boot Retaining Ring	11. Outer Race
4. Tri-Pot Joint Boot	8. Six Ball Bearings	12. Deflector Ring

CAUTION: After leak checking converter, bleed air pressure from test plug before removing tool from converter hub.

Fig. 6: Installing Converter Pressure Test Plug

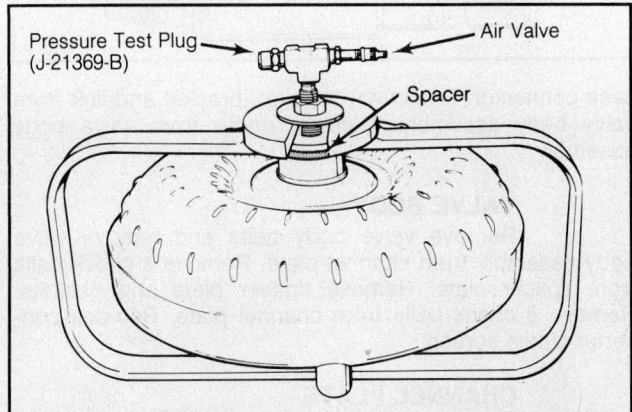

Apply 80 psi (5.6 kg/cmS#2) air pressure to air valve.

END PLAY CHECK

1) Install End Play Adapter (J-29830) into converter hub and hand tighten counterclockwise. Mount a dial indicator onto hub of tool so that dial indicator plunger rests on converter. Zero dial indicator.

Fig. 7: Measuring Torque Converter End Play

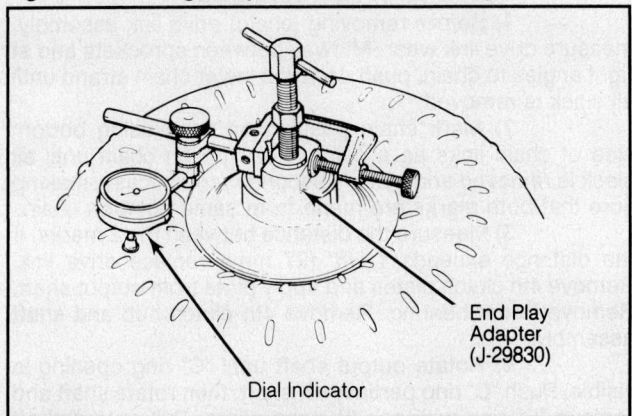

End play must not exceed 0.050" (1.27 mm).

2) Lift up on tool and read play at dial indicator. Converter end play should be less than 0.050" (1.27 mm). If clearance is greater than 0.050" (1.27 mm), replace torque converter.

TRANSAXLE DISASSEMBLY

Thoroughly clean transaxle exterior. Remove torque converter. Place transaxle in holding fixture and drain fluid from transaxle.

SPEEDOMETER DRIVE GEAR, GOVERNOR ASSEMBLY & MODULATOR

Remove speedometer driven gear attaching bolt and retainer. Remove speedometer sleeve and driven gear assembly from governor cover. Remove governor cover and oil seal. Lift out governor and speedometer drive gear as an assembly. Remove modulator retainer bolt and retainer. Remove modulator and "O" ring. Using a magnet, remove modulator valve.

REVERSE & 1-2 SERVO ASSEMBLIES

1) Position transaxle so oil pan is up. Remove oil pan and oil strainer from lower case. Remove accumulator cover bolts and governor control body bolts.

2) Remove accumulator oil pipes, cover body and gasket as an assembly. Remove accumulator cover gaskets and spacer plate. Remove lube oil pipe, retainer, "O" ring and spring. Remove accumulator assemblies. Do not interchange springs. Remove oil scavenging scoop.

3) Remove servo cover snap ring, cover and "O" ring. Remove servo assembly. *See Fig. 8.* Keep reverse and 1-2 servo assemblies separate. Reverse servo apply pin is longer than 1-2 servo apply pin.

NOTE: Make band apply pin selection check at this time to determine correct pin to use during reassembly.

Band Apply Pin Selection Check

Install Band Apply Pin Gauge (J-33382) with reverse servo pin. *See Fig. 9.* Apply 20 ft. lbs. (27 N.m) of torque to hex nut on gauge. Check pin length using band apply pin gauge. See REVERSE AND 1-2 BAND APPLY PIN

2-372

Automatic Transmissions
GENERAL MOTORS TURBO HYDRA-MATIC 440-T4
TRANSAXLE (Cont.)

Fig. 8: Removing Reverse & 1-2 Servo Assemblies

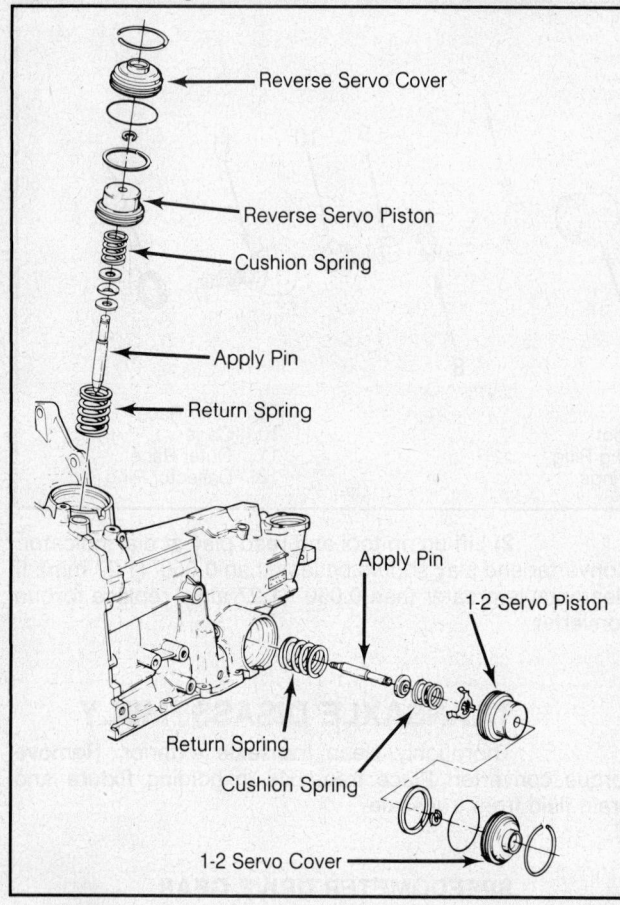

Fig. 9: Checking Band Apply Pin Length

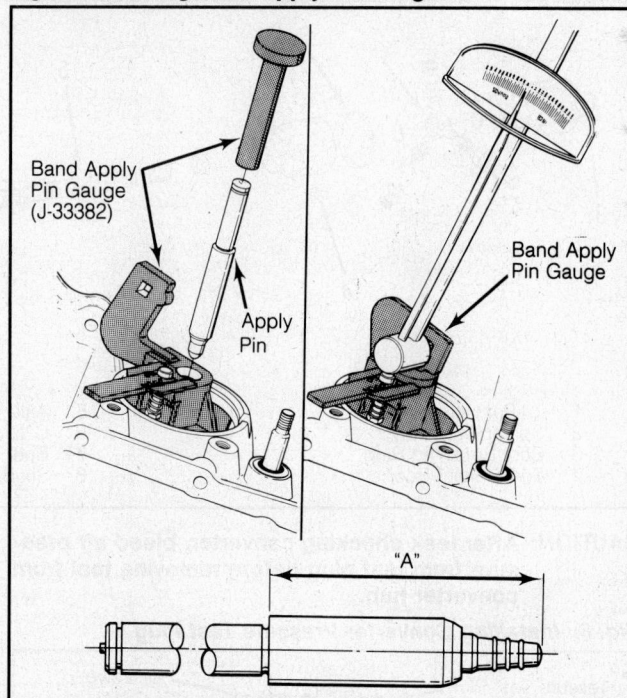

TABLE. If gauge "GO" side will slide under head and "NO-GO" side will not, pin is correct size.

REVERSE AND 1-2 BAND APPLY PIN TABLE

Apply Pin Identification	Dimension "A" In. (mm)
Reverse Apply Pin	
2 Wide Bands	2.79-2.80 (70.9-71.1)
3 Grooves & Wide Band	2.83-2.84 (71.9-72.1)
2 Grooves & Wide Band	2.87-2.88 (72.9-73.1)
1 Groove & Wide Band	2.91-2.92 (74.0-74.2)
No Groove	2.95-2.96 (75.0-75.2)
1 Groove	2.99-3.00 (76.0-76.2)
2 Grooves	3.03-3.04 (77.1-77.3)
3 Grooves	3.07-3.08 (78.1-78.3)
4 Grooves	3.11-3.12 (79.2-79.3)
1-2 Apply Pin	
1 Ring & Wide Band	2.21-2.22 (56.2-56.4)
1 Ring	2.25-2.26 (57.2-57.4)
2 Rings	2.29-2.30 (58.3-58.4)
3 Rings	2.33-2.34 (59.3-59.5)
Wide Band	2.37-2.38 (60.3-60.5)
2 Rings & Wide Band	2.41-2.42 (61.3-61.5)

OIL PUMP ASSEMBLY

Remove case side cover and gaskets. Disconnect wiring harness from solenoid pressure switches and case connector. Remove T.V. lever, bracket and link from valve body assembly. Remove pump from valve body assembly.

VALVE BODY

Remove valve body bolts and remove valve body assembly from channel plate. Remove 4 check balls from spacer plate. Remove spacer plate and gaskets. Remove 8 check balls from channel plate. Remove converter clutch screen.

CHANNEL PLATE

Remove oil pump shaft. Place detent lever in "P" position and remove manual valve clip. Remove channel plate from case. Remove modulator port gasket, upper and lower gaskets from channel plate. Remove input accumulator piston and spring. Remove converter clutch accumulator piston and spring.

4th CLUTCH, OUTPUT SHAFT & DRIVE LINK ASSEMBLIES

1) Before removing (chain) drive link assembly, measure drive link wear. Midway between sprockets and at right angles to chain, push down on lower chain strand until all slack is removed.

2) Mark chain position on case using bottom side of chain links as a guide. Push up on chain until all slack is removed and place a second mark on case, making sure that both marks are made from same point on chain.

3) Maesure the distance between the 2 marks. If the distance exceeds 1 1/6" (27 mm), replace drive link. Remove 4th clutch plates and apply plate from output shaft. Remove thrust bearing. Remove 4th clutch hub and shaft assembly.

4) Rotate output shaft until "C" ring opening is visible. Push "C" ring partially off shaft, then rotate shaft and remove "C" ring with needle-nose pliers. Pull output shaft from transaxle. See Fig. 10.

Automatic Transmissions
GENERAL MOTORS TURBO HYDRA-MATIC 440-T4 TRANSAXLE (Cont.)

2-373

Fig. 10: Exploded View of 4th Clutch, Output Shaft And Drive Link Assemblies

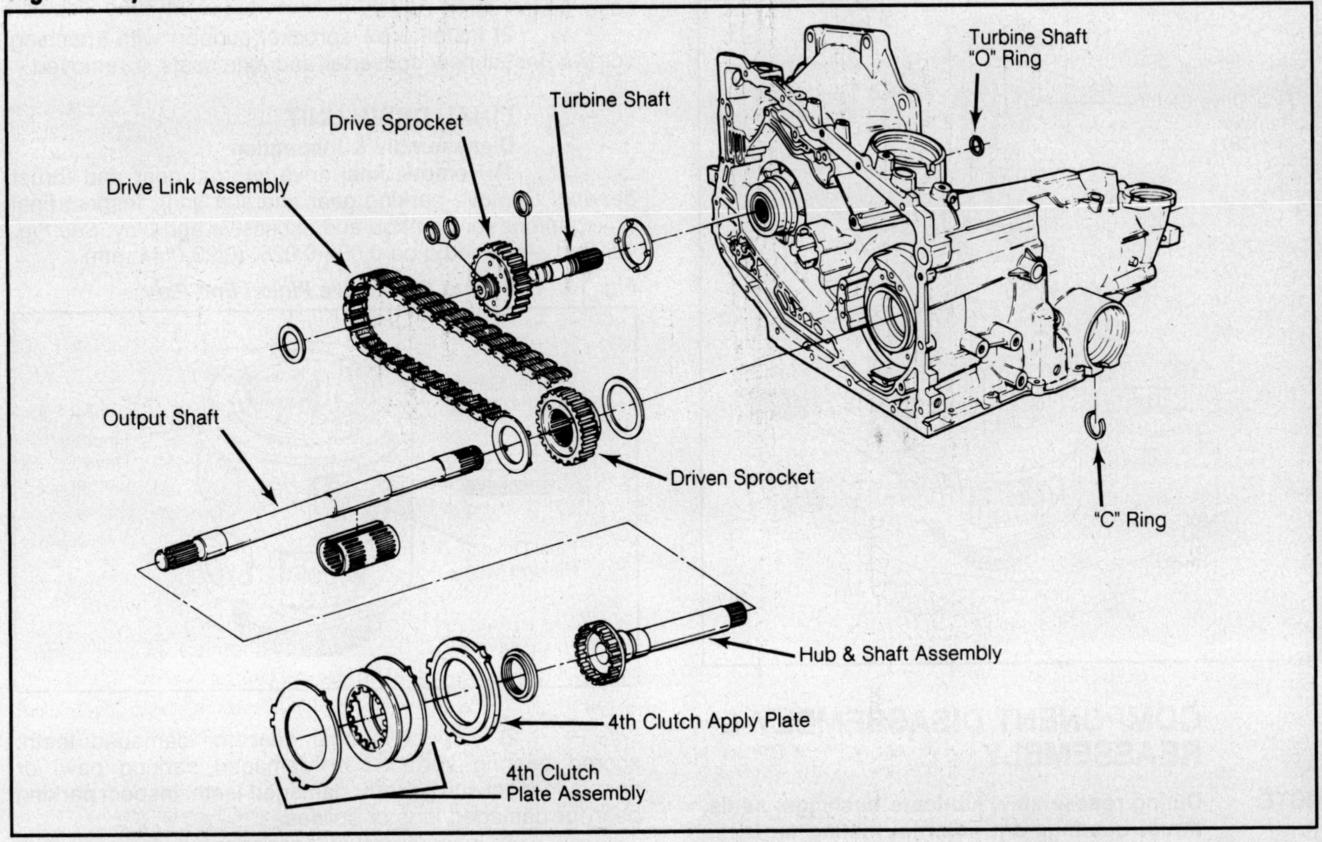

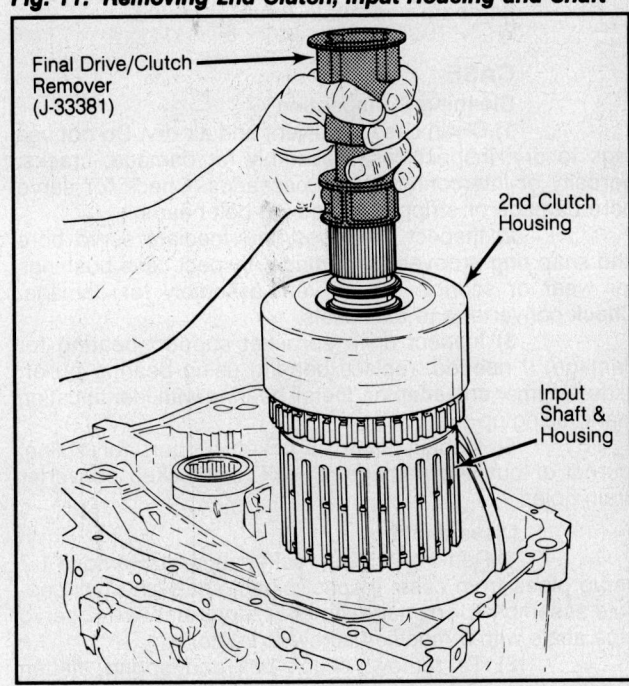

5) Remove turbine shaft "O" ring. Remove sprockets and link assembly from case, noting position of colored link (should face up). Remove thrust washers. Remove chain scavenging scoop and oil reservoir baffle from driven sprocket support. Remove driven sprocket support and thrust washer.

2nd, INPUT & ROLLER CLUTCHES & SPRAG ASSEMBLY

1) Using Final Drive/Clutch Remover (J-33381), remove 2nd and input clutches, sprag and roller clutch assembly and sun gear. *See Fig. 11.*

2) Remove reverse band if it did not come out with 2nd clutch. Remove reverse reaction drum. Remove input carrier assembly. Remove thrust bearing, reaction carrier and other thrust bearing.

3) Remove reaction sun gear/drum assembly. Remove 1-2 band. DO NOT clean band in solvent. Remove reaction sun gear/internal gear bearing. Remove final drive sun gear shaft.

FINAL DRIVE UNIT

Remove final drive internal gear-to-case snap ring. Using Final Drive/Clutch Installer (J-33381), remove final drive unit. *See Fig. 12.*

MANUAL SHAFT/DETENT LEVER & ACTUATOR ROD

NOTE: Do not remove these parts unless replacement is necessary

Fig. 11: Removing 2nd Clutch, Input Housing and Shaft

Remove pin and lock nut from manual shaft. Remove actuator rod from detent lever. Remove retaining pin from case. Remove actuator rod assembly from case. Remove "O" ring from actuator rod guide. Parking lock pawl assembly cannot be removed from final drive internal gear.

2-374

Automatic Transmissions
GENERAL MOTORS TURBO HYDRA-MATIC 440-T4
TRANSAXLE (Cont.)

Fig. 12: Removing Final Drive Unit

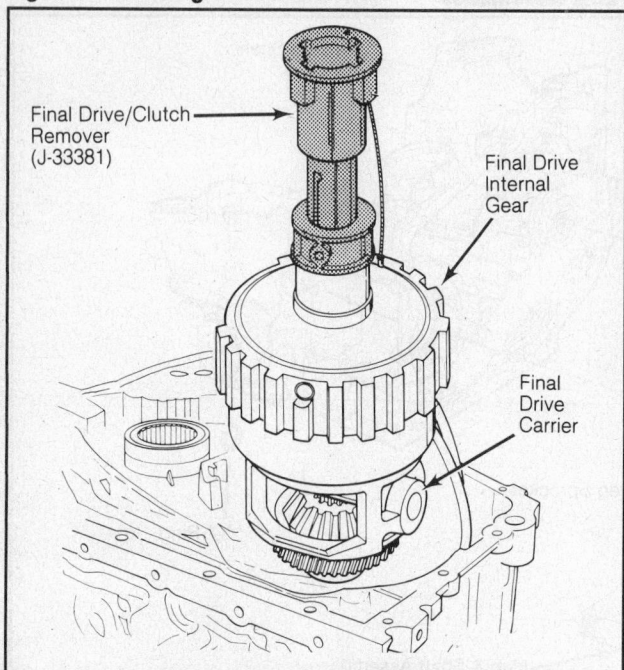

opens into servo bore. Install new 1-2 servo pipe seals into case. Install servo pipes.

2) Install drive sprocket support with attaching screws. Install new converter and axle seals, if removed.

FINAL DRIVE UNIT
Disassembly & Inspection
1) Remove final drive internal gear and thrust bearing. Remove parking gear and sun gear. Inspect final drive pinions for damage and excessive end play. *See Fig. 13.* End play should be 0.009-0.025" (0.23-0.64 mm).

Fig. 13: Checking Final Drive Pinion End Play

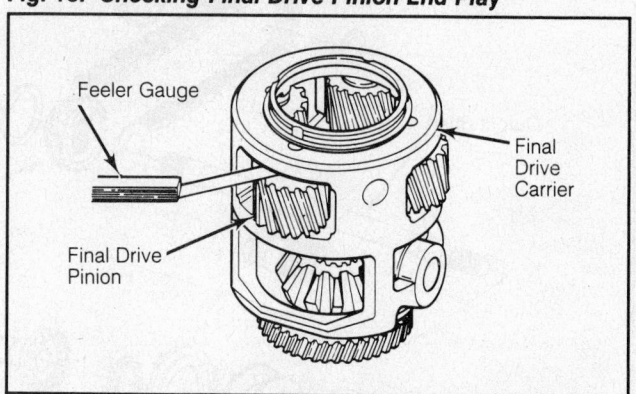

COMPONENT DISASSEMBLY & REASSEMBLY

NOTE: During reassembly, lubricate bushings, seals, thrust bearings and internal mating surfaces with transmission fluid. Use petroleum jelly to lubricate and retain thrust washers.

CASE
Cleaning & Inspection
1) Clean case in solvent and air dry. Do not use rags to dry. Inspect case assembly for damage, cracks, porosity or interconnected oil passages. Check for servo bore damage or stripped threads in bolt heads.

2) Inspect case lugs, intermediate servo bore and snap ring grooves for damage. Inspect case bushings for wear or scoring. Check vent assembly for damage. Check converter and axle seals.

3) Inspect drive sprocket support bearing for damage. If needed, replace bearing using bearing puller, slide hammer and adapter. Install bearing with identification mark facing up.

4) Inspect drive sprocket support for spline, journal or bushing damage. Check for blocked converter drain holes.

Disassembly
1) Remove drive sprocket support. Remove 1-2 servo pipes from case. Inspect pipes, seals and ball capsule assembly for damage. If necessary, remove 1-2 servo pipe seals with a modified screw extractor.

2) To remove check ball and spring, flatten dimples that retain check ball and spring in capsule. Remove check ball and spring with magnet. Remove capsule from case with screw extractor.

Reassembly
1) Install new capsule assembly into case with a 1/2" (13 mm) diameter steel rod. Position capsule slot so it

2) Inspect internal gear for damaged teeth, scored bearing surfaces or damaged parking pawl or spring. Inspect sun gear for damaged teeth. Inspect parking gear for damaged lugs or splines.

3) Inspect thrust bearings for damage. Sun gear/carrier thrust bearing cannot be removed from carrier. Inspect governor drive gear for wear or damage. If damaged, place a thick washer on hub and remove governor drive gear with gear remover. *See Fig. 15.*

4) Inspect differential pinion gears and side gears for damage. If gears are damaged, remove pinion retaining pin with a punch. Remove pinion shaft, pinion gears, side gears and thrust washers. Inspect thrust washers and final drive carrier for damage.

Reassembly
1) Assemble differential side gears and thrust washers into carrier. Using petroleum jelly, stick thrust washers onto pinion gears. Assemble pinion gears and washers into carrier.

2) Slide pinion shaft through both pinion gears for alignment, then remove shaft. Rotate pinion gears into position, then install pinion shaft. Tap retaining pin into position using a plastic mallet.

3) Tap governor drive gear into position using plastic mallet. Install sun gear with stepped side facing out. Assemble parking gear into sun gear. Assemble thrust bearing into internal gear. Install internal gear onto carrier.

4) Inspect carrier-to-case selective thrust washer for damage. Install thrust washer onto carrier hub and retain washer with petroleum jelly. Install thrust bearing onto thrust washer and retain with petroleum jelly.

5) Move detent lever out of "P" position. Use pin to hold parking pawl in place and install final drive assembly into case using Final Drive/Clutch Installer (J-33381).

6) Install snap ring into case. To measure final drive end play, install dial indicator so pointer contacts Adapter (J-26958-10). *See Fig. 16.* Lift governor drive gear with Snap Ring Remover (J-28585) and read dial indicator.

Fig. 14: Exploded View of Differential and Final Drive Unit

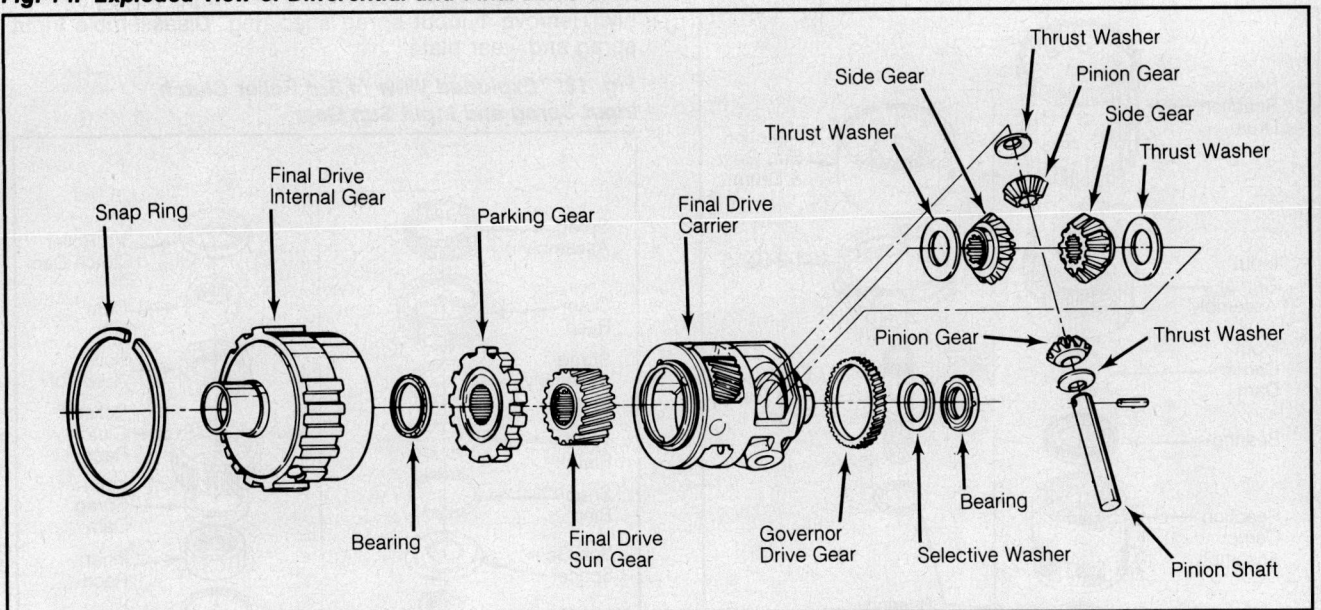

Fig. 15: Removing Governor Drive Gear

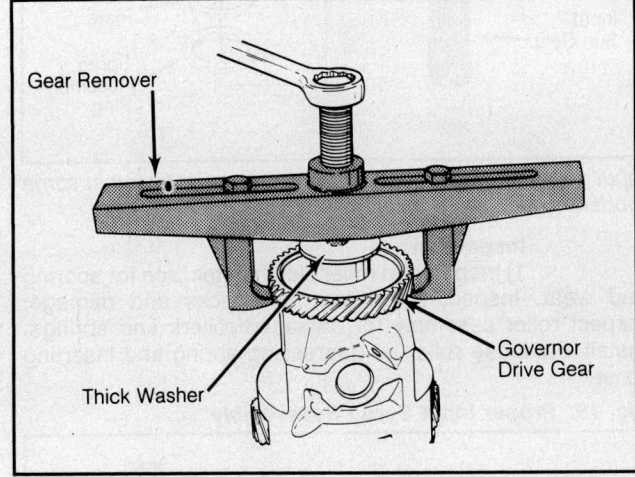

Fig. 16: Measuring Final Drive End Play

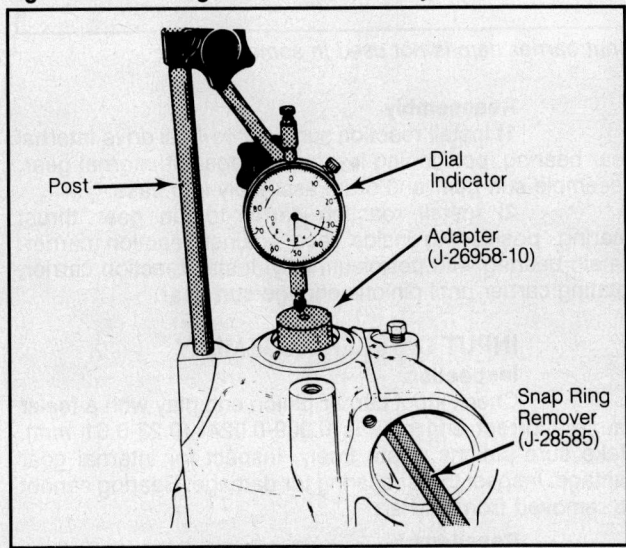

7) Correct end play is .005-.025" (.12-.62 mm). If needed, adjust end play with selective carrier-to-case thrust washer. See CARRIER-TO-CASE SELECTIVE THRUST WASHER SIZES table.

SUN GEAR SHAFT
Inspection & Reassembly

Inspect final drive sun gear shaft for damaged splines or journals. Install final drive sun gear shaft into final drive, ensuring splines engage with parking gear and sun gear.

CARRIER-TO-CASE SELECTIVE THRUST WASHER SIZES

Washer Identification	Thickness In. (mm)
1	0.059-0.062 (1.5-1.6)
2	0.062-0.066 (1.6-1.7)
3	0.066-0.070 (1.7-1.8)
4	0.070-0.074 (1.8-1.9)
5	0.074-0.078 (1.9-2.0)
6	0.078-0.082 (2.0-2.1)

1-2 BAND ASSEMBLY
Inspection & Reassembly

DO NOT wash 1-2 band in solvent. Inspect 1-2 band assembly for heat damage, lining cracks and separation. Check band stop for damage and replace as required. Assemble 1-2 band into case, making sure band anchor pins engage band.

REACTION SUN GEAR & DRUM
Inspection

Inspect reaction sun gear and drum assembly for damaged teeth and bushings and scored or warped drum. Check thrust bearings for damage. Using a feeler gauge, check reaction carrier pinion end play. End play should be .009-.024" (.23-.61 mm). Check for damaged pinion and internal gear.

2-376

Automatic Transmissions
GENERAL MOTORS TURBO HYDRA-MATIC 440-T4 TRANSAXLE (Cont.)

Fig. 17: Exploded View of Input and Reaction Carriers

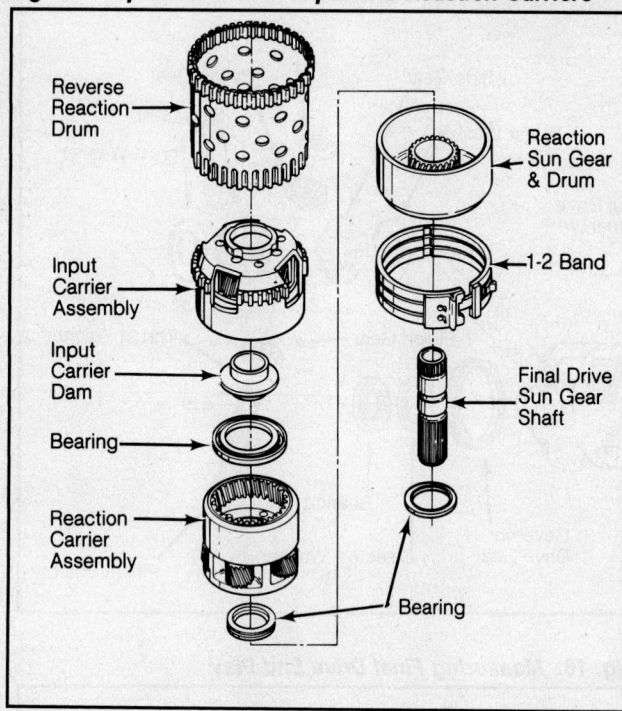

Input carrier dam is not used in some models.

Reassembly

1) Install reaction sun gear-to-final drive internal gear bearing, positioning inside race against internal gear. Assemble sun gear and drum assembly into case.

2) Install reaction carrier-to-sun gear thrust bearing, positioning inside race against reaction carrier. Retain bearing with petroleum jelly. Install reaction carrier, rotating carrier until pinions engage sun gear.

INPUT CARRIER ASSEMBLY
Inspection

Check input carrier pinion end play with a feeler gauge. Correct end play is 0.009-0.024" (0.23-0.61 mm). Make sure pinions rotate freely. Inspect for internal gear damage. Inspect thrust bearing for damage. Bearing cannot be removed from carrier.

Reassembly

Install thrust bearing with inside race against carrier. Retain thrust bearing with petroleum jelly. Install input carrier into case and rotate into position.

REVERSE REACTION DRUM
Inspection & Reassembly

Inspect reverse reaction drum for damaged teeth and distortion. Install reverse reaction drum, making sure spline teeth engage input carrier.

3rd ROLLER CLUTCH, INPUT SPRAG & INPUT SUN GEAR
Disassembly

1) Disassemble 3rd roller clutch and input sprag from input sun gear. Remove input sun gear spacer and retainer from sun gear. Remove 3rd roller clutch outer race and cam from roller assembly.

2) Remove inner race from input sprag assembly. Remove 1 input sprag snap ring. Disassemble input sprag and wear plate.

Fig. 18: Exploded View of 3rd Roller Clutch, Input Sprag and Input Sun Gear

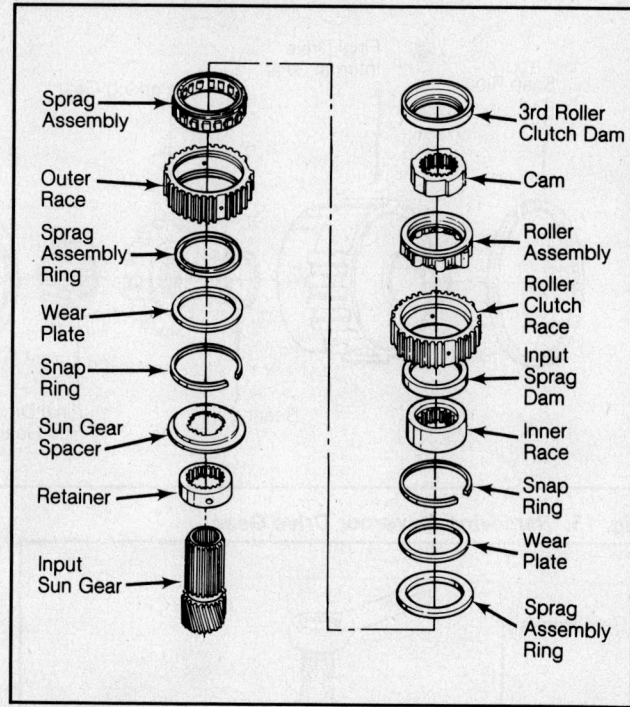

Input sprag and 3rd roller clutch dams are not used in some models.

Inspection

1) Inspect 3rd roller clutch outer race for scoring and wear. Inspect roller cam for cracks and damage. Inspect roller assembly for damaged rollers and springs. Install any loose roller by depressing spring and inserting roller.

Fig. 19: Proper Input Sprag Reassembly

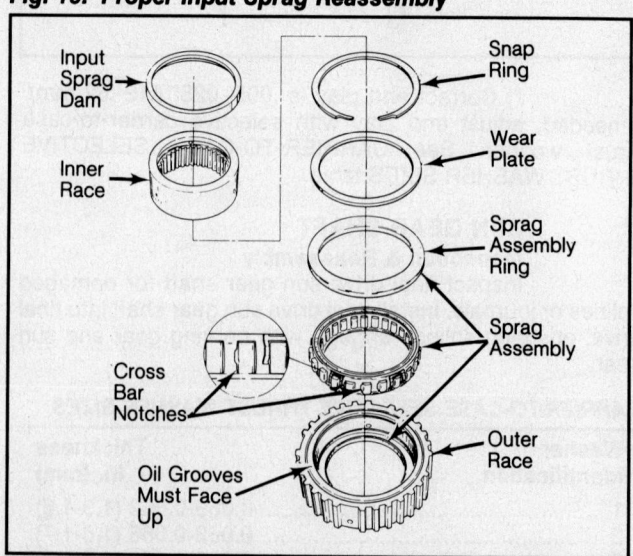

Input sprag dam is not used in some models.

Automatic Transitions
GENERAL MOTORS TURBO HYDRA-MATIC 440-T4
TRANSAXLE (Cont.)

2-377

Fig. 20: Checking Sprag and Roller Clutch

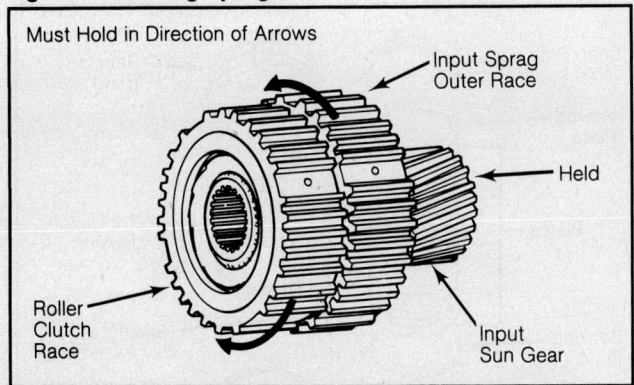

Sprag and roller clutch must hold in directions shown.

2) Inspect input sprag inner and outer races for damage. Check sprag assembly for damaged sprags or cages. Check wear plates for scoring. Inspect input sun gear splines and bushing for damage.

Reassembly

1) Install roller cam into roller cage assembly, rotating cage so rollers are at lowest ramp position. Install roller clutch outer race over cage and cam.

2) Assemble 1 wear plate against snap ring. Install sprag assembly against wear plate with cross bar notches positioned as shown in *Fig. 19.* Install other wear plate. Install snap ring.

3) Assemble spacer onto input sun gear. Assemble input sprag retainer, sprag assembly and roller clutch onto sun gear. Check that sprag and 3rd roller clutch hold when turned as shown in *Fig. 20.*

INPUT CLUTCH ASSEMBLY
Disassembly

1) Remove input shaft thrust washer and input clutch backing plate snap ring. Remove input clutch backing plate. Remove input clutch steel and composition plates. Remove input clutch apply plate.

2) Remove 3rd clutch backing plate snap ring and backing plate. Remove 3rd clutch steel and composition plates. Remove 3rd clutch spring snap ring. Using Clutch Spring Compressor (J-23327) and Adapter (J-25018-A), compress and remove spring retainer.

3) Remove 3rd clutch piston from housing. Remove 3rd clutch piston inner seal from shaft. Compress piston housing and remove snap ring. Remove "O" ring. Remove spring and retainer assembly. Remove input clutch piston and inner seal.

Inspection

Inspect all clutch plates for cracks, wear, lining separation, pitting or other damage. Inspect thrust washer for damage. Inspect input clutch housing and shaft for interconnected oil passages, damaged clutch hub, worn bushings, damaged 4th clutch shaft seal or oil seal rings.

4th Clutch Shaft Seal Replacement

1) Using Bushing Remover (J-29369-2) and slide hammer, remove lock-up sleeve. Expand bushing remover just enough to contact lock-up sleeve.

2) Install new seal into input shaft, aligning seal tab with shaft slot. Install lock-up sleeve into shaft with Bushing Installer (J-25019-6) and bench press.

Input Shaft Seal Replacement

1) Cut solid oil seal rings from input shaft. Inspect seal ring grooves for nicks or burrs. Lubricate oil seal ring and position it on Seal Protector (J-34741-1).

Fig. 21: Exploded View of Input Clutch Assembly

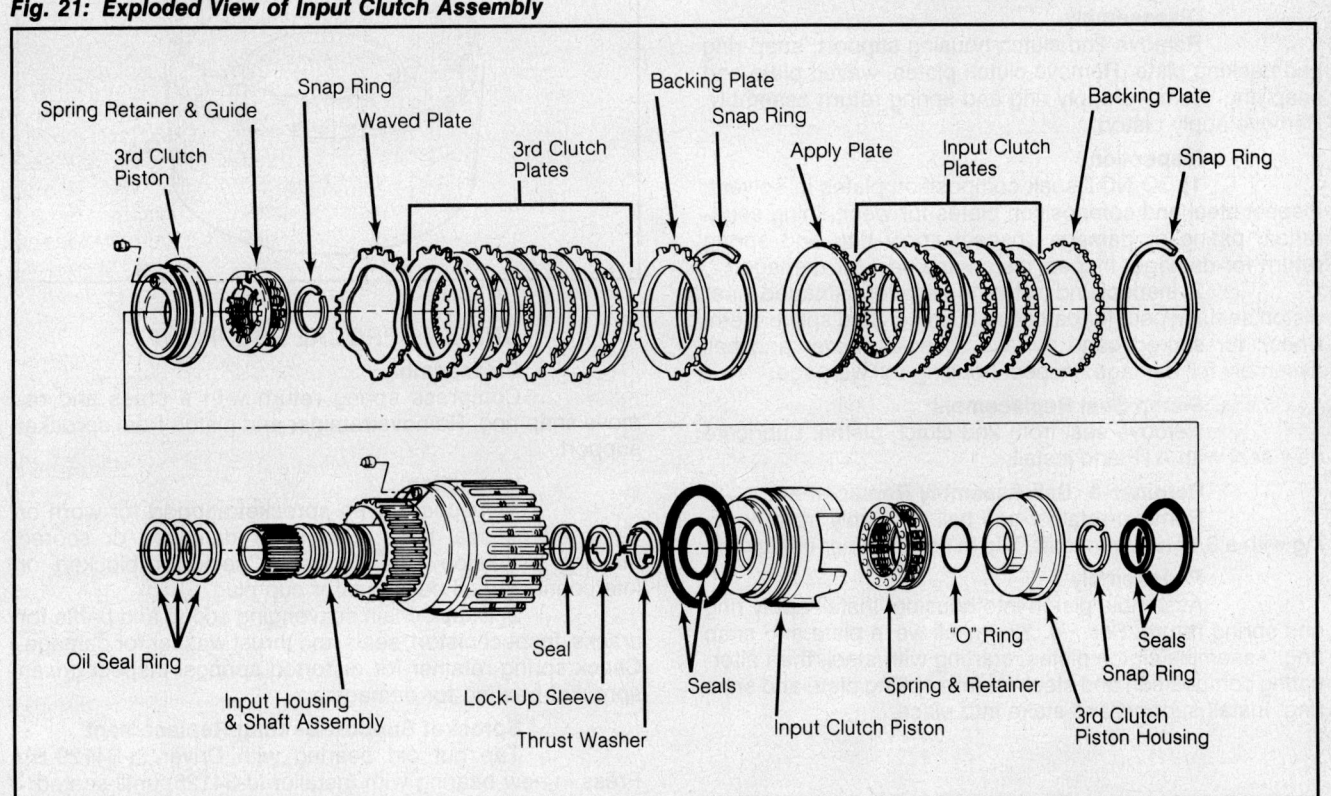

2) Quickly slide seal into position with Seal Driver (J-34741-2) over seal protector. Size seal with Seal Sizer (J-34741-3), gently twisting sizer over seal.

Retainer & Ball Assembly Replacement
Remove retainer and ball assembly from housing using a 3/8" (9.5 mm) drift. Tap in new retainer using drift.

Piston Seal Replacement
Remove seals from input clutch piston or 3rd clutch piston. Lubricate new seals with ATF and install seals.

Reassembly
1) Lubricate input clutch piston inner seal with ATF and install seal using Seal Driver (J-34093) and Protector (J-34092). Assemble input piston into input housing. Assemble "O" ring seal onto input shaft.

2) Install spring retainer into piston. Install 3rd clutch piston housing into input housing. Using Clutch Compressor (J-23327), compress 3rd clutch housing and install snap ring.

3) Install 3rd clutch inner seal. Install 3rd clutch piston into housing. Compress 3rd clutch spring retainer and install snap ring.

4) Install wave plate. Assemble 3rd clutch plates, starting with steel, then alternating composition and steel. Install 3rd clutch backing plate with stepped side facing up. Install snap ring.

5) Assemble input clutch plates, starting with composition, then alternating steel and composition. Install input clutch backing plate with identification mark facing up.

6) Install snap ring. Apply air pressure to oil passages in input shaft and check for proper operation of clutch. Air pressure must not exceed 90 psi (6.3 kg/cm^2).

2nd CLUTCH ASSEMBLY
Disassembly
Remove 2nd clutch housing support, snap ring and backing plate. Remove clutch plates, waved plate and snap ring. Remove apply ring and spring return assembly. Remove apply piston.

Inspection
1) DO NOT soak composition plates in solvent. Inspect steel and composition plates for wear, lining separation, pitting or damage. Inspect apply ring and spring return for damage. Inspect piston and seal for damage.

2) Inspect 2nd clutch housing for damaged inner piston seal. Inspect for damaged bushings and spline teeth. Check for scored band surface. Check retainer and ball assembly for damage. Inspect housing for warpage.

Piston Seal Replacement
Remove seal from 2nd clutch piston. Lubricate new seal with ATF and install.

Retainer & Ball Assembly Replacement
Remove retainer and ball assembly from housing with a 3/8" (9.5 mm) drift. Tap in new retainer using drift.

Reassembly
Assemble piston into housing. Install apply ring and spring return. See Fig. 23. Install wave plate and snap ring. Assemble clutch plates, starting with steel, then alternating composition and steel. Install backing plate and snap ring. Install support and stake into place.

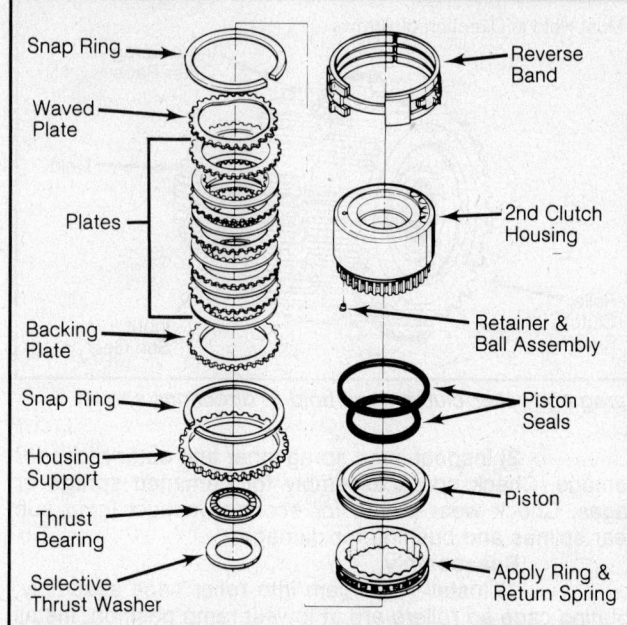
Fig. 22: Reverse Band & Second Clutch Exploded View

Snap Ring
Waved Plate
Plates
Backing Plate
Snap Ring
Housing Support
Thrust Bearing
Selective Thrust Washer
Reverse Band
2nd Clutch Housing
Retainer & Ball Assembly
Piston Seals
Piston
Apply Ring & Return Spring

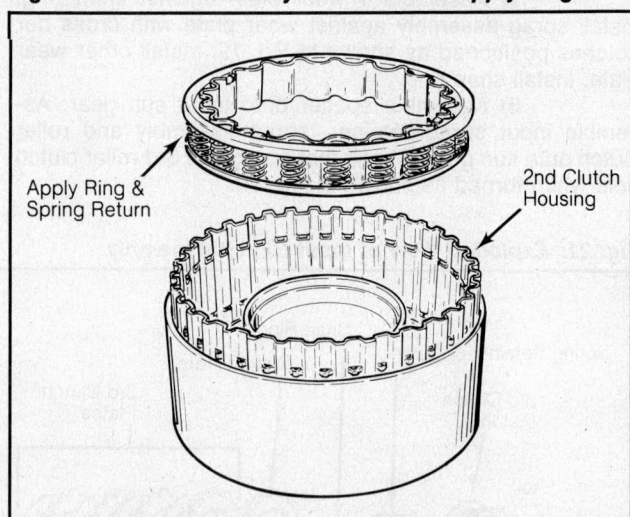
Fig. 23: Correct Assembly of 2nd Clutch Apply Ring

Apply Ring & Spring Return
2nd Clutch Housing

DRIVEN SPROCKET SUPPORT
Disassembly
Compress spring return with a press and remove snap ring. Remove retainer and piston from sprocket support.

Inspection
1) Inspect driven sprocket support for worn or damaged oil seal rings. Check for damaged or scored bushing or piston seal surface. Check for blocked or interconnected oil passages or cup plug.

2) Check chain scavenging scoop and baffle for cracks. Inspect piston, seals and thrust washer for damage. Check spring retainer for distorted springs. Inspect driven sprocket bearing for damage.

Sprocket Support Bearing Replacement
Tap out old bearing with Driver (J-34129-B). Press in new bearing with Installer (J-34126) until seated.

Automatic Transmissions
GENERAL MOTORS TURBO HYDRA-MATIC 440-T4 TRANSAXLE (Cont.)

2-379

Reassembly

Press piston into driven sprocket support using arbor press. Install spring retainer onto piston. Compress spring retainer with arbor press and install snap ring.

OUTPUT SHAFT
Inspection

Inspect output snap ring groove, splines, journal, and bearings for damage. Replace as necessary.

DRIVE LINK ASSEMBLY & SPROCKETS
Inspection

Inspect drive and driven sprockets for damaged or chipped teeth. Check sprockets for damaged bearings surfaces or spline damage. Check thrust washers and drive link for excessive wear or damage. Inspect 4th clutch shaft and turbine shaft for damaged bushings, splines or seals.

VALVE BODY
Disassembly

1) Thoroughly clean and air dry valve body. Remove valve trains, beginning with upper left hand corner. Cover bores when removing roll pins because some valves are under pressure.

2) Remove blind hole roll pins with a modified drill bit. Lay valves, springs and bushings on a clean surface exactly as removed. Remove servo pipe lip seals. Clean valves, springs and bushings in solvent. Do not use shop rags to clean valve body components.

Inspection

Inspect valves and bushings for scoring, nicks and scratches. Inspect springs for damaged or distorted coils. Inspect valve body casting for porosity, interconnected oil passages and damaged machined surfaces.

Reassembly

Assemble valve body assembly as shown in *Fig. 25*. Install new servo pipe lip seals.

OIL PUMP ASSEMBLY
Disassembly

Clean and air dry oil pump. Remove oil pump cover bolts. Remove vane ring, vanes and rotor. Remove seal and springs. Remove slide, slide seal support and slide seal. Remove pivot pin and roll pin. Remove 3-2 coast-down valve, spring and bore plug.

Inspection

Inspect pump body for porosity, interconnected oil passages, pump pocket damage or damaged machine face. Check slide, springs, rotor and vanes for damage. Inspect slide seal, slide support and seals for damage.

NOTE: Oil pump components are matched sets. Do not switch parts with another pump as damage may occur.

Reassembly

1) Assemble 3-2 coast-down valve train into pump body. Install vane ring onto pump pocket. Install pump slide into pump body. Install seal and support into slide.

2) Install inner priming spring into outer priming spring. Press springs into pump body. Install seal onto slide. Install rotor into pump body. Install vanes into rotor, ensuring vanes are flush with top of rotor.

Fig. 24: Exploded View of Oil Pump Assembly

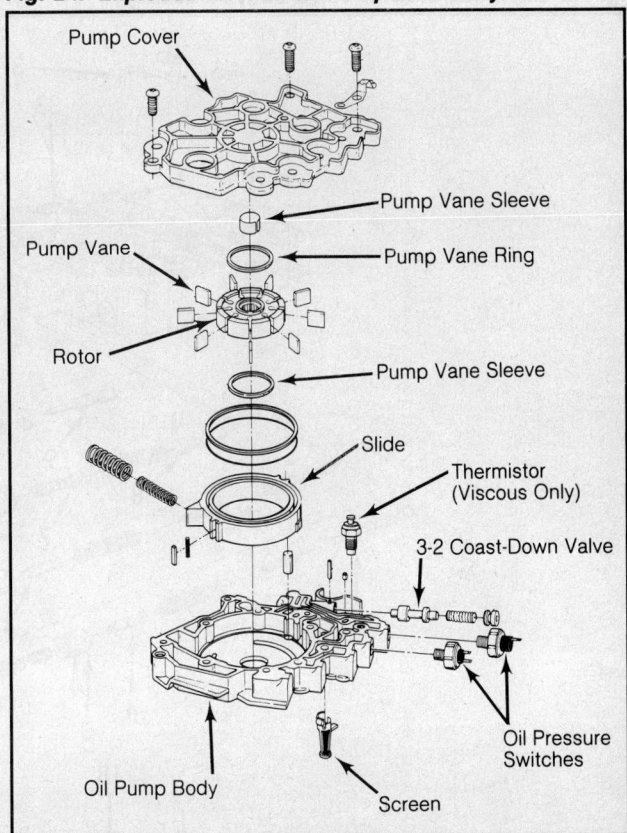

3) Install pump cover onto body with cover bolts. Install pump pressure screen into pump. (Screen has one-way tab for locating.) Install pump onto valve body assembly. Install pump attaching bolts.

1-2 & 3-4 ACCUMULATORS & GOVERNOR CONTROL BODY
Disassembly

Remove oil pipes from accumulator cover and governor retainer. Remove governor screen from pipe.

Inspection

Inspect governor pipes, orifice cup plug and lube oil pipes for damage. Inspect accumulator cover for damage or porosity. Inspect accumulator pistons, seals and springs for damage. Inspect lube pipe retainer and thermo element for damage.

Thermo Element Replacement

Remove washers, pins and thermo element. Remove plate element. For new element, set thermo pin height with Height Gauge (J-34094). *See Fig. 26.* Install element plate. Install pin and washer assemblies, and set height with gauge. Install new thermo element.

Reassembly

Assemble oil pipe into accumulator cover. Install governor screen (closed end first) into governor feed pipe. Install oil pipes into governor retainer.

1-2 & REVERSE SERVOS
Inspection

Inspect servo pistons and seals for damage or cracks. Do not remove seals unless replacement is required. Inspect springs for damaged coils.

2-380

Automatic Transmissions
GENERAL MOTORS TURBO HYDRA-MATIC 440-T4 TRANSAXLE (Cont.)

Fig. 25: Exploded View of Valve Body Assembly

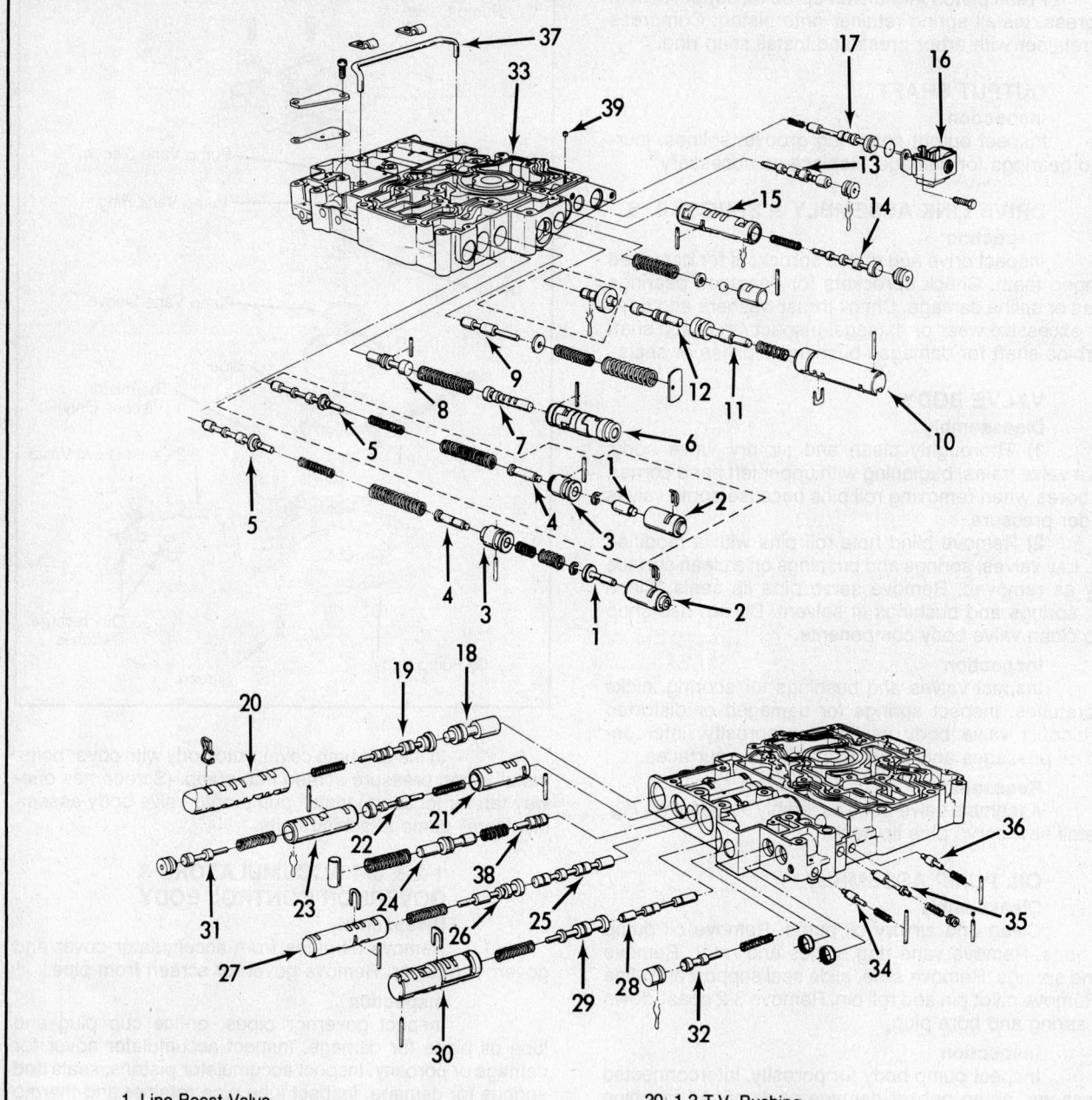

1. Line Boost Valve
2. Line Boost Valve Bushing
3. Reverse Boost Bushing
4. Reverse Boost Valve
5. Pressure Regulator Valve
6. T.V. Plunger Bushing
7. T.V. Plunger
8. Throttle Valve
9. T.V. Feed Valve
10. Converter Clutch T.V. Bushing
11. Converter Clutch T.V. Spring
12. Converter Clutch Shift Valve
13. Converter Clutch Reg. Valve
    (NOTE: Some models use a spring on inner end of valve.)
14. 1-2 Accumulator Valve
15. 1-2 Accumulator Bushing
16. Solenoid
17. Converter Clutch Valve
18. 1-2 Shift Valve
19. 1-2 Throttle Valve

20. 1-2 T.V. Bushing
21. 2-3 Accumulator Bushing
22. 2-3 Accumulator Valve
23. 3-4 Man. T.V. Bushing
24. 3-2 Control Valve
25. 2-3 Shift Valve
26. 2-3 Throttle Valve
27. 2-3 T.V. Bushing
28. 3-4 Shift Valve
29. 3-4 Throttle Valve
30. 3-4 T.V. Bushing
31. 3-4 Man. T.V. Valve
32. 4-3 Man. T.V. Valve
33. Valve Body
34. Reverse Servo Boost Valve
35. 1-2 Servo Control Valve
36. 1-2 Servo Boost Valve
37. 2nd Clutch Pipe
38. 3-2 Isolator Valve
39. Plug, Orificed (NOTE: AC & AY models only.)

Automatic Transmissions
GENERAL MOTORS TURBO HYDRA-MATIC 440-T4 TRANSAXLE (Cont.)

2-381

Fig. 26: Installing Thermo Element

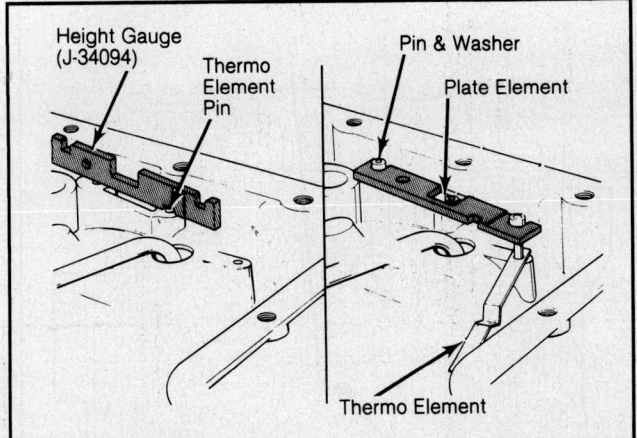

Fig. 27: Measuring Input Shaft End Play

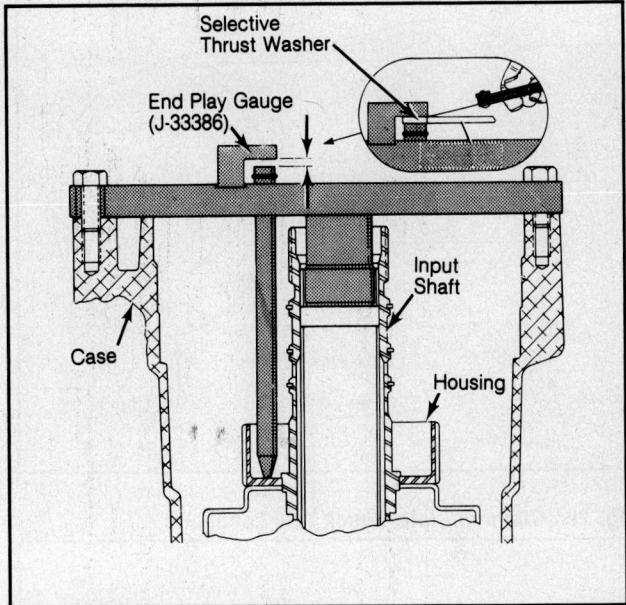

Reassembly

DO NOT interchange servo parts. Assemble spring retainer onto pin. The 1-2 servo spring retainer step must face spring. Reverse servo wave spring must be installed between 2 spring retainers. Install cushion spring, servo piston and snap ring onto pin.

TRANSAXLE REASSEMBLY

NOTE: All selective snap ring and thrust washer measurements taken during disassembly should be rechecked at appropriate stage of reassembly.

1) Install thrust washer onto input shaft and retain with petroleum jelly. Install sprag, roller clutch and input sun gear assembly into input clutch assembly. Clutch hubs must engage clutch plates.

2) Install input clutch roller clutch and sprag assemblies into case using Final Drive/Clutch Installer (J-33381). DO NOT install 2nd clutch, thrust bearing or thrust washer yet.

3) Check input shaft end play. See Fig. 27. Install and tighten Loader (J-26958). Install End Play Gauge (J-33386), then measure with selective thrust washer. If a 0.006" (0.152 mm) feeler gauge can be inserted between thrust washer and tool, use next larger thrust washer.

4) Install reverse reaction plate and thrust washer. Install thrust bearing with large race facing down. Install 2nd clutch assembly onto input clutch assembly. Clutch plates must engage input clutch hub and clutch housing must engage reverse reaction drum splines.

5) Install reverse band into case, locating band on anchor pins. Install thrust washer to driven sprocket support and retain washer with petroleum jelly. Install driven sprocket support into case, ensuring support lube hole aligns with hole in bottom of case.

6) Install output shaft into case. Install "C" ring onto output shaft through bottom of case. Push "C" ring onto output shaft.

7) Coat Seal Installer (J-29569-1 and J-29829-1) with petroleum jelly and place installer over turbine shaft. Slide oil ring seals into position. Size seals using Seal Sizer (J-29569-2 and J-29829-1) by gently twisting sizer over seal.

8) Install thrust washer onto drive sprocket and retain washer with petroleum jelly. Install sprockets and drive link onto case. Ensure colored link faces up.

INPUT SHAFT THRUST WASHER SELECTION GUIDE

Washer Color	Thickness In. (mm)
Orange/Green	0.114-0.118 (2.90-3.00)
Orange/Black	0.120-0.124 (3.05-3.15)
Orange	0.126-0.130 (3.20-3.30)
White	0.132-0.136 (3.35-3.45)
Blue	0.138-0.142 (3.50-3.60)
Pink	0.144-0.148 (3.65-3.75)
Brown	0.150-0.154 (3.80-3.90)
Green	0.155-0.159 (3.95-4.05)
Black	0.161-0.165 (4.10-4.20)
Purple	0.167-0.171 (4.25-4.35)
Purple/White	0.173-0.177 (4.40-4.50)
Purple/Blue	0.179-0.183 (4.55-4.65)
Purple/Pink	0.185-0.189 (4.70-4.80)
Purple/Brown	0.191-0.195 (4.85-4.95)
Purple/Green	0.197-0.201 (5.00-5.10)

9) Install thrust washer onto driven sprocket and retain with petroleum jelly. Insert 4th clutch shaft through driven sprocket and install clutch apply plate with identification mark down. Install 4th clutch plates.

10) If necessary, pry out axle seal and tap new seal into place. Install pistons and pins into channel plate. Install springs into case. Install channel plate gaskets and modulator port gasket. Install thrust washer onto channel plate.

11) Install channel plate onto case. Channel plate lugs must align with tangs on 4th clutch plates and apply plate. See Fig. 28. Install sleeve into channel plate. Install oil reservoir baffle, detent spring and roller.

12) Install and tighten channel plate bolts. Install check balls in channel plate, using petroleum jelly to retain check balls. See Fig. 29. Install converter clutch screen. Install detent spring and roller assembly.

13) Install new spacer plate/channel plate gasket onto channel plate, using alignment pins. Install spacer plate onto gasket. Install new spacer plate/valve body gasket onto spacer plate.

2-382

Automatic Transmissions
GENERAL MOTORS TURBO HYDRA-MATIC 440-T4
TRANSAXLE (Cont.)

Fig. 28: Aligning Channel Plate & Fourth Clutch Plates

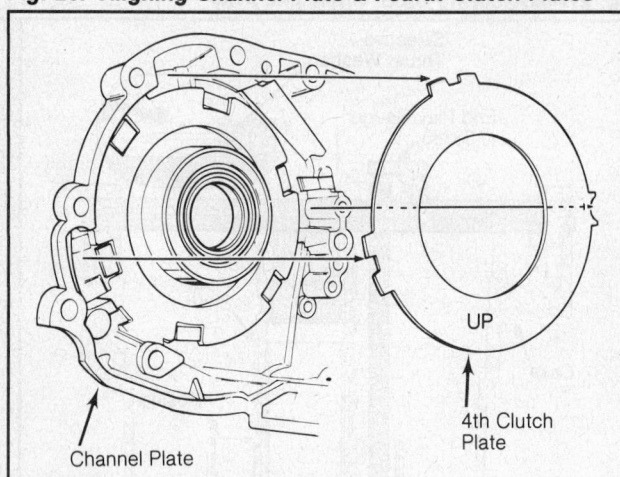

Channel Plate

4th Clutch Plate

UP

Fig. 29: Channel Plate Check Ball Locations

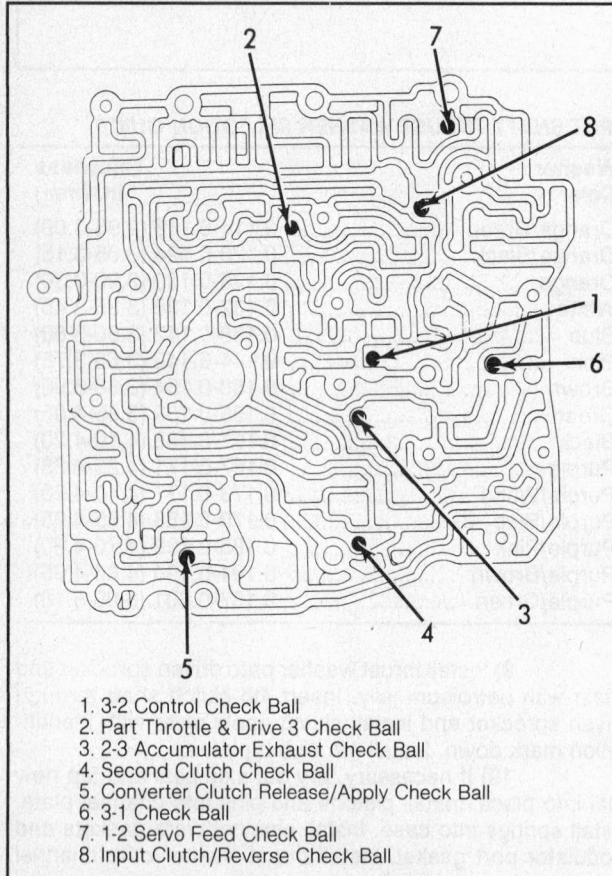

1. 3-2 Control Check Ball
2. Part Throttle & Drive 3 Check Ball
3. 2-3 Accumulator Exhaust Check Ball
4. Second Clutch Check Ball
5. Converter Clutch Release/Apply Check Ball
6. 3-1 Check Ball
7. 1-2 Servo Feed Check Ball
8. Input Clutch/Reverse Check Ball

One check ball is located in capsule in case.

14) Install oil pump drive shaft and converter clutch solenoid screen. Install check balls into valve body assembly, using petroleum jelly to retain check balls. *See Fig. 30.*

15) Install valve body assembly onto channel plate, using alignment pins. Install servo pipes into valve body with retainer and bolt.

16) Install gaskets onto case and channel plate. Install side cover. Install accumulator pins into case. Install

Fig. 30: Valve Body Check Ball Locations

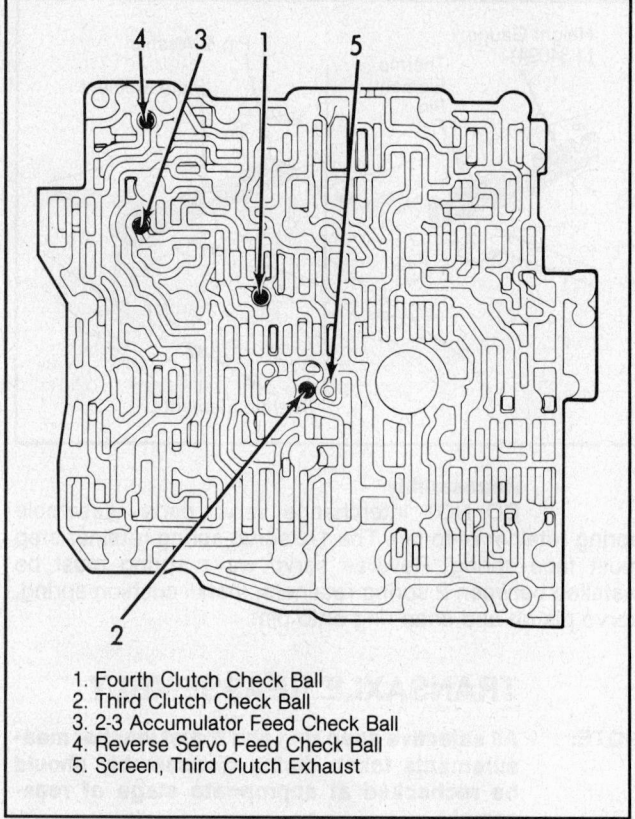

1. Fourth Clutch Check Ball
2. Third Clutch Check Ball
3. 2-3 Accumulator Feed Check Ball
4. Reverse Servo Feed Check Ball
5. Screen, Third Clutch Exhaust

One check ball is located in capsule in case.

accumulator springs into case. (Larger spring is for 3-4 accumulator.)

17) Install lube oil pipe retainer spring into pocket. Install lube oil pipe retainer onto lube oil pipe and "O" ring onto retainer. Install lube oil pipe into case. Ensure pipe is installed into driven sprocket support lube hole.

18) Install spacer plate and new gaskets onto case. Install oil scavenger scoop. Install accumulator cover, pipes and governor retainer as an assembly onto case. Ensure lube oil pipe is installed into final drive internal gear.

19) Install new filter lip seal, filter and gasket into case. Install magnet over dimple in bottom of pan. *See Fig. 31.* Install bottom pan.

Fig. 31: Location of Bottom Pan Magnet

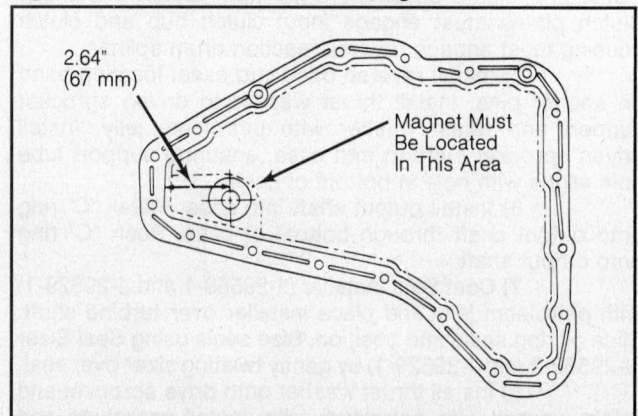

2.64" (67 mm)

Magnet Must Be Located In This Area

Automatic Transmissions
GENERAL MOTORS TURBO HYDRA-MATIC 440-T4 TRANSAXLE (Cont.)

20) Install 1-2 and reverse servo return springs into respective servo bore. Assemble each servo, then install into case. Install new oil seal ring onto each servo cover. Install 1-2 and reverse servo covers into case. Install snap rings.

21) Install governor assembly into case. Install speedometer drive gear onto governor. Install bearing onto gear. Install new "O" ring onto governor cover. Install governor cover onto case, ensuring governor shaft fits into cover.

Fig. 32: Installing Governor and Modulator

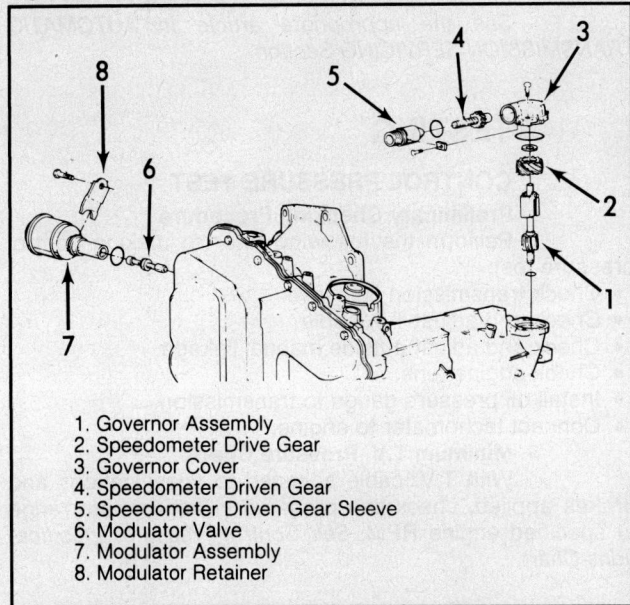

1. Governor Assembly
2. Speedometer Drive Gear
3. Governor Cover
4. Speedometer Driven Gear
5. Speedometer Driven Gear Sleeve
6. Modulator Valve
7. Modulator Assembly
8. Modulator Retainer

22) Install modulator valve into case. Install new "O" ring seal onto modulator. Install modulator into case. Install retainer and bolt. DO NOT use modulator to lift transaxle. Install torque converter and Converter Holding Strap (J-21366).

TIGHTENING SPECIFICATIONS

Application	Ft. Lbs. (N.m.)
Accumulator Cover-to-Case	20 (27)
Case-to-Drive Sprocket Support	20 (27)
Case Side Cover-to-Channel Plate	10 (14)
Channel Plate-to-Case	20 (27)
Channel Plate-to-Driven Sprocket Support	20 (27)
Connector Cooler Fitting	30 (41)
Governor-to-Case	20 (27)
Governor Control Body-to-Cover	20 (27)
Governor Oil Pipe Retainer	10 (14)
Hub & Bearing Assembly Bolts	
Celebrity, Century,	
Cutlass Ciera & 6000	63 (85)
DeVille, Electra,	
Fleetwood & Ninety-Eight	70 (95)
Hub Nut	
Celebrity, Century,	
Cutlass Ciera & 6000	192 (260)
DeVille, Electra,	
Fleetwood & Ninety-Eight	180 (245)
Manual Detent Spring-to-Valve Body	10 (14)
Manual Shaft-to-Detent Lever	25 (34)
Modulator-to-Case	20 (27)
Oil Scoop-to-Case	10 (14)
Pipe Plug	10 (14)
Pressure Switch	10 (14)
Pump Body-to-Case	20 (27)
Pump Cover-to-Channel Plate	10 (14)
Pump Cover-to-Pump Body	20 (27)
Pump Cover-to-Valve Body	10 (14)
Servo Pipe Bracket-to-Valve Body	10 (14)
Solenoid-to-Valve Body	10 (14)
Side Cover-to-Case	10 (14)
Valve Body-to-Case	20 (27)
Valve Body-to-Channel Plate	10 (14)

Automatic Transmissions

GENERAL MOTORS TURBO HYDRA-MATIC 700-R4

Chevrolet, GMC, Pontiac

TRANSMISSION IDENTIFICATION

The Turbo Hydra-Matic 700-R4 transmission can be identified by a two letter code stamped into the transmission case just above the oil pan on the right rear side. See the following the following table for list of the two letter codes.

TRANSMISSION MODEL CODES

Application	Code
All Models	YC,YX,YN,YK,Y6,YP,YZ,VE
	MG,VJ,MH,T8,TM,TH,MK,VH,TK,MD
	TE,ME,MW,TZ,TW,VZ,VK,MX,VF,ML,ML
	MP,MS,T7,TD,MR,TG,YT,PQ,TL,Y8,TS
	VG,VL,MM,VC,MT,PR

DESCRIPTION

The 700-R4 is a fully automatic transmission consisting of a 3-element hydraulic torque converter with the addition of a converter clutch. Two planetary gear sets, 5 multiple-disc clutches, 2 roller clutches and a band are used to provide the friction elements necessary to produce 4 forward speeds, the last of which is overdrive. The torque converter, through oil, couples engine power to gear sets and provides additional torque multiplication when required. The converter clutch drive and driven members operate as one unit when applied, providing mechanical drive from engine through transmission. A hydraulic system, pressurized by a variable capacity vane type pump, provides working pressure required to operate friction elements and automatic controls.

NOTE: **See General Motors Torque Converter Clutch System article in this section for additional information on the converter clutch system used in the 700-R4 transmission.**

LUBRICATION & ADJUSTMENT

See the appropriate article in AUTOMATIC TRANSMISSION SERVICING Section.

TESTING

CONTROL PRESSURE TEST
Preliminary Checking Procedure
Perform the following prior to making control pressure test:
- Check transmission fluid level.
- Check and adjust T.V. cable.
- Check and adjust outside manual linkage.
- Check engine tune.
- Install oil pressure gauge to transmission.
- Connect tachometer to engine.
   Minimum T.V. Pressure Check
With T.V. cable adjusted to specifications and brakes applied, check line pressure in appropriate range at specified engine RPM. *See Control Pressure Specifications Chart.*

Fig. 1: Cutaway View of General Motors 700-R4 Automatic Transmission

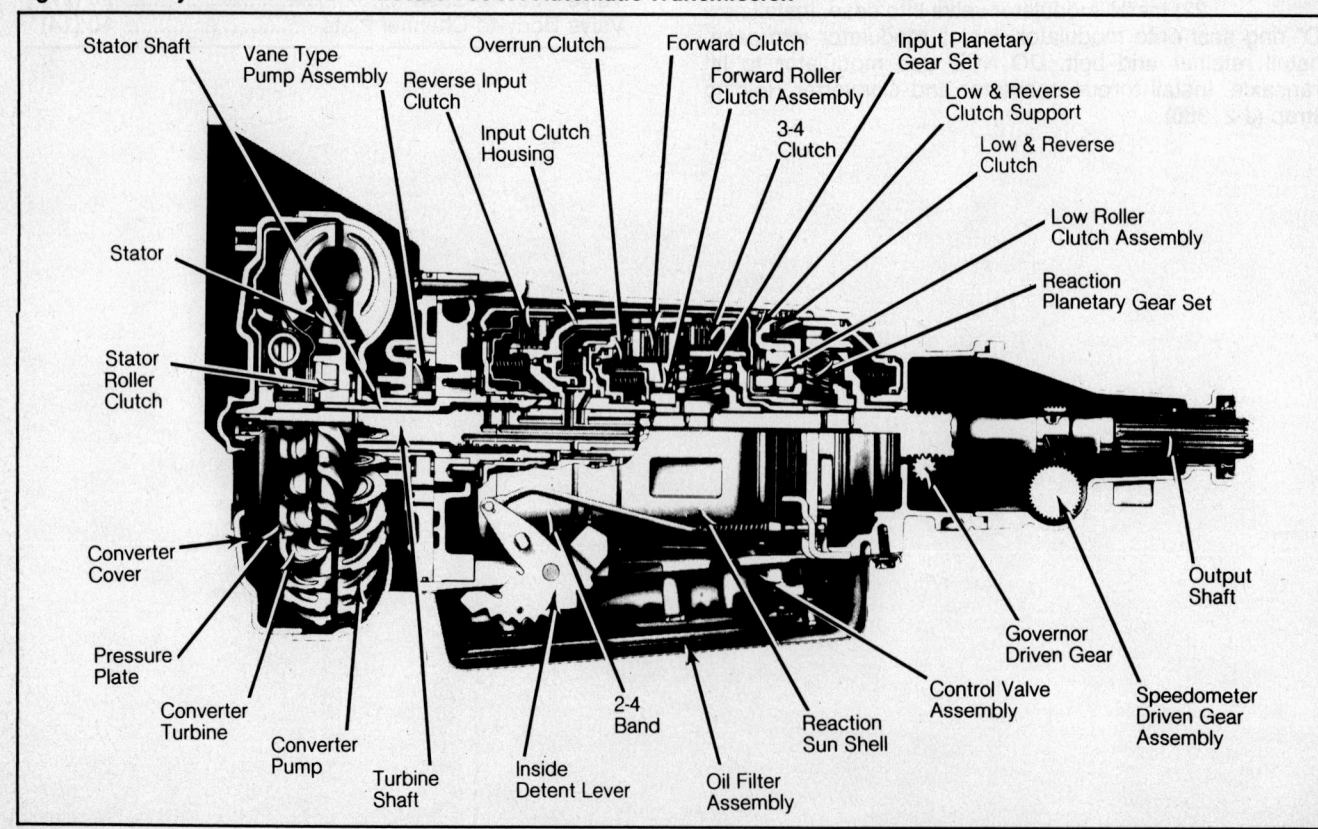

GENERAL MOTORS TURBO HYDRA-MATIC 700-R4 (Cont.)

Full T.V. Pressure Check

With T.V. cable held at full extent of its travel and brakes applied, check line pressure in appropriate range at specified engine RPM. *See Control Pressure Specifications Chart.*

Pressure Differential Check

Check oil pressure differential between line pressure and 2nd, 3rd and 4th clutch pressure while driving vehicle. If pressure differential between line pressure and any of the clutch circuits is more than 10 psi (provided your gauges are accurate) there is a possible leak in that clutch oil circuit. *See Fig. 2.*

CONTROL PRESSURE SPECIFICATIONS

Application	Oil Pressure Minumum T.V. psi (kg/cm²)	Oil Pressure Maximum T.V. psi (kg/cm²)
Park, Neutral Overdrive & Manual 3rd @ 1000 RPM		
YC	56-64 (3.9-4.5)	148-201 (10.4-14.1)
YX	65-75 (4.6-5.3)	137-182 (9.6-12.8)
YN,YK,Y6,YP,YZ	56-64 (3.9-4.5)	127-171 (8.9-12.0)
All Others	65-75 (4.6-5.3)	128-170 (9.0-12.0)
Reverse @ 1000 RPM		
YC	92-106 (6.5-8.3)	243-330 (17.1-25.8)
YX	107-123 (7.5-8.6)	225-298 (15.8-23.3)
YN,YK,Y6,YP,YZ	92-106 (6.5-7.5)	209-282 (14.7-19.8)
All Others	107-123 (7.5-8.6)	211-280 (14.8-19.7)
Manual 2nd & Manual Low @ 1000 RPM		
VE,MG,VJ MH,T8,TM	93-106 (6.5-7.5)	93-106 (6.5-7.5)
All Others	103-117 (7.2-8.2)	103-117 (7.2-8.2)

CONTROL PRESSURE TEST RESULTS

High or Low Oil Pressures

- Pump assembly pressure regulator valve binding, dirty or broken spring.
- Pump assembly T.V. and reverse boost plugs and bushings dirty, sticking, damaged or assembled incorrectly.
- Pump assembly pressure relief ball not seated or damaged.
- Pump assembly slide sticking.
- Pump assembly not regulating.
- Pump assembly excessive rotor clearance.
- Manual valve not engaged or damaged.

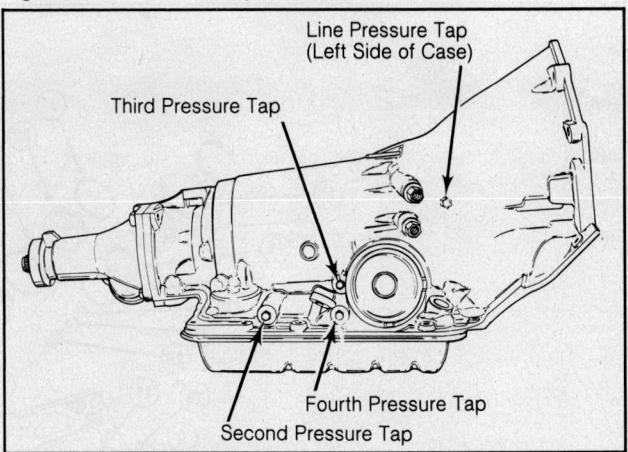

Fig. 2: Oil Pressure Tap Locations

- T.V. exhaust valve binding or damaged.
- Throttle lever and bracket assembly binding, damaged, incorrectly assembled or check valve missing.
- Throttle valve or plunger sticking in valve body.
- T.V. limit valve sticking in valve body.
- Throttle link not engaged, damaged, incorrect link, burr on upper end or hanging on T.V. sleeve.
- Oil filter restricted, missing "O" ring or hole in intake pipe.

SERVICE (IN VEHICLE)

The following components can be removed from transmission without removing transmission from vehicle:

- Governor Cover and Seals
- Governor Assembly
- Governor Pressure Switch (Diesel Only)
- Intermediate Servo Cover and Seal
- Intermediate Servo Piston Assembly
- 3rd Accumulator Check Valve Assembly
- Oil Pan and Oil Screen (Intake Pipe) Assembly
- Control Valve Assembly (Valve Body)
- Check Balls and Valve Body Spacer Plates and Gaskets
- Inside Detent/Range Lever
- Manual Detent Roller and Spring Assembly
- Throttle Lever and Bracket Assembly
- TV/Detent Cable and "O" Ring
- Parking Pawl Actuator Rod
- Parking Pawl Bracket
- Parking Pawl
- Manual Shaft and Seal
- Manual Valve
- Manual Valve Link
- Extension Housing and Gasket
- Rear Seal
- 1-2 Accumulator Assembly
- Intermediate Band Anchor Pin
- Cooler Fittings
- Oil Filter Pipe and "O" Ring
- Speedometer Driven Gear Assembly
- Speedometer Drive Gear
- Converter Clutch Solenoid
- Solenoid Wire Clips
- Electrical Connectors

Automatic Transmissions

GENERAL MOTORS TURBO HYDRA-MATIC 700-R4 (Cont.)

Fig. 3: *Exploded View of Turbo Hydra-Matic 700-R4 External Parts*

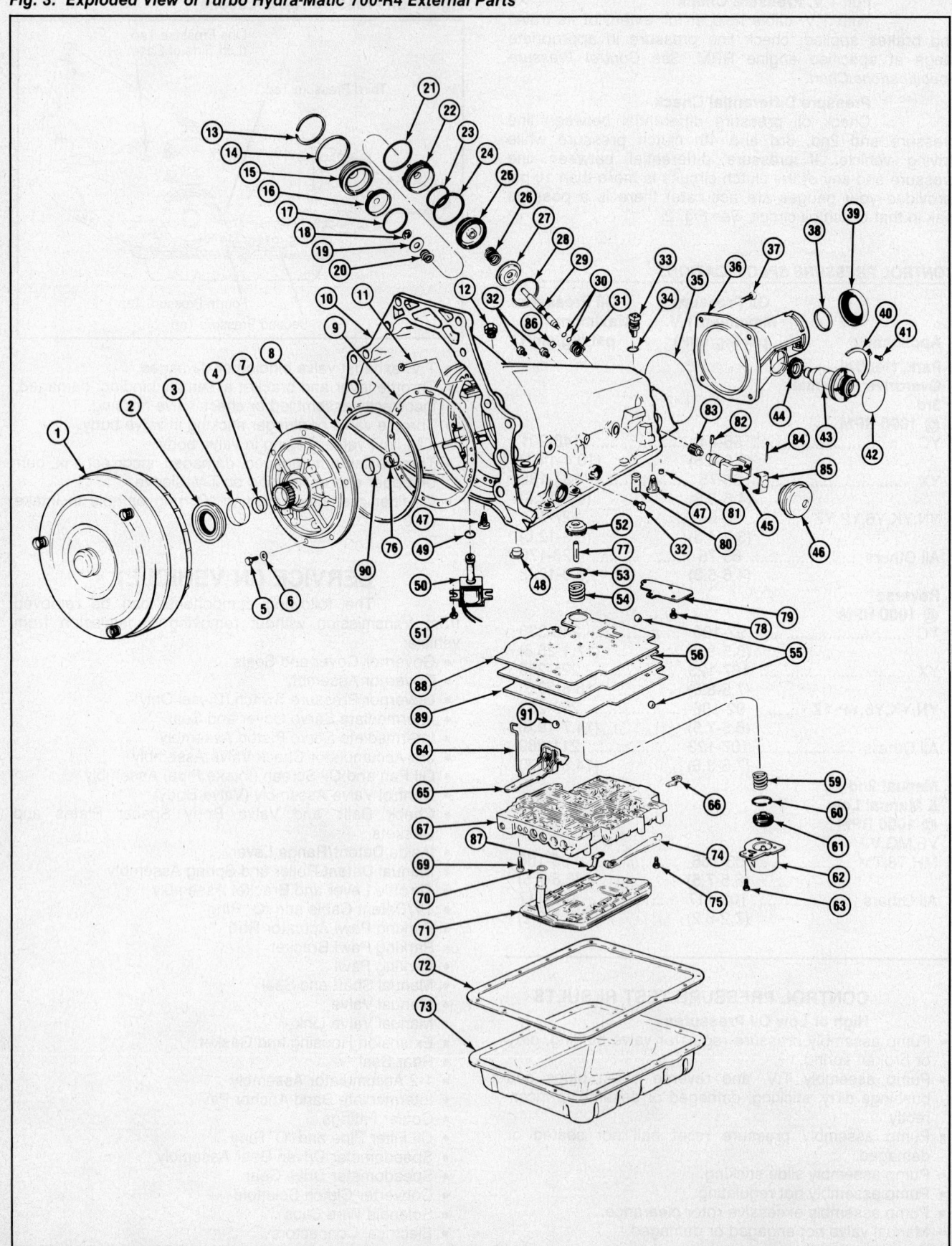

GENERAL MOTORS TURBO HYDRA-MATIC 700-R4 (Cont.)

Turbo Hydra-Matic 700-R4 External Parts (Use With Fig. 3)

1. Converter Assembly	45. Governor Assembly
2. Oil Seal Assembly	46. Governor Cover
3. Oil Pump Body Bushing	47. Converter & Governor Oil Pressure Screen
4. Stator Shaft Front Bushing	48. Band Anchor Pin
5. Pump-to-Case Bolt	49. Solenoid "O" Ring Seal
6. Pump-to Case Bolt Washer	50. Solenoid Assembly
7. Oil Pump Assembly	51. Solenoid Hex Washer Head Bolt
8. Pump-to-Case Oil Seal	52. 3-4 Accumulator Piston
9. Pump Cover-to-Case Gasket	53. 3-4 Accumulator Piston Oil Seal Ring
10. Transmission Case	54. 3-4 Accumulator Spring
11. Transmission Case Vent	55. .25 Diameter Ball
12. Oil Cooler Pipe Connector	56. Valve Body Spacer Plate
13. Servo Cover Retaining Ring	59. 1-2 Accumulator Spring
14. 2-4 Servo Cover "O" Ring	60. 1-2 Accumulator Piston Oil Seal Ring
15. 2-4 Servo Cover	61. 1-2 Accumulator Piston
16. 4th Apply Piston	62. 1-2 Accumulator Cover & Pin Assembly
17. 4th Apply Piston Oil Seal Outer Ring	63. Accumulator Cover Bolt
18. Apply Pin Retainer Ring	64. Throttle Lever-to-Cable Link
19. Servo Apply Pin Washer	65. Throttle Lever & Bracket Assembly
20. Servo Apply Pin Spring	66. Electrical Wire Clip
21. "O" Ring Seal	67. Valve Body
22. Servo Piston Inner Housing	69. Valve Body Bolt
23. 2nd Apply Piston Oil Seal Inner Ring	70. Oil Filter "O" Ring Seal
24. 2nd Apply Piston Oil Seal Outer Ring	71. Oil Filter Assembly
25. 2nd Apply Piston	72. Oil Pan Gasket
26. Servo Cushion Spring	73. Oil Pan
27. Servo Cushion Spring Retainer	74. Manual Detent Spring Assembly
28. 2nd Apply Piston Retainer Ring	75. Manual Detent Spring Bolt
29. 2nd Apply Piston Pin	76. Case Bushing
30. 2nd Apply Piston Pin Seal	77. Accumulator Piston Pin
31. Servo Return Spring	78. Oil Passage Cover Bolt
32. Pressure Plug	79. Oil Passage Cover
33. Electrical Connector	80. 3rd Accumulator Retainer & Ball Assembly
34. Electrical Connection "O" Ring Seal	81. Case Accumulator Bleed Plug
35. Case Extension-to-Case Seal	82. Governor Gear Retainer Pin
36. Extension Housing	83. Governor Driven Gear
37. Extension Housing-to-Case Bolt	84. Governor Weight Pin
38. Extension Housing Bushing	85. Governor Thrust Cap
39. Extension Housing Oil Seal	86. Case Servo Plug
40. Speedo Driven Gear Fitting Retainer	87. Filter Retainer Clip
41. Bolt & Washer Assembly	88. Spacer Plate-to-Case Gasket
42. Speedo Adapter-to-Extension "O" Ring	89. Spacer Plate-to-Valve Body
43. Speedo Adapter Assembly	90. Rear Stator Shaft Bushing
44. Speedo Driven Gear	91. Carbon Steel T.V. Exhaust Ball

For removal and installation of these components, *see Transmission Disassembly and Transmission Reassembly procedures.*

REMOVAL & INSTALLATION

See the appropriate article in AUTOMATIC TRANSMISSION REMOVAL Section.

TORQUE CONVERTER

NOTE: **The torque converter is a sealed unit and cannot be disassembled for service.**

LEAKAGE CHECK

See procedure given in G.M. Turbo Hydra-Matic 400 article.

END CLEARANCE CHECK

See procedure given in G.M. Turbo Hydra-Matic 400 article.

CONVERTER FLUSHING

See procedure given in G.M. Turbo Hydra-Matic 400 article.

NOTE: **For additional information on the Torque Converter Clutch (TCC) system used on this transmission, see General Motors Torque Converter Clutch System article in this section.**

TRANSMISSION DISASSEMBLY

VALVE BODY & WIRING HARNESS

1) Mount transmission in a holding fixture and remove torque converter. Rotate transmission so that oil pan is facing up. Remove oil pan and gasket. Remove oil filter intake pipe and "O" rings which may be located in pump bore.

2) Disconnect inner harness connector at the outside location of the transmission case. Remove the outside connector and "O" ring seal from transmission case. Remove solenoid and attaching bolts, and "O" ring

Automatic Transmissions

GENERAL MOTORS TURBO HYDRA-MATIC 700-R4 (Cont.)

Fig. 4: General Motors 700-R4 Hydraulic Circuits Diagram

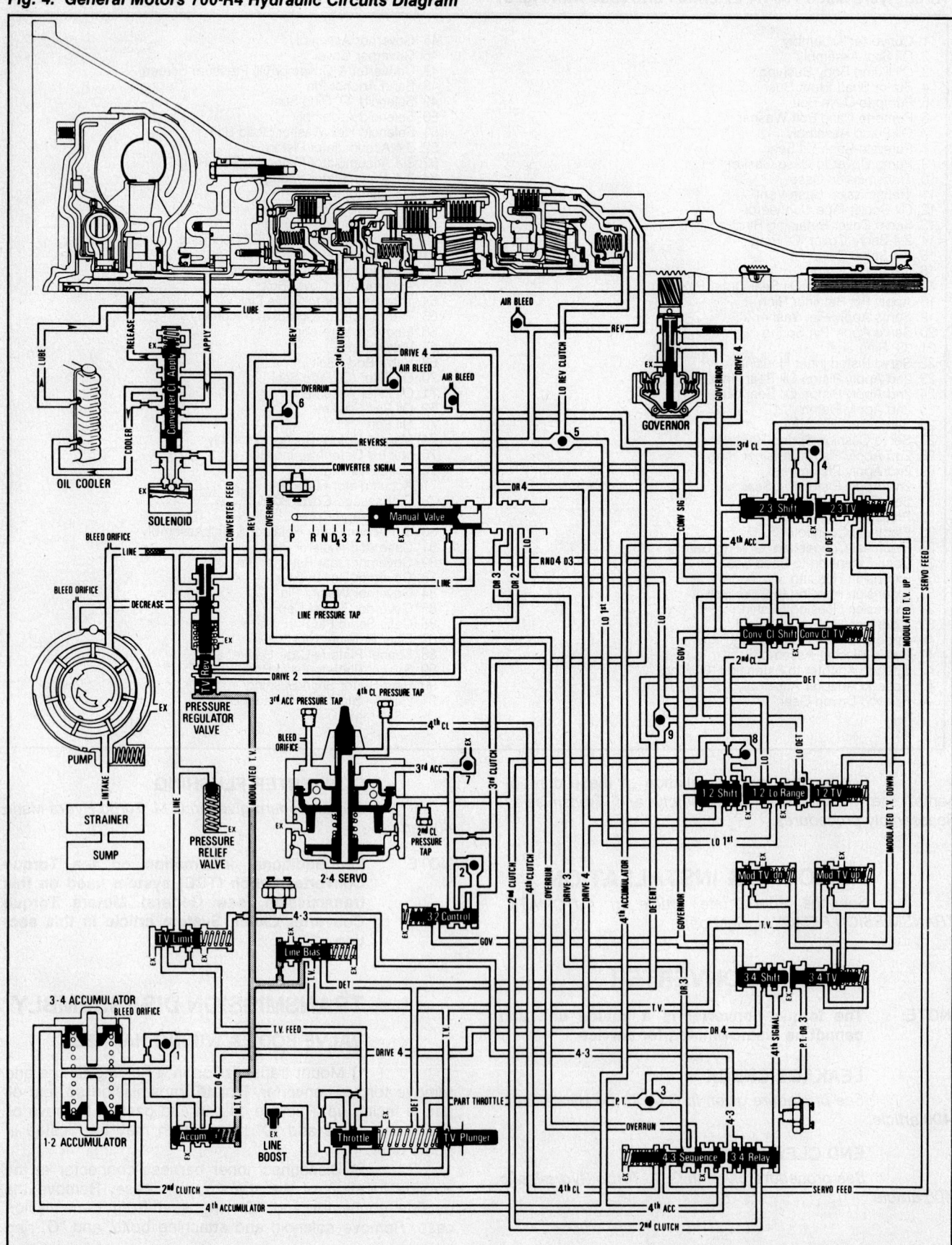

from case and pump. Disconnect all wires from pressure switches and remove complete wiring harness and solenoid assembly.

Fig. 5: Valve Body Bolt Locations

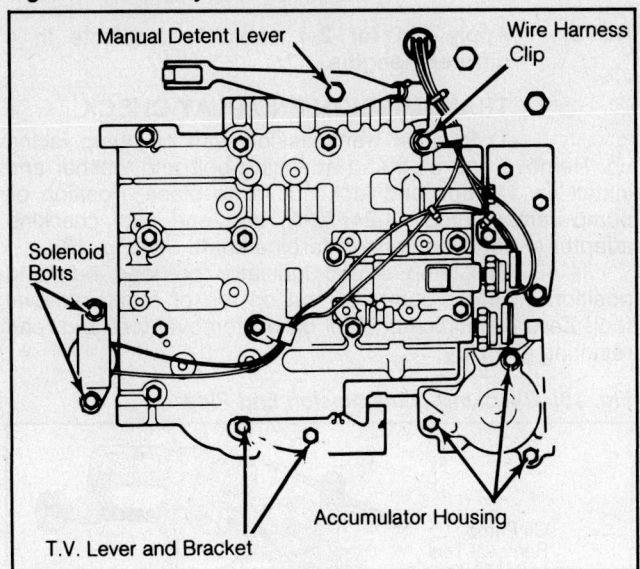

Fig. 6: Valve Body Check Ball Locations

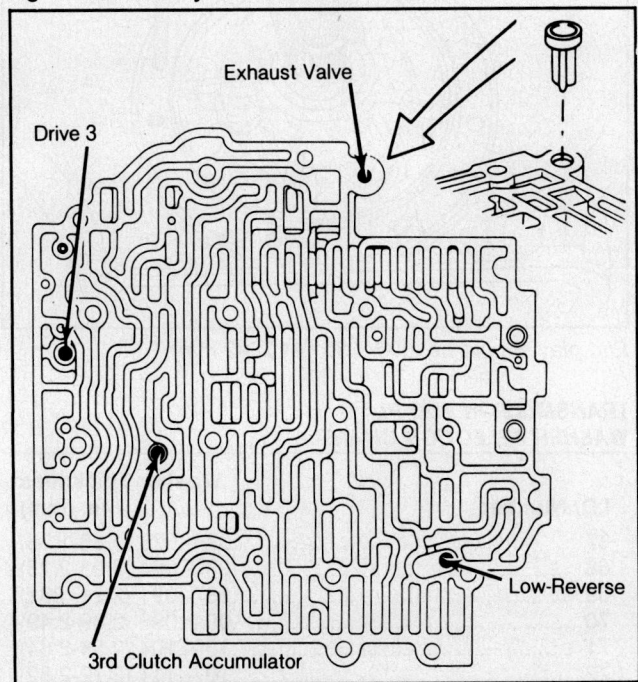

3) Remove 1-2 accumulator housing, attaching bolts, 1-2 accumulator spring, piston, gasket and plate. Remove the oil passage cover and attaching bolts from transmission case.

4) Remove manual detent roller assembly and attaching bolt. Remove wire harness retaining clips and attaching bolts. Remove throttle lever bracket assembly and T.V. link. Remove retaining valve body attaching bolts.

Fig. 7: Model 700-R4 Case Attaching Parts

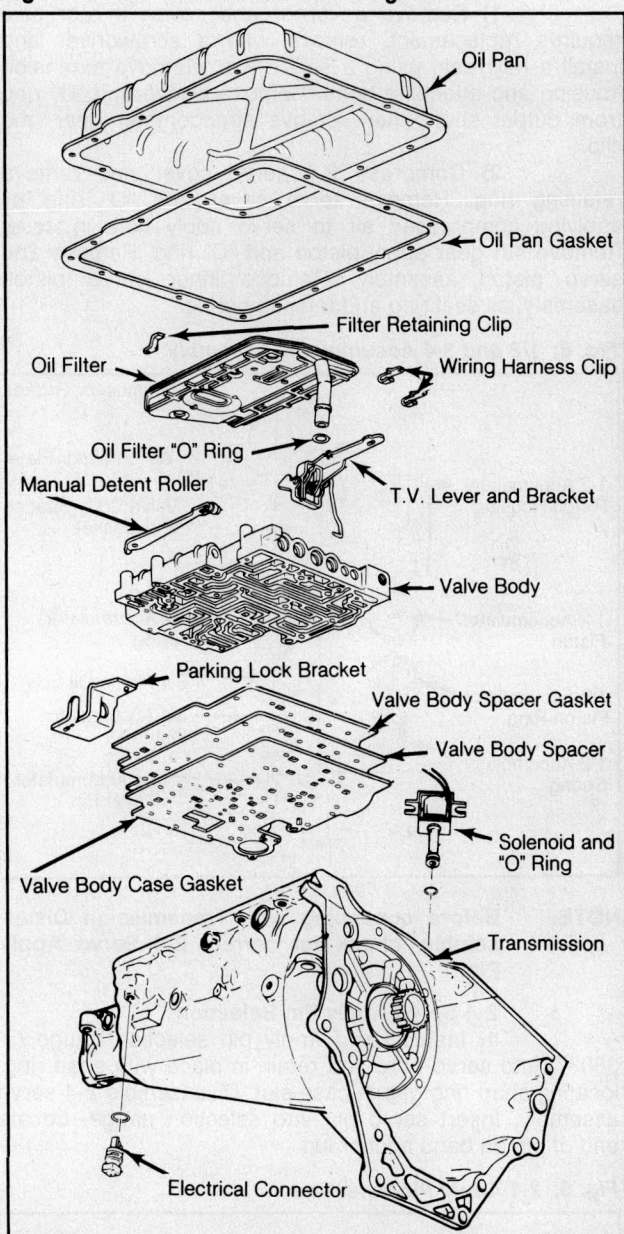

Disconnect manual valve retaining clip at inside detent lever and remove valve body assembly, spacer plate and gaskets.

NOTE: There are 3 check balls located in the valve body that can and will fall free.

5) Remove 3-4 accumulator spring, piston and pin from transmission case. Remove 5 check balls and check valve from case passages. Remove converter clutch and governor screens from case.

GENERAL MOTORS TURBO HYDRA-MATIC 700-R4 (Cont.)

GOVERNOR & EXTERNAL PARTS

1) Remove governor and cover. If rear seal requires replacement, remove with a screwdriver and install a new seal using a seal driver. Remove extension housing and attaching bolts. Remove sleeve and "O" ring from output shaft, then remove speedometer gear and clip.

2) Compress 2-4 servo cover and remove retaining ring. Remove servo cover and "O" ring by applying compressed air to servo apply hole in case. Remove 4th gear apply piston and "O" ring. Remove 2nd servo piston assembly. Remove inner servo piston assembly, oil seal ring and release spring.

Fig. 8: 1-2 and 3-4 Accumulator Assembly

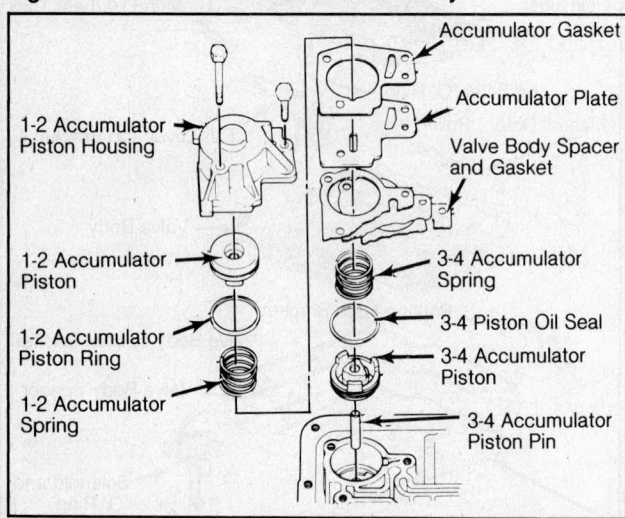

NOTE: Before continuing with Transmission Disassembly, check for correct 2-4 Servo Apply Pin.

2-4 Servo Apply Pin Selection

1) Install servo apply pin selection gauge (J-33037) into servo bore and retain in place with snap ring, locating snap ring gap in case slot. Disassemble 2-4 servo assembly. Insert servo pin into selection gauge. Locate end of pin on band anchor lug.

Fig. 9: 2-4 Apply Pin Selection

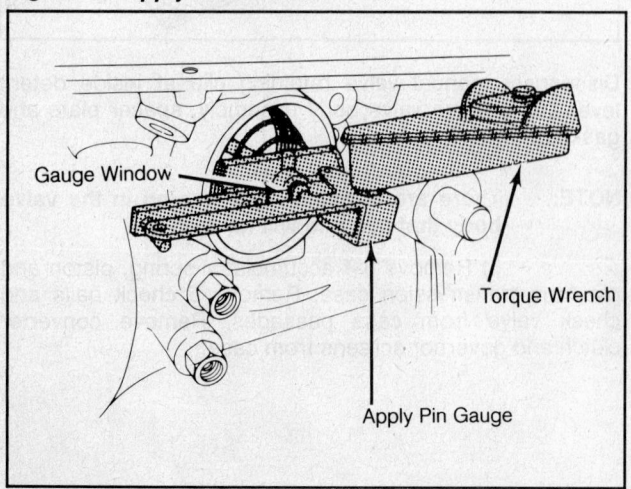

If white line on servo pin appears in gauge window, correct apply pin is installed.

2) Apply 100 INCH Lbs. (11.2 N.m) torque to hex nut on selection gauge. If any part of white line on servo pin appears in window of gauge, correct pin is installed. If white line cannot be seen, select another pin until correct pin is obtained.

NOTE: Apply pin for 2-4 servo is available in 4 different lengths.

TRANSMISSION END PLAY CHECK

1) Position transmission with oil pump facing up. Remove one oil pump attaching bolt and washer and install an 11" bolt and lock nut in its place. Position oil pump removal tool (J-24773-A) and end play checking adapter (J-25022) on end of turbine shaft. *See Fig. 10.*

2) Clamp a dial indicator on long bolt and position indicator point cap nut on top of pump removal tool. Zero dial indicator. Pull up on removal tool and read resulting end play.

Fig. 10: Checking Transmission End Play

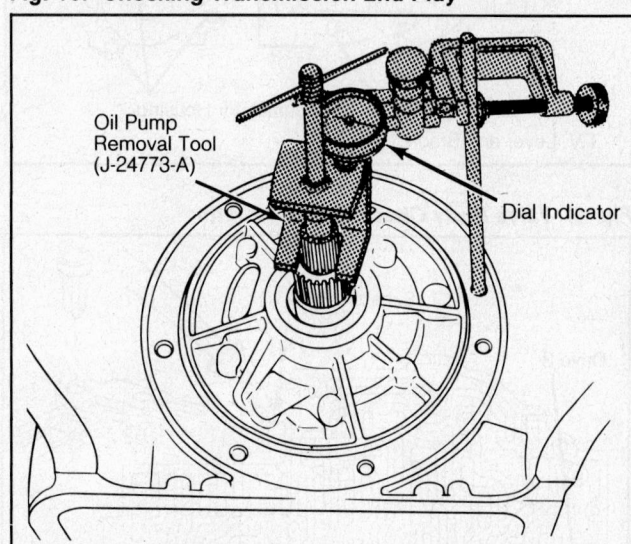

End play should be .005-.036" (.13-.92 mm).

TRANSMISSION END PLAY WASHER SELECTION CHART

I.D. Number	Washer Thickness In. (mm)
67	.074-.078 (1.88-1.98)
68	.080-.084 (2.03-2.13)
69	.087-.091 (2.21-.231)
70	.094-.098 (2.39-2.49)
71	.100-.104 (2.54-2.64)
72	.107-.111 (2.72-2.82)
73	.113-.118 (2.87-3.00)
74	.120-.124 (3.05-3.15)

3) Transmission end play should be .005-.036" (.13-.91 mm). The selective thrust washer controlling transmission end play is located between input housing and thrust washer on the pump hub. If end play is not within specifications, select proper thrust washer from *Transmission End Play Washer Selection Chart.* Remove dial indicator and tools.

GENERAL MOTORS TURBO HYDRA-MATIC 700-R4 (Cont.)

OIL PUMP, REVERSE CLUTCH & INPUT CLUTCH

CAUTION: The filter and solenoid must be removed before the pump can be removed.

1) If required, remove oil pump seal using a screwdriver. Remove pump-to-case attaching bolts and washers. Using removal tool (J-24773-A), pull pump assembly from case. Remove pump-to-case gasket.

2) Remove reverse input drum-to-pump washer from the pump. Remove reverse and input clutch assemblies by lifting out with turbine shaft.

NOTE: Do not remove Teflon oil seal rings on turbine shaft unless required.

2-4 BAND & INPUT GEAR SET

1) Remove 2-4 band assembly from case. Remove band anchor pin from case. Remove input sun gear.

NOTE: To prevent the possibility of the output shaft falling free, install output shaft support tool (J-29837) on the case, holding the output shaft in place.

2) Remove input carrier to output shaft snap ring with narrow snap ring pliers. If free, remove output shaft and tool. Remove input carrier and thrust washer. Remove reaction shaft thrust bearing from input internal gear.

Fig. 11: Installing Output Shaft Support Tool

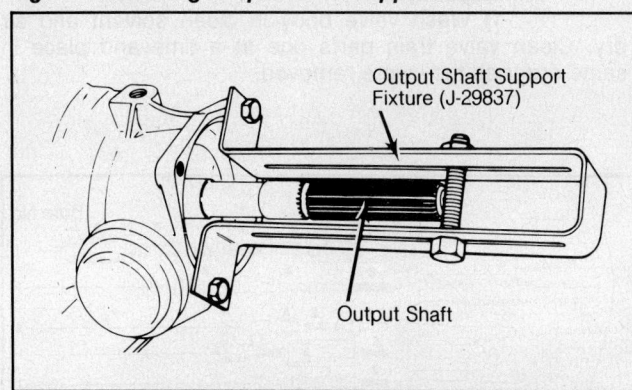

REACTION GEAR SET

1) Remove reaction shaft-to-reaction sun gear washer and reaction shell. Remove reaction shell-to-inner race washer. Remove low and reverse support-to-case retaining ring and support spring. Remove reaction sun gear.

2) Remove low and reverse inner race, roller assembly, support assembly and reaction carrier assembly. Remove low and reverse clutch composition plates and steel plates. Remove reaction internal gear, output shaft (if not previously removed) and bearing assembly. Remove support bearing assembly from case hub.

LOW/REVERSE CLUTCH

1) Remove parking lock bracket and 2 attaching bolts. Position parking lock pawl inboards. Using a compressor tool, compress low/reverse clutch spring retainer.

2) Remove spring retaining ring and low/reverse spring assembly. Remove tools. Remove low/reverse clutch piston by applying air pressure in the case apply passage.

INNER MANUAL LINKAGE

1) Rotate transmission to a horizontal position, loosen manual shaft retaining nut and move manual shaft inboard. Move inner detent lever, connected actuator rod assembly and manual shaft retainer, inboard.

2) Tap manual shaft outboard until retaining nut is free. If necessary, install a retaining nut on outside end of manual shaft. Using a screwdriver, remove manual shaft retainer and connect inner detent lever and actuator rod. Remove manual shaft and nut.

3) If necessary, remove inside detent lever from actuator rod by rotating rod and indexing notches in rod with hole in lever. If required, remove manual shaft seal by driving outward from case.

PARKING PAWL & RETURN SPRING

Using a screw extractor, remove parking pawl shaft and return spring.

3RD ACCUMULATOR CHECK VALVE REPLACEMENT

1) Inspect 3rd accumulator check valve for the following: missing check ball, check ball binding or stuck in tube, oil feed slot in tube missing or restricted, improperly assembled, loose fitting or not fully seated in case. If check valve requires replacement, proceed to step 2).

2) Using a No. 4 screw extractor, remove check valve assembly from case by turning and pulling straight out. *See Fig. 12.*

3) Install new check valve assembly, small end first, into case. Position oil feed slot in tube so it faces servo. On a 3/8" diameter metal rod, scribe a mark 1 41/64" (42 mm) from one end. Drive check valve assembly until mark is flush with machined surface of case.

Fig. 12: Installing 3rd Accumulator Check Valve Assembly

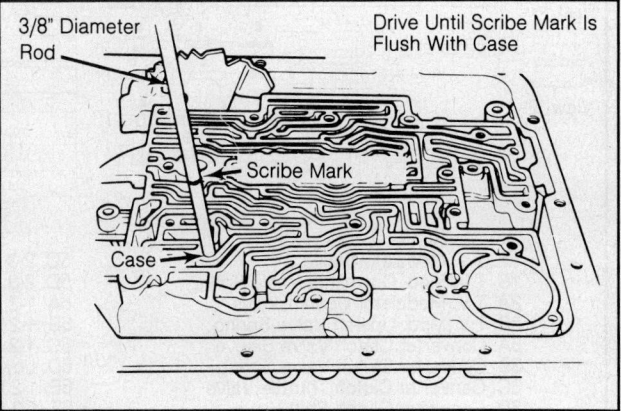

Remove using a No. 4 screw extractor.

GENERAL MOTORS TURBO HYDRA-MATIC 700-R4 (Cont.)

COMPONENT DISASSEMBLY & REASSEMBLY

VALVE BODY ASSEMBLY

NOTE: As valve trains are removed from each valve body bore, place individual parts in correct order and in relative position to valve body to simplify reassembly. Valves and springs are not interchangeable and all parts must be installed in correct order in proper valve body bore.

During disassembly, note the following:
- Remove all outside roll pins by pushing through from rough casting side of valve body.
- Remove inner roll pins by grinding a taper on one end of a 1/16" drill, then tap drill into pin and pull straight out.
- Some roll pins are spring loaded and care should be taken when removing to prevent losing them.
- Remove spring retaining sleeves by compressing with needle-nose pliers and moving upward through exposed hole.
- Do not remove pressure switches unless they require replacement.

Disassembly

1) Remove 3 check balls from passage side of body (if present). Position valve body with machined face up and manual valve at lower right. Remove link and retaining clip from manual valve.

2) From bore No. 1 (upper left), remove retaining pin, valve bore plug, T.V. modulator downshift valve and T.V. valve spring.

3) From bore No. 2, remove retaining pin, valve bore sleeve, T.V. modulator upshift valve and T.V. valve spring.

4) From bore No. 3, remove retaining pin, converter clutch throttle sleeve, converter throttle valve spring and valve. Remove converter clutch shift valve.

5) From bore No. 4, remove retaining pin, 3-4 throttle valve sleeve, 3-4 valve spring, 3-4 throttle valve and shift valve.

6) From bore No. 5, remove retaining pin, 2-3 throttle valve sleeve, 2-3 valve spring, 2-3 valve and 2-3 shift valve.

7) From bore No. 6, remove outer roll pin, 1-2 throttle valve sleeve, 1-2 valve spring, 1-2 valve and low range valve. Remove inner retaining pin and remove low range valve sleeve and 1-2 shift valve.

8) From bore No. 7 (upper right), remove outer roll pin from rough casting side, throttle valve plunger sleeve, throttle plunger and valve spring. Remove inner roll pin and valve.

9) From bore No. 8, remove retaining roll pin and plug. Remove 3-4 relay valve, 4-3 sequence valve and spring.

10) From bore No. 9, using needle nose pliers. Compress and remove spring retainer. Remove T.V. limit plug and spring valve.

11) From bore No. 10, remove retaining roll pin and plug. Remove 1-2 accumulator valve, spring and sleeve.

12) From bore No. 11, using needle nose pliers, compress the line bias valve spring retainer and remove plug, line bias and spring.

13) From bore No. 12, remove roll pin, 3-2 control valve spring and 3-2 control valve.

14) From bore No. 13, remove manual valve.

Inspection

1) Wash valve body in clean solvent and air dry. Clean valve train parts one at a time and place in same order as they were removed.

Fig. 13: Exploded View of Model 700-R4 Valve Body Assembly

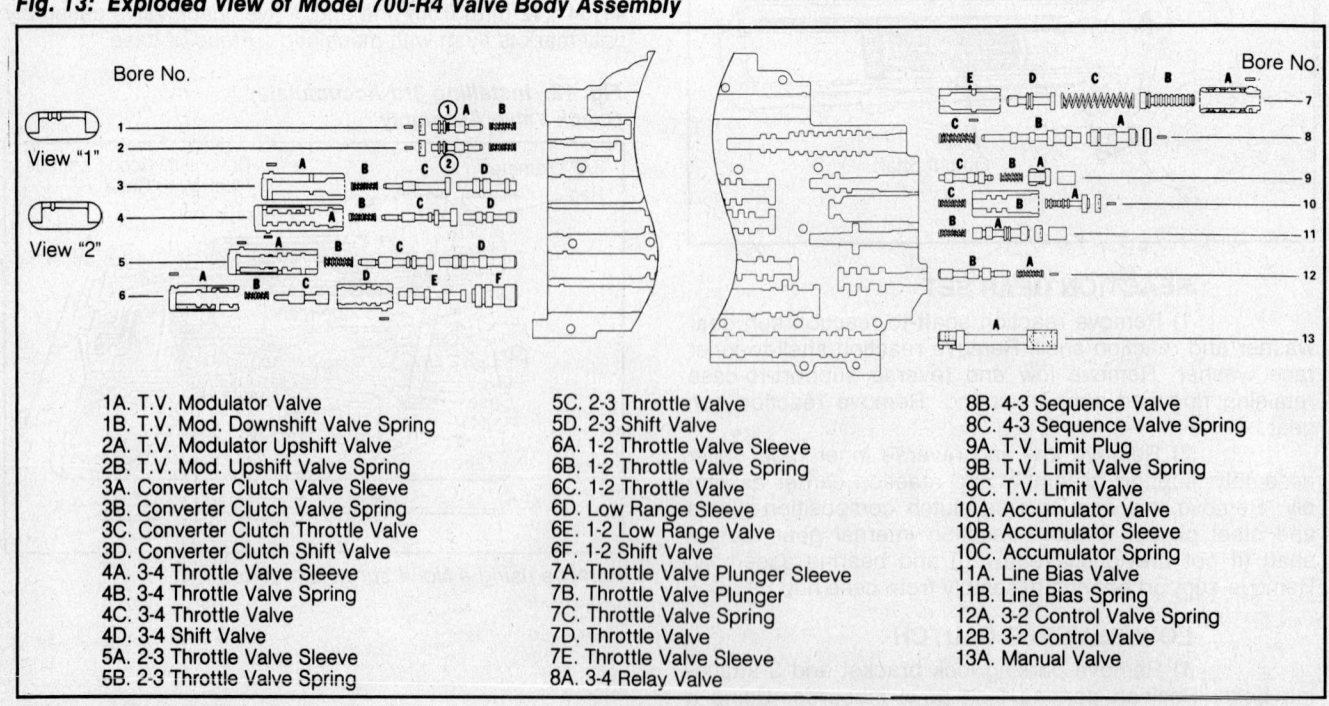

1A. T.V. Modulator Valve	5C. 2-3 Throttle Valve	8B. 4-3 Sequence Valve
1B. T.V. Mod. Downshift Valve Spring	5D. 2-3 Shift Valve	8C. 4-3 Sequence Valve Spring
2A. T.V. Modulator Upshift Valve	6A. 1-2 Throttle Valve Sleeve	9A. T.V. Limit Plug
2B. T.V. Mod. Upshift Valve Spring	6B. 1-2 Throttle Valve Spring	9B. T.V. Limit Valve Spring
3A. Converter Clutch Valve Sleeve	6C. 1-2 Throttle Valve	9C. T.V. Limit Valve
3B. Converter Clutch Valve Spring	6D. Low Range Sleeve	10A. Accumulator Valve
3C. Converter Clutch Throttle Valve	6E. 1-2 Low Range Valve	10B. Accumulator Sleeve
3D. Converter Clutch Shift Valve	6F. 1-2 Shift Valve	10C. Accumulator Spring
4A. 3-4 Throttle Valve Sleeve	7A. Throttle Valve Plunger Sleeve	11A. Line Bias Valve
4B. 3-4 Throttle Valve Spring	7B. Throttle Valve Plunger	11B. Line Bias Spring
4C. 3-4 Throttle Valve	7C. Throttle Valve Spring	12A. 3-2 Control Valve Spring
4D. 3-4 Shift Valve	7D. Throttle Valve	12B. 3-2 Control Valve
5A. 2-3 Throttle Valve Sleeve	7E. Throttle Valve Sleeve	13A. Manual Valve
5B. 2-3 Throttle Valve Spring	8A. 3-4 Relay Valve	

On vehicles with ECM control of TCC apply, the converter clutch shift valve train (3A, B, C & D) is eliminated.

GENERAL MOTORS TURBO HYDRA-MATIC 700-R4 (Cont.)

2) Inspect valves for scoring, cracks and free movement in their bores. Inspect all bushings for cracks or scored bores.

3) Inspect valve body for cracks, damage or scored bores. Lands should be flat with no cross leaks.

Reassembly

1) Install all parts in reverse order of removal. Assemble all bore plugs against retaining pins with recessed holes outboard. All roll pins must be installed so they do not extend above flat machined face of valve body pad.

2) Install all flared coiled pins with the flared end out. Ensure all retaining or roll pins are installed into proper slots in the sleeves, not in oil passage holes.

NOTE: **The bushing for the 1-2 accumulator valve train must be assembled with small hole for roll pin facing rough casting side of valve body.**

GOVERNOR ASSEMBLY

Disassembly

Cut off one end of each governor weight pin and remove pins, primary weights and secondary weights. Remove governor valve from sleeve.

Inspection

1) Wash all parts in clean solvent, air dry and blow out passages. Inspect governor body and valve for free operation, nicks, burrs, scoring or galling. Inspect springs for distortion.

2) Inspect driven gear for nicks, damage, or excessive looseness and replace as necessary.

Governor Driven Gear Replacement

1) Drive out driven gear retaining pin using a small punch. Support governor assembly on plates installed in exhaust slots of governor sleeve.

2) Place assembly in an arbor press. With a long punch, press driven gear out of sleeve. Clean sleeve of any chips that may be present.

Fig. 14: Governor Assembly Exploded View

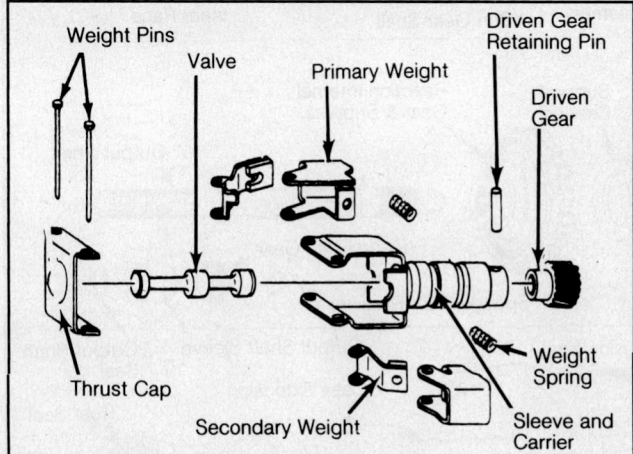

3) To install new gear, support governor on plates installed in exhaust slots. Position new gear on sleeve and press gear into sleeve until seated against shoulder.

4) Locate a new pin hole 90 degrees from existing hole. Center punch new hole, then drill a new hole through sleeve and gear using a standard 1/8" drill. Install

new retaining pin and stake in 2 locations. Thoroughly wash governor assembly to remove any chips or shavings.

Reassembly
Reverse disassembly procedure.

TRANSMISSION CASE

Inspection

1) Inspect case assembly for damage, cracks, porosity or interconnected oil passages. Inspect valve body case pad for flatness or land damage. Air check case passages for restrictions or blockage. Inspect case internal clutch plate lugs for damage or wear.

2) Inspect speedometer, servo and accumulator bores for damage and clearance relative to mating parts. Inspect all bolt holes for damaged threads. Inspect cooler line connectors. Inspect all snap ring grooves for damage. Inspect governor locating pin for proper length. An incorrect length results in a damaged governor gear.

Fig. 15: Front View of Transmission Case

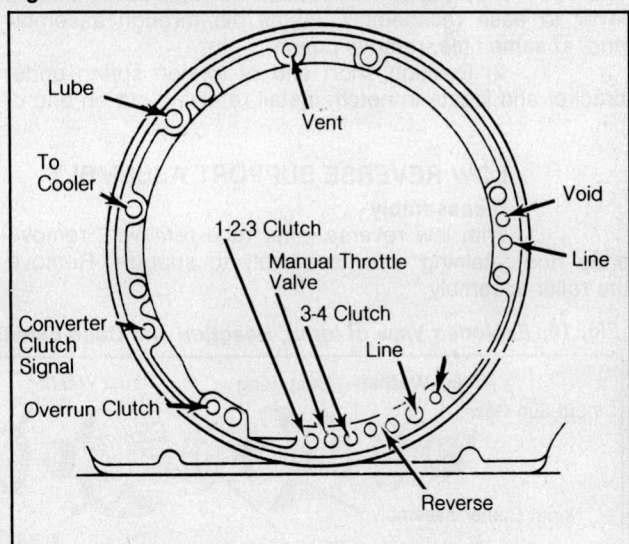

Oil pump-to-case oil passages are shown.

CASE ATTACHING PARTS

Inspection

1) Check 1-2 and 3-4 accumulator parts for porosity or damage to pistons, housing or oil seal rings. Inspect for flatness and condition of accumulator and oil passage plate and gasket.

2) Inspect wiring harness leads and connectors for damage. Inspect "O" ring. Inspect coil and all connections for damage. Inspect speedometer gear and clip for tooth damage or distortion.

REACTION & INPUT GEAR SETS, LOW REVERSE CLUTCH & SUPPORT

Inspection

1) Check reaction and input carriers for pinion gear damage, excessive wear, incorrect number of pinion pin washers and proper staking of pinion pins. Inspect bearings of carrier for heat damage, flatness, and roller condition by rotating top thrust washer.

2) Inspect sun and internal gears and supports for tooth condition and bushing wear. If necessary, remove retaining rings of internal gears. Check all snap

GENERAL MOTORS TURBO HYDRA-MATIC 700-R4 (Cont.)

rings for damage or distortion. Inspect low reverse clutch plates for damage or burning.

3) Remove seals from low reverse piston and inspect for damage. Reinstall or replace seals as required. Inspect piston for damage or porosity. Check low reverse spring retainer and springs for flatness or distortion. Inspect finish on thrust washers for damage.

THROTTLE LEVER & BRACKET ASSEMBLY

Disassembly
Unhook and remove line boost spring. Remove retaining nut from pin and remove pin, torsion lever spring, line boost lever, throttle lever and bracket.

Inspection
Inspect throttle lever and bracket assembly for sticking, binding or damage. Ensure operation is free and without restriction.

Reassembly
1) Insert a small punch through all parts, leave torsion lever spring unhooked and rearward of top throttle lever to ease reassembly. Install pin through assembly and, at same time, remove punch.

2) Position short end of torsion spring under bracket and locate in notch. Install retaining nut on end of pin.

LOW REVERSE SUPPORT ASSEMBLY

Disassembly
With low reverse inner race removed, remove snap ring retaining roller assembly to support. Remove the roller assembly.

Fig. 17: Exploded View of Throttle Lever and Bracket Assembly

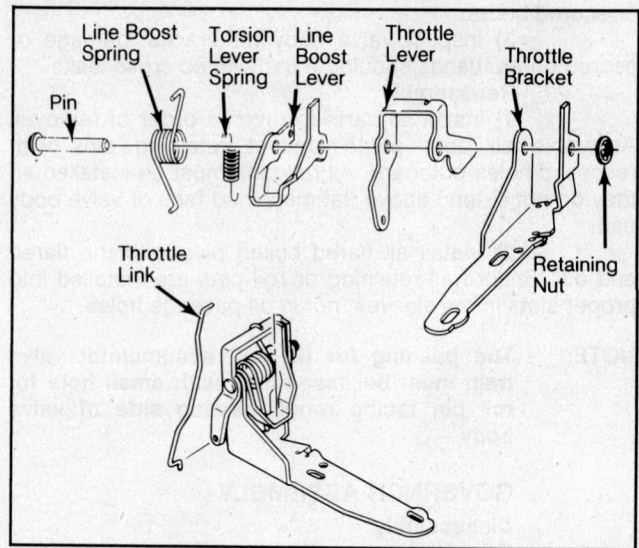

Inspection
Check inner and outer races for damage and surface finish. Inspect roller and springs for damage or distortion.

Reassembly
1) Position low reverse support on bench with chamfered side up. Install low reverse roller assembly into support with oil lube hole down (rearward).

Fig. 16: Exploded View of Input, Reaction and Case Extension Parts

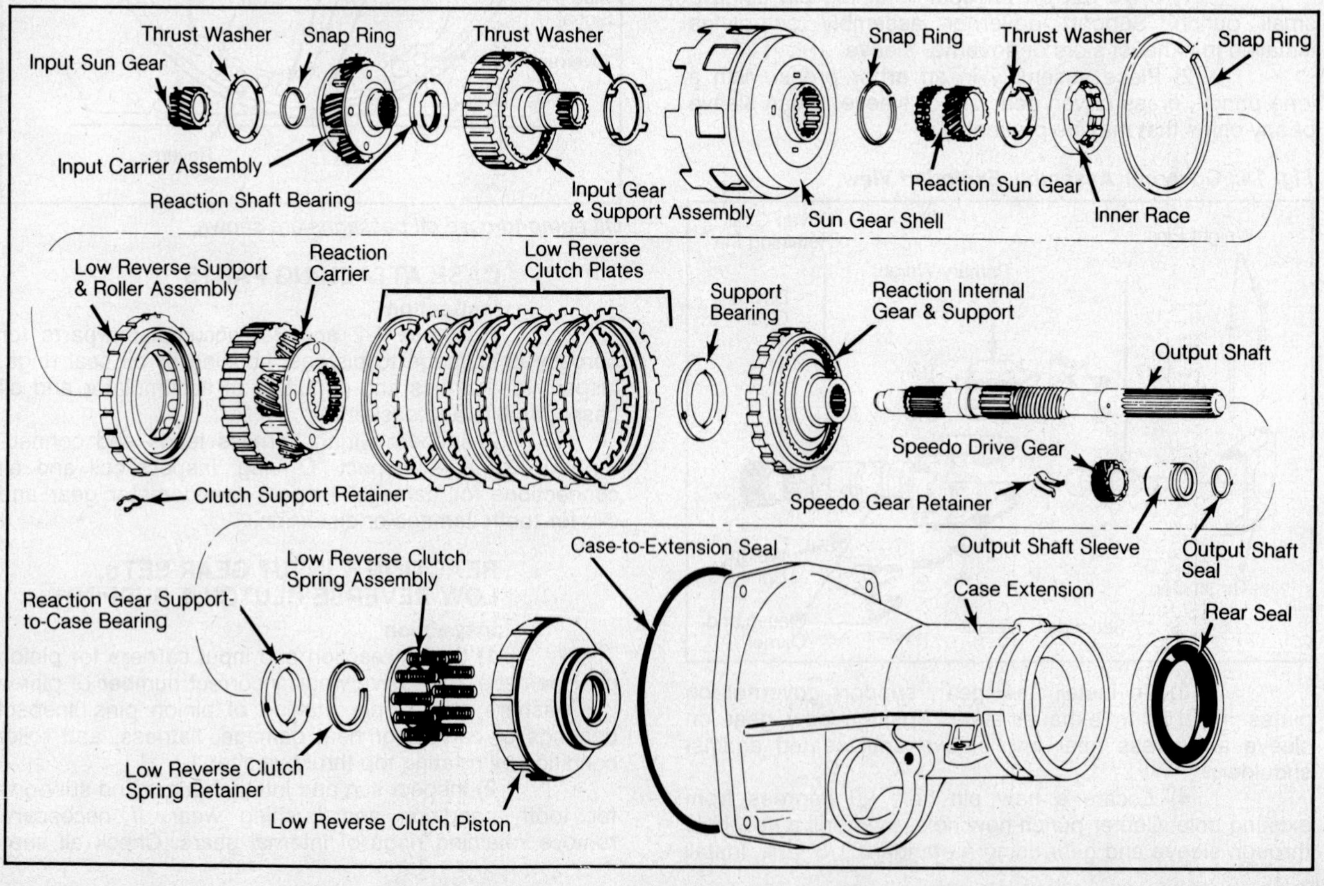

Thrust Washer — Input Sun Gear — Input Carrier Assembly — Snap Ring — Reaction Shaft Bearing — Thrust Washer — Input Gear & Support Assembly — Snap Ring — Sun Gear Shell — Snap Ring — Thrust Washer — Reaction Sun Gear — Inner Race — Snap Ring

Low Reverse Support & Roller Assembly — Reaction Carrier — Low Reverse Clutch Plates — Support Bearing — Reaction Internal Gear & Support — Output Shaft — Clutch Support Retainer — Speedo Drive Gear — Speedo Gear Retainer — Output Shaft Sleeve — Output Shaft Seal

Reaction Gear Support-to-Case Bearing — Low Reverse Clutch Spring Assembly — Case-to-Extension Seal — Case Extension — Rear Seal — Low Reverse Clutch Spring Retainer — Low Reverse Clutch Piston

GENERAL MOTORS TURBO HYDRA-MATIC 700-R4 (Cont.)

Fig. 18: Low Reverse Clutch Support Assembly

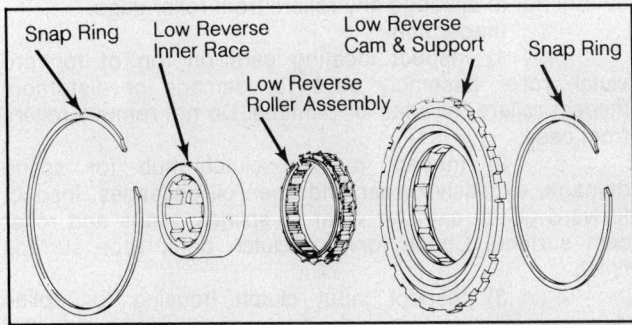

CAUTION: Care should be taken to insure roller and springs are not damaged and that rollers do not become dislodged.

2) Install low reverse inner race into roller assembly by rotating clockwise. When installed, the inner race should rotate in the clockwise direction and lock up in the counterclockwise direction.

REVERSE INPUT CLUTCH

Disassembly

1) Remove snap ring from reverse input housing. Remove reverse input clutch backing plate. Remove reverse input steel and composition clutch plates. Using clutch spring compressor (J-23327) compress reverse input spring assembly and remove snap ring.

2) Remove all tools. Remove reverse input clutch release spring assembly. Remove reverse input clutch piston and remove inner and outer seals.

Inspection

1) Inspect reverse input clutch backing plate for damage, distortion, flatness and burred edges on clutch plate face. Inspect reverse plates. Inspect reverse input composition plates. Check release spring retainer for distortion and damage. Check reverse input clutch piston and seals for damage or distortion.

2) Inspect reverse input housing and drum for cracks. Check surface finish on hub and for worn or damaged bushing. Check freeness and condition of ball check. The ball must move freely with applied air pressure.

Reassembly

1) Lube and install inner and outer seals on clutch piston with seal lips facing away from hub. Install piston into reverse input clutch housing with hub upwards, using an .031" (.8 mm) feeler gauge to position seals. Install spring assembly, large opening first, onto clutch piston.

2) Using clutch spring compressor and adapter (J-23327 and J-250l8-A) on spring retainer, compress spring retainer and install retaining snap ring. Remove all tools.

3) Install 1 waved steel reverse plate. No indexing is necessary. Install a composition plate, followed by the balance of plates, alternating composition faced and flat steel. Install reverse input backing plate with chamfered side up. Install backing plate snap ring.

NOTE: The reverse clutch plates are the largest plates with equally spaced tangs.

REVERSE INPUT CLUTCH PLATE USAGE CHART

Application	Flat Steel [1]	Composition [1]
T2,VA,ML,MP,MS, T7,YH,YF,PQ,Y7, MB,MC,MJ,VN	2 [2]	3 [2]
All Others	3 [2]	4 [2]

[1] – Plate thickness is .077" (1.97 mm).
[2] – Plus 1 Waved steel plate .079" (2.03 mm) thick installed first.

INPUT CLUTCH & FORWARD CLUTCH CAM ASSEMBLY

Disassembly

1) Position input clutch assembly on bench with turbine shaft located in hole on bench and resting on turbine shaft housing. Remove snap ring retaining the 3-4

Fig. 19: Exploded View of Reverse Input Clutch Assembly

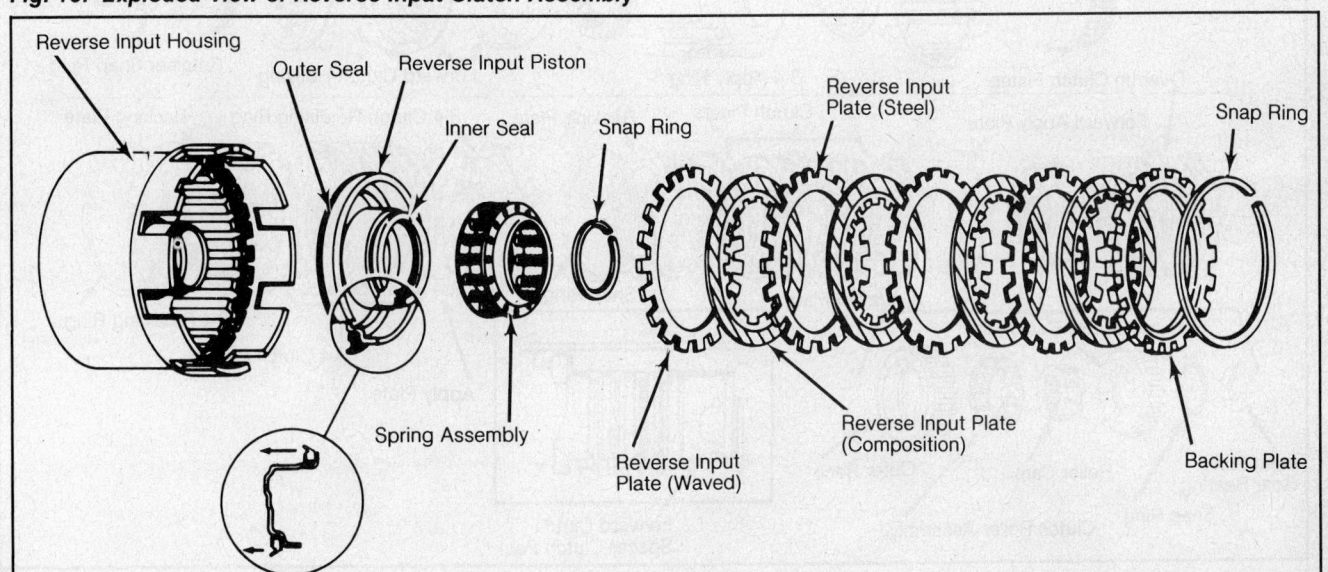

GENERAL MOTORS TURBO HYDRA-MATIC 700-R4 (Cont.)

clutch backing plate and remove plate. Remove 3-4 clutch plates and the 3-4 apply plate. Remove the retaining apply ring and remove the forward clutch backing plate and backing plate snap ring.

2) Remove forward clutch cam assembly and outer race by pulling up. The complete assembly will consist of the forward clutch roller cam, overrun clutch hub and snap ring, and forward clutch outer race and roller assembly. Remove input sun gear bearing (it can be located on back side of input inner race). Remove output shaft nylon seal.

3) Remove forward clutch plates (steel and composition). Remove apply plate and spacer if used. Remove overrun clutch plates (2 steel and 2 composition). Using clutch spring compressor and adapter (J-23456 and J-25018) compress overrun clutch spring retainer. Remove overrun clutch snap ring and all tools. Remove overrun spring and piston assemblies.

4) Remove inner and outer seals from overrun clutch piston. Remove forward clutch piston assembly. Remove inner and outer seals from forward clutch piston assembly.

NOTE: **Apply air pressure to 3-4 feed hole in turbine shaft. It is 3rd hole from shaft end. If unable to remove parts, strike housing on soft surface squarely on open end.**

5) Remove forward clutch housing assembly. Remove 3-4 spring assembly. Remove 3-4 apply ring and piston. Remove "O" ring from input housing. Inspect 4 teflon oil seal rings on turbine shaft for damage or distortion. Remove and replace only if necessary.

6) Remove overrun clutch hub snap ring and overrun hub. Remove forward clutch cam (inner race).

Remove roller assembly from forward clutch cam. Be careful not to dislodge any rollers from roller cage.

Inspection

1) Inspect locating ears on top of forward clutch roller assembly cage for damage or distortion. Inspect rollers for wear or damage. Do not remove rollers from case.

2) Inspect overrun clutch hub for spline damage, excessive wear and open oil passages. Inspect forward clutch cam for wear to splines, tangs and roller cam surface. Check forward clutch outer race surface finish.

3) Inspect input clutch housing for spline damage, wear and open feed passages. Check rear end of turbine shaft for presence of 3 sealing balls (1 hole is an open feed hole and is not sealed). Inspect the 4 Teflon seals on turbine shaft for wear and correct installation. *See Fig. 21.*

NOTE: **Do not remove turbine shaft Teflon oil seals unless damaged.**

4) Inspect converter check ball on front end of turbine shaft for restrictions and free operation. Ball must move with air pressure. If damaged, replace check ball as follows:

- Straighten tangs of retainer and check ball capsule and remove check ball.
- Using a No. 4 screw extractor, remove check valve retainer from shaft by turning and pulling straight out.
- Position new check valve assembly, check valve seat first, into turbine shaft.
- Using a 3/8" (9.5 mm) diameter rod, drive retainer and check valve assembly into shaft until it is 1/8" (3 mm) below top surface of shaft.

Fig. 20: Exploded View of Input Clutch and Forward Clutch Cam Assembly

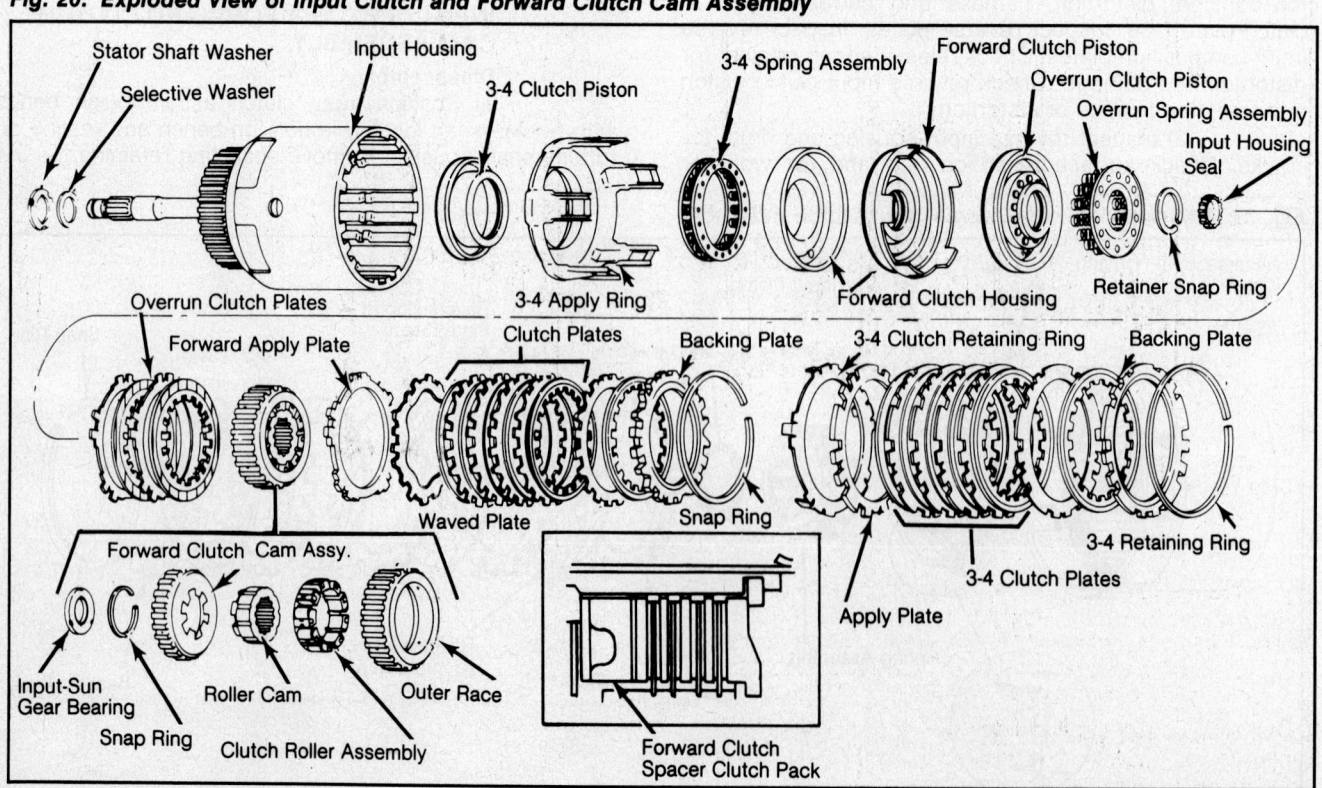

GENERAL MOTORS TURBO HYDRA-MATIC 700-R4 (Cont.)

Fig. 21: View of Turbine Shaft Showing Correct Installation of Teflon Oil Seals

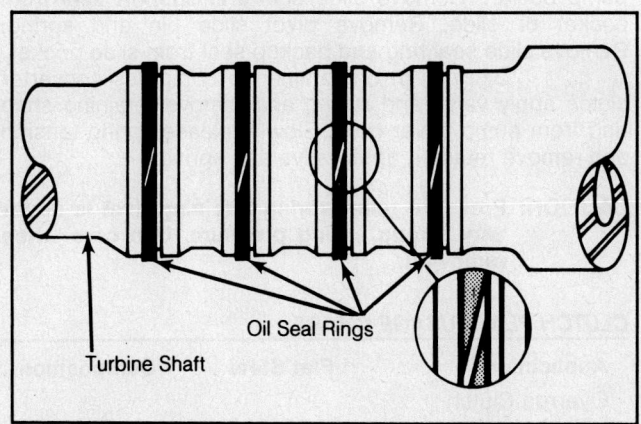

Oil Seal Rings

Turbine Shaft

5) Check 3-4 check ball in input housing for free operation. Inspect all clutch pistons for wear, damage or porosity. Check piston seals for wear or damage.

6) Inspect all clutch release springs for damage, distortion and spring retainer for flatness and damage. Inspect steel clutch plates for damaged tang ends, high or burned spots, excessive wear, or distortion caused by heat. Inspect composition clutch plates for damaged tang ends, burning, flaking or excessive wear (thickness).

7) Inspect all snap rings for distortion and damage. Check backing plates for flatness, distortion and sharpness or burrs on inside edge. Inspect clutch apply rings for distortion and damaged apply tangs.

8) Inspect forward clutch housing ball check for proper operation. Inspect housing for distortion or damage. Inspect needle bearings for excessive wear, flatness, damage or flat rollers.

Reassembly

1) Position forward clutch cam with tangs facing upward. Install forward clutch roller assembly over cam, indexing roller cage to engage tangs in ramps of forward clutch cam. When properly seated, the square ears will be flush with inner race.

2) Position the overrun clutch hub assembly or cam and roller assembly and install snap ring. Install assembled hub, cam and roller assembly into the forward clutch outer race by rotating clockwise. When assembled, the forward clutch hub must rotate freely in the clockwise direction and lockup in the counterclockwise direction.

3) If removed, install the 4 Teflon oil seals rings on turbine shaft. *See Fig. 21.* Assemble with a long edge and the large "O" ring on inside of housing. If removed, install small "O" ring on end of turbine shaft.

4) Position input clutch housing over bench hole with turbine shaft downward. Install inner and outer seals on 3-4 piston, with lips facing away from hub. Install 3-4 piston in input housing, rotate and gently push downward making sure piston is properly seated. Install inner and outer seals on forward clutch piston with lips facing away from tangs.

5) Lube and install forward clutch piston into forward clutch housing. Install 3-4 spring retainer into 3-4 clutch apply ring. Install assembled forward clutch housing and piston on spring retainer in 3-4 apply ring. Notches of the forward clutch piston must be indexed with the long apply tangs of the 3-4 apply ring. Install seal protector (J-29883) on input shaft.

6) Hold 3-4 apply ring and assembled parts by tangs and install into input clutch housing and firmly seat forward clutch piston. Remove tools. Do not let pistons separate. Install overrun clutch seal protector (J-29882) on input housing shaft and install overrun clutch piston with hub facing upward and remove tool.

7) Overrun piston should be 3/16" below snap ring groove on input housing hub. If not seated properly, install clutch spring compressor (J-23327) and tap until all parts are fully seated. Install overrun clutch spring retainer on overrun clutch piston locating release springs on piston tabs. Use clutch spring compressor press and adapter (J-23456 and J-25018) on the overrun spring assembly and compress spring retainer.

NOTE: Do not over compress springs as distortion to the retainer can occur.

8) With springs compressed, install retaining snap ring and remove all tools. Install splined nylon output shaft seal, with seal lip facing up. On forward clutch piston in input housing, install 4 overrun clutch plates. Starting with steel plate and positioning so that long recessed slot is indexed with wide notch in housing. Install remaining clutch plates alternating steel and composition.

9) Install input sun gear bearing assembly on input clutch hub on top of nylon seal positioning outside "L" race in downward position. Make sure bearing is centered. Using a screwdriver, align and center inside drive tangs of 2 overrun clutch plates (composition).

10) Install assembled forward clutch cam assembly and outer race clutch hub, indexing overrun clutch plates. Install forward clutch spacer (thick steel) into input clutch housing, indexing lug on spacer with large slot in input housing.

NOTE: A 5 plate forward clutch will use a single thick apply plate. A 4 plate clutch will use a thick spacer and a thin apply plate and must be assembled with thin apply plate first and spacer with holes facing thin apply plate.

11) Install "Waved" steel forward clutch plate into input housing, indexing wide slot with 2 small ears with wide notch in housing. Install forward clutch plate assembly (composition) on forward clutch hub. Install remaining forward clutch plates alternating composition and steel. The last plate installed will be composition.

12) Install forward clutch backing plate into input housing, with chamfered side up. Install snap ring into input clutch housing (smaller ring with larger gap). Install 3-4 gear ring retaining plate (flat plate with legs) into clutch housing indexing each apply lug with ends of 3-4 gear apply ring.

13) Install 3-4 gear apply plate (thick steel) into input housing indexing long wide gear of plate with wide slot in housing. Install 3-4 assembly (composition), then install remaining plates alternating steel and composition indexing long wide ear of plate with wide slot in housing. The last plate installed will be composition.

14) Install 3-4 gear backing plate with chamfered side up. Install 3-4 retaining ring into input housing assembly. Using feeler gauges, measure end clearance between backing plate and first composition plate. If end clearance is not within specifications, select proper backing plate from chart. Air check all clutches by applying air pressure at feed holes in turbine shaft.

GENERAL MOTORS TURBO HYDRA-MATIC 700-R4 (Cont.)

3-4 BACKING PLATE SELECTION CHART

Application	Backing Plate Travel In. (mm)	Backing Plate Diameter/I.D. In. (mm)
T2,VA,ML,MP,MS, T7,YF,PQ,Y7,MB, MC,MJ,VN,TC	.055-.109 (1.39-2.78)	.278/1 (7.125)
		.239/2 (6.125)
All Others	.049-.113 (1.25-2.87)	.200/3 (5.125)
		.161/4 (4.125)

OIL PUMP ASSEMBLY

Disassembly

1) Remove reverse input clutch drum-to-pump thrust washer, pump-to-case gasket and pump-to-case oil seal ring from pump assembly. Do not remove the 2 Teflon oil seal rings from pump hub unless replacement is necessary. Remove attaching bolts and separate pump cover from pump body.

CAUTION: Pump slide spring is under very high pressure. Place a shop towel over spring when removing to prevent possible injury.

2) Using needle-nose pliers, compress pump slide spring and remove from pump by pulling straight out. Remove pump guide rings, pump vanes, pump rotor and rotor guide from pump body pocket. Remove slide from pump pocket. Remove slide seal and support seal from pocket or slide. Remove pivot slide pin and spring. Remove slide seal ring and backup seal from slide pocket.

3) Push in on retainer to compress converter clutch apply valve and spring and remove retaining snap ring from pump cover bore. Slowly release spring tension and remove retainer, apply valve and spring.

CAUTION: Pressure relief spring retaining rivet is under very strong spring pressure. Use care when removing.

CLUTCH PLATE USAGE CHART

Application	Flat Steel	Composition
Overrun Clutch		
All Models	2 [1]	[2] 2
Forward Clutch		
T2,VA,ML,MP,MS T7,YF,YH,PQ,Y7		
MB,MC,MJ,VN,TC	3 [3] [4]	[2] 4
All Others	4 [3] [4]	[2] 5
3-4 Clutch		
T2,VA,ML,MP,MS, T7,YF,PQ,Y7,MB, MC,MJ,VN,TC	4 [4]	[2] 5
All Others	5 [4]	[2] 6

[1] – Plate thickness is .091" (2.31 mm).
[2] – Plate thickness is .079" (2.03 mm).
[3] – Plus 1 waved steel plate .079" (2.03 mm).
[4] – Plate thickness is .077" (1.97 mm).

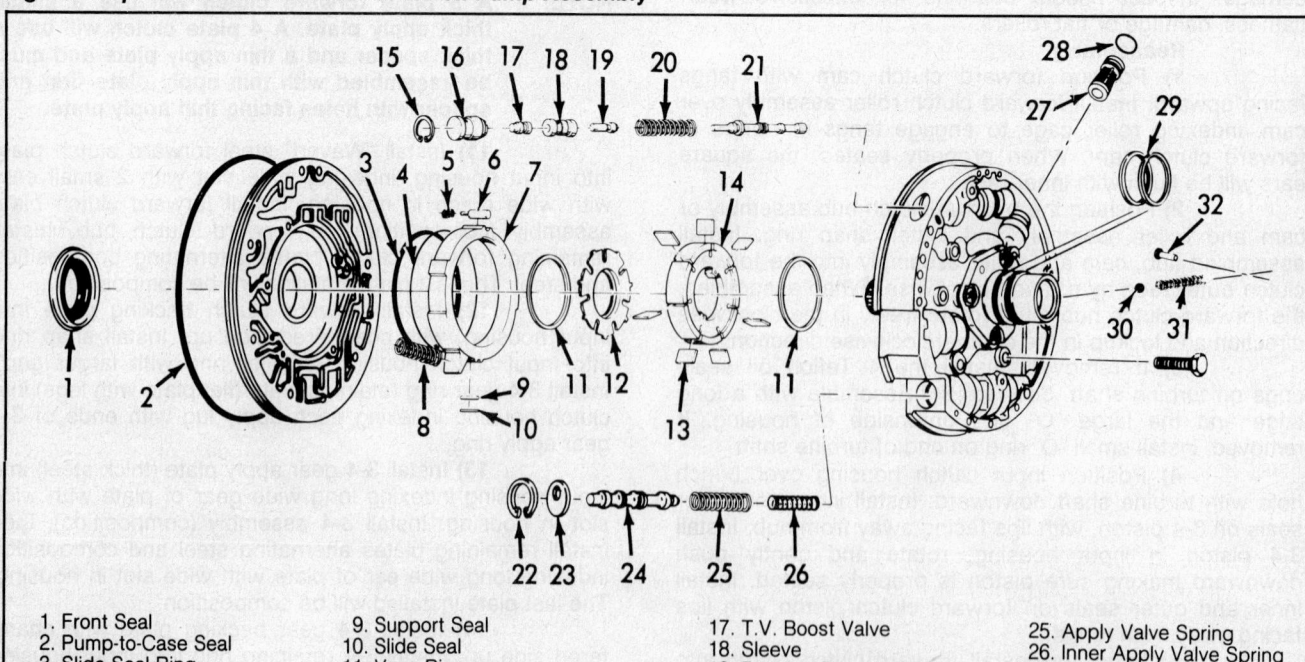

Fig. 22: Exploded View of Model 700-R4 Oil Pump Assembly

1. Front Seal	17. T.V. Boost Valve
2. Pump-to-Case Seal	18. Sleeve
3. Slide Seal Ring	19. Reverse Boost Valve
4. Slide Backup Seal	20. Pressure Regulator Spring
5. Pivot Pin Spring	21. Pressure Regulator Valve
6. Pivot Pin	22. Snap Ring
7. Slide	23. Converter Valve Stop
8. Slide Spring	24. Conv. Clutch Apply Valve
9. Support Seal	25. Apply Valve Spring
10. Slide Seal	26. Inner Apply Valve Spring
11. Vane Ring	27. Pump Screen
12. Rotor Guide	28. Screen Seal
13. Vane	29. Stator Shaft Oil Seal
14. Rotor	30. Pressure Relief Ball
15. Snap Ring	31. Pressure Relief Spring
16. Bushing	32. Ball Retainer

GENERAL MOTORS TURBO HYDRA-MATIC 700-R4 (Cont.)

Fig. 23: Oil Pump Cover and Body Oil Passages

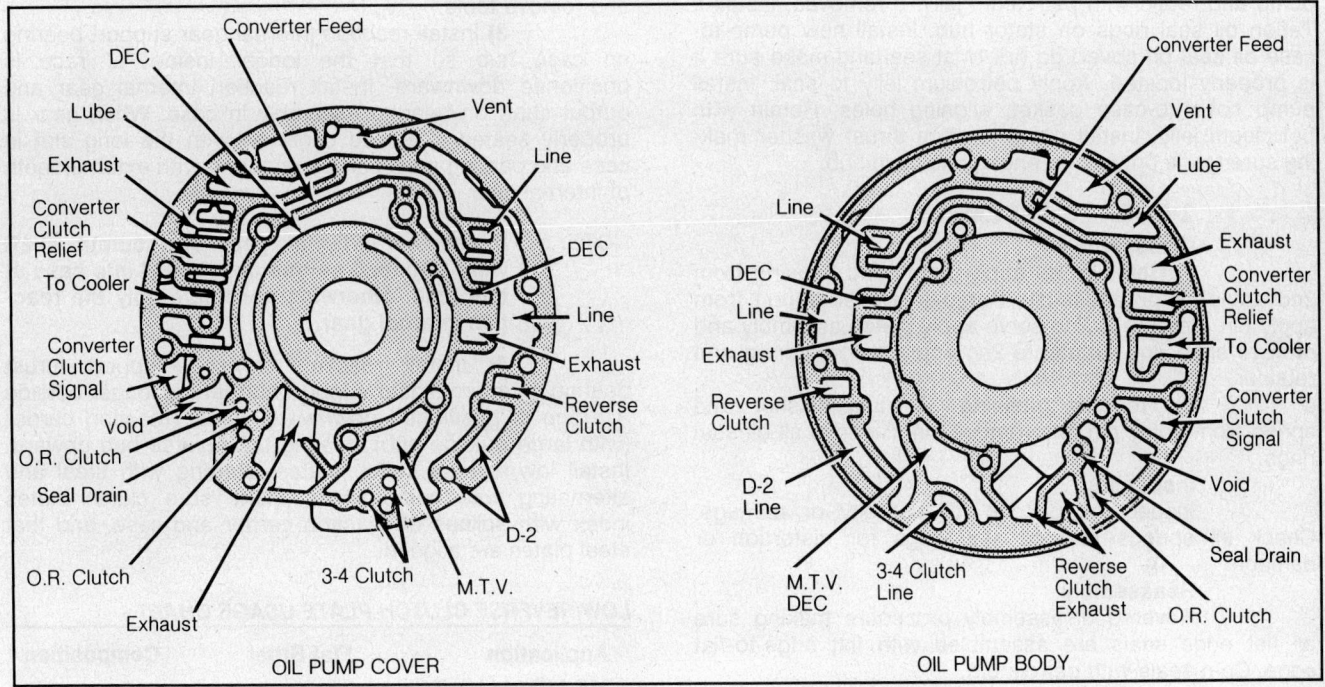

OIL PUMP COVER   OIL PUMP BODY

4) Using a small punch, remove pressure relief spring retaining rivet. Remove relief spring and ball. If ball is not free, remove by applying air pressure to oil passage located in pump cover. Remove oil screen and "O" ring from pump cover.

5) Position pump with stator shaft down through hole in work bench and secure with a holding bolt. Using a small screwdriver, compress T.V. boost valve bushing and remove snap ring. Remove bushing and valve using a magnet. Using the same procedure, remove reverse boost valve and sleeve and pressure regulator valve and spring.

Inspection

1) Inspect all valves, springs, sleeves and bushings for chips, burrs, distortion and freeness in bores. Check pressure relief ball and spring for damage or distortion. Inspect pump cover screen and "O" ring for wear or damage.

2) Clean pump body and cover and check all bores for obstructions. Inspect mating sides of cover and body for scoring, flatness, porosity or voids between channels. Check channels for dirt, interconnected passages or damage.

3) Inspect rotor and slide for scoring, cracks or damage. Check rotor guide and pump vane rings for excessive wear or damage. Inspect all seals for damage. Inspect front seal for damage or excessive wear and seal retaining spring for proper location.

Reassembly

1) Install "O" ring and flat steel ring into groove on back side of pump slide and retain in place with petroleum jelly. Install small pivot pin and spring into small hole located in pump body pocket.

2) Install slide into pump body, indexing notch in slide with pivot pin hole and with flat oil seal ring facing down into pocket. Install slide seal and support into slide adjacent to rotor.

NOTE: **Position pump slide seal (composition) against outer diameter of pump pocket.**

3) Install a vane ring into pump pocket, centering on stator hole. Install composition rotor guide into deep pocket or rotor, indexing notches. Retain with petroleum jelly. Install rotor and guide into pump pocket with guide positioned downward.

4) Install vanes into rotor, positioning so they are flush with rotor and with the full wear pattern against slide. Install vane guide ring into rotor. Compress pump slide spring and install into pump pocket.

NOTE: **All parts must be flush with pump body face.**

5) Assemble "O" ring on pump screen and install screen into pump cover with seal end last. Install pressure relief ball and spring into cover and install retaining rivet.

6) Position spring on long end of converter clutch apply valve and retain with petroleum jelly. Install apply valve and spring into pump and install retaining snap ring.

7) Position pump cover so that pressure regulator valve bore is in a vertical position. Install regulator valve into bottom of cover bore with large land and orifice hole end installed first. Install pressure regulator valve spring into bore.

8) Install T.V. boost valve into bushing with long land of valve into large hole of bushing and retain with petroleum jelly. Install reverse boost valve into sleeve (small end first). Retain with petroleum jelly.

9) Using a small magnet install reverse and T.V. boost valve assemblies into pump cover bore. Compress T.V. boost valve and install retaining snap ring. Make sure snap ring seats in groove.

10) Place body assembly over hole in work bench with stator shaft downward. Assemble pump cover to body and install attaching bolts finger tight. Align pump body and cover using aligning strap (J-21368), and place a holding bolt or screwdriver through pump-to-case bolt hole and hole in bench. Remove strap and tighten cover-to-body bolts.

GENERAL MOTORS TURBO HYDRA-MATIC 700-R4 (Cont.)

11) Position new pump-to-case gasket on pump and retain with petroleum jelly. If removed, install 2 Teflon oil seal rings on stator hub. Install new pump-to-case oil seal on cover; do not twist seal and make sure it is properly located. Apply petroleum jelly to seal. Install pump cover-to-case gasket, aligning holes. Retain with petroleum jelly. Install pump-to-drum thrust washer making sure tangs on washer engage holes in hub.

2-4 SERVO ASSEMBLY

Disassembly

1) Remove 4th apply piston and housing from 2nd apply piston assembly. Remove release spring from apply pin. Compress 2nd servo apply piston assembly and remove snap ring. Separate 2nd apply piston, spring and retainer.

2) Remove retaining "E" ring, washer and spring from apply pin and remove pin. Remove all oil seal rings.

Inspection

Inspect all pistons for porosity or damage. Check all springs and oil seal rings for distortion or damage.

Reassembly

Reverse disassembly procedure making sure all flat edge seals are assembled with flat edge-to-flat edge. Coat seals with petrolatum.

Fig. 24: Exploded View of 2-4 Servo Assembly

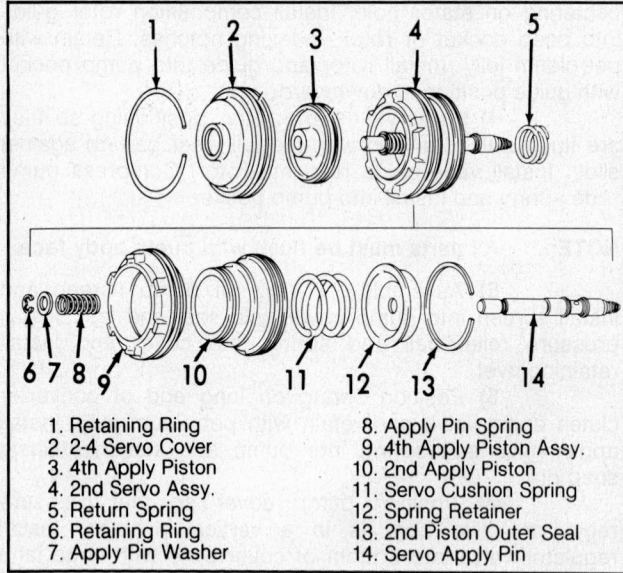

1. Retaining Ring
2. 2-4 Servo Cover
3. 4th Apply Piston
4. 2nd Servo Assy.
5. Return Spring
6. Retaining Ring
7. Apply Pin Washer
8. Apply Pin Spring
9. 4th Apply Piston Assy.
10. 2nd Apply Piston
11. Servo Cushion Spring
12. Spring Retainer
13. 2nd Piston Outer Seal
14. Servo Apply Pin

TRANSMISSION REASSEMBLY

LOW/REVERSE CLUTCH

1) Place transmission in a vertical position. Oil and install inner, center and outer seals on low/reverse clutch piston. Install piston into transmission case, indexing piston with notch at bottom of case and hub facing down. Make sure piston is fully seated and parking pawl will index into opening in piston wall.

2) Install low/reverse clutch spring retainer assembly into case with flat side of retainer upward. Install clutch spring compressor (J-23327) and compress springs, indexing tool retaining plate so that tool is free to

slide over case hub. Install low/reverse clutch snap ring and remove tools.

3) Install reaction internal gear support bearing on case hub so that the longer inside "L" race is positioned downward. Install reaction internal gear and output shaft on bearing assembly in case. When gear is properly seated it will be centered with the long slot in case and parking pawl can be engaged with external teeth of internal gear.

NOTE: **If reaction internal gear and output shaft were removed as one unit, install into case at this time, otherwise assemble only the reaction internal gear.**

4) Install reaction carrier-to-support thrust bearing on internal gear support so that the longer outside "L" race is positioned downward. Install reaction carrier (with large outside hub) locating the reverse hub upward. Install low/reverse clutch plates, starting with steel and alternating with composition. Make sure clutch plates index with splines of reaction carrier and case, and that steel plates are aligned.

LOW/REVERSE CLUTCH PLATE USAGE CHART

Application	Flat Steel	Composition
MB,MC,MJ,VN,TC, T2,VA,ML,MP,MS, T7,YH,YF,PQ,Y7	4 [1]	4 [2]
All Others	5 [1]	5 [2]

[1] – Plate thickness is .069" (1.77 mm).
[2] – Plate thickness is .088" (2.25 mm).

5) Remove low/reverse inner race and install low/reverse support and roller assembly with chamfered side up in case, indexing with case splines. Install low/reverse inner race into roller assembly and rotate until internal splines are engaged. Push down for full engagement. The bottom tangs will be flush with reaction hub when seated. Install low/reverse snap ring and support spring into transmission case.

REACTION & INPUT GEAR SETS

1) If removed, install snap ring on reaction sun gear. Install sun gear into reaction carrier, indexing pinions. Install nylon thrust washer with 4 locating ears on low/reverse clutch inner race. Install reaction sun gear shell (large housing with end slots and holes), engaging splines of shell shaft and sun gear.

2) Install reaction shaft-to-shell thrust washer (bronze washer with wide thrust face), indexing the tangs in shell. Install input internal gear and shaft (shaft end first). If output shaft and reaction gear were removed as separate parts during disassembly, go to step 3).

3) Position output shaft into transmission, indexing with all parts. Install output shaft support tool (J-29837) and adjust so that output shaft is positioned upward as far as possible. See Fig. 11.

4) Install input carrier-to-reaction shaft thrust bearing with long "L" race on outside. Install input carrier assembly, with hub end down. Install new snap ring on output shaft. Install input sun gear, indexing gear end with input carrier pinions. Install input carrier thrust washer on input carrier.

GENERAL MOTORS TURBO HYDRA-MATIC 700-R4 (Cont.)

REVERSE INPUT ASSEMBLY & INPUT CLUTCH

1) Install selective washer on turbine housing. Install oil pump hub bearing on selective washer with black finish side up.

2) Position reverse input assembly on bench hole with clutch plates facing upward. Align and center clutch plates with screwdriver and install input clutch assembly with turbine shaft downward. Index reverse clutch plates with hub of input housing. Make certain all clutch plates are fully engaged.

REVERSE & INPUT CLUTCHES

Install reverse and input clutch assemblies into case as an assembly, indexing 3-4 clutch plates of input assembly with input internal gear. Complete assembly is properly seated when reverse housing is just below pump face of case. Make sure all clutch plates are fully engaged.

2-4 BAND & SERVO ASSEMBLY

1) Position 2-4 band in case, indexing anchor pin end with case pin hole. Install band achor pin in case and index with 2-4 band end.

2) Install 2-4 servo assembly into case and index apply pin on band end. Check for proper engagement of apply pin on band end. Recheck 2-4 servo apply pin selection to ensure correct pin is installed.

3) Install servo cover and "O" ring. Install compressor tool and compress cover. Install cover retaining ring, indexing ring ends with slot in case.

OIL PUMP ASSEMBLY

1) Install aligning pins into 2 opposing pump attaching bolt holes in case. Install pump into case, aligning filter and pressure regulator holes with holes in case. Install and tighten pump attaching bolts.

2) Rotate transmission to a horizontal position and rotate turbine or output shaft by hand. If shaft will not rotate, loosen pump attaching bolts and attempt to rotate shaft again. If shaft now turns, reverse and input assemblies have not been indexed properly or some other assembly problem has occurred, such as a mispositioned thrust washer. Rotate transmission to a vertical position.

VALVE BODY & WIRING HARNESS

1) Install 1-2 accumulator pin into case. Install accumulator piston and seal over pin with lug end up. Install spring on accumulator piston.

2) Install governor and converter clutch oil screens into case. Install 5 check balls into case pockets. See Fig. 25. Install valve body alignment pins, then install spacer plate-to-case gasket (identified with a small "c") on case. Install valve body spacer on case, aligning holes.

3) Install valve body-to-spacer gasket (identified with a "V") on spacer plate. Install 3 exhaust check balls and check valve into valve body pockets. See Fig. 6. Retain with petroleum jelly. Install valve body and connect link to inside detent lever. Remove aligning pins and install and tighten valve body-to-case bolts.

4) Attach retaining clip to manual valve link and inside detent lever. Install throttle lever, bracket and T.V. link, locating slot in bracket with roll pin on valve body top

Fig. 25: View of Transmission Case Showing Oil Passages and Check Ball Locations

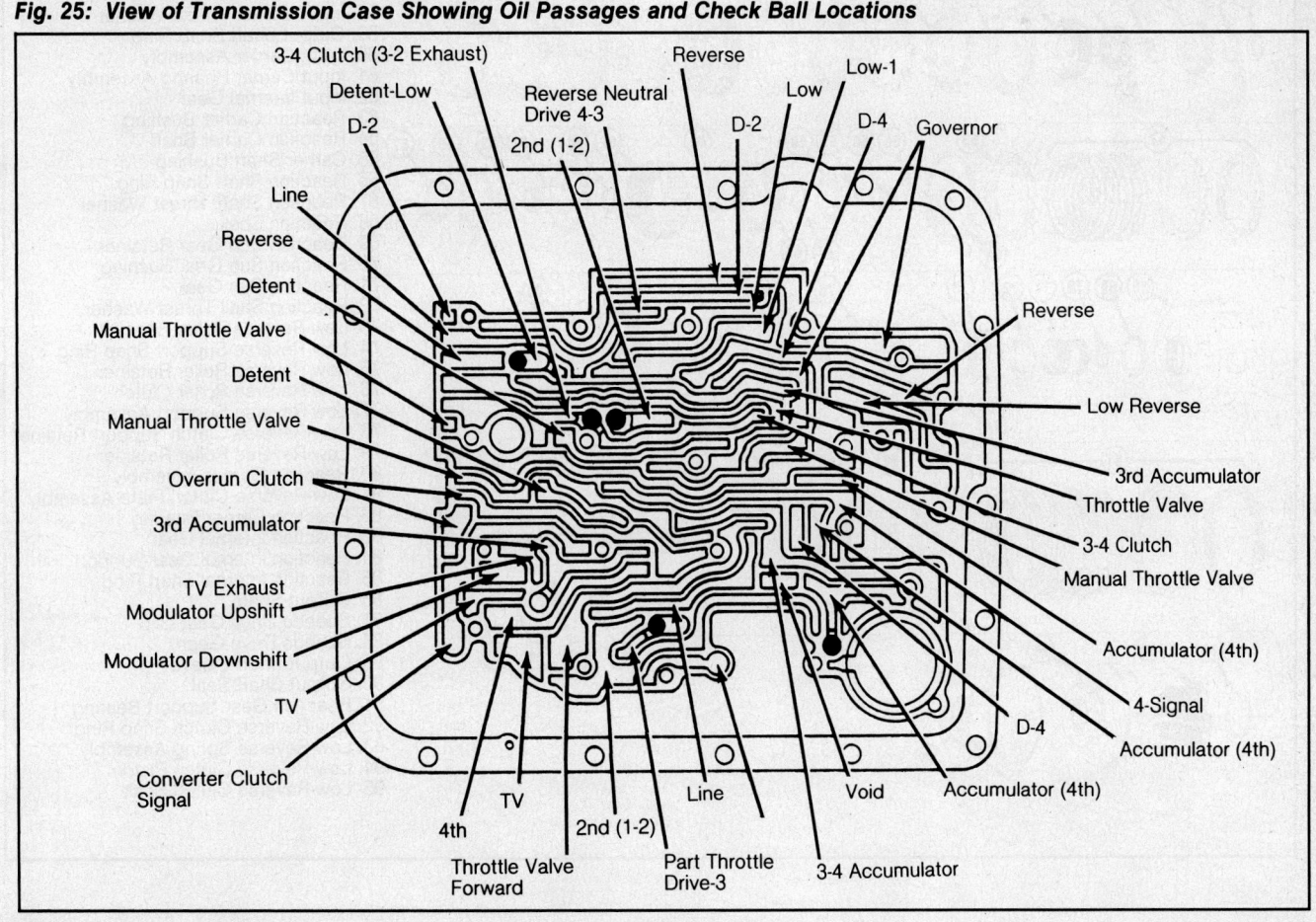

Fig. 26: *Exploded View of Transmission Internal Components*

1. Pump Thrust Washer
2. 2-4 Band Assembly
3. Reverse Input Clutch Bushing
4. Check Valve Assembly
5. Reverse Input Clutch Housing
6. Reverse Input Clutch Bushing
7. Reverse Input Clutch Piston
8. Reverse Input Clutch Seals
9. Reverse Input Clutch Spring Assembly
10. Reverse Input Snap Ring
11. Reverse Input Waved Plate
12. Reverse Input Clutch Plate Assembly
13. Reverse Input Backing Plate
14. Reverse Input Snap Ring
15. Stator Shaft Bearing
16. Selective Washer
17. Check Valve Assembly
18. Turbine Shaft "O" Ring
19. Turbine Shaft Oil Seals
20. Check Ball
21. Input Housing
22. Input Housing "O" Ring
23. 3-4 Clutch Piston
24. 3-4 Clutch Seals
25. 3-4 Clutch Apply Ring
26. 3-4 Clutch Spring Assembly
27. Forward Clutch Check Ball
28. Forward Clutch Housing
29. Forward Clutch Seals
30. Forward Clutch Piston
31. Overrun Clutch Seals
32. Overrun Clutch Piston
33. Overrun Clutch Ball
34. Overrun Clutch Spring Assembly
35. Overrun Clutch Snap Ring
36. Input Housing Seal
37. Input Sun Gear Bearing
38. Overrun Clutch Snap Ring
39. Overrun Clutch Hub
40. Forward Roller Cam
41. Forward Roller Assembly
42. Forward Clutch Outer Race
43. Overrun Clutch Plate Assembly
44. Forward Clutch Apply Plate
45. Forward Clutch Spacer (4-PLT)
46. Forward Clutch Plate (Waved)
47. Forward Clutch Plate Assembly
48. Forward Clutch Backing Plate
49. Forward Clutch Snap Ring
50. 3-4 Clutch Retainer Plate
51. 3-4 Clutch Apply Plate
52. 3-4 Plate Assembly
53. 3-4 Clutch Backing Plate
54. 3-4 Clutch Snap Ring
55. Input Sun Gear Bushing
56. Input Sun Gear
57. Input Sun Gear Bushing
58. Input Carrier Thrust Washer
59. Output Shaft Snap Ring
60. Input Carrier Assembly
61. Input Carrier Bearing Assembly
62. Input Internal Gear
63. Reaction Carrier Bushing
64. Reaction Carrier Shaft
65. Carrier Shaft Bushing
66. Reaction Shaft Snap Ring
67. Reaction Shaft Thrust Washer
68. Reaction Shell
69. Reaction Sun Gear Retainer
70. Reaction Sun Gear Bushing
71. Reaction Sun Gear
72. Reaction Shell Thrust Washer
73. Low-Reverse Roller Race
74. Low-Reverse Support Snap Ring
75. Low-Reverse Roller Retainer
76. Low-Reverse Roller Clutch
77. Low-Reverse Support Assembly
78. Low-Reverse Clutch Support Retainer
79. Low-Reverse Roller Retainer
80. Reaction Carrier Assembly
81. Low-Reverse Clutch Plate Assembly
82. Reaction Carrier Bearing
83. Reaction Internal Gear
84. Reaction Internal Gear Support
85. Reaction Internal Snap Ring
86. Output Shaft
87. Speedo Drive Gear Clip
88. Speedo Drive Gear
89. Output Shaft Sleeve
90. Output Shaft Seal
91. Reaction Gear Support Bearing
92. Low-Reverse Clutch Snap Ring
93. Low-Reverse Spring Assembly
94. Low-Reverse Clutch Piston
95. Low-Reverse Clutch Seals

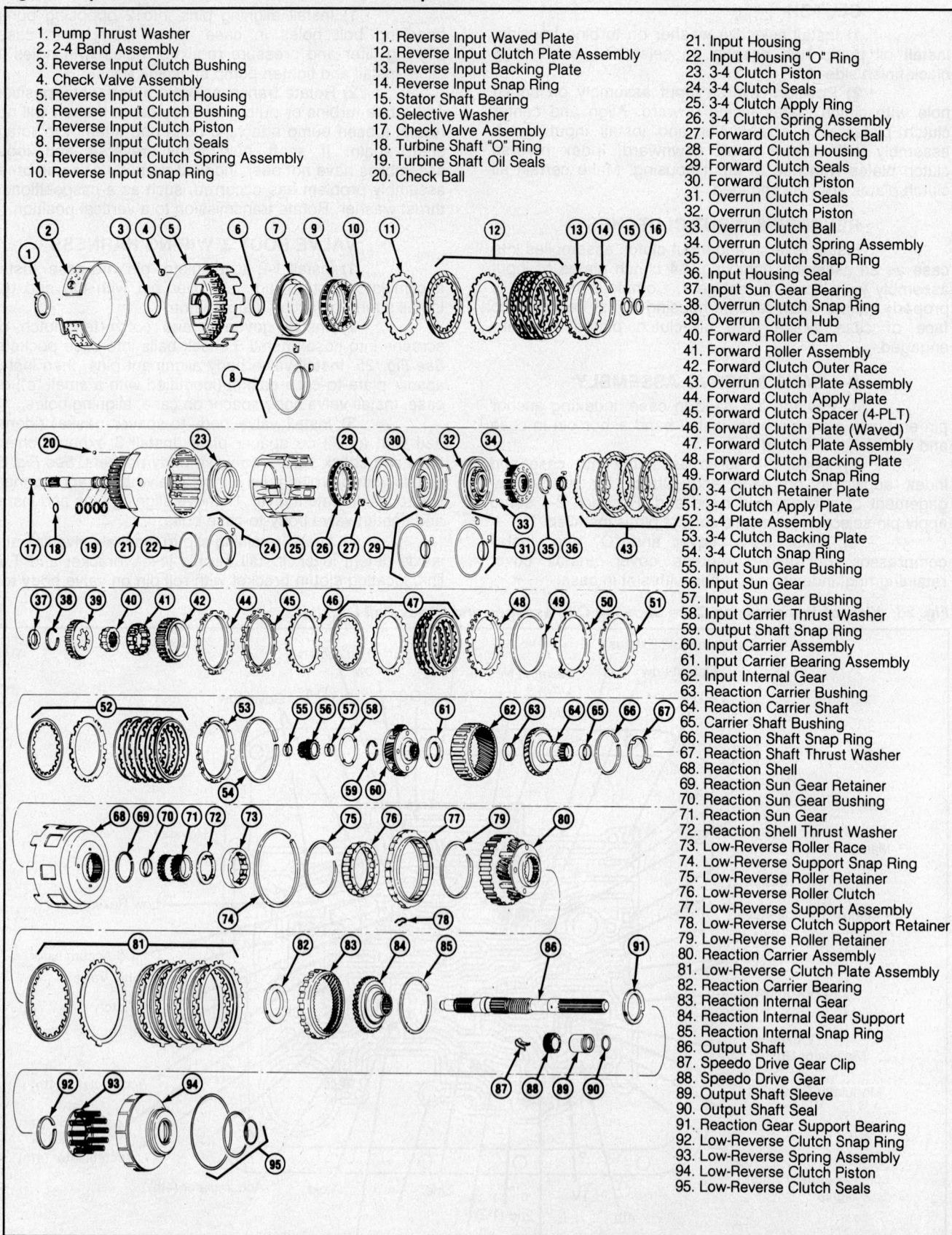

GENERAL MOTORS TURBO HYDRA-MATIC 700-R4 (Cont.)

Fig. 27: *Cutaway View of Transmission Showing Thrust Washer, Bearing and Oil Seal Locations*

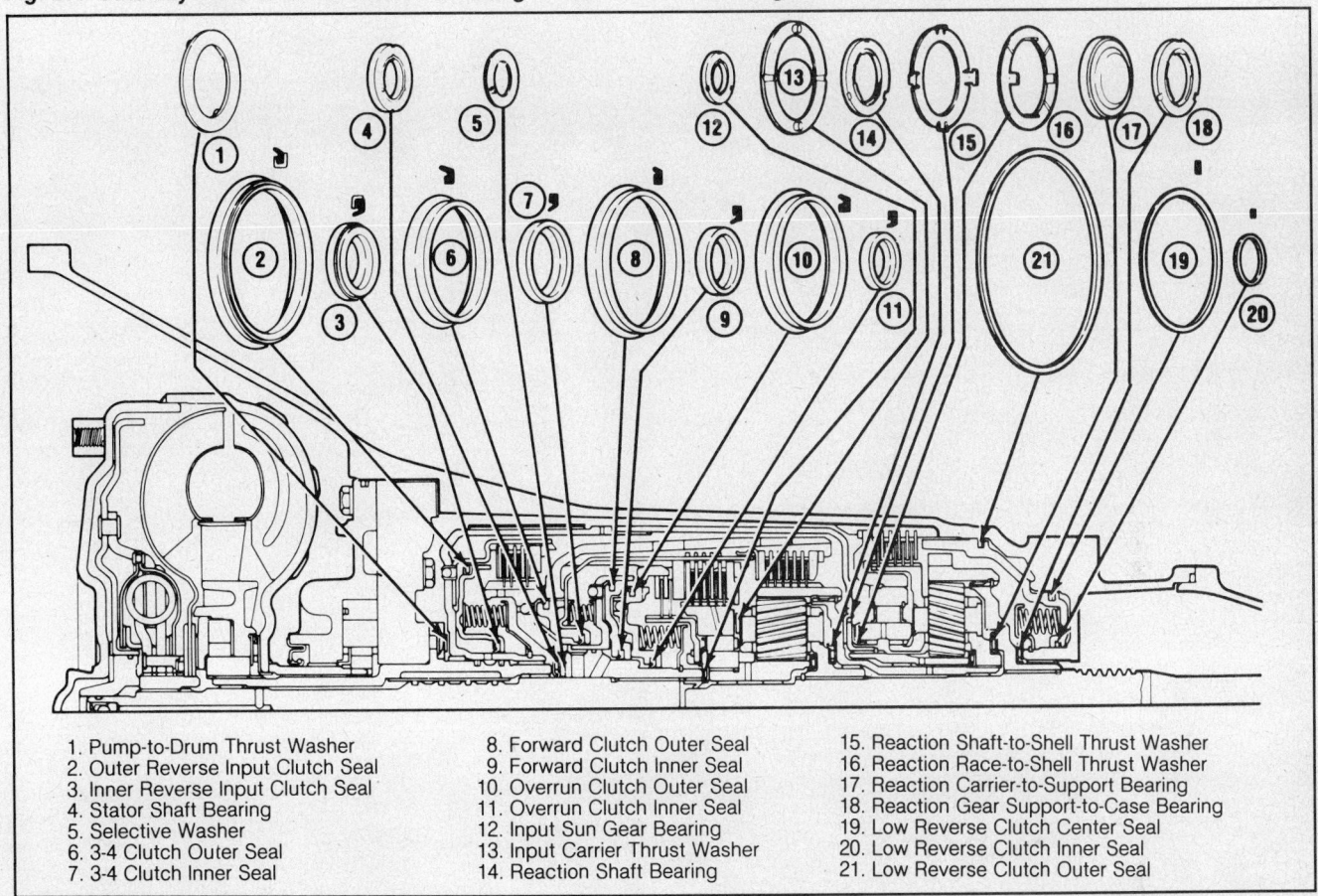

1. Pump-to-Drum Thrust Washer	8. Forward Clutch Outer Seal	15. Reaction Shaft-to-Shell Thrust Washer
2. Outer Reverse Input Clutch Seal	9. Forward Clutch Inner Seal	16. Reaction Race-to-Shell Thrust Washer
3. Inner Reverse Input Clutch Seal	10. Overrun Clutch Outer Seal	17. Reaction Carrier-to-Support Bearing
4. Stator Shaft Bearing	11. Overrun Clutch Inner Seal	18. Reaction Gear Support-to-Case Bearing
5. Selective Washer	12. Input Sun Gear Bearing	19. Low Reverse Clutch Center Seal
6. 3-4 Clutch Outer Seal	13. Input Carrier Thrust Washer	20. Low Reverse Clutch Inner Seal
7. 3-4 Clutch Inner Seal	14. Reaction Shaft Bearing	21. Low Reverse Clutch Outer Seal

face. Align link through T.V. linkage case bore. Attach assembly with 2 valve body attaching bolts.

     5) Install valve body attaching bolt and harness clip. Install parking pawl bracket. Install manual detent spring and roller assembly. Install "O" ring on solenoid. Install assembly into pump, locating attaching wire harness toward transmission. Install wiring harness and connect to all pressure switches.

NOTE: **Each pressure switch is color coded. Match color of switch with same color of wire.**

     6) Install "O" ring on outside electrical connector and install into case by compressing inside tang. Locate tab with case notch. Attach inside connector terminal to outside connector. Install oil passage cover on transmission with 3 bolts and tighten.

     7) Install 3-4 accumulator piston into housing with lug end up. Install 3-4 piston spring into housing on piston. Position 3-4 accumulator plate and gasket on transmission placing gasket on top. Install housing, spring and piston on transmission case and secure with 3 bolts and tighten.

     8) Install speedometer gear and retaining clip on output shaft, positioning large notch on speedometer gear rearward. Install output shaft seal in output shaft sleeve and install on output shaft with oil pump seal installer (J-25016).

     9) Install oil seal ring on case extension and install on case. Position so speedometer hole is located on same side as governor. Install governor assembly.

Apply cup sealant to edge of cover, then install cover. Install "O" ring on filter and install.

     10) Position new oil pan gasket on transmission case. Install oil pan and pan attaching bolts. Tighten attaching bolts.

     11) Install remaining outside connectors such as driven speedometer gear and adapter, outside manual lever and nut. Remove transmission from holding fixture and install torque converter.

TIGHTENING SPECIFICATIONS

Application	Ft. Lbs. (N.m)
Converter-to-Flywheel	41-52 (55-70)
Extension-to-Case	26 (34)
Man. Shaft-to-Detent Lever	23 (31)
Oil Cooler Pipes	28 (38)
Park Bracket-to-Case	18 (22)
Transmission-to-Engine	35 (50)
	INCH Lbs.
Accumulator Cover-to-Case	96 (11)
Detent Spring-to-Valve Body	216 (22)
Oil Pan-to-Case	216 (22)
Oil Passage Cover-to-Case	96 (11)
Pressure Plugs	96 (11)
Pump-to-Case	216 (22)
Solenoid Assy.-to-Pump	96 (11)
Valve Body-to-Case	96 (11)

SECTION 3

DOMESTIC MANUAL TRANSMISSIONS

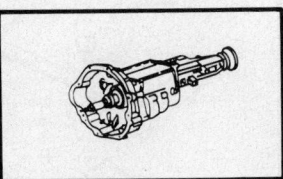

NOTE: ALSO SEE GENERAL INDEX.

Manual Transmissions
AMC/RENAULT ALLIANCE & ENCORE 4 & 5-SPEED TRANSAXLE

IDENTIFICATION

The 3 manual transaxles can be identified by a plate affixed to the top of the transaxle by one of the clutch housing bolts. Top line of plate identifies transaxle model and date codes. Bottom line on plate is the transaxle fabrication number.

Fig. 1: JB Series Transaxle Identification Plate

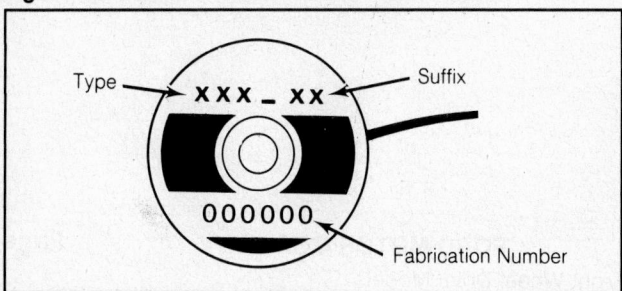

DESCRIPTION

TRANSAXLE IDENTIFICATION CODES

Application	Axle Ratio	Code
JB 0 4-Speed	3.29:1	JB 0-00
JB 1 5-Speed	3.87:1	JB 1-00
JB 3 5-Speed	3.29:1	JB 3-00

The manual transaxle combines a 4-speed (JB 0) or 5-speed (JB 1, JB 3) manual transmission and differential into a single component designed for front drive applications. The transmission and differential are housed in a 2-piece, light weight aluminum alloy housing which is bolted to the back of the engine.

The transaxle is fully synchronized in all forward gears with reverse provided by a separate shaft and gear. All gears, except reverse, are helical cut for quiet operation. Both input and main shafts, are supported in case by roller bearings.

The differential assembly is supported by 2 opposed roller bearings. Side plates are used to hold ends of axle shafts in place. The left side uses a constant velocity joint on the end of the axle. The right side axle shaft has splines to engage with the transaxle.

LUBRICATION & ADJUSTMENT

See appropriate MANUAL TRANSMISSION SERVICING article in DOMESTIC GENERAL SERVICING section.

TROUBLE SHOOTING

See MANUAL TRANSMISSION TROUBLE SHOOTING article in DOMESTIC GENERAL SERVICING section.

SERVICE (IN VEHICLE)

GEARSHIFT LEVER & LINKAGE
Removal

Shift transaxle to 2nd gear, and prevent input lever from moving. Disconnect spring and rod beneath vehicle. Remove boot, console and gearshift lever housing. Place gearshift lever in a vise and remove components. See Fig. 3.

Installation

Install components and gearshift lever housing. Connect rod to gearshift lever and tighten clip. Connect spring, adjust shift rod and install console and boot.

5TH GEAR CLUSTER

CAUTION: **Place the gear shift lever in 3rd or 4th position to prevent the interlocking ball from falling into the transaxle case.**

Removal

1) Remove transaxle front mount and lower the transaxle enough to remove the rear cover. Place a pan under rear cover and remove cover and gasket.

2) Raise transmission slightly. Insert a block of wood between 5th gear fork and driving gear. Tap out roll pin with a 3/16" pin punch.

3) Remove block of wood and place gearshift lever in the neutral position. Select the 1st gear position with the shift lever and 5th gear in the transaxle by sliding the 5th shift fork. See Fig. 2.

Fig. 2: Shift Fork Assemblies

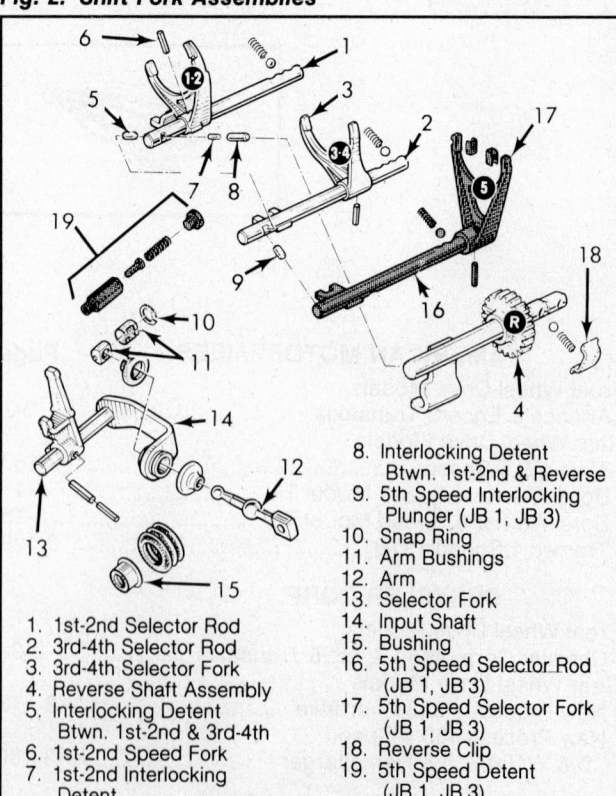

1. 1st-2nd Selector Rod
2. 3rd-4th Selector Rod
3. 3rd-4th Selector Fork
4. Reverse Shaft Assembly
5. Interlocking Detent Btwn. 1st-2nd & 3rd-4th
6. 1st-2nd Speed Fork
7. 1st-2nd Interlocking Detent
8. Interlocking Detent Btwn. 1st-2nd & Reverse
9. 5th Speed Interlocking Plunger (JB 1, JB 3)
10. Snap Ring
11. Arm Bushings
12. Arm
13. Selector Fork
14. Input Shaft
15. Bushing
16. 5th Speed Selector Rod (JB 1, JB 3)
17. 5th Speed Selector Fork (JB 1, JB 3)
18. Reverse Clip
19. 5th Speed Detent (JB 1, JB 3)

4) Remove the input shaft nut. Place gearshift lever in neutral. If 5th speed idling gear is not chamfered

Manual Transmissions
AMC/RENAULT ALLIANCE & ENCORE 4 & 5-SPEED TRANSAXLE (Cont.)

3-3

Fig. 3: Gearshift Lever & Linkage Assembly

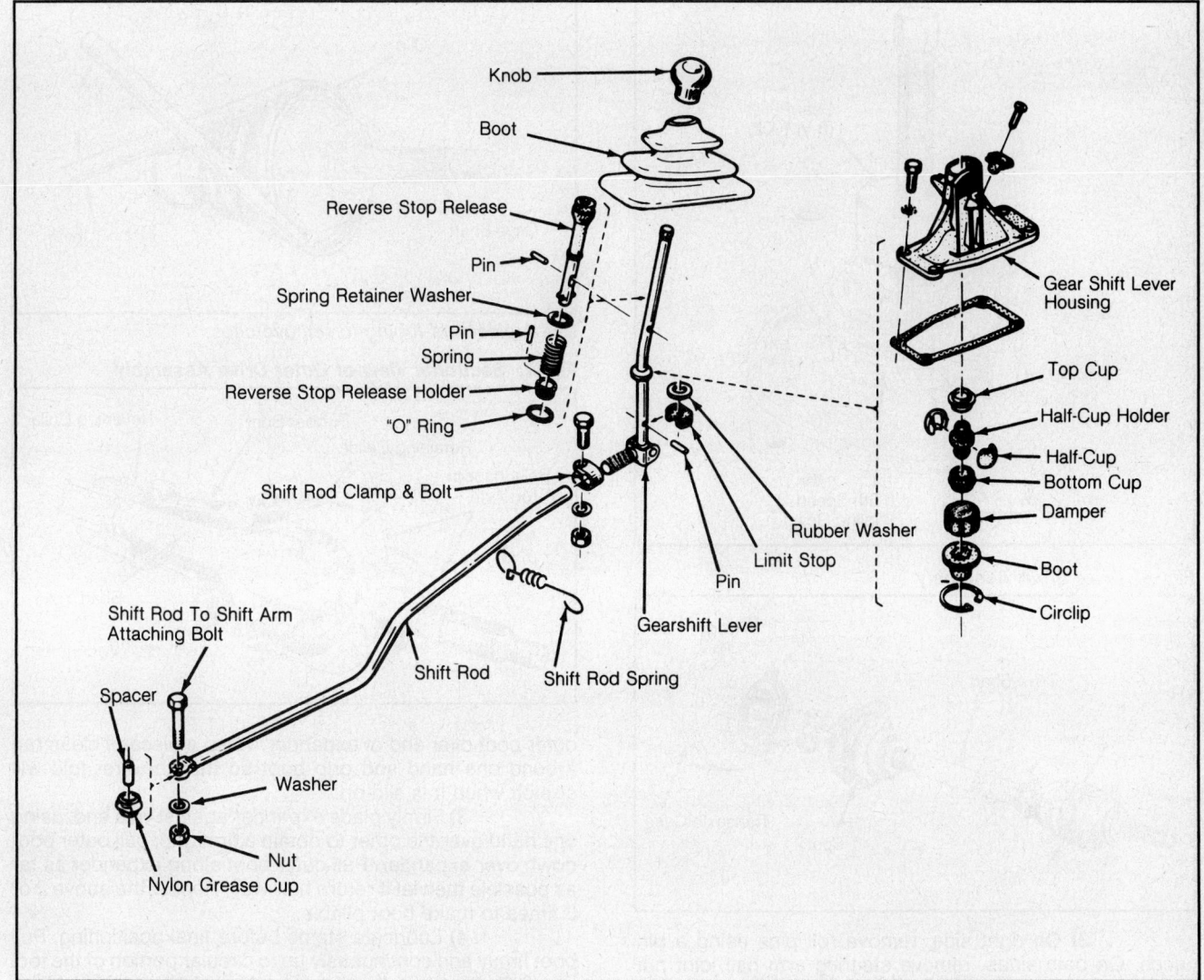

on lower edge, use Puller (B.Vi.1002) to remove gear. *See Fig. 4.* If gear is not chamfered, use Puller (B.Vi.1007).

5) Remove retaining bolt from mainshaft. Pull 5th speed fixed gear off shaft using gear puller.

Installation
1) If the mainshaft is equipped with a 10 mm bolt, apply 3 drops of Loctite to 5th speed fixed gear splines. Install gear on mainshaft with washer and circlip. Install flanged washer. Apply 3 drops of Loctite 271 to bolt threads and install. Tighten to 59 ft. lbs. (80 N.m).

2) If mainshaft is equipped with a 8 mm bolt, apply 3 drops of Loctite 271 to 5th speed fixed gear splines and place on shaft. Install flanged washer. Install bolt and tighten to 15 ft. lbs. (20 N.m).

3) Remove bolt and flanged washer. Install washer and circlip using tool (B.Vi.948). Install bolt and tighten to specification.

4) To assemble input shaft components on all models, apply Loctite 271 to hub splines. Install the hub-sliding gear assembly and fork on the primary shaft. Install the synchronizer ring bosses in the hub.

5) Select 1st gear position with gear shift lever and 5th gear in the transaxle by sliding the 5th gear shift fork. Install nut and tighten to 100 ft. lbs. (135 N.m).

6) Place transaxle in neutral using gearshift lever. Raise transaxle slightly and install wood block between 5th speed fork and the driving gear as a support. Install the roll pin using pin punch.

7) Install rear cover using a new "O" ring. Align oil channel in the input shaft on oil feed tube in oil passage. Install front mount. Fill transaxle to proper level with lubricant. Start engine and check for leaks.

DRIVE AXLE SHAFT
Removal
1) Raise and support vehicle. Remove wheel and caliper asssemblies. Support caliper up out of the way. Remove spindle nut using Holding Tool (Rou. 604-01) attached to lug nuts.

2) On left side, drain oil from transaxle. Remove 3 mounting bolts. Remove boot and drive shaft.

CAUTION: During removal be sure that the 3 rollers on CV joint are not dislodged. Tape CV to prevent the components from falling apart.

3-4

Manual Transmissions
AMC/RENAULT ALLIANCE & ENCORE 4 & 5-SPEED TRANSAXLE (Cont.)

Fig. 4: Removing 5th Gear Assembly

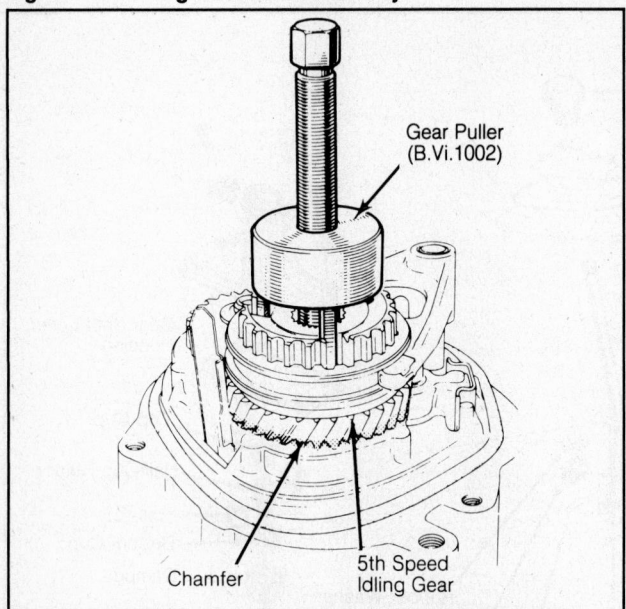

Fig. 5: Drive Shaft Assembly

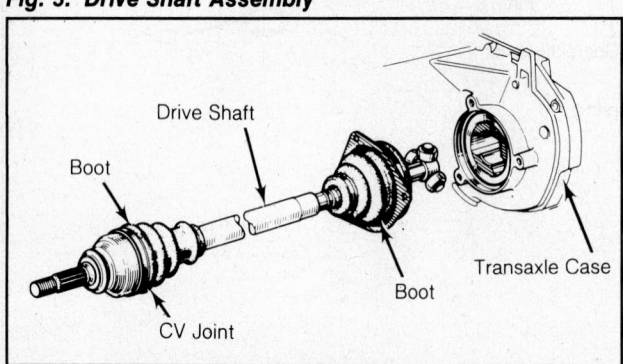

Fig. 6: Removing Clips From Drive shaft Boots

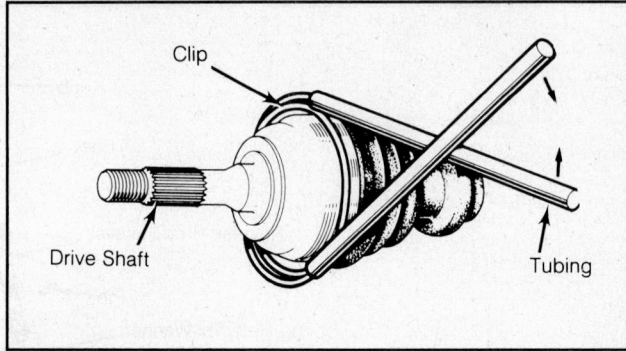

Use 2 pieces of tubing to remove clips.

Fig. 7: Sectional View of Outer Drive Assembly

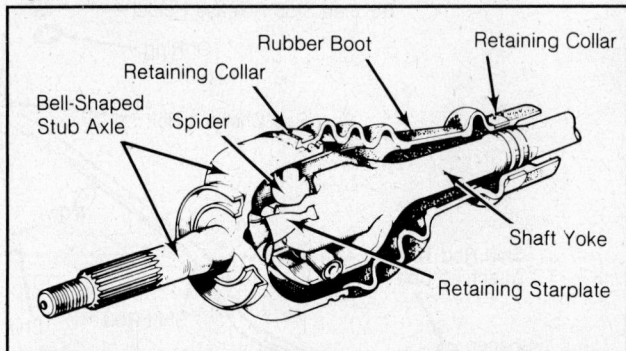

3) On right side, remove roll pins using a pin punch. On both sides, remove steering arm ball joint nut and disconnect ball joint assembly using Extractor Tool (T.AV.476). Remove strut assembly bottom mounting bolts.

4) Tilt stub axle carrier. Remove drive shaft from transaxle at the same time. Install impact tool on hub. Remove drive shaft. Tilt stub axle carrier. Remove drive shaft from its sunwheel at the same time.

CAUTION: Never use solvents or thinners for cleaning the CV joint components.

Disassembly (Right & Left Outer Joints)
1) Remove clip ring from around outer boot using 2 locally made drilled rods. Install 1 rod on each clip to expand and remove the clip.

2) Remove as much grease as possible. Remove bell-shaped stub axle from drive shaft by raising starplate arms one by one (DO NOT twist starplate arms).

Reassembly (Right & Left Outer Joints)
1) To reassemble both outer joints, place drive shaft at a convenient angle in a soft-jawed vise. Install Expander (T.AV. 537-02) on outer end of yoke. Lubricate the whole expander, inside the boots, and the neck in particular.

2) Place a thumb over bottom hole of outer boot. Pour some oil into boot and spread it around inside. Slip

outer boot over end of expander. Wrap a piece of clean rag around one hand and grip boot so that the first fold will stretch when it is slid on.

3) Firmly place expander against vise and, using one hand over the other to obtain a firm grip, pull outer boot down over expander. Pull outer boot along expander as far as possible then let it return half-way. Repeat the above 2 or 3 times to make boot pliable.

4) Lubricate stems before final positioning. Pull boot firmly and continuously up to circular portion of the tool in one motion. Install spring and thrust ball in spider. Move roller cages toward center.

5) Position retaining starplate so that each arm is centered between each spider trunnion. Insert outer drive shaft yoke in bell-shaped stub axle. Tilt shaft to fit 1 starplate arm into its slot, then press it in to locate it.

6) The other 2 arms may be installed easily by using a screwdriver with tip ground to fit end of arm. Make sure that each starplate arm is located in slot. Check that spider coupling moves freely by hand in all directions.

7) Distribute grease evenly between boot and bell-shaped stub axle. Position boot lips in grooves in stub axle and drive shaft. Insert a smooth round-ended piece of rod between boot and stub axle to restrict the amount of air inside. Install retaining collars over boot using the 2 fabricated rods.

Disassembly (Right Inner Joint)
1) On right side inner joint, remove retaining spring holding boot to yoke. Cut the boot off of shaft. Lift the 3 ears of the anti-separation plate and disassemble the yoke.

2) Do not remove roller cages from their individual trunnions. Cages and bearings are matched and must not be mixed. Wrap tape around trunion to hold in place.

3) Remove the snap ring. Remove spider using a press.

Reassembly (Right Inner Joint)

1) To reassemble right inner joint, lubricate the drive shaft and install the retaining collar and boot. Install spider on the shaft. Install snap ring. Spread 5 oz. (140 grams) of grease inside boot and on yoke.

2) Fabricate a .098" (2.5mm) thick shim and insert it between the anti-separation plate and the yoke. *See Fig. 8.*

Fig. 8: Assembling Right Side Inner Drive Axle CV Joint

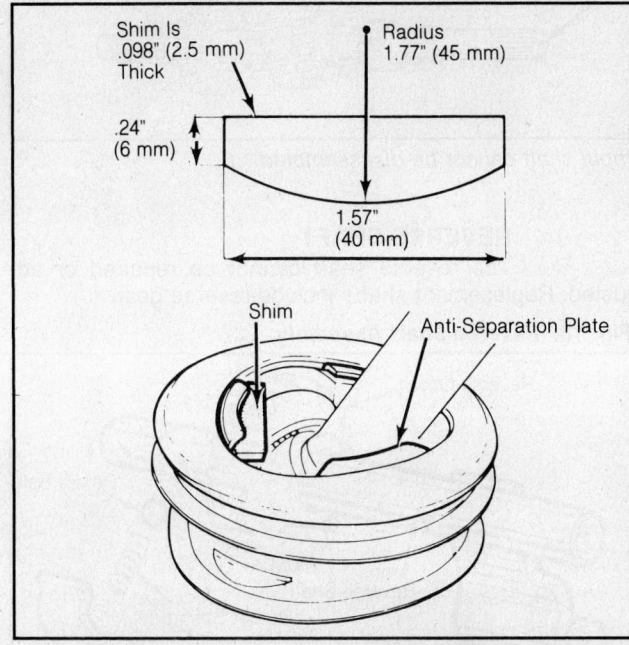

3) Locate boot lips in their respective grooves in the shaft and metal cover. Insert a smooth piece of rod between the boot and yoke to expel air inside boot.

4) With rod still in boot, lengthen or shorten coupling to obtain 6.04" (153.5 mm) between boot end face and largest machined diameter on the yoke. *See Fig. 9.*

Fig. 9: Adjusting Right Side Drive Shaft Length

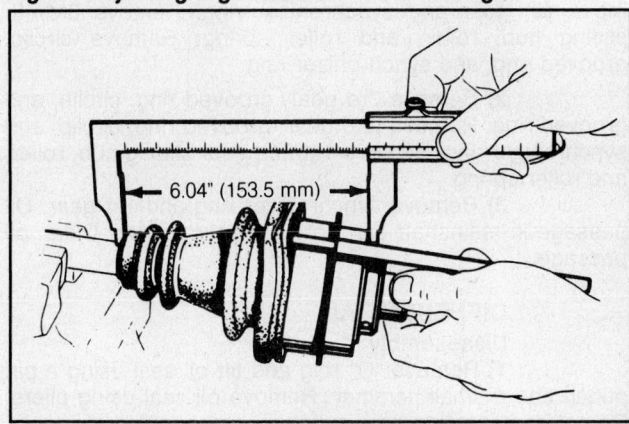

5) Remove the rod. Install retaining springs on boot. Spring must not be streched and coils must be touching after assembly.

Disassembly (Left Inner Joint)

On left side inner joint, remove the snap ring. Press spider assembly off shaft. Press boot and bearing assembly off shaft.

Reassembly (Left Inner Joint)

1) Press the boot-bearing assembly on the shaft. Bearing is correctly installed when edge of bearing is 5.85" (123.2 mm) from end of drive shaft.

CAUTION: Never drive bearing into place using a hammer.

2) Install the spider on the shaft splines. Install snap ring.

Installation

1) On left side, remove tape securing CV joint components. Install drive shaft in sunwheel. Pull it into hub using installer tool (T.AV. 602).

CAUTION: During installation be sure that none of the 3 rollers are dislodged. Needle bearings from joint could fall into case causing damage.

2) On right side, at transaxle end, coat splines of joint with Molykote BR.2 grease. Align drive shaft for installation in transaxle (roll pin holes). Use 3/16" punch to align holes.

3) Install 2 roll pins one inside the other with slots at 90° angle from each other. Pull drive shaft stub into hub using installer tool (T.AV. 602).

4) On both sides, install shock absorber bottom mounting nuts to stub axle carrier, with nuts towards caliper. Install steering arm ball joint and nut.

5) Tighten nuts and install holding tool to spindle using lug nuts. Tighten stub axle nut. On left side clean boot contact surface. Install the boot. Keep boot level as possible while tightening mounting bolts.

6) On both sides, install calipers. Install wheel assemblies and lower vehicle. Press brake pedal several times to push caliper piston into contact with brake pads. Transaxle must be filled with oil if left drive shaft has been removed.

REMOVAL & INSTALLATION

TRANSAXLE

See the appropriate MANUAL TRANSMISSION REMOVAL article in DOMESTIC GENERAL SERVICING section.

TRANSAXLE DISASSEMBLY

1) Remove rear cover. On 4-speed models, remove input shaft and mainshaft circlips and washers. On 5-speed models, engage 1st gear with gear selector lever and 5th gear with shift fork.

2) Remove 5th gear retaining nut. Remove 5th gear roll pin using a 3/16" pin punch. Place a block of wood at the back of shaft for support. Remove shift fork with sliding gear hub and spring from input shaft. Discard shift fork pads.

3) Remove all 5-speed components as described under SERVICE (IN VEHICLE) in this article. Remove clutch housing bolts. Remove reverse clip.

4) On 4-speed models, remove threaded limit stop. On 5-speed models, remove 5th gear detent. On all models, remove fork control rod. Insert 2 dummy rods at

3-6

Manual Transmissions
AMC/RENAULT ALLIANCE & ENCORE 4 & 5-SPEED TRANSAXLE (Cont.)

rear of case to prevent interlocking balls for the 4 forward gears from falling out. *See Fig. 10.*

Fig. 10: Placement of 2 Dummy Rods in Transaxle

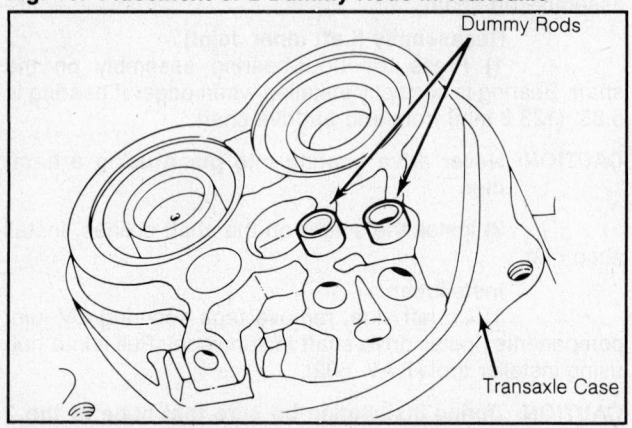

Rods will keep interlocking balls from falling out.

5) On 5-speed models, pull case upward and remove it with 5th gear fork rod. Retain 5th gear interlocking plunger. On all models, remove roll pin from 3rd/4th selector fork using a 3/16" pin punch. Move the 1st/2nd selector rod and reverse rod to neutral position.

6) Remove 3rd/4th selector rod, fork, and retaining detent. Remove roll pin from 1st/2nd gear rod using a 3/16" pin punch. Reverse shaft must be in neutral. Remove 1st/2nd selector rod. Remove fork and retaining detent from rod. Push interlocking detent toward 3rd/4th selector rod.

Fig. 11: Removing Input, Main, and Reverse Shafts as an Assembly

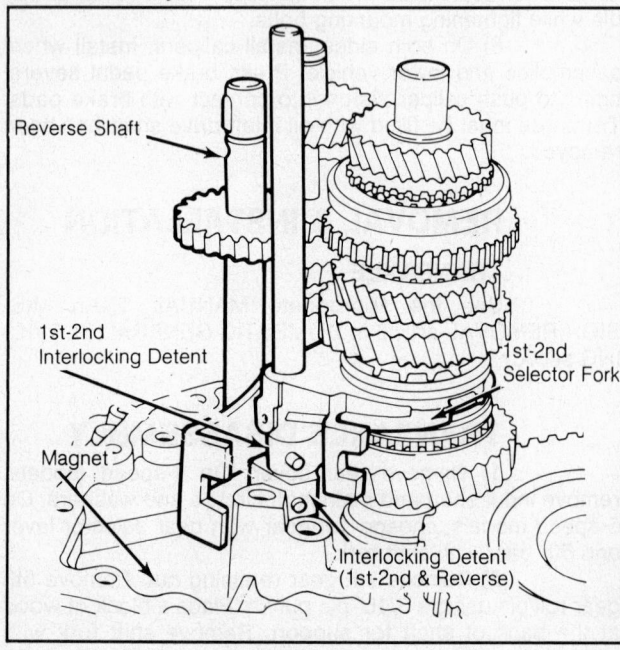

7) Remove input, main, and reverse shafts together. Hold mainshaft vertical with 1st gear at bottom. Remove magnet, clean it and reinstall in case. Remove gear selector control assembly from case.

COMPONENT DISASSEMBLY & ADJUSTMENT

INPUT SHAFT

The input shaft used in both 4 and 5-speed models, cannot be repaired or adjusted. On 5-speed models, the oil passage cannot be disassembled. Clean oil passage for 5th gear.

Fig. 12: Input Shaft Assembly

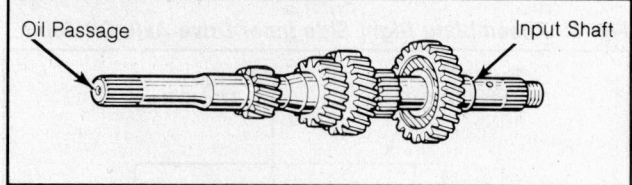

Input shaft cannot be disassembled.

REVERSE SHAFT

The reverse shaft cannot be repaired or adjusted. Replacement shafts include reverse gear.

Fig. 13: Reverse Shaft Assembly

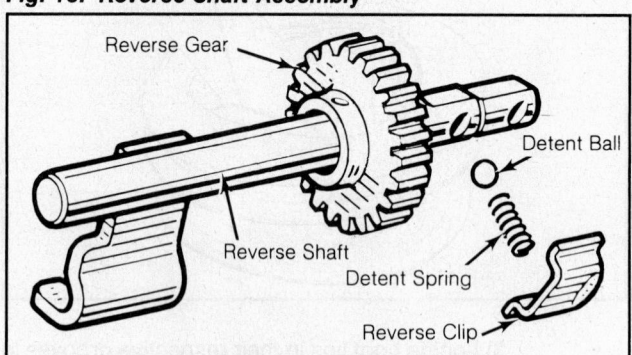

Reverse gear cannot be removed from shaft.

MAINSHAFT
Disassembly

1) Clamp mainshaft in a soft-jawed vise. Remove 4th gear and synchronizer ring. Remove 3rd/4th sliding hub, roller, and roller spring. Remove circlip, grooved ring, and synchronizer ring.

2) Remove 3rd gear, grooved ring, circlip, and grooved ring. Remove 2nd gear, grooved ring, circlip, and synchronizer ring. Remove 1st/2nd gear sliding hub, roller, and roller spring.

3) Remove synchronizer ring and 1st gear. Oil passage in mainshaft can not be disassembled. Clean oil passage.

DIFFERENTIAL
Disassembly

1) Remove "O" ring and tilt oil seal using a pin punch and a small hammer. Remove oil seal using pliers. Do not damage side gear splines.

2) Position clutch housing in arbor press, shaft end up. Support ring gear (on differential case) with wood block. With press pushing on housing, apply just enough downward force to allow removal of small snap ring on stemmed planetary gear.

Manual Transmissions
AMC/RENAULT ALLIANCE & ENCORE 4 & 5-SPEED TRANSAXLE (Cont.)

3-7

Fig. 14: Exploded View of Shaft and Gear Clusters

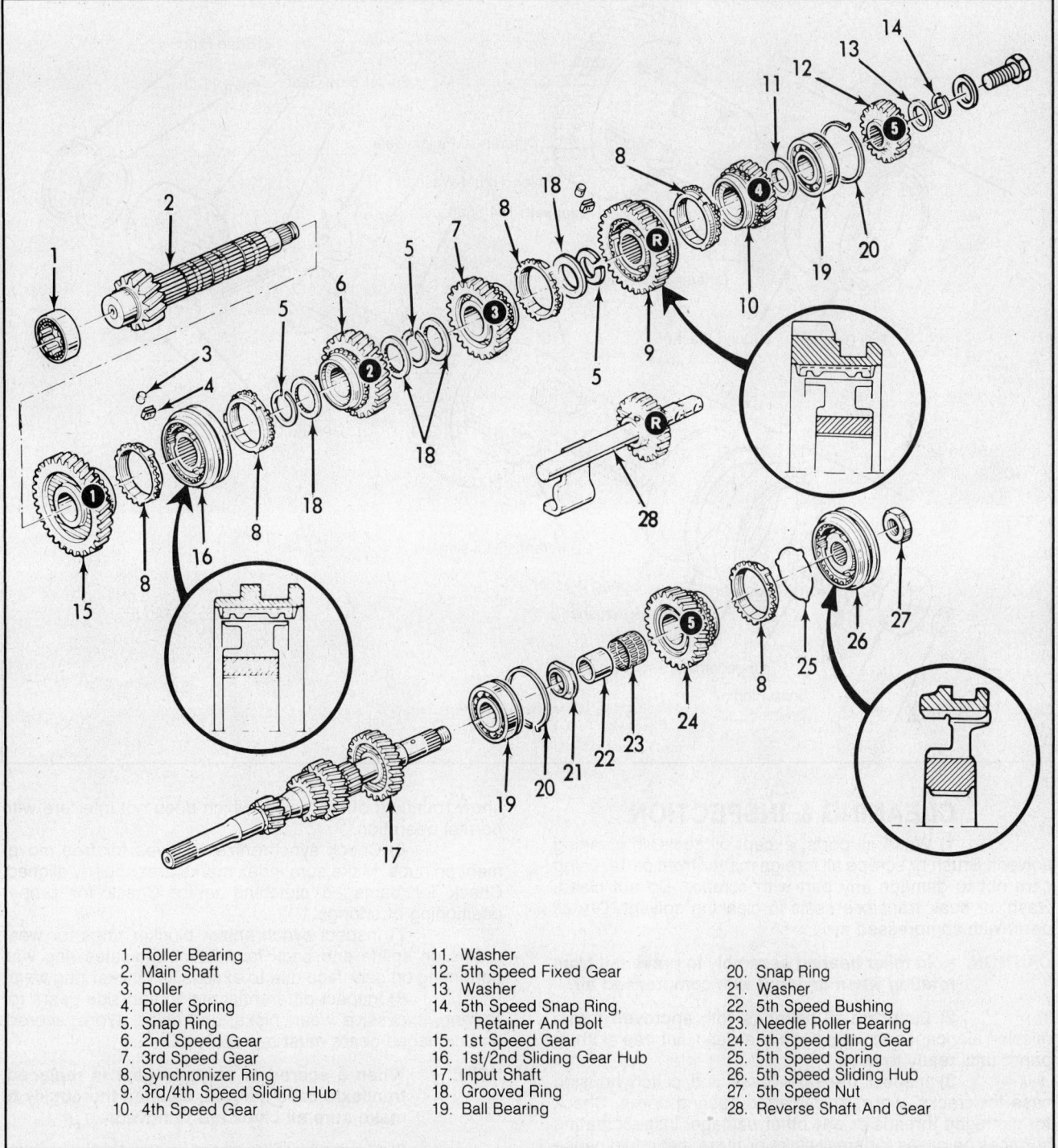

1. Roller Bearing	11. Washer
2. Main Shaft	12. 5th Speed Fixed Gear
3. Roller	13. Washer
4. Roller Spring	14. 5th Speed Snap Ring,
5. Snap Ring	Retainer And Bolt
6. 2nd Speed Gear	15. 1st Speed Gear
7. 3rd Speed Gear	16. 1st/2nd Sliding Gear Hub
8. Synchronizer Ring	17. Input Shaft
9. 3rd/4th Speed Sliding Hub	18. Grooved Ring
10. 4th Speed Gear	19. Ball Bearing

20. Snap Ring
21. Washer
22. 5th Speed Bushing
23. Needle Roller Bearing
24. 5th Speed Idling Gear
25. 5th Speed Spring
26. 5th Speed Sliding Hub
27. 5th Speed Nut
28. Reverse Shaft And Gear

3) Turn assembly over. Mount differential housing in a soft-jawed vise. Remove snap ring, shim, spider side gear, and pinion shaft. Remove pinion gears, thrust washers, and side gear with tail shaft. Attach each thrust washer to its matching differential pinion gear for reassembly reference.

BEARINGS

Transaxle Case Bearing

Remove the snap rings and tap bearings down inside the case using a hammer.

Secondary Shaft Bearing

Using a grinder or sharp chisel, remove case material which retains the bearing. Use a slide hammer to remove roller bearing.

Differential Bearings

Remove snap ring from small bearing and press out into case. Large differential bearing can also be pressed out of case.

Manual Transmissions
AMC/RENAULT ALLIANCE & ENCORE 4 & 5-SPEED TRANSAXLE (Cont.)

Fig. 15: Exploded View of Differential Components

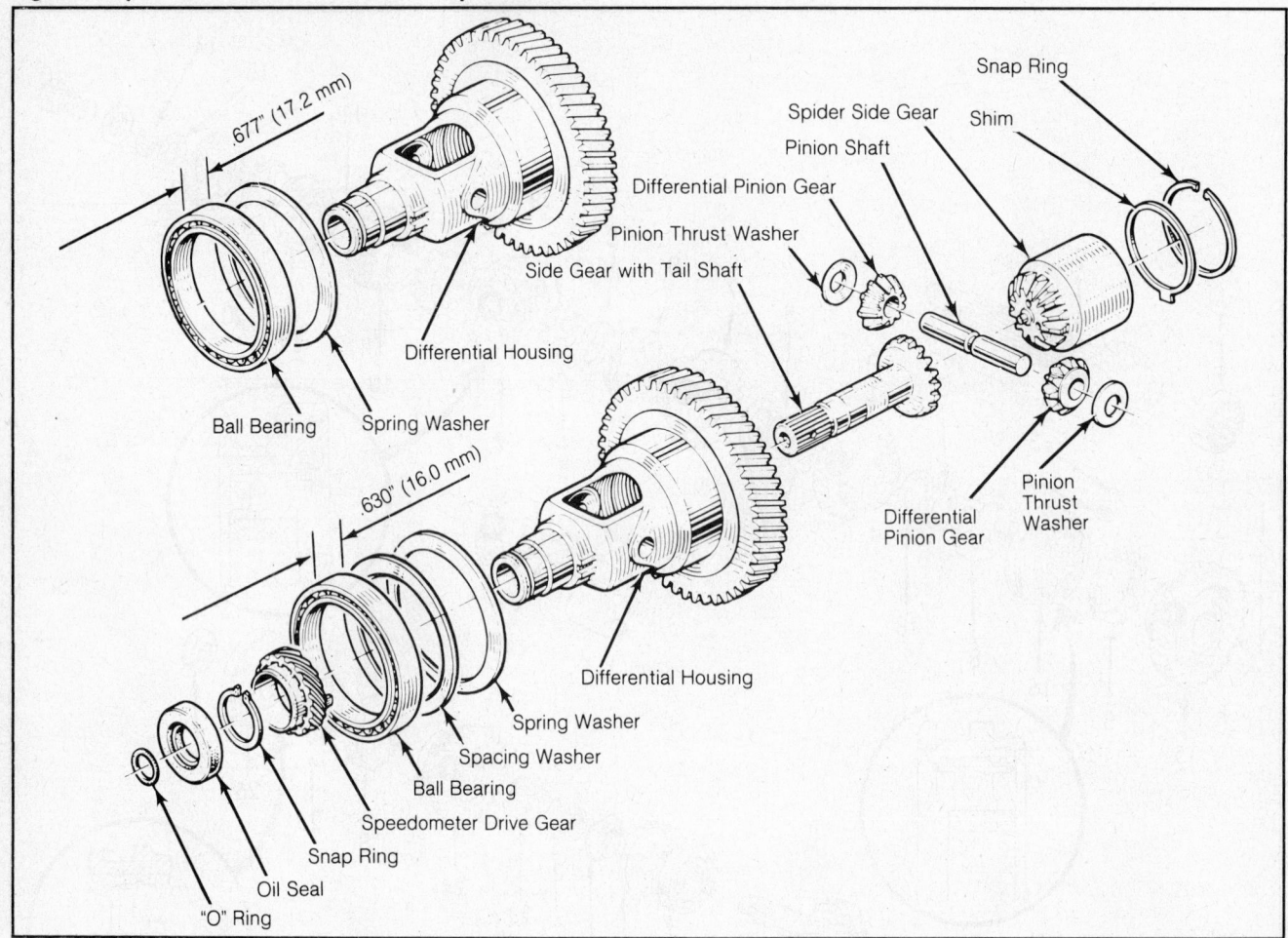

CLEANING & INSPECTION

1) Wash all parts, except oil seals, in cleaning solvent. Brush or scrape all foreign matter from parts, using care not to damage any part with scraper. Do not clean, wash, or soak transaxle seals in cleaning solvent. Dry all parts with compressed air.

CAUTION: Hold roller bearing assembly to prevent it from rotating when drying it with compressed air.

2) Lubricate all bearings with approved transmission lubricant and wrap them in a clean, lint free cloth or paper until ready to use.

3) Inspect transaxle case and clutch housing case for cracks, worn, or damaged bearing bores. Check for damaged threads or any other damage. Inspect mating surfaces on cases for small nicks or burrs that could cause misalignment of the 2 halves. Remove all small nicks or burrs with a fine stone or file.

4) Check reverse gear and sliding gears for chipped, broken, or bent teeth. Check wear of reverse gear shaft. It is normal for front of teeth to show wear, this does not interfere with proper function.

5) Check teeth, splines and journals of mainshaft for damage. Check all other gears for chipped, broken, or worn teeth. Check for eroded clutching teeth and damaged bearing surfaces. Clutching teeth will usually show rounding of the points which does not interfere with normal operation.

6) Check synchronizer sleeves for free movement on hubs. Make sure index marks are properly aligned. Check for damaged clutching teeth. Check for proper positioning of springs.

7) Inspect synchronizer blocker rings for wear marks on spline end back face which indicates ring was bottoming on gear face due to excessive blocker ring wear.

8) Inspect differential pinion and side gears for scoring, excessive wear, nicks, and chips. Worn, scored, and damaged gears must be replaced.

NOTE: **When a scored or chipped gear is replaced, transaxle case must be cleaned thoroughly to make sure all chips are removed.**

9) Make sure differential case bearing journals are smooth. Inspect case bearing shoulders for damage caused by bearing removal. Check fit (free rotation) of side gears in their cavities.

10) Check differential bearings and bearing races for wear or other damage. Check bearings for smooth rotation in races. Examine bearing roller ends for step wear.

NOTE: **If inspection reveals either a damaged bearing or race, both parts must be replaced as they are a matched set.**

Manual Transmissions
AMC/RENAULT ALLIANCE & ENCORE 4 & 5-SPEED TRANSAXLE (Cont.)

3-9

TRANSAXLE REASSEMBLY

BEARINGS

Differential Bearings
Position small bearing over opening and install using an arbor press and piece of 2.56" (65 mm) diameter tube. Press large bearing into housing using arbor press and a steel bar 5.12" (130 mm) long.

Secondary Shaft Bearing
Clean bearing seat using emery cloth and compressed air. Using arbor press, install bearing flush with the inside face of the case. Stake the bearing in place using a chisel. Depth of stake must be within .04-.05" (.9-1.3 mm).

Transaxle Case Bearings
Install snap rings in case with open ends facing each other. Spread the snap ring in the case using tool (B.Vi.947) and install bearings.

DIFFERENTIAL
1) Install spring washer with base of tapered section against gear. Install spacing washer, if equipped, and speedometer gear. If a new .677" (17.2 mm) bearing must be installed, discard spacing washer.

2) If original .630" (16 mm) bearing is installed, do not discard spacing washer. Install it with bearing. Install side gear with tail shaft. Install pinion gears with matching thrust washers. Install spider side gear, shim, and snap ring.

3) Install differential assembly in housing. Install new snap ring on speedometer gear. Install differential oil seal.

MAINSHAFT
1) Install 1st gear and synchronizer ring. Install roller spring, roller, and 1st/2nd gear sliding hub. Install synchronizer ring, circlip, grooved ring, and 2nd gear.

2) Install grooved ring, circlip, grooved ring, and 3rd gear. Install synchronizer ring, grooved ring, and circlip. Install roller spring, roller, and 3rd/4th sliding hub. Install synchronizer ring and 4th gear.

TRANSAXLE
1) Install magnet in case. Install selector control assembly in housing using new bushings and oil seal.

2) Holding mainshaft vertically with 1st gear at bottom, install input, main, and reverse shafts together as an assembly. Tilt mainshaft to aid installing it in mainshaft bearing in case.

3) Install 1st/2nd/reverse interlocking detent. Install 1st/2nd selector fork with shift rod fingers facing gear. Install 1st/2nd rod in fork and install small plunger.

4) The interlocking ball recesses face shafts. Lift reverse shift rod. Lower 1st/2nd shift rod. Be sure that 1st/2nd/reverse interlocking detent is in recess in reverse shift rod.

5) Be sure that reverse shift rod is locked in place. Install medium sized interlocking shift detent between 1st/2nd and 3rd/4th shift rods. Install 3rd/4th fork with thicker side toward gear.

6) Install 3rd/4th shift rod with interlocking detent recesses facing shift rods. Install fork roll pins using 3/16 pin punch.

NOTE: Roll pin slots must face longitudinal axis of each rod. New roll pins must be used whenever transaxle is disassembled.

7) Apply Permatex 6 Form A Gasket onto joint faces of rear case and clutch case. On 5-speed models, install 5th gear interlocking ball and spring in rear case. Install 5th gear selector fork.

8) Pull selector control outward and center input shaft, mainshaft, and selector fork shift rods. Install rear case. Remove dummy rods used during disassembly. Tap rear case with soft mallet to seat input and mainshafts in bearings.

9) Using a piece of wire, lift up reverse shaft and install interlocking ball, spring, and clip. Install 2 case bolts and operate shift mechanism to ensure transaxle shifts correctly.

10) Install threaded limit stop, or 5th speed detent, and tighten stop. On 4-speed models, install new mainshaft circlip. Install new circlip on input shaft nut. Use Installer Tool (B.Vi. 902-01) and hammer.

Fig. 16: Using Wire Hook To Lift Reverse Gear

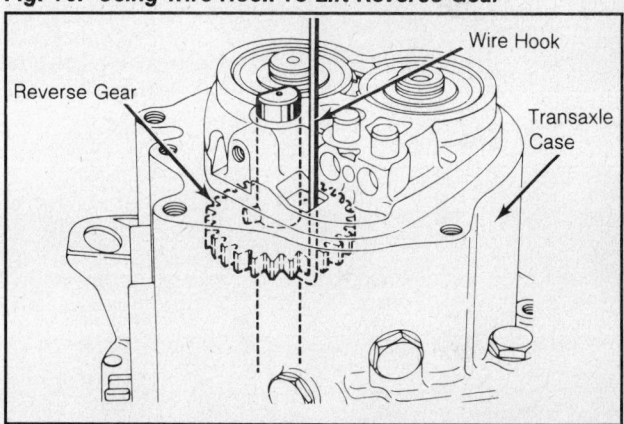

11) Support shaft on clutch spline side with screw from plate (B.Vi. 902-01). Ensure circlip is secure in groove. Install and tighten remaining case bolts.

12) On 5-speed models, install 5th speed fixed gear, washer, 5th gear circlip, retainer, and bolt using Installer Tool (B.Vi. 948). Ensure 5th gear circlip is seated in groove.

13) Install flange facing bearing, washer, 5th gear bushing, roller bearing, 5th gear, and synchronizer ring. Install 5th gear spring in 5th gear sliding hub. Install fork in sliding gear hub. Use new fork pads. See Fig. 17.

14) Install fork on shaft and install roll pin using 3/16" pin punch. Support shaft with a block of wood when installing roll pin. Install input shaft nut. Shift transaxle into 2 gears at once and tighten mainshaft nut.

15) On both models, install rear case "O" ring by rolling it into place with a small screwdriver. Install rear cover. Install and tighten retaining case bolts.

Manual Transmissions
AMC/RENAULT ALLIANCE & ENCORE 4 & 5-SPEED TRANSAXLE (Cont.)

Fig. 17: Exploded View of 5th Gear Assembly

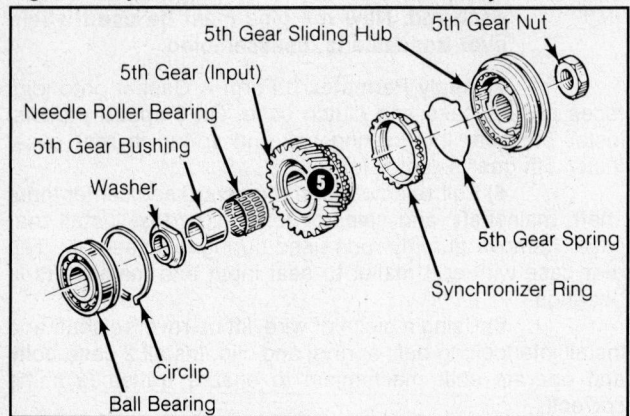

5th Gear Sliding Hub
5th Gear Nut
5th Gear (Input)
Needle Roller Bearing
5th Gear Bushing
Washer
5th Gear Spring
Synchronizer Ring
Circlip
Ball Bearing

TIGHTENING SPECIFICATIONS

Application	Ft. Lbs. (N.m)
Brake Caliper Bolts	25 (35)
Hub Nut	154 (210)
Rear Case Bolts	18 (25)
Steering Tie Rod Nut	25 (35)
Switch Bodies	18 (25)
Transaxle Bellows Bolts	18 (25)
5th Speed Detent Stop	14 (19)
5th Speed Input Shaft Nut	100 (135)
5th Speed Secondary Shaft Bolt	18 (25)
5th Speed Mainshaft Bolt	59 (80)

BORG-WARNER 4-SPEED MODEL T4

Jeep
CJ-7 & Scrambler

IDENTIFICATION

Transmission identification tag is attached to right side of adapter/extension housing by housing-to-transmission case bolt.

DESCRIPTION

The model T4 transmission is a constant mesh, fully synchronized unit which provides synchomesh in all 4 forward gears. The forward gears are helical-cut and are in constant mesh. The reverse gears are spur-cut and are not in constant mesh. An interlock system prevents accidental engagement of reverse gears when selecting any of the forward gear ranges.

LUBRICATION & ADJUSTMENT

See the appropriate article in MANUAL TRANS-MISSION SERVICING Section.

TROUBLE SHOOTING

See MANUAL TRANSMISSION TROUBLE SHOOTING in TRANSMISSION SERVICING Section

REMOVAL & INSTALLATION

See appropriate article in MANUAL TRANSMIS-SION REMOVAL Section.

TRANSMISSION DISASSEMBLY

NOTE: **All threaded holes and bolts, except for gearshift lever attaching bolts and fill plug, are metric threaded.**

1) Remove drain plug and drain lubricant. Using pin punch, remove roll pin attaching offset lever-to-shift rail. Remove extension/adapter housing-to-transmission case bolts.

2) Remove housing and offset lever as an assembly. Remove detent ball and spring from offset lever and remove roll pin from extension/adapter housing or offset lever. *See Fig. 1.*

NOTE: **Do not attempt to remove offset lever while adapter housing is still bolted in place. Positioning lug prevents moving lever far enough rearward for removal.**

3) Remove and retain countershaft rear thrust bearing and bearing race. Remove transmission cover, shift fork assembly attaching bolts and remove cover.

NOTE: **Two of the shift control cover bolts are dowel-type alignment bolts. Note positions of these bolts for reassembly reference.**

4) Remove "C" clip attaching reverse lever to reverse lever pivot bolt. Remove bolt, then remove reverse lever and lever fork as an assembly. Matchmark

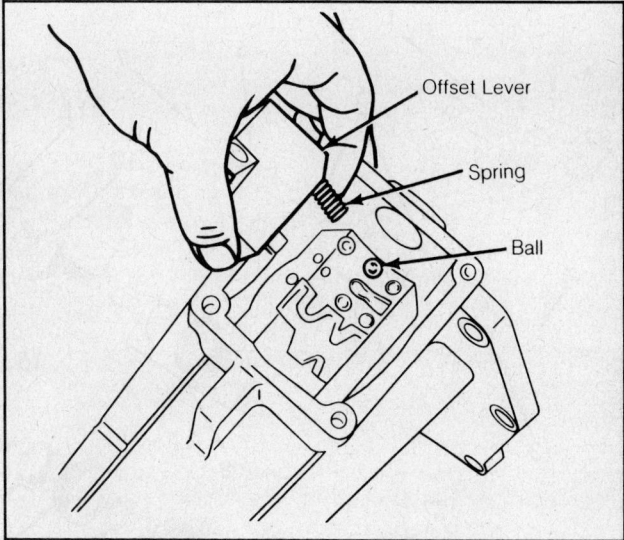

Fig. 1: Offset Lever Spring & Ball

front bearing cap and transmission case with a punch and remove front bearing cap bolts and cap.

5) Remove front bearing race, shims and oil seal from bearing cap. Rotate clutch shaft until flat on gear teeth is facing countershaft and remove shaft. Remove thrust bearing and 15 roller bearings from clutch shaft.

6) Remove output shaft bearing race. If necessary, tap output shaft with rubber hammer to remove bearing race. Tilt output shaft assembly upward and remove from transmission case. Remove coutershaft rear bearing with a brass drift and arbor press.

7) Note position of bearing for reassembly reference. Bearing number should face outward when correctly installed. Move countershaft rearward, tilt upward and remove shaft from case.

8) Note position of washer for reassembly reference. Remove countershaft rear bearing spacer. Remove reverse idler shaft and gear, noting position for reassembly reference.

9) Remove countershaft front bearing using arbor press. Using bearing removal tool (J-2972 and J-22912), remove clutch shaft front bearing. Remove rear extension/adapter housing seal with drift and hammer. Remove backup lamp switch from transmission case.

COMPONENT DISASSEMBLY & REASSEMBLY

OUTPUT SHAFT (MAINSHAFT)
Disassembly

1) Remove thrust bearing washer from front end of output shaft. Scribe alignment marks on 3rd-4th synchronizer hub and sleeve for reassembly reference.

2) Remove 3rd-4th synchronizer blocking ring, sleeve and hub as an assembly. Remove 3rd-4th synchronizer, insert springs, and remove inserts and sleeve from hub.

3) Remove 3rd gear from shaft. Remove 2nd gear retaining snap ring and remove tabbed 2nd gear thrust washer and 2nd gear. Remove output shaft bearing using puller (J-29721 with adapters 293-39).

Manual Transmissions

BORG-WARNER 4-SPEED MODEL T4 (Cont.)

Fig. 2: Exploded View of Model T4 4-Speed Transmission Assembly

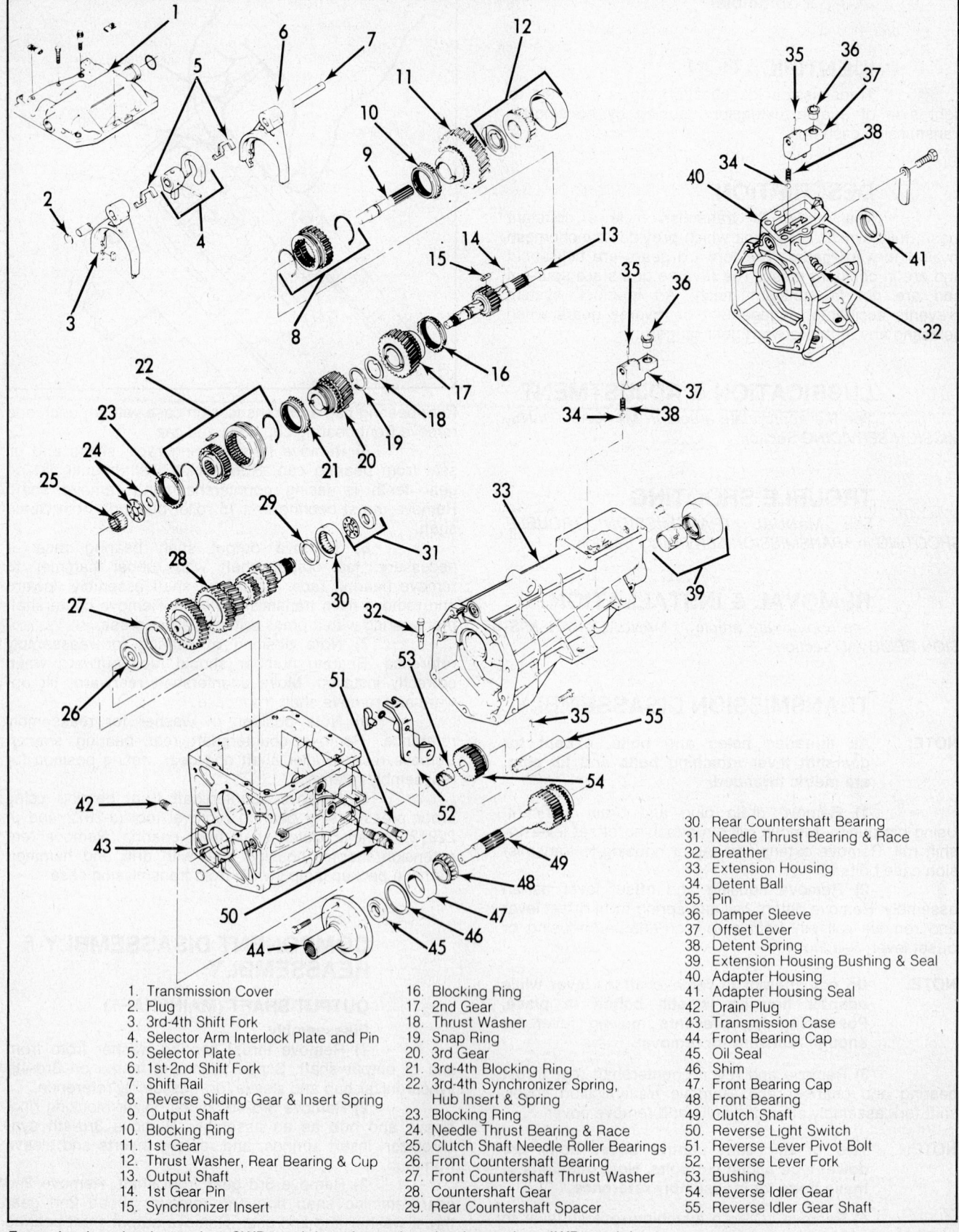

1. Transmission Cover	16. Blocking Ring
2. Plug	17. 2nd Gear
3. 3rd-4th Shift Fork	18. Thrust Washer
4. Selector Arm Interlock Plate and Pin	19. Snap Ring
5. Selector Plate	20. 3rd Gear
6. 1st-2nd Shift Fork	21. 3rd-4th Blocking Ring
7. Shift Rail	22. 3rd-4th Synchronizer Spring, Hub Insert & Spring
8. Reverse Sliding Gear & Insert Spring	23. Blocking Ring
9. Output Shaft	24. Needle Thrust Bearing & Race
10. Blocking Ring	25. Clutch Shaft Needle Roller Bearings
11. 1st Gear	26. Front Countershaft Bearing
12. Thrust Washer, Rear Bearing & Cup	27. Front Countershaft Thrust Washer
13. Output Shaft	28. Countershaft Gear
14. 1st Gear Pin	29. Rear Countershaft Spacer
15. Synchronizer Insert	

30. Rear Countershaft Bearing	
31. Needle Thrust Bearing & Race	
32. Breather	
33. Extension Housing	
34. Detent Ball	
35. Pin	
36. Damper Sleeve	
37. Offset Lever	
38. Detent Spring	
39. Extension Housing Bushing & Seal	
40. Adapter Housing	
41. Adapter Housing Seal	
42. Drain Plug	
43. Transmission Case	
44. Front Bearing Cap	
45. Oil Seal	
46. Shim	
47. Front Bearing Cap	
48. Front Bearing	
49. Clutch Shaft	
50. Reverse Light Switch	
51. Reverse Lever Pivot Bolt	
52. Reverse Lever Fork	
53. Bushing	
54. Reverse Idler Gear	
55. Reverse Idler Gear Shaft	

Extension housing is used on 2WD models; adapter housing is used on 4WD models.

BORG-WARNER 4-SPEED MODEL T4 (Cont.)

4) Remove 1st gear thrust washer and, using diagonal cutters, remove 1st gear roll pin. Remove 1st gear and blocking ring. Scribe alignment marks on 1st-2nd gear synchronizer sleeve and hub for reassembly reference.

NOTE: Do not removed 1st-2nd hub from output shaft. Hub and output shaft are machined and assembled as a matched set.

5) Remove insert springs and inserts from 1st-reverse sliding gear and remove gear from output shaft hub.

Reassembly
1) Coat output shaft gear needle bearings and bores and shaft with transmission lubricant. Install and align 1st-2nd synchronizer sleeve on output shaft hub using index marks. Install three 1st-2nd synchronizer inserts and 2 insert springs in 1st-reverse synchronizer sleeve.

2) Engage tang end of each insert spring in same synchronizer insert but position open ends of springs to face 180° away from each other. See Fig 3. Align sleeve hub with index marks. Install blocking ring and 2nd gear on mainshaft.

Fig. 3: Installing Synchronizer Insert Spring

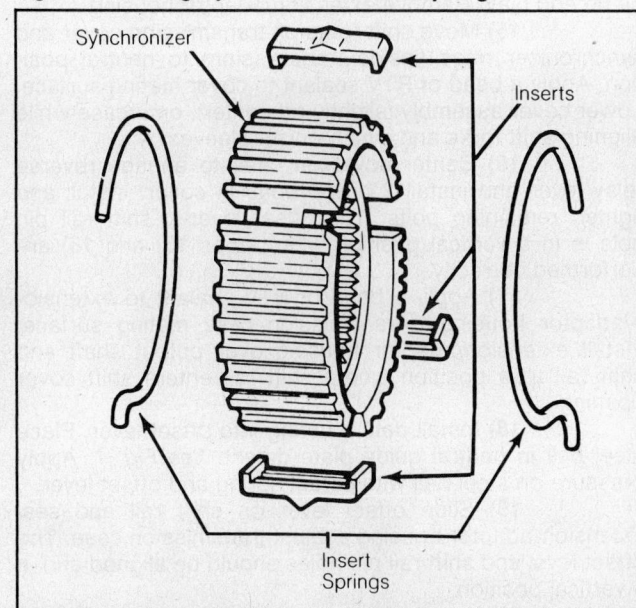

3) Install tabbed thrust washer and 2nd gear snap ring on mainshaft. Ensure washer tab is correctly seated in mainshaft notch. Install blocking ring and 1st gear on output shaft. Install 1st gear roll pin in output shaft.

4) Install rear bearing on output shaft using bearing installer (J-2995) and arbor press. Install 1st gear thrust washer. Install 3rd gear, 3rd and 4th gear synchronizer hub inserts and sleeve on shaft. Hub offset must face forward. Install thrust bearing washer on forward end of output shaft.

TRANSMISSION COVER ASSEMBLY
Disassembly
1) Place selector arm plates and shift rail in centered (neutral) position. Rotate shift rail counterclockwise until selector arm disengages from selector arm

plates and selector arm roll pin is accessible. Pull rail rearward until selector contacts 1st-2nd shift fork.

2) Using a 3/16" pin punch, remove roll pin. Remove shift rail, shift forks, selector arm plates, selector arm and roll pin, and interlock plate. Using a screwdriver, remove shift rail oil seal and "O" ring.

3) Remove shift rail plug with hammer and punch. Remove nylon inserts and selector arm plates from shift forks, noting positioning for reassembly reference.

Fig. 4: Exploded View of Transmission Cover Assembly

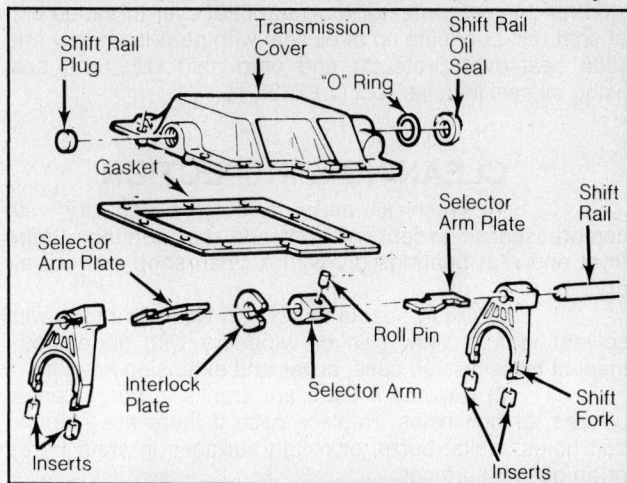

Reassembly
1) Install nylon inserts and selector arm plates in shift forks. See Fig. 5. Coat edge of shift rail plug with sealer and install. Coat shift rail and shift rail bores with petroleum jelly and insert shift rail in cover.

Fig. 5: Assembling Shift Forks & Selector Arm Plates

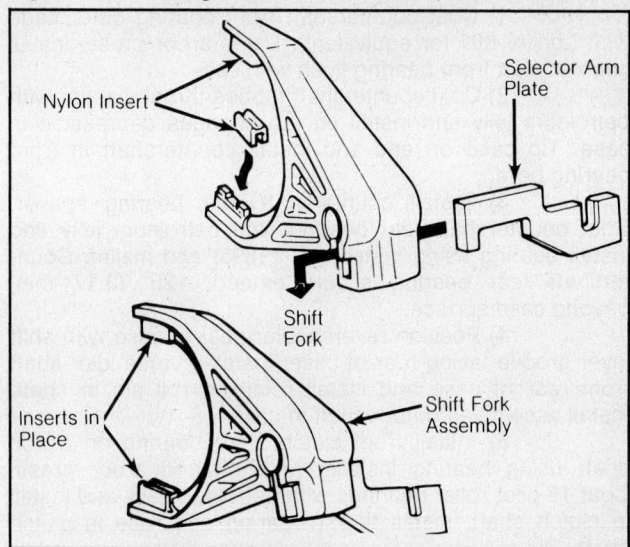

2) Install rail until end of rail is flush with inside edge of cover. Position 1st-2nd shift fork in cover with fork offset facing rear of cover and push shift rail through fork. The 1st-2nd shift fork is the larger of the 2 forks.

3) Position selector arm and "C" shaped interlock plate in cover and insert shift rail through selector arm. Widest part of interlock plate must face away from cover and selector arm roll pin must face downward and toward rear of cover.

Manual Transmissions

BORG-WARNER 4-SPEED MODEL T4 (Cont.)

4) Position 3rd-4th shift fork in cover with fork offset facing rear of cover. The 3rd-4th shift fork selector arm plate must be positioned under 1st-2nd shift fork selector arm plate. Insert shift rail through 3rd-4th shift fork and into front shift rail bore in cover.

5) Rotate shift rail until selector arm plate at forward end of rail faces away from, but is parallel to, cover. Align selector arm and shift rail roll pin holes and install roll pin. Ensure roll pin is flush with selector arm surface. Install "O" ring in groove of shift rail oil seal.

6) Install shift rail oil seal as follows: Install shift rail oil seal protector tool (J-26628) over threaded end of shift rail. Lubricate lip of oil seal with petroleum jelly and slide seal over protector and onto shift rail. Seat seal using oil seal installer tool (J-22628-1).

CLEANING & INSPECTION

1) Wash all parts in solvent and dry with compressed air except for front and rear bearings. Wipe front and rear bearings dry with a clean shop cloth or air dry.

2) Clean needle thrust and roller bearings with solvent in a shallow pan or wipe dry with shop cloth. Inspect transmission case, cover and extension housing.

3) Replace if there are cracks in bores, sides, bosses, or bolt holes. Replace case if there are stripped bolt holes, nicks, burrs, or rough surfaces in shaft bores or on gasket surfaces.

4) Inspect gear train and shift mechanism. Replace any parts exhibiting wear, chips, galling, distortion or bending. Check for worn bearings and bores. Check for weak snap rings and stripped offset lever.

TRANSMISSION REASSEMBLY

1) Coat countershaft front bearing outer cage with Loctite 601 (or equivalent). Using arbor press, install countershaft front bearing flush with case.

2) Coat countershaft tabbed thrust washer with petroleum jelly and install so tab engages depression in case. Tip case on end and install countershaft in front bearing bore.

3) Install countershaft rear bearing spacer. Coat countershaft rear bearing with petroleum jelly and install bearing using installer (J-29895) and mallet. Countershaft rear bearing should extend .125" (3.17 mm) beyond case surface.

4) Position reverse idler gear in case with shift lever groove facing rear of case. Install reverse idler shaft from rear of case and install retaining roll pin in shaft. Install assembled output shaft in case.

5) Install front clutch shaft bearing on clutch shaft using bearing installer (J-2995) and arbor press. Coat 15 pilot roller bearings with petroleum jelly and install in clutch shaft. Install thrust bearing and race in clutch shaft.

6) Install 4th gear blocking ring on output shaft. Install rear output shaft bearing race. Install clutch shaft in case and engage shaft in 3rd-4th synchronizer sleeve and blocking ring.

7) Using seal installer (J-26625), install replacement oil seal in front bearing cap. Using seal installer (J-29184), install replacement oil seal in rear adapter housing.

8) Install front bearing race in front bearing cap, but do not install shims. Install front bearing cap. Do not install sealer at this time. Install reverse lever, pivot pin, and retaining "C" clip.

9) Coat countershaft rear bearing race and thrust bearing with petroleum jelly and install in extension/adapter housing. Temporarily install extension/adapter housing. Do not seal housing to case or tighten bolts.

10) Turn transmission case on end. Mount dial indicator on extension/adaptor housing with indicator stylus on end of output shaft. Rotate clutch and output shaft until end play is removed.

11) To completely eliminate output shaft and clutch shaft end play, bearings must be preloaded from .001"-.005" (.03-.13 mm). Read end play dimension on dial indicator.

12) Select shim pack measuring .001-.005" (.03-.13") thicker than end play measurement. Place transmission horizontally on workbench and remove front bearing cap and front bearing race.

13) Add shims to bearing cap to obtain necessary preload and install clutch shaft bearing race in cap. Apply bead of RTV sealant on case mating surface on front bearing cap.

14) Install front bearing cap using index marks. Tighten retaining bolts. Recheck end play. There should be no end play. Remove extension/adaptor housing.

15) Move shift forks on transmission cover and synchronizer rings (inside transmission) to neutral position. Apply a bead of RTV sealant to cover mating surface. Lower cover assembly (slightly off center), onto case while aligning shift forks and synchronizer sleeves.

16) Center cover on case to engage reverse relay lever and install 2 dowel bolts in cover. Install and tighten remaining bolts. The offset lever-to-shift rail pin hole is in a vertical position when steps **15)** and **16)** are performed correctly.

17) Apply a bead of RTV sealant to extension/adaptor housing-to-transmission case mating surface. Install extension/adaptor housing over output shaft and shift rail to a position where shift rail enters shift cover opening.

18) Install detent spring into offset lever. Place steel ball in neutral guide plate detent. *See Fig. 1.* Apply pressure on steel ball with detent spring and offset lever.

19) Slide offset lever on shift rail and seal extension/adaptor housing against transmission case. The offset level and shift rail pin holes should be aligned and in a vertical position.

20) Install and tighten adaptor housing retainer bolts. Install roll pin in offset lever and shift rail. Install damper sleeve in offset lever. Coat back-up light switch with RTV sealer and install in case.

TIGHTENING SPECIFICATIONS

Application	Ft. Lbs. (N.m)
Adapter Housing Bolt	13 (18)
Back-Up Lamp Switch	15 (20)
Fill Plug	23 (31)
Front Bearing Cap Bolt	13 (18)
Shift Cover-to-Case	10 (14)
Reverse Pilot Bolt-to-Case	20 (27)
Transmission-to-Clutch Housing Bolt	55 (75)
	INCH Lbs. (N.m)
Transmission Cover	84 (10)

BORG-WARNER 5-SPEED MODEL T5

American Motors
  Eagle
Ford Motor Co.
  Capri, Cougar, Mustang
  Thunderbird
Jeep
  CJ-7, Scrambler

IDENTIFICATION

American Motors Passenger Cars – An identification tag is attached to the rear of the transmission. For certain models, special identification numbers are stamped on a boss on the left side of transmission case.

Ford Motor Co. – Identification code is located on extension bolt on left-hand side of transmission.

Jeep – An identification tag displaying model part number is attached to right side of adapter housing by an adapter housing-to-transmission case bolt.

DESCRIPTION

The T5 5-speed transmission is a constant mesh, fully synchronized unit which provides synchromesh engagement in all forward gear ranges. The reverse gear is spur-cut and is not in constant mesh. The transmission utilizes an internal-type non-adjustable shift mechanism with a reverse gear lock-out. The lock-out feature prevents accidental engagement in reverse when selecting any of the forward gears. On some Ford vehicles there is a Top Gear Sensing Switch attached to the transmission case cover.

LUBRICATION & ADJUSTMENT

See Appropriate MANUAL TRANSMISSION SERVICING article in DOMESTIC GENERAL SERVICING section.

TROUBLE SHOOTING

See MANUAL TRANSMISSION TROUBLE SHOOTING article in DOMESTIC GENERAL SERVICING section.

SERVICE (IN VEHICLE)

GEAR SHIFT LEVER
Removal & Installation
Remove bolts attaching shift boot to floor pan (if applicable). Remove bolts attaching shift lever to transmission and remove shift lever assembly. To install, reverse removal procedure.

REMOVAL & INSTALLATION

TRANSMISSION
See appropriate MANUAL TRANSMISSION REMOVAL article in DOMESTIC GENERAL SERVICING section.

TRANSMISSION DISASSEMBLY

CAUTION: If bolts are replaced, use only those of the same size and length as the originals.

NOTE: Remove top gear sensing switch and pigtail connector (if equipped) from front right side of transmission cover. Remove top gear sensing switch pin using a pencil magnet. To install, reverse procedure.

1) Remove drain bolt on transmission case to drain lubricant. Do not reuse lubricant when transmission is reassembled. Use only recommended lubricant.

2) Do not remove offset lever while extension housing is bolted in place. Using a pin punch and hammer, remove roll pin attaching offset lever to shift rail. Remove damper sleeve. Remove extension or adapter housing-to-transmission bolts and remove housing and offset lever as an assembly.

3) On AMC and Jeep models remove plastic funnel, thrust bearing race and thrust bearing from rear of countershaft, found on end of countershaft or inside adapter housing. On Ford models, remove offset lever, roll pin detent spring and detent ball from extension housing detent plate.

4) Remove bolts attaching cover and shift fork assembly to transmission and remove cover assembly. Remove back-up lamp switch. Remove roll pin from 5th gear shift fork. Place a wood block under 5th gear shift fork during roll pin removal to prevent damage to 5th gear-/reverse shift rail. *See Fig. 1.*

Fig. 1: Removing 5th Gear Shift Fork Roll Pin

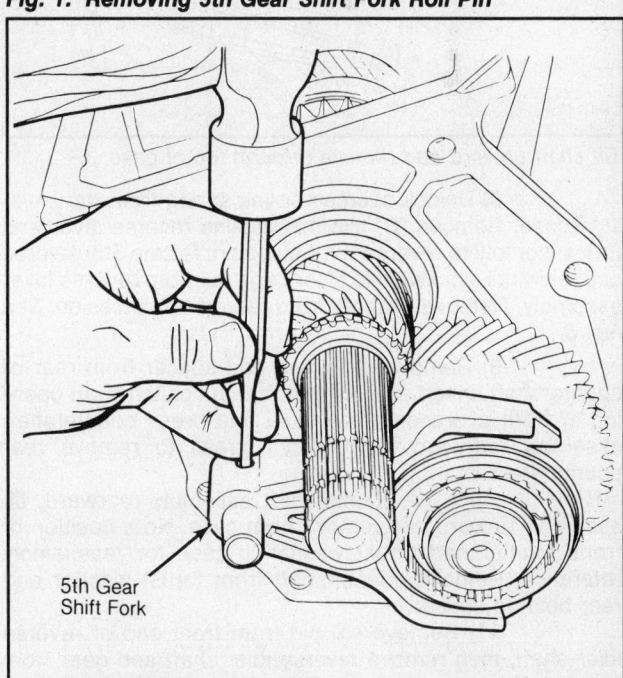

5th Gear
Shift Fork

Place wood block under gear during removal.

5) Remove 5th gear synchronizer snap ring, shift fork, 5th gear synchronizer sleeve, blocking ring and 5th speed drive gear from rear of countershaft. Remove 5th gear synchronizer insert retainer springs and inserts from sleeve and hub. Mark position of hub and sleeve for assembly reference.

6) Remove snap ring and 5th speed driven gear from rear of output shaft using Puller (J-25215 or equivalent). Mark front bearing cap for assembly reference. Remove front bearing cap bolts and bearing cap. Remove front bearing race, end play shims and oil seal from bearing cap.

7) Rotate input shaft until flat surface on main drive gear faces countershaft and remove 4th gear blocking ring from 3rd/4th synchronizer. Remove input shaft from transmission. Remove input shaft needle bearings, thrust bearing and race. Remove output shaft rear bearing race, then tilt output shaft upward and remove through top of transmission case. *See Fig. 2.*

Fig. 2: Removing & Installing Output Shaft

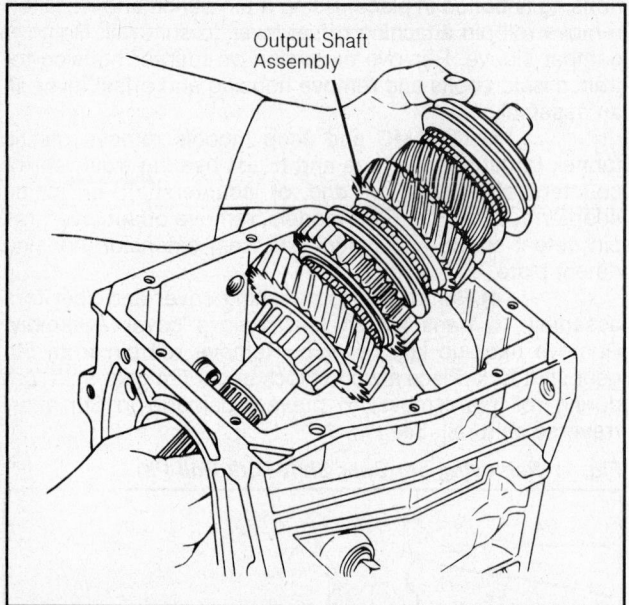

Output Shaft
Assembly

Tilt shaft upward and remove through top of case.

8) Unlock overcenter link spring from transmission case. Remove "C" clip that retains reverse lever and fork assembly to reverse lever pivot pin. Rotate 5th/reverse gear shift rail clockwise to disengage rail from reverse lever assembly. Remove shift rail from rear of transmission. *See Fig. 3.*

9) Remove snap ring and spacer from rear of countershaft. Insert a brass drift through clutch shaft opening in front of transmission case and press countershaft assembly rearward, using arbor press to remove rear countershaft bearing.

10) Slide countershaft assembly rearward, tilt assembly upward and remove from case. Note position of front countershaft thrust washer in case for reassembly reference. Remove countershaft front thrust washer and rear bearing spacer.

11) Remove roll pin from front end of reverse idler shaft, then remove reverse idler shaft and gear from transmission case. Note position of reverse idler gear for reassembly reference.

12) Using an arbor press, remove countershaft front bearing from transmission case. Remove bearing from front of clutch shaft. Using a flat drift and hammer, remove rear extension or adapter housing seal.

Fig. 3: Removing & Installing Reverse Shift Rail

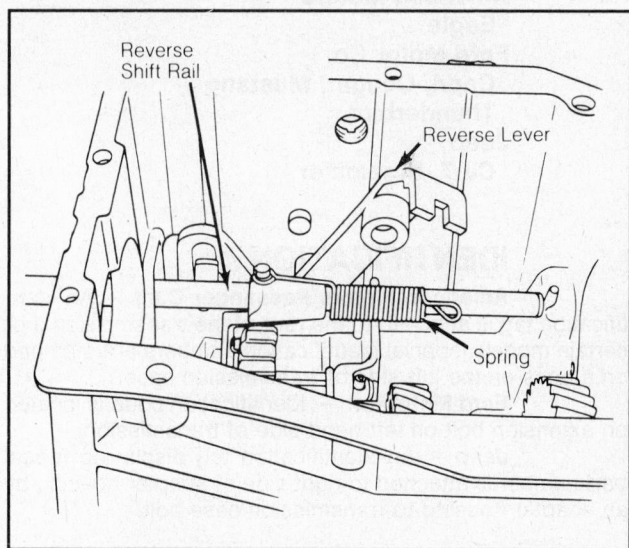

Reverse
Shift Rail

Reverse Lever

Spring

COMPONENT DISASSEMBLY & REASSEMBLY

OUTPUT SHAFT
Disassembly
1) Remove thrust bearing washer from front of output shaft. Scribe alignment mark on 3rd-4th synchronizer hub and sleeve for reassembly reference. Remove 3rd-4th gear synchronizer blocking ring, sleeve, hub and 3rd gear as an assembly.

2) Remove snap ring that retains 2nd gear on shaft, then remove tabbed 2nd gear thrust washer and 2nd gear. Using Puller (J-22912 or equivalent) and arbor press, remove 5th gear. Slide rear bearing off mainshaft.

3) Remove 1st gear thrust washer, 1st gear roll pin (using diagonal cutters), 1st gear and blocking ring. Scribe alignment marks on 1st-2nd gear synchronizer sleeve and hub for reassembly reference.

4) Remove insert springs and insert from 1st/reverse sliding gear and remove gear from output shaft hub. Do not attempt to remove 1st-2nd/reverse hub from output shaft. Hub and shaft are machined as a matched set.

Reassembly
1) Coat ouput shaft and gear bores with transmission lubricant. Install and align 1st-2nd gear synchronizer sleeve on output shaft hub using reference marks made at disassembly. Install 1st-2nd synchronizer inserts and springs in 1st/reverse synchronizer sleeve.

2) Engage tang end of each insert spring in same synchronizer insert, but position open ends of springs to face 180° from each other. Be sure that reference marks are aligned. *See Fig. 5.*

NOTE: **If any output shaft gear is replaced, the countershaft gear must also be replaced to maintain proper gear mesh and avoid noisy operation.**

3) Install blocking ring and 2nd gear on output shaft. Install tabbed thrust washer and 2nd gear retaining snap ring on output shaft. Be sure that washer tab is properly seated in output shaft notch.

Fig. 4: Exploded View of Borg-Warner 5-Speed Model T5 Transmission

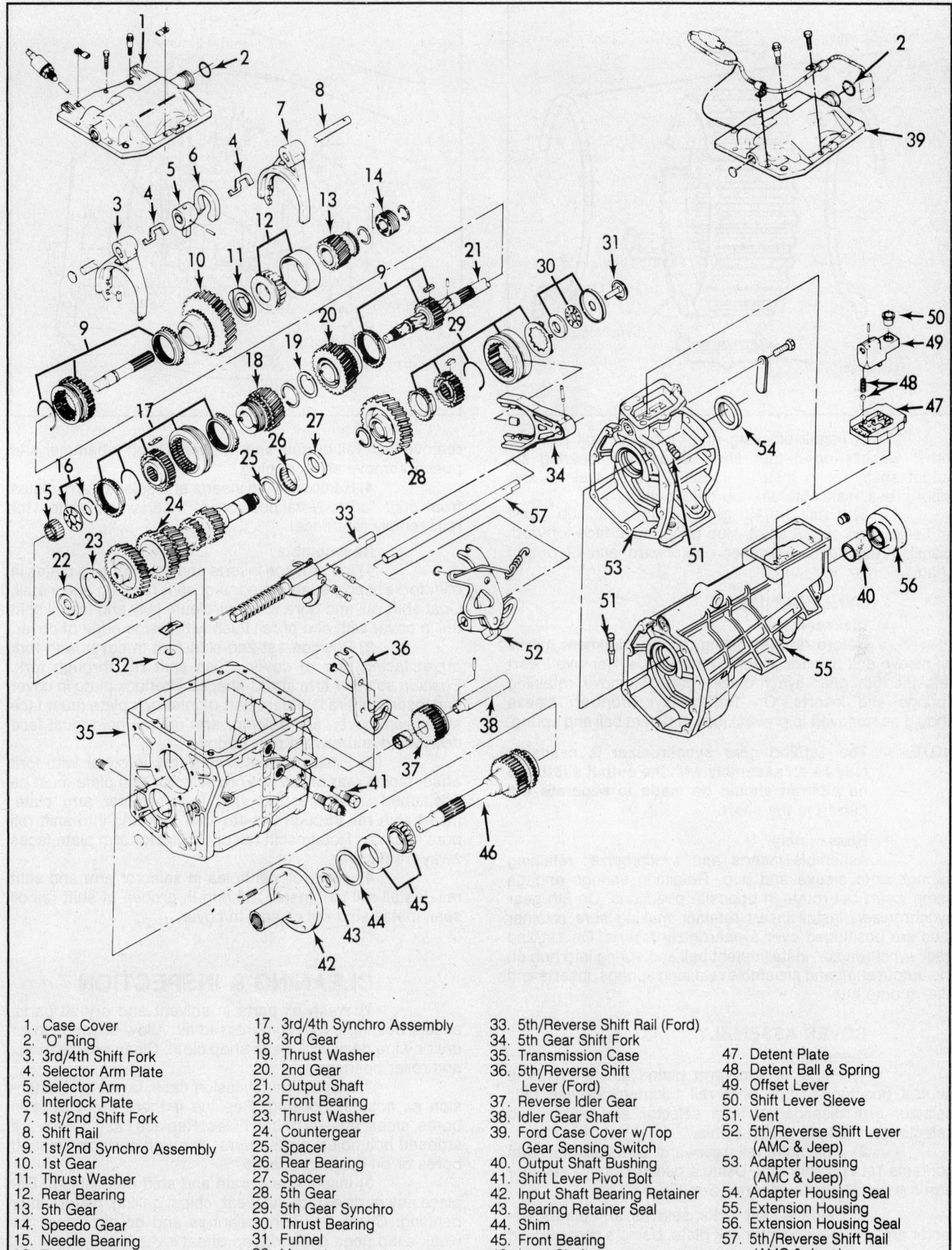

1. Case Cover	17. 3rd/4th Synchro Assembly	33. 5th/Reverse Shift Rail (Ford)
2. "O" Ring	18. 3rd Gear	34. 5th Gear Shift Fork
3. 3rd/4th Shift Fork	19. Thrust Washer	35. Transmission Case
4. Selector Arm Plate	20. 2nd Gear	36. 5th/Reverse Shift
5. Selector Arm	21. Output Shaft	Lever (Ford)
6. Interlock Plate	22. Front Bearing	37. Reverse Idler Gear
7. 1st/2nd Shift Fork	23. Thrust Washer	38. Idler Gear Shaft
8. Shift Rail	24. Countergear	39. Ford Case Cover w/Top
9. 1st/2nd Synchro Assembly	25. Spacer	Gear Sensing Switch
10. 1st Gear	26. Rear Bearing	40. Output Shaft Bushing
11. Thrust Washer	27. Spacer	41. Shift Lever Pivot Bolt
12. Rear Bearing	28. 5th Gear	42. Input Shaft Bearing Retainer
13. 5th Gear	29. 5th Gear Synchro	43. Bearing Retainer Seal
14. Speedo Gear	30. Thrust Bearing	44. Shim
15. Needle Bearing	31. Funnel	45. Front Bearing
16. Thrust Bearing	32. Magnet	46. Input Shaft

47. Detent Plate
48. Detent Ball & Spring
49. Offset Lever
50. Shift Lever Sleeve
51. Vent
52. 5th/Reverse Shift Lever
(AMC & Jeep)
53. Adapter Housing
(AMC & Jeep)
54. Adapter Housing Seal
55. Extension Housing
56. Extension Housing Seal
57. 5th/Reverse Shift Rail
(AMC & Jeep)

Fig. 5: Installing Synchronizer Insert Spring

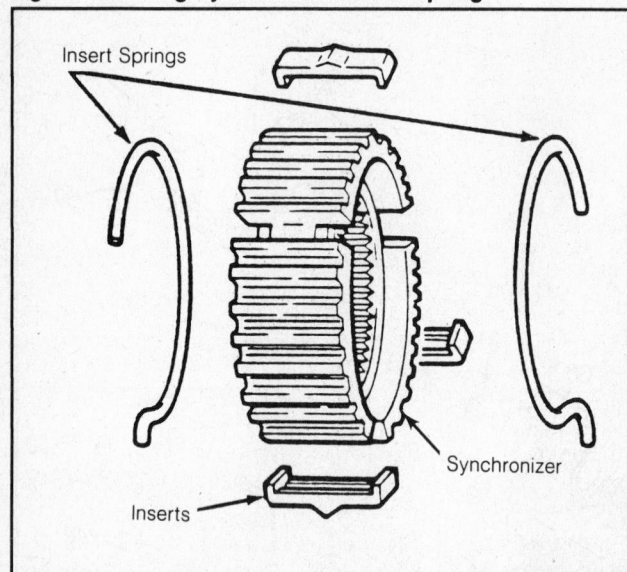

Fig. 6: Removing Shift Rail Retaining Roll Pin

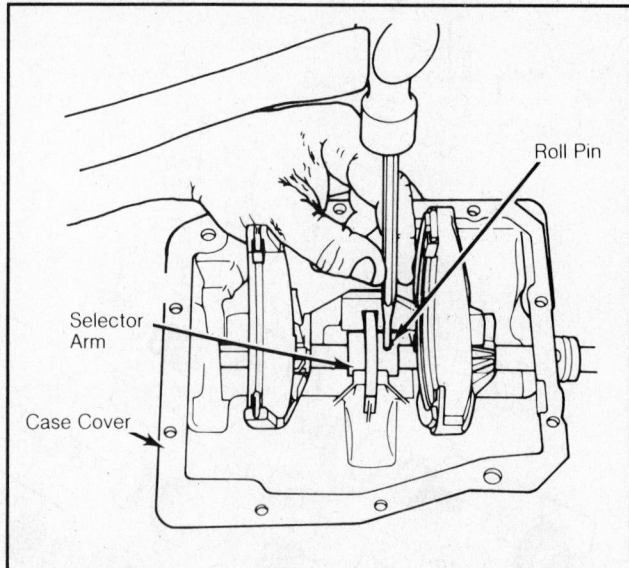

4) Install blocking ring, 1st gear, roll pin and thrust washer on output shaft. Slide rear bearing on output shaft. Using Installer (J-22912 or equivalent) and arbor press, install 5th gear on output shaft.

5) Install 3rd/4th gear synchronizer hub insert and sleeve on output shaft. Hub offset must face forward. Install thrust bearing washer on forward end of output shaft.

SYNCHRONIZERS
Disassembly
Before disassembling, scribe alignment marks on sleeve and hub for assembly reference. Remove insert retainer (5th gear synchronizer only). Remove retaining springs and inserts. On 1st/2nd synchronizer, sleeve should be removed to prevent loss of detent ball and spring.

NOTE: **The 1st/2nd gear synchronizer is available only as an assembly with the output shaft and no attempt should be made to separate the hub from the shaft.**

Reassembly
Assemble inserts and synchronizer retaining springs onto sleeve and hub. Retaining springs engage same insert but rotate in opposite directions. On 5th gear synchronizer, install insert retainer making sure retainer tabs are positioned over synchronizer inserts. On 1st/2nd gear synchronizer, install detent ball and spring into hub on the output shaft and assemble retaining springs, inserts and sleeve onto hub.

COVER ASSEMBLY
Disassembly
1) Place selector arm plates and shift rail in neutral position. Rotate shift rail counterclockwise until selector arm disengages from selector arm plates and selector arm roll pin is accessible.

2) Pull shift rail rearward until selector arm contacts 1st-2nd shift fork. Using a punch, remove selector arm roll pin. Remove shift rail. *See Fig. 6.*

3) Remove shift forks, selector arm plates, selector arm, roll pin and interlock plate. Using a screwdriver,

remove shift rail oil seal and "O" ring. Using a hammer and punch, remove shift rail plug.

4) Remove nylon inserts and selector arm plates from shift forks. Note position of inserts and plates for reassembly reference.

Reassembly
1) Install nylon inserts and selector arm plates in shift forks. Apply sealer to edge of shift rail plug and install. Coat shift rail and bore with petroleum jelly and install shift rail in cover with end of rail flush with inside edge of cover.

2) Position 1st-2nd shift fork in cover with fork offset facing rear of cover. Push shift rail through fork. Position selector arm and C-shaped interlock plate in cover and insert shift rail. Widest part of interlock plate must face away from cover, and selector arm roll pin hold must face downward and toward rear of cover.

3) Position 3rd-4th shift fork in cover with fork offset facing rear of cover. Fork selector arm plate must be positioned under 1st-2nd shift fork selector arm plate. Insert shift rail through 3rd-4th shift fork and into shift rail bore in cover. Rotate shift rail until selector arm plate faces away from cover.

4) Align roll pin holes in selector arm and shift rail. Install roll pin. Install "O" ring in groove of shift rail oil seal. Install shift rail oil seal in cover.

CLEANING & INSPECTION
1) Wash all parts in solvent and dry all parts, except bearings, with compressed air. Allow bearings to air dry or wipe dry with a clean shop cloth. Clean needle thrust and roller bearings.

2) Inspect transmission case, cover and extension or adapter housing. Replace if there are cracks in bores, sides, bosses or bolt holes. Replace case if there are stripped bolt holes, nicks, burrs, or rough surfaces in shaft bores or on gasket surfaces.

3) Inspect gear train and shift mechanism. Replace any parts exhibiting wear, chips, galling, distortion or bending. Check for worn bearings and bores. Check for weak snap rings and stripped offset lever.

BORG-WARNER 5-SPEED MODEL T5 (Cont.)

TRANSMISSION REASSEMBLY

1) Coat countershaft front bearing outer cage with Loctite 601, or equivalent. Using an arbor press, install countershaft front bearing flush with case. Coat tabbed countershaft thrust washer with petroleum jelly and install with tab engaged with depression in case.

2) Place transmission case on end and install countershaft in front bearing. Install countershaft rear bearing spacer. Coat rear bearing with petroleum jelly and install using Bearing Installer Tool (J-29895 or equivalent).

3) Use sleeve tool to prevent needle bearings from catching on countershaft shoulder. When properly installed, bearing should extend .125" (3.17 mm) beyond surface of case.

4) Place reverse idler gear in case with shift lever groove facing rearward. Install reverse idler shaft from rear of case and install retaining roll pin. Install assembled output shaft in transmission case.

5) Install output shaft rear bearing race in case. Install 4th gear in case and engage 3rd-4th synchronizer sleeve and blocking ring on output shaft. Install front bearing race in front bearing cap without shims.

6) Temporarily install front bearing cap. Install 5th speed/reverse lever, pivot bolt and retaining "C" clip. Coat pivot bolt threads with RTV sealer. Be sure to engage reverse lever fork in reverse idler gear.

7) Install front bearing race in front bearing cap without shims. Temporarily install front bearing cap. Install 5th speed driven gear and retaining snap ring on rear of output shaft. Install 5th speed gear on countershaft.

8) Insert 5th gear/reverse rail through rear of case and install 5th/reverse gear lever. To simplify engagement with lever, rotate rail during installation. Install 5th/reverse gear lever over center spring.

9) Assemble 5th gear synchronizer sleeve, insert springs and insert retainer using marks made at disassembly. Install plastic inserts in notches on each side of 5th gear shift fork. Place 5th gear synchronizer sleeve on 5th gear shift fork and slide onto countershaft and 5th/reverse gear rail.

10) Align roll pin hole in 5th/reverse gear rail and 5th gear shift fork. Place assembled 5th/reverse gear rail and shift fork on block of wood and install retaining roll pin. Install thrust race against 5th gear synchronizer hub and install retaining snap ring.

11) Install needle thrust bearing against thrust race on countershaft. Coat thrust bearing and race with petroleum jelly. Install lipped thrust race over needle thrust bearing and install plastic funnel into hole in end of countershaft gear.

12) Temporarily install extension or adapter housing. Turn transmission case on end and mount dial indicator on extension or adapter housing with indicator stylus on end of output shaft. Rotate clutch and output shaft and zero dial indicator. Pull upward on output shaft and read end play on dial indicator. *See Fig. 7.*

13) Select a shim pack measuring .001-.005" (.03-.13 mm) thicker than end play measured in step **12**). Horizontally place transmission on bench and remove front bearing cap and race.

14) Add shims to cap and install clutch shaft bearing race in cap. Apply RTV sealant, or equivalent, to front bearing cap and install on transmission case. Tighten bolts. Recheck end play. There should be no end play.

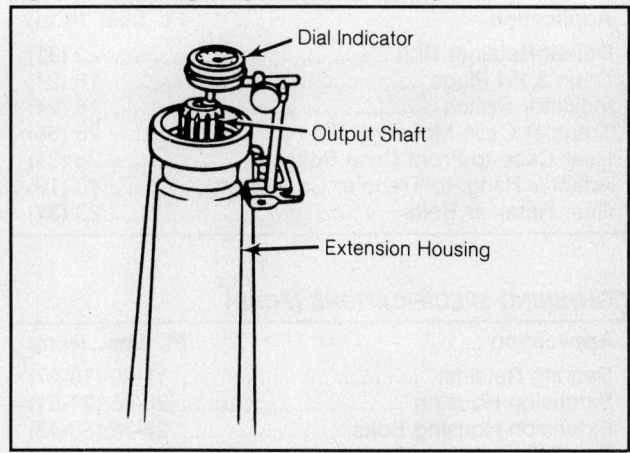

Fig. 7: Measuring Output Shaft End Play

15) Remove extension or adapter housing and install extension or adapter housing seal using a seal installer. Move transmission shift fork to place transmission in neutral.

16) Apply RTV sealant, or equivalent, to cover. Install cover assembly onto case while aligning shift forks and synchronizer sleeves. Install cover attaching bolts and tighten. Be sure that reverse relay lever is engaged.

17) Apply RTV sealant, or equivalent, to extension or adapter housing and install housing over output shaft and shift rail into position where shift rail just enters shift cover opening.

18) Install detent spring into offset lever and place steel ball in neutral guide plate detent. *See Fig. 8.* Apply pressure to steel ball with detent spring and offset lever.

Fig. 8: Offset Lever, Ball & Spring Location

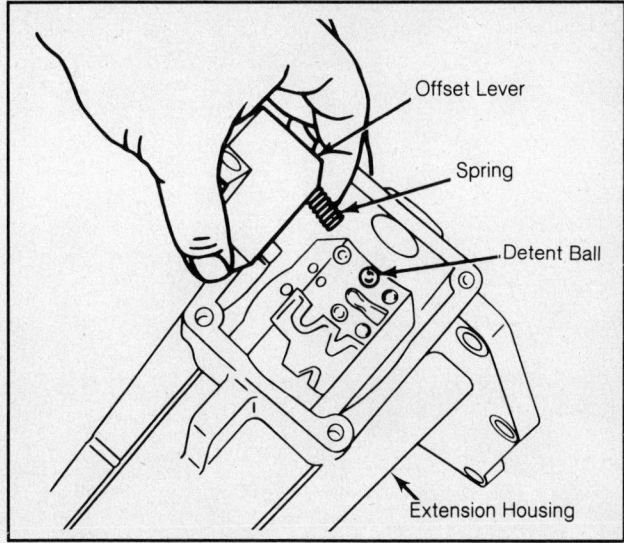

19) Slide offset lever onto shift rail and seat extension or adapter housing to transmission case. Install and tighten housing attaching bolts. Install roll pin in offset lever and shift rail.

20) Install damper sleeve in offset lever. Coat back-up lamp switch threads with RTV sealant, or equivalent, and install switch.

TIGHTENING SPECIFICATIONS (AMC)

Application	Ft. Lbs. (N.m)
Detent Retainer Bolt	23 (31)
Drain & Fill Plugs	18 (24)
Indicator Switch	18 (24)
Transfer Case Mounting Nuts	26 (35)
Rear Case-to-Front Case Bolts	23 (31)
Adapter Hsng.-to-Transfer Case Bolts	13 (18)
Rear Retainer Bolts	23 (31)

TIGHTENING SPECIFICATIONS (FORD)

Application	Ft. Lbs. (N.m)
Bearing Retainer	11-20 (15-27)
Extension Housing	20-45 (27-61)
Extension Housing Bolts	28-36 (38-48)
Turret Cover	11-15 (15-20)
Transmission Support	36-50 (48-68)
Drain Plug	15-30 (20-41)
Top Gear Sensing Switch	12-18 (17-24)
Back-Up Lamp Switch	12-18 (17-24)

TIGHTENING SPECIFICATIONS (JEEP)

Application	Ft. Lbs. (N.m)
Adapter Housing Bolt	13 (18)
Back-Up Lamp Switch	15 (20)
Fill Plug	23 (31)
Transmission-to-Clutch Hsng. Bolt	13 (18)
Front Bearing Cap Bolt	13 (18)
Shift Cover-to-Case	10 (14)
Reverse Pilot Bolt-to-Case	20 (27)

Manual Transmissions

BORG-WARNER 4-SPEED MODEL T18

Bronco and
F150/F350, 2WD & 4WD

IDENTIFICATION

An identification tag is attached to one of the shift control housing-to-case attaching bolts.

DESCRIPTION

Transmission is a 4-speed unit, synchronized in 2nd, 3rd, and 4th gears only. First and reverse gears are spur type, while 2nd, 3rd, and 4th gears are helical type. The input shaft is supported with a ball bearing. The mainshaft is supported at the front by a pilot bearing in input shaft and at the rear by a ball bearing pressed onto shaft and into case. All other gears are supported by needle bearings.

LUBRICATION & ADJUSTMENT

See appropriate MANUAL TRANSMISSION SERVICING article in DOMESTIC/IMPORT GENERAL SERVICING section.

TROUBLE SHOOTING

See MANUAL TRANSMISSION TROUBLE SHOOTING article in DOMESTIC GENERAL SERVICING section.

REMOVAL AND INSTALLATION

SHIFT LEVER

NOTE: Remove shift ball, boot and lever as an assembly. Disassemble only if individual component replacement is required.

Removal
Remove plastic insert from shift ball. Warm ball with heat gun to 140-180°F (60-82°C). Using wooden block and hammer, carefully drive ball from lever. Remove rubber boot and floor pan cover. Shift unit into 2nd gear, remove lock pin and remove lever from housing.

Installation
Install lever in housing, making certain slot in lever aligns with tab in housing. Install lock pin. Install rubber boot and floor pan cover. Warm ball with heat gun. Using 7/16 socket and mallet, tap ball on lever. Install plastic insert.

TRANSMISSION

See appropriate MANUAL TRANSMISSION REMOVAL article in DOMESTIC GENERAL SERVICING section.

TRANSMISSION DISASSEMBLY

1) Mount transmission in holding fixture and drain lubricant. Position shift lever in 2nd gear and remove shift control housing. Lock transmission in 2 gears, then remove companion flange and oil seal.

2) Remove speedometer driven gear and bearing assembly. Remove mainshaft bearing retainer or extension housing. Remove speedometer drive gear snap ring, retainer and drive gear.

3) Remove the mainshaft bearing snap ring retainers and remove bearing spacer. Using puller and attachments (T75L-7025-B, F, H and J), remove mainshaft bearing. See Fig. 1.

Fig. 1: Removing Mainshaft Bearing

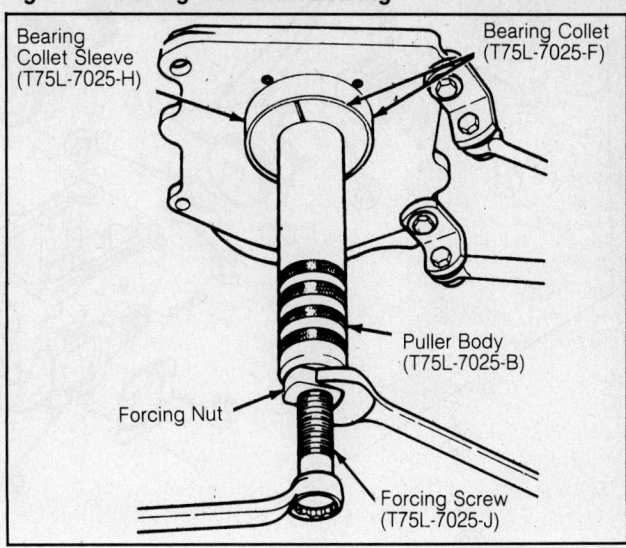

4) Remove input shaft bearing retainer. Using same puller, remove input shaft bearing. Remove input shaft oil baffle. Carefully remove input shaft assembly from case by pushing rearward and removing from inside case.

5) Remove lock plate from countershaft and reverse idler shaft. Using slide hammer and adapter (T50T-100-A and T50T-7140-C), remove reverse idler gear shaft. See Fig. 3. Remove reverse idler gear from case.

6) Using same tool combination, remove countershaft. Insert proper O.D. dummy shaft, about 10" long, into countershaft. Remove countershaft gear assembly from case, ensuring countershaft needle bearings and spacers remain in place.

CLEANING & INSPECTION

1) All parts should be thoroughly cleaned in solvent and air dried. If any transmission gear requires replacement, also replace gear with which it meshes. Replace gaskets, oil seals and snap rings.

2) Inspect transmission case for cracks, worn or scored bearing bosses. Examine bearings for cracked races, excessive wear and improper fit in case bores.

3) Inspect gear teeth for cracks or chips. Check countershaft and reverse idler shaft for pitting, wear, scores, nicks, cracks and flat spots. Replace shafts if worn or damaged. Replace parts as required.

COMPONENT DISASSEMBLY & REASSEMBLY

COUNTERSHAFT GEAR
Disassembly
Remove dummy shaft, roller bearings, spacers and center spacer from countershaft gear.

Manual Transmissions

BORG-WARNER 4-SPEED MODEL T18 (Cont.)

Fig. 2: Exploded View of Warner Model T 18 4-Speed Transmission

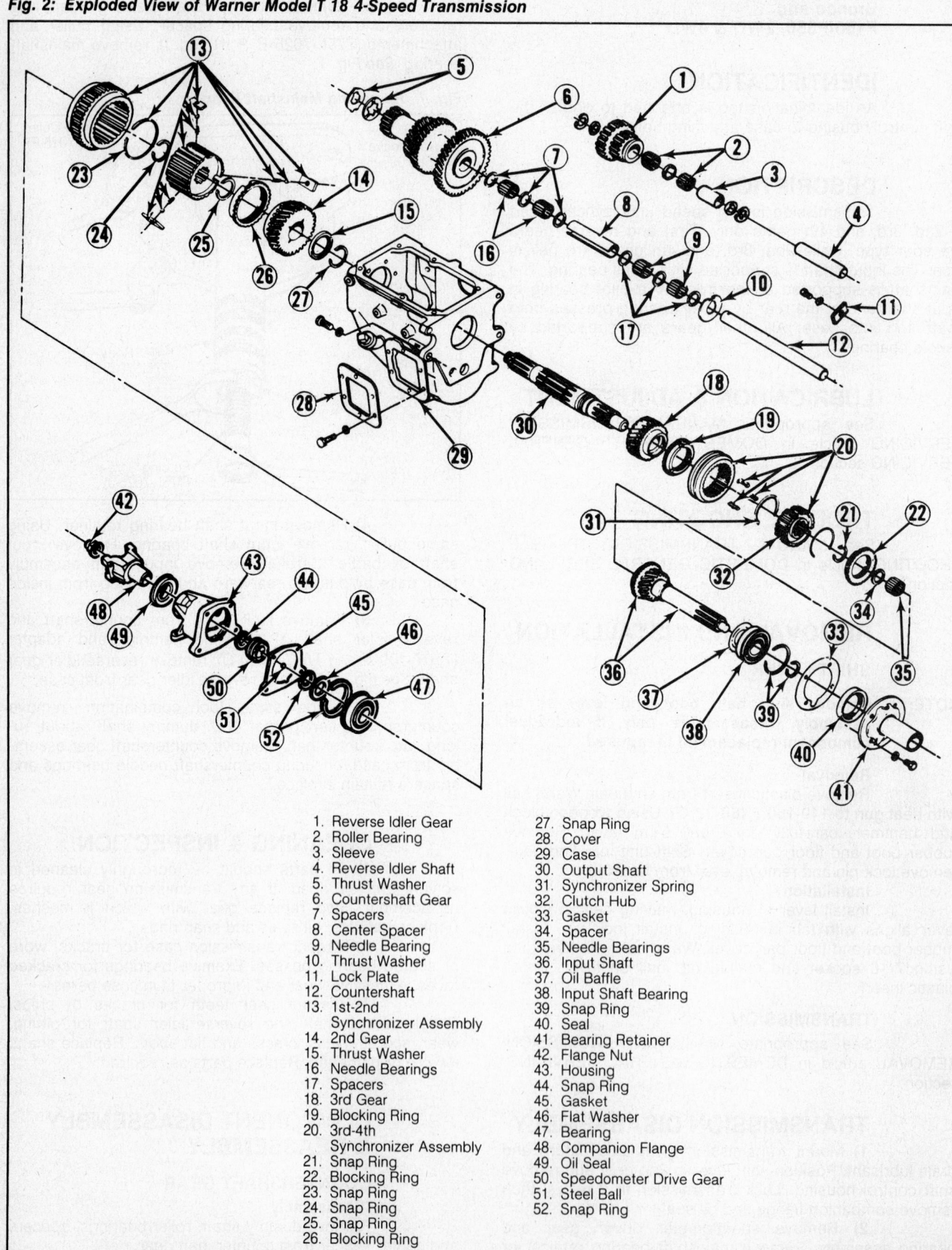

1. Reverse Idler Gear	27. Snap Ring
2. Roller Bearing	28. Cover
3. Sleeve	29. Case
4. Reverse Idler Shaft	30. Output Shaft
5. Thrust Washer	31. Synchronizer Spring
6. Countershaft Gear	32. Clutch Hub
7. Spacers	33. Gasket
8. Center Spacer	34. Spacer
9. Needle Bearing	35. Needle Bearings
10. Thrust Washer	36. Input Shaft
11. Lock Plate	37. Oil Baffle
12. Countershaft	38. Input Shaft Bearing
13. 1st-2nd	39. Snap Ring
Synchronizer Assembly	40. Seal
14. 2nd Gear	41. Bearing Retainer
15. Thrust Washer	42. Flange Nut
16. Needle Bearings	43. Housing
17. Spacers	44. Snap Ring
18. 3rd Gear	45. Gasket
19. Blocking Ring	46. Flat Washer
20. 3rd-4th	47. Bearing
Synchronizer Assembly	48. Companion Flange
21. Snap Ring	49. Oil Seal
22. Blocking Ring	50. Speedometer Drive Gear
23. Snap Ring	51. Steel Ball
24. Snap Ring	52. Snap Ring
25. Snap Ring	
26. Blocking Ring	

BORG-WARNER 4-SPEED MODEL T18 (Cont.)

Fig. 3: Removing Reverse Idler Shaft

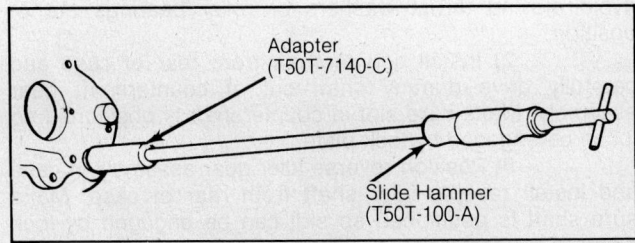

Adapter
(T50T-7140-C)

Slide Hammer
(T50T-100-A)

Remove countershaft using same tool combination.

Reassembly

1) Insert center spacer into bore of countershaft gear. Insert dummy shaft into center of spacer. Lightly coat bore of countershaft with petroleum jelly. Install 1 bearing spacer and 22 roller bearings in bore.

2) Position spacer on top of rollers, install 22 more rollers and another spacer. Repeat same operation at opposite end of countershaft gear. Leave dummy shaft installed in gear.

MAINSHAFT

Disassembly

1) Remove 3rd-4th synchronizer snap ring from mainshaft and slide 3rd-4th synchronizer assembly and 3rd gear from mainshaft. Remove synchronizer sleeve and inserts from hub.

2) Check end play of 2nd gear, it should be .005-.024" (.127-.609 mm). Remove snap rings from end of hub. Slide 1st-2nd gear from hub, being careful not to loose any balls, springs, inserts or anti-rattle spring and ball.

3) Remove snap ring from behind synchronizer hub. Pull synchronizer hub from shaft and remove blocking ring. Remove snap ring from 2nd gear and remove gear and thrust washer from mainshaft.

Reassembly

1) Place mainshaft in soft-jaw vise with threaded end up. Install snap ring in 3rd groove from threaded end of shaft. Place 2nd gear thrust on shaft with recessed end over snap ring.

2) Position 2nd gear against washer and install snap ring. Place blocking ring on 2nd gear. Assemble 2nd gear synchronizer assembly over splines of mainshaft while aligning blocking ring cut-outs with inserts.

3) Install snap ring in mainshaft groove behind clutch hub. Turn mainshaft over and place 3rd gear against shoulder of mainshaft. Install 3rd gear blocking ring.

4) Install 3rd-4th synchronizer assembly over mainshaft splines. Align blocking ring slots with inserts and position end of hub with long chamfer to front of transmission. Install snap ring and spacer.

Fig. 4: Exploded View of Shift Control Housing

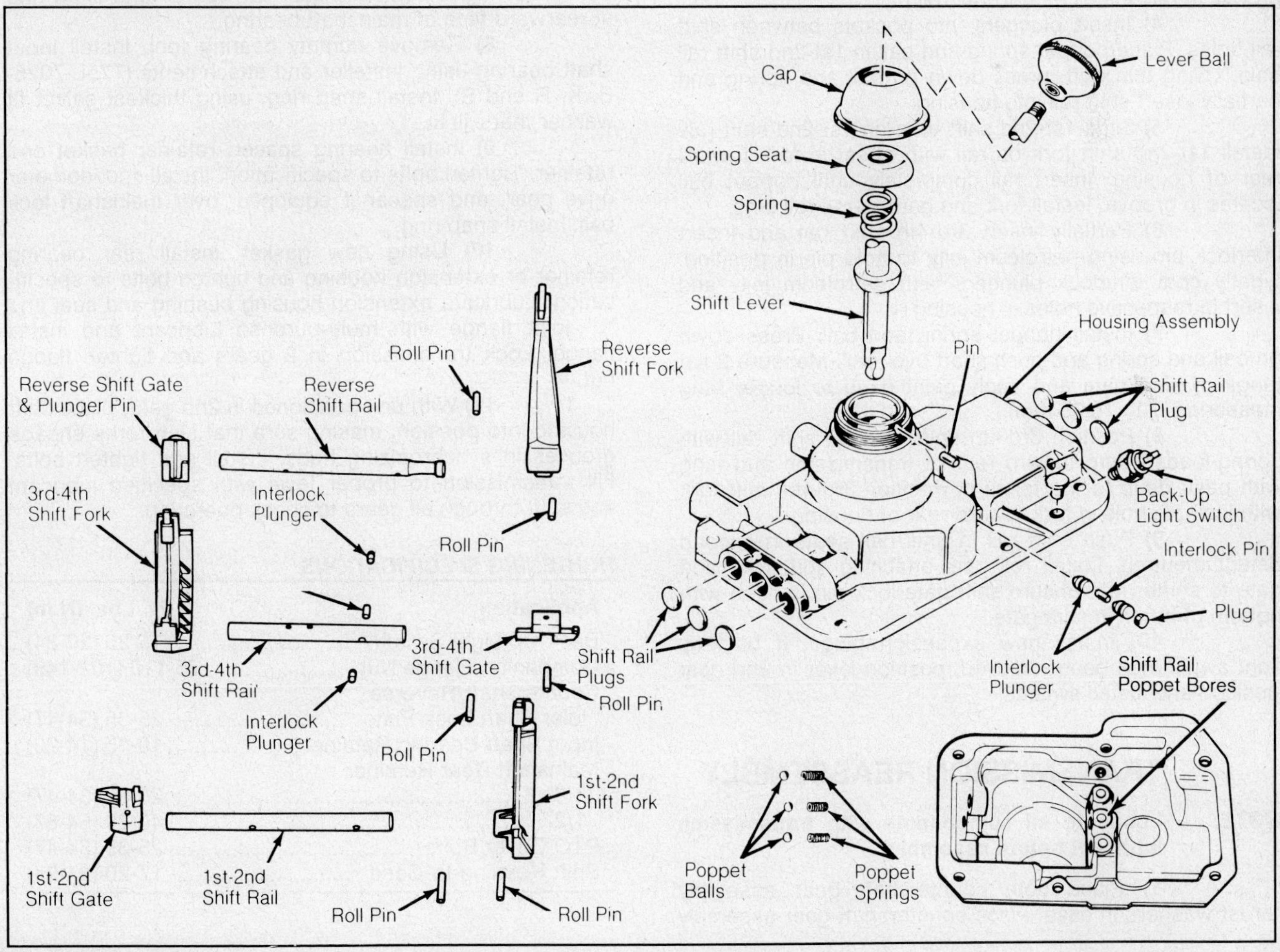

Cap

Lever Ball

Spring Seat

Spring

Shift Lever

Pin

Housing Assembly

Shift Rail Plug

Back-Up Light Switch

Interlock Pin

Plug

Reverse Shift Fork

Roll Pin

Reverse Shift Gate & Plunger Pin

Reverse Shift Rail

3rd-4th Shift Fork

Interlock Plunger

Roll Pin

3rd-4th Shift Rail

3rd-4th Shift Gate

Interlock Plunger

Roll Pin

Shift Rail Plugs

Roll Pin

Interlock Plunger

Shift Rail Poppet Bores

1st-2nd Shift Fork

1st-2nd Shift Gate

1st-2nd Shift Rail

Roll Pin

Roll Pin

Poppet Balls

Poppet Springs

BORG-WARNER 4-SPEED MODEL T18 (Cont.)

SHIFT CONTROL HOUSING

Disassembly

1) Place housing in soft-jawed vise with shift forks facing upward. Remove back-up light switch. Using a hammer and a punch, remove shift rail expansion plugs from forward end of housing.

2) Using pin punch, drive out roll pins securing shift forks and shift gates. Tap shift rails out front of housing while holding shop towel over poppet springs and balls to prevent losing them.

3) Remove interlock pin from 3rd-4th shift rail. Remove shift forks and shift gates. Note location of forks and gates for reassembly. Remove poppet balls and springs from housing.

4) Remove interlock plungers from housing. If required, remove retaining clip, spring and plunger from reverse shift gate.

Reassembly

1) Replace breather in housing if damaged or restricted. If reverse shift gate is disassembled, install spring and plunger, compress spring and install retaining clip.

2) Position spring and ball in reverse shift rail hole in housing. Partially insert shift rail into housing and install reverse shift fork on rail. Using long thin drift, push down on poppet ball and spring.

3) Position reverse shift ball notch so it does not pass over ball. Slide reverse gate onto rail with long end forward. Drive rail into housing until ball locates in groove in rail. Install gate-to-rail roll pin.

4) Insert plungers into pockets between shift rail holes. Place poppet spring and ball in 1st-2nd shift rail hole. Using thin drift, press down on ball and spring and partially insert shift rail into housing.

5) Slide 1st-2nd shift gate on 1st-2nd shift rail. Install 1st-2nd shift fork on rail with offset in fork toward rear of housing. Insert rail completely until poppet ball locates in groove. Install fork and gate-to-rail roll pins.

6) Partially insert 3rd-4th shift rail and insert interlock pin using petroleum jelly to hold pin in position. Lightly coat interlock plungers with petroleum jelly and insert in respective holes in housing.

7) Install poppet spring and ball. Press down on ball and spring and push shaft over ball. Measure 2 flat tangs of shift gate and apply paint daub to longer tang measuring .72" (18.26 mm).

8) Position 3rd-4th shift gate on shift rail with spring-loaded tang toward rear of transmission and tang with paint daub facing forward. Position 3rd-4th shift fork with lock pin hole in fork toward rear of housing.

9) Push shift rail in until ball seats in second detent (neutral). Install roll pins attaching shift fork and gate to shifter rail. Ensure shift gate lock pin is flush with bottom of notch in shift gate.

10) Install new expansion plugs. If back-up light switch has been removed, position lever in 2nd gear position and install switch.

TRANSMISSION REASSEMBLY

NOTE: Lubricate all components with transmission lubricant before assembly.

1) Place both countershaft gear assembly thrust washers in case. Place countershaft gear assembly into position, with dummy shaft still installed. Use care to avoid moving thrust washers or roller bearings out of position.

2) Install countershaft from rear of case and carefully drive dummy shaft out of countershaft gear assembly. Make sure slot in countershaft is positioned so it can be engaged by lock plate.

3) Position reverse idler gear assembly in case and install reverse idler shaft from rear of case. Make sure shaft is positioned so slot can be engaged by lock plate.

4) Install countershaft and reverse idler gear shaft lock plate. Install 22 pilot roller bearings in end of input shaft. Use petroleum jelly to hold bearings in place.

5) Place input shaft in case. Place 4th gear synchronizer blocking ring on input shaft. Install mainshaft in transmission case, taking care not to move pilot roller bearings out of position.

6) Install input shaft oil baffle. Install dummy bearing (T75L-7025-Q) on transmission input shaft to hold input shaft and mainshaft in place while installing mainshaft bearing.

NOTE: If dummy bearing is not used, slide a protector over 3rd-4th synchronizer to prevent wedging 4th blocking ring onto tapered seat.

7) Install snap ring on mainshaft bearing. Using installer set (T75L-7025-B and L), install bearing into case until snap ring is seated. Install flat washer and snap ring at rearward face of mainshaft bearing.

8) Remove dummy bearing tool. Install input shaft bearing using installer and attachments (T75L-7025-B, K, R and S). Install snap ring, using thickest select fit washer that will fit.

9) Install bearing spacer, retainer gasket and retainer. Tighten bolts to specification. Install speedometer drive gear, and spacer if equipped, over mainshaft lock ball. Install snap ring.

10) Using new gasket, install rear bearing retainer or extension housing and tighten bolts to specification. Lubricate extension housing bushing and seal and "U" joint flange with multi-purpose lubricant and install flange. Lock transmission in 2 gears and tighten flange nut.

11) With unit positioned in 2nd gear, place shift housing into position, making sure that shift forks engage grooves in synchronizing hubs. Install and tighten bolts. Fill transmission to proper level with specified lubricant and shift through all gears to check operation.

TIGHTENING SPECIFICATIONS

Application	Ft. Lbs. (N.m)
Back-Up Light Switch	15-25 (20-34)
Companion Flange Nut	75-110 (102-149)
Countershaft/Reverse	
Idler Shaft Lock Plate	25-35 (34-47)
Input Shaft Bearing Retainer	10-15 (14-20)
Mainshaft Rear Retainer	
3/8"	25-35 (34-47)
1/2"	40-50 (54-67)
PTO Cover Bolts	25-35 (34-47)
Shift Housing-to-Case	17-20 (24-27)

BORG-WARNER 4-SPEED MODEL T19B/D

F250/350 HD (2WD & 4WD)

IDENTIFICATION

The transmission identification code can be found on the Vehicle Compliance Certification Label located on the driver's door lock pillar. The code for a Borg-Warner 4-speed model T19B/D is "P". There is also a service identification tag located on the left middle cover-to-case transmission bolt. *See Fig. 1.*

Fig. 1: Transmission Identification Tag

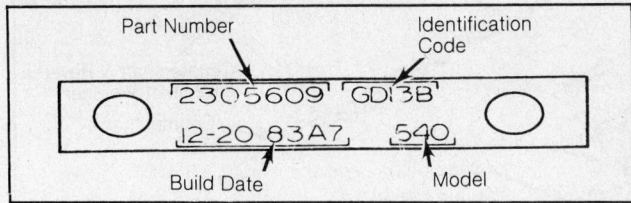

DESCRIPTION

The 4-speed fully synchronized model T19B/D transmission is equipped with a center, floor mounted gear shift lever. The reverse and 1st, 2nd, 3rd, and 4th gears are helical cut for quiet running. The input shaft is supported by a ball bearing. Front end of the output shaft is supported by a pilot bearing installed in the input shaft. The rear end of the output shaft is supported by a ball bearing. The ball bearing and shaft are retained in the case by a snap ring.

LUBRICATION & ADJUSTMENT

See appropriate MANUAL TRANSMISSION SERVICING article in DOMESTIC GENERAL SERVICING section.

REMOVAL & INSTALLATION

TRANSMISSION

See appropriate MANUAL TRANSMISSION REMOVAL article in DOMESTIC GENERAL SERVICING section.

SERVICE (IN VEHICLE)

GEAR SHIFT LEVER

NOTE: **Remove shift ball only if shift ball, boot, or lever is to be replaced. If either the ball, boot, or lever is not being replaced, remove the ball, boot, and lever as an assembly.**

Removal
1) Remove plastic insert from shift ball. Warm ball with heat gun to 140-160°F (60-82°C), knock ball off lever with a block of wood and a hammer, taking care not to damage finish on shift lever.
2) Remove rubber boot and floor pan cover. Shift transmission into 2nd gear, remove lock pin, and shift lever from shift lever housing.

Installation
1) Install shift lever in shifter housing, making sure that slot in lever aligns with tab in housing. Install lock pin. Install rubber boot and floor pan cover.

2) Warm ball with heat gun to 140-180°F (60-82°C) and tap ball on lever with a 7/16" socket and mallet. Install plastic shift pattern insert.

TRANSMISSION DISASSEMBLY

1) Install transmission in bench mounted holding fixture. Remove drain plug and drain lubricant from transmission. Remove bolts retaining gear shift housing to case and remove housing.

2) Lock transmission in two gears and remove U-joint flange and oil seal. Remove speedometer driven gear and bearing assembly. Remove output shaft bearing retainer or extension housing and gasket.

3) Remove speedometer drive gear snap ring retainer. Slide drive gear off output shaft. Remove output shaft bearing snap ring from output shaft and snap ring from bearing. Remove bearing spacer.

4) Install tools (T75L-7025-B, F, H & J) on output shaft and over output shaft bearing. Remove output shaft bearing. Remove input shaft bearing retainer and gasket. Remove input shaft bearing snap ring from input shaft and snap ring from bearing.

5) Install remover tube on input shaft and over input shaft bearing. Remove input shaft bearing. Remove input shaft oil baffle. Baffle is installed in an offset position away from bearing.

6) Remove spring clip from reverse shifter arm pivot screw. Remove pivot screw from shifter arm and case. Lift shifter arm and shoe assembly out of case by prying with screwdriver.

7) Remove input shaft (with flat facing upward) assembly from case. DO NOT lose the 22 pilot bearing rollers from inner end of shaft. Remove thrust spacer. Remove output shaft and gear assemblies from case.

8) Use dummy countershaft (T83T-7111-B) to drive out countershaft (from the front). Keep dummy shaft in contact with countershaft to avoid dropping rollers. The dummy shaft should be 9.379-9.380" (238.23-238.25 mm) long and 1.133-1.135" (28.78-28.83 mm) in diameter.

9) Remove countershaft and cluster gear. Make sure front and rear thrust washers are removed from case. Be careful not to lose any rollers.

10) Remove idler shaft (from front of transmission) using shaft remover (T50T-7140-C) and slide hammer. Remove reverse idler gear, and thrust washers, being careful not to lose any rollers.

CLEANING & INSPECTION

1) Wash all parts (except bearings) in cleaning solvent and dry with compressed air. Brush or scrape all foreign matter from parts. Wash bearings in clean solvent, hold bearings and dry with compressed air. Inspect transmission case for cracks, damaged bearing bores, and/or threads.

2) Check operation and condition of shift levers, forks and side rails. Ensure that vent hole in the case is open.

3) Remove all small nicks or burrs from front and/or rear of case. Check bearings for excessive wear or roughness by slowly turning race by hand.

4) Inspect needle bearing rollers, shafts, and washers for wear and/or damage. Check all other parts for wear, damage, chipped, and/or broken teeth. Replace parts as necessary.

Manual Transmissions

BORG-WARNER 4-SPEED MODEL T19B/D (Cont.)

Fig. 2: Exploded View of Borg-Warner T19B 4-Speed Transmission

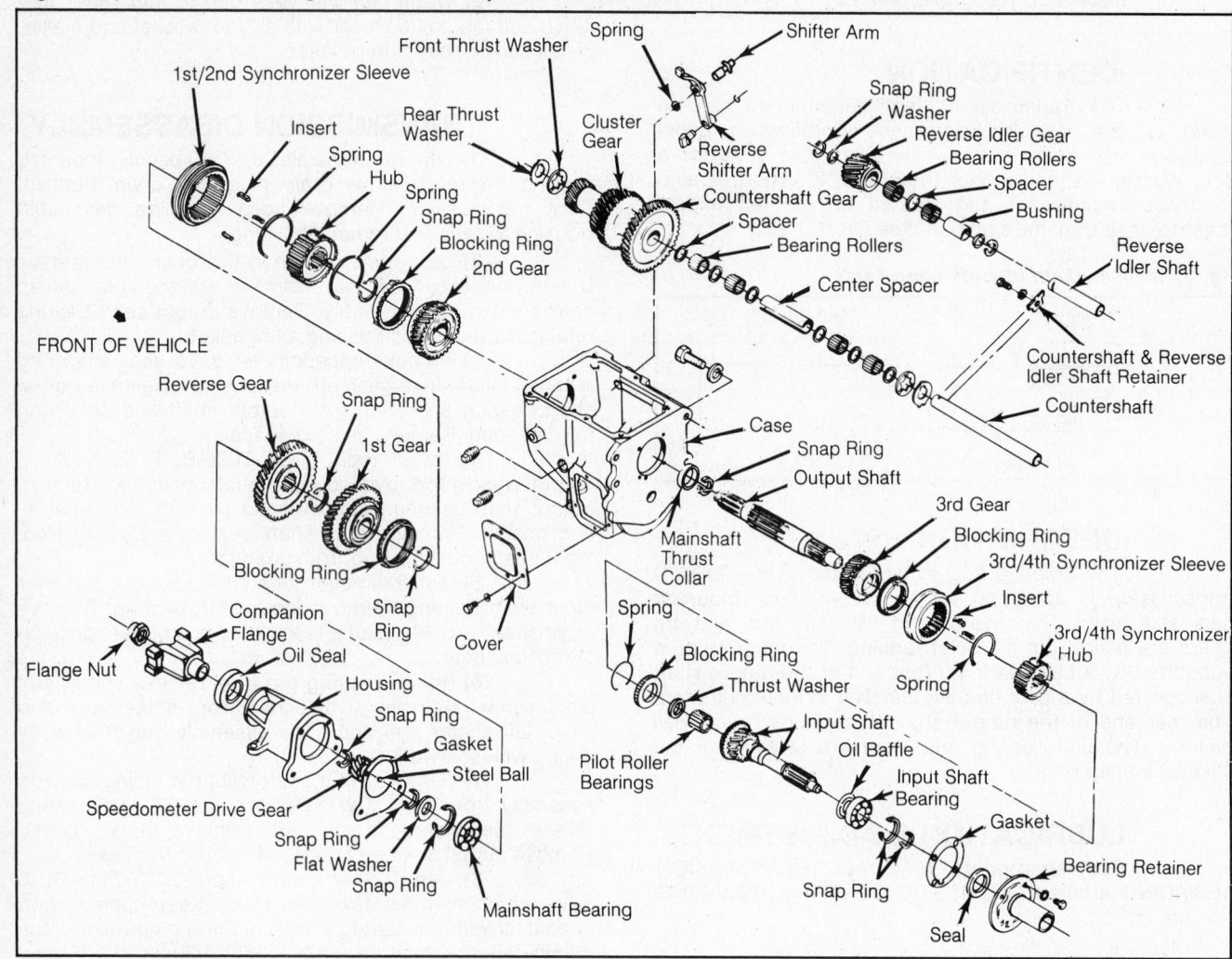

COMPONENT DISASSEMBLY & REASSEMBLY

INPUT SHAFT

Disassembly

Remove thrust spacer and pilot rollers from gear bore. Using a puller, remove input shaft ball bearing. Remove oil baffle.

Reassembly

Press ball bearing and oil baffle onto input shaft and against gear. Coat bore of gear with grease, and place 22 pilot rollers in bore. Install thrust spacer in bore against rollers. Use grease to hold it in position.

OUTPUT SHAFT

Disassembly

1) Remove snap ring. Slide 3rd/4th synchronizer assembly, blocking ring, and 3rd gear off shaft. Place output shaft in an arbor press and press reverse gear off shaft or pull reverse gear off shaft with puller.

2) Remove 1st gear selective snap ring. Slide 1st gear and blocking ring off output shaft. Remove 1st/2nd gear synchronizer snap ring. Slide synchronizer off shaft.

3) Remove snap ring from rear of 2nd gear. Remove blocking ring and synchronizer gear from output shaft.

Reassembly

1) Hold shaft in a vertical position with front of shaft down, and slide 2nd gear onto shaft (gear cone toward rear). Install selective snap ring of .092-.094" (2.34-2.39 mm) onto output shaft at rear of 2nd gear.

2) Place a blocking ring in 1st/2nd synchronizer assembly next to side of hub with counterbore. Make sure that ring slots are aligned with insert.

3) Hold blocking ring in 1st/2nd synchronizer assembly (with ring slots aligned with inserts) on side with hub counterbore and install assembly on output shaft. The hub counterbore must be toward 2nd gear. Install thickest selective snap ring that can be fit into groove.

4) Install second blocking ring in synchronizer assembly, making sure that ring slots are aligned with inserts. Install 1st gear (coned portion toward 1st/2nd synchronizer assembly) and .101-.103" (2.57-2.61 mm) thick snap ring on shaft.

5) Mount output shaft in a press and press reverse gear (longer hub toward 1st gear) on shaft. Press rear bearing cone on output shaft. If output shaft bearing

BORG-WARNER 4-SPEED MODEL T19B/D (Cont.)

is to be replaced, be sure it is a maximum load-rated bearing.

6) Remove output shaft from press. Install 3rd gear (cone toward front). Place a blocking ring in 3rd/4th synchronizer assembly on side with larger hub diameter. Make sure that slots are aligned with inserts.

7) Hold blocking ring in position, and slide synchronizer assembly onto output shaft. Blocking ring and large hub diameter must be toward 3rd gear. Install thrust race on shaft against synchronizer hub. The flange must be toward front. Install thrust bearing against race.

8) Apply grease to face of blocking ring and install it on shaft and in 3rd/4th synchronizer assembly.

COUNTERSHAFT
Disassembly

Remove dummy shaft, bearing rollers, bearing spacers, and center spacer from countershaft gear.

Reassembly

1) Slide long bearing spacer into countershaft bore and insert dummy shaft in spacer. Dummy shaft should be lubricated liberally with grease.

2) Hold gear in a vertical position and install one of the bearing spacers. Position the 22 pilot bearing rollers in gear bore. *See Fig. 3.*

Fig. 3: Countershaft Gear Bearing Rollers Installation

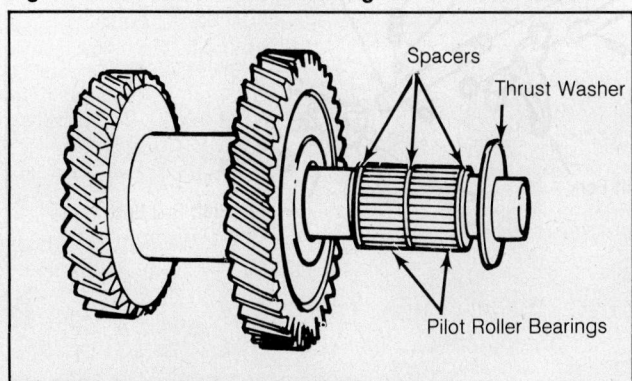

Install 22 rollers, a spacer, and 22 more rollers.

3) Place a spacer on top of rollers and install 22 pilot bearing rollers and another spacer. Coat face of large thrust washer with grease.

4) Hold a large thrust washer against the end of countershaft gear to prevent rollers from dropping out and turn assembly over. Install rollers, spacers, and thrust washer in the other end of gear.

REVERSE IDLER GEAR
Disassembly

1) Check idler gear roller bearings for roughness by holding bushing to prevent its turning while rotating gear. The gear should then be installed on shaft to check for roughness between shaft and bushing.

2) If gear turns freely and smoothly, disassembly of unit is not necessary. If any roughness is noticed, disassemble unit by removing snap ring from one end of gear.

3) Remove idler gear bearing rollers, thrust washers, bearing spacer, bushing, and remaining snap ring from gear.

Reassembly

1) Install snap ring in one end of idler gear and set gear on end, with snap ring at bottom. Position a

thrust washer in gear on top snap ring. Coat outside of bushing with grease and install bushing on top of washer.

2) Insert 37 bearing rollers between bushing and gear bore. Install a spacer on top of rollers and install 37 more rollers. Place remaining thrust washer on rollers and install snap ring.

1ST/2ND & 3RD/4TH SYNCHRONIZER HUBS
Disassembly

Remove spring from each side of assembly, and remove the 3 inserts. Slide hub out of sleeve.

Reassembly

1) Install gear clutch hub in sleeve. On 1st/2nd synchro, hub counterbore should be on the same side as sleeve chamfer. On 3rd/4th synchro, the 2 grooves on chamfered portion of clutch sleeve can be assembled in either direction on hub. Place 3 inserts in hub slots. *See Fig. 4.*

Fig. 4: Synchronizer Hub and Sleeve Assembly

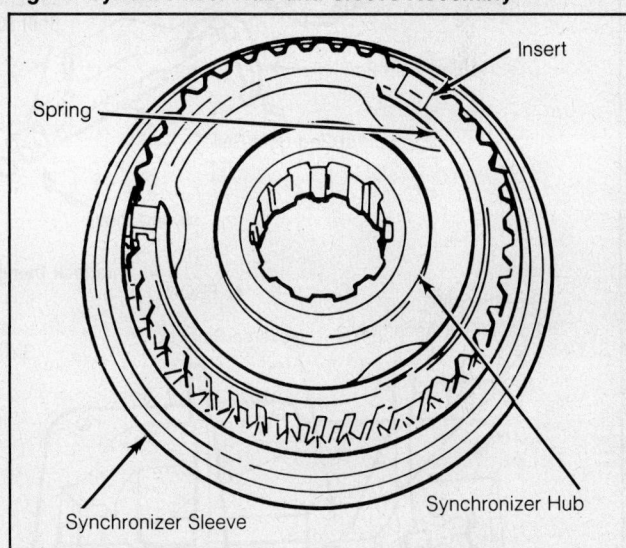

Hub counterbore should be on the side as sleeve chamfer.

2) Hook end of spring under an insert and position spring around hub and under each inserts. Turn assembly over and hook end of second spring over the other end of insert used for hooking first spring.

3) Position spring around hub and under each insert, but on opposite direction of first spring.

GEAR SHIFT HOUSING
Disassembly

1) Remove gear shift lever housing cap and lift lever out of housing. Be sure all shafts are in neutral before disassembly. Remove spring pins from shift forks and shift rail ends. Remove expansion plugs from ends of housing.

2) Tap shift rails out of housing while holding one hand over holes in housing to prevent loss of poppet springs and balls. Remove shift rail ends and forks. Lift the 2 shaft interlock plungers and pin out of housing.

3) To disassemble reverse shift rail end, remove circlip to release plunger and spring. Remove cotter pin, spring, and ball.

Manual Transmissions

BORG-WARNER 4-SPEED MODEL T19B/D (Cont.)

Fig. 5: *Exploded View of Gear Shift Housing and Shift Rail Locations*

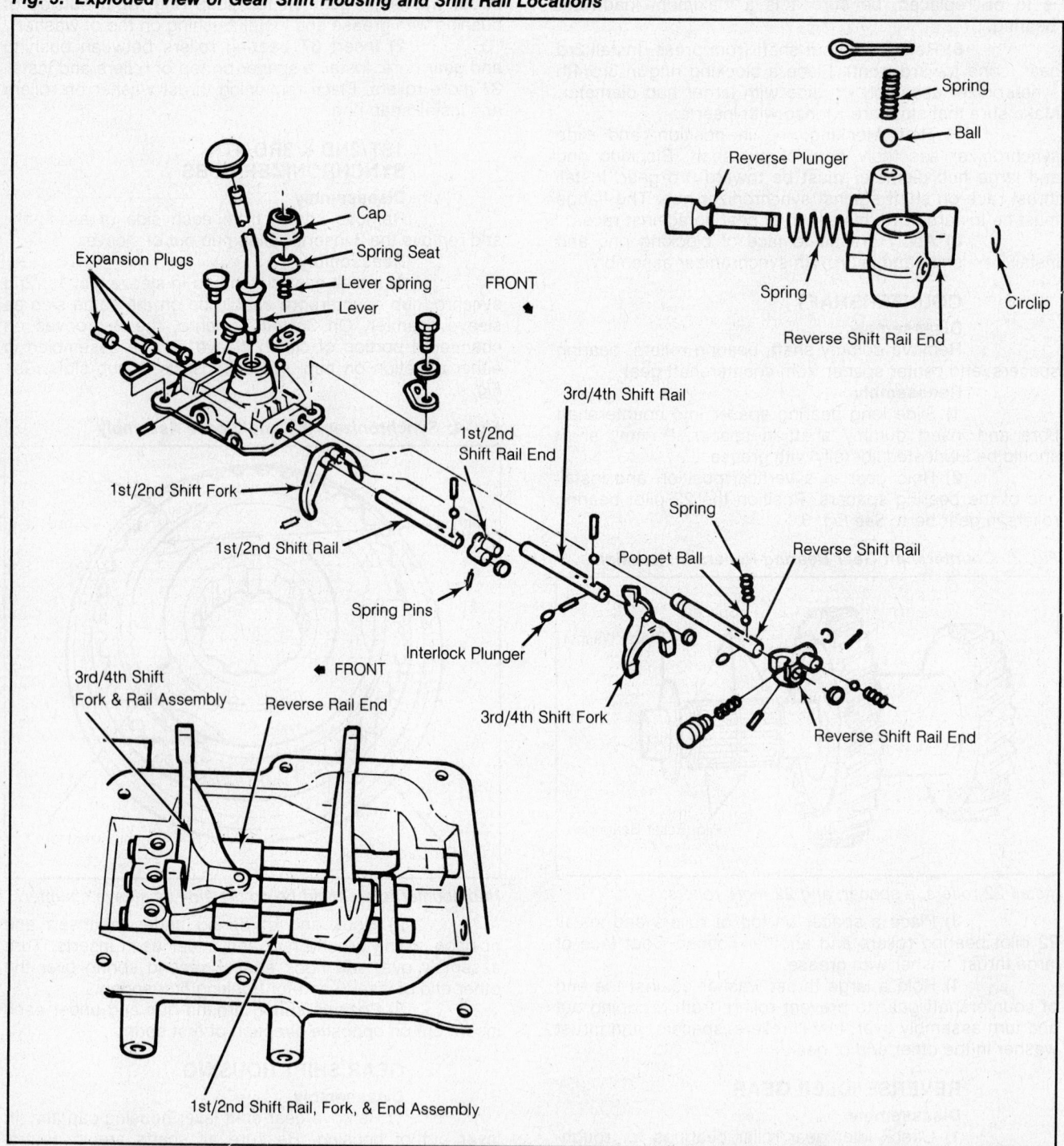

Reassembly

1) Position notched end of 1st/2nd shift rail through rear bore of housing. Slide 1st/2nd shift fork (use outer hole) onto shift rail. DO NOT slide shaft into its bore at front end at this time.

2) The 3 poppet notches should face the top of housing. Slide 1st/2nd shift rail end into rail. Place poppet spring and ball in hole at front of cover. Depress ball and spring, and slide rail into its bore over ball.

3) Drive a spring pin through hole in 1st/2nd shift rail end and into hole in rail. Secure shift fork to rail with spring pin. Slide shift rail to its neutral position (center poppet).

4) Install interlock plunger in housing making sure that end of plunger is in the side notch of 1st/2nd shift rail. Install 3rd/4th shift rail (notched end toward front) in center bore of housing, and assemble shift fork, interlock pin, and poppet spring and ball.

5) Note that 3rd/4th shift rail passes through a second hole in 1st/2nd shift fork and that poppet notches are toward housing top. Secure 3rd/4th shift fork to rail

BORG-WARNER 4-SPEED MODEL T19B/D (Cont.)

with a spring pin. Slide rail to neutral position (center poppet).

6) Install interlock plunger and make sure it is positioned in notch in 3rd/4th shift rail. Assemble reverse plunger and spring in reverse shift rail end. Retain with a circlip inserted in plunger groove.

7) Assemble ball, spring, and cotter pin in shift rail end. Install reverse shift rail (notched end toward front), reverse shift rail end, poppet spring, and ball in housing.

8) Note that the 2 poppet notches are towards the housing top. Secure shift rail end to rail with a spring pin. Slide rail to neutral position. Install expansion plugs into the 3 shift rail openings at each end of housing.

9) Install gear shift lever, spring, spring seat, and lever housing cap.

TRANSMISSION REASSEMBLY

1) Coat all parts, especially bearings, with transmission lubricant to prevent scoring when transmission is first operated. Start countershaft (small end first) into its bore at rear of case. Insert shaft just enough to position rear countershaft steel thrust washer on shaft and against case.

2) Apply grease to washer to hold it in position. Using reverse idler shaft as a temporary holding tool, insert small end of shaft into front countershaft bore just enough to hold front countershaft steel thrust washer in position. Install thrust washer.

NOTE: Ensure that the notch in thrust washers are aligned with the boss at each end of case.

3) Position countershaft gear assembly in case. DO NOT lose any rollers. Slide out reverse idler shaft and countershaft gear dummy shaft by installing countershaft gear from the rear. Keep shaft ends in contact so that rollers cannot drop out of position. DO NOT drive countershaft completely into press fit at rear of case at this time.

4) Position reverse idler gear assembly in case and install idler (small end of shaft toward front). Shift fork groove of gear should be toward front of case. DO NOT drive shaft completely into position.

5) Make sure that countershaft and reverse idler gear shaft are properly aligned so that retainer can be positioned in shaft slots. Drive shafts into position in case. Install retainer and bolt. Install output shaft assembly in case.

6) With output shaft shifted slightly to the right, position reverse shifter arm and shoe assembly on reverse idler gear. Install pivot screw through hole in left side of case and into shifter arm hole. Install clip to retain shifter arm to pivot. Center output shaft to case bore.

7) Install input shaft through front bore with flats on shaft facing upward. When past countershaft, turn input shaft so flats are facing downward. Guide input shaft onto output shaft. Install input shaft oil baffle.

8) Install dummy bearing tool (T75L-7025-Q) on transmission input shaft. This tool is necessary to keep input and output shafts in alignment when installing output shaft bearing.

9) Assemble locating snap ring to outer race of output shaft bearing in groove provided. Using tools (T75L-7025-B & L) install output shaft bearing. Install flat washer against rearward face of output shaft bearing.

NOTE: The properly installed washer will be external to the main body of transmission.

10) Install snap ring at rearward surface of washer in output shaft groove provided. Remove dummy bearing from input shaft. Install input shaft bearing. Install snap ring. Use the thickest select fit snap rings which will fit on bearing.

11) Install input shaft bearing spacer, retainer gasket and retainer. Tighten bolts. Position speedometer drive gear and spacer (if used) on output shaft over lock ball. Install speedometer drive gear retaining snap ring.

12) Using a new gasket install output shaft bearing retainer (or extension housing). Tighten bolts. Lubricate retainer, bushing, seal, and U-joint flange with grease. Install U-joint flange. Lock transmission in 2 gears and tighten retaining nut.

13) Install gear shift housing assembly (with housing assembly and unit shifted into second gear). Fill transmission to proper level. Add 1/2 pint (1/4L) of lubricant through speedometer cable hole in rear transmission extension housing.

TIGHTENING SPECIFICATIONS

Application	Ft. Lbs. (N.m)
Countershaft and Reverse Idler Shaft	
Retainer Bolt	25-35 (34-47)
Drain Plug	25-40 (34-54)
Filler Plug	25-40 (34-54)
Flywheel Housing-to-Engine	40-50 (54-67)
Gear Shift Housing-to-Case	25-35 (34-47)
Input Shaft Bearing Retainer	15-25 (21-34)
Output Shaft Bearing	
Retainer-to-Case	34-45 (46-61)
Output Shaft Flange Nut	75-115 (102-149)
Power Take Off Cover	25-35 (34-47)
Trans.-to-Flywheel Housing	37-42 (51-56)

Manual Transmissions

CHRYSLER A-460 & A-525 MANUAL TRANSAXLE

Chrysler
  Caravelle, Laser, LeBaron,
  LeBaron GTS, New Yorker
Dodge
  Aries, Caravan, Charger, Daytona,
  Omni, Lancer, Ram Van, 600
Plymouth
  Horizon, Reliant, Turismo, Voyager

IDENTIFICATION

The transaxle model, assembly number, build date, and final-drive ratio are stamped on a tag that is attached to the steel end-cover on the 4-speed, and the differential cover on 5-speeds. The last 8 digits of the vehicle identification number are stamped on a raised boss on top of clutch housing area.

DESCRIPTION

The A-460 transaxle has 4 forward speeds, the A-525 has five. These manual transaxles are fully synchronized and combine gear reduction, ratio selection and differential functions in 1 unit housed in a die-cast aluminum case.

Larger diameter 1st/2nd synchronizers and 1st/2nd stop rings provide greater capacity and reduce 1st/2nd gear shift effort. The larger diameter synchronizer utilizes a cast iron 1st/2nd shift fork and plastic pads, or "struts", that are wider than the other shift fork struts on the transaxle. All synchronizers use a "winged" strut design that prevents the struts from popping out of position.

LUBRICATION & ADJUSTMENT

See appropriate MANUAL TRANSMISSION SERVICING article in DOMESTIC GENERAL SERVICING section.

TROUBLE SHOOTING

See MANUAL TRANSMISSION TROUBLE SHOOTING article in DOMESTIC GENERAL SERVICING section.

SERVICE (IN VEHICLE)

SPEEDOMETER PINION GEAR

NOTE: Speedometer pinion gear is located in right extension housing. Speedometer pinion must be removed before removing right-side drive axle shaft.

Fig. 1: Cutaway View of A-460 4-Speed Manual Transaxle

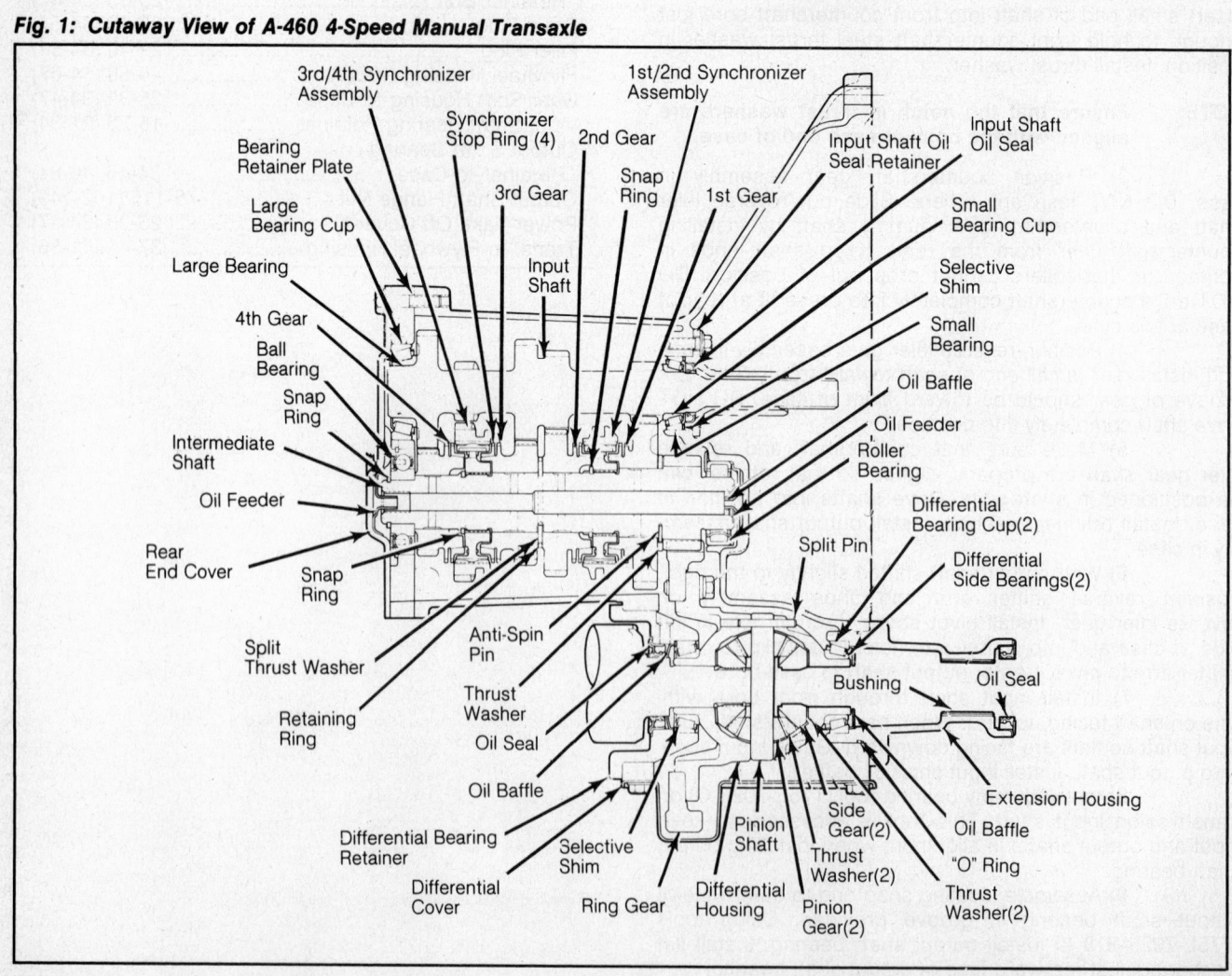

CHRYSLER A-460 & A-525 MANUAL TRANSAXLE (Cont.)

Fig. 2: Cutaway View of A-525 5-Speed Transaxle

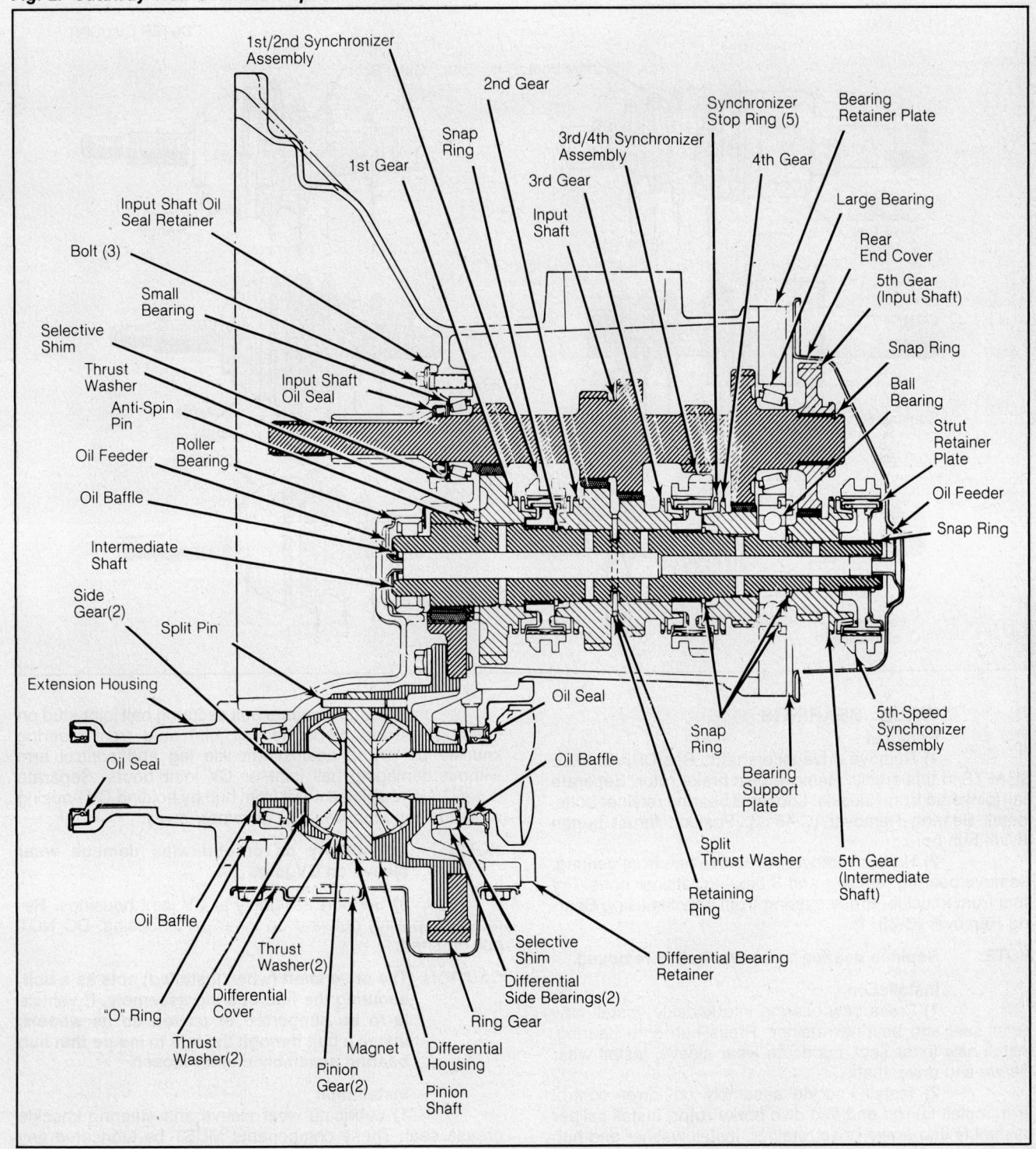

Removal

Remove bolt and washer securing speedometer pinion adapter in extension housing. With cable housing connected, carefully work adapter and pinion out of extension housing. Remove retainer and remove pinion from adapter.

Seal Replacement

If transmission oil is found in cable housing, install a new speedometer pinion and seal assembly. If oil is found between cable and adapter, replace small "O" ring on cable.

Installation

Before installing pinion, adapter and cable assembly, make sure adapter flange and its mating areas on extension housing are clean. Dirt or sand will cause misalignment, resulting in speedometer pinion gear damage. Install and tighten bolt.

3-32

Manual Transmissions
CHRYSLER A-460 & A-525 MANUAL TRANSAXLE (Cont.)

Fig. 3: Axle Shaft Identification

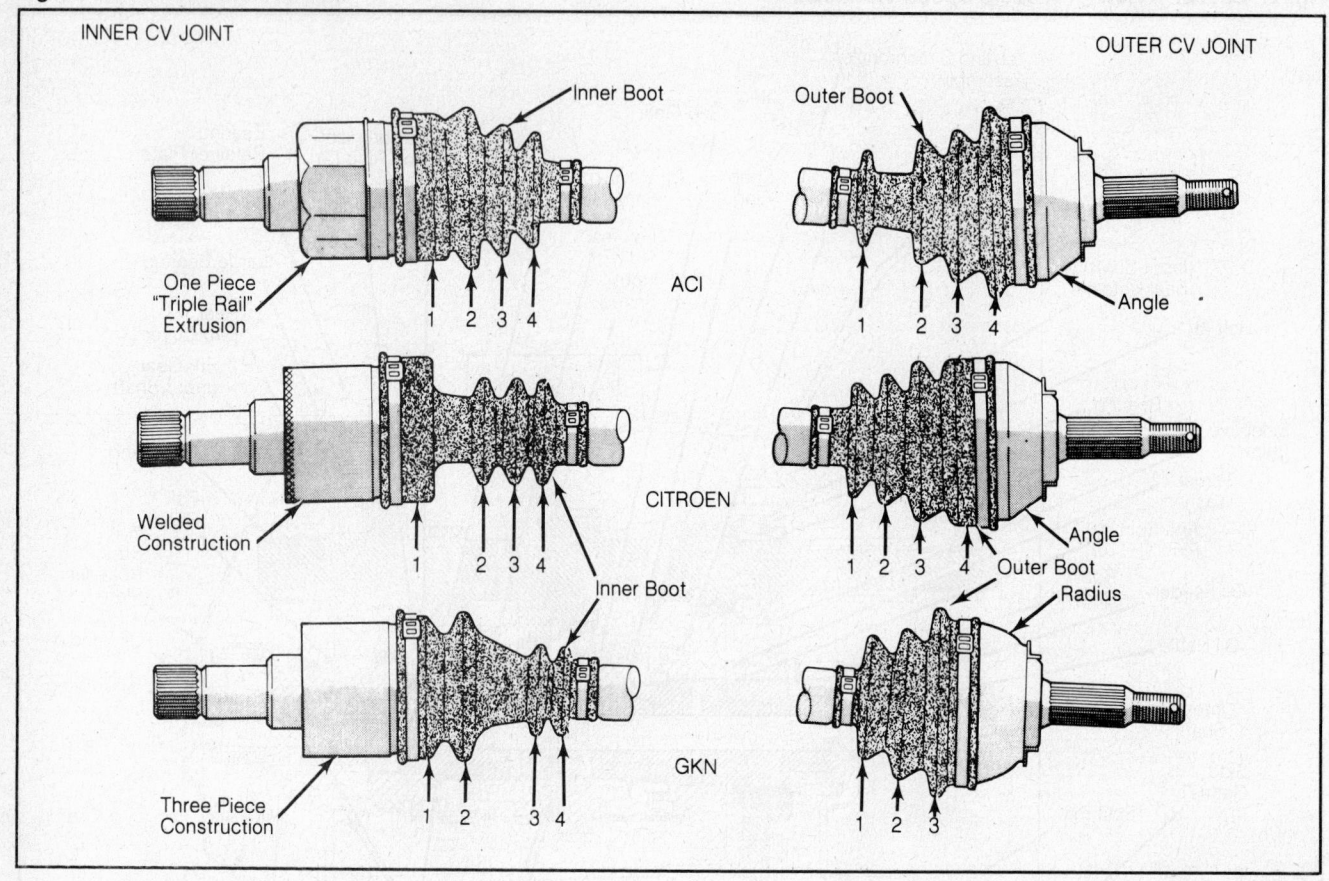

WHEEL BEARINGS
Removal

1) Remove drive axle shafts. See DRIVE AXLE SHAFTS in this article. Remove disc brake rotor. Separate ball joint stud from knuckle. Loosen 3 bearing retainer bolts. Install Bearing Remover (C-4811). Position thrust button inside hub bore.

2) Tighten remover to remove hub from bearing. Remove bearing remover and 3 bearing retainer bolts. Pry seal from knuckle. Press bearing from knuckle using Bearing Remover (C-4811).

NOTE: Replace bearing whenever hub is removed.

Installation

1) Press new bearing into knuckle. Install new outer seal and bearing retainer. Press hub onto bearing. Install new inner seal. Lubricate wear sleeve. Install wear sleeve and drive shaft.

2) Install knuckle assembly on lower control arm. Install tie rod end and disc brake rotor. Install caliper assembly and brake hose retainer. Install washer and hub nut. Tighten to specification. Install spring washer, lock nut and cotter pin

DRIVE AXLE SHAFTS
Removal

1) Remove hub retaining nuts at wheel assemblies. Drive shafts are retained in differential side gears by constant force of spring in inboard CV joint. To remove right-side drive shaft, first remove speedometer pinion.

2) Remove clamp bolt securing ball joint stud on steering knuckle. Separate ball joint stud from steering knuckle by prying against knuckle leg and control arm without damaging ball joint or CV joint boots. Separate outer CV joint splined shaft from hub by holding CV housing while moving knuckle (hub) assembly away.

NOTE: Do not pry on or otherwise damage wear sleeve on CV joint.

3) Support assembly at CV joint housings. Remove by pulling outward on inner joint housing. DO NOT pull on shaft.

CAUTION: The drive shaft (when installed) acts as a bolt, securing the hub/bearing assembly. If vehicle is to be supported or moved on its wheels, install a bolt through the hub to insure that hub bearing assembly cannot loosen.

Installation

1) Lubricate wear sleeve and steering knuckle grease seal. These components MUST be lubricated any time knuckle and driveshaft are separated.

2) Hold inner joint assembly at housing while aligning and guiding inner joint spline into transaxle (or intermediate shaft assembly on Turbo models). If equipped with ACI CV joint, ensure that tripod is engaged in housing and boot is not twisted.

3) To install outer CV joint, push knuckle (hub) assembly out and install splined outer CV joint shaft in hub. Reinstall knuckle assembly on ball joint stud. Install and tighten clamp bolt.

CHRYSLER A-460 & A-525 MANUAL TRANSAXLE (Cont.)

Fig. 4: Exploded View of Front Axle Drive Shaft Assembly

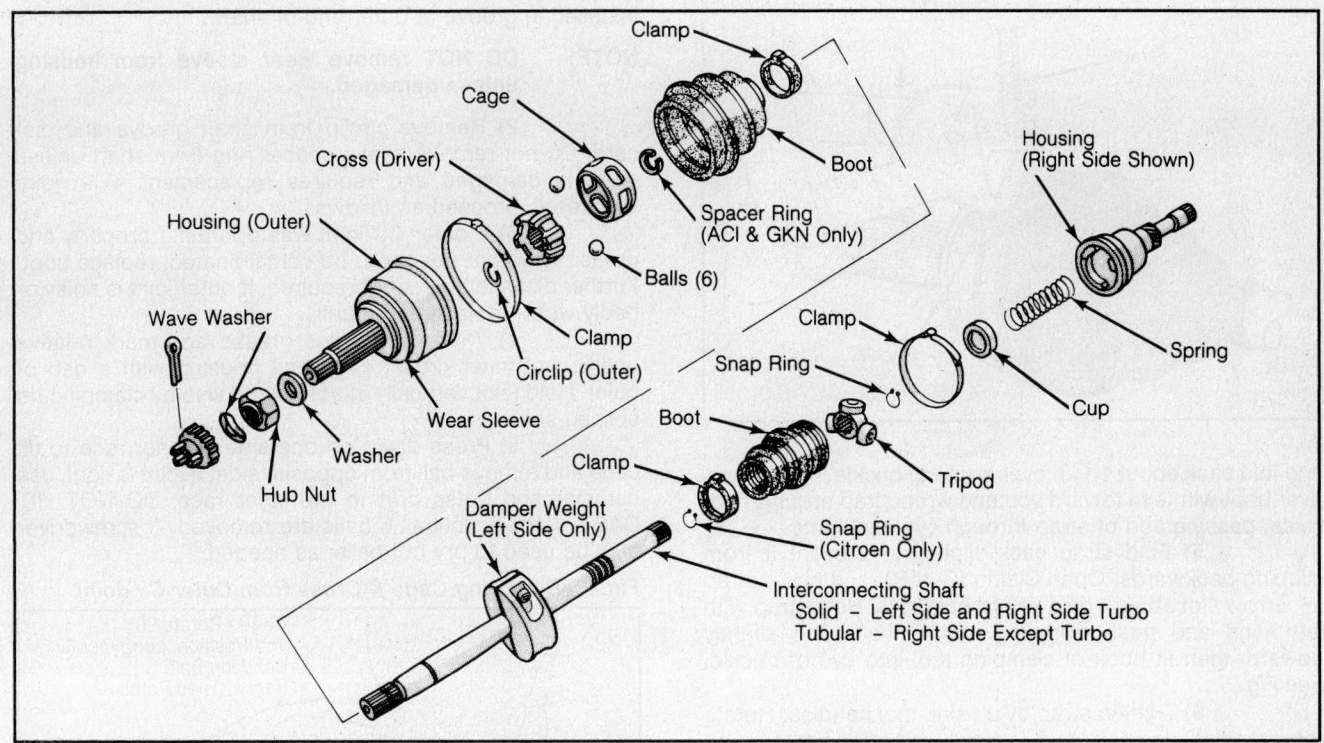

4) Install speedometer pinion gear. Install and tighten hub retaining nut. Check transaxle fluid level and add as needed.

5) If inboard boot is collapsed or deformed, boot must be vented. Remove boot clamp (if rubber clamp is used, venting may be accomplished without removing clamp) and insert a blunt, small diameter rod between boot and axle shaft.

6) Squeeze boot to remove air pockets, ensuring that no dirt enters, or grease escapes from boot. Install new clamp.

INNER CV JOINT
Disassembly
1) With axle shaft assembly removed from vehicle, remove clamps and pull back boots to provide access to tripod retention system. On ACI and GKN joints, bend retaining tabs away from rollers. On Citroen joints, slightly deform retaining ring at each roller.

2) Support housing as retention spring pushes it off of tripod. Hold rollers in position when removing housing to prevent rollers from falling off of studs. Secure rollers to studs by wrapping with tape. If a new retainer ring is to be used on Citroen joints, carefully cut away old retainer ring.

3) Remove snap ring from end of shaft and remove tripod. Tap tripod with brass punch and small hammer as needed to remove. Remove as much grease as possible from assembly. Inspect joint housing, ball raceway, tripod components, spring, spring cup and rounded end of shaft for excessive wear. Replace components as needed.

Reassembly
1) Slide new rubber seal onto stub shaft, past splines, and seat in groove (Turbo models only). Slide small rubber clamp onto shaft (some ACI or GKN joints), or install small metal clamp or buckle. Slide end of boot over shaft.

2) On tubular shafts (right side except Turbo), position boot lip even with locating mark on shaft. On solid shafts (left side and right side Turbo), position small boot end in machined groove in shaft.

3) Clamp boot in place by positioning rubber clamp over boot, or by tightening metal clamp. If using a bridge-type clamp, position clamp over boot, making sure that it is properly located over boot and shaft, and is not twisted. Locate clamp tangs in slot, making clamp as tight as possible by hand. Complete tightening by clamping bridge with Clamp (C-4124). *See Fig. 5.*

Fig. 5: Tightening Bridge-Type Boot Clamp

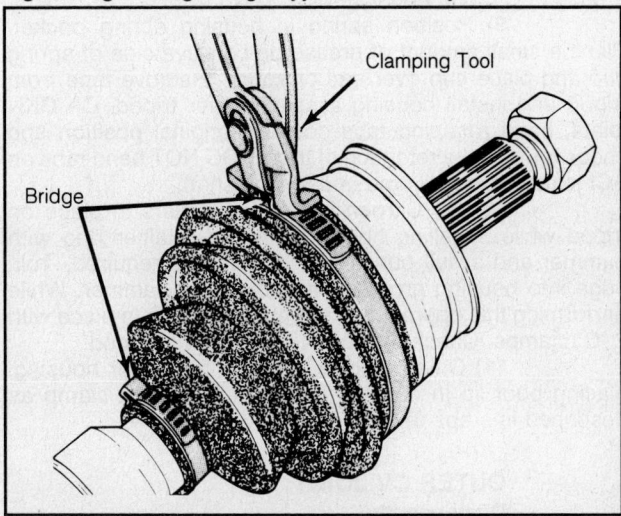

Tighten by hand before using clamping tool.

4) If using Citroen-type binding clamp, wrap binding strap around boot twice, plus an additional 2 1/2", then remove strap. Pass one end of strap through buckle

3-34

Manual Transmissions
CHRYSLER A-460 & A-525 MANUAL TRANSAXLE (Cont.)

Fig. 6: Tightening Strap on Citroen-Type Boot Clamp

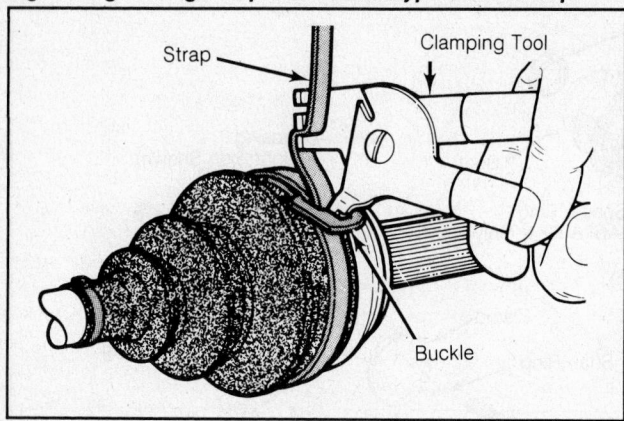

and fold back about 1 1/8" over inside of buckle. Place strap over boot with eye toward you and wrap strap around boot twice, passing end of strap through eye each time.

5) Fold strap back slightly to prevent it from slipping backwards. Open Clamp (C-4653) and place strap in narrow slot about 1/2" away from buckle. Hold strap with left hand and push clamping tool forward and slightly upward, then fit hook of clamping tool into eye of buckle. *See Fig. 6.*

6) Tighten strap by closing tool handles. Rotate tool (handles) downward while slowly releasing pressure on handles. Allow handles to open progressively. Open tool entirely and remove sideways from strap.

7) If strap is not tight enough, repeat procedure, always with tool about 1/2" away from buckle. When strap is tight enough, remove tool and cut strap off about 1/8" away from buckle. Complete by folding strap back neatly (end of strap must not extend beyond eye).

8) Slide tripod on shaft with non-chamfered end (ACI and GKN) facing retainer groove at end of shaft (both ends of Citroen tripod are the same). Install snap ring in groove at end of shaft. Lubricating grease is provided in Boot Joint Kit. Distribute 1 packet (ACI), 2 packets (GKN) or 2/3 packet (Citroen) of grease in boot. Distribute remaining grease in CV joint housing.

9) Position spring in housing spring pocket. Place a small amount of grease on concave side of spring cup and place cup over end of spring. Remove tape from tripod and install housing assembly over tripod. On GKN joints, bend retaining tabs down to original position and check for positive retention of tripod. DO NOT bend tabs on ACI joints. Boot will hold housing on shaft.

10) On Citroen joints, hold rollers in place on tripod while installing housing. Reform retainer ring with hammer and a dull punch. If a new ring is required, "roll" edge into housing groove with punch and hammer. While performing this operation, hold retaining collar in place with 2 "C" clamps. Check for positive retention of tripod.

11) On all models, position boot over housing, placing boot lip in housing groove. Install boot clamp as described in steps **3)** through **7)**.

OUTER CV JOINT
Disassembly
1) Cut boot clamp on boot and discard. Wipe grease away to expose joint. Support shaft in soft-jawed vise. Support outer joint. Using a hammer, tap top of joint

body sharply to dislodge joint from internal circlip. Circlip is installed in groove at outer end of shaft.

NOTE: **DO NOT remove wear sleeve from housing unless damaged.**

2) Remove circlip from shaft groove and discard. Do not remove heavy spacer ring from shaft unless shaft is damaged and requires replacement. With joint separated, proceed as follows:

3) If outer CV joint was operating properly and grease does not appear to be contaminated, replace boot. Further disassembly is not required. If outer joint is noisy or badly worn, replace entire unit.

4) Wipe off surplus grease and mark relative position of inner cross, cage and housing with a dab of paint. Hold joint vertically in soft-jawed vise by clamping on splined shaft.

5) Press down on one side of inner race to tilt cage and remove ball from opposite side. If joint is tight, use hammer and brass drift to tap inner race. DO NOT HIT CAGE. Repeat until all 6 balls are removed. A screwdriver may be used to pry out balls, as needed.

Fig. 7: Removing Cage & Cross from Outer CV Joint

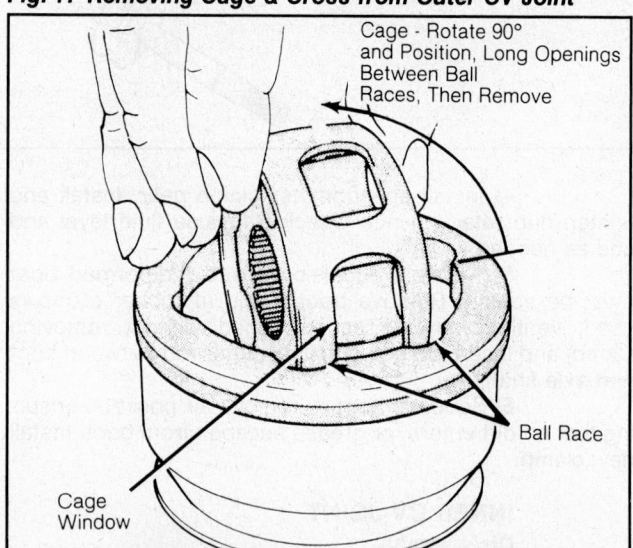

6) Tilt cage and inner race assembly vertically and position 2 opposing cage windows in area between ball grooves. *See Fig. 7.* Remove cage and inner race assembly by pulling upward, away from housing.

7) Turn inner cross (driver) 90° to cage and align 1 spherical land of race with cage window. Raise land into cage window and remove inner race by swinging out.

Cleaning & Inspection
1) Wash all parts in solvent and dry with compressed air. Inspect housing ball races for excessive wear and scoring. Check splined shaft and nut threads for damage. During any service procedure where steering knuckle and axle shaft are separated, thoroughly clean seal and wear sleeve with solvent.

2) Inspect all 6 balls for pitting, cracks, scoring and wear. Dulling of surface is normal. Inspect cage for excesive wear on inside and outside spherical surfaces, surface ripples on cage window, cracks and chipping.

3) Inspect inner race (cross) for excessive wear or scoring of ball races. If any of the preceding is found, the complete CV joint should be replaced.

CHRYSLER A-460 & A-525 MANUAL TRANSAXLE (Cont.)

Fig. 8: Exploded View of Outer CV Joint

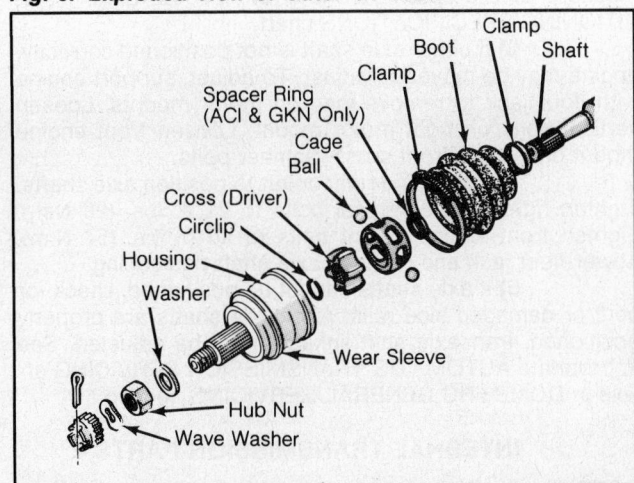

NOTE: Polished areas in races (cross and housing) and on cage spheres are normal and do not indicate need for joint replacement unless they are suspected of causing noise and/or vibration.

Reassembly

1) If wear sleeve was removed, position new sleeve on housing and install with Installer (C-4698). Lightly oil all components before reassembling outer joint. Align parts according to paint markings made at disassembly.

2) Insert 1 inner race (cross) land into a cage window and feed race into cage. Pivot cross 90° to complete cage assembly.

3) Align opposing cage window with housing land and feed race assembly into housing. Pivot cage 90° to complete installation. When properly assembled, large

Fig. 9: Cutaway View of Outer CV Joint Showing Correct Cage and Cross Installation

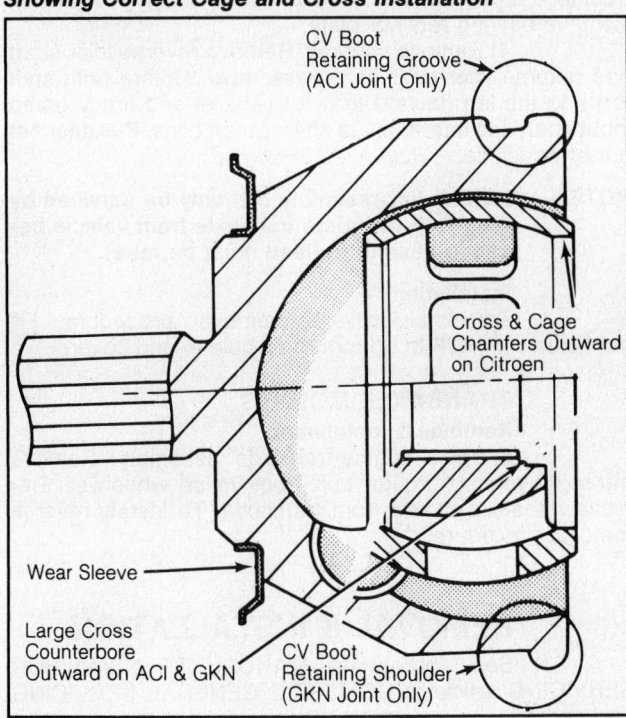

cross counterbore (ACI and GKN) or cross and cage chamfers (Citroen) will be facing outward from joint. *See Fig. 9.*

4) Apply lubricant to ball races from packet provided in kit and distribute equally between all sides of ball grooves. One packet is sufficient to lubricate joint. Insert balls into races by tilting cage and inner race assembly.

5) Install boot on shaft as described in steps 3) through 7) of INNER CV JOINT REASSEMBLY procedure. Install new circlip (provided with kit) on shaft, using care not to expand or twist clip during installation. Lubricate wear sleeve and steering knuckle grease seal. *See Fig. 10.*

Fig. 10: Lubricating Wear Sleeve and Grease Seal

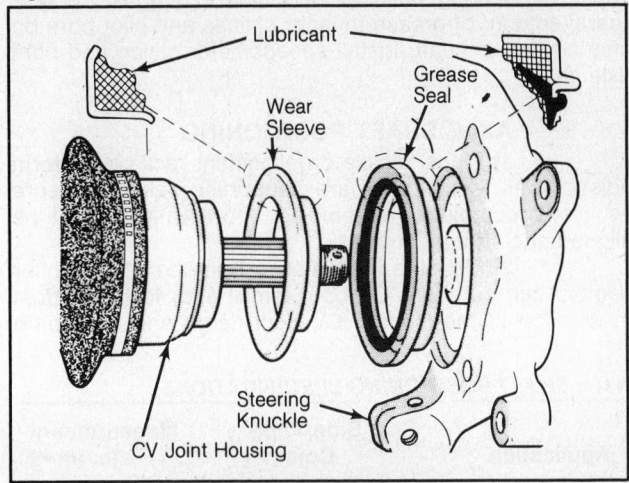

Clean and lubricate sleeve and seal any time knuckle and driveshaft are separated.

6) Install hub nut on end of stub shaft to protect threads. Position outer joint on splined end of shaft, engage splines and tap hub nut sharply with a mallet. Check that circlip is properly seated by attempting to pull joint from shaft.

7) Locate large end of boot over joint housing, checking that boot is not twisted. Install boot clamp as described in steps 3) through 7) of inner CV joint reassembly procedure.

INTERMEDIATE SHAFT ASSEMBLY (TURBO ONLY)
Removal

Remove right axle shaft and speedometer drive pinion as previously described. Remove screws from bearing support-to-engine bracket. Pull intermediate shaft assembly from transaxle.

Disassembly (Universal Joint)

Mark axle shafts for correct reassembly. Remove universal joint retaining clips from inner edge of bearing caps. Use 1 1/8" socket and hammer to remove caps from yoke.

Reassembly

Place universal joint cross between yokes. Position caps and drive into position with hammer, guiding cross into caps. Install new retaining clips.

Disassembly (Bearing Assembly)

Remove 2 bearing assembly-to-bracket screws. Press stub shaft from bearing assembly. Do not damage inner slinger, rubber seal or end of stub shaft. Remove slinger if damaged.

Reassembly

To install slinger, use a 2" (51 mm) diameter by 3" (76 mm) long pipe. Press bearing assembly onto shaft until there is a minimum 1/32" (1 mm) clearance between bearing and slinger. Press outer slinger into position until it bottoms on shoulder of shaft.

Installation

1) Loosely attach support bracket to bearing. Guide axle shaft into transaxle. Attach support bracket assembly to engine and tighten bracket-to-engine bolts to 40 ft. lbs. (54 N.m).

2) Push shaft into transaxle as far as possible. Hold shaft in position and tighten support bracket-to-bearing bolts to 21 ft. lbs. (28 N.m). Apply a liberal amount of grease to inner splines and pilot bore on bearing end of shaft. Install speedometer pinion and right axle shaft.

AXLE SHAFT POSITIONING

1) Place vehicle on alignment rack or platform hoist, so all four wheels are supporting vehicle. Ensure vehicle is completely assembled. Front wheels must be aligned and straight ahead.

2) Measure the distance from the bottom inner edge of the outboard CV boot (small end) to the bottom inner edge of the inboard CV boot (large end). Compare measurement to specifications given in AXLE SHAFT POSITIONING SPECIFICATIONS chart.

3) If either axle shaft is not positioned correctly, engine may be moved to adjust. To adjust, support engine with floor jack to remove load on motor mounts. Loosen vertical bolts on right motor mount. Loosen front engine mount bracket-to-front cross member bolts.

4) Pry engine right or left to position axle shafts. Tighten right engine vertical bolts to 21 ft. lbs. (28 N.m). Tighten front engine mount bolts to 40 ft. lbs. (54 N.m). Lower floor jack and recheck axle shaft positioning.

5) If axle shafts cannot be positioned, check for bent or damaged side rails. After axle shafts are properly positioned, transaxle shift linkage must be adjusted. See appropriate AUTOMATIC TRANSMISSION SERVICING article in DOMESTIC GENERAL SERVICING section.

INTERNAL TRANSMISSION PARTS

NOTE: The selector shaft housing, all synchronizers, intermediate shaft and gears, 5th gear, input shaft, reverse idler gear and shaft, shift forks and pads, shift fork rail and speedometer pinion can be removed without removing transaxle from vehicle.

Removal

1) Disconnect negative battery cable. On Charger, Horizon, Omni and Turismo models, loosen left motor mount. On all models, remove nut attaching shift lever to selector shaft. Remove lever.

2) Remove selector shaft housing bolts, noting position of 2 pilot bolts, and remove selector shaft housing. On A-525 models, remove 5th gear shifter pin, fill plug, end cover, 5th gear synchronizer and input and intermediate shaft 5th gears as described in TRANSAXLE DISASSEMBLY in this article, steps 3) through 5).

3) Raise vehicle on hoist. Remove left wheel and tire. Remove left splash shield. Place drain pan under transaxle and remove end cover (if not already removed). Remove bearing retainer plate.

4) Remove shift rail. Remove reverse idler shaft and reverse idler gear as an assembly. Rotate both shift forks to the left (toward front of vehicle) and firmly grasp input shaft and intermediate shaft assemblies. Pull gear set out of transaxle.

NOTE: Differential assembly can only be serviced by removing complete transaxle from vehicle because bearing preload must be reset.

Installation

To install, reverse removal procedure. Fill transaxle with ATF to bottom of fill hole in end cover.

TRANSAXLE MOUNTS

Removal & Installation

Support engine/transaxle assembly. Remove transaxle mount through bolt from inside wheelwell. Remove transaxle mount from transaxle. To install, reverse removal procedure.

REMOVAL & INSTALLATION

See appropriate MANUAL TRANSMISSION SERVICING article in DOMESTIC GENERAL SERVICING section.

AXLE SHAFT POSITIONING SPECIFICATIONS

Application	Side/Tape Color	Measurement In. (mm)
Caravan, Ram Van & Voyager	Rt./Blue	20.5-20.9 (520-532)
	Lt./Blue	10.0-10.6 (255-270)
	Rt./Green	21.3-21.6 (542-549)
	Lt./Green	10.6-11.2 (270-285)
Charger, Horizon Omni, Turismo (Exc. Turbo)	Rt./Yellow	19.6-20.0 (498-509)
	Lt./Yellow	9.5-10.0 (240-253)
	Rt./Red	18.5-19.0 (469-478)
	Lt./Red	8.2-8.6 (208-218)
	Rt./Green	18.3-18.8 (465-477)
	Lt./Green	8.3-8.7 (211-220)
	Rt./Blue	18.2-18.6 (463-472)
	Lt./Blue	8.0-8.4 (204-213)
All Models With 2.2L Turbo	Rt./Tan	10.1-10.4 (257-265)
	Lt./Silver	10.0-10.6 (254-269)
	Rt./Red	9.5-9.9 (241-252)
	Lt./Yellow	9.4-10.0 (238-255)
	Rt./Org.	8.3-8.7 (211-220)
	Lt./Org.	8.3-8.7 (211-220)
All Others 2.2L	Rt./Blue	19.9-20.3 (498-515)
	Lt./Blue	10.2-10.9 (259-277)
	Rt./Green	18.8-19.1 (477-485)
	Lt./Green	9.0-9.6 (229-244)
	Rt./Org.	19.4-19.7 (492-500)
	Lt./Org.	9.6-10.2 (243-258)
	Rt./White	18.9-19.4 (480-492)
	Lt./White	9.4-10.0 (238-255)
2.6L	Rt./Silver	19.7-20.1 (501-510)
	Lt./Silver	10.0-10.6 (254-269)
	Rt./Yellow	18.9-19.4 (480-492)
	Lt./Yellow	9.4-10.0 (238-255)

CHRYSLER A-460 & A-525 MANUAL TRANSAXLE (Cont.)

TRANSAXLE DISASSEMBLY

1) Place transaxle in holding fixture. Remove differential cover bolts and differential cover. Remove 8 differential bearing retainer bolts. Using Spanner (L-4435), rotate differential bearing retainer to remove retainer.

2) Remove extension housing bolts, then remove extension housing and differential assembly. DO NOT damage bearing cups. Remove 6 selector shaft housing bolts (2 bolts are pilot bolts), then remove housing.

Fig. 11: Removing Differential Bearing Retainer

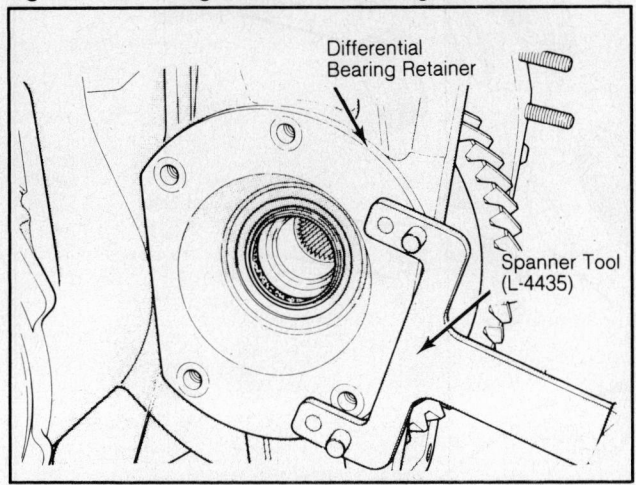

3) Remove 5th gear shifter pin and fill plug (A-525 models). Remove rear end cover bolts and nuts. Using a screwdriver, pry up on cover (at notch on A-460 models) and remove end cover.

4) On A-525 models, remove 5th gear synchronizer strut retainer plate snap ring. Remove retainer plate. Remove synchronizer assembly and shift fork with shift rail. *See Fig. 12.* Using Puller (C-4693), remove 5th gear synchronizer and struts from intermediate shaft. *See Fig. 13.* Remove 5th gear (intermediate shaft).

Fig. 12: Removing 5th Gear Synchronizer Sleeve Assembly

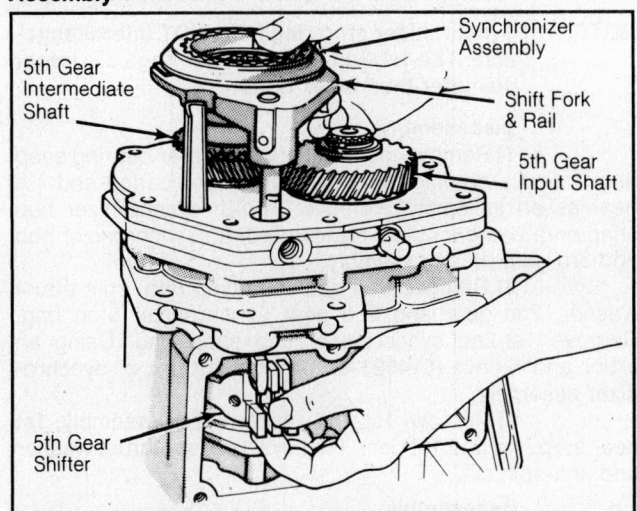

5) Remove input shaft 5th gear snap ring, then remove gear with Pulley Puller (C-4333). Remove 2 bearing support plate bolts and pry off plate.

Fig. 13: Removing 5th Gear Synchronizer

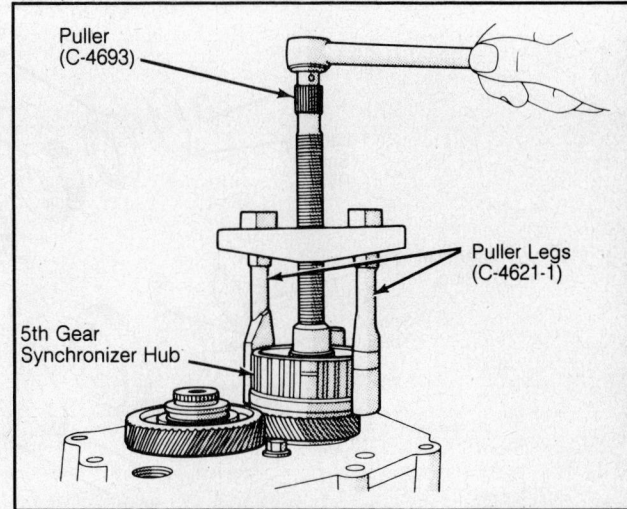

Synchronizer is on intermediate shaft.

6) On all models, remove intermediate shaft rear bearing snap ring. Remove bearing retainer plate (tap with plastic hammer as needed). With retainer plate removed, remove 3rd/4th shift fork rail. Remove reverse idler gear shaft, idler gear and plastic stop as an assembly.

Fig. 14: Removing Reverse Idler Gear Assembly

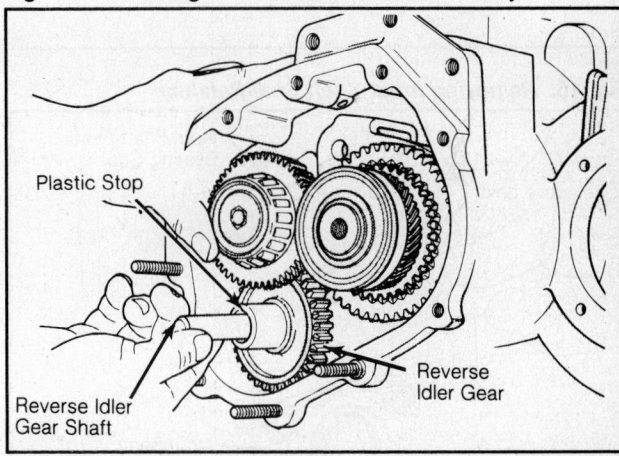

7) Grasp intermediate shaft assembly and input shaft assembly together and remove from transaxle case. Remove shift forks and pads from intermediate shaft assembly.

8) Remove clutch release shaft "E" clip with screwdriver and remove shaft from housing. Separate shaft from release lever by removing "E" clip from end of shaft. Disassemble components. Remove release bearing, fork and bushings from housing.

9) Remove input shaft seal retainer bolts, then remove seal retainer and selective shim. Measure shim thickness for transaxle reassembly reference. Remove reverse shift lever "E" clip, then remove flat washer, wave washer and reverse shift lever.

CLEANING & INSPECTION

1) All parts should be thoroughly washed in cleaning solvent and dried with compressed air. Do not spin

Fig. 15: Disassembled View of Intermediate Shaft Assembly

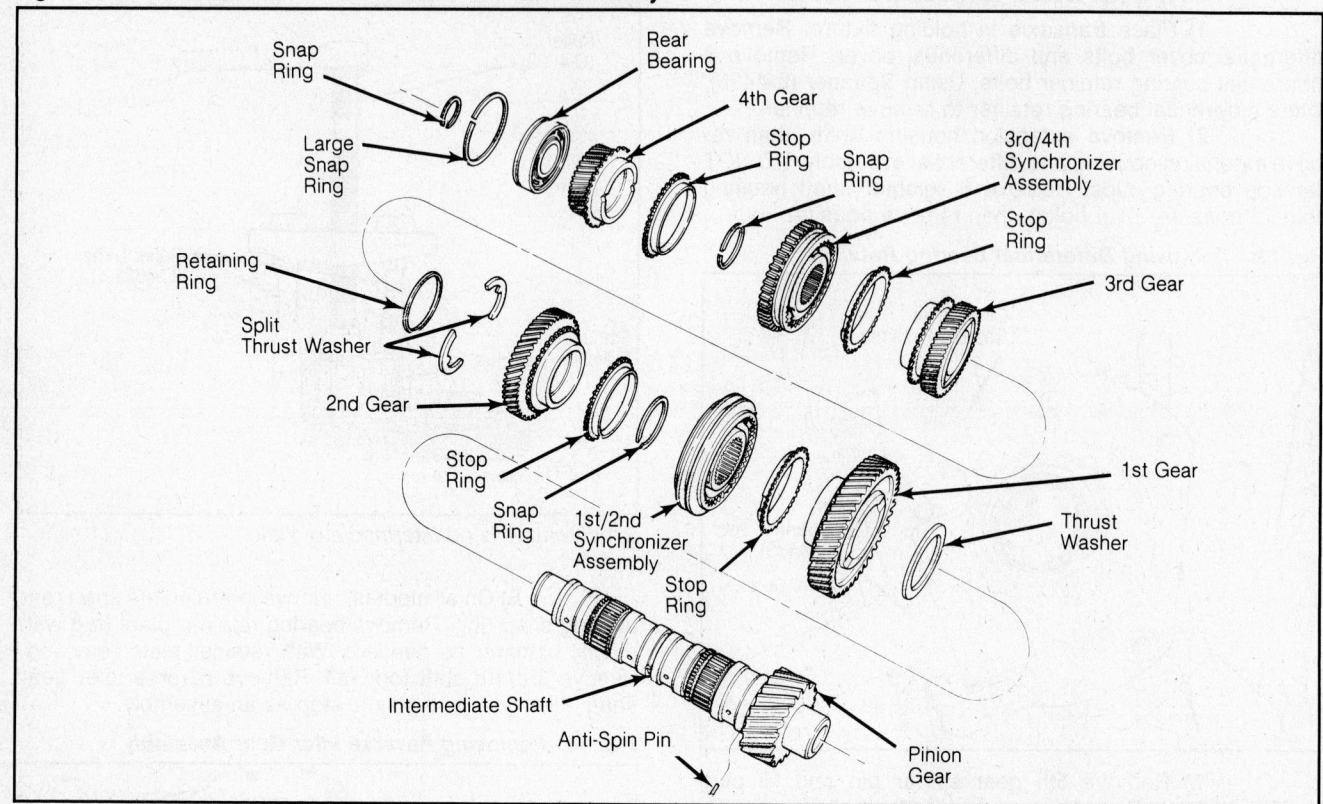

Fig. 16: Removing Input Shaft Seal Retainer

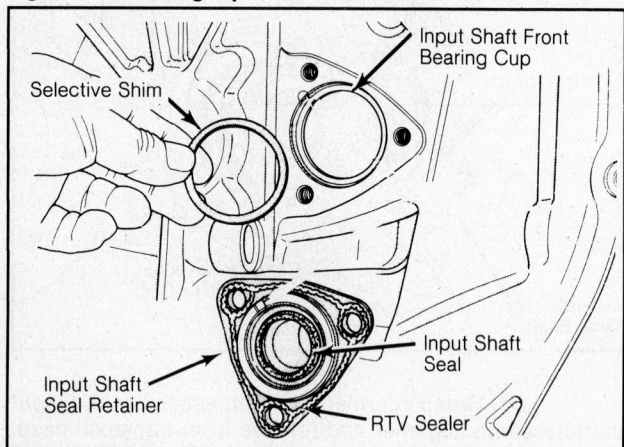

bearings with compressed air. Remove portions of old gaskets with stiff brush or scraper.

2) Clean bearings separately from other parts. Hold bearing races so bearings will not rotate and use soft brush to remove all foreign material. Inspect all bearings, rollers, races and spacers for galling or flat spots. Lubricate bearings with light oil and check for roughness by slowly turning race by hand. Lubricate bearings with light grade oil and wrap in clean paper until ready to reinstall.

3) Examine all gear teeth and splines for chips, wear, breaks, or nicks. Examine case, housing, retainers, and covers for cracks, distortion, or other damage. Inspect thrust washers, snap rings, and snap ring grooves for wear or damage.

4) Check all synchronizers for wear, damage, and proper fit. Coat all moving parts before installation with lubricant and always use new gaskets, oil seals, and snap rings. Replace parts as required.

COMPONENT DISASSEMBLY & REASSEMBLY

INTERMEDIATE SHAFT ASSEMBLY

NOTE: Synchronizer stop rings are NOT interchangeable. The 1st/2nd synchronizer rings are larger diameter than other rings.

Disassembly

1) Remove intermediate shaft rear bearing snap ring. Using a bearing puller, remove rear bearing and 4th gear as an assembly. Remove 3rd/4th synchronizer hub snap ring. Using a puller, remove 3rd/4th synchronizer hub and 3rd gear as an assembly.

2) Remove 2nd gear retaining ring, split thrust washer, 2nd gear and 2nd gear synchronizer stop ring. Remove 1st/2nd synchronizer hub snap ring. Using an arbor and Sleeve (C-4621-3), press shaft out of synchronizer assembly.

3) Remove 1st/2nd synchronizer assembly, 1st gear stop ring and 1st gear. Remove 1st gear thrust washer and anti-spin pin.

Reassembly

Reverse disassembly procedure to reassemble, noting the following:

• Install 1st gear thrust washer with chamfered edge toward pinion gear.

CHRYSLER A-460 & A-525 MANUAL TRANSAXLE (Cont.)

- When assembling 1st/2nd synchronizer assembly and intermediate shaft, fit a 1 7/8" (47.6 mm) diameter pipe, 8 1/2" (21.6 cm) long, over shaft with arbor press against end of pipe.
- Relief on 1st/2nd synchronizer assembly faces toward 2nd gear.
- Ensure that all gears turn freely and have a minimum end

play of .003" (.076 mm).
- Use arbor press and Installer (C-4672 for A-460; L-4507 for A-525) to install rear bearing.

SYNCHRONIZERS
Disassembly

Mark hub and sleeves for reassembly reference. Using care, pry out both synchronizer springs. Separate hubs, sleeve and 3 winged struts, noting their positions. Clean, inspect and replace parts, as needed.

Fig. 17: Removing 1st/2nd Synchronizer Assembly

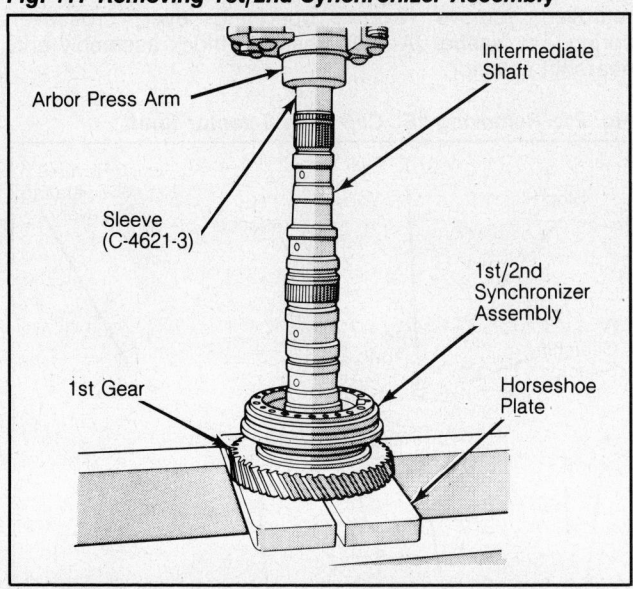

Use Adapter (C-4621-3) between press ram and shaft.

Fig. 19: Assembled View of 3rd/4th Synchronizer Assembly (1st/2nd Synchronizer Similar)

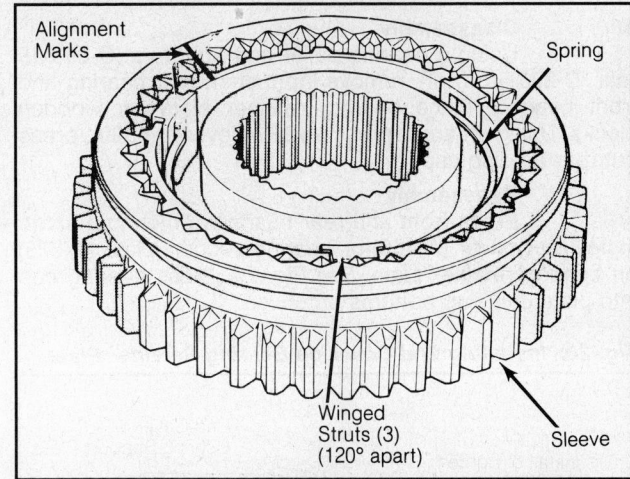

Fig. 18: Disassembled View of 5th Gear Assembly

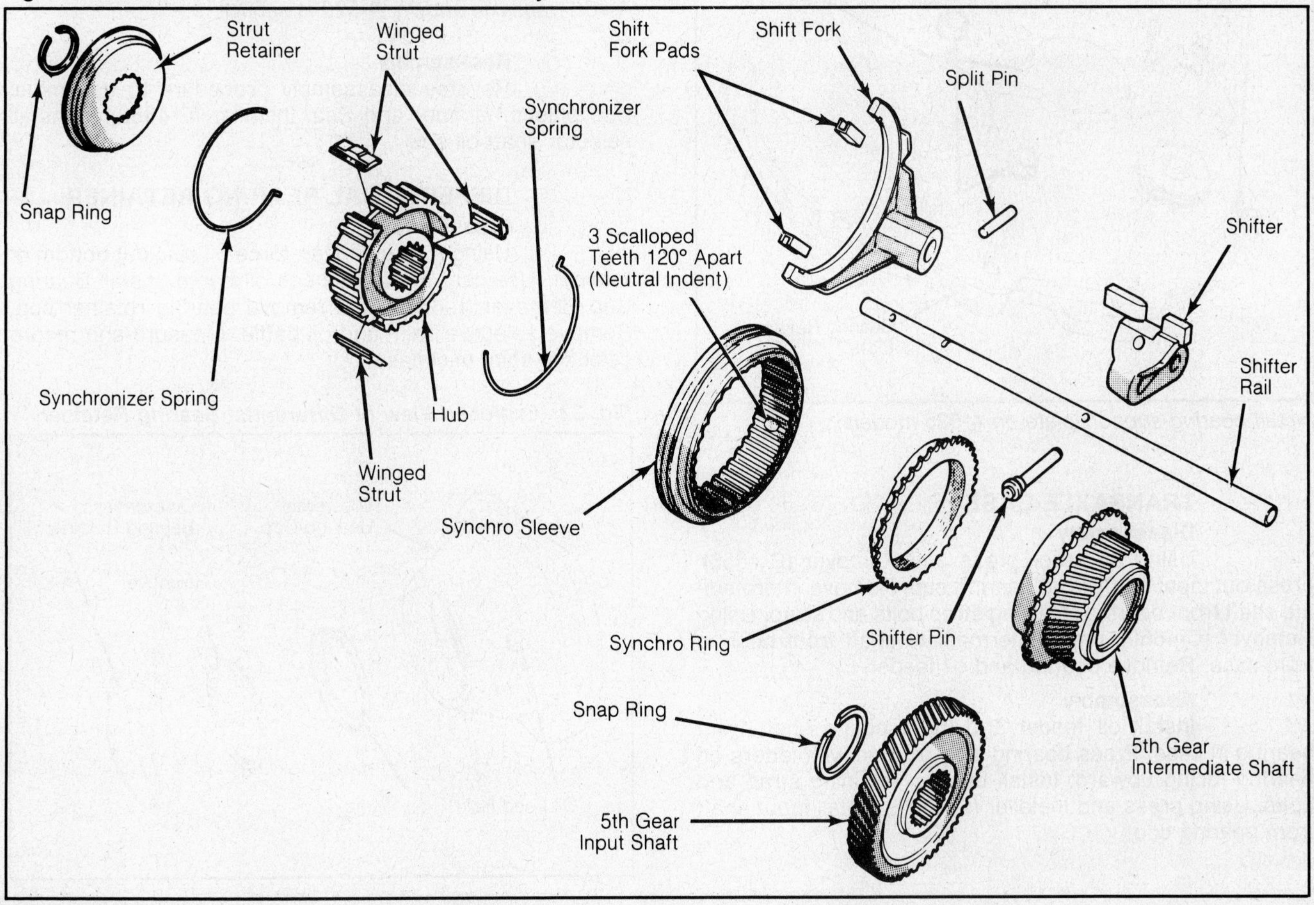

CHRYSLER A-460 & A-525 MANUAL TRANSAXLE (Cont.)

Reassembly
Align marks made during disassembly. Assemble hub to sleeve. Install winged struts, then carefully install springs. Do not install tanged end of both springs in the same strut.

INPUT SHAFT ASSEMBLY

NOTE: Input shaft shim thickness need only be determined if any of the following parts are replaced: Transaxle case, input shaft seal retainer, bearing retainer plate, rear end cover, input shaft or input shaft bearings.

Disassembly
Using a bearing puller and Adapters (C-293-45 rear, C-293-50 front), remove input shaft rear bearing and front bearing. Place bearing retainer plate on wooden blocks. Using an arbor press and Remover (L-4520), press out rear bearing cup.

Reassembly
Press front and rear bearings onto input shaft. Install rear cover (A-460) or bearing support plate (A-525) on bearing retainer plate. See Fig. 20. Press bearing cup into plate until cup bottoms on cover.

Fig. 20: Installing End Cover on Bearing Retainer Plate

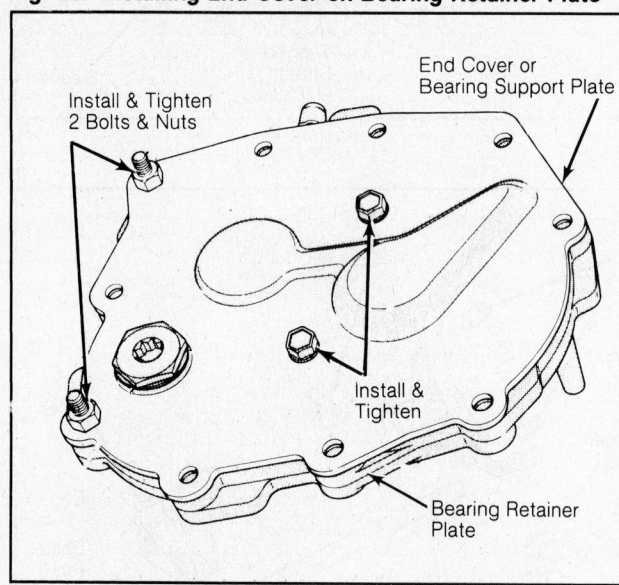

Install bearing support plate on A-525 models.

TRANSAXLE CASE
Disassembly
Using an arbor press and Remover (C-4656), press out input shaft front bearing cup. Remove intermediate shaft front bearing retaining strap bolts and strap. Using Remover (C-4660), press intermediate shaft front bearing from case. Remove bearing and oil feeder.

Reassembly
Install oil feeder and intermediate shaft front bearing in case. Press bearing into position with letters on bearing facing upward. Install bearing retaining strap and bolts. Using press and Installer (C-4655), install input shaft front bearing cup.

SELECTOR SHAFT HOUSING
Disassembly
1) Remove dust boot snap ring and dust boot. Using a screwdriver, pry oil seal off selector shaft. Remove lock pin, back-up lamp switch and gasket.

2) Hold reverse operating lever away from housing. Using a screwdriver, remove "E" clip. Carefully remove selector shaft from shaft housing bore. With selector shaft removed, remove reverse operating lever, crossover spring, flat washer (A-460), gearshift block assembly and gearshift selector.

Fig. 21: Removing "E" Clip from Selector Shaft

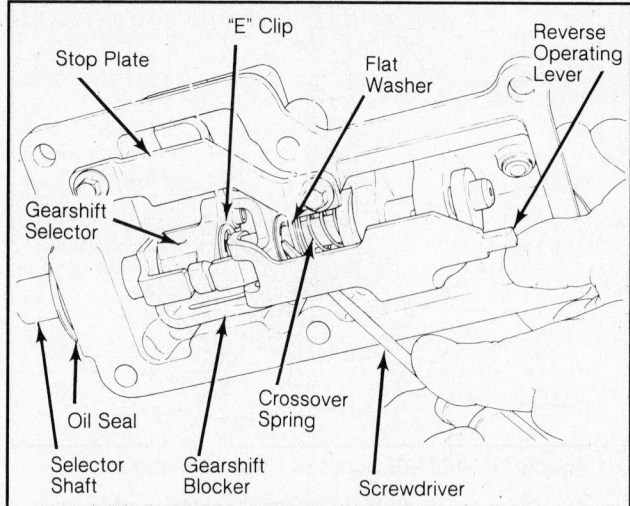

A-460 transaxle shown. A-525 is similar.

Reassembly
Reverse disassembly procedure to assemble. Use plastic hammer and Seal Installer (C-4662) to install selector shaft oil seal.

DIFFERENTIAL BEARING RETAINER
Disassembly
Using a screwdriver, force oil seal out bottom of retainer. Use care not to damage oil baffle. Install Bearing Cup Remover (L-4518) and remove bearing retainer cup. Remove selective shim and oil baffle. Measure and record selective shim thickness.

Fig. 22: Exploded View of Differential Bearing Retainer

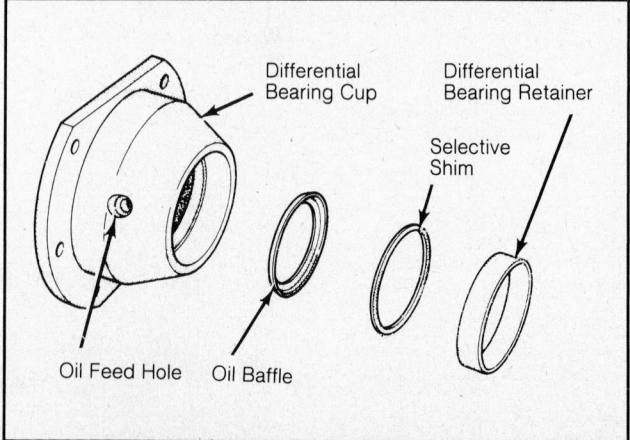

CHRYSLER A-460 & A-525 MANUAL TRANSAXLE (Cont.)

Reassembly
Using an arbor press and Installer (L-4520), press oil baffle into bearing retainer (installer must be inverted to prevent damage to baffle). Turn installer over (cone facing down) and press in selective shim and bearing retainer cup. Turn bearing retainer over, invert installer (cone facing up) and press in oil seal.

EXTENSION HOUSING
Disassembly
Using a screwdriver, remove extension housing oil seal. Using Remover (L-4518), remove bearing cup without damaging oil baffle. Remove oil baffle and "O" ring.

Reassembly
Install "O" ring. Using Installer (L-4520) with cone facing up, press oil baffle into housing, then turn installer over and press bearing cup into housing. Install new oil seal in housing using the same installer and a hammer.

DIFFERENTIAL CASE & RING GEAR
NOTE: Differential shim thickness need only be determined if any of the following parts are replaced: Transaxle case, differential bearing retainer, extension housing, differential case or differential bearings.

Fig. 23: Disassembled View of Differential Assembly

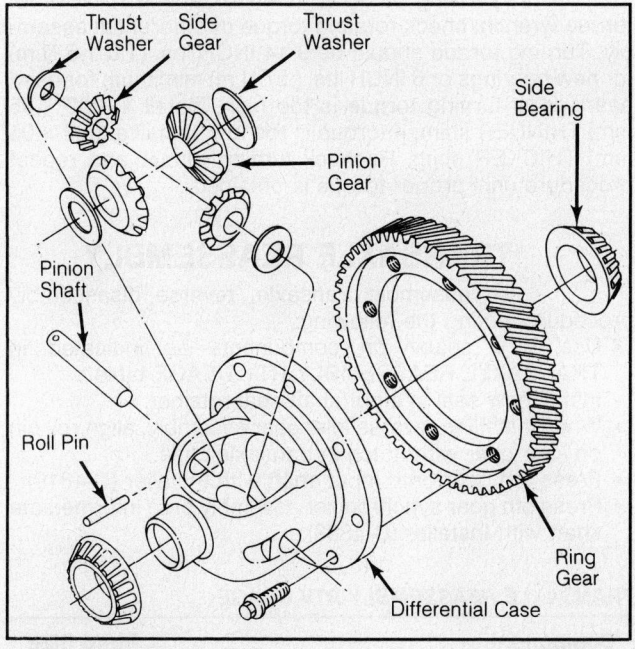

Disassembly
1) Using Bearing Remover (L-4406-1) and Adapters (L-4406-3) remove differential side bearings. Remove 8 ring gear attaching bolts and separate ring gear from differential case.

2) Using a small punch, drive out pinion shaft split pin. Remove pinion shaft. Roll gears around and remove pinion gears, side gears and thrust washers through case opening. Clean and inspect all parts, replace as necessary.

Reassembly
1) Install thrust washers, side gears and pinion gears in differential case. Install pinion shaft and insert split pin.

2) Install ring gear on differential case using NEW bolts. Using arbor press and Bearing Installer (L-4410), install differential side bearings.

TRANSAXLE ADJUSTMENTS
NOTE: All bearing adjustments must be made with no other component interference or gear intermesh. Replace bearings in pairs. Bearing cups MUST be replaced if removed. Turning torque readings should be obtained while smoothly rotating (break-away reading is not indicative of true turning torque). Replace oil baffle, if damaged.

INPUT SHAFT BEARING END PLAY
1) Using Bearing Installer (L-4656) with Handle (C-4171), press input shaft front bearing cup slightly forward in case. Then press bearing cup back into case, from front, to properly position cup before checking input shaft end play.

NOTE: This step is not necessary if Installer (L-4655) was used during reassembly of input shaft front bearing and no input shaft selective shim has been installed since pressing cup into case.

2) Select a gauging shim which will give .001-.010" (.025-.25 mm) end play. A shim .010" (.25 mm) thinner than original selective shim should give this reading. Install gauging shim on bearing cup and install input shaft seal retainer. Alternately tighten input shaft seal retainer bolts until retainer is bottomed against case.

NOTE: Input shaft seal retainer is used to draw input shaft front bearing cup the proper distance into case bore during this step.

3) Oil input shaft bearings with ATF and install input shaft in case. Install bearing retainer plate with input shaft rear bearing cup pressed in and end cover (A-460) or bearing support plate (A-525) installed. Tighten all bolts and nuts to 21 ft. lbs. (28 N.m).

4) Mount dial indicator on transaxle case with plunger touching end of input shaft. See Fig. 24. Apply moderate pressure, by hand, to input shaft splines. Push input shaft toward rear of case while rotating shaft back and forth several times to seat bearings.

5) Zero dial indicator. Pull input shaft toward front of case while rotating shaft back and forth several times to seat bearings. Record end play.

6) The required shim for proper input shaft end play is total of gauging shim thickness, plus end play reading recorded in step 5), MINUS .002" (.050 mm). Combine shims (as required) to obtain a shim within .0016" (.040 mm) of required shim thickness. Shims are available in 30 thicknesses ranging from .024-.069" (.60-1.75 mm). Remove dial indicator.

7) Remove input shaft seal retainer and gauging shim. Install required shim(s). Apply a 1/16" bead of RTV

3-42

Manual Transmissions
CHRYSLER A-460 & A-525 MANUAL TRANSAXLE (Cont.)

Fig. 24: *Measuring Input Shaft Bearing End Play*

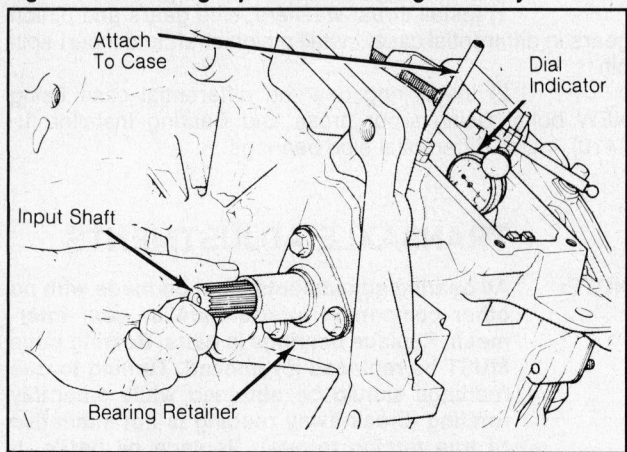

Fig. 25: *Measuring Differential Bearing End Play*

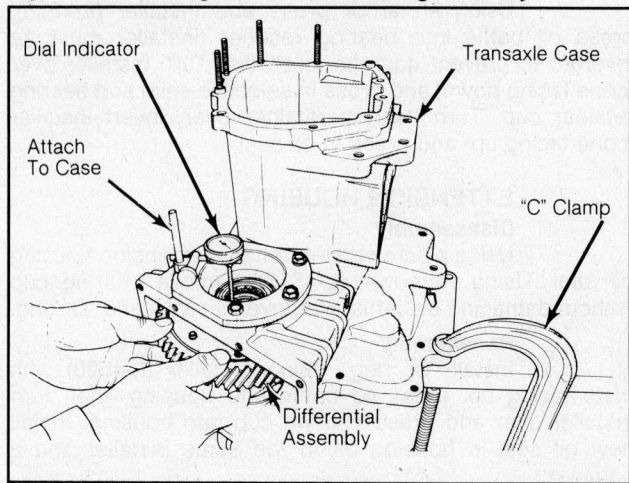

sealer to input shaft seal retainer and install. Tighten bolts alternately until retainer is bottomed against case.

NOTE: Do not allow RTV sealant to get in oil slot.

8) Using Adapter (L-4508) and an INCH lb. torque wrench, check input shaft turning torque. Turning torque for new bearings should be 1-5 INCH lbs. (.11-.56 N.m). Torque for old bearings should be 1 INCH lb. (.11 N.m) minimum. If turning torque is too high, install a .0016" (.040 mm) THINNER shim; if torque is too low, install a .0016" (.040 mm) THICKER shim.

9) If shims require replacement after initial torque reading check, repeat step 1) to assure that input shaft front bearing cup is properly seated. Repeat step 8) until proper bearing turning torque is obtained.

DIFFERENTIAL BEARING PRELOAD

1) Remove bearing cup and existing shim from differential bearing retainer. Select a gauging shim shich will give .001-.010" (.025-.25 mm) end play. A shim .015" (.38 mm) thinner than original selective shim should give this reading. Install gauging shim in differential bearing retainer and press in bearing cup.

NOTE: Do not install oil baffle when checking differential end play.

2) Oil differential bearings with ATF and install differential assembly in transaxle case. Install extension housing and bearing retainer. Tighten bolts to 21 ft. lbs. (28 N.m). Mount transaxle case on workbench with "C" clamps (clutch housing facing down). Mount dial indicator with plunger touching differential case. *See Fig. 25.*

3) Apply medium pressure to ring gear, by hand, in downward direction while rolling differential assembly back and forth several times to seat bearings. Zero dial indicator. Apply medium pressure, by hand, in upward direction while rotating differential several times to seat bearings. Record end play.

4) The required shim to obtain proper bearing preload is the total of gauging shim thickness, plus end play reading recorded in step 3), PLUS .010" (.25 mm). Combine shims (as required) to obtain a shim within .002" (.05 mm) of required shim thickness. Shims are available in 29 thicknesses ranging from .020-.083" (.50-2.10 mm). Remove dial indicator.

5) Remove differential bearing retainer. Remove bearing cup and gauging shim. Install oil baffle, using care not to damage baffle. Install required shim(s). Press bearing cup into differential bearing retainer.

6) Check bearing retainer "O" ring for damage and replace if necessary. Apply 1/16" bead of RTV sealer to bearing retainer and install. Install extension housing and tighten bolts.

7) Using Adapter (L-4436) and an INCH lb. torque wrench, check rotating torque of differential assembly. Turning torque should be 9-14 INCH lbs. (1.0-1.6 N.m) for new bearings or 6 INCH lbs. (.67 N.m) mimimum for used bearings. If turning torque is too high, install a .002" (.05 mm) THINNER shim; if torque is too low, install a .002" (.05 mm) THICKER shim. Recheck turning torque and repeat procedure unitl proper torque is obtained.

TRANSAXLE REASSEMBLY

To assemble transaxle, reverse disassembly procedure, noting the following:
- Use RTV sealer on components as indicated in TRANSAXLE REASSEMBLY RTV USAGE table.
- Install new seal in input shaft seal retainer.
- When installing reverse idler gear assembly, align roll pin on idler gear with notch in transaxle case.
- Press 5th gear onto input shaft with Installer (C-4810).
- Press 5th gear synchronizer assembly onto intermediate shaft with Installer (C-4888).

TRANSAXLE REASSEMBLY RTV USAGE

Component	Bead Size
Input Shaft Seal Retainer	1/16"
Bearing Retainer Plate	1/8"
Rear Cover	1/8"
Selector Shaft Housing	1/16"
Extension Housing	1/16"
Differential Cover	1/8"

Manual Transmissions

CHRYSLER A-460 & A-525 MANUAL TRANSAXLE (Cont.)

TIGHTENING SPECIFICATIONS

Application	Ft. Lbs. (N.m)
Axle Shaft (Hub) Nut [1]	180 (245)
Differential Bearing Retainer Bolts	21 (28)
Differential Extension Bolts	21 (28)
End Cover-to-Bearing Retainer Bolts	21 (28)
End Cover-to-Case Bolts & Stud Nuts	21 (28)
Fill Plug	24 (33)
Gearshift Housing-to-Case	21 (28)
Gearshift Operating Lever Attaching Nut [1]	21 (28)
Input Shaft Seal Retaining Bolt	21 (28)
Mount-to-Block & Case	70 (95)
Ring Gear Bolts	70 (95)
Steering Knuckle Clamp Bolt	70 (95)
Strut-to-Block & Case Bolts	70 (95)
Transaxle Case-to-Engine Block	70 (95)

Application	INCH Lbs. (N.m)
Anti-Rotational Strut Bracket	214 (23)
Differential Oil Pan Nut & Screw	188 (19)
Intermediate Shaft Bearing Strap Screw	108 (7)
Shift Linkage Adjusting Pin	108 (7)

[1] – Always replace with new nut.

Manual Transmissions
FORD MOTOR CO. 3.03 3-SPEED

E150, E350, F150, F250

IDENTIFICATION

The transmission identification code can be found on the Vehicle Compliance Certification Label located on the driver's door lock pillar. There is also a service identification tag located on the right front side of transmission case. The code for a 3-Speed 3.03 transmission is "C". See Fig. 1.

Fig. 1: Transmission Identification Tag

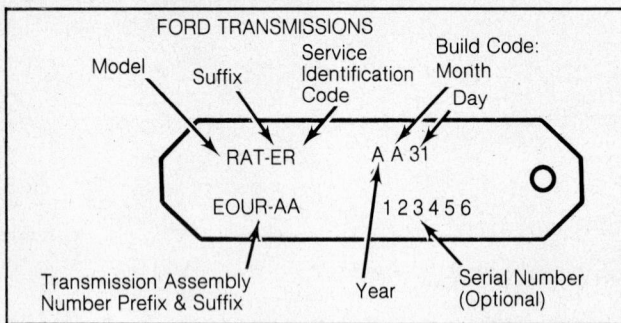

DESCRIPTION

Transmission is a 3-speed, fully synchronized unit. All forward gears are constant mesh helical type. Forward speed changes are accomplished through use of synchronizer sleeves. Synchronizers allow quicker shifts and reduce gear clash.

Reverse gears are spur type and are not synchronized. Transmission uses a system of detents and interlocks within the case, which maintains gear position and prevents selection of more than one speed at a time.

LUBRICATION & ADJUSTMENT

See appropriate MANUAL TRANSMISSION SERVICING article in DOMESTIC GENERAL SERVICING section.

TROUBLE SHOOTING

See MANUAL TRANSMISSION TROUBLE SHOOTING article in DOMESTIC GENERAL SERVICING section.

REMOVAL & INSTALLATION

See appropriate MANUAL TRANSMISSION REMOVAL article in DOMESTIC GENERAL SERVICING section.

TRANSMISSION DISASSEMBLY

1) With transmission in a sturdy holding fixture, remove lower extension bolt and drain transmission lubricant. Remove cover-to-case capscrews. Remove cover and gasket from case. Remove long spring and detent plug using a magnet.

2) Remove extension housing-to-case bolts. Remove extension housing retainer and gasket. Remove front bearing retainer-to-case bolts and withdraw front bearing retainer and gasket.

Fig. 2: Exploded View of Transmission Case Assembly

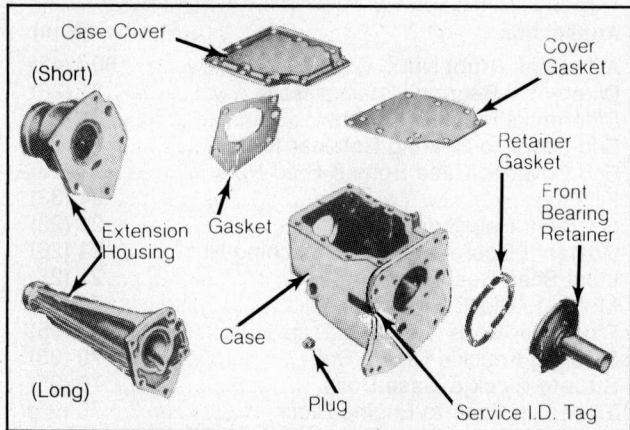

3) Remove filler plug from right side of case. Working through opening, drive roll pin out of case and countershaft using a 1/4" (6.35 mm) punch. Hold countershaft gear with hook, and with dummy shaft, drive countershaft out rear of case. Lower countershaft gear and washers to bottom of case.

Fig. 3: Shift Rails and Shift Forks Installation

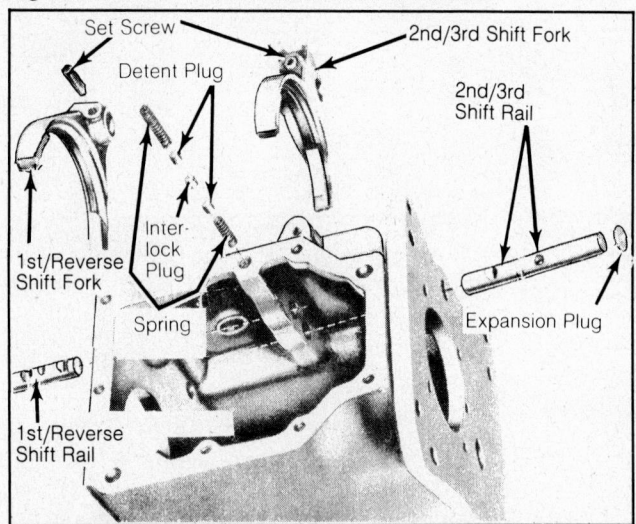

Rotate shift rail 90° to remove.

4) Remove speedometer drive gear snap ring and slide gear off shaft. Remove gear lock ball from shaft. Remove output shaft bearing snap ring. Using pullers (T75L-7025-B, C, E, G, and J) remove bearing from shaft. Place shift levers in center (neutral) position.

5) Remove set screw that secures 1st/Reverse shift fork to shift rail. Slide shift rail out through rear of case. Slide 1st/Reverse synchronizer as far forward as possible and rotate shift fork upward and remove.

6) Move 2nd/3rd shift fork to second speed position and remove set screw from fork. Rotate shift rail 90° and lift interlock plug from case with a magnet.

7) Tap on inner end of 2nd/3rd shift rail to remove expansion plug from front of case. Remove shift rail. Remove 2nd/3rd speed shift rail detent plug and spring from detent bore using a magnet.

8) Pull input gear shaft blocking ring, bearing and snap ring from case. Rotate 2nd/3rd shift fork upward and lift from case.

FORD MOTOR CO. 3.03 3-SPEED (Cont.)

9) Carefully lift output shaft assembly out through top of case. Remove roll pin and reverse idler gear shaft and lift idler gear and 2 thrust washers from case. Lift out countershaft gear, thrust washer and dummy shaft from case.

10) Remove snap ring from front of output shaft and slide 2nd/3rd speed synchronizer and 2nd speed gear off shaft. Remove snap ring and tabbed thrust

washer from output shaft and withdraw first gear and blocking ring.

11) Remove next snap ring from output shaft. Using an arbor press, withdraw synchronizer hub assembly from shaft. Do not remove hub by hammering or prying. Remove rail pin from bottom of case.

Fig. 4: Disassembled View of Ford 3.03 3-Speed Manual Transmission

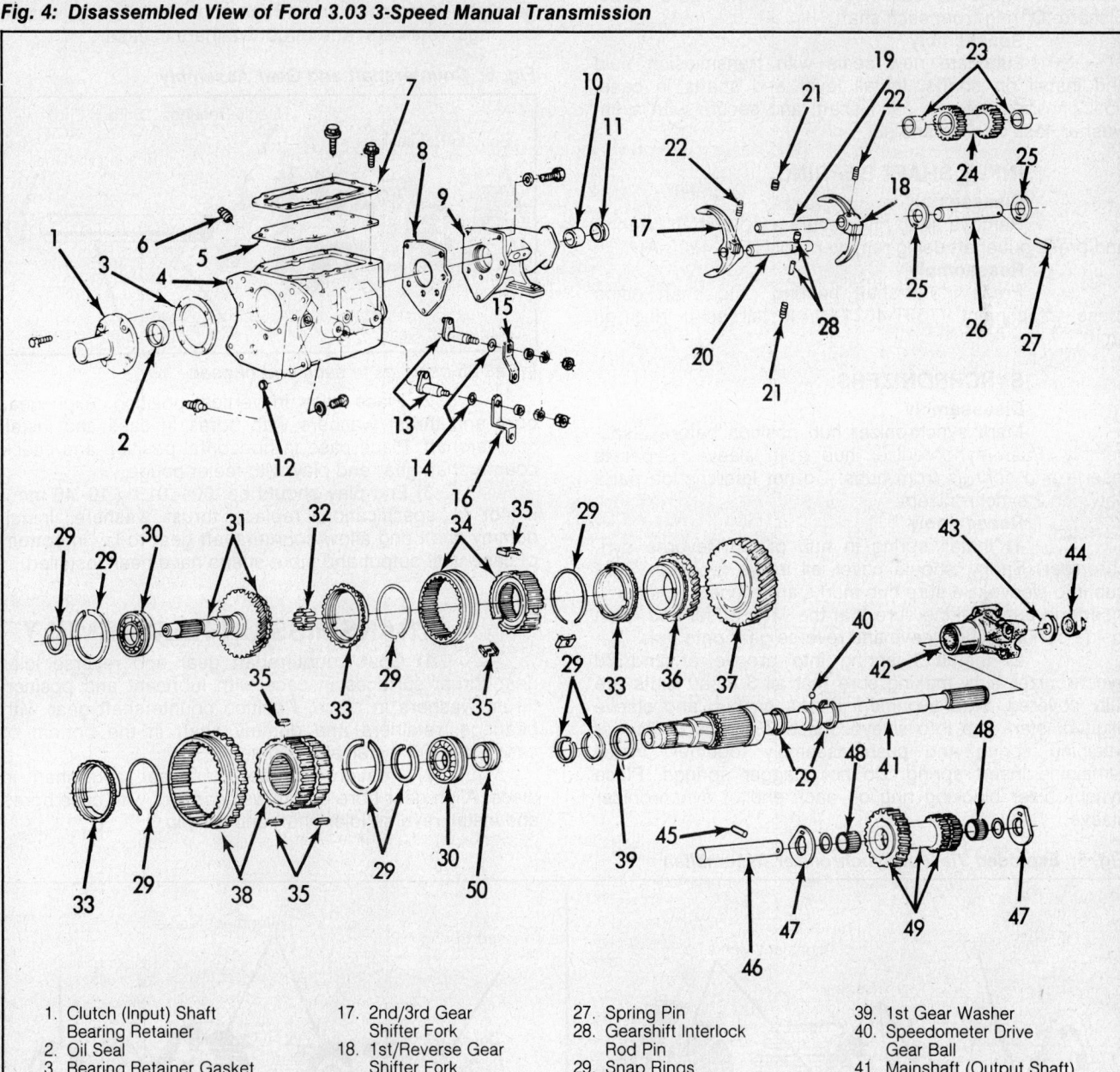

1. Clutch (Input) Shaft Bearing Retainer	17. 2nd/3rd Gear Shifter Fork	27. Spring Pin	39. 1st Gear Washer
2. Oil Seal	18. 1st/Reverse Gear Shifter Fork	28. Gearshift Interlock Rod Pin	40. Speedometer Drive Gear Ball
3. Bearing Retainer Gasket	19. 1st/Reverse Gear Shifter Shaft	29. Snap Rings	41. Mainshaft (Output Shaft)
4. Transmission Case	20. 2nd/3rd Gear Shifter Shaft	30. Ball Bearings	42. Mainshaft Flange
5. Shift Housing Gasket	21. Shifter Interlock Spring	31. Clutch (Input) Shaft	43. Washer
6. Fill Plug	22. Set Screws	32. Needle Bearings (15)	44. Lock Nut
7. Gear Shift Housing	23. Reverse Idler Gear Bushings	33. Synchronizing Blocking Ring	45. Countershaft-to-Case Pin
8. Extension Housing Gasket	24. Reverse Idle Gear	34. 2nd/3rd Sliding Gear Synchronizer	46. Countershaft
9. Extension Housing	25. Washers	35. Inserts	47. Countershaft Gear Thrust Plate
10. Bushing	26. Reverse Idler Gear Shaft	36. Mainshaft (Input) Gear and Bushing	48. Needle Bearings (25)
11. Oil Seal		37. 1st Gear	49. Countershaft Cluster Gear
12. Expansion Plug		38. 1st/Reverse Sliding Gear Synchronizer	50. Speedometer Drive Gear
13. Shift Control Fingers			
14. Seals			
15. 1st/Reverse Lever			
16. 2nd/3rd Lever			

Manual Transmissions

FORD MOTOR CO. 3.03 3-SPEED (Cont.)

COMPONENT DISASSEMBLY & REASSEMBLY

SHIFT LEVERS & SEALS

Disassembly

Remove nut, flat washer and lock washer securing each shift lever to lever and shaft in case. Lift off shift lever and slide each lever and shaft out of case. Discard "O" ring from each shaft.

Reassembly

Lubricate new seals with transmission fluid and install on shafts. Install lever and shafts in case, position shift lever on each shaft, and secure with a flat washer, lock washer and nut.

INPUT SHAFT BEARING

Disassembly

Remove snap ring securing input shaft bearing and press out shaft using remover tool (T57L-4220-A).

Reassembly

Press input shaft bearing onto shaft using press attachment (T53T-4621-B). Install snap ring on shaft.

SYNCHRONIZERS

Disassembly

Mark synchronizer hub position before disassembly. Push synchronizer hub from sleeve. Separate inserts and springs from hubs. Do not interchange parts between 2 synchronizers.

Reassembly

1) Install spring in hub of 1st/Reverse synchronizer. Spring should cover all insert grooves. Start hub into sleeve. Be sure hub marks are aligned. Position 3 inserts in hub, making sure that the wide offset end is on inside of hub. Slide sleeve and reverse gear onto hub.

2) Install 1 spring into groove of 2nd/3rd synchronizer hub, making sure that all 3 insert slots are fully covered. With alignment marks on hub and sleeve aligned, start hub into sleeve. Place 3 inserts on top of retaining spring and push assembly together. Install remaining insert spring. Do not stagger springs. Place synchronizer blocking ring on each end of synchronizer sleeve.

COUNTERSHAFT GEAR BEARINGS

Disassembly

Remove dummy shaft, 50 needle bearings and 2 bearing retainer washers from countershaft gear.

Reassembly

1) Coat bore in each end of countershaft gear with grease. Hold dummy shaft in the gear and install 25 needle bearings and a retainer washer in each end of the gear. Position countershaft gear, dummy shaft, needle bearings, retainers, ane thrust washers in case.

Fig. 6: Countershaft and Gear Assembly

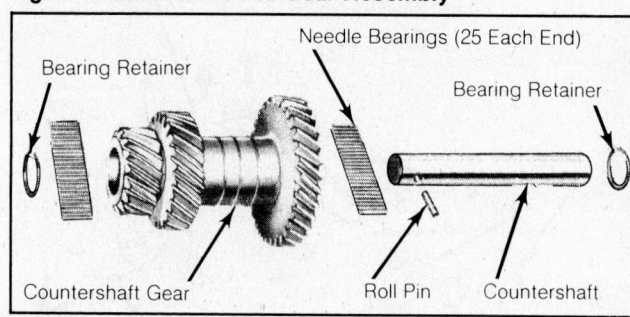

Install 25 bearings in each end of gear.

2) Place case in vertical position. Align gear bore and thrust washers with bores in case and install countershaft. Place case in horizontal position and check countershaft gear end play with feeler gauge.

3) End play should be .004-.018" (.10-.46 mm). If not to specification, replace thrust washers. Install dummy shaft and allow countershaft gear to lay in bottom of case until output and input shafts have been installed.

TRANSMISSION REASSEMBLY

1) Coat countershaft gear and reverse idler gear thrust surfaces in case with lubricant and position thrust washers in place. Position countershaft gear with bearings, retainers and dummy shaft in the bottom of case. DO NOT install at this time.

2) Postion reverse idler gear and shaft in place. Align gear bore and thrust washers with case bores and install reverse idler shaft and roll pin.

Fig. 5: Exploded View of Synchronizer Assemblies

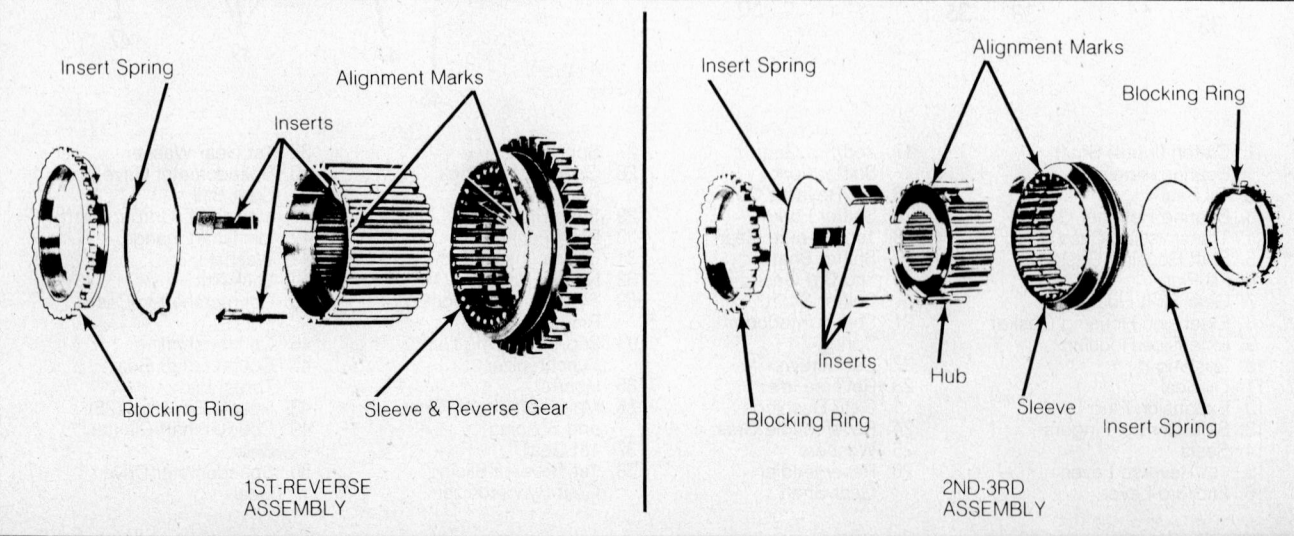

1ST-REVERSE ASSEMBLY

2ND-3RD ASSEMBLY

FORD MOTOR CO. 3.03 3-SPEED (Cont.)

3) Measure reverse idler gear end play with a feeler gauge. End play should be within .004-.018" (.10-.46 mm). If end play is not to specification, replace thrust washers. If end play is within limits leave gear installed.

4) Lubricate output shaft splines and machined surfaces. Install 1st/Reverse synchronizer hub on shaft with teeth end of gear facing toward rear of shaft. Press on shaft using arbor press, DO NOT attempt to hammer or pry. Install snap ring.

5) Place blocking ring on tapered machined surface of 1st gear and slide 1st gear onto output shaft with blocking ring toward rear of shaft. Rotate gear as necessary to engage 3 notches in blocking ring with synchronzier inserts. Secure 1st gear with thrust washer and snap ring.

6) Slide blocking ring onto tapered machined surface of 2nd gear. Slide 2nd gear, with blocking ring and 2nd/3rd gear synchronizer onto output shaft. Tapered machined surface of 2nd gear must face toward front of shaft. Ensure that the notches in blocking ring engage synchronizer inserts and secure with snap ring.

7) Coat bore of input shaft with thin film of grease and install 15 roller bearings. Install input shaft and blocking ring through front of transmission and install snap ring in bearing groove. Position output shaft assembly in case, and place shift fork on 2nd/3rd synchronizer assembly.

NOTE: **Use only a thin film of grease; a thick application will block lubricating holes.**

Fig. 7: Reverse Idler Gear and Shaft Assembly

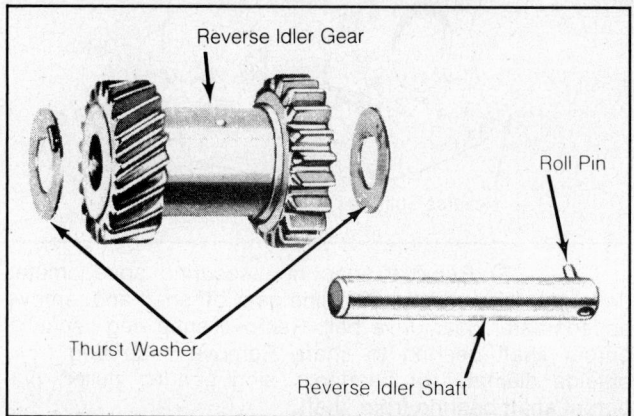

Idler gear end play should be .004-.018" (.10-.46 mm).

8) Place detent spring and plug into case. Position 2nd/3rd synchronizer in 2nd gear position (toward rear of transmission). Align shift fork, depress detent plug and install shift rail. Move rail inward until detent plug engages forward notch (2nd gear position).

9) Secure fork to shaft with set screw. Move synchronizer to neutral position, and install interlock plug in case. Move 1st/Reverse synchronizer to 1st speed position and place shift fork in synchronizer groove.

10) Rotate shift fork into position and install shift rail. Move rail inward until center notch (neutral) is aligned with detent bore. Secure fork to rail with set screw. Install a new shift rail expansion plug in front of case.

11) Hold input shaft and blocking ring in position. Move output shaft forward to seat pilot in roller bearings of input gear. Tap input gear bearing into place. Hold output shaft to prevent roller bearings from dropping.

12) Install front bearing retainer with new gasket. Ensure that oil return slot is at the bottom of case. Install and tighten retainer-to-case attaching screws.

Fig. 8: Input Shaft and Gear Assembly

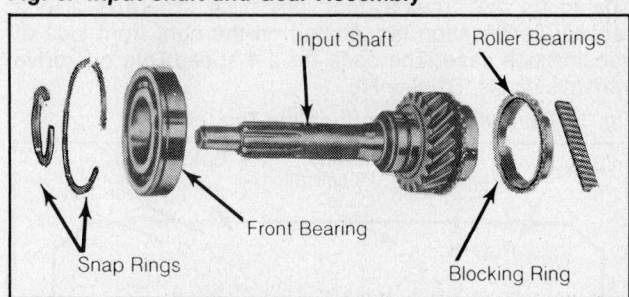

See Fig. 2 for view of front bearing retainer.

13) Install large snap ring on rear bearing and place bearing on output shaft with snap ring toward rear of shaft. Using bearing installer (T75L-7075-B, K & P) press bearing into place. Secure bearing to shaft with snap ring.

14) Hold speedometer drive gear lock ball in detent and slide speedometer drive gear into place. Secure gear with snap ring. Place transmission in vertical position. Working with screwdriver through bottom drain hole, align bore of countershaft gear with bore of case.

15) Working from rear of case, push dummy shaft out of countershaft gear with countershaft. Be sure roll pin hole is aligned with hole in case before inserting countershaft. Drive shaft into place and install roll pin.

16) Place output shaft bearing retainer into front of extension housing. Coat new extension housing gasket with sealer and install. Install lock washers on 5 attaching screws and dip threads in sealer.

17) Bolt housing to case and tighten to specification. Place transmission in gear and pour approved lubricant over entire gear train while rotating either input or output shaft.

18) Install remaining detent plug and long spring into case. Coat new cover gasket with sealer. Position gasket and cover on transmission case, and install and tighten attaching screws. Check operation of transmission in all gear positions. Fill transmision to the bottom of fill hole with approved lubricant.

TIGHTENING SPECIFICATIONS

Application	Ft. Lbs. (N.m)
Cover-to-Case	20-25 (27-33)
Extension Housing-to-Case	42-50 (57-67)
Filler Plug	10-20 (14-27)
Front Bearing Retainer-to-Case	30-36 (41-48)
Outer Shift Lever Nut	18-23 (24-31)
Reverse Lamp Switch	8-12 (11-16)
Shift Fork-to-Shift Rail	10-18 (14-24)
Transmission-to-Clutch Housing	42-50 (57-67)

Manual Transmissions
FORD MOTOR CO. RUG OVERDRIVE 4-SPEED

E150 & E350

IDENTIFICATION

The transmission identification code can be found on the Vehicle Compliance Certification Label located on the driver's door lock pillar. There is also a service identification tag located on the right front side of transmission case. The code for a 4-speed Rug overdrive transmission is "B". *See Fig. 1.*

Fig. 1: Transmission Identification Tag

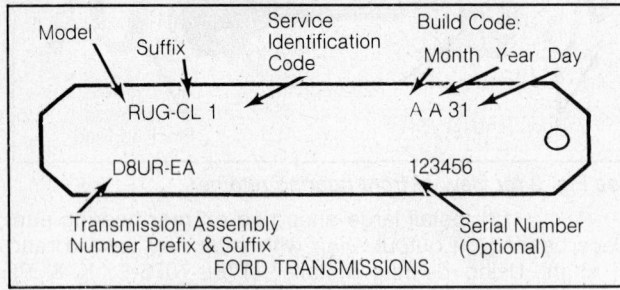

DESCRIPTION

The 4-speed overdrive transmission is fully synchronized with all gears except the reverse sliding gear being in constant mesh. All forward speed changes are accomplished with synchronizer sleeves. All forward speed gears are helical type. Reverse sliding gear and the external teeth of the 1st and 2nd speed synchronizer sleeve are spur type.

LUBRICATION & ADJUSTMENT

See appropriate MANUAL TRANSMISSION SERVICING article in DOMESTIC GENERAL SERVICING section.

TROUBLE SHOOTING

See MANUAL TRANSMISSION TROUBLE SHOOTING article in DOMESTIC GENERAL SERVICING section.

REMOVAL & INSTALLATION

TRANSMISSION

See appropriate MANUAL TRANSMISSION REMOVAL article in DOMESTIC GENERAL SERVICING section.

TRANSMISSION DISASSEMBLY

1) Mount transmission in a holding fixture. Drain lubricant by removing lower extension housing attaching bolt. Remove cover and gasket from case. Remove long spring which retains detent plug in case and remove detent plug using small magnet.

2) Remove extension housing bolts and washers. Remove extension housing from case and discard gasket. Remove input shaft bearing retainer screws and slide retainer off input shaft. Support countershaft gear with wire hook. Push countershaft out rear of case. Lower countershaft gear to bottom of case and remove hook.

3) Remove set screw from 1st/2nd shift fork. Slide 1st/2nd shift rail out rear of case. Using magnet, remove interlock detent from between 1st/2nd and 3rd/overdrive shift rails. *See Fig. 2.* Shift transmission into overdrive position.

4) Remove set screw from 3rd/overdrive shift fork. Remove the side detent bolt, plug and spring. Rotate 3rd/overdrive shift rail 90° clockwise, and tap it out through front of case. Remove interlock pin from top of case with magnet.

Fig. 2: Exploded View of Shift Rails & Forks

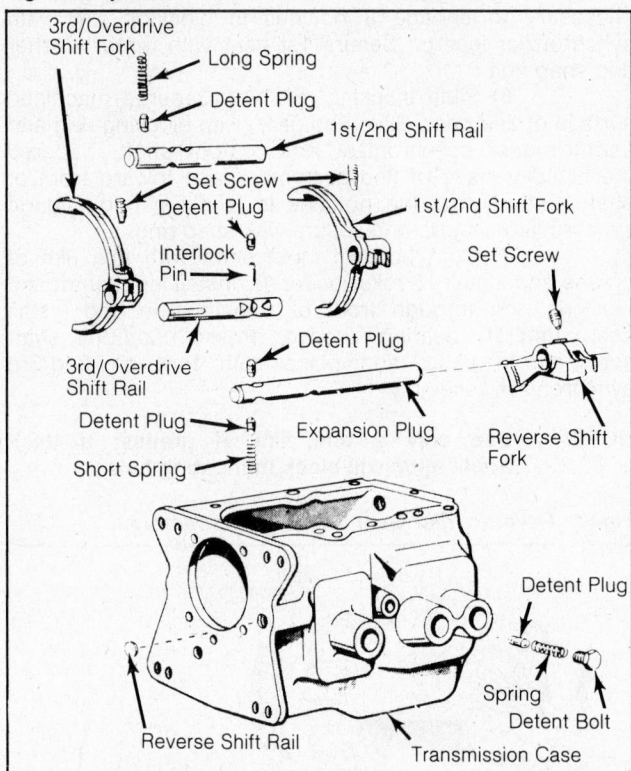

5) Remove snap ring securing speedometer drive gear on output shaft. Slide gear off shaft and remove speedometer gear drive ball. Remove snap ring securing output shaft bearing to shaft. Remove snap ring from outside diameter of bearing. Using bearing puller, pull output shaft bearing from shaft.

6) Remove snap ring securing input shaft bearing to shaft. Remove snap ring from outside diameter of bearing. Remove retaining ring. Use bearing puller to remove bearing from input shaft and transmission case. Remove input shaft and blocking ring from front of case. Move output shaft to right side of case, and rotate shift forks up and out of case.

7) Support thrust washer and 1st gear to prevent them from sliding off shaft. Lift output shaft assembly from case. Remove reverse gear shift fork set screw. Rotate shift rail 90° and slide rail out rear of case. Lift reverse shift fork from case. Remove reverse detent plug and spring from case with magnet. *See Fig. 3.*

8) Remove reverse idler gear shaft from case using dummy shaft. Lift countershaft gear and thrust washers out of case being careful not to drop bearings and dummy shaft from countershaft gear. Lift reverse idler gear and thrust washer from case.

FORD MOTOR CO. RUG OVERDRIVE 4-SPEED (Cont.)

Fig. 3: Reverse Shift Rail Removal

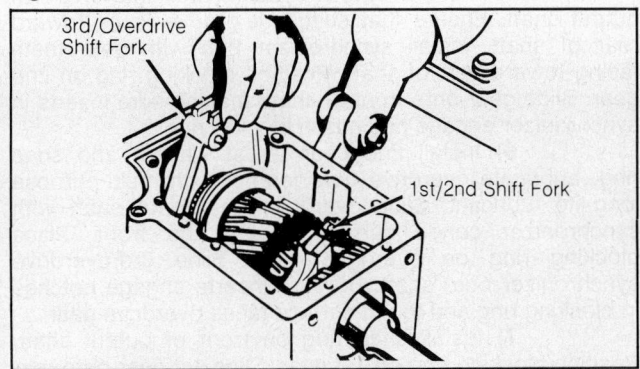

Rotate shift rail 90°.

9) Remove snap ring from front of output shaft. Slide 3rd/overdrive synchronizer blocking ring and gear from shaft. Remove next snap ring from output shaft. Slide 2nd gear thrust washer, 2nd gear and blocking ring off shaft. Remove remaining snap ring from output shaft. Remove thrust washer, 1st gear and blocking ring from rear of shaft.

CLEANING & INSPECTION

1) Wash all parts in cleaning solvent and dry with compressed air (except bearings). Brush or scrape all foreign matter from parts. Let bearings air dry in clean shop cloth. Inspect transmission case for cracks, damaged bearing bores, or threads.

2) Remove all small nicks or burrs from front or rear of case. Check bearings for roughness by slowly turning race by hand.

3) Inspect needle bearing rollers, shafts, and washers for wear or damage. Check all other parts for wear, damage, chipped, or broken teeth. Replace parts as necessary.

COMPONENT DISASSEMBLY & REASSEMBLY

SHIFT LEVERS AND SEALS

Disassembly

Remove nut, lock washer and flat washer. Lift shift levers off shafts. Slide each lever and shaft from case. Remove and discard "O" ring seal from each lever and shaft.

Reassembly

Lubricate new "O" ring seals with transmission lubricant and install seals on shafts. Install levers and shafts into case. Position shift lever on each shaft and secure with flat washer, lock washer and nut.

SYNCHRONIZER ASSEMBLY

Disassembly

Put alignment marks on hub and sleeve of synchronizer before disassembly. Push hub from each synchronizer sleeve. Separate inserts and insert springs from hubs. Do not mix the parts of 1st/2nd synchronizer with 3rd/overdrive synchronizer.

Reassembly

Install hub in sleeve. Ensure that alignment marks are properly indexed. Place 3 inserts into place on

hub. Install insert springs. Ensure that irregular surface (hump) is seated in one of the inserts. DO NOT stagger springs. *See Fig. 4.*

Fig. 4: Exploded View of Synchronizer Assemblies

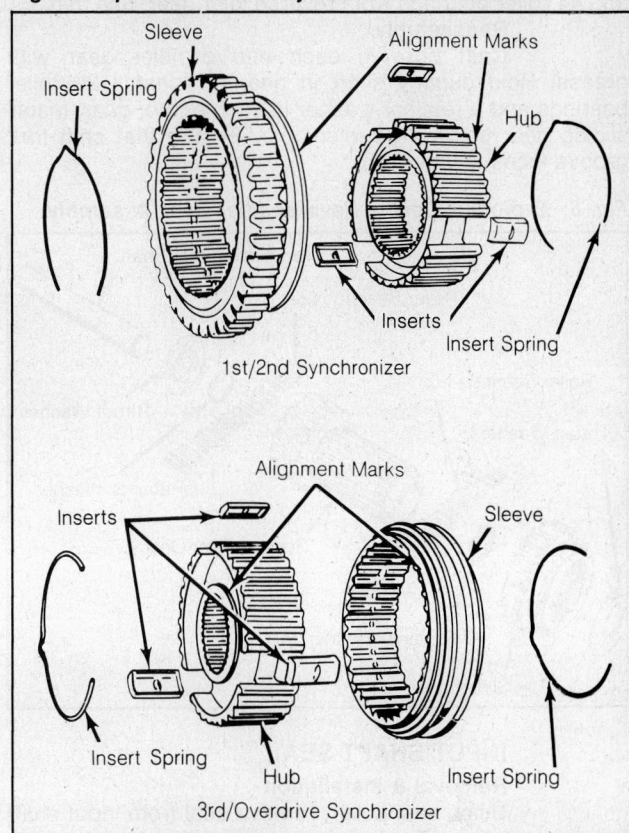

COUNTERSHAFT GEAR BEARINGS

Disassembly

Remove dummy shaft, 2 bearing retainer washers and 21 roller bearings from each end of countershaft gear. *See Fig. 5.*

Reassembly

Coat bore in each end of gear with grease. Hold dummy shaft in gear and install 21 roller bearings and a retainer washer in each end of gear.

Fig. 5: Exploded View of Countershaft Gear

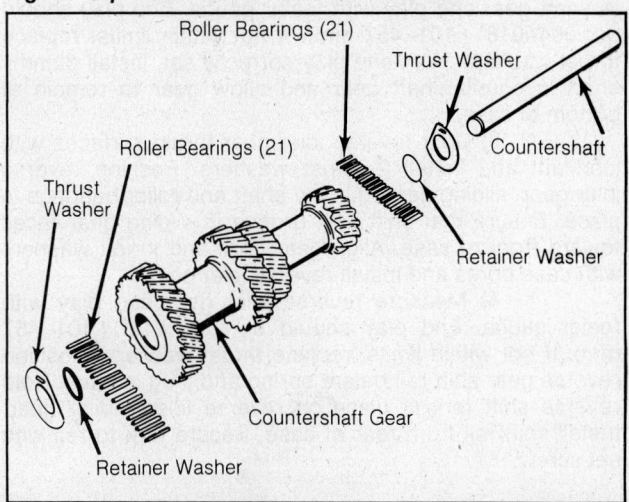

FORD MOTOR CO. RUG OVERDRIVE 4-SPEED (Cont.)

REVERSE IDLER GEAR BEARINGS

Disassembly

Slide reverse idler sliding gear off reverse idler gear. Remove dummy shaft, 2 bearing retainer washers and 44 roller bearings from reverse idler gear. See. Fig. 6.

Reassembly

Coat bore in each end of idler gear with grease. Hold dummy shaft in gear and install 22 roller bearings and a retainer washer in each end of gear. Install sliding gear on reverse idler gear. Ensure that shift fork groove faces toward front.

Fig. 6: Exploded View of Reverse Idler Gear Assembly

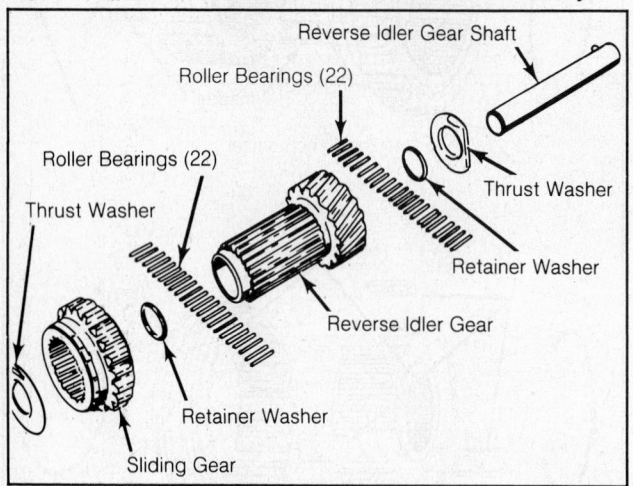

INPUT SHAFT SEAL

Removal & Installation

Using seal puller, remove seal from input shaft bearing retainer. To install, coat sealing surface with lubricant and drive seal into place.

TRANSMISSION REASSEMBLY

1) Coat countershaft gear thrust surfaces in case with thin film of lubricant. Position thrust washer at each end of case. Position countershaft gear, dummy shaft and roller bearings in case. Place case in vertical position. Align gear bore and thrust washers with bores in case and install countershaft.

2) Place case horizontal and check countershaft gear end play with feeler gauge. End play should be .004-.018" (.101-.457 mm). If not within limits, replace thrust washers. With end play correctly set, install dummy shaft in countershaft gear and allow gear to remain at bottom of case.

3) Coat reverse idler gear thrust surfaces with lubricant and install 2 thrust washers. Position reverse idler gear, sliding gear, dummy shaft and roller bearings in place. Ensure that shift fork groove in sliding gear faces toward front of case. Align gear bore and thrust washers with case bores and install reverse idler shaft.

4) Measure reverse idler gear end play with feeler gauge. End play should be .004-.018" (.101-.457 mm). If not within limits, replace thrust washers. Position reverse gear shift rail detent spring and plug in case. Hold reverse shift fork in place on reverse idler sliding gear. Install shift rail from rear of case. Secure fork to rail with set screw.

5) Install 1st/2nd synchronizer into front of output shaft. Ensure that shift fork groove faces toward rear of shaft. Install synchronizer hub with gear teeth facing toward rear of shaft. Position blocking ring on 2nd gear. Slide gear onto front of shaft, making sure inserts in synchronizer engage notches in blocker ring.

6) Install 2nd gear thrust washer and snap ring. Lubricate overdrive gear journal with multi-purpose long-life lubricant. Slide overdrive gear onto shaft with synchronizer coned surface toward the front. Place blocking ring on overdrive gear. Slide 3rd/overdrive synchronizer onto shaft. Be sure inserts engage notches in blocking ring and thrust surface faces overdrive gear.

7) Install snap ring on front of output shaft. Position blocking ring on 1st gear. Slide 1st gear onto rear of output shaft. Be sure notches of blocking ring engage synchronizer inserts. Install heavy thrust washer on rear of output shaft. Support thrust washer and 1st gear to prevent them from sliding. Carefully lower output shaft assembly into case.

8) Position 1st/2nd shift fork and 3rd/overdrive shift forks on proper gears and rotate them into place. Install spring and detent plug into detent bore. Place reverse shift rail into neutral position. See Fig. 7.

Fig.7: Output Shaft Assembly Installation

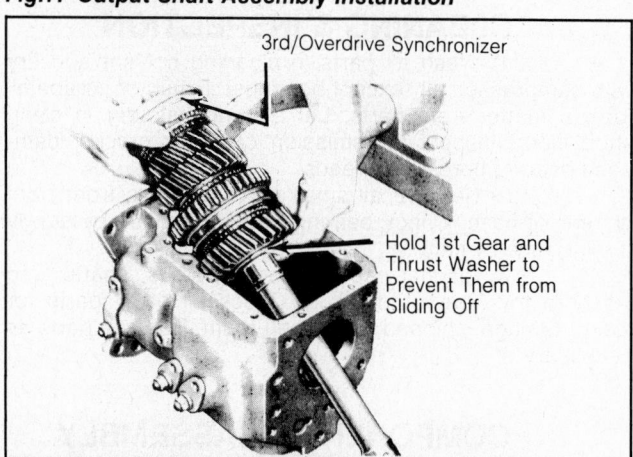

Hold 1st gear and thrust washer to prevent sliding.

9) Coat 3rd/overdrive shift rail interlock pin (tapered ends) with grease and position in shift rail. Align 3rd/overdrive shift fork with shift rail bores and slide rail into place. Be sure 3 detents face toward outside of case. Place front synchronizer into overdrive position and install set screw in 3rd/overdrive shift fork. Move synchronizer to neutral position. Install 3rd/overdrive detent plug, spring and bolt in left side of case. Place detent plug (tapered ends) in detent bore in case.

NOTE: **A missing or improperly installed interlock pin could allow the transmission to be shifted into 1st and Reverse gear at the same time.**

10) Align 1st/2nd shift fork with case bores and slide shift rail into place, securing shift fork with set screw. Coat input gear bore with thin film of grease. Install 15 roller bearings into bore. Place front blocking ring in 3rd/overdrive synchronizer. Place dummy bearing (T77L-7025-B) on output shaft to support and align shaft assembly in case. See Fig. 8.

FORD MOTOR CO. RUG OVERDRIVE 4-SPEED (Cont.)

Fig. 8: Exploded View of Output Shaft Assembly

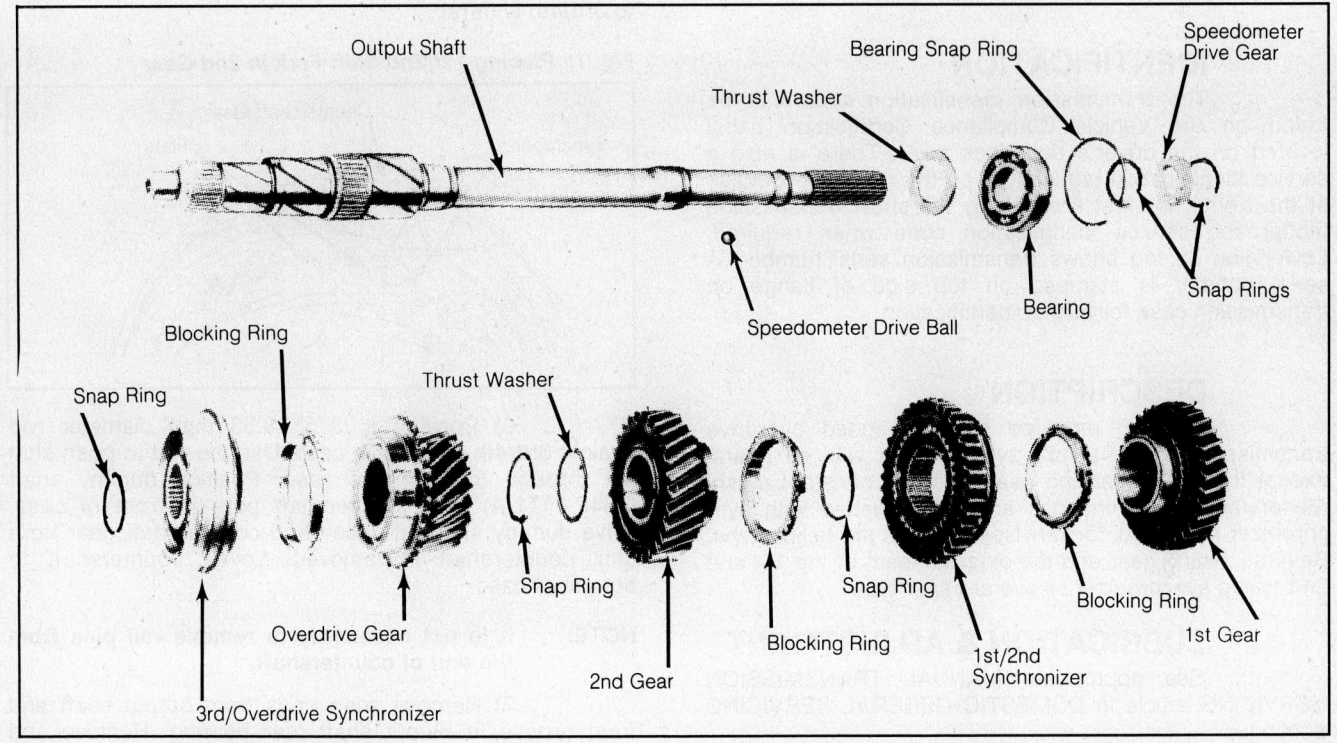

NOTE: A thick film of grease could plug lubrication holes and restrict lubrication of bearings.

11) Place input shaft gear into case. Output shaft pilot must enter roller bearings in input gear bore. Position input shaft bearing on input shaft. Slowly and evenly press bearing onto shaft and into case. Install snap rings on input shaft and input shaft bearing. Place new gasket on input shaft bearing retainer. Dip retainer attaching bolts in sealer and install retainer on case. See Fig. 9.

12) Remove dummy bearing from output shaft. Press output shaft bearing onto output shaft and into case. Install snap rings on output shaft and output shaft bearing. Ensure that output shaft bearing aligns with bore and countershaft is not interferring with output shaft assembly.

Fig. 9: Exploded View of Input Shaft Assembly

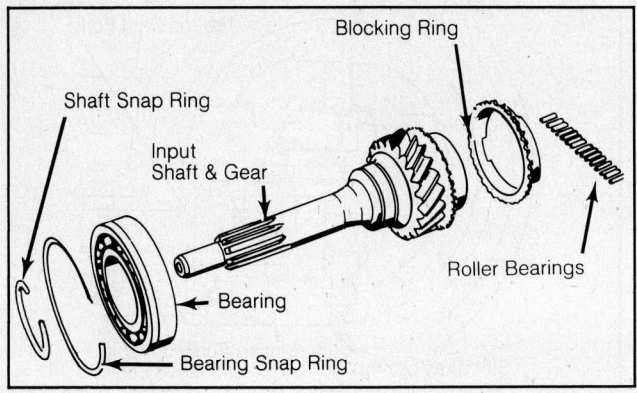

13) Position transmission in vertical position. Align countershaft gear bore and thrust washers with bore in case. Install countershaft into case. Install extension housing to case using new gasket. Pour lubricant over entire gear train while rotating input shaft.

14) Try each shift fork in all positions to ensure proper operation. Install remaining detent plug in case. Install long spring (retained by case) to secure detent plug. Install cover with new gasket. Coat 3rd/overdrive shift rail plug bore with sealant and install new expansion plug.

TIGHTENING SPECIFICATIONS

Application	Ft. Lbs. (N.m)
Access Cover-to-Case Screw	20-25 (28-33)
Detent Bolt-to-Case	10-15 (14-20)
Extension Housing Bolts	42-50 (57-67)
Filler Plug	10-20 (14-27)
Gear Shift Lever Attaching Nuts	18-23 (25-31)
Input Shaft Bearing Retainer	19-25 (26-33)

Manual Transmissions

FORD MOTOR CO. 4-SPEED – T.O.D. OVERDRIVE

Bronco, F150/F250

IDENTIFICATION

The transmission identification code can be found on the Vehicle Compliance Certification Label located on the driver's door lock pillar. There is also a service identification tag located on the right side of case at the front. The first line on tag will show transmission model and service identification code when required. Lower line on tag shows transmission serial number. A serial number is stamped on top side of flange on transmission case for further identification.

DESCRIPTION

The top mounted shifter 4-speed overdrive transmission (TOD) is fully synchronized with all gears, except the reverse sliding gear, being in constant mesh. All forward speed changes are accomplished with synchronizer sleeve. All forward speed gears are helical type. Reverse sliding gear and the external teeth of the 1st and 2nd speed synchronizer sleeve are spur type.

LUBRICATION & ADJUSTMENT

See appropriate MANUAL TRANSMISSION SERVICING article in DOMESTIC GENERAL SERVICING section.

TROUBLE SHOOTING

See MANUAL TRANSMISSION TROUBLE SHOOTING article in DOMESTIC GENERAL SERVICING section.

REMOVAL & INSTALLATION

See appropriate MANUAL TRANSMISSION REMOVAL article in DOMESTIC GENERAL SERVICING section.

TRANSMISSION DISASSEMBLY

1) Mount transmission in a holding fixture. Remove ball, boot and lever as an assembly. Remove retaining screws from boot and pad. Shift transmission into Neutral. Remove boot from cap. Place oil filter wrench (D79L-6731-A or B) around gearshift housing cap and twist off cap. Remove shift lever.

2) Insert a screwdriver into 2nd gear and shift transmission into 2nd gear. Force shift bias spring over and engage slot in 1st/2nd fork and move fork forward. *See Fig. 1.*

3) Remove 6 gear shift housing assembly-to-transmission bolts. Remove housing assembly from case by inserting a screwdriver under bosses on housing and prying up gently. Remove all gasket material.

4) Shift transmission into Neutral position. With a drain pan under extension housing, remove the 5 extension housing-to-transmission case bolts. Separate housing from case and drain the transmission fluid into pan. Remove all gasket material. If installed, remove shipping seal and discard.

5) Remove snap ring securing speedometer drive gear to output shaft. Slide gear off shaft, then remove .025" (.64 mm) speedometer gear drive ball. Use a

punch and drive out roll pin that secures 3rd/4th shift fork to 3rd/4th shift rail.

Fig. 1: Placing 1st/2nd Shift Fork in 2nd Gear

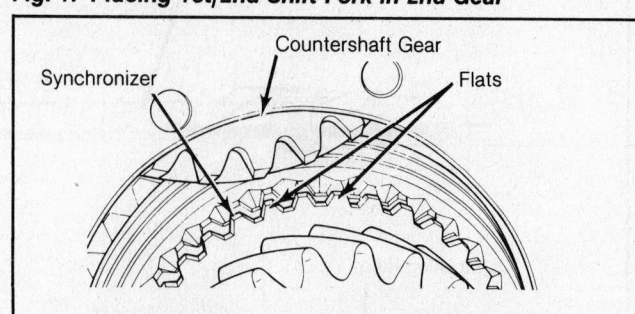

6) Position a .375" (9.53 mm) diameter rod against 3rd/4th shift rail in case. Use the rod to push shift rail through the front of case. Position dummy shaft (T64P-7111-A) over countershaft bore in front of case. Drive dummy shaft into case and countershaft gear bore until countershaft is removed. Lower countershaft to bottom of case.

NOTE: It is not necessary to remove roll pins from the end of countershaft.

7) Remove snap rings from output shaft and from groove in output shaft rear bearing. Remove and discard output shaft rear bearing. Remove 4 input shaft retainer-to-case bolts and remove retainer by prying in the 2 notches located at 11 and 1 o'clock. Remove all gasket material.

8) Remove snap rings securing input shaft bearing to shaft and snap ring from groove in bearing. Remove retainer from input shaft ball bearing. Remove front input shaft ball bearing from case and discard.

NOTE: Remove front bearing only if replacement is necessary.

9) Rotate input shaft until flat on synchronizer teeth align with teeth on countershaft gear. *See Fig. 2.* Remove input shaft from case, be careful not to drop the 15 roller bearings. Remove the 3rd/4th blocking ring from the rear of input shaft. Mark blocking ring to ensure position during reassembly.

Fig. 2: Aligning Teeth on Countershaft Gear

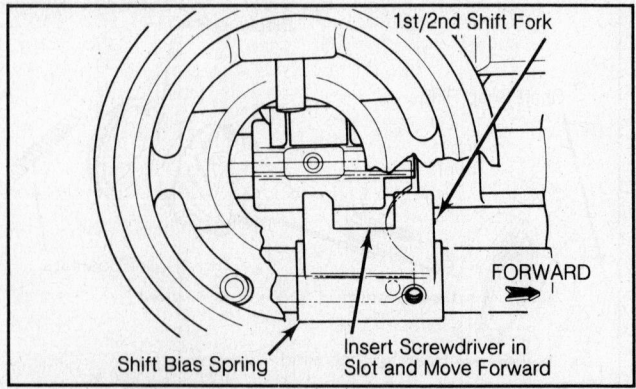

10) Remove 3rd/4th shift fork from intermediate and high clutch sleeve. Tilt output shaft and gear train assembly upwards and remove from case. Lift countershaft gear (with dummy shaft tool still inside) from

FORD MOTOR CO. 4-SPEED – T.O.D. OVERDRIVE (Cont.)

Fig. 3: *Exploded View of T.O.D. 4-Speed Transmission Assembly*

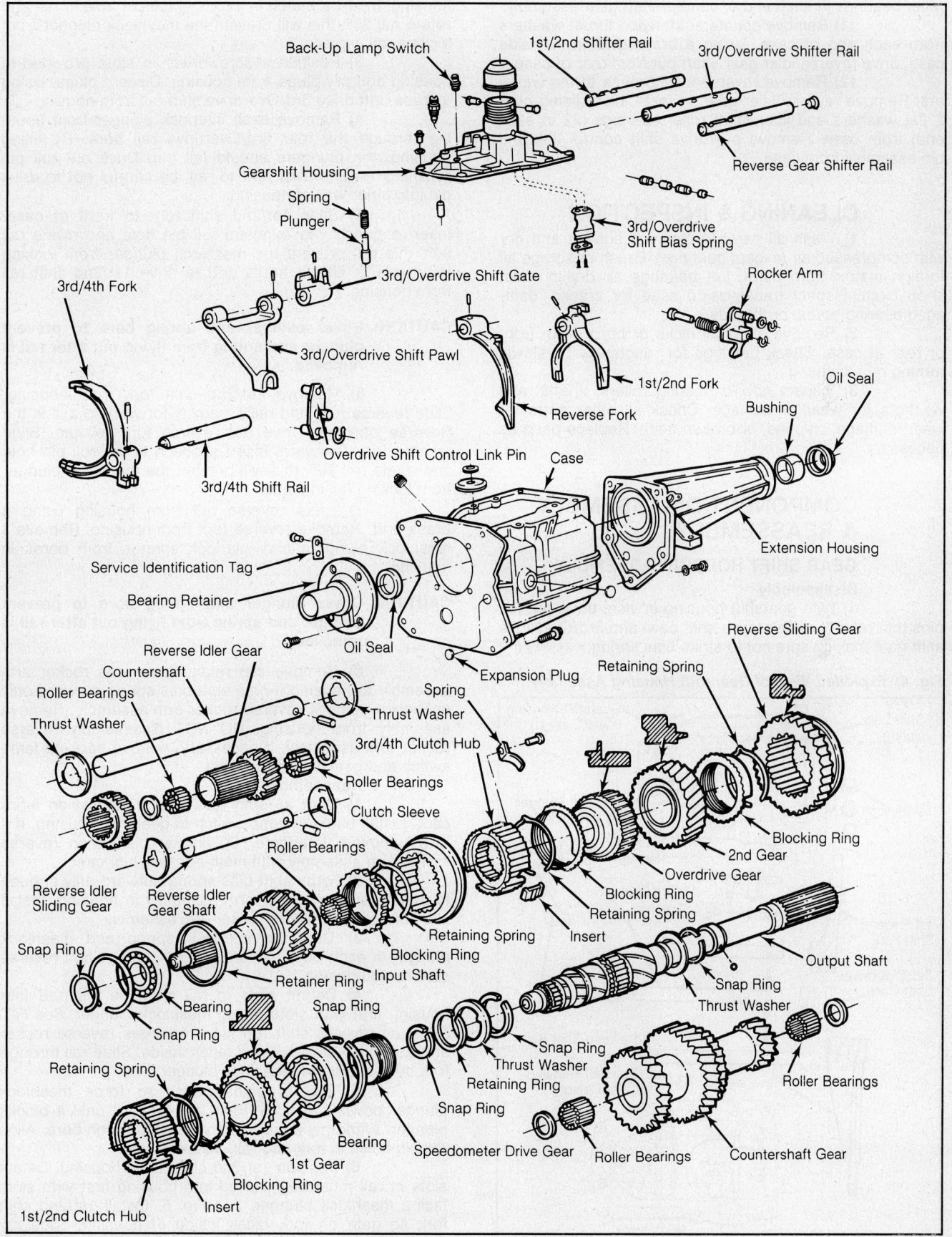

Back-Up Lamp Switch
1st/2nd Shifter Rail
3rd/Overdrive Shifter Rail
Reverse Gear Shifter Rail
Gearshift Housing
Spring
Plunger
3rd/Overdrive Shift Bias Spring
Rocker Arm
3rd/4th Fork
3rd/Overdrive Shift Gate
3rd/Overdrive Shift Pawl
1st/2nd Fork
Oil Seal
Bushing
Reverse Fork
Overdrive Shift Control Link Pin
Case
3rd/4th Shift Rail
Extension Housing
Service Identification Tag
Bearing Retainer
Oil Seal
Reverse Sliding Gear
Reverse Idler Gear
Countershaft
Expansion Plug
Retaining Spring
Roller Bearings
Spring
Thrust Washer
Thrust Washer
3rd/4th Clutch Hub
Roller Bearings
Roller Bearings
Blocking Ring
Clutch Sleeve
2nd Gear
Overdrive Gear
Roller Bearings
Blocking Ring
Retaining Spring
Blocking Ring
Insert
Reverse Idler
Sliding Gear
Reverse Idler
Gear Shaft
Retaining Spring
Snap Ring
Output Shaft
Snap Ring
Retainer Ring
Input Shaft
Snap Ring
Thrust Washer
Snap Ring
Bearing
Snap Ring
Snap Ring
Thrust Washer
Retaining Ring
Roller Bearings
Retaining Spring
Snap Ring
Bearing
Speedometer Drive Gear
Roller Bearings
Countershaft Gear
1st Gear
Blocking Ring
Insert
1st/2nd Clutch Hub

FORD MOTOR CO. 4-SPEED – T.O.D. OVERDRIVE (Cont.)

bottom of transmission case. Be careful not to drop the 21 roller bearings in each end of countershaft gear assembly.

11) Remove countershaft nylon thrust washers from each end of case. Using a brass drift from inside case, drive reverse idler gear shaft out from rear of case.

12) Remove reverse idler bronze thrust washers. Remove reverse idler gear, reverse idler sliding gear 2 flat washers and idler shaft roller bearings (22 in each end) from case. Remove overdrive shift control link and pin assembly from case.

CLEANING & INSPECTION

1) Wash all parts in cleaning solvent and dry with compressed air (except bearings). Brush or scrape all foreign matter from parts. Let bearings air dry in clean shop cloth. Inspect transmission case for cracks, damaged bearing bores, or threads.

2) Remove all small nicks or burrs from front or rear of case. Check bearings for roughness by slowly turning race by hand.

3) Inspect needle bearing rollers, shafts, and washers for wear or damage. Check all other parts for wear, damage, chipped, or broken teeth. Replace parts as necessary.

COMPONENT DISASSEMBLY & REASSEMBLY

GEAR SHIFT HOUSING ASSEMBLY
Disassembly

1) With gearshift housing in vise, drive out roll pins that retain 3rd/Overdrive shift pawl and 3rd/Overdrive shift gate making sure not to strike bias spring.

Fig. 4: Exploded View of Gearshift Housing Assembly

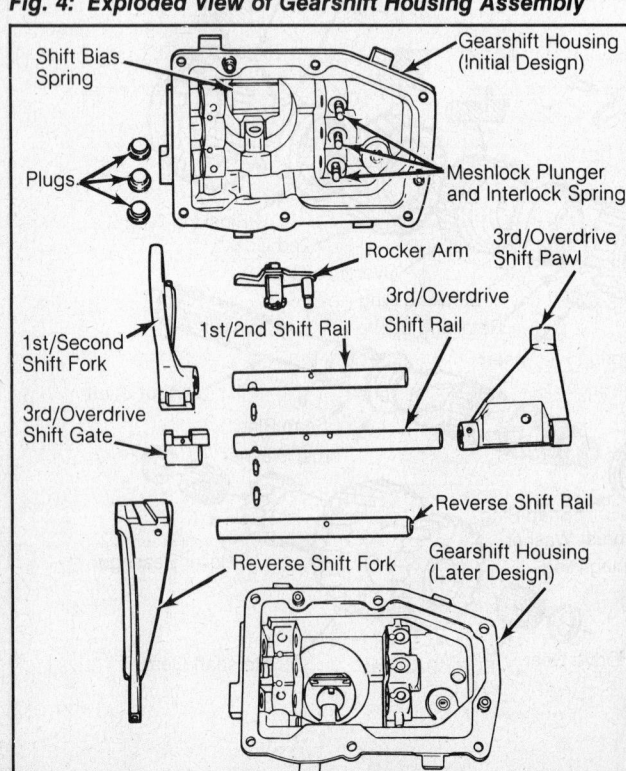

Shift Bias Spring

Gearshift Housing (Initial Design)

Plugs

Meshlock Plunger and Interlock Spring

Rocker Arm

3rd/Overdrive Shift Pawl

1st/2nd Shift Rail

3rd/Overdrive Shift Rail

1st/Second Shift Fork

3rd/Overdrive Shift Gate

Reverse Shift Rail

Reverse Shift Fork

Gearshift Housing (Later Design)

2) Slide 3rd/Overdrive shift pawl to front of housing. Insert a punch in exposed roll pin hole in rail and rotate rail 90°, this will prevent the meshlock plunger from locking rail in place.

3) Position a screwdriver in slots provided in housing and pry plugs from housing. Discard plugs. Using a brass drift drive 3rd/Overdrive shift rail from housing.

4) Remove each interlock plunger from housing through the rear 3rd/Overdrive rail bore. By tilting housing, the plungers should fall out. Drive out roll pin retaining 1st/2nd shift fork to rail, be careful not to drive pin into inner wall of housing.

5) Slide 1st/2nd shift fork to front of case. Insert a punch into exposed roll pin hole and rotate rail 90°, this will prevent the meshlock plunger from locking rail in place. Use a brass drift to drive 1st/2nd shift rail from housing.

CAUTION: Cover plunger and spring bore to prevent plunger and spring from flying out after rail is removed.

6) Remove 1st/2nd shift fork from housing. Slide reverse fork and rail assembly forward so it is in the Reverse position. Drive out reverse fork roll pin. Slide reverse fork rearward, insert a punch in the roll pin hole and rotate rail 90°, this will prevent the meshlock plunger from locking rail in place.

7) Drive reverse rail from housing using a brass drift. Remove reverse fork from housing. Remove 3 meshlock plungers and interlock springs from bores in housing.

CAUTION: Cover plunger and spring bore to prevent plunger and spring from flying out after rail is removed.

8) Remove clip retaining reverse rocker arm assembly to housing. Force shift bias spring outward only enough to remove reverse rocker arm assembly. Remove assembly from housing. DO NOT disassembly reverse rocker arm assembly. If necessary, remove back-up lamp switch and gasket from housing.

Reassembly

1) Coat all shift rails with transmission lubricant. Install back-up lamp switch in gearshift housing, if it was removed. Lubricate "O" ring and shaft on reverse rocker arm assembly with multi-purpose lubricant.

2) Force shift bias spring outward only enough to install reverse rocker arm assembly in housing. Install clip that retains reverse rocker arm assembly.

3) Drop an interlock spring and meshlock plunger in each bore in front of housing. Position reverse shift rail in housing.

4) Detent slots in rail must be inserted into housing first with slots facing meshlock plunger. *See Fig. 5.* Install reverse shift fork so it engages reverse rocker arm assembly and fork pad faces inside. Slide rail through fork bore and up to meshlock plunger.

5) Use a small punch to force meshlock plunger down into bore. Push rail forward until it blocks plunger. Withdraw punch and push rail through bore. Align roll pin holes in fork and rail. Install roll pin.

6) Position 1st/2nd shift rail in housing. Detent slots in rail must be inserted into housing first with slots facing meshlock plunger. *See Fig. 5.* Install 1st/2nd shift fork so gate on fork faces inside of housing. Slide rail through fork and up to meshlock plunger. Repeat step **5)**.

FORD MOTOR CO. 4-SPEED – T.O.D. OVERDRIVE (Cont.)

Fig. 5: Shift Rails Showing Detent Slots

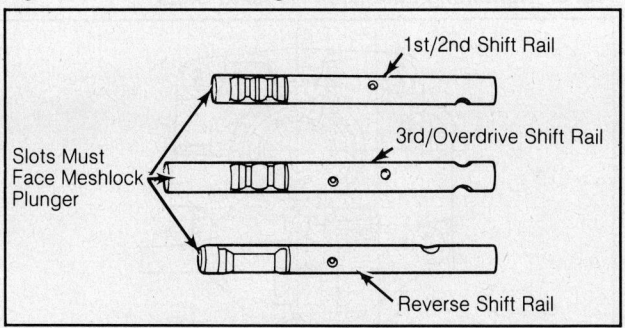

7) Ensure that 1st/2nd and reverse shift forks are in Neutral position. The 1st/2nd fork should be in alignment. The 1st/2nd fork should be in center detent position. The reverse fork should be shifted fully rearward.

8) Install interlock plungers through 3rd/Overdrive bore in rear of housing. One plunger will be positioned against the reverse shift rail. The other plunger will be positioned against the 1st/2nd shift rail.

9) Position 3rd/Overdrive shift rail in housing. Detent slots in rail must be inserted into housing first with slots facing meshlock plunger. Place 3rd/Overdrive shift gate in housing so slot in gate faces down and the small tab is rearward in housing. Slide rail forward until it is just through gate.

10) Install interlock pin to the rear of 3rd/Overdrive shift rail. Place 3rd/Overdrive shift pawl in housing. Position pawl so that slot is on reverse rail side of housing. Slide rail through pawl up to plunger.

11) Repeat step 5). Align roll pin holes in pawl, gate and rail. Install roll pin. Apply stud and bearing mount sealer to the outside diameter of shift rail cup plugs. Drive cups into bores located in rear of housing. Place gearshift housing assembly in 2nd gear for installation.

SYNCHRONIZER ASSEMBLY
Disassembly

Scribe alignment marks on hub and sleeve of synchronizer before disassembly. Push synchronizer hub

Fig. 6: Exploded View of Synchronizers

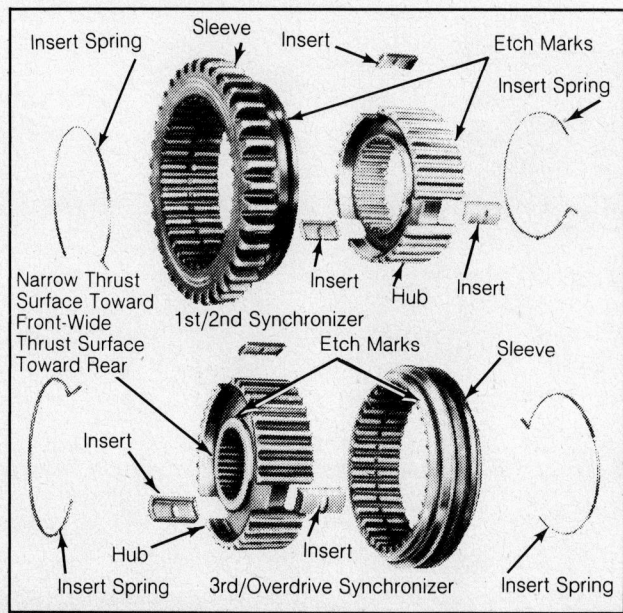

from each synchronizer sleeve. Separate inserts and insert springs from hubs. DO NOT mix parts of 1st and 2nd synchronizer with 3rd and Overdrive synchronizer.

Reassembly

Position hub in sleeve, ensure that alignment marks are properly indexed. Place 3 inserts into place on hub. Install insert springs making sure that tab is located in a common insert rotating in opposite directions. DO NOT stagger springs.

OUTPUT SHAFT AND GEAR TRAIN
Disassembly

1) Before disassembling output shaft and gear train assembly, end play of 1st, 2nd and overdrive gears must be checked. See Fig. 7. End play is measured with the 1st gear thrust washer clamped tight against the shoulder of output shaft. If measurements exceed specifications, rebuild assembly with new components. See End Play Specification Chart.

Fig. 7: Checking Gear Train End Play

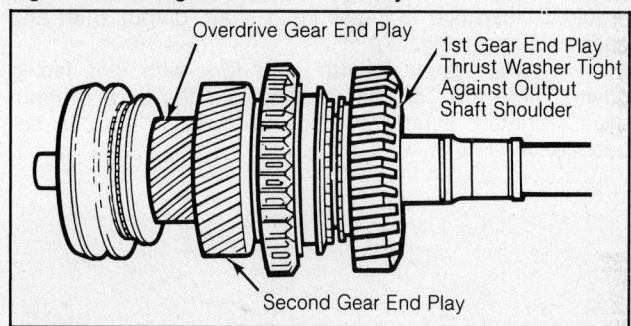

END PLAY SPECIFICATIONS

Application	End Play In. (mm)
1st Gear	.005-.024 (.127-.609)
2nd Gear	.003-.021 (.076-.553)
Countershaft Gear	.004-.018 (.10-.46)
Overdrive Gear	.009-.023 (.228-.584)
Reverse Idler Gear	.005-.023 (.127-.584)

2) Remove snap ring from front of output shaft. Remove 3rd/4th synchronizer assembly. Remove Overdrive gear from shaft. Remove next snap ring and second gear thrust washer from shaft. Slide the 2nd gear and blocking ring from shaft.

3) Remove next snap ring. Using a press, remove 1st/2nd synchronizer assembly. Synchronizer assembly is a press fit on output shaft.

Reassembly

1) Lubricate 1st gear journal with multi-purpose lubricant. Press 1st/2nd synchronizer assembly onto front of output shaft, making sure shift fork groove is facing towards rear of shaft. Install 1st gear and blocking ring on rear of shaft.

2) Install snap ring in front of 1st/2nd synchronizer assembly. Position blocking ring on 2nd gear. Lubricate 2nd gear journal on output shaft with multi-purpose lubricant. Slide 2nd gear with blocking ring onto front of shaft. Ensure that the inserts in synchronizer engage notches in blocking ring.

3) Install 2nd gear thrust washer and snap ring. Lubricate Overdrive gear journal with multi-purpose grease. Slide overdrive gear onto shaft with coned synchronizer surface facing towards the front.

FORD MOTOR CO. 4-SPEED – T.O.D. OVERDRIVE (Cont.)

4) Slide 3rd/4th synchronizer assembly onto shaft making sure inserts in synchronizer engage notches in blocking ring and small thrust surface is facing forward. Install snap ring on front of output shaft.

TRANSMISSION REASSEMBLY

1) Reverse disassembly procedures, noting the following: coat all moving parts with a multi-purpose grease. Use anaerobic sealer (gasket eliminator) to form a mating surface gasket instead of using a gasket. Coat bolts with threadlock and sealer prior to installation.

2) Ensure that square shouldered pin is positioned towards bottom of case. Align tabs on reverse idler gear thrust washer with slots in case. There are 22 roller bearings on each end of reverse idler shaft. Grooved portion of sliding gear for reverse fork must face front of case when installed.

3) There are 21 roller bearings on each end of countershaft. Countershaft gear must be at bottom of case with countershaft removed in order to obtain required clearance to install input shaft, output shaft and gear train assembly.

4) Install 3rd/4th shift fork with slot facing down. There are 15 roller bearings for the bore of input shaft. Tighten extension housing bolts in proper sequence. *See Fig. 8.*

Fig. 8: *Tightening Extension Housing Bolts*

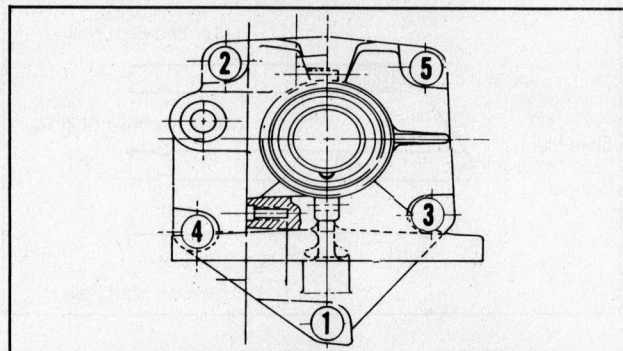

5) Welch plug must not protrude above face of case or more than .06" (1.52 mm) below face. Position 3rd/4th shift rail so that the flat on rail faces front and bottom of case. Install gearshift housing assembly in 2nd gear position. Ensure that reverse idler gear is positioned rearward.

TIGHTENING SPECIFICATIONS

Application	Ft. Lbs. (N.m)
Back-Up Lamp Switch	8-12 (11-16)
Extension Housing Bolts	42-50 (54-67)
Filler Plug	10-20 (14-27)
Gearshift Housing-to-Case Bolts	18-22 (25-29)
Input Shaft Bearing Retainer	12-16 (16-21)

FORD MOTOR CO. 4-SPEED 85ET

Capri, Mustang

TRANSMISSION IDENTIFICATION

This transmission is manufactured in Germany. Unit may be identified by tag located under lower left side of extension housing-to-case bolts. The first line on tag shows transmission model prefix, suffix and build date code. Lower line on tag shows transmission serial number.

DESCRIPTION

Four speed fully synchronized, except reverse. Forward gears are in constant mesh. Gear changes are through forged blocker ring synchronized units. Engagement of two gears at once is prevented by means of a selector interlock plate pivoted in the transmission case. This plate engages with selector forks which are not in use and holds them positively in disengaged position.

Selective snap rings compensate for tolerances which must be allowed in manufacture. Whenever overhauling the gear case where snap ring removal is required, ensure correct size new snap ring is properly installed.

LUBRICATION & ADJUSTMENT

See the appropriate article in MANUAL TRANSMISSION SERVICING Section.

REMOVAL & INSTALLATION

See the appropriate article in MANUAL TRANSMISSION REMOVAL Section.

TRANSMISSION DISASSEMBLY

1) With transmission case mounted to holding fixture (T57L-500-B), remove clutch release bearing and lever. Remove flywheel housing mount bolts. Separate housing from transmission case.

Fig. 1: Removing Detent Plunger Assembly from Case

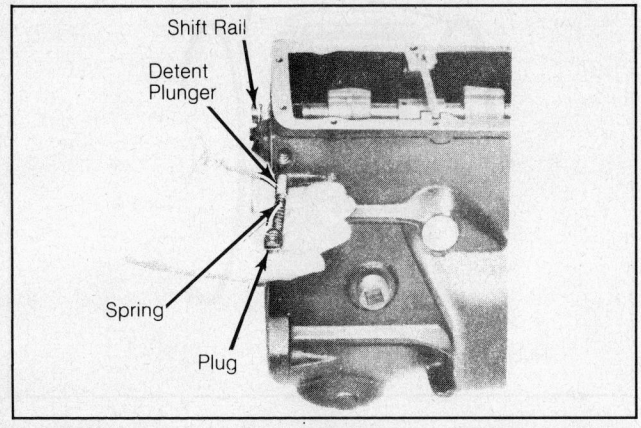

2) Remove cover mount bolts. Remove cover, discard gasket and drain gear oil. Remove threaded plug, spring and shift rail detent plunger from upper left front side of transmission case. See Fig. 1.

3) Working from inside transmission case, drive access plug from rear of case using proper size drift and hammer. See Fig. 2.

Fig. 2: Removing Access Plug from Case

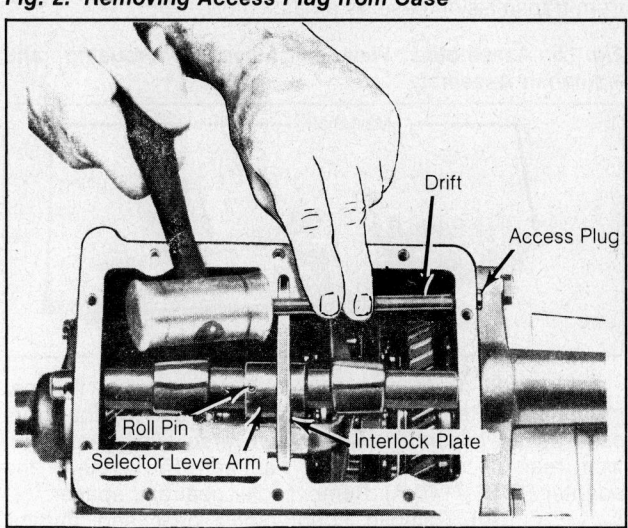

4) Working through access plug hole, drive retaining pin from case. Remove interlock plate. See Fig. 3.

Fig. 3: Removing Interlock Retaining Pin

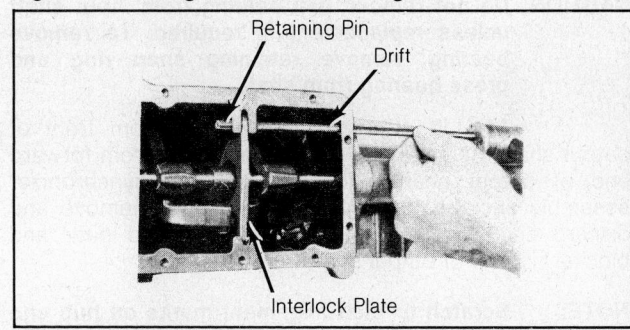

5) Remove roll pin from selector lever arm. Tap front end of shift rail to displace plug at rear of extension housing. Remove shift rail from extension housing and case. See Fig. 4. Lift selector arm and shift forks from case.

Fig. 4: Removing Shift Rail from Extension Housing

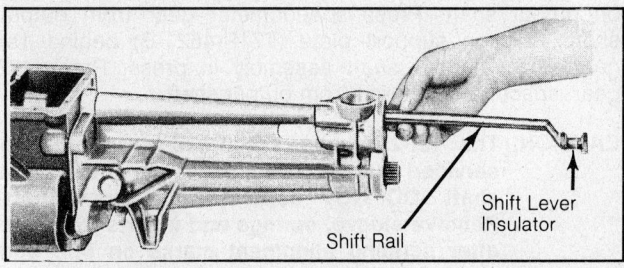

6) Remove 4 extension housing mount bolts. Tap housing with plastic mallet to loosen it from case.

FORD MOTOR CO. 4-SPEED 85ET (Cont.)

Rotate housing until countershaft is aligned with cutaway in housing flange.

7) With brass drift, drive countershaft rearward until it just clears front of case. Install dummy shaft (T71P-7111-B or equivalent) into case and countershaft gear. Drive countershaft from case.

8) Lower dummy shaft and countershaft gear to bottom of case. Lift extension housing and mainshaft from transmission case as an assembly.

Fig. 5: Assembled View of Extension Housing and Mainshaft Assembly

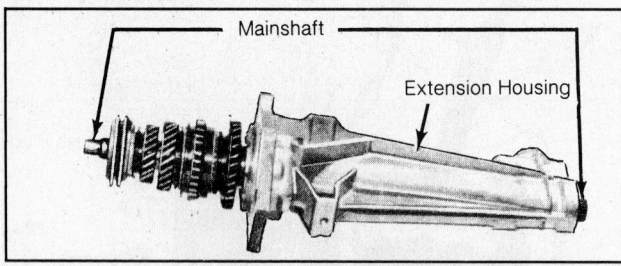

9) Remove 4 input shaft bearing retainer mount bolts. Remove input shaft bearing and retainer from case as an assembly. Remove reverse idler gear shaft from rear of case using slide hammer (T50T-100-A) and adapter (T71P-7140-A). Remove idler gear and spacer.

10) Remove countershaft gear and dummy shaft from bottom of case. Separate bearing retainer washers, bearings and dummy shaft from countershaft gear. Remove bearing retainer and pilot bearing from input shaft gear. Pry oil seal from bearing retainer.

CAUTION: Do not remove ball bearing from input shaft unless replacement is required. To remove bearing, remove retaining snap ring and press bearing from shaft.

11) Lift 4th gear blocker ring from front of output shaft. Remove and discard snap ring from forward end of output shaft. Slide 3rd-4th gear synchronizer assembly and 3rd gear from output shaft. Remove and discard snap ring. Slide thrust washer, 2nd gear and blocker ring off of output shaft.

NOTE: Scratch or etch alignment marks on hub and sleeve of synchronizer before disassembly.

12) Disassemble synchronizer assembly by pulling sleeve off hub. Remove inserts and springs. Remove and discard snap ring retaining output shaft bearing in extension housing. Press or tap output shaft assembly from housing with plastic hammer.

13) Remove snap ring which retains bearing on output shaft. Press speedometer gear from output shaft. Position support plate (T71P-4621-B) behind 1st gear. Place output shaft assembly in press. Press 1st gear, spacer and bearing from output shaft.

CAUTION: The 1st-2nd gear synchronizer and hub is serviced as an assembly with the output shaft. DO NOT separate hub from shaft. Remove sleeve, springs and inserts from hub after scribing alignment marks on hub and sleeve. Only springs and inserts are serviceable.

14) Inspect shift rail bushing and, if necessary for replacement, drive bushing from rear of extension housing with 9/16" socket and extension. Do not remove bushing if serviceable. Pry shift rail seal from extension housing. Remove remaining shift linkage from case.

15) Check extension housing oil seal (lower) for wear or damage. If necessary, remove seal using oil seal remover (T71P-7657-A). Install new seal using oil seal installer (T71P-7095-A) and adapter. Ensure adapter shoulder faces away from seal when installing.

CLEANING & INSPECTION

Wash all parts except seals, "O" rings and ball bearings in cleaning solvent and dry with compressed air. Rotate ball bearings in solvent until lubricant is removed. Hold bearing assembly to prevent rotation and blow dry. Dip bearings in transmission lubricant and wrap in clean, lint-free cloth until ready for installation.

If equipped, clean magnet in bottom of transmission case with kerosene. Inspect case for cracks, wear, damaged bearing bores or damaged threads. Remove all small nicks or burrs from front of case. Check all gears for wear, chipped or broken teeth and damage. Replace parts as necessary. Inspect speedometer gear for stripped teeth or other damage. Replace with correct size gear as necessary.

TRANSMISSION REASSEMBLY

1) With 3/4" socket, drive new shift rail seal into rear of transmission case. If shift rail bushing was removed from extension housing, drive new one into place with 9/16" socket and extension.

2) If 1st-2nd gear synchronizer was disassembled, slide synchronizer sleeve over hub. Ensure alignment marks made at disassembly are aligned and shift fork groove is toward front of shaft.

3) Locate an insert in each of 3 slots cut in hub. Install an insert spring inside synchronizer sleeve beneath inserts. The tab on end of spring must locate in "U" section of insert. Fit other spring on opposite face making sure tab is in same recess and spring is in opposite rotational direction. See Fig. 6.

Fig. 6: Synchronizer Spring Installation

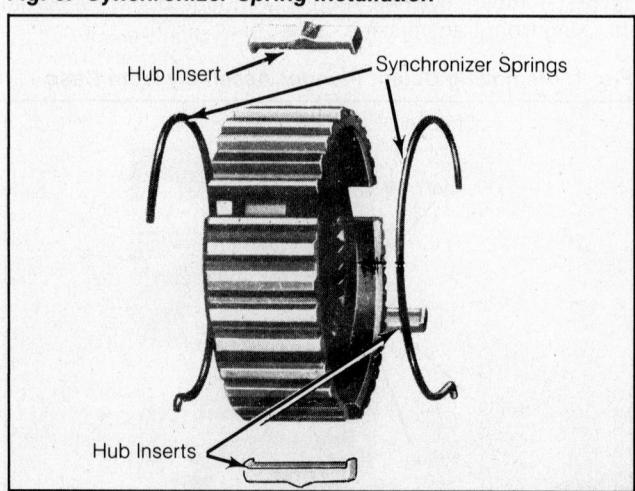

FORD MOTOR CO. 4-SPEED 85ET (Cont.)

4) Assemble a blocker ring on 1st gear side of 1st-2nd gear synchronizer. Slide 1st gear onto output shaft so cone surface engages blocker ring. Install spacer on shaft. Ensure large diameter is toward rear of shaft.

5) Place master spacer tool (T70P-7154) in output shaft bearing bore of extension housing. *See Fig. 7.* Measure width of output shaft bearing outer race with micrometer.

Fig. 7: Using Special Gauge to Determine End Play Snap Ring Thickness

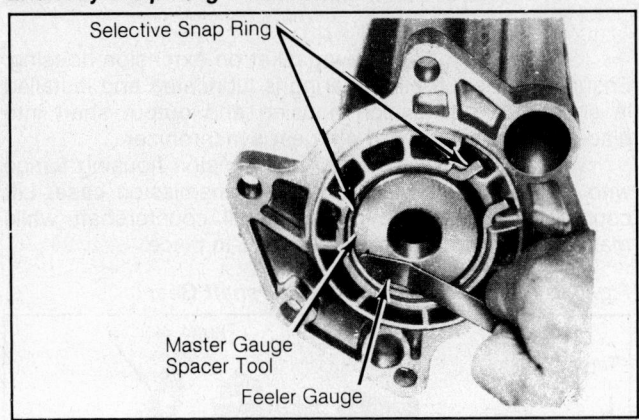

6) The difference in thickness between master gauge and bearing outer race will determine thickness of selective snap ring required to eliminate end play. If bearing race thickness is more than that stamped on master gauge, decrease snap ring thickness. If thickness is less, increase snap ring thickness to remove end play.

OUTPUT SHAFT BEARING-TO-CASE SNAP RING TABLE

Part No. [1]	Identification (Color or Letter)	Thickness In. (mm)
A	Copper	.0679 (1.725)
B	W	.0689 (1.750)
C	V	.0699 (1.775)
D	U	.0709 (1.801)
E	None	.0719 (1.826)
F	Blue	.0728 (1.849)
G	Black	.0738 (1.875)
H	Brown	.0748 (1.899)

[1] - All part numbers are preceded by "D1FZ-7030-".

7) Position selected snap ring and output shaft bearing on shaft. Place assembly in hydraulic press. Press bearing into place and secure with thickest snap ring that will fit groove in output shaft.

Fig. 9: Cutaway View of Transmission Showing Snap Ring Locations

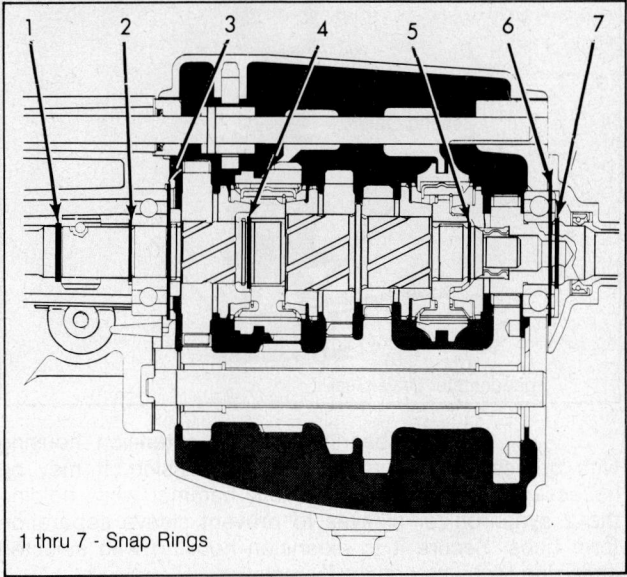

1 thru 7 - Snap Rings

8) Install 2nd gear and blocker ring on output shaft so that dog teeth face rearward. Install washer and snap ring. Install 3rd gear on output shaft so that dog teeth face forward. Install blocker ring on 3rd gear cone.

NOTE: **Apply lubricant to cones of all gears and output shaft gear journals before installation of gears. Ensure new snap rings are used in all positions.**

9) Install 3rd-4th gear synchronizer assembly on output shaft with hub boss (small diameter) facing forward. Retain 3rd-4th gear synchronizer assembly with snap ring. Pull up on synchronizer assembly so snap ring is tight in its groove. Install 4th gear blocker ring on input shaft gear cone.

10) Press speedometer drive gear onto shaft using support tool (T71P-17271-A). Press until dowels on

Fig. 8: Exploded View of Output Shaft

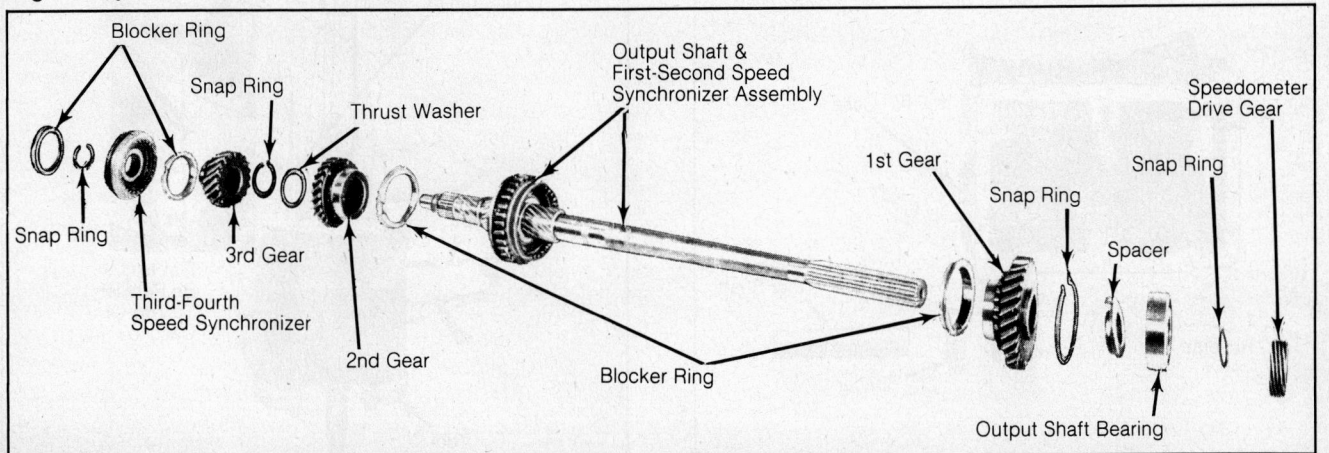

FORD MOTOR CO. 4-SPEED 85ET (Cont.)

tool just contacts bearing outer race to properly locate speedometer drive gear on shaft. *See Fig. 10.*

Fig. 10: *Installing Speedometer Drive Gear*

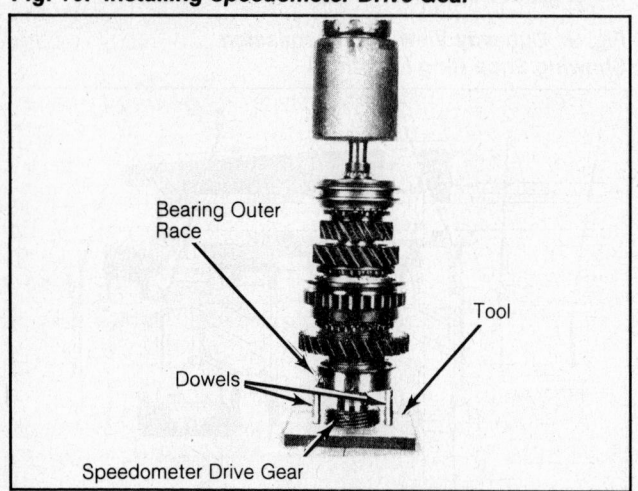

11) Coat bearing bore of extension housing with grease. Install output shaft in housing. It may be necessary to tap shaft with plastic hammer while holding the 2 synchronizer sleeves to prevent sleeve separation from hubs. Secure it to extension housing with selected snap ring that was previously installed.

12) Press bearing on input shaft. Ensure snap ring groove is toward front end of shaft. Retain with thickest snap ring that will fit groove in input shaft. Slide spacer and dummy shaft into countershaft gear. Install bearing retainer washer at each end of dummy shaft. Lubricate and load long roller bearings in small end of gear and short roller bearings in large end of gear.

13) Install retaining washer over each end of dummy shaft. Coat thrust washers with grease and install 1 on each end of dummy shaft. Make sure tabs are in same relative position so they may engage slots in case when gear is lowered into place.

14) Loop piece of rope or wire around each end of gear. Carefully install gear through rear end of case. Lower gear into place. Do not to disturb thrust washers. Ensure tabs engage slots in case. If reverse selector relay lever was removed, install it on pivot pin and secure with spring clip.

Fig. 11: *Reverse Idler Gear Assembly*

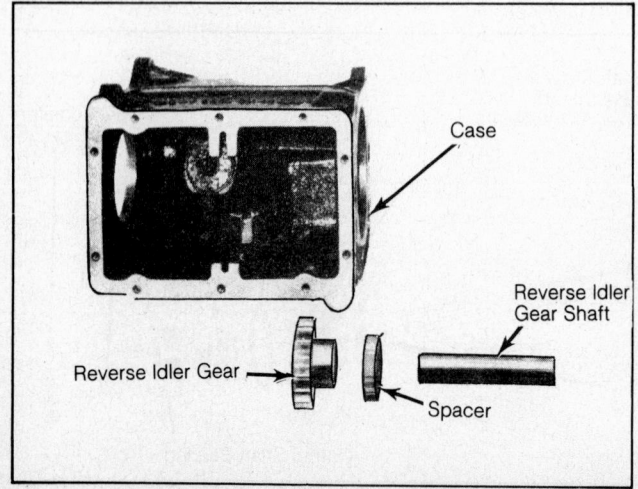

15) Hold reverse idler gear in lever with long hub toward rear of case. Slide reverse idler gear shaft into place and install spacer. *See Fig. 11.* Seat shaft into case with soft face hammer. Assemble and install input shaft into transmission case. If necessary, tap outer race of bearing with soft hammer alternately and evenly until outer snap ring seats against case.

CAUTION: Do not tap on input shaft or load will pass through bearings and may damage races and/or bearings.

16) Position new gasket on extension housing. Ensure input shaft pilot bearing is lubricated and installed in shaft. Slide extension housing and output shaft into place. Do not disturb 3rd-4th gear synchronizer.

17) Align cutaway in extension housing flange with countershaft bore in rear of transmission case. Lift countershaft gear into place. Install countershaft while making sure both thrust washers are in place.

Fig. 12: *Exploded View of Countershaft Gear*

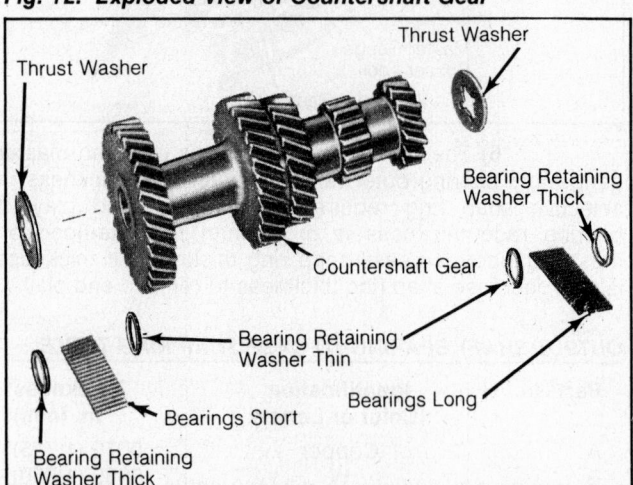

18) Make sure that flat on countershaft is toward top of case and in a horizontal position. *See Fig. 13.* Tap countershaft into case with brass hammer until front of shaft is flush with case. Rotate extension housing to align bolt holes. Coat bolts with sealer and install them loosely.

Fig. 13: *Installing Countershaft into Case*

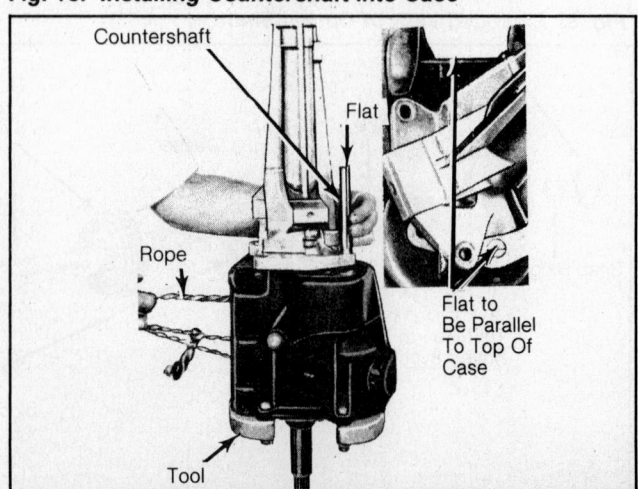

FORD MOTOR CO. 4-SPEED 85ET (Cont.)

19) Before tightening housing bolts, ensure shift rail slides freely in bore. If it binds, rotate housing slightly to free rail, then push housing into case. Tighten bolts after making sure housing does not interfere with reverse idler or countershafts.

20) Install shift forks in synchronizer sleeves. Install interlock lever with new retaining pin. Lubricate shift rail oil seal. Slide shift rail through extension housing, transmission case and 1st-2nd shift fork. Install selector arm on rail. Slide rail through 3rd-4th gear shift fork.

21) Slide rail through front of case until center detent is aligned with detent plunger bore. Install new retaining pin in selector arm. Install detent plunger, spring and plug (apply sealant to plug threads). Install new interlock lever access plug in rear of case. See Fig. 14.

Fig. 14: Installing Interlock Access Plug

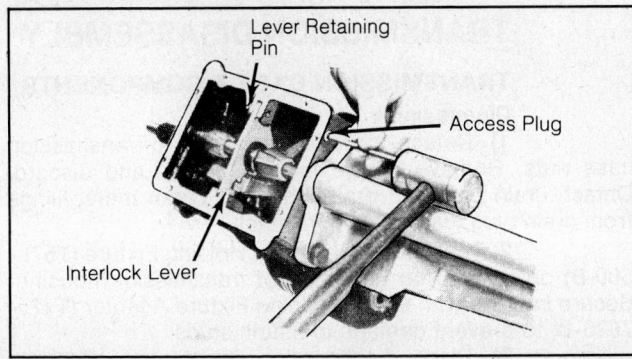

22) With seal installer tool (T71P-7050-A), drive new seal into input shaft bearing retainer until it bottoms. Ensure tension spring and lip of seal face toward transmission case. Install new "O" ring in groove provided in face of transmission case.

23) Lubricate input shaft seal journal area. DO NOT damage seal lip when installing retainer. Install input shaft bearing retainer on case. See Fig. 15 and 16. Ensure oil groove in retainer is in line with oil passage in case. Apply sealant and loosely install mount bolts but do not tighten at this time.

Fig. 15: Exploded View of Input Shaft Assembly

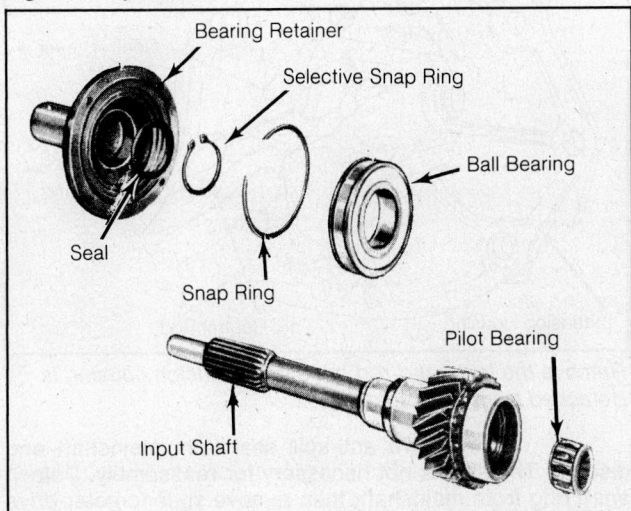

Fig. 16: Installing Input Shaft Gear

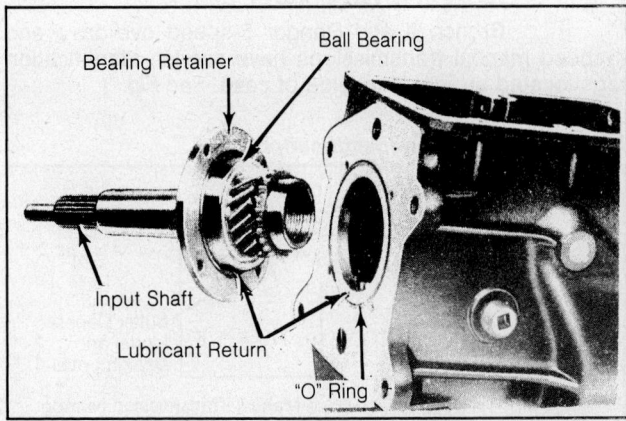

Oil groove in retainer must be in line with oil passage in case.

24) Install flywheel housing and tighten mount bolts. Tighten front bearing retainer bolts. Coat machined area of front bearing retainer with grease and install clutch release arm and bearing. Apply sealant to new extension housing plug. Using installer (T70P-6011-A), install plug in extension housing, behind shift rail.

25) Place new cover gasket on case. Install cover with vent toward rear. Apply sealant to threads of left front cover bolt to seal bolt hole that aligns with detent plunger hole. Install and tighten 10 cover mount bolts. Fill transmission with 2.8 pts. (1.3L) of gear oil until level is to the bottom of filler hole.

TIGHTENING SPECIFICATIONS

Application	Ft. Lbs. (N.m)
Detent Plug	12-14 (16-18)
Extension Housing-to-Case Bolt	33-36 (45-48)
Filler Plug-to-Case	24-27 (33-36)
Flywheel Housing-to-Engine Block	38-55 (52-75)
Flywheel Housing-to-Transmission Case	35-45 (47-61)
Shift Lever Bolts	17-25 (24-33)

	INCH Lbs. (N.m)
Cover-to-Case Screw	96-120 (11-13)
Input Shaft Bearing Retainer	96-120 (11-13)
Shift Lever Boot Mount Bolt	35-80 (4-9)

Manual Transmissions
FORD MOTOR CO. 4 & 5-SPEED BRONCO II & RANGER – GASOLINE

IDENTIFICATION

Bronco II and Ranger 5-speed overdrive and 4-speed manual transmissions have service identification tags located at right front side of case. *See Fig. 1.*

Fig. 1: Transmission Identification Tag

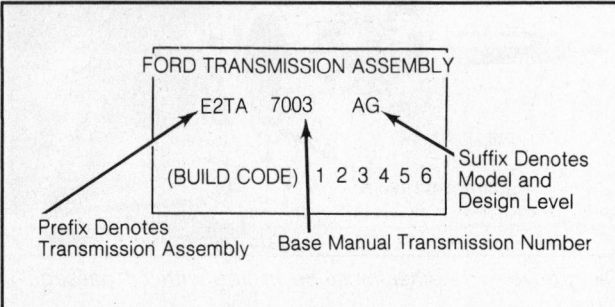

Tag is found at right front side of transmission case.

TRANSMISSION IDENTIFICATION CODES

Application	Code
4-Speed	X
5-Speed Overdrive	5

DESCRIPTION

The 4 and 5 speed transmissions are very similar. The 5-speed overdrive transmission has an additional 5th gear located in the extension housing. On both transmissions, all forward gears are synchronized. The reverse gear is a constant mesh type. All forward gears are helical-cut for quiet running. The reverse gear and reverse idler gear are spur-cut.

The transmission case is of light metal construction with removable clutch and extension housings. The gearshift mechanism is a direct control with a floor shift. The floor shift mechanism is built into the extension housing.

LUBRICATION & ADJUSTMENT

See appropriate MANUAL TRANSMISSION SERVICING article in DOMESTIC GENERAL SERVICING section.

TROUBLE SHOOTING

See MANUAL TRANSMISSION TROUBLE SHOOTING article in DOMESTIC GENERAL SERVICING section.

REMOVAL & INSTALLATION

TRANSMISSION

See appropriate MANUAL TRANSMISSION REMOVAL article in DOMESTIC GENERAL SERVICING section.

SERVICE (IN VEHICLE)

GEAR SHIFT LEVER
Removal

1) Place gear shift lever in Neutral position. Detach boot retainer screws. Remove bolts attaching retainer cover to gearshift lever retainer.

2) Pull gear shift lever assembly, shim and bushing straight up and away from gear shift lever retainer. Cover shift tower opening in extension housing with a cloth to avoid dirt falling into transmission.

Installation

Install gear shift lever assembly by reversing removal procedure.

TRANSMISSION DISASSEMBLY

TRANSMISSION CASE & COMPONENTS
Disassembly

1) Detach clutch bellhousing-to-transmission case nuts. Remove clutch housing gasket and discard. Detach drain plug and drain lubricant. Clean metal filings from drain plug magnet, then reinstall.

2) Position Bench Mount Holding Fixture (T57L-500-B) onto studs on right side of transmission housing. Secure in place with Bench Holding Fixture Adapter (T77J-7025-D) to prevent damage to metric studs.

3) Place transmission in Neutral. Remove speedometer sleeve and driven gear assembly from extension housing. Remove 3 bolts (14 mm) and 4 nuts (14 mm) retaining extension housing to case.

4) Raise control lever to left and slide towards rear of transmission. Slide extension housing off mainshaft, being careful not to damage oil seal. Pull control lever and rod out front end of extension housing. *See Fig. 2.* If necessary, remove back-up light switch from extension housing.

Fig. 2: Removing Control Lever & Rod

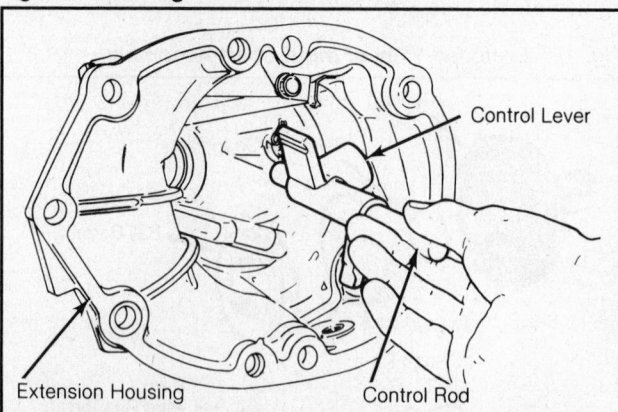

Remove the lever and rod once the extension housing is detached from the transmission.

5) Remove anti-spill seal from mainshaft and discard. The seal is not necessary for reassembly. Detach snap ring from mainshaft, then remove speedometer drive gear. Use magnet to remove lock ball from mainshaft.

6) Evenly loosen 14 retaining bolts (10 mm) from case cover. Remove cover and discard gasket. Mark shift

rails and fork for reassembly reference. Remove roll pins attaching shift rod ends to shift rod. Remove shift rod ends.

7) Gently pry bearing housing away from transmission case, being careful not to damage housing or case. Slide bearing housing off mainshaft. Remove snap ring and washer retaining mainshaft rear bearing to mainshaft.

8) Assemble Bearing Puller Ring (T77J-7025-J), Bearing Puller (T77J-7025-H) and Forcing Screw (T84T-7025-B) on Remover/Installer Tube (T75L-7025-B). Slide tool assembly over mainshaft and engage puller jaws behind rear bearing. See Fig. 3.

Fig. 3: Removing Mainshaft Rear Bearing

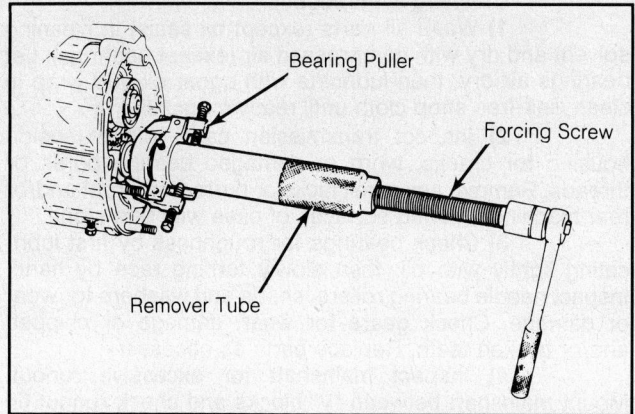

Jaws of puller must be fully behind bearing before removing.

9) Tighten jaws evenly onto bearing with wrench. Turn forcing screw to remove mainshaft rear bearing. Remove snap ring from rear end of countershaft. Assemble bearing puller, bearing puller ring and forcing screw onto remover tube.

10) Slide tool assembly over countershaft and engage puller jaws behind countershaft rear bearing. Tighten jaws evenly onto bearing with wrench. Turn forcing screw to remove bearing.

11) Remove countershaft 5th gear and spacer from rear of countershaft. Tap housing with soft mallet and remove center housing. Remove reverse idler gear and 2 spacers with housing. Detach cap screw (12 mm) from center housing, then remove idler gear shaft. See Fig. 4.

Fig. 4: Removing Idler Gear Shaft

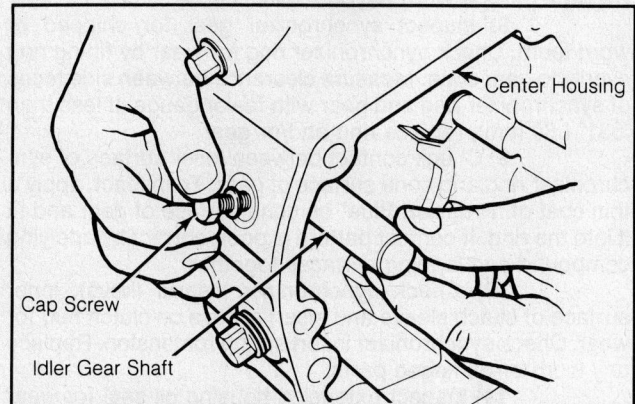

Remove cap screw from side of case and pull out shaft.

12) Remove 3 spring cap bolts. The 2 bolts on case upper portion are 17 mm and the bolt on case side is

14 mm. Using a magnet, remove detent springs and balls from case.

13) Remove 4 bolts (10 mm) retaining blind covers to case. Remove blind covers and discard gaskets. Remove roll pin from 5th/Reverse shift fork. Slide 5th/Reverse shift fork shaft out of case.

14) Shift transmission into 4th gear to provide space to drive out roll pin. Through hole in side of case, drive out roll pin from 3rd/4th shift fork. Slide 3rd/4th shift fork shaft out of rear of case.

15) Through other hole in side of case, drive out roll pin for 1st/2nd shift fork. Slide 1st/2nd shift fork shaft assembly out rear of case. Remove both interlock pins. Remove snap ring securing 5th gear to mainshaft.

16) Remove thrust washer, lock ball, 5th gear and synchronizer ring from rear of mainshaft. Install Synchronizer Ring Holder/Countershaft Spacer (T77J-7025-E) between 4th gear synchronizer ring and synchromesh gear on mainshaft. See Fig. 5.

Fig. 5: Installing Synchronizer Ring Holder

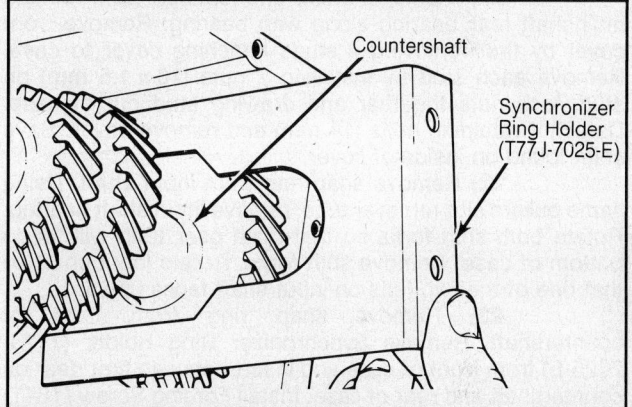

Place holder behind 3rd/4th clutch hub.

17) Shift transmission into 2nd gear to lock mainshaft and prevent assembly from rotating. Straighten staked portion of mainshaft bearing lock nut with Staking Tool (T77J-7025-F). Using Lock Nut Wrench (T77J-7025-C), remove mainshaft bearing lock nut.

18) Slide reverse gear and clutch hub assembly off mainshaft. Remove countershaft reverse gear from countershaft. If installed, remove transmission from holding fixture and set on workbench. Detach bolts (12 mm) retaining mainshaft center bearing cover to transmission. Remove bearing cover.

19) Remove countershaft center bearing using Puller (T77J-7025-H), Puller Rings (T77J-7025-J), Remover Tube (T77J-7025-B) and Forcing Screw (T84T-7025-B) on countershaft. Squarely insert jaws of puller behind center bearing retainer ring in 2 recessed areas of case. Turn forcing screw to remove bearing.

CAUTION: Do not distort retainer ring during mainshaft, countershaft and input shaft bearing removal. If necessary, before puller is installed, turn retainer ring to position split in ring midway between recessed areas of case.

20) Remove mainshaft center bearing using Puller (T77J-7025-H), Puller Rings (T77J-7025-J), Long Remover Tube (T75L-7025-C) and Forcing Screw (T84T-7025-B). Squarely insert jaws of puller behind rear mainshaft

Manual Transmissions
FORD MOTOR CO. 4 & 5-SPEED BRONCO II & RANGER – GASOLINE (Cont.)

Fig. 6: Removing Countershaft Center Bearing

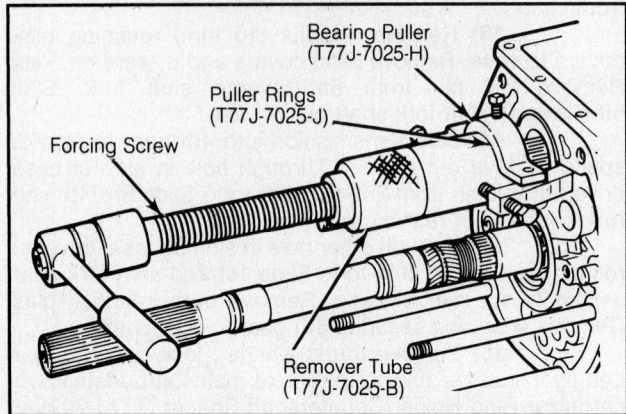

bearing retainer ring in the 2 recessed areas of case. Turn forcing screw clockwise to remove bearing.

21) Remove shim and spacer from behind mainshaft rear bearing along with bearing. Remove front cover by first removing 4 studs attaching cover to case. Remove each stud by installing 2 nuts (10 x 1.5 mm) on stud, lock nuts together and drawing stud out of case. Detach 4 retaining bolts (14 mm) and remove cover. Save shim found on inside of cover.

22) Remove snap ring from input shaft. Using same pullers and remover tube, remove input shaft bearing. Rotate both shift forks so that main gear train will fall to bottom of case. Remove shift forks. Rotate input shaft so that one of the two flats on input shaft faces upward.

23) Remove snap ring from front of countershaft. Remove Synchronizer Ring Holder (T77J-7025-E) from front of case and insert between first gear on countershaft and rear of case. Install Forcing Screw (T84T-7025-B), Press Frame (T77J-7025-N) and Press Frame Adapter (T82T-7003-BH) against countershaft assembly. *See Fig. 7.*

Fig. 7: Pressing Countershaft Rearward

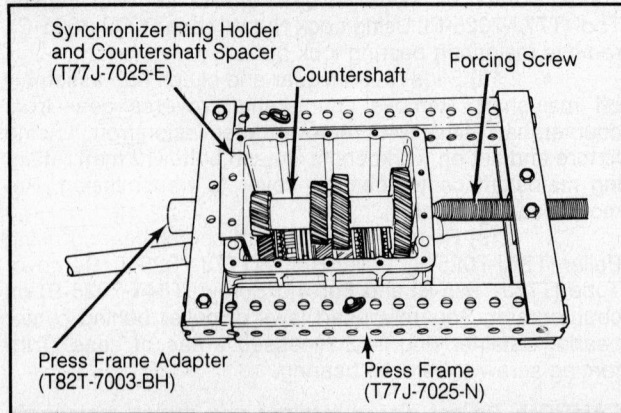

Press countershaft about 3/16".

24) Turn forcing screw clockwise to press countershaft rearward. Press countershaft about 3/16" (4.8 mm), until it contacts synchronizer ring holder/countershaft spacer.

25) Remove press frame. To remove countershaft front bearing, install puller, puller rings, remover tube and forcing screw. Squarely insert jaws of puller

behind front bearing retainer ring in 2 recessed areas in case.

26) Turn forcing screw clockwise to remove bearing. Remove shim from behind countershaft front bearing. Remove countershaft from case. Remove input shaft from case.

27) Remove synchronizer ring and caged bearing from mainshaft. Remove mainshaft and gear assembly from case. Disassembly mainshaft and countershaft as necessary. Clean and inspect gears, bearings, shafts and transmission case.

Cleaning & Inspection

1) Wash all parts (except oil seals) in cleaning solvent and dry with compressed air (except bearings). Let bearings air dry, then lubricate with qgear oil and wrap in clean, link-free shop cloth until ready to install.

2) Inspect transmission case and extension housing for cracks, worn or damaged bearing bores or threads. Remove any small nicks or burrs from front and/or rear machined mating surfaces of case with fine stone.

3) Check bearings for roughness by first lubricating lightly with oil, then slowly turning race by hand. Inspect needle bearing rollers, shafts and washers for wear or damage. Check gears for wear, damage or chipped and/or broken teeth. Replace parts as necessary.

4) Inspect mainshaft for excessive runout. Mount mainshaft between "V" blocks and check runout (in several places) using a dial indicator. Standard runout is .0012" (.030 mm). If runout exceeds specification, straighten mainshaft in a press or replace component.

5) Inspect input shaft for damaged splines, worn or rough needle bearing bore surface and/or damaged cone surface. Replace shaft as necessary. Check countershaft gear for worn or damaged gear teeth. Check countershaft for excessive runout. Replace countershaft if bent, scored or worn.

6) Inspect contact surface of shift fork (with detent ball) for wear or damage. Check contact surface of shift fork shaft (with control lever) for wear using a feeler gauge. Clearance between shift fork shaft and control lever must be less than .031" (.80 mm). Replace parts as needed.

7) Check contact surface of shift forks with clutch sleeve for wear or damage. Clearance between shift fork and clutch sleeve must be less than .020" (.50 mm). Replace parts if worn beyond specification.

8) Inspect synchronizer gear for chipped or worn teeth. Check synchronizer ring for wear by fitting ring evenly to gear cone. Measure clearance between side faces of synchronizer ring and gear with feeler gauge. If less than .031" (.80 mm), replace ring and/or gear.

9) Check contact between inner surface of synchronizer ring and cone surface of gear. To inspect, apply a thin coat of "Prussian Blue" on cone surface of gear and fit it into the ring. If contact pattern is poor, correct by applying compound and lapping surfaces together.

10) Check synchronizer inserts (keys), inner surface of clutch sleeve and insert groove on clutch hub for wear. Check synchronizer insert spring for tension. Replace any worn or damaged parts.

11) Inspect extension housing oil seal for wear or damage and replace as needed. Remove seal using Oil Seal Remover (T71P-7657-A) and install using Oil Seal Installer (T71P-7095-A). If removed, install new oil seal after extension housing is installed on transmission.

3-65

Manual Transmissions
FORD MOTOR CO. 4 & 5-SPEED BRONCO II & RANGER — GASOLINE (Cont.)

12) If extension housing rear bushing needs replacement, remove using Bushing Remover (T72J-7697). Check speedometer shaft and drive and driven gears for wear or damage. Replace parts as needed.

COMPONENT DISASSEMBLY & REASSEMBLY

CAUTION: Before beginning component and transmission reassembly procedures, 3 measurements must be performed: Mainshaft thrust play, countershaft thrust play and mainshaft bearing clearance.

NOTE: When measuring mainshaft and countershaft thrust play and mainshaft bearing clearance, ensure micrometer probe touches retainer ring shoulder (second step of bore) and micrometer rests on case outer surface. Measure bearing height from where retainer ring inner surface contacts bore shoulder to bearing outer surface.

COUNTERSHAFT
Disassembly

Remove inner race of countershaft center bearing from countershaft in press frame using Axle Bearing Seal Plate (T75L-1165-B) and Pinion Bearing Cone Remover (D79L-4621-A). *See Fig. 8.*

Fig. 8: Removing Countershaft Bearing Inner Race

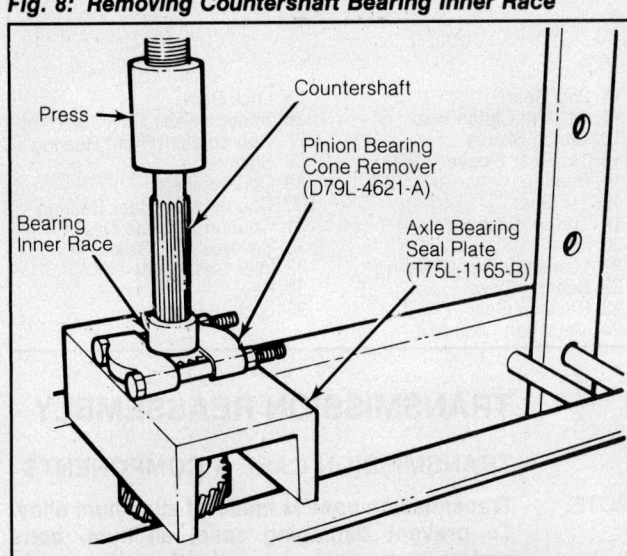

Countershaft Thrust Play

1) Check countershaft thrust play by measuring depth of countershaft front bearing bore in case (from case surface to retainer ring shoulder), using a Depth Micrometer (D80P-4201-A).

2) Measure countershaft front bearing height (from where retainer ring inner surface contacts bore shoulder to bearing outer surface).

NOTE: The difference between the two measurements indicates the required thickness of the adjusting shims.

3) The standard thrust play is 0-.004" (0-.10 mm). Adjusting shims are available in .004" (.10 mm) and .012" (.30 mm) sizes.

Reassembly

Press inner race of countershaft rear bearing onto countershaft using Center Bearing Installer (T77J-7025-K).

MAINSHAFT
Disassembly

1) Remove 1st gear and 1st/2nd synchronizer ring. Remove snap ring retainer from mainshaft. Do not mix synchronizer rings. Install Bearing Remover (T71P-4621-B) between 2nd/3rd gear.

2) Press mainshaft out of 3rd gear and 3rd/4th clutch hub sleeve. Press 1st/2nd clutch hub and sleeve assembly and 1st gear sleeve from mainshaft. Clean and inspect components.

Mainshaft Thrust Play

1) Using a Depth Micrometer (D80P-4201-A), check mainshaft thrust play. Measure depth of bearing retainer ring shoulder in transmission rear cage mainshaft bearing bore. Measure distance from retainer ring inner surface to bearing front surface.

2) The difference between the two measurements indicates the required adjusting shim thickness. Standard thrust play clearance is 0-.004" (0-.10 mm). If an adjusting shim is required, select one to bring clearance within specifications.

NOTE: Adjusting shims are available in .004" (.10 mm) and .012" (.30 mm) sizes.

Mainshaft Bearing Clearance

1) Using a Depth Micrometer (D80P-4201-A), check mainshaft bearing clearance. Measure depth of bearing retainer ring shoulder in clutch adapter plate mainshaft bearing bore. Measure distance from retainer ring inner surface to bearing front surface.

2) The difference between the two measurements indicates required adjusting shim thickness. Standard thrust play clearance is 0-.004" (0-.10 mm). If an adjusting shim is required, select one to bring clearance to within specifications.

NOTE: Adjusting shims are available in .004" (.10 mm) and .012" (.30 mm) sizes.

Reassembly

1) Assemble 1st/2nd and 3rd/4th sychromesh mechanisms by first installing clutch hub to sleeve. Place 3 synchronizer keys into clutch hub key slots, then install key springs to clutch hub.

NOTE: When installing key springs, open end tab of springs should be inserted into hub holes with springs turned in the same direction to keep spring tension on each key uniform.

2) Place synchronizer ring on 2nd gear. Position 2nd gear onto mainshaft with synchronizer ring toward rear of shaft. Slide 1st/2nd clutch hub and sleeve assembly onto mainshaft with oil grooves of clutch hub toward front of mainshaft.

CAUTION: Ensure 3 synchronizer keys in synchromesh mechanism engage notches in 2nd synchronizer ring.

Manual Transmissions
FORD MOTOR CO. 4 & 5-SPEED BRONCO II & RANGER – GASOLINE (Cont.)

Fig. 9: Exploded View of 4 & 5-Speed Transmission Mainshaft

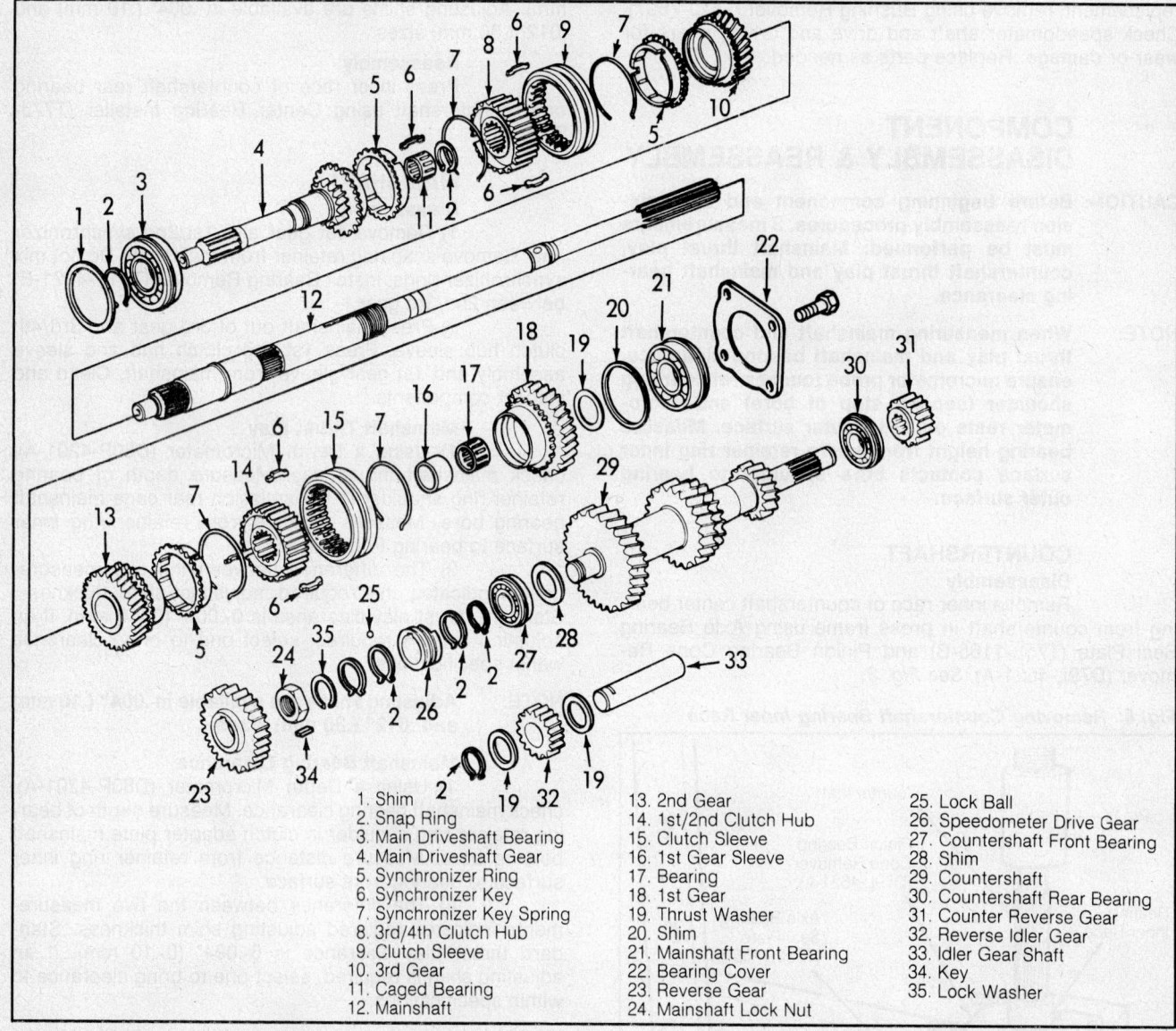

1. Shim	13. 2nd Gear	25. Lock Ball
2. Snap Ring	14. 1st/2nd Clutch Hub	26. Speedometer Drive Gear
3. Main Driveshaft Bearing	15. Clutch Sleeve	27. Countershaft Front Bearing
4. Main Driveshaft Gear	16. 1st Gear Sleeve	28. Shim
5. Synchronizer Ring	17. Bearing	29. Countershaft
6. Synchronizer Key	18. 1st Gear	30. Countershaft Rear Bearing
7. Synchronizer Key Spring	19. Thrust Washer	31. Counter Reverse Gear
8. 3rd/4th Clutch Hub	20. Shim	32. Reverse Idler Gear
9. Clutch Sleeve	21. Mainshaft Front Bearing	33. Idler Gear Shaft
10. 3rd Gear	22. Bearing Cover	34. Key
11. Caged Bearing	23. Reverse Gear	35. Lock Washer
12. Mainshaft	24. Mainshaft Lock Nut	

3) Press 2nd gear and 1st/2nd gear clutch hub and sleeve assembly into position using press and Pinion Bearing Cone Replacer Set (T53T-4621-C, T57L-4621-B, T62F-4621-A and T75L-7025-Q).

4) Insert 1st gear sleeve on mainshaft. Place synchronizer ring on 3rd gear along with caged roller bearing. Slide 3rd gear onto front of mainshaft, with synchronizer ring toward front.

5) Using press and Replacer Tube (T77J-7025-B), press 3rd/4th clutch hub and sleeve assembly onto front of mainshaft. Ensure 3 synchronizer keys in synchromesh mechanism engage notches in synchronizer ring. Install snap ring onto front of mainshaft.

6) Slide needle bearing for 1st gear onto mainshaft. Place synchronizer ring on 1st gear. Slide 1st gear onto mainshaft with synchronizer ring facing front of shaft. Rotate 1st gear, as necessary, to engage 3 notches in synchronizer ring with synchronizer keys. Install original thrust washer onto mainshaft.

TRANSMISSION REASSEMBLY

TRANSMISSION CASE & COMPONENTS

NOTE: **Transmission case is made of aluminum alloy. To prevent damaging case, all nuts, bolts and/or lock washers contacting case must have a flat washer placed next to case so that turning attaching bolt or nut will not damage aluminum surface.**

Reassembly

1) Position mainshaft and gear assembly in case. Position 1st/2nd shift fork and 3rd/4th shift fork in groove of clutch hub and sleeve assembly. Position caged bearing in front end of mainshaft.

2) Place synchronizer ring on input shaft (4th gear) and install input shaft onto front end of mainshaft. Ensure 3 synchronizer keys in 3rd/4th synchromesh mechanism engage notches in synchronizer ring.

Manual Transmissions
FORD MOTOR CO. 4 & 5-SPEED BRONCO II & RANGER — GASOLINE (Cont.)

3-67

Fig. 10: Countershaft Front Bearing Installation

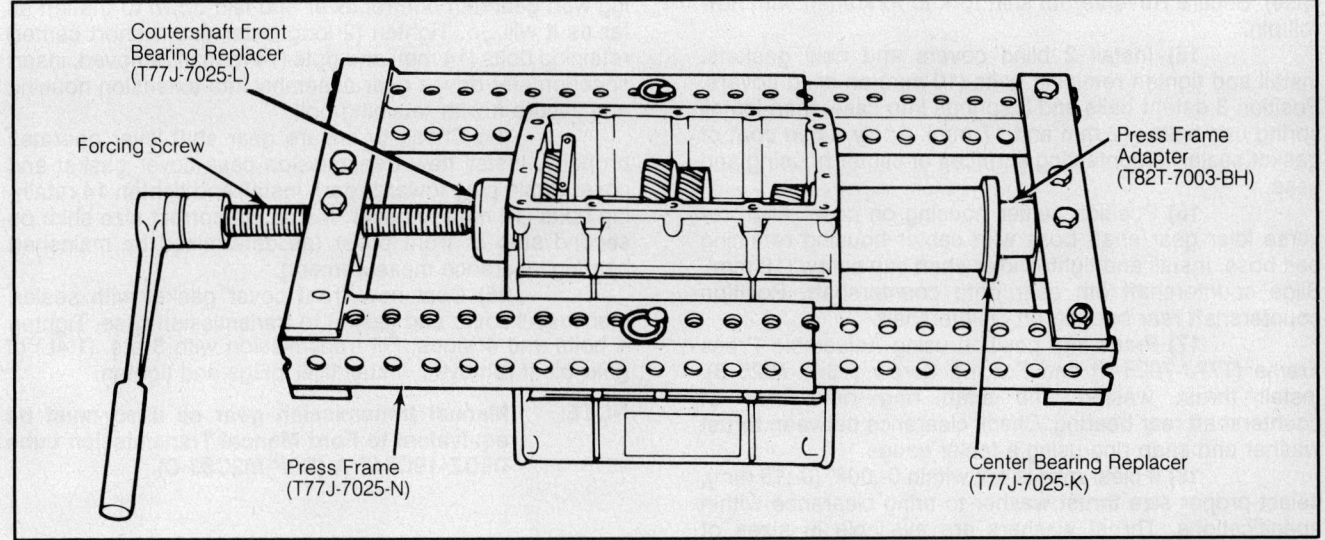

Position countershaft bearings in bores. Install installation tools.

3) Press inner race of countershaft rear bearing onto countershaft using Center Bearing Replacer (T77J-7025-K). Position countershaft gear in case. Ensure countershaft gear engages each gear of mainshaft assembly.

4) Install correct shim on mainshaft center bearing (as determined by mainshaft thrust play measurement). Position input shaft bearing and mainshaft center bearing into proper bearing bores. Ensure synchronizer and shift forks have not been moved out of position.

5) Install Synchronizer Ring Holder (T77J-7025-E) between 4th synchronizer ring and synchromesh gear on mainshaft. Install Dummy Bearing Replacer (T75L-7025-Q), Input Shaft Bearing Replacer (T82T-7003-DH), Replacer Tube (T77J-7025-M) and Press Frame (T77J-7025-N) on case. Turn forcing screw on press frame until both bearings are properly seated.

CAUTION: Synchronizer and shift forks must be properly positioned during seating of bearings. After bearings are seated, ensure both synchronizers operate freely.

6) Install input shaft bearing snap ring. Place correct shim in countershaft front bearing bore (as determined by countershaft thrust play measurement). Position countershaft front and center bearings in bores. Install press frame, press frame adapter, center and front bearing replacers and forcing screw on case. *See Fig. 10.*

7) Turn forcing screw until bearing is properly seated. Use center bearing as a pilot. Install snap ring to secure countershaft front bearing. Remove synchronizer ring holder. Install bearing cover onto transmission case. Tighten 4 retaining bolts (12 mm).

8) Install reverse idler gear and shaft with a spacer on each side of shaft. Slide countershaft Reverse gear (chamfer side forward) and spacer onto countershaft. Slide thrust washer, reverse gear, caged roller bearings and clutch hub assembly onto mainshaft.

9) Install a new lock nut onto mainshaft (hand-tight). Shift into 2nd gear and reverse gear to lock rotation of mainshaft. Tighten lock nut using Lock Nut Wrench (T77J-

7025-C). Stake lock nut into mainshaft keyway using Staking Tool (T77J-7025-F). Place 4th/3rd clutch sleeve in 3rd gear using synchronizer ring holder and Countershaft Spacer (T77J-7025-E).

10) If new synchronizers have been installed, check clearance between synchronizer key and exposed edge of synchronizer ring with a feeler gauge. If measurement is greater than .079" (2 mm), synchronizer key can pop out of position. To correct this condition, change selective fit thrust washer between mainshaft center bearing and 1st gear.

NOTE: **Thrust washers are available in sizes of .098" (2.50 mm), .118" (3 mm) and .138" (3.50 mm).**

11) If thrust washer was changed, recheck clearance again with feeler gauge. If clearance is within specifications, bend lock washer tab. Position 5th synchronizer ring on 5th gear. Slide 5th gear onto mainshaft with synchronizer ring toward front of shaft. Rotate 5th gear, as necessary, to engage 3 notches in synchronizer ring with synchronizer keys in Reverse and clutch hub assembly.

12) Install lock ball and thrust washer on rear of 5th gear. Install snap ring on rear of thrust washer. Check clearance between thrust washer and snap ring. If clearance is not within .004"-.012" (.10-.30 mm), select proper size thrust washer to bring clearance within specifications.

NOTE: **Thrust washers are available in sizes of .2362" (6 mm), .2441" (6.20 mm), .252" (6.40 mm), .2559" (6.50 mm), .2598" (6.60 mm), .2638" (6.70 mm), .2677" (6.80 mm), .2756" (7 mm) and .2835" (7.20 mm).**

13) Slide 1st/2nd shift fork shaft assembly into case (front rear of case). Secure 1st/2nd shift fork to fork shaft with a new roll pin. Insert interlock pin into transmission using Lock-Out Pin Replacer Set (T72J-7280). Shift transmission into 4th gear.

14) Slide 3rd/4th shift fork shaft into case (from rear of case). Secure 3rd/4th shift fork to fork shaft with a new roll pin. Insert interlock pin. Shift synchronizer hub into 5th gear (if equipped). Position Reverse/5th fork on clutch

Manual Transmissions
FORD MOTOR CO. 4 & 5-SPEED BRONCO II & RANGER – GASOLINE (Cont.)

hub and slide Reverse/5th fork shaft into case (from rear of case). Secure Reverse/5th shift fork to fork shaft with new roll pin.

15) Install 2 blind covers and new gaskets. Install and tighten retaining bolts (10 mm) on blind covers. Position 3 detent balls and 3 springs into case, then install spring cap bolts (12 mm and 17 mm). Apply a thin coat of gasket sealer to contacting surfaces of center housing and case.

16) Position center housing on case. Align reverse idler gear shaft boss with center housing retaining bolt boss. Install and tighten idler shaft cap screw (12 mm). Slide countershaft 5th gear onto countershaft. Position countershaft rear bearing on countershaft.

17) Press into position using Adjustable Press Frame (T77J-7025-N) and Forcing Screw (T84T-7025-B). Install thrust washer and snap ring onto rear of countershaft rear bearing. Check clearance between thrust washer and snap ring using a feeler gauge.

18) If clearance is not within 0-.006" (0-.15 mm), select proper size thrust washer to bring clearance within specifications. Thrust washers are available in sizes of .0748" (1.90 mm), .0787" (2 mm), .0827" (2.10 mm) and .0866" (2.20 mm).

19) If installed, remove filler plugs. Position mainshaft rear bearing on mainshaft. Press into place using Adjustable Press Frame (T77J-7025-N), Dummy Bearing (T75L-7025-Q1) and Forcing Screw (T84T-7025-B).

20) Install thrust washer and snap ring onto rear of mainshaft rear bearing. Check clearance between thrust washer and snap ring. Clearance should be 0-.004" (0-.10 mm). If clearance is not within specifications, replace thrust washer with selective thrust washer.

NOTE: **Thrust washers are available in sizes of .0787" (2 mm), .0846" (2.15 mm) and .0906" (2.30 mm).**

21) Apply a thin coat of gasket sealer to contacting surfaces of bearing housing and center housing. Position bearing housing on center housing. Install each shift fork end onto proper shift fork shaft. Match up reassembly reference marks made during disassembly. Secure with new roll pins.

22) Install lock ball, speedometer drive gear and snap ring onto mainshaft. If removed, install control lever and rod in extension housing. Apply a thin coat of gasket sealer to contacting surfaces of bearing housing and extension housing.

23) Position extension housing in bearing housing with gearshift control lever end laid down to the left as far as it will go. Tighten (2 long outer and 1 short center) retaining bolts (14 mm) and nuts (14 mm). If removed, insert speedometer driven gear assembly into extension housing and secure it with retaining bolt.

24) Check to ensure gear shift lever operates properly. Install new transmission case cover gasket and cover (drain plug toward rear). Install and tighten 14 retaining bolts (10 mm) to cover. Install the correct size shim on second step of front cover (as determined by mainshaft bearing clearance measurement).

25) Coat new front cover gasket with sealer, then install cover and gasket to transmission case. Tighten 4 bolts and 4 studs. Fill transmission with 3 pts. (1.4L) of gear oil. If removed, install filler plugs and tighten.

NOTE: **Manual transmission gear oil used must be equivalent to Ford Manual Transmission Lube D8DZ-19C547-A (ESP-M2C83-C).**

TIGHTENING SPECIFICATIONS

Application	Ft. Lbs. (N.m)
Back-Up Light Switch	22-29 (30-39)
Blind Cover Mounting Bolt	23-34 (32-46)
Clutch Release Lever Pivot	23-34 (32-46)
Drain Plug	29-43 (39-58)
Extension Housing Mounting Bolt/Nut	60-80 (82-108)
Filler Plug	18-29 (25-39)
Idler Shaft Cap Screw	41-59 (56-79)
Mainshaft Lock Nut	115-172 (156-233)
Shift Rail Detent Spring Cap	29-43 (39-58)
Transmission Case Cover Mounting Bolt	23-34 (32-46)
Nut/Bolt Size	
8 mm	12-17 (17-23)
10 mm	23-34 (32-45)
12 mm	41-59 (56-79)
	INCH Lbs. (N.m)
Interlock Pin Bore Plug	97-132 (11-14)
Nut/Bolt Size	
6 mm	62-97 (7-11)

FORD MOTOR CO. 4-SPEED
BRONCO II & RANGER — DIESEL

IDENTIFICATION

Manual transmissions have a service identification tag to identify transmissions for servicing. Tag is found at right front side of case. The 4-speed transmission I.D. code is "X". *See Fig. 1.*

Fig. 1: Transmission Identification Tag

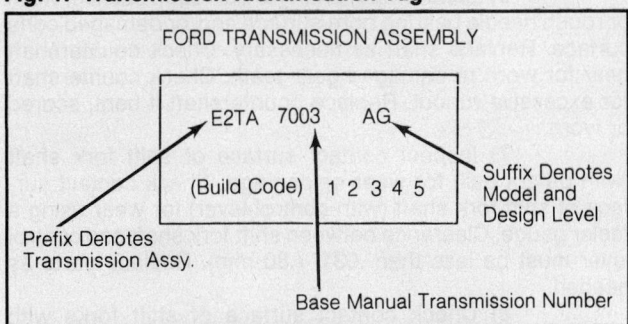

I.D. tag is found at right front side of transmission case.

DESCRIPTION

The 4-speed manual transmission is fully synchronized with all gears, except reverse gear which is in constant mesh. All forward gears are helical-cut for quiet running operation. The reverse gear and reverse idler gear are spur-cut.

Transmission case is of light metal construction and features an integral clutch housing and gear case with a separate extension housing. The gear shift mechanism is a direct control with a floor shift. The floor shift mechanism is built into the extension housing.

LUBRICATION & ADJUSTMENT

See appropriate MANUAL TRANSMISSION SERVICING article in DOMESTIC GENERAL SERVICING section.

TROUBLE SHOOTING

See MANUAL TRANSMISSION TROUBLE SHOOTING article in DOMESTIC GENERAL SERVICING section.

REMOVAL & INSTALLATION

TRANSMISSION

See appropriate MANUAL TRANSMISSION REMOVAL article in DOMESTIC GENERAL SERVICING section.

SERVICE (IN VEHICLE)

GEARSHIFT LEVER

Removal

1) Place gear shift lever in Neutral position. Detach boot retainer screws. Remove bolts attaching retainer cover to gearshift lever retainer.

2) Pull gear shift lever assembly, shim and bushing straight up and away from gear shift lever retainer.

Cover shift tower opening in extension housing with a cloth to avoid dirt falling into transmission.

Installation

Install gear shift lever assembly by reversing removal procedure.

TRANSMISSION DISASSEMBLY

TRANSMISSION CASE
& INTERNAL COMPONENTS
Disassembly

1) Remove drain plug and drain gear oil. Remove fork and release bearing from clutch housing. Install transmission in Holding Fixture (T57L-500-B).

2) Detach 6 front cover-to-case retaining bolts (12 mm). Remove cover and shim, then discard gasket. Remove front cover oil seal using Inner Seal Remover (T75P-3504-G) and Slide Hammer (T50T-100-A). Using expanding-type snap ring pliers, remove input shaft snap ring.

3) Remove outer snap ring on input shaft bearing. Install Bearing Collet (T75L-7025-E) on main input shaft front bearing, then install Remover Tube (T75L-7025-B) and Forcing Screw (T75L-7025-J).

4) Slide Bearing Collet Sleeve (T75L-7025-G) over remover tube and bearing collet. Turn forcing screw to remove input shaft bearing. If speed control sensor must be removed, detach retaining bolt and pull sensor from extension housing. Remove 8 retaining bolts (12 mm) attaching extension housing to transmission case.

5) Slide extension housing off mainshaft (with control lever end laid down and to the left as far as possible). Remove bolt (10 mm) retaining control lever end to control rod. Remove control lever end and rod from extension housing.

6) Remove speedometer driven gear assembly from extension housing. Remove back-up light switch and neutral sensing switch. Detach snap ring that secures speedometer drive gear on mainshaft.

7) Slide speedometer drive gear off mainshaft. Use a magnet to remove lock ball. Install Bearing Pusher (T83T-7111-A) over countershaft front bearing. Turn forcing screw to force countershaft, together with countershaft front bearing, from transmission housing.

8) Slide bearing holder and gear shaft assembly from transmission housing. Remove 3 spring cap bolts, 3 springs (reverse spring is shortest) and shift locking balls.

NOTE: Mark 3rd/4th and 1st/2nd shift forks, before removal, for reassembly reference.

9) Remove reverse shift rod and shift fork assembly and reverse gear from bearing housing. Remove roll pins retaining shift forks to rods. Push each shift rod rearward through fork and bearing housing. Remove shift rods and forks.

10) Remove lower reverse shift rod locking ball, spring and interlock pin from bearing housing. Using Staking Tool (T77J-7025-F), straighten tab of lock washer. Lock transmission synchronizers into any 2 gears. Remove mainshaft lock nut using Adapter (T83T-7025-A) and Tool Shaft (T77J-7025-C).

11) Remove reverse gear and key from mainshaft. Detach snap ring from rear end of countershaft. Slide off countershaft reverse gear. Detach 5 bearing cover

3-70

Manual Transmissions
FORD MOTOR CO. 4-SPEED
BRONCO II & RANGER — DIESEL (Cont.)

Fig. 2: Removing Shift Lock Balls & Springs

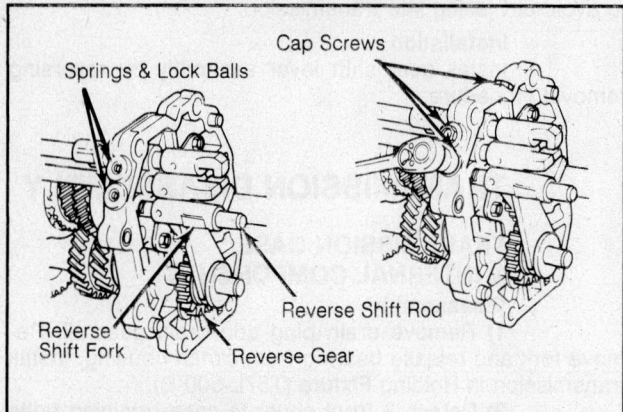

Use care during removal, lower shift locking ball will pop out when removed.

bolts (12 mm). Remove cover and reverse idler gear shaft from bearing housing.

12) Using a soft hammer, carefully tap rear end of mainshaft and countershaft in turn. DO NOT damage shafts. Remove shafts from bearing housing. Carefully separate input shaft and caged needle roller bearing from mainshaft.

13) Remove rear countershaft bearing from bearing housing using Remover Tube (T77J-7025-B). Remove rear mainshaft bearing from bearing housing using Bearing Remover (T77F-4222-A) and Remover Tube (T77J-7025-B).

14) Remove thrust washer, 1st gear, sleeve and synchronizer ring from rear of mainshaft. Remove snap ring from front of mainshaft. Using a press and Remover (T71P-4621-B), remove 3rd/4th clutch hub, sleeve synchronizer ring and 3rd gear from front of mainshaft. *See Fig. 3.*

15) Using a press and Remover (T71P-4621-B), remove 1st/2nd clutch hub and sleeve assembly synchronizer ring and 2nd gear from rear of mainshaft. Press front bearing from countershaft using Remover (D79L-4621-A or T71P-4621-B) and driver.

16) Clean transmission case and extension housing, then check for cracks, burrs or other damage. Check all gears, shafts, bearings and synchronizer components for wear or damage.

CLEANING & INSPECTION

1) Wash all parts (except oil seals) in cleaning solvent and dry with compressed air (except bearings). Let bearings air dry, then lubricate with gear oil and wrap in clean, link-free shop cloth until ready to install.

2) Inspect transmission case and extension housing for cracks, worn or damaged bearing bores or threads. Remove any small nicks or burrs from front and/or rear machined mating surfaces of case with fine stone.

3) Check bearings for roughness by first lubricating lightly with oil, then slowly turning race by hand. Inspect needle bearing rollers, shafts and washers for wear or damage. Check gears for wear, damage or chipped and/or broken teeth. Replace parts as necessary.

4) Inspect mainshaft for excessive runout. Mount mainshaft between "V" blocks and check runout (in several places) using a dial indicator. Standard runout is

.0012" (.030 mm). If runout exceeds specification, straighten mainshaft in a press or replace component.

5) Check fit of mainshaft and gear bores. Standard fit is .0012-.0031" (.030-.080 mm). If clearance increases beyond .006" (.15 mm), due to wear, replace the gear.

6) Inspect input shaft for damaged splines, worn or rough needle bearing bore surface and/or damaged cone surface. Replace shaft as necessary. Check countershaft gear for worn or damaged gear teeth. Check countershaft for excessive runout. Replace countershaft if bent, scored or worn.

7) Inspect contact surface of shift fork shaft (with detent ball) for wear or damage. Check contact surface of shift fork shaft (with control lever) for wear using a feeler gauge. Clearance between shift fork shaft and control lever must be less than .031" (.80 mm). Replace parts as needed.

8) Check contact surface of shift forks with clutch sleeve for wear or damage. Clearance between shift fork and clutch sleeve must be less than .020" (.50 mm). Replace parts if worn beyond specification.

9) Inspect synchronizer ring for chipped or worn gear teeth. Check synchronizer ring for wear by fitting ring evenly to gear cone. Measure clearance between side faces of synchronizer ring and gear with feeler gauge. If less than .031" (.80 mm), replace ring and/or gear.

10) Check contact between inner surface of synchronizer ring and cone surface of gear. To inspect, apply a thin coat of "Prussian Blue" on cone surface of gear and fit it into ring. If contact pattern is poor, correct by applying compound and lapping surfaces together. Ensure sleeve slides easily on clutch hub.

11) Check synchronizer inserts (keys), inner surface of clutch sleeve and insert groove on clutch hub for wear. Check synchronizer insert spring for tension. Replace any worn or damaged parts.

12) Inspect extension housing oil seal for wear or damage and replace as needed. Remove seal using Oil Seal Remover (T71P-7657-A) and install using Oil Seal Installer (T71P-7095-A). If removed, install new oil seal after extension housing is installed on transmission.

13) If extension housing rear bushing needs replacement, remove using Bushing Remover (T72J-7697). Check speedometer shaft and drive and driven gears for wear or damage. Replace parts as needed.

TRANSMISSION REASSEMBLY

TRANSMISSION CASE & INTERNAL COMPONENTS

NOTE: Transmission case is made of aluminum alloy. To prevent damaging case, all nuts, bolts and/or lock washers contacting case must have a flat washer placed next to case so that turning attaching bolt or nut will not damage aluminum surface.

Reassembly

1) Assemble 3rd/4th and 1st/2nd clutch hub in the same manner. Install clutch hub and synchronizer into sleeve, placing the 3 keys into clutch hub slots and install springs onto hub.

Fig. 3: Exploded View of Transmission Gear Assemblies

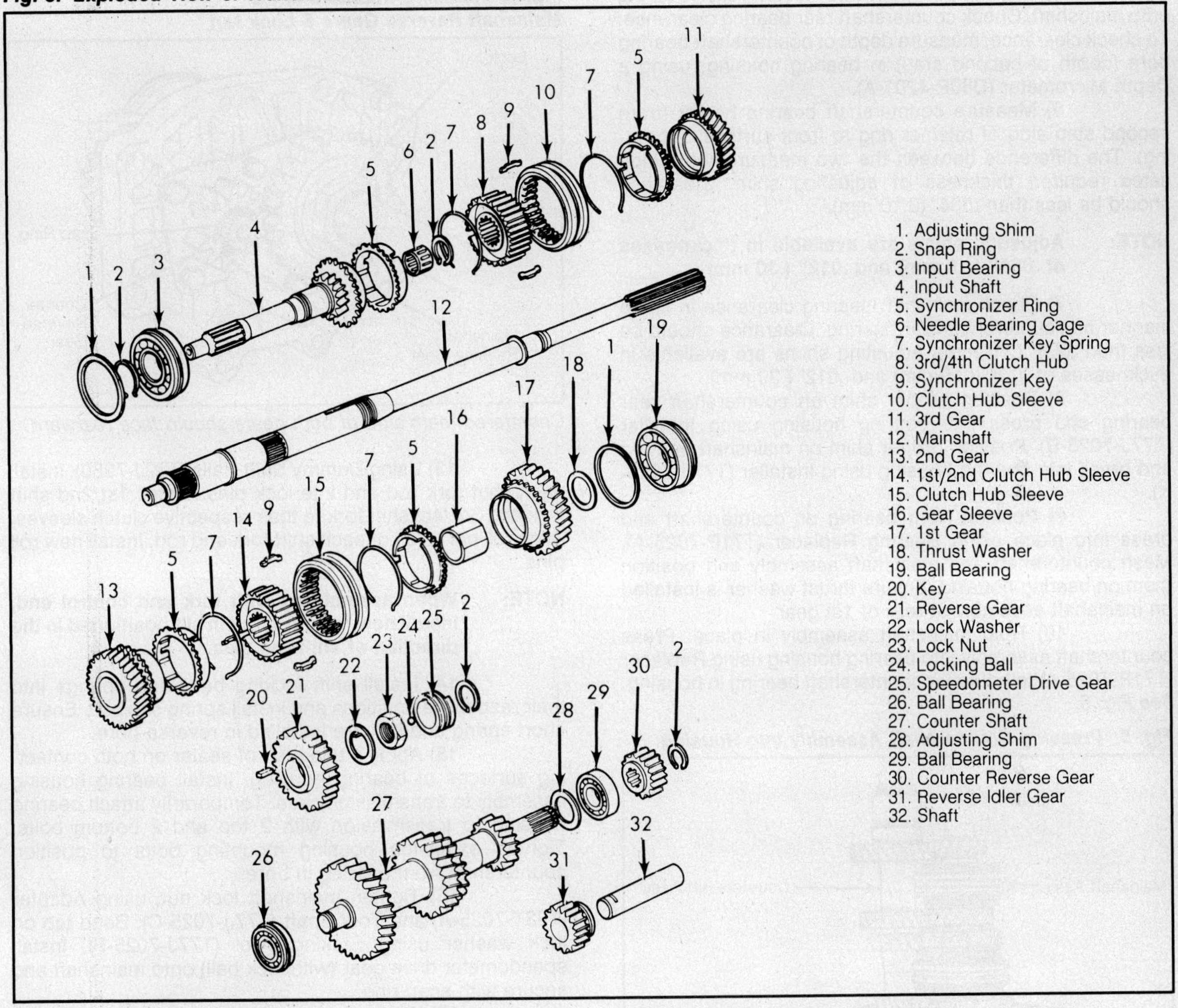

1. Adjusting Shim
2. Snap Ring
3. Input Bearing
4. Input Shaft
5. Synchronizer Ring
6. Needle Bearing Cage
7. Synchronizer Key Spring
8. 3rd/4th Clutch Hub
9. Synchronizer Key
10. Clutch Hub Sleeve
11. 3rd Gear
12. Mainshaft
13. 2nd Gear
14. 1st/2nd Clutch Hub Sleeve
15. Clutch Hub Sleeve
16. Gear Sleeve
17. 1st Gear
18. Thrust Washer
19. Ball Bearing
20. Key
21. Reverse Gear
22. Lock Washer
23. Lock Nut
24. Locking Ball
25. Speedometer Drive Gear
26. Ball Bearing
27. Counter Shaft
28. Adjusting Shim
29. Ball Bearing
30. Counter Reverse Gear
31. Reverse Idler Gear
32. Shaft

NOTE: When installing key springs, ensure open end tab of springs is inserted into hub hole with springs turned in same direction to keep spring tension on each key uniform.

CAUTION: When installing clutch hubs, ensure small shoulder of 3rd/4th clutch hub and oil groove of 1st/2nd clutch hub faces front.

2) Install 3rd gear and synchronizer ring onto front section of mainshaft. Assemble Replacer (T53T-4621-C), Installer Tube (T77J-7025-B) and 3rd/4th clutch hub assembly on mainshaft. Hold tools and mainshaft components together, then slowly press into place.

3) Fit snap ring on mainshaft. Install 2nd gear and synchronizer ring onto rear section of mainshaft. Assemble Replacer Tool Set (T75L-7025-Q, T57L-4621-B and T62F-4621-A or T53T-4621-C) and 1st/2nd clutch hub assembly (with 2nd gear and 3rd gear) onto mainshaft.

4) Using a press, install 1st/2nd clutch hub assembly onto mainshaft. Install synchronizer ring, 1st gear with sleeve and thrust washer onto mainshaft. See Fig. 4.

Fig. 4: Mainshaft Gear Assembly

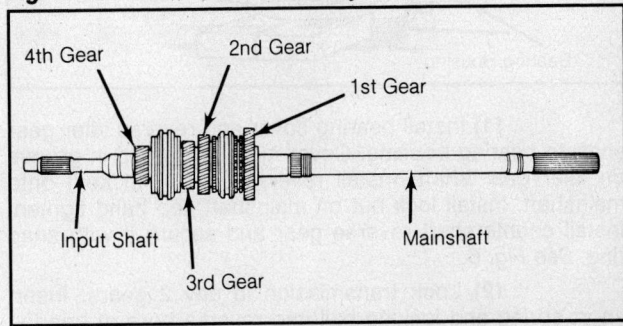

NOTE: When measuring countershaft rear bearing clearance, ensure micrometer probe touches retainer ring shoulder (second step of bore) and micrometer rests on case outer surface. Measure bearing height from where retainer ring inner surface contacts bore shoulder to bearing outer surface.

Manual Transmissions
FORD MOTOR CO. 4-SPEED
BRONCO II & RANGER – DIESEL (Cont.)

5) Install input shaft and needle roller bearing onto mainshaft. Check countershaft rear bearing clearance. To check clearance, measure depth of countershaft bearing bore (depth of second step) in bearing housing, using a Depth Micrometer (D80P-4201-A).

6) Measure countershaft bearing height (from second step side of retainer ring to front surface of bearing). The difference between the two measurements indicates required thickness of adjusting shim. Clearance should be less than .004" (0.10 mm).

NOTE: Adjusting shims are available in thicknesses of .004" (.10 mm) and .012" (.30 mm).

7) Check mainshaft bearing clearance in same manner as countershaft rear bearing. Clearance should be less than .004" (.10 mm). Adjusting shims are available in thicknesses of .004" (.10 mm) and .012" (.30 mm).

8) Position proper shim on countershaft rear bearing and press into bearing housing using Installer (T77J-7025-B). Position proper shim on mainshaft bearing and press into bearing housing using Installer (T77J-7025-K).

9) Position front bearing on countershaft and press into place using Bearing Replacer (T71P-7025-A). Mesh countershaft and mainshaft assembly and position them on bearing housing. Ensure thrust washer is installed on mainshaft assembly at rear of 1st gear.

10) Hold mainshaft assembly in place. Press countershaft assembly into bearing housing using Replacer (T71P-7025-A) to hold rear countershaft bearing in housing. See Fig. 5.

Fig. 5: Pressing Countershaft Assembly into Housing

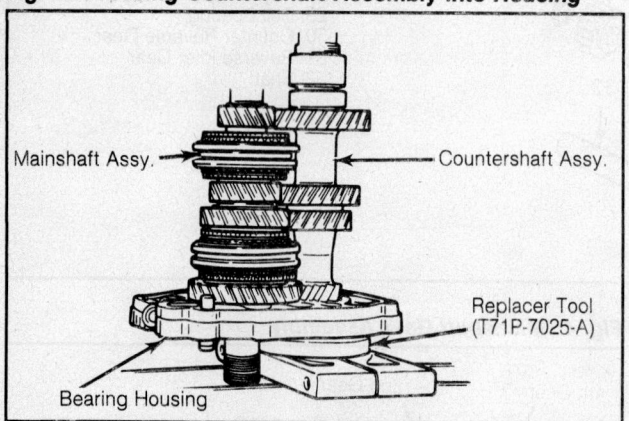

11) Install bearing cover and reverse idler gear shaft to bearing housing. Cover must be seated in groove on idler gear shaft. Install reverse gear (with key) onto mainshaft. Install lock nut on mainshaft and hand tighten. Install countershaft reverse gear and secure it with snap ring. See Fig. 6.

12) Lock transmission in any 2 gears. Insert short spring and locking ball into reverse bore of bearing housing. Hold down ball with a punch. Install reverse shift rod and shift lever assembly, with reverse idler gear, at the same time.

NOTE: If necessary, remove plugs from bell housing shift rod bores to align shift rods. After installation of bearing housing assembly is complete, reinstall bore plugs using silicone sealer.

Fig. 6: Installing Countershaft & Mainshaft Reverse Gears & Lock Nut

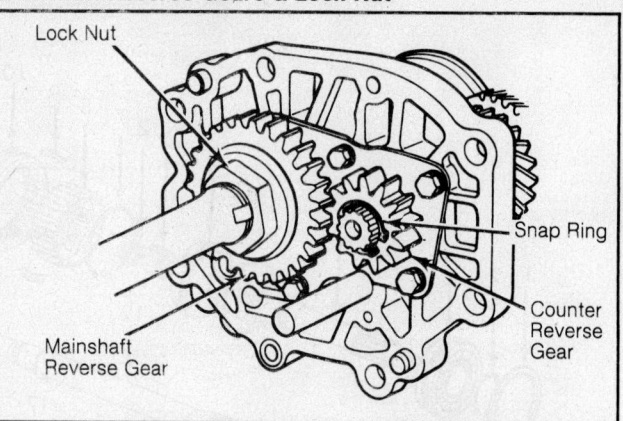

Chamfered teeth side of both gears should face rearward.

13) Using Dummy Shift Rails (T72J-7280), install each shift fork rod and interlock pins. Install 1st/2nd shift fork and 3rd/4th shift fork to their respective clutch sleeves. Align roll pin holes of each shift fork and rod. Install new roll pins.

NOTE: When assembling shift fork and control end, install new roll pin with pin slit positioned in the direction of shift rod axis.

14) Install shift locking balls and springs into their respective positions and install spring cap bolt. Ensure short spring and ball are installed in reverse bore.

15) Apply a thin coat of sealer on both contacting surfaces of bearing housing. Install bearing housing assembly to transmission case. Temporarily attach bearing housing to transmission with 2 top and 2 bottom bolts. Tighten extension housing mounting bolts to position countershaft front bearing in bore.

16) Tighten mainshaft lock nut, using Adapter (T83T-7025-A) and Tool Shaft (T77J-7025-C). Bend tab on lock washer using Staking Tool (T77J-7025-F). Install speedometer drive gear (with lock ball) onto mainshaft and secure with snap ring.

17) With outer snap ring in place on mainshaft front bearing, place bearing, Shim (389117-2S) and Adapter Tool (T75L-7025-N) over input shaft. Thread Replacer Shaft (T75L-7025-K) onto adapter tool. Install Replacer Tube (T75L-7025-B) over replacer shaft. Install nut and washer on forcing screw.

18) Slowly tighten nut until adapter is secure on input shaft. Ensure all tools are aligned. Tighten nut on forcing screw until bearing outer snap ring is seating against housing. Remove tools.

19) Install input shaft snap ring. Install speedometer driven gear assembly into extension housing and attach with bolt and lock plate. Insert shift control lever through holes in extension housing (from front side).

20) Install control lever end to control lever and tighten retaining bolt. Install back-up light switch and neutral sensing switch into extension housing and tighten. Remove bolts installed previously to temporarily hold bearing housing.

21) Apply a thin coat of sealer on contacting surface of bearing housing and extension housing. Install extension housing to bearing housing with control lever laid down to the left as far as possible. Tighten 8 retaining bolts (12 mm). Check to ensure that control rod operates properly.

Manual Transmissions

3-73

FORD MOTOR CO. 4-SPEED
BRONCO II & RANGER — DIESEL (Cont.)

22) Install gearshift lever retainer and new gasket to extension housing with 4 bolts (12 mm). Install gear shift lever. Install new oil seal in front cover using Oil Seal Installer (T71P-7050-A).

23) Apply gear lubricant to lip of oil seal inside front cover. Install front cover to case with 6 bolts (12 mm). With front cover installed, ensure clearance between bearing outer race and front cover is less than .004" (.10 mm).

NOTE: **If necessary, clearance between bearing outer race and front cover can be adjusted by inserting an adjusting shim of .006" (.15 mm) or .012" (.30 mm).**

24) Install release bearing and release fork. Install drain plug (and remove filler plug) if necessary, then fill transmission with 1.6 qts. (1.5L) of Ford Manual Transmission Lube D8DZ-19C547-A (ESP-M2C83-C).

TIGHTENING SPECIFICATIONS

Application	Ft. Lbs. (N.m)
Back-Up Light Switch	20-25 (28-34)
Clutch Release Lever Pivot	23-34 (32-46)
Control Lever	
End-to-Control Lever Bolt	20-25 (28-34)
Drain Plug	29-43 (40-58)
Filler Plug	18-29 (25-40)
Mainshaft Gear Lock Nut	116-174 (160-240)
Neutral Sensing Switch	20-25 (28-34)
Shift Rail Detent Spring Cap	29-43 (40-58)
Nut/Bolt Size	
8 mm	12-17 (17-23)
10 mm	23-34 (32-45)
12 mm	41-59 (56-79)
	INCH Lbs. (N.m)
Nut/Bolt Size	
6 mm	62-97 (7-11)

Manual Transmissions
FORD MOTOR CO. 5-SPEED BRONCO II & RANGER - DIESEL

IDENTIFICATION

Manual transmissions have a service identification tag to identify transmissions for servicing. Tag is found at right front side of case. Transmission I.D. code for 5-speed transmission is "D". *See Fig. 1.* This transmission (Model FM145) is used on 4 x 4 models only.

Fig. 1: Transmission Identification Tag

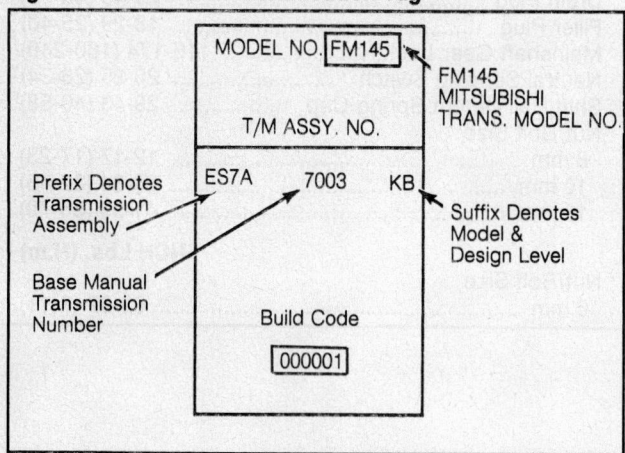

Tag is found at right front side of transmission case.

DESCRIPTION

The 5-speed manual transmission is fully synchronized in all forward gears. The 5th gear is an overdrive gear. All gear changes are accomplished with synchronizer sleeves. Reverse gear uses a reverse idler gear which is in constant mesh with countershaft gear.

Top mounted shifter operates shift rails through a set of shift forks. Shift forks mounted on rails operate synchronizer sleeves, allowing shifts of 1st-2nd, 3rd-4th and Overdrive-Reverse. A shift interlock system, located in the side of transmission case, prevents shift rails from engaging 2 gears at a time.

Transmission is composed of 3 main components, a front bearing retainer, transmission case and transfer case adapter. All components are made of aluminum.

LUBRICATION & ADJUSTMENT

See appropriate MANUAL TRANSMISSION SERVICING article in DOMESTIC GENERAL SERVICING section.

TROUBLE SHOOTING

See MANUAL TRANSMISSION TROUBLE SHOOTING in MANUAL TRANSMISSION SERVICING section.

REMOVAL & INSTALLATION

See appropriate MANUAL TRANSMISSION REMOVAL article in DOMESTIC GENERAL SERVICING section.

SERVICE (IN VEHICLE)

GEAR SHIFT LEVER ASSEMBLY

NOTE: **Remove shift ball only if shift ball, boot or lever is to be replaced. If either ball, boot or lever is not being replaced, remove the ball, boot and lever as an assembly.**

Removal

1) To remove shift lever ball, first remove plastic insert. Warm ball with heat gun to 140-180°F (60-82°C), knock ball off lever with a block of wood and a hammer, taking care not to damage finish on shift lever.

2) Remove rubber boot. Detach bolts retaining shift lever to transfer case adapter, then remove gear shift lever assembly.

Installation

1) Lubricate shift lever with multi-purpose grease. Position lever in in transfer case adapter. Ensure selector ball on lever is in the socket in the adapter. Install bolts and tighten to 71-89 INCH lbs. (8-14 N.m).

2) Install rubber boot and floor pan cover. Warm ball with heat gun to 140-180°F (60-82°C), then tap ball onto lever with a 7/16" socket and mallet. Install plastic shift pattern insert.

TRANSMISSION DISASSEMBLY

TRANSMISSION CASE & TRANSFER CASE ADAPTER

NOTE: **During disassembly, all gaskets must be removed and discarded. Thoroughly clean all traces of gasket material from mating surfaces of transfer case adapter, input shaft front bearing retainer and transmission case.**

Disassembly

1) With transmission removed from vehicle and in Neutral position, detach nuts retaining clutch bellhousing to transmission case. Remove housing. If not removed, pull clutch slave cylinder from input shaft.

2) Remove back-up light switch, neutral position switch (2.3L E.F.I. engine only) and shift indicator switch from transfer case adapter. Remove drain plug from pan and drain gear oil.

3) Detach bolts retaining pan to transmission case, then remove pan and discard gasket. Remove all traces of gasket from pan and case mating surfaces. With shift lever assembly removed, detach bolts retaining top cover to transfer case adapter.

4) Remove cover (with stopper bracket inside) and discard gasket. Clean all traces of gasket from cover and adapter mating surfaces. Remove detent spring and ball from adapter.

5) Using a 6 mm Allen-head wrench, remove 3 shift gate roll pin access plugs (2 on side and 1 on bottom). Using a punch, drive roll pins from shift gates (through access holes).

6) From right side of adapter, remove bolt, neutral return spring and plunger. *See Fig. 2.* Note that plunger has a slot in center for detent ball.

7) From left side of adapter, remove bolt, neutral return spring and plunger. Note that this plunger has no ball slot. From top of adapter, lift gate selector lever out of shift

Manual Transmissions
FORD MOTOR CO. 5-SPEED BRONCO II & RANGER - DIESEL (Cont.)

Fig. 2: Exploded View Of Transfer Case Adapter & Components

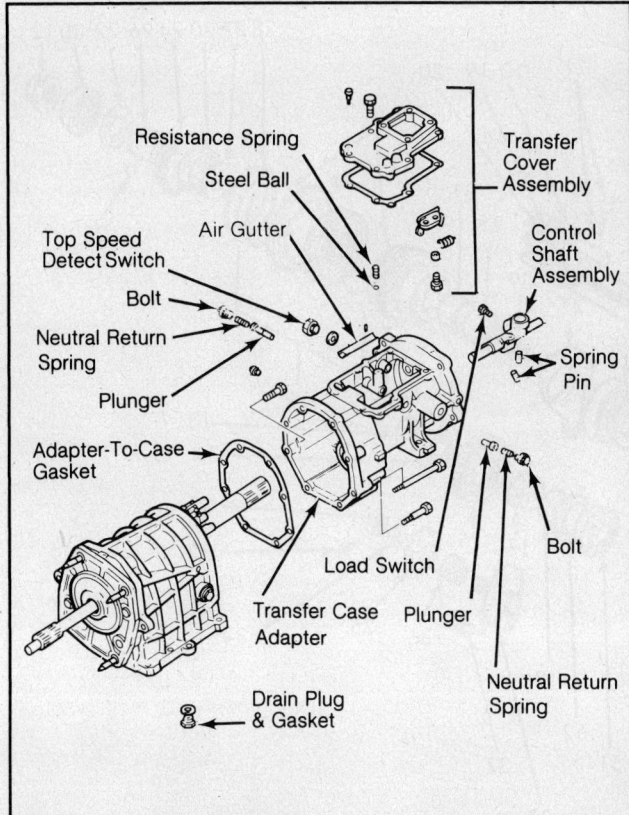

gates. Move lever as far to rear of adapter as it will go. This will allow clearance to remove adaptor from case.

8) Detach bolts retaining transfer case adapter to transmission case. Mark bolt holes for 3 different length bolts used (35 mm, 55 mm and 110 mm). Remove adapter from case and discard gasket.

NOTE: When detaching adapter from case, ensure shift gates do not bind in adapter during removal. Rotate gates on rails as needed.

9) Clean all traces of gasket from case and adapter mating surfaces. Identify and mark each shift rail and gate, then remove gates from rails. From inside transmission case, drive out roll pins retaining 1st/2nd and 3rd/4th shift forks to the rails.

CAUTION: Roll pin in switch actuator does not need to be removed to disassemble transmission.

10) Drive out Overdrive/Reverse shift fork roll pin. Note installed depth of .24" (6.1 mm), then remove poppet spring set screw (on top of case). Remove 1 poppet spring and 1 steel ball from bore. Detach 2 bolts (on side of case) and remove 2 poppet springs and 2 steel balls. See Fig. 4.

11) Pull Overdrive/Reverse shift rail and 3rd/4th shift rail from case. Remove Overdrive/Reverse shift fork. When the 2 shift rails are removed, the interlock pins can be removed from case.

CAUTION: Do not attempt to remove 1st/2nd shift rail at this time.

12) Using Mainshaft Lock Nut Staking Tool (T77J-7025-F), unstake lock nuts on mainshaft and countershaft. To remove lock nuts, first position 2 synchronizers to engage transmission in 2 gears (to lock-up gear sets).

13) Using a 30 mm socket, remove and discard countershaft lock nut. Using Mainshaft Lock Nut Wrench (T77J-7025-C), remove and discard mainshaft lock nut. Using Tube (T77J-7025-B), Forcing Screw (T84T-7025-B), Bearing Puller (T77J-7025-H) and Puller Ring (T77J-7025-J), pull rear bearing off mainshaft and discard it.

14) Slide spacer off mainshaft and, using a magnet if necessary, remove lock ball from bore. Using Puller (T77J-4220-B1), with jaws of puller behind gear, turn forcing screw to remove countershaft overdrive gear and ball bearing from countershaft. While removing gear, pull 1st/2nd shift rail from case.

15) Remove 1st/2nd shift forks from case. Remove Overdrive gear, caged needle bearing, spacer and synchronizer ring from mainshaft. Detach overdrive synchronizer sleeve from synchronizer hub on mainshaft.

CAUTION: When separating synchronizer sleeve from hub, do not lose 3 keys (located in hub) and/or 2 springs (1 on each side of hub).

16) Pull overdrive synchronizer hub and overdrive gear bearing sleeve from mainshaft with previously used forcing screw, tube, bearing puller and puller ring. See Fig. 3. Slide Reverse gear and caged needle bearing assembly off mainshaft.

Fig. 3: Removing Rear Mainshaft Bearing, Overdrive Synchronizer Hub & Overdrive Gear Bearing Sleeve

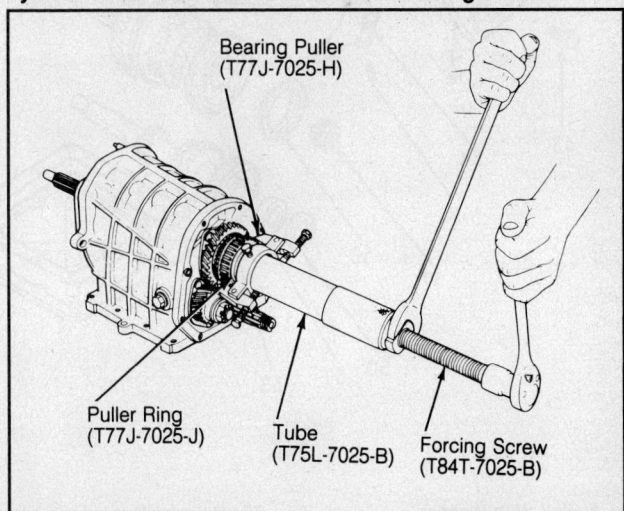

17) Slide countershaft reverse gear and distance spacer off countershaft. Remove cotter pin and detach nut from reverse idler shaft. Remove thrust washer, reverse idler gear and 2 sets of caged needle bearings. See Fig. 5.

18) Detach Allen-head bolts (6 mm) attaching mainshaft rear bearing retainer to case. Remove retainer and discard gasket. Clean gasket surfaces. Detach Allen-head bolts retaining reverse idler gear shaft assembly to case.

19) Using Slide Hammer (T50T-100-A) and Reverse Idler Gear Shaft Remover (T85T-7140-A), pull reverse

Manual Transmissions
FORD MOTOR CO. 5-SPEED BRONCO II & RANGER - DIESEL (Cont.)

Fig. 4: Exploded View Of Transmission Case & Components

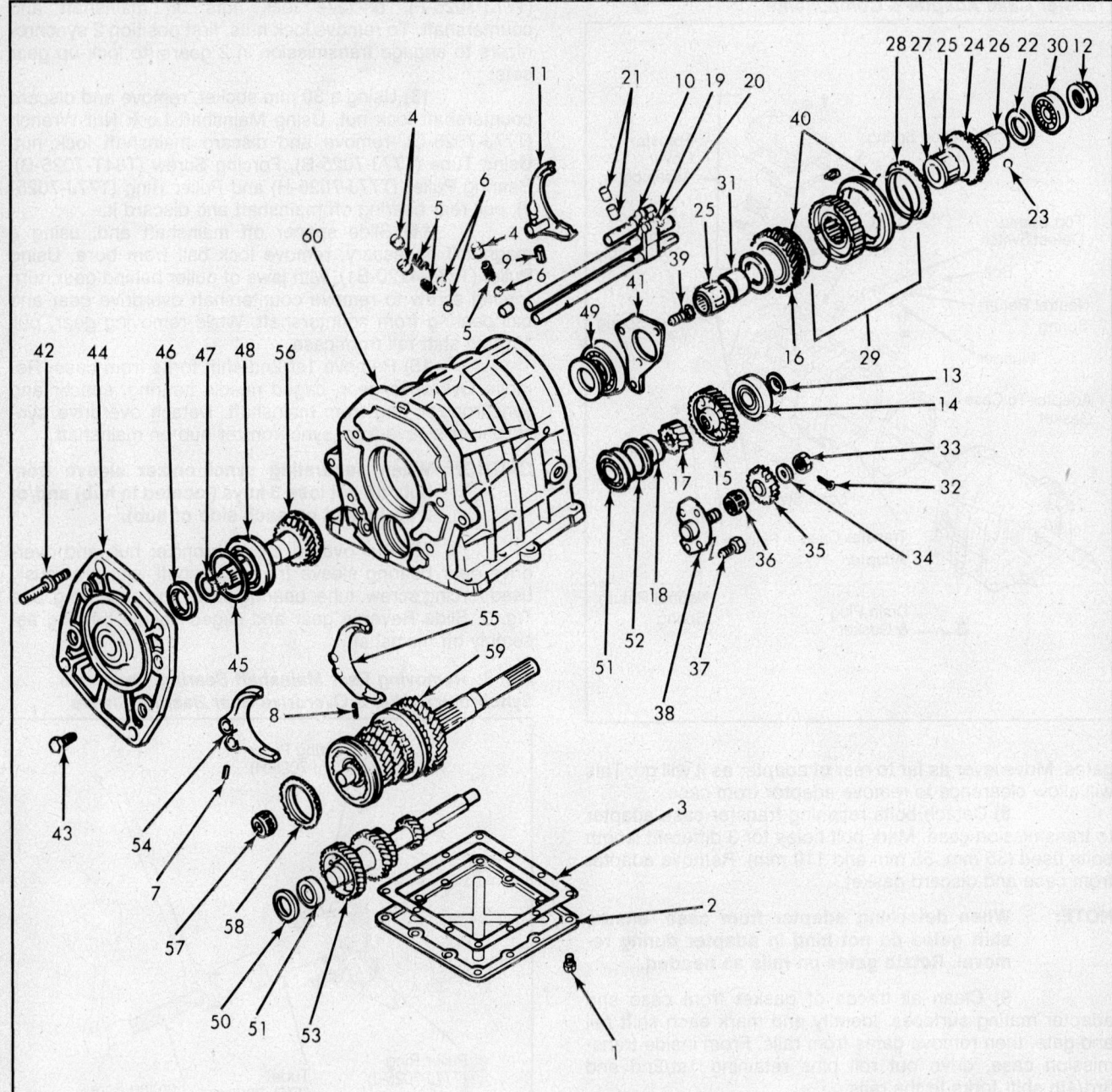

1. Bolt With Washer	16. Reverse Gear	31. Sleeve
2. Transmission Case Pan	17. Countershaft Reverse Gear	32. Split Pin
3. Transmission Case Pan Gasket	18. Spacer	33. Nut
4. Plug	19. 3rd/4th Shift Rail	34. Thrust Washer
5. Poppet Spring (3)	20. 1st/2nd Shift Rail	35. Reverse Idler Gear
6. Steel Ball (3)	21. Interlock Plunger	36. Needle Bearing (2)
7. 3rd/4th Shift Fork Spring Pin	22. Thrust Washer	37. Screw (4)
8. 1st/2nd Shift Fork Spring Pin	23. Steel Ball	38. Reverse Idler Shaft
9. Overdrive/Reverse Shift Fork Spring Pin	24. Overdrive Gear	39. Screw (4)
10. Overdrive/Reverse Shift Rail	25. Needle Bearing	40. Synchronizer Spring
11. Overdrive/Reverse Shift Fork	26. Overdrive Gear Sleeve	41. Rear Bearing Retainer
12. Mainshaft Lock Nut	27. Bearing Spacer	42. Stud (4)
13. Countershaft Lock Nut	28. Synchronizer Ring	43. Bolt (4)
14. Ball Bearing	29. Overdrive Synchronizer Assembly	44. Front Bearing Retainer
15. Countershaft Overdrive Gear	30. Bail Bearing	45. Spacer

46. Oil Seal
47. Snap Ring
48. Ball Bearing
49. Double Bearing (Angular-Type)
50. Spacer
51. Countershaft Rear Roller Bearing
52. Shim
53. Countershaft Assembly
54. 3rd/4th Shift Fork
55. 1st/2nd Shift Fork
56. Mainshaft Drive Gear
57. Needle Bearing
58. Synchronizer Ring
59. Mainshaft Assembly
60. Transmission Case Assembly

Manual Transmissions
FORD MOTOR CO. 5-SPEED BRONCO II & RANGER - DIESEL (Cont.)

3-77

Fig. 5: Removing Reverse Gears, Reverse Idler Gear, Spacer & Bearings

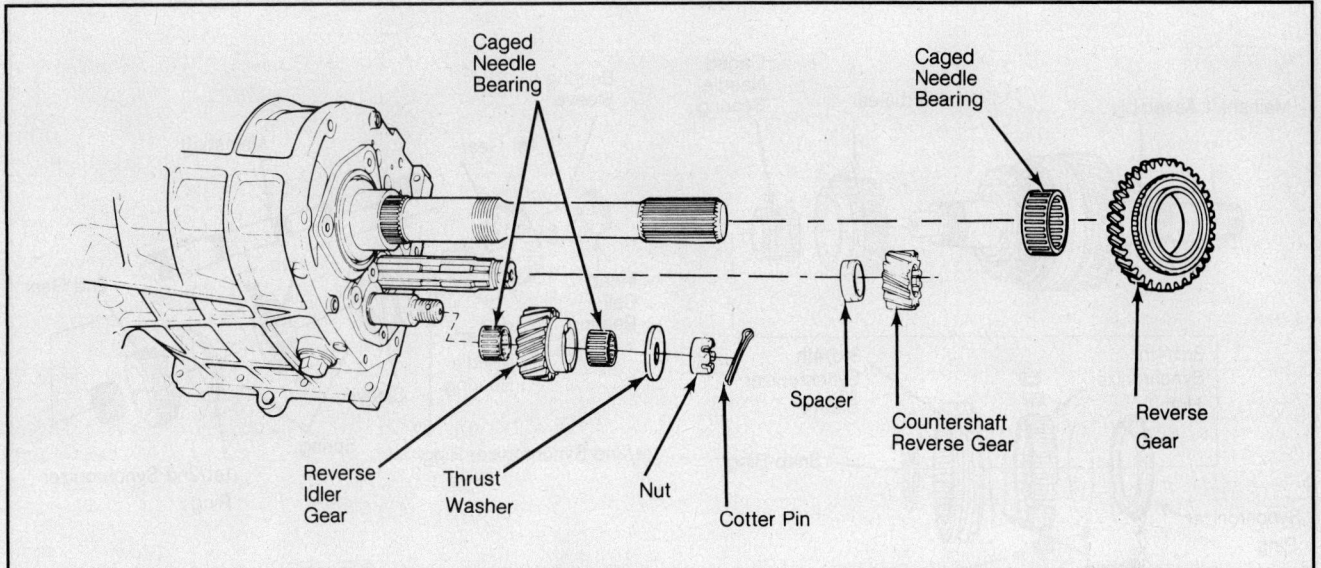

idler gear shaft out of case. Remove 4 studs retaining input shaft front bearing retainer to case.

20) Remove input shaft front bearing retainer from case. Remove and discard gasket. Clean gasket surfaces. Remove selective shim from inside of retainer. Do not discard selective shim. Detach small selective snap ring retaining input shaft to bearing. Do not discard selective snap ring.

21) Detach large selective snap ring retaining input shaft bearing to case. Remove bearing from input shaft using Tube (T75L-7025-B), Bearing Collets (T75L-7025-D), Bearing Collet Sleeve (T75L-7025-G) and Forcing Screw (T84T-7025-B). Remove and discard bearing.

22) Rotate input shaft so flats on shaft face countershaft (to provide clearance to remove input shaft). Remove input shaft. If necessary, pull mainshaft toward rear of case. Remove small caged needle bearing from input gear I.D.

23) Remove snap ring from mainshaft outer bearing race. Remove outer mainshaft bearing race, ball bearing and bearing sleeve using tube, Mainshaft Bearing Collet Remover (T85T-7065-A), Bearing Collet Sleeve (T77F-7025-C) and forcing screw. Inner front bearing race will remain on mainshaft. Discard outer bearing race and ball bearing.

24) Remove countershaft front spacer and bearing race. Move mainshaft assembly slightly to the side, if necessary, to allow clearance for countershaft assembly removal. Remove countershaft assembly from bottom of case. Remove mainshaft assembly from case.

MAINSHAFT ASSEMBLY
Disassembly
1) Detach and discard selective snap ring retaining 3rd/4th synchronizer assembly to mainshaft (a new snap ring will be used during assembly). *See Fig. 6 and 7.*

NOTE: **Ensure position of synchronizer hub and sleeve is noted during disassembly for reassembly reference.**

Fig. 6: Cutaway View Of Mainshaft Assembly

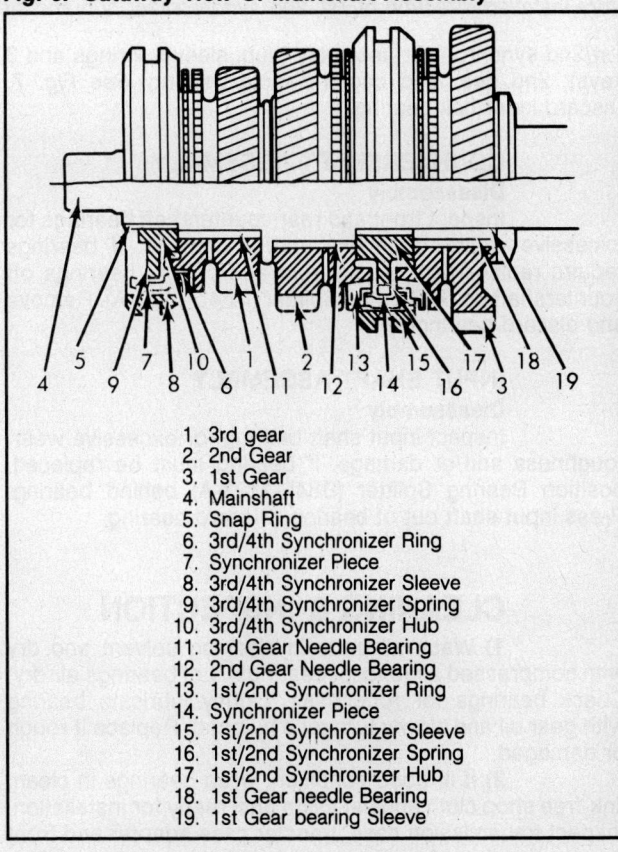

1. 3rd gear
2. 2nd Gear
3. 1st Gear
4. Mainshaft
5. Snap Ring
6. 3rd/4th Synchronizer Ring
7. Synchronizer Piece
8. 3rd/4th Synchronizer Sleeve
9. 3rd/4th Synchronizer Spring
10. 3rd/4th Synchronizer Hub
11. 3rd Gear Needle Bearing
12. 2nd Gear Needle Bearing
13. 1st/2nd Synchronizer Ring
14. Synchronizer Piece
15. 1st/2nd Synchronizer Sleeve
16. 1st/2nd Synchronizer Spring
17. 1st/2nd Synchronizer Hub
18. 1st Gear needle Bearing
19. 1st Gear bearing Sleeve

2) Remove 3rd/4th synchronizer assembly (hub, sleeve, spring and keys), synchronizer ring, 3rd gear and caged needle bearing from front of mainshaft. *See Fig. 6 and 7.*

3) Position mainshaft assembly in press so 2nd gear is supported by press bed. Press mainshaft down and out from 1st and 2nd gear assembly. Separate inner ball bearing, bearing sleeve, 1st gear, caged needle bearing,

Manual Transmissions
FORD MOTOR CO. 5-SPEED BRONCO II & RANGER - DIESEL (Cont.)

Fig. 7: Exploded View Of Mainshaft Assembly

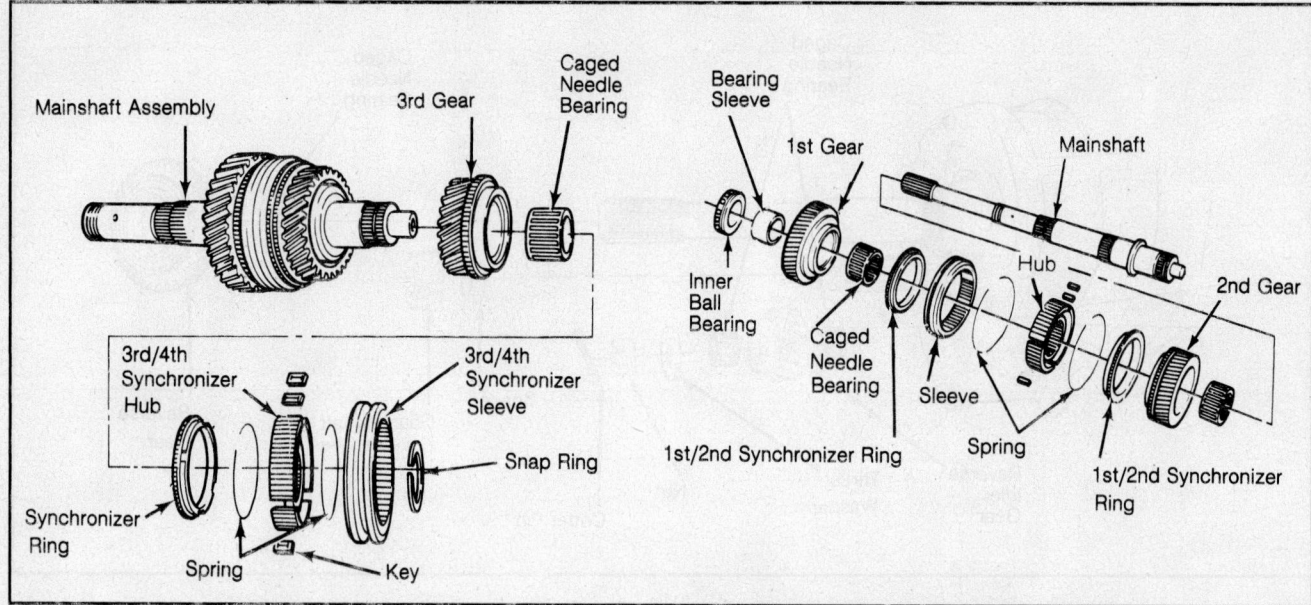

Note installed direction of 1st/2nd synchronizer hub and sleeve during disassembly for reassembly reference.

1st/2nd synchronizer assembly (hub, sleeve, 2 rings and 3 keys), 2nd gear and caged needle bearing. *See Fig. 7.* Discard inner ball bearing.

COUNTERSHAFT ASSEMBLY
Disassembly
Inspect front and rear countershaft bearings for excessive wear, roughness and/or damage. If bearings require replacement, press front and/or rear bearings off countershaft using Bearing Splitter (D84L-1123-A). Remove and discard bearing(s).

INPUT SHAFT ASSEMBLY
Disassembly
Inspect input shaft bearing for excessive wear, roughness and/or damage. If bearing must be replaced, position Bearing Splitter (D84L-1123-A) behind bearing. Press input shaft out of bearing. Discard bearing.

CLEANING & INSPECTION
1) Wash all parts in cleaning solvent and dry with compressed air (except bearings). Let bearings air dry. Check bearings for roughness. Lightly lubricate bearing with gear oil and slowly turn race by hand. Replace if rough or damaged.

2) If in good condition, wrap bearings in clean, link-free shop cloth and set aside until ready for installation. Inspect transmission case, transfer case adapter and front bearing retainer for cracks, damaged bearing bores or threads. Remove all small nicks or burrs from front and rear of case.

3) Inspect needle bearing rollers, shafts and washers for wear and damage. Check all other parts for wear, damage and chipped or broken teeth. Replace parts as necessary.

4) Inspect synchronizer blocking rings for widened index slots, rounded clutch teeth and smooth internal surfaces (must have machined grooves). With blocker ring

on cone, distance between face of gear clutching teeth and face of blocking ring must not be less than .009" (.23 mm).

5) Check synchronizer sleeves for free movement on hubs. Ensure alignment marks (etched or painted marks) are properly indexed. Replace synchronizer components as necessary. Replace seal in input shaft bearing retainer.

TRANSMISSION REASSEMBLY

INPUT SHAFT ASSEMBLY
Reassembly
Position new bearing on input shaft. Press bearing onto shaft using Tube (T75L-7025-B) with Replacing Shaft Sleeve (T75L-7025-K) and Shaft Coller (T75L-7025-M) inside tube and Rack Bushing Holder (T81P-3504-D) or an appropriate size washer against bearing.

COUNTERSHAFT ASSEMBLY
Reassembly
If bearing must be replaced, install bearing splitter on end of countershaft opposite bearing being installed. Position countershaft assembly upright, with bearing splitter resting on press bed. Press new bearing onto countershaft using hydraulic press and Countershaft Bearing Replacer (T85T-7121-A).

MAINSHAFT ASSEMBLY
Reassembly
1) Check clearance between synchronizer rings and gears. Install ring on gear, then insert feeler gauge between ring teeth and gear. If clearance is less than .009" (.23 mm), replace synchronizer ring and/or gear. *See Fig. 8.*

2) Install caged needle bearing for 2nd gear (from rear of mainshaft). Position 2nd gear on mainshaft with synchronizer ring surface facing rear of shaft. Install synchronizer ring on 2nd gear.

Manual Transmissions
FORD MOTOR CO. 5-SPEED BRONCO II & RANGER - DIESEL (Cont.)

3-79

Fig. 8: Checking Synchonizer Ring-To-Gear Clearance

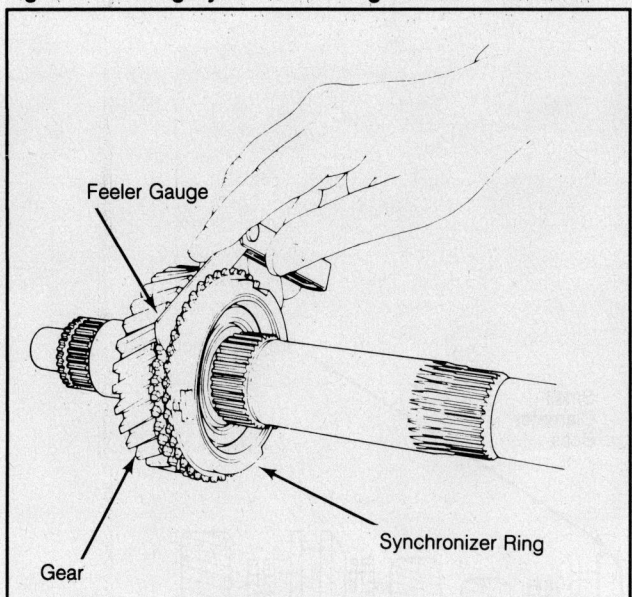

If clearance is less than .009" (.23 mm), replace the synchronizer ring and/or gear.

Fig. 9: Installing 3rd/4th Synchronizer Assembly Onto Mainshaft

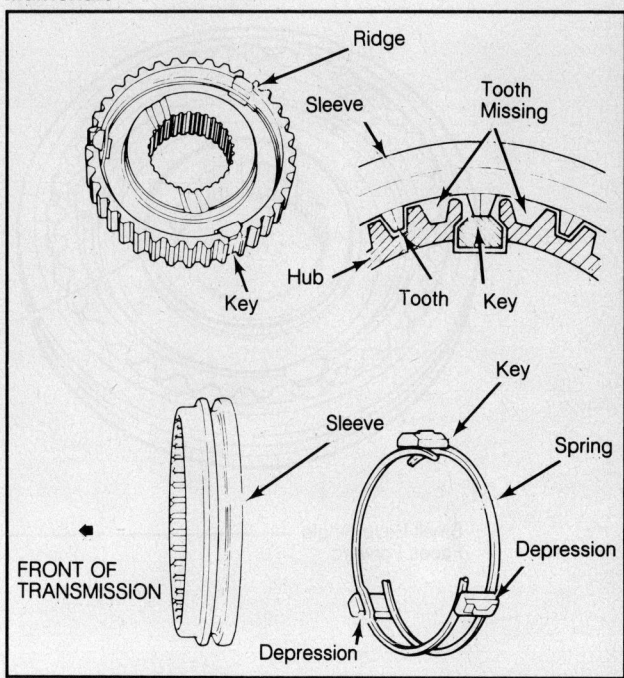

When installing 3rd/4th synchronizer assembly, ensure mainshaft splines and synchronizer are properly aligned.

3) Position 1st/2nd synchronizer assembly on rear of mainshaft. Ensure mainshaft splines and synchronizer are properly aligned. Rear of 1st/2nd hub is identified by a ridge machined on rear surface. *See Fig. 10.* Ridge must face rear of mainshaft.

4) Install sleeve with large bevel angle facing front of mainshaft. Synchronizer sleeve has a tooth missing at 6 positions. Assemble hub to sleeve so single tooth, between 2 missing portions, will touch synchronizer key. *See Fig. 10.*

NOTE: When synchronizer keys and springs are properly installed, the open ends of spring do not face each other.

5) Press 1st/2nd synchronizer assembly into position on mainshaft using Replacing Shaft Sleeve (T75L-7025-K), Shaft Collar (T75L-7025-M) and Tube (T75L-7025-C). If properly installed, 2nd gear should rotate freely.

6) Position 1st gear bearing sleeve on mainshaft. Press sleeve on shaft using replacing shaft sleeve, shaft collar, Rack Bushing Holder (T81P-3504-D) and tube. When properly installed, sleeve should be against synchronizer hub. Ensure gears rotate freely.

7) Install synchronizer ring on 1st/2nd synchronizer assembly. Install caged needle bearing and 1st gear. Slide a new inner ball bearing into position on mainshaft. Press bearing onto mainshaft usng rack bushing holder, tube, replacing sleeve shaft and shaft collar. After installation, ensure gears rotate freely.

8) Install 3rd gear and caged needle bearing over front of mainshaft. Install synchronizer ring against 3rd gear. When installing 3rd/4th synchronizer assembly, ensure mainshaft splines and synchronizer are properly aligned. Small diameter hub boss and small bevel angle of sleeve faces front of mainshaft. *See Fig. 9.*

NOTE: Synchronizer sleeve has a tooth missing at 6 positions. Assemble hub to sleeve so single tooth, between 2 missing portions, will touch

synchronizer key. When synchronizer keys and springs are properly installed, the open ends of spring do not face each other.

9) Install 3rd/4th synchronizer assembly onto front of mainshaft. Install a new selective snap ring that retains 3rd/4th synchronizer assembly to mainshaft. Select thickest snap ring that will fit in groove. See MAINSHAFT SELECTIVE SNAP RING table.

MAINSHAFT SELECTIVE SNAP RING

Identification Color	Thickness In. (mm)
White	.091 (2.30)
Brown	.093 (2.35)
None	.094 (2.40)
Blue	.096 (2.45)
Yellow	.098 (2.50)

TRANSMISSION CASE & TRANSFER CASE ADAPTER
Reassembly

1) Install mainshaft assembly into transmission case. Install 1st/2nd and 3rd/4th shift forks into their respective synchronizer sleeves. Ensure roll pin bosses on forks face each other. Install countershaft assembly into case.

NOTE: If necessary, move mainshaft to 1 side in order to ease countershaft installation.

2) Choose and install a new selective snap ring in front of input shaft bearing. Select thickest snap ring that

3-80

Manual Transmissions
FORD MOTOR CO. 5-SPEED BRONCO II & RANGER - DIESEL (Cont.)

Fig. 10: Installing 1st/2nd Synchronizer Assembly On Mainshaft

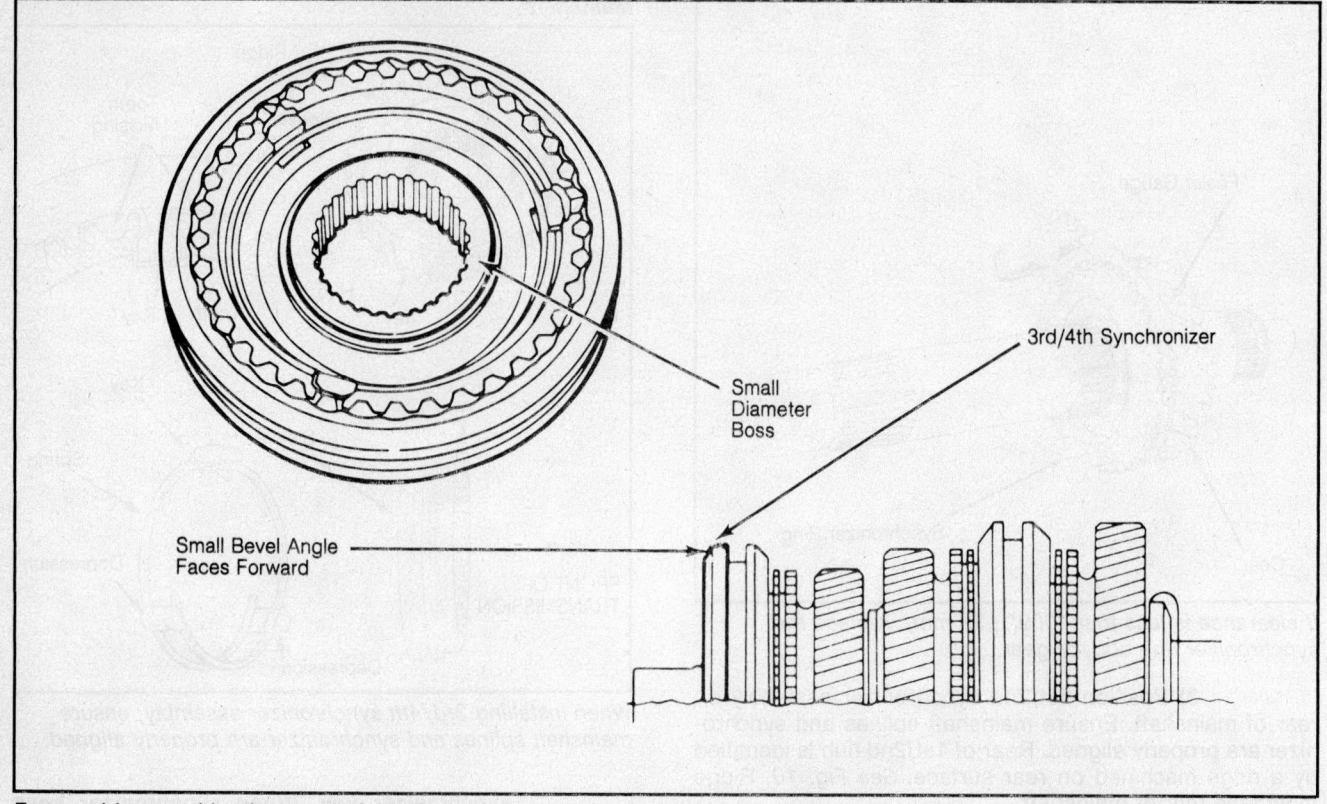

3rd/4th Synchronizer

Small Diameter Boss

Small Bevel Angle Faces Forward

Ensure ridge machined on rear of 1st/2nd synchronizer hub faces rear of mainshaft.

will fit in groove. See INPUT SHAFT SELECTIVE SNAP RING table for available sizes and identification colors.

INPUT SHAFT SELECTIVE SNAP RING

Identification Color	Thickness In. (mm)
Blue	.085 (2.15)
None	.087 (2.22)
Brown	.090 (2.29)
White	.093 (2.36)

3) Install small caged needle bearing inside input gear. Install synchronizer ring on input shaft. Check clearance between ring and gear. If clearance is less than .009" (.23 mm), replace ring and/or input shaft.

4) Install synchronizer ring and input shaft in case. Rotate input shaft so flats face countershaft (to provide installation clearance). If necessary, tap input shaft into position with brass hammer.

5) Install a new snap ring on new outer bearing race, then install race in case. Ensure longest portion of race is installed toward case. Slide new outer ball bearing onto mainshaft.

6) Press bearing on mainshaft and in race using previously used tube, replacing shaft sleeve and shaft collar. After pressing into position, ensure all gears rotate freely.

7) Using Oil Seal Installer (T85T-7011-A) and Driver Handle (T80T-4000-W), drive new oil seal into input shaft front bearing retainer. Install large snap ring that retains input shaft bearing to case.

8) Check input shaft front bearing retainer-to-bearing clearance. Remove front bearing retainer selective shim. Using a depth micrometer, measure distance between top machined surface to spacer surface (second landing) of front bearing retainer. See Fig. 11. Record reading.

9) Bottom input shaft bearing so snap ring is flush against transmission case. Using depth micrometer, measure distance from top of outer front bearing race to machined surface of case. See Fig. 11.

10) Subtract distance of bearing-to-case from retainer dimensions. This will give required maximum shim size to obtain a 0-.004" (0-.10 mm) clearance. Measure and install appropriate size selective shim in front bearing retainer. Refer to INPUT SHAFT FRONT BEARING RETAINER-TO-BEARING SELECTIVE SHIM table for available shim sizes and identification colors.

11) Install countershaft front outer bearing race and non-selective spacer. Install countershaft rear outer bearing race. Install new gasket between front bearing retainer and case. Position retainer on case (with selective shim installed). Install 4 bolts and 4 studs, then tighten to 22-30 ft. lbs. (30-41 N.m).

12) Check and adjust countershaft end play. Place transmission so rear of mainshaft and countershaft face upward. Install countershaft rear selective spacer. See Fig. 12. Force countershaft downward so it bottoms against front bearing retainer.

Manual Transmissions
FORD MOTOR CO. 5-SPEED BRONCO II & RANGER - DIESEL (Cont.)

3-81

Fig. 11: Checking Input Shaft Front Bearing Retainer-To-Bearing Clearance

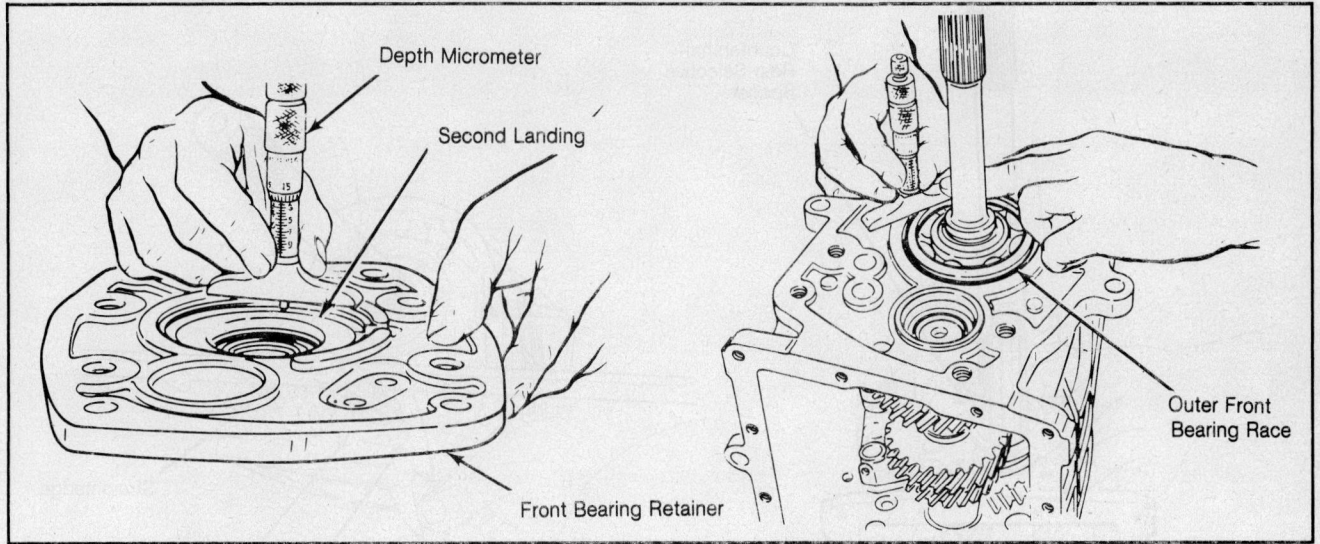

INPUT SHAFT FRONT BEARING RETAINER-TO-BEARING SELECTIVE SHIM

Identification Color	Thickness In. (mm)
Black	.033 (.84)
None	.037 (.93)
Red	.040 (1.02)
White	.044 (1.11)
Yellow	.047 (1.20)
Blue	.051 (1.29)
Green	.054 (1.38)

13) Place straightedge across rear countershaft selective spacer in case. *See Fig. 12.* Try to turn spacer. If spacer turns lightly, replace spacer with next larger size.

14) Install a spacer so clearance between spacer and straightedge is 0-.002" (0-.05 mm). Refer to COUNTERSHAFT END PLAY SELECTIVE SPACER table for available sizes and identification markings on spacer. Install correct size spacer over countershaft rear bearing race.

15) Install and tighten rear bearing retainer onto case with 4 Allen-head bolts (6 mm). Ensure spacer installed in step **14)** does not fall out of place when installing rear bearing retainer.

16) Position reverse idler gear shaft assembly on case. Install Allen-head bolts (6 mm) to act as a pilot. Install Reverse Idler Gear Shaft Remover (T85T-7140-A) on shaft and drive assembly into place. Tighten bolts to 11-16 ft. lbs. (15-21 N.m).

17) Install 2 caged needle bearings, reverse idler gear and thrust washer on idler shaft. Boss on idler gear faces away from transmission. Install lock nut and tighten to 15-42 ft. lbs. (20-58 N.m). If necessary, advance nut to next castillation and install new cotter pin.

CAUTION: When installed, ensure cotter pin does not cause interference with countershaft overdrive gear. Bend and/or cut end of cotter pin if necessary.

COUNTERSHAFT END PLAY SELECTIVE SPACER

Identification Mark	Thickness In. (mm)
84	.0724 (1.840)
87	.0736 (1.870)
90	.0748 (1.900)
93	.0760 (1.930)
96	.0772 (1.960)
99	.0783 (1.990)
02	.0795 (2.020)
06	.0807 (2.050)
08	.0819 (2.080)
11	.0831 (2.110)
14	.0843 (2.140)
17	.0854 (2.170)
20	.0866 (2.200)
23	.0878 (2.230)
26	.0890 (2.260)
29	.0902 (2.290)
32	.0913 (2.320)
35	.0925 (2.350)
38	.0937 (2.380)
41	.0949 (2.410)
44	.0961 (2.440)
47	.0972 (2.470)
50	.0984 (2.500)
53	.0996 (2.530)
56	.1008 (2.560)
59	.1020 (2.590)
62	.1031 (2.620)
65	.1043 (2.650)
68	.1055 (2.680)

18) Install spacers and countershaft reverse gear on mainshaft. Press reverse gear sleeve onto mainshaft using Tube (T85T-7025-A), Shaft Sleeve Replacer (T75L-7025-K), Shaft Collar (T75L-7025-M) and Forcing Screw (T84T-7025-B).

19) Install caged needle bearing and reverse gear onto mainshaft. Assemble overdrive synchronizer hub

Manual Transmissions
FORD MOTOR CO. 5-SPEED BRONCO II & RANGER - DIESEL (Cont.)

Fig. 12: Checking Countershaft End Play

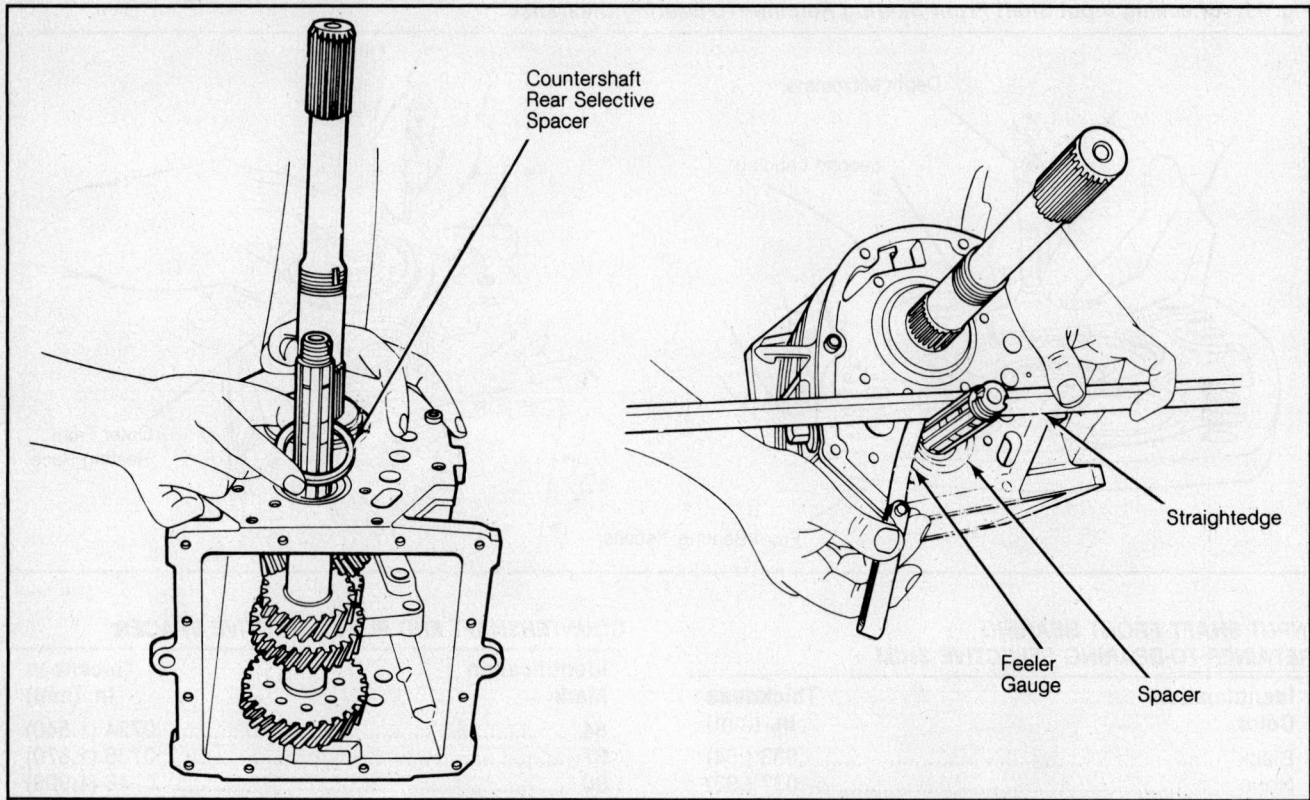

and sleeve by first installing hub into sleeve. Ensure recessed boss on sleeve faces front of transmission. Large boss on hub must also face front of transmission.

20) When installing hub in sleeve and 3 keys, ensure single tooth between 2 spaces will touch key. Install springs so open ends do not face each other. Install overdrive synchronizer on mainshaft with recessed boss of sleeve facing front of transmission.

21) Press overdrive gear sleeve onto mainshaft using previously used tube, shaft sleeve replacer, shaft collar and Overdrive Gear Bearing Replacer (T85T-7061-A). Install ring onto overdrive synchronizer.

22) Slide small spacer, caged needle bearing and overdrive gear onto mainshaft. Check clearance between overdrive gear and synchronizer ring. If clearance is less than .009" (.23 mm), replace ring and/or overdrive gear.

23) Install countershaft overdrive gear and ball bearing onto countershaft along with 1st/2nd shift rail. Seat bearing into position using Countershaft Bearing Replacer Collet (T85T-7121-A), Rear Countershaft Bearing Installer Adapter (T85T-7111-A) and Remover/Replacer Tube (T77J-7025-B). Ensure rail engages forks.

24) Install lock ball and spacer onto mainshaft. Place rear bearing over mainshaft. Press bearing into position using Rack Bushing Holder (T81P-3504-D), tube, shaft sleeve replacer and shaft collar.

25) Install new lock nuts on countershaft and mainshaft. Double engage transmission in 2 gears to prevent shafts from turning. Tighten mainshaft lock nut to 180-195 ft. lbs. (245-265 N.m) using Mainshaft Lock Nut Wrench (T77J-7025-C).

26) Tighten countershaft lock nut to 115-137 ft. lbs. (157-168 N.m) using a 30 mm socket. Disengage

transmission. Stake lock nuts on mainshaft and countershaft using Lock Nut Staking Tool (T77J-7025-F).

27) Install and interlock plunger in bore between 1st/2nd and 3rd/4th shift rails. Reposition 1st/2nd shift rail so flats for poppet ball and spring and interlock plunger are in correct position. Ensure roll pin holes for shift forks are in alignment.

28) Install Overdrive/Reverse shift fork on synchronizer sleeve. Slide 3rd/4th shift rail through Overdrive/Reverse shift fork, into case and into 3rd/4th shift fork (inside case). Position shift rail flats to accept poppet balls and interlock plunger.

29) Insert interlock plunger in bore between 3rd/4th shift rail and Overdrive/Reverse shift rail. Ensure roll pin holes in fork are in alignment. Insert Overdrive/Reverse shift rail so it engages forks in case. Check that roll pin holes in fork and rail are in alignment.

30) Insert poppet ball and spring in 1st/2nd (upper) bore of case. Ensure small end of spring is installed toward ball. Install set screw and tighten until set screw head is .24" (6 mm) below top of bore.

31) Insert poppet springs and balls into 3rd/4th and Overdrive/Reverse bore (2 bores on side of case). Ensure small end of each spring faces its ball. Install and tighten bolts.

32) Install roll pins in shift forks. If removed, install switch actuator and roll pin. Install shift gates on appropriate shift rails. Move 1st/2nd gate to rear of rail. Position new gasket between transmission case and transfer case adapter.

33) Ensure selector arm is out of gates and change shifter is at rear of adapter. Position adapter on case (ensure shift gate clears adapter). Check that shift rails and rear bearings line up with bores in adapter.

Manual Transmissions
FORD MOTOR CO. 5-SPEED BRONCO II & RANGER - DIESEL (Cont.)

3-83

Fig. 13: Transfer Case Adapter Mounting Bolt Hole Locations

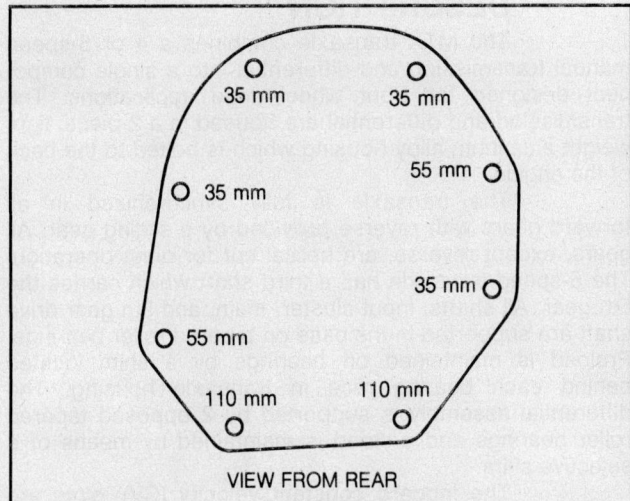

VIEW FROM REAR

Install 3 different sizes of bolts in appropriate holes shown in adapter, then tighten to specification.

34) Install 3 different sizes of bolts in appropriate holes in adapter, then tighten to 11-16 ft. lbs. (15-21 N.m). *See Fig. 13.* Install neutral return plungers, springs and bolts in adapter. Longer plunger (with slot for detent ball) is installed on right side of adapter.

35) Position shift gates so roll pin holes in gates and rails are in alignment. Install roll pins through access holes. Install access hole plugs. Position pan and new gasket on case. Install and tighten mounting bolts. Do not overtighten. Install drain plug (if necessary) and tighten.

36) Insert plunger detent ball and spring in hole above neutral return plunger in adapter case. Ensure stopper bracket assembly on cover (for transfer case adapter)

moves smoothly. Position new gasket on adapter and install housing cover. Install and tighten mounting bolts.

37) Install back-up light switch and shift indicator light switch in adapter. Remove filler plug and fill transmission to bottom of fill hole with SAE 80W gear oil (fluid capacity is 9 pts).

38) Install filler plug and tighten. Position clutch slave cylinder on input shaft. Position clutch bellhousing on transmission case, then install and tighten mounting bolts.

TIGHTENING SPECIFICATIONS

Application	Ft. Lbs. (N.m)
Clutch Bellhousing	
To-Engine Mounting Bolt	28-38 (38-51)
To-Trans. Case Mounting Bolt	30-40 (41-54)
Countershaft Lock Nut	115-137 (157-168)
Damper-To-Insulator Nut	71-94 (97-127)
Drain Plug	25-32 (35-44)
Filler Plug	22-25 (30-35)
Front Bearing Retainer	
To-Trans. Case Mounting Bolt	22-30 (30-41)
Housing Cover	
To-Transfer Case Adapter Bolt	11-16 (15-21)
Insulator-To-Transmission Bolt	60-80 (81-108)
Mainshaft Lock Nut	180-195 (245-265)
Output Shaft Lock Nut	94-152 (127-210)
Pan-To-Trans. Case Mounting Bolt	11-16 (15-21)
Rear Bearing-To-Case Mounting Bolt	22-30 (30-41)
Reverse Idler Gear Nut	15-42 (20-58)
Reverse Idler Gearshaft Assembly	
To-Trans. Case Mounting Bolt	11-16 (15-21)
Shift Lever Assembly	
To-Transfer Case Adapter Bolt	6-10 (8-14)
Starter Motor	
To-Clutch Housing Mounting Bolt	15-20 (20-27)
Stud-To-Front Retainer & Case	22-30 (30-41)

Manual Transmissions

FORD MOTOR CO.
MTX 4 & 5-SPEED MANUAL TRANSAXLE

Escort, EXP, Lynx, Tempo, Topaz

IDENTIFICATION

The MTX 4 and 5-speed manual transaxles can be identified by a tag affixed to top of transaxle case. Top line of tag identifies transaxle model, next line identifies transaxle assembly, third line shows the build date code, and bottom line is the transaxle serial number. Transaxle axle ratios are shown in TRANSAXLE RATIO table.

TRANSAXLE RATIO

Application	Model	Axle Ratio
4-Speed		
1.6L & 2.3L	RGT-AV	.... 3.04:1
1.6L	RGT-AS	.... 3.59:1
5-Speed		
Diesel Engine	RWB-AV	.... 3.52:1
Diesel Engine	RWB-AW	.... 3.73:1
Gas Engine	RWB-AS, AU	.... 3.33:1
Gas Engine	RWB-AR	.... 3.73:1

DESCRIPTION

The MTX transaxle combines a 4 or 5-speed manual transmission and differential into a single component designed for front wheel drive applications. The transmission and differential are housed in a 2-piece, light weight aluminum alloy housing which is bolted to the back of the engine.

The transaxle is fully synchronized in all forward gears with reverse provided by a sliding gear. All gears, except reverse, are helical cut for quiet operation. The 5-speed transaxle has a third shaft which carries the 5th gear. All shafts, input cluster, main, and 5th gear drive shaft are supported in the case on tapered roller bearings. Preload is maintained on bearings by a shim located behind each bearing race in transaxle housing. The differential assembly is supported by 2 opposed tapered roller bearings and preload is maintained by means of a selective shim.

The inboard constant velocity (CV) joints are positively connected with the differential side gears by means of splines and secured in case with 2 snap rings. The ring gear is riveted to the differential case (bolted on after service).

Fig. 1: Sectional View of MTX 4-Speed Manual Transaxle Assembly

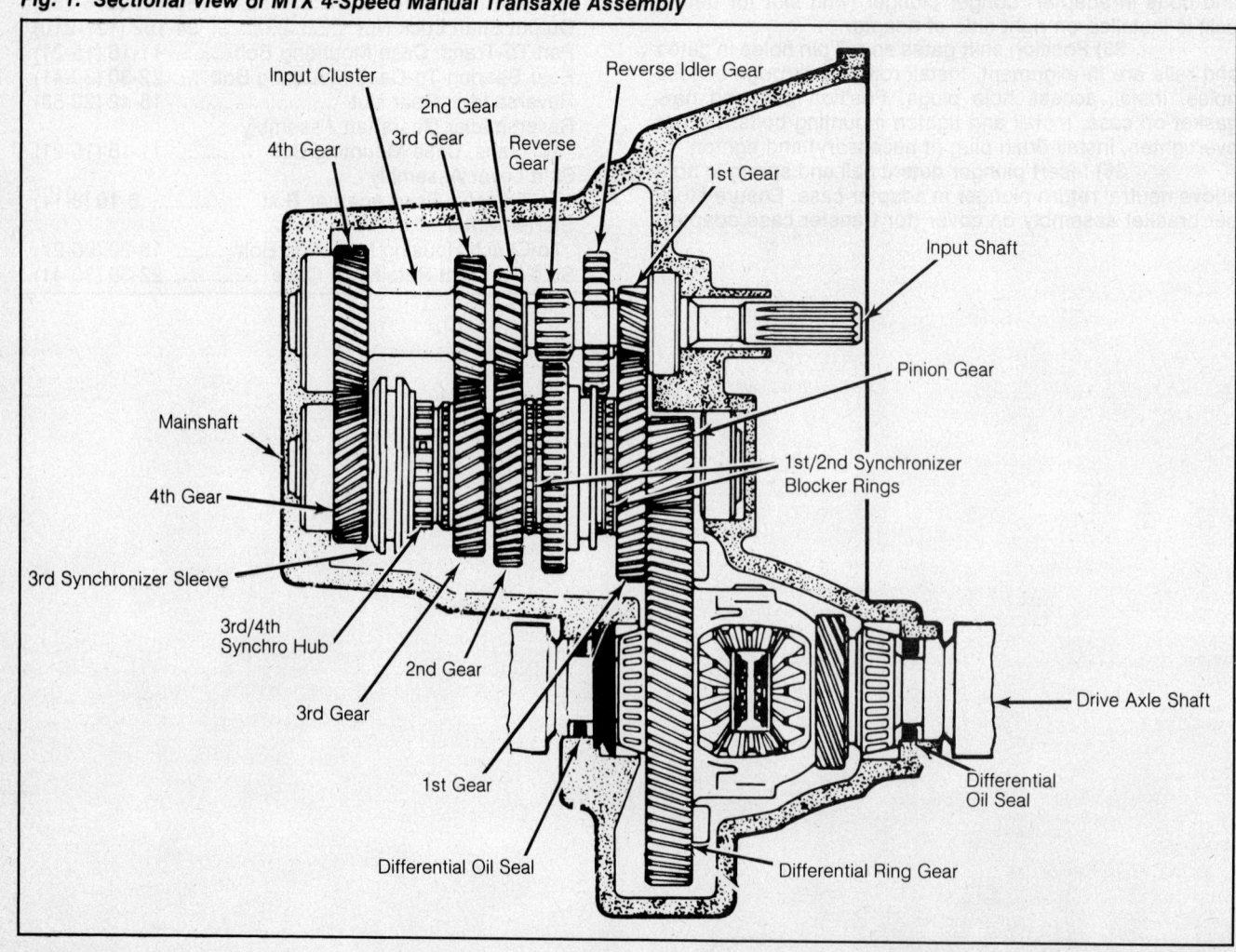

Manual Transmissions
3-85

FORD MOTOR CO.
MTX 4 & 5-SPEED MANUAL TRANSAXLE (Cont.)

Fig. 2: Sectional View of MTX 5-Speed Manual Transaxle Assembly

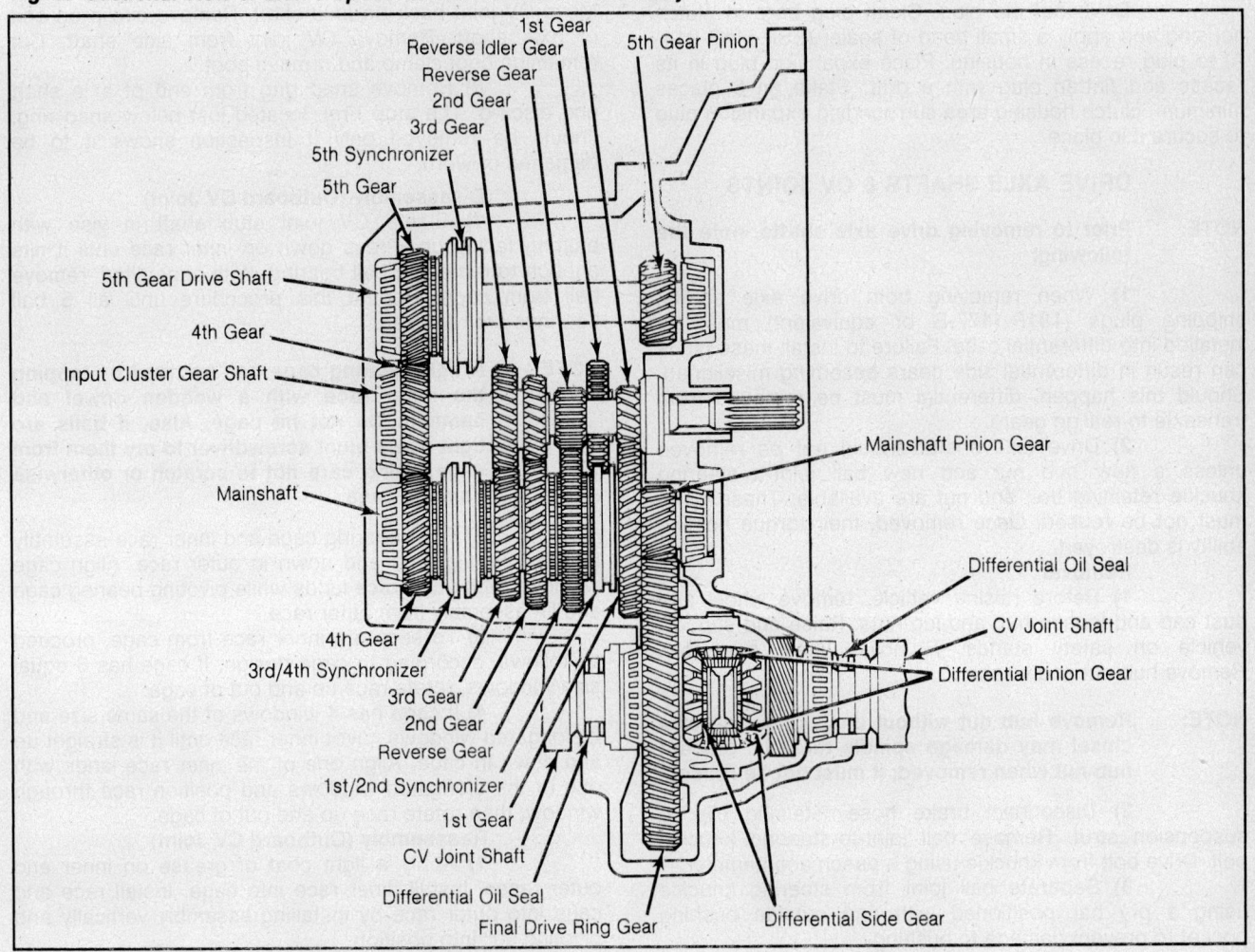

Labels (top): 1st Gear, Reverse Idler Gear, Reverse Gear, 2nd Gear, 3rd Gear, 5th Synchronizer, 5th Gear, 5th Gear Pinion

Labels (left): 5th Gear Drive Shaft, 4th Gear, Input Cluster Gear Shaft, Mainshaft

Labels (right): Mainshaft Pinion Gear, Differential Oil Seal, CV Joint Shaft, Differential Pinion Gear

Labels (bottom): 4th Gear, 3rd/4th Synchronizer, 3rd Gear, 2nd Gear, Reverse Gear, 1st/2nd Synchronizer, 1st Gear, CV Joint Shaft, Differential Oil Seal, Final Drive Ring Gear, Differential Side Gear

LUBRICATION & ADJUSTMENT

See appropriate MANUAL TRANSMISSION SERVICING article in DOMESTIC GENERAL SERVICING section.

TROUBLE SHOOTING

See MANUAL TRANSMISSION TROUBLE SHOOTING article in DOMESTIC GENERAL SERVICING section.

SERVICE (IN VEHICLE)

BACK-UP LIGHT SWITCH
Removal
Disconnect electrical lead to back-up light switch. Place transaxle in reverse. Remove switch from transaxle case using a 30 mm wrench.

CAUTION: To prevent internal problems, do not shift transaxle until a new switch is installed.

Installation
Reverse removal procedure and wrap switch threads with teflon tape in a clockwise direction.

SPEEDOMETER RETAINER & DRIVEN GEAR
Removal
Clean off top of retainer. Remove retaining bolt from driven gear retainer assembly. Pry on retainer with a screwdriver to remove gear and retainer assembly from case bore. If necessary, carefully pry from inside of case on bottom of gear.

Installation
Clean and inspect case bore and all parts. Lightly grease "O" ring on retainer. Using a 13/16" deep-well socket, gently tap retainer and gear assembly into case. Install and tighten retaining bolt.

CLUTCH HOUSING EXPANSION PLUG

NOTE: The 15 mm expansion plug installed on bottom side of clutch housing case should never be removed during normal service. However, if for any reason it becomes necessary to install a new plug, proceed as follows:

3-86

Manual Transmissions

FORD MOTOR CO.
MTX 4 & 5-SPEED MANUAL TRANSAXLE (Cont.)

Expansion Plug Replacement

Drive out old plug. Clean plug bore in clutch housing and apply a small bead of sealer (ESP-M4G-214-A) to plug recess in housing. Place expansion plug in its recess and flatten plug with a drift. Stake (in 3 places minimum) clutch housing area surrounding expansion plug to secure it in place.

DRIVE AXLE SHAFTS & CV JOINTS

NOTE: **Prior to removing drive axle shafts, note the following:**

1) When removing both drive axle shafts, shipping plugs (T81P-1177-B or equivalent) must be installed into differential case. Failure to install these plugs can result in differential side gears becoming misaligned. Should this happen, differential must be removed from transaxle to realign gears.

2) Drive axle shafts should not be removed unless a new hub nut and new ball joint-to-steering knuckle retaining bolt and nut are available. These parts must not be reused. Once removed, their torque holding ability is destroyed.

Removal

1) Before raising vehicle, remove wheel hub dust cap and loosen hub and lug nuts. Raise and support vehicle on safety stands. Remove wheel assembly. Remove hub nut and washer.

NOTE: **Remove hub nut without unstaking. Use of a chisel may damage spindle threads. Discard hub nut when removed; it must not be reused.**

2) Disconnect brake hose retaining clip to suspension strut. Remove ball joint-to-steering knuckle bolt. Drive bolt from knuckle using a punch and hammer.

3) Separate ball joint from steering knuckle using a pry bar positioned with end outside bushing pocket to prevent damage to bushing.

NOTE: **Plastic disc brake shield must be bent back away from ball joint while prying ball joint from steering knuckle.**

4) Using a pry bar, separate drive axle shaft from differential housing. Position pry bar between housing and shaft. Use care not to damage dust deflector between shaft and housing, differential oil seal, CV joint boot, or CV joint dust deflector. Support end of axle shaft with a piece of wire to prevent damage to outboard CV joint. Using a puller, separate outboard CV joint from hub, and remove shaft.

CAUTION: **Never use a hammer to separate outboard CV joint from hub. Damage to CV joint internal components may result.**

5) To remove CV joint and boot from axle shaft, clamp shaft in a soft-jawed vise, making sure vise jaws do not contact boot or clamp. Cut large clamp from boot and pull boot back over shaft.

6) Separate CV joint from shaft using hammer and drift (except MTX 5-speed) by hitting inner race. Cut remaining boot clamp and remove boot.

7) On MTX 5-speed, remove wire ring at edge of CV housing. Remove outer housing. Spread lock ring on back side of CV joint and move back on axle shaft. Move CV joint back on axle shaft. Remove circlip on end of axle shaft. Remove CV joint from axle shaft. Cut remaining boot clamp and remove boot.

8) Remove snap ring from end of axle shaft and discard. The stop ring, located just below snap ring, should be removed only if inspection shows it to be damaged or worn.

Disassembly (Outboard CV Joint)

1) Clamp CV joint stub shaft in vise with bearing facing up. Press down on inner race until it tilts enough to remove a ball bearing. With cage tilted, remove ball from cage. Repeat this procedure until all 6 ball bearings are removed.

NOTE: **A tight bearing cage can be tilted by tapping the inner race with a wooden dowel and hammer. Do not hit cage. Also, if balls are tight use a blunt screwdriver to pry them from cage, using care not to scratch or otherwise damage cage.**

2) Pivot bearing cage and inner race assembly until it is straight up and down in outer race. Align cage windows with outer race lands while pivoting bearing cage and lift assembly from outer race.

3) To separate inner race from cage, proceed as follows, according to cage design. If cage has 6 equal size windows, rotate race up and out of cage.

4) If cage has 4 windows of the same size and 2 elongated windows, pivot inner race until it is straight up and down in cage. Align one of the inner race lands with one of the elongated windows and position race through window, then rotate race up and out of cage.

Reassembly (Outboard CV Joint)

1) Apply a light coat of grease on inner and outer races. Install inner race into cage. Install race and cage into outer race by installing assembly vertically and pivoting 90° into position.

NOTE: **When properly installed, shallow counterbore cut into inner race will be facing up.**

2) Align bearing cage and inner race with outer race. Tilt race and cage, and install ball bearing. Repeat procedure to install all ball bearings.

3) After installing bearings, pack CV joint with 3.2 ounces (90 grams) of specified grease (supplied in service kit). Pack grease into joint by forcing it through splined hole in inner race.

Disassembly (Inboard CV Joint)

1) Remove snap ring from end of CV joint stub shaft. Using side cutters, cut and remove ball bearing retainer.

NOTE: **Discard ball bearing retainer when removed. A new retainer is not required for reassembly.**

2) Gently tap CV joint on bench until cage and inner race assembly can be removed by hand. Remove ball bearings by prying from cage with a blunt screwdriver, using care not to scratch or otherwise damage race and cage spheres.

3) Rotate inner race to align lands with cage windows. Lift inner race from bearing cage through wider end of cage.

Manual Transmissions
FORD MOTOR CO.
MTX 4 & 5-SPEED MANUAL TRANSAXLE (Cont.)

3-87

Fig. 3: Exploded View of Drive Axle Shaft and CV Joint Assembly

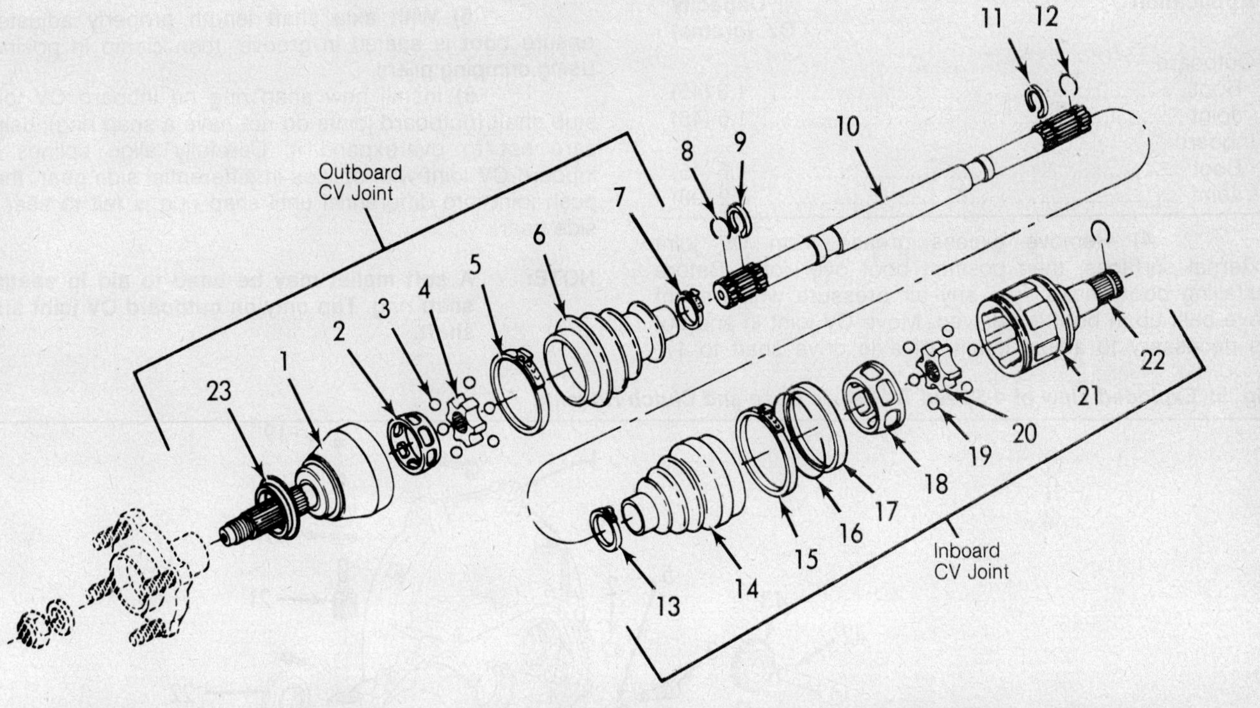

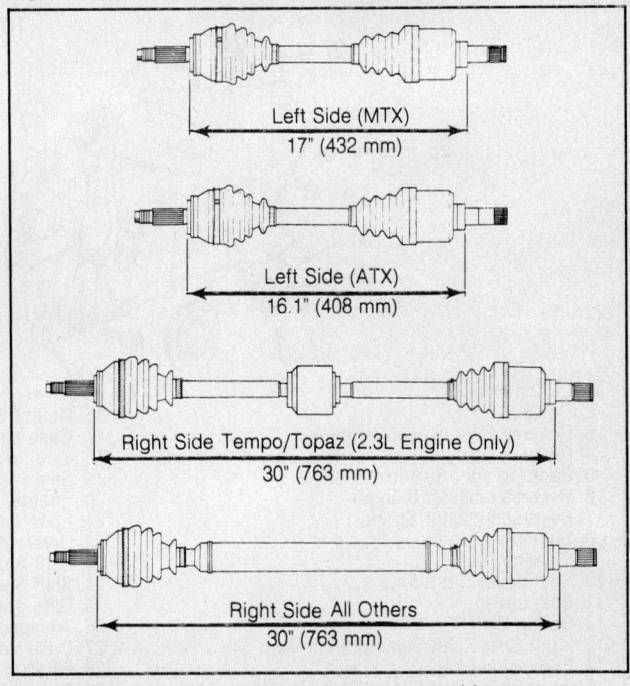

Outboard CV Joint

Inboard CV Joint

1. Outer Bearing Race & Stub	8. Snap Ring	16. Bearing Retainer (MTX 5-Speed)
2. Bearing Cage	9. Stop Ring	17. Bearing Retainer (All Others)
3. Ball Bearings (6)	10. Axle Shaft	18. Bearing Cage
4. Inner Bearing Race	11. Stop Ring	19. Ball Bearings (6)
5. Large Boot Clamp	12. Snap Ring	20. Inner Bearing Race
6. Boot	13. Small Boot Clamp	21. Outer Race & Stub Shaft Assy.
7. Small Boot Clamp	14. Boot	22. Snap Ring
	15. Large Boot Clamp	23. Dust Shield

Left side assembly shown, right side is similar.

Reassembly (Inboard CV Joint)

1) Install snap ring on stub shaft, using care not to over-expand it. Install inner race through large end of cage with race hub facing large end of cage. With inner race and cage properly aligned, press ball bearings through cage with hand.

2) Pack outer race with 1 packet of grease (supplied in service kit). Position inner race and bearing assembly in outer race, then push assembly fully into outer race.

NOTE: When properly assembled, inner race hub will face into outer race.

Installation

1) If removed, install a new stop ring into groove on axle drive shaft. Install new snap ring in groove nearest end of shaft, using care not to over-expand it. If removed, install CV joint boot on axle shaft. Make sure boot is seated in groove, then clamp boot in position using crimping pilers.

2) Install CV joint in housing and secure with retainer clip (MTX 5-speed inboard CV joint only). With CV joint boot peeled back, position joint on axle shaft and tap into position using a plastic mallet. When fully seated, snap ring locks in groove cut into CV joint inner race.

3) Before positioning boot over CV joint, pack joint and boot with lubricant supplied in service kit. See CV JOINT GREASE CAPACITY table.

Fig. 4: Drive Axle Shaft Assembled Length

Left Side (MTX)
17" (432 mm)

Left Side (ATX)
16.1" (408 mm)

Right Side Tempo/Topaz (2.3L Engine Only)
30" (763 mm)

Right Side All Others
30" (763 mm)

Check axle length and that boots are seated in groove.

Manual Transmissions
FORD MOTOR CO.
MTX 4 & 5-SPEED MANUAL TRANSAXLE (Cont.)

CV JOINT GREASE CAPACITY

Application	Capacity Oz. (grams)
Outboard	
Boot	1.6 (45)
Joint	1.6 (45)
Inboard	
Boot	1.6 (45)
Joint	3.2 (90)

4) Remove excess grease from CV joint external surfaces, then position boot over joint. Before installing boot, make sure any air pressure which might have built up in boot is relieved. Move CV joint in and out as necessary to adjust length of axle drive shaft to 17"

(432 mm) on left side axle shaft and 30" (763 mm) on right side axle shaft. *See Fig. 4.*

5) With axle shaft length properly adjusted, ensure boot is seated in groove, then clamp in position using crimping pliers

6) Install new snap ring on inboard CV joint stub shaft (outboard joints do not have a snap ring), using care not to overexpand it. Carefully align splines of inboard CV joint with splines in differential side gear, then push joint into differential until snap ring is felt to seat in side gear.

NOTE: A soft mallet may be used to aid in seating snap ring. Tap only on outboard CV joint stub shaft.

Fig. 5: Exploded View of 4-Speed Transaxle Case and Clutch Housing

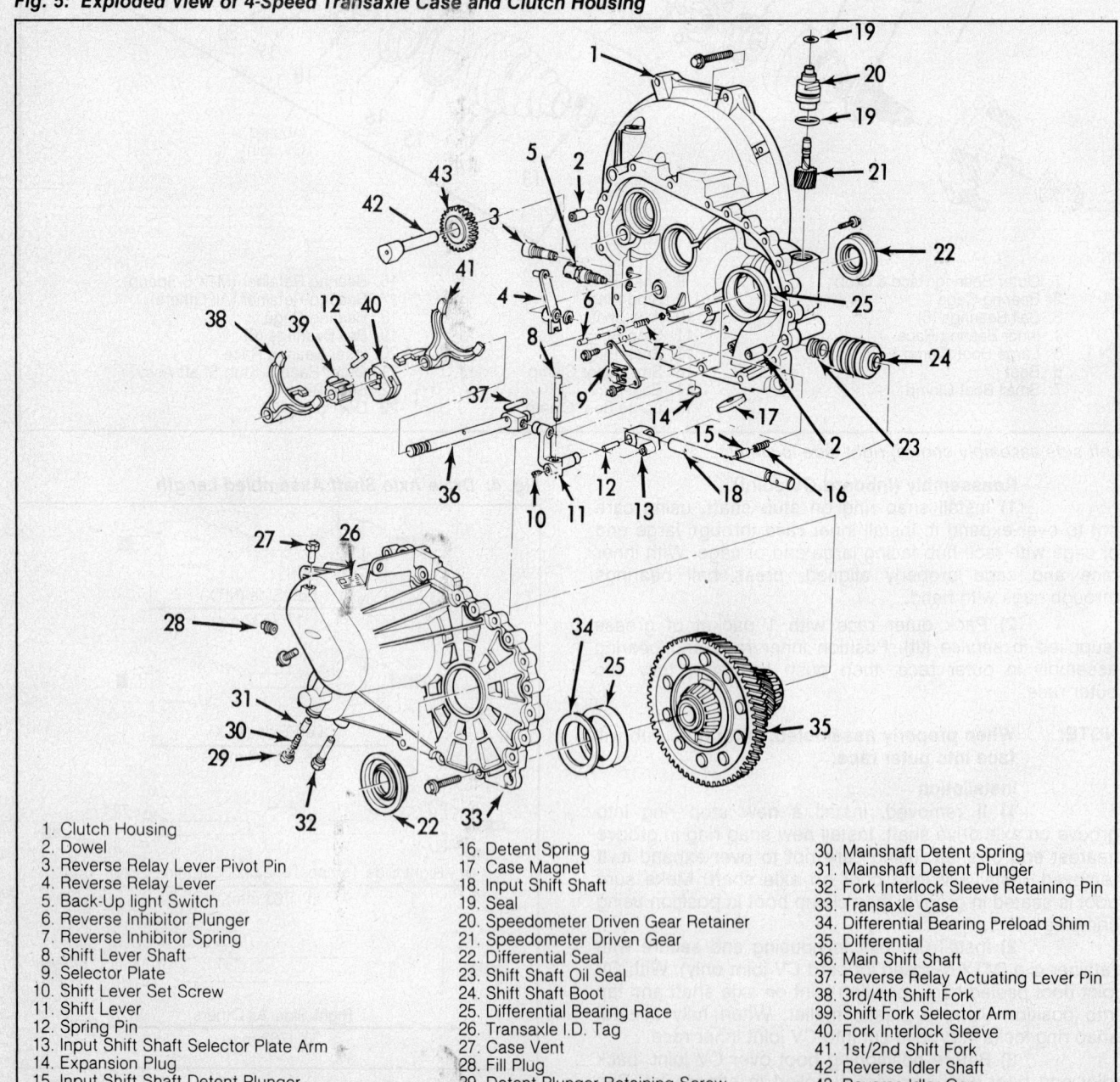

1. Clutch Housing
2. Dowel
3. Reverse Relay Lever Pivot Pin
4. Reverse Relay Lever
5. Back-Up light Switch
6. Reverse Inhibitor Plunger
7. Reverse Inhibitor Spring
8. Shift Lever Shaft
9. Selector Plate
10. Shift Lever Set Screw
11. Shift Lever
12. Spring Pin
13. Input Shift Shaft Selector Plate Arm
14. Expansion Plug
15. Input Shift Shaft Detent Plunger
16. Detent Spring
17. Case Magnet
18. Input Shift Shaft
19. Seal
20. Speedometer Driven Gear Retainer
21. Speedometer Driven Gear
22. Differential Seal
23. Shift Shaft Oil Seal
24. Shift Shaft Boot
25. Differential Bearing Race
26. Transaxle I.D. Tag
27. Case Vent
28. Fill Plug
29. Detent Plunger Retaining Screw
30. Mainshaft Detent Spring
31. Mainshaft Detent Plunger
32. Fork Interlock Sleeve Retaining Pin
33. Transaxle Case
34. Differential Bearing Preload Shim
35. Differential
36. Main Shift Shaft
37. Reverse Relay Actuating Lever Pin
38. 3rd/4th Shift Fork
39. Shift Fork Selector Arm
40. Fork Interlock Sleeve
41. 1st/2nd Shift Fork
42. Reverse Idler Shaft
43. Reverse Idler Gear

Manual Transmissions
FORD MOTOR CO.
MTX 4 & 5-SPEED MANUAL TRANSAXLE (Cont.)

Fig. 6: Exploded View of 5-Speed Transaxle Case and Clutch Housing

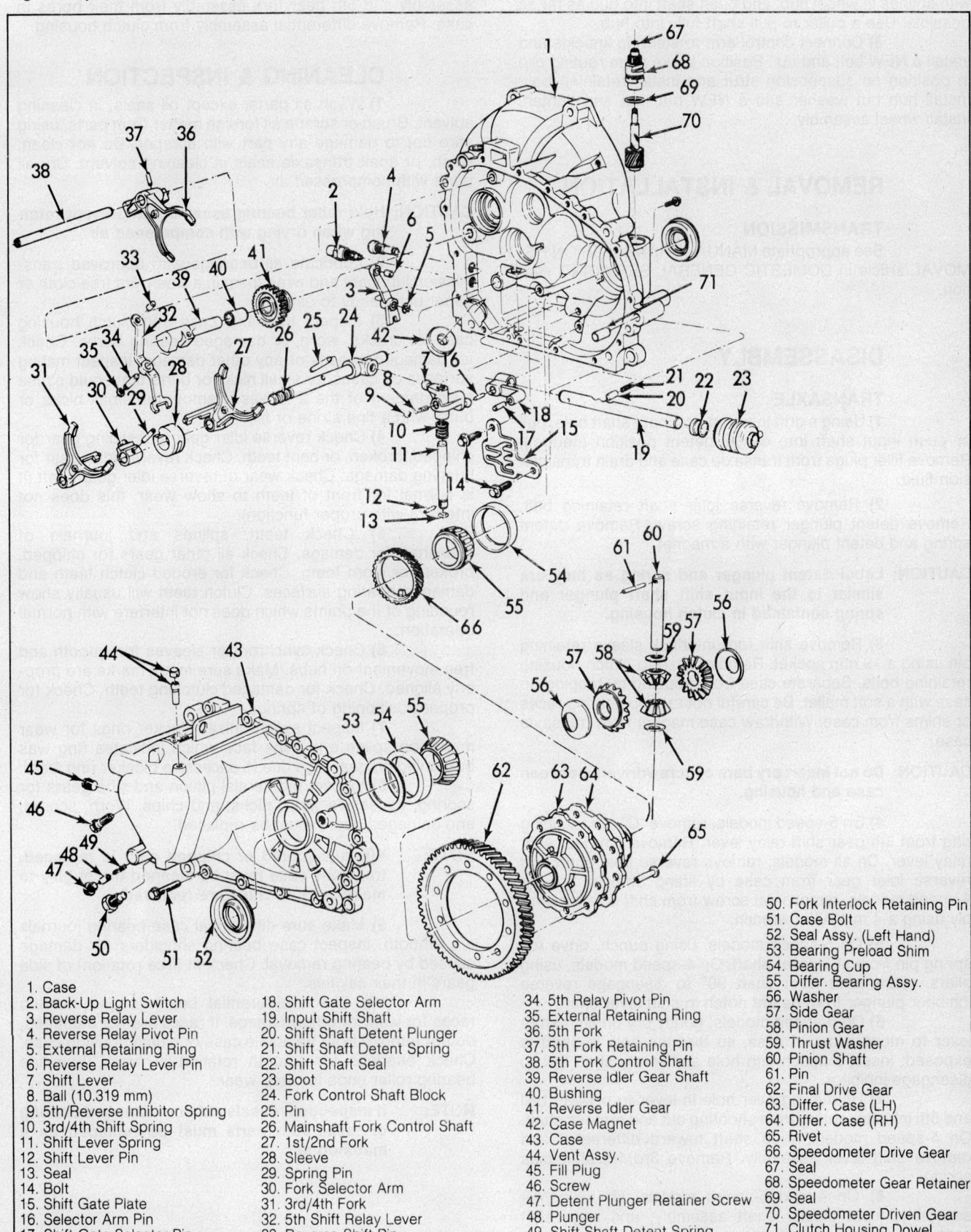

1. Case
2. Back-Up Light Switch
3. Reverse Relay Lever
4. Reverse Relay Pivot Pin
5. External Retaining Ring
6. Reverse Relay Lever Pin
7. Shift Lever
8. Ball (10.319 mm)
9. 5th/Reverse Inhibitor Spring
10. 3rd/4th Shift Spring
11. Shift Lever Spring
12. Shift Lever Pin
13. Seal
14. Bolt
15. Shift Gate Plate
16. Selector Arm Pin
17. Shift Gate Selector Pin
18. Shift Gate Selector Arm
19. Input Shift Shaft
20. Shift Shaft Detent Plunger
21. Shift Shaft Detent Spring
22. Shift Shaft Seal
23. Boot
24. Fork Control Shaft Block
25. Pin
26. Mainshaft Fork Control Shaft
27. 1st/2nd Fork
28. Sleeve
29. Spring Pin
30. Fork Selector Arm
31. 3rd/4th Fork
32. 5th Shift Relay Lever
33. Reverse Shift Pin
34. 5th Relay Pivot Pin
35. External Retaining Ring
36. 5th Fork
37. 5th Fork Retaining Pin
38. 5th Fork Control Shaft
39. Reverse Idler Gear Shaft
40. Bushing
41. Reverse Idler Gear
42. Case Magnet
43. Case
44. Vent Assy.
45. Fill Plug
46. Screw
47. Detent Plunger Retainer Screw
48. Plunger
49. Shift Shaft Detent Spring
50. Fork Interlock Retaining Pin
51. Case Bolt
52. Seal Assy. (Left Hand)
53. Bearing Preload Shim
54. Bearing Cup
55. Differ. Bearing Assy.
56. Washer
57. Side Gear
58. Pinion Gear
59. Thrust Washer
60. Pinion Shaft
61. Pin
62. Final Drive Gear
63. Differ. Case (LH)
64. Differ. Case (RH)
65. Rivet
66. Speedometer Drive Gear
67. Seal
68. Speedometer Gear Retainer
69. Seal
70. Speedometer Driven Gear
71. Clutch Housing Dowel

Manual Transmissions
FORD MOTOR CO.
MTX 4 & 5-SPEED MANUAL TRANSAXLE (Cont.)

7) Align splines of outboard CV joint stub shaft with splines in wheel hub, and push shaft into hub as far as possible. Use a puller to pull shaft fully into hub.

8) Connect control arm to steering knuckle and install a NEW bolt and nut. Position brake hose routing clip in position on suspension strut and install retaining bolt. Install hub nut washer and a NEW hub nut and tighten. Install wheel assembly.

REMOVAL & INSTALLATION

TRANSMISSION

See appropriate MANUAL TRANSMISSION REMOVAL article in DOMESTIC GENERAL SERVICING section.

DISASSEMBLY

TRANSAXLE

1) Using a drift inserted into input shaft hole, pull or push input shaft into center detent position (neutral). Remove filler plugs from transaxle case and drain transmission fluid.

2) Remove reverse idler shaft retaining bolt. Remove detent plunger retaining screw. Remove detent spring and detent plunger with a magnet.

CAUTION: Label detent plunger and spring as they are similar to the input shift shaft plunger and spring contained in clutch housing.

3) Remove shift fork interlock sleeve retaining pin using a 19 mm socket. Remove case-to-clutch housing retaining bolts. Separate case from housing by tapping on case with a soft mallet. Be careful not to drop bearing races or shims from case. Withdraw case magnet from transaxle case.

CAUTION: Do not insert pry bars or screwdrivers between case and housing.

4) On 5-speed models, remove "C" clip retaining ring from 5th gear shift relay lever. Remove 5th gear shift relay lever. On all models, remove reverse idler shaft and reverse idler gear from case by lifting straight up. On 4-speed models, remove set screw from shift lever assembly using a 4 mm Allen wrench.

5) On 5-speed models, using punch, drive roll spring pin from shift lever shaft. On 4-speed models, using pliers, rotate shift lever shaft 90° to disengage reverse inhibitor plunger from detent notch in shift lever shaft.

6) On 5-speed models, gently pry on shift shaft lever to move it out of case, so that the hole in shaft is exposed. Insert a punch into hole and rotate shaft 90° to disengage inhibitor.

7) Hold a rag over hole in lever to prevent ball and 5th inhibitor spring from shooting out and remove shaft. On 4-speed models, slide shaft toward differential and remove shift lever assembly. Remove 3rd/4th shift bias spring.

8) On 4 and 5-speed models, lift mainshaft assembly, input cluster shaft assembly, and main shift control shaft assembly from case as a single unit.

9) On 5-speed models, remove 5th gear shaft assembly and 5th gear fork assembly from their bores in case. Remove differential assembly from clutch housing.

CLEANING & INSPECTION

1) Wash all parts, except oil seals, in cleaning solvent. Brush or scrape all foreign matter from parts, using care not to damage any part with scraper. Do not clean, wash, or soak transaxle seals in cleaning solvent. Dry all parts with compressed air.

CAUTION: Hold roller bearing assembly to prevent rotating when drying with compressed air.

2) Lubricate all bearings with approved transmission lubricant and wrap them in a clean, lint free cloth or paper until ready to use.

3) Inspect transaxle case and clutch housing case for cracks, worn, or damaged bearing bores. Check for damaged threads or any other damage. Inspect mating surfaces on cases for small nicks or burrs that could cause misalignment of the 2 halves. Remove all small nicks or burrs with a fine stone or file.

4) Check reverse idler gear and sliding gear for chipped, broken, or bent teeth. Check reverse idler gear for bushing damage. Check wear of reverse idler gear shaft (it is normal for front of teeth to show wear; this does not interfere with proper function).

5) Check teeth, splines and journals of mainshaft for damage. Check all other gears for chipped, broken, or worn teeth. Check for eroded clutch teeth and damaged bearing surfaces. Clutch teeth will usually show rounding of the points which does not interfere with normal operation.

6) Check synchronizer sleeves for smooth and free movement on hubs. Make sure index marks are properly aligned. Check for damaged clutching teeth. Check for proper positioning of springs.

7) Inspect synchronizer blocker rings for wear marks on spline end back face which indicates ring was bottoming on gear face due to excessive blocker ring wear.

6) Inspect differential pinion and side gears for scoring, excessive wear, nicks, and chips. Worn, scored, and damaged gears must be replaced.

NOTE: When a scored or chipped gear is replaced, transaxle case must be cleaned thoroughly to make sure all chips are removed.

9) Make sure differential case bearing journals are smooth. Inspect case bearing shoulders for damage caused by bearing removal. Check fit (free rotation) of side gears in their cavities.

10) Check differential bearings and bearing races for wear or other damage. If races are not damaged, do not remove from transaxle case or clutch housing case. Check bearings for smooth rotation in races. Examine bearing roller ends for step wear.

NOTE: If inspection reveals either a damaged bearing or race, both parts must be replaced as a matched set.

Manual Transmissions

FORD MOTOR CO.
MTX 4 & 5-SPEED MANUAL TRANSAXLE (Cont.)

3-91

Fig. 7: Exploded View of Mainshaft Assembly

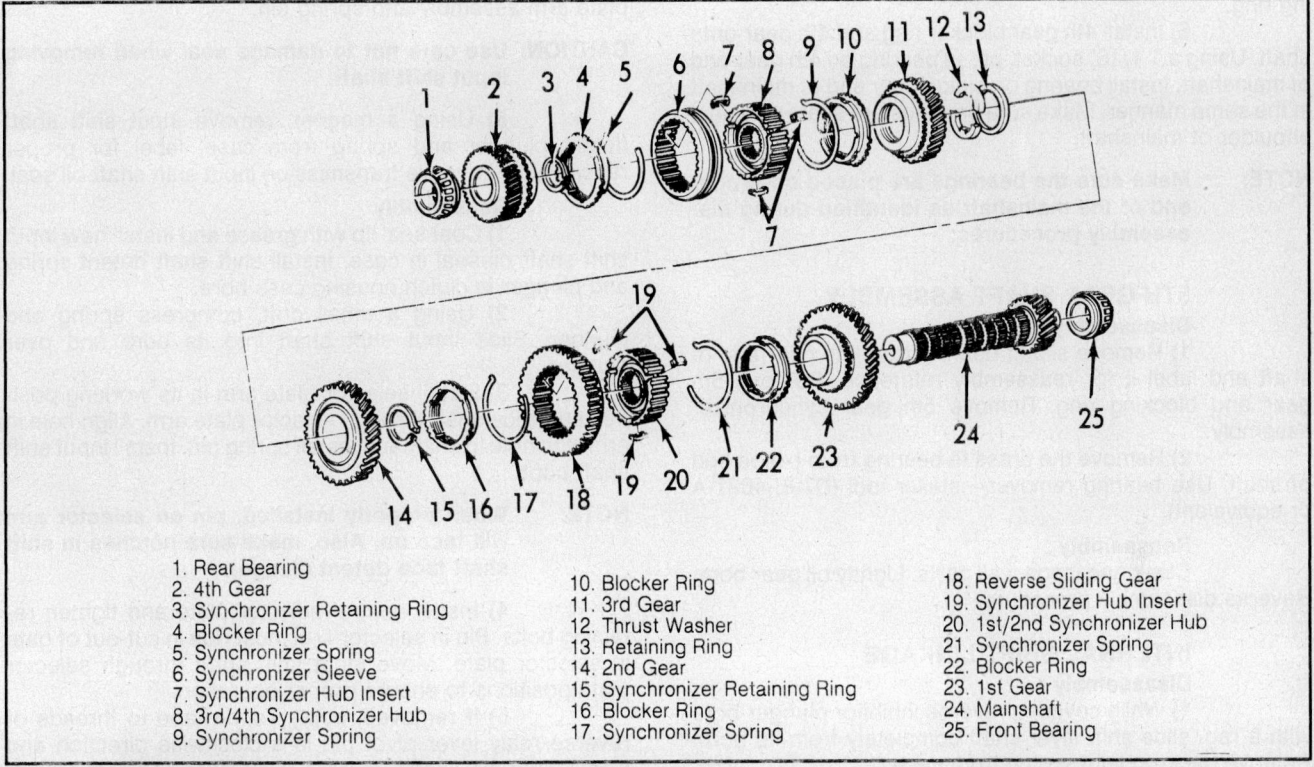

1. Rear Bearing
2. 4th Gear
3. Synchronizer Retaining Ring
4. Blocker Ring
5. Synchronizer Spring
6. Synchronizer Sleeve
7. Synchronizer Hub Insert
8. 3rd/4th Synchronizer Hub
9. Synchronizer Spring
10. Blocker Ring
11. 3rd Gear
12. Thrust Washer
13. Retaining Ring
14. 2nd Gear
15. Synchronizer Retaining Ring
16. Blocker Ring
17. Synchronizer Spring
18. Reverse Sliding Gear
19. Synchronizer Hub Insert
20. 1st/2nd Synchronizer Hub
21. Synchronizer Spring
22. Blocker Ring
23. 1st Gear
24. Mainshaft
25. Front Bearing

NOTE: If inspection reveals either a damaged bearing or race, both parts must be replaced as a matched set.

COMPONENT DISASSEMBLY & REASSEMBLY

MAINSHAFT ASSEMBLY

Disassembly

1) If damaged, press tapered roller bearing from pinion end of mainshaft using an arbor press. Press bearing from 4th gear end of shaft.

NOTE: Mainshaft bearings should be identified for reassembly when pressed from shaft.

2) Slide 4th gear and synchronizer blocker ring from mainshaft. Remove 3rd/4th synchronizer retaining ring. Slide synchronizer assembly, blocker ring, and 3rd gear from shaft.

3) Remove 2nd/3rd thrust washer retaining ring and 2-piece thrust washer. Remove 2nd gear and blocker ring. Remove retaining ring. Slide 1st/2nd synchronizer assembly, blocker ring, and 1st gear from shaft.

Reassembly

1) Prior to installing components on mainshaft, reassemble synchronizer assemblies and note the following:

2) Align index mark on synchronizer sleeve and hub. Place tab on synchronizer spring into groove of one of the inserts and snap spring into place. Place tab of the other spring into same insert (on opposite side of synchronizer assembly), and rotate spring in the opposite direction and snap into place.

Fig. 8: Exploded View of Synchronizer Assembly

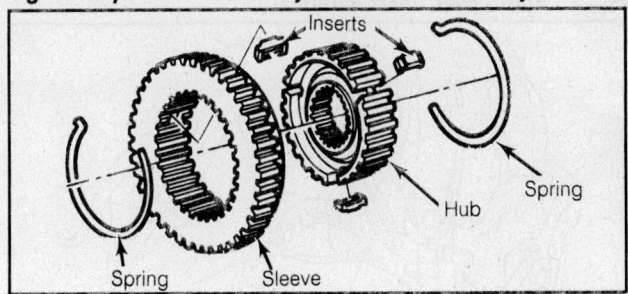

NOTE: When assembling synchronizer, notice that sleeve and hub have an extremely tight fit and must be held square to prevent jamming. Do not force sleeve onto hub.

3) To reassemble mainshaft, lightly oil gear bores and other parts with appropriate transmission fluid. Slide blocker ring and 1st gear onto shaft.

4) Slide 1st/2nd synchronizer assembly into place, making sure shift fork groove on reverse sliding gear faces 1st gear. Install synchronizer retaining ring.

NOTE: When installing synchronizer assembly, align the 3 grooves in 1st gear blocker ring with synchronizer inserts. This allows synchronizer assembly to seat properly in blocker ring.

5) Install 2nd gear blocker ring and 2nd gear onto shaft. Install thrust washer halves and retaining ring. Slide 3rd gear onto shaft followed by blocker ring and

3-92

Manual Transmissions
FORD MOTOR CO.
MTX 4 & 5-SPEED MANUAL TRANSAXLE (Cont.)

3rd/4th synchronizer assembly. Install synchronizer retaining ring.

6) Install 4th gear blocker ring and 4th gear onto shaft. Using a 1 1/16" socket, press bearing on 4th gear end of mainshaft. Install bearing on pinion gear end of mainshaft in the same manner. Make sure bearings are seated against shoulder of mainshaft.

NOTE: **Make sure the bearings are placed on proper end of the mainshaft as identified during disassembly procedures.**

5TH GEAR SHAFT ASSEMBLY
Disassembly

1) Remove slip fit bearing from 5th gear end of shaft and label it for reassembly reference. Remove 5th gear and blocking ring. Remove 5th gear synchronizer assembly.

2) Remove the press fit bearing from pinion end of shaft. Use bearing remover/installer tool (D79L-4621-A or equivalent).

Reassembly

Clean and inspect all parts. Lightly oil gear bore. Reverse diassembly procedure.

INTERNAL SHIFT LINKAGE
Disassembly

1) While covering reverse inhibitor plunger bore with a rag, slide shift lever shaft completely from its bore. Remove back-up light switch from case.

Fig. 9: Shift Lever Shaft Removal

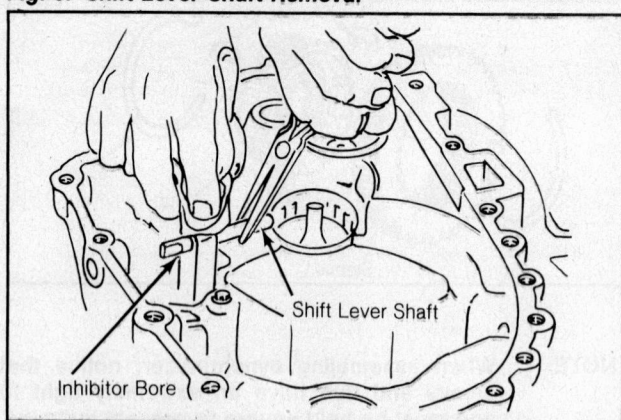

Cover inhibitor bore before removing shaft.

CAUTION: **Removal of shift lever shaft could allow reverse inhibitor plunger to spring from its bore in case. Ensure inhibitor bore is covered to prevent possible injury.**

2) Using a screwdriver, remove "C" clip and remove reverse relay lever (it is not necessary to remove pivot pin). Remove 2 control selector plate retaining bolts and remove plate from case.

3) Place input shift shaft in center detent position. Drive spring pin through selector plate arm assembly, through shift shaft into recess in clutch housing case. Remove shift shaft boot.

4) Using a drift, rotate input shift shaft 90°. Depress detent plunger from shaft detent notches inside

housing and pull shift shaft out. Remove shift shaft selector plate arm assembly and spring pin.

CAUTION: **Use care not to damage seal when removing input shift shaft.**

5) Using a magnet, remove input shift shaft detent plunger and spring from case, label for proper reassembly. Remove transmission input shift shaft oil seal.

Reassembly

1) Coat seal lip with grease and install new input shift shaft oil seal in case. Install shift shaft detent spring and plunger in clutch housing case bore.

2) Using a small drift, compress spring and plunger. Slide input shift shaft into its bore and over plunger.

3) Install selector plate arm in its working position and slide shaft through selector plate arm. Align hole in arm with hole in shaft and install spring pin. Install input shift shaft boot.

NOTE: **When properly installed, pin on selector arm will face up. Also, make sure notches in shift shaft face detent plunger.**

4) Install control selector plate and tighten retaining bolts. Pin in selector arm must ride in cut-out of gate in selector plate. Move input shift shaft through selector plate positions to ensure proper operation.

5) If removed, apply Teflon tape to threads of reverse relay lever pivot pin in a clockwise direction and install pivot pin. Install reverse relay lever and secure with "C" clip, making sure pin at end of lever faces outward.

6) Apply Teflon tape to threads of back-up light switch in a clockwise direction. Install and tighten switch. Depress reverse inhibitor plunger and slide shift lever shaft (with oil relief flat first) through case pedestal.

7) Slide shaft far enough so that mainshaft or differential will not interfere with shift lever shaft when installed.

MAIN SHIFT CONTROL SHAFT
Disassembly

1) Rotate 3rd/4th shift fork on shaft until notch in fork is positioned over interlock sleeve. Rotate 1st/2nd shift fork on shaft until notch in fork is positioned over selector arm finger.

2) With forks in this position, slide 3rd/4th fork and interlock sleeve off shaft. Drive out selector arm retaining pin using a punch. Remove selector arm and 1st/2nd shift fork from shaft.

Fig. 10: Assembled View of Main Shift Control Shaft

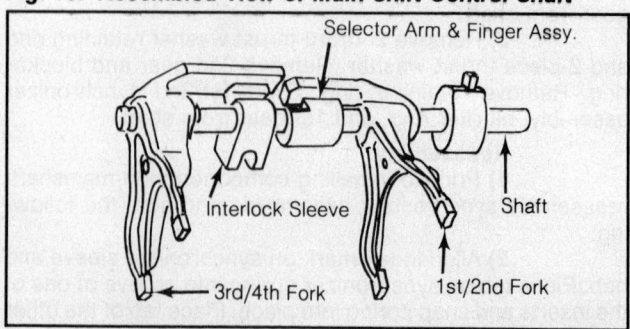

Reassembly

1) Clean and inspect all parts. Lightly oil all parts. Install 1st/2nd shift fork and selector arm on shift

FORD MOTOR CO.
MTX 4 & 5-SPEED MANUAL TRANSAXLE (Cont.)

shaft. Align hole in selector arm with hole in shaft and install retaining pin.

CAUTION: Before installing retaining pin, make sure selector arm finger is aligned with oil relief flats on detent end of shaft. This will prevent arm from being installed 180° from correct operating position.

2) Position slot in 1st/2nd fork over selector arm finger. Position slot in 3rd/4th fork over interlock sleeve. Slide 3rd/4th fork and sleeve onto shaft. Align interlock sleeve splines with splines on fork selector arm and slide into position.

5TH GEAR SHIFT CONTROL SHAFT
Disassembly
Using a punch, remove roll pin. Slide fork from shaft.

Reassembly
Holding shaft with hole on the left, install 5th gear shift fork so that the protruding spline is pointing toward the long end of the shaft. Install roll pin.

DIFFERENTIAL ASSEMBLY
4-Speed (Disassembly)
1) Using a puller, remove differential side bearings from differential case. Remove speedometer drive gear from case.

2) Remove side gears and thrust washers from differential case by rotating gears toward case windows. Using a punch, drive out differential pinion gear shaft retaining pin. Remove pinion shaft, pinion gears and thrust washers from case.

3) If necessary, remove ring gear from differential case as follows: Mount differential assembly in a vise, using a 5/16" (8 mm) drill bit, drill formed side of attaching rivets. Remove heads of rivets with a chisel. Using a punch, drive remaining rivet shank from case and remove ring gear.

4-Speed (Reassembly)
1) To reassemble differential, reverse disassembly procedures and note the following: Lubricate all thrust washers and thrust surfaces on gears and in case with automatic transmission fluid.

2) If removed, press ring gear onto differential case and secure to case with special service replacement bolts and nuts. Special service parts MUST be used to provide proper clearance with transmission case. Install bolts with heads on ring gear side of case and nuts on differential side, partially tighten nuts.

3) Using a standard circular pattern sequence, tighten only the nuts. Install speedometer gear on case with flat side of gear with chamfer facing ring gear.

NOTE: Differential side gears must be aligned in case. This alignment must be held while installing differential in transaxle case. Failure to maintain alignment will make it impossible to install axle drive shafts through side gears.

5-Speed (Disassembly)
1) Use a 1/2" (12 mm) drill and drill through each final drive gear rivet. Using a chisel remove rivet heads. With differential assembly mounted in a vise, use a punch to drive out rivet shanks. Repeat procedure until all 10 rivet shanks are driven out.

Fig. 11: Exploded View of 4-Speed Differential Assembly

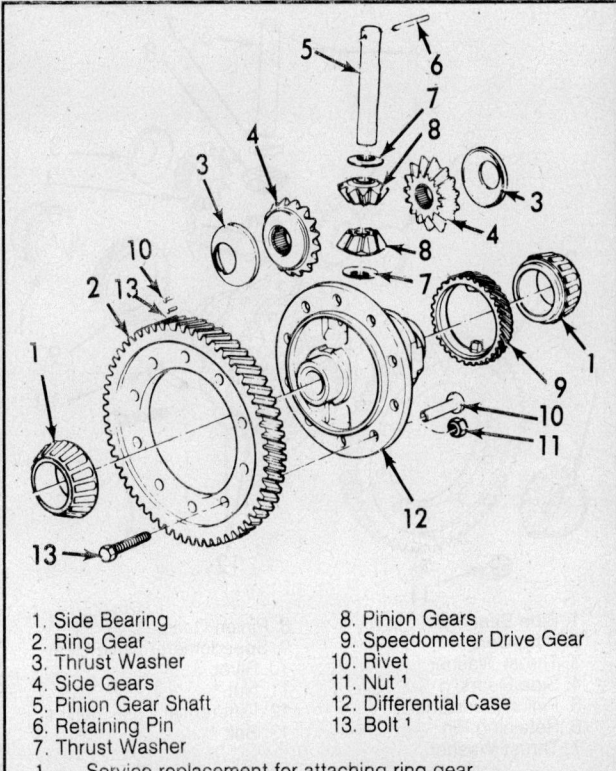

1. Side Bearing
2. Ring Gear
3. Thrust Washer
4. Side Gears
5. Pinion Gear Shaft
6. Retaining Pin
7. Thrust Washer
8. Pinion Gears
9. Speedometer Drive Gear
10. Rivet
11. Nut [1]
12. Differential Case
13. Bolt [1]

[1] — Service replacement for attaching ring gear.

2) Use an arbor press to press off final drive gear. Separate differential case halves by inserting a 9/16" (15 mm) deep-well socket into final drive gear side bearing journal. Install bearing remover (T77F-4220-B1 or T57L-4220-A) and step plate. Begin to remove bearing, case halves will separate before bearing unseats.

3) Do not remove final drive gear side bearing unless it needs to be replaced. Use bearing puller (T57L-4220-A or T77F-4220-B1) and step plate to remove bearing if necessary. Remove speedometer gear.

4) Remove left side gear from case. Rotate right side gear around pinions and remove. Using a 3/32" drill, drill through the center of pinion shaft retaining roll pin and case wall.

NOTE: On some differential cases, the pinion shaft retaining pin may be set in a blind hole. A through-hole must be drilled to facilitate pin removal.

5) Using drilled hole in case as a pilot, use special drill tool (T83P-4204-A) to drill through case to roll pin. Drive roll pin out of pinion shaft with a 5/32" (4 mm) drift. Remove pinion shaft, pinion gears and thrust washers.

5-Speed (Reassembly)
1) Clean and inspect all parts for wear and damage. Lubricate back face of gears and thrust surfaces on differential case with grease (ESA-M1C75B). Assemble pinion gears and thrust washers on pinion shaft as shaft is being installed in right case half.

2) Align hole in pinion shaft with hole in case. Drive roll pin into hole, approximately 3/8" (9.5 mm) below case flange mating surface. Position side gear and thrust washer on pinions. Ensure proper tooth mesh and rotate toward right bearing journal.

3-94

Manual Transmissions
FORD MOTOR CO.
MTX 4 & 5-SPEED MANUAL TRANSAXLE (Cont.)

Fig. 12: Exploded View of 5-Speed Differential Assembly

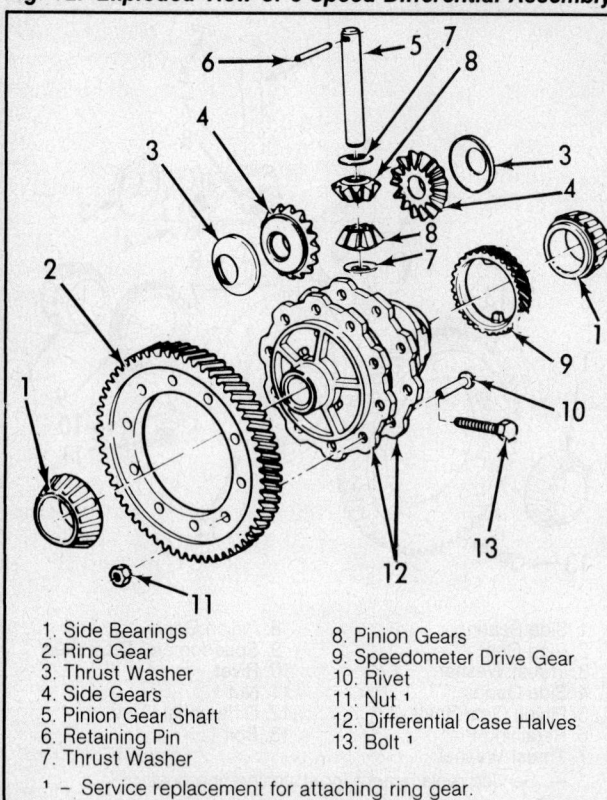

1. Side Bearings
2. Ring Gear
3. Thrust Washer
4. Side Gears
5. Pinion Gear Shaft
6. Retaining Pin
7. Thrust Washer
8. Pinion Gears
9. Speedometer Drive Gear
10. Rivet
11. Nut [1]
12. Differential Case Halves
13. Bolt [1]

[1] – Service replacement for attaching ring gear.

NOTE: Ensure proper alignment of side gear splines to right bearing journal. In not properly aligned, case must be disassembled to align gear splines for later CV shaft installation. Install left side gear and thrust washer. Check for correct engagement.

3) Assemble case halves, aligning retaining pin hole in right case half with retaining pin access hole in left differential case half. Install speedometer drive gear so tangs are positioned on upper side of gear.

4) Using Press Tool (T81P-4221-A), install differential bearings. If final drive gear has been removed, position machined surface of gear toward case with holes in gear aligned with holes in case flange. Contact final drive gear in at least 2 opposite points and press in onto case.

5) Special service bolts and nuts replace rivets for ring gear-to-case assembly. Special service parts MUST be used to provide proper clearance with transmission case. Install bolts with head against differential case and nut against final drive gear, partially tighten nuts. Using a standard circular pattern sequence, tighten only the nuts.

REASSEMBLY & ADJUSTMENT

DIFFERENTIAL BEARING PRELOAD

1) Differential bearing preload is set at the factory and need not be checked or adjusted unless one of the following components is replaced: transaxle case, differential case, differential side bearings or clutch housing.

2) To check and adjust preload, remove differential seal from transaxle case. Drive differential bearing

outer race from case and remove preload adjusting shim located under race.

3) Position differential assembly in clutch housing. Install height Gauge Spacer (T81P-4451-B) on clutch housing dowel. Position bearing outer race removed from transaxle case on differential bearing. Install Shim Selector (T81P-4451-B) over race. See Fig. 13.

Fig. 13: Positioning Differential Preload Measuring Tools

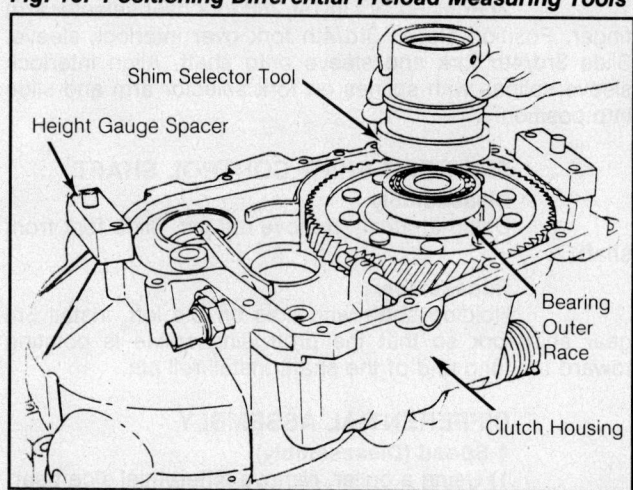

Use 4 retaining bolts supplied with measuring tool.

4) Place transaxle case in position on clutch housing and install the 4 retaining bolts supplied with preload checking tools. Tighten retaining bolts to 17-21 ft. lbs. (23-28 N.m). Rotate differential several times to ensure setting of differential bearing.

5) Place Gauge Bar (T80L-77003-A) across shim selector tool. Using a feeler gauge, measure clearance between gauge bar and shim selector tool. Obtain measurements from 3 positions around tool and take the average of the reading. See Fig. 14.

Fig. 14: Measuring Differential Bearing Preload

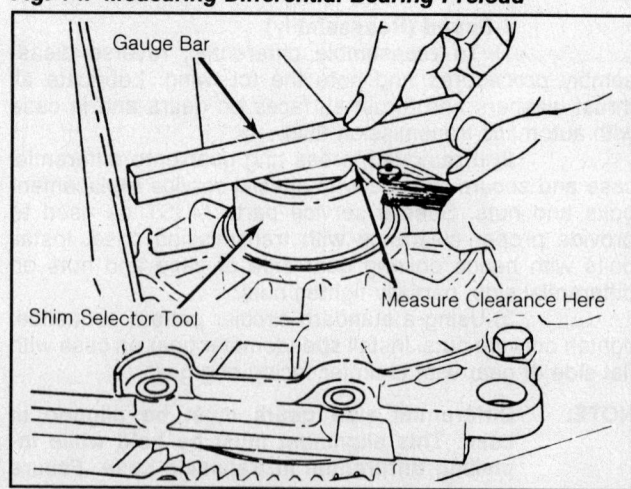

Use feeler gauge to measure bearing preload.

6) The average measurement obtained in preceding step is the thickness of shim needed to obtain specified differential bearing preload. Differential bearing preload shims are available in thicknesses of .012" to .049" (.30 to 1.24 mm) in .002" (.05 mm) increments.

NOTE: If preload adjusting shim required is not available, always use next thickest shim.

7) Separate transaxle case from clutch housing and remove measuring tools. Install selected preload shim in transaxle case. Lubricate gearing bores and press outer race into case until fully seated. Install new differential oil seal in transaxle case.

MAINSHAFT & INPUT CLUSTER SHAFT BEARING PRELOAD

NOTE: The use of a nominal thickness service shim eliminates the need for gauging mainshaft and input cluster shaft bearing clearances prior to reassembly. While this method produces wider variations of bearing settings than are present in factory assembled units, the extreme possible settings have been tested and found to be acceptable.

1) Preload of mainshaft and input cluster shaft bearings is maintained by shims located behind bearing outer races in transaxle case.

2) A replacement bearing preload shim will be provided for service and should be installed in place of original shim as outlined in PRELOAD SHIM SELECTION CHART.

PRELOAD SHIM SELECTION CHART

Parts Replaced	Shims Replaced with Service Shims		
	Input Cluster Shaft	**Main Shaft**	**5th Gear Shaft**
1 Input Cluster Bearing	Yes	No	No
2 Input Cluster Bearings	Yes	No	No
1 Input Cluster Bearing 1 Mainshaft Bearing 1 5th Gear Shaft Bearing	Yes Yes Yes	Yes Yes Yes	Yes Yes Yes
2 Input Cluster Bearings 2 Mainshaft Bearings 2 5th Gear Shaft Bearings	Yes Yes Yes	Yes Yes Yes	Yes Yes Yes
1 Mainshaft Bearing	No	Yes	No
2 Mainshaft Bearings	No	Yes	No
1 5th Gear Shaft Bearing	No	No	Yes
2 5th Gear Shaft Bearings	No	No	Yes
Clutch Housing Assembly	Yes	Yes	Yes
Transaxle Case Assembly	Yes	Yes	Yes

CAUTION: If bearing outer races are removed from case for any reason, it is very important to keep the race and its matching shim together. It is also important to label bearing races as they are removed from transaxle case or clutch hous-

ing. Maintaining proper race-to-shim relationship and proper race labeling will ensure correct bearing preload when transaxle is assembled.

3) The following points should be noted when replacing shaft bearing preload shims. When repairs require use of service replacement shim, discard original shim. DO NOT use more than 1 shim per shaft.

4) If parts are replaced other than parts shown in selection chart, original shim should be re-used. Preload shims must be installed only under bearing races at transaxle case end of both shafts.

5) Bearing races are not pressed into cases. The slip-fit existing between race and case allows removal and installation of races by hand.

REASSEMBLY

TRANSAXLE

1) Position differential assembly in clutch housing case. On 5-speed models, install 5th gear shaft assembly and fork shaft assembly in case. On 4 and 5-speed models, place main shift control shaft assembly on mainshaft so that shift forks engage in respective slots in synchronizer sleeves. See Fig. 15.

Fig. 15: Assembling Main Shift Control Shaft Assembly to Mainshaft Assembly

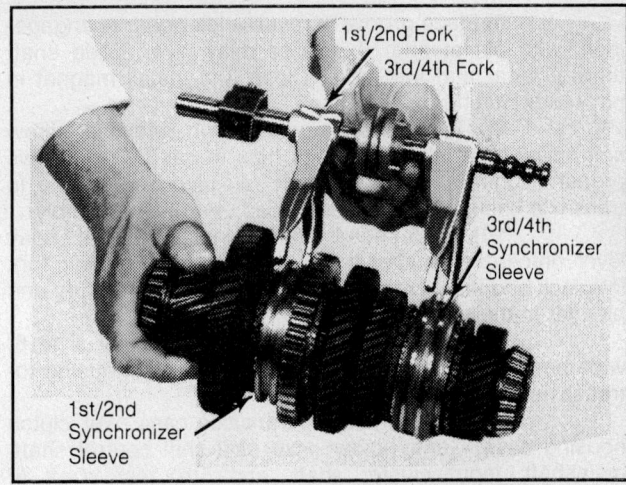

2) Mesh mainshaft assembly with input cluster shaft. Hold shaft assemblies together in their respective working positions and lower them into bores in clutch housing case as a unit. Use care not to damage input shaft oil seal or main shaft oil funnel.

3) Position shift lever assembly in its working position. One shift lever pin should be in socket of input shift shaft selector plate arm assembly. The other pin should be in socket of main shift control shaft block.

4) Slide shift lever shaft through shift lever and into its bore in clutch housing. Rotate shaft so reverse inhibitor notch faces inhibitor plunger.

5) On 4-speed models, position shift lever shaft so set screw hole on shaft aligns with hole in shift lever. Install set screw. Before tightening set screw, position shift lever on shaft to make sure set screw is centered in shaft center drilled hole.

3-96

Manual Transmissions
FORD MOTOR CO.
MTX 4 & 5-SPEED MANUAL TRANSAXLE (Cont.)

6) On 5-speed models, install spring and ball in 5th and reverse inhibitor shaft lever hole. Slide shift lever shaft (notch down) through shift lever. Tap shift shaft into its bore in clutch housing. Align shift shaft bore with case bore and tap in roll pin. Ensure that roll pin is slightly below case surface.

7) Before proceeding with transaxle reassembly on 4 and 5-speed models, verify the following: Selector pin should be in neutral gate of control selector plate. Finger of fork selector arm should be partially engaged with 1st/2nd shift fork and 3rd/4th shift fork. See Fig. 16.

Fig. 16: Checking Selector Pin Position

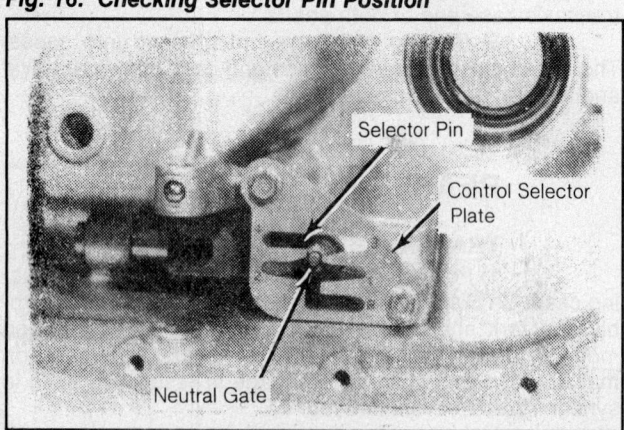

Pin selector should be in neutral gate.

8) Place groove in reverse idler gear in engagement with pin at end of reverse relay lever. Slide shaft through gear and into bore. Clean and install magnet in pocket of clutch housing case.

9) On 4-speed models, align retaining screw hole in reverse idler shaft with hole in case. This allows proper alignment between shaft retaining screw hole in transaxle case, when case is placed over this assembly.

10) On 5-speed models, install 5th shift relay lever onto reverse idler shaft. Align it with 5th gear fork interlock and install retaining ring. Install detent spring and plunger in their bore in case.

11) On 4 and 5-speed models, apply a 1/16" wide bead of sealer (E1FZ-19562-A) to clutch housing-to-transaxle case mounting surface.

12) Carefully lower transaxle case over clutch housing case. Gently lower case until shift control shaft, mainshaft, input cluster shaft, and 5th gear shaft (if equipped) align with bores in transaxle case.

13) Gently slide transaxle case over dowels. Case should sit flush on clutch housing, without binding on magnet. Install and tighten transaxle case-to-clutch housing retaining bolts.

14) If necessary, use a drift to align bore in reverse idler shaft with retaining screw hole in transaxle case. Install and tighten reverse idler shaft retaining bolt.

15) Apply Teflon tape to threads of interlock sleeve retaining pin. If necessary, align slot in interlock sleeve with hole in transaxle case using a drift. Install and tighten retaining pin. Install differential oil seal.

16) Apply Teflon tape to threads of detent plunger retaining screw. Install and tighten screw. Place transaxle upright and position drift through hole in input shift shaft. Shift transaxle through all gears to ensure proper installation.

TIGHTENING SPECIFICATIONS

Application	Ft. Lbs. (N.m)
Back-Up Light Switch	[1] 14-18 (19-24)
Ball Joint-to-Steering Knuckle	37-44 (50-60)
Control Arm-to-Knuckle	37 (50)
Differential Bearing Retainer-to-Case	15-19 (20-26)
Fork Interlock Sleeve Pin	[1] 12-15 (16-20)
Reverse Idler Shaft-to-Case	16-20 (22-27)
Reverse Relay Lever Pivot Pin	[1] 14-18 (19-24)
Ring Gear-to-Differential Case	
4-Speed	55-70 (75-95)
5-Speed	80-100 (108-136)
Stabilizer-to-Control Arm	59-73 (80-99)
Trans. Case-to-Clutch Hsg.	13-17 (18-23)
Transaxle-to-Engine	28-31 (38-42)

Application	INCH Lbs. (N.m)
Control Selector Plate	72-96 (8-11)
Detent Plunger Retainer Screw	
4-Speed	[1] 108-144 (12-16)
5-Speed	[1] 72-96 (8-11)
Shift Lever Set Screw	84-120 (10-14)
Transaxle Filler Plug	108-168 (12-19)

[1] – Coat threads with Teflon tape prior to installation and tightening.

GENERAL MOTORS 3-SPEED — 76 MM

Chevrolet, GMC

DESCRIPTION

The 76 mm 3-speed transmission is identified by the measured distance (76 mm) between the centerlines of the mainshaft and countergear and by the number of forward gears.

It is a fully-synchronized transmission, providing synchromesh engagement in all forward gears. All gears are helical cut, with the forward gears being in constant mesh.

LUBRICATION & ADJUSTMENTS

See the appropriate article in MANUAL TRANSMISSION SERVICING Section

TROUBLE SHOOTING

See MANUAL TRANSMISSION TROUBLE SHOOTING in TRANSMISSION SERVICING Section

REMOVAL & INSTALLATION

See the appropriate article in MANUAL TRANSMISSION REMOVAL Section

TRANSMISSION DISASSEMBLY

1) With assembly drained of oil and placed in clean work area, shift transmission into neutral detent positions before removing cover. Remove side cover mount bolts and cover assembly. Remove input shaft bearing retainer and gasket.

2) Remove input shaft bearing-to-gear stem snap ring. To remove input shaft bearing, pull outward on shaft until a screwdriver can be inserted between bearing snap ring and case to complete removal.

NOTE: The input shaft bearing is a slip fit on the gear and into the case bore.

3) To remove speedometer driven gear, detach lock plate-to-housing mount bolt and washer. Remove lock plate. Insert screwdriver into lock plate slot of fitting. Pry fitting, gear and shaft from housing. Remove and discard "O" ring.

4) Remove extension housing-to-case mount bolts. Remove "E" clip from reverse idler shaft. Remove input shaft, mainshaft and extension assembly through rear of case.

5) Remove drive gear, input shaft needle bearings and synchronizer ring from mainshaft. Expand snap ring, in extension housing, retaining mainshaft rear bearing. Remove extension housing.

Fig. 1: Cutaway View of General Motors 3-Speed 76 MM Transmission

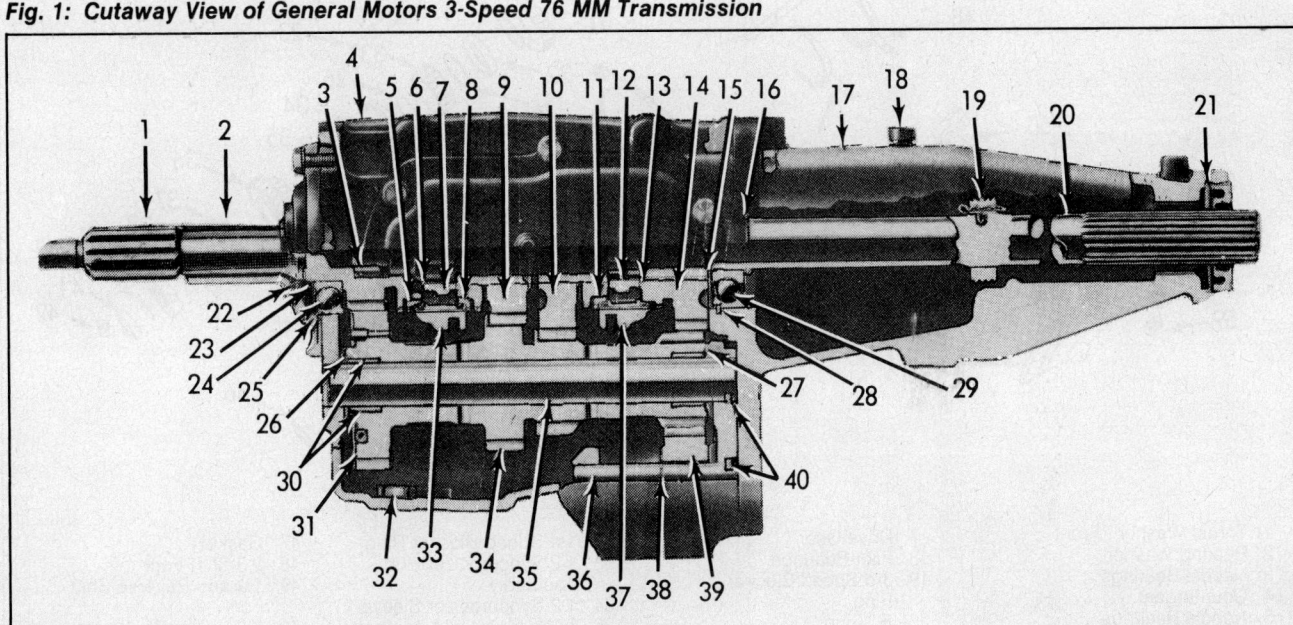

1. Input Shaft	15. Reverse Gear Thrust & Spring Washers	29. Rear Bearing
2. Bearing Retainer	16. Bearing-to-Mainshaft Snap Ring	30. Countergear Roll Bearings
3. Pilot Bearings	17. Extension Housing	31. Anti-Lash Plate Assembly
4. Case	18. Vent	32. Magnet
5. 3rd Gear Blocker Ring	19. Speedo Drive Gear & Clip	33. 2nd-3rd Synchro Sleeve
6. 2nd-3rd Synchro Snap Ring	20. Mainshaft	34. Countergear
7. 2nd-3rd Synchro Hub	21. Rear Oil Seal	35. Countershaft
8. 2nd Gear Blocker Ring	22. Retainer Oil Seal	36. Reverse Idler Shaft
9. 2nd Gear	23. Bearing-to-Gear Snap Ring	37. 1st Gear Synchro Sleeve
10. 1st Gear	24. Input Shaft Bearing	38. "E" Ring
11. 1st Gear Blocker Ring	25. Bearing-to-Case Snap Ring	39. Reverse Idle Gear
12. 1st Gear Synchro Hub	26. Front Thrust Washer	40. Woodruff Key
13. 1st Gear Synchro Snap Ring	27. Rear Thrust Washer	
14. Reverse Gear	28. Extension Housing Snap Ring	

Manual Transmissions

GENERAL MOTORS 3-SPEED — 76 MM (Cont.)

6) Using dummy countershaft (J-22246), drive countershaft and its woodruff key out rear of case. Dummy shaft will hold roller bearings in position in gear.

7) Remove countergear, bearings and thrust washers. Using a long drift through front bearing case bore, drive reverse idler shaft and woodruff key out rear of case. Lift out reverse idler gear.

CLEANING & INSPECTION

1) Wash all components in solvent and dry with compressed air. Inspect transmission case for cracks, damaged bearing bores or damaged threads. Remove all small nicks and burrs from front and rear face of case.

2) Check ball bearings for roughness by lubricating with light oil and slowly turning race by hand.

Fig. 2: Exploded View of General Motors 3-Speed 76 MM Transmission

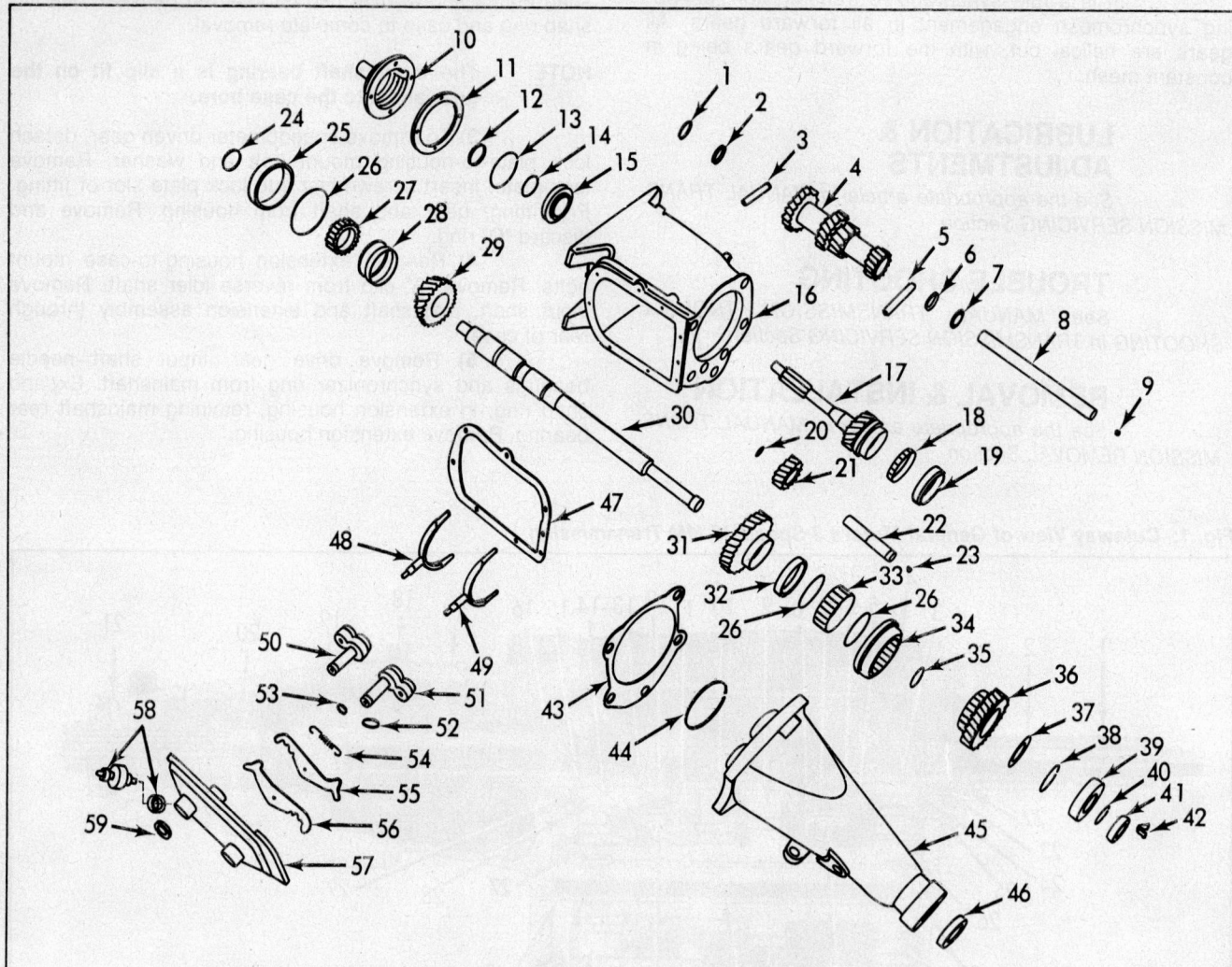

1. Thrust Washer - Front	17. Drive Gear	32. 1st Speed Blocker Ring	47. Gasket
2. Bearing Washer	18. Pilot Bearings	33. 1-2 Synchronizer Hub	48. 2-3 Shift Fork
3. Needle Bearings	19. 3rd Speed Blocker	Assembly	49. 1st and Reverse Shift
4. Countergear	Ring	34. 1-2 Synchronizer Sleeve	Fork
5. Needle Bearings	20. "E" Ring	35. Snap Ring - Hub to Shaft	50. 2-3 Shifter Shaft
6. Bearing Washer	21. Reverse Idler Gear	36. Reverse Gear	Assembly
7. Thrust Washer - Rear	22. Reverse Idler Shaft	37. Thrust Washer	51. 1st and Reverse Shifter
8. Counter Shaft	23. Woodruff Key	38. Spring Washer	Shaft
9. Woodruff Key	24. Snap Ring - Hub	39. Rear Bearing	52. "O" Ring Seal
10. Bearing Retainer	to Shaft	40. Snap Ring - Bearing	53. "E" Ring
11. Gasket	25. 2-3 Synchronizer Sleeve	to Shaft	54. Spring
12. Oil Seal	26. Synchronizer Key Spring	41. Speedometer Drive Gear	55. 2nd and 3rd Detent Cam
13. Snap Ring - Bearing	27. 2-3 Synchronizer Hub	42. Retaining Clip	56. 1st and Reverse Detent
to Case	Assembly	43. Gasket	Cam
14. Snap Ring - Bearing	28. 2nd Speed Blocker Ring	44. Snap Ring - Rear Bearing	57. Side Cover
to Gear	29. 2nd Speed Gear	to Extension	58. TCS Switch and Gasket
15. Drive Gear Bearing	30. Mainshaft	45. Extension	59. Lip Seal
16. Case	31. 1st Speed Gear	46. Oil Seal	

GENERAL MOTORS 3-SPEED — 76 MM (Cont.)

Inspect bearing rollers, shafts and washers for wear or damage.

3) Inspect bushing in reverse gear and reverse idler gear for wear or damage. If worn or damaged, entire assembly must be replaced. Bushings are not serviced separately.

4) Inspect clutch sleeves of synchronizer assemblies to see if they slide freely on their hubs. Check all other components for wear, chipped or broken teeth and damage. Replace parts as necessary.

COMPONENT DISASSEMBLY & REASSEMBLY

MAINSHAFT

Disassembly

1) Remove 2nd-3rd gear sliding clutch snap ring from mainshaft. Remove clutch assembly, 2nd gear blocker ring and 2nd gear from front of mainshaft. *See Fig. 2.*

2) Depress speedometer gear retaining clip and remove speedometer gear from mainshaft. Remove rear bearing snap ring from groove in mainshaft. Support reverse gear with press plates. Press on rear of mainshaft to remove reverse gear, thrust washer, spring washer, rear bearing and snap ring.

3) Remove 1st-Reverse sliding clutch hub snap ring from mainshaft. Remove clutch assembly. Remove 1st gear blocker ring and 1st gear from rear of mainshaft.

NOTE: In some cases, it may be necessary to press synchronizer hub and gear from mainshaft.

Reassembly

1) On front end of mainshaft, install 2nd gear with clutching teeth upward. Rear face of gear will butt against flange on mainshaft. Install blocker ring, with teeth down, over synchronizing surface of 2nd gear. All 3 blocker rings are the same.

2) Install 2nd-3rd gear synchronizer assembly on mainshaft, with fork slot downward. Press assembly into place until it bottoms out. Both synchronizer assemblies used in transmission are the same. *See Fig. 3.*

NOTE: If sleeve is removed from 2nd-3rd gear hub, notches on hub O.D. face toward front of mainshaft. Ensure notches on blocker ring align with keys on synchronizer assembly.

3) Install synchronizer hub snap ring. Both synchronizer snap rings are identical. Install 1st gear on rear end of mainshaft, with clutching teeth up. Front face of gear will butt against flange on mainshaft. Install blocker ring with teeth downward over 1st gear.

4) Install 1st-Reverse synchronizer assembly on mainshaft splines, with fork slot downward. Assembly should be a sliding fit onto mainshaft. Install synchronizer hub snap ring. Ensure blocker ring notches align with synchronizer keys.

5) Install reverse gear with teeth downward. Install reverse gear thrust washer (steel) and spring washer. Using hydraulic press if necessary, press rear bearing on mainshaft with snap ring slot down. Install bearing snap ring. Install speedometer drive gear tand retaining clip.

Fig. 3: *Synchronizer Clutch Assembly*

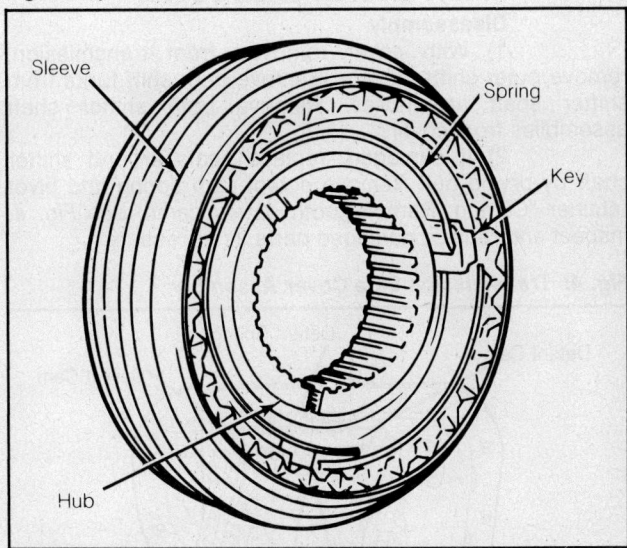

The groove around outside of synchronizer hub must be opposite fork slot in sleeve during assembly.

SYNCHRONIZER CLUTCH ASSEMBLIES

NOTE: The clutch hubs and sliding sleeves are a selected assembly and should be kept together as originally assembled. However, the keys and 2 springs may be replaced if worn or broken.

Disassembly

Mark hub and sleeve, so they can be aligned upon reassembly. Push hub from sliding sleeve, then remove keys and springs.

Reassembly

1) Place 3 keys and 2 springs in position, 1 on each side of hub, so all 3 keys are engaged by both springs. The tanged end of each synchronizer spring should be installed into different key cavities on either side.

2) A groove around outside of synchronizer hub identifies end that must be opposite fork slot in sleeve when assembled. Groove indicates end of hub with greater recess depth. Slide sleeve onto hub, aligning marks before assembly.

EXTENSION HOUSING OIL SEAL OR BUSHING

1) If bushing in rear of extension housing requires replacement, remove seal. Using driver tool (J-21465 or J-23062-14), drive bushing from its bore into extension housing. Remove old bushing.

2) Using same tool, drive new bushing into housing from rear. Coat I.D. of bushing and new seal with transmission lubricant. Coat O.D. of seal with sealant. Using oil seal installer (J-21426 or J-21359), install seal into housing.

INPUT SHAFT RETAINER OIL SEAL

If seal in retainer requires replacement, pry out old seal. Using installer (J-23096), drive new seal into retainer until seal seats in bore. During installation, make sure seal lip faces rear of transmission.

GENERAL MOTORS 3-SPEED — 76 MM (Cont.)

TRANSMISSION CASE COVER

Disassembly

1) With cover removed from transmission, remove outer shifter levers. Remove both shift forks from shifter shaft assemblies. Remove both shifter shaft assemblies from cover.

2) If damaged, replace seals around shifter shaft by prying out. Remove detent cam spring and pivot retainer "C" ring. Remove both detent cams. *See Fig. 4.* Inspect and replace damaged parts as necessary.

Fig. 4: Transmission Side Cover Assembly

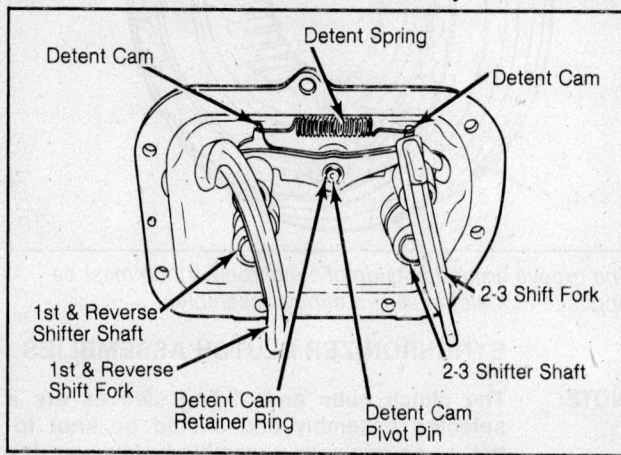

Shift the transmission into its neutral detents before removing or installing side cover assembly.

Reassembly

1) With detent spring tang projecting up over 2nd-3rd shifter shaft cover opening, install 1st-Reverse detent cam onto detent cam pivot pin. With detent spring tang projecting up over the 1st-Reverse shifter shaft cover hole, install the 2nd-3rd detent cam onto detent cam pivot pin.

2) Install detent cam retaining "C" ring to pivot pin. Hook detent spring into detent cam notches. Install both shifter shaft assemblies into cover. Do not damage oil seals.

3) Install both shift forks to shifter shaft assemblies. Lift up on detent cam to allow forks to fully seat into position. Install outer shifter levers, flat washers lock washers and bolts. Install cover assembly.

TRANSMISSION REASSEMBLY

NOTE: Apply sealant to all through-bolts used during reassembly.

1) Coat countershaft bore with heavy grease. Insert dummy countershaft into countergear. Install 27 needle bearings and a thrust washer in each end of gear.

2) Place countergear assembly through rear opening in case along with a tanged thrust washer at each end. Tang should be away from gear. Install countergear shaft and woodruff key from rear of case. Ensure countershaft picks up both thrust washers and that tangs are aligned with their notches in the case.

3) Install reverse idler gear and shaft with woodruff key from rear of case. Do not install idler shaft "E" clip at this time. Expand snap ring in extension housing. Install extension housing over rear of mainshaft and onto rear bearing. Seat snap ring in groove.

4) Coat input shaft cavity with heavy grease. Install 14 mainshaft pilot needle bearings into cavity. Install 3rd gear blocking ring on input shaft with teeth facing input gear.

5) Guide input shaft, pilot bearings and 3rd gear blocking ring assembly over front of mainshaft assembly. *See Fig. 5.* Do not assemble bearing to gear yet. Blocker ring notches should align with keys in 2nd-3rd synchronizer assembly.

Fig. 5: Input Shaft Assembly

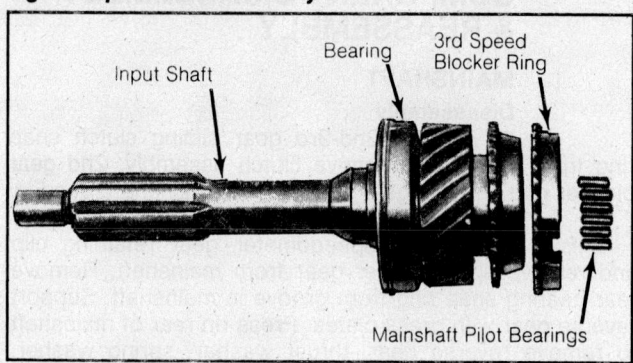

Install input shaft from rear of the transmission case.

6) Install extension housing-to-case gasket. From the rear, install input shaft, mainshaft and extension housing to case as an assembly. Install extension housing-to-case mount bolts.

7) Install snap ring on front bearing. Place bearing over input shaft. Slide bearing into bore in case. Install snap ring on input shaft. Install input shaft bearing retainer and new gasket to case. Ensure bearing retainer oil hole is on the bottom.

8) Install reverse idler gear "E" clip on shaft. Shift synchronizer sleeves to neutral position and install cover, gasket and fork assembly to case. Ensure forks align with synchronizer sleeve grooves.

9) Install new "O" ring in groove in fitting of speedometer driven gear. Coat "O" ring and shaft with gear oil. Insert shaft in extension housing, holding assembly so slot in fitting is toward lock plate boss in housing.

10) With fitting pushed into housing, insert lock plate in groove and install mount bolt. Tighten all bolts to specifications. Fill transmission with SAE 80W or 80W-90 gear oil. Rotate input shaft and shift transmission into all gears to check operation.

TIGHTENING SPECIFICATIONS

Application	Ft. Lbs. (N.m)
Case-to-Clutch Housing Bolts	75 (101)
Ext. Housing-to-Case Bolts	45 (61)
Gear Oil Filler Plug	13 (17)
Input Shaft Retainer-to-Case Bolts	15 (20)
Mount-to-Transmission Bolt	40 (54)
Shift Lever-to-Shifter Shaft Bolts	25 (32)
Side Cover-to-Case Bolts	15 (20)

GENERAL MOTORS 4-SPEED – 70 MM

Chevrolet Chevette
Pontiac 1000

TRANSMISSION IDENTIFICATION

Transmission can be identified by a 2 letter code, stamped on machined pad centered on right side of case.

DESCRIPTION

Transmission is a 4-speed unit, synchronized in all forward gears. Reverse gear is not synchronized. Helical gears are used throughout transmission and, with the exception of reverse gears, all transmission gears are in constant mesh.

All gears are carried on shafts inside transmission case, except reverse gears, which are mounted on outside of rear case face, inside extension housing. Transmission utilizes single rail shift linkage, supported on one end by extension housing, and on opposite end by clutch housing.

LUBRICATION & ADJUSTMENT

See appropriate article in MANUAL TRANSMISSION SERVICING section.

REMOVAL & INSTALLATION

See appropriate article in MANUAL TRANSMISSION REMOVAL Section.

TRANSMISSION DISASSEMBLY

1) Place transmission on clean bench with clutch housing facing downward. Drive roll pin from shifter shaft arm assembly and shifter shaft. See Fig. 14. Remove shifter shaft arm assembly.

2) Remove 5 mount bolts attaching extension housing to case. Withdraw extension housing. Press down on speedometer gear retainer and slide gear and retainer off mainshaft. Remove shifter shaft snap rings. Remove reverse shifter shaft cover, shifter shaft detent cap, spring with ball and interlock lock pin. See Fig. 2.

Fig. 1: Cross Sectional View of General Motors 70 MM 4-Speed Transmission Assembly

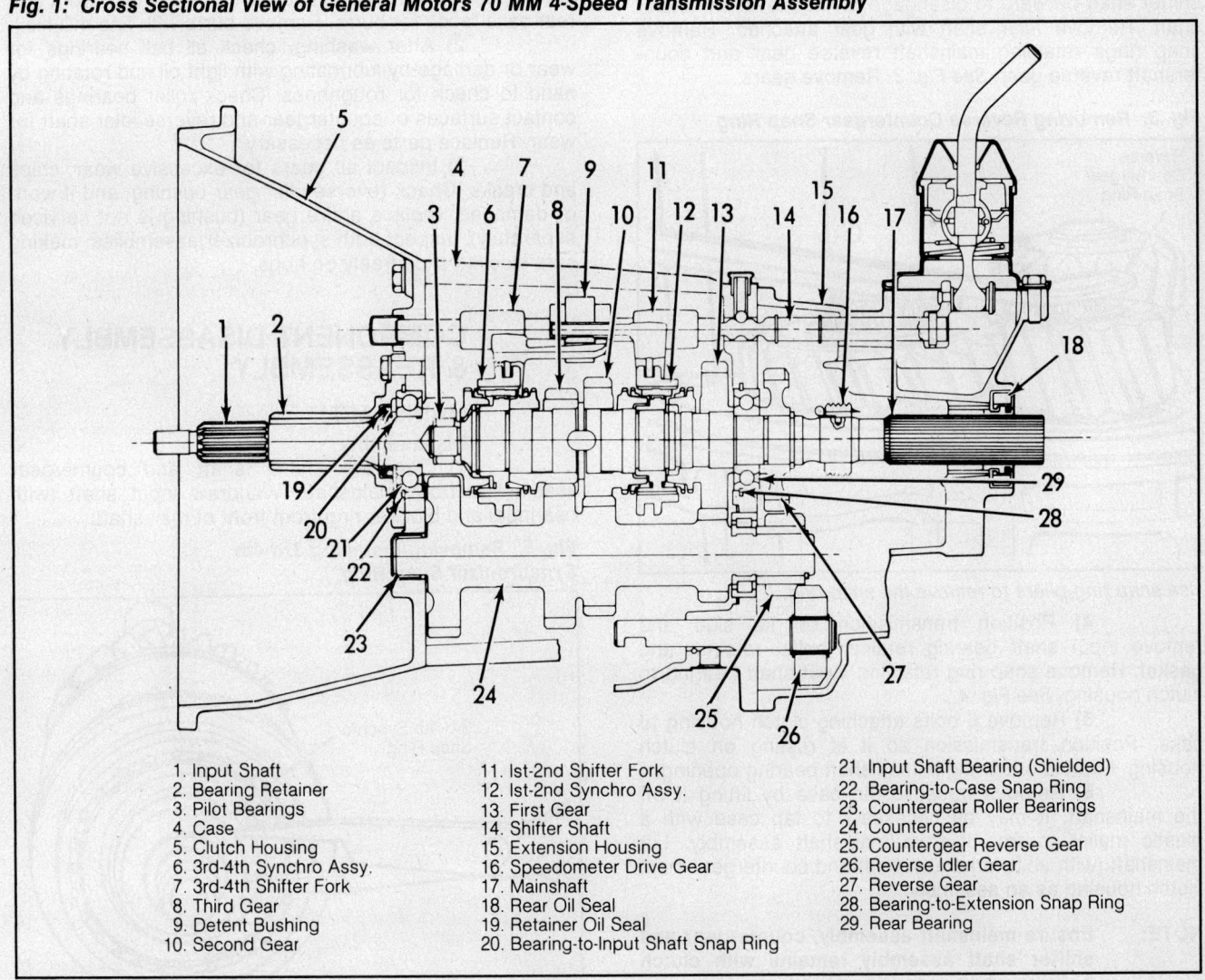

1. Input Shaft
2. Bearing Retainer
3. Pilot Bearings
4. Case
5. Clutch Housing
6. 3rd-4th Synchro Assy.
7. 3rd-4th Shifter Fork
8. Third Gear
9. Detent Bushing
10. Second Gear
11. lst-2nd Shifter Fork
12. lst-2nd Synchro Assy.
13. First Gear
14. Shifter Shaft
15. Extension Housing
16. Speedometer Drive Gear
17. Mainshaft
18. Rear Oil Seal
19. Retainer Oil Seal
20. Bearing-to-Input Shaft Snap Ring
21. Input Shaft Bearing (Shielded)
22. Bearing-to-Case Snap Ring
23. Countergear Roller Bearings
24. Countergear
25. Countergear Reverse Gear
26. Reverse Idler Gear
27. Reverse Gear
28. Bearing-to-Extension Snap Ring
29. Rear Bearing

GENERAL MOTORS 4-SPEED – 70 MM (Cont.)

Fig. 2: View of Transmission Case Showing Location of Cover, Detent Cap and Interlock Pin

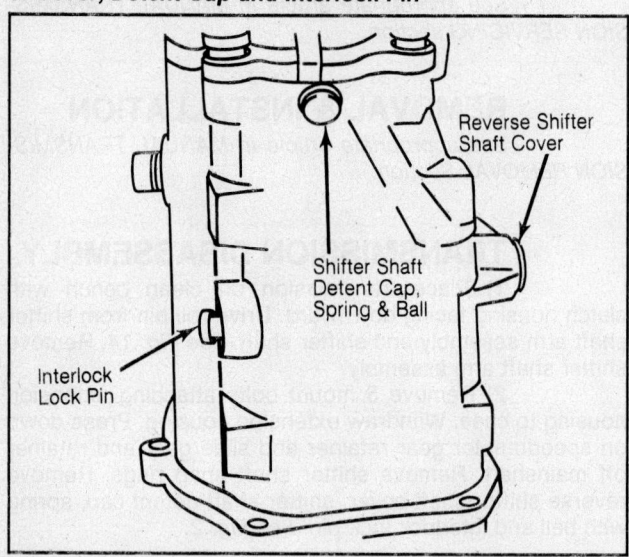

3) Using pliers, pull exposed end of reverse shifter shaft outward to disengage reverse lever from idler shaft. Remove idler shaft with gear attached. Remove snap rings retaining mainshaft reverse gear and countershaft reverse gear. *See Fig. 3.* Remove gears.

Fig. 3: Removing Reverse Countergear Snap Ring

Use snap ring pliers to remove the snap ring.

4) Position transmission on its side and remove input shaft bearing retainer bolts, retainer and gasket. Remove snap ring retaining input shaft bearing to clutch housing. *See Fig. 4.*

5) Remove 6 bolts attaching clutch housing to case. Position transmission so it is resting on clutch housing. Expand snap ring in mainshaft bearing opening.

6) Remove transmission case by lifting it off the mainshaft. It may be necessary to tap case with a plastic mallet to free it from mainshaft assembly. Lift mainshaft (with shift forks attached) and countergear from clutch housing as an assembly.

NOTE: Ensure mainshaft assembly, countergear and shifter shaft assembly remains with clutch housing when case is removed.

Fig. 4: Removing Bearing-to-Clutch Housing Snap Ring

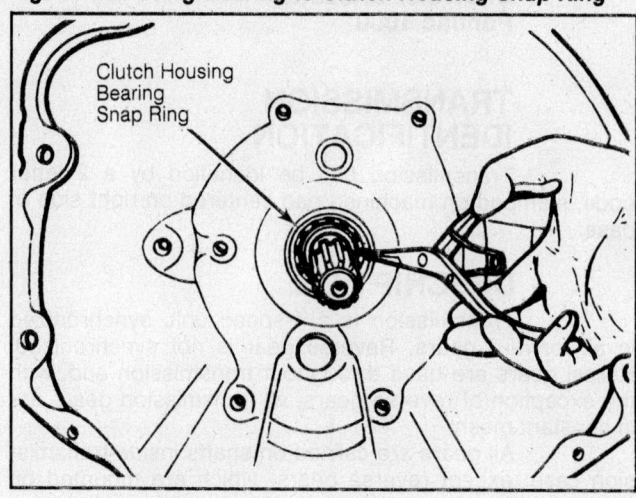

INSPECTION

1) Wash all parts thoroughly in solvent and blow dry with compressed air. DO NOT spin bearings with air. Inspect transmission case for cracks. Check front and rear case faces for burrs. Remove burrs with fine mill file.

2) After washing, check all ball bearings for wear or damage by lubricating with light oil and rotating by hand to check for roughness. Check roller bearings and contact surfaces of countergear and reverse idler shaft for wear. Replace parts as necessary.

3) Inspect all gears for excessive wear, chips and cracks. Check reverse idler gear bushing, and if worn or damaged, replace entire gear (bushing is not serviced separately). Inspect both synchronizer assemblies, making sure sleeves slide freely on hubs.

COMPONENT DISASSEMBLY & REASSEMBLY

MAINSHAFT

Disassembly

1) Separate shifter shaft and countergear assemblies from mainshaft. Withdraw input shaft (with bearings) and blocker ring from front of mainshaft.

Fig. 5: Removing/Installing 3rd-4th Synchronizer Snap Ring

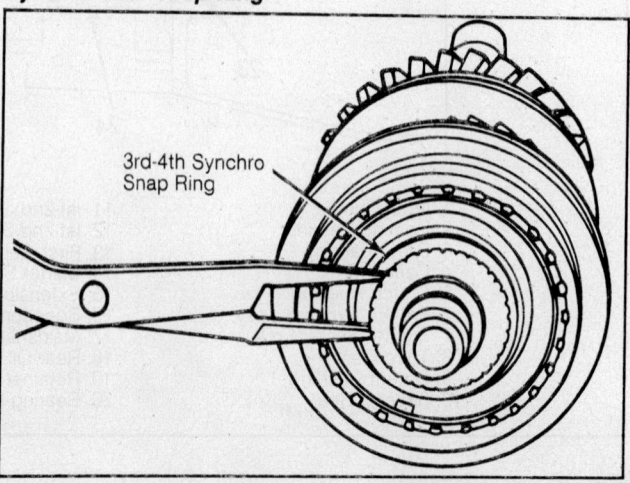

GENERAL MOTORS 4-SPEED – 70 MM (Cont.)

NOTE: Input shaft has 15 roller bearings. Note positions for reassembly referrence. During disassembly, DO NOT loose bearings as they may fall out of gear.

2) Remove snap ring retaining 3rd-4th synchronizer assembly on mainshaft. *See Fig. 5.* If necessary, remove synchronizer with hydraulic press. Remove blocker ring and 3rd gear from mainshaft. Using press plates, withdraw ball bearing from rear end of mainshaft.

3) With rear bearing removed, withdraw 1st gear and blocker ring from mainshaft. Remove snap ring retaining 1st-2nd synchronizer hub on mainshaft. Withdraw synchronizer assembly with press if necessary. Withdraw 2nd gear and blocking ring from mainshaft.

NOTE: Before reassembly of mainshaft, see SYNCHRONIZER CLUTCH ASSEMBLIES.

Reassembly
1) With rear end of mainshaft upward, install 2nd gear (clutching teeth upward) so rear face of gear butts against mainshaft flange. Install a blocker ring with clutching teeth downward over synchronizing surface of 2nd gear.

NOTE: All 4 blocker rings used in this transmission are identical.

2) Install 1st-2nd synchronizer assembly with fork slot downward over mainshaft. Press assembly onto mainshaft splines until it bottoms out. Ensure notches of blocker ring align with keys of synchronizer assembly.

3) Install synchronizer hub-to-mainshaft retaining snap ring. Install a blocker ring with notches downward so they align with keys of 1st-2nd synchronizer assembly.

4) Install 1st gear over end of mainshaft with clutching teeth downward. Position rear bearing over end of mainshaft with snap ring groove downward. Press bearing into position.

NOTE: There are two ball bearings used in this transmission. A shielded input shaft bearing and a non-shielded mainshaft bearing. DO NOT interchange.

5) Turn mainshaft so front faces upward. Install 3rd gear over shaft with clutching teeth upward. Move into place so front face of gear butts against mainshaft flange. Install a blocker ring with clutching teeth downward over synchronizing surface of 3rd gear.

6) Install 3rd-4th synchronizer assembly onto shaft with fork slot downward. *See Fig. 5.* Install synchronizer hub-to-mainshaft retaining snap ring. Install blocker ring with notches downward so they align with keys of synchronizer.

SYNCHRONIZER CLUTCH ASSEMBLIES

NOTE: Synchronizer hub and sliding sleeves are select fit and should be kept together as originally assembled. However, keys and springs may be replaced if worn or broken.

Disassembly
If not already marked, mark hub and sleeve for reassembly reference in same position. Push the hub, springs and keys from sleeve. Keys will fall free and springs should be easily removed.

Reassembly
Place 2 springs in position (one on each side of hub) so that all 3 keys will engage both springs. *See Fig. 6.* Place keys in position and while holding in place, push sleeve over hub. Ensure index marks made before disassembly are aligned.

Fig. 6: Synchronizer Assembly

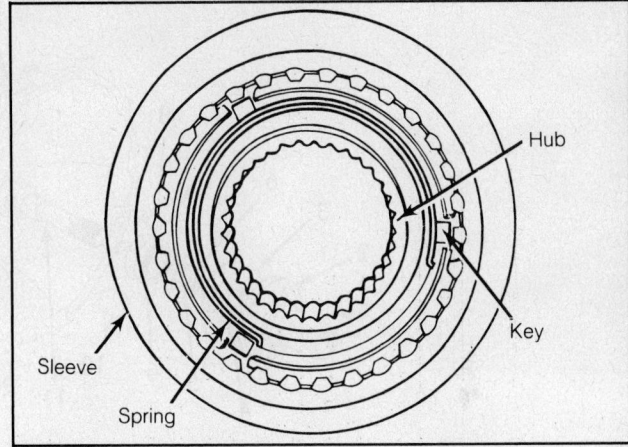

Mark the relative position of the hub to the sleeve for reassembly reference.

EXTENSION HOUSING SEAL & BUSHING
Removal & Installation
Pry rear seal from extension housing using a screwdriver. Using a bushing driver (J-5778), remove bushing from rear of housing. Use same tool to drive new bushing into housing. Coat I.D. of new bushing and seal with transmission lubricant. Install seal into housing using a seal driver (J-21426 or J-5154).

FRONT BEARING RETAINER SEAL
Removal & Installation
Pry out old seal using a screwdriver. Using seal driver (J-23096), install new oil seal into retainer until it bottoms in bore. Lubricate I.D. of new seal with transmission lubricant.

TRANSMISSION REASSEMBLY
1) Using arbor press, install shielded ball bearing on input shaft with snap ring groove upward. Install snap ring to retain bearing on shaft. Install mainshaft pilot roller bearings into input shaft cavity, using heavy grease to hold them in place.

2) Carefully assemble input shaft to mainshaft assembly. Install detent lever to shifter shaft and retain with roll pin. From rear of shifter shaft, slide 1st-2nd shifter fork onto shaft so fork arm engages detent lever.

3) Assemble 3rd-4th shifter fork to detent bushing. From front of shifter shaft, slide 3rd-4th fork and detent bushing onto shaft, locating 3rd-4th fork arm below the 1st-2nd fork arm. *See Fig. 8.*

4) With front of clutch housing resting on 2 wood blocks, place thrust washer over hole for countergear. Index washer tabs with holes provided in clutch housing. Place both synchronizers in neutral.

5) Mate shifter shaft assembly with mainshaft assembly. Index shifter forks into synchronizer sleeve grooves. Mesh countergear with mainshaft gears and install complete assembly onto clutch housing as a unit. *See Fig. 9.*

Manual Transmissions

GENERAL MOTORS 4-SPEED — 70 MM (Cont.)

Fig. 7: Exploded View of General Motors 70 mm 4-Speed Transmission Assembly

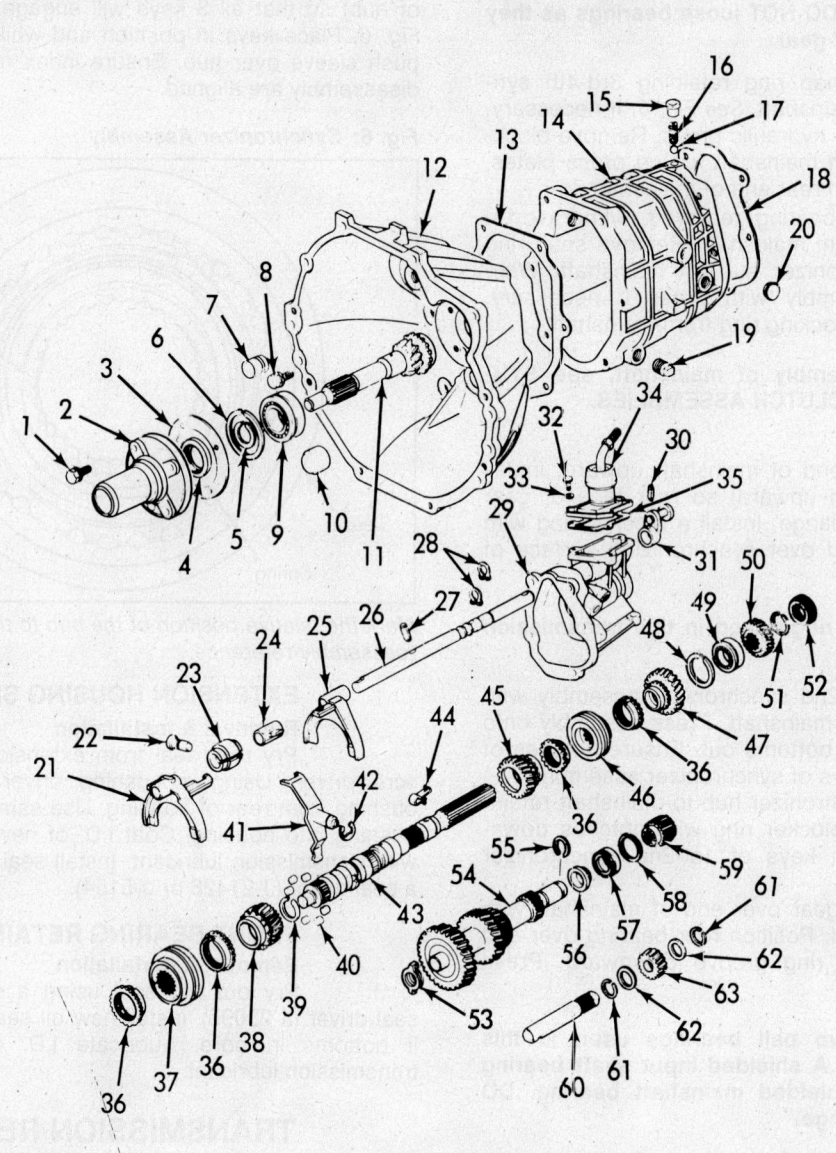

1. Bearing Retainer Bolt
2. Bearing Retainer
3. Retainer Gasket
4. Retainer Seal
5. Snap Ring
6. Bearing Outer Snap Ring
7. Shifter Shaft Stop Plug
8. Clutch Housing-to-Case Bolt
9. Input Shaft Bearing
10. Countergear Front Needle Bearings
11. Input Shaft
12. Clutch Housing
13. Housing-to-Case Gasket
14. Case
15. Shifter Shaft Detent Cap
16. Shifter Shaft Detent Spring
17. Shifter Shaft Detent Ball
18. Case-to-Extension Gasket
19. Magnet Plug
20. Reverse Lever Cap
21. 3rd-4th Shift Fork

22. Interlock Lock Pin
23. Detent Bushing
24. Detent Lever
25. 1st-2nd Shift Fork
26. Shifter Shaft
27. Detent Lever Pin
28. Shifter Shaft Snap Rings
29. Extension Housing
30. Shifter Shaft Arm Roll Pin
31. Shifter Shaft Arm
32. Shift Lever-to-Extension Bolt
33. Washer
34. Shift Lever Assembly
35. Shift Lever Gasket
36. Blocker Rings
37. 3rd-4th Synchro Assembly
38. Third Speed Gear
39. Synchro Hub-to-Shaft Snap Ring
40. Input Shaft Roller Bearings
41. Reverse Lever Assy.
42. Reverse Lever Snap Ring

43. Mainshaft
44. Speedometer Gear Retainer
45. Second Speed Gear
46. 1st-2nd Synchro Assembly
47. First Speed Gear
48. Bearing Outer Snap Ring
49. Rear Bearing
50. Reverse Gear
51. Reverse Gear Snap Ring
52. Speedometer Gear
53. Countergear Thrust Washer
54. Countergear
55. Snap Ring
56. Inner Bearing Race
57. Countergear Bearing
58. Bearing Outer Snap Ring
59. Countergear Reverse Gear
60. Idler Gear Shaft
61. Idler Gear Thrust Washer
62. Snap Ring
63. Reverse Idler Gear

GENERAL MOTORS 4-SPEED – 70 MM (Cont.)

Fig. 8: Assembling Shift Forks on Shifter Shaft

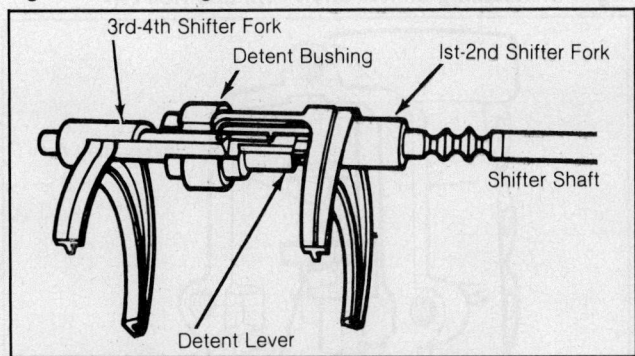

Fig. 9: Installed View of Mainshaft, Countergear and Shifter Shaft

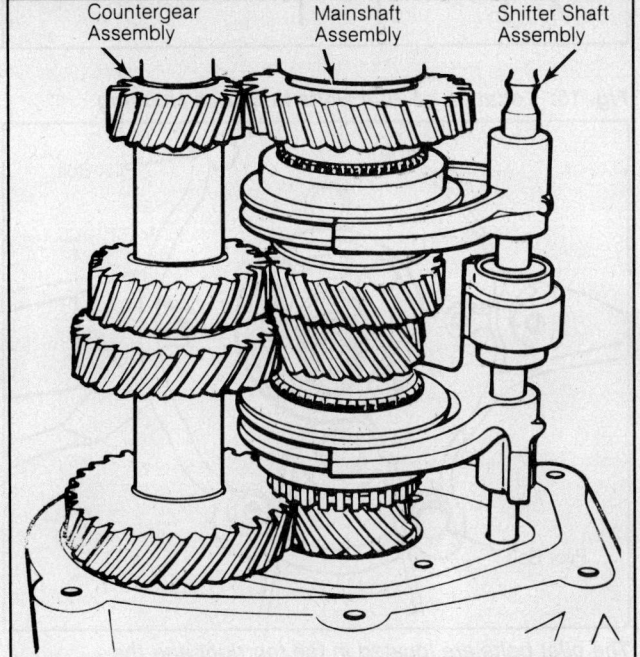

Fig. 10: View of Installed Reverse Lever

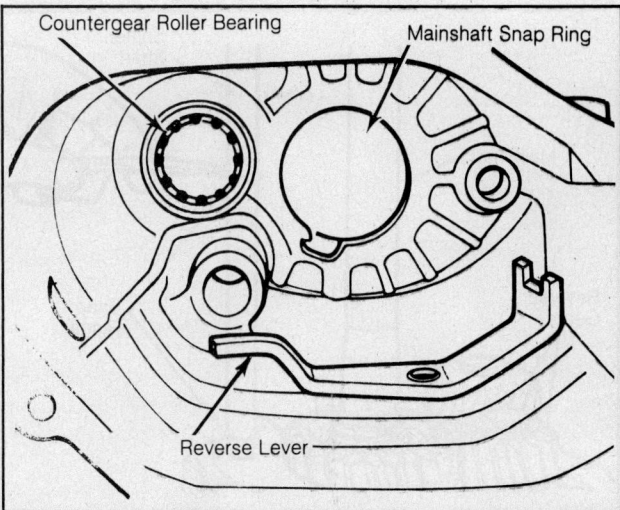

Ensure screwdriver slot for reverse lever is parallel with the front of the transmission case.

10) Install interlock lock pin to hold shifter shaft in place. Use sealer cement. Install idler shaft so it will engage with reverse lever inside of case. Install cover over reverse shifter shaft to hold the reverse lever in place.

11) Install the detent ball, spring and cap into case. Position reverse gear over end of mainshaft, with chamfer on gear teeth upward. Push gear onto splines of mainshaft and secure with snap ring.

12) Install smaller reverse gear onto countergear shaft with shoulder resting against countergear bearing. Secure snap ring. If removed, install snap ring, thrust washer and reverse idler gear (chamfer of gear teeth downward) onto idler shaft. Secure parts with thrust washer and snap ring. *See Fig. 11.*

Fig. 11: Installing Reverse Idler Gear

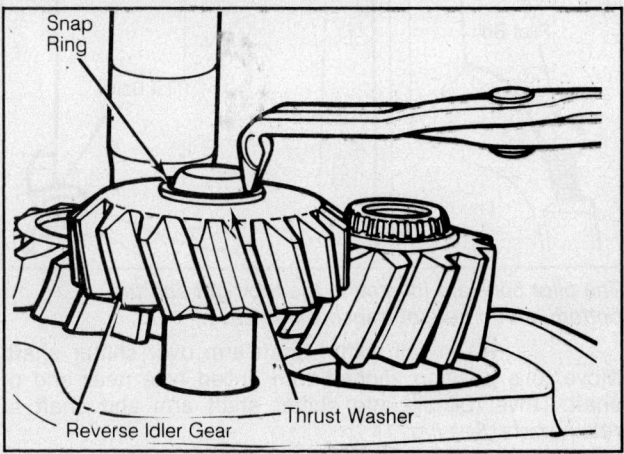

Position the reverse idler gear with the chamfer on the gear teeth facing upward.

13) Install snap rings on shifter shafts. *See Fig. 12.* Be sure they are tight in grooves. Position speedometer gear retainer in mainshaft hole. With retainer loop facing forward, slide speedometer gear over mainshaft and into position. Heat gear to 175°F (80°C) with heat lamp or oven prior to installation.

6) Place clutch housing on its side and install snap ring to ball bearing on input shaft. Install gasket and bearing retainer onto clutch housing, using sealer on retainer bolts.

7) Turn clutch housing case so it sets on wood blocks. If removed, install reverse lever into case, using grease to hold it in place. *See Fig. 10.* Ensure screwdriver slot for reverse lever is parallel with front of case. Install reverse lever snap ring.

8) Install roller bearing into countergear opening with snap ring groove inside of case (snap ring will be assembled to roller bearing). Install case-to-clutch housing gasket on clutch housing using rubber cement to hold it in place.

NOTE: Before installing case, ensure synchronizers are in neutral, detent bushing slot is facing outward and reverse lever is flush with inside wall of case.

9) Install case onto assembly, and at same time, expand snap ring in mainshaft opening of case to allow ring to pilot over mainshaft bearing. Use a plastic hammer if necessary to seat parts.

Fig. 12: *Installing Shifter Shaft Snap Rings*

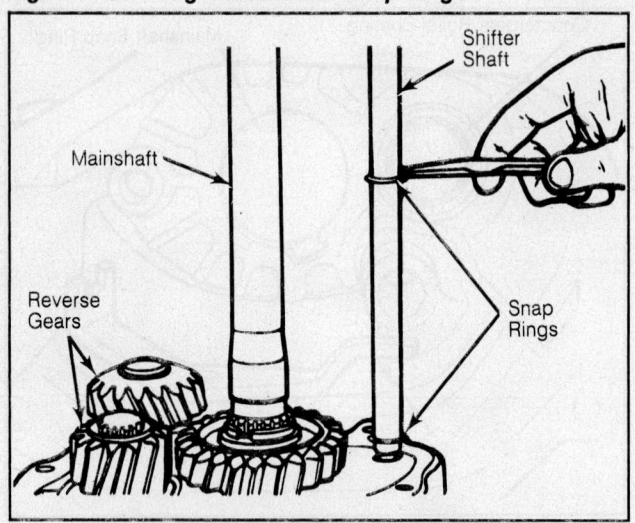

Fig. 14: *Installing Shifter Shaft Arm and Roll Pin*

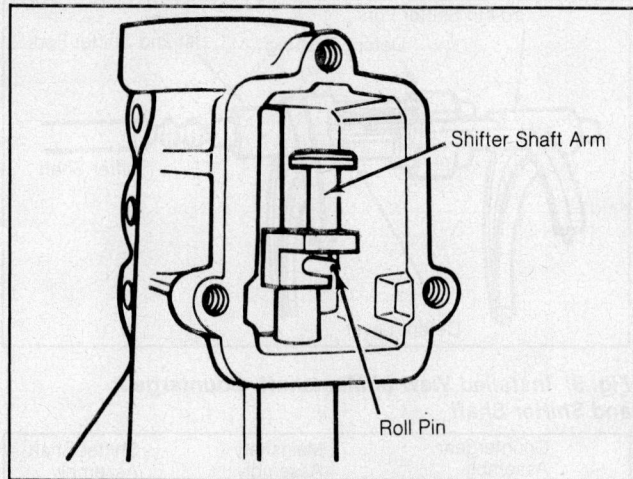

14) Position extension housing and gasket on case and install 2 partially threaded pilot bolts. *See Fig. 13.* Install other 3 remaining bolts. Ensure pilot bolts are installed in upper right corner and lower left corner of case.

CAUTION: If pilot bolts are installed in wrong holes, splitting of case may occur.

Fig. 13: *Extension Housing Pilot Bolt Locations*

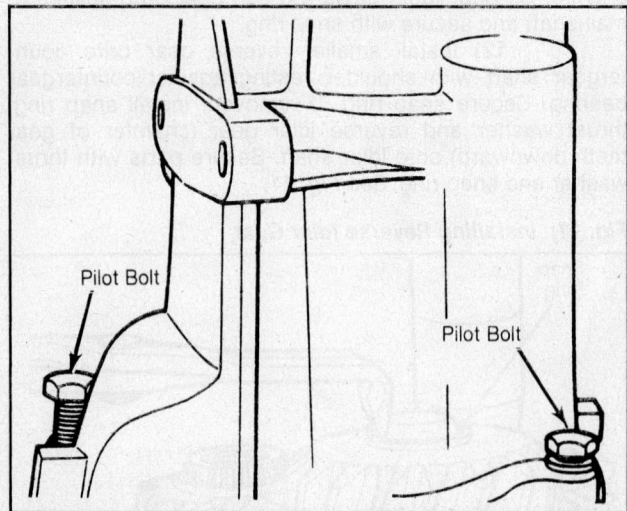

The pilot bolts are located in the top right and the bottom left corners of transmission case.

15) Install shifter shaft arm over shifter shaft. Move to a position aligned with drilled hole near end of shaft. Drive roll pin into shifter shaft arm and shaft to retain parts. *See Fig. 14*

16) Place transmission on its side. Install 2 pilot bolts before installing other 4 attaching bolts to clutch housing and case. *See Fig. 15.*

NOTE: **Pilot bolts are partially threaded and are installed in upper right and lower left holes in clutch housing.**

Fig. 15: *Location of Pilot Bolts in Clutch Housing*

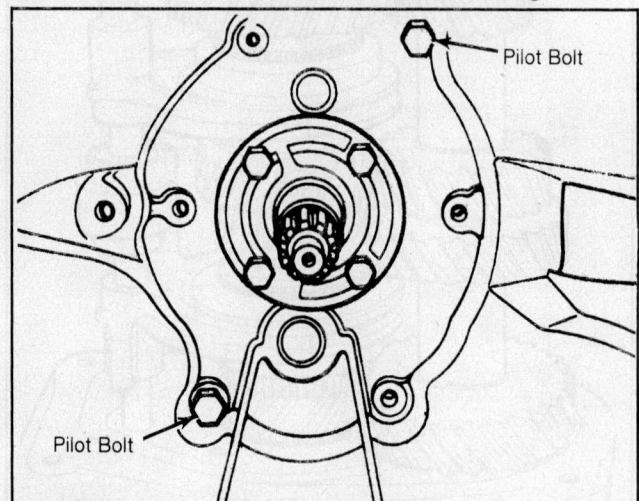

The pilot bolts are located in the top right and the bottom left corners.

TIGHTENING SPECIFICATIONS

Application	Ft. Lbs. (N.m)
Back-up Lamp Switch	25 (34)
Clutch Cover-to-Flywheel	18 (24)
Clutch Fork Ball Stud Lock Nut	24 (33)
Clutch Housing-to-Case	26 (35)
Clutch Housing-to-Engine	25 (34)
Crossmember-to-Frame	40 (55)
Crossmember-to-Transmission	
Center Nut	33 (45)
End Nut	21 (28)
Extension Housing-to-Case	26 (35)
Rear Support-to-Transmission	32 (43)
Shift Lever Retaining Bolts	10 (14)
	INCH Lbs. (N.m)
Bearing Retainer-to-Clutch Housing	105 (12)
Clutch Cable Lock Nut	53 (6)
Clutch Housing Lower Cover Bolts	90 (10)
Converter Bracket-to-Rear Support	150 (17)
Speedometer Driven Gear Retainer Bolt	44 (5)

GENERAL MOTORS (ISUZU) 4-SPEED – 77.5 MM

Chevrolet & GMC, "S" Trucks

IDENTIFICATION

Transmission identification tag is attached to transmission by an extension housing mounting bolt. Transmission can also be identified by the measured distance (3.05", 77.5 mm) between centerlines of mainshaft and countershaft.

DESCRIPTION

The 4-speed 77.5 MM transmission is a floor shifted, fully synchronized unit with blocker ring synchronizers and a sliding mesh type reverse gear. Unit consists of a case with integral clutch housing, center support and an extension housing that holds the various gears and bearings.

LUBRICATION & ADJUSTMENT

See appropriate article in MANUAL TRANSMISSION SERVICING Section.

TROUBLE SHOOTING

See MANUAL TRANSMISSION TROUBLE SHOOTING in TRANSMISSION SERVICING Section

SERVICE (IN VEHICLE)

SHIFT CONTROL LEVER

Removal & Installation

Remove screws from transmission shift lever boot retainer. Slide boot up lever and remove bolts attaching lever to transmission. Remove lever. To install shift lever, reverse removal procedure.

EXTENSION HOUSING OIL SEAL

Removal

Raise vehicle. Disconnect propeller shaft. Using a screwdriver, pry oil seal from extension housing.

Installation

Install new oil seal in extension housing using seal installer tool (J-33035). Connect propeller shaft. Check transmission fluid level and add fluid as necessary. Lower vehicle.

REMOVAL & INSTALLATION

See appropriate article in MANUAL TRANSMISSION REMOVAL section.

TRANSMISSION DISASSEMBLY

1) Disconnect retaining springs from bearing side. Remove bearing, boot and clutch fork. Remove drain plug and drain lubricant from transmission. Remove bearing retainer bolts, retainer and gasket. Remove ball stud, if necessary.

2) Remove speedometer driven gear and back-up light switch. Remove 4 shift cover bolts, cover and gasket. Remove rear extension bolts, rear extension and gasket. Remove speedometer drive gear from mainshaft.

3) Using a punch, remove pin from reverse shift block while supporting end of shaft with bar or wood block. Remove reverse block retaining bolts. Remove reverse shifter shaft, shift block, shift fork and reverse gear as an assembly. See Fig. 1. Remove retaining rings from drive gear shaft bearing outer race and countershaft front bearing outer race.

Fig. 1: Removing Reverse Shifter Assembly

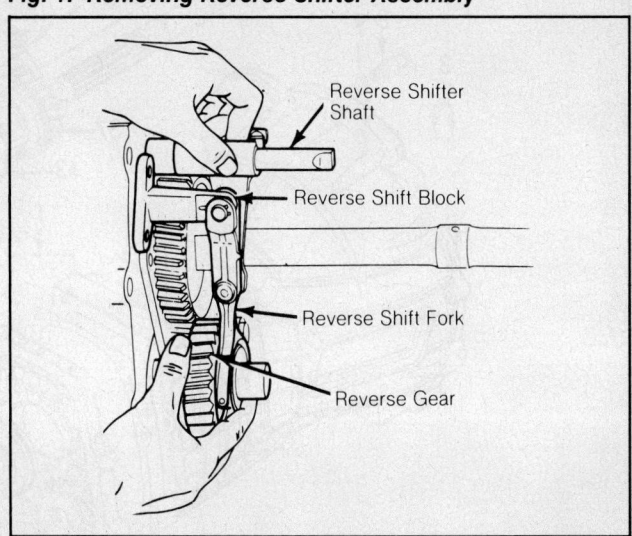

Remove shifter shaft, block, fork and gear as an assembly.

4) Remove support assembly from transmission case. Drive pins from 1st-2nd and 3rd-4th shift forks using a punch. See Fig. 2. Support ends of shafts during removal. Loosen retaining bolts and remove plate, gasket and springs.

Fig. 2: Removing Pin From Shifter Shafts

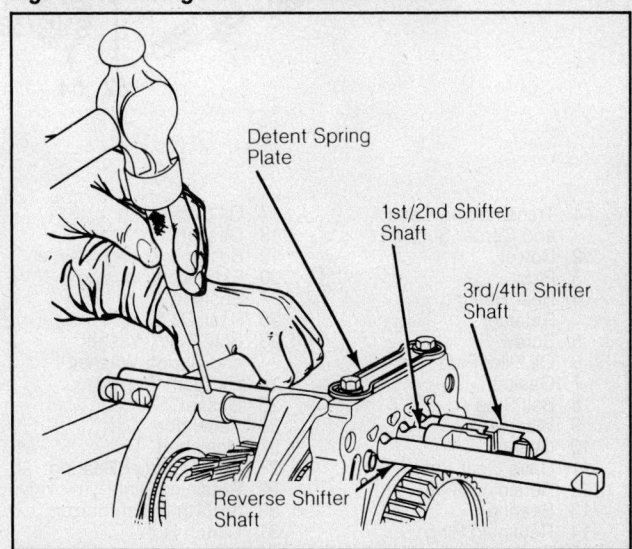

Remove pins from shift fork using a punch.

5) Position 3 shifter shafts into neutral position. Remove reverse shaft, 1st-2nd shaft and 3rd-4th

Manual Transmissions

GENERAL MOTORS (ISUZU) 4-SPEED – 77.5 MM (Cont.)

Fig. 3: Exploded View of General Motors (Isuzu) 77.5 MM 4-Speed Transmission

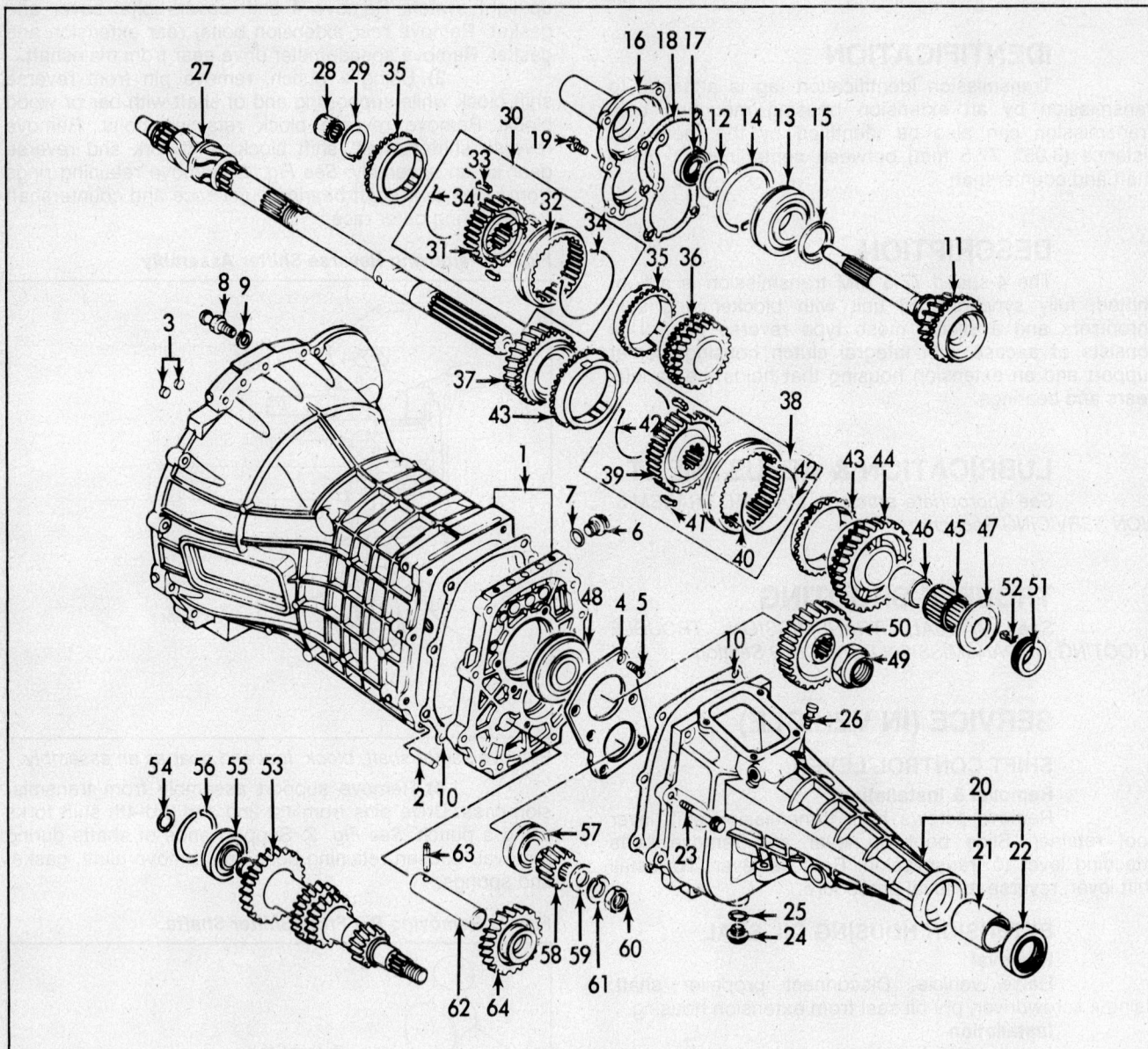

1. Transmission Case and Center Support	17. Oil Seal	33. Insert	49. Nut
2. Dowel	18. Gasket	34. Spring	50. Reverse Gear
3. Plug	19. Bolt and Spring Washer	35. Blocker Ring	51. Speedometer Drive Gear
4. Rear Bearing Retainer	20. Extension Housing	36. 3rd Gear	52. Clip
5. Screw	21. Bushing	37. 2nd Gear	53. Counter Shaft
6. Oil Filler Plug	22. Rear Oil Seal	38. 1st/2nd Synchronizer	54. Retaining Ring
7. Gasket	23. Bolt, Plain Washer and Spring Washer	39. Clutch Hub	55. Bearing
8. Ball Stud	24. Oil Drain Plug	40. Sleeve	56. Retaining Ring
9. Washer	25. Gasket	41. Insert	57. Bearing
10. Gasket	26. Ventilator	42. Spring	58. Reverse Gear
11. Drive Gear Shaft	27. Mainshaft	43. Blocker Ring	59. Plain Washer
12. Retaining Ring	28. Needle Roller Bearing	44. 1st Gear	60. Nut
13. Bearing	29. Retaining Ring	45. Needle Roller Bearing	61. Spring Washer
14. Retaining Ring	30. 3rd/4th Synchronizer	46. Bearing Collar	62. Reverse Idler Shaft
15. Spacer	31. Clutch Hub	47. Thrust Washer	63. Spring Pin
16. Front Bearing Retainer	32. Sleeve	48. Bearing	64. Reverse Idler Gear

GENERAL MOTORS (ISUZU) 4-SPEED – 77.5 MM (Cont.)

shifter shaft in that order. Remove 3 detent balls and 2 interlock pins. *See Fig. 7.* Remove shift forks. Engage synchronizers, and temporarily install transmission case to center support.

6) Raise staking on mainshaft rear nut using screwdriver or punch and remove nut. Remove reverse gear from mainshaft. Remove countershaft nut, spring washer, plain washer and reverse gear. Remove case from center support. Set synchronizers in neutral position.

Fig. 4: Exploded View of Shifter Assemblies

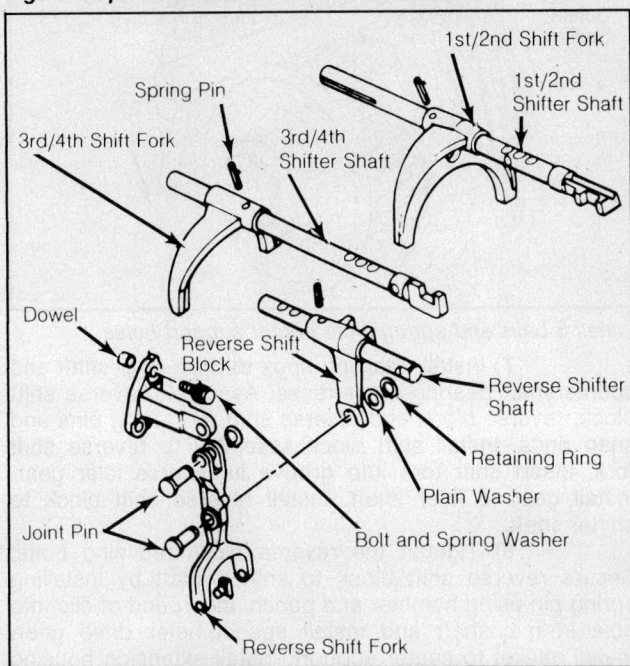

7) Remove rear bearing retainer from center support. *See Fig. 5.* Slide rear bearing outer race rearward by moving countershaft back and forth. Remove outer race using screwdrivers or equivalent. Remove countershaft and drive gear shaft. Remove 4th blocker ring and needle roller bearing.

Fig. 5: Removing Rear Bearing Retainer

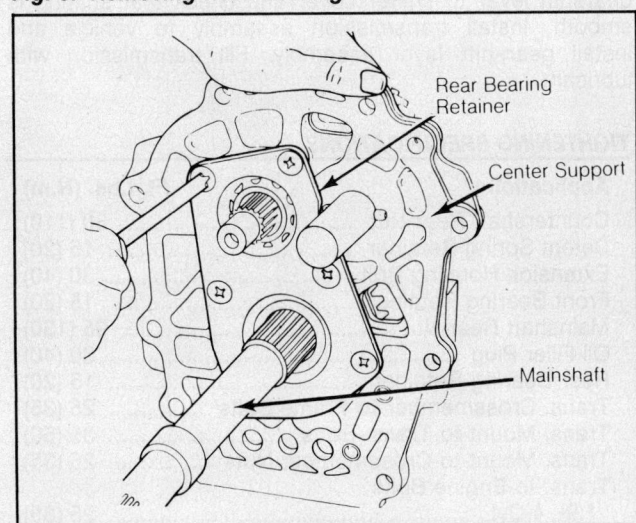

Remove retainer from center support.

COMPONENT DISASSEMBLY & REASSEMBLY

MAINSHAFT
Disassembly

1) Position support tool (J-22912-01) at rear face of 2nd gear on mainshaft. Remove mainshaft from center support using arbor press. *See Fig. 6.* Remove 2nd gear, 1st-2nd synchronizer and 1st and 2nd blocker rings. Remove 1st gear needle roller bearing, bearing collar and thrust washer. Remove mainshaft rear bearing from center support.

Fig. 6: Removing Mainshaft From Center Support

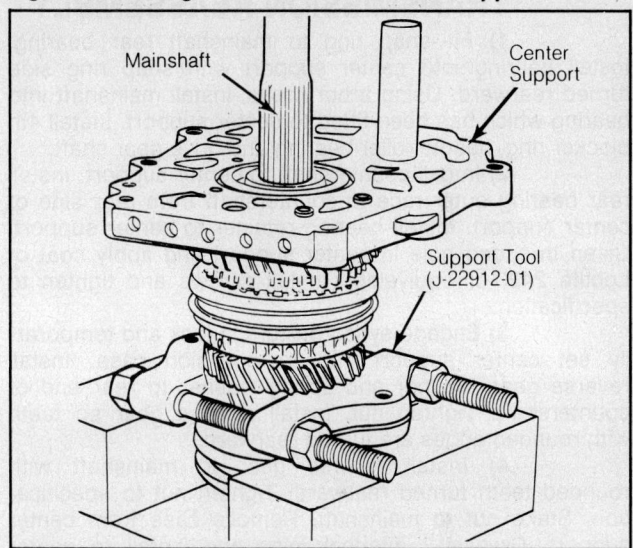

Use arbor press to remove mainshaft from support.

2) Remove snap ring from front of mainshaft. Set rear face of 3rd gear in blocks and remove mainshaft using arbor press. Remove 3rd gear, 3rd blocker ring and 3rd-4th synchronizer.

Reassembly

1) Install 3rd gear and 3rd gear blocker ring to front of mainshaft. Install 3rd-4th synchronizer assembly to mainshaft using arbor press. Install retaining ring to front of mainshaft. Install 2nd gear and 2nd gear blocker ring to rear of mainshaft.

2) Install 1st-2nd synchronizer assembly to mainshaft using arbor press. Install 1st gear bearing collar to mainshaft using installer (J-8853-01) and arbor press. Install 1st blocker ring, needle roller bearing and 1st gear.

3) Install thrust washer with oil grooves turned toward gear. If reverse idler shaft has been removed, reinstall shaft into center support with press. Be sure spring pin is fitted to shaft.

CLEANING & INSPECTION

1) Wash parts in solvent and dry all parts, except front and rear bearings, with compressed air. Wipe front and rear bearings with a clean cloth or air dry. Do not allow bearings to spin. Turn them slowly by hand. Spinning may damage race and balls. Lubricate bearings with light oil and check for roughness by slowly turning race by hand.

GENERAL MOTORS (ISUZU) 4-SPEED – 77.5 MM (Cont.)

2) Inspect transmission case, cover and extension housing. Replace if there are cracks in bores, sides, bosses or bolt holes. Replace case if there are stripped bolt holes, nicks burrs, or rough surfaces in shaft bores or on gasket surfaces. Inspect gear train and shift mechanism.

3) Replace any parts exhibiting wear, chips, galling, distortion or bending. Check for worn bearings and bores. Check for weak snap rings and stripped offset lever. Synchronizer hubs and sliding sleeves are a selected assembly. Keep together as originally assembled. Keys and springs may be replaced if worn or broken.

TRANSMISSION REASSEMBLY

1) Fit snap ring to mainshaft rear bearing. Install bearing into center support with snap ring side turned rearward. Using arbor press, install mainshaft into bearing which has been fitted to center support. Install 4th blocker ring, needle roller bearing and drive gear shaft.

2) Install countershaft to center support. Install rear bearing outer race to countershaft from rear side of center support. Install bearing retainer to center support. Clean threaded hole in center support and apply coat of Loctite 242, or equivalent. Install screws and tighten to specification.

3) Engage synchronizers in lock and temporarily set center support into transmission case. Install reverse gear, washer and spring washer to rear end of countershaft. Tighten nut. Install reverse gear so teeth with rounded edges are turned rearward.

4) Install reverse gear to mainshaft with rounded teeth turned rearward. Tighten nut to specification. Stake nut to mainshaft. Remove case from center support. Grease 2 interlock pins and install to center support. See Fig. 7. Install shift fork to synchronizers.

Fig. 7: Installing Interlock Pins

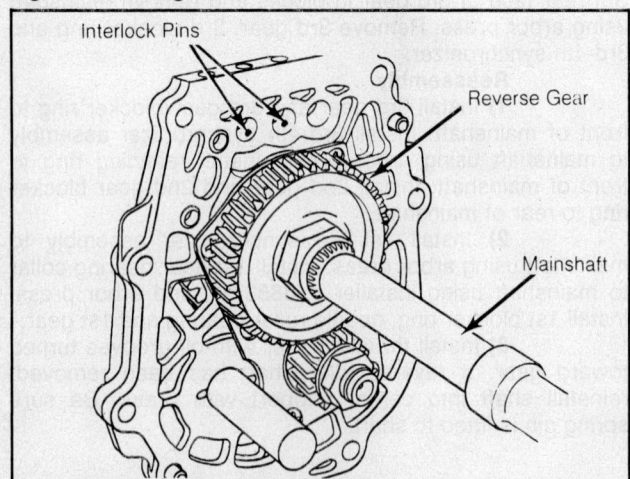

Install greased pins to center support.

5) Install 3rd-4th shifter shaft to center support and shift fork. Bring shaft into neutral position. Install 1st-2nd shifter shaft and reverse shifter shaft to center support. Drive spring pin into 1st-2nd and 3rd-4th shift forks. Support shaft end when installing spring pin.

6) Install 3 detent balls and springs into holes in center support. See Fig. 8. The spring for reverse is shorter in length than others. Install gasket and plate.

Tighten bolts to specification. Install gasket to transmission case. Install center support by aligning it with dowels on case.

Fig. 8: Installing Detent Balls and Springs

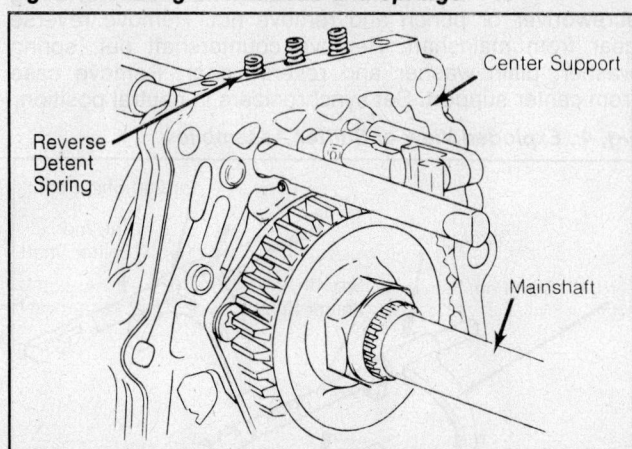

Install 3 balls and springs into center support holes.

7) Install retaining rings to drive gear shaft and countershaft bearing outer races. Assemble reverse shift block, reverse block and reverse shift fork using pins and snap rings. Install shift block assembly to reverse shift fork. Insert shift fork into groove in reverse idler gear. Install gear to idler shaft. Install reverse shift block to shifter shaft.

8) Tighten the reverse block retaining bolts. Secure reverse shift block to shifter shaft by installing spring pin using hammer and punch. Insert end of clip into hole in mainshaft and install speedometer drive gear. Install gasket to center support. Install extension housing to support by aligning it with dowels. Tighten bolts.

9) Install back-up light switch. Install gasket to upper face of extension housing. Install shifter cover. Install speedometer driven gear. Install ball stud, if removed. Install gasket to transmission case. Apply Permatex 2, or equivalent, to thread of bolts. Install and tighten bolts.

10) Install bearing, boot and clutch fork. Install gearshift lever to shifter cover and check that shifting is smooth. Install transmission assembly to vehicle and install gearshift lever assembly. Fill transmission with lubricant.

TIGHTENING SPECIFICATIONS

Application	Ft. Lbs. (N.m)
Countershaft Rear Nut	80 (110)
Detent Spring Retainer	15 (20)
Extension Housing Bolts	30 (40)
Front Bearing Retainer	15 (20)
Mainshaft Rear Nut	95 (130)
Oil Filler Plug	30 (40)
Rear Bearing Retainer	15 (20)
Trans. Crossmember-to-Frame Bolts	25 (35)
Trans. Mount-to-Trans. Bolts	35 (50)
Trans. Mount-to-Crossmember Nuts	25 (35)
Trans.-to-Engine Bolts	
1.9L 4-Cyl.	25 (35)
2.5L 4-Cyl.	37 (50)
2.8L V6	55 (75)

GENERAL MOTORS 83 MM 4-SPEED
AUTOMATIC OVERDRIVE – TRANSMISSION

Corvette

DESCRIPTION

The 83 MM 4-Speed transmission is a synchronized constant-mesh design. The input shaft has an integral main drive gear and rotates when the clutch is engaged. The drive gear is in constant mesh with the countershaft drive gear. The gears are helical designed and are used with synchronizers for all forward speeds. The transmission is identified by the distance between centerlines of the mainshaft and the countergear (83 MM).

LUBRICATION & ADJUSTMENT

See the appropriate article in MANUAL TRANSMISSION SERVICING Section.

TROUBLE SHOOTING

See MANUAL TRANSMISSION TROUBLE SHOOTING in TRANSMISSION SERVICING Section

SERVICE (IN VEHICLE)

SIDE COVER

Removal

1) Shift transmission into 2nd gear. Raise vehicle on hoist. Disconnect electrical leads at side cover switches. Remove switches.

2) Remove shift levers from shifter shafts. Remove cover attaching bolts, remove cover assembly and allow transmission to drain.

Disassembly

1) Remove outer shifter lever nuts and lockwashers. Pull levers from shafts. Carefully push shifter shafts into cover, allowing detent balls to fall free, then remove both shifter shafts.

2) Remove interlock sleeve, interlock pin and poppet spring. Clean and inspect components and replace damaged parts.

Reassembly

To reassemble, reverse disassembly procedure.

Installation

1) Move shifter levers into 2nd gear position. Position cover gasket on case. Carefully position side cover into place making sure shift forks are aligned with their respective mainshaft synchronizer sliding sleeves.

2) Install cover attaching bolts and tighten evenly. Install switches and connect electrical leads at side cover. Connect shift levers to shifter shafts. Remove filler plug and add lubricant to level of filler plug hole. Lower and remove vehicle from hoist.

SHIFTER ASSEMBLY

Removal

1) Disconnect battery negative cable. Remove left seat from vehicle. If equipped with power seats, disconnect electrical leads. Remove knob from shift lever. Remove console cover. Remove glove box lock.

2) Remove left side panel from console. Remove shifter cover. Disconnect 3 rods at shifter. Disconnect park lock cable from shifter. Remove shifter

cross bolt. Remove shifter mounting bracket. Remove shifter mounting bolt at body panel and remove shifter assembly from vehicle.

Installation

1) Position shifter to body. Install mounting bolt and tighten. Position mounting bracket to shifter. Install bracket bolts and tighten. Install shifter cross bolt and tighten. Connect 3 rods to shifter. Adjust shift linkage.

2) Connect park lock cable to shifter and adjust as follows: Place steering column lock lever in "Lock Park Position", shift transmission into reverse gear and push down on lock tab on park lock cable.

3) Install shifter cover, left side panel from console, glove box lock and console cover. Install shift lever knob. Reconnect electrical leads on power seat equipped vehicles. Replace left seat. Reconnect negative battery cable.

REMOVAL & INSTALLATION

See the appropriate article in MANUAL TRANSMISSION REMOVAL Section.

DISASSEMBLY

TRANSMISSION

1) With transmission removed from vehicle and separated from overdrive unit, remove drain plug from lower right side of case and drain lubricant. Shift transmission into 2nd gear. Remove shift cover attaching bolts, cover, gasket and both shift forks.

2) Remove backup switch from reverse housing. Rotate reverse shifter shaft and remove shift fork and gear from mainshaft. Remove lock pin from reverse shift lever boss and pull shaft from housing. Remove drive gear bearing retainer bolts, retainer and gasket from front of transmission.

3) Remove front bearing snap ring, selective fit snap ring and spacer washer. Using puller (J-6654-01 and J-8433-1), pull drive gear bearing from transmission. See Fig. 2. Remove 6 bolts attaching reverse housing to case. Using a small drift and hammer, tap locating pin for reverse housing into case.

4) Rotate reverse housing on mainshaft until hole for reverse idler gear shaft in housing lines up with countergear shaft. Using driver tool (J-24658), drive countergear shaft rearward out of gear and through reverse housing. Countergear will drop to bottom of case allowing clearance for removal of mainshaft.

5) Remove mainshaft with reverse housing and drive gear from case. Remove front reverse idler gear and thrust washer from case. Remove countergear and 2 tanged thrust washers from case. Check bottom of case for loose pilot bearings. Remove locating pin for reverse housing and any other loose components.

MAINSHAFT & COUNTERGEAR

1) Using snap ring pliers, remove 3-4 synchronizer assembly retaining ring at front of mainshaft. Slide washer, synchronizer assembly, synchronizer ring and 3rd speed gear from mainshaft. Spread rear bearing retainer snap ring and slide retainer from mainshaft.

Manual Transmissions
GENERAL MOTORS 83 MM 4-SPEED
AUTOMATIC OVERDRIVE – TRANSMISSION (Cont.)

Fig. 1: Exploded View of General Motors 83 MM 4-Speed Manual Transmission

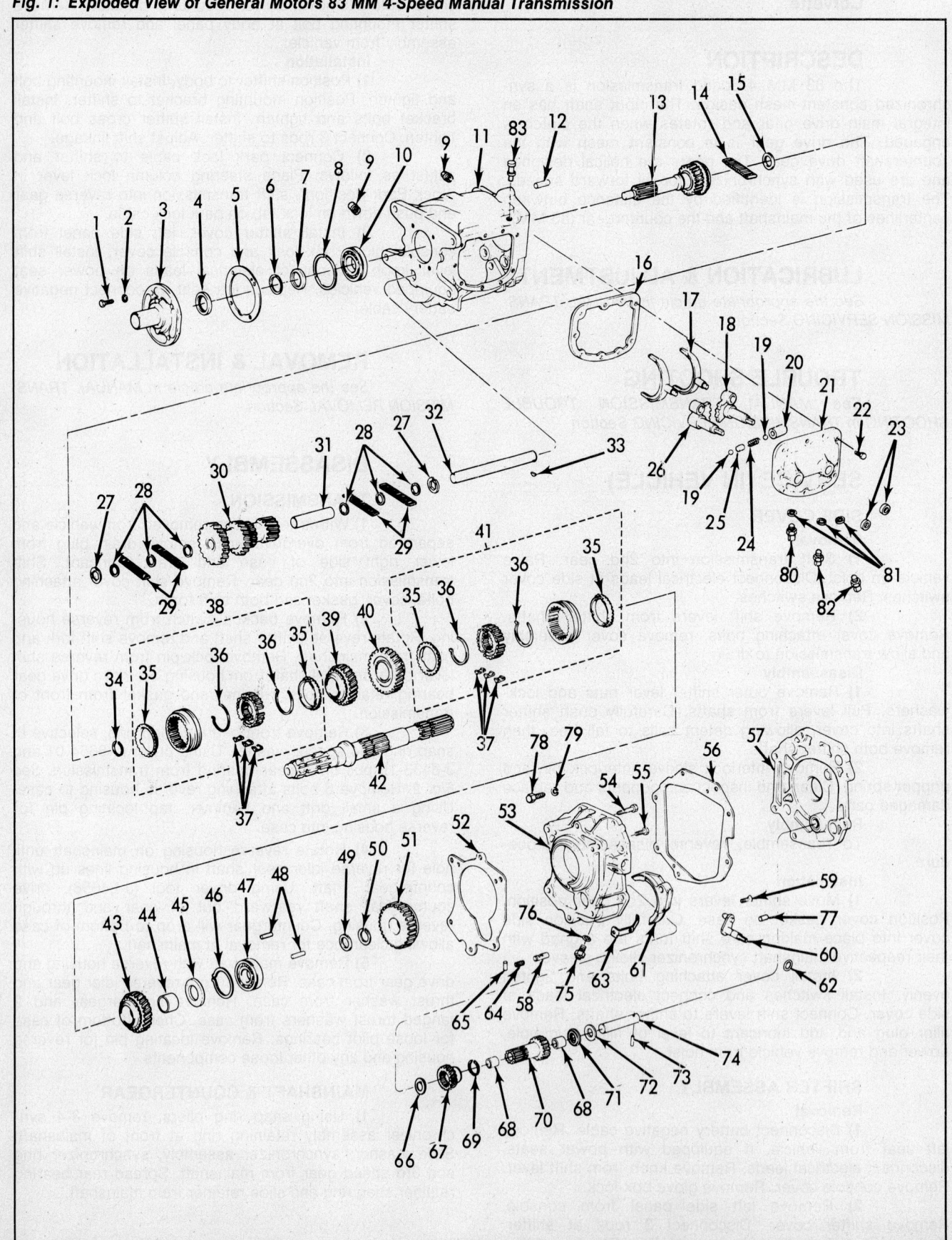

Manual Transmissions

3-113

GENERAL MOTORS 83 MM 4-SPEED
AUTOMATIC OVERDRIVE – TRANSMISSION (Cont.)

General Motors 83 MM Manual Transmission Components (Use With Fig. 1)

1. Bolt	43. 1st Speed Gear
2. Lock Washer	44. 1st Speed Gear Sleeve
3. Main Drive Gear Bearing Front Retainer	45. 1st Speed Gear Thrust Washer
4. Main Drive Gear Bearing Front Oil Seal	46. Rear Bearing Snap Ring
5. Main Drive Gear Bearing Retainer Gasket	47. Mainshaft Rear Bearing
6. Main Drive Gear Bearing Retainer Snap Ring	48. Dowel Pin
7. Main Drive Gear Bearing Spacer	49. Main Drive Gear Bearing Spacer
8. Main Drive Gear Bearing Lock Ring	50. Mainshaft Snap Ring
9. Magnetic Drain Plug	51. Reverse Gear
10. Main Drive Gear Bearing	52. Rear Bearing Retainer-to-Transmission Case Gasket
11. Transmission Case	53. Rear Bearing Retainer
12. Dowel Pin	54. Rear Bearing Retainer Bolt
13. Main Drive Gear	55. Rear Bearing Retainer Bolt
14. Main Drive Gear Pilot Rear Roller	56. Adapter Plate Gasket
15. Mainshaft Pilot Bearing Spacer	57. Adapter Plate
16. Side Cover Gasket	58. Reverse Detent Pin
17. Shift Forks (1-2, 3-4)	59. Rear Bearing Retainer Screw
18. 1st & 2nd Shift Shaft	60. Reverse Shift Shaft
19. Steel Ball	61. Reverse Shift Fork
20. Interlock Sleeve	62. Reverse Shift Shaft Oil Seal
21. Side Cover	63. Harness Clip Bracket
22. Transmission Cover Bolt	64. Reverse Detent Pin Poppet Spring
23. Shift Lever Shaft Oil Seals (1-2, 3-4)	65. Reverse Detent Spring Pin
24. Shift Lever Poppet Spring	66. Front Reverse Idler Gear Thrust Washer
25. Interlock Pin	67. Reverse Idler Front Gear
26. 3rd & 4th Shift Shaft	68. Reverse Idler Bushing
27. Countergear Rear Washer	69. Reverse Idler Gear Retainer Ring
28. Countershaft Bearing Roller Washer	70. Reverse Idler Rear Gear
29. Countergear Bearing Roller	71. Reverse Idler Thrust Bearing
30. Countergear	72. Rear Reverse Idler Gear Thrust Washer
31. Countergear Bearing Spacer	73. Spring Pin
32. Countergear Shaft	74. Reverse Idler Shaft
33. Woodruff Key	75. Overdrive Override Reverse Gear Switch
34. Mainshaft Snap Ring	76. Reverse Gear Switch Seal
35. Synchronizer Blocking Ring	77. Solid Tapper Pin
36. Synchronizer Spring	78. Transmission-to-Overdrive Bolt
37. Synchronizer Key	79. Transmission-to-Overdrive Bolt Lock Washer
38. Synchronizer (3rd & 4th)	80. Overdrive Override (3-4) Switch
39. 3rd Speed Gear	81. Overdrive Override Switch Seal
40. 2nd Speed Gear	82. Overdrive Override (1-2) Switch
41. Synchronizer (1st & 2nd)	83. Transmission Ventilator
42. Mainshaft	

Fig. 2: Removing Front Bearing

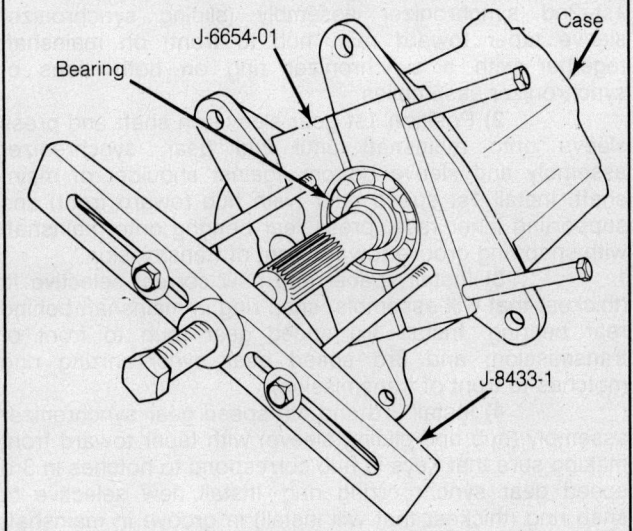

2) Remove rear bearing-to-mainshaft snap ring. Support mainshaft under 2nd gear and press mainshaft from rear bearing, 1st gear and sleeve, 1-2 synchronizer assembly and 2nd gear. Remove driver tool

(J-24658) from countergear. Tip countergear on end and let 6 spacers, 112 rollers and roller sleeve slide out from gear.

CLEANING & INSPECTION

1) Wash transmission thoroughly inside and outside with cleaning solvent, then inspect case for cracks. Check front and rear faces for burrs, and if present, dress them off with a fine mill file.

2) All main drive gear and countergear bearing rollers should be inspected closely and replaced if they show wear. Inspect countershaft and reverse idler shaft at same time. Replace if necessary. Replace all worn spacers.

3) Inspect all gears for excessive wear, chips or cracks and replace any that are worn or damaged. Inspect reverse gear bushing and if worn or damaged, replace entire gear (reverse gear bushing is not serviced separately). Check both synchronizer sleeves to see that they slide freely on their hubs.

4) Wash front and rear ball bearings thoroughly in a cleaning solvent. Blow out bearing with compressed air. Do not allow bearing to spin. Turn them slowly by hand. Spinning bearing may damage race and balls.

Manual Transmissions

GENERAL MOTORS 83 MM 4-SPEED
AUTOMATIC OVERDRIVE – TRANSMISSION (Cont.)

COMPONENT DISASSEMBLY & REASSEMBLY

SYNCHRONIZER KEYS & SPRINGS

NOTE: The synchronizer hubs and sliding sleeves are a selected assembly and should be kept together as originally assembled, but keys and 2 springs may be replaced if worn or broken.

If relation of hub and sleeve are not already marked, mark for assembly purposes. Push hub from sliding sleeve, keys will fall free and springs may be easily removed. Place 2 springs in position (one on each side of hub) so all 3 keys are engaged by both springs. Place keys in position and while holding them in place, slide sleeve onto hub. Align marks made before disassembly.

DRIVE GEAR BEARING RETAINER OIL SEAL

Pry out old seal. Using a seal installer, install a new seal into retainer until it bottoms in bore. Lubricate inside diameter of seal with transmission fluid.

REVERSE SHIFTER SHAFT AND SEAL

1) With reverse housing removed from transmission, reverse shifter shaft lock pin will already be removed. Carefully drive shifter shaft into reverse housing allowing ball detent to drop into case. Remove shaft and ball detent spring. Remove "O" ring seal from shaft.

2) Place ball detent spring into detent spring hole and start reverse shifter shaft into hole in boss. Place detent ball on spring and while holding ball down, push shifter shaft into place and turn until ball drops into place in detent on shaft detent plate.

3) Install "O" ring seal on shaft. Install shift fork. Do not drive shifter shaft lock pin into place until reverse housing has been installed on transmission case.

REVERSE IDLER SHAFT

Place a small punch into hole in front cover of overdrive unit and drive pin into shaft until shaft can be pulled from front cover. Insert new idler shaft into cover until hole in shaft lines up with hole in boss. Insert roll pin into boss opening and drive pin into cover until shaft is securely locked in place.

REASSEMBLY

COUNTERGEAR

1) Install roller spacer in countergear (if removed). Insert loading tool (J-24658) into countergear. Using heavy grease to retain rollers, install spacer, 28 rollers, spacer, 28 rollers, and spacer in either end of countergear. Repeat in other end of countergear.

2) Rest transmission case on its side with side cover opening toward assembler. Put countergear tanged thrust washers in place, retaining them with heavy grease, making sure tangs are resting in notches of case.

3) Set countergear in place in bottom of transmission case, making sure that tanged thrust washers are not knocked out of place. Lubricate and insert countergear (pushing loading tool out front of case) until

woodruff key slot is in its relative installed position (do not install key).

4) Attach a dial indicator and check end play of countergear. If end play is greater than .025" (.64 mm), a new thrust washer must be installed. See Fig. 3.

Fig. 3: Measuring Countergear End Play

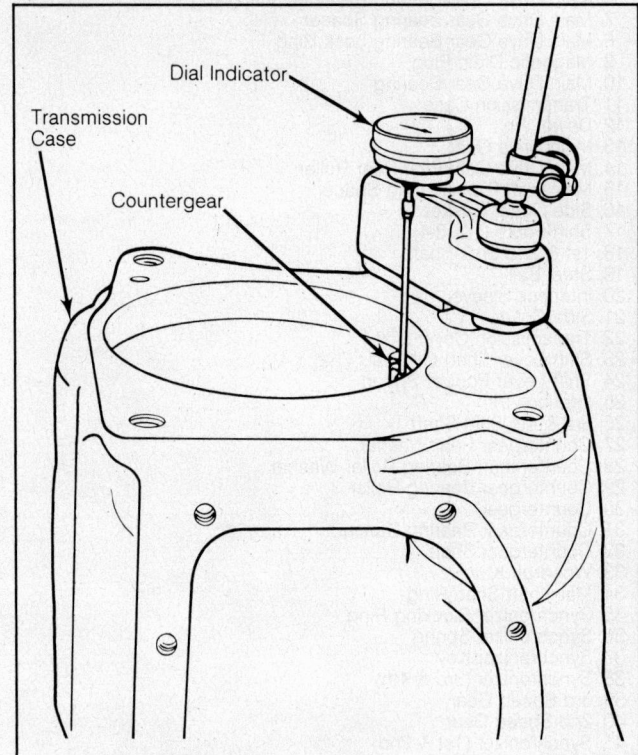

MAINSHAFT

1) From rear of mainshaft, assemble 2nd speed gear (with hub of gear toward rear of shaft). Install 1st–2nd synchronizer assembly (sliding synchronizer sleeve taper toward rear, hub to front) on mainshaft together with a synchronizer ring on both sides of synchronizer assemblies.

2) Position 1st gear sleeve on shaft and press sleeve onto mainshaft until 2nd gear, synchronizer assembly and sleeve bottom against shoulder of mainshaft. Install 1st speed gear (with hub toward front) and supporting inner race, press rear bearing onto mainshaft with snap ring groove toward front of transmission.

3) Install spacer and new correct selective fit (thickest that will assemble) snap ring in mainshaft behind rear bearing. Install 3rd speed gear (hub to front of transmission) and 3rd speed gear synchronizing ring (notches to front of transmission).

4) Install 3rd and 4th speed gear synchronizer assembly (hub and sliding sleeve) with taper toward front making sure that keys in hub correspond to notches in 3rd speed gear synchronizing ring. Install new selective fit snap ring (thickest that will install) in groove in mainshaft in front of 3rd and 4th speed synchronizer assembly.

5) Install rear bearing retainer (reverse housing) over end of mainshaft. Spread snap ring to drop around rear bearing. Release snap ring when it aligns with groove in rear bearing.

Manual Transmissions

3-115

GENERAL MOTORS 83 MM 4-SPEED
AUTOMATIC OVERDRIVE – TRANSMISSION (Cont.)

TRANSMISSION

1) Place transmission case on its side with shift cover opening toward assembler. Position countergear tanged washers in place, using a heavy grease to retain them. Be sure tangs are in notches of thrust face. Position countergear in bottom of case.

2) Install front reverse idler gear (teeth forward) and thrust washer in case. Use a heavy grease to hold thrust washer in position. Using a heavy grease, install 16 roller bearings and washer into main drive gear. Mate main drive gear with mainshaft assembly.

3) Position 3rd-4th synchronizer sliding sleeve forward. This will provide clearance for installation as well as hold assembly together. Position a new reverse housing to case gasket on rear of case. Install mainshaft and drive gear assembly into case.

4) Place bearing snap ring on front main bearing. Position front main bearing at case opening and with a hollow shaft, tap bearing into case. Install spacer washer and selective fit snap ring to secure main drive bearing.

5) Raise countergear in case, aligning holes in case with center of gear. With thrust washers in place, slide countershaft through rear of case. Install woodruff key and tap shaft into case, until flush with rear face of transmission case.

6) Align reverse housing and gasket with transmission case. Install locating pin for reverse housing. Tap pin in until flush with housing. Install 6 bolts attaching reverse housing to case. Tighten bolts to specifications. Install reverse shift shaft and "O" ring into housing. Install retaining pin.

7) Install reverse gear and shift fork. Slide gear and fork forward on mainshaft until shift fork and shifter shaft can be indexed into position. Position drive gear bearing retainer and gasket at front of case. Apply sealer to bolts. Install bolts and tighten to specifications.

8) Install rear reverse idler gear. Align splines on rear gear with front gear and slide together. Assemble overdrive unit to reverse housing. Guide idler shaft on overdrive unit into idler gears and align splines on mainshaft with splines in input sun gear. Slide units together and install retaining bolts. Tighten bolts to specifications.

9) Slide 1-2 synchronizer forward into 2nd gear. Install shift forks into grooves of synchronizers. Place side cover with a gasket on transmission. Guide shift forks into cover and install retaining bolts. Tighten bolts to specifications. Check operation of transmission by manually shifting transmission into all gears.

TIGHTENING SPECIFICATIONS

Application	Ft. Lbs. (N.m)
Drive Gear Bearing Retainer	15-20 (20-27)
Side Cover	15-20 (20-27)
Rev. Gear Housing-to-Case (1) Bolt	30-40 (40-54)
Rev. Gear Housing-to-Case (2) Bolts	40-50 (54-67)
Rev. Gear Housing-to-Case (3) Bolts	35-45 (47-61)
Drain Plug	15-25 (20-33)
Filler Plug	25-35 (33-47)
Transmission-to-Bell Housing	45-60 (60-80)

Manual Transmissions
GENERAL MOTORS 83 MM 4–SPEED AUTOMATIC OVERDRIVE – OVERDRIVE

Corvette

DESCRIPTION

The overdrive unit is a 2-Speed overdrive system electronically controlled by the ECM which operates with a 1:1 or 0.68:1 ratio. It is mounted to the rear of the manual transmission. By combining these 2 transmissions, the complete unit is actually capable of operating with 7 separate gear ratios. One of which is an overdrive.

The 2-Speed overdrive unit performs its function using a planetary gear system in combination with 2 sets of clutch packs. The output shaft from the manual unit is linked to a 40-tooth input sun gear in the overdrive unit. This in turn, is meshed with 4 double planet gears which mesh with a 34-tooth output shaft gear.

The overdrive mode cannot occur when 4-Speed transmission is in first gear. It can, however, occur in the remaining 3 gears. Rapid acceleration will cause a shift from overdrive to direct mode. Overdrive is automatically engaged at speeds above 110 MPH. Overdrive mode can be turned off by a switch on the vehicle's console.

LUBRICATION & ADJUSTMENT

See the appropriate article in MANUAL TRANS-MISSION SERVICING Section.

TROUBLE SHOOTING

See MANUAL TRANSMISSION TROUBLE SHOOTING in TRANSMISSION SERVICING Section

SERVICE (IN VEHICLE)

COOLER LINE FLUSHING

NOTE: If replacement of transmission steel tubing cooler lines is required, use only double wrapped and brazed steel tubing meeting GM specification 123M. Steel tubing should be flared using the double flare method.

CAUTION: Under no condition should copper or aluminum tubing be used to replace steel tubing. These materials do not have satisfactory fatigue durability to withstand normal vehicle vibrations.

NOTE: In a major transmission failure, where particles of metal have been carried with oil throughout units of transmission, it will be necessary to flush out oil cooler and connecting lines.

1) Disconnect both cooler lines from transmission. Place a hose over end of cooler inlet line (from bottom of cooler) and insert hose into an empty container.

2) Flush clean solvent through return line (from top of cooler) using an oil suction gun until clean solvent comes out of hose. This will "backflush" cooler. Remove hose from inlet cooler line and place it on return line.

3) Flush clean solvent through inlet line until clean solvent comes out of return line. Remove remaining solvent from cooler with compressed air applied to return line and flush with transmission fluid. Reconnect oil cooler lines and tighten nuts.

Fig. 1: Hydraulic Circuit Diagram

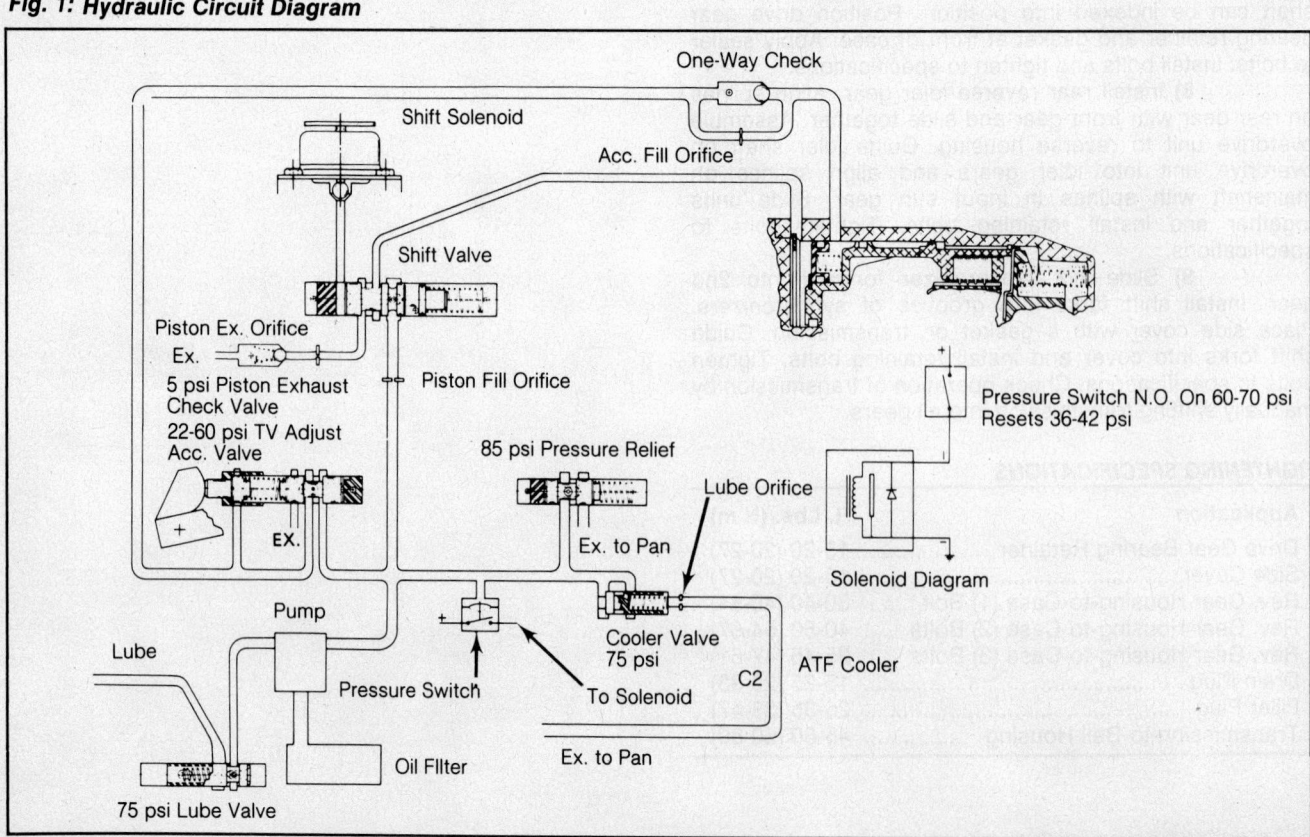

Manual Transmissions
3-117

GENERAL MOTORS 83 MM 4-SPEED
AUTOMATIC OVERDRIVE — OVERDRIVE (Cont.)

Fig. 2: *Cross Section View of Overdrive Unit*

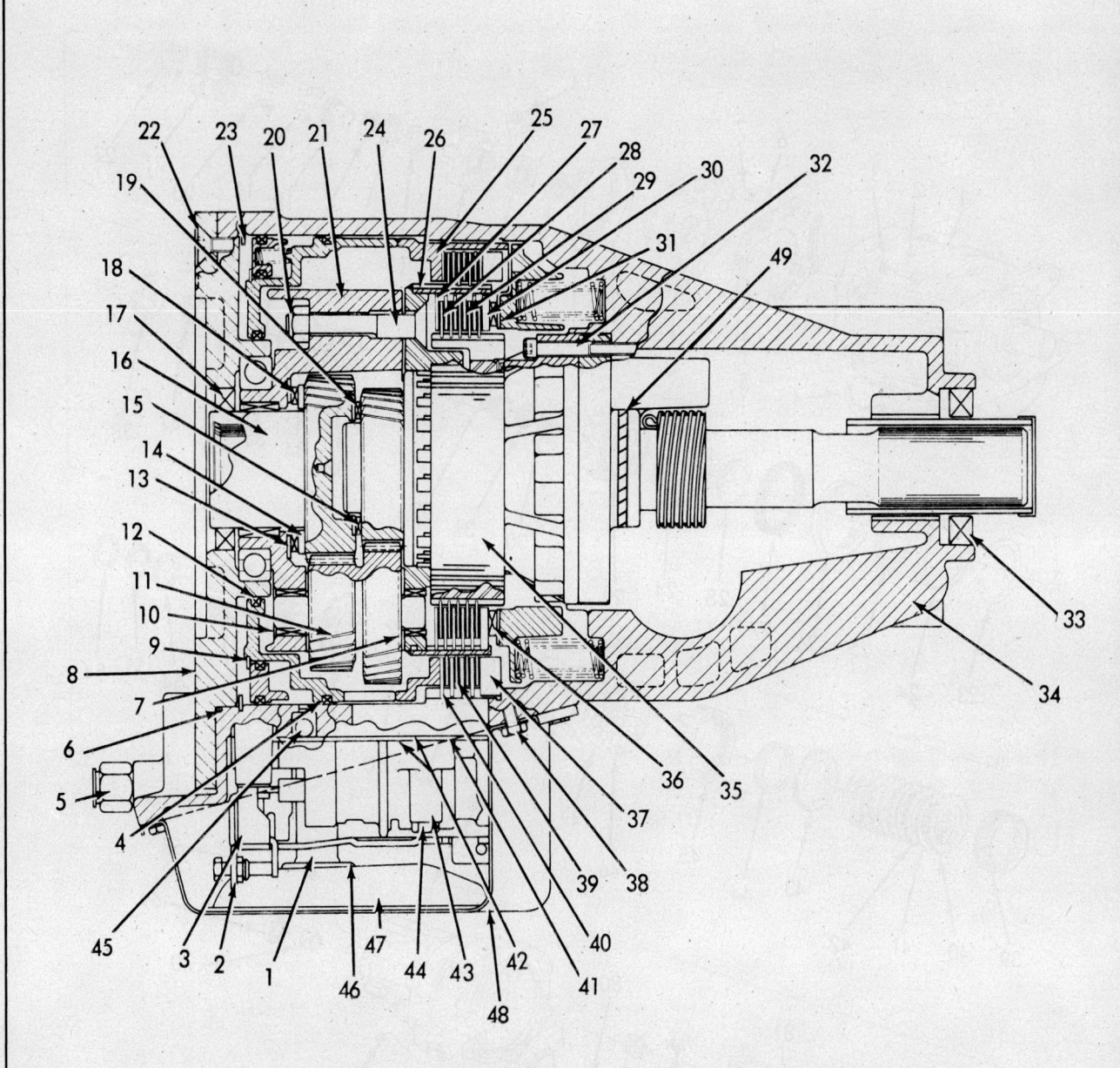

1. Pickup Tube	17. Input Seal	33. Output Seal
2. Lever Arm Assembly	18. Thrust Bearing	34. Housing Assembly
3. Lever Cam	19. Thrust Bearing	35. Shaft Assembly
4. Quad Seal	20. Lock Nut	36. Thrust Bearing
5. Fitting	21. Carrier Bearing Assembly	37. Stop Clutch
6. "O" Ring Seal	22. Screw	38. Screw (6 mm x 12 mm)
7. Thrust Plate	23. Retaining Ring	39. Clutch Disc
8. Adapter Plate	24. Screw	40. Clutch Plate
9. Piston-Accumulator Assembly	25. Finger Pressure Plate	41. Valve Plate
10. Thrust Washer	26. Clutch Hub Assembly	42. Valve Gasket
11. Planet Gear	27. Clutch Plate	43. Valve Body Assembly
12. Quad Seal	28. Clutch Disc	44. Screw (6 mm x 45 mm)
13. Thrust Washer	29. Clutch Plate	45. 5/16" Steel Ball
14. Thrust Washer	30. Bearing Plate	46. Grommet
15. Thrust Washer	31. Thrust Washer	47. Oil Filter
16. Sun Gear	32. Allen Screw (6 mm x 40 mm)	48. Oil Pan
		49. Pump Seal

Manual Transmissions

GENERAL MOTORS 83 MM 4–SPEED
AUTOMATIC OVERDRIVE – OVERDRIVE (Cont.)

Fig. 3: Exploded View of Automatic Overdrive Unit

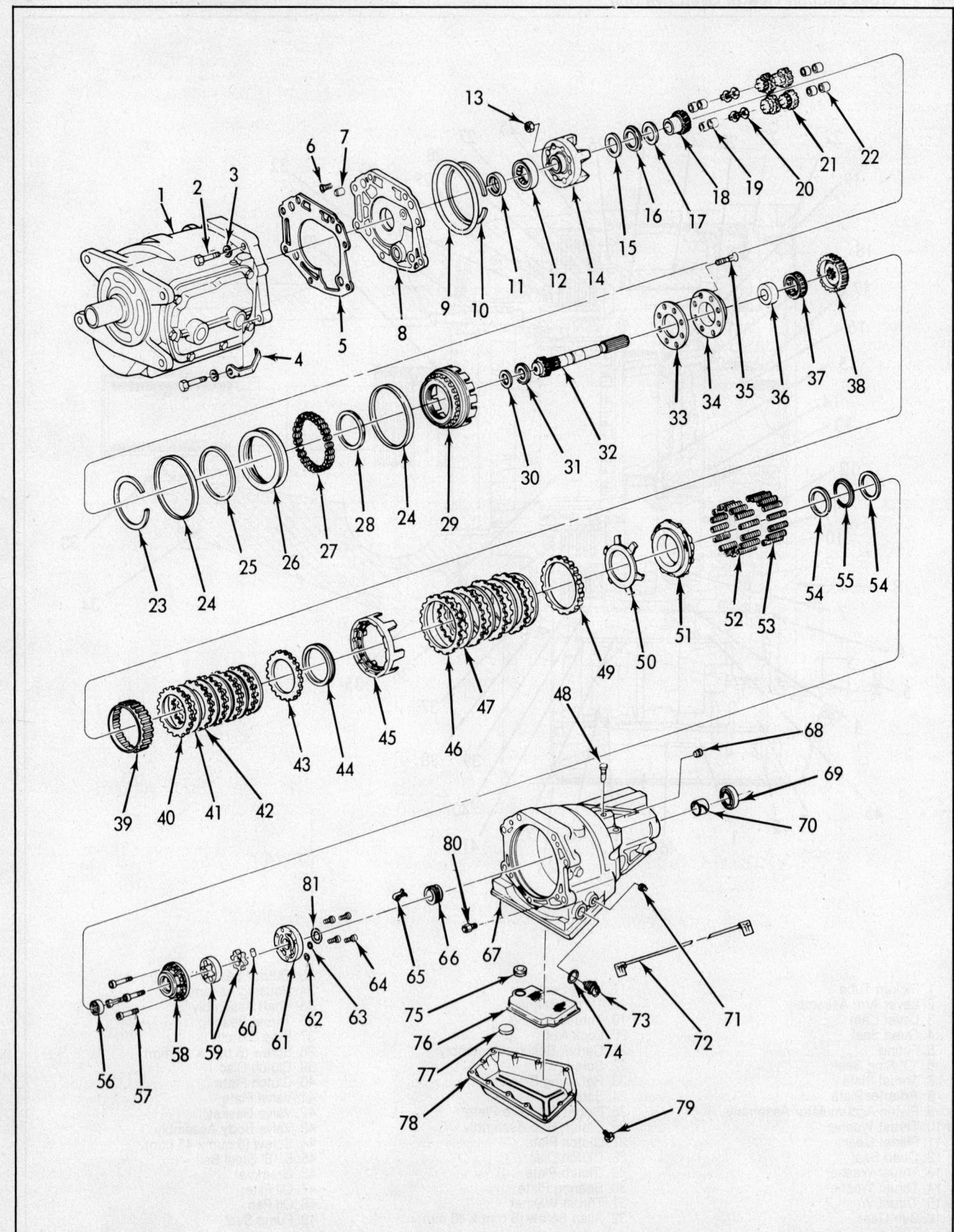

GENERAL MOTORS 83 MM 4-SPEED
AUTOMATIC OVERDRIVE — OVERDRIVE (Cont.)

Automatic Overdrive Unit Components (Use With Fig. 3)

1. Transmission (Less Overdrive Unit)	41. Direct Clutch Plate
2. Transmission-to-Overdrive Bolt	42. Direct Clutch Driven Plate
3. Transmission-to-Overdrive Bolt Lock Washer	43. Direct Clutch Pressure Plate
4. Harness Clip Bracket	44. Direct Clutch Bearing
5. Adapter Plate Gasket	45. Overdrive Clutch Piston
6. Adapter Plate Screw	46. Overdrive Clutch Driven Plate
7. Dowel Pin	47. Overdrive Clutch Plate
8. Adapter Plate	48. Overdrive Vent Tube
9. Adapter Plate "O" Ring	49. Overdrive Clutch Pressure Plate
10. Accumulator Piston Retaining Ring	50. Direct Clutch Thrust Washer
11. Input Sun Gear Oil Seal	51. Overdrive Direct Clutch Piston
12. Annular Bearing	52. Overdrive Direct Clutch Outer Spring
13. Carrier Bearing Lock Nut	53. Overdrive Direct Clutch Inner Spring
14. Planetary Gear Carrier	54. Overdrive Direct Clutch Hub Thrust Washer
15. Input Sun Gear Thrust Washer	55. Overdrive Direct Clutch Hub Thrust Bearing
16. Input Sun Gear Thrust Bearing	56. Pump Bearing Cup
17. Input Sun Gear Thrust (Selective) Washer	57. Overdrive Pump & Output Shaft Screw
18. Input Sun Gear	58. Overdrive Pump (Gerotor) Housing, with Bearing
19. Bearing Cup	59. Overdrive Oil (Gerotor) Pump
20. Planetary Gear Thrust Washer	60. Oil Pump Drive Pin
21. Planetary Gear	61. Pump (Gerotor) Spool
22. Bearing Cup	62. Overdrive Oil Pump "O" Ring
23. Accumulator Piston Retaining Ring	63. Overdrive Oil Pump "O" Ring
24. Accumulator Piston Seal	64. Overdrive Pump Spool (Gerotor) Screw
25. Accumulator Piston Seal	65. Speedometer Drive Gear Clip
26. Accumulator Cushion Piston	66. Speedometer Drive Gear
27. Accumulator Piston Spring	67. Overdrive Case
28. Accumulator Piston Seal	68. Headless Slotted Plug
29. Accumulator Piston	69. Overdrive Output Shaft Oil Seal
30. Output Shaft Thrust Washer	70. Case Bushing
31. Output Shaft Thrust Bearing	71. Overdrive Valve Body Pressure Switch Wire
32. Output Shaft	72. Square Head Filler Plug
33. Planetary Gear Thrust Plate	73. Overdrive Solenoid Electrical Connector
34. Clutch Drum Plate	74. Overdrive Solenoid Electrical Connector "O" Ring
35. Clutch Drum Bolt	75. Overdrive Oil Screen Tube Grommet
36. Inner Race	76. Overdrive Oil Screen
37. Direct Clutch Sprag	77. Overdrive Oil Pan Magnet
38. Direct Clutch Hub	78. Overdrive Oil Pan
39. Direct Clutch Drum	79. Overdrive Oil Pan Bolt
40. Direct Clutch Inner Driven (Selective) Plate	80. Oil Cooler Fitting
	81. Pump Seal

REMOVAL & INSTALLATION

See the appropriate article in MANUAL TRANS-MISSION REMOVAL Section.

PRESSURE SWITCH

Removal

Remove oil pan and filter. Disconnect 2 electrical leads at switch. Unscrew switch from valve body.

Installation

To install, reverse removal procedures. Fill transmission with Dexron II automatic transmission fluid.

O/D UNIT OUTPUT SHAFT SEAL

Removal

Remove drive shaft. Pry out old seal using a seal removal tool.

Installation

Coat lip of new seal with automatic transmission fluid. Place a new seal on installer (J-21426), and install seal. Install drive shaft. Replace lost fluid.

O/D SOLENOID

Removal

Remove transmission oil pan and filter. Disconnect T.V. cable at throttle body lever. Remove valve body. Using spring compressor (J-34529), compress shift valve spring and remove pin. Using same tool, compress

relief valve springs and remove pin. Remove bolts attaching solenoid valve to valve body. Remove solenoid and check ball from valve body.

Installation

To install, reverse removal procedure. Fill overdrive unit with Dexron II automatic transmission fluid.

DISASSEMBLY

OVERDRIVE UNIT

1) Remove fill plug and drain oil from case. Remove retaining bolt and bracket for speedometer sensor and driven gear. Remove sensor and gear. Remove 1/8" pipe plugs (3) from rear of unit. Install 3 pressure plate retaining bolts until flush with case. Turn bolts 2 additional turns, by rotating each bolt 1 turn at a time.

NOTE: This sequence must be followed in order to prevent pressure plate from cocking and causing damage to unit.

2) Remove 4 Allen head bolts retaining adapter plate to case. Remove adapter plate, using a plastic hammer and screwdriver. Tap adapter plate to separate from case.

NOTE: Do not pry between case and adapter plate, damage to sealing surfaces may occur.

Manual Transmissions
GENERAL MOTORS 83 MM 4–SPEED
AUTOMATIC OVERDRIVE – OVERDRIVE (Cont.)

3) Mount overdrive unit in a holding fixture. Remove large snap ring from overdrive unit forward of accumulator piston.

CAUTION: If pressure is felt at snap ring, do not remove. Check to ensure pressure plate retaining bolts are installed. If bolts are installed, tighten each bolt one additional turn until pressure is relieved. The pressure plate is under a 1200 lb (544 kg.) spring load. If 3 retaining bolts are not installed, personal injury could occur.

4) Remove piston and accumulator assembly. Using an Allen wrench, pry assembly up evenly by lifting under flange. *See Fig. 4.* Do not pry at or near seal surface. Remove carrier and bearing assembly (includes input sun and pinion gears) as an assembly.

Fig. 4: Removing Piston & Accumulator Assembly

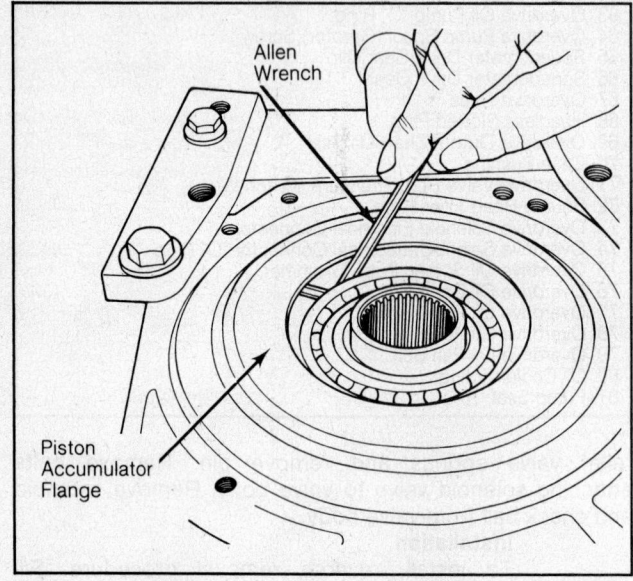

5) Remove finger pressure plate from clutch pack. Remove overdrive clutches (4 composition, 4 steel and 1 clutch stop plate). Remove direct clutch plates (5 composition, 5 steel and 1 steel bearing plate).

6) Measure each selective clutch plate in direct clutch pack and record readings. Selective clutch plates are used to control clutch pack clearance. When replacing clutch plates, replace each selective clutch plate with one of the same size.

7) Inspect overdrive and direct clutch plates as follows: Dry composition plates and inspect for pitting, flaking wear, glazing, cracking, charring and chips or metal particles imbedded in lining. If a compositioned plate shows any of these signs, replacement is required.

8) Wipe steel plate dry and check for discoloration. If surface is smooth and an even color smear is indicated, plate should be reused. If severe heat spot discoloration or surface scuffing is indicated, plate must be replaced.

9) Remove thrust washer and bearing from output sun gear. Thrust washer may stick to input sun gear hub. Remove 4 Allen head pump housing retaining bolts by rotating hub to gain access to bolts. Remove

output shaft assembly (Includes: output sun gear, sprag clutch, clutch hub, gerotor pump and speedometer drive gear).

10) Remove pressure plate and springs by positioning plate tool (J-21420-2) on pressure plate with bolt from (J-23327) through center of plate. Position (J-23327) on rear of case and install retaining nut. *See Fig. 5.* Remove 3 retaining bolts from rear of case. Loosen retaining nut on (J-23327) bolt to relieve spring pressure.

Fig. 5: Removing Pressure Plate & Springs

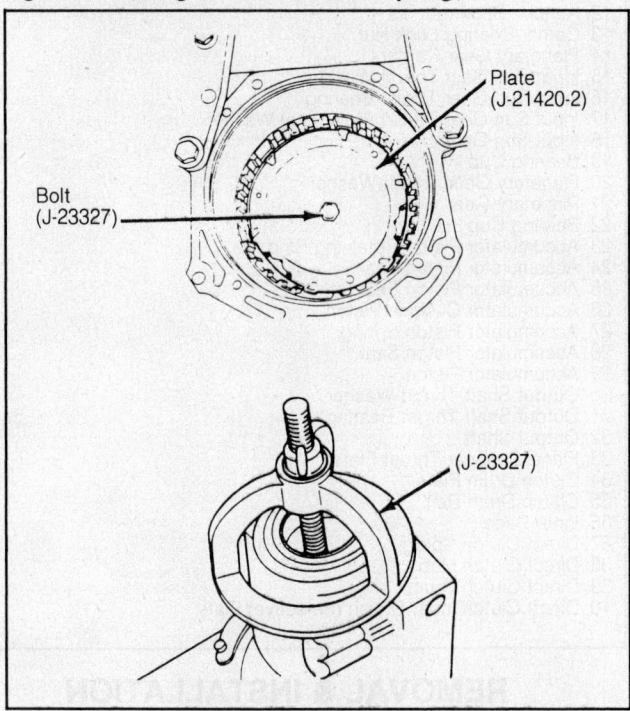

11) Remove cooler valve assembly by loosening 2 nuts on tube and then removing 2 bolts holding valve to case. Remove 12 oil pan retaining bolts and pry pan from case. Remove oil filter and tube from valve body.

12) Disconnect T.V. cable from lever. Remove cable retaining bolt and remove cable assembly. Remove T.V. lever retaining bolt and then lever from valve body. Remove remaining valve body bolts and remove valve body with spacer plate.

NOTE: There are 2 check balls, one on each side of spacer plate. One ball is located in case and the other is spring loaded in valve body.

COMPONENT DISASSEMBLY & REASSEMBLY

VALVE BODY
Disassembly
1) Using tool (J-34529), relieve pressure on shift valve and remove pin, spring and valve. Relieve pressure on relief valve and remove pin, spring and valve. Relieve pressure on accumulator valve and remove pin, spring, valve, plug, sleeve and plunger.

2) Disconnect solenoid electrical lead at pressure switch. Remove solenoid attaching bolts. Remove

Manual Transmissions

3-121

GENERAL MOTORS 83 MM 4–SPEED
AUTOMATIC OVERDRIVE – OVERDRIVE (Cont.)

solenoid and checkball. Disconnect the other electrical lead at pressure switch. Remove switch from valve body.

Reassembly

To reassemble, reverse removal procedures. Coat all components with clean Dexron II automatic transmission fluid before reassembling.

OUTPUT SHAFT

Disassembly

1) Remove speedometer gear retaining clip and gear. Remove 4 Allen head bolts retaining pump cover to pump housing. Remove cover. Mark pump gears with a grease pencil. Gears must be installed in same direction as removed.

2) Position output shaft with splines down. Rotate pump housing until gears slide out. Remove drive pin from output shaft. Remove pump housing from output shaft. Remove thrust washer from pump housing. Remove thrust bearing and washer from clutch hub.

3) Remove clutch hub from output shaft. Note direction of hub on shaft. Oil grooves face sprag clutch or forward on shaft. Remove sprag clutch from output shaft. Note direction of sprag clutch. Lip on sprag clutch cage goes toward oil grooves on clutch hub.

Reassembly

1) Coat all parts with clean Dexron II automatic transmission fluid before reassembling. Install sprag clutch on output shaft. Lip on sprag clutch cage faces rearward or toward oil grooves on clutch hub. Install clutch hub on output shaft. Oil grooves on hub face sprag clutch or forward on shaft.

2) Install thrust washer, then thrust bearing on clutch hub. Install thrust washer on pump housing. Use petrolatum to retain thrust washer to housing. Install pump housing on output shaft. Install pin in output shaft. Install pump gears in housing. Gears must be installed in same direction as removed. Install oil pump seal in cover.

3) Place pump cover on housing. Align 4 bolt holes in cover with pump housing. Install bolts and tighten to specifications. Install speedometer gear on output shaft. Install retaining clip. Install new "O" rings on pump. Use petrolatum to retain "O" rings to cover.

CARRIER ASSEMBLY

Disassembly

1) Remove 4 nuts retaining carrier cover and remove cover. Remove thrust washer, thrust bearing, selective washer and input sun gear. Remove 4 pinion gears.

2) Remove steel thrust plate from carrier. Clean and inspect parts. Replace any parts that are cracked, chipped or show excessive wear.

Reassembly

Carrier assembly must be reassembled in transmission case.

PISTON & ACCUMULATOR ASSEMBLY

Disassembly

Remove snap ring retaining accumulator to piston. Remove accumulator and 24 springs from piston. Remove 2 "O" rings from accumulator. Remove 2 "O" rings from piston.

Reassembly

To reassemble, reverse removal procedures. Coat "O" rings with clean Dexron II automatic transmission fluid before installing.

REASSEMBLY

OVERDRIVE UNIT

1) Install pressure plate springs into pockets of transmission case as shown in *Fig 6*. Place pressure plate on top of springs. Seat springs into pockets of pressure plate.

Fig. 6: Pressure Plate Spring Installation

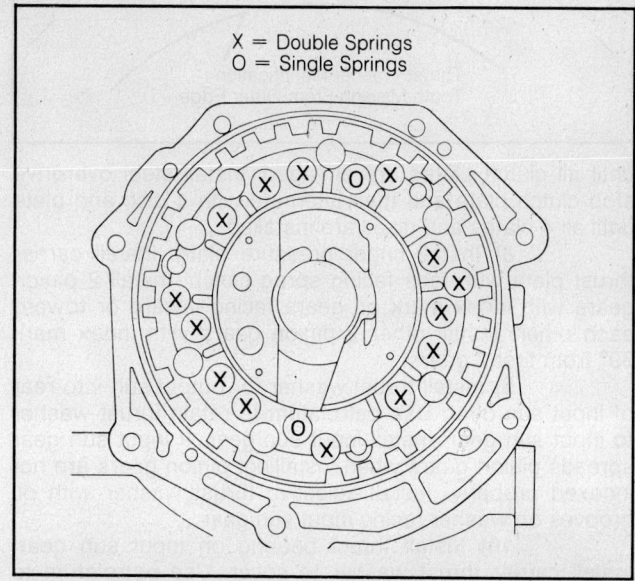

X = Double Springs
O = Single Springs

2) Position Plate Tool (J-21420-2) on top of pressure plate with bolt from Tool (J23327) through center of plate. Next position Plate Tool on rear of case. Install retaining nut. Tighten nut until pressure plate is drawn approximately 1/8" below step for overdrive clutch plates. Install 3 pressure plate retaining bolts. Remove tools from case. *See Fig. 5.*

3) Install output shaft assembly into transmission case. Be sure "O" rings are positioned properly on pump cover before installing output shaft assembly. Install 4 pump retaining bolts. Tighten to specification.

4) Install thrust bearing on output sun gear. Install tanged direct clutch thrust washer with tangs facing pressure plate. Tang with hole in it should be positioned at bottom of case (6 o'clock position). Ensure tabs on back of washer are seated in pressure plate. Install direct clutch thrust bearing.

5) Install direct clutch thrust washer. Thrust washer will have tooth missing from its outer edge. Side of thrust washer with circular grind pattern must face thrust bearing. Side with grind pattern can be identified by notch ground into tooth. *See Fig. 7.*

6) Install 1 composition clutch disc and a selective clutch plate. Selective clutch plates come in 5 sizes from .080-.120" (2.03-3.05) and are used to control clutch pack clearance. Direct clutch pack clearance is .050-.070" (1.27-1.78). Incorrect clutch travel will cause failure to clutch plates and discs.

7) Alternate remaining clutch discs and plates until all 5 plates and discs are installed. Install lower half of carrier assembly onto direct clutch pack. Index carrier

3-122

Manual Transmissions
GENERAL MOTORS 83 MM 4-SPEED AUTOMATIC OVERDRIVE — OVERDRIVE (Cont.)

Fig. 7: Thrust Washer Identification

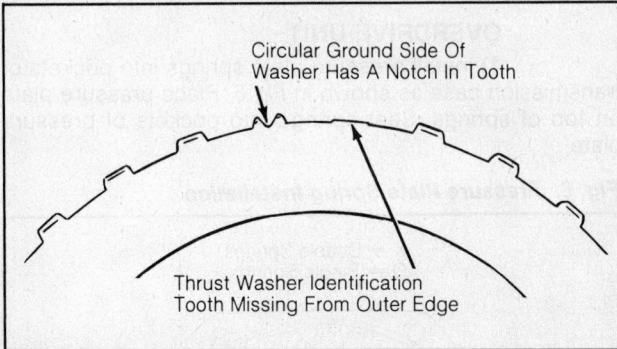

Circular Ground Side Of Washer Has A Notch In Tooth

Thrust Washer Identification Tooth Missing From Outer Edge

Fig. 8: Measuring End Play

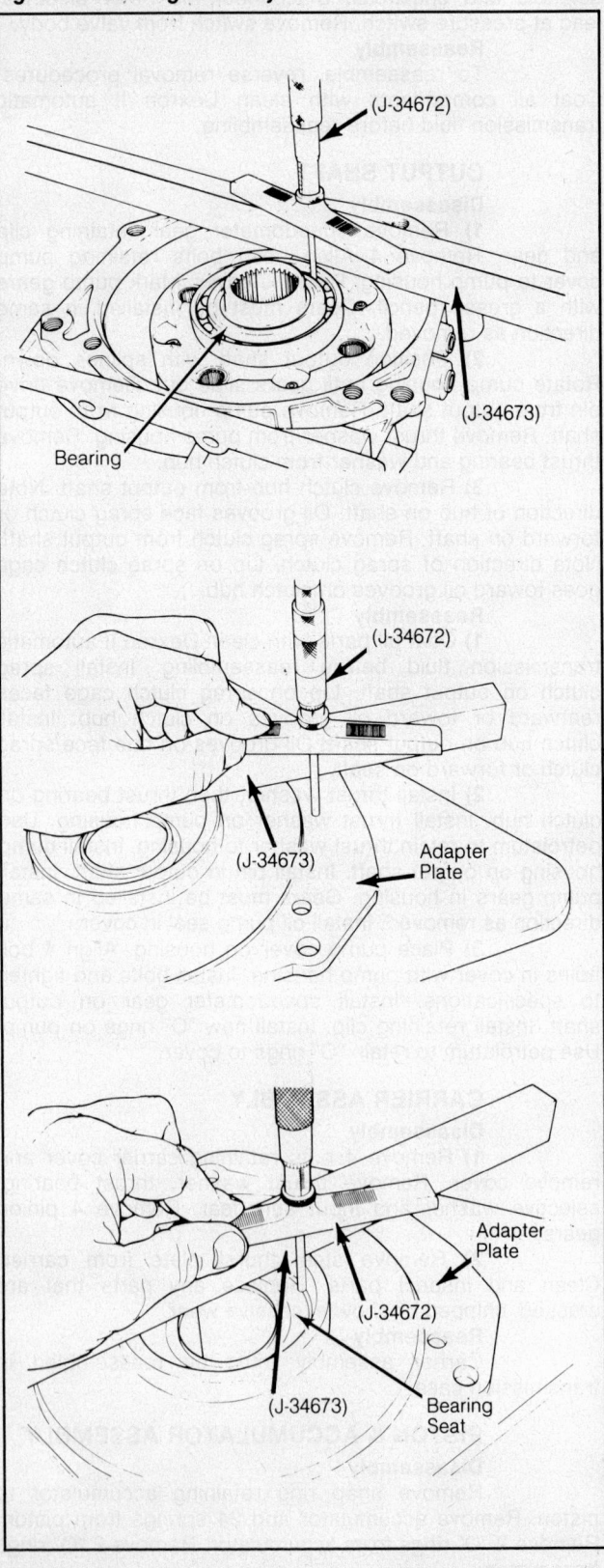

until all clutch plates are engaged. Install steel overdrive stop clutch plate and then alternate with a disc and plate until all 4 plates and discs are installed.

    8) Install finger pressure plate. Install carrier thrust plate with tabs facing sprag clutch. Install 2 pinion gears with index mark on gears facing inward or toward each other. Install other 2 pinion gears with index mark 90° from first 2 gears.

    9) Install thrust washer for output sun into rear of input sun gear. Use petrolatum to retain thrust washer to input sun gear. Install input sun gear. If input sun gear spreads pinion gears when installing, pinion gears are not indexed properly. Install selective thrust washer with oil grooves on washer facing input sun gear.

    10) Install thrust bearing on input sun gear. Install carrier thrust washer to cover. Use petrolatum to retain thrust washer to cover. Install 4 pinion gear thrust washers onto carrier cover. Use petrolatum to retain washers to cover.

    11) Install carrier cover. If pinion gears are not indexed properly, 4 bolt holes in cover will not align with bolts in lower half of carrier. Install 4 new retaining nuts and tighten to specifications.

    12) Measure end play for overdrive unit as follows. Place straightedge (J-34673) across face of overdrive unit as shown in *Fig. 8.* Use depth micrometer (J-34672) and measure distance from bearing to top of bar (S_1). Next, measure thickness of straightedge (S_2) with a 0-1" outside micrometer and subtract S_2 from S_1 and record this reading (S_3).

    13) Place straightedge across rear of adapter plate as shown in *Fig. 8.* Use depth micrometer and measure distance from top of bar to adapter plate mounting surface and record reading (S_4).

    14) Next measure distance from top of bar to bearing seat in adapter plate as shown in *Fig. 8* and record reading (S_5). Subtract S_5 from S_4 and record difference (S_6).

    15) Subtract S_6 from S_3 and record reading (S_7). S_7 is the end play. End play S_7 should be .000-.003". If S_7 is not within specifications, it will be necessary to remove carrier cover and change input sun selective thrust washer.

    16) Install accumulator and piston assembly. Coat lips of seals with clean Dexron II automatic transmission fluid before installing. Install large snap ring that goes in front of overdrive unit. Snap ring must be installed as shown in *Fig. 9.*

    17) Install a new seal in adapter plate. Place seal on seal installer and install from front side of adapter plate. Place seal protector on input sun gear. Install

adapter plate. Apply a light coating of RTV sealant around heads of adapter plate bolts.

    18) Install 4 adapter plate bolts and tighten to specifications. Remove seal protector. Remove first 1/8"

(J-34672)

(J-34673)

Bearing

(J-34672)

(J-34673)

Adapter Plate

(J-34672)

(J-34673)

Adapter Plate

Bearing Seat

Fig. 9: Snap Ring Installation

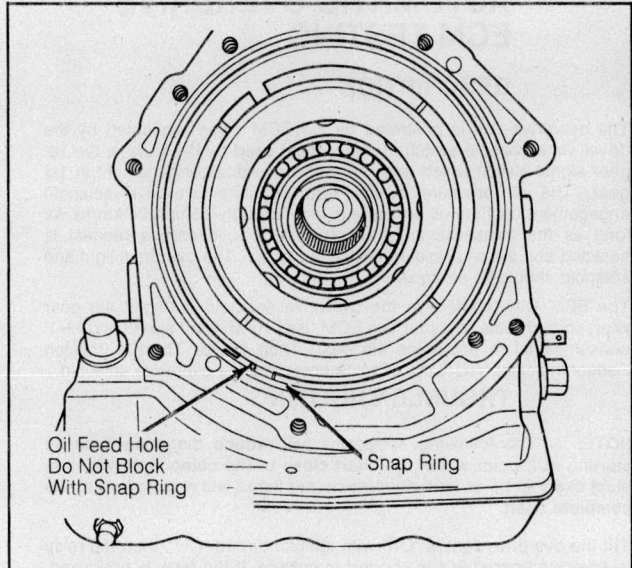

pipe plug from left side of overdrive unit. Install air line fitting (J-34742) into plug hole and tighten.

19) Measure clutch pack clearance as follows. Loosen 3 pressure plate retaining bolts evenly until spring pressure is released. Assemble dial indicator (J-8001) to rear of overdrive unit as shown in *Fig. 10*.

Fig. 10: Checking Clutch Pack Clearance

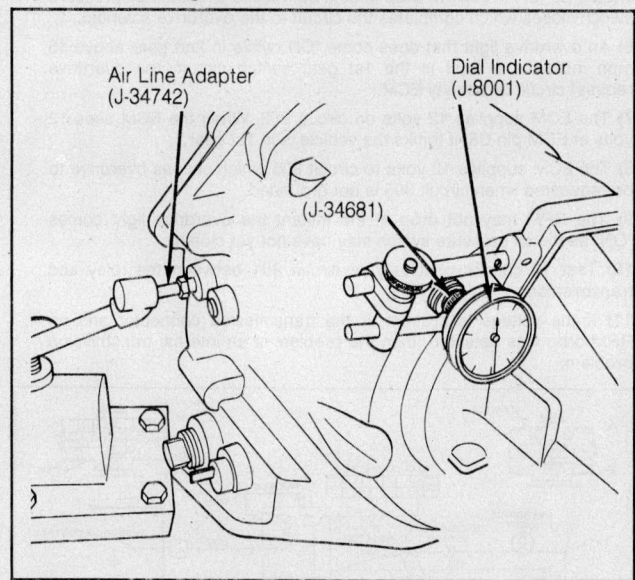

20) Apply a minimum of 100 psi (7.0 kg/cm²) to air line fitting (J-34742) and read dial indicator. Reading should be between .050-.070". If reading is different, it will be necessary to disassemble overdrive unit to change direct clutch selective clutch plates.

21) Selective clutch plates are available in 5 sizes from .080-.120" in .010" increments. If clutch pack clearance is within specification, remove 3 clutch pack retaining bolts. Coat 3 pipe plugs (1/8") with anti-sieze compound and install plugs. Tighten plugs to specifications.

22) Remove air line adapter. Coat plug with anti-sieze compound and install plug. Tighten to specifica-

tion. Install speedometer gear and sensor. Install a new output seal using a seal installer. Coat lip of seal with Dexron II automatic transmission fluid.

Fig. 11: Location of Check Ball

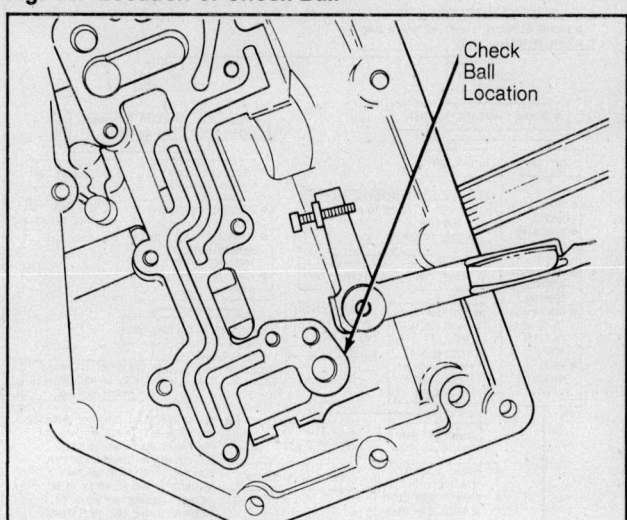

23) Install valve body as follows. Install check ball into case as shown in *Fig. 11*. Position 2 gaskets, one on each side of separator plate. Position separator plate on valve body. Position valve body to case and install retaining bolts and tighten to specifications.

24) Install T.V. cable and install retaining clip and bolt. Tighten bolt to specifications. Install T.V. lever and tighten bolt to specification. Connect T.V. cable to lever. Install throttle setting gauge (J-34671-1) into T.V. cable bore on side of case. See *Fig. 12*.

25) Set hook on T.V. cable onto high step of gauge. Place cam stop on valve body as close to lever as possible and install retaining bolt. Tighten to specifications. Set hook on T.V. cable onto lower step of gauge. Place gauge (J-34671-2) between piston and solenoid bracket.

26) Adjust screw/bolt on T.V. lever until bolt makes contact with stop on cam. After removing tools, install pickup tube and oil filter on valve body. Apply a bead of RTV sealant to oil pan flange and assemble wet.

27) Install magnet in oil pan. The bead of RTV should be applied around inside of bolt holes. Install pan bolts and tighten to specifications.

TIGHTENING SPECIFICATIONS

Application	Ft. Lbs. (N.m)
Cooler Block-to-Case	6-8 (8-10)
Pressure Tap Plugs	7-9 (9-12)
Pressure Plate Access Plugs	7-9 (9-12)
Valve Body-to-Case	6-8 (8-10)
Adapter Plate-to-Case	18-20 (24-27)
Oil Pan-to-Case	6-8 (8-10)
Pump Housing-to-Case	6-8 (8-10)
Pump Cover-to-Pump Cavity	10-12 (13-16)
O/D Case-to-Reverse Housing	34-36 (46-48)

Manual Transmissions

GENERAL MOTORS 83 MM 4–SPEED
AUTOMATIC OVERDRIVE – OVERDRIVE (Cont.)

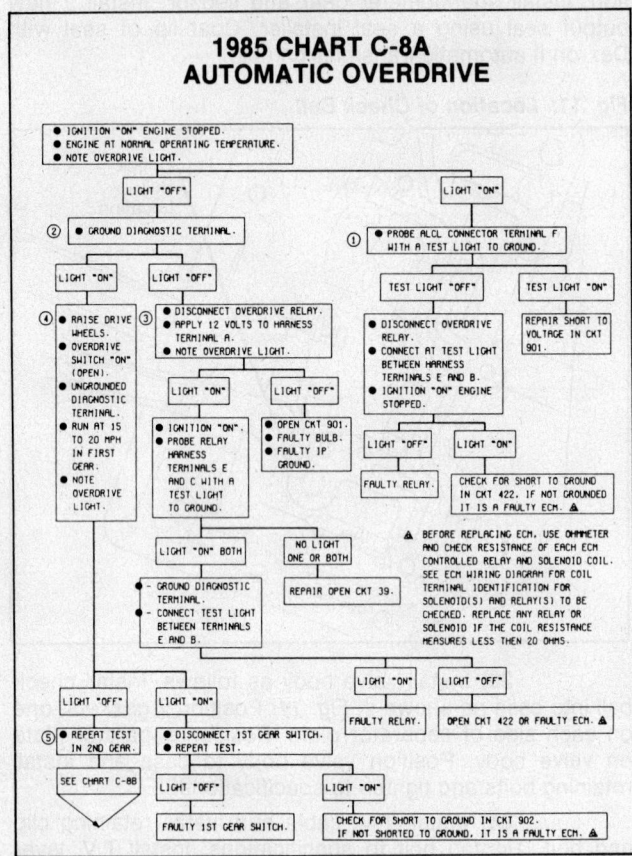

1985 CHART C-8A
AUTOMATIC OVERDRIVE

1985 CHART C-8B
AUTOMATIC OVERDRIVE

AUTOMATIC OVERDRIVE ECM TESTING

DESCRIPTION

The overdrive unit is controled by the ECM when requested by the driver via a console switch. Another input used by the ECM is the 1st gear signal switch which does not allow overdrive engagement in 1st gear. The oil pressure switch also prohibits overdrive solenoid engagement until the oil pressure is high enough (15mph 24 km/h). As long as the transmission is not in first gear, overdrive request is selected and the oil pressure switch is closed . The overdrive light and solenoid should be energized.

The ECM will de-energize the overdrive solenoid during a 4th gear wide open throttle situation.The ECM uses RPM, road speed,and MAF sensor signal to determine 4th gear. Then as the Throttle Position Sensor indicates WOT, the ECM de-energizes the overdrive solenoid.

TROUBLE SHOOTING

NOTE: The following symptoms will reduce diagnosis time by starting at a point within the chart close to the component which is most likely to be at fault. Symptoms not listed will require use of the complete chart.

1)If the overdrive light is "ON" with ignition turned "ON", then the relay is energized circuit 901 is shorted to voltage. If the relay is energized, the test light should not light at this point.

2) Grounding the diagnostic terminal with ignition "ON" should energize the relay and turn "ON" the overdrive light.

3) Connecting 12 volts to circuit 901 will check the continuity of the bulb circuit.

4) The 1st gear switch input (open) should not allow the overdrive to be energized.

5) With the vehicle in 2nd gear and above 15 mph, the overdrive light should be "ON". An RPM drop should be noticed when the oil pressure switch closes which completes the circuit to the overdrive solenoid.

6) An overdrive light that does come "ON" while in 2nd gear above 15 mph indicates a fault in the 1st gear switch circuit, the overdrive request circuit or a faulty ECM.

7) The ECM supplies 12 volts on circuit 902. When the ECM sees 12 volts at ECM pin C8, it thinks the vehicle is in 1st gear.

8) The ECM supplies 12 volts to circuit 905 which causes overdrive to be requested when circuit 905 is not grounded.

9) The RPM may not drop at the instant the overdrive light comes "ON" as the oil pressure switch may have not yet closed.

10) Test 10 checks continuity of circuit 901 between the relay and transmission.

11) If the voltage is present at the transmission connector and no RPM drop was detected, then the problem is an internal transmission problem.

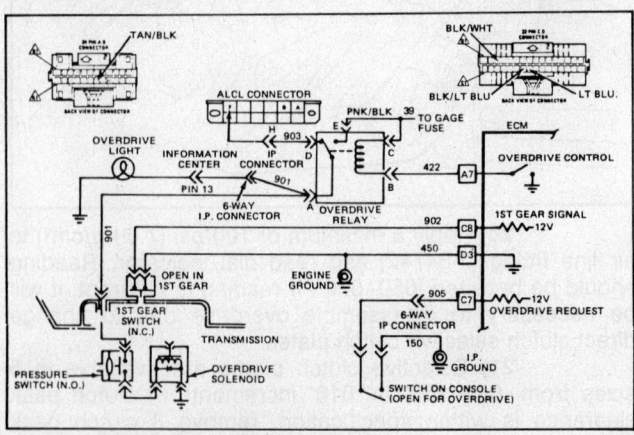

Manual Transmissions

GENERAL MOTORS 4-SPEED — 117 MM

Chevrolet & GMC 10-30 Series Truck

IDENTIFICATION

Transmission can be identified by a 2 letter code, stamped on a machined pad, on right side of case.

DESCRIPTION

The 117 MM 4-speed transmission is identified by the measured distance (117 mm) between centerlines of mainshaft and countergear and also by the number of forward gears. The 1st gear is a constant mesh type that engages with the 2nd gear synchronizer sleeve. The 2nd, 3rd, and 4th gears are synchronized.

LUBRICATION & ADJUSTMENT

See the appropriate article in MANUAL TRANS-MISSION SERVICING Section.

TROUBLE SHOOTING

See MANUAL TRANSMISSION TROUBLE SHOOTING in TRANSMISSION SERVICING Section

SERVICE (IN VEHICLE)

SHIFT LEVER
Removal
1) On 4WD models, remove transfer case shift lever boot retaining screws and retainer from compartment floor.
2) On all models, remove transmission shift lever boot retaining screws. Slide boot and retainer up on shift lever and remove shift lever.
Installation
1) Install transmission shift lever. Slide boot and retainer down shift lever and install attaching screws.
2) On 4WD models, install transfer case shift lever boot, retainer and attaching screws.

EXTENSION HOUSING OIL SEAL
Removal
1) Raise vehicle and support with safety stands. Drain lubricant from transmission. Disconnect propeller shaft and secure out of way. Disconnect speedometer cable and remove speedometer driven gear.
2) Using flange/yoke holding tool, remove output yoke/companion flange nut. Pull output yoke and companion nut off mainshaft. Support transmission while removing mounting bolts and bearing retainer bolts.
3) Remove bearing retainer and gasket. Discard gasket. Remove and discard oil seal.
Installation
1) Clean gasket surfaces. Coat outer diameter of new oil seal with sealing cement. Install oil seal using drive tool (J-22834-2). Install retaining bolts and tighten.
2) Install output yoke on mainshaft. Using a flange/yoke holding tool, install retaining nut. Tighten nut to specifications. Install speedometer driven gear, and connect speedometer cable.
3) Connect propeller shaft to transmission. Fill transmission with lubricant and lower vehicle.

REMOVAL & INSTALLATION

COVER & SHIFT FORK ASSEMBLY
Removal
1) Mount transmission in holding fixture and remove cover bolts. Move reverse shifter fork so reverse idler gear is partially engaged before removing cover.
2) Forks must be set so rear edge of slot in reverse fork is in line with front edge of slot in forward forks as viewed through tower opening.
3) If necessary, insert 2 bolts in cover flange threaded holes and turn evenly to raise cover dowel pins from case.
Installation
1) Move transmission gears to neutral except reverse idler gear which should be engaged about 3/8". Install cover with new gasket.
2) Shift forks must slide into their proper positions on clutch sleeves and reverse idler gear. Forks must be positioned as in removal. Install cover bolts and tighten.

DRIVE GEAR OIL SEAL
Removal & Installation
Remove retainer, oil seal assembly and gasket. Pry oil seal from retainer. Install new seal using installer (J-22833), with lip of seal toward flange of installer tool. Install retainer with new gasket.

TRANSMISSION
See the appropriate article in MANUAL TRANS-MISSION REMOVAL Section.

TRANSMISSION DISASSEMBLY

1) Mount transmission in holding fixture and remove cap screws retaining transmission cover assembly to case. If required, insert two 5/16" x 18 bolts in cover flange threaded holes and turn evenly to raise cover dowel pin from case.
2) Move reverse shifter fork so that reverse idler gear is partially engaged before attempting to remove cover. Forks must be positioned so rear edge of slot in reverse fork is in line with front edge of slot in forward forks as viewed throught tower opening.
3) Place transmission in 2 gears at once to lock gears. Remove universal joint flange and brake drum assembly. On 4WD models, use main bearing lock nut remover/installer (J-23070) to remove mainshaft rear lock nut. *See Fig. 2.*
4) If equipped, remove parking brake and brake flange plate assembly. On all models, remove rear bearing retainer and gasket. Slide speedometer drive gear off mainshaft.
5) Remove drive gear bearing retainers and gasket. Remove countergear front bearing cap and gasket. Pry countergear front bearing out, by inserting a two-pronged puller (J-28509) through cast slots in case.
6) Remove countergear rear bearing snap ring from shaft and bearing. Using puller (J-8433-1) with bearing puller (J-22832), remove countergear rear bearing. *See Fig. 3.* Let countergear assembly rest on bottom of case.
7) Remove drive gear bearing outer race to case retaining ring. Remove drive gear and bearing by tapping gently on bottom side of drive gear shaft and

Manual Transmissions

GENERAL MOTORS 4-SPEED – 117 MM (Cont.)

Fig. 1: Exploded View of General Motors 117 MM Manual Transmission

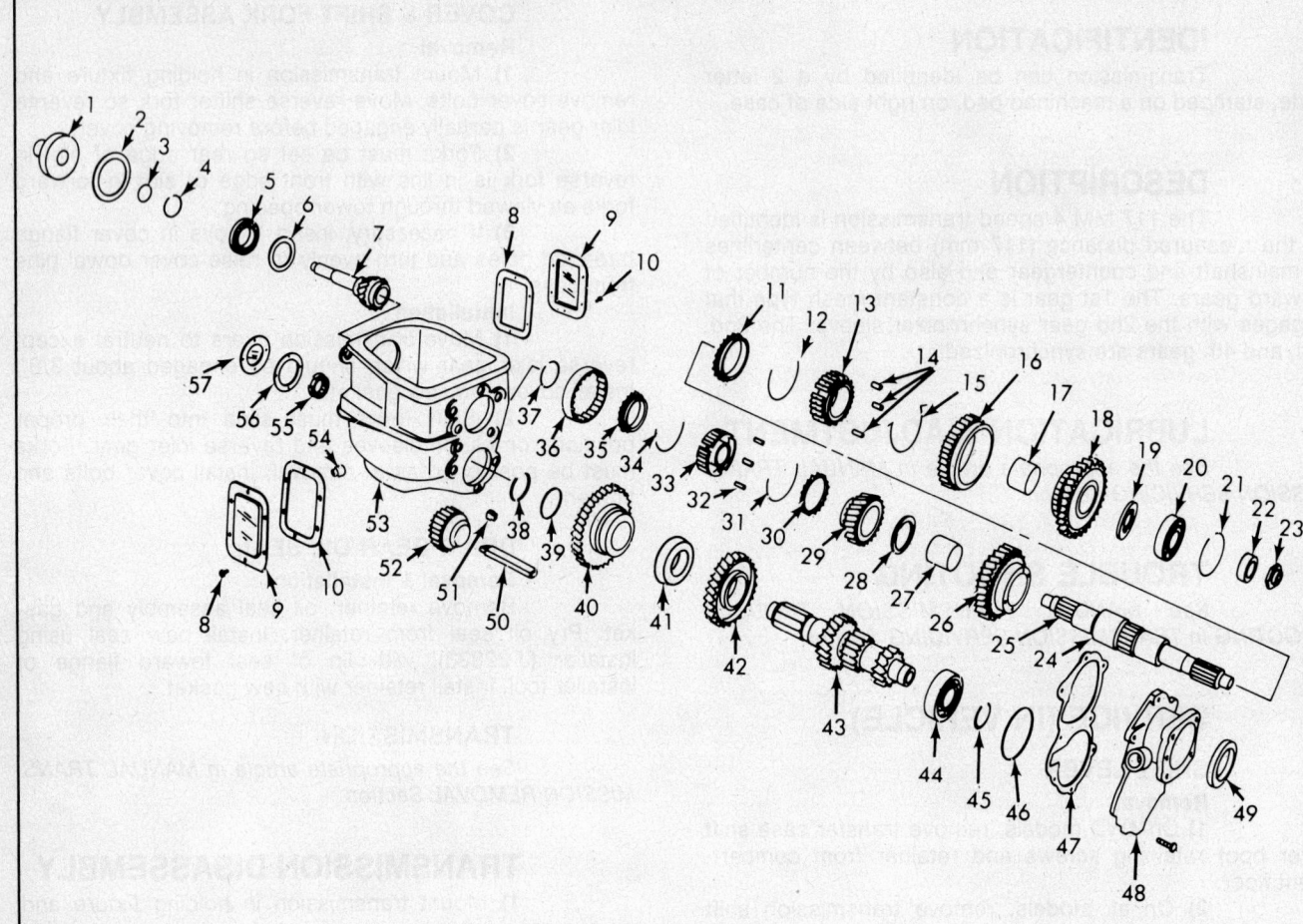

1. Drive Gear Bearing Retainer
2. Retainer Gasket
3. Lip Seal
4. Snap Ring
5. Drive Gear Bearing
6. Oil Slinger
7. Drive Gear & Pilot Bearings
8. Power Take-Off Cover Gasket
9. Power Take-Off Cover
10. Retaining Screws
11. 1st-2nd Gear Blocker Ring
12. Synchronizer Spring
13. 1st-2nd Gear Synchronizer Hub
14. Synchronizer Keys
15. Synchronizer Spring
16. Reverse Driven Gear
17. 1st Gear Bushing
18. 1st Gear
19. Thrust Washer
20. Rear Main Bearing
21. Bearing Snap Ring
22. Speedometer Gear
23. Rear Mainshaft Lock Nut
24. 2nd Gear Bushing (On Shaft)
25. Mainshaft
26. 2nd Gear
27. 3rd Gear Bushing
28. Thrust Washer
29. 3rd Gear
30. 3rd Gear Blocker Ring

31. Synchronizer Spring
32. Synchronizer Keys
33. 3rd-4th Synchronizer Hub
34. Synchronizer Spring
35. 3rd-4th Gear Blocker Ring
36. 3rd-4th Gear Synchronizer Sleeve
37. Snap Ring
38. Snap Ring
39. Thrust Washer
40. Clutch Countergear
41. Spacer
42. 3rd Gear Countergear
43. Countergear Shaft
44. Bearing
45. Snap Ring
46. Snap Ring
47. Rear Retainer Gasket
48. Rear Retainer
49. Lip Seal
50. Reverse Idler Shaft
51. Drain Plug
52. Reverse Idler Gear
53. Case
54. Fill Plug
55. Countergear Front Bearing
56. Gasket
57. Front Cover

GENERAL MOTORS 4-SPEED – 117 MM (Cont.)

prying directly opposite against case and bearing snap ring groove at the same time.

Fig. 2: Removing 4WD Mainshaft Rear Bearing Lock Nut

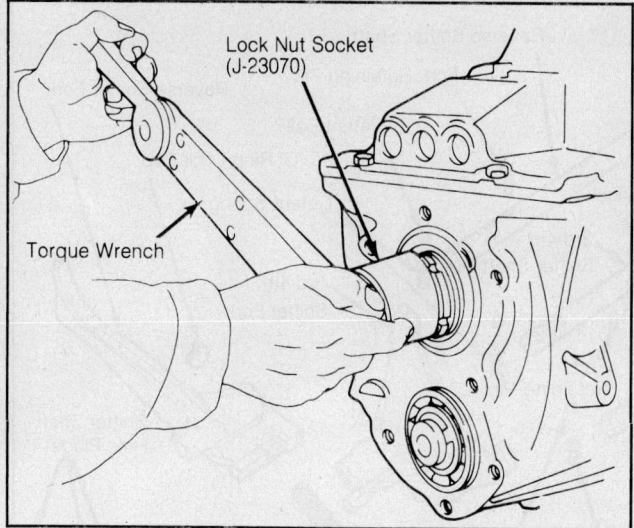

Fig. 3: Removing Rear Countergear Bearing

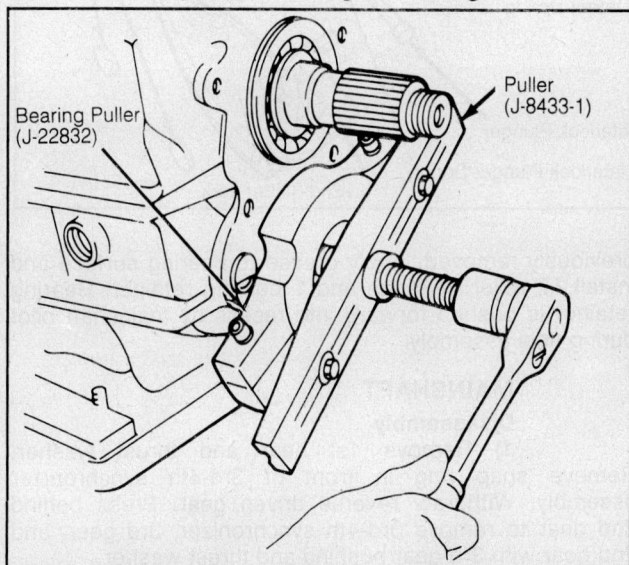

Let countergear rest on case for mainshaft removal.

8) Remove 4th gear synchronizer ring. Index cut-out section of drive gear in down position with countergear to obtain clearance for removing clutch gear. Remove rear mainshaft bearing retainer ring and using bearing remover, remove bearing from case.

9) Slide 1st gear thrust washer off mainshaft. Raise rear of mainshaft assembly and push rearward in case bore, swing front end and lift from case. Remove synchronizer cone from shaft.

10) Slide reverse idler gear rearward and move countergear rearward until front end is free of case, then lift to remove from case. Remove reverse idler gear, drive reverse idler gear shaft out of case from front to rear using a driver. Remove reverse idler gear from case.

11) Remove mainshaft rear bearing snap ring. Using puller (J-8433-1) and bearing remover (J-22832), remove bearing from case. Slide 1st gear thrust washer off mainshaft. Raise rear of mainshaft and move rearward.

12) Lift front of shaft up and out of case. Remove synchronizer cone from shaft. Slide reverse idler gear rearward and move countergear back until front end is free of case. Remove assembly. Drive reverse idler gear shaft out of case from front to rear, using a drift. Remove reverse idler gear.

CLEANING & INSPECTION

Wash case and all internal parts in solvent. Dry with compressed air. Check all parts for damage or excessive wear. Check bearings and synchronizers for rough operation. File off any burrs on mating surfaces. Replace damaged parts as necessary.

COMPONENT DISASSEMBLY & REASSEMBLY

COVER & SHIFT FORK ASSEMBLY

Disassembly

1) Drive out pins retaining 1st-2nd and 3rd-4th gear shifter forks to shifter shafts. Remove shaft expansion plugs. Note that pin retaining 3rd-4th gear shifter must be removed before removing shifter head pin. With shifter shafts in neutral position, drive shafts out of cover to remove shifter forks.

2) Ensure that detent balls, springs, and interlock pins are not lost as shifter shafts are removed. Drive out pin holding reverse shifter head and drive out shaft. Ensure that detent balls are not lost as they are under spring tension in rear rail boss holes.

Reassembly

1) Install shifter shafts in correct order. *See Fig. 4.* Install reverse shaft, 3rd-4th shaft, and 1st-2nd shaft. Place fork detent ball springs and balls in hole positions in cover. Start shafts into cover, depressing yoke detent balls with a small punch, and push shaft on over balls.

2) Starting with reverse shifter shaft, hold fork in position and push shaft through yoke. Install split pin in fork and shaft, position fork in neutral position.

3) Hold 3rd-4th fork in position and push shaft through yoke, but not through front support bore. Place 2 interlock balls between reverse and 3rd-4th shifter shafts in cross bore of front support boss. Install interlock pin in 3rd-4th shaft hole and grease to hold in place.

4) Push 3rd-4th shaft through fork and cover bore, keeping both balls and pin in fork and shaft. Position fork in neutral position. Place 2 interlock balls between 1st-2nd shaft and 3rd-4th shaft in cross bore of front support boss.

5) Hold 1st-2nd fork in position and push shaft through cover bore and fork until retainer hole and fork line up with hole in shaft. Install retainer pin and move to neutral position. Install new shaft hole expansion plugs.

DRIVE GEAR (INPUT SHAFT)

Disassembly

1) Remove mainshaft pilot bearing rollers (17) from drive gear if not already removed, and remove roller retainer. Do not remove snap ring on inside of drive gear.

2) Remove snap ring securing bearing on stem of drive gear. To remove bearing, position bearing support tool under bearing and using an arbor press, press gear and shaft out of bearing.

Manual Transmissions

GENERAL MOTORS 4-SPEED — 117 MM (Cont.)

Fig. 4: Exploded View of Cover and Shift Assembly

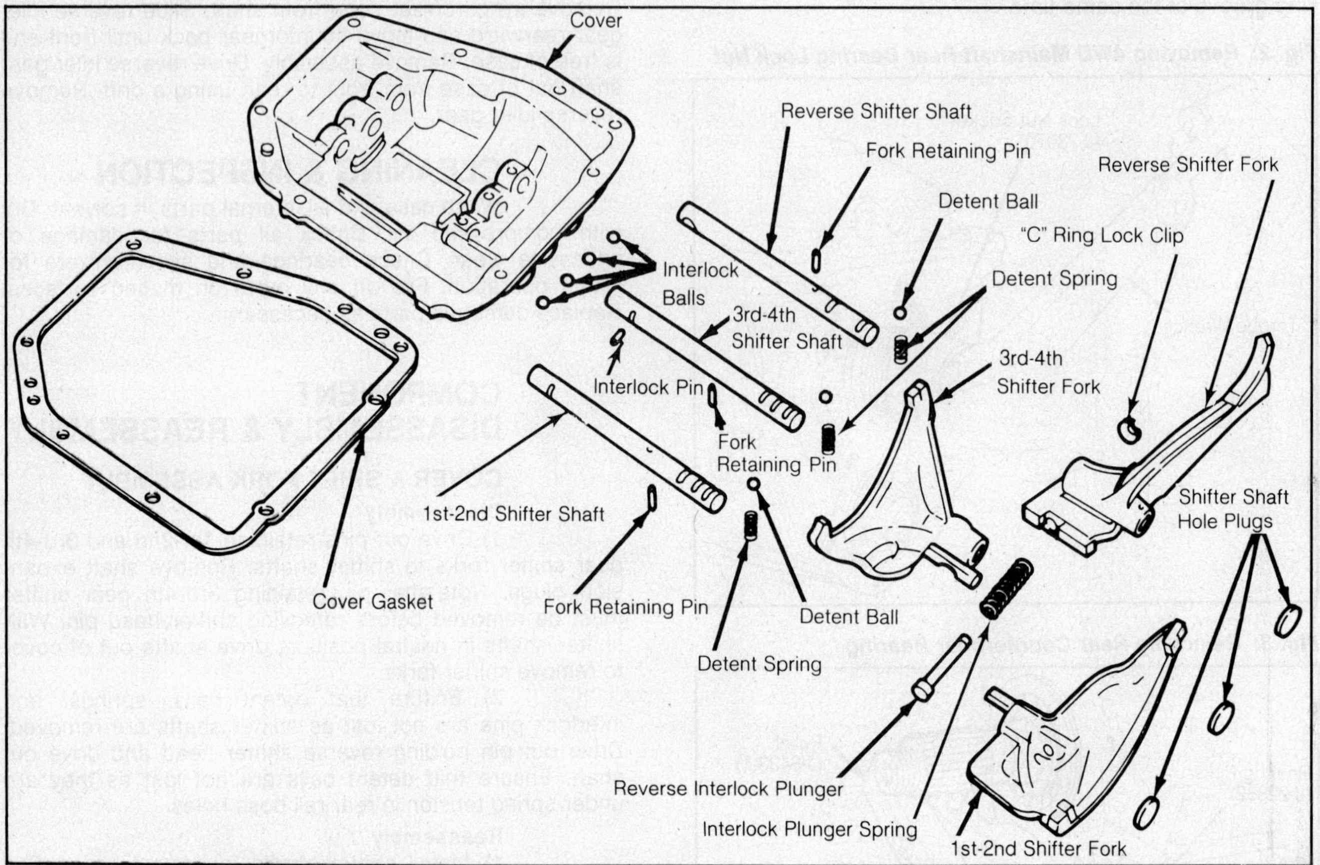

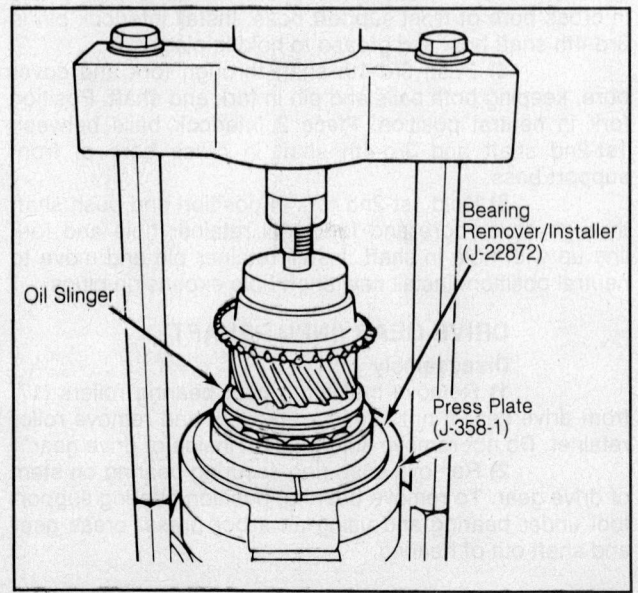

Reassembly

1) Press bearing and new oil slinger onto drive gear shaft. Slinger should be flush with bearing shoulder on drive gear. Install snap ring on shaft to secure bearing. Install bearing retainer ring in O.D. bearing groove. *See Fig. 5.*

2) Ensure bearing turns freely after installed on shaft. Install snap ring in mainshaft pilot bearing bore, if

Fig. 5: Installing Drive Gear Bearing

Oil Slinger

Bearing Remover/Installer (J-22872)

Press Plate (J-358-1)

previously removed. Apply grease to bearing surface and install 17 roller bearings and 1 bearing retainer. Bearing retainer is pushed forward into recess by mainshaft pilot during final assembly.

MAINSHAFT

Disassembly

1) Remove 1st gear and thrust washer. Remove snap ring in front of 3rd-4th synchronizer assembly. Withdraw reverse driven gear. Press behind 2nd gear to remove 3rd-4th synchronizer, 3rd gear, and 2nd gear with 3rd gear bushing and thrust washer.

2) Remove 2nd gear synchronizer ring. Support 2nd gear synchronizer hub on front face and press mainshaft through, removing 1st gear bushing and 2nd gear synchronizer hub. Split 2nd gear bushing with a chisel and remove bushing from shaft.

Reassembly

1) Bushing for 1st, 2nd, and 3rd gears are sintered iron and care should be taken when installing to prevent damaged. Lubricate all bushings with oil before installing gears. Press 2nd gear onto mainshaft until it bottoms on shoulder.

2) Press 1st-2nd synchronizer hub onto mainshaft until it bottoms on shoulder. Install 1st-2nd synchronizer keys and springs, if removed. Using arbor press and driver (J-22873), press 1st gear bushing on mainshaft until it bottoms against hub.

3) Install synchronizer blocker ring and 2nd gear on mainshaft, against synchronizer hub. Index synchronizer key slots with keys in hub. Install 3rd gear thrust washer on mainshaft with tang in slot on shaft and

Fig. 6: Disassembling Mainshaft

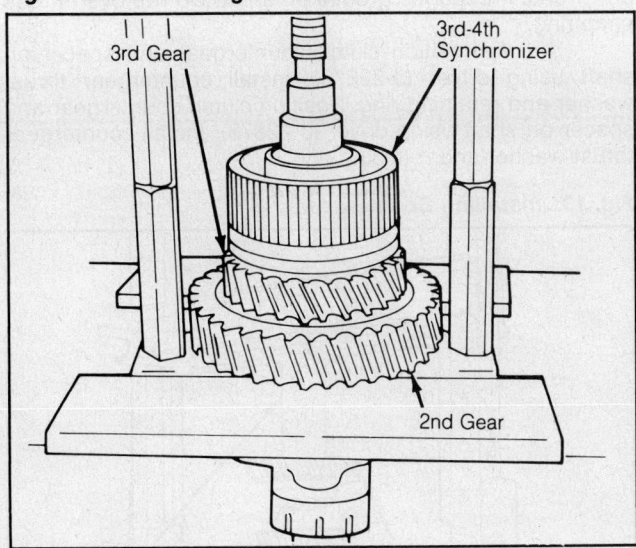

The 3rd gear should be a running fit on mainshaft.

Fig. 7: Installing 2nd Gear Bushing

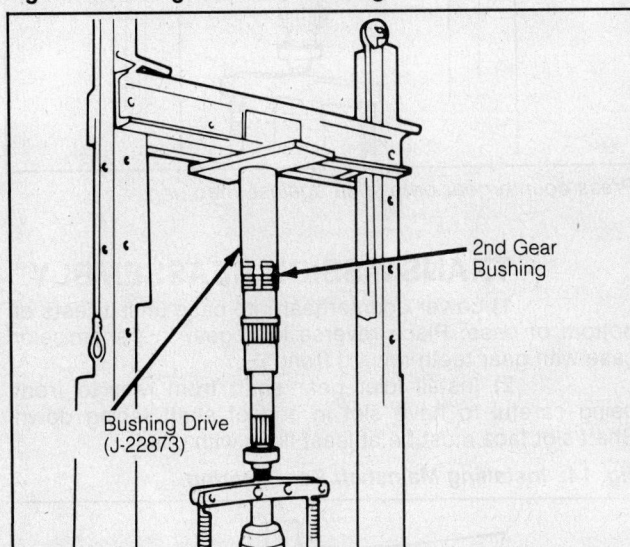

Bushing should bottom on mainshaft shoulder.

Fig. 8: Installing 1st Gear Bushing

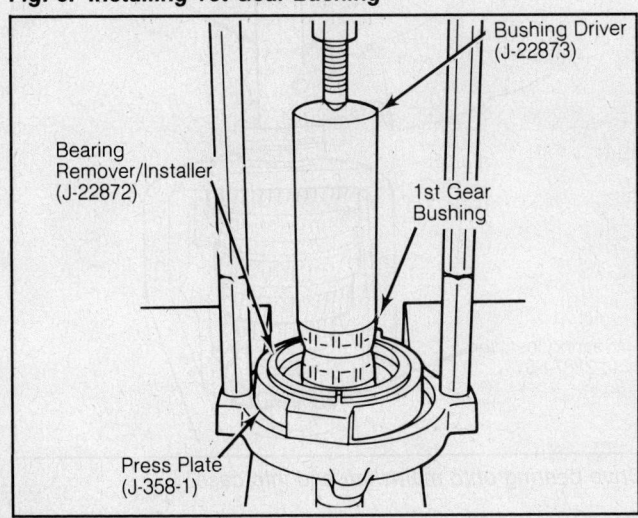

Bushing must bottom against hub.

against 2nd gear bushing. Press 3rd gear bushing on mainshaft using arbor press and driver (J-22875), until it bottoms thrust washer. *See Fig. 9 .*

Fig. 9: Installing 3rd Gear Bushing

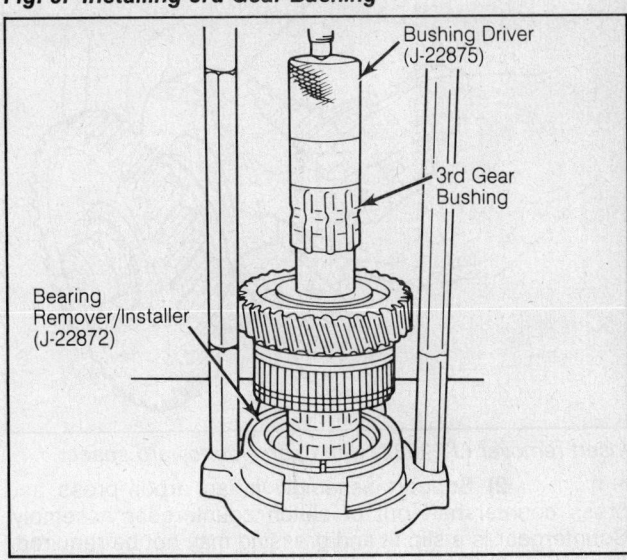

Bushing must bottom on thrust washer.

   4) Install 3rd gear and 3rd synchronizer blocker ring on mainshaft, against 3rd gear thrust washer. Index synchronizer ring key slots with keys. Using arbor press and driver (J-22875), press 3rd-4th synchronizer hub assembly onto mainshaft and against 3rd gear with bushing thrust face toward 3rd gear.

   5) Retain synchronizer assembly with snap ring. Install reverse driven gear with fork groove toward rear. Install 1st gear on mainshaft and against 1st-2nd synchronizer hub. Install 1st gear thrust washer.

Fig. 10: Installing 3rd-4th Synchronizer

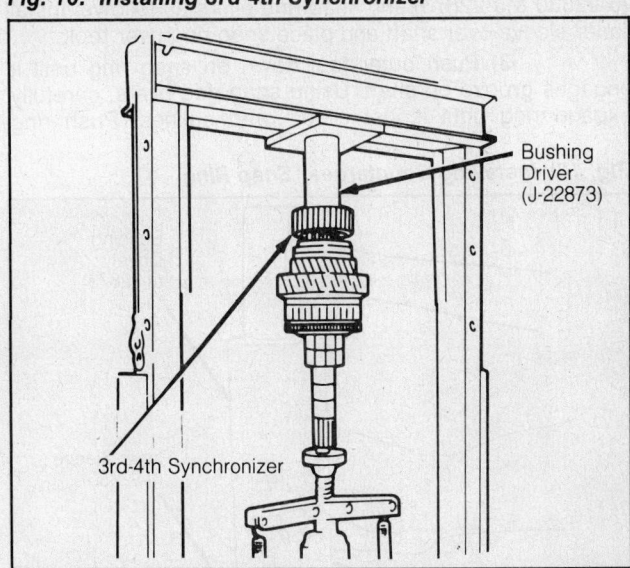

Press assembly onto mainshaft using driver (J-22875).

COUNTERSHAFT
Disassembly
   1) Remove front countergear shaft snap ring and thrust washer. Discard snap ring. Install press plates (J-22832) on countershaft with open side to spacer. *See Fig. 11.*

Fig. 11: Removing Countergear

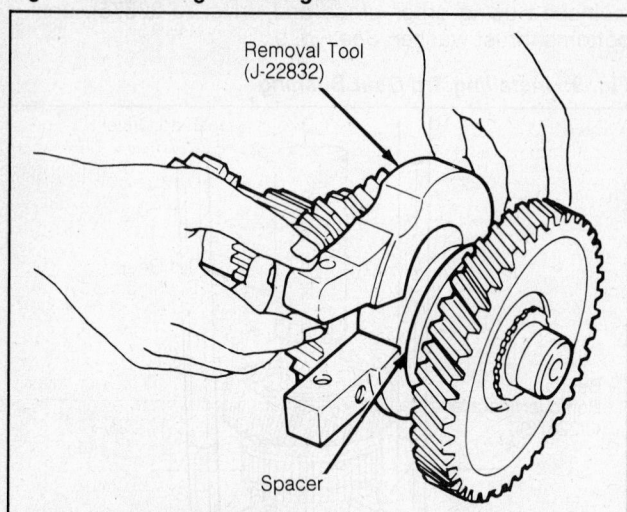

Insert remover (J-22832) with open side toward spacer.

2) Support assembly in an arbor press and press countershaft out of clutch countergear assembly. Countergear is a slip fit and pressing may not be required.

3) Remove clutch countergear rear retaining ring and discard. Remove and discard 3rd gear countergear retaining ring. Position assembly on an arbor press and press shaft from 3rd speed gear.

Reassembly

1) Position 3rd gear countergear on shaft with undercut surface toward front of shaft. Press gear on shaft with arbor press using a minimum force of 1500 lbs. (680 kg). If gear can be installed with less than 1500 lbs. (680 kg), replace gear.

2) Install spacer and press front gear on countershaft. Using snap ring pliers, install snap ring. Install new countergear rear snap ring using sleeve tools (J-22830 & J-22873) and snap ring pliers as follows: Install inner sleeve over shaft and place snap ring over tool.

3) Push outer tool down on snap ring until it engages groove on shaft. Using snap ring pliers, carefully expand ring until it just slides onto splines. Push ring

Fig. 12: Installing Countergear Snap Ring

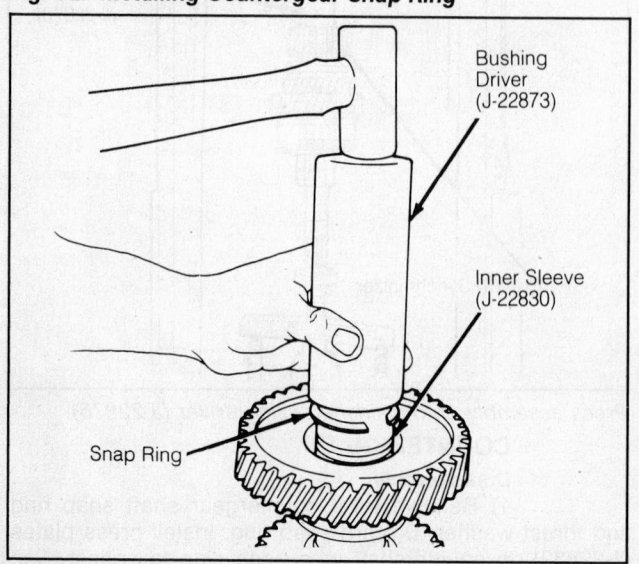

down until it engages groove on shaft. Do not over-stress snap ring.

4) Position clutch countergear and spacer on shaft using driver (J-22873). Install countergear thrust washer and retaining ring. Position clutch countergear and spacer on shaft using driver (J-22873). Install countergear thrust washer and retaining ring.

Fig. 13: Installing Countergear

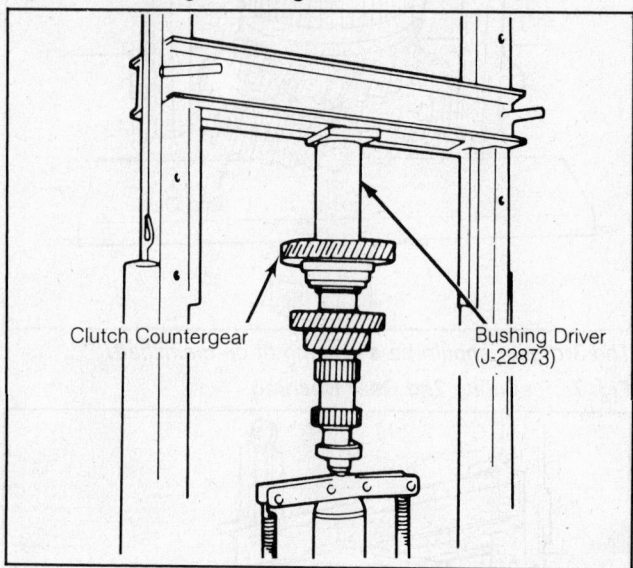

Press countergear onto shaft against snap ring.

TRANSMISSION REASSEMBLY

1) Lower countergear into case until it rests on bottom of case. Place reverse idler gear in transmission case with gear teeth toward front.

2) Install idler gear shaft from rear to front, being careful to have slot in end of shaft facing down. Shaft slot face must be at least flush with case.

Fig. 14: Installing Mainshaft Rear Bearing

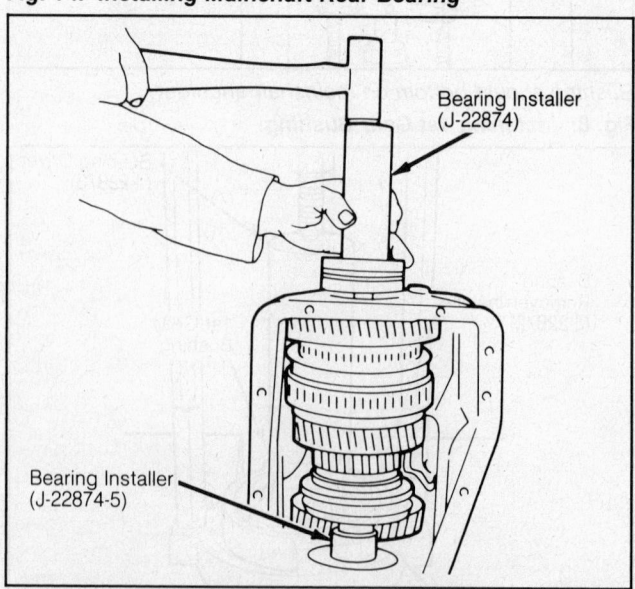

Drive bearing onto mainshaft and into case.

GENERAL MOTORS 4-SPEED – 117 MM (Cont.)

3) Install mainshaft assembly into case with rear of shaft protruding out rear bearing hole in case. Position installer tool (J-22874) in clutch gear case opening and engage front mainshaft. Rotate case onto front end. *See Fig. 14.*

4) Install 1st gear thrust washer on shaft, if not previously installed. Install snap ring on bearing outside diameter and position rear mainshaft bearing on shaft.

5) Using driver (J-22874-1), seat bearing on shaft and into case. Rotate case and remove tool. Install synchronizer cone on pilot end of mainshaft and slide rearward to clutch hub.

6) Make sure the 3 cut-out sections of 4th gear synchronizer cone align with 3 clutch keys in clutch assembly. Install snap ring on drive gear bearing outside diameter.

7) Index cut-out portion of drive gear teeth to obtain clearance over countershaft drive gear teeth. Start clutch gear, then tap bearing outer race with mallet.

8) Install drive gear bearing retainer using a new gasket. Install and tighten bolts. Install countergear front support (J-22874-10) into countergear front bearing opening in case. Rotate case onto front end. *See Fig. 15.*

Fig. 15: Installing Rear Countergear Bearing

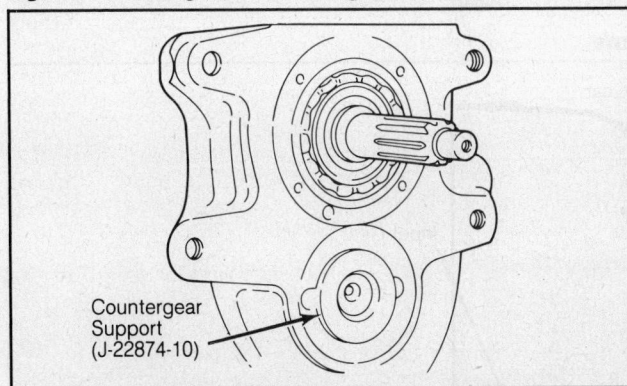

Countergear Support (J-22874-10)

Use bearing support to secure front of countergear shaft when installing rear countergear bearing.

9) Install snap ring on O.D. of countergear rear bearing. Position bearing on countergear and using driver (J-22874-1), seat bearing. *See Fig. 16.* Rotate case, install snap ring on countershaft at rear bearing and remove tool.

10) Tap countergear front bearing assembly into case. Install countergear front bearing cap and new gasket. Slide speedometer drive gear over mainshaft to bearing.

11) Install rear bearing retainer with new gasket. Be sure snap ring ends are in lube slot and cut-out in bearing retainer. Install bolts and tighten. Install brake backing plate assembly on models equipped with propeller shaft brake.

12) On 4WD models, install rear lock nut and washer using lock nut remover/installer (J-23070). *See Fig. 2.* Tighten lock nut and bend washer tangs to fit slots in nut.

13) Install parking brake drum and/or universal joint flange. Apply light coat of oil to seal surface. Lock transmission in 2 gears at once. Install universal joint flange lock nut and tighten.

Fig. 16: Installing Rear Countergear Bearing

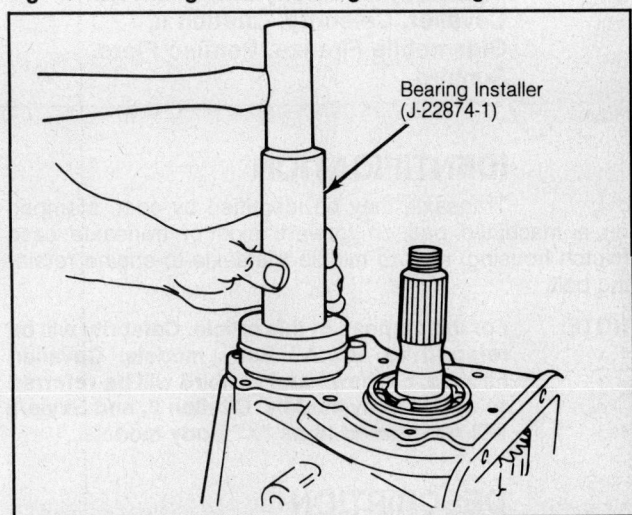

Bearing Installer (J-22874-1)

TIGHTENING SPECIFICATIONS

Application	Ft. Lbs. (N.m)
Cover-to-Case Bolts	20 (27)
Crossmember-to-Frame Nuts	55 (75)
Crossmember-to-Mount Bolts	40 (55)
Drain & Filler Plug	30 (40)
Drive Gear Bearing Retainer-to-Case Bolts	25 (34)
Extension and Retainer-to-Case Bolts	
Upper	20 (27)
Lower	30 (40)
Shift Lever-to-Shifter Shaft Nut	20 (27)

Manual Transmissions

GENERAL MOTORS 4-SPEED MANUAL TRANSAXLE

**Buick Skyhawk, Skylark, Chevrolet
Cavalier, Celebrity, Citation II,
Oldsmobile Firenza, Pontiac Fiero,
Sunbird**

IDENTIFICATION

Transaxle may be identified by code stamped on a machined pad on forward side of transaxle case (clutch housing) next to middle transaxle-to-engine retaining bolt.

NOTE: For the purpose of this article, Celebrity will be referred to as "A" Body models. Cavalier, Firenza, Skyhawk and Sunbird will be referred to as "J" Body models. Citation II, and Skylark will be referred to as "X" Body models.

DESCRIPTION

Final drive and 4-speed transmission are mounted in a common 2-piece aluminum case. Transmission is fully synchronized in all forward gears. Forward gears are helically cut and in constant mesh. Reverse gears are spur cut and are engaged by sliding reverse idler gear. Fourth gear is indirect (overdrive).

The input gear, output gear and differential assembly are all supported by preloaded tapered roller bearings. Final output gear with its integral shaft, turns ring gear and differential assembly, drive axles and front wheel assemblies. *See Fig. 1.*

Gears are shifted by 2 cable assemblies, the trans-selector and trans-shifter cables.

SERVICE (IN VEHICLE)

TRANSAXLE MOUNTS

To check mounts, raise vehicle on hoist. Push up and pull down on transaxle case, observing mounts as you do. If rubber separates from metal plate or mount, or if case moves up but not down, replace mount.

DRIVE AXLE SHAFTS

CAUTION: DO NOT move vehicle, or allow the weight of the vehicle, to rest on the wheels and hubs, without the hub nut installed to proper torque. Damage to the ball bearings and races may occur.

Fig. 1: Cutaway View of General Motors 4-Speed Manual Transaxle

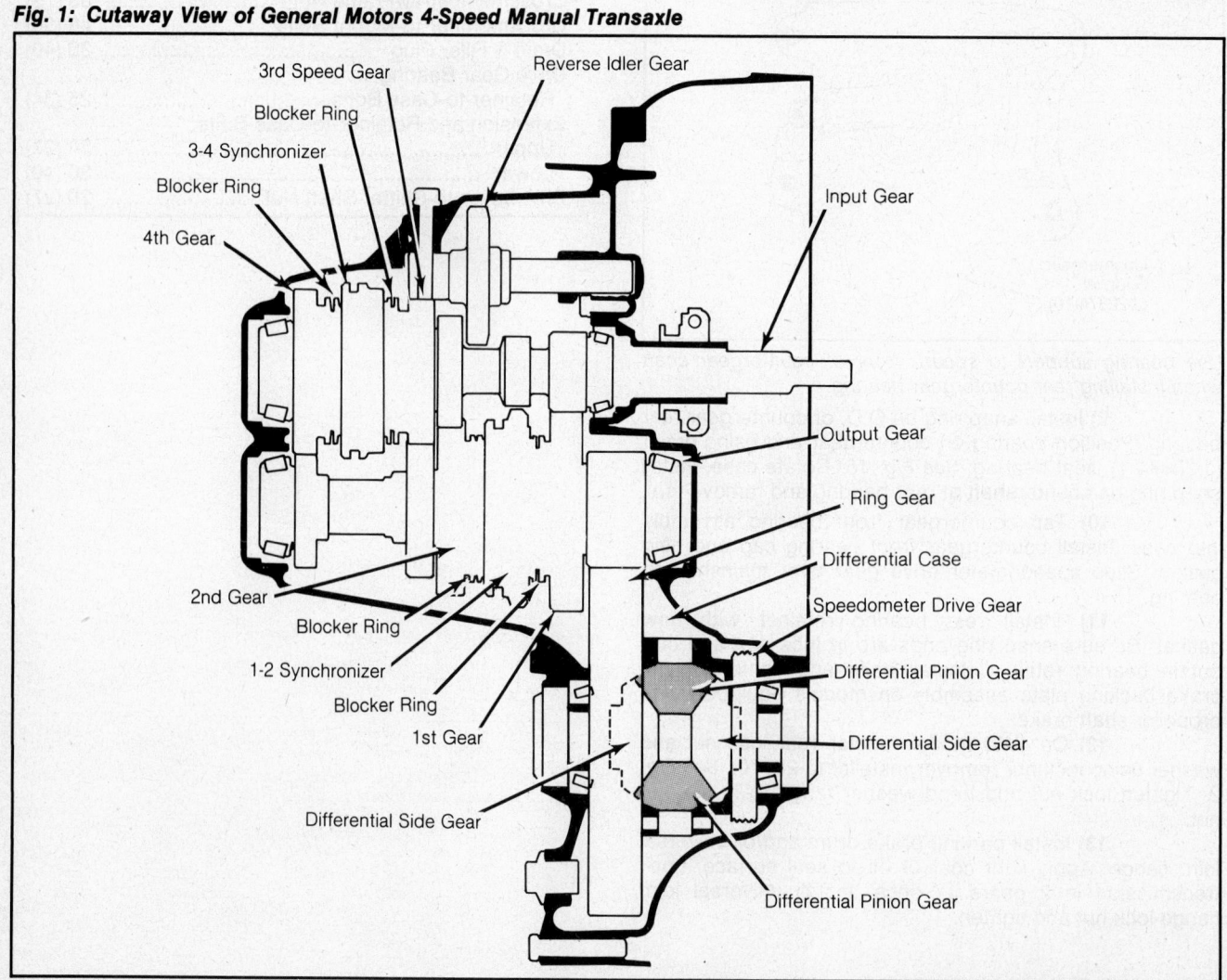

GENERAL MOTORS 4-SPEED MANUAL TRANSAXLE (Cont.)

Fig. 2: Removing Drive Axles from Transaxles

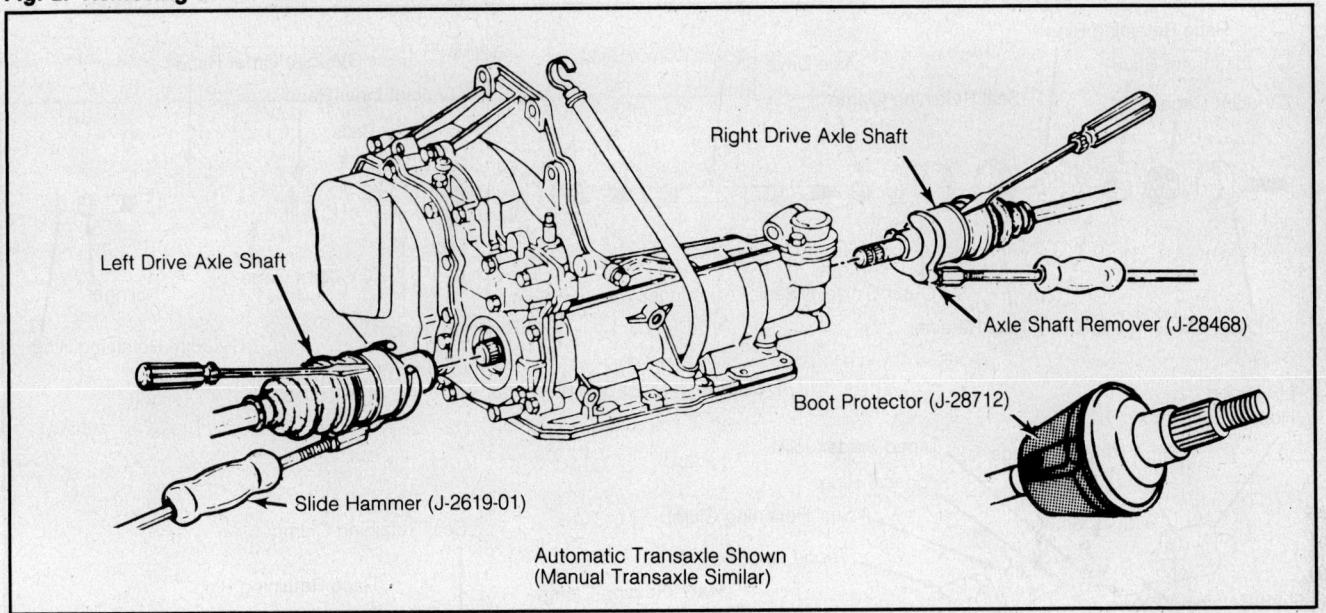

Right Drive Axle Shaft

Left Drive Axle Shaft

Axle Shaft Remover (J-28468)

Boot Protector (J-28712)

Slide Hammer (J-2619-01)

Automatic Transaxle Shown
(Manual Transaxle Similar)

Removal

1) Remove hub nut with washer. Raise and support vehicle. Remove wheels and tires. Install boot seal protectors (J-28712) for all outer CV joints, boot protectors (J-33162) for all Tripod inner joints and boot protectors (J-28712) for all Double Offset joints. *See Fig. 2.*

NOTE: **Boot protectors are only required on silicone (gray) boots, generally right inner CV joint. All other boots are made of thermoplastic material (black) and do not require boot protectors.**

2) Remove brake caliper and rotor. On "A" and "X" models disconnect brake line clip at stut. Support caliper out of way. If necessary, mark strut-to-steering knuckle relation to insure proper camber alignment on reassembly. Remove strut-to-steering knuckle mount bolts/nuts. Separate strut from knuckle. If necessary, detach stabilizer bar/tie rod from steering knuckle/lower control arm.

3) On all models, pull steering knuckle assembly out of strut bracket. Using slide hammer type puller with special tool (J-28468 or J-33008 with J-29749), pull drive axle from transaxle. *See Fig. 2.* Support drive axle end with wire.

NOTE: **Support Tripod joint in level position when handling drive axle. If allowed to hang, weight of housing can separate it from spider bearing assembly.**

4) With axle shaft supported, remove clamp bolt from lower control arm ball stud. Separate knuckle from lower control arm. Pull strut, knuckle and caliper assembly away from body and secure in this position.

5) Using spindle remover (J-28733), remove axle shaft from hub and bearing assembly. *See Fig. 3..* Remove drive axle for vehicle.

Disassembly (Double Offset)

1) Procedure is similar for outer CV joints and inner Double Offset joints. *See Figs. 4 and 5.* For Tripod Joint disassembly, *See Figs. 4 and 6.* If equipped with

Fig. 3: Removing Axle Shaft from Hub and Bearing

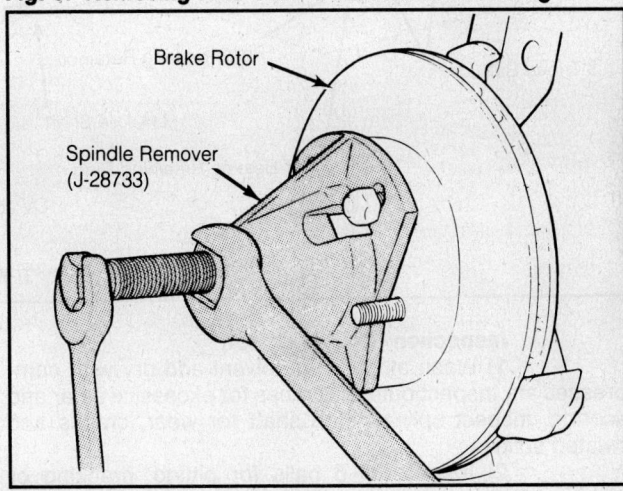

Brake Rotor

Spindle Remover
(J-28733)

rubber deflector ring, remove by pulling from groove of outer race and discard.

2) If equipped with steel deflector ring, remove by tapping off with brass drift. Using side cutters, cut seal retainer clamp on small end of seal and discard. Using brass drift, tap lightly around edge of seal retainer to remove retainer from CV joint assembly. Spread snap ring and pull shaft from joint assembly.

3) For outer CV joint, use brass drift to tap lightly on bearing cage until it tilts enough to remove one ball bearing. Rotate cage and repeat procedure to remove remaining balls from cage.

4) To remove inner cage and race, pivot components until 90° to normal installed position is obtained (cage windows will align with lands of outer race). *See Fig. 5, No. 5.* Lift cage and inner race from outer race. Rotate inner race upward and out of cage.

5) On inner Double Offset joint, remove components as previously described. Remove ball race retaining ring. Balls will come out when cage and inner race are removed from outer race.

Manual Transmissions

GENERAL MOTORS 4-SPEED MANUAL TRANSAXLE (Cont.)

Fig. 4: Exploded View of Constant Velocity Joints

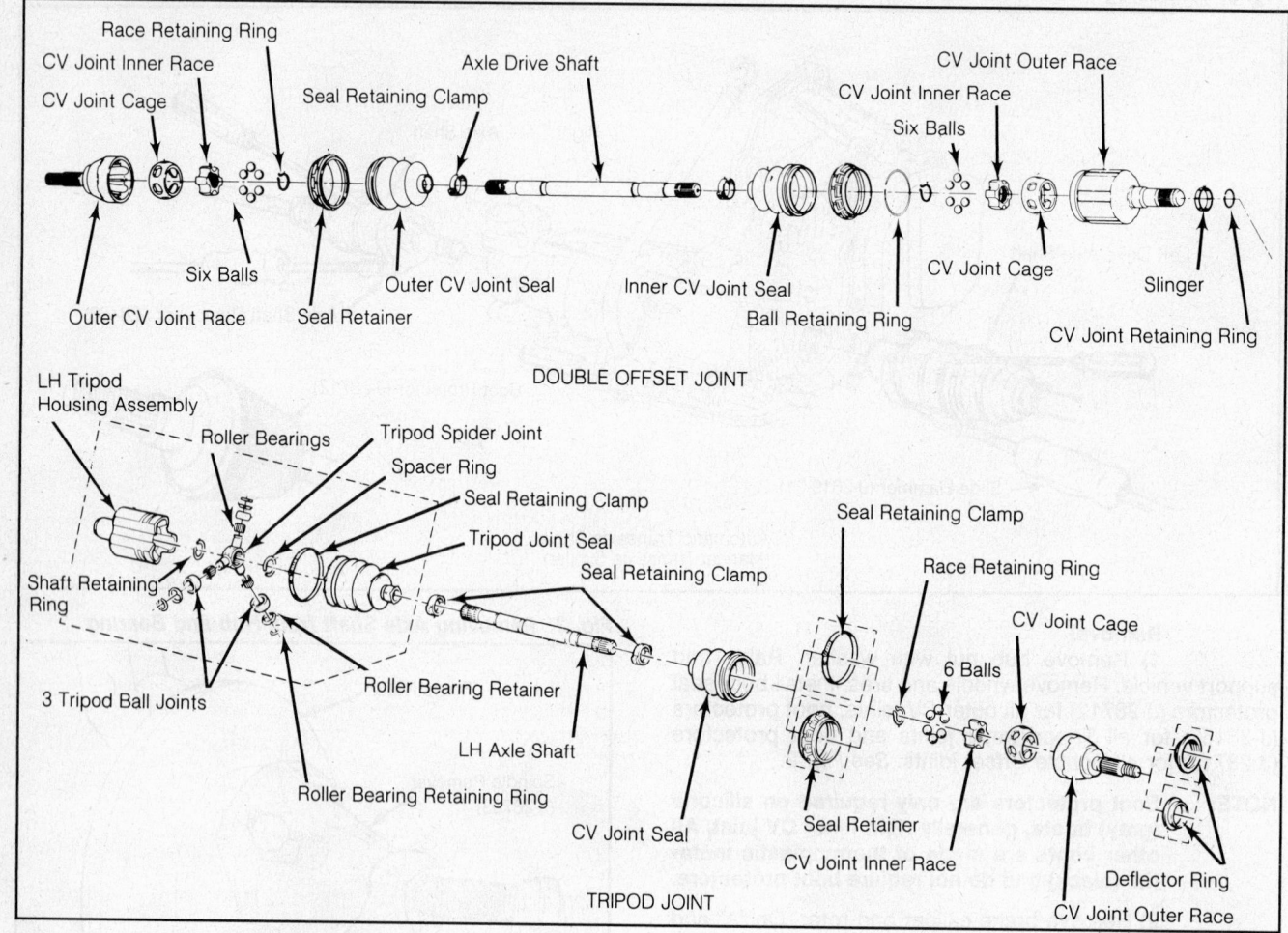

DOUBLE OFFSET JOINT

TRIPOD JOINT

Inspection (Double Offset)

1) Wash all parts in solvent and dry with compressed air. Inspect outer ball races for excessive wear and scoring. Inspect splined stub shaft for wear, cracks and twisted splines.

2) Inspect all 6 balls for pitting, cracking or scoring. Dulling of surface is normal. Inspect cage for excessive wear on inside and outside spherical surfaces. Look for heavy brinelling of cage windows. Check components for cracks or chips.

3) Inspect inner race for excessive wear or scoring. If any damage is found, replace entire CV or Double Offset joint assembly. Polished areas in races and on cage spheres are normal and do not require joint replacement.

Inspection (Tripod)

Inspect drive axle boot for tears or excessive wear. Check spider assembly for worn or damaged needle bearings. Inspect snap rings, spacer ring and drive shaft grooves for excessive wear. Replace components as necessary. If drive axle is replaced, install new knuckle seal.

Reassembly

1) Apply a light coat of grease on ball grooves of inner and outer races. Install inner race into cage using a rotating action opposite of removal. Inner race snap ring should face axle side.

2) On inner CV joints, be sure ball bearing retaining ring is installed on inner race side facing small end of cage. Align windows of cage with outer race lands. Pivot cage with inner race into tilted position (opposite of removal).

3) Install ball bearings, one at a time, into outer CV joint as cage is tilted and rotated. On inner CV joint, insert ball bearings through cage windows. After balls are installed into cage of outer joint, pivot cage and inner race into installed position.

4) On Tripod Joints, slide spider gear onto axle with counter bore facing inner (transaxle) end of shaft. Install shaft retaining ring. Install inner and outer boot seal protectors.

5) Slide new seal clamp (for small end of boot seal), boot seal and seal retainer onto axle shaft. Coat inside lip (large diameter end) of seal with grease. Slide seal retainer on end of seal. Spread ears of bearing race snap ring and slide CV joint onto axle shaft until snap ring seats in groove.

6) Pack joint with approximately one-half grease provided in seal kit. Apply remaining grease inside seal. Slide seal toward joint until small end of seal is in groove in axle shaft. Position small clamp over small end of seal and into groove and tighten.

7) Place assembly vertically into an arbor press, with joint up so seal retainer is supported. See Fig. 5, No. 7.

Fig. 5: Disassembly of Drive Shaft Assembly With Double Offset and CV Joints

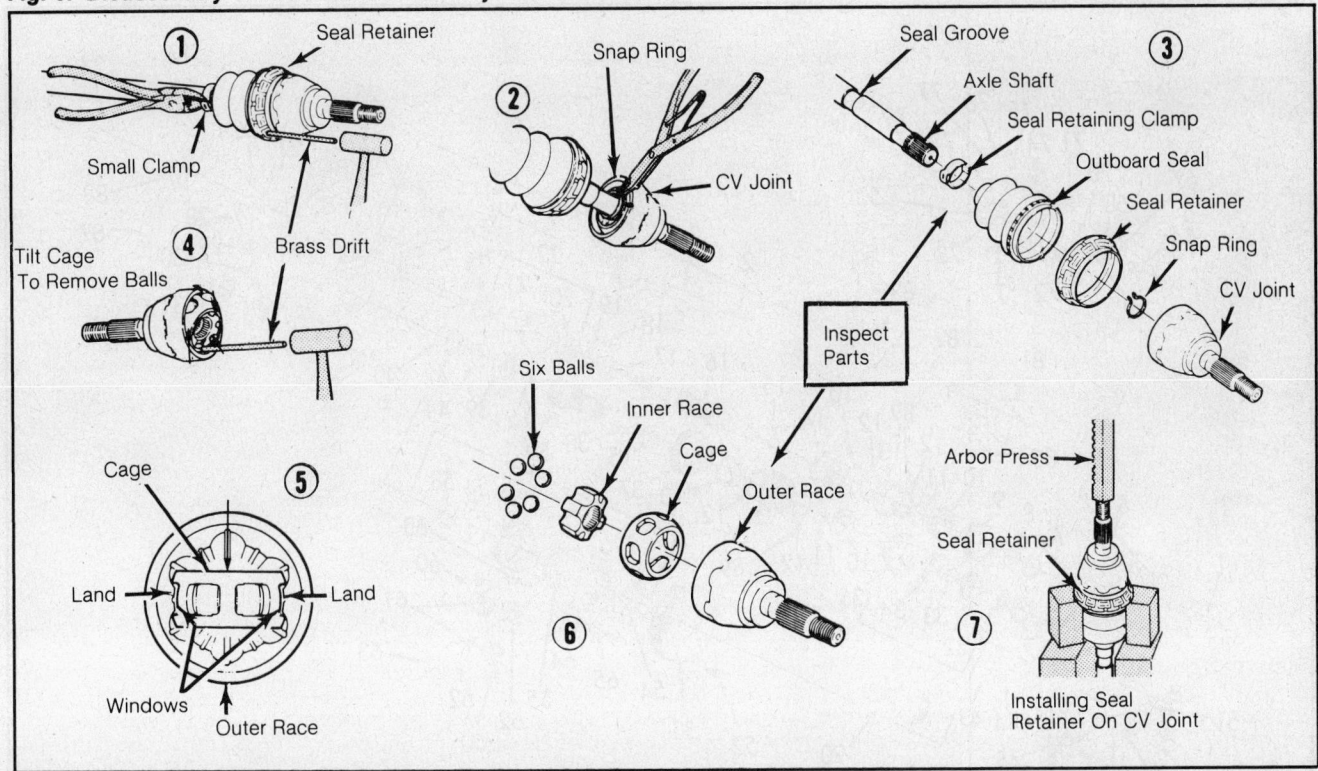

The outer CV joint is illustrated, the inner Double Offset joint is similar.

Press joint down onto retainer. Ensure seal stays on retainer during reassembly. If equipped, stretch rubber deflector ring and set in groove.

8) Install steel deflector ring using 2 1/2" pipe coupling over ring. Install a .118" (3 mm) sheet steel plate with .945" (24 mm) drilled hole (in center) over drive shaft end. Install nut on drive shaft end and tighten until ring seats in position.

Fig. 6: View of Tripod Joint

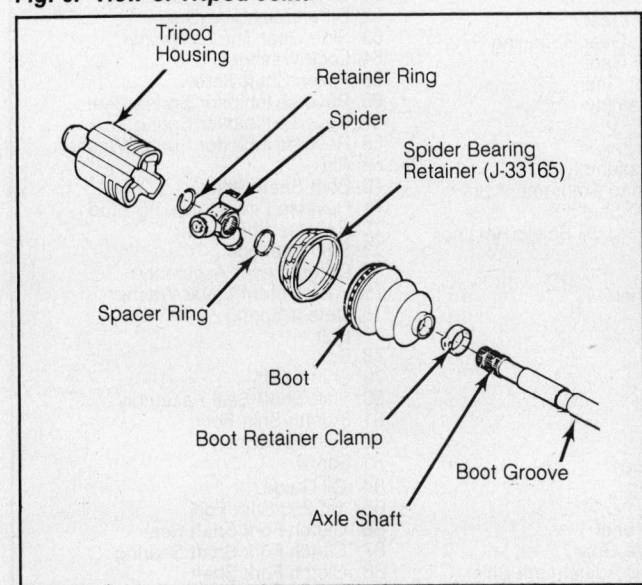

Installation

1) Position drive axle loosely into steering knuckle and transaxle. Install steering knuckle onto strut bracket. Tighten strut bracket bolts fingertight only. Assemble stabilizer bar/tie rod as necessary.

2) Install rotor and brake caliper. Tighten mount bolts. Install drive axle through steering knuckle. Insert a drift in rotor slot to prevent hub from turning. Install hub nut and partially tighten.

3) Seat drive axle at transaxle using a screwdriver in groove provided on inner retainer. *See Fig. 2.* Tap screwdriver until shaft is seated. Connect brake line clip to strut. Install wheel and tires. Lower vehicle and retighten hub nut to final torque.

REMOVAL & INSTALLATION

See appropriate MANUAL TRANSMISSION REMOVAL article in DOMESTIC GENERAL SERVICING section.

DISASSEMBLY

TRANSAXLE

1) Place transaxle assembly into work stand (J-28408) to prevent assembly from falling over. Remove 15 bolts retaining clutch cover.

2) Using soft mallet, tap clutch cover from case. *See Fig. 8.* Remove ring gear and differential assembly.

Fig. 7: Exploded View of General Motors 4-Speed Manual Transaxle

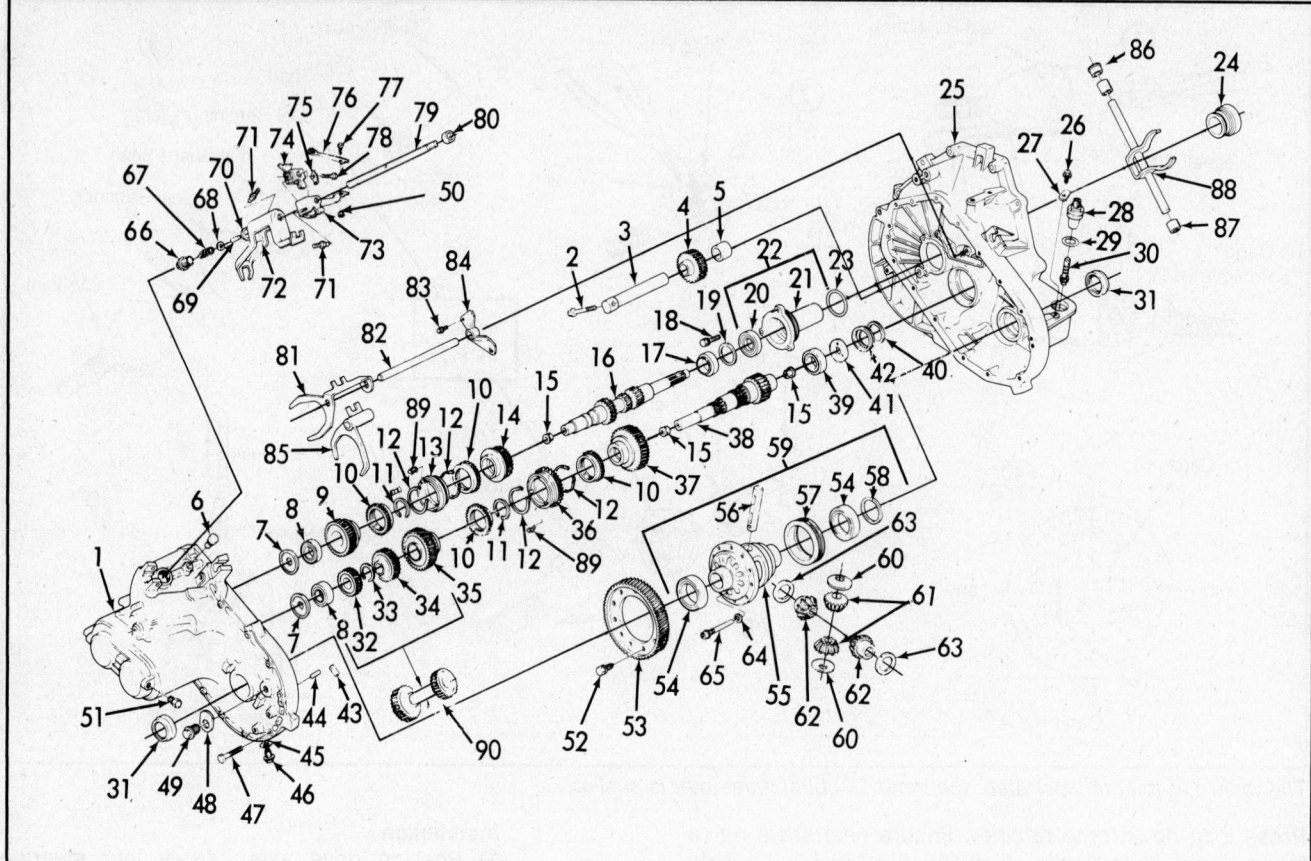

1. Transaxle Case	31. Axle Shaft Seal	61. Differential Pinion Gear
2. Reverse Idler Screw	32. 4th Speed Output Gear	62. Differential Side Gear
3. Reverse Idler Shaft	33. 3rd Speed Output Gear Retaining Ring	63. Side Gear Thrust Washer
4. Reverse Idler Gear	34. 3rd Speed Output Gear	64. Lock Washer
5. Reverse Idler Shaft Spacer	35. 2nd Speed Output Gear	65. Pinion Shaft Screw
6. Vent Assembly	36. Synchronizer Assembly	66. Reverse Inhibitor Spring Seat
7. Oil Shield	37. 1st Gear Output	67. Reverse Inhibitor Spring
8. Bearing Assembly	38. Output Gear	68. Reverse Inhibitor Spring Washer
9. 4th Gear Input	39. Output Bearing Assembly	69. Pin
10. Synchronizer Blocking Ring	40. Output Gear Bearing Adjustment Shim	70. Shift Shaft Shim
11. Synchronizer Retaining Ring	41. Output Bearing Oil Shield	71. Reverse Lever Locating Stud
12. Synchronizer Key Retaining Ring	42. Output Gear Bearing Oil Shield Retainer	72. Reverse Shift Lever
13. Synchronizer Assembly	43. Magnet	73. Shift Interlock
14. 3rd Gear Input	44. Pin	74. Detent Lever Assembly
15. Oil Shield Sleeve	45. Drain Screw Washer	75. Lock Detent Lever Washer
16. Input Cluster Gear	46. Drain Screw	76. Detent Spring
17. Input Bearing Assembly	47. Bolt	77. Bolt
18. Screw	48. Fill Plug Washer	78. Bolt
19. Input Gear Bearing Adjustment Shim	49. Fill Plug	79. Shift Shaft
20. Input Gear Seal Assembly	50. Nut	80. Shift Shaft Seal Assembly
21. Input Gear Retainer	51. Plug	81. 3rd-4th Shift Fork
22. Input Gear Bearing Retainer Assembly	52. Bolt	82. Shift Fork Shaft
23. Input Gear Bearing Retainer Seal	53. Differential Ring Gear	83. Screw
24. Clutch Release Bearing Assembly	54. Differential Bearing	84. Oil Guide
25. Clutch & Differential Housing	55. Differential Case	85. 1st-2nd Shift Fork
26. Screw	56. Differential Pinion Shaft	86. Clutch Fork Shaft Seal
27. Speedometer Gear Retainer	57. Speedometer Drive Gear	87. Clutch Fork Shaft Bearing
28. Speedometer Driven Gear Sleeve	58. Differential Bearing Adjustment Shim	88. Clutch Fork Shaft
29. Speedometer Gear Sleeve Seal	59. Differential Assembly	89. Synchronizer Keys
30. Speedometer Driven Gear	60. Pinion Thrust Washer	90. 3rd & 4th Output Gear (MX6 ONLY)

GENERAL MOTORS 4-SPEED MANUAL TRANSAXLE (Cont.)

Fig. 8: Transaxle with Clutch Cover Removed

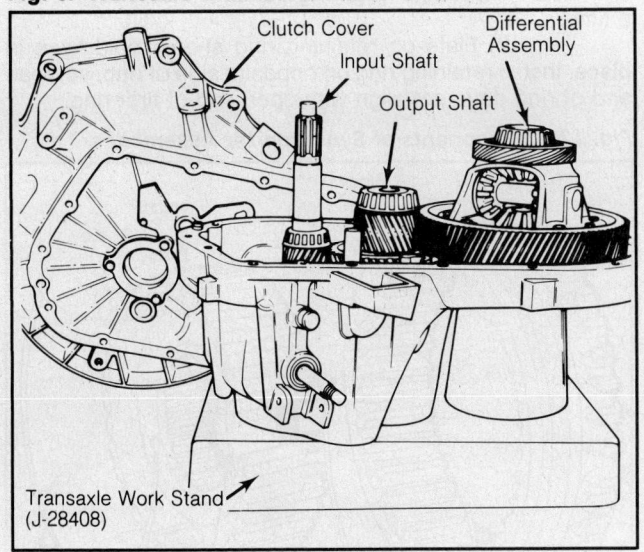

Clutch Cover
Input Shaft
Differential Assembly
Output Shaft
Transaxle Work Stand (J-28408)

3) Position shifter shaft in neutral position, so shifter moves easily and is not engaged in any drive gear. Remove bolt from shifter shaft. Remove shaft and shift forks from synchronizer forks.

4) Remove reverse shift fork by disengaging it from guide pin and interlock bracket. Remove the lock bolt securing the reverse idler gear shaft. Remove the gear, shaft and spacer assembly.

5) Remove detent shift lever and interlock assembly. Leave shift forks engaged with synchronizers. Grasp input and output shafts and lift them from transaxle case as an assembly. See Fig. 9. After noting shift fork positions for reassembly reference, remove shift forks.

Fig. 9: Input and Output Shafts With Shift Forks

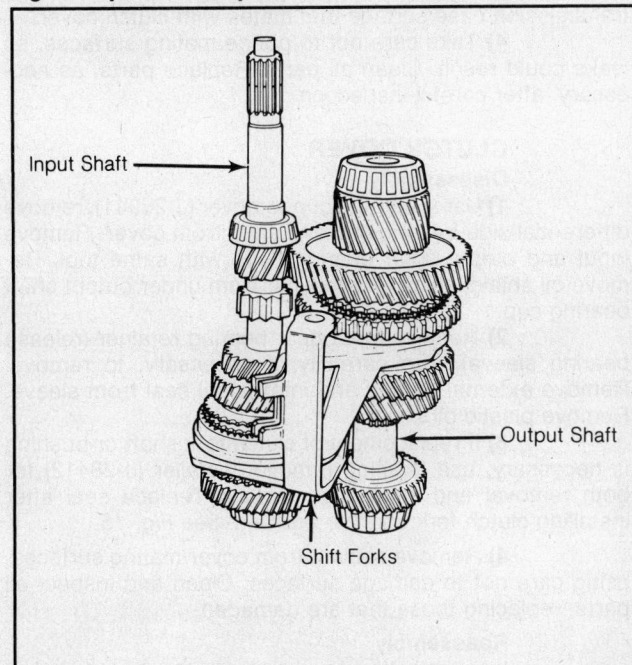

Input Shaft
Output Shaft
Shift Forks

COMPONENT DISASSEMBLY & REASSEMBLY

INPUT SHAFT

Disassembly

1) Support 4th gear with bearing remover (J-22912-01). Press on end of shaft furthest from clutch in normal installed position. Remove 4th gear and outer bearing from shaft.

2) Remove brass blocker ring and snap ring from 3-4 synchronizer. Supporting 3rd gear, press 3rd gear and 3-4 synchronizer from shaft. See Fig. 10.

3) Using bearing remover (J-26946) to hold bearing, press shaft from bearing nearest clutch end.

Reassembly

1) Lubricate all parts and install bearing on clutch end of shaft, using bearing installer (J-28406). Turn shaft end for end in press and install 3rd gear. Install brass blocker ring onto gear cone and install 3-4 synchronizer.

Fig. 10: Components of Input Shaft

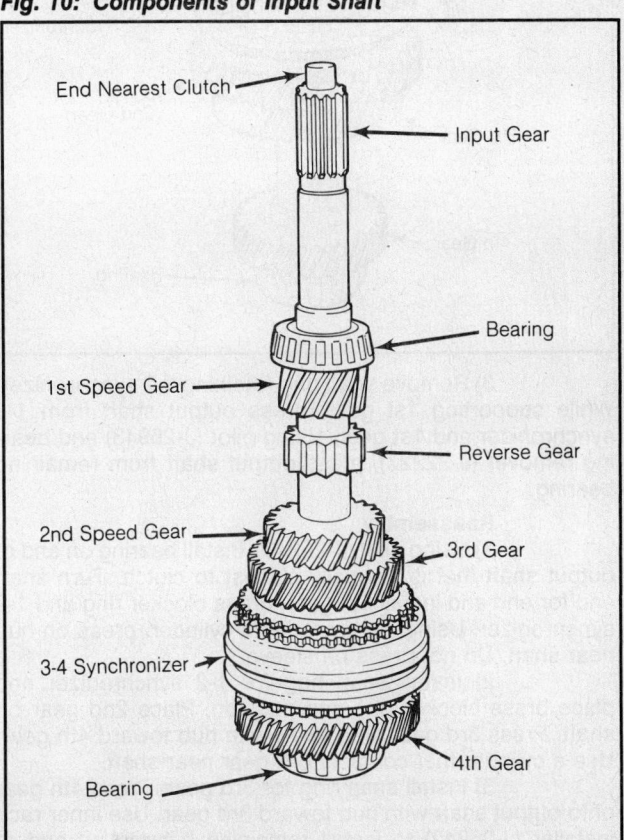

End Nearest Clutch
Input Gear
Bearing
1st Speed Gear
Reverse Gear
2nd Speed Gear
3rd Gear
3-4 Synchronizer
4th Gear
Bearing

NOTE: Use an appropriate cylinder to contact hub near shaft. Do not press on sleeve portion. Both synchronizers are press fits to shaft.

2) Install snap ring to hold 3-4 synchronizer, making sure beveled edge of ring is away from synchronizer. Install blocker ring. Install 4th gear onto shaft, and using inner race installer (J-26942), install bearing furthest from clutch end onto shaft

Manual Transmissions

GENERAL MOTORS 4-SPEED MANUAL TRANSAXLE (Cont.)

OUTPUT SHAFT
Disassembly

1) Place support under 4th gear and install pilot (J-26943) on end of shaft. Press output shaft from 4th gear and bearing. See Fig. 11.

2) Remove snap ring retaining 3rd gear. Slide 1-2 synchronizer assembly into 1st gear position, so press plates support 2nd gear. Press 2nd gear and 3rd gear from output shaft and remove brass blocker ring.

Fig. 11: Components of Output Shaft

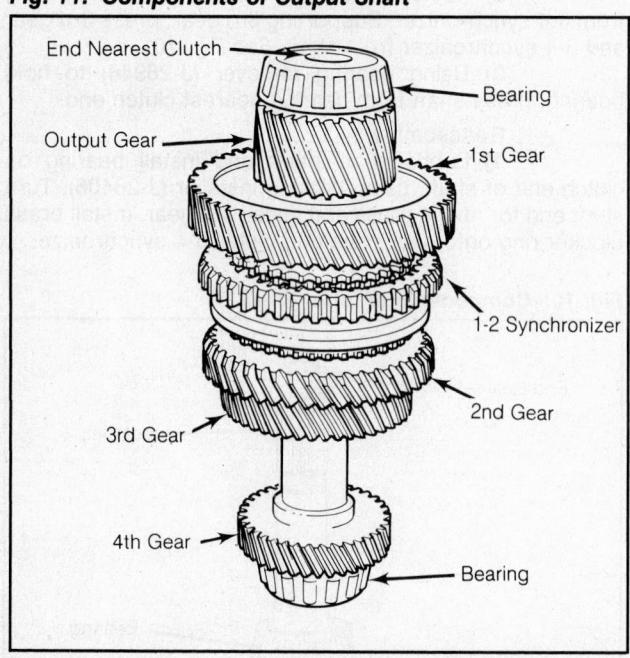

3) Remove snap ring retaining 1-2 synchronizer. While supporting 1st gear, press output shaft from 1-2 synchronizer and 1st gear. Using pilot (J-26943) and bearing remover (J-22227), press output shaft from remaining bearing.

Reassembly

1) Using pilot (J-26943), install bearing on end of output shaft that is normally closest to clutch. Turn shaft end for end and install 1st gear, brass blocker ring and 1-2 synchronizer. Using an appropriate cylinder, press on hub near shaft. Do not press on sleeve.

2) Install snap ring for 1-2 synchronizer and place brass blocker ring into position. Place 2nd gear on shaft. Press 3rd gear onto shaft with hub toward 4th gear. Use a cylinder that contacts 3rd gear near shaft.

3) Install snap ring for 3rd gear. Press 4th gear onto output shaft with hub toward 3rd gear. Use inner race installer (J-26942) to install remaining bearing on end of shaft furthest from clutch.

SYNCHRONIZERS
Disassembly

Using care, pry out both synchronizer retaining rings. Separate hub, sleeve, and 3 keys, noting their position. See Fig. 12. Scribe hub to sleeve location and separate. Clean, inspect, and replace parts, as necessary.

Reassembly

1) Assemble hub to sleeve with lip of hub away from shift fork groove in sleeve. Align scribe marks. Care-

fully install retaining ring, prying it back to insert keys one at a time.

2) Flats on retaining ring should hold keys in place. Install retaining ring on opposite side of hub, so open end of ring does not align with open end of first ring.

Fig. 12: Components of Synchronizer Assemblies

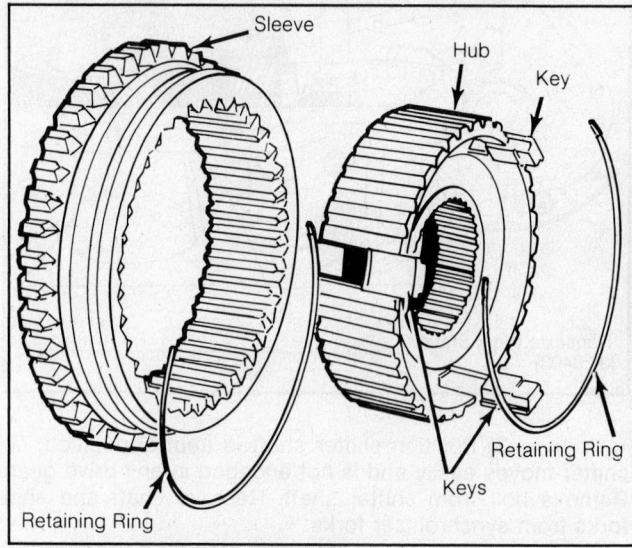

TRANSMISSION CASE

1) Remove reverse inhibitor seat, spring, pilot, and shimming washers. Remove input and output shaft bearing cups using Tool (J-26941). See Figs. 13 and 14.

2) Remove oil slingers. Using bearing cup remover (J-26941), remove differential side bearing cup. Turn tool's set screw counterclockwise to insert tool below bearing cup. Then turn clockwise to grasp cut.

3) Inspect 2 guide pins for interlock bracket and reverse shift fork. Also check magnet. Remove sealant from transmission case surface that mates with clutch cover.

4) Take care not to gouge mating surfaces, as leaks could result. Clean all parts. Replace parts, as necessary, after careful inspection.

CLUTCH COVER
Disassembly

1) Using bearing cup remover (J-26941), remove differential side bearing cup and shim from cover. Remove input and output shaft bearing cups with same tool. Remove oil shield, shim, and retainer from under output shaft bearing cup.

2) Remove input gear bearing retainer (release bearing sleeve). Tap carefully, if necessary, to remove. Remove external oil ring and internal oil seal from sleeve. Remove plastic oil scoop

3) If replacement of clutch fork shaft or bushing is necessary, use bushing remover/installer (J-28412) for both removal and installation. Always replace seal after installing clutch fork shaft or bushing. See Fig. 15.

4) Remove sealant from cover mating surfaces, using care not to damage surfaces. Clean and inspect all parts, replacing those that are damaged.

Reassembly

Install plastic oil scoop, replace external square cut oil ring on sleeves. Install input bearing retainer (release

GENERAL MOTORS 4-SPEED MANUAL TRANSAXLE (Cont.)

Fig. 13: Removing Reverse Inhibitor Assembly

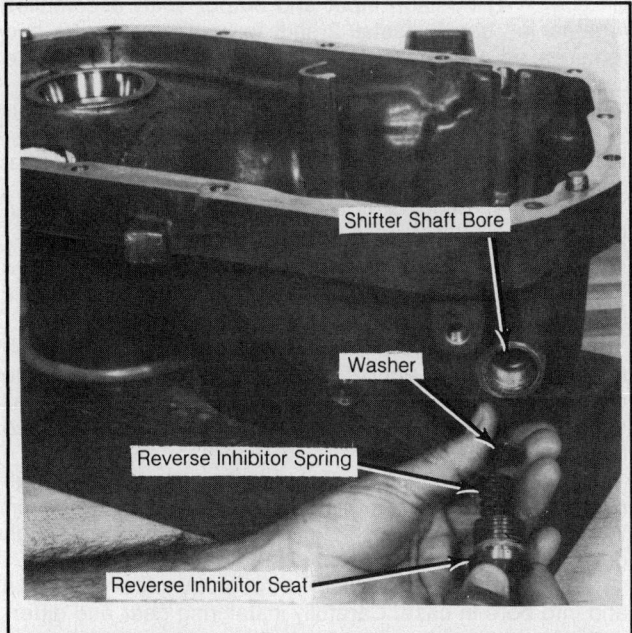

Reassembly

Install gears and thrust washers into case. Install pinion shaft and lock bolt. Attach ring gear to differential case using appropriate lock compound on bolts. Torque to specifications.

REASSEMBLY

TRANSAXLE
Shim Selection

NOTE: Shims may be selected for proper preload as soon as input and output shaft assemblies and differential assembly are reassembled and ready for installation in transaxle case.

1) Place transaxle case into holding fixture (J-28408). *See Fig. 8.* Install 3 bearing races into case, and install input, output and differential assemblies in position. Install remaining 3 bearing races onto their respective bearings.

2) Install gauges over each bearing (J-26935-2 for input shaft; J-26935-4 for output shaft; and J-26935-3 for differential shaft). *See Fig. 16.* Be sure bearing races fit smoothly in bores of gauges.

3) Install metal oil shield retainer into bore on top of output shaft gauge (J-26935-4). Carefully assemble clutch cover over gauges and onto transaxle case, using 7 spacers evenly around case mating surfaces.

4) Install bolts supplied and tighten bolts alternately to gradually draw clutch cover to transaxle case. Tighten bolts to 10 ft. lbs. (14 N.m) to compress gauge sleeves.

5) Rotate each gauge to seat bearings. Rotate differential case 3 revolutions in each direction. With gauges compressed, measure gap between outer sleeve and base pad of each shaft. This will provide the shim thickness required for proper bearing preloading at each shaft. *See Fig. 17.*

6) On the output and differential shafts use one size smaller than the largest shim that can be placed into

Fig. 14: Removing Bearing Cups

Use bearing cup remover (J-26941). When installing cups, use bearing cup installer (J-26938).

bearing sleeve). Using bearing cup installer (J-26936), install internal oil seal. Reverse remainder of disassembly procedures.

DIFFERENTIAL CASE & RING GEAR
Disassembly

1) Separate ring gear from differential case. Remove pinion shaft lock bolt and pinion shaft. Roll gears and thrust washers out through opening in case.

2) If differential side bearings are to be replaced, use puller (J-22888 and J-22888-30). Use cone installer (J-22919) when installing bearings. Clean and inspect all parts. Replace parts, where necessary.

Fig. 15: Replacing Clutch Fork Shaft and Bushings

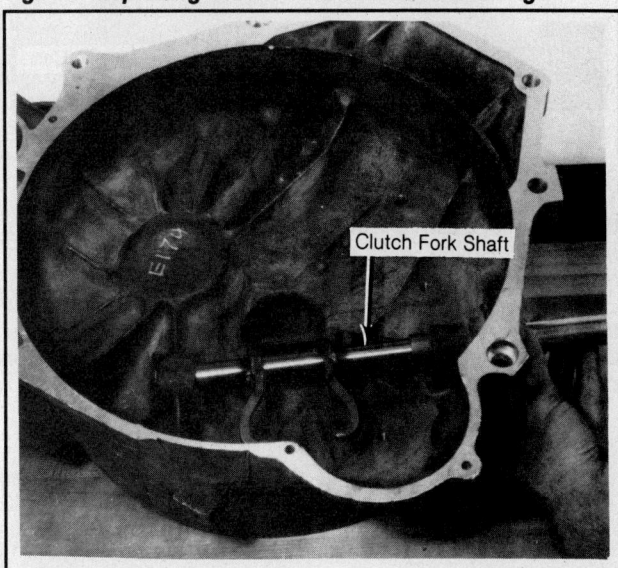

Fig. 16: Installing Gauges Over Shaft Bearings

Fig. 17: Measuring Gap to Determine Preload Shim Requirements

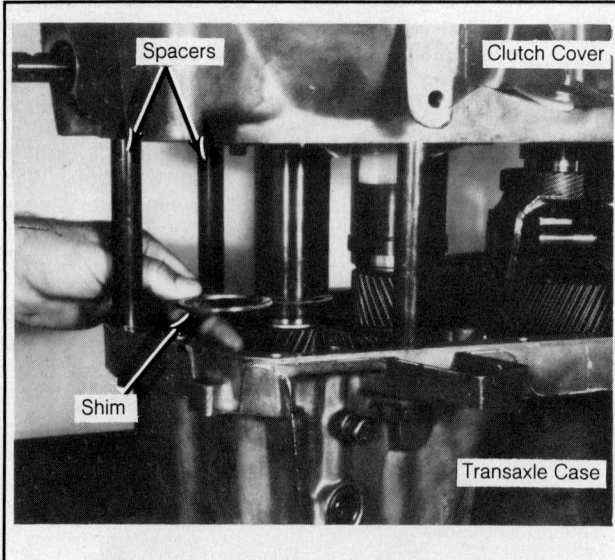

Rotate case 3 times in each direction.

the gap and drawn through without binding. On the input shaft, use a shim 2 sizes smaller. When shims are selected, remove clutch cover, spacers and gauges.

7) Install shims into their respective bores in clutch cover. Add metal shield, and install bearing cups, using Cup Installer (J-26936 on input shaft; J-23423-A on output shaft; and J-26938 on differential bearing cup).

Case
1) Position input and output shaft assemblies together on bench. Install 2 shift forks. Grasp shafts and forks as an assembly, and carefully lower into transaxle case. Do not damage gears.

2) Place interlock bracket onto Guide Pin (J-28411). Be sure bracket engages fingers on shift forks. Place detent shift lever into interlock. Using a straightedge, check alignment of detent to interlock.

3) Place detent shift lever into the interlock. Install shifter shaft through interlock bracket and detent shift lever, but no further. Install reverse shift fork onto guide pin. Be sure reverse shift fork engages interlock bracket.

4) Install reverse idler gear and shaft into position. Be sure long end of shaft points upward and large champfered ends of gear tooth are facing upward. Install spacer onto shaft. Flat on reverse idler shaft must face input gear shaft.

5) Complete installation of shifter shaft through reverse shift fork until it pilots into inhibitor spring spacer. With shaft in neutral position, install bolt and lock through detent shift lever. Bend tab of lock over bolt head.

6) Install fork shaft through synchronizer forks and into bore in case. Carefully install ring gear and differential case assembly. Install magnet.

7) Apply a thin bead of sealant to clutch cover and carefully install cover onto transaxle case. Use dowel pins to guide cover into position. Tap clutch cover lightly with soft mallet to seat parts securely.

8) Install 15 retaining bolts and tighten idler shaft retaining bolt in case. Shift through gear ranges to test that all parts move freely.

TIGHTENING SPECIFICATIONS

Application	Ft. Lbs. (N.m)
Case-to-Clutch Cover	
Shim Selection	10 (14)
Final Assembly	16 (22)
Engine-to-Transaxle	55 (75)
Stabilizer Bar Bushing Retainer	
Crossmember	40 (54)
Control Arm	35 (47)
Suspension	
Cam Bolt	140 (190)
Upper Bolt	140 (190)
Toe Link Rod-	
Brake Caliper	30 (41)
Hub Nut	
Initial	70 (95)
Final	185-225 (250-305)
Cradle	
Sidemember-to-Crossmember	34-47 (46-64)
Body Mount	66 (90)
Engine Support Bolts	50 (68)
Transaxle Mounts	
4-Cylinder Engine	35 (47)
V6 Engine	18 (24)

Manual Transmissions

GENERAL MOTORS 5-SPEED – 69.5 MM

Chevrolet Chevette

IDENTIFICATION

Transmission can be identified by a 2 letter code, stamped on machined pad centered on right side of case. Clutch housing and gearbox are a single piece casting.

DESCRIPTION

The transmission is a 5-speed fully synchronized unit with blocker ring synchronizers and a constant mesh reverse gear. First through 4th gears are housed within the case. Reverse and 5th gears are contained in the extension housing.

The input-output shaft and the countershaft are supported by 3 ball bearings. The bearings are located in the front wall of the case, the center support and the extension housing. All forward gears are helical cut.

LUBRICATION & ADJUSTMENT

See the appropriate article in MANUAL TRANS-MISSION SERVICING Section.

TROUBLE SHOOTING

See MANUAL TRANSMISSION TROUBLE SHOOTING in TRANSMISSION SERVICING Section

REMOVAL & INSTALLATION

TRANSMISSION

See the appropriate article in MANUAL TRANS-MISSION REMOVAL Section.

SHIFT LEVER

Removal

Removal shifter console. Remove inner and outer shift boots. Remove retaining bolts and shift lever. See Fig. 2.

Installation

Install shift lever and retaining bolts. Check operation of shifter. Install outer boot and shifter console.

TRANSMISSION DISASSEMBLY

1) Remove plug and drain transmission. Remove release bearing and fork assembly. Remove input shaft bearing retainer and Belleville spring washer. See Fig. 3.

2) Remove speedometer driven gear and back-up light switch. Remove shift control box from extension housing. Remove extension housing from transmission case. See Fig. 2.

3) Remove snap rings, speedometer drive gear and retainer clip, and bearing. Remove snap ring, thrust washer, and lock ball from output shaft. Remove outer snap ring from input shaft bearing. Remove center support from case with all gears attached.

Fig. 1: Cutaway View of General Motors 69.5 mm 5-Speed Transmission

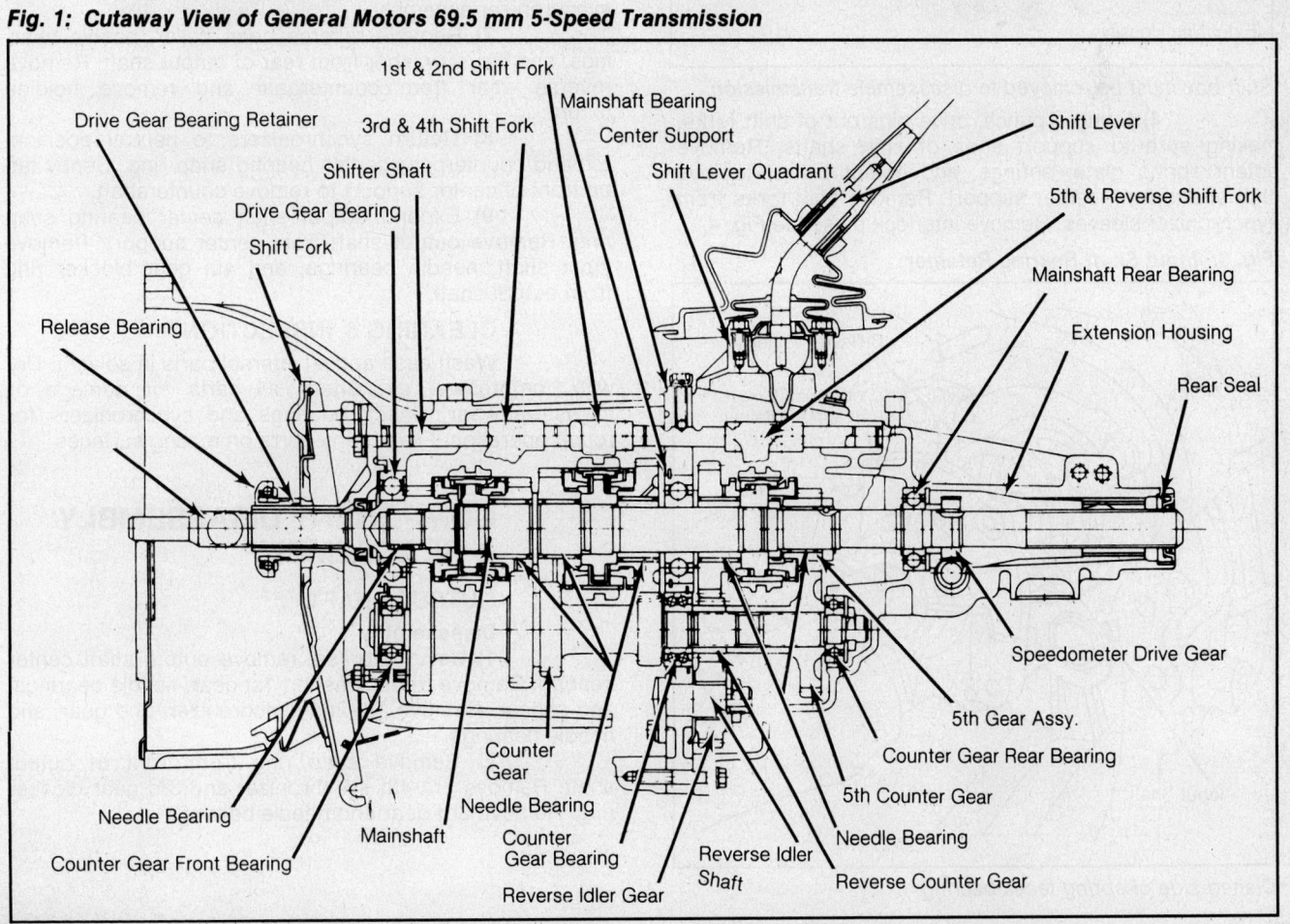

GENERAL MOTORS 5-SPEED – 69.5 MM (Cont.)

Fig. 2: Exploded View of Shifter

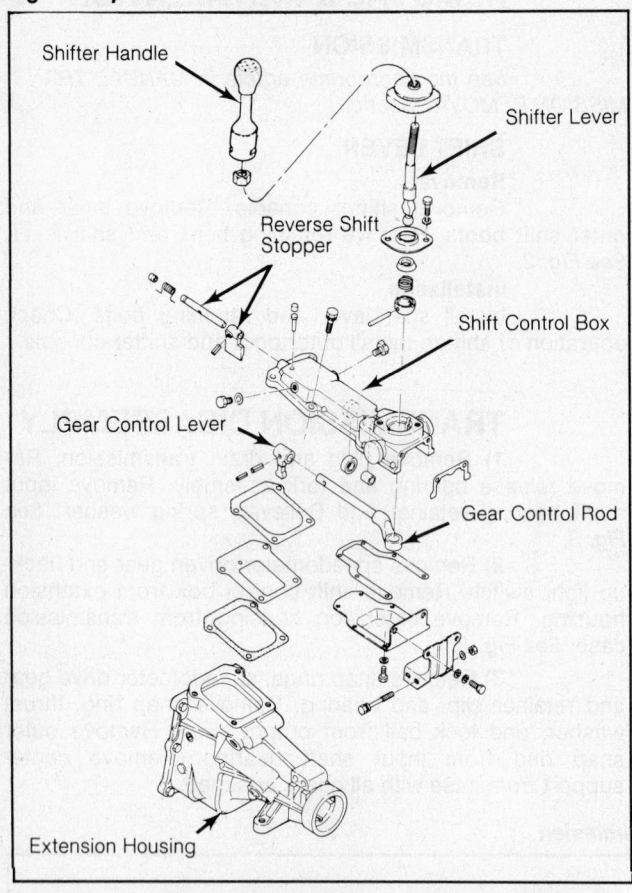

Shift box must be removed to disassemble transmission.

4) Using a punch, drive pins out of shift forks, making sure to support ends of shift shafts. Remove detent spring plate, springs, and detent balls. Remove shift shafts from center support. Remove shift forks from synchronizer sleeves. Remove interlock pins. *See Fig. 4.*

Fig. 3: Input Shaft Bearing Retainer

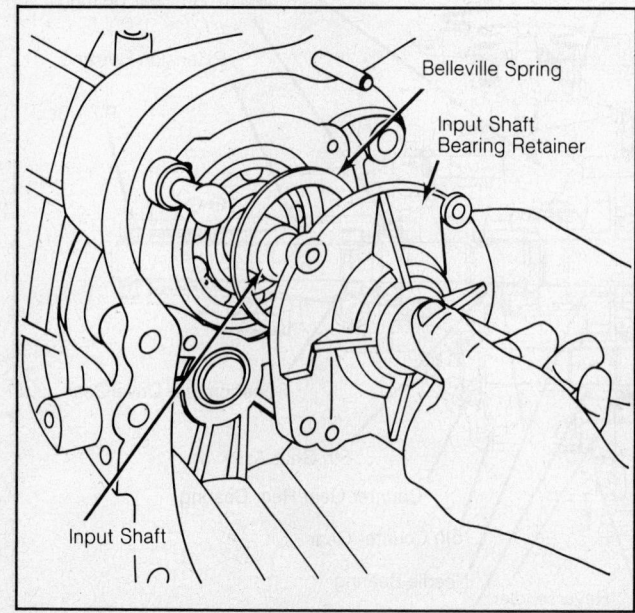

Dished side of spring faces bearing.

Fig. 4: Exploded View of Shift Shaft Assembly

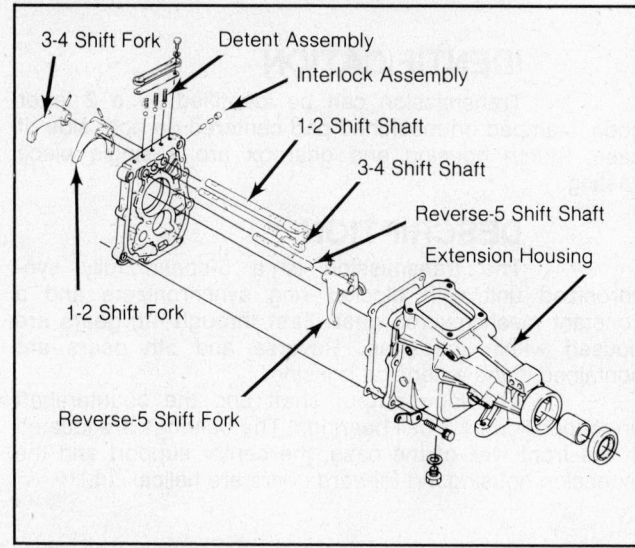

5) Engage 1st and 3rd gears to prevent rotation of countershaft. Install holding fixture (J-29768) onto front of gear assembly. Remove self-locking nut from countergear. Using a puller, remove 5th gear together with ball bearing.

6) Remove 5th gear, needle bearings, and blocker ring from output shaft. Remove thrust washers, reverse idler gear, and retaining nut from reverse idler shaft. Remove output shaft nut, retainer, and reverse-5th synchronizer assembly.

7) Remove reverse gear, collar, needle bearings, and thrust washer from rear of output shaft. Remove reverse gear from countergear and remove holding fixture.

8) Return synchronizers to neutral position. Expand countergear center bearing snap ring. Gently tap on front of center support to remove countershaft.

9) Expand output shaft center bearing snap ring. Remove output shaft from center support. Remove input shaft, needle bearings, and 4th gear blocker ring from output shaft.

CLEANING & INSPECTION

Wash case and all internal parts in solvent. Dry with compressed air. Check all parts for damage or excessive wear. Check bearings and synchronizers for rough operation. File off any burrs on mating surfaces.

COMPONENT DISASSEMBLY & REASSEMBLY

OUTPUT SHAFT

Disassembly

1) Using a press, remove output shaft center bearing. Remove thrust washer, 1st gear, needle bearings, and spacer. Remove 1st-2nd synchronizer, 2nd gear, and needle bearings.

2) Remove snap ring from front of output shaft. Remove 3rd-4th synchronizer and 3rd gear blocker ring. Remove 3rd gear and needle bearing.

GENERAL MOTORS 5-SPEED – 69.5 MM (Cont.)

Fig. 5: Exploded View of 69.5 mm 5-Speed Transmission

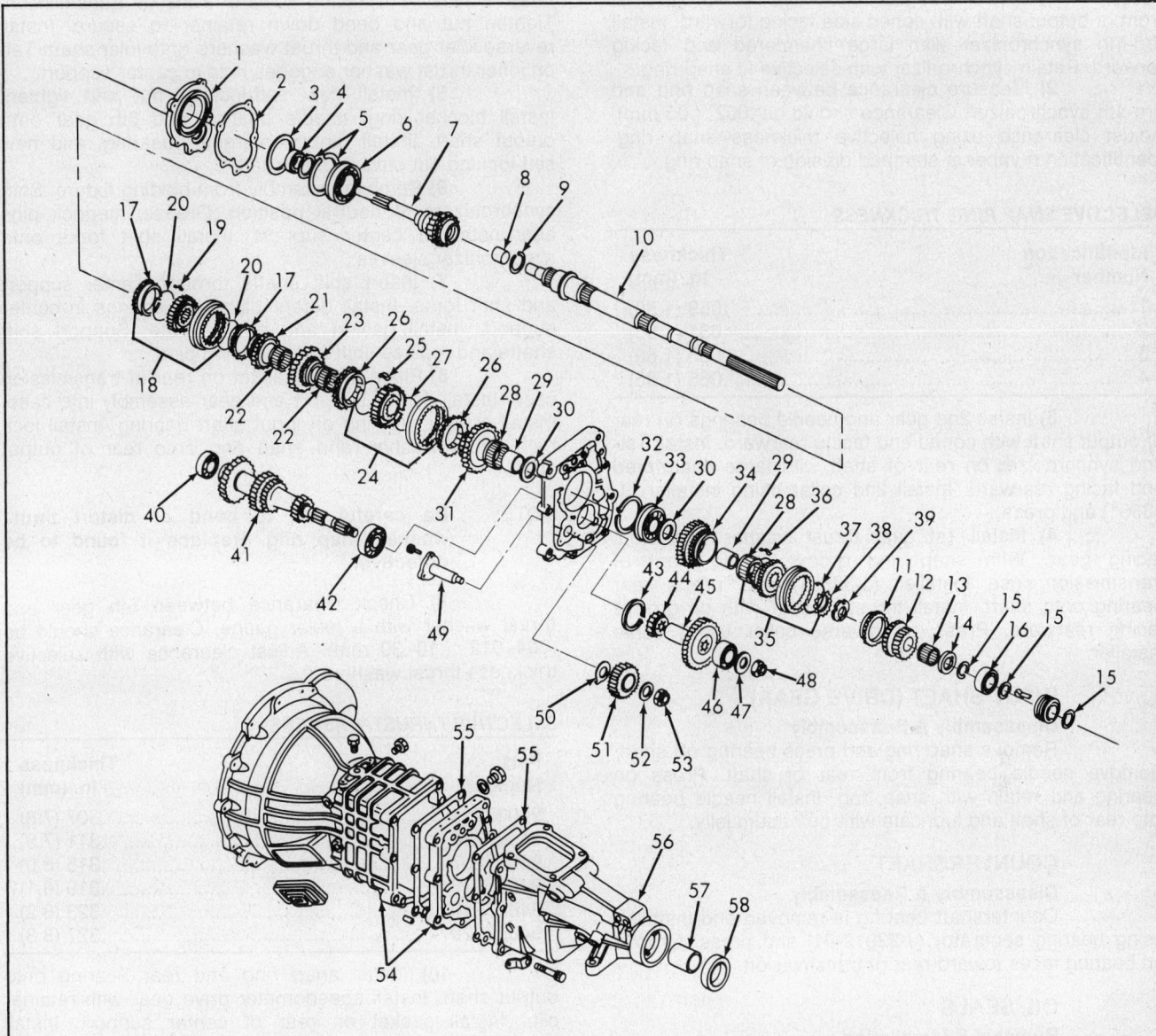

1. Input Bearing Retainer
2. Gasket
3. Belleville Spring
4. Seal
5. Snap Ring
6. Input Bearing
7. Input Shaft
8. Needle Bearing
9. Snap Ring
10. Output Shaft
11. 5th Gear Blocker Ring
12. 5th Gear
13. Needle Bearing
14. Thrust Washer
15. Snap Ring
16. Rear Output Bearing
17. Blocker Ring
18. 3-4 Synchro Assy.
19. Synchro Key
20. Synchro Spring

21. 3rd Gear
22. Needle Bearing
23. 2nd Gear
24. 1-2 Synchro Assy.
25. Synchro Key
26. Blocker Ring
27. Synchro Spring
28. Needle Bearing
29. Collar
30. Thrust Washer
31. 1st Gear
32. Snap Ring
33. Center Output Bearing
34. Reverse Gear
35. Reverse-5th Synchro Assy.
36. Synchro Key
37. Synchro Spring
38. Lock Washer
39. Nut

40. Front Counter Bearing
41. Countershaft
42. Center Counter Bearing
43. Snap Ring
44. Reverse Countergear
45. 5th Countergear
46. Rear Counter Bearing
47. Washer
48. Nut
49. Reverse Idler Shaft
50. Thrust Washer
51. Reverse Idler Gear
52. Thrust Washer
53. Nut
54. Case & Center Support
55. Gasket
56. Extension Housing
57. Ext. Hsg. Bushing
58. Ext. Hsg. Seal

Manual Transmissions

GENERAL MOTORS 5-SPEED – 69.5 MM (Cont.)

Reassembly

1) Install 3rd gear and needle bearing, onto front of output shaft with coned side facing forward. Install 3rd-4th synchronizer with large chamfered end facing forward. Retain synchronizer with selective fit snap ring.

2) Measure clearance between snap ring and 3rd-4th synchronizer. Clearance should be .002" (.05 mm). Adjust clearance using selective thickness snap ring. Identification number is stamped on side of snap ring.

SELECTIVE SNAP RING THICKNESS

Identification Number	Thickness In. (mm)
1	.059 (1.50)
2	.061 (1.55)
3	.063 (1.60)
4	.065 (1.65)

3) Install 2nd gear and needle bearings on rear of output shaft with coned end facing rearward. Install 1st-2nd synchronizer on rear of shaft with large chamfered end facing rearward. Install 2nd collar using installer (J-33851) and press.

4) Install 1st gear thrust washer with slots facing gear. With snap ring groove facing front of transmission, use installer (J-33851) and press rear bearing onto shaft. Install thrust washer with oil groove facing rearward. Press on reverse collar using same installer.

INPUT SHAFT (DRIVE GEAR)

Disassembly & Reassembly

Remove snap ring and press bearing off shaft. Remove needle bearing from rear of shaft. Press on bearing and retain with snap ring. Install needle bearing into rear of shaft and lubricate with petroleum jelly.

COUNTERSHAFT

Disassembly & Reassembly

Countershaft bearing is removed and installed using bearing separator (J-22912-01) and press. Groove on bearing faces toward rear of transmission.

OIL SEALS

Removal & Installation

Remove seals by prying with a screwdriver or small chisel. Coat outside of new extension housing seal with sealer (Permatex No. 2). Install seals with seal drivers (J-21426 for Ext. Hsg. and J-26540 for Input Shaft).

TRANSMISSION REASSEMBLY

1) If removed, install center support snap rings and reverse idler shaft. Tighten reverse idler shaft retaining bolts. Install input shaft onto front of output shaft and engage with countergear.

2) Install center support onto gear assemblies while expanding snap rings until bearing grooves seat in snap rings. Engage 1st and 3rd gears to prevent rotation. Install reverse gear on countergear.

3) Install needle bearing and reverse gear on output shaft. Install reverse-5th synchronizer so side of clutch hub with raised face is toward front (reverse gear side).

4) Install locking retainer and nut with chamfered side of nut facing toward front of transmission. Tighten nut and bend down retainer to secure. Install reverse idler gear and thrust washers onto idler shaft. Tab on inner thrust washer engages hole in center support.

5) Install new self-locking nut and tighten. Install blocker ring, needle bearing and 5th gear onto output shaft. Install 5th countergear, bearing, and new self-locking nut onto countershaft.

6) Remove assembly from holding fixture. Shift synchronizers to neutral position. Grease interlock pins and install in center support. Install shift forks onto synchronizer sleeves.

7) Insert shift shafts through center support and shift forks. Install detent balls and springs in center support. Install gasket and detent plate. Support shift shafts and replace shift fork retaining pins.

8) Place a new gasket on rear of transmission case. Install center support and gear assembly into case. Install outer snap ring on input shaft bearing. Install lock ball, thrust washer, and snap ring onto rear of output shaft.

NOTE: **Be careful not to bend or distort thrust washer snap ring. Replace if found to be defective.**

9) Check clearance between 5th gear and thrust washer with a feeler gauge. Clearance should be .004-.012" (.10-.30 mm). Adjust clearance with selective thickness thrust washers.

SELECTIVE THRUST WASHERS

Part Number	Thickness In. (mm)
94027215	.307 (7.8)
94027216	.311 (7.9)
94027217	.315 (8.0)
94027218	.319 (8.1)
94027219	.323 (8.2)
94027220	.327 (8.3)

10) Install snap ring and rear bearing onto output shaft. Install speedometer drive gear with retainer clip. Install gasket on rear of center support. Install extension housing. Install speedometer drive gear and back-up light switch.

11) Install Belleville spring washer over input shaft, with dished side toward bearing. Install bearing retainer with gasket. Apply sealer (Permatex No. 2) to threads of 3 lower retainer bolts. Install retainer bolts and tighten. Install release bearing and fork assembly.

TIGHTENING SPECIFICATIONS

Application	Ft. Lbs. (N.m)
Countergear Nut	80 (108)
Extension Housing Bolts	27 (37)
Input Shaft Bearing Retainer	14 (19)
Mainshaft-to-Center Support	94 (127)
Output Shaft Nut	94 (127)
Reverse Idler Shaft Retaining Bolts	14 (19)
Reverse Idler Shaft Nut	80 (108)
Shift Box Bolts	14 (19)

Chevrolet
  Camaro, Chevette, S10/15
Pontiac
  Firebird, 1000

IDENTIFICATION

Transmission may have an identification plate on side of case or be ink stamped on bellhousing.

DESCRIPTION

The 5-speed 77 mm transmission is fully synchronized unit with blocker ring synchronizers and a sliding mesh reverse gear. It has an aluminum case and extension housing. The gearshift lever assembly is floor-mounted and is located on top the extension housing. The shift mechanism does not require adjustment and can be serviced independently of the transmission.

LUBRICATION & ADJUSTMENT

See appropriate MANUAL TRANSMISSION SERVICING article in DOMESTIC GENERAL SERVICING section.

TROUBLE SHOOTING

See appropriate MANUAL TRANSMISSION TROUBLE SHOOTING article in DOMESTIC GENERAL SERVICING section.

SERVICE (IN VEHICLE)

GEAR SHIFT LEVER
Removal & Installation
Remove screws from transmission shift lever boot retainer. Slide boot up lever. Remove shift lever attaching bolts at transmission and remove lever. To install shift lever, reverse removal procedure.

REMOVAL & INSTALLATION

TRANSMISSION
See appropriate MANUAL TRANSMISSION REMOVAL article in DOMESTIC GENERAL SERVICING section.

TRANSMISSION DISASSEMBLY

1) Drain lubricant from transmission. Clean exterior of transmission. Using pin punch and hammer, remove roll pin attaching offset lever to shift rail.

2) Remove extension housing-to-transmission case bolts. Remove housing and offset lever as an assembly.

CAUTION: Do not remove offset lever while extension housing is bolted in place. Lever has a positioning lug engaged in the housing detent plate which prevents moving the lever far enough for removal.

3) Remove detent ball and spring from offset lever. Remove roll pin from extension housing or offset lever. Remove plastic funnel, thrust bearing race and thrust bearing from rear of countershaft.

4) Remove transmission cover attaching bolts and lift off cover. Note location of 2 alignment-type dowel bolts for reassembly.

5) Support end of 5th-reverse shift rail with a wood block. Drive roll pin from 5th gear shift fork.

6) Remove 5th gear synchronizer snap ring, shift fork, 5th gear synchronizer sleeve, blocking ring and 5th speed drive gear from rear of countershaft. Remove snap ring from 5th speed driven gear on output shaft.

7) Using a hammer and punch, place mating marks on bearing cap and case for reassembly reference. Remove front bearing cap bolts and lift off bearing cap. Lift off front bearing race and end play shims from bearing cap.

8) Rotate drive gear until flat surface faces countershaft. Remove input shaft with drive gear from case.

9) Remove reverse lever "C" clip and pivot bolt. See Fig. 1. Remove mainshaft rear bearing race. Tilt output shaft assembly upward and remove from case.

Fig. 1: Removing Reverse Lever Retaining Clip and Bolt

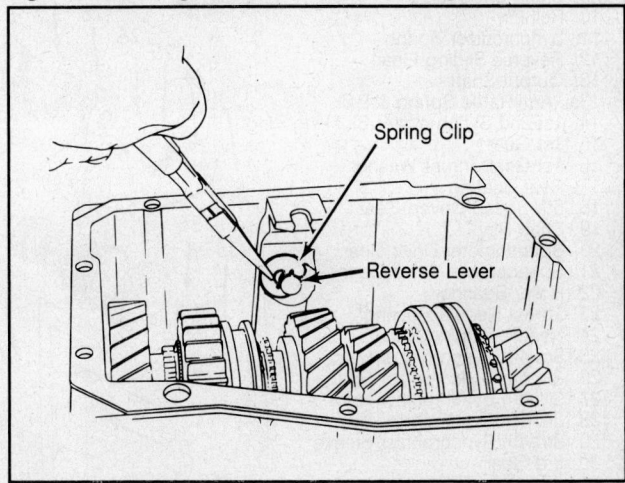

10) Unhook overcenter link spring from front of case. Rotate 5th-reverse shift rail to disengage rail from reverse lever assembly. Remove shift rail from rear of transmission case. See Fig. 2.

Fig. 2: Removing 5th-Reverse Shift Rail

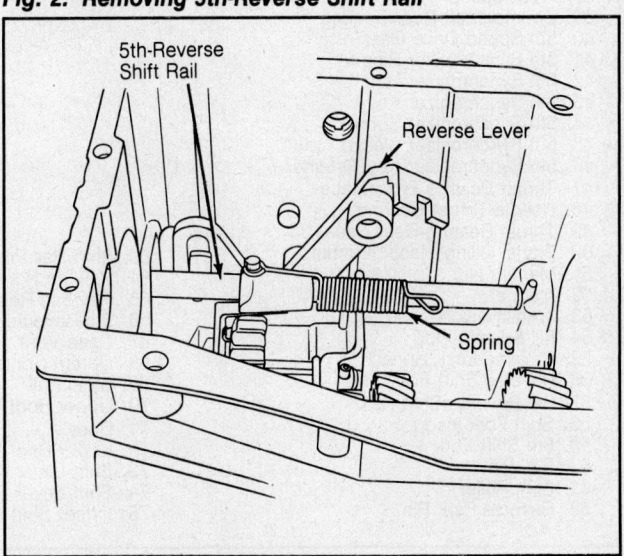

Manual Transmissions

GENERAL MOTORS 5-SPEED — 77 MM (Cont.)

Fig. 3: *Exploded View of 77mm 5-Speed Transmission*

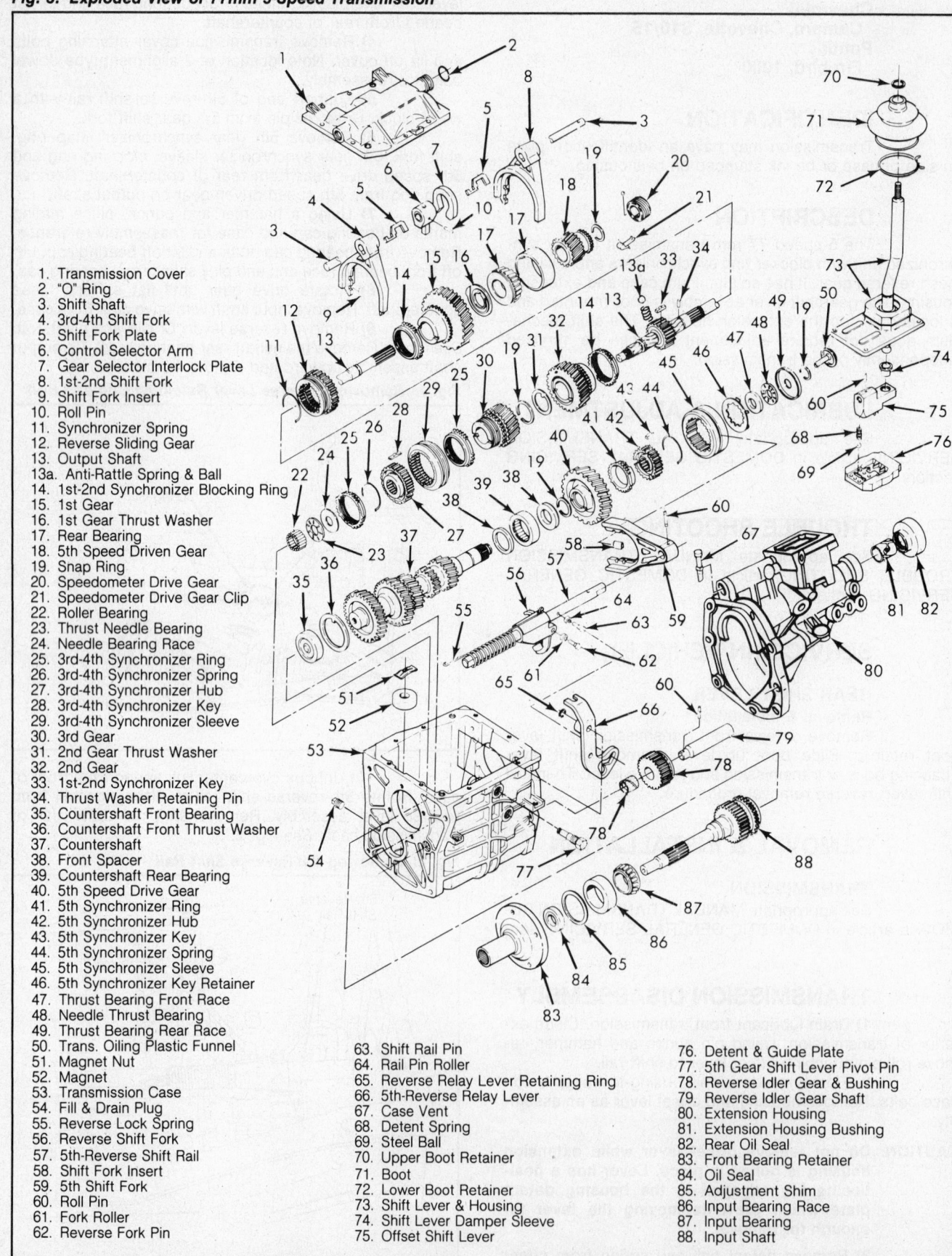

1. Transmission Cover
2. "O" Ring
3. Shift Shaft
4. 3rd-4th Shift Fork
5. Shift Fork Plate
6. Control Selector Arm
7. Gear Selector Interlock Plate
8. 1st-2nd Shift Fork
9. Shift Fork Insert
10. Roll Pin
11. Synchronizer Spring
12. Reverse Sliding Gear
13. Output Shaft
13a. Anti-Rattle Spring & Ball
14. 1st-2nd Synchronizer Blocking Ring
15. 1st Gear
16. 1st Gear Thrust Washer
17. Rear Bearing
18. 5th Speed Driven Gear
19. Snap Ring
20. Speedometer Drive Gear
21. Speedometer Drive Gear Clip
22. Roller Bearing
23. Thrust Needle Bearing
24. Needle Bearing Race
25. 3rd-4th Synchronizer Ring
26. 3rd-4th Synchronizer Spring
27. 3rd-4th Synchronizer Hub
28. 3rd-4th Synchronizer Key
29. 3rd-4th Synchronizer Sleeve
30. 3rd Gear
31. 2nd Gear Thrust Washer
32. 2nd Gear
33. 1st-2nd Synchronizer Key
34. Thrust Washer Retaining Pin
35. Countershaft Front Bearing
36. Countershaft Front Thrust Washer
37. Countershaft
38. Front Spacer
39. Countershaft Rear Bearing
40. 5th Speed Drive Gear
41. 5th Synchronizer Ring
42. 5th Synchronizer Hub
43. 5th Synchronizer Key
44. 5th Synchronizer Spring
45. 5th Synchronizer Sleeve
46. 5th Synchronizer Key Retainer
47. Thrust Bearing Front Race
48. Needle Thrust Bearing
49. Thrust Bearing Rear Race
50. Trans. Oiling Plastic Funnel
51. Magnet Nut
52. Magnet
53. Transmission Case
54. Fill & Drain Plug
55. Reverse Lock Spring
56. Reverse Shift Fork
57. 5th-Reverse Shift Rail
58. Shift Fork Insert
59. 5th Shift Fork
60. Roll Pin
61. Fork Roller
62. Reverse Fork Pin

63. Shift Rail Pin
64. Rail Pin Roller
65. Reverse Relay Lever Retaining Ring
66. 5th-Reverse Relay Lever
67. Case Vent
68. Detent Spring
69. Steel Ball
70. Upper Boot Retainer
71. Boot
72. Lower Boot Retainer
73. Shift Lever & Housing
74. Shift Lever Damper Sleeve
75. Offset Shift Lever

76. Detent & Guide Plate
77. 5th Gear Shift Lever Pivot Pin
78. Reverse Idler Gear & Bushing
79. Reverse Idler Gear Shaft
80. Extension Housing
81. Extension Housing Bushing
82. Rear Oil Seal
83. Front Bearing Retainer
84. Oil Seal
85. Adjustment Shim
86. Input Bearing Race
87. Input Bearing
88. Input Shaft

11) Remove reverse lever and fork assembly from transmission case. Using hammer and punch, drive roll pin from forward end of reverse idler shaft. Remove reverse idler shaft, "O" ring and gear from transmission case.

12) Remove rear countershaft snap ring and spacer. Insert brass drift through input shaft opening in front of case. Using an arbor press, press countershaft rearward to remove rear countershaft bearing.

13) Move countershaft assembly rearward. Tilt countershaft upward and remove from case. Remove countershaft front thrust washer and rear bearing spacer. Press countershaft front bearing from case.

CLEANING & INSPECTION

TRANSMISSION CASE

Wash transmission inside and out using cleaning solvent. Inspect for cracks. Clean magnetic disc at bottom of transmission case. Check front and rear faces of transmission case for burrs. If present, dress them off with a fine mill file.

BEARINGS, ROLLERS AND SPACERS

1) All drive gear bearing rollers should be inspected closely and replaced if they show wear. Inspect reverse idler shaft at the same, replace if necessary. Replace all worn spacers.

2) Wash the front and rear bearings thoroughly in a cleaning solvent. Blow out bearings with compressed air.

CAUTION: Do not spin bearings with compressed air.

3) Lubricate bearings with a light engine oil. Check them for roughness by slowly turning the race by hand.

GEARS

Inspect all gears for excessive wear, chips or cracks. Replace gears that are worn or damaged. Check clutch sleeves to ensure they slide freely on their hubs.

COMPONENT DISASSEMBLY & REASSEMBLY

OUTPUT SHAFT
Disassembly

1) Remove thrust bearing washer from front end of output shaft. Scribe reference mark on 3rd-4th synchronizer hub and sleeve for reassembly.

2) Press 3rd-4th synchronizer blocking ring, sleeve, hub and 3rd gear as an assembly from shaft. Remove snap ring, tabbed thrust washer and 2nd gear from output shaft. Press 5th gear off of shaft.

3) Remove 1st gear thrust washer, thrust washer locating roll pin, 1st gear and synchronizer ring from shaft. Scribe reference mark on 1st-2nd synchronizer hub and sleeve for reassembly.

4) Remove synchronizer spring and keys from 1st-reverse sliding gear. Remove gear from output shaft hub. Remove anti-rattle spring and ball from hub.

NOTE: Do not remove the 1st-2nd-reverse hub from shaft. Hub and shaft are assembled and machined as a matched set.

Reassembly

1) Coat output shaft and gear bores with transmission lubricant. Install anti-rattle spring and ball in hub. Slide 1st-2nd synchronizer sleeve on output shaft hub, aligning marks made at disassembly.

2) Install 1st-2nd synchronizer keys and springs. Engage tang end of each spring in same synchronizer key but position open end of springs opposite of each other. *See Fig. 4.*

Fig. 4: Installing Synchronizer Springs

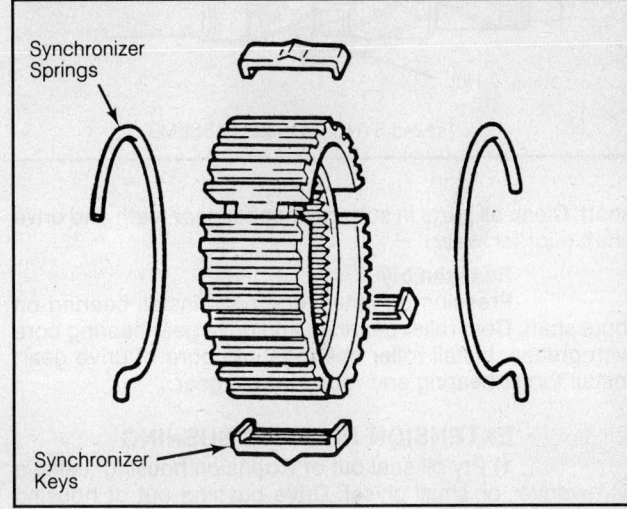

Synchronizer Springs

Synchronizer Keys

3) Install blocker ring and 2nd gear on output shaft. Install tabbed thrust washer and 2nd gear retaining snap ring on shaft. Ensure washer tab is properly seated in shaft notch.

4) Install blocker ring and 1st gear on shaft. Install 1st gear roll pin and then 1st gear thrust washer. Slide rear bearing on shaft.

5) Press 5th gear on shaft using arbor press. Install snap ring on shaft. Install 3rd gear, 3rd-4th synchronizer assembly and thrust bearing on shaft. Synchronizer hub offset must face forward.

SYNCHRONIZERS

NOTE: The synchronizer hubs and sliding sleeves are a selected assembly and should be kept together as originally assembled. Keys and springs may be replaced if worn or broken.

Disassembly & Reassembly

1) If relation of hub and sleeve are not already marked, mark for reassembly purposes. Push sliding sleeve from hub. The keys will fall free and the spings may then be removed.

2) To assemble synchronizers, place a blocker ring on side of the hub and sleeve. Install keys and retain with a spring. Place a blocker ring on opposite side of hub and sleeve. Install remaining spring.

INPUT SHAFT (DRIVE GEAR)
Disassembly

Remove bearing race, thrust bearing and roller bearings from cavity of drive gear. Press bearing from input

Fig. 5: Exploded View of Synchronizer Assemblies

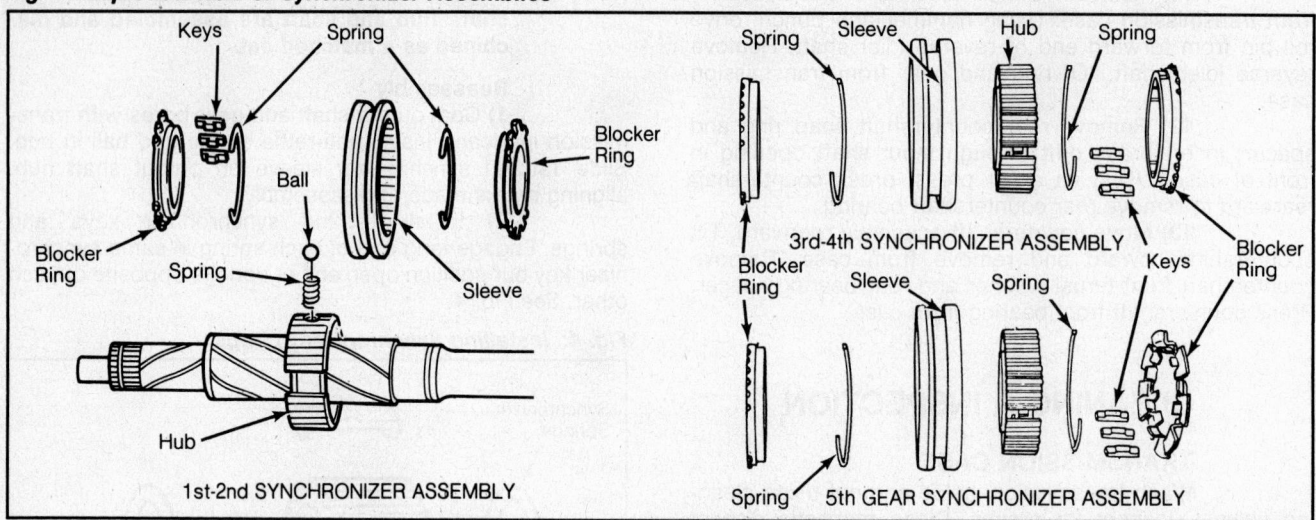

shaft. Clean all parts in solvent. Inspect gear teeth and drive shaft pilot for wear.

Reassembly
Pressing on inner race only, install bearing on input shaft. Coat roller bearings and drive gear bearing bore with grease. Install roller bearings into bore of drive gear. Install thrust bearing and race in drive gear.

EXTENSION HOUSING BUSHING
1) Pry oil seal out of extension housing, using a screwdriver or small chisel. Drive bushing out of housing using Remover/Installer (J-8092 and J-23062-14).

2) Use same tool to install bushing. Coat outer diameter of new oil seal with sealant. Install new oil seal into extension housing. Lubricate I.D. of seal with transmission lubricant.

TRANSMISSION COVER
Disassembly
1) Place selector arm plates and shift rail in neutral (centered) position. Rotate shift rail until selector arm disengages from selector arm plates and roll pin is accessible.

2) Remove selector arm roll pin using a pin punch and hammer. Remove shift rail, shift forks, selector arm plates, selector arm, interlock plate and roll pin.

3) Remove shift cover-to-extension housing "O" ring seal. Remove nylon inserts and selector arm plates from shift forks. Note position of inserts and plates for reassembly reference.

Reassembly
1) Install nylon inserts and selector arm plates in shift forks. If removed, install shift rail plug. Coat edges of plug with sealant before installing.

2) Coat shift rail and rail bores with lightweight grease and insert shift rail in cover. Install rail until flush with inside edge of cover.

3) Place 1st-2nd shift fork in cover with fork offset facing rear of cover and push shift rail through fork. The 1st-2nd shift fork is the larger of the 2 forks.

4) Position selector arm and "C" shaped interlock plate in cover and insert shift rail through arm. Widest part of interlock plate must face away from cover. Selector

arm roll pin must must face downward and toward rear of cover.

5) Position 3rd-4th shift fork in cover with fork offset facing rear of cover. The 3rd-4th shift fork selector arm plate must be under 1st-2nd shift fork selector arm plate.

6) Push shift rail through 3rd-4th shift fork and into front bore in cover. Rotate shift rail until selector arm plate at forward end of rail faces away from, but is parallel to cover.

7) Align roll pin holes in selector arm and shift rail. Install roll pin. Roll pin must be flush with surface of selector arm to prevent pin from contacting selector arm plates during shifts.

8) Install a new shift cover to extension housing "O" ring seal. Coat "O" ring seal with transmission lubricant.

TRANSMISSION REASSEMBLY
1) Coat countershaft front bearing bore with Loctite 601. Install front counterhsaft bearing flush with facing of case using an arbor press.

2) Coat countershaft tabbed thrust washer with grease and install washer so tab engages depression in case. Tip transmission case on end. Install countershaft in front bearing bore.

3) Install countershaft rear bearing spacer. Coat countershaft rear bearing with grease. Install bearing using Installer Tool (J-29895). When correctly installed, bearing will extend .125" (3.0 mm) beyond case surface.

4) Position reverse idler gear in case with shift lever groove facing rear of case. Install reverse idler shaft from rear of case. Install roll pin in idler shaft.

5) Install assembled output shaft in case. Install rear output shaft bearing in case. Install drive gear in case. Engage in 3rd-4th synchronizer sleeve and blocker ring.

6) Install front bearing race in front bearing cap. Do not install shims in front bearing cap at this time. Temporarily install front bearing cap.

7) Install 5th gear-reverse shift rail in case. Engage with 5th gear-reverse shift lever. Rotate rail during installation to simplify engagement with lever. Connect spring to front of case.

GENERAL MOTORS 5-SPEED – 77 MM (Cont.)

8) Position 5th gear shift fork on 5th gear synchronizer assembly. Install synchronizer on countershaft and shift fork on shift rail. Make sure roll pin hole in shift fork and shift rail are aligned.

9) Support 5th gear shift rail and fork on a block of wood and install roll pin. Install thrust race against 5th gear synchronizer hub and install snap ring.

10) Install thrust bearing against race on countershaft. Coat both bearing and race with petroleum jelly.

11) Install lipped thrust race over needle-type thrust bearing. Install plastic funnel into hole in end of countershaft gear.

12) Temporarily install extension housing and attaching bolts. Turn transmission case on end. Mount a dial indicator on extension housing with stem of indicator on end of output shaft.

13) Rotate output shaft and zero dial indicator. Pull upward on mainshaft until end play is removed and record reading. Shaft bearings require a preload of .001-.005" (.03-.13 mm). To set preload, select a shim pack measuring .001-.005" (.03-.13 mm) greater than recorded dial indicator reading.

14) Remove front bearing cap and front bearing race. Install necessary shims to obtain preload and reinstall bearing race.

15) Apply a 1/8" bead of RTV sealant on case-to-front bearing cap mating surface. Install bearing cap aligning marks made during disassembly. Tighten bolts to specification.

16) Remove extension housing. Move shift forks on transmission cover and synchronizer sleeves inside transmission to the neutral position. Apply a 1/8" bead of RTV sealant on cover mating surface of transmission.

17) Lower cover onto case while aligning shift forks and synchronizer sleeves. Center cover and install the 2 dowel bolts. Install and tighten remaining bolts.

NOTE: **The offset lever-to-shift rail roll pin hole must be in the verticle position after cover installation.**

18) Apply a 1/8" bead of RTV sealant on extension housing-to-transmission case mating surface. Install extension housing over output shaft and shift rail to a position where shift rail just enters shift cover opening.

19) Install detent spring into offset lever and place steel ball in neutral guide plate detent. Position detent lever on steel ball. Apply pressure on offset lever and at the same time seat extension housing against transmission case.

20) Install and tighten extension housing bolts. Align and install roll pin in offset lever and shift rail. Fill transmission to proper level with recommended lubricant.

TIGHTENING SPECIFICATIONS

Application	Ft. Lbs. (N.m)
Crossmember-to-Frame Bolts	35 (50)
Extension-Housing-to-Case Bolts	25 (30)
Fill Plug	20 (27)
Front Bearing Cap-to-Case	15 (20)
Reverse Pivot Bolt	20 (27)
Shift Cover-to-Case Bolts	10 (13)
Trans.-to-Engine Bolts	55 (75)
Trans. Mount-to-Trans. Bolts	35 (50)
Trans. Mount-to-Crossmember Bolts	35 (50)

Manual Transmissions

GENERAL MOTORS 5-SPEED MANUAL TRANSAXLE

Buick Skyhawk, Cadillac Cimarron,
Chevrolet Cavalier, Oldsmobile Firenza,
Pontiac Sunbird

IDENTIFICATION

Transaxle may be identified by code stamped on a machined pad on forward side of transaxle case (clutch housing) next to middle transaxle-to-engine retaining bolt.

DESCRIPTION

Final drive and 5-speed transmission are mounted in a common 2-piece aluminum case. Transmission is fully synchronized in all forward gears. Forward gears are helically cut and in constant mesh. Reverse gears are spur cut and are engaged by sliding reverse idler gear.

The input gear, output gear and differential assembly are all supported by preloaded tapered roller bearings. Final output gear with its integral shaft, turns ring gear and differential assembly, drive axles, and front wheel assemblies. See Fig. 1.

Gears are shifted by 2 cable assemblies, the trans-selector and trans-shifter cables.

SERVICE (IN VEHICLE)

TRANSAXLE MOUNTS

To check mounts, raise vehicle on hoist. Push up and pull down on transaxle case. If rubber separates from metal plate or mount, or if case moves up but not down, replace mount.

Removal & Installation

1) Install Alignment Bolt (M6X1X65) in the right front engine mount. Remove the negative battery cable. Install Engine Support Fixture (J-22825-1). Raise engine enough to take the pressure off motor mounts. Remove through bolt at transaxle mount. Remove bolts attaching transaxle to side frame.

2) To install, position mount to side frame and install bolts. Tighten the through bolt at transaxle mount. Loosen 2 top transaxle mount nuts. Loosen the engine support to center mount. To complete installation, reverse removal procedure.

DRIVE AXLE SHAFTS

CAUTION: DO NOT move vehicle, or allow the weight of the vehicle, to rest on the wheels and hubs, without the hub nut installed to proper torque. Damage to the ball bearings and races may occur.

Fig. 1: Sectional View of General Motors 5-Speed Manual Transaxle

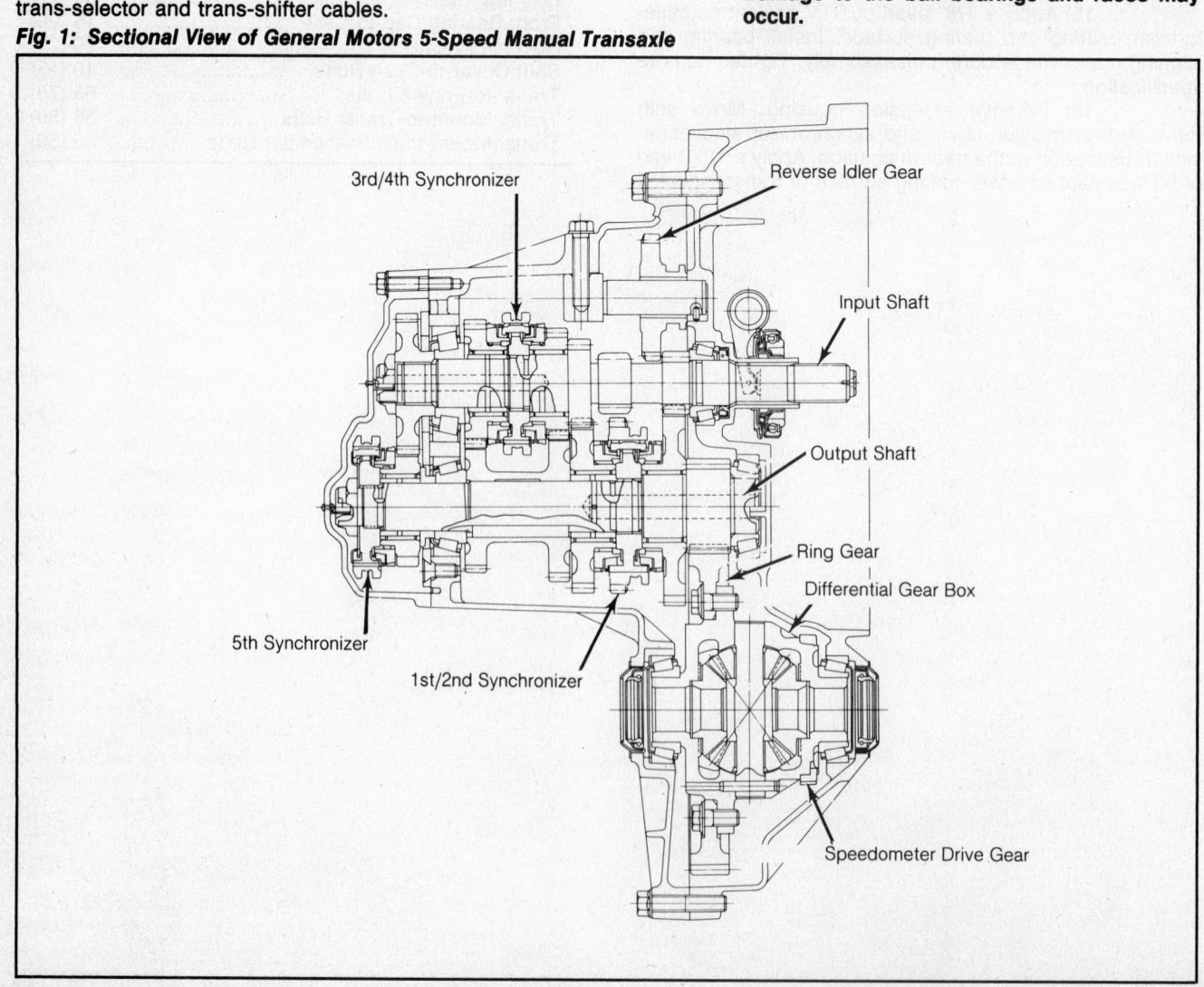

Fig. 2: Removing Drive Axles from Transaxles

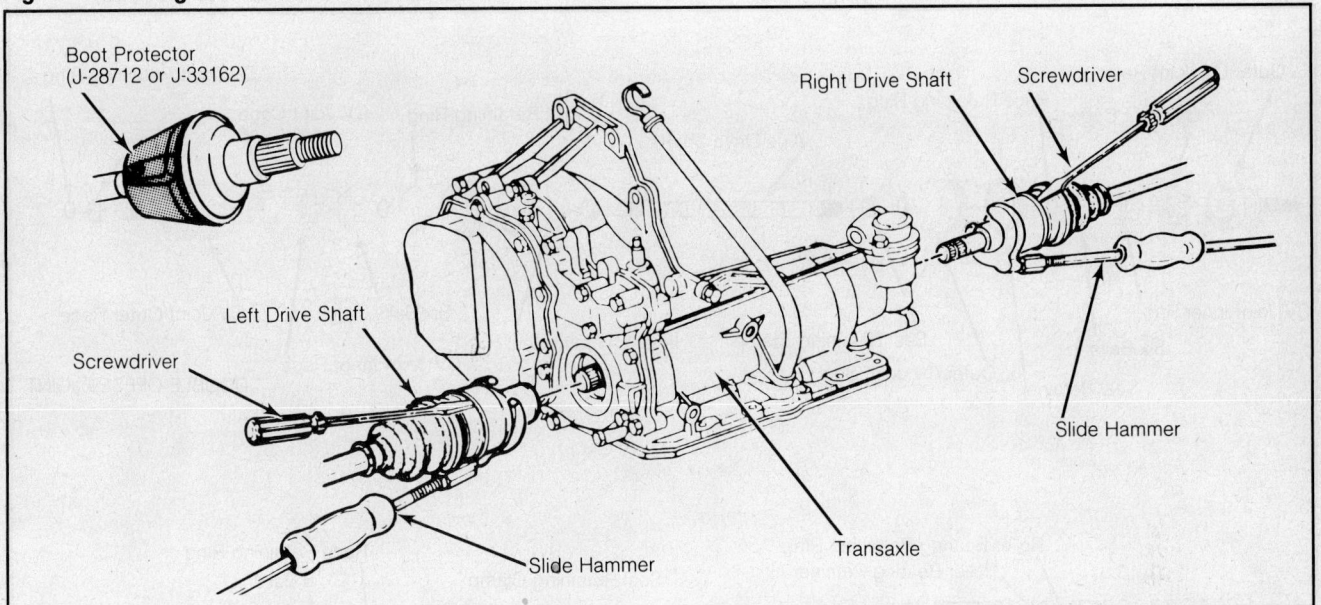

Removal

NOTE: **Boot protectors are only required on silicone (gray) boots, generally right inner CV joint. All other boots are made of thermoplastic material (black) and do not require boot protectors.**

1) Remove hub nut with washer. Raise and support vehicle. Remove wheels and tires. Install Boot Seal Protectors (J-28712) for all outer CV joints, Boot Protectors (J-33162) for all Tripod inner joints and Boot Protectors (J-28712) for all Double Offset joints. *See Fig. 2.*

2) Remove brake caliper and rotor. Support caliper out of way. If necessary, mark strut-to-steering knuckle relation to insure proper camber alignment on reassembly.

3) Remove strut-to-steering knuckle mount bolts/nuts. Separate strut from knuckle. If necessary, detach stabilizer bar/tie rod from steering knuckle/lower control arm.

4) Pull steering knuckle assembly out of strut bracket. Using slide hammer type puller with Special Tool (J-28468 or J-33008 with J-29749), pull drive axle from transaxle. *See Fig. 2.* Support drive axle end with wire.

NOTE: **Support Tripod joint in level position when handling drive axle. If allowed to hang, weight of housing can separate it from spider bearing assembly.**

5) With axle shaft supported, remove clamp bolt from lower control arm ball stud. Separate knuckle from lower control arm. Pull strut, knuckle and caliper assembly away from body and secure in this position.

6) Using Spindle Remover (J-28733), remove axle shaft from hub and bearing assembly. *See Fig. 3.* Remove drive axle for vehicle.

Disassembly (Double Offset)

1) Procedure is similar for outer CV joints and inner Double Offset joints. *See Figs. 4 and 5.* For Tripod Joint disassembly, *See Fig. 4 and 6.* If equipped with rubber deflector ring, remove by pulling from groove of outer race and discard.

Fig. 3: Removing Axle Shaft from Hub and Bearing

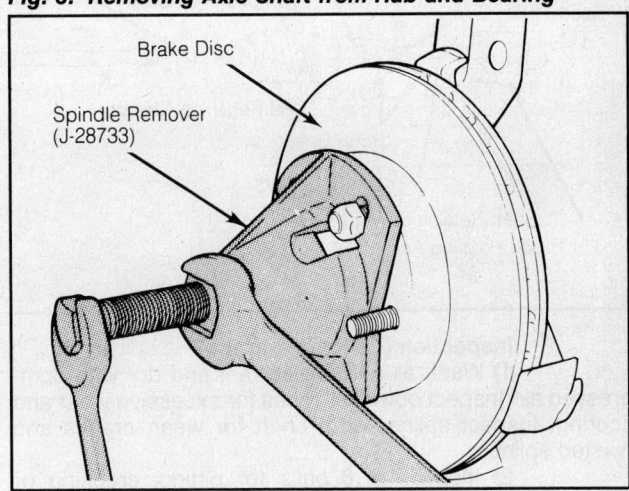

2) If equipped with steel deflector ring, remove by tapping off with brass drift. Using side cutters, cut seal retainer clamp on small end of seal and discard. Using brass drift, tap lightly around edge of seal retainer to remove retainer from CV joint assembly. Spread snap ring and pull shaft from joint assembly.

3) For outer CV joint, use brass drift to tap lightly on bearing cage until it tilts enough to remove one ball bearing. Rotate cage and repeat procedure to remove remaining balls from cage.

4) To remove inner cage and race, pivot components until 90° to normal installed position is obtained (cage windows will align with lands of outer race). *See Fig. 5, No. 5.* Lift cage and inner race from outer race. Rotate inner race upward and out of cage.

5) On inner Double Offset joint, remove components as previously described. Remove ball race retaining ring. Balls will come out when cage and inner race are removed from outer race.

Manual Transmissions

GENERAL MOTORS 5-SPEED MANUAL TRANSAXLE (Cont.)

Fig. 4: *Exploded View of Constant Velocity Joints*

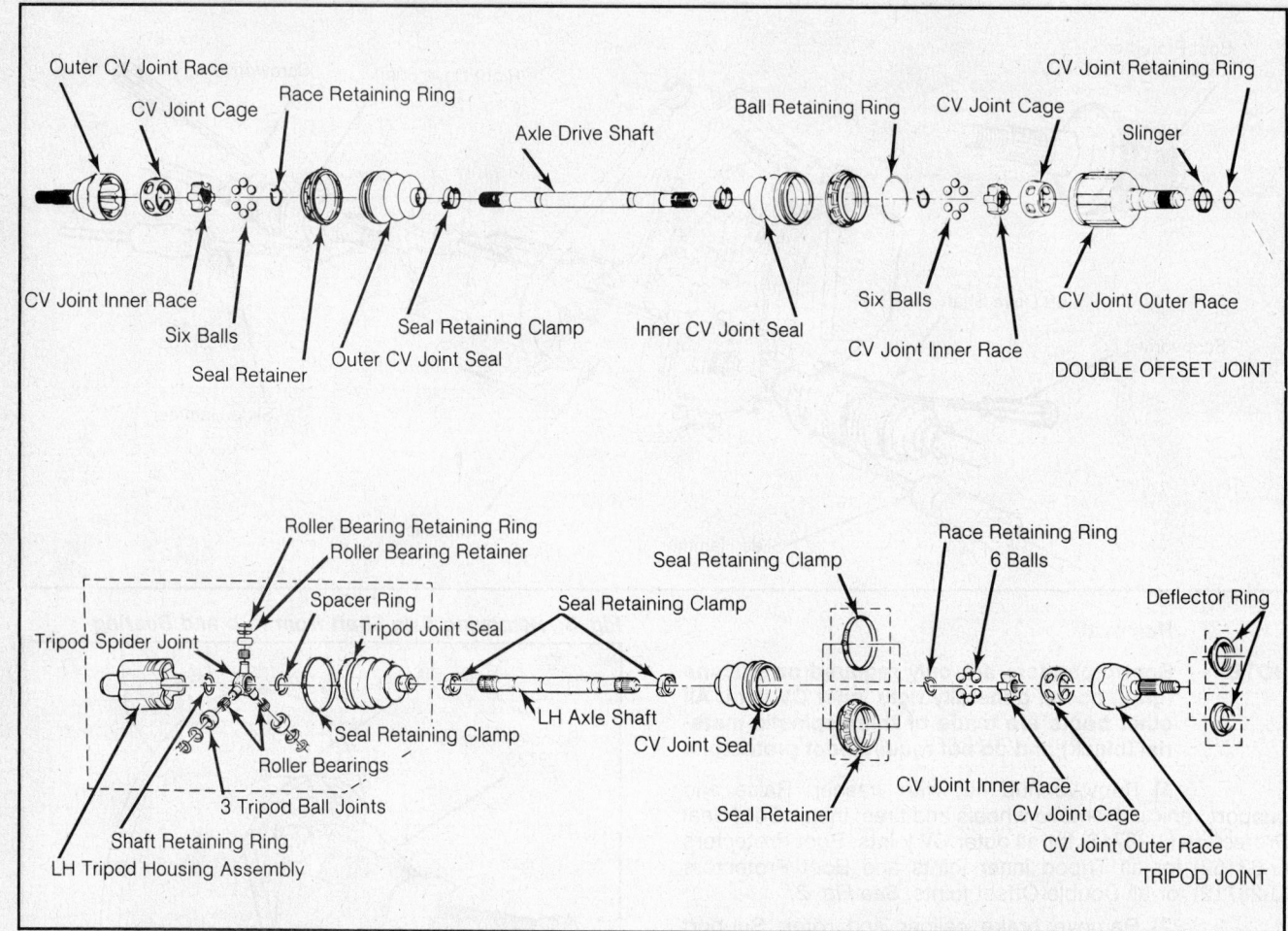

Inspection (Double Offset)

1) Wash all parts in solvent and dry with compressed air. Inspect outer ball races for excessive wear and scoring. Inspect splined stub shaft for wear, cracks and twisted splines.

2) Inspect all 6 balls for pitting, cracking or scoring. Dulling of surface is normal. Inspect cage for excessive wear on inside and outside spherical surfaces. Look for heavy brinelling of cage windows. Check components for cracks or chips.

3) Inspect inner race for excessive wear or scoring. If any damage is found, replace entire CV or Double Offset joint assembly. Polished areas in races and on cage spheres are normal and do not require joint replacement.

Inspection (Tripod)

Inspect drive axle boot for tears or excessive wear. Check spider assembly for worn or damaged needle bearings. Inspect snap rings, spacer ring and drive shaft grooves for excessive wear. Replace components as necessary. If drive axle is replaced, install new knuckle seal.

Reassembly

1) Apply a light coat of grease on ball grooves of inner and outer races. Install inner race into cage using a rotating action opposite of removal. Inner race snap ring should face axle side.

2) On inner CV joints, be sure ball bearing retaining ring is installed on inner race side facing small end of cage. Align windows of cage with outer race lands. Pivot cage with inner race into tilted position (opposite of removal).

3) Install ball bearings, one at a time, into outer CV joint as cage is tilted and rotated. On inner CV joint, insert ball bearings through cage windows. After balls are installed into cage of outer joint, pivot cage and inner race into installed position.

4) On Tripod Joints, slide spider gear onto axle with counter bore facing inner (transaxle) end of shaft. Install shaft retaining ring. Install inner and outer boot seal protectors.

5) Slide new seal clamp (for small end of boot seal), boot seal and seal retainer onto axle shaft. Coat inside lip (large diameter end) of seal with grease. Slide seal retainer on end of seal. Spread ears of bearing race snap ring and slide CV joint onto axle shaft until snap ring seats in groove.

6) Pack joint with approximately one-half grease provided in seal kit. Apply remaining grease inside seal. Slide seal toward joint until small end of seal is in groove in axle shaft. Position small clamp over small end of seal and into groove and tighten.

7) Place assembly vertically into an arbor press, with joint up so seal retainer is supported. *See Fig. 5, No. 7.* Press joint down onto retainer. Ensure seal stays on retainer during reassembly. If equipped, stretch rubber deflector ring and set in groove.

GENERAL MOTORS 5-SPEED MANUAL TRANSAXLE (Cont.)

Fig. 5: Disassembly of Drive Shaft Assembly With Double Offset and CV Joints

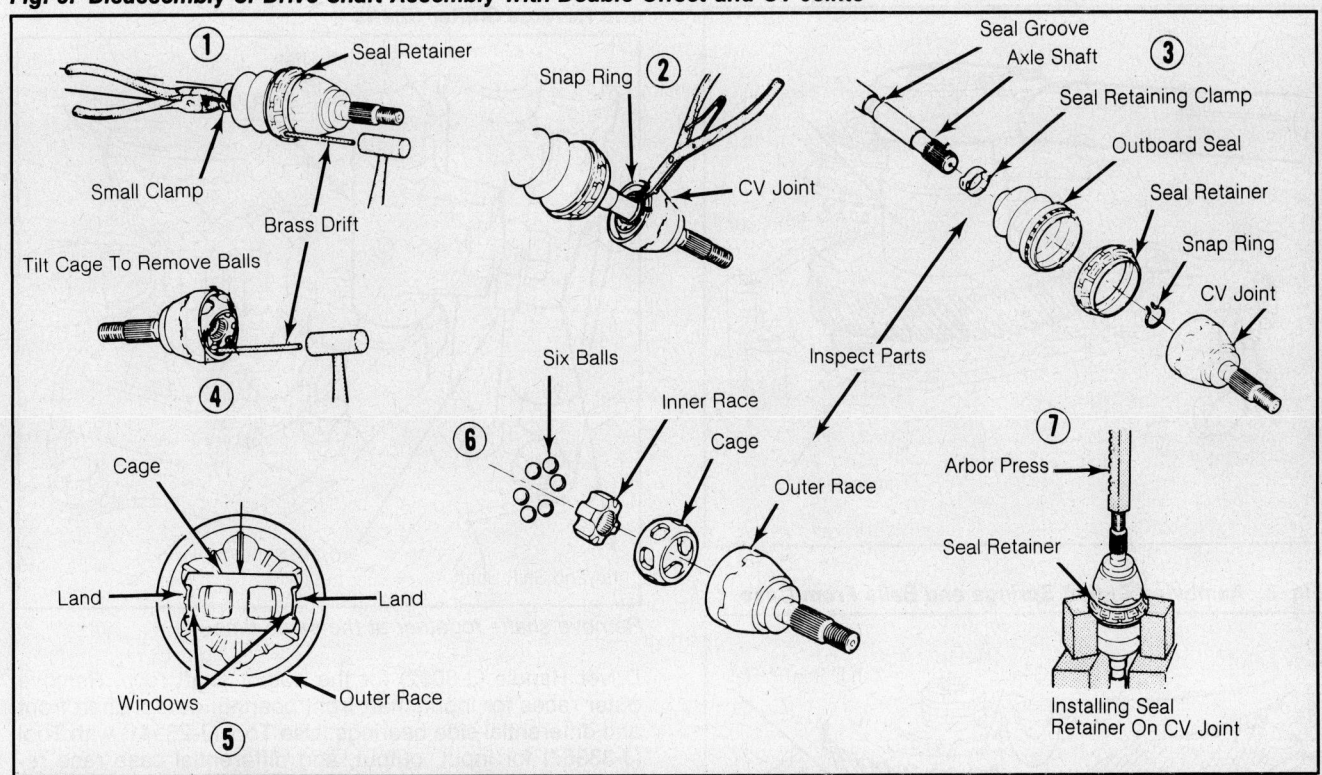

The outer CV joint is illustrated, the inner Double Offset joint is similar.

8) Install steel deflector ring using 2 1/2" pipe coupling over ring. Install a .118" (3 mm) sheet steel plate with .945" (24 mm) drilled hole (in center) over drive shaft end. Install nut on drive shaft end and tighten until ring seats in position.

Installation

1) Position drive axle loosely into steering knuckle and transaxle. Install steering knuckle onto strut bracket. Tighten strut bracket bolts fingertight only. Assemble stabilizer bar/tie rod as necessary.

Fig. 6: View of Tripod Joint

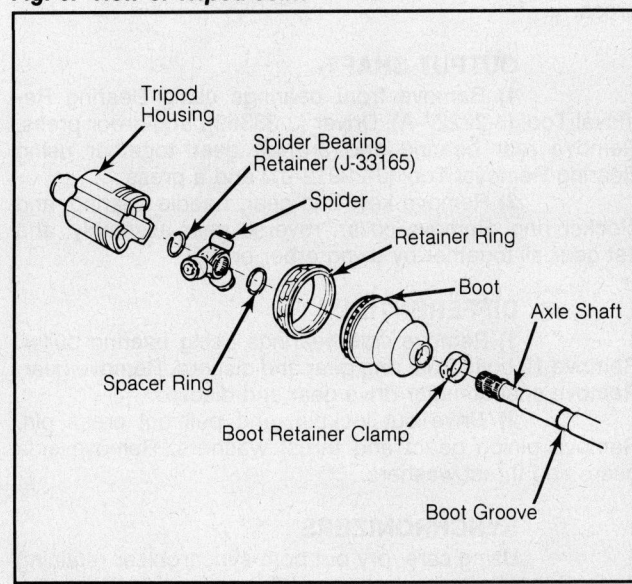

2) Install rotor and brake caliper. Tighten mount bolts. Install drive axle through steering knuckle. Insert a drift in rotor slot to prevent hub from turning. Install hub nut and partially tighten.

REMOVAL & INSTALLATION

See appropriate MANUAL TRANSMISSION REMOVAL article in DOMESTIC GENERAL SERVICING section.

DISASSEMBLY

TRANSAXLE

1) Attach transaxle assembly to Holding Fixture (J-33366) and attach fixture to Base Plate (J-3389-20). Remove 7 bolts retaining clutch cover.

2) Remove control box assembly together with 4 bolts from transaxle case. Shift transaxle into gear and remove 5th gear drive and driven gear retaining nuts from input and output shaft. *See Fig. 7.*

3) Shift transaxle to neutral. Remove detent spring retaining bolts for 1st/2nd, 3rd/4th, reverse, and 5th gear, and remove detent springs and balls. *See Fig. 8.*

4) Place 5th gear synchronizer in neutral and remove roll pin at 5th gear shift fork. Remove 5th gear synchronizer hub, sleeve roller bearing, and gear with shift fork as an assembly from output shaft.

5) Remove 5th gear from input shaft using Removal Tool (J-35274). Remove 7 screws using Removal Tool (J-25359-6) from bearing retainer. Remove bearing retainer and shims from input and output shafts.

Manual Transmissions

GENERAL MOTORS 5-SPEED MANUAL TRANSAXLE (Cont.)

Fig. 7: Removing 5th Gear Retaining Nut

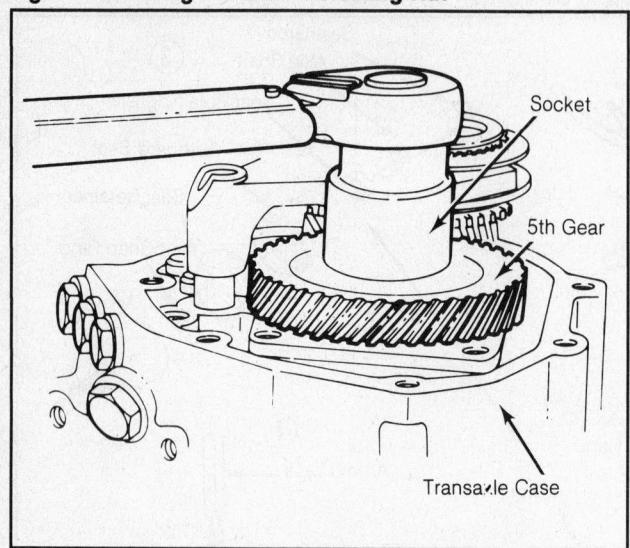

Fig. 8: Removing Detent Springs and Balls From Case

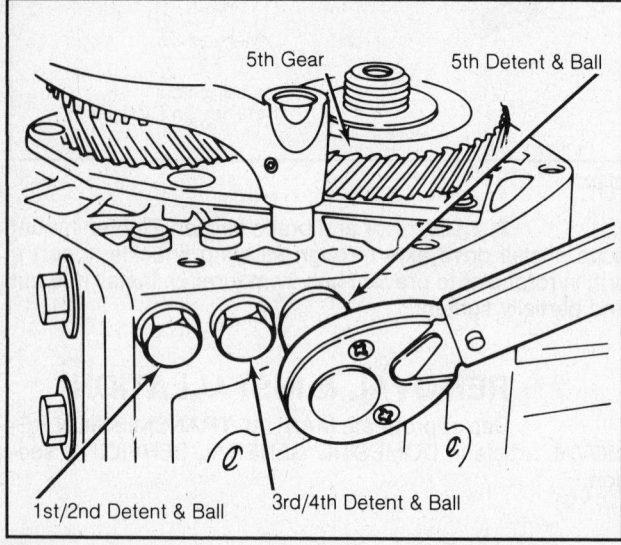

Reverse is located on opposite side of case.

6) Remove bolt used to retain reverse idler shaft at case. Remove collar and thrust washer from output shaft using Pullers (J-22888 and J-22888-30). Remove 14 bolts retaining transaxle case and separate case from clutch housing.

7) Remove reverse idler gear and reverse idler shaft. Lift 5th gear shaft. With detent aligned facing the same way and remove 5th and reverse shafts at the same time. *See Fig. 9.*

8) Remove roll pin from 1st/2nd shift fork, slide 1st/2nd shaft upward to clear housing and remove fork and shaft from case. Remove roll pin and reverse shift lever.

9) Remove input and output shafts with 3rd/4th shift fork and shaft as an assembly. Remove differential case assembly. Remove reverse shift bracket together with 4 bolts, and take out 3 interlock pins.

10) Remove rear bearing outer races from transaxle case. Use Puller (J-24256-2) with Driver Handle (J-8092) for the input shaft race. Use Puller (J-33370) with

Fig. 9: Proper Position to Remove 5th and Reverse Shifter Shafts

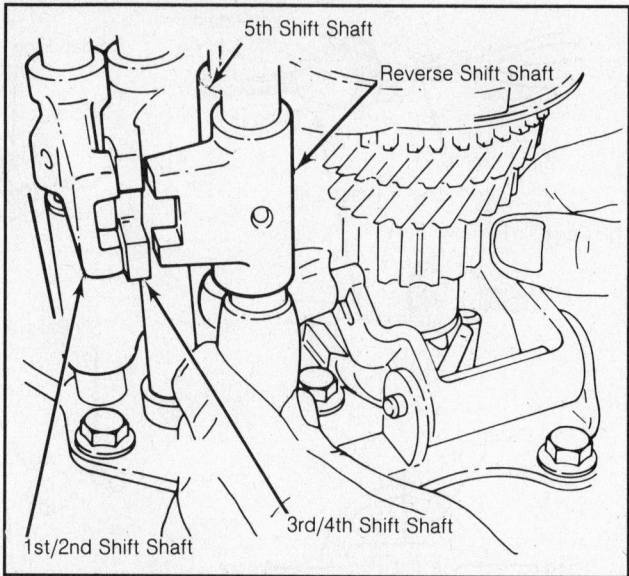

Remove shafts together at the same time.

Driver Handle (J-8092) for the output shaft race. Remove outer races for input shaft front bearing, output shaft front and differential side bearings. Use Tool (J-26941) with Tool (J-33367) for input, output, and differential case race removal, and Tool (J-26941) with slide hammer to remove the differential race in the housing.

11) Remove input shaft seals from housing. Remove clutch shaft seal only when replacement is required. Drive out bushing toward inside of case. Remove fork assembly only when replacing clutch fork assembly.

COMPONENT DISASSEMBLY

INPUT SHAFT

Remove front bearing using gear remover and press. Remove rear bearing 4th gear, 3rd/4th synchronizer assembly and 3th gear all together, using gear remover and press.

OUTPUT SHAFT

1) Remove front bearings using Bearing Removal Tool (J-22227-A), Driver (J-33369), and arbor press. Remove rear bearing and 3rd/4th gear together using Bearing Removal Tool (J-22912-01) and a press.

2) Remove key, 2nd gear, needle bearing, and blocker ring. Remove collar, reverse gear assembly, and 1st gear all together by using arbor press.

DIFFERENTIAL

1) Remove side bearings using bearing puller. Remove 10 bolts from ring gear and discard. Remove gear. Remove speedometer drive gear and discard.

2) Drive out lockpin, and pull out cross pin. Remove pinion gears and thrust washers. Remove side gears and thrust washers.

SYNCHRONIZERS

Using care, pry out both synchronizer retaining rings. Separate hub, sleeve, and 3 keys, noting their posi-

GENERAL MOTORS 5-SPEED MANUAL TRANSAXLE (Cont.)

Fig. 10: Exploded View 5-Speed Manual Transaxle Gear Assemblies

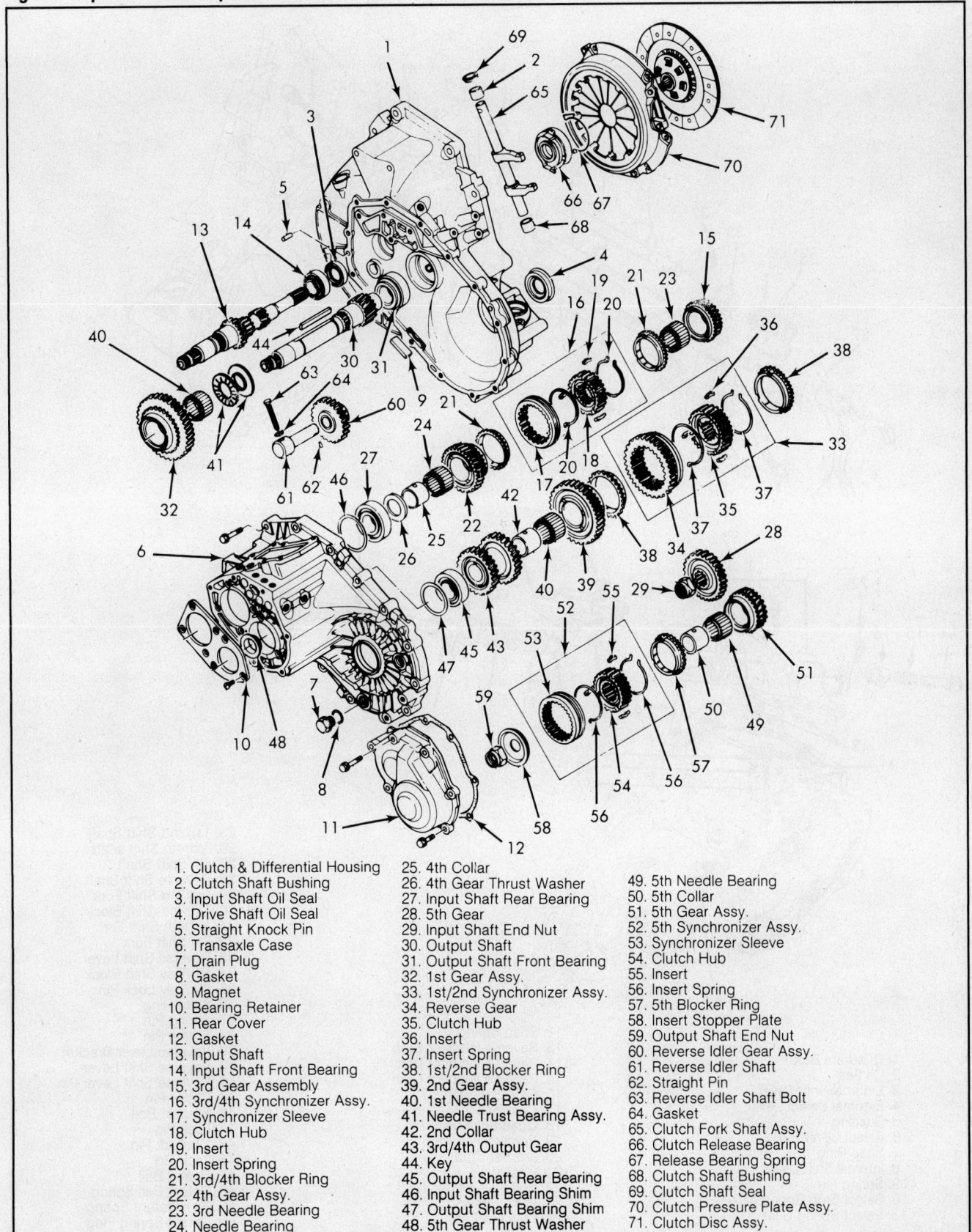

1. Clutch & Differential Housing
2. Clutch Shaft Bushing
3. Input Shaft Oil Seal
4. Drive Shaft Oil Seal
5. Straight Knock Pin
6. Transaxle Case
7. Drain Plug
8. Gasket
9. Magnet
10. Bearing Retainer
11. Rear Cover
12. Gasket
13. Input Shaft
14. Input Shaft Front Bearing
15. 3rd Gear Assembly
16. 3rd/4th Synchronizer Assy.
17. Synchronizer Sleeve
18. Clutch Hub
19. Insert
20. Insert Spring
21. 3rd/4th Blocker Ring
22. 4th Gear Assy.
23. 3rd Needle Bearing
24. Needle Bearing
25. 4th Collar
26. 4th Gear Thrust Washer
27. Input Shaft Rear Bearing
28. 5th Gear
29. Input Shaft End Nut
30. Output Shaft
31. Output Shaft Front Bearing
32. 1st Gear Assy.
33. 1st/2nd Synchronizer Assy.
34. Reverse Gear
35. Clutch Hub
36. Insert
37. Insert Spring
38. 1st/2nd Blocker Ring
39. 2nd Gear Assy.
40. 1st Needle Bearing
41. Needle Trust Bearing Assy.
42. 2nd Collar
43. 3rd/4th Output Gear
44. Key
45. Output Shaft Rear Bearing
46. Input Shaft Bearing Shim
47. Output Shaft Bearing Shim
48. 5th Gear Thrust Washer
49. 5th Needle Bearing
50. 5th Collar
51. 5th Gear Assy.
52. 5th Synchronizer Assy.
53. Synchronizer Sleeve
54. Clutch Hub
55. Insert
56. Insert Spring
57. 5th Blocker Ring
58. Insert Stopper Plate
59. Output Shaft End Nut
60. Reverse Idler Gear Assy.
61. Reverse Idler Shaft
62. Straight Pin
63. Reverse Idler Shaft Bolt
64. Gasket
65. Clutch Fork Shaft Assy.
66. Clutch Release Bearing
67. Release Bearing Spring
68. Clutch Shaft Bushing
69. Clutch Shaft Seal
70. Clutch Pressure Plate Assy.
71. Clutch Disc Assy.

Fig. 11: Exploded View of 5-Speed Manual Transaxle Gear Shifter Assemblies

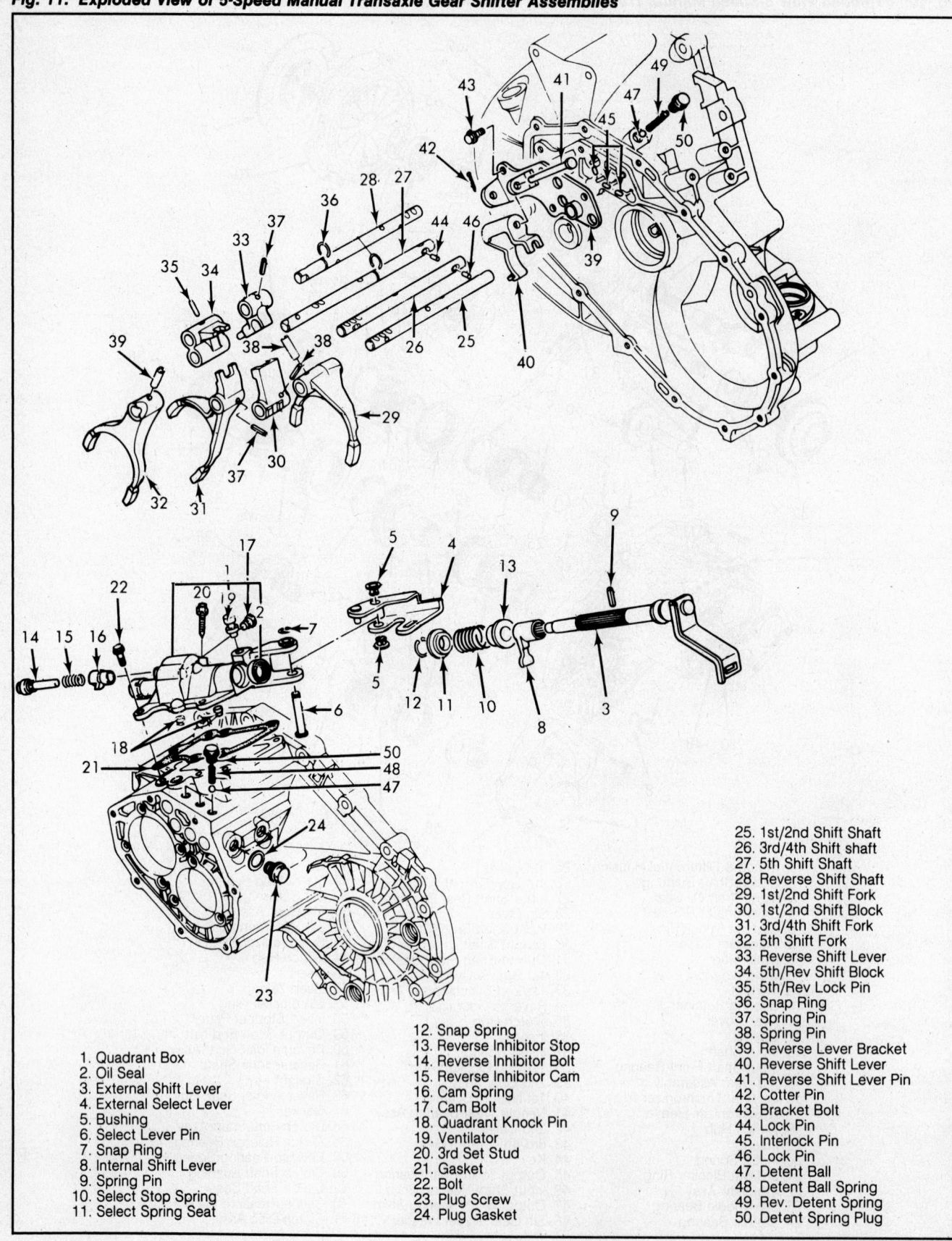

1. Quadrant Box
2. Oil Seal
3. External Shift Lever
4. External Select Lever
5. Bushing
6. Select Lever Pin
7. Snap Ring
8. Internal Shift Lever
9. Spring Pin
10. Select Stop Spring
11. Select Spring Seat

12. Snap Spring
13. Reverse Inhibitor Stop
14. Reverse Inhibitor Bolt
15. Reverse Inhibitor Cam
16. Cam Spring
17. Cam Bolt
18. Quadrant Knock Pin
19. Ventilator
20. 3rd Set Stud
21. Gasket
22. Bolt
23. Plug Screw
24. Plug Gasket

25. 1st/2nd Shift Shaft
26. 3rd/4th Shift shaft
27. 5th Shift Shaft
28. Reverse Shift Shaft
29. 1st/2nd Shift Fork
30. 1st/2nd Shift Block
31. 3rd/4th Shift Fork
32. 5th Shift Fork
33. Reverse Shift Lever
34. 5th/Rev Shift Block
35. 5th/Rev Lock Pin
36. Snap Ring
37. Spring Pin
38. Spring Pin
39. Reverse Lever Bracket
40. Reverse Shift Lever
41. Reverse Shift Lever Pin
42. Cotter Pin
43. Bracket Bolt
44. Lock Pin
45. Interlock Pin
46. Lock Pin
47. Detent Ball
48. Detent Ball Spring
49. Rev. Detent Spring
50. Detent Spring Plug

tion. *See Fig. 12.* Scribe hub to sleeve location and separate. Clean, inspect, and replace parts, as necessary.

Fig. 12: Components of Synchronizer Assemblies

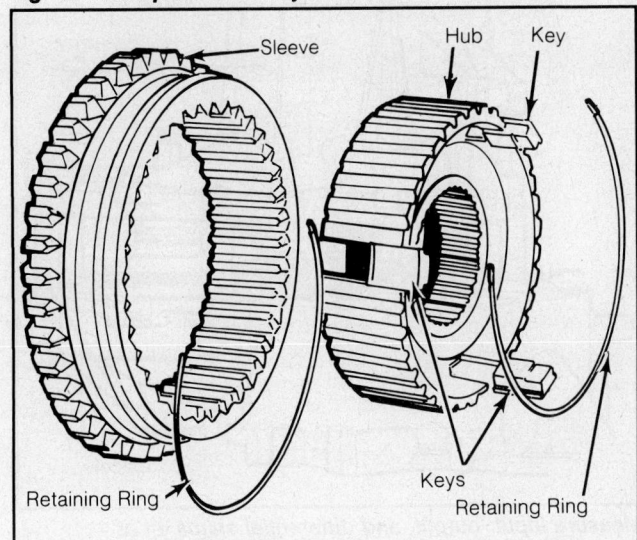

CLEANING & INSPECTION

1) Wash all parts, except oil seals, in cleaning solvent. Brush or scrape all foreign matter from parts, using care not to damage any part with scraper. Do not clean, wash, or soak transaxle seals in cleaning solvent. Dry all parts with compressed air.

CAUTION: Hold roller bearing assembly to prevent it from rotating when drying it with compressed air.

2) Lubricate all bearings with approved transmission lubricant and wrap them in a clean, lint free cloth, or paper until ready to use.

3) Inspect transaxle case and clutch housing case for cracks, worn, or damaged bearing bores. Check for damaged threads or any other damage. Inspect mating surfaces on cases for small nicks or burrs that could cause misalignment of the 2 halves. Remove all small nicks or burrs with a fine stone or file.

4) Check reverse idler gear and sliding gear for chipped, broken, or bent teeth. Check reverse idler gear for bushing damage. Check wear of reverse idler gear shaft (it is normal for front of teeth to show wear, this does not interfere with proper function).

5) Check teeth, splines, and journals of mainshaft for damage. Check all other gears for chipped, broken, or worn teeth. Check for eroded clutching teeth and damaged bearing surfaces. Clutching teeth will usually show rounding of the points which does not interfere with normal operation.

6) Check synchronizer sleeves for free movement on hubs. Make sure index marks are properly aligned. Check for damaged clutching teeth. Check for proper positioning of springs.

7) Inspect synchronizer blocker rings for wear marks on spline end back face which indicates ring was bottoming on gear face due to excessive blocker ring wear.

8) Inspect differential pinion and side gears for scoring, excessive wear, nicks, and chips. Worn, scored, and damaged gears must be replaced.

NOTE: **When a scored or chipped gear is replaced, transaxle case must be cleaned thoroughly to make sure all chips are removed.**

9) Make sure differential case bearing journals are smooth. Inspect case bearing shoulders for damage caused by bearing removal. Check fit (free rotation) of side gears in their cavities.

10) Check differential bearings and bearing races for wear or other damage. If races are not damaged, do not remove from transaxle case or clutch housing case. Check bearings for smooth rotation in races. Examine bearing roller ends for step wear.

NOTE: **If inspection reveals either a damaged bearing or race, both parts must be replaced as they are a matched set.**

COMPONENT REASSEMBLY

SYNCHRONIZERS

1) Assemble hub to sleeve with lip of hub away from shift fork groove in sleeve. Align scribe marks. Carefully install retaining ring, prying it back to insert keys one at a time.

2) Flats on retaining ring should hold keys in place. Install retaining ring on opposite side of hub, so open end of ring does not align with open end of first ring.

INPUT SHAFT

1) Install needle bearing, 3th gear, and block ring onto shaft. Match inserts of 3rd/4th sleeve and hub assembly with grooves of blocker ring. Press on sleeve, hub assembly and collar. Apply oil to collar and hub before and after installation. Use Driver (J-33374) and press.

2) Install blocker ring and needle bearing. Install 4th gear and thrust washer. Install thrust washer with recessed area facing 4th gear. Install front and rear bearings using Driver (J-33374) and press.

OUTPUT SHAFT

NOTE: **Before assembly apply oil to all thrust surfaces of gears, synchronizer interiors, and to bearing races.**

1) Install thrust washer, thrust needle bearing, 1st gear and blocker ring. Match the inserts of the sleeve and hub assembly with grooves in blocker ring and press assembly together with the collar using Support (J-8853-01) and Pilot (J-33369).

2) Install blocker ring needle bearing and 2nd gear, and install key on key groove. Apply oil to 3th/4th gear interior, match key with key groove, and fit key together with rear bearing. Using Driver (J-33374) and press, press bearing on shaft. Press front bearing on shaft using Driver (J-33368) and press.

DIFFERENTIAL

NOTE: **Before assembly apply oil to bearing interiors and race surfaces.**

1) Install 2 side gears on differential case together with thrust washers. Position 2 thrust washers and pinion gears opposite each other, and install them in to position by turning side gear.

2) Insert cross pin, and ensure backlash is within rated range of .0012-.0031" (.03-.08 mm). Install lock pin and stake it. Heat speedometer drive gear to about 203°F (95°C), and install it on differential.

3) Apply oil to cross pin, differential gears, thrust portion, side gear shaft portion, side gear spline portion before installation. Install ring gear on differential case. Install 10 ring gear bolts and tighten.

4) Install the side bearings on the differential case using Tool (J-22919) and press, install bearings.

REASSEMBLY

TRANSAXLE

1) Place transaxle case in holding fixture. Using Seal Installer (J-26540), drive input shaft seal into case. Install front outer bearing races for input shaft, output shaft, and differential into clutch housing.

2) Apply oil to bearing races before installation. Using Tool (J-33371) with Driver (J-8092), press input race into housing. Using Tool (J-7817) with Driver (J-8092), press output race into housing. Using Tool (J-8611-01) with Driver (J-8092), press differential race into housing. Apply grease to 3 interlock pins, and install them on clutch housing.

3) Install reverse shift bracket on clutch. Use 3rd/4th shaft rod to align bracket to housing. Make sure rod operates smoothly after installation. Install retaining bolts and torque to specifications. Install differential assembly first, then install input and output shaft with 3rd/4th shift fork and shaft together as an assembly into clutch housing.

4) The 3rd/4th shift shaft is installed into raised collar of reverse shift lever bracket. Install 1st/2nd shift fork onto synchronizer sleeve and insert shifter shaft into reverse shift lever bracket.

5) Align hole in fork with shaft and install roll pin. Install reverse lever on shift bracket. Install reverse and 5th gear shifter shaft and at the same time, engage reverse shaft with reverse shift lever. Install reverse idler shaft together with gear into clutch housing. Make sure reverse lever is engaged in collar of gear.

6) Measure and determine shim size using the 7 spacers and Shim Selector Gauges (J-33373). Position outer bearing races on input, output, and differential bearings. Position shim selection gauges on bearing races. See Fig. 13.

7) The 3 gauges are identified: Input, Output, and Differential. Install bearing and shims retainer on ends of shafts. Tighten bolts to 11-16 ft. lbs. (15-22 N.m).

8) Place 7 spacers (provided with gauges), evenly around perimeter of clutch housing. See Fig. 13. Carefully position transaxle case over gauges and on spacers. Install 7 bolts provided with gauge kit and tighten bolts alternately until case is seated on spacers. Tighten kit bolts to 10 ft. lbs. (14 N.m).

9) Rotate each gauge to seat bearings. Rotate differential case through 3 revolutions in each direction. With 3 gauges compressed, measure gap between outer sleeve and the base pad using available shim sizes. Use the largest shim that can be placed into gap and drawn through without binding. See Fig. 14.

10) Preload shims for input shaft are available in thicknesses of .0394" to .0977" (1.00 to 2.48 mm) in .0016" (.04 mm) increments. Preload shims for output shaft are available in thicknesses of .0457" to .0961" (1.16 to 2.44

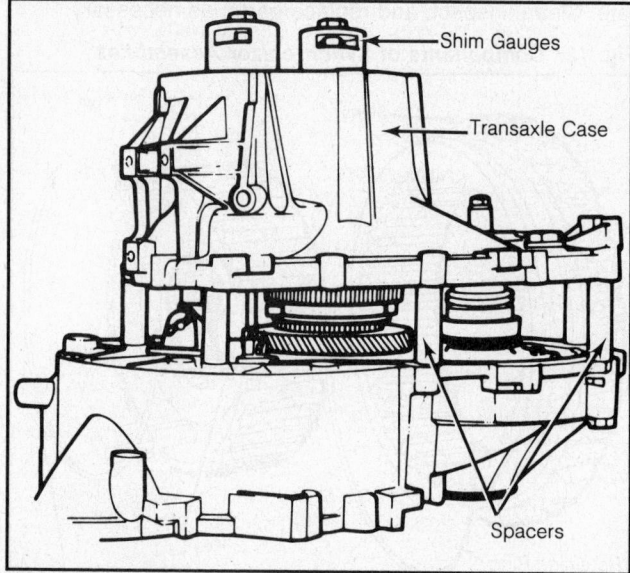

Fig. 13: Shim Gauges Sets Used to Measure Shims

Measure input, output, and differential shims all at the same time.

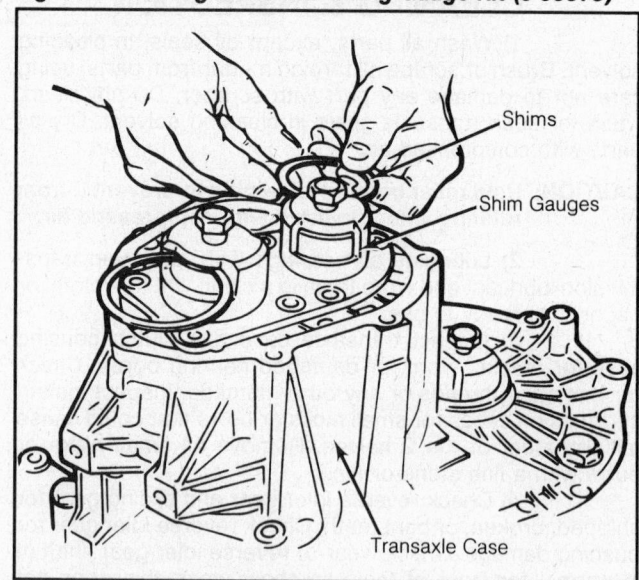

Fig. 14: Checking Shim Size Using Gauge Kit (J-33373)

Use largest shim without binding in gauge.

mm) in .0031" (.08 mm) increments. Preload shims for differential are available in thicknesses of .0426" to .0788" (1.08 to 2.00 mm) in .0016" (.04 mm) increments. The input shaft shim should be one size smaller than the largest shim that will fit in the gap. The differential should use a shim three sizes larger than that which will smoothly fit in the gap. The output shaft should use the largest shim that can be placed into the gap and drawn through without binding.

11) When each of the 3 shims have been selected, remove transaxle case, the 7 spacers, and 3 gauges. Position shims selected for input shaft, output shaft, and differential into bearing race bores in transaxle case. Install rear input shaft bearing race using Installer (J-24256-A) and Driver (J-8092).

GENERAL MOTORS 5-SPEED MANUAL TRANSAXLE (Cont.)

12) Press bearing until seated in its bore. Install rear output shaft bearing race using Installer (J-33370) and Driver (J-8092). Press bearing until seated in its bore. Install rear differential case bearing race using Installer (J-8611-01) and Driver (J-8092). Press bearing until seated in its bore.

13) Apply a 1/8" bead of sealant to the mating surfaces of clutch housing and transaxle case. Be sure magnet is installed in transaxle case. Install transaxle case on clutch housing.

14) Install reverse idle shaft bolt into transaxle case. Install 14 case bolts and tighten in diagonal sequence. Install drive axle seals. Install thrust washer and collar to output shaft.

15) Install 5th gear to input shaft. Install needle bearing, 5th gear, blocker ring, hub/sleeve assembly with shift fork in its groove and back plate on output shaft.

16) Apply Locktite No. 262 or equivalent to threads of the input and output shafts , do not allow Locktite to flow on splines of 5th gear and intput shaft. Install new retaining nuts.

17) Align shift fork on shifter shaft and install roll pin. Install detent balls and detent springs for reverse, 1st/2nd, 3rd/4th, and 5th gears. Install retaining bolts and tighten. Stake nuts after reaching final torque.

18) Install gasket and control box assembly on transaxle case, and tighten 4 bolts. Make sure transaxle shifts properly before installing rear cover. Install gasket and rear cover with 7 bolts, and tighten bolts.

19) Install clutch fork assembly if it has been removed. Lubricate and install bushing into upper hole using Bushing Installer (J-28412). Install oil seal. Install the clutch release bearing.

TIGHTENING SPECIFICATIONS

Application	Ft. Lbs. (N.m)
Brake Caliper	30 (41)
Control Box-to-Case Bolts	11-16 (15-22)
Cradle	
Sidemember-to-Crossmember	34-47 (46-64)
Body Mount	66 (90)
Detent Spring Retaining Bolts	15-21 (21-29)
Engine Support Bolts	50 (68)
Engine-to-Transaxle	55 (75)
Hub Nut	
Initial	70 (95)
Final	185-225 (250-305)
Input/Output Shaft Nuts	87-101 (118-137)
Rear Cover Bolts	11-16 (15-22)
Reverse Idler Shaft Bolt	22-33 (30-45)
Ring Gear Bolts	73-79 (98-107)
Stabilizer Bar Bushing Retainer	
Crossmember	40 (54)
Control Arm	35 (47)
Suspension	
Cam Bolt	140 (190)
Upper Bolt	140 (190)
Transaxle Mounts	
4-Cylinder Engine	35 (47)
V6 Engine	18 (24)
Transaxle-to-Clutch Hsg. Bolts	22-33 (30-45)

Manual Transmissions

JEEP AISIN 4 & 5-SPEED

Cherokee & Wagoneer

IDENTIFICATION

Two separate identification codes are used on AX4 and AX5 units. Model number and coded shipping date are found to rear of shift tower. Second code, which shows build date and serial number, is stamped on bottom of case next to intermediate plate.

First number of 2nd code is year of manufacture, while 2nd and 3rd numbers are month of manufacture. Five numbers remaining indicate serial number in sequence of building.

DESCRIPTION

Model AX4 is 4-speed unit and AX5 is 5-speed unit. Both models use top shifter. Transmission case is l-piece unit. Dark Gray cast iron intermediate plate is used between transmission and adapter housing. Both models are fully synchronized in all forward speeds.

LUBRICATION & ADJUSTMENT

See appropriate article in MANUAL TRANSMIS-SION SERVICING Section.

REMOVAL & INSTALLATION

See appropriate article in MANUAL TRANSMIS-SION REMOVAL Section.

DISASSEMBLY

TRANSMISSION

1) Remove clutch fork and release bearing. Remove back-up light switch. Remove shift lever retainer and restrict pins. Note restrict pins are different, with left side being black. Remove clutch housing-to-transmission case bolts.

2) Remove clutch housing from transmission case. Remove screw plug, spring, and detent ball. Use

Fig. 2: Location of Switches and Detent Ball Plug

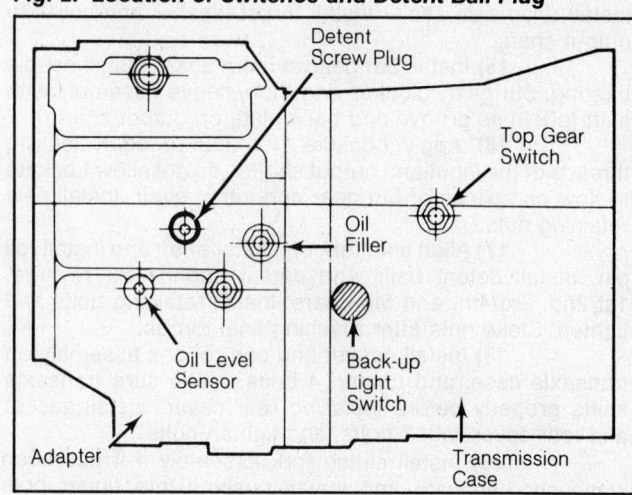

Use Torx bit and magnet to remove plug, ball and spring.

Fig. 1: Exploded View of AX4 & AX5 Transmissions

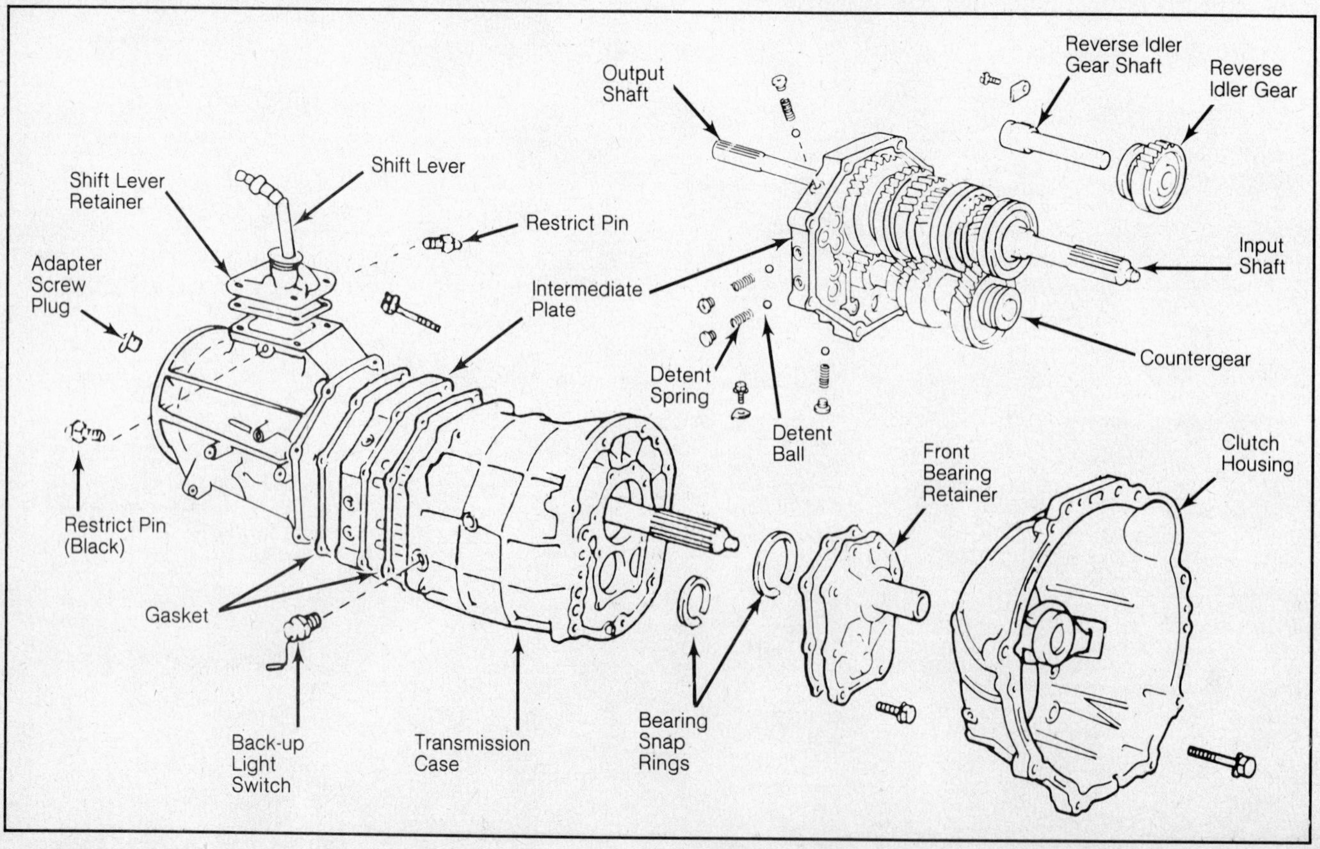

JEEP AISIN 4 & 5-SPEED (Cont.)

Torx bit and magnetic finger to remove spring and ball. *See Fig. 2.*

   3) Remove 5 bolts and 1 nut holding adapter housing to intermediate plate. Remove shift lever housing set bolt and lock plate. Remove plug from back of shift fork shaft. Remove large magnet and withdraw shaft.

   4) While rotating shift lever, remove it from top of transmission. Remove 2 studs from adapter housing. Use plastic hammer to tap and remove extension housing from intermediate plate. Leave gasket attached to intermediate plate.

   5) Remove front bearing retainer and outer snap rings on 2 front bearings. Loosen intermediate plate from transmission case with plastic hammer. Remove transmission case.

COMPONENT DISASSEMBLY

SHIFTING MECHANISM

NOTE: **Detent balls in intermediate housing will usually fall out when plugs or shift fork shafts are removed. Be careful to retain all detent balls, springs, and interlock pins. Magnet should be used to remove parts that do not come out easily.**

   1) Place intermediate plate in vise. Clamp intermediate plate securely. Make sure that machined surfaces of intermediate plate are protected from damage to sealing surfaces with soft jaws or by other means. Remove screw plugs, detent balls, and springs from side and bottom of intermediate plate.

   2) Drive out roll pins holding shift forks to shift rails. Remove both "E" type snap rings from shift rails. On AX5 models, pull shift fork shaft No. 4 from intermediate plate and catch detent ball. Remove shift fork shaft No. 4 and 5th gear fork. *See Fig. 3.*

   3) On both models, remove shift fork shaft No. 5 from intermediate plate with reverse shift head attached. Remove shift fork shaft No. 3 from intermediate plate, catching interlock pins if necessary. Remove shift fork shaft No. 1 from intermediate plate.

   4) Remove shift fork shaft No. 2 along with shift forks No. 2 and No. 1. Remove reverse idle gear shaft stopper, reverse idler gear and reverse gear shaft. Remove reverse shift arm from reverse shift arm bracket.

GEARS & SHAFTS

   1) Before removing gears and shafts from intermediate plate on AX5 model, thrust clearance between fifth gear on countershaft and rear counter gear bearing spacer should be measured. Standard clearance is .004-.012" (.10-.30 mm). If clearance is not correct, check parts for wear or damage.

   2) Engage any 2 gears so that output shaft is locked up. Loosen staked portion of nut on countershaft. Remove nut and disengage gears. Using puller (J 22888), remove countershaft 5th gear, needle bearing, synchro ring, and gear spline piece No. 5. Remove spacer and ball underneath spacer. Remove reverse shift arm bracket.

   3) On both models, remove bolts from rear output shaft bearing retainer. Remove snap ring from rear output shaft bearing after retainer is removed. Remove output shaft, counter gear, and input shaft as unit by tapping on intermediate plate while holding counter gear.

Fig. 3: Shift Shafts and Forks

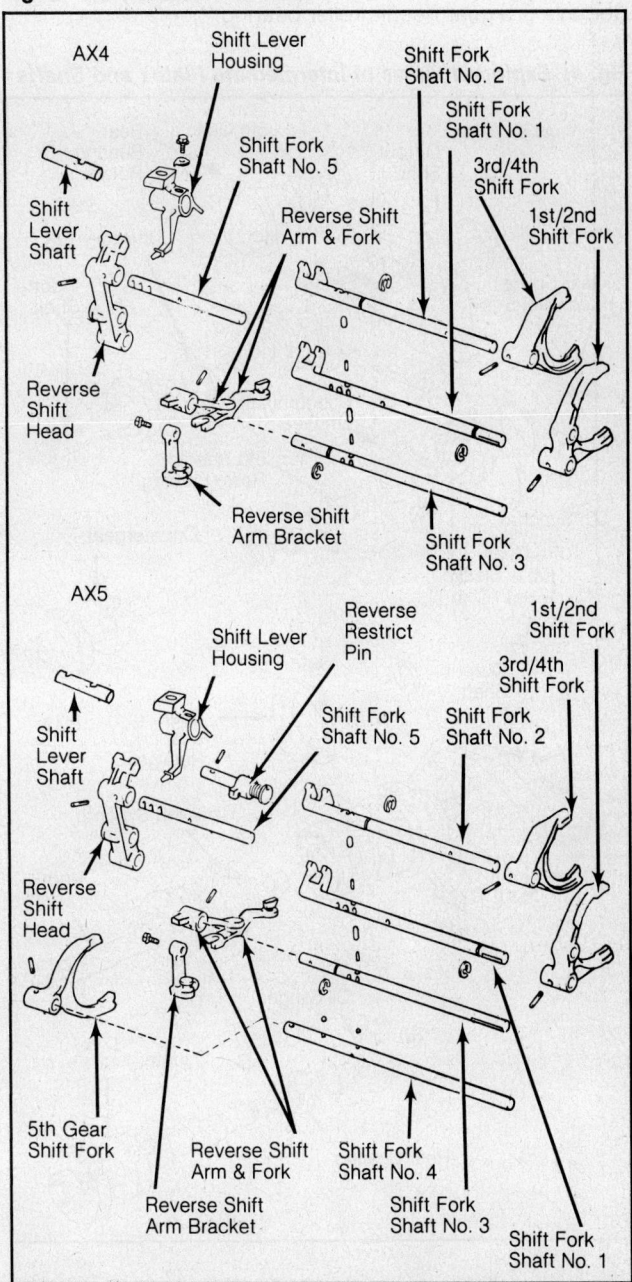

Use care to avoid losing parts when disassembling shift mechanisms.

   4) Remove input shaft, with 14 needle roller bearings, from output shaft. Remove countergear rear bearing from intermediate plate. With shaft removed from intermediate plate, measure thrust clearance of each gear. Standard clearance should be .004-.010" (.10-.30 mm).

   5) Remove small snap ring from output shaft. Press against 1st gear and remove inner race, 1st gear, rear bearing, and 5th gear (on AX5 model) off output shaft. Remove 1st gear needle roller bearing. Remove 1st gear synchro ring and locking ball.

   6) Pressing against 2nd gear, remove 1st/2nd gear hub, 2nd gear synchro ring, and 2nd gear. Remove 2nd gear needle roller bearing. Remove snap ring next to 3rd/4th gear hub. Pressing against 3rd gear, remove

Manual Transmissions
JEEP AISIN 4 & 5-SPEED (Cont.)

3rd/4th gear hub, 3rd gear synchro ring, and 3rd gear. Remove 3rd gear needle roller bearing.

Fig. 4: Exploded Views of Intermediate Plates and Shafts

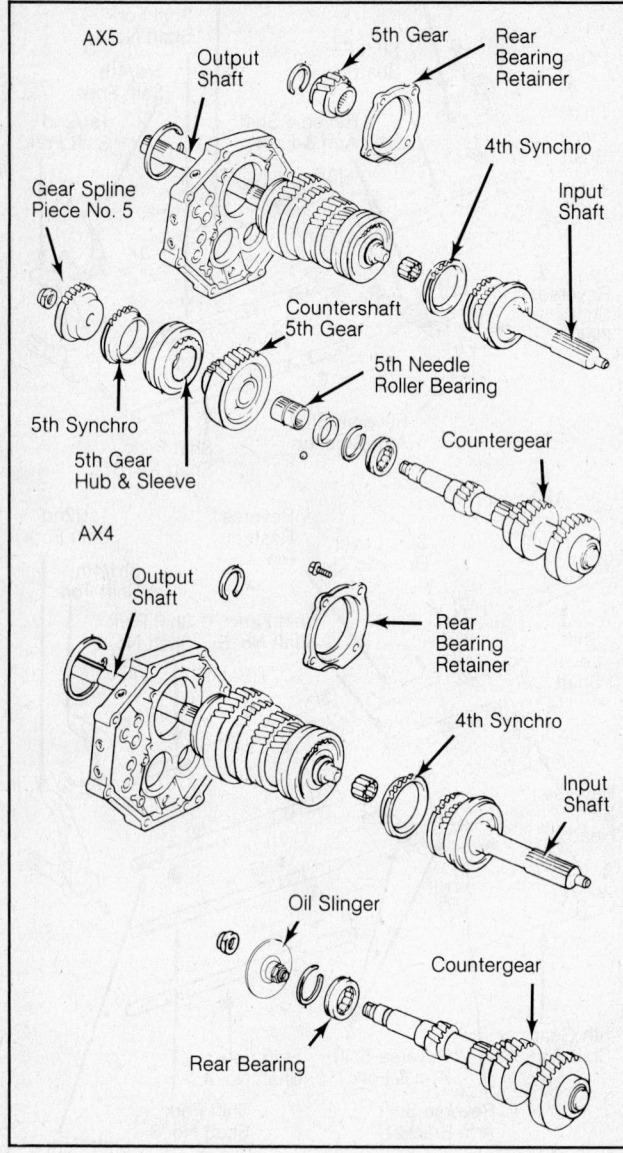

Fig. 5: Exploded View of Output Shaft

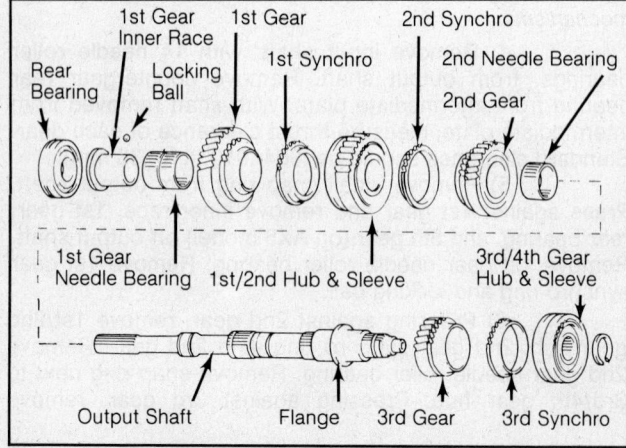

INSPECTION

1) Check output shaft and 1st gear inner race for wear or damage. Measure flange thickness on both output shaft and inner race with vernier caliper. Minimum thickness of output shaft flange is .189" (4.80 mm). Minimum thickness of inner race flange is .157" (3.99 mm).

2) Measure outer diameter of output shaft journals for 2nd and 3rd gears. Minimum diameter for 2nd gear journal is 1.495" (37.96 mm). Minimum diameter for 3rd gear journal is 1.377" (34.98 mm). Measure outer diameter of 1st gear inner race. Minimum diameter for inner race is 1.535" (38.99 mm).

3) Mount output shaft in "V" blocks or lathe. Mount dial indicator with tip on portion of shaft where 1st gear inner race sears. Rotate output shaft and measure runout. Maximum runout allowed is .002" (.05 mm).

4) Oil clearance between gears and bearing races must be measured with dial indicator. Install 1st gear needle bearing and inner race into 1st gear. With tip of indicator on inner race and gear held securely, move race up and down to measure oil clearance. *See Fig. 6.* Standard clearance range is .0004-.0013" (.009-.032 mm).

Fig. 6: Measuring 1st Gear Oil Clearance

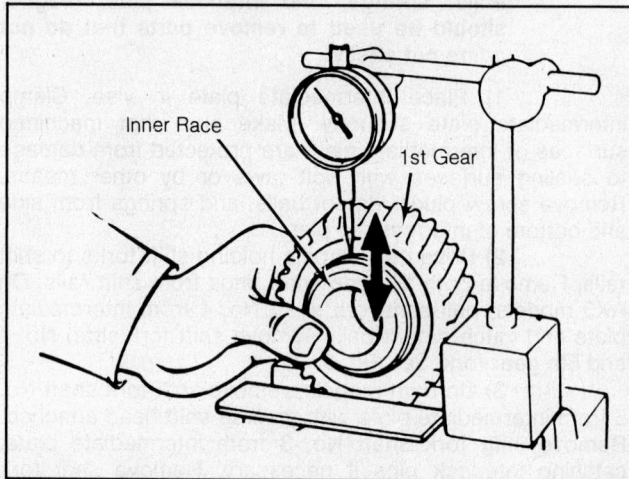

Procedure is similar for other gears with needle roller bearings.

5) Measure oil clearance of 2nd, 3rd, and countershaft 5th gears. Install gear on shaft with needle roller bearing in place. Position dial indicator tip on tooth of gear to be measured.

6) With shaft held securely, move gear up and down to measure clearance. Standard clearance range for 2nd and 3rd gears is .0004-.0013" (.009-.033 mm). Standard clearance range for countershaft 5th gear is .0004-.0013" (.009-.033 mm).

7) Check synchro ring braking action by pushing in and turning ring on tapered cone of gear. Measure synchro-to-gear face clearance with feeler gauge. This measurement should be made while ring is firmly pushed toward gear on cone. Standard clearance is .039-.079" (1.0-2.0 mm) while wear limit is .031" (.80 mm).

8) Measure clearance between inner edge of hub sleeve and face of shift fork. Maximum clearance between sleeve and fork is .039" (1.0 mm). Check input shaft for wear or damage. To remove bearing, snap ring must be removed and bearing pressed off input shaft.

JEEP AISIN 4 & 5-SPEED (Cont.)

9) Check countergear and bearing for wear or damage. If necessary, remove snap ring and press bearing off countergear with tool (J 22912 01). Check front bearing retainer for any damage or wear. Check adapter housing for wear or damage.

COMPONENT REASSEMBLY

NOTE: **Manufacturer recommends replacing all lip type oil seals, lock nuts, roll pins and snap rings when overhauling transmission. Use of Loctite Thread Lock or Loctite 242 Sealer is recommended when liquid sealer is required.**

GEARS & SHAFTS

1) If input shaft bearing is replaced, use press tool (J 34603) and press to install new bearing. Select snap ring that allows minimum axial play of bearing. There are 6 snap rings available, marked 0 through 5, in different thicknesses. *See Bearing Snap Ring Sizes* chart.

Bearing Snap Ring Sizes

Input Mark	Countergear Mark	Thickness In. (mm)
0	1	.0807-.0827 (2.05-2.10)
1	2	.0827-.0846 (2.10-2.15)
2	3	.0846-.0866 (2.15-2.20)
3	4	.0866-.0886 (2.20-2.25)
4	5	.0886-.0906 (2.25-2.30)
5	6	.0906-.0925 (2.30-2.35)

2) If countergear front bearing is to be replaced, use press tool (J 28406) and press to install new bearing and inner race. Select snap ring which will allow minimal axial play. There are 6 snap rings available, marked 1 through 6, in different thicknesses. *See Bearing Snap Ring Sizes* chart.

3) Press new seal into front bearing retainer with installer (J 34602). Oil seal should be installed so that top edge of seal is .441-.480" (11.18-12.19 mm) from bearing retainer-to-transmission mating surface.

Fig. 7: Assembling Synchronizer Hubs & Shift Sleeves

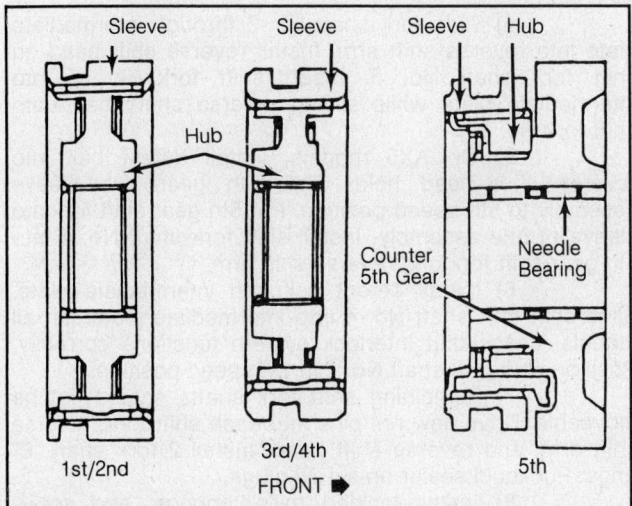

1st/2nd   3rd/4th   5th

FRONT ➡

Make sure to stagger end gaps of key springs.

4) On AX5 models, reverse restrict pin must be replaced if worn or damaged. Remove screw plug and drive out roll pin. Remove lever housing and slide out shaft. Install lever housing with new reverse restrict pin. Install new roll pin and tighten screw plug. On all models, replace adapter housing oil seal using driver (J 29184).

5) Install 1st/2nd gear hub into hub sleeve with shifting keys in place. Install 3rd/4th gear hub into hub sleeve with keys. Make sure end gaps of key springs are staggered on opposite sides of hub. Make sure that hubs and sleeves are in correct positions. *See Fig. 7.*

6) Put gear oil on output shaft and 3rd gear needle roller bearing. Place 3rd gear synchro ring on gear, making sure that ring slots align with shifting keys. Install needle roller bearing into 3rd gear and 3rd/4th gear hub.

7) Press gear and synchro hub assembly onto output shaft. Install new snap ring selected to allow minimal axial play. Snap rings are available in 7 thicknesses. *See 3rd Gear Snap Rings* table.

3rd Gear Snap Rings

Mark	Thickness In. (mm)
C-1	.0689-.0709 (1.75-1.80)
D	.0709-.0728 (1.80-1.85)
D-1	.0728-.0748 (1.85-1.90)
E	.0748-.0768 (1.90-1.95)
E-1	.0768-.0787 (1.95-2.00)
F	.0788-.0807 (2.00-2.05)
F-1	.0807-.0827 (2.05-2.10)

8) Measure 3rd gear thrust clearance between face of gear and flange on output shaft. Standard clearance range is .004-.010" (.10-.25 mm). Lightly coat output shaft and 2nd gear needle bearing with gear oil. Put 2nd gear synchro ring on 2nd gear. Align slots in ring with keys in hub.

9) Install needle roller bearing into 2nd gear. Press 2nd gear and 1st/2nd gear hub onto output shaft. Install 1st gear locking ball into output shaft. Lightly coat 1st gear needle roller bearing with gear oil. Assemble 1st gear, synchro ring, needle roller bearing, and 1st gear bearing inner race.

10) Install assembly on output shaft and align shynchro ring slots with shifting keys. Turn inner race so that it aligns with locking ball. Install rear output shaft bearing on shaft with snap ring groove of outer race toward rear of shaft. Hold 1st gear inner race to keep it from falling during assembly.

11) Using press tool (J 34603), press rear bearing onto output shaft. Measure thrust clearance of both 1st and 2nd gears. Thrust of 2nd gear is measured between face of gear and flange on output shaft. Thrust of 1st gear is measured between face of gear and flange of needle bearing inner race.

12) On AX5 model, press 5th gear onto output shaft with press tool (J 34603). On all models, select snap ring that allows minimum axial play. There are eleven different sizes of snap ring available. *See Rear Output Shaft Snap Rings* table. Install selected snap ring onto output shaft.

Rear Output Shaft Snap Rings

Mark	Thickness In. (mm)
A	.1051-.1071 (2.67-2.72)
B	.1075-.1094 (2.73-2.78)
C	.1098-.1118 (2.79-2.84)
D	.1122-.1142 (2.85-2.90)
E	.1146-.1165 (2.91-2.96)
F	.1169-.1189 (2.97-3.02)
G	.1193-.1213 (3.03-3.08)
H	.1217-.1236 (3.09-3.14)
J	.1240-.1260 (3.15-3.20)
K	.1264-.1283 (3.21-3.26)
L	.1287-.1307 (3.27-3.32)

13) Apply multipurpose grease to 14 needle roller bearings which were removed from input shaft. Install bearings into input shaft. Install output shaft into intermediate plate. Tap on intermediate plate while pulling on output shaft. Install input shaft to output shaft, using care to avoid cocking bearings in input shaft.

14) Make sure synchro ring slots on input shaft align with keys in 3rd/4th gear hub sleeve assembly. Install countergear into intermediate plate. With intermediate plate securely clamped and countergear held in place, drive rear countergear bearing into intermediate plate.

15) Install small snap ring for rear countergear bearing. Install large output shaft bearing snap ring. Make sure that snap ring is flush with surface of intermediate plate. Install bearing retainer and tighten bolts. Install reverse shift arm bracket and tighten bolts.

16) On AX5 models, install ball and spacer on countergear. Install shift keys and 5th gear hub sleeve onto countershaft 5th gear. Make sure key springs are positioned so end gaps are staggered and install key springs under shifting keys.

17) Apply light coating of gear oil to needle roller bearing. Install countershaft 5th gear with shifting hub sleeve assembly and needle roller bearing. Install synchro ring on gear spline piece No. 5. Drive gear spline piece No. 5 onto countergear, using driver (J 28406). Make sure synchro ring slots line up with shift keys.

NOTE: When driving gear spline piece No. 5 onto countergear, support front of countergear with hammer or other solid object.

18) Engage 2 gears to lock output shaft. Install lock nut on countergear and tighten to 90 ft. lbs. (122 N.m). Stake lock nut and disengage gears. Measure thrust clearance of countergear 5th gear between spacer and face of gear. Standard clearance should be .004-.012" (.10-.30 mm).

SHIFTING MECHANISM

1) Install reverse shift arm on pivot of reverse shift arm bracket. Put reverse idler gear onto shaft. Align reverse shift fork in groove of reverse idler gear. Install reverse idler gear shaft into intermediate plate. Install reverse idler shaft stop and tighten bolt.

2) Insert shift forks into 1st/2nd and 3rd/4th gear hub sleeves. Install fork shaft No. 2 through intermediate plate and both shift forks. Lightly coat detent balls and interlock pins with multipurpose grease. Install detent ball into intermediate plate. Make sure that

Fig. 8: Installation of Detents and Interlocks

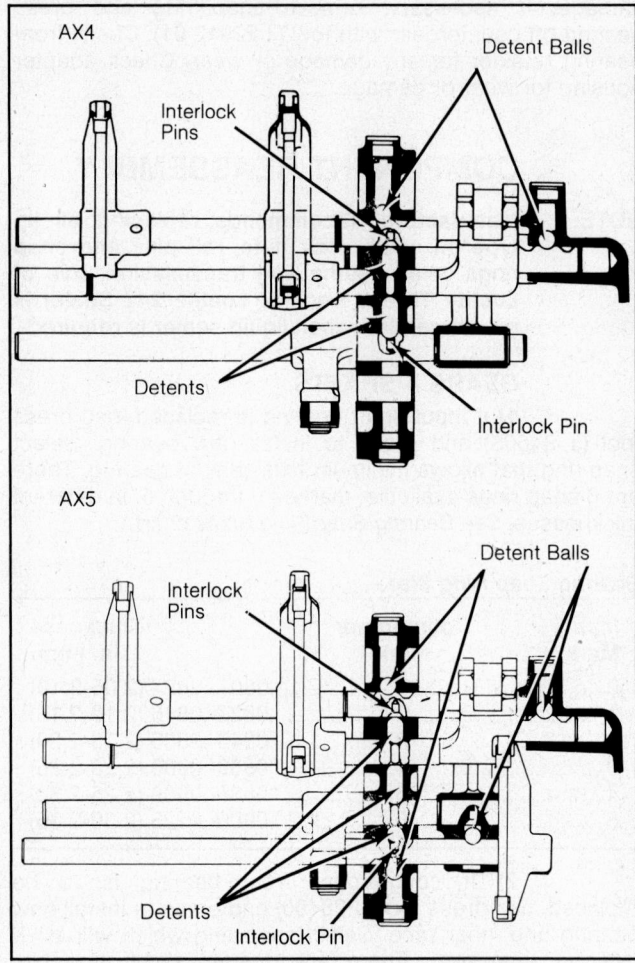

Note position by size and shape of balls and pins.

interlock pins and balls are installed in correct locations. See Fig. 8.

3) Install interlock pin into hole of shift fork shaft No. 1. Slide fork shaft No. 1 through intermediate plate into 1st/2nd gear fork. Install detent ball into intermediate plate. Install interlock pin into hole of shift fork shaft No. 3.

4) Slide fork shaft No. 3 through intermediate plate into reverse shift arm. Install reverse shift head on shift fork shaft No. 5. Insert shift fork No. 5 into intermediate plate while sliding reverse shift head onto shift fork No. 3.

5) On AX5 models, install detent ball into reverse shift head hole. Shift 5th gear hub sleeve assembly to 5th speed position. Put 5th gear shift fork into sleeve of hub assembly. Install shift fork shaft No. 4 into 5th gear shift fork and reverse shift arm.

6) Install detent ball into intermediate plate. Slide shift fork shaft No. 4 into intermediate plate. On all models, check that interlock system functions correctly. Position shift fork shaft No. 1 in 1st speed position.

7) Remaining shift fork shafts should not be moveable. Drive new roll pins into each shift fork, reverse shift arm, and reverse shift head. Install 2 fork shaft "E" rings. Put liquid sealer on screw plugs.

8) Install locking balls, springs, and screw plugs to intermediate plate. Short spring goes into top

JEEP AISIN 4 & 5-SPEED (Cont.)

hole on intermediate plate. Remove intermediate plate from vise and clean old gasket from plate surface.

REASSEMBLY

NOTE: Manufacturer recommends replacing all lip type oil seals, lock nuts, roll pins and snap rings when overhauling transmission. Use of Loctite Thread Lock or Loctite 242 Sealer is recommended when liquid sealer is required.

TRANSMISSION

1) Place new gasket on front of intermediate plate. Align bearing outer races, shift fork shaft ends, and reverse idler gear with holes in transmission case. Install case against intermediate plate, tapping on case with plastic hammer if necessary.

2) Install 2 new bearing snap rings outside transmission housing. Install front bearing retainer with new gasket. Apply liguid sealer on retainer-to-transmission boltsand tighten retainer plate to transmission. Install new gasket on back of intermediate plate. Install adapter housing.

3) Tighten adapter-to-intermediate plate bolts. Install shift lever housing. Insert shift lever into adapter and shift lever housing. Tighten shift lever housing bolt, using new lock plate. Lock plate in place. Install and tighten adapter screw plug.

4) Apply liquid sealer to detent plug. Install detent ball, spring, and plug into adapter housing. Tighten plug and make sure that input and output shafts rotate smoothly. Make sure that shifting can be done smoothly into all gears.

5) Install restrict pins into adapter housing. Black pin belongs on reverse/5th gear side of housing. Install shift lever retainer with new gasket. Install backup light switch. Install clutch housing and tighten bolts evenly.

TIGHTENING SPECIFICATIONS

Application	Ft. Lbs. (N.m)
Backup Lamp Switch	27 (37)
Clutch Housing	27 (37)
Restrict Pins	20 (27)
Screw Plugs	14 (19)
Shift Lever Housing	28 (38)
Front Bearing Retainer	12 (16)
Adapter Bolts	27 (37)
Reverse Shaft Stopper	13 (18)

Manual Transmissions
NEW PROCESS 435

Chrysler Corp. Ramcharger,
D & W100/350,
Ford Bronco, F150/F350

IDENTIFICATION

Chrysler Corp. 4-speed manual transmissions use aluminum identification tag secured by 2 bolts on power take-off cover. Information on tag includes part number, model and build date.

Ford 4-speed manual transmissions have service identification tag found on 2 bolts retaining power take-off cover to case. See Fig. 1.

Fig. 1: Ford Motor Company Identification Tag

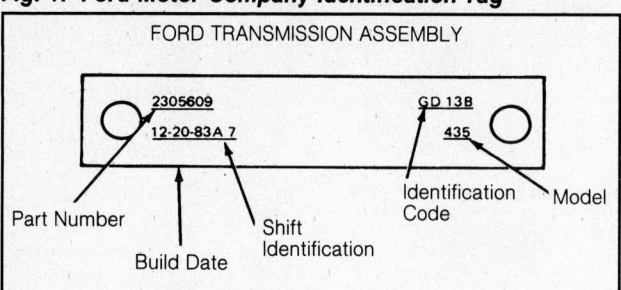

DESCRIPTION

New Process 435 4-speed transmission uses top-mounted shift lever and cover. Spur cut gears are used for 1st and Reverse speeds. Helical cut gears, synchronized for easier shifting, are used for 2nd, 3rd, and 4th speeds.

Input shaft is supported at front by tapered roller bearing. End play is controlled by gasket thickness between case and bearing retainer. Front of mainshaft is supported by pilot roller bearing in input shaft. Rear of mainshaft is supported by ball bearing that is pressed onto shaft and held in case by snap ring.

Countershaft and gears are integral one-piece design. Countershaft gear is supported by caged roller bearings at each end. Roller-type thrust bearing and race are provided at rear of countershaft gear, with thrust washer at front of gear.

Reverse idler gear uses bronze bushing. The 3rd-4th speed synchronizer is mounted at front of mainshaft. The 2nd speed synchronizer and 1st speed sliding gear is mounted at rear of mainshaft.

LUBRICATION & ADJUSTMENT

See appropriate MANUAL TRANSMISSION SERVICING article in DOMESTIC GENERAL SERVICING section.

TROUBLE SHOOTING

See MANUAL TRANSMISSION TROUBLE SHOOTING article in DOMESTIC GENERAL SERVICING section.

REMOVAL & INSTALLATION

See appropriate MANUAL TRANSMISSION REMOVAL article in DOMESTIC GENERAL SERVICING section.

SERVICE (IN VEHICLE)

GEAR SHIFT LEVER

NOTE: **Following gear shift lever procedure applies to Ford vehicles only. Remove shift ball only if shift ball, boot or lever is to be replaced. If either ball, boot or lever is not being replaced, remove ball, boot, and lever as assembly.**

Removal

1) Remove plastic insert from shift ball. Warm ball with heat gun to 140-180°F (60-80°C). Knock ball off lever with block of wood and hammer, taking care not to damage finish on shift lever.

2) Remove rubber boot and floor pan cover. Shift into 2nd gear. Remove lock pin and remove shift lever from shifter housing.

Installation

1) Lubricate shift lever. Install shift lever in shifter housing, making sure that slot in lever aligns with tab in housing. Install lock pin. Install rubber boot and floor pan cover.

2) Remove shift pattern insert from ball. Warm ball with heat gun to 140-180°F (60-80°C) and tap ball on lever with 7/16" socket and mallet. Install insert.

TRANSMISSION DISASSEMBLY

1) Mount transmission assembly in holding fixture and remove drain and filler plugs. Place gearshift lever in Neutral position. Remove shift control cover bolts.

2) Remove cover by lifting and rotating slightly counterclockwise to provide clearance for shift forks. Remove cover and discard gasket. See Fig. 9.

3) Lock transmission in 2 gears. Remove mainshaft flange nut and mainshaft flange. Remove extension housing and slide speedometer drive gear off mainshaft.

4) Measure and record synchronizer outer stop ring and 3rd gear end play for reference during reassembly. See Fig. 15.

5) Remove input shaft bearing retainer and gasket. Rotate gear to align notch in input shaft gear clutch teeth with countershaft drive gear teeth.

6) Remove input shaft assembly and tapered roller bearing. Remove snap ring, washer, and pilot roller bearing from recess in rear of input shaft. See Fig. 2.

7) Place brass drift in front center of mainshaft and drive mainshaft to rear. Remove rear bearing with puller. Move mainshaft to rear and tilt front of mainshaft upward.

8) Remove roller-type thrust bearing. Remove synchronizer and stop rings separately. Remove mainshaft assembly. See Figs. 3 and 4.

9) Remove Reverse idler lock screw and lock plate. Use brass drift, held at angle, to drive idler shaft to rear. Remove shaft. Lift Reverse idler gear from case.

Fig. 2: Input Shaft Assembly

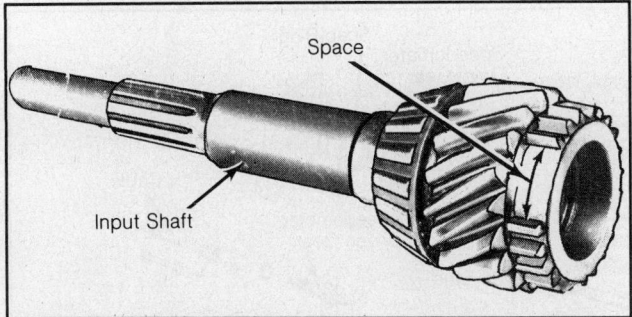

Align space in input gear clutch teeth with countershaft gear teeth.

10) Remove bearing retainer from rear of countershaft. Roller bearing remains with retainer. Tilt cluster gear assembly and work out of case. Use driver to remove front bearings from case.

Fig. 3: Removing Rear Mainshaft Bearing

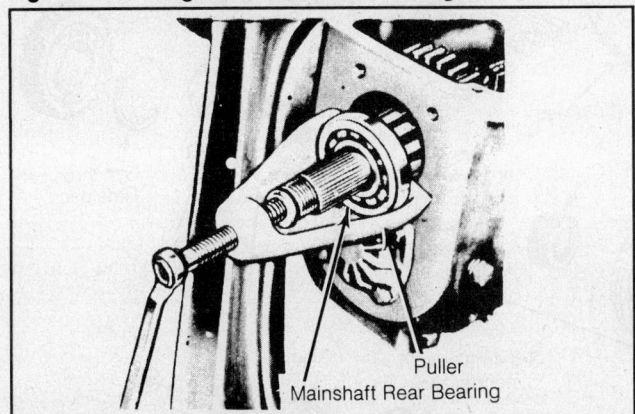

Attach puller to rear bearing and remove bearing.

Fig. 4: Removing Mainshaft from Case

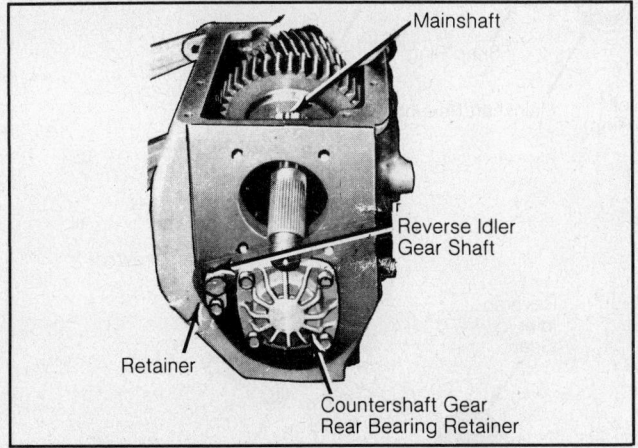

Move mainshaft to rear and tilt front upward.

CLEANING & INSPECTION

1) All parts should be thoroughly washed in cleaning solvent and air dried. Remove portions of old gaskets with stiff brush or scraper. Clean bearings separately from other parts. Hold bearing races so bearings will not rotate and brush with soft brush to remove all foreign material.

2) Loose particles may be removed by striking bearing flat against wood block. Rinse bearings in clean solvent and air dry. Lubricate with light grade oil and wrap in clean paper until ready to reinstall. Do not spin bearings.

3) Examine all gear teeth and splines for chips, wear, breaks, or nicks. Examine case, housing, retainers, and covers for cracks or other damage. Inspect thrust washers, snap ring grooves, and spacers for wear or damage.

4) Check all bearings and synchronizers for wear, damage, and proper fit. Coat all moving parts before installation with lubricant and always use new gaskets, oil seals, and snap rings.

COMPONENT DISASSEMBLY & REASSEMBLY

SHIFT CONTROL COVER

NOTE: Gearshift housing should be disassembled only if it is necessary to replace rails, poppets, interlock plungers, broken springs or if shift forks or cover itself need replacing.

Disassembly
1) Using No. 2 screw extractor, remove roll pins from 1st-2nd shift fork and gate. Push shift rail out through front to force plug out of housing. See Fig. 6. Cover detent ball hole to prevent ball and spring from flying out. Remove rail, fork and gate.

2) Remove back-up light switch. Remove remaining shift rails in same manner. Compress Reverse gear plunger and remove retaining clip. Withdraw plunger and spring from gate.

Cleaning & Inspection
1) Examine housing for cracks or other damage. Inspect shift forks for wear and/or distortion. Check detent ball springs for distortion or collapsed coils.

2) Examine detent balls for corrosion and wear. If shift lever shaft detents show signs of wear, replace them. Replace all gaskets, expansion plugs, and roll pins. See Fig. 9.

Reassembly
1) Place spring on Reverse gear plunger, install and compress assembly in Reverse shift gate. Install retaining clip. Start Reverse shift rail in cover. Place detent spring and ball in position, depress ball and slide shift rail over it.

2) Install gate and shift fork on rail and install new roll pins. Apply film of sealer to plug seat at front of cover. Install new plug in Reverse shift rail bore.

3) Place Reverse fork in Neutral position and install 2 interlock plungers in bores. Insert interlock pin in 3rd-4th shift rail. Install remaining rails in same manner as Reverse rail, making sure that interlock plunger in 1st-2nd shift rail is in place.

4) Install back-up light switch. Install new expansion plugs and rail interlock hole plug.

INPUT SHAFT DRIVE GEAR
Disassembly
Remove tapered roller bearing from pinion shaft with puller. Remove snap ring, pilot roller bearing washer

Manual Transmissions
NEW PROCESS 435 (Cont.)

Fig. 5: Exploded View of New Process 435 4-Speed Transmission

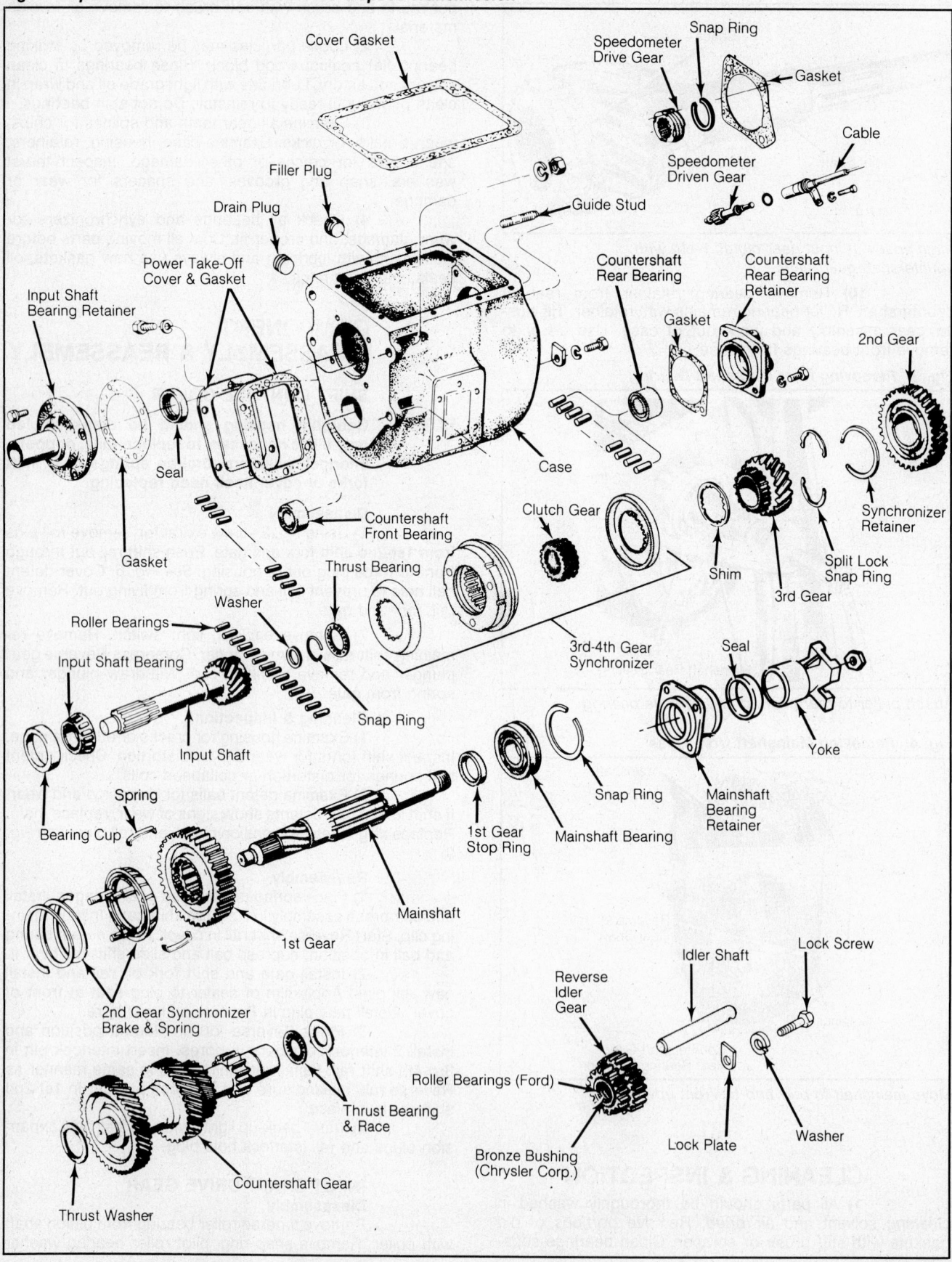

Fig. 6: Removing Shift Rail Roll Pins

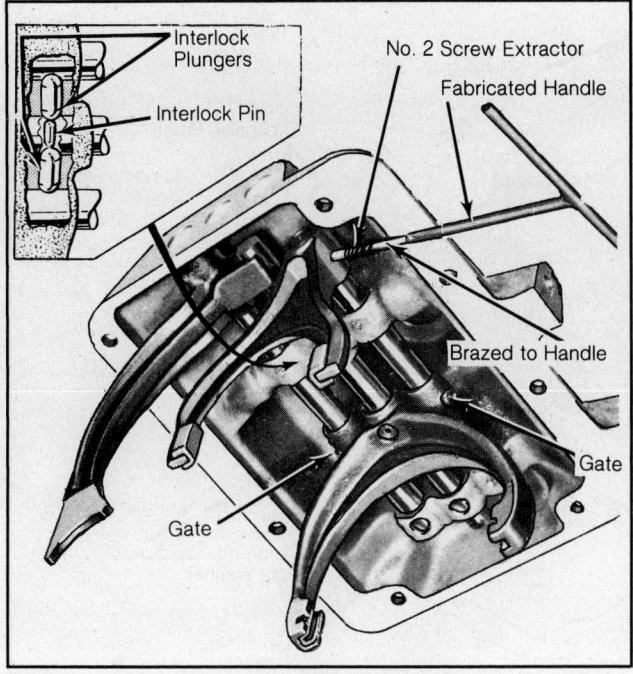

Remove pins using No. 2 screw extractor.

and pilot bearing rollers from gear. Remove bearing race from front bearing retainer with puller. Remove pinion shaft seal.

Reassembly

Position drive pinion in arbor press. Place wooden block on pinion gear and press bearing until it contacts bearing inner race. *See Fig. 7.* Lubricate pilot bearing rollers with light grease and insert in cavity at rear of drive pinion gear. Install washer and snap ring. Press new seal into place with lip of seal toward mounting surface. Press bearing race into retainer.

Fig. 7: Installing Tapered Roller Bearing on Input Shaft

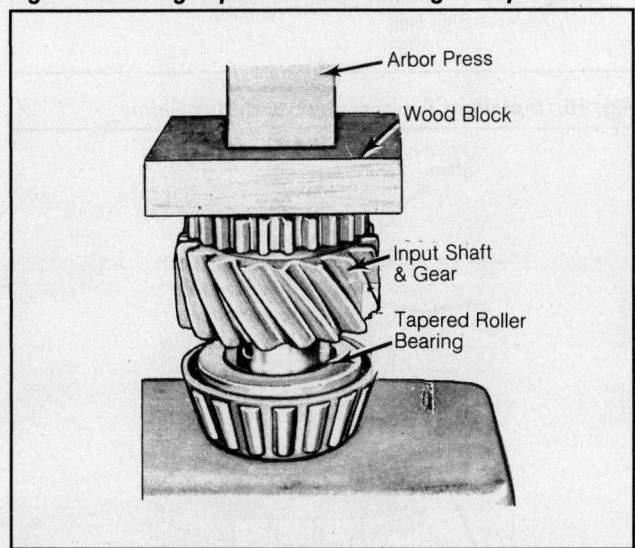

Place block on input gear and press gear into bearings.

INPUT SHAFT
BEARING RETAINER
Roller Bearing Race

Bearing race is installed in bearing retainer. Use puller to remove race from retainer. Press new race squarely into retainer. *See Fig. 8.*

Fig. 8: Installing Input Shaft Bearing Race

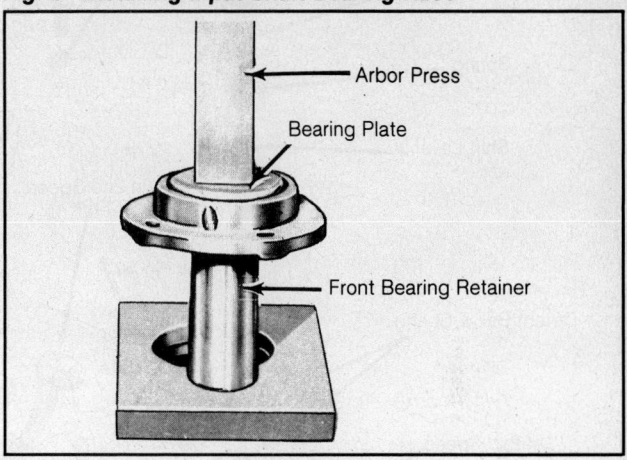

Oil Seal Replacement

Pry oil seal out of retainer and press new seal into place using sleeve. Lip of oil seal should point toward gasket surface of retainer.

MAINSHAFT
Disassembly

Remove clutch gear snap ring. Remove clutch gear, synchronizer outer stop ring-to-3rd gear shim(s), and 3rd gear. Remove split lock ring with 2 screwdrivers. Withdraw 2nd gear and synchronizer assembly. Remove 1st-Reverse sliding gear from shaft.

Reassembly

1) Place mainshaft assembly in soft-jawed vise with rear end up. Install 1st-Reverse gear making sure 2 spline springs are in place inside gear as it is installed on shaft.

2) Move mainshaft in vise so that forward end is up. Install synchronizer spring and synchronizer on 2nd gear. Secure with snap ring, making sure snap ring tangs are away from gear.

3) Slide 2nd gear assembly onto mainshaft making sure synchronizer is toward rear. Secure gear to shaft with split lock snap rings, then install 3rd gear.

NOTE: **Synchronizer clutching gear must be installed with BOTH oil slots facing 3rd gear. Oil slots must NOT face thrust bearing.**

4) Install correct shim(s) between 3rd gear and 3rd-4th synchronizer stop ring. Refer to end play measurement obtained during disassembly to bring end play within specification. Exact determination of end play will be made after mainshaft and main drive gear are installed in case.

REVERSE IDLER GEAR

Gear is serviced by replacement only. Replacement gear is equipped with integral bearings rather than bushing as on original gear.

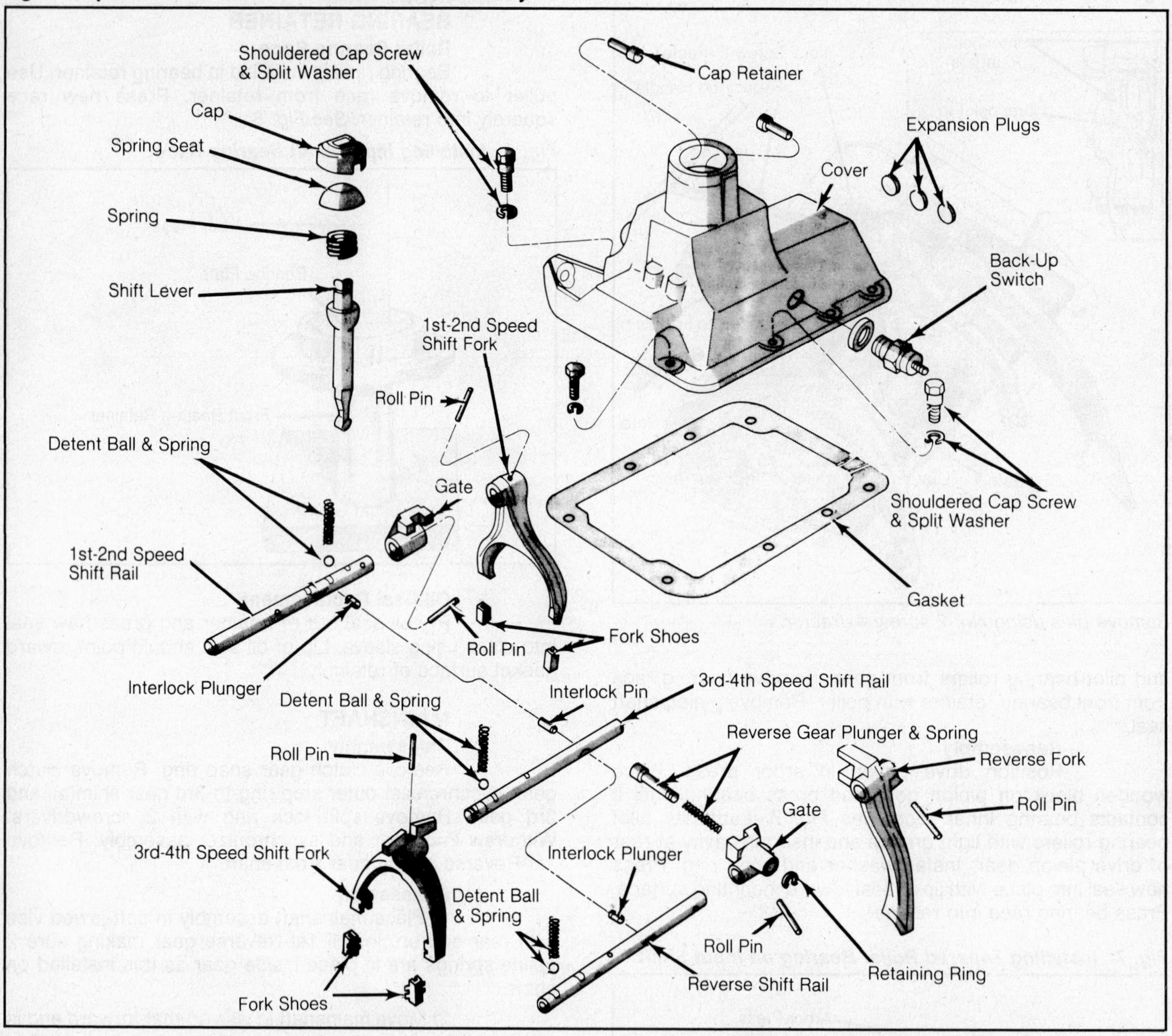

Fig. 9: Exploded View of Shift Control Cover Assembly

Shouldered Cap Screw & Split Washer

Cap Retainer

Cap

Expansion Plugs

Spring Seat

Cover

Spring

Back-Up Switch

Shift Lever

1st-2nd Speed Shift Fork

Roll Pin

Detent Ball & Spring

Gate

1st-2nd Speed Shift Rail

Shouldered Cap Screw & Split Washer

Fork Shoes

Gasket

Interlock Plunger

Roll Pin

Detent Ball & Spring

Interlock Pin

3rd-4th Speed Shift Rail

Reverse Gear Plunger & Spring

Roll Pin

Reverse Fork

Roll Pin

Gate

3rd-4th Speed Shift Fork

Interlock Plunger

Detent Ball & Spring

Roll Pin

Retaining Ring

Fork Shoes

Reverse Shift Rail

NOTE: Do not attempt to disassemble roller bearing assembly. Bearing lock ring cannot be removed without damaging gear or bearing.

COUNTERSHAFT
Front Bearing
Press or drive old bearing out of case and discard. Install new bearing, pressing bearing cage into case until flush with front of case. Coat roller bearings with multi-purpose grade 2 grease or equivalent.

Rear Bearing
Using puller, remove rear bearing from retainer and discard. Position new bearing squarely in retainer bore and press into place until bearing bottoms in retainer. Coat roller bearings with multi-purpose grade 2 grease or equivalent.

TRANSMISSION REASSEMBLY
1) Press front countershaft roller bearing into case until cage is flush with front of case. Lubricate roller

Fig. 10: Installing Synchronizer End Play Shims

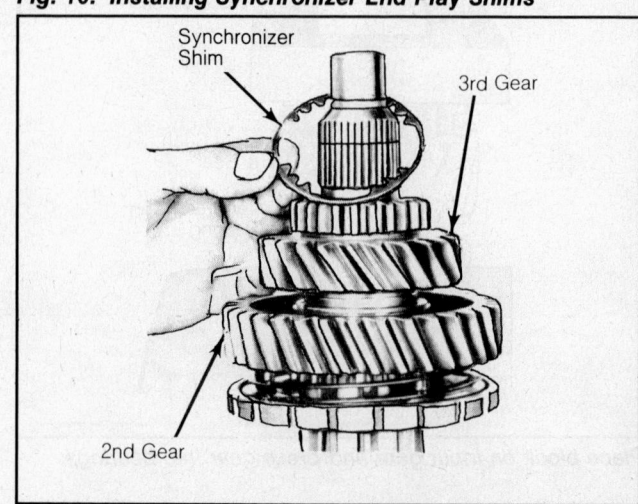

Synchronizer Shim

3rd Gear

2nd Gear

NEW PROCESS 435 (Cont.)

bearings with light coating of grease. Place transmission with front of case facing down. If uncaged bearings are re-used, hold loose rollers in place with light film of grease.

2) Lower countershaft assembly into case placing thrust washer tangs in slots in case, and inserting front end of shaft into bearing. Install countershaft gear rear thrust bearing and race on pilot diameter of countershaft. *See Fig. 11.*

Fig. 11: Installing Rear Countershaft Bearing

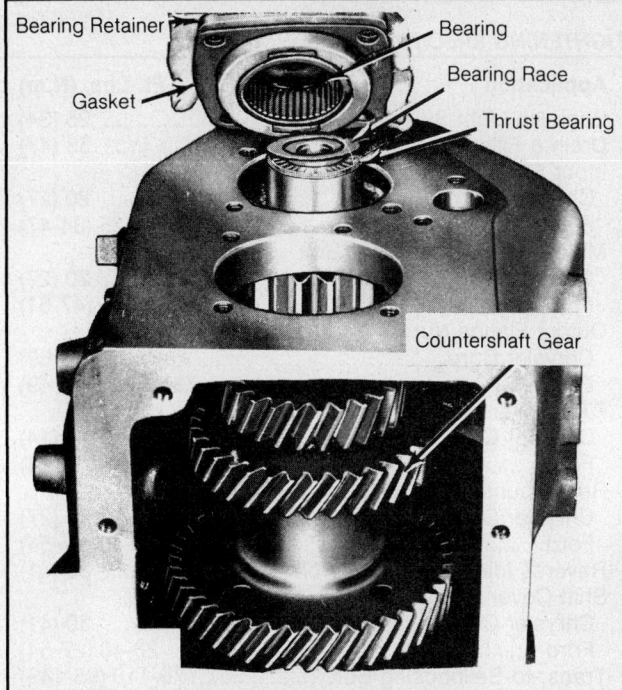

Install bearing and race on countergear.

3) Install new rear bearing retainer gasket, rear bearing retainer and bearing assembly. Install bolts and tighten.

4) Install Reverse idler gear assembly in transmission case. Align Reverse idler shaft so lock plate groove in shaft is in proper alignment to install lock plate.

5) Hold gear in position and tap shaft through case and gear. Install lock plate and washer. Tighten bolt. Ensure that gear turns freely on shaft.

6) Lower rear end of mainshaft into case (holding 1st gear on shaft) and maneuver through rear bearing opening. Ensure that synchronizer and shims remain in position on mainshaft. Install roller thrust bearing. *See Fig. 12.*

7) Place block of wood between front end of mainshaft and front of case. Install rear bearing on mainshaft and drive into case until bearing snap ring is flush with case.

8) Install drive pinion shaft and bearing assembly. Ensure that pilot rollers remain in place. Install rear bearing retainer and gasket. Install drive pinion bearing retainer (without gasket).

9) While holding bearing retainer tight against bearing, measure clearance between retainer and face of case with feeler gauge. *See Fig. 13.*

10) Remove bearing retainer. Install gasket shim pack .010-.015" (.254-.381 mm) thicker than measured

Fig. 12: Installing Rear Mainshaft Bearing

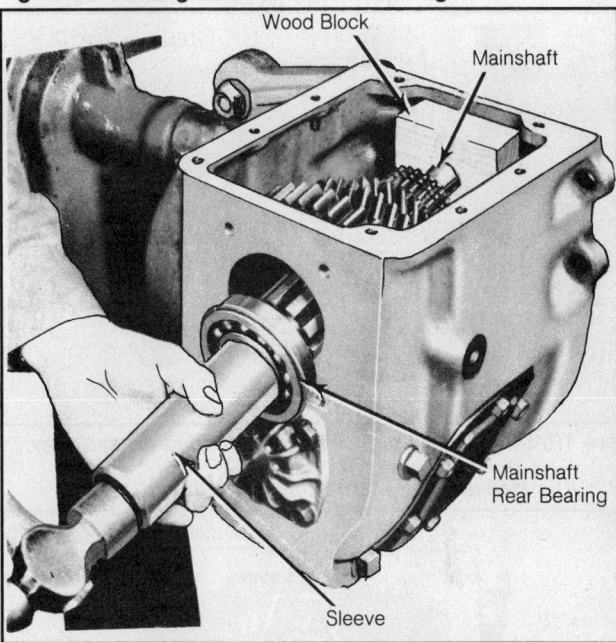

Place wood block between front of mainshaft and case.

Fig. 13: Measuring Bearing Retainer Clearance

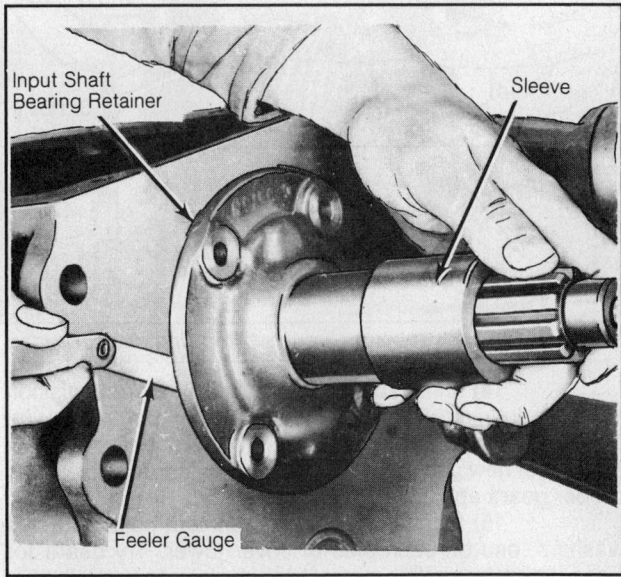

Measure clearance between retainer and case.

clearance between retainer and case. Reinstall and tighten retainer. Recheck end play.

11) Using dial indicator, measure input shaft and gear end play. *See Fig. 14.* End play of input shaft and gear is necessary to allow for normal heat expansion of parts during operation.

12) Check synchronizer end play after all mainshaft components are in position and properly tightened. Two equal size feeler gauges are used to measure synchronizer end play.

13) Keep feeler gauges as close as possible to both sides of mainshaft. Disassemble mainshaft and add or subtract shims to bring end play within specification. *See Fig. 15.* Shift gears into all gear positions and check for free rotation.

Fig. 14: Measuring Input Shaft Drive Gear End Play

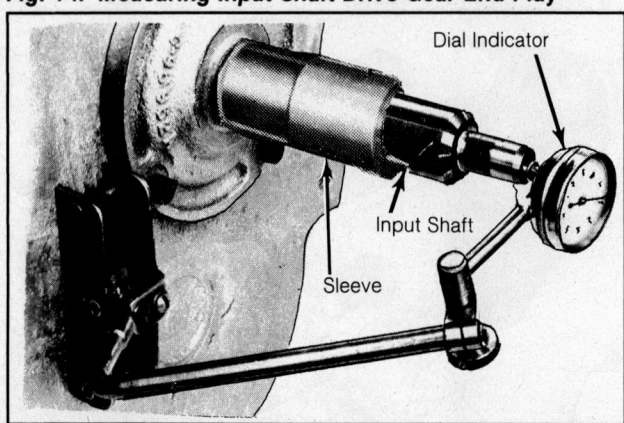

Dial Indicator

Input Shaft

Sleeve

See TRANSMISSION SPECIFICATIONS table for end play.

Fig. 15: Measuring Synchronizer End Play

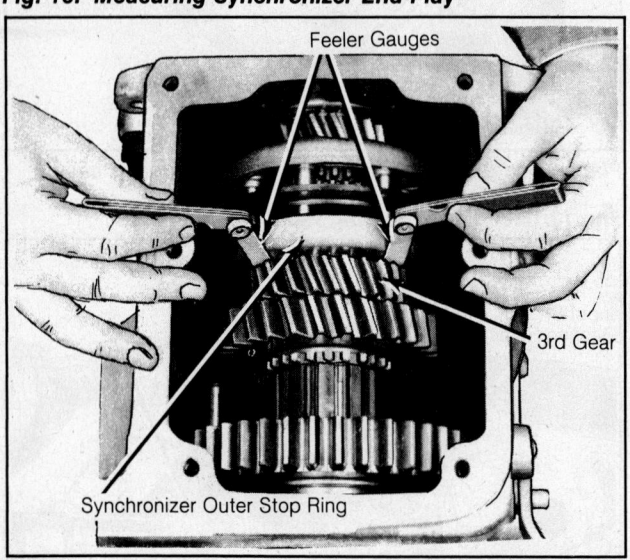

Feeler Gauges

3rd Gear

Synchronizer Outer Stop Ring

Measure play between synchronizer stop ring and 3rd gear.

14) Make sure all internal parts of transmission are well lubricated before installing shift control cover. Place all transmission gears in Neutral position. Install cover with new gasket on case. Carefully engage forks into proper gears and lower cover into place.

15) Install shouldered alignment bolts and split washers, one on each side of cover tower. Try gears for free rotation by shifting gears through cover tower with long screwdriver. Install remaining bolts and washers.

TRANSMISSION SPECIFICATIONS

Application	Inches (mm)
Input Shaft & Gear End Play	
Chrysler Corp.	.007-.017 (.177-.432)
Ford	.007-.014 (.177-.355)
Synchronizer End Play	
Chrysler Corp.	.050-.070 (1.27-1.77)
Ford	.063-.081 (1.60-2.06)

TIGHTENING SPECIFICATIONS

Application	Ft. Lbs. (N.m)
Back-Up Light Switch	25 (34)
Drain & Filler Plugs	35 (47)
Input Shaft Bearing Retainer Screw	
Chrysler Corp.	20 (27)
Ford	25-35 (34-47)
Mainshaft Rear Retainer Bolt	
Chrysler Corp.	20 (27)
Ford	35-45 (47-61)
Output Flange Nut	
Chrysler Corp.	125 (169)
Ford	75-110 (102-149)
PTO Cover Bolt	
Chrysler Corp.	10 (14)
Ford	12-18 (16-24)
Rear Countershaft Retainer Bolt	
Chrysler Corp.	20 (27)
Ford	20-40 (27-54)
Reverse Idler Shaft Lock Bolt	30 (41)
Shift Cover Screw	
Chrysler Corp.	30 (41)
Ford	20-40 (27-54)
Trans.-to-Bellhousing Bolt	70-110 (95-149)

NEW PROCESS A833 OVERDRIVE

Chrysler Corp., General Motors

IDENTIFICATION

Transmission may be identified by number stamped on machined pad on right side of case. First two letters of code identify manufacturing plant, next three numbers designate transmission type (833), next four numbers indicate manufacturing date, and last four numbers are production sequence series.

DESCRIPTION

Transmission is 4-speed unit providing clash-free shifting in all forward gears due to use of 2 synchronizer assemblies. Drive pinion (input shaft) is supported by ball bearing in front of transmission case and oilite bushing pressed in rear of crankshaft.

Front end of mainshaft is supported by roller bearings in end of drive pinion and by ball bearing in front of extension housing.

Rear end of mainshaft is supported by sliding yoke of propeller shaft, which is supported by bushing in extension housing. Countershaft gear is supported by double row of needle-type roller bearings at each end.

Gear thrust is taken up by means of thrust washers located between ends of gear and case. Reverse idler gear is supported on bronze bushing, pressed into gear.

LUBRICATION & ADJUSTMENT

See appropriate MANUAL TRANSMISSION SERVICING article in DOMESTIC GENERAL SERVICING section.

TROUBLE SHOOTING

See MANUAL TRANSMISSION TROUBLE SHOOTING article in DOMESTIC GENERAL SERVICING section.

SERVICE (IN VEHICLE)

SPEEDOMETER PINION GEAR
Removal

Place drain pan under speedometer adapter. Remove bolt and retainer securing pinion adapter to extension housing. With cable housing connected, work adapter and pinion out of extension housing.

NOTE: General Motors models use "O" ring on adapter but do not use internal oil seal. SEAL REPLACEMENT procedure is for Chrysler Corp. models only.

Seal Replacement

1) If transmission fluid is found in cable housing, replace seal in adapter. Start new seal and retainer ring in adapter, then push into adapter with Seal Installer (C-4004) until installer bottoms.

2) Be sure adapter flange and mating area on extension housing are clean and lubricated. Dirt or sand will cause misalignment and pinion gear damage.

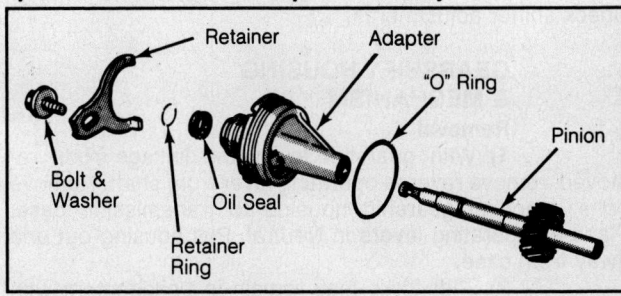

Fig. 1: Exploded View of Chrysler Corp. Speedometer Pinion & Adapter Assembly

General Motors models do not use oil seal.

Installation

1) On Chrysler Corp. models, note number on adapter. This number corresponds to correct number of teeth on gear. Count gear teeth and install correct speedometer pinion gear into adapter. Rotate pinion gear and adapter assembly so that number on adapter is in 6 o'clock position.

2) Install assembly in housing. Install retainer with tangs in adapter positioning slots. Tap adapter firmly into extension housing and tighten retaining bolt. Check fluid level in transmission.

3) On General Motors models, place assembly in housing so slot in adapter is toward retainer boss on housing. Push adapter into housing until retainer fits into groove on adapter. Tighten bolt holding retainer to housing. Check fluid level in transmission.

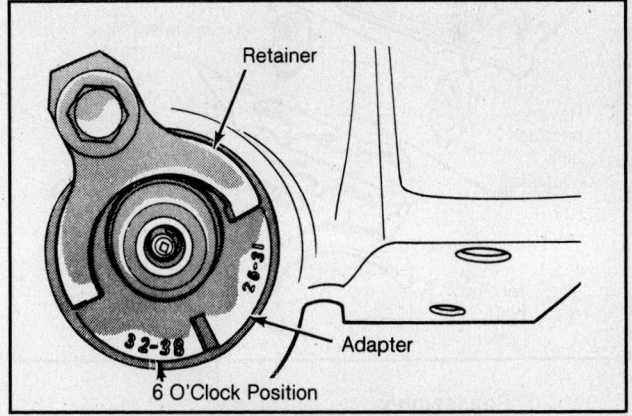

Fig. 2: Installed View of Chrysler Corp. Speedometer Pinion & Adapter

Secure pinion adapter in extension housing with retainer.

GEARSHIFT LEVER & LINKAGE
Removal

1) Disconnect battery ground cable. Remove floor pan boot, sliding it up and off shift lever. Slide .010" (.25 mm) feeler gauge down left side of shift lever into floor shift assembly to release gearshift lever.

2) Pull up on lever to remove it from floor shift assembly. Remove clips, washers and control rods from shift unit levers. Remove 2 bolts holding shift unit to mounting plate on extension housing. Remove shift unit.

Installation

Attach shift unit to mounting plate. Tighten bolts to 30 ft. lbs. (41 N.m). Install shift rods, washers and clips.

NEW PROCESS A833 OVERDRIVE (Cont.)

Install shift lever in shift assembly. Slide boot down shift lever and attach to floor. Reconnect battery ground cable. Check shifter adjustments.

GEARSHIFT HOUSING & MECHANISM

Removal

1) With gearshift lever and linkage rods removed, remove reverse operating lever from shaft. Remove bolts attaching gearshift housing to transmission case. Place all operating levers in Neutral. Pull housing out and away from case.

2) Shift forks may remain in engagement with synchronizer sleeves. If so, work forks out of sleeves and remove from case. Remove reverse detent spring and ball from bore in side of case.

Disassembly

1) If oil leakage is visible around lever shafts or if interlock levers are cracked, remove shift levers and shafts. Make sure shafts are free of burrs before removing to avoid damaging housing bores.

2) Remove "O" ring retainers and "O" rings from housing. Remove "E" clip from interlock lever pivot pin. Remove interlock levers and spring from housing.

Fig. 3: Exploded View of Gearshift Housing & Mechanism

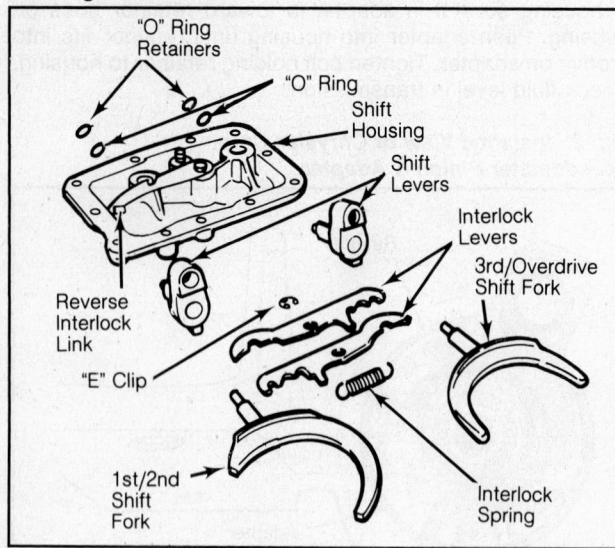

Reassembly

1) Install interlock levers on pivot pin and fasten with "E" clip. Use pliers to install spring on interlock lever hangers. Coat new oil seal "O" rings and "O" ring retainers with multipurpose grease.

2) Lubricate shift shaft bores in cover and install each shift lever shaft, followed by "O" ring and "O" ring retainer. Install operating levers and retaining nuts. Make sure 3rd/Overdrive operating lever points downward.

Installation

1) Rotate each shaft fork bore to Neutral (straight up). Install 3rd/Overdrive shift fork into bore under both interlock levers. Set both synchronizer sleeves in Neutral. Place 1st/2nd shift fork in groove of 1st/2nd synchronizer sleeve.

2) Slide reverse idler gear to Neutral. Place transmission on right side. Position gearshift housing gasket on case using grease to retain gasket. Install reverse detent ball and spring into bore in side of case.

3) Lower shift housing into place. Guide 3rd/Overdrive shift fork into 3rd/Overdrive synchronizer groove. Place shaft of 1st/2nd shift fork into bore of 1st/2nd shift lever. Hold reverse interlock link against 1st/2nd shift lever to provide clearance while cover is lowered.

4) Using screwdriver, raise interlock lever against spring tension to allow 1st/2nd shift fork shaft to slip under levers. Ensure that reverse detent spring is positioned in cover bore. Cover should seat against case gasket.

5) Install housing bolts finger tight and shift transmission through all gears to ensure proper operation. Grease reverse shaft. Install operating lever and retaining nut. Shift transmission into each gear to check for correct shift travel and smooth action.

NOTE: **Eight shift housing bolts are shoulder bolts for locating shift mechanism. One bolt has longer shoulder and acts as locating dowel into case in center rear hole of flange. Two bolts at lower rear of cover are standard.**

EXTENSION HOUSING YOKE SEAL

Removal

Place drain pan under seal. Mark propeller shaft for reassembly and remove propeller shaft. Remove oil seal from housing using seal remover or screwdriver.

Installation

Drive new seal into opening of extension housing with Seal Installer (C-3972 on Chrysler Corp. models; J-21426 on General Motors models). Install propeller shaft, aligning marks made at removal. Check transmission fluid level.

REMOVAL & INSTALLATION

TRANSMISSION

See appropriate MANUAL TRANSMISSION REMOVAL article in DOMESTIC GENERAL SERVICING section.

TRANSMISSION DISASSEMBLY

1) Remove speedometer pinion and adapter from extension housing. Remove bolts attaching extension housing to transmission case. Rotate extension housing on output shaft to expose rear of countershaft. Install 1 extension housing bolt to hold extension housing in this position.

2) With center punch or drill, make hole in countershaft expansion plug at front of case. Working through hole, drive countershaft forward and remove Woodruff key. Push countershaft forward until expansion plug is driven out of case.

3) Using Arbor Adapter (C-3938 on Chrysler Corp. models; J-29793 on General Motors models), push countershaft out rear of case. Lower countershaft gear to bottom of case. Rotate extension housing back to normal position. Remove drive pinion bearing retainer and gasket from transmission.

Fig. 4: Exploded View Of A833 Overdrive Transmission

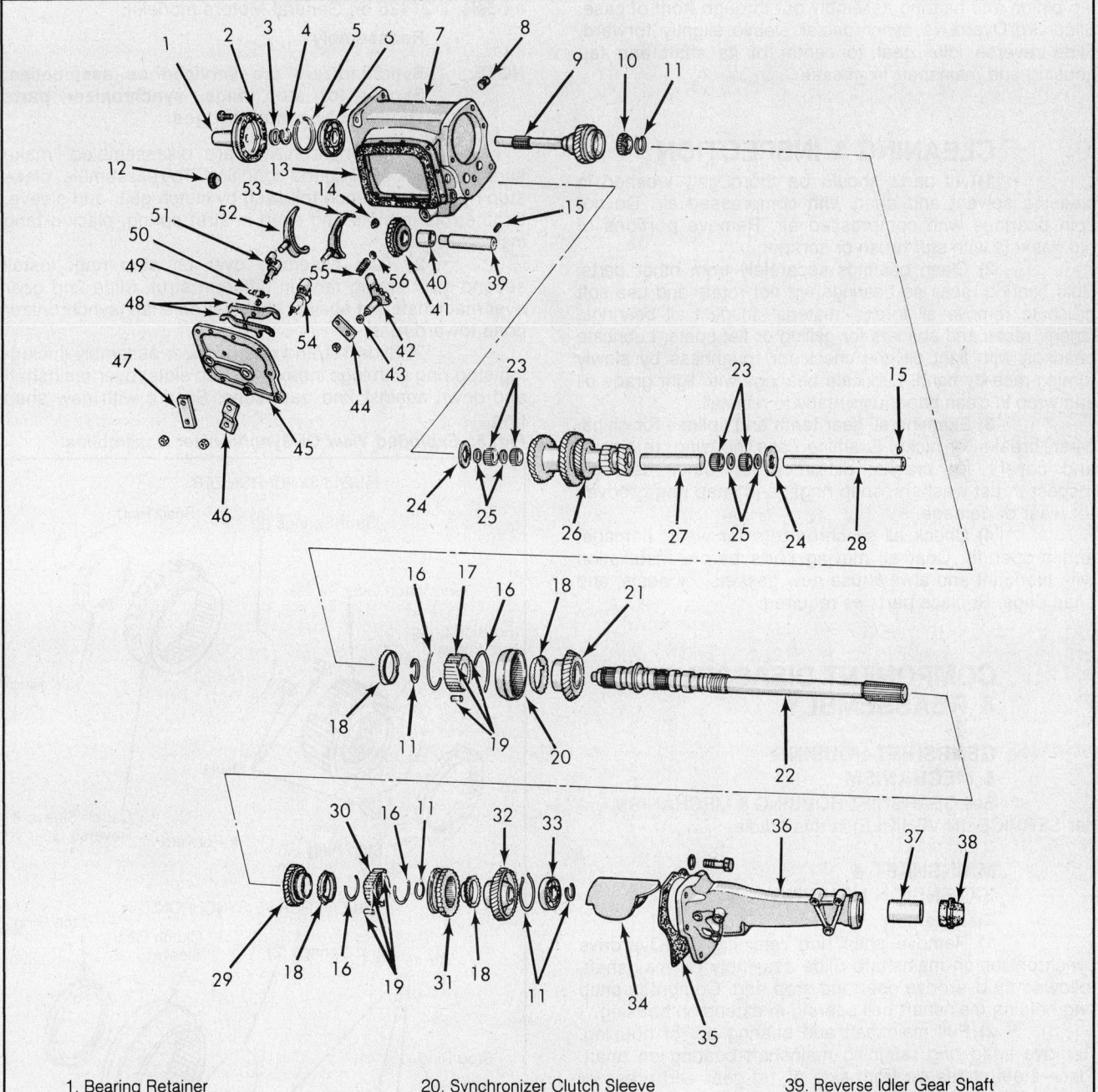

1. Bearing Retainer	20. Synchronizer Clutch Sleeve	39. Reverse Idler Gear Shaft
2. Retainer Gasket	21. Overdrive Gear	40. Reverse Idler Gear Bushing
3. Retainer Oil Seal	22. Mainshaft (Output)	41. Reverse Idler Gear
4. Bearing Inner Snap Ring	23. Needle Roller Bearing	42. Reverse Lever
5. Bearing Outer Snap Ring	24. Countershaft Thrust Washer	43. Reverse Lever Oil Seal
6. Drive Pinion Bearing	25. Needle Bearing Spacer Ring	44. Reverse Operating Lever
7. Case	26. Countershaft Cluster Gear	45. Shift Mechanism Housing
8. Filler Plug	27. Bearing Spacer	46. 1st/2nd Operating Lever
9. Main Drive Pinion	28. Countershaft	47. 3rd/Overdrive Operating Lever
10. Needle Roller Bearing	29. 2nd Gear	48. Interlock Levers (2)
11. Snap Ring	30. Synchronizer Clutch Gear	49. "E" Clip
12. Expansion Plug	31. 1st/2nd Synchronizer Sleeve Gear	50. Interlock Lever Spring
13. Shift Mechanism Gasket	32. 1st Gear	51. 3rd/Overdrive Lever
14. Drain Plug	33. Rear Bearing	52. 3rd/Overdrive Shift Fork
15. Woodruff Key	34. Baffle	53. 1st/2nd Shift Fork
16. Synchronizer Shift Strut Spring	35. Gasket	54. 1st/2nd Lever
17. Synchronizer Clutch Gear	36. Extension Housing	55. Reverse Detent Ball Spring
18. Synchronizer Stop Ring	37. Yoke Bushing	56. Reverse Detent Ball
19. Synchronizer Shift Struts	38. Yoke Seal	

4) Remove seal from retainer. Using brass drift, tap pinion and bearing assembly out through front of case. Slide 3rd/Overdrive synchronizer sleeve slightly forward. Slide reverse idler gear to center of its shaft and tap housing and mainshaft from case.

CLEANING & INSPECTION

1) All parts should be thoroughly washed in cleaning solvent and dried with compressed air. Do not spin bearings with compressed air. Remove portions of old gaskets with stiff brush or scraper.

2) Clean bearings separately from other parts. Hold bearing races so bearings will not rotate and use soft brush to remove all foreign material. Inspect all bearings, rollers, races and spacers for galling or flat spots. Lubricate bearings with light oil and check for roughness by slowly turning race by hand. Lubricate bearings with light grade oil and wrap in clean paper until ready to reinstall.

3) Examine all gear teeth and splines for chips, wear, breaks, or nicks. Examine case, housing, retainers, and covers for cracks, distortion, or other damage. Inspect thrust washers, snap rings, and snap ring grooves for wear or damage.

4) Check all synchronizers for wear, damage, and proper fit. Coat all moving parts before installation with lubricant and always use new gaskets, oil seals, and snap rings. Replace parts as required.

COMPONENT DISASSEMBLY & REASSEMBLY

GEARSHIFT HOUSING & MECHANISM

See GEARSHIFT HOUSING & MECHANISM under SERVICE (IN VEHICLE) in this article.

MAINSHAFT & EXTENSION HOUSING
Disassembly

1) Remove snap ring retaining 3rd/Overdrive synchronizer on mainshaft. Slide assembly off mainshaft, followed by overdrive gear and stop ring. Compress snap ring holding mainshaft ball bearing in extension housing.

2) Pull mainshaft and bearing out of housing. Remove snap ring retaining mainshaft bearing on shaft. Place steel plates on front side of 1st gear and press or drive mainshaft through bearing.

3) Remove bearing, snap ring, 1st gear and stop ring from shaft. Remove snap ring retaining 1st/2nd synchronizer assembly on mainshaft. Slide synchronizer assembly and 2nd gear off mainshaft.

NOTE: DO NOT disassemble synchronizer assemblies unless replacement of parts is required.

Extension Housing Bushing Replacement

1) Remove extension housing yoke seal. Drive bushing out of housing using Bushing Remover (C-3974 on Chrysler Corp. models; J-8092 and J-21424-9 on General Motors models). Slide new bushing on installing end of remover.

2) Align oil hole in bushing with oil slot in housing and drive bushing into place. Drive new oil seal into housing using Seal Installer (C-3972 on Chrysler Corp. models; J-21426 on General Motors models).

Reassembly

NOTE: Synchronizers are serviced as assemblies. Except for stop rings, synchronizer parts should not be interchanged.

1) If synchronizers are disassembled, make sure that parts are in good condition. To reassemble, place stop ring flat on bench followed by clutch gear and sleeve. Drop struts in slots and snap in strut spring, placing tang inside one strut.

2) Turn assembly over on stop ring. Install second strut spring tang in different strut. Slide 2nd gear over mainshaft and against shoulder on shaft (synchronizer cone toward rear).

3) Slide 1st/2nd synchronizer assembly (including stop ring with lugs indexed in hub slots) over mainshaft and down against 2nd gear cone. Secure with new snap ring.

Fig. 5: Exploded View Of Synchronizer Assemblies

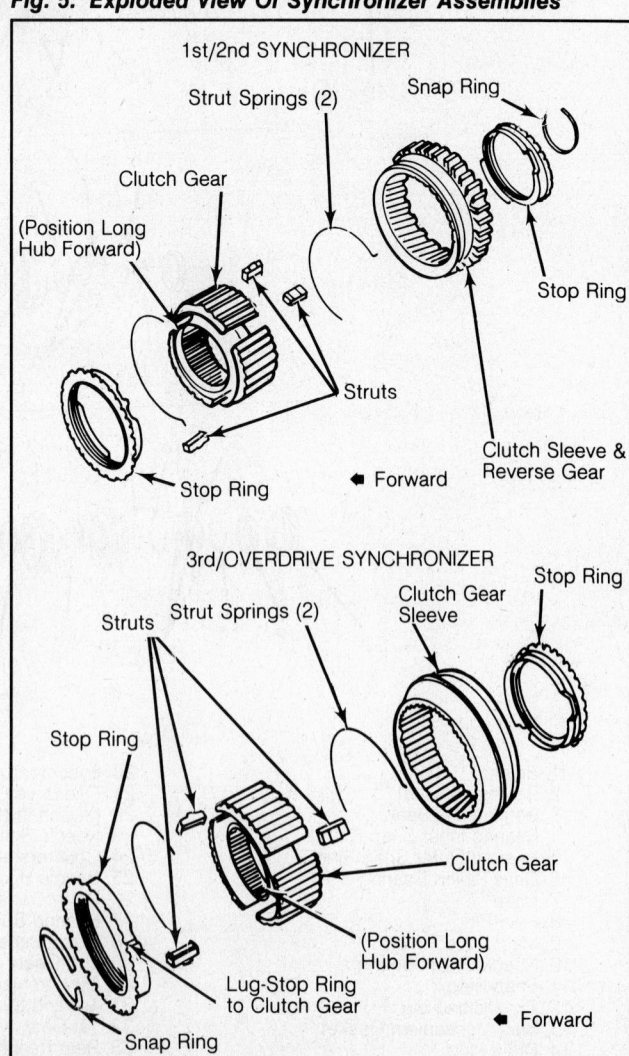

Long hub must face forward.

4) Slide next stop ring over shaft and index lugs into clutch hub slots. Slide 1st gear into position over

NEW PROCESS A833 OVERDRIVE (Cont.)

mainshaft, against clutch sleeve gear. Install mainshaft bearing retaining ring and mainshaft rear bearing.

5) Using arbor and driving tool, press bearing into position. Install new snap ring on shaft to secure bearing. Snap ring is selective fit for minimum end play.

6) Install partially assembled mainshaft into extension housing far enough to engage bearing retaining ring in slot in housing. Compress ring with pliers so that mainshaft ball bearing can bottom against thrust shoulder in housing. Release ring and ensure that it is completely seated in groove in housing.

7) Slide overdrive gear over mainshaft with synchronizer cone toward front. Install stop ring. Install 3rd/Overdrive synchronizer assembly on mainshaft with shift fork slot toward rear.

8) Ensure that stop ring is indexed with shift struts. Install retaining ring. Grease front stop ring and install on synchronizer, indexing ring lugs with shift struts.

DRIVE PINION & COUNTERSHAFT GEAR
Disassembly

1) Remove pinion bearing inner snap ring. Using arbor press, remove ball bearing from pinion. Remove snap ring and 16 bearing rollers from cavity in pinion. Remove countershaft gear from bottom of case.

2) Remove arbor adapter. Remove thrust washers, spacers and 76 needle bearings from center of countershaft gear.

Reassembly

1) Coat inner bore of countershaft gear with light film of grease. Install roller bearing spacer with arbor into gear. Center spacer and arbor in gear. Coat needle bearings with grease. At each end of gear, install 19 rollers, followed by spacer ring, then 19 more roller bearings and another spacer ring.

2) Coat thrust washers with grease. Install thrust washers over arbor with tang side toward case boss. Place countershaft assembly on bottom of case, making sure thrust washers stay in place.

Fig. 6: Assembled View of Drive Pinion

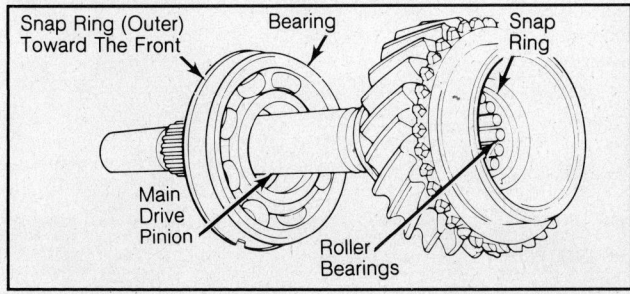

Select inner snap ring to give minimum end play.

3) Press drive pinion bearing onto pinion shaft, with outer snap ring groove toward front. Seat bearing fully against shoulder of gear. Select and install new inner snap ring on shaft to retain bearing and give minimum end play. Be sure snap ring is fully seated.

4) Place pinion shaft in soft-jawed vise and install 16 bearing rollers in cavity of shaft. Coat rollers with grease and install retaining snap ring. Using Seal Installer (C-3789 on Chrysler Corp. models; J23096 on General Motors models), drive new oil seal into gear retainer bore until installer bottoms out.

REVERSE GEAR, LEVER & FORK
Disassembly

1) Remove reverse idler gear shaft using 3/8" X 3 1/2" bolt with free spinning nut and 7/16" deep socket. Place bolt and socket in case with socket against end of shaft and head of bolt against case. Press shaft out of case using nut to extend tool. Remove Woodruff key from shaft. *See Fig. 7.*

Fig. 7: Removing Reverse Idler Gear Shaft

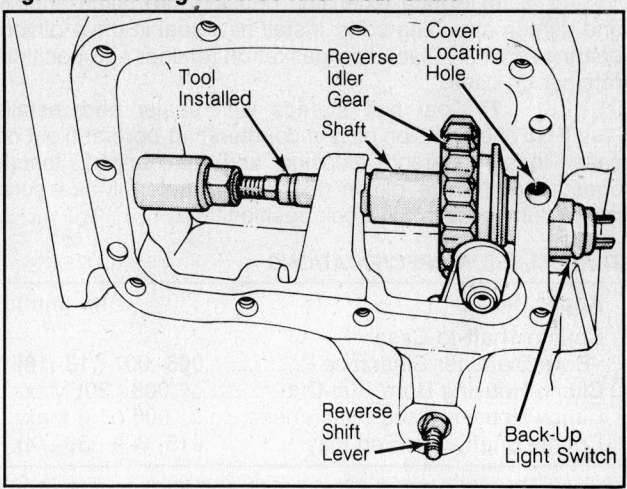

Use locally made tool to press shaft from case.

2) Remove back-up light switch and gasket. If oil leakage is visible around reverse gearshift lever shaft, remove burrs from shaft. Push shaft inward and remove from case. Remove "O" ring and "O" ring retainer from case bore.

Reassembly

1) Coat oil seal "O" ring and "O" ring retainer with multipurpose grease. Install reverse shift lever in case bore followed by "O" ring and "O" ring retainer.

2) Place reverse idler gear shaft in end of case. Drive shaft in far enough to position reverse idler gear on shaft with fork slot toward rear. Engage slot with reverse shift fork.

3) When reverse idler gear is correctly positioned, drive shaft further into case and install Woodruff key. Press shaft in until flush with end of case. Install back-up light switch and gasket.

TRANSMISSION REASSEMBLY

1) Install countershaft gear in bottom of case. Make sure thrust washers remained in place. Coat new extension housing-to-case gasket with grease. Install gasket on extension housing. Slide reverse idler gear to center of its shaft. Move 3rd/Overdrive synchronizer sleeve as far forward as possible without losing struts.

2) Insert mainshaft assembly into case, tilting it to clear idler and cluster gears. Place 3rd/Overdrive synchronizer in Neutral. Rotate extension housing on output shaft to expose rear of countershaft. Install 1 extension housing bolt to hold extension housing in inverted position.

3) Install drive pinion and bearing assembly into case. Position it in front bore. Install outer snap ring in drive pinion bearing groove. Tap lightly into position with soft-faced hammer. Snap ring should bottom on case. If not, internal parts are not in correct position.

Manual Transmissions
NEW PROCESS A833 OVERDRIVE (Cont.)

4) Turn transmission upside down while holding countershaft gear assembly to prevent damage. Lower countershaft gear assembly into position (teeth meshed with drive pinion gear). Make sure thrust washers remain in position and tangs are aligned with slots in case.

5) Install countershaft into bore from rear of case and push forward until installed approximately half-way. Install Woodruff key. Push shaft forward until end is flush with rear of case face. Remove arbor tool.

6) Rotate extension housing into place. Install and tighten attaching bolts. Install new seal in drive pinion bearing retainer. Place new gasket on retainer and position retainer on case.

7) Coat bolt threads with sealer and install. Install NEW expansion plug in countershaft bore at front of case. Install gearshift housing and mechanism. Install speedometer drive pinion gear and adapter. Make sure range number is in 6 o'clock position.

TRANSMISSION SPECIFICATIONS

Application	In. (mm)
Countershaft-to-Case	
Bore Diameter Clearance	.005-.007 (.13-.18)
Clutch Housing Bore Run-Out	.008 (.20) Max.
Clutch Housing Face Squareness	.006 (.15) Max.
Countershaft Gear End Play	.015-.029 (.38-.74)

TIGHTENING SPECIFICATIONS

Application	Ft. Lbs. (N.m)
Back-Up Light Switch	15 (20)
Drain Plug	
Chrysler Corp.	25 (34)
General Motors	15 (20)
Extension Hsg.-to-Case Bolts	50 (68)
Gearshift Mount-to-Ext. Hsg. Bolts	12 (16)
Gearshift Mount-to-Plate Bolts	24 (32)
Input Bearing Retainer Bolts	30 (41)
Shift Cover Housing Bolts	15 (20)
Shift Lever Nuts	18 (24)
Transmission-to-Bellhousing Bolts	
Chrysler Corp.	50 (68)
General Motors	75 (100)

TREMEC 4-SPEED MODEL T-176

Jeep
J 10 Pickup & Fleet Grand Wagoneer

IDENTIFICATION

Transmission identification tag showing Jeep part number is attached to transmission shift control housing by one of the mounting bolts.

DESCRIPTION

Transmission is a 4-speed unit, fully synchronized in all forward gears. All forward gears are constant mesh helical cut type and speed changes are accomplished through use of blocker type synchronizer assemblies. Input shaft and mainshaft are supported by ball bearings in front and rear of case. All other gears are supported by needle type roller bearings.

LUBRICATION & ADJUSTMENT

See the appropriate article in MANUAL TRANS-MISSION SERVICING Section.

TROUBLE SHOOTING

See MANUAL TRANSMISSION TROUBLE SHOOTING in TRANSMISSION SERVICING Section

REMOVAL & INSTALLATION

See the appropriate article in MANUAL TRANS-MISSION REMOVAL Section.

TRANSMISSION DISASSEMBLY

1) Remove transfer case if not already removed. Remove shift control housing, noting positions of 2 dowel-type alignment bolts for reassembly reference. Using arbor tool (J-29342), remove countershaft through rear of case.

2) Remove locating ring and retaining snap ring from rear bearing. Remove rear bearing using puller (J-25152). Matchmark front bearing retainer and case for reassembly reference. Remove front bearing retainer and gasket.

Fig. 1: *Removing Input Shaft and Front Bearing*

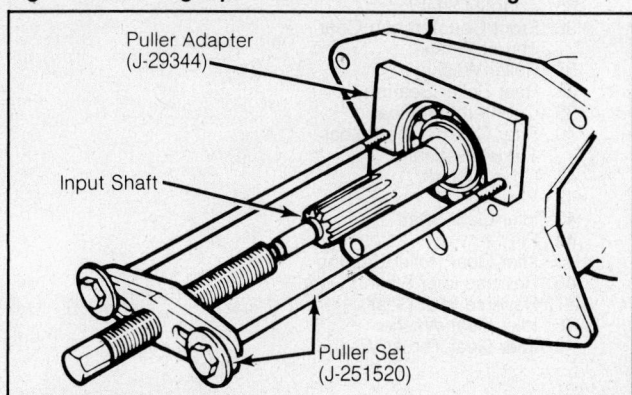

Rear bearing is removed using same puller set without adapter (J-29344).

3) Remove and discard front bearing retainer oil seal. Remove locating ring and retaining snap ring from front bearing. Remove input shaft and front bearing using puller and adapter (J-25152 & J-29344). See Fig. 1.

4) Remove 4th gear synchronizer ring from input shaft or synchronizer hub. Remove mainshaft pilot bearing rollers from input shaft. See Fig. 2. Remove mainshaft and geartrain assembly.

Fig. 2: *Input Shaft & Bearing Assembly*

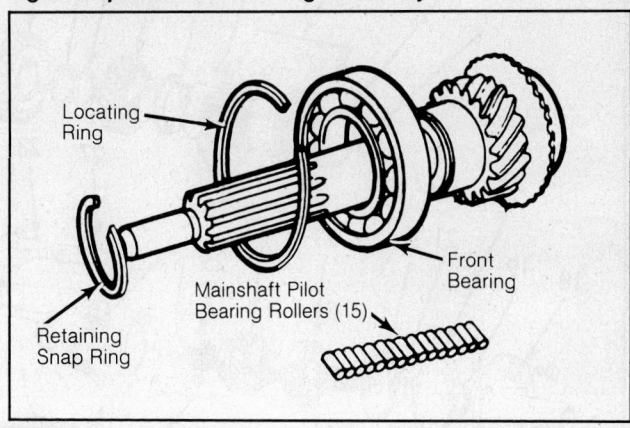

5) Move 3rd-4th synchronizer sleeve rearward to 3rd gear position. Lift front end of shaft upward and remove mainshaft assembly from case. Remove countershaft gear, arbor tool, thrust washers and any needle bearing rollers that may have fallen into case.

6) Tap reverse idler shaft out rear of case. Remove reverse idler gear and thrust washers from case. Remove needle bearings and bearing retainers from gear assembly. Remove sliding gear from idler gear noting position for reassembly.

CLEANING & INSPECTION

1) Wash all parts in cleaning solvent. Dry all parts, except bearings, with compressed air. Let bearings air dry in clean shop cloth. Inspect transmission case for cracks, damaged bearing bores or damaged threads. Remove all small nicks or burrs from front or rear of case.

2) Check ball bearings for roughness by slowly turning race by hand. Inspect needle bearing rollers, shafts and washers for wear or damage. Check all other parts for wear, damage, chipped or broken teeth. Replace parts as necessary.

COMPONENT DISASSEMBLY & REASSEMBLY

MAINSHAFT ASSEMBLY
Disassembly

1) Remove 3rd-4th synchronizer snap ring from front of mainshaft and slide 3rd-4th synchronizer assembly from shaft. Slide hub out of sleeve. Remove insert springs, inserts and blocking rings, noting positions for reassembly reference.

2) Remove 3rd gear from mainshaft. Remove snap ring holding 2nd gear and remove 2nd gear and blocking ring from shaft. Remove tabbed washer from mainshaft. Remove snap ring retaining 1st-2nd synchronizer hub.

Manual Transmissions

TREMEC 4-SPEED MODEL T-176 (Cont.)

Fig. 3: Disassembled View of Warner T-176 4-Speed Manual Transmission

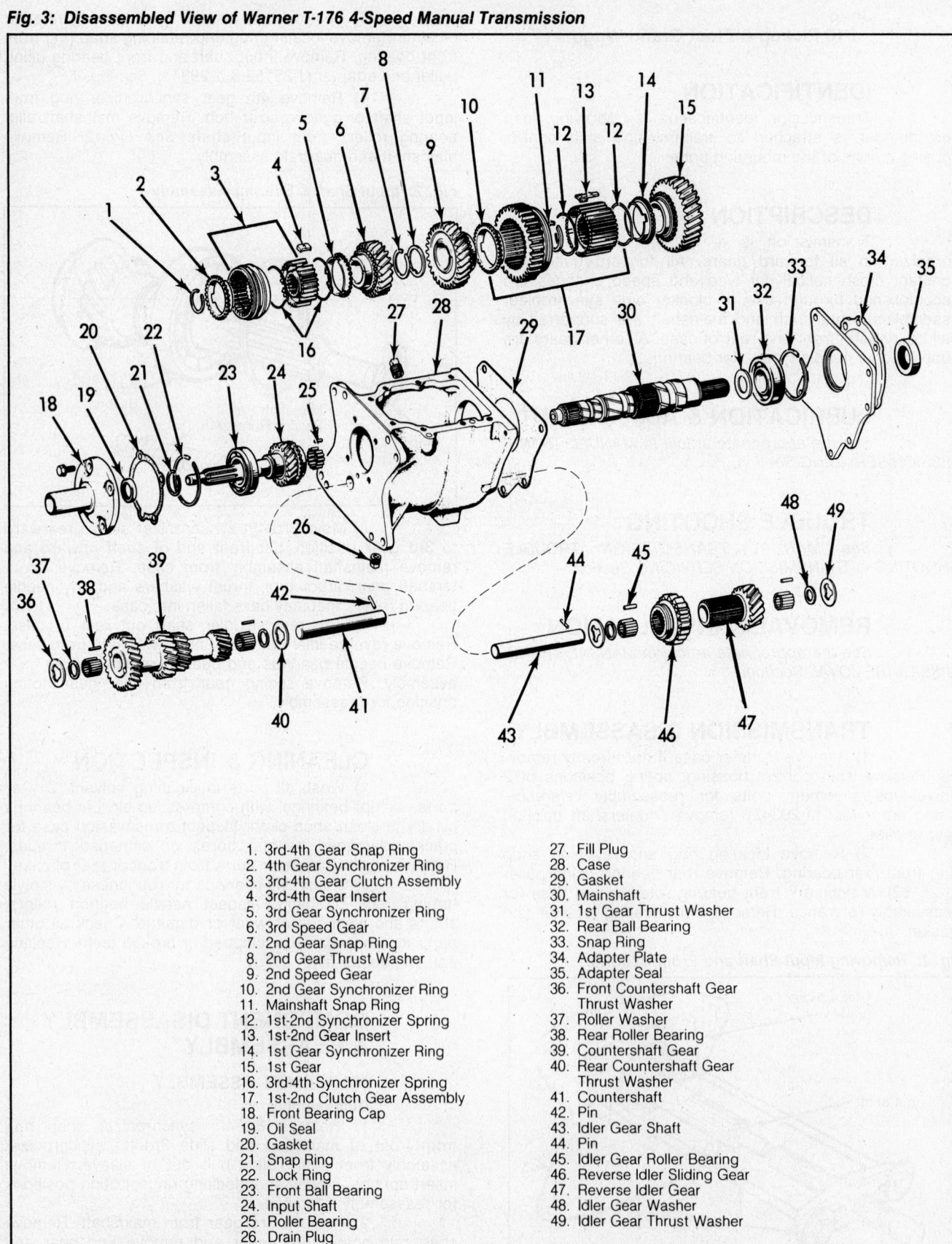

1. 3rd-4th Gear Snap Ring
2. 4th Gear Synchronizer Ring
3. 3rd-4th Gear Clutch Assembly
4. 3rd-4th Gear Insert
5. 3rd Gear Synchronizer Ring
6. 3rd Speed Gear
7. 2nd Gear Snap Ring
8. 2nd Gear Thrust Washer
9. 2nd Speed Gear
10. 2nd Gear Synchronizer Ring
11. Mainshaft Snap Ring
12. 1st-2nd Synchronizer Spring
13. 1st-2nd Gear Insert
14. 1st Gear Synchronizer Ring
15. 1st Gear
16. 3rd-4th Synchronizer Spring
17. 1st-2nd Clutch Gear Assembly
18. Front Bearing Cap
19. Oil Seal
20. Gasket
21. Snap Ring
22. Lock Ring
23. Front Ball Bearing
24. Input Shaft
25. Roller Bearing
26. Drain Plug
27. Fill Plug
28. Case
29. Gasket
30. Mainshaft
31. 1st Gear Thrust Washer
32. Rear Ball Bearing
33. Snap Ring
34. Adapter Plate
35. Adapter Seal
36. Front Countershaft Gear
Thrust Washer
37. Roller Washer
38. Rear Roller Bearing
39. Countershaft Gear
40. Rear Countershaft Gear
Thrust Washer
41. Countershaft
42. Pin
43. Idler Gear Shaft
44. Pin
45. Idler Gear Roller Bearing
46. Reverse Idler Sliding Gear
47. Reverse Idler Gear
48. Idler Gear Washer
49. Idler Gear Thrust Washer

TREMEC 4-SPEED MODEL T-176 (Cont.)

3) Remove hub, reverse gear and sleeve as an assembly. Matchmark hub and sleeve. Remove insert springs, 3 inserts, sleeve and gear from hub. Remove 1st gear thrust washer from shaft and remove 1st gear and blocking ring.

Reassembly

1) Lubricate mainshaft, synchronizer assemblies and gear bores with transmission lubricant. Align matchmarks and assemble 1st-2nd synchronizer hub and reverse gear and sleeve. Install gear and sleeve on hub and place assembly on flat surface.

2) Place inserts into hub slots. Install insert spring with loop end in 1 insert. Compress spring and insert spring under lips of 2 remaining inserts. Ensure spring is under lip of each insert. Turn assembly over and install 2nd spring in same manner with open ends opposite each other 180°.

Fig. 4: Exploded View of Synchronizer Assembly

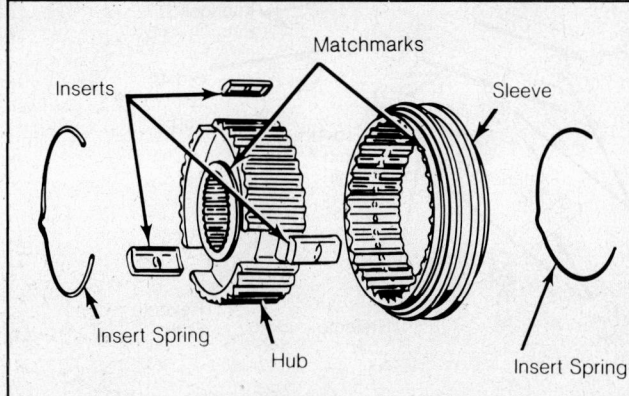

Be sure spring is under lip of each insert.

3) Install 1st-2nd synchronizer assembly, reverse gear, sleeve and new snap ring on mainshaft. Install insert spring, placing loop end of spring in 1 insert. Install spring under lips of remaining inserts.

4) Install 1st gear, 1st gear blocking ring, thrust washer and new tabbed thrust washer on mainshaft. Make sure tabbed washer is seated in mainshaft tab bore and sharp end of thrust washer is facing outward.

5) Install 2nd gear, 2nd gear blocking ring and new snap ring on mainshaft. Install 3rd gear and 3rd gear blocking ring on mainshaft. Align matchmarks and assemble 3rd-4th synchronizer hub and sleeve. Place assembly on flat surface and install inserts and springs as previously described.

6) Install 3rd-4th synchronizer assembly and new snap ring on mainshaft. Measure end play between hub and snap ring with feeler gauge. End play should be .004-.014" (.10-.36 mm). Replace mainshaft thrust washers and snap rings, if end play is excessive.

SHIFT CONTROL HOUSING

Disassembly

1) Remove shift lever cover, control housing cap, retainer, shift lever and spring. Position transmission case cover in vise so shift forks are facing upward. Use wooden blocks to protect cover.

2) Place shift rails in neutral position and remove shift forks and rails. Note position of components for reassembly. Remove poppet balls and springs. Remove roll pins attaching shift forks to shift rails and remove shift forks.

Fig. 5: Measuring Mainshaft End Play

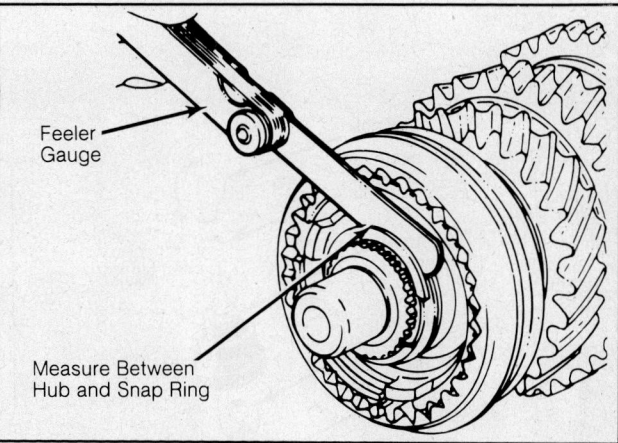

Clearance should be .004-.014" (.10-.36 mm).

Reassembly

1) With transmission case cover in vise, lubricate shift rails and rail grooves with petroleum jelly. Install poppet springs and balls (one on each spring).

2) Position reverse gear shift rail and fork on reverse rocker arm in cover. Be sure notch on shift rail is over reverse poppet ball and reverse rocker arm is engaged in reverse fork slot.

3) Install 3rd-4th shift rail and shift fork in cover. Be sure interlock pin is in position in shift rail. Install 1st-2nd shift rail and shift fork. Be sure rail notch is over poppet ball. Install shifter interlock rings in cover and between poppet balls.

4) Press downward evenly on rails to compress poppet balls and springs. Position shift rail retaining plates on housing and secure with bolts and tabbed washers.

5) Tighten bolts. Check tabbed washer position before bending over tabs. Check shift rail operation. Install shift lever, spring, spring retainer and control housing cap.

TRANSMISSION REASSEMBLY

1) Lubricate reverse idler gear bore and sliding gear with transmission lubricant. Install sliding gear on reverse idler gear. Install arbor tool (J-29343) in reverse idler gear, and place 22 roller bearings and 1 bearing retainer at each end of gear.

2) Coat reverse idler gear thrust washers with petroleum jelly. Place gear in case with flats of washers facing mainshaft and tabs engaging slots in case. Install reverse idler gear assembly. Align gear bore and install shaft from rear of case. Make sure shaft roll pin is aligned with counterbore in case.

3) Measure reverse idler gear end play by inserting feeler gauge between thrust washer and gear. End play should be .004-.018" (.10-.46 mm). If end play exceeds .018" (.46 mm), replace thrust washer.

4) Coat countershaft gear bore, needle bearings and bearing bores in gear with petroleum jelly. Insert arbor tool (J-29342) in bore and install 22 needle rollers and 1 bearing retainer at each end of gear. Coat countershaft gear thrust washers with petroleum jelly. Place in case with tabs engaging slots in case.

5) Install countershaft gear assembly. Align gear bore, and install shaft from rear, part way into case.

Manual Transmissions

TREMEC 4-SPEED MODEL T-176 (Cont.)

Fig. 6: Disassembled View of Shift Control Housing

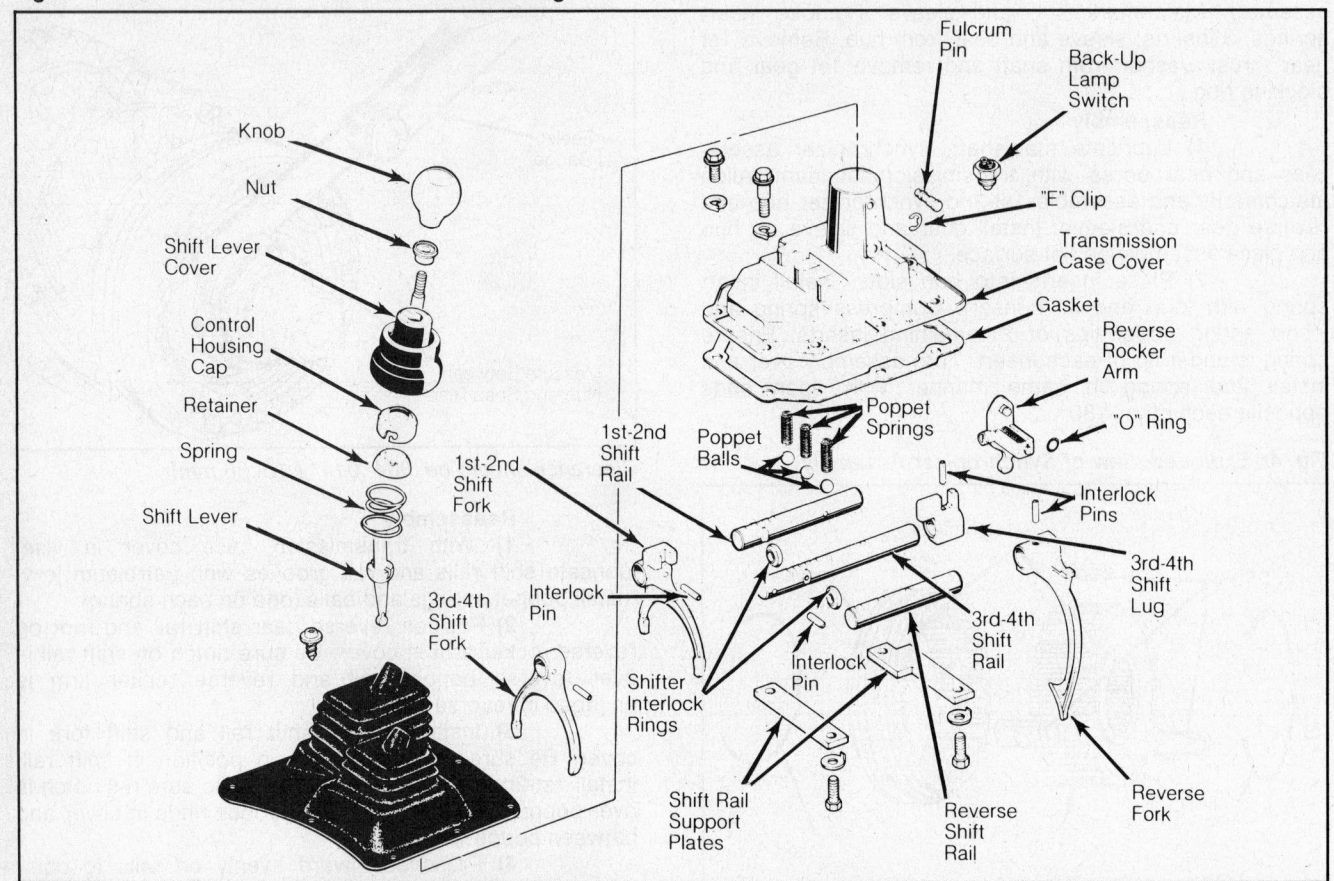

Make sure arbor tool enters shaft bore at front of case. Measure countergear end play by inserting feeler gauge between thrust washer and gear. End play should be .004-.018" (.10-.46 mm). If end play exceeds .018" (.46 mm), replace thrust washer.

6) After correct end play is obtained, push arbor tool back into countergear. Remove shaft at rear of case and allow countergear to lie at bottom of case. Leave countergear at bottom of case to provide clearance for installation of mainshaft assembly.

7) Install mainshaft assembly in case. Make sure synchronizers are in neutral position. Coat 3rd-4th blocking ring with transmission lubricant and install on input shaft. Install roller bearings in end of input shaft using petroleum jelly to retain bearings.

NOTE: Using grease less soluble than petroleum jelly, to retain roller bearings, can plug lubrication holes in shaft and cause bearing failure.

8) Support mainshaft assembly. Install input shaft through front bearing bore in case. Align and seat mainshaft pilot hub in input shaft bore. Tap front bearing and input shaft into case using rawhide mallet, or equivalent. Install front bearing retainer and bolts. Tighten bolts finger tight.

9) Position rear bearing on mainshaft and install into case using installer tool (J-29345). Remove tool and complete installation using rawhide mallet, or equivalent. When bearing is fully seated, install bearing retaining snap ring.

10) Remove front bearing retainer and seat front bearing fully on input shaft. Install bearing retaining snap ring. Apply sealer to front bearing retainer gasket and position on case. Install front bearing retainer oil seal in retainer. Position seal on case aligning notch with oil drain back hole. Install bolts and tighten to specification.

11) Install locating ring on rear bearing and reseat bearing if necessary. Position case on end with input shaft facing downward. Align countershaft gear bores with thrust washers. Install shaft from rear and tap into place being careful not to damage thrust washers.

12) Shift synchronizer sleeves through all gear positions, making sure no binding exists. If input shaft and mainshaft appear to bind in neutral position, check blocking rings for any possibly sticking on tapered portion of gears. Free blocking rings using screwdriver. Place transmission back in neutral position.

13) Install new shift control housing gasket and install housing assembly. Install and tighten bolts to specification making sure 2 dowel type bolts are placed in their correct holes. Install transmission on transfer case.

TIGHTENING SPECIFICATIONS

Application	Ft.Lbs. (N.m)
Back-Up Lamp Switch	15 (20)
Drain/Filler Plugs	15 (20)
Front Bearing Retainer Bolts	13 (18)
Shift Control Housing	13 (18)

SECTION 4

DOMESTIC TRANSFER CASES

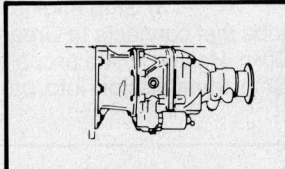

NOTE: **ALSO SEE GENERAL INDEX.**

Transfer Cases
AMERICAN MOTORS MODEL 129

Eagle

DESCRIPTION

Eagle models are equipped with model 129 full-time 4WD transfer case. This unit provides fully differentiated 4WD under all operating conditions. The model 129 is a single range unit. Selection of 4WD is automatic and does not require any external linkage to achieve 4WD operation.

Differentiated operation occurs through a coupling connected to an open differential. Torque is distributed to the front and rear propeller shafts through 2 drive sprockets and drive chain. Case assembly is cast aluminum and consists of front and rear halves, and a rear retainer.

Eagles may be equipped with optional Select Drive system. Select Drive consists of a dash mounted switch, vacuum actuated shift lever in transfer case and vacuum actuated front axle disconnect.

Select Drive provides drive train selection appropriate for road conditions. Selection of "2WD" mode activates transfer case shift lever to provide torque to rear propeller shaft only. Selection of "4WD" mode activates transfer case shift lever to provide torque to both front and rear propeller shafts. See Fig. 1.

LUBRICATION

SERVICE INTERVAL

Check transfer case fluid level at first 5 month or 5000 mile interval; then, every 7 1/2 months or 7500 miles. Change fluid every 12 1/2 months or 12,500 miles.

FLUID TYPE
Use Dexron II ATF.

CAPACITY
Capacity is 6 pints (2.8L) or up to bottom edge of fill plug hole.

TROUBLE SHOOTING

LUBRICANT LEAKS PAST YOKE OR OUT OF VENT
Overfilled condition or vent could be closed or restricted. Yoke seal could be worn or damaged.

NOISY OPERATION
Incorrect or insufficient lubrication. Incorrect tire pressure. Mismatched or unequal tire sizes and type.

SEVERE LOW SPEED SHUDDER
Low level or loss of viscous silicone fluid level.

WILL NOT ENGAGE 2WD
1) Raise vehicle so that all 4 wheels are free to rotate. Start engine. Disconnect mode selector vacuum harness at steel tube connection. Check for vacuum at Red hose that attaches to canister. See Fig. 3. If vacuum exists, go to step 3). If no vacuum, go to step 2).

2) Check intake manifold vacuum supply fitting, vacuum hose and storage tank. Repair or replace damaged or leaking components. If vacuum leak still exists, check and replace vacuum hose between tank and steel tube. If vacuum now exists at Red hose, proceed with system check.

3) Stop engine. Connect vacuum pump to steel tube that connects to Green hose in vacuum harness. Apply 20 in. Hg and rotate propeller shaft to engage transfer case. Shift transmission into park or first gear. If transfer case

Fig. 1: Select Drive Transfer Case

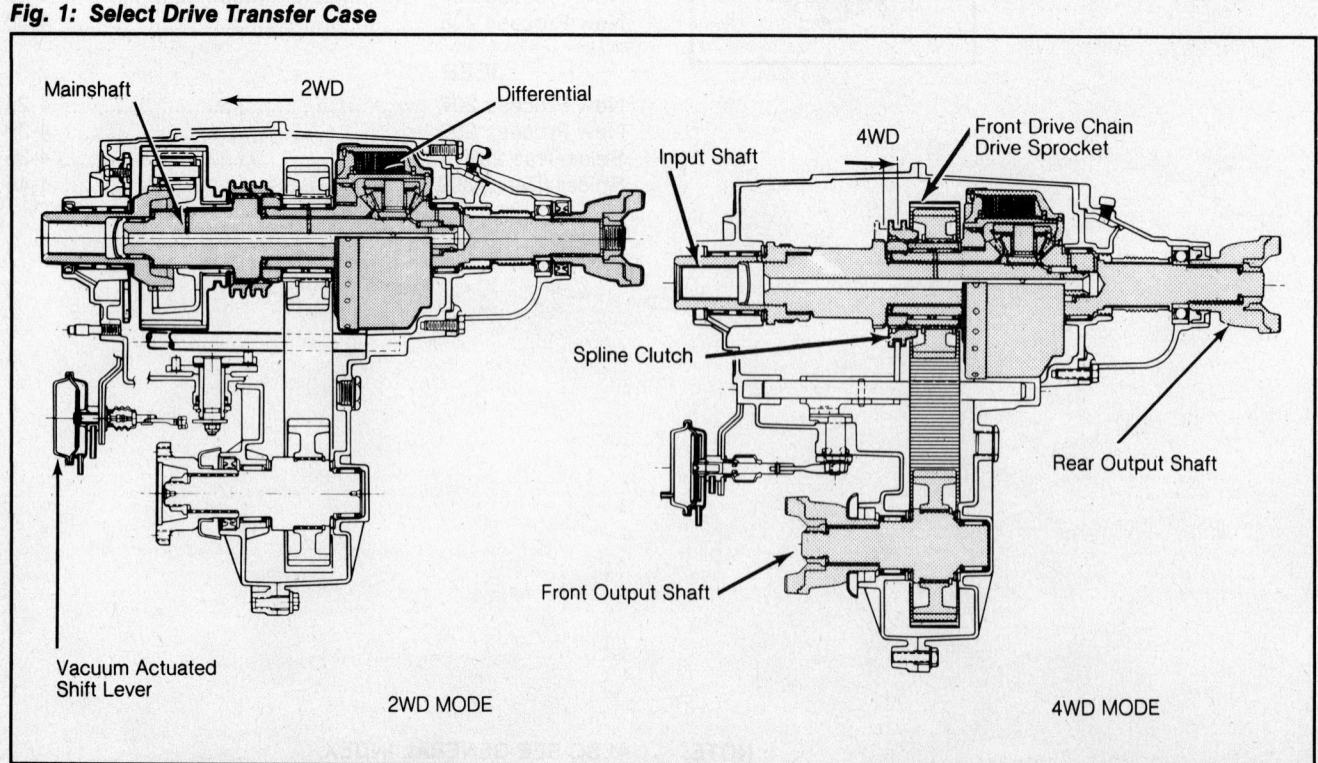

2WD MODE

4WD MODE

AMERICAN MOTORS MODEL 129 (Cont.)

engages, go to step **6**). If transfer case does not engage, go to step **4**).

4) Check transfer case shift motor. If stem is extended, shift motor is okay. If stem is not extended, check vacuum tubes for leaks and damage. Repair as necessary. If transfer case shift motor is still inoperative, check shift motor function. See SHIFT MOTOR FUNCTION TEST. If shift motor is defective, replace motor.

5) If shift motor is okay and transfer case will not engage in 2WD, check transfer case shift linkage and repair as necessary. If linkage is okay and transfer case will not shift into 2WD, repair case. If transfer case now engages in 2WD, check axle for 2WD mode engagement (disconnected). If front axle is not in 2WD mode, check axle shift motor and replace as necessary.

6) Rotate right front wheel. Front axle should be disengaged, if front axle shift motor is okay. Check shift mode selector switch and vacuum harness. Repair as necessary. If front axle shift motor will not disengage, check vacuum lines and repair as necessary. If axle shift motor is still inoperative, check axle shift motor operation. See SHIFT MOTOR FUNCTION TEST.

7) If axle shift motor is still inoperative, replace shift motor. If axle shift motor is okay and axle still will not disengage, remove axle housing cover and shift motor. Inspect shift fork, collar and axle components. Repair as necessary.

WILL NOT ENGAGE 4WD

1) Raise vehicle so that all 4 wheels are free to rotate. Start engine. Disconnect mode selector vacuum harness at steel tube connection. Check for vacuum at Red hose that attaches to storage tank. *See Fig. 3*. If vacuum exists, go to step **3**). If no vacuum, go to step **2**).

2) Check intake manifold vacuum supply fitting, vacuum hose and storage tank. Repair or replace damaged or leaking components. If vacuum leak still exists, check and replace vacuum hose between tank and steel tube. If vacuum now exists at Red hose, proceed with system check.

3) Stop engine. Connect vacuum pump to steel tube that connects to Yellow hose in vacuum harness. Apply 20 in. Hg and rotate right front wheel to engage axle. If front axle engages, go to step **6**). If front axle does not engage, go to step **4**).

4) Check front axle shift motor operation. See SHIFT MOTOR FUNCTION TEST. If shift motor is okay, check vacuum lines and tubes for leaks or damage. Repair as necessary.

5) If axle shift motor is inoperative, replace motor and recheck for axle engagement. If axle still will not engage, remove axle housing cover and shift motor. Inspect shift fork, collar, and axle components. Repair as necessary.

6) Check that transfer case shift motor stem is retracted. If motor stem is retracted, check transfer case shift linkage and repair as necessary. If transfer case shift motor is inoperative (stem is not retracted), check vacuum hoses and repair as necessary.

7) If transfer case shift motor is still inoperative, check motor operation. See SHIFT MOTOR FUNCTION TEST. If shift motor is defective, replace motor and retest. If transfer case motor is okay and transfer case does not engage in 4WD, check axle shift linkage and repair as necessary. If linkage is okay, repair transfer case as necessary.

SHIFT MOTOR FUNCTION TEST

1) Disconnect vacuum harness from shift motor. Connect vacuum pump to front port and apply 15 in. Hg to motor. On transfer case mounted motor, rotate propeller shaft to engage transfer case in 4WD mode. On front axle mounted motor, rotate right wheel to fully disengage axle.

2) On all models, shift motor should maintain vacuum applied to the front port for at least 30 seconds. If vacuum is not maintained, replace motor. If motor does hold vacuum, go to step **3**).

3) Disconnect vacuum pump from front port of vacuum motor. Connect pump to rear port of motor and plug connecting port. *See Fig. 2*. Apply 15 in. Hg to motor. On transfer case mounted motor, shift automatic transmission into park, manual transmission into Neutral.

4) On all models, shift motor should maintain vacuum applied to the rear port for at least 30 seconds. If vacuum is not maintained, replace motor. If motor does hold vacuum, go to step **5**).

5) Remove plug from connecting port and check for vacuum at this port. If vacuum is not present: Rotate propeller shaft on transfer case mounted motor to ensure complete transfer case engagement. Rotate right wheel on front axle mounted motor to ensure axle has shifted completely.

6) On transfer case mounted motor, if vacuum is present at connecting port after fully engaging transfer case, continue TESTING procedure. If vacuum is still not present at connecting port, pull back boot on stem and measure distance that stem has extended.

7) Stem should extend a distance of 5/8" (16 mm) as measured from edge of shift motor housing to "E" ring on stem. If stem does not extend the specified distance or if stem extends the specified distance but no vacuum is present at connecting port, replace motor.

8) On front axle mounted motor, check for vacuum at connecting port once more. If vacuum is still not present at connecting port, replace shift motor. If vacuum is present at connecting port, continue TESTING procedure.

Fig. 2: Typical Select Drive Vacuum Shift Motor

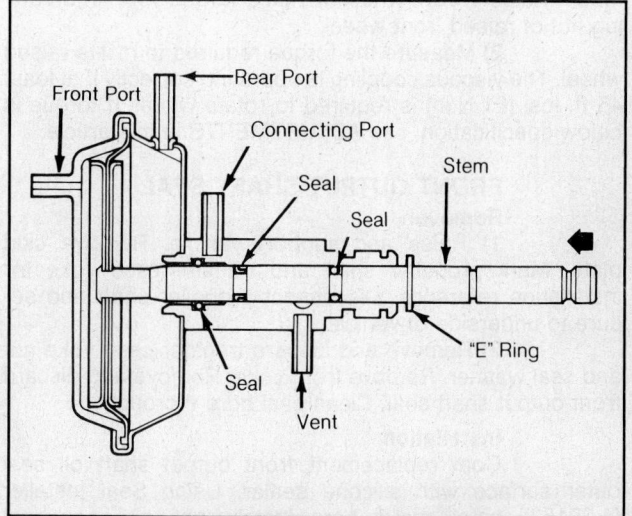

Connecting port is supplied with air when stem is extended. Stem is shown in retracted position.

Transfer Cases
AMERICAN MOTORS MODEL 129 (Cont.)

Fig. 3: Select Drive System Vacuum Diagrams

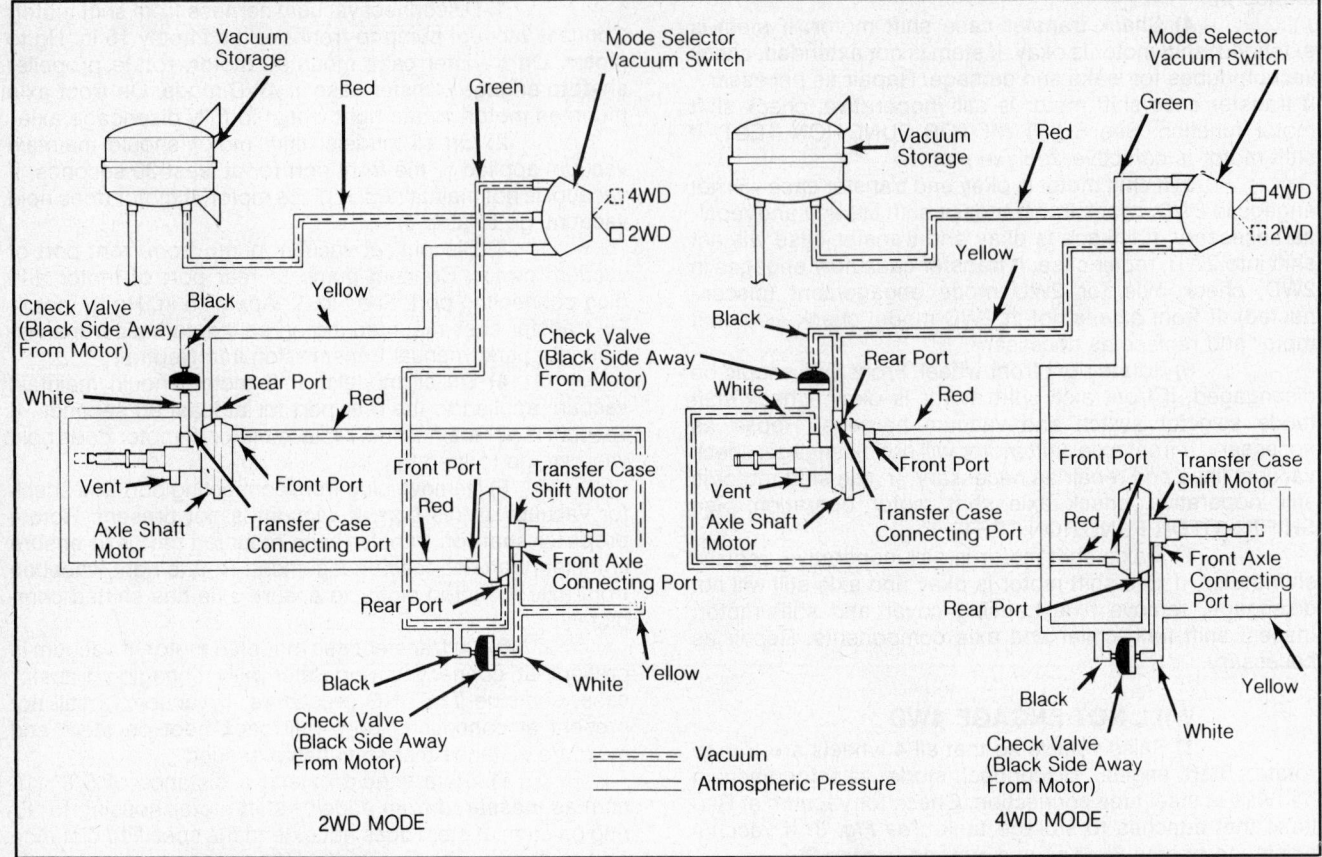

SERVICE (IN VEHICLE)

VISCOUS COUPLING TORQUE BIAS CHECK

1) Place vehicle on a level surface. Stop engine. Place transmission in Neutral with Select Drive lever in 4WD mode. Raise 1 front wheel. Install a torque wrench on any lug nut of raised front wheel.

2) Measure the torque required to rotate raised wheel. The viscous coupling is operating correctly if at least 45 ft. lbs. (61 N.m) is required to rotate wheel. If torque is below specification, see ADJUSTMENTS in this article.

FRONT OUTPUT SHAFT SEAL
Removal

1) Raise and support vehicle. Remove skid plate. Mark propeller shaft and transfer case yoke for installation reference. Disconnect propeller shaft and secure to underside of vehicle.

2) Remove and discard transfer case yoke nut and seal washer. Remove front yoke. Remove and discard front output shaft seal. Clean seal bore thoroughly.

Installation

Coat replacement front output shaft oil seal outer surface with silicone sealer. Using Seal Installer (J-29162), install seal in bore. Install front yoke, new seal washer, and new yoke nut. Tighten yoke nut. Install propeller shaft and skid plate. Lower vehicle.

FRONT AND REAR YOKE SEALS, REAR RETAINER, REAR BEARING & SPEEDOMETER GEAR
Removal

1) Raise and support vehicle. Remove skid plate. Remove drain plug and drain lubricant. Mark propeller shaft and transfer case yoke for installation reference.

2) Disconnect propeller shaft and secure to underside of vehicle. Remove speedometer cable and adapter from rear retainer. Remove and discard speedometer adapter seal.

3) Support engine and transmission (under clutch or converter housing) with support stand. Remove rear crossmember bolts. Using a jack, lower transmission/transfer case assembly to gain access to rear retainer bolts. Mark rear retainer and case for installation reference.

4) Remove rear yoke nut and seal washer. Remove rear yoke. Remove rear retainer bolts and tap off rear retainer with plastic mallet. Do not pry retainer from case.

5) Remove differential shim(s) and speedometer gear from rear output shaft. Remove bearing snap ring (if equipped), bearing and rear yoke seal from retainer. Remove sealant from retainer and case mating surfaces.

Installation

1) Install rear output bearing in rear retainer with shielded side facing case interior. Install bearing snap ring (if equipped). Using Seal Installer (J-29162), install yoke seal.

2) Coat rear retainer mating surface with sealant, align marks made during removal and install rear

AMERICAN MOTORS MODEL 129 (Cont.)

retainer. Tighten retainer bolts. Install yoke, new seal washer and new nut. Tighten nut.

3) Install drain plug and fill transfer case. Install fill plug. Raise transmission/transfer case and rear crossmember. Install and tighten crossmember attaching bolts.

4) Remove engine support and jack. Connect propeller shaft after aligning marks made during removal. Install new seal on speedometer adapter. Install adapter and speedometer cable in rear retainer. Install skid plate and lower vehicle.

REMOVAL & INSTALLATION

TRANSFER CASE

Removal (Automatic Transmission)

1) Raise and support vehicle. Support engine and transmission with transmission jack or support stand. Disconnect catalytic converter support bracket at adapter housing.

2) Remove skid plate, rear brace rod, speedometer cable, and adapter. Remove and discard adapter seal. Mark propeller shafts and yokes for installation reference. Disconnect propeller shafts at yokes and secure to underside of vehicle.

3) Disconnect gearshift and throttle linkage at transmission. Remove rear crossmember and transfer case-to-adapter housing nuts. Lower and remove transfer case from vehicle.

Installation

To install transfer case, reverse removal procedure. Always replace speedometer adapter seal.

Removal (Manual Transmission)

1) Raise and support vehicle. Remove skid plate and rear brace rod. Mark position of speedometer adapter for installation reference. Remove speedometer adapter retainer, adapter, and speedometer cable. Plug adapter opening to prevent excessive fluid spills.

2) Mark propeller shafts and yokes for installation reference. Disconnect propeller shafts at yokes and secure to underside of vehicle. Remove transfer case shift motor vacuum harness. Support transfer case with transmission jack. Remove transfer case mounting nuts and remove from vehicle.

Installation

To install transfer case, reverse removal procedure. Always replace speedometer adapter seal.

OVERHAUL

TRANSFER CASE

Disassembly

1) Drain lubricant from transfer case. Remove nut and bolt attaching shift motor bracket to transfer case and remove motor and bracket as an assembly. Remove front and rear yoke nuts. Remove and discard seal washers. Remove yokes.

2) Mount transfer case on wooden blocks. Cut "V" notches in blocks to clear front case mounting studs. Mark rear retainer and rear case for reassembly reference, then remove retainer bolts. Using 2 screwdrivers inserted in retainer and case slots, pry retainer loose.

3) Remove retainer, differential shim(s) and speedometer drive gear. *See Fig 4.* Remove bolts attaching

rear case to front case. Bolts at end of case use flat washers. Using 2 screwdrivers inserted in slots at each end of rear case, loosen case halves. Remove rear case.

CAUTION: Do not attempt to wedge case halves apart. Case mating surfaces may be damaged.

Fig. 4: Speedometer Gear and Differential Shims

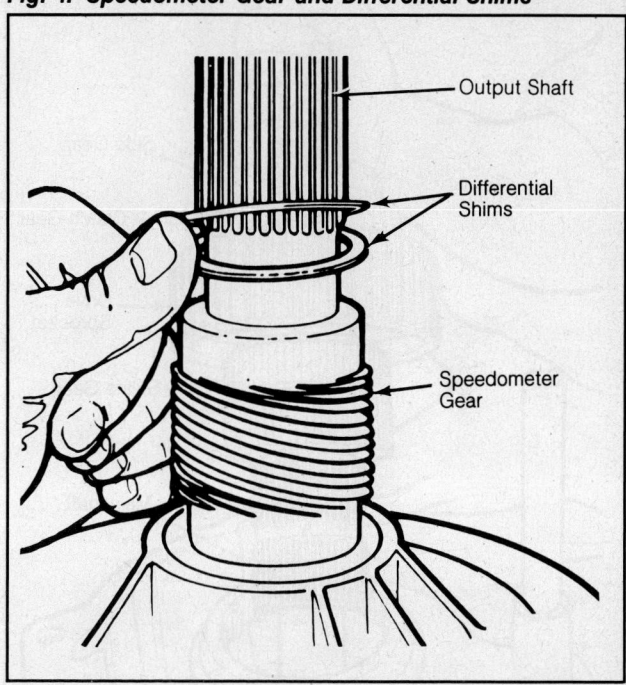

Output Shaft

Differential Shims

Speedometer Gear

4) Remove thrust bearing and races from front output shaft. Note position of bearing and races for reassembly reference. Remove oil pump from rear output shaft. Note position of pump for reassembly reference (recessed side faces case interior).

5) Remove rear output shaft from viscous coupling. Remove 15 mainshaft pilot bearing rollers from shaft or coupling. Remove mainshaft "O" ring from end of shaft. Remove viscous coupling from mainshaft and side gear.

6) Lift front output shaft, sprocket and chain as an assembly. Tilt front shaft toward mainshaft, slide chain off drive sprocket and remove assembly. Remove front output shaft front thrust bearing assembly from front case or shaft, if bearing and races remained on shaft during removal. Remove drive chain from front output shaft and sprocket.

7) Remove driven sprocket snap ring from front output shaft. Mark sprocket and shaft for reassembly reference, then remove sprocket. Remove mainshaft, side gear, clutch gear, drive sprocket, and spline gear as an assembly. *See Fig. 5.* Place assembly aside on clean surface.

8) Remove range fork, rail and clutch sleeve as an assembly. Mark sleeve and fork for reassembly reference, then remove sleeve from fork. Drive roll pin out of fork and rail. Remove rail from fork. Remove mainshaft thrust washer from input gear. Remove input gear, input thrust bearing and race. Remove detent bolt, spring and plunger. Remove range sector shaft retaining nut and washer.

9) Remove ranger sector. Tap sector shaft with plastic mallet to remove shaft from case bore. Remove range sector shaft "O" ring seal and seal retainer from case bore. Remove rear output bearing and rear yoke seal from rear retainer. Note position of bearing for reassembly reference (bearing is shielded on one side). Remove input gear. Pry front yoke seals out of front case.

Fig. 5: Removing Mainshaft Assembly

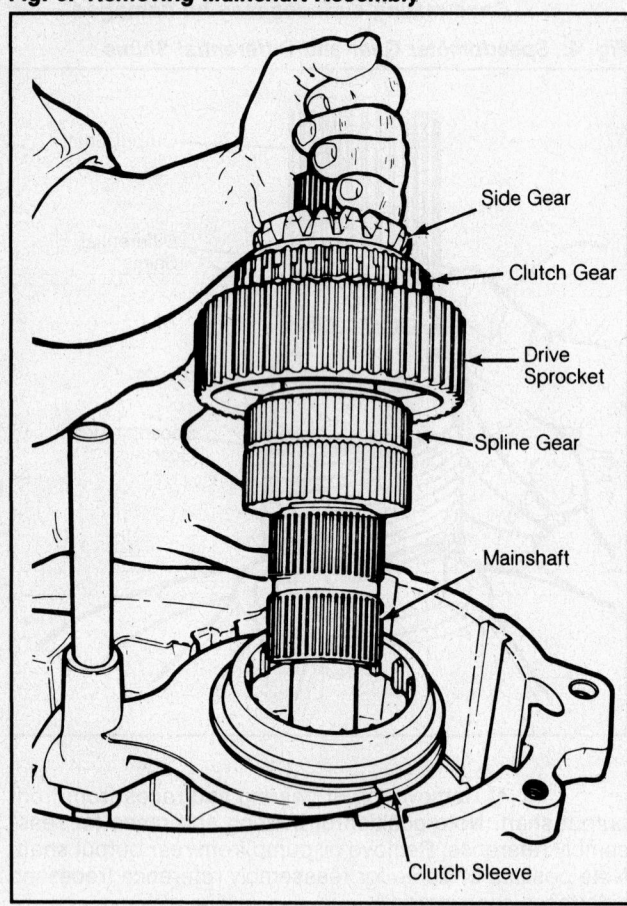

Fig. 6: Removing Drive Sprocket, Clutch Gear, Side Gear and Sprocket Carrier from Mainshaft

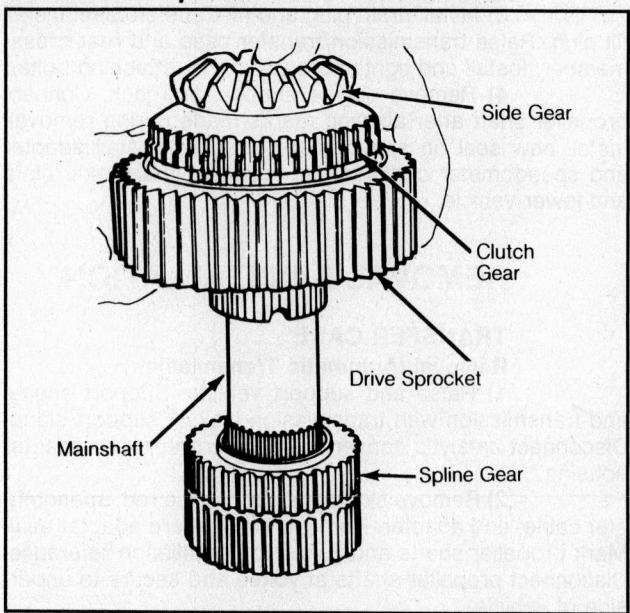

MAINSHAFT
Disassembly
1) Grasp drive sprocket and lift sprocket, clutch gear and side gear upward and off mainshaft. Remove mainshaft needle bearings (82) and bearing spacers (3) from mainshaft. Note spacer position for reassembly reference. See Fig. 6.

2) Remove spline gear and thrust washer from mainshaft. Remove side gear, clutch gear and clutch gear thrust washer from sprocket carrier and sprocket. Remove clutch gear and thrust washer from side gear.

3) Remove 1 sprocket carrier snap ring and remove drive sprocket from carrier. Mark sprocket and carrier for reassembly reference. Remove 3 bearing spacers and all sprocket carrier needle bearings from carrier. A total of 120 needle bearings are used.

NOTE: **The sprocket carrier and mainshaft needle bearings are different sizes. Take care to avoid intermixing them.**

CLEANING & INSPECTION
1) Clean all parts in cleaning solvent. Be sure all old lubricant or foreign material is removed from surfaces of every part. Apply compressed air to blow dry parts.

2) Inspect all gears for signs of excessive wear or damage and check all gear splines for burrs, nicks, wear or damage. Remove minor nicks or scratches using an oilstone. Replace any part exhibiting excessive wear or damage.

NOTE: **Front output shaft thrust bearing race surfaces are heat treated, causing Brown or Blue discoloration. Do not replace front output shaft because of this discoloration.**

3) Inspect case halves and rear retainer for cracks, porosity, damaged mating surfaces, stripped bolt threads or distortion. Inspect condition of all bearings and all bearing bores. Replace any part that exhibits signs of wear or damage.

CAUTION: **All bearings used in transfer case halves must be correctly positioned to avoid blocking bearing oil feed holes. After replacing bearing, check that feed hole is not covered by bearing.**

MAINSHAFT
Reassembly
1) Install thrust washer, new "O" ring, needle bearings and bearing spacers on mainshaft. Coat shaft bearing surfaces and all needle bearings with petroleum jelly. Install short bearing spacer on shaft and install first 41 needle bearings. See Fig. 8.

2) Install long bearing spacer, remaining 41 needle bearings and remaining short spacer. Be careful to avoid displacing bearings as spacers are installed. If necessary, use additional petroleum jelly to hold bearings in place. Install spline gear on mainshaft. Take care to avoid displacing bearings while installing spline gear.

3) Install sprocket carrier in drive sprocket and install sprocket carrier snap rings. Be sure to align carrier and sprocket according to reference marks made during disassembly. See Fig. 9.

AMERICAN MOTORS MODEL 129 (Cont.)

Fig. 7: American Motors Model 129 Transfer Case

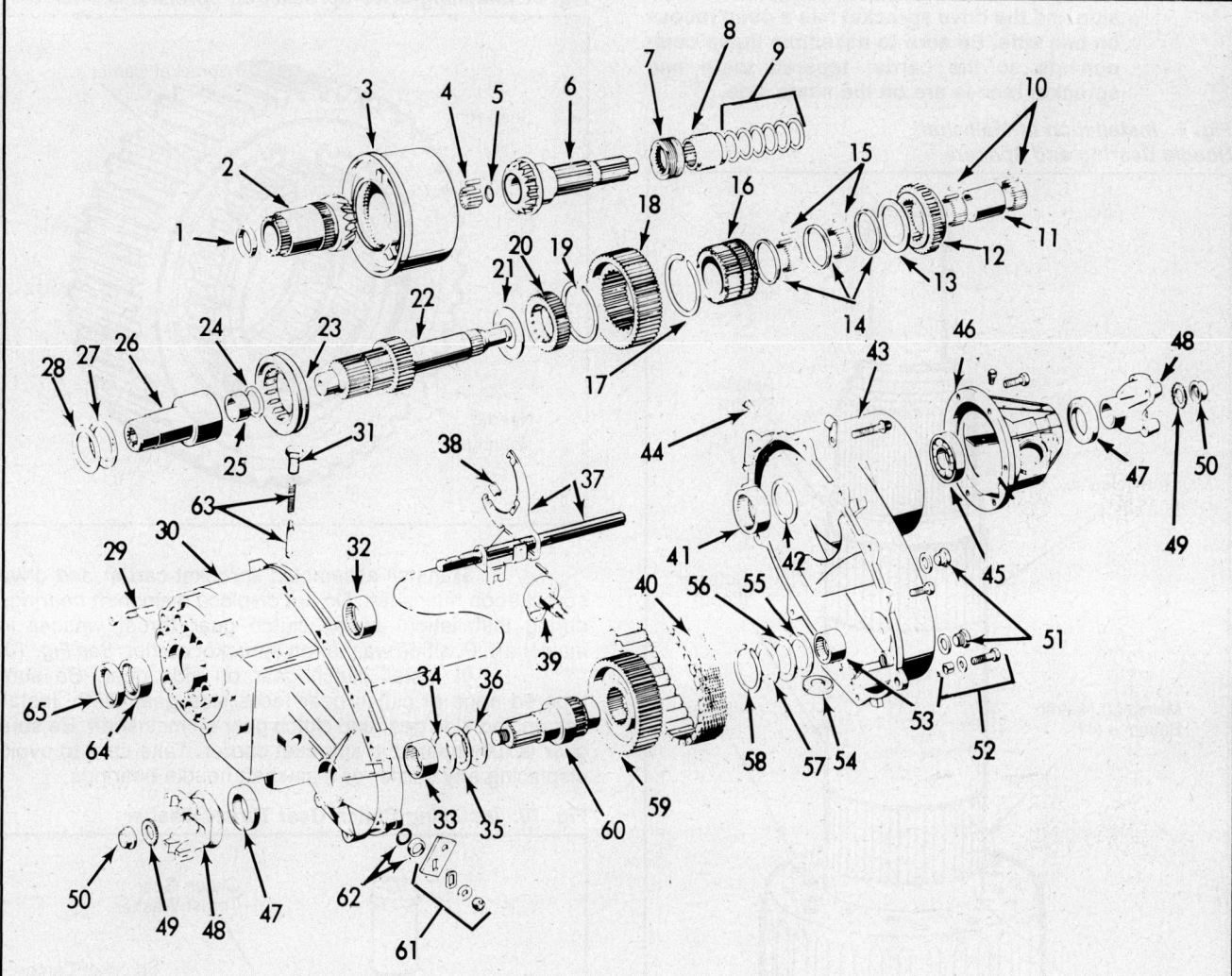

1. Mainshaft Bearing Spacers (Short) (2)
2. Side Gear
3. Viscous Coupling
4. Mainshaft Pilot Bearings
5. Mainshaft "O" Ring
6. Rear Output Shaft
7. Oil Pump
8. Speedometer Drive Gear
9. Differential Drive Shims
10. Mainshaft Needle Bearings (82)
11. Mainshaft Needle Bearing Spacer (Long) (1)
12. Clutch Gear
13. Clutch Gear Thrust Washer
14. Sprocket Carrier Needle Bearing Spacer (3)
15. Sprocket Carrier Needle Bearings (120)
16. Sprocket Carrier
17. Sprocket Carrier Snap Ring
18. Drive Sprocket
19. Sprocket Carrier Snap Ring
20. Spline Gear
21. Mainshaft Thrust Washer
22. Mainshaft
23. Clutch Sleeve
24. Mainshaft Thrust Bearing
25. Mainshaft Bushing
26. Input Gear
27. Input Gear Thrust Bearing
28. Input Gear Thrust Bearing Race
29. Mounting Gear
30. Front Case
31. Plug and Washer
32. Input Gear Rear Bearing
33. Front Output Shaft Front Bearing
34. Front Output Shaft Front Thrust Bearing Race (Thick)
35. Front Output Shaft Front Thrust Bearing
36. Front Output Shaft Front Thrust Bearing Race (Thin)
37. Range Fork and Rail
38. Shift Fork Pad
39. Range Sector
40. Drive Chain
41. Rear Output Shaft Bearing
42. Rear Output Shaft Bearing Seal
43. Rear Case
44. Plug
45. Rear Output Bearing
46. Rear Retainer
47. Yoke Seal
48. Yoke
49. Seal Washer
50. Yoke Nut
51. Fill and Drain Plugs
52. Alignment Dowel, Washer and Bolt
53. Front Output Shaft Rear Bearing
54. Magnet
55. Front Output Shaft Rear Thrust Bearing Race (Thick)
56. Front Output Shaft Rear Thrust Bearing
57. Front Output Shaft Rear Thrust Bearing Race (Thin)
58. Drive Sprocket Retaining Snap Ring
59. Drive Sprocket
60. Front Output Shaft
61. Range Sector Shaft Retaining Lock Nut and Washers
62. Range Sector Shaft Seal and Retainer
63. Detent Spring and Plunger
64. Input Gear Front Bearing
65. Input Gear Seal

NOTE: The sprocket carrier teeth are tapered on one side and the drive sprocket has a deep recess on one side. Be sure to assemble these components so the carrier tapered teeth and sprocket recess are on the same side.

Fig. 8: Installation of Mainshaft Needle Bearing and Spacers

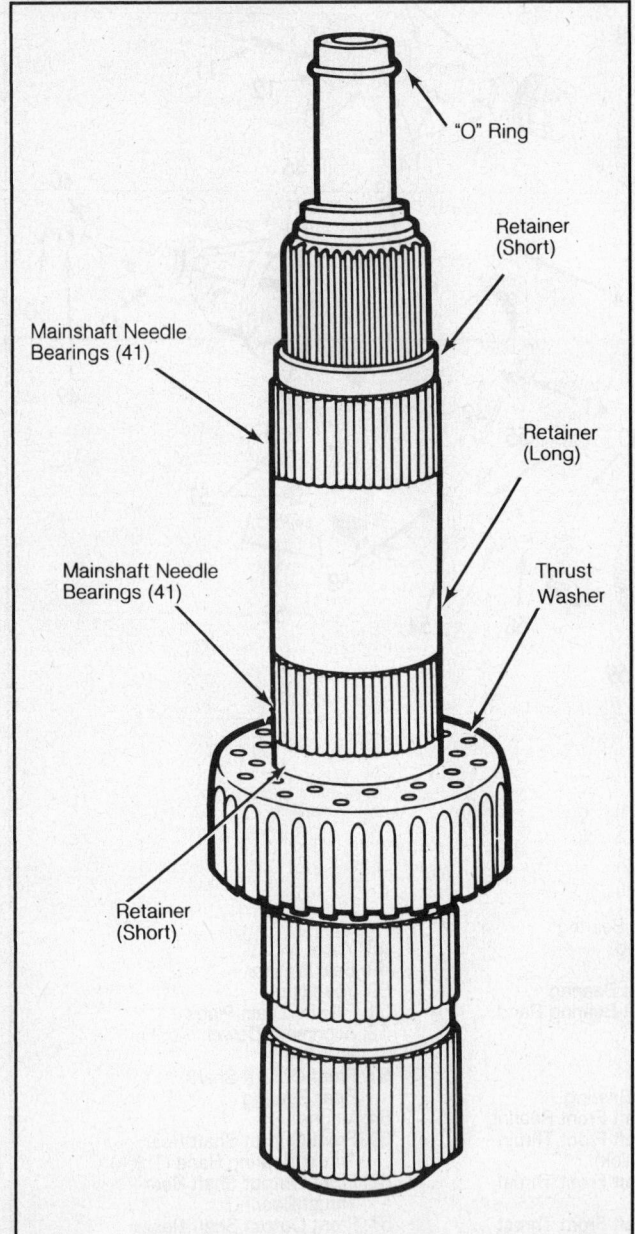

Fig. 9: Installing Drive Sprocket on Sprocket Carrier

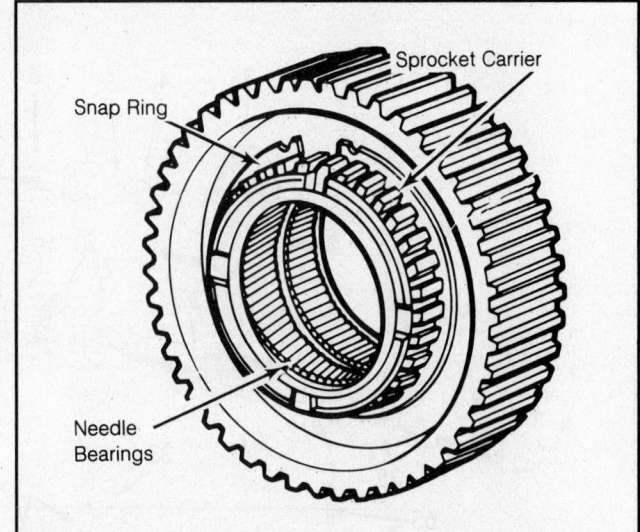

5) Install assembled sprocket carrier and drive sprocket on mainshaft. Do not displace mainshaft bearings during installation. Install clutch gear thrust washer in mainshaft. Position washer on sprocket carrier. *See Fig. 10.*

6) Install clutch gear on side gear. Be sure tapered edge of clutch gear faces side gear teeth. Install assembled side gear and clutch gear on mainshaft. Be sure gear is fully seated in sprocket carrier. Take care to avoid displacing any carrier or mainshaft needle bearings.

Fig. 10: Installing Clutch Gear Thrust Washer

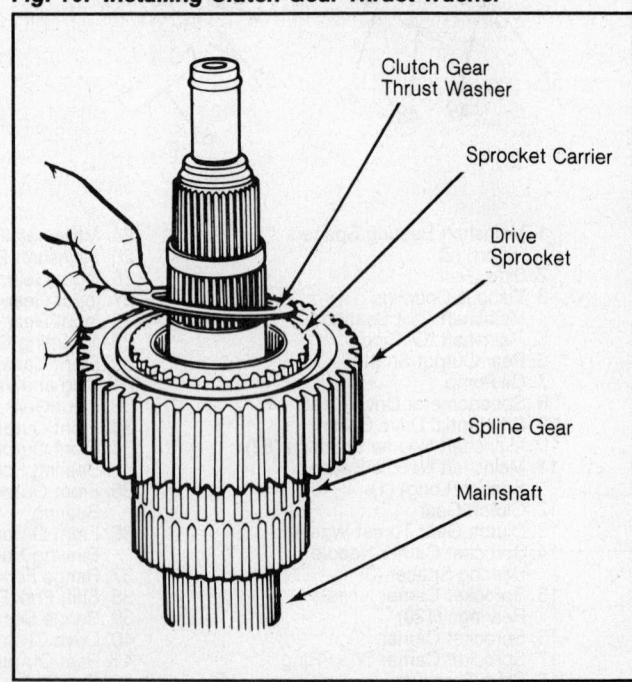

4) Install sprocket carrier bearings and spacers. Coat carrier bore and all 120 carrier needle bearings with petroleum jelly. Install center spacer. Install 60 bearings in each end of carrier and install 2 remaining spacers (1 at each end of carrier). If necessary, use additional petroleum jelly to hold bearings in place.

AMERICAN MOTORS MODEL 129 (Cont.)

TRANSFER CASE
Reassembly

NOTE: **Before reassembling transfer case, verify viscous coupling operation. See ADJUSTMENTS in this article.**

1) Install new range sector shaft "O" ring and retainer in case shaft bore. Install range sector, "O" ring, retainer, range lever, washer and lock nut on sector shaft. Tighten lock nut.

2) Install thrust bearing and race on input gear and install gear in front case. Install mainshaft thrust washer in input gear. Assemble range fork, rail and clutch sleeve. Install assembly in case. Be sure rail is fully seated in case bore.

NOTE: **The rail bore in the front case must be absolutely dry and free of oil. A small amount of oil in the bore will prevent the rail from seating completely and also prevent rear case installation.**

3) Install mainshaft and gear assembly in case. Be sure mainshaft is fully seated in input gear. Install driven sprocket on front output shaft according to reference marks made during disassembly. Install sprocket retaining snap ring. Install front output shaft thrust bearing assembly in front case.

4) Install thick race in case, then install bearing and thin race. Install drive chain, front output shaft and driven sprocket. Raise and tilt driven sprocket and chain and install opposite end of chain on drive sprocket. Align front output shaft with shaft bore in front case and install shaft in case. Be sure front shaft thrust bearing assembly is fully seated in case.

5) Install front output shaft rear thrust bearing assembly on front output shaft. Install thin race first, then install bearing and thick race. Check viscous coupling torque bias check. See ADJUSTMENTS in this article. Install viscous coupling on side gear and clutch gear. Coupling must be fully seated on clutch gear.

NOTE: **Clutch gear should be flush with coupling and gear teeth should not be visible.**

6) Coat mainshaft pilot bearing surface and all 15 pilot roller bearings with petroleum jelly and install bearings on shaft. Install rear output shaft on mainshaft and into viscous coupling. Tap shaft with mallet to seat it if necessary. Install oil pump on rear output shaft. Install new rear output bearing oil seal in rear case.

7) Apply bead of sealer to mating surface of rear case. Install magnet, if removed. Install rear case on front case. Install and tighten rear case-to-front case bolts. Flat washers are used on bolts at case ends where alignment dowels are located.

NOTE: **If rear case will not seat properly in the front case, check for the following: Oil in the range fork rail bore, front output shaft rear thrust bearing assembly is not aligned with the rear case, mainshaft is not completely seated, rear case not aligned with oil pump.**

8) Install speedometer drive gear on rear output shaft. Measure thickness of differential shim pack and record measurement. Install a shim pack measuring approximately .030" (.762 mm) and install on rear output shaft.

See Fig. 4. Align rear retainer on rear case and install retainer.

9) Install retainer bolts and tighten securely; DO NOT tighten to specified torque. Install front and rear output shaft yokes and original yoke nuts. Tighten yoke nuts finger tight. Place transfer case in 4WD-High range position. Check and adjust differential end play. See ADJUSTMENTS in this article.

10) After checking or adjusting end play, remove front and rear yokes. Discard original yoke nuts. Remove rear retainer and apply sealer to retainer mating surfaces. Install rear retainer. Apply sealer to retainer bolts and tighten.

11) Install front and rear yokes, new yoke seal and new nut. Tighten nut. Install plunger and spring on case. Apply sealer to bolt and install on case. Install drain plug and fill transfer case with lubricant. Install fill plug.

ADJUSTMENTS

VISCOUS COUPLING
TORQUE BIAS CHECK

1) Install clutch gear on side gear. Install assembled clutch gear and side gear in viscous coupling. Mount assembled viscous coupling and gears in vise which has wooden blocks installed to prevent side gear damage. Firmly clamp assembly on side gear. *See Fig. 11.*

2) Check engagement of clutch gear in viscous coupling. Clutch gear must be fully engaged in coupling. If necessary, reposition wood blocks so they support gear in coupling. Install rear output shaft and install yoke retaining nut. Install torque wrench on yoke nut.

3) Rotate output shaft and measure torque required to rotate shaft in coupling. Rotating torque should be 25 ft. lbs. (34 N.m) MINIMUM. If rotating torque is less than specified, replace coupling. If torque is at or above specification, coupling is operating properly.

Fig. 11: Viscous Coupling Torque Bias Check

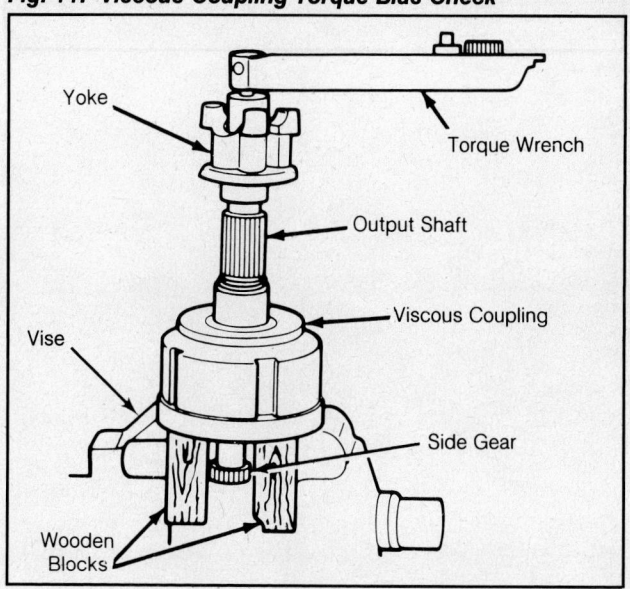

Transfer Cases

AMERICAN MOTORS MODEL 129 (Cont.)

DIFFERENTIAL END PLAY

1) Mount dial indicator on rear retainer and position indicator stylus so it contacts rear yoke nut. *See Fig. 12.* Support transfer case to prevent front output yoke from turning.

2) Using a wrench for leverage, slowly turn rear output shaft while maintaining moderate inward pressure on rear yoke. Turn rear output shaft at least 2 full turns to determine maximum run-out of shaft.

3) Set shaft at its minimum run-out point and zero dial indicator. Pull upwrd on rear output yoke, note reading on dial indicator and record it. End play should be between .002-.010" (.05-.25 mm). If end play is incorrect, remove retainer and add or subtract shims as necessary to correct end play.

Fig. 12: Measuring Differential End Play

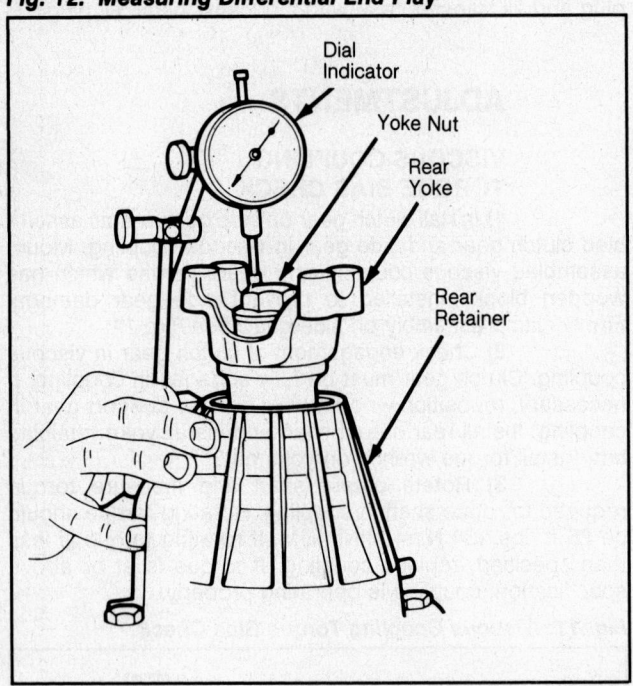

TIGHTENING SPECIFICATIONS

Application	Ft. Lbs. (N.m)
Crossmember Bolts	30 (41)
Plunger Bolt	23 (31)
Drain and Fill Plugs	18 (24)
Front and Rear Yoke Nuts	120 (163)
Operating Lever Lock Nut	15-20 (20-27)
Propeller Shaft-to-Yoke	15 (20)
Rear Brace Rod Bolts	30 (41)
Rear Case-to-Front Case Bolts	23 (31)
Rear Retainer Bolts	23 (31)
Skid Plate Bolts	30 (41)
Transfer Case-to-Adapter Housing	33 (45)
4WD Indicator Light Switch	15-20 (20-27)

Transfer Cases

BORG-WARNER 1345

Ford Motor Co.

DESCRIPTION

Transfer case is a 2-piece, part-time unit using planetary gearing, a chain drive, and an aluminum case. The unit is lubricated by a positive-displacement oil pump that channels oil flow through drilled holes in rear output shaft. Pump turns with the rear output shaft, permitting towing of the vehicle for extended distances without disconnecting rear propeller shaft.

LUBRICATION

SERVICE INTERVALS

Check fluid level whenever malfunction is suspected or when fluid leakage or contamination is observed. Also check after operation in water.

FLUID TYPE

Use Dexron II ATF.

CAPACITY

Refill capacity is 6.5 pints (3.1L).

ADJUSTMENTS

Adjust shift linkage so that all positions may be selected without interference or binding. Inspect all swivels, rods and mountings for wear or damage. Replace as necessary.

REMOVAL & INSTALLATION

TRANSFER CASE

Removal

1) Raise vehicle. Remove drain plug and drain fluid from transfer case. Replace plug. Disconnect 4WD indicator switch connector at transfer case. If equipped, remove skid plate.

2) Disconnect front and rear propeller shafts from transfer case output shaft yokes, and wire out of way. Do not allow shafts to hang free as damage to universal joints may result.

3) Disconnect speedometer driven gear from rear bearing retainer. Remove retaining clips and shift rod from transfer case control and transfer case shift levers. Disconnect vent hose from case.

4) Remove heat shield. Support transfer case with transmission jack. Remove transfer case-to-transmission adapter bolts and slide transfer case off of transmission output shaft (toward rear). Lower transfer case and remove gasket from between transfer case and adapter.

Installation

Reverse removal procedure to install transfer case. Fill case with 6.5 pints (3.1L) of Dexron II type ATF.

DISASSEMBLY

TRANSFER CASE

1) Remove transfer case from vehicle and drain fluid. Remove both output shaft yoke nuts and washers. Remove output yokes from transfer case. Remove 4WD indicator switch. Separate cover from case by removing attaching bolts. Pry case and cover apart by inserting a screwdriver in pry bosses.

2) Remove magnetic chip collector from bottom case half. Slide shift collar hub off rear output shaft. Compress shift fork spring, and remove upper and lower spring retainers from shaft. *See Fig. 1.*

3) Remove 4WD lock-up fork and lock-up shift collar from case as an assembly. Take care not to lose nylon wear pads on fork. Remove snap ring and thrust washer from front output shaft. Grip chain and sprockets, and lift straight up to remove drive sprocket, driven sprocket, and chain from output shafts.

Fig. 1: Removing Spring Retainers

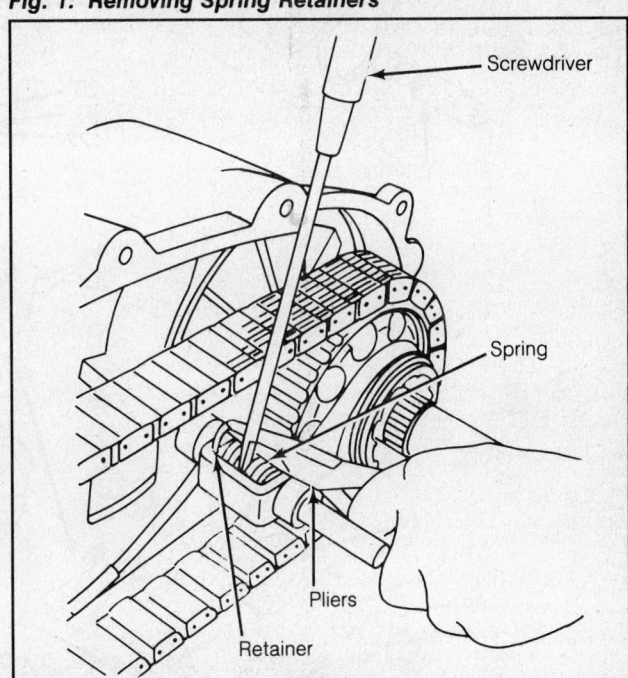

Use a screwdriver and needle nose pliers.

4) Remove thrust washer from rear output shaft. Remove front output shaft from case. Remove oil pump attaching bolts and remove oil pump rear cover, pick-up tube, pump body and filter, 2 pump pins, pump spring and oil pump front cover from rear output shaft. Disconnect oil pick-up tube from pump body.

5) Remove bearing retainer snap ring from inside case. Lift out rear output shaft, while tapping on bearing retainer with a plastic hammer. Lift rear output shaft and bearing retainer from case, noting that 2 dowel pins will fall into case.

6) Remove rear output shaft from bearing retainer. If necessary, press needle bearing assembly from bearing retainer. Remove "C" clip holding shift cam to shift actuating lever inside the case. Remove shift lever retaining screw and remove lever from case. *See Fig. 3.*

Transfer Cases
BORG-WARNER 1345 (Cont.)

Fig. 2: Exploded View of Borg-Warner 1345 Transfer Case

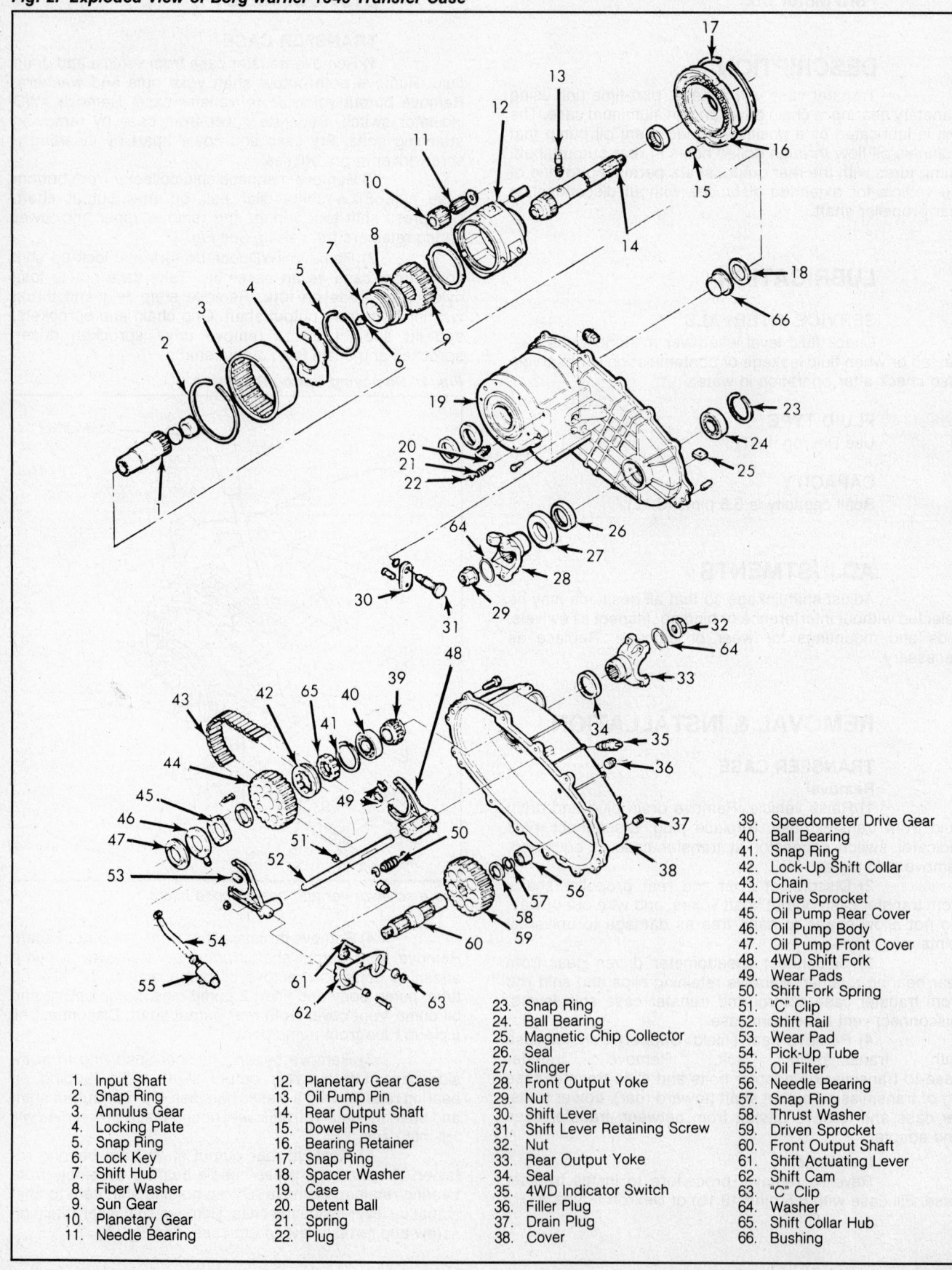

1. Input Shaft
2. Snap Ring
3. Annulus Gear
4. Locking Plate
5. Snap Ring
6. Lock Key
7. Shift Hub
8. Fiber Washer
9. Sun Gear
10. Planetary Gear
11. Needle Bearing
12. Planetary Gear Case
13. Oil Pump Pin
14. Rear Output Shaft
15. Dowel Pins
16. Bearing Retainer
17. Snap Ring
18. Spacer Washer
19. Case
20. Detent Ball
21. Spring
22. Plug
23. Snap Ring
24. Ball Bearing
25. Magnetic Chip Collector
26. Seal
27. Slinger
28. Front Output Yoke
29. Nut
30. Shift Lever
31. Shift Lever Retaining Screw
32. Nut
33. Rear Output Yoke
34. Seal
35. 4WD Indicator Switch
36. Filler Plug
37. Drain Plug
38. Cover
39. Speedometer Drive Gear
40. Ball Bearing
41. Snap Ring
42. Lock-Up Shift Collar
43. Chain
44. Drive Sprocket
45. Oil Pump Rear Cover
46. Oil Pump Body
47. Oil Pump Front Cover
48. 4WD Shift Fork
49. Wear Pads
50. Shift Fork Spring
51. "C" Clip
52. Shift Rail
53. Wear Pad
54. Pick-Up Tube
55. Oil Filter
56. Needle Bearing
57. Snap Ring
58. Thrust Washer
59. Driven Sprocket
60. Front Output Shaft
61. Shift Actuating Lever
62. Shift Cam
63. "C" Clip
64. Washer
65. Shift Collar Hub
66. Bushing

Transfer Cases

BORG-WARNER 1345 (Cont.)

NOTE: When removing lever, shift cam will disengage from shift lever shaft. This may release detent ball and spring.

Fig. 3: Removing Shift Cam "C" Clip

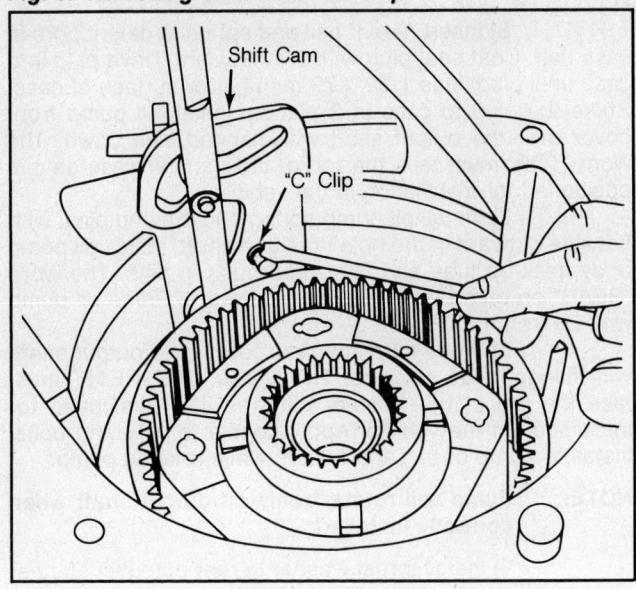

Use a flat-bladed screwdriver to remove "C" clip.

7) Remove planetary gear set, shift rail, shift cam, input shaft and shift forks from case as an assembly. Take care not to lose 2 nylon wear pads on shift fork. *See Fig. 4.* Remove spacer washer from bottom of case and remove bushing. Using a drift, drive plug out from detent spring bore.

Fig. 4: Disassembling Shifter Mechanism

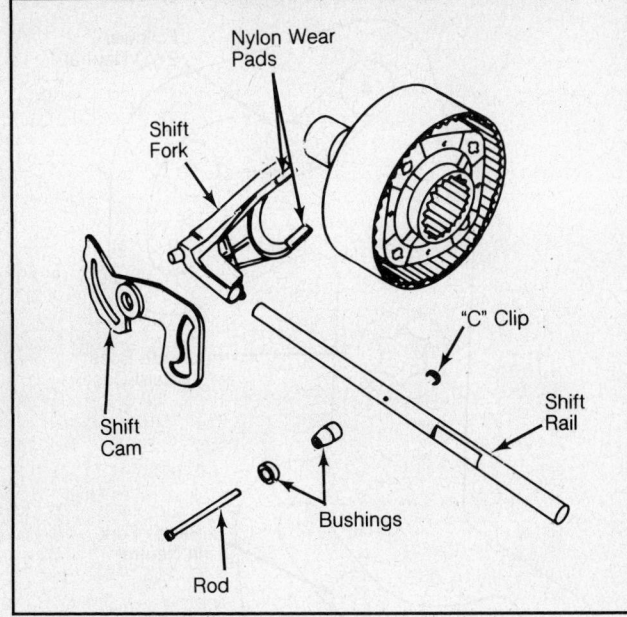

Do not lose nylon wear pads located on shift forks.

PLANETARY GEAR SET

1) Slide input shaft rearward out of planetary gear set. Remove snap ring from annulus gear. Remove

shift hub and planetary gear case from annulus gear. Remove locking plates from hub. *See Fig. 5.*

2) Remove shift hub snap ring. Remove "T" shaped lock key. Lift shift hub from the assembly. Remove outer fiber washer, sun gear and inner fiber washer, while rotating inner washer slightly to allow positioning tabs to clear planetary gears.

Fig. 5: Disassembling Planetary Gear Set

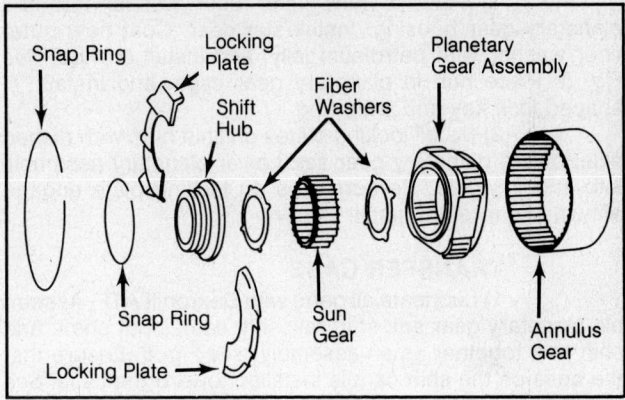

Remove locking plates from shift hub.

COVER

1) Remove snap ring retaining rear output shaft ball bearing assembly in cover. Turn cover over and remove rear output shaft seal using Seal Remover (1175-AC) and Slide Hammer (T50T-100-A). Remove speedometer drive gear.

2) Press rear output shaft ball bearing from cover. Remove speedometer gear adapter. Using Slide Hammer (T50T-100-A) and Puller (D80L-100T from D80-100-A Puller Set), remove front output shaft inner needle bearing.

CASE

Remove snap ring retaining front output shaft ball bearing assembly in case. Remove output shaft seal and 2 input shaft seals. Press front output shaft bearing and input shaft bushing from case.

CLEANING & INSPECTION

1) Clean all parts in cleaning solvent. Be sure to remove all traces of gaskets from gasket surfaces. Dry parts with compressed air, being careful not to spin bearings. Check all gear teeth and splines for burrs, nicks, or excessive damage. Inspect all snap rings and thrust washers for excessive wear, distortion or damage.

2) Inspect 2 case halves for cracks, porosity, damaged mating surfaces, stripped bolt threads or distortion. Inspect condition of all bearings and retainers. Inspect condition of chain and oil pump.

REASSEMBLY

CASE

Press new input shaft bushing into case. Ensure that lug is in downward position. Install new output shaft ball bearing and snap ring. Press input shaft seals into case. Press front output shaft seal into case.

Transfer Cases
BORG-WARNER 1345 (Cont.)

COVER

Press a new needle bearing into cover. Using Bearing Installer (T80T-7127-B), press new ball bearing into cover and install snap ring. Turn cover over and install speedometer drive gear. Install new output shaft seal. Install speedometer gear adapter.

PLANETARY GEAR ASSEMBLY

1) Place a new inner fiber washer into the planetary gear housing. Install sun gear. Coat new outer fiber washer with petroleum jelly, and install on hub. *See Fig. 5.* Place hub in planetary gear cage, and install "T" shaped lock key and snap ring.

2) Install locking plates on shift hub, with dished side toward planetary gear set. Lower planetary assembly into annulus gear. Be sure tabs on locking plate engage annulus gear teeth. Install snap ring.

TRANSFER CASE

1) Lubricate all parts with Dexron II ATF. Assemble planetary gear set, shift rail, shift cam, input shaft, and shift fork together as an assembly. *See Fig. 6.* Ensure that the boss on the shift cam is installed toward the case. *See Fig. 7.* Install spacer washer on input shaft.

2) Place rear output shaft in planetary gear set, making sure shift cam engages shift fork actuating pin. Lay case on its side. Insert rear output shaft and planetary gear set into case. Be sure spacer washer remains on input shaft.

3) Install shift rail into hole in case. Install outer roller bushing into guide in case. Remove rear output shaft, and position shift fork in Neutral. Place shift control lever shaft through cam, and install clip ring. Ensure shift control lever is pointed downward and parallel to front face of case.

5) Insert output shaft through bearing retainer from the bottom side outward. Insert rear output shaft pilot into the input shaft rear bushing. Align dowel holes, and lower bearing into position. Install dowel pins. Install bearing retainer snap ring.

6) Insert detent ball and spring in detent bore in case half. Coat seal plug with RTV sealant. Drive plug into case until plug lip is 1/32" (.79 mm) below surface of case. Stake the plug to case in 2 places. Install oil pump front cover over the output shaft with flanged side down. The word "TOP" must face the top of the transfer case as it is positioned for installation in the vehicle.

7) Install oil pump spring and 2 pump pins, with flat side outward in the hole in output shaft. Install oil pump body, pick-up tube and filter, and push in pins. The word "REAR" on pump body must face upward. Prime oil pump with Dexron II ATF.

8) Place oil pump rear cover onto output shaft, with flanged side outward. The words "TOP REAR" must face the top of the transfer case as it is positioned for installation in the vehicle. Apply Loctite to oil pump bolts, install to pump cover, and tighten while rotating pump.

NOTE: **Pump will rotate freely on output shaft when correctly installed.**

9) Install thrust washer to rear output shaft near oil pump. Install chain on drive and driven sprockets. Lower chain and sprockets into position in case. The driven sprocket is installed over front output shaft and the drive sprocket is placed over rear output shaft.

10) Install washer and snap ring behind driven sprocket. Engage 4WD shift fork on shift collar. Slide shift fork over shift shaft. Install shift collar over rear output shaft. Ensure nylon wear pads are installed on shift fork

Fig. 6: *Installing Planetary Gear Set and Shifter Mechanism*

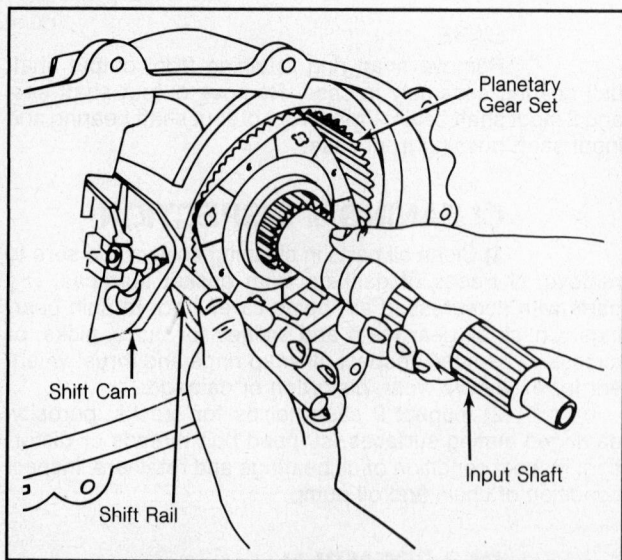

Planetary Gear Set

Shift Cam

Shift Rail

Input Shaft

Install components as an assembly.

4) Check shift fork and planetary gear engagement. Unit should operate freely without binding. Using Bearing Installer (T80T-7127-C), press new needle bearing into bearing retainer (if removed).

Fig. 7: *Installing and Engaging Shift Cam*

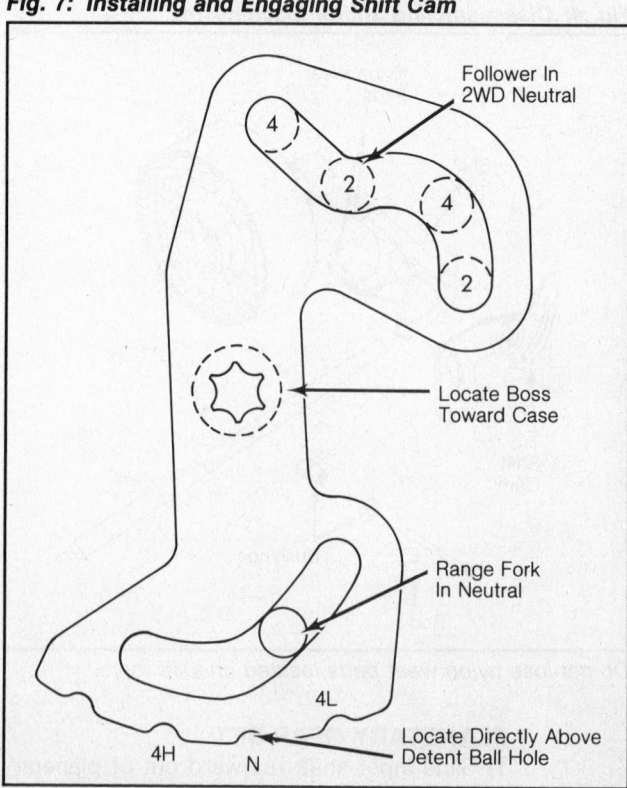

Follower In 2WD Neutral

4

2

4

2

Locate Boss Toward Case

Range Fork In Neutral

4L

4H   N

Locate Directly Above Detent Ball Hole

Install shift cam with boss toward case.

BORG-WARNER 1345 (Cont.)

tips, and that necked down portion of shift collar is facing rearward.

11) Push 4WD shift spring downward and install upper spring retainer. Push spring upward and install lower spring retainer. Install shift collar hub on rear output shaft.

12) Apply RTV sealant to the case mounting surface. Lower the cover over rear output shaft. Align shift rail with blind hole in cover. Ensure the front output shaft is seated in support bearing. Install bolts and tighten. Install 4WD indicator switch.

13) Press oil slinger on front yoke. Install front and rear output shaft yokes. Apply Loctite to threads of output shafts and faces of yoke nuts, then tighten. Refill transfer case, install in vehicle, and test for correct operation.

TIGHTENING SPECIFICATIONS

Application	Ft. Lbs. (N.m)
Case Half Attaching Bolts	35-40 (47-54)
Drain Plug	14-22 (19-29)
Fill Plug	15-25 (20-34)
Front Propeller Shaft-to-Front Output Yoke	8-15 (11-20)
Heat Shield-to-Transfer Case	40-45 (54-61)
Output Yokes-to-Transfer Case	120-150 (163-203)
Rear Propeller Shaft-to-Rear Output Yoke	20-28 (27-38)
Skid Plate-to-Frame	15-20 (20-27)
Transfer Case-to-Transmission Adapter	25-43 (34-58)
4WD Indicator Switch	8-12 (11-16)

Transfer Cases
BORG-WARNER 1350

Bronco II, Ranger

DESCRIPTION

The Borg-Warner 1350 is a chain driven, part time 4WD unit. It provides 4 driving modes. This unit offers 2WD and 4WD high ranges, 4WD low range and Neutral. The 1350 has a 3 piece aluminum case, an internal oil pump driven off the rear output shaft and an angular front output shaft with a cardan joint. Floor mounted shift levers select the driving ranges, high and low, and the driving modes, 2WD and 4WD. The oil pump is driven by the rear output shaft. This allows the vehicle to be towed for long distances without disconnecting propeller shafts.

LUBRICATION

SERVICE INTERVALS

Check and refill transfer case when malfunction is suspected, fluid leakage or contamination is observed or after axle is submerged in water.

FLUID TYPE

Use Dexron II ATF.

CAPACITY

Refill capacity is 3 pts. (1.4L).

SERVICE (IN VEHICLE)

FRONT OUTPUT SHAFT OIL SEAL
Removal

1) Raise vehicle on hoist. Remove front drive shaft from axle input yoke. Loosen clamp retaining drive shaft boot to transfer case. Pull drive shaft and boot assembly out of transfer case front output shaft.

2) Place a drain pan under transfer case, remove drain plug and drain fluid from case. Remove oil seal from front output housing bore with Seal Remover (1175-AC) and Slide Hammer (T50T-100-A).

Installation

1) Make sure housing face and bore are free from nicks and burrs. Coat oil seal with multipurpose grease. Position oil seal into front output housing bore, making sure oil seal is not cocked in bore. Drive oil seal into bore with Driver (T80T-4000-W) and Output Shaft Seal Installer (T83T-7065-B).

2) Clean transfer case front output female spline and apply small amount of multipurpose grease. Insert front drive shaft male spline. Connect front drive shaft to axle input yoke and tighten bolts.

3) Push drive shaft boot to engage external groove on transfer case front output shaft. Secure boot with clamp. Install drain plug and tighten. Remove fill plug and fill transfer case with Dexron II ATF to bottom of fill hole. Install fill plug and tighten. Lower vehicle from hoist.

REAR OUTPUT SHAFT OIL SEAL
Removal

1) Raise vehicle on hoist. Remove rear drive shaft from transfer case output shaft yoke. Wire drive shaft out of the way.

2) Remove output shaft yoke by removing retaining nut, steel washer, and rubber seal from rear of output shaft. Remove oil seal from rear output housing bore with Seal Remover (1175-AC) and Slide Hammer (T50T-100-A).

Installation

1) Make sure output housing bore and face are free from nicks and burrs. Coat oil seal with a small amount of multipurpose grease. Position oil seal into rear output housing bore. Make sure oil seal is not cocked in bore. Drive seal into bore with Driver (T80T-4000-W) and Output Shaft Seal Installer (T83T-7065-B).

2) Install yoke, rubber seal, steel washer, and nut on output shaft. Tighten nut. Connect rear drive shaft to transfer case output shaft yoke and tighten bolts. Lower vehicle from hoist.

REMOVAL & INSTALLATION

TRANSFER CASE
Removal

1) Raise vehicle on hoist. Remove skid plate, if used. Remove drain plug and drain transfer case lubricant. Disconnect 4WD indicator switch wire at transfer case. Disconnect front drive shaft from axle input yoke.

2) Loosen clamp retaining front drive shaft boot to transfer case. Pull drive shaft and front boot assembly out of transfer case front output shaft. Disconnect rear drive shaft from transfer case output yoke. Disconnect speedometer driven gear from case rear cover.

3) Disconnect vent hose from control lever. Loosen or remove large bolt and small bolt retaining shifter to extension housing. Pull on control lever until bushing slides off transfer case shift lever pin. If necessary, unscrew shift lever from control lever. Remove heat shield from transfer case.

4) Support transfer case with a transmission jack. Remove bolts retaining transfer case to transmission and extension housing. Slide transfer case rearward off transmission and lower case from vehicle. Remove gasket from between transfer case and extension housing.

Installation

1) Place a new gasket between transfer case and extension housing. Raise transfer case with jack and position it so splines on transfer case input shaft align with transmission output shaft. Slide case forward onto transmission output shaft and dowel pin.

2) Install bolts that retain transfer case to transmission. Tighten bolts evenly and in a clockwise sequence from locating pin as viewed from front of vehicle.

3) Remove jack from transfer case. Install heat shield on transfer case and tighten bolts. Move control lever until bushing is in position over transfer case shift lever pin. Install both attaching bolts by hand. Tighten large bolt retaining shifter to extension housing first. Tighten small bolt next.

4) Install vent assembly so White marking on hose is in position in notch on shifter. Vent hose should be positioned so that upper end of hose is 2" above top of shifter and inside drive boot. Connect speedometer gear to transfer case rear cover and tighten screw.

5) Connect rear drive shaft to transfer case output shaft yoke and tighten bolts. Clean transfer case front output shaft female splines. Apply a small amount of

BORG-WARNER 1350 (Cont.)

Fig. 1: Exploded View of Borg-Warner 1350 Transfer Case

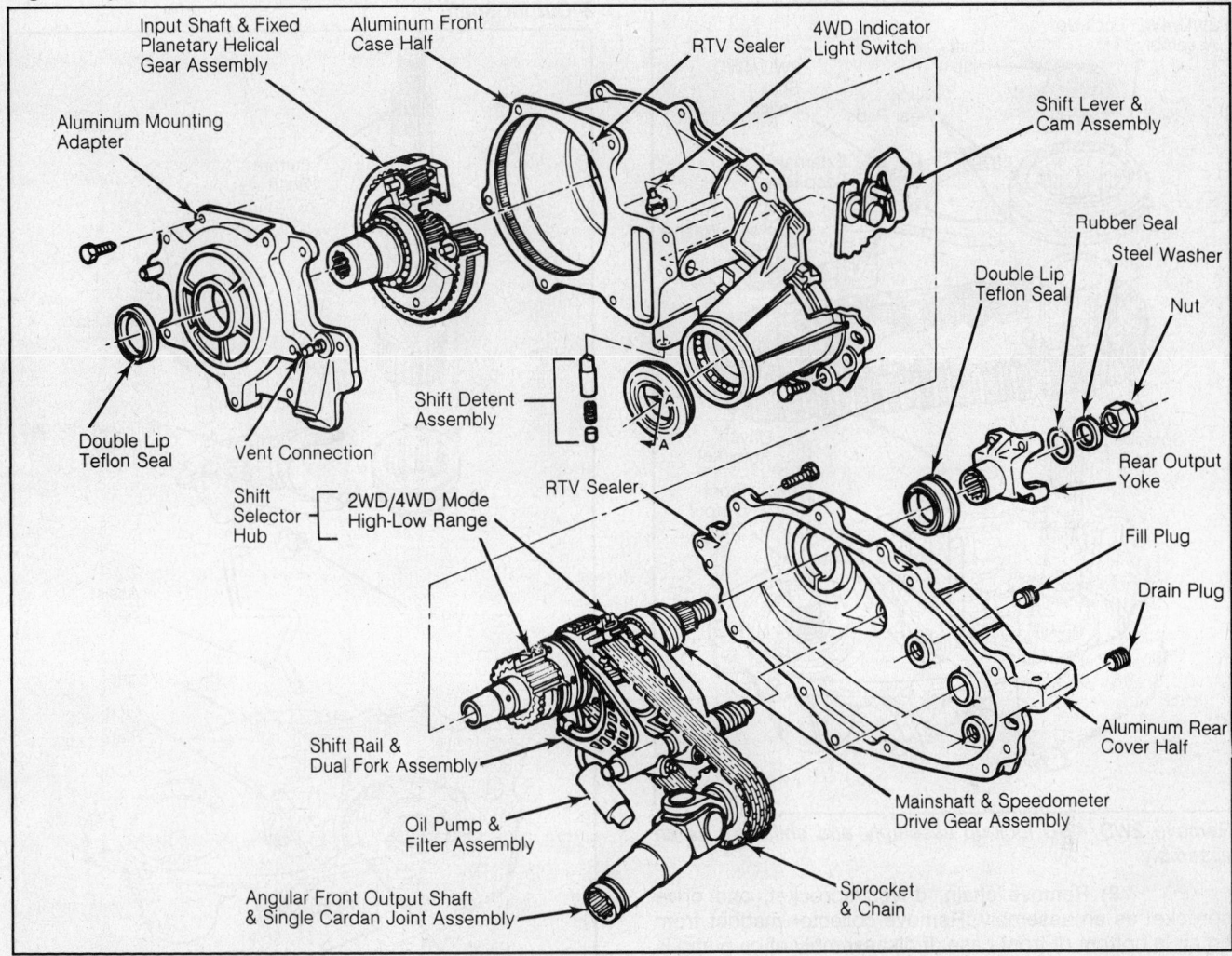

multipurpose grease to splines. Insert front drive shaft male spline.

6) Connect front drive shaft to axle input yoke and tighten bolts. Push drive shaft boot to engage external groove on transfer case front output shaft. Secure boot with clamp. Connect 4WD indicator switch wire connector at transfer case. Install drain plug and tighten.

7) Remove fill plug. Fill transfer case with 3 pts. (1.4L) of Dexron II ATF. Install fill plug. Install skid plate to frame and tighten bolts, if used. Lower vehicle from hoist.

DISASSEMBLY

TRANSFER CASE

1) Drain transfer case and remove from vehicle. Place transfer case on bench. Remove 4WD indicator switch and breather vent. Remove rear output shaft yoke by removing retaining nut, steel washer and rubber seal from output shaft.

2) Remove 9 bolts retaining front case to rear cover. Insert a 1/2" drive breaker bar between 3 pry bosses to separate front case and rear cover. Remove all traces of RTV gasket sealer from mating surfaces.

3) If speedometer drive gear or ball bearing assembly is to be replaced, remove output shaft oil seal. Seal can be removed from inside of rear cover with a brass drift and hammer. Remove speedometer drive gear assembly. Note that round end of speedometer gear clip faces inside of rear cover.

4) Remove internal snap ring retaining output shaft ball bearing rear in bore. Remove ball bearing with Driver (T80T-4000-W) and Output Shaft Bearing Replacer (T83T-7025-B) from outside of case.

5) If necessary, remove front output shaft caged needle bearing from rear cover using Puller (D80L-100-S) and slide hammer. Remove 2WD/4WD shift fork from boss in rear cover.

6) Remove shift collar hub from output shaft. Remove 2WD/4WD lock-up assembly and 2WD/4WD shift fork as an assembly. Remove 2WD/4WD lock-up assembly from 2WD/4WD shift fork. *See Fig. 2.* If necessary, remove external clip and roller bushing assembly from 2WD/4WD shift fork.

7) If disassembly of 2WD/4WD lock-up assembly is necessary, remove internal snap ring and pull lock-up hub and spring from lock-up collar. Remove external snap ring and thrust washer that retains driven sprocket to front output shaft.

Transfer Cases
BORG-WARNER 1350 (Cont.)

Fig. 2: Removing Shift Collar Hub & Drive Chain

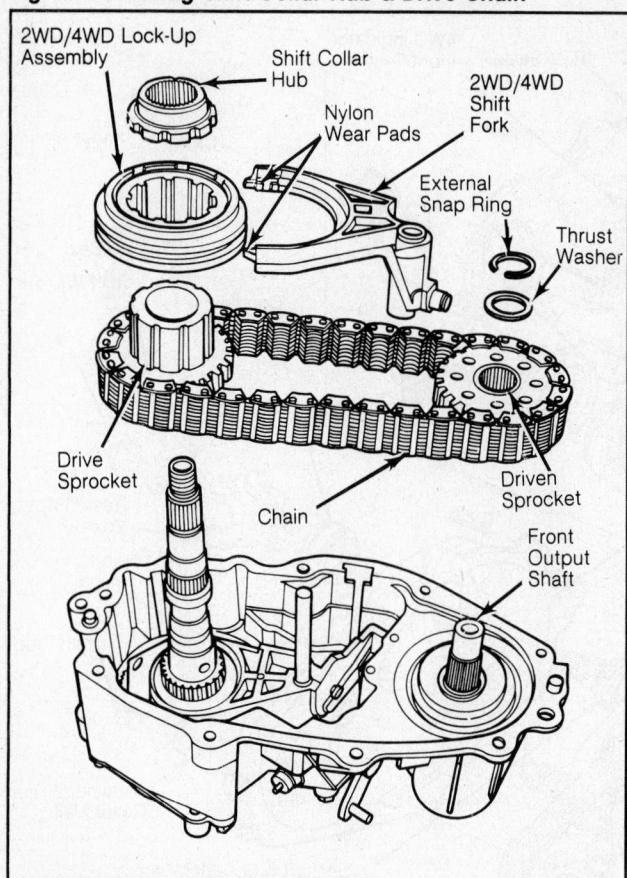

Remove 2WD/4WD lock-up assembly and shift fork as an assembly.

8) Remove chain, driven sprocket, and drive sprocket as an assembly. Remove collector magnet from notch in bottom of front case. If disassembly of oil pump is necessary, remove bolts from pump body. Note position and markings of front cover, body, pins, rear cover, and pump retainer.

9) Pull out shift rail. Slip the high-low range shift fork out of inside track of shift cam. If required, remove external clip and roller bushing assembly (bushing, shaft and external clip) from high-low range shift fork. Remove high-low shift hub from planetary gear set in front case. *See Fig. 3.*

10) Push and pull out anchor end of assist spring from locking post in front case half. Remove spring and roller out of shift cam. Turn case over and remove 6 bolts retaining mounting adapter to front case. Remove mounting adapter, input shaft and planetary gear set as an assembly.

11) If required, remove the ring gear from front case using a press. Note relationship of serrations to chamfered pilot diameter during removal. Expand tangs of large snap ring in mounting adapter and pry under planetary gear set with screwdrivers. Separate input shaft and planetary gear set from mounting adapter.

12) If required, remove oil seal from mounting adapter with Seal Remover (1175-AC) and slide hammer. Remove internal snap ring from planetary carrier and separate planetary gear set from input shaft assembly. Remove external snap ring from input shaft. *See Fig. 4.*

Fig. 3: High-Low Range Shift Assembly & Output Shaft

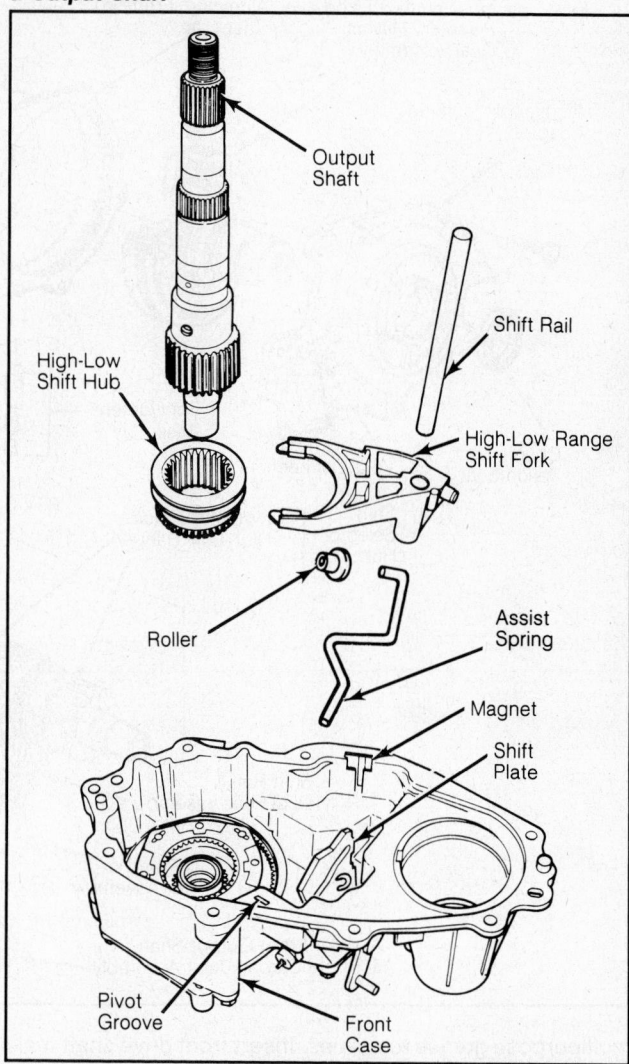

Remove roller bushing, shaft and clip as an assembly.

Fig. 4: Exploded View of Planetary Gear Set

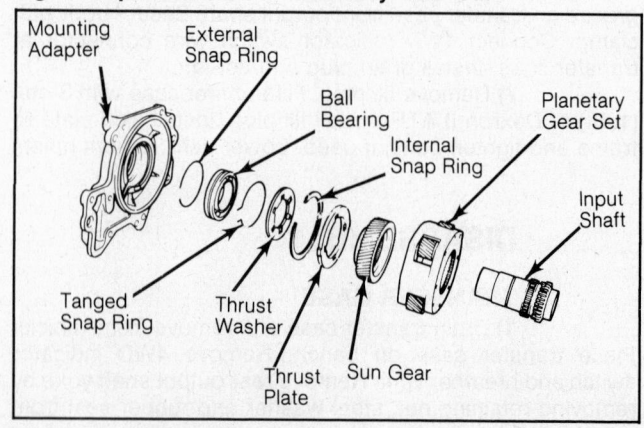

13) Place input shaft assembly in a press and remove ball bearing from input shaft with Bearing Splitter (D79L-4621-A). Remove thrust washer, thrust plate and sun gear off input shaft.

BORG-WARNER 1350 (Cont.)

14) Move shift lever by hand until shift cam is in 4WD-High detent position. Scribe a line on outside of front case using the side of shift lever and a grease pencil. *See Fig. 5.* Remove 2 Phillips head set screws from front case and shift cam.

Fig. 5: Shift Lever & Cam Assembly

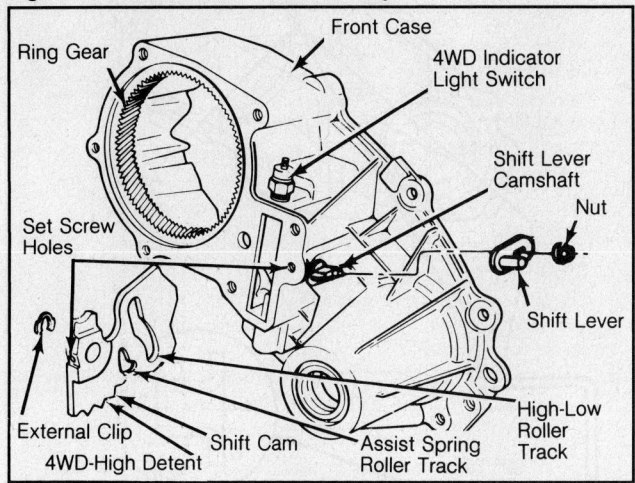

Mark case with cam in 4WD-High detent position.

15) Turn front case over and remove external clip. Pry shift lever out of front case and shift cam. Do not pound on external clip during removal. Remove "O" ring from 2nd groove in shift lever shaft. Remove detent plunger and compression spring from inside of front case.

Fig. 6: Removing/Installing Front Output Shaft Assembly

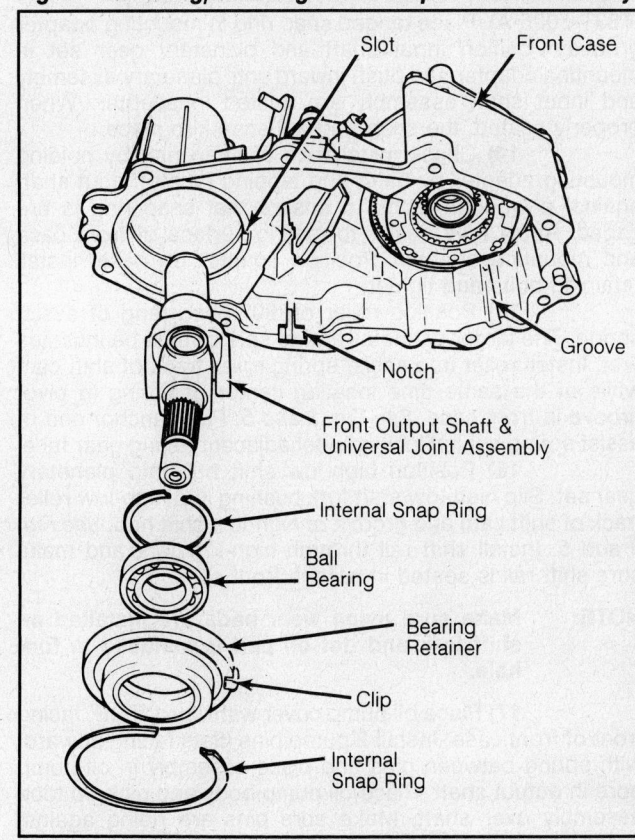

Do not discard clip.

16) Remove internal snap ring and ball bearing retainer from front case by tapping on face of front output

shaft and universal joint assembly using a plastic hammer. Remove internal snap ring and drive ball bearing out of bearing retainer using Driver (T80T-4000-W) and Output Shaft Bearing Replacer (T83T-7025-B). *See Fig. 6.*

NOTE: The clip on bearing retainer is required to prevent bearing retainer from rotating. Do not discard clip.

17) Remove front output shaft and universal joint assembly from front case. If necessary, remove oil seal with Seal Remover (1175-AC) and slide hammer. If necessary, remove internal snap ring and drive ball bearing out of front case bore. Use driver and output shaft replacer.

18) If required, place front output shaft and universal joint assembly in a vise. Use copper or wood vise jaws to prevent damage to assembly. Remove internal snap rings that retain bearings in shaft.

19) Position "U" Joint Remover/Installer (T74P-4635-C) over shaft and press bearing out. If bearing cannot be pressed all the way out, remove it with a pair of vise grips or channel lock pliers. Reposition tool on spider to remove opposite bearing. Repeat procedure until all bearings are removed.

REASSEMBLY

TRANSFER CASE

1) Lubricate all parts with Dexron II ATF. Support front output shaft in a vise equipped with copper or wood jaws. If removed, start a new bearing into end of a shaft. Position spider into bearing and press bearing below snap ring groove using "U" joint installer. Remove tool and install a new internal snap ring in groove.

2) Start new bearing into opposite end of shaft. Using "U" joint installer, press bearing until opposite bearing contacts snap ring. Remove tool and install new internal snap ring in groove. Reposition front output shaft assembly and install other 2 bearings in same manner.

3) Check universal joint for freedom of movement and binding. If universal joint shows any sign of binding, tap both shafts sharply to relieve bind. Do not install front output shaft assembly if universal joint shows any sign of binding.

4) If removed, drive ball bearing into front output case bore using Driver (T80T-4000-W) and Output Shaft Bearing Replacer (T83T-7025-B). Make sure bearing is not cocked in bore. Install internal snap ring that retains ball bearing to front case. If removed, install front output oil seal in front case bore. Use Driver (T80T-4000-W) and Output Shaft Seal Installer (T83T-7065-W).

5) If removed, install ring gear in front case. Align serrations on outside diameter of ring gear to serrations previously cut in front case bore. Using a press, start piloted chamferred end of ring gear first and press in until it is fully seated. Make sure ring gear is not cocked in bore.

6) If removed, install ball bearing in bearing retainer bore. Drive bearing into retainer using driver and output shaft bearing replacer. Make sure ball bearing is not cocked in bore. Install internal snap ring that retains ball bearing to retainer. Install front output shaft and universal joint assembly through front case seal.

7) Position ball bearing and retainer assembly over front output shaft and install in front case bore. Make sure clip on bearing retainer aligns with slot in front case. Tap bearing retainer into place with a plastic hammer. Install internal snap ring that retains ball bearing and retainer assembly to front case. *See Fig. 6.*

Fig. 7: Assist Spring Installation

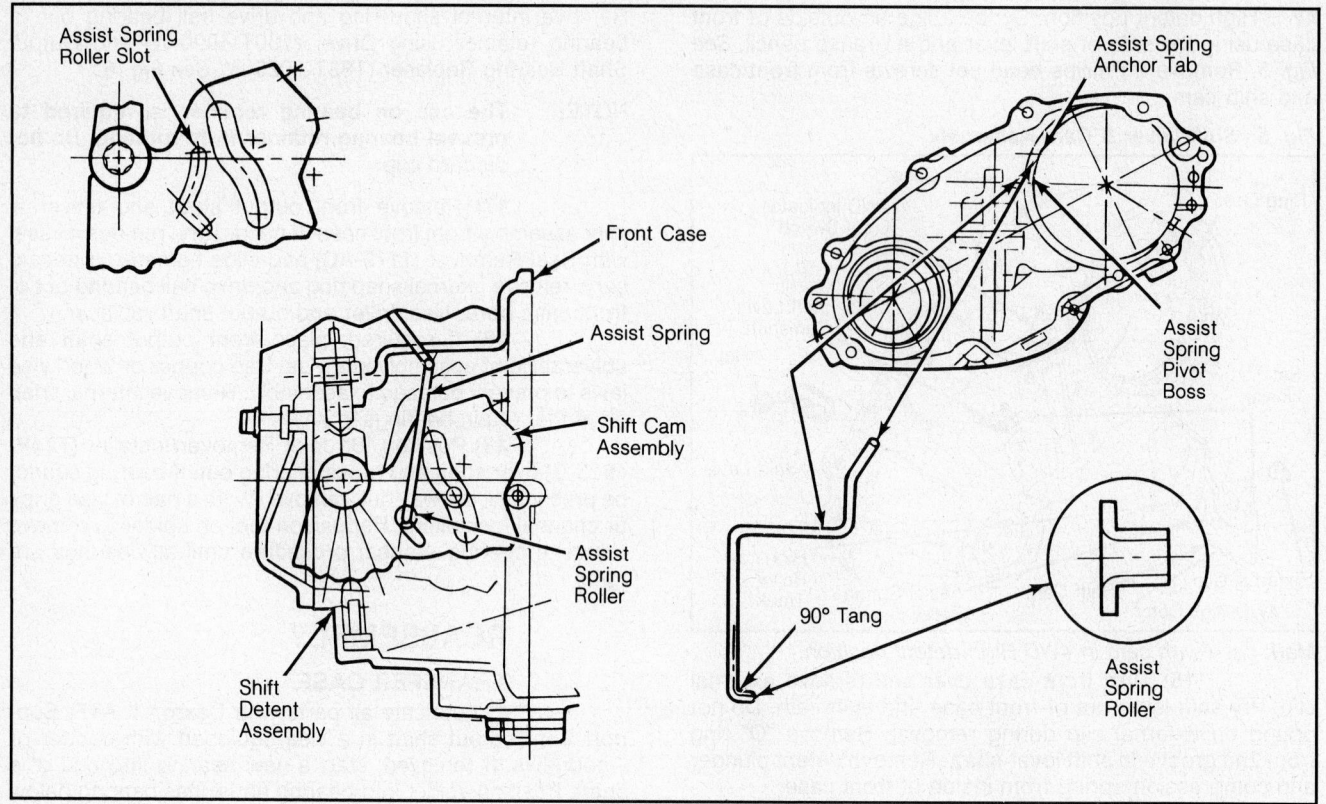

8) Install compression spring and detent plunger into bore from inside of front case. If disassembled, install shift lever cam shaft to shift lever and tighten nut. Install a new "O" ring in second groove of shift lever shaft. Coat shaft and "O" ring with a small amount of multipurpose grease. Use a rubber band to fill the first groove so as not to cut "O" ring. Discard rubber band.

9) With shift cam, shift lever and snap ring installed in front case, position shift lever in 4WD-High detent position (line scribed during disassembly). Place assist spring roller on the 90° bend tang of assist spring and insert roller into assist spring roller slot of shift cam. See Fig. 7.

10) Position middle section of assist spring into the groove of front case pivot boss. Push in and lock the upper end of assist sping behind the front case spring anchor tab. See Fig. 7.

11) Install 2 Phillips head screws in front case and in shift cam. Tighten screws. Make sure set screw in front case is in first groove of shift lever shaft and not bottomed out against shaft itself. Shift lever should be able to move freely to all detent positions.

12) Slide sun gear, thrust plate and thrust washer over input shaft. Press ball bearing over input shaft. Install external snap ring to input shaft. Install planetary gear set to sun gear and install input shaft assembly. Install internal snap ring to planetary carrier.

NOTE: **The sun gear recessed face and ball bearing snap ring groove should be toward rear of transfer case. The stepped face of thrust washer should face toward the ball bearing.**

13) Drive oil seal into bore of mounting adapter with Driver (T80T-4000-W) and Input Shaft Seal Installer

(T83T-7065-A). Place tanged snap ring in mounting adapter groove. Position input shaft and planetary gear set in mounting adapter and push inward until planetary assembly and input shaft assembly are seated in adapter. When properly seated, the snap ring will snap into place.

14) Check installation of snap ring by holding mounting adapter by hand and tapping face of input shaft against a wooden block to ensure that snap ring is engaged. Apply RTV sealer to mating surface of front case and mounting adapter. Position adapter on case, install retaining bolts and tighten.

15) Position roller on 90° bend tang of assist spring. The larger diameter end of spring must be installed first. Install roller into assist spring roller track of shift cam while at the same time locating center of spring in pivot groove in front case. See Fig. 3 and 5. Push anchor end of assist spring behind locking post adjacent to ring gear face.

16) Position high-low shift hub into planetary gear set. Slip high-low shift fork bushing into high-low roller track of shift cam and groove of high-low shift hub. See Fig. 3 and 5. Install shift rail through high-low fork and make sure shift rail is seated in bore in front case.

NOTE: **Make sure nylon wear pads are installed on shift fork and dot on pad is installed in fork hole.**

17) Place oil pump cover with word "TOP" facing front of front case. Install 2 pump pins (flats facing upward) with spring between pins and place assembly in oil pump bore in output shaft. Place oil pump body and pick-up tube assembly over shaft. Make sure pins are riding against inside of pump body.

18) Place oil pump rear cover with words "TOP REAR" facing rear of front case. The word "TOP" on front

BORG-WARNER 1350 (Cont.)

and rear covers should be on the same side. Install pump retainer, 4 bolts and rotate output shaft while tighening bolts to prevent pump from binding. The output shaft must turn freely within oil pump. If binding occurs, loosen 4 bolts and retighten.

19) Install output shaft and oil pump assembly in input shaft. Make sure external splines of output shaft engage internal splines of high-low shift hub. Make sure oil pump retainer and oil filter leg are in groove and notch of front case. Install collector magnet in notch in front case.

20) Install chain, drive sprocket and driven sprocket as an assembly over shafts. Install thrust washer on front output shaft and external snap ring over thrust washer to retain driven sprocket.

21) If disassembled, assemble 2WD/4WD lock-up assembly. Install spring in lock-up collar. Place lock-up hub over spring and engage lock-up hub in notches in lock-up collar. Retain lock-up hub to lock-up collar with an internal snap ring. *See Fig. 8.*

Fig. 8: Exploded View 2WD/4WD Lock-Up Assembly

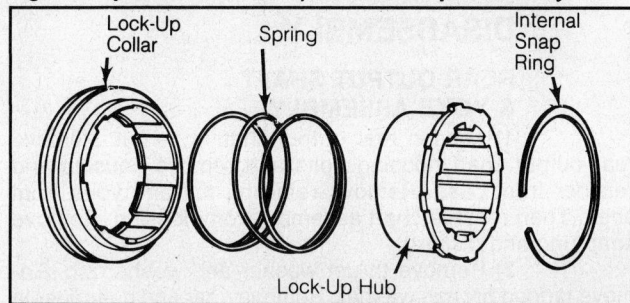

22) Install 2WD/4WD shift fork to 2WD/4WD lock-up assembly. If removed, make sure nylon wear pads are installed on fork and dot on pad is installed in hole in fork. Install 2WD/4WD lock-up collar and hub assembly over output shaft and onto shift rail. *See Fig. 2.*

23) If removed, install shaft, bushing and external clip to 2WD/4WD lock-up fork. Install shift collar hub to output shaft. If removed, drive caged needle bearing into rear cover bore with Driver (T80T-4000-W) and Needle Bearing Replacer (T83T-7127-A).

24) If removed, install ball bearing in rear cover bore. Drive bearing into rear cover bore with driver and Output Shaft Bearing Replacer (T83T-7025-B). Make sure ball bearing is not cocked in bore. Install internal snap ring that retains ball bearing to rear cover.

25) Install speedometer drive gear assembly into rear cover bore with round end of speedometer gear clip facing toward inside of rear cover. Drive oil seal into rear cover bore with driver and output shaft seal installer (T83T-7065-B).

26) Prior to final assembly of rear cover to front case half, transfer case shift lever assembly should be shifted into 4WD-High detent position to assure positioning of shift rail to rear cover.

27) Coat mating surface of front case with a bead of RTV sealer. Install 2WD/4WD shift fork spring on shift rail and shift fork with spring mounted in vertical position.

28) Position rear cover on front case so that spring boss engages 2WD/4WD shift fork spring and shift rod. Install bolts and tighten. If rear cover assembly does not seat properly, move rear cover up and down slightly to permit end of shift rail to enter shift rail hole in rear cover boss.

29) Install rear yoke on output shaft. Install rubber seal, washer, and nut. Tighten nut. Install 4WD indicator switch and breather plug. Install drain plug. Remove fill plug and fill transfer case with 3 pts. (1.4L) of Dexron II ATF. Install fill plug and install transfer case.

TIGHTENING SPECIFICATIONS

Application	Ft. Lbs. (N.m)
Breather Vent	6-14 (8-19)
Case-to-Cover Bolts	23-30 (31-41)
Drain & Fill Plug	14-22 (19-30)
Front & Rear Drive Shaft Bolts	12-15 (16-20)
Shift Control Bolts (Large)	70-90 (95-122)
Shift Control Bolts (Small)	31-42 (42-57)
Shift Lever Nut	19-26 (25-35)
Skid Plate-to-Frame Bolt	22-30 (30-41)
Transfer Case-to-Transmission	25-35 (34-47)
Upper Shift Control Lever & Heat Shield Bolts	27-37 (37-50)
Yoke Nut	120-150 (163-203)
4WD Indicator Switch	25-35 (34-47)

	INCH Lbs. (N.m)
Oil Pump Bolts	36-40 (4.0-4.5)
Shift Shaft & Shift Cam Set Screw	60-84 (6.8-9.5)
Speedometer Screw	20-25 (2.3-2.8)

Transfer Cases

NEW PROCESS MODEL 205

Chrysler Corp., General Motors

DESCRIPTION

Transfer case provides two gears, high (1:1) for highway driving and low (1.96:1) for off-road or heavy duty operation. With this transfer case, direct drive is available in both 2WD and 4WD.

Sliding clutch gears are used in controlling the various selections of gear combinations. The transfer case contains constant-mesh helical cut gears with shafts mounted on ball and roller bearings. When driving in a 4WD mode, hubs on the front wheels must be turned to the "LOCKED" position.

LUBRICATION

SERVICE INTERVALS
Chrysler Corp.
Check fluid level and fill as necessary. Drain and refill transfer case every 37,500 miles.

General Motors
Check fluid level and fill as necessary every 4 months or 7500 miles.

FLUID TYPE
Chrysler Corp.
Use multipurpose gear lubricants meeting API specification GL-5 or engine oils labeled "SE" and "CC".

If multipurpose gear lubricant is used and the minimum anticipated air temperature is:
• Above 90°F (32°C), use SAE 140.
• Below 90°F (32°C) but above -10°F (-23°C), use SAE 90.
• Below -10°F (-23°C), use SAE 80.
If engine oil is used and the air temperature is:
• Above 32°F (0°C), use SAE 50.
• Below 32°F (0°C), use SAE 30.

General Motors
Use Dexron II Automatic Transmission Fluid.

CAPACITY
Chrysler Corp.
Capacity is 4.5 pints (2.1L).

General Motors
Capacity is 5.1 pints (2.4L).

ADJUSTMENTS

SHIFT LINKAGE
Chrysler Corp.
Install lower shift lever to bracket. Loosely install bracket on adapter. Install shift rod. Position bracket as far forward as possible and tighten bracket bolts. Place lever in all positions to ensure that linkage operates properly.

General Motors
Adjust shift linkage so that all positions may be selected without interference or binding.

REMOVAL & INSTALLATION

TRANSFER CASE
Removal
1) Raise vehicle, remove plug and drain transfer case. Replace plug. Disconnect speedometer cable. Remove skid plate, crossmember and strut rods as needed. Disconnect propeller shafts and wire out of way. Do not allow propeller shafts to hang free, as damage to universal joints may result.
2) Disconnect shift lever rod from shift rail link. Support transfer case and remove transfer case-to-transmission adapter bolts. Move transfer case to rear until input shaft clears adapter. Lower transfer case from vehicle.

Installation
Reverse removal procedure to install transfer case. Ensure that all attaching bolts are tight. Fill transfer case with lubricant.

DISASSEMBLY

REAR OUTPUT SHAFT & YOKE ASSEMBLY
1) Loosen rear output shaft yoke nut. Remove rear output shaft housing bolts and remove housing and retainer from case. Remove retaining nut and yoke from shaft. Then remove shaft assembly from housing. Remove snap ring and discard.
2) Remove thrust washer and washer pin. Remove tanged bronze washer. Remove gear and gear needle bearings (32 per row). Remove spacer and 2nd row of needle bearings. Remove tanged bronze thrust washer from shaft.
3) Remove needle bearings from shaft (15 per row). Remove retainer ring and washer. Discard retainer ring. Remove oil seal retainer, ball bearing, speedometer gear and spacer. Discard all gaskets. Press out bearing and remove oil seal.

FRONT OUTPUT SHAFT ASSEMBLY
1) Remove lock nut, washer and yoke. Remove front bearing retainer attaching bolts and retainer. Remove front output shaft rear bearing retainer attaching bolts.
2) Using a soft-faced hammer, tap on output shaft and remove shaft, gear assembly and rear bearing retainer from case. See Fig. 1. Remove the sliding clutch from output high gear. Remove washer and bearing remaining in case.
3) Remove gear retaining snap ring from shaft. Discard retaining snap ring. Remove thrust washer and pin from shaft. Remove gear, needle bearings (32 per row) and spacer.
4) If necessary to replace front output shaft rear bearing, support cover and press bearing from cover. Position new bearing to outside face of cover and using a pipe or piece of wood, press bearing into cover until flush with opening. Use a new retainer when replacing bearing.

SHIFT RAIL & FORK ASSEMBLIES
1) Remove 2 poppet nuts and springs on top of case. Using a magnet, remove the poppet balls. Drive cup plugs into case using a 1/4" (6.35 mm) punch. Position both shift rails in Neutral. Using a long, narrow punch, drive shift fork pins through shift rails into case.

NEW PROCESS MODEL 205 (Cont.)

Fig. 1: Removing Front Output Shaft Assembly

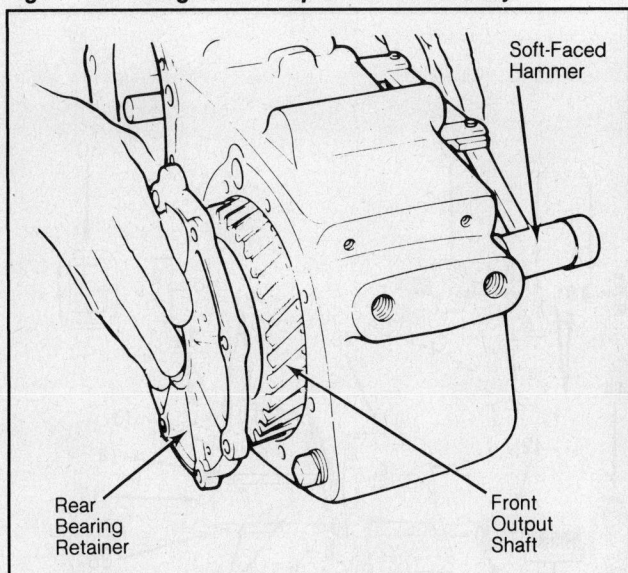

Using a soft-faced hammer, tap shaft of transfer case.

2) Remove clevis pins and shift rail link. Remove shift rails, upper range rail, then lower (4WD) rail. Remove shift forks and sliding clutch from case. Remove front output high gear, washer, and bearing from case.

3) Remove shift rail cup plugs and pins from case. Remove snap ring in front of bearing. Using a soft-faced hammer, tap shaft out rear of case. Tap bearing out front of case. Tip case on PTO and remove 2 interlock pins from inside case.

IDLER GEAR

Remove idler gear shaft nut. Remove idler shaft rear cover. Remove idler gear shaft using a soft-faced hammer and a driver. Tilt case at 45° angle and roll idler gear to front output shaft hole and remove from case. Remove 2 bearing cups from idler gear.

CLEANING & INSPECTION

1) Clean all parts with solvent, and blow parts dry with compressed air. Direct air across bearings, ensuring that they do not spin. Remove all traces of gaskets from surfaces where used.

2) Examine all bearings for wear or evidence of chipping or cracks. Replace bearings as necessary. Bearings are nonadjustable. If they are worn or damaged, they must be replaced.

3) Inspect teeth of all gears for excessive wear or damage. Replace any gear where these conditions exist. Sliding clutch wear occurs on engagement side, if wear is present, use opposite side of clutch in reassembly. Both sides of clutch are identical.

4) Carefully examine splines and shaft for scoring or evidence of wear. Sliding clutch gears must move freely on splines. Parts should be replaced if spline or shaft is scored or heavily worn.

REASSEMBLY

IDLER GEAR

1) If removed, press 2 bearing cups in idler gear. Assemble 2 bearing cones, spacer, shims and idler gear on dummy shaft with bore up. Check end play; limits are .001-.002" (.025-.050 mm). *See Fig. 2.*

Fig. 2: Checking Idler Gear End Play

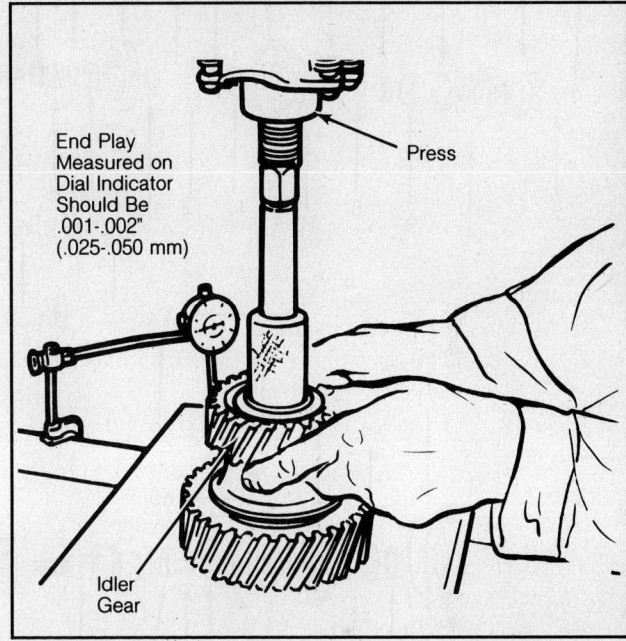

Install idler gear with dummy shaft, large end first.

2) Install idler gear assembly with dummy shaft into case. Install through front output bore, large end first. Install idler shaft from large bore side and drive through using soft-faced hammer.

3) Install washer and new lock nut. Check for end play and free rotation. Tighten lock nut. Install idler shaft cover, flat spot on cover must be located toward front output shaft rear cover. Install gasket and tighten bolts.

SHIFT RAIL & FORK ASSEMBLIES

1) Press 2 rail seals into case. Seals should be installed with metal lip outward. Install interlock pins through large bore or PTO opening. Start front output drive shift rail into case from back, slotted end first with poppet notches up.

2) Install shift fork into rail with long end inward. Push rail through to Neutral position. Install input shaft bearing and shaft into case. Start range rail into case from front with poppet notches up.

3) Install sliding clutch onto fork, placing clutch over input shaft in case. Position to receive range rail and push rail through to Neutral position. Install new lock pins through holes at top of case and drive them into forks. Tip case on PTO opening when installing range rail lock pin.

FRONT OUTPUT SHAFT & GEAR ASSEMBLY

1) Install 2 rows of needle bearings (32 each), separated by spacer, in front low output gear. Use grease to retain bearings. Place front output shaft in a soft-jawed

Transfer Cases

NEW PROCESS MODEL 205 (Cont.)

Fig. 3: *New Process Model 205 Transfer Case*

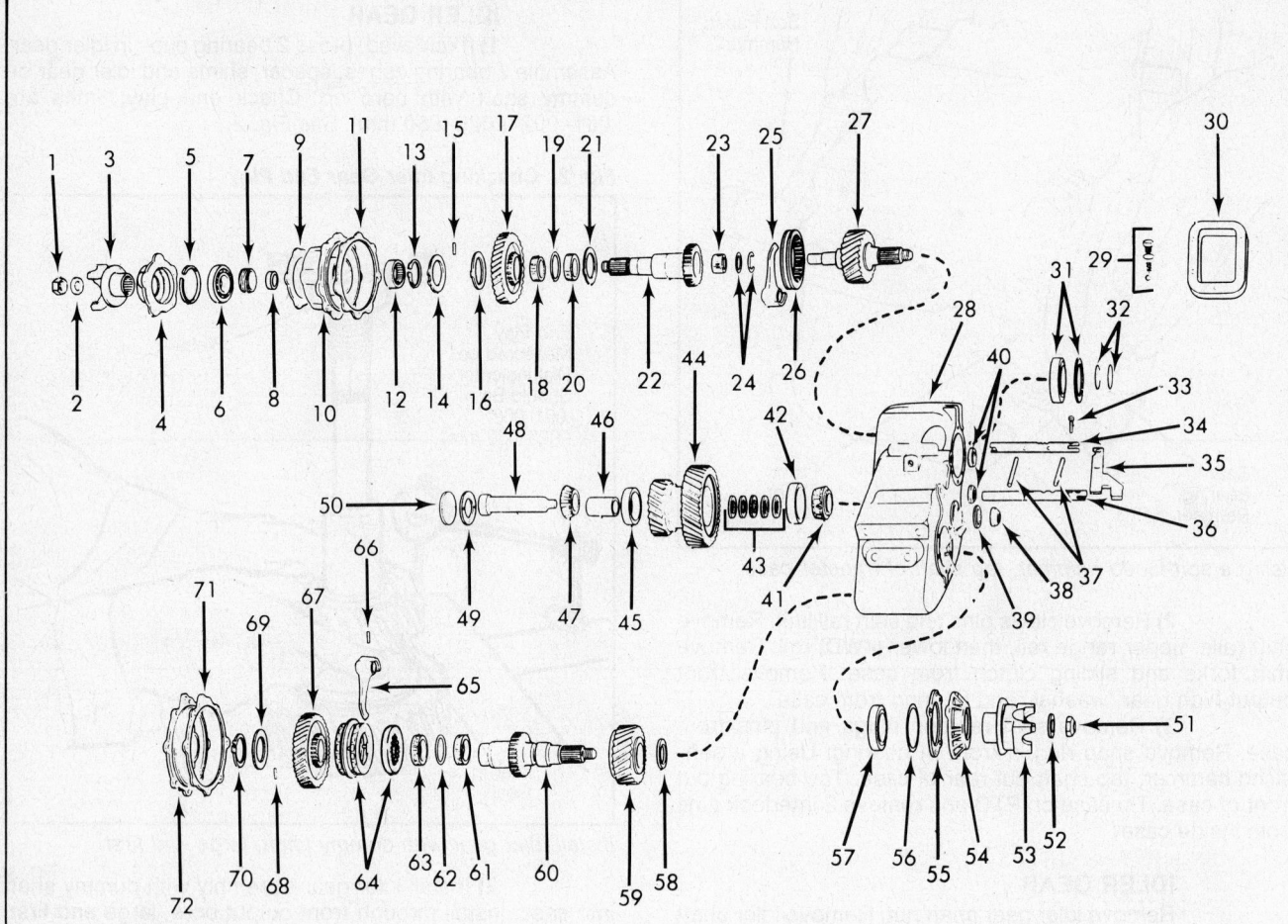

1. Rear Output Shaft Lock Nut	25. Shift Fork	49. Cover Gasket
2. Washer	26. Sliding Clutch	50. Rear Cover
3. Rear Output Shaft Yoke	27. Input Shaft	51. Front Output Shaft Lock Nut
4. Bearing Retainer & Seal	28. Transfer Case	52. Washer
5. Snap Ring	29. Poppet Plug, Spring & Ball	53. Yoke
6. Bearing	30. PTO Gasket & Cover	54. Bearing Retainer & Seal
7. Speedometer Gear	31. Input Shaft Bearing & Snap Ring	55. Gasket
8. Spacer	32. Snap Ring & Rubber "O" Ring (General Motors Only)	56. Snap Ring
9. Gasket	33. Shift Link Clevis Pin	57. Front Bearing
10. Rear Output Shaft Housing	34. Range Shift Rail	58. Thrust Washer
11. Gasket	35. Shift Rail Connector Link	59. 4WD-High Gear
12. Bearing	36. 4WD Shift Rail	60. Front Output Shaft
13. Snap Ring	37. Interlock Pins	61. Needle Bearing
14. Thrust Washer	38. Rear Idler Lock Nut	62. Spacer
15. Thrust Washer Lock Pin	39. Washer	63. Needle Bearing
16. Thrust Washer (Tanged)	40. Shift Rail Seals	64. Sliding Clutch Gear
17. Low Speed Gear	41. Idler Shaft Bearing	65. Shift Fork
18. Needle Bearings	42. Bearing Cup	66. Roll Pin
19. Spacer	43. Shims	67. Front Output Low Gear
20. Needle Bearings	44. Idler Gear	68. Thrust Washer Lock Pin
21. Thrust Washer (Tanged)	45. Bearing Cup	69. Thrust Washer
22. Rear Output Shaft	46. Spacer	70. Snap Ring
23. Needle Bearings	47. Idler Shaft Bearing	71. Rear Cover Gasket
24. Washer & Retainer	48. Idler Shaft	72. Rear Cover & Bearing

NEW PROCESS MODEL 205 (Cont.)

vise, splined end down. Install front low gear over shaft with clutch gear facing down.

2) Install thrust washer pin, thrust washer, and new snap ring. Position snap ring so opening is opposite the pin. Position front wheel high gear and washer in case. Install sliding clutch in fork, then put shift fork and rail in 4WD position with clutch teeth meshed with teeth of front wheel high gear.

3) Line up washer, high gear and sliding clutch with bearing bore. Insert front output shaft and low gear assembly through high gear assembly. Using seal driver, install new seal in bearing retainer. Install front output bearing and retainer in case.

4) Clean and grease rollers in front output rear bearing retainer. Install onto case using 1 gasket. Dip bolts into sealant. Install bolts and tighten. Install front output yoke, washer, and lock nut. Tighten nut.

REAR OUTPUT SHAFT ASSEMBLY

1) Install 2 rows of needle bearings (32 each), separated by spacer. Use grease to retain bearings. Install thrust washer onto rear output shaft, with tang down in clutch gear groove. Install output low gear onto shaft with clutch teeth facing down.

2) With tab pointing up and away from gear, install thrust washer over gear. Install washer pin and large thrust washer over shaft and pin. Rotate washer until tab fits into slot, approximately 90° away from pin. Install new snap ring and check end play. End play should be within .002-.027" (.051-.686 mm).

3) Grease pilot bore of rear output shaft and install needle bearings (15 each). Install thrust washer and new snap ring. Clean, grease and install new bearing in retainer housing.

4) Install housing onto output shaft assembly. Install spacer and speedometer gear. Using 1 or 2 gaskets depending on clearance, install bearing, rear bearing retainer seal, and bearing retainer onto housing. Tighten bolts. Install yoke, washer, and lock nut on output shaft.

5) Position range rail in high gear and install output shaft and retainer assembly on transfer case. Tighten bolts. Install PTO cover and gasket. Install and seal cup plugs at rail pin holes. Install drain and fill plug. Install shift rail cross link, clevis pins and lock pins.

Fig. 4: Rear Output Spacer and Speedometer Gear

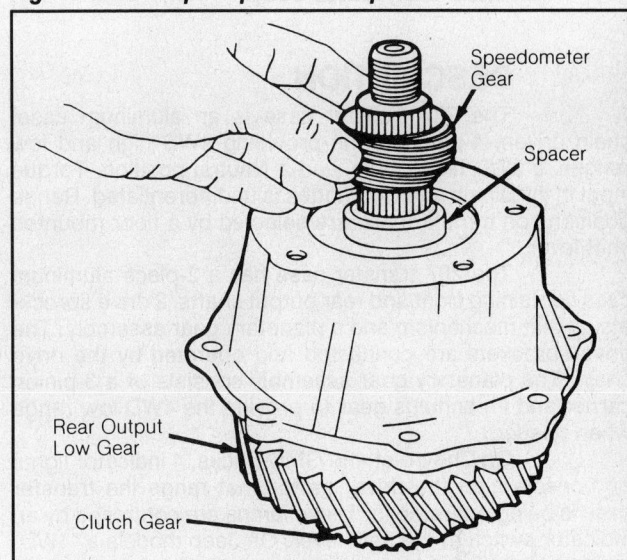

Install housing onto output shaft assembly

TIGHTENING SPECIFICATION

Application	Ft. Lbs. (N.m)
Drain & Fill Plugs	30 (41)
Idler Shaft Cover Bolts	20 (27)
Idler Shaft Lock Nut	150 (203)
Input & Output Bearing Retainer Bolts	30-35 (41-47)
Output Yoke Lock Nuts	150 (203)
PTO Cover Bolts	15 (20)
Transfer Case-to-Adapter Bolts	45 (61)

Transfer Cases

NEW PROCESS MODEL 207

Chevrolet, GMC, Jeep

DESCRIPTION

The 207 transfer case is an aluminum case, chain driven, 4-position unit providing 4WD high and low ranges, a 2WD high range, and a Neutral position. Torque input in 4WD high and low ranges is undifferentiated. Range positions on transfer case are selected by a floor mounted shift lever.

The 207 transfer case has a 2-piece aluminum case containing front and rear output shafts, 2 drive sprockets, a shift mechanism and a planetary gear assembly. The drive sprockets are connected and operated by the drive chain. The planetary gear assembly consists of a 3-pinion carrier and an annulus gear to provide the 4WD low range when needed.

On Chevrolet and GMC trucks, 4 indicator lights on console alert the driver as to what range the transfer case is being operated in. These lamps are controlled by an indicator switch at the shift lever. On Jeep models a "4WD" indicator light is used.

LUBRICATION

SERVICE INTERVALS
Check fluid and refill as necessary every 12 months or 7500 miles.

FLUID TYPE
Use Dexron II ATF.

CAPACITY
Refill capacity is 2.3 quarts (2.2L).

REMOVAL & INSTALLATION

TRANSFER CASE
Removal
1) Shift transfer case into 4WD high range and disconnect battery negative cable. Raise vehicle and remove skid plate, if used. Drain lubricant from transfer case.
2) Mark front and rear output shaft yokes and front and rear propeller shafts for reassembly reference. Remove propeller shafts. Disconnect speedometer cable and vacuum (hoses) harness at transfer case. Remove shift lever or linkage rod from case.
3) On Jeep trucks, remove shift lever bracket bolts. Support transfer case and remove transfer case attaching bolts. Remove transfer case from vehicle. On Chevrolet or GMC trucks, remove catalytic converter hanger bolts at converter. Raise transmission and transfer case and remove mount attaching bolts.
4) Remove transmission mount and catalytic converter hanger. Lower transmission and transfer case. Support transfer case and remove transfer case attaching bolts.
5) On vehicles equipped with automatic transmissions, it will be necessary to remove shift lever bracket mounting bolts from case in order to remove the upper left transfer case attaching bolt. Remove transfer case from vehicle.

Installation
1) On Jeep trucks, reverse removal procedure to complete installation. Road test vehicle. On Chevrolet or GMC trucks, clean all old gasket material from transmission and transfer case mating surfaces.
2) Position new gasket on transfer case with orientation tab at upper left bolt hole. See Fig. 1. Install transfer case, aligning splines of input shaft with transmission. Slide transfer case forward until seated against transmission.

Fig. 1: Assembling Transfer Case to Transmission

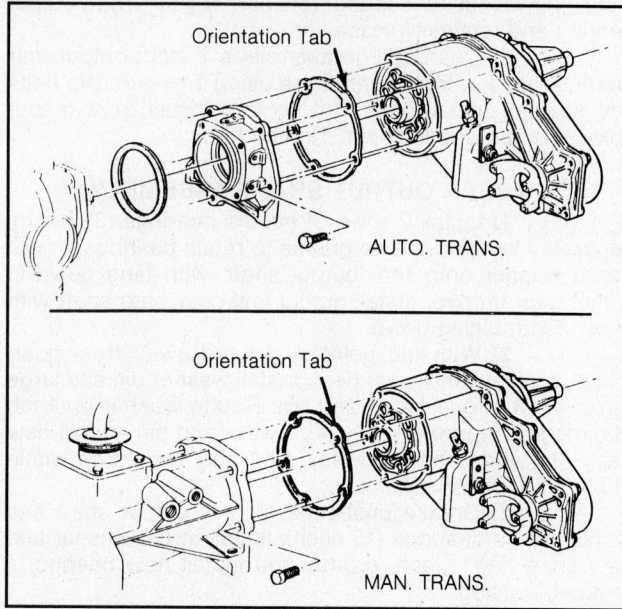

Note position of orientation tab.

3) Install transfer case attaching bolts and tighten. On vehicles equipped with automatic transmission, install shift lever bracket. Raise transmission and transfer case and install mount and hanger bracket. Install attaching bolts and tighten.
4) Install catalytic converter hanger bolts. Attach shift lever, connect speedometer and vacuum harness at transfer case. Using reference marks, made during removal, reinstall front and rear propeller shafts. Refill transfer case. Install skid plate and lower vehicle. Connect negative battery cable. Road test vehicle.

DISASSEMBLY

TRANSFER CASE
1) Remove drain and fill plugs. Remove front yoke. Discard seal washer and yoke nut. Turn transfer case on end and position transfer case on wood blocks. Shift transfer case to 4WD low.
2) Remove extension housing bolts and, using a hammer, tap shoulder on housing to break sealer loose. Remove rear bearing snap ring from mainshaft and discard. Remove rear retainer attaching bolts and, using a hammer, tap shoulder on retainer to break sealer loose.
3) Remove rear retainer and pump housing from transfer case. Remove pump seal from pump housing and discard seal. Remove speedometer drive gear and pump gear from mainshaft.

NEW PROCESS MODEL 207 (Cont.)

Fig. 2: Exploded View of New Process 207 Transfer Case

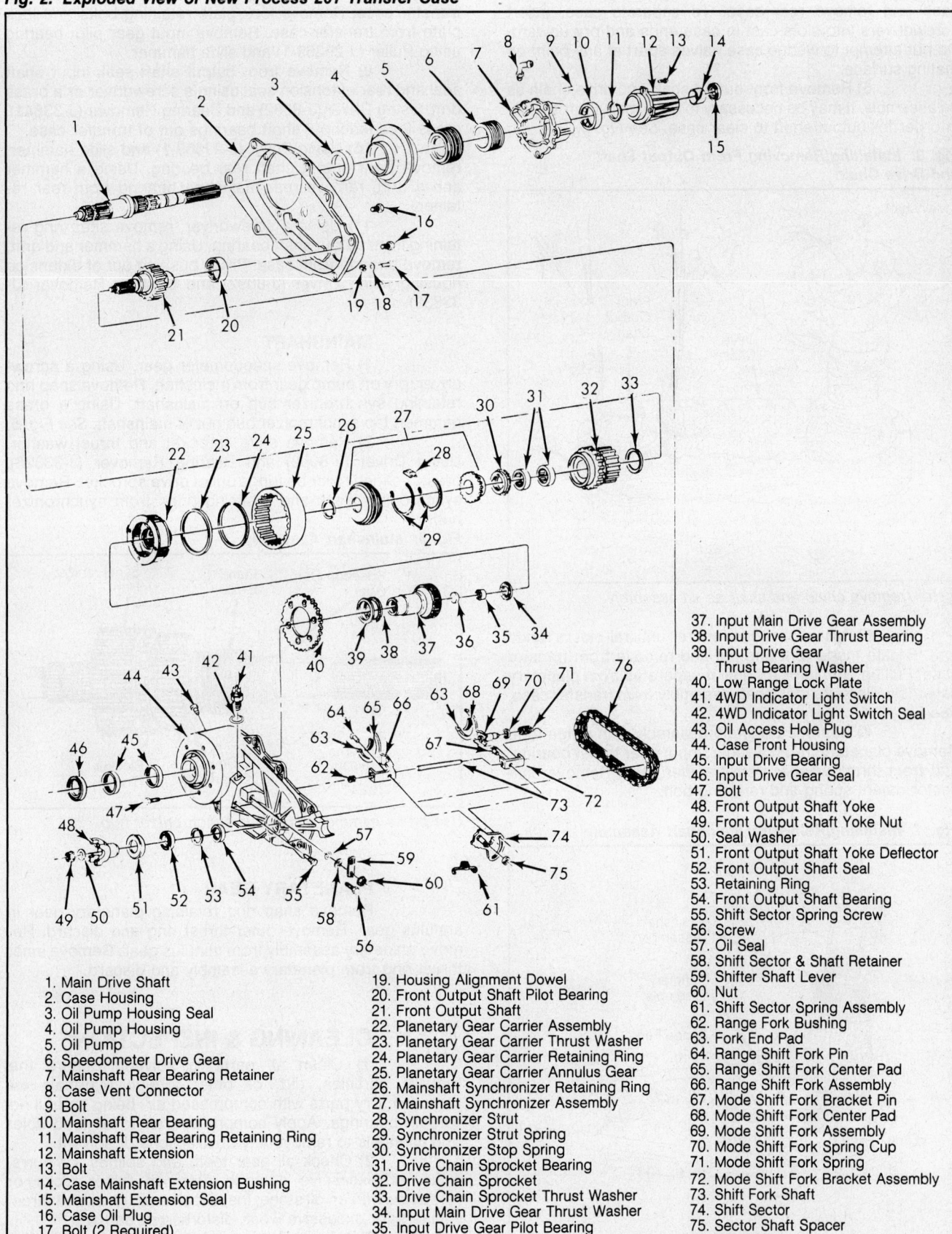

1. Main Drive Shaft
2. Case Housing
3. Oil Pump Housing Seal
4. Oil Pump Housing
5. Oil Pump
6. Speedometer Drive Gear
7. Mainshaft Rear Bearing Retainer
8. Case Vent Connector
9. Bolt
10. Mainshaft Rear Bearing
11. Mainshaft Rear Bearing Retaining Ring
12. Mainshaft Extension
13. Bolt
14. Case Mainshaft Extension Bushing
15. Mainshaft Extension Seal
16. Case Oil Plug
17. Bolt (2 Required)
18. Housing Alignment Dowel Washer

19. Housing Alignment Dowel
20. Front Output Shaft Pilot Bearing
21. Front Output Shaft
22. Planetary Gear Carrier Assembly
23. Planetary Gear Carrier Thrust Washer
24. Planetary Gear Carrier Retaining Ring
25. Planetary Gear Carrier Annulus Gear
26. Mainshaft Synchronizer Retaining Ring
27. Mainshaft Synchronizer Assembly
28. Synchronizer Strut
29. Synchronizer Strut Spring
30. Synchronizer Stop Spring
31. Drive Chain Sprocket Bearing
32. Drive Chain Sprocket
33. Drive Chain Sprocket Thrust Washer
34. Input Main Drive Gear Thrust Washer
35. Input Drive Gear Pilot Bearing
36. Plug

37. Input Main Drive Gear Assembly
38. Input Drive Gear Thrust Bearing
39. Input Drive Gear Thrust Bearing Washer
40. Low Range Lock Plate
41. 4WD Indicator Light Switch
42. 4WD Indicator Light Switch Seal
43. Oil Access Hole Plug
44. Case Front Housing
45. Input Drive Bearing
46. Input Drive Gear Seal
47. Bolt
48. Front Output Shaft Yoke
49. Front Output Shaft Yoke Nut
50. Seal Washer
51. Front Output Shaft Yoke Deflector
52. Front Output Shaft Seal
53. Retaining Ring
54. Front Output Shaft Bearing
55. Shift Sector Spring Screw
56. Screw
57. Oil Seal
58. Shift Sector & Shaft Retainer
59. Shifter Shaft Lever
60. Nut
61. Shift Sector Spring Assembly
62. Range Fork Bushing
63. Fork End Pad
64. Range Shift Fork Pin
65. Range Shift Fork Center Pad
66. Range Shift Fork Assembly
67. Mode Shift Fork Bracket Pin
68. Mode Shift Fork Center Pad
69. Mode Shift Fork Assembly
70. Mode Shift Fork Spring Cup
71. Mode Shift Fork Spring
72. Mode Shift Fork Bracket Assembly
73. Shift Fork Shaft
74. Shift Sector
75. Sector Shaft Spacer
76. Drive Chain

Transfer Cases

NEW PROCESS MODEL 207 (Cont.)

4) Remove bolts attaching rear case to front case and remove rear case. To separate case, insert screwdrivers into slots cast in case ends and pry upward. Do not attempt to wedge case halves apart at any point on mating surface.

5) Remove front output shaft and drive chain as an assembly. It may be necessary to raise mainshaft slightly in order for output shaft to clear case. See Fig. 3.

Fig. 3: Installing/Removing Front Output Shaft and Drive Chain

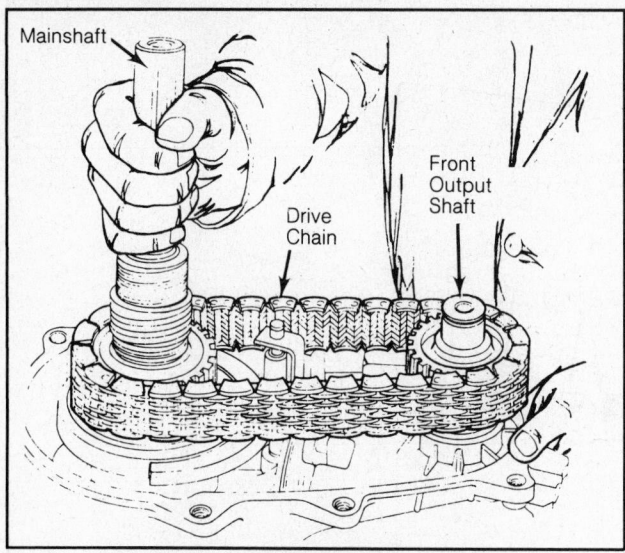

Install/remove chain and shaft as an assembly.

6) Pull up on mode fork rail until rail clears range fork. Rotate mode fork and rail and remove from transfer case. Pull up on mainshaft until it separates from planetary assembly. Remove mainshaft assembly from transfer case. See Fig. 4.

7) Remove planetary assembly with range fork. Remove planetary thrust washer, input gear thrust bearing, and front thrust washer from transfer case. Remove shift sector detent spring and retaining bolt.

Fig. 4: Installing/Removing Mainshaft Assembly

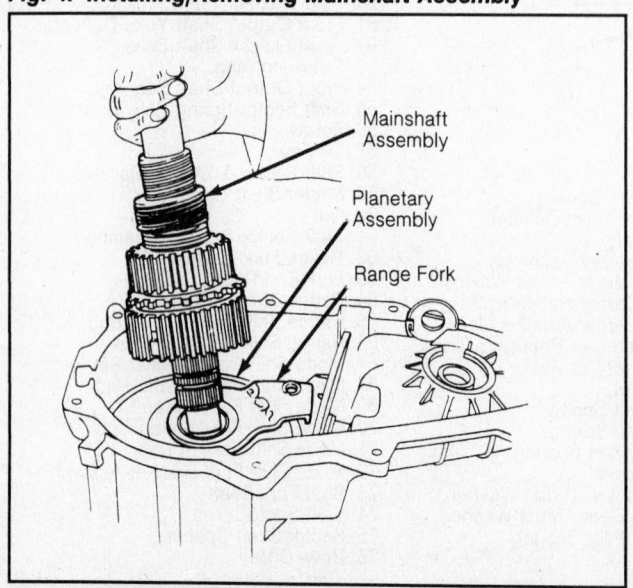

8) Remove shift sector, shaft, and spacer from transfer case. Remove lock plate retaining bolts and lock plate from transfer case. Remove input gear pilot bearing using Puller (J-29369-1) and slide hammer.

9) Remove front output shaft seal, input shaft seal and rear extension seal using a screwdriver or a brass drift. Using Driver (J-8092) and Bearing Remover (J-33841), press 2 caged input shaft bearings out of transfer case.

10) Using Puller (J-29369-1) and slide hammer, remove front output shaft rear bearing. Using a hammer and a drift, remove rear mainshaft bearing from rear retainer.

11) Using a screwdriver, remove snap ring retaining front output shaft bearing. Using a hammer and drift, remove bearing from case. Press bushing out of extension housing using Driver (J-8092) and Bushing Remover (J-33839).

MAINSHAFT

1) Remove speedometer gear. Using a screwdriver, pry off pump gear from mainshaft. Remove snap ring retaining synchronizer hub on mainshaft. Using a brass hammer, tap synchronizer hub out of mainshaft. See Fig. 5.

2) Remove drive sprocket and thrust washer. Using Driver (J-8092) and Bearing Remover (J-33826), press 2 caged roller bearings out of drive sprocket. Remove synchronizer keys and retaining rings from synchronizer hub.

Fig. 5: Mainshaft Assembly

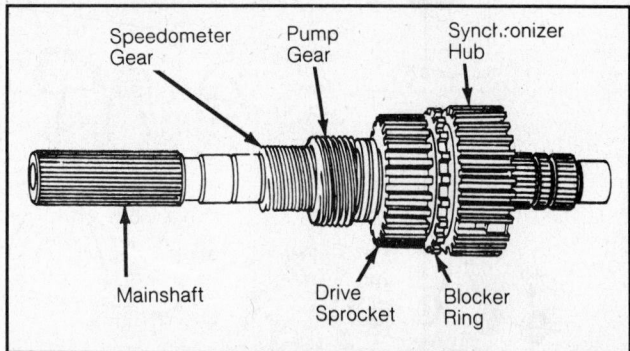

Use brass hammer to remove synchronizer hub.

PLANETARY GEAR

Remove snap ring retaining planetary gear in annulus gear. Remove outer thrust ring and discard. Remove planetary assembly from annulus gear. Remove inner thrust ring from planetary assembly and discard.

CLEANING & INSPECTION

1) Clean all parts in solvent. Ensure that metallic particles, dirt, or other foreign materials are removed. Dry parts with compressed air, being careful not to spin bearings. Apply compressed air to oil feed holes and channels to remove any obstructions or solvent.

2) Check all gear teeth and splines for burrs, nicks, or excessive damage. Remove minor nicks or scratches with an oil stone. Inspect all snap rings and thrust washers for excessive wear, distortion or damage.

3) Inspect 2 case halves for cracks, porosity, damaged mating surfaces, stripped bolt threads or distor-

NEW PROCESS MODEL 207 (Cont.)

tion. Inspect condition of all bearings and retainers. Inspect condition of chain and oil pump. Replace parts as necessary.

REASSEMBLY

PLANETARY GEAR

Install inner thrust ring on planetary assembly. Install planetary assembly into annulus gear. Install outer thrust ring and then snap ring. *See Fig. 6.*

Fig. 6: Installing Thrust Washers in Planetary Assembly

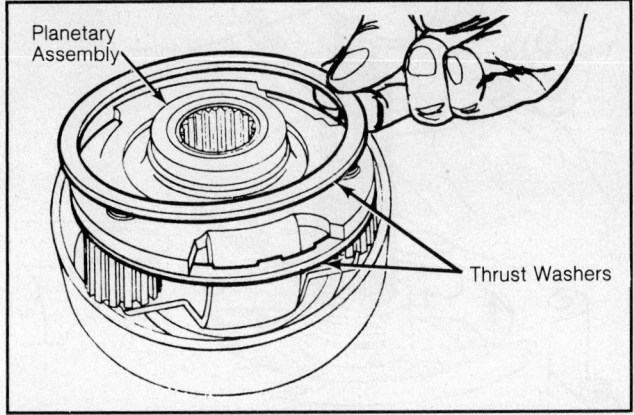

Planetary Assembly

Thrust Washers

Install one thrust washer on each side of planetary assembly.

MAINSHAFT

1) Using Driver (J-8092) and Bearing Installer (J-33828), install front drive sprocket bearing. Press bearing until tool bottoms. Bearing should be flush with front surface.

2) Reverse installer on driver and press rear bearing into sprocket until tool bottoms. Rear bearing should be recessed after installation. Install thrust washer and drive sprocket on mainshaft.

3) Install blocker ring and synchronizer assembly on mainshaft. Install new snap ring. Install pump gear on mainshaft. Tap gear with hammer to seat it on mainshaft. Install speedometer gear on mainshaft.

TRANSFER CASE

CAUTION: **All bearings used in transfer case must be correctly positioned to avoid covering bearing oil feed holes. After installation of bearings, check bearing position to be sure feed hole is not blocked by bearing.**

1) Install lock plate in transfer case. Coat case and lock plate surfaces around bolt holes with Loctite 515. Position lock plate on case and align bolt holes with case. Install attaching bolts and tighten.

2) Install roller bearings for input shaft into case using Driver (J-8092) and Bearing Installer (J-33830). Press bearings until tool bottoms. Using Driver (J-8092) and Bearing Installer (J-33832), install front output shaft rear bearing. Press bearing until tool bottoms.

3) Install front output shaft front bearing using Driver (J-8092) and Bearing Installer (J-33833). Press bearing until tool bottoms. Install snap ring that retains front output shaft bearing in case. Install front output and input shaft seals using Seal Installers (J-33831 and J-33834).

4) Install spacer on shift sector shaft and install sector in case. Install shift lever and retaining nut. Tighten nut. Install shift sector detent spring and retaining bolt. Using Driver (J-8092) and Bearing Installer (J-33829), press pilot bearing onto input gear. Press bearing until tool bottoms.

5) Install input gear front thrust bearing and input gear in case. Install planetary gear thrust washer on input gear. Position range fork on planetary assembly and install planetary assembly into case.

6) Ensure that thrust washer is aligned with input gear and planetary assembly. Install mainshaft into case. Install mode fork on synchronizer sleeve and rotate until mode fork is aligned with range fork. Slide mode fork rail down through range fork until rail seats in bore of case.

7) Position drive chain on front output shaft and install chain on drive sprocket. Install front output shaft in case. It may be necessary to slightly raise mainshaft to seat output shaft in case. Install magnet into pocket of transfer case.

8) Apply 1/8" bead of Loctite 515 to mating surface of front case. Install rear case on front case aligning dowel pins. Install and tighten bolts. Install 2 bolts with washers into dowel pin holes.

9) Install output bearing into rear retainer using Driver (J-8092) and Bearing Installer (J-33833). Press bearing until seated in bore. Install pump seal using Seal Installer (J-33835). Apply petroleum jelly to pump housing tabs and install housing in rear retainer.

10) Apply Loctite 515 sealer to mating surface of rear retainer. Align retainer with case. Install retaining bolts and tighten. Install a new snap ring on mainshaft. Pull up on mainshaft and seat snap ring in groove.

11) Install bushing in extension housing using Driver (J-8092) and Bushing Installer (J-33826). Press bushing until tool bottoms. Install new seal in extension housing using Seal Installer (J-33843).

12) Apply Loctite 515 to mating surface of extension housing. Align housing with rear retainer. Install attaching bolts and tighten. Install front yoke on output shaft. Install a new yoke seal washer and nut. Tighten nut. Install drain and fill plugs.

TIGHTENING SPECIFICATIONS

Application	Ft. Lbs. (N.m)
Adapter-to-Transfer Case Bolt	19-29 (26-39)
Drain/Fill Plug	30-40 (41-54)
Extension Housing Bolt	20-25 (27-34)
Front Output Yoke Nut	90-130 (122-176)
Indicator Light Switch	15-25 (20-34)
Lock Plate-to-Transfer Case	20-30 (27-41)
Rear Retainer Bolt	15-20 (20-27)
Shift Bracket Bolt	47-62 (64-84)
Shift Lever Adjustment Bolt	25-35 (34-47)
Shift Lever Nut	15-20 (20-27)
Shift Lever Pivot Bolt	88-103 (119-140)
Transfer Case Bolt	20-25 (27-34)

Transfer Cases

NEW PROCESS MODEL 208

Chevrolet, Chrysler Corp., Ford, GMC, Jeep

DESCRIPTION

The Model 208 is a part-time 4WD unit having an integral 4WD-Low range. This model is a 4-position unit, providing 2 gear ratios in 4WD (High and Low), a 2WD-High and Neutral.

A chain drive is used with front and rear output shafts mounted in ball and roller bearings. Two drive sprockets and a planetary gear assembly, consisting of a 4-pinion carrier and annulus gear are housed in a 2-piece aluminum case. All models have manual locking hubs as standard equipment and 4WD indicator lamps. These lamps inform the driver of the operating mode of the vehicle.

LUBRICATION

SERVICE INTERVALS

Check fluid level. Case should be filled to edge of fill plug opening. Add fluid as necessary every 4 months or 6,000 miles. Drain and refill transfer case every 36,000 miles.

FLUID TYPE
All Models
Use Dexron II ATF.

CAPACITY
Chrysler Corp. & Jeep
Capacity is 6 pints (2.8L).
Ford
Capacity is 9 pints (4.3L).
General Motors
Capacity is 10 pints (4.7L).

ADJUSTMENTS

Adjust shift linkage so that all positions may be selected without interference or binding. Inspect all swivels, rods and mountings for wear or damage. Replace as necessary.

REMOVAL & INSTALLATION

See approriate article in MANUAL TRANSMIS-SION REMOVAL section.

DISASSEMBLY

TRANSFER CASE

1) Remove fill and drain plugs. Remove front and rear yokes. Discard yoke seal washers and nuts. Place transfer case on end and position front case on wood blocks. It may be necessary to cut "V" notches in wooden blocks to clear mounting studs in front case.

2) Remove lock mode indicator switch and washer. Remove detent bolt, spring and ball. Mark rear retainer and case for assembly alignment reference. Remove rear bearing retainer and pump housing as an assem-

bly. Use mallet to remove retainer from case. Do not pry on retainer. *See Fig. 1.*

Fig. 1: Rear Retainer Case Removal & Installation

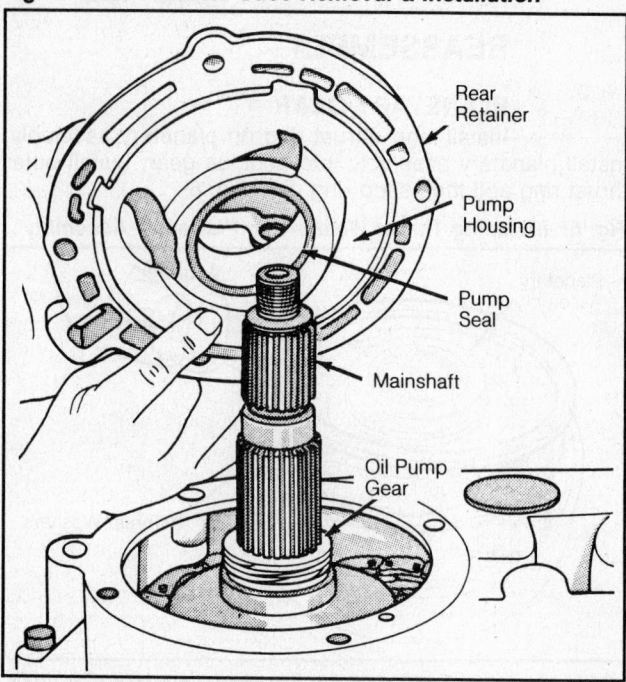

Tap retainer from case using plastic mallet.

3) Remove pump housing from retainer and pump seal from housing. Discard pump seal. Remove speedometer drive gear from mainshaft. Remove oil pump from mainshaft. Mark position of pump for reassembly. Side of oil pump facing case interior is recessed. Remove bolts attaching rear case to front case. Remove rear case.

NOTE: To remove rear case, insert screwdrivers into slots in case ends and gently pry upward. Do not pry case halves apart at any point on mating surface.

4) Remove front output shaft rear thrust bearing assembly. Mark position of bearing and races for reassembly. Remove driven sprocket retaining snap ring, drive sprocket retaining snap ring, and thrust washers.

5) Remove sprockets and drive chain as an assembly. Lift evenly on both sprockets to remove. On Chrysler Corp. and General Motors models, do not lose needle bearings (120 each) from within drive sprocket.

6) On all models, remove front output shaft front thrust bearing assembly. On Chrysler Corp. and General Motors models, remove blocker ring and synchronizer. *See Fig. 3.* On Ford and Jeep models, remove sprocket carrier stop ring and clutch spring. *See Fig. 4 and 5.*

7) On all models, remove sliding clutch, mode fork, mode fork spring and bracket as an assembly. Remove shift rail. On Ford and Jeep models, remove snap ring, sprocket carrier, thrust washer and mainshaft needle bearings as an assembly. Do not lose bearings (120 each).

8) On all models, remove mainshaft. Remove annulus gear retaining ring and thrust washer. Remove annulus gear and range fork as an assembly. Turn fork counterclockwise to disengage fork lug from range sector, and lift assembly out of case. Remove planetary thrust washer, and remove planetary assembly.

NEW PROCESS MODEL 208 (Cont.)

Fig. 2: Sprocket & Chain Removal & Installation

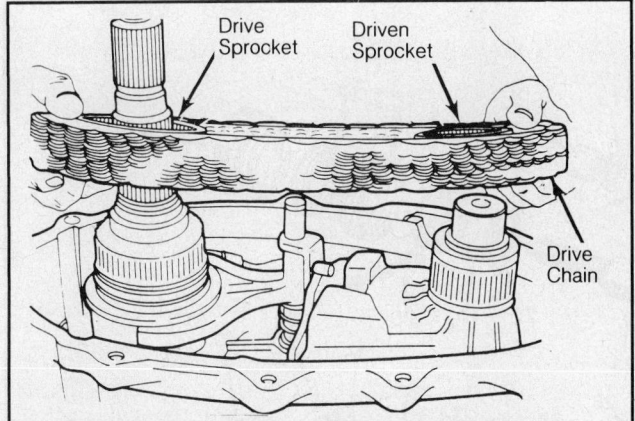

Drive Sprocket

Driven Sprocket

Drive Chain

Remove sprocket and chain as assembly.

9) Remove mainshaft thrust bearing from input gear. Remove input gear by lifting straight up and out of case. Remove input gear thrust bearing and race. Note position of bearing and race for reassembly. Remove range sector operating lever nut and washer.

10) Remove lever, sector shaft seal and seal retainer. Remove range sector. Inspect lock plate. If lock plate is loose, worn or cracked, remove lock plate. See SUB-ASSEMBLY OVERHAUL in this article. Remove output shaft seals from front and rear case seal bores.

CLEANING & INSPECTION

1) Wash all parts in cleaning solvent. Be sure to remove all traces of gasket from surfaces where used. Apply compressed air to each oil feed port and channel in each case half to remove any obstruction or residue.

2) Check all gear teeth and splines for burrs, nicks, excessive wear or damage. Inspect all snap rings and thrust washers for excessive wear, distortion or damage.

3) Inspect both case halves for cracks, porosity, damaged mating surfaces, stripped bolt threads or distortion. Check lock plate teeth and hub for cracks, chips or excessive wear.

4) Inspect condition of all bearings in both case halves and input gear. Check condition of bearing bores in both case halves, input gear, rear output shaft, side gear and rear retainer. Replace bearings as required.

SUB-ASSEMBLY OVERHAUL

NOTE: All of the bearings used in the trasnfer case must be correctly positioned to avoid covering bearing oil feed holes. After replacing any bearing check the bearing position to be sure that oil feed is not blocked by bearing.

ANNULUS GEAR BUSHING

On Jeep, remove bushing using Driver (J-8092) and Bushing Remover/Installer (J-29185) Install new bushing and remove any chips generated by bushing replacement. On Chrysler Corp., if annulus gear bushing requires replacement, replace annulus gear.

LOCK PLATE

1) Remove and discard lock plate attaching bolts. Remove lock plate from case. Coat case and lock plate surfaces around bolt holes with RTV sealant.

2) Position new lock plate in case and align bolt holes in lock plate with case. Coat new lock plate attaching bolts with Loctite. Install and tighten lock plate bolts.

REAR OUTPUT BEARING & REAR SEAL

Remove rear seal using screwdriver or brass drift. Remove bearing retaining snap ring. Remove bearing using brass drift. Install new bearing. Ensure that shielded side of bearing faces interior of case. Install bearing retaining snap ring. Install new rear seal.

FRONT OUTPUT SHAFT FRONT BEARING

Remove bearing. Install new front bearing and check bearing position to ensure that oil feed hole is not blocked.

FRONT OUTPUT SHAFT REAR BEARING

Remove bearing. Install new front bearing and check bearing position to ensure that oil feed hole is not blocked. Ensure that bearing is flush with case.

INPUT GEAR FRONT & REAR BEARING

Remove both bearings at the same time. Install new bearings one at a time. Install rear bearing first; then install front bearing. Remove installer and check bearing position to ensure that oil feed holes are not covered. Ensure that bearings are flush with case.

MAIN SHAFT PILOT BEARING

Remove pilot bearing and plug. Install new bearing and check bearing position to ensure that oil feed hole is not blocked. Ensure that bearing is flush with edge of bearing bore. Install bearing plug.

REASSEMBLY

TRANSFER CASE

NOTE: During assembly, lubricate all components with Dexron II type oil or petroleum jelly where indicated only. Do not use any other type of lubricants.

1) Install input gear race and thrust bearing in front case. Install input gear. Install mainshaft thrust bearing in input gear. Install range sector shaft seal and seal retainer. Install range sector.

2) Install operating lever on range sector shaft. Install and tighten shaft washer and lock nut. Install planetary assembly over input gear making sure planetary set is fully seated and meshed with gear. Install planetary thrust washer on planetary hub.

3) If removed, install inserts in range fork. Engage range fork in annulus gear. Install annulus gear over planetary assembly. Install annulus gear thrust washer and retaining snap ring. Align shift rail bores in case and range fork. Install shift rail.

NOTE: Ensure shift rail bore is completely dry and contains no oil. Oil may prevent rail from seating completely and also prevent front case installation.

Transfer Cases
NEW PROCESS MODEL 208 (Cont.)

Fig. 3: Exploded View of Chrysler Corp. & General Motors Model 208 Transfer Case

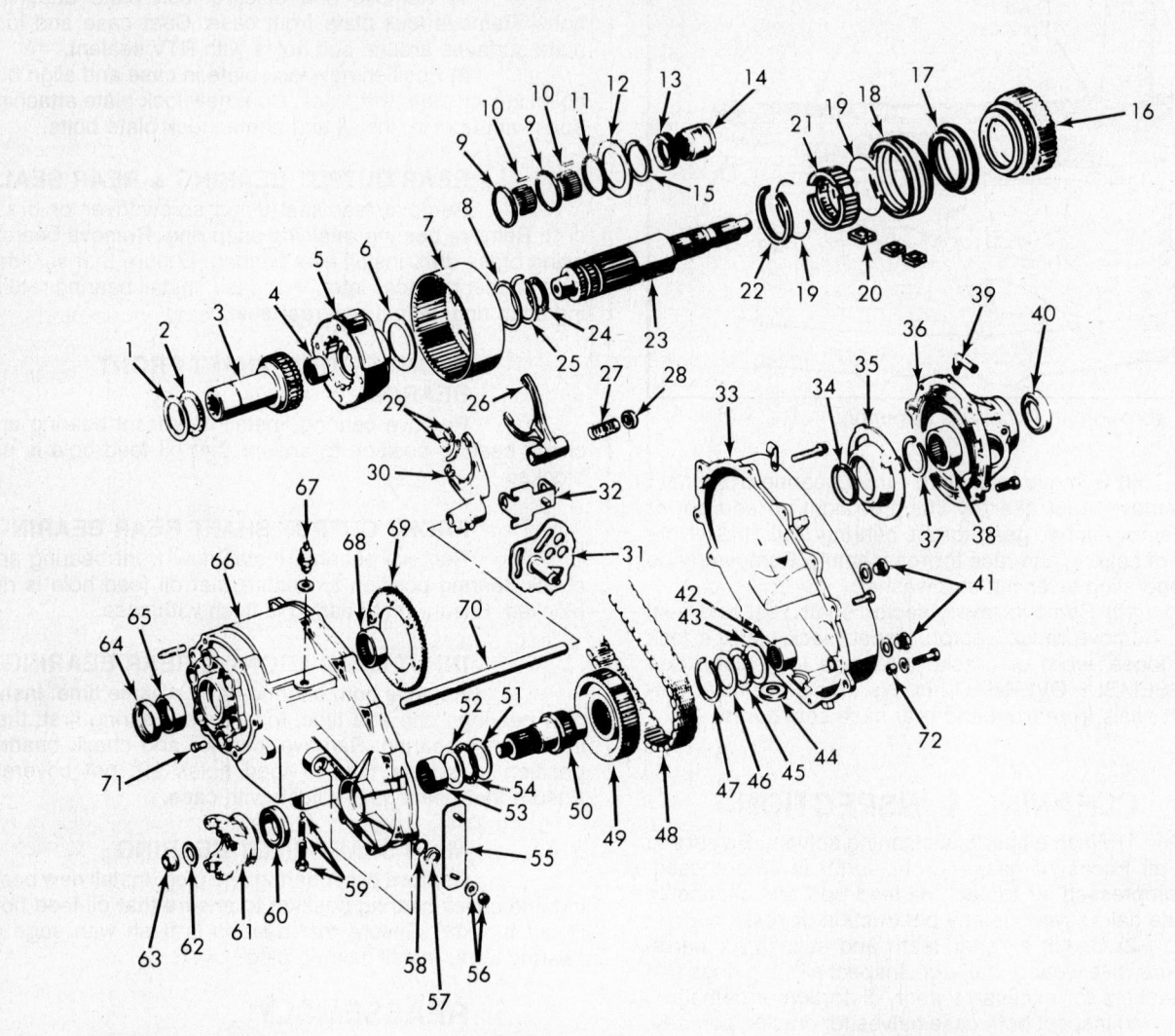

1. Input Gear Thrust Washer
2. Input Gear Thrust Bearing
3. Input Gear
4. Mainshaft Pilot Bearing
5. Planetary Assembly
6. Planetary Thrust Washer
7. Annulus Gear
8. Annulus Gear Thrust Washer
9. Needle Bearing Spacers
10. Mainshaft Needle Bearings (120)
11. Needle Bearing Spacer
12. Spacer Washer
13. Oil Pump Gear
14. Speedometer Gear
15. Drive Sprocket Snap Ring
16. Drive Sprocket
17. Blocker Ring
18. Synchronizer Sleeve
19. Synchronizer Spring
20. Synchronizer Key
21. Synchronizer Hub
22. Synchronizer Hub Snap Ring
23. Mainshaft
24. Mainshaft Thrust Bearing
25. Internal Gear Snap Ring
26. Mode Fork
27. Spring
28. Spring Retainer

29. Range Fork Pads
30. Range Fork
31. Range Sector
32. Mode Fork Bracket
33. Rear Case
34. Seal
35. Oil Pump Housing
36. Rear Retainer
37. Bearing Snap Ring
38. Rear Output Bearing
39. Vent Tube
40. Rear Seal
41. Drain & Fill Plugs
42. Front Output Shaft
   Rear Bearing
43. Front Output Shaft Rear
   Thrust Bearing Race (Thick)
44. Magnet
45. Front Output Shaft
   Rear Thrust Bearing
46. Front Output Shaft Rear
   Thrust Bearing Race (Thin)
47. Driven Sprocket Retaining Ring
48. Drive Chain
49. Driven Sprocket
50. Front Output Shaft
51. Front Output Shaft Front
   Thrust Bearing Race (Thin)

52. Front Output Shaft Front
   Thrust Bearing Race (Thick)
53. Front Output Shaft Front Bearing
54. Front Output Shaft Front
   Bearing Thrust Race
55. Operating Lever
56. Washer & Lock Nut
57. Range Sector Shaft
   Seal Retainer
58. Range Sector Shaft Seal
59. Detent Ball, Spring
   & Retainer Bolt
60. Front Seal
61. Front Yoke
62. Yoke Seal Washer
63. Yoke Nut
64. Input Gear Oil Seal
65. Input Gear Front Bearing
66. Front Case
67. 4WD Indicator Light
   Switch & Washer
68. Input Gear Rear Bearing
69. Lock Plate
70. Shifter Fork Shaft
71. Lock Plate Bolts
72. Alignment Dowels

Transfer Cases

NEW PROCESS MODEL 208 (Cont.)

Fig. 4: Exploded View of Ford Model 208 Transfer Case

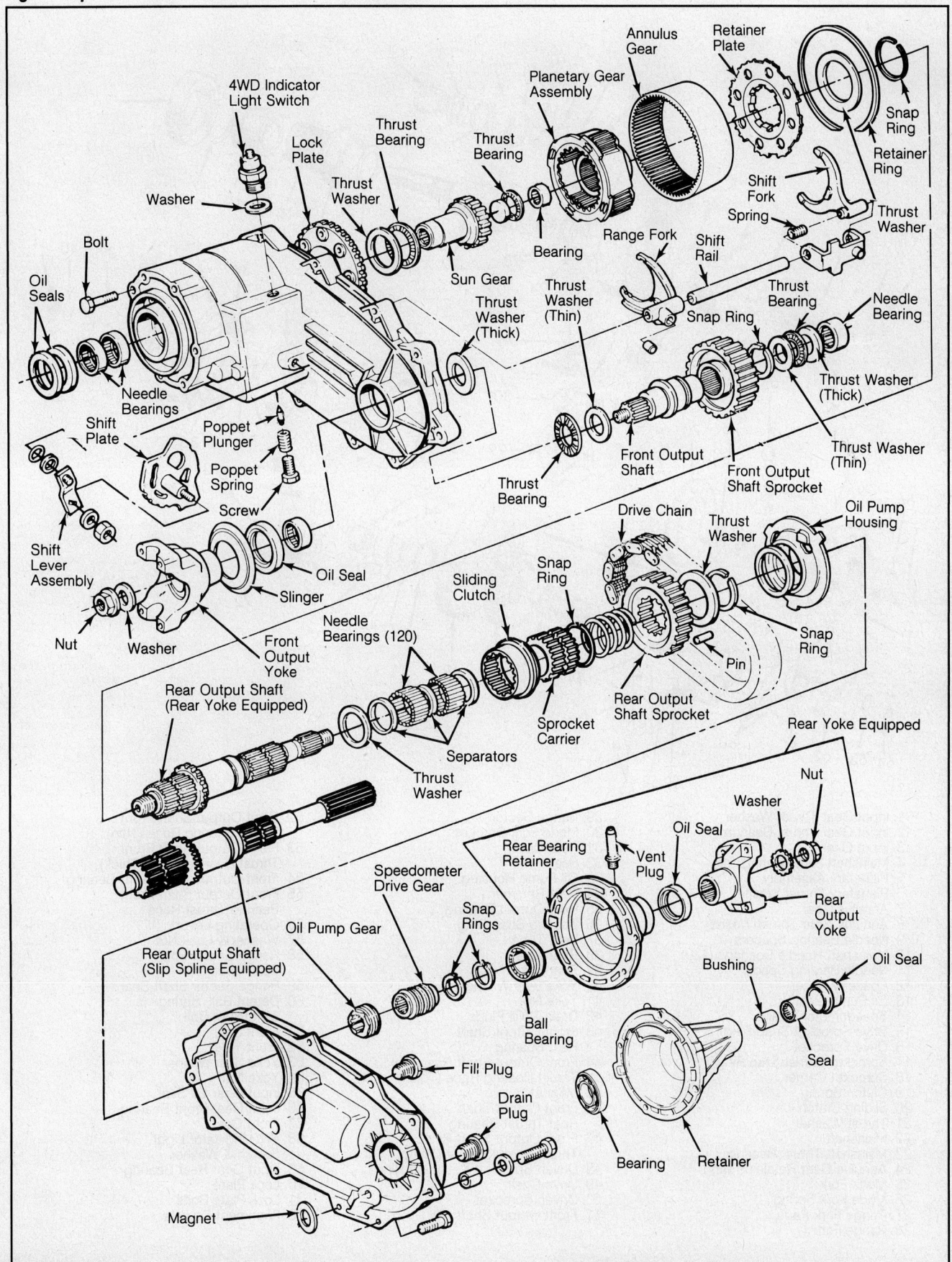

4-33

Transfer Cases
NEW PROCESS MODEL 208 (Cont.)

Fig. 5: Exploded View of Jeep Model 208 Transfer Case

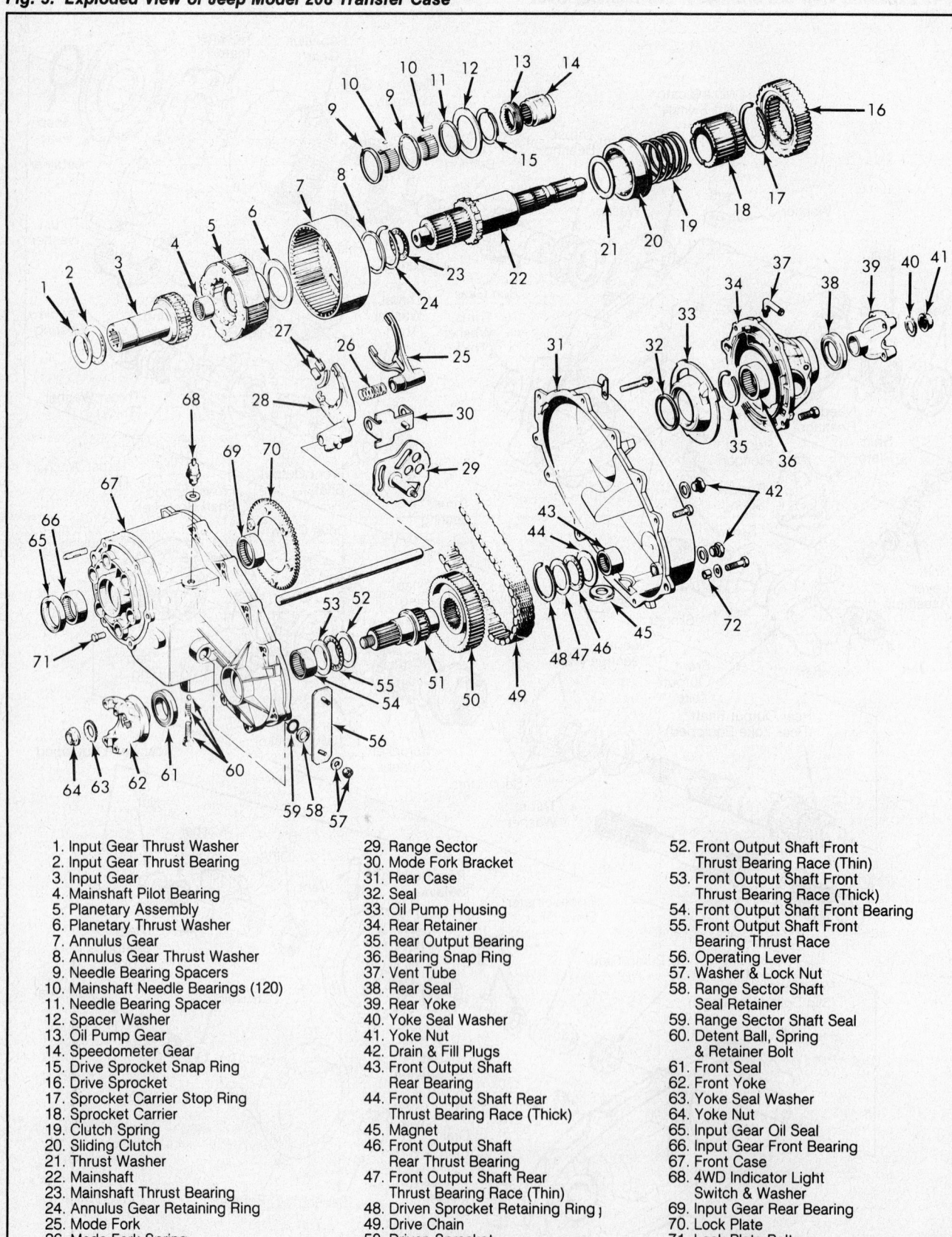

1. Input Gear Thrust Washer	29. Range Sector	52. Front Output Shaft Front
2. Input Gear Thrust Bearing	30. Mode Fork Bracket	Thrust Bearing Race (Thin)
3. Input Gear	31. Rear Case	53. Front Output Shaft Front
4. Mainshaft Pilot Bearing	32. Seal	Thrust Bearing Race (Thick)
5. Planetary Assembly	33. Oil Pump Housing	54. Front Output Shaft Front Bearing
6. Planetary Thrust Washer	34. Rear Retainer	55. Front Output Shaft Front
7. Annulus Gear	35. Rear Output Bearing	Bearing Thrust Race
8. Annulus Gear Thrust Washer	36. Bearing Snap Ring	56. Operating Lever
9. Needle Bearing Spacers	37. Vent Tube	57. Washer & Lock Nut
10. Mainshaft Needle Bearings (120)	38. Rear Seal	58. Range Sector Shaft
11. Needle Bearing Spacer	39. Rear Yoke	Seal Retainer
12. Spacer Washer	40. Yoke Seal Washer	59. Range Sector Shaft Seal
13. Oil Pump Gear	41. Yoke Nut	60. Detent Ball, Spring
14. Speedometer Gear	42. Drain & Fill Plugs	& Retainer Bolt
15. Drive Sprocket Snap Ring	43. Front Output Shaft	61. Front Seal
16. Drive Sprocket	Rear Bearing	62. Front Yoke
17. Sprocket Carrier Stop Ring	44. Front Output Shaft Rear	63. Yoke Seal Washer
18. Sprocket Carrier	Thrust Bearing Race (Thick)	64. Yoke Nut
19. Clutch Spring	45. Magnet	65. Input Gear Oil Seal
20. Sliding Clutch	46. Front Output Shaft	66. Input Gear Front Bearing
21. Thrust Washer	Rear Thrust Bearing	67. Front Case
22. Mainshaft	47. Front Output Shaft Rear	68. 4WD Indicator Light
23. Mainshaft Thrust Bearing	Thrust Bearing Race (Thin)	Switch & Washer
24. Annulus Gear Retaining Ring	48. Driven Sprocket Retaining Ring	69. Input Gear Rear Bearing
25. Mode Fork	49. Drive Chain	70. Lock Plate
26. Mode Fork Spring	50. Driven Sprocket	71. Lock Plate Bolts
27. Range Fork Pads	51. Front Output Shaft	72. Alignment Dowels
28. Range Fork		

Transfer Cases

NEW PROCESS MODEL 208 (Cont.)

4) Install mainshaft making sure thrust bearing is properly seated in input gear. On Chrysler Corp. and General Motors models, position synchronizer keys and install synchronizer and mode fork as an assembly. Install blocker ring.

5) Coat sprocket carrier with petroleum jelly and position bearing retainer at center of carrier bore bore. Coat needle bearings with petroleum jelly and install 60 needle bearings in each end of drive sprocket bore; a total of 120 bearings are used. Install bearing retainer in each end of sprocket, and position thrust washer on bottom of drive sprocket.

6) Align assembled carrier and needle bearings with mainshaft and install on mainshaft. Do not displace needle bearings during installation. Assemble mode fork, fork spring and bracket. Engage sliding clutch and install assembly on shift rail and mainshaft.

7) On Ford and Jeep models, install clutch spring and stop ring in sprocket carrier. On all models, install front output shaft thrust bearing assembly in front case. Correct sequence is: thick race, thrust bearing, thin race. Install front output shaft.

8) Position sprockets in chain, align sprockets with shafts and install as an assembly. Make sure drive sprocket recessed side is facing into case. Install spacer and thrust washer on drive sprocket. Install snap ring.

9) Install driven sprocket retaining snap ring. Install front output shaft rear thrust bearing assembly on front output shaft. Correct sequence is: thin race, thrust bearing, thick race.

10) Install oil pump on mainshaft. Make sure recessed side of pump faces into case. Install speedometer drive gear. Install magnet in front case, if removed. Apply RTV silicone or equivalent sealant to 1 side of case and mate rear case on front case.

11) Make sure front output shaft rear thrust bearing assembly is seated in rear case. Align bolt holes and dowels. Install flat washers on 2 bolts installed at opposite ends of case. Install all bolts and tighten.

12) Install seal in pump housing. Coat pump housing tabs with petroleum jelly and install housing in rear retainer. Apply sealer to mating surface of rear retainer, align with case index marks, install retainer and bolts.

13) Install oil seal in rear retainer bore. Coat seal lip with petroleum jelly before installation. Install indicator switch and washer. Apply small amount of sealer to detent retainer bolt and install detent ball, spring and bolt.

14) Install drain plug and gasket. Install oil seal in front case output shaft bore. Install front and rear yokes. Be sure yoke with collar is on front output shaft. Install yoke seal washers and nuts. Fill transfer case and install fill plug.

TIGHTENING SPECIFICATIONS

Application	Ft. Lbs. (N.m)
Detent Retainer Bolt	20-25 (27-34)
Drain & Fill Plugs	
Chrysler	15-20 (20-27)
All Others	30-40 (41-54)
Indicator Switch	15-20 (20-27)
Lock Plate Bolts	30 (41)
Operating Lever Lock Nut	15-20 (20-27)
Rear Case-to-Front Case Bolts	20-25 (27-34)
Rear Retainer Bolts	20-25 (27-34)
Sector Shaft Nut	20-25 (27-34)
Yoke Nuts	120 (163)

Transfer Cases

SELEC-TRAC MODEL 229

Jeep

DESCRIPTION

The Selec-Trac Model 229 transfer case is a full-time/part-time 4WD unit, with integral low range. Selec-Trac is only available with automatic transmission and includes: Model 44 front axle with 2WD disconnect, a vacuum control system, model 229 transfer case, and a 2/4WD mode selector on the instrument panel. This unit provides 4 driving ranges: 4WD high, 4WD low, 2WD high and Neutral.

The vacuum control system consists of 2 vacuum shift motors, a vacuum storage tank, lines and hoses, check valves and a 2/4WD mode selector. *See Fig. 1.* This system will allow for low range operation only after 4WD mode has been selected. The design of the vacuum motors allows for sequential engagement of the vacuum controlled components. *See Fig. 2.* When shifting into 4WD, the axle is shifted first. When shifting into 2WD, the transfer case is shifted first.

LUBRICATION

SERVICE INTERVALS

Check fluid every 5 months or 5000 miles. Replace as necessary. Drain and refill transfer case every 30 months or 30,000 miles.

FLUID TYPE

Use only Jeep Automatic Transmission fluid or equivalent labeled Dexron II.

CAPACITY

Capacity is 6 pints (2.8L).

Fig. 1: Drive Mode Selector on Instrument Panel

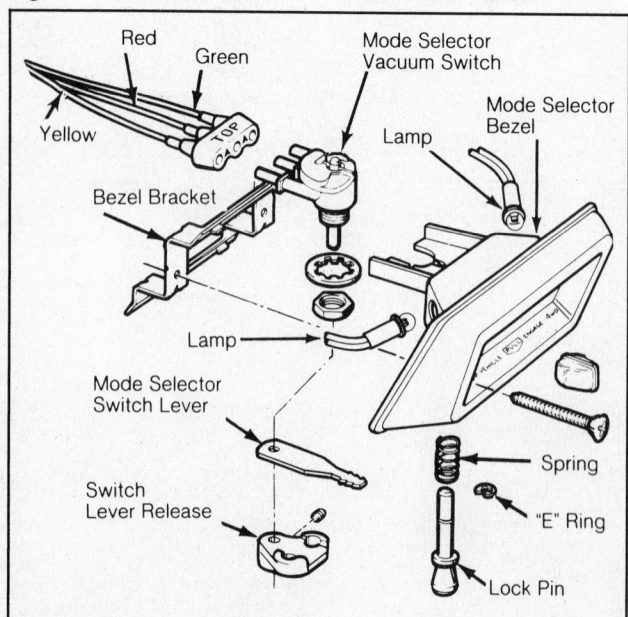

LO range can only be selected when operating in 4WD mode.

Fig. 2: Vacuum Shift Motor

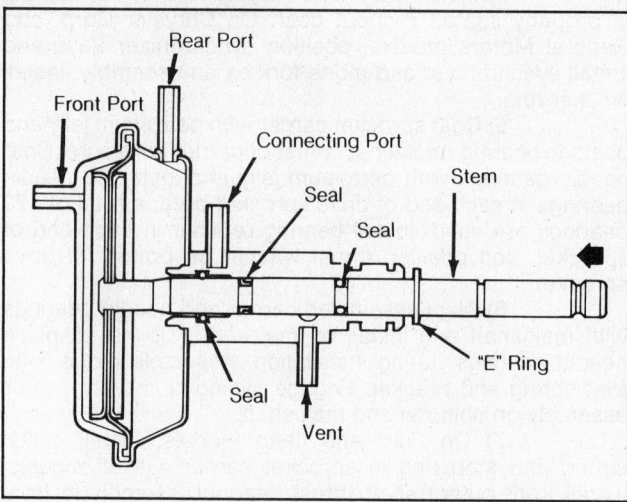

Vacuum at connecting port only when stem is fully extended.

TROUBLE SHOOTING

WILL NOT ENGAGE IN 2WD

1) Raise vehicle so that all 4 wheels are free to rotate. Start engine. Disconnect mode selector vacuum harness at steel tube connection. Check for vacuum at Red hose that attaches to canister. If vacuum exists, go to step 3). If no vacuum, go to step 2).

2) Check intake manifold vacuum supply fitting, vacuum hose and storage tank. If damaged, repair or replace components as necessary. If vacuum leak still exists, repair vacuum line between canister and steel tube. If vacuum exists at Red hose, proceed with system check.

3) Stop engine. Connect vacuum pump to steel tube that connects to Green hose in vacuum harness. Apply 20 in. Hg and rotate propeller shaft to engage transfer case. Shift transmission into park or first gear. If transfer case engages, go to step 6). If transfer case does not engage, go to step 4).

4) Check transfer case shift motor. Motor stem should be extended. If stem is not extended, check vacuum tubes for leaks and damage. Repair as necessary. If transfer case shift motor is still inoperative, check shift motor function. If shift motor is defective, replace motor. If shift motor is operative go to step 5).

5) If transfer case will not engage in 2WD, check transfer case shift linkage and repair as necessary. If linkage is okay and transfer case will not shift into 2WD, repair case. If transfer case now engages in 2WD, check axle for 2WD mode engagement (disconnected). If front axle is not in 2WD mode, check axle shift motor and replace as necessary.

6) If front axle shift motor is okay, check the shift mode selector switch and vacuum harness. Repair as necessary. If front axle shift motor will not disengage, check vacuum lines and repair as necessary.

7) If vacuum lines are okay and axle will not disengage, remove axle housing cover and shift motor. Inspect shift fork, collar and axle components. Repair as necessary.

SELEC-TRAC MODEL 229 (Cont.)

Fig. 3: Selec-Trac System Vacuum Diagram

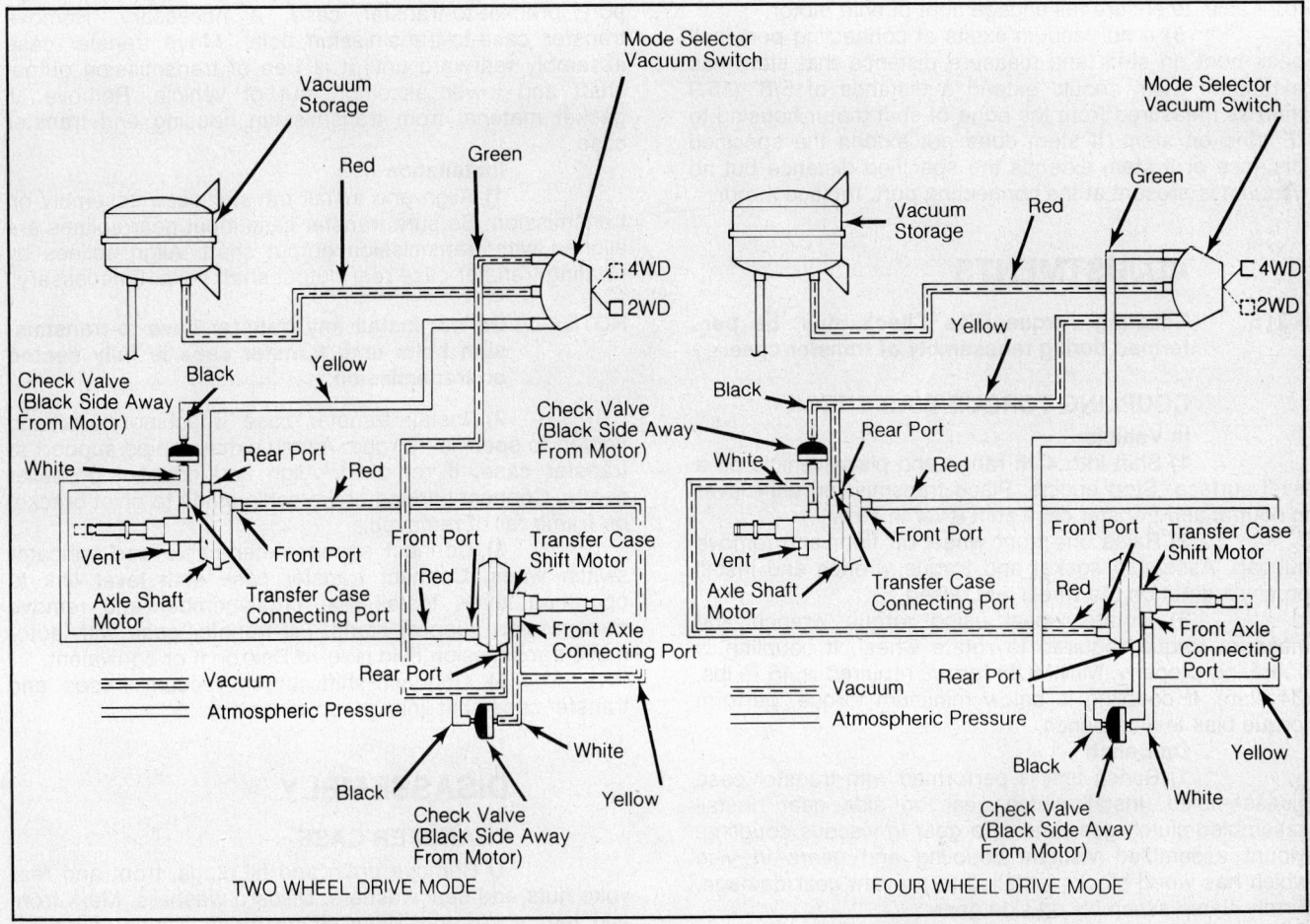

WILL NOT ENGAGE IN 4WD

1) Raise vehicle so that all 4 wheels are free to rotate. Start engine. Disconnect mode selector vacuum harness at steel tube connection. Check for vacuum at Red hose that attaches to canister. If vacuum exists, go to step 3). If no vacuum, go to step 2).

2) Check intake manifold vacuum supply fitting, vacuum hose and storage tank. If damaged, repair or replace components as necessary. If vacuum leak still exists, repair vacuum line between canister and steel tube. If vacuum exists at Red hose, proceed with system check.

3) Stop engine. Connect vacuum pump to steel tube that connects to Yellow hose in vacuum harness. Apply 20 in. Hg and rotate right front wheel to engage axle. If front axle is engaged, go to step 6). If front axle is not engaged proceed with system check.

4) Check front axle shift motor for operation. If shift motor is okay, check vacuum lines and tubes for leaks or damage. Repair as necessary. If axle shift motor is inoperative, replace motor and recheck for axle engagement.

5) If axle will not engage, remove axle housing cover and shift motor. Inspect shift fork, collar, and axle components. Repair as necessary.

6) Check that transfer case shift motor stem is retracted. If so, check transfer case shift linkage and repair as necessary. If not, check vacuum hoses and repair as necessary.

7) If transfer case motor is still inoperative, test motor operation with vacuum pump. If vacuum motor is defective, replace motor and retest. If transfer case motor is okay and transfer case does not engage in 4WD, check axle shift linkage and repair as necessary. If linkage is okay, repair transfer case as necessary.

TESTING

VACUUM SHIFT MOTOR

1) Disconnect vacuum harness from shift motor. Connect vacuum pump to front port and apply 15 in. Hg to motor. On transfer case rotate propeller shaft to engage transfer case in 4WD mode. On front axle, rotate right wheel to fully disengage axle.

2) Shift motor should maintain vacuum applied for at least 30 seconds. If motor does not maintain vacuum, replace motor. If motor does hold vacuum, go to step 3).

3) Disconnect vacuum pump from the front port of the vacuum motor. Connect pump to the rear port of the motor and plug the connecting port. Apply 15 in. Hg to motor; vacuum should be maintained for 30 seconds. If vacuum is not maintained, replace motor. If motor holds vacuum, go to step 4).

4) Remove plug from connecting port and check for vacuum at this port. If vacuum is not present,

Transfer Cases

SELEC-TRAC MODEL 229 (Cont.)

rotate propeller shaft on transfer case or right wheel on front axle, to ensure full engagement of shift motor.

5) If no vacuum exists at connecting port, pull back boot on stem and measure distance that stem has extended. Stem should extend a distance of 5/8" (15.9 mm) as measured from the edge of shift motor housing to "E" ring on stem. If stem does not extend the specified distance or if stem extends the specified distance but no vacuum is present at the connecting port, replace motor.

ADJUSTMENTS

NOTE: Coupling Torque Bias Check must be performed during reassembly of transfer case.

COUPLING TORQUE BIAS CHECK

In Vehicle

1) Shift into 4 HI range and place vehicle on a level surface. Stop engine. Place transmission shift lever in neutral and transfer case shift lever in 4 HI.

2) Raise one front wheel off floor and remove hubcap. Assemble socket and torque wrench and install on any lug nut on the wheel just raised.

3) Rotate wheel using torque wrench and measure torque required to rotate wheel. If coupling is operating properly, MINIMUM torque required is 45 ft. lbs. (34 N.m). If coupling is below minimum torque, perform torque bias test on bench.

On Bench

1) Bench test is performed with transfer case disassembled. Install clutch gear on side gear. Install assembled clutch gear and side gear in viscous coupling. Mount assembled viscous coupling and gears in vise which has wood blocks installed to prevent gear damage. Firmly clamp assembly on side gear.

2) Check engagement of clutch gear in viscous coupling. Clutch gear must be fully engaged in coupling. If necessary, reposition wood blocks so they support gear in coupling. Install rear output shaft and install yoke retaining nut. Install torque wrench on yoke nut.

3) Rotate output shaft and measure torque required to rotate shaft in coupling. Rotating torque should be 25 ft. lbs. (34 N.m) MINIMUM. If rotating torque is less than specified, replace coupling. If torque is at or above specification, coupling is operating properly.

REMOVAL & INSTALLATION

TRANSFER CASE

Removal

1) Raise vehicle and drain transfer case lubricant. Disconnect speedometer cable, indicator switch and transfer case shift lever link at operating lever. Disconnect parking brake cable guide from pivot located on right frame rail, if necessary.

2) Place support stand under transmission and remove rear crossmember. Mark the output shaft yokes for reassembly reference. Mark the yokes and the propeller shafts.

3) Disconnect front and rear propeller shafts, support them in vehicle with wire. Do not allow shafts to hang on universal joint as damage to joint may result. Disconnect shift motor vacuum lines and transfer case shift linkage.

4) Remove bolts attaching exhaust pipe support bracket-to-transfer case, if necessary. Remove transfer case-to-transmission bolts. Move transfer case assembly rearward until it is free of transmission output shaft and lower assembly out of vehicle. Remove all gasket material from transmission housing and transfer case.

Installation

1) Align and install transfer case assembly on transmission. Be sure transfer case input gear splines are aligned with transmission output shaft. Align splines by rotating transfer case rear output shaft yoke, if necessary.

NOTE: Do not install any transfer case-to-transmission bolts until transfer case is fully seated on transmission.

2) Install transfer case attaching bolts and tighten to specified torque. Attach exhaust pipe support to transfer case, if removed. Align and connect propeller shafts. Connect parking brake cable guide to pivot bracket on frame rail, if removed.

3) Connect speedometer cable and indicator switch wires. Connect transfer case shift lever link to operating lever. Install rear crossmember and remove transmission support stand. Fill transfer case with automatic transmission fluid labeled Dexron II or equivalent.

4) Connect shift motor vacuum hoses and transfer case shift linkage. Lower vehicle.

DISASSEMBLY

TRANSFER CASE

1) Remove drain and fill plugs, front and rear yoke nuts and seal washers. Discard washers. Mark front and rear yokes and drive shafts for assembly alignment reference. Remove front and rear yokes, using puller if necessary.

2) Mount transfer case on wood blocks. Cut V-notches in blocks to clear front case mounting studs.

Fig. 4: Separating Rear and Front Cases

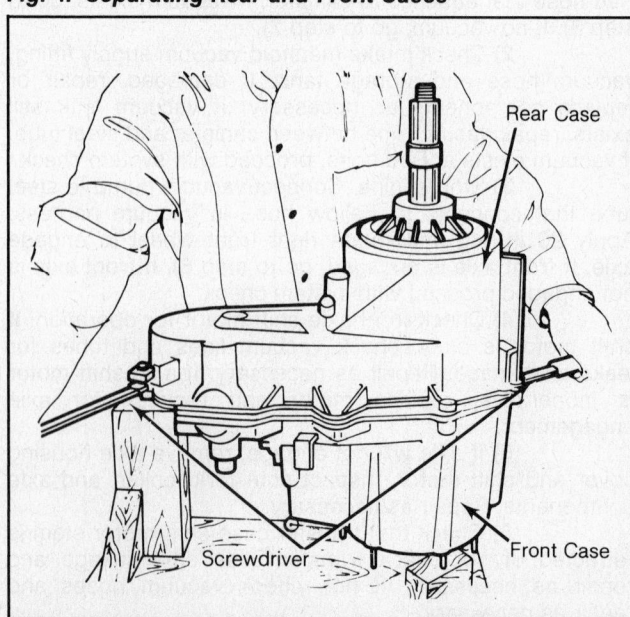

Make sure case is not damaged when separated.

SELEC-TRAC MODEL 229 (Cont.)

Mark rear retainer and rear case for assembly reference. Remove rear retainer bolts and retainer. Use 2 screw drivers to pry retainer off case. Position screwdrivers in slots in retainer and case to pry retainer loose.

3) Remove differential shims and speedometer gear from rear output shaft. Remove bolts attaching rear case to front case. Remove rear case from front case by prying with screwdriver. See Fig. 4.

CAUTION: Insert screwdrivers in the slots at each end of the rear case to loosen it. Do not attempt to wedge the case halves apart. The case mating surfaces will be damaged.

4) Remove thrust bearing and races from front output shaft. Note position of bearing and races for assembly reference. See Fig. 5. Remove oil pump from rear output shaft. Note that the recessed side of the pump faces case interior. Remove rear output shaft from the viscous coupling.

Fig. 5: Thrust Bearing and Races on Front Output Shaft

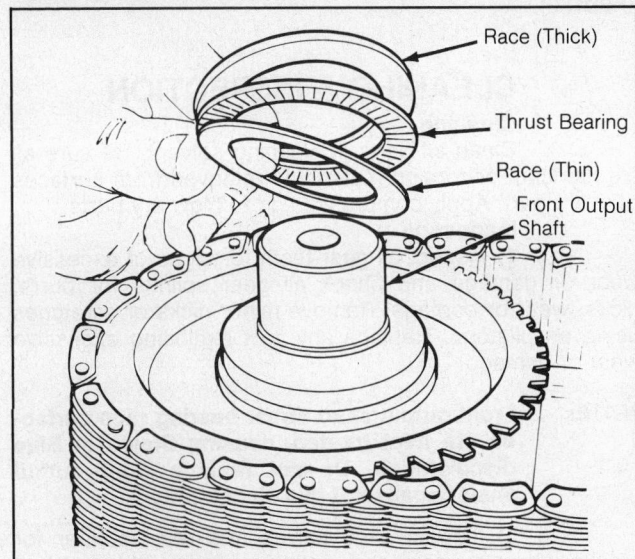

Note position of races when removing.

5) Remove 15 mainshaft pilot bearing rollers from shaft or coupling if rollers dropped off during removal of rear output shaft. Remove mainshaft "O" ring from end of shaft. Remove viscous coupling from mainshaft and side gear.

6) Remove front output shaft, driven sprocket and drive chain assembly. Lift front shaft, sprocket and chain upward. See Fig. 6. Tilt front shaft toward mainshaft. Slide chain off sprocket and remove assembly. Remove front output shaft front thrust bearing assembly from front case. Remove thrust bearing from shaft, if bearing and races remained on shaft during removal.

7) Remove drive chain from front output shaft and sprocket. Remove snap ring that retains driven sprocket on front output shaft. Mark sprocket and shaft for assembly reference and remove sprocket from shaft. Remove mainshaft, side gear, clutch gear drive sprocket and spline gear as assembly. Set aside until front case disassembly is completed.

8) Remove mode fork, shift rail and clutch sleeve as an assembly. Mark sleeve and fork for assembly reference and remove sleeve from fork. Remove locking fork, clutch sleeve, fork brackets and fork springs as

Fig. 6: Removing Front Output Shaft, Chain and Driven Sprocket

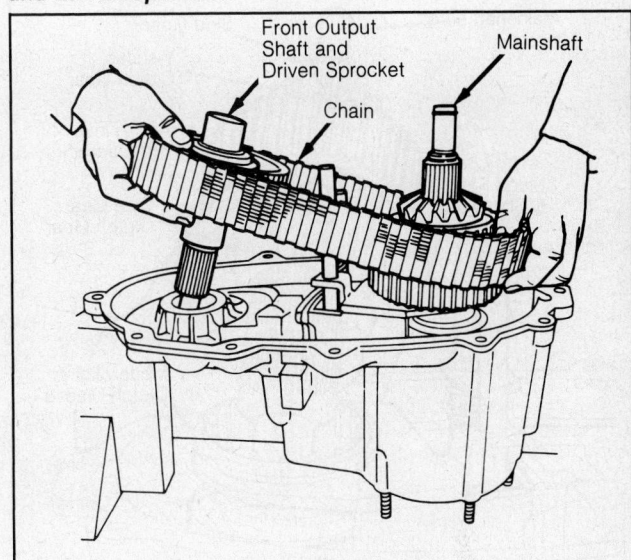

Slide chain off sprocket and remove assembly.

assembly. Note position of components for reassembly. Disassemble components for cleaning and inspection.

9) Remove range selector detent screw and remove detent spring, plunger and ball. See Fig. 7. Move range operating lever downward to last detent position. Disengage low range fork lug from range sector slot. Remove planetary assembly by grasping hub and lifting it upward.

Fig. 7: Removing Detent Ball, Spring, Retainer and Screw

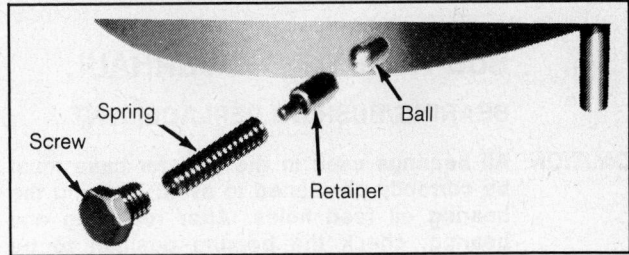

Note order for reassembly.

10) Remove mainshaft thrust bearing from input gear. Remove input gear and remove input gear thrust bearing and race. Remove range sector and operating lever attaching nut and lock washer and remove lever. Remove range sector and shaft from front case. Remove range sector "O" ring and retainer.

11) Remove rear output bearing and rear yoke seal from rear retainer. The bearing is shielded on one side. Note bearing position for reassembly. Remove input gear and front yoke seals from front case. Use screwdriver to pry seals out of case.

MAINSHAFT & GEARS

1) Grasp drive sprocket and lift sprocket clutch gear and side gear upward and off mainshaft. See Fig. 8. Remove mainshaft needle bearings and 2 bearing spacers from mainshaft. A total of 82 bearings are used. Note spacer position for reassembly.

SELEC-TRAC MODEL 229 (Cont.)

Fig. 8: Removing Mainshaft and Gear Assembly

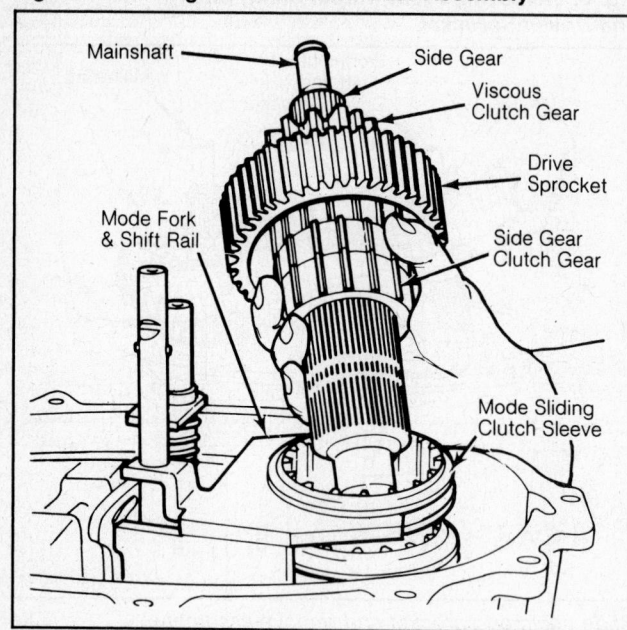

Note order for reassembly.

2) Remove spline gear and thrust washer from mainshaft. Remove side gear, clutch gear and clutch gear thrust washer from sprocket carrier and sprocket. Remove clutch gear and thrust washer from side gear.

3) Remove one sprocket carrier snap ring and remove drive sprocket from carrier. Mark for assembly references. Remove 3 bearing spacers and all sprocket carrier needle bearings from carrier. A total of 120 needle bearings are used.

SUB-ASSEMBLY OVERHAUL

BEARING/BUSHING REPLACEMENT

CAUTION: All bearings used in the transfer case must be correctly positioned to avoid blocking the bearing oil feed holes. After replacing any bearing, check the bearing position to be sure the feed hole is not covered by the bearing.

Rear Output Shaft Bearing
1) Remove bearing using slide hammer and bearing remover (J-26941). Remove rear output lip seal using a small screwdriver.
2) Install new lip seal. Install new bearing using driver J-29166. After bearing installation, check that bearing does not cover oil feed hole.

Front Output Shaft Front Bearing
Drive front output shaft front bearing out of case using driver (J-29168). Install bearing using same tool, check that bearing does not cover oil passage.

Front Output Shaft Rear Bearing
1) Support front case so that it will not be damaged. Using slide hammer and puller (J-26941), remove front output shaft rear bearing.
2) Install new bearing using driver (J-29163). Remove installer tool and check that bearing does not block oil passage.

Input Gear Front/Rear Bearing
1) Remove both bearings simultaneously using driver (J-29169). Install new bearings one at a time, rear bearing first. Use same tool for installation.
2) Remove bearing installer and check that bearing does not block oil passage. Check that bearings are flush with case. Install new oil seal using seal installer (J-29162).

Mainshaft Pilot Bushing
1) After carefully supporting input gear to prevent damage, remove bushing using slide hammer and remover tool (J-29369-1).
2) Install new bushing using driver (J-29174). Check that bushing is clear of oil passage.

Rear Output Bearing & Rear Yoke Seal
1) Remove bearing using brass drift and hammer. Remove seal from retainer using brass drift and hammer.
2) Install new bearing using driver (J-7818). Install bearing so that shielded side is facing the case interior after installation. Install seal in retainer using driver (J-29162).

CLEANING & INSPECTION

Cleaning
Clean all parts in cleaning solvent. Be sure all old lubricant or foreign material is removed from surfaces of every part. Apply compressed air to blow dry parts.

Inspection
1) Inspect all gear teeth for signs of excessive wear or damage and check all gear splines for burrs, nicks, wear or damage. Remove minor nicks or scratches using an oilstone. Replace any part exhibiting excessive wear or damage.

NOTE: **Front output shaft thrust bearing race surfaces are heat treated, causing Brown or Blue discoloration. Do not replace front output shaft because of this discoloration.**

2) Inspect case halves and rear retainer for cracks, porosity, damaged mating surfaces, stripped bolt threads or distortion.
3) Inspect the condition of all bearings. Also check the condition of all bearing bores. Replace any part that exhibits signs of wear or damage.
4) Inspect the viscous coupling and differential drive pinions. If the pinions or carrier are damaged or worn excessively, replace the coupling as an assembly only. If the coupling is cracked, leaking or damaged, replace the coupling as an assembly only.

REASSEMBLY

TRANSFER CASE

NOTE: **During assembly, prelubricate all transfer case internal components with Jeep Dexron II automatic transmission fluid or petroleum jelly where indicated. Do not use chassis lubricant or other "heavy" grease.**

1) Install new input gear and rear output shaft bearing oil seals. Seat seals flush with edge of seal bore

SELEC-TRAC MODEL 229 (Cont.)

or in groove in case. Coat seal lips with petroleum jelly after installation. Install input gear thrust bearing race in case counterbore.

    2) Install input gear thrust bearing on input gear and install gear and bearing in case. *See Fig. 9.* Install mainshaft thrust bearing in bearing recess in input gear. Install planetary assembly on input gear. Be sure planetary pinion teeth mesh fully with input gear. Install planetary thrust washer on planetary hub. *See Fig. 10.*

Fig. 9: Installing Input Gear and Thrust Bearing in Centerbore

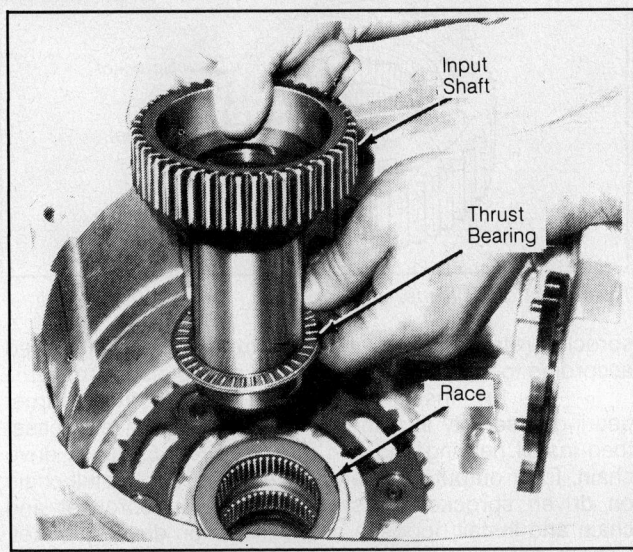

Install gear and bearing as an assembly.

    3) Install new sector shaft "O" ring and install retainer in shaft bore in case. Install "O" ring on mode sector shaft and install mode sector through range sector. Install range sector in front case. Install operating lever and snap ring on range sector shaft.

Fig. 10: Installing Planetary Gear Assembly

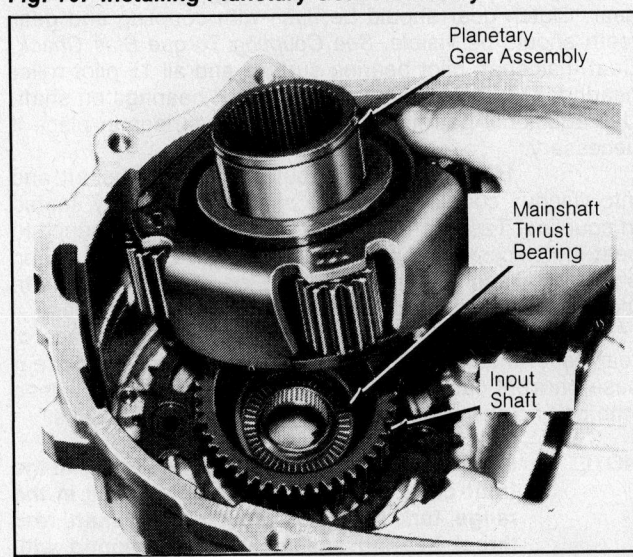

Be sure planetary pinion teeth mesh fully with input gear.

    4) Install lever attaching washer and lock nut on mode sector shaft. Tighten lock nut to specified torque. Assemble annulus gear, range fork, and rail. *See Fig. 11.*

Install assembled fork on and over planetary assembly. Be sure annulus gear is fully meshed with planetary pinions. Install annulus thrust washer and annulus retaining ring on annulus gear hub.

Fig. 11: Installing Annulus Gear Assembly, Range Rail and Fork

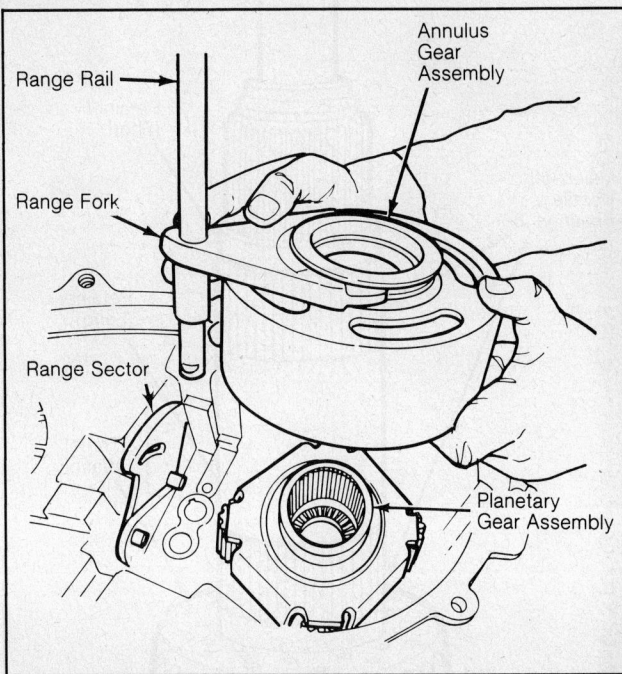

Be sure annulus gear is fully meshed with planetary pinions.

    5) Install detent spring plunger ball and retainer screw in front case detent bore. *See Fig. 7.* Torque bolt to specifications. Assemble and install locking fork, fork brackets, fork springs and clutch sleeve. Be sure lug on fork is seated in range sector detent slot.

    6) Install range fork lug in range sector detent notch. Move range sector to high range position. Assemble and install mode fork, shift rail and mode clutch sleeve. Install thrust washer and new "O" ring on mainshaft.

    7) Install needle bearings and bearing spacers on mainshaft. *See Fig. 12.* Coat shaft bearing surface and all needle bearings with petroleum jelly. Install first 41 needle bearings. Install long bearing spacer, remaining 41 needle bearings and remaining short spacer. Be careful to avoid displacing bearings as spacers are installed. Use additional petroleum jelly to hold bearings in place if necessary.

    8) Install spline gear on mainshaft. Take care to avoid displacing bearings while installing gear. Install sprocket carrier in drive sprocket and install sprocket carrier snap rings. Be sure to align carrier and sprocket according to reference marks made during disassembly. Be sure that the tapered teeth on the drive sprocket carrier and the recess on the sprocket are on the same side.

    9) Install sprocket carrier bearings and spacers. Coat carrier bore and all 120 carrier needle bearings with petroleum jelly. Install center spacer. Install 60 bearings in each end of carrier and install remaining 2

SELEC-TRAC MODEL 229 (Cont.)

Fig. 12: *Installing Needle Bearings and Spacers on Mainshaft*

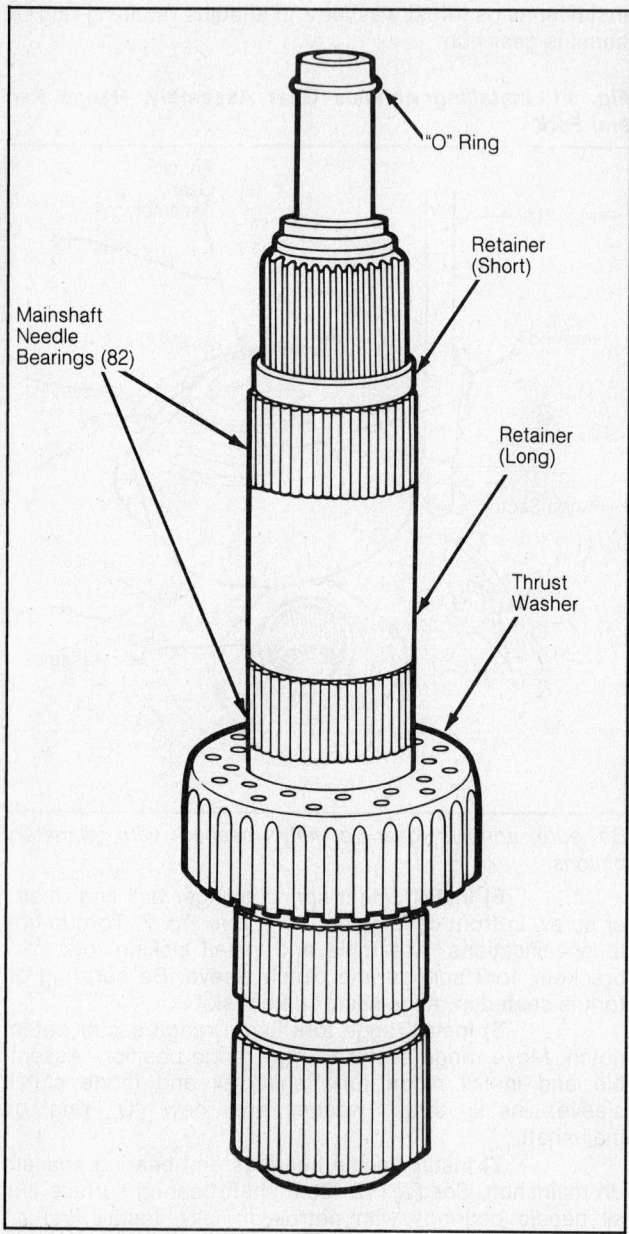

Use new "O" ring.

Fig. 13: *Installing Side Gear on Clutch Gear*

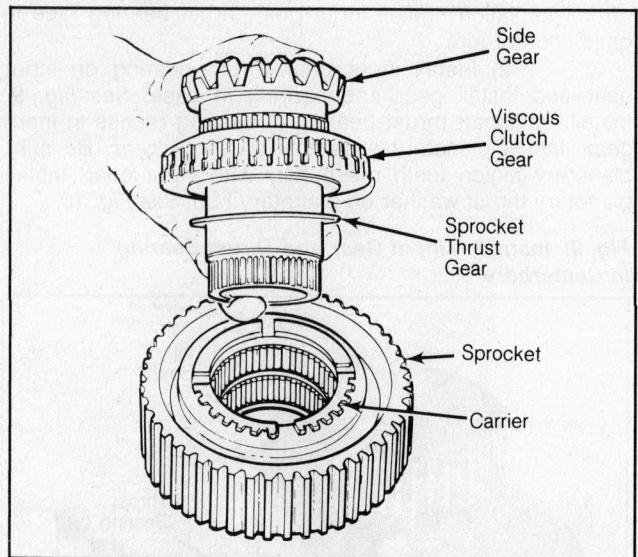

Note position of thrust washer.

spacers, one at each side of carrier. Use additional petroleum jelly to hold bearings in place if necessary.

10) Install assembled sprocket carrier and drive sprocket on mainshaft. Do not displace mainshaft bearings during installation. Be sure recessed side of drive sprocket is facing downward. Install clutch gear thrust washer in mainshaft. Position washer on sprocket carrier.

11) Install clutch gear on side gear. *See Fig. 13.* Be sure tapered edge of clutch gear faces side gear teeth. Install assembled side gear and clutch gear on mainshaft. Be sure side gear is fully seated in sprocket carrier. Take care to avoid displacing any of the carrier or mainshaft needle bearings.

12) Install mainshaft and gear assembly in case. Be sure mainshaft is fully seated in input gear. Install driven sprocket on front output shaft and install

sprocket retaining snap ring. Be sure sprocket is installed according to reference marks made during disassembly.

13) Install front output shaft front thrust bearing assembly in front case. Install thick race in case, then install bearing and thin race. *See Fig. 5.* Install drive chain, front output shaft and driven sprocket. Install chain on driven sprocket. Raise and tilt driven sprocket and chain and install opposite end of chain on drive sprocket. *See Fig. 6.*

14) Align front output shaft with shaft bore in front case and install shaft in case. Be sure front shaft thrust bearing assembly is seated in case. Install front output shaft rear thrust bearing assembly on front output shaft. Install thin race first; then install bearing and thick race. *See Fig. 5.*

15) Install viscous coupling on side gear and clutch gear. Be sure coupling is fully seated on clutch gear. Clutch gear should be flush with coupling and gear teeth should be visible. *See Coupling Torque Bias Check.* Coat mainshaft pilot bearing surface and all 15 pilot roller bearings with petroleum jelly and install bearings on shaft. Use additional petroleum jelly to hold bearings in place if necessary.

16) Install rear output shaft on mainshaft and into viscous coupling. Be sure shaft is completely seated in coupling. Tap shaft with plastic mallet or brass punch to seat it if necessary. Do not displace pilot bearings during shaft installation. Install oil pump on rear output shaft. Install new rear output shaft bearing oil seal in rear case.

17) Apply suitable sealer to mating surface of rear case. Install magnet in case, if removed. Install rear case on front case. Be sure alignment dowels are aligned with bolt holes in rear and seat rear case on front case.

NOTE: **If the rear case will not seat completely in the front case, check for the following: oil in the range fork rail bore, front output shaft rear thrust bearing assembly is not aligned with the rear case, mainshaft is not completely seated, rear case not aligned with oil pump.**

18) Install rear case-to-front bolts and torque to specifications. Be sure that flat washers are used on

SELEC-TRAC MODEL 229 (Cont.)

Fig. 14: Exploded View of Model 229 Transfer Case

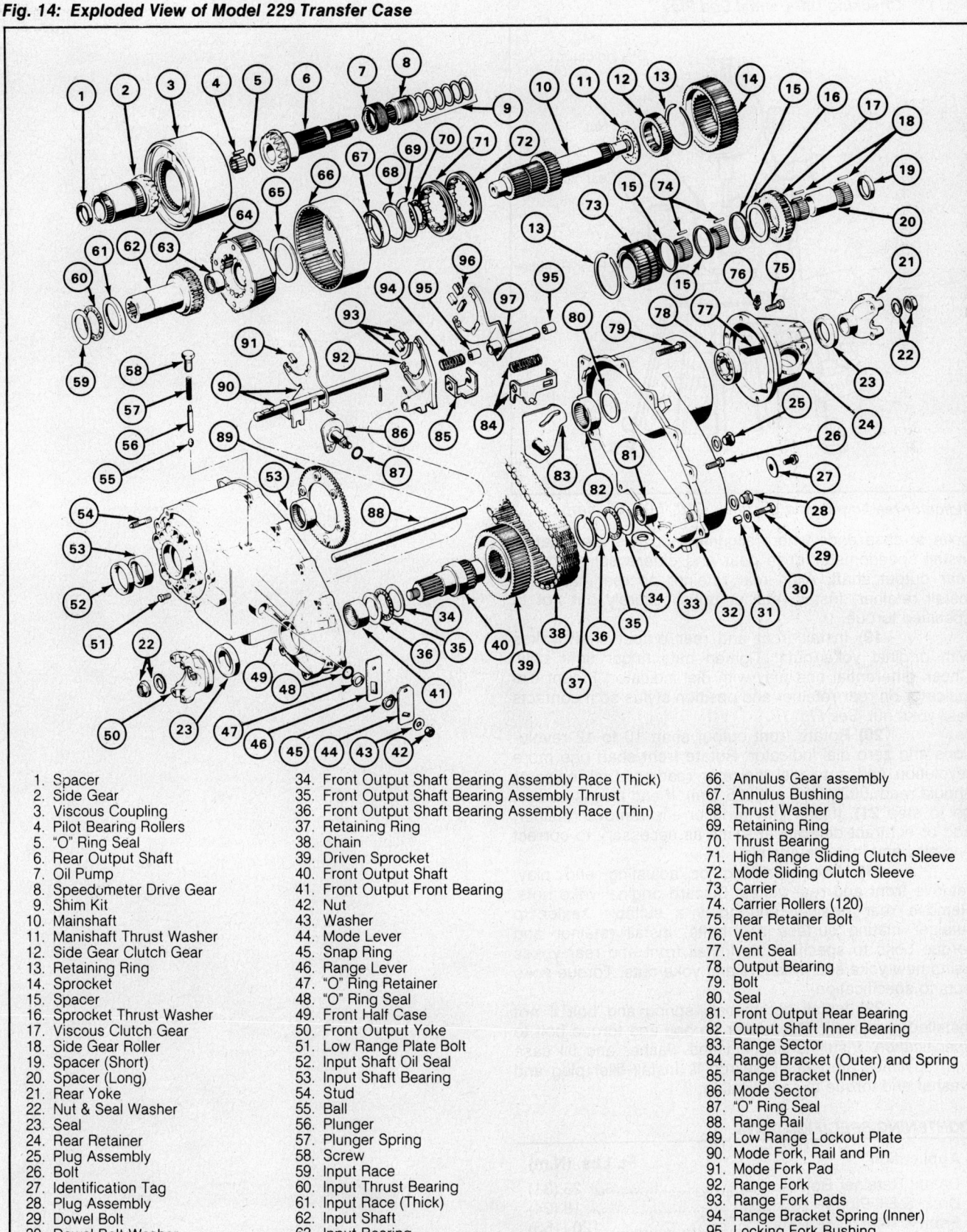

1. Spacer
2. Side Gear
3. Viscous Coupling
4. Pilot Bearing Rollers
5. "O" Ring Seal
6. Rear Output Shaft
7. Oil Pump
8. Speedometer Drive Gear
9. Shim Kit
10. Mainshaft
11. Manishaft Thrust Washer
12. Side Gear Clutch Gear
13. Retaining Ring
14. Sprocket
15. Spacer
16. Sprocket Thrust Washer
17. Viscous Clutch Gear
18. Side Gear Roller
19. Spacer (Short)
20. Spacer (Long)
21. Rear Yoke
22. Nut & Seal Washer
23. Seal
24. Rear Retainer
25. Plug Assembly
26. Bolt
27. Identification Tag
28. Plug Assembly
29. Dowel Bolt
30. Dowel Bolt Washer
31. Case Half Dowel
32. Rear Half Case
33. Magnet

34. Front Output Shaft Bearing Assembly Race (Thick)
35. Front Output Shaft Bearing Assembly Thrust
36. Front Output Shaft Bearing Assembly Race (Thin)
37. Retaining Ring
38. Chain
39. Driven Sprocket
40. Front Output Shaft
41. Front Output Front Bearing
42. Nut
43. Washer
44. Mode Lever
45. Snap Ring
46. Range Lever
47. "O" Ring Retainer
48. "O" Ring Seal
49. Front Half Case
50. Front Output Yoke
51. Low Range Plate Bolt
52. Input Shaft Oil Seal
53. Input Shaft Bearing
54. Stud
55. Ball
56. Plunger
57. Plunger Spring
58. Screw
59. Input Race
60. Input Thrust Bearing
61. Input Race (Thick)
62. Input Shaft
63. Input Bearing
64. Planetary Gear Assembly
65. Input Gear Thrust Washer

66. Annulus Gear assembly
67. Annulus Bushing
68. Thrust Washer
69. Retaining Ring
70. Thrust Bearing
71. High Range Sliding Clutch Sleeve
72. Mode Sliding Clutch Sleeve
73. Carrier
74. Carrier Rollers (120)
75. Rear Retainer Bolt
76. Vent
77. Vent Seal
78. Output Bearing
79. Bolt
80. Seal
81. Front Output Rear Bearing
82. Output Shaft Inner Bearing
83. Range Sector
84. Range Bracket (Outer) and Spring
85. Range Bracket (Inner)
86. Mode Sector
87. "O" Ring Seal
88. Range Rail
89. Low Range Lockout Plate
90. Mode Fork, Rail and Pin
91. Mode Fork Pad
92. Range Fork
93. Range Fork Pads
94. Range Bracket Spring (Inner)
95. Locking Fork Bushing
96. Locking Fork Pads
97. Locking Fork

Transfer Cases

SELEC-TRAC MODEL 229 (Cont.)

Fig. 15: *Checking Differential End Play*

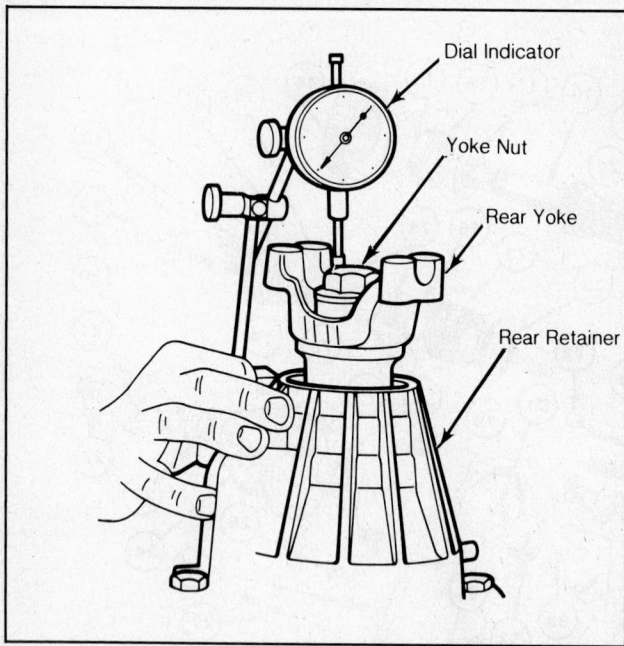

Dial Indicator

Yoke Nut

Rear Yoke

Rear Retainer

Indicator reading should be .002"-.010" (.05-.25 mm).

bolts at case ends where alignment dowels are located. Install speedometer drive gear and differential shims on rear output shaft. Align rear retainer on rear case and install retainer. Install retainer bolts securely but not to specified torque.

19) Install front and rear output shaft yokes with original yoke nuts. Tighten nuts finger tight only. Check differential end play with dial indicator. Mount dial indicator on rear retainer and position stylus so it contacts rear yoke nut. *See Fig. 15.*

20) Rotate front output shaft 10 to 12 revolutions and zero dial indicator. Rotate front shaft one more revolution and note dial indicator reading. Dial indicator should read .002"-.010" (.05-.25 mm). If end play is correct go to step **21)**. If end play is incorrect, remove retainer, add or subtract differential shims as necessary to correct end play and recheck end play.

21) After checking or adjusting end play, remove front and rear yokes. Discard original yoke nuts. Remove rear retainer and apply a suitable sealer to retainer mating surface and bolts. Install retainer and torque bolts to specification. Install front and rear yokes using new yoke seal washers and yoke nuts. Torque yoke nuts to specification

22) Install detent ball, spring and bolt if not installed previously. Use sealer on bolt and torque bolt to specification. Install drain plug and washer and fill case with specified amount of Dexron II. Install filler plug and washer and torque to specification.

TIGHTENING SPECIFICATIONS

Application	Ft. Lbs. (N.m)
Detent Retainer Bolt	23 (31)
Drain & Fill Plugs	18 (24)
Front & Rear Yoke Nuts	120 (163)
Operating Lever Lock Nut	18 (24)
Rear Case-to-Front Case Bolts	23 (31)
Rear Retainer Bolts	23 (31)

SPICER (DANA) MODEL 300

Jeep

DESCRIPTION

The Model 300 is a 4-position, dual range, part-time 4WD unit with integral low range. It provides 4-wheel undifferentiated high and low ranges, a Neutral position and 2-wheel high range. The 300 is used with both manual and automatic transmission applications. Locking front hubs are standard equipment.

LUBRICATION

SERVICE INTERVALS

Check fluid level every 5 months or 5000 miles and refill as necessary. Change fluid every 30 months or 30,000 miles.

FLUID TYPE

Use SAE 85W-90, API grade GL-5 gear lubricant.

CAPACITY

Refill capacity is 4.0 pints (1.9L).

REMOVAL & INSTALLATION

TRANSFER CASE
Removal

1) On models with manual transmission, remove shift lever knob, trim ring and boot from transmission and transfer case shift levers. Remove floor covering, if equipped, and remove transmission access cover. Raise vehicle and drain transfer case.

2) Support transmission and remove rear crossmember. Mark propeller shaft yokes for reassembly. Disconnect propeller shafts at transfer case. Disconnect speedometer cable at transfer case.

3) Disconnect parking brake cable at equalizer. Disconnect exhaust pipe support bracket at transfer case, if equipped. Remove bolts attaching transfer case to transmission. Remove transfer case.

Installation

1) Shift transfer case to "4L" position. Rotate transfer case output shaft by turning yoke until transmission output shaft engages transfer case input shaft. Move transfer case forward until case seats against transmission.

NOTE: **Do not install transfer case attaching bolts until case is completely seated against transmission as damage to transfer case will occur.**

2) Install transfer case attaching bolts and tighten. Install drain plug and refill case. Connect speedometer driven gear to case. Connect shift lever and control links to shift rods.

3) Align reassembly marks and connect propeller shafts to transfer case. Install rear crossmember and remove support. Install parking brake cable at equalizer and connect exhaust pipe support bracket at transfer case, if disconnected.

4) Lower vehicle and install transmission access cover and floor covering, if equipped. Install shift lever boot, trim ring, levers, and shift knob.

DISASSEMBLY

TRANSFER CASE

1) Remove shift lever assembly. Remove bottom cover, using a putty knife to break seal. Use Puller (J-8614-01) to remove front and rear yokes, discard lock nuts.

2) Remove screws attaching input shaft support to case. Remove support, rear output shaft gear and input shaft as an assembly, using a putty knife to break seal. See Fig. 1.

Fig. 1: Rear Output Shaft Gear & Input Assembly

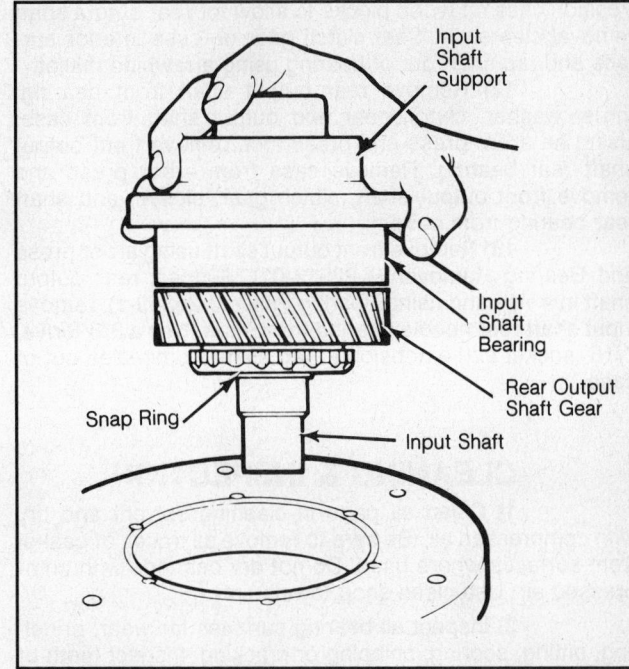

Input Shaft Support

Input Shaft Bearing

Rear Output Shaft Gear

Snap Ring

Input Shaft

Loosen support using a putty knife.

3) Remove rear output shaft clutch sleeve from case. Remove and discard snap ring holding rear output shaft gear on input shaft. Remove gear. Remove and discard input shaft bearing snap ring.

4) Remove input shaft and bearing from support using a plastic mallet to tap shaft loose. Remove bearing and shims from input shaft using an arbor press. Remove and discard seal from input shaft support. Remove intermediate shaft lock plate bolt and lock plate.

5) Tap intermediate shaft out of case using a brass punch and plastic mallet. Remove and discard intermediate shaft seal. Remove thrust washers and intermediate gear assembly. Note location of tabs on thrust washers for reassembly.

6) Remove 48 needle bearings and 3 bearing spacers from intermediate gear. Remove rear bearing cap bolts. Remove rear bearing cap using a putty knife to break seal and a plastic mallet to tap output shaft loose. Remove end play shims and speedometer drive gear from rear output shaft.

7) Remove and discard rear output shaft oil seal. Remove bearings and races from rear bearing cap. Remove set screws retaining front and rear output shaft shift forks from shift rods.

8) Using a punch, inserted in pin holes in rods, rotate rods to remove them from case. Take care not to lose poppet balls and springs. Remove shift forks from case.

9) Remove bolts attaching front bearing cap-to-case. Remove front cap using a putty knife to break seal. Remove front output shaft from front cap. Remove and discard shift rod oil seals from front cap.

10) Remove bearing race from front cap using Bearing Remover (J-29168) and Driver (J-8092). Remove cover plate and shims from case. Keep shims together for reassembly. Move front output shaft toward front of case and remove rear bearing race from case.

11) Remove rear output shaft front bearing. Position case on wood blocks to allow for rear output shaft removal clearance. Seat clutch gear on case interior surface and tap shaft out of bearing using a rawhide mallet.

12) Remove rear output shaft front bearing, thrust washer, clutch gear and output shaft from case. Using an arbor press and press tool, remove front output shaft rear bearing. Remove case from arbor press and remove front output shaft, clutch gear, sleeve, and shaft rear bearing from case.

13) Remove front output shaft using arbor press and Bearing Remover (J-22912-01). Support rear output shaft in a vise and using Bearing Puller (J-29369-1), remove input shaft rear needle bearing from shaft. Use a 3/8" drive, 7/16" socket and extension to tap shift rod thimbles out of case.

CLEANING & INSPECTION

1) Clean all parts in cleaning solvent and dry with compressed air. Be sure to remove all traces of gasket from surfaces where used. Do not dry bearings with compressed air. Use clean shop towels only.

2) Inspect all bearing surfaces for wear, brinelling, pitting, scoring, chipping or cracking. Inspect teeth of all gears for excessive wear or damage. Replace as necessary.

3) Replace any shaft that has damaged splines, threads or bearing surfaces. Check shift rods and rod bores for wear or damage. Minor scratches or nicks on rods may be cleaned with crocus clotch. Replace as necessary.

REASSEMBLY

TRANSFER CASE

1) Apply sealant (Loctite 220) to shift rod thimbles and install parts. Install front output shaft gear on front output shaft. Make sure that gear clutch teeth face shaft gear teeth.

2) Install front bearing on front output shaft using arbor press and press tool. *See Fig. 2.* Make sure bearing is seated against gear. Install front output shaft in case and install clutch sleeve and gear on shaft.

3) Install front output shaft rear bearing using arbor press and press tool. Install input shaft rear needle bearing in rear output shaft using bearing installer.

4) Position rear output shaft clutch gear in case and insert rear output shaft into gear. Install thrust washer and front bearing on rear output shaft. Install shims and bearing on input shaft. Use arbor press and press tool to install parts.

Fig. 2: Installing Front Output Shaft Rear Bearing

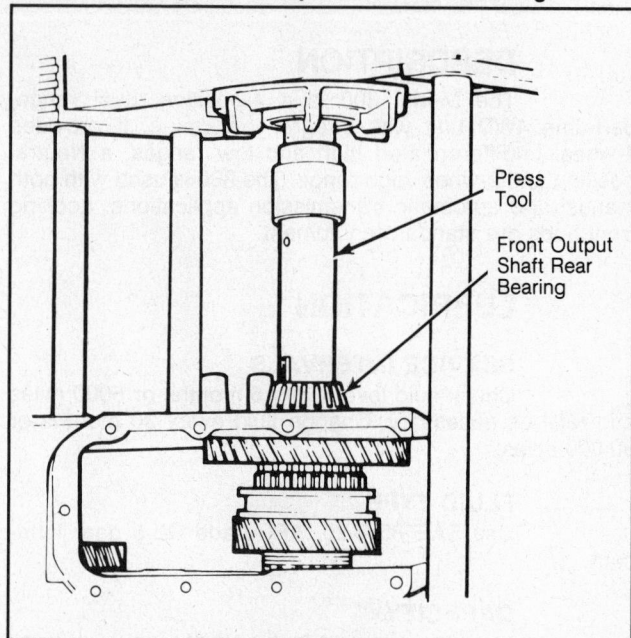

Press Tool

Front Output Shaft Rear Bearing

Be sure bearing is seated against gear.

5) Install new oil seal in input shaft support using Seal Installer (J-29184). Install input shaft, bearing and new snap ring in support. Install rear output shaft gear and new snap ring on input gear.

6) Measure clearance between input gear and gear retaining snap ring using a feeler gauge. If clearance exceeds 0.003" (0.076 mm), disassemble input shaft and add shims between input shaft and shaft bearing until proper measurement is obtained.

7) Install clutch sleeve on rear output shaft. Apply sealant to mating surface of input shaft support. Install assembled support, shaft, and gear in case. Using 2 support bolts to align support on case, tap support into position with a plastic mallet.

8) Install and tighten support socket head screws. Install rear bearing cap front bearing race using Bearing Installer (J-9276-3) and Driver (J-8092). Install rear bearing cap rear bearing race using Bearing Installer (J-29182) and driver.

9) Position rear output shaft rear bearing in rear bearing cap. Install rear output shaft yoke oil seal using Seal Installer (J-25160). Install speedometer gear and end play shims on rear output shaft. Install rear bearing cap.

10) Apply sealant to mating surface of rear bearing cap. Align bolt holes with 2 cap bolts and tap rear bearing cap into position using a plastic mallet. Tighten cap bolts.

11) Install rear output shaft yoke. Tighten yoke nut while holding yoke with Holder (J-8614-01). Clamp dial indicator onto bearing cap. Position indicator stylus so it contacts end of shaft. *See Fig. 4.*

12) Pry rear output shaft back and forth to check end play. End play should be 0.001-0.005" (0.025-0.127 mm). If end play is not correct, remove or add shims between speedometer drive gear and output shaft rear bearing.

13) Install front output shaft rear bearing race. Install front output shaft end, shims and cover plate. Apply

Transfer Cases

SPICER (DANA) MODEL 300 (Cont.)

Fig. 3: Exploded View of Model 300 Transfer Case

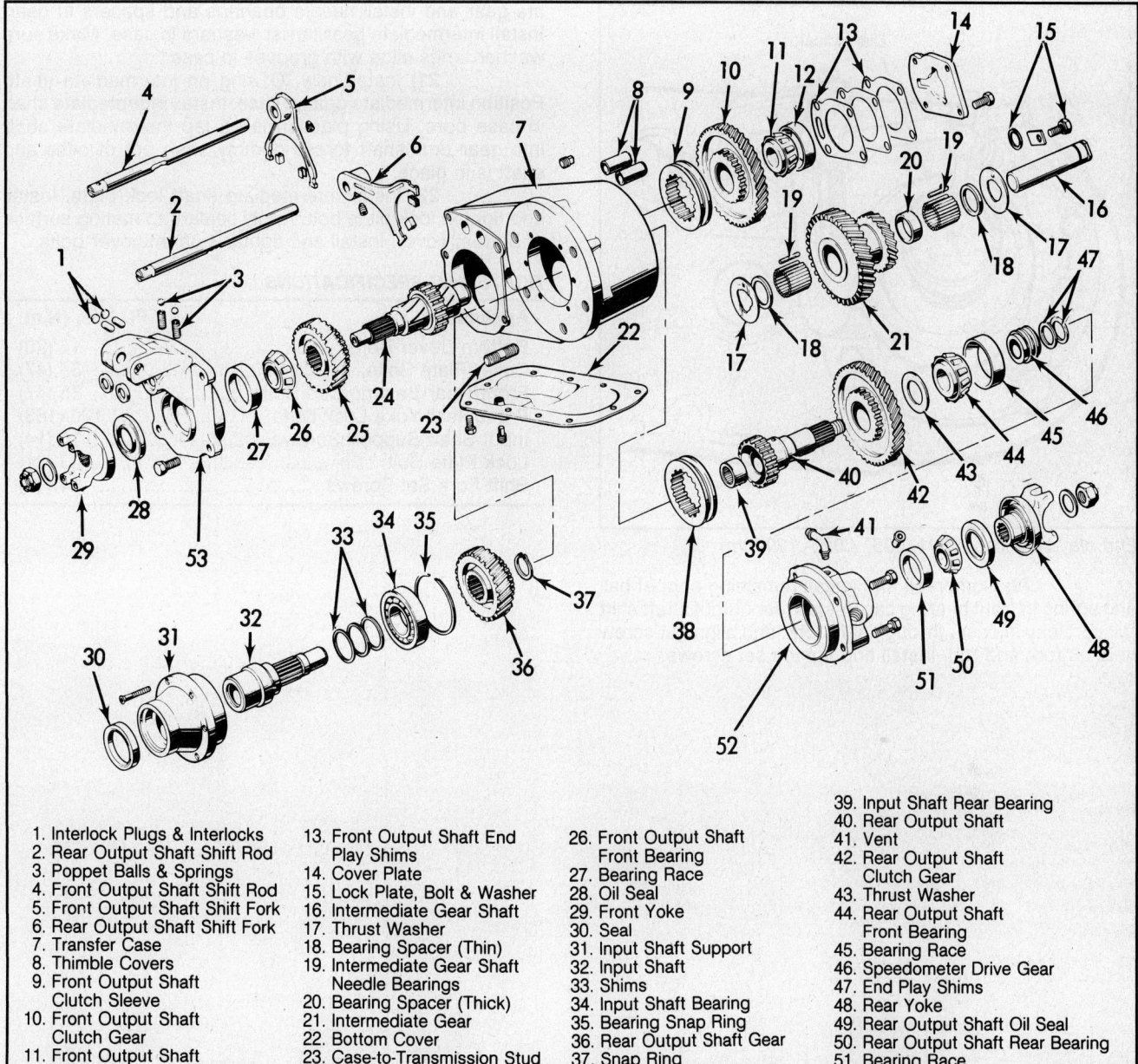

1. Interlock Plugs & Interlocks
2. Rear Output Shaft Shift Rod
3. Poppet Balls & Springs
4. Front Output Shaft Shift Rod
5. Front Output Shaft Shift Fork
6. Rear Output Shaft Shift Fork
7. Transfer Case
8. Thimble Covers
9. Front Output Shaft Clutch Sleeve
10. Front Output Shaft Clutch Gear
11. Front Output Shaft Rear Bearing
12. Bearing Race
13. Front Output Shaft End Play Shims
14. Cover Plate
15. Lock Plate, Bolt & Washer
16. Intermediate Gear Shaft
17. Thrust Washer
18. Bearing Spacer (Thin)
19. Intermediate Gear Shaft Needle Bearings
20. Bearing Spacer (Thick)
21. Intermediate Gear
22. Bottom Cover
23. Case-to-Transmission Stud
24. Front Output Shaft
25. Front Output Shaft Gear
26. Front Output Shaft Front Bearing
27. Bearing Race
28. Oil Seal
29. Front Yoke
30. Seal
31. Input Shaft Support
32. Input Shaft
33. Shims
34. Input Shaft Bearing
35. Bearing Snap Ring
36. Rear Output Shaft Gear
37. Snap Ring
38. Rear Output Shaft Clutch Sleeve
39. Input Shaft Rear Bearing
40. Rear Output Shaft
41. Vent
42. Rear Output Shaft Clutch Gear
43. Thrust Washer
44. Rear Output Shaft Front Bearing
45. Bearing Race
46. Speedometer Drive Gear
47. End Play Shims
48. Rear Yoke
49. Rear Output Shaft Oil Seal
50. Rear Output Shaft Rear Bearing
51. Bearing Race
52. Rear Bearing Cap
53. Front Bearing Cap

sealant (Loctite 220) to cover plate bolt threads and install bolts. Install front output shaft front bearing race using Bearing Installer (J-29181) and Driver (J-8092).

14) Install front output shaft yoke oil seal using Seal Installer (J-25160). Install shift rod oil seals using Seal Installer (J-25167). Install front bearing cap. Apply sealant to mating surface of front bearing cap. Use 2 bolts to align cap with case bolt holes and tap front bearing cap into position.

15) Install and tighten bearing cap bolts. Seat rear bearing cup against cover plate by tapping end of front output shaft with plastic mallet. Mount dial indicator on front bearing cap and postion indicator stylus against end of output shaft.

16) Pry front output shaft back and forth to check end play. End play should be 0.001-0.005" (0.025-0.127 mm). If end play is not correct, remove or add shims between cover plate and case. If shims are added, reseat rear bearing cup before checking end play again.

17) Install front output shaft yoke. Install new lock nut. Tighten yoke nut while holding yoke. Insert front and rear output shaft shift forks into case. Install front output shaft shift rod poppet ball and spring in front bearing cap.

18) Compress poppet ball and spring. Install front output shaft shift rod part way in case. Insert shift rod through shift fork. Align set screw hole in shift fork and rod. Install and tighten set screw.

Fig. 4: Checking Rear Output Shaft End Play

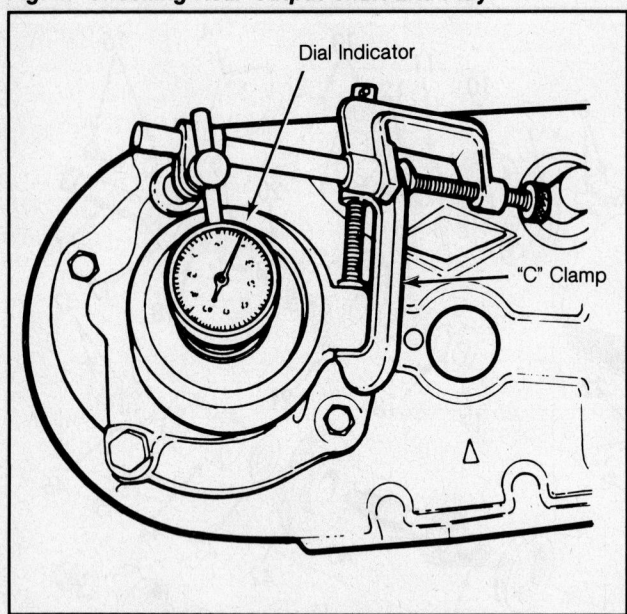

End play should be .001-.005" (.025-.129 mm).

19) Compress and install remaining poppet ball and spring in front bearing cap. Install rear output shaft shift rail part way in case, through shift fork, and align set screw hole on fork and rod. Install and tighten set screws.

20) Insert Dummy Shaft (J-25142) in intermediate gear and install needle bearings and spacers in gear. Install intermediate gear thrust washers in case. Make sure washer tangs align with grooves in case.

21) Install new "O" ring on intermediate shaft. Position intermediate gear in case. Install intermediate shaft in case bore. Using plastic mallet, tap intermediate shaft into gear until shaft forces dummy shaft out of case and shaft is in place.

22) Install intermediate shaft lock plate. Install and tighten lock plate bolt. Apply sealant to mating surface of bottom cover. Install and tighten bottom cover bolts.

TIGHTENING SPECIFICATIONS

Application	Ft. Lbs. (N.m)
Bottom Cover Bolts	15 (20)
Cover Plate Bolts	35 (47)
Front/Rear Bearing Cap Bolts	35 (47)
Front/Rear Yoke Lock Nuts	120 (163)
Input Shaft Support Screws	10 (14)
Lock Plate Bolt	23 (31)
Shift Fork Set Screws	14 (19)

FOR 1985 & EARLIER DOMESTIC MODELS

NOTE: The Latest Changes and Corrections represent a collection of the last minute 1985 information which arrived too late to be included into the regular data pages. In addition, we have included information on prior year models which we have received since last year's edition.

This information is numbered to assist you in relating them to the regular data pages. To correctly use them, simply write the corresponding number within the small box and the year of the edition on the appropriate page(s) of the text.

AUTOMATIC TRANSMISSIONS

AMC/RENAULT

1⟩ *1984 MB1 AUTOMATIC TRANSAXLE: INCORRECT TESTING PROCEDURE* – In the 1984 edition of Mitchell's TRANSMISSION SERVICE & REPAIR MANUAL, the MB1 automatic transaxle testing procedure should be corrected. Under ELECTRONIC CONTROL COMPONENT TESTING (6-Way Connector), step **2)** should read:

2) Connect voltmeter between terminal "A" and ground. With ignition "ON", voltage should be 10-14 volts. If not, check back-up light fuse and accessory plate wiring. Repair as needed.

CHRYSLER CORP.

2⟩ *1984 ARIES, E-CLASS, LEBARON, NEW YORKER, RELIANT AND 600 MODELS WITH 2.6L ENGINE AND A-470 TRANSAXLE: GRINDING NOISE AND/OR FAILURE OF FRONT PUMP AND TORQUE CONVERTER* – Some Chrysler products with 2.6L engine and A-470 transaxle may exhibit a grinding noise and/or failure of the front pump and torque converter. This condition may be caused by an undersized torque converter-to-crankshaft adapter. A new adapter (MD024893) is available to correct this condition. To diagnose and repair this problem, proceed as follows:

1) Remove the transaxle and torque converter. Measure the inside diameter of torque converter-to-crankshaft adapter. The inside diameter should not be smaller than 1.34" (34 mm). Inspect the torque converter pilot for wear. Disassemble the front pump and inspect for worn pump gears.

2) Replace the adapter with a new adapter if less than the minimum size. Replace the torque converter or front pump if necessary.

3⟩ *1983-84 ARIES, CARAVAN, "E" CLASS, LEBARON, MINI RAM VAN, NEW YORKER, RELIANT, VOYAGER, 400 AND 600 WITH AUTOMATIC TRANSAXLE: NO MANUAL 1ST GEAR OPERATION* – These Chrysler products with a column shift may not have 1st gear operation due to a misadjusted gear selector cable. Condition may diagnosed and repaired as follows:

1) Place gear selector in "DRIVE 1" position. Accelerate vehicle to about 45 MPH. If transaxle shifts from 1st to 2nd gear, readjust selector cable.

2) Loosen the cable housing clamp. Grasp the cable housing and move it to rear 1/8". Retighten cable housing clamp.

FORD MOTOR CO.

4⟩ *1980-84 FORD AOD TRANSMISSIONS: 2-3 MODULATOR VALVE ASSEMBLY* – Due to an error in the factory service manual, the exploded view of the valve body in the 1980 through 1984 editions of Mitchell's TRANSMISSION SERVICE & REPAIR manual are incorrect. The 2-3 modulator valve and spring positions are reversed. The modulator spring should be installed in the valve body BEFORE the modulator valve. The illustration has been corrected for the 1985 edition.

5⟩ *1981-83 ESCORT, EXP, LYNX AND LN7 WITH ATX TRANSAXLES: REVISED CLUTCH SNAP RING* – Selective retainer snap rings are no longer required for the reverse clutch assembly. During overhaul or other service procedures, use the revised retainer snap ring (E1FFZ-7D483-G). When assembling the clutch pack, install the reverse clutch return spring and holder assembly. Install the clutch wave spring, clutch pack, pressure plate and REVISED retaining snap ring.

6⟩ *1981-84 ESCORT, EXP, LYNX, LN7, TEMPO AND TOPAZ WITH ATX TRANSAXLES: NEW FINAL GEAR HOUSING BOLTS* – When servicing 1981-84 Ford products with the ATX transaxle, always use new revised final gear housing bolts. The new design bolts (E4FZ-7A291-A) are now available. These bolts are coated with a high strength thread adhesive. Always use new bolts when servicing the final gear housing.

7⟩ *1981-84 ESCORT, LINX, EXP, LYNX, LN7, TEMPO AND TOPAZ WITH ATX TRANSAXLE: REVISED DIRECT CLUTCH SEALS* – Revised direct clutch seals are available for 1981-84 ATX automatic transaxles. The new design inner seal (E55FZ-7A548-A) and outer seal (E55FZ-7C099-A) may be identified by a short lip as shown in illustration.

1981-84 Ford ATX Transaxle Direct Clutch Seals

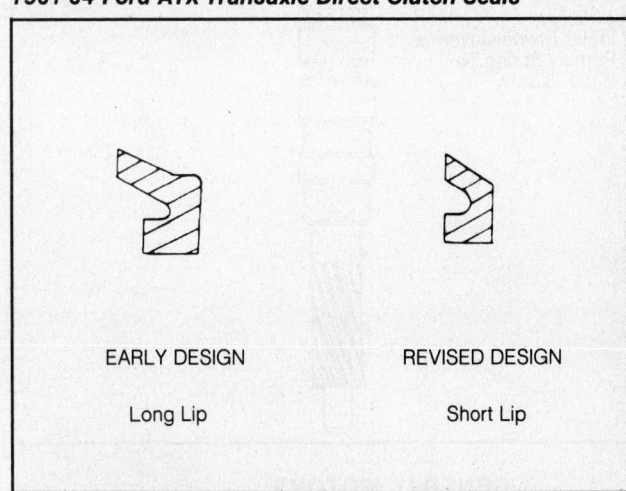

EARLY DESIGN
Long Lip

REVISED DESIGN
Short Lip

8⟩ *1983-84 FORD CAPRI, COUGAR, LTD, MARQUIS, MUSTANG AND THUNDERBIRD WITH C-5 TRANSMISSION: SENSITIVE 3-2 DOWNSHIFT* – Some Ford C-5 transmissions in 1983-84 may exhibit a sensitive 3-2 downshift. This condition may be caused by the throttle

Latest Changes & Corrections

FOR 1985 & EARLIER DOMESTIC MODELS (Cont.)

pressure booster spring. A new design spring (LE4ZZ-7A331-A) is now available to correct this condition. To repair, proceed as follows:

    1) Remove transmission oil pan. Remove main control valve body. Inspect the throttle pressure booster spring coils for either a Red or no color.

    2) If present, remove throttle pressure booster valve retainer, valve and spring. Replace throttle pressure booster valve spring with the new design (Blue color) spring. Reassemble transmission.

9 *1984 FORD C-5 TRANSMISSION: INCORRECT REVERSE-HIGH CLUTCH ILLUSTRATION* – In the 1984 edition of Mitchell's TRANSMISSION SERVICE & REPAIR manual, Fig. 12 of the Ford C-5 transmission article is incorrect. There should be a disc spring installed between the pressure plate and large snap ring.

10 *1984 FORD TEMPO AND TOPAZ WITH AUTOMATIC TRANSAXLES: TRANSAXLE HUNTING BETWEEN 2-3 OR 3-2 SHIFT AT 24 MPH* – Some 1984 Tempo and Topaz models with automatic transaxle may exhibit a hunting condition between 2-3 or 3-2 gears on light throttle operation around 24 MPH. This condition may be corrected by installating a Brown primary spring (E43Z-7E467-A). To repair transaxle, remove governor assembly. Remove Pink governor primary spring and replace with new Brown primary spring.

1984 Tempo & Topaz Governor Assembly

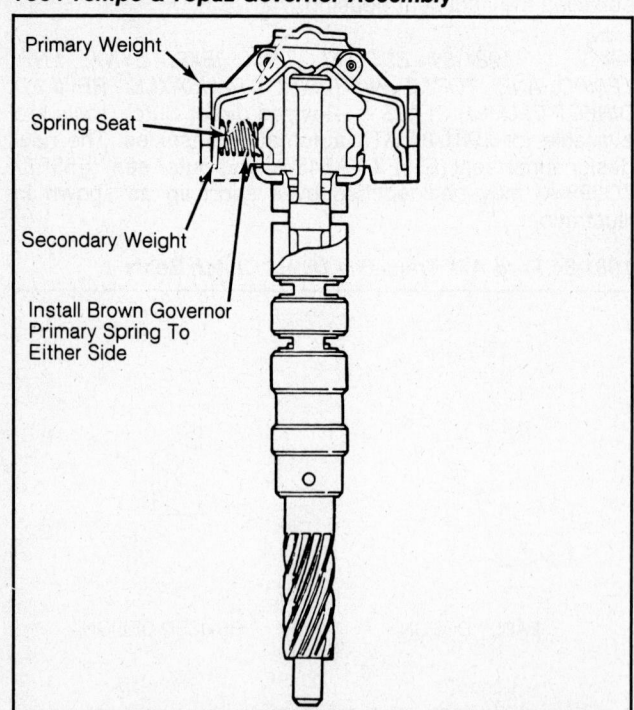

Primary Weight

Spring Seat

Secondary Weight

Install Brown Governor Primary Spring To Either Side

GENERAL MOTORS

11 *1983 CAVALIER, CELEBRITY, CENTURY, CIMARRON, CITATION, CUTLASS CIERA, FIRENZA, OMEGA, PHOENIX, SKYHAWK, SKYLARK, 2000 AND 6000 WITH THM 125C AUTOMATIC TRANSAXLE: INTERMITTENT 2ND GEAR STARTS* – Some General Motors vehicles with the 125C automatic transaxle may exhibit a condition where the transmission starts out in 2nd gear. To correct this

condition, remove the transaxle from the vehicle. Remove governor assembly. Remove the primary spring from the governor assembly. Assemble transaxle and install in vehicle.

1983 General Motors 125C Automatic Transaxle Governor Assembly

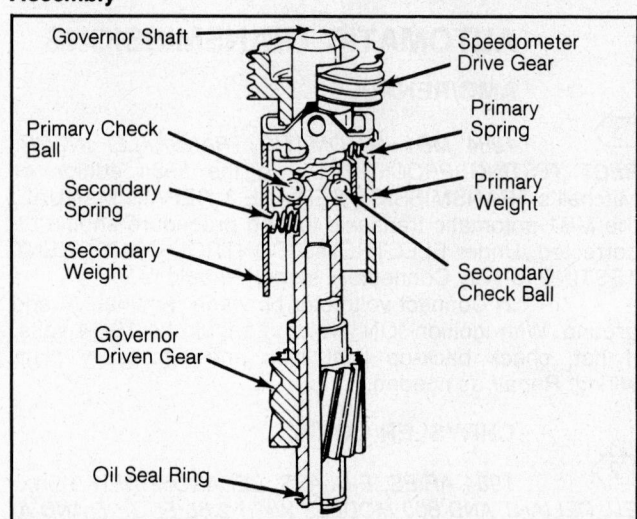

Governor Shaft

Speedometer Drive Gear

Primary Check Ball

Primary Spring

Secondary Spring

Primary Weight

Secondary Weight

Secondary Check Ball

Governor Driven Gear

Oil Seal Ring

12 *1984 GENERAL MOTORS VEHICLES WITH THM 125C TRANSAXLES: INCORRECT DIRECT AND FORWARD CLUTCH ASSEMBLY INSTALLATION* – Mitchell's 1983 and 1984 editions of the TRANSMISSION SERVICE & REPAIR manual contain an error on page 2-210. The direct clutch-to-housing measurement shown in Fig. 51 should be changed to 1 11/16" (42 mm).

13 *1984 GENERAL MOTORS VEHICLES WITH THM 200-4R AUTOMATIC TRANSMISSION: HARSH 1-2 AND/OR 3-4 SHIFTS* – Some General Motors vehicles with THM 200-4R transmissions built before April, 1984 may exhibit harsh 1-2 and/or 3-4 shifts. This condition may be caused by a damaged or incorrectly installed T.V. boost valve spring. New design control valve assemblies are now available to correct this condition. Use the following method to repair transmission.

    Remove the transmission oil pan. Remove the control valve body. Inspect the T.V. boost valve spring for correct installation or damage. If present, replace control valve body with the new design control valve assembly.

THM 200-4R CONTROL VALVE ASSEMBLY APPLICATION

Transmission Model	Part Number
AA, AP	8639343
BQ	8639914
BT, BY	8639912
CH	8639393
CQ	8639400
CR	8639414
HE	8639424
HG	8639431
OF, OY	8639326
OG	8639452
OJ	8639462
OM	8639915
OZ	8639343

FOR 1985 & EARLIER DOMESTIC MODELS (Cont.)

14 *GENERAL MOTORS VEHICLES WITH 325-4L TRANSMISSIONS: VALVE BODY* – In the 1984 edition of Mitchell's TRANSMISSION SERVICE & REPAIR manual, Fig. 34 on page 2-305 contains a mistake. The assembly order of the Line Bias Valve (No. 35) and Line Bias Valve Spring (No. 36) should be reversed. The spring is installed in the valve body BEFORE the Line Bias Valve is inserted. If not installed as described, transmission may not shift or shift incorrectly.

15 *GENERAL MOTORS VEHICLES WITH 440-T4 TRANSMISSIONS: THROTTLE VALVE LINE PRESSURES* – Some Throttle Valve Line Pressures listed on page 2-355 of the 1984 edition of Mitchell's TRANSMISSION SERVICE & REPAIR manual are incorrect. For correct pressures, see revised THROTTLE VALVE LINE PRESSURE TESTS chart in this edition.

16 *1983-84 GENERAL MOTORS VEHICLES WITH THM 700-R4 AUTOMATIC TRANSMISSION: GRINDING NOISE OR NO DRIVE IN GEAR* – Some 1983-84 General Motors passenger vehicles with the THM 700-R4 transmission may have a grinding noise or drive in gear. This condition may be caused by a broken reaction internal gear. A new design reaction internal gear (8654161) is available to correct this problem. The new design reaction internal gear may be identified by an equally spaced broached line on 3 of the parking lugs.

New Reaction Internal Gear For 1983-84 General Motors Vehicles With 700-R4 Transmission

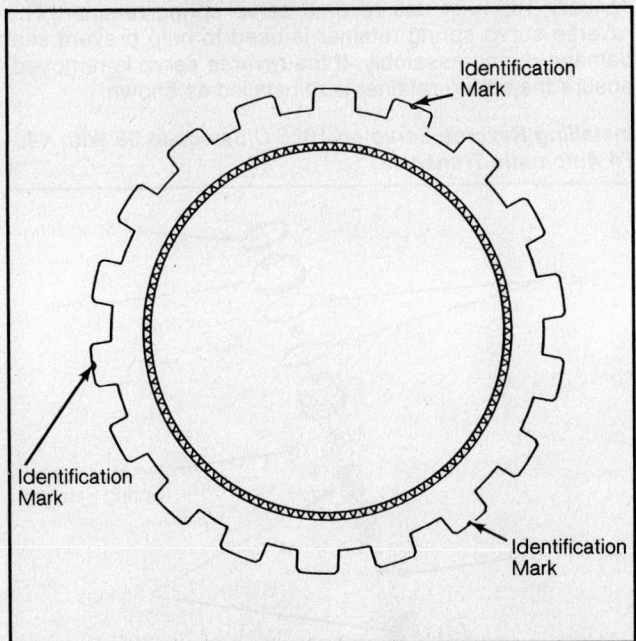

17 *1982-84 CADILLAC CIMARRONS WITH 125C AUTOMATIC TRANSAXLE: SHUDDER* – Some Cadillac Cimarron models may shudder during Torque Converter Clutch (TCC) application. This condition may be caused by excessive torque converter end play. Using a dial indicator or End Play Checking Tool (J-29830-A), check torque converter end play. Replace converter if end play is more than .020" (.50 mm).

18 *1982-84 CADILLAC CIMARRON WITH 125C AUTOMATIC TRANSAXLE: NO TCC APPLICATION OR SHUDDER DURING TCC APPLICATION* – This condition may be caused by the TCC case cover sleeve feed hole being out of alignment with the oil channel. To repair transaxle, remove valve body cover and case cover. Ensure TCC case cover sleeve feed hole is aligned with the oil channel. If not, replace sleeve or drill a hole through sleeve into oil channel.

1982-84 125C Oil Feed Hole Repair

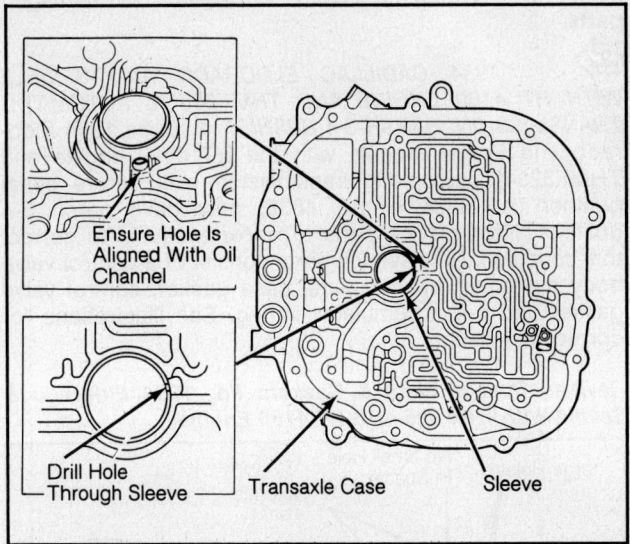

19 *1982-84 CADILLAC CIMARRON WITH 125C AUTOMATIC TRANSAXLE: SHUDDER DURING TCC OPERATION* – This condition may be caused by weak TCC regulator load spring in the auxiliary valve body. A new design load spring (8637888) is now available. To repair transaxle, remove control valve cover and auxiliary valve body. Depess regulator load spring retainer and remove pin. Remove old regulator load spring. Install new design spring and reassemble the transaxle.

20 *1983-84 CADILLAC BROUGHAM AND DEVILLE WITH 5.7L DIESEL ENGINE AND THM 200-4R AUTOMATIC TRANSMISSIONS: SOFT OR SLIPPING 1-2 SHIFT* – Some 1983-84 Brougham and DeVilles with 5.7L diesel engine and THM 200-4R automatic transmission ("OM" models only in 1984) may exhibit a soft or slipping 1-2 shift. A new design service package (8639915) is now available to correct this condition. Service package contains a control valve body and 3-4 accumulator spring. To repair transmission, proceed as follows:

    1) Remove transmission oil pan. Remove control valve body and 3-4 accumulator spring.

    2) Install new design control valve body and 3-4 accumulator spring. Replace oil pan. Refill transmission with Dexron II to correct level.

21 *1982-85 CADILLAC ELDORADO AND SEVILLE WITH THM 325-4L AUTOMATIC TRANSMISSION: FINAL DRIVE NOISE OR NO 1-2 SHIFT* – Some 1984 Eldorado and Seville models with THM 325-4L transmissions may develope a final drive noise. This condition may be caused by overheated final drive pinion bearings. The governor may also be damaged and prevent a normal 1-2 upshift.

The excessive heat may also prevent a normal final drive and transmission removal procedure. To correct this condition, proceed as follows:

1) Do not use excess force to remove the final drive from the transmission. If necessary, remove the assembly as a unit from the vehicle.

2) Disassemble the transmission until the output shaft-to-internal gear retaining snap ring may be removed. Remove the retaining snap ring. Separate the final drive from the transmission case. Disassemble the final drive and replace final drive bearings. Inspect all parts for overheating. Repair or replace all damaged parts.

22 *1984 CADILLAC ELDORADO AND SEVILLE WITH HT 4100 ENGINE AND THM 325-4L AUTOMATIC TRANSMISSION: HARSH 3-4 UPSHIFT* – Some 1984 Eldorado and Seville models with the HT 4100 engine and THM 325-4L automatic transmission built before serial number (AJ 8438 or AE 4838) may have harsh 3-4 upshifts. New service parts are now available to correct this condition. New service parts consist of a control valve body assembly, spacer plate, case gasket, control valve gasket and 3-4 accumulator spring. See illustrations for correct installation.

Revised Spacer Plate & Gaskets For 1984 Eldorado & Seville With THM 325-4L & HT 4100 Engine

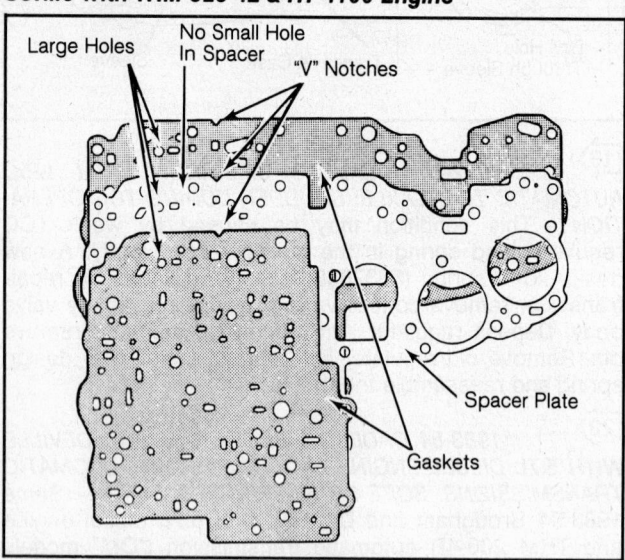

Revised Accumulator Spring For 1984 Eldorado & Seville With THM 325-4L & HT 4100 Engine

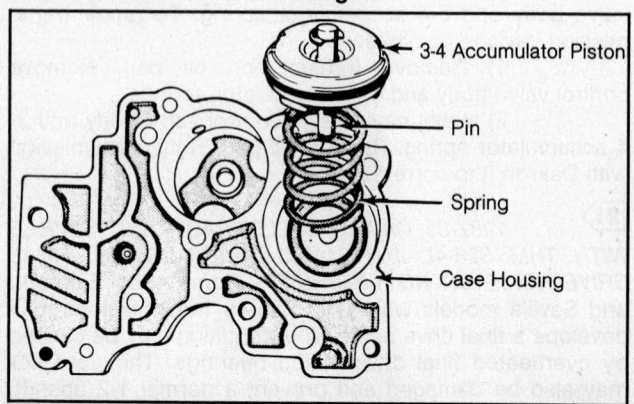

23 *1983-84 OLDSMOBILE CUTLASS SUPREME AND 88 WITH THM 200-4R TRANSMISSION: OIL EXHAUSTING FROM VENT* – Some 1983-84 Cutlass Supreme and 88 models with THM 200C automatic transmissions may develope a problem with oil exhausing from the vent during a rapid deceleration or sharp turns. This condition may be caused by warped or defective oil pump assembly. A new design oil pump assembly (8638922) and oil pump cover are now available to correct this condition. Oil pump will have to be removed from transmission to check for damage or warpage.

THM 200C Oil Pump Cover Application

Model	Part Number
CZ, JY	8633956
OR, OU	8633957
BH, OI, PS	8633958

24 *1983-84 OLDSMOBILE CUTLASS WITH THM 200-4R TRANSMISSION: WORN OR CRACKED THRUST WASHER* – Some 1983-84 Cutlass models with the THM 200-4R transmission (identification code "OZ") may have a worn or cracked thrust washer (rear carrier-to-low race). A new design service package (8639909) is now available to correct this condition.

25 *1985 OLDSMOBILE 98 WITH THM 440-T4 AUTOMATIC TRANSAXLE: REVISED SERVO* – All AY, BA and BS models of the THM 440-T4 transaxles built after January 16, 1984 use reverse servo spring retainer. The reverse servo spring retainer is used to help prevent seal damage during assembly. If the reverse servo is removed, ensure the spring retainer is reinstalled as shown.

Installing Reverse Servo on 1985 Oldsmobile 98 With 440-T4 Automatic Transaxle

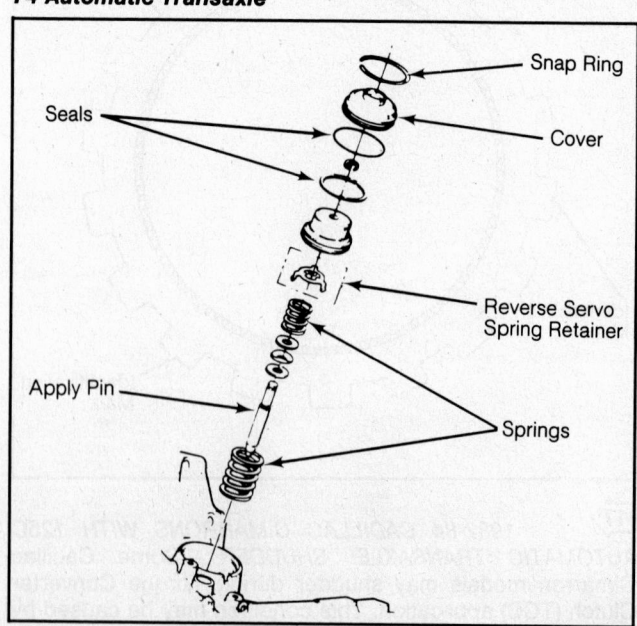

26 *1985 OLDSMOBILE 98 WITH THM 440-T4 AUTOMATIC TRANSAXLE: HARSH SHIFTING* – Some 1985 Oldsmobiles may have a harsh shifting condition between Park-to-Reverse or Neutral-to-Reverse gears,

FOR 1985 & EARLIER DOMESTIC MODELS (Cont.)

harsh upshifting between all gears, slipping in Drive or Reverse, harsh 3-2 coastdown shifts, rough 4-3 or 3-2 manual down shifts or 2nd gear starts. These conditions may be caused by a reduced vacuum signal to the vacuum modulator. The condition may be corrected as follows:

1) Disconnect the vacuum hose from the vacuum modulator. Connect a vacuum gauge to hose and check for proper engine vacuum signal. The vacuum gauge should read 13-17 in. Hg. If vacuum is okay, go to step **3)**.

2) If vacuum is less, check for an out-of-tune engine or for kinked or disconnected vacuum hoses. Also check A/C aspirator tee connections for proper routing. Ensure modulator hose is connected to the "MOD" fitting and the intake manifold hose is connected to the "MAN" fitting.

3) Remove modulator assembly and valve. Check the valve for nicks or scoring. Using a hand vacuum pump, apply 15-20 in. Hg to modulator. Ensure modulator plunger pulls in and modulator holds vacuum for at least 30 seconds. If not, replace modulator.

27▷ *1985 OLDSMOBILE 98 WITH THM 440-T4 TRANSAXLE: REVISED REASSEMBLY PROCEDURE* – During reassembly of the THM 440-T4 transaxle, ensure the 4th clutch apply plate is installed with the side stamped "UP" facing the 4th clutch piston. Ensure the input clutch apply plate is installed with the side stamped "UP" facing the 3rd clutch backing plate snap ring.

Revised Assembly Procedure For 1985 Oldsmobile 98 With THM 440-T4 Transaxle

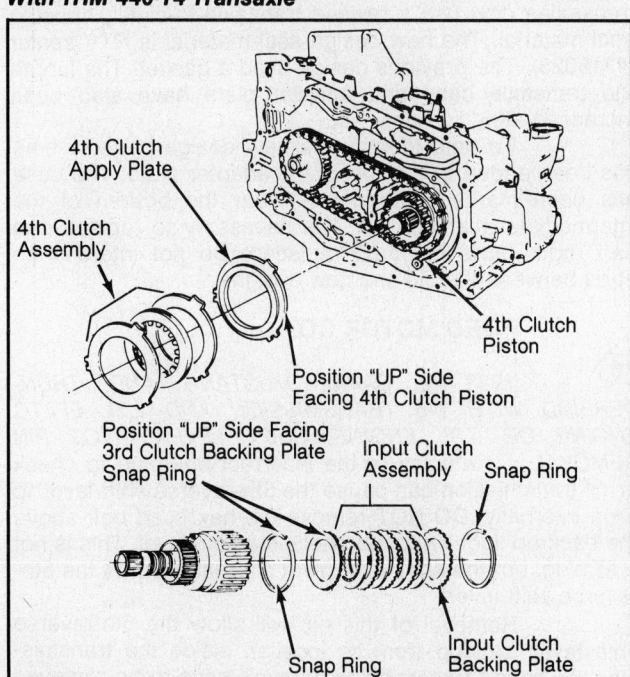

28▷ *1983-84 PONIAC VEHICLES WITH THM 200-4R AUTOMATIC TRANSMISSION: HARSH 1-2 UPSHIFT* – Some 1983-84 Pontiac vehicles with a THM 200-4R transmission may exhibit harsh 1-2 shifts. This condition may be caused by the 2nd clutch ball peening the 2nd clutch apply oil hole on the spacer plate. To correct the problem, replace the valve body-to-spacer plate gasket, spacer plate-to-case gasket and spacer plate.

Spacer Plate For 1983-84 Pontiacs With THM 200-4R Transmission

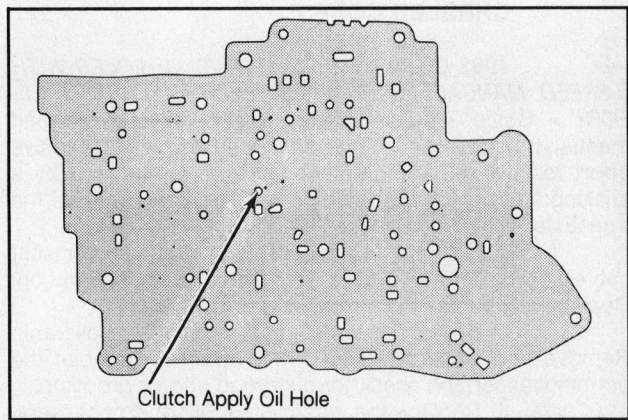

Clutch Apply Oil Hole

29▷ ALL 1985 PONTIAC MODELS WITH THM 200C, 200-4R, 325-4L, 350C OR 700-R4 AUTOMATIC TRANSMISSIONS: NEW DESIGN TORQUE CONVERTER LUGS – Beginning in early March 1985, all Pontiac vehicles with 9.65" and 11.73" (245 mm and 298 mm) torque converter assemblies will be equipped with redesigned torque converter lugs.

All 11.73" (298 mm) torque converter assemblies for diesel engine applications will have only 3 converter lugs. Six lugs were previously standard for all diesel applications.

30▷ *1985 PONTIAC GRAND AM WITH 3.0L ENGINE AND AUTOMATIC TRANSAXLE: TORQUE CONVERTER COVER NOISE* – Some 1985 Grand Am models with 3.0L engine and automatic transaxle may creat a noise at the torque converter cover area. This condition may be caused by placing the torque converter cover tabs on the transaxle side of the oil pan flange. To prevent cover noise, ensure torque converter cover tabs are placed on the engine side of the oil pan flange as illustrated.

1985 Pontiac Grand Am Torque Converter Cover Installation

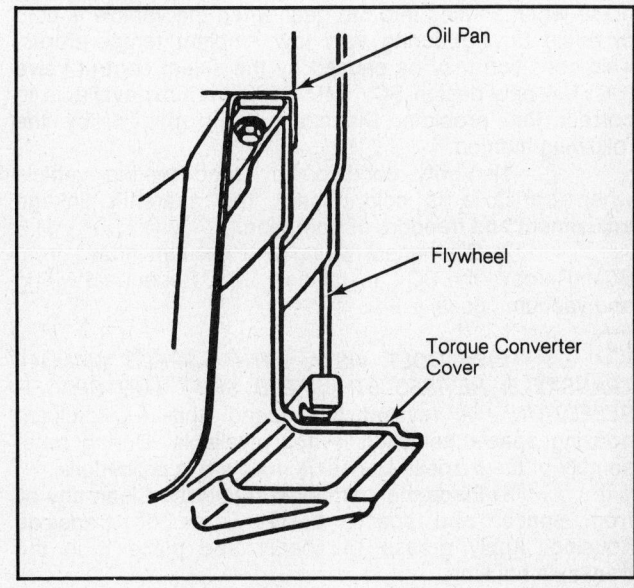

MANUAL TRANSMISSIONS

CHRSLER CORP.

1 ▷ *1983 CHRYSLER CORP. FWD VEHICLES WITH 5-SPEED MANUAL TRANSAXLES: EXCESSIVE SHIFT EFFORT* – Some Chrysler Corp. vehicles with 5-speed manual transaxle and cable shift may require excessive effort to shift gears. This condition may be caused by a sticking shift cable or binding of the bellcrank at the transaxle. This condition may be corrected as follows:

1) Disconnect the crossover and selector shift cables. Check the cables for freedom of operation. Replace any cables that are kinked or sticking.

2) Remove the pivot screw from the bellcrank. Remove and discard the top wave washer. Remove the bottom washer and check for distortion and/or grooving.

3) Replace the washer (6500814) if necessary. Clean and lubricate all bellcrank bearing surfaces and the pivot bolt.

4) Reinstall the bellcrank assembly and tighten the pivot bolt to 70 ft. lbs. (95 N.m). Reconnect the cables and make any necessary adjustments.

5) Road test the vehicle and verify proper operation of the gearshift linkage.

2 ▷ *1984 ARIES, CARAVAN, DAYTONA, HORIZON, OMNI, RAM VAN, RELIANT AND VOYAGER: REMOVING PRESS-FIT 5TH-SPEED SYNCHRONIZER* – Beginning May 15, 1984, all A-525 transaxles for these Chrysler vehicles are equipped with press-fit 5th-speed synchronizer hub. The press-fit hub reduces gear rattle and overall noise emitted from the transaxle.

The new press-fit hub is interchangeable with prior A-465 and A-525 hubs. Service procedures for the new hub are the same as for previous units, except for removal and installation.

3 ▷ *1984 COLT VISTA WITH 5-SPEED MANUAL TRANSAXLE: JUMPS OUT OF 5TH GEAR* – Some 1984 Colt Vista models equipped with a 5-speed manual transaxle may exhibit a condition where the transaxle jumps out of 5th gear. Another symptom may be clashing noise when shifting into 5th gear when the vehicle is cold or while driving during very low ambient temperatures. This condition may be caused by the select control valve (SCV). A new design SCV (MD703922) is now available to correct this problem. Diagnosis and repair is by the following method.

1) Verify condition by road testing vehicle when transaxle is cold. Check the gearshift linkage adjustment and freedom of operation.

2) Disconnect wiring and vacuum hoses from SCV. Remove the SCV. Install new SCV. Reconnect wiring and vacuum hoses.

4 ▷ *1984 COLT VISTA WITH 5-SPEED MANUAL TRANSAXLE: REVISED 5TH SPEED SHIFT LUG SPACER SELECTION* – A revised 5th speed shift lug-to-clutch housing spacer selection is now available. During reassembly of the 5-speed transaxle, follow this procedure:

1) Place the shift lever in neutral. Clean any oil from spacer and spacer contact area on transaxle housing. Apply grease to spacer and place it in the transaxle housing.

2) Using a feeler gauge, check the clearance between the 3-4 shift lug and the 5th shift lug as illustrated. The correct clearance should be .004-.020" (.10-.50 mm). If not, select a different spacer. Spacers are available from .024-.106" (.60-2.70 mm) in .012" (.30 mm) increments.

Measuring 1984 Colt Vista 3-4 Shift Lug-to-5th Shift Lug Clearance

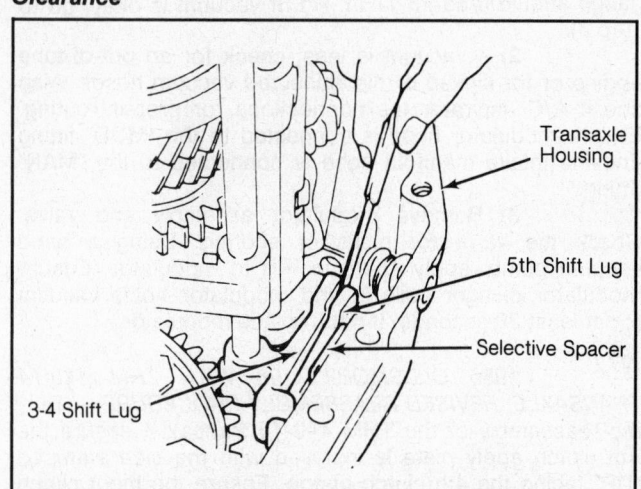

5 ▷ *1984 COLT AND VISTA WITH MANUAL TRANSAXLES: REVISED TRANSAXLE-TO-CLUTCH HOUSING SEAL* – All 1984 Colt and Vista models with manual transaxles now use a revised transaxle-to-clutch housing seal material. The new design seal material is RTV sealer (4318025). The previous design used a gasket. The length the transaxle case and adapter plate have also been increased .008" (.2 mm).

To help identify the new design parts, a hole has been added to the top of the adapter plate. The case has been marked with an "A" near the bottom of the intermediate gear boss. If it is necessary to replace one part, both parts must be replaced. Do not interchange parts between the old and new designs.

FORD MOTOR CO.

6 ▷ *1983 1/2 CAPRI, MUSTANG AND THUNDERBIRD WITH T-5 TRANSMISSION AND 2.3L EFI-TC ENGINE OR 5.0L ENGINE: SHIFT LEVER PIVOT PIN REMOVAL* – Removal of the incorrect bolt/plug to check or fill transmission can cause the 5th-reverse shift lever to drop internally. DO NOT remove the hex head bolt above the back-up light switch to check the fluid level. This is not a fill plug, but the shift lever pivot pin that secures the 5th-reverse shift lever.

Removal of this pin will allow the 5th-reverse shift lever to drop from its location inside the transmission. To repair transmission, unit will have to be removed from vehicle. Fluid is added or checked by removing the top plug on the right-hand side of the transmission. Fluid level should be to the bottom of the fill plug hole.

7 ▷ *1985 CAPRI, COUGAR, MUSTANG, MUSTANG SVO AND THUNDERBIRD WITH T-5 MANUAL TRANSMISSION: GEAR CLASH AT COLD TEMPERATURES* – Some vehicles equipped with the T-5 (5-speed) transmission may exhibit gear clashing during brisk 2-3 and 3-4 shifts at

FOR 1985 & EARLIER DOMESTIC MODELS (Cont.)

temperatures below 40°F (4.5°C). Transmissions affected were built prior to December 12, 1984. Condition may be corrected by replacing the 3rd and 4th blocker rings with new design rings.

8) *1984 FORD F250 HEAVY DUTY AND F350 WITH T19 TRANSMISSION: TICKING, TAPPING OR GRINDING NOISE* – Some 1984 Ford trucks with the T19 transmission may make a ticking, tapping or grinding noise. This may be cause by partial engagement of the reverse idler gear due to bent reverse shifter arm. A new design reverse shift fork (E3TZ-7409-A) and shifter arm (E3TZ-7243-A) are availble to correct this condition. Use the following method to determine if shifter arm and fork are defective.

1) Listen for noises from transmission during deceleration while driving vehicle between 45-55 MPH. If any noise is present, inspect reverse gears for damage.

2) To inspect reverse gears, remove transmission shift cover access panel. Remove gear shift cover from transmission. Check reverse idler gear and reverse mainshaft gear for any damage.

3) If any sign of nicks, chips or missing teeth are present, replace shifter arm and fork with new design reverse shifter arm and fork. If necessary, remove transmission to replace defective gears.

Checking Gear Teeth On 1984 Ford F250 Heavy Duty & F350 With T19 Transmision

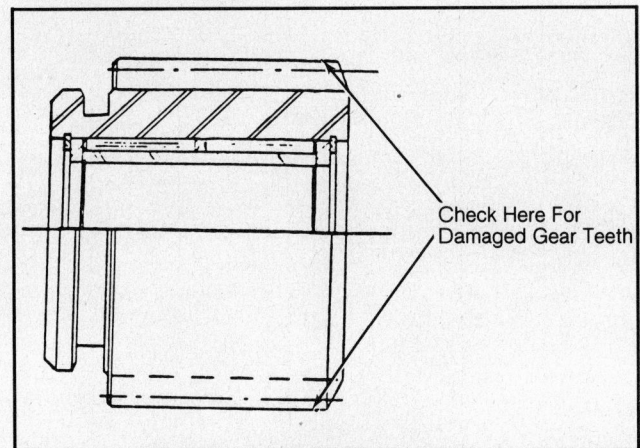

Check Here For Damaged Gear Teeth

GENERAL MOTORS

9) *1982 CADILLAC CIMARRON WITH 4-SPEED TRANSAXLE: INCOMPLETE 1ST GEAR ENGAGEMENT* – Some 1982 Cadillac Cimarron models with 4-speed transaxles may exhibit incomplete 1st gear engagement. This condition may be caused by improper synchronizer operation. A new design 1-2 synchronizer (14062629) and blocker ring (464835) are now available to correct this condition. To diagnose and repair this condition, use the following method.

1) Ensure linkage is properly adjusted. If necessary, have a helper hold the shift lever up as far as possible in 1st gear position and toward the driver's side of the vehicle. This is to preload the shift lever in 1st gear.

2) If trouble is still present, remove and disassemble the transaxle. Replace the 1-2 synchronizer and blocker ring with the new design type.

3) Inspect the 1st speed output gear assembly. If necessary, replace the output gear assembly (14008270).

4) Using Kent-Moore Tool (J-33373), install input shaft shims. Select a shim which is 2 sizes smaller than the maximum size possible. Check the input shaft end play.

5) End play should not be greater than .004-.005" (.10-.13 mm). If so, install a size larger input shaft shim.

10) *1983-84 PONTIAC FIREBIRD WITH "WARNER GEAR" 5-SPEED MANUAL TRANSMISSION: OIL LEAK AT SPEEDOMETER DRIVEN GEAR SLEEVE* – Some 1983-84 Firebird models with "Warner Gear" 5-speed transmissions may develope a leak at the speedometer driven gear sleeve. This condition may be caused by a worn speedometer driven gear sleeve. A new design speedmometer driven gear sleeve and seal (34345215) are now available to correct this condition.

11) *1984 CHEVETTE AND 1000 MODELS WITH 4-SPEED MANUAL TRANSMISSION: REVERSE GEAR DISENGAGEMENT* – Some 1984 Chevette and 1000 models with a 4-speed transmission may exhibit reverse gear disengagement during some vehicle operations. This condition may be caused by bent reverse shift lever. To correct this condition, replace the following parts: reverse shift lever assembly, reverse gear, reverse idler gear, reverse idler shaft and reverse countergear.

TRANSFER CASES

JEEP

1) *1984-85 CHEROKEE AND WAGONEER 70 SERIES WITH NEW PROCESS MODEL 207: TRANSFER CASE BEARING NOISE* – Some 1984-85 Cherokee and Wagoneer 70 series with New Process model 207 transfer case built before August 9, 1984 may have drive chain sprocket bearings which generate some noise in the 2WD drive mode at any speed. To repair this condition, proceed as follows:

1) Remove the transfer case. Remove drain and fill plugs. Remove front yoke. Discard seal washer and yoke nut.

2) Turn transfer case on end and position front case half on wooden blocks. Shift transfer case to "4WL" position. Remove extension housing attaching bolts.

3) Using a plastic mallet, tap extension housing shoulder to break sealer loose and remove the housing. Remove and discard rear bearing snap ring from mainshaft. Remove rear retainer attaching bolt.

4) Using a mallet, tap the shoulder of the retainer to break seal loose. Remove rear retainer and pump housing. Remove and discard pump seal from pump housing.

5) Remove speedometer and pump gears from mainshaft. Separate case halves. Insert screwdrivers into slots cast in case ends and pry upward. Do not attempt to wedge case halves apart at any point on mating surfaces.

6) Remove front output shaft and drive chain as an assembly. If necessary, raise mainshaft slightly for output shaft to clear the case. Pull up on mode fork rail until rail clears range fork. Rotate mode fork and rail and remove from case.

7) Rotate drive sprocket slowly and check for any roughness. Spin the sprocket and verify bearing noise.

8) Remove snap ring retaining synchronizer hub to mainshaft. Remove synchronizer hub and drive chain sprocket from mainshaft as an assembly.

9) Using Bearing Remover (J-33826) and Driver Handle (J-8092), press the 2 roller bearings out of drive sprocket. Clean and inspect mainshaft and drive chain sprocket bearing surfaces for wear, distortion, discoloration or damage. Replace sprocket or mainshaft, if damaged.

10) Using an abrasive stone, remove any burrs or rough edges on drive chain sprocket oil groove surfaces "A" as shown. Clean the hub thoroughly.

11) Using Bearing Installer (J-33828) and Driver Handle (J-8092), install drive chain sprocket front bearing. Press bearing inward until press tool bottoms. Bearing should be flush with front surface of hub.

12) Reverse bearing installer on handle and press drive chain sprocket rear bearing into sprocket until the tool bottoms. Rear bearing should be recessed after installation.

13) Install drive chain sprocket on mainshaft and repeat roughness and noise (spin) checks to verify repair. Assemble and install transfer case.

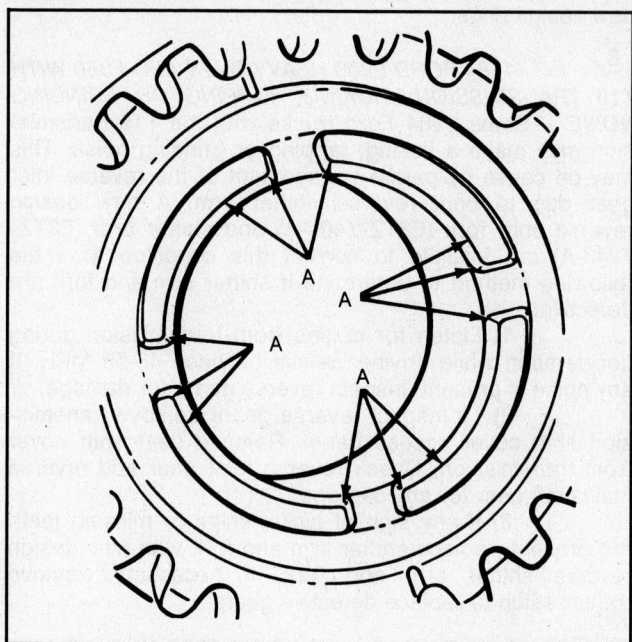

Checking Drive Chain Sprocket Oil Grooves On 1984-85 Cherokee & Wagoneer 70 With New Process 207 Transfer Case

1984 IMPORT GENERAL INDEX

The first step in using these pages
is to locate the listed components that you require
information on. Go down the list under the specific component heading
to the model or transmission type of the vehicle you are working on. On the
right-hand side of the column is the number of the article you require.

1984 Imported General Index

1984 Imported General Index

SECTION 5

IMPORT GENERAL SERVICING

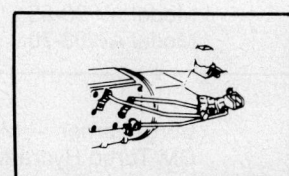

NOTE: ALSO SEE GENERAL INDEX.

Transmission Application

AUTOMATIC TRANSMISSIONS – IMPORTED CARS & TRUCKS

MANUFACTURER & MODEL	TRANSMISSION MODEL
AUDI	
Coupe GT & 5000 Series	Model 087 Transaxle
4000 Series	Model 089 Transaxle
BMW	
318i	Model ZF 3 HP-22
All Others	Model ZF 4 HP-22
CHRYSLER CORP. IMPORTS	
Colt	Mitsubishi – Model KM170 Transaxle
Colt Vista	Mitsubishi – Model KM172
Conquest	Mitsubishi – Model JM600
Ram-50 Pickup	2WD – Torqueflite Model MA904A
	4WD – Torqueflite Model KM146
GENERAL MOTORS IMPORTS	
Spectrum	Model MXI Transaxle
HONDA	
Accord & Prelude	Model AS 4-Speed Transaxle
Civic	Model AW Transaxle
ISUZU	
I-Mark & P'UP	Model AW03-55
Impulse	Model AW03-70
JAGUAR	
XJ6	Borg-Warner – Model 66
XJS	GM Turbo Hydra-Matic – Model 400
MAZDA	
GLC & 626	Mazda – Model F3A Transaxle
RX7	JATCO – Model L4N71B
Pickup	JATCO – Model 3N71B
MERCEDES-BENZ	
190 Series	MB – Model W4A020 4-Speed
300, 380 & 500 Series	MB – Model W4A040 4-Speed
MITSUBISHI	
Cordia & Tredia	Mitsubishi – Model KM171 Transaxle
Pickup	2WD – Torqueflite Model MA904A
	4WD – Mitsubishi Model KM146 Transaxle
Starion	Mitsubishi – Model JM600
NISSAN/DATSUN	
Maxima & 200SX	JATCO – Model L4N71B
Pickup	JATCO – Model L3N71B
Pulsar & Stanza	JATCO – Model RL3F01A
Sentra	
Diesel	JATCO – Model RN3F01A
Gas	JATCO – Model RL3F01A
300ZX & 300ZX Turbo	JATCO – Model E4N71B
PEUGEOT	
505	Model ZF 3 HP-22

AUTOMATIC TRANSMISSIONS – IMPORTED CARS & TRUCKS (Cont.)

MANUFACTURER & MODEL	TRANSMISSION MODEL
PORSCHE 928S 944	Model A28.01 Transaxle Model 087 Transaxle
RENAULT Fuego & Sportwagon	Renault – Model 4139-65 Transaxle
SAAB 900 Series	Borg-Warner – Model 37 Transaxle
SUBARU 1800 – 2WD, 4WD & Turbo	Gunma Model M41A
TOYOTA Camry Celica Corolla FWD Corolla RWD Cressida & Pickup Supra Tercel Van	Model A140E Transaxle Model A40D Model A130L & A131L Model A42L Model A43D Model A43DE Model A55 Transaxle Model A43DL Transmission
VOLKSWAGEN Jetta, Rabbit & Scirocco Quantum Vanagon	Model 010 Transaxle Model 089 Transaxle Model 090 Transaxle
VOLVO 760 GLE All Others	Aisin-Warner Model AW71 Borg-Warner Model 55 ZF 4HP 22 4-Speed Aisin-Warner Models AW70, 71 Borg-Warner Model 55

Transmission Application

MANUAL TRANSMISSIONS – IMPORTED CARS & TRUCKS

MANUFACTURER & MODEL	TRANSMISSION MODEL
ALFA ROMEO Spider 2.0 & GTV-6 2.5	5-Speed
AUDI 4000 Series Coupe GT & 5000 Series Quattro	Model 014 Transaxle Model 093 Transaxle Model 5H Transaxle
BMW 318i All Others	Getrag 240 / ZFS5-16 Getrag 260

CHRYSLER CORP. IMPORTS
 Colt
 Colt Vista
 Ram-50 Pickup
   2WD
   4WD
	Model KM160, KM165 Or KM166 Transaxle
	 Model KM163 Or Km166 Transaxle
	
	 Model KM130 Or KM132
	 Model KM144 Or KM 145

GM IMPORTS Sprint	Model MV2 Transaxle
HONDA Accord Civic Prelude	Model GS Transaxle Model GV Transaxle Model GW Transaxle Model GM Transaxle
ISUZU I-Mark Impulse P'UP (2WD) P'UP (4WD) & Trooper II	Model MSG-4K Model MSG-5K Model MSG-5K Model MSG-4K Or MSG-5K Model MSG-4ET
MAZDA B2000 Pickup & B2200 Pickup GLC RX7 626	4 & 5-Speed 4 & 5-Speed Transaxle 5-Speed 5-Speed Transaxle
MERCEDES-BENZ 190D 190E	Model GL 68/20 A-5 Model GL 68/20 B-5
MITSUBISHI Cordia & Tredia Pickup (2WD) Pickup (4WD) & Montero Starion	Model KM163 Or KM166 Transaxle Model KM132 Model KM145 Model KM132

MANUAL TRANSMISSIONS – IMPORTED CARS & TRUCKS (Cont.)

MANUFACTURER & MODEL	TRANSMISSION MODEL
NISSAN/DATSUN	
Maxima & 200SX	Model FS5W71B
Pickup (2WD & 4WD)	Model FS5W71B
Pulsar	Model RS5F30A Transaxle
Sentra	Model RN4F30A Transaxle
	Model RS5F30A Transaxle
Stanza	Model RS5F30A Transaxle
200SX & 200SX Turbo	Model FS5W71B
300ZX & 300ZX Turbo	FS5R90A (Borg Warner Model T-5)
	FS5W71C
PEUGEOT	
505	5-Speed
PORSCHE	
911	Model 915/68 Or 915/70 Transaxle
928S	Model G28.05 Transaxle
944	Model 016 Y Transaxle
RENAULT	
Fuego	NG Series Transaxle
SAAB	
900 Series	Model G Transaxle
SUBARU	
1800 & 1800 4WD	4 & 5-Speed Transaxle
TOYOTA	
Camry & Corolla FWD	Model S41/S50 Transaxle
Celica, Cressida, & Supra	Model W58
Corolla RWD	Model T50
Land Cruiser	Model H42
Pickup (Diesel)	Model G40/G52
Pickup (2WD Gas)	Model G42/G50
Pickup (4WD Gas)	Model K45/K52
Starlet	Model K40/K50
Tercel (2WD)	4-Speed – Model Z44 Transaxle
	5-Speed – Model Z52 Transaxle
Tercel (4WD)	5-Speed – Model Z52F Transaxle
Van	Model G53
VOLKSWAGEN	
Jetta, Quantum, Rabbit & Scirocco	Model Transaxle
	Model 020 Transaxle
Vanagon	Model 091, 091/1 Or 094 Transaxle
VOLVO	
All Models	Model M46

Automatic Transmission Servicing

AUDI

IDENTIFICATION

TRANSMISSION CODES

Application	Code
4000S	089
Coupe & 5000 Series	087

LUBRICATION

SERVICE INTERVALS

Check fliud in transmission and final drive every 15,000 miles. Change fluid in transmission every 30,000 miles.

CHECKING FLUID LEVEL

When checking fluid levels, be sure that vehicle is level, place selector lever in "P" position and apply parking brake. Run engine until fluids reach normal operating temperature.

Transmission

Pull out dipstick and wipe clean. Reinsert dipstick until fully seated, pull out dipstick and check fluid level. Fluid level should be between marks.

Final Drive

Remove fill plug on side of final drive assembly and note oil level. Oil should be even with bottom of fill hole.

RECOMMENDED FLUID

Use Dexron II automatic transmission fluid. Use Hypoid SAE 90 (API GL-5) in final drive.

FLUID CAPACITY

TRANSMISSION REFILL CAPACITIES

Application	Quantity
Transmission	3.2 qts. (3.0L)
Final Drive	1.6 pts. (0.76L)

DRAINING & REFILLING

Transmission

1) Loosen 2 front pan bolts. Remove rear bolts while holding pan in place. Carefully lower pan at rear and drain old ATF. Remove front pan bolts and remove pan.

2) Remove screws holding strainer. Clean pan and strainer with clean solvent. Install strainer using a new gasket, tighten screws to 26 INCH lbs. (3 N.m). Install pan using a new gasket, tighten bolts to 14 ft. lbs (19 N.m).

3) Add 3.2 qts. (3.0L) of ATF. Set parking brake and place transmission in Neutral. Start engine and check for leaks. Allow engine to reach normal operating tenperature and check ATF level.

Final Drive

Remove drain plug and allow oil to drain. Replace oil drain plug and fill housing until oil is even with bottom of fill hole.

ADJUSTMENTS

SECOND GEAR BAND

Lock nut and tighten adjustment screw to 87 INCH lbs. (10 N.m). Loosen and retighten to 43 INCH lbs.

(5 N.m). Turn adjustment screw out 2 turns and tighten lock nut on 087 transmission. Turn adjustment screw out 2 1/2 turns and tighten lock nut on 089 transmission.

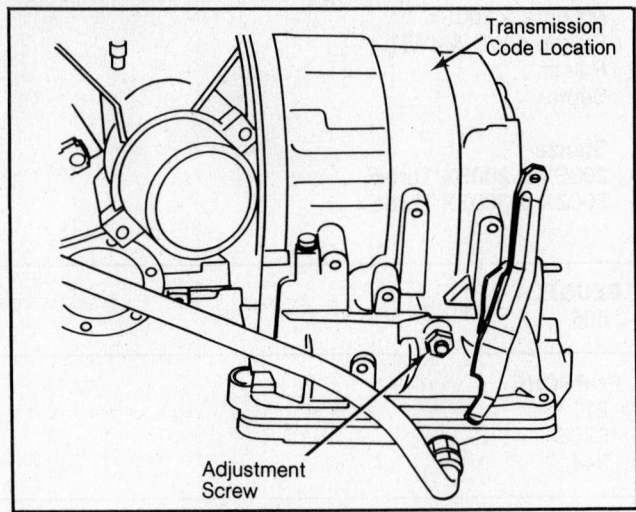

Fig. 1: Second Gear Band Adjustment

THROTTLE LINKAGE

087 TRANSMISSION

1) Check pull rod for free movement in ball joints of throttle valve lever and linkage. With throttle in idle position, loosen push rod clamping bolt at transmission end. Hold selector lever in Neutral position and tighten clamping bolt.

2) Remove pedal stop and intermediate piece beneath accelerator pedal. Attach 2 nuts to a M8 X 135 bolt so that distance from top of bolt to bottom of nuts is 4 7/8" (124 mm).

3) Install bolt in place of pedal stop so that bottom of pedal plate rests on bolt head. Remove slack out of accelerator cable using adjustment nut on transmission bracket. Remove adjustment bolt and install accelerator pedal stop.

089 TRANSMISSION

1) Check operating lever for free movement. With throttle in idle position, loosen lock nuts on cylinder head valve cover bracket. Pull sleeve of throttle cable away from engine until resistance is felt. Turn lock nut against bracket and lock using second nut.

2) Remove pedal stop and switch (A/C equipped vehicles only) beneath accelerator pedal. Attach 2 nuts to a M8 X 135 bolt so that distance from top of bolt to bottom of nuts is 4 7/8" (124 mm).

3) Install bolt in place of pedal stop so that bottom of pedal plate rests on bolt head. Remove slack out of accelerator cable using adjustment nut on transmission bracket. Remove adjustment bolt and install accelerator pedal stop.

NEUTRAL SAFETY SWITCH

1) Remove shift selector handle and center console. Loosen selector cable clamp nut and move lever on transmission into "P" position. Tighten cable clamp nut to 72 INCH lbs. (8 N.m).

2) Loosen neutral safety switch mounting screws. Adjust switch by moving it forward or rearward so that engine can only be started in "N" or "P" positions. Tighten mounting screws. Install console and shift selector handle.

IDENTIFICATION

TRANSMISSION CODES

Application	Code
318i	ZF 3 HP-22
All Other Models	ZF 4 HP-22

LUBRICATION

SERVICE INTERVALS
Check fluid level at least at every oil change. Drain and refill transmission every 30,000 miles.

CHECKING FLUID LEVEL
Transmission must be at normal operating temperature with vehicle on a level surface, engine at idle and gear selector in "P". Fluid level should be between the "MAX" and "MIN" marks on the dipstick. Distance between marks represents .42 qts. (.40L) on ZF 3 HP-22 and 1.1 qts. (1.0L) on ZF 4 HP-22 transmissions.

RECOMMENDED FLUID
All transmissions use Dexron or Dexron II automatic transmission fluid.

FLUID CAPACITY

TRANSMISSION REFILL CAPACITIES

Application	Refill Quantity	Dry Fill Quantity
318i	2.3 qts. (2.2L)	6.4 qts.(6.0L)
All Other Models	3.2 qts. (3.0L)	8.0 qts.(7.5L)

DRAINING & REFILLING
1) With transmission at normal operating temperature, remove drain plug and allow fluid to drain. Remove oil pan bolts and tap on pan to break seal loose.
2) Remove oil screen and clean or replace as necessary. Clean oil pan. Reinstall filter screen and oil pan. Fill transmission with new transmission fluid.

ADJUSTMENTS

SHIFT LINKAGE
ZF 3 HP-22
1) Check tightness of shift console lever before adjusting. Disconnect selector rod from lever at adjustment pin. Move transmission shifter lever to "N" position. Press shifter against shift gate stop.
2) Alter length of selector rod with adjusting pin until adjusting pin aligns with hole in selector lever. Shorten selector rod by 1 turn of adjusting pin. Attach selector rod, adjusting pin and selector lever together.
ZF 4 HP-22
1) Move selector lever to "P". Loosen cable attaching nut on shift lever at transmission. Push lever forward to "P" and push cable rod the opposite direction.
2) Tighten shift cable rod nut to 7-9 ft. lbs. (10-12 N.m). Check proper operation of shifter in teach gear selection, readjust if necessary.

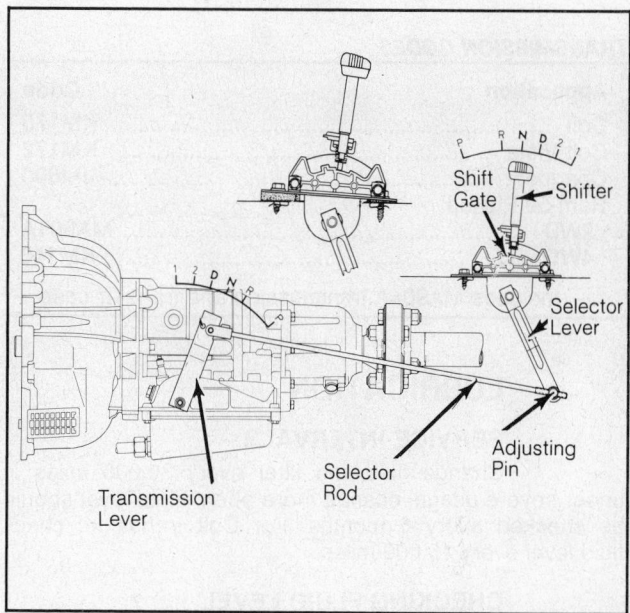

Fig. 1: Shift Linkage Adjustment

Adjustment for 318i shown.

THROTTLE CABLE & KICKDOWN STOP
Adjust cable play to .010-.030" (.25-.75 mm). See Fig. 2. Check kickdown stop. If adjustment is necessary, loosen lock nut and screw on kickdown stop. Push down accelerator pedal to transmission pressure point. Unscrew kickdown stop in this position, until it contacts the accelerator pedel. Push down accelerator pedal to kickdown position. Distance from lead seal to end of sleeve must be at least 1.73" (44 mm).

NEUTRAL SAFETY SWITCH
Neutral saftey switch is connected to selector lever and relay. If not operating properly, check relay and selector adjustment.

Fig. 2: Throttle Cable and Kickdown Stop Adjustment

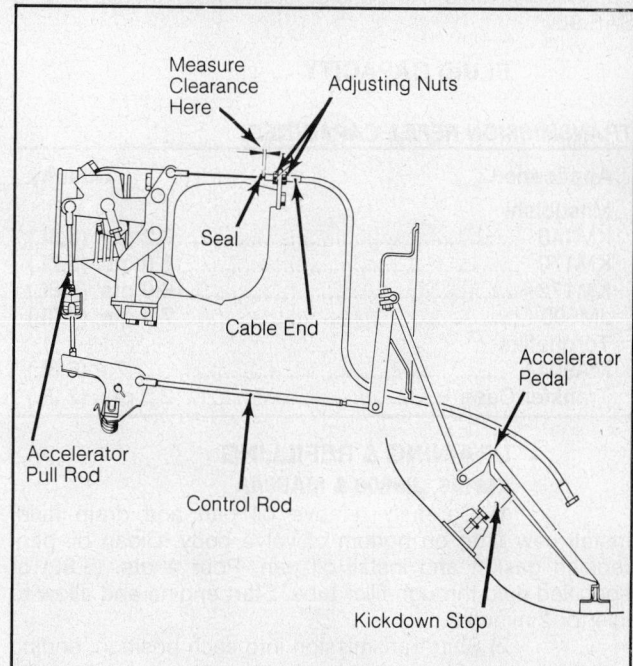

Model 733i is shown. All other models are similar.

Automatic Transmission Servicing

CHRYSLER CORP. IMPORTS

IDENTIFICATION

TRANSMISSION CODES

Application	Code
Colt	KM170
Colt Vista	KM172
Conquest	JM600
Ram-50 Pickup	
2WD	MA904A
4WD	¹ KM146

¹ – Includes MA904A transmission and transfer case.

LUBRICATION

SERVICE INTERVALS

Change fluid and filter every 30,000 miles; if under severe usage, change more often. Fluid level should be checked every 6 months. For Colt transaxle, check fluid level every 15,000 miles.

CHECKING FLUID LEVEL

1) Park vehicle on level area. Oil must be at normal operating temperature, parking brake engaged and engine at idle. Shift transmission selector through each position, stopping briefly in each position.

2) Place selector in "N" position and clean area around dipstick tube. Ensure that fluid level is between lower and upper marks, but never over upper mark. Add or drain fluid as necessary.

CAUTION: If severe darkening of the fluid and a strong odor is noted, fluid and filter should be changed and bands adjusted.

RECOMMENDED FLUID

All transmissions use Dexron II automatic transmission fluid. All transfer cases use API GL-4 & -5 SAE 90.

FLUID CAPACITY

TRANSMISSION REFILL CAPACITIES

Application	Quanity
Mitsubishi	
KM146	7.2 qts. (6.8L)
KM170	6.0 qts. (5.7L)
KM172	6.0 qts. (5.6L)
JM600	7.4 qts. (7.0L)
Torqueflite	
MA904A	7.2 (6.8L)
Transfer Case	2.3 qts. (2.2L)

DRAINING & REFILLING
KM146, JM600 & MA904A

1) Carefully remove oil pan and drain fluid. Install new filter on bottom of valve body. Clean oil pan, replace gasket and install oil pan. Pour 4 qts. (3.8L) of specified fluid through filler tube. Start engine and allow to idle for 2 minutes.

2) Shift transmission into each position, ending in "N" position. Check fluid level with engine running at idle and add sufficient fluid to bring level to "ADD 1 PINT"

mark. Recheck fluid level after transmission is at normal operating temperature.

KM170 & KM172

1) Remove drain plug from differential and drain fluid. *See Fig. 1.* If replacing filter, remove bolts and lower oil pan. Install new filter on bottom of valve body. Replace pan gasket and install pan.

2) Tighten differential plug to 22-25 ft. lbs. (30-34 N.m). Ensure that dipstick hole area is clean and pour in approximately 4.2 qts. (4.0L) of "DEXRON II" fluid.

3) Run engine for 2 minutes at idle. Shift transmission to each position, ending in "N" position. Add sufficient fluid to reach lower mark. After reaching normal operating temperature, fluid should be between upper and lower marks of "HOT" range.

Fig. 1: KM170 & KM172 Drain Plug Locations

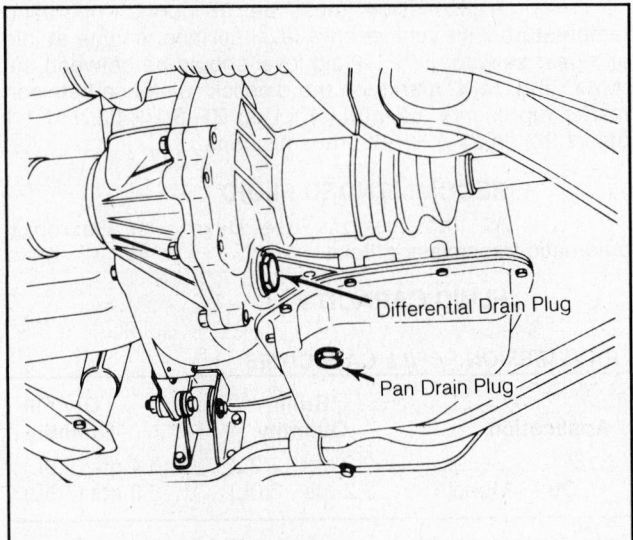

Differential Drain Plug

Pan Drain Plug

ADJUSTMENTS

FRONT (KICKDOWN) BAND
KM146 & MA904A

1) Front (kickdown) band adjuster screw is located on left side of transmission case. To adjust band, loosen and back off lock nut about 5 turns. Check that adjuster screw turns freely.

2) Using wrench (C-3380-A) with adapter (C-3705), tighten band adjuster screw to 52 INCH lbs. (5.9 N.m). *See Fig. 2.*

3) If adapter (C-3705) is not used, tighten adjuster screw to 51 INCH lbs. (5.8 N.m), which is the true torque. Back off adjusting screw 3 1/2 turns, hold adjuster screw and tighten lock nut to 37 ft. lbs. (50 N.m).

Fig. 2: KM146 & MA904A
Front (Kickdown) Band Adjusting Screw Location

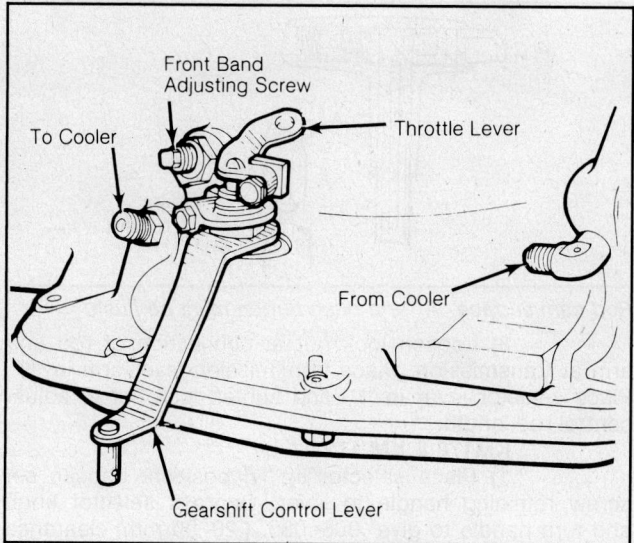

KM170 & KM172

1) Clean all dirt from kickdown servo cover and remove snap ring. Remove cover and loosen lock nut. Hold servo piston from turning and tighten adjusting screw to 88 INCH lbs. (10 N.m) and back it off.

2) Repeat torquing twice to seat kickdown band against drum. Tighten adjusting screw to 44 INCH lbs. (5 N.m) and back off 3 1/2 turns. Hold screw and tighten lock nut. Install cover and snap ring.

NOTE: Install new seal ring with "D" shaped section to outside of cover. If reusing old seal ring, make certain it is not distorted.

Fig. 3: KM170 & KM172 Kickdown Band Adjustment

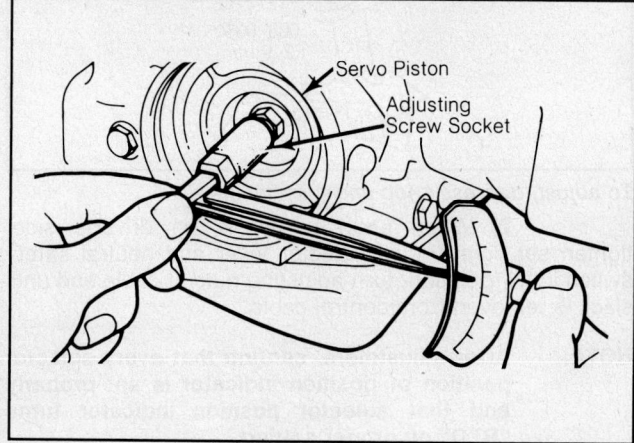

Hold piston and turn adjusting screw.

REAR BAND
KM146 & MA904A

1) Remove oil pan. Loosen lock nut and adjusting screw at servo end of lever and tighten screw to 43 INCH lbs. (4.9 N.m) of torque.

2) Back off screw 7 turns. Hold adjusting screw and tighten lock nut to 29 ft. lbs. (40 N.m). Reinstall oil pan.

Fig. 4: KM146 & MA904A
Rear Band Adjusting Screw Location

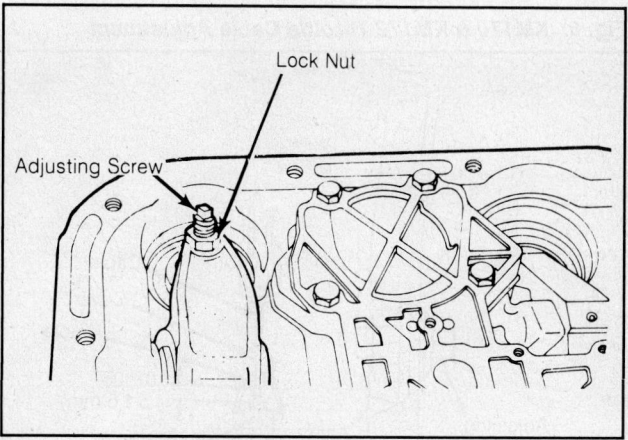

Oil pan must be removed for adjustment.

TRANSMISSION THROTTLE CONTROL
KM146 & MA904A

1) With engine at normal operating temperature and idle speed set correctly, loosen bolt retaining throttle rod "C" to "B". Lightly push throttle rod "A" or transmission throttle lever and rod toward idle stop and set rods to "IDLE" position.

2) Tighten bolt retaining rod "B" to "C". Open throttle to "WIDE OPEN" position. Make sure that transmission lever moves from "IDLE" to "WIDE OPEN" position (total movement 47.5° to 54°). Some play should still exist in throttle lever stroke at wide open throttle.

Fig. 5: KM146 & MA904A Throttle Rod Adjustment

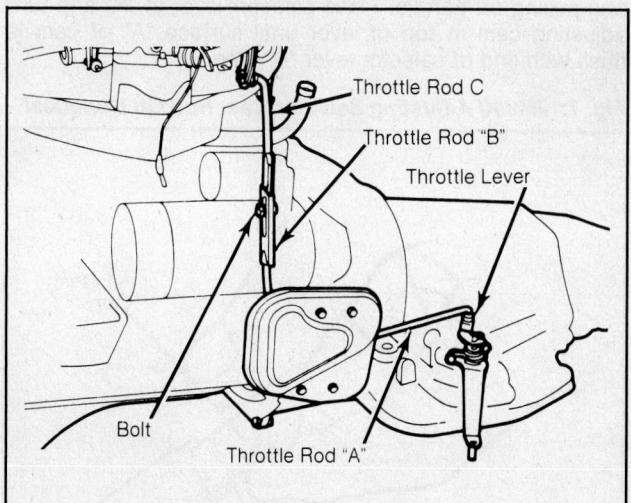

Make sure that transmission lever moves from "IDLE" to "WIDE OPEN" position.

KM170 & KM172

1) Ensure that carburetor throttle lever is at "CURB IDLE" position, engine is at operating temperature, and fast idle condition has been reset. Raise cover "B" and loosen cable bracket mounting bolt.

2) Move lower cable bracket until distance between nipple and top cover "A" of throttle cable is adjusted to .02-.06" (.5-1.5 mm). *See Fig. 6.* Tighten lower cable bracket mounting bolt.

3) With throttle lever in "WIDE OPEN" position, pull cable upward to ensure freedom of cable movement.

Fig. 6: KM170 & KM172 Throttle Cable Adjustment

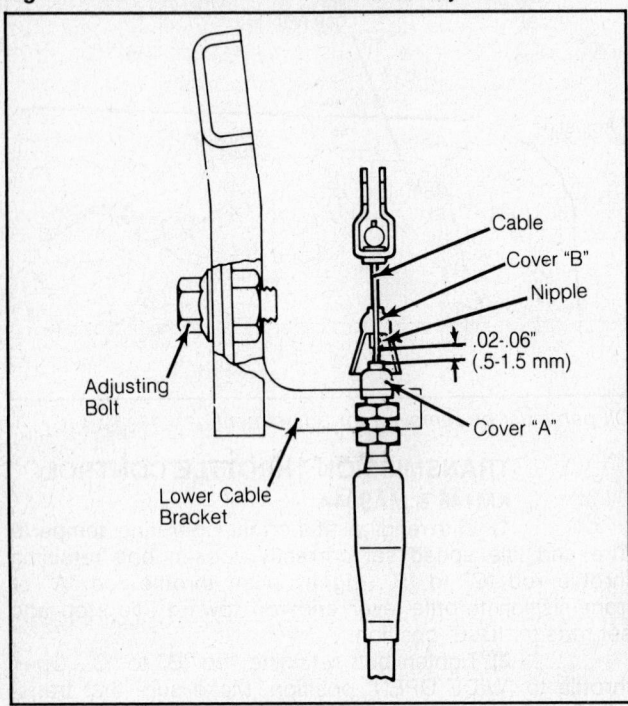

Cable
Cover "B"
Nipple
.02-.06"
(.5-1.5 mm)
Cover "A"
Adjusting Bolt
Lower Cable Bracket

SHIFT LINKAGE
KM146, MA904A & JM600

1) Remove shift handle by loosening set screw and pulling off handle. Place selector lever in "N" and turn adjusting cam in top of lever until surface "A" of cam is flush with end of selector lever "B". *See Fig. 7.*

Fig. 7: JM600 Adjusting Selector Cam Rod On Conquest

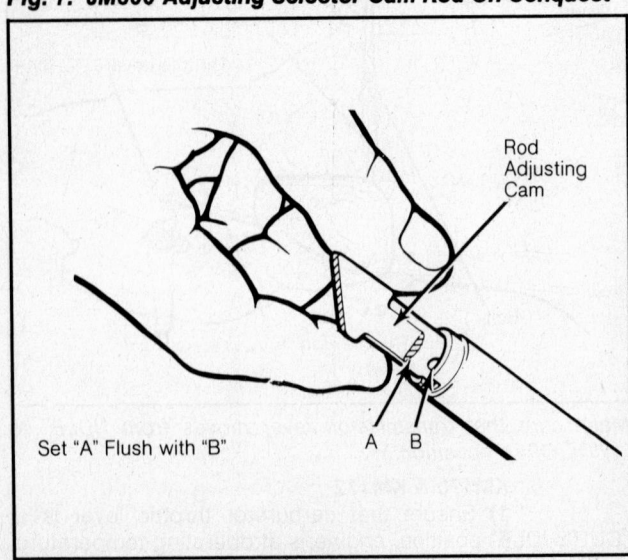

Rod Adjusting Cam

Set "A" Flush with "B"

A B

Adjust surface "A" flush with surface "B".

2) For Pickups, place selector lever in "N" and turn adjusting cam in top of lever until surface "A" of cam is flush with push button. *See Fig. 8.*

Fig. 8: KM146 & MA904A
Adjusting Selector Cam Rod On Pickups

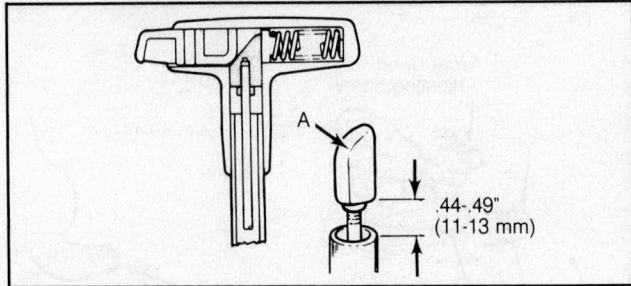

A

.44-.49"
(11-13 mm)

Rod cam surface "A" and push button must be flush.

3) Loosen lock nut at connection of rod and arm at transmission. Place transmission lever arm in "N". Place selector lever in "N" and tighten lock nut to adjust control rod length.

KM170 & KM 172

1) Place selector in "N" position. Loosen set screw retaining handle to lever. Depress selector knob and turn handle to give .008-.035" (.20-.90 mm) clearance between selector lever end pin and detent plate. *See Fig. 9.*

Fig. 9: Adjusting Selector Lever
On KM170 & KM172 Transaxle

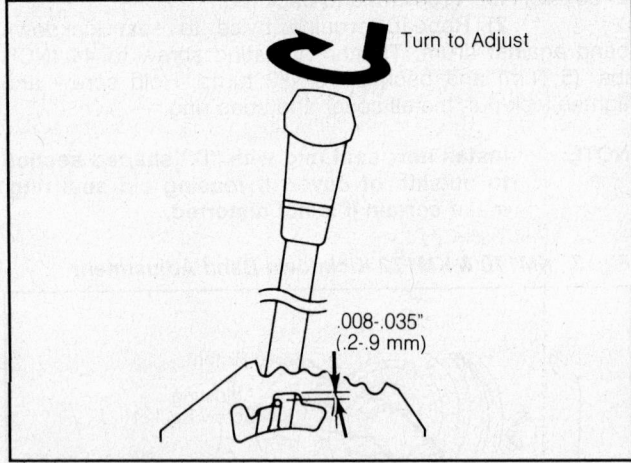

Turn to Adjust

.008-.035"
(.2-.9 mm)

To adjust, depress knob and turn handle.

2) When knob button is on driver's side, tighten set screw. With selector lever and neutral safety switch in "N" position, turn adjusting nuts at cable end until slack is removed from control cable.

NOTE: After adjustment, confirm that every selector position of position indicator is set properly and that selector position indicator turns "RED" on proper setting.

NEUTRAL SAFETY SWITCH
KM146 & MA904A

NOTE: Safety switch is located under shift lever console and is operated by shift lever. In addition to the neutral safety switch function, switch also operates back-up lights and seat belt warning system.

1) To adjust switch, remove console, loosen switch attaching screws, and place selector lever in "N" position. Slide switch back and forth to measure contact range of "N" position. *See Fig. 11.*

Fig. 10: Positioning Neutral Safety Switch
On KM146 & MA904A

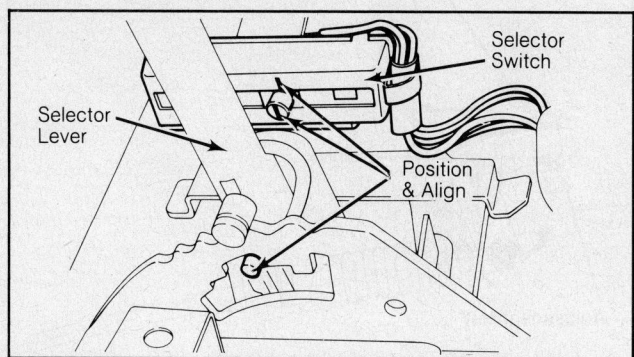

Place shift lever in "N" and align switch mark with rod indicator.

Fig. 11: Adjusting Neutral Safety Switch Movement
On KM146 & MA904A

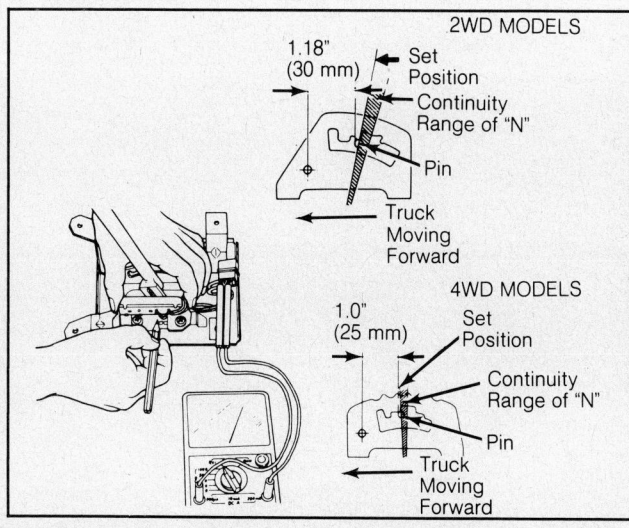

Connect tester to switch terminals (BY-BY) and move switch back and forth to check continuity.

Fig. 12: Adjusting Neutral Safety Switch
On KM146 & MA904A

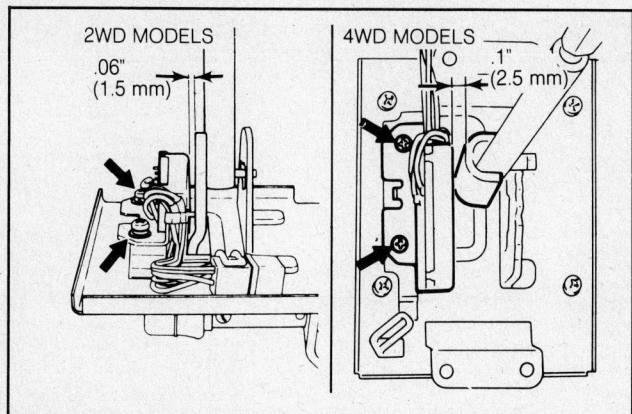

2) Temporarily install switch and adjust so there is .06" (1.5 mm) for 2WD Pickup, .1" (2.5 mm) for 4WD Pickup, side clearance between selector lever and switch. *See Fig. 12.* Set selector lever in "P", "R", and "N" positions and check continuity of terminals. After confirming continuity, tighten switch attaching screws and reinstall console.

NOTE: **If correct continuity cannot be achieved, reposition safety switch.**

KM170, KM172 & JM600
Place transmission control lever in "N" position and loosen switch retaining bolts. Turn switch body so that aligning hole end of lever overlaps switch body flange (on JM600 insert alignment pin) and tigthten bolts. *See Fig. 13.*

Fig. 13 Adjusting Neutral Saftry Switch
On KM170 & KM172 Transaxle

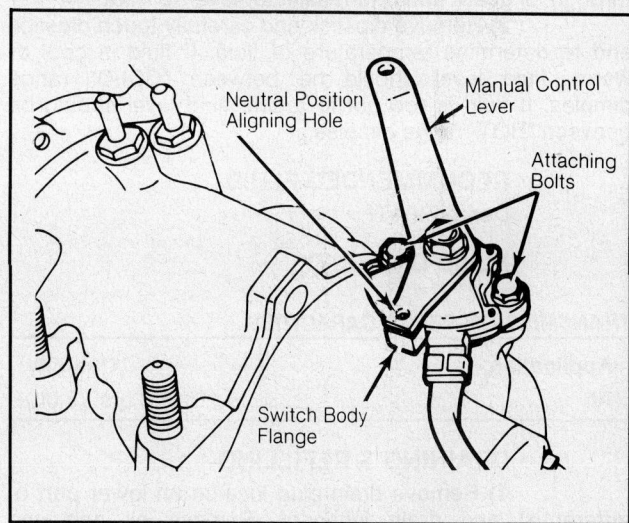

Align lever hole with housing hole. JM600 is similar.

VACUUM DIAPHRAGM ROD
JM600
Disconnect vacuum hose at vacuum diaphragm and remove diaphragm from transmission case. Using depth gauge, measure depth "L". Be sure vacuum throttle valve is pushed into valve body as far as possible. See VACUUM DIAPHRAGM ROD SELECTION table.

VACUUM DIAPHRAGM ROD SELECTION

Depth "L" in. (mm)	Rod Length in. (mm)	Part No.
Under 1.0059 (25.55)	1.142 (29.0)	MD610614
1.0098-1.0256 (25.67-26.05)	1.161 (29.5)	MD610615
1.0295-1.0453 (26.15-26.55)	1.181 (30.0)	MD610616
1.0492-1.0650 (26.65-27.05)	1.201 (30.5)	MD610617
Over 1.0689 (27.15)	1.220 (31.0)	MD610618

GENERAL MOTORS IMPORTS

IDENTIFICATION

TRANSMISSION CODES

Application	Code
Spectrum	MXI

LUBRICATION

SERVICE INTERVALS

Check transaxle lubricant each time engine oil is changed or every 7,500 miles. Replace lubricant and sump filter every 30,000 miles.

CHECKING FLUID LEVEL

1) Park vehicle on level surface and apply parking brake. Place selector lever in Park, start engine and allow engine to idle for 2 minutes. Apply brakes, shift through all gears and return selector lever to Park.

2) Remove dipstick and carefully touch dipstick end to determine temperature of fluid. If fluid is cool or warm, fluid level should be between "COLD" range dimples. If fluid is too hot to touch, fluid level should be between "HOT" range dimples.

RECOMMENDED FLUID

Dexron II ATF.

FLUID CAPACITY

TRANSMISSION REFILL CAPACITIES

Application	Quantity
All	6.3 qts. (6.0L)

DRAINING & REFILLING

1) Remove drain plug located on lower part of differential and drain lubricant. Remove oil pan and discard pan gasket. Remove (3) bolts retaining sump filter to valve body. Remove filter and discard.

2) Install new sump filter and tighten bolts to 26-35 INCH lbs. (3-4 N.m). Install oil pan using a new gasket. Install drain plug, fill transaxle and check fluid level.

ADJUSTMENTS

SHIFT CONTROL CABLE

Loosen adjustment nuts at control rod link. With transaxle in Neutral detent, place selector lever in "N". Rotate link assembly clockwise to remove slack in cable. Tighten rear adjustment nut until it makes contact with link, then tighten front adjustment nut until it makes contact with link. *See Fig. 1.*

PARK LOCK CABLE

Place ignition key in "LOCK" position and selector lever in Park. Pull park cable forward at shifter bracket. Tighten forward nut until it makes contact with bracket, then tighten rear nut until it makes contact with bracket.

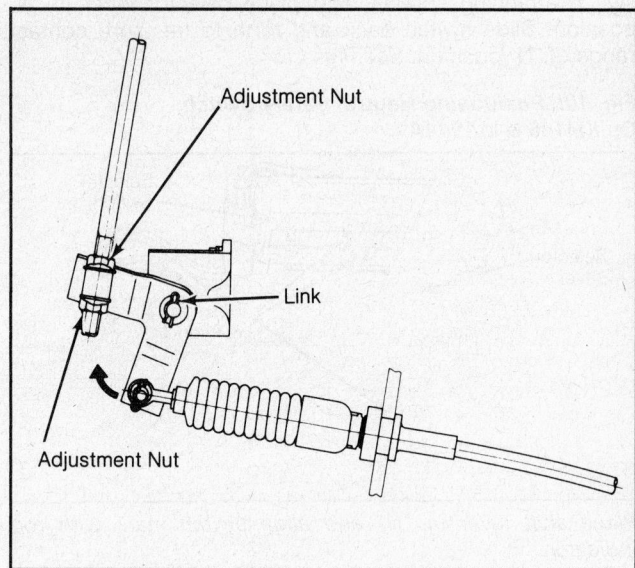

Fig. 1: Shift Control Cable Adjustment

HONDA

IDENTIFICATION

TRANSMISSION CODES

Application	Code
Accord & Prelude	Model AS Transaxle
Civic	Model AW Transaxle

LUBRICATION

SERVICE INTERVALS

Check fluid level at every oil change. Transmission fluid should be changed at 15,000 miles, then every 30,000. No filter service or band adjustment is required.

CHECKING FLUID LEVEL

1) With vehicle on level floor and at normal operating temperature, stop engine. Clean area around dipstick and unscrew dipstick. Remove dipstick and wipe clean, then insert into hole but do not screw down.

2) Remove dipstick and check level. Fluid should be between upper and lower marks. Add fluid as necessary. After Checking fluid level, screw the dipstick in securely. DO NOT use a wrench.

FLUID TYPE

All models use Dexron type automatic transmission fluid (ATF).

FLUID CAPACITY

TRANSMISSION REFILL CAPACITIES

Application	Refill Quantity	Dry Fill Quantity
Accord & Prelude ...	3.0 qts. (2.8L)	6.1 qts. (5.8L)
Civic	2.9 qts. (2.8L)	5.6 qts. 5.4L)

DRAINING & REFILLING

1) Ensure that operating temperature is up to normal and remove transmission drain plug. Use new gasket and replace drain plug when fluid is drained.

2) Fill with about 2 qts. (1.9L) of fluid through dipstick hole and check level. Add fluid to bring to upper mark on dipstick.

NOTE: **Refill capacity will always be slightly less than specified capacity due to fluid remaining in recesses of housing and converter.**

ADJUSTMENTS

SHIFT CONTROL CABLE

1) Ensure that reverse gear engages. Remove center console. Place shift lever in "D" position. Remove lock clip and control cable pin. Check that hole in cable end is perfectly aligned with holes in selector lever arm.

2) If not, loosen lock nuts on control cable and adjust as required. Tighten lock nuts and install pin with lock clip. If pin does not go in easily, further adjustment is required. Check gear operation. *See Fig. 1.*

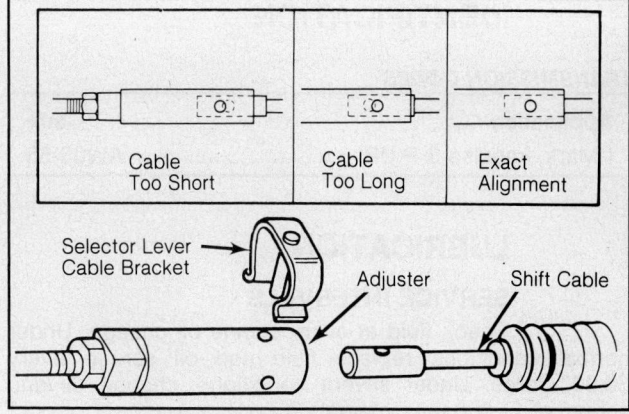

Fig. 1: Shift Control Cable Alignment

Cable Too Short | Cable Too Long | Exact Alignment

Selector Lever Cable Bracket — Adjuster — Shift Cable

THROTTLE CONTROL CABLE & BRACKET

1) Ensure that engine is warmed to normal operating temperature and cable securing clamps are in position. Disconnect control cable from lever and lay end on top of shock absorber tower.

2) Using throttle gauge (07974-6890300), adjust cable control bracket so that distance between bracket and lever is 3.29" (83.5 mm). Depress accelerator until there is no slack in carburetor throttle cable.

3) Adjust distance between control cable end and nut "A" to 3.3" (84.5 mm). Install cable and tighten lock nut "B", ensuring that lock nut "A" does not turn. *See Fig. 2.*

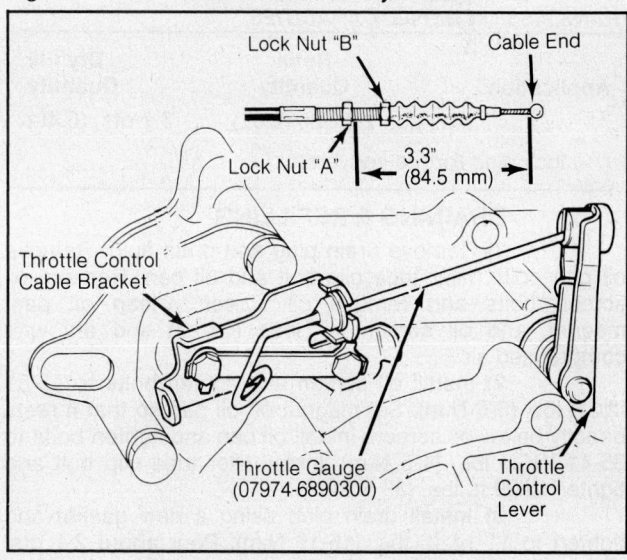

Fig. 2: Throttle Cable & Bracket Adjustment

Lock Nut "B" — Cable End
Lock Nut "A" — 3.3" (84.5 mm)
Throttle Control Cable Bracket
Throttle Gauge (07974-6890300) — Throttle Control Lever

NEUTRAL SAFETY SWITCH

Move selector lever to "P", "R" and "N" to check switch continuity. On all models, continuity between Black/White and Black/White terminals should be present in "P" and "N". On Accord and Prelude models, continuity between Green/Black and Green/Black terminals should be present when in "R". On Civic models, continuity between Yellow and Green/Black should be present when in "R".

Automatic Transmission Servicing

ISUZU

IDENTIFICATION

TRANSMISSION CODES

Application	Code
I-Mark, Impulse & P'UP	AW03-55

LUBRICATION

SERVICE INTERVALS

Check fluid at every engine oil change. Under normal conditions replace fluid and oil screen every 30,000 miles. Under severe conditions, change oil and screen at 15,000 mile intervals.

CHECKING FLUID LEVEL

1) Park vehicle on level surface, place selector lever in "P" position, set parking brake and allow engine to reach normal operating temperature. Apply brake pedal and move shift lever through each gear, then place shift lever in "P" position.

2) With engine idling, pull out dipstick, wipe clean and insert. Remove dipstick and check level reading. Fluid level should be between dimples of "HOT" range. If not, add ATF as necessary to bring fluid to proper level.

RECOMMENDED FLUID

Dexron II automatic transmission fluid.

FLUID CAPACITY

TRANSMISSION REFILL CAPACITIES

Application	Refill Quantity	Dry Fill [1] Quantity
All	2.1 qts. (2.0L)	6.7 qts. (6.4L)

[1] – Including torque converter.

DRAINING & REFILLING

1) Remove drain plug and drain fluid. Remove oil pan bolts, filler tube clip bolt and oil pan. Remove oil screen bolts and remove oil screen. Clean oil pan, magnet, and oil screen in clean solvent and dry with compressed air.

2) Install oil screen and tighten bolts to 43-51 INCH lbs. (5-6 N.m). Set magnet on oil pan so that it rests directly below oil screen. Install oil pan and tighten bolts to 35-41 INCH lbs. (4-5 N.m). Install filler tube clip bolt and tighten to 29 ft. lbs. (39 N.m).

3) Install drain plug using a new gasket and tighten to 11-14 ft. lbs. (15-19 N.m). Pour about 2.1 qts. (2.0L) of ATF through filler tube. Park vehicle on level surface and check fluid level. Add ATF as necessary to bring fluid to proper level.

ADJUSTMENTS

THROTTLE VALVE CABLE

Gasoline Engines

1) Loosen throttle valve cable adjusting nuts. Ensure that carburetor throttle adjusting screw is in contact with stopper for normal idling.

2) Adjust setting of outer cable, using adjusting nuts, so that distance between upper face of rubber boot on outer cable and cable stopper on inner cable is .032-.059" (0.8-1.5 mm). See Fig. 1.

Fig. 1: Gasoline Throttle Valve Cable Adjustment

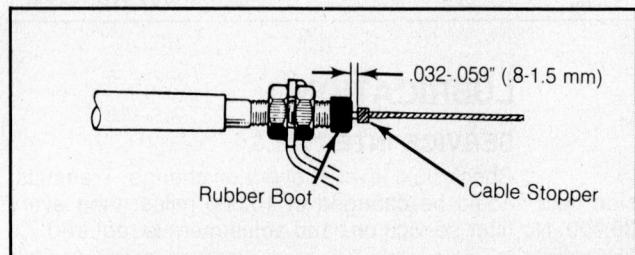

3) Tighten adjusting nuts. Check that stroke of inner cable from normal idling position to wide open throttle is 1.30-1.36" (32.0-34.5 mm).

Diesel Engines

1) Loosen throttle valve cable adjusting nuts. With accelerator pedal fully depressed, ensure that injection pump lever is in contact with maximum speed adjust screw.

2) Hold lever in this position. Adjust setting of outer cable, using adjusting nuts, so that distance between end of rubber boot on outer cable and cable stopper on inner cable is 0-.04" (0-1 mm). See Fig. 2.

Fig. 2: Diesel Throttle Valve Cable Adjustment

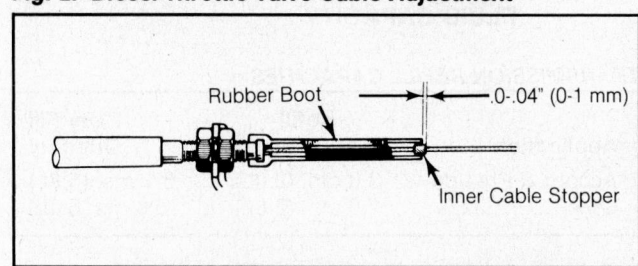

3) Tighten adjusting nuts. Check that stroke of inner cable from normal idling position to wide open throttle is 1.30-1.36" (32.0-34.5 mm).

SHIFT LINKAGE

1) Loosen shift control rod adjusting nuts on transmission. Turn manual shaft fully clockwise as viewed from right side (left side on P'UP) of transmission. Turn back to 3rd stop and set shaft in "N" position.

2) With transmission in "N", check that manual shift lever is in vertical position. Hold manual shaft in this position and place shift lever in "N".

3) To remove play, tighten adjusting nuts with control shaft lever pushed rearward together with shift control lever. Road test vehicle to ensure that shift lever moves properly and transmission operates smoothly in all gears.

NEUTRAL SAFETY SWITCH

Loosen switch retaining screws (near base of selector lever). Place selector lever in "N". Bring center of switch moving piece into alignment with line scribed on steel case of switch. Tighten retaining screws. Ensure that vehicle will only start in "P" or "N" position.

JAGUAR

IDENTIFICATION

TRANSMISSION CODES

Application	Code
XJ6	Borg-Warner 66
XJS	GM THM 400

LUBRICATION

SERVICE INTERVALS

Check fluid level at first 1,000 miles and then every 7,500 miles. Change fluid and filter at 30,000 mile intervals.

CHECKING FLUID LEVEL

1) Park vehicle on level ground. Apply hand brake and run engine at 750 RPM for several minutes. Place selector lever in all ranges and return to "P" position.

2) With engine idling, withdraw and wipe off dipstick. Replace dipstick in filler tube, withdraw it and check fluid level. If necessary, add fluid to reach "MAX" level on "COLD" side of dipstick. After adding fluid, repeat checking procedure to ensure overfilling has not occurred.

RECOMMENDED FLUID

XJ6
Type G automatic transmission fluid.
XJS
Dexron II automatic transmission fluid.

FLUID CAPACITY

TRANSMISSION REFILL CAPACITIES

Application	[1] Quantity
Borg-Warner 66	8.4 qts. (8.0L)
GM THM 400	19.2 pts. (9.1L)

[1] – Dry fill.

DRAINING & REFILLING

Borg-Warner 66
1) Disconnect dipstick/filler tube at oil pan and drain oil. Remove oil pan bolts and pan. Remove screws securing suction tube to valve body. Lower suction tube, discard gasket and remove filter.

2) Install oil filter and suction tube, using a new gasket. Clean and install oil pan. Connect dipstick/filler tube, add transmission fluid and check fluid level.

GM THM 400
1) Remove vacuum capsule clamp and bolt. Disconnect capsule and drain oil. Remove oil pan bolts, carefully lower pan and drain remaining oil. Remove oil filter bolt and filter.

2) Install oil filter. Clean and install oil pan, using a new gasket. Connect capsule, install clamp and tighten using bolt. Add transmission fluid and check fluid level.

ADJUSTMENTS

FRONT BAND
Borg-Warner 66
Remove nut securing selector lever to selector shaft and remove lever. Loosen lock nut retaining band adjustment screw and loosen screw 2 or 3 turns. Tighten screw to 60 INCH lbs. (7 N.m). Back off screw 3/4 of a turn. Tighten lock nut while holding screw in place.

REAR BAND
Borg-Warner 66
Loosen lock nut securing band adjustment screw and loosen screw 2 or 3 turns. Tighten screw to 60 INCH lbs. (7 N.m). Back off 3/4 of a turn. Tighten lock nut while holding screw in place.

DOWNSHIFT CABLE
Borg-Warner 66
1) Engine must be correctly tuned before attempting downshift cable adjustment. Using Allen wrench, remove plug from transmission and connect pressure gauge to transmission with adapter.

2) Feed gauge hose through passenger window, keeping hose clear of exhaust pipe. Block wheels and apply hand and foot brakes. Run engine to normal operating temperature.

3) With transmission selector in "D" position, pressure gauge should read 60-75 psi (4.2-5.3 kg/cm²) at idle speed. Increase engine speed to 1200 RPM. Gauge should now read 75-115 psi (5.3-8.1 kg/cm²).

4) If correct pressures are not obtained, turn engine off and place transmission in "N". Loosen lock nut on downshift cable, and turn adjustment nut on outer cable to alter pressure. See Fig. 1.

5) Increasing length of cable increases pressure. Decreasing length decreases pressure. When pressures are correct, tighten cable lock nut, install plug and road test vehicle.

Fig. 1: Downshift Cable Adjustment

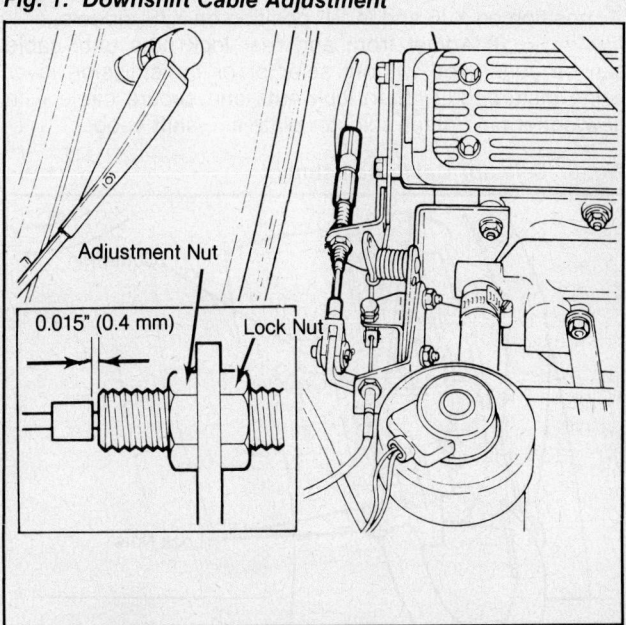

Ferrule crimped on inner cable should be 0.015" (0.4 mm) from threaded portion of outer cable.

Automatic Transmission Servicing

JAGUAR (Cont.)

KICKDOWN SWITCH
GM THM 400

1) With ignition on, check that power is available at input terminal (Green wire). With one lead of test lamp grounded, connect other lead to output terminal (Green/White wire).

2) Fully depress accelerator pedal, test lamp should light. If test lamp fails to light, release accelerator pedal and gently depress switch arm. If test lamp still does not light, replace kickdown switch.

3) If test lamp lights when switch arm is depressed, loosen switch screws and move switch toward cable until at full throttle opening test lamp lights. Tighten switch screws and recheck.

Fig. 2: Kickdown Switch Adjustment

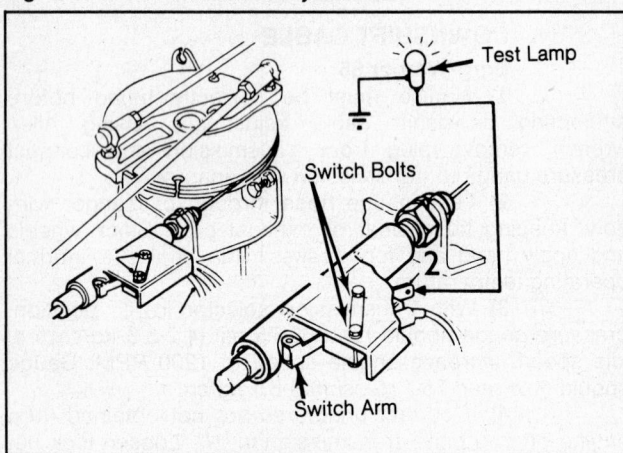

SELECTOR CABLE

1) Remove console and place selector lever in "1" position on XJ6 models, and in "N" position on XJS models. Unscrew shift knob and remove indicator plate.

2) Remove cotter pin and washer retaining cable to bracket on lever. Ensure transmission lever is in "1" position on XJ6 and in "N" position on XJS models.

3) Adjust front and rear lock nuts until cable can be connected without selector or transmission lever being disturbed. Tighten lock nuts and secure cable with new cotter pin. Install selector plate and shift knob.

Fig. 3: Selector Cable Adjustment

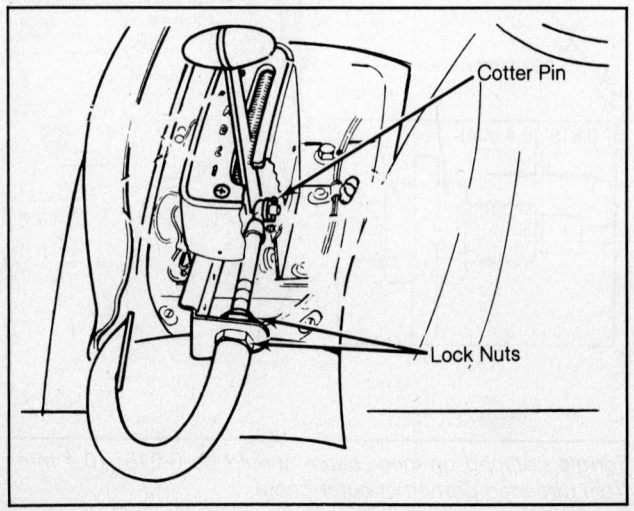

NEUTRAL SAFETY SWITCH

1) Remove selector indicator and position electric window switch panel away from console. Move control panel to gain access to cigar lighter wiring and door lock switch wiring. Note position of wires and disconnect.

2) Remove control panel. Disconnect feed wire to switch and connect self-powered test light to terminal. Place selector lever in "N" position and loosen lock nuts which secure the switch. Adjust switch until test lamp lights.

3) Tighten switch lock nuts and check that light remains on with lever in "P", and goes off with lever in any driving position. Remove test lamp, reconnect feed wire, and install all removed parts.

Fig. 4: Neutral Safety Switch Adjustment

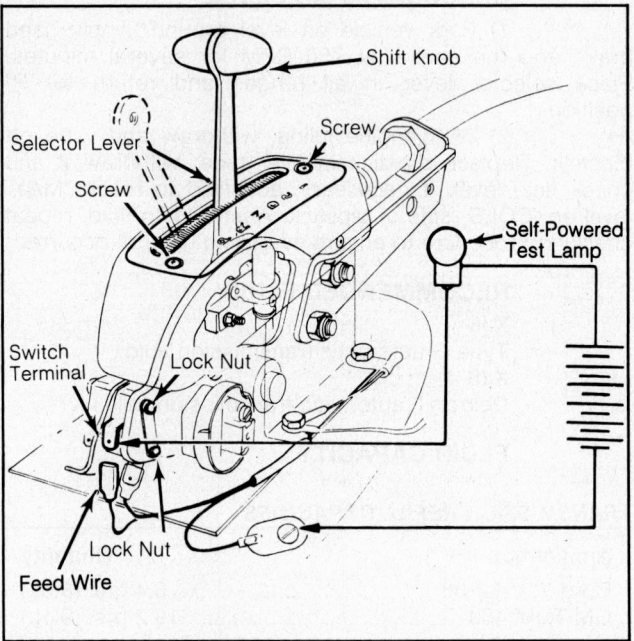

MAZDA

IDENTIFICATION

TRANSMISSION CODES

Application	Codes
B2000	3N71B
GLC & 626	F3A
RX7	L4N71B

LUBRICATION

SERVICE INTERVALS

Check fluid level every 7,500 miles or every 8 months, whichever occurs first.

CHECKING FLUID LEVEL

1) Park vehicle on level ground. Apply parking brake firmly and run engine at idle for approximately 2 minutes. Briefly place selector lever in all gears, and return to "P" position.

2) Clean dipstick cap and remove dipstick. Wipe dipstick and insert in filler tube. Remove dipstick and note reading. Level should be between "L" and "F" marks. Add fluid through filler tube, if necessary. Do not overfill.

RECOMMENDED FLUID

Type F automatic transmission fluid.

FLUID CAPACITY

TRANSMISSION REFILL CAPACITIES

Application	Quantity
B2000 & RX7	6.6 qts. (6.2L)
GLC & 626	6.0 qts. (5.7L)

DRAINING & REFILLING

B2000 & RX7

Remove oil pan bolts and drain fluid. Remove oil pan and discard gasket. Clean oil pan and install, using a new gasket. Tighten oil pan bolts to 43-72 INCH lbs. (5-8 N.m). Add fluid through filler tube and check fluid level. Do not overfill.

GLC & 626

1) Remove drain plug on bottom of differential and drain fluid. If transaxle is to be completely drained, remove oil pan bolts and drain remaining fluid. Remove oil pan and discard gasket.

2) Clean oil pan and install, using a new gasket. Tighten oil pan bolts to 43-72 INCH lbs. (5-8 N.m). Add fluid through filler tube and check fluid level. Do not overfill.

ADJUSTMENTS

BRAKE BAND

B2000

Remove oil pan to adjust brake band. Loosen servo piston stem lock nut. Tighten servo piston stem to 108-132 INCH lbs. (12-15 N.m), then back off piston stem 2 turns. Hold piston stem in this position and tighten lock nut to 11-29 ft. lbs. (15-39 N.m).

GLC & 626

NOTE: **Make this adjustment with oil pump installed. Apply sealant to anchor bolt threads.**

Loosen lock nut on brake band anchor bolt. Tighten brake band anchor bolt to 108-132 INCH lbs. (12-15 N.m), then back off bolt 2 turns. Hold brake band anchor bolt in this position and tighten lock nut to 41-59 ft. lbs. (56-80 N.m).

Fig. 1: GLC & 626 Brake Band Adjustment

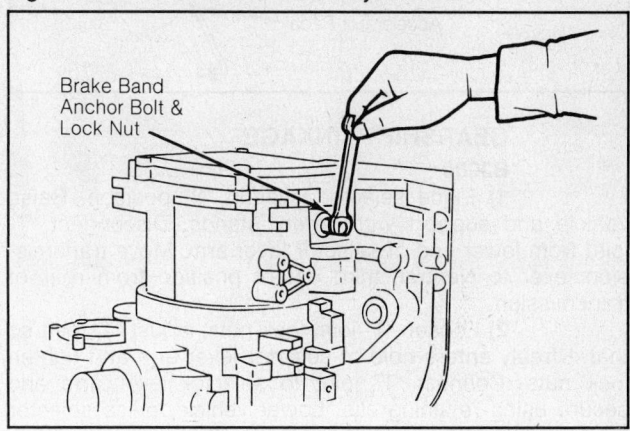

Brake Band
Anchor Bolt &
Lock Nut

RX7

1) Remove overdrive brake band servo cover to adjust overdrive brake band. Remove oil pan to adjust 2nd gear brake band. Loosen overdrive brake band and 2nd gear brake band servo piston stem lock nuts.

2) Tighten overdrive brake band servo piston stem to 61-86 INCH lbs. (7-10 N.m), then back off piston stem 2 turns. Hold piston stem in this position and tighten lock nut to 11-29 ft. lbs. (15-39 N.m).

3) Tighten 2nd gear brake band servo piston stem to 108-132 INCH lbs. (12-15 N.m), then back off piston stem 3 turns. Hold piston stem in this position and tighten lock nut to 11-29 ft. lbs. (15-39 N.m).

Fig. 2: RX7 Brake Band Adjustment

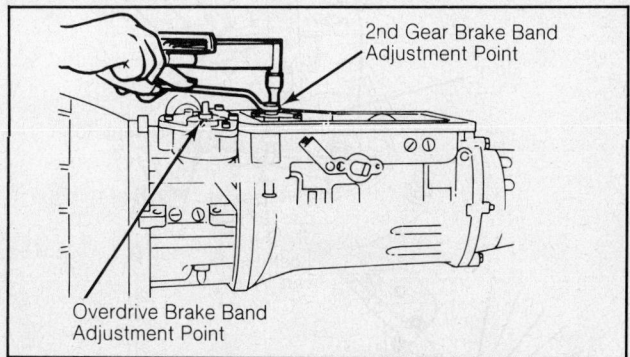

2nd Gear Brake Band
Adjustment Point

Overdrive Brake Band
Adjustment Point

KICKDOWN SWITCH & DOWNSHIFT SOLENOID

All Models

1) Depress accelerator pedal to limit. Near wide open throttle, click should be heard from solenoid. Switch must operate at or after 7/8 of pedal travel.

2) If not, loosen switch retaining nut and adjust switch to engage when pedal is at 7/8 of its full travel, tighten retaining nut and check solenoid.

Automatic Transmission Servicing

MAZDA (Cont.)

Fig. 3: Kickdown Switch and Downshift Solenoid

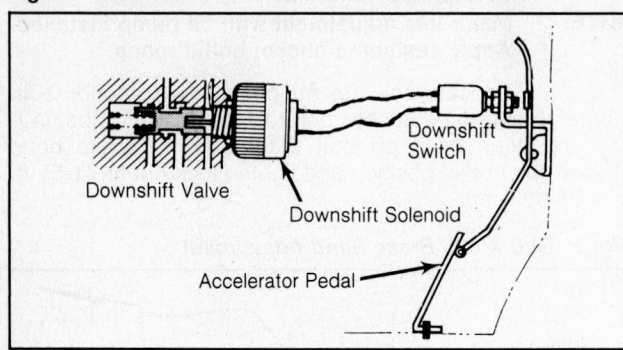

GEARSHIFT LINKAGE

B2000

1) Place selector lever in "N" position. Raise vehicle and support with safety stands. Disconnect "T" joint from lower end of selector lever arm. Move transmission lever to Neutral, third detent position from rear of transmission.

2) Loosen "T" joint lock nuts, adjust "T" joint so that it freely enters hole of selector lever arm and tighten lock nuts. Connect "T" joint to selector lever arm and secure using retaining clip. Lower vehicle, place selector lever in each position to ensure that selector lever functions properly.

GLC & 626

1) Loosen lock nuts "A" and "B" at "T" joint and place selector lever in "N" position. Move transaxle lever to Neutral, fourth detent position away from transaxle.

2) Turn lock nut "A" until it comes in contact with "T" joint, then tighten lock nut "B". Move selector lever toward "P" until lever on transaxle begins to move and check amount of movement.

Fig. 4: GLC & 626 Gearshift Linkage Adjustment

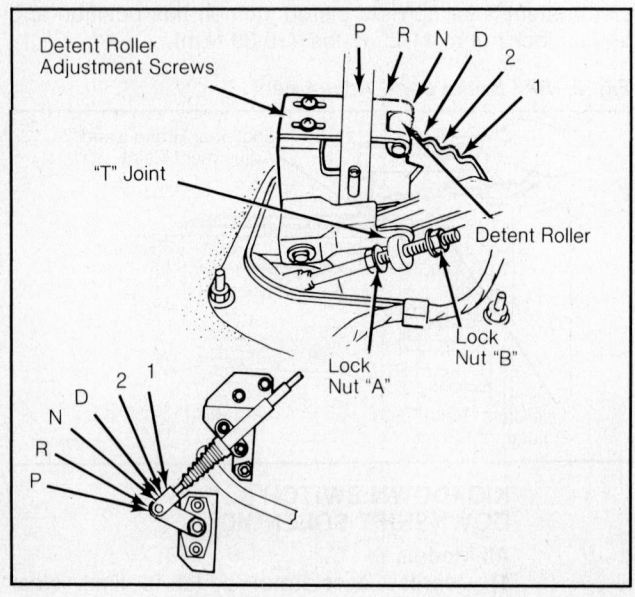

3) Move lever toward "D" until lever on transaxle begins to move and check amount of movement. Amount of movement should be equal. If movement toward "P" is greater than movement toward "D", loosen lock nut "B" and tighten lock nut "A" so that movement becomes smaller.

4) If movement toward "D" is greater than movement toward "P", loosen lock nut "A" and tighten lock nut "B" so that movent becomes smaller. Ensure that when selector lever is shifted from "P" to "1" position that a "click" can be felt in each position and that gear corresponds to that of position plate.

5) Ensure that lever can be shifted between "D" and "N" without depressing push button. If lever can be shifted from "D" to "R" without depressing push button, or if push button is loose. Adjust selector lever handle.

RX7

1) Remove boot plate. Place selector lever in "P" position. Loosen selector lever plate adjustment bolt. Raise vehicle and support with safety stands. Move transmission selector rod to "P" position, first detent from rear of transmission.

2) Tighten selector lever plate adjustment bolt to 23-34 ft. lbs. (32-47 N.m). Lower vehicle, place selector lever in each position to ensure that selector lever functions properly.

SELECTOR LEVER HANDLE

B2000 & RX7

1) Place selector lever in "N" or "D" position. Loosen lock nut below selector lever handle and turn handle until no play exist in push button. Unscrew selector lever handle 1 full turn until button is on driver's side.

2) Push button and and ensure that lever can be shifted into "P" position. If lever cannot be shifted into "P", turn lever in 1 full turn. Repeat procedure until lever can be shifted into "P" position.

3) Ensure that lever cannot be shifted from "N" to "R" or from "D" to "2" without depressing push button. If lever can be shifted into "R" or "2" without depressing button, selector lever has been turned in too much, turn selector lever out.

4) After adjustment is complete, check protrusion of push button. Protrusion should be 3/16-9/32 in. (4.8-7.1 mm). Place selector lever in each position and ensure that selector lever functions properly. Tighten lock nut to 11-15 ft. lbs. (15-20 N.m).

GLC & 626

1) Place selector lever in "P" position. Loosen lock nut below selector lever handle and turn nut and handle until they bottom. Unscrew selector lever handle 1 full turn until button is on driver's side. Tighten lock nut to 11-15 ft. lbs. (15-20 N.m).

2) Ensure that selector lever functions properly. If button does not operate smoothly, set lever in "P" position and loosen detent roller adjustment screws and adjust by moving detent roller.

NEUTRAL SAFETY SWITCH

B2000 & RX7

1) Check and adjust gearshift linkage on B2000. Place transmission lever in Neutral, third detent position from rear of transmission on B2000. Place selector lever in "N" position on RX7.

2) Loosen neutral safety switch attaching bolts and remove screw from alignment pin hole from bottom of switch. Rotate switch and insert a 0.059 in. (1.5 mm) alignment pin through alignment holes.

3) Tighten attaching bolts and remove alignment pin. Install alignment pin hole screw and check operation of switch. Vehicle should start in "P" and "N" positions only.

MAZDA (Cont.)

GLC & 626

NOTE: The following instructions are for checking neutral safety switch. No adjustments are possible.

   1) Ensure that vehicle starts in "P" and "N" positions only. Make sure that back-up lights illuminate with selector lever in "R". If switch is faulty, disconnect it and check continuity between each terminal.

   2) With selector lever in "P" or "N", continuity should exist between terminals "A" and "B". With lever in "R" position, continuity shold exist between terminals "C" and "D".

Fig. 5: Neutral Safety Switch Continuity Check

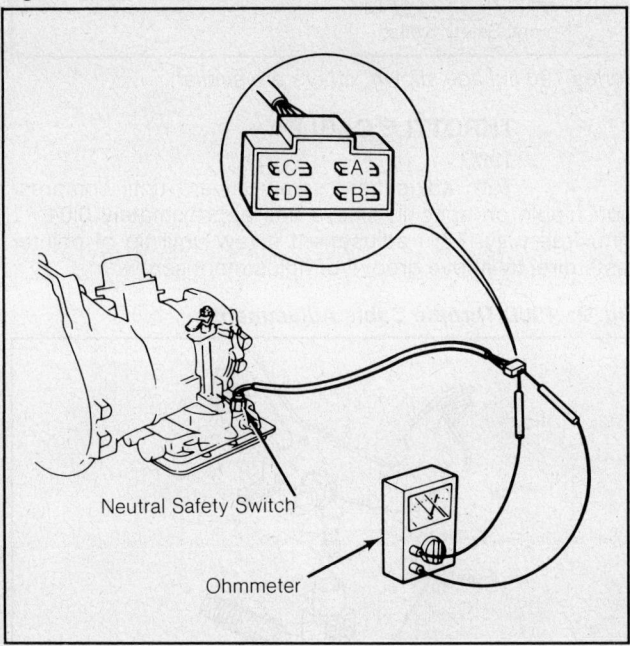

Neutral Safety Switch

Ohmmeter

Automatic Transmission Servicing

MERCEDES-BENZ

IDENTIFICATION

TRANSMISSION CODES

Application	Code
190 Series	W4A020
300, 380 & 500 Series	W4A040

LUBRICATION

SERVICE INTERVALS

Check fluid level at first 800-1000 miles and every 15,000 miles thereafter. Change fluid and filter every 30,000 miles. Under severe service conditions, change fluid every 15,000 miles.

CHECKING FLUID LEVEL

With transmission fluid at a normal operating temperature of 176°F (80°C), park vehicle on level surface. Place selector lever in "P" position and set parking brake. Allow engine to idle for 2 minutes, measure fluid level with dipstick completely inserted and locking lever released.

RECOMMENDED FLUID

Dexron II automatic transmission fluid.

FLUID CAPACITY

TRANSMISSION REFILL CAPACITIES

Application	Refill	Dry fill
190 Series	5.8 qts. (5.5L)	7.0 qts. (6.6L)
300 Series	6.6 qts. (6.2L)	7.7 qts. (7.3L)
380 & 500 Series	8.1 qts. (7.7L)	9.1 qts. (8.6L)

DRAINING & REFILLING

1) Disconnect fill tube from oil pan and drain fluid. Rotate engine until torque converter drain plug is at bottom of torque converter housing. Remove plug and drain fluid. Install plug, using a new sealing ring. Remove oil pan and filter.

2) Install filter and oil pan, using a new gasket. Attach fill tube, using new sealing rings on hollow screw. Add approximately 4.2 qts. (4.0L) of automatic transmission fluid.

3) Apply parking brake and start engine with lever in "P" position. Run engine at idle speed and gradually add fluid. Momentarily place selector lever in each gear, then return to "P" position. Check fluid level and adjust if necessary. Do not overfill.

ADJUSTMENTS

SHIFT LINKAGE

Disconnect control rod from selector lever. Place transmission lever in "N" (vertical) position. Loosen lock nut at end of control rod and adjust control rod length so that approximately 0.04" (1 mm) clearance exists between selector lever and "N" stop on gate plate. Connect control rod, secure and tighten lock nut.

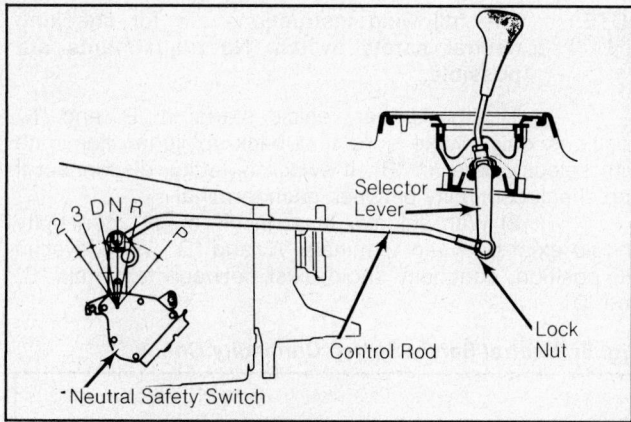

Fig. 1: Shift Linkage Adjustment

Series 190 linkage shown, others are similar.

THROTTLE CABLE
190D

Turn adjustment screw inward until compression nipple on spacing sleeve has approximately 0.04" (1 mm) free play. Turn adjustment screw until tip of pointer rests directly above groove of adjustment screw.

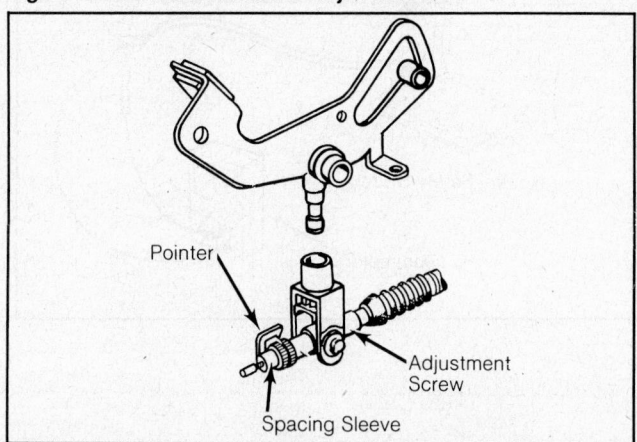

Fig. 2: 190D Throttle Cable Adjustment

190E

Disconnect control cable. Extend telescoping rod to maximum length. Pull control cable forward until a slight resistance is felt. Hold ball socket in this position. Ball socket should fit freely into ball. Adjust rod length, if necessary.

300 Series

Disconnect control cable. Push ball socket rearward, then pull forward until resistance is felt. Hold ball socket in this position. Ball socket should fit freely into ball. Adjust cable length, if necessary.

380 & 500 Series

Remove air cleaner. Loosen adjustment screw on connecting rod. Extend connecting rod then retract, until resistance is felt. Tighten adjustment screw and install air cleaner.

NEUTRAL SAFETY SWITCH

Loosen neutral safety switch screws and insert a 5/32" (4 mm) drill through adjustment hole and into housing. Tighten screws and remove drill. Ensure that vehicle starts in "P" and "N" positions only.

MITSUBISHI

IDENTIFICATION

TRANSMISSION CODES

Application	Code
Cordis & Tredia	KM172
Pickup	
2WD	MA904A
4WD	[1] KM146
Starion	JM600

[1] – Includes MA904A transmission and transfer case.

LUBRICATION

SERVICE INTERVAL

Check oil level every 15,000 miles. Change oil every 30,000 miles or if under severe usage, change every 15,000 miles.

CHECKING FLUID LEVEL

1) Position vehicle on a level surface and set parking brake. Run engine at idle. Move selector lever through all positions, ending in "N".

2) With engine at normal operating temperature, remove dipstick and wipe with a clean cloth, and check oil level. Oil level must be between "FULL" and "ADD" mark of dipstick.

CAUTION: **If severe darkening of the fluid and a strong odor is noted, fluid and filter should be changed and bands adjusted.**

RECOMMENDED FLUID

All transmissions use Dexron or Dexron II automatic transmission fluid. Transfer Case uses API GL-4 SAE 90.

FLUID CAPACITY

TRANSMISSION REFILL CAPACITIES

Application	Quanity
Mitsubishi	
KM146	7.2 qts. (6.8L)
KM172	6.0 qts. (5.6L)
JM600	7.4 qts. (7.0L)
Torqueflite	
MA904A	7.2 (6.8L)
Transfer Case	2.3 qts. (2.2L)

DRAINING & REFILLING
KM146, JM600 & MA904A

1) Carefully remove oil pan and drain fluid. Install new filter on bottom of valve body. Clean oil pan, replace gasket and install oil pan. Pour 4 qts. (3.8L) of specified fluid through filler tube. Idle engine for 2 minutes.

2) Shift transmission into each position, ending in "N" position. Check fluid level with engine running at idle and add sufficient fluid to bring level to "ADD 1 PINT" mark. Recheck fluid level after transmission is at normal operating temperature. See Fluid Checking Level.

KM172

1) Remove drain plugs from both differential and oil pan and drain fluid. If replacing filter, remove bolts and lower oil pan. Install new filter on bottom of valve body. Replace pan gasket and install pan.

2) Tighten differential plug to 22-25 ft. lbs. (30-34 N.m) and pan plug to 18-21 ft. lbs. (24-28 N.m). Ensure that dipstick hole area is clean and pour in approximately 4.2 qts. (4.0L) of "DEXRON II" fluid.

3) Run engine for 2 minutes at idle. Shift transmission to each position, ending in "N" position. After reaching normal operating temperature, fluid should be between upper and lower marks of "HOT" range.

ADJUSTMENTS

FRONT (KICKDOWN) BAND
KM146 & MA904A

1) Front (kickdown) band adjuster screw is located on left side of transmission case. To adjust band, loosen and back off lock nut about 5 turns.

2) Using wrench (C-3380-A) with adapter (C-3705), tighten band adjuster screw to 52 INCH lbs. (5.9 N.m). See Fig. 1.

3) If adapter (C-3705) is not used, tighten adjuster screw to 51 INCH lbs. (5.8 N.m), which is the true torque. Back off adjusting screw 3 1/2 turns, hold adjuster screw and tighten lock nut to 37 ft lbs. (50 N.m).

Fig. 1: KM146 & MA904A
Front (Kickdown) Band Adjusting Screw Location

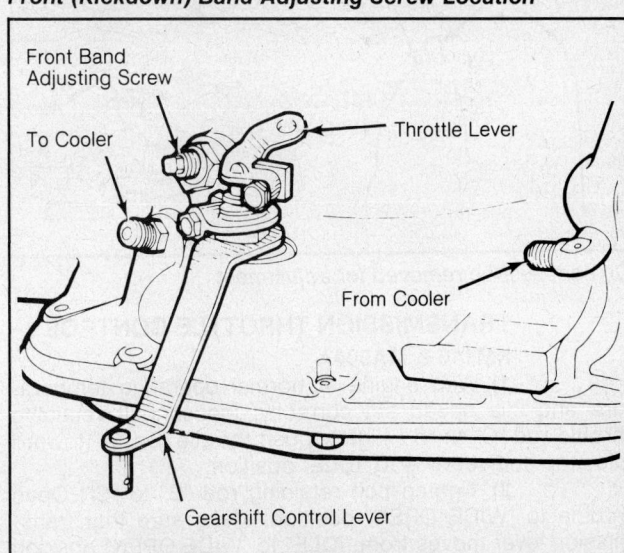

KM172

1) Clean all dirt from kickdown servo cover and remove snap ring. Remove cover and loosen lock nut. Hold servo piston from turning and tighten adjusting screw to 88 INCH lbs. (10 N.m) and back it off.

2) Repeat torquing twice to seat kickdown band against drum. Tighten adjusting screw to 44 INCH lbs. (5 N.m) and back off 3 1/2 turns. Hold screw and tighten lock nut. Install cover and snap ring.

NOTE: **Install new seal ring with "D" shaped section to outside of cover. If reusing old seal ring, make certain it is not distorted.**

Fig. 2: KM172 Kickdown Band Adjustment

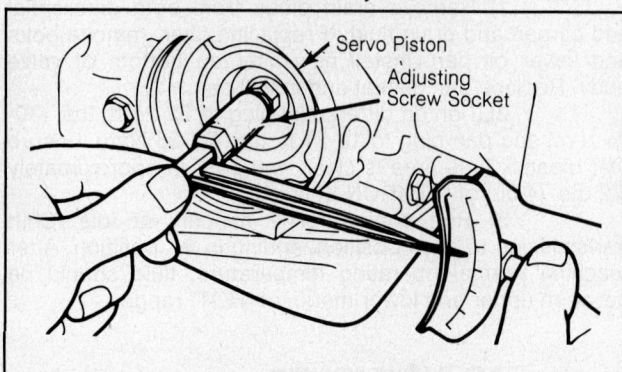

Hold piston and turn adjusting screw.

REAR BAND
KM146 & MA904A
1) Remove oil pan. Loosen lock nut and adjusting screw at servo end of lever and tighten screw to 43 INCH lbs. (4.9 N.m) of torque.
2) Back off screw 7 turns. Hold adjusting screw and tighten lock nut to 29 ft. lbs. (40 N.m). Reinstall oil pan.

Fig. 3: KM146 & MA904A
Rear Band Adjusting Screw Location

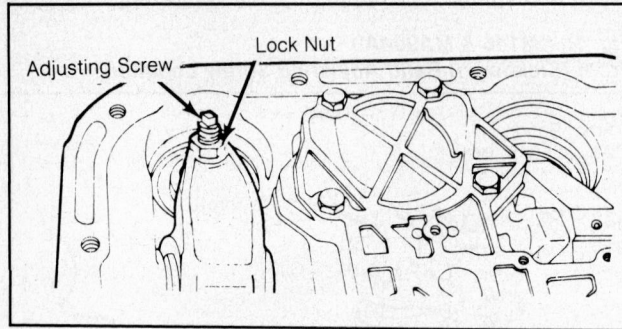

Oil pan must be removed for adjustment.

TRANSMISSION THROTTLE CONTROL
KM146 & MA904A
1) With engine at normal operating temperature and idle speed set correctly, loosen bolt retaining throttle rod "C" to "B". Lightly push throttle rod "A" toward idle stop and set rods to "IDLE" position.
2) Tighten bolt retaining rod "B" to "C". Open throttle to "WIDE OPEN" position. Make sure that transmission lever moves from "IDLE" to "WIDE OPEN" position (total movement 47.5° to 54°). Some play should still exist in throttle lever stroke at wide open throttle.

Fig. 4: KM146 & MA904A
Throttle Rod Adjustment

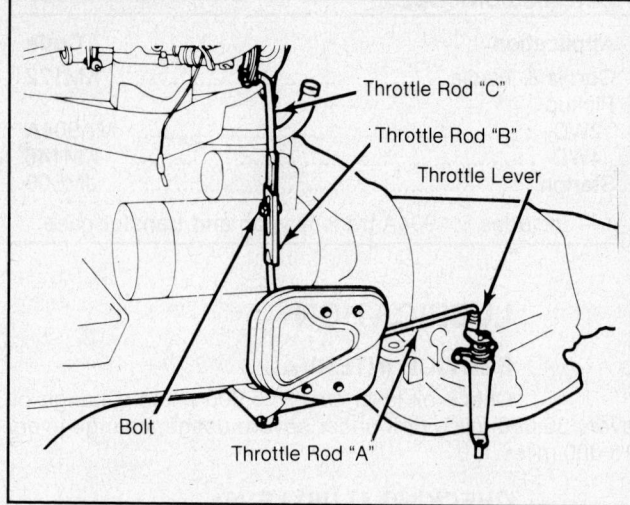

Make sure that transmission lever moves from "IDLE" to "WIDE OPEN" position.

KM172
1) Ensure that carburetor throttle lever is at "CURB IDLE" position, engine is at operating temperature, and fast idle condition has been reset. Raise cover "B" and loosen cable bracket mounting bolt.
2) Move lower cable bracket until distance between nipple and top cover "A" of throttle cable is adjusted to .02-.06" (.5-1.5 mm). See Fig. 5. Tighten lower cable bracket mounting bolt.
3) With throttle lever in "WIDE OPEN" position, pull cable upward to ensure freedom of cable movement.

Fig. 5: KM172 Throttle Cable Adjustment

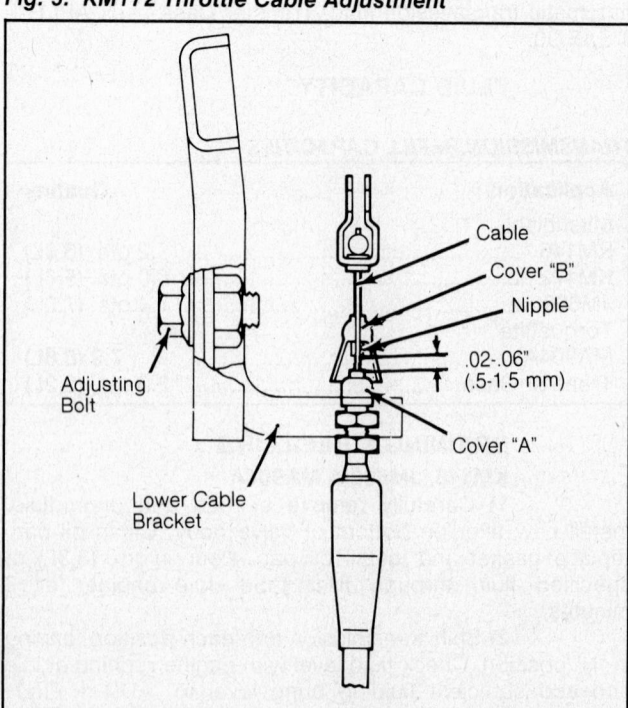

Pull back cover "B" to loosen bracket nut.

MITSUBISHI (Cont.)

SHIFT LINKAGE
KM146, MA904A & JM600

1) Remove shift handle by loosening set screw and pulling off handle. Place selector lever in "N" and turn adjusting cam in top of lever until surface "A" of cam is flush with end of selector lever "B". See Fig. 7.

Fig. 6: Adjusting Selector Cam Rod On KM146 & MA904A

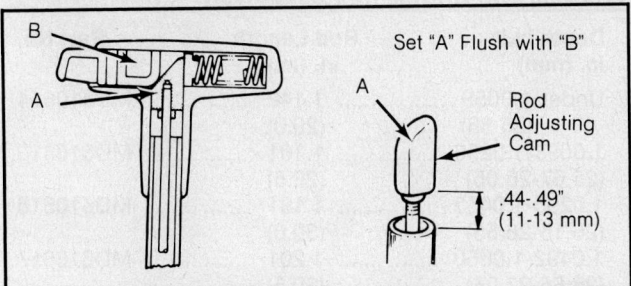

Rod cam Surface "A" and push button must be flush. JM600 is similar.

2) Loosen lock nut at connection of rod and arm at transmission. Place transmission lever arm in "N". Place selector lever in "N" and tighten lock nut to adjust control rod length.

KM172

1) Place selector in "N" position. Loosen set screw retaining handle to lever. Push selector knob and turn handle to give .008-.035" (.2-.9 mm) clearance between selector lever end pin and detent plate. See Fig. 7.

Fig. 7: Adjusting Selector Lever On KM172 Transaxle

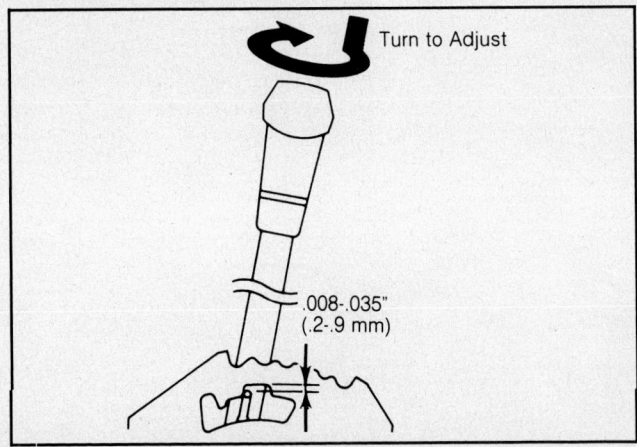

To adjust, depress knob and turn handle.

2) When knob button is on driver's side, tighten set screw. With selector lever and neutral safety switch in "N" position, turn adjusting nuts at cable end until slack is removed from control cable.

NOTE: After adjustment, confirm that every selector position of position indicator is set properly.

NEUTRAL SAFETY SWITCH
KM146 & MA904A

NOTE: Safety switch is located under shift lever console and is operated by shift lever. This switch also operates back-up lights and seat belt warning system.

1) To adjust switch, remove console, loosen switch attaching screws, and place selector lever in "N" position. Slide switch back and forth to measure contact range of "N" position. See Fig. 8.

Fig. 8: Adjusting Neutral Safety Switch Movement On KM146 & MA904A

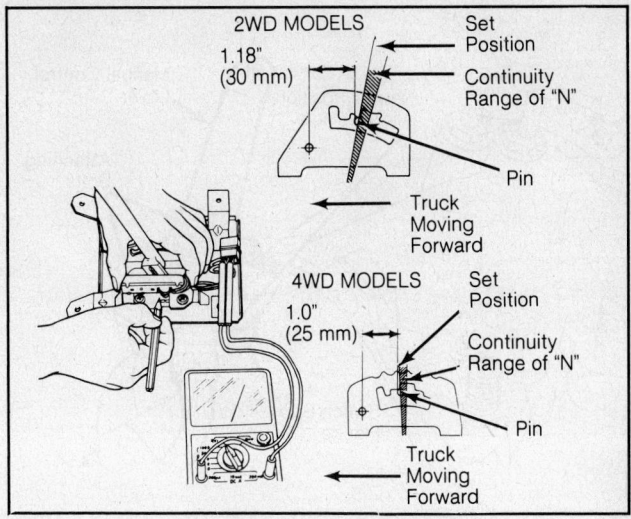

Connect tester to switch terminals (BY-BY).

2) Install switch and adjust so there is .06" (1.5 mm) for 2WD Pickup and .1" (2.5 mm) for 4WD Pickup, side clearance between selector lever and switch. See Fig. 9. Set selector lever in "P", "R", and "N" positions and check continuity of terminals. After confirming continuity, tighten switch attaching screws and reinstall console.

NOTE: If correct continuity cannot be achieved, reposition safety switch.

Fig. 9: Adjusting Neutral Safety Switch On KM146 & MA904A

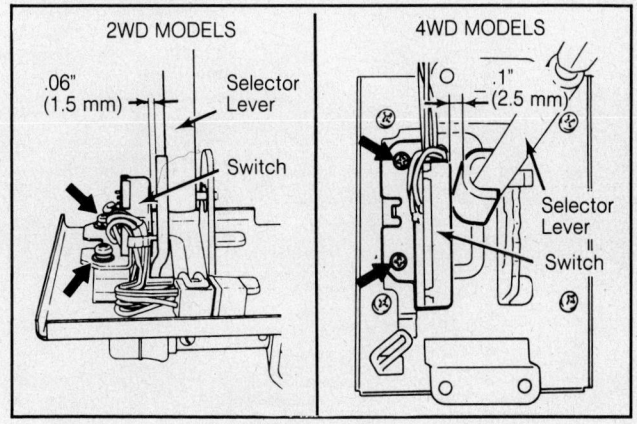

MITSUBISHI (Cont.)

KM172 & JM600

Place transmission control lever in "N" position and loosen switch retaining bolts. Turn switch body so that aligning hole end of lever overlaps switch body flange (on JM600 insert alignment pin) and tigthten bolts. See Fig. 10.

Fig. 10 Adjusting Neutral Saftry Switch On KM172 Transaxle

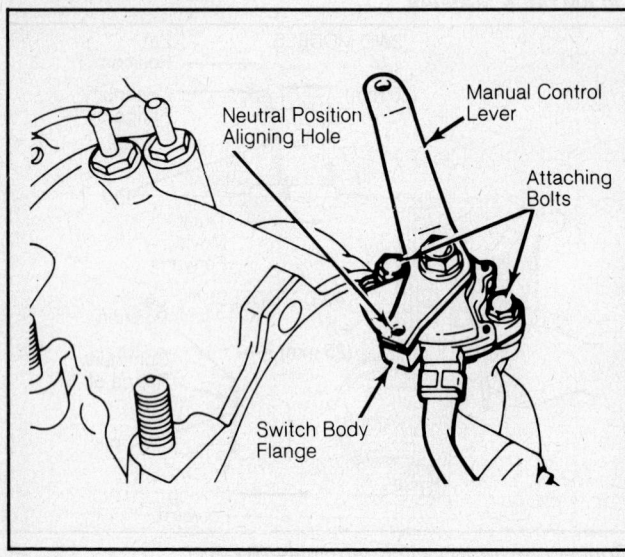

Align lever hole with housing hole. JM600 is similar.

VACUUM DIAPHRAGM ROD

JM600

Disconnect vacuum hose at vacuum diaphragm and remove diaphragm from transmission case. Using depth gauge, measure depth "L". Be sure vacuum throttle valve is pushed into valve body as far as possible. See VACUUM DIAPHRAGM ROD SELECTION table.

VACUUM DIAPHRAGM ROD SELECTION

Depth "L" in. (mm)	Rod Length in. (mm)	Part No.
Under 1.0059 (25.55)	1.142 (29.0)	MD610614
1.0098-1.0256 (25.67-26.05)	1.161 (29.5)	MD610615
1.0295-1.0453 (26.15-26.55)	1.181 (30.0)	MD610616
1.0492-1.0650 (26.65-27.05)	1.201 (30.5)	MD610617
Over 1.0689 (27.15)	1.220 (31.0)	MD610618

NISSAN/DATSUN

IDENTIFICATION

TRANSMISSION CODES

Application	Code
FWD	
Pulsar & Stanza	RL3F01A
Sentra	
Diesel	RN4F30A
Gas	RL3F01A
RWD	
Maxima	L4N71B
Pickup	L3N71B
200SX & 200SX Turbo	L4N71B
300ZX & 300ZX Turbo	E4N71B

LUBRICATION

SERVICE INTERVAL

Inspect fluid level every 15,000 miles or 12 months. If under severe usage, change every 30,000 miles or 24 months.

CHECKING FLUID LEVEL

Transaxle & Transmission

1) Check fluid with engine and transmission at normal operating temperatures (this is reached after several minutes of driving). With vehicle standing level and at idle, shift transmission through all positions and return to "P" position.

2) Clean area around dipstick. Remove dip stick, wipe clean, insert and withdraw. Level should be between "H" and "L" marks, if not, add as necessary.

NOTE: Normal fluid should be clear with a pink color and should not have a strong odor.

Transfer Case

Oil level should be at bottom of fill hole.

NOTE: If fluid has a strong, burned odor or is dark in color, overheating and internal wear may be indicated. If milky in appearance, moisture from cooling system or road may have entered the system. Foamy or excessively bubbled fluid indicates overfilling and aeration.

FLUID CAPACITY

TRANSMISSION REFILL CAPACITIES

Application	Code
FWD	
RL3F01A	6.4 qts. (6.0L)
RN4F30A	6.4 qts. (6.0L)
RWD	
L3N71B	5.9 qts. (5.5L)
L4N71B	7.4 qts. (7.0L)
E4N71B	7.4 qts. (7.0L)
Transfer Case	1.5 (1.4L)

RECOMMENDED FLUID

All transmissions use Dexron or Dexron II automatic transmission fluid. All transfer cases use SAE 80W/90 (API GL-4).

DRAINING & REFILLING

Transaxle & Transmission

1) Loosen oil pan bolts and allow ATF to drain. Remove oil pan and clean pan and screen thoroughly. Install pan using a new gasket. Add fluid through filler tube.

2) Run engine at idle speed for about 2 minutes, then at fast idle (1200 RPM) for several more minutes, until normal operating temperatures are reached. Shift transmission through all gears and return to "P" (Park). Check fluid level and add to obtain appropriate level.

ADJUSTMENTS

BRAKE BAND

Transmission

Loosen piston stem lock nut and tighten piston stem (adjusting screw) to 106-132 INCH lbs. (12-15 N.m). Back off piston stem 2 turns. While holding servo piston stem stationary, tighten lock nut to 177 INCH lbs. (20 N.m).

Transaxle

Loosen lock nut. Torque anchor end pin to 35-53 INCH lbs. (4-6 N.m). Back off anchor end pin 2 1/2 turns. Tighten lock nut (while holding anchor pin), to 141-195 INCH lbs. (16-22 N.m).

SHIFT LINKAGE

RWD

1) Starting in "P" position, shift through all positions to "1" position. If detents cannot be felt or pointer is improperly aligned, linkage must be adjusted.

2) Place shift lever in "D" position and loosen lock nuts on rod. Turn lock nuts until pointer aligns properly and all detents can be felt. Tighten lock nuts and recheck positions, ensuring that full detent is felt in "P" position.

NOTE: If unable to adjust, grommets at ends of rod may be worn or damaged and require replacement.

FWD

1) Place control lever at "P" position. Connect control cable end to manual lever of transaxle unit and tighten control cable retaining bolts. Move control lever from "P" to "1".

2) Make sure that control lever can move smoothly and without any sliding noise. Place control lever at "P". Make sure that control lever locks at "P". Remove lock nut at control cable and loosen adjusting nut. Connect control cable to trunnion.

3) Adjust and tighten adjusting nut. Install and tighten lock nut. Move control lever from "P" to "1" again. Make sure that control lever can move smoothly and without sliding noise. Apply grease to spring washer.

Automatic Transmission Servicing

NISSAN/DATSUN (Cont.)

KICKDOWN SWITCH

RWD

Kickdown switch is located at top of accelerator pedal post. A "click" should be heard just before accelerator bottoms out when depressed. If not, loosen switch lock nut and adjust.

NOTE: Do not allow switch to close too soon, for downshift will occur at part throttle.

NEUTRAL SAFETY SWITCH

1) Switch operates back-up lights and prevents starting except in "P" or "N". To adjust, ensure that transmission is in "N" with lever at transmission in vertical position.

2) Remove alignment hole screw at bottom of switch and loosen retaining bolts. Move switch until alignment pin, .08" (2 mm) for RWD or .098" (2.5 mm) for FWD, can be inserted in rotor. Tighten retaining bolts and replace alignment hole screw.

Fig. 1: Adjusting Neutral Safety Switch

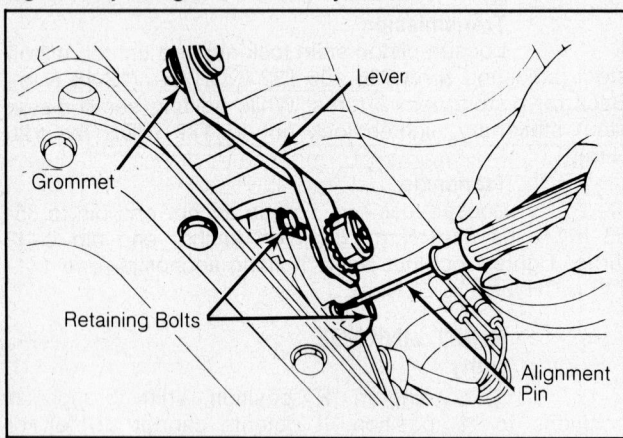

Safety switch for transaxle is similar.

VACUUM DIAPHRAGM ROD

E4N71B

Disconnect vacuum hose at vacuum diaphragm and remove diaphragm from transmission case. Using depth gauge, measure depth "L". Be sure vacuum throttle valve is pushed into valve body as far as possible. See VACUUM DIAPHRAGM ROD SELECTION table.

VACUUM DIAPHRAGM ROD SELECTION

Depth "L" in. (mm)	Rod Length in. (mm)	Part No.
Under 1.0059 (25.55)	1.142 (29.0)	31932-X0103
1.0098-1.0256 (25.67-26.05)	1.161 (29.5)	31932-X0104
1.0295-1.0453 (26.15-26.55)	1.181 (30.0)	31932-X0100
1.0492-1.0650 (26.65-27.05)	1.201 (30.5)	31932-X0102
Over 1.0689 (27.15)	1.220 (31.0)	31932-X0101

PEUGEOT

IDENTIFICATION

TRANSMISSION CODES

Application	Codes
505	ZF 3HP 22

LUBRICATION

SERVICE INTERVALS

Check transmission level at every oil change. Drain and refill transmission every 30,000 miles or 2 years, whichever comes first. In severe driving conditions change fluid at 12,500 miles.

CHECKING FLUID LEVEL

1) Position vehicle on level floor and have engine at operating temperature. Apply parking brake, move selector lever through all positions ending in "P".

2) Remove dipstick and wipe with a clean lint free cloth. Reinstall dipstick and check fluid level. "MAX" mark is maximum hot level. "MIN" mark is minimum cold level. "MIDDLE" mark is minimum hot level or maximum cold level.

RECOMMENDED FLUID

All transmissions use Dexron "B" or "D" automatic transmission fluid.

FLUID CAPACITY

TRANSMISSION REFILL CAPACITIES

Application	Refill Quantity	Dry Fill Quantity
All Models	1.7 qts. (1.6L)	5.4 qts. (5.2L)

NEUTRAL SAFETY SWITCH

Engine should start in "N" or "P" positions only. To adjust, install or remove shims at base of switch until proper operation is achieved.

DRAINING & REFILLING

1) Have engine at normal operating temperature. Remove drain plug from transmission oil pan, allow all fluid to drain and install drain plug. Pour approximate amount of fluid as listed in Fluid Capacity chart.

2) Start and run engine at normal idle. Shift selector lever through all positions, check fluid level, add fluid as needed. DO NOT overfill.

ADJUSTMENTS

KICKDOWN CABLE

With throttle control drum in normal hot idle position, adjust cable housing to give maximum clearance of .020" (.5 mm) between end of cable housing and clip on cable.

SHIFT LINKAGE

Disconnect selector rod at transmission lever. Place transmission lever in "N" position. Place gear selector lever in "N" and adjust rod length to fit both levers without tension.

Automatic Transmission Servicing

PORSCHE

IDENTIFICATION

TRANSMISSION CODES

Application	Code
928S	A28
944	087

LUBRICATION

SERVICE INTERVALS

Check fluid level every 15,000 miles. Change fluid and filter every 30,000 miles.

CHECKING FLUID LEVEL

Check fluid level through transparent reservoir, located at rear end of transmission housing. With fluid at normal operating temperature, vehicle on level surface, engine idling and selector lever in Neutral. Fluid level should be between "MIN" and "MAX" marks. Do not overfill.

RECOMMENDED FLUID

Dexron B automatic transmission fluid.

FLUID CAPACITY

TRANSMISSION REFILL CAPACITIES

Application	Refill	Dry Fill
928S	3.0 qts. (2.8L)	6.3 qts. (6.0L)
944	5.8 qts. (5.5L)	6.3 (6.0L)

DRAINING & REFILLING

1) Remove drain plug and drain fluid. Turn crankshaft until torque converter drain plug is at bottom opening of torque converter housing. Remove drain plug. Remove oil pan and filter.

2) Install new oil filter. Install oil pan, using a new gasket and tighten bolts to 6 ft. lbs. (8 N.m). Install drain plugs, using new seals and add approximately 5.3 qts. (5.0L) of automatic transmission fluid.

3) Start engine with selector lever in "P" and run engine at idle. Check fluid level in reservoir and add more fluid. Apply brake pedal and momentarily place selector lever in each gear. Check fluid level.

ADJUSTMENTS

SELECTOR LEVER

928S

Place selector lever in "N" position. Detach cable from operating lever on transmission. Place transmission lever in "N" position. Adjust cable so that socket attaches to operating lever without tension and attach cable to lever. *See Fig. 1.*

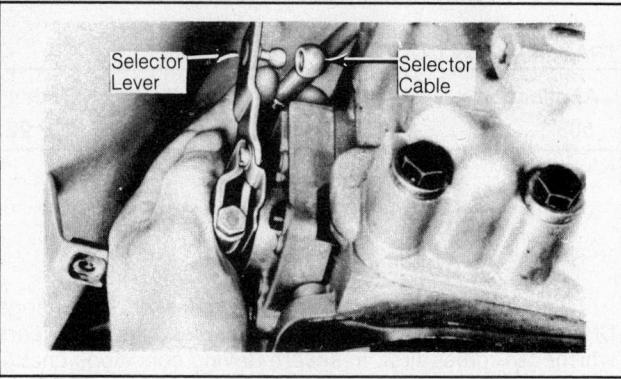

Fig. 1: 928S Selector Lever Adjusting Point

944

1) Place selector lever in "P" position. Loosen nut on clamping sleeve for selector lever cable. Place operating lever on transmission in "P" position (against stop). *See Fig. 2.*

2) Tighten nut on clamping sleeve. Move selector through all positions with engine running, engagement should be felt after 5 seconds.

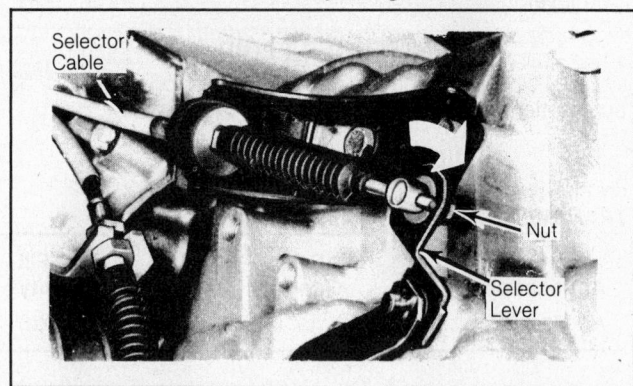

Fig. 2: 944 Selector Lever Adjusting Point

THROTTLE CABLE

944

1) Completely screw in mounting nut for cable sleeve on transmission bracket and ball socket, for transmission lever and mount. Relax cable sleeve on firewall and long cable sleeve on cam plate bracket.

2) Place and position cable around cam plate. Adjust long cable sleeve until clamping nipple is positioned in opening without tension. Adjust accelerator pedal cable to sleeve control without tension.

3) When cable is adjusted correctly, accelerator pedal will be in idle position, throttle will be closed, and transmission operating lever will be on lower step.

928S

Detach cable at transmission lever. Adjust lever with adjusting bolt "A" after loosening bolt "B" so that cable can be attached without tension or free play. *See Fig. 3.*

PORSCHE (Cont.)

Fig. 3: 928S Throttle Cable Pressure Adjustment

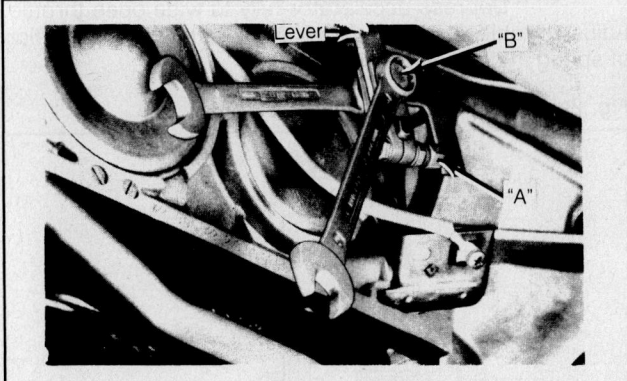

Fig. 4: 928S Brake Band Measurement

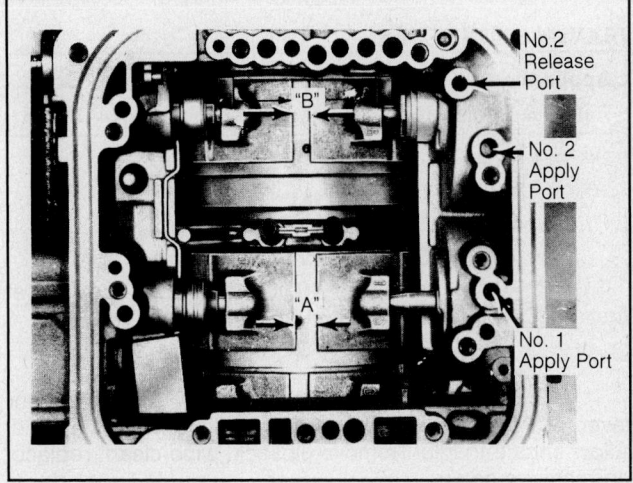

BRAKE BAND

1) On all models. loosen lock nut, tighten adjusting screw to 84 INCH lbs. (10 N.m). Back off adjusting screw and tighten to 48 INCH lbs. (5 N.m). Loosen adjusting screw 1 3/4 turns and tighten lock nut.

2) On 928S models, there are 2 additional bands to adjust. Measure distance of free play for piston No. 2 by applying air pressure to No. 2 release port. Check distance at "B", apply air pressure to No. 2 apply port and recheck distance "B", difference between measurements equals free play.

3) Brake band No. 1 is checked by measuring distance at "A". Apply air pressure to No. 1 apply port and recheck distance "A", difference between measurements equals free play. Free play of both bands should be .118-.157" (3-4 mm). Adjustments are made using pins.

NEUTRAL SAFETY SWITCH
928S

Place selector lever in "N" position. Loosen adjusting screw, insert .157" (4 mm) pin through drive dog into hole in case. Tighten adjusting screw and remove locating pin. Check that engine starts in "N" or "P" positions only.

944

Starter should operate only in "P" or "N" positions. If starter operates in any other position, remove selector lever gate and loosen retaining bolts on safety switch. Adjust switch as necessary.

Automatic Transmission Servicing

RENAULT

IDENTIFICATION

TRANSMISSION CODES

Application	Code
Fuego & Sportwagon	4139-65

LUBRICATION

SERVICE INTERVALS

Check fluid every 6,000 miles. Change fluid at first 1,000 miles and every 30,000 miles thereafter.

FLUID LEVEL

1) With vehicle on level floor, place selector lever in "P" position. Apply parking brake and start engine. Allow engine to idle. Remove dipstick, wipe clean, replace, and remove again.

2) With engine at normal operating temperature, fluid level should be between "MINI HOT" and "MAXI HOT" marks. With fluid level at ambient temperatures, level should be between "MINI COLD" marks.

RECOMMENDED FLUID

Dexron II automatic transmission fluid.

FLUID CAPACITY

TRANSMISSION REFILL CAPACITIES

Application	Refill Quantity	Dry Fill Quantity
All	2.7 qts. (2.6L)	5.2 qts. (5.0L)

ADJUSTMENTS

KICKDOWN SWITCH

Make sure that throttle cable has sufficient play to allow a 0.12-0.16" (3-4 mm) movement in stop sleeve when accelerator pedal is completely depressed. Make sure that cover is in position to prevent tarnishing of contacts. *See Fig. 1.*

Fig. 1: Kickdown Switch Adjustment

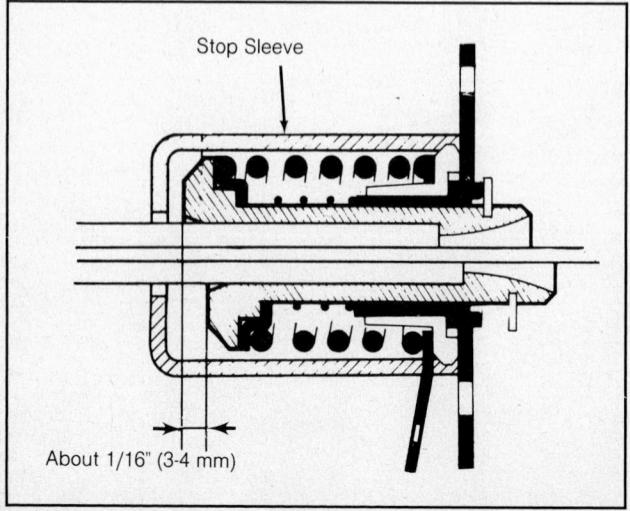

Adjust kickdown switch before adjusting other components.

THROTTLE CABLE

Depress accelerator fully to wide open throttle. Adjust throttle cable to obtain 0.08" (2 mm) compression of spring in cable stop. *See Fig. 2.*

Fig. 2: Throttle Cable Adjustment

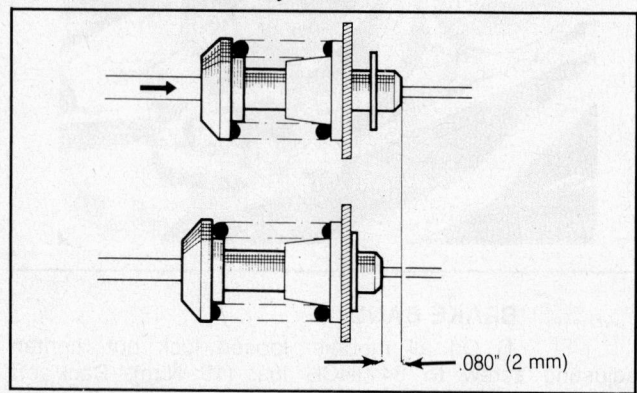

Make sure kickdown switch is functioning correctly.

GOVERNOR CABLE

Adjust cable adjusters on both governor and throttle sides to midway. Adjust cable stop to obtain a clearance of .008-.028" (.20-.70 mm). *See Fig. 3.*

Fig. 3: Governor Cable Adjustment

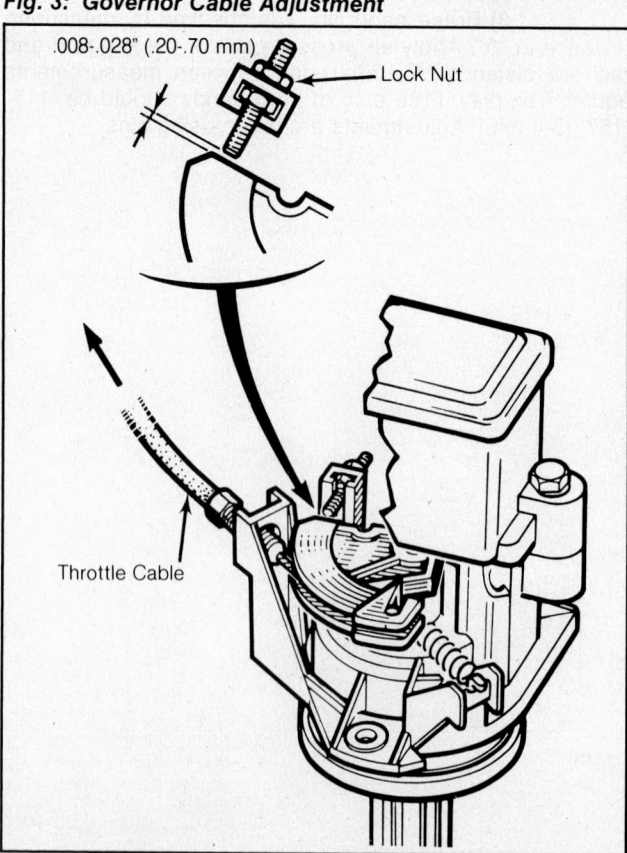

All other components must be operating properly before adjusting governor.

SAAB

IDENTIFICATION

TRANSMISSION CODES

Application	Code
All (Borg-Warner)	37

LUBRICATION

SERVICE INTERVALS

Adjust automatic transmission gear selector control cable every 1,000 miles. Check fluid level in transmission every 7,500 miles, or when servicing engine.

CHECKING FLUID LEVEL

1) Park vehicle on level surface, apply hand brake and allow engine to idle. Place selector lever in all positions for at least 15 seconds, and return to "P" position.

2) Remove dipstick, wipe and check fluid level. Fluid level should be between maximum and minimum marks on dipstick. Use hot or cold markings on dipstick, depending on transmission oil temperature. Do not overfill.

RECOMMENDED FLUID

Type F automatic transmission fluid.

FLUID CAPACITY

TRANSMISSION REFILL CAPACITIES

Application	Quantity
All	8.5 qts. (8.0L)

DRAINING & REFILLING

Transmission drain plug is 13 mm across flat spots. Remove drain plug from oil pan and drain fluid. Replace drain plug, add transmission fluid and check fluid level. Do not overfill.

ADJUSTMENTS

THROTTLE CABLE

1) Connect a pressure gauge to transmission. Place selector lever in "P" position, block wheels and apply hand brake. Start engine, check that idle is 850 RPM.

2) Disconnect throttle cable from throttle lever, check that throttle is not binding. Withdraw cable to obtain maximum line pressure, then return it to original position, pressure should return to initial pressure. If pressure stays above 69 psi (4.9 kg/cm²), throttle must be cleaned or adjusted.

3) Connect throttle cable to throttle lever. Place selector lever in "D" position. Check that cable is released, to obtain lowest pressure. Increase pressure to 1.4 psi (0.1 kg/cm²) by adjusting throttle cable. Place selector lever in "P" position. Pressure should be between 59-69 psi (4.1-4.9 kg/cm²).

SELECTOR LEVER

1) Place selector lever in "N" position. Depress pawl button and move selector lever slightly back and forth, increased resistance should be felt in both direc-

tions. Hold lever mid-way between positions in which resistace is felt.

2) Disconnect gear selector cable from lever, using an Allen wrench. Release pawl button and move lever to "N" position. Tighten gear selector cable set screw.

Fig. 1: Selector Lever Adjustment

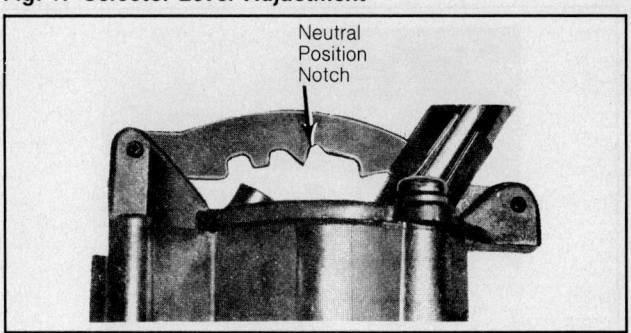

FRONT BAND

Up To Serial No. 001-1700 & 002-2800
Drain fluid and remove oil pan. Loosen lock nut. Place a 0.25" (6.35 mm) spacer (87 90 073) between adjustment screw and rod on servo piston. Tighten adjustment screw to 10 INCH lbs. (1 N.m). Back off screw 1 turn and while holding in position, tighten lock nut to 15-20 ft. lbs. (20-27 N.m).

NOTE: Serial No. 001-1700 and 002-2800 transmissions having a BWS suffix punched into I.D. plate should be adjusted using Serial No. 001-1701 and 002-2801 adjustment procedure.

From Serial No. 001-1701 & 002-2801
Drain fluid and remove oil pan. Loosen lock nut. Place a 0.35" (8.9 mm) spacer (87 91 030) between adjustment screw and rod on servo piston. Tighten adjustment screw to 10 INCH lbs. (1 N.m) and while holding in position, tighten lock nut to 15-20 ft. lbs. (20-27 N.m). Do not back off adjustment screw.

Fig. 2: Front Band Adjustment

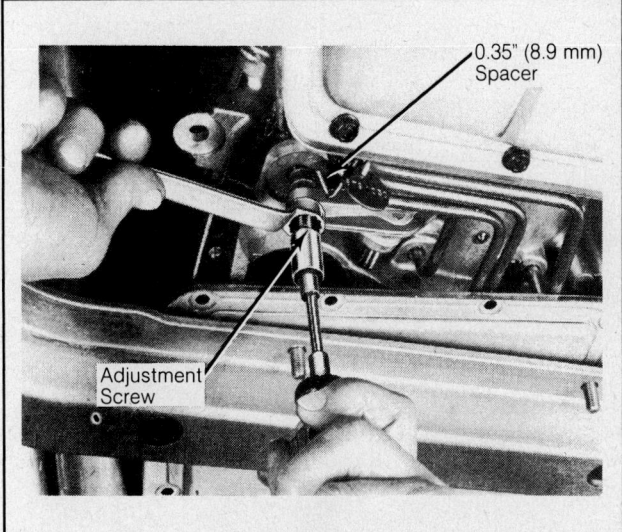

Oil pan must be removed to adjust front band.

Automatic Transmission Servicing
SAAB (Cont.)

REAR BAND

Loosen lock nut a few turns and tighten adjustment screw to 114-124 INCH lbs. (13-14 N.m). Back screw off 1 1/4 turn and while holding in position, tighten lock nut to 29-40 ft. lbs. (39-54 N.m).

Fig. 3: Rear Band Adjustment

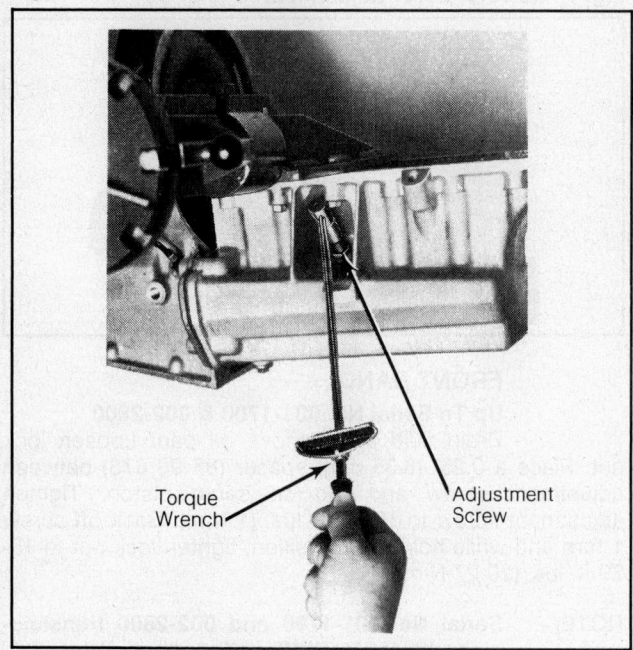

Adjustment is made on left side of transmission.

NEUTRAL SAFETY SWITCH

Place selector lever in "N" position. Loosen securing screws. Rotate switch housing to line up lever with mark on switch housing. Tighten securing screws.

SUBARU

IDENTIFICATION

TRANSMISSION CODES

Application	Transmission (Code)
1800 2WD	Model Gunma (C)
1800 4WD & Turbo	Model Gunma (F)

LUBRICATION

SERVICE INTERVALS

Check fluid level in transmission every 5 months or 15,000 miles, whichever comes first. Transmission fluid should be changed every 30,000 miles and band adjusted as necessary.

CHECKING FLUID LEVEL

1) Normal operating temperature for fluid is 140-176°F (60-80°C) and is reached after driving for 10 minutes or idling for 25 minutes. With vehicle parked on level floor and at normal operating temperature.

2) Set transmission selector lever in "P" position with engine idling. Remove dipstick and clean with lint-free cloth. Insert and remove dipstick, note fluid level and add through dipstick hole to bring to full mark. When filling transmission, do not overfill.

RECOMMENDED FLUID

All models use Dexron type automatic transmission fluid (ATF).

FLUID CAPACITY

TRANSMISSION REFILL CAPACITIES

Application	Quantity
1800	5.9-6.3 qts. (5.6-6.0L)
1800 4WD & Turbo	6.3-6.8 qts. (6.0-6.4L)

NOTE: Fluid capacity of transfer case is part of 1800 4WD and Turbo specification.

DRAINING & REFILLING

Remove drain plug and drain fluid. Replace drain plug and fill transmission with about 4 quarts of ATF. Start engine and check fluid level with engine idling. Add fluid as necessary. Do not overfill.

ADJUSTMENTS

REAR BAND

Adjustment is made ast left side of transaxle. Loosen lock nut on band adjusting screw and tighten screw to 78 INCH lbs. (9 N.m). Loosen screw 2 turns and hold in position while tightening lock nut.

KICKDOWN SWITCH

Switch ignition "ON" and depress accelerator fully. A "click" should be heard just as accelerator bottoms out. Adjust switch inward or outward for proper operation.

NOTE: If switch operates too soon, downshift will occur at part throttle.

SHIFT LINKAGE

1) Move selector lever from "P" to "1" position. Lever should set into each position with a "click". At each position, check that selector dial gives proper indication of gear position.

2) If linkage is out of adjustment, set selector lever to "N" position. Loosen the linkage adjusting nut, adjust until the "N" is aligned within .24" (6 mm).

3) Adjust rod until the "N" mark of the guide plate is aligned correctly with the detent position. Recheck in all positions.

4) If indicator needle is not aligned with guide plate marking, remove console box, loosen mounting screws and adjust as required.

Fig. 1: Shift Linkage Adjustment

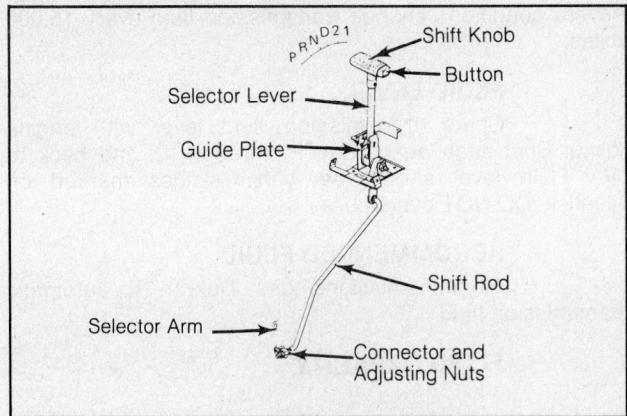

When shifting into each position a click should be heard.

NEUTRAL SAFETY SWITCH

1) Switch is mounted on right side of selector lever plate. To adjust, remove switch from plate and insert .08" (2 mm) diameter pin in alignment hole on switch.

2) Ensure that selector lever is in "N" position, pushed lightly toward "P". Match locator to bracket hole and moving plate pin to arm hole. Tighten retaining bolts in position and remove alignment pin.

Fig. 2: Neutral Safety Switch Adjustment

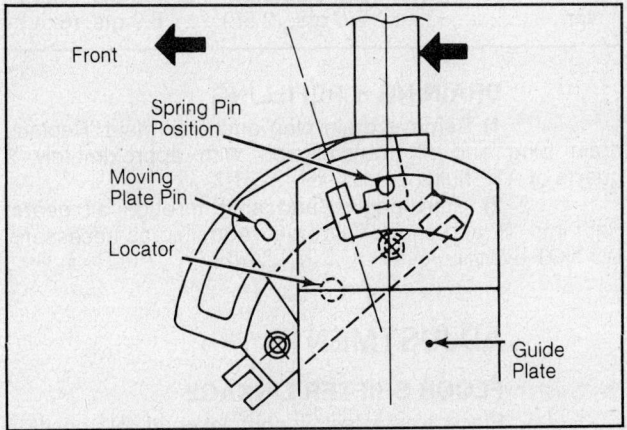

Insert a .08" (2 mm) diameter pin to align hole in switch.

Automatic Transmission Servicing
TOYOTA

IDENTIFICATION

TRANSMISSION CODES

Application	Code
Camry (FWD)	A140E
Celica (RWD)	A40D
Corolla (FWD)	A130L & A131L
Corolla (RWD)	A42L
Cressida & Supra (RWD)	A43DE
Pickup (RWD)	A43D
Tercel (FWD)	A55
Van	A43DL

LUBRICATION

SERVICE INTERVALS

Check transmission fluid every 15,000 miles. In severe conditions change transmission fluid every 15,000 miles.

FLUID LEVEL

Check transmission fluid level with engine idling. Shift each gear from "P" through "L" and back to "P". Fluid level should be within ranges marked on dipstick. DO NOT overfill.

RECOMMENDED FLUID

All transmissions use Dexron II automatic transmission fluid.

FLUID CAPACITY

TRANSMISSION REFILL CAPACITIES

Application	Refill Quantity	Dry Fill Quantity
Camry	2.5 qts. (2.4L)	6.3 qts. (6.0L)
Celica	2.5 qts. (2.4L)	6.7 qts. (6.3L)
Corolla FWD		
Diesel	2.5 qts. (2.4L)	6.2 qts. (5.9L)
Gas	2.4 qts. (2.3L)	5.8 qts. (5.5L)
Corolla RWD	2.5 qts. (2.4L)	6.0 qts. (5.7L)
Cressida, Pickup &		
Supra	2.5 qts. (2.4L)	6.9 qts. (6.5L)
Tercel	2.3 qts. (2.2L)	4.8 qts. (4.5L)
Van	2.6 qts. (2.5L)	6.9 qts. (6.5L)

DRAINING & REFILLING

1) Remove drain plug and drain fluid. Replace drain plug and fill transmission with approximately 2 quarts of ATF fluid.

2) Start engine and shift through all gears. Shift into "P" and check fluid level. Add fluid as necessary. DO NOT overfill.

ADJUSTMENTS

FLOOR SHIFTER LINKAGE

Place transmission shift lever in "N" position and adjust shift rod until shift lever indicates "N" position correctly. Holding shift selector lightly toward "R" position, tighten lock nuts. Check that all ranges engage correctly.

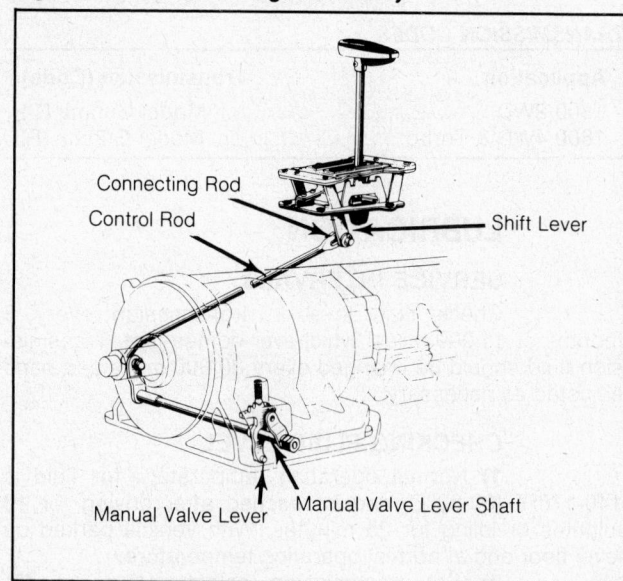

Fig. 1: Floor Shift Linkage Assembly

Connecting Rod — Control Rod — Shift Lever — Manual Valve Lever — Manual Valve Lever Shaft

THROTTLE CABLE

Remove air cleaner. Check throttle cable bracket and linkage for looseness or bending. Depress accelerator to wide open throttle position. Adjust cable housing so distance between rubber boot end and inner cable stopper is .04" (1 mm). Tighten lock nut.

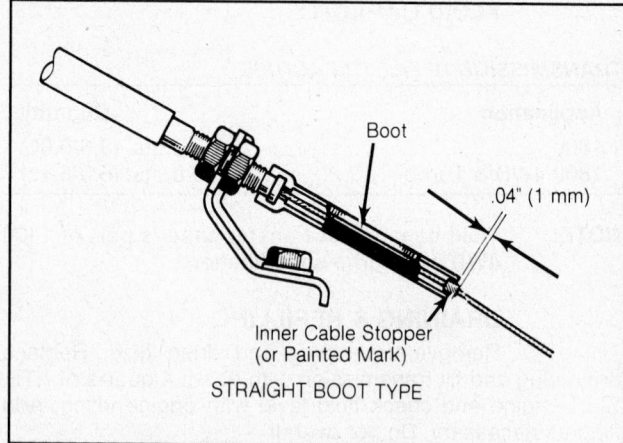

Fig. 2: Adjusting Throttle Cable

Boot — .04" (1 mm) — Inner Cable Stopper (or Painted Mark) — STRAIGHT BOOT TYPE

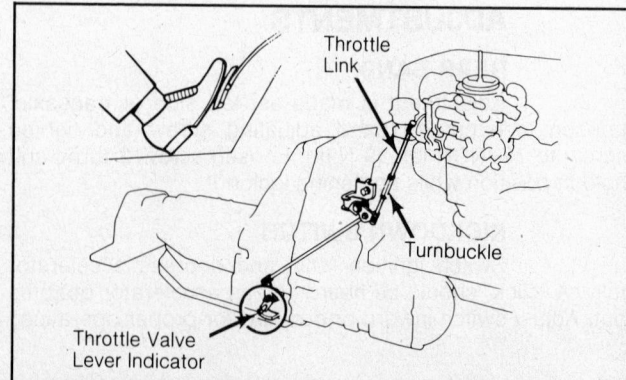

Fig. 3: Tercel Throttle Link Adjustment

Throttle Link — Turnbuckle — Throttle Valve Lever Indicator

THROTTLE LINK

Tercel

1) Remove air cleaner. Check throttle cable bracket and linkage for looseness or bending. Depress accelerator to wide open throttle position.

2) Adjust linkage by turning turnbuckle until throttle valve lever indicator lines up with mark on transmission case. Tighten lock nut.

NEUTRAL SAFETY SWITCH

Celica, Supra & Van

Loosen adjusting bolt. Position shift lever in "N" position. Align switch shaft groove to neutral basic line. Tighten adjusting bolt.

Fig. 4: Neutral Safety Switch Adjustment

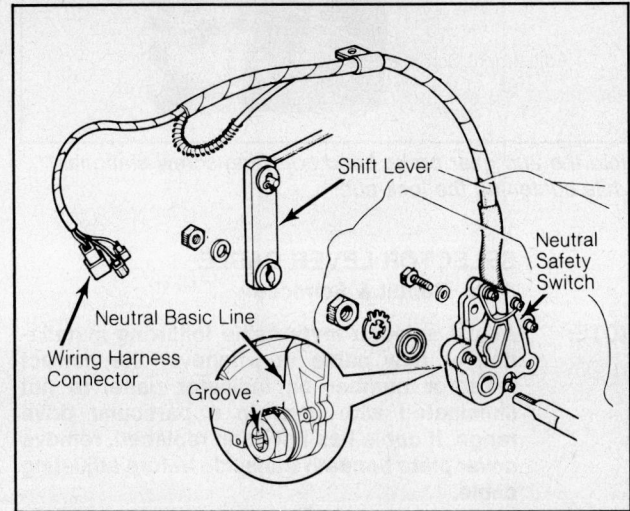

All Other Models

Disconnect switch connector. Connect an ohmmeter between terminals and adjust switch to the point where there is continuity between terminals. Tighten screws and connect switch connector.

Fig. 5: Neutral Safety Switch Test Terminals

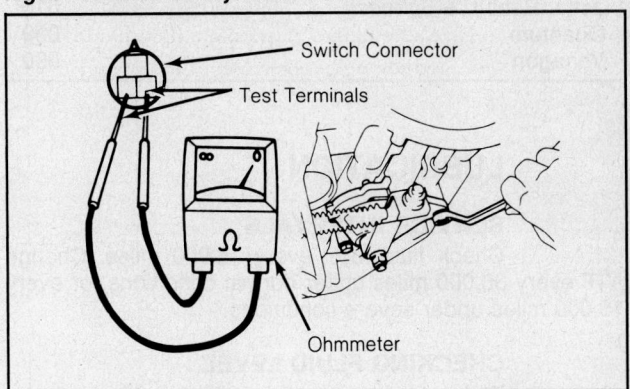

Automatic Transmission Servicing
VOLKSWAGEN

IDENTIFICATION

TRANSAXLE CODES

Appication	Code
Jetta, Rabbit, & Scirocco	010
Quantum	089
Vanagon	090

LUBRICATION

SERVICE INTERVALS

Check fluid level every 15,000 miles. Change ATF every 30,000 miles under normal conditions, or every 15,000 miles under severe conditions.

CHECKING FLUID LEVEL

With transmission at normal operating temperature, park vehicle on level surface. Place selector lever in "P" or "N" position, apply parking brake and allow engine to idle. Remove dipstick, wipe clean and insert. Remove dipstick and check that fluid level is between high and low marks on dipstick.

RECOMMENDED TRANSAXLE FLUIDS

Automatic transmission fluid (ATF): Dexron or Dexron type II. All approved ATFs may be mixed with one another. Do not use additives.

Differential final drive: Hypoid gear oil SAE 80 or SAE 80/90.

FLUID CAPACITY

TRANSMISSION REFILL CAPACITIES

Application	Refill	Dry Fill
All Models	3.2 qts. (3.0L)	6.4 qts. (6.0L)

DRAINING & REFILLING

1) Remove transaxle protection plate. Remove rear pan bolts and loosen front pan bolts. Carefully lower pan and drain as much fluid as possible. Remove oil pan. Remove and discard filter.

2) Clean oil pan in solvent and blow dry with compressed air. Install new filter. Tighten screws to 27 INCH lbs. (3 N.m). Install oil pan, using new gasket.

3) Tighten pan mounting bolts to 15 ft. lbs. (20 N.m). Install protection plate, tighten bolts to 18 ft. lbs. (25 N.m). Add new ATF. Warm engine to operating temperature and check fluid level.

ADJUSTMENTS

2nd GEAR BRAKE BAND

CAUTION: If transmission is out of vehicle, unit must be horizontal during adjustment or 2nd gear brake band may jam when adjusting screw is moved. If brake band jams, it is necessary to partially disassemble transmission in order to realign band.

1) Loosen adjusting screw lock nut. Center brake band by tightening adjusting screw to 89 INCH lbs. (10 N.m). Loosen adjustment screw once more, then tighten to 44 INCH lbs. (5 N.m).

2) From this position, back off adjusting screw exactly 2 1/2 turns. While holding adjusting screw in position, tighten lock nut to 177 INCH lbs. (20 N.m).

Fig. 1: Adjusting 2nd Gear Brake Band

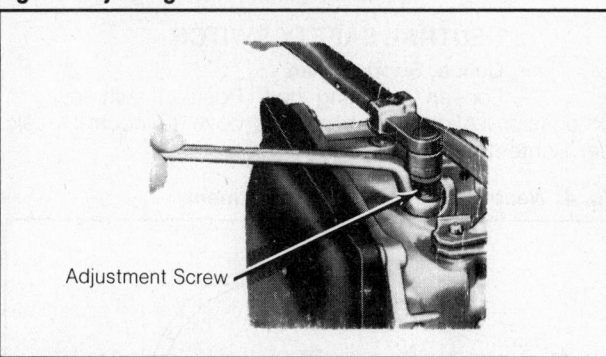

Adjustment Screw

Hold the 2nd gear brake band adjusting screw stationary while tightening the lock nut.

SELECTOR LEVER CABLE
Jetta, Rabbit & Scirocco

NOTE: **Adjust selector lever cable following installation of new cable or whenever the correct letter or number on indicator panel is not illuminated with lever in a particular drive range. If cable has not been replaced, remove cover plate beneath transaxle before adjusting cable.**

1) Place transmission selector lever in "P" position. If cable has broken, ensure transmission is in "P" by hand-moving lever on transaxle to the left.

NOTE: **Push vehicle forward or backward to ensure parking pawl has engaged inside transmission.**

2) If necessary, remove cable boot. Loosen nut for clamping pin which retains selector cable to operating lever on transaxle.

3) Ensure that selector lever and operating lever are fully engaged in "P" position. Tighten cable clamping pin mounting nut to 71 INCH lbs. (8 N.m).

Quantum

Place shift selector lever into "P" position. Loosen clamping nut and press shift lever on transmission into Park. Tighten nut on cable to 72 INCH lbs. (8 N.m).

Vanagon

Place transmission lever in "P" position. Loosen bolt which retains shift rod to operating lever on transaxle. Ensure that selector lever and operating lever are in "P" position. Push shift rod to rear and tighten bolt.

THROTTLE CABLE
Quantum

1) Loosen lock nuts on cylinder head cover. Pull sleeve of throttle cable until resistance is felt. Turn adjustment nut against bracket and lock using second nut.

2) Attach 2 nuts to a M8 X 135 mm bolt so that distance between bolt head and outer nut is 4 7/8" (124 mm). Remove accelerator pedal stop and install bolt in place of pedal stop. Bolt head must rest on plate, not rod. Adjust throttle cable at transmission adjustment nut.

3) Install pedal stop. Depress accelerator pedal until resistance is felt at full throttle position (no kickdown), throttle lever must contact stop. Depress accelerator pedal to full throttle stop. Linkage spring must be compressed and operating lever on transmission must contact stop (kickdown).

Vanagon

1) Loosen adjustment nut and remove override spring. Start engine, adjust idle speed to 800-1000 rpm and turn engine off. Push throttle lever forward until it stops.

2) Using a screwdriver, turn adjustment rod until it contacts throttle lever pivot. Install overide spring, start engine and check idle speed. If necessary, adjust idle speed by turning rod. Tighten lock nut on adjustment rod.

3) Depress accelerator pedal to floor. Transmission kickdown lever must be in kickdown position with 1/32-3/32" (1-2 mm) free play between lever and stop. Release accelerator pedal, kickdown lever must return to idle position. If necessary, adjust throttle cable at clamping bolt.

NEUTRAL SAFETY SWITCH

Neutral safety switch is located in shift console. Remove console cover and adjust switch so that engine starts in "P" and "N" positions only.

Automatic Transmission Servicing

VOLVO

IDENTIFICATION

TRANSMISSION CODES

Application	Code
760 GLE	AW71 & ZF 4 HP-22
All Others	BW55

LUBRICATION

SERVICE INTERVAL

Under normal use it is not necessary to change the transmission fluid. Transmission fluid should be checked every 7,500 miles or twice a year. For vehicles in heavy duty service, transmission fluid should be changed every 25,000 miles.

CHECKING FLUID LEVEL

1) Position vehicle on level floor. Apply parking brake and shift selector lever into "P" position. Start engine and let idle. Shift selector lever through all gears pausing 4-5 seconds for engagement at each position.

2) Return selector lever to "P". Wait 2 minutes, then remove dipstick. Wipe dipstick off with lint free cloth and reinsert. Withdraw dipstick and check reading. Level must be between "MIN" and "MAX" marks. If not, add (or remove) fluid to obtain correct level.

RECOMMENDED FLUID

All transmission use fluid type "F" or "G".

FLUID CAPACITY

TRANSMISSION REFILL CAPACITIES

Application	Refill Quantity	Dry Fill Quantity
BW55	3.2 qts (3L)	7.1 qts. (6.8L)
AW71		7.9 qts. (7.5L)
ZF 4 HP-22		6.3 qts. (6.0L)

ADJUSTMENTS

THROTTLE & KICKDOWN CABLES

1) Transmission cable should be stretched in idle position. Distance between clip and sheath should be .010-.040" (.25-1.0 mm). See Fig. 1.

Fig. 1: Checking Throttle Controls

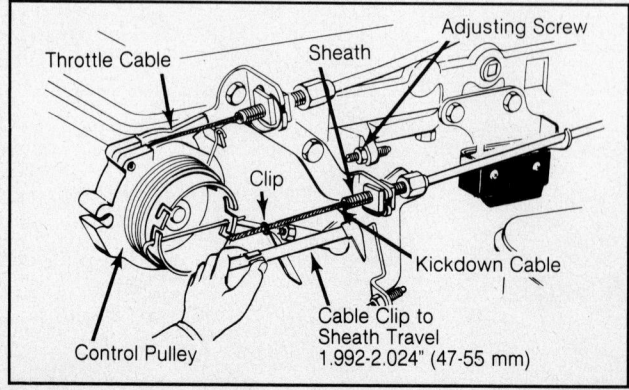

Throttle Cable — Sheath — Adjusting Screw — Clip — Kickdown Cable — Cable Clip to Sheath Travel 1.992-2.024" (47-55 mm) — Control Pulley

2) Pull transmission cable out by hand approximately .39-.59" (10-15 mm), and release. A distinct "click" should be heard from transmission, indicating cable moves freely and throttle cam returns to initial position.

3) Depress accelerator pedal completely. The transmission cable should travel 1.992-2.024" (47-55 mm), from idle position to full throttle position. See Fig. 1.

GEAR SELECTOR

1) Press on gear selector and check that clearance from "D" to stop is approximately the same as from "2" to stop. If clearance is incorrect, control rod needs adjustment.

2) Adjustment is made by turning clevis in or out on control rod. Maximum visible thread length permitted is 1.1" (28 mm).

3) Increasing rod length reduces position "D" clearance. Decreasing rod length increases position "D" clearance. Shift to position "1" then to position "P" for recheck. See Fig. 2.

Fig. 2: Gear Selector Adjustment

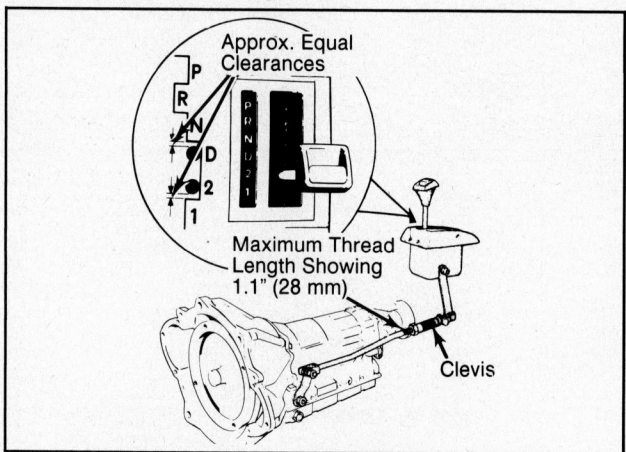

Approx. Equal Clearances — Maximum Thread Length Showing 1.1" (28 mm) — Clevis

NEUTRAL SAFETY SWITCH

1) Switch is located at and directly controlled by the gear shift control lever. Place selector lever in "P" position. Adjust neutral safety switch to set "P" mark at center of switch lever.

2) Place selector lever in "N" position. Confirm "N" mark is at center of switch lever. Move selector lever from "P" to "1" and back again.

3) Check that control pin does not slide out of switch lever. See Fig. 3. Check that engine only starts in "P" and "N", and that the back-up lights illuminate in position "R" only.

Fig. 3: Adjusting Neutral Safety Switch

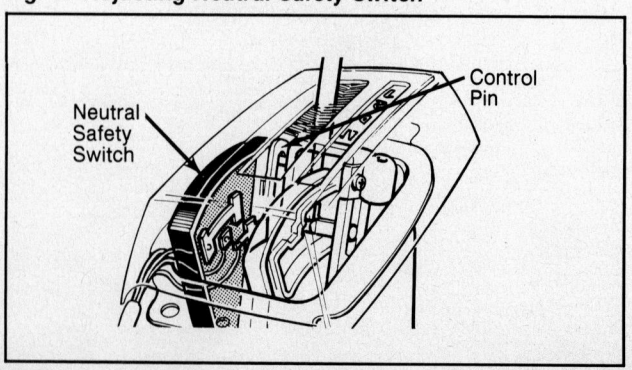

Neutral Safety Switch — Control Pin

AUDI

AUDI COUPE & 4000

REMOVAL

1) Disconnect battery ground cable. Disconnect accelerator linkage rod. Disconnect speedometer cable. Remove upper engine-to-transaxle bolts.

2) Support engine from above. Disconnect automatic transaxle cooler lines. Disconnect exhaust pipe from manifold. Disconnect exhaust pipe bracket at transaxle.

3) Unbolt exhaust pipe from catalytic converter. Remove axle shaft guard plate, then disconnect axle shafts from transaxle flanges. Wire axle shafts back out of way. Remove starter. Remove 3 bolts securing torque converter to drive plate.

4) Remove subframe rear mounting bolts and loosen front bolts (do not remove). Disconnect linkage rod from transaxle. Remove selector cable holder and circlip. Disconnect cable and "O" ring. Place transaxle jack under transaxle and raise transaxle slightly. Remove accelerator cable holder, then disconnect accelerator cable.

5) Remove lower engine-to-transaxle bolts. Remove transaxle rubber mount bolts. Separate transaxle from engine. Secure torque converter to transaxle to prevent converter from falling when removing transaxle. Lower transaxle out of vehicle.

INSTALLATION

To install transaxle, reverse removal procedure. Ensure torque converter is fully seated to transaxle and all linkage is properly installed and adjusted.

5000

REMOVAL

1) Disconnect battery ground cable. Disconnect hoses from transaxle cooler. Disconnect accelerator linkage and speedometer cable. Support engine from above. Remove upper engine-to-transaxle bolts. Remove guard plate from subframe and remove exhaust pipe.

2) Remove right guard plate at right axle drive shaft and remove drive shaft bolts. Mark left ball joint position on control arm. Remove bolts attaching ball joints to control arm. Remove starter, selector lever cable holder and selector lever cable at transaxle lever.

3) Disconnect lower accelerator linkage rod and accelerator cable from transaxle lever. Remove right side guard plate from subframe. Remove torque converter-to-drive plate bolts.

4) Support transaxle with jack and raise slightly. Remove lower engine-to-transaxle bolts and rear subframe bolts. Position drive shafts to rear of vehicle. Separate transaxle from engine, secure torque converter in place and lower transaxle from vehicle.

INSTALLATION

To install, reverse removal procedure. When attaching torque converter to drive plate use new bolts and lock washers. After transaxle installation, check and adjust accelerator cable and throttle linkage (if necessary).

BMW

318i WITH ZF 3HP-22

REMOVAL

1) Disconnect battery ground cable. Detach transmission throttle cable from accelerator cross shaft and bracket. Remove oil filler tube from transmission and plug hole in transmission. Remove all transmission-to-engine bolts that can be removed from above.

2) Drain transmission fluid. Detach exhaust system bracket from transmission extension housing. Disconnect exhaust pipe from exhaust manifold. Turn steering wheel to full left lock to provide clearance for removal. Disconnect propeller shaft from transmission output flange by removing 3 bolts and nut.

3) Remove bolts from center support to body. Position propeller shaft out of way. Remove retaining bolt and withdraw speedometer cable from transmission extension housing. Disconnect transmission shift lever from selector lever rod. Disconnect electrical leads from neutral safety switch.

4) Note position of speed sensor and reference mark sensor. Disconnect and remove speed and reference mark sensors from torque converter housing. Remove thrust bracket (if equipped) and converter cover plate. Rotate engine and remove 4 converter-to-drive plate bolts.

5) Disconnect oil cooler lines from transmission. Position a jack under transmission and disconnect crossmember. Remove remaining transmission-to-engine attaching bolts and remove transmission.

INSTALLATION

1) To install, reverse removal procedure. Check for correct engagement of torque converter in transmission by measuring distance from front of transmission case to torque converter-to-drive plate lugs. Distance should be about .50" (12 mm).

2) Coat speed and reference mark sensors with anti-seize compound prior to installation. When installing speed and reference mark sensors, Black plug of speed sensor faces ring gear and Gray plug of reference mark sensor faces flywheel.

3) When installing oil cooler lines, check condition of line-to-case gaskets and replace if necessary. Fill transmission with fluid and adjust transmission control linkage.

325e, 528e, 533i, 633CSi & 733i WITH ZF 4HP-22

REMOVAL

1) Disconnect battery ground cable. Detach transmission throttle cable from accelerator cross shaft and bracket. Remove exhaust assembly and heat shields. Remove oil filler tube from transmission and plug hole in transmission. Remove all transmission-to-engine bolts that can be removed from above.

2) Drain transmission fluid. Detach exhaust system bracket from transmission extension housing. Discon-

BMW (Cont.)

nect exhaust pipe from exhaust manifold. Turn steering wheel to full left lock to provide clearance for removal. Disconnect propeller shaft from transmission output flange by removing 3 bolts and nut.

3) Remove bolts from center support to body. Position propeller shaft out of way. Disconnect transmission shift lever from selector lever rod. Disconnect electrical leads from neutral safety switch.

4) Note position of speed sensor and reference mark sensor. Disconnect and remove speed and reference mark sensors from torque converter housing. Remove thrust bracket (if equipped) and converter cover plate. Rotate engine and remove 4 converter-to-drive plate bolts.

5) Disconnect oil cooler lines from transmission. Position a jack under transmission and disconnect crossmember. Remove remaining transmission-to-engine attaching bolts and remove transmission.

INSTALLATION

1) To install, reverse removal procedure, noting the following: Clean out all transmission oil cooler lines. Check for correct engagement of torque converter in transmission by measuring distance from front of transmission case to torque converter-to-drive plate lugs. Distance should be about .50" (12 mm).

2) Coat speed and reference mark sensors with anti-seize compound prior to installation. When installing speed and reference mark sensors, Black plug of speed sensor faces ring gear and Gray plug of reference mark sensor faces flywheel.

3) When installing oil cooler lines, check condition of line-to-case gaskets and replace if necessary. Fill transmission with new fluid and adjust transmission control linkage.

CHRYSLER CORP. IMPORTS

CONQUEST & RAM-50 PICKUP

REMOVAL

NOTE: **Transmission and converter must be removed as an assembly to prevent damage to drive plate, pump bushing, and oil seal. Do not allow weight of transmission to rest on drive plate at any time during removal or installation.**

1) Disconnect battery ground cable. Remove oil cooler lines at transmission. Remove starter motor and cooler line bracket. Loosen pan to drain transmission.

2) Mark converter and drive plate for reassembly reference. Using socket wrench on crankshaft vibration damper bolt, rotate engine clockwise to position converter attaching bolts for removal. Remove bolts and propeller shaft.

3) Disconnect electrical leads. Disconnect gearshift rod and torque shaft assembly, throttle rod lever from left side of transmission, and linkage bellcrank (if so equipped) from transmission.

4) Remove oil filler tube and speedometer cable. Support rear of engine with engine support fixture. With a transmission support on a service jack, support transmission. Raise transmission slightly to relieve load on supports.

5) Remove bolts securing transmission mount to crossmember and crossmember to frame, then remove crossmember. Remove all converter housing bolts, then carefully work transmission and converter assembly rearward off engine block dowels and disengage converter hub from end of crankshaft.

6) Attach a small "C" clamp to edge of converter housing to hold converter in place during transmission removal. Lower transmission and remove from under vehicle. To remove converter assembly, remove "C" clamp from edge of converter housing and carefully slide assembly from transmission.

INSTALLATION

1) To install, reverse removal procedure. To install converter, rotate pump rotors with Front Pump Aligner (C-3756) until 2 small holes in handle are vertical.

Carefully slide converter over input shaft and reaction shaft. Ensure converter hub slots are also vertical and fully engage pump inner rotor lugs.

2) Test for full engagement by placing straight edge on face of converter housing. Surface of converter front cover lug should be at least 1/2" from rear of straight-edge when converter is pushed all the way into transmission. Attach a small "C" clamp to converter housing to hold converter in place during transmission installation.

Fig. 1: Using Front Pump Aligner to Align Pump Rotors for Torque Converter Installation

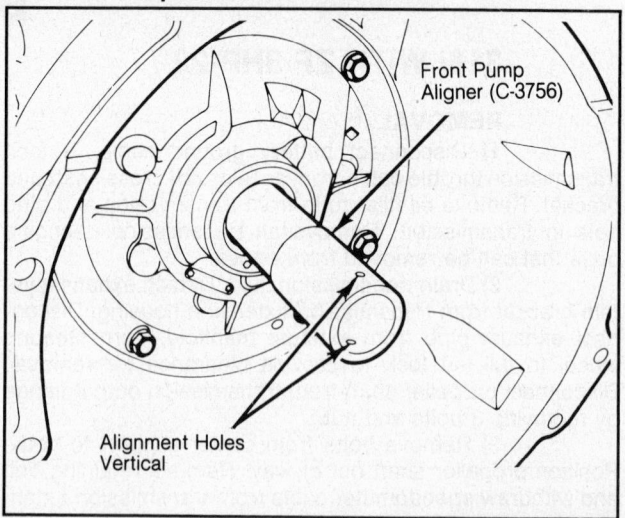

3) Inspect converter drive plate for distortion or cracks and replace if necessary. Coat converter hub hole in crankshaft with multi-purpose grease. When drive plate replacement has been necessary, ensure both transmission dowel pins are in engine block and they are protruding far enough to hold transmission in alignment.

4) Place transmission and converter assembly on a jack and position under vehicle for installation. Raise or tilt as necessary to align transmission to engine. Rotate

CHRYSLER CORP. IMPORTS (Cont.)

Fig. 2: Measuring for Full Converter Engagement

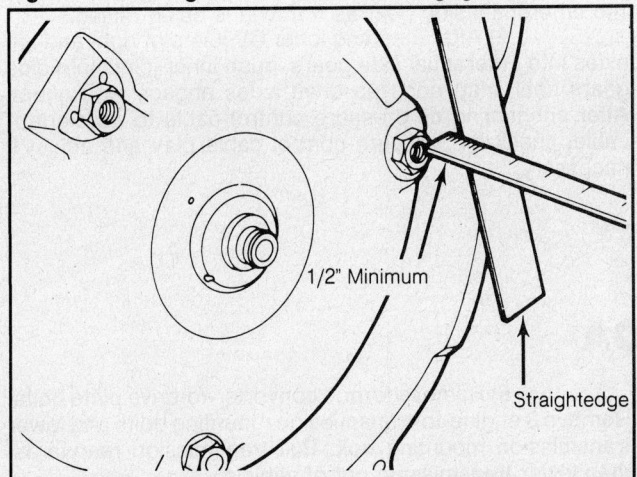

1/2" Minimum

Straightedge

converter so that mark on converter (made during removal) will align with mark on drive plate.

5) Carefully work transmission assembly forward over engine block dowels with converter hub entering crankshaft opening. After transmission is in position on engine, install and tighten all bolts. Adjust shift and throttle linkage, then refill transmission with DEXRON II type automatic transmission fluid.

COLT & COLT VISTA

REMOVAL

1) Disconnect negative battery cable. Disconnect throttle cable at carburetor and manual control cable at transaxle. On Colt Vista models, remove battery, battery tray, reservoir tank and air cleaner housing.

2) On all models, remove inhibitor switch connector, cooler hoses and 4 top engine-to-transaxle mounting bolts. Raise vehicle and remove front wheels. Remove under cover and drain transaxle fluid. Remove strut and stabilizer bars from lower control arm.

3) Remove both drive shafts from transaxle case. Remove starter and disconnect speedometer cable from transaxle. Remove converter housing. Remove 3 special bolts attaching converter to drive plate. Ensure torque converter is loose from engine and will come out with transmission.

4) Install an engine support. Place transmission jack under transaxle assembly. Remove remaining bolts holding engine-to-transaxle assembly. Remove transaxle mounting bolts. Lower transaxle assembly (with torque converter) out of vehicle.

INSTALLATION

To install transaxle assembly, reverse removal procedure. Install torque converter to transaxle, not to engine. Install new drive shaft retainer rings on reassembly. Ensure transaxle assembly is filled with fluid and all cables are properly connected and adjusted.

GENERAL MOTORS IMPORTS

SPECTRUM

REMOVAL

1) Disconnect negative cable at battery. Remove air intake hose from air cleaner. Disconnect shift cable from transaxle. Disconnect speedometer cable. Disconnect vacuum hose at vacuum diaphragm.

2) Disconnect engine wiring harness clamp at transaxle. Disconnect ground cable at transaxle. Disconnect inhibitor switch wire connector at left fender. Disconnect kickdown solenoid wire connector at left fender.

3) Disconnect transaxle cooler lines. Remove 3 upper transaxle to engine attaching bolts. Raise vehicle. Remove both front wheel and tire assemblies. Remove splash shield at left front fender.

4) Disconnect both tie rod ends at steering knuckle. Remove both front tension rod brackets. Disconnect both tension rods from control arms. Disengage both drive axle shafts from transaxle. Remove flywheel dust cover.

5) Remove converter to flywheel attaching bolts. Remove rear mount thru bolts at transaxle. Disconnect starter motor. Support transaxle. Remove lower transaxle to engine attaching bolts. Remove transaxle from vehicle.

INSTALLATION

To install, reverse removal procedure. Adjust shift linkage. Fill transaxle with Dexron II automatic transmission fluid.

SPRINT

REMOVAL

1) Disconnect air suction guide from air cleaner. Disconnect negative and positive cables from battery. Remove battery and tray. Disconnect negative cable at transaxle. Disconnect solenoid wire coupler and shift lever switch wire couplers. Disconnect wire harness and speedometer cable from transaxle.

2) Disconnect oil pressure control cable from accelerator cable, and then, accelerator cable from transaxle. Disconnect select cable from transaxle. Remove starter motor. Drain transaxle fluid.

3) Disconnect oil outlet and inlet hoses from oil pipes. After disconnecting, plug 2 oil hoses to prevent fluid in hoses and oil cooler from draining. Raise vehicle. Disconnect exhaust No. 1 pipe. Remove clutch housing lower plate.

4) Remove 6 drive plate bolts. To lock drive plate, engage a screwdriver with drive plate gear through notch provided at under side of transaxle case. Remove left front drive axle. Detach inner CV joint of right axle from differential. Remove transaxle mounting member.

5) Securely support transaxle with a suitable jack for removal. Disconnect transaxle left mounting. Remove bolts fastening engine and transaxle. Disconnect transaxle from engine by sliding toward left side, and then, carefully lower jack.

6) When removing transaxle assembly from engine, move it in parallel with crankshaft and use care so

Automatic Transmission Removal

GENERAL MOTORS IMPORTS (Cont.)

as not to apply excessive force to drive plate and torque converter. After removing transaxle assembly, be sure to keep it so oil pan is at bottom. If transaxle is tilted, fluid in it may flow out.

INSTALLATION

1) To install, reverse removal procedure. Before installing, apply grease around cup at center of torque converter. When installing transaxle, guide right drive axle into differential side gear as tranaxle is being raised.

2) After inserting inner CV joints of right and left axles into differential side gears, push inner joints into side gears until snap rings on drive axles engage side gears. After connecting oil pressure control cable to accelerator cable, check oil pressure control cable play and adjust if necessary.

HONDA

ALL MODELS

REMOVAL

1) Disconnect battery ground cable and ground strap at transmission. Release steering lock and place selector lever in "N". Disconnect battery cable from starter and wires from starter solenoid. Disconnect wire from water temperature sender and wire from ignition timing thermosensor.

2) Disconnect cooler hoses and wire them up out of way, making sure they won't drain. Remove starter mounting bolt, on transmission side, and top transmission mounting bolt. Raise and support front of vehicle. Remove wheels. Remove fender well shield from right front wheel well on Accord models only.

3) On all models, drain transmission and rein-stall plug. Remove throttle control cable from transmission. Remove speedometer cable from transmission. Do not remove speedometer cable holder or speedometer gear may fall into transmission housing.

4) On Accord models only, remove starter side mounting bolt and remove 2 upper transmission mounting bolts. Place a jack under transmission and attach an engine support to engine. Remove crossbeam. Disconnect radius rods, then disconnect axle shafts from transmission.

5) Remove remaining starter bolt and remove starter. Remove transmission damper bracket, located in front of torque converter cover plate, then remove cover plate. Remove center console and shift indicator. Place selector lever in "R" and remove shift cable from shift lever. Loosen nuts and pull shift cable out of transmission housing.

6) Remove torque converter-to-drive plate bolts. Remove 3 engine-to-transmission mounting bolts and lower transmission mounting bolt. Pull transmission rearwards, then lower transmission out of vehicle.

7) On Civic and Prelude models only, remove splash shields, stabilizer bar nuts, mounting brackets and then remove stabilizer bar. Remove axle shafts from transmission. Remove engine torque rods and brackets. Remove engine side starter mounting bolt, then remove starter.

8) Attach engine support to engine and place a jack under transmission. Remove nuts from front and rear engine mounts. Remove crossbeam bolts and crossbeam. Remove torque converter cover plate and center damper bracket.

9) Remove center console and shift indicator. Place selector lever in "R" and remove shift cable from selector lever. Loosen "U" bolt nuts and pull shift cable out of transmission housing. Remove torque converter-to-drive plate bolts. Remove remaining transmission mounting bolts and pull transmission rearward. Lower transmission out of vehicle.

INSTALLATION

1) To install, reverse removal procedures. Be sure ignition is off when connecting ground cable to battery and transmission.

2) With installation complete and transmission filled with oil, start engine and shift through all gear ranges. Check shift cable adjustment. Road test vehicle. With engine at operating temperature, check fluid level.

ISUZU

I-MARK

REMOVAL

1) Disconnect negative battery cable. Disconnect throttle valve control cable from engine. Remove transmission oil dipstick and tube. Raise vehicle on hoist and drain transmission.

2) Remove starter attaching hardware. Remove starter by moving it toward front of vehicle. Remove propeller shaft. Disconnect shift control rod from shifter lever. Disconnect speedometer cable from transmission. Remove exhaust pipe bracket.

3) Remove transmission oil cooler lines from transmission and position aside to avoid damage. Remove under cover on front of engine. Remove converter housing cover. Remove 6 bolts attaching converter to drive plate. Access to bolts is obtained by rotating crankshaft pulley.

4) Remove bolt from center part of rear mounting frame bracket. Raise engine and transmission assembly. Support rear of engine with a jack. Remove 4 nuts (gas engine) or 4 bolts (diesel engine) attaching rear mounting frame bracket to frame. Remove bracket.

5) Lower transmission and engine slightly. Remove transmission-to-engine bolts. Remove transmission from vehicle by moving it toward rear of vehicle.

ISUZU (Cont.)

INSTALLATION

Reverse removal procedure and note the following: Tighten all nuts and bolts evenly. After installation, fill transmission with fluid. Adjust throttle linkage and shift control linkage.

IMPULSE

REMOVAL

1) Drain transmission fluid. Disconnect throttle cable at engine side. Disconnect negative battery cable. Remove transmission oil dipstick and tube. Raise vehicle on hoist.

2) Remove starter attaching hardware. Remove starter by moving it toward front of vehicle. Remove propeller shaft. Disconnect shift control rod from shifter lever. Disconnect speedometer cable from transmission. Remove exhaust pipe.

3) Loosen joint nut on transmission side. Disconnect by-pass pipe and wire aside to avoid damage. Remove dust cover and under cover on front of engine. Remove 6 bolts attaching converter to drive plate. Access to bolts is obtained by rotating crankshaft pulley.

4) Remove bolt from center part of rear mounting frame bracket. Remove housing bolt. Raise engine and transmission assembly. Support rear of engine with a jack.

5) Lower transmission and engine slightly. Remove transmission-to-engine bolts. Remove transmission from vehicle by moving it toward rear of vehicle. Do not let torque converter slip out of transmission.

INSTALLATION

Reverse removal procedure and note the following: Tighten all nuts and bolts evenly. Check that distance from end of converter housing to front face of converter is about 1.4" (35 mm). After installation, fill transmission with fluid. Adjust throttle linkage and shift control linkage.

P'UP

REMOVAL

1) Disconnect negative battery cable. Detach throttle valve cable from bracket on carburetor. Remove air cleaner and transmission dipstick. Remove dipstick tube upper mounting bolt.

2) Raise and support vehicle. Remove dust cover from lower side of converter housing. Remove starter mounting bolts, then move starter assembly forward.

3) Mark propeller shaft for reassembly reference and remove. Disconnect speedometer cable, and oil cooler lines from transmission. Disconnect shift control linkage.

4) Support transmission with jack and remove rear transmission support bolt and mount. Remove exhaust pipe bracket.

NOTE: Mark converter and flywheel for reassembly to same position.

5) Remove torque converter bolts under pan. Lower transmission until jack barely supports it and remove transmission-to-engine attaching bolts. Raise transmission to normal position. Support engine with jack. Slide transmission away from engine and lower out of vehicle.

NOTE: Use converter holder to prevent converter from sliding out of transmission during removal.

INSTALLATION

1) Reverse removal procedure and note the following: Before installing drive plate-to-converter bolts, ensure welded brackets on converter are flush with drive plate. Check that converter rotates freely by hand in this position.

2) Hand start all 3 bolts and finger tighten before final tightening to ensure correct converter alignment. After installation, adjust shift linkage and downshift cable. Fill transmission with fluid.

JAGUAR

XJS

REMOVAL

1) Drive vehicle onto ramp. Remove transmission dipstick. Unscrew and remove bolt securing dipstick upper tube to lifting eye bracket. Remove dipstick upper tube.

2) Loosen fender supports to firewall securing bolt. Remove fender support-to-fender attaching bolts. Remove support from fender clamps. Secure fender supports away from fenders.

3) Unscrew and remove handles from Engine Lifting Hooks (MS 53 A). Attach hooks to rear lifting eyes. Attach engine support. Attach and tighten handles. Raise ramp.

4) Unscrew and remove nuts and bolts holding intermediate exhaust pipes, rotating flanges for access. Disconnect exhaust pipes and remove sealers. Remove intermediate and rear heat shields.

5) Secure exhaust pipes aside. Remove front heat shields. Remove rear mount center nut and spacer. Put block of wood between jack and transmission rear mount. Remove rear mount bolts and spacers. Lower jack. Remove rear mounts, wooden block and jack.

6) Remove crossmember. Remove propeller shaft and set aside. Working from above engine compartment, loosen hooks 10 turns only. From beneath vehicle, disconnect speedometer cable from transmission.

7) Unscrew nut holding selector pin to lever and disconnect cable. Unscrew bolt holding selector cable to support bracket and secure cable aside. Disconnect kickdown solenoid feed wire and remove clamp bolt holding feed wire to transmission.

8) Disconnect modulator capsule vacuum tube. Remove bolt and clamp plate holding modulator. Place container under modulator, remove modulator and partially drain transmission fluid. Remove and discard modulator "O" ring.

9) Unscrew cooler pipe union nuts from unions. Unscrew bolt holding cooler pipe bracket to engine sump. Remove spacer. Disconnect and plug cooler pipes. Remove access cover.

Automatic Transmission Removal

JAGUAR (Cont.)

10) Remove bolts holding converter to drive plate. Turn drive plate for access. Remove right side heat shield. Remove and secure catalytic converter from manifold.

11) Remove all engine-to-transmission attaching bolts except 2 lower left side bolts and lower starter attaching bolt. Remove dipstick tube and position tube/vacuum pipe mounting bracket along the vacuum pipe.

12) Using an Epco Lift (V1000), remove front and rear clamps. Attach lift to transmission and remove weight from transmission. Adjust tilt angle and side clamps. Tighten clamps.

13) Fit chain to right side arm, fit securing peg and pass chain over transmission into front arm. Tighten chain adjuster. Remove remaining securing bolts, lower unit and remove transmission from beneath vehicle.

INSTALLATION

1) With lift unit attached, position speedometer cable, selector cable, kickdown solenoid feed wire and vacuum pipe. Align transmission mating flange over locating dowels.

2) Install and tighten 3 lower left transmission bolts. Install starter. Loosen lift chain and remove pin from left side arm. Remove chain assembly. Lower and remove lift. Tighten remaining securing bolts.

3) Place dipstick pipe clamp on torque converter housing and fit lower dipstick tube. Connect dipstick tube to transmission and pull vacuum pipe through bracket. Install, but do not tighten, 2 accessible torque converter/drive plate bolts.

4) Install remaining drive plate bolts. Turn drive plate and tighten first 4 bolts. Install torque converter cover plate. Loosen left side nut attaching strap to cover and position strap aside.

5) Remove plugs from cooler pipes and connect pipes to transmission. Position cooler pipe mounting bracket, fit spacer and bolt and secure bracket to engine sump.

6) Fit new "O" ring to modulator capsule and fit modulator to transmission with clamp plate and bolt. Connect vacuum pipe to modulator. Connect kickdown solenoid feed wire to transmission.

7) Install selector cable bracket to mount and connect cable to lever. Fit and tighten selector pin securing nut. Working from above engine, tighten hook handles to raise engine.

8) Working from beneath vehicle, connect propeller shaft to transmission flange. Position and align crossmember and install attaching bolts. Place ramp jack under rear mount with wooden block. Raise jack and align attachment holes.

9) Install rear spacers and bolts. Remove jack and wooden block. Install rear mounting spacer and center nut. Install right side catalyst to manifold. Attach converter cover strap to catalyst.

10) Install exhaust pipes and heat shields. Lower ramp. Remove support hook handles and support. Install dipstick upper tube and fender stays. Fill transmission with fluid.

XJ6

REMOVAL

1) Disconnect battery cable. Remove transmission dipstick from tube and bolts securing tube to manifold. Remove upper fan shroud and disconnect kickdown cable from throttle bellcrank.

2) Raise vehicle on hoist. Remove transmission fill tube, exhaust intermediate pipe and heat shields. Secure transmission jack-to-transmission, and raise enough to support weight of transmission. Remove rear transmission support plate. Remove mount-to-transmission securing bolts and remove mount.

3) Remove drive shaft from vehicle as a unit. Lower transmission jack to position required to remove transmission, but do not remove transission at this time. Remove rubber pad from top of transmission.

4) Position Engine Support (MS 53A) and attach to rear lifting eye on engine. Turn adjusting nut to support weight of engine. Take care not to damage water heater valve.

5) From transmission unit selector lever, remove nut to release ball peg on inner selector cable. Remove set screw and spring washer securing outer selector cable clamp. Disconnect speedometer cable from transmission.

6) Remove dipstick tube and cover on front of converter housing. Remove 4 bolts retaining torque converter to drive plate. Disconnect oil cooler lines from transmission case and plug lines.

7) Remove all converter housing-to-engine bolts. Move starter out of way. Separate and lower transmission from engine.

INSTALLATION

Secure transmission to jack, fit torque converter to transmission and reverse removal procedure to complete installation.

MAZDA

GLC & 626

REMOVAL

1) Drain all fluid from tranxaxle assembly (oil pan must be removed to completely drain transaxle as drain plug alone will not drain all fluid). Disconnect negative cable from battery. Disconnect speedometer cable, inhibitor switch connector, neutral switch connector and kickdown solenoid connector.

2) Remove vacuum diaphragm line. Raise front end of vehicle and support. Remove wheels, disconnect lower control arm ball joints and pull drive shafts out of transaxle. Use care when removing drive shafts to avoid stressing outer constant velocity joint to its limit, as this will damage the joint. Remove engine undercover.

3) Attach engine support to engine hanger and support engine. Remove shift linkage from transaxle assembly. Remove crossmember. Disconnect oil hose from oil pipe and plug ends of hose and pipe. Remove rear

MAZDA (Cont.)

transmission mount. Remove starter, end cover and torque converter-to-drive plate retaining bolts.

4) Support transaxle with jack and remove transaxle-to-engine retaining bolts. Lower transaxle assembly out of vehicle. Use care when removing transaxle so that torque converter does not fall out.

INSTALLATION
To install, reverse removal procedure.

RX-7

REMOVAL
1) Disconnect negative battery cable. Remove air cleaner, converter housing upper and side covers, and top bolts attaching transmission to engine. On models so equipped, disengage torsion shaft from accelerator linkage. Raise vehicle and support with safety stands.

2) Drain fluid from transmission. Remove propeller shaft. Use output shaft plug to prevent oil leakage from rear of transmission. Remove any exhaust mounts attached to transmission. Disconnect exhaust pipe from manifold. Disconnect shift linkage from manual shaft on transmission.

3) Disconnect all electrical and vacuum leads from transmission. Disconnect speedometer cable. Remove oil filler tube from transmission, then disconnect both oil cooler pipes.

4) Disconnect governor tube from converter housing and transmission case (if equipped). Support transmission with wood block between oil pan and transmission jack.

5) Remove converter inspection plate. Mark converter and flywheel for realignment reference during installation. Remove torque converter-to-flywheel attaching bolts.

6) Remove rear mount and crossmember mounting bolts. Remove starter (lower transmission as needed to gain access to starter bolts). Remove transmission-to-engine bolts and slowly lower transmission out of vehicle.

INSTALLATION
Reverse removal procedure to install transmission, noting the following: When installing torque converter, ensure notch in converter lines up with notch in oil pump. When bolting converter to flywheel, align mark made during removal to ensure proper alignment. After transmission is installed, rotate crankshaft several times to be sure that transmission rotates freely without binding.

PICKUP

REMOVAL
1) Raise vehicle and support with safety stands. Disconnect negative battery cable. Remove shift rod from right side of transmission case. Remove bolts and nuts attaching exhaust pipe and catalytic converter.

2) Remove solenoid and inhibitor switch connectors. Remove speedometer cable. Remove propeller shaft. Fit main Shaft Holder (49 0259 440) into main shaft in transmission case to prevent oil leak. Remove starter and gusset plates.

3) Remove lower covers from front and rear of engine. Remove converter housing bolts. Remove vacuum pipe clip. Remove bolt, pipe clip and installation bolt from left side of transmission.

4) Remove connector bolts and washers from left side of transmission. Remove engine hanger. Remove clip and bolt from top of converter housing. Remove oil filter pipe and level gauge.

5) Securely support transmission with hydraulic jack. Remove transmission mounts. Cover oil filler pipe and connector bolt mounting hole on transmission case.

6) Insert screwdriver through torque converter installation hole in drive plate. Press against torque converter to prevent it from separating when transmission is removed. Remove transmission-to-engine bolts and slowly lower transmission out of vehicle.

INSTALLATION
Reverse removal procedure to install transmission. After transmission is installed, rotate crankshaft several times to be sure that transmission rotates freely without binding.

MERCEDES-BENZ

190 SERIES

REMOVAL

NOTE: To avoid damaging compartment wall (firewall), attach a sheet metal panel to vehicle's compartment wall to protect insulating mat during all jobs where the transmission is lowered at the rear. Disconnect exhaust assembly at rear mounting bracket and fasten by means of a wire approximately 2 inches lower than bracket.

1) Disconnect negative cable on battery. Unscrew holder for oil filler pipe on cylinder head. Force off ball socket. Disconnect cable control for control pressure.

2) Pull out lock and loosen cable control. Unscrew drain plug on oil pan and torque converter. Drain fluid. Screw back drain plugs with new seals and tighten.

3) Remove 6 torque converter bolts. Remove crossmember with rear engine mount. Remove exhaust support. Remove companion plate on universal flange of transmission.

Automatic Transmission Removal

MERCEDES-BENZ (Cont.)

NOTE: Loosen soft companinon plate installed at transmission end by using a mandrel.

4) Disconnect exhaust system at rear mount. Remove shielding plate. Loosen propeller shaft clamping nut and push propeller shaft together as much as possible.

5) Pull cable from kickdown solenoid valve. Loosen tachometer shaft. Disconnect control rod on floor shift. Remove fastening clip for tachometer shaft.

6) Swivel locking bracket in upward direction and pull plug from starter lockout switch. Pull vacuum line from vacuum control unit. Pull out filler pipe in upward direction.

7) Remove oil cooler lines and clamps. Remove all transmission-to-engine mounting bolts. Slightly lift transmission with mounting. Slide transmission to the rear and carefully let dowm.

Installation

1) Place transmission on removing and installing fixture, turn torque converter so that one of 3 threaded plates is in alignment with bottom of bell housing. Lightly grease centering pin on torque converter. Connect control rod to transmission and secure.

2) Lift transmission, slide forward at engine level until converter housing rests against engine. Bolt transmission to engine. Fasten control pressure cable control and vacuum line to holder.

3) Fasten grounding strap by means of lower bolt. Connect oil cooler lines with new sealing rings. Bolt on fastening clamps. Insert oil filler pipe. Connect oil cooler line with new sealing rings.

4) Push plug on starter lockout switch and fold locking bracket in downward direction. Plug cable to kickdown solenoid valve. Slip in tachometer shaft and secure.

5) Attach control rod to floor shift and secure with clip. Install companion plate to universal flange of transmission. Install crossmember with rear engine mount, fasten cable for kickdown solenoid valve.

6) Fasten tachometer shaft with clip. Tigthen propeller shaft clamping nut. Install shielding plate under propeller shaft intermediate bearing. Install exhaust system. Attach cable control for control pressure insert lock. Push on ball socket.

300, 380 & 500 SERIES

REMOVAL

1) Disconnect negative battery cable. Remove transmission oil filler pipe clamp from cylinder head. Force off ball socket on control wire linkage pivot. Pull out wire lock and loosen control wire. Compress tabs on plastic clip and pull retainer control wire from bracket.

2) Raise vehicle on hoist. Remove cross yoke center body support. Remove oil pan drain plug and drain oil from transmission. Remove drain plug from torque converter and drain. Reinstall drain plugs. Remove torque converter cover plates. Remove 6 bolts that secure torque converter-to-drive plate.

3) Place a block of wood between engine oil pan and front crossmember. Disconnect exhaust pipes at coupler at rear of transmission and remove exhaust pipes. Remove rear crossmember and rear transmission mount as an assembly. Remove cable strap and unscrew kickdown solenoid valve cable. Remove impulse transmitter retaining screws and remove transmitter.

4) Remove bolts attaching transmission companion flange to propeller shaft 3-arm flange. Remove exhaust shielding plate. Loosen propeller shaft clamping nut and slide propeller shaft as far rearward as possible. Turn starter lock-out switch plug retainer ring in upward direction. Carefully remove plug with 2 screwdrivers.

5) Disconnect shift control rod from range selector lever. Unscrew holder and remove vacuum line from vacuum control unit. Disconnect oil cooler lines from transmission. Remove oil filler tube retainer bolt and push tube upward to remove.

6) Remove all engine-to-transmission attaching bolts except for 2 bottom bolts. Slightly raise transmission with transmission jack. Remove 2 bottom engine-to-transmission bolts. Push transmission and jack toward rear of vehicle as far as possible. Remove transmission from vehicle. Place transmission in vertical position. Install Converter Handles (065) and lift converter from transmission.

INSTALLATION

Reverse removal procedures and note the following: When installing torque converter to transmission, coat converter tangs, turbine and stator shaft with assembly lubricant. Be sure that converter is fully seated in transmission before installing in vehicle.

MITSUBISHI

CORDIA & TRENDIA

REMOVAL

1) Remove battery and battery tray. Remove reservoir tank and windshield washer tank. Remove air cleaner case. Disconnect throttle control cable from carburetor.

2) Disconnect control cable from transaxle. Disconnect inhibitor switch connector, oil cooler hoses and speedometer from transaxle. Plug oil cooler hoses. Disconnect starter harness and remove starter.

3) Lift vehicle and remove wheels. Drain transmission fluid. Remove strut bars and stabilizer bars from lower control arms. Remove right and left drive shafts from transaxle and set them aside.

4) Remove bell housing cover. Remove 3 special bolts (3 pieces) connecting converter with drive plate. Turn engine for access to all 3 bolts. Push torque converter into transaxle after bolt removal.

5) Remove upper 5 bolts connecting transaxle to engine. Support a wide area of lower part of transaxle with transmission jack. Remove remaining engine connecting bolts. Remove transaxle mount insulator bolts.

6) Remove blank cap from inside right fender shield and remove installation bolts. Remove transaxle insulator and mounting brackets. Slide transaxle assembly to the right and lower it to remove.

MITSUBISHI (Cont.)

INSTALLATION

Reverse removal procedures and note the following: Be sure to install torque converter first to transaxle and then to engine. Refill transaxle fluid to specified level. Adjust control cables. Ensure that inhibitor switch harness does not contact transaxle insulator bracket.

PICKUP

REMOVAL

1) Drain transmission. Raise and support vehicle. Disconnect control rod, throttle linkage and cooler lines to transmission fittings. Remove starter motor. Remove converter to drive plate bolts.

2) Mark propeller shaft and universal joints for reassembly reference. Remove propeller shaft. Disconnect control rod from manual control lever. Disconnect throttle rod from transmission throttle lever.

3) Support transmission with hydraulic jack. Remove oil filter tube and speedometer cable. Remove extension housing mount from rear insulator, raise transmission and remove rear engine support bracket from body. Lower and remove transmission from vehicle.

INSTALLATION

Reverse removal procedures and note the following: Tighten converter housing bolts to 31-40 ft. lbs. (42-54 N.m). Align reference marks before connecting propeller shaft.

STARION

REMOVAL

1) Disconnect battery ground cable. Remove oil cooler lines at transmission. Remove starter motor and cooler line bracket. Loosen pan to drain transmission.

2) Mark converter and drive plate for reassembly reference. Using socket wrench on crankshaft vibration damper bolt, rotate engine clockwise to position converter attaching bolts for removal. Remove bolts and propeller shaft.

3) Disconnect electrical leads. Disconnect gearshift rod and torque shaft assembly, throttle rod lever from left side of transmission, and linkage bellcrank (if so equipped) from transmission.

4) Remove oil filler tube and speedometer cable. Support rear of engine with engine support fixture. With a transmission support on a service jack, support transmission. Raise transmission slightly to relieve load on supports.

5) Remove bolts securing transmission mount to crossmember and crossmember to frame, then remove crossmember. Remove all converter housing bolts, then carefully work transmission and converter assembly rearward off engine block dowels and disengage converter hub from end of crankshaft.

6) Attach a small "C" clamp to edge of converter housing to hold converter in place during transmission removal. Lower transmission and remove from under vehicle. To remove converter assembly, remove "C" clamp from edge of converter housing and carefully slide assembly from transmission.

INSTALLATION

1) To install, reverse removal procedure. Install converter and test for full engagement by placing straight edge on face of converter housing. Surface of converter front cover lug should be at least 1/2" from rear of straightedge when converter is pushed all the way into transmission.

2) Attach a small "C" clamp to converter housing to hold converter in place during transmission installation. Inspect converter drive plate for distortion or cracks and replace if necessary.

3) Coat converter hub hole in crankshaft with multi-purpose grease. When drive plate replacement has been necessary, ensure both transmission dowel pins are in engine block and they are protruding far enough to hold transmission in alignment.

4) Place transmission and converter assembly on a jack and position under vehicle for installation. Raise or tilt as necessary to align transmission to engine. Rotate converter so that mark on converter (made during removal) will align with mark on drive plate.

5) Carefully work transmission assembly forward over engine block dowels with converter hub entering crankshaft opening. After transmission is in position on engine, install and tighten all bolts. Adjust shift and throttle linkage, then refill transmission with DEXRON II type automatic transmission fluid.

NISSAN/DATSUN

REAR WHEEL DRIVE MODELS

REMOVAL

1) On models so equipped, disengage torsion shaft from accelerator linkage. Raise vehicle and support with safety stands. Drain fluid from transmission. Remove propeller shaft.

2) Use output shaft plug to prevent oil leakage from rear of transmission. Remove any exhaust mounts attached to transmission. Disconnect exhaust pipe from manifold. Disconnect shift linkage from manual traft on transmission.

3) Disconnect all electrical and vacuum leads from transmission. Disconnect speedometer cable. Remove oil filler tube from transmission, then disconnect both oil cooler pipes.

4) Disconnect governor tube from converter housing and transmission case (if equipped). Support transmission with wood block between oil pan and transmission jack. On Maxima and 200SX models, remove gussets from front of transmission.

Automatic Transmission Removal

NISSAN/DATSUN (Cont.)

5) On all models, remove converter inspection plate. Mark converter and flywheel for realignment reference during installation. Remove torque converter-to-flywheel attaching bolts.

6) Remove rear mount and crossmember mounting bolts. Remove starter (lower transmission as needed to gain access to starter bolts). Remove transmission-to-engine bolts and slowly lower transmission out of vehicle.

INSTALLATION

1) Reverse removal procedure to install transmission, noting the following: Check flywheel runout with dial indicator before installing transmission. Runout must not exceed .02" (.5 mm).

2) When installing torque converter, ensure that notch in converter lines up with notch in oil pump. Measure distance from front of converter housing to flywheel bolt mounting surface on converter. If distance is less than 1.38" (35.0 mm), converter or other components are incorrectly assembled.

FRONT WHEEL DRIVE MODELS

REMOVAL

1) Disconnect battery ground cable. Raise and support vehicle. Remove wheels and tires. Drain transaxle fluid. Remove left fender protector. Remove brake caliper and pry cotter pin out of hub. Loosen, do not remove, wheel hub nut from axle shaft while preventing hub from turning.

2) Remove tie rod end from steering knuckle. Remove lower ball joint and discard nut. Remove axle shaft from transaxle and discard axle shaft snap ring. Do not damage oil seal during axle shaft removal. Insert a bar or equivalent tool into each side of differential case to prevent dropping of side gear.

3) Remove knuckle attaching bolts and remove hub, knuckle and axle shaft as an assembly. Disconnect speedometer cable, throttle cable and control linkage. Remove fluid dipstick and tube assembly. Place transmission jack under engine and transaxle assembly. DO NOT place jack under oil pan drain plug.

4) Disconnect oil cooler lines. Remove inspection plate from torque converter. Rotate crankshaft and remove torque converter-to-drive plate bolts. Mark position of torque converter in relation to housing for installation reference. Remove engine mount bolts. Remove starter motor.

5) Remove transaxle-to-engine bolts. Gradually move jack to rear until transaxle can be removed. Carefully remove transaxle from vehicle by taking out through left wheel housing.

INSTALLATION

1) To install, reverse removal procedure. Measure drive plate runout with a dial indicator before installing torque converter. Runout should not exceed .020" (.5 mm). After installing torque converter to transaxle, ensure distance from converter housing surface to converter face ring is more than .83" (21 mm).

2) Apply sealant to torque converter bolts prior to installation. Align reference marks made during removal when installing converter. After converter is installed, rotate crankshaft several times and make sure transaxle rotates freely without binding.

PEUGEOT

ALL MODELS

REMOVAL

1) Open hood as far as possible without forcing and support open with block placed under safety hook. Disconnect negative battery cable. Remove air duct between metering unit and butterfly housing. Remove 2 bolts from control pressure regulator.

2) Remove upper and lower radiator mounts and fan shroud. Place a piece of cardboard between radiator and fan to protect radiator from damage during transmission removal. Disconnect kickdown control cable at throttle linkage.

3) Remove exhaust-to-manifold nuts. Disconnect all exhaust system hangers. Remove heat shield from above muffler. Remove front seat stiffener located above muffler.

4) Remove vibration damper from propeller shaft tube. Remove extension housing bracket bolts. Disconnect differential from its mount. Mark position of lower steering column flange coupling and remove bolts.

5) On models with power steering, remove front crossmember-to-front mount bolts and replace with 2" (50 mm) bolts. Remove remaining crossmember bolts. Lower crossmember about 2" (50 mm) by unscrewing 2 bolts in crossmember. On all other models, remove steering box mounting bolts and lower steering gear without disconnecting links.

6) On all models, drain transmission fluid. Disconnect and plug cooler lines at transmission. Remove starter motor bolts. Disconnect filler tube from transmission. Remove torque converter cover plate and sensor from bellhousing. DO NOT alter sensor adjustment.

7) Remove torque converter-to-flywheel bolts. Using a retainer, secure torque converter in housing so it will not fall out during transmission removal. Place jack under transmission and remove 4 propeller shaft-to-transmission bolts.

8) Separate transmission from tube about .8" (20 mm) and install Retaining Plate (8.0403SZ) between the 2 units. Install 2 bolts to hold plate in place.

9) Pull differential and propeller shaft assembly to the rear of vehicle and allow front of tube to rest on rear crossmember. Disconnect gear shift linkage, speedometer and electrical connections from transmission. Lower and tilt transmission as far as possible.

10) Install engine lift equipment to front of engine. Lift engine far enough to gain access to upper transmission-to-engine bolts. Remove bolts and remove transmission from vehicle.

INSTALLATION

Reverse removal procedure to install, noting the following: Apply grease to torque converter pilot bushing. Adjust shift and throttle linkage as needed. Fill transmission with fluid and check for leaks.

PORSCHE

944

REMOVAL

1) Remove heat shield and rear muffler bracket. Detach axle shafts at transaxle. Suspend axle shafts in horizontal position to prevent damage to dust covers. Remove transaxle oil filter shield.

2) Detach selector and transaxle lever cables. Remove converter bolts through hole in torque converter housing. Support transaxle with jack and remove transaxle-to-engine bolts and transaxle mounts. Slide transaxle toward rear of vehicle and remove.

INSTALLATION

Reverse removal procedures to install, noting the following: Ensure pump shaft and torque converter are fully seated in transaxle or damage to internal components may result during installation.

928S

REMOVAL

1) Disconnect and remove battery. Remove self-locking nuts from spring struts in trunk. Disconnect multiple plug in spare wheel well and pull toward rear. Disconnect parking brake cable and lock. Remove rear wheels and splash shield. Drain torque converter and transmission oil sump. Remove oil filler tube. Disconnect transmission oil cooler lines.

2) Remove lower body brace. Disconnect exhaust pipe from catalytic converter. Remove exhaust pipe heat shields. Remove battery box. Remove rubber cap from inspection hole in front converter housing and turn crankshaft to position coupling so that socket head screw can be removed. Disconnect brake calipers and suspend with wire. Disconnect axle shafts and swing out of the way. Remove rear reinforcement plate. Disconnect stabilizer bar from lower control arm.

3) Support transaxle with Support (9164) and remove 2 bolts from transaxle mounts. Remove 2 bolts holding rear axle crossmember to frame. Mark position of eccentric bolts and remove bolts. Mark position of rear axle crossmember for reinstallation. Place jack under transaxle crossmember and remove mounting bolts from crossmember.

4) Lower rear axle carefully and take care that spring struts, crossmember and bearing brackets do not tilt. Mount Special Tool (9163) on adjustable floor jack. Lift transaxle and remove Special Tool (9164). Lower transaxle slightly and remove selector lever. Disconnect modulator vacuum line. Remove 6 bolts from central tube. Pull transaxle out of coupling splines and lower carefully.

NOTE: **Transaxle has to be lowered as far as possible to gain access to all tube bolts.**

INSTALLATION

To install, reverse removal procedure and check rear end alignment.

RENAULT

FUEGO & SPORTWAGON

REMOVAL

1) Raise and support vehicle. Disconnect battery. Drain transmission fluid. Disconnect vacuum capsule hose from intake manifold. Disconnect transaxle wiring connectors and remove support. Insert Spacer (T. Av. 509-01) between lower shock mounting base and lower control arm pivot shaft on each side.

2) Remove drive shaft retaining roll pins with drift. Separate tie rod end ball joints and upper control arm ball joints from steering knuckle using puller. Tilt axle carriers away from transaxle to separate drive shafts from side gears.

3) With shift lever in neutral position, disconnect shift rod at entry to transaxle and at the shift lever. Remove dipstick and inspection plate. Remove 3 torque converter retaining bolts. Remove exhaust pipe bracket nut at transaxle.

4) Position Transmission Jack (Desvil 701 ST) under rear of transaxle and raise until assembly is supported on the 4 studs. Remove transaxle mounts. Lower assembly enough to remove speedometer and governor cables. Remove engine-to-transaxle retaining bolts. Lower transaxle from vehicle. Attach Torque Converter Retaining Strap (B. Vi. 465 Ref. D) to hold torque converter in place in case.

INSTALLATION

1) Reverse removal procedures to install, noting the following: Lightly lubricate axle shaft splined ends before installing. Tilt stub axle carrier as needed to line up roll pin holes. If equipped with TDC sensor, make sure it is adjusted correctly when installed.

2) If a new TDC sensor is used, install into position until pegs (3) on sensor contact flywheel. Tighten retaining screw. If reusing an old sensor, install until it contacts flywheel, mark position with a fine line on sensor body, and back sensor out about .04" (1 mm). Tighten retaining screw.

3) Adjust selector lever and governor cable. Check computer and governor connections and make sure ground wire is connected.

Fig. 1: Location of Spacer in Front Suspension

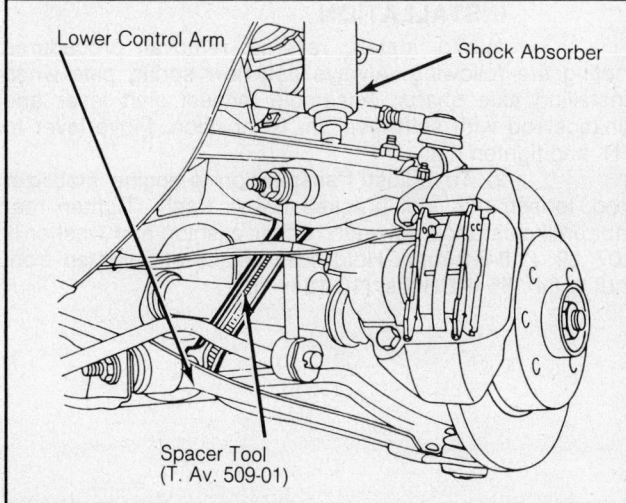

Install tool between lower shock mount and lower control are pivot shaft.

Automatic Transmission Removal

SAAB

ALL MODELS

REMOVAL

NOTE: Engine and transaxle must be removed as an assembly.

1) Disconnect positive battery terminal from battery. Drain radiator. Disconnect windshield washer hose from hood. Remove hood.

2) Disconnect all engine or transaxle electrical connections as needed for engine removal. Remove air cleaner, preheater hose and crankcase ventilation hose.

3) Disconnect fuel line and plug. Disconnect choke, throttle cable, hose to expansion tank and brake servo vacuum hose. Remove clamps from drivers side inner universal joint.

4) Place special tool 83 93 209 between the upper control arm underside and frame (insert tool from engine compartment side). Raise and support vehicle.

5) Remove lower control arm-to-ball joint bolts. Pull control arm assembly from control arm and support with jack stand.

6) Remove gear selector cable screw at transaxle. Pull cable out of transaxle and slide back spring loaded sleeve, then disconnect from control lever. Disconnect speedometer cable from transaxle. Remove rear engine mounting bolts.

7) Loosen front engine mounting nut so mount can be lifted from bracket. Attach engine lifting device on 2 engine lifting lugs and raise engine slightly. Move engine assembly side to side to free universal joints. Lift assembly from vehicle and place on engine stand.

8) To separate transaxle from engine, drain engine oil and remove inspection cover. Remove starter. Disconnect throttle cable. Remove engine-to-transaxle bolts. Remove 4 converter-to-flex plate bolts. Turn flex plate until plate angles are horizontal and lift engine off of transaxle.

INSTALLATION

1) To install, reverse removal procedure and note the following: Mating surfaces of transaxle and engine must be thoroughly clean. Use gasket sealer on new gasket when assembling transaxle and engine. Apply sealer to bolts indicated in *Fig. 1* of SAAB MANUAL TRANSAXLE REMOVAL procedure.

2) Pack inner universal joints with grease, adjust shift cable if necessary and check cooling system for leaks.

SUBARU

1800

REMOVAL

1) Remove spare tire from engine compartment. Disconnect negative battery cable. Remove spare tire mount. Disconnect transmission diaphragm vacuum hose. Disconnect speedometer cable from transmission and unfasten clip on cable.

2) Disconnect back-up light switch connector from transmission, ground cable from body and starter harness. Remove torque converter-to-drive plate retaining bolts (4) through hole in torque converter housing (timing hole). Be careful that bolts do not fall into housing. Disconnect transmission fluid lines from transmission and drain transmission fluid.

3) Remove starter (cable still attached) and set aside. Remove upper transmission-to-engine retaining bolts and loosen lower nuts. Loosen retaining nut on transmission-to-engine stabilizer rod (transmission side of bracket) not more than .4" (10 mm). Tighten nut on opposite side by an equal amount. Tilt engine back slightly.

4) Disconnect oxygen sensor harness and unclamp. Raise front of vehicle and remove exhaust pipe assembly. Use care not to damage oxygen sensor during exhaust removal. Drain transmission fluid and disconnect oil supply pipe. With shift lever in "P" position, mark location of connector nut on manual lever. Separate manual lever from linkage rod.

5) Remove suspension stabilizer bar and transverse link-to-front crossmember retaining bolts (both sides). Lower transverse links. Drive out left and right axle shaft retaining spring pins. Push wheels toward outside of vehicle to separate axle shafts from transmission drive shafts.

6) Remove transmission mount-to-crossmember attaching nut and support transmission on a jack. Remove the crossmember. Remove 2 transmission-to-engine retaining nuts that were loosened in step 3). Pull transmission away from engine and lower out of vehicle.

INSTALLATION

1) To install, reverse removal procedures noting the following: Always use new spring pins when installing axle shafts. Assemble manual shift lever and linkage rod with shift lever in "P" position. Move lever to "N" and tighten nut.

2) To adjust transmission-to-engine stabilizer rod, loosen nut until bracket moves freely. Tighten rear nut until clearance between rubber cushion and washer is .07-.09" (1.8-2.2 mm). Hold nut in place and tighten front nut to 84-156 INCH lbs. (10-18 N.m).

TOYOTA

CAMRY

REMOVAL

1) Remove front and rear mounts. Remove left dust cover and mounting bracket. Remove side gear shaft, intermediate shaft and universal joint from transaxle. Remove control cable bracket and stiffener plate. Remove torque converter dust cover and locking plate.

2) Remove 6 torque converter mounting bolts. Turn crankshaft to gain access to each bolt. Hold crankshaft pulley nut with a wrench. Remove starter. Remove transaxle mounting bolts.

3) Install guide pin in one of the torque converter bolt holes. Pry on end of guide pin to begin moving transmission with converter. Remove transaxle assembly from engine.

INSTALLATION

1) Install torque converter in transmission. Using calipers and a straightedge, measure from installed surface to front surface of transmission housing. Correct distance should be .51" (13 mm).

2) Install guide pin in torque converter. Align guide pin with one of the drive plate holes. Align 2 knock pins on block with the converter housing. Temporarily install one bolt.

3) Install transmission housing mounting bolts. Tighten 12 mm bolts to 47 ft. lbs. (64 N.m) and 10 mm bolts to 25 ft. lbs. (34 N.m). Install starter. Remove guide pin. Install 6 torque converter bolts finger tight. Turn crankshaft to gain access. Tighten bolts evenly to 13 ft. lbs. (18 N.m).

4) Install torque converter dust cover. Lock transaxle mounting bolt near differential with the locking plate and one dust cover mounting bolt. Tighten bolts to 18 ft. lbs. (24 N.m).

5) Install stiffener plate and tighten bolts to 27 ft. lbs. (37 N.m). Install control cable bracket. Install side gear shaft and universal joint. Install left dust cover. Install front and rear mounts.

CELICA

REMOVAL

1) Disconnect negative battery cable. Drain coolant. Disconnect upper radiator hose. Remove air intake connector. Disconnect transmission throttle cable. Raise vehicle and drain transmission.

2) Disconnect wiring connectors to neutral start and back-up light switches. Remove intermediate shaft with center bearing from propeller shaft. Disconnect manual shift linkage. Disconnect speedometer cable.

3) Remove sliding yoke from gear housing and shift. Disconnect 2 oil cooler lines. Disconnect front exhaust pipe from rear pipe. Remove pipe clamp from transmission housing. Disconnect pipe from exhaust manifold and remove exhaust pipe from vehicle.

4) Remove power steering oil cooler clamp. Remove automatic transmission oil cooler pipe clamp at left of cylinder block. Remove power steering pressure line clamp.

5) Using Remover (SST09611-22012), disconnect both tie rod ends. Remove gear housing and suspend at crossmember. Remove both stiffener plates from transmission housing. Jack up transmission slightly to take weight off rear crossmember.

6) Remove rear support member, removing rubber exhaust hanger and ground strap if equipped. Remove engine under cover to gain access to crankshaft pulley. Lower transmission on wood piece. Pry out rubber plugs from service holes for torque converter.

7) Turn crankshaft as necessary to gain access to torque converter bolts and remove bolts. Install guide pin or cut off bolt in a torque converter bolt hole. Remove transmission housing mounting bolts. Pry on end of guide pin to start transmission movement to rear of vehicle.

8) Move transmission toward rear of vehicle, being careful not to catch throttle cable or neutral start switch cable. Keep oil pan positioned down. Place pan under converter housing and remove converter, pulling straight off and allowing fluid to drain into pan. If not already removed, remove filter tube and rear transmission support with ground strap.

INSTALLATION

1) Measure drive plate runout with dial indicator. If runout exceeds .0079" (.20 mm), or if ring gear is damaged, replace drive plate. If installing new drive plate, note positioning of spacers and tighten with new bolts.

2) Measure torque converter sleeve runout. If runout exceeds .012" (.30 mm), try to correct by repositioning converter. If runout cannot be corrected in this manner, torque converter must be replaced. Be sure to mark position of converter to ensure correct installation.

3) Install filler tube. Apply grease to center hub of torque converter and pilot hole in drive plate. Install torque converter in transmission. Refill with fresh ATF. Check torque converter installation.

4) Using calipers and straightedge, check that distance from center of hub to front surface of transmission housing is .79" (20 mm). Install guide pin in torque converter. Install transmission assembly. Align guide pin with a drive plate hole.

5) Align upper starter stud with hole on engine plate. Align 2 sleeves on block with converter housing. Tighten transmission housing mounting bolts. Install and tighten torque converter bolts.

6) To complete installation, reverse removal procedure. Fill transmission with automatic transmission fluid. Road test vehicle for proper operation of all functions.

COROLLA

REMOVAL

1) Disconnect negative battery cable. Drain coolant. Disconnect upper radiator hose. Remove air cleaner. Disconnect transmission throttle cable. Raise vehicle and drain transmission.

2) Disconnect wiring connectors to neutral start and back-up light switches. Remove propeller shaft. Remove front exhaust pipe. Disconnect 2 oil cooler lines. Remove power steering gear housing.

3) Disconnect manual shift linkage. Disconnect speedometer cable. Remove both stiffener plates from transmission housing. Jack up transmission slightly. Remove rear support member, rubber exhaust hanger and ground strap.

4) Remove engine under cover. Pry out rubber plug from service hole at rear of engine. Turn crankshaft

Automatic Transmission Removal

TOYOTA (Cont.)

to gain access to each torque converter mounting bolt. Remove 6 mounting bolts.

5) Install guide pin or cut off bolt in a torque converter bolt hole. Remove transmission housing mounting bolts. Pry on end of guide pin to start transmission movement to rear of vehicle.

6) Move transmission toward rear of vehicle, being careful not to catch throttle cable or neutral start switch cable. Keep oil pan positioned down.

7) Place pan under converter housing and remove converter, pulling straight off and allowing fluid to drain into pan. Remove filter tube and rear transmission support with ground strap.

INSTALLATION

1) Measure drive plate runout with dial indicator. If runout exceeds .0079" (.20 mm), or if ring gear is damaged, replace drive plate. If installing new drive plate, note positioning of spacers and tighten with new bolts.

2) Measure torque converter sleeve runout. If runout exceeds .012" (.30 mm), try to correct by re-positioning converter. If runout cannot be corrected in this manner, torque converter must be replaced. Be sure to mark position of converter to ensure correct installation.

3) Install rear transmission mount on extension housing. Install filler tube. Apply grease to center hub of torque converter and pilot hole in drive plate. Install torque converter in transmission. Refill with fresh ATF. Check torque converter installation.

4) Ensure that distance from center of hub to front surface of transmission housing is .91" (23 mm). Install guide pin in torque converter. Install transmission assembly. Align guide pin with a drive plate hole.

5) Align upper starter stud with hole on engine plate. Align 2 sleeves on block with converter housing. Tighten transmission housing mounting bolts. Install and tighten torque converter bolts.

6) To complete installation, reverse removal procedure. Fill transmission with automatic transmission fluid. Road test vehicle for proper operation of all functions.

CRESSIDA & SUPRA

REMOVAL

1) Disconnect negative battery cable. Drain coolant. Disconnect upper radiator hose. Remove air intake connector. Disconnect transmission throttle cable. Raise vehicle and drain transmission.

2) Disconnect wiring connectors to neutral start and back-up light switches. Remove intermediate shaft with center bearing from propeller shaft. Disconnect exhaust pipe at rear side of converter. Remove 2 rubber hangers and pipe clamp from transmission case.

3) Disconnect 2 oil cooler lines. Disconnect manual shift linkage and speedometer cable. Remove exhaust pipe bracket and converter cover stiffener plates from transmission housing and cylinder block.

4) Remove sliding yoke from gear housing. Using Remover (SST09611-22012), disconnect both tie rod ends. Remove fluid line clamps. Remove 4 bolts and remove 2 brackets and rubber insulator. Remove gear housing from crossmember and suspend it from frame.

5) Jack up transmission enough to remove weight from rear support member. Remove ground cable from rear support member. Install a wooden block between cowl panel and cylinder head rear end to prevent damage to heater hose. Remove rear support member.

6) Remove engine under cover. Remove 6 torque converter mounting bolts. Turn crankshaft to gain access to each bolt. Install guide pin in one of the torque converter bolt holes.

7) Remove starter and transmission housing mounting bolts. Pry on end of guide pin to start transmission movement to rear of vehicle. Move transmission toward rear of vehicle, being careful not to catch throttle cable or neutral start switch cable.

8) Keep oil pan positioned down. Place pan under converter housing and remove converter, pulling straight off and allowing fluid to drain into pan. If not already removed, remove filter tube and rear transmission support with ground strap.

INSTALLATION

1) Measure drive plate runout with dial indicator. If runout exceeds .0079" (.20 mm), or if ring gear is damaged, replace drive plate. If installing new drive plate, note positioning of spacers and tighten with new bolts.

2) Measure torque converter sleeve runout. If runout exceeds .012" (.30 mm), try to correct by re-positioning converter. If runout cannot be corrected in this manner, torque converter must be replaced. Be sure to mark position of converter to ensure correct installation.

3) Install rear transmission mount on extension housing. Install filler tube. Apply grease to center hub of torque converter and pilot hole in drive plate. Install torque converter in transmission. Refill with fresh ATF. Check torque converter installation.

4) Ensure that distance from center of hub to front surface of transmission housing is 1.02" (26 mm). Install guide pin in torque converter. Install transmission assembly. Align guide pin with a drive plate hole.

5) Align upper starter stud with hole on engine plate. Align 2 sleeves on block with converter housing. Tighten transmission housing mounting bolts. Install and tighten torque converter bolts.

6) To complete installation, reverse removal procedure. Fill transmission with automatic transmission fluid. Road test vehicle for proper operation of all functions.

PICKUP

REMOVAL

1) Disconnect negative battery cable. Remove air cleaner. Loosen transmission throttle cable adjusting nuts. Disconnect cable housing from bracket. Remove clip from cable guide and disconnect guide grommet. Disconnect cable from carburetor linkage.

2) Remove upper mounting nut on starter. Raise vehicle and drain transmission. Disconnect wiring connectors to neutral start and back-up light switches. Remove starter. Remove propeller shaft. Disconnect speedometer cable. Disconnect manual shift linkage.

3) Disconnect 2 oil cooler lines. Disconnect exhaust pipe clamp and remove oil filler tube. Jack up

TOYOTA (Cont.)

transmission slightly. Remove rear engine mount with bracket. Remove engine under cover.

4) Insert wooden block between engine oil pan and crossmember. Lower transmission and rest engine on crossmember. Pry out rubber plugs from service holes at rear of engine. Turn cranksahft to gain access to each bolt and remove 6 torque converter mounting bolts.

5) Install guide pin in one of the torque converter bolt holes. Remove transmission housing mounting bolts. Pry on end of guide pin to start transmission movement to rear of vehicle.

6) Move transmission toward rear of vehicle, being careful not to catch throttle cable or neutral start switch cable. Keep oil pan positioned down. Place pan under converter housing and remove converter, pulling straight off and allowing fluid to drain into pan.

INSTALLATION

1) Measure drive plate runout with dial indicator. If runout exceeds .0079" (.20 mm), or if ring gear is damaged, replace drive plate. If installing new drive plate, note positioning of spacers and tighten with new bolts.

2) Measure torque converter sleeve runout. If runout exceeds .012" (.30 mm), try to correct by repositioning converter. If runout cannot be corrected in this manner, torque converter must be replaced. Be sure to mark position of converter to ensure correct installation.

3) Apply grease to center hub of torque converter and pilot hole in drive plate. Install torque converter in transmission. Refill with fresh ATF. Check torque converter installation.

4) Using calipers and a straightedge, measure from center hub to front surface of transmission housing. Ensure that distance is .79" (20 mm). Install guide pin in torque converter. Install transmission assembly. Align guide pin with a drive plate hole.

5) Align upper starter stud with hole on engine plate. Align 2 sleeves on block with converter housing. Tighten transmission housing mounting bolts. Install and tighten torque converter bolts.

6) To complete installation, reverse removal procedure. Fill transmission with automatic transmission fluid. Road test vehicle for proper operation of all functions.

TERCEL

REMOVAL

1) Disconnect battery ground cable and neutral safety switch. Partially drain radiator, then disconnect upper radiator hose at engine. Remove air cleaner. Disconnect throttle linkage, transmission cooler pipes and clamps. Disconnect cooler pipes from transmission.

2) Remove transmission-to-engine top bolts. Remove drive axle assemblies. Raise and support vehicle. Disconnect exhaust pipe from manifold. Remove 2 right side stiffener plate bolts. Disconnect shift control link bolt and speedometer cable (from transmission).

3) Remove engine under cover. Remove torque converter cover and torque converter-to-drive plate bolts. Hold crankshaft from turning when removing bolts. Disconnect oil cooler outlet pipe.

4) Place transmission jack under transmission and remove remaining transmission-to-engine bolts. Disconnect rear bond cable. Remove rear transmission

support. Pull transmission to the rear to separate torque converter from drive plate. Lower transmission out of vehicle.

INSTALLATION

1) Before installing transmission, apply grease to torque converter shaft and crankshaft pilot hole. Install Guide Pin (SST09350-12010) in outside converter mounting hole. Align guide pin with 1 of the drive plate holes.

2) Be careful not to tilt transaxle forward or torque converter will slide out. Install transaxle to engine so that tip of converter goes into crankshaft hole. Remove guide pin. Temporarily insert 2 bolts about 3/8" (10 mm) and tighten evenly a little at a time.

3) Install 4 transaxle-to-engine bolts and install exhaust pipe bracket and throttle link bracket on the right side of the transaxle case. Install rear transaxle support member and tighten to 26-36 ft. lbs. (35-48 N.m). Remove temporarily installed bolts from torque converter and install 6 bolts finger tight.

4) Turn crankshaft to gain access. Tighten bolts evenly to 11-15 ft. lbs. (15-20 N.m). Install torque converter cover and connect bond cable. Connect cooler outlet pipe and tighten to 15-21 ft. lbs. (20-28 N.m). Install engine under cover. Install 2 right side stiffener plate bolts. Install exhaust pipe. Connect speedometer and rear bond cable.

5) Align shift lever and control link at neutral position. Connect control link. Lower vehicle. Install both drive shafts. Connect oil cooler inlet pipe. Install cooler pipe clamp. Connect throttle linkage. Connect all wiring connectors. To complete installation, reverse removal procedure.

6) Check and adjust wheel alignment, throttle link rod and selector lever if necessary. Fill transmission with automatic transmission fluid Type F. Fill differential with 1 quart of SAE 80W-90 gear oil.

VAN

REMOVAL

1) Disconnect negative battery cable. Loosen transmission throttle cable adjustment nuts. Disconnect cable housing from bracket. Disconnect cable from throttle body.

2) Disconnect Neutral start switch, back-up light and overdrive solenoid connectors. Raise vehicle and drain transmission. Remove propeller shaft. Disconnect exhaust pipe clamp from transmission housing. Remove exhaust pipe clamp.

3) Disconnect shift cable from transmission. Disconnect speedometer and bond cables. Loosen oil cooler nuts. Remove clamps and disconnect oil cooler lines. Remove starter.

4) Support transmission with jack. Remove 2 fuel tank mount bolts and support fual tank. Remove transmission mount through bolt. Remove stiffner plates from transmission housing.

5) Remove access cover from lower rear side of engine. Remove 6 torque converter attaching bolts. Install guide pin in torque converter. If necessary, a guide pin can be made by cutting off the head of a bolt.

6) Remove transmission mount bolts. Pry on end of guide pin to begin moving transmission and torque converter toward rear. Remove transmission and torque converter.

Automatic Transmission Removal

TOYOTA (Cont.)

NOTE: **Position transmission down and toward rear. Do not catch throttle cable or Neutral safety switch cable. Keep oil pan positioned downward.**

7) Place pan under converter housing and remove converter. Drain converter. Remove filler tube. Remove transmission mount.

INSTALLATION

1) Measure drive plate runout with dial indicator. If runout exceeds 0.0079" (0.20 mm), or if ring gear is damaged, replace drive plate. If installing a new drive plate, note position of spacers and tightn with new bolts.

2) Measure torque converter sleeve runout, If runout exceeds 0.012" (0.30 mm), try to correct by repositioning converter. If runout cannot be corrected in this manner, replace torque converter. Mark torque converter for correct installation.

3) Install rear transmission mount on extension housing. Install filler tube. Apply grease to center hub of torque converter and pilot hole in drive plate. Fill torque converter with ATF. Install torque converter in transmission.

4) Check torque converter installation by measuring the distance between transmission case and torque converter bolt hole pad. Correct distance is 1.02" (26 mm). Install guide pin in torque converter.

5) Aling guide pin with a hole in drive plate. Install transmission assembly and align upper starter stud with hole on engine plate. Align 2 sleeves on block with converter housing.

6) Tighten transmission housing mount bolts. Install and tighten torque converter bolts. To complete installation, reverse removal procedure. Fill transmission with ATF. Road test vehicle.

VOLKSWAGEN

JETTA, RABBIT & SCIROCCO

REMOVAL

1) Disconnect battery ground strap and starter cable at battery. Disconnect speedometer cable from transmission. Remove 2 upper engine-to-transmission attaching bolts. Loosen left side transmission mount. Install Support Fixture (10-222).

2) Remove 5 rear transmission mounting bolts. Mark axle drive shafts for reassembly reference, and disconnect from final drive flanges. Remove starter bolts and position starter out of the way.

3) Remove transmission protection plate and converter cover plate, then remove drive plate-to-torque converter bolts. Place selector lever in "P" position and disconnect selector cable from transmission lever. Remove cable bracket from transmission, then disconnect accelerator and pedal cables from bracket.

4) Support transmission with Fixture (US 4470) attached to engine hoist. Remove left side engine/transmission mount. Detach side carrier and mount from transmission. Remove front mount. Remove lower transmission-to-engine bolt. Remove remaining transmission-to-engine bolts. Lift transmission slightly and, taking care not to allow converter to drop, lower transmission from vehicle.

INSTALLATION

1) Reverse removal procedure and note the following: Ensure that torque converter is fully seated on one-way clutch support. Adjust selector lever cable.

2) To check converter installation, lay a straight edge across converter housing and measure distance from straight edge to center converter hub. If distance is less than 1.2" (30 mm), converter is not fully engaged.

QUANTUM

REMOVAL

1) Disconnect negative battery cable. Disconnect accelerator linkage rod. Disconnect speedometer cable then remove upper engine-to-transaxle bolts.

2) Support engine from above. Disconnect automatic transaxle cooler lines. Disconnect exhaust pipe from manifold, exhaust pipe bracket at transaxle and unbolt exhaust pipe from catalytic converter.

3) Remove axle shaft guard plate, then disconnect axle shafts from transaxle flanges. Wire axle shafts back out-of-way. Remove starter. Remove 3 bolts securing torque converter-to-drive plate.

4) On 089 transaxle, mark left ball joint position on control arm. Remove ball joint-to-control arm bolts. On all models, remove sub-frame rear mounting bolts and loosen front (do not remove).

5) Disconnect linkage rod from transaxle. Remove selector cable holder and circlip, then disconnect cable and "O" ring.

6) Place transaxle jack under transaxle and raise slightly. Remove accelerator cable holder, then disconnect accelerator cable. Remove lower engine-to-transaxle bolts. Remove transaxle rubber mount bolts. Separate transaxle from engine. Lower transaxle out of vehicle.

CAUTION: **Secure torque converter to transaxle to prevent converter from falling out when removing transaxle.**

INSTALLATION

To install transaxle, reverse removal procedures. Ensure torque converter is fully seated in transaxle and all linkage is properly installed and adjusted.

VOLKSWAGEN (Cont.)

VANAGON

REMOVAL

1) Disconnect battery ground and remove fan housing grill. Remove torque converter bolts. To gain access to bolts, rotate engine until each bolt is visible in hole at top of transmission housing.

NOTE: **When turning crankshaft, use "T" handle and adapter 3052. This adapter has a pin that must engage recess on cooling fan hub.**

2) Disconnect both drive shafts from transmission. Disconnect wires from starter, remove starter. Loosen bracket for automatic transmission filler tube. Disconnect accelerator linkage, accelerator cable and selector lever cable from operating lever.

3) Install engine support and disconnect engine ground wire. Support transmission with jack. Remove mounting bracket bolts, then disconnect rear transmission mount from body. Remove lower engine-to-transmission bolts and lower transmission out of vehicle.

NOTE: **When lowering transmission from vehicle, torque converter must be secured to transmission so it will not slide off transmission.**

INSTALLATION

To install transaxle assembly, reverse removal procedures. Make sure torque converter is fully seated on one-way clutch support or damage to oil pump could occur when assembly is bolted to engine.

VOLVO

ALL MODELS

REMOVAL

NOTE: **Removal and installation information on 760 GLE with ZF 4 HP22 automatic transmission was not available from manufacturer.**

1) Remove air cleaner. Disconnect throttle cable at pulley and cable sheath at bracket. Remove 2 upper transmission-to-engine bolts. Remove transmission oil dipstick.

2) Raise and support vehicle. Disconnect oil filler pipe from oil pan and drain transmission fluid. Remove vehicle splash guard.

3) Disconnect muffler from hanger. Disconnect propeller shaft from transmission rear drive flange. Remove exhaust pipe clamps from bracket. Remove transmission support member attaching bolts. Pull support member back, twist and lift out. Remove rear transmission mount and exhaust pipe bracket.

4) Disconnect speedometer cable from transmission. Disconnect oil cooler lines from transmission and oil cooler, then remove from vehicle. Disconnect gear shift control rod from transmission.

5) Remove torque converter cover plate. Remove starter motor attaching bolts and starter motor cover. Remove 4 torque converter-to-drive plate attaching bolts.

6) Support transmission with transmission jack. Remove 2 lower transmission-to-engine attaching bolts. Using a screwdriver, separate torque converter from drive plate. Lower transmission from vehicle.

INSTALLATION

Reverse removal procedure and note the following: Tighten all nuts and bolts evenly. After installation, fill transmission with fluid. Adjust throttle linkage and shift control linkage.

Manual Transmission Servicing

ALFA ROMEO

LUBRICATION

SERVICE INTERVALS

Inspect transmission lubricant level at 20,000, 60,000 and 100,000 miles. Lubricant does not have to be changed.

CHECKING FLUID LEVEL

Check lubricant level at fill hole. Lubricant should be level with bottom of fill hole.

RECOMMENDED FLUID

Hypoid SAE 85W/90.

FLUID CAPACITY

TRANSMISSION REFILL CAPACITIES

Application	Quantity
GTV-6 2.5	2.9 qts. (2.70L)
Spider 2.0	1.9 qts. (1.85L)

ADJUSTMENTS

LINKAGE

Both models use floor-mount shifters with no external adjustment.

AUDI

IDENTIFICATION

TRANSMISSION CODES

Application	Code
5-Speed	013
5-Speed (4WD)	016
5-Speed	093

LUBRICATION

SERVICE INTERVALS

Check transmission lubricant level when vehicle is serviced. Lubricant does not have to be changed.

CHECKING FLUID LEVEL

Check fluid level at fill hole. Lubricant should be slightly below bottom of fill hole.

RECOMMENDED FLUID

Hypoid oil SAE 80 or SAE 80W/90 (API GL-4).

FLUID CAPACITY

TRANSMISSION REFILL CAPACITIES

Application	Quantity
Coupe & 5000S	[1] 5.0 qts. (2.4L)
4000S	[1] 4.2 qts. (2.0L)
4000S Quattro	[2] 7.0 qts. (3.3L)

[1] – Including differential.
[2] – Including front and center differential.

ADJUSTMENTS

GEARSHIFT LEVER

1) Place gearshift lever in 1st gear position, push to left stop and release. Lever must spring back 1/4-3/8" (6-10 mm) to right. Place lever in 5th gear position, push shift lever to right stop and release. Lever must spring back 1/4-3/8" (6-10 mm) to left. Lever must spring back approximately same distance in both directions.

2) If gearshift lever does not spring back as indicated, loosen gearshift lever housing (stop plate) bolts and move housing slightly sideways in slots. If this adjustment does not correct hard shifting, perform *GEAR-SHIFT LINKAGE ADJUSTMENT*.

Fig. 1: Gearshift Linkage Adjustment

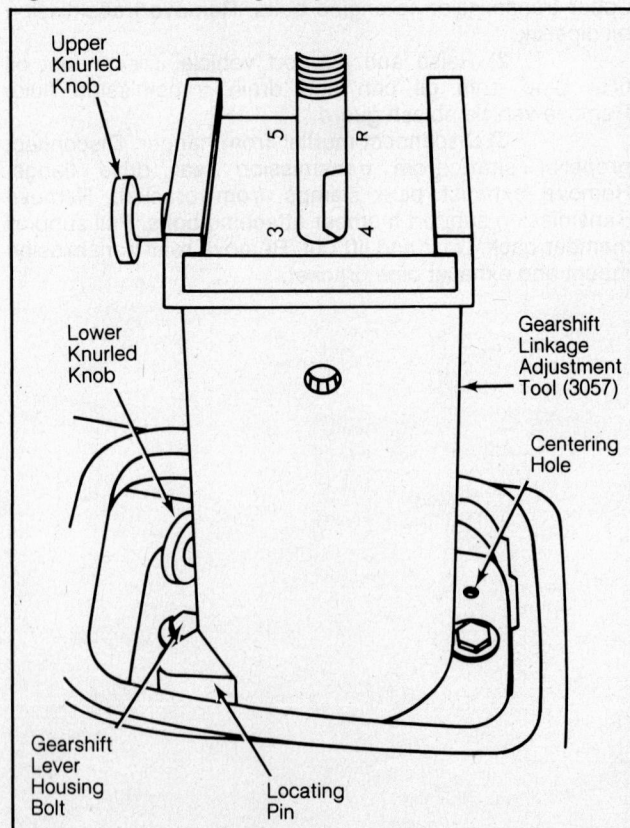

AUDI (Cont.)

GEARSHIFT LINKAGE

All (Except 4WD Transmission)

1) Place gearshift lever in Neutral. Loosen shift rod clamp so that shift finger slides freely on shift rod. Remove shift lever knob and rubber boot.

2) Loosen gearshift lever housing bolts, align centering holes and tighten bolts. Install linkage adjustment tool (3057) with locating pin toward front. Push shift lever into 5/R gear position of tool. Tighten lower knurled knob on tool.

3) Move shift lever and slide to right stop. Tighten upper knurled knob on tool. Push shift lever into 3/4 gear position of tool. Adjust shift rod and finger. Tighten clamp nut and remove tool.

4) Place shift lever in 1st gear position, press to left stop and release. Shift lever must spring back to right. Place lever in 5th gear position, push shift lever to right stop and release. Shift lever must spring back to left.

5) If gearshift lever does not spring back as indicated, move gearshift lever housing slightly sideways in slots. Check that all gears engage easily and without jamming, particularly reverse gear stop. Install shift boot and lever knob.

NOTE: All 4WD transmission linkage adjustment should be performed only when gearshift lever adjustment cannot be corrected or after a repair which involved loosening shift rod clamp.

Fig. 2: Linkage Rod Length Adjustment

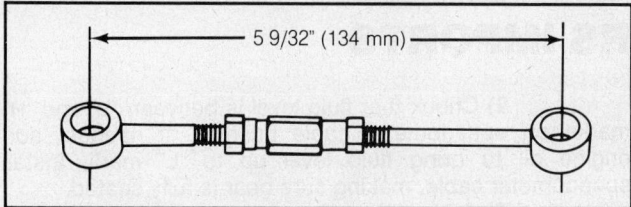

Adjust rod length to 5 9/32" (134 mm).

All 4WD Transmission

1) Place gearshift lever in Neutral. Measure linkage rod length and adjust to 5 9/32" (134 mm), if necesary. Remove shift lever knob and rubber boot. Loosen stop plate bolts, align centering holes and tighten bolts.

2) Loosen shift rod clamp between front and rear rods, so that rods move freely. Install linkage adjustment tool (3048) by inserting locating pins (right side pins first) into centering holes of stop plate.

3) Check that gearshift rod remains in Neutral, tighten shift rod clamp and remove adjustment tool. Check that all gears engage easily and without jamming, particularly reverse gear safety catch. Adjust stop plate, if necessary. Install shift lever knob and rubber boot.

Fig. 3: Gearshift Linkage Adjustment

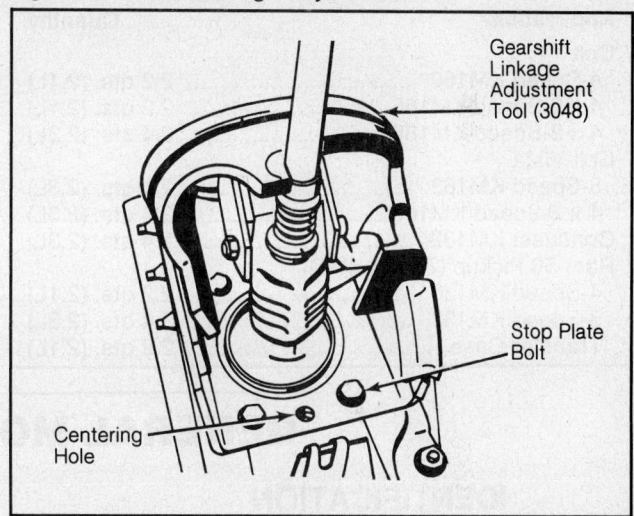

BMW

LUBRICATION

SERVICE INTERVALS

Inspect transmission lubricant level when vehicle is serviced. Change transmission oil at first 600 miles, then at every 30,000 mile interval.

CHECKING FLUID LEVEL

Check lubricant at fill hole. Lubricant should be at bottom of fill plug hole.

RECOMMENDED FLUID

SAE 80W (API GL-4, in cold climates use HD).

FLUID CAPACITY

TRANSMISSION REFILL CAPACITIES

Application	Quantity
318i	1.4 qts. (1.2L)
All Others	1.7 qts. (1.6L)

ADJUSTMENTS

LINKAGE

All models use floor-mount shifter with no external linkage. No adjustment is provided.

Manual Transmission Servicing

CHRYSLER CORP. IMPORTS

LUBRICATION

SERVICE INTERVALS
Check the fluid level every 30,000 miles.

CHECKING FLUID LEVEL
Check lubricant level at fill hole. Lubricant must be at bottom of fill hole.

RECOMMENDED FLUID
Transaxle – SAE 75W/85W (API GL-4).
Transmission – SAE 80W (API GL-4).

FLUID CAPACITY

TRANSMISSION REFILL CAPACITIES

Application	Quantity
Colt	
4-Speed KM160	2.2 qts. (2.1L)
4 x 2-Speed KM165	2.2 qts. (2.1L)
4 x 2-Speed KM166	2.4 qts. (2.3L)
Colt Vista	
5-Speed KM163	2.4 qts. (2.3L)
4 x 2-Speed KM166	2.4 qts. (2.3L)
Conquest KM132	2.4 qts. (2.3L)
Ram-50 Pickup (2WD & 4WD)	
4-Speed KM130	2.2 qts. (2.1L)
5-Speed KM132	2.4 qts. (2.3L)
Transfer Case	2.2 qts. (2.1L)

NOTE: KM130 (4-Speed) transmission with transfer case is referred to as KM144; KM132 (5-Speed) transmission with transfer case is referred to as KM145.

ADJUSTMENTS

LINKAGE
4, 5 & 4 x 2-Speed Transaxles
To adjust range selector control, place selector in "E" position, loosen adjustment nut and establish .2" (5 mm) free play at top of selector control handle. After adjustment, tighten adjustment nut. For shift lever, no linkage adjustment is required.
4 & 5-Speed Transmissions
Shifter is integral with transmission housing and has no external linkage. No adjustment is required.

GENERAL MOTORS IMPORTS

IDENTIFICATION

TRANSMISSION CODES

Application	Code
Spectrum	MR8
Sprint	MV2

LUBRICATION

SERVICE INTERVALS
Spectrum
Check transaxle oil each time engine oil is changed, when vehicle is on hoist or every 7,500 miles. Replace transaxle oil after first 7,500 miles and every 30,000 miles thereafter.
Sprint
Check transaxle oil each time engine oil is changed, when vehicle is on hoist or every 7,500 miles. Replace transaxle oil every 15,000 miles.

CHECKING FLUID LEVEL
Spectrum
1) Check fluid level with engine off, vehicle on level surface and transaxle cool enough to touch. Remove speedometer cable assembly located on driver's side of case, above drive shaft.

2) Check that fluid level is between "L" and "H" marks on speedometer cable bushing. If needed, add engine oil to bring fluid level up to "L" mark. Install speedometer cable, making sure gear is fully seated.
Sprint
1) Remove oil level gauge from side case of transaxle. Insert oil level gauge through opening until threaded part of gauge rests on top of side case.
2) Remove gauge and check oil level. Oil level should be between "FULL" level and "LOW" level lines. If oil level is below "LOW" level line, add oil until it reaches "FULL" level line.

RECOMMENDED FLUID
Spectrum
SAE 5W/30 SF rated engine oil.
Sprint
Hypoid oil SAE 80W or 80W/90 (API GL-5).

FLUID CAPACITY

TRANSMISSION REFILL CAPACITIES

Application	Quantity
Spectrum	2.8 qts. (2.7L)
Sprint	2.4 qts. (2.3L)

Manual Transmission Servicing

GENERAL MOTORS IMPORTS (Cont.)

DRAINING & REFILLING
Spectrum
Remove drain plug, drain oil and install drain plug. Remove speedometer cable, add engine oil and check oil level.
Sprint
1) Remove oil level gauge. Using a 10 mm hexagon socket, remove drain plug and drain oil. Clean plug and apply sealant (GM 1052080) to thread portion of plug. After draining, install gasket and drain plug.
2) If transaxle is cold, tighten drain plug to 18-22 ft. lbs. (24-30 N.m). If transaxle is warm, tighten drain plug to 15-18 ft. lbs. (20-24 N.m). Refill transaxle with oil and check oil level.

ADJUSTMENTS

GEARSHIFT LINKAGE
Spectrum
Place transaxle and lever in Neutral. Turn adjustment nuts until shift lever lever is in vertical position. Tighten adjustment nuts. *See Fig. 1.*

NOTE: Sprint gearshift adjustment should be performed only when each shift stroke is short or when gears are not in complete mesh.

Sprint
1) Loosen gearshift housing nuts and guide plate bolts. Adjust guide plate by moving it from front to rear so that base of gearshift control lever is brought to middle of guide plate and at a right angle.

2) Once guide plate is positioned properly, tighten guide plate bolts to 6-7 ft. lbs. (8-9 N.m). Tighten left front and right rear housing nut to 11-14 ft. lbs. (15-19 N.m). Tighten right front and left rear housing nut to 3-4 ft. lbs. (4-5 N.m).

Fig. 1: Spectrum Gearshift Linkage Adjustment

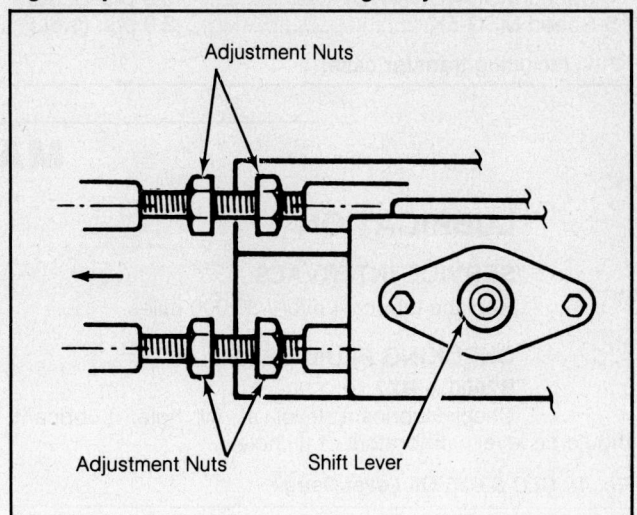

HONDA

LUBRICATION

SERVICE INTERVALS
Change lubricant every 30,000 miles.

CHECKING FLUID LEVEL
Check lubricant level at transmission fill hole. Lubricant should be to bottom of filler hole.

RECOMMENDED FLUID
SAE 10W/40 engine oil rated SE or SF.

FLUID CAPACITY

TRANSMISSION REFILL CAPACITIES

Application	Quantity
All Models	2.6 qts. (2.5L)

ADJUSTMENTS

LINKAGE
No external adjustments required.

ISUZU

LUBRICATION

SERVICE INTERVALS
Replace lubricant after first 7,500 miles and every 30,000 miles thereafter. Check lubricant every 7,500 miles or 12 months, whichever comes first.

CHECKING FLUID LEVEL
Check lubricant level at fill hole. Lubricant should be to bottom edge of fill hole.

RECOMMENDED FLUID
Impulse & I-Mark
0°-90°F (-18°-32°C) SAE 5W/30 engine oil.
Above 90°F (32°C) SAE 40 engine oil.
P'UP & Trooper II
Below 50°F (10°C) SAE 10W/30 engine oil.
0°-90°F (-18°-32°C) SAE 30 engine oil.
Above 50°F (10°C) SAE 40 engine oil.

Manual Transmission Servicing

ISUZU (Cont.)

FLUID CAPACITY

TRANSMISSION REFILL CAPACITIES

Application	Quantity
4-Speed MSG-4K	2.7 pts. (1.3L)
4-Speed MSG-4ET (4WD)	[1] 5.3 pts. (2.5L)
5-Speed MSG-5K	3.3 pts. (1.6L)

[1] – Including transfer case.

ADJUSTMENTS

LINKAGE

Shift linkage is integral with transmission housing and requires no external adjustment.

MAZDA

LUBRICATION

SERVICE INTERVALS

Replace lubricant every 30,000 miles.

CHECKING FLUID LEVEL

B2000 & RX7

Check lubricant level at fill hole. Lubricant should be level with bottom of fill hole.

Fig. 1: GLC & 626 Oil Level Gauge

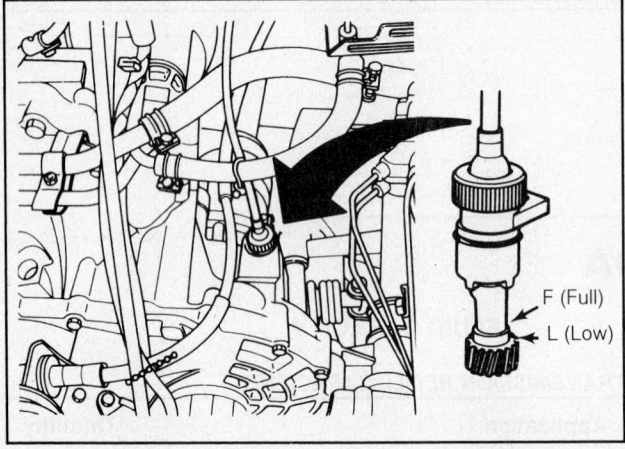

F (Full)
L (Low)

GLC location shown, 626 is similar.

GLC & 626

Remove speedometer cable and driven gear from transaxle case. Use "L" and "F" marks on driven gear to determine lubricant level. If necessary, add oil through driven gear opening.

RECOMMENDED FLUID

Hypoid SAE 80W/90 (API GL-4 or GL-5).

FLUID CAPACITY

TRANSMISSION REFILL CAPACITIES

Application	Quantity
B2000	
4-Speed	1.6 qts. (1.5L)
5-Speed	1.8 qts. (1.7L)
GLC	3.4 qts. (3.2L)
RX7	1.8 qts. (1.7L)
626	3.6 qts. (3.4L)

ADJUSTMENTS

LINKAGE

No external linkage adjustment is required.

MERCEDES-BENZ

IDENTIFICATION

TRANSMISSION CODES

Application	Code
190D	GL 68/20 A-5
190E	GL 68/20 B-5

LUBRICATION

SERVICE INTERVALS

Check and correct fluid level every 15,000 miles. Change fluid at first 800-1000 miles. Change fluid every 5000 miles thereafter, on 190D. Change fluid every 7500 miles thereafter, on 190E.

CHECKING FLUID LEVEL

Check lubricant level at fill hole. Lubricant should be level with bottom of fill hole.

RECOMMENDED FLUID

Type A Suffix A, automatic transmission fluid.

FLUID CAPACITY

TRANSMISSION REFILL CAPACITIES

Application	Quantity
All	1.6 qts. (1.5L)

MERCEDES BENZ (Cont.)

ADJUSTMENTS

LINKAGE

Place transmission in Neutral. Disconnect rods at transmission and align levers by inserting a centering pin at shift bracket. Adjust rods so that they fit into transmission levers freely. Install rounded locking clips, remove centering pin and check for proper operation.

MITSUBISHI

LUBRICATION

SERVICE INTERVALS

2WD Pickup
Inspect and replenish oil every 30,000 miles or 12 months, whichever comes first.
All Others
Replace oil every 30,000 miles or 12 months.

CHECKING FLUID LEVEL

Lubricant should be up to bottom of fill hole.

RECOMMENDED FLUID

Hypoid SAE 75W/85W or 80W (API GL-4).

FLUID CAPACITY

TRANSMISSION REFILL CAPACITIES

Application	Quantity
Cordia & Tredia	
4 x 2-Speed KM165	2.2 qts. (2.1L)
5-Speed KM162	2.2 qts. (2.1L)
Montero	
5-Speed KM132	2.3 qts. (2.2L)
Transfer Case	2.3 qts. (2.2L)
Pickup (2WD & 4WD)	
4-Speed KM130	2.2 qts. (2.1L)
5-Speed KM132	2.4 qts. (2.3L)
Transfer Case	2.3 qts. (2.2L)
Starion KM132	2.4 qts. (2.3L)

NOTE: KM130 (4-Speed) transmission with transfer case is referred to as KM144; KM132 (5-Speed) transmission with transfer case is referred to as KM145.

ADJUSTMENTS

LINKAGE

4, 5 & 4 x 2-Speed Transaxles
To adjust range selector control, place selector in "E" position, loosen adjustment nut and establish .2" (5 mm) free play at top of selector control handle. After adjustment, tighten adjustment nut. For shift lever, no linkage adjustment is required. *See Fig. 1.*

Fig. 1: Selector Switch Position

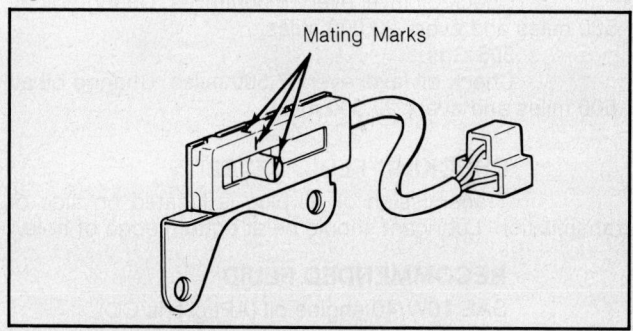

Selector lever must be in "ECONOMY" position.

4 & 5-Speed Transmissions
Shifter is integral with transmission housing and has no external linkage. No adjustment is required.

NISSAN/DATSUN

LUBRICATION

SERVICE INTERVALS

Add or replace oil level every 15,000 miles.

CHECKING FLUID LEVEL

Lubricant level should be to bottom of fill hole.

RECOMMENDED FLUID

Hypoid SAE 80W/90 (API GL-4).

ADJUSTMENTS

LINKAGE

NOTE: All RWD models have a floor shift which has no external linkage and requires no adjustment.

Pulsar, Sentra & Stanza
1) Loosen selector stopper bolts. Place transaxle in "1st" gear. Slide selector stopper to establish clearance of .039" (1 mm) between control lever and select stopper. *See Fig. 1.*

FLUID CAPACITY

TRANSMISSION REFILL CAPACITIES

Application	Quantity
Maxima FS5W71B	2.1 qts. (2.0L)
Pickup (2WD & 4WD)	
5-Speed FS5W71B	2.1 qts. (2.0L)
Transfer Case	1.5 qts. (1.4L)
Pulsar 5-Speed RS5F30A	2.7 qts. (2.5L)
Sentra	
4-Speed RN4F30A	2.4 qts. (2.3L)
5-Speed RS5F30A	2.9 qts. (2.7L)
Stanza 5-Speed RS5F31A	2.9 qts. (2.7L)
200SX 5-Speed FS5W71B	2.0 qts. (1.9L)
300ZX & 300ZX Turbo	
FS5W71C	2.1 qts. (2.0L)
BW T-5	2.1 qts. (2.0L)

Fig. 1: Control Lever Adjustment

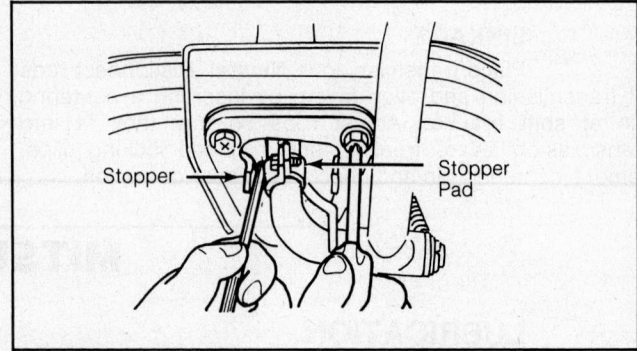

Place shifter in 1st gear.

2) Tighten bolts. After adjustment, shift control lever to be sure no binding or dragging exists.

PEUGEOT

LUBRICATION

SERVICE INTERVALS

505 Diesel

Check oil level every 5,000 miles. Change oil at 1,500 miles and every 20,000 miles.

505 Gas

Check oil level every 7,500 miles. Change oil at 1,500 miles and every 22,500 miles.

CHECKING FLUID LEVEL

Transmission oil fill plug is located on side of transmission. Lubricant should be at bottom edge of hole.

RECOMMENDED FLUID

SAE 10W/40 engine oil (API grade CC).

FLUID CAPACITY

TRANSMISSION REFILL CAPACITIES

Application	Quantity
505 Diesel	
4-Speed	1.2 qts. (1.1L)
5-Speed	1.8 qts. (1.7L)
505	
5-Speed	1.8 qts. (1.7L)

ADJUSTMENTS

LINKAGE

4-Speed

Install Shift Lever Gauge (00315) and place shift lever in correct position. *See Fig. 1.* Loosen reverse

Fig 1: Shift Lever Adjustment

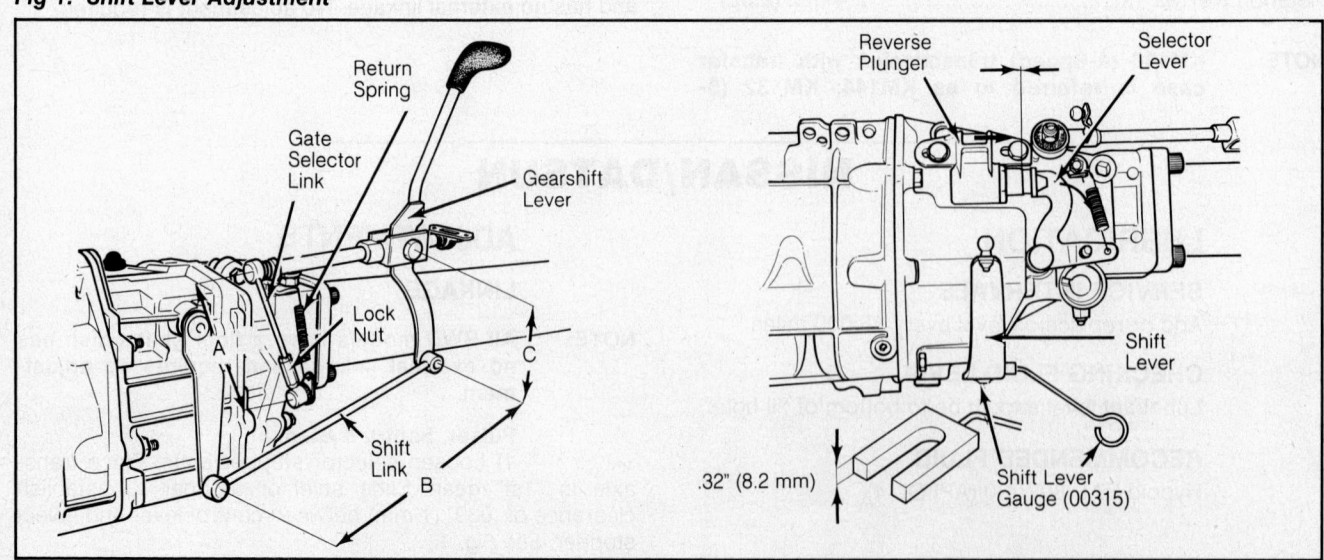

PEUGEOT (Cont.)

plunger bolts and place reverse plunger against selector lever. Tighten 2 bolts and remove gauge.

4 & 5-Speed

Lubricate ball sockets. Install shift link with center-to-center dimension "B" of 11.22" (285 mm) for 4-Speed; 11" (280 mm) for 5-Speed. See Fig. 1. Adjust gate selector link with center-to-center dimension "A" to 4.37" (111 mm). Holding ball sockets in proper directions, tighten lock nut. Install gate selector link with fixed ball socket side mounted to gearshift lever.

NOTE: **Gearshift lever dimension "C" is 3.11" (79 mm) for 4-Speed and 4.13" (105 mm) for 5-Speed.**

PORSCHE

LUBRICATION

SERVICE INTERVALS

911 Carrera & 928S

Check lubricant level and clean magnetic drain plug at first 1,000 miles. Check lubricant level every 15,000 miles and replace every 30,000 miles.

944

Change oil and clean magnetic drain plug at first 1,250 miles. Check and correct oil level every 15,000 miles. Change oil every 30,000 miles.

CHECKING FLUID LEVEL

Check lubricant level at fill hole. Lubricant should be level with bottom of fill hole.

RECOMMENDED FLUID

911 Carrera
 Hypoid SAE 90W (API GL-5).
928S
 Hypoid SAE 75W/90 (API GL-5).
944
 Hypoid SAE 80 (API GL-4).

FLUID CAPACITY

TRANSMISSION REFILL CAPACITIES

Application	Quantity
911 Carrera	3.2 qts. (3.0L)
928S	4.0 qts. (3.8L)
944	2.8 qts. (2.6L)

ADJUSTMENTS

LINKAGE

No adjustment required.

RENAULT

LUBRICATION

SERVICE INTERVALS

Change lubricant after first 1,000 miles and at 12,000 mile intervals thereafter.

CHECKING FLUID LEVEL

Check lubricant level at fill hole. Lubricant should be even with bottom of fill hole.

RECOMMENDED FLUID

Hypoid SAE 80 (API GL-5).

FLUID CAPACITY

TRANSMISSION REFILL CAPACITIES

Application	Quantity
All	2.2 qts. (2.0L)

ADJUSTMENTS

LINKAGE

1) Place shift lever in Neutral position. Loosen lock nut on yoke so that shift linkage turns freely. Put lever at transmission case exit, against 3rd-4th gear line.
2) Place a 0.39" (10 mm) shim between end piece of shift linkage and surface of housing. Tighten yoke nut. Make sure that clearance between end piece and lever housing equals size of shim.

Manual Transmission Servicing

SAAB

LUBRICATION

SERVICE INTERVALS

Change transmission lubricant and clean magnetic drain plug at first 1,000 miles. Check lubricant level every 5,000 miles on 900 Turbo, every 7,500 miles on other models.

CHECKING FLUID LEVEL

Check oil level with dipstick, located on right side of engine. Oil level should be between "MIN" and "MAX" marks.

RECOMMENDED FLUID

SAE 10W/30 engine oil.

FLUID CAPACITY

TRANSMISSION REFILL CAPACITIES

Application	Quantity
All	2.6 qts. (2.5L)

ADJUSTMENTS

LINKAGE

1) Select Reverse gear. Loosen clamp on gear shift rod joint, so that gear shift rod can be moved in joint. Lock gear lever in Reverse by inserting a 15/64" (6 mm) drift pin into locking holes of gear shift lever housing and gear shift rod. Locking holes are accessible once gear lever console cover has been removed.

2) Check that Reverse gear at transmission is fully engaged. Tighten clamp on gear shift rod joint to 12-16 ft. lbs. (16-22 N.m). After adjustment check that gear shift lever is in alignment with 3rd-4th gear gate, when placed in Neutral.

3) If lever adjustment is required, remove driver's seat and fold back carpeting enough to allow heating duct to be dismantled. Select 3rd gear and remove bolts holding control unit to gear shift lever housing.

4) Adjust control unit so that rollers reach bottom of plunger groove, and spring is at its shortest length. Tighten control unit, return gear shift lever to Neutral. Check that spring moves gear shift lever in alignment with 3rd-4th gear gate. Fit carpeting and install seat.

SUBARU

LUBRICATION

SERVICE INTERVALS

Replace lubricant at first 1,000 miles and every 30,000 miles thereafter. Check lubricant level every 15,000 miles.

FLUID LEVEL

Check lubricant level at dipstick located in engine compartment. Transmission and differential (transaxle) are lubricated through a common oil supply.

FLUID TYPE

Hypoid SAE 80W/90.

FLUID CAPACITY

TRANSMISSION REFILL CAPACITIES

Application	Quantity
2WD 4 & 5-Speed	2.6 qts. (2.5L)
4WD 4-Speed	3.0 qts. (2.8L)

ADJUSTMENTS

LINKAGE

All models use shift linkage which does not require external adjustment. If equipped with dual-range, confirm that lower surface of drive selector grip is approximately 1.57" (40 mm) from rod cover surface. If dimension is beyond adjustment distance, readjust positioning plate.

TOYOTA

LUBRICATION

SERVICE INTERVALS

Check lubricant level every 15,000 miles. Inspect and replace if necessary.

FLUID LEVEL

Check lubricant level at fill hole. Lubricant should be to bottom of hole.

RECOMMENDED FLUID

Camry
Type ATF Dexron II, transmission fluid.

Land Cruiser
Type SAE 90W (API GL-4 or GL-5), transmission fluid.

Tercel
Above 0° F (-18° C) SAE 80W/90 or 90W (API Hypoid GL-5), and Below 0° F (-18° C) SAE 80W/90 or 80W (API Hypoid GL-5), transmission fluid.

All Others
Type SAE 75W/90 (API GL-4 or GL-5) or SAE 80W/90 (API GL-4 or GL-5), transmission fluid.

TOYOTA (Cont.)

FLUID CAPACITY

TRANSMISSION REFILL CAPACITIES

Application	Quantity
Camry	2.7 qts. (2.6L)
Celica, Cressida & Supra	2.5 qts. (2.4L)
Corolla FWD	2.4 qts. (2.3L)
Corolla RWD	1.8 qts. (1.7L)
Land Cruiser	3.3 qts. (3.1L)
Pickup	
2WD	
4-Speed W42	[1] 2.9 qts. (2.7L)
5-Speed W52	[2] 2.7 qts. (2.6L)
4WD	4.1 qts. (3.9L)
Starlet	2.6 qts. (2.5L)
Tercel 2WD	3.5 qts. (3.3L)
Tercel 4WD	4.1 qts. (3.9L)
Van	2.3 qts. (2.2L)

[1] – Add .2 qts. (.2L) for diesel engine.
[2] – Add .6 qts. (.5L) for diesel engine.

ADJUSTMENTS

LINKAGE

No external adjustment in required.

VOLKSWAGEN

LUBRICATION

SERVICE INTERVALS

No oil changes are required. Check oil every 15,000 miles.

FLUID LEVEL

Check lubricant level at fill hole. Lubricant should be level with bottom of fill hole.

RECOMMENDED FLUID

Hypoid SAE 80W or 80W/90 (API GL-4).

FLUID CAPACITY

TRANSMISSION REFILL CAPACITIES

Application	Quantity
Jetta, Quantum, Rabbit, & Scirocco	
4-Speed	1.6 qts. (1.5L)
5-Speed	2.1 qts. (2.0L)
Vanagon	3.7 qts. (3.5L)

ADJUSTMENTS

LINKAGE

Jetta, Rabbit & Scirocco

1) Adjust gearshift lever. Loosen bolts holding lever housing, and pull boot off of housing. Loosen shift rod clamp bolt so selector lever moves freely on shift rod. Adjust shift finger in center of lock out plate so that an equal distance is obtained on both sides of shift finger. *See Fig. 1.*

2) Adjust shift rod end so that a distance of 25/32" (20 mm) for 4-Speed models, or 19/32" (15 mm) for 5-Speed models exists between shift finger and stop plate. *See Fig. 2.* Tighten shift rod clamp. Shift through gears and check for proper engagement.

Fig. 1: Linkage Adjustment

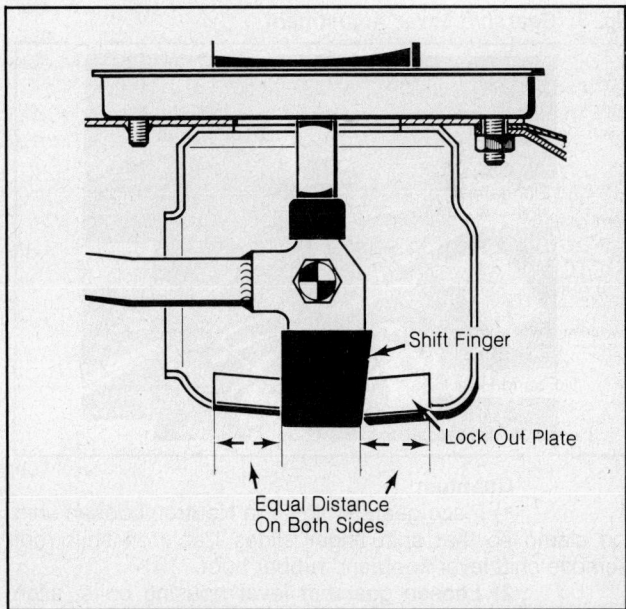

Shift Finger

Lock Out Plate

Equal Distance On Both Sides

Vanagon

1) Place shift lever in Neutral position. Align holes of upper lever bearing plate with holes in lower lever bearing plate.

2) Loosen shift rod clamp so selector lever moves freely on shift rod. Remove spare tire. Move shift finger of front shift rod to center of rubber stop in housing.

3) Adjust shift rod end so that a distance of 7/8" (22 mm) exists between shift rod end and stop plate. Check for proper operation.

Manual Transmission Servicing

VOLKSWAGEN (Cont.)

Fig. 2: Linkage Adjustment

25/32" (20 mm) 4-Speed Models
19/32" (15 mm) 5-Speed Models

GEARSHIFT LEVER

Jetta, Rabbit & Scirocco

1) Move lever bearing assembly on its elongated bolt holes until round holes are perfectly aligned with corresponding round holes in lever plate and housing.

2) If after adjustment, bolts are not centered in elongated holes, remove bolts and turn lever bearing assembly 180°. Install bolts and readjust lever.

Fig. 3: Gearshift Lever Adjustment

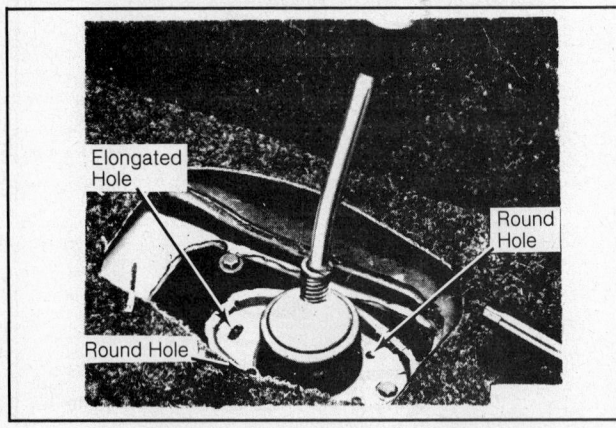

Elongated Hole

Round Hole

Round Hole

Quantum

1) Place gearshift lever in Neutral. Loosen shift rod clamp so that shift finger slides freely on shift rod. Remove shift lever knob and rubber boot.

2) Loosen gearshift lever housing bolts, align centering holes and tighten bolts. Install linkage adjustment tool (3057) with locating pin toward front. Push shift lever into 5/R gear position of tool. Tighten lower knurled knob on tool.

3) Move shift lever and slide to right stop. Tighten upper knurled knob on tool. Push shift lever into 3/4 gear position of tool. Adjust shift rod and finger. Tighten clamp nut and remove tool.

4) Place shift lever in 1st gear position, press to left stop and release. Shift lever must spring back to right. Place lever in 5th gear position, push shift lever to right stop and release. Shift lever must spring back to left.

5) If gearshift lever does not spring back as indicated, move gearshift lever housing slightly sideways in slots. Check that all gears engage easily and without

jamming, particularly reverse gear stop. Install shift boot and lever knob.

Fig. 4: Gearshift Lever Adjustment

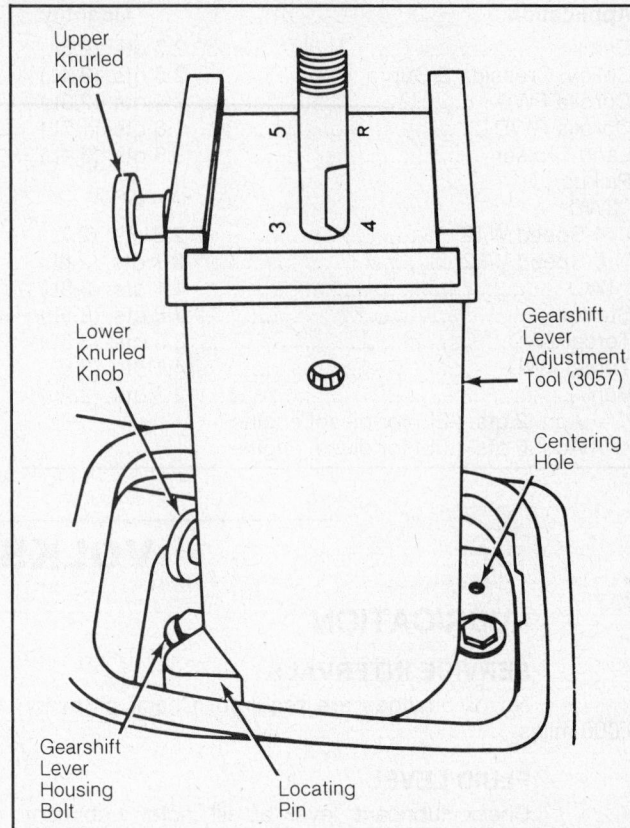

Upper Knurled Knob

Lower Knurled Knob

Gearshift Lever Adjustment Tool (3057)

Centering Hole

Gearshift Lever Housing Bolt

Locating Pin

Vanagon

1) Place shift lever in Neutral position. Align holes of upper lever bearing plate with holes in lower lever bearing plate. Loosen shift rod clamp so selector lever moves freely on shift rod.

2) Remove spare tire. Place transmission lever in vertical position and push shift rod into transmission until spring tension is felt. Keep shift rod in this position.

3) Push shift rod to right and move in a longitudinal direction so that measurement between Reverse gear lock stop and shift rod is 1/8" (3 mm). Let shift rod spring back into left shift position and push rod slightly to right. Boot must touch shift mechanism housing, tighten clamp nut to 18 ft. lbs. (25 N.m).

4) Place shift lever in 2nd gear and check distance between shift lever and heater covering. Measurement must be a minimum of 5/8" (15 mm). If not, move lever in slotted holes. Check that all gears engage easily and without jamming, particularly reverse gear stop.

Manual Transmission Servicing

VOLVO

LUBRICATION

SERVICE INTERVALS
Replace transmission oil at first 600-1200 miles ONLY. Check every 7,500 miles thereafter.

CHECKING FLUID LEVEL
Check lubricant level at fill hole. Oil should be up to bottom of fill hole. When adding oil, allow sufficient time for oil to flow into overdrive unit.

RECOMMENDED FLUID
F or G Automatic Transmission Fluid (FLM).

FLUID CAPACITY

TRANSMISSION REFILL CAPACITIES

Application	Quantity
4-Speed M46	2.4 qts. (2.3L) (With overdrive)

ADJUSTMENTS
No external linkage adjustment is required.

Manual Transmission Removal

AUDI

4000

REMOVAL

1) Disconnect battery ground strap. Disconnect exhaust pipe from transaxle bracket and engine. Remove square bolt and press shifter coupling from rear of transaxle shifting shaft. Unhook clutch cable and disconnect speedometer. On models equipped with a 5-cylinder engine, support front of engine when transaxle is removed.

2) Disconnect CV joints at inner drive flanges. Support axle shafts from vehicle with wire. Remove starter, front mounting plate and transaxle mounting bolts. Disconnect back-up light switch connector. Support transaxle on floor jack and remove crossmember mount. Remove transaxle from engine and lower from vehicle.

INSTALLATION

1) Install crossmember to transaxle. Raise transaxle up to vehicle and install crossmember bolts finger tight. Slide transaxle up to engine and install mounting bolts. Install front mounting plate and starter. Install inner CV joint mounting bolts into CV joint and drive flange. Tighten crossmember mounting bolts.

2) Install shift rod coupling bolt and lock with safety wire. Connect exhaust pipe, allowing 3/8" (10 mm) clearance between pipe and floor. Reconnect all wires, cables and linkages that were removed during removal procedure.

NOTE: Always use longer hex head bolt when replacing shift rod coupling instead of original square head bolt. Secure with safety wire.

5000

REMOVAL

1) Remove air cleaner (diesel only). Disconnect battery ground cable. Remove windshield washer reservoir. Remove upper engine-to-transaxle bolts. Disconnect speedometer cable.

2) Remove right side guard plate. Disconnect drive axle shafts from drive flanges and support on top of subframe. Disconnect wire from back-up light switch. Disconnect shift linkage from transaxle case.

3) Remove lower engine-to-transaxle bolts, starter and guard plate from subframe. Lift transaxle slightly and remove transaxle supports. Remove rear subframe mounting bolts. Remove right transaxle bracket, then remove transaxle from below.

INSTALLATION

Reverse removal procedure and note the following: Lubricate mainshaft splines lightly with grease. Make sure transaxle seats on engine dowels. Adjust shift linkage as necessary.

QUATTRO

REMOVAL

1) Disconnect battery ground strap and RPM sensor. Remove upper engine-to-transmission bolts. Disconnect speedometer cable with wrench (#3016). Disconnect tie rod coupling from steering rack. Always remove self-locking nuts (below tie rod coupling) first, then mounting bolts.

2) Drive out clutch slave cylinder lock pin. Remove clutch slave cylinder (leave hydraulic line connected). Disconnect backup light switch and shift linkage. Install engine support tool (#10-222). Remove deflector for axle shaft and right transmission mount.

3) Remove right transmission mount. Disconnect exhaust pipe at flange. Disconnect right axle shaft at transmission. Remove left transmission mount. Disconnect left axle shaft at transmission and drive shaft at rear of transmission.

4) Disconnect cable for differential lock. Remove transmission cover plate. Turn spindle of engine support tool (#10-222) to raise engine slightly. Place hoist (VWAG-1383) under transmission. Remove the lower engine-to-transmission bolts and push transmission back.

INSTALLATION

To install transmission, reverse removal procedure and note the following: Check that the engine-to-transmission mounts are free of tension. Readjust shift linkage. Clean drive shaft and axle flanges and lightly coat with oS_2 grease or spray. If pickup eye is still in place on transmission (near starter), remove with hacksaw to gain easier access to exhaust pipe.

BMW

ALL MODELS

REMOVAL

1) Push up shift lever boot and foam ring, then remove circlip from shift lever ball socket. Remove exhaust bracket from transmission and exhaust pipe from manifold. Remove upper clutch housing bolts.

2) Remove propeller shaft from transmission (coupling or flexible disc remains with shaft). Remove propeller shaft center support bearing, pull shaft downward and away from centering pin.

3) Remove shift lever bearing pin and push shift lever upward. Remove clutch linkage and slave cylinder as required. Loosen angle support and remove transmission front cover plate.

4) Support engine using a block between engine and front axle subframe. Remove speedometer shaft and electrical connections. Loosen crossmember and turn steering to full right lock position.

5) On 325e models, remove remaining bolts securing transmission to engine and frame; remove transmission. On all other models, remove transmission-to-clutch housing bolts and separate transmission from clutch housing.

INSTALLATION

Reverse removal procedure and note the following: Use new lock nuts on propeller shaft; tighten nuts on propeller shaft only, never bolts; use shims under shift lever circlip to remove play in shift lever; preload center bearing .079" (2 mm); adjust clutch pedal free play.

CHRYSLER CORP. IMPORTS

ALL FWD MODELS

REMOVAL

1) Disconnect battery negative cable. Remove the following parts from transaxle: Clutch cable, speedometer cable, back-up light switch harness, starter, and 4 top engine-to-transaxle mounting bolts.

2) Raise vehicle and remove wheels. Remove shift rod and extension. Drain transaxle fluid. Remove drive shafts. Disconnect gear selector cable. Remove engine rear cover.

3) Connect engine to hoist and remove remaining transaxle-to-engine bolts. Remove transaxle mount insulator bolt. Lower and remove transaxle.

INSTALLATION

To install, reverse removal procedure and note the following: The coupling bolt at each end of front roll rod should be temporarily tightened at installation. After the transaxle has been installed, tighten bolts to specifications.

ALL RWD MODELS – 4-SPEED

REMOVAL

1) In engine compartment, disconnect negative battery cable. Remove air cleaner and starter. Remove 2 upper transmission mounting bolts.

2) Inside vehicle, take out console box (if equipped) and carpet. Remove dust cover retainer plate at base of shift lever. Lift up dust cover and remove attaching bolts at lower part of extension housing and remove gearshift lever.

NOTE: Make sure gearshift lever is in 2nd speed position before removing.

3) With vehicle raised and supported, drain transmission. Remove bolts from rear of propeller shaft and draw shaft out of transmission.

4) Disconnect speedometer and back-up light switch harness at transmission side. Disconnect front exhaust pipe. From clutch control lever, disconnect clutch cable.

5) Support rear of engine with jack, place transmission jack under transmission and remove rear supports and crossmember.

6) Remove clutch housing inspection cover and bolts attaching clutch housing to engine block. Pulling rearward and downward, remove transmission from vehicle.

INSTALLATION

1) To install, reverse removal procedure and note the following: When installing control lever assembly, place shift lever in 2nd gear position so that nylon bushing hole is vertical.

CAUTION: During this operation, use care that dirt does not enter through opening.

2) When installing clutch housing inspection cover, make sure that it is not bent. When installing shift lever dust boot, make sure cover is tightly installed to prevent noise entry into vehicle. After installing transmission, refill with SAE 80 gear oil.

RAM-50 (2WD) 5-SPEED

REMOVAL

1) In engine compartment, disconnect negative battery cable. Remove air cleaner and starter. Remove 2 upper transmission mounting bolts.

2) Inside vehicle, take out console box (if equipped), and carpet. Remove dust cover retainer plate at base of shift lever. Lift up dust cover and remove attaching bolts at lower part of extension housing and remove gearshift lever.

NOTE: Make sure gearshift lever is in 2nd speed position before removing.

3) With vehicle raised and supported, drain transmission. Remove bolts from rear of propeller shaft and draw shaft out of transmission.

4) Disconnect speedometer and back-up light switch harness at transmission side. Disconnect front exhaust pipe. From clutch control lever, disconnect clutch cable.

5) Support rear of engine with jack, place transmission jack under transmission and remove rear supports and crossmember.

6) Remove clutch housing inspection cover and bolts attaching clutch housing to engine block. Pulling rearward and downward, remove transmission from vehicle.

INSTALLATION

1) To install, reverse removal procedure and note the following: When installing control lever assembly, place shift lever in 2nd gear position so that nylon bushing hole is vertical.

CAUTION: During this operation, use care that dirt does not enter through opening.

2) When installing clutch housing inspection cover, make sure that it is not bent. When installing shift lever dust boot, make sure cover is tightly installed to prevent noise entry into vehicle. After installing transmission, refill with SAE 80 gear oil.

RAM-50 (4WD)

REMOVAL

1) Inside vehicle, take out console box (if equipped), and carpet. Remove dust cover retainer plate at base of shift lever. Lift up dust cover and remove attaching bolts at lower part of extension housing and remove gearshift lever. Shift levers should be in neutral position (transmission) and "4H" position (transfer case).

2) Raise and support vehicle. Remove drain plugs and drain transission and transfer case fluid. Remove front and rear propeller shafts.

3) Disconnect speedometer cable, back-up light switch wiring and 4WD indicator light switch harness from transmission. Disconnect front exhaust pipe. Disconnect clutch cable from clutch control lever.

4) Support rear of engine with safety stand. Support transmission with transmission jack. Disconnect plate and remove transfer case mounting bracket. Remove second crossmember.

5) Remove clutch housing cover, then remove remaining transmission mounting bolts. Pull transmission assembly back and lower out of vehicle.

INSTALLATION

Reverse removal procedure to install, noting the following: Shift lever assembly must be installed with transmission lever in neutral position and transfer case lever in "4H" position.

GENERAL MOTORS IMPORTS

SPRINT

REMOVAL

1) Disconnect ground cable from battery and transaxle. Remove air cleaner and heat pipe. Remove clutch cable from clutch release lever. Remove starter.

2) Disconnect speedometer cable at transaxle. Disconnect all wires from trasmaxle. Remove front and rear torque rod bolts from transaxle. Raise and support vehicle.

3) Drain transaxle oil. Disconnect exhaust pipe at exhaust manifold and at the first exhaust hanger. Remove clutch housing lower plate. Disconnect gear shift control shift and extension rod at transaxle.

4) Remove left front wheel. Detach the snap rings on RH and LH drive axles from the differential side gears. To detach the snap ring fitted on the spline of differintial side joint (inboard joint) from differential side gear. Pry the inboard joint out by using a pry bar.

5) Remove stabilizer bar mount bolts and ball stud bolt on left side. After removing these bolts, detach ball stud from the steering knuckle by pushing down on the stabilizer bar.

6) Draw out the inboard joint of the lift drive axle from the transaxle. Remove front torque rod. Securely support the transaxle caes with a jack for removal.

7) Remove mounting member bolts from the body and transaxle. Remove bolts and nuts fastening transaxle to the engine. Disconnect transaxle from engine by silding towards the left side and carefully lowering the jack.

INSTALLATION

To install, reverse removal procedure and note the following: Guide the right drive axle into the transaxle as the transaxle is being raised. Push the R and L drive axles into differential side gears until the snaprings on drive axles ingage side gears. Refill transaxle with new oil.

HONDA

ACCORD & PRELUDE

REMOVAL

1) Disconnect ground cable from battery and transaxle. Release steering lock and place shift selector lever in neutral. Disconnect the following electrical leads: Positive battery cable at starter, starter solenoid and backup light switch.

2) Disconnect clutch cable at release arm. Remove starter mounting bolt from transaxle and upper transaxle mounting bolts. Raise and support vehicle, drain transaxle and remove front wheels.

3) Support transaxle with jack. Remove speedometer drive holder retaining bolt and pull assembly out of transaxle. Disconnect torque rod from clutch housing. Remove shift rod clevis bolt.

4) Disconnect and remove tie-rod ball joints. Remove lower arm ball joint pinch bolts and free arms by tapping downward with soft (brass) hammer. Turn steering knuckle to outward-most position, pry CV joint out about 1/2" and pull axle shaft out of transaxle housing. Repeat on other side.

5) Remove right-side radius rod. Remove torque arm brackets from clutch housing. Remove damper bracket from center beam. Remove clutch housing bolts at both transaxle mounting brackets. Remove clutch cover.

6) Remove remaining starter mounting bolt and remove starter. Remove front transaxle mounting bolt. Pull transaxle back until it clears dowel pins and lower assembly out of vehicle.

INSTALLATION

Reverse removal precedures to install transaxle, noting the following: Clean and lightly grease release bearing sliding surface. Always use spring clips when installing axle shafts.

CIVIC

REMOVAL

1) Disconnect ground cable from battery and transaxle. Release steering lock and place gear shift in neutral Position. Disconnect the following electrical leads: Starter motor, starter solenoid, temperature sending unit, ignition timing thermosensor and back-up light switch.

2) Remove speedometer cable and clip without disassembling speedometer gear holder. Remove clutch cable at release arm. Remove tannsaxle-side starter mounting bolt and top transaxle mounting bolt. Remove forward bolt from rear torque arm bracket.

3) Raise and support vehicle on hoist. Drain transaxle fluid and remove wheels. Remove engine shields,

HONDA (Cont.)

(if equipped). Remove stabilizer bar and brackets. Disconnect tie rod ends and lower ball joints from suspension arms. Remove CV joints from transaxle and remove axle shafts.

4) Disconnect shift lever torque rod from clutch housing. Slide pin retainer back and drive out spring with punch. Disconnect shift rod. Remove bolt from shift rod. Raise engine slihgtly and remove engine torque rods and brackets. Remove engine damper bracket from center beam. Remove transaxle and rear engine mount and bracket.

5) Place 1" x 2" x 4" wooden board between engine oil pan and center beam. Lower engine until it rests on beam. Remove engine-side starter mounting bolt and starter. Place transmisson jack under transaxle and remove remaining transaxle mounting bolts. Raise transaxle just enough to remove weight from engine and pull assembly away from engine until mainshaft clears clutch pressure plate. Lower transaxle out of vehicle.

INSTALLATION

To install, reverse removal procedure and note the following: When connecting axle shafts to transaxle, ensure they are fully seated in transaxle case. After insatllation, refill transaxle with fluid and adjust shift linkage as needed.

ISUZU

I-MARK 4-SPEED & 5-SPEED, P'UP 5-SPEED

REMOVAL

1) Disconnect negative battery cable. From inside vehicle, remove shift lever assembly. Loosen clutch cable adjusting nuts at lift side of engine compartment. Disconnect upper starter mounting nut and starter wiring.

2) Raise and support vehicle. Disconnect speedometer cable and clutch cable. Remove propeller shaft. Remove lower starter mounting bolt and remove starter. Disconnect exhaust pipe from manifold. Remove exhaust pipe bracket.

3) Remove flywheel inspection cover. Remove rear support mounting bolt. Support transmission under case and remove rear support. Lower transmission about 4" from normal position and remove any wires connected to transmission. Remove transmission-to-engine bolts. Remove transmission by sliding straight back and lowering from vehicle.

INSTALLATION

Reverse removal procedure and note the following: Lubricate input shaft splines and release bearing support with a light coat of grease. Adjust clutch. Refill transmission with lubricant.

INPULSE 5-SPEED

REMOVAL

1) Remove magnetic plug and drain oil. Disconnect negative battery cable. Remove gearshift lever boot. Remove console assembly. Raise vehicle on hoist and remove exhaust hanger at transmission.

2) Disconnect speedometer cable, ground cable and propeller shaft. Remove propeller shaft. Remove slave cylinder assembly.

3) Remove transmission rear mounting bolts and nuts at clutch cover plate. Remove bolts for shift quadrant cover, lever attaching bolts and lever. Remove control box assembly.

4) Lower engine and transmission and support rear of engine. Disconnect back-up light switch. Remove transmission-to-engine bolts. Pull transmission back until disengaged from clutch. Remove transmission.

INSTALLATION

Reverse removal procedure and note the following: Lubricate imput shaft splines and release bearing support with a light coat of grease. Adjust clutch. Refill transmission with lubricant.

P'UP 4-SPEED (2WD)

REMOVAL

1) Disconnect negative battery terminal. Slide gearshift boot up on lever and remove lever attaching bolts, then withdraw lever. Remove starter attaching bolts and place starter out of way.

2) Raise vehicle on hoist. Disconnect exhaust pipe hanger at transmission, speedometer cable at extension housing, battery ground cable at transmission and propeller shaft from rear axle. Remove propeller shaft and either drain transmission fluid or install plug in extension housing to prevent fluid loss.

3) Remove return spring from clutch fork. Remove bolts attaching flywheel cover and remove frame bracket-to-transmission rear mount bolts. Raise engine and transmission as required and remove crossmember-to-frame bracket bolts. Remove rear mounting from extension housing.

4) Lower engine and transmission assembly and support rear of engine with support stand. Disconnect electrical connectors at back-up light and "coasting richer solenoid" (Federal models) switches. Remove transmission-to-engine attaching bolts. Pull transmission straight back until disengaged from clutch. Tip front of transmission down and remove transmission from vehicle.

INSTALLATION

Reverse removal procedure and note the following: Adjust clutch cable and clutch pedal height if required. Refill transmission to correct fluid level.

Manual Transmission Removal

ISUZU (Cont.)

P'UP & TROOPER II 4-SPEED WITH TRANSFER CASE (4WD)

REMOVAL

1) Disconnect battery negative terminal. Slide gearshift boot up on lever and remove lever attaching bolts. Disconnect transfer gear shift lever return spring. Remove both gear shift levers.

2) Remove starter attaching bolts and lay starter out of way. Raise vehicle on hoist. Disconnect exhaust pipe from manifold and at hanger on transmission. Disconnect speedometer cable at transfer case, ground cable at transmission and propeller shaft from rear axle. Disconnect front propeller shaft and remove both shafts from vehicle.

3) Disconnect clutch fork return spring, then remove clutch cable from hooked portion of fork. Pull cable forward through stiffener bracket. Remove the lower 2 bolts attaching transmission rear mount to frame.

4) Raise engine and transmission just enough so the 4 crossmember-to-frame bolts can be removed. Remove the 2 transfer case rear mounting bolts, then remove bolts attaching transfer side case to transfer case and remove transfer side case.

NOTE: Be sure not to lose shift rod dentent spring and ball from transfer side case.

5) Remove stud bolt from transfer case then lower engine and transmission, supporting rear of engine. Disconnect electrical connectors at back-up light and "coasting richer solenoid" (Federal models) switches. Remove 4 bolts holding shift cover to transfer case and remove cover and gasket.

6) Remove all bolts attaching transmission to engine then remove transmission with transfer case. To ease removal, turn transfer case side of transmission downward, slide transmission backward until clear of clutch, then tilt front of transmission down and slide forward and out of vehicle.

INSTALLATION

To install, reverse removal procedure while noting the following: Install transmission with transmission shift lever in neutral and transfer case shift lever in "4H" position. Fill transmission with lubricant and adjust clutch fork and pedal height as needed.

MAZDA

GLC

REMOVAL

1) Disconnect negative battery cable, speedometer cable and any wires or connectors that may be connected to transaxle. Remove 2 clutch brackets and disconnect clutch cable from release lever. Remove water pipe bracket and harness clips.

2) Raise and support vehicle. Drain fluid from transaxle. Remove wheels and any shields or grards that may interfere with transmission removal. Remove ball joint from lower control arm. Disconnect drive shaft from differential by pulling outward on knuckle.

3) Support drive shaft out of the way. Support rear of engine with a support beam. Separate shift control rod and extension bar from transaxle.

4) Remove transaxle support crossmember and separate mount. Remove starter. Support transaxle with a jack. Remove transaxle-to-engine bolts. Lower transaxle out of vehicle.

INSTALLATION

Reverse removal procedure and note the following: Refill transaxle with lubricant. Check operation of shifter and clutch linkages and adjust as needed.

626

REMOVAL

1) Disconnect negative battery cable, speedometer cable and any wires or connectors that may be connected to transaxle. Remove 2 clutch cable bracket bolts and disconnect clutch cable from release lever. Remove ground wire installation bolt and harness clips.

2) Remove starter. Mount engine support (49-G030-025), and attach the support hook to the engine hanger. Remove transaxle-to-engine attaching bolts. Raise vehicle and support with safety stands. Drain fluid from transaxle. Remove wheels and any shields or guards that may interfere with transmission removal.

3) Remove control link of stabilizer bar. Remove the under cover (if equipped). Remove ball joint from lower control arm by pulling arm downward. Remove left drive shaft from transaxle by inserting a lever between the drive shaft and the transaxle case and tap the end of the lever to uncouple the drive shaft and the differential side gear. Pull front hub forward and disconnect drive shaft from differential by pulling outward on knuckle.

NOTE: In order not to mark the oil seal, hold the joint at the differential side with one hand and pull the shaft straight out.

4) Remove the right drive shaft and the joint shaft by inserting a lever between them. Pull the front hub forward and separate the drive shaft from the joint shaft and set it aside. Remove joint shaft bracket mounting bolts and remove joint shaft and shaft bracket assembly from transaxle as an assembly.

5) Remove transaxle mounting bracket nuts at the crossmember. Remove the crossmember and the left lower arm as an assembly. Separate change control rod from change rod. Remove extension bar from transaxle. Remove transaxle under cover. Attach a rope to transaxle mount bracket at 2 places and over the engine support. Place a board on a floor jack and use this to support the transaxle as it is lowered from the vehicle.

CAUTION: Because the transaxle is not well balanced, be careful concerning the point of support.

6) Remove transaxle-to-engine attaching bolts (2). Seprate transaxle from engine. Loosen rope while lowering transaxle on jack. Remove transaxle mount brackets from the transaxle.

MAZDA (Cont.)

INSTALLATION

Reverse removal procedure and note the following: Install new clips on ends of drive shafts. After installing drive shafts, pull outward on shaft to ensure that shaft doesn't come out. Refill transaxle with lubricant. Check operation of shifter and clutch linkages and adjust as necessary.

ALL RWD MODELS

REMOVAL

1) Disconnect negative battery cable. Place gearshift lever in neutral position, and remove gearshift knob. Remove console box (if equipped) and gearshift lever. B2000 gearshift lever components include a wave washer, shim and bushing.

2) On RX7, remove air cleaner and upper transmission-to-engine bolts. On all models, raise and support vehicle and drain transmission. Disconnect and remove propeller shaft. Disconnect and/or remove under cover, exhaust components and emission control components as required.

3) On all models, reomve clutch slave cylinder and place out of the way without removing line. On all models, disconnect and remove starter, speedometer cable, back-up light wires and other electrical connections.

4) Place jack under rear of engine, protecting oil pan with wooden block. Position transmission jack under transmission and remove transmission-to-engine mounting bolts. If equipped, remove transmission-to-crossmember bolts, crossmember-to-frame bolts and crossmember. Slide transmission back until input shaft is cleared. Remove from vehicle.

INSTALLATION

To install, reverse removal precedure, ensureing that splines in input shaft align with those in clutch disc.

MERCEDES-BENZ

NOTE: Information not available.

MITSUBISHI

CORDIA & TREDIA

REMOVAL

1) Remove the battery, battery tray, windshield washer reservoir, and air cleaner. Disconnect the clutch cable, speedometer cable, and back-up light harness from transaxle. Disconnect starter motor harness.

2) Remove upper 5 transaxle-to-engine bolts. Remove stater. Raise and support vehicle. Remove wheels. Drain transaxle oil. Remove the extension, shift control rod, and range selector control cable from under the engine compartment.

3) Disconnect the stabilizer bar and strut rod from the lower control arm. Remove drive axle shafts. See appropriate Mitsubishi article in MANUAL TRANSMISSIONS section. Support the transaxle with a jack. Do not compress the oil pan.

4) Remove bell housing cover. Remove transaxle-to-engine bolts, transaxle mount insulator bracket, and transaxle mount bracket. Lower transaxle from under vehicle.

INSTALLATION

To install, reverse removal procedure. Fill transaxle with Hypoid gear oil. Adjust clutch cable. Adjust linkage as necessary.

MONTERO

REMOVAL
Transmission & Transfer Case

1) Disconnect negative battery cable. Place transmission gearshift lever in Neutral position and transfer case lever in 4WD high range position. Remove both gearshift lever assemblies.

2) Raise and support vehicle. Remove skid plate. Drain transmission and transfer case oil. Remove front and rear drive shafts. Disconnect speedometer cable, back-up light switch harness, and 4WD indicator light harness.

3) Detact clutch slave cylinder from case. Remove bell housing cover, starter, and front exhaust pipe mounting bracket. Remove rear transmission mount bolts. Support transmission with a jack and remove the crossmember. Remove transfer case mount.

4) Remove transmission-to-engine mounting bolts. Pull transmission and transfer case away from engine and remove from vehicle.

INSTALLATION

To install, reverse removal procedure. Fill transaxle with Hypoid gear oil. Adjust clutch cable. Adjust linkage as necessary.

Manual Transmission Removal

MITSUBISHI (Cont.)

PICKUP

REMOVAL

4 & 5-Speed (2WD & 4WD)

1) Disconnect negative battery cable. Remove air cleaner, starter, and upper 2 transmission-to-engine mounting bolts. From inside passenger compartment, remov console box or carpeting covering transmission access plate.

2) Remove the shift lever assembly from the extension housing. Raise and support vehicle. Drain all gear oil. Remove drive shaft(s). Disconnect the speedometer cable.

3) On 2WD models, disconnect the back-up light harness. On 4WD models, disconnect back-up light and indicator light harnesses. On both models, disconnect front exhaust pipe. Remove clutch slave cylinder or disconnect clutch release cable.

4) Support rear of engine with a jack. On 4WD models, remove the transfer case mounting bracket. On both models, place jack under transmission. Do not crush oil pan. Remove crossmember.

3) Remove bell housing cover and remaining transmission-to-engine bolts. Slide transmission away from engine and remove from vehicle.

INSTALLATION

1) To install, reverse removal procedure. On 2WD models, install the gear shift lever assembly in the 4-speed transmission in the 2nd gear position, or 5-speed transmission in 1st gear position.

2) On 4WD models, install the gear shift lever assembly with the transmission in the Neutral position and transfer case in the "4H" position. On both models, adjust clutch. Refill transmission and transaxle with gear oil.

STARION

REMOVAL

1) Drain transmission gear oil. Remove drive shaft. Disconnect speedometer cable and back-up light wires. Remove the clutch slave cylinder from transmission. Remove the bell housing cover and starter.

2) Remove the 2 upper transmission-to-engine mounting bolts. Raise and support the vehicle. Support the transmission with a jack. Remove the engine support bracket, insulator assembly, and ground cable.

3) Remove the gear shift lever assembly with transmission in Neutral position. Remove remaining transmission-to-engine mounting bolts. Remove crossmember. Lower transmission out of vehicle.

INSTALLATION

To install, reverse removal procedure. Fill transaxle with Hypoid gear oil. Adjust linkage as necessary.

NISSAN/DATSUN

ALL RWD MODELS

REMOVAL

1) Disconnect negative battery cable. Remove console (if equipped) and shift lever boot. Place transmission in neutral. Remove snap ring or nut from control lever pin. Remove control lever pin and control lever.

2) Raise vehicle and remove exhaust pipe. Disconnect wiring at back-up light switch, high gear switch, neutral switch (if equipped) and overdrive switch (210 5-speed). Disconnect speedometer cable.

3) On 4WD pickups, disconnect wires from 4WD indicator switch. Disconnect propeller shaft between transmission and transfer case. Remove front differential carrier crossmember. Disconnect propeller shaft between transfer case and front differential carrier.

4) On all other models, disconnect propeller shaft from transmission. On all models, remove clutch cylinder from transmission case. Support engine and transmission. Remove rear transmission mounting bolts and crossmember bolts. Remove starter. Remove transmission-to-engine mounting bolts.

5) Slide transmission to rear away from engine. Remove transmission from vehicle. Use care when removing transmission to avoid striking any adjacent parts or main drive shaft.

INSTALLATION

Reverse removal procedures to install transmission, noting the following:

- Clean mating surfaces of engine rear plate and transmission case. Apply a light coat of grease to splined parts of clutch disc, input shaft and moving surfaces of control lever and striking rod.
- Lubricate oil seal lip and bushing of extension housing before installing propeller shaft.
- Fill transmission with gear oil to level of filler hole.

PULSAR, SENTRA & STANZA

REMOVAL

1) Remove battery and battery holding plate. Remove radiator reservoir tank. Remove drive shafts from transaxle without damaging oil seals. Insert a shaft into each side of differential to prevent side gears from falling into differential case.

2) Remove wheel well protector. Separate shifter control rod and support rod from transaxle. Remove exhaust pipe securing nuts and bolts. Remove engine gusset bolts and transmission protector. Remove clutch control cable from withdraw lever.

3) Disconnect speedometer cable. Disconnect wires from reverse and neutral switches. Support engine with a jack and a block of wood placed under the oil pan. Spuuort the transaxle with a jack.

4) Remove starter motor. Remove engine mount securing bolts. Remove bolts securing transaxle to engine. Separate teansaxle from engine and remove transaxle from under vehicle.

INSTALLATION

To install, reverse removal procedure and note the following: Clean mating surface between engine and clutch housing. Apply grease to splines on input shaft and clutch disc. Remove filler plug and fill transaxle with recommended amount and type of gear lube.

PEUGEOT

ALL MODELS

REMOVAL

1) Open hood as far as possible and support with wooden blocks under safety hooks. Disconnect battery cable and fan shroud. Remove header pipe bolts and disconnect oxygen sensor (if equipped). Remove heat shield and air injection hose.

2) Remove front seat track floor brace. Remove rear tailpipe brackets. Remove rear axle mounts. Mark position of strap on steering column flange and remove bolts.

3) On each side of crossmember, remove bolt and install bolt 2" longer than original. Remove 2 remaining bolts. Lower crossmember by backing off new bolts about 2 inches.

4) Place transmission jack under transmission and remove propeller shaft tube bolts. Separate propeller shaft from transmission by 13/16" (20 mm). Insert transmission shaft retaining plate (80403-SZ) to clear transmission output shaft.

5) Remove front mount for gear selector rod. Remove shifting link rod, selector link rod and back-up light switch. Remove speedometer cable. Remove bolts from inspection plates on clutch housing. Remove plates

6) Remove slave cylinder circlip and flexible hose bracket. With engine suspended from hoist and hooks, lower hoist to tilt the transmission as far as possible. Remove starter. Remove clutch housing bolts and lower transmission.

INSTALLATION

To install, reverse removal procedures. Lubricate input shaft splines and clutch release bearing guide with grease (Molykote or equivalent). Prior to fully engaging transmission into place, install slave cylinder into its housing. Refill transmission to proper level. Adjust linkage as needed.

PORSCHE

911SC

REMOVAL

1) Transaxle and engine must be removed as a unit. After removal, assemblies may be separated. Vehicle must be raised and supported with safety stands to remove assembly from below vehicle.

2) Disconnect battery ground cable. Remove engine block vent hose and plug hose. On A/C equipped vehicles, detach compressor at console but leave hoses connected.

NOTE: Air conditioning system is under pressure. DO NOT unhook hoses unless system is discharged first.

3) Remove relay plate cover and disconnect engine wires at relay plate, adapter plug, relay, socket and ignition control unit. Remove fuel hoses at filter and return line. Disconnect accelerator linkage.

4) Remove rear center tunnel cover in passenger compartment. Remove rubber boot in tunnel by pulling forward over selector rod. Loosen shift rod coupling and pull coupling off of transmission inner shift rod.

5) Disconnect speedometer sensor wires in tunnel. Remove rubber plug with wire plug. Drain crankcase and plug hoses on engine and oil tank. Remove heater hoses at exchangers. Remove rear stabilizer.

6) Disconnect ground strap at body and battery wires at starter. Disconnect accelerator linkage at pedal and clutch cable from transmission.

CAUTION: Be careful when jacking assembly upward not to damage secondary air injection pipes.

7) Place a jack under engine/transmission assembly and apply a little upward pressure to relieve tension on motor mounts. Remove transmission and engine mount bolts. Lower engine/transmission assembly out of vehicle.

CAUTION: Do not move vehicle unless drive shafts are suspended horizontally, to prevent damage to dust covers.

INSTALLATION

To install, reverse removal procedure and note the following: Do not clamp heater hoses. Slide them onto exchangers just before engine/transmission assembly is in final installation position.

928S

TRANSAXLE ASSEMBLY
Removal

1) Remove battery from case. Loosen rear wheels and position transmission in 5th gear. Loosen screw clamping selector rod to transmission linkage at rear of tunnel.

2) Open inspection cover (rubber cap) in transmission. Turn 1 wheel and hold opposite wheel to position coupling bolt between drive and input shafts for removal. Remove bolt.

Manual Transmission Removal

PORSCHE (Cont.)

3) Position shift lever in neutral. Remove rear wheels and detach brake calipers and suspend them to relieve hoses of any tension. Disconnect axle shafts from transaxle and suspend horizontally from car to prevent damage to boots.

4) Push dust cover back and remove set screw from shift rod coupling. Detach shift rod and slide rod forward in tunnel to clear linkage at rear. Disconnect back-up light wires and speedometer pulse transmitter wires from transmission. Remove switch and pulse transmitter.

Fig. 1: Location of Input Shaft Coupling Bolt and Shift Rod Coupling Set Screw

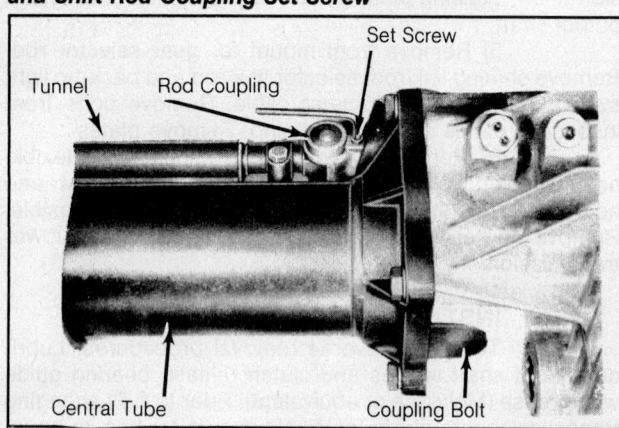

5) Detach exhaust assembly and remove entire assembly after the catalytic converter. This requires removal of 4 bolts between converter and intermediate muffler, 2 bolts on front rubber mount, 1 bolt on rear rubber mount and 2 bolts on holder for main muffler. Remove battery box.

6) Remove 2 transmission mounting bolts on rear axle crossmember and 2 bolts between rear axle crossmember and frame. Place transmission jack beneath rear axle crossmember and mark position of crossmember. Remove remaining 4 bolts on crossmember. Tilt rear axle carefully and support in tilted position taking weight off the lower control arm link pins.

7) Mount transmission support bracket to transmission with fixtures (9148 and 9149). *See Fig. 2.* Remove 6 bolts between central tube and transmission. Pull transmission back to one side and lower from vehicle.

Installation

To install, reverse removal procedure noting that propeller shaft extends .50-.53" (12.5-13.5 mm) beyond rear flange surface. Improper position may cause clutch drag due to improper engagement of spline and clutch disc. Tighten all nuts and bolts to specifications.

TRANSAXLE CENTRAL TUBE

Removal

1) With transaxle removed from vehicle, disconnect negative battery cable. Suspend engine from front eyelet with fixture (VW 10-222) and hold tightly in installation position.

2) Support tube at front tunnel reinforcing brace with a front block. Detach central tube from front clutch housing and slide back about 4".

3) Remove rear cross traverse in tunnel, then loosen rear axle mountings and lower torsion bar tube. Pull

Fig. 2: Installing Transmission Support Brackets

selector rod out to the rear. Remove central tube by lowering and pulling out to the rear.

Inspection

Propeller shaft must extend .50-.53" (12.5-13.5 mm) beyond face of clutch housing flange in order to properly engage clutch disc splines. Correct shaft position by tapping end with soft faced hammer. Check free rotation of shaft turning by hand.

NOTE: **Shaft must turn easily without noise or flat spots. If bearings or shaft are damaged, entire assembly must be replaced. Separate component replacement is not possible as individual parts are not available.**

Installation

To install, reverse removal procedure.

944

TRANSAXLE

Removal

1) Detach exhaust pipe from catalytic converter and loosen exhaust system brackets at central tube. Remove muffler clamp from transaxle end plate and remove entire converter and muffler assembly.

2) Push shift linkage dust boot back and remove lock wire from shift linkage connecting bolt. Remove connecting bolt. From inside vehicle, fold back dust boot and inner cover on shift lever. Remove clamp from shift lever knob, then remove knob.

3) Remove circlip holding selector rod to shift lever. Pull shift rod and spring washer from shift lever pin. Turn shift lever 180° and tilt out to right. Press down on rubber seal between central tube and tunnel. Slide selector rod forward in tunnel about 12" to clear linkage at rear.

PORSCHE (Cont.)

4) Remove plug from rear of central tube housing. Push shift rod protective tube back far enough so shift rod tube is outside central tube housing. Remove inspection plugs (1 located at bottom of central tube housing; the other on upper left side of transmission case). Remove propeller shaft-to-mainshaft coupling screws through inspection holes. Slide coupling back toward transmission case.

5) Detach axle shafts from transaxle and suspend from vehicle in horizontal position. Disconnect wires from back-up light switch. Place a jack with transmission adapter (US 618 and 618/1) under transmission and raise slightly to release pressure from transmission suspension.

6) Remove transmission-to-central tube housing flange bolts. Remove transaxle mount bolts. Lower transaxle assembly and central tube until central tube rests on rear axle cross tube. Remove transaxle out rear.

Installation

1) To install, reverse removal procedure and note the following: Before installing transaxle, check propeller shaft protrusion at rear flange. Shaft should extend .49-.53" (12.5-13.5 mm) beyond flange lips. Make small corrections by tapping on end of shaft with soft-faced hammer.

2) After installation, adjust shift linkage as follows: Place transmission in Neutral and install intermediate shift lever with a 5° rearward offset from center of shaft. Ensure shift lever is in neutral, then move shift lever base to adjust shift lever to an 85° angle from rear of central tube.

3) With shift lever in Neutral, transverse selector shaft will be held in 3rd/4th gear (middle shift pattern) by spring pressure. With shift linkage connected and adjusted properly, shift lever will not lean to either side. If shift lever leans to either side, adjust at intermediate shift lever.

CENTRAL TUBE
Removal
1) With transaxle assembly removed from vehicle, disconnect negative battery strap. Suspend engine from front eyelet with support fixture (VW10-222) and hold tight in installation position.

2) Support tube at front tunnel reinforcing brace with locally made block. Detach central tube from clutch housing. Remove rear reinforcement strut, then loosen rear axle mountings and lower torsion bar tube. Pull selector rod rearward. Remove central tube by lowering and pulling out to rear.

Inspection
Check for free rotation of central tube bearings by turning propeller shaft by hand. Shaft must turn easily without binding. If bearings or shaft are damaged, central tube with shaft and bearings must be replaced.

Installation
To install, reverse removal procedure and check propeller shaft protrusion. Check and adjust shift linkage.

RENAULT

FUEGO

REMOVAL
1) Disconnect battery ground cable and starter wiring harness. Remove starter attaching bolts and starter. Disconnect clutch cable at release lever.

2) Remove axle shafts from transaxle. Do not disconnect outer end from hub unless outer CV joint service is required. See appropriate Renault article in MANUAL TRANSMISSIONS section. Disconnect speedometer cable, shift linkage, and any wires that are connected to transaxle.

NOTE: **DO NOT remove any of the gear shift linkage ball joints from their sockets.**

3) Remove clutch cover and any shields or guards that may interfere with transaxle removal. Support transaxle with a transmission jack. Remove transmission mounts. Remove engine-to-transaxle bolts. Slide transaxle rearward and remove from vehicle.

Installation
To install, reverse removal procedure. Lightly coat input shaft splines with assembly lube prior to reinstalling transaxle. Adjust and check operation of shifter and clutch linkage. Adjust Top Dead Center sensor as needed. End of sensor should be .04" (1 mm) from flywheel face.

SAAB

ALL MODELS

REMOVAL
1) Remove hood, then disconnect battery cables and lift out battery. Drain coolant from radiator and engine. Disconnect power brake unit vacuum hose from intake manifold. Remove rubber bellows between air flow sensor and intake manifold. Disconnect and plug fuel line. Disconnect air flow sensor electrical leads. Remove air cleaner and mixture control unit.

2) Remove air intake, preheater hose, crankcase ventilation hose and intake hose. Disconnect cable from oil pressure sender. On California models, disconnect all EGR system hoses. If equipped with power steering, disconnect and plug hoses at steering pump.

3) Disconnect and remove ignition coil. Disconnect the following electrical connections: Temperature sending unit, radiator fan, thermostat contact, oil pressure sender, headlights and starter leads. Disconnect and plug all fuel injection lines (if equipped). Disconnect choke and throttle cables. Disconnect all water hoses. Disconnect hose to expansion tank.

4) Remove grill and hood locking cable. Remove radiator/headlight assembly. Disconnect hose from clutch slave/cylinder and plug hose and hole in cylinder. Disconnect exhaust pipe from manifold and ground cable from

SAAB (Cont.)

Fig. 1: Installing New Transmission Housing Gasket

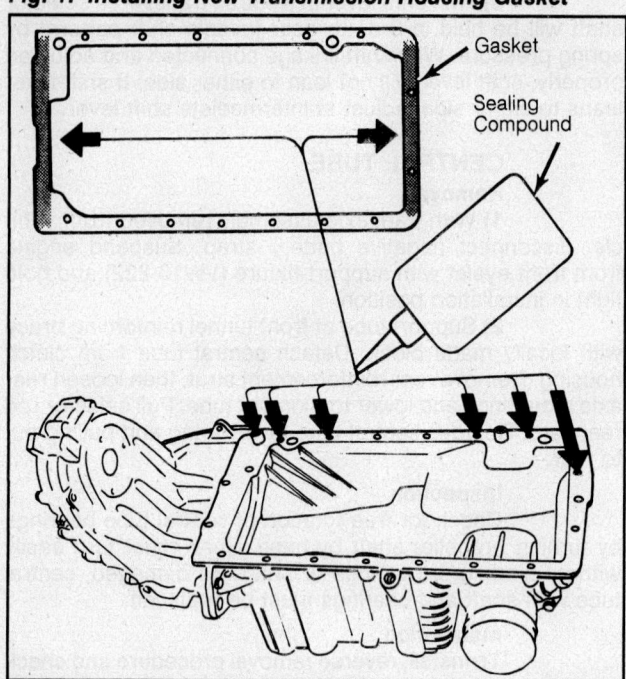

Apply sealing compound on ends of gasket and in bolt holes indicated.

transaxle. Remove bellows clamp and bellows from inner CV joints.

5) Place spacer (8393209) between upper control arm underside and body to unload suspension when vehicle is raised. Insert spacer from engine compartment side. Raise and support front of vehicle.

6) Remove lower end piece from control arm. Pull out steering knuckle assembly and support end piece against control arm outer end. Place shifter in Neutral. Remove nut and knock out taper pin in gear shift rod joint.

NOTE: Gear shift rod joints are made of steel or plastic. DO NOT knock out taper pin from plastic joints.

7) Remove rear engine mounting bolts. Loosen nut on front engine mounting so mounting can be lifted from bracket. Slightly raise engine and move engine/transaxle unit to each side to free CV joints. Lift engine/transaxle unit from vehicle.

8) To separate transaxle from engine, drain engine oil. Remove clutch cover, starter and clutch shaft. Remove 3 clutch slave cylinder retaining screws. Remove engine-to-transaxle attaching bolts and carefully lift engine off transaxle unit.

INSTALLATION

To install, reverse removal procedure. Be sure CV joints are packed with grease prior to installation. Apply sealing compound to 3 clutch slave cylinder retaining bolts. Use new gasket on transmission housing, applying sealing compound to both sides of gasket ends. Also apply sealing compound to 6 bolts shown in *Fig. 1*.

SUBARU

ALL MODELS

REMOVAL

1) Disconnect battery cables. Remove spare tire and air cleaner. Remove clutch cable return spring and clutch cable. Disconnect speedometer cable from transaxle housing. Disconnect back-up light switch, ground strap from vehicle body and starter harness. DO NOT remove battery cable from starter.

2) Remove starter and upper engine-to-transmission mounting bolts. Loosen lower mounting bolts. Loosen transmission side stabilizer bar .39" (10 mm) and tighten engine side stabilizer bar the same amount. Slightly tilt engine backward to facilitate transaxle removal.

NOTE: DO NOT tighten engine side stabilizer bar more than .39" (10 mm).

3) On 4WD vehicles, remove hand brake tray cover and brake cover. Remove the rod cover. Set the drive selector lever at 4WD position. Remove the nut connecting gear shift and drive selector rods.

4) Remove 2 nuts securing drive selector rod and drive selector to plate. Remove gearshift lever boot screws and nut connecting gearshift lever with operating lever. Remove gearshift lever and boot.

5) On all models, disconnect the oxygen sensor harness. Raise and support vehicle. Disconnect hot air intake hose. Separate front exhaust pipe from rear exhaust pipe.

6) Remove bolts front exhaust pipe-to-bracket bolts. Support the front exhaust pipe and remove nuts from exhaust port of engine. Remove exhaust pipe, being carefull not to damage oxygen sensor. Remove stove from exhaust manifold.

7) On 4WD models, remove transmission skid plate. Remove rear drive shaft from transmission. Plug open end of transmission assembly. On all models except 4WD, remove exhaust system shield. Remove gearshift retaining bolts from transmission. Free gearshift system from transmission.

8) On all models, remove stabilizer bar. Disconnect and lower transverse links from front crossmember. Drive out inner axle shaft-to-drive axle shaft retaining pin. Push wheel assembly toward outside of vehicle and separate axle shaft from drive axle. Remove clamp on left side of parking brake cable to facilitate removal of rear crossmember.

9) Remove left and right transmission mounts. Support transaxle assembly with a jack. Remove crossmember. Remove 2 nuts securing engine to transaxle. Move transaxle assembly rearward to clear mainshaft, then lower transaxle from vehicle.

INSTALLATION

To install, reverse removal procedure. Replace all lock nuts and roll pins. Tighten nut connecting control arm to crossmember only when vehicle has been lowered to floor.

TOYOTA

CAMRY

REMOVAL

NOTE: **The engine and transaxle are removed as an assembly.**

1) Mark hood hinge positions. Remove hood and battery. Drain cooling system. Disconnect accelerator cable from throttle body.

2) If equipped with cruise control, remove actuator cover. Disconnect wiring connector and vacuum hose. Remove actuator with bracket. If equipped with air conditioning, disconnect main and sub fan motor connectors. Disconnect reservoir and upper and lower radiator hoses.

3) Remove radiator supports, rubber cushions, and radiator. Remove air cleaner assembly with air flow meter and hose.

4) Mark for reassembly reference and remove all electrical connectors, cables, and vacuum hoses that interfer with engine removal. Pull out EFI wire harness to right side fender apron.

5) Disconnect 2 heater hoses. Detach fuel inlet hose from filter and return hose from return pipe. Remove speedometer cable from transaxle.

6) Detach clutch slave cylinder and hose bracket. Do not disconnect hoses from the hydraulic system. Disconnect transaxle control cable. If equipped, detach A/C belt, compressor, power steering belt, and steering pump with bracket. Set assemblies aside. Do not discharge A/C system.

7) Raise and support vehicle. Drain oil from transaxle. Wrap drive axle boots with shop towels. Remove 6 nuts from each drive shaft flange while depressing brake pedal. Disconnect both front drive shafts.

8) Disconnect front exhaust pipe and remove 2 gaskets from manifold. Remove exhaust pipe stay from cylinder block. Remove 2 hole covers and disconnect front and rear engine mounts. Remove crossmember if necessary. Lower vehicle.

NOTE: **Do not damage power steering gear housing or neutral start switch during removal. Ensure all wiring, hoses, and cables are clear of engine before lifting.**

9) Attach engine hoist to lift brackets on engine. Remove engine and transaxle mounts from brackets. Remove left side transaxle mount bracket. Carefully lift engine/transaxle assembly out of vehicle.

10) Remove front and rear brackets. Remove side gear shaft and universal joint. Remove starter. Separate engine from transaxle.

INSTALLATION

1) Install mounts and starter on engine/transaxle assembly. Install side gear shaft and universal joint. With engine hoist chained to lift brackets, slowly lower engine/transaxle assembly into engine compartment.

2) Tilt transaxle down while lowering to clear neutral start switch, mount brackets, and power steering gear housing. Install engine mounts, brackets, and crossmembers.

3) To complete installation, reverse removal procedures. Connect all wiring and fuel and vacuum hoses. Adjust drive belts. Fill radiator with coolant and transaxle with gear oil.

CELICA & COROLLA (RWD)

REMOVAL

1) Drain coolant from upper portion of radiator. Remove upper radiator hose. Disconnect battery at ground terminal. Remove shift lever from inside of vehicle. Drain transmission lubricant. Mark propeller shaft and rear flange for orientation and remove propeller shaft.

2) On Celica models, disconnect exhaust pipe clamp from stiffener plate, speedometer cable and back-up light switch wire. Remove lower clutch housing cover plate. Disconnect the clutch release cylinder from clutch housing leaving hydraulic line connected. Remove starter.

3) On Corolla models, disconnect speedometer cable, back-up light switch wire and exhaust pipe clamp at clutch housing. Remove exhaust pipe at manifold. Remove lower clutch housing cover plate. Disconnect the clutch release cylinder from clutch housing leaving hydraulic line connected. Remove starter.

4) On both models, support transmission and remove rear support member. Remove remaining bolts attaching clutch housing to engine. Move transmission rearward and lower from vehicle, clear of clutch assembly.

INSTALLATION

To install, reverse removal procedure. Lightly grease friction surfaces and reverse removal procedure. Ensure propeller shaft and rear flange marks are aligned. Refill transmission lubricant.

CRESSIDA & SUPRA

REMOVAL

1) Remove negative battery terminal. Drain coolant from upper tank. Remove upper radiator hose. Remove console box and shift lever from inside of vehicle. Raise and support vehicle.

2) Drain transmission gear oil. Remove steering gear housing without disconnecting fluid hoses and suspend it. Mark drive shaft and rear flange for reassembly reference and remove drive shaft.

3) Remove exhaust pipe clamp bolt from stiffener plate. Disconnect speedometer cable and back-up light switch from transmission. Remove clutch slave cylinder. Do not disconnect hydraulic line.

4) Remove starter. Place jack under transmission and raise slightly. Remove rear transmission mount. Remove transmission-to-engine mounting bolts and remove transmission from vehicle.

INSTALLATION

To install, reverse removal procedure. Lightly grease friction surfaces and reverse removal procedure. Ensure propeller shaft and rear flange marks are aligned. Refill transmission lubricant.

COROLLA (FWD)

REMOVAL

1) Remove negative battery terminal. Drain coolant from radiator (C51). Remove air cleaner with air hose. Raise and support vehicle.

TOYOTA (Cont.)

2) Disconnect back-up light switch connector. Remove speedometer cable. Disconnect control cables. Remove water inlet from transaxle (C51).

3) Remove clip from clutch pipe bracket (S41 and 50). Disconnect bracket from the transaxle (S41 ans 50). Remove 2 bolts and clutch release cylinder.

4) Remove under cover. Remove front and rear mounting. Remove engine mounting center member. Disconnect drive shaft from transaxle.

5) Disconnect steering knuckle from the lower arm. Pull steering knuckle outward, and remove left drive shaft. Remove starter. Disconnect bond cable. Remove engine rear plate No. 2 (C51).

6) Raise transaxle and engine slightly, use wooden block between jack and engine. Disconnect left engine mount. Disconnect transaxle mount bolts from engine. Lower engine left side and remove the transaxle from the engine.

INSTALLATION

To install, reverse removal procedure. Lightly grease friction surfaces and reverse removal procedure. Refill transmission lubricant.

LAND CRUISER

REMOVAL

1) Disconnect battery cable. Raise and support vehicle. Drain gear oil from transmission and transfer cases. Remove transmission skid plate. Disconnect the drive shafts, speedometer cable, and parking brake cable from transmission/transfer case assembly.

2) From inside vehicle, remove scuff plate, side panel trim, heater duct, and carpets. Remove shift lever knobs, dust boots, and transmission shift lever.

3) Disconnect electrical wiring and vacuum hoses (if necessary) from transmission/transfer case assembly. Remove attaching bolts, then remove transmission/transfer case assembly from vehicle.

4) To separate transfer case from transmission, move transfer case lever to "4L" position. Remove back-up light switch from transmission case. Remove stake marks from transmission output shaft nut, then hold power take-off companion flange stationary and remove output shaft nut.

NOTE: **When removing transmission output shaft nut, have front drive engaged.**

5) Remove 5 transfer case-to-transmission case attaching bolts. Using a puller, separate transfer case from transmission case, holding power take-off gear to prevent it from dropping out of case.

INSTALLATION

To install, reverse removal procedure. After transfer case is attached to transmission case, stake transmission output shaft nut in place. With transmission/transfer case assembly installed in vehicle, fill transmission case and transfer case with gear oil. Adjust shift linkage.

PICKUP

REMOVAL

1) Disconnect negative battery cable. Remove floor mat and shifter boot(s). Remove shift lever(s) and retainer from inside vehicle. Remove upper starter mounting nut.

2) Raise and support vehicle. Drain transmission (and transfer case on 4WD models). Remove clutch slave cylinder (with hydraulic line connected) and position out of way. Remove starter. Mark drive shaft and transmission yoke for reassembly reference and remove shaft.

3) Disconnect speedometer cable. Disconnect back-up light switch wire. Disconnect exhaust pipe clamp from transmission housing. Remove 4 mounting bolts from extension housing.

4) On 2WD models, raise transmission slightly by raising engine with jack and wooden block under engine. Remove the 4 bracket bolts from support member and remove rear mounting with bracket.

5) On 4WD models, jack up transmission enough to remove the weight from the rear support. Remove 8 bolts, and remove support member. On all models, remove remaining transmission housing bolts. Place a safety support with a wooden block under engine and lower jack until engine is resting on support.

6) Draw out transmission and transfer case assembly, down and toward the rear. Remove engine rear mounting. Remove transfer case from transmission.

INSTALLATION

To install, reverse removal procedure. Apply a small amount of multi-purpose grease to end of input shaft, shaft splines, release bearing and diaphragm spring contact surfaces before installation. Refill transmission and transfer case with lubricant after installation.

STARLET

REMOVAL

1) Remove shift boot and snap ring. Remove shift lever from transmission. Disconnect negative battery terminal. Remove water hose from thermostat housing.

2) Remove air cleaner. Disconnect accelerator pump lever. Disconnect wiring harness connector. Wrap steering rack boot with a towel.

3) Remove exhaust muffler clamp. Remove clutch and speedometer cables. Disconnect propeller shaft and plug extension housing with extension housing plug (09325-12010).

4) Remove starter motor and engine rear support. Remove engine-to-transmission bolts. Remove rear transmission support member and remove transmission.

INSTALLATION

To install, reverse removal procedures, ensuring that splines on input shaft align with those in clutch disc.

TOYOTA (Cont.)

TERCEL

NOTE: **Transmission assembly may be removed without removing differential assembly. Procedure given here covers removal of complete transaxle assembly.**

REMOVAL

All 2WD & 4WD Models

1) Drain coolant from upper radiator tank. Disconnect negative battery cable, air cleaner inlet duct, and upper radiator hose (from engine). Disconnect clutch cable. Remove starter motor. Remove 4 upper clutch housing-to-engine bolts.

2) On 4WD models, remove console box and shift lever from passenger compartment. On both models, raise and support vehicle. Remove axle drive shafts. See appropriate Toyota article in MANUAL TRANSMISSION section. Remove drain plugs and drain transaxle (and transfer case) fluid.

3) On 4WD models, remove drive shaft and insert tool (SST09325-12010). On both models, disconnect exhaust pipe at manifold and remove exhaust system. Remove transaxle stiffener plate on right side.

4) On 4WD models, disconnect 4WD link. Disconnect back-up light switch and 4WD switch wire. On 2WD models, disconnect gear shift rod at housing rod yoke. Disconnect and remove shift lever housing rod retaining bolt. Disconnect and remove back-up light wiring connector.

5) On both models, disconnect speedometer cable at transaxle housing. Support transaxle on jack. Remove lower transaxle-to-engine mounting bolts. Disconnect ground wire.

6) Remove engine rear support member and lower transaxle assembly out from under vehicle. Place a 1.2" (30 mm) block of wood between crossmember and oil pan to support engine for installation of transaxle assembly.

INSTALLATION (ALL MODELS)

To install transaxle assembly, reverse removal procedure. Install all drain plugs and fill transaxle assembly with gear oil (SAE 90 GL-5 or SAE 80W-90).

VAN

REMOVAL

1) Disconnect battery cable. Raise and support vehicle. Drain gear oil from transmission and transfer cases. Disconnect the drive shaft.

2) Disconnect select cable from select outer lever. Remove clip and select cable. Disconnect shift cable from shift outer lever. Remove clip and shift cable.**3)** Remove clutch release cylinder. Disconnect starter wires. Remove starter bolts and starter. Disconnect bond and speedometer cable. Disconnect back-up light switch connector.

4) Remove exhaust pipe clamp and bracket. Remove stiffener plate. With hydraulic jack, raise transmission to remove the weight from rear support. Remove engine rear mount and bracket.

5) Remove transmission mounting bolts. Remove transmission. Pull out transmission down and to the rear.

INSTALLATION

To install, reverse removal procedure. Lightly grease friction surfaces. Ensure that splines on input shaft align with those in clutch disc. Refill transmission lubricant.

VOLKSWAGEN

QUANTUM

REMOVAL

1) Disconnect battery ground strap. Disconnect exhaust pipe from transaxle bracket and engine. Remove square bolt and press shifter coupling from rear of transaxle shifting shaft. Unhook clutch cable and disconnect speedometer.

2) Disconnect CV joints at inner drive flanges. Support axle shafts from vehicle with wire. Remove starter, front mounting plate and transaxle mounting bolts. Disconnect back-up light switch connector. Support transaxle on floor jack and remove crossmember mount. Remove transaxle from engine and lower from vehicle.

INSTALLATION

1) Install crossmember to transaxle. Raise transaxle up to vehicle and install crossmember bolts finger tight. Slide transaxle up to engine and install mounting bolts. Install front mounting plate and starter. Install inner CV joint mounting bolts into CV joint and drive flange. Tighten crossmember mounting bolts.

2) Install shift rod coupling bolt and lock with safety wire. Connect exhaust pipe, allowing 3/8" (10 mm) clearance between pipe and floor. Reconnect all wires, cables and linkages that were removed during removal procedure.

NOTE: **Always use longer hex head bolt when replacing shift rod coupling instead of original square head bolt. Secure with safety wire.**

JETTA, RABBIT, & SCIROCCO

REMOVAL

1) Disconnect negative battery cable. Install engine support bar. Remove 3 transmission mount bolts located on left side of vehicle near battery. Disconnect speedometer cable from case and plug opening. Remove upper transaxle-to-engine bolts, electrical connection at back-up light switch and clutch cable. Remove shift linkage parts from relay lever on transaxle and rod lever.

2) Disconnect ground strap from transaxle. Remove starter and 2 engine-to-transaxle bolts on either side of starter opening. Remove exhaust pipe bracket from bottom of transaxle. Place floor jack with adapter under transaxle and raise until transaxle is supported. Remove rear transaxle mount and bracket.

3) Disconnect both axle drive shafts from drive flanges and wire up out of the way. Remove bolts attaching cover plates to transaxle. Remove small cover plate, then remove remaining transaxle-to-engine bolts and nuts. Lower transaxle and remove from under vehicle.

INSTALLATION
Reverse removal procedure to install. Fill with lubricant and adjust shift linkage.

VANAGON
REMOVAL
1) Disconnect negative battery cable. Remove upper right transmission-to-engine bolt. Disconnect clutch hydraulic line from transmission case, then remove clutch slave cylinder from bracket and suspend out of way with wire.

4-SPEED
REMOVAL
1) Disconnect battery ground cable. From under vehicle, disconnect gearshift lever from rod by removing lock bolt and pressing out pivot pin.

2) Working inside vehicle, lift shift lever boot and remove left side of center console. Disconnect back-up light and overdrive connectors (if equipped) and remove reverse detent plate. Remove lock ring and lift out gearshift lever. Remove plastic bushing and rubber ring.

3) From under vehicle, remove crossmember at rear of transmission and disconnect clutch fork return spring and release cable. Disconnect speedometer cable and unbolt propeller shaft from drive flange. Remove exhaust pipe attachment to clutch housing and unhook rubber supports for front muffler.

4) Remove starter from engine and take out all except 2 bottom bolts holding clutch housing to engine. Attach transmission jack and support transmission. Remove 2 bottom bolts and pull transmission to rear, turning slightly to clear tunnel while separating from vehicle.

INSTALLATION
To install, reverse removal procedure.

NOTE: Do not disconnect hydraulic line from slave cylinder.

2) Remove upper left, then lower left transmission-to-engine bolts. Remove the bolts from left axle shaft, remove axle shaft from transmission and suspend with wire. Disconnect starter cables. Remove the bolts from right axle shaft, remove axle shaft from transmission and suspend with wire.

3) Remove lower right transmission-to-engine nut. Support engine. Disconnect back-up light wires, shift linkage and ground strap from transmission. Remove front transmission support-to-body bolts and support transmission. Separate transmission from engine and remove transmission.

INSTALLATION
To install transmission, reverse removal procedures and note the following: Clean and lubricate splines with grease. Make sure air deflector plates are positioned correctly. Make sure engine compartment seals are not damaged or missing.

VOLVO

Drive Axles

GEAR TOOTH CONTACT PATTERNS

INSPECTION

PRELIMINARY INSPECTION

Wipe lubricant from internal parts. Rotate gears, and inspect for wear or damage. Mount dial indicator to housing, and check backlash at several points around ring gear. Backlash must be within specifications at all points. If no defects are found, check gear tooth contact pattern.

GEAR TOOTH CONTACT PATTERN

NOTE: **Drive pattern should be well centered on ring gear teeth. Coast pattern should be centered, but may be slightly toward toe of ring gear teeth.**

1) Paint ring gear teeth with marking compound. Wrap cloth or rope around drive pinion flange to act as brake. Rotate ring gear until clear tooth contact pattern is obtained.

2) Contact pattern will indicate whether correct pinion bearing mounting shim has been installed and if drive gear backlash has been set properly. Backlash between drive gear and pinion must be maintained within specified limits, until correct tooth pattern is obtained.

ADJUSTMENTS

GEAR BACKLASH & PINION SHIM CHANGES

NOTE: **Backlash is adjusted by either shifting shims from 1 side of differential case to other or by turning adjusting nuts on which differential side bearings ride. Changing pinion shims changes distance from face of pinion to centerline of ring gear.**

1) With no change in backlash, moving pinion further from ring gear moves drive pattern toward heel and top of tooth, and moves coast pattern toward toe and top of tooth.

2) With no change in backlash, moving pinion closer to ring gear moves drive pattern toward toe and bottom of tooth, and moves coast pattern toward heel and bottom of tooth.

3) With no change in pinion shim thickness, an increase in backlash moves ring gear further from pinion. Drive pattern moves toward heel and top of tooth, and coast pattern moves toward heel and top of tooth.

4) With no change in pinion shim thickness, decrease in backlash moves ring gear closer to pinion gear. Drive pattern moves toward toe and bottom of tooth, and coast pattern moves toward toe and bottom of tooth.

Fig. 1: Drive Axle Gear Tooth Pattern

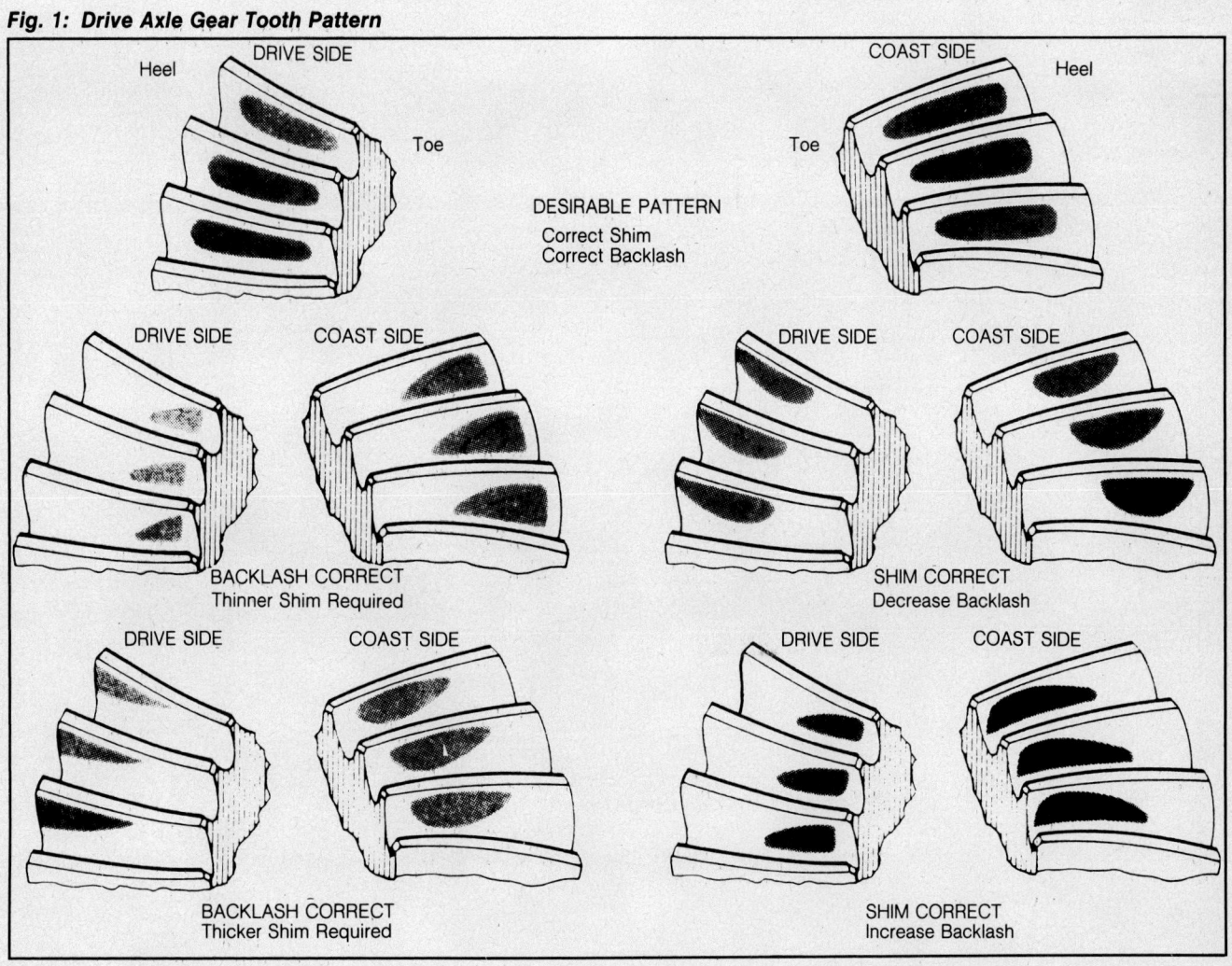

SECTION 6

IMPORT AUTOMATIC TRANSMISSIONS

NOTE: **ALSO SEE GENERAL INDEX.**

Automatic Transmissions

AISIN-WARNER 55, 70, 71 & BORG-WARNER 55

Isuzu I-Mark, Impulse, P'UP
Volvo DL, GL, Turbo, 760 GLE

TRANSMISSION IDENTIFICATION

Transmissions are manufactured by either Aisin-Warner (AW) or Borg-Warner (BW). Units are interchangeable with exception of oil cooler pipes, which must be changed to match particular unit installed.

Transmissions may be identified by plate attached to left side of transmission case. Plate shows manufacturer (AW or BW), transmission model number, and transmission serial number.

DESCRIPTION

AW 55 and BW 55 transmissions are fully automatic 3-speed units consisting of 3-element torque converter, compound planetary gear set, 2 multiple-disc clutches, 2 one-way roller clutches, and 3 multiple-disc brakes. Clutches may use either single or multiple piston return springs.

AW 70 and AW 71 transmissions are fully automatic 4-speed units consisting of 3-element torque converter, compound planetary gear set, 3 multiple-disc clutches, 3 one-way roller clutches, and 4 multiple-disc brakes.

Hydraulic system, pressurized by gear type pump, provides working pressure required to operate automatic controls. Valve bodies will vary in different models.

AW 70 and 71 transmissions are equipped with overdrive. Overdrive is automatically engaged in 3rd gear direct drive and gives drive ratio of 0.69:1. Overdrive will not operate in kickdown 3rd gear (throttle open more than 85%).

Overdrive can be manually disengaged by depressing button on shift lever. This will illuminate "OD OFF" warning lamp on instrument panel and remove power from relay to overdrive solenoid on transmission. Relay automatically resets and returns transmission to overdrive mode when ignition is turned off.

LUBRICATION & ADJUSTMENT

See appropriate AUTOMATIC TRANSMISSION SERVICING article in IMPORT GENERAL SERVICING section.

TROUBLE SHOOTING

NOTE: **Most transmission problems will show up in one or more of following tests: Check for proper fluid level, gear selector adjustment, throttle cable adjustment, line pressure, stall speed, or governor pressure. These tests show condition of most important transmission components and should be checked to determine proper repair for reported malfunction.**

NO MOVEMENT IN "D" OR SLIPS IN "D"

Low fluid level. Manual linkage out of adjustment. Faulty direct (rear) clutch, intermediate brake, one-way clutch for planetary gear set, forward (front) clutch, secondary regulator valve or valve body assembly.

NO MOVEMENT IN "R" OR SLIPS IN "R"

Low fluid level. Manual linkage out of adjustment. Faulty direct (rear) clutch, intermediate brake, oil pump, or valve body assembly. Line pressure too low.

NO MOVEMENT IN ANY RANGE

Low fluid level. Manual linkage out of adjustment. Parking pawl jammed or defective. Faulty torque converter, valve body assembly, or oil pump. Multiple unit damage. Shaft and or spline damage. Faulty forward clutch.

Fig. 1: Mechanical System Schematic for AW 71 & BW 55 Transmissions

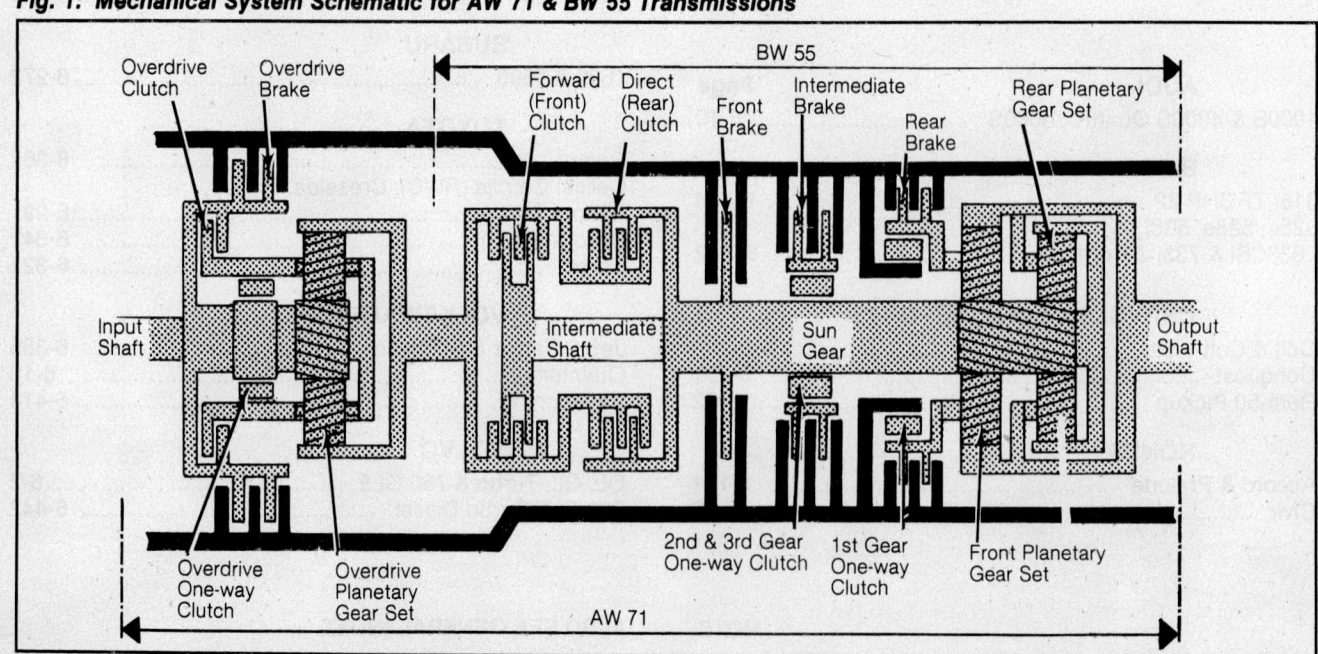

Note additional elements of overdrive portion for AW 71.

HARSH SHIFT FROM "N" TO "D" OR "R"

Manual linkage out of adjustment. Accumulator pistons for forward (front) or direct (rear) clutch seized or leaking. Defective valve bodies or accumulator pistons.

HARSH "1-2" OR "2-1" SHIFT

Second speed brake accumulator piston seized or leaking. Intermediate coast shift valve seized. Governor valve or 1-2 shift valve stuck.

HARSH "2-3" OR "3-2" SHIFT

Direct (rear) clutch accumulator piston seized or leaking. Defective governor valve body assembly. Check intermediate coast modulator valve. Governor valve or 2-3 shift valve stuck.

SLIP ON "1-2" UPSHIFT

Intermediate coast shift valve seized, thereby not engaging No. 1 brake. Defective No. 1 brake. Defective No. 2 brake. Center support one-way clutch defective.

SLIP ON "2-3" UPSHIFT

Defective direct (rear) clutch or its oil circuit. Faulty valve body assembly (2-3 shift valve, etc.).

NO ENGINE BRAKING IN "1"

Defective No. 3 brake. Low coast modulator valve seized or low coast valve frozen in top position.

NO ENGINE BRAKING IN "2"

No. 1 brake or its oil circuit defective. Intermediate coast modulator valve seized.

NO "2-1" SHIFT IN "1"

Defective No. 3 brake. Low coast modulator valve or low coast shift valve seized.

VEHICLE STARTS OUT IN "2" OR "3"

Governor pressure inaccurate (should be 0 with vehicle stationary). Defective valve body assembly, 1-2 throttle valve, 2-3 shift valve, primary throttle valve or primary regulator valve.

TRANSMISSION NOISE

Growling On Acceleration

Low fluid level, clogged oil filter or worn oil pump. Defective torque converter. Broken gears. Worn bushings.

NOTE: If torque converter is replaced, oil cooler and lines must be cleaned.

Gear Noise

Torque converter-to-drive plate bolts loose. Faulty coupling of one-way clutches. Faulty planetary gear sets. Worn thrust needle bearings or bushings. Partially engaged park pawl.

Whining or Humming Noise

Defective torque converter (noise may disappear in "N"). Defective oil pump (noise varies with engine speed). Low fluid level.

TESTING

ROAD TEST

1) Before road testing, ensure fluid level and condition are okay. Control linkage adjustments have been checked and corrected as necessary. During test, transmission should upshift and downshift at speed shown in SHIFT SPEED SPECIFICATIONS chart.

2) All shifts may vary somewhat due to production tolerances or tire size. Important factor is quality of shifts. All shifts should be smooth, responsive, and with no slippage or engine speed runaway.

3) Slippage or engine runaway in any gear usually indicates clutch or brake problems. Slipping unit in particular gear can usually be identified by noting transmission operation in other selector positions and comparing which internal units are applied in those positions. See CLUTCH & BRAKE APPLICATION chart.

4) This process of elimination can be used to detect any unit which slips, and to confirm proper operation of good units; however, actual cause of malfunction usually cannot be easily decided.

5) Almost any condition can be caused by leaking hydraulic circuits or sticking valves. Therefore, unless obvious condition exists, do not disassemble transmission until hydraulic pressure tests have been made.

STALL SPEED TEST

CAUTION: Before making stall speed test, ensure that line pressure is correct. If line pressure is too low when performing stall test, transmission can be damaged. During stall test, do not hold throttle open for more than 5 seconds at time. Return transmission to neutral between stall speed tests to allow for cooling of ATF.

Stall Test Procedure

1) Road test vehicle and warm transmission to normal operating temperature. Connect tachometer to engine. Position tachometer so that it can be read from driver's seat.

2) Set parking and service brakes. Start engine and place selector lever in "D". Depress accelerator pedal completely and note maximum RPM obtained. RPM should be approximately as shown in STALL SPEED SPECIFICATIONS chart.

3) Place selector lever in "N" and allow engine to idle to cool off transmission. Then, place selector lever in "R" and repeat stall test. Stall RPM should be approximately as shown in STALL SPEED SPECIFICATIONS chart.

Stall Test Results

1) If stall test RPM is about 600 RPM lower than specifications, torque converter one-way clutch is slipping and torque converter should be replaced. If stall RPM is about 300 RPM lower than specifications, engine performance may be unsatisfactory.

2) If stall test RPM is about 300 RPM above specifications in "R", direct (rear) clutch or 1st-Reverse brake is slipping. If RPM is about 300 RPM above specifications in "D", forward (front) clutch or rear one-way clutch is slipping.

3) If stall speed is about 300 RPM above specifications, and no clutch or brake is slipping, fluid level is incorrect, line pressure is too low or valve body oil strainer is clogged.

6-4

Automatic Transmissions
AISIN-WARNER 55, 70, 71 & BORG-WARNER 55 (Cont.)

CLUTCH AND BAND APPLICATION (ELEMENTS IN USE)

Selector Lever Position	Forward (Front) Clutch	Direct (Rear) Clutch	Overdrive (OD) Clutch (70 & 71 Only)	Planetary Gear	Brake	One-Way Clutch	Overdrive Brake (70 & 71 Only)
D – DRIVE							
First	Applied		Applied	Both	No. 2	Rear/OD	
Second	Applied		Applied	Rear	No. 2	Front/OD	
Third	Applied	Applied	Applied	Direct [1]	No. 2	OD	
Overdrive (70 & 71 Only)	Applied	Applied		Direct/OD	No. 2		Applied
2 – SECOND							
First	Applied		Applied	Both		Rear/OD	
Second	Applied		Applied	Rear	No. 1 & No. 2	Front/OD	
1 – LOW	Applied		Applied	Both	No. 3	Rear/OD	
R – REVERSE		Applied	Applied	Front	No. 3	OD	
P – PARK			Applied [2]		No. 3 [2]		
N – NEUTRAL			Applied				

[1] – Direct means planetary gear set is locked up with 1:1 ratio.
[2] – With engine running.

STALL SPEED SPECIFICATIONS

Application	[1] Stall Speed (RPM)
Isuzu	
Impulse	2000-2300
I-Mark	
Gas Engine	1700-2000
Diesel Engine	1900-2200
P'UP	
Gas Engine	1950-2250
Diesel Engine	1900-2200
Volvo	
DL & GL	
Gas Engine	2250
Diesel Engine	2200
Turbo	2050-2500
760 GLE	
Gas Engine	2000 min.
Diesel Engine	2200-2700

[1] – Speed measured at sea level. Stall speed will drop 120 RPM for each 3200 ft. of elevation.

LINE PRESSURE TEST

1) Road test vehicle to bring transmission to normal operating temperature. Connect pressure gauge to front plug on transmission. *See Fig. 2.* Place gauge so that it is visible from driver's seat. Connect tachometer to engine.

2) Start engine and if necessary, adjust idle speed to 900 RPM (1000 RPM on I-Mark). Depress brake pedal and place selector lever in "D". Note line pressure reading on gauge. Pressure should be approximately as shown in LINE PRESSURE SPECIFICATIONS chart.

3) Repeat line pressure test with selector lever in "R". Pressure should be approximately as shown in LINE PRESSURE SPECIFICATIONS chart.

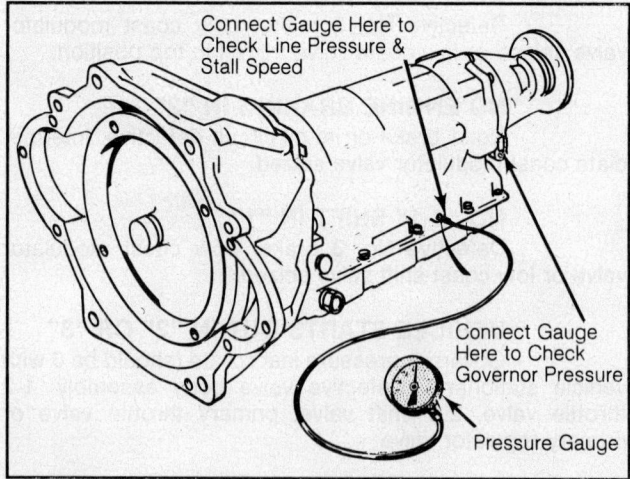

Fig. 2: Transmission Case Pressure Test Port Locations

Connect Gauge Here to Check Line Pressure & Stall Speed

Connect Gauge Here to Check Governor Pressure

Pressure Gauge

Test port locations apply to all transmissions.

LINE PRESSURE SPECIFICATIONS

Application	psi (kg/cm²)
AW 55	
In "D"	57-64 (4.0-4.5)
In "R"	82-97 (5.8-6.8)
AW 70 & 71	
In "D"	65-77 (4.6-5.4)
In "R"	108-117 (7.6-8.2)
BW 55	
In "D"	75-90 (5.3-6.3)
In "R"	104-129 (7.3-9.1)

LINE PRESSURE TEST RESULTS

Pressure Too High

If pressure is too high, check throttle cable adjustment. If cable is correctly adjusted and pressure is still high, primary regulator valve or throttle valve may be seized.

SHIFT SPEED SPECIFICATIONS [1]

Application	MPH
Isuzu	
I-Mark [5]	
Gas Engine	
1-2 Upshift	36-43
2-3 Upshift	67-73
3-2 Downshift	60-67
3-1 or 2-1 Downshift	22-29
Diesel Engine	
1-2 Upshift	29-35
2-3 Upshift	53-58
3-2 Downshift	49-55
3-1 or 2-1 Downshift	20-25
P'UP [5]	
Gas Engine	
1-2 Upshift	31-37
2-3 Upshift	58-64
3-2 Downshift	55-61
3-1 or 2-1 Downshift	24-30
Diesel Engine	
1-2 Upshift	23-29
2-3 Upshift	46-53
3-2 Downshift	40-46
3-1 or 2-1 Downshift	16-23
Volvo	
DL & GL	
Gas Engine [2]	
1-2 Upshift	40
2-3 Upshift	67
3-4 Upshift (3/4 Throttle)	70
4-3 Downshift (Coasting)	25
3-2 Downshift	64
2-1 Downshift	32
Diesel Engine [3]	
1-2 Upshift	36
2-3 Upshift	66
3-2 Downshift	61
3-1 Downshift	31
Turbo [4]	
1-2 Upshift	37
2-3 Upshift	62
3-4 Upshift (3/4 Throttle)	65
4-3 Downshift (Coasting)	23
3-2 Downshift	58
2-1 Downshift	30
760 GLE	
Gas Engine [4]	
1-2 Upshift	42
2-3 Upshift	70
3-4 Upshift (3/4 Throttle)	74
4-3 Downshift (Coasting)	18
3-2 Downshift	66
2-1 Downshift	33
Diesel Engine [3]	
1-2 Upshift	38
2-3 Upshift	69
3-2 Downshift	63
3-1 Downshift	38

[1] – At full throttle (kick-down) unless otherwise noted.
[2] – AW 70.
[3] – BW 55.
[4] – AW 71.
[5] – AW 55.

Pressure Too Low

If line pressure is too low, check for seizing of primary regulator valve or throttle valve in valve body. If valves are not seized, check pressure relief valve and oil pump assembly for damage. Defective oil pump assembly will usually make noise.

GOVERNOR PRESSURE TEST

NOTE: Governor pressure is "modified" line pressure. Therefore, governor pressure will be incorrect if line pressure is incorrect. Line pressure must be correct before checking governor pressure.

Testing Procedures

Road test vehicle to warm transmission to normal operating temperature. Connect pressure gauge to rear pressure port on transmission case. See Fig. 2. Position gauge so it is visible from driver's seat. Test drive vehicle in "D" and note pressure readings. Pressures should be about as shown in GOVERNOR PRESSURE SPECIFICATIONS chart.

SERVICE (IN VEHICLE)

NOTE: Following units can be replaced without removing transmission from vehicle: Oil Pan, Valve Body Assembly, Accumulator Pistons, Parking Pawl, Rear Extension Housing and Oil Seal, Speedometer Driven Gear, Overdrive Solenoid (AW 70 & 71 models only) and Governor Body. See procedures given in TRANSMISSION DISASSEMBLY and TRANSMISSION REASSEMBLY in this article.

REMOVAL & INSTALLATION

See appropriate AUTOMATIC TRANSMISSION REMOVAL article in IMPORT GENERAL SERVICING section.

TORQUE CONVERTER

NOTE: Torque converter is sealed unit and cannot be disassembled for service. Replace if found defective.

TRANSMISSION DISASSEMBLY

CAUTION: All Isuzu models use Dexron II ATF. All Volvo models except those using BW 55 transmission use Dexron II ATF. Volvo models using BW 55 transmission use Type "F" ATF. Use only specified ATF. Damage to friction linings may occur if incorrect type of ATF is used.

1) Clean outside of transmission thoroughly before disassembly to prevent dirt or foreign material from entering transmission. Pull torque converter from transmission. Place transmission in holding fixture.

2) Remove 6 converter housing-to-transmission case bolts. Separate converter housing from case. Remove speedometer driven gear assembly retaining bolt. Using screwdriver, pry speedometer driven gear assembly from case.

GOVERNOR PRESSURE SPECIFICATIONS

Vehicle Speed	psi (kg/cm²)
Isuzu	
I-Mark	
Gas Engine	
19 MPH	13-21 (0.9-1.5)
39 MPH	23-33 (1.6-2.3)
68 MPH	58-75 (4.1-5.3)
Diesel Engine	
18 MPH	14-23 (1.0-1.6)
37 MPH	33-43 (2.3-3.0)
64 MPH	64-81 (4.5-5.7)
P'UP	
Gas Engine	
19 MPH	13-21 (0.9-1.5)
39 MPH	23-33 (1.6-2.3)
68 MPH	58-75 (4.1-5.3)
Diesel Engine	
17 MPH	17-26 (1.2-1.8)
35 MPH	37-47 (2.6-3.3)
61 MPH	67-84 (4.7-5.9)
Volvo	
DL & GL	
Gas Engine	
19 MPH	14-18 (1.0-1.3)
37 MPH	21-27 (1.5-1.9)
68 MPH	37-65 (3.6-4.6)
Diesel Engine	
19 MPH	16-20 (1.1-1.4)
37 MPH	26-31 (1.8-2.2)
68 MPH	53-61 (3.8-4.3)
Turbo	
19 MPH	13-21 (0.9-1.5)
31 MPH	23-31 (1.6-2.2)
62 MPH	59-75 (4.1-5.3)
760 GLE	
Gas Engine	
21 MPH	15-24 (1.1-1.7)
33 MPH	24-33 (1.7-2.3)
66 MPH	54-71 (3.8-5.0)
Diesel Engine	
18 MPH	14-18 (1.0-1.3)
48 MPH	24-32 (1.7-2.2)
66 MPH	48-57 (3.4-4.0)

Fig. 3: Accumulator Pistons & Springs Removal

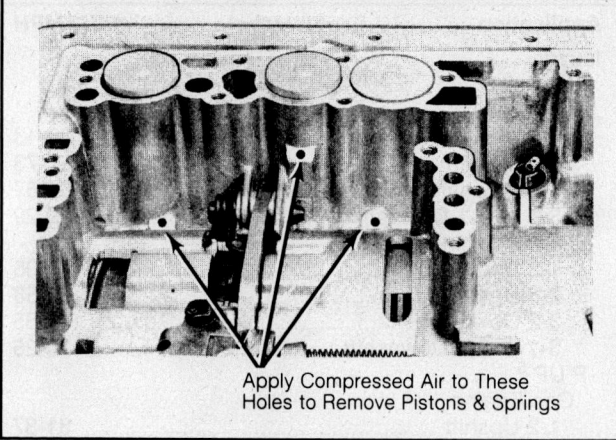

Apply Compressed Air to These Holes to Remove Pistons & Springs

Note spring position for reassembly as sizes vary.

mm socket. Invert transmission case so oil pump faces up. Remove oil pump attaching bolts. Using puller, remove oil pump assembly from case.

7) Hold input shaft with hand and pull forward (front) clutch assembly from case. Remove thrust bearing and race from clutch. Remove direct (rear) clutch bearing and race. Pull direct (rear) clutch assembly from case. Remove center support bolts. *See Fig. 4.* Lift center support assembly from case.

Fig. 4: Location of Center Support Attaching Bolts

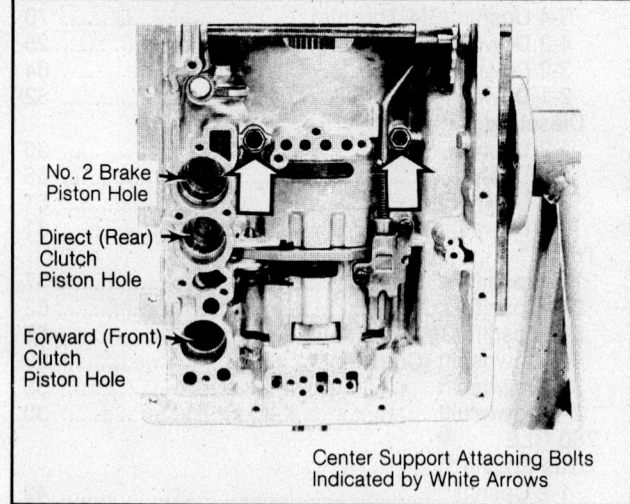

No. 2 Brake Piston Hole

Direct (Rear) Clutch Piston Hole

Forward (Front) Clutch Piston Hole

Center Support Attaching Bolts Indicated by White Arrows

Note positions for reassembly reference.

3) Hold output shaft drive flange stationary and remove flange bolt. Using puller, pull drive flange from output shaft. Remove extension housing-to-case bolts. Lift off extension housing.

4) If equipped, remove speedometer drive gear snap ring and slide gear and spacer ring from output shaft. If equipped, remove 2nd snap ring. Remove governor retaining clip and pull governor assembly off shaft.

5) Remove oil pan and gasket. Invert transmission. Remove attaching bolts and lift oil strainer and particle magnet from transmission case. Remove valve body-to-case bolts. Carefully lift valve body and disconnect throttle cable from valve body cam. Lift valve body assembly from case.

6) Apply low pressure, 14 psi (.98 kg/cm²), compressed air to holes under accumulator pistons to force pistons from case bores. *See Fig. 3.* Remove pistons and springs. Press out plastic throttle cable sheath, using 10

8) Remove No. 3 brake snap ring from groove in case. Lift No. 3 brake disc pack and planetary gear assembly from case as unit. Remove brake apply tube (shell), thrust bearing and races from transmission case.

9) Turn transmission so rear face of case is up. Remove governor oil duct cover screws and cover from case. Noting position for reassembly reference, remove oil cooler line nipples from case. Remove plugs from governor and line pressure ports.

10) Turn transmission so oil pan attaching surface is up. Remove parking pawl rod plate bolts. Remove plate and rod. Using drift, drive detent lever lock pin out of lever and shaft. Pull shaft out of lever and case. Lift up

parking pawl, press out shaft and spring, then lift parking pawl from case. Pry shaft oil seals out of case.

COMPONENT DISASSEMBLY & REASSEMBLY

OIL PUMP ASSEMBLY

CAUTION: **Do not use punch to make matching marks on oil pump gears. High spots in metal may occur and cause binding when pump is reassembled. Make marks with paint or pen.**

Disassembly

Remove 2 oil seal rings from pump cover. Remove cover bolts and separate cover from pump housing. Remove large "O" ring from housing. Mark pump drive and driven gears for reassembly in same position. Remove gears from pump housing. Pry oil seal from housing.

Fig. 5: Exploded View of Oil Pump Assembly

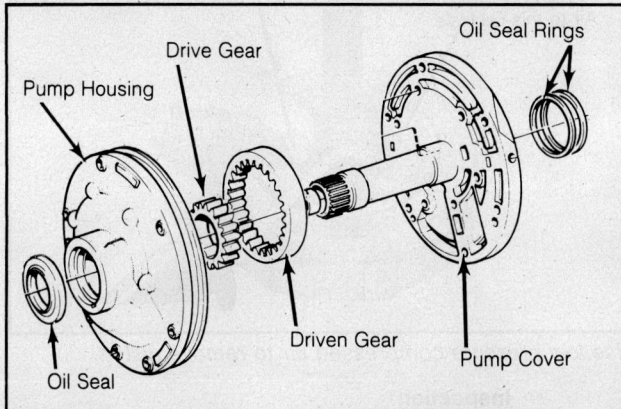

Mark gears with paint for reassembly reference. DO NOT use punch for markings.

Inspection

Clean all parts thoroughly and dry with compressed air. Inspect all parts for wear, cracks, or scoring. If pump housing, cover, drive gear or driven gear requires replacement, complete oil pump assembly must be replaced as unit.

Reassembly

1) Install drive and driven gear into housing, aligning marks made during disassembly. Measure clearance between driven (outer) gear and pump housing with feeler gauge. Clearance should be .003-.006" (.07-.15 mm) for AW models and .003-.012" (.07-.30 mm) for BW models. Replace oil pump assembly if clearance is excessive.

2) Check clearance between driven (outer) gear teeth and crescent. Clearance should be .004-.006" (.11-.14 mm) for AW models and .004-.020" (.11-.50 mm) for BW models. Replace oil pump if clearance is excessive.

3) Using straightedge and feeler gauge, check pump housing face-to-gear face clearance. Clearance should be .0008-.0020" (.020-.050 mm) for AW models and .0008-.0040" (.020-.100 mm) for BW models. Replace oil pump assembly if clearance is excessive.

4) Lubricate all parts with ATF. Press new oil seal into pump housing. Assemble pump cover to housing, then install bolts finger tight. Fit Centering Clamp (Isuzu J-25280 or Volvo 5077) around housing and cover. Tighten

centering clamp screw to align housing and cover. *See Fig. 7.*

Fig. 6: Measuring Housing-to-Gear Face Clearance

Use straightedge and feeler gauge.

Fig. 7: Aligning Oil Pump Housing & Cover

Bolts must be installed in cover finger tight.

5) Tighten bolts and remove centering clamp. Lubricate large "O" ring with ATF and install in groove on pump housing. Lubricate oil seal rings with petroleum jelly and install on pump cover.

OVERDRIVE CLUTCH ASSEMBLY
Disassembly

1) Remove snap ring and overdrive brake hub. Remove overdrive input shaft assembly and thrust washer. Remove overdrive clutch drum and clutch assembly.

2) Install clutch drum to the oil pump. Remove the clutch piston by blowing compressed air into oil pump from the oil port. Lift clutch plates and discs from drum. Note number and arrangement of plates and discs for reassembly reference.

3) Compress return spring retainer. Remove snap ring and lift out retainer and return spring(s). Remove snap ring, thrust washer, one-way clutch, one-way clutch race and thrust washer.

Inspection

1) Check the overdrive planetary gear pinion, clutch disc groove, snap ring groove and input shaft splines for wear or damage. Check one-way overdrive clutch sprag, ribbon spring and outer race for wear or damage.

Fig. 8: Exploded View of Overdrive Clutch Assembly

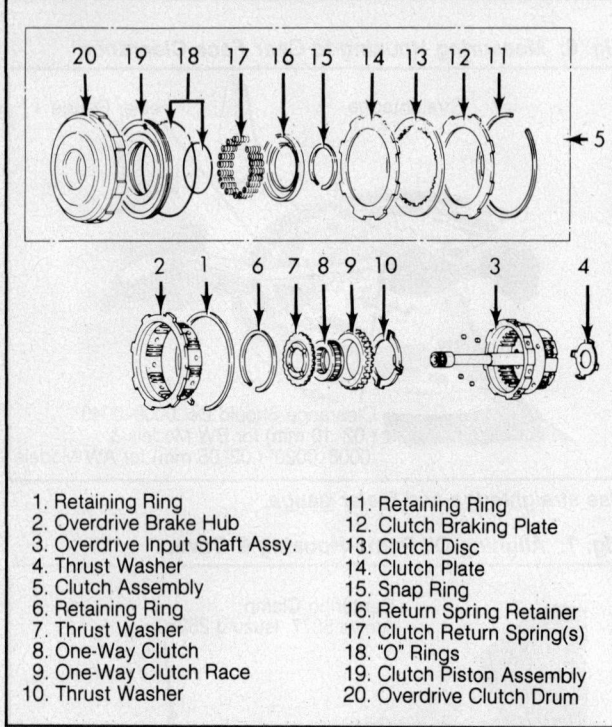

1. Retaining Ring
2. Overdrive Brake Hub
3. Overdrive Input Shaft Assy.
4. Thrust Washer
5. Clutch Assembly
6. Retaining Ring
7. Thrust Washer
8. One-Way Clutch
9. One-Way Clutch Race
10. Thrust Washer
11. Retaining Ring
12. Clutch Braking Plate
13. Clutch Disc
14. Clutch Plate
15. Snap Ring
16. Return Spring Retainer
17. Clutch Return Spring(s)
18. "O" Rings
19. Clutch Piston Assembly
20. Overdrive Clutch Drum

AW 70 & AW 71 models only.

2) Check overdrive clutch drum gear, pinion sliding face, thrust washer and one-way clutch fitting face, snap ring groove, bushing and oil seal sliding face for wear or damage.

3) Check clutch piston and springs for wear or damage. Clutch piston spring free length should be .571-.587" (14.5-14.9 mm). Inspect check ball for sticking by shaking the piston. Check for leakage by blowing compressed air into the oil port.

4) Check the overdrive brake hub clutch disc fitting face and drum fitting face for wear. Check thrust washers for excessive wear.

Reassembly
1) Assemble clutch piston, "O" rings and drum. Lubricate "O" rings with ATF before installing. Install clutch return springs, retainer and snap ring into clutch drum using Spring Compressor (J-25048).

2) Install clutch plates and discs in original order. Ensure flange is installed with the stepped face turned up. Install snap ring. Install brake hub and snap ring. Measure clutch clearance in the following manner: Install dial indicator so tip is resting on direct (rear) clutch hub lip.

3) Apply 57-114 psi (4-8 kg/cm²) compressed air and read dial indicator. Piston stroke should be .061-.090" (1.55-2.28 mm). If stroke exceeds specification, clutch pack is excessively worn. If stroke does not meet specification, clutch components have been incorrectly installed or too much ATF was applied to clutch plates and discs.

4) Remove dial indicator. Install bearing and race on input shaft. Install thrust washer, one-way clutch race, one-way clutch assembly, thrust washer and snap ring. Install clutch assembly, planetary gear assembly and thrust washer.

FORWARD (FRONT) CLUTCH ASSEMBLY
Disassembly
1) Remove bearing and race from input shaft. Remove snap ring and lift direct (rear) clutch hub from clutch assembly. Pull forward (front) clutch hub from clutch drum, then remove bearing and races.

2) Lift clutch plates and discs from drum. Note number and arrangement of plates and discs for reassembly reference. Compress return spring retainer. Remove snap ring and lift out retainer and return spring(s).

3) Position clutch drum with input shaft facing up. Apply low pressure compressed air to 1 oil hole on inside of drum. Cover other hole with finger and force piston from drum. *See Fig. 9.* Remove and discard "O" rings from clutch piston.

Fig. 9: Forward (Front) Clutch Piston Removal

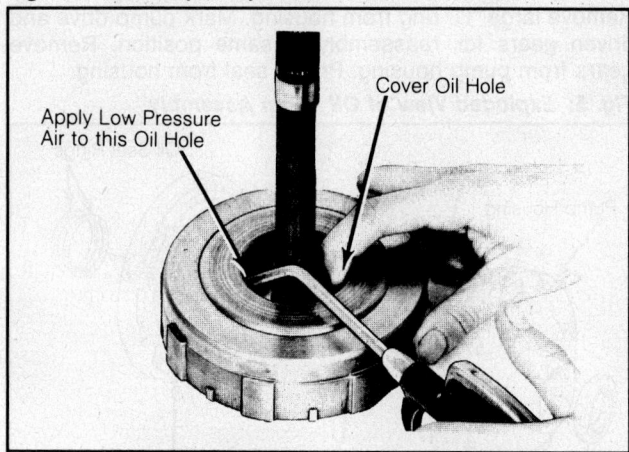

Apply Low Pressure Air to this Oil Hole

Cover Oil Hole

Use low pressure compressed air to remove piston.

Inspection
1) Clean all parts (except discs) with clean solvent and dry with compressed air. Inspect clutch plates and discs to ensure they are flat with no burns or cracks.

2) Minimum thickness of discs is .08" (2.1 mm). Inspect all other parts for wear or damage. Check clutch piston to ensure check ball is not stuck. Replace defective or worn parts.

Reassembly
1) Coat all friction surfaces with ATF. Install new "O" rings on clutch piston. Install piston into clutch drum with check valve toward input shaft end. Install return spring(s) and retainer.

2) Using compressor, compress return spring retainer and install snap ring. Remove compressor. Install clutch plates and discs into clutch drum. Alternate plates and discs until they are installed in same positions and amounts as found during disassembly.

3) Install bearing and races onto top of return spring retainer. Install forward (front) clutch hub and ensure hub meshes with all clutch discs. Install direct (rear) clutch hub and snap ring. Ensure snap ring fits properly in groove and that ends are not near groove which holds clutch plate lug.

4) On Isuzu applications of AW 55 model, install dial indicator so tip is resting on direct (rear) clutch hub lip. Apply compressed air and read dial indicator. Piston stroke should be .056-.092" (1.42-2.33 mm). Thin inner snap ring should be left out for this procedure.

Fig. 10: Exploded View of Forward (Front) Clutch Assembly

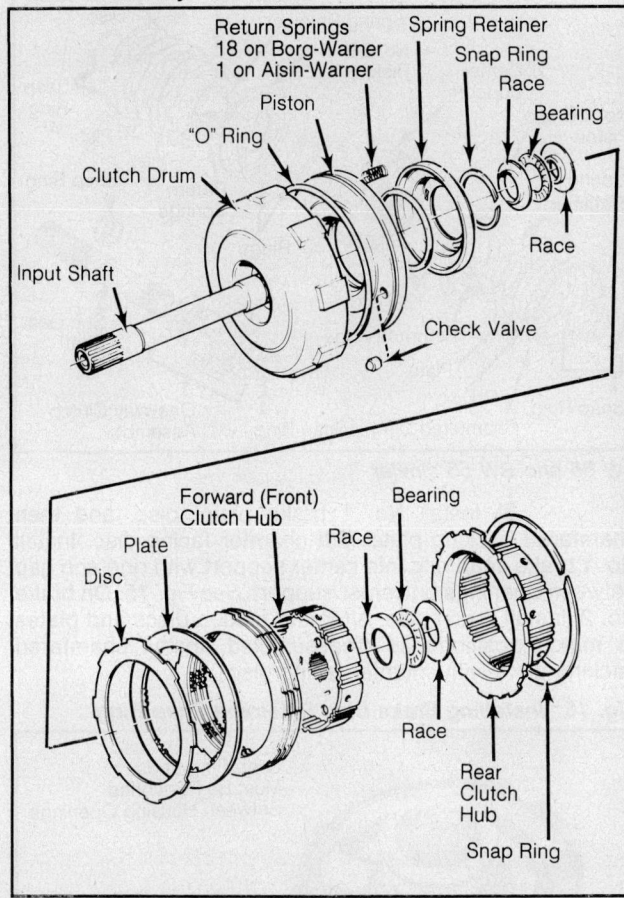

Clutch may use a single large piston return spring or 18 small piston return springs.

Fig. 11: Exploded View of Direct (Rear) Clutch Assembly

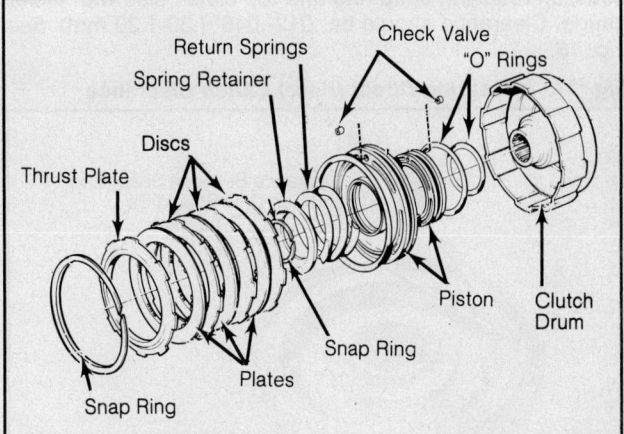

Single or multiple piston return springs may be used.

Fig. 12: Direct (Rear) Clutch Piston Removal from Drum

Apply Low Pressure Air Here While Covering Remaining Oil Hole

Use low pressure compressed air to remove piston.

5) On Volvo applications of BW and AW 55 models, check operation of piston by applying low pressure compressed air to 1 oil hole while covering other. When air is applied, distinct "plop" should be heard as piston applies. Install bearing and race on input shaft.

6) If stroke exceeds specification, clutch pack is excessively worn. If stroke does not meet specification, clutch components have been incorrectly installed or too much ATF was applied to clutch plates and discs. Remove dial indicator. Install bearing and race on input shaft.

DIRECT (REAR) CLUTCH ASSEMBLY
Disassembly
1) Using screwdriver, remove clutch disc pack snap ring. Lift out backing plate, clutch discs and plates. Note number and arrangement of discs and plates for reassembly reference.

2) Using compressor, compress return spring retainer. Remove snap ring. Remove compressor. Lift retainer and clutch return spring(s) from drum.

3) Apply low pressure compressed air to 1 oil hole in clutch drum while covering other oil hole. *See Fig. 12.* Force piston from drum. Remove "O" rings from piston.

Inspection
Clean all parts (except plates and discs) in clean solvent and dry with compressed air. Inspect clutch discs for signs of burning and wear. Check thickness of clutch discs. Minimum thickness is .08" (2.1 mm). Inspect all other parts for wear or damage. Shake piston to ensure check ball is free. Replace any defective part.

Reassembly
1) Lubricate all friction surfaces with ATF. Lubricate and install new "O" rings on clutch piston. Install piston into drum. Install return spring(s) on piston and install retainer over spring(s). Compress spring retainer and install snap ring.

2) Install clutch plates and discs into clutch drum. Alternate plates and discs until number and position of plates and discs are installed as they were removed. Install backing plate with bevelled side facing discs and plates. Install clutch pack snap ring with ends away from groove in which clutch plate lug is installed.

3) On BW transmissions, check operation of piston by applying compressed air to 1 oil hole while blocking other. When air is applied, distinct "plop" should be heard as piston applies.

4) On Isuzu applications, install direct clutch assembly on center support. Install dial indicator so tip is resting on edge of backing plate. Apply compressed air and read dial indicator. Piston stroke should be .037-.067" (.93-1.70 mm).

6-10

Automatic Transmissions
AISIN-WARNER 55, 70, 71 & BORG-WARNER 55 (Cont.)

5) On Volvo applications, measure clearance between retaining snap ring and top clutch disc with feeler gauge. Clearance should be .012-.048" (.30-1.20 mm). *See Fig. 13.*

Fig. 13: Measuring Direct (Rear) Clutch Clearance

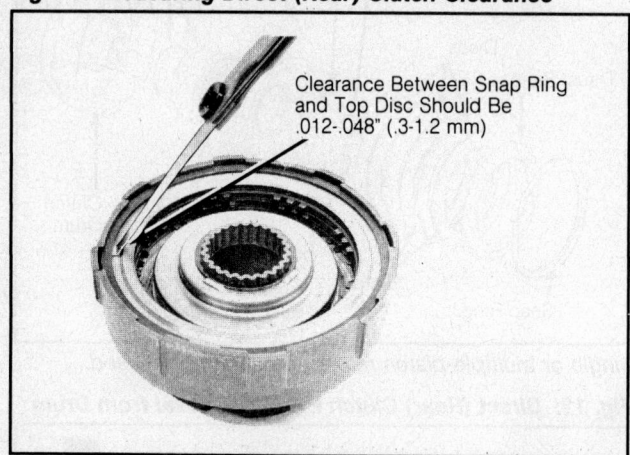

Clearance Between Snap Ring and Top Disc Should Be .012-.048" (.3-1.2 mm)

Measure between snap ring and top disc.

6) If stroke exceeds specification, clutch pack is excessively worn. If stroke is less than specification, clutch components have been incorrectly installed or too much ATF was applied to clutch plates and discs. Remove dial indicator and install bearing and race on input shaft.

CENTER SUPPORT ASSEMBLY
Disassembly

1) Remove snap ring from sun gear shaft. Pull center support from shaft. Remove snap ring for No. 1 brake. Remove discs and plates from center support. Note number and position of discs and plates for reassembly reference. Invert center support.

2) Remove snap ring for No. 2 brake. Remove discs and plates from center support. Using compressor, compress No. 2 brake return spring retainer and remove snap ring. Remove compressor and lift return springs and retainer from center support. Repeat procedure on No. 1 brake return springs.

3) Using compressed air, force No. 2 and No. 1 brake pistons from center support. Slide one-way clutch hub from sun gear shaft after noting direction of rotation. Remove 3 oil seal rings from center support hub and 2 oil seal rings from sun gear shaft. Remove "O" rings from brake pistons.

Inspection

Clean all parts (except discs) in clean solvent and dry with compressed air. Inspect all parts for wear or other damage and replace as necessary. Check thickness of all brake discs. Replace discs if thickness is less than .08" (2.1 mm).

Reassembly

1) Lubricate all moving parts with ATF. Install new oil seals and "O" rings on center support hub, sun gear shaft and brake piston. Lubricate "O" rings and install No. 2 brake piston into center support. Use care not to damage "O" rings.

2) Install return springs into position on piston, then place retainer onto return springs. Compress return springs and install snap ring. Repeat procedure for No. 1 brake piston.

Fig. 14: Exploded View of Center Support Assembly

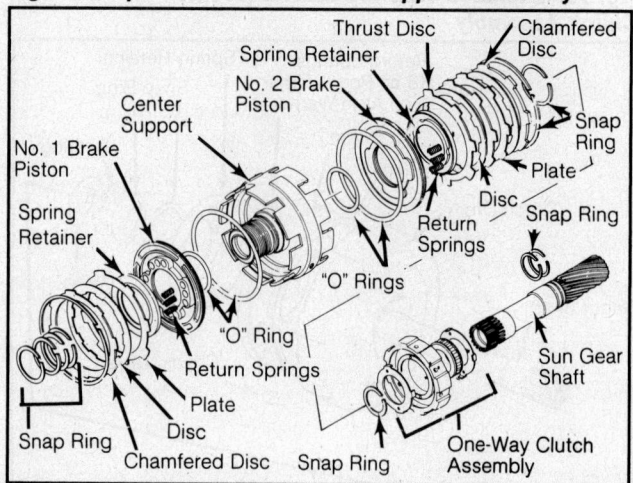

AW 55 and BW 55 similar.

3) Install No. 1 brake plate, disc, and then chamfered backing plate with chamfer facing disc. Install No. 1 brake snap ring into center support with ring end gap between openings on center support. *See Fig. 15.* On brake No. 2, install thrust disc. Alternate friction discs and plates to match positions as disassembled. Install chamfered backing plate with chamfer facing disc.

Fig. 15: Installing Brake Disc Retaining Snap Ring

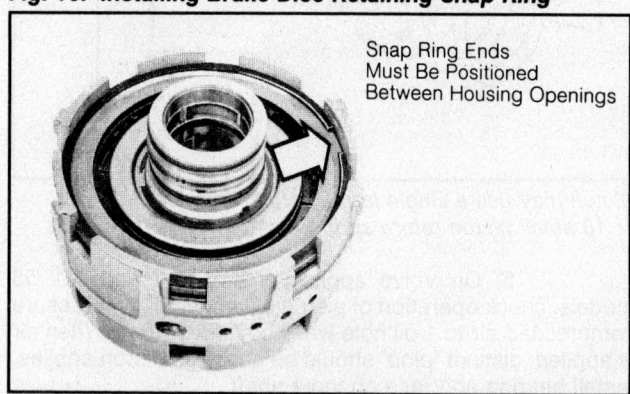

Snap Ring Ends Must Be Positioned Between Housing Openings

Note position of snap ring openings.

4) Install No. 2 brake snap ring. On Isuzu applications, install dial indicator so tip is resting on backing plate. Apply compressed air and record piston stroke as measured on dial indicator. Piston stroke should be .026-.051" (.65-1.30 mm) for No. 1 (front) brake and .037-.068" (.93-1.7 mm) for No. 2 (rear) brake.

5) In Volvo applications, BW 55 models use .055" (1.4 mm) snap ring on No. 2 brake while AW 55 models use .047" (1.2 mm) snap ring which has blue marking to identify it further. End clearance between snap rings and discs on both brakes should be .012-.048" (.30-1.20 mm). *See Fig. 16.*

6) Check operation of No. 1 and No. 2 brake pistons by applying compressed air to oil holes. When air is applied, distinct clicking should be heard as piston is activated. *See Fig. 17.*

7) If stroke exceeds specification, clutch pack is excessively worn. If stroke is less than specification, clutch components have been incorrectly installed or too much ATF was applied to clutch plates and discs.

Fig. 16: Measuring Center Support Brake Clearance

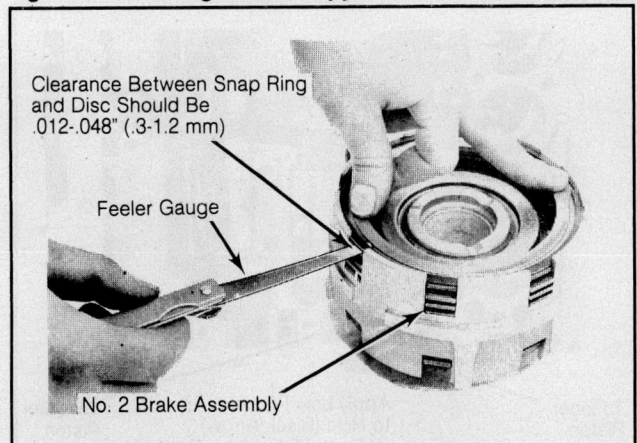

Measure between snap ring and top brake disc.

Fig. 17: Checking Brake Piston Operation

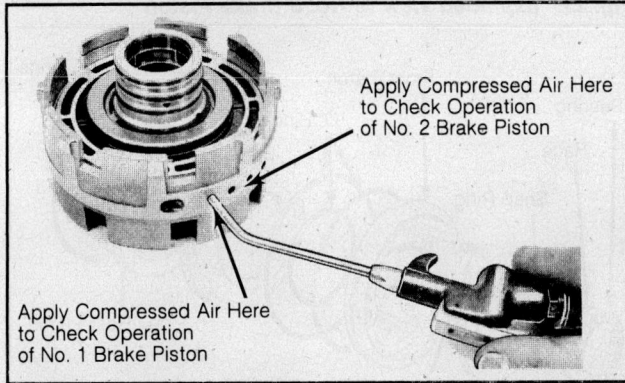

Apply compressed air as shown.

8) Install brake hub assembly on sun gear with cupped side facing splines of sun gear. Install one-way clutch on sun gear shaft. Check that one-way clutch is not loose or stiff when installed on shaft. Check one-way clutch by holding No. 2 brake hub and rotating sun gear. Sun gear should rotate counterclockwise but lock up if clockwise rotation is attempted.

9) Install one-way clutch and sun gear shaft into center support. Align grooves of brake hub with lugs on discs. Install snap ring on sun gear shaft in groove on splined portion of shaft.

PLANETARY GEAR ASSEMBLY
Disassembly

1) Separate front planetary gear set, one-way clutch, and No. 3 brake discs from output shaft assembly. Invert shaft assembly so that assembly is resting on output shaft. Compress snap ring and lift front planetary ring gear from assembly.

2) Pull intermediate shaft and rear planetary gear set from output shaft housing. Remove bearing and race from output shaft housing. Remove plastic and steel thrust washers from intermediate shaft. Pull rear planetary gear set from rear ring gear.

3) Remove bearing and race. Remove snap ring and slide rear ring gear from intermediate shaft. Slide rear bearing race from shaft. Remove oil seal rings from output shaft. Remove steel thrust plate from front planetary gear set.

4) Remove No. 3 brake discs and plates from around planetary gear set. Remove one-way clutch inner hub from front planetary gear set. Remove snap ring from one-way clutch. Remove both bearing cages, one-way clutch and plastic ring from gear set.

Fig. 18: Exploded View of Planetary Gear Set

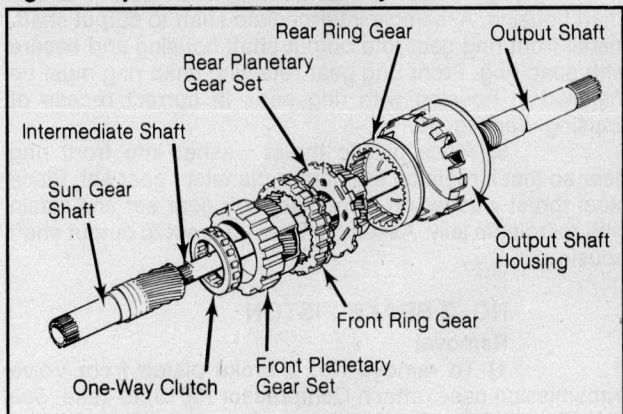

Note component position during disassembly.

Inspection

Clean all parts (except discs) with clean solvent and dry with compressed air. Inspect all parts for wear, cracks, or other damage and replace as necessary. Check thickness of each brake disc. Replace discs if thickness is less than .08" (2.1 mm).

Reassembly

1) Lubricate all moving parts with ATF. Install plastic ring and lower bearing cage into front planetary gear set. Install one-way clutch into gear set with arrow on side of clutch pointing down. Collar end of clutch should be up. Install one-way clutch upper bearing cage on top of clutch and retain with snap ring.

2) Install one-way clutch and front planetary gear set into front ring gear. With one-way clutch installed in front ring gear, front planetary gear set should rotate freely in counterclockwise direction. Front planetary gear set should be locked in clockwise direction. Assemble No. 3 brake discs to front planetary gear set.

Fig. 19: Installing Front Ring Gear Snap Ring

Snap ring ends must fit in correct housing recess.

3) Install new oil seal rings on output shaft and ensure that ring ends are properly hooked. Position rear race on intermediate shaft. Slide rear ring gear onto shaft. Secure with snap ring. Position bearing and front race on intermediate shaft in rear ring gear. Install rear planetary gear set into ring gear.

4) Position thrust bearing and race in output shaft housing. Assemble intermediate shaft to output shaft. Install front ring gear into output shaft housing and secure with snap ring. Front ring gear retaining snap ring must be installed in housing with ring ends in correct recess of housing. *See Fig. 19.*

5) Place plastic thrust washer into front ring gear so that it rests on top of rear planetary gear set. Place steel thrust washer on front planetary gear set and retain with petroleum jelly. Assemble front gear set to output shaft housing.

NO. 3 BRAKE PISTON
Removal
1) To remove No. 3 brake piston from Volvo transmission case, attach Compressor (5073) to case. *See Fig. 20.* Alternately tighten compressor bolts until snap ring on piston return spring retainer is free of tension. Isuzu uses Internal Compressor (J-25048). Using screwdriver, pry out snap ring. Remove compressor.

Fig. 20: Installing Volvo Compressor (5073)

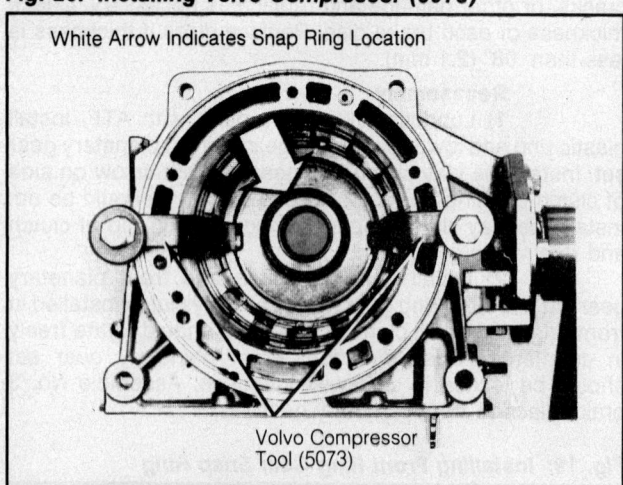

Isuzu uses internal compressor.

2) Lift return spring retainer and 16 return springs from transmission case. Turn transmission so front end is facing down. Apply compressed air to oil holes. *See Fig. 21.* Force pistons from seat in case and lift pistons out of case.

Disassembly & Reassembly
Pull front and rear pistons from piston sleeve. Remove "O" rings from pistons. Clean and inspect all parts and replace as necessary. Install new "O" rings on pistons. Coat all friction surfaces with ATF. Assemble front and rear pistons to piston sleeve.

Installation
1) Install piston assembly into transmission case using care not to damage "O" rings. Install return springs onto piston and use petroleum jelly to hold springs in place on pistons. Ensure springs are fitted vertically.

Fig. 21: Removing No. 3 Brake Piston

Use compressed air to force out pistons.

Fig. 22: Exploded View of No. 3 Brake Piston

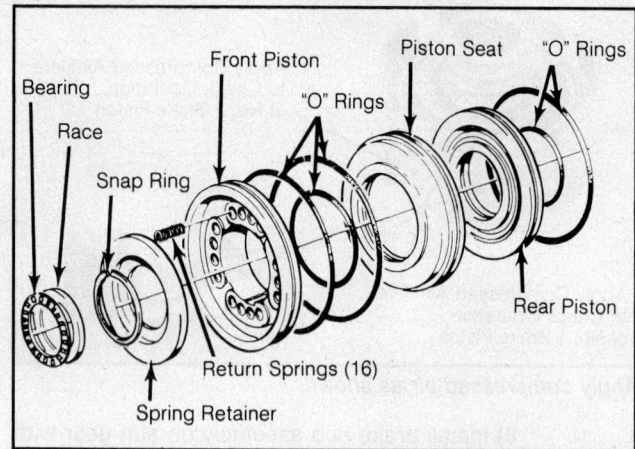

2) Install spring retainer on top of springs. Compress piston springs with compressor used at removal. Install retaining snap ring. Remove compressor.

Fig. 23: Disassembled View of Governor Assembly

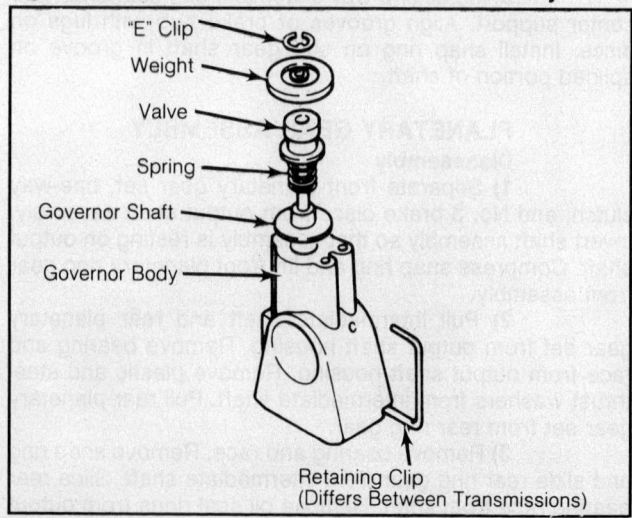

Retaining clip style varies with different models.

AISIN-WARNER 55, 70, 71 & BORG-WARNER 55 (Cont.)

GOVERNOR ASSEMBLY
Disassembly
Remove retaining clip from governor assembly. Remove "E" clip from end of governor shaft. Remove shaft with governor valve, spring and weight from valve bore side of body.

Inspection
Clean all parts with solvent and dry with compressed air. Inspect all parts for wear or damage.

Reassembly
Lubricate all parts with ATF. Install spring and valve on shaft. Install shaft into governor body. Place weight on shaft. Install "E" clip to retain parts. Install retaining clip on governor housing. Install new oil seal in extension housing.

VALVE BODY ASSEMBLY
NOTE: Valve body assemblies used on BW and AW transmissions differ slightly. These differences will be called out in following procedures.

Disassembly
1) Remove detent spring assembly. Pull manual valve out of valve body bore. Remove front and rear upper valve body attaching bolts from top of lower valve body. Invert valve body assemblies and remove retaining bolts from bottom of lower valve body.

2) Carefully lift lower body off both upper bodies with plate and gasket. Ensure gasket does not stick to upper bodies. Place lower body aside with gasket up. To disassemble front upper valve body, place valve body upside down on work bench. Remove check ball and throttle valve retaining plate. Using screwdriver, push out cutback valve retainer. Remove cutback valve and spring.

3) Remove throttle cam, spring and spacer sleeve from front upper valve body. Pull out throttle valve, kickdown valve, springs, and spacers, noting number of spacers removed with throttle valve. Equal amount of spacers must be reinstalled for correct throttle valve adjustment.

4) Remove 1 secondary regulator valve cover plate bolt. Loosen other bolt while keeping tension on plate. Carefully swing plate aside without allowing spring to pop out of cavity. Remove regulator valve.

5) To disassemble rear upper valve body, place body upside down on work bench. On AW transmissions, remove 4 check balls (3 rubber and 1 steel). On BW transmissions, remove 2 check balls from valve body passages, if equipped. See Fig. 27.

6) On both models, push in intermediate coast shift valve and remove retainer. Slide coast valve and spring for 2-3 shift valve out of valve body. Remove 2-3 shift valve retainer and shift valve. Push out detent regulator valve retainer using small screwdriver. Remove detent regulator valve with spring.

7) Remove remaining cover plate from rear upper valve body. Remove following valves and springs from valve body bores, keeping valve and springs together for identification: Low coast modulator valve, governor modulator valve (if equipped), reverse clutch sequence valve, and intermediate coast modulator valve.

8) To disassemble lower valve body, lift off spacer plate and gaskets. Remove cooler by-pass valve and spring. On AW transmissions, remove 2 check balls from valve body passages. On BW transmissions, remove 4 check balls from valve body passages (if equipped). See Fig. 27.

9) On all transmissions, push in 1-2 shift valve and allow retainer to drop out of valve body. Remove plug, 1-2 shift valve, and spring. Remove low coast shift valve cover plate. Slide low coast shift valve, reverse gear pilot valve (or brake sequence valve), and spring from valve body.

NOTE: Isuzu AW transmission models use brake sequence valve while Volvo AW transmission models use reverse gear pilot valve.

10) On Isuzu AW transmissions, remove pressure relief valve (ball type) retainer. Remove relief ball and spring. Remove primary regulator valve train retainer. Slide valve train and spring out of valve body. Remove cover plate.

Inspection
1) Thoroughly clean all parts in clean solvent, then use compressed air to dry parts. Blow out all channels and passages in valve bodies.

2) Check spacer plate to ensure all holes are open. Check all valves and valve bores for wear and damage. After cleaning and lubricating valves with ATF, ensure they slide freely in bores.

Reassembly
1) Reverse disassembly procedure and note the following: Lubricate all valves and valve bores with ATF before reassembly. Ensure all check balls are installed in correct valve body passages. See Fig. 27.

2) When installing throttle valve in front upper valve body, install same number of spacers that were removed. This ensures correct throttle valve adjustment.

TRANSMISSION REASSEMBLY
1) Install new oil seals for manual shaft in case. Install new "O" rings on oil cooler line nipples. Install nipples in transmission case so they point in same direction as when removed. Install line pressure and governor pressure plugs with new "O" rings.

2) Install cover for governor oil ducts on transmission case. Always use new gasket. Install throttle cable in case. Assemble parking pawl, spring and shaft in case. Install detent lever and shaft, using new collar and pin. Drive new retaining pin through lever and shaft.

3) Fit parking pawl rod to pawl and detent lever. Install parking pawl cam plate. Invert transmission case so case opening is up. Install rearmost bearing and race. Install No. 3 brake apply tube into case. Lower lugs on tube go inside No. 3 brake piston bore. Parking pawl pin fits in middle of drum recess.

4) Install planetary gear and No. 3 brake disc assembly into transmission case with recess in reaction plate lug toward oil pan. Install planetary assembly retaining snap ring in groove of case. Snap ring ends must be between splines. See Fig. 28.

5) Check operation of No. 3 brake piston by applying low pressure compressed air to oil holes. See Fig. 29. When air is applied, audible "plop" noise should be heard.

6) Hold sun gear shaft and lower center support assembly into transmission case until it mates with planetary gear assembly. Install center support bolts into case by hand to avoid thread damage. DO NOT tighten bolts at this time.

Automatic Transmissions
AISIN-WARNER 55, 70, 71 & BORG-WARNER 55 (Cont.)

Fig. 24: Exploded View of Volvo AW 55 & BW 55 Valve Body Assemblies

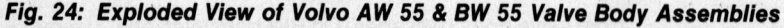

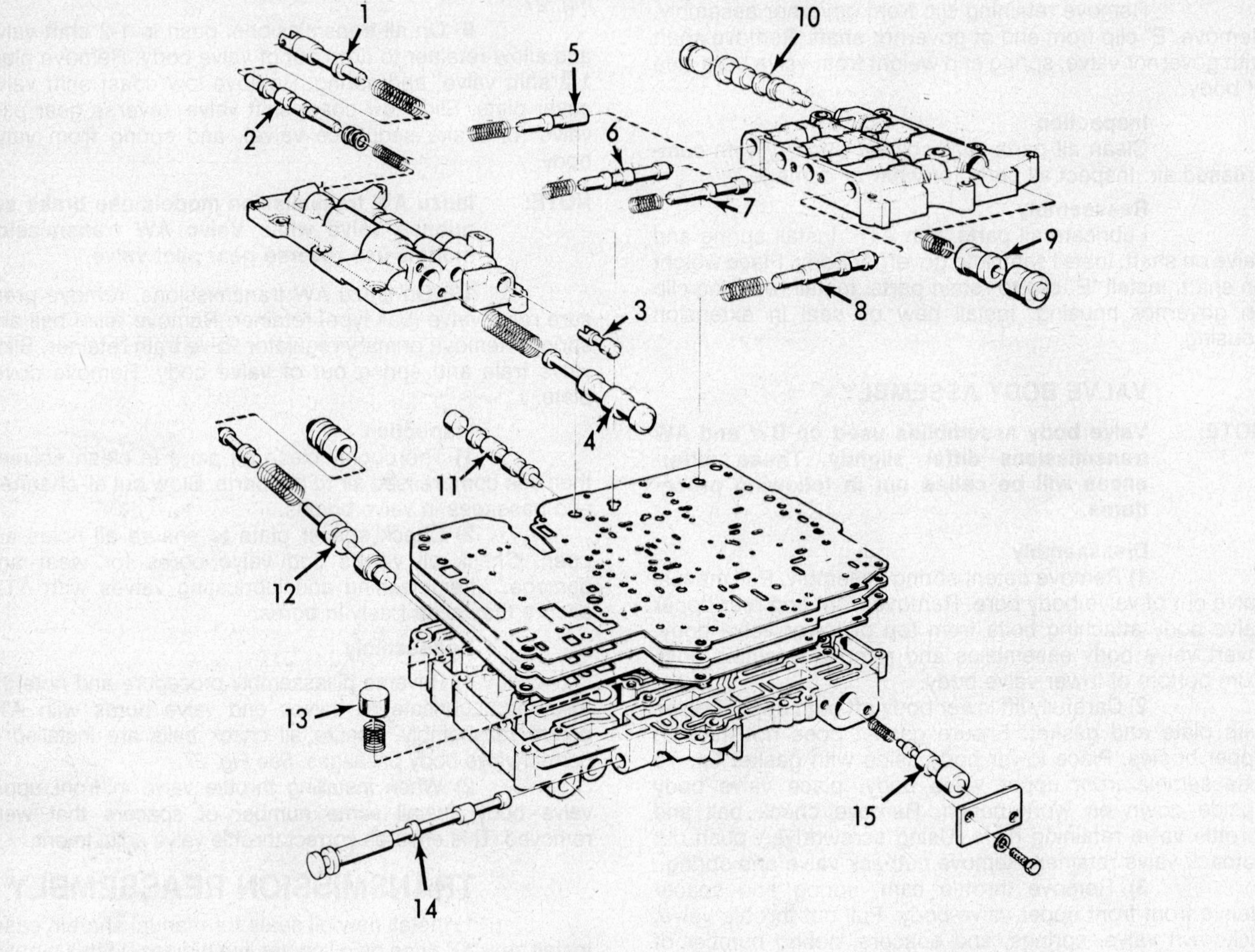

1. Secondary Throttle Valve	6. Intermediate Coast Modulator Valve	11. 1-2 Shift Valve
2. Primary Throttle Valve	7. Reverse Clutch Sequence Valve	12. Primary Regulator Valve
3. Cutback Valve	8. Low Coast Modulator Valve	13. Cooler Bypass Valve
4. Secondary Regulator Valve	9. Intermediate Coast Shift Valve	14. Manual Valve
5. Detent Regulator Valve	10. 2-3 Shift Valve	15. Low Coast Shift Valve

7) Align discs on center support and install direct (rear) clutch assembly into transmission case. If direct (rear) clutch is properly assembled, clutch splines and sun gear shaft splines should mesh. Position bearings and races on direct (rear) clutch hub.

8) Align discs and install forward (front) clutch in case, engaging lugs of direct (rear) clutch to grooves in hub of forward (front) clutch. Isuzu specifies that face of correctly installed forward (front) clutch will be about .06" (1.5 mm) from face case where oil pump attaches.

9) Install bearing and race on input shaft, with race toward oil pump. Position oil pump in case, then install and tighten attaching bolts. Tighten bolts alternately and evenly. Be careful to avoid damaging or warping of "O" rings.

10) Tighten center support bolts in 4 steps, starting with bolt next to accumulator piston bores. Check operation of brake and clutch pistons by applying low pressure compressed air to respective oil hole. *See Fig. 30.* When air is applied to each oil hole, distinct "plop" should be heard.

11) Mount dial indicator on transmission case with indicator tip touching end of input shaft. Zero dial indicator. Move input shaft up and down and note maximum dial indicator reading. This reading is input shaft end play. End play should be .009-.020" (.22-.53 mm) for BW 55 and .012-.035" (.30-.90 mm) for all others. Input shaft should rotate without binding.

12) Attach torque converter housing to transmission case and tighten bolts. Rotate transmission on holding fixture until oil pan mounting surface is up. Install accumulator piston springs into case bore. Install new "O" rings on accumulator pistons and install pistons into bores.

NOTE: On AW 70 and 71 transmissions, No. 2 brake spring is longer than forward (front) clutch spring. On AW and BW 55 transmissions, forward (front) clutch spring is longer than No. 2 brake spring. Short spring is installed in center bore on all transmissions. Install small piston in center bore on all transmissions. Two large pistons are different sizes and cannot be incorrectly installed.

Fig. 25: *Exploded View of Isuzu AW & BW Valve Body Assembly*

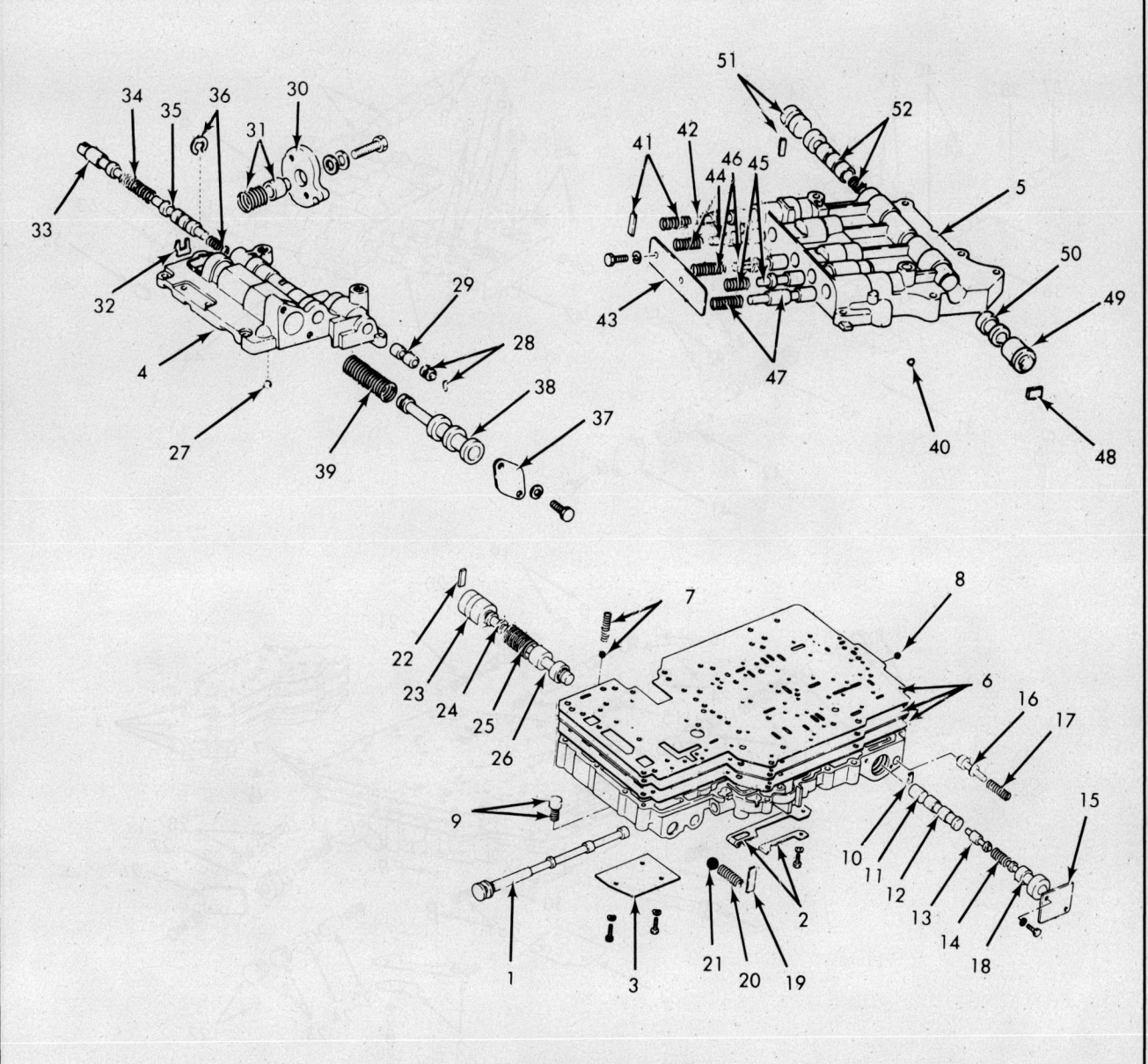

1. Manual Valve	19. Pressure Relief Valve Retainer	37. Front Valve Cover
2. Spring & Plate Assembly	20. Pressure Relief Valve Spring	38. Secondary Valve
3. Lower Valve Cover	21. Steel Check Ball	39. Secondary Spring
4. Front Upper Valve Body	22. Sleeve Retainer	40. 7/32" Rubber Check Ball
5. Rear Upper Valve Body	23. Primary Regulator Valve Sleeve	41. Retainer & Spring
6. Separator Plate & Gaskets	24. Primary Regulator Valve Plunger	42. Detent Valve
7. Spring & 1/4" Check Ball	25. Primary Regulator Valve Spring	43. Rear Valve Cover
8. 7/32" Rubber Check Ball	26. Primary Regulator Valve	44. Intermediate Valve & Spring
9. By-pass Valve & Spring	27. 7/32" Rubber Check Ball	45. Reverse Clutch Valve & Spring
10. Valve Retainer	28. Plug & Retainer	46. Governor Valve & Spring
11. 1-2 Shift Valve Plug	29. Cutback Valve	47. Low Coast Valve & Spring
12. 1-2 Lower Shift Valve	30. Kickdown & Throttle Valve Cam	48. Intermediate Retainer
13. 1-2 Upper Shift Valve	31. Spacer & Spring	49. Plug
14. 1-2 Shift Valve Spring	32. Throttle Valve Plate	50. Intermediate Valve
15. Valve Cover	33. Kickdown Valve Assembly	51. 2-3 Shift Plug & Retainer
16. Reverse Valve	34. Primary Throttle Valve Spring	52. 2-3 Shift Valve & Spring
17. Reverse Valve Spring	35. Throttle Valve	
18. Low Coast Shift Valve	36. Retaining Clip & Spring	

Automatic Transmissions
AISIN-WARNER 55, 70, 71 & BORG-WARNER 55 (Cont.)

Fig. 26: Exploded View of Isuzu Overdrive Transmission Valve Body Assembly

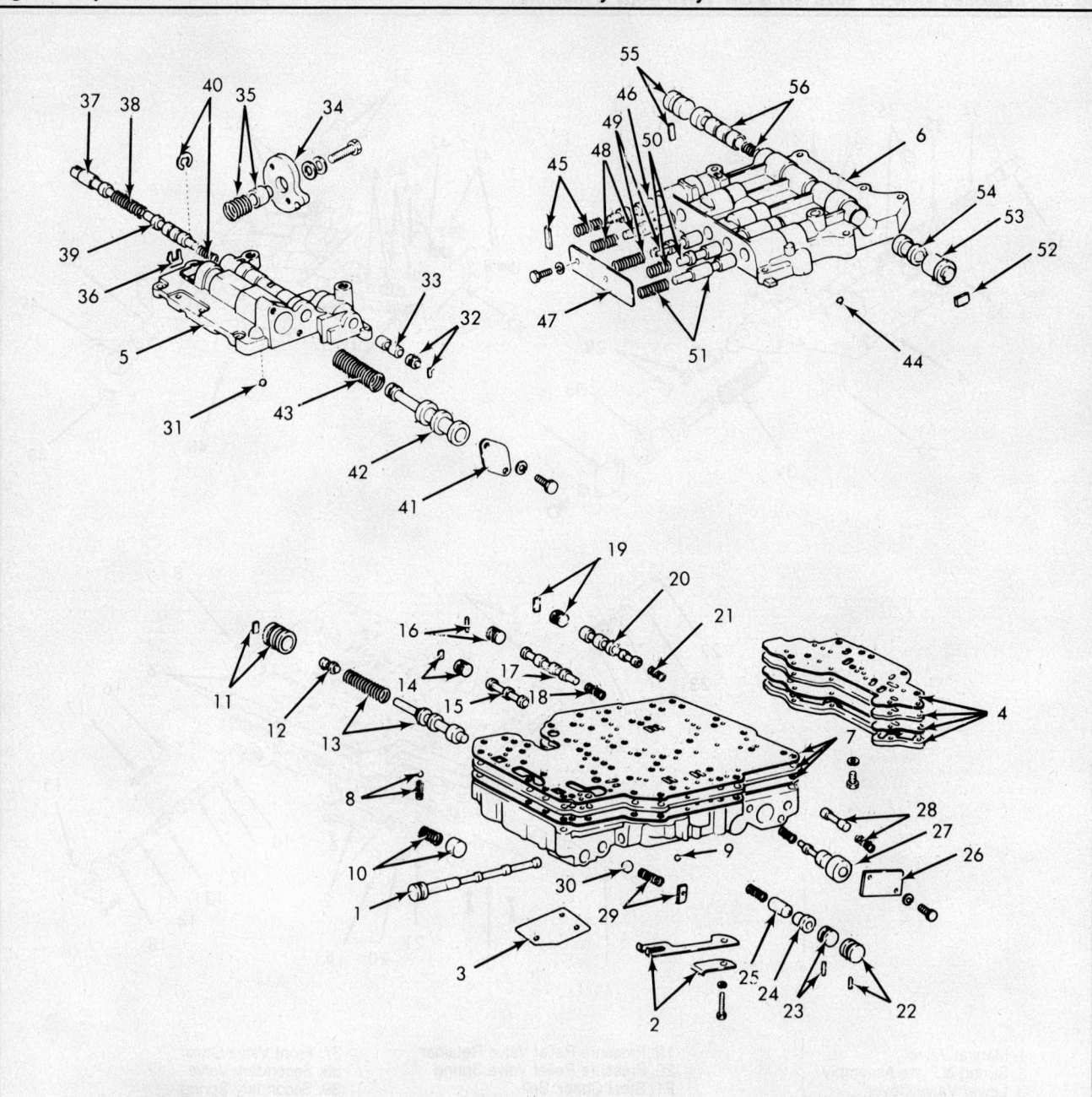

1. Manual Valve	20. 1-2 Shift Valve	38. Primary Throttle Valve Spring
2. Spring & Plate Assembly	21. 1-2 Shift Valve Spring	39. Throttle Valve
3. Lower Valve Cover	22. Manual Valve Plug & Pin	40. Retaining Clip & Spring
4. Gasket & Cover Plate	23. 3rd Coast Shift Valve Plug & Pin	41. Front Valve Cover
5. Front Upper Valve Body Assy.	24. 3rd Coast Shift Valve	42. Secondary Valve
6. Rear Upper Valve Body Assy.	25. 3-4 Shift Control Valve	43. Secondary Spring
7. Plate & Gasket	26. Valve Cover	44. 7/32" Rubber Check Ball
8. Spring & 1/4" Rubber Check Ball	27. Low Coast Shift Valve	45. Retainer & Spring
9. 7/32" Rubber Check Ball	28. Reverse Valve & Spring	46. Detent Valve
10. By-Pass Valve & Spring	29. Pressure Relief Valve	47. Rear Valve Cover
11. Sleeve & Retainer	Spring & Retainer	48. Intermediate Valve & Spring
12. Primary Regulator Valve Plunger	30. Steel Check Ball	49. Reverse Clutch Valve & Spring
13. Primary Regulator Valve & Spring	31. 7/32" Rubber Check Ball	50. Governor Valve & Spring
14. Plug & Retainer	32. Plug & Retainer	51. Low Coast Valve & Spring
15. D-2 Downshift Timing Valve	33. Cutback Valve	52. Intermediate Retainer
16. Plug & Roll Pin	34. Kickdown & Throttle Valve Cam	53. Plug
17. 3-4 Shift Valve	35. Spacer & Spring	54. Intermediate Valve
18. 3-4 Shift Valve Spring	36. Throttle Valve Plate	55. Plug & Retainer
19. Plug & Retainer	37. Kickdown Valve Assembly	56. 2-3 Shift Valve & Spring

AISIN-WARNER 55, 70, 71 & BORG-WARNER 55 (Cont.)

Fig. 27: Check Ball Installation in AW 55 & BW 55 Valve Bodies

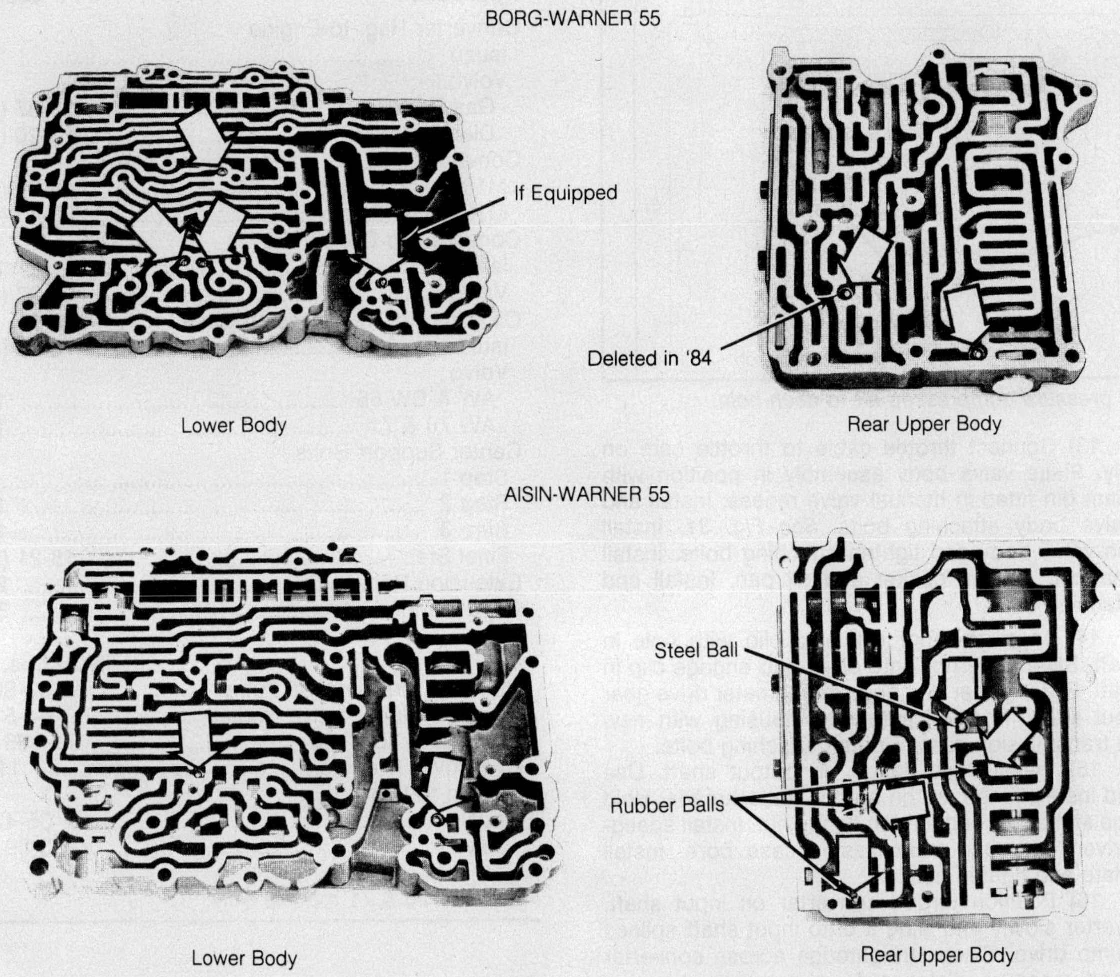

BORG-WARNER 55
If Equipped
Deleted in '84
Lower Body
Rear Upper Body
AISIN-WARNER 55
Steel Ball
Rubber Balls
Lower Body
Rear Upper Body

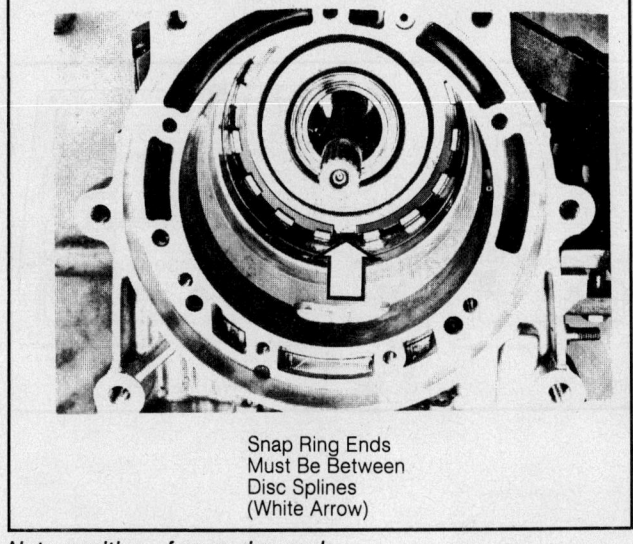

Fig. 28: Installing Planetary Assembly Snap Ring

Snap Ring Ends
Must Be Between
Disc Splines
(White Arrow)

Note position of snap ring ends.

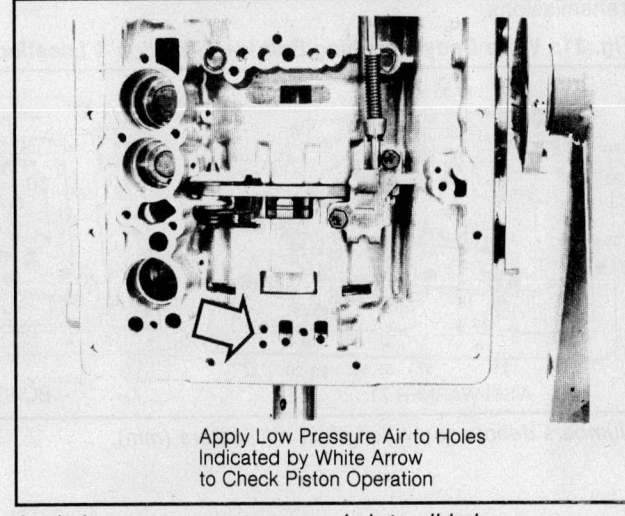

Fig. 29: Checking No. 3 Brake Piston Operation

Apply Low Pressure Air to Holes
Indicated by White Arrow
to Check Piston Operation

Apply low pressure compressed air to oil hole.

6-18

Automatic Transmissions
AISIN-WARNER 55, 70, 71 & BORG-WARNER 55 (Cont.)

Fig. 30: Checking Clutch & Brake Piston Operation

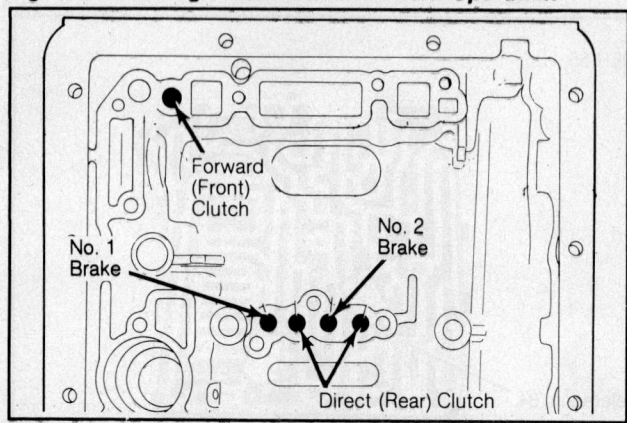

Apply low pressure compressed air to each hole.

13) Connect throttle cable to throttle cam on valve body. Place valve body assembly in position with selector cam pin fitted in manual valve recess. Install and tighten valve body attaching bolts. *See Fig. 31.* Install strainer on valve body and tighten attaching bolts. Install particle magnet, oil pan gasket and oil pan. Install and tighten attaching bolts.

14) Align governor retaining clip with hole in output shaft. Slide governor onto shaft and engage clip in hole in shaft. Slide spacer ring and speedometer drive gear onto output shaft. Position extension housing with new gasket on transmission case. Tighten attaching bolts.

15) Install drive flange on output shaft. Use Loctite and install flange nut on output shaft threads. Hold drive flange stationary and tighten flange nut. Install speedometer driven gear into transmission case bore. Install retainer plate and tighten bolt.

16) Position torque converter on input shaft. Turn converter slowly and slide it onto input shaft splines and oil pump drive. Place straightedge across converter housing and measure distance from converter housing surface to converter face ring. Distance should be .64-.77" (16.3-19.6 mm) for BW 55 and 1.24" (31.5 mm) for AW 55 transmissions.

TIGHTENING SPECIFICATIONS

Application	Ft. Lbs. (N.m)
Converter Hsg.-to-Engine	
Isuzu	29 (39)
Volvo	
Gas Engine	30-37 (41-50)
Diesel Engine	13-20 (18-27)
Converter Hsg.-to-Transmission Case	
M10 Bolts	19-29 (26-39)
M12 Bolts	35-43 (47-58)
Converter-to-Drive Plate	
Isuzu	14 (19)
Volvo	30-37 (41-50)
Oil Pump-to-Transmission Case	
Isuzu	13-18 (18-24)
Volvo	
AW & BW 55	18 (24)
AW 70 & 71	16 (22)
Center Support Bolts	
Step 1	5 (7)
Step 2	10 (14)
Step 3	15 (20)
Final Step	18-21 (24-29)
Extension Hsg.-to-Case	26 (35)
Drive Flange Nut	33 (45)

Application	INCH Lbs. (N.m)
Oil Pump Cover-to-Oil Pump	53-80 (6-9)
Lower-to-Upper Valve Bodies	44-53 (5-6)
Valve Body-to-Case	71-106 (8-12)
Overdrive Solenoid [1]	115 (13)
Oil Pan-to-Case	
Isuzu	35-43 (4-5)
Volvo	53-89 (6-10)

[1] – AW 70 & 71 models only.

Fig. 31: Valve Body Attaching Bolt Identification & Location

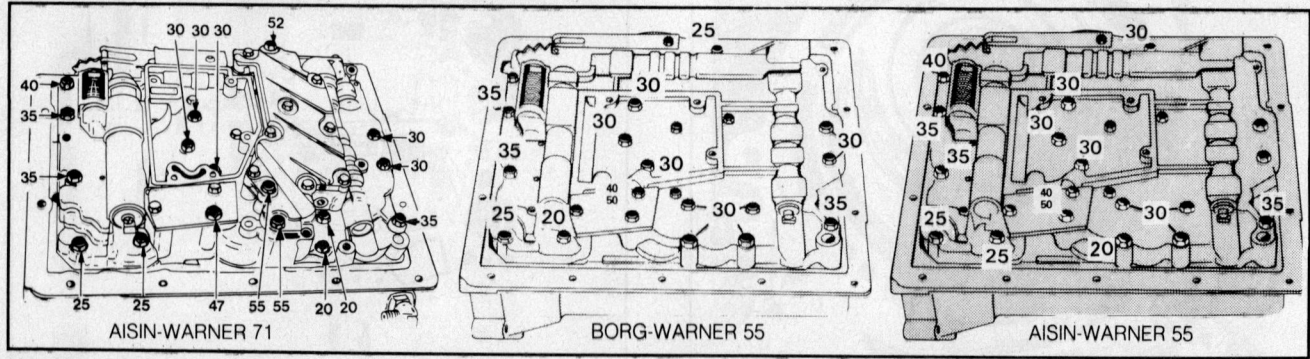

Numbers denote screw length in millimeters (mm).

AUDI 4000S, 4000S QUATTRO, 5000S, PORSCHE 944 & VOLKSWAGEN QUANTUM

TRANSAXLE IDENTIFICATION

Transaxle type may be identified by group of numbers cast into top rear of case. Transaxle model code is identified by group of figures stamped into torque converter housing. These figures consist of model code and build date code.

Audi uses type 087 and 089 transaxles. Volkswagen Quantum uses type 087 and 089 transaxles. Porsche 944 is equipped with type 087 transaxle. Turbine shaft length is main difference between 2 transaxles. Type 087 uses 16.71" (424.5 mm) shaft while type 089 uses 15.82" (401.7 mm) shaft. Testing, disassembly and reassembly procedures are same.

TRANSAXLE MODEL CODES

Application	Code
Audi	
Coupe GT, 4000S & 4000S Quattro	
087	RR
089	KJ
089 E-Mode	RC
5000S	
087	RY
087 E-Mode	RC
Porsche	
087	RCB
Volkswagen	
087	RR
089	KJ/KAF
089 E-Mode	KU/KAC

DESCRIPTION

Transaxle assembly consists of automatic transmission and final drive assembly. Transmission housing contains 2 planetary gear sets, 2 multiple-disc clutches, 1 brake band and servo, 1 multiple-disc brake, one-way clutch, and hydraulic control system.

Final drive housing contains torque converter, transmission governor, ring gear, and differential carrier with pinion and side gears.

Models with diesel engines are offered with E-Mode transaxles, which are used to improve fuel economy. When selector lever is in "E" position, transmission disengages from differential whenever accelerator pedal is released. In all other selector lever positions, transmission operates same as conventional model. Main modifications to E-Mode transaxle are in valve body and forward clutch.

LUBRICATION & ADJUSTMENT

See the appropriate article in AUTOMATIC TRANSMISSION SERVICING Section.

SERVICE (IN VEHICLE)

For service procedures for DRIVE AXLE SHAFTS, CONSTANT VELOCITY (CV) JOINTS and WHEEL BEARINGS, see appropriate article in MANUAL TRANSMISSION section.

TROUBLE SHOOTING

NO MOVEMENT

In Any Gear

Low fluid level. Manual lever not connected to manual valve. Torque converter disconnected from drive plate. Main pressure valve sticking. Oil pump and/or pump drive shaft defective.

In Forward Gears

Forward clutch internal damage (worn plates, broken diagram spring, seals leaking, etc.). Forward planetary gears damaged.

In First Gear in "D" or "2"

One-way clutch not holding. Forward clutch internal damage.

In First Gear in "1"

First/Reverse brake plates worn or burnt. Forward clutch damage.

In Second Gear

Second gear brake band out of adjustment or burnt, or servo defective.

In Third Gear

Direct/Reverse clutch plates burnt or worn.

In Reverse

First/Reverse brake plates worn or burnt. Direct/Reverse clutch internal damage. Forward clutch seized in applied position.

NO UPSHIFT

Into Second Gear

Faulty governor drive. Governor incorrectly assembled or dirty. Loose accumulator cover plate. 1-2 gear shift valve sticking. Brake band for 2nd gear burnt or worn.

Into Third Gear

Governor or valve body dirty. 2-3 shift valve sticking. Loose oil pump bolts.

NO DOWNSHIFT

Into Second Gear

Governor dirty. 2-3 shift valve sticking.

Into First Gear

Governor dirty. 1-2 shift valve sticking.

DELAYED ENGAGEMENT ON UPSHIFTS

1-2 Upshift

Low fluid level. Dirty valve body. Second gear brake band worn, burnt or out of adjustment. Second gear servo defective, possible wrong piston.

2-3 Upshift

Low fluid level. Dirty valve body. Second gear brake band worn, burnt or out of adjustment. Second gear servo defective. Direct/Reverse clutch plates worn or burnt. Wrong Direct/Reverse clutch installed.

ERRATIC DRIVE

Low fluid level. Bushing in one-way clutch support and turbine shaft worn. Oil filter dirty. Governor dirty. Valve body dirty. Planetary gears or separation plate gasket damaged.

AUDI 4000S, 4000S QUATTRO, 5000S, PORSCHE 944 & VOLKSWAGEN QUANTUM (Cont.)

E-MODE

Transaxle Does Not Disengage With Throttle Closed & Selector In "E" Position

Accelerator cable or selector lever incorrectly adjusted. Main pressure too high. Declutching valve in valve body sticking. Forward clutch damage.

TESTING

ROAD TESTING

1) Before road testing, ensure that fluid level and condition are correct. Check control linkage adjustments and correct as necessary. During test, transmission should upshift and downshift at approximate speeds shown in *Shift Speeds* chart.

2) All shifts may vary somewhat due to production tolerances or tire size. Quality of shifts is most important factor. All shifts should be smooth, responsive, and with no slippage or engine speed runaway.

3) Slippage or engine runaway in any gear usually indicates clutch, band, or brake problems. Slipping unit in particular gear can be identified by noting transmission operation in other selector positions and comparing which internal units are applied. *See Clutch and Band Application* chart.

4) This process of elimination can be used to detect any unit which slips and to confirm proper operation of good units. Actual cause of malfunction usually cannot be easily decided.

5) Practically any condition can be caused by leaking hydraulic circuits or sticking valves. Therefore, unless definite problem exists, do not disassemble transmission until hydraulic pressure test has been made.

HYDRAULIC PRESSURE TEST

1) Connect pressure gauge to main pressure test point on case (adjacent to servo cover). Transmission must be at normal operating temperature.

Fig. 1: Testing Transmission Pressures

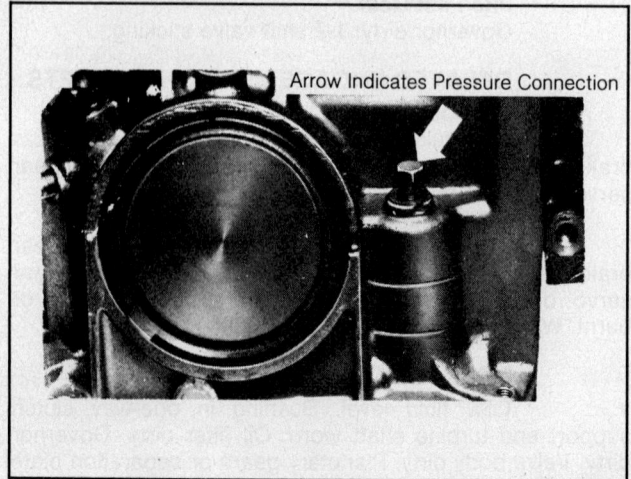

Arrow Indicates Pressure Connection

Arrow indicates connector location.

2) Pressures obtained in each phase of test should be approximately as shown in *Main Pressures Test*

chart. If pressures are incorrect, check for oil leaks, defective oil pump, or sticking valves in valve body assembly.

SHIFT SPEEDS

Application	Shift Points (MPH)	
	Full Throttle	Kickdown
Coupe GT, 4000S & 4000S Quattro		
087		
1-2 Upshift	19-28	40-42
2-3 Upshift	47-60	72-73
3-2 Downshift	34-47	68-70
2-1 Downshift	14-16	37-38
089		
1-2 Upshift	20-28	34-37
2-3 Upshift	48-61	66-67
3-2 Downshift	35-48	62-64
2-1 Downshift	14-16	37-38
089 E-Mode		
1-2 Upshift	23-26	37-40
2-3 Upshift	53-65	65-66
3-2 Downshift	35-48	60-62
2-1 Downshift	17-30	32-35
5000S		
087		
1-2 Upshift	19-27	38-40
2-3 Upshift	45-57	69-70
3-2 Downshift	32-45	65-67
2-1 Downshift	13-16	35-37
087 E-Mode		
1-2 Upshift	22-25	40-42
2-3 Upshift	51-63	66-67
3-2 Downshift	34-47	62-63
2-1 Downshift	27-31	35-37
944		
087		
1-2 Upshift	22-30	45-48
2-3 Upshift	52-65	81-83
3-2 Downshift	37-52	77-80
2-1 Downshift	16-17	42-44
Quantum		
087		
1-2 Upshift	19-28	40-42
2-3 Upshift	47-60	72-73
3-2 Downshift	34-47	68-70
2-1 Downshift	14-16	37-38
089		
1-2 Upshift	20-28	34-37
2-3 Upshift	48-61	66-67
3-2 Downshift	35-48	62-64
2-1 Downshift	14-16	29-31
089 E-Mode		
1-2 Upshift	23-26	37-40
2-3 Upshift	53-65	65-66
3-2 Downshift	35-48	60-62
2-1 Downshift	17-30	32-35

AUDI 4000S, 4000S QUATTRO, 5000S, PORSCHE 944 & VOLKSWAGEN QUANTUM (Cont.)

CLUTCH AND BAND APPLICATION (ELEMENTS IN USE)

Selector Lever Position	Forward Clutch	Direct/Reverse Clutch	First/Reverse Brake	Second Gear Band	One-Way Clutch
"D" – DRIVE					
1st Gear	X				Holding
2nd Gear	X			X	Overrun
3rd Gear	X	X			Overrun
"2" – INTERMEDIATE					
1st Gear	X				Holding
2nd Gear	X			X	Overrun
"1" – LOW (First)	X		X		
"R" – REVERSE		X	X		

NEUTRAL OR PARK – All clutches, brakes, and bands released and/or ineffective.

MAIN PRESSURE TEST

Selector Lever Position	Accelerator Pedal Position	Main Pressure psi (kg/cm²)	Test Conditions [1]
"D" – DRIVE All Models	At Idle	42.06-43.51 (3.0-3.1)	Accelerate to 35 mph, release throttle and check pressure
"D" – DRIVE All Except E-Mode 087 (Coupe GT, 4000S, 5000S, & Quantum) 089 (Coupe GT, 4000S, 5000S, & Quantum) 087 (944) All Models E-Mode [2]	W.O.T.	81.95-83.40 (5.8-5.9) 84.85-86.30 (6.0-6.1) 105.88-107.33 (7.4-7.6) 84.85-86.30 (6.0-6.1)	Vehicle speed above 35 mph
"R" – REVERSE All Except E-Mode 087 (Coupe GT, 4000S, & 5000S) 089 (Coupe GT & 4000S) 087 & 089 (Quantum) 087 (944) All Models E-Mode	At Idle	131.99-140.69 (9.3-9.9) 131.99-140.69 (9.3-9.9) 130.54-145.04 (9.2-10.2) 133.44-142.14 (9.4-10.0) 130.54-145.04 (9.2-10.2)	Vehicle Stationary
"R" – REVERSE 087 (944)	W.O.T.	290.0 (20.0) Min.	At stall speed

[1] – Manufacturer recommends that "D" tests be performed on chassis dynamometer.
[2] – No specifications available for Quantum E-Mode at time of publication.

STALL SPEED

CAUTION: Do not hold throttle open for longer than time needed to read tachometer. Maximum stall speed test time is 5 seconds. Wait at least 20 seconds with transmission in neutral before repeating test. If engine speed exceeds limits, release accelerator immediately as clutch or band slippage is indicated.

Testing Procedure

Engine must be at normal operating temperature. Connect tachometer. Start engine and set parking and service brakes. Place selector in "D". Depress accelerator briefly to full throttle and note maximum RPM obtained. Engine speed should be within limits. See Stall Speeds table.

Stall Speed Test Results

1) If stall speed is higher than specified, forward clutch or one-way clutch for 1st gear is slipping. If

Automatic Transmissions

AUDI 4000S, 4000S QUATTRO, 5000S, PORSCHE 944 & VOLKSWAGEN QUANTUM (Cont.)

stall speed in "D" range is too high, repeat stall test in "1". If RPM is within specifications, one-way clutch for 1st gear is defective. If RPM exceeds specification in "1", forward clutch is defective.

2) If stall speed is approximately 200 RPM below specifications, engine performance may be unsatisfactory. If stall speed is more than 200 RPM below specifications, torque converter stator one-way clutch is faulty and complete converter should be replaced.

STALL SPEEDS

Application	Stall RPM [1]
Coupe & 4000	
087	2250-2500
089	2450-2700
089 E-Mode	2530-2780
5000	
087	2250-2500
087/Turbo	3000-3400
087 E-Mode	2400
944	
087	2600-3000
Quantum	
087	2250-2500
089	2450-2700
089 E-Mode	2530-2780

[1] – Stall speeds will drop 125 RPM for each 3300 ft. (1006 m) increase in elevation. High ambient temperature may cause slight drop in stall speed.

REMOVAL & INSTALLATION

See the appropriate article in AUTOMATIC TRANSMISSION REMOVAL Section.

TORQUE CONVERTER

BUSHING REPLACEMENT

1) Check bushing wear using inside micrometer. Wear limit is 1.343" (34.12 mm). Maximum allowable out-of-round is .001" (.03 mm). If bushing wear exceeds limit, use bushing puller (US 691, VW 201 and adapter US 4452) to withdraw bushing from converter hub.

2) Press new bushing into place using bushing driver (VW 474). Measure inside diameter of new bushing after installation. Remove any burrs from edge of converter hub after installation of new bushing.

3) Minimum allowed inside diameter of new bushing is 1.340-1.341" (34.03-34.05 mm). Bushing may seize if inside diameter is less than minimum limit. Do not ream out bushing to fit. Repeat replacement procedure with another new bushing if necessary.

TRANSMISSION DISASSEMBLY

1) To separate transmission from final drive assembly, withdraw torque converter from final drive housing and remove oil pump shaft from center of turbine shaft. Disconnect filler pipe from oil pan. Mount transaxle

assembly in holding fixture with back of transmission assembly bolted to fixture.

Fig. 2: Removing Torque Converter Bushing

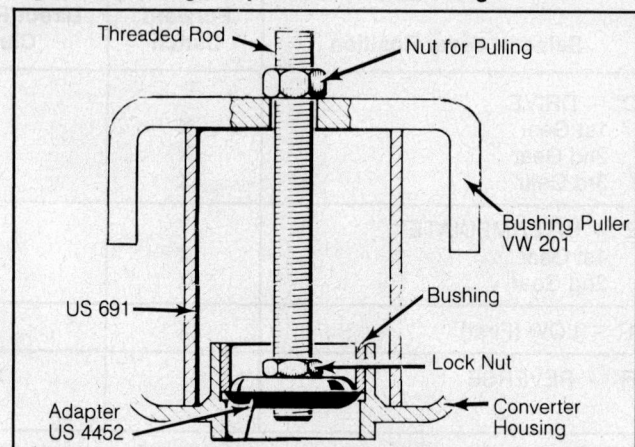

2) Remove attaching nuts from final drive-to-transmission studs. Separate final drive unit from transmission case. Withdraw turbine shaft from final drive. For final drive disassembly and reassembly, see *Final Drive* in this article.

Fig. 3: Installed View of One-Way Clutch Assembly Showing Location of Retaining Snap Ring

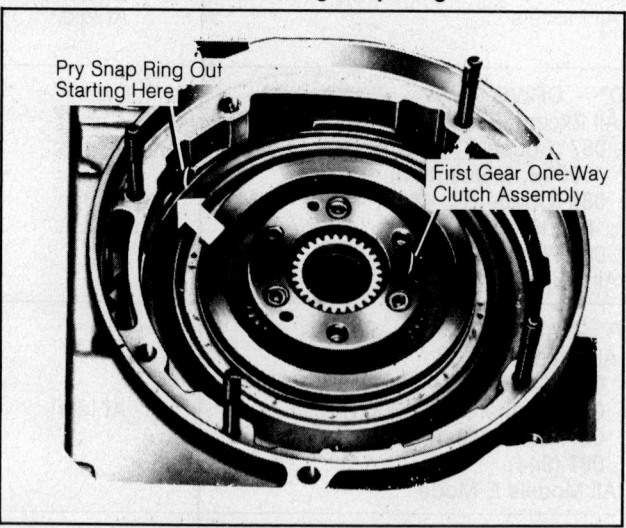

3) Remove separation plate and gasket from transmission case. Remove reverse planetary ring gear, needle bearing and thrust washer. Using screwdriver, carefully remove large snap ring retaining 1st gear one-way clutch assembly in case.

4) Lift out one-way clutch, 1st/Reverse gear brake plates, and reverse planetary gear set. Remove thrust washers, then lift following components from case as assembly: sun gear, driving shell, forward planetary gear set, and forward clutch.

5) Remove 2nd gear brake band servo cover snap ring. Use rubber mallet to tap cover until cover and piston pop out under spring pressure. Loosen 2nd gear brake band lock nut and remove adjusting screw and lock nut. Withdraw pushrod for adjusting screw.

AUDI 4000S, 4000S QUATTRO, 5000S, PORSCHE 944 & VOLKSWAGEN QUANTUM (Cont.)

Fig. 4: Using Rubber Mallet to Remove Brake Band Servo Cover

Tap Cover Until Cover and Piston Pop Out Under Spring Pressure

Cover will pop out under spring tension.

6) Lift out remaining components that are housed in 1st/Reverse gear brake shell. Remove bolts from 1st/Reverse brake spring plate, withdraw spring plate and springs. Pull brake shell, brake piston, and oil pump from case.

7) Invert transmission so that oil pan is facing up. Remove attaching bolts and lift off oil pan and gasket. Remove oil strainer and cover from valve body. Remove 11 valve body attaching bolts.

8) Lift valve body assembly from case. DO NOT drop manual valve. Remove accumulator spring and piston from transmission case. If necessary for replacement, disassemble kickdown and selector linkage. *See Fig 5.*

COMPONENT DISASSEMBLY & REASSEMBLY

OIL PUMP ASSEMBLY

CAUTION: Pump cover is under spring tension.

Disassembly
1) Remove pump cover attaching screws and separate cover from pump housing. Remove check ball and spring from pump body. Lift out pump gears and drive plate.

2) Unhook piston ring ends and remove rings from pump body. Remove thrust washer from end of pump housing.

Inspection
Wash all parts in solvent and blow out oil passages with compressed air. Inspect all parts for wear, scoring, chipped teeth and any other damage. Replace parts as necessary.

Fig. 5: Bottom View of Transmission Housing Showing Kickdown and Selector Linkage

Parking Lock Operating Lever

Parking Pawl Pin

Parking Pawl Spring

Spring Retaining Bolt

Parking Pawl

Roller Spring

Kickdown Lever

Manual Lever

Operating Lever

Manual Lever Nut

Kickdown Operating Lever

Kickdown Lever Nut

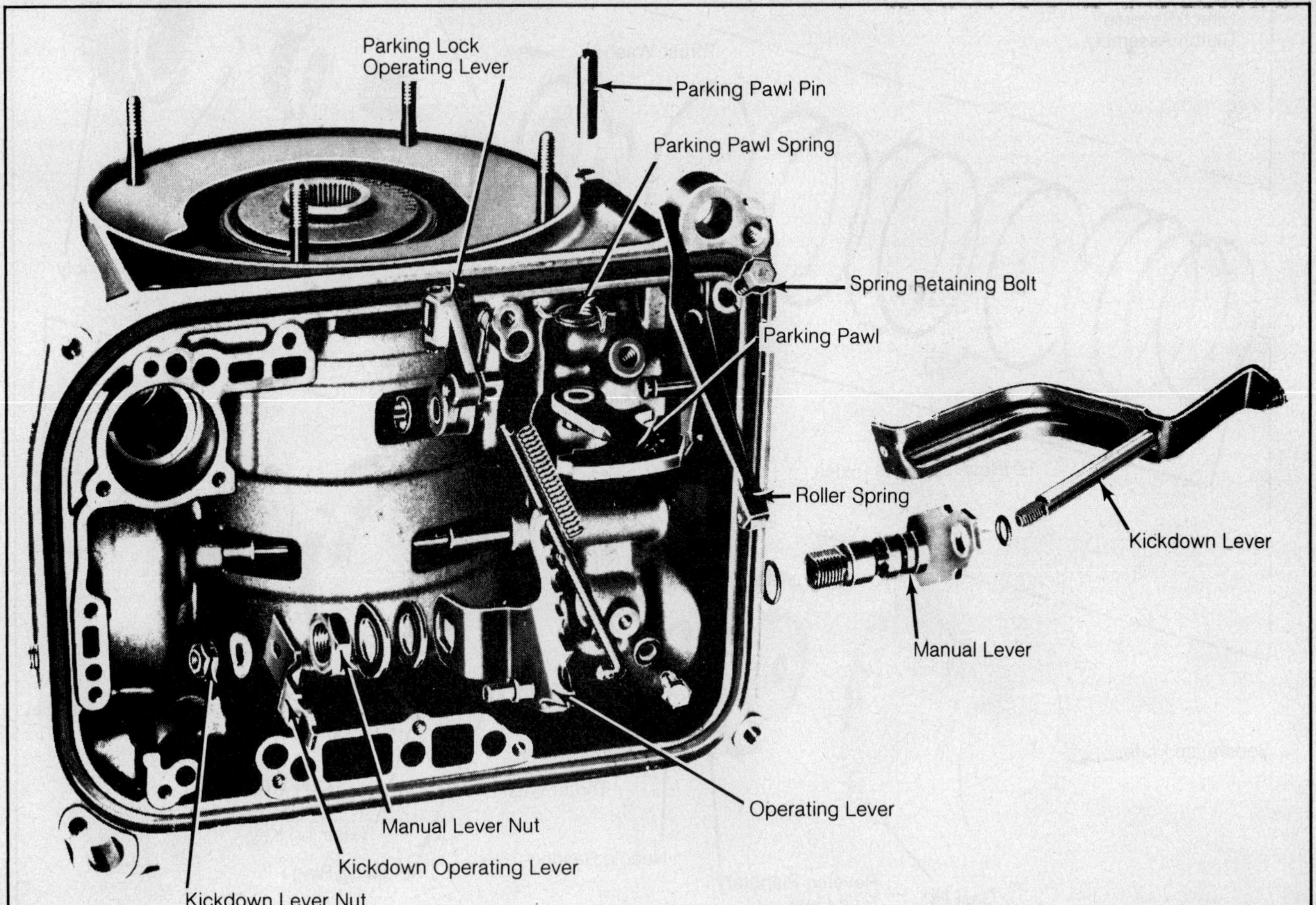

Automatic Transmissions

AUDI 4000S, 4000S QUATTRO, 5000S, PORSCHE 944 & VOLKSWAGEN QUANTUM (Cont.)

Fig. 6: Exploded View of Transmission Case and Main Components

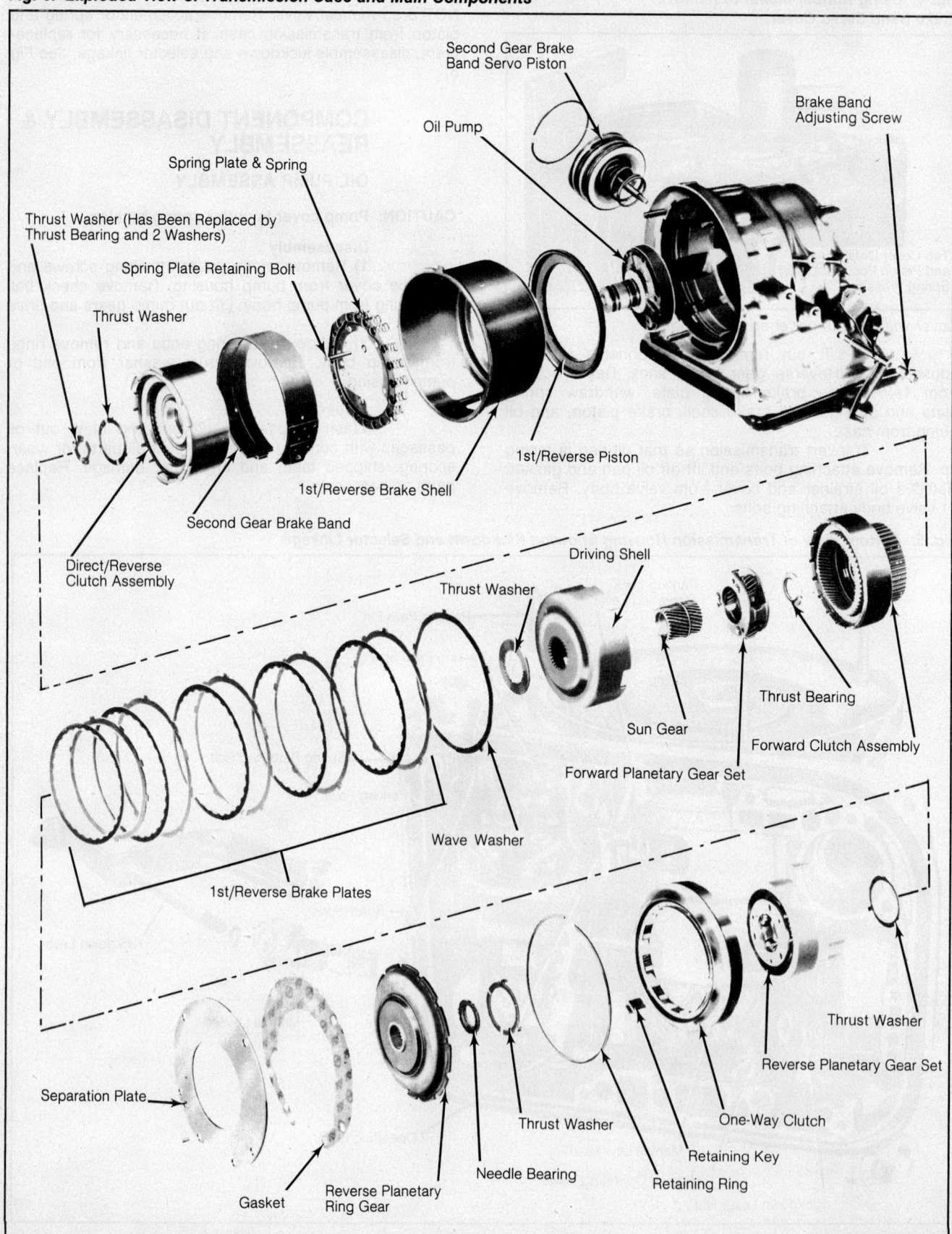

AUDI 4000S, 4000S QUATTRO, 5000S, PORSCHE 944 & VOLKSWAGEN QUANTUM (Cont.)

NOTE: If either pump gear, pump housing or cover is damaged, entire oil pump assembly must be replaced. Drive plate, piston rings and thrust washer (thrust bearing and washers) may be replaced individually as needed.

Reassembly

1) Install thrust washer on pump housing. Carefully install large piston rings and then small piston rings. Make sure that ring ends are hooked together correctly. Lubricate all parts with ATF.

2) Install inner and outer gears into housing. Side of outer gear with marking (code letter) must face cover plate. Install drive plate with extended hub inserted into pump body away from cover plate. Install check ball and spring. Align cover with housing. Install and tighten attaching screws.

NOTE: After reassembly, insert pump shaft into oil pump and ensure that gears rotate smoothly without binding. Gear movement should also be checked after pump is installed in transmission case.

DIRECT/REVERSE CLUTCH

Disassembly

1) Using screwdriver, pry clutch pack retaining snap ring from clutch drum. Withdraw clutch pressure plate, lined clutch plates and steel clutch plates from drum.

2) Place clutch drum in press, apply downward pressure to piston spring retainer and remove retaining snap ring. Release press and remove spring retainer. Using twisting motion, remove piston with return springs from drum. Remove piston seals and springs from piston.

Fig. 7: Exploded View Showing Components of Oil Pump Assembly

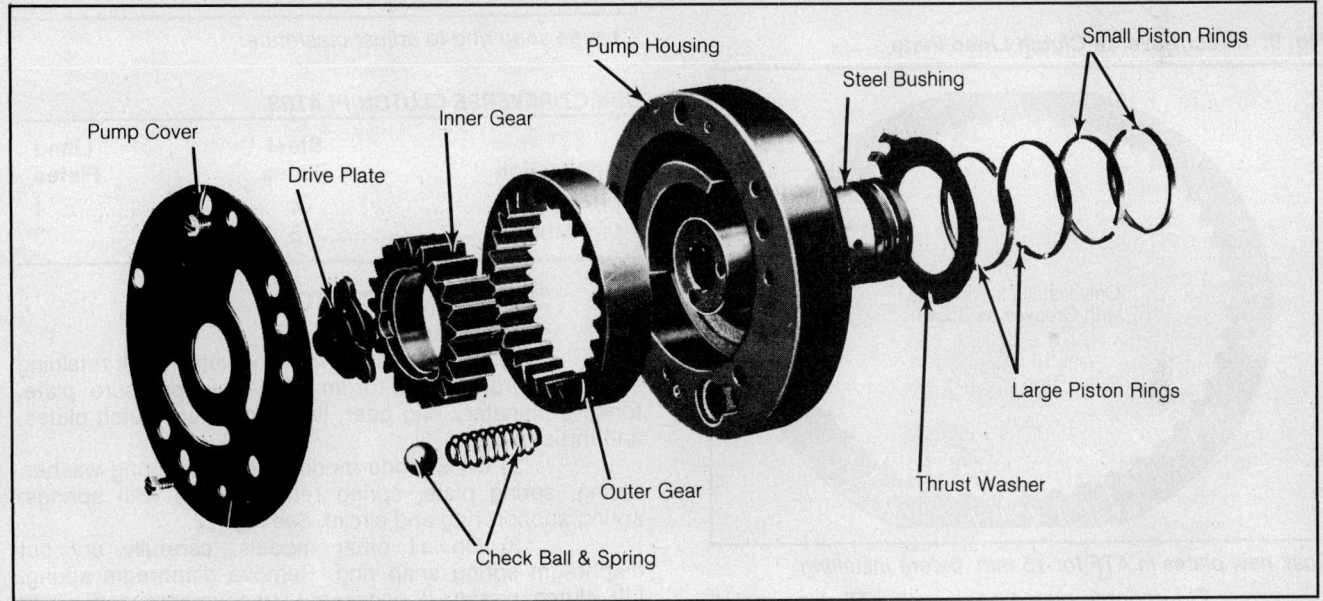

Fig. 8: Exploded View Showing Components of Direct/Reverse Clutch Assembly

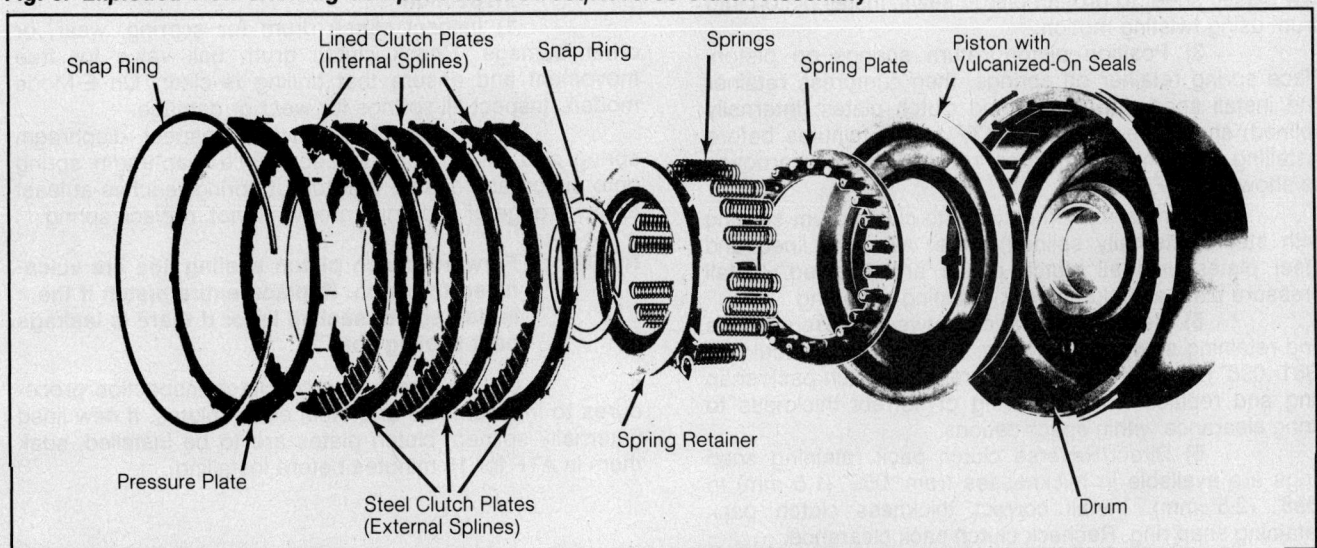

Transmission model 089 is shown. Model 087 uses 4 inner splined and 4 outer splined plates.

Automatic Transmissions

AUDI 4000S, 4000S QUATTRO, 5000S, PORSCHE 944 & VOLKSWAGEN QUANTUM (Cont.)

3) If necessary for replacement, place clutch drum in press and drive bushing out of drum using bushing driver.

Inspection

1) Inspect friction surfaces of piston and drum for wear or damage. Check clutch drum ball valve for free movement. Inspect piston springs for wear or collapsed coils and replace as necessary.

2) Inspect steel (externally splined) clutch plates. If plates are scored or have radial grooves, they must be replaced. Plates that are only discolored can be reused.

3) Inspect lined (internally splined) clutch plates. Replace any plate that is worn, damaged, or burned.

Reassembly

1) If removed, press new bushing into clutch drum until it is .067" (1.7 mm) below lip of drum hub on all models.

Fig. 9: Direct/Reverse Clutch Lined Plate

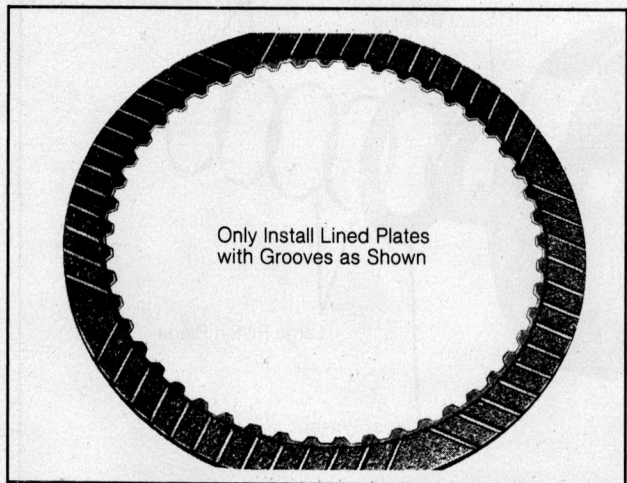

Only Install Lined Plates with Grooves as Shown

Soak new plates in ATF for 15 min. before installing.

2) Lubricate piston seals with ATF, then install them into clutch drum with lips facing into drum. Using stiff plastic sheet to protect piston seals, install piston into drum using twisting motion.

3) Position piston return springs on piston. Place spring retainer on springs, then compress retainer and install snap ring. New lined clutch plates (internally splined) should be soaked in ATF for 15 minutes before installing. Use only lined plates with identification grooves as shown. *See Fig. 9.*

4) Install clutch plates into clutch drum starting with steel (externally splined) plate. Alternate lined and steel plates until all clutch plates are installed. Install pressure plate and clutch pack retaining snap ring.

5) Measure clearance between pressure plate and retaining snap ring. *See Fig. 10.* Clearance should be .081-.098" (2.05-2.50 mm). If not, remove clutch pack snap ring and replace with snap ring of correct thickness to bring clearance within specifications.

6) Direct/Reverse clutch pack retaining snap rings are available in thicknesses from .059" (1.5 mm) to .098" (2.5 mm). Install correct thickness clutch pack retaining snap ring. Recheck clutch pack clearance.

Fig. 10: Measuring Direct/Reverse Clutch Clearance

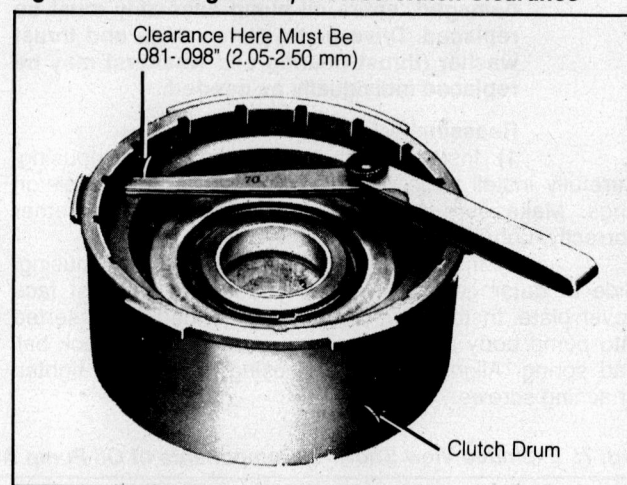

Clearance Here Must Be .081-.098" (2.05-2.50 mm)

Clutch Drum

Change snap ring to adjust clearance.

DIRECT/REVERSE CLUTCH PLATES

Application	Steel Plates	Lined Plates
087 Models	4	4
089 Models	3	3

FORWARD CLUTCH

Disassembly

1) Using screwdriver, pry clutch pack retaining snap ring from clutch drum. Withdraw pressure plate, forward planetary ring gear, lined and steel clutch plates, and thrust plate.

2) On E-Mode models, remove spring washer, spring, spring plate, spring retaining ring with springs, spring support ring and circlip. *See Fig. 12.*

3) On all other models, carefully pry out diaphragm spring snap ring. Remove diaphragm spring. Lift clutch piston. If necessary, use compressed air to force clutch piston from drum. *See Fig. 11.*

Inspection

1) Inspect clutch drum for scoring, wear, or other damage. Check clutch drum ball valve for free movement and ensure that drilling is clear. On E-Mode models, inspect all springs for wear or damage.

2) On all other models, inspect diaphragm spring and piston for damage. Place diaphragm spring onto piston and ensure that top of spring reaches at least to lower edge of snap ring groove. If not, replace spring.

NOTE: **Forward clutch piston sealing lips are vulcanized to piston. Replace entire piston if there is damage to sealing lip or if there is leakage past sealing lips.**

3) Use direct-reverse clutch inspection procedures to inspect lined and steel clutch plates. If new lined (internally splined) clutch plates are to be installed, soak them in ATF for 15 minutes before installing.

AUDI 4000S, 4000S QUATTRO, 5000S, PORSCHE 944 & VOLKSWAGEN QUANTUM (Cont.)

Fig. 11: Exploded View of Forward Clutch Assembly

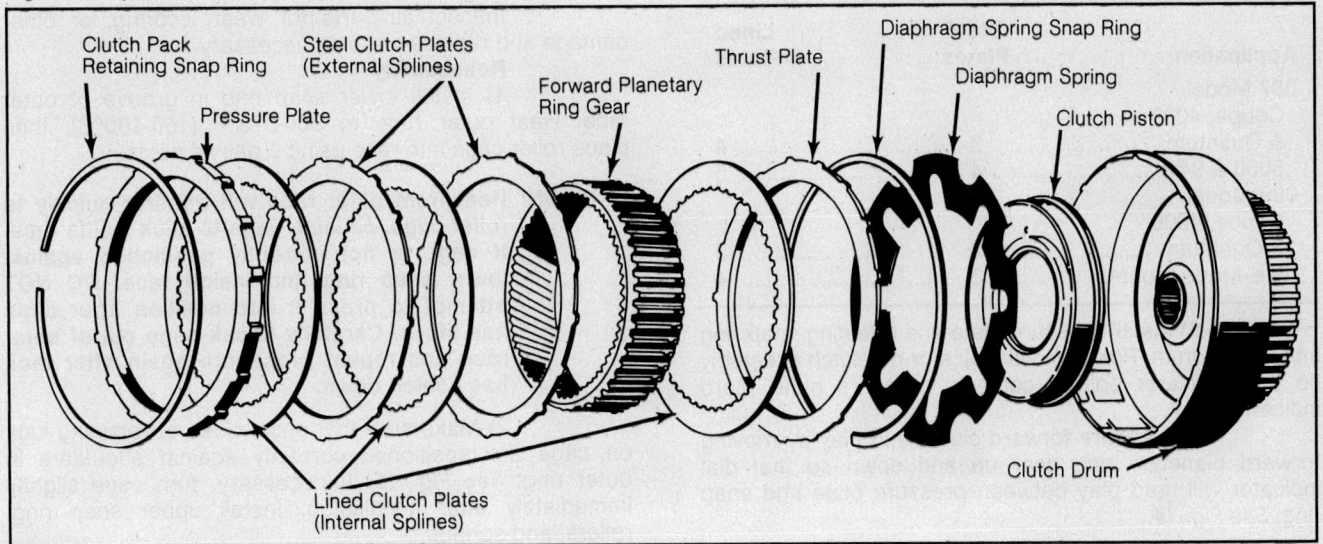

Fig. 12: Exploded View of E-Mode Forward Clutch Assembly

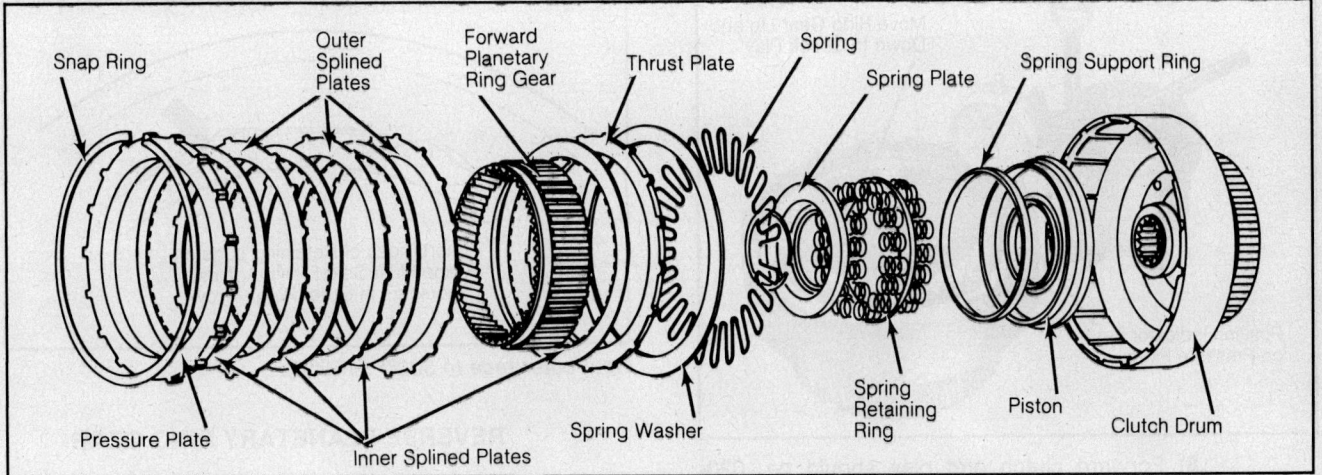

Reassembly

1) Lubricate piston sealing lips with ATF. Install piston into drum using twisting motion. On all models except E-Mode, install diaphragm spring, with convex side toward piston, into clutch drum. Install retaining snap ring.

2) With snap ring installed, diaphragm spring should be lightly tensioned; if not, replace spring. Install thrust plate into drum. If one side of thrust plate is chamfered, install chamfered side toward diaphragm spring.

3) On E-Mode models, install spring support ring and spring retaining ring. Springs must be installed with small diameter toward spring plate. Install spring plate and circlip. Install spring and spring washer with convex side toward piston. Install thrust plate.

4) On all models, install one lined (internally splined) clutch plate. Use only lined plates with identification grooves as shown. See Fig. 13. Install forward planetary ring gear so that short splines beneath its retaining ridge are engaged in lined clutch plate.

5) Install remaining clutch plates starting with steel (externally splined) clutch plate and alternating lined and steel plates until all clutch plates are installed. See Forward Clutch Plates chart.

Fig. 13: Forward Clutch Lined Plate

Only Install Lined Plates with Grooves as Shown

Soak new plates in ATF for 15 min. before installing.

Automatic Transmissions

AUDI 4000S, 4000S QUATTRO, 5000S, PORSCHE 944 & VOLKSWAGEN QUANTUM (Cont.)

FORWARD CLUTCH PLATES

Application	Steel Plates	Lined Plates
087 Model		
Coupe, 4000		
& Quantum	3	4
5000 & 944	4	5
089 Model		
Coupe, 4000		
& Quantum	2	3
All E-Mode Models	3	4

6) Install pressure plate and retaining snap ring into clutch drum. Position dial indicator on clutch assembly so that indicator pointer contacts pressure plate. Zero indicator.

7) Measure forward clutch end play by moving forward planetary ring gear up and down so that dial indicator will read play between pressure plate and snap ring. See Fig. 14.

Fig. 14: Measuring Forward Clutch End Play

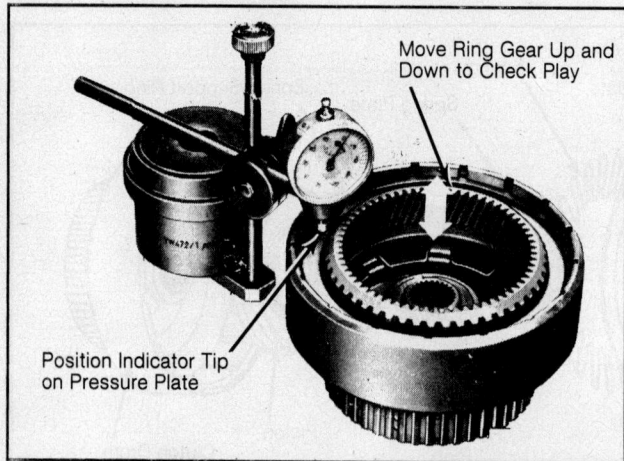

Move Ring Gear Up and Down to Check Play

Position Indicator Tip on Pressure Plate

8) Forward clutch end play should be .020-.035" (.50-.90 mm) on all models. If not, replace pressure plate (except E-Mode models) with one of correct thickness to bring play within specifications. After correct pressure plate has been installed, recheck end play.

9) Forward clutch pressure plates are available in thicknesses of 2.3-3.9 mm with .4 mm increments for all 087 models except for those in Quantum vehicles. Quantum 087 models use pressure plates ranging from 6.0-7.6 mm with .4 mm increments.

10) In 5000 087 models, both 2.3-3.9 mm and 6.0-7.6 mm ranges are available. On 089 models in Coupe, 4000 and Quantum vehicles, forward clutch pressure plates are available in thicknesses of 6.0-7.6 mm with .4 mm increments.

11) All E-Mode transaxles adjust forward clutch end play by replacing snap ring. Snap rings are available in 1.5, 1.7, 2.0, 2.3, 2.5, 2.9, 3.2, and 3.5 mm.

FIRST GEAR ONE-WAY CLUTCH

Disassembly
Remove one-way clutch rollers and spring. Remove snap rings. Using plastic hammer, carefully drive roller cage out of outer race.

Inspection
Inspect all parts for wear, scoring, or other damage and replace parts as necessary.

Reassembly
1) Install lower snap ring in groove of outer race. Heat outer race to 300-375°F (150-190°C), then place roller cage into race using 2 pair of pliers.

CAUTION: **Heat from outer race will transfer quickly to roller cage, causing cage to stick inside race. If cage is not correctly positioned against lower snap ring and inside race, DO NOT attempt to press it into position after cage has stuck. Carefully knock cage out of outer race and repeat procedure again after race has cooled down.**

2) Make sure that short sides of retaining lugs on cage are positioned correctly against shoulders in outer ring. See Fig. 15. If necessary, turn cage slightly immediately after installation. Install upper snap ring, rollers, and springs.

Fig. 15: Installing Cage Into Outer Race

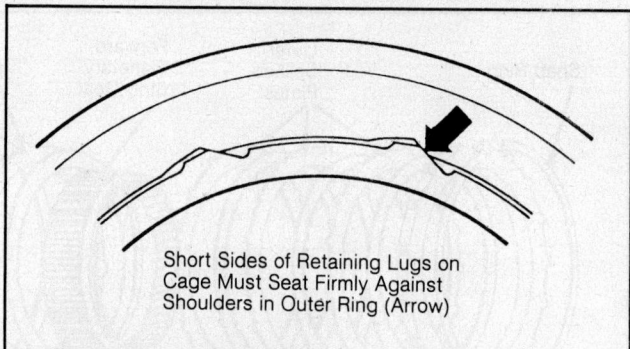

Short Sides of Retaining Lugs on Cage Must Seat Firmly Against Shoulders in Outer Ring (Arrow)

Heat outer race to 300°F (150°C).

REVERSE PLANETARY RING GEAR

NOTE: **Only disassemble reverse planetary ring gear if one of components requires replacement.**

Disassembly & Reassembly
Remove snap ring and lift ring gear hub from ring gear. Inspect parking lock notches on ring gear for wear. Replace if worn. To reassemble, reverse disassembly procedure.

VALVE BODY ASSEMBLY

CAUTION: **As valve body components are removed from each valve body bore, place individual parts in tray (2008) in correct order to simplify reassembly. DO NOT interchange valves or valve springs. Several valve springs have identical dimensions but different tolerances. Individual valve body components are not available. Valve bodies are available only as exchange units.**

Disassembly
1) Remove transfer plate-to-main valve body attaching screws. Lift transfer plate and separator plate

AUDI 4000S, 4000S QUATTRO, 5000S, PORSCHE 944 & VOLKSWAGEN QUANTUM (Cont.)

from main valve body. Remove main valve body check balls from passages in valve body. *See Fig. 18.*

Fig. 16: Exploded View of One-Way Clutch

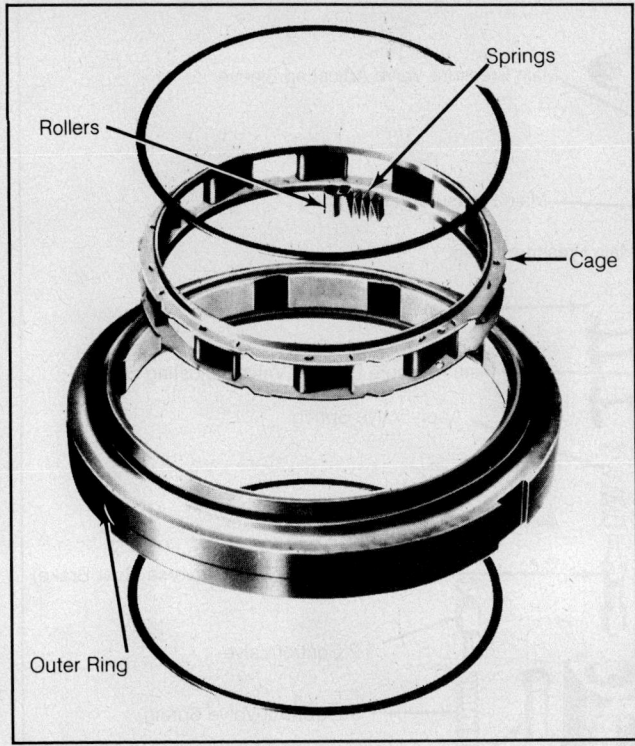

Fig. 17: Removing Valve Body Assembly

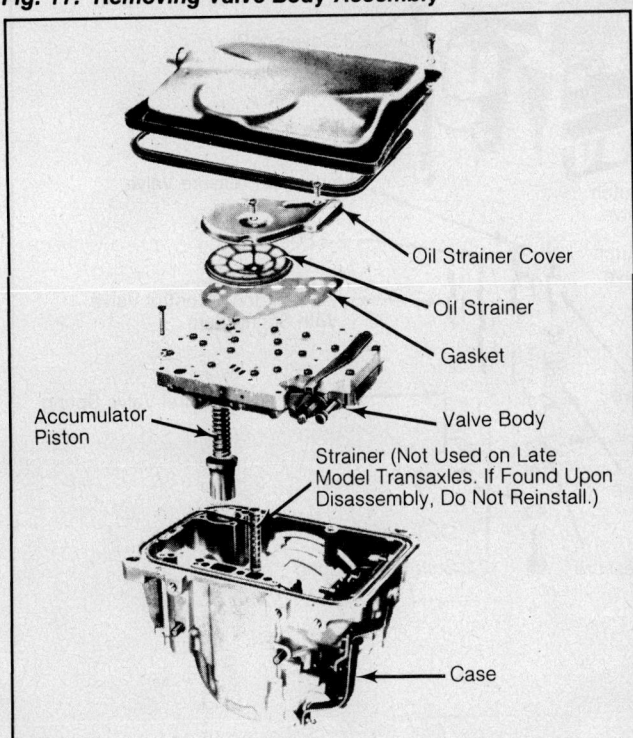

Fig. 18: Main Valve Body Check Ball Locations

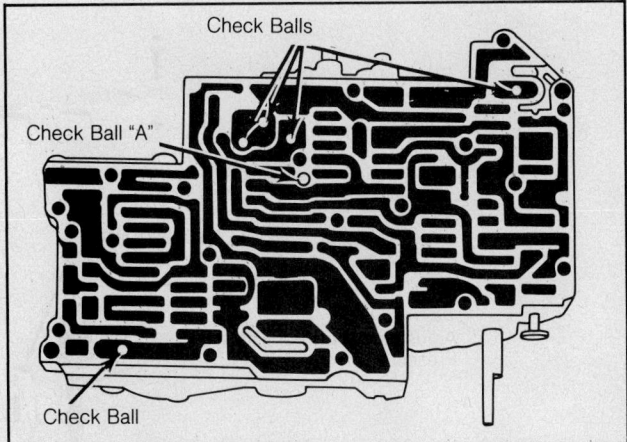

Small check ball "A" is .12" (3.0 mm) in diameter.

CAUTION: DO NOT alter settings of adjusting screws. Adjusting screws change pressures and can only be properly adjusted on test stand.

2) Remove rear end cover plate and withdraw valves, springs, and adjusting screws. Remove remaining end plates one at time and withdraw all valves, plugs, springs and adjusting screws. Tag all parts for reassembly reference or use tray (2008) to hold parts. This tray holds springs and valves in correct order and location.

Inspection

1) Wash all parts in clean solvent and dry them with compressed air only. DO NOT use rags or water. Lint from rags can cause problems in flow of ATF after reassembly. Check all parts for burrs and scores. Replace assembly if damaged.

NOTE: Valves which are slightly scored may be reused, if they slide under their own weight after cleaning and lubrication with fresh ATF. This scoring will not affect operation of transmission.

Fig. 19: Sealing Balls in Valve Body Transfer Plate

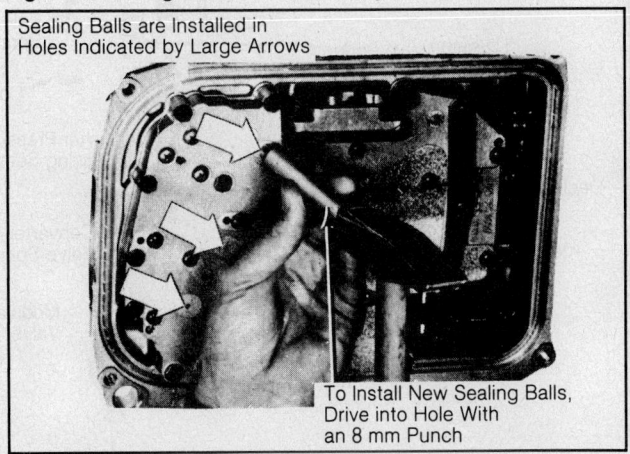

Automatic Transmissions

AUDI 4000S, 4000S QUATTRO, 5000S, PORSCHE 944 & VOLKSWAGEN QUANTUM (Cont.)

Fig. 20: Exploded View of Valve Body

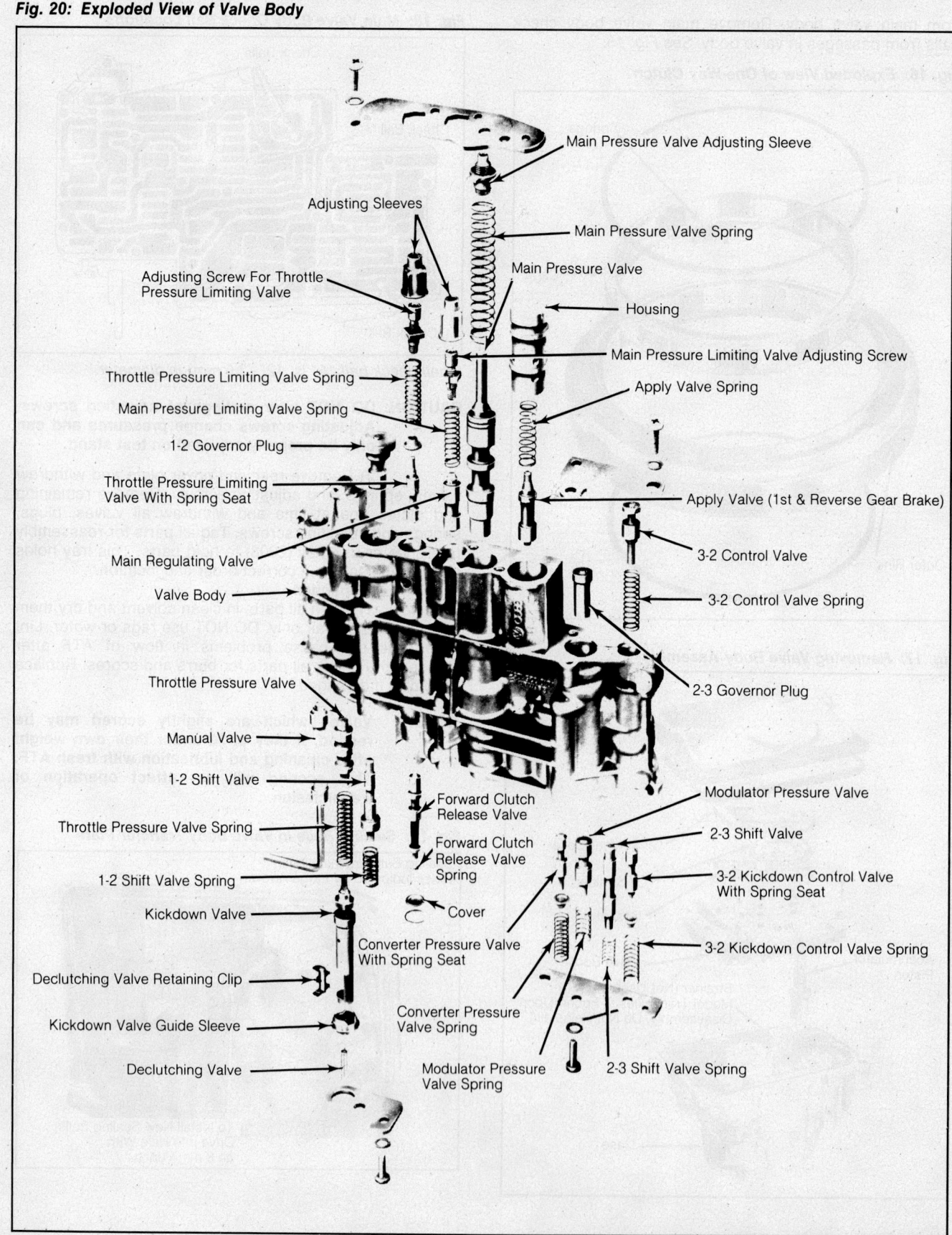

Main Pressure Valve Adjusting Sleeve

Adjusting Sleeves

Main Pressure Valve Spring

Adjusting Screw For Throttle Pressure Limiting Valve

Main Pressure Valve

Housing

Throttle Pressure Limiting Valve Spring

Main Pressure Limiting Valve Adjusting Screw

Apply Valve Spring

Main Pressure Limiting Valve Spring

1-2 Governor Plug

Throttle Pressure Limiting Valve With Spring Seat

Apply Valve (1st & Reverse Gear Brake)

3-2 Control Valve

Main Regulating Valve

Valve Body

3-2 Control Valve Spring

Throttle Pressure Valve

2-3 Governor Plug

Manual Valve

1-2 Shift Valve

Modulator Pressure Valve

Forward Clutch Release Valve

2-3 Shift Valve

Throttle Pressure Valve Spring

Forward Clutch Release Valve Spring

3-2 Kickdown Control Valve With Spring Seat

1-2 Shift Valve Spring

Kickdown Valve

Cover

3-2 Kickdown Control Valve Spring

Declutching Valve Retaining Clip

Converter Pressure Valve With Spring Seat

Kickdown Valve Guide Sleeve

Converter Pressure Valve Spring

Declutching Valve

Modulator Pressure Valve Spring

2-3 Shift Valve Spring

E-Mode is shown. Other models are similar.

AUDI 4000S, 4000S QUATTRO, 5000S, PORSCHE 944 & VOLKSWAGEN QUANTUM (Cont.)

2) Check all valve body springs for damage or collapsed coils. Some transfer plates are equipped with three sealing balls. *See Fig. 19.* If transmission did not shift into 3rd gear, trouble may be caused by missing sealing ball.

3) To install new sealing balls, stick .118" (3 mm) diameter sealing ball on 8 mm diameter punch with small amount of grease and drive ball flush into hole of transfer plate.

Reassembly

1) Lubricate all parts with ATF and install into proper valve body bores in reverse order of disassembly. DO NOT overtighten plate attaching screws. Overtightening can strip threads or distort valve body enough to cause valve to stick.

2) Ensure all check balls are installed in proper valve body passages. Check ball "A" is .12" (3 mm) in diameter. All other check balls are .24" (6 mm) in diameter. *See Fig. 18.* Install transfer plate-to-main valve body screws and tighten from center outward. DO NOT overtighten.

GOVERNOR ASSEMBLY

NOTE: Governor is mounted in final drive assembly.

Removal

Remove cover bolts and washers. Remove governor cover and "O" ring from final drive housing. Withdraw governor from housing with clockwise turning motion to allow governor drive gear to disengage from drive pinion gear.

Disassembly

Remove 2 attaching screws and withdraw thrust plate and governor housing. Remove transfer plate (noting position), balance weight and oil strainer (if equipped). Remove "E" clip and pull centrifugal weight, valve, spring and dished washer from pin.

Reassembly

Reverse disassembly procedure and lubricate all parts with ATF when reassembling. Transfer plate must be reinstalled in same position. DO NOT reinstall oil strainer. Be sure angle in thrust plate is in center of housing so cover will bear against it.

Installation

Check governor oil seal and needle bearing in housing for damage or wear. Replace if necessary. Reverse removal procedure to install. Rotate governor to engage drive gear.

BAND SERVO

Disassembly

Pull servo piston assembly out of cover, then remove "O" ring seals from outer diameter of cover. Remove retaining "E" clip and separate piston pin, accumulator spring, spring seat and adjusting shim from servo piston. Remove 2 seals from servo piston.

Inspection

Clean all parts and check for wear, scoring, or other damage. All parts in assembly must be replaced if piston is damaged.

Reassembly

1) Position spring seat, accumulator spring and shim on piston pin. Install assembly into servo piston and install retaining "E" clip onto pin.

2) Install lip seals onto piston with smaller (upper) seal with lip facing upward into servo cover. Larger seal is positioned with lip facing downward, out of servo cover.

3) Lubricate assembly thoroughly and install piston into cover. Install "O" rings on outer diameter of servo cover.

Fig. 21: Exploded View of Governor Assembly

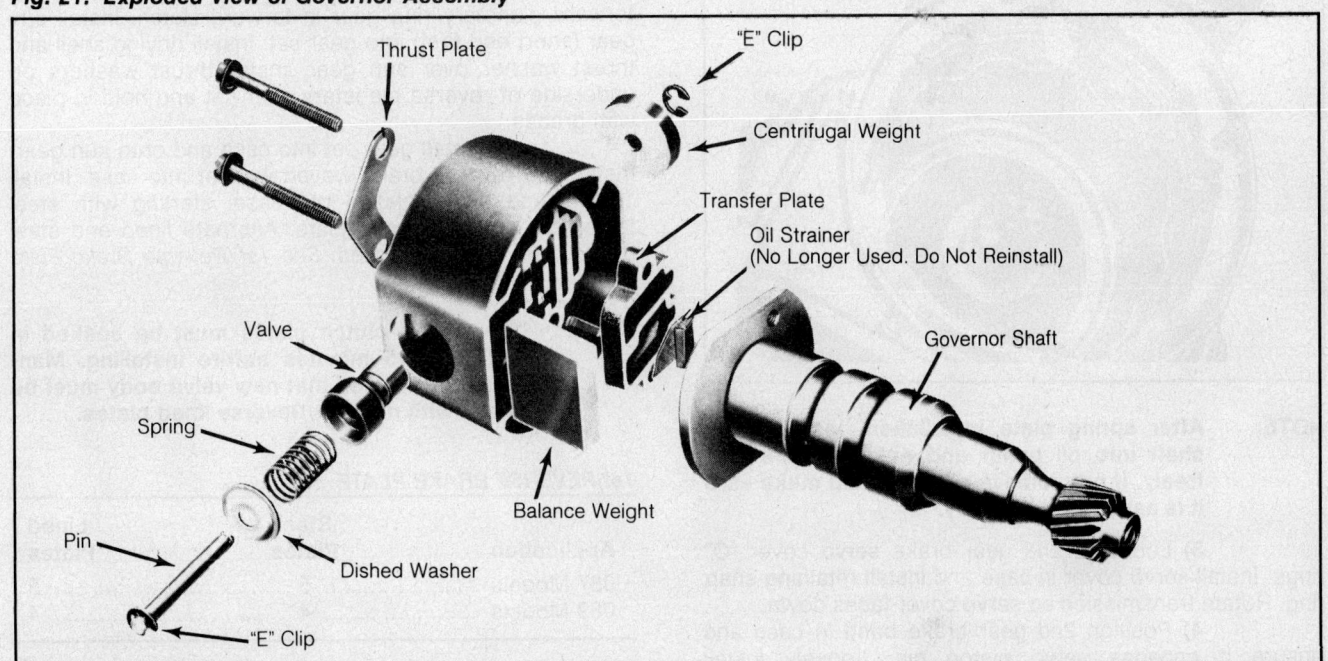

Note transfer plate position for reassembly.

Automatic Transmissions

AUDI 4000S, 4000S QUATTRO, 5000S, PORSCHE 944 & VOLKSWAGEN QUANTUM (Cont.)

Fig. 22: Exploded View of Band Servo Assembly

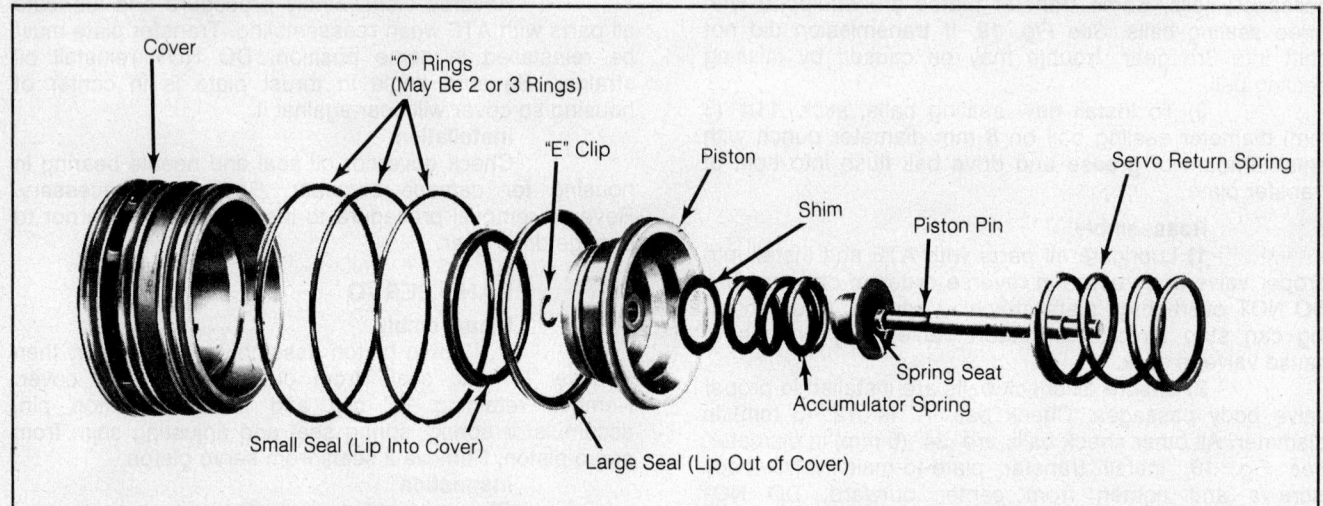

Cover
"O" Rings (May Be 2 or 3 Rings)
"E" Clip
Piston
Shim
Piston Pin
Servo Return Spring
Spring Seat
Accumulator Spring
Small Seal (Lip Into Cover)
Large Seal (Lip Out of Cover)

TRANSMISSION REASSEMBLY

1) Lubricate 1st/Reverse brake piston with ATF. Install brake piston on oil pump. Install oil pump and piston assembly into case. Position pump so thin rib on pump body is toward top of case. Install thrust washer on pump face.

2) Install 1st/Reverse brake shell into transmission case so lug engages in groove at top of case. Install 1st/Reverse brake piston return springs on spring plate. Insert assembly into case with springs downward. Install attaching bolts and tighten in diagonal pattern.

Fig. 23: Installing Brake Shell in Transmission Case

Lug Must Engage Groove at Top of Case

NOTE: After spring plate installation, insert pump shaft into oil pump and ensure gears turn freely. If not, remove oil pump and make sure it is assembled properly.

3) Lubricate 2nd gear brake servo cover "O" rings. Install servo cover in case and install retaining snap ring. Rotate transmission so servo cover faces down.

4) Position 2nd gear brake band in case and ensure it engages servo piston pin. Loosely install pushrod for adjusting screw. Install adjusting screw and

lock nut. Place 2 thrust washers and thrust bearing in position on end of oil pump and hold in place with grease.

5) Install forward clutch into Direct/Reverse clutch, making sure splines on forward clutch drum fully engage splines in Direct/Reverse clutch lined plates. Turn transmission case so open end points down at angle. Lubricate and install Direct/Reverse and forward clutch assemblies as unit.

6) Slide clutch assembly unit onto oil pump neck and into 2nd gear brake band. Tighten 2nd gear brake band adjusting screw just enough to prevent band from shifting its position on Direct/Reverse clutch drum. Rotate transmission case so open end is up.

7) Install forward planetary-to-forward clutch needle bearing into forward clutch. Needle bearing is installed with smaller inside diameter toward forward planetary gear.

8) Install forward planetary gear set into forward planetary ring gear in forward clutch. Install sun gear (short end first) into gear set. Install driving shell and thrust washer over sun gear. Install thrust washers on underside of reverse planetary gear set and hold in place with grease.

9) Install gear set into case and onto sun gear. Install 1st/Reverse brake waved washer into case. Install 1st/Reverse brake plates into case, starting with steel (externally splined) brake plate. Alternate lined and steel plates until all are installed. See 1st/Reverse Brake Plate chart.

NOTE: New lined clutch plates must be soaked in ATF for 15 minutes before installing. Manufacturer states that new valve body must be used with new 1st/Reverse lined plates.

1st/REVERSE BRAKE PLATE

Application	Steel Plates	Lined Plates
087 Models	5	5
089 Models	4	4

AUDI 4000S, 4000S QUATTRO, 5000S, PORSCHE 944 & VOLKSWAGEN QUANTUM (Cont.)

10) Install 1st gear one-way clutch assembly into transmission case. Insert retaining key between case and one-way clutch. Push clutch downward while rotating reverse planetary gear set to fully engage parts.

NOTE: With one-way clutch installed, it should not be possible to rotate reverse planetary gear set counterclockwise due to locking of one-way clutch.

11) Install one-way clutch-to-case snap ring. Snap ring opening must be opposite to retaining key. If all parts are correctly installed, one-way clutch snap ring groove will be exposed. Do not force snap ring into groove of incorrectly assembled transmission.

12) Position thrust washer and needle bearing on rear side of reverse planetary gear set. Larger inside diameter collar faces toward reverse planetary gear set. Install reverse planetary ring gear into case so it fully engages reverse planetary gear set.

13) Install new separation plate gasket over case studs and place separation plate over gasket. Install and tighten retaining screws.

Fig. 24: Installing One-Way Clutch Snap Ring

Parts are Installed Correctly if Groove for One-Way Clutch Snap Ring is Exposed

Opening of snap ring must be opposite retaining key (White arrow).

NOTE: Second gear brake band must be adjusted at this time. Transmission case must be horizontal during adjustment to prevent band from jamming.

14) Tighten brake band adjusting screw to 87 INCH Lbs. (10 N.m). Loosen screw. Retighten to 43 INCH Lbs. (5 N.m). Back off adjusting screw exactly 2 1/2 turns on 089 models and on 087 models found in 5000 vehicles. Back off adjusting screw exactly 2 turns on all other 087 models. Tighten adjusting screw lock nut.

15) If case linkage was disassembled, reinstall in case. *See Fig. 5.* Install accumulator piston with seal lip pointing toward case. Install accumulator piston spring in piston.

16) Install valve body assembly into case, making sure manual valve engages manual lever and kickdown valve engages kickdown lever. Install valve body-to-case bolts and tighten from center outward.

17) Position new pan gasket on transmission case. Install oil pan and tighten oil pan bolts.

NOTE: See Final Drive Assembly for installation of turbine and pump shaft and measurement of play between transmission and final drive.

FINAL DRIVE

DISASSEMBLY

NOTE: Backlash and turning torque should be measured and recorded before final drive disassembly. If parts are used again, set backlash and turning torque to same values as measured. See Pinion Shaft Turning Torque and Pinion Depth and Bearing Preload procedures for measuring instructions.

1) Place final drive housing in holding fixture. Mark position of side bearing adjusting rings before removing. Remove governor assembly from final drive housing. Use slide hammer to remove governor oil seal and needle bearing together.

2) Remove ATF oil cooler from case. Remove final drive housing front cover. Use slide hammer to remove front cover if necessary. Remove pinion rear cover. Remove retaining bolt from center of each axle drive flange. Pull flanged shafts out of final drive housing.

3) Remove bolts and lock plates from adjusting rings. Remove adjusting rings with spanner (VW 544). Pull pinion out slightly. Tilt differential case assembly with ring gear to one side and remove. Lift pinion shaft out of housing.

4) Place differential case assembly in soft jaw vise with ring gear attaching bolts up. Loosen attaching bolts and remove ring gear by tapping lightly on bolt heads.

5) Remove pinion gears, side gears, thrust washers and nuts for axle shaft drive flange retaining bolts. Remove differential side bearings and speedometer drive gear (if equipped) with press or gear puller. Mark side bearings so that they may be reinstalled in same position and with matching outer race.

CAUTION: If original shims are to reused, note number and thickness of pinion adjusting shims on pinion shaft for reassembly reference. When pressing drive pinion bearings on or off, use extreme care to avoid damage to any teeth on shaft.

6) Remove drive pinion bearings using press. Remove rear pinion bearing and oil sleeve together. Pinion bearing outer races and oil seals will also have to be replaced if pinion bearings are replaced. Remove torque converter seal from front cover. Remove front cover pinion seal.

7) Press pinion bearing outer race from front cover. Drive both pinion oil seals from rear cover using driver. Press pinion bearing outer race from rear cover using driver.

NOTE: If pinion bearing outer races are being removed from both front and rear covers, be sure to keep races with their respective bearings.

Automatic Transmissions

AUDI 4000S, 4000S QUATTRO, 5000S, PORSCHE 944 & VOLKSWAGEN QUANTUM (Cont.)

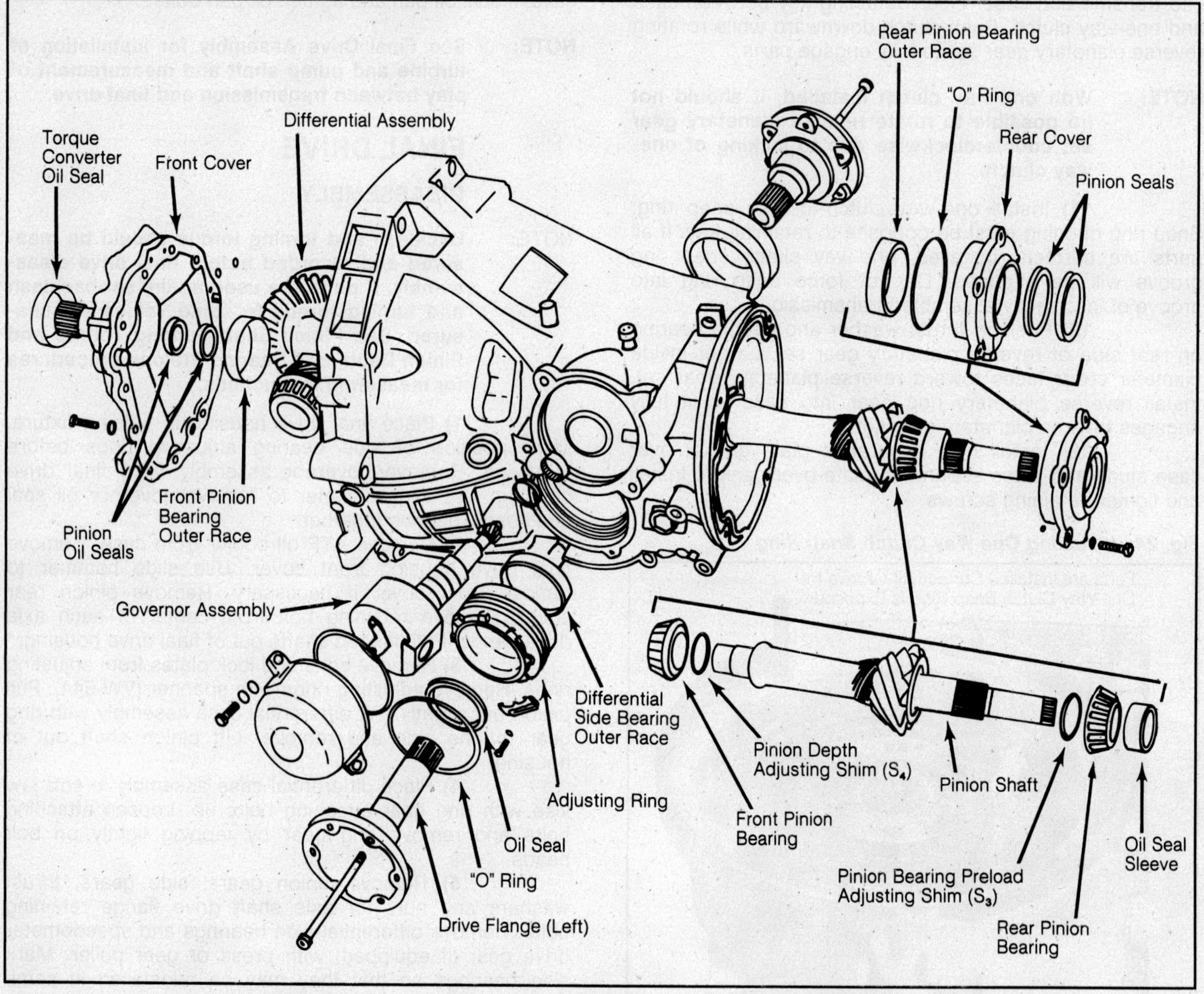

Fig. 25: Exploded View of Typical Final Drive Assembly

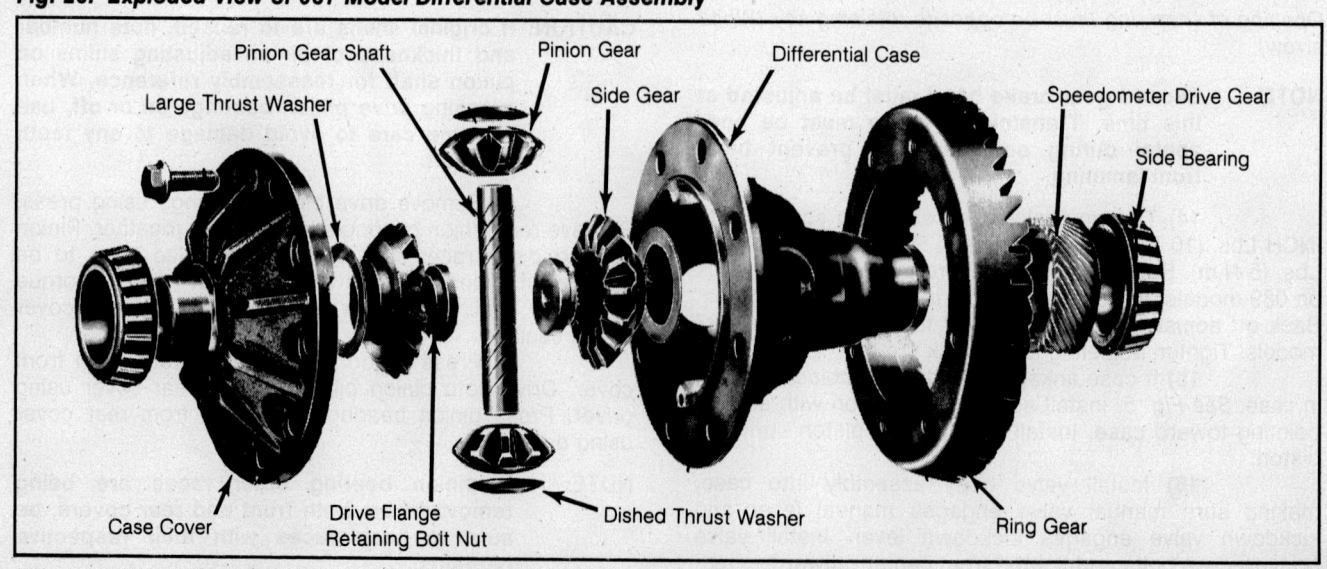

Torque Converter Oil Seal

Front Cover

Differential Assembly

Rear Pinion Bearing Outer Race

"O" Ring

Rear Cover

Pinion Seals

Front Pinion Bearing Outer Race

Pinion Oil Seals

Governor Assembly

Differential Side Bearing Outer Race

Adjusting Ring

Oil Seal

"O" Ring

Drive Flange (Left)

Pinion Depth Adjusting Shim (S_4)

Front Pinion Bearing

Pinion Bearing Preload Adjusting Shim (S_3)

Pinion Shaft

Rear Pinion Bearing

Oil Seal Sleeve

Fig. 26: Exploded View of 087 Model Differential Case Assembly

Large Thrust Washer

Pinion Gear Shaft

Pinion Gear

Side Gear

Differential Case

Speedometer Drive Gear

Side Bearing

Case Cover

Drive Flange Retaining Bolt Nut

Dished Thrust Washer

Ring Gear

AUDI 4000S, 4000S QUATTRO, 5000S, PORSCHE 944 & VOLKSWAGEN QUANTUM

REASSEMBLY & ADJUSTMENTS

Differential Assembly

1) Inspect all thrust surfaces on differential case, cover, ring gear, pinion shaft and thrust washers. Replace all worn parts. Inspect gear teeth for burrs and excessive wear. Replace as necessary.

NOTE: **If either pinion shaft or ring gear requires replacement, replace both as set.**

2) Position differential side gears, large thrust washers, dished thrust washers and pinion gear into differential case. Align pinion gear holes with holes in case. Drive pinion shaft through pinion gears. If pinion shaft does not fit tightly, replace it.

3) Place differential cover on differential case. Install 2 centering pins in opposite ring gear attaching bolt holes. Heat ring gear to about 212° F (100° C), then position it on housing. Remove centering pins and tighten attaching bolts.

NOTE: **On 087 models with pressed on speedometer gear, new speedometer gear must be pressed onto differential case before side bearing installation.**

4) Heat side bearings in hot oil and press them onto differential case and cover. Press side bearing outer races into position in side bearing adjusting rings.

NOTE: **If original parts are reused, use same thickness pinion depth and bearing preload adjusting shims as were removed during disassembly.**

Pinion Depth and Bearing Preload

1) Heat pinion shaft bearings to about 212° F (100° C) in oil bath. Press rear (larger) bearing onto shaft without any shim until seated at back of gear with 3 tons of pressure. Press front (smaller) bearing onto pinion shaft with 1.1 mm test shim installed behind bearing.

CAUTION: **If pinion shaft is installed into housing without this test shim installed, it will contact housing and cause incorrect reading.**

2) Install final drive housing front cover (without oil seals) and tighten attaching bolts. Position pinion shaft in place in housing. Install rear cover (without oil seals) and tighten attaching bolts.

3) Install magnetic plate (VW 385/17) onto rear end of pinion shaft. Attach dial indicator to final drive housing so indicator tip is touching magnetic plate on pinion shaft. Zero indicator. Move pinion shaft up and down (without turning) and note indicator reading.

CAUTION: **If pinion shaft is turned during measurement, readings will be incorrect due to settling of bearings.**

4) Add end play measured on dial indicator, plus .25 mm for settling allowance (constant value), plus .15 mm for bearing preload, plus 1.1 mm for thickness of test shim. Total is thickness of shims required to obtain proper pinion depth and bearing preload. Record total shim pack thickness.

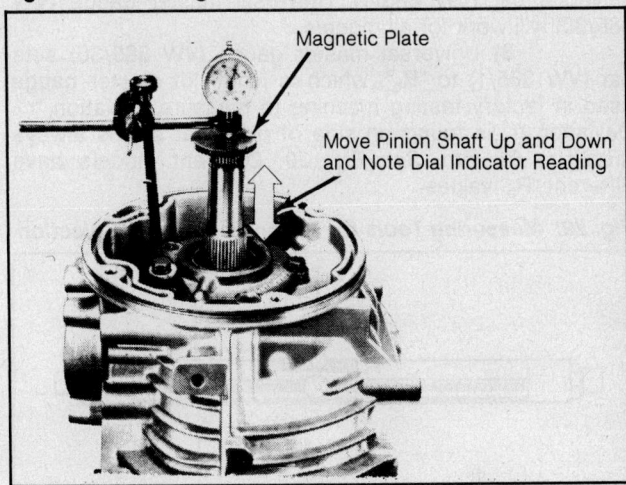

Fig. 27: Measuring Pinion Shaft End Play

Magnetic Plate

Move Pinion Shaft Up and Down and Note Dial Indicator Reading

Turning drive pinion will cause incorrect reading.

5) Remove rear cover and pinion shaft from housing. Press front pinion bearing from shaft, remove test shim, and install shims equal to total thickness determined in step 4). Heat and press bearing back onto pinion shaft.

6) Reinstall pinion shaft in housing. Reinstall rear cover and tighten bolts. Turn pinion in both directions several times. Install special gauge plate (VW 385/28) on pinion shaft. See Fig. 28. Adjust clamp ring on universal measuring bar (VW 385/1) until distance "A" is 3.23" (82 mm) for 087 models or 2.28" (58 mm) for 089 models. See Fig. 29.

Fig. 28: Installation of Measuring Tools for 089 Model Pinion Depth

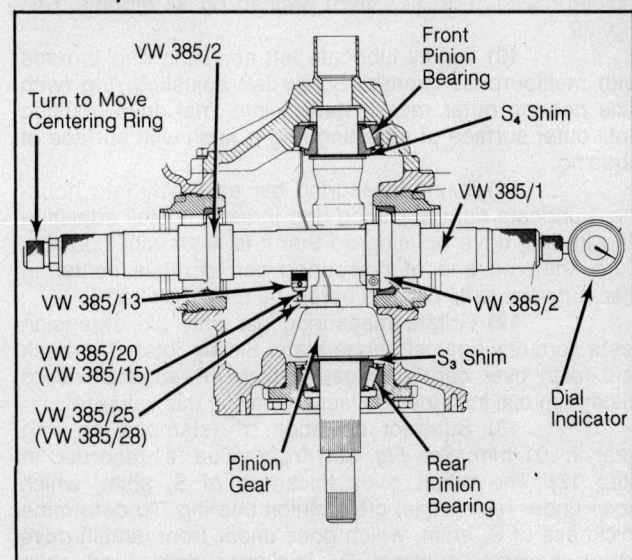

VW 385/2

Front Pinion Bearing

Turn to Move Centering Ring

S₄ Shim

VW 385/1

VW 385/13

VW 385/2

VW 385/20 (VW 385/15)

S₃ Shim

VW 385/25 (VW 385/28)

Dial Indicator

Pinion Gear

Rear Pinion Bearing

Tool numbers in parentheses are for 087 models.

7) Assemble dial indicator, centering discs (VW 385/2), measuring pin (VW 385/13), extension (VW 385/15 for 087 models; VW 385/20 for 089 models) and master (setting) gauge to measuring bar (VW 385/1). Master gauge usage varies with model and is needed to adjust

AUDI 4000S, 4000S QUATTRO, 5000S, PORSCHE 944 & VOLKSWAGEN QUANTUM (Cont.)

universal bar (VW 385/1). Universal master gauge (VW 385/30) will work for all models.

8) Universal master gauge (VW 385/30) sets bar (VW 385/1) to "R_o", which is length of master gauge used in factory testing machine to measure deviation "r". Deviation "r" is found on side of ring gear and is always given in .01 mm. *See Fig. 30*. Different models have different "R_o" values.

Fig. 29: *Measuring Tools for Pinion Depth Shim Selection*

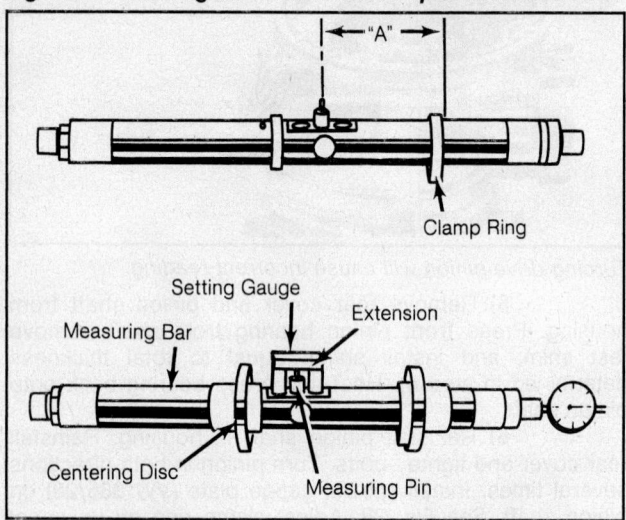

9) All 087 models have "R_o" of 46.60 mm. All 089 models have "R_o" of 40.55 mm. Individual master gauges are available. All 087 models use master gauge VW 385/26. All 089 models use master gauge VW 385/5. With bar assembled and master gauge in place, set dial indicator with .118" (3.0 mm) preload on all models. *See Fig. 29*.

10) Lightly lubricate left adjusting ring threads with multipurpose grease. Screw left adjusting ring (with side bearing outer race installed) into final drive housing until outer surface of adjusting ring is flush with surface of housing.

11) Insert measuring bar assembly into housing. Lubricate right adjusting ring threads. Install adjusting ring in final drive housing so that it is flush with housing. Turn knob on end of measuring bar to move centering disc outward, until bar can barely be turned by hand.

12) Rotate measuring bar until pin extension rests squarely against gauge plate. Slowly rotate bar back and forth over center of gauge plate. Read and record maximum dial indicator deflection, calling this value "e".

13) Subtract deviation "r" (stamped on ring gear in .01 mm; *See Fig. 30*.) from value "e" recorded in step **12)**. The result gives thickness of S_3 shim, which goes under rear (large) drive pinion bearing. To determine thickness of S_4 shim, which goes under front (small) drive pinion bearing, subtract S_3 thickness from total shim thickness as determined in step **4)**.

14) Shims for S_3 and S_4 are available in thicknesses from 1.100-1.900 mm in increments of .025 mm. Measure selected shims at several points, looking for burrs or other damage. Install selected shims and bearings on drive pinion shaft. Install drive pinion in housing and lubricate bearings with hypoid oil.

15) Reinstall universal measuring bar (VW 385/1) and make sure that indicator reading agrees with deviation "r", ±.04 mm. Remove measuring bar.

Fig. 30: *Meaning of Numbers on Side of Ring Gear*

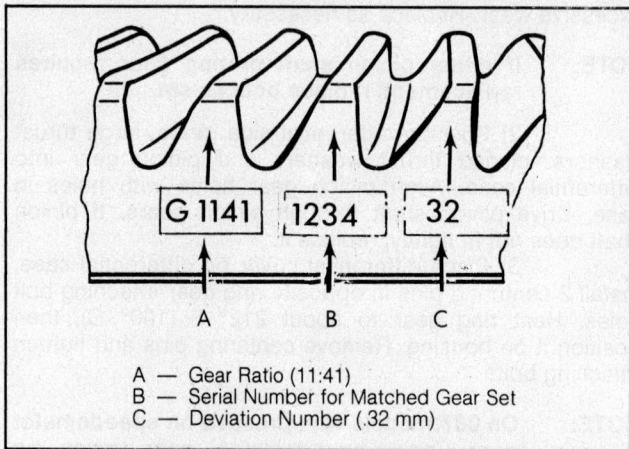

A — Gear Ratio (11:41)
B — Serial Number for Matched Gear Set
C — Deviation Number (.32 mm)

Deviation number is called "r" in calculations.

Pinion Shaft Turning Torque

After installing correct pinion adjusting shims, check turning torque of pinion shaft. Turning torque for all models should be 22-49 INCH Lbs. (2.5-5.5 Nm). If turning torque is incorrect, recheck shim thicknesses for proper bearing preload.

NOTE: **Turning torque value is for new bearings only. If used bearings are reinstalled, turning torque should be same as that measured before disassembly.**

Fig. 31: *Checking Pinion Shaft Turning Torque*

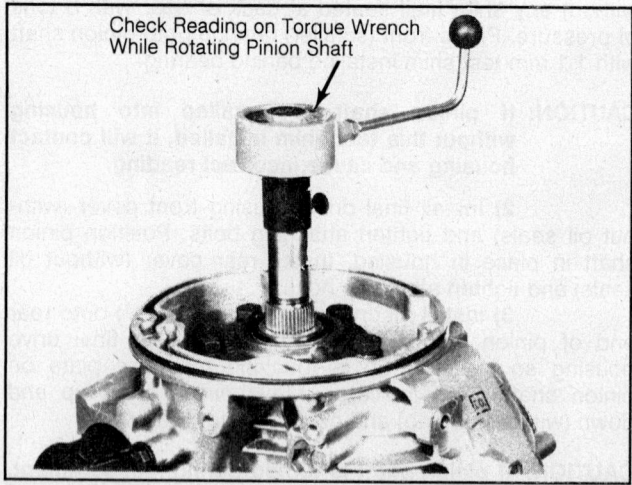

Turning torque should be 22-49 INCH Lbs. (2.5-5.5 Nm) with new bearings.

Side Bearing Preload & Ring Gear Backlash

1) After adjusting pinion shaft depth and bearing preload, remove front and rear covers from final drive housing. Withdraw pinion shaft. Install differential assembly and pinion shaft into final drive housing.

AUDI 4000S, 4000S QUATTRO, 5000S, PORSCHE 944 & VOLKSWAGEN QUANTUM (Cont.)

2) Install new oil seals into front and rear covers. Install new "O" ring on rear cover. Lubricate "O" ring and pinion shaft bearings. Apply sealer to bolt flange of front cover. Install front and rear covers and tighten attaching bolts.

3) Install new "O" rings on differential side bearing adjusting rings. Lightly coat "O" rings and threads on adjusting rings with multi-purpose grease. Lubricate bearings with hypoid gear oil. Install each adjusting ring into housing until surfaces between tooth divisions are flush with housing surface.

4) Turn in right adjusting ring slowly until ring gear meshes fully with pinion gear without backlash. Screw in left adjusting ring (opposite ring gear) as far as possible. Preload left ring slightly to take play out of differential side bearings.

Fig. 32: Adjusting Side Bearing Preload and Ring Gear Backlash

Adjusting Ring (Left Side Shown) Arrow
Indicates 2 Tooth Division Adjustment

Use spanner (VW 544) to turn adjusting rings.

5) Turn right adjusting ring 1/2 tooth division out. Turn left adjusting ring 2 tooth divisions in. This should correctly set side bearing preload and ring gear backlash.

6) To check ring gear backlash, turn pinion shaft several times in both directions to settle bearings. Using holding tool (VW 386a), clamp pinion shaft so that it cannot turn.

7) Insert clamping sleeve (VW 521/4) with slotted sleeve (VW 521/7 on 089 models; 521/8 on 087 models) into differential through adjusting ring and secure with nut. Adjust length of backlash measuring bar (VW 388) to 2.44" (62 mm) on 089 models or to 2.68" (68 mm) on 087 models.

NOTE: See Figures 33 and 34 for assembly and positioning of ring gear backlash measuring tools.

8) Attach measuring bar (VW 388) to clamping sleeve (VW 521/4). Install dial indicator with square end extension (VW 382/10) in holder (VW 387) and attach holder to final drive housing.

NOTE: Dial indicator tip must be located at right angle to backlash measuring lever.

Fig. 33: Adjusting Measuring Bar Length for Ring Gear Backlash Check

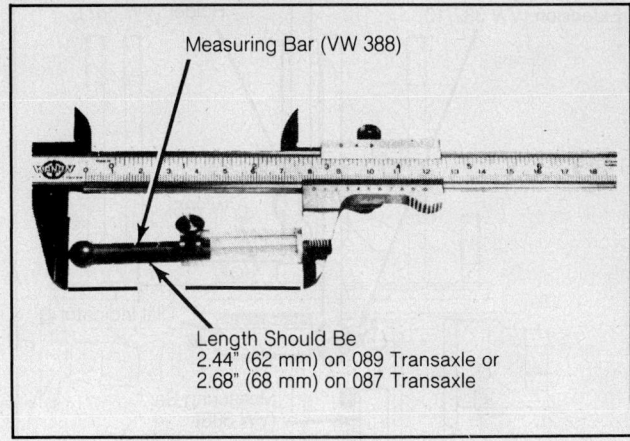

Measuring Bar (VW 388)

Length Should Be
2.44" (62 mm) on 089 Transaxle or
2.68" (68 mm) on 087 Transaxle

9) Turn ring gear to take up backlash. Zero dial indicator and clamp in holder. Turn ring gear in opposite direction until it touches pinion gear again and note indicator reading. This reading is ring gear backlash.

10) Check ring gear backlash at 4 locations (90° apart) around circumference of ring gear. Add 4 measurements together, then divide total by 4. Resulting figure is average ring gear backlash. Ring gear backlash should be .006-.010" (.15-.25 mm).

NOTE: Backlash specifications apply to new ring and pinion set. If ring and pinion are reused, backlash should be set to same value as found prior to disassembly.

CAUTION: Difference between individual backlash measurements must not exceed .002" (.05 mm). If measurements differ more than this, ring gear or pinion shaft is incorrectly installed.

11) If backlash is not within specifications, correct by turning both side bearing adjusting rings by equal amounts in opposite directions. Adjusting rings must be moved in equal amounts to maintain bearing preload.

NOTE: If new differential side bearings have been installed as well as new pinion shaft bearings, recheck pinion shaft turning torque. With differential installed, pinion shaft turning torque should be approximately 3.5-4.4 INCH lbs. (.4-.5 N.m) greater than it was when only pinion shaft was installed.

12) Install side bearing adjusting ring lock plate. Recheck total bearing preload to ensure no alterations were made during backlash adjustment.

Final Assembly of Transaxle

1) To measure end play between final drive housing and transmission, place straightedge on transmission attaching face of final drive housing. Using depth gauge, measure distance from top surface of straightedge down to edge of pinion shaft oil seal sleeve.

Automatic Transmissions

AUDI 4000S, 4000S QUATTRO, 5000S, PORSCHE 944 & VOLKSWAGEN QUANTUM (Cont.)

Fig. 34: Positioning of Ring Gear Backlash Measuring Tools

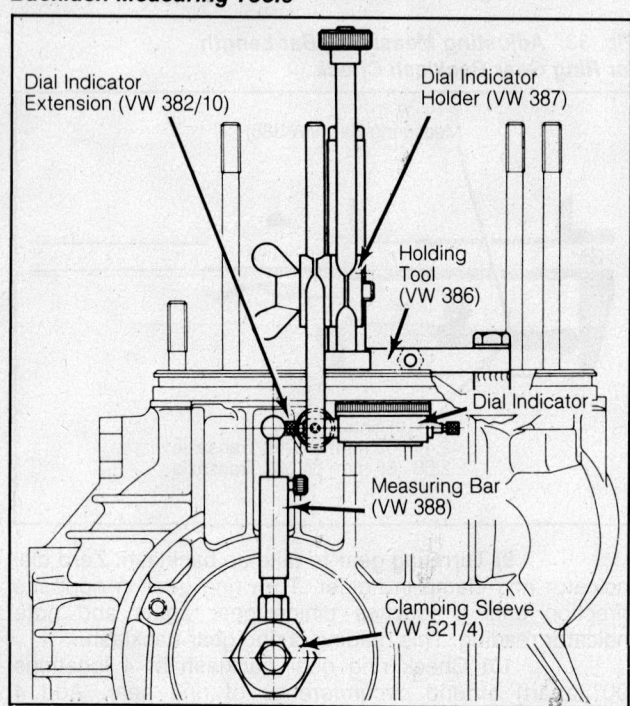

Fig. 35: Measurements to Adjust Transmission-to-Final Drive End Play

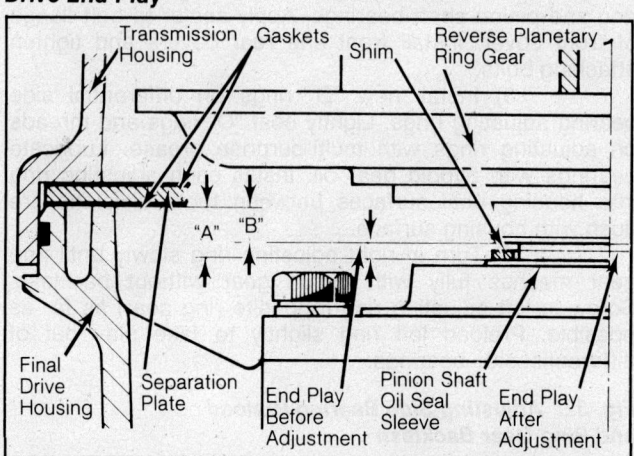

Transmission-to-final drive end play limits end play of reverse planetary ring gear.

2) Measure distance from top surface of straightedge to face of final drive housing. Subtract straightedge-to-face distance from straightedge-to-oil seal sleeve distance. Result is measurement "A". *See Fig. 35.* Note result for future reference.

3) With new gasket on transmission separation plate, position straightedge on transmission case. Measure distance from top surface of straightedge down to gasket surface.

4) Measure distance from top surface of straightedge down to shim surface on shoulder of reverse planetary gear set ring gear. Subtract straightedge-to-shoulder measurement from straightedge-to-gasket measurement. Result is measurement "B". *See Fig. 35.* Note answer for next step.

5) Subtract measurement "B" obtained in step 4) from measurement "A" obtained in step 2). Result is end play (without shims) between final drive and transmission.

6) Select proper end play shim(s) to use by finding applicable end play reading in left column of *End Play Shim Selection* chart. Use shim(s) of thickness noted in right column. Use minimum number of shims possible.

7) Transmission-to-final drive end play adjusting shims are available in 2 thicknesses: .016" (.4 mm) and .047" (1.2 mm). Combine shim thicknesses to obtain total thickness required. Install selected end play adjusting shim(s) on top of pinion shaft oil seal sleeve in final drive case.

8) Install sealing "O" ring into groove around final drive housing. Install turbine shaft and pump shaft fully into pinion shaft of final drive. End of turbine shaft with piston rings must be toward transmission with rings inside pinion shaft.

9) Turbine shaft used in 087 models is 16.71" (424.5 mm) with 20.2" (513 mm) pump shaft. Turbine shaft used in 089 models is 15.82" (401.7 mm) with 19.32" (490.6 mm) pump shaft.

10) Mate final drive and transmission cases. Install final drive-to-transmission case nuts and tighten. Drive governor needle bearing into final drive case until it stops, using driver (VW 545). Using driver and collar (VW 545 and VW 545/2), install governor oil seal with lip facing out toward governor. Place new "O" ring seals onto governor cover and speedometer driven gear assembly.

11) Install governor, cover, and speedometer driven gear into case. Install transaxle oil cooler. Ensure pump shaft is fully inserted into pump splines before installing converter. Install torque converter onto stator support to complete assembly. Make sure torque converter engages splines on pump shaft.

END PLAY SHIM SELECTION

If End Play Is In. (mm)	Install This Shim In. (mm)
.009-.003 (.23-.84)	None
.033-.049 (.85-1.24)	.016 (.4)
.049-.065 (1.25-1.64)	.032 (.8)
.065-.080 (1.65-2.04)	.048 (1.2)
.081-.096 (2.05-2.44)	.064 (1.6)
.096-.112 (2.45-2.84)	.080 (2.0)
.112-.128 (2.85-3.24)	.096 (2.4)
.128-.143 (3.25-3.64)	.112 (2.8)
.144-.153 (3.65-3.88)	.128 (3.2)

TIGHTENING SPECIFICATIONS

Application	Ft. Lbs. (N.m)
Band Adjusting Screw Lock Nut	14 (19)
Drive Flange-To-Differential	18 (25)
Front or Rear Cover-To-Housing	18 (25)
Kickdown Lever Nut	11 (15)
Manual Valve Lever Nut	14 (19)
Rear Mount-To-Case	40 (54)
Ring Gear-To-Differential Case	
Porsche 944	58-69 (78-93)
All Others	52 (70)
Torque Converter-To-Drive Plate	22 (30)
Transmission-To-Engine	40 (54)
Transmission-To-Final Drive	22 (30)

BORG-WARNER MODEL 66

Jaguar XJ6

DESCRIPTION

Transmission is a fully automatic 3-speed unit consisting basically of a 3 element torque converter and a compound planetary gear set. Two multiple-disc clutches, one roller clutch, and two brake bands provide friction elements required to obtain desired function of planetary gear set. Hydraulic control system, pressurized by gear-type oil pump, provides working pressure required to operate automatic controls. Transmission kickdown is actuated by cable attached to accelerator assembly and a cam in transmission case.

LUBRICATION & ADJUSTMENTS

See appropriate AUTOMATIC TRANSMISSION SERVICING article in IMPORT GENERAL SERVICING section.

TROUBLE SHOOTING

ROUGH INITIAL ENGAGEMENT

Engine idle speed too high. Throttle cable out of adjustment. Valve body assembly faulty, valves sticking or worn.

NO ENGAGEMENT

In Any Position

Incorrect fluid level. Manual linkage out of adjustment. Throttle cable out of adjustment. Input shaft broken. Primary regulator valve sticking. Front pump worn.

In Forward Gears

Governor valve stuck or damaged. Output shaft seal rings or governor pressure tube seals worn or faulty. Also check front clutch, stator support shaft bearing, and front seal rings on sun gear shaft.

In 1st Gear in "D"

One-way clutch faulty or installed backwards.

In 2nd Gear

Front band faulty or out of adjustment. Front servo piston or seals worn or damaged. Oil pipes loose, damaged, or missing. Foreign matter or damage in valve body.

In 3rd Gear

Foreign matter in valve body or governor. Check rear clutch feed pipes, rear clutch, and piston rings in hub of intermediate shaft.

No Overrun Braking in "1"

Rear band out of adjustment or worn. Rear servo seals or feed pipes damaged or missing.

SLIPPING OR LATE SHIFTS

Throttle cable out of adjustment. Main pressure not within specifications (check oil pump and seals on pump tubes). Governor faulty. Valve body faulty. Check output

Fig. 1: Cross-Sectional View of Borg-Warner Model 66 Automatic Transmission

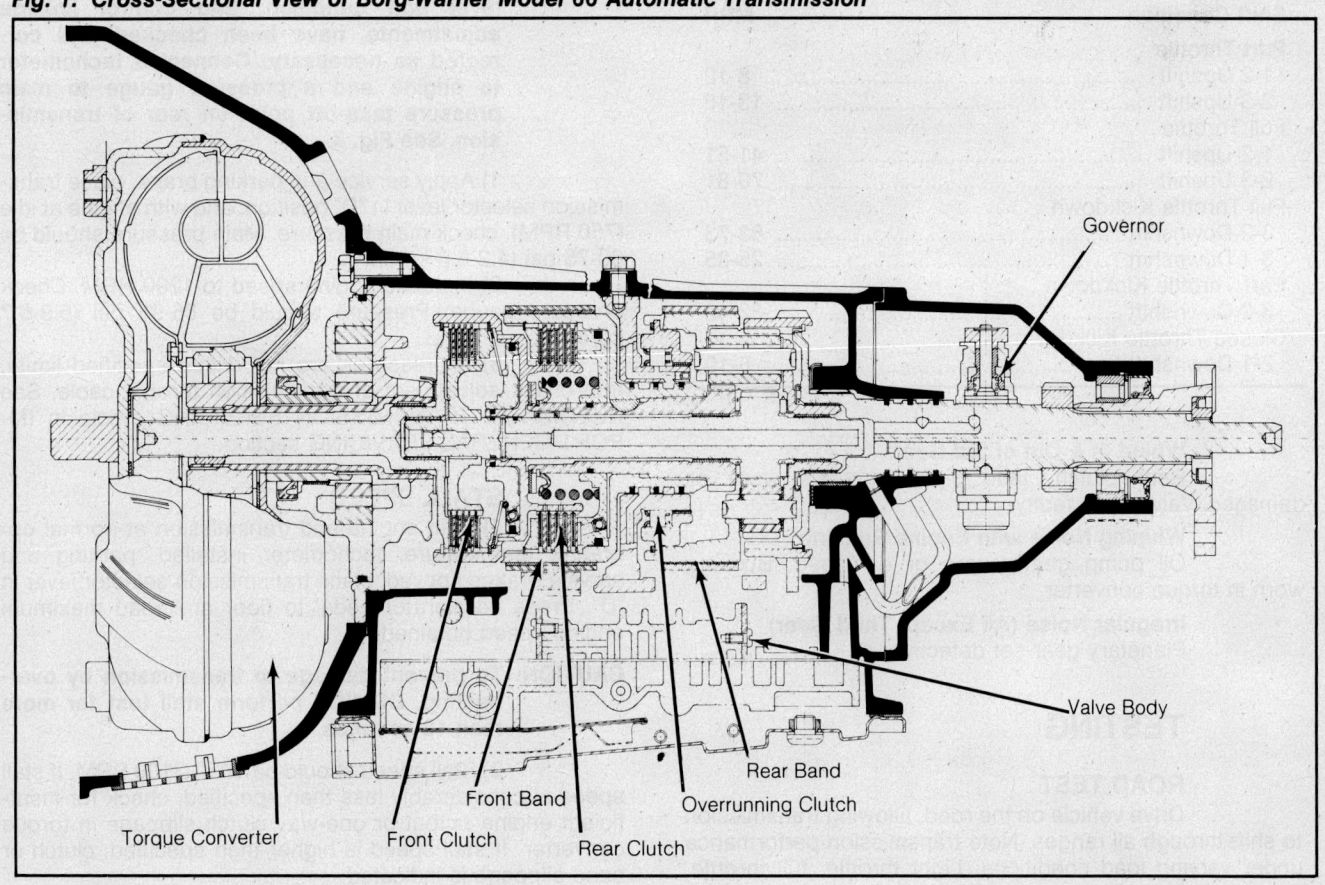

Governor

Valve Body

Rear Band

Overrunning Clutch

Torque Converter

Front Band

Front Clutch

Rear Clutch

CLUTCH AND BAND APPLICATION CHART
(ELEMENTS IN USE)

Selector Lever Position	Front Clutch	Rear Clutch	Front Band	Rear Band	One-Way Clutch
D – DRIVE					
First Gear	X				X
Second Gear	X		X		
Third Gear	X	X			
2 – INTERMEDIATE					
Second Gear	X		X		
1 – LOW	X			X	
R – REVERSE		X		X	

NEUTRAL OR PARK – All clutches, brakes, and bands released and/or ineffective.

shaft oil seal rings and governor tubes for wear or damage. Check front and rear bands and servos for wear or damage.

TRANSMISSION NOISE
Whine In & Out of 2nd Gear
Front band out of adjustment. Front servo parts worn or damaged. Oil pipes loose. Front band worn or damaged. Valve body faulty.

SHIFT SPEED SPECIFICATIONS

Shift Condition	MPH
Part Throttle	
1-2 Upshift	8-12
2-3 Upshift	13-18
Full Throttle	
1-2 Upshift	41-51
2-3 Upshift	73-81
Full Throttle Kickdown	
3-2 Downshift	63-73
3-1 Downshift	25-35
Part Throttle Kickdown	
3-2 Downshift	32-42
Closed Throttle Kickdown	
2-1 Downshift	5-10

Whine In & Out of 3rd Gear
Rear clutch, feed pipe, or seals worn or damaged. Valve body faulty.
Whining Noise with Engine Running
Oil pump gears worn or damaged. Bushing worn in torque converter.
Irregular Noise (All Except Third Gear)
Planetary gear set defective.

TESTING

ROAD TEST
Drive vehicle on the road, allowing transmission to shift through all ranges. Note transmission performance under varying load conditions: Light throttle, full throttle,

and kickdown. Transmission should operate smoothly but firmly, with no apparent slipping or engine speed flare-up. Check for proper transmission shift points. See SHIFT SPEED SPECIFICATIONS table.

NOTE: **Shift speeds may vary slightly due to production tolerances, rear axle ratio, or tire size.**

HYDRAULIC PRESSURE TESTS
NOTE: **Before making pressure test, ensure fluid level and condition, and control linkage adjustments, have been checked and corrected as necessary. Connect a tachometer to engine and a pressure gauge to main pressure take-off point on rear of transmission. See Fig. 3.**

1) Apply service and parking brake, place transmission selector lever in "D" position, and with engine at idle (750 RPM), check main pressure. Main pressure should be 60-75 psi (4.2-5.3 kg/cm^2).

2) Increase engine speed to 1200 RPM. Check pressure gauge. Pressure should be 85-95 psi (5.9-6.7 kg/cm^2).

3) If pressures are not within specified limits, first check adjustment of transmission throttle cable. See AUTOMATIC TRANSMISSION SERVICING article in IMPORT GENERAL SERVICING section.

STALL SPEED
1) With engine and transmission at normal operating temperature, tachometer installed, parking and service brakes applied, place transmission selector lever in "D". Press accelerator pedal to floor and read maximum engine speed obtained.

CAUTION: **To prevent damage to transmission by overheating, DO NOT perform stall test for more than 10 seconds.**

2) Stall speed should be 1950-2100 RPM. If stall speed is considerably less than specified, check for insufficient engine output or one-way clutch slippage in torque converter. If stall speed is higher then specified, clutch or band slippage is indicated.

Automatic Transmissions

BORG-WARNER MODEL 66 (Cont.)

Fig. 2: Borg-Warner Model 66 Automatic Transmission Hydraulic Circuits Diagram

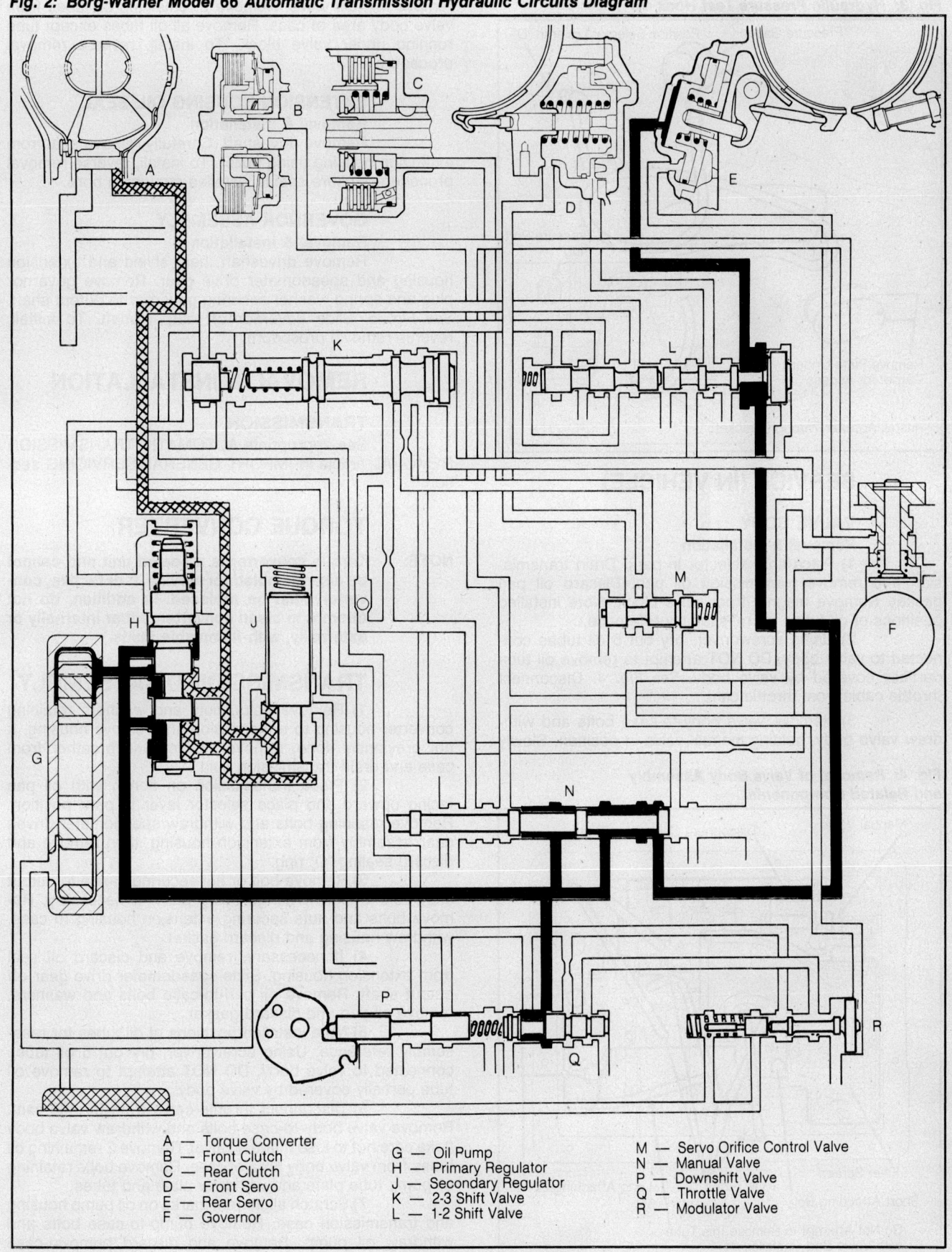

A — Torque Converter
B — Front Clutch
C — Rear Clutch
D — Front Servo
E — Rear Servo
F — Governor

G — Oil Pump
H — Primary Regulator
J — Secondary Regulator
K — 2-3 Shift Valve
L — 1-2 Shift Valve

M — Servo Orifice Control Valve
N — Manual Valve
P — Downshift Valve
Q — Throttle Valve
R — Modulator Valve

Automatic Transmissions
BORG-WARNER MODEL 66 (Cont.)

Fig. 3: Hydraulic Pressure Test Hook-Up

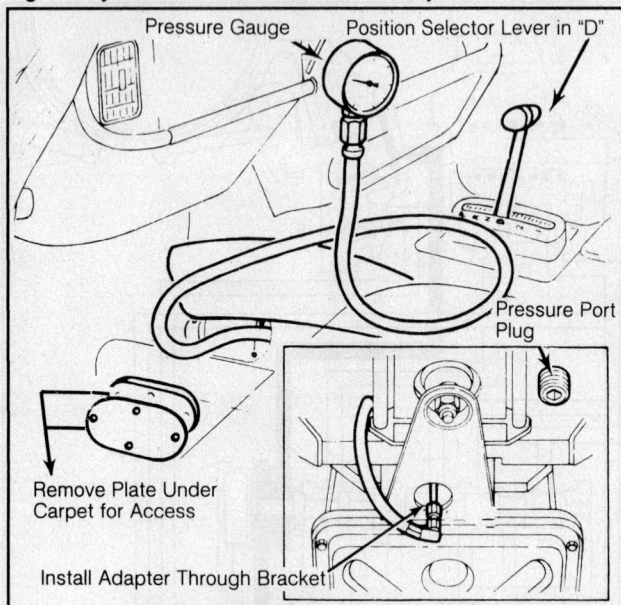

SERVICE (IN VEHICLE)

VALVE BODY
Removal & Installation

1) Place shift selector in park. Drain transmission and remove transmission oil pan. Discard oil pan gasket. Remove magnet from valve block. Note installed positions of oil tubes for reassembly reference.

2) Using screwdriver, pry out 5 oil tubes connected to valve body. DO NOT attempt to remove oil tube partially covered by valve body. *See Fig. 4.* Disconnect throttle cable from throttle cam.

3) Remove valve body-to-case bolts and withdraw valve body, holding manual valve in position. Slowly

Fig. 4: Removal of Valve Body Assembly and Related Components

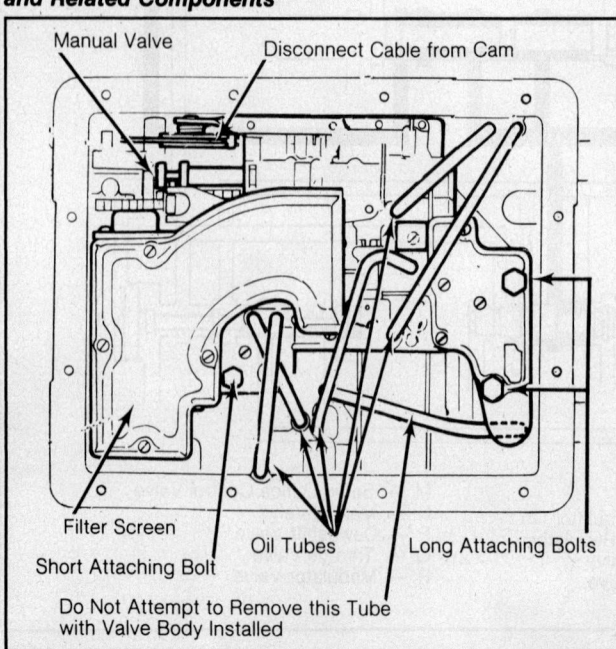

remove manual valve. Remove 2 remaining oil tubes from valve body area of case. Remove all oil tubes except tube running under valve block. To install, reverse removal procedure.

EXTENSION HOUSING OIL SEAL
Removal & Installation

Remove driveshaft. Carefully remove seal from extension housing using puller. To install, reverse removal procedure. Ensure seal is installed straight in bore.

GOVERNOR ASSEMBLY
Removal & Installation

Remove driveshaft, heat shield and extension housing and speedometer drive gear. Remove governor plug and spring washer securing governor to output shaft. *See Fig. 5.* Slide governor off output shaft. To install, reverse removal procedure.

REMOVAL & INSTALLATION

TRANSMISSION

See appropriate AUTOMATIC TRANSMISSION REMOVAL article in IMPORT GENERAL SERVICING section.

TORQUE CONVERTER

NOTE: **Torque converter is a sealed unit and cannot be disassembled for service. If defective, converter must be replaced. In addition, do not attempt to clean converter, either internally or externally, with flammable fluids.**

TRANSMISSION DISASSEMBLY

1) Remove bolts, nuts and washers retaining converter housing to transmission and remove housing. If not previously done, remove dipstick and breather from case and drain transmission fluid.

2) Place transmission on bench with oil pan facing upward and place selector lever in park position. Remove retaining bolts and withdraw speedometer driven gear assembly from extension housing, then remove and discard sealing "O" ring.

3) Remove bolt or nut securing flange to output shaft and withdraw flange using puller if necessary. Remove bolts and nuts securing extension housing to case, withdraw housing and discard gasket.

4) If necessary, remove and discard oil seal from extension housing. Slide speedometer drive gear off output shaft. Remove oil pan-to-case bolts and washers, remove oil pan and discard gasket.

5) Note installed positions of oil tubes for reassembly reference. Using screwdriver, pry out 5 oil tubes connected to valve body. DO NOT attempt to remove oil tube partially covered by valve body.

6) Disconnect throttle cable from throttle cam. Remove valve body-to-case bolts and withdraw valve body (take care not to lose manual valve). Remove 2 remaining oil tubes from valve body area of case. Remove bolts retaining oil pump tube plate and withdraw plate and tubes.

7) Scratch alignment marks on oil pump housing and transmission case. Remove pump-to-case bolts and withdraw oil pump. Remove and discard pump-to-case gasket and pump-to-front clutch thrust washer.

Fig. 5: Removal of Governor and Oil Tubes

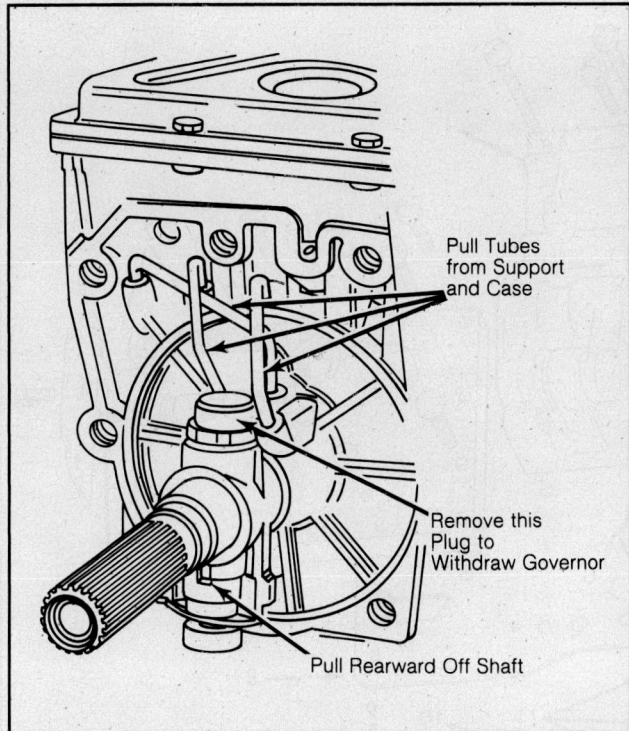

Pull Tubes from Support and Case

Remove this Plug to Withdraw Governor

Pull Rearward Off Shaft

8) At rear end of transmission, remove plug and spring washer retaining governor to output shaft. Note installed position of governor, and remove from shaft. Using screwdriver, carefully pry oil tubes from case and governor support.

9) Loosen both band adjusting screw lock nuts. Remove adjusting screws from case then withdraw both band struts. Withdraw front clutch and input shaft assembly from case. Remove bronze and steel thrust washers, then withdraw rear clutch assembly.

Fig. 6: Disassembled View of Transmission Gear Train Components

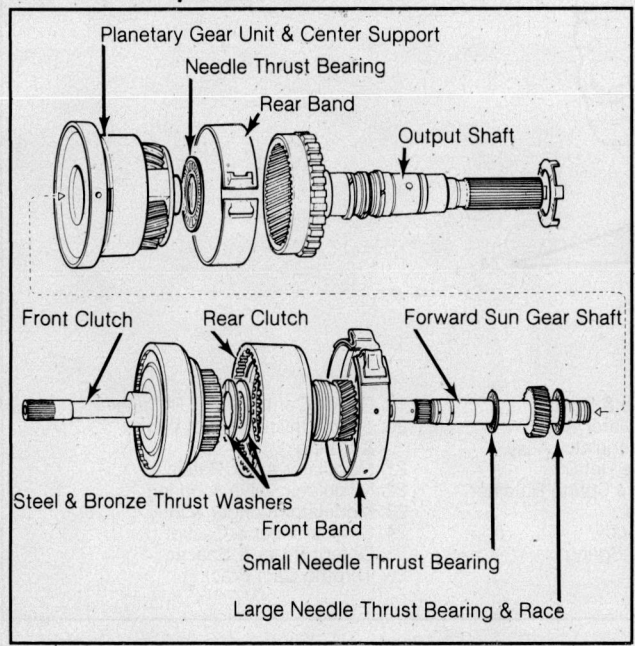

Planetary Gear Unit & Center Support
Needle Thrust Bearing
Rear Band
Output Shaft

Front Clutch   Rear Clutch   Forward Sun Gear Shaft
Steel & Bronze Thrust Washers
Front Band
Small Needle Thrust Bearing
Large Needle Thrust Bearing & Race

10) Compress ends of front band together and remove from case. Withdraw forward sun gear shaft from case, along with small needle thrust bearing from front end of shaft and large needle thrust bearing and race from rear end of shaft.

11) Remove bolts securing center support in case. Push forward on output shaft to break support loose, then withdraw center support and planetary assembly from case. Remove planetary-to-output shaft needle thrust bearing, then separate support and planetary.

12) Move output shaft back into original position. Compress ends of rear band together, and remove band from case. Remove output shaft assembly from case along with output shaft-to-case thrust washer.

13) Remove bolts securing front servo cover to case. Remove cover, and withdraw servo piston, rod and spring. Scribe alignment marks on rear servo cover and transmission case. Remove bolts attaching servo cover.

14) Remove rear servo cover, piston, rod and spring from case. Remove retaining bolts from plate covering parking pawl, withdraw pivot pin, and remove rear servo operating lever.

Fig. 7: Removing Rear Servo Operating Lever

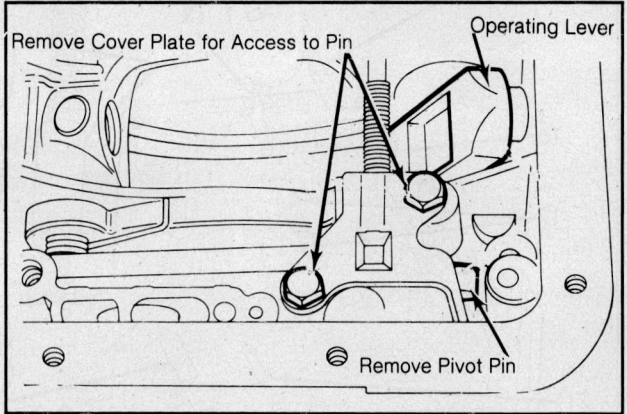

Remove Cover Plate for Access to Pin
Operating Lever
Remove Pivot Pin

COMPONENT DISASSEMBLY & REASSEMBLY

VALVE BODY ASSEMBLY
Disassembly
1) Remove manual valve from body. Remove screws retaining filter screen (and adapter if equipped) to body and remove filter screen. Remove 6 upper valve body retaining screws from lower valve body, invert valve body, and remove 4 screws retaining upper body and cam mounting arm. Remove cam mounting arm, withdraw downshift valve and spring, then separate upper body from assembly.

2) Remove screws securing end plates to upper body and remove plates. Remove 1-2 shift valve, plunger and spring, and 2-3 shift valve, plunger and spring. Remove retaining screws and lift transfer plate off main valve body.

3) Loosen, but do not remove, governor pressure plate retaining screws. Hold separator plate in contact with main valve body, remove governor pressure plate retaining screws, and remove plate. Carefully remove separator plate from main body, noting position of ball valve and spring.

Automatic Transmissions

BORG-WARNER MODEL 66 (Cont.)

Fig. 8: Exploded View of Valve Body Assembly

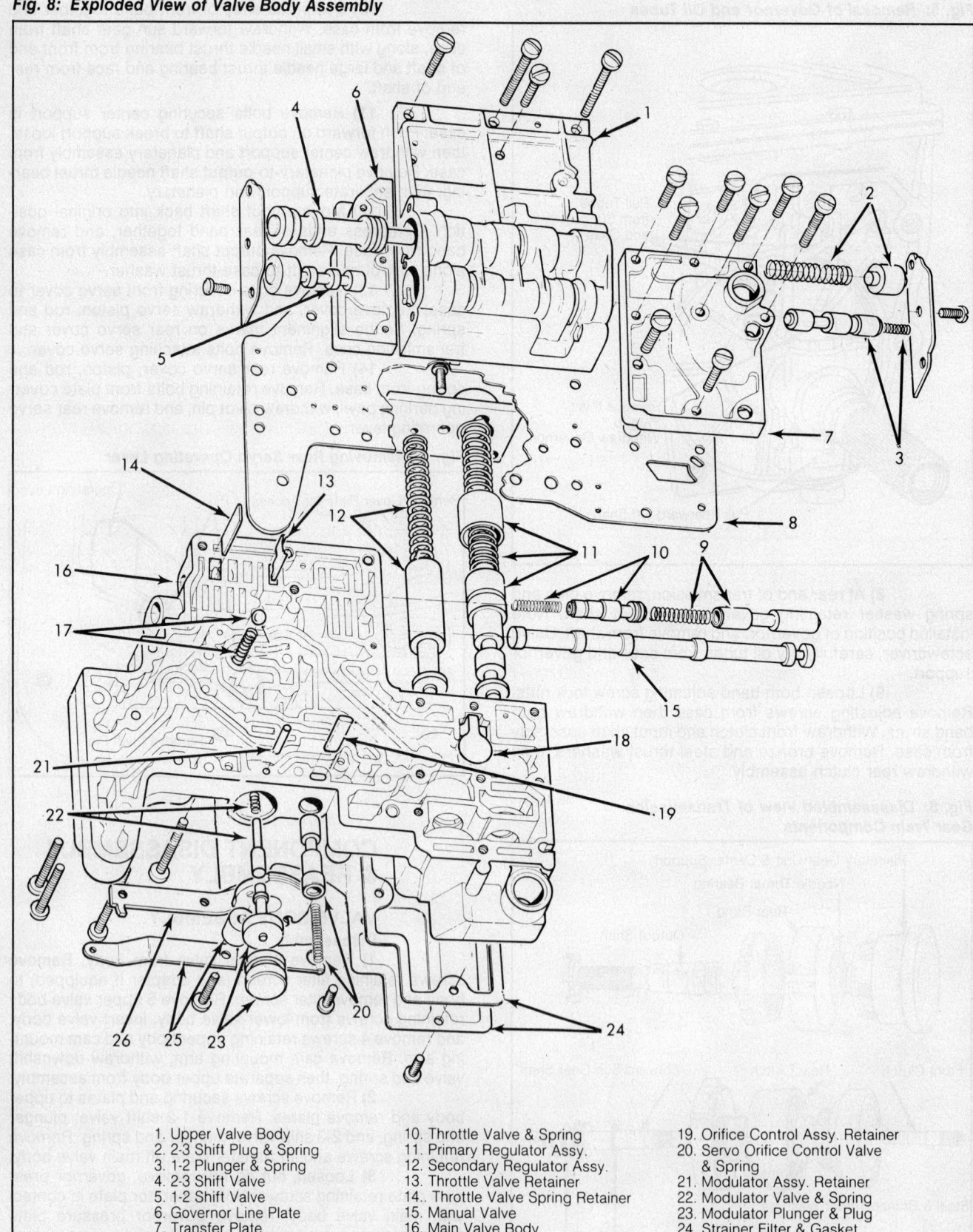

1. Upper Valve Body	10. Throttle Valve & Spring	19. Orifice Control Assy. Retainer
2. 2-3 Shift Plug & Spring	11. Primary Regulator Assy.	20. Servo Orifice Control Valve
3. 1-2 Plunger & Spring	12. Secondary Regulator Assy.	& Spring
4. 2-3 Shift Valve	13. Throttle Valve Retainer	21. Modulator Assy. Retainer
5. 1-2 Shift Valve	14. Throttle Valve Spring Retainer	22. Modulator Valve & Spring
6. Governor Line Plate	15. Manual Valve	23. Modulator Plunger & Plug
7. Transfer Plate	16. Main Valve Body	24. Strainer Filter & Gasket
8. Separator Plate	17. Check Ball & Spring	25. Detent Roller & Spacer
9. Downshift Valve & Spring	18. Check Valve	26. Throttle Cam Bracket

JAGUAR VALVE BODY SPRING IDENTIFICATION CHART

Valve Spring	Length In. (mm)	Diameter In. (mm)	Number Of Coils	Color
Secondary Regulator Valve	2.59 (65.8)	.480-.490 (12.3-12.4)	23	Blue
Primary Regulator Valve	2.94 (74.6)	.604-.610 (15.3-15.5)	14	Blue
Servo Orifice Control Valve	1.00 (25.5)	.198-.208 (5.0-5.3)	17	Yellow
2-3 Shift Valve	1.59 (40.4)	.275-.285 (6.9-7.2)	22.5	Yellow
1-2 Shift Valve	1.09 (27.7)	.230-.240 (5.8-6.1)	13	Natural
Throttle Return Valve	0.80 (20.5)	.136-.146 (3.4-3.7)	28	Yellow
Modulator Valve	1.07 (27.1)	.150-.160 (3.8-4.1)	19	Natural
Throttle Valve	1.18 (29.9)	.230-.240 (5.8-6.1)	18	Green
Dump Ball Valve	0.70 (17.7)	.210-.230 (5.3-5.8)	16	Natural/White

4) From main valve body, remove following parts: Retainer, spring, and servo orifice control valve; retaining pin, plug, spring, and modulator valve; 2 retainers, spring, and throttle valve. Remove retaining screw and detent roller and spring assembly.

5) Remove screws securing regulator valve retaining plate to main valve body, slowly release pressure on plate. Withdraw plate, spring, sleeve and primary regulator valve, and spring and secondary regulator valve.

Cleaning & Inspection

Clean all parts in solvent and air dry. Check all valves, plugs, and sleeves for wear, burrs, and scoring. Ensure all valves and plugs move freely in valve body bores. Also check all valve springs for distortion or collapsed coils.

NOTE: If any valve body component is damaged or worn, entire valve body assembly must be replaced; parts are not serviced separately.

Reassembly

Reverse disassembly procedure and note following: Coat all components with transmission fluid before installing into bodies. Ensure check ball and spring are installed in correct main body passage. See Fig. 8. Always use new strainer filter gasket when assembling.

CAUTION: Do not overtighten valve body attaching bolts and screws.

PLANETARY CARRIER & ONE-WAY CLUTCH
Cleaning & Inspection

1) Check planetary gear teeth for chipping or scoring (light scoring is acceptable). Ensure all gears rotate freely by hand, and that end play of gears is not excessive. Inspect bushing in hub of planetary carrier for wear. If any part of carrier is worn or damaged, complete carrier must be replaced.

2) Withdraw one-way clutch roller assembly from carrier and inspect for worn or broken rollers and damage to outer race. If any one-way clutch component is damaged, replace roller and outer race assembly.

NOTE: When installing roller assembly into outer race (in carrier), ensure lip of roller cage faces outward.

FORWARD SUN GEAR SHAFT
Cleaning & Inspection

Check oil passages in shaft for obstructions; clear out with compressed air only. Inspect splines, seal ring grooves, and gear teeth for damage (minor damage may be removed with fine abrasive). Check large and small needle thrust bearings for damage and replace as necessary.

REAR CLUTCH
Disassembly

1) Remove clutch pack retaining snap ring. Withdraw pressure plate, 5 steel clutch plates, and 5 line discs. Using a spring compressor, compress piston return spring.

2) Remove snap ring, then withdraw compressor, spring retainer, and piston return spring. Remove clutch piston by applying air pressure to fluid supply passage in clutch hub. Remove inner seal from clutch drum and outer seal from piston.

Cleaning & Inspection

1) Check clutch drum for scoring or wear and all fluid passages for obstructions. Clear passages with compressed air only. Inspect piston for damage and free operation of check ball. Check all lined discs for wear and distortion; all lined discs must be flat.

2) Check steel clutch plates for scoring or burrs; replace any plates found damaged. Also check steel plates for coning; plates must be coned at least .010" (.25 mm). Inspect needle roller bearing in clutch hub for wear. If bearing is worn or damaged, replace complete clutch housing.

Reassembly

1) Coat new piston seals with petrolatum and install onto piston and clutch hub. Position piston installer into clutch drum, coat piston with transmission fluid, and install into bottom of drum. Position piston return spring and retainer on top of piston, compress assembly, and install retaining snap ring.

NOTE: If new lined discs are used, soak in transmission fluid before installation.

2) Install clutch pack into drum, starting with steel plate and alternating lined discs and steel plates until correct number are installed (5 steel and 5 fiber-lined). Ensure all steel plate cones are facing in same direction.

Fig. 9: Disassembled View of Planetary Carrier and One-Way Clutch Assembly

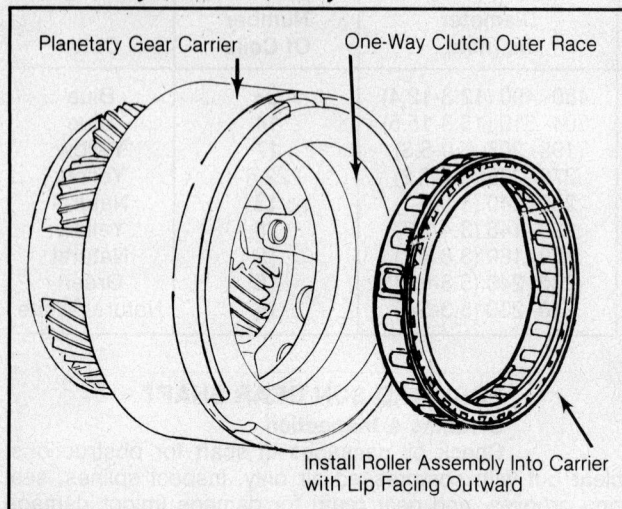

Planetary Gear Carrier

One-Way Clutch Outer Race

Install Roller Assembly Into Carrier with Lip Facing Outward

Fig. 10: Exploded View of Rear Clutch Assembly

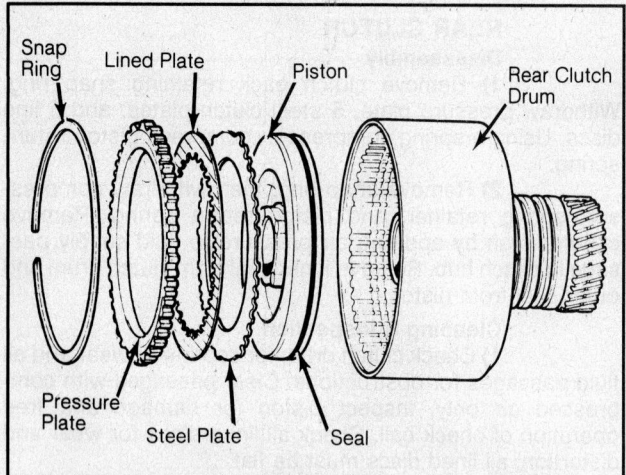

Snap Ring

Lined Plate

Piston

Rear Clutch Drum

Pressure Plate

Steel Plate

Seal

Fig. 11: Checking Rear Clutch Steel Plate Coning

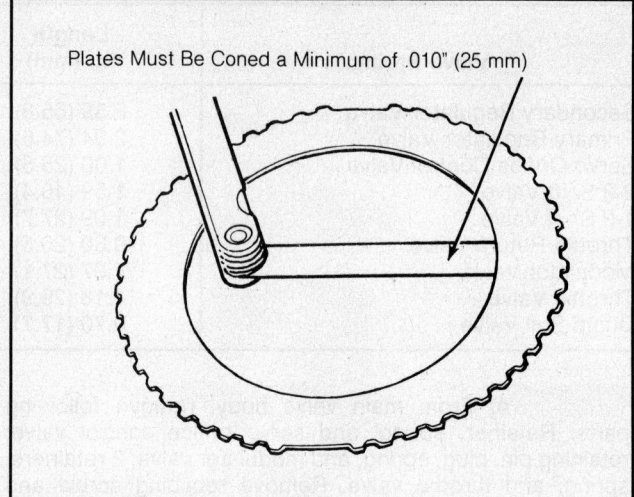

Plates Must Be Coned a Minimum of .010" (25 mm)

Cleaning & Inspection

1) Check clutch drum for scoring or wear, and all fluid passages for obstructions. Clear passages with compressed air. Inspect piston for damage and free operation of check ball. Check diaphragm release spring for cracks or distortion and replace as necessary.

2) Inspect all clutch plates for wear or other damage. Ensure all plates are flat; coned plates are used in rear clutch only. Check bushing in turbine shaft for wear; if damaged, replace.

Reassembly

1) Coat new seal with petrolatum and install onto clutch piston. On models with "O" ring type seal on clutch hub, coat seal with petrolatum and install. On all other models, install spring washers into bottom of piston and follow with inner seal.

NOTE: Open end of seal should face out of piston.

2) Position piston installer into clutch drum, coat all parts with transmission fluid, and install piston into drum. Install diaphragm spring into drum with cone facing upward, then install retaining snap ring.

3) With rear clutch and sun gear shaft assembly again positioned on bench, install steel backing washer and bronze thrust washer over sun gear shaft and against rear clutch. Ensure seal ring gaps on sun gear shaft are staggered, and that rear clutch lined disc splines are aligned. Install forward clutch drum and piston assembly into rear clutch.

NOTE: Ensure all parts are fully mated.

4) Install pressure plate into front clutch drum and against diaphragm spring snap ring. Follow with clutch pack, starting with a lined plate and alternating steel and lined plates until all plates are installed.

5) Align inner splines of lined plates and install clutch hub, making sure it fully engages all plates. Position new thrust washer into recess of hub. Install turbine shaft and snap ring, making sure ring is correctly seated in groove of clutch drum.

CAUTION: With all parts assembled, do not allow front and rear clutches to separate as damage to seal rings on sun gear shaft may occur.

Install pressure plate into clutch drum (flat side downward) and install clutch pack retaining snap ring.

3) Install new sealing rings onto clutch drum hub and lock ends (if used). Install new seal rings onto forward sun gear shaft. Position shaft in holding fixture with long end of shaft upward. Coat small needle thrust bearing with petrolatum and install over shaft and against sun gear. Coat sun gear shaft with transmission fluid, then install rear clutch assembly onto shaft and against thrust washer. Place assembly aside.

FRONT CLUTCH

Disassembly

1) Remove clutch pack retaining snap ring and withdraw turbine shaft, thrust washer, clutch hub, and clutch pack from drum. Remove large retaining snap ring and diaphragm return spring.

2) Remove clutch piston by applying air pressure to fluid supply passage in clutch hub. Remove spring washers from clutch drum (if equipped). Remove seals from clutch hub and piston.

Fig. 12: Exploded View of Front Clutch Assembly

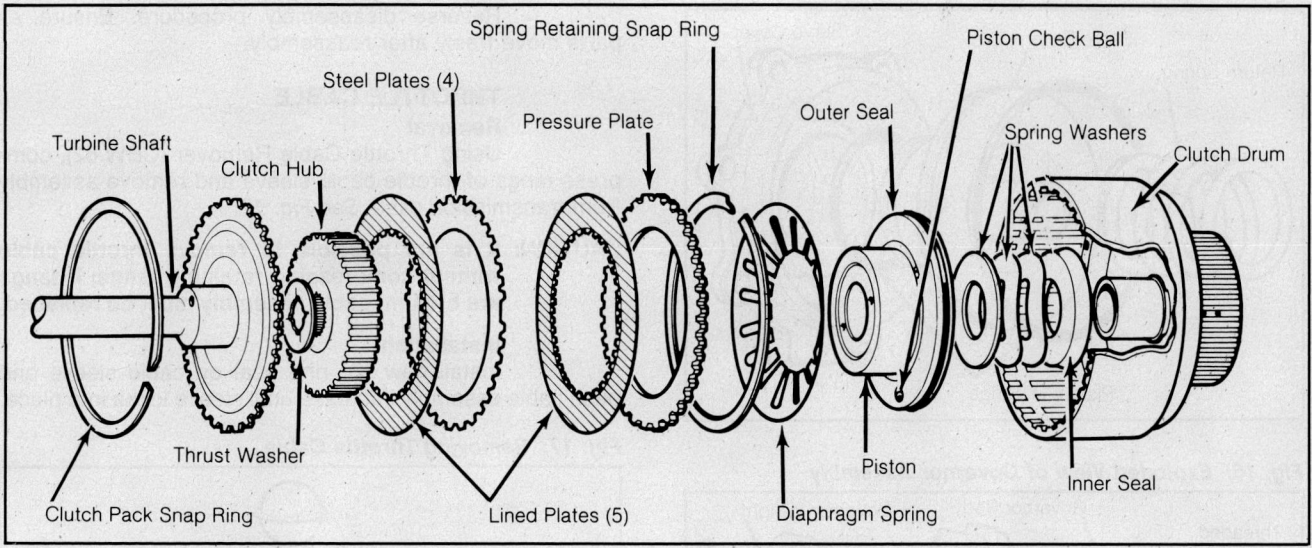

OIL PUMP

Disassembly

1) Remove bolts and screw retaining pump housing to cover. Separate cover and housing. Mark mating surfaces of pump drive and driven gears with die marker for reassembly reference.

CAUTION: Do not punch or scribe marks in gears.

2) Remove "O" ring seal from outer diameter of pump housing, and converter lip seal from front of pump housing.

Cleaning & Inspection

Check surfaces of housing and cover, gears, splines, and bushings for scoring, wear or other damage. If any part shows evidence of wear, entire assembly must be replaced; parts are not serviced separately.

Fig. 13: Exploded View of Oil Pump Assembly

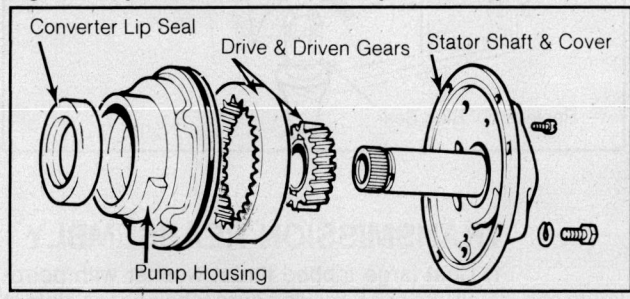

Reassembly

Soak new converter lip seal and housing "O" ring seal in transmission fluid and install into pump housing. Install drive and driven gears into housing, aligning marks made at disassembly. Install cover into housing, align bolt and screw holes, then install and tighten attaching bolts and screw. Rotate pump gears to check for freedom of movement.

FRONT & REAR SERVOS

Disassembly

Remove spring from servo piston. Remove piston from servo body. Remove seals from piston and body.

Cleaning & Inspection

Clean all parts in solvent. Blow dry with compressed air, clearing out all lubrication passages.

Fig. 14: Exploded View of Front Servo Assembly

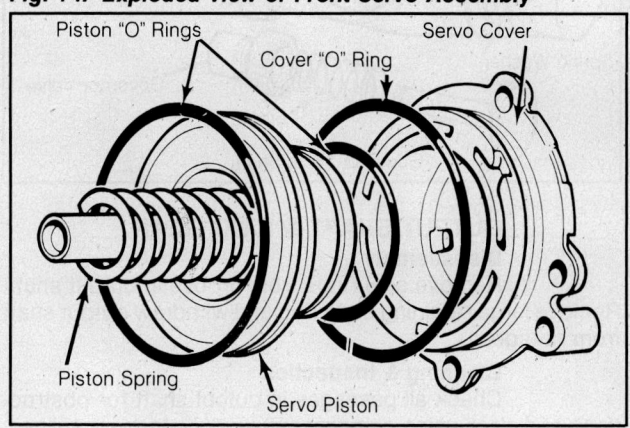

Reassembly

Coat new seals with petrolatum and install onto piston and servo body. Position spring on servo piston, then place assembly aside.

GOVERNOR

Disassembly

Depress governor shaft to expose snap ring, remove snap ring and weight from outside of assembly, withdraw governor shaft, spring, and valve from inside governor body.

Cleaning & Inspection

Wash all parts in solvent and air dry. Check all parts for wear or damage, and spring especially for distortion. If any part of governor is found to be damaged, entire governor assembly must be replaced.

Reassembly

Lubricate all parts with transmission fluid. Install governor valve, spring, and shaft into body, position weight on shaft, then install snap ring. Check all parts for freedom of movement. If governor shaft shows signs of sticking, governor assembly must be replaced.

Fig. 15: Exploded View of Rear Servo Assembly

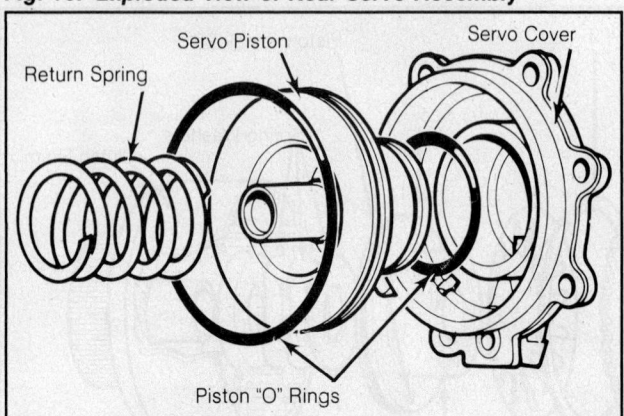

Fig. 16: Exploded View of Governor Assembly

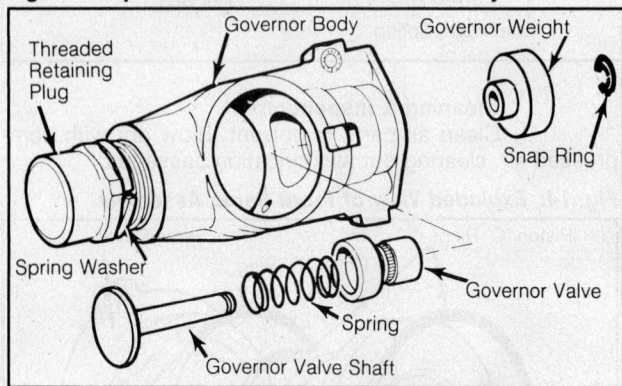

OUTPUT SHAFT & RING GEAR
Disassembly

Remove seal rings from groove in output shaft. Remove large retaining snap ring and withdraw output shaft from ring gear.

Cleaning & Inspection

Check all passages in output shaft for obstructions and clear using compressed air only. Inspect splines, seal ring grooves, and gear teeth of shaft and ring gear for burrs, scoring, or other damage (minor damage may be removed with a fine abrasive). If any part is worn or damaged, replace.

Reassembly

Position output shaft in ring gear and install retaining snap ring. Install new seal rings into grooves of output shaft, taking care to stagger ring gaps.

MANUAL LINKAGE
Disassembly

1) Note position of parking pawl spring, then detach spring from pawl. Remove parking pawl shaft from outside of case, and withdraw pawl and spring from inside case. Remove clip from manual shaft and pin retaining detent lever. Withdraw manual shaft, detent lever, spacer, and washers from case.

2) Disconnect parking rod from parking pawl. Note position of parking pawl operating lever and spring, and detach spring from lever. Using a punch, drive out operating lever pin and withdraw operating lever and spring.

Reassembly

Reverse disassembly procedure. Ensure all parts move freely after reassembly.

THROTTLE CABLE
Removal

Using Throttle Cable Remover (CBW.62), compress tangs of throttle cable sleeve and remove assembly from transmission case. *See Fig. 17.*

CAUTION: It is not possible to remove throttle cable without compressing retaining tangs; if tangs are broken, cable assembly must be replaced.

Installation

Install new "O" ring seal on cable sleeve and push cable assembly into case until sleeve locks into place.

Fig. 17: Removing Throttle Cable

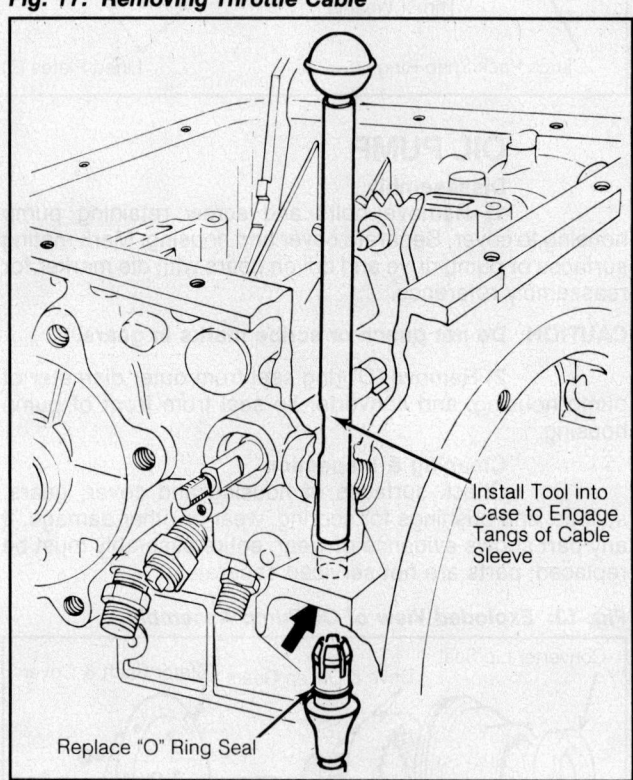

TRANSMISSION REASSEMBLY

1) Coat large tabbed thrust washer with petrolatum and install into case, making sure tabs engage slots in case. Install output shaft and ring gear assembly into case and through thrust washer. Ensure washer is positioned correctly.

2) Place front and rear bands in position in case. While holding clutch assemblies (previously assembled), install large needle thrust bearing and race onto sun gear shaft, with flange facing away from clutches.

3) Install center support, clutch and sun gear assembly into planet carrier. Rotate center support until holes on outer diameter are in approximate alignment with center support bolt holes in case, then install entire assembly (clutches, planetary carrier, and support) into transmission case.

Fig. 18: Exploded View of Manual Linkage Components

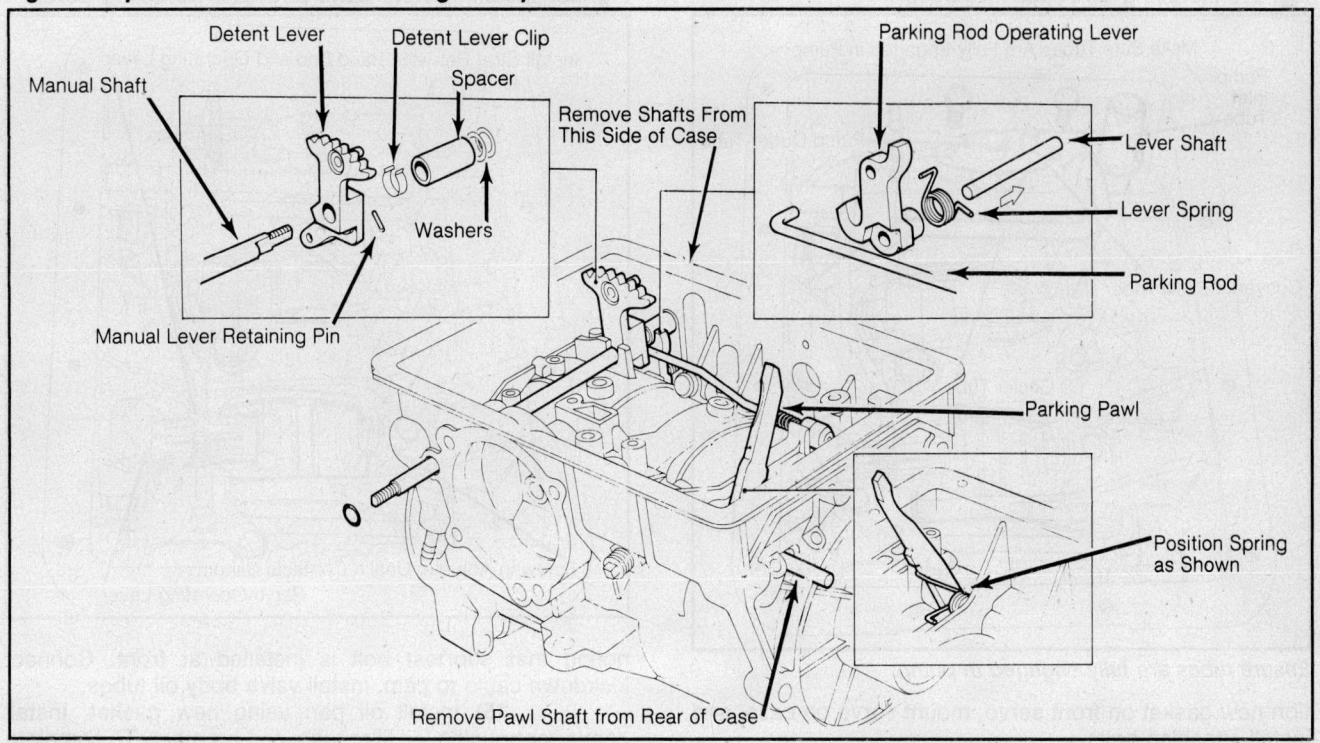

Fig. 19: Installation of Output Shaft Into Transmission Case

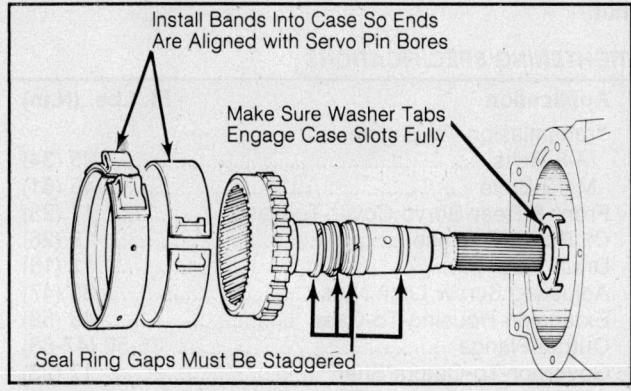

Fig. 20: Installing Oil Pump Onto Transmission Case

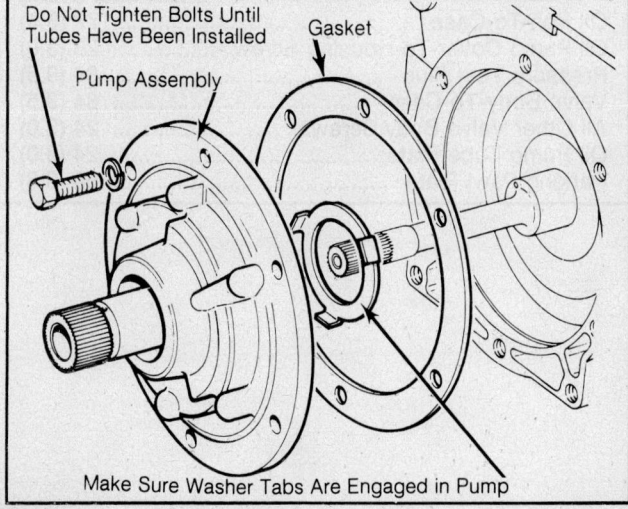

4) Position new thrust washer and gasket onto rear of oil pump. Mount oil pump to transmission case, and install but do not tighten attaching bolts. Install new "O" ring seal on pump inlet tube.

5) Install inlet tube along with outlet tube and converter feed tube into oil pump housing (inside case). Ensure tubes are correctly positioned. Install tube retaining plate and attaching bolts, then tighten oil pump-to-case bolts. At this time, also install oil cooler tube into case.

CAUTION: To prevent damage to internal parts, do not allow components to separate when installing.

6) On rear of case, install 3 oil tubes into case and governor support. Slide governor unit onto output shaft and install plug and spring washer, making sure plug enters BLIND hole in output shaft.

7) Install speedometer drive gear onto output shaft and against governor. Install new seal into extension housing, position new extension-to-case gasket, then install housing onto case, tightening nuts and bolts in a diagonal sequence.

8) Install output flange onto shaft, engage parking pawl with parking gear, then install flange attaching bolt or nut and tighten. Position dial indicator assembly on front of transmission case with button of indicator contacting turbine shaft.

9) With screwdriver inserted between front clutch and front of case, pry gear train fully rearward. Zero dial indicator. Next, with screwdriver between parking gear and rear clutch, pry gear train forward and note reading on gauge. Reading should be .008-.029" (.20-.73 mm). If not, repeat steps 4), 5), 6), 7) and 8), installing thicker or thinner washer (as required) behind oil pump.

10) Coat new "O" ring with petrolatum and install onto speedometer driven gear housing. Install driven gear assembly into extension housing and install retainer. Posi-

Fig. 21: Installing Oil Tubes Into Case

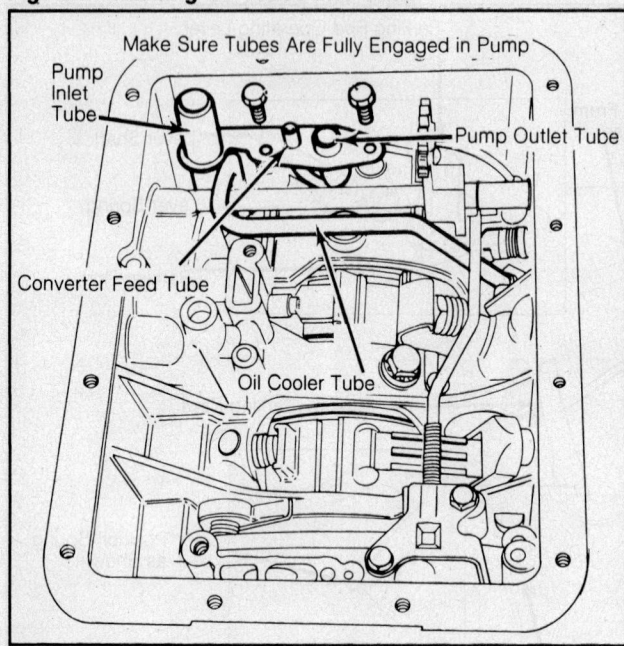

Ensure tubes are fully engaged in pump.

tion new gasket on front servo, mount servo on case, and install attaching bolts.

11) Install front band strut into servo rod and band. Screw in front band adjusting screw until it engages band end. Do not tighten screw or lock nut at this time. *See Fig. 22.*

Fig. 22: Installing Front Band Strut and Adjusting Screw

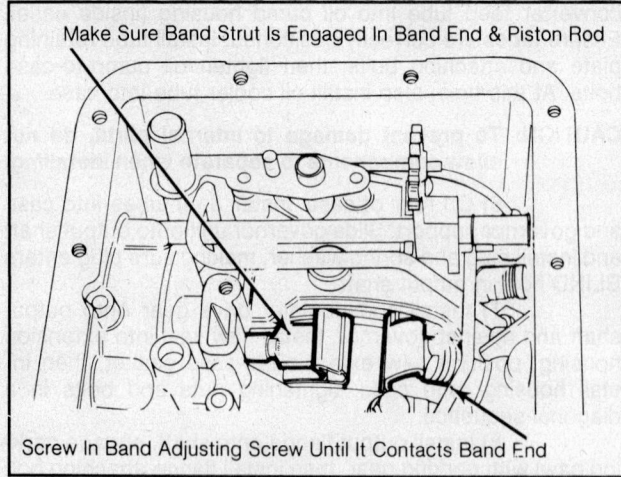

12) If removed, install rear servo operating lever in transmission case. Install new "O" rings and gasket on rear servo body and mount servo on case. Ensure servo rod engages operating lever. Install rear band strut between band end and operating lever. *See Fig. 23.*

13) Screw in band adjusting screw until contact is just made with band, tighten servo body-to-case bolts. At this time, install oil tube "D", which will be partially covered by valve body. *See Fig. 24.*

14) Install valve body into case. Ensure manual valve engages detent lever and that valve body fully engages oil pump tubes. Install valve body-to-case bolts,

Fig. 23: Installing Rear Band Strut and Adjusting Screw

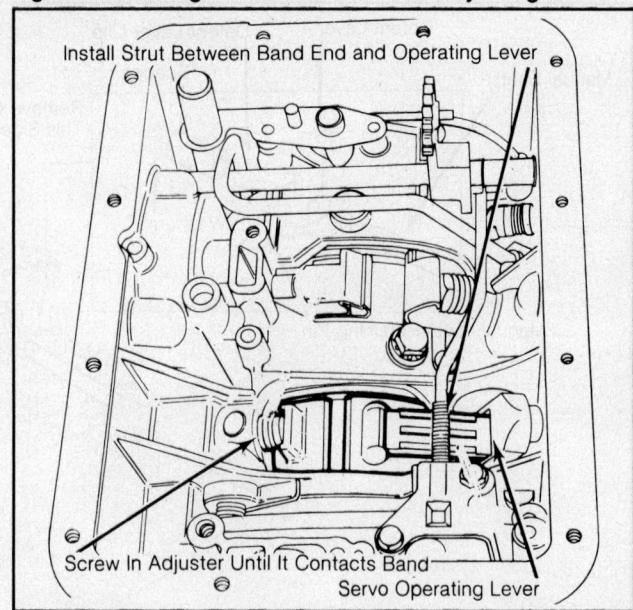

noting that shortest bolt is installed at front. Connect kickdown cable to cam. Install valve body oil tubes.

15) Install oil pan using new gasket. Install converter housing, oil filler tube, and breather. To complete assembly, adjust both bands as follows: Tighten band adjusting screw to 60 INCH lbs. (7 N.m), back out screw 3/4 of a turn, hold in position and tighten adjusting screw lock nut.

TIGHTENING SPECIFICATIONS

Application	Ft. Lbs. (N.m)
Transmission-To-Engine	
M-8 Bolts	25 (34)
M-12 Bolts	45 (61)
Front & Rear Servo Cover-To-Case	17 (23)
Oil Pump-To-Case	19 (26)
Drain Plug	11 (15)
Adjusting Screw Lock Nuts	35 (47)
Extension Housing-To-Case	43 (58)
Output Flange	35-50 (47-68)
Governor-To-Output Shaft	17 (23)

	INCH Lbs. (N.m.)
Oil Pan-To-Case	72 (8.1)
Oil Pump Cover-To-Housing Screw	25 (3.0)
Pressure Test Plug	84 (9.5)
Valve Body-To-Case	84 (9.5)
All Other Valve Body Screws	24 (3.0)
Oil Pump Tube Plate	24 (3.0)
Parking Pawl Plate	60 (6.8)

Fig. 24: Installing Oil Tubes

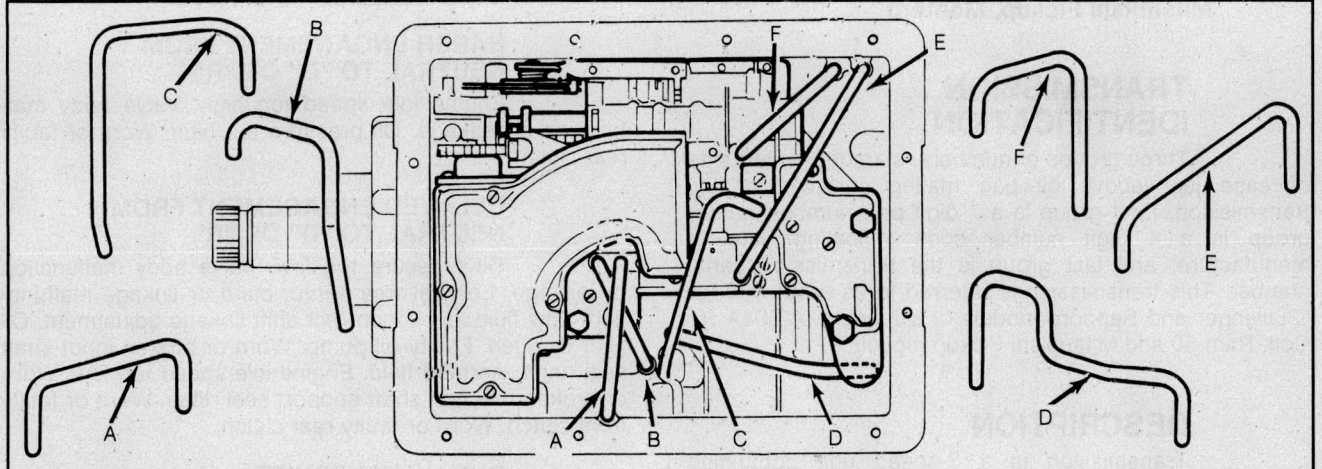

Automatic Transmissions

CHRYSLER CORP. & MITSUBISHI TORQUEFLITE

Chrysler Corp. Ram-50 Pickup
Mitsubishi Pickup, Montero

TRANSMISSION IDENTIFICATION

Three groups of numbers, stamped on left side of case just above oil pan mating surface, identify transmission. First group is a 7 digit part number, center group is a 4 digit number code indicating date of manufacture, and last group is the transmission serial number. This transmission is referred to as a MA-904 for Challenger and Sapporo models or a model MA-904A for Colt, Ram-50 and Mitsubishi Pickup models.

DESCRIPTION

Transmission is a 3-speed unit combining torque converter and compound planetary gear system. Transmission case and converter housing are an integral aluminum casting. Transmission consists basically of 2 multiple-disc clutches, 2 bands and servos, and overrunning clutch, 2 planetary gear sets, and a hydraulic control system.

LUBRICATION & ADJUSTMENT

See the appropriate article in AUTOMATIC TRANSMISSION SERVICING Section.

TROUBLE SHOOTING

HARSH ENGAGEMENT FROM NEUTRAL TO "D" OR "R"

Engine idle speed too high. Valve body malfunction or leakage. Oil pressure too high. Worn or faulty rear clutch.

DELAYED ENGAGEMENT FROM NEUTRAL TO "D" OR "R"

Oil pressure too low. Valve body malfunction or leakage. Low-reverse servo, band or linkage malfunction. Low fluid level. Incorrect shift linkage adjustment. Oil filter clogged. Faulty oil pump. Worn or broken input shaft seal rings. Aerated fluid. Engine idle speed too low. Worn or broken reaction shaft support seal rings. Worn or faulty front clutch. Worn or faulty rear clutch.

RUNAWAY UPSHIFT

Oil pressure too low. Valve body malfunction or leakage. Low fluid level. Oil filter clogged. Aerated fluid. Incorrect throttle rod adjustment. Worn or broken reaction shaft support seal rings. Kickdown servo, band or linkage malfunction. Worn or faulty front clutch.

NO UPSHIFT

Oil pressure too low. Valve body leakage or malfunction. Low fluid level. Incorrect shift linkage adjustment. Incorrect throttle rod adjustment. Governor support

Fig. 1: Cutaway View of Torqueflite Transmission Showing Major Components

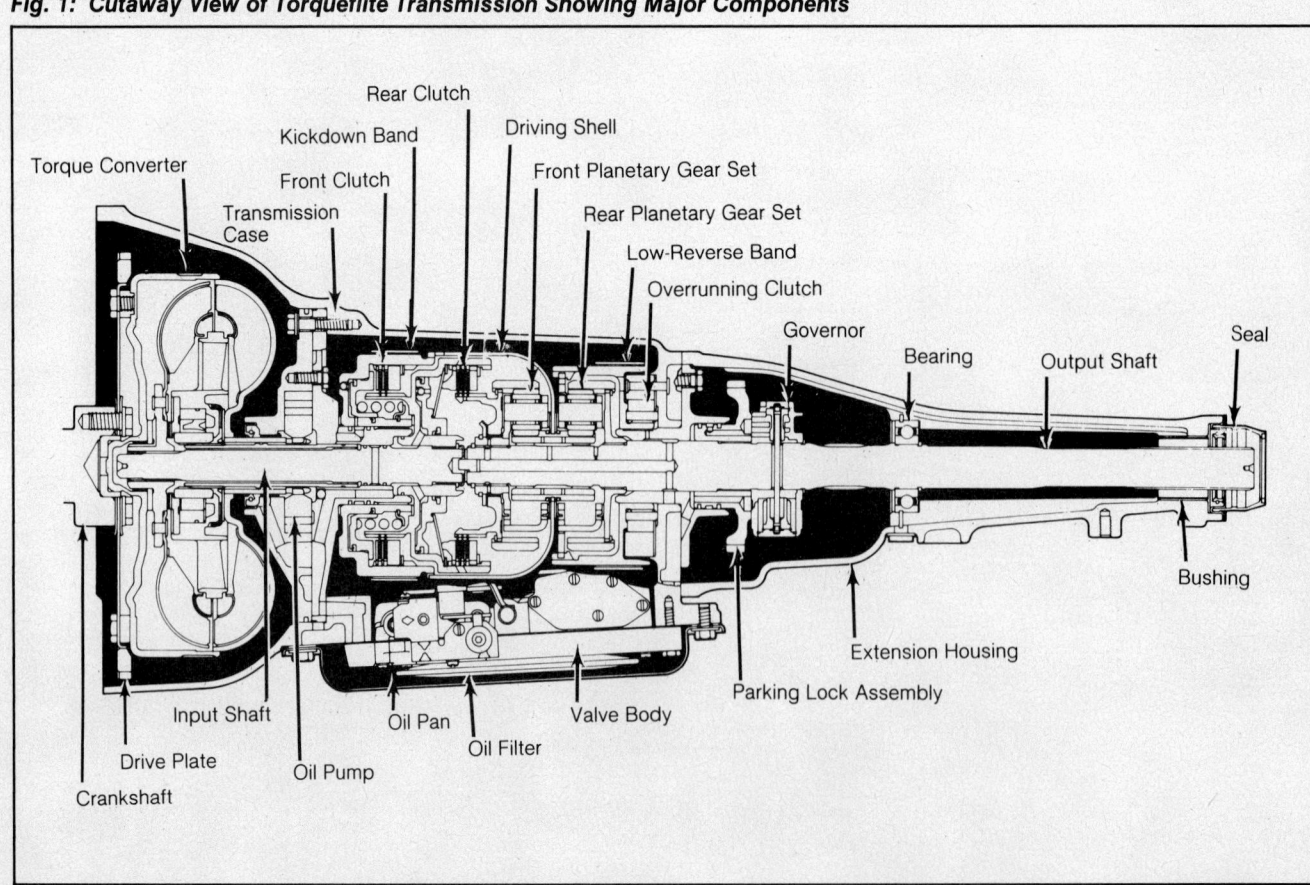

CHRYSLER CORP. & MITSUBISHI TORQUEFLITE (Cont.)

Fig. 2: Torqueflite Automatic Transmission Hydraulic Circuits Diagram

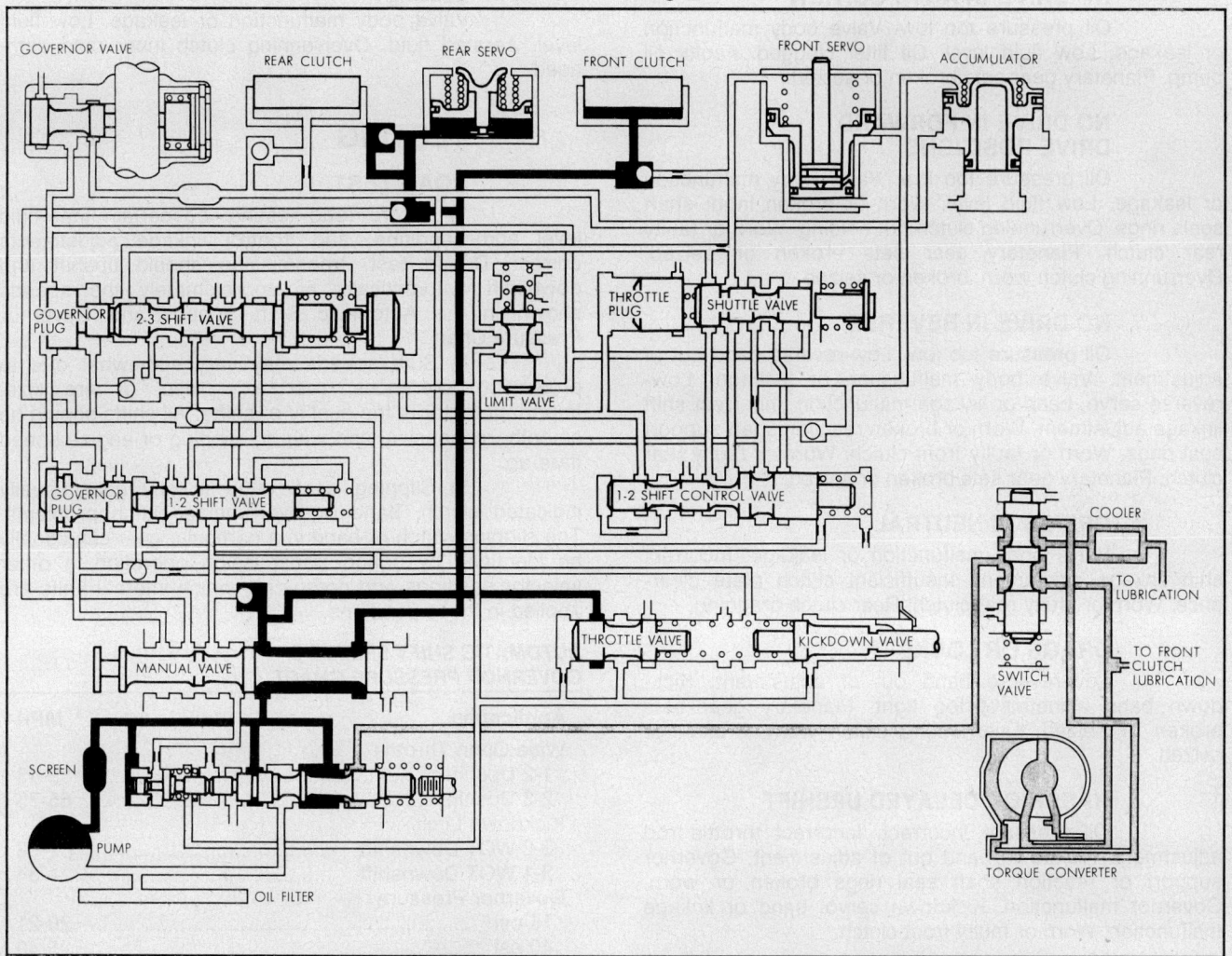

seal rings broken or worn. Worn or broken reaction shaft support seal rings. Governor malfunction. Kickdown servo, band or linkage malfunction. Worn or faulty front clutch.

3-2 KICKDOWN RUNAWAY

Oil pressure too low. Valve body malfunction or leakage. Low fluid level. Aerated fluid. Incorrect throttle rod adjustment. Kickdown band out of adjustment. Worn or broken reaction shaft support seal rings. Kickdown servo, band or linkage malfunction. Worn or faulty front clutch.

NO KICKDOWN OR NORMAL DOWNSHIFT

Valve body malfunction or leakage. Incorrect throttle rod adjustment. Governor malfunction. Kickdown servo, band or linkage malfunction.

SHIFTS ERRATIC

Oil pressure too low. Valve body malfunction or leakage. Low fluid level. Incorrect shift linkage adjustment. Oil filter clogged. Faulty oil pump. Aerated fluid. Incorrect throttle rod adjustment. Governor support seal rings broken or worn. Worn or broken reaction shaft support seal rings. Governor malfunction. Kickdown

servo, band or linkage malfunction. Worn or faulty front clutch.

SLIPS IN FORWARD DRIVE POSITIONS

Oil pressure too low. Valve body malfunction or leakage. Low fluid level. Incorrect shift linkage adjustment. Oil filter clogged. Faulty oil pump. Worn or broken input shaft seal rings. Aerated fluid. Incorrect throttle rod adjustment. Overrunning clutch not holding. Worn or faulty rear clutch. Overrunning clutch worn, broken or seized.

SLIPS IN REVERSE ONLY

Oil pressure too low. Low-reverse band out of adjustment. Valve body malfunction or leakage. Low-reverse servo, band or linkage malfunction. Low fluid level. Incorrect shift linkage adjustment. Faulty oil pump. Aerated fluid. Worn or broken reaction shaft support seal rings. Worn or faulty front clutch.

SLIPS IN ALL POSITIONS

Oil pressure too low. Valve body malfunction or leakage. Low fluid level. Oil filter clogged. Faulty oil pump. Worn or broken input shaft seal rings. Aerated fluid.

Automatic Transmissions

CHRYSLER CORP. & MITSUBISHI TORQUEFLITE (Cont.)

NO DRIVE IN ANY POSITION

Oil pressure too low. Valve body malfunction or leakage. Low fluid level. Oil filter clogged. Faulty oil pump. Planetary gear sets broken or seized.

NO DRIVE IN FORWARD DRIVE POSITIONS

Oil pressure too low. Valve body malfunction or leakage. Low fluid level. Worn or broken input shaft seals rings. Overrunning clutch not holding. Worn or faulty rear clutch. Planetary gear sets broken or seized. Overrunning clutch worn, broken or seized.

NO DRIVE IN REVERSE

Oil pressure too low. Low-reverse band out of adjustment. Valve body malfunction or leakage. Low-reverse servo, band or linkage malfunction. Incorrect shift linkage adjustment. Worn or broken reaction shaft support seal rings. Worn or faulty front clutch. Worn or faulty rear clutch. Planetary gear sets broken or seized.

DRIVES IN NEUTRAL

Valve body malfunction or leakage. Incorrect shift linkage adjustment. Insufficient clutch plate clearance. Worn or faulty rear clutch. Rear clutch dragging.

DRAGS OR LOCKS

Low-reverse band out of adjustment. Kickdown band adjustment too tight. Planetary gear sets broken or seized. Overrunning clutch worn, broken or seized.

HARSH OR DELAYED UPSHIFT

Oil pressure incorrect. Incorrect throttle rod adjustment. Kickdown band out of adjustment. Governor support or reaction shaft seal rings broken or worn. Governor malfunction. Kickdown servo, band or linkage malfunction. Worn or faulty front clutch.

TRANSMISSION NOISE

Grating, Scraping, Or Growling

Low-reverse band out of adjustment. Output shaft bearing and/or bushing damaged. Planetary gear sets broken or seized. Overrunning clutch worn, broken or seized.

Buzzing

Valve body malfunction or leakage. Low fluid level. Aerated fluid. Overrunning clutch inner race damaged.

TESTING

ROAD TEST

1) Before road testing, be certain that fluid level and condition, and control linkage adjustments correct. During test, transmission should upshift and downshift automatically at approximately the speeds shown in the Automatic Shift Speeds and Governor Pressure Chart.

2) Shift speeds may vary somewhat due to production tolerances, rear axle ratio, or tire size. Important factor is the quality of shifts. All shifts should be smooth, responsive, and with no slipping or engine speed flare-up.

3) Slipping or flare-up in any gear usually indicated clutch, band or overrunning clutch problems. The slipping clutch or band in a particular gear can usually be identified by noting transmission operation in other selector positions and comparing which internal units are applied in those positions.

AUTOMATIC SHIFT SPEEDS & GOVERNOR PRESSURE CHART

Application	[1] MPH
Wide Open Throttle	
1-2 Upshift	35-45
2-3 Upshift	65-75
Kickdown Limit	
3-2 WOT Downshift	52-68
3-1 WOT Downshift	24-34
Governor Pressure	
15 psi	20-21
40 psi	35-40
60 psi	52-57

[1] – All speeds given are approximate. Changes in tire size or axle ratio will correspondingly raise or lower vehicle speed.

CLUTCH AND BAND APPLICATION CHART (ELEMENTS IN USE)

Selector Lever Position	Front Clutch	Rear Clutch	Over-running Clutch	Front (Kickdown) Band	Rear (Low-reverse) Band
D – DRIVE					
First		X	X		
Second		X		X	
Direct	X	X			
2 – SECOND					
First		X	X		
Second		X		X	
L – LOW (First)		X			X
R – REVERSE	X				X

NEUTRAL OR PARK – All clutches and bands released and/or ineffective.

CHRYSLER CORP. & MITSUBISHI TORQUEFLITE (Cont.)

4) For example, if transmission slips in "D" third gear, either front or rear clutch is slipping. By selecting another gear which does not use one of those units, the unit which is slipping can be identified. If transmission slips in reverse, the front clutch is slipping. If transmission does not slip in reverse, the rear clutch is slipping.

5) Although this process of elimination can be used to detect any unit which slips and to confirm proper operation of good units, the actual cause of malfunction usually cannot be decided. Practically any condition can be caused by leaking hydraulic circuits or sticking valves. Therefore, unless an obvious condition exists, transmission should never be disassembled until hydraulic pressure tests have been made.

HYDRAULIC PRESSURE TESTS

Before making pressure tests, be certain that fluid level and condition, and control linkage adjustments have been checked and corrected if necessary. Install an engine tachometer, raise vehicle on hoist which allows rear wheels to turn, and position tachometer so it can be read under vehicle. Disconnect throttle rod and shift rod from transmission levers so they can be controlled under vehicle. Make sure transmission fluid is at normal operating temperature (170°F).

Pressure Test (Selector in "L")

1) Attach 0-100 psi gauges to line and rear servo ports. Operate engine at 1000 RPM for test. Move selector lever on transmission all the way forward ("L" position). Read pressures on both gauges as throttle lever on transmission is moved from full rearward position to full forward position.

2) Line pressure should read 54-60 psi (3.8-4.2 kg/cm²) with throttle lever rearward and gradually increase, as lever is moved forward to 90-95 psi (6.3-6.7 kg/cm²). Rear servo pressure should read the same as line pressure within 3 psi (0.2 kg/cm²). This tests pump output, pressure regulation, and condition of rear clutch and rear servo hydraulic circuits.

Fig. 3: View of Right Side of Transmission Case Showing Pressure Test Ports

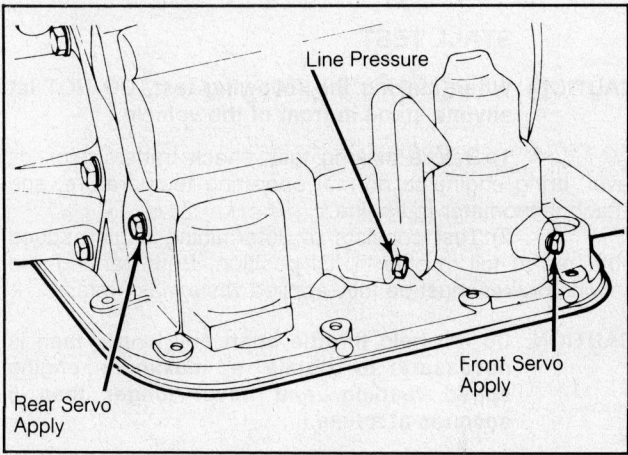

Pressure Test (Selector in "2")

1) Install "T" connection at rear cooler line fitting. Attach 0-100 psi gauges to "T" connection and line pressure port. Operate engine at 1000 RPM for test. Move selector lever on transmission 1 detent rearward from full forward position (into selector "2" position).

2) Read pressures on both gauges as throttle lever on transmission is moved from full rearward position to full forward position. Line pressure should read 54-90 psi (3.8-6.3 kg/cm²) with throttle lever rearward and gradually increase, as lever is moved forward to 90-96 psi (6.3-6.8 kg/cm²).

3) Lubrication pressure should be 6-16 psi (0.4-1.1 kg/cm²) with lever rearward, and 10-30 psi (0.7-2.1 kg/cm²) with lever forward. This tests pump output, pressure regulation, and condition of rear clutch and lubrication hydraulic circuits.

Pressure Test (Selector in "D")

1) Attach 0-100 psi gauges to line and front servo release ports. Operate engine at 1600 RPM for test. Move selector lever on transmission 2 detents rearward from full forward position (selector in "D" position).

Fig. 4: Rear View of Transmission Case Showing Pressure Test Ports

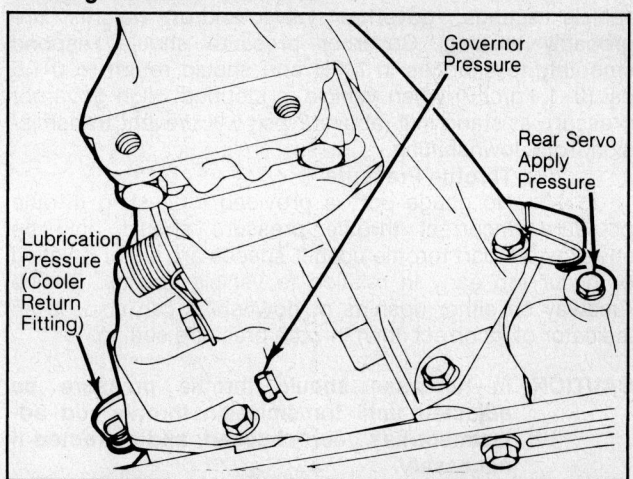

2) Read pressure on both gauges as throttle lever on transmission is moved from full rearward position to full forward position. Line pressure should rear 54-60 psi (3.8-4.2 kg/cm²) with throttle lever rearward and gradually increase, as lever is moved forward.

3) Front servo release is pressurized only in direct drive and should be same as line pressure within 3 psi (.2 kg/cm²), up to downshift point. This tests pump output, pressure regulation, and condition of rear clutch and front clutch hydraulic circuits.

NOTE: A 0-300 psi gauge is required for the following test.

Pressure Test (Selector in Reverse)

1) Attach gauge to rear servo apply port. Operate engine at 1600 RPM for test. Move selector lever on transmission 4 detents rearward from full forward position (into selector "R" position).

2) Rear servo pressure should read 230-260 psi (16.2-18.3 kg/cm²). This tests pump output, pressure regulation, and condition of front clutch and rear servo hydraulic circuits.

3) Move selector lever on transmission to "D" position to check that rear servo pressure drops to zero. This tests for leakage into rear servo, due to case porosity, which can cause reverse band to burn out.

Pressure Test Indication

1) If proper line pressure, minimum to maximum, is found in any one test, pump and pressure

CHRYSLER CORP. & MITSUBISHI TORQUEFLITE (Cont.)

regulator are working properly. Low pressure in "D", "L" and "2" but correct pressure in "R", indicates rear clutch circuit leakage.

2) Low pressure in "D" and "R", but correct pressure in "L", indicates front clutch circuit leakage. Low pressure in "R" and "L", but correct pressure in "2", indicates rear servo circuit leakage, low line pressure in all positions indicates defective pump, clogged filter, or stuck pressure regulator valve.

Governor Pressure

NOTE: **Test only if transmission shifts at wrong vehicle speeds when throttle rod is correctly adjusted.**

1) Connect 0-100 psi (0-7.0 kg/cm²) gauge to governor pressure port. Operate transmission in third gear to read pressures. *See Automatic Shift Speeds and Governor Pressure Chart.*

2) If governor pressures are incorrect at given vehicle speeds, governor valve and/or weights are probably sticking. Governor pressure should respond smoothly to changes in MPH and should return to 0-1.5 psi (0-.1 kg/cm²) when vehicle is stopped. High governor pressure at stand still (above 2 psi) will prevent transmission from downshifting.

Throttle Pressure

No gauge port is provided for testing throttle pressure. Incorrect throttle pressure should only be suspected if part throttle upshift speeds are either delayed or occur too early in relation to vehicle speeds. Engine runaway on either upshifts or downshifts can also be an indicator of incorrect (low) throttle pressure setting.

CAUTION: **In no case should throttle pressure be adjusted until transmission throttle rod adjustment has been checked, and corrected if necessary.**

HYDRAULIC PRESSURE ADJUSTMENTS

NOTE: **An incorrect throttle pressure setting will cause incorrect line pressure readings even though line pressure adjustment is correct. Always inspect and correct throttle pressure adjustment before adjusting line pressure.**

Throttle Pressure

1) Remove valve body from transmission. Insert gauge (C-3763) between throttle lever cam and kickdown valve.

Fig. 5: View of Valve Body Showing Throttle Pressure Adjustment

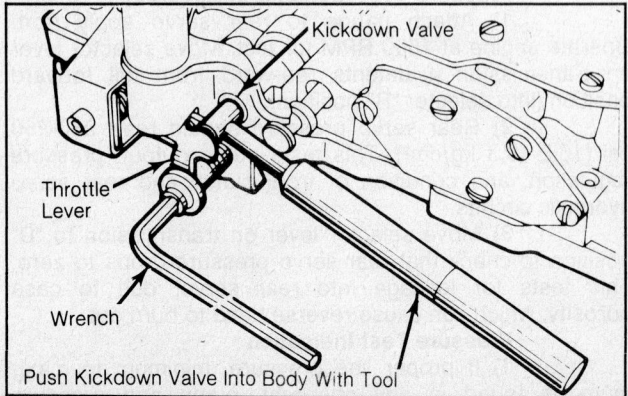

2) By pushing in on tool, compress kickdown valve against spring so valve is completely bottomed inside the valve body. As force is being exerted to compress spring, turn throttle lever stop screw with an Allen wrench until head of screw touches throttle lever tang with throttle lever cam touching tool and throttle valve bottomed.

Line Pressure

1) Turn Allen screw in end of pressure regulator spring bracket so measurement between valve body and inner edge of adjusting nut is 1 5/16". *See Fig. 6.*

NOTE: **Due to manufacturing tolerances, adjustment can be varied to obtain specified line pressure.**

Fig. 6: View of Valve Body Showing Line Pressure Adjustment

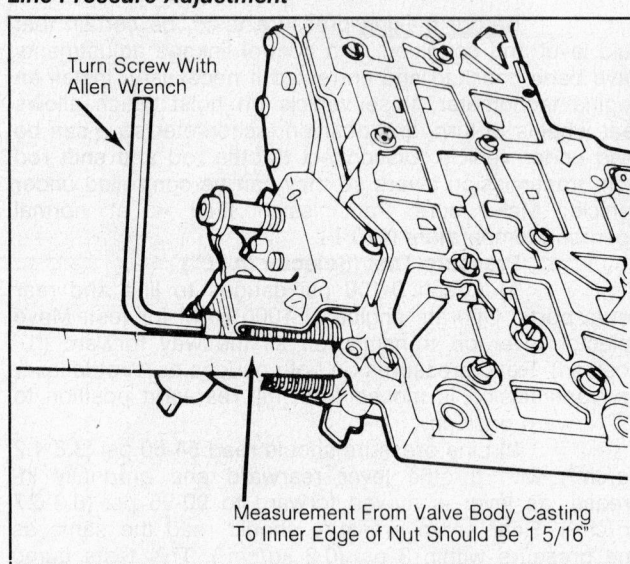

2) One complete turn of adjusting screw changes closed throttle line pressure approximately 1.4 psi (.098 kg/cm²). Turning adjusting screw counterclockwise increases pressure; clockwise decreases pressure.

STALL TEST

CAUTION: **When making the following test, DO NOT let anyone stand in front of the vehicle.**

1) Before making test, check transmission oil level, bring engine to normal operating temperature, and attach tachometer to engine.

2) Test consists of determining engine speed obtained at full throttle in "D" position. Both parking and service brakes must be fully applied while making test.

CAUTION: **Do not hold throttle open any longer than is necessary to obtain a maximum engine speed reading, and never longer than 5 seconds at a time.**

3) If more than one stall check is required, operate engine at approximately 1000 RPM in neutral for 20 seconds to cool transmission fluid between runs. If engine speed exceeds maximum limits shown, release accelerator immediately since transmission clutch slippage is indicated.

CHRYSLER CORP. & MITSUBISHI TORQUEFLITE (Cont.)

Stall Speed Above Specification

If stall speed exceeds maximum limits shown by more than 200 RPM, transmission clutch slippage is indicated. Make hydraulic pressure and air pressure checks to determine cause of slippage.

Stall Speed Below Specification

1) Low stall speeds (with a properly tuned engine) indicate torque converter stator clutch problems. A road test will be necessary to identify exact problem.

2) If stall speeds are 250-350 RPM below specifications, and vehicle operates properly at highway speeds, but has poor through-gear acceleration, stator overrunning clutch is slipping.

3) If stall speed and acceleration are normal, but abnormally high throttle opening is required to maintain highway speeds, stator clutch has seized. Both of these stator defects require replacement of torque converter.

Noise

Whining or siren-like noise due to fluid flow is normal during stall operation with some converters; however, loud metallic noises from loose parts or interference within the assembly indicate a defective converter. To be sure noise originates within the converter, raise vehicle on hoist and operate at light throttle in "D" and "N" while listening under transmission bell housing.

STALL SPEED SPECIFICATIONS

Application	Stall RPM
2.0L Engine	1950-2450
2.6L Engine	1800-2200

SERVICE (IN VEHICLE)

SPEEDOMETER PINION GEAR

Removal

Remove bolt and retainer securing speedometer pinion adapter in extension housing. With cable housing connected, carefully work adapter and pinion out of extension housing.

Fig. 7: Disassembled View of Speedometer Drive

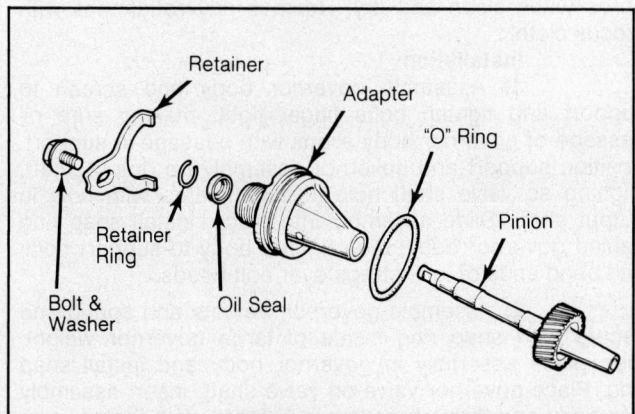

Seal Replacement

If transmission fluid is found in cable housing, replace seal in adapter. Start seal and retainer ring in adapter, then push into adapter using tool (C-4004) until tool bottoms.

Fig. 8: Speedometer Pinion Seal Installation

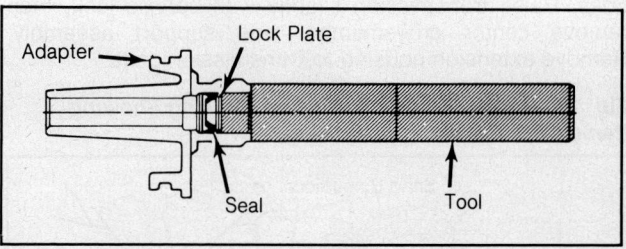

CAUTION: To avoid misalignment, make sure adapter flange and its mating area on extension housing are clean.

Intallation

1) Note number of gear teeth and install speedometer pinion gear into adapter. Rotate pinion gear and adapter assembly so that number on adapter, corresponding with number of teeth on gear, is in 6 o'clock position as assembly is installed.

2) Install retainer and bolt, with tangs in adapter positioning slots. Tap adapter firmly into extension housing, then tighten retainer bolt.

Fig. 9: View of Extension Housing Showing Speedometer Pinion and Adapter Installation

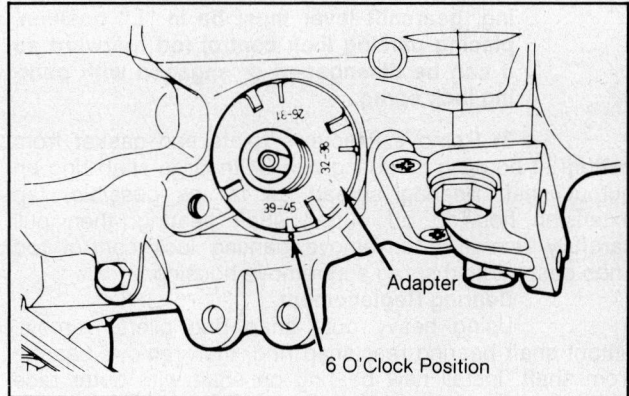

NEUTRAL SAFETY SWITCH

See Automatic Transmission Servicing.

EXTENSION HOUSING YOKE SEAL

CAUTION: Use care not to damage yoke and splines.

Removal

Marking parts for reassembly reference, remove propeller shaft. Cut boot end of extension housing yoke seal, then use puller to remove seal from extension housing.

Installation

Using seal installer, drive new seal into extension housing. Install propeller shaft, aligning marks made at removal.

EXTENSION HOUSING

Removal

1) Marking parts for reassembly reference, remove propeller shaft, then remove extension housing seal. Remove speedometer pinion adapter assembly, then drain approximately 2 quarts of transmission fluid.

CHRYSLER CORP. & MITSUBISHI TORQUEFLITE (Cont.)

2) Remove extension housing-to-crossmember bolts. Raise transmission slightly with service jack, then remove center crossmember and support assembly. Remove extension housing-to-transmission bolts.

Fig. 10: Bottom View of Extension Housing Showing Removal of Retaining Snap Ring

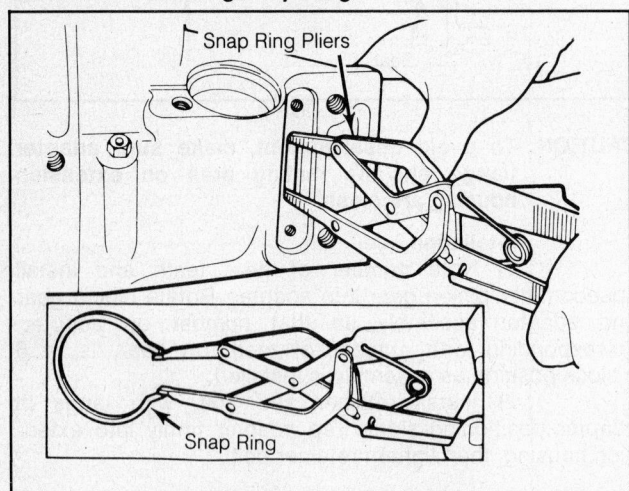

NOTE: When removing or installing extension housing, gearshift lever must be in "L" position, placing parking lock control rod rearward so it can be disengaged or engaged with parking lock sprag.

3) Remove 2 screws, plate and gasket from bottom of housing mounting pad. With large snap ring on output shaft bearing spread as far as possible, tap extension housing off output shaft bearing, then pull carefully rearward to remove parking lock control rod knob past parking sprag and remove housing.

Bearing Replacement

Using heavy duty snap ring pliers, remove output shaft bearing rear snap ring, then remove bearing from shaft. Install new bearing on shaft with outer race ring groove toward front, then install rear snap ring.

Bushing Replacement

Using driver, remove bushing from extension housing. Align hole in new bushing with oil slot in extension housing, drive or press bushing into housing, then install new seal.

Installation

1) Install a new gasket on transmission case. Position output shaft bearing retaining snap ring in extension housing. Slide extension housing on output shaft guiding the parking lock control rod knob past parking sprag. While spreading large snap ring in housing, carefully tap housing into place, then release snap ring.

CAUTION: Make sure snap ring is fully seated in bearing outer race ring groove.

2) Install and tighten extension housing-to-transmission bolts, then install gasket, plate, and screws on bottom of extension housing mounting pad. Install center crossmember and rear mount assembly, then lower transmission and install and tighten extension housing-to-support bolts.

3) Install speedometer pinion and adapter. Carefully guide front universal joint yoke into extension

housing and on the output shaft splines. Align marks made at removal and connect propeller shaft to rear axle pinion shaft yoke. Adjust transmission fluid level as necessary.

Fig. 11: Rear View of Transmission Showing Output Shaft Bearing Installation

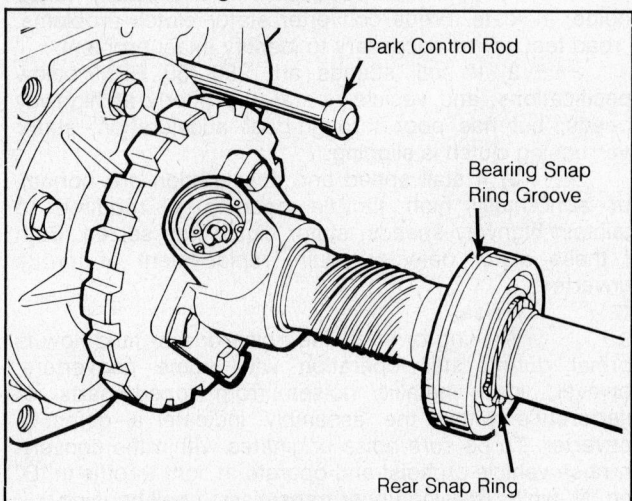

GOVERNOR & PARKING GEAR
Removal

1) Remove extension housing and output shaft bearings as previously outlined. Carefully pry snap ring from weight end of governor valve shaft, then slide valve and shaft assembly out of governor body.

2) Remove large snap ring from weight end of governor body, then lift out governor weight assembly. Remove snap ring from inside governor weight, then remove inner weight and spring from outer weight.

3) Remove snap ring from behind governor body, slide governor and support assembly off output shaft. Remove bolts and separate governor body and screen from parking gear.

Inspection

Inspect all parts for wear or damage, and spring for distortion. Weights and valve should fall freely in bores when clean and dry. Remove any roughness with crocus cloth.

Installation

1) Assemble governor body and screen to support and tighten bolts finger tight, making sure oil passage of governor body aligns with passage in support. Position support and governor assembly on output shaft, aligning so valve shaft hole in body mates with hole in output shaft. Slide assembly into place, install snap ring behind governor body, then tighten body-to-support bolts and bend ends of lock straps over bolt heads.

2) Assemble governor weights and spring and secure with snap ring inside of large governor weight, then place assembly in governor body and install snap ring. Place governor valve on valve shaft, insert assembly into body and through governor weights, then install valve shaft retaining snap ring. Inspect valve and weight assembly for free movement, then install output shaft bearing and extension housing.

Fig. 12: Installed View of Governor Assembly

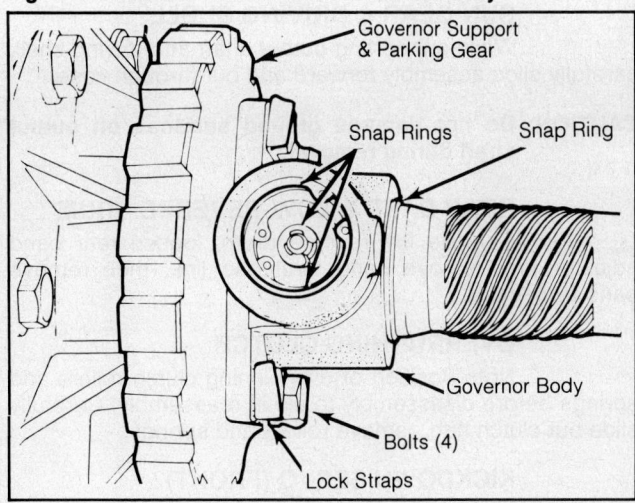

Fig. 13: Disassembled View of Governor Assembly

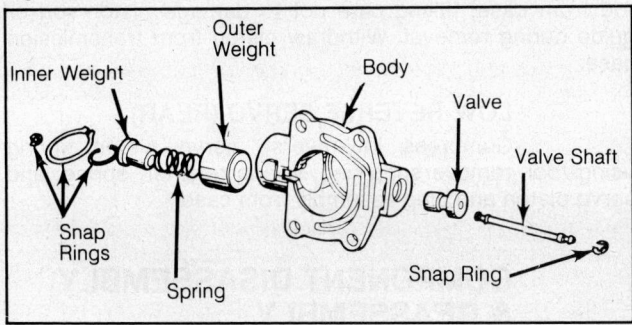

PARKING LOCK

Removal

With extension housing removed, slide shaft out of housing to remove parking sprag and spring. Remove snap ring, then slide reaction plug and pin assembly out of housing.

Installation

Install reaction plug and spring assembly in housing, then secure with snap ring. Position sprag and spring in housing then insert shaft, making sure square lug on sprag is toward parking gear, and spring is positioned so it moves sprag away from gear. Install extension housing.

Fig. 14: Disassembled View Showing Components of Parking Lock Assembly

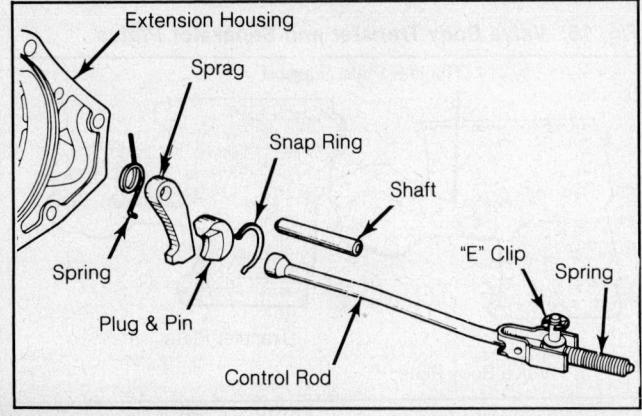

VALVE BODY ASSEMBLY & ACCUMULATOR PISTON

Removal

1) Loosen oil pan bolts, tap pan to break it loose allowing fluid to drain, then remove pan. Loosen clamp bolts, then remove throttle and shift levers from transmission.

2) Remove neutral safety switch, then remove valve body-to-transmission case bolts and lower valve body down and forward out of case. If necessary, rotate propeller shaft to align parking gear and sprag to permit knob on end of parking control rod to pass sprag.

3) Remove accumulator piston and spring from transmission case, then inspect for damage. If valve body manual lever shaft seal requires replacement, drive out of case with a punch. Drive new seal into case with a 15/16" (24 mm) socket and hammer.

NOTE: Seal may be replaced without removing valve body from case by using a small screwdriver to pry seal out of case. Take care not to damage shaft or seal bore in case.

Installation

1) With neutral safety switch removed from case, place valve body manual lever in low position to move parking rod to rear position. Use screwdriver to push sprag into engagement with parking gear, turning output shaft to ensure engagement. This will allow knob on end of parking rod to move past sprag as valve body is installed. Install accumulator piston in case. Position accumulator spring between piston and valve body.

2) Place valve body in position, working park rod through opening and past sprag, then install retaining bolts finger tight. Install neutral safety switch. Place manual lever in neutral position, shifting valve body if necessary to center neutral finger over switch plunger.

3) Install and tighten valve body-to-case bolts evenly. Install gearshift lever and tighten clamp bolt. Move lever through all detent positions to ensure shaft does not bind in case. If binding exists, loosen valve body bolts and realign.

4) Be sure throttle shaft seal is in place, then install flat washer and throttle lever and tighten clamp bolt. Connect throttle and gearshift linkage, adjust as required. Install oil pan with new gasket, then adjust transmission fluid level.

REMOVAL & INSTALLATION

See the appropriate article in AUTOMATIC TRANSMISSION REMOVAL Section.

TORQUE CONVERTER

Converter Pressure Test

Drain all oil from converter. If flushing is required, flush before checking for leakage. Install pressure test tool (C-4102) and tighten. Apply a maximum of 100 psi (7.0 kg/cm²) air pressure to converter, then submerge in a tank of water and observe hub, ring gear and seam welds for bubbles. Five to ten minutes may be required for bubbles to appear from small leaks. If leakage occurs, converter must be replaced.

CHRYSLER CORP. & MITSUBISHI TORQUEFLITE (Cont.)

TRANSMISSION DISASSEMBLY

INPUT SHAFT END PLAY CHECK

Measuring input shaft end play before disassembly will usually indicate when thrust washer change is required (except when major parts are replaced). Thrust washer is located between input and output shafts. Attach dial indicator to transmission converter housing with plunger seated against end of input shaft. Move input shaft in and out to obtain end play reading. End play should be .022-.091" (.56-2.3 mm). Record end play reading for reassembly reference.

Fig. 15: *Using a Dial Indicator to Measure Input Shaft End Play*

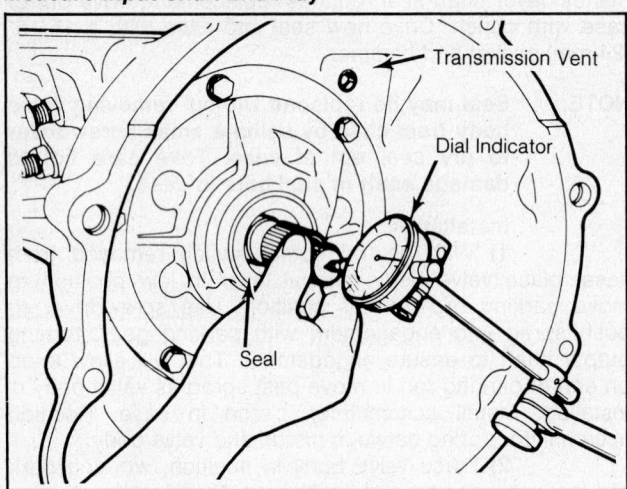

VALVE BODY ASSEMBLY & ACCUMULATOR PISTON
See Service (In Vehicle)

EXTENSION HOUSING
See Service (In Vehicle)

GOVERNOR
See Service (In Vehicle)

OIL PUMP & REACTION SHAFT SUPPORT

Tighten front band adjusting screw until band is tight on front clutch retainer, preventing retainer from coming out with pump, damaging clutches. Remove oil pump housing retaining bolts, then install slide hammers in threaded holes in pump housing flange. Operating both hammers evenly, withdraw pump and reaction shaft support assembly from case.

FRONT BAND & FRONT CLUTCH

Loosen front band adjuster, remove band strut then slide band out of case. Slide front clutch assembly out of case.

INPUT SHAFT & REAR CLUTCH

Grasp input shaft, then slide input shaft and rear clutch assembly out of case.

CAUTION: Do not lose thrust washer located between rear end of input shaft and forward end of output shaft.

PLANETARY GEAR ASSEMBLIES, SUN GEAR & DRIVING SHELL

While supporting output shaft and driving shell, carefully slide assembly forward and out through case.

CAUTION: Do not damage ground surfaces on output shaft during removal.

REAR BAND & LOW-REVERSE DRUM

Remove low-reverse drum, loosen rear band adjuster and remove band strut and link, then remove band from case.

OVERRUNNING CLUTCH

Note position of overrunning clutch rollers and springs before disassembly to aid in reassembly. Carefully slide out clutch hub, remove rollers and springs.

KICKDOWN SERVO (FRONT)

Using tool, compress kickdown servo spring, remove snap ring. Remove rod guide, springs, and piston rod from case, taking care not to damage piston rod or guide during removal. Withdraw piston from transmission case.

LOW-REVERSE SERVO (REAR)

Compress low-reverse servo piston spring using tool, remove snap ring, spring retainer, spring, and servo piston and plug assembly from case.

COMPONENT DISASSEMBLY & REASSEMBLY

VALVE BODY DISASSEMBLY

NOTE: Tag all springs for reassembly reference as they are removed.

CAUTION: DO NOT clamp any portion of valve body or transfer plate in vise. Any distortion of valve body or transfer plate will result in sticking valves. Always place valve in repair stand when repair procedures are to be performed.

Filter, Transfer Plate & Pressure Regulators
1) Remove 3 screws from fluid filter and remove filter from valve body. Remove top and bottom screws from adjustment screw bracket. Hold bracket firmly while removing last retaining screw from side of valve body.

Fig. 16: *Valve Body Transfer and Separator Plates*

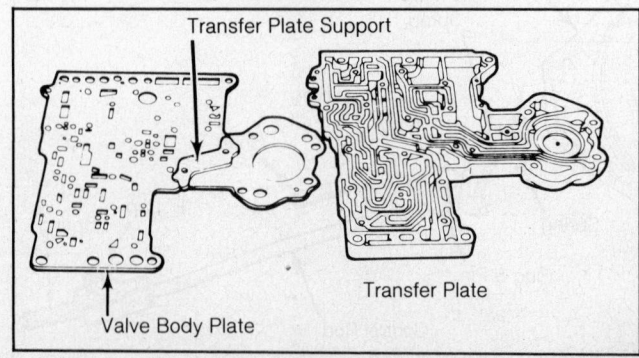

CHRYSLER CORP. & MITSUBISHI TORQUEFLITE (Cont.)

2) Remove bracket with line and throttle pressure adjusting screws (do not disturb screw settings). Also remove regulator valve and switch valve springs. Remove switch valve and regulator valve. Remove transfer plate retaining screws and remove transfer plate and valve body plate. *See Fig. 16.*

3) Remove 6 screws from transfer plate support and valve body plate and separate parts for cleaning. Remove rear clutch check ball and rear servo check ball from transfer plate. Also remove screen from valve body plate. *See Fig. 16.* Remove 7 check balls from valve body. *See Fig. 20.*

Fig. 17: Exploded View of Valve Body Showing Shuttle Valve and Governor Plugs

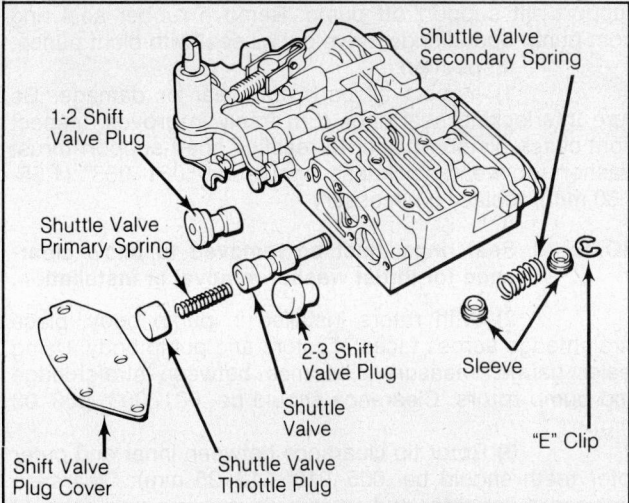

Shuttle Valve & Governor Plugs

1) Turn valve body over. Remove "E" clip and park sprag rod from manual lever. Remove shuttle valve cover plate. Remove shift valve plug cover.

2) Remove 1-2 and 2-3 shift valve plugs. Remove shuttle valve "E" clip and slide shuttle valve, along with the secondary spring and sleeve, from bore.

Manual Lever & Throttle Lever

1) Remove "E" clip and washer from throttle lever shaft. Remove any burrs from shaft. While holding manual lever detent ball and spring in bore, slide manual lever off throttle shaft.

2) Remove detent ball and spring, slide manual valve from bore. Slide out kickdown detent, kickdown valve, throttle valve spring, and throttle valve.

Shift Valves & Regulator Plugs

1) Remove regulator valve cover. Slide out sleeve, line pressure plug, throttle pressure plug, and spring. Remove limit valve body and throttle pressure plug.

2) Remove retainer, limit valve and spring. Remove each shift valve and spring. Withdraw 1-2 shift control valve out of its bore.

VALVE BODY INSPECTION

1) Wash all parts in solvent and blow dry with compressed air. Inspect all parts for nicks, burrs, scratches, or distortion. Small nicks and burrs may be removed with crocus cloth, taking care not to round off any machined sharp edges. Make sure all passages are clean and free from obstructions, and all metering holes in steel plate and valve body are open.

2) Inspect all valve springs for distortion or collapsed coils. Inspect manual and throttle valve operating levers and shafts. If lever is loose on its shaft, it may be SILVER SOLDERED ONLY, or lever and shaft assembly should be replaced. DO NOT attempt to straighten bent levers. When bores, valves and plugs are clean and dry, valves and plugs should fall freely in their bores.

VALVE BODY REASSEMBLY

Shift Valves & Regulator Plugs

1) Insert 1-2 and 2-3 shift valves and springs into proper valve body bores. Assemble limit valve body as follows: Insert limit valve and spring into proper bore. Fit spring retainer in groove in limit valve body. Place throttle plug in limit valve body. Place this assembly against shift valve spring.

2) Mount shift valve cover to valve body. Tighten screws to 26-42 INCH lbs. (2.9-4.9 N.m). Install springs, throttle pressure plug, line pressure plug and sleeve. Secure regulator valve cover to valve body.

Manual Lever & Throttle Lever

1) Install throttle valve, throttle valve spring, kickdown valve, and kickdown detent plug. Slide manual valve into bore. *See Fig. 18.* Install throttle lever on valve body. Insert detent ball and spring in bore in valve body.

2) Depress ball and spring and slide manual lever over throttle shaft so it engages manual valve and detent ball. Install seal, retaining washer, and "E" clip on throttle shaft.

Shuttle Valve & Shift Plugs

Place 1-2 and 2-3 shift valve plugs in their bores. Install shuttle valve, spring and shuttle valve throttle plug. Install shift valve end plate. Install "E" clip on end of shuttle valve, then install shuttle valve cover plate.

Fig. 18: Exploded View of Valve Body Showing Pressure Regulators and Manual Control

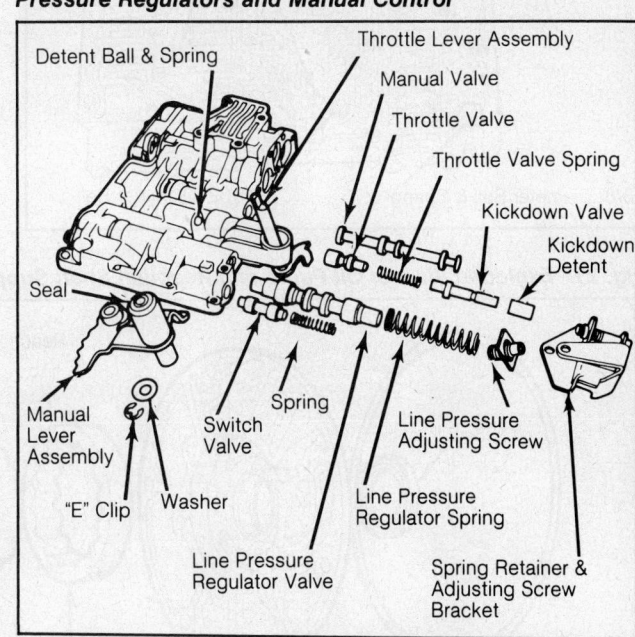

Filter, Transfer Plate, & Pressure Regulators

1) Install 7 check balls in valve body. *See Fig. 20.* Install rear clutch check ball and rear servo check ball in transfer plate. Install regulator valve screen to valve body plate.

CHRYSLER CORP. & MITSUBISHI TORQUEFLITE (Cont.)

2) Assemble transfer plate to valve body plate with 6 screws. Place transfer plate assembly on valve body and install 14 screws. Tighten screws to 26-42 INCH lbs. (2.9-4.9 N.m) working from center screws outward.

Fig. 19: Exploded View of Valve Body Showing Shift Valves and Pressure Regulator Valve Plugs

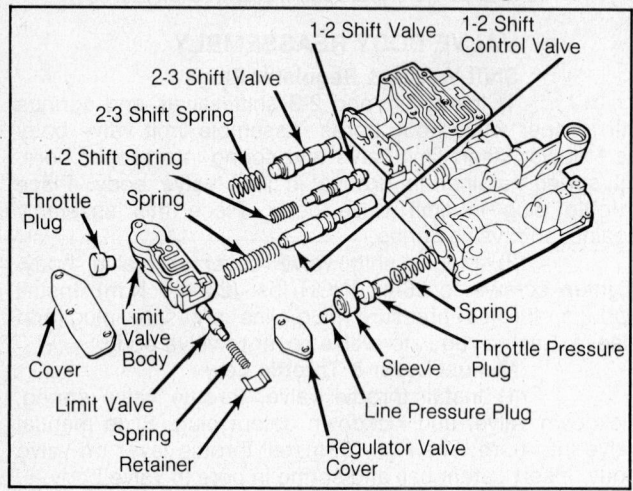

Fig. 20: View of Valve Body Showing Check Ball Locations

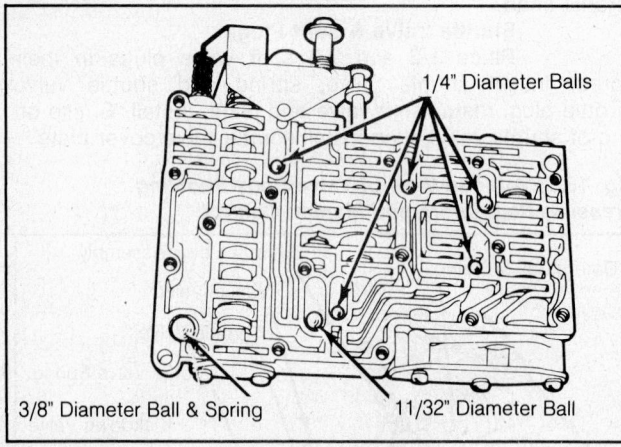

3) Place switch valve, regulator valve and spring in their respective bores. *See Fig. 18*. Place adjustment screw bracket on spring and temporarily install side mounting screw. After top and bottom screws have been installed and tightened, tighten side screw.

4) Install oil filter and tighten attaching screws. After valve body is completely assembled, measure throttle and line pressure adjustments. If pressures were satisfactory before disassembly, use original settings. Install park sprag rod and "E" clip on manual lever.

OIL PUMP & REACTION SHAFT SUPPORT

Disassembly

Remove bolts from rear side of reaction shaft support, lift support off pump. Remove rubber seal ring from pump body flange, drive out oil seal with blunt punch.

Inspection

1) Inspect all parts for wear or damage. Be sure interlocking seal rings turn freely in groves. Inspect front clutch piston retainer to reaction shaft support thrust washer for wear; thickness should be .061-.063" (1.55-1.60 mm), replace if necessary.

NOTE: **Seal rings must be removed to allow clearance for thrust washer removal or installation.**

2) With rotors installed in pump body, place straightedge across faces of rotors and pump body. Using feeler gauge, measure clearance between straightedge and pump rotors. Clearance should be .001-.003" (.03-.08 mm).

3) Rotor tip clearance between inner and outer rotor teeth should be .005-.010" (.13-.25 mm). Clearance between outer rotor and rotor bore in pump body should be .004-.008" (.10-.20 mm).

Pump Bushing Replacement

1) Place pump housing (seal face down) on a clean, smooth surface. Using removing tool (SP-3551) and handle (SP-3549 or C-4171), drive bushing straight down and out of bore, being careful not to cock tool in bore. Using installing head (SP-5117), drive new bushing into place in pump rotor housing.

2) Stake bushing in place using blunt punch or other similar tool. Using narrow bladed knife or similar

Fig. 21: Exploded View of Oil Pump and Reaction Shaft Support

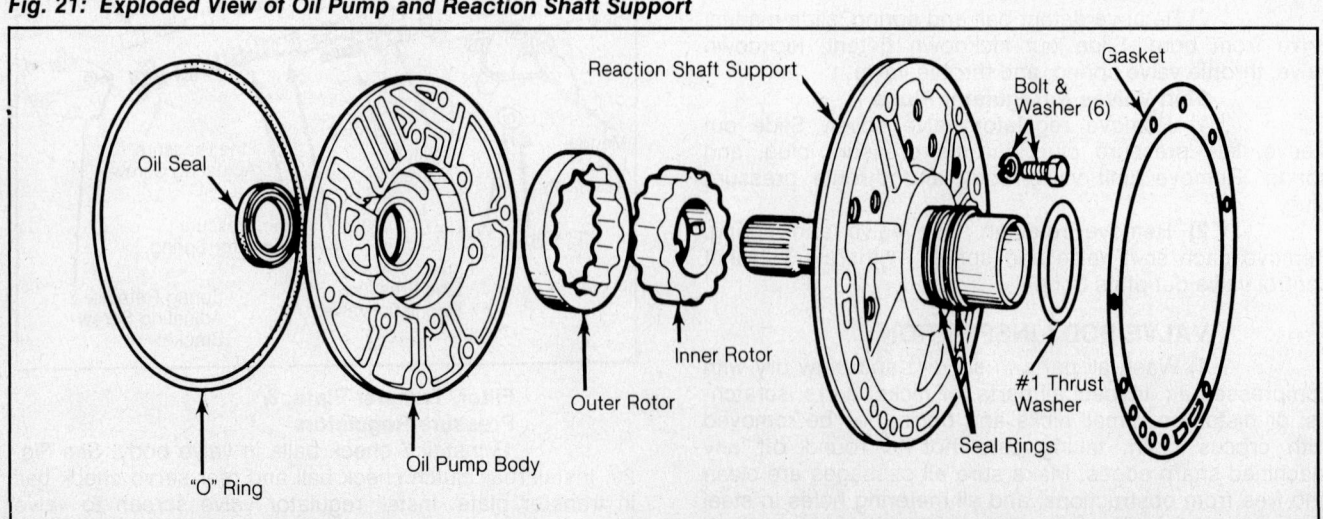

Automatic Transmissions

CHRYSLER CORP. & MITSUBISHI TORQUEFLITE (Cont.)

tool, remove high points or burrs around staked area. Do not use file or any tool that would remove more metal than necessary.

Fig. 22: Rear View of Oil Pump Housing Showing Staking Positions in Bushing

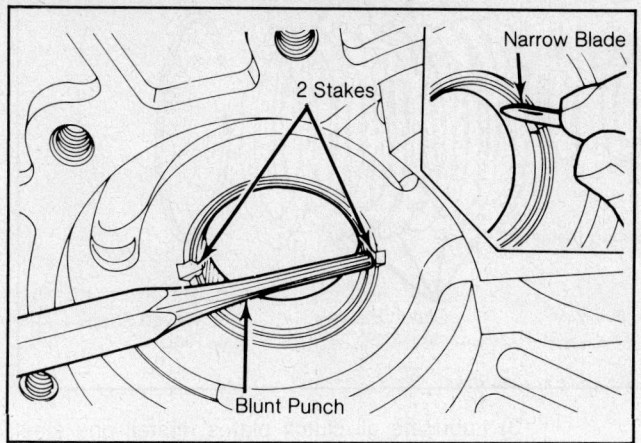

Reaction Shaft Bushing Replacement

Thread bushing remover tool into bushing. See Fig. 23. Withdraw bushing from reaction shaft. Support reaction shaft upright. Using driving tool, drive new bushing into place in reaction shaft.

NOTE: If bushing failed in service, inspect support for wear from input shaft seal ring lands. If worn or grooved, replace support assembly.

Fig. 23: Tool Set-Up for Reaction Shaft Bushing Replacement

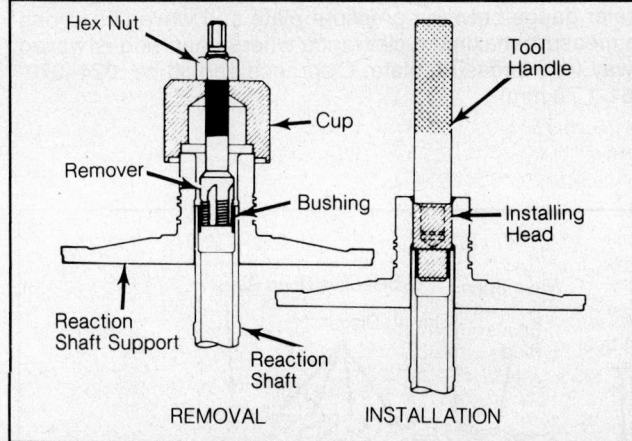

Reassembly

1) Place reaction shaft support in an assembling tool (C-3759) with hub of support and tool on a smooth, flat surface. Install 2 pilot studs in threaded holes in support flange. See Fig. 24.

2) Assemble rotors in center of support and lower pump body over pilot studs. Using tool (C-3756), center rotors in pump body. With pump body firmly against reaction shaft support, tighten assembling tool securely.

3) Invert pump and tool assembly. Install support-to-pump bolts and tighten evenly. Remove assembling tool, pilot studs, and aligning tool. Using tool (C-4193), install new pump oil seal.

Fig. 24: Tool Set-Up for Assembling Oil Pump and Reaction Shaft Support

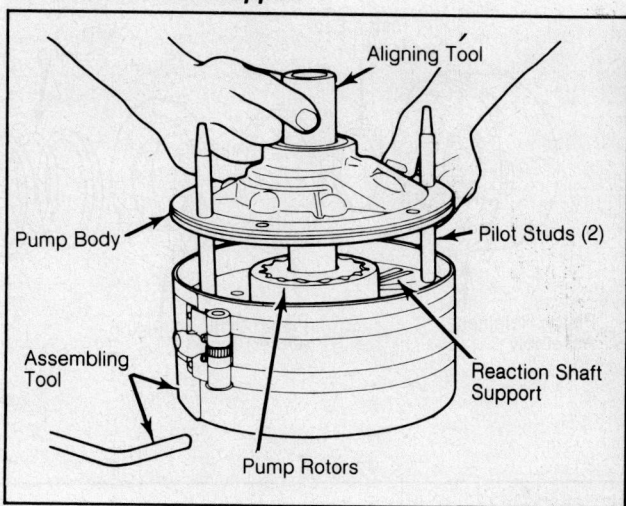

FRONT CLUTCH
Disassembly

1) Remove large waved snap ring that secures pressure plate in clutch piston retainer. Remove pressure plate, clutch discs and clutch plates from retainer. Install compression tool (C-3573-A) over piston spring retainer. Compress spring and remove snap ring.

2) Slowly release compressor tool until spring retainer is free from hub. Remove tool, retainer and spring. Invert clutch retainer assembly. Bump assembly on block of wood to remove piston. Remove all seals from piston and clutch retainer hub.

Inspection

1) Inspect plates and discs for flatness; they must not be warped or cone-shaped. Inspect facing material on all driving discs, replace if damaged.

2) Inspect discs and plates for wear on splines or lugs. Check clutch retainer for damaged lug grooves, or damaged band contacting surfaces. Make sure ball check in clutch retainer moves freely.

3) Check neoprene seals for wear, hardness or deterioration. Inspect piston spring(s), retainer and snap ring for distortion.

Front Clutch Retainer Bushing Replacement

Lay clutch retainer (open end down) on a clean smooth surface. Using removing head tool (SP-3627), drive bushing straight down and out of bore, being careful not to cock tool. To install, lay clutch retainer (open end up) on clean smooth surface, using installing head tool (SP-3626), drive bushing into place in clutch retainer bore.

Reassembly

1) Lubricate and install inner seal on hub of clutch retainer, making sure lip of seal faces down and is properly seated in groove. Install outer seal on clutch piston, with lip of seal toward bottom of clutch retainer. Apply a coating of wax type lubricant to outer edge of seal. Place piston assembly in retainer and carefully seat piston in bottom of retainer.

2) Place spring on piston hub and position spring retainer and snap ring on spring. Using tool (C-3575-A), compress spring, seat snap ring in hub groove, remove tool.

Automatic Transmissions

CHRYSLER CORP. & MITSUBISHI TORQUEFLITE (Cont.)

Fig. 25: Exploded View of Front Clutch Assembly

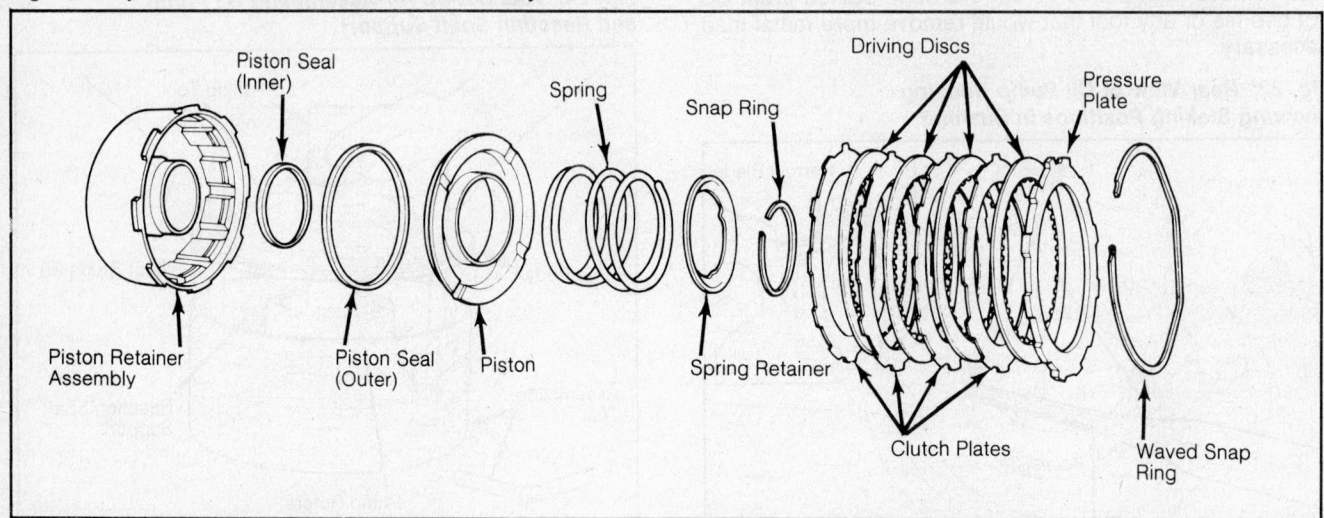

Fig. 26: Using a Feeler Gauge to Measure Front Clutch Clearance

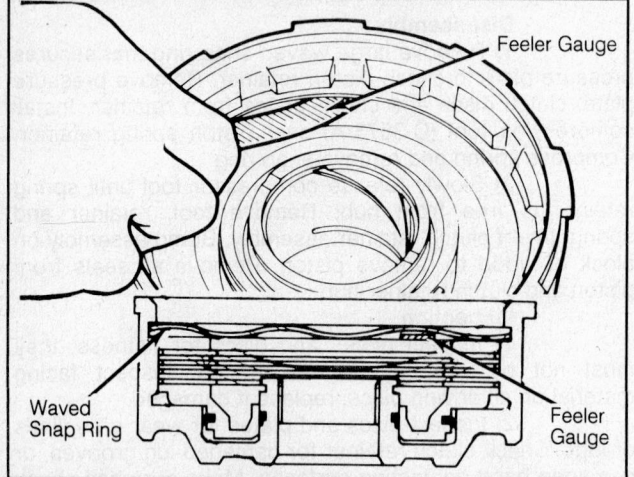

3) Lubricate all clutch plates. Install one steel plate followed by one lined disc until number given in Front Clutch Chart is installed. Install pressure plate and snap ring, making sure snap ring is properly seated. Insert feeler gauge between pressure plate and waved snap ring to measure maximum clearance where snap ring is waved away from pressure plate.

FRONT CLUTCH PLATE USAGE CHART

Application	Plates	Discs
All Models	2	2

4) With clutch assembly completed, insert feeler gauge between pressure plate and waved snap ring to measure maximum clearance where snap ring is waved away from pressure plate. Clearance should be .024-.070" (.61-1.78 mm).

Fig. 27: Exploded View of Rear Clutch Assembly

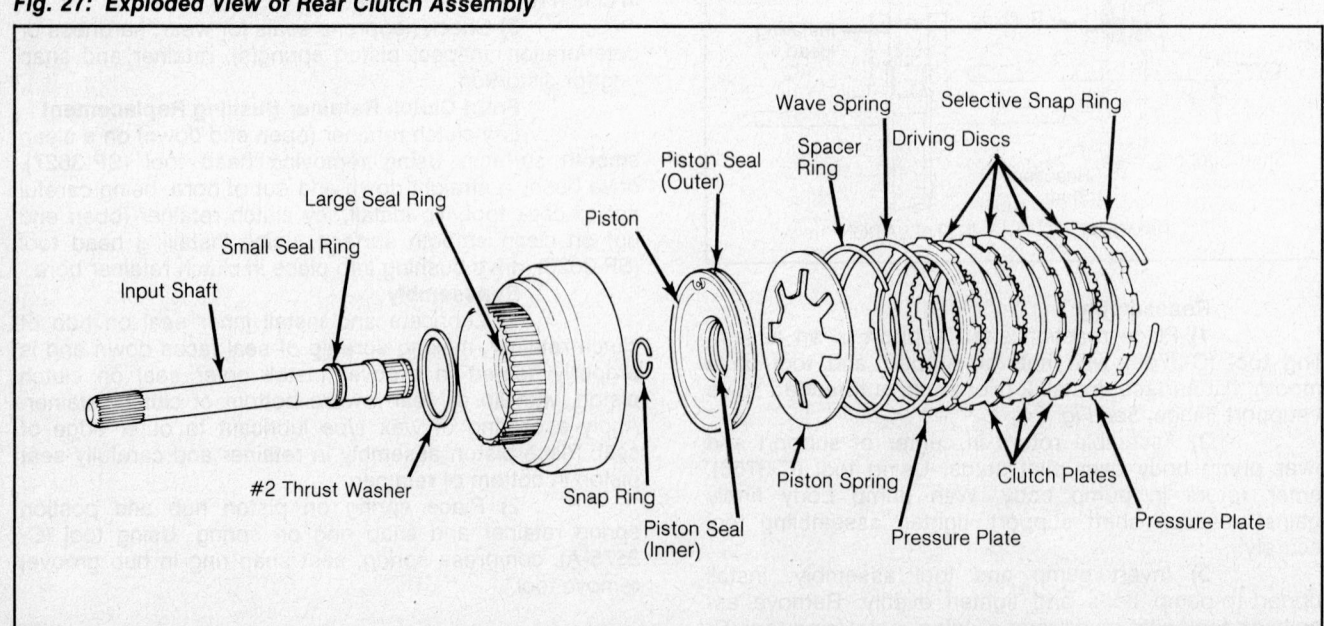

CHRYSLER CORP. & MITSUBISHI TORQUEFLITE (Cont.)

REAR CLUTCH
Disassembly
1) Remove large selective snap ring securing pressure plate in clutch piston retainer. Lift pressure plate, clutch plates, and inner pressure plate out of retainer. Carefully pry one end of wave spring out of groove in clutch retainer. Remove wave spring and clutch piston spring.

2) Invert clutch piston retainer assembly and bump it on a wood block to remove piston, then remove seals from piston. If necessary, remove snap ring and press input shaft from piston retainer.

Inspection
1) Inspect all parts for wear or damage. Plates and discs must not be warped or cone-shaped. Note ball check in clutch retainer, make sure ball moves freely. Inspect neoprene seals for deterioration, wear and hardness.

2) Inspect piston spring and wave spring for distortion or breakage. Inspect seal rings for wear or breakage, make sure they turn freely in grooves. Inspect rear clutch-to-front clutch thrust washer for wear. Thickness should be .061-.063" (1.55-1.60 mm), replace as necessary.

NOTE: Do not remove rings unless conditions warrant. Replacement seal rings are cast iron hooked joint type.

Reassembly
1) If removed, press input shaft into piston retainer and install snap ring. Lubricate and install inner and outer seals on clutch piston, making sure lips of seals face toward head of clutch retainer and are properly seated in grooves. Place piston assembly in retainer, with a twisting motion, seat piston in bottom of retainer.

2) Place clutch piston spring on top of piston in clutch retainer. Start one end of wave spring in retainer groove. Progressively push or tap spring into place making sure it is fully seated in groove.

3) Install inner pressure plate in clutch retainer with raised portion of plate resting on spring. Lubricate all clutch plates. Install one lined disc followed by one steel plate until all plates are installed. Install outer pressure plate and selective snap ring.

Fig. 28: Installing Piston Spring and Wave Spring in Rear Clutch Drum

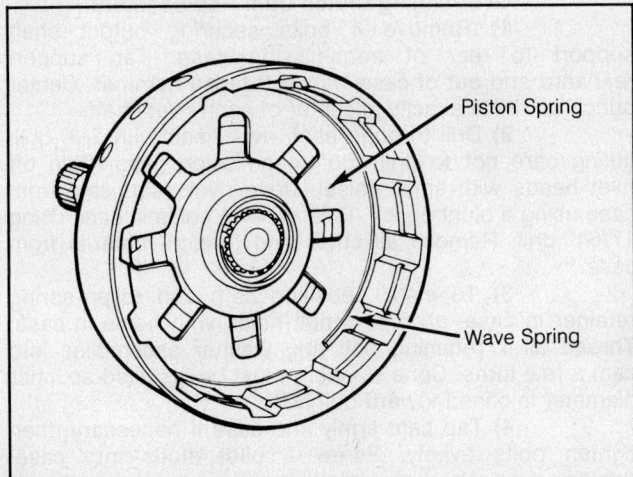

Fig. 29: Using Feeler Gauge to Measure Rear Clutch Clearance

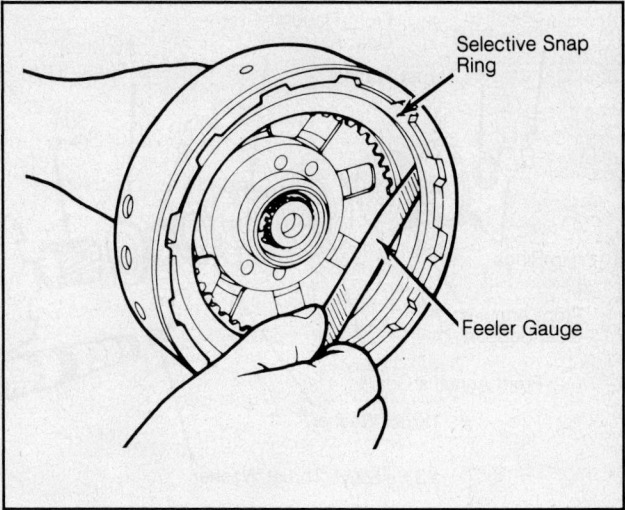

REAR CLUTCH PLATE CHART

Application	Plates	Discs
All Models	2	3

4) Measure rear clutch clearance by pressing down frimly on outer pressure plate. Inserting feeler gauge between plate and snap ring. Clearance should be .032-.055" (.82-1.39 mm), with low limit clearance desirable. Install new snap ring of proper thickness to obtain specified clearance. Snap rings are available in thicknesses of .061", .077" and .099" (1.55, 1.96 and 2.51 mm).

PLANETARY GEAR TRAIN
End Play
1) Measure end play of planetary gear assemblies, sun gear and driving shell before removing from output shaft. Stand assembly upright with forward end of output shaft on a wood block so that all parts will move forward against snap ring at front of shaft.

2) Insert feeler gauge between rear annulus gear support hub and shoulder on output shaft. Clearance should be .006-.033" (.16-.83 mm). If clearance exceeds specifications, replace thrust washers and/or necessary parts. See Fig. 30.

Fig. 30: Using a Feeler Gauge to Measure Planetary Gear Train End Play

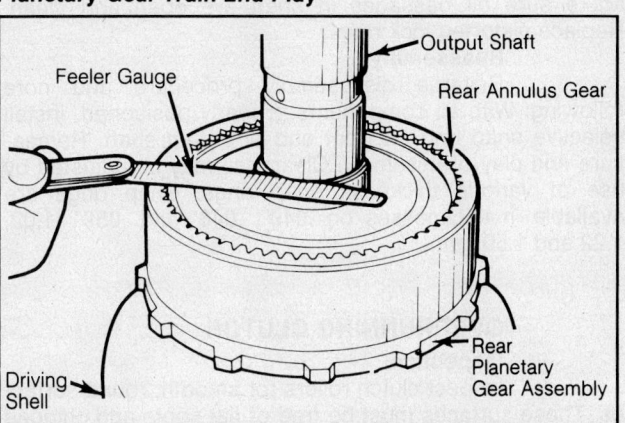

Fig. 31: Exploded View of Planetary Gear Train and Output Shaft

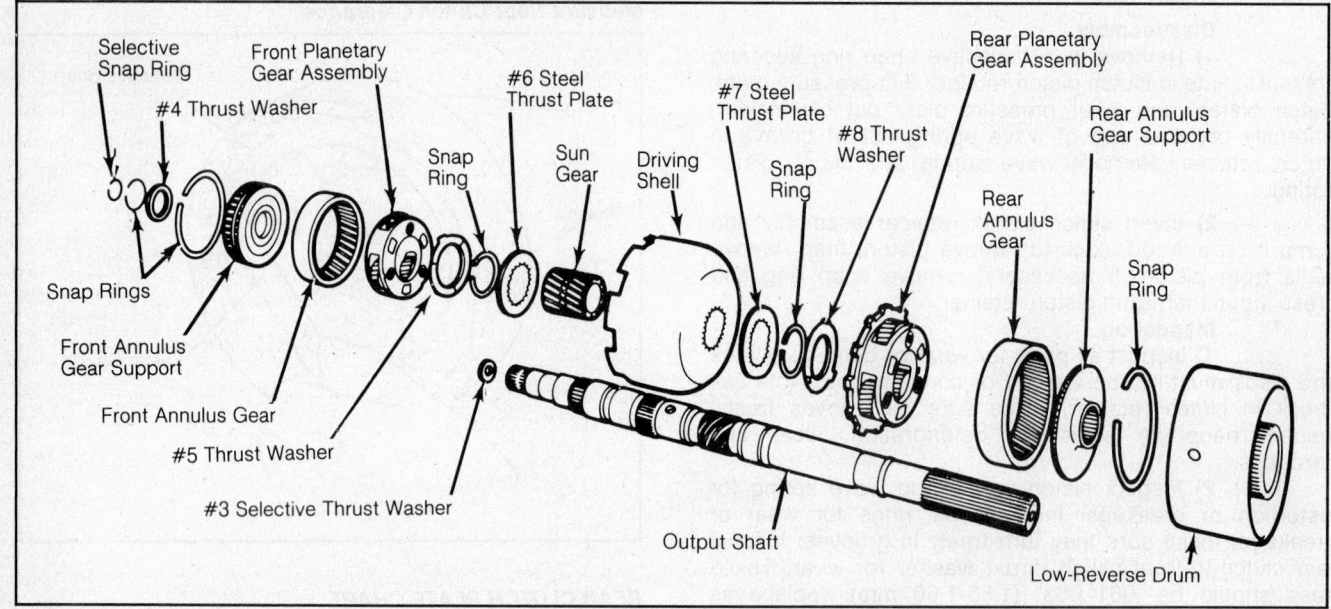

Disassembly

1) Remove selective thrust washer from forward end of output shaft. Remove selective snap ring and thrust washer from forward hub of front planetary gear assembly. Slide front annulus gear and support off planetary gear set.

2) If necessary, remove snap ring from front of annulus gear to separate support from annulus gear. Slide sun gear, driving shell and rear planetary assembly off output shaft. Lift sun gear and driving shell off rear planetary assembly. Remove snap ring and thrust plate from sun gear (rear side of driving shell).

3) Slide sun gear out of driving shell. Remove snap ring and thrust plate from opposite end of sun gear if necessary. Remove thrust washer from forward side of rear planetary assembly. Remove planetary gear set from rear annulus gear. If necessary, remove snap ring from rear of annulus gear to separate support from annulus gear.

Inspection

Inspect all parts for nicks, burrs, scores or other damage. Light scratches, small nicks or burrs can be removed with crocus cloth or fine stone. Inspect bushings in sun gear for wear or scores, replace assembly if bushings are damaged. Inspect all thrust washers for wear and scores, replace if damaged or worn. Make sure oil passages in shaft are open and clean. Replace distorted lock rings.

Reassembly

Reverse disassembly procedure and note following: With all components properly positioned, install selective snap ring on front end of output shaft. Remeasure end play of assembly. Clearance may be adjusted by use of various thickness snap rings. Snap rings are available in thicknesses on .040", .048" and .059" (1.02, 1.22 and 1.50 mm).

OVERRUNNING CLUTCH
Inspection

Inspect clutch rollers for smooth, round surfaces. These surfaces must be free of flat spots and chipped edges. Inspect roller contacting surfaces in cam and race for wear. Inspect roller springs for distortion, wear or other damage.

Fig. 32: Disassembled View of Replacement Type Overrunning Clutch Cam

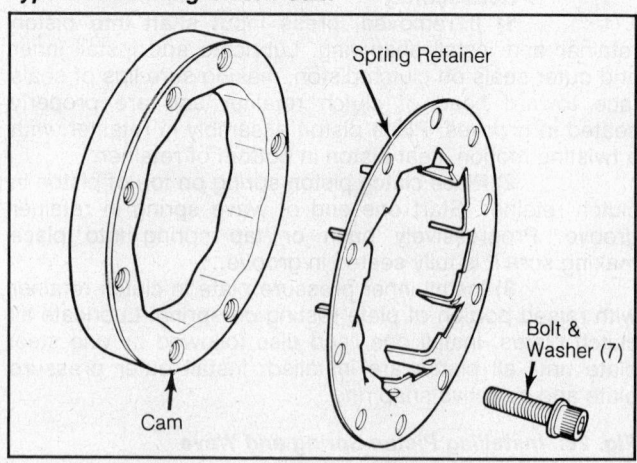

Overrunning Clutch Cam Replacement

1) Remove 4 bolts securing output shaft support to rear of transmission case. Tap support rearward and out of case with soft faced hammer. Center punch on rivets exactly in center of each rivet head.

2) Drill through each rivet head with 3/8" drill, taking care not to drill into transmission case. Chip off rivet heads with small chisel. Drive rivets and cam from case using a blunt punch. Enlarge rivet holes in case using 17/64" drill. Remove all chips and foreign material from case.

3) To install, position cam and roller spring retainer in case, align cam bolt holes with holes in case. Thread all 7 retaining bolt and washer assemblies into cam a few turns. Cone washers must be installed so inner diameter is coned toward bolt head.

4) Tap cam firmly into case if necessary, then tighten bolts evenly. Screw 2 pilot studs into case. Position support cover studs and tap firmly into place

CHRYSLER CORP. & MITSUBISHI TORQUEFLITE (Cont.)

using a soft faced hammer. Remove pilot studs, then install and tighten bolts evenly.

Fig. 33: Installed View of Overrunning Clutch Assembly

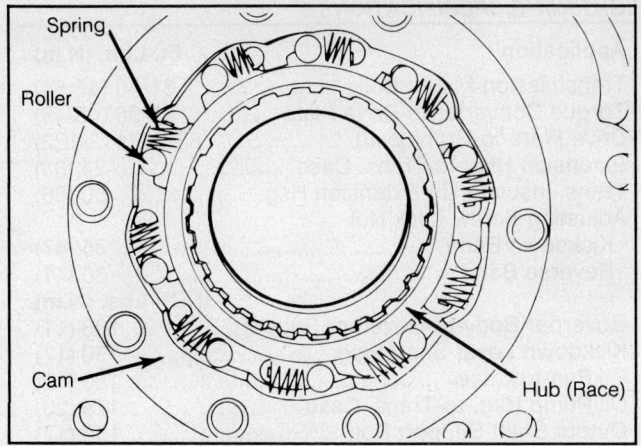

KICKDOWN SERVO & BAND

Disassembly

Disassemble servo piston by removing small snap ring from servo piston, then remove washer, spring and piston rod from servo piston.

Inspection

Inspect all parts for nicks, burrs, wear or damage. Be sure piston and guide seal rings turn freely in grooves. Do not remove seal rings unless conditions warrant. Inspect fit of guide on piston rod and piston spring for distortion. Inspect band lining for wear or damage. If lining is worn so grooves are not visible at ends or any portion of band, replace band.

Fig. 34: Exploded View of Kickdown Servo

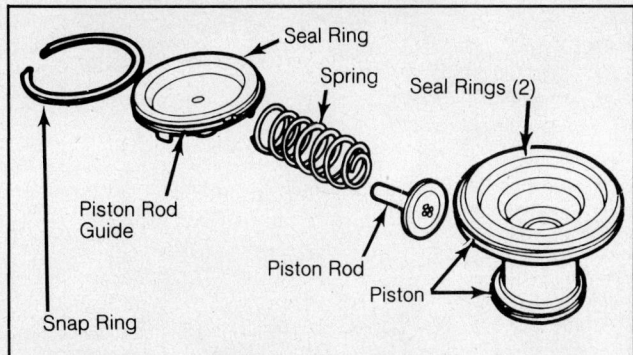

Fig. 35: Exploded View of Low-Reverse Servo

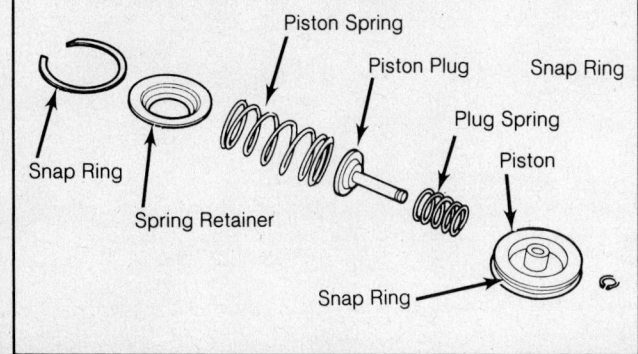

Reassembly

Carefully push servo piston into transmission case bore, then install piston rod, springs and guide. Compress kickdown servo springs with spring compressor and install snap ring.

LOW-REVERSE SERVO & BAND

Disassembly

Remove snap ring, piston, plug retainer and spring.

Inspection

Inspect seal for deterioration, wear and hardness. Inspect piston for cracks, burrs, scores and wear. Inspect piston bore for scores or damage. Check springs for distortion. Inspect band lining for wear and bond of lining to band. If linging is worn so grooves are not visible at ends or any portion of band, replace band.

Reassembly

Low-Reverse Servo & Band are reassembled when reassembling transmission. See *LOW-REVERSE SERVO & BAND* under *TRANSMISSION REASSEMBLY* in this article.

TRANSMISSION REASSEMBLY

NOTE: Use only Dexron type Automatic Transmission Fluid to lubricate transmission parts during reassembly.

OVERRUNNING CLUTCH

With transmission case in upright position, insert clutch hub inside cam. Install overrunning clutch rollers exactly as shown in *Fig. 33.*

Fig. 36: Assembled View of Low-Reverse Band and Linkage Assembly

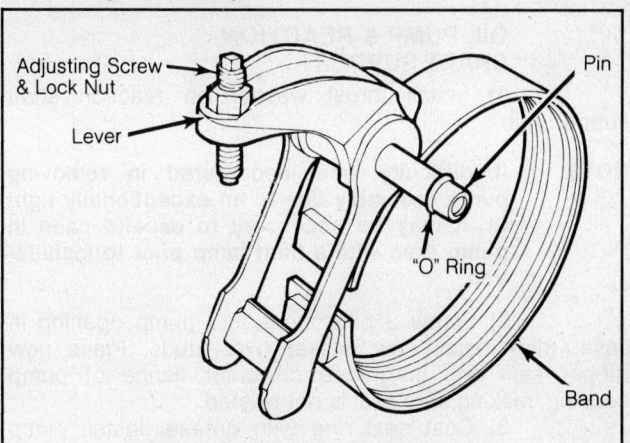

LOW-REVERSE SERVO & BAND

Low-Reverse Servo

Carefully work servo piston into transmission case with a twisting motion, then place spring, retainer and snap ring over piston. Uning spring compressor, compress low-reverse servo piston and install snap ring.

Low-Reverse Band

Position rear band in transmission case, install short strut, connect long link and anchor to band. Screw in band adjuster just enough to hold strut in place, then install low-reverse drum. Make sure long link and anchor are installed so as to provide running clearance for low-reverse drum.

PLANETARY GEAR, SUN GEAR & DRIVING SHELL

While supporting assembly in case, insert output shaft through rear support. Carefully work assembly rearward, engaging rear planetary carrier lugs into low-reverse drum slots.

CAUTION: Do not damage ground surfaces on output shaft durng installation.

FRONT & REAR CLUTCH ASSEMBLIES

NOTE: Front and rear clutches, front band, oil pump and reaction shaft support are more easily installed with transmission in upright position.

1) Apply a coat of grease to seletive thrust washer and install on front end of output shaft. If input shaft end play was not with in specifications, .022-.091" (.56-2.3 mm), when tested prior to disassembly, replace thrust washer with one of proper thickness.

2) Align front clutch plate inner splines. Place assembly in position on rear clutch, making sure front clutch plate splines are fully engaged on rear clutch splines.

3) Align rear clutch plate splines, grasp input shaft, lower assemblies into case. Carefully work clutch assemblies in circular motion to engage rear clutch splines over splines of front annulus gear. Make sure front clutch drive lugs are fully engaged in slots of driving shell.

FRONT (KICKDOWN) BAND

Slide front band over front clutch assembly. Install band strut, then screw in adjuster just enough to hold strut and anchor in place.

OIL PUMP & REACTION SHAFT SUPPORT

1) Install thrust washer on reaction shaft support hub.

NOTE: If difficulty was incountered in removing pump assembly due to an exceptionally tight fit, it may be necessary to expand case in pump area with a heat lamp prior to installation.

2) Screw 2 pilot studs into pump opening in case, then install new gasket over studs. Place new rubber seal ring in groove on outer flange of pump housing, making sure seal is not twisted.

3) Coat seal ring with grease. Install pump assembly into case, tapping lightly with soft mallet, if necessary. Remove pilot studs, install bolts and snug down evenly.

4) Rotate input and output shafts to see that no binding exists, then tighen bolts. Check shafts again for free rotation, then adjust both bands.

GOVERNOR

See Service (In Vehicle).

EXTENSION HOUSING

See Service (In Vehicle).

TORQUE CONVERTER

See Transmission Removal & Installation

TIGHTENING SPECIFICATIONS

Application	Ft. Lbs. (N.m)
Transmission Mount Bolts	31-40 (42-54)
Torque Converter-to-Drive Plate	33-36 (45-49)
Drive Plate-to-Crankshaft	83-90 (113-122)
Extension Hsg.-to-Trans. Case	24 (33)
Trans. Insulator-to-Extension Hsg.	50 (68)
Adjusting Screw Lock Nut	
Kickdown Band	35 (47)
Reverse Band	30 (41)
	INCH Lbs. (N.m)
Governor Body-to-Governor Support	100 (11)
Kickdown Lever Shaft Plug	150 (17)
Oil Pan-to-Case	150 (17)
Oil Pump Hsg.-to-Trans. Case	175 (20)
Output Shaft Support Bolt	150 (17)
Pressure Test Plug	110 (12)
Reaction Shaft Support-to-Oil Pump	160 (18)
Valve Body Screws	35 (4)
Valve Body-to-Trans. Case	100 (11)

GM TURBO HYDRA-MATIC 400 - JAGUAR

Jaguar XJS-HE

DESCRIPTION

Transmission is a fully automatic unit consisting primarily of a 3 element hydraulic torque converter and a compound planetary gear set. Three multiple disc clutches, 2 roller clutches, and 2 bands provide friction elements required to obtain desired function of planetary gear set. A hydraulic system pressurized by a gear-type pump provides working pressure required to operate friction elements and automatic controls.

LUBRICATION & ADJUSTMENTS

BAND ADJUSTMENT
Band Apply Selection Test

1) Raise and support vehicle. Remove oil pan and allow fluid to drain. Remove valve body assembly with governor lines attached. Remove rear servo cover and gasket, rear servo assembly and servo accumulator spring.

2) Position selection gauge and gauge of Service Set (18G-1310) in servo bore and secure with 2 bolts. Ensure gauge is free to move up and down in both selection gauge and servo bore.

3) Using 9/16" socket on torque wrench, tighten nut on gauge to 25 ft. lbs. (34 N.m). This will cause lever on top of gauge to depress stepped gauge pin into servo pin bore, simulating actual operating conditions.

4) Note letter and relation of steps on gauge pin and select appropriate size apply pin. *See Fig. 2.* If new band apply pin is required, make note of pin size. Remove selection gauge and gauge pin.

Fig. 2: Band Apply Pin Selection

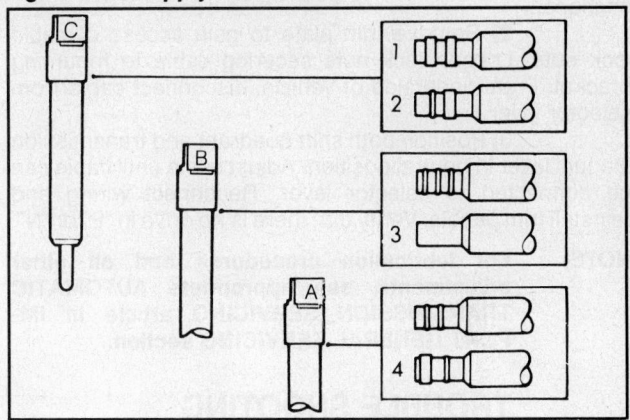

Pins 1, 2, 3 and 4 are factory installed, but are not available as replacement parts.

Fig. 1: Cutaway View of Turbo Hydra-Matic 400 Automatic Transmission

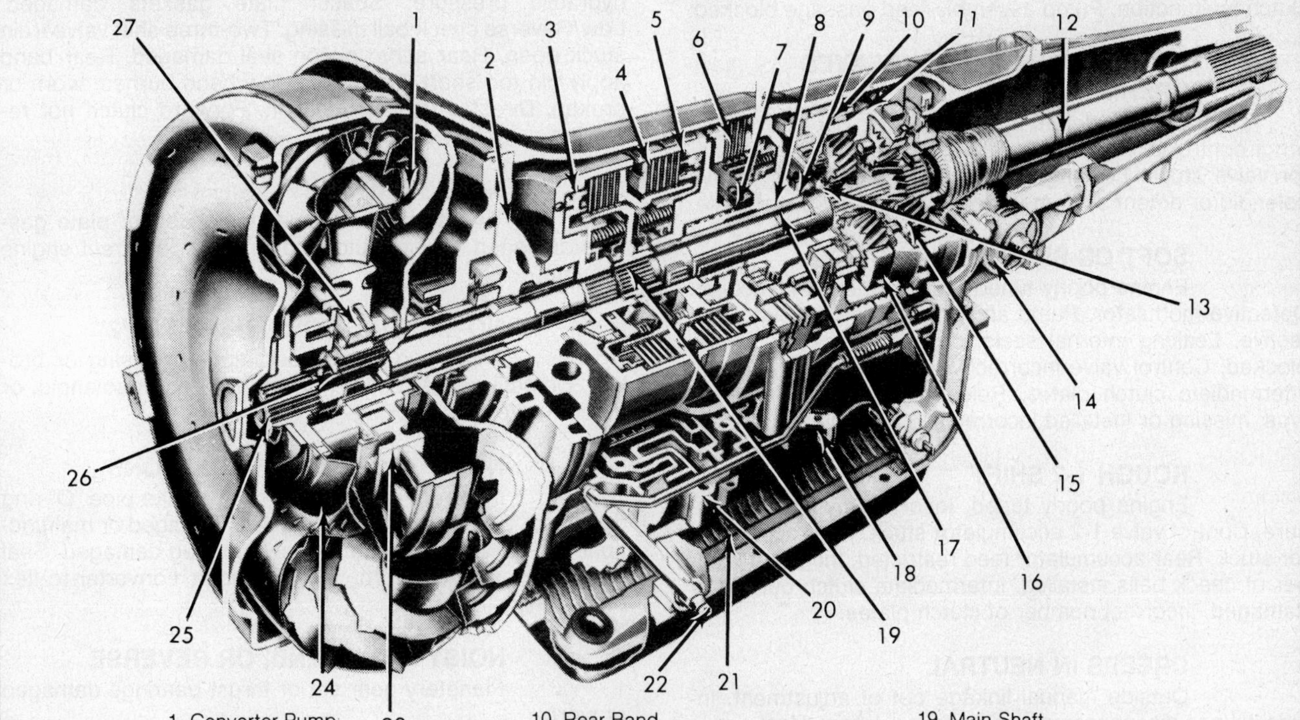

1. Converter Pump	10. Rear Band	19. Main Shaft
2. Pump Assembly	11. Output Carrier & Internal Gear	20. Control Valve
3. Forward Clutch	12. Output Shaft	21. Filter Assembly
4. Direct Clutch	13. Sun Gear	22. Manual Shaft
5. Front Band	14. Speedometer Driven Gear	23. Stator
6. Intermediate Clutch	15. Rear Internal Gear	24. Turbine
7. Intermediate Sprag	16. Reaction Carrier	25. Turbine Shaft
8. Center Support	17. Sun Gear Shaft	26. Stator Shaft
9. Low Roller Clutch	18. Detent Solenoid	27. Stator Roller Clutch

5) Install selected apply pin, servo accumulator spring and servo assembly. Install servo cover with new gasket. Install valve body and governor pipes. Install oil pan with new gasket. Replenish transmission fuid.

SELECTOR CABLE ADJUSTMENT

1) Disconnect negative battery cable. Remove gear selector knob. Remove screws from selector trim plate, withdraw plate slightly and disconnect electrical connections.

2) Remove trim plate to gain access of cable lock nuts. Loosen lock nuts securing cable to mounting bracket. From underside of vehicle, disconnect cable from selector lever.

3) Position both shift quadrant and transmission manual lever in neutral position. Adjust cable until cable can be connected to selector lever. Reconnect wiring and reinstall trim panels. Verify that there is no drive in "P" or "N".

NOTE: **For lubrication procedures and all other adjustments, see appropriate AUTOMATIC TRANSMISSION SERVICING article in IMPORT GENERAL SERVICING section.**

TROUBLE SHOOTING

NO DRIVE IN "D"

Manual linkage out of adjustment. Low hydraulic pressures. Manual valve disconnected from lever. Forward clutch malfunction. Pump assembly feed passage blocked.

NO 1-2 UPSHIFT - OR DELAYED UPSHIFT

Short in detent switch or wiring. Defective governor control valve or feed system. Vacuum leaks. Modulator valve stuck. Leaking modulator diaphragm. Defective solenoid or detent system. Blocked orifice in spacer plate.

SOFT OR SLIPPING 1-2 SHIFT

Engine poorly tuned. Incorrect engine vacuum. Defective modulator. Pump and/or pressure regulator defective. Leaking internal seals, gaskets or circuits. Filter blocked. Control valve incorrectly torqued. Wrong type of intermediate clutch plates. Release springs of incorrect type, missing or installed incorrectly. Leaking case.

ROUGH 1-2 SHIFT

Engine poorly tuned. Incorrect hydraulic pressure. Control valve 1-2 accumulator stuck. Rear accumulator stuck. Rear accumulator feed restricted. Incorrect number of check balls installed. Intermediate clutch burned or damaged. Incorrect number of clutch plates.

CREEPS IN NEUTRAL

Outside manual linkage out of adjustment. Inside linkage disconnected or pin broken. Internal leakage in pump assembly. Damaged or incorrect clutch plates.

ROUGH 2-3 SHIFT

Defective vacuum modulator. Modulator valve stuck. Pump pressure regulator or boost valve stuck. Front servo accumulator spring damaged or missing. Front servo accumulator piston stuck. Extra waved steel plate installed in in direct clutch. Drilled controlled valve assembly blocked.

SLIPPING 2-3 SHIFT

Incorrect hydraulic pressure. Direct clutch leaking. Leaky passages or stuck valves in control valve assembly. Spacer plate damaged in control valve. Blocked direct clutch feed orifice. Servo pin leaking. Broken or missing front servo spring. Incorrect number of direct clutch plates. Damaged or missing piston seals. Broken or undersize oil rings. Case-to-center support leaking.

WILL NOT HOLD IN PARK

Misadjusted linkage. Parking pawl broken or chamfer missing.

WILL NOT RELEASE FROM PARK

Misadjusted linkage.

NO ENGINE BRAKING IN "L1"

Low/Reverse check ball missing. Rear servo oil seal ring, bore or piston damaged. Rear band apply pin to short or improperly installed. Rear band damaged.

NO ENGINE BRAKING IN "L2"

Front servo or accumulator oil rings/bore damaged. Front servo piston stuck. Front band damaged or incorrectly installed

NO REVERSE - OR SLIPS IN REVERSE

Manual linkage incorrectly adjusted. Incorrect hydraulic pressure. Spacer plate gaskets damaged. Low/Reverse check ball missing. Two-three shift valve train stuck open. Rear servo piston seal damaged. Rear band apply pin too short. Reverse or low band burned, worn or broken. Direct clutch malfunction. Forward clutch not releasing.

NO 2-3 SHIFT

Two-three shift valve stuck. Spacer plate gaskets damaged. Direct clutch malfunction. Incorrect engine vacuum.

NO MANUAL DOWNSHIFT TO "2"

Three-two valve stuck, spring missing or broken. Defective detent switch, defective detent solenoid, or detent valve train sticking.

NOISY IN ALL GEAR POSITIONS

Incorrect or restricted filter. Intake pipe "O" ring damaged. Leaking case. Pump gears damaged or malfunctioning. Pressure regulator orifice cup plug damaged. Seal rings damaged or worn. Loose torque converter-to-flex plate bolts.

NOISY IN 1ST, 2ND, OR REVERSE

Planetary gear set or thrust bearings damaged or worn.

NOISY DURING ACCELERATION

Transmission cooler lines contacting body. Motor mounts loose.

SQUEAK AT LOW SPEEDS

Speedometer shaft seal damaged. Extension housing seal damaged.

GM TURBO HYDRA-MATIC 400 - JAGUAR (Cont.)

TESTING

ROAD TEST

1) Place selector lever in "D", and accelerate vehicle from a stop. The 1-2 and 2-3 shift should occur at all throttle openings. See SHIFT SPEED SPECIFICATIONS table. As vehicle speed decreases below 16 MPH, a 3-2 and 2-1 downshift should occur.

2) Place selector lever in "2" (Intermediate) and accelerate from a stop. A 1-2 upshift should occur and no 2-3 shift should occur. See SHIFT SPEED SPECIFICA-TIONS table. As vehicle speed decreases below 10 MPH, a 2-1 downshift should occur.

3) Place selector lever in "1" (Low), and acceler-ate vehicle from a stop. No upshifts should occur below 6200 RPM. Testing for upshift is not necessary.

4) With selector lever in "D", and vehicle speed approximately 35 MPH, close throttle and move selector lever to "2" (Intermediate). Transmission should immediately downshift to 2nd gear, increase engine RPM and an engine braking effect should be noticed.

5) With selector lever in "2" (Intermediate), and vehicle speed approximately 30 MPH, close throttle and move selector lever to "1" (Low). Transmission should downshift to 1st gear between 18-13 MPH, increase engine RPM and an engine braking effect should be noticed.

SHIFT SPEED SPECIFICATIONS

Application	Speed (MPH)
Upshift	
Light Throttle	
1-2	5-12
2-3	10-20
Full Throttle	
1-2	40-50
2-3	55-70
Full Throttle Kick-Down	
1-2	50-60
2-3	80-95
Kick-Down	
3-2	70-85
2-1	28-38
Downshift	
Manual	
2-1	13-18
Part Throttle Kick-Down	
3-2	40-50
Closed Throttle	
3-2	8-12
2-1	3-8

LINE PRESSURE TESTS

1) With transmission fluid at correct level and operating temperature, and pressure gauge installed as previously described, line pressure can be checked.

2) With vehicle stationary, service brakes ap-plied (except as noted), check line pressures according to selector position and RPM conditions. See LINE PRES-SURES table.

3) Total running time when performing combina-tion of, Low or "2" at 1000 RPM and Reverse at 1000 RPM tests, must not exceed 2 minutes.

4) When stationary testing is complete, perform Drive at 30 MPH Test, with vehicle on road or with vehicle raised on hoist and brakes released. Raise engine speed to 3000 RPM. Close throttle. Read pressure between 1200-2000 RPM.

LINE PRESSURES

Range at RPM	psi (kg/cm^2)
Neutral at 1000 RPM [1]	55-70 (3.9-4.9)
Drive at Idle [1]	60-85 (4.2-6.0)
Drive at 1000 RPM [1]	[2] 60-90 (4.2-6.3)
Low or "2" at 1000 RPM [1]	135-160 (9.5-11.2)
Reverse at 1000 RPM [1]	95-150 (6.7-10.5)
Drive at 1000 RPM [3]	90-100 (6.3-7.0)
Drive at 30 MPH [4]	55-70 (3.9-4.9)

[1] - Brakes applied.
[2] - If line pressure is high, check vacuum and, if necessary check modulator.
[3] - Brakes applied and downshift swith activated.
[4] - Vehicle on hoist, driving wheels off ground, brakes released. Raise speed to 3000 RPM, close throttle and read pressure between 1200-2000 RPM.

LINE PRESSURE TESTS RESULTS

Too Low

- Transmission fluid level low. Faulty vacuum modulator assembly. Oil filter blocked or restricted, "O" ring on filter intake pipe omitted or damaged, intake pipe split or leaking.
- Not enough spacers in oil pump pressure regulator. Pressure regulator spring too weak. Oil pump gear clearance incorrect. Oil pump damaged or worn.
- Internal leak in direct clutch circuit (pressure normal in neutral, low, intermediate and drive, but low in reverse).
- Internal leak in forward clutch circuit (pressure normal in neutral and reverse, low in drive).

Too High

- Vacuum system leak or improper engine vacuum. Vac-uum modulator not operating properly or defective. Stuck modulator valve. Defective EGR valve.
- Detent switch actuated or shorted, detent solenoid stuck open. Detent feed orifice in spacer plate blocked, detent solenoid loose. Detent valve bore plug damaged. Detent regulator valve pin too short.
- Oil pump pressure regulator and/or boost valve stuck. Incorrect pump pressure regulator spring. Pressure boost valve installed backward. Too many oil pump pressure regulator valve spacers. Oil pump casting defective.
- Valve body assembly-to-spacer gasket out of propor-tion. Valve body assembly gaskets switched.

STALL TEST

CAUTION: Test must not last longer than 10 seconds. Allow engine to idle in neutral at least 2 min-utes between tests to cool transmission.

1) Install a 0-300 psi pressure gauge with exten-sion pressure line, to pressure take-off point at left side of transmission near manual lever. Place gauge where it can be seen from driver's seat. See Fig, 3.

CLUTCH AND BAND APPLICATION CHART (ELEMENTS IN USE)

Selector Lever Position	Forward Clutch	Direct Clutch	Front Band	Intermed. Clutch	Intermed. Roller Clutch Or Sprag	Low Roller Clutch	Rear Band
"D" – DRIVE							
1st Gear	X					X	
2nd Gear	X			X	X		
3rd Gear	X	X		X			
"2" – INTERMEDIATE							
1st Gear	X					X	
2nd Gear	X		X	X	X		
"1" – LOW (First)	X					X	X
"R" – REVERSE		X					X

NEUTRAL OR PARK – All clutches and bands released and/or ineffective.

Fig. 3: Transmission Case Pressure Take-Off Point

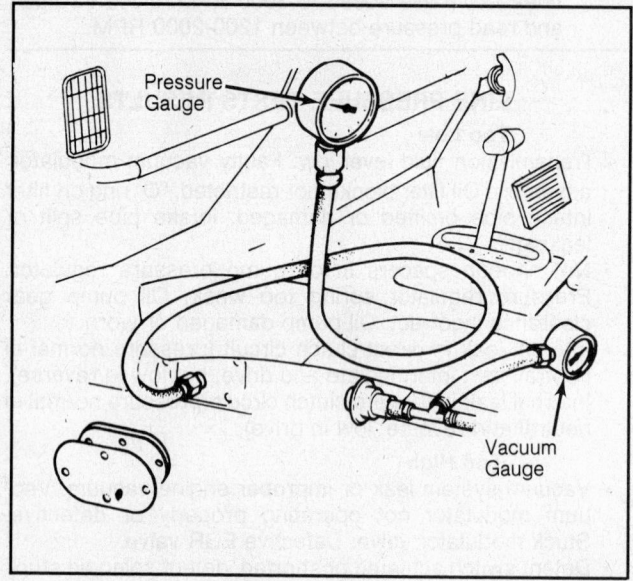

Pressure Gauge

Vacuum Gauge

2) Ensure engine is properly tuned and engine and transmission are at operating temperature. Chock wheels, set hand brake and apply service brake. Start engine and place selector in drive.

3) Gradually apply full throttle and note maximum RPM and line pressure. If transmission slip occurs, stop engine and locate cause. Restart engine and repeat procedure with selector in reverse.

STALL SPEED SPECIFICATIONS

Selector Position	Stall Speed RPM	Stall Pressure psi (kg/cm²)
Drive	2100-2400	145-155 (10.2-10.9)
Reverse	2100-2400	240-260 (16.8-18.2)

GOVERNOR

1) With vehicle on hoist (rear wheels off ground), disconnect vacuum line to modulator. Connect pressure gauge to transmission and tachometer to engine.

STALL SPEED RESULTS

RPM	Condition
Under 1800	Stator Slipping
1800-1900	Poorly Tuned Engine
2100-2400	Normal Stall Speed
Over 2400	Transmission Slipping

2) Start engine. Move selector lever to "D", and release brake. Check line pressure at 1000 RPM. Line pressure should be 150 psi (10.5 kg/cm²). Slowly increase engine speed to 3000 RPM. Check line pressure.

3) Line pressure should drop 10 psi (.7 kg/cm²). If no pressure drop occurs, inspect governor for sticking valve or weight, restricted orifice in valve, scored or cracked bore or restricted feed pipe or screen.

VACUUM MODULATOR
Vacuum Diaphragm Leak Test

Insert a pipe cleaner into vacuum connector pipe as far as possible and check for presence of transmission oil. If oil is found, replace modulator.

NOTE: Gasoline or water vapor may settle in vacuum side of modulator. If this is found without presence of oil, modulator should not be changed.

Atmospheric Leak Test

1) Apply a liberal coating of soapy solution to threaded screw seal and vacuum connector pipe seam at crimped upper-to-lower housing seam.

2) Using a short piece of rubber hose, apply air pressure to vacuum pipe by blowing into hose and check for leak bubbles. If bubbles appear, replace modulator.

CAUTION: Do not use a compressor for applying air pressure. Pressures over 6 psi (.4 kg/cm²) may damage modulator.

Bellows Comparison Test

Where the vacuum bellows are suspected, substitute vacuum modulator in question with a new or good modulator.

Sleeve Alignment Test

Roll main body of modulator on a flat surface and observe sleeve for concentricity to cam. If sleeve is concentric and plunger is free, modulator is okay.

KICK-DOWN SOLENOID

1) Turn ignition to "ON", but do not start engine. From under hood, check that there is current at input terminal (Green cable) of switch. Connect a test lamp between output terminal (Green/White cable) and ground.

2) Move throttle linkage to wide open position. If test lamp fails to light, allow throttle to return to closed position. Depress the switch by hand. If lamp still fails to light, replace switch.

3) If lamp lights when operated by hand, loosen attaching bolts and adjust switch toward cable until lamp lights at full throttle. Test light should go out when throttle is released.

SERVICE (IN VEHICLE)

VALVE BODY

1) With oil pan, filter and intake tube removed, remove detent spring and roller assembly retaining bolt. Remove remaining valve body attaching bolts but leave solenoid attached.

NOTE: **Front servo parts may drop out of the transmission case as valve body assembly is removed.**

2) Remove valve body assembly with governor pipes attached, using care not to drop manual valve as valve body assembly is removed. Remove front servo piston assembly, if still in case.

3) Remove governor screen from governor feed pipe hole in case or from end of feed pipe. Remove governor pipes from valve body assembly. Governor pipes are interchangeable.

EXTENSION HOUSING OIL SEAL

1) Support engine/transmission assembly using rear engine lifting eye. Remove rear engine/transmission mount. Lower engine slightly. Remove driveshaft from gearbox output flange.

2) Remove output shaft drive flange bolt, washer and flange. Using a puller remove extension housing oil seal. To install, reverse removal procedure. Ensure seal is installed straight in bore.

GOVERNOR ASSEMBLY

Remove extension housing. Slide speedometer gear from output shaft. Place transmission in neutral. Remove governor plug and spring washer. Slide governor off output shaft. To install, reverse removal procedure.

OIL PAN, FILTER & INTAKE PIPE

Remove oil pan attaching bolts and remove pan. Remove filter retaining bolt and withdraw intake pipe and filter assembly. Discard filter and "O" ring seal from intake pipe.

REAR SERVO

1) With oil pan and valve body assembly removed, remove rear servo cover and gasket, rear servo assembly and servo accumulator spring.

2) Make a band apply pin selection check at this time to determine correct pin for proper band application. This is equivalent to band adjustment.

SPEEDOMETER DRIVE PINION

Disconnect speedometer cable from drive pinion. Remove pinion clamp bolt and clamp plate. Remove pinion assembly from case. Discard seals.

REMOVAL & INSTALLATION

TRANSMISSION

See appropriate AUTOMATIC TRANSMISSION REMOVAL article in IMPORT GENERAL SERVICING section.

TORQUE CONVERTER

Remove transmission from vehicle. See appropriate AUTOMATIC TRANSMISSION REMOVAL article in IMPORT GENERAL SERVICING section. Slide torque converter off input shaft. Remove bolts attaching torque converter housing to transmission case. To install, reverse removal procedure.

TRANSMISSION DISASSEMBLY

NOTE: **Perform input shaft end play check before proceeding with transmission disassembly. Record end play for use in determining proper selective thrust washer during reassembly.**

INPUT SHAFT END PLAY

1) With transmission removed from vehicle and torque converter removed, remove 1 front pump attaching bolt and bolt seal at either 10 o'clock or 5 o'clock position.

2) Install slide hammer bolt into threaded bolt hole in front pump. Mount a dial indicator to bolt and index indicator to register with end of turbine shaft. While holding output shaft forward, push turbine shaft rearward.

3) Zero dial indicator. Pull turbine shaft forward and read resulting end play on indicator. End play should be .003-.025" (.08-.64 mm). If end play is not within specified limits, select correct thickness washer for use at reassembly.

4) Selective thrust washer controlling this end play is located between pump cover and forward clutch housing. Front end play selective thrust washers are available in varying thicknesses and are color coded.

VALVE BODY ASSEMBLY & SPACER PLATE

1) Invert transmission and remove oil pan, filter and intake tube. Remove bolt securing detent spring and roller assembly. Remove valve body retaining bolts and remove valve body.

2) Remove detent solenoid attaching bolts and remove solenoid. Being careful to prevent distorting, re-

Automatic Transmissions
GM TURBO HYDRA-MATIC 400 - JAGUAR (Cont.)

FRONT UNIT END PLAY SELECTIVE THRUST WASHERS

Washer Thickness [1]	Color Code
.060-.064"	Yellow
.071-.075"	Blue
.082-.086"	Red
.093-.097"	Brown
.104-.108"	Green
.115-.119"	Black
.126-.130"	Purple

[1] – An oil soaked washer may tend to discolor, so it will be necessary to measure washer for its actual thickness.

move valve body spacer plate. Remove 6 check balls from transmission casing.

FRONT PUMP

If front seal requires replacement, pry seal out before removing pump assembly. Remove pump attaching bolts. Install 2 slide hammers into 2 opposite threaded pump bolt holes, and evenly remove pump assembly from case. Remove and discard pump-to-case seal ring and gasket.

TURBINE SHAFT, FORWARD & DIRECT CLUTCH ASSEMBLIES, SUN GEAR SHAFT & FRONT BAND

Remove forward clutch and turbine shaft assembly from case, then remove forward clutch hub-to-direct clutch housing thrust washer. Remove direct clutch and intermediate roller assembly, then remove sun gear shaft and front band.

NOTE: **Make rear end play check before removing center support or proceeding with transmission disassembly. Record end play for use in determining proper selective thrust washer.**

REAR UNIT END PLAY CHECK

1) With extension housing removed, install threaded end of a 3/8"-16 rod into one of the extension housing bolt holes in rear of case. Install dial indicator on rod with indicator pin contacting end of output shaft.

2) Zero indicator dial, then move output shaft in and out and note end play reading. End play should be .003-.019" (.08-.48 mm). If end play needs adjustment, select a thrust washer that will bring end play within specifications.

SELECTIVE THRUST WASHERS (REAR UNIT END PLAY)

Washer Thickness	I.D. Notches
.080-.082"	None
.086-.090"	Side of 1 Tab
.094-.098"	Side of 2 Tabs
.102-.106"	End of 1 Tab
.110-.114"	End of 2 Tabs
.118-.122"	End of 3 Tabs

3) Selective thrust washer controlling rear unit end play is a steel washer having 3 tabs. It is located between output shaft thrust washer and rear face of transmission case. Notches and/or numerals on tabs of washer identify thickness.

CENTER SUPPORT, INTERMEDIATE CLUTCH, GEAR CARRIER/OUTPUT SHAFT ASSEMBLY & REAR BAND

1) Using 3/8", 12 point socket, remove recessed center support retaining bolt from hole in valve body mating surface of transmission case between rear servo and detent solenoid mounting position.

2) Remove intermediate clutch backing plate-to-case snap ring. Withdraw backing plate and clutch plates. Remove center support-to-case snap ring. Install Gear Carrier Remover (J-21795) on end of main shaft so tangs engage groove in shaft.

3) Tighten screw on remover to prevent movement of roller clutch during gear carrier assembly removal. Also, cover shaft splines to prevent damaging case bushing.

4) With transmission case in horizontal position, remove complete assembly from case. Remove output shaft-to-case thrust washer and rear unit selective thrust washer. Remove rear band from case.

DETENT LEVER, MANUAL LEVER SHAFT & PARK LINKAGE

1) If necessary for parts replacement, remove manual linkage. Loosen jam nut holding detent lever to manual shaft. Remove manual shaft retaining pin from case. Remove jam nut and detent lever from manual shaft. Remove manual shaft.

2) Remove parking pawl actuator rod and detent lever assembly. Remove attaching bolts and parking bracket. Remove parking pawl return spring. Remove parking pawl shaft retainer. Remove parking pawl shaft cup plug. Pry outward to remove plug. Remove parking pawl shaft and parking pawl.

Fig. 4: Detent and Manual Levers and Parking Pawl Assembly

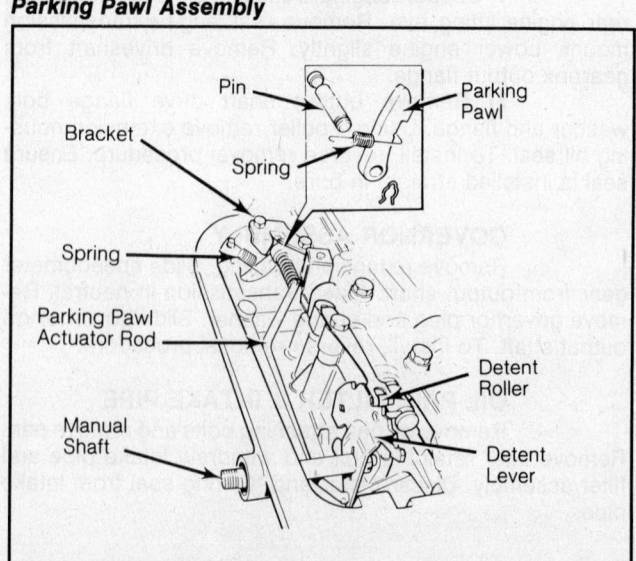

COMPONENT DISASSEMBLY & REASSEMBLY

VALVE BODY
Disassembly

NOTE: As each valve train is removed, place the individual valve train in a separate location relative to its position in valve body. None of valves or springs are interchangeable.

1) Position valve body assembly with machined surface facing up, with manual valve away from you and accumulator pocket toward you. Remove manual valve from upper bore.

NOTE: Steps 2) and 3) require using a pin punch to remove valve train retaining pins.

2) Install Piston Spring Compressor (18G 1295) on accumulator piston. Compress spring, remove "E" ring and remove piston and spring. Remove retaining pins, and remove 1-2 valve train from upper right hand bore.

3) From center right hand bore, remove 2-3 valve train. From lower right hand bore, remove 3-2 valve train. From upper left hand bore, remove detent valve train. From lower left hand bore, remove 1-2 accumulator valve train.

Cleaning & Inspection

1) Inspect all valves and bushings carefully to make sure they are free from dirt and are not damaged in any way. If burrs are present, remove with a fine stone or fine grade crocus cloth and light oil.

CAUTION: When removing burrs from valves, use care not to round off shoulders of valves.

2) Test all valves and bushings in their bores to make sure they slide freely of their own weight. Manual valve is only valve that can be serviced separately. If other valves require replacement, complete valve body assembly should be replaced.

3) Inspect valve body for cracks or scored bores. Check all springs for distortion or collapsed coils. Inspect accumulator piston and oil ring for damage.

NOTE: Do not remove Teflon oil seal from front accumulator piston unless seal needs replacing. For service, the oil seal ring is cast iron.

Reassembly

1) Install front accumulator spring and piston into valve body, then compress piston and spring and install retaining "E" clip.

2) In lower left bore, install 1-2 accumulator primary spring (if required) and 1-2 accumulator valve, stem end out, then install bore plug.

3) Install detent regulator spring and spacer in upper left bore. Install detent regulator valve (stem end out) and detent valve (narrow land first). Install bore plug with open end out and install retaining pin.

4) Install 3-2 valve in lower right bore, then install spacer, valve spring, bore plug (open end out) and retaining pin. In next bore up, install 2-3 shift valve (hole end out) and 3-2 intermediate spring. Install 2-3 modulator valve into bushing and install both parts into valve bore. Install 2-3 valve spring, then install retaining pin.

5) In next bore, install 1-2 valve (stem end out). Install 1-2 regulator valve (large stem first), spring and 1-2 detent valve (hole end first) into 1-2 modulator bushing, aligning spring in bore of detent valve and install parts into valve body bore.

6) Compress bushing against spring and install retaining pin. Install manual valve with detent pin groove to the right.

REAR SERVO
Disassembly

Remove rear accumulator piston from rear servo piston. Remove "E" ring retaining rear servo piston to

Fig. 5: Exploded View of Valve Body Assembly

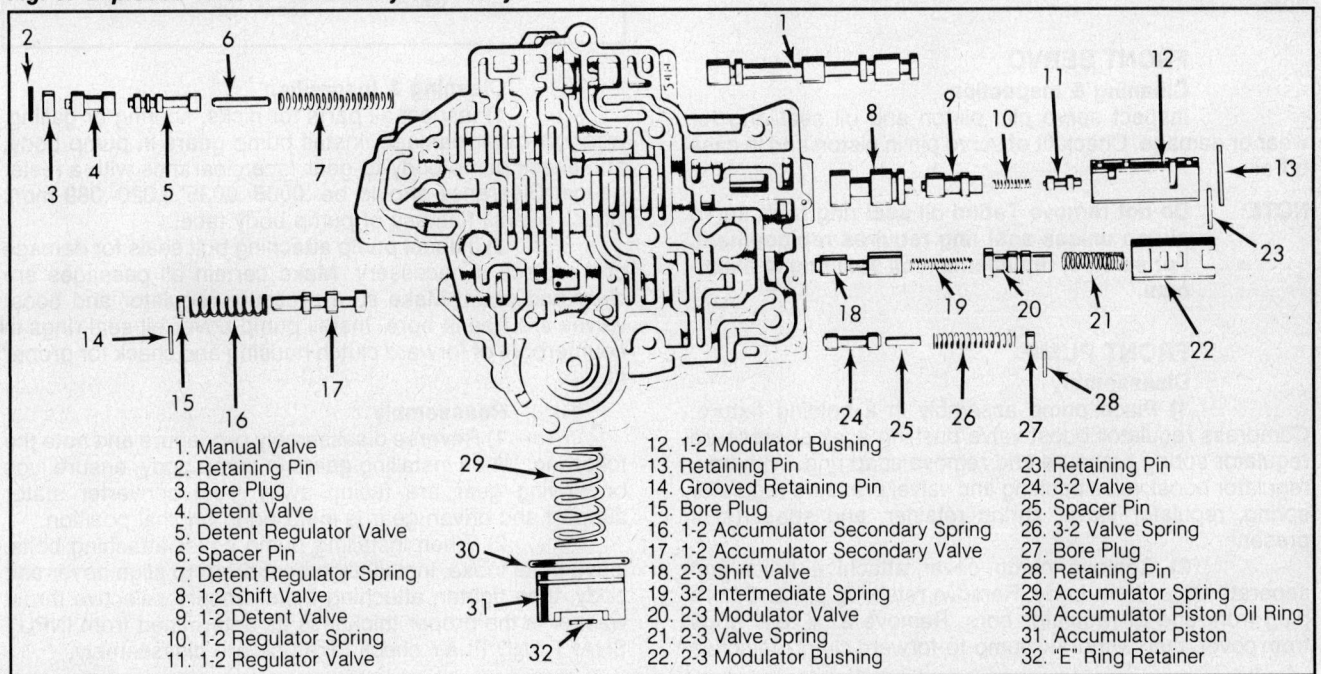

1. Manual Valve	12. 1-2 Modulator Bushing	23. Retaining Pin
2. Retaining Pin	13. Retaining Pin	24. 3-2 Valve
3. Bore Plug	14. Grooved Retaining Pin	25. Spacer Pin
4. Detent Valve	15. Bore Plug	26. 3-2 Valve Spring
5. Detent Regulator Valve	16. 1-2 Accumulator Secondary Spring	27. Bore Plug
6. Spacer Pin	17. 1-2 Accumulator Secondary Valve	28. Retaining Pin
7. Detent Regulator Spring	18. 2-3 Shift Valve	29. Accumulator Spring
8. 1-2 Shift Valve	19. 2-3 Intermediate Spring	30. Accumulator Piston Oil Ring
9. 1-2 Detent Valve	20. 2-3 Modulator Valve	31. Accumulator Piston
10. 1-2 Regulator Spring	21. 2-3 Valve Spring	32. "E" Ring Retainer
11. 1-2 Regulator Valve	22. 2-3 Modulator Bushing	

band apply pin, then remove rear servo piston and seal from pin. Remove washer, spring and retainer.

CAUTION: Do not remove Teflon oil seals unless they require replacement. If small ring requires replacement, use service aluminum ring. If large ring requires replacement, use only Teflon oil ring.

Fig. 6: Exploded View of Rear Servo Assembly

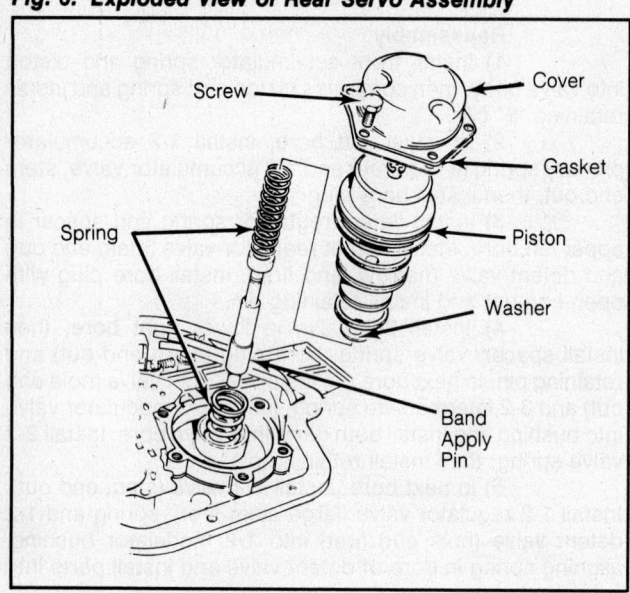

Cleaning & Inspection

Check for free movement of accumulator rings in piston and their respective bores. Inspect fit of band apply pin in servo piston and case bore. Inspect band apply pin for scores or cracks. Inspect servo piston for cracks or porosity.

Reassembly

To reassemble, reverse disassembly procedure.

FRONT SERVO

Cleaning & Inspection

Inspect servo pin, piston and oil seal ring for wear or damage. Check fit of servo pin in piston and in case bore.

NOTE: Do not remove Teflon oil seal ring from servo piston unless seal ring requires replacement. For service, replacement oil seal ring is aluminum.

FRONT PUMP

Disassembly

1) Place pump assembly in a holding fixture. Compress regulator boost valve bushing against pressure regulator spring pressure and remove snap ring. Withdraw regulator boost valve bushing and valve, pressure regulator spring, regulator valve, spring retainer, and spacer(s) if present.

2) Remove pump cover attaching bolts and separate cover from body. Remove retaining pin and bore plug from end of regulator bore. Remove 2 oil seal rings from cover, then withdraw pump-to-forward clutch selective

thrust washer. Note installed positions of drive and driven gears and remove from pump body

Fig. 7: Exploded View of Front Servo Assembly

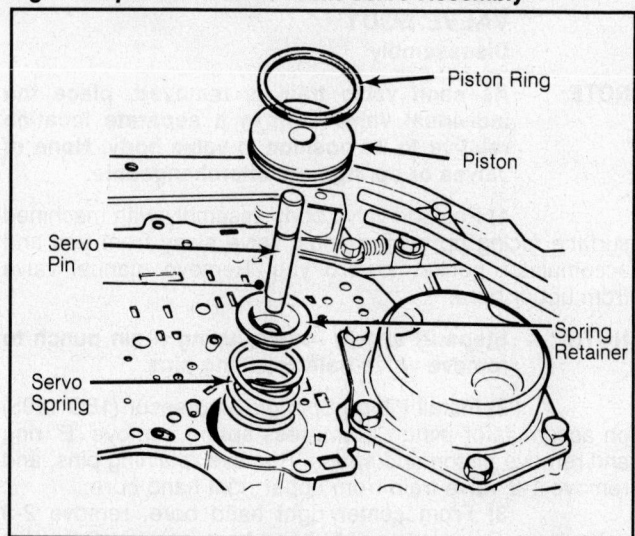

Fig. 8: Exploded View of Front Pump Cover and Pressure Regulator Valve

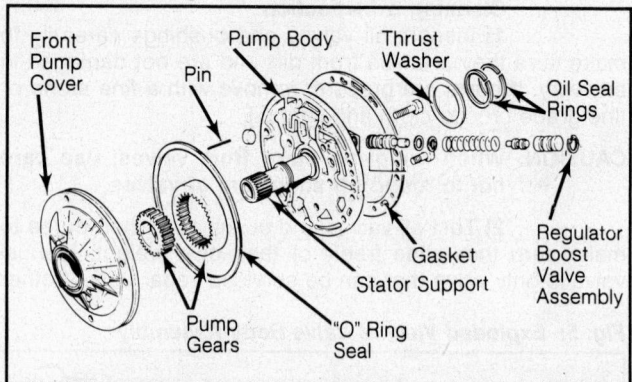

Cleaning & Inspection

1) Inspect all parts for nicks, scoring or galling, wear, or other damage. Install pump gears in pump body, and check pump body-to-gear face clearance with a feeler gauge. Clearance should be .0008-.0035" (.020-.089 mm). Check overall flatness of pump body face.

2) Inspect pump attaching bolt seals for damage and replace if necessary. Make certain all passages are clear and open. Make sure pressure regulator and boost valves are free in bore. Install pump cover oil seal rings in counterbore of forward clutch housing and check for proper fit.

Reassembly

1) Reverse disassembly procedure and note the following: When installing gears in pump body, ensure lugs on driving gear are facing away from converter stator support and driven gear is installed in original position.

2) When installing pump cover attaching bolts, leave bolts loose, install alignment strap to align cover and body, then tighten attaching bolts. Ensure selective thrust washer is the proper thickness as determined from INPUT SHAFT END PLAY check taken before disassembly.

GM TURBO HYDRA-MATIC 400 - JAGUAR (Cont.)

FORWARD CLUTCH
Disassembly
1) Remove forward clutch housing-to-direct clutch hub snap ring and withdraw hub. Remove forward clutch hub and thrust washers from each side of hub. Withdraw composition and steel clutch plates.

2) If necessary, place clutch housing in an arbor press and press turbine shaft out of housing. Using a compressor, compress spring retainer and remove snap ring.

3) Remove compressor and lift out spring retainer and 16 clutch release springs. Remove forward clutch piston from housing. Remove inner and outer seals from piston and center seal from clutch housing.

NOTE: Keep forward clutch release springs separate from direct clutch release springs.

Fig. 9: Exploded View of Forward Clutch Assembly

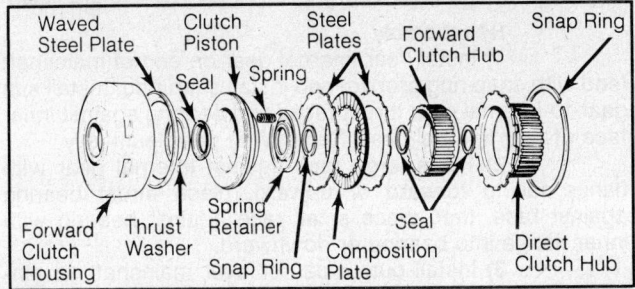

Cleaning & Inspection
1) Inspect clutch plates for burning, scoring, or wear. Check release springs for distortion or collapsed coils. Inspect clutch hubs for worn splines and thrust faces, and for clear lubrication passages.

2) Check piston for cracks or porosity. Check turbine shaft and clutch housing for wear, scoring or other damage. Make sure check ball in housing moves freely.

Reassembly
1) Oil and install inner and outer seals on clutch piston with seal lips facing away from spring pockets. Oil and install center seal on clutch housing with seal lips facing upward.

2) Place seal protectors over clutch hub and into clutch housing, then install piston into housing. Install 16 clutch release springs into piston pockets, place spring retainer and snap ring over springs, then compress springs and install snap ring into groove.

3) If turbine shaft was removed, install shaft into housing using an arbor press. Install forward clutch hub thrust washers. Make sure bronze washer is installed on side of hub facing forward clutch housing. Retain washers in place with petroleum jelly. Place forward clutch hub into clutch housing.

4) Lubricate with transmission fluid and install clutch plates, starting with a waved steel plate (plate with "U" notch), then alternating composition and flat steel plates (plate with "V" notch) until all clutch plates are installed. See FORWARD CLUTCH PLATE chart.

5) Install direct clutch hub and retaining snap ring. Place forward clutch housing on oil pump delivery sleeve. Air check operation of forward clutch by applying air through forward clutch passage in pump to actuate piston and move forward clutch.

FORWARD CLUTCH PLATE

Flat Steel	Composition	Waved Steel
5	5	1

DIRECT CLUTCH & INTERMEDIATE ROLLER ASSEMBLY
Disassembly
1) Remove intermediate roller assembly retainer snap ring and retainer. Remove roller outer race and roller assembly. Turn unit over and remove backing plate-to-direct clutch housing snap ring. Remove direct clutch backing plate and clutch pack.

2) Using a compressor, compress spring retainer in arbor press and remove snap ring. Remove retainer and piston and 16 clutch release springs. Remove direct clutch piston from clutch housing, then remove inner and outer seals from piston. Remove center piston seal from direct clutch housing.

NOTE: Keep springs separate from forward clutch release springs.

Fig. 10: Exploded View of Direct Clutch and Intermediate Roller Clutch Assembly

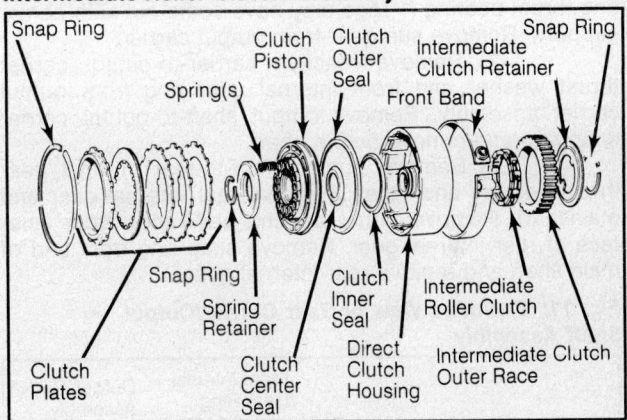

Cleaning & Inspection
1) Inspect roller assembly for popped or loose rollers; inner cam and outer race for scratches or wear and clutch housing for cracks, wear, proper opening of oil passages or wear on clutch plate drive lugs.

2) Inspect clutch plates for wear or burning; backing plate for scratches or damage; clutch piston for cracks; clutch housing for free operation of check ball and springs for collapsed coils and distortion.

Reassembly
1) Lubricate seals with transmission fluid and install new inner and outer seals on clutch piston with seal lips facing away from spring pockets. Install new center seals on clutch hub with seal lip facing upward.

2) Place seal protectors over clutch hub and into clutch housing, then install clutch piston into housing with a rotating motion. If production clutch release springs are being used, install 14 springs into spring pockets of piston, leaving 2 opposite pockets with no springs.

3) If service relacement springs are used, install all 16 springs into spring pockets. Place spring retainer on top of springs and snap ring on top of retainer. Using compressor used at disassembly, compress springs and install snap ring.

4) Lubricate clutch plates with transmission fluid. Install plates into clutch housing starting with a waved steel plate. Alternate composition and flat steel plates until all plates are installed. See DIRECT CLUTCH PLATE chart. Install backing plate and retaining snap ring.

DIRECT CLUTCH PLATES

Flat Steel [1]	Composition	Waved Steel
5	5	1

[1] – Four of steel plates are .077" (1.9 mm) thick. One of steel plates is .091" (2.2 mm) thick.

5) Install rollers in case by compressing energizing spring and inserting roller from outer side. Turn unit over and install roller clutch assembly onto intermediate clutch inner cam, then install outer race with a clockwise turning motion. Install clutch retainer and snap ring. Place assembly on center support and air check operation of clutch.

GEAR CARRIER/OUTPUT SHAFT ASSEMBLY
Disassembly

1) Remove center support-to-sun gear races and thrust bearing (1 race may have come out with center support). Remove sun gear from output carrier.

2) Remove reaction carrier-to-output carrier thrust washer and front internal gear ring from output carrier assembly. Remove output shaft-to-output carrier snap ring and remove output shaft.

3) Remove output shaft-to-rear internal gear thrust bearing and races. Remove rear internal gear and mainshaft. Remove thrust bearing and races from inner face of rear internal gear. Remove snap ring from end of main shaft and remove rear internal gear.

Fig. 11: Exploded View of Gear Carrier/Output Shaft Assembly

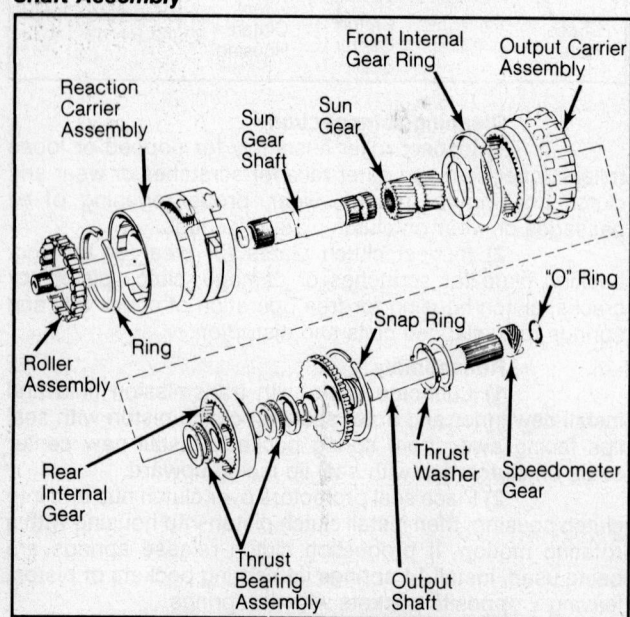

Speedometer Drive Gear Replacement
1) If equipped with a nylon speedometer gear, depress retaining clip and slide gear off shaft. To install, place retaining clip (square end toward flange of shaft) into hole in shaft, align slot in gear with clip, and install gear.

2) If equipped with a steel gear, use a puller and remove gear from shaft. To install, support output shaft on front face and use driver to drive gear onto shaft.

3) Drive speedometer gear onto shaft until distance from rear face of gear to end of output shaft is 5 21/32" (83.34 mm).

Cleaning & Inspection
1) If reaction carrier is equipped with a spacer ring in an undercut at bottom of roller cam ramps, inspect ring for wear or damage. Inspect reaction carrier bushing for damage; if bushing is damaged, carrier must be replaced.

2) Check pinions for damage, rough bearings, or tilt. Check pinion end play; end play should be .009-.024" (.23-.61 mm). Inspect band surface on reaction carrier for burning or scoring. Check all other parts for wear, scoring, or other damage. Make sure all lubrication holes are open.

Reassembly
1) Install rear internal gear on end of mainshaft (end with snap ring groove) and install snap ring. Install sun gear-to-internal gear thrust races and bearing against inner face of rear internal gear. Retain with petroleum jelly.

2) Place large race against internal gear with flange facing forward or upward, place thrust bearing against race, then place small race against bearing with inner flange into bearing or downward.

3) Install output carrier over mainshaft so pinions mesh with rear internal gear. With mainshaft in downward position, install rear internal gear to output shaft thrust races and bearings. Retain with petroleum jelly.

4) Place small diameter race against internal gear with center flange facing up. Place bearing on race, then place second race on bearing with outer flange cupped over bearing. Install output shaft into output carrier assembly. Install output shaft to output carrier snap ring.

5) Install speedometer drive gear. Install output shaft "O" ring (if required). With output shaft in a downward position, install reaction carrier to output carrier thrust washer with tabs facing down in pockets, and retain with petroleum jelly.

6) Install sun gear with chamfer down. Install gear ring over output carrier. Install sun gear shaft with long splined-end down. Install reaction carrier. Install center support-to-sun thrust races and bearing (retain with petroleum jelly).

7) Install large race over sun gear shaft with center flange upward, install thrust bearing against race, then install second race with center flange upward.

8) Install rollers that may have come out of roller case by compressing energizing spring with forefinger and inserting roller from outer side. Install roller clutch into reaction carrier outer race.

9) Install center support-to-reaction carrier thrust washer into recess in center support and retain with petroleum jelly. Install center support into reaction carrier and roller clutch assembly.

10) Install a holding fixture to keep units in place, then install output shaft-to-case thrust washers (bent tabs in pockets) and retain with petroleum jelly.

CENTER SUPPORT & INTERMEDIATE CLUTCH
Disassembly

If necessary, remove 4 center support oil seal rings. Compress spring retainer and remove snap ring.

GM TURBO HYDRA-MATIC 400 - JAGUAR (Cont.)

Remove spring retainer and 3 clutch release springs. Remove intermediate clutch spring guide and clutch piston from center support. Remove inner and outer piston seals from piston.

Cleaning & Inspection

1) Check all parts for wear, scoring or damage. Inspect release springs for distortion or collapsed coils. Check oil ring grooves and oil rings for wear or damage. Rings should fit freely in grooves.

2) Make sure all passages, lubrication grooves and holes are clear of obstructions. Check roller clutch inner race for scratches and indentations. Make sure constant bleed orifice is open .020" (.51 mm).

Fig. 12: Exploded View of Center Support and Intermediate Clutch

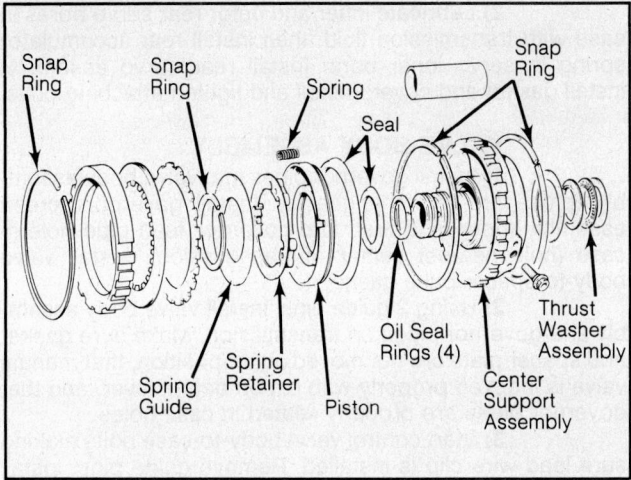

Reassembly

1) Lubricate and install inner and outer seals on piston with seal lips facing away from spring pockets. Place a seal protector over center support hub. Install piston indexing spring pockets in drum and piston.

2) Install spring guide and evenly space 3 release springs in spring guides. Place spring retainer and snap ring over springs, then compress springs and install snap ring in groove.

3) If removed, install 4 oil seal rings on center support. Air check operation of intermediate clutch piston by applying air through center oil feed hole to actuate clutch piston.

NOTE: When installing Teflon oil seal rings on center support, be sure split ends are assembled in the same relation as cut.

TRANSMISSION CASE
Cleaning & Inspection

Inspect case for cracks, porosity, or interconnected passages. Check governor and modulator valve bores for scratches or scoring. Check band anchor pins for retention, and intermediate clutch driven plate lugs for damage. Inspect snap ring grooves for damage. Ensure intermediate clutch cup plug is properly staked and sealed.

CAUTION: If case assembly requires replacement, make sure that center support-to-case spacer and name plate are removed from old case and installed in new case.

EXTENSION HOUSING
Cleaning & Inspection

Check housing for cracks or porosity. Inspect gasket mounting face for burrs or other damage. Make sure rear seal drain-back part is not obstructed. Check rear bushing for wear or damage. Replace as necessary.

TRANSMISSION REASSEMBLY

PARKING PAWL

1) Install parking pawl, tooth toward inside of case, then install parking pawl shaft and shaft retainer. Install a new cup plug using a 3/8" (9.5 mm) diameter rod, and drive plug into case until shaft bottoms on case rib.

2) Install parking pawl return spring, with square end hooked on pawl and other end on case. Install parking pawl bracket with guides over parking pawl, then install and tighten attaching bolts.

CENTER SUPPORT, INTERMEDIATE CLUTCH, GEAR CARRIER/OUTPUT SHAFT ASSEMBLY & REAR BAND

1) Install rear band so that lugs index with anchor pins. Install support-to-case spacer against shoulder at bottom of case splines and with ring gap adjacent to band anchor pin.

2) Install previously selected rear unit end play washer into slots provided inside rear of case and retain washer with petroleum jelly. Place transmission in a horizontal position and install holding fixture on output shaft.

3) Install complete gear unit assembly into case by lining up slots and carefully guiding assembly horizontally into case making sure center support bolt hole is aligned with hole in case.

4) Position transmission vertically and remove output shaft holding fixture. Install center support-to-case retaining ring, with beveled side up. Locate gap adjacent to band anchor pin.

5) Lubricate and install intermediate clutch plates, starting with a waved steel plate, then alternating composition and flat steel plates until all clutch plates are installed.

6) Install intermediate clutch backing plate with flat machined surface against clutch plates. Install backing plate-to-case snap ring, locating ring gap opposite band anchor pin. Before proceeding with transmission reassembly, recheck rear unit end play.

CLUTCH ASSEMBLIES & FRONT BAND

1) Install front band with band anchor hole over band anchor pin and apply lug facing servo hole. Install direct clutch and intermediate roller assembly. Install forward clutch hub to direct clutch housing thrust washer on forward clutch hub and retain with petroleum jelly.

NOTE: Rotate housing to index roller outer race with composition clutch plates.

2) Install forward clutch and turbine shaft, indexing direct clutch hub so end of mainshaft will go all the way into forward clutch hub. When forward clutch is seated, it will be 1 1/4" (25.4-31.8 mm) from pump mounting face in case.

Automatic Transmissions

GM TURBO HYDRA-MATIC 400 - JAGUAR (Cont.)

FRONT PUMP

1) Install square cut "O" ring around outer circumference of pump body and attach new gasket to oil pump cover, retaining gasket with petroleum jelly. Lubricate turbine shaft journals and pump oil seal rings.

2) Using 2 alignment dowels, install pump assembly into case. Install pump attaching bolts with new seals (omit 1 bolt for end play check), and tighten bolts evenly.

CAUTION: If turbine shaft cannot be rotated as pump is being pulled into place, forward or direct clutch housings have not been installed properly to index with all clutch plates. Correct this condition before pulling pump fully into place.

3) Recheck front unit end play. If necessary, adjust end play by changing thrust washer located between pump cover and forward clutch housing. Install remaining pump attaching bolt. Apply a non-hardening sealer to outside of new front oil seal. Install seal into pump using a driver.

PARKING LINKAGE, DETENT LEVER & MANUAL SHAFT

1) If removed, install a new manual shaft seal into transmission case using a 3/4" (19 mm) diameter rod to seat seal. Install actuator rod into manual detent lever from side opposite pin.

2) Install actuator rod plunger under parking bracket and over parking pawl. Install manual shaft through case and detent lever. Install detent retaining lock nut on manual shaft and tighten. Install retaining pin, indexing with groove in manual shaft.

NOTE: It may be necessary to bend manual shaft retaining pin to install. Straighten pin during installation.

EXTENSION HOUSING

1) Install a new gasket on extension housing and retain with petroleum jelly. Install housing on transmission case and tighten attaching bolts. If applicable, check "O" ring on output shaft for any nicks or flattening and replace ring if necessary.

2) Apply a non-hardening sealer to outside diameter of rear oil seal, position on extension housing, then seat seal in housing using driver.

VALVE BODY SPACER PLATE & DETENT SOLENOID

1) Install 2 guide pins opposite each other into 2 valve body assembly attaching bolt holes. Install check balls into ball seat pockets in case. Install control valve spacer plate-to-case gasket, gasket with extension for detent solenoid and marked with a "C".

2) Install control valve spacer plate and control valve-to-spacer plate gasket, marked with a "VB". Install detent solenoid gasket, then install solenoid with connector facing outer edge of case. Do not tighten bolts at this time.

NOTE: Some overhaul kits supply a solenoid gasket. This gasket must not be installed.

3) Install "O" ring seal on solenoid connector. Compress connector tangs and install in case with locator tab in notch on side of case. Connect detent solenoid wire to connector terminal.

FRONT SERVO

1) Install front servo spring and spring retainer into transmission case. Install retainer ring in front servo pin groove and install pin in case so tapered end contacts band.

2) Make sure retainer ring is still installed in groove. Install seal ring on piston. Install piston on pin with flat side of piston positioned toward oil pan.

REAR SERVO

1) Before installing servo, check band apply pin. See Band Apply Selection Test in ADJUSTMENTS section. Ensure rear band apply lug is aligned with servo pin bore in transmission case.

2) Lubricate inner and outer rear servo bores in case with transmission fluid, then install rear accumulator spring in servo inner bore. Install rear servo assembly, install gasket and cover. Install and tighten attaching bolts.

VALVE BODY ASSEMBLY

1) Install governor pipes into valve body assembly (pipes are interchangeable). Install governor screen assembly (open end first) into governor feed pipe hole in case (hole nearest center of transmission). Install valve body-to-spacer plate gasket.

2) Using 2 guide pins, install valve body assembly and governor pipes on transmission. Make sure gasket and spacer plate are not moved out of position, that manual valve is indexed properly with pin on detent lever, and that governor pipes are properly seated in case holes.

3) Start control valve body-to-case bolts making sure lead wire clip is installed. Remove guide pins, install detent roller and spring assembly, then install and tighten remaining attaching bolts.

GOVERNOR

Install governor assembly into case. Install cover with new gasket and tighten attaching bolts.

SPEEDOMETER DRIVE PINION

Install new seals to housing. Lubricate and install pinion into housing. Install pinion assembly into case and secure with clamp plate and bolt.

OIL PAN, FILTER & INTAKE PIPE

Install case-to-intake pipe "O" ring seal on intake pipe. Install pipe into filter assembly. Place filter and intake pipe in case, install retaining bolt and tighten. Install oil pan with new gasket. Install and tighten attaching screws.

VACUUM MODULATOR & VALVE

Install modulator valve into case with stem end out. Install new "O" ring seal on vacuum modulator. Install modulator into case with vacuum hose pipe facing front and angled 5° toward top of case. Install modulator retainer with curved side of tangs inboard. Install and tighten attaching bolt.

CONVERTER ASSEMBLY

Install converter into front pump assembly. Make sure converter hub drive slots are fully engaged with pump drive gear tangs and converter is installed fully toward rear of transmission.

GM TURBO HYDRA-MATIC 400 - JAGUAR (Cont.)

TIGHTENING SPECIFICATIONS

Application	Ft. Lbs. (N.m)
Center Support Bolts	25 (34)
Converter-To-Drive Plate Bolts	35 (48)
Extension Housing-To-Case Bolts	23 (32)
Transmission-To-Engine Bolts	35 (48)

	INCH Lbs.
Detent Solenoid Bolts	84 (10)
Filter Retainer Bolt	120 (14)
Governor Cover Bolts	240 (27)
Line Pressure Take-Off Plug	120 (14)
Manual Lever-To-Detent Lever	240 (27)
Manual Lever-To-Manual Shaft Nut	96 (11)
Modulator Retainer Bolts	240 (27)
Oil Pan Bolts	144 (16)
Parking Pawl Bracket Bolts	240 (27)
Pump Cover Bolts	240 (27)
Pump-To-Case Bolts	240 (27)
Rear Servo Cover Bolts	240 (27)
Valve Body Bolts	96 (11)

Automatic Transmissions
HONDA 3-SPEED

Civic

IDENTIFICATION

Transaxle may be identified by a group of characters stamped in a pad on top of transaxle. First 2 characters show transaxle type. Next 7 characters are transaxle serial number.

TRANSAXLE MODEL CODE

Application	Code
Civic	AW

DESCRIPTION

The Honda 3-speed automatic transaxle is a combination of a 3-section torque converter, dual shift transmission and a differential-type final drive assembly. Transmission housing is comprised of 2 sections; the torque convertor housing and the transmission housing. Transmission is controlled by main valve body, regulator valve body and servo valve. Countershaft is in constant mesh with differential ring gear.

Fig. 1: Cutaway View of Transaxle Gears

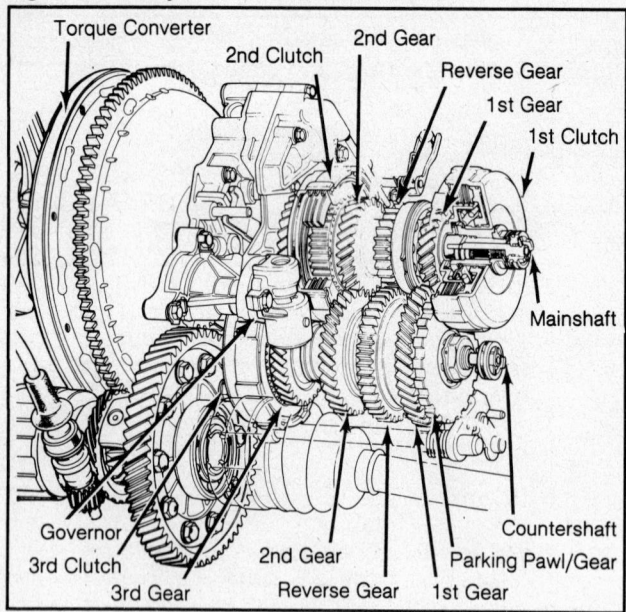

LUBRICATION & ADJUSTMENTS

See appropriate AUTOMATIC TRANSMISSION SERVICING article in IMPORT GENERAL SERVICING section.

TROUBLE SHOOTING

NO MOVEMENT
In Any Gear
Low fluid level. Faulty pump. Regulator valve stuck or damaged spring. Servo shaft stuck. Reverse hub splines stuck. Mainshaft damaged. Manual shift cable out of adjustment or broken. Damaged final drive gear. Broken flex plate. Oil filter clogged.

In "D1"; OK in Other Gears
Low fluid level. Manual shift cable out of adjustment. Worn or damaged one-way clutch. Low gear damaged. 1st clutch piston stuck, damaged "O" ring, damaged feed pipe or "O" rings, check valve stuck, worn or burnt clutch discs.

In "2"; OK in Other Gears
Low fluid level. Manual shift cable out of adjustment. Damaged 2nd gear. Faulty 2nd clutch.

In "R"; OK in Other Gears
Low fluid level. Servo shaft stuck. Faulty 2nd clutch. Damaged reverse gear.

ENGINE RACES IN "D"
Stall RPM High in "D" and "2"
Low fluid level. Faulty pump. Regulator valve stuck or spring damaged. Manual shift cable out of adjustment. Torque converter check valve.

Stall RPM High in "D" Only
Low fluid level. Faulty pump. Manual shift cable out of adjustment. 1st clutch piston stuck, damaged clutch "O" ring, clutch feed pipe or "O" ring damaged, check valve stuck, worn or burnt clutch discs.

Stall RPM High in "2"
Manual shift cable out of adjustment. Faulty 2nd clutch.

Stall RPM OK
1-2 shift valve faulty. Faulty governor valve. Fluid level too high. Faulty torque converter one-way clutch.

Stall RPM Low
Throttle cable at carburetor out of adjustment. Throttle control cable at automatic transmission out of adjustment. Engine performance not to specifications.

HARSH "D1-D2" UPSHIFT
Faulty 2nd clutch. Defective 2nd accumulator. No 2nd ball check valve.

ENGINE RACES IN "2"
Faulty 2nd clutch.

UPSHIFT SPEED TOO HIGH
Governor valve faulty. Throttle cable at carburetor out of adjustment. Defective throttle valve.

JUMPS FROM "D1" TO "D3"
Defective 2-3 shift valve.

UPSHIFT TOO EARLY
"D1-D2" and "D2-D3"
Faulty governor valve. Throttle cable at carburetor out of adjustment. Defective throttle valve. Defective modulator valve.

"D1-D2"
Faulty 1-2 shift valve.

"D2-D3"
Faulty 2-3 shift valve.

KICKDOWN TOO LOW
Faulty 1-2 shift valve or 2-3 shift valve.

ENGINE RACES IN "D2-D3" SHIFT
Throttle valve "B" defective. Faulty 2nd accumulator, 3rd accumulator or orifice control valve faulty. Main orifice plugged. Faulty 3rd clutch.

ENGINE VIBRATES IN "D2-D3" SHIFT
Orifice control valve faulty or second orifice plugged.

VEHICLE CREEPS IN "N"
Low fluid level. Manual shift cable out of adjustment. Faulty 1st or 2nd clutch. Throttle cable at carburetor out of adjustment. Damaged needle bearing or thrust washer. Improper clutch clearance.

DELAYED ENGAGEMENT
From "N" to "D"
Manual shift cable out of adjustment. Faulty 1st clutch. Low orifice plugged.

From "N" to "R"
Servo shaft stuck. Manual shift cable out of adjustment. Faulty 2nd clutch.

PROBLEMS AFTER REASSEMBLY
Loud Noise in All Selector Positions
Oil pump gear installed backwards. Damaged 3rd gear. Damaged ball bearings.

Vehicle Will Not Move in Any Gear
Fluid level too low. Manual shift control out of adjustment.

Movement only in Reverse
Faulty 1st clutch assembly. Counter shaft one-way clutch upside down.

Acceleration to 30 MPH Only
Stator assembled backwards in torque converter, or seized.

Vibration in All Gears
Torque converter not fully tightened or seated.

No Park Position
Manual shift control out of adjustment or binding. Parking pawl installed backward.

Vehicle Has 3rd Gear Only
Faulty governor valve.

TESTING

ROAD TEST
1) Before road testing, be certain that fluid level and condition, and control linkage adjustments have been checked and corrected as necessary. While testing, ensure that upshifts and downshifts occur at specified speeds. See SHIFT SPEED SPECIFICATIONS chart.

2) Shift speeds may vary slightly due to production tolerances or tire size. The important factor is the quality of the shifts. All shifts should be smooth, responsive and with no slippage or engine speed runaway.

3) Slippage or engine runaway in any gear usually indicates clutch or sprague problems. The slipping unit in a particular gear can usually be identified by noting transmission operation in other selector positions and comparing which internal units are applied in those positions. See CLUTCH & BAND APPLICATION chart.

SHIFT SPEED SPECIFICATIONS

Application	Shift Speed (MPH)
Upshift	
Full Throttle	
1-2 Shift	30-38
2-3 Shift	57-67
Half Throttle	
1-2 Shift	17-22
2-3 Shift	30-45
Closed Throttle	
1-2 Shift	10-15
2-3 Shift	20-27
Downshift	
Full Throttle	
3-2 Shift	50-60
2-1 Shift	25-27
Closed Throttle	
3-2 Shift	15-20
2-1 Shift	5-10

4) This process of elimination can be used to detect any unit which slips, and to confirm proper operation of good units; however, the actual cause of the malfunction usually cannot be easily decided.

5) Practically any condition can be caused by leaking hydraulic circuits or sticking valves. Therefore, unless an obvious condition exists, do not disassemble transmission until hydraulic pressure tests have been made.

HYDRAULIC PRESSURE TESTS
1) Before performing pressure tests, be sure that fluid level and condition have been checked and corrected as necessary. With engine at normal operating temperature, connect a tachometer to engine.

2) Connect pressure gauges to the following pressure test points: line pressure port, 1st clutch pressure port, 2nd clutch pressure port and 3rd clutch pressure port. See Fig. 2.

3) Raise front of vehicle so front wheels are off ground and support with safety stands. Start and run engine at 2000 RPM. Place selector lever in the following positions: "P", "N", "D", "2" and "R". Verify correct pressure readings for each selector position. See MAIN PRESSURES chart.

4) If reading in "P" or "N" is not to specifications, check torque converter, oil pump pressure regulator or torque converter check valve. If reading in "D" (high gear) is not to specifications, check 3rd clutch. If reading in "D1" is not to specifications, check 1st clutch. If reading in "2" (manual), is not to specifications. Check 2nd clutch. If reading in "R" is not to specifications, check servo valve.

NOTE: Allow engine to return to idle before changing selector positions.

5) Stop engine and remove pressure gauge connections. Connect pressure gauge to throttle pressure port and disconnect throttle cable at carburetor. Start engine, place selector lever in "D" and run engine at 1000 RPM. Depress accelerator pedal so throttle control lever is in full throttle position and note pressure reading. Verify correct reading. See MAIN PRESSURES chart.

6) If throttle pressure reading in "D" is not to specifications, check throttle valve "A" or throttle modulator

CLUTCH AND BAND APPLICATION CHART (ELEMENTS IN USE)

Selector Lever Position	Low Clutch	Second Clutch	Third Clutch	Sprag Clutch
D — DRIVE				
First	X			X
Second	X	X		
Third	X		X	
2 — MANUAL		X		
REVERSE		X		

NEUTRAL OR PARK — All clutch and sprag clutch released and/or ineffective.

Fig. 2: Pressure Test Point Locations

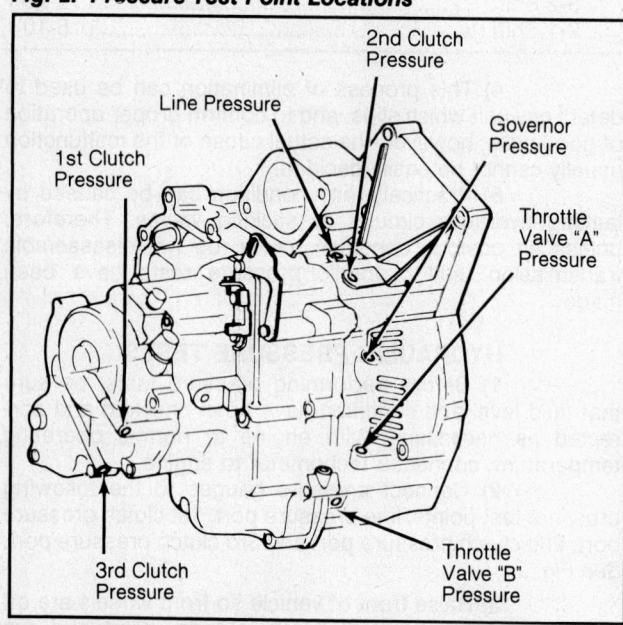

valve. Stop engine and remove pressure gauge from throttle pressure port and reconnect throttle cable at carburetor.

7) Place vehicle on a chassis dynamomator or raise and support front of vehicle on safety stands. Connect pressure gauge to governor pressure port. Start engine, place selector lever in "D" and increase engine speed to 38 MPH. compare pressure reading to specifications. See MAIN PRESSURES chart.

8) If governor pressure reading was not to specifications, check governor valve.

MAIN PRESSURES

Application	psi (kg/cm^2)
Line ("P", "N")	107-114 (7.5-8.0)
1st & 3rd Clutch ("D1", "D2", "D3")	100-114 (97.0-8.0)
2nd Clutch ("D1", "D2", "D3")	100-114 (7.0-8.0)
Throttle (In "D")	85-88 (6.0-6.2)
Governor (In "D")	47-49 (3.5-3.6)

STALL TEST
Testing Precautions
Maximum stall speed test time is 10 seconds. Allow engine to run at idle for at least 2 minutes in "N" to cool transmission between tests. If engine speed exceeds limits, release accelerator immediately as clutch slippage is indicated. See STALL SPEEDS chart.

Testing Procedure
With engine at normal operating temperature, connect a tachometer to engine. Start engine and set parking brake and service brakes. Place selector lever in "D". Depress accelerator briefly (6 to 8 seconds) to full throttle and note maximum RPM obtained.

NOTE: Maximum stall speed test time is 10 seconds.

Allow 2 minutes for cooling and repeat test in "2" and "R". Engine speed should be within limits. See STALL SPEEDS chart.

STALL SPEEDS

Application	Stall RPM
Civic	2300-2900

SERVICE (IN VEHICLE)

DRIVE AXLE SHAFTS
Removal
1) Drain transmission, then unfold tabs on spindle nut lock washer and loosen nut. Raise and support vehicle. Remove nut and wheel.

2) Support lower ball joint with jack, remove ball joint nut, and separate steering knuckle from ball joint. Slowly lower jack under ball joint. Pull steering knuckle outward until axle shaft is clear of front hub.

3) Pry inboard constant velocity (CV) joint out of transaxle case approximately 1/2" (12 mm), this will collapse spring clip (on axle shaft inside transaxle case) and allow axle shaft to be withdrawn from case.

4) Pull axle shaft out of transaxle case and front hub assembly. Repeat procedures for other axle shaft.

Installation
Install outer rubber boot and metal bands. Adjust driveshafts to proper lengths. See AXLE SHAFT

HONDA 3-SPEED (Cont.)

LENGTH chart. Install a new spring clip on inner end of axle shaft. To complete installation, reverse removal procedure.

Fig. 3: Measuring Axle Shaft Length

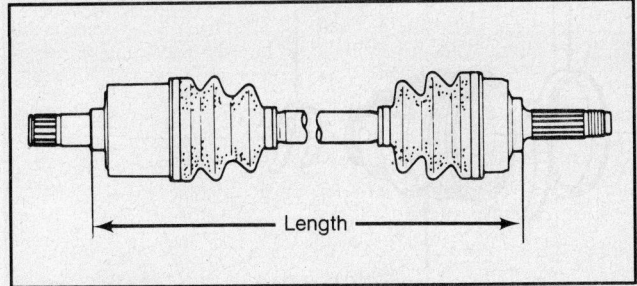

Length

AXLE SHAFT LENGTH

Application	Length In. (mm)
Right Axle Shaft	18.54-18.74 (471-476)
Left Axle Shaft	30.35-30.55 (771.0-776.0)

CV JOINTS
Disassembly
Roller-Type Joint
1) Remove metal bands securing both rubber boots to axle shaft and CV joints. Slide boots toward each other, onto axle shaft, and remove snap rings from each side of roller assembly (inner end of shaft). *See Fig. 4.*

NOTE: Outer CV joint is not removable.

2) Index mark position of rollers to roller grooves for reassembly reference. Pull axle shaft from inner CV joint. Inspect all parts for wear, pitting or other damage. Replace parts as necessary.

Reassembly
Install rubber boots and metal bands. Adjust driveshafts to proper lengths. Assemble CV joint. Ensure roller joints are in their proper groove. Pack bearings and CV joints with molybdenum disulfide grease. To complete installation, reverse removal procedure. Install a new spring clip on inner end of axle shaft.

NOTE: Pack CV joints with molybdenum disulfide grease before installation of rubber boots.

Disassembly
Ball-Type Joint
1) Remove metal bands securing rubber boot to axle shaft and inner CV joint. Slide boot back onto axle shaft and remove snap rings. Pull axle shaft from inner CV joint. *See Fig. 4.*

NOTE: Outer CV joint is not removable.

2) Remove retaining ring, then ball bearing cage with bearing race and balls. Remove balls from bearing race by prying out with a screwdriver. Remove band from damper and remove damper toward inside of axle shaft. Remove outer rubber boot. Inspect all parts for wear, pitting or other damage. Replace parts as necessary.

Reassembly
1) Assemble CV joint bearing with cage and insert balls, packed with molybdenum disulfide grease. Install boot to axle shaft.

2) Install snap ring, bearing assembly, then snap ring to axle shaft. Slide CV joint onto axle shaft. Attach rubber boot to CV joint and to axle shaft.

WHEEL BEARINGS
Removal
1) Remove wheel and spindle nut. Remove caliper bolts and hang caliper out of way. Remove 2 brake retaining screws, screw in 2 metric bolts (8 by 1.25 mm) to remove brake rotor from hub.

2) Disconnect tie rod ball joint and lower control arm ball joint from steering knuckle. Disconnect shock absorber from steering knuckle and remove steering knuckle from vehicle.

3) Press hub from steering knuckle. Remove splash guard and snap ring from steering knuckle. Press seal, and bearing out of steering knuckle (toward outside). *See Fig. 5.*

4) Using a puller, remove steering knuckle inside outer race from hub, then pry seal from hub.

NOTE: Pack both wheel bearings with grease before installing. Also, apply grease to lips of seals.

Installation
1) Press bearing outer race into steering knuckle. Install bearing, outside inner race and snap ring to steering knuckle.

2) Install seal to outside of steering knuckle. Install inner bearing and race to inside of steering knuckle. Install splash guard. Press hub into steering knuckle and install seal.

3) Place steering knuckle in position on vehicle and attach shock absorber. Attach lower control arm ball joint and tie rod ball joint to steering knuckle. Install rotor, caliper and axle shafts to steering knuckle. Install new spindle nut, then wheel.

TRANSAXLE REMOVAL & INSTALLATION
See appropriate AUTOMATIC TRANSMISSION REMOVAL article in IMPORT GENERAL SERVICING section.

TORQUE CONVERTER

DISASSEMBLY & REASSEMBLY
With transmission removed and torque converter pulled off stator shaft, scribe an alignment mark across edge of converter for reassembly reference. Remove drive plate and washer from converter. *See Fig. 6.* To assemble, reverse removal procedure. Tighten converter bolts in a star pattern.

TRANSAXLE DISASSEMBLY
1) Remove dipstick. Remove bolts from end cover, then remove cover. Shift transmission to "P". Lock mainshaft using Holder (07923-6890202). *See Fig. 6.*

2) Remove end cover gasket, dowel pins and "O" rings. Pry staked edge of lock nut flange out of notch in 1st clutch. Remove mainshaft lock nut (LEFT HAND thread), then remove 1st clutch. Remove 1st clutch thrust washer,

Fig. 4: Exploded View of Axle Shaft Assemblies

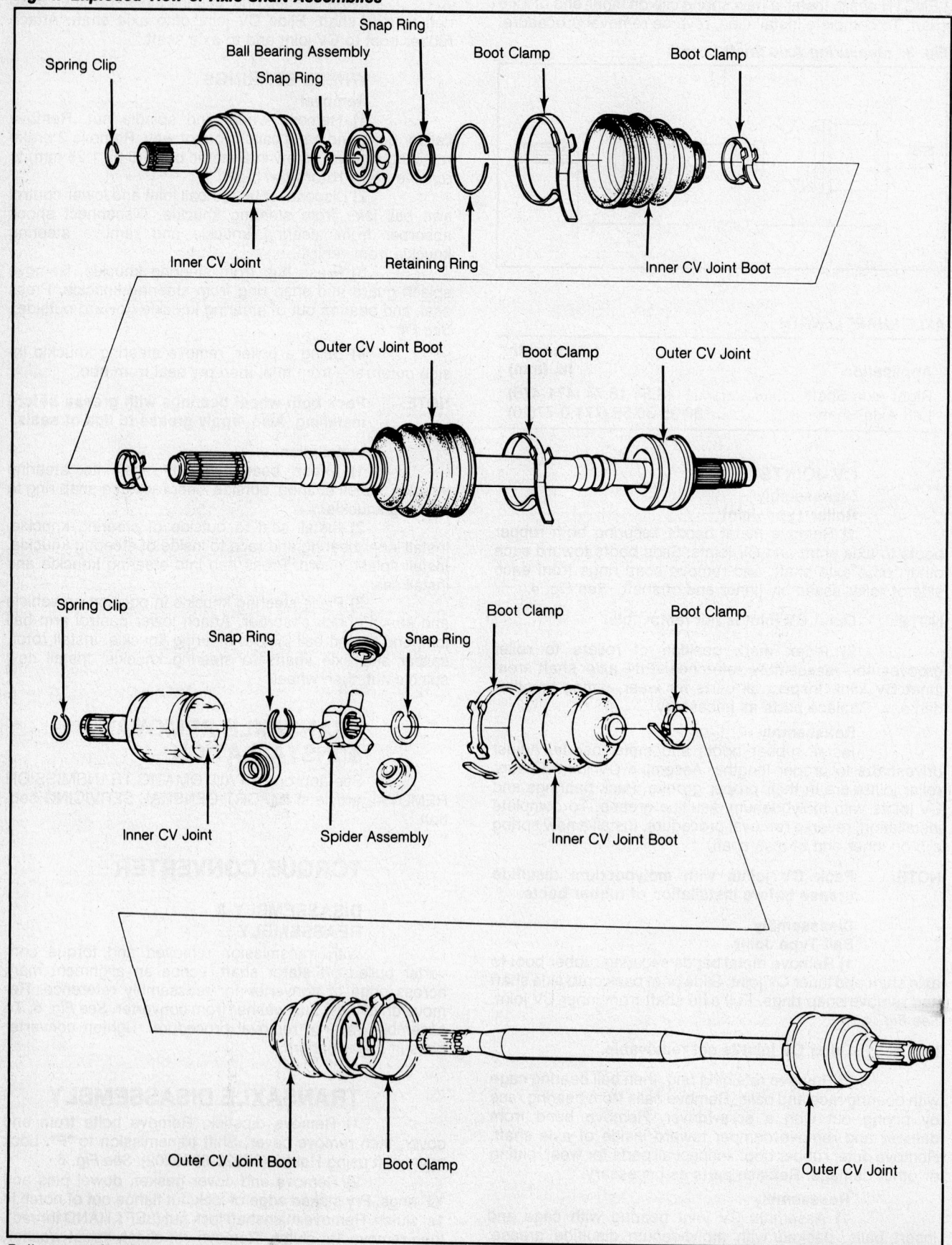

Ball-type and roller-type joints are both shown.

HONDA 3-SPEED (Cont.)

Fig. 5: Exploded View of Front Hub and Bearing Assembly

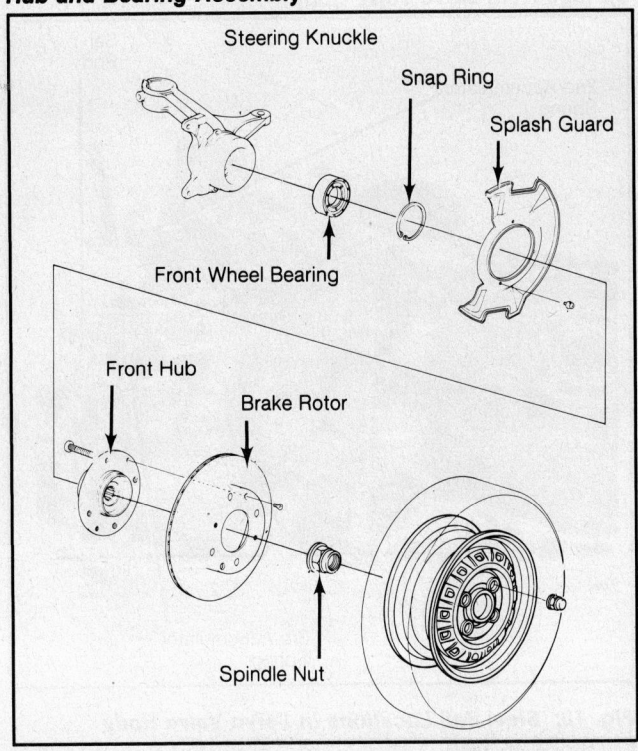

Fig. 7: Locking Mainshaft Using Special Holding Tool

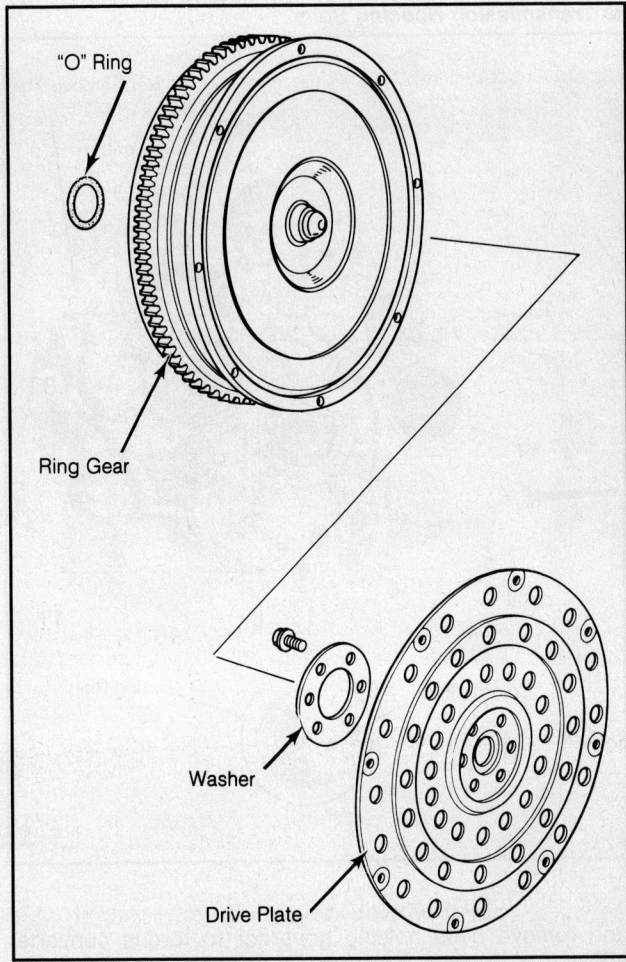

needle bearing and 1st gear. Remove bearing and thrust washer from mainshaft.

3) Pry staked edge of lock nut out of notch in parking gear. Remove coutershaft lock nut and parking pawl stop pin. Remove parking pawl, shaft and spring. Remove parking gear and countershaft 1st gear as a unit. Remove bearing and 1st gear collar from countershaft. Remove "O" ring and 1st gear collar from mainshaft.

Fig. 6: Exploded View of Torque Converter

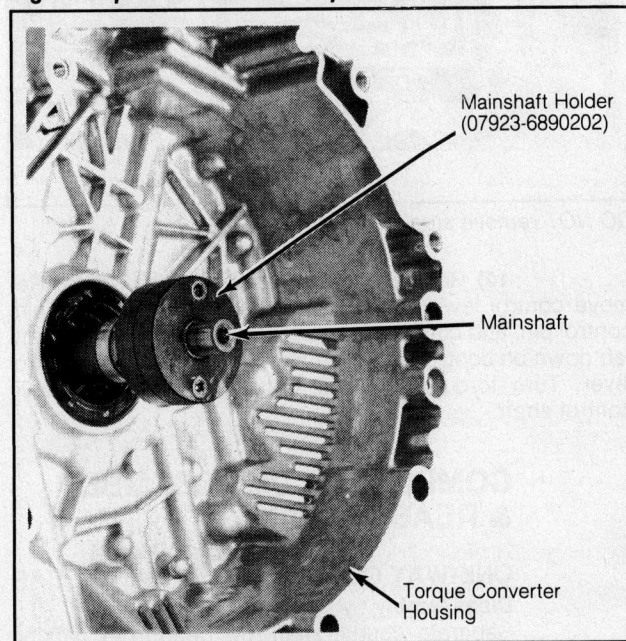

4) Remove reverse idler bearing holder. Bend down tab on lock plate under parking shift arm bolt. Remove bolt and parking shift arm. Lift out parking shift arm, then remove shift arm spring.

5) Bend down tab on throttle control lever bolt lock plate and remove bolt. Remove throttle control lever and spring from shaft. Remove torque converter housing-to-transmission housing bolts. *See Fig. 8.*

NOTE: Do not remove bolt number 1, just loosen enough so bolt threads are free of torque converter housing. If bolt is removed completely, throttle control bracket will have to be readjusted.

6) Align control shaft spring pin with cut-out in transmission housing. Install a puller (that will bolt to transmission housing and press against the countershaft) and separate transmission housing from torque converter housing. After separating housings, remove transmission housing completely.

7) On gear side of torque converter housing, remove gasket, dowel pins and 1st and 3rd oil feed pipes. Remove reverse gear collar, needle bearing and countershaft reverse gear. Bend down tab on lock plate and remove bolt from reverse shift fork. Remove reverse shift fork and selector sleeve as a unit.

8) Remove countershaft 2nd gear. Remove mainshaft and countershaft together. To clear governor, pull shafts up at a slight angle. Bend governor tabs down

Fig. 8: Location of Converter Housing to Transmission Housing Bolts

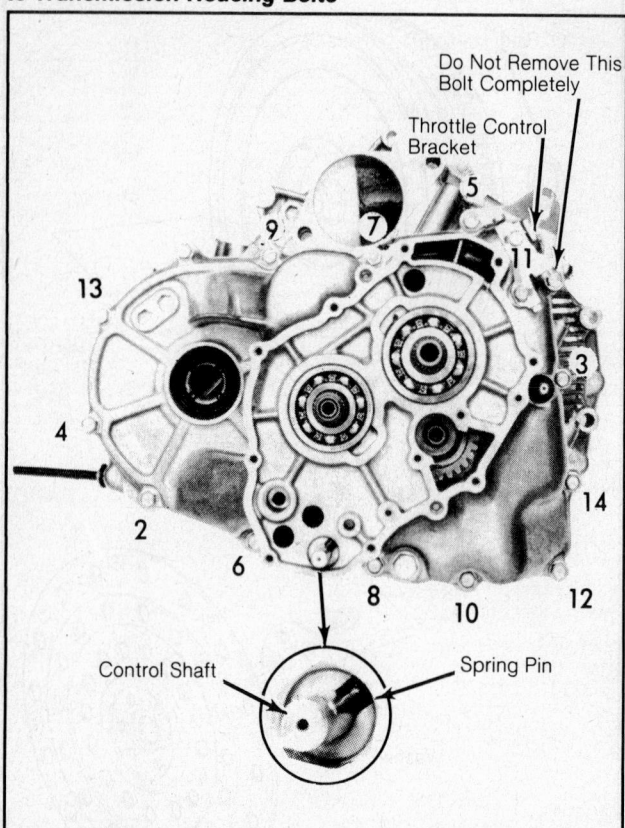

Fig. 9: Removing Accumulator Springs from Servo Valve Body

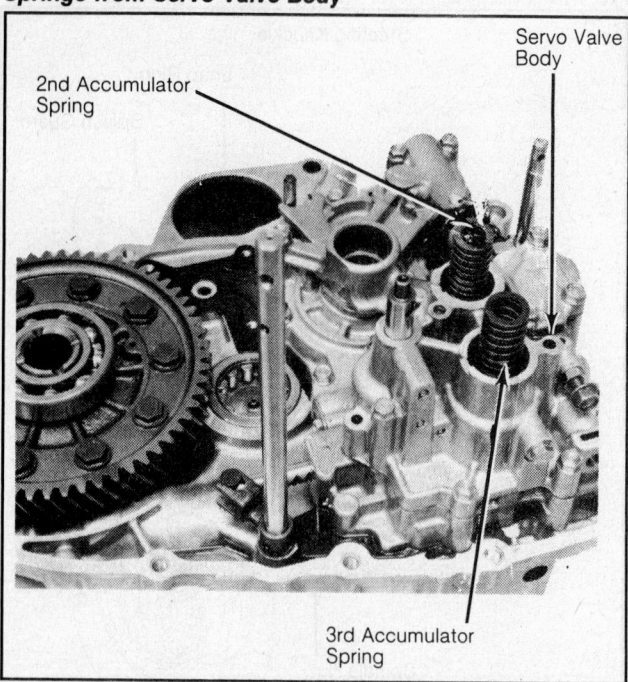

Fig. 10: Steel Ball Locations in Servo Valve Body

DO NOT remove steel balls with a magnet.

and remove bolts holding governor to torque converter housing.

CAUTION: Accumulator cover is spring loaded. Hold cover down while removing bolts in an alternating pattern.

9) Remove accumulator cover, 2nd and 3rd accumulator springs. *See Fig. 9.* Remove 4 lock-up valve body mounting bolts. Slide the valve body away from clutch pressure control valve to remove the oil feed pipe and lock-up valve body.

10 Remove 1st gear oil feed pipe (pipe nearest clutch pressure control valve). Remove 3rd gear oil feed pipe (pipe nearest differential gear). Remove clutch pressure control valve and separator plate.

11 Remove 7 servo body bolts and servo body. Remove "E" clip from throttle control shaft and remove shaft. Remove servo valve separator plate and dowel pins. Remove steel balls from valve body oil passage. Note ball locations for reassembly reference. *See Fig. 10.*

12) Remove steel ball from regulator valve body. Remove regulator valve body bolts. Remove stator shift arm, dowel pins, stop pin and 4 bolts holding valve body to torque converter housing.

13) Remove cotter pin, washer, rollers and pin from manual valve. Remove valve body, being careful not to lose the torque converter check valve and spring. Remove pump gears and shaft. Remove servo valve separator plate, dowel pins, check valve and spring.

14) Remove oil screen and suction pipe. Remove control lever cable holder, then remove cotter pin, control pin, and control lever roller from control lever. Bend tab down on control lever bolt and remove bolt and control lever. Turn torque converter housing over and remove control shaft.

COMPONENT DISASSEMBLY & REASSEMBLY

ONE-WAY CLUTCH AND PARKING GEAR
Disassembly
Separate countershaft 1st gear from parking gear by gripping 1st gear in left hand and turning parking gear counterclockwise. Remove one-way clutch from

HONDA 3-SPEED (Cont.)

Fig. 11: Exploded View of Transmission Housing and Components

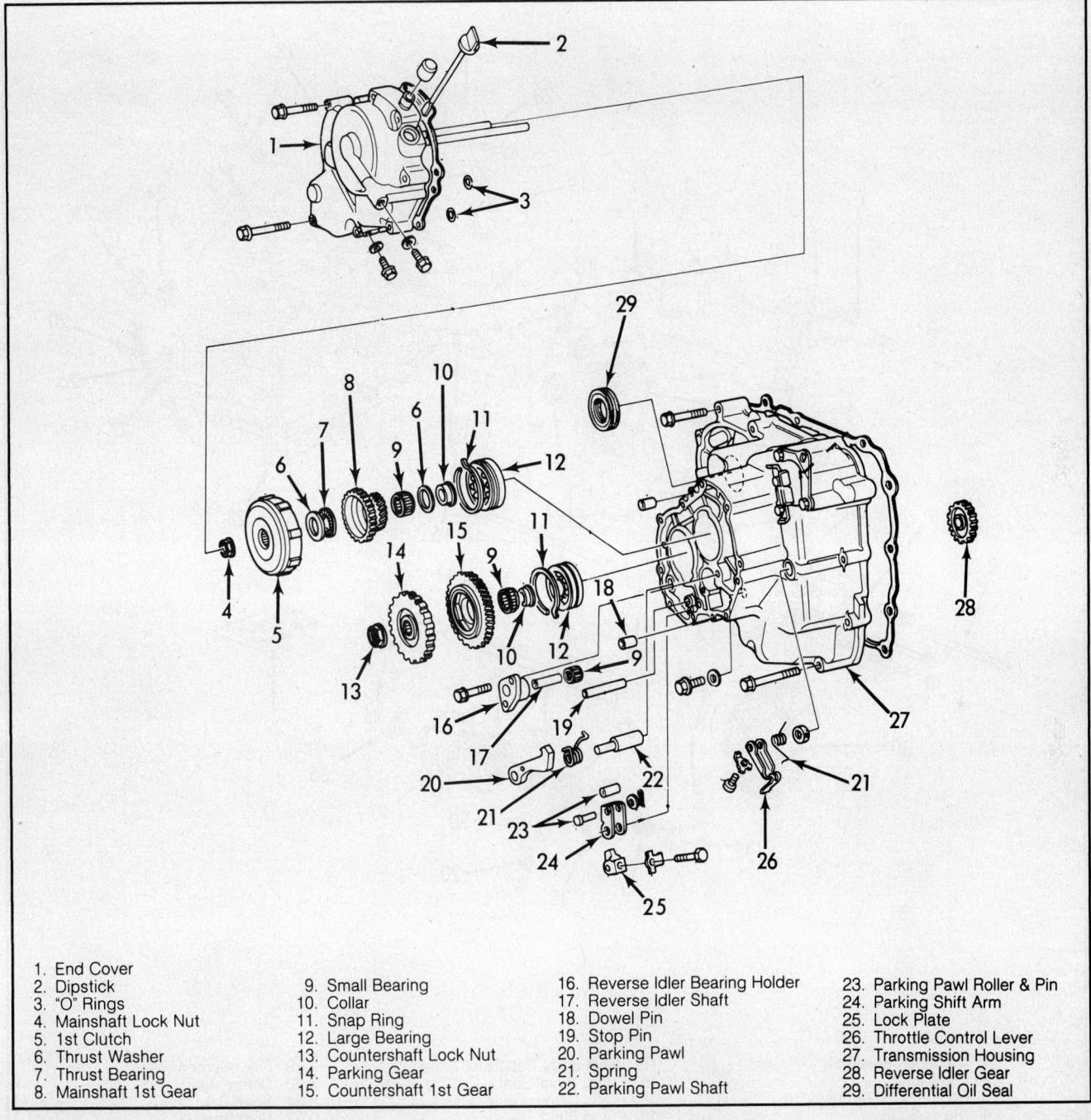

1. End Cover
2. Dipstick
3. "O" Rings
4. Mainshaft Lock Nut
5. 1st Clutch
6. Thrust Washer
7. Thrust Bearing
8. Mainshaft 1st Gear

9. Small Bearing
10. Collar
11. Snap Ring
12. Large Bearing
13. Countershaft Lock Nut
14. Parking Gear
15. Countershaft 1st Gear

16. Reverse Idler Bearing Holder
17. Reverse Idler Shaft
18. Dowel Pin
19. Stop Pin
20. Parking Pawl
21. Spring
22. Parking Pawl Shaft

23. Parking Pawl Roller & Pin
24. Parking Shift Arm
25. Lock Plate
26. Throttle Control Lever
27. Transmission Housing
28. Reverse Idler Gear
29. Differential Oil Seal

counter 1st gear by prying out with a screwdriver. Inspect countershaft 1st gear and parking gear for wear, damage or scoring. Inspect one-way clutch for damage.

Reassembly

To reassemble one-way clutch and parking gear, reverse disassembly procedures. When reassembled, check one-way clutch for free movement in one direction only.

VALVE BODY

NOTE: When disassembling valve body, lay out components in order of removal for reassembly reference.

Disassembly

1) Remove torque converter check valve and spring. Remove relief valve cap, spring and valve. Remove orifice control valve plate, spring and valve. Remove detent spring and rollers. Remove manual valve.

2) Remove 1-2 shift valve plate, then carefully remove 1-2 shift valve with sleeve. Remove 1-2 shift spring. On 1-2 shift valve, carefully slide sleeve off valve, being careful to catch 2 steel balls and spring as sleeve is removed.

3) Remove and disassemble 2-3 shift valve in same manner as 1-2 shift valve. Check all components for wear or damage. Replace spring if not to specifications. See SPRING IDENTIFICATION table. Replace complete

Fig. 12: *Exploded View of Torque Converter Housing and Components*

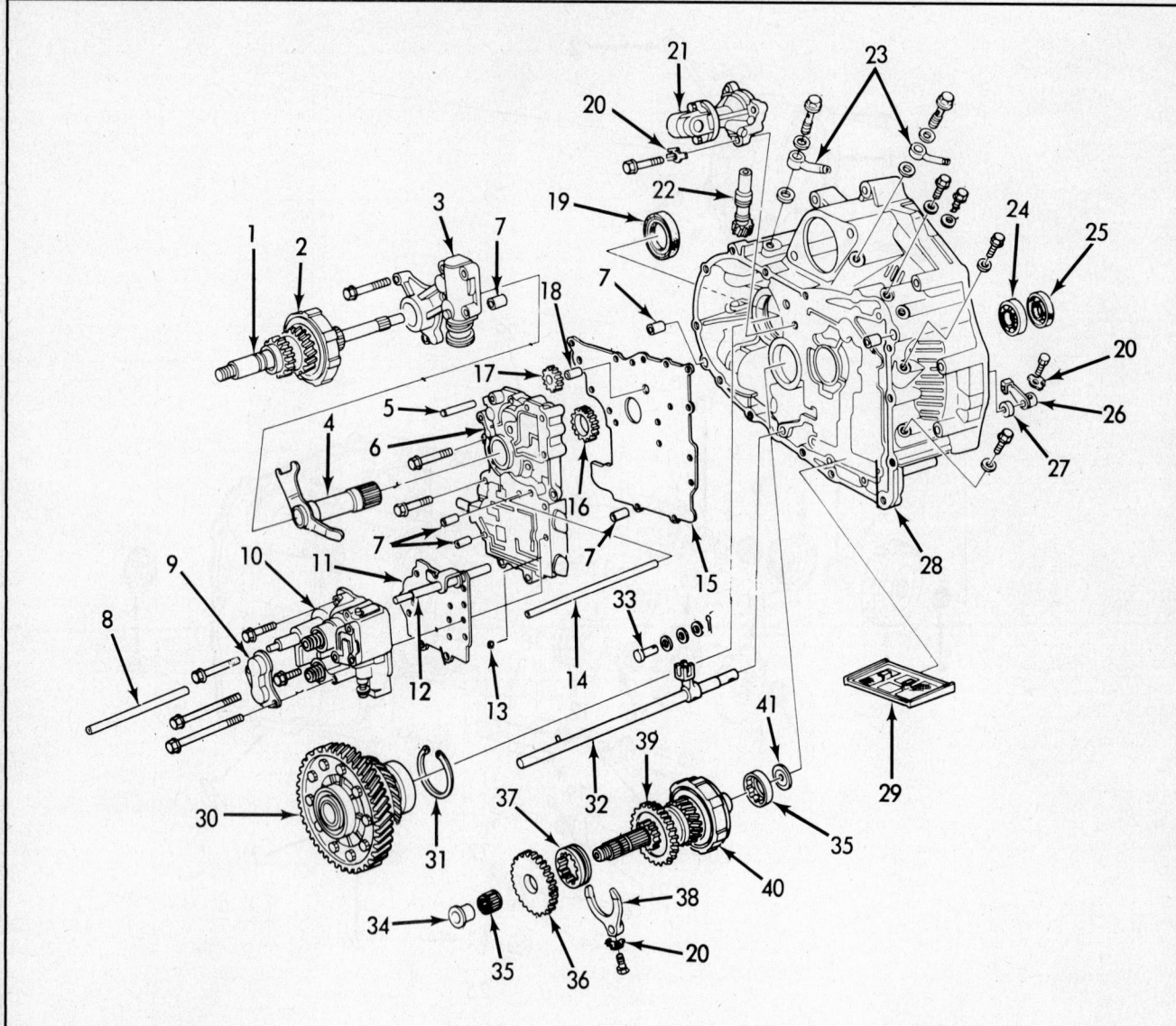

1. Mainshaft Assembly
2. 2nd Clutch
3. Regulator Assembly
4. Stator Shaft
5. Stop Pin
6. Valve Body Assembly
7. Dowel Pin
8. Feed Pipe for 1st Gear
9. Accumulator Cover
10. Servo Valve Assembly
11. Servo Separator Plate
12. Throttle Control Shaft
13. Steel Ball
14. Feed Pipe for 3rd Gear

15. Valve Body Separator Plate
16. Pump Drive Gear
17. Pump Driven Gear
18. Pump Shaft
19. Differential Oil Seal
20. Lock Plate
21. Governor Assembly
22. Speedometer Drive Gear
23. Transmission Cooler Lines
24. Mainshaft Bearing
25. Mainshaft Oil Seal
26. Shift Lever
27. Oil Seal
28. Torque Converter Housing

29. Filter Screen
30. Differential
31. Snap Ring
32. Shift Shaft
33. Manual Valve Pin
34. Reverse Gear Collar
35. Bearing
36. Countershaft Reverse Gear
37. Selector Hub
38. Reverse Shift Fork
39. Countershaft Assembly
40. 3rd Clutch
41. Oil Guide Plate

SPRING IDENTIFICATION CHART

Valve Spring	Length In. (mm)	Outer Diameter In. (mm)	Number Of Coils	Wire Thickness In. (mm)
Regulator Valve Outer Spring	3.28 (83.2)	.58 (14.7)	17	.07 (1.8)
Regulator Valve Inner Spring	1.73 (44.0)	.38 (9.6)	9	.07 (1.8)
Stator Reacting Spring	1.19 (30.3)	1.51 (38.4)	2	.24 (6.0)
Torque Converter Check Valve Spring	1.53 (38.9)	.35 (8.89)	15	.04 (.9)
Throttle Modulator Valve Spring	1.20 (30.5)	.37 (9.4)	8	.05 (1.2)
Relief Valve Spring	1.86 (47.2)	.33 (8.4)	15	.03 (.8)
Governor Spring	1.11 (28.3)	.74 (18.8)	3.5	.05 (1.2)
Orifice Control Spring	1.28 (32.5)	.27 (6.8)	16	.04 (.9)
Throttle Control Valve "A" Outer Spring	.84 (21.4)	.33 (8.4)	6	.04 (1.0)
Throttle Control Valve "A" Inner Spring	1.18 (29.9)	.24 (6.2)	8	.03 (1.4)
Throttle Control Valve "B" Spring	1.20 (30.5)	.33 (8.4)	8.5	.06 (1.4)
Servo Return Spring	1.24 (31.4)	1.13 (28.6)	2.4	.10 (2.5)

valve body assembly if valve body or any valve is worn or damaged. *See Fig. 14.*

NOTE: **Coat all parts in ATF before reassembly.**

Reassembly
1) Slide 1-2 shift valve spring into hole in 1-2 shift valve. Press steel balls (1 on each side of spring) into hole of shift valve and slide sleeve over shift valve and balls. Place 1-2 shift spring in valve body, then install shift valve (with sleeve) into valve body. Install 1-2 shift valve plate and bolts to valve body. *See Fig. 13.*

Fig. 13: Exploded View of Shift Valve Assembly

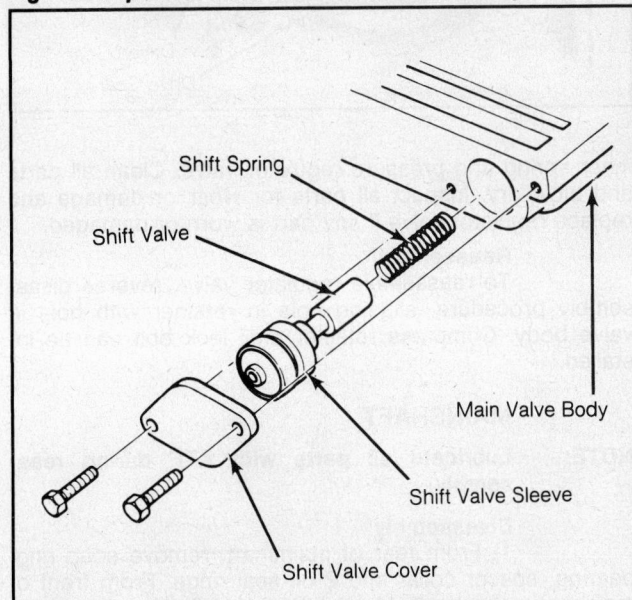

Shift Spring

Shift Valve

Main Valve Body

Shift Valve Sleeve

Shift Valve Cover

2) Assemble 2-3 shift valve in same manner as 1-2 shift valve and install it to valve body. Place relief spring in relief valve and install in valve body. Compress spring with a screwdriver and insert valve spring cap (with cut-out aligned with screwdriver).
3) Install manual valve into valve body, then install detent rollers and spring. Install oil pump driven gear shaft and driven gear (make sure chamfered side of gear faces away from valve body). Install oil pump drive gear.
4) Measure driven gear-to-valve body thrust clearance. Clearance should be .001-.002" (.03-.05 mm).

Measure side clearance of driven and drive gears. Driven gear side clearance should be .002-.004" (.05-.10 mm), drive gear side clearance should be .004-.006" (.10-.14 mm). *See Fig. 15.* If clearance is not to specifications, check valve body for excessive wear. If wear exists, replace valve body assembly.

SERVO VALVE ASSEMBLY

NOTE: **Clean all parts in solvent and blow dry with air. Replace servo valve as an assembly if any parts are worn or damaged.**

Disassembly
1) Push out 2nd and 3rd accumulator pistons, then remove "O" rings. Remove servo valve and spring, then remove "O" ring from valve. Remove throttle control valve "B", then separate control valve "B" from inner and outer springs and plug. *See Fig. 16.*
2) Remove retainer bolt and retainer of throttle control valve "A". Remove plug, outside spring, throttle control valve "A" and inside spring. Remove throttle control cover, then separator plate. Remove oil passage pipe from valve body.
3) Remove plug and washer from servo valve body. Remove modulator valve retainer plate, spring and modulator valve. Inspect all components for wear or damage. verify that springs meet specifications. See SPRING IDENTIFICATION table. Replace springs that are not to specifications or complete servo assembly if any part is worn or damaged.

Reasembly
To reassemble servo valve, reverse disassembly procedure. Always replace "O" rings with new ones.

NOTE: **Do not remove or adjust shift adjustment bolt. Adjustment bolt is factory set and should not be changed or shift points will be changed.**

GOVERNOR ASSEMBLY

NOTE: **Replace governor assembly if any part is worn or damaged, or if governor does not operate smoothly.**

Disassembly
1) Remove governor housing lock plate bolts and remove governor housing. Remove "E" ring from governor housing, then remove small snap ring, spring and

Fig. 14: Exploded View of Valve Body and Components

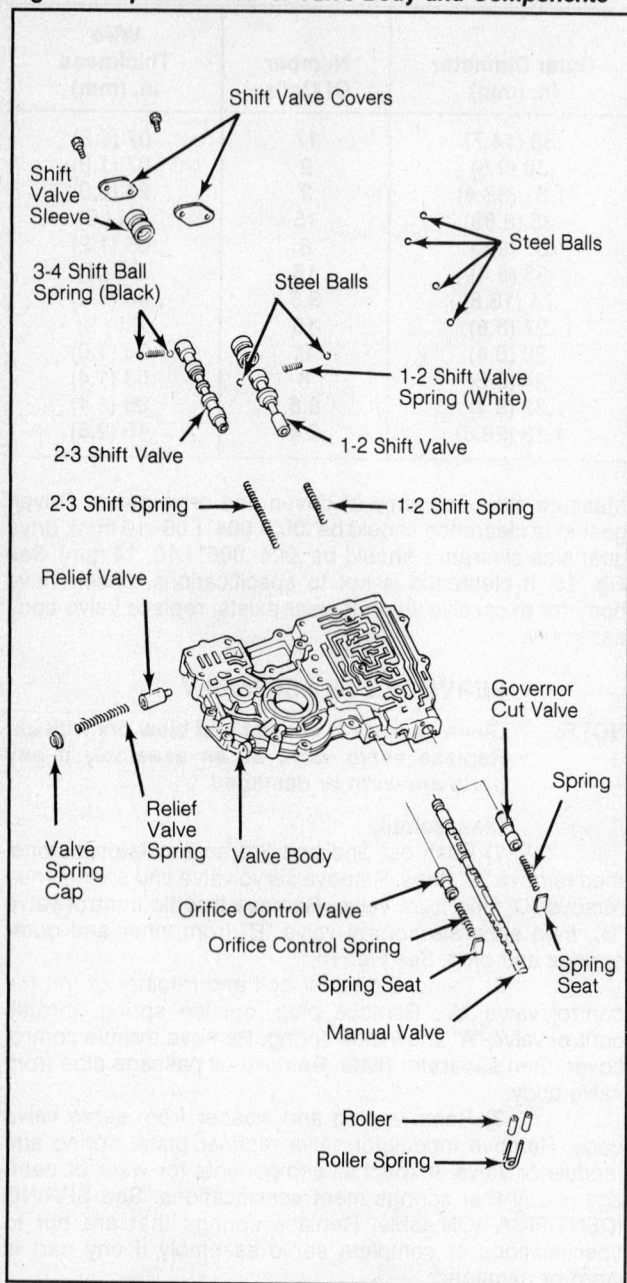

Fig. 15: Measuring Oil Pump-to-Valve Body Gear Clearance

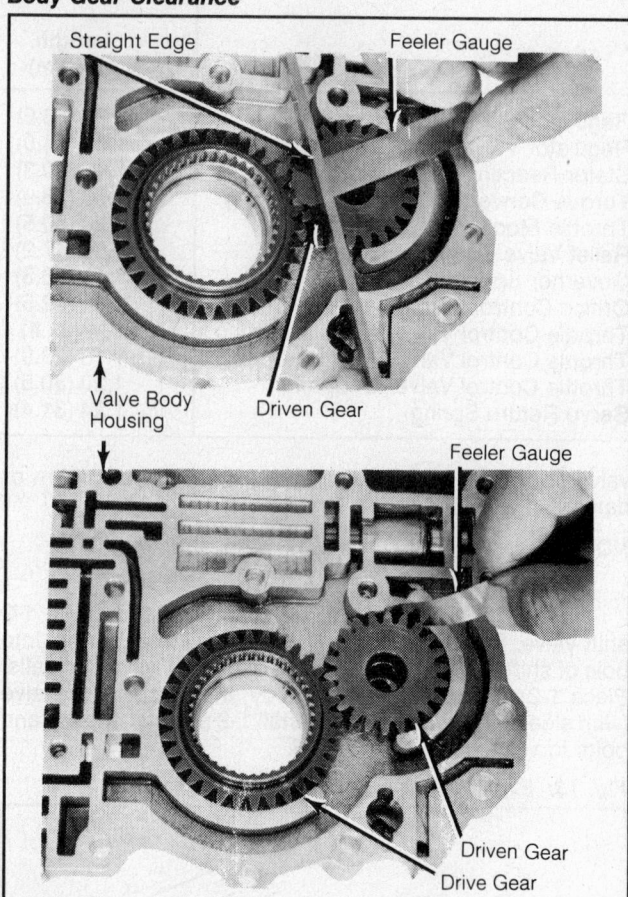

inner spring and pressure regulator valve. Clean all parts and blow dry. Inspect all parts for wear or damage and replace regulator valve if any part is worn or damaged.

Reassembly
To reassemble regulator valve, reverse disassembly procedure, aligning hole in retainer with hole in valve body. Compress retainer until lock bolt can be installed.

MAINSHAFT
NOTE: Lubricate all parts with ATF during reassembly.

Disassembly
1) From rear of mainshaft, remove snap ring, bearing, spacer collar and 2 oil seal rings. From front of mainshaft, remove lock nut (LEFT HAND thread) and 1st clutch.

2) Remove thrust washer, thrust needle bearing, 1st gear, bearing, thrust washer and spacer collar. Remove bearing, 2 "O" rings, snap ring, washer, thrust needle bearing and 2nd gear.

3) Remove 2 bearings, thrust needle bearing and splined thrust washer. Remove 2nd clutch and 2 "O" rings from mainshaft.

NOTE: When installing thrust needle bearings, install unrolled edge of bearing cage facing thrust washer.

secondary weight. Remove large snap ring and primary weight. Remove governor valve. *See Fig. 17.*

2) On governor holder, remove snap ring, gear and thrust washer. From governor shaft, remove pipe. Pull governor shaft out of governor holder and remove Woodruff key and thrust washer. Inspect all parts for wear or damage. Check for smooth operation of all parts.

Reassembly
To reassemble governor, reverse disassembly procedure, replace lock plates with new ones and check for smooth operation after reassembly.

REGULATOR VALVE BODY
Disassembly
Hold retainer in compressed position while removing lock bolt, then slowly release retainer. Remove retainer, spring seat, stator reaction spring, outer spring,

HONDA 3-SPEED (Cont.)

Fig. 16: Exploded View of Servo Valve Assembly

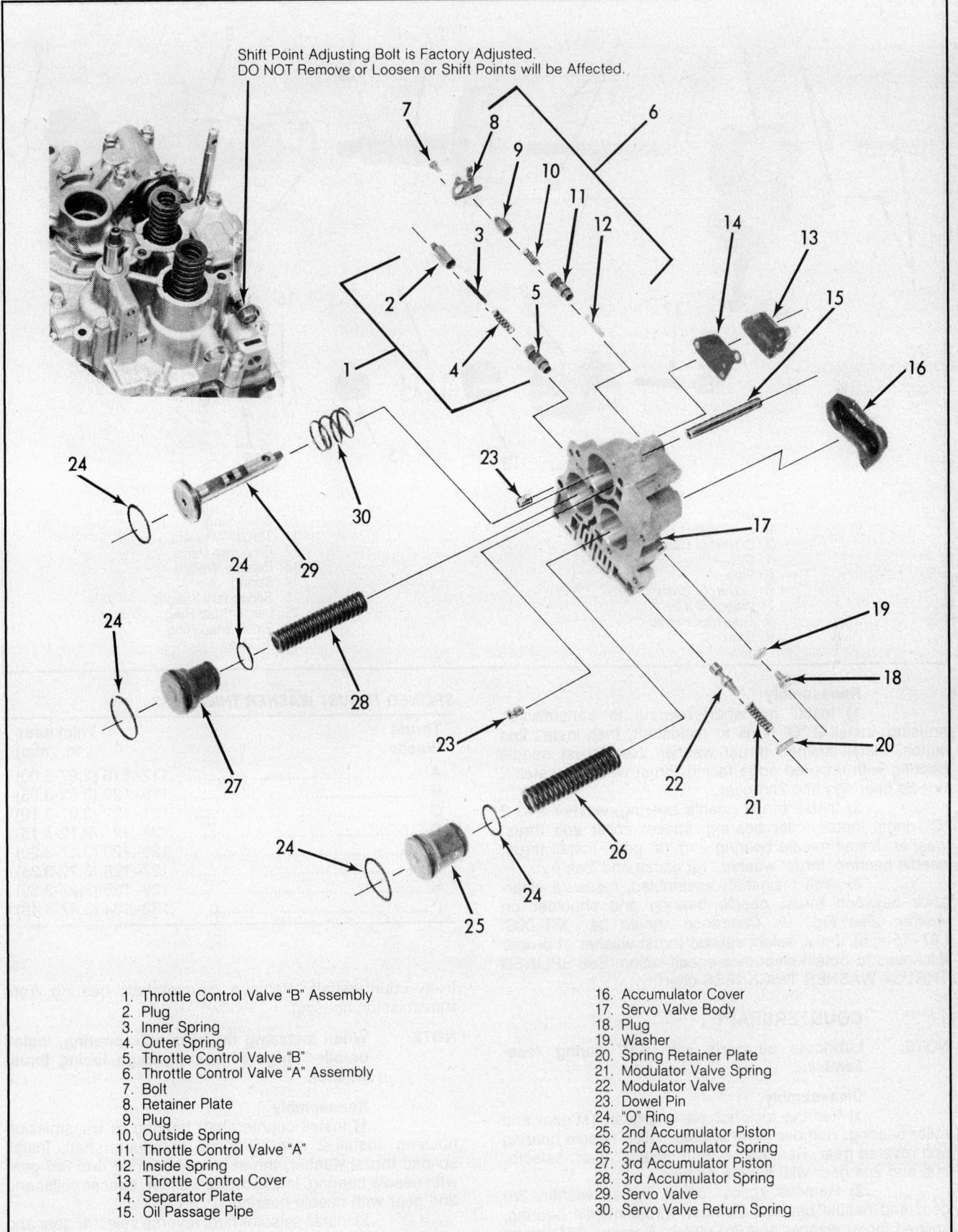

Shift Point Adjusting Bolt is Factory Adjusted.
DO NOT Remove or Loosen or Shift Points will be Affected.

1. Throttle Control Valve "B" Assembly
2. Plug
3. Inner Spring
4. Outer Spring
5. Throttle Control Valve "B"
6. Throttle Control Valve "A" Assembly
7. Bolt
8. Retainer Plate
9. Plug
10. Outside Spring
11. Throttle Control Valve "A"
12. Inside Spring
13. Throttle Control Cover
14. Separator Plate
15. Oil Passage Pipe
16. Accumulator Cover
17. Servo Valve Body
18. Plug
19. Washer
20. Spring Retainer Plate
21. Modulator Valve Spring
22. Modulator Valve
23. Dowel Pin
24. "O" Ring
25. 2nd Accumulator Piston
26. 2nd Accumulator Spring
27. 3rd Accumulator Piston
28. 3rd Accumulator Spring
29. Servo Valve
30. Servo Valve Return Spring

Automatic Transmissions
HONDA 3-SPEED (Cont.)

Fig. 17: Exploded View of Governor Assembly

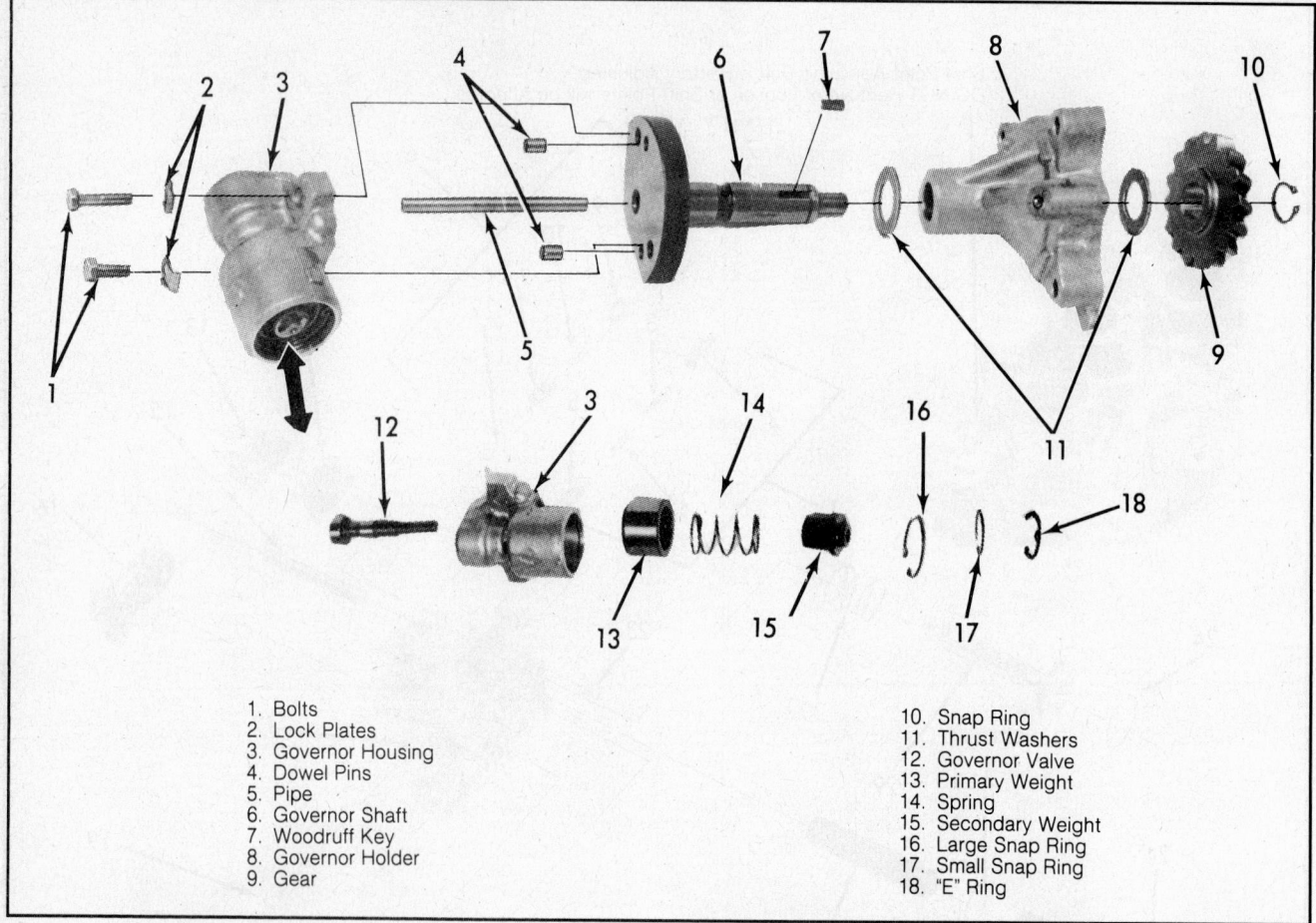

1. Bolts
2. Lock Plates
3. Governor Housing
4. Dowel Pins
5. Pipe
6. Governor Shaft
7. Woodruff Key
8. Governor Holder
9. Gear
10. Snap Ring
11. Thrust Washers
12. Governor Valve
13. Primary Weight
14. Spring
15. Secondary Weight
16. Large Snap Ring
17. Small Snap Ring
18. "E" Ring

Reassembly

1) Install mainshaft bearing to transmission housing. Install 2 "O" rings to mainshaft, then install 2nd clutch. Install splined thrust washer then thrust needle bearing with unrolled edge facing thrust washer. Install 2 needle bearings and 2nd gear.

2) Install thrust needle bearing, washer and 2 "O" rings. Install roller bearing, spacer collar and thrust washer. Install needle bearing and 1st gear. Install thrust needle bearing, thrust washer, 1st clutch and lock nut.

3) With mainshaft assembled, measure clearance between thrust needle bearing and shoulder on washer. *See Fig. 19.* Clearance should be .003-.006" (.07-.15 mm), if not, select splined thrust washer of proper thickness to obtain clearance specification. See SPLINED THRUST WASHER THICKNESS chart.

COUNTERSHAFT

NOTE: Lubricate all parts with ATF during reassembly.

Disassembly

1) Remove lock nut, parking gear, 1st gear and roller bearing. Remove reverse gear collar, needle bearing and reverse gear. Remove reverse selector gear, selector hub and 2nd gear with needle bearing.

2) Remove spacer collar, thrust washer, 3rd gear and needle bearing. Remove thrust needle bearing, splined thrust washer and 3rd clutch. Remove 2 "O" rings

SPLINED THRUST WASHER THICKNESS

Thrust Washer	Thickness In. (mm)
A	.117-.118 (2.97-3.00)
B	.119-.120 (3.02-3.05)
C	.121-.122 (3.07-3.10)
D	.123-.124 (3.12-3.15)
E	.125-.126 (3.17-3.20)
F	.127-.128 (3.22-3.25)
H	.129-.130 (3.27-3.30)
I	.132-.134 (3.37-3.40)

from countershaft. Remove countershaft bearing from transmission housing.

NOTE: When installing thrust needle bearing, install unrolled edge of bearing cage facing thrust washer.

Reassembly

1) Install countershaft bearing to transmission housing. Install 2 new "O" rings to countershaft. Install splined thrust washer, thrust needle bearing and 3rd gear with needle bearing. Install thrust washer, spacer collar and 2nd gear with needle bearing.

2) Install selector hub, reverse selector gear and reverse gear with needle bearing. Install reverse gear collar,

Fig. 18: Exploded View of Mainshaft Assembly

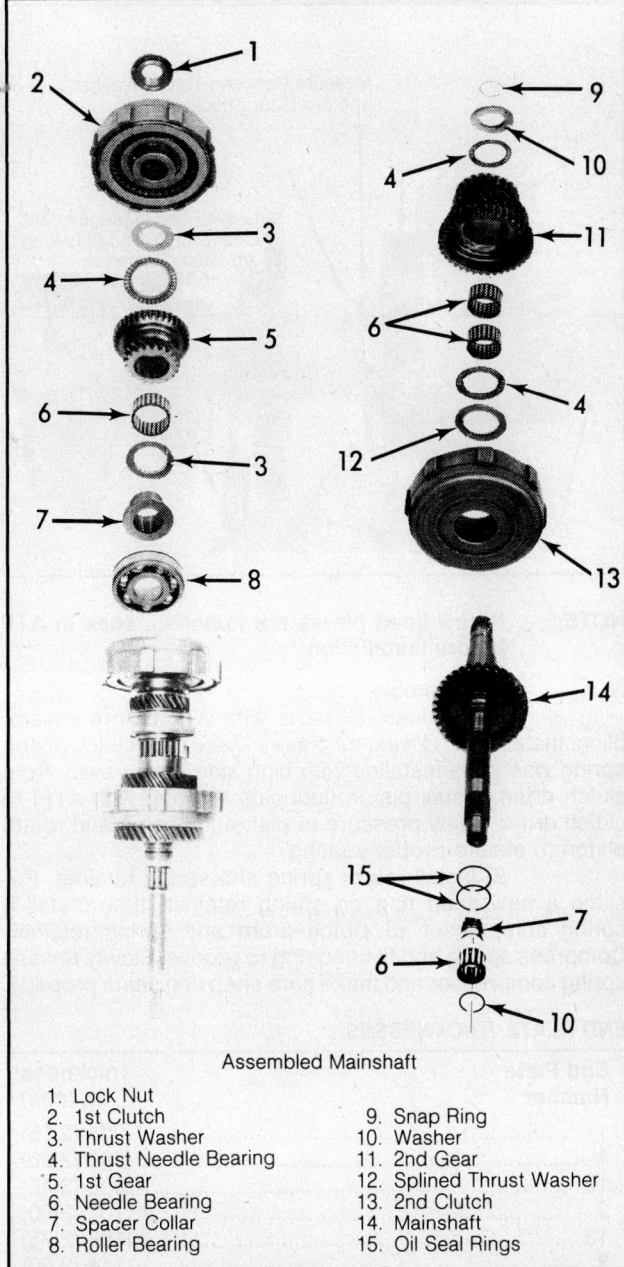

Assembled Mainshaft

1. Lock Nut
2. 1st Clutch
3. Thrust Washer
4. Thrust Needle Bearing
5. 1st Gear
6. Needle Bearing
7. Spacer Collar
8. Roller Bearing
9. Snap Ring
10. Washer
11. 2nd Gear
12. Splined Thrust Washer
13. 2nd Clutch
14. Mainshaft
15. Oil Seal Rings

Fig. 19: Measuring Mainshaft Gear Clearance

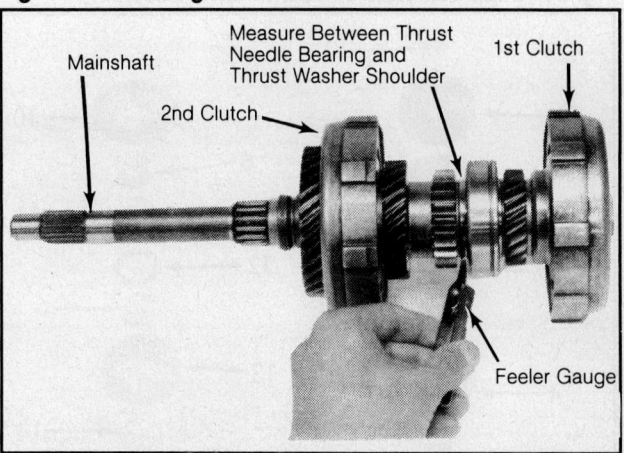

THRUST WASHER THICKNESS

Thrust Washer	Thickness In. (mm)
A	.089-.091 (2.27-2.30)
B	.091-.092 (2.32-2.35)
C	.093-.094 (2.37-2.40)
D	.095-.096 (2.42-2.45)
E	.097-.098 (2.47-2.50)
F	.099-.100 (2.52-2.55)
G	.101-.102 (2.57-2.60)

Fig. 20: Measuring Countershaft 2nd Gear Clearance

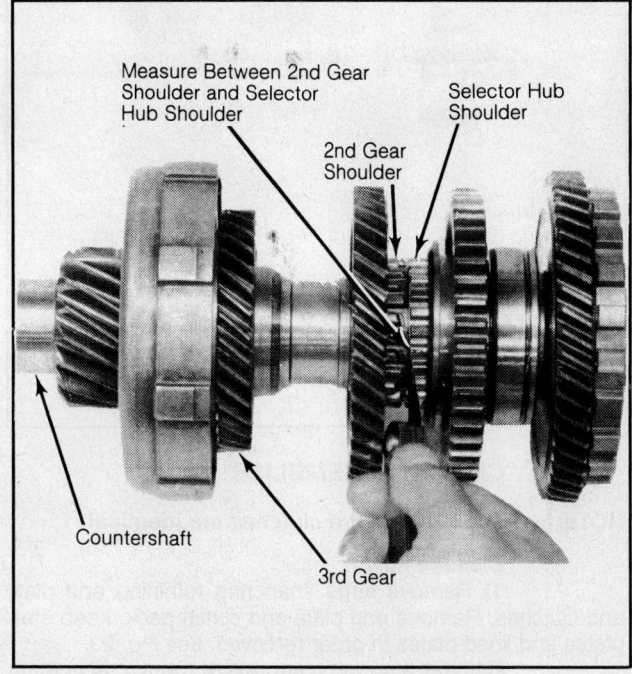

roller bearing, 1st gear, parking gear and lock nut. *See Fig. 21.*

   3) With countershaft assembled, measure clearance between selector hub and shoulder on 2nd gear. *See Fig. 20.* Clearance should be .003-.006" (.07-.15 mm). If clearance is more than specifications, install a thrust washer of proper thickness to achieve correct clearance. See THRUST WASHER THICKNESS chart.

   4) Leave feeler gauge of .003-.006" (.07-.15 mm) thickness (standard 2nd gear clearance) installed between selector hub and 2nd gear, then install another feeler gauge between thrust washer and shoulder of 3rd gear to measure 3rd gear clearance. *See Fig. 22.* Clearance should be .003-.006" (.07-.15 mm).

   5) If clearance is not to specifications, install a splined thrust washer of proper thickness. See SPLINED THRUST WASHER THICKNESS chart, to determine amount of mainshaft 2nd gear clearance.

Fig. 21: Exploded View of Countershaft Assembly

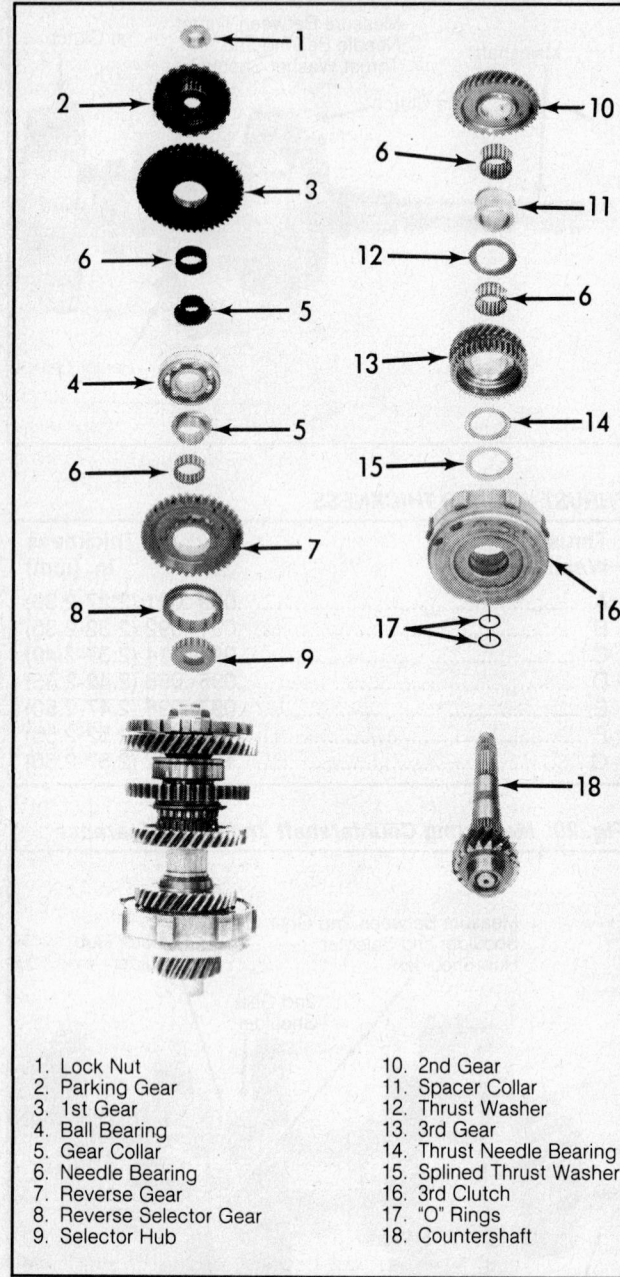

1. Lock Nut
2. Parking Gear
3. 1st Gear
4. Ball Bearing
5. Gear Collar
6. Needle Bearing
7. Reverse Gear
8. Reverse Selector Gear
9. Selector Hub
10. 2nd Gear
11. Spacer Collar
12. Thrust Washer
13. 3rd Gear
14. Thrust Needle Bearing
15. Splined Thrust Washer
16. 3rd Clutch
17. "O" Rings
18. Countershaft

CLUTCH ASSEMBLIES

NOTE: 1st, 2nd and 3rd clutches are identical.

Disassembly

1) Remove large snap ring retaining end plate and clutches. Remove end plate and clutch pack, keep steel plates and lined plates in order removed. See Fig. 23.

2) Install a spring compressor that seats against clutch drum and against spring retainer. Compress spring and remove small snap ring. Slowly release spring compressor, then remove spring retainer, return spring, large "O" ring, small "O" ring and piston.

3) Check condition of piston and check valve. Check for excessive wear or scoring on steel plates and lined plates. Replace steel or lined plates if necessary. Replace clutch assembly if piston is damaged.

Fig. 22: Measuring Countershaft 3rd Gear Clearance

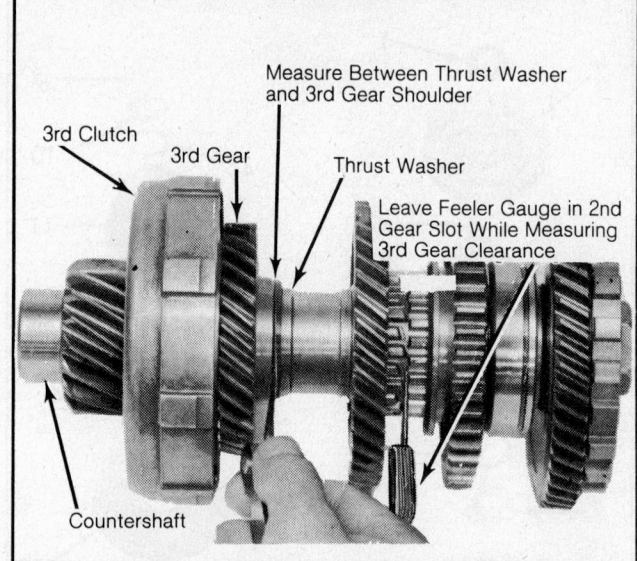

NOTE: If new lined plates are installed, soak in ATF before installation.

Reassembly

1) Lubricate all parts with ATF before assembling. Install new "O" ring on piston. Make sure clutch piston spring washer is installed with high side facing away from clutch drum. Install piston (lubricate "O" ring with ATF) to clutch drum. Apply pressure to piston (by hand) and rotate piston to ensure proper seating.

2) Install return spring and spring retainer. Position a new snap ring on spring retainer, then install a spring compressor to clutch drum and spring retainer. Compress spring and fit snap ring to groove. Slowly release spring compressor and make sure snap ring seats properly.

END PLATE THICKNESSES

End Plate Number	Thickness In. (mm)
11	.084 (2.15)
1	.090 (2.30)
12	.096 (2.45)
2	.102 (2.60)
13	.108 (2.75)
3	.114 (2.90)
14	.120 (3.05)
4	.125 (3.20)
15	.132 (3.35)
5	.137 (3.50)
16	.143 (3.65)

3) Install clutch pack, starting with a steel plate and alternating with lined plates, ending with the end plate. Install large snap ring to clutch drum. Measure clearance between end plate and lined plate. Clearance should be .016-.028" (.4-.7 mm).

4) If clearance is not to specifications, select an end plate to obtain correct clearance. See END PLATE THICKNESS chart. With correct end plate installed, check operation of clutch by blowing compressed air into oil

Fig. 23: Exploded View of 1st, 2nd and 3rd Clutch Assemblies

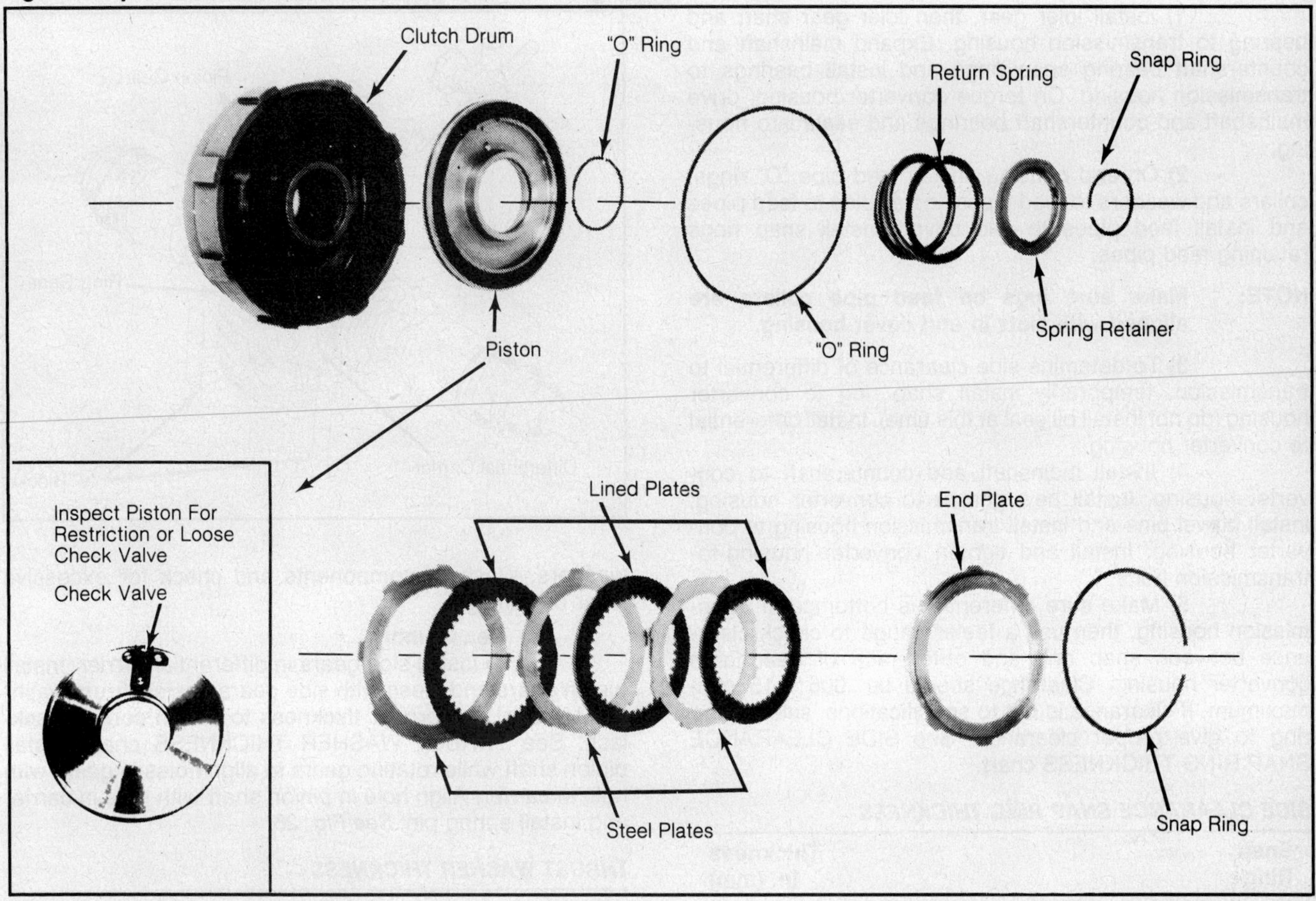

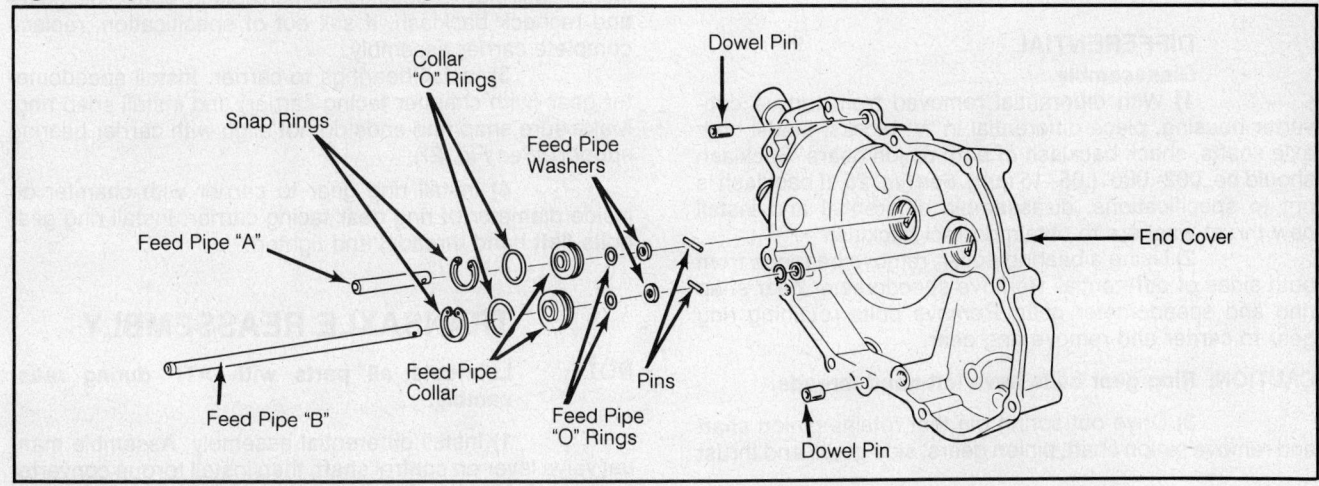

passage in clutch drum. Clutch should apply. Remove air pressure and clutch should release.

TRANSMISSION, END & TORQUE CONVERTER HOUSING
Disassembly

1) If seals are to be replaced or if differential needs repair, lift differential out of torque converter housing. Remove differential seal snap ring and drive seal out.

2) On end cover, remove snap rings to feed pipes "A" and "B". Remove feed pipes with collars, then remove pins and collars from feed pipes. *See Fig. 24.*

3) On torque converter housing, drive in oil seals and bearings from mainshaft and countershaft. On transmission housing, expand snap rings (do not remove) and push bearings out by hand. Push out idler gear shaft and bearing from inside transmission housing then remove idler gear.

Fig. 24: Exploded View of End Housing Assembly

Automatic Transmissions
HONDA 3-SPEED (Cont.)

Reassembly

1) Install idler gear, then idler gear shaft and bearing to transmission housing. Expand mainshaft and countershaft bearing snap rings and install bearings to transmission housing. On torque converter housing, drive mainshaft and countershaft bearings and seals into housing.

2) On end housing, install feed pipe "O" rings, collars and washers to feed pipes. Install pins to feed pipes and install feed pipes to end cover. Install snap rings retaining feed pipes.

NOTE: Make sure lugs on feed pipe collars are aligned with slots in end cover housing.

3) To detemine side clearance of differential to transmission, temporarily install snap ring to converter housing (do not install oil seal at this time). Install differential to converter housing.

4) Install mainshaft and countershaft to converter housing. Install new gasket to converter housing, install dowel pins and install transmission housing to converter housing. Install and tighten converter housing-to-transmission bolts.

5) Make sure differential is bottomed in transmission housing, then use a feeler gauge to check clearance between snap ring and outer race of bearing in converter housing. Clearance should be .006" (.15 mm) maximum. If clearance is not to specifications, select snap ring to give proper clearance. See SIDE CLEARANCE SNAP RING THICKNESS chart.

SIDE CLEARANCE SNAP RING THICKNESS

Snap Ring	Thickness In. (mm)
1	.096 (2.45)
2	.100 (2.55)
3	.104 (2.65)
4	.108 (2.75)
5	.112 (2.85)
6	.116 (2.95)

6) Disassemble temporarily assembled transmission and install oil seal and correct snap ring to converter housing. Install differential and snap ring to converter housing.

DIFFERENTIAL
Disassembly

1) With differential removed from torque converter housing, place differential in "V" blocks. Install both axle shafts, check backlash of both pinion gears. Backlash should be .002-.006" (.05-.15 mm). See Fig. 25. If backlash is not to specifications, disassemble differential and install new thrust washers to obtain correct backlash.

2) Using a bearing puller, remove bearings from both sides of differential. Remove speedometer gear snap ring and speedometer gear. Remove bolts retaining ring gear to carrier and remove ring gear.

CAUTION: Ring gear bolts have left hand threads.

3) Drive out spring pin that retains pinion shaft and remove pinion shaft, pinion gears, side gears and thrust

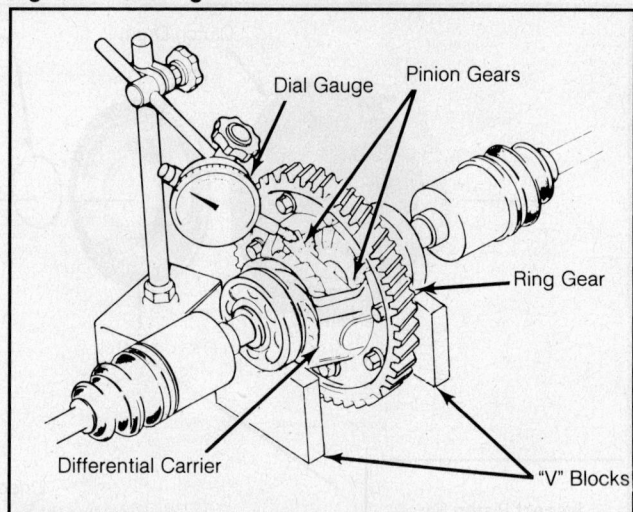

Fig. 25: Checking Backlash of Differential

washers. Wash all components and check for excessive wear or damage.

Reassembly

1) Install side gears in differential carrier. Install pinion gears and mesh with side gears. Install thrust washers of equal and proper thickness to obtain correct backlash. See THRUST WASHER THICKNESS chart. Install pinion shaft while rotating gears to align holes in gears with hole in carrier. Align hole in pinion shaft with hole in carrier and install spring pin. See Fig. 26.

THRUST WASHER THICKNESS

Thrust Washer	Thickness In. (mm)
1	.028 (.7)
2	.031 (.8)
3	.035 (.9)
4	.040 (1.0)

2) With differential assembled with new thrust washers, again measure backlash. If backlash is still not to specifications, replace both pinion gears and recheck backlash. If still not to specifications, replace both side gears and recheck backlash. If still out of specification, replace complete carrier assembly.

3) Install bearings to carrier. Install speedometer gear (with chamfer facing carrier) and install snap ring. Make sure snap ring ends do not align with carrier bearing support. See Fig. 27.

4) Install ring gear to carrier with chamfer on inside diameter of ring gear facing carrier. Install ring gear bolts (left hand threads) and tighten.

TRANSAXLE REASSEMBLY

NOTE: Lubricate all parts with ATF during reassembly.

1) Install differential assembly. Assemble manual valve lever on control shaft, then install torque converter housing. Install control lever and new lock plate on other

Fig. 26: Exploded View of Differential Assembly

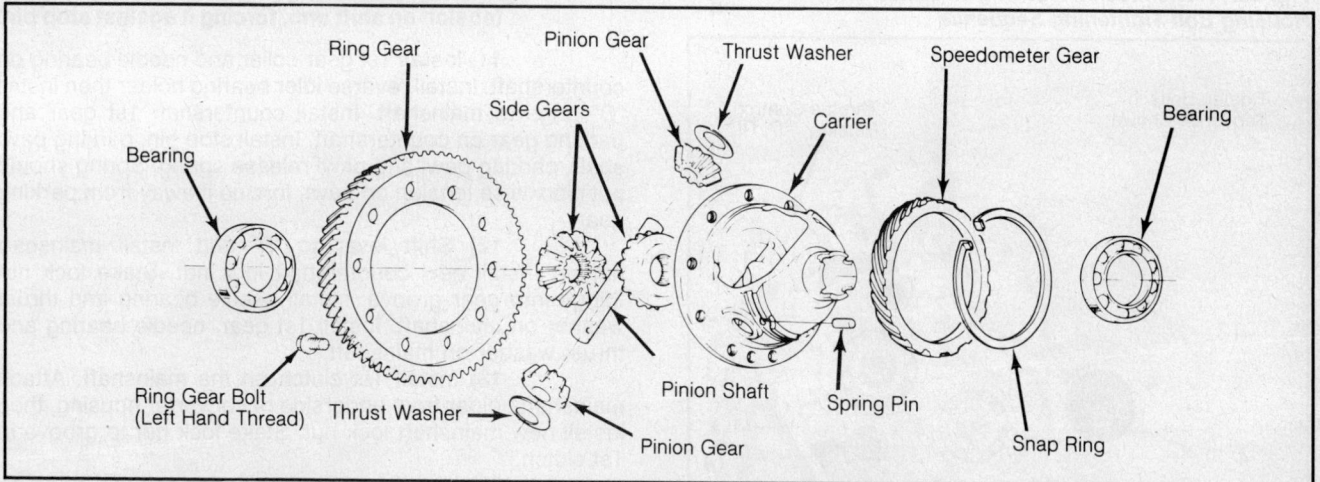

Fig. 27: Installation of Snap Ring on Differential Carrier

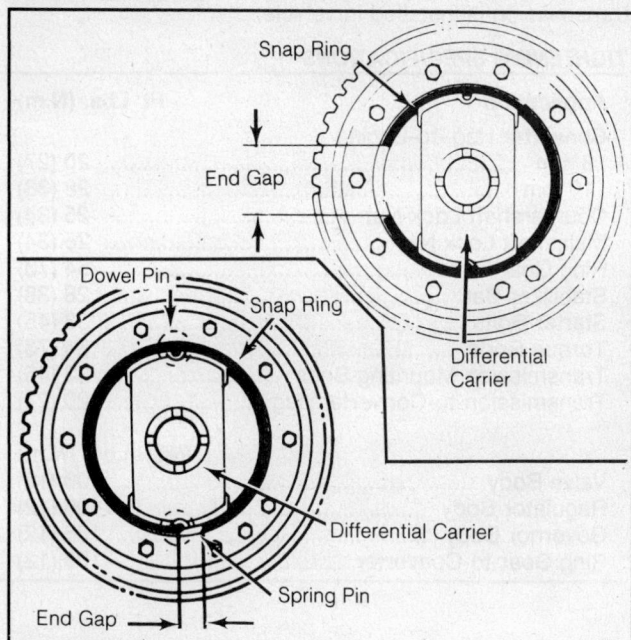

Fig. 28: Installation of Servo-to-Converter Housing Showing Attaching Bolt Lengths

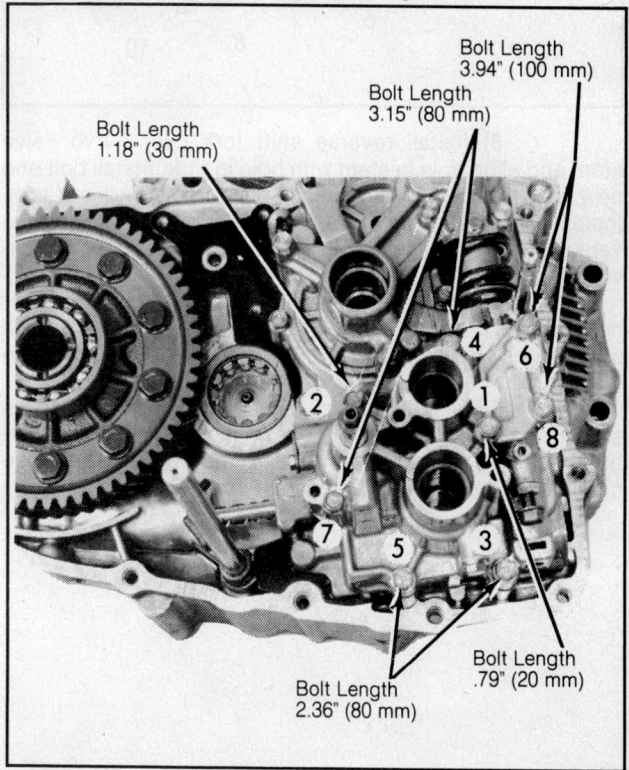

end of control shaft, install and tighten bolt. Bend tab of lock plate up to prevent bolt from turning.

2) Install new filter screen in converter housing. Install separator plate, dowel pin, oil pump gears and shaft. Make sure chamfered side of driven gear and shouldered side of drive gear is facing down. Install check valve and spring, then install valve body on converter housing.

3) Install and tighten valve body bolts. Install stator shaft arm, stop pin and dowel pins. Install regulator valve. Install steel balls in valve body oil passage. *See Fig. 10.* Install separator plate, throttle control shaft and dowel pins.

4) Install servo. Ensure correct length bolt is installed or servo will not seal to housing. *See Fig. 28.* Place a roller on each side of manual valve stem, then attach valve to lever with pin. Secure with cotter pin.

5) Install 2nd and 3rd accumulator spring in servo body. See VALVE BODY SPRING IDENTIFICATION chart for accumulator spring diameters and lengths. Install

accumulator cover; compress accumulator springs before tightening bolts.

6) Install governor valve, using new lock plates, then bend lock plate tabs over so bolts will not turn. Install mainshaft and countershaft in converter housing, as an assembly.

NOTE: **Do not tap on shaft ends to force shafts to seat.**

7) Remove lock nuts from mainshaft and countershaft, if installed, then install countershaft 2nd gear and reverse selector sleeve with reverse shift fork (assembled before installation). Groove on selector sleeve faces down.

Automatic Transmissions
HONDA 3-SPEED (Cont.)

Fig. 29: Transmission Housing-to-Converter Housing Bolt Tightening Sequence

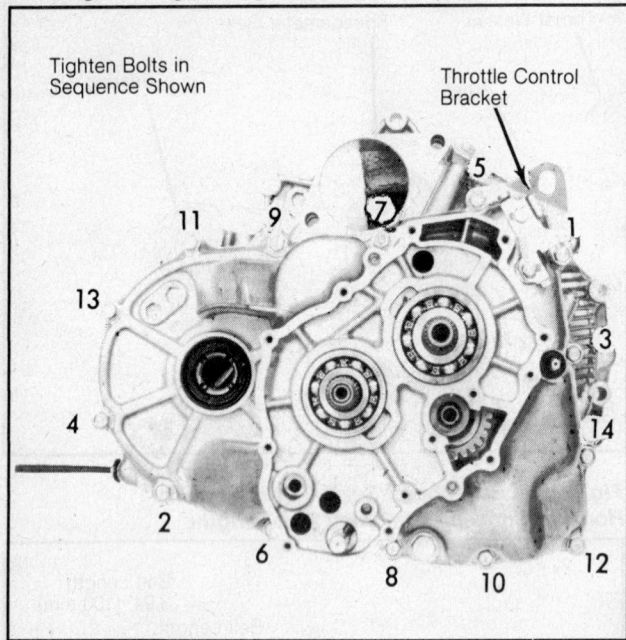

Tighten Bolts in Sequence Shown

Throttle Control Bracket

8) Install reverse shift fork over servo valve stem and align hole in stem with hole in fork. Install bolt and new lock plate. Bend tab on lock plate so bolt will not turn. Install countershaft reverse gear, needle bearing and reverse gear collar. Install gasket and 2 dowel pins in converter housing.

9) Place transmission housing on converter housing and install oil feed pipes. Make sure throttle control shaft aligns with hole in converter housing. Tighten bolts in 2 steps in order. *See Fig. 29.*

10) Install control lever and spring on control shaft, then install bolt and new lock plate. Bend tab against bolt. Install parking shift arm and spring on shift shaft, use new lock tab and bend tab against bolt.

NOTE: Parking shift arm spring should put clockwise tension on shift arm, forcing it against stop pin.

11) Install 1st gear collar and needle bearing on countershaft. Install reverse idler bearing holder then install "O" rings to mainshaft. Install countershaft 1st gear and parking gear on countershaft. Install stop pin, parking pawl shaft, parking pawl and pawl release spring. Spring should put clockwise tension on pawl, forcing it away from parking gear.

12) Shift lever to "P" and install mainshaft holder. Install new countershaft lock nut. Stake lock nut flange into gear groove. Install needle bearing and thrust washer on mainshaft. Install 1st gear, needle bearing and thrust washer on mainshaft.

13) Install 1st clutch on the mainshaft. Attach mainshaft holder from underside of converter housing, then install new mainshaft lock nut. Stake lock nut to groove in 1st clutch.

14) Install gasket, dowel pins and "O" rings on transmission housing. Install end cover and bolts. Install dipstick, coller fittings. Do not tighten cooler fittings until transmission is installed in vehicle.

TIGHTENING SPECIFICATIONS

Application	Ft. Lbs. (N.m)
Converter Hsg.-to-Engine	
8 mm	20 (27)
10 mm	28 (38)
Countershaft Lock Nut	25 (34)
Mainshaft Lock Nut	25 (34)
Ring Gear Bolts	54 (73)
Stabilizer Bar	28 (38)
Starter Bolts	33 (45)
Torque Rods	54 (73)
Transmission Mounting Bolts	33 (45)
Transmission-to-Converter Hsg.	20 (27)
	INCH Lbs. (N.m)
Valve Body	106 (12)
Regulator Body	106 (12)
Governor Body	106 (12)
Ring Gear-to-Converter	106 (12)

HONDA 4-SPEED

Accord & Prelude

IDENTIFICATION

The automatic transmission may be identified by a group of letters and numbers stamped on a pad on top of transaxle case. First 2 letters are transmission type. Next 7 numbers are transmission serial number.

TRANSMISSION MODEL CODE

Application	Code
All Models	AS

DESCRIPTION

The Honda automatic transaxle is a combination of a 3-element torque converter, dual-shaft 4-speed automatic transmission and a differential-type final drive assembly. Transmission consists of two parallel shafts; a mainshaft and a countershaft. The mainshaft is in line with crankshaft. *See Fig. 7.* Transmission is controlled by main valve body, regulator valve body and servo valve. Countershaft is in constant mesh with differential ring gear.

The torque convertor consists of a pump, turbine and stator, assembled in a single unit. A lock-up mechanism is built into torque converter. When transmission is in 4th gear, above 43 MPH, pressurized fluid is drained from back of torque converter, through an oil passage. This causes lock-up piston to press against torque converter cover. As this takes place, the mainshaft rotates at the same speed as crankshaft.

A pressure control valve body is bolted to top of regulator body and includes the pressure control shift valve and pressure control timing valve. The pressure control shift valve controls the range of lock-up according to vehicle speed and throttle pressure. The timing valve senses when transmission is in 4th gear.

LUBRICATION & ADJUSTMENTS

See appropriate AUTOMATIC TRANSMISSION SERVICING article in IMPORT GENERAL SERVICING section.

SERVICE (IN VEHICLE)

DRIVE AXLE SHAFT
Removal

1) Loosen front wheel lug nuts. Raise locking tab on spindle nut, then loosen nut with a 1.25" (32 mm) socket wrench. Raise and support front of vehicle.

2) Remove front wheels. Using a 3/8" drive socket wrench, remove drain plug and drain transmission fluid. Remove oil filler plug to speed draining. Remove spindle nut.

3) On Accord, detach ball joint pinch bolt. Remove tie rod end stud cotter pin and nut. Detach tie rod stud from steering knuckle arm bore using Ball Joint Remover (07941-6920001). Remove stabilizer bar bolts. Using plastic hammer, tap lower control arm to separate steering knuckle from ball joint.

4) On Prelude, remove shock absorber lower fork bolt and shock absorber pinch bolt, then remove damper fork. Remove tie rod end stud cotter pin and castle nut. Detach tie rod stud from steering knuckle arm bore using Ball Joint Remover (07941-6920001).

5) Pry out cotter pin from lower ball joint stud, then loosen castle nut half the length of stud threads. Using a 2-arm puller (with pawls hooked to lower control arm), separate ball joint from lower control arm. Do not damage ball joint rubber grease boot during removal.

6) On all models, pull hub/rotor assembly and steering knuckle outward, all the way off axle shaft. Pry inboard constant velocity (CV) joint out of transaxle case approximately 1/2" to force spring clip past groove in differential side gear splines.

7) Do not damage oil seal during prying operation. Do not pull on axle shaft or inboard CV joint may come apart. Pull on inboard CV joint housing to pull axle shaft assembly away from transaxle case, then lift assembly out of vehicle. Remove spring clip from stub axle and discard. Repeat procedures for other axle shaft.

NOTE: Mark CV joint rollers, spider and roller grooves during disassembly to ensure proper positioning during reassembly.

Disassembly

1) Remove metal boot bands securing rubber dust boot to axle shaft and inner constant velocity joint and discard. Slide boot back onto axle shaft and remove snap rings. Pull axle shaft from inner CV joint assembly. *See Fig. 1.* Remove inboard dust boot.

NOTE: Outer constant velocity joint is not removable from axle shaft.

2) Remove spider and rollers from inboard CV joint housing. Detach boot bands, then remove outer rubber boot from axle shaft assembly. Discard boot bands. Inspect all parts for excessive wear, deterioration or other damage.

Inspection

1) Check inboard axle shaft and CV joint housing splines for damage and/or excessive wear. Inspect inboard CV joint housing inside bore for excessive wear and joint housing outside surface for cracks. Inspect spider and roller assembly for wear or damage.

2) Check inboard and outboard rubber dust boots for cracks, splitting and wear. Inspect outboard CV joint for faulty movement, excessive wear and damaged splines or stripped threads on stub axle.

3) Check outboard CV joint ball bearings (while rotating), for noise, roughness and/or excessive wear. Check axle for damage or excessive runout. Replace axle shaft/outboard CV joint assembly and/or inboard CV joint components as necessary.

NOTE: Thoroughly pack spider assembly bearings and both inboard and outboard CV joint housings with molybdenum disulfide grease when reassembling drive axle shaft.

CAUTION: Avoid getting grease on rubber parts or deterioration may result.

Fig. 1: Exploded View of Axle Shaft Assembly

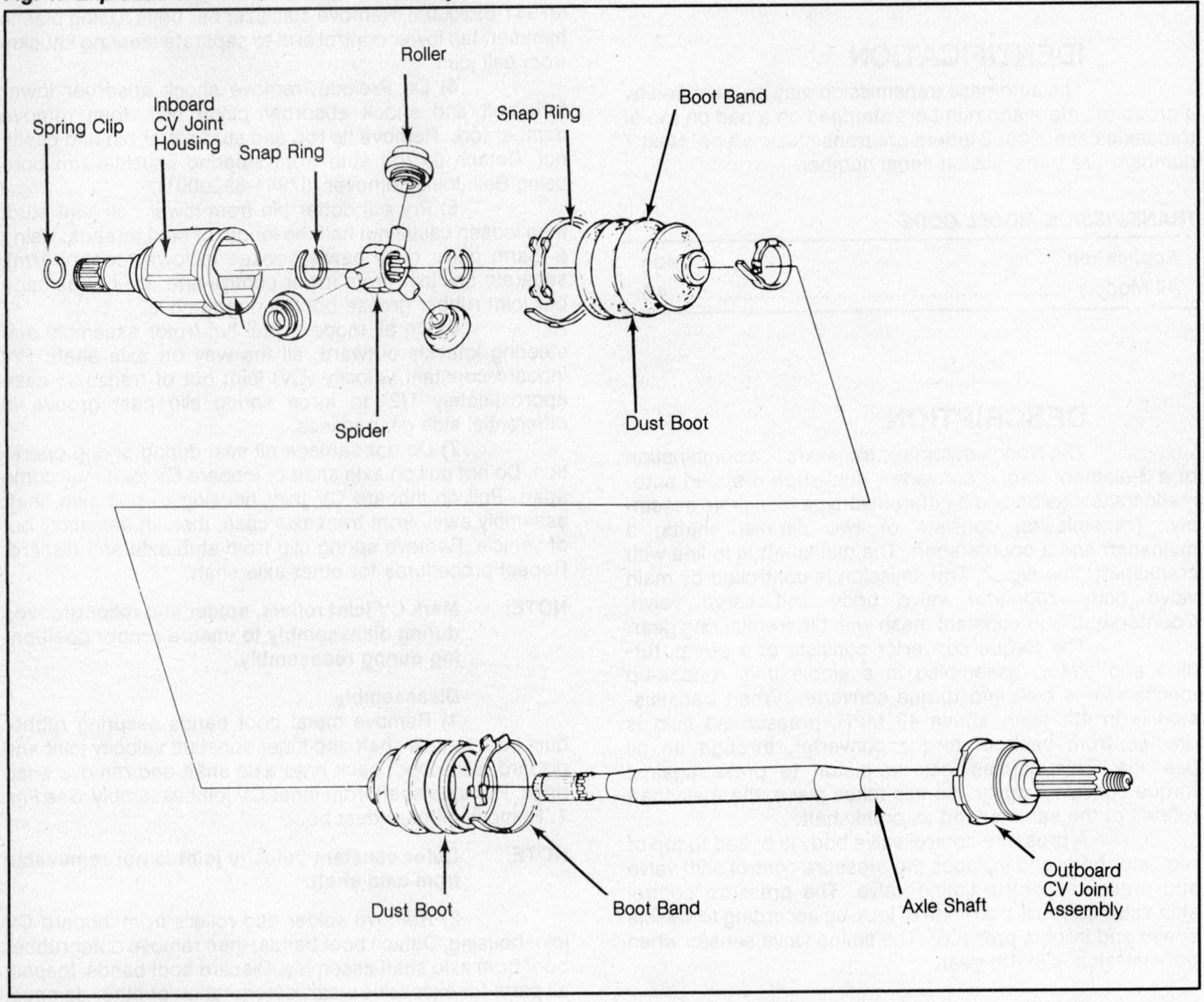

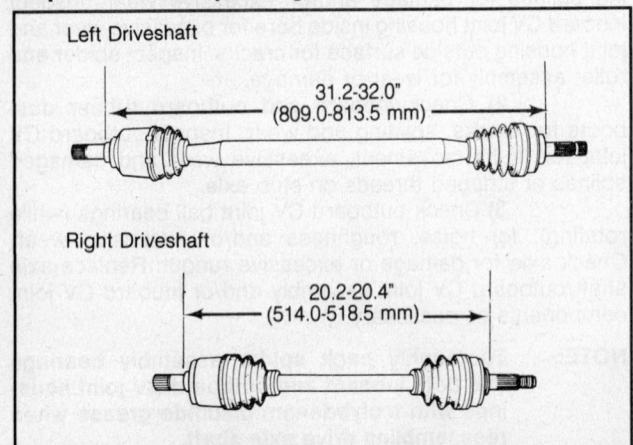

Fig. 2: Measuring Axle Shaft For Proper CV Joint Separating Distances

Left Driveshaft

31.2-32.0"
(809.0-813.5 mm)

Right Driveshaft

20.2-20.4"
(514.0-518.5 mm)

Always install new dust boot bands whenever the axle shafts must be adjusted or when bands are loosened or removed.

Reassembly

1) Pack outboard CV joint cavity with proper grease, then install outboard dust boot and new metal boot bands (loosely). Assemble CV joint spider components (with high shoulder of each roller facing outward). Insert into inboard CV joint housing. Ensure CV joint assembly is packed with grease.

2) Install inboard dust boot onto axle shaft. Install snap ring, spider/roller assembly and snap ring to axle shaft. Slide CV joint housing onto axle shaft assembly. Attach rubber boot to CV joint and axle shaft with new boot bands (loosely).

NOTE: **When installing rubber dust boots and new boot bands, position bands so they are centered between locating humps at each end of axle shaft. Expand and compress boots until they return to their normal shape and length.**

3) Adjust length of axle shaft to specifications. *See Fig. 2.* Adjust dust boots to halfway between full compression and full extension, then tighten all boot bands.

4) Ensure both sets of locking tabs are bent. Lightly tap on doubled-over portions to reduce their height. Do not strike boot. Install new spring clip on inner end of axle shaft (end fitting into transaxle case).

Fig. 3: Exploded View of Front Wheel Hub, Steering Knuckle & Bearing Assembly

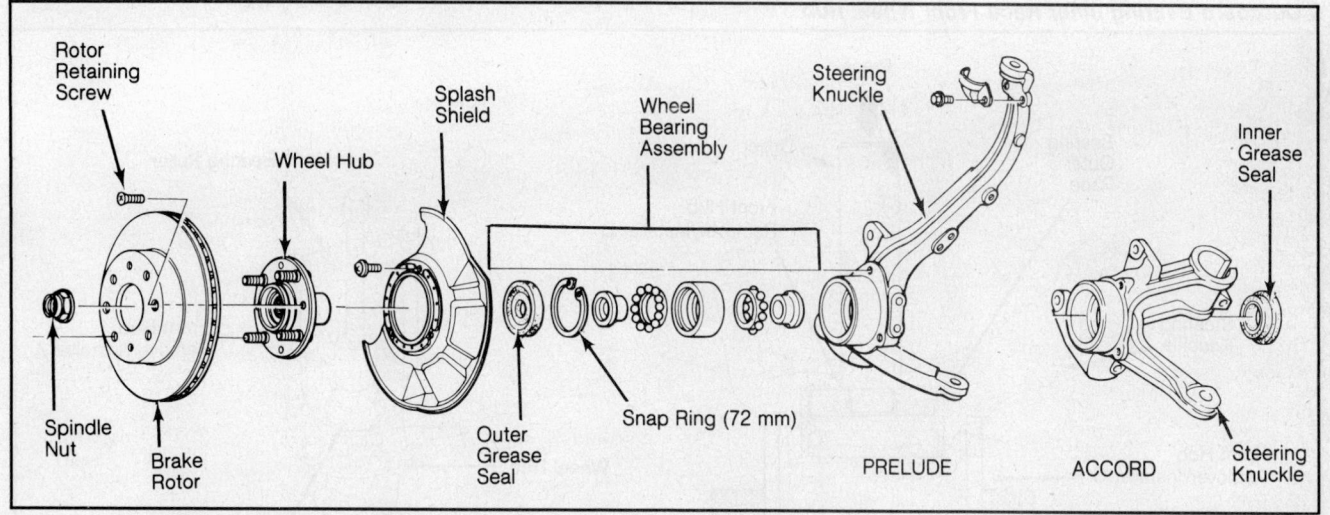

Installation

To install axle shaft and CV joint assemblies, reverse removal procedures. Ensure that when axle shaft assembly is installed, inboard CV joint subaxle bottoms in differential and that spring clip locks in differential side gear groove. Check and add ATF if necessary.

WHEEL HUB, STEERING KNUCKLE & BEARINGS
Removal

1) Loosen wheel lug nuts slightly. Pry spindle nut lock tab away from spindle, then loosen spindle nut using a 1.25" (32 mm) socket. Raise and support vehicle. Remove lug nuts, wheel and spindle nut. *See Fig. 3.*

2) Detach brake caliper mounting bolts. Remove caliper and hang out of work area with wire. Detach two 6 mm brake rotor retaining screws. *See Fig. 3.* Install 2 rotor removal bolts (8 x 1.25 x 12 mm) into rotor. Remove rotor from hub by turning bolts 2 turns at a time to prevent cocking disc excessively.

3) Remove cotter pin and castle nut from tie rod end stud, then separate tie rod end from steering knuckle arm bore using Ball Joint Remover (07941-6920001).

4) On Accord, detach stabilizer bar bolts if necessary. Remove lower ball joint pinch bolt and nut. Using plastic hammer, tap lower control arm down to disconnect lower ball joint from steering knuckle.

5) Detach shock absorber pinch bolt. Using lead or brass hammer, tap knuckle down until it comes off shock absorber. Pull hub/knuckle assembly off axle shaft splines and remove assembly from vehicle.

6) On Prelude, pry cotter pin from lower ball joint stud and loosen castle nut half the length of joint stud threads. Using a 2-arm puller (with pawls hooked to lower control arm), separate ball joint from control arm.

7) Remove upper ball joint shield. Pry out cotter pin and remove upper ball joint stud nut. Separate ball joint from steering knuckle using ball joint remover. Slide knuckle and hub assembly off axle shaft.

NOTE: **Do not distort splash shield during hub removal. Hold onto hub to keep it from falling when pressed clear of knuckle.**

8) On all models, detach 2 back splash shield mounting bolts from knuckle. Using hydraulic press, Driver (07965-6340100) and Hub Remover/Installer Base (07965-6340301), press hub from steering knuckle. Detach remaining mounting bolt and remove splash shield.

9) Remove outboard grease seal (note installed position), snap ring (72 mm) and outboard bearing assembly from steering knuckle. Using a bearing puller, Front Hub Remover/Installer A (07965-6920100) and Front Hub Remover/Installer B (07965-6920200), pull outboard bearing inner race from hub. *See Fig. 4.*

10) Turn knuckle over and remove inboard grease seal and inboard bearing (with inner race). Using a hydraulic press, Driver (07749-0010000), Front Hub Remover/Installer C (07965-6920300) and Front Hub Remover/Installer D (07965-6920400), press wheel bearing outer race from knuckle. *See Fig. 4.* Wash hub and knuckle thoroughly before assembly.

CAUTION: When pressing bearing outer race into knuckle, maximum press load is 2.5 tons.

Installation

1) Using a hydraulic press, Driver (07749-0010000), front hub remover/installer B, Remover/Installer Tool Base A (07965-6340301) and Front Hub Remover/Installer F (07965-SA00600), press bearing outer race into steering knuckle. *See Fig. 5.*

NOTE: **Pack both wheel bearings with grease before installing. Apply grease to seal lips and bearing races.**

2) Install outboard bearing and inner race into steering knuckle. Position snap ring securely in knuckle groove. Using Driver (07749-0010000) and front hub remover/installer F, drive in new outboard grease seal until flush with knuckle surface.

CAUTION: When pressing wheel hub into steering knuckle, maximum press load is 2 tons.

3) Install splash shield. Turn knuckle over and install inboard bearing and inner race into steering knuckle. Using Driver (07749-0010000), front hub remover/installer (A and B), remover/installer tool base A and Front Hub Remover/Installer E (07965-6920500), press hub into steering knuckle. *See Fig. 5.*

Fig. 4: Removing Bearing Outer Race From Knuckle & Outboard Bearing Inner Race From Wheel Hub

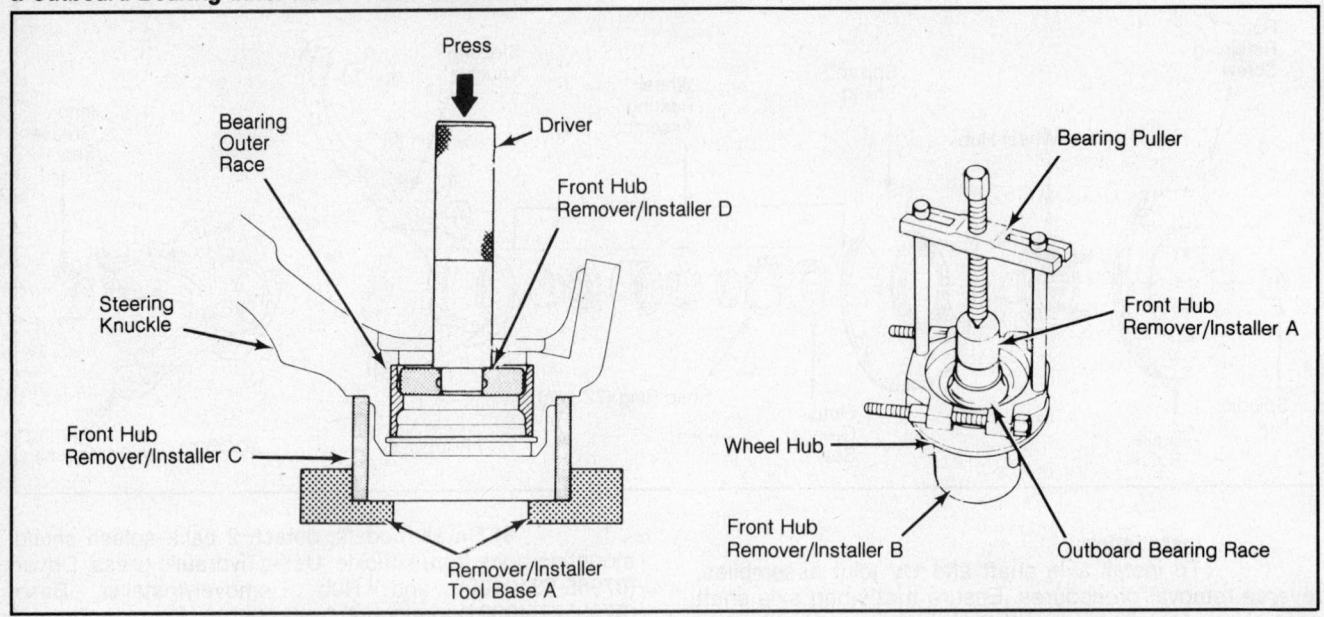

4) Using Driver (07749-0010000) and front hub remover/installers (B and F), install new inboard grease seal. *See Fig. 5.* To complete installation, reverse removal procedure.

TROUBLE SHOOTING

NOTE: If manual shift cable is out of adjustment, check for broken cable or loose end pin. If faulty 1st or 3rd clutch assembly is suspected, check for stuck clutch piston, damaged clutch

"O" ring, damaged clutch feed pipe or "O" ring, plugged check valve and worn or burnt clutch discs. If faulty 2nd or 4th clutch assembly is suspected, check for stuck clutch piston, damaged clutch "O" ring, plugged check valve, worn or damaged sealing rings and worn or burnt clutch discs.

NO MOVEMENT

In Any Gear (With Engine Running)

Low fluid level. Faulty ATF pump. Regulator valve stuck or damaged spring. Mainshaft damaged.

Fig. 5: Installing Wheel Bearing Outer Race, Grease Seal & Wheel Hub Into Knuckle

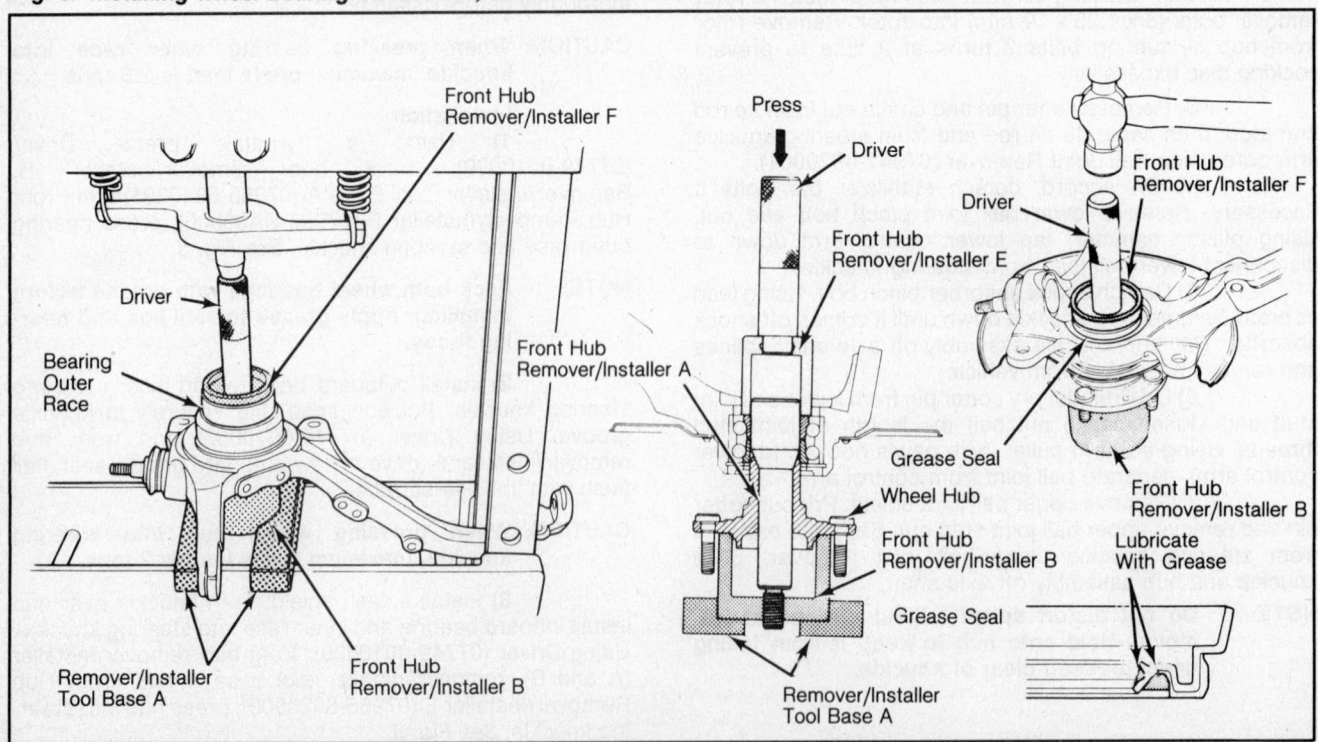

Manual shift cable out of adjustment. Damaged final drive gear. Torque convertor not fully seated (causing flex plate to deform).

In "D3" Or "D4";
OK In 2nd (No Low Gear)
Manual shift cable out of adjustment. Worn or damaged 1-way clutch. Low gear damaged. Faulty 1st clutch. Defective clutch pressure control (CPC) valve.

In 2nd (OK In "D3" or "D4")
Manual shift cable out of adjustment. Damaged 2nd gear. Faulty 1st clutch assembly.

In "R" (OK in "D3", "D4" & 2nd)
Stuck servo shaft. Manual shift cable out of adjustment (broken cable, loose end pin). Reverse gear damaged. Defective 2nd-3rd shift valve. Defective 4th clutch assembly.

POOR ACCELERATION
ENGINE RACES WHEN STARTING
OFF IN "D3" & "D4"
Stall RPM High In "D3", "D4" & 2nd
Low fluid level. Faulty ATF pump. Regulator valve stuck or spring damaged. Manual shift cable out of adjustment. Oil filter clogged. Falty torque converter check valve.

Stall RPM High In "D3" & "D4"
Manual shift cable out of adjustment. Worn or damaged 1-way clutch. Faulty 1st clutch.

Stall RPM High In 2nd
Check for manual shift cable out of adjustment or faulty 2nd clutch.

Stall RPM OK
ATF fluid level too high.

Stall RPM Low
Burnt or seized torque convertor 1-way clutch. Improperly adjusted throttle cable (at carburetor). Lack of engine power.

ENGINE VIBRATES AT IDLE
Faulty ATF pump. Lack of engine power. Torque convertor not fully seated (causing flex plate to deform).

UPSHIFT SPEED TOO HIGH
Governor valve faulty. Improperly adjusted throttle control cable (at automatic transmission). Defective throttle valve "A". Defective modulator valve.

JUMPS FROM 1ST-3RD IN "D3"
Defective 2nd-3rd shift valve.

JUMPS FROM 1ST-4TH IN "D4"
Defective 2nd-3rd shift valve. Defective 3rd-4th shift valve.

UPSHIFT POINTS
(TO EARLY OR TO LATE)
1st-2nd, 2nd-3rd & 3rd-4th
Faulty governor valve. Throttle control cable out of adjustment (at automatic transmission). Defective throttle valve "A". Defective modulator valve.

"D1-D2" Only
Faulty governor valve or 1st-2nd shift valve.

"D2-D3" Only
Faulty governor valve or 2nd-3rd shift valve.

"D3-D4" Only
Faulty governor valve or 3rd-4th shift valve.

HARSH UPSHIFT
From 1st-2nd
Faulty 2nd clutch. Defective throttle shift valve "B" or 2nd accumulator.

From 2nd-3rd
Defective throttle shift valve "B". Defective 3rd accumulator. Defective 2nd orifice control valve. Defective 3rd clutch.

From 3rd -4th
Defective throttle shift valve "B". Defective 4th accumulator. Defective 4th clutch assembly. Lack of engine power.

HARSH DOWNSHIFT
From 2nd-1st
Defective throttle shift valve "B". Defective 2nd accumulator. Defective 2nd orifice control valve. No 2nd ball check valve.

From 3rd-2nd
Defective throttle shift valve "B". Defective 3rd accumulator. Defective 3rd orifice control valve. No 3rd ball check valve.

From 4th-3rd
Defective throttle valve "B". Defective 4th accumulator. No 4th ball check valve.

ENGINE RACES DURING SHIFT
From 2nd-3rd (Shift Timing OK)
Defective throttle valve "B", 3rd accumulator or 2nd orifice control valve. Main or 3rd orifice plugged. Defective 3rd clutch assembly.

From 3rd-4th (Shift Timing OK)
Defective throttle valve "B" or 4th accumulator. Defective 3rd orifice control valve. Defective 4th clutch assembly.

ENGINE VIBRATES DURING SHIFT
From 2nd-3rd (Shift Timing OK)
Faulty 2nd clutch assembly. Defective throttle valve "B". Defective 3rd accumulator. Plugged 2nd orifice or separator port orifice. No 3rd ball check valve.

From 3rd-4th (Shift Timing OK)
Defective 3rd orifice control valve. Defective throttle valve "B". No 4th ball check valve. Plugged separator port orifice.

VEHICLE CREEPS FORWARD IN "N"
With Shift Cable Properly Adjusted
ATF level too high. Faulty 2nd or 4th clutch assembly. Faulty 1st or 3rd clutch assembly. Damaged (burnt) needle bearing and/or thrust washer. Improper clutch clearance.

EXCESSIVE TIME LAG WHEN SHIFTING
From "N" to "D3" or "D4"
(Shift Cable Adjusted Correctly)
Faulty 1st clutch assembly. Plugged 1st orifice.

Automatic Transmissions

HONDA 4-SPEED (Cont.)

From "N" to "R"
(Shift Cable Adjusted Correctly)
Servo shaft stuck. Defective 4th clutch assembly. Faulty 2nd-3rd shift valve.

PROBLEMS AFTER REASSEMBLY
Loud Noise in All Selector Positions
Faulty ATF pump. Damaged 3rd gear. Damaged mainshaft ball bearings and/or countershaft bearings.

Acceleration to 30 MPH Only
Burnt or seized torque converter 1-way clutch.

Vibration in All Gears
Torque converter not fully seated (causing flex plate to deform).

Shift Lever Requires Excessive Force
Manual shift cable out of adjustment or cable housing damaged.

Vehicle Has 4th Gear Only
Faulty governor valve.

No Park Position
Manual shift cable out of adjustment or cable housing damaged.

High Stall Speed, OK Pressure Readings
Faulty torque converter check valve.

IMPROPER OPERATION
OF LOCK-UP CLUTCH
Lock-Up Clutch Engages
Or Disengages Abnormally
Improperly adjusted throttle control cable (at automatic transmission). Defective thottle valve "B", pressure control timing valve, governor cut switch or pressure control shift valve.

Engine Vibrates When
Lock-Up Clutch Engages
Defective governor cut valve, pressure control shift valve, Lock-up piston, lock-up piston damper spring or pressure control valve.

Lock-Up Clutch Slips
Stuck regulator valve or damaged spring. Faulty torque convertor check valve. Defective pressure control shift valve or pressure control valve.

TESTING

ROAD TEST
NOTE: **Before testing transmission, ensure ATF level is between full and low marks on dipstick. With transmission at operating temperature, check ATF level immediately after shutting off engine. Standard ATF capacity is 3.0 qts. (2.8L) after oil change and 6.1 qts. (5.8L) after overhaul.**

CAUTION: Do not screw in dipstick to check ATF level.

Before Transmission Removal
1) Before road testing, be certain that fluid level, condition and control linkage adjustments have been checked and corrected as necessary. During test, transmission should upshift and downshift at approximately the speeds shown. See SHIFT SPEED SPECIFICATIONS table.

2) All shifts may vary somewhat due to production tolerances and/or tire size. The important factor is shift quality. All shifts should be smooth and responsive, with no slippage or engine speed runaway.

3) Slippage or engine runaway in any gear usually indicates clutch or sprag problems. The slipping unit in a particular gear can usually be identified by noting transmission operation in other selector positions.

4) This process of elimination can be used to detect any unit which slips and to confirm proper operation of good units; however, the actual cause of the malfunction usually cannot be easily decided.

5) Practically any condition can be caused by leaking hydraulic circuits or sticking valves. Therefore, unless an obvious condition exists, do not disassemble transmission until hydraulic pressure tests have been made.

After Transmission Installation
1) Check floor mat to ensure it does not interfer with accelerator pedal travel. Fully depress accelerator pedal and check carburetor to ensure throttle lever is fully opened.

2) Release accelerator pedal and check both inner control cables to ensure they have slight play. Warm engine to operating temperature.

3) With transmission in "D3" and "D4" range, apply parking brake and block wheels. Move selector to "D4" while depressing brake pedal. Start engine, depress accelerator pedal, then release it suddenly. Engine should not stall.

NOTE: **Check that shift points occur at approximate speeds shown in SHIFT SPEEDS SPECIFICATION table. Also check for abnormal noise and/or clutch slippage.**

4) With transmission in "D3" and "D4" range, accelerate vehicle to about 35 MPH (transmission in 4th), then shift from "D4" to 2nd. Vehicle should immediately begin slowing down from engine braking.

CAUTION: Do not shift from "D4" or "D3" to 2nd at speeds over 60 MPH or transmission damage may result.

5) With vehicle in 2nd gear, accelerate from a stop at full throttle. Check for abnormal noise or clutch slippage. Upshifts and downshifts should not occur with selector in this range.

6) With vehicle in Reverse, accelerate from a stop at full throttle and check for abnormal noise and clutch slippage. With vehicle in parked on a slope (approximately 16°), apply parking brake and shift into Park. Release brake. Vehicle should not move.

HYDRAULIC PRESSURE TESTS
1) Before performing pressure tests, be sure that fluid level and condition have been checked and corrected as necessary. With engine at normal operating temperature, connect a tachometer to engine.

NOTE: **Stop engine when connecting hoses for pressure tests. Tighten all hose fittings to 12 ft. lbs. (18 N.m).**

CAUTION: Do not reuse aluminum washers.

2) Connect the Pressure Test Hoses (07406-0020201), from the Pressure Gauge Set (07406-0020002),

HONDA 4-SPEED (Cont.)

SHIFT SPEED SPECIFICATIONS

Application	Shift Speed (MPH)
Full Throttle Upshift [1]	
Accord	
1st-2nd Shift	37-42
2nd-3rd Shift	58-65
3rd-4th Shift	86-92
Lock-Up Clutch On	89-95
Prelude	
1st-2nd Shift	36-40
2nd-3rd Shift	60-65
3rd-4th Shift	92-98
Half Throttle [1]	
Accord	
1st-2nd Shift	18-22
2nd-3rd Shift	33-42
3rd-4th Shift	50-60
Lock-Up Clutch On	54-60
Prelude	
1st-2nd Shift	19-22
2nd-3rd Shift	38-43
3rd-4th Shift	57-63
Closed Throttle [2]	
Accord	
1st-2nd Shift	12-15
2nd-3rd Shift	21-24
3rd-4th Shift	23-30
Lock-Up Clutch On	31-34
Prelude	
1st-2nd Shift	12-14
2nd-3rd Shift	22-25
3rd-4th Shift	26-30
Full Throttle Downshift [3]	
Accord	
4th-3rd Shift	77-83
3rd-2nd Shift	51-58
2nd-1st Shift	24-30
Prelude	
4th-3rd Shift	83-89
3rd-2nd Shift	53-58
2nd-1st Shift	23-28
Closed Throttle [4]	
Accord	
4th-3rd Shift	.....
3rd-2nd Shift	18-21
2nd-1st Shift	5-8
Prelude	
4th-3rd Shift	.....
3rd-2nd Shift	16-19
2nd-1st Shift	5-8

[1] – Acceleration from a stop.
[2] – Coasting down-hill from a stop.
[3] – When vehicle is slowed by increased grade, wind, etc.
[4] – Coasting or braking from a stop.

to 3 of the following pressure test points (depending on pressure readings required): Line pressure port, 1st clutch pressure port, 2nd clutch pressure port, 3rd clutch pressure port and/or 4th clutch pressure port. See Fig. 6.

3) To test 1st-4th clutch pressures and line pressure, first apply parking brake, then raise front wheels

Fig. 6: Pressure Test Point Locations

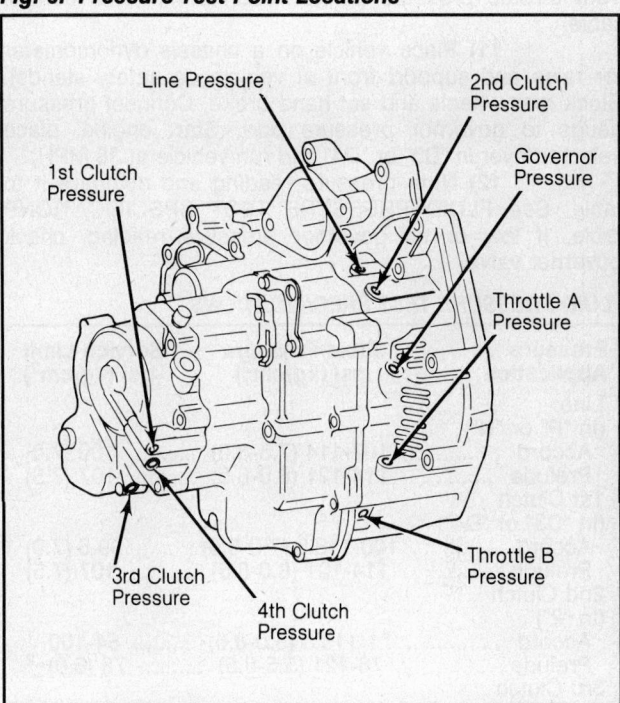

Line Pressure
2nd Clutch Pressure
Governor Pressure
1st Clutch Pressure
Throttle A Pressure
3rd Clutch Pressure
4th Clutch Pressure
Throttle B Pressure

Before checking the line, clutch, governor or throttle pressures, ensure transmission is filled to proper level.

off ground and support with safety stands. Start and run engine at 2000 RPM.

4) Place selector lever in 1 of the following positions: "P", "N", "2", "D3", "D4" or "R". Note pressure readings at each selector lever position and compare readings to FLUID PRESSURE TEST SPECIFICATIONS table.

NOTE: Allow engine to return to idle before changing selector positions.

5) If low or no line pressure reading (with selector in "P" or "N"), check torque converter, oil pump pressure regulator or torque converter check valve. If 1st clutch pressure reading (with selector in "D3 or D4") shows low or no pressure, check 1st clutch assembly.

6) If 2nd clutch pressure reading (with selector in "2") shows low or no pressure, check 2nd clutch assembly. If 3rd clutch pressure reading (with selector in in "D3") shows low or no pressure, check 3rd clutch assembly.

7) If 4th clutch pressure reading (with selector in "D4") shows low or no pressure, check 4th clutch assembly. If 4th clutch pressure reading (with selector in "R") shows low or no pressure, check servo valve.

8) Stop engine and remove pressure gauge hose connections from transmission. Reconnect 2 pressure gauge hoses to throttle pressure port "A" and "B". Disconnect throttle control cable (at throttle lever).

9) Start engine, place selector lever in "D3" or "D4" and run engine at 1000 RPM. Read pressure with lever released. Manually push lever up (simulating full throttle) and note pressure reading. Compare reading with FLUID PRESSURE TEST SPECIFICATIONS table.

10) If low or no throttle pressure reading in "D3" or "D4", check throttle valve "A", throttle valve "B" or throttle modulator valve. Stop engine. Remove pressure gauge from throttle pressure ports. Reconnect throttle control cable.

11) Place vehicle on a chassis dynomometer (or raise and support front of vehicle on safety stands). Block rear wheels and set hand brake. Connect pressure gauge to governor pressure port. Start engine, place selector lever in "D3" or "D4" and run vehicle at 38 MPH.

12) Note pressure reading and compare it to table. See FLUID PRESSURE TEST SPECIFICATIONS table. If low or no governor pressure reading, check governor valve.

FLUID PRESSURE TEST SPECIFICATIONS

Pressure Application	Fluid Pressure psi (kg/cm²)	Service Limit psi (kg/cm²)
Line		
(In "P" or "N")		
Accord	107-114 (7.5-8.0)	100 (7.0)
Prelude	114-121 (8.0-8.5)	107 (7.5)
1st Clutch		
(In "D3" or "D4")		
Accord	100-113.8 (7.0-8.0)	99.6 (7.0)
Prelude	114-121 (8.0-8.5)	107 (7.5)
2nd Clutch		
(In "2")		
Accord	71-113.8 (5.0-8.0)	64-100 [1]
Prelude	78-121 (5.5-8.5)	78 (5.0) [2]
3rd Clutch		
(In "D3")		
Accord	[3]	[5]
Prelude	[3]	107 (7.5)
4th Clutch		
(In "D4")		
Accord	[3]	[5]
Prelude	[3]	107 (7.5)
(In "R")		
Accord	[4]	[5]
Prelude	[4]	[5]
Throttle Port "A"		
(In "D3" or "D4")		
Accord	[6]	75.3 (5.4)
Prelude	[7]	73 (5.1) [8]
Throttle Port "B"		
(In "D3" or "D4")		
Accord	[9]	100 (7.0)
Prelude	[10]	107 (7.5)
Governor		
(In "D3" or "D4")		
Accord	31-33 (2.2-2.3)	29.2 (2.05)
Prelude	31-33 (2.2-2.3)	30.6 (2.15)

[1] – Service limit is 4.5-7.0 kg/cm².
[2] – With lever released.
[3] – Varies with throttle opening.
[4] – No fluid pressure specification.
[5] – No fluid pressure service limit.
[6] – Fluid pressure is 0 psi (0 kg/cm²) with lever released and 86-88 psi (6.05-6.20 kg/cm²) with lever in full throttle position.
[7] – Fluid pressure is 0 psi (0 kg/cm²) with lever released and 73-75 psi (5.15-5.30 kg/cm²) with lever in full throttle position.
[8] – With lever in full throttle position.
[9] – Fluid pressure is 0 psi (0 kg/cm²) with lever released and 79.6-115.9 psi (5.60-8.15 kg/cm²) with lever in full throttle position.
[10] – Fluid pressure is 0 psi (0 kg/cm²) with lever released and 114-121 psi (8.0-8.5 kg/cm²) with lever in full throttle position.

STALL TEST

Testing Precautions

When making test, do not hold throttle open any longer than the time it takes to read tachometer. Maximum stall speed test is 10 seconds at a time. Allow engine to run at idle for at least 2 minutes in "N" to cool transmission between tests. If engine speed exceeds limits shown, release accelerator immediately as clutch slippage is indicated. See STALL SPEEDS table.

Testing Procedure

1) Connect a tachometer to engine. Set parking brake and block front wheels. With engine at normal operating temperature, start engine. Place selector lever in "D3".

2) Depress accelerator briefly (6 to 8 seconds) to full throttle and note maximum RPM obtained. Allow 2 minutes for cooling and repeat test in "D4", "2" and "R". Stall speed in "D3", "D4", "2" and "R" should be the same and within limits shown. See STALL SPEED RPM table.

STALL SPEED RPM

Application	Specification	Service Limit
Accord	2400	2250-2550
Prelude	2400	2100-2700

3) If stall speed RPM is high in "2", "D3", "D4", and "R", check for low ATF level, low pump output, clogged oil strainer or pressure regulator and slipping clutch assembly or slipping 1-way clutch in torque convertor.

4) If stall speed RPM is high in "D3" and "D4" only, check for slipping 1st clutch assembly. If stall speed RPM is low in "2", "D3", "D4" and "R", check for low engine output, misadjusted throttle control cable (at carburetor) and seized oil pump or convertor thrust washer.

REMOVAL & INSTALLATION

AUTOMATIC TRANSMISSION

See the appropriate article in AUTOMATIC TRANSMISSION REMOVAL section.

TORQUE CONVERTER

Removal

1) Before detaching engine-to-transmission mounting bolts, remove torque convertor cover plate. Detach 8 torque convertor-to-drive plate mounting bolts.

2) Remove transmission from engine and lower from vehicle, then pull torque convertor from transmission. Remove and discard convertor "O" ring (32 x 1.9 mm).

3) If necessary, detach drive plate-to-crankshaft flange mounting bolts, then remove drive plate and washer. Inspect components for wear or damage.

Inspection

Inspect torque convertor for broken and/or chipped ring gear teeth or fluid leakage. Check drive plate and washer for cracks. Replace components as necessary.

Installation

Install new "O" ring to convertor. If removed, install drive plate and washer onto crankshaft flange and tighten mounting bolts in a crisscross pattern. To install torque convertor, reverse removal procedure.

HONDA 4-SPEED (Cont.)

CONTROL SHAFT

Removal

Remove control cable holder. Detach cotter pin, control pin and control lever roller from control lever. Bend down lock plate tab under bolt in control lever, then remove bolt and lever. Turn torque convertor housing over remove control shaft.

Installation

Install control shaft in reverse of removal procedure. Replace lock plate.

TRANSAXLE DISASSEMBLY

TORQUE CONVERTER

The torque converter is a sealed unit. If torque converter is full of contaminated fluid or a possible cause of transaxle problems, do not attempt disassembly and repair, replace torque converter as a unit.

TRANSMISSION HOUSING & TORQUE CONVERTOR HOUSING

Disassembly

1) Remove dipstick. Detach 9 bolts from transmission housing end cover, then remove cover. If necessary, detach mounting bolts and remove 1st accumulator (Prelude only) from end cover, then disassembly unit as needed.

NOTE: On Prelude only, 1st accumulator can be removed with end cover installed.

2) Shift transmission to "P". Lock mainshaft using Mainshaft Holder (07923-6890201). See Fig. 7. Remove end cover gasket, 2 dowel pins (8 x 14 mm) and 3 "O" rings (6 x 2.3 mm). Discard "O" rings.

Fig. 7: Locking Mainshaft For Lock Nut Removal

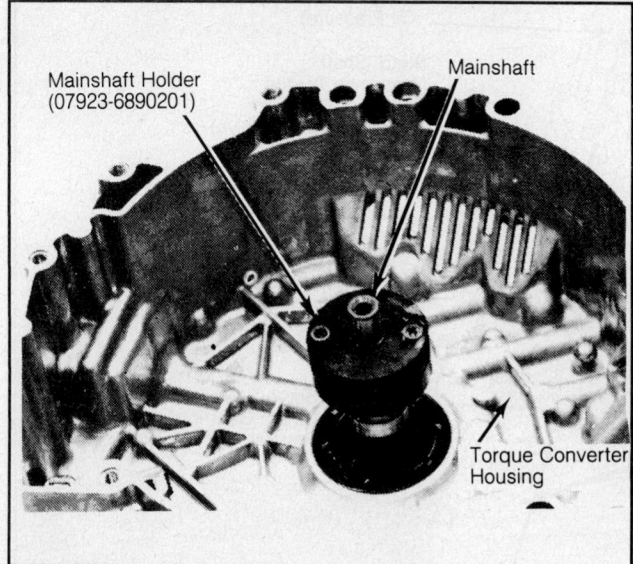

Mainshaft Holder (07923-6890201)

Mainshaft

Torque Converter Housing

Mainshaft lock nut has left-hand threads.

3) Pry staked edge of lock nut flange out of notch in 1st clutch assembly. Using breaker bar and socket (22 mm), remove mainshaft lock nut (LEFT-HAND thread). Remove 1st clutch assembly. Remove 1st clutch thrust washer (26 mm), needle bearing (31 x 47 x 2 mm) and 1st gear. Remove 1st gear needle bearing (31 x 36 x 18.5 mm) and thrust washer from mainshaft.

4) Pry staked edge of lock nut out of notch in parking gear. Using breaker bar and socket (30 mm), remove countershaft lock nut. Remove parking pawl stop pin. Remove parking pawl, shaft and spring. See Fig. 12. Remove parking gear and countershaft 1st gear as a unit.

5) Remove needle bearing (30 x 35 x 11 mm) and 1st gear collar from countershaft. Remove 2 "O" rings (19.8 x 1.9 mm) and 1st gear collar (26 mm) from mainshaft. Discard "O" rings. See Fig. 9.

6) Detach and remove reverse idler gear shaft locating bolt (with washer and spring) and bearing holder mounting bolts. Remove reverse idler gear bearing holder. See Fig. 9.

7) Bend down tab on parking shift arm bolt lock plate (under bolt). Remove bolt. Lift out parking shift arm and shift arm spring. See Fig. 12.

NOTE: The torque convertor housing-to-transmission housing mounting bolt pattern may be slightly different between models but removal sequence is the same.

8) Bend down tab on throttle control lever bolt lock plate and remove bolt. Remove throttle control lever and spring from throttle valve shaft. Remove 15 torque converter housing-to-transmission housing mounting bolts (8 x 1.25 mm) in proper sequence. See Fig. 10.

NOTE: Do not remove bolt number 1, loosen just enough so bolt threads are free of torque converter housing. If bolt is removed completely, throttle control bracket will have to be readjusted.

9) Align control shaft spring pin with cut-out in transmission housing. Install Transmission Housing Puller (07933-6890201) onto housing with 4 bolts (6 x 1.0 x 18 mm). Screw puller bolt against end of countershaft until transmission housing comes free from torque converter housing.

10) After separating housings, remove transmission housing completely. On gear side of torque converter housing, remove gasket, 1 dowel pin (14 x 20 mm) and 2 dowel pins (14 x 25 mm).

11) To remove mainshaft and countershaft, first remove reverse gear collar and countershaft reverse gear with needle bearing. See Fig. 21. Bend down tab on reverse shift fork bolt lock plate, then remove bolt.

12) Remove reverse shift fork and selector sleeve as a unit. Remove selector hub, countershaft 4th gear, needle bearing and spacer collar. See Fig. 21. Remove mainshaft and countershaft as an assembly.

NOTE: When removing mainshaft and countershaft, pull countershaft up at a slight angle to clear governor.

13) Bend governor mounting bolt lock tabs down and detach bolts holding governor to torque converter housing. Remove governor. See Fig. 13.

Automatic Transmissions
HONDA 4-SPEED (Cont.)

Fig. 8: Internal Views Of 4-Speed Automatic Transmission

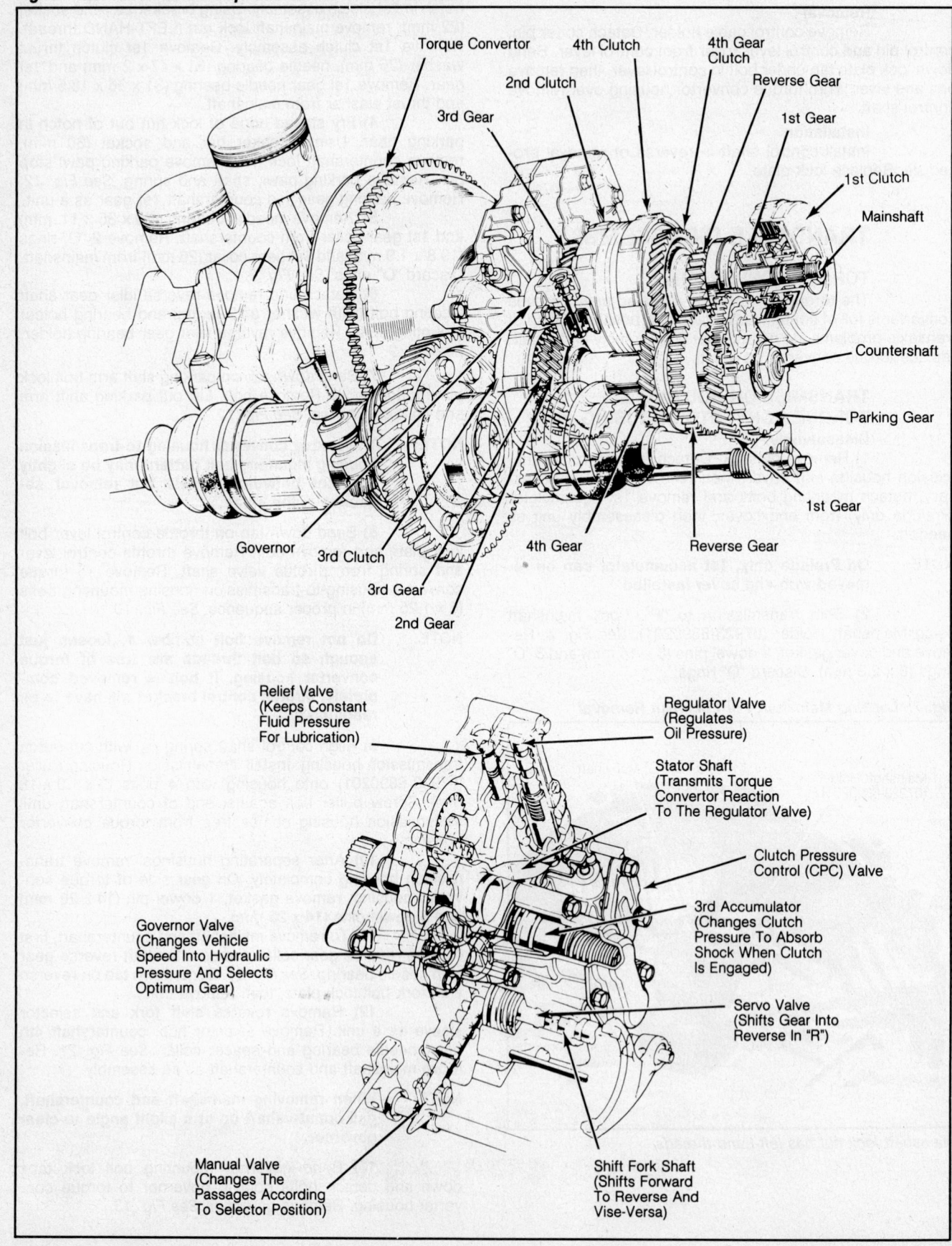

Torque Convertor

4th Clutch

4th Gear Clutch

2nd Clutch

Reverse Gear

3rd Gear

1st Gear

1st Clutch

1st Clutch

Mainshaft

Countershaft

Parking Gear

1st Gear

Governor

3rd Clutch

3rd Gear

Reverse Gear

2nd Gear

4th Gear

Relief Valve (Keeps Constant Fluid Pressure For Lubrication)

Regulator Valve (Regulates Oil Pressure)

Stator Shaft (Transmits Torque Convertor Reaction To The Regulator Valve)

Clutch Pressure Control (CPC) Valve

3rd Accumulator (Changes Clutch Pressure To Absorb Shock When Clutch Is Engaged)

Servo Valve (Shifts Gear Into Reverse In "R")

Governor Valve (Changes Vehicle Speed Into Hydraulic Pressure And Selects Optimum Gear)

Manual Valve (Changes The Passages According To Selector Position)

Shift Fork Shaft (Shifts Forward To Reverse And Vise-Versa)

HONDA 4-SPEED (Cont.)

Fig. 9: Removing Collars, Needle Bearings & "O" Rings From Mainshaft & Countershaft

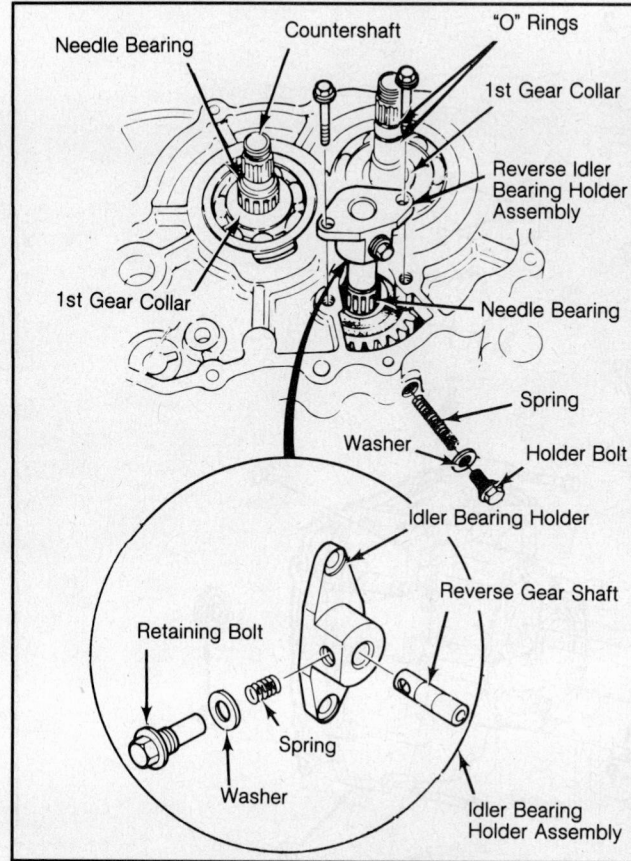

Fig. 10: Removal Sequence of Torque Converter Housing-to-Transmission Housing Mounting Bolts

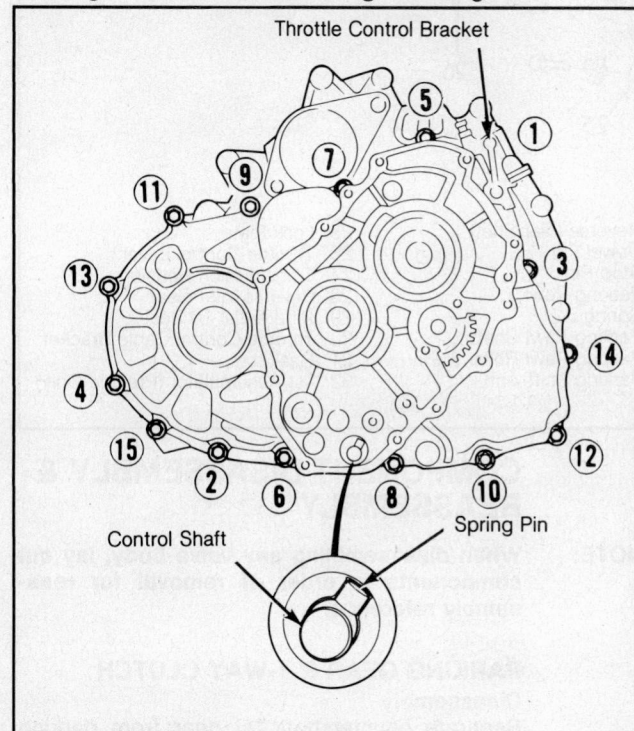

CAUTION: Accumulator covers are spring loaded. To prevent stripping threads in torque convertor housing, hold covers down while removing bolts (in a crisscross pattern).

14) To remove main valve body assembly, first detach 2nd/3rd accumulator cover and 4th accumulator cover. Note locations and sizes, then remove 2nd, 3rd and 4th accumulator springs. *See Fig. 13.*

15) Detach 3 pressure control valve body mounting bolts. To remove 2 oil passage pipes (5 x 168 mm and 8 x 136 mm), slide pressure control valve body to the side. Remove 1st, 3rd and 4th clutch pipes. Remove clutch pressure control valve body. *See Fig. 11.*

16) Detach "E" clip from throttle control shaft. Remove shaft from servo valve body. Detach 3 servo valve body mounting bolts from main valve body, then remove servo valve body assembly.

17) Remove 2 oil pipes (8 x 50 mm and 8 x 29.5 mm). Remove servo separator plate and 2 dowel pins (8 x 14 mm). Remove all 7/32" (5.5 mm) steel balls and the spring from servo valve body oil passages in main valve body (note locations for reassembly).

CAUTION: Do not use a magnet to remove steel balls or balls may become magnetized. Note all steel ball locations for reassembly reference.

18) Remove steel ball from regulator valve (Prelude) and note location for reassembly reference. Detach 3 regulator valve body mounting bolts. Remove stator shift arm, 2 dowel pins (8 x 14 mm), stop pin and 4 mounting bolts holding main valve body to torque converter housing.

19) Remove cotter pin, washer, rollers and pin from manual valve. Remove main valve body, being careful not to lose torque converter check valve and spring. Remove pump gears and shaft. Remove separator plate, dowel pins, check valve and spring. Remove filter screen and suction pipe. Discard filter screen.

Fig. 11: Removing Pressure Control Valve Body, Oil Passage Pipes & Clutch Pipes

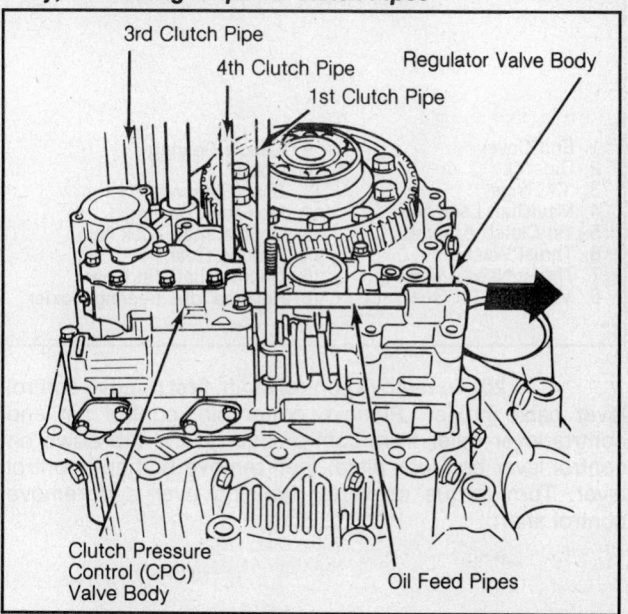

Detach oil passage pipes by moving pressure control valve body in direction of arrow.

Automatic Transmissions
HONDA 4-SPEED (Cont.)

Fig. 12: Exploded View of Transmission End Housing, End Housing Cover & Components

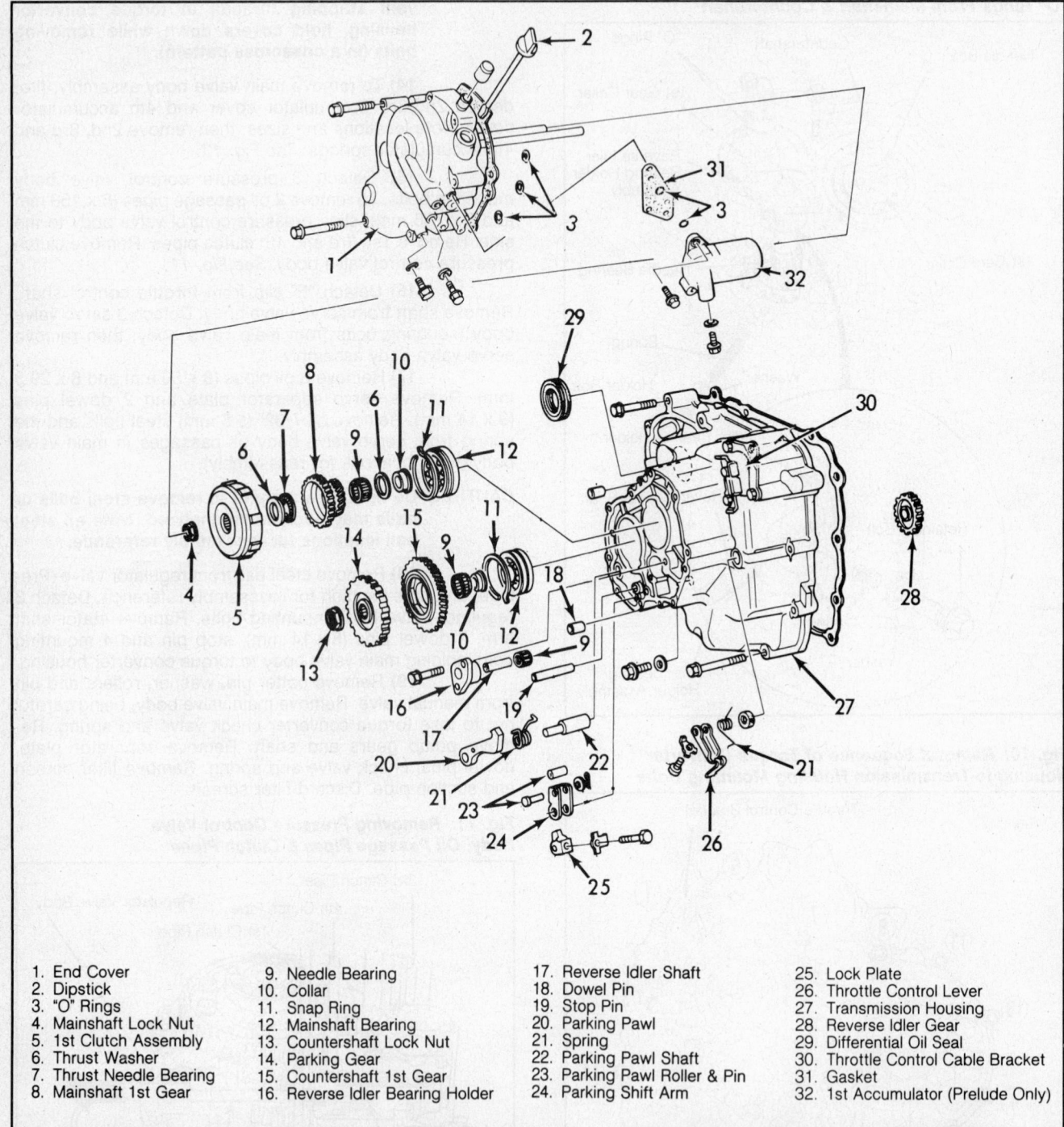

1. End Cover
2. Dipstick
3. "O" Rings
4. Mainshaft Lock Nut
5. 1st Clutch Assembly
6. Thrust Washer
7. Thrust Needle Bearing
8. Mainshaft 1st Gear
9. Needle Bearing
10. Collar
11. Snap Ring
12. Mainshaft Bearing
13. Countershaft Lock Nut
14. Parking Gear
15. Countershaft 1st Gear
16. Reverse Idler Bearing Holder
17. Reverse Idler Shaft
18. Dowel Pin
19. Stop Pin
20. Parking Pawl
21. Spring
22. Parking Pawl Shaft
23. Parking Pawl Roller & Pin
24. Parking Shift Arm
25. Lock Plate
26. Throttle Control Lever
27. Transmission Housing
28. Reverse Idler Gear
29. Differential Oil Seal
30. Throttle Control Cable Bracket
31. Gasket
32. 1st Accumulator (Prelude Only)

20) To remove control shaft, first remove control lever cable holder. Remove cotter pin, control pin and control lever roller from control lever. Bend tab down on control lever bolt lock plate, then remove bolt and control lever. Turn torque converter housing over and remove control shaft.

COMPONENT DISASSEMBLY & REASSEMBLY

NOTE: When disassembling any valve body, lay out components in order of removal for reassembly reference.

PARKING GEAR & 1-WAY CLUTCH
Disassembly
Separate countershaft 1st gear from parking gear by gripping 1st gear in left hand and turning parking

HONDA 4-SPEED (Cont.)

Fig. 13: Exploded View of Torque Converter Housing & Components

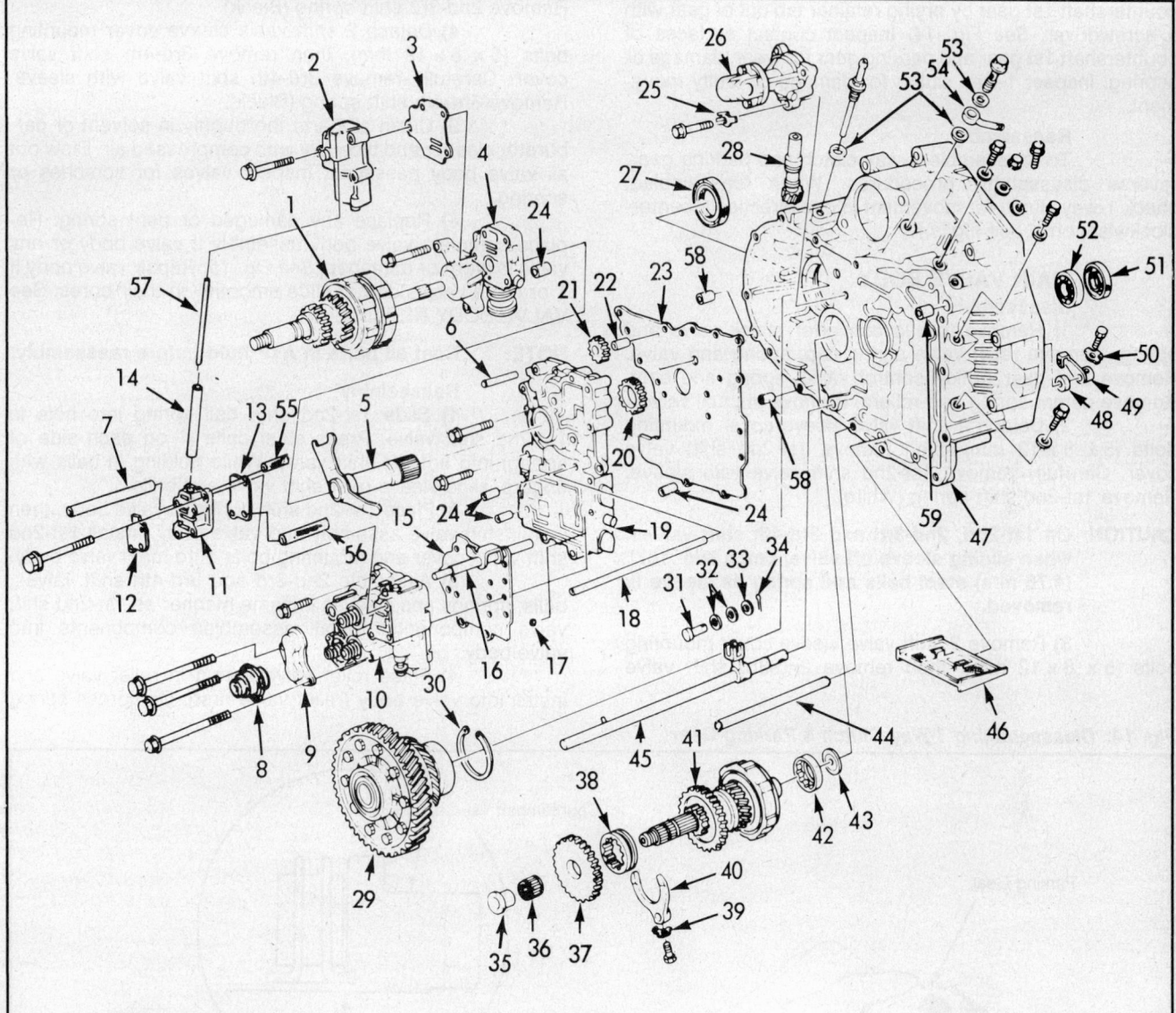

1. Mainshaft Assembly
2. Regulator Valve Cover
3. Separator Plate
4. Regulator Valve Assembly
5. Stator Shaft
6. 3rd Clutch Pipe
7. 4th Clutch Pipe
8. 4th Accumulator Cover
9. 2nd/3rd Accumulator Cover
10. Servo Valve Assembly
11. Clutch Pressure Control Valve (Prelude Similar)
12. Cover
13. Plate
14. Oil Feed Pipe (8 x 136 mm)
15. Servo Separator Plate
16. Throttle Control Shaft
17. Steel Ball (No. 6)
18. 1st Clutch Pipe
19. Main Valve Body
20. Pump Drive Gear
21. Pump Driven Gear
22. Pump Shaft
23. Main Valve Separator Plate
24. Dowel Pin (8 x 14 mm))
25. Lock Plate
26. Governor Assembly
27. Differential Oil Seal
28. Speedometer Drive Gear
29. Differential Assembly
30. Snap Ring (72 mm)
31. Manual Valve Pin
32. Rollers
33. Washer (5 mm)
34. Cotter Pin
35. Reverse Gear Collar
36. Needle Bearing
37. Countershaft Reverse Gear
38. Selector Hub
39. Lock Plate
40. Reverse Shift Fork
41. Countershaft Assembly
42. Countershaft Needle Bearing
43. Oil Guide Plate
44. Suction Pipe
45. Throttle Control Shaft
46. Filter Screen
47. Torque Convertor Housing
48. Control Shaft Oil Seal
49. Shift Lever
50. Lock Plate
51. Mainshaft Oil Seal
52. Mainshaft Bearing
53. Washer (12 mm)
54. Hose Joint
55. Oil Passage Pipe (8 x 29.5 mm)
56. Oil Passage Pipe (8 x 50 mm)
57. Oil Feed Pipe (5 x 168 mm)
58. Dowel Pin (14 x 20 mm)
59. Dowel Pin (14 x 25 mm)

Automatic Transmissions
HONDA 4-SPEED (Cont.)

gear counterclockwise. Remove 1-way clutch from countershaft 1st gear by prying retainer tab out of gear with a screwdriver. *See Fig. 14.* Inspect contact surfaces of countershaft 1st gear and parking gear for wear, damage or scoring. Inspect 1-way clutch for damage or faulty movement.

Reassembly
To reassemble 1-way clutch and parking gear, reverse disassembly procedures. When reassembled, check 1-way clutch for movement in one direction (counterclockwise) only. *See Fig. 14.*

MAIN VALVE BODY
Disassembly
1) Remove torque converter check valve and spring. Remove relief valve spring cap, spring and valve. Remove 2nd gear orifice control valve, spring and seat. Remove detent spring and rollers. Remove manual valve.

2) Detach 2 shift valve sleeve cover mounting bolts (5 x .8 x 12 mm), then remove 1st-2nd shift valve cover. Carefully remove 1st-2nd shift valve with sleeve. Remove 1st-2nd shift spring (White).

CAUTION: On 1st-2nd, 2nd-3rd and 3rd-4th shift valves, when sliding sleeve off valve, catch two .187" (4.76 mm) steel balls and spring as sleeve is removed.

3) Remove 2 shift valve sleeve cover mounting bolts (5 x .8 x 12 mm), then remove 2nd-3rd shift valve

cover. Carefully remove 2nd-3rd shift valve with sleeve. Remove 2nd-3rd shift spring (Black).

4) Detach 2 shift valve sleeve cover mounting bolts (5 x .8 x 12 mm), then remove 3rd-4th shift valve cover. Carefully remove 3rd-4th shift valve with sleeve. Remove 3rd-4th shift spring (Black).

5) Clean all parts thoroughly in solvent or carburetor cleaner and blow dry with compressed air. Blow out all valve body passages. Inspect valves for scraches or scoring.

6) Replace any damaged or bent spring. Replace complete valve body assembly if valve body or any valve is worn or damaged. *See Fig. 15.* Repair valve body if 1 or more valves do not slide smoothly in their bores. See VALVE BODY REPAIR.

NOTE: Coat all parts in ATF fluid before reassembly.

Reassembly
1) Slide 1st-2nd shift ball spring into hole in 1st-2nd shift valve. Press steel balls (1 on each side of spring) into hole of shift valve. While holding in balls with fingers, slide sleeve over shift valve and balls.

2) Place 1st-2nd shift spring in valve body, then install shift valve assembly into valve body. Install 1st-2nd shift valve cover and mounting bolts onto main valve body.

3) Assemble 2nd-3rd and 3rd-4th shift valves, balls, springs and sleeves in same manner as 1st-2nd shift valve components. Install assembled components into valve body.

4) Place relief valve spring in relief valve and install into valve body (relief valve first). Compress spring

Fig. 14: Disassembling 1-Way Clutch & Parking Gear

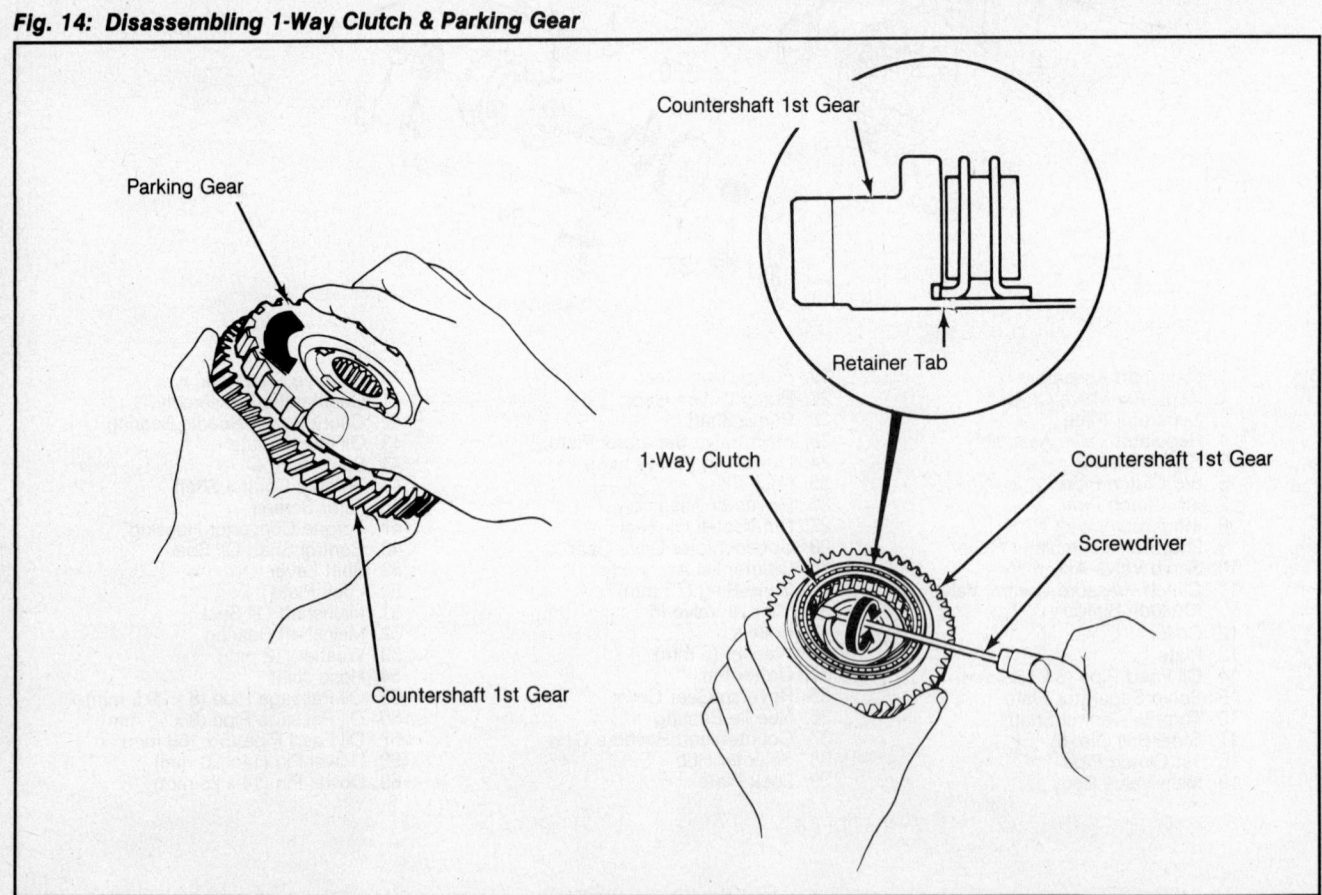

HONDA 4-SPEED (Cont.)

Fig. 15: Exploded View of Main Valve Body & Components

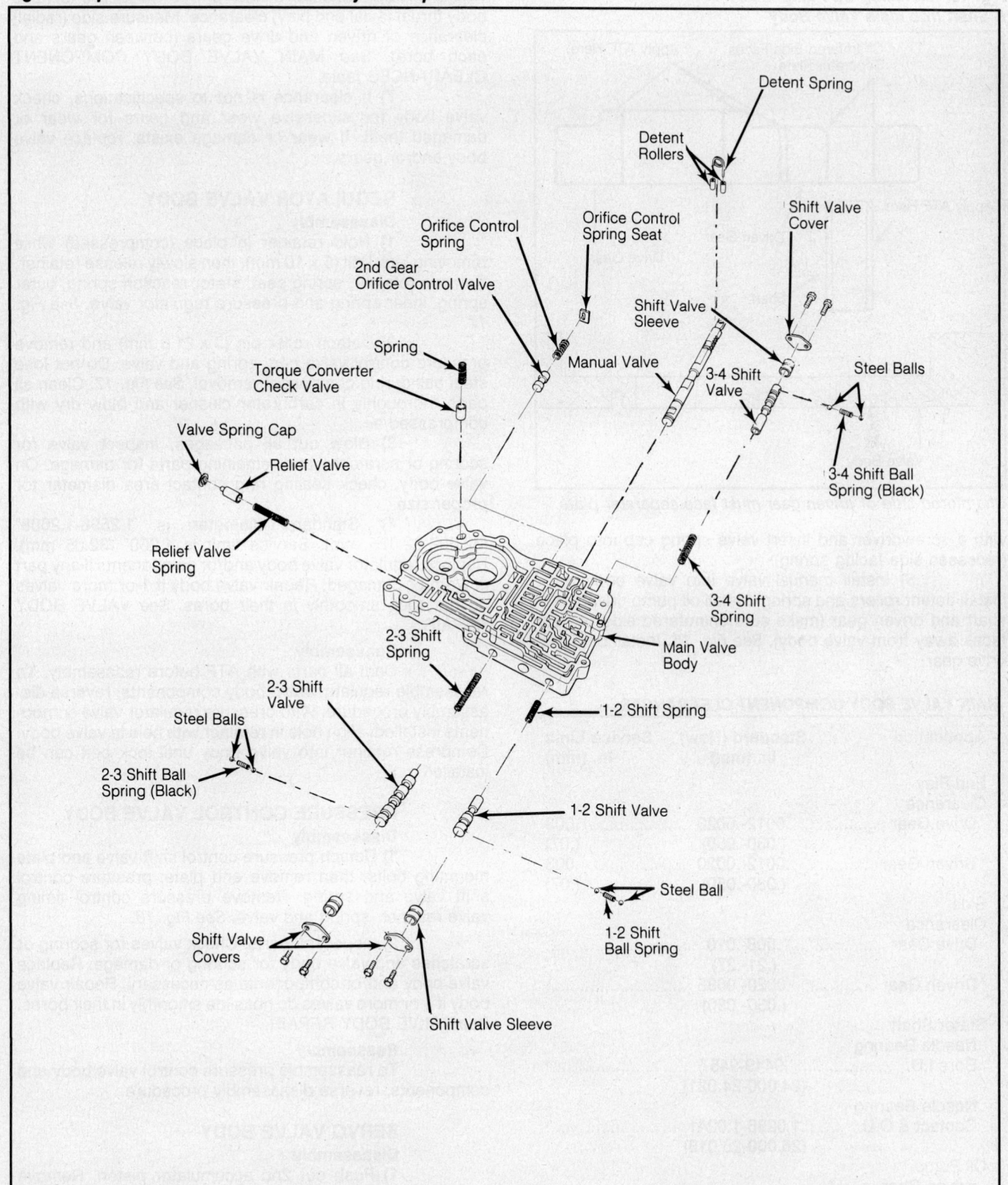

Do not lose shift valve balls and springs during component disassembly.

Fig. 16: Installing Oil Pump Gears & Shaft Into Main Valve Body

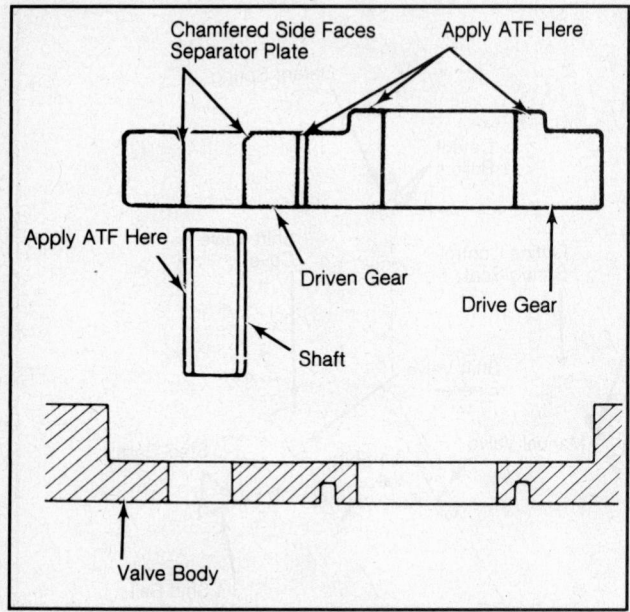

Chamfered side of driven gear must face separater plate.

with a screwdriver and insert valve spring cap into place (recessed side facing spring).

5) Install manual valve into valve body, then install detent rollers and spring. Install oil pump driven gear shaft and driven gear (make sure chamfered side of gear faces away from valve body). *See Fig. 16.* Install oil pump drive gear.

MAIN VALVE BODY COMPONENT CLEARANCES

Application	Standard (New) In. (mm)	Service Limit In. (mm)
End Play Clearance		
Drive Gear	.0012-.0020 (.030-.050)	.003 (.07)
Driven Gear	.0012-.0020 (.030-.050)	.003 (.07)
Side Clearance		
Drive Gear	.008-.010 (.21-.27)	
Driven Gear	.0020-.0035 (.050-.090)	
Stator Shaft Needle Bearing		
Bore I.D.	.9449-9457 (24.000-24.021)	[1]
Needle Bearing		
Contact & O.D.	1.0236-1.0241 (26.000-26.013)	[1]
Oil Pump Driven Gear		
(I.D.)	.5518-.5525 (14.016-14.034)	[1]
Shaft O.D.	.5503-.5507 (13.980-13.990)	[1]

[1] – Replace component if worn or damaged.

6) Measure driven and drive gears-to-valve body thrust (axial end play) clearance. Measure side (radial) clearance of driven and drive gears (between gears and each bore). See MAIN VALVE BODY COMPONENT CLEARANCES table.

7) If clearance is not to specifications, check valve body for excessive wear and gears for wear or damaged teeth. If wear or damage exists, replace valve body and/or gears.

REGULATOR VALVE BODY
Disassembly

1) Hold retainer in place (compressed) while removing lock bolt (6 x 10 mm), then slowly release retainer. Remove retainer, spring seat, stator reaction spring, outer spring, inner spring and pressure regulator valve. *See Fig. 17.*

2) Detach roller pin (3 x 21.8 mm) and remove pressure control valve cap, spring and valve. Do not lose steel ball during component removal. *See Fig. 17.* Clean all parts thoroughly in carburetor cleaner and blow dry with compressed air.

3) Blow out all passages. Inspect valve for scoring or scratches and remaining parts for damage. On valve body, check sealing ring contact area diameter for proper size.

4) Standard diameter is 1.2598-1.2608" (32.000-32.025 mm). Service limit is 1.260" (32.05 mm). Replace regulator valve body and/or components if any part is worn or damaged. Repair valve body if 1 or more valves do not slide smoothly in their bores. See VALVE BODY REPAIR.

Reassembly

Coat all parts with ATF before reassembly. To reassemble regulator valve body components, reverse disassembly procedure. With pressure regulator valve components installed, align hole in retainer with hole in valve body. Compress retainer into valve body until lock bolt can be installed.

PRESSURE CONTROL VALVE BODY
Disassembly

1) Detach pressure control shift valve end plate mounting bolts, then remove end plate, pressure control shift valve and spring. Remove pressure control timing valve retainer, spring and valve. *See Fig. 18.*

2) Inspect all parts. Check valves for scoring or scratches and valve body for scoring or damage. Replace valve body and/or components as necessary. Repair valve body if 1 or more valves do not slide smoothly in their bores. See VALVE BODY REPAIR.

Reassembly

To reassemble pressure control valve body and components, reverse disassembly procedure.

SERVO VALVE BODY
Disassembly

1) Push out 2nd accumulator piston. Remove spring, collar (2 mm), outer "O" ring (33.2 x 2.4 mm) and inner "O" ring (23.5 x 2.1 mm). Push out 3rd accumulator piston. Remove spring, outer "O" ring (35.2 x 2.4 mm) and inner "O" ring (23.5 x 2.1 mm). Discard "O" rings.

2) Remove servo valve with "O" ring (31 x 2.7 mm) and return spring. Remove "O" ring from valve and

Fig. 17: Exploded View Of Regulator Valve Body & Components

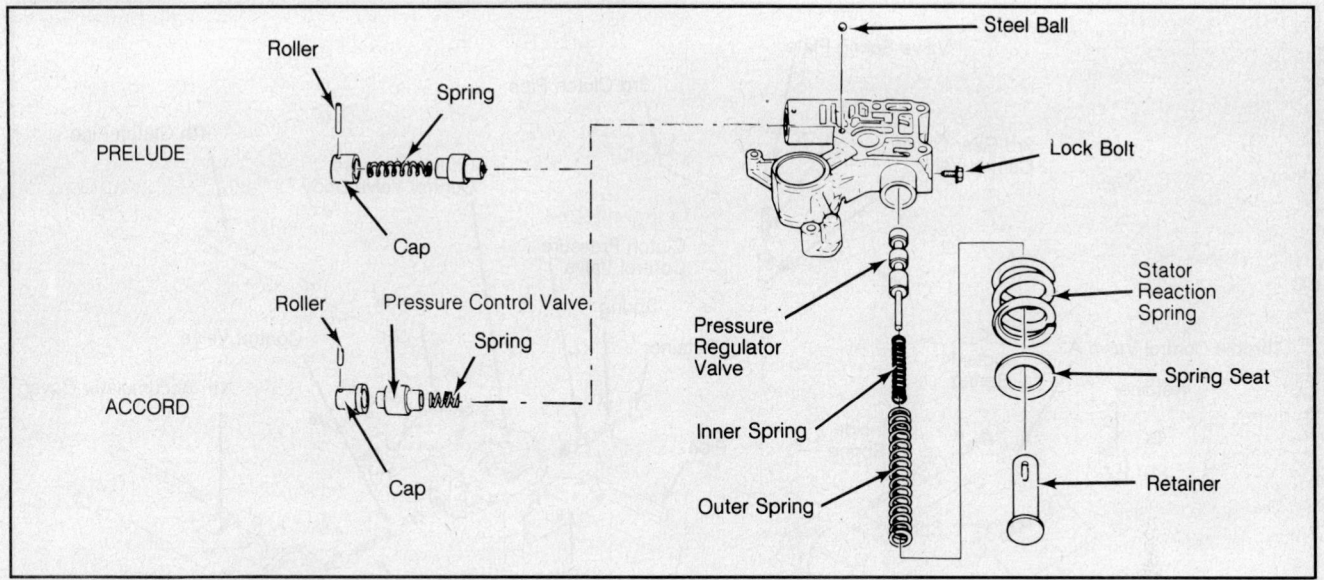

When assembling, note pressure control valve and spring location differences between Accord and Prelude.

Fig. 18: Exploded View Of Pressure Control Valve Body & Components

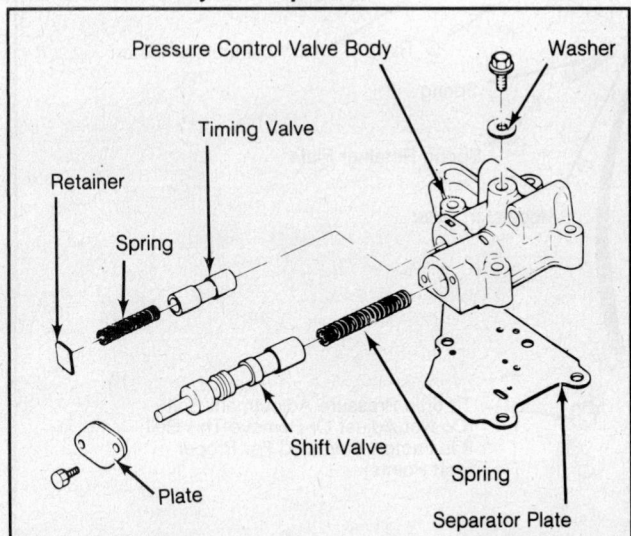

discard. Detach throttle control valve "B" retainer mounting bolt (6 x 1.25 mm). Remove retainer and throttle control valve "B" assembly.

3) Separate control valve "B" components from spring. *See Fig. 19.* Remove throttle control valve "A" assembly from servo body and separate valve components from inner and outer springs. Detach 4th accumulator piston cover mounting bolts, then remove cover.

4) Remove "O" ring (31 x 2.7 mm) and spring from cover. Discard "O" ring. Pull 4th accumulator piston, outer "O" ring (21.2 x 2.4 mm) and inner "O" ring (29 x 2.4 mm) from servo body. Remove and discard "O" rings.

5) Detach clutch pressure control (CPC) valve body mounting bolts. Remove cover, CPC valve body and plate from servo valve body. Remove CPC valve retainer,

spring and valve. Remove clutch oil passage pipes from valve body as necessary.

CAUTION: Do not adjust or remove throttle pressure adjustment bolt (on servo valve body). See Fig. 19. Bolt has been adjusted at factory for proper shift points.

6) Remove modulator valve retainer plate, spring and modulator valve. Clean all parts thoroughly in solvent or carburetor cleaner, then blow dry with compressed air. Blow out all passages. Inspect all components.

7) Inspect valves for free movement, damage, scratches or scoring. Check clutch oil passage pipes for damage to ends. Replace servo valve body and/or components if any part is worn or damaged.

NOTE: When removing springs, be sure to note location, diameter and length of each spring for reassembly reference.

8) Check springs for proper length. See SERVO VALVE BODY COMPONENTS & SPRING SPECIFICATIONS table. Replace springs that are not to specifications. Repair valve body if 1 or more valves do not slide smoothly in their bores. See VALVE BODY REPAIR.

NOTE: Clean all parts in solvent and blow dry with compressed air. Replace servo valve as an assembly if any parts are worn or damaged.

CAUTION: Do not remove or adjust throttle pressure adjustment bolt. Adjustment bolt is factory set for proper shift points.

Reassembly
To reassemble servo valve, reverse disassembly procedure. Always install new "O" rings.

Automatic Transmissions
HONDA 4-SPEED (Cont.)

Fig. 19: Exploded View Of Servo Valve Body & Components

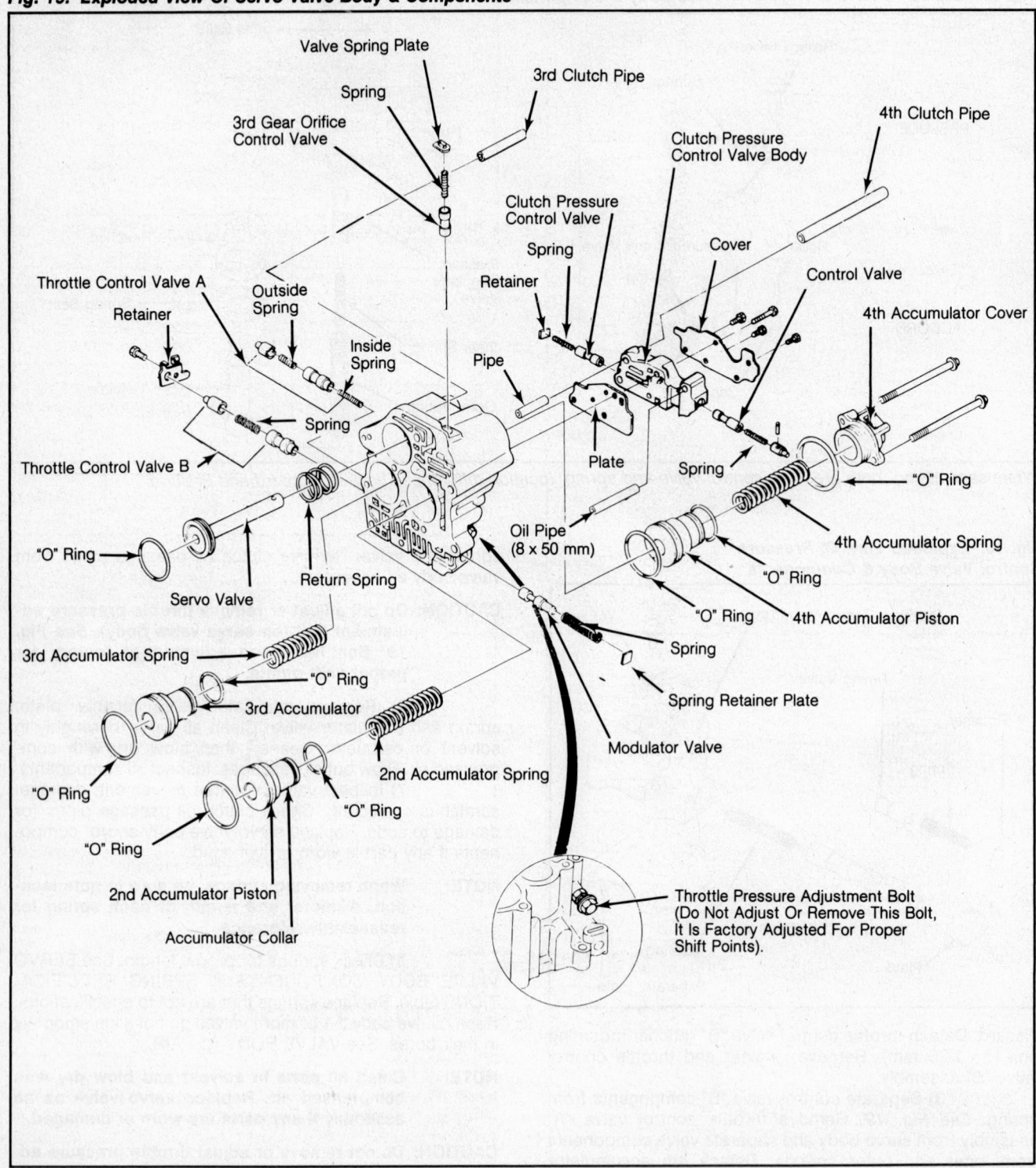

SERVO VALVE BODY COMPONENT & SPRING SPECIFICATIONS

Application	Standard In. (mm)	Service Limit In. (mm)
2nd Accumulator Spring Length [1]		
Accord	3.28 (83.4)	3.20 (81.4)
Prelude	3.20 (81.2)	3.15 (80.0)
3rd Accumulator Spring Length [2]		
Accord	4.21 (107)	4.13 (105)
Prelude	3.47 (88.1)	3.41 (86.5)
4th Accumulator Spring Length [3]		
Accord	3.72 (94.6)	3.65 (92.6)
Prelude	3.80 (96.4)	3.72 (94.4)
Servo Valve Return Spring		
Accord	1.59 (40.3)	1.44 (36.7)
Prelude	1.59 (40.3)	1.44 (36.7)
Servo Valve Body Shift Fork Shaft Bore I.D.		
A	.5512-.5514 (14.000-14.005)	
B	.5514-.5516 (14.000-14.010)	
C	.5516-.5518 (14.011-14.015)	
Shift Fork Shaft Valve Bore I.D.	1.4567-1.4582 (37.000-37.039)	1.4583 (37.045)

[1] – Accord and Prelude spring dia. is .79" (20 mm).
[2] – Accord spring dia. is .81" (20.6 mm). Prelude spring dia. is .80" (20.4 mm).
[3] – Accord and Prelude spring dia. is .732" (18.6 mm).

VALVE BODY REPAIR

NOTE: **Valve body repair is only necessary if one or more valves in valve body do not slide smoothly in their bores. This procedure may be used to free valves in main valve body, regulator valve body, pressure control valve body and servo valve body.**

CAUTION: Do not attempt to repair governor assembly, replace unit if valves are stuck.

1) With unit removed, carefully tap valve body so that sticking valve drops out of its bore. If necessary, use a small screwdriver to pry valve free.

NOTE: **Do not damage bore if screwdriver is used during valve removal.**

2) Soak a sheet of #600 grit sandpaper in ATF for about 30 minutes. Inspect valve for any scuff marks. Use ATF-soaked sandpaper to polish off any scuffs or burrs

found on valve, then wash in solvent and blow dry with compressed air.

3) Roll up half a sheet of ATF-soaked sandpaper and insert it in bore of sticking valve. Twist paper slightly so that it unrolls and fits bore tightly, then polish bore by twisting paper as it is moved in and out.

NOTE: **The aluminum valve body does not require much polishing to remove any scuffs or burrs.**

4) Remove sandpaper and thoroughly wash entire valve body in solvent and blow dry with compressed air. Coat valve with ATF and drop it into its bore.

5) Valve should drop to bottom of bore under its own weight. If not, repeat step 3), then retest. Final clean valve and valve body in solvent and blow dry. Assemble components using ATF as a lubricant.

GOVERNOR ASSEMBLY
Disassembly

1) Bend governor housing mounting bolt lock plates away from bolt heads. Detach mounting bolts (6 x 1.0 mm) and remove governor housing from shaft. Discard lock plates.

NOTE: **Push down on secondary weight to ease removal of 20 mm snap ring.**

Fig. 20: Exploded View of Governor Valve & Housing Assembly

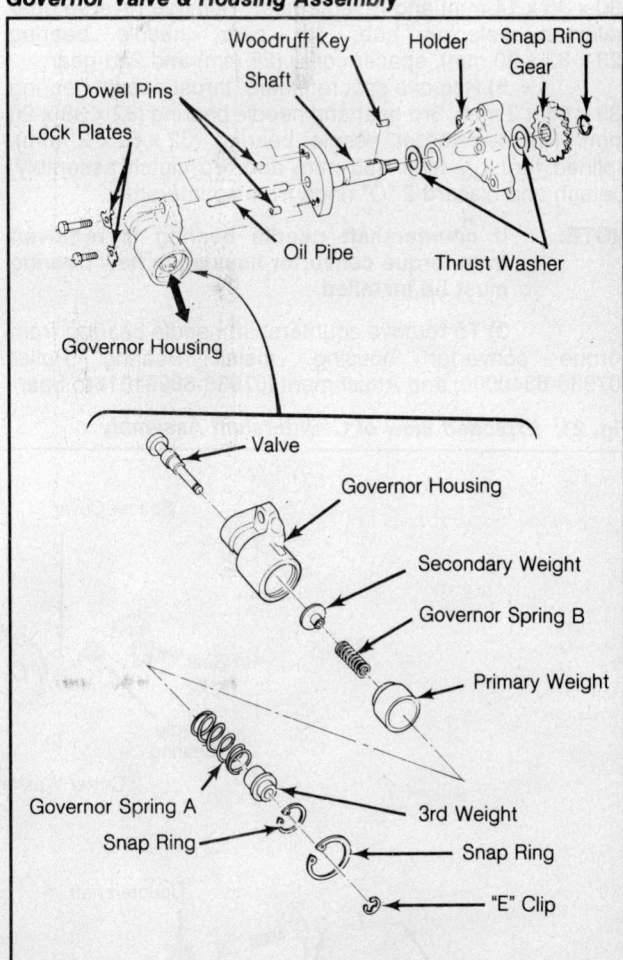

Replace governor assembly if any part is worn or damaged or unit does not operate smoothly. Do not attempt repair.

Automatic Transmissions
HONDA 4-SPEED (Cont.)

2) Remove "E" ring (5 mm) from end of governor valve. Slide out valve. Detach small snap ring (20 mm), then remove governor spring "A" and 3rd weight from inside of primary weight.

3) Detach large snap ring (28 mm), then remove primary weight, governor spring "B" and secondary weight from governor housing bore. *See Fig. 20.*

4) On governor holder, detach snap ring (14 mm). Remove gear and thrust washer (14 mm). Remove pipe (5 x 65 mm) from governor shaft. Pull governor shaft out of governor holder and remove Woodruff key (3 mm) and thrust washer (14 mm). Inspect all parts.

5) Check oil pipe for damaged ends. Inspect governor housing and holder for scoring or warpage. Check gear teeth for chipped teeth, damage or excessive wear. Inspect primary, secondary and 3rd weights for wear, scoring or scratches. Replace parts as needed.

Reassembly
To reassemble governor, reverse disassembly procedure. Use a new "E" clip (5 mm) when installing valve in housing. Install new lock plates when replacing governor housing onto shaft. Check governor assembly for smooth operation after reassembly.

COUNTERSHAFT ASSEMBLY
Disassembly
1) Remove reverse gear collar, needle bearing (30 x 36 x 14 mm) and reverse gear. Remove reverse gear selector, selector hub, 4th gear, needle bearing (28 x 33 x 20 mm), spacer collar (28 mm) and 2nd gear.

2) Remove split retainers, thrust needle bearing (39 x 54 x 2 mm), 3rd gear and needle bearing (32 x 38 x 20 mm). Remove thrust needle bearing (32 x 52 x 2 mm), splined thrust washer (35 mm) and 3rd clutch assembly. Detach and discard 2 "O" rings from countershaft.

NOTE: **If countershaft needle bearing is removed from torque convertor housing, a new bearing must be installed.**

3) To remove countershaft needle bearing from torque convertor housing, install Bearing Puller (07936-6340000) and Attachment (07936-6890101) to bear-

ing. Tap bearing out of case. Note position of oil guide plate for reassembly reference.

4) To remove countershaft bearing from transmission case, expand bearing locating snap ring (62 mm) with snap ring pliers. Push bearing out through case (away from snap ring) by hand. Do not remove snap ring unless it is necessary to clean housing.

Inspection
Check needle bearings for galling and/or rough movement. Inspect countershaft splines for excessive wear or damage. Check bearing surfaces for scoring, scratches or excessive wear. Replace countershaft and/or components as necessary.

NOTE: **On all thrust needle bearings, ensure unrolled edge of bearing cage faces thrust washer. Lubricate all parts with ATF during reassembly.**

Reassembly
1) To install countershaft bearing to transmission housing, first expand snap ring with snap ring pliers. With part number facing out, insert new bearing part-way into housing (from snap ring side), then release pliers.

2) Push bearing down into transmission until ring snaps in place around it. Ensure snap ring is properly seated in bearing and housing grooves. To install countershaft bearing into torque converter housing, first ensure oil guide plate is in proper position.

3) Using Driver (07749-0010000) and Attachment (07746-0010400), tap bearing in until flush with case. To reassemble countershaft, first install 2 new "O" rings. Install 3rd clutch assembly, splined thrust washer, thrust needle bearing. Check splined thrust washer for proper fit. See MAINSHAFT & COUNTERSHAFT CLEARANCE MEASUREMENTS. Install 3rd gear with needle bearing.

4) Install thrust needle bearing, split retainers and 2nd gear with space collar and needle bearing. Install 4th gear, selector hub (groove facing convertor housing), reverse gear selector (chamfer toward torque convertor housing) and reverse gear with needle bearing. Install reverse gear collar and ball bearing. *See Fig. 21.*

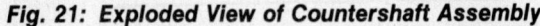

Fig. 21: Exploded View of Countershaft Assembly

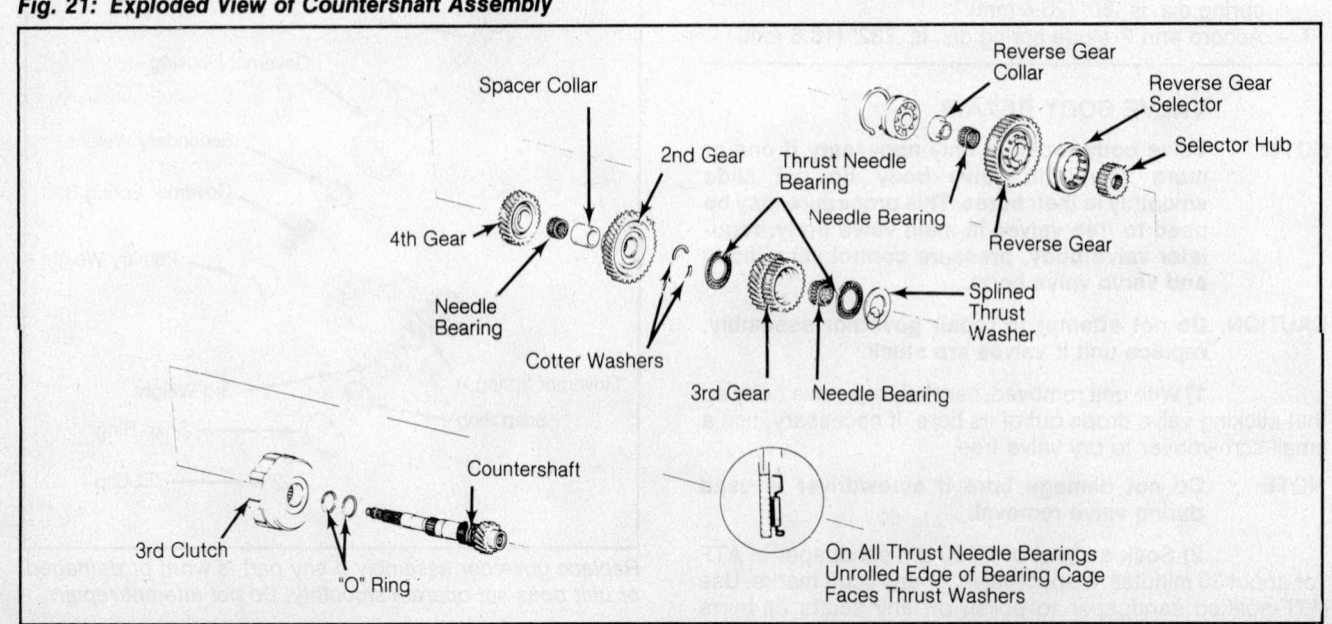

Spacer Collar
Reverse Gear Collar
Reverse Gear Selector
Selector Hub
2nd Gear
Thrust Needle Bearing
Needle Bearing
4th Gear
Reverse Gear
Needle Bearing
Cotter Washers
Splined Thrust Washer
3rd Gear
Needle Bearing
Countershaft
3rd Clutch
"O" Ring
On All Thrust Needle Bearings Unrolled Edge of Bearing Cage Faces Thrust Washers

HONDA 4-SPEED (Cont.)

5) With countershaft assembled, measure clearance between selector collar and shoulder of 4th gear. Clearance should be .003-.006" (.07-.15 mm). Adjust clearance as necessary. See MAINSHAFT & COUNTERSHAFT CLEARANCE MEASUREMENTS.

MAINSHAFT ASSEMBLY
Disassembly
1) From rear of mainshaft, detach snap ring (20 mm), needle bearing (20 x 26 x 20 mm) and spacer washer. Detach 2 metal sealing rings (32 mm) and discard. From front of mainshaft, detach snap ring (26 mm). See Fig. 22.

2) Remove thrust washer (26 x 45 x 3 mm), thrust needle bearing (32 x 44 x 2 mm) and 4th gear with 2 needle bearings (32 x 38 x 20 mm). Remove thrust needle bearing (39 x 54 x 2 mm) and 4th gear collar.

3) Remove thrust washer, 2nd/4th clutch assembly and 3 oil seal "O" rings (34 x 1.9 mm). Remove thrust washer (36 mm), thrust needle bearing (36 x 52 x 2 mm), 2nd gear, needle bearing (36 x 41 x 18.3 mm) and thrust needle bearing (42 x 58 x 2 mm). Remove and discard 2 "O" rings (19.8 x 1.9 mm) from mainshaft. See Fig. 22.

4) Using hammer, driver and Attachment (07947-6340500), remove mainshaft bearing and seal from torque convertor housing (drive out from valve body side). Discard oil seal.

5) To remove mainshaft bearing from transmission housing, expand snap ring (60 mm) with snap ring pliers. Push bearing out of housing (away from snap ring) by hand.

Inspection
Check mainshaft splines for excessive wear or damage. Inspect bearing surface for scoring, scratches or excessive wear. Check all needle bearings for galling and/or rough movement. Replace parts as needed.

NOTE: When installing thrust needle bearings, ensure unrolled edge of bearing cage faces thrust washer. Lubricate all parts with ATF fluid during reassembly.

Reassembly
1) To install new mainshaft bearing to transmission housing, expand locating snap ring with snap ring pliers and insert bearing part-way into it, then release pliers. Push bearing into housing until ring snaps in place around it. Ensure snap ring is seated in bearing and housing grooves.

2) Using hammer, driver and Attachment (07947-6340500), drive in new bearing (from torque convertor side) until it bottoms in convertor housing. Install new mainshaft oil seal (from torque convertor side) using hammer, driver and Oil Seal Installer (07947-6340201).

3) Install 2 new "O" rings onto mainshaft. Install thrust needle bearing, needle bearing and 2nd gear. Install thrust needle bearing, thrust washer and 3 new "O" rings. Check measurement. See MAINSHAFT & COUNTERSHAFT CLEARANCE MEASUREMENTS. Install 2nd/4th clutch assembly.

4) Install thrust washer, 4th gear collar, thrust needle bearing and 4th gear (with 2 needle bearings). Install thrust needle bearing, thrust washer and snap ring onto mainshaft.

MAINSHAFT & COUNTERSHAFT CLEARANCE MEASUREMENTS.

NOTE: To check mainshaft and countershaft clearances, both shaft assemblies must be removed from transmission housing and checked in assembled form.

Fig. 22: Exploded View of Mainshaft Assembly

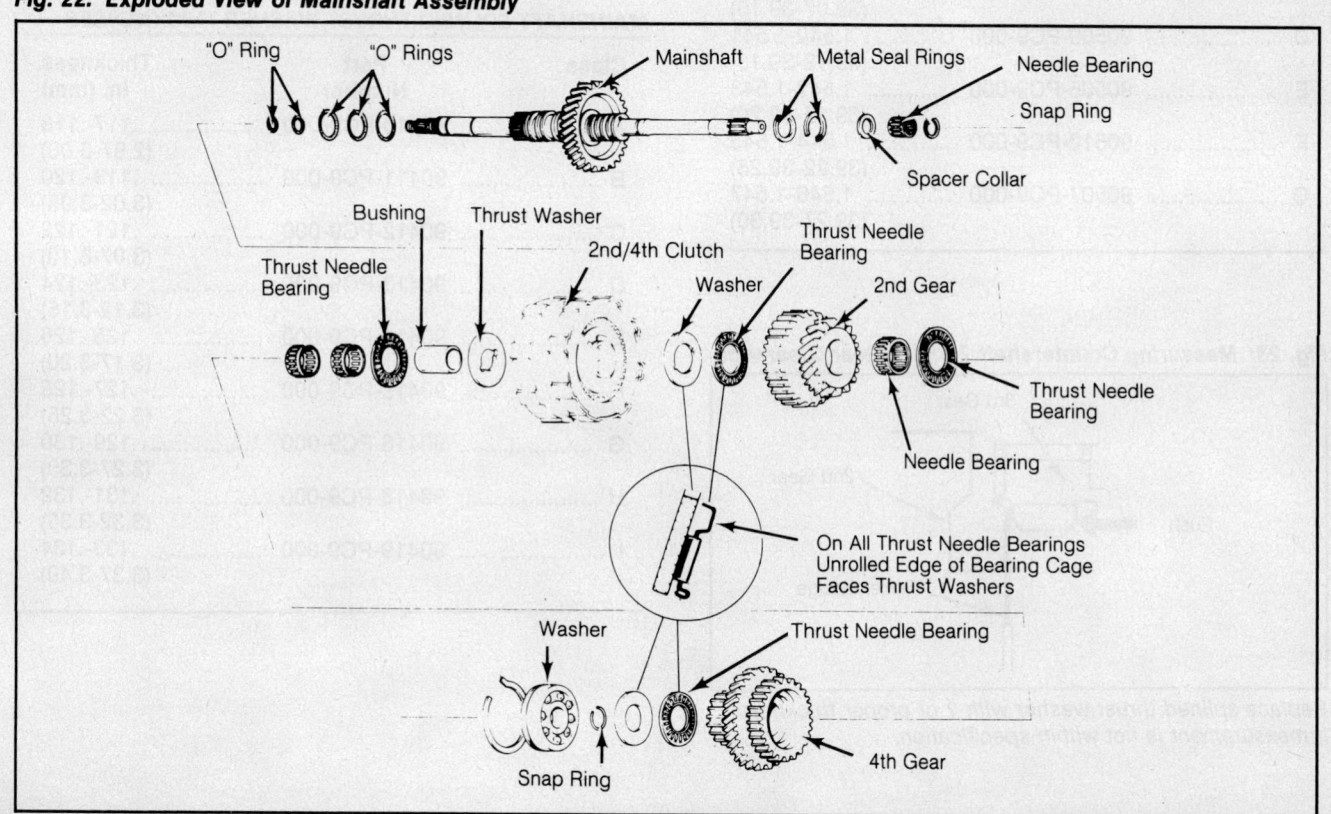

1) Install mainshaft and countershaft assemblies into torque convertor housing. Install Mainshaft Holder (07923-6890201) and tighten mainshaft and countershaft lock nuts to 25 ft. lbs. (35 N.m). Remove assemblies from housing and lay each flat on work surface. Using a feeler gauge, measure clearances.

2) On countershaft, measure clearance between shoulder on gear selector hub and shoulder of 4th gear. Standard countershaft 4th gear clearance is .003-.006" (.07-.15 mm).

3) If countershaft clearance is more than specifications, measure thickness of spacer collar and select a replacement which gives proper clearance. See COUNTERSHAFT SPACER COLLAR THICKNESSES table.

4) Leave feeler gauge used in step **2)** between selector hub and 4th gear. Slide 3rd gear out fully. Using another feeler gauge, measure clearance between 2nd and 3rd gears. Record this measurement. Slide 3rd gear in fully and measure clearance between 2nd and 3rd gears. See Fig. 23.

5) Calculate difference between the 2 readings. This is the actual clearance between the 2 gears. Clearance should be .003-.006" (.07-.15 mm). If clearance is not to specifications, install a splined thrust washer (35 mm I.D.) of proper thickness. See COUNTERSHAFT SPLINED THRUST WASHER THICKNESSES.

COUNTERSHAFT SPACER COLLAR THICKNESSES

Class	Part Number	Thickness In. (mm)
A	90503-PC9-000	1.534-1.535 (38.97-39.00)
B	90508-PC9-000	1.536-1.537 (39.02-39.05)
C	90504-PC9-000	1.538-1.539 (39.07-39.10)
D	90509-PC9-000	1.540-1.541 (39.12-39.15)
E	90505-PC9-000	1.542-1.543 (39.17-39.20)
F	90510-PC9-000	1.544-1.545 (39.22-39.25)
G	90507-PC9-000	1.546-1.547 (39.27-39.30)

COUNTERSHAFT SPLINED THRUST WASHER THICKNESSES

Class	Part Number	Thickness In. (mm)
A	90411-PA9-0100	.117-.118 (2.97-3.00)
B	90412-PA9-0100	.119-.120 (3.02-3.05)
C	90413-PA9-0100	.121-.122 (3.07-3.10)
D	90414-PA9-0100	.123-.124 (3.12-3.15)
E	90415-PA9-0100	.125-.126 (3.17-3.20)
F	90418-PA9-0100	.127-.128 (3.22-3.25)
G	90419-PA9-0100	.129-.130 (3.27-3.30)
H	90420-PA9-0100	.131-.132 (3.32-3.35)
I	90421-PA9-0100	.133-.134 (3.37-3.40)

NOTE: Make all measurements before changing thrust washers. Recheck after making adjustments.

6) On mainshaft assembly, measure clearance between shoulder on 2nd gear and mainshaft 3rd gear. Standard (new) clearance is .003-.006" (.07-.15 mm). If not to specification, measure thickness of 2nd clutch (splined) thrust washer (36 mm I.D.) and select a washer which gives correct clearance. See MAINSHAFT SPLINED THRUST WASHER THICKNESSES table.

MAINSHAFT SPLINED THRUST WASHER THICKNESSES

Class	Part Number	Thickness In. (mm)
A	90410-PC9-000	.117-.118 (2.97-3.00)
B	90411-PC9-000	.119-.120 (3.02-3.05)
C	90412-PC9-000	.121-.122 (3.07-3.10)
D	90413-PC9-000	.123-.124 (3.12-3.15)
E	90414-PC9-000	.125-.126 (3.17-3.20)
F	90415-PC9-000	.127-.128 (3.22-3.25)
G	90416-PC9-000	.129-.130 (3.27-3.30)
H	90418-PC9-000	.131-.132 (3.32-3.35)
I	90419-PC9-000	.133-.134 (3.37-3.40)

Fig. 23: Measuring Countershaft 2nd/3rd Gear Clearance

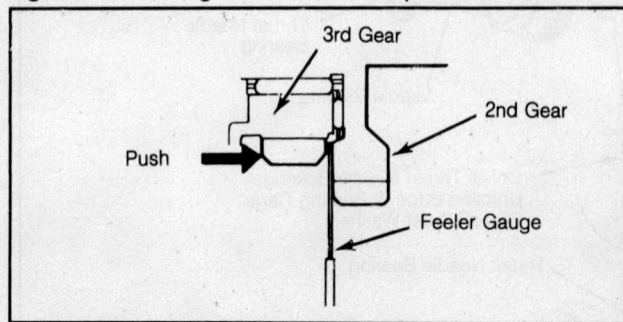

Replace splined thrust washer with 1 of proper thickness if measurement is not within specification.

HONDA 4-SPEED (Cont.)

Fig. 24: Exploded View of 1st & 3rd Clutch Assemblies

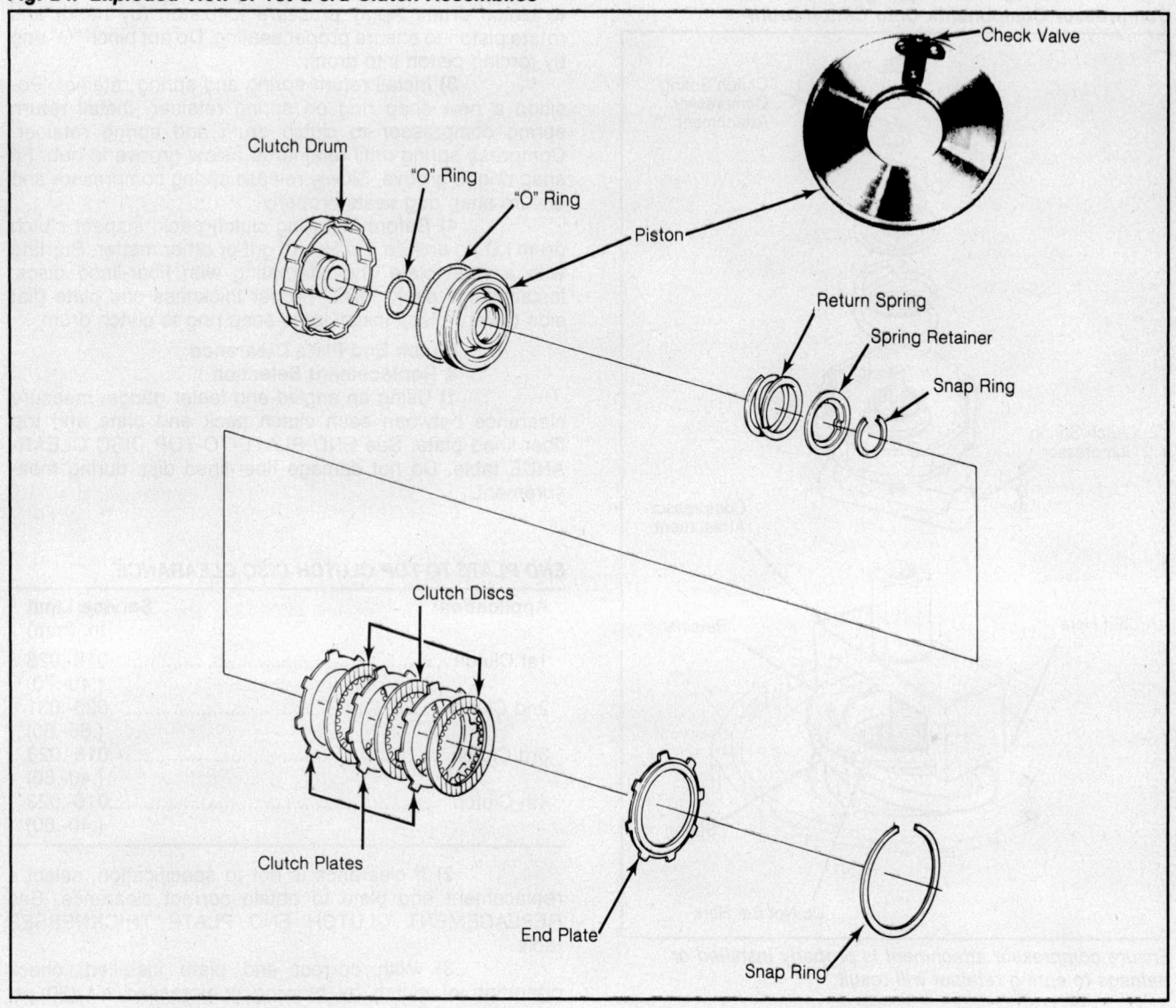

CLUTCH ASSEMBLIES

NOTE: 1st and 3rd clutches are identical in appearance but are not interchangeable.

Disassembly

1) On 1st and 3rd clutch assemblies, use a screwdriver to detach large snap ring (119 mm) retaining end plate, clutch discs and plates. Remove end plate and clutch pack. Keep steel plates and fiber-lined discs in order removed. *See Fig. 24.*

CAUTION: If either end of compressor attachment is set over open area not touched by spring, spring retainer may be damaged.

2) Install Clutch Return Spring Compressor (07960-6120000) and Attachment (07960-6890100) onto clutch drum. *See Fig. 25.* Compress spring and remove small snap ring (40 mm).

3) Slowly release spring compressor. Remove spring retainer and return spring. To remove clutch piston, first wrap shop rag around clutch drum. Carefully apply air

pressure (30 psi maximum) to oil passage in clutch drum while holding finger over other passage opening.

4) Remove piston, then detach large "O" ring (104 x 2.2 mm) from piston O.D. and small "O" ring (39.8 x 2.2 mm) from piston I.D. Discard "O" rings. Inspect clutch components for damage or wear. Check clutch return spring for proper free length. See CLUTCH RETURN SPRING SPECIFICATIONS.

5) On 2nd/4th clutch assembly, disassemble components by follow steps 1) through 4) for each clutch assembly. *See Fig. 26.* Inspect clutch components for damage or wear. Check clutch return springs for proper free length. See CLUTCH RETURN SPRING SPECIFICATIONS.

Inspection

Clean all parts thoroughly in solvent and blow dry with compressed air. Blow out all passages. Check piston for restriction and/or loose check valve. Check for excessive wear or scoring on steel plates and lined plates. Replace steel or lined plates if necessary. Replace clutch assembly if piston is damaged.

Fig. 25: Installing Clutch Spring Compressor Components Onto Clutch Drum

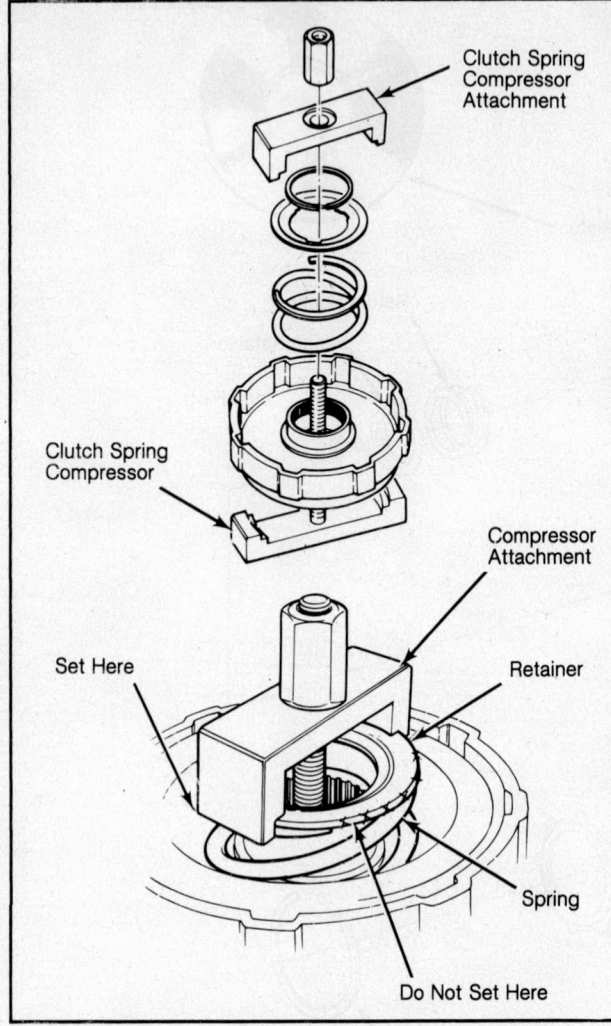

Ensure compressor attachment is properly installed or damage to spring retainer will result.

CLUTCH RETURN SPRING SPECIFICATIONS

Application	Standard	Service Limit
1st Clutch Spring		
Free Length	1.26	1.18
	(32.0)	(30.0)
2nd/4th Clutch Spring		
Free Length	1.20	1.12
	(30.5)	(28.5)
3rd Clutch Spring		
Free Length	1.20	1.12
	(30.5)	(28.5)

NOTE: Soak new fiber-lined plates in ATF for 30 minutes before installation.

Reassembly
1) Lubricate all parts with ATF fluid before assembling. Install new "O" ring on piston. Make sure clutch piston spring washer is installed with high side facing away from clutch drum.

2) Install piston (lubricate "O" ring with ATF fluid) to clutch drum. Apply pressure to piston (by hand) and rotate piston to ensure proper seating. Do not pinch "O" ring by forcing piston into drum.

3) Install return spring and spring retainer. Position a new snap ring on spring retainer. Install return spring compressor to clutch drum and spring retainer. Compress spring until retainer is below groove in hub. Fit snap ring to groove. Slowly release spring compressor and ensure snap ring seats properly.

4) Before installing clutch pack, inspect clutch drum I.D. to ensure it is free of grit or other matter. Starting with a steel plate and alternating with fiber-lined discs, install clutch pack. Install proper thickness end plate (flat side toward disc). Install large snap ring to clutch drum.

Clutch End Plate Clearance & Replacement Selection
1) Using an angled-end feeler gauge, measure clearance between each clutch pack end plate and top fiber-lined plate. See END PLATE-TO-TOP DISC CLEARANCE table. Do not damage fiber-lined disc during measurement.

END PLATE-TO-TOP CLUTCH DISC CLEARANCE

Application	Service Limit In. (mm)
1st Clutch	.016-.028 (.40-.70)
2nd Clutch	.026-.031 (.65-.80)
3rd Clutch	.016-.023 (.40-.60)
4th Clutch	.016-.023 (.40-.60)

2) If clearance is not to specification, select a replacement end plate to obtain correct clearance. See REPLACEMENT CLUTCH END PLATE THICKNESSES table.

3) With correct end plate installed, check operation of clutch by blowing compressed air (30 psi maximum) into oil passage in clutch drum. Clutch should engage. Remove air pressure and check that clutch releases.

TRANSMISSION, END COVER & TORQUE CONVERTER HOUSINGS
Disassembly
1) If differential seals are to be replaced or if differential needs repair, lift differential out of torque converter housing. Remove differential seal snap ring (72 mm) from torque convertor housing.

NOTE: Seal installed depth should be noted for reassembly reference.

2) Using Driver (07749-0010000) and Attachment (07947-6340500), drive seal out through torque convertor housing. Using hammer and drift, drive differential seal (away from snap ring) out of transmission housing.

CAUTION: Use care not to damage end cover components during disassembly.

3) On end cover, detach snap rings retaining 1st and 3rd clutch feed pipe assemblies. Remove feed pipe

Fig. 26: Exploded View of 2nd & 4th Clutch Assemblies

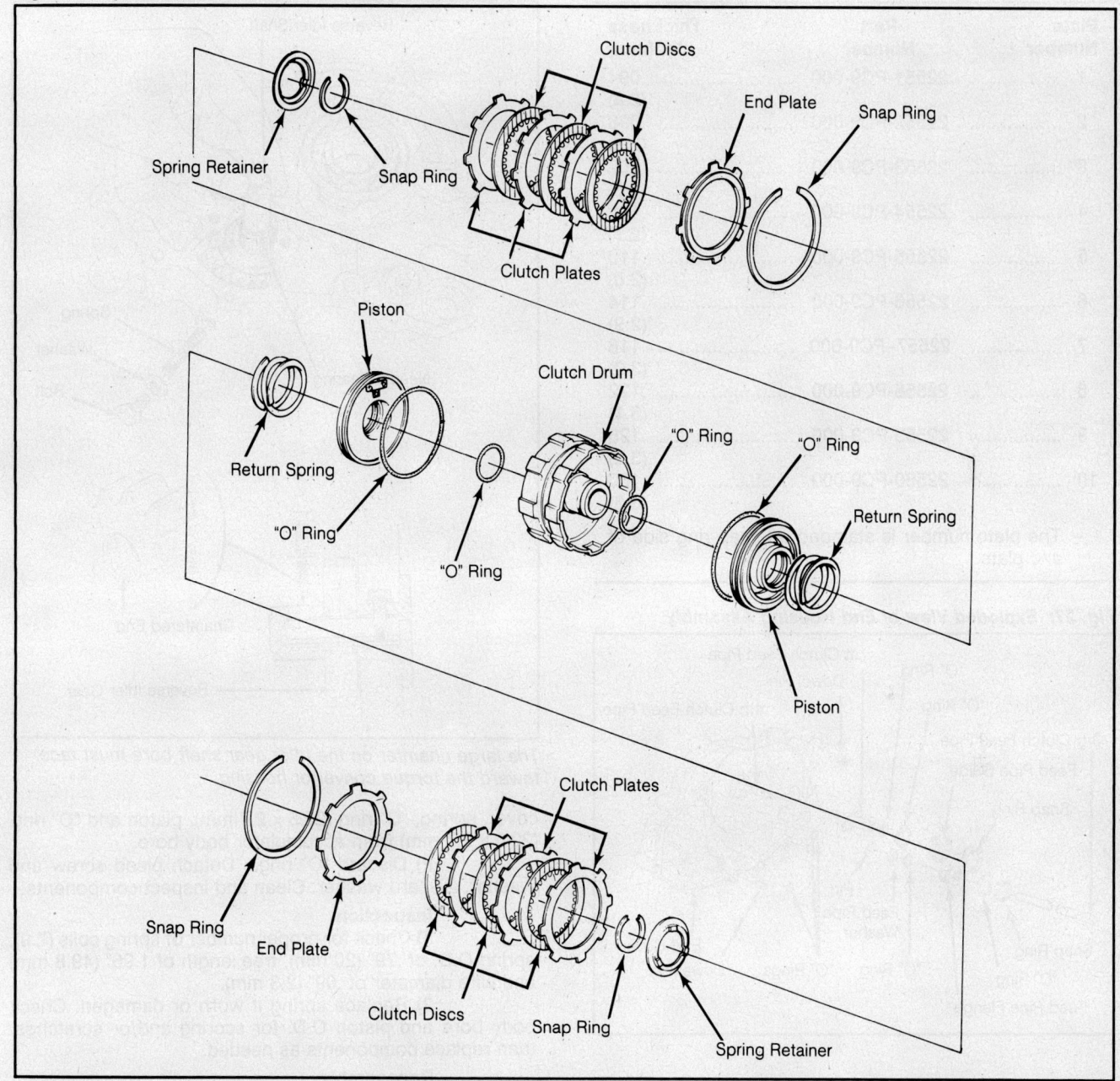

assemblies from cover, then disassemble "O" rings, guide, pin and flange from feed pipes. Discard "O" rings. *See Fig. 27.*

4) If not previously removed, detach reverse idler bearing holder mounting bolts and remove holder. Detach 2 idler gear shaft locating bolts and remove washers and springs.

5) Pull out reverse idler gear shaft from outside transmission housing. From inside housing, remove idler gear and needle bearing (14 x 18 x 15 mm). Inspect components and replace if worn or damaged.

Inspection

Inspect end cover components. Check 1st and 3rd clutch feed pipes for damage to ends. Check end cover for cracks, grooves and/or scoring. Ensure all passages are

clear by blowing out with compressed air. Check and replace dowel pins (8 x 14 mm) if necessary.

Reassembly

1) Install reverse idler gear so that large chamfer on shaft bore faces away from transmission housing. *See Fig. 28.* Position idler gear shaft and needle bearing to transmission housing, then install shaft locating bolts, washers and springs.

2) Install reverse idler gear bearing holder and tighten mounting bolts. Expand mainshaft and countershaft bearing snap rings and install bearings to transmission housing.

3) On torque converter housing, install snap ring (72 mm) if removed. Using hammer, driver and Attachment (07947-6110500), drive new mainshaft and countershaft seals into housing.

REPLACEMENT CLUTCH END PLATE THICKNESSES

Plate Number [1]	Part Number	Thickness In. (mm)
1	22551-PC9-000	.094 (2.4)
2	22552-PC9-000	.098 (2.5)
3	22553-PC9-000	.102 (2.6)
4	22554-PC9-000	.106 (2.7)
5	22555-PC9-000	.110 (2.8)
6	22556-PC9-000	.114 (2.9)
7	22557-PC9-000	.118 (3.0)
8	22558-PC9-000	.122 (3.1)
9	22559-PC9-000	.126 (3.2)
10	22560-PC9-000	.130 (3.3)

[1] – The plate number is stamped on snap ring side of end plate.

Fig. 27: Exploded View of End Housing Assembly

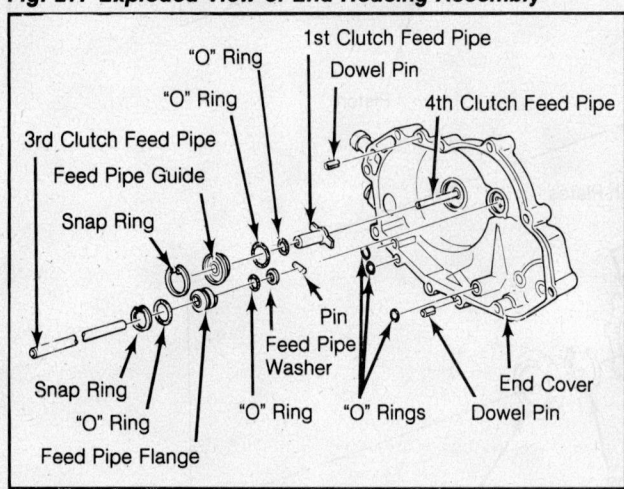

NOTE: With feed pipes assembled, ensure lugs on feed pipe collars are aligned with slots in end cover housing.

4) On end cover housing, install 3 new "O" rings (6 x 2.3 mm). Install new "O" ring (34 x 1.9 mm), 1st clutch feed pipe, new "O" ring (8.5 x 1.9 mm) and feed pipe guide onto 4th clutch feed pipe. Retain assembly in housing with new snap ring (38 mm).

5) Install 3rd clutch feed pipe pin (19.8 mm), washer, new "O" ring (7.7 x 1.9 mm), feed pipe flange and new "O" ring (19.8 x 1.9 mm) onto 3rd clutch feed pipe, then retain in housing with new snap ring (26 mm).

1ST ACCUMULATOR
Disassembly (Prelude)

1) Apply pressure to accumulator cover and spring while detaching snap ring (30 mm), then remove

Fig. 28: Installing Reverse Idler Gear & Components

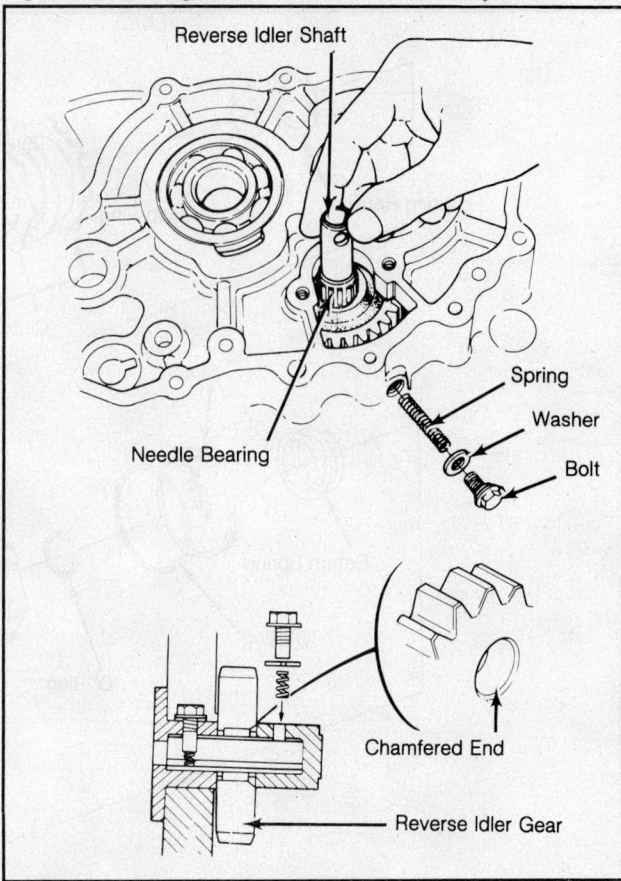

The large chamfer on the idler gear shaft bore must face toward the torque convertor housing.

cover, spring, "O" ring (22.5 x 2.7 mm), piston and "O" ring (22.5 x 2.7 mm) from accumulator body bore.

2) Discard "O" rings. Detach bleed screw and washer. Discard washer. Clean and inspect components.

Inspection

1) Check for proper number of spring coils (7.9), spring O.D. of .79" (20 mm), free length of 1.96" (49.8 mm) and wire diameter of .09" (2.3 mm).

2) Replace spring if worn or damaged. Check body bore and piston O.D. for scoring and/or scratches, then replace components as needed.

Reassembly

Install new washer and bleed screw to body, then tighten screw to 12 ft. lbs. (18 N.m). Assemble piston, spring, cover and new "O" rings into body bore, then retain with new snap ring.

DIFFERENTIAL ASSEMBLY

NOTE: Pinion gear thrust washer backlash inspection must be performed before differential disassembled.

Backlash Inspection

1) Remove differential assembly from torque converter housing. Position differential with carrier side bearings resting in "V" blocks. Install both axle shafts. Using a dial indicator, check backlash of both pinion gears. See Fig. 29.

HONDA 4-SPEED (Cont.)

Fig. 29: Checking Differential Assembly Pinion Gear Backlash

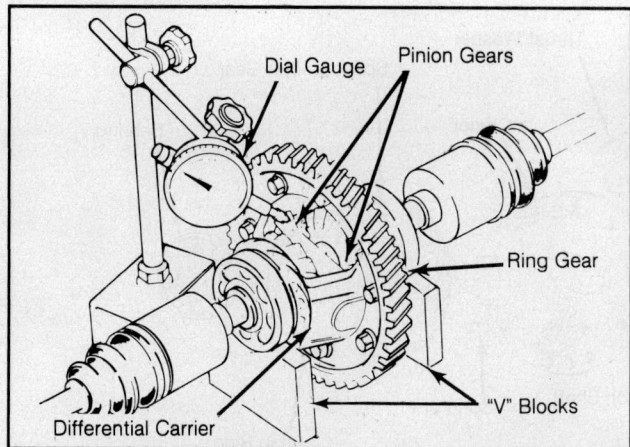

2) Standard backlash is .002-.006" (.05-.15 mm). If backlash is not to specification, disassemble differential. Measure orignal thrust washers to determine thickness. Select new pinion gear thrust washers to obtain correct backlash. See DIFFERENTIAL PINION GEAR THRUST WASHER THICKESSES table.

NOTE: New thrust washers must be of equal thickness.

DIFFERENTIAL PINION GEAR THRUST WASHER THICKESSES

Part Number	Thickness In. (mm)
41351-689-000	.028 (.70)
41355-PC8-000	.030 (.75)
41352-689-000	.031 (.80)
41356-PC8-000	.033 (.85)
41353-689-000	.035 (.90)
41357-PC8-000	.037 (.95)
41254-689-000	.039 (1.0)

NOTE: Before disassembly, inspect differential side bearings for wear or rough rotation. If bearings are in good condition, removal is not necessary.

Disassembly

1) Remove differential assembly from torque converter housing and check backlash. If necessary, remove bearings from both sides of differential using a 2-jaw bearing puller. Detach 10 LEFT-HAND thread ring gear mounting bolts (10 x 1.25 mm). Remove ring gear from carrier. Inspect teeth for damage or excessive wear.

CAUTION: The speedometer drive gear has sharp edges. Use care when handling it during disassembly and reassembly procedures.

2) Using a screwdriver, pry snap ring (80 mm) off carrier. Carefully remove speedometer drive gear and dowel pin (5 x 10 mm). Using hammer and a 4 mm Pin Punch (07499-SA00000), drive out pinion shaft spring pin. See Fig. 30.

3) Remove pinion shaft, pinion gears, side gears and thrust washers. Wash all components thoroughly in solvent and blow dry with compressed air. Inspect all parts for excessive wear or damage. Check pinion shaft for scoring or burrs. Check bearings for damage or rough movement. Replace any parts that are defective.

NOTE: Completely coat all gears with molybdenum disulfide grease before reassembly.

Reassembly

1) Install side gears in differential carrier. Position pinion gears in place (exactly opposite each other), in mesh with side gears. Install new thrust washers (of equal and proper thickness) behind each one. See DIFFERENTIAL PINION GEAR THRUST WASHER THICKESSES table.

2) Install pinion shaft, while rotating gears, to align shaft holes in gears with shaft holes in carrier. Insert pinion shaft and align spring pin hole in one end with matching hole in carrier. Install spring pin. See Fig. 30.

3) If removed, install side bearings onto carrier. With differential assembled, remeasure backlash. If backlash is still out of tolerance (from initial backlash inspection), replace both pinion gears and recheck backlash.

4) If still out of tolerance, replace both side gears and recheck backlash. If still out of tolerance, replace complete carrier assembly. Install dowel pin.

5) Install speedometer drive gear. Ensure chamfer (on gear I.D.) is facing carrier. Install and align snap ring properly on carrier. See Fig. 31. Ensure snap ring end gap does not align with spring pin or dowel pin.

6) Install ring gear onto carrier. Check that chamfer on inside diameter of ring gear is facing carrier. Install ring gear bolts (LEFT-HAND threads) from RIGHT-HAND side of carrier and tighten.

7) Temporarily install large snap ring into torque converter housing bore. Do not install oil seal at this time. Install differential assembly into converter housing using Driver (07749-0010000) and Attachment E (07947-6340500). Tap on differential assembly with driver and attachment to seat snap ring in housing.

CAUTION: If torque convertor housing, transmission housing and/or differential side bearings were replaced, differential side clearance must be checked.

NOTE: The torque convertor housing-to-transmission housing mounting bolt pattern may be slightly different but tightening sequence is the same.

8) Install mainshaft and countershaft assemblies into converter housing. Install new gasket onto converter housing. Install dowel pins. Install transmission housing onto torque converter housing.

9) Install and tighten the convertor housing-to-transmission housing mounting bolts the same as removal sequence. See Fig. 11. Tighten mounting bolts in 2 or more steps. Check differential side clearance.

Differential Side Clearance Check

1) Ensure differential is bottomed in transmission housing. Using a feeler gauge, check clearance between snap ring and outer race of bearing in torque convertor housing. Standard side clearance is .006" (.15 mm) maximum. If clearance is not to specification, select snap ring to give proper clearance. See SIDE CLEARANCE SNAP RING THICKNESSES table.

Fig. 30: Exploded View of Differential Assembly

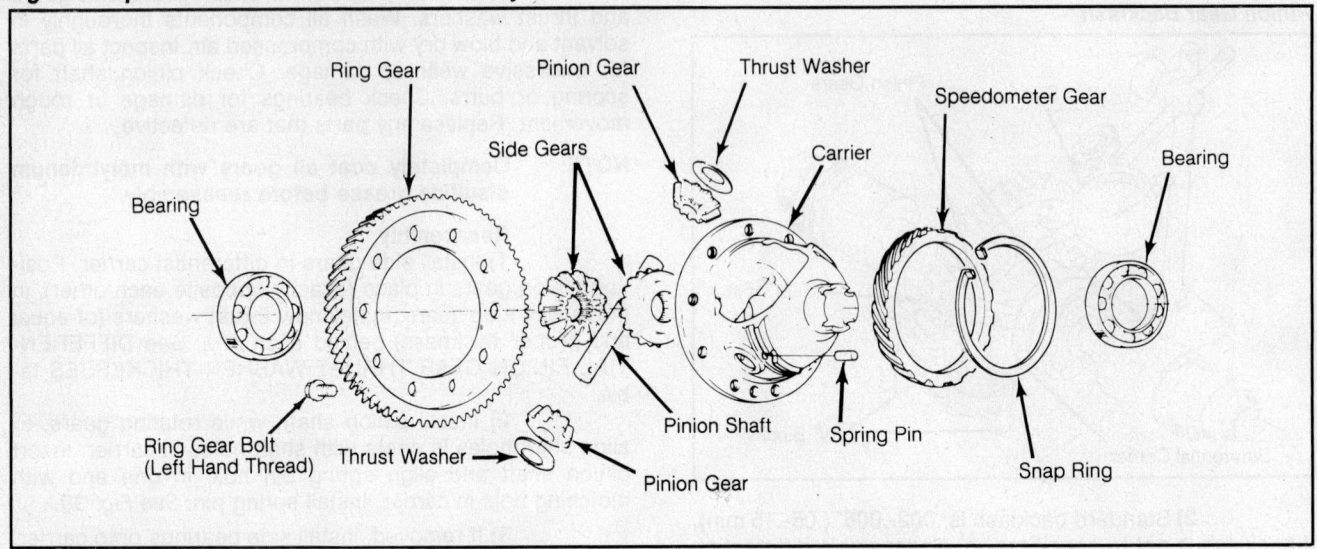

Fig. 31: Installation of Snap Ring On Differential Carrier

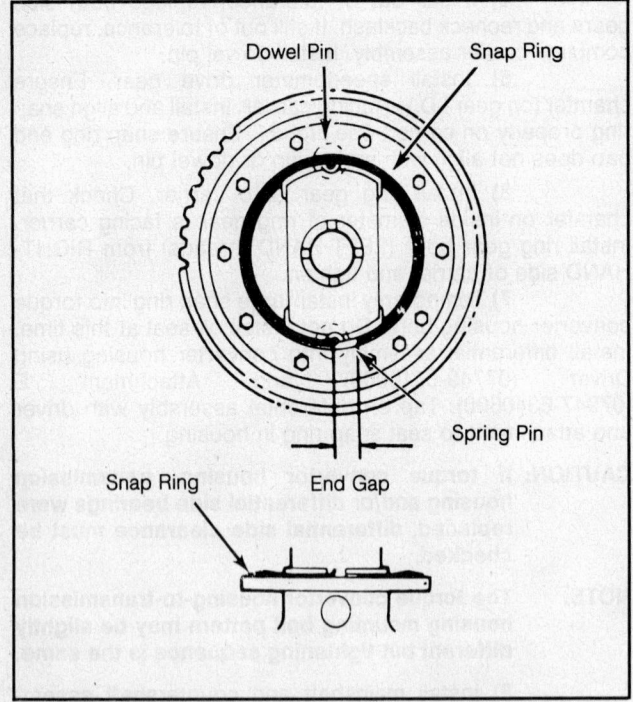

Ensure the snap ring end gap does not aligned with the pinion shaft spring pin or carrier dowel pin.

2) If snap ring replacement is necessary, split housings. Remove differential assembly and old snap ring. Install and seat new, correct snap ring in torque convertor housing groove. Reseat differential, assemble housings and recheck side clearance.

3) If side clearance is correct, disassemble temporarily assembled transmission. Apply oil to new differential seals. Using hammer, driver and Oil Seal Installer (07947-6110500), install new oil seals into torque convertor housing and transmission housing.

SIDE CLEARANCE SNAP RING THICKNESSES

Part Number	Thickness In. (mm)
Accord	
90414-634-000	.096 (2.45)
90415-634-000	.100 (2.55)
90416-634-000	.104 (2.65)
90417-634-000	.108 (2.75)
90418-634-000	.112 (2.85)
90419-634-000	.116 (2.95)
Prelude	
90414-689-000	.098 (2.50)
90415-689-000	.102 (2.60)
90416-689-000	.106 (2.70)
90417-689-000	.110 (2.80)
90418-689-000	.114 (2.90)

TRANSAXLE REASSEMBLY

NOTE: Lubricate all parts with ATF during reassembly.

1) Install differential assembly. Assemble manual valve lever on control shaft, then install in torque converter housing. Install control lever and new lock plate on other end of control shaft. Install and tighten bolt (6 x 10 mm). Bend tab of lock plate up to prevent bolt from turning.

2) Install suction pipe and new filter screen in converter housing. Install separator plate, dowel pin, oil pump gears and shaft. Ensure chamfered side of driven gear and shouldered side of drive gear face housing.

3) Install check valve and spring, then install main valve body onto converter housing. Install and tighten 4 valve body mounting bolts in sequence. *See Fig. 32.*

NOTE: Ensure oil pump drive gear rotates smoothly in normal operating direction and pump shaft moves smoothly in both axial and normal operating directions. See Fig. 32.

Fig. 32: Main Valve Body Mounting Bolt Tightening Sequence

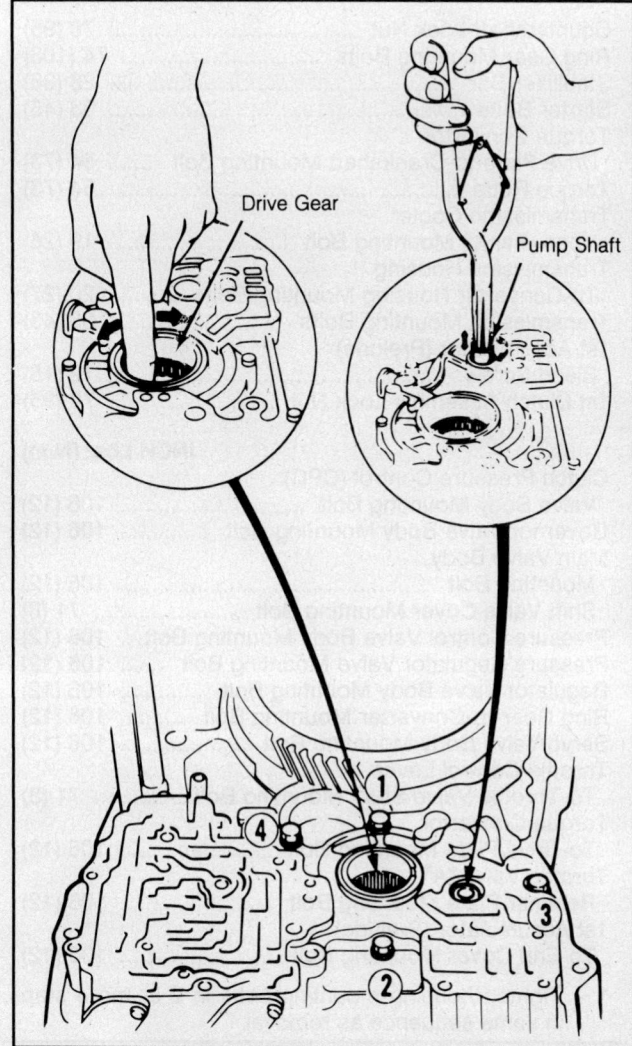

Drive Gear

Pump Shaft

mm and 5 x 168 mm) between pressure control valve and CPC valve body. Slide pressure control valve into position (opposite of removal). *See Fig. 13.* Install pressure control valve body mounting bolts in their proper positions and tighten.

8) Install 2nd, 3rd and 4th accumulator springs in servo body. Check to ensure proper spring diameters and lengths. See SERVO VALVE BODY COMPONENTS & SPRING SPECIFICATIONS table. When installing 2nd/3rd and 4th accumulator covers, compress accumulator springs (by pushing on each cover) before tightening mounting bolts (in a crisscross pattern).

9) Install 3 governor valve mounting bolts (6 mm), with new lock plates, and tighten. Bend lock plate tabs over against bolt heads so bolts will not turn. Install mainshaft and countershaft assemblies into torque converter housing, as an assembly.

NOTE: **Do not tap on shaft ends to force shafts to seat.**

10) If installed, remove lock nuts from mainshaft and countershaft. Install selector hub, countershaft 4th gear and needle bearing. Assemble reverse selector sleeve with reverse shift fork (un-marked side up). Install as an assembly onto countershaft. Ensure flat face on selector sleeve faces up.

11) Install reverse shift fork over servo valve stem. Align hole in valve stem by turning stem so chamfered hole faces fork bolt hole. Install bolt and new lock plate. Bend lock plate tab over bolt head. Install countershaft reverse gear, needle bearing (30 x 36 x 14 mm) and reverse gear collar. Install new gasket, 1 dowel pin (14 x 20 mm) and 2 dowel pins (14 x 25 mm) on convertor housing.

12) Place transmission housing on torque convertor housing. Ensure main valve control shaft lines up with hole in housing and that reverse idler gear meshes with mainshaft and countershaft or housing will not go on. Tighten housing mounting bolts, in 2 or more steps, in the same sequence as removal.

NOTE: **When tightening transmission housing mounting bolts, ensure throttle control bracket is not distorted or damage or transmission shift points will be changed.**

13) Install throttle control lever and spring on throttle control shaft. Install bolt and new lock plate. Bend tab against bolt head. Install parking shift arm, parking lever and spring onto shift shaft. Ensure flat pad of parking lever faces closed end of shift arm. Using a new lock tab, bend tab against bolt head.

NOTE: **Parking shift arm spring should put clockwise tension on shift arm, forcing it against stop pin.**

14) Install 1st gear collar and needle bearing on countershaft. Install collar (26 mm) onto mainshaft. Install reverse idler bearing holder over shaft and onto case. Tighten mounting bolts. Install new "O" rings (19.8 x 1.9 mm) onto mainshaft.

15) Install countershaft 1st gear and parking gear on countershaft. Install stop pin, parking pawl shaft, parking pawl and pawl release spring. Ensure end of parking pawl release spring fits into hole in parking pawl. Release spring should put clockwise tension on pawl, forcing it away from parking gear.

NOTE: **On Accord, when installing .22" (5.5 mm) steel balls, place 5 steel balls in main valve body passages. On Prelude, install 1 steel ball in regulator valve oil passage and 4 balls in main valve body oil passages.**

4) Install stator shaft arm, stop pin and dowel pins. Install regulator valve and tighten 3 mounting bolts. Install steel balls in oil passage(s). Install separator plate and dowel pins. On Prelude, install throttle control shaft.

5) On all models, install servo valve body. Ensure correct length bolt is installed in proper hole or servo will not seal to housing. On Accord, install 2 oil pipes and throttle control shaft. On all models, attach "E" clip to control shaft.

6) Place rollers on each side of manual valve stem. Attach valve to lever with pin and secure with cotter pin. If necessary, install 2 oil passage pipes (8 x 50 mm and 8 x 29.5 mm). Install clutch pressure control (CPC) valve body, body cover and separator plate onto servo valve body. Tighten mounting bolts.

7) Install 1st, 3rd and 4th clutch feed pipes. Install separator plate. Position 2 oil passage pipes (8 x 136

16) Shift lever to "P" and install mainshaft holder. Using breaker bar and 30 mm socket wrench (07907-6890100), install and tighten new countershaft lock nut. Stake lock nut flange into gear groove. Install needle bearing (31 x 36 x 18.5 mm) and thrust washer on mainshaft. Install 1st gear, needle bearing (31 x 37 x 72 mm) and thrust washer (26 mm) on mainshaft.

NOTE: **When installing thrust washer and needle bearing, ensure that unrolled edge of bearing faces thrust washer.**

17) Install 1st clutch on mainshaft. Attach Mainshaft Holder (07932-6890202) from underside of converter housing, then install new mainshaft lock nut (LEFT-HAND threads). Stake lock nut flange to groove in 1st clutch. Install gasket, dowel pins and "O" rings on transmission housing.

18) Install end cover and tighten mounting bolts. If removed, install 1st accumulator (if equipped) onto end cover with new gasket and "O" rings (8.5 x 1.9 mm). Install dipstick and cooler fittings. Do not tighten cooler fittings until transmission is installed in vehicle.

TIGHTENING SPECIFICATIONS

Application	Ft. Lbs. (N.m)
Countershaft Lock Nut	70 (95)
Ring Gear Mounting Bolts	74 (103)
Stabilizer Bar	28 (38)
Starter Bolts	33 (45)
Torque Convertor	
Drive Plate-to-Crankshaft Mounting Bolt	54 (73)
Torque Rods	54 (73)
Transmission Cooler	
Hose (Banjo) Mounting Bolt	19 (26)
Transmission Housing [1]	
To-Converter Housing Mounting Bolts	20 (27)
Transmission Mounting Bolts	33 (45)
1st Accumulator (Prelude)	
Bleed Screw	12 (18)
1st Clutch Assembly Lock Nut	70 (95)

	INCH Lbs. (N.m)
Clutch Pressure Control (CPC)	
Valve Body Mounting Bolt	106 (12)
Governor Valve Body Mounting Bolt	106 (12)
Main Valve Body	
Mounting Bolt	106 (12)
Shift Valve Cover Mounting Bolt	71 (8)
Pressure Control Valve Body Mounting Bolt	106 (12)
Pressure Regulator Valve Mounting Bolt	106 (12)
Regulator Valve Body Mounting Bolt	106 (12)
Ring Gear-to-Converter Mounting Bolt	106 (12)
Servo Valve Body Mounting Bolt	106 (12)
Throttle Control Lever	
To-Throttle Valve Shaft Mounting Bolt	71 (8)
Torque Convertor	
To-Drive Plate Mounting Bolt	106 (12)
Throttle Valve "A"	
Retainer Plate Mounting Bolt	106 (12)
1st Accumulator (Prelude)	
To-End Cover Mounting Bolt	106 (12)

[1] – Tighten housing mounting bolts in 2 or more steps, in same sequence as removal.

JATCO 3N71B, E4N71B, JM600, L3N71B & L4N71B

APPLICATION

TRANSMISSION APPLICATION

Vehicle	Transmission
Chrysler Corp.	
Conquest	JM600
Mazda	
B2000 Pickup	3N71B
B2200 Pickup	3N71B
RX7	L4N71B
Mitsubishi	
Starion	JM600
Nissan/Datsun	
Maxima	L4N71B
Pickup	L3N71B
200SX & 200SX Turbo	L4N71B
300ZX & 300ZX Turbo	E4N71B

IDENTIFICATION

These transmissions are manufactured by Japan Automatic Transmission Company (JATCO). Transmission model may be identified by stamped metal plate attached to right side of transmission case. Plate lists model code on top line and serial number on bottom line.

DESCRIPTION

JATCO 3N71B and L3N71B transmissions are 3-speed units, consisting of 3-element torque converter and 2 planetary gear sets. The E4N71B and L4N71B are 4-speed units, consisting of 3-element torque converter and 3 planetary gear sets.

The L3N71B and L4N71B models use lock-up type torque converter. Model 3N71B uses conventional type converter. Model E4N71B is based on L4N71B and provides electronic control of converter lock-up in all forward gears.

The E4N71B model uses microcomputer to select shift pattern ("standard" or "power") depending upon rate at which accelerator is depressed. Shift pattern programs are set in lock-up control unit depending upon vehicle speed and throttle position.

To provide friction elements required to obtain desired function of planetary gear sets, 3N71B and L3N71B models utilize 2 multiple disc clutches, 1 multi-disc brake, 1 brake band and 1-way clutch. On E4N71B and L4N71B models, 3 multiple disc clutches, 1 multi-disc brake, 2 brake bands and 1-way clutch are used.

On all models, hydraulic system, pressurized by gear-type pump, provides working pressure required to operate friction elements and automatic controls.

LUBRICATION & ADJUSTMENT

See appropriate AUTOMATIC TRANSMISSION SERVICING article in IMPORT GENERAL SERVICING section.

TROUBLE SHOOTING

Possible causes of problem are listed in order of probability for particular malfunction.

ENGINE WILL NOT START WITH SELECTOR LEVER IN "N" OR "P"

Check ignition and starter systems. Adjust selector lever linkage. Check inhibitor switch and wiring.

ENGINE STARTS IN POSITIONS OTHER THAN "N" OR "P"

Check selector lever linkage, inhibitor switch and wiring.

SHARP SHOCK WHEN SHIFTED FROM "N" TO "D"

Engine idle RPM too high. Check vacuum diaphragm and hoses. Check transmission line pressure. Check control valve body. Check forward clutch.

VEHICLE HAS "2", "1", AND "R", BUT NO "D"

Check selector lever linkage. Check control valve body. Check 1-way clutch operation.

VEHICLE HAS "R", BUT NO FORWARD GEARS. TRANSMISSION SLIPS BADLY, POOR ACCELERATION

Check ATF level and quality. Check selector lever adjustment. Check transmission line pressure. Check control valve body. Check forward clutch, oil passage leakage or high-Reverse clutch.

NO MOVEMENT IN ANY RANGE

Check ATF level and quality. Check selector lever linkage adjustment. Check control valve body. Check forward clutch, oil passage leakage or park linkage failure.

SLIPPAGE OF CLUTCHES OR BRAKES WHEN STARTING AWAY

Check ATF level and quality. Check line pressure. Check vacuum diaphragm and hoses. Check oil pump or oil passage leakage.

VEHICLE MOVES IN "N"

Check selector linkage adjustment. Check ATF level and quality. Check control valve body. Check forward clutch.

POOR ACCELERATION, VEHICLE WILL NOT ATTAIN TOP SPEED

Check ATF level and quality. Check selector lever linkage adjustment. Check line pressure. Incorrect stall RPM. Check band servo. Check control valve body. Check 2nd gear band brake, low and Reverse brake, forward clutch, high-Reverse clutch or oil pump.

VEHICLE BRAKES WHEN SHIFTED INTO "R"

Check ATF level and quality. Check band servo. Check forward clutch, 2nd band brake or park linkage.

VEHICLE HAS EXCESSIVE "CREEP"

Adjust engine idle RPM.

VEHICLE HAS NO "CREEP"

Check ATF level and selector lever adjustment. Adjust engine idle RPM. Check control valve body. Check

Automatic Transmissions

JATCO 3N71B, E4N71B, JM600, L3N71B & L4N71B (Cont.)

Fig. 1: Exploded View Of L3N71B 3-Speed As Used In Nissan/Datsun Pickup

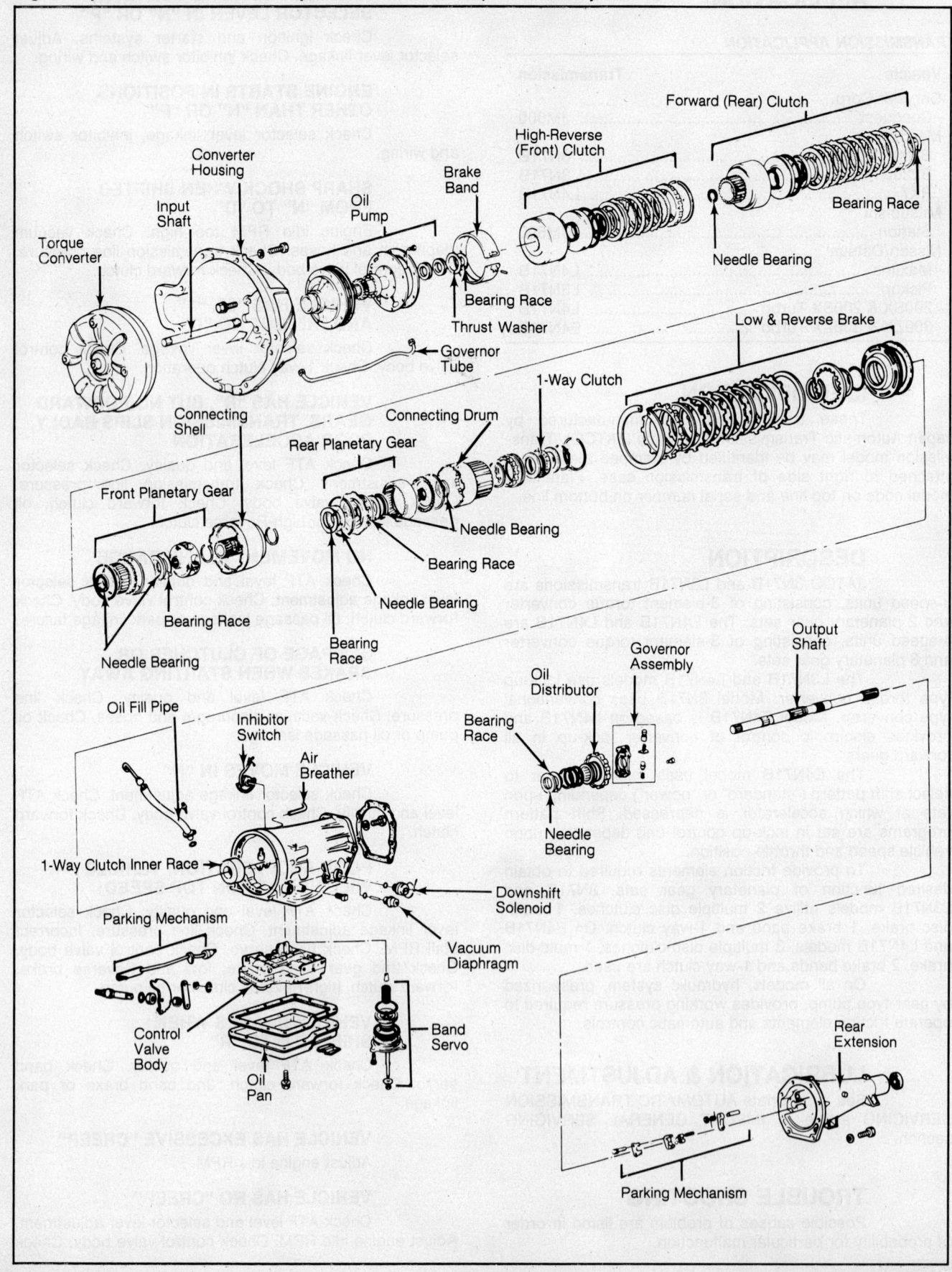

Parking Mechanism

Automatic Transmissions

JATCO 3N71B, E4N71B, JM600, L3N71B & L4N71B (Cont.)

Fig. 2: Exploded View Of E4N71B 4-Speed As Used In Nissan/Datsun 300ZX.

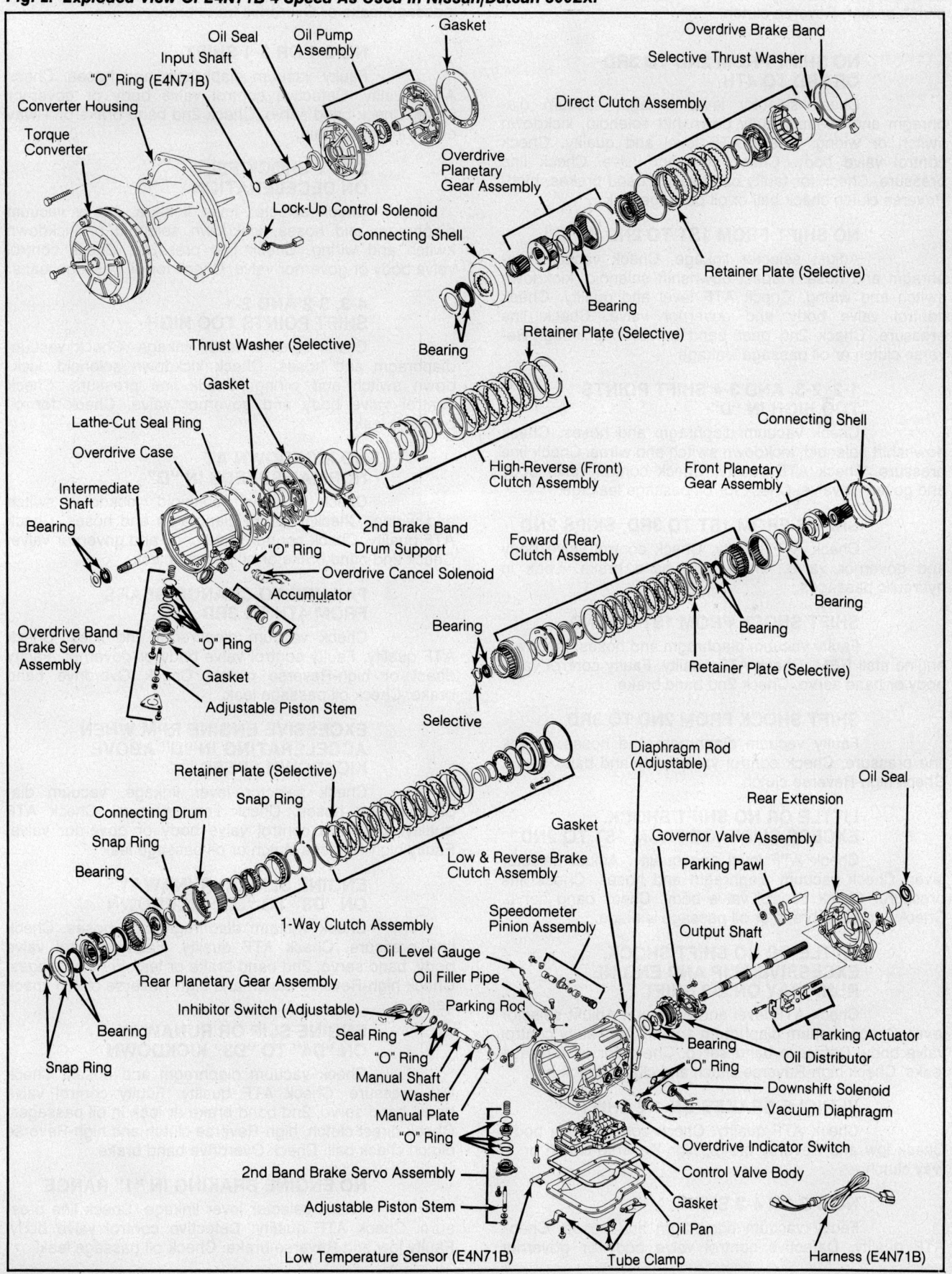

JATCO 3N71B, E4N71B, JM600, L3N71B & L4N71B (Cont.)

oil pump, oil passage leakage, direct clutch, forward clutch or high-Reverse clutch.

NO SHIFT FROM 2ND TO 3RD OR 3RD TO 4TH

Check selector lever linkage, vacuum diaphragm and hoses. Faulty downshift solenoid, kickdown switch or wiring. Check ATF level and quality. Check control valve body. Check governor valve. Check line pressure. Check for faulty band servo, band brakes, high-Reverse clutch check ball or oil passage leak.

NO SHIFT FROM 1ST TO 2ND IN "D"

Adjust selector linkage. Check vacuum diaphragm and hose. Inspect downshift solenoid, kickdown switch and wiring. Check ATF level and quality. Check control valve body and governor valve. Check line pressure. Check 2nd gear band servo. Check high-Reverse clutch or oil passage leakage.

1-2, 2-3, AND 3-4 SHIFT POINTS TOO HIGH IN "D"

Check vacuum diaphragm and hoses. Check downshift solenoid, kickdown switch and wires. Check line pressure. Check ATF quality. Check control valve body and governor valve. Check for oil passage leakage.

SHIFTS FROM 1ST TO 3RD, SKIPS 2ND

Check ATF quality. Check control valve body and governor valve. Check 2nd band brake. Leak in hydraulic passages.

SHIFT SHOCK FROM 1ST TO 2ND

Faulty vacuum diaphragm and hoses. Incorrect engine stall RPM. Check ATF quality. Faulty control valve body or band servo. Check 2nd band brake.

SHIFT SHOCK FROM 2ND TO 3RD

Faulty vacuum diaphragm and hoses. Check line pressure. Check control valve body and band servo. Check high-Reverse clutch.

LITTLE OR NO SHIFT SHOCK. EXCESS SLIPPAGE FROM 1ST TO 2ND

Check ATF level and quality. Adjust selector lever. Check vacuum diaphragm and hoses. Check line pressure. Check control valve body. Check band servo. Check 2nd band brake or oil passage leakage.

LITTLE OR NO SHIFT SHOCK. EXCESSIVE SLIP AND ENGINE RUNAWAY ON 2-3 SHIFT

Check ATF level and pressure. Adjust selector lever. Check vacuum diaphragm and hoses. Faulty control valve body. Defective band servo. Check for oil passage leaks. Check high-Reverse clutch and clutch check ball.

VEHICLE BRAKES ON 1-2 SHIFT

Check ATF quality. Check control valve body. Check low and Reverse brake, high-Reverse clutch or 1-way clutch.

NO 3-2 OR 4-2 SHIFT

Faulty vacuum diaphragm and hoses. Check ATF quality. Defective control valve body or governor valve. Faulty high-Reverse clutch, 2nd band brake, oil passage leaks or Overdrive band brake.

NO 2-1 OR 3-1 SHIFT

Faulty vacuum diaphragm and hoses. Check ATF quality. Defective control valve body or governor valve. Check band servo. Check 2nd band brake or 1-way clutch in power train.

SHIFT SHOCK FELT ON DECELERATION

Check selector lever linkage. Faulty vacuum diaphragm and hoses, kickdown solenoid or kickdown switch and wiring. Check line pressure. Check control valve body or governor valve. Check for oil passage leaks.

4-3, 3-2 AND 2-1 SHIFT POINTS TOO HIGH

Check selector lever linkage. Check vacuum diaphragm and hoses. Check kickdown solenoid, kickdown switch and wiring. Check line pressure. Check control valve body and governor valve. Check for oil passage leak.

NO KICKDOWN AT NORMAL SPEEDS IN "D"

Check kickdown solenoid, kickdown switch and wiring. Check vacuum diaphragm and hoses. Check ATF quality. Check control valve body and governor valve. Check 2nd band brake or oil passage leak.

FAILURE TO CHANGE GEARS FROM 4TH TO 3RD

Check vacuum diaphragm and lines. Check ATF quality. Faulty control valve body or governor. Faulty direct or high-Reverse clutch. Check Overdrive band brake. Check oil passage leak.

EXCESSIVE ENGINE RPM WHEN ACCELERATING IN "D" ABOVE KICKDOWN SPEED

Check selector lever linkage, vacuum diaphragm and hoses. Check line pressure. Check ATF quality. Defective control valve body or governor valve. Faulty high-Reverse clutch or oil passage leak.

ENGINE SLIP OR RUNAWAY ON "D3" TO "D2" KICKDOWN

Check vacuum diaphragm and hoses. Check line pressure. Check ATF quality. Faulty control valve body, band servo, 2nd band brake or leak in oil passages. Check high-Reverse clutch and high-Reverse clutch check ball.

ENGINE SLIP OR RUNAWAY ON "D4" TO "D3" KICKDOWN

Check vacuum diaphragm and hoses. Check line pressure. Check ATF quality. Faulty control valve body, band servo, 2nd band brake or leak in oil passages. Check direct clutch, high-Reverse clutch and high-Reverse clutch check ball. Check Overdrive band brake.

NO ENGINE BRAKING IN "1" RANGE

Check selector lever linkage. Check line pressure. Check ATF quality. Defective control valve body. Faulty low and Reverse brake. Check oil passage leak.

JATCO 3N71B, E4N71B, JM600, L3N71B & L4N71B (Cont.)

TRANSMISSION OVERHEATS

Check ATF level and quality. Faulty rear lubrication or line pressure. Incorrect engine stall speed. Defective control valve body. Faulty band servo, high-Reverse clutch, band brake, low and Reverse brake, oil pump. Possible hydraulic passage leaks. Defective 1-way clutch in torque converter or planetary gear. Faulty torque converter.

TRANSMISSION NOISY IN "P" AND "N"

Check fluid level. Faulty line pressure. Faulty pump.

TRANSMISSION NOISY IN "R" AND ALL "D" RANGES

Check fluid level. Faulty line pressure, forward clutch, oil pump, 1-way clutch in power train or planetary gear.

NOTE: Following problems and possible causes apply ONLY to models with lock-up control and Overdrive functions. These are E4N71B, JM600, L3N71B and L4N71B transmission models.

TORQUE CONVERTER DOES NOT LOCK UP

Governor tube disconnected or damaged. Governor faulty. Incorrect line pressure. Check "O" ring in input shaft and oil pump condition. Speed cut valve (L3N71B model only) or lock-up control valve faulty or defective. Check lock-up orifice in oil pump cover. Faulty torque converter.

CLUTCH AND BAND APPLICATION – 3N71B & L3N71B (ELEMENTS IN USE)

Selector Lever Position	High-Reverse (Front) Clutch	Forward (Rear) Clutch	Low-Reverse Brake	Brake Band	One-Way Clutch
P – PARK			X		
R – REVERSE	X		X		
N – NEUTRAL [1]					
D – DRIVE					
First		X			X
Second		X		X	
Direct	X	X			
2 – SECOND		X		X	
1 – LOW					
First		X	X		
Second		X		X	

[1] – NEUTRAL or PARK – All clutches and bands released and/or ineffective.

CLUTCH AND BAND APPLICATION – E4N71B, JM600 & L4N71B (ELEMENTS IN USE)

Selector Lever Position	Direct Clutch	Overdrive Band	High-Reverse (Ft.) Clutch	Forward (Rear) Clutch	Low & Reverse Brake	Brake Band	One-Way Clutch
P – PARK	X	X			X		
R – REVERSE	X	X	X		X		
N – NEUTRAL [1]	X	X					
D – DRIVE							
First	X	X		X			X
Second	X	X		X		X	
Direct	X	X	X	X		X	
Overdrive		X	X	X		X	
2 – SECOND	X	X		X		X	
1 – LOW							
Second	X	X		X		X	
First	X	X		X	X		X

[1] – NEUTRAL or PARK – All clutches and bands released and/or ineffective.

Automatic Transmissions

JATCO 3N71B, E4N71B, JM600, L3N71B & L4N71B (Cont.)

LOCK-UP PISTON SLIPS

Incorrect line pressure. Check condition of "O" ring in input shaft. Check lock-up orifice in oil pump cover. Check oil pump condition. Faulty torque converter.

LOCK-UP POINT TOO HIGH OR TOO LOW

Governor tube disconnected or damaged. Governor faulty. Check speed cut valve (L3N71B model only) and lock-up control valve condition.

ENGINE STOPPED IN ANY GEAR RANGE

Faulty lock-up control valve. Defective torque converter.

TRANSMISSION SHIFTS TO OVERDRIVE EVEN WHEN CANCEL SWITCH IS ON

Check Overdrive cancel switch and wiring. Check Overdrive cancel solenoid.

TRANSMISSION OVERHEATS

Check line pressure. Check "O" ring in input shaft. Check lock-up orifice in oil pump cover. Oil pump faulty. Torque converter faulty or damaged.

TESTING

LOCK-UP & OVERDRIVE CONTROLS

200SX Lock-Up & Overdrive Control

1) Operation of torque converter lock-up and Overdrive (D_4) is handled by ECU that senses vehicle speed. ECU will activate lock-up solenoid if conditions are correct. Overdrive control switch activates Overdrive cancel solenoid when turned off and transmission can not shift into D_4 range.

2) If lock-up or Overdrive malfunction, perform Lock-Up Control Unit Test first. See NISSAN/DATSUN 200SX LOCK-UP CONTROL UNIT TEST CHART. If ECU tests properly, proceed to lock-up control testing and 3rd/Overdrive control testing as shown in flow charts and associated text.

3) ECU is located in left side of luggage compartment on hatchback models; on coupe models, it is located behind right panel in rear seat area. Testing is to be performed with wiring harness connected to ECU. Using voltmeter, check voltage between terminal No. 5 (Ground) and each terminal as listed in test chart.

4) No. 6 terminal is not used on ECU connector. No. 1 terminal is directly above No. 6. Upper row of connector contains terminals 1 through 5, counting left to right viewed from front. Lower row contains terminals 6 through 10.

NISSAN/DATSUN 200SX LOCK-UP CONTROL UNIT TEST CHART

Terminal	Unit Tested	Test Condition	Result
1	Power Source	Meter between terminals 1 & 5	12 volts at all times
2	Overdrive Cancel Solenoid	Operate Overdrive control switch	Switch ON: 0 volts Switch OFF: 12 volts
3	Lock-Up Solenoid	Driving in "D"	0 volts when ON 12 volts when OFF
4	Throttle Sensor (Ground)	.....	.....
5	Ground	.....	.....
6	Not Used		
7	Speed Sensor	Check voltage variation over 3 feet at very low speed	0 volts to 5.1 (or more) volts
8	Throttle Sensor (Power Source)	Meter between terminals 8 & 5	5 volts at all times
9	Throttle Sensor	Depress and release accelerator pedal	Closed throttle: .4 volts Full throttle: 4 volts
10	Lock-Up Cancel Signal	Depress and release accelerator pedal	Coolant 149°F (65°C) or less: 12 volts at all times Coolant 158°F (70°C) or more: Full throttle: 12 volts Partial throttle: 0 volts

200SX LOCK-UP CONTROL
INSPECTION POINTS

Inspection Item-1

Connect voltmeter between terminals No. 3 and No. 5. Check lock-up signals while running vehicle with partial throttle and Overdrive control switch on. At speeds above 48 MPH, lock-up solenoid should be ON. At speeds below 45 MPH, lock-up solenoid should be OFF.

Inspection Item-2

Check wiring between ECU and lock-up solenoid. Check connections and continuity.

Inspection Item-3

Make sure "O" ring is installed on tip of lock-up solenoid. Check that solenoid clicks when 12 volts is applied to it.

Inspection Item-4

Check wiring between ECU and following sensors: throttle and vehicle speed. Check wiring between ECU and Overdrive control switch. Check connections and continuity.

Inspection Item-5

Check signals of input sensors and switches. See NISSAN/DATSUN 200SX LOCK-UP CONTROL UNIT TEST CHART for correct results.

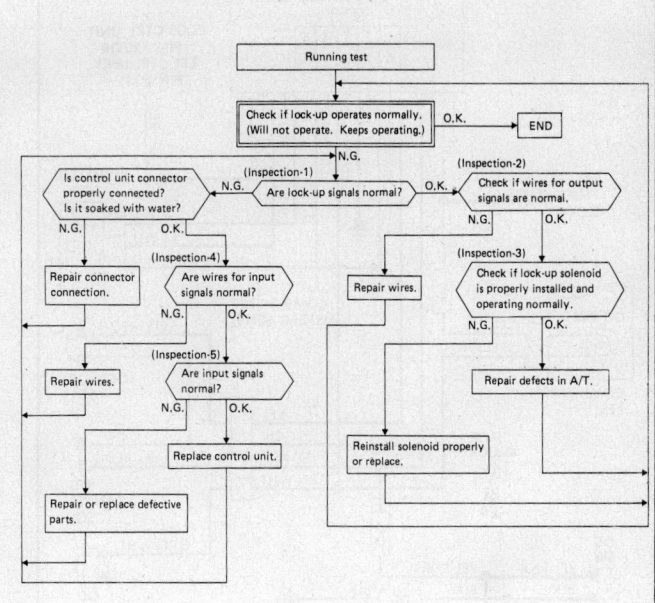

200SX 3RD/OVERDRIVE CONTROL
INSPECTION POINTS

Inspection Item-1

Check operation of Overdrive solenoid by applying 12 volts to solenoid. Good solenoid will click if working.

Inspection Item-2

Check continuity between terminals of Overdrive control switch. There should be no continuity when control switch is ON. There should be continuity when control switch is OFF.

Inspection Item-3

Check wiring between ECU and vehicle speed sensor. Check wiring between ECU and terminal No. 20 on EFI control unit connector terminal. Check connections and continuity.

Inspection Item-4

Check ECU connector terminals No. 4 and No. 10 for continuity and voltage. See NISSAN/DATSUN 200SX LOCK-UP CONTROL UNIT TEST CHART for correct results of tests.

Inspection Item-5

Check wiring between ECU and Overdrive cancel solenoid. Check connections and continuity.

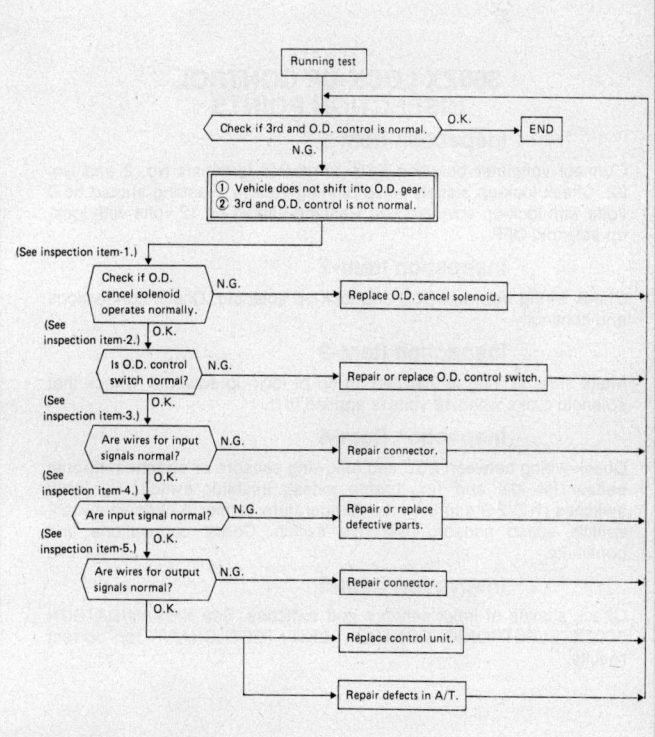

Automatic Transmissions

JATCO 3N71B, E4N71B, JM600, L3N71B & L4N71B (Cont.)

Fig. 3: 1985 Nissan/Datsun 200SX A/T Lock-Up Control Wiring Diagram

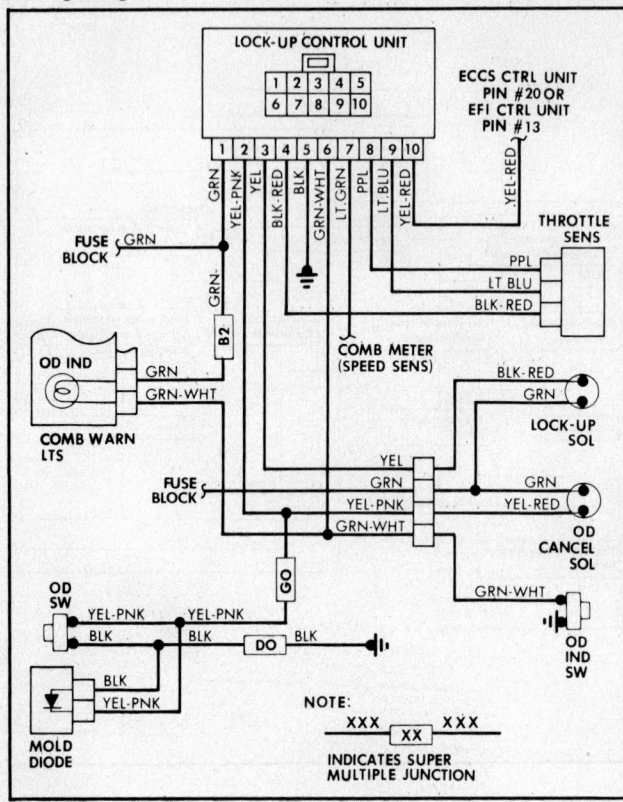

300ZX Electronic Lock-Up & Overdrive Control

1) Operation of torque converter lock-up and Overdrive (D_4) is handled by electronic control unit (ECU), located on floor near driver's seat. ECU will activate lock-up solenoid in all forward ranges if conditions are correct. Either "standard" or "power" shift pattern is selected by ECU depending upon rate at which accelerator is depressed.

2) Vehicle speed and throttle position are both inputs to ECU. Power shift switch activates Overdrive cancel solenoid when turned off and transmission will not shift into D_4 range. If lock-up or Overdrive malfunction, test lock-up control unit first. See NISSAN/DATSUN 300ZX ELECTRONIC LOCK-UP CONTROL UNIT TEST CHART.

3) Testing is to be performed with wiring harness connected to ECU. Using voltmeter, check voltage between terminal No. 22 (Ground) and each terminal as listed in test chart. If ECU tests properly, proceed to lock-up, Overdrive, downshift, shift pattern change, A.S.C.D. (Automatic Speed Control Device), and kickdown control testing as shown in flow charts and associated text.

4) Terminal No. 20 is not used on ECU connector. Terminal No. 1 is directly above No. 6. Top row of connector contains terminals 1 through 17, viewed from front. Bottom row contains terminals 6 through 22.

300ZX LOCK-UP CONTROL INSPECTION POINTS

Inspection Item-1

Connect voltmeter between ECU connector terminals No. 2 and No. 22. Check lock-up signals while running vehicle. Reading should be 0 volts with lock-up solenoid ON. Reading should be 12 volts with lock-up solenoid OFF.

Inspection Item-2

Check wiring between ECU and lock-up solenoid. Check connections and continuity.

Inspection Item-3

Make sure "O" ring is installed on tip of lock-up solenoid. Check that solenoid clicks when 12 volts is applied to it.

Inspection Item-4

Check wiring between ECU and following sensors or switches: throttle sensor (at idle and full throttle sides); inhibitor switch (D_2); shift switches (1-2, 2-3 and 3-4); low-temperature sensor; kickdown switch; vehicle speed sensor; Overdrive switch. Check connections and continuity.

Inspection Item-5

Check signals of input sensors and switches. See NISSAN/DATSUN 300ZX ELECTRONIC CONTROL UNIT TEST CHART for correct results.

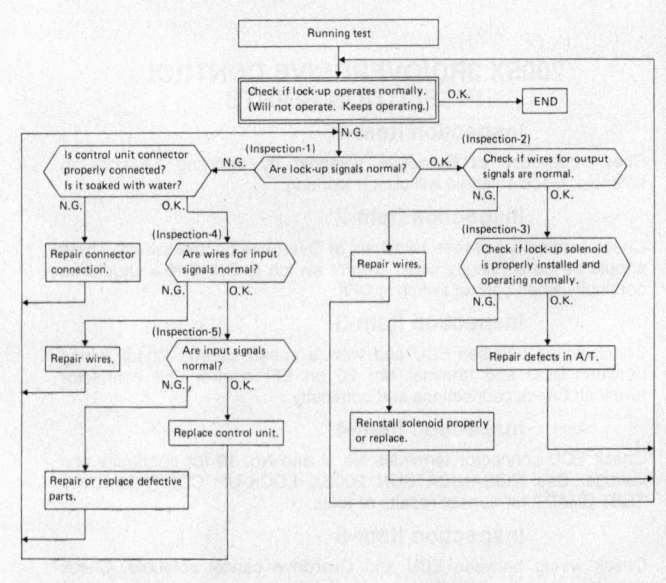

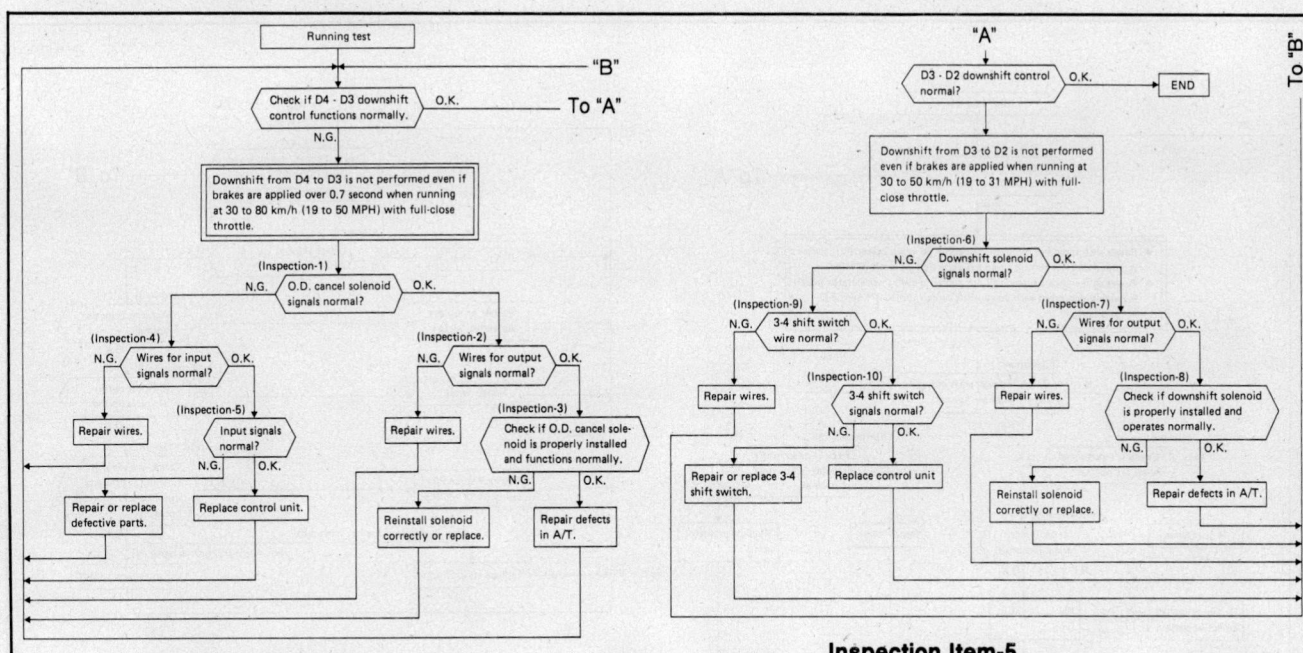

300ZX DOWNSHIFT CONTROL INSPECTION POINTS

Inspection Item-1

Jack up rear wheels. Set selector lever in "D" range. Accelerate to D_4 speed at partial throttle. When vehicle speed is in 19-50 MPH range, close throttle fully. Apply brakes for longer than .7 seconds. Check output signals to Overdrive cancel solenoid. See NISSAN/DATSUN 300ZX ELECTRONIC CONTROL UNIT TEST CHART for correct results.

Inspection Item-2

Check wiring between ECU and Overdrive cancel solenoid. Check connections and continuity.

Inspection Item-3

Apply 12 volts to Overdrive cancel solenoid. Proper operation is indicated by click from Overdrive cancel solenoid.

Inspection Item-4

Check wiring between ECU and and following sensors and switches: inhibitor switch (D_2); shift switches (1-2, 2-3 and 3-4); brake switch; idle contact switch; throttle sensor; vehicle speed sensor. Check connections and continuity.

Inspection Item-5

Check signals from input sensors and switches. See NISSAN/DATSUN 300ZX ELECTRONIC CONTROL UNIT TEST CHART for correct results.

Inspection Item-6

Jack up rear wheels. Set selector lever in "D" range. Accelerate to D_3 speed at partial throttle. When vehicle speed is in 19-31 MPH range, close throttle fully and apply brakes. See NISSAN/DATSUN 300ZX ELECTRONIC CONTROL UNIT TEST CHART to check downshift solenoid operation.

Inspection Item-7

Check wiring between ECU and downshift solenoid. Check connections and continuity.

Inspection Item-8

Apply 12 volts to downshift solenoid. Proper operation is indicated by click from downshift solenoid.

Inspection Item-9

Check wiring between ECU and 3-4 shift switch. Check connections and continuity.

Inspection Item-10

Check signals from 3-4 switch. See NISSAN/DATSUN 300ZX ELECTRONIC CONTROL UNIT TEST CHART for correct results.

300ZX KICKDOWN CONTROL INSPECTION POINTS

Inspection Item-1

Turn ignition ON and depress accelerator fully. Proper operation is indicated by click from downshift solenoid.

Inspection Item-2

Connect voltmeter to ECU connector terminals No. 21 and No. 22. Reading should be 0 volts with wide open throttle. Reading should be 5 volts at any less than full throttle.

Inspection Item-3

Check wiring between ECU and kickdown switch. Check connections and continuity.

Inspection Item-4

Check wiring between ECU and downshift solenoid. Check connections and continuity.

Inspection Item-5

Apply 12 volts to downshift solenoid. Proper operation is indicated by click from downshift solenoid.

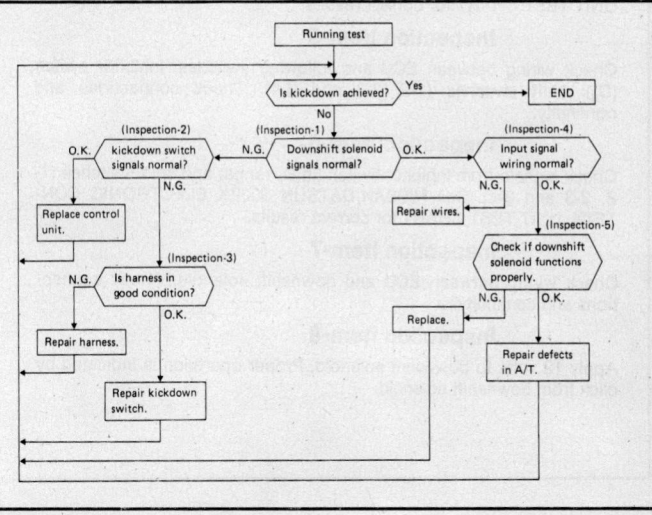

Automatic Transmissions

JATCO 3N71B, E4N71B, JM600, L3N71B & L4N71B (Cont.)

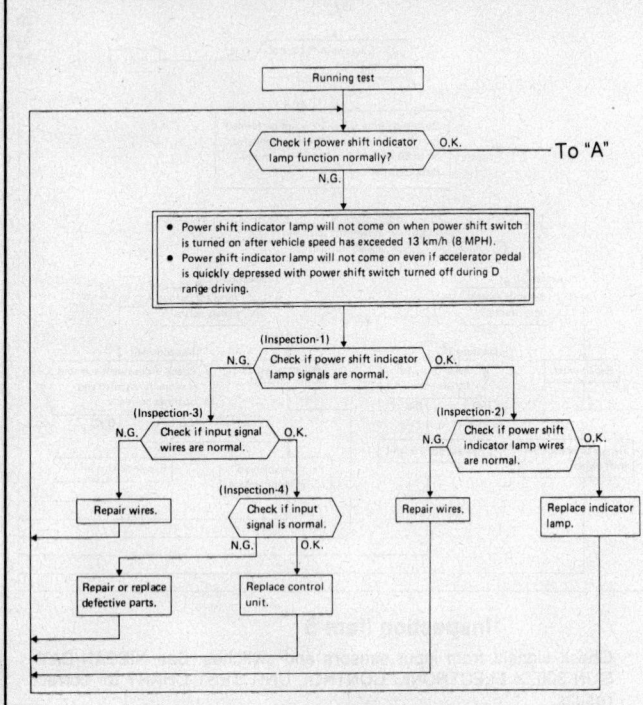

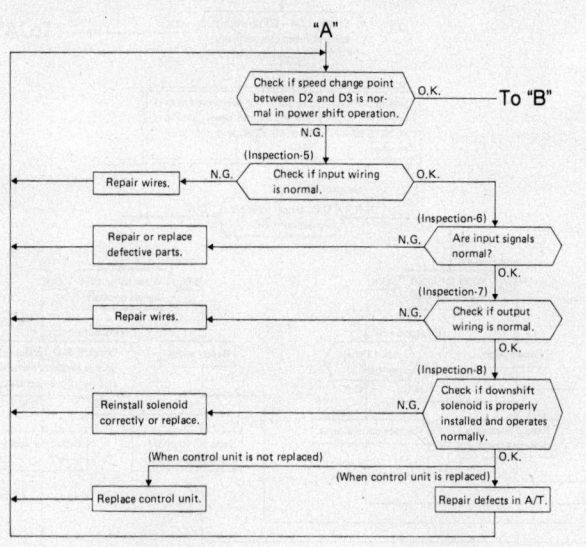

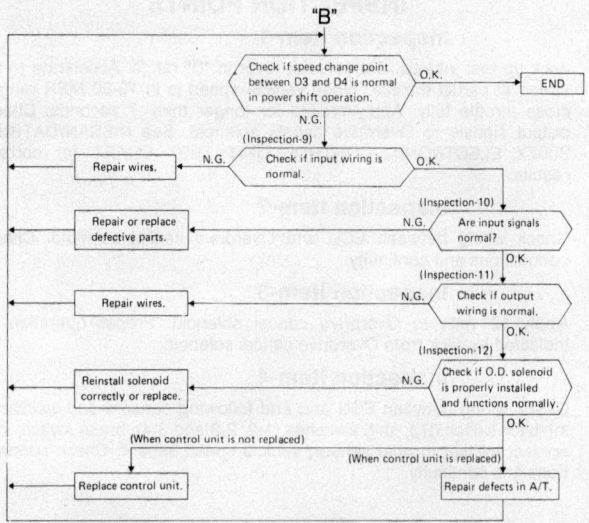

300ZX SHIFT PATTERN CHANGE CONTROL INSPECTION POINTS

Inspection Item-1

Jack up rear wheels and accelerate in "D" range. Turn on power shift switch as speed goes over 8 MPH. Depress and release accelerator pedal quickly at same time. Check power shift indicator light. See NISSAN/DATSUN 300ZX ELECTRONIC CONTROL UNIT TEST CHART for correct results.

Inspection Item-2

Check wiring between ECU and power shift indicator lamp. Check connections and continuity.

Inspection Item-3

Check wiring between ECU and following sensors and switches: power shift switch; throttle sensor; vehicle speed sensor. Check connections and continuity.

Inspection Item-4

Check signals from power shift switch, throttle sensor and vehicle speed sensor. See NISSAN/DATSUN 300ZX ELECTRONIC CONTROL UNIT TEST CHART for correct results.

Inspection Item-5

Check wiring between ECU and following switches: inhibitor switch (D_2); shift switches (1-2, 2-3 and 3-4). Check connections and continuity.

Inspection Item-6

Check signals from inhibitor switch (in D_2 range) and shift switches (1-2, 2-3 and 3-4). See NISSAN/DATSUN 300ZX ELECTRONIC CONTROL UNIT TEST CHART for correct results.

Inspection Item-7

Check wiring between ECU and downshift solenoid. Check connections and continuity.

Inspection Item-8

Apply 12 volts to downshift solenoid. Proper operation is indicated by click from downshift solenoid.

Inspection Item-9

Check wiring between ECU and 3-4 shift switch. Check connections and continuity.

Inspection Item-10

Check signals from 3-4 shift switch. See NISSAN/DATSUN 300ZX ELECTRONIC CONTROL UNIT TEST CHART for correct results.

Inspection Item-11

Check wiring between ECU and Overdrive cancel solenoid. Check connections and continuity.

Inspection Item-12

Apply 12 volts to Overdrive cancel solenoid. Proper operation is indicated by click from downshift solenoid.

300ZX A.S.C.D. PARTS INSPECTION POINTS

Inspection Item-1

Jack up rear wheels. Set selector lever in "D" range. Accelerate to D_4 speed at partial throttle. When vehicle speed is in 19-50 MPH range, close throttle fully. Apply brakes for longer than .7 seconds. Check output signals to Overdrive cancel solenoid. See NISSAN/DATSUN 300ZX ELECTRONIC CONTROL UNIT TEST CHART for correct results.

Inspection Item-2

Connect voltmeter to ECU connector terminals No. 13 and No. 22. Release vehicle speed setting repeatedly while driving in A.S.C.D. (Automatic Speed Control Device) mode. If A.S.C.D. is set, reading should be 12 volts. If A.S.C.D. is released, reading should be 0 volts.

Inspection Item-3

Inspect physical condition of A.S.C.D. wiring harness. Check connections and continuity.

Inspection Item-4

Test A.S.C.D. controller.

Inspection Item-5

Connect voltmeter to ECU connector terminals No. 15 and No. 22. Release vehicle speed setting repeatedly while driving in A.S.C.D. mode in D_4 range. If accelerator pedal is depressed, reading should be 0 volts. If accelerator pedal is released, reading should be 5 volts.

Inspection Item-6

Inspect physical condition of A.S.C.D. wiring harness. Check connections and continuity.

Inspection Item-7

Check wiring between ECU and Overdrive cancel solenoid. Check connections and continuity.

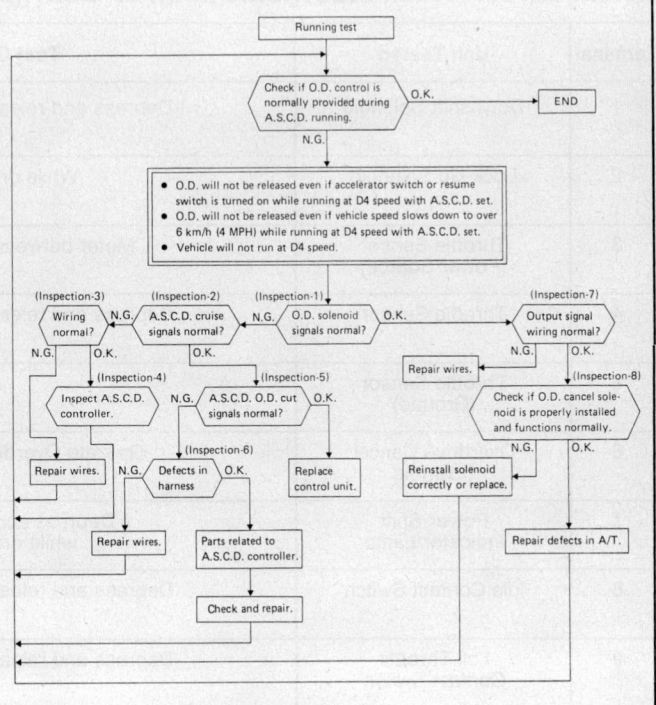

Inspection Item-8

Apply 12 volts to Overdrive cancel solenoid. Proper operation is indicated by click from Overdrive cancel solenoid.

300ZX OVERDRIVE CONTROL INSPECTION POINTS

Inspection Item-1

Turn ignition key ON. Set Overdrive switch to "Overdrive Release" position. Proper operation is indicated by click from Overdrive solenoid.

Inspection Item-2

Check signals of following input sensors and switches: shift switches (1-2, 2-3 and 3-4); vehicle speed sensor; low-temperature sensor; full throttle contact switch; kickdown switch. See NISSAN/DATSUN 300ZX ELECTRONIC CONTROL UNIT TEST CHART for correct results.

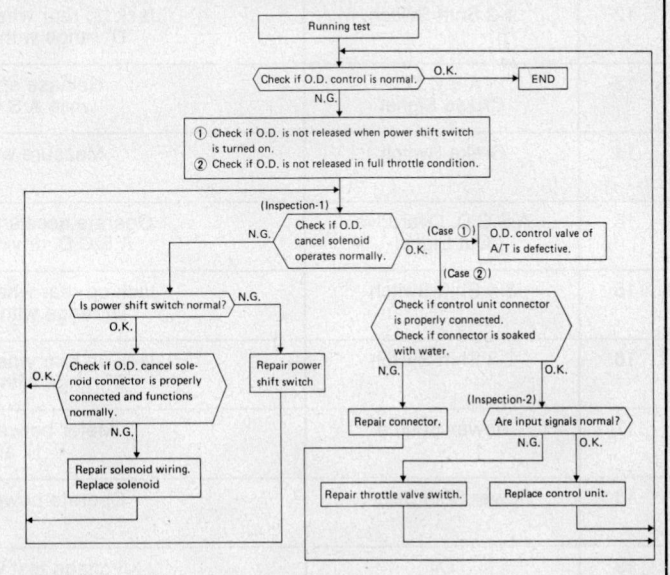

300ZX Self-Diagnosing

1) If power shift indicator flickers at intervals of 1 second up to D_2 speed (8-9 MPH), check for broken wiring between shift switch and ECU connector harness. If wiring is good, shift switch is malfunctioning.

2) If power shift indicator flickers at intervals of 1 second above D_2 speed (8-9 MPH), vehicle speed sensor is defective or wiring between vehicle speed sensor and ECU is broken.

3) To check vehicle speed sensor, connect voltmeter between terminals No. 11 and No. 22 of ECU connector. Good vehicle speed sensor will give voltage reading varying from 0 volts to over 5 volts while driving vehicle very slowly over 3 feet.

4) If power shift indicator light flickers at 1/4 second intervals, throttle sensor is defective, wiring harness is broken between throttle sensor and ECU, or ECU is malfunctioning.

5) To check throttle sensor, connect voltmeter to ECU connector terminals No. 4 and No. 22. Reading should be 0 volts in fully closed throttle position. Reading should be 4 volts in full open throttle position.

Automatic Transmissions

JATCO 3N71B, E4N71B, JM600, L3N71B & L4N71B (Cont.)

NISSAN/DATSUN 300ZX ELECTRONIC LOCK-UP CONTROL UNIT TEST CHART

Terminal	Unit Tested	Test Condition	Result
1	Downshift Solenoid	Depress and release accelerator pedal	0 volts when ON 12 volts when OFF
2	Lock-Up Solenoid	While driving in "D"	O volts when ON 12 volts when OFF
3	Throttle Sensor (Power Source)	Meter between terminals 3 & 5	5 volts at all times
4	Throttle Sensor	Depress and release accelerator pedal	Closed throttle: .4 volts Full throttle: 4 volts
5	Throttle Sensor (Ground)	......	......
6	Overdrive Cancel Solenoid	Operate Overdrive cancel switch	Switch ON: 0 volts Switch OFF: 12 volts
7	Power Shift Indicator Lamp	Depress accelerator pedal while driving in "D"	0 volts when ON 12 volts if OFF
8	Idle Contact Switch	Depress and release accelerator pedal	Closed throttle: 12 volts Partial throttle: 0 volts
9	Full Throttle Contact Switch	Depress and release accelerator pedal	Above 1/2 throttle: 12 volts Below 1/4 throttle: 0 volts
10	Inhibitor "2" Range Switch	Shift lever in "2" or other ranges	12 volts in "2" 0 volts in other ranges
11	Speed Sensor	Check voltage variation over 3 feet at very low speed	0 volts to 5.1 (or more) volts
12	1-2 Shift Switch	Jack up rear wheels, accelerate in "D" range with partial throttle	0 volts in D1 5 volts in D2, D3, D4
13	A.S.C.D. Cruise Signal	Release speed setting while A.S.C.D driving	A.S.C.D. released: 0 volts A.S.C.D. set: 12 volts
14	Brake Switch	Measure while braking	Braking: 12 volts Not braking: 0 volts
15	A.S.C.D. Overdrive Cut Signal	Operate accelerator switch while A.S.C.D. driving at D4 speed	Switch ON: 0 volts Switch OFF: 5 volts
15	3-4 Shift Switch	Jack up rear wheels, accelerate in "D" range with partial throttle	0 volts in D1, D2, D3 5 volts in D4
16	2-3 Shift Switch	Jack up rear wheels, accelerate in "D" range with partial throttle	0 volts in D1 & D2 5 volts in D3 & D4
17	Power Source	Meter between terminals 17 and 22	12 volts at all times
18	Power Shift Switch	Operate power shift switch	Switch ON: 0 volts Switch OFF: 12 volts
19	Oil Low Temperature Sensor	Voltage test while installed Continuity test while removed	Oil over 68°F (20°C): 5 volts Oil under 50°F (10°C): 0 volts 68°F (20°C) & higher: OPEN 50°F (10°C) & lower: CLOSED
20	Not Used	......	......
21	Kickdown Switch	Depress and release accelerator pedal	Full throttle: 0 volts Less than full throttle: 5 volts
22	Ground	......	......

JATCO 3N71B, E4N71B, JM600, L3N71B & L4N71B (Cont.)

Fig. 4: Nissan/Datsun 300ZX Electronic A/T Lock-Up Wiring Diagram

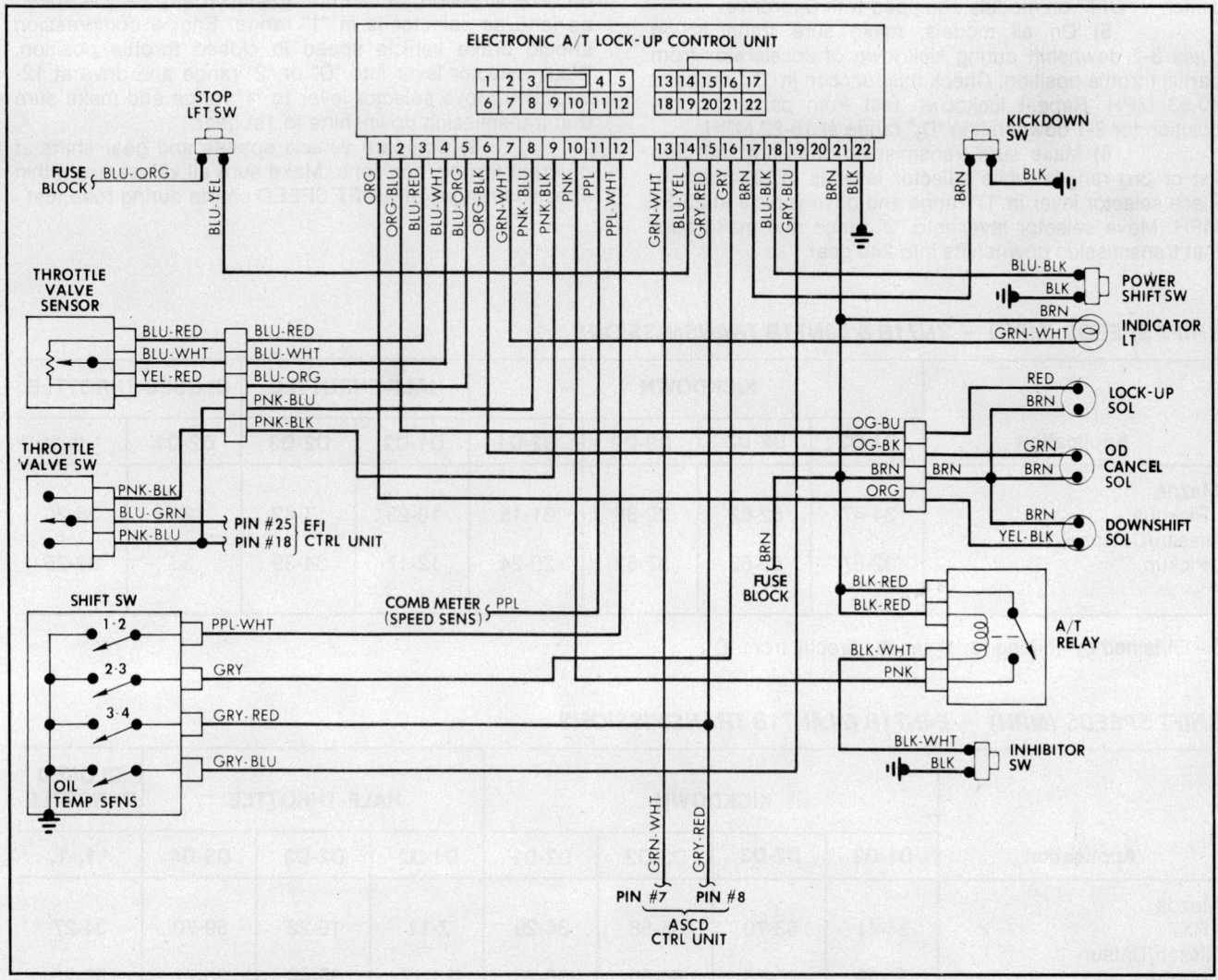

ATF CONDITION

1) Before performing road test, check color, texture and odor of ATF. Dark or Black ATF with burned odor indicates worn friction material is in ATF. Milky Pink ATF indicates water contamination, often from road water entering filler tube or breather. Leaks in lower radiator tank or in ATF lines inside tank can also cause water contamination.

2) ATF that is tacky and light-to-dark Brown (varnished) indicates oxidation. This can be caused by overfilling or underfilling. Overheating of ATF will also cause oxidation to occur.

3) If ATF leak is suspected, clean area of transmission in question. Raise vehicle, supporting it securely, and start engine. Apply foot brake and place selector lever in Drive. After several minutes, stop engine and look for fresh leakage.

4) Ensure that ATF level, shift linkage, control linkage and detent cable adjustments have been checked and adjusted as needed. Attach vacuum gauge to engine to measure intake manifold vacuum.

ROAD TEST

1) Place selector lever in "P" range and start engine. Stop engine and repeat starting procedure in all gear ranges, including Neutral. Drive vehicle to slight upgrade and park vehicle. Place selector lever in "P" and release parking brake. Make sure vehicle remains locked in place.

2) Shift from "P" to "R" range and note quality of shift engagement. Drive vehicle in Reverse long enough to detect any slippage or other problems. Shift from "R" and "D" ranges in and out of "N" range while noting shift quality. Release parking brake while vehicle is in "N" range. Make sure vehicle does not move or "creep" when accelerator is lightly depressed.

NOTE: **If transmission is new or recently rebuilt, vehicle might have some slight movement. This is NOT cause for concern.**

3) Move selector lever from "N" to "D" range. Check shift quality. Take vehicle on road test in "D" range. Compare actual vehicle speeds at upshift and downshift points with those listed in SHIFT SPEED charts. Note points at which shifting shock and clutch engagement occur.

4) On E4N71B models, compare shift speed as accelerator is depressed slowly or quickly. Make sure that Overdrive range cannot be selected when power shift

Automatic Transmissions

JATCO 3N71B, E4N71B, JM600, L3N71B & L4N71B (Cont.)

switch is "ON" (E4N71B models) or Overdrive cancel switch is "OFF" on models equipped with Overdrive.

   5) On all models, make sure transmission gives 3-2 downshift during kickdown of accelerator from partial throttle position. Check this function in "D_3" range at 40-53 MPH. Repeat kickdown test from partial throttle position for 2-1 downshift in "D_2" range at 16-22 MPH.

   6) Make sure transmission does not shift into 1st or 3rd ranges while selector lever is in "2" position. Place selector lever in "D" range and drive vehicle at 25-31 MPH. Move selector lever into "2" range and make sure that transmission downshifts into 2nd gear.

   7) Place selector lever in "1" range and drive on. Transmission should not upshift at any vehicle speed as long as selector is in "1" range. Engine compression should brake vehicle speed in closed throttle position. Place selector lever into "D" or "2" range and drive at 12-19 MPH. Move selector lever to "1" range and make sure that transmission downshifts to 1st gear.

   8) Compare vehicle speeds and gear shifts at different throttle positions. Make sure all values are within specified ranges of SHIFT SPEED charts during road test.

SHIFT SPEEDS (MPH) – 3N71B & L3N71B TRANSMISSIONS

Application	KICKDOWN				HALF-THROTTLE		CLOSED THROTTLE	
	D1-D2	D2-D3	D3-D2	D2-D1	D1-D2	D2-D3	D2-D1	[1] 1_2-1_1
Mazda								
Pickups	34-47	52-62	72-55	31-15	10-23	17-42	12-5	35-25
Nissan/Datsun								
Pickup	32-37	58-62	57-52	29-24	12-17	34-39	.....	29-25

[1] – Obtained by shifting to "1" range, directly from "D".

SHIFT SPEEDS (MPH) – E4N71B & L4N71B TRANSMISSIONS

Application	KICKDOWN				HALF-THROTTLE			CLOSED THROTTLE
	D1-D2	D2-D3	D3-D2	D2-D1	D1-D2	D2-D3	D3-D4	[1] 1_2-1_1
Mazda								
RX7	34-41	63-70	65-58	36-29	7-11	19-22	59-70	34-27
Nissan/Datsun								
Maxima	34-39	60-65	60-55	30-25	13-17	35-40	66-71	30-25
200SX	32-37	57-62	57-52	29-24	9-19	37-46	51-59	31-24
200SX Turbo	28-32	47-51	47-42	26-22	11-18	16-32	26-38	39-34
300ZX	37-42	63-68	60-55	31-26	7-14	29-37	42-52	29-24
300ZX Turbo	37-43	64-70	58-53	34-29	10-16	13-21	25-35	34-27

[1] – Obtained by shifting to "1" range, directly from "D".

SHIFT SPEEDS (MPH) – JM600 TRANSMISSION

Application	KICKDOWN				HALF-THROTTLE			CLOSED THROTTLE
	D1-D2	D2-D3	D3-D2	D2-D1	D1-D2	D2-D3	D3-D4	[1] 1_2-1_1
Chrysler Corp.								
Conquest	14-21	42-50	31-21	12-7	10-16	12-21	25-35	32-26
Mitsubishi								
Starion	14-21	42-50	31-21	12-7	10-16	12-21	25-35	32-26

[1] – Obtained by shifting to "1" range, directly from "D".

JATCO 3N71B, E4N71B, JM600, L3N71B & L4N71B (Cont.)

HYDRAULIC PRESSURE TESTS
Line Pressure Tests

1) Make sure engine fluids and ATF are at correct levels. Connect oil pressure gauges to line pressure and 2nd servo release test ports. *See Fig. 5.* Connect vacuum gauge so intake manifold vacuum can be monitored. Warm up engine until coolant and ATF are at operating temperatures.

Fig. 5: Line Pressure Test Ports

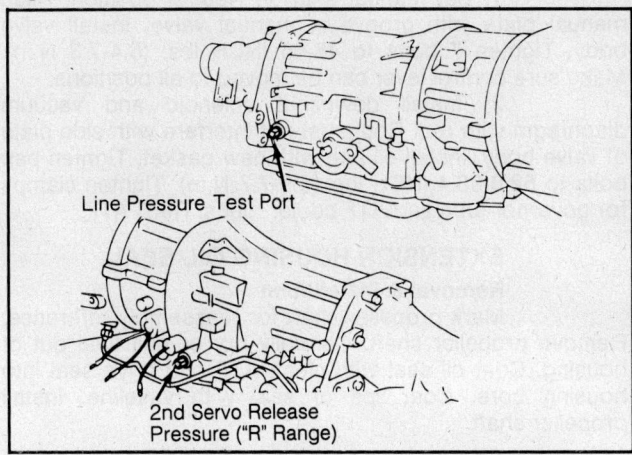

Line Pressure Test Port

2nd Servo Release
Pressure ("R" Range)

Use 2nd servo release port for measurements in "R" range.

LINE PRESSURE SPECIFICATIONS
(CHRYSLER CORP./MITSUBISHI)

Application	psi (kg/cm²)
At Idle Speed	
In "R"	44-64 (3.0-4.5)
In "D"	40-54 (2.8-3.8)
In "2"	114-164 (8.0-11.5)
In "1"	40-54 (2.8-3.8)
At Stall Speed	
In "R"	284-341 (20.0-24.0)
In "D"	242-273 (17.0-19.2)
In "2"	242-259 (17.0-18.2)
In "1"	249-273 (17.5-19.2)

2) Block front and rear wheels. Set parking brake firmly. Place selector lever in range to be checked. Note pressure reading on gauge at idle. Apply brake pedal fully and check pressure reading at full throttle (stall point).

LINE PRESSURE SPECIFICATIONS (MAZDA)

Application	psi (kg/cm²)
At Idle Speed	
In "R"	57-110 (4.0-7.7)
In "D"	43-57 (3.0-4.0)
In "2"	114-171 (8.0-12.0)
In "1"	43-57 (3.0-4.0)
At Stall Speed	
In "R"	228-270 (16.0-19.0)
In "D"	128-156 (9.0-11.0)
In "2"	114-171 (8.0-12.0)
In "1"	128-156 (9.0-11.0)

3) Use readings at 2nd servo release port for testing in "R" range. All pressures should be in range shown in appropriate LINE PRESSURE SPECIFICATIONS

table. Pressure readings should increase steadily as car speed increases under light load. Maximum pressure drop between shift points is 14 psi (.98 kg/cm²). Excessive pressure drop could be caused by internal leak at servo or clutch seal.

CAUTION: Do not maintain wide open throttle condition longer than 5 seconds for any reading.

LINE PRESSURE SPECIFICATIONS (NISSAN/DATSUN)

Application	psi (kg/cm²)
At Idle Speed	
In "R"	
200SX	60-80 (4.2-5.6)
200SX Turbo	57-71 (4.0-5.0)
300ZX	65-85 (4.6-6.0)
300ZX Turbo	44-64 (3.1-4.5)
All Others	60-80 (4.2-5.6)
In "D"	
200SX	46-54 (3.2-3.8)
200SX Turbo	43-57 (3.0-4.0)
300ZX	40-54 (2.8-3.8)
300ZX Turbo	40-54 (2.8-3.8)
All Others	46-54 (3.2-3.8)
In "2"	
200SX	85-166 (6.0-11.7)
200SX Turbo	85-171 (6.0-12.0)
300ZX	114-156 (8.0-11.0)
300ZX Turbo	114-164 (8.0-11.5)
All Others	85-166 (6.0-11.7)
In "1"	
200SX	46-54 (3.2-3.8)
200SX Turbo	43-57 (3.0-4.0)
300ZX	40-54 (2.8-3.8)
300ZX Turbo	40-54 (2.8-3.8)
All Others	46-54 (3.2-3.8)
At Stall Speed	
In "R"	
200SX	171-230 (14.1-16.2)
200SX Turbo	313-356 (22.0-25.0)
300ZX	284-347 (20.0-24.4)
300ZX Turbo	284-341 (20.0-24.4)
All Others	203-230 (14.3-16.2)
In "D"	
200SX	141-158 (9.9-11.1)
200SX Turbo	259-282 (18.2-19.8)
300ZX	156-178 (11.0-12.5)
300ZX Turbo	242-273 (17.0-19.2)
All Others	141-158 (9.9-11.1)
In "2"	
200SX	144-165 (10.1-11.6)
200SX Turbo	259-282 (18.2-19.8)
300ZX	156-185 (11.0-13.0)
300ZX Turbo	242-273 (17.0-19.2)
All Others	145-166 (10.2-11.7)
In "1"	
200SX	141-158 (9.9-11.1)
200SX Turbo	259-282 (18.2-19.8)
300ZX	156-178 (11.0-12.5)
300ZX Turbo	242-273 (17.0-19.2)
All Others	141-158 (9.9-11.1)

Governor Pressure Test

1) Governor pressure test should only be used if vehicle shift speeds are different than those indicated in SHIFT SPEED chart. Install pressure gauge in governor

JATCO 3N71B, E4N71B, JM600, L3N71B & L4N71B (Cont.)

pressure port on transmission case. Use Pipe Adapter (49 HO75 406) to connect both pressure gauge and governor pipe at same time.

2) Read pressure with vehicle running at speeds indicated in GOVERNOR PRESSURE SPECIFICATIONS table. If pressures are incorrect, disassemble and clean governor assembly. Repeat tests after reinstalling governor.

GOVERNOR PRESSURE SPECIFICATIONS

Application	psi (kg/cm²)
Chrysler Corp.	1
Mazda	
RX7	
At 20 MPH	11-17 (0.8-1.2)
At 35 MPH	20-28 (1.4-2.0)
At 55 MPH	46-58 (3.2-4.1)
Pickup	
At 20 MPH	11-17 (0.8-1.2)
At 35 MPH	20-28 (1.4-2.0)
At 55 MPH	38-48 (2.7-3.4)
Mitsubishi	1
Nissan/Datsun	1

1 – Information not available from manufacturer.

STALL TEST

1) Check engine and transmission for proper lubricant levels. Bring engine to normal operating temperature. Attach tachometer to engine and position so it is visible from driver's seat. Block front and rear wheels, and apply hand brake.

2) Place one foot firmly on brake pedal and place selector lever in "D" position. Gradually increase engine speed to wide open throttle. When engine speed will not increase further, note tachometer reading. Release throttle to idle position immediately.

CAUTION: Do not hold wide open throttle position for more than 5 seconds. Severe transmission damage due to heat and load may result. DO NOT test more than 2 ranges without driving vehicle to cool engine and ATF.

3) Move selector lever to "N" range and run engine at 1200 RPM for at least 1 minute to cool engine and ATF. Repeat stall test procedure with shift lever in "2", "1" and "R" ranges.

STALL SPEED SPECIFICATIONS

Application	Stall RPM
Chrysler Corp.	
Conquest	2350-2650
Mitsubishi	
Starion	2350-2650
Nissan/Datsun	
Maxima	1800-2100
Pickup	2000-2300
200SX	2000-2300
200SX Turbo	2000-2200
300ZX	2150-2450
300ZX Turbo	2500-2800
Mazda	
RX7	2400-2650
Pickups	2000-2250

SERVICE (IN VEHICLE)

VALVE BODY

Removal
Drain ATF by removing pan. Remove downshift solenoid and vacuum diaphragm with vacuum rod. Remove 7 bolts holding valve body to transmission case. Remove valve body from transmission.

Installation
1) Set manual shaft in Neutral position. Align manual plate with groove in manual valve. Install valve body. Tighten 7 bolts to 48-65 INCH lbs. (5.4-7.3 N.m). Make sure control lever can be moved to all positions.

2) Install downshift solenoid and vacuum diaphragm with rod. Rod must not interfere with side plate of valve body. Install oil pan with new gasket. Tighten pan bolts to 52.8-68.4 INCH lbs. (5.9-7.7 N.m). Tighten clamps for governor tube and ATF cooler tubes. Refill ATF.

EXTENSION HOUSING OIL SEAL

Removal & Installation
Mark propeller shaft for reassembly reference. Remove propeller shaft. Carefully pry or pull seal out of housing. Coat oil seal with clean ATF and drive seal into housing bore. Coat lips of seal with vaseline. Install propeller shaft.

PARKING COMPONENTS

Removal
1) Drain ATF while removing pan. Mark propeller shaft for reassembly reference. Remove propeller shaft. Disconnect speedometer cable from sleeve assembly. Remove sleeve assembly from housing.

2) Support weight of transmission with jack and wooden block. Remove rear extension housing and rear mount. Remove valve body. Remove parking pawl, pin, spring and washer. Note location for reassembly procedure.

Installation
Install parking pawl, pin, spring and washer, using new parts if necessary. Install valve body. Install rear extension and mounting parts. Install speedometer housing and attach cable. Install propeller shaft after aligning marks made during disassembly. Install oil pan with new gasket. Refill transmission with ATF.

GOVERNOR VALVE ASSEMBLY

Removal & Installation
Drain ATF by removing pan. Remove rear mountings and rear extension. Remove governor assembly from transmission housing. To install, reverse removal procedure.

REMOVAL & INSTALLATION

TRANSMISSION
See appropriate AUTOMATIC TRANSMISSION REMOVAL article in IMPORT GENERAL SERVICING section.

TRANSMISSION DISASSEMBLY

1) Remove torque converter. Drain ATF through end of rear extension. Mount transmission in

JATCO 3N71B, E4N71B, JM600, L3N71B & L4N71B (Cont.)

holding fixture. Remove lock-up solenoid from E4N71B models. On all models, remove governor tube. Remove converter housing. Remove oil pan and check contents for signs of contamination or internal part damage.

2) Loosen 2nd band servo lock nut. Tighten piston stem of 2nd band servo. If more than 2 turns are required to tighten stem, band is worn out. Back off stem to release pressure. On models without Overdrive, go to step 5). On models with Overdrive, remove Overdrive assembly. Remove high-Reverse (front) clutch thrust washer, needle bearing and race.

3) Take out input shaft and intermediate shaft. Attach slide hammers to pump and remove pump. Remove Overdrive servo cover. Loosen Overdrive band servo piston stem. Remove Overdrive planetary gear and direct clutch assembly. Remove needle bearing, race and direct clutch thrust washer.

4) Remove Overdrive brake band and strut. Remove Overdrive servo assembly by lightly tapping retainer. Remove accumulator snap ring. Apply air pressure to remove accumulator plug, piston and spring. Remove Overdrive cancel solenoid and "O" ring. Remove drum support.

5) On all models, remove downshift solenoid, vacuum diaphragm, diaphragm rod and "O" rings. Remove speedometer lock plate and speedometer pinion. Remove valve body bolts. Remove valve body from transmission. Remove manual valve from valve body to prevent it from dropping out accidentally.

6) On L3N71B and 3N71B transmissions, loosen brake band adjusting screw lock nut and tighten screw enough to prevent high-Reverse clutch drum from coming out with oil pump. Remove input shaft from oil pump. Remove pump with slide hammers. Remove high-Reverse clutch thrust washer and bearing race. Back off band servo piston stem to release band.

7) On all transmissions, remove brake band strut. Before removing brake band, secure ends together with clip. This will keep band from flexing enough to crack or peel. Remove brake band, high-Reverse (front) clutch, forward (rear) clutch and front planetary gear set (if equipped) as assembly.

8) On 3N71B and L3N71B models, remove front pump thrust bearing and forward clutch thrust washer. Remove forward clutch hub, front planetary carrier and connecting shell. Remove forward clutch thrust bearing, front planetary carrier thrust washer and thrust bearing.

9) On all models, back out band servo attaching bolts about half-way. Carefully apply air pressure at band servo release port to loosen servo. See Fig. 19. Remove band servo retaining bolts and pull band servo out.

10) On E4N71B models, check 1-way clutch for correct operation. On all models, remove rear planetary carrier snap ring. Remove rear planetary carrier. Remove output shaft snap ring. Remove rear connecting drum and internal annulus gear as assembly.

11) Pry off one end of low and Reverse brake snap ring. Remove snap ring by gripping loose end of ring with pliers and turning it in direction away from gap in ring while pulling outward. Remove low and Reverse brake clutch assembly. Remove extension housing being careful not to lose parking pawl, spring and retaining washer.

12) Remove output shaft and governor as assembly. Remove governor thrust washer and needle bearing. Remove 1-way clutch inner race attaching bolts.

Remove 1-way clutch inner race, return thrust washer, low and Reverse return spring and spring thrust ring.

13) Apply air pressure to passage in transmission case to remove low and Reverse brake piston. See Fig. 19. Remove snap rings from both ends of parking brake lever and remove lever. Remove lock nut, manual plate and parking rod. Remove inhibitor switch and manual shaft. On Overdrive models, remove Overdrive indicator switch and "O" ring.

COMPONENT DISASSEMBLY & REASSEMBLY

OIL PUMP ASSEMBLY

Disassembly

1) Take cover off pump housing. On 3N71B and L3N71B models, remove speed cut valve and lock-up control valve. On E4N71B models, remove lock-up valve retaining pin with punch.

2) Remove lock-up control valve and spring. On all models, match mark inner and outer gears with quick-drying ink or paint for reassembly reference. Remove gears from housing.

CAUTION: Oil pump gears MUST be reinstalled in original positions. Mark gears with ink or paint before removing. NEVER use punch to mark gears.

Inspection

1) Check all parts for wear, cracks or other damage. Replace any defective parts. Check gear teeth for excessive wear or damage. Replace rubber seal ring if worn. Check clearances of oil pump.

2) Using straight edge and feeler gauge, measure pump gear face-to-cover clearance. Clearance should be .0008-.0016" (.02-.04 mm). If clearance exceeds .003" (.08 mm), replace gears.

3) Measure clearance between outer gear and crescent. Clearance should be .006-.008" (.14-.21 mm). If clearance exceeds .010" (.25 mm), replace gears.

4) Measure clearance between outer gear and pump housing. Clearance should be .002-.008" (.05-.20 mm). If clearance exceeds .010" (.25 mm), replace gears.

5) Check that oil seal rings and oil feed grooves are not damaged. Make sure that rings still have tension. Check side clearance of oil rings. Clearance should be .002-.006" (.04-.16 mm). Replace seal rings if clearance exceeds .006" (.16 mm).

Reassembly

1) Install valves and springs in cover with NEW retaining pins. On all models except JM600, place pump housing in Oil Pump Assembler (Nissan/Datsun: ST2558001; Mazda: 49 0378 405A). Fit inner and outer gears in housing in same position as when disassembled. On JM600 models, use Aligning Dowels (MD998393) to align cover with pump body.

2) On all models except JM600, check pump cover runout. Temporarily assemble pump cover and housing. DO NOT tighten bolts completely at this time. Attach dial indicator to assembler. Measure total pump cover runout. Total runout must not exceed .003" (.07 mm).

3) Runout can be adjusted by tapping cover lightly with plastic hammer. Tighten pump cover bolts. Recheck runout. On all models, install seal rings on stator

support and new large seal ring on pump housing outside diameter.

DRUM SUPPORT
Disassembly
Inspect drum support bushing and ring groove areas for wear. Remove drum support and gasket from Overdrive case. Stake off retaining pin using punch having .059-.071" (1.5-1.8 mm) outer diameter. DO NOT stake off from contacting face side. Remove Overdrive cancel valve and spring.

Inspection
Inspect Overdrive cancel valve and spring and all internal surfaces for faults and visible wear. Spring should have free length of .906" (23 mm) and outer coil diameter of .1949" (4.95 mm). Measure clearance between seal ring and ring groove. Clearance should be .0020-.0079" (.05-.20 mm). Replace if clearance exceeds .0079" (.2 mm).

Reassembly
1) Install Overdrive cancel valve and spring into drum support, and tap retaining pins. Install fiber lubrication plug into drum support. Install 1-way plug in Overdrive case. On all models except JM600, mount oil pump assembly in oil pump assembly tool with .79" (20 mm) spacer below tool to protect oil pump. Mount Overdrive case, drum support and gasket in oil pump assembly.

2) Temporarily assemble drum support. Make sure Overdrive case is inserted properly into oil pump assembly. Insert 4.33" (110 mm) bar in oil pump at shaft location and install intermediate shaft onto it. See Fig. 6.

3) Set runout of drum support to less than .002" (.05 mm). On JM600 models, use aligning dowels to center drum support in Overdrive case. Tighten drum support securing bolts. Recheck runout. Replace "O" ring and gasket.

Fig. 6: Assembling Drum Support

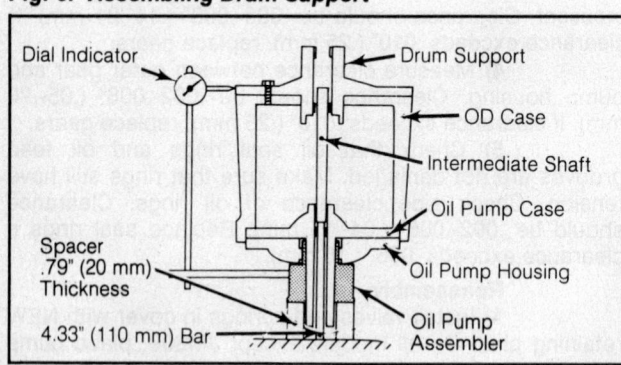

Runout should be less than .002" (.05 mm).

DIRECT CLUTCH & HIGH-REVERSE CLUTCH
Disassembly
Remove snap ring and take out retaining plate, lined plates, steel plates and dished plate. Compress and hold clutch springs. Remove coil spring retainer snap ring. Remove compressor tool. Remove spring retainer and springs. Remove high-Reverse (front) clutch piston by applying compressed air into oil hole.

Inspection
Inspect lined plates for wear or fatigue. Check coil spring retainer and replace if deformed. Ensure that coil spring has not lost tension. Inspect seal around piston and "O" ring inside clutch drum for damage. Replace all parts which show undue wear or fatigue. Standard plate thickness is .059-.065" (1.50-1.65 mm). Minimum thickness is .055" (1.4 mm).

Reassembly
1) Coat new seals with clean ATF and install seals onto clutch piston and clutch drum. Install piston into drum. Position return springs and retainer on top of piston. Compress return springs and retainer and install snap ring. Install dished plate into drum.

2) Install flat steel plate, then alternate lined and steel plates until all plates are installed. See HIGH-REVERSE (FRONT) CLUTCH PLATE USAGE chart. Position retaining ring in drum and install clutch pack snap ring. Using feeler gauge, measure clearance between clutch pack retaining snap ring and retaining plate in drum.

3) Clearance should be .063-.071" (1.6-1.8 mm) for direct and high-Reverse clutches on Mazda models and direct clutches on Chrysler Corp. and Mitsubishi models; .063-.079" (1.6-2.0 mm) for direct and high-Reverse clutches on Nissan/Datsun models and high-Reverse clutches on Chrysler Corp. and Mitsubishi models.

4) If clearance is incorrect, adjust by installing retaining plate of different thickness. Retaining plates for direct clutches are available in thicknesses ranging from .197-.244" (5.0-6.2 mm). Additional retaining plates, measuring .283" (7.2 mm) and .291" (7.4 mm), are available for direct clutches used in Nissan/Datsun 300ZX Turbo model.

5) Retaining plates for high-reverse clutches used in Mazda Pickups are available in thicknesses ranging from .283-.323" (7.2-8.2 mm) in increments of .008" (.2 mm). Retaining plates for high-reverse clutches in all other models are available in thickness ranging from .197-.244" (5.0-6.2 mm). Retaining plate thicknesses change in increments of .008" (.2 mm) for all models.

DIRECT & HIGH-REVERSE CLUTCH PLATE USAGE

Application	Lined Plates	Steel Plates
High-Rev. Clutch		
Chrysler Corp		
Conquest	3	5
Mazda		
All Models	3	3
Mitsubishi		
Starion	3	5
Nissan/Datsun		
Maxima	3	5
Pickup	3	5
200SX	3	3
200SX Turbo	3	3
300ZX	3	5
300ZX Turbo	4	5
Direct Clutch		
Nissan/Datsun		
300ZX Turbo	3	3
All Others	2	2

Fig. 7: Exploded View Of High-Reverse (Front) Clutch Assembly

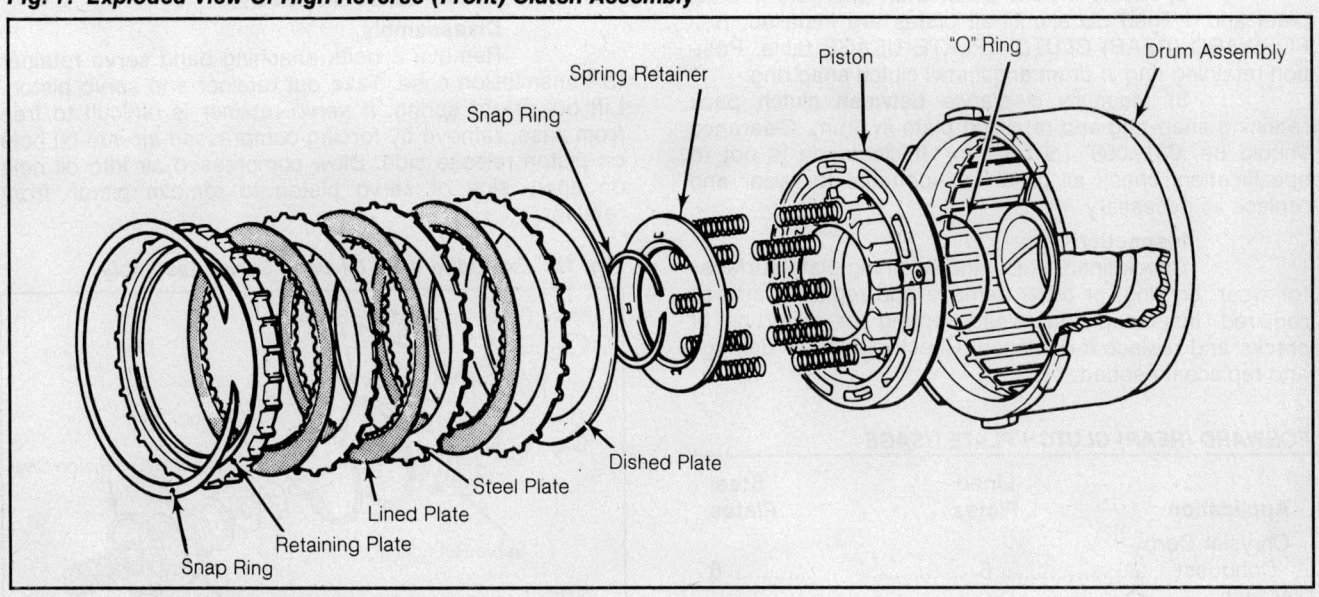

Number of clutch plates and discs varies with application.

FORWARD (REAR) CLUTCH
Disassembly
Remove snap ring, retaining plate, steel plate, lined plate, and dished plate in same order used for high-Reverse (front) clutch. Remove coil spring retainer using compressing tool. Take out retainer and all springs. Remove piston by blowing compressed air into oil hole.

Inspection
Make same inspection of components as for high-Reverse (front) clutch. Replace any parts showing signs of undue wear or fatigue.

Reassembly
1) Coat new seals with clean ATF and install seals on clutch piston and clutch drum. Install piston into drum. Position return springs and retainer on top of piston. Compress return springs and retainer.

Fig. 8: Exploded View Of Forward (Rear) Clutch Assembly

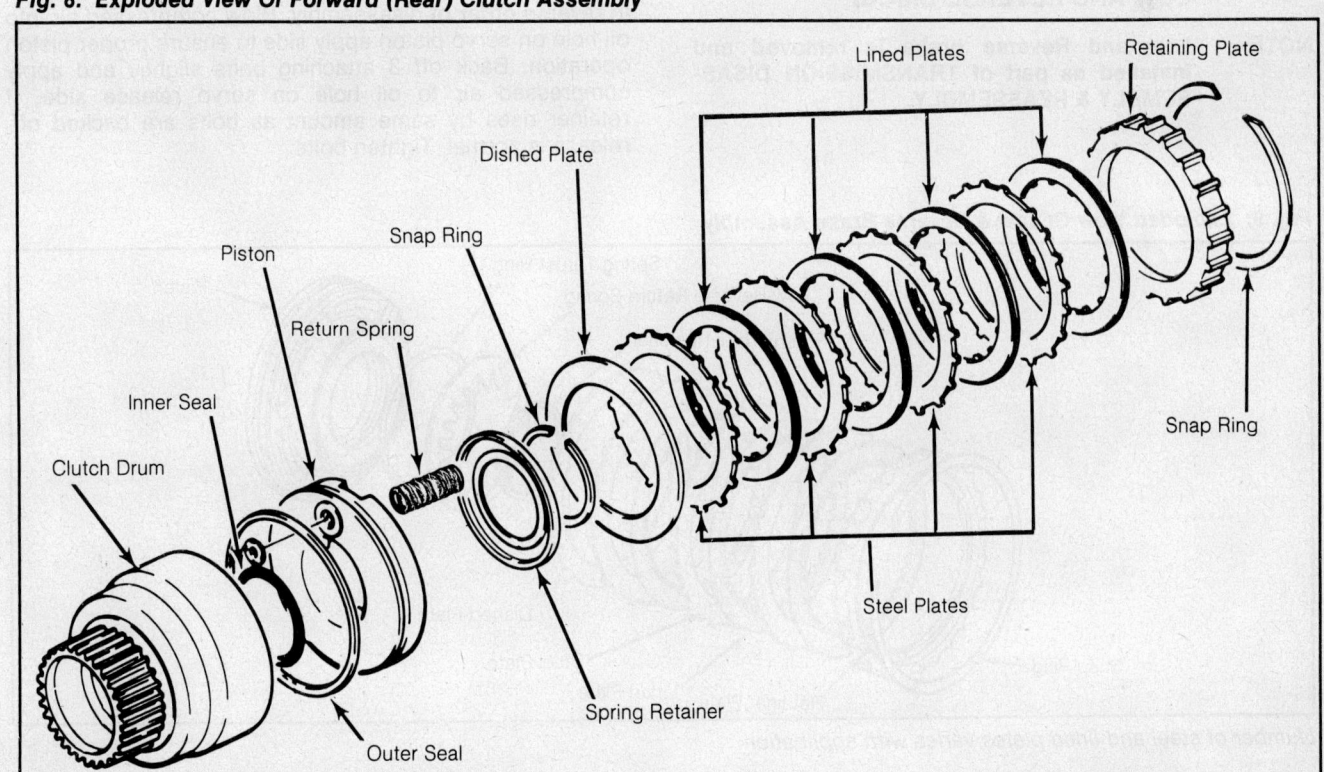

Number of lined and steel plates varies with application.

Automatic Transmissions

JATCO 3N71B, E4N71B, JM600, L3N71B & L4N71B (Cont.)

2) Install dished plate, then alternate 1 steel plate and 1 lined plate until all plates are installed. See FORWARD (REAR) CLUTCH PLATE USAGE table. Position retaining ring in drum and install clutch snap ring.

3) Measure clearance between clutch pack retaining snap ring and retaining plate in drum. Clearance should be .031-.059" (.8-1.5 mm). If clearance is not to specification, check all clutch components for wear and replace as necessary.

Inspection

Check lined, steel, and retaining plate surfaces for wear, scoring, or other damage and replace parts as required. Inspect piston release spring for distortion or cracks and replace if damaged. Check piston for damage and replace if needed.

FORWARD (REAR) CLUTCH PLATE USAGE

Application	Lined Plates	Steel Plates
Chrysler Corp		
Conquest	6	6
Mazda		
All Models	4	4
Mitsubishi		
Starion	6	6
Nissan/Datsun		
Maxima	6	6
Pickup	6	6
200SX	5	5
200SX Turbo	4	4
300ZX	6	6
300ZX Turbo	6	6

LOW AND REVERSE BRAKE

NOTE: Low and Reverse brake is removed and installed as part of TRANSMISSION DISASSEMBLY & REASSEMBLY.

BAND SERVO PISTON

Disassembly

Remove 3 bolts attaching band servo retainer to transmission case. Take out retainer and servo piston. Lift out return spring. If servo retainer is difficult to free from case, remove by forcing compressed air into oil hole on piston release side. Blow compressed air into oil hole on apply side of servo piston to remove piston from retainer.

Fig. 10: Exploded View Of Band Servo Assembly

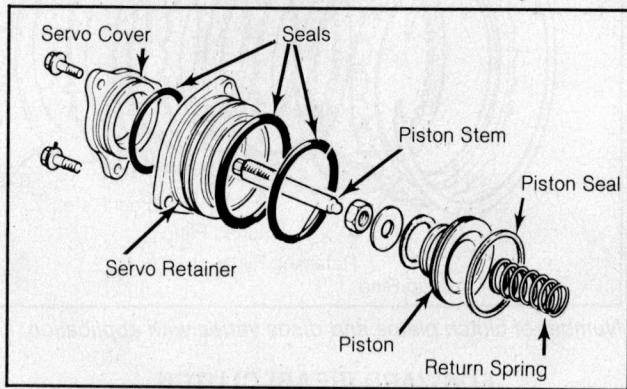

Mazda model shown. Other models are similar.

Inspection

Ensure that 2 "O" rings on servo retainer and rubber seal on servo piston are not damaged. Check all parts for undue wear or fatigue. Inspect return spring for adequate tension. Inspect brake band lining for excessive wear or damage. Replace parts as needed.

Reassembly

Coat all parts with clean ATF and reassemble in reverse order of disassembly. Blow compressed air into oil hole on servo piston apply side to ensure proper piston operation. Back off 3 attaching bolts slightly and apply compressed air to oil hole on servo release side. If retainer rises by same amount as bolts are backed off, release is normal. Tighten bolts.

Fig. 9: Exploded View Of Low & Reverse Brake Assembly

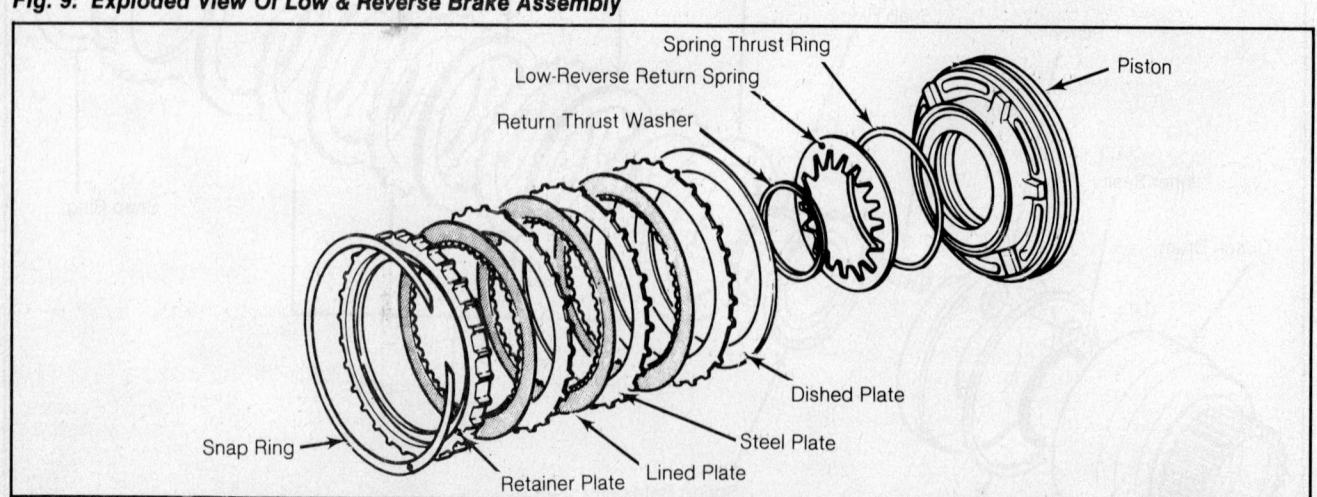

Number of steel and lined plates varies with application.

JATCO 3N71B, E4N71B, JM600, L3N71B & L4N71B (Cont.)

GOVERNOR VALVE ASSEMBLY
Disassembly
Separate governor from oil distributor by removing 4 attaching bolts. Remove secondary governor valve retainer plate. Remove spring and secondary governor valve from governor body. Remove primary governor valve spring seat, primary governor valve, spring and spring seat.

Fig. 11: Exploded View Of Governor Assembly

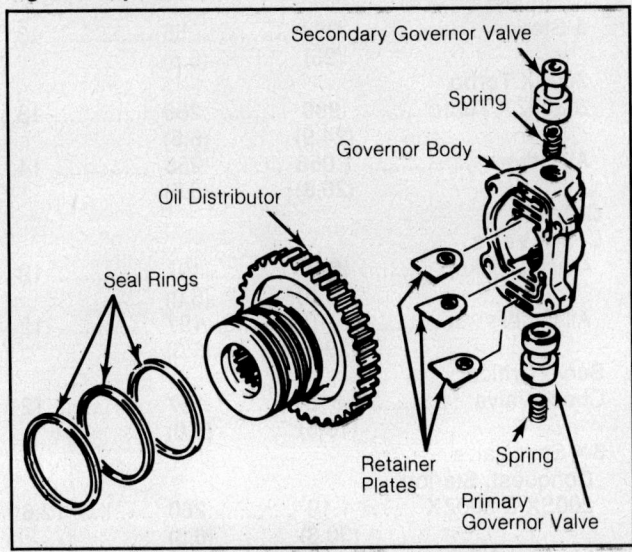

Keep primary and secondary components separate.

Inspection
Check valve and body for valve sticking or catching. Ensure that spring has not lost tension and that retainer plates are not deformed.

Reassembly
1) Coat all parts with clean ATF and reassemble in reverse order of disassembly. Be careful not to confuse primary valve and secondary valve.
2) Primary governor spring has free length of .858" (21.8 mm) and outer coil diameter of .345" (8.8 mm).
3) Secondary governor spring has free length of .783" (19.9 mm) and outer coil diameter of .362" (9.2 mm). Install and tighten governor attaching bolts.

ACCUMULATOR
Remove accumulator snap ring. Apply air pressure to remove accumulator plug, piston, spring and spacer. Check accumulator components for wear and scoring. Accumulator spring should have free length of 1.56" (39.7 mm) and outer coil diameter of .5846" (14.85 mm).

PLANETARY CARRIER
Planetary carrier is 1-piece unit. Clearance check is between pinion washer and carrier. Standard clearance is .008-.028" (.20-.70 mm). If clearance exceeds .031" (.80 mm), replace carrier.

CONNECTING DRUM & 1-WAY CLUTCH ASSEMBLY
Disassembly & Reassembly
Draw out 1-way clutch by removing snap ring from each end. Remove outer race snap ring and draw outer race rearward out of drum. Inspect 1-way clutch for undue wear or damage. Check contacting surfaces of inner and outer races. When reassembling 1-way clutch, ensure that clutch roller cage is fitted so that arrow on side of cage points toward front of vehicle.

Fig. 12: Exploded View Of Valve Body Assembly For L3N71B & 3N71B

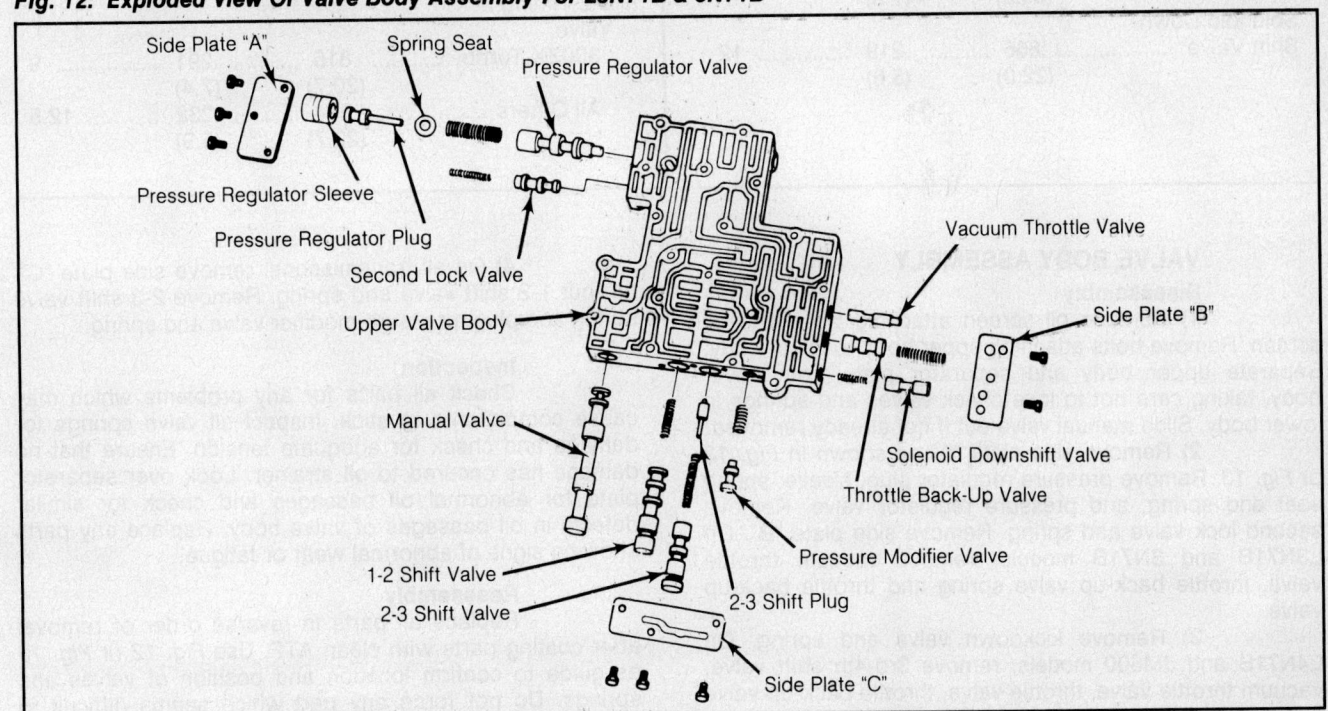

Keep all parts in rack in sequence of assembly.

Automatic Transmissions

JATCO 3N71B, E4N71B, JM600, L3N71B & L4N71B (Cont.)

VALVE BODY SPRING IDENTIFICATION

Application	Length In. (mm)	Diameter In. (mm)	Number of Coils
Manual Detent	1.276 (32.4)	.287 (7.3)	15
Pressure Regulator Valve	1.693 (43.0)	.461 (11.7)	13
Pressure Modifier Valve			
Conquest & Starion	.772 (19.6)	.339 (8.6)	5.5
300ZX Turbo	.728 (18.5)	.339 (8.6)	5.5
All Others	.728 (18.5)	.331 (8.4)	5
1-2 Shift Valve			
Conquest, Starion & 300ZX Turbo	1.11 (28.3)	.276 (7.0)	11.8
200SX Turbo	1.11 (28.3)		
All Others	1.260 (32.0)	.260 (6.6)	16
2-3 Shift Valve	1.614 (41.0)	.272 (6.9)	18
Throttle Back-Up Valve			
RX7	1.25 (31.8)	.287 (7.3)	14
Conquest, Starion & 300ZX	1.25 (31.8)	.287 (7.3)	13.5
All Others	1.417 (36.0)	.287 (7.3)	14
Solenoid Down-Shift Valve	.866 (22.0)	.219 (5.6)	12
Second Lock Valve	1.319 (33.5)	.219 (5.6)	16
Throttle Relief Check Valve			
Conquest & Starion	.984 (25)	.256 (6.5)	13
200SX Turbo & 300ZX Turbo	.980 (24.9)	.256 (6.5)	13
All Others	1.055 (26.8)	.256 (6.5)	14
Orifice Check Valve			
Mazda Pickup	.847 (21.5)	.197 (5.0)	12
All Others	.610 (15.5)	.197 (5.0)	12
Servo Orifice Check Valve	.610 (15.5)	.197 (5.0)	12
3-4 Shift Valve			
Conquest, Starion, 200SX & 300ZX	1.19 (30.3)	.260 (6.6)	12.6
Maxima & 300ZX Turbo	1.055 (26.8)	.240 (6.1)	13.6
RX7	1.02 (25.8)	.287 (7.3)	
All Others	1.055 (30.6)	.274 (6.9)	12.7
3-2 Timing Valve			
300ZX Turbo	.815 (20.7)	.291 (7.4)	9
All Others	.894 (22.7)	.232 (5.9)	12.5

VALVE BODY ASSEMBLY
Disassembly
1) Remove oil screen attaching bolts and oil screen. Remove bolts attaching upper body to lower body. Separate upper body and separator plate from lower body, taking care not to lose check valves and springs in lower body. Slide manual valve out if not already removed.

2) Remove side plate "A" as shown in *Fig. 12* or *Fig. 13*. Remove pressure regulator plug, sleeve, spring seat and spring, and pressure regulator valve. Remove second lock valve and spring. Remove side plate "B". On L3N71B and 3N71B models, remove vacuum throttle valve, throttle back-up valve spring and throttle back-up valve.

3) Remove kickdown valve and spring. On L4N71B and JM600 models, remove 3rd-4th shift valve, vacuum throttle valve, throttle valve, throttle back-up valve with spring, and kickdown valve with spring.

4) On all transmissons, remove side plate "C". Lift out 1-2 shift valve and spring. Remove 2-3 shift valve spring and plug, pressure modifier valve and spring.

Inspection
Check all parts for any problems which may cause components to stick. Inspect all valve springs for damage and check for adequate tension. Ensure that no damage has occured to oil strainer. Look over separator plate for abnormal oil passages and check for similar defects in oil passages of valve body. Replace any parts showing signs of abnormal wear or fatigue.

Reassembly
Replace all parts in reverse order of removal after coating parts with clean ATF. Use *Fig. 12* or *Fig. 13* as guide to confirm location and position of valves and springs. Do not force any part which seems difficult to place or insert. Use light, straight pressure to fit parts.

Automatic Transmissions

JATCO 3N71B, E4N71B, JM600, L3N71B & L4N71B (Cont.)

Fig. 13: Exploded View Of Valve Body Assembly For E4N71B, L4N71B & JM600

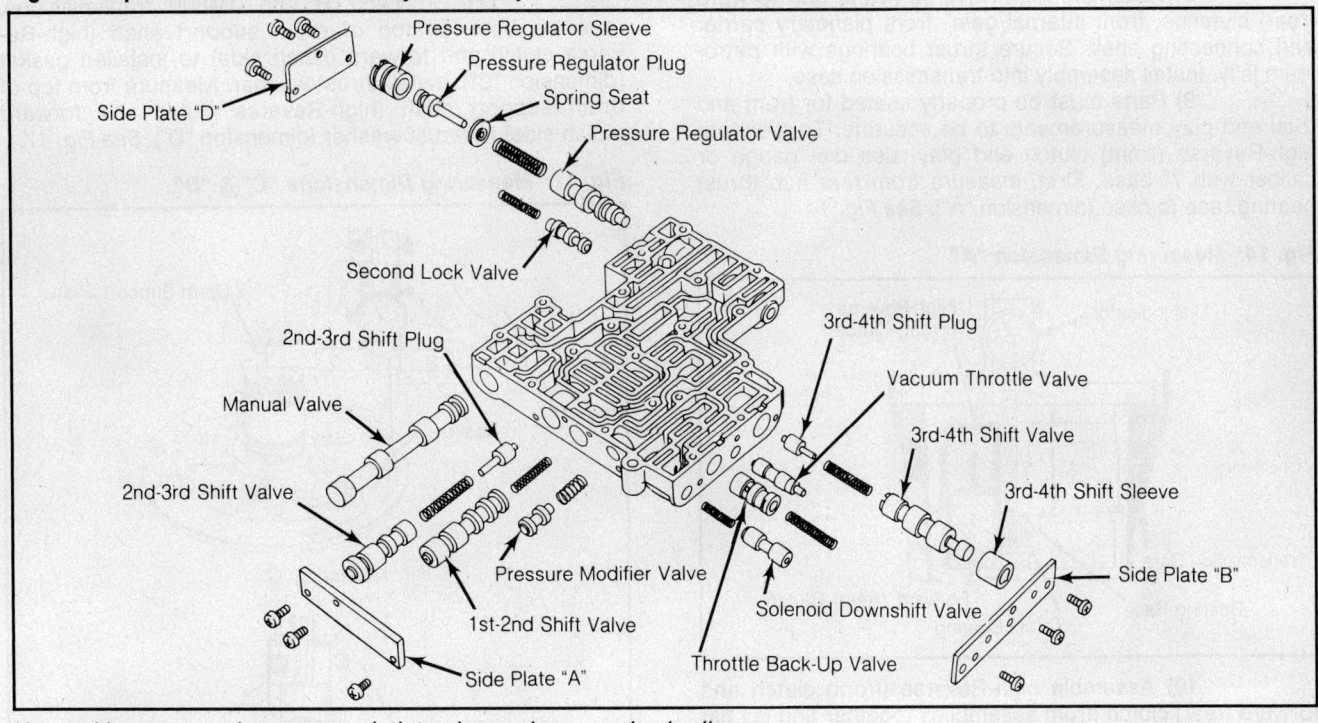

Use nothing coarser than crocus cloth to clean valves or valve bodies.

INPUT SHELL & SUN GEAR ASSEMBLY

Disassembly & Reassembly

Remove external snap ring from sun gear, withdraw thrust washer, then remove sun gear from shell. Remove internal snap ring from sun gear. To assemble, coat all parts with clean ATF and reverse disassembly procedure.

INTERNAL DRIVE FLANGE ASSEMBLY

Disassembly & Reassembly

Remove snap ring and disconnect flange from internal gear. Inspect part for wear or fatigue. Reverse disassembly procedure to assemble after coating all parts with clean ATF.

TRANSMISSION REASSEMBLY

1) Lubricate low and Reverse brake piston with clean ATF and install in transmission case. Position thrust ring, piston return spring, snap ring, and 1-way clutch inner race into transmission case.

2) Hold inner race in position and install 1-way clutch inner race attaching bolts. Check that return spring is centered on race before tightening. Tighten bolts. Install steel dished plate, steel and friction plates. See LOW & REVERSE BRAKE PLATE USAGE table.

3) Install retaining plate and snap ring. Check clearance between retaining plate and snap ring. Clearance should be .032-.049" (.80-1.25 mm). If clearance is incorrect, it may be adjusted by installing retaining plate of different thickness.

4) Plates are available in sizes from .465" (11.8 mm) to .504" (12.8 mm) in .008" (.2 mm) increments for JM600 models. On all other models, plates are available in sizes from .307" (7.8 mm) to .346" (8.8 mm) in .008" (.2 mm) increments. Install correct plate and recheck clear-

ance. Using air gun with tapered rubber tip, check low and Reverse brake operation.

5) Install governor thrust washer and needle bearing. Slide governor distributor assembly on output shaft from front of shaft. Install shaft and governor distributor into case, using care not to damage distributor rings.

6) Install connecting drum with sprag by rotating drum clockwise using slight pressure and wobbling to align plates with hub and sprag assembly. Connecting drum should now be free to rotate clockwise only. This verifies that sprag is correctly installed and operative.

7) Install rear internal gear and snap ring on shaft. Secure thrust bearing and washer with petroleum jelly and install rear planetary carrier. Install rear planetary carrier snap ring. Note that this snap ring is thinner than clutch drum snap rings.

LOW & REVERSE BRAKE PLATE USAGE

Application	Lined Plates	Steel Plates
Chrysler Corp		
Conquest	6	6
Mazda		
All Models	4	4
Mitsubishi		
Starion	6	6
Nissan/Datsun		
Maxima	5	5
Pickup	5	5
200SX	5	5
200SX Turbo	5	5
300ZX	6	6
300ZX Turbo	7	7

8) Assemble high-Reverse (front) and forward (rear) clutches, front internal gear, front planetary carrier and connecting shell. Secure thrust bearings with petroleum jelly. Install assembly into transmission case.

9) Parts must be properly seated for front and total end play measurements to be accurate. To measure high-Reverse (front) clutch end play, use dial gauge or caliper with 7" base. First, measure from rear hub thrust bearing race to case (dimension "A"). *See Fig. 14.*

Fig. 14: *Measuring Dimension "A"*

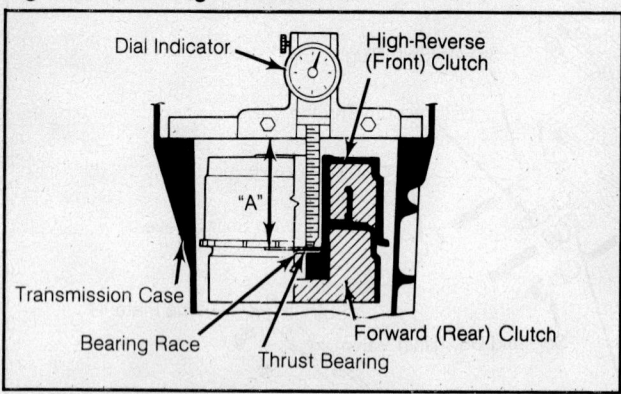

10) Assemble high-Reverse (front) clutch and forward (rear) clutch drum assemblies together and lay flat on bench. Make sure rear hub thrust bearing is properly seated. Measure from front face of clutch drum to top of thrust bearing race (dimension "B"). *See Fig. 15.*

Fig. 15: *Measuring Dimension "B"*

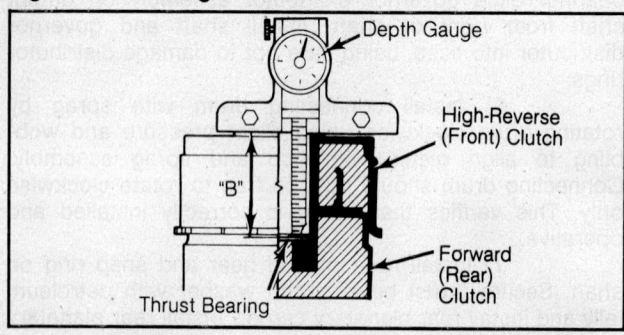

11) On L3N71B and 3N71B transmissions, measure from top of oil pump shaft to installed gasket (dimension "C"). Install thrust washer. Measure from top of oil pump shaft to thrust washer (dimension "D".) *See Fig. 16.*

Fig. 16: *Measuring Dimensions "C" & "D"*

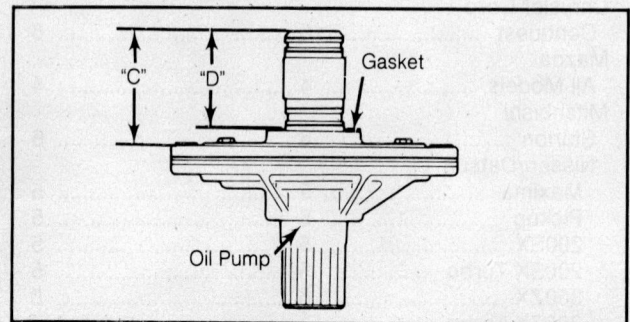

This procedure is for models 3N71B and L3N71B.

12) On L4N71B and JM600 transmissions, measure between top of drum support shaft (high-Reverse clutch and forward clutch side) to installed gasket (dimension "C"). Install thrust washer. Measure from top of drum support shaft (high-Reverse clutch and forward clutch side) to thrust washer (dimension "D"). *See Fig. 17.*

Fig. 17: *Measuring Dimensions "C" & "D"*

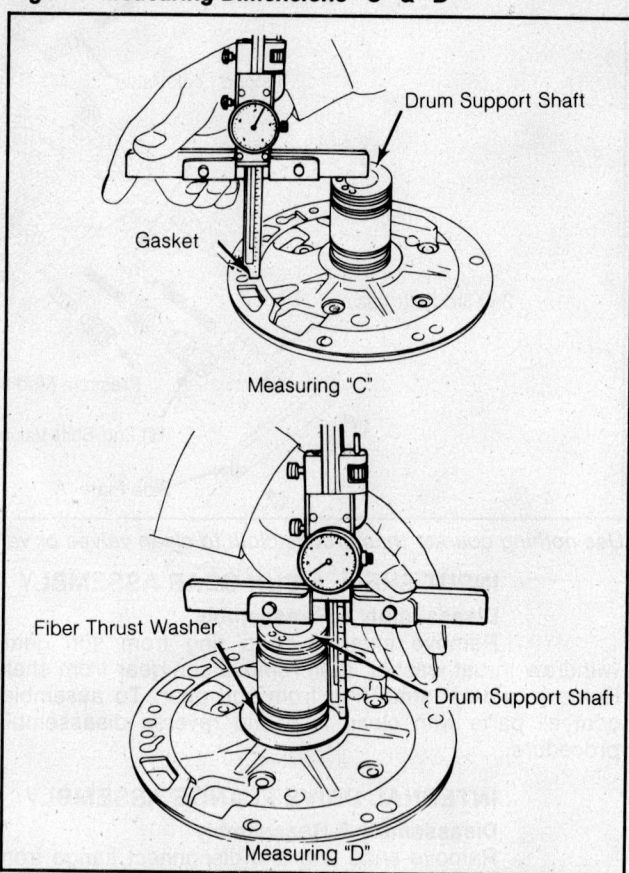

This procedure is for models E4N71B, L4N71B and JM600.

13) First, subtract .004" (.1 mm) from dimension "A". Then subtract dimension "B" from result. Note this result. Then subtract dimension "D" from dimension "C". The result of sum ("A" minus .004" (.1 mm) minus "B") less sum ("C" minus "D") is high-Reverse (front) clutch end play.

14) Front end play range is .020-.031" (.5-.8 mm). Front end play can be adjusted by changing thicknesses of high-Reverse (front) clutch thrust washers. These washers are available in thicknesses from .051-.106" (1.3-2.7 mm) in .008" (.2 mm) increments.

15) Total end play is result of sum ("A" minus .004" (.1 mm)) less dimension "C". Total end play range is .0098-.0197" (.25-.50 mm). Change total end play with oil pump cover bearing races of different thicknesses. Bearing races are available in thicknesses of .047-.087" (1.2-2.2 mm) in .08" (.2 mm) increments.

16) Install brake band, band strut and band servo. Lubricate servo "O" rings before installing. Install and tighten retainer bolts. Loosen piston stem. Finger tighten brake band servo piston stem enough to prevent brake band and strut from falling out.

17) DO NOT adjust at this time. On 3N71B and L3N71B models, go to step **26)**. On L4N71B, JM600 and

JATCO 3N71B, E4N71B, JM600, L3N71B & L4N71B (Cont.)

E4N71B models, apply petroleum jelly to bearing race and thrust washer and mount them to drum support. Mount drum support gasket to drum support after coating with petroleum jelly. Apply clean ATF to "O" ring of drum support.

18) Align drum support with Overdrive case to transmission case and install. Install Overdrive case and temporarily tighten it using 2 converter housing securing bolts. Insert intermediate shaft. Make sure shaft is installed in correct direction.

19) Overdrive pack end play and Overdrive total end play must be correct. To check Overdrive pack end play, assemble direct clutch assembly, Overdrive planetary gear set and connecting drum.

20) Install this assembly on Overdrive pack. Install oil pump bearing, gasket and Overdrive pack on oil pump. Measure dimensions "F" and "H". See Fig. 18. Attach thrust washer and needle bearing to drum support and Overdrive case. Measure dimensions "E" and "G". See Fig. 18.

21) Result of sum ("E" minus .004" (.1 mm)) less dimension "F" is Overdrive pack end play. Overdrive pack end play range is .020-.031" (.5-.8 mm). Overdrive pack end play can be changed with Overdrive thrust washers of different thicknesses. These washers, which are same as high-Reverse (front) clutch thrust washers, are available in thicknesses of .051-.106" (1.3-2.7 mm) in .008" (.2 mm) increments.

22) Result of sum ("G" minus .004" (.1 mm)) less "H" is Overdrive total end play. Total Overdrive end play range is .0098-.0197" (.25-.50 mm). Adjust total Overdrive end play with different thicknesses of Overdrive bearing race. Races are available in thicknesses from .047-.087" (1.2-2.2 mm) in .008" (.2 mm) increments.

23) Adjust band. See appropriate AUTOMATIC TRANSMISSION SERVICING article in IMPORT GENERAL SERVICING section for band adjustment procedure. Make sure brake band strut is correctly installed. Tighten piston stem to 60-84 INCH lbs. (7-10 N.m). Back off 2 full turns and tighten piston stem lock nut.

24) Lubricate Overdrive servo "O" rings with clean ATF. Install brake band, band strut and Overdrive band servo. Apply clean ATF to seal ring of direct clutch. Install Overdrive bearing and race, Overdrive thrust washer and Overdrive pack on drum support.

25) Make sure brake band strut is correctly installed. Apply clean ATF to "O" ring of oil pump. Install needle bearing, race and oil pump. Make sure oil pump housing and oil pump have been centered correctly. Adjust Overdrive band. Tighten piston stem to 61.2-86.4 INCH lbs. (7-10 N.m). Back of 2 full turns and tighten piston stem lock nut.

Fig. 18: Measuring Dimensions "E", "F", "G" & "H"

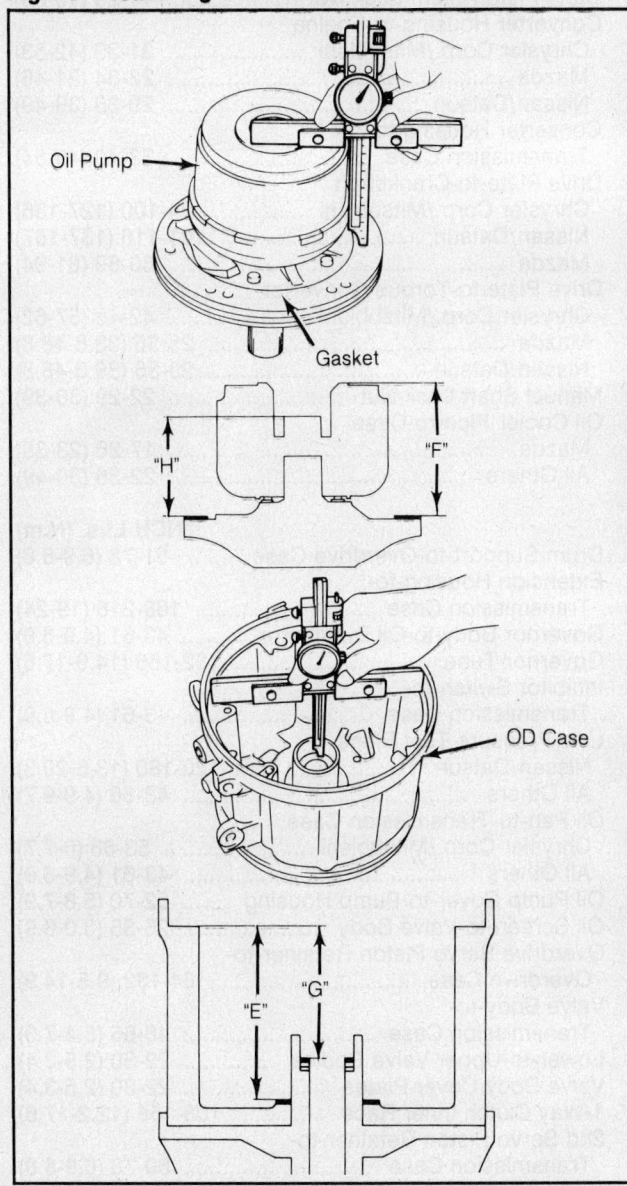

Fig. 19: Air Check Points

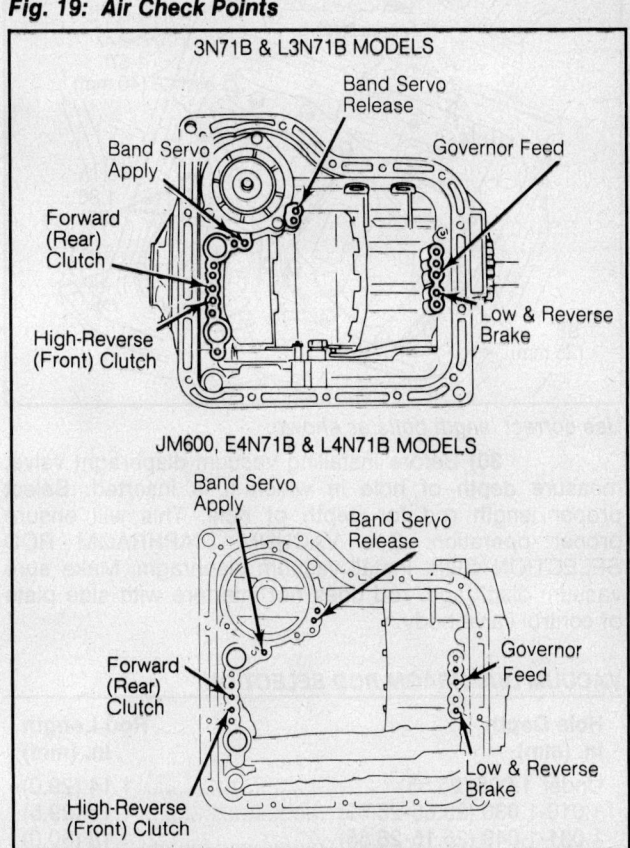

Test clutch and band functions with compressed air before installing valve body.

JATCO 3N71B, E4N71B, JM600, L3N71B & L4N71B (Cont.)

26) Using air gun with tapered rubber tip, test Overdrive band servo operation. Install accumulator parts. Install accumulator snap ring. Remove 2 converter housing bolts used to tighten Overdrive case. Apply sealant to seating surfaces of converter housing at bolt locations. Install converter housing on Overdrive case and tighten securing bolts. Install input shaft.

27) On L3N71B and 3N71B models, mount oil pump gasket on oil pump with petroleum jelly. Align pump to transmission case and install. Adjust band. See appropriate AUTOMATIC TRANSMISSION SERVICING article in IMPORT GENERAL SERVICING section for band adjustment procedure. Make sure that brake band strut is correctly installed. Tighten piston stem to 108-132 INCH lbs. (12-15 N.m). Back off 2 full turns. Tighten lock nut.

28) On all models, use air gun with tapered rubber tip to perform final air check of all assembled components. See Fig. 19. Do this BEFORE proceeding with installation of valve body assembly. This will ensure that all bolts are tightened and that seals have not been damaged during assembly.

29) Check that parking pawl, pin, spring and washer are assembled correctly. Install rear extension. Install control valve body with correct length attaching bolts. See Fig. 20. Be sure manual valve is in alignment with selector pin. Tighten control valve body attaching bolts. Make sure manual lever can be moved to all positions after control valve body attaching bolts are tightened.

Fig. 20: Control Valve Body Attaching Bolts

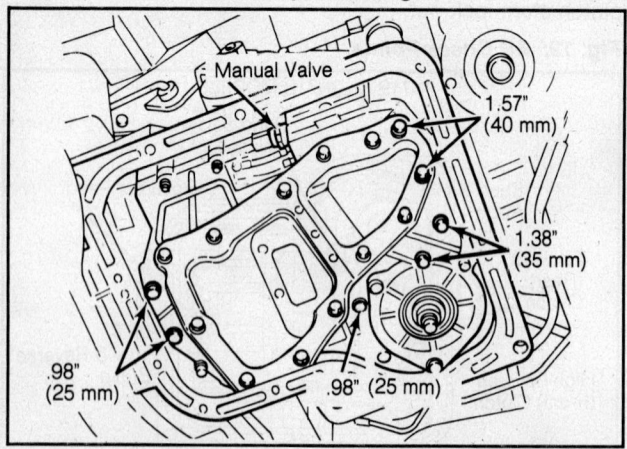

Use correct length bolts as shown.

30) Before installing vacuum diaphragm valve, measure depth of hole in which it is inserted. Select proper length rod for depth of hole. This will ensure proper operation. See VACUUM DIAPHRAGM ROD SELECTION chart. Install vacuum diaphragm. Make sure vacuum diaphragm rod does not interfere with side plate of control valve body.

VACUUM DIAPHRAGM ROD SELECTION

Hole Depth In. (mm)	Rod Length In. (mm)
Under 1.006 (25.55)	1.14 (29.0)
1.010-1.030 (25.65-26.05)	1.16 (29.5)
1.031-1.049 (26.15-26.55)	1.18 (30.0)
1.050-1.069 (26.65-27.05)	1.20 (30.5)
Over 1.070 (27.15)	1.22 (31.0)

31) Install downshift solenoid, Overdrive cancel solenoid and Overdrive indicator switch. Install inhibitor switch and check for proper operation. See appropriate AUTOMATIC TRANSMISSION SERVICING article in IMPORT GENERAL SERVICING section for checking and adjustment procedures.

32) Before installing oil pan, check alignment and operation of control lever and parking pawl engagement. Clean mechanism with compressed air. Make final check to be sure all bolts are correctly installed in control valve body. Install oil pan with new gasket.

33) Install governor tube. Carefully inspect torque converter for damage. Check converter hub for grooves caused by hardened seals. Check bushing contact area. Lubricate oil pump lip seal and converter neck before installing converter. Install converter, making sure that converter is properly meshed with oil pump drive gear.

TIGHTENING SPECIFICATIONS

Application	Ft. Lbs. (N.m)
Band Piston Stem Lock Nut	11-29 (15-39)
Converter Housing-to-Engine	
Chrysler Corp./Mitsubishi	31-39 (42-53)
Mazda	23-34 (31-46)
Nissan/Datsun	29-36 (39-49)
Converter Housing-to-Transmission Case	33-40 (45-54)
Drive Plate-to-Crankshaft	
Chrysler Corp./Mitsubishi	94-100 (127-136)
Nissan/Datsun	101-116 (137-157)
Mazda	60-69 (81-94)
Drive Plate-to-Torque Converter	
Chrysler Corp./Mitsubishi	42-46 (57-62)
Mazda	25-36 (33.8-48.8)
Nissan/Datsun	29-36 (39.3-48.8)
Manual Shaft Lock Nut	22-29 (30-39)
Oil Cooler Pipe-to-Case	
Mazda	17-26 (23-35)
All Others	22-36 (30-49)

Application	INCH Lbs. (N.m)
Drum Support-to-Overdrive Case	61-78 (6.9-8.8)
Extension Housing-to-Transmission Case	168-216 (19-24)
Governor Body-to-Oil Distributor	43-61 (4.9-6.9)
Governor Tube	132-156 (14.9-17.6)
Inhibitor Switch-to-Transmission Case	43-61 (4.9-6.9)
Line Pressure Test Plugs	
Nissan/Datsun	120-180 (13.6-20.3)
All Others	43-86 (4.9-9.7)
Oil Pan-to-Transmission Case	
Chrysler Corp./Mitsubishi	53-68 (6-7.7)
All Others	43-61 (4.9-6.9)
Oil Pump Cover-to-Pump Housing	52-70 (5.8-7.9)
Oil Screen-to-Valve Body	26-35 (3.0-3.9)
Overdrive Servo Piston Retainer-to-Overdrive Case	84-132 (9.5-14.9)
Valve Body-to-Transmission Case	48-65 (5.4-7.3)
Lower-to-Upper Valve Bodies	22-30 (2.5-3.4)
Valve Body Cover Plates	22-30 (2.5-3.4)
1-Way Clutch Inner Race	108-156 (12.2-17.6)
2nd Servo Piston Retainer-to-Transmission Case	60-78 (6.9-8.8)

MAZDA F3A 3-SPEED

GLC (FWD)

DESCRIPTION

The transaxle consists of 3 main units: Automatic transmission, torque converter and differential assembly. The automatic transmission consists of front, rear and one-way clutches, low-reverse brake assembly, oil pump and hydraulic controls (valve body and servo piston assemblies). The torque converter and differential are housed together in the torque converter housing.

LUBRICATION & ADJUSTMENT

See appropriate AUTOMATIC TRANSMISSION SERVICING article in DOMESTIC GENERAL SERVICING section.

SERVICE (IN VEHICLE)

DRIVE AXLE SHAFTS

See Service (In Vehicle) in Mazda GLC 4 & 5-Speed manual transaxle article for complete axle shaft and wheel bearing service procedures.

Fig. 1: Exploded View of Transmission Housing & Primary Components

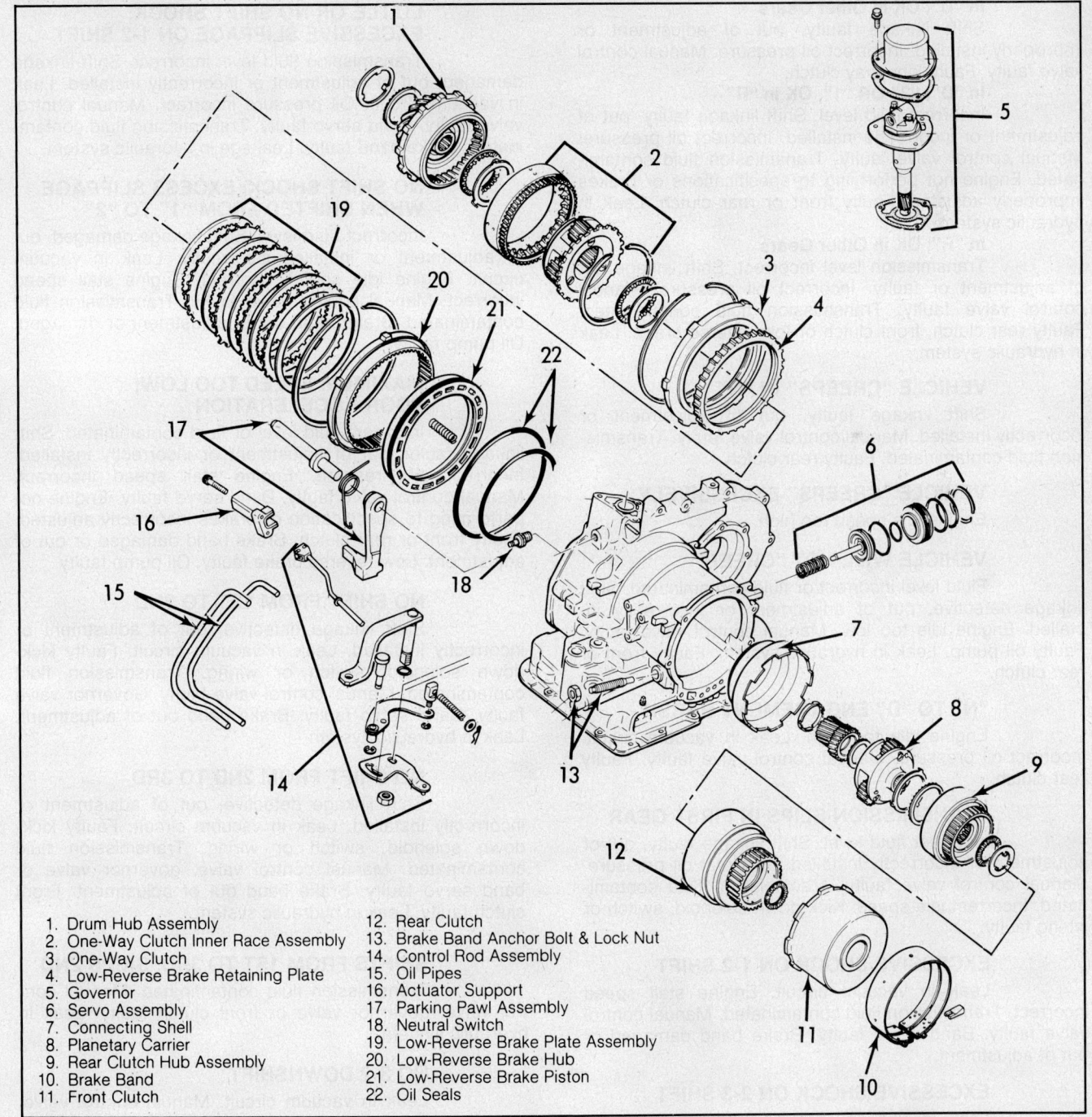

1. Drum Hub Assembly
2. One-Way Clutch Inner Race Assembly
3. One-Way Clutch
4. Low-Reverse Brake Retaining Plate
5. Governor
6. Servo Assembly
7. Connecting Shell
8. Planetary Carrier
9. Rear Clutch Hub Assembly
10. Brake Band
11. Front Clutch
12. Rear Clutch
13. Brake Band Anchor Bolt & Lock Nut
14. Control Rod Assembly
15. Oil Pipes
16. Actuator Support
17. Parking Pawl Assembly
18. Neutral Switch
19. Low-Reverse Brake Plate Assembly
20. Low-Reverse Brake Hub
21. Low-Reverse Brake Piston
22. Oil Seals

Automatic Transmissions

MAZDA F3A 3-SPEED (Cont.)

TROUBLE SHOOTING

ENGINE STARTS IN "D", "2", "1" OR "R", OR WILL NOT START IN "N" OR "P"

Check ignition and starter circuit. Shift linkage faulty or installed improperly. Leak in vacuum circuit.

NO MOVEMENT

In Any Gear

Incorrect fluid level. Shift linkage faulty, out of adjustment or incorrectly installed. Incorrect oil pressure. Manual control valve faulty. Faulty oil pump. Leak in hydraulic system. Parking linkage improperly adjusted.

In "D", OK in Other Gears

Shift linkage faulty, out of adjustment or improperly installed. Incorrect oil pressure. Manual control valve faulty. Faulty one-way clutch.

In "D", "2" OR "1", OK in "R"

Incorrect fluid level. Shift linkage faulty, out of adjustment or incorrectly installed. Incorrect oil pressure. Manual control valve faulty. Transmission fluid contaminated. Engine not performing to specifications or brakes improperly adjusted. Faulty front or rear clutch. Leak in hydraulic system.

In "R", OK in Other Gears

Transmission level incorrect. Shift linkage out of adjustment or faulty. Incorrect oil pressure. Manual control valve faulty. Transmission fluid contaminated. Faulty rear clutch, front clutch or low-reverse brake. Leak in hydraulic system.

VEHICLE "CREEPS" IN "N"

Shift linkage faulty, out of adjustment or incorrectly installed. Manual control valve faulty. Transmission fluid contaminated. Faulty rear clutch.

VEHICLE "CREEPS" EXCESSIVELY

Engine idle speed too high.

VEHICLE WILL NOT "CREEP"

Fluid level incorrect or fluid contaminated. Shift linkage defective, out of adjustment or incorrectly installed. Engine idle too low. Manual control valve faulty. Faulty oil pump. Leak in hydraulic system. Faulty front or rear clutch.

"N" TO "D" ENGAGEMENT HARSH

Engine idle too high. Leak in vacuum circuit. Incorrect oil pressure. Manual control valve faulty. Faulty rear clutch.

TRANSMISSION SLIPS IN FIRST GEAR

Incorrect fluid level. Shift linkage faulty, out of adjustment or incorrectly installed. Incorrect oil pressure. Manual control valve faulty. Transmission fluid contaminated. Incorrect idle speed. Kick-down solenoid, switch or wiring faulty.

EXCESSIVE SHOCK ON 1-2 SHIFT

Leak in vacuum circuit. Engine stall speed incorrect. Transmission fluid contaminated. Manual control valve faulty. Band servo faulty. Brake band damaged or out of adjustment.

EXCESSIVE SHOCK ON 2-3 SHIFT

Leak in vacuum circuit. Kickdown solenoid, switch or wiring faulty. Incorrect oil pressure. Manual control valve faulty. Band servo or front clutch faulty.

SHIFT SHOCK FELT ON DECELERATION

Shift linkage damaged, out of adjustment or incorrectly installed. Leak in vacuum circuit. Kickdown solenoid, switch or wiring faulty. Incorrect oil pressure. Manual control valve faulty. Governor valve faulty. Leak in hydraulic system.

EXCESSIVE 2-1 SHIFT SHOCK WITH LEVER IN "1" POSITION

Leak in vacuum circuit. Engine stall speed incorrect. Manual control valve faulty. Transmission fluid contaminated. Low-reverse brake faulty.

LITTLE OR NO SHIFT SHOCK; EXCESSIVE SLIPPAGE ON 1-2 SHIFT

Transmission fluid level incorrect. Shift linkage damaged, out of adjustment or incorrectly installed. Leak in vacuum circuit. Oil pressure incorrect. Manual control valve faulty. Band servo faulty. Transmission fluid contaminated. Brake band faulty. Leakage in hydraulic system.

NO SHIFT SHOCK; EXCESS SLIPPAGE WHEN SHIFTED FROM "1" TO "2"

Incorrect fluid level. Shift linkage damaged, out of adjustment or installed incorrectly. Leak in vacuum circuit. Engine idle speed incorrect. Engine stall speed incorrect. Manual control valve faulty. Transmission fluid contaminated. Brake band out of adjustment or damaged. Oil pump faulty.

MAXIMUM SPEED TOO LOW; POOR ACCELERATION

Incorrect fluid level or fluid contaminated. Shift linkage faulty, out of adjustment or incorrectly installed. Incorrect oil pressure. Engine stall speed incorrect. Manual control valve faulty. Band servo faulty. Engine not performing to specification or brakes incorrectly adjusted. Faulty front or rear clutch. Brake band damaged or out of adjustment. Low-reverse brake faulty. Oil pump faulty.

NO SHIFT FROM 1ST TO 2ND

Shift linkage defective, out of adjustment or incorrectly installed. Leak in vacuum circuit. Faulty kickdown solenoid, switch or wiring. Transmission fluid contaminated. Manual control valve faulty. Governor valve faulty. Band servo faulty. Brake band out of adjustment. Leak in hydraulic system.

NO SHIFT FROM 2ND TO 3RD

Shift linkage defective, out of adjustment or incorrectly installed. Leak in vacuum circuit. Faulty kickdown solenoid, switch or wiring. Transmission fluid contaminated. Manual control valve, governor valve or band servo faulty. Brake band out of adjustment. Front clutch faulty. Leak in hydraulic system.

SHIFTS FROM 1ST TO 3RD; SKIPS 2ND

Transmission fluid contaminated. Manual control valve, governor valve or front clutch faulty. Leak in hydraulic system.

NO 3-2 DOWNSHIFT

Leak in vacuum circuit. Manual control valve, governor valve or band servo faulty. Transmission fluid contaminated. Brake band out of adjustment or damaged. Front clutch damaged. Leak in hydraulic system.

MAZDA F3A 3-SPEED (Cont.)

Fig. 2: Mazda F3A Automatic Transmission Hydraulic Circuits Diagram

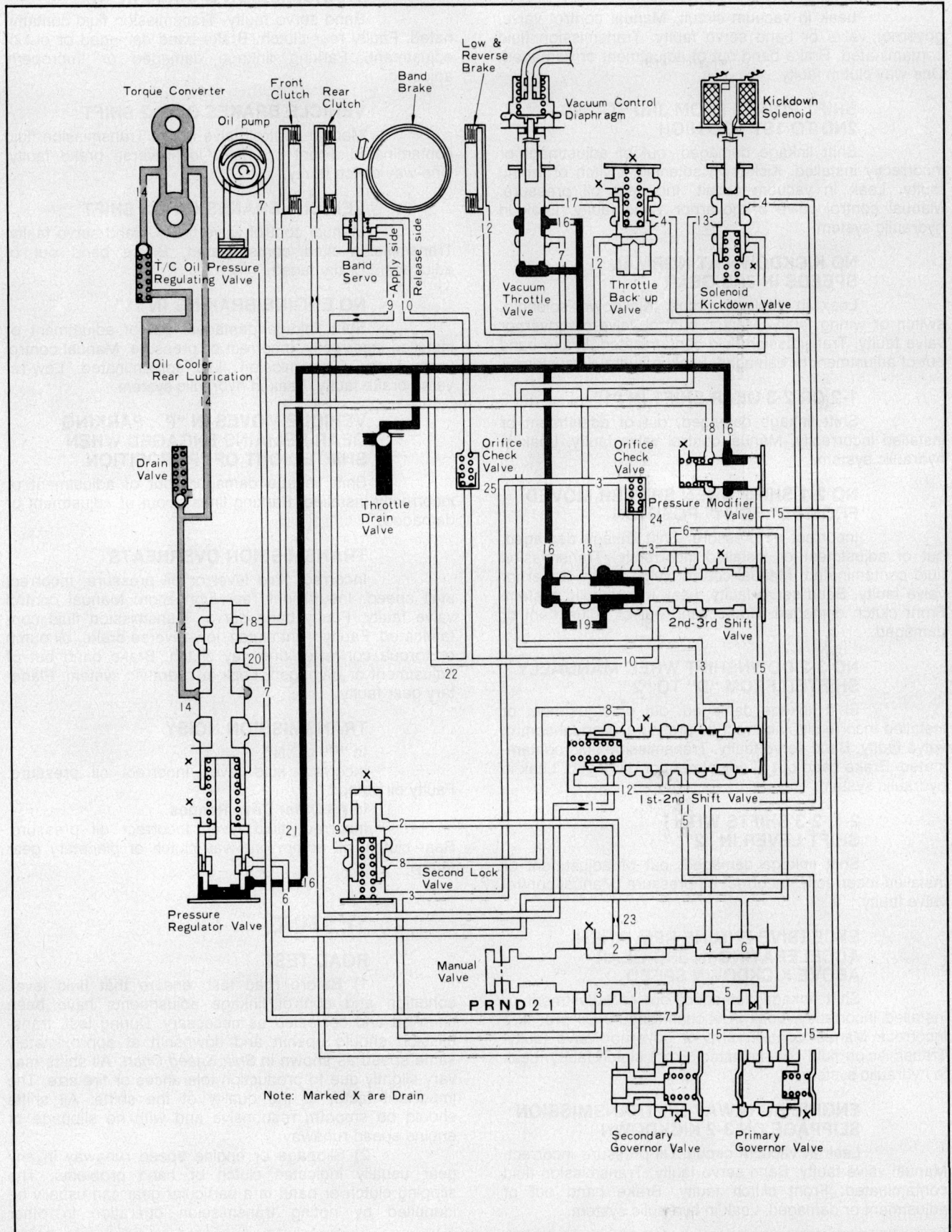

Automatic Transmissions

MAZDA F3A 3-SPEED (Cont.)

NO 2-1 OR 3-1 DOWNSHIFT

Leak in vacuum circuit. Manual control valve, governor valve or band servo faulty. Transmission fluid contaminated. Brake band out of adjustment or damaged. One-way clutch faulty.

SHIFT POINTS FROM 3RD TO 2ND, 2ND TO 1ST TOO HIGH

Shift linkage damaged, out of adjustment or incorrectly installed. Kickdown solenoid, switch or wiring faulty. Leak in vacuum circuit. Incorrect oil pressure. Manual control valve or governor valve faulty. Leak in hydraulic system.

NO KICKDOWN AT NORMAL SPEEDS IN 3RD GEAR

Leak in vacuum circuit. Kickdown solenoid, switch or wiring faulty. Manual control valve or governor valve faulty. Transmission fluid contaminated. Brake band out of adjustment or damaged. Leak in hydraulic system.

1-2 OR 2-3 GEAR SHIFT IN "1"

Shift linkage damaged, out of adjustment or installed incorrectly. Manual control valve faulty. Leak in hydraulic system.

NO 2-1 SHIFT WHEN SHIFTER MOVED FROM "D" TO "1" POSITION

Incorrect oil pressure. Shift linkage damaged, out of adjustment or installed incorrectly. Transmission fluid contaminated. Manual control valve faulty. Governor valve faulty. Band servo faulty. Leak in hydraulic system. Front clutch damaged. Brake band out of adjustment or damaged.

NO 3-2 DOWNSHIFT WHEN MANUALLY SHIFTED FROM "D" TO "2"

Shift linkage damaged, out of adjustment or installed incorrectly. Incorrect oil pressure. Manual control valve faulty. Band servo faulty. Transmission fluid contaminated. Brake band out of adjustment or damaged. Leak in hydraulic system.

2-1, 2-3 SHIFTS WITH SHIFT LEVER IN "2"

Shift linkage damaged, out of adjustment or installed incorrectly. Incorrect oil pressure. Manual control valve faulty.

EXCESSIVE ENGINE RPM WHEN ACCELERATING IN 3RD GEAR ABOVE KICKDOWN SPEED

Shift linkage damaged, out of adjustment or installed incorrectly. Leak in vacuum circuit. Oil pressure incorrect. Manual control valve or governor valve faulty. Transmission fluid contaminated. Front clutch faulty. Leak in hydraulic system.

ENGINE RUNAWAY OR TRANSMISSION SLIPPAGE ON 3-2 KICKDOWN

Leak in vacuum circuit. Oil pressure incorrect. Manual valve faulty. Band servo faulty. Transmission fluid contaminated. Front clutch faulty. Brake band out of adjustment or damaged. Leak in hydraulic system.

TRANSMISSION BRAKES IN "R"

Band servo faulty. Transmission fluid contaminated. Faulty rear clutch. Brake band damaged or out of adjustment. Parking linkage damaged or improperly adjusted.

VEHICLE BRAKES ON 1-2 SHIFT

Manual control valve faulty. Transmission fluid contaminated. Front clutch or low-reverse brake faulty. One-way clutch faulty.

VEHICLE BRAKES ON 2-3 SHIFT

Manual control valve faulty. Band servo faulty. Transmission fluid contaminated. Brake band out of adjustment or damaged.

NO ENGINE BRAKING IN "1"

Shift linkage damaged, out of adjustment or installed incorrectly. Incorrect oil pressure. Manual control valve faulty. Transmission fluid contaminated. Low-reverse brake faulty. Leak in hydraulic system.

VEHICLE MOVES IN "P"; PARKING GEAR REMAINS ENGAGED WHEN SHIFTED OUT OF "P" POSITION

Shift linkage damaged, out of adjustment or incorrectly installed. Parking linkage out of adjustment or damaged.

TRANSMISSION OVERHEATS

Incorrect fluid level or oil pressure. Incorrect stall speed. Insufficient rear lubrication. Manual control valve faulty. Faulty band servo. Transmission fluid contaminated. Faulty front clutch, low-reverse brake, oil pump or torque converter one-way clutch. Brake band out of adjustment or damaged. Leak in hydraulic system. Planetary gear faulty.

TRANSMISSION NOISY

In "P" or "N"

Incorrect fluid level. Incorrect oil pressure. Faulty oil pump.

In All Other Drive Ranges

Incorrect fluid level. Incorrect oil pressure. Rear clutch, oil pump, one-way clutch or planetary gear faulty.

TESTING

ROAD TEST

1) Before road test, ensure that fluid level, condition and control linkage adjustments have been checked and corrected as necessary. During test, transmission should upshift and downshift at approximately same speed as shown in *Shift Speed Chart*. All shifts may vary slightly due to production tolerances or tire size. The important factor is the quality of the shifts. All shifts should be smooth, responsive and with no slippage or engine speed runaway.

2) Slippage or engine speed runaway in any gear usually indicates clutch or band problems. The slipping clutch or band in a particular gear can usually be identified by noting transmission operation in other

MAZDA F3A 3-SPEED (Cont.)

selector positions and comparing internal units which are applied in these positions. *See Clutch and Band Application Chart.*

3) With vehicle at a standstill, accelerate under half and full throttle conditions to ensure that 1-2 and 2-3 shifts occur within specified range.

4) With shift lever in "D" position and vehicle speed at about 55 MPH, depress accelerator pedal to floor and ensure that a 3-2 downshift occurs. Slow vehicle to about 25 mph. Repeat and ensure that a 2-1 downshift occurs.

SHIFT SPEED CHART

Application	Shift Points (MPH)	
	Half Throttle	Full Throttle
1-2 Upshift	9-21	30-43
2-3 Upshift	17-38	54-74
3-2 Downshift	[1] 6-13	[2] 48-64
2-1 Downshift	[3] 23-32	[2] 13-29

[1] – Coastdown. Throttle fully closed.
[2] – Kickdown.
[3] – Shift lever in "1" position. Throttle fully closed.

STALL TEST

Testing Precautions

When making test, do not hold throttle open any longer than 5 seconds. Shift to "N" and allow engine to idle for at least 1 minute between tests to cool transmission. If engine speed exceeds maximum limit shown in *Stall Speed Specifications* table, release accelerator immediately as clutch or band slippage is indicated.

Testing Procedures

With engine at normal operating temperature, tachometer installed and parking and service brakes applied, make transmission stall test in "D", "2", "1" and "R" ranges at full throttle and note maximum RPM obtained.

STALL SPEED SPECIFICATIONS

Application	Stall RPM
All Models	2200-2450

Stall Test Results

1) If stall speed is below specifications, engine performance is unsatisfactory or torque converter one-way clutch is faulty (slipping).

2) If stall speed is high in all drive ranges, oil pressure is incorrect. Check oil pump (weak), oil pump control valve and transmission case for leaks. Check pressure regulator valve (sticking).

3) If stall speed is high in forward gears only, the rear clutch is slipping; in "D" only, the one-way clutch is slipping; in "2" only, the brake band is slipping. If high in "R" only, either the low-reverse brake or the front clutch is slipping.

HYDRAULIC PRESSURE TESTS

Line Pressure

1) Attach oil pressure gauge at line pressure checking plug located at rear of transaxle case on left side. *See Fig. 3.* Attach tachometer. Position gauges so that they may be observed from the driver's seat.

Fig. 3: Transaxle Assembly

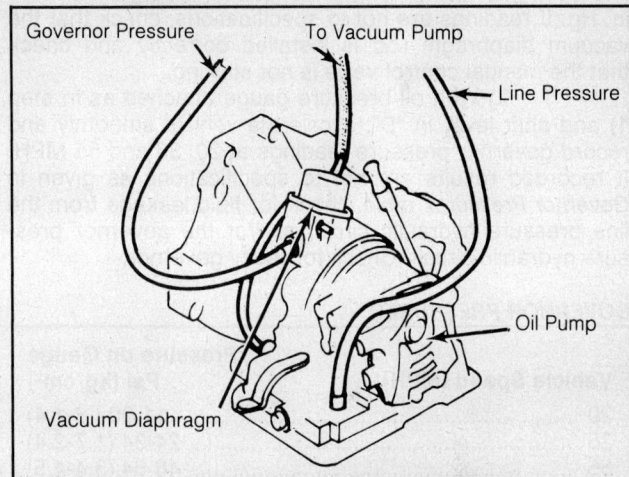

Attach lines as shown for hydraulic pressure tests.

2) With engine at normal operating temperature, transmission fluid level correct and transmission in "D", check line pressure at idle and stall speed. Repeat test in "2" and "R", allowing sufficient time for engine and transmission to cool between tests. Record results.

3) Disconnect line from vacuum diaphragm and connect a vacuum pump at connection. With shift lever in "D", increase engine RPM gradually and observe gauge reading. If line pressure drops abruptly, check governor pressure.

CLUTCH AND BAND APPLICATION CHART (ELEMENTS IN USE)

Selector Lever Position	Front Clutch	Rear Clutch	Low-Reverse Brake	Brake Band	One-Way Clutch
D – DRIVE					
First		X			X
Second		X		X	
Third	X	X			
2 – INTERMEDIATE		X		X	
1 – LOW					
Second		X		X	
First		X	X		
R – REVERSE	X		X		
P – PARK			X		

NEUTRAL – All clutches and bands released and/or ineffective.

LINE PRESSURES TABLE

Gear Range	Line Pressure In psi (kg/cm²) At Idle	At Stall Speed
"D"	43-57 (3.0-4.0)	128-156 (9.0-11.0)
"2"	114-171 (8.0-12.0)	114-171 (8.0-12.0)
"R"	57-110 (4.0-7.7)	228-270 (16.0-19.0)

Governor Pressure Tests

1) Attach vacuum pump at vacuum diaphragm and oil pressure gauge at governor port. With gauge on pump at zero, check governor pressure and record result. Increase vacuum to 7.9 in. Hg (200 mm Hg) and record gauge reading. Pressure observed should be 14-23 psi (1.0-1.6 kg/cm²) at zero and 6-14 psi (.4-1.0 kg/cm²) at 7.9 in. Hg. If readings are not to specifications, check that the vacuum diaphragm rod is installed correctly and check that the manual control valve is not sticking.

2) With oil pressure gauge attached as in step **1)** and shift lever in "D", accelerate vehicle smoothly and record governor pressure readings at 20, 35 and 55 MPH. If recorded results are not to specifications as given in *Governor Pressures* table, check for fluid leakage from the line pressure hydraulic circuit and/or the governor pressure hydraulic circuit. Check for faulty governor.

GOVERNOR PRESSURES

Vehicle Speed (MPH)	Pressure on Gauge Psi (kg/cm²)
20	11-20 (.8-1.4)
35	24-34 (1.7-2.4)
55	48-64 (3.4-4.5)

REMOVAL & INSTALLATION

See the appropriate article in AUTOMATIC TRANSMISSION REMOVAL Section.

TORQUE CONVERTER

The torque converter is a sealed unit and cannot be disassembled for service. If the converter or any component thereof is found to be faulty, the entire assembly must be replaced.

TRANSAXLE DISASSEMBLY

Whenever working with transmission, it is important that normal standards of cleanliness be observed. Complete transaxle assembly should be thoroughly steam cleaned before beginning any disassembly. Disassemble only those parts which require repair or replacement. Compressed air is preferred for drying components and oil passages, however, nylon cloth may be used. Never use fluffy rags or cloths to wipe parts dry.

1) Remove torque converter. Attach transaxle to hanger (49 F401 495) and place on engine stand. Remove inhibitor switch, kickdown solenoid and vacuum diaphragm with rod, from transmission case. Remove oil dipstick and tube. Remove speedometer drive gear retaining bolt and lift out gear assembly.

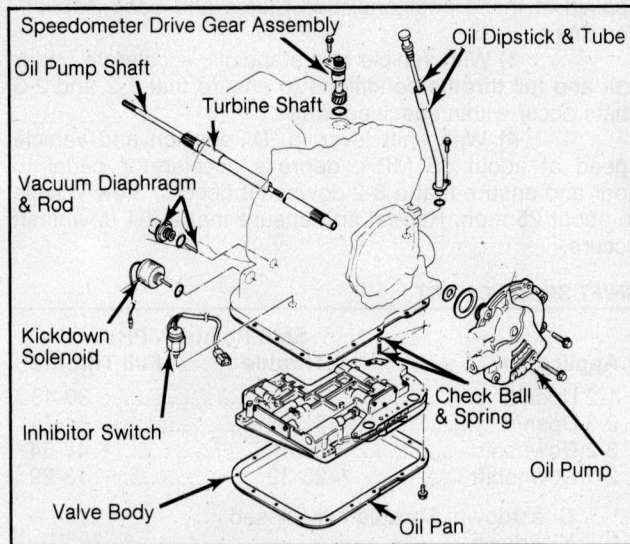

Fig. 4: Transaxle Outer Components

Use care when removing valve body so as not to lose check ball and spring.

2) Remove oil pump drive shaft and turbine shaft. Remove oil pan. Remove valve body, being careful not to lose check ball and spring. Measure and record front clutch drum end play. To determine front clutch drum end play, pry clutch drum toward oil pump with screwdriver and measure gap between drum and the connecting shell.

3) End play should be .020-.031" (.5-.8 mm). Determine adjusting shims required to bring end play to specifications and record for reassembly. Shims are available in thicknesses of .051" (1.3 mm) to .106" (2.7 mm) in increments of .008" (.02 mm).

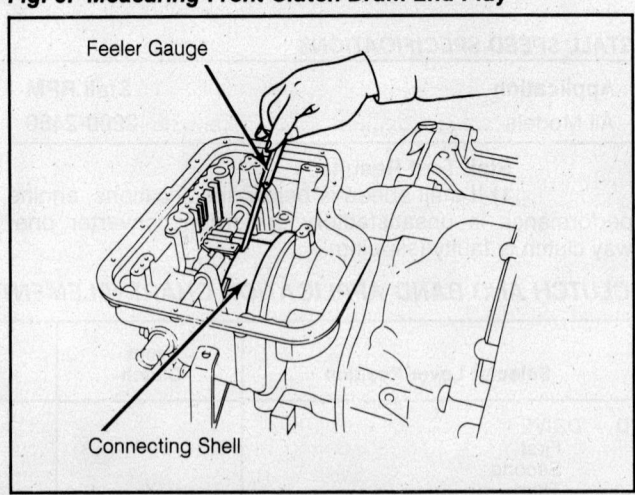

Fig. 5: Measuring Front Clutch Drum End Play

Clearance must be .020-.031" (.5-.8 mm).

4) Remove oil pump. If oil pump is difficult to remove, tighten brake band adjusting bolt until front clutch locks, then remove pump. Measure total end play. To do so, remove pump cover from oil pump. Place bearing in front brake drum. Fit bearing outer race on pump cover and install in front brake drum.

5) Place straightedge on face of transmission case and measure distance between straightedge and pump cover or straightedge and transmission case. Pump

MAZDA F3A 3-SPEED (Cont.)

cover should be between .004" (.10 mm) below transmission case and .006" (.15 mm) above case. Limits are .008" (.20 mm) and .012" (.30 mm), respectively.

6) If end play is not to specifications, select new bearing race as needed to obtain correct end play. Selective bearing races are available in thicknesses of .047" (1.2 mm) to .087" (2.2 mm) in increments of .008" (.2 mm). Record race chosen for reassembly reference.

Fig. 6: *Measuring Transaxle Total End Play*

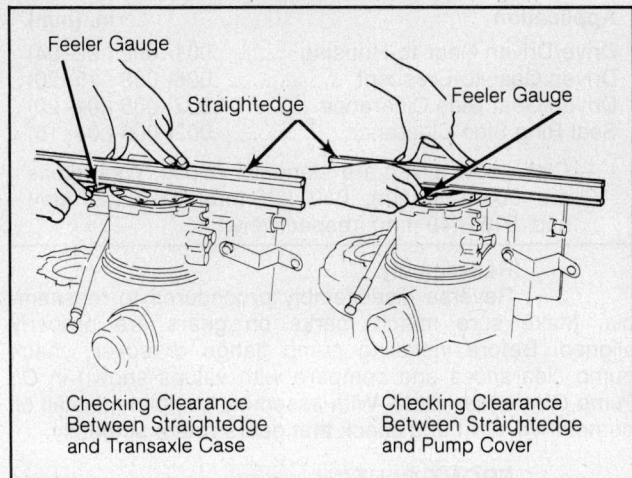

Checking Clearance
Between Straightedge
and Transaxle Case

Checking Clearance
Between Straightedge
and Pump Cover

7) Remove brake band adjusting bolt and lock nut. Remove brake band. DO NOT allow brake band to rest in fully expanded state. Hold band partially closed with a piece of wire. Remove front clutch, rear clutch and rear clutch hub assembly.

8) Remove planetary gear carrier, sun gear with spacer and connecting shell. Compress servo piston with "C" clamp and remove snap ring. Release "C" clamp and remove servo piston.

9) Separate transmission case from torque converter case. Remove neutral switch and governor assembly from transmission case. Remove oil pipes and parking pawl assembly. Remove drum hub assembly. Remove one-way clutch inner race assembly.

Fig. 7: *Removing Servo Piston*

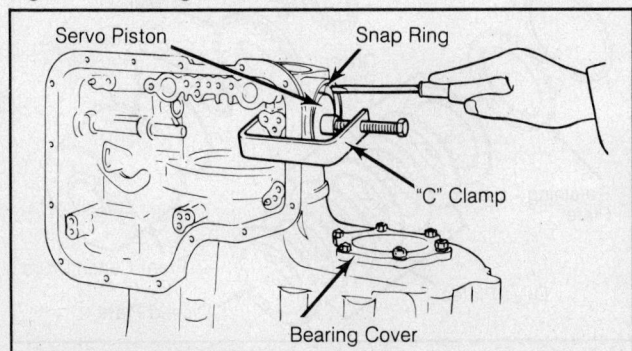

Servo Piston

Snap Ring

"C" Clamp

Bearing Cover

Compress piston with "C" clamp while removing snap ring.

10) Attach dial indicator and measure clearance between one-way clutch and low-reverse brake assembly. With gauge pin resting on drive plate, move plate up and down by hand while observing indicator dial. Clearance should be .031-.041" (.80-1.05 mm).

11) If clearance is not to specifications, select a retaining plate of different thickness to obtain correct clearance. Retaining plates are available in thicknesses of

.181" (4.6 mm) to .221" (5.6 mm) in increments of .008" (.2 mm). Record plate chosen for reassembly reference.

Fig. 8: *Checking Low-Reverse Brake Clearance*

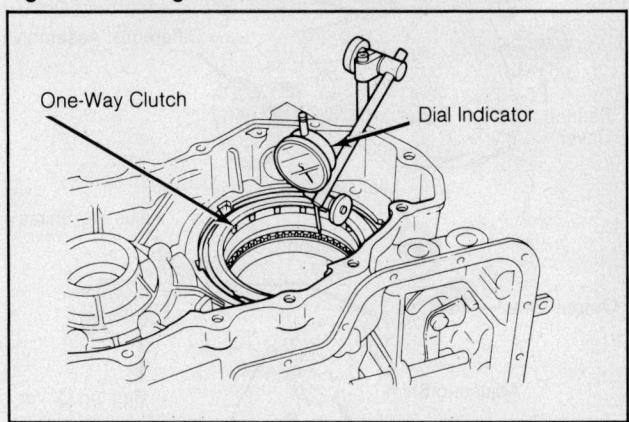

One-Way Clutch

Dial Indicator

Clearance must be .031-.041" (.80-1.05 mm).

12) Remove snap ring, one-way clutch and low-reverse brake retaining plate. Remove low-reverse brake plates. Attach low-reverse brake hub and piston removal tool (49 FT01 377). Remove snap ring with screwdriver, then remove brake hub and piston.

13) Drive out manual shaft retaining spring pin and remove manual shaft assembly. Do not lose check ball and spring. Remove shift control rod assembly and assembly support. Retain all components in correct order to aid in installation procedures.

14) Remove differential assembly from torque converter housing. Remove bearing housing assembly (with idler and output gears). If necessary, strike idler shaft lightly with soft hammer to ease bearing housing removal. Drive out idler gear retaining spring pin and remove idler from bearing housing. Remove output gear assembly and press off bearing race. Save adjusting shim for reassembly.

15) Remove 6 bearing cover-to-transmission case retaining bolts and remove bearing cover. Press off bearing race. Remove and retain adjusting shims for reassembly. Drive out oil seal. Remove bearing cover from torque converter side of torque converter housing. Press out bearing race. Drive oil seal from last bearing cover removed. Remove bearing race from differential assembly.

Fig. 9: *Removing Low-Reverse Brake Hub & Piston*

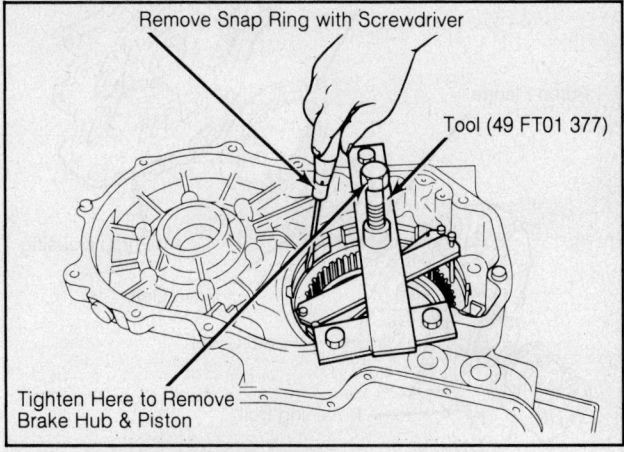

Remove Snap Ring with Screwdriver

Tool (49 FT01 377)

Tighten Here to Remove
Brake Hub & Piston

Tighten tool slowly as brake and piston assembly is removed.

Fig. 10: Torque Converter Housing Components

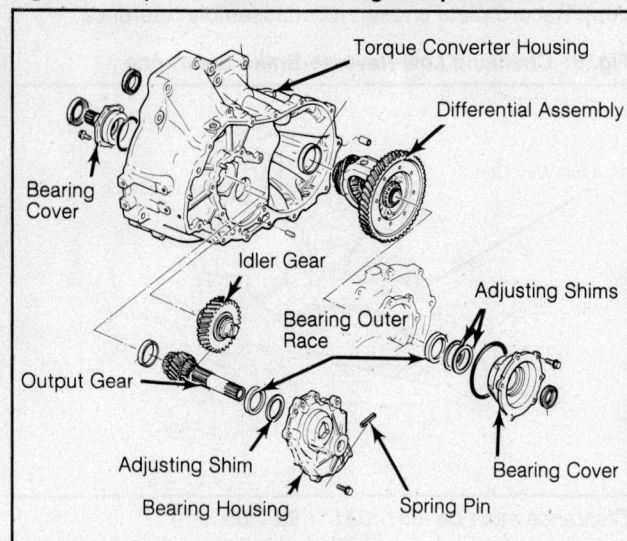

COMPONENT DISASSEMBLY & REASSEMBLY

When reassembling transaxle components, observe the folllowing practices and precautions:
- Wash all parts thoroughly.
- Use new drive plates in all clutch assemblies.
- Soak drive plates and brake band in ATF for at least 2 hours before assembly in the transaxle.
- Use petroleum jelly as needed to hold thrust bearings and/or washers in place during installation. Do not use grease.

OIL PUMP
Disassembly

1) Remove pump cover retaining bolts and separate cover from pump body. Remove pump flange. If gears are to be reused, scribe marks on gears to ensure reassembly in same position. Remove drive and driven gears.

Fig. 11: Exploded View of Oil Pump Assembly

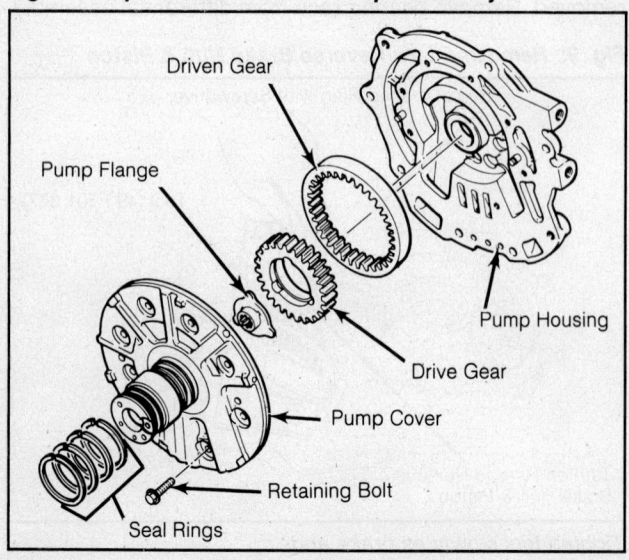

2) Check condition of gear teeth and surfaces. Check seal ring for cracks or breaks and replace as needed. Check condition of pump housing sleeve and inner gear bushing. Check sleeve outer diameter and bushing inner diameter. If sleeve diameter is less than 1.499" (38.075 mm) or bushing diameter is greater than 1.492" (37.90 mm), replace sleeve and bushing as a set.

OIL PUMP CLEARANCES

Application	[1] In. (mm)
Drive/Driven Gear-to-Housing	.001-.002 (.02-.04)
Driven Gear-to-Crescent	.006-.008 (.15-.20)
Driven Gear Side Clearance	.002-.008 (.04-.20)
Seal Ring Side Clearance	.002-.006 (.04-.15)

[1] – Clearances given are standard values. Wear limits are .003" (.08 mm), .010" (.25 mm), .010" (.25 mm) and .016" (.40 mm), respectively.

Reassembly

Reverse disassembly procedures to reassemble. Make sure match marks on gears are properly aligned. Before installing pump flange or cover, check pump clearances and compare with values shown in *Oil Pump Clearances* table. With assembly complete, install oil pump drive shaft and check that gears rotate smoothly.

FRONT CLUTCH
Disassembly

1) Before disassembling clutch, check clearance. Place front clutch on oil pump, install dial indicator so that the plunger rests on retaining plate and apply compressed air to oil hole of oil pump. Measurement shown on gauge face is front clutch clearance.

2) If clearance is not .063-.071" (1.6-1.8 mm), it may be adjusted by replacing the retaining plate with one of a different size. Retaining plates are available in thicknesses of .205" (5.2 mm) to .244" (6.2 mm) in increments of .008" (.2 mm).

Fig. 12: Exploded View of Front Clutch

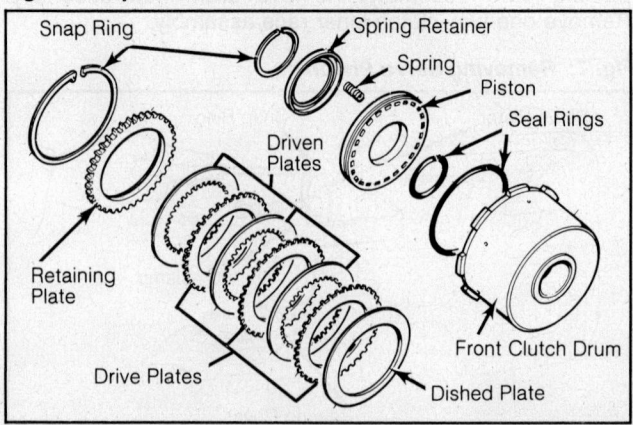

3) Compress clutch assembly with clutch spring compressor (49 0378 375) and remove large snap ring. Lift out retaining plate, clutch plates and dished plate. Remove small snap ring, spring retainer and clutch return springs. Apply compressed air at oil hole in clutch drum tand remove piston. Remove seal rings.

4) Inspect all parts for wear or damage and replace as needed. Return springs must have free length

MAZDA F3A 3-SPEED (Cont.)

of .992-1.071" (25.2-27.2 mm). If not, they are fatigued and should be replaced. Check inside diameter of clutch drum bushing. If diameter exceeds 1.735" (44.075 mm), replace bushing.

Fig. 13: Checking Clutch Clearance

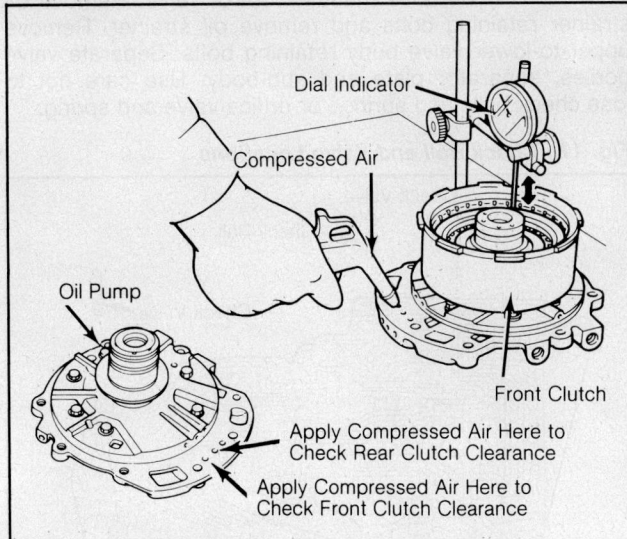

Apply compressed air at oil passages indicated.

Reassembly
Reverse disassembly procedures to reassemble. Be careful to avoid damage to oil seal ring when installing clutch piston. When installing dished plate, make sure that dished face is away from piston. Install retaining plate as determined during disassembly. Place clutch assembly on oil pump and apply compressed air to oil hole to determine proper clutch operation.

REAR CLUTCH
Disassembly
1) Before disassembling clutch, check clearance. To do so, follow same procedure used for checking front clutch clearance. Clearance should be .031-.059" (.80-1.50 mm). If clearance is incorrect, adjust by selecting a new retaining plate. Available retaining plates are same as those for front clutch.

Fig. 14: Exploded View of Rear Clutch

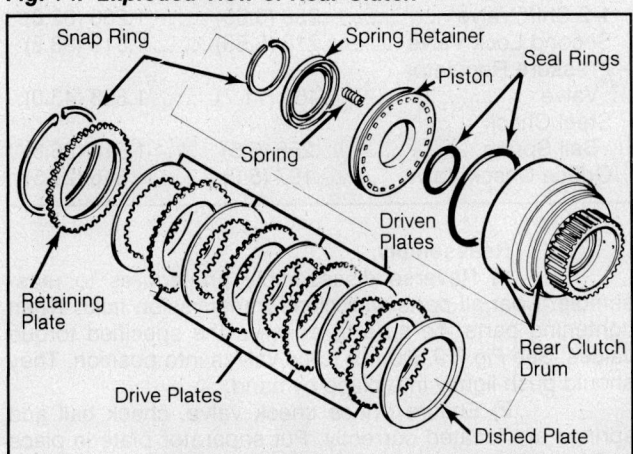

2) Compress clutch assembly with clutch spring compressor (49 0378 375) and remove large snap ring. Lift out retaining plate, clutch plates and dished plate.

Remove small snap ring, spring retainer and clutch return springs.

3) Apply compressed air to oil hole in clutch drum and remove piston. Remove seal rings. Inspect all parts for wear or damage and replace as needed. Return springs must have free length of .992-1.071" (25.2-27.2 mm). If not, they are fatigued and should be replaced.

Reassembly
Reverse disassembly procedures to reassemble. Be careful not to damage oil seal ring when installing clutch piston. When installing dished plate, make sure that dished face is facing away from piston. Install retaining plate as determined during disassembly. Place clutch assembly on oil pump and apply compressed air at oil hole in pump to determine proper clutch operation.

DRUM HUB
Disassembly
Remove parking gear spring. Push in parking gear retaining pin with screwdriver and remove parking gear. Remove snap ring and lift internal gear assembly from drive hub. Check gears for excessive wear or damage and replace if needed.

Fig. 15: Exploded View of Drum Hub Assembly

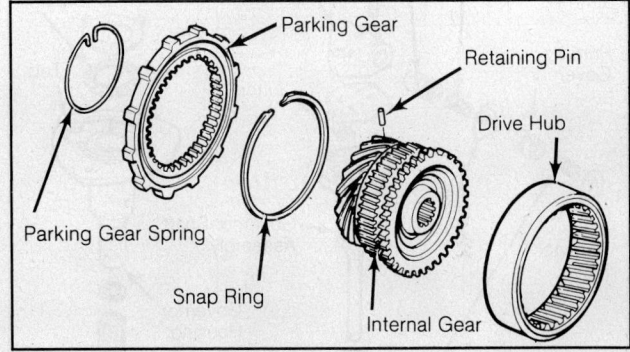

Reassembly
Reverse disassembly procedures to reassemble drum hub.

REAR CLUTCH HUB
Disassembly & Reassembly
Remove snap ring and separate hub from internal gear. Check for worn or damaged snap ring or gear. Replace as needed. Reassemble in reverse order of disassembly.

ONE-WAY CLUTCH
Disassembly
1) One-way clutch and one-way clutch inner race are removed from transmission case separately. The clutch requires no further disassembly. The inner race is disassembled by removing the snap ring and separating the inner race from the planetary carrier.

2) Check for worn or damaged gears on inner race. Check pinion operation in planetary carrier. Check clearance between the pinion washer and planetary carrier. Clearance must not exceed .031" (.8 mm).

Reassembly
Reverse disassembly procedures to reassemble. Install one-way clutch in inner race and ensure that it will turn in one direction only.

LOW-REVERSE BRAKE

Disassembly

Low-Reverse brake assembly was disassembled during transaxle disassembly. Check all components for signs of damage or excessive wear. Check return springs free length. If length is not 1.051-1.130" (26.7-28.7 mm), the spring is fatigued and should be replaced.

Reassembly

Reassembly will be accomplished when transaxle is reassembled. *See Transaxle Reassembly.*

GOVERNOR ASSEMBLY

Disassembly

Remove 2 governor housing retaining bolts and separate governor body with shaft from housing. Separate body from shaft using care not to lose filter. Disassemble governor body and retain components in correct order for reassembly. Check filter and clean if clogged. Check return springs free length and outside diameter. If not to specification, replace spring.

Fig. 16: Exploded View of Governor Assembly

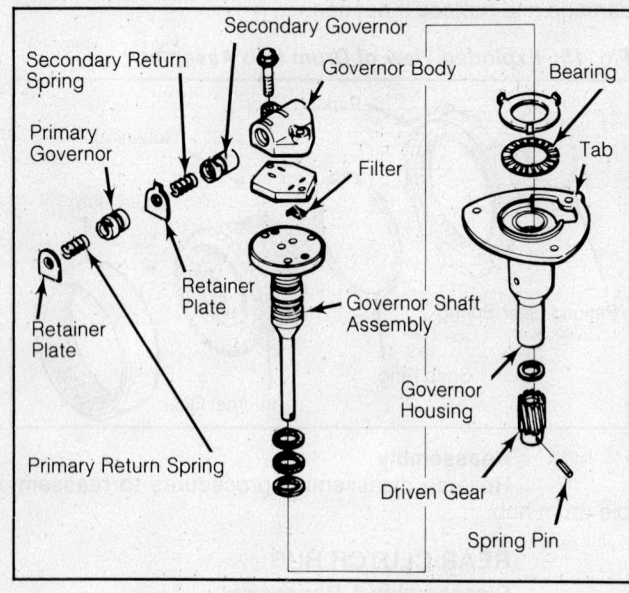

Reassembly

Reverse disassembly procedure to assemble. Apply compressed air at top oil hole in housing and ensure that valve is operating properly.

GOVERNOR RETURN SPRING SPECIFICATIONS

Application	Free Length In. (mm)	Diameter In. (mm)
Primary Spring	.650-.728 (16.5-18.5)	.350-.366 (8.7-9.3)
Secondary Spring	.488-.567 (12.4-14.4)	.352-.396 (8.95-9.55)

VALVE BODY

Many components of the valve body assembly are very similar in appearance. Therefore, care should be taken that the different components are kept separate from each other during disassembly. Arrange valves, springs and plugs relative to their positions in the valve body to aid in reassembly.

Disassembly

1) Remove manual control valve. Remove oil strainer retaining bolts and remove oil strainer. Remove upper-to-lower valve body retaining bolts. Separate valve bodies, separator plate and sub-body. Use care not to lose check balls and springs or orifice valve and spring.

Fig. 17: Check Ball and Valve Locations

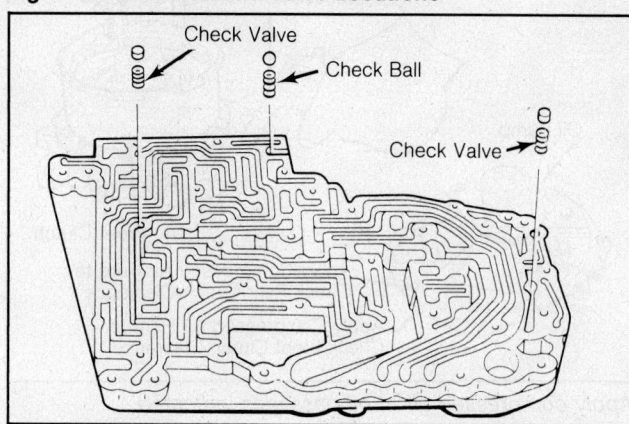

2) Remove side plate. Remove vacuum throttle valve, throttle backup valve and spring, and downshift valve and spring. Remove end plate. Remove pressure modifier valve, 2-3 shift valve, spring and plug, and 1-2 shift valve and spring.

3) Remove side plate. Remove second lock valve and spring. Remove pressure regulator valve assembly (sleeve, plug, seat, spring and valve).

VALVE BODY SPRING IDENTIFICATION

Spring	Outer Diameter In. (mm)	Free Length In. (mm)
Throttle Backup Valve	.287 (7.3)	1.417 (36.0)
Downshift Valve	.218 (5.55)	.866 (22.0)
2-3 Shift Valve	.272 (6.9)	1.164 (41.0)
1-2 Shift Valve	.258 (6.55)	1.260 (32.0)
Second Lock Valve	.218 (5.55)	1.319 (33.5)
Pressure Regulator Valve	.461 (11.7)	1.693 (43.0)
Steel Check Ball Spring	.256 (6.5)	1.516 (26.8)
Orifice Check Valve	.197 (5.0)	.846 (21.5)

Reassembly

1) Reverse disassembly procedures to reassemble. Coat all parts with clean transmission fluid. When tightening parts, be sure to observe the specified torque values. *See Fig. 19.* Do not force valves into position. They should push lightly into place by hand.

2) Ensure orifice check valve, check ball and springs are located correctly. Put separator plate in place and hold there with hand clamps. Install upper valve body and bolt in place.

MAZDA F3A 3-SPEED (Cont.)

Fig. 18: Exploded View of Valve Body and Main Controls

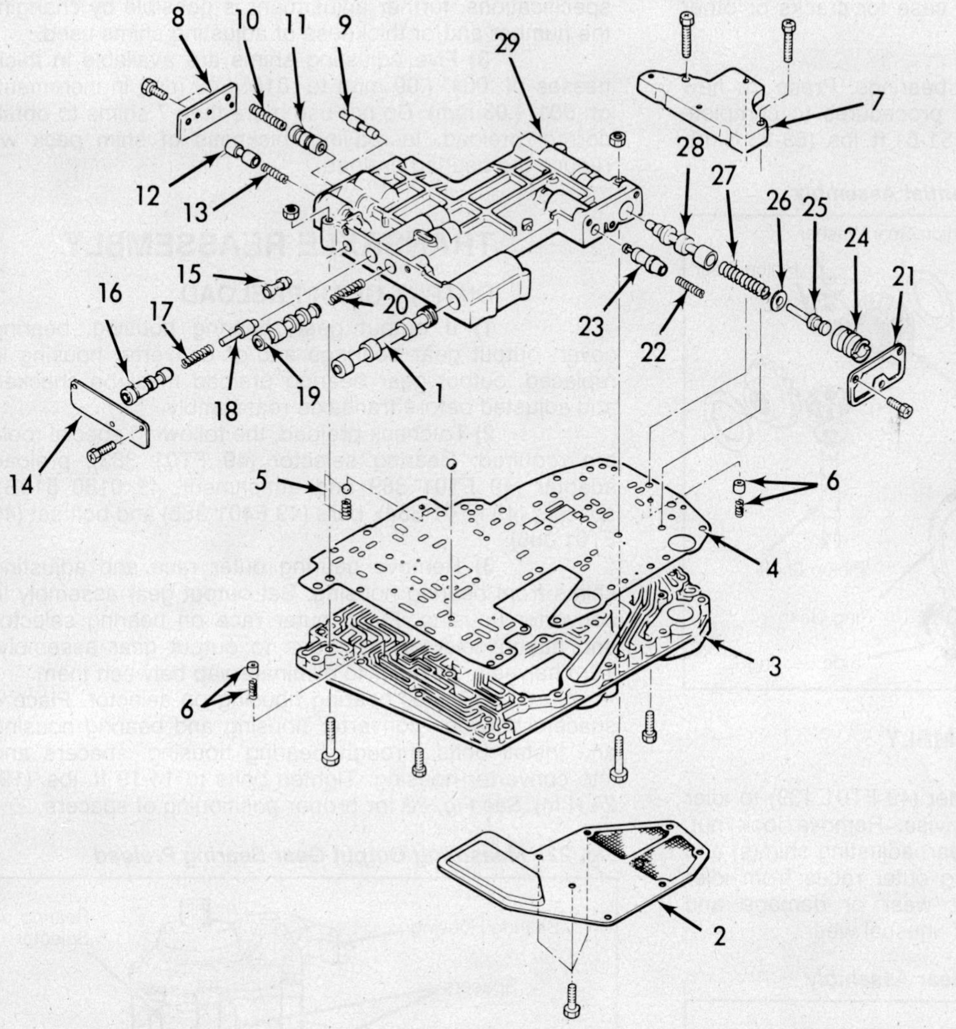

1. Manual Control Valve
2. Oil Strainer
3. Lower Valve Body
4. Separator Plate
5. Check Ball & Spring
6. Orifice Check Valve & Spring
7. Sub-Body
8. Side Plate
9. Vacuum Throttle Valve
10. Spring
11. Throttle Backup Valve
12. Downshift Valve
13. Spring
14. End Plate
15. Pressure Modifier Valve
16. 2-3 Shift Valve
17. Spring
18. 2-3 Shift Plug
19. 1-2 Shift Valve
20. Spring
21. Side Plate
22. Spring
23. Second Lock Valve
24. Pressure Regulator Sleeve
25. Pressure Regulator Plug
26. Spring Seat
27. Spring
28. Pressure Regulator Valve
29. Upper Valve Body

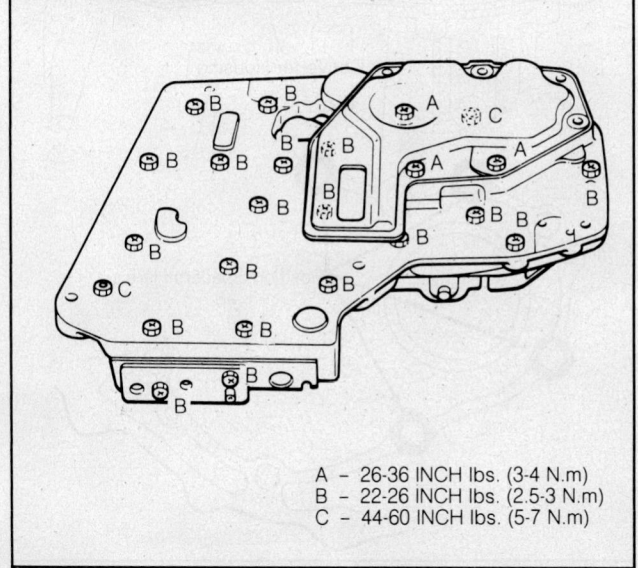

Fig. 19: Valve Body Tightening

A – 26-36 INCH lbs. (3-4 N.m)
B – 22-26 INCH lbs. (2.5-3 N.m)
C – 44-60 INCH lbs. (5-7 N.m)

DIFFERENTIAL

Disassembly

1) Measure side gear and pinion gear backlash before disassembling differential assembly. To do so, insert both drive shafts into differential and support by shafts in "V" blocks. Position dial indicator with plunger resting on teeth of pinion gear. Measure backlash. Repeat procedure with plunger on other pinion gear.

2) Backlash readings should be less than .004" (.1 mm). If not, adjust by changing thrust washers. There are 3 sizes of thrust washers available: .079" (2.0) mm), .083" (2.1 mm) and .087" (2.2 mm). Use thrust washers of the same thickness on both sides whenever possible.

3) Disassemble differential assembly. Remove ring gear retaining bolts, knock out locating pin and remove right gear. Push out pinion gear shaft. Remove pinion and side gears, with washers, from case. Place differential housing in press and support by bearing on opposite side from ring gear. Press differential case out from bearing. Remove ring gear side bearing with a bearing puller.

4) Side bearings are severely damaged when removed, therefore, new bearings must always be used when differential is reassembled. Remove speedometer drive gear. Check all gears for signs of excessive wear or damage. Check differential gear case for cracks or other damage. Replace as needed.

Reassembly

DO NOT reuse side bearings. Press on new side bearings. Reverse removal procedures to complete reassembly. Tighten ring gear to 51-61 ft. lbs. (69-83 N.m)

Fig. 20: Exploded View of Differential Assembly

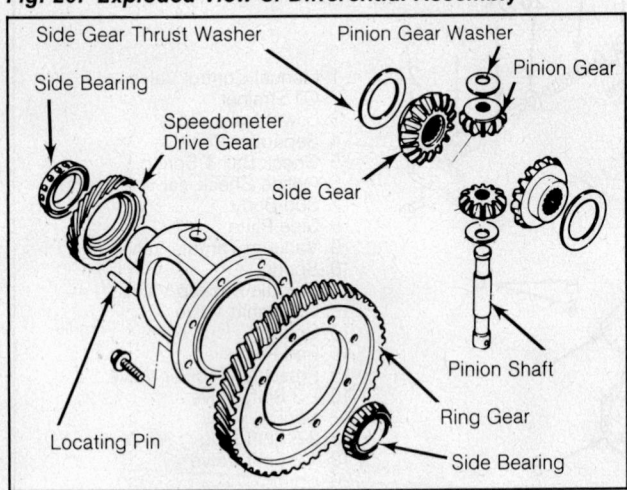

IDLER GEAR ASSEMBLY

Disassembly

Attach idler shaft holder (49 FT01 439) to idler shaft and support assembly in vise. Remove lock nut. Remove bearing, spacer, idler gear, adjusting shim(s) and remaining bearing. Press bearing outer races from idler gear. Check all gear teeth for wear or damage and bearings for breakage or signs of unusual wear.

Fig. 21: Exploded View of Idler Gear Assembly

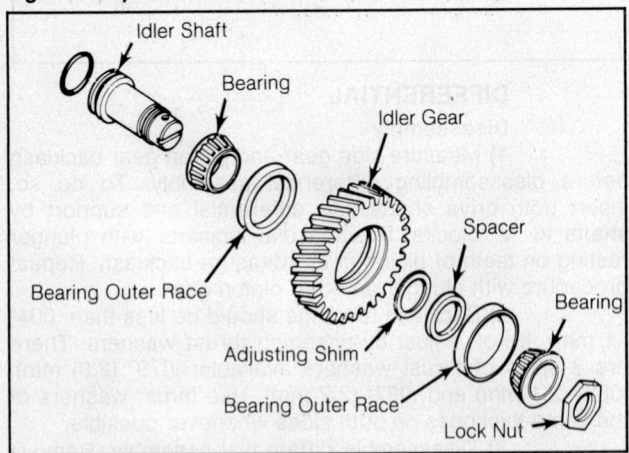

Reassembly

1) Reverse disassembly procedures to reassemble. Check bearing preload. Clamp idler gear assembly in a soft-jawed vise and tighten lock nut to 130 ft. lbs. (176 N.m). Attach idler shaft holder (49 FT01 439) and preload attachment (49 0180 510B) to idler shaft. Connect spring scale to preload attachment and measure bearing preload.

2) Bearing preload should be .07-2.1 lbs. (.03-.95 kg). If preload is too high, loosen lock nut to a

minimum of 94 ft. lbs. (127 N.m) to obtain correct reading. If correct preload cannot be obtained within these torque specifications, further adjustment is possible by changing the number and/or thickness of adjusting shims used.

3) Five adjusting shims are available in thicknesses of .004" (.09 mm) to .018" (.45 mm) in increments of .001" (.03 mm). Do not use more than 7 shims to obtain correct preload. Increasing thickness of shim pack will reduce the bearing preload.

TRANSAXLE REASSEMBLY

OUTPUT GEAR PRELOAD

1) If output gear, bearing housing, bearing cover, output gear bearings and/or converter housing is replaced, output gear bearing preload must be checked and adjusted before transaxle reassembly.

2) To check preload, the following special tools are required: Bearing selector (49 FT01 383), preload adapter (49 FT01 389 and attachment, 49 0180 510B), spacers (49 FT01 384), bars (49 F401 385) and bolt set (49 FT01 386).

3) Remove bearing outer race and adjusting shims from bearing housing. Set output gear assembly in converter housing. Place outer race on bearing selector and attach selector with race to output gear assembly. Turn halves of selector to eliminate gap between them.

4) Install bearing housing on selector. Place 4 spacers between converter housing and bearing housing and install bolts through bearing housing, spacers and into converter housing. Tighten bolts to 14-19 ft. lbs. (19-26 N.m). See Fig. 22 for proper positioning of spacers.

Fig. 22: Measuring Output Gear Bearing Preload

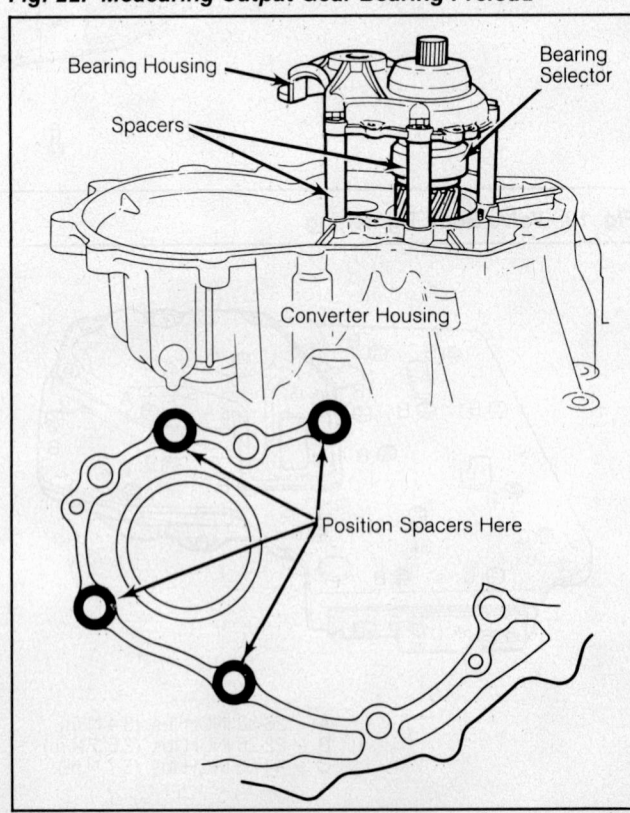

Position spacers between converter and bearing housings (in positions as shown).

MAZDA F3A 3-SPEED (Cont.)

5) To seat bearing, insert bars in holes in each half of bearing selector. Turn halves as gap between them widens. Continue to increase gap until selector stops. Reverse direction and close gap.

6) Set preload adapter and attachment on output gear. Measure bearing preload while gradually increasing gap in bearing selector. When preload is 1.1-2.0 lbs. (.5-.9 kg), measure gap in selector (check at several different points). Select adjusting shims to fill gap at widest point.

7) Shims are available in thicknesses of .004" (.10 mm) to .008" (.20 mm) in .001" (.02 mm) increments, and .020" (.50 mm). Do not exceed 7 shims in the pack. Remove selector, install shims and install bearing housing. Check that preload with components properly installed is .07-.20 lbs. (.03-.09 kg).

DIFFERENTIAL SIDE BEARING PRELOAD

1) If differential gear case, side bearing(s), bearing cover, torque converter housing and/or transmission case is replaced, differential side bearing preload must be checked and adjusted before transaxle reassembly.

2) To check preload, the following special tools will be required: Bearing selector (49 F401 381), preload adapter (49 FT01 515), spacers (49 F401 384), bars (49 F401 385) and bolt set (49 FT01 387).

3) Remove bearing outer race and adjusting shims from differential bearing cover. Place differential assembly in converter housing. Place outer race on bearing selector and place selector with race in differential assembly. Turn halves of selector to eliminate gap between them.

Fig. 23: Measuring Differential Side Bearing Preload

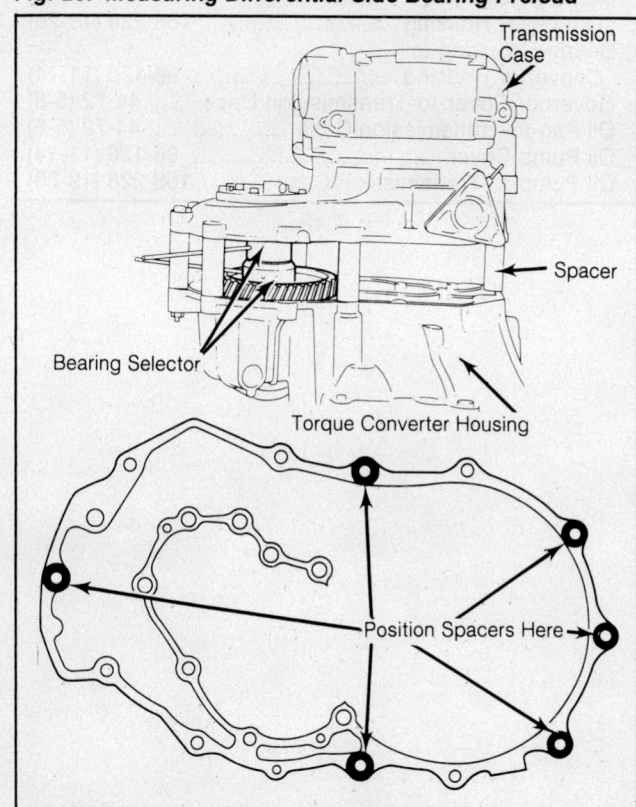

Position spacers between transmission case and converter housing as shown.

4) Install transmission case on selector using 6 spacers between transmission case and torque converter housing. Install bolts through transmission case, spacers and into converter housing. Tighten bolts to 23-34 ft. lbs. (31-46 N.m). See *Fig. 23* for proper positioning of spacers.

5) To seat bearing, insert bars in holes in each half of bearing selector and turn so that gap between them widens. Continue to increase gap until selector stops. Reverse direction and close gap.

6) Set preload adapter and attachment on output gear. Measure bearing preload while gradually increasing gap in bearing selector. When preload is 1.1-2.0 lbs. (.5-.9 kg), measure gap in selector (check at several different points). Select adjusting shim to fill gap at widest point.

7) Shims are available in thicknesses of .004" (.10 mm) to .008" (.20 mm) in increments of .001" (.03 mm) and .012" (.30 mm) to .036" (.90 mm) in increments of .04" (1.0 mm). Use as few shims as possible to meet gap requirements. Remove selector, install shim pack and install transmission case. Check that preload with components properly installed is .07-1.7 lbs. (.03-.76 kg).

TRANSAXLE REASSEMBLY

1) Throughout reassembly procedure, handle all parts carefully to avoid damaging bearing and mating surfaces. Lubricate all components with ATF fluid. Gaskets and thrust washers may be held in place with petroleum jelly where needed. DO NOT use grease. Install all new gaskets and seals.

2) Install oil seal on output gear bearing cover and in opening in converter case adjacent to differential assembly. Press differential bearing outer race into bearing cover. Press output gear bearing outer race into bearing cover. Install output gear bearing cover on torque converter housing and place housing on stand.

3) Install output gear adjusting shims in bearing housing and press in bearing outer race. Install output gear assembly and idler gear assemblies in bearing housing. Install idler gear retaining spring pin. Install complete assembly in converter housing.

4) Install differential assembly in converter housing. Install oil seal in differential bearing cover. Install adjusting shims and bearing outer race, then install completed bearing cover assembly in transmission case. Tighten bolts in a diagonal pattern.

5) Working with transmission case, install shift control rod assembly and support. Install manual shaft assembly with check ball and spring. Retain with new spring pin. Assemble low-reverse brake hub and piston, then attach to tool (used in low-reverse brake hub and piston removal) and install in transmission case. Retain with large snap ring.

6) Install dished plate on top of low-reverse brake hub with dished face down (toward hub). Install drive and driven plates beginning with internally lugged plate and alternating with an externally lugged plate until all plates have been installed.

7) Install correct retaining plate as determined in step **7)** of Transaxle Disassembly. Install one-way clutch with bushing side toward retaining plate. Retain with snap ring. Install washer, bearing and one-way clutch inner race assembly. Install washer, bearing, drum hub assembly and last washer and bearing. Install parking pawl assembly and oil pipes.

8) Install governor assembly. Governor is installed correctly when tab on governor sleeve is aligned

MAZDA F3A 3-SPEED (Cont.)

with mark on transmission case. *See Fig. 16.* Install neutral switch. Apply a thin film of sealer on contact surfaces of transmission case and converter housing.

    9) Assemble transmission case to torque converter housing. Place servo assembly in position in case and compress with "C" clamp. Install retaining snap ring and remove "C" clamp.

    10) Install connecting hub, sun gear with spacer and planetary gear carrier assembly. Install rear clutch hub assembly, rear clutch and front clutch. Install bearing race used for end play adjustment as determined during oil pump disassembly.

    11) Install brake band. Install oil pump. Install and adjust brake band adjusting bolt. Install bolt and tighten to 9-11 ft. lbs. (12-15 N.m). Loosen exactly 2 turns. Tighten lock bolt.

    12) Install steel check ball and spring in case, then install valve body assembly. Install oil pan. Install turbine and oil pump shafts. Install speedometer drive gear, oil dipstick and tube, and vacuum diaphragm.

    13) A check must be made to determine which rod to install. Measure dimension "A" shown in *Fig. 24*, and compare to *Diaphragm Rod Chart* to determine which rod to install. Install kickdown solenoid and inhibitor switch hand tight.

    14) Install torque converter in torque converter housing. With converter properly installed, dimension "A" in *Fig. 24* should be .425-.492" (10.8-12.5 mm).

DIAPHRAGM ROD CHART

Dimension "A" In. (mm)	Rod Size In. (mm)
Under 1.00 (25.4)	1.16 (29.5)
1.00-1.02 (25.4-25.9)	1.18 (30.0)
1.02-1.04 (25.9-26.4)	1.20 (30.5)
1.04-1.06 (26.4-26.9)	1.22 (31.0)
Over 1.06 (26.9)	1.24 (31.5)

Fig. 24: Vacuum Diaphragm Installation

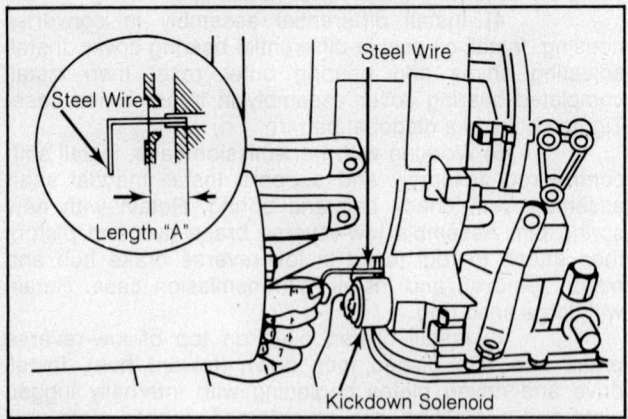

Check length "A" to determine diaphragm rod usage.

Fig. 25: Torque Converter Installation

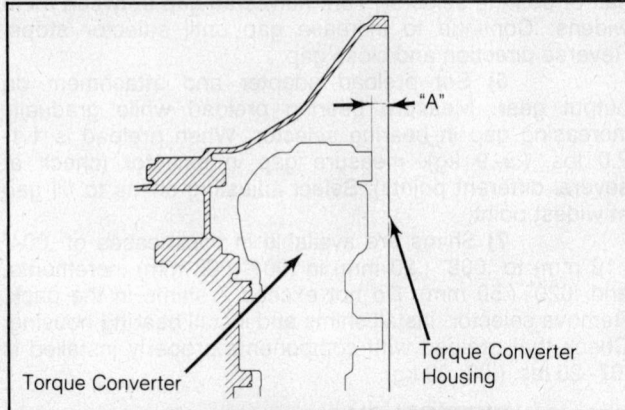

Dimension "A" will be .425-.492" (10.8-12.5 mm) with converter properly installed.

TIGHTENING SPECIFICATIONS

Application	Ft. Lbs. (N.m)
Torque Converter-to-Drive Plate	25-36 (34-49)
Drive Plate-to-Crankshaft	60-69 (81-94)
Trans. Case-to-Converter Housing	23-34 (31-46)
Converter Housing-to-Engine	
12 mm Bolts	47-69 (64-94)
14 mm Bolts	65-87 (88-118)
Idler Gear Lock Nut	94-130 (127-176)

	INCH Lbs. (N.m)
Bearing Cover-to-Transmission Case	168-228 (19-26)
Bearing Cover-to-Converter Housing	168-228 (19-26)
Bearing Housing-to-Converter Housing	96-120 (11-14)
Governor Cover-to-Transmission Case	44-72 (5-8)
Oil Pan-to-Transmission Case	44-72 (5-8)
Oil Pump Cover	96-120 (11-14)
Oil Pump-to-Transmission Case	168-228 (19-26)

Automatic Transmissions
MERCEDES-BENZ TYPE W 4 A 040

300, 380, 500 Series

DESCRIPTION

This is a fully automatic 4-speed unit consisting primarily of a 3-element welded torque converter and 2 compound planetary gear sets. Two multiple-disc clutches, 1 overrunning clutch, and 3 brake bands provide friction elements required to obtain desired function of planetary gear set. A hydraulic system, pressurized by a primary gear type pump and a secondary piston type pump provide working pressure required to operate friction elements and automatic controls.

On 380 Series models, to relieve load on the vehicle's service brakes on lengthy downgrades, the engine's braking effect is utilized by providing an additional shift lever position "B" (Braking). When the shift lever is placed in position "B", the solenoid valve in the transmission is energized through the switch at the shift lever. The transmission will remain in 1st gear independent of accelerator position. It will shift to 2nd gear when the regular kickdown shift point is reached.

On 500 series, the transmission is the same as 300 and 380 series except for the following: 500 series transmission's have a torque converter that is 11.4" (290 mm) in diameter. Clutches "K-1" and "K-2" have five inner discs each. The diaphragm diameter of the vacuum modulator valve is 1.08" (27.5 mm), the identifying color is White. Dependng on driving style, the transmission can start in 2nd or 1st gear. The electrical circuit for the lock out and back up light switch has an additional contact pin, which energized in shift lever positions "3" and "2", allowing the transmission to start in 1st gear at moderate acceleration.

OPERATION

STARTING IN 1ST GEAR

In shift lever positions "3" and "2", the switching unit is activated by terminal 15 by the starter lock out and back up light switch. The switching unit then activates the kickdown valve which switches to 1st gear, while the vehicle is stationary.

Starting at a speed of approximately 7 MPH, the switching unit is activated by the cruise control connection of the speedometer. The switching unit interrupts the current flow to the kickdown valve and the transmission will shift to 2nd gear.

LUBRICATION & ADJUSTMENT

See appropriate MANUAL TRANSMISSION SERVICING article in IMPORT GENERAL SERVICING section.

TROUBLE SHOOTING

TRANSMISSION SLIPS

Slips In All Selector Positions

Incorrect modulating pressure. Modulating pressure control valve or pressure relief valve for modulating pressure dirty or sticking. Line to transmission vacuum unit clogged or leaking. Working pressure control valve dirty or sticking. Defective primary pump.

Fig. 1: Shift Lever Position "B" Circuit

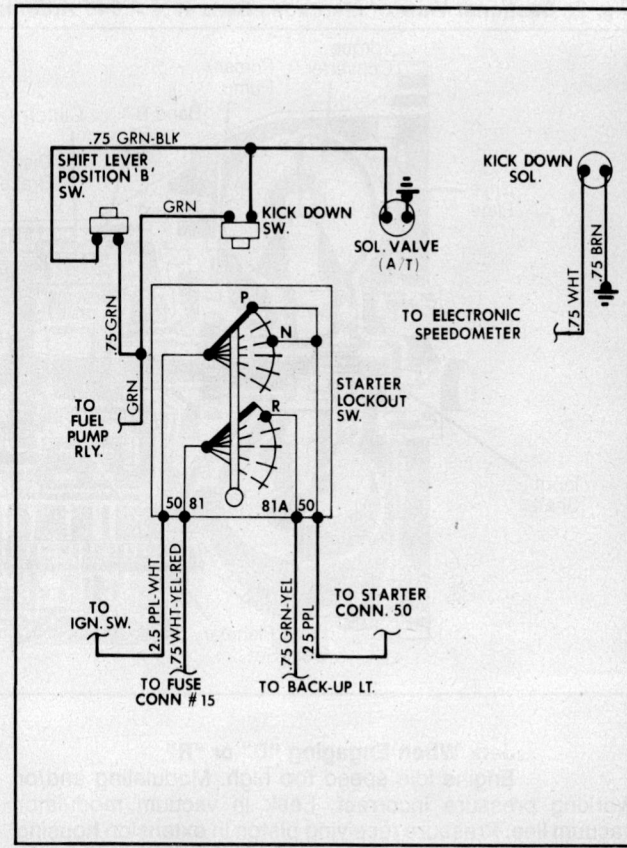

Transmission Slips in 1st & 2nd Gear When Starting Off or Starting Off Impossible, Okay in Reverse

Band "B-2" shift valve sticking. Valve body malfunction. Band "B-2" piston worn or damaged. Band "B-2" adjustment incorrect, worn or damaged.

Transmission Slips in 2nd Gear Or Shifts From 1st to 3rd

Brake band "B-1" control valve sticking. Valve body malfunction. Brake band "B-1" piston sealing ring worn or damaged. Band "B-1" worn or damaged.

Transmission Slips When Upshifting From 2nd To 3rd Or From 3rd To 4th Gear

Governor and/or working pressure incorrect. Valve body assembly worn or damaged. Defective front or rear clutch assembly.

No Positive Engagement In Reverse

Front band out of adjustment. Sealing ring on rear band piston worn or damaged. One-way roller clutch in gear assembly worn or damaged.

SHIFT JERK

Rough Jerks When Changing Gears

Incorrect modulating pressure. Incorrect working pressure. If working pressure is too high, replace valve body assembly. Vacuum line to modulator leaking. Control pressure linkage out of adjustment. Control valve converter adjustment incorrect.

MERCEDES-BENZ TYPE W 4 A 040 (Cont.)

Fig. 2: Sectional View of Mercedes-Benz W 4 A 040 Automatic Transmission

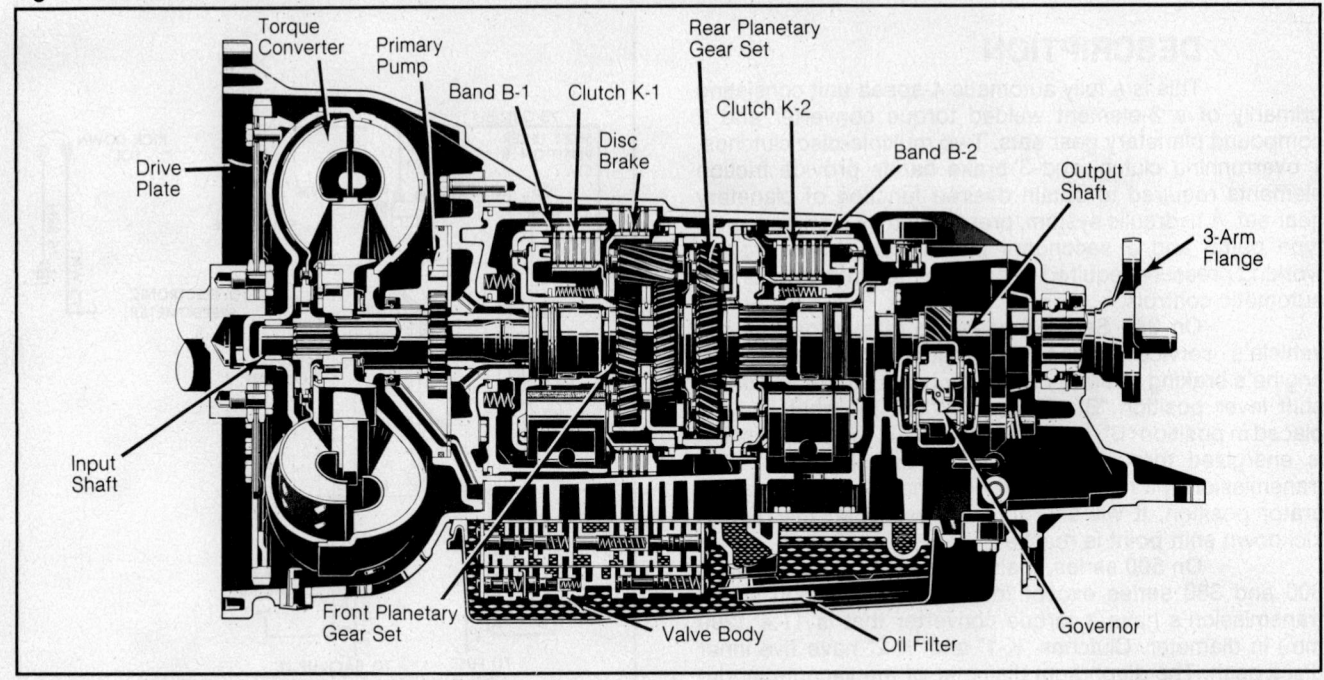

Jerk When Engaging "D" or "R"
Engine idle speed too high. Modulating and/or working pressure incorrect. Leak in vacuum modulator vacuum line. Pressure receiving piston in extension housing worn, damaged, or installed incorrectly. Feed bore in pressure receiving piston plugged.

Rough Jerk on 4-3 Downshift
Sealing ring on release end of band "B-2" worn or damaged. Band "B-2" piston worn or damaged.

UPSHIFTS & DOWNSHIFTS
No Upshift
Incorrect governor pressure. Defective governor assembly. Valve body dirty or valves sticking.

Upshifts Only In Upper
Speed Range Of Gears
Control pressure linkage out of adjustment. Defective governor assembly. Propeller shaft flange retaining nut loose.

No Kickdown Shifts
Fuse for power supply to solenoid valve blown. Defective solenoid valve. Control pressure linkage damaged or out of adjustment. Kickdown control valve in valve body sticking.

No Brake Shifts (4-3 & 3-2)
Control pressure out of adjustment. Make brake shaft piston operable and exchange shift valve housing, if required.

TESTING

ROAD TEST
NOTE: Before road testing, make sure fluid level and condition, and control linkage adjustments have been checked and corrected as necessary.

1) During road test, transmission should upshift and downshift at approximately the speeds shown in SHIFT SPEEDS SPECIFICATION (MPH). All shifts may vary somewhat due to production tolerances or tire size. The important factor is quality of shifts. All shifts should be smooth, responsive, and with no engine speed flare-up.

NOTE: Shifts at full throttle and kickdown are somewhat firmer than part throttle shifts.

2) Slipping or engine speed flare-up in any gear usually indicates clutch or band problems. The slipping clutch or band in a particular gear can usually be identified by noting transmission operation in all selector positions and comparing which internal units are applied in those positions. See CLUTCH & BAND APPLICATION CHART.

3) Although this process of elimination can be used to detect any unit which slips, and to confirm proper operation of good units, actual cause of malfunction usually cannot be decided. Practically any condition can be caused by leaking hydraulic circuits or sticking valves. Therefore, unless an obvious condition exists, transmission should never be disassembled until hydraulic pressure tests have been made.

HYDRAULIC PRESSURE TESTS
Preparation For Tests
Before making tests, be sure fluid level and condition, manual and throttle linkages, EGR system, and neutral safety/back-up light switch have been checked and adjusted or corrected as necessary. Connect a pressure gauge test set to pressure take-off points on transmission. *See Fig. 3.*

NOTE: Make sure pressure gauge hoses do not drag on pavement or contact exhaust system.

NOTE: Modulating pressure must be measured (and corrected if necessary) before making working pressure and governor pressure tests.

Automatic Transmissions

MERCEDES-BENZ TYPE W 4 A 040 (Cont.)

SHIFT SPEED SPECIFICATIONS (MPH)

Application	300 Series	380 & 500 Series
Lever in "D"		
Idle		
1-2 Upshift	9	13
2-3 Upshift	17	17
3-4 Upshift	23	25
4-3 Downshift	17	17
3-2 Downshift	12	11
2-1 Downshift	.....	.....
Full Throttle		
1-2 Upshift	22	34
2-3 Upshift	43	58
3-4 Upshift	73	101
4-3 Downshift	43	65
3-2 Downshift	20	32
2-1 Downshift	7	19
Kickdown		
1-2 Upshift	25	44
2-3 Upshift	43	65
3-4 Upshift	73	106
4-3 Downshift	63	95
3-2 Downshift	20	55
2-1 Downshift	11	30
Lever in "3" [1]		
Idle		
1-2 Upshift	9	13
2-3 Upshift	17	17
3-2 Downshift	12	11
2-1 Downshift	.....	.....
Full Throttle		
1-2 Upshift	22	34
2-3 Upshift	43	58
3-2 Downshift	20	32
2-1 Downshift	7	19
Kickdown		
1-2 Upshift	25	44
2-3 Upshift	43	65
3-2 Downshift	33	55
2-1 Downshift	11	30
Lever in "2" [2]		
Idle		
1-2 Upshift	25	29
2-1 Downshift	9	13
Full Throttle		
1-2 Upshift	25	34
2-1 Downshift	14	19
Kickdown		
1-2 Upshift	25	44
2-1 Downshift	18	30
Lever in "B" [3]		
Idle-to-Kickdown		
Upshift	.....	44
Downshift	.....	30

[1] – Lever in "S" on 300 Series
[2] – Lever in "L" on 300 Series
[3] – On 380 and 500 Series only.

Modulating Pressure Test

Accelerate vehicle on the road or on a dynamometer to 53 MPH. Run engine at full throttle, and keep speed at 30 MPH by lightly applying service brakes. Read resulting pressure on gauge attached to modulating pressure take-off point on transmission. Pressure should check as shown in MODULATING & WORKING PRESSURE chart. Adjust pressure as necessary.

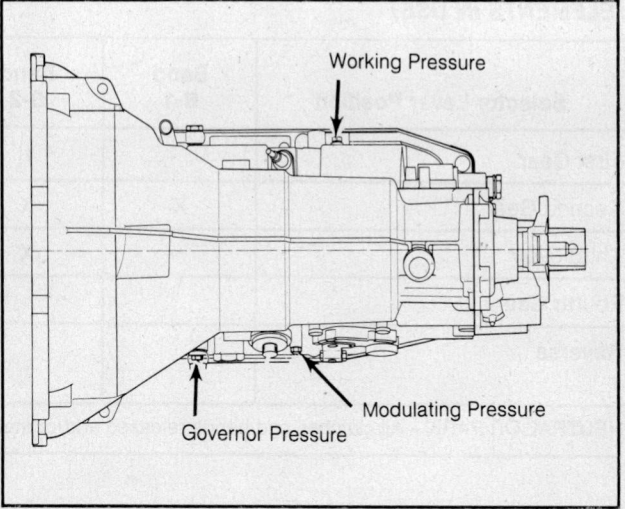

Fig. 3: Pressure Test Take-Off Points

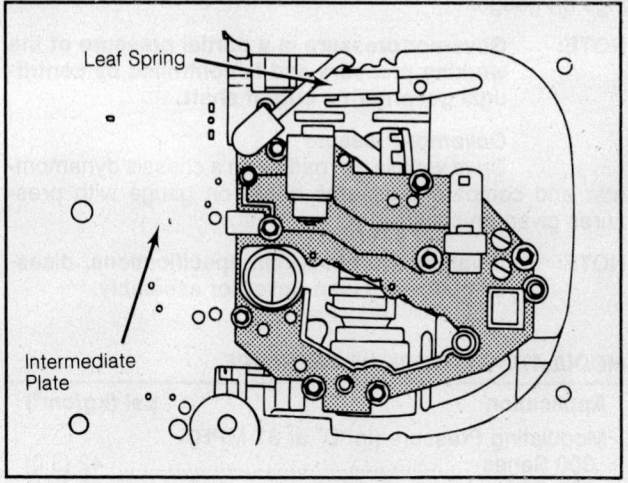

Fig. 4: Bottom View of Transmission Case Showing Location of Leaf Spring

NOTE: On models with diesel engines it may be necessary to adjust vacuum supply to modulator to obtain correct vacuum. If adjustment is needed, see appropriate AUTOMATIC TRANSMISSION SERVICING article in IMPORT GENERAL SERVICING.

Modulating Pressure Adjustment

1) Remove rubber cap on vacuum control unit. Pull locking plate out of locking slots to permit rotation.

2) Adjusting screw in vacuum modulator can now be adjusted by means of locking plate. One turn of adjusting screw results in a pressure change of 6 psi (.4 kg/cm^2).

3) After turning adjusting screw, push locking plate back into locking slots. Put rubber cap back on vacuum control unit. Measure modulating pressure once again. Plug-on vacuum line and screw to holder.

NOTE: Working pressure is not adjustable. Pressure is automatically established with correctly adjusted modulating pressure.

6-174

Automatic Transmissions
MERCEDES-BENZ TYPE W 4 A 040 (Cont.)

CLUTCH AND BAND APPLICATION CHART (ELEMENTS IN USE)

Selector Lever Position	Band B-1	Band B-2	Disc Brake	Clutch K-1	Clutch K-2	One-Way Clutch
First Gear		X			X	X
Second Gear	X	X				
Third Gear		X		X		
Fourth Gear				X	X	
Reverse			X		X	X

NEUTRAL OR PARK – All clutches and bands released and/or ineffective.

Working Pressure

To check pressure, drive vehicle in indicated range and speed shown in chart, and note pressure readings on gauge.

NOTE: **Governor pressure is a partial pressure of the working pressure and is controlled by centrifugal governor on output shaft.**

Governor Pressure

Drive vehicle on road or on a chassis dynamometer and compare pressures noted on gauge with pressures given on chart.

NOTE: **If values are not within specifications, disassemble and clean governor assembly.**

MODULATING & WORKING PRESSURE

Application	psi (kg/cm²)
Modulating Pressure (In "D" at 31 MPH)	
300 Series	42 (3.0)
380 Series	58 (4.1)
Working Pressure (In "D" stationary)	
300 Series	167-196 (11.7-13.8)
380 Series	177-206 (12.4-14.5)

Control Pressure

Control pressure is a partial pressure of modulating pressure and is controlled by the position of accelerator pedal. If control pressure rod is correctly adjusted, control pressure will be arrived at automatically. No take-off point is provided for measuring control pressure.

GOVERNOR PRESSURE

Speed (MPH)	300 Series psi (kg/cm²)	380 & 500 Series psi (kg/cm²)
12	7-10 (.5-.7)	5-8 (.4-.6)
25	25-28 (1.8-2.0)	12-162 (.8-1.1)
37	29-32 (2.0-2.2)	25-28 (1.6-2.0)
56	39-42 (2.7-3.0)	30-33 (2.1-2.3)
75	52-55 (3.7-3.9)	36-39 (2.5-2.7)

STALL TEST
Testing Precautions

When making test, do not hold throttle open longer than 5 seconds or severe transmission damage may result from heat generated. If engine speed exceeds maximum limits shown, release accelerator immediately as this is an indication of clutch or band slippage.

Testing Procedure

With engine at normal operating temperature, tachometer installed, and parking and service brakes applied firmly, stall test transmission by pushing accelerator to floor and noting engine speed on tachometer. Engine speed should be within limits in chart.

Stall Test Results

If stall speed is higher than specified, general transmission problems are indicated and hydraulic pressure tests should be made to locate faulty units. If stall speed is lower than specified, torque converter roller clutch is faulty.

CAUTION: **Make sure engine performance is satisfactory before condemning converter assembly. Torque converter is a sealed unit and cannot be disassembled for service.**

STALL SPEED SPECIFICATIONS

Application	Stall RPM
300 Series	2200-2300
380 Series	1300-1700

SERVICE (IN VEHICLE)

The following units may be removed from transmission without removing transmission from vehicle: Oil Pan and Gasket, Shift Valve Body, Vacuum Modulator Unit, Speedometer Driven Gear Assembly, Secondary Pump Assembly, Extension Housing, Pressure Receiving Piston, Modulating Pressure Housing and Bi-metallic Spring, Speedometer Drive Gear, Secondary Pump Eccentric, Governor Assembly, Parking Pawl, and Parking Linkage. See procedures given in TRANSMISSION DISASSEMBLY and TRANSMISSION REASSEMBLY

Fig. 5: Secondary Pump Assembly

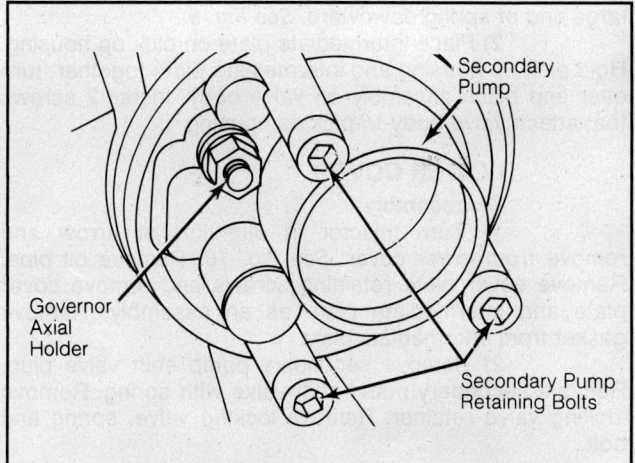

Showing location of nuts and bolts for removal.

REMOVAL & INSTALLATION

See appropriate AUTOMATIC TRANSMISSION REMOVAL article in IMPORT GENERAL SERVICING section.

TORQUE CONVERTER

NOTE: **Torque converter is a sealed unit and cannot be disassembled for service. If hub of converter is scored, or if metallic particles are found in transmission fluid, replace converter assembly.**

TRANSMISSION DISASSEMBLY

1) Position transmission in a holding fixture (116 589 06 59 00 and 126 589 10 63 00) with oil pan facing upward, then remove oil pan and gasket. Remove oil filter and bolts attaching valve body to transmission case, then lift valve body from case.

2) Remove leaf spring screw and remove leaf spring and holder together. *See Fig. 4.* Remove screws and remove lower transmission case cover along with intermediate plate and oil pipe. Remove one-way valve and band "B-1" guide. Push in band "B-2" piston cover and remove locking ring. Remove band piston cover and pull piston out of bore.

3) Attach compressor (126 589 00 59 00) to transmission housing. Apply compressor to band "B-1" piston cover and remove locking ring. Remove compressor and withdraw band "B-1" piston cover, piston and back pressure springs. Remove guide for band "B-1". Remove closing cover for band "B-1" thrust bolt.

4) Remove range selector lever. Remove starter lock-out switch. Remove retaining screws and remove vacuum control unit holding plate. Withdraw vacuum control unit from transmission case. Remove band "B-1" thrust body and modulating pressure control valve.

5) Remove kickdown solenoid valve. Remove slot nut and 3-arm flange. Remove bolts attaching rear cover-to-transmission case. Loosen rear cover by lightly tapping cover with a plastic hammer. Remove rear cover.

6) Remove parking lock gear and parking pawl as an assembly. Remove expanding ring. Remove nut from axial holder for governor. Remove Allen head bolts that retain secondary pump and remove pump. *See Fig. 5.* Remove "O" ring and intermediate plate of secondary pump.

7) Remove plastic guide and roller assembly from bottom of transmission case. Push in governor cover and remove retaining ring. Pull cover out of bore. Swivel axial holder back. Remove governor assembly. Remove axial holder. Remove helical gear. *See Fig. 6.*

Fig. 6: View of Transmission Case

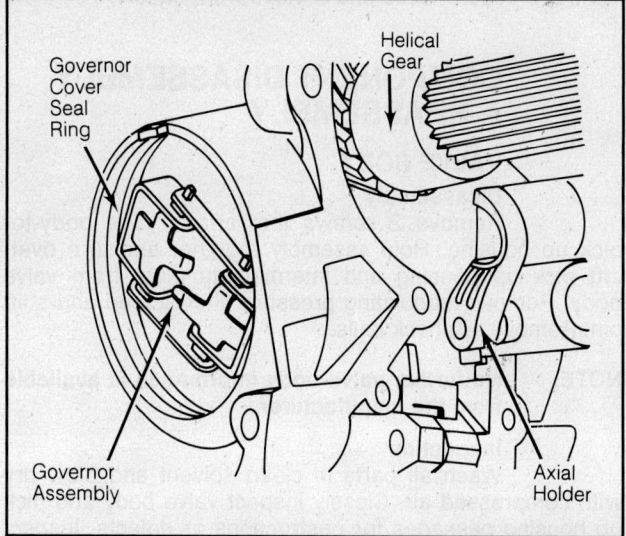

Note location of governor, axial holder and helical gear.

8) Remove circlip from output shaft. Remove bolts attaching front cover to transmission case. Install 2 longer bolts into threaded holes in front cover (to serve as handles). Pull front cover from transmission case. Hold planetary gear set on input shaft and carefully remove assembly from front of transmission case.

9) Remove clutch "K-1" and band "B-1" from case as an assembly. Remove disc brake plates. Remove clutch "K-2" thrust pin and clutch "K-2". Remove bolt retaining detent plate to transmission case. Remove output shaft from transmission case. Remove detent plate.

Fig. 7: View Into Transmission Case

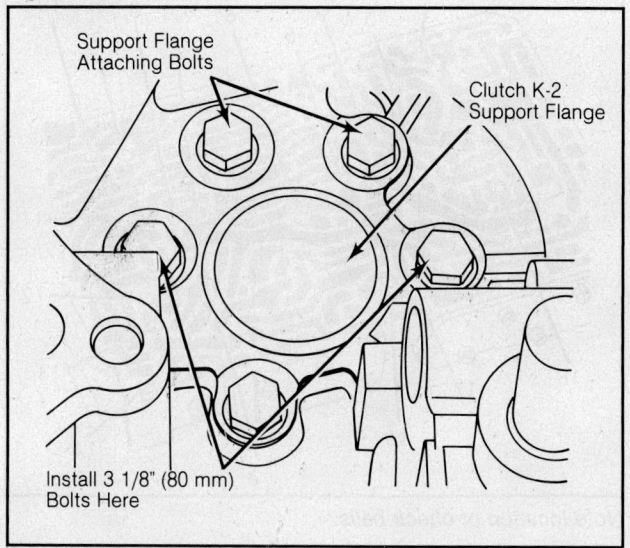

Showing location of clutch "K-2" support flange attaching bolts.

6-176

Automatic Transmissions
MERCEDES-BENZ TYPE W 4 A 040 (Cont.)

10) Tilt band "B-2" on an angle and remove from case. Remove band "B-2" thrust washer and band "B-2" thrust body. Remove bolts attaching clutch "K-2" support flange to case. Install 2 bolts, approximately 3 3/8" (80 mm) long, into support flange. Loosen support flange by hitting bolts with hammer. *See Fig. 7.* Remove support flange from case using bolts as handles.

11) Release tabs on detent cable retainer from inside of case. Pull detent cable out of case. Disconnect control pressure cable and remove from case.

COMPONENT DISASSEMBLY & REASSEMBLY

VALVE BODY

Disassembly

Remove 2 screws that attach valve body-to-pick up housing. Hold assembly together and turn over. Lift pick up housing and intermediate plate from valve body. Remove modulating pressure filter screen and shift pin. Remove all check balls.

NOTE: No further valve body information is available from the manufacturer.

Inspection

Wash all parts in clean solvent and blow dry with compressed air. Closely inspect valve body and pick up housing passages for obstructions or defects. Inspect intermediate plate for damage. Also check all balls for any kind of damage. If internal valve body problems are found or suspected, valve body assembly must be replaced as an assembly.

NOTE: One valve body illustration is shown but there are several; all are similar to the one shown. The number of check balls may vary by one or two, so be sure of number and locations during disassembly.

Fig. 8: Pick-Up Housing with Valve Body Removed

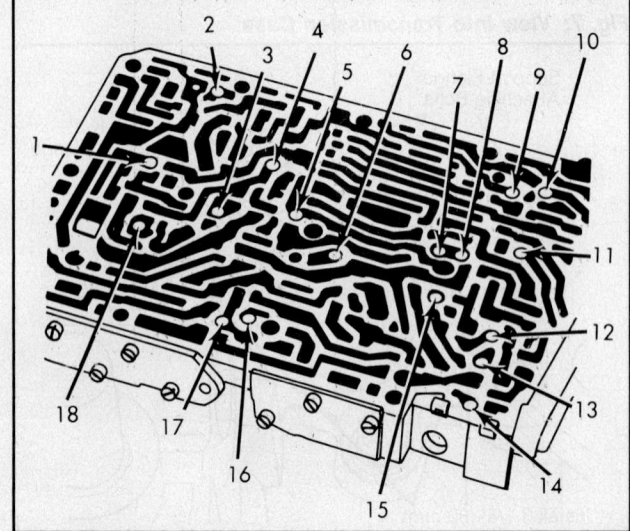

Note location of check balls.

Reassembly

1) Install all check balls into pick up housing. *See Fig. 8.* Install modulating pressure filter screen and

shift pin. Place conical spring under check ball No. 7 with large end of spring downward. *See Fig. 9.*

2) Place intermediate plate on pick up housing. Hold pick up housing and intermediate plate together, turn over and place assembly on valve body. Install 2 screws that attach valve body-to-pick up housing.

LOWER COVER

Disassembly

1) Turn injector in direction of arrow and remove from lower cover. *See Fig. 10.* Remove oil pipe. Remove cover plate retaining screws and remove cover plate and intermediate plate as an assembly. Remove gasket from intermediate plate.

2) Remove secondary pump shift valve plug. Remove secondary pump shift valve with spring. Remove locking valve retainer. Remove locking valve, spring and bolt.

Fig. 9: Top View of Pick-Up Housing

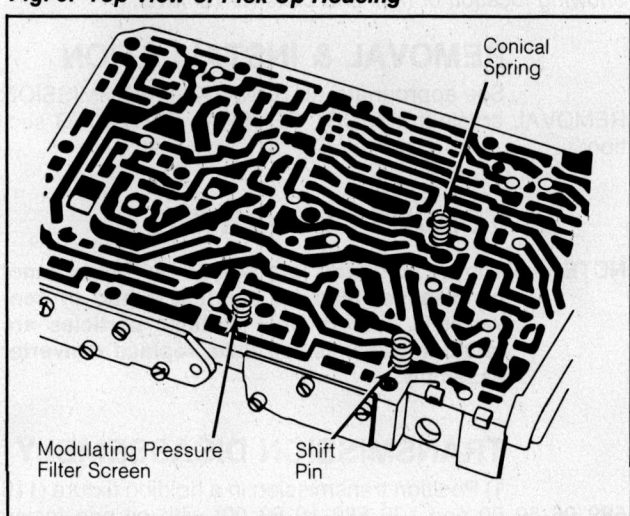

Inspection

Check that intermediate plate is not plugged or distorted in any way. Inspect secondary pump shift valve and spring for damage or distortion. Inspect locking valve and spring for damage or distortion.

Fig. 10: Injector Located on Bottom of Lower Cover

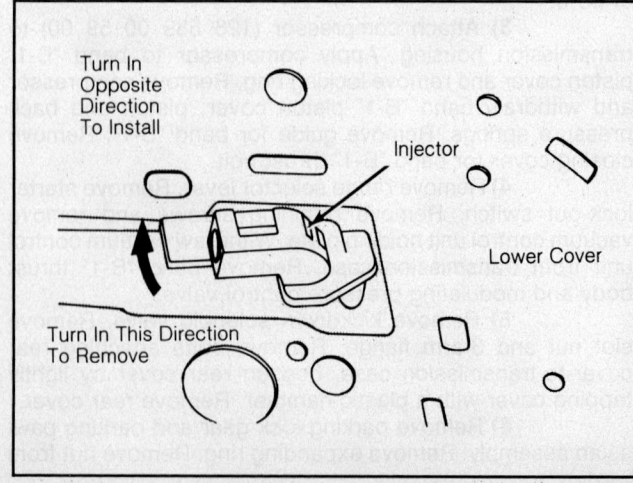

Reassembly

1) Install secondary pump shift valve, spring and plug into lower cover. Install locking valve, spring and bolt. Install locking valve retainer. Place intermediate plate, with a new gasket, on lower cover.

2) Install cover plate on intermediate plate and lower cover assembly. Install oil pump. Install injector in lower cover and rotate in opposite direction of arrow. *See Fig. 10.*

SECONDARY PUMP
Disassembly

Remove pump gears from pump housing. Remove shutoff piston cover retaining ring and cover. Remove shutoff piston with compression spring, spring retainer and ball from pump housing. *See Fig. 11.*

Inspection

Check pump gears and pump housing for damage or unusual wear. Check compression spring for distortion. Check shutoff piston and piston seal for damage and replace as necessary.

Reassembly

Place "O" ring into pump housing. Install Teflon sealing ring on shutoff piston. Install shutoff piston into pump housing. Install compression spring, spring retainer and ball into shutoff piston. Install piston cover and piston cover retaining ring. Lubricate pump gears and place in pump housing. *See Fig. 11*

Fig. 11: Exploded View of Secondary Pump

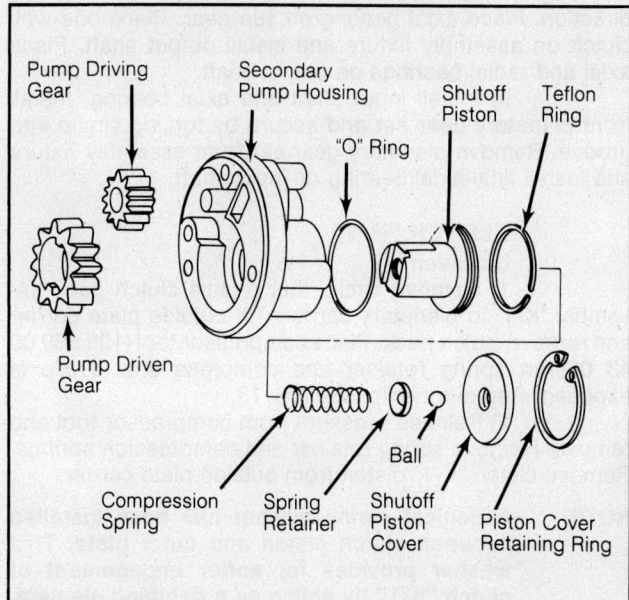

PRIMARY PUMP
Disassembly

1) Remove 2 Teflon rings from stator shaft. Push disc brake spring retainer down and remove locking ring. Remove spring retainer and back pressure springs for disc brake piston.

2) Remove disc brake piston. Remove bolts attaching pump housing-to-front cover and lift pump from cover. Remove both primary pump gears from pump housing. *See Fig. 12.*

Fig. 12: Removing Driven Gear From Front Pump Housing

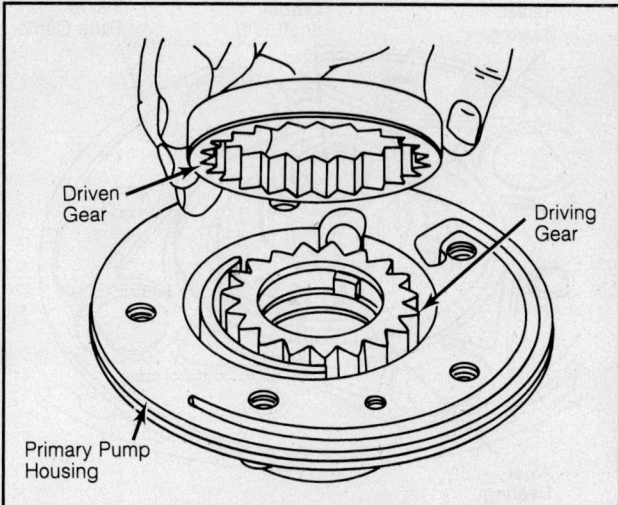

Housing shown with front cover removed.

Inspection

Check bearing bushing for scores or damage. Check radial sealing ring for damage. Check that "O" ring is properly seated in groove. Check that pump gears are not scored or damaged.

Reassembly

1) Install both pump gears into pump housing. Make sure that chamfered edge of driven gear faces down in pump housing. *See Fig. 12.* Place intermediate plate on primary pump assembly. Place primary pump housing onto front cover being careful not to damage bearing bushing on stator shaft. Install pump-to-front cover attaching bolts.

2) Install lip sealing rings on disc brake piston. Place insertion sleeve (126 589 04 14 00) on front cover. Lubricate lip sealing rings. Install piston over insertion sleeve so that pin on piston lines up with bore in front cover. Carefully push piston down without tilting piston.

3) Install back pressure springs and spring retainer. Slide locking ring over insertion sleeve. Hold locking ring at bottom of sleeve and remove sleeve. Push spring retainer and locking ring down until locking ring seats in its groove. Install Teflon rings on stator shaft.

PLANETARY GEAR SET
Disassembly

1) Clamp gear set in assembly fixture (126 589 00 35 00), at 2 flat sides, in a vise. Place planetary gear set assembly into assembly fixture. Remove circlip that retains planetary gear. Lift front planetary gear set off input shaft. Remove radial bearing and axial bearing. *See Fig. 13.*

2) Remove output shaft. Remove axial bearing from sun gear. Remove sun gear. Remove circlip that retains clutch "K-2" inside plate carrier. Remove clutch "K-2" inside plate carrier with one-way clutch from connecting carrier. Remove support disc, compensating ring and "O" ring from one-way clutch. *See Fig. 14.* Rotate inner race of one-way clutch in counterclockwise direction and pull out. Remove one-way clutch and rollers.

Inspection

Check all bearings, bearing surfaces and bearing races for scoring or damage. Check one-way clutch roller bearings for scoring, roundness and extreme wear. If

6-178

Automatic Transmissions
MERCEDES-BENZ TYPE W 4 A 040 (Cont.)

Fig. 13: Top View of Inside Plate Carrier

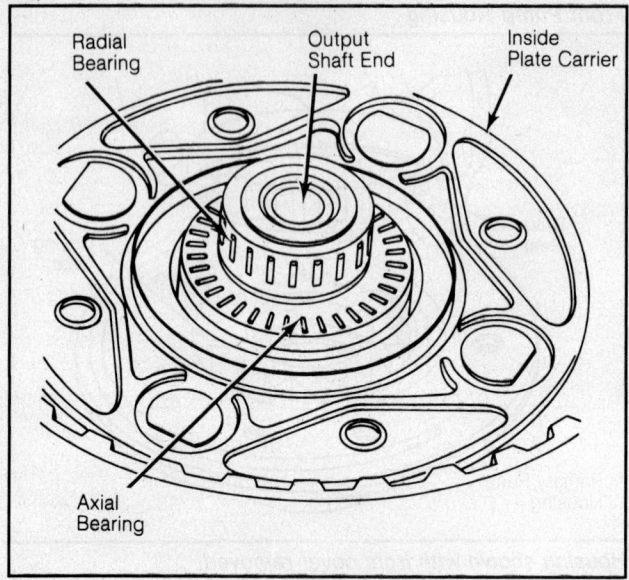

Showing location of radial and axial bearings.

Fig. 14: Top View of One-Way Clutch

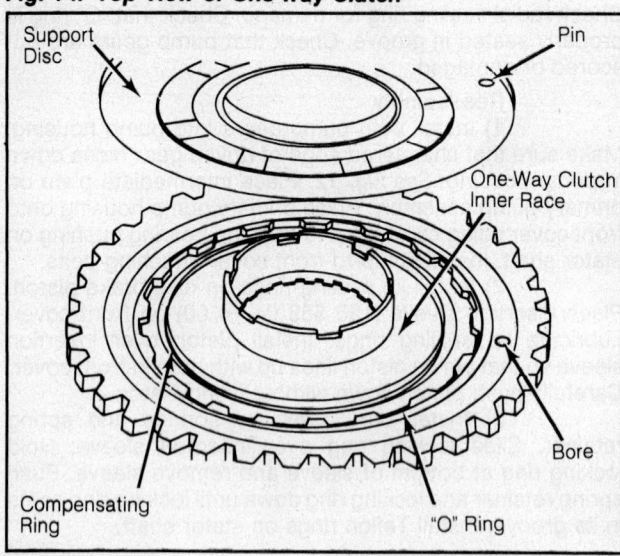

Note component location.

damage to one-way clutch rollers is noted, replace one-way clutch as an assembly.

Reassembly
1) Press compression springs together with a screwdriver and install one-way clutch rollers. Press rollers against compression springs and insert locking plates with offset pointing outward. *See Fig. 15.* Install one-way clutch inner race. Remove locking plates.

2) Install compensating ring and "O" ring. Mount support plate so that pin on support plate enters in one-way clutch outer race. *See Fig. 14.* Install compensating washers into connecting carrier. Hold one-way clutch together and place assembly into connecting carrier. Install circlip and force into groove with screwdriver.

3) Check clearance between one-way clutch and connecting carrier. *See Fig. 17.* Clearance should be

Fig. 15: View of One-Way Clutch

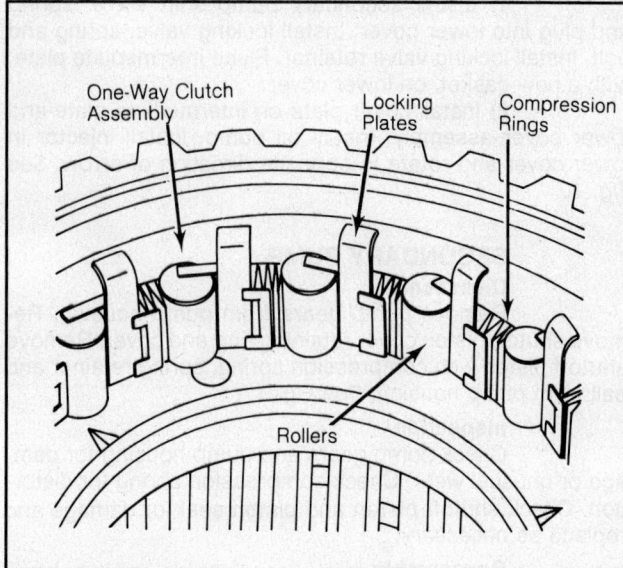

Note location of rollers, compression springs and locking plates.

.002-.008" (.05-.20 mm). If clearance is not within limits, add or remove compensating washer until specified clearance is obtained.

4) Place sun gear into one-way roller assembly. One-way clutch should lock when rotated in clockwise direction. Place axial bearing on sun gear. Place one-way clutch on assembly fixture and install output shaft. Place axial and radial bearings on output shaft.

5) Install input shaft and axial bearing. Install front planetary gear set and secure by forcing circlip into groove. Remove planetary gear set from assembly fixture and install final axial bearing on input shaft.

CLUTCH "K-1"
Disassembly
1) Remove circlip that retains clutch pack assembly "K-1" in planetary carrier. Tilt outside plate carrier and remove clutch pack. Place compressor tool (126 589 00 43 00) on spring retainer and compress until circlip is exposed. Remove circlip. *See Fig. 18.*

2) Release pressure from compressor tool and remove. Remove spring retainer and compression springs. Remove clutch "K-1" piston from outside plate carrier.

NOTE: A conical spring washer has been installed between clutch piston and outer plate. This washer provides for softer engagement of clutch "K-1" by acting as a damping element. Be sure it is reinstalled at reassembly.

Reassembly
1) Install new lip sealing rings into piston so lip of sealing ring points downward. Place installation sleeves (126 589 02 14 00 and 126 589 03 14 00) into outer plate carrier. Lubricate installation sleeves and sealing rings with ATF. Install piston into outer plate carrier being careful not to tilt piston. Remove installation sleeves.

2) Install compression springs into piston. Install spring retainer, making sure that each compression spring is centered by a guide pin. Install compressor tool and compress compression springs. Install circlip and release

Automatic Transmissions
MERCEDES-BENZ TYPE W 4 A 040 (Cont.)

6-179

Fig. 16: Exploded View of Planetary Gear Set

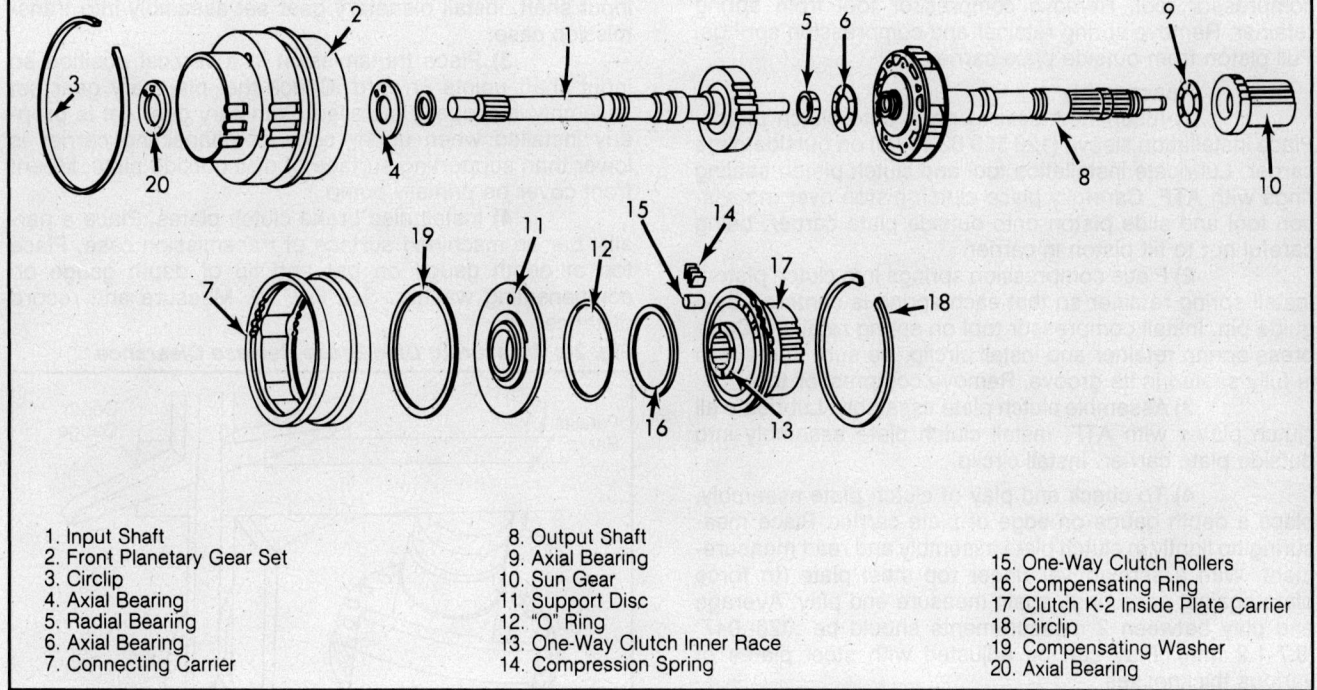

1. Input Shaft
2. Front Planetary Gear Set
3. Circlip
4. Axial Bearing
5. Radial Bearing
6. Axial Bearing
7. Connecting Carrier
8. Output Shaft
9. Axial Bearing
10. Sun Gear
11. Support Disc
12. "O" Ring
13. One-Way Clutch Inner Race
14. Compression Spring
15. One-Way Clutch Rollers
16. Compensating Ring
17. Clutch K-2 Inside Plate Carrier
18. Circlip
19. Compensating Washer
20. Axial Bearing

Fig. 17: Measuring One-Way Clutch-to-Connecting Carrier Clearance

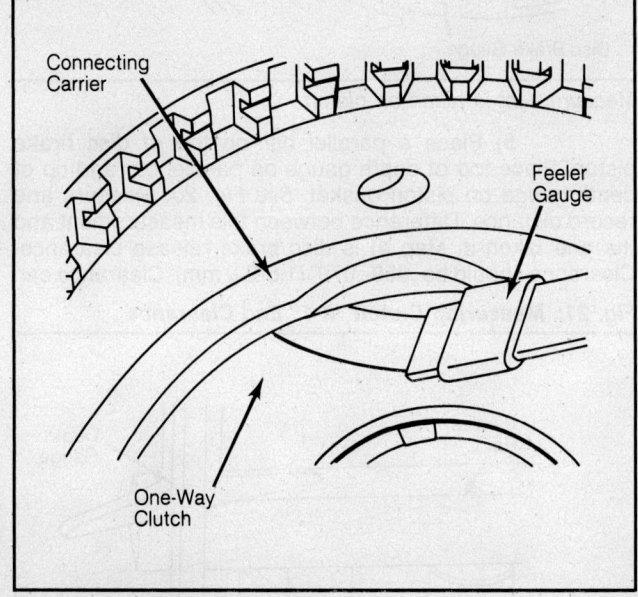

Note position of feeler gauge.

compressor tool, making sure that circlip is properly seated in groove. Remove compressor tool.

3) Assemble clutch plates. Lubricate all clutch plates with ATF. Install clutch plates into outside plate carrier. Install circlip, making sure that it is fully seated in groove.

4) To check end play of clutch plate assembly, place a depth gauge on edge of plate carrier. Place measuring tip lightly in clutch plate assembly and read measurement. With a screwdriver under top steel plate (to force

Fig. 18: Installing Spring Compressor Tool on Clutch Pack "K-1"

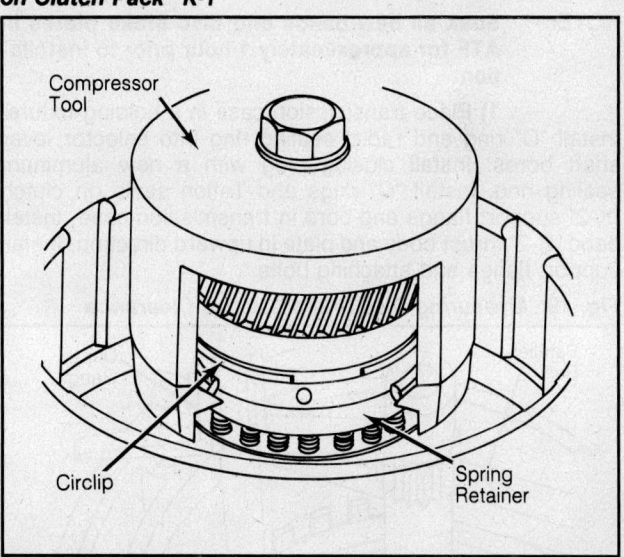

Compressor tool is necessary to remove compressor springs and spring retainer.

plate against snap ring), again measure end play. Average end play between 2 measurements should be .028-.047" (.7-1.2 mm). Play can be adjusted with steel plates of various thicknesses.

CLUTCH "K-2"
Disassembly

1) Remove circlip that retains clutch plate assembly in outside plate carrier. Tilt plate carrier and remove clutch plate assembly. Install compressor tool (126 589 00 43 00) on spring retainer and compress until circlip is exposed.

6-180

Automatic Transmissions
MERCEDES-BENZ TYPE W 4 A 040 (Cont.)

2) Remove circlip and release pressure from compressor tool. Remove compressor tool from spring retainer. Remove spring retainer and compression springs. Pull piston from outside plate carrier.

Reassembly

1) Insert new sealing rings onto clutch piston. Place installation sleeve (126 589 02 14 00) on outside plate carrier. Lubricate installation tool and clutch piston sealing rings with ATF. Carefully place clutch piston over installation tool and slide piston onto outside plate carrier, being careful not to tilt piston in carrier.

2) Place compression springs into clutch piston. Install spring retainer so that each spring is centered by a guide pin. Install compressor tool on spring retainer. Compress spring retainer and install circlip. Be sure that circlip is fully seated in its groove. Remove compressor tool.

3) Assemble clutch plate assembly. Lubricate all clutch plates with ATF. Install clutch plate assembly into outside plate carrier. Install circlip.

4) To check end play of clutch plate assembly, place a depth gauge on edge of plate carrier. Place measuring tip lightly in clutch plate assembly and read measurement. With a screwdriver under top steel plate (to force plate against snap ring), again measure end play. Average end play between 2 measurements should be .028-.047" (9.7-1.2 mm). Play can be adjusted with steel plates of various thicknesses.

TRANSMISSION REASSEMBLY

NOTE: Soak all new bands and disc brake plates in ATF for approximately 1 hour prior to installation.

1) Place transmission case in a holding fixture. Install "O" ring and radial sealing ring into selector lever shaft bores. Install closing plug with a new aluminum sealing ring. Install "O" rings and Teflon seals on clutch "K-2" support flange and bore in transmission case. Install band "B-2" thrust body and plate in upward direction. Install support flange and attaching bolts.

Fig. 19: Measuring Disc Brake Release Clearance

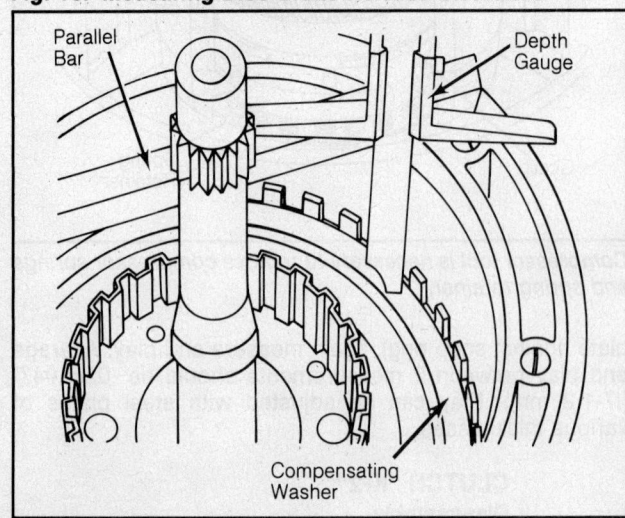

Measurement is taken in case.

2) Install thrust washer so plate for torsion lock is fixed in housing. Compress band "B-2" on supporting lugs as much as possible and install in transmission case. Place

clutch "K-2" on planetary gear set assembly. While rotating input shaft, install planetary gear set assembly into transmission case.

3) Place transmission in a vertical position so input shaft points upward. Check that planetary gear set assembly is properly installed. Planetary gear set is properly installed when upper edge of connecting carrier is lower than supporting surface of disc outside plate. Mount front cover on primary pump.

4) Install disc brake clutch plates. Place a parallel bar on machined surface of transmission case. Place top of depth gauge on bar and tip of depth gauge on compensating washer. *See Fig. 19.* Measure and record distance.

Fig. 20: Measuring Disc Brake Release Clearance

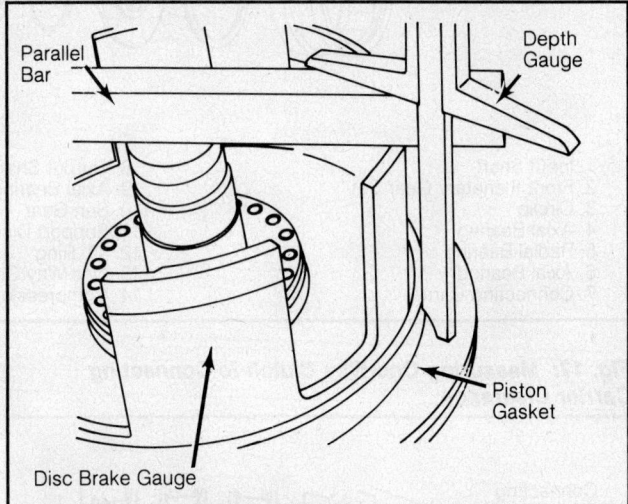

Measurement is taken on piston.

5) Place a parallel bar on top of disc brake piston. Place top of depth gauge on parallel bar and tip of depth gauge on piston gasket. *See Fig. 20.* Measure and record distance. Difference between this measurement and the one taken in step **4)** is disc brake release clearance. Clearance should be .059-.079" (1.5-2.0 mm). Clearance can

Fig. 21: Measuring Clutch "K-1" End Clearance

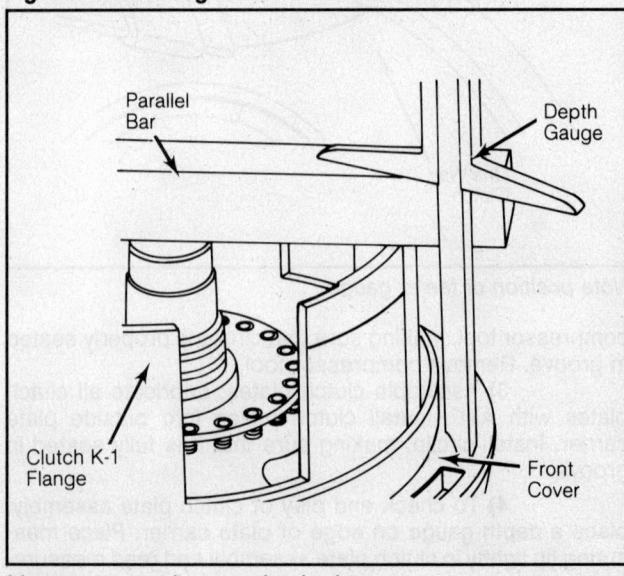

Measurement taken on clutch piston.

MERCEDES-BENZ TYPE W 4 A 040 (Cont.)

be adjusted with compensating washers and steel plates of various thicknesses.

6) Place axial bearing into planetary gear carrier. Pack groove in input shaft with grease and install grease pressure ring. Connect assembly lock to band "B-1". Rotate clutch "K-1" to provide meshing of teeth. Install band "B-1" so pin of assembly lock is facing toward band "B-1" thrust body. Install axial bearing.

7) Place gasket on front cover. Place a parallel bar on clutch "K-1" flange. Place top of depth gauge on bar and tip of depth gauge on gasket of front cover. See Fig. 21. Measure and record distance.

8) Place parallel bar on machined surface of transmission case. Place top of depth gauge on bar and tip of depth gauge on roller of axial bearing. See Fig. 22. Measure and record distance. Difference between this measurement and measurement taken in step 7) is clutch "K-1" end clearance. Clearance should be .031" (.8 mm). Clearance can be adjusted with compensating washers under washer for axial bearing.

9) Position front cover on transmission case. Install front cover-to-transmission case attaching bolts. Position transmission case so output shaft is pointing upward. Place circlip into its groove on output shaft. Install helical gear on output shaft. Install governor axial holder.

10) Install "O" ring in governor bore and install governor. Swivel axial holder toward governor so it will enter groove in governor shaft. Install governor and retaining ring. Pull cover out so it rests on retaining ring all the way around.

Fig. 22: Measuring Clutch "K-1" End Clearance

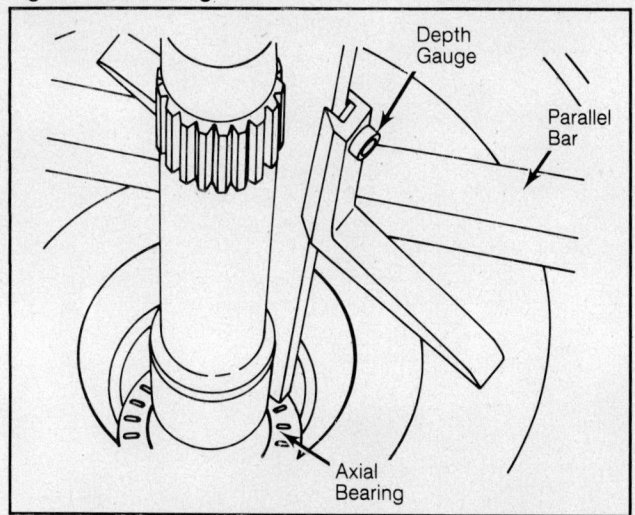

Measurement taken in transmission case.

11) Install intermediate plate and "O" ring. Install secondary pump and pump attaching bolts. Check that governor axial holder is properly seated. Install governor axial holder nut. Install oil pipe and attaching bolt. Install detent plate and shaft. Install detent plate-to-case attaching bolt.

12) Mount resilient linkage on detent plate. Mount roller on resilient linkage. Install plastic guide over roller. Place compensating washers on helical gear. Mount parking lock pawl, insert expanding spring and attach spring to parking lock pawl. Install parking lock wheel.

13) Install measuring sleeve (126 589 06 14 00) over output shaft and tighten slot nut. Engage parking lock pawl to hold assembly from turning. Place a parallel bar across rear cover mounting surface on transmission case. Measure distance from top on parallel bar to lip of measuring sleeve. See Fig. 23. Add .59" (15 mm) to measurement to compensate for height of parallel bar and lip in measuring sleeve.

Fig. 23: Measuring Output Shaft End Play

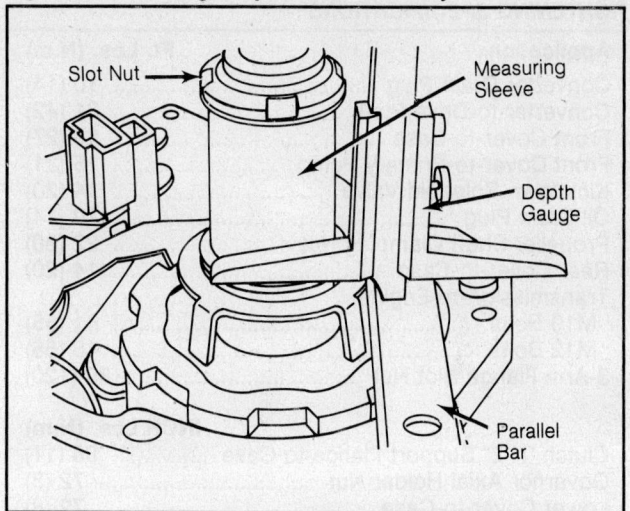

Seen from rear of transmission.

14) Assemble rear cover. Using a depth gauge, measure distance from rear cover sealing surface to inner race of radial bearing. Subtract this measurement from measurement made in step 13) to obtain output shaft end play. End play should be .011-.019" (.3-.5 mm). End play can be adjusted by adding or removing compensating washers under parking lock wheel.

15) Install rear cover assembly and rear cover-to-transmission case attaching bolts. Install washer for 3-arm flange on output shaft. Insert "O" ring into 3-arm flange. Slide 3-arm flange onto output shaft and install slot nut. Install kickdown solenoid valve. Stake 3-arm flange slot nut into groove in output shaft.

16) Install thrust pin in band "B-1" thrust body. Install thrust body in transmission case. Install modulating pressure control valve. Install vacuum control unit and retaining plate. Install starter lock-out switch. Install range selector lever. Install range selector lever retaining bolt and nut. Install cotter pin in range selector lever.

17) Install band "B-1" guide into transmission case. Install lip seal on band "B-1" piston. Using a compressor tool, install band "B-1" compression spring and piston. Install locking ring and remove compressor tool. Insert thrust pin for band "B-2" into transmission case. Make sure large end of pin is toward band.

18) Install Teflon ring onto band "B-2" piston. Install thrust pin in piston. Place band "B-2" piston into transmission case bore making sure that thrust pin enters band "B-2". Install band "B-2" piston cover and locking ring. Measure release clearance of band from inside transmission case. Band "B-2" release clearance should be .24-.28" (6-7 mm). Adjust clearance by exchanging thrust pins.

19) Install one-way valve and guide for band "B-2". Connect control pressure cable-to-connecting rod. Push plastic sleeve of control pressure cable into transmis-

Automatic Transmissions
MERCEDES-BENZ TYPE W 4 A 040 (Cont.)

sion case bore. Install lower cover making sure that oil pipe enters bore in transmission case.

       20) Place intermediate plate on transmission case. Install plate attaching bolts. Install leaf spring with holder and attaching bolt. Install valve body making sure that range selector valve engages drive detent plate. Install valve body-to-transmission case attaching bolts. Install oil filter and attaching bolts. Install oil pan with new gasket.

TIGHTENING SPECIFICATIONS

Application	Ft. Lbs. (N.m)
Converter Drain Plug	10 (14)
Converter-to-Drive Plate	31 (42)
Front Cover-to-Case	20 (27)
Front Cover-to-Primary Pump	15 (21)
Kickdown Solenoid Valve	14 (20)
Oil Drain Plug	10 (14)
Propeller Shaft Clamping Nut	22 (30)
Rear Cover-to-Case	14 (20)
Transmission-to-Engine	
M10 Bolts	41 (55)
M12 Bolts	48 (65)
3-Arm Flange Slot Nut	89 (120)

Application	INCH Lbs. (N.m)
Clutch "K-2" Support Flange-to-Case	96 (11)
Governor Axial Holder Nut	72 (8)
Lower Cover-to-Case	72 (8)
Oil Filter-to-Valve Body	36 (4)
Oil Pan-to-Case	72 (8)
Range Selector Lever Nut	72 (8)
Secondary Pump-to-Case	72 (8)
Vacuum Control Unit-to Case	72 (8)
Valve Body-to-Case	72 (8)

MERCEDES-BENZ W 4 A 020

190 Series

DESCRIPTION

This is a fully automatic 4-speed unit consisting primarily of a 3-element welded torque converter and 2 compound planetary gear sets. There are 2 multiple-disc clutches, 1 overrunning clutch, and 3 brake bands provide friction elements required to obtain desired function of planetary gear set. A hydraulic system, pressurized by a primary pump and a secondary piston type pump provide working pressure required to operate friction elements and automatic controls.

OPERATION

The W 4 A 020 transmission is similar to the W 4 A 040 transmission. The similarity applies to arrangemnet and layout of planetary gear sets, clutches and brake bands, as well as to shift valves of individual gears.

The 190D models start in first gear in all forward driving positions and shifts up depending on the accelerator pedal position and speed. On 190E models, with shift lever in positions "D" and "3", transmission starts in 2nd gear when driving in lower partial load range and in first gear beginning in higher partial load range. When stopped, 2nd gear remains engaged at idle to prevent creeping.

LUBRICATION & ADJUSTMENT

See appropriate MANUAL TRANSMISSION SERVICING article in IMPORT GENERAL SERVICING section.

TROUBLE SHOOTING

NOTE: If the transmission fluid is Black or has a burnt smell or if there is an abnormal number of metal chips in oil pan, either recondition or exchange transmission.

TRANSMISSION SLIPS

Slips In All Selector Positions
Transmission has incorrect modulating pressure. Modulating pressure control valve or pressure relief valve is dirty or sticking. Fluid line to transmission vacuum unit clogged or leaking. Working pressure control valve dirty or sticking. Defective primary pump.

Transmission Slips In 2nd Gear On Shifts From 1st To 3d.
Check control slide "B-1" for easy operation. Exchange shift valve housing, if necessary. Remove and install brake band piston "B-1", check lip sealing ring and replace if necessary. Replace brake band "B-1" and thrust body for "B-1".

Transmission Slips When Starting In 1st Or 2nd (No Forward, But Reverse Is Working)
Make shift valve "B-2" operable. Exchange shift valve housing. If necessary, replace brake band piston. Readjust brake band "B-2" by installation of a longer thrust pin. If the brake band is heavily worn or broken, replace brake band.

Transmission Slips During 2-3 Shift, Or Slips At First And Then Grabs Hold
Check modulating pressure. Adjust modulating pressure, if necessary. Check whether temperature unit is installed. Exchange shift valve housing, if necessary. Replace inner plate of clutch "K-1". Recondition clutch, if necessary.

Transmission Slips During 3-4 Shift
Check modulating pressure and adjust, if necessary. Exchange shift valve housing. Replace inner plates of clutch "K-2", recondition clutch according to condition.

OTHER SHIFTING PROBLEMS

Transmission Has No Positive Contact Following Installation Or Fails After A Short Period Of Operation
Torque converter not installed correctly. Transmission "drivers" not aligned with drive gear of primary pump. The "drivers" on torque converter and primary pump are distorted. Replace primary pump or torque converter, if necessary.

No Power Transmission In All Selector Lever Positions Immediately After Starting Engine
Torque converter drains partially by leaking or defective lubrication pressure ring on input shaft or by leaking lubricating pressure valve in shift valve housing.

Check lubrication pressure ring on input shaft, replace pressure ring if necessary. Check and clean lubrication pressure valve in shift valve housing.

No Positive Contact In Reverse Gear
Check lining plates and lip sealing rings on piston of "LB 3" and replace if necessary. Replace one-way roller clutch in gear assembly.

Heavy Cut-In Jerk When Engaging Selector Lever Position "D" or "R"
Adjust idle speed and emission value as specified. Check modulating pressure. Correct modulating pressure, if necessary. Check whether cone spring under valve ball in shift valve housing is installed. Check vacuum line and connecting points for leaks. Check pressure pickup piston in shift valve housing for easy operation and correct installation and exchange shift valve housing, if necessary.

NOTE: If during repeated shifts selections from "N" and "D" a hard cut-in jerk results, this is normal. The pressure pickup requires a running period of approximatley 2 seconds. If this time is maintained, the cut-in jerk is okay.

Heavy Shift Jerks When Changing Gears
Check modulating pressure. Adjust modulating pressure, if necessary. Check vacuum line and connecting point for leaks.

Heavy Shift Jerk During Downshift From 4th To 3rd
Replace lip sealing ring release side "B-2". Replace brake band piston "B-2". Thrust body "B-2" twisted, replace thrust body.

Transmission Jerks When Shifting In Partial Load Range
1) Check adjustment of control pressure cable control. When on a test drive always set control pressure cable control slightly shorter until optimal shift quality is obtained.

Automatic Transmissions

MERCEDES-BENZ W 4 A 020 (Cont.)

2) DO NOT set control pressure cable control too short, since otherwise there will be no more brake shifts. Check modulating pressure and adjust, if necessary. Check vacuum line and connecting points for leaks.

No Upshifts
Check regulating pressure. Clean centrifugal governor and make operable. Disassemble and clean shift valve housing and replace, if necessary.

Upshifts In Upper Speed Range Of Gears Only
Check cable control for control pressure and adjust as necessary. Check regulator pressure. If regulator pressure is too low, exchange centrifugal governor. Make control pressure regulating valve operable.

Upshifts In Lower Speed Range Of Gears Only
1) Check cable control for control pressure whether disengaged or torn and make accurate adjustments. Check full throttle stop.

2) Accelerate by means of accelerator lever and check whether throttle valve rests against full throttle stop. Readjust throttle stop, if necessary. Check regulator pressure. If regulator pressure is too high, exchange centrifugal governor.

No Kickdown Downshifts
1) Check fuse for current supply to magnetic valve. Remove magnetic valve. Connect to voltage supply and check for proper function. Replace magnetic valve if necessary.

2) Check cable control for control pressure whether disengaged, torn or wrongly adjusted. Check kickdown regulating slide in shift valve housing for easy operation and exchange shift valve housing, if necessary.

No Brake Shifts (4-3 and 3-2)
Adjust cable control for control pressure. Check vacuum lines and connections of leaks. Make brake shift piston operable and exchange shift valve housing, if necessary.

Automatic And Unwanted Downshifts Outside Partial Throttle Downshift Range Without Actuating Kickdown Switch
1) Remove kickdown magnetic valve. Check "O" ring on magnetic valve for damage. Check whether kickdown switch sticks in pushed-in position. Replace switch, if necessary.

2) Check whether magnetic valve sticks in opened position. Replace magnetic valve, if necessary.

Poor Acceleration When Starting
Check stalling speed. If stalling speed drops by approximately 400-700 RPM below specified value, one-way roller clutch in torque converter will slip. Replace torque converter, if necessary.

Parking Lock Not Engaging
Check rear engine mount. Replace mount, if necessary. Check adjustment of selector rod. Adjust selector rod, if necessary.

Selector Lever Positions "R" and "P" Cannot Be Engaged
With engine running, clean centrifugal governor and make operable. With engine not running, make detent piston on lower cover operable.

Engine Cannot Be Started In Selector Lever Position "P" and "N"
Adjust shift rod and starter lock out switch. Replace starter lock out switch, if necessary.

Oil Loss With Smoke in Exhaust
Diaphragm in vacuum control unit defective. Transmission oil drawn from engine by vacuum line. Replace control unit, if necessary.

Oil Loss Between Torque Converter and Primary Pump
1) Screw in oil drain plug on torque converter with new sealing ring. Coat threads with Hylomar paste and tighten. In the event of additional leaks, go to step **2)**.

2) Replace radial sealing ring and "O" ring of primary pump, while checking groove for "O" ring on primary pump for porous spots. Replace primary pump, if necessary.

TESTING

ROAD TEST

NOTE: **Before road testing, make sure fluid level and condition, and control linkage adjustments have been checked and corrected as necessary.**

1) During test drive, in addition to shift points, special attention should be paid to changeover during gear change. Shifting up at part throttle should be noticed only when listening carefully.

2) At full throttle and kickdown the gear changes are clearly heard, but the new gear speed should obtain a smooth hold and the impression of an energetic engine should remain. Sudden revving up of the engine, for example, when shifting up indicates slipping of a servo member (brake band or clutch) and should be checked.

3) Automatic downshifts without acceleration occur at very low speeds and will be heard only when listening very carefully (speed increase of engine). On the other hand, downshifts under kickdown are coupled with clearly felt shifting impulse in addition to an increase in engine speed. At certain speed ranges a downshift under part throttle to full throttle is possible.

4) Downshifts with selector lever are either acceleration downshifts (on hills) or deceleration brake shifts (downhill or during deceleration). Accelerating downshifts require only a few fractions of a second for changing gears, while deceleration brake shifts require from 1 to 2 seconds.

5) During check make sure that transmission, particularly under load, is not constantly shifted. While shifting, the servo members develop considerable heat. A reference value is: repeat a gear shift under maximum load only once within 15 seconds.

NOTE: **In the following chart, all speed data are approximates. They apply to the respectively valid rear axle series ratio and tires. Deviations from the named values are caused by dispersions both at transmission and at tachometer readout.**

HYDRAULIC PRESSURE TESTS
Preparation For Tests
1) Before making tests, be sure to check fluid level and condition. Check throttle linkages, EGR system and neutral safety switch. Check adjustment and correct as necessary. Connect Pressure Gauge (123 589 04 21 00) to pressure take-off points on transmission. *See Fig. 1.*

MERCEDES-BENZ W 4 A 020 (Cont.)

SHIFT SPEED SPECIFICATIONS (MPH)

Application	190E Series	190D Series
Lever in "D"		
Idle		
1-2 Upshift	9	8
2-3 Upshift	16	13
3-4 Upshift	20	13
4-3 Downshift	16	9
3-2 Downshift	12	7
2-1 Downshift	.....	.....
Full Throttle		
1-2 Upshift	19	18
2-3 Upshift	48	35
3-4 Upshift	75	59
4-3 Downshift	50	42
3-2 Downshift	24	19
2-1 Downshift	2	11
Kickdown		
1-2 Upshift	27	22
2-3 Upshift	50	39
3-4 Upshift	75	63
4-3 Downshift	70	57
3-2 Downshift	43	34
2-1 Downshift	18	18
Lever in "3" [1]		
Idle		
1-2 Upshift	9	8
2-3 Upshift	16	13
3-2 Downshift	9	9
2-1 Downshift	.....	.....
Full Throttle		
1-2 Upshift	19	18
2-3 Upshift	48	35
3-2 Downshift	24	19
2-1 Downshift	12	11
Kickdown		
1-2 Upshift	27	22
2-3 Upshift	50	39
3-2 Downshift	43	34
2-1 Downshift	18	18
Lever in "2" [2]		
Idle		
1-2 Upshift	10	6
2-1 Downshift	12	11
Full Throttle		
1-2 Upshift	27	22
2-1 Downshift	12	11
Kickdown		
1-2 Upshift	27	22
2-1 Downshift	18	18

2) Attach pressure tester to inside mirror in such a manner that it can be easily read from driver's seat. Run pressure hoses through passenger window. Connect to measuring points.

3) Make sure that the pressure hoses are not too slack and are not resting against exhaust pipe. Following checkup, run engine and check measuring points for leaks.

Modulating Pressure Test
Pull line from vacuum control unit. In selector lever position "D", drive at approximately 40 MPH while reading pressure value.

Modulating Pressure Adjustment
1) Remove rubber cap from vacuum control unit. Pull locking plate out of locking slots to permit rotation. The adjusting screw in vacuum control unit can now be adjusted by means of locking plate.

Fig. 1: Pressure Take-Off Points

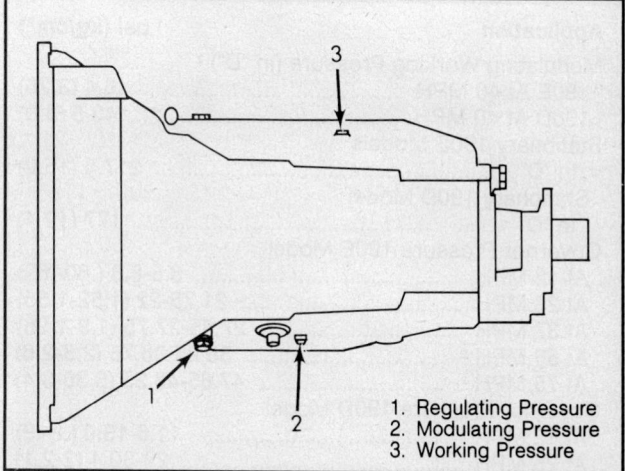

1. Regulating Pressure
2. Modulating Pressure
3. Working Pressure

2) One turn of adjusting screw results in a pressure change of approximately 6 psi (.42 kg/cm²). After turning adjusting screw, push locking plate back into locking slots.

3) Put rubber cap back on vacuum control unit. Check modulating pressure again. Replace plug vacuum line.

Working Pressure Test
Pull vacuum line from vacuum control unit. Start engine and run at approximately 1000 RPM while reading pressure.

NOTE: The working pressure cannot be adjusted. Measuring pressure simply provides information concerning operation of working pressure regulator valve in the shift valve housing. When measuring working pressure, make sure that the modulating pressure has been accurately set.

Governor Pressure Test
Drive vehicle at speeds used in SHIFT SPEED SPECIFICATIONS chart. If no governor pressure is indicated, remove centrifugal governor and clean. If all pressure data is different from the values named on tables, replace centrifugal governor.

NOTE: If values are not within specifications, disassemble and clean governor assembly.

STALL TEST
Precautions
During this check, the entire output torque of the engine is converted into heat, and for this reason the checkup should not last longer that 5 seconds. Make sure that rear wheels are not rotating during test.

Testing Procedure
1) With engine at normal operating temperature, tachometer installed, parking and service brakes applied firmly, stall test transmission by pushing accelerator to floor and noting engine speed on tachometer. Engine speed should be within limits in chart.

2) Run engine prior to measuring for approximately 2 minutes at approximately 2000 RPM. Set parking brake. Place selector in "D" position. Accelerate to full

Automatic Transmissions

MERCEDES-BENZ W 4 A 020 (Cont.)

HYDRAULIC PRESSURE SPECIFICATIONS

Application	¹ psi (kg/cm²)
Modulating Working Pressure (In "D") ²	
190E At 40 MPH	46.4 (3.26)
190D At 40 MPH	43.5 (3.0)
Stationary 190E Models	
In "D"	217.5 (15.0)
Stationary 190D Model	
In "D"	177 (12.4)
Governor Pressure 190E Model	
At 12 MPH	8.5-8.8 (.60-.62)
At 25 MPH	21.75-22 (1.52-1.55)
At 37 MPH	27.55-27.75 (1.9-1.95)
At 56 MPH ²	36.25-36.75 (2.5-2.6)
At 75 MPH ²	47.85-48.25 (3.36-3.4)
Governor Pressure 190D Model	
At 12 MPH	11.6-13.0 (.8-.9)
At 25 MPH	29-30.4 (2-2.1)
At 37 MPH	33.3-34 (2.3-2.4)
At 56 MPH	46.4-47 (3.26-3.3)
At 75 MPH	65.25-66.75 (4.6-4.7)

¹ – Specifications given are minimum pressures.
² – Can be measured at full throttle only.

STALL SPEED SPECIFICATIONS

Application	Stall RPM
190 Series	1500-1700

throttle with right foot, during which the specified stalling speed must be attained.

NOTE: **If the stalling speed remains by approximately 400 to 700 RPM below specified value, the one-way roller clutch in the torque converter is slipping.**

3) If the stall speed is okay, but the maximum speed is not attained, the one-way roller clutch locks in both directions or is stuck. Repair or replace one-way roller clutch as necessary.

Stall Test Results
If stall speed is higher than specified, general transmission problems are indicated and hydraulic pressure tests should be made to locate faulty units. If stall speed is lower than specified, torque converter roller clutch is faulty.

NOTE: **Make sure engine performance is satisfactory before condemning converter assembly. Torque converter is a sealed unit and cannot be diassembled for service.**

SERVICE (IN VEHICLE)

The following units may be removed from transmission without removing transmission from vehicle: Oil Pan and Gasket, Shift Valve Body, Vacuum Modulator Unit, Speedometer Driven Gear Assembly, Secondary Pump Assembly, Extension Housing, Pressure Receiving Piston, Modulating Pressure Housing, and Bimetallic Spring, Speedometer Drive Gear, Secondary Pump Eccen-

tric, Governor Assembly, Parking Pawl and Parking Linkage. See procedures given in TRANSMISSION DISASSEMBLY & REASSEMBLY.

REMOVAL & INSTALLATION

See appropriate article in AUTOMATIC TRANSMISSION REMOVAL section.

TORQUE CONVERTER

NOTE: **Torque converter is a sealed unit and cannot be diassembled for service. If hub of converter is scored, or if metallic particles are found in transmission fluid, replace converter assembly.**

TRANSMISSION DISASSEMBLY & REASSEMBLY

1) Remove pressure control control cable by pushing link toward sleeve and turning sleeve 90° in anticlockwise direction. Pull pressure control cable out in upward direction.

2) Screw mounting plate to assembly bracket. Insert transmission into mounting plate and fasten. Unscrew combination screws and remove oil pan.

3) Remove Phillips screws and oil filter. Unscrew combination screws and remove shift valve housing. Remove holder with leaf spring.

4) Remove combination screws, lift off lower cover with intermediate plate and oil pipe. Diassemble lower cover. Push in brake band piston cover and remove locking pin.

5) Remove brake band piston cover. Pull out brake band piston. Mount Assembly Device (126 589 00 59 00) and screw to transmission housing. Clamp Assembly Device (126 589 00 59 00) and remove locking ring.

6) Unclamp Assembly Device (126 589 00 59 00), remove brake band piston "B-1" with cover and backpressure screws. Unscrew assembly unit. Pull out brake band guide. Remove closing plug for thrust body.

7) Remove holding plate and vacuum control unit with thrust pin. Remove combination screw and remove starter lock out switch. Remove thrust body and modulating pressure control valve.

8) Remove kickdown magnetic valve. Remove double hex collar nut and pull off universal flange. Remove washer and combination screws. Loosen rear cover by means of light blows with a plastic hammer. Disassemble rear cover.

9) Remove oil pipe for tachometer lubrication, helical gear for tachometer drive, parking lock gear with parking lock pawl and expanding spring. Pull out plastic guide in upward direction, then remove roller.

10) Remove compensating washer and spacing sleeve. Take circlip from output shaft and remove helical gear. Take locking ring from output shaft. Remove combination screw and remove oil pipe. Remove secondary pump. Remove "O" ring and intermediate plate of secondary pump.

11) Push in cover and remove locking ring, then pull out cover. Compress locking ring and remove centrifugal governor. Force off lock and remove resilient linkage.

Fig. 2: *Valve Body Assembly Showing Plastic Valve & Steel Ball Locations*

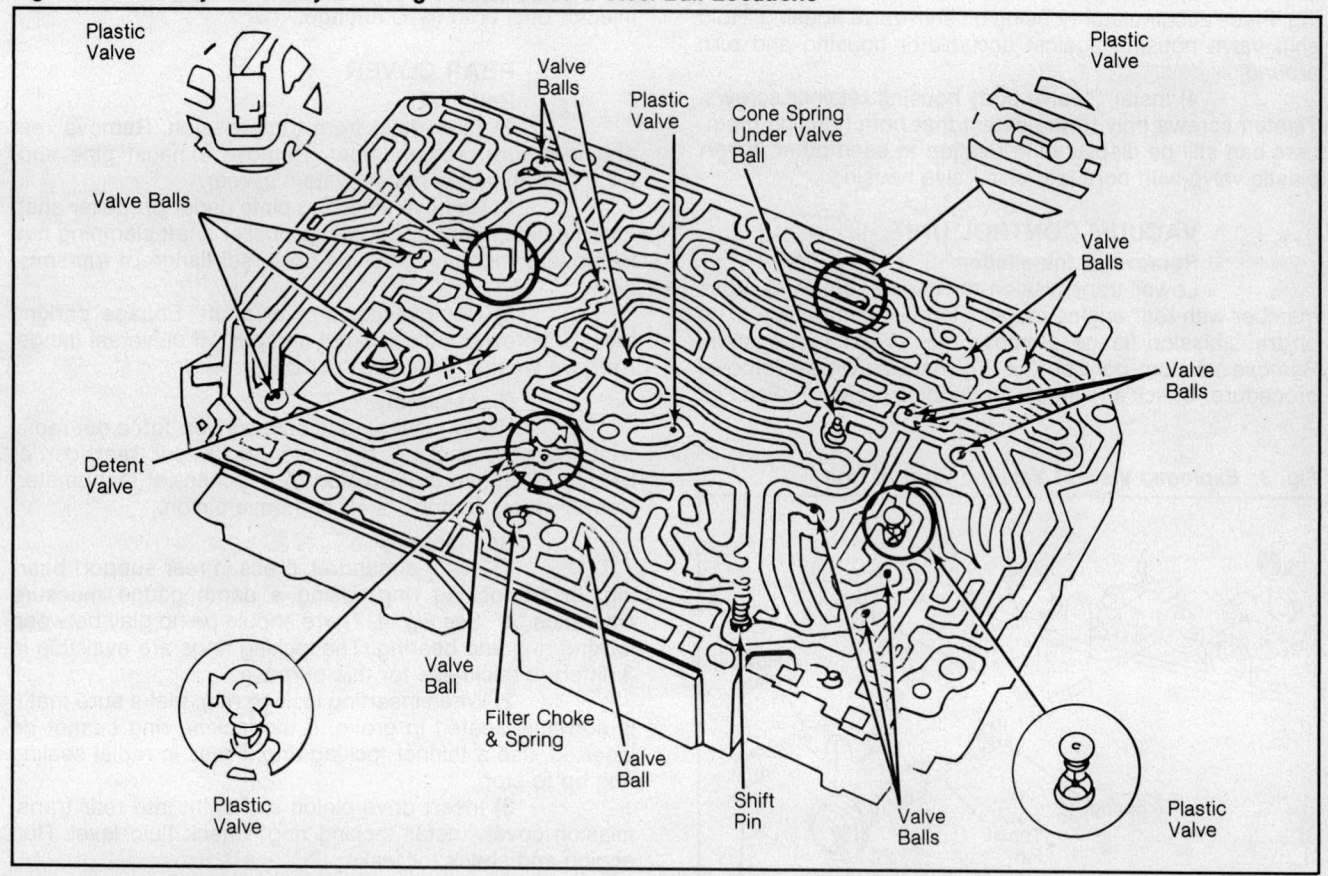

12) Remove brake band guide and one-way valve. Remove temperature throttle and oil deflector. Completely remove front cover. Screw 2 screws into threaded holes and use to pull off cover. Hold gear assembly at input shaft and pull out carefully in forward direction.

13) Pull clutch "K-1" with brake band "B-1" from gear assembly. Remove clutch plates of clutch "B-3". Remove thrust pin. Pull out clutch "K-2". Remove screws for shift range selector lever and remove detent plate.

14) Remove thrust washer. On opposite of side of transmission screw in 2 screws approximately 3.15" (80 mm) long. Loosen supporting flange from housing by means of hammer blows against the 2 screws.

15) Set brake band "B-2" diagonally and remove. Pull out thrust body "B-2". Remove sealing rings, measuring connection plugs still in housing.

COMPONENT DISASSEMBLY & REASSEMBLY

VALVE BODY

Preparation

Observe particular cleanliness for all jobs on shift valve housing. The work should be done as much as possible on a plastic surface. DO NOT use fuzzy cloth, leather would be best. Upon disassembly, wash all parts and blow out with compressed air.

NOTE: The shift valve body has 19 steel balls. Be careful not to loose them during disassembly.

Make sure of proper placement during reassembly.

Disassembly

Remove 2 screws that attach valve body-to-pickup housing. Hold assembly together and turn over. Lift pickup housing and intermediate plate from valve body. Remove plastic valves, shift pin and detent valve "K-1". Remove all valve balls. *See Fig. 2.*

NOTE: Plastic valves are similar in shape and dimension, they differ only by a bore in one valve holder. Keep removed valves in proper order for proper replacement.

Inspection

Wash all parts in clean solvent and blow dry with compressed air. Closely inspect valve body and pickup housing passages for obstructions or defects. Inspect intermediate plate for damage. Also check all balls for any kind of damage. If internal valve body problems are found or suspected, valve body assembly must be replaced as an assembly.

Reassembly

1) Install all valve balls into valve body housing. *See Fig. 2.* Install cone spring with large diameter in downward direction underneath valve ball. Insert plastic valves and springs. Springs are located under plastic valves.

2) Install filter choke with spring and shift pin detent valve. Insert lube pressure valve and excess pressure modulating pressure valve. Insert vent valve "K-1" into accumlator housing.

MERCEDES-BENZ W 4 A 020 (Cont.)

3) Place intermidiate plate on shift valve housing. Place accumulator housing on shift valve housing. Hold shift valve housing against accumlator housing and turn around.

4) Install 2 valve body housing retainer screws. Tighten screws only to the extent that both housing members can still be displaced in relation to each other. Insert plastic valve with bore into shift valve housing.

VACUUM CONTROL UNIT
Removal & Installation

Lower transmission at rear by removing cross member with rear engine mount. Remove companion plate on transmission flange. Remove rear of exhaust system. Remove vacuum control unit. To install, reverse removal procedure. Check and adjust modulating pressure. *See Fig. 3.*

Fig. 3: Exploded View of Vacuum Control Unit

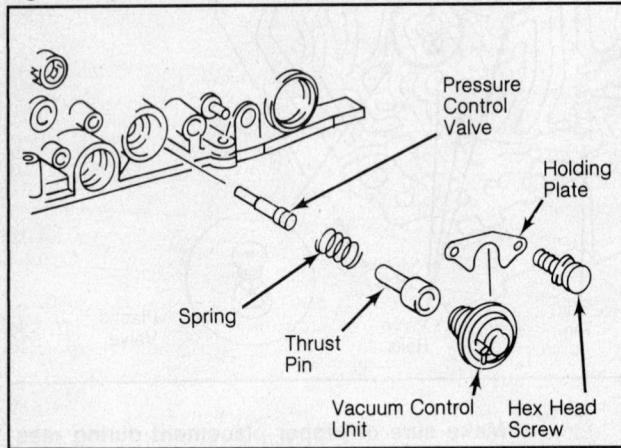

LOWER COVER
Removal

1) Remove shift valve housing. Remove oil filter and holder with leaf spring. Remove combination screws and lower cover with oil pipe. Press against both flaps and remove injector.

2) Pull out oil pipe. Remove cover plate with intermediate plate. Loosen gasket from intemediate plate. Pull holding plate, remove shift valve secondary pump with spring and plug. Remove lock and detent valve with spring and bolt.

Disassembly

1) Press against both flaps and remove injector. Pull out oil pipe. Unsrew fastening screws, remove cover plate with intermediate plate.

2) Loosen gasket from intermediate plate. Pull off holding plate, remove shift valve secondary pump with spring and plug. Remove lock. Remove detent valve with spring and bolt.

Reassembly

1) Insert shift valve secondary pump with spring and plug. Secure with holding plate. Insert detent valve with spring and bolt. Insert lock. Check detent valve for tight seat. Insert both screen filters into lower cover.

2) Place intermediate plate with gasket on lower cover. Locate gasket in relation to intermediate plate.

Mount cover plate and tighten fastening screw. Insert injector until both flaps engage.

REAR COVER
Removal

1) Drain fluid from transmission. Remove rear engine mount crossmember. Remove exhaust pipe support. Disconnect exhaust system at rear.

2) Remove shielding plate under propeller shaft intermediate bearing. Loosen propeller shaft clamping nut. Remove companion plate on universal flange of transmission.

3) Remove tachometer shaft. Engage parking lock. Unscrew double hex nut and pull off universal flange. Remove washer. Remove rear cover.

Disassembly

Using a flat bladed screwdriver, force out radial seal. Remove locking ring and knock out rear carrier bearing. Remove drive pinion for mechanical tachometer. Remove lock, remove shaft and drive pinion.

Reassembly

1) Using a mandrel, press in rear support bearing. Insert locking ring. Using a depth gauge measure clearance "A". *See Fig. 4.* There should be no play between locking ring and bearing. The locking rings are available in 3 different thickness for this purpose.

2) When inserting locking ring, make sure that it is correctly seated in grove. If the locking ring cannot be inserted, use a thinner locking ring. Press in radial sealing ring up to stop.

3) Insert drive pinion and shaft into rear transmission cover. Install locking ring. Check fluid level. Run engine and check for leaks.

Installation

1) Install new gasket. Install rear cover. Insert washer. Install universal flange. Lock double hex nut, using a mandrel to knock flange into recess in output shaft. Install companion plate to universal flange on transmission.

2) Install tachometer shaft and tighten. Install crossmember with rear engine mount. Tighten propeller shaft clamping nut. Screw on shielding plate under propeller shaft intermediate bearing.

3) Install exhaust system and exhaust support. Replenish transmission fluid.

CENTRIFUGAL GOVERNOR
Removal

1) Remove rear engine mount. Unscrew companion plate on universal flange of transmission. Disconnect rear of exhaust system. Press in cover and remove circlip. *See Fig. 5.*

2) Turn universal flange so that centrifugal governor takes a vertical position. Align locking ring, until distance is the same at top and bottom. Compress locking ring with pliers and pull out centrifugal governor as far as possible.

3) Place a piece of wood against tunnel and push transmission toward the right by means of an assembly lever and remove centrifugal governor. Remove lock and pull off worm gear.

4) Move centrifugal weights while checking control valve in openings for easy operation. Control valve should move easily, wash centrifugal weights and blow out with compressed air. If control valve is still hard to move, exchange centrifugal governor. *See Fig. 6.*

MERCEDES-BENZ W 4 A 020 (Cont.)

Fig. 4: Measuring Clearance "A" For Rear Cover

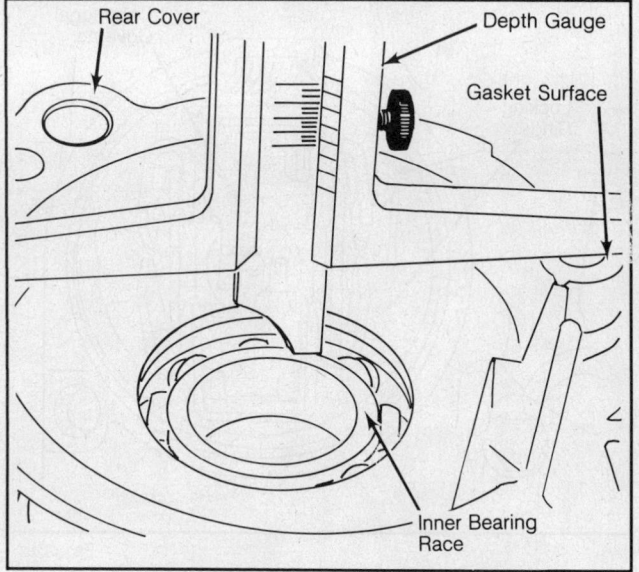

Rear Cover
Depth Gauge
Gasket Surface
Inner Bearing Race

NOTE: If replacing the centrifugal governor, mount worm gear so that drive pin enters bore in worm gear. Then insert lock.

Installation
1) Turn bearing ring so that lug is pointing downwards. Position pliers and compress locking ring.

Push transmission to the right and insert centrifugal governor with pliers under pressure, while introducing lug into groove in housing.

2) Take away pliers and move centrifugal governor axially until locking ring engages. Insert cover and locking ring, then pull cover in outward direction against locking ring. See Fig. 8.

3) Screw companion plate to universal flange transmission. Install rear engine mount. Install exhaust system. Check fluid level. Run engine and check transmission for leaks.

PRIMARY PUMP
Removal
1) Remove mounting bolts. Screw 2 bolts into threaded holes and use to pull out front cover. Remove the 2 Teflon rings. Place Assembly Device (201 589 12 43 00) and remove retainers.

2) Remove spring washer and backpressure spring for piston "B-3". Pull out piston. Remove primary pump from front cover. Remove both pump wheels from pump housing. Fig. 7.

Installation
1) Check radial sealing ring and replace as necessary. Replace primary pump "O" ring, do not twist during installation. See Fig. 9.

2) Lubricate both pump wheels and place into pump housing. Insert pump wheel in such a manner that chamfer points toward radial roller bearing. Place intermediate plate on primary pump.

Fig. 5: Exploded View of Centrifugal Governor Unit

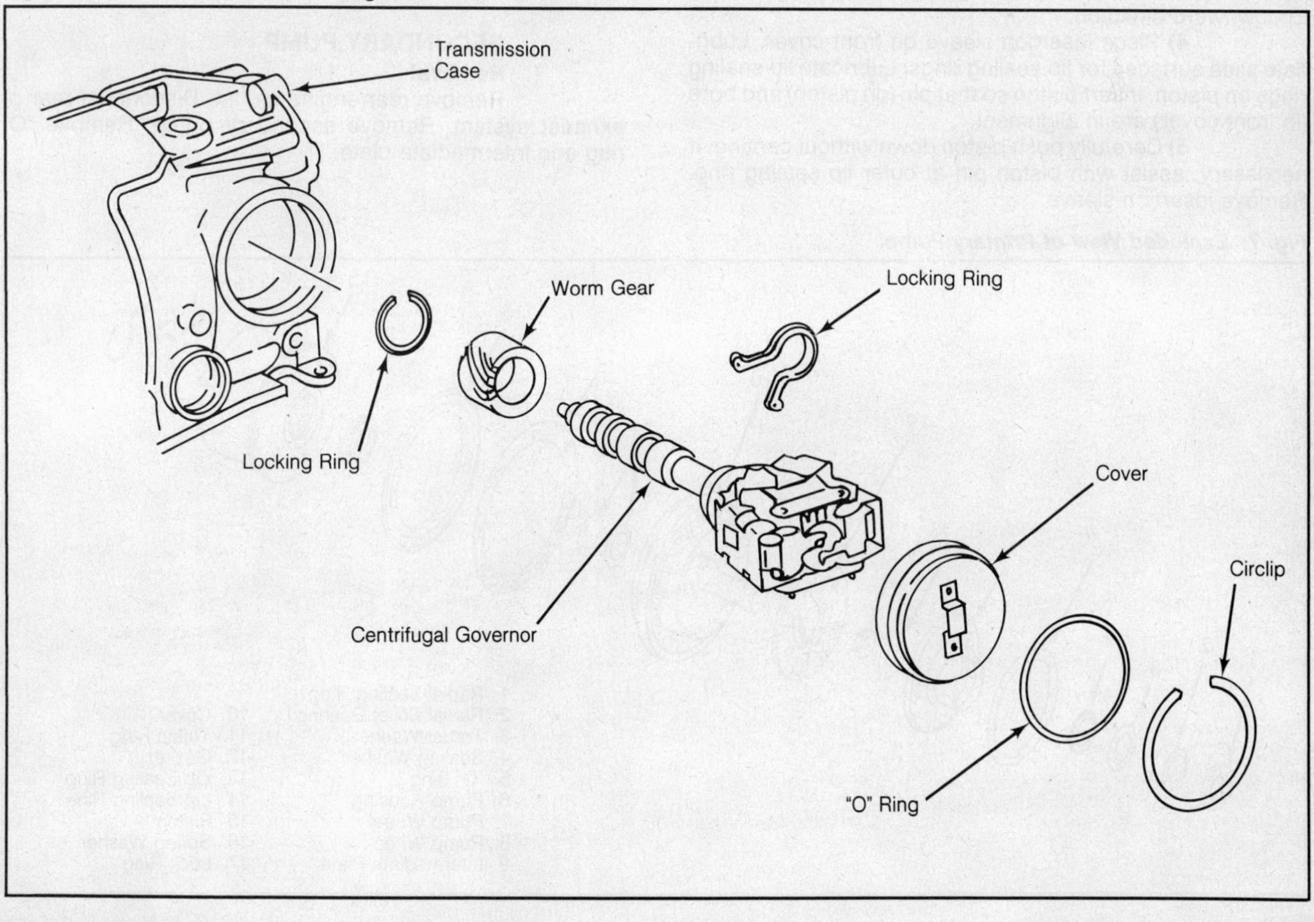

Transmission Case
Worm Gear
Locking Ring
Locking Ring
Cover
Circlip
Centrifugal Governor
"O" Ring

MERCEDES-BENZ W 4 A 020 (Cont.)

Fig. 6: Sectional View of Centrifugal Governor

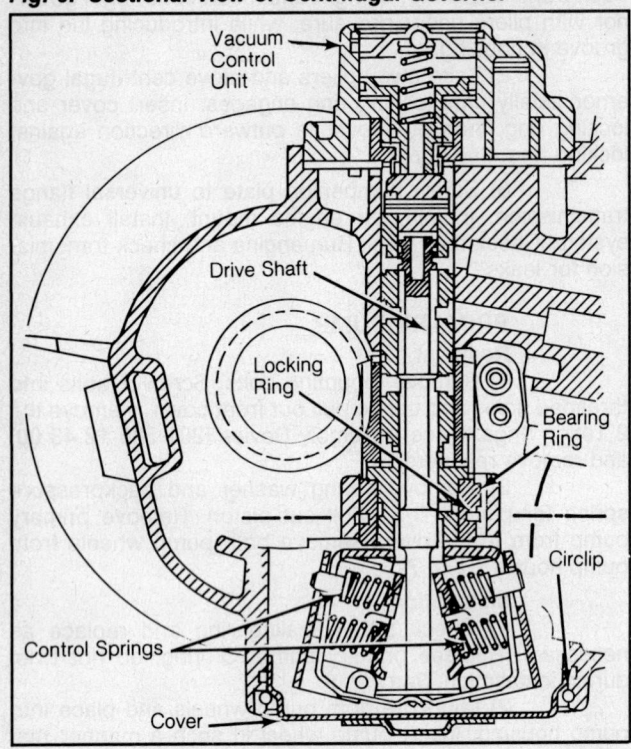

Fig. 8: Positioning Centrifugal Governor

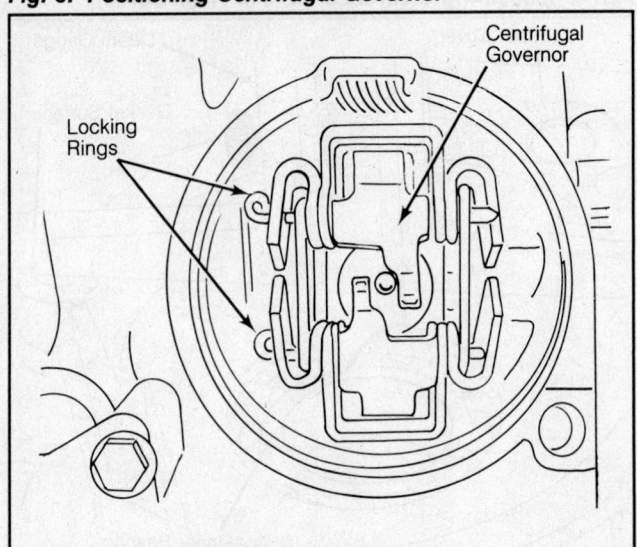

6) Mount backpressure springs and spring retainer. Place Assembly Device (201 589 12 43 00) on spring retainer and tension. Insert locking ring. Slacken and remove Assembly Device (201 589 12 43 00).

7) Insert Teflon rings with grease. Make sure that ring gap remains closed. If necessary, remove rings once again and shape to smaller diameter. Place gasket with matching hole pattern on front cover. Install front cover. *See Fig. 9.*

SECONDARY PUMP
Removal

Remove rear engine mount. Disconnect rear of exhaust system. Remove secondary pump. Remove "O" ring and intermediate plate.

3) Place primary pump into front cover. Check valve for correct seat. Check lip sealing rings, replace if necessary. Install lip sealing rings with sealing lip pointing in downward direction.

4) Place insertion sleeve on front cover. Lubricate slide surfaces for lip sealing rings. Lubricate lip sealing rings on piston. Insert piston so that pin (on piston) and bore (in front cover) are in alignment.

5) Carefully push piston down without canting. If necessary, assist with piston pin at outer lip sealing ring. Remove insertion sleeve.

Fig. 7: Exploded View of Primary Pump

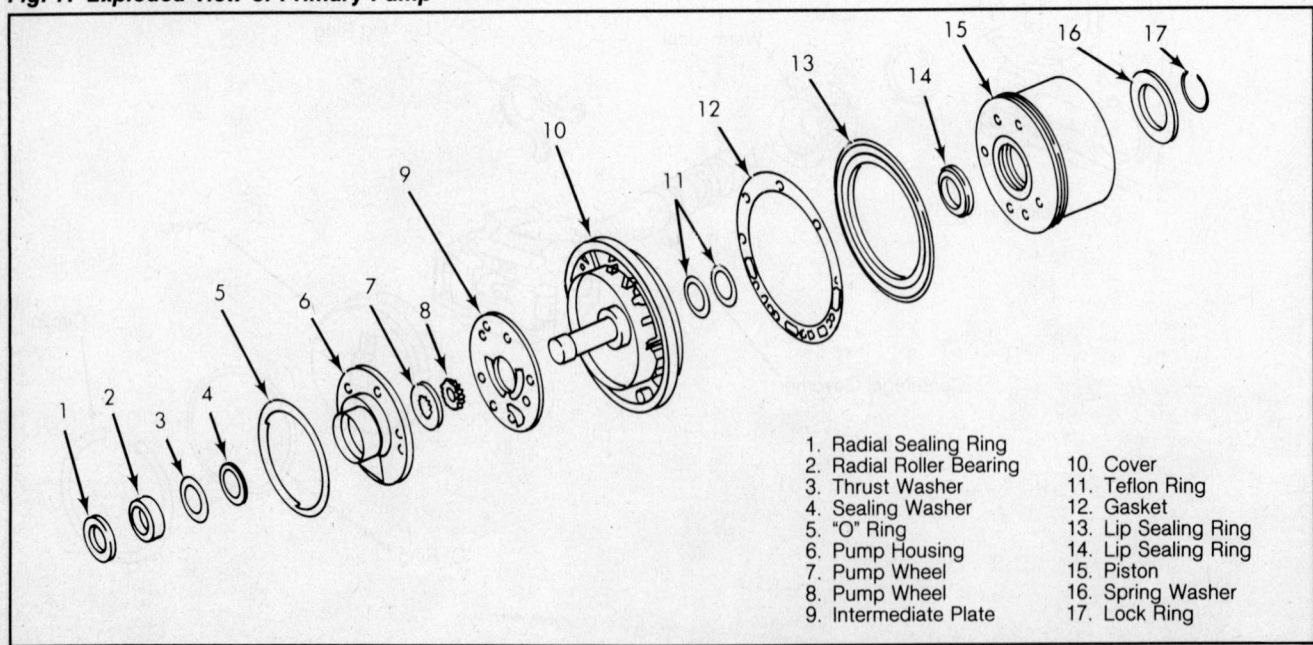

1. Radial Sealing Ring	
2. Radial Roller Bearing	10. Cover
3. Thrust Washer	11. Teflon Ring
4. Sealing Washer	12. Gasket
5. "O" Ring	13. Lip Sealing Ring
6. Pump Housing	14. Lip Sealing Ring
7. Pump Wheel	15. Piston
8. Pump Wheel	16. Spring Washer
9. Intermediate Plate	17. Lock Ring

Fig. 9: Location of Primary Pump Sealing Rings

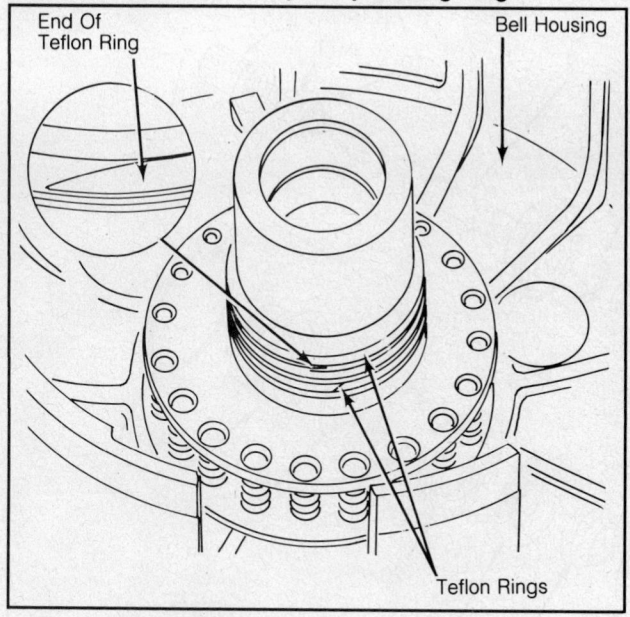

Fig. 11: Snap Ring Location for Secondary Pump

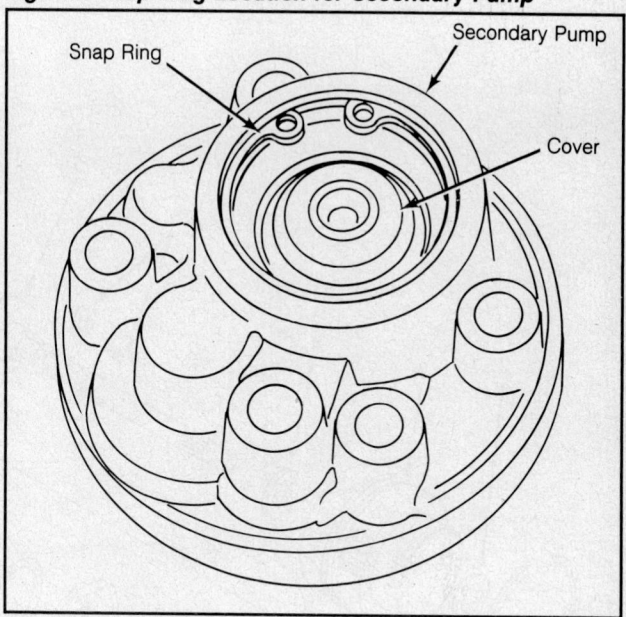

Disassembly

Remove pump gear (driving and driven) from housing. Remove locking ring and cover. Remove shutoff piston with compression spring and spring retainer. Remove out of transmission. *See Fig. 10.*

NOTE: Check all parts for damage and wear. Joint of both Teflon rings should completely come together. If necessary insert rings slights greased into grooves.

Reassembly

1) Insert "O" ring into pump housing. Insert Teflon rings into shutoff piston. Install shutoff pisto into pump housing. Place compression spring with spring retainer into shutoff piston.

2) Insert cover and locking ring. Lubricate pump gears and insert into pump housing. Insert pump gear, driving so that the driver is pointing upwards. *See Fig. 11.*

Installation

To install, reverse removal procedure. Insert intermediate plate and "O" ring into gear housing. Install secondary pump and tighten hex socket screws. Install rear engine mount. Install rear exhaust support. Run engine and check fluid level.

TORQUE CONVERTER
Removal

Remove transmission from vehicle. Set transmission to a vertical position. Using a 8 mm Allen wrench, turn plastic holding pin a 1/4 turn counterclockwise and remove plastic holding pin. Screw Removal Handle (126 589 01 62 00) on torque converter. Pull out torque converter.

Cleaning & Inspection

1) If transmission fluid has a burnt smell or is mixed up with abrasive material, flush torque converter, oil cooler lines and oil cooler.

Fig. 10: Exploded View of Secondary Pump

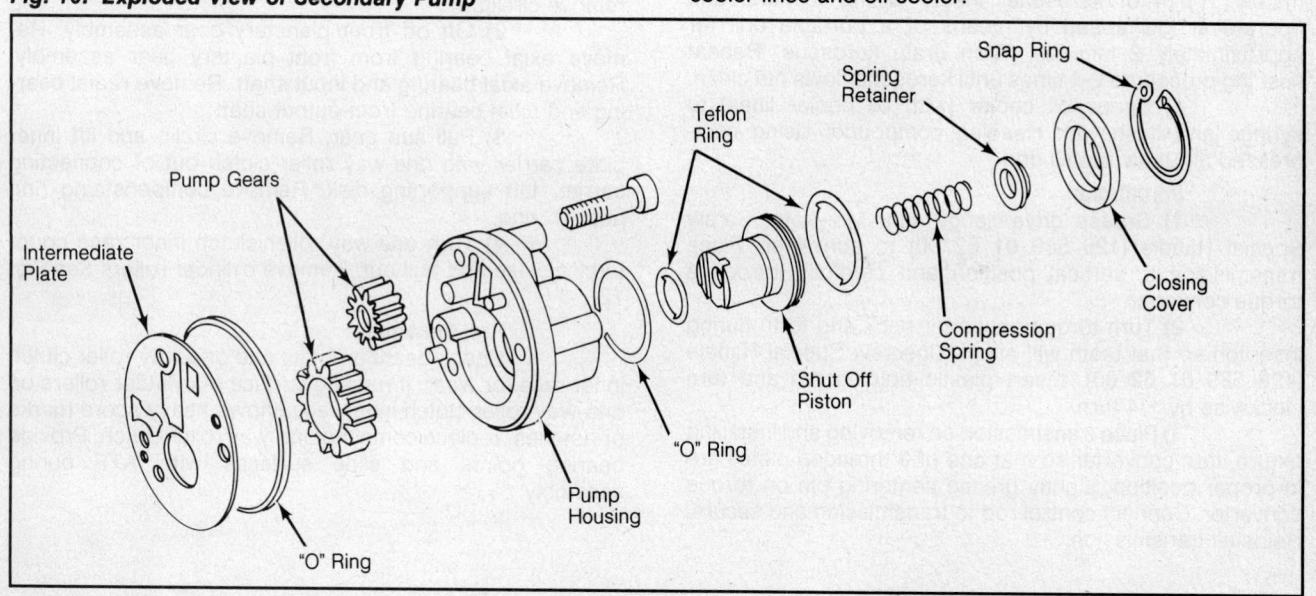

Fig. 12: *Exploded View of Gear Assembly*

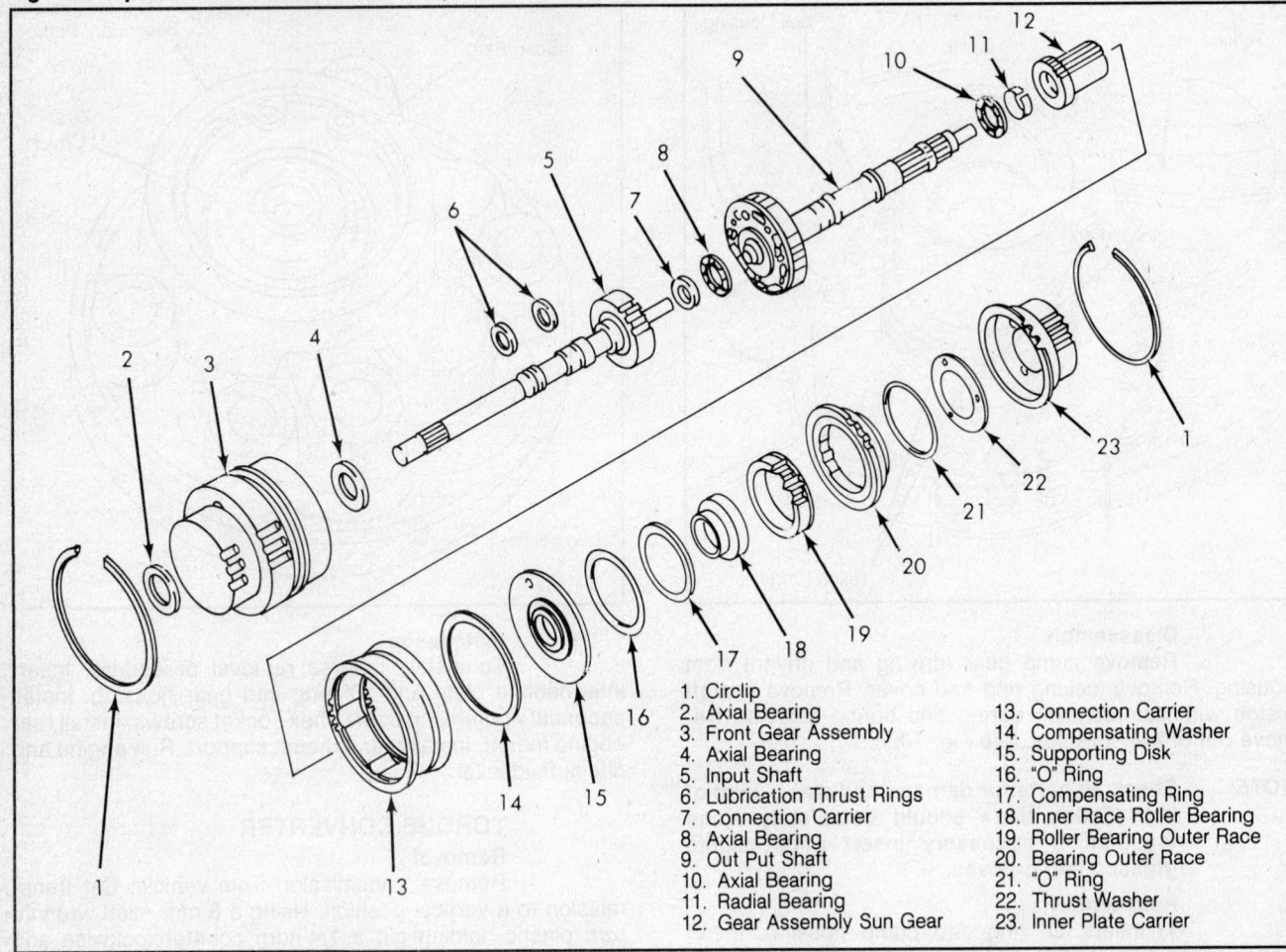

1. Circlip
2. Axial Bearing
3. Front Gear Assembly
4. Axial Bearing
5. Input Shaft
6. Lubrication Thrust Rings
7. Connection Carrier
8. Axial Bearing
9. Out Put Shaft
10. Axial Bearing
11. Radial Bearing
12. Gear Assembly Sun Gear
13. Connection Carrier
14. Compensating Washer
15. Supporting Disk
16. "O" Ring
17. Compensating Ring
18. Inner Race Roller Bearing
19. Roller Bearing Outer Race
20. Bearing Outer Race
21. "O" Ring
22. Thrust Washer
23. Inner Plate Carrier

2) If the transmission oil pan contains metal chips, replace torque converter. Metal chips are not completely removed by flushing and may lead to transmission damage later on.

3) Flush torque converter by adding approximately 1 pint of kerosene. Insert flusing mandrel and operate at low speed by means of a portable drill for approximately 2 minutes. Then drain kerosene. Repeat flushing procedure 2-4 times until kerosene flows out clean.

4) Screw oil cooler (with oil cooler lines) to syringe and flush with cleaning compound. Using compressed air, blow out till dry.

Installation
1) Grease drive flange with Molykote. Screw Special Handle (126 589 01 62 00) to converter. Place transmission in vertical position and carefully introduce torque converter.

2) Turn torque converter back and forth during insertion so that teeth will mesh. Unscrew Special Handle (126 589 01 62 00). Insert plastic holding pin and turn clockwise by 1/4 turn.

3) Place transmission on removing and installing fixture, turn converter so that one of 3 threaded plates are in proper position. Lightly grease centering pin on torque converter. Connect control rod to transmission and secure. Reinstall transmission.

GEAR ASSEMBLY
Disassembly
1) Clamp assembly bracket into a vise, with disk in upward direction. Place gear assembly into assembly bracket. Remove lubrication thrust rings from input shaft, remove circlip.

2) Lift off front planetary gear assembly. Remove axial bearing from front plantery gear assembly. Remove axial bearing and input shaft. Remove radial bearing and axial bearing from output shaft.

3) Pull sun gear. Remove circlip and lift inner plate carrier with one-way roller clutch out of connecting carrier. Lift supporting disk. Remove compenstaing ring and "O" ring.

4) Turn one-way roller clutch inner race counterclockwise and pull out. Remove cylinder rollers *See Fig. 12.*

Pre-Assembly
Check bearing points and one-way roller clutch inner race for wear. If running surface of cylinder rollers on one-way roller clutch inner race shows heavy score marks or notches, replace complete one-way roller clutch. Provide bearing points and slide surfaces with ATF during assembly.

MERCEDES-BENZ W 4 A 020 (Cont.)

Fig. 13: Exploded View of Clutch "K-1"

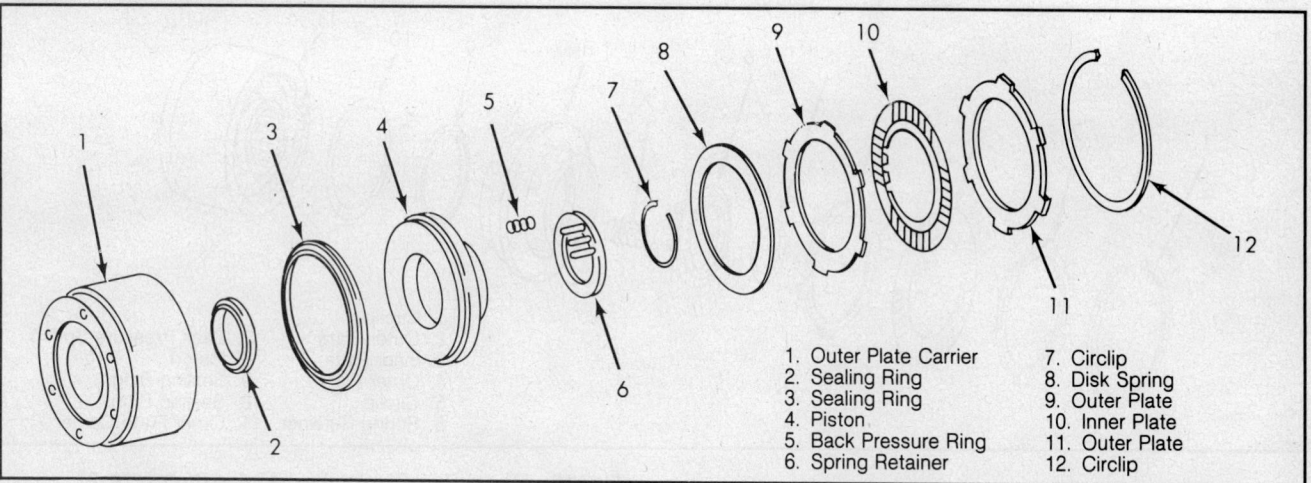

1. Outer Plate Carrier
2. Sealing Ring
3. Sealing Ring
4. Piston
5. Back Pressure Ring
6. Spring Retainer
7. Circlip
8. Disk Spring
9. Outer Plate
10. Inner Plate
11. Outer Plate
12. Circlip

Reassembly

1) Place thrust washer into inner plate carrier. Insert "O" ring only after end play of one-way roller clutch has been checked. Insert cylinder rollers in roller cage.

2) Place one-way roller clutch outer race on inner plate carrier and insert roller cage. Push cylinder roller against compression springs and insert locking plates with offset in outward direction.

3) Insert one-way roller clutch inner race while rotating in a counterclockwise direction. Pull out locking plates. Insert compensating ring.

NOTE: Insert "O" ring only after end play of one-way roller clutch has been checked.

4) Mount supporting disk so that lugs are entering bore in one-way roller clutch outer race. Place compensating washers into connecting carrier. Hold one-way roller clutch together and place into connecting carrier.

5) Insert circlip and push into groove by means of screwdriver. Check end play of one-way roller clutch. Using a feeler gauge, check clearance between one-way roller clutch and connecting carrier.

6) Compensate clearance by means of compensating washers to .0020-.008" (.05-.2 mm). Insert "O" ring. Insert sun gear into one-way roller clutch and rotate clockwise. One-way roller clutch should lock in.

7) Place axial bearing and radial bearing on input shaft. Place one-way roller clutch on Assembly Bracket (126 589 10 63 00) and insert output shaft. Place axial bearing and radial bearing on output shaft. Mount input shaft and axial bearing.

8) Insert axial bearing into front plantary gear assembly. Mount front gear assembly and secure with circlip. Push circlip into groove by means of a screw driver. Insert lubrication thrust rings into input shaft and lift gear assembly out of assembly bracket.

CLUTCH "K-1"
Disassembly

1) Remove circlip. Tilt outer plate carrier and remove plate assembly. Place Assembly Device (201 589 12 43 00) on spring retainer and tension until circlip is exposed.

2) Tilt outer plate carrier and remove plate assembly. Place Assembly Device (201 589 12 43 00) on spring retainer and tension until circlip is exposed. Remove circlip.

3) Slacken Assembly Device (201 589 12 43 00) and remove. Remove spring retainer and compression springs. Pull piston out of outer plate carrier. See Fig. 13.

Measuring

Determine clearance "A" with a slip gauge. Clearance "A" is set by using circlip which is available in 3 degrees of thickness: .080, .091 and .119" (2.0, 2.5 and 3.0 mm). If specified clearance "A" is not obtained with circlip, compensate with center outer plates, which are available in different thickness. See Fig. 14.

Fig. 14: Measuring Dimension "A" for Clutch "K-1"

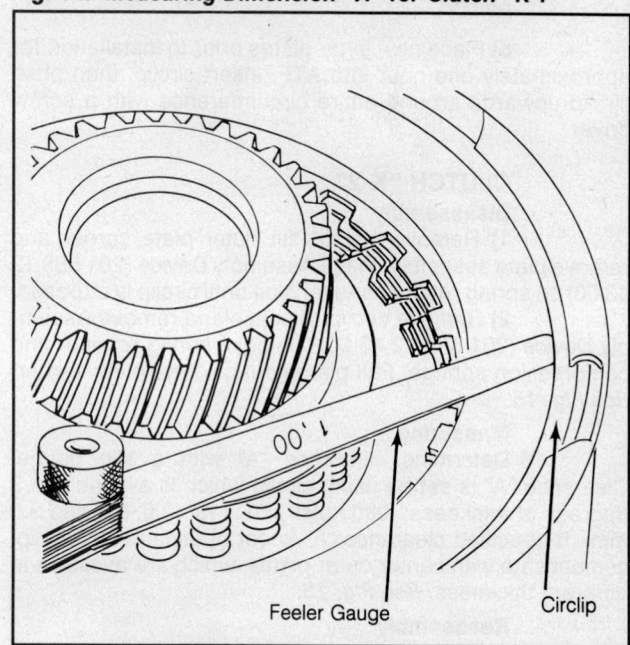

Feeler Gauge   Circlip

Reassembly

1) Insert lip sealing rings into piston so that sealing lips are pointing downwards. Place insertion sleeve into outer plate carrier. Using ATF, lubricate insertion sleeve as well as lip sealing rings.

2) Carefully insert piston and force into outer plate carrier without canting. Remove insertion sleeve. Place compression springs into piston. Mount spring re-

Fig. 15: Exploded View of Clutch "K-2"

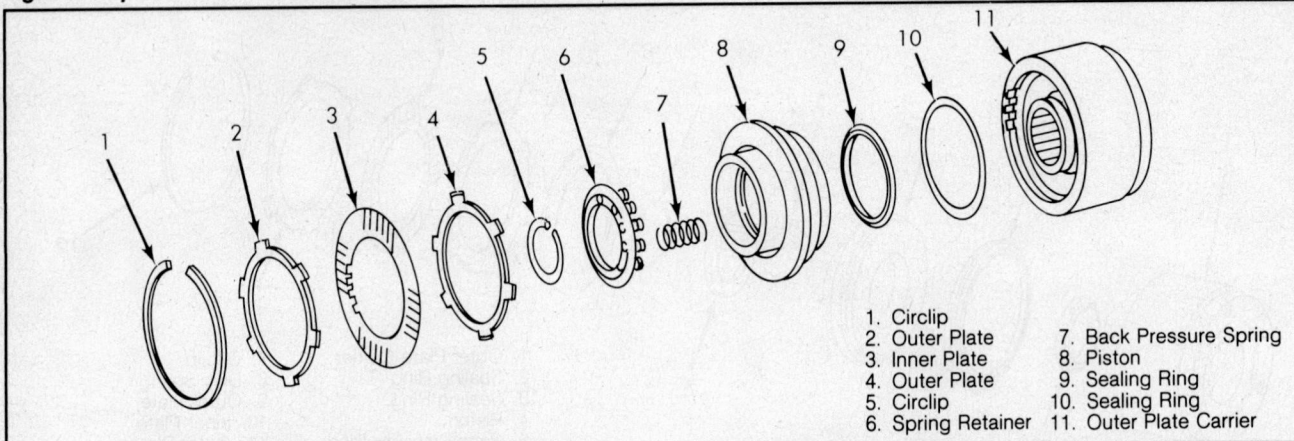

1. Circlip
2. Outer Plate
3. Inner Plate
4. Outer Plate
5. Circlip
6. Spring Retainer
7. Back Pressure Spring
8. Piston
9. Sealing Ring
10. Sealing Ring
11. Outer Plate Carrier

tainer, making sure that each spring is centered by one guide lug.

3) Mount Assembly Device (201 589 12 43 00) and tension. Insert circlip. Slacken assembly device and make sure that circlip is correctly seated.

4) Remove assembly device. Place plate disk spring on piston with crown. Assemble plate assembly in accordance with transmission type designation and place into outer plate carrier.

NOTE: Outer and inner plates which are badly burnt or bent must be replaced. Inner plates which are .080" (2 mm) thickness or less must be replaced.

5) Place new inner plates prior to installation for approximately one hour into ATF. Insert circlip, then push circlip upwards around entire circumference with a screw driver.

CLUTCH "K-2"
Disassembly

1) Remove circlip. Tilt outer plate carrier and remove plate assembly. Place Assembly Device (201 589 12 43 00) on spring retainer and tension until circlip is exposed.

2) Remove circlip. Slacken and remove Assembly Device (201 589 12 43 00). Remove spring retainer and compression springs. Pull piston out of outer plate carrier. See Fig. 15.

Measuring

Determine clearance "A" with a slip gauge. Clearance "A" is set by using circlip which is available in 3 degrees of thickness: .080, .091 and .119" (2.0, 2.5 and 3.0 mm). If specified clearance "A" is not obtained with circlip, compensate with center outer plates, which are available in different thickness. See Fig. 16.

Reassembly

1) Insert sealing ring, making sure that sealing ring is not twisted. Place lip sealing ring into piston in such a manner that sealing lip is pointing downwards.

2) Lubricate sealing rings with ATF. Place piston carefully into outer plate carrier, without canting slightly turn piston. Place compression springs into piston. Mount spring retainer so that each spring is centered by one guide lug.

Fig. 16: Measuring Clearance "A" for Clutch "K-2"

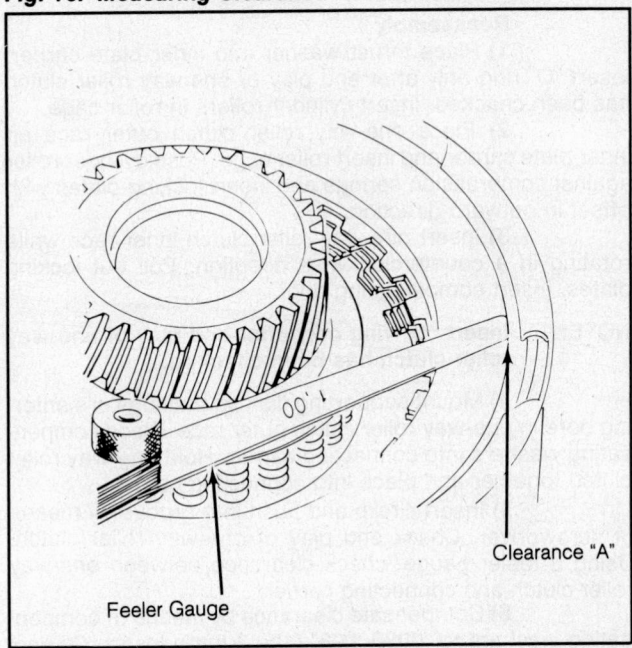

Feeler Gauge

Clearance "A"

3) Mount Assembly Device (201 589 12 43 00) and tension. Insert circlip. Slacken and remove assembly device, making sure that the circlip is correctly seated.

4) Assemble plate assembly for "K-2" according to transmission version. Place plate assembly into outer plate carrier. Insert circlip, then push circlip in upward direction along entire circumference by means of a screwdriver

TRANSMISSION REASSEMBLY

NOTE: During reassembly, lubricate bearing points and slide surfaces with ATF. Place new brake bands and lining plates of plate brake for approximately 1 hour into ATF fluid prior to sealing should point in direction of brake band piston cover.

1) Install all "O" rings into appropriate grooves. Insert thrust body "B-2" with link in upward direction. Screw

MERCEDES-BENZ W 4 A 020 (Cont.)

in closing plug with a new aluminum sealing ring and tighten.

2) Compress (as much as possible) brake band "G" enters into bore in supporting flange. Check seat of Teflon rings on supporting flange once again.

3) Place clutch "K-2" on gear assembly. Insert gear assembly into transmission housing while rotating input shaft. Set transmission vertical with input shaft in upward direction.

4) Check installation position of gear assembly. Gear assemby is correctly installed if the upper edge of connection carrier is deeper than the supporting surface of the outer plate.

5) Assemble front cover with primary pump. Assembly plates for plate brake "B3". Measure release clearance "L" of "B-3" and compensate.

6) To determine dimension "D", place parallel bar on machined surface, measure with depth gauge on compensating washer. To determine dimension "E", place parallel bar on piston of plate brake. Measure with depth gauge on gasket. *See Fig. 17 and 18.*

Fig. 17: Measuring Clearance For "B-3"

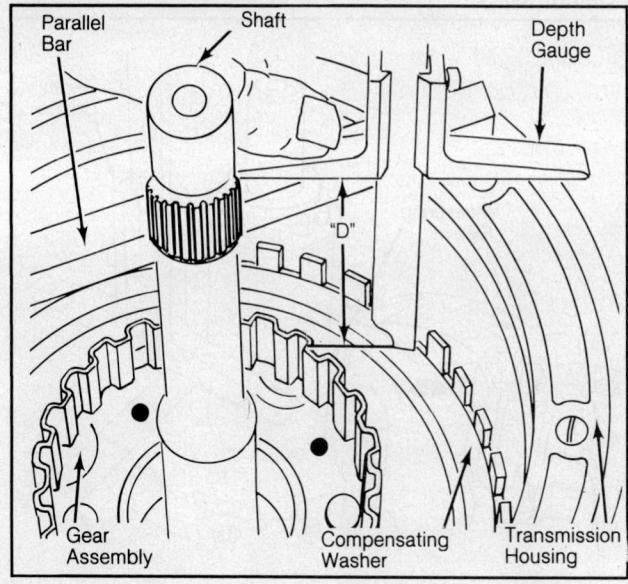

Fig. 18: Measuring Dimension "E" For "B-3"

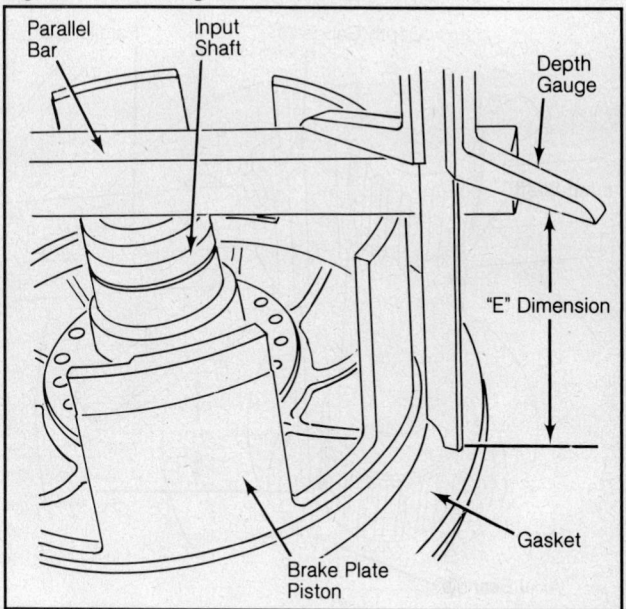

7) The difference from the 2 measurements provides release clearance "L". Set release clearance "L" to its nominal value of .060-.078" (1.5-2.0 mm). Compensate by means of outer plates and compensating washers available in varying degrees of thickness. *See Fig. 18.*

8) Provide groove in input shaft with grease and insert grease thrust rings. Attach assembly lock to brake band "B-1". Insert clutch "K-1" while rotating clutch so that the teeth can mesh.

9) Insert brake band "B-1" so that the tonque of assembly lock points toward body "B-1". Insert thrust pin into thrust body "B-1". Replace "O" rings.

10) Insert thrust body "B-1". Screw in closing plug and tighten. Insert brake band guide, making sure that locating lugs are entering bores in housing and are pushed in until guide noticeably engages.

11) Measure end play "B" for clutch "K-1" and compensate. Place gasket on front cover. Place parallel bar on flange. Measure with depth gauge from parallel bar to gasket (dimension "A"). *See Fig. 19.*

Fig. 19: Measuring Dimension "A" For Clutch "K-1"

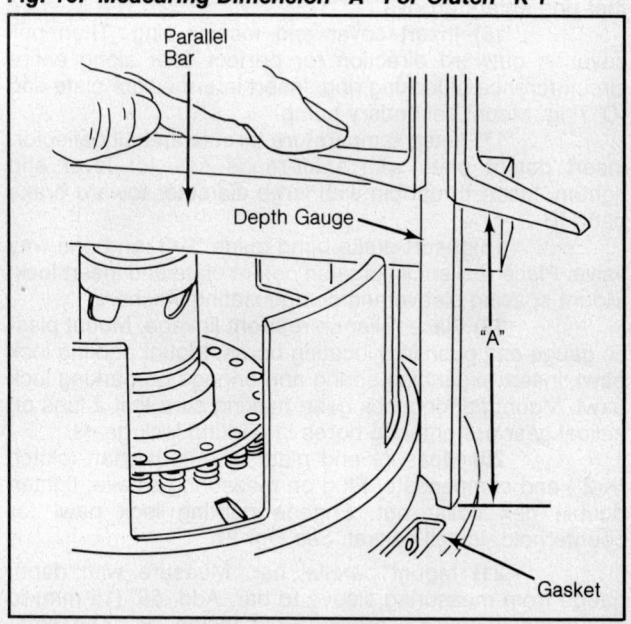

12) Place parallel bar on machined surface. Measure with depth gauge from parallel bar to a roller of axial bearing (dimension "B"). The difference from the 2 measurements provides clearance "B".

13) Adjust clearance by inserting pertinent compensating washers under washer of axial bearing. Check Teflon rings on front cover and on input shaft for correct seat. *See Fig. 20.*

14) Insert front cover with gasket and tighten. Turn assembly device so that input shaft is pointing in upward direction. Slip circlip up to its groove on input shaft.

15) Insert oil pipe and tighten retainer screw. Mount helical gear and insert circlip. Insert "O" ring and centrifugal governor while turning bearing ring so that lug

Fig. 20: Measuring Axial Bearing Play For Clutch "K-1"

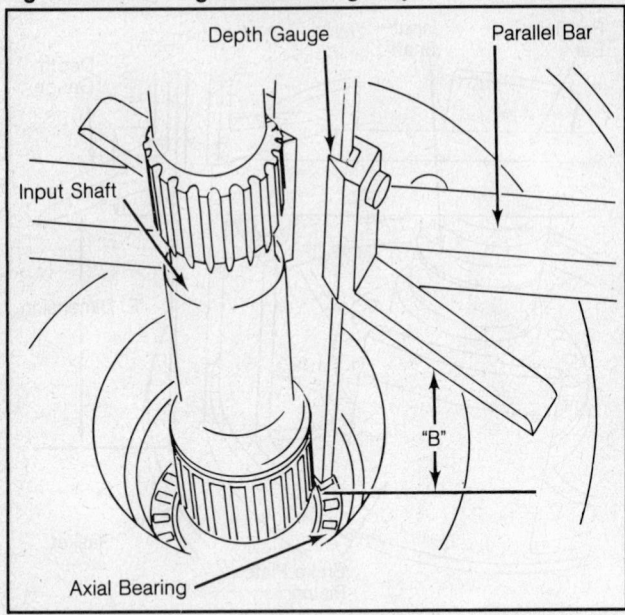

Fig. 21: Measuring End Plate For Output Shaft (Clutch "K-2")

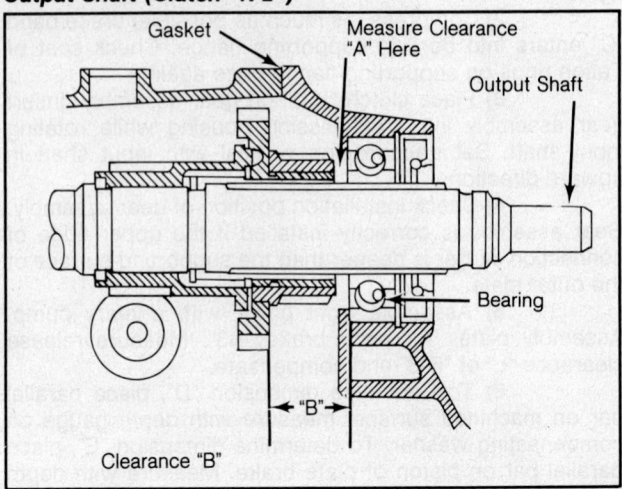

Fig. 22: Measuring Dimension "B" For Output Shaft (Clutch "K-2")

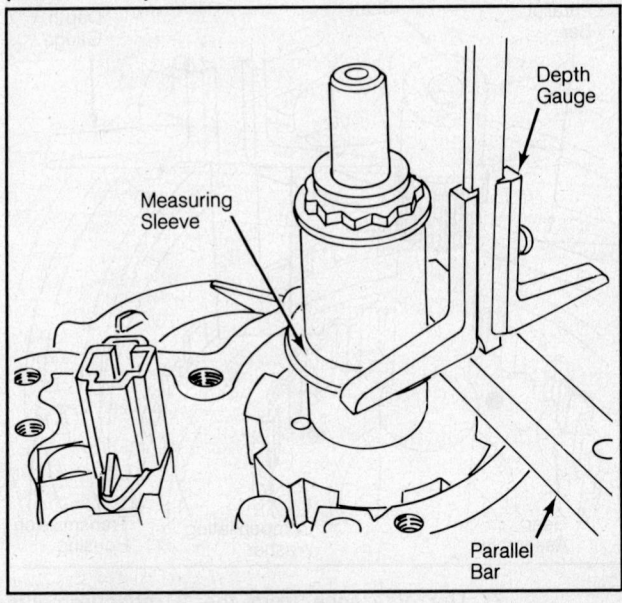

enters groove in housing. Insert locking ring, making sure that ring enters groove.

16) Insert cover and locking ring. Then pull cover in outward direction for perfect seat along entire circumference of locking ring. Insert intermediate plate and "O" ring. Mount secondary pump.

17) Insert temperature throttle and oil deflector. Insert detent plate with shaft-range selector lever and tighten. Insert thrust pin with large diameter toward brake band "B-2".

18) Insert brake band guide "B-2" and one-way valve. Place resilent linkage on detent plate and insert lock. Mount spacing sleeve and compensating washers.

19) Place roller on resilient linkage. Mount plastic gauge and push into locating bores. Mount parking lock pawl, insert expanding spring and engage on parking lock pawl. Mount parking lock gear, making sure that 2 lugs on helical gear are entering bores in parking lock gears.

20) Measure end plate of output shaft (clutch "K-2") and compensate. Plug on measuring sleeve, tighten double hex collar nut. Engage parking lock pawl for counterhold. Install gasket. *See Fig. 21.*

21) Mount parallel bar. Measure with depth gauge from measuring sleeve to bar. Add .59" (15 mm) to measured dimension provides dimension "B". The additional clearance is a result of the height of parallel bar .78" (20 mm) minus edge of measuring sleeve .20" (5 mm).

22) Assemble rear cover. Measure with depth gauge from sealing surface of rear cover to inner ring of radial ball bearing (dimension "A"). Dimension "A" is deducted from dimension "B" provides end play "C".

23) Compensate end play "C" by adding or removing compensating washers under parking lock gear. Place "O" ring on tachometer oil pipe. Insert tachometer oil pipe, making sure that the 2 lugs are entering bores in parking lock gear.

24) Install rear cover and insert washer. Install "O" ring into output flange and install output flange. Tighten double hex collar nut. Using a mandrel, knock collar of double hex nut into recess of output shaft. Screw in kickdown magnetic valve and tighten. *See Fig. 22.*

25) Insert modulating pressure control valve and thrust pin. Mount vacuum control with holding plate and tighten. Mount starter lock out switch, making sure that the driver enters into range selector lever. Screw in both fastening screws, but do not tighten.

NOTE: On transmission 722.402 a spring is installed for the modulating pressure control valve, starting with end No. 2201.

26) Insert a .16" (4 mm) cotter pin or drill as a locating pin through locating hole in driver. Tighten fastening screw and remove locating pin. Insert lip sealing ring on brake band piston "B-1" in such a manner that sealing lip is pointing in a counterclockwise direction.

NOTE: Brake band pistons with several different lenght of thrust pins are available for compensating release clearance on brake band "B-1" These thrust pins are identified with grooves. The brake band piston with the shortest thrust.

MERCEDES-BENZ W 4 A 020 (Cont.)

pin has no identifying groove, the brake band piston with longest thrust pin has 6 identifying grooves.

27) Mount Assembly Device (126 589 10 63 00) and screw to transmission housing. Insert brake band piston "B-1" with compression springs.

28) Screw in spindle of Assembly Device (126 589 10 63 00), making sure that the thrust pin of the brake band piston "B-1" is introduced into brake band and that the lip sealing ring is not damaged. Insert locking ring, relieve assembly device and remove.

29) Measure release clearance "L" on brake band "B-1" and adjust. Threads on Measuring Device (201 589 07 21 00) have .039" (1 mm) pitch, so that one revolution means .039" (1 mm) of travel. Screw in screw on measuring device manually until resistance is felt.

30) Continue screwing in screw with torque wrench while counting revolutions and tighten. Idle travel on brake band should amount to .12-.16" (3-4 mm), therefore a torque of 44 INCH lbs. (5 N.m) must be attained after 3-4 revolutions.

31) If the idle travel is too long, install a brake band piston with a longer thrust pin or if the idle travel is too short, a brake band piston with shorter thrust pin. Mount Assembly Device (126 589 10 63 00) and tighten. Insert brake band piston cover instead of Measuring Device (126 589 10 63 00).

32) Screw in spindle of Assembly Device (126 589 10 63 00). Insert locking ring. Relieve assembly device and remove. Insert thrust pin into brake band piston "B-2".

33) Insert brake band piston "B-2", while making sure that thrust pin enters brake band. Push in brake band piston cover "B-2" and insert locking ring. Measure release clearance "L" on brake band "B-2" and adjust.

34) Push brake band "B-2" at supporting link to brake band piston, so that brake band piston rests against brake band piston cover. Measure dimension "A" on brake band by means of slide rule.

35) Push brake band "B-2" likewise on supporting link to thrust body. Measure dimension "A" once again. The difference from both measurements provides release clearance "L". Adjust release clearance "L" by changing thrust pin on brake band piston "B-2" to .24-.28" (6-7 mm).

36) Insert locating pin into housing. Assemble lower cover and install while making sure that oil pipe is

introduced into bore. Center intermediate plate by means of 2 screws. Insert combination screws and tighten.

37) Mount leaf spring with holder and tighten. Check clearance "A" between detent piston and stop on resilent linkage. Adjust clearance, if necessary. Adjust clearance "A" in position "N" by means of plastic clip to .0016-.039" (.4-1.0 mm). Plastic clip is available in 3 difference degrees of thickness.

38) Mount shift valve housing, making sure that the range selection slide enters driver on detent plate. Insert combination screws and tighten. Pay attention to length of screws. The 3 screws marked with "7a" are only 1.97" (50 mm) long, the other 12 screws are 2.17" (55 mm) long.

39) Install oil filter and oil pan. Engage cable control for control pressure in connecting rod, check "O" ring and replace, if necessary. Push plastic sleeve of control pressure cable control into housing. Turn plastic sleeve clockwise until link engages in housing. Install transmission.

TIGHTENING SPECIFICATIONS

Application	Ft. Lbs. (N.m)
Converter-to-Drive Plate	31 (42)
Front Cover-to-Case	20 (27)
Front Cover-to-Primary Pump	15 (21)
Kickdown Solenoid Valve	14 (20)
Propeller Shaft Clamping Nut	22 (30)
Rear Cover-to-Case	14 (20)
Transmission-to-Engine	
M10 Bolts	41 (55)
M12 Bolts	48 (65)
3-Arm Flange Slot Nut	89 (120)

	INCH Lbs. (N.m)
Clutch K-2 Support Flange-to-Case	96 (11)
Converter Drain Plug	120 (14)
Governor Axial Holder Nut	72 (8)
Lower Cover-to-Case	72 (8)
Oil Drain Plug	120 (14)
Oil Filter-to-Valve Body	36 (4)
Oil Pan-to-Case	72 (8)
Range Selector Lever Nut	72 (8)
Secondary Pump-to-Case	72 (8)
Vacuum Control Unit-to Case	72 (8)
Valve Body-to-Case	72 (8)

Automatic Transmissions
MITSUBISHI KM170, KM171 & KM172

Dodge Colt, Colt Vista
Mitsubishi Cordia, Tredia

DESCRIPTION

Mitsubishi models KM170, KM171 and KM172 automatic transaxle assemblies consist of automatic transmission, torque converter, transfer assembly and differential. The complete transaxle assembly is contained in a single housing.

The automatic transmission consists of a front and rear clutch, kickdown band, low-reverse brake, one-way clutch, valve body and a planetary gear set.

The transfer assembly consists of a drive gear, idler gear, driven gear and a transfer shaft. The differential consists of a differential case, ring gear, pinion shaft and gears, speedometer gear and 2 side gears.

The Colt Vista, Cordia and Tredia models use a lock-up torque converter.

LUBRICATION & ADJUSTMENT

See appropriate AUTOMATIC TRANSMISSION SERVICING article in IMPORT GENERAL SERVICING section.

TROUBLE SHOOTING

NO STARTER OPERATION IN "P" OR "N"
Faulty or misadjusted inhibitor switch. Manual linkage out of adjustment.

NO DRIVE IN "D"
Throttle control cable out of adjustment. Low fluid level. Manual linkage out of adjustment. Line pressure too low. Faulty rear clutch and piston. Faulty overrunning clutch. Valve body malfunction. Defective oil pump.

NO DRIVE IN "R"
Throttle control cable out of adjustment. Low fluid level. Manual linkage out of adjustment. Line pressure too low. Valve body malfunction. Faulty front clutch and piston. Faulty low reverse brake and piston. Missing "O" ring in front clutch circuit between valve and body case. Defective oil pump.

HARSH ENGAGEMENT
From "N" to "D", "2", "L" or "R"
Idle speed too high. Throttle control cable out of adjustment. Line pressure too high.

3-2 Kickdown
Throttle control cable out of adjustment. Low fluid level. Line pressure too low. Valve body malfunction. Kickdown band out of adjustment.

POOR PERFORMANCE OR OVERHEATING IN "D"
Faulty torque converter.

TRANSMISSION SLIPS IN "D"
Throttle control cable out of adjustment. Low fluid level. Manual linkage out of adjustment. Line pressure too low. Faulty rear clutch and piston. Faulty overrunning clutch. Valve body malfunction.

TRANSMISSION SLIPS IN "R"
Throttle control cable out of adjustment. Low fluid level. Manual linkage out of adjustment. Line pressure too low. Valve body malfunction. Faulty front clutch and piston. Faulty low-reverse brake and piston. Missing "O" ring in front clutch circuit between valve body and case.

TRANSMISSION SLIPS ON 1-2 UPSHIFT
Throttle control cable out of adjustment. Low fluid level. Line pressure too low. Valve body malfunction. Faulty kickdown band or servo. Kickdown band out of adjustment.

TRANSMISSION SLIPS ON 2-3 UPSHIFT
Throttle control cable out of adjustment. Low fluid level. Line pressure too low. Valve body malfunction. Faulty front clutch and piston.

TRANSMISSION SLIPS OR SHUDDERS ON STARTS IN "L"
Throttle control cable out of adjustment. Low fluid level. Manual linkage out of adjustment. Valve body malfunction.

NO DOWNSHIFT IN "D" TO "L" SHIFT
Manual shift linkage out of adjustment. Valve body malfunction. Faulty kickdown band or servo. Kickdown band out of adjustment.

NO 1-2 UPSHIFT OR WRONG SPEED 1-2 UPSHIFT
Throttle control cable out of adjustment. Low fluid level. Line pressure too low. Valve body malfunction. Governor valve malfunction. Faulty kickdown band or servo. Kickdown band out of adjustment.

NO 2-3 UPSHIFT OR WRONG SPEED 2-3 UPSHIFT
Throttle control cable out of adjustment. Low fluid level. Line pressure too low. Valve body malfunction. Faulty front clutch or piston. Governor valve malfunction.

UPSHIFT IN "L"
Manual linkage out of adjustment.

"P" WILL NOT ENGAGE
Manual linkage out of adjustment. Faulty parking mechanism.

CONVERTER NOISE
Loose converter bolts or warped flex plate. Defective oil pump. Interference of oil pump gear teeth, and wear of bushing.

MITSUBISHI KM170, KM171 & KM172 (Cont.)

Fig. 1: *Cross-Sectional View of Mitsubishi KM170 Automatic Transaxle for Colt*

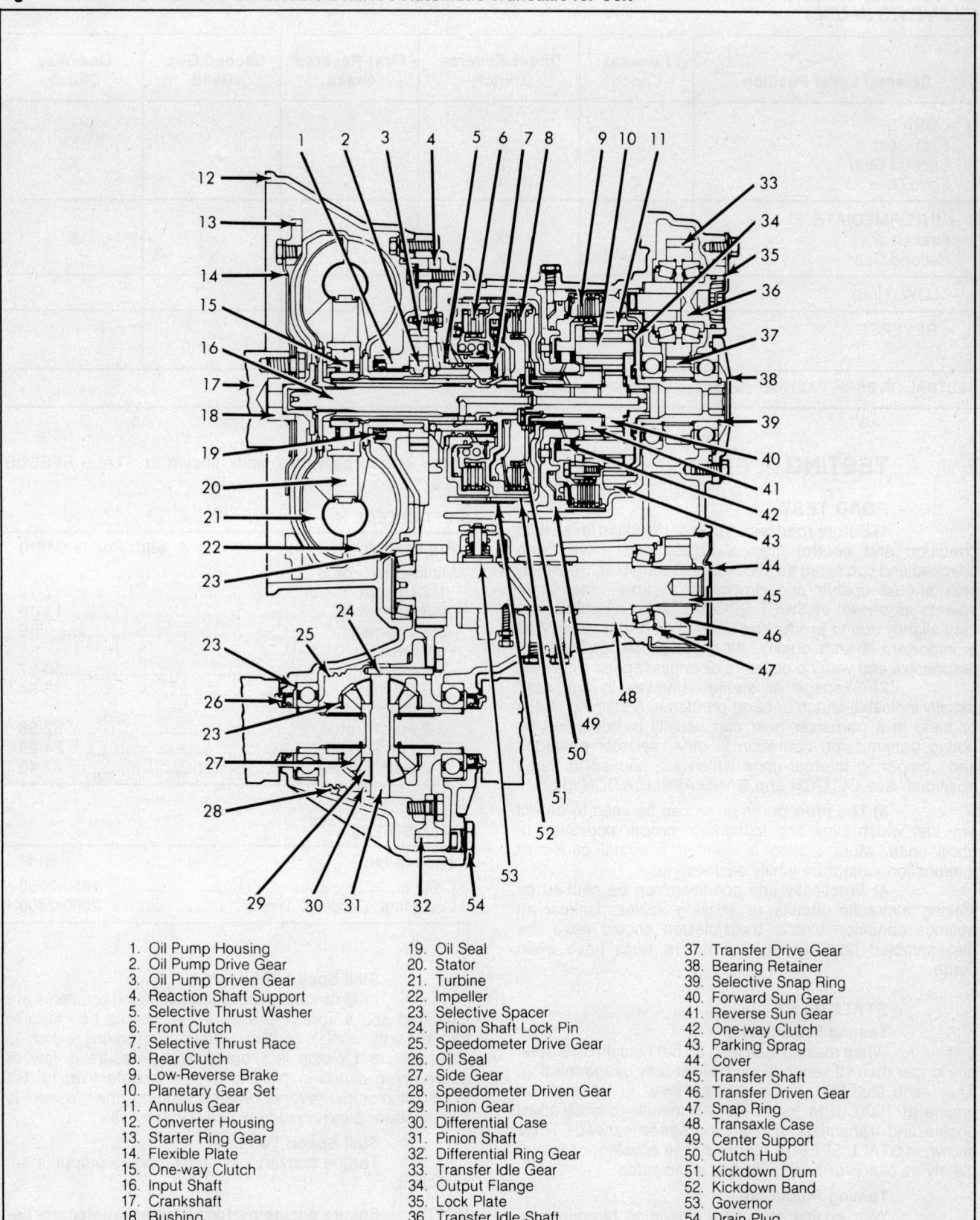

1. Oil Pump Housing	19. Oil Seal	37. Transfer Drive Gear
2. Oil Pump Drive Gear	20. Stator	38. Bearing Retainer
3. Oil Pump Driven Gear	21. Turbine	39. Selective Snap Ring
4. Reaction Shaft Support	22. Impeller	40. Forward Sun Gear
5. Selective Thrust Washer	23. Selective Spacer	41. Reverse Sun Gear
6. Front Clutch	24. Pinion Shaft Lock Pin	42. One-way Clutch
7. Selective Thrust Race	25. Speedometer Drive Gear	43. Parking Sprag
8. Rear Clutch	26. Oil Seal	44. Cover
9. Low-Reverse Brake	27. Side Gear	45. Transfer Shaft
10. Planetary Gear Set	28. Speedometer Driven Gear	46. Transfer Driven Gear
11. Annulus Gear	29. Pinion Gear	47. Snap Ring
12. Converter Housing	30. Differential Case	48. Transaxle Case
13. Starter Ring Gear	31. Pinion Shaft	49. Center Support
14. Flexible Plate	32. Differential Ring Gear	50. Clutch Hub
15. One-way Clutch	33. Transfer Idle Gear	51. Kickdown Drum
16. Input Shaft	34. Output Flange	52. Kickdown Band
17. Crankshaft	35. Lock Plate	53. Governor
18. Bushing	36. Transfer Idle Shaft	54. Drain Plug

Mitsubishi MK171 Automatic Transaxle is virtually the same.

Automatic Transmissions
MITSUBISHI KM170, KM171 & KM172 (Cont.)

**CLUTCH AND BAND APPLICATION CHART
(ELEMENTS IN USE)**

Selector Lever Position	Forward Clutch	Direct-Reverse Clutch	First-Reverse Brake	Second Gear Band	One-Way Clutch
D – DRIVE					
First Gear		X			X
Second Gear		X		X	X
Third Gear	X	X			
2 – INTERMEDIATE					
First Gear		X			X
Second Gear		X		X	
1 – LOW (First)		X	X		
R – REVERSE	X		X		

NEUTRAL OR PARK – All clutches, brakes, and bands released or ineffective.

TESTING

ROAD TEST

1) Before road testing, be certain fluid level, fluid condition and control linkage adjustments have been checked and corrected as necessary. During test, transmission should upshift and downshift at about the same speeds as shown in SHIFT SPEEDS table. All shifts may vary slightly due to production tolerances or tire size. What is important is shift quality. All shifts should be smooth, responsive and with no slippage or engine speed runaway.

2) Slippage or engine runaway in any gear usually indicates clutch or band problems. A slipping clutch or band in a particular gear can usually be identified by noting transmission operation in other selector positions and comparing internal units which are applied in these positions. See CLUTCH and BAND APPLICATION chart.

3) The procedures given can be used to detect any unit which slips and to confirm proper operation of good units. More testing is needed if actual cause of malfunction cannot be easily decided.

4) Practically any condition can be caused by leaking hydraulic circuits or sticking valves. Unless an obvious condition exists, transmission should never be disassembled until hydraulic pressure tests have been made.

STALL TEST

Testing Precautions

When making stall test, do not hold throttle open any longer than 10 seconds to obtain steady gauge reading. After each stall test, move selector lever to "N" and run engine at 1000 RPM for at least 1 minute to cool down engine and transmission. If engine speed exceeds limits shown in STALL SPEEDS table, release accelerator immediately as clutch or band slippage is indicated.

Testing Procedure

With engine at normal operating temperature, tachometer installed, and parking and service brakes applied, make transmission stall test in "D" and "R" ranges at full throttle and note maximum RPM obtained. Engine speed should be within limits shown in STALL SPEEDS table.

SHIFT SPEEDS

Application	Shift Points (MPH)
Minimum Throttle	
1-2 Upshift	7-12
2-3 Upshift	11-16
3-1 Downshift	5-9
Full Throttle	
1-2 Upshift	30-37
2-3 Upshift	58-64
Kickdown	
3-2 Full Throttle	52-58
3-1 Full Throttle	24-29
3-2 Half Throttle	32-40

STALL SPEEDS

Application	RPM
Colt	1650-2050
Colt Vista, Cordia & Tredia	2000-2400

Stall Speed Too High

In all ranges: general transmission problems are indicated and a control pressure test should be made to locate faulty unit(s). In "D"; Stator overrunning clutch is defective, rear clutch is slipping, line pressure is low or overrunning clutch in planetary gear is defective. In "R"; front clutch or low-reverse brake is slipping, line pressure is low or stator overrunning clutch is defective.

Stall Speed Too Low

Torque converter is faulty, engine output is not sufficient.

NOTE: Ensure engine performance is satisfactory before condemning converter. Converter cannot be overhauled and must be replaced if defective.

HYDRAULIC PRESSURE TESTS

NOTE: Ensure transmission fluid level is correct, control cable is adjusted and transmission is at normal operating temperature. Connect a tachometer, disconnect throttle control cable from carburetor and raise vehicle on a hoist so front wheels are off ground.

Line Pressures

1) Connect oil pressure gauge(s) to each of the following: line pressure port, low-reverse brake pressure port, front clutch pressure port, and "tee" into transmission "To Cooler" line. *See Fig. 2* for pressure port locations. See HYDRAULIC PRESSURES table for pressure specifications.

2) Place manual control lever to "L" position (all the way rearward). Take pressure reading at idle, half throttle then with full throttle (engine speed should be at stall speed). Also note low-reverse brake pressure.

3) Place manual control lever to "2" position (1 detent forward). Note pressures at idle, half and full throttle. Also note lubrication (from "To Cooler" line) pressure.

4) Place manual control lever in "D" position (2 detents forward). Note pressures at idle, half and full throttle.

5) Place manual control lever in "R" position (4 detents forward). With pressure gauge attached to low-reverse pressure port, note pressures at idle, half and full throttle.

Line Pressure Test Results

1) If line pressure was correct in any test, pump and pressure regulator are working properly.

HYDRAULIC PRESSURES

Application	psi (kg/cm^2)
Line Pressure in All Ranges	
Idle	58-67 (4.1-4.7)
Half Throttle	96 (6.7)
Full Throttle [1]	98-100 (6.9-7.0)
Low-Reverse Brake Pressure	
In "L"	24-33 (1.7-2.3)
In "R"	199-284 (14.0-20.0)
Lubrication Pressure	
In "2"	7-21 (.5-1.5)

[1] – Pressure should increase as cable is moved from idle to full throttle. Full throttle should be at stall speed specification.

2) A low pressure reading in "L", "2" and "D" but correct pressure in "R" indicates rear clutch circuit leakage.

3) A low pressure reading in "D" and "R" but correct pressure in "L" indicates front clutch circuit leakage.

4) A low pressure reading in "L" and "R" but correct pressure in "2" indicates low-reverse brake circuit leakage.

5) Low pressure readings in all positions indicates a defective pump, clogged filter or a stuck pressure regulator valve.

Governor Pressure Test

1) Make this test only if vehicle shifts at wrong speeds with throttle cable properly adjusted. Connect pressure gauge to governor pressure port. *See Fig. 2.*

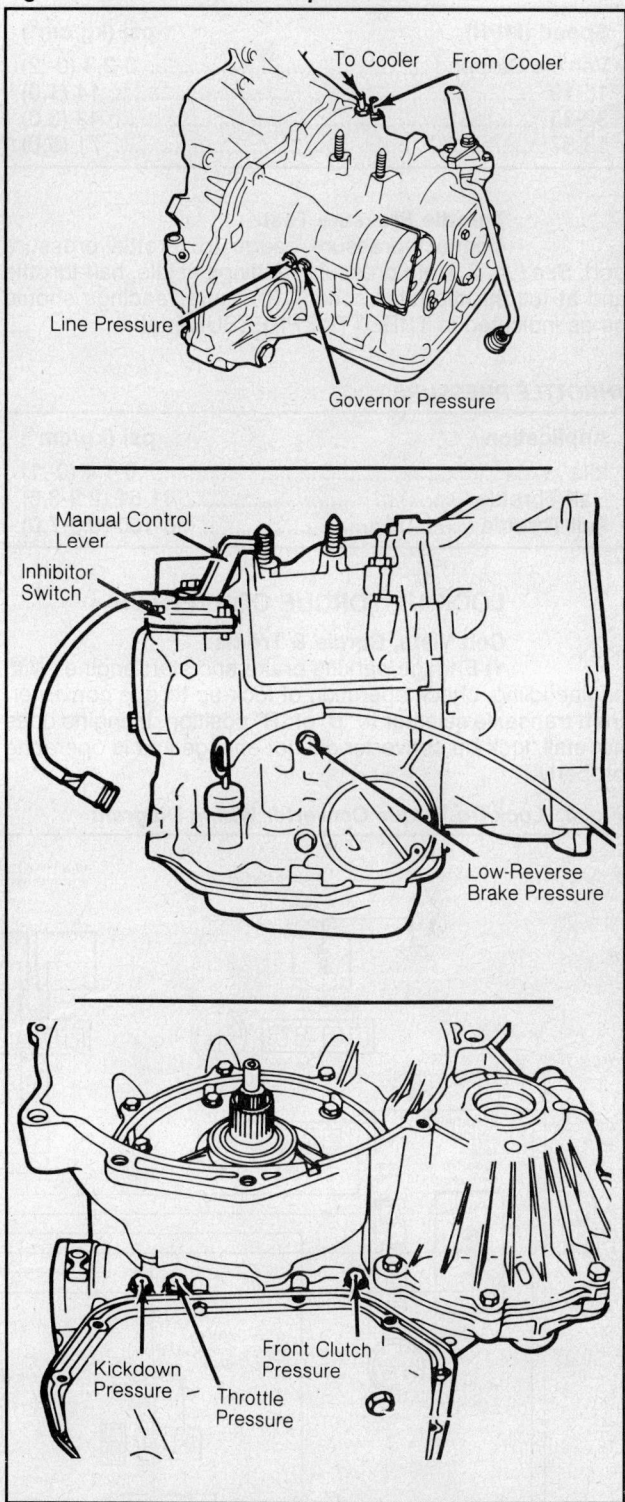

Fig. 2: Pressure Test Hookup Locations

2) Place manual control lever in "D" position and increase vehicle speed and note pressures at which transmission shifts. Transmission should shift at indicated speeds and governor pressure should be as indicated in GOVERNOR PRESSURE table. If not, governor valve is sticking, or filter in governor body is clogged.

Automatic Transmissions
MITSUBISHI KM170, KM171 & KM172 (Cont.)

GOVERNOR PRESSURE

Speed (MPH)	psi (kg/cm^2)
Vehicle Stopped	0-2.8 (0-.2)
16-19	14 (1.0)
32-35	43 (3.0)
53-57	71 (5.0)

Throttle Pressure Test

Connect pressure gauge to throttle pressure port. *See Fig. 2.* Note pressure readings at idle, half throttle and at full throttle (stall speed). Pressure readings should be as indicated in THROTTLE PRESSURE table.

THROTTLE PRESSURE

Application	psi (kg/cm^2)
Idle	0-1.4 (0-.1)
Half Throttle	41-51 (2.9-3.6)
Full Throttle	98-100 (6.9-7.0)

LOCK-UP TORQUE CONVERTER

Colt Vista, Cordia & Tredia

1) Engage parking brake and start engine. With engine idling, check operation of lock-up torque converter. Shift transaxle selector to "D" or "R" position. If engine does not stall, lock-up converter did not engage and is operating properly.

2) If engine stalled, solenoid valve is not completely closed, lock-up torqueconverter control valve is stuck, lock-up torque converter is heat seized or idle speed is incorrectly adjusted.

3) Using the ELC-A/T Checker (MD998405), check lock-up torque converter, lock-up torque converter hydraulic control circuit and the control unit-to-solenoid valve control circuit that is used to control hydraulic pressure.

4) Connect ELC-A/T checker as follows: Connect White inspection connector, located near master cylinder reservior, to tester connector "C". Disconnect harness connector from transaxle solenoid valve connector. Connect transaxle solenoid valve connector to tester connector "A".

5) Connect transaxle solenoid valve harness connector to tester connector "B". Connect tester clip to positive battery terminal.

SERVICE (IN VEHICLE)

DRIVE AXLE SHAFTS
Removal

1) Remove front wheel dust cap and loosen lock nut. Raise vehicle and remove wheels. Remove underside shield (Colt). Remove lower ball joint and strut from lower control arm. Drain transaxle fluid.

Fig. 3: *Lock-Up Torque Converter Wiring Diagram*

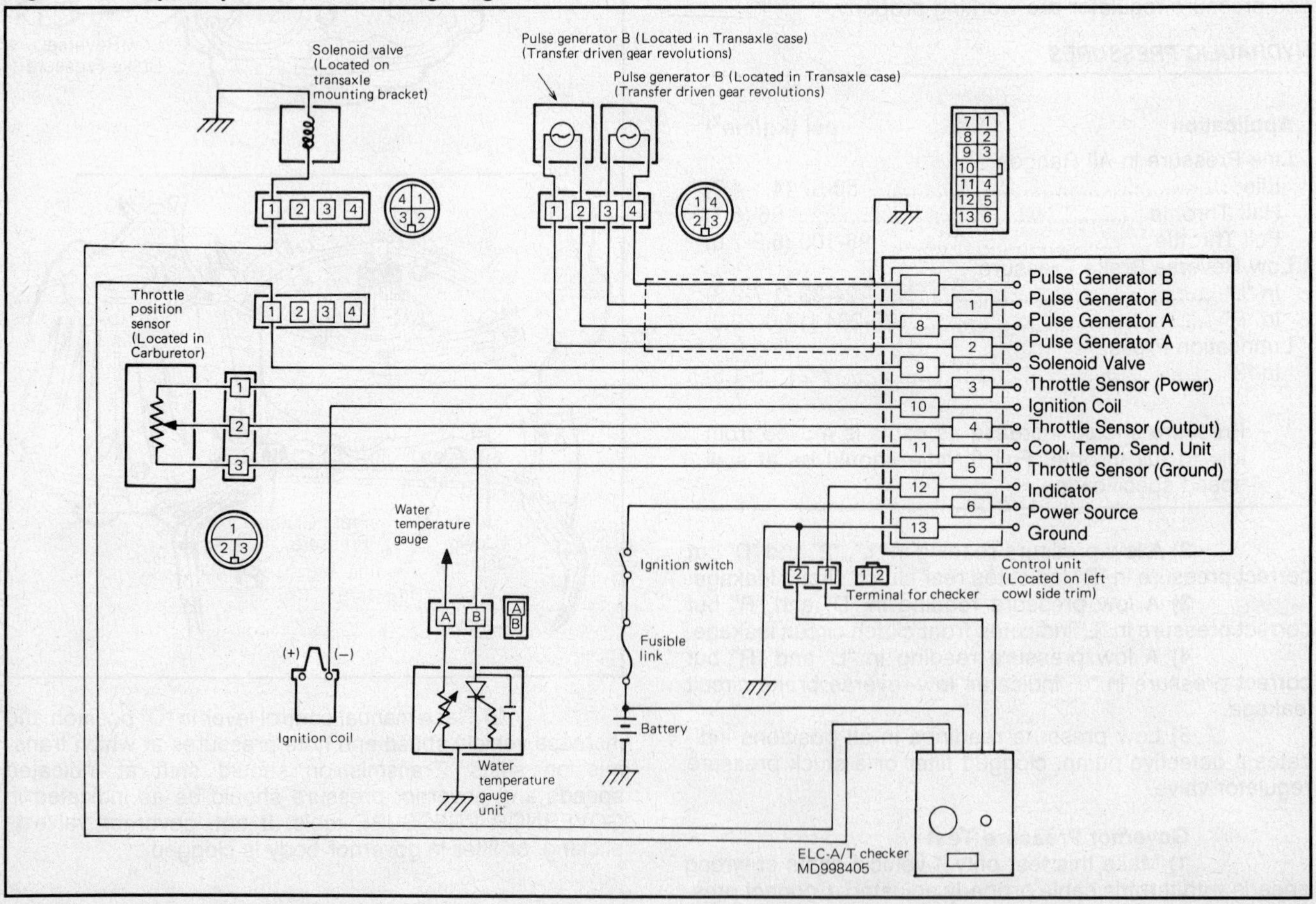

MITSUBISHI KM170, KM171 & KM172 (Cont.)

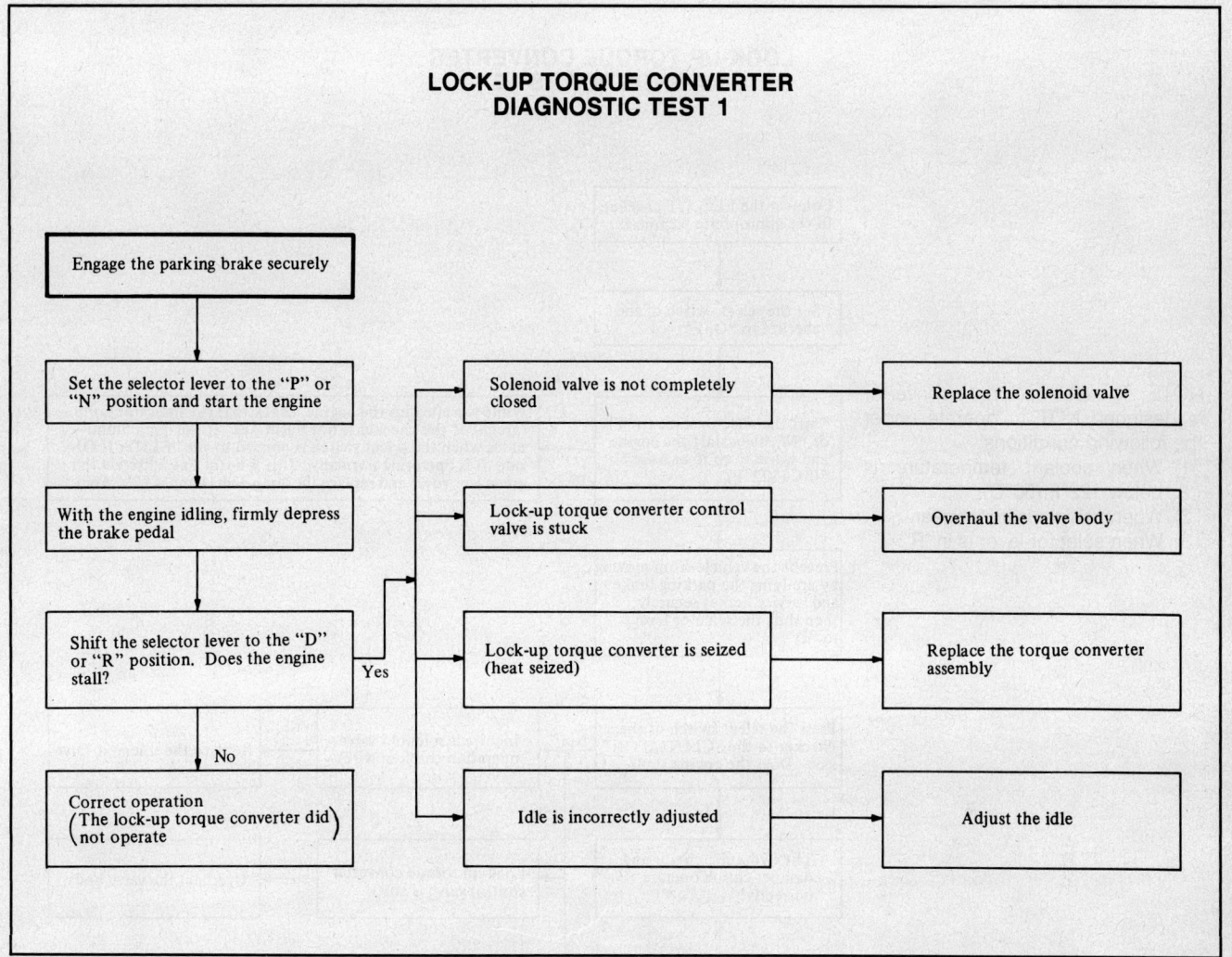

**LOCK-UP TORQUE CONVERTER
DIAGNOSTIC TEST 1**

Engage the parking brake securely

↓

Set the selector lever to the "P" or "N" position and start the engine

↓

With the engine idling, firmly depress the brake pedal

↓

Shift the selector lever to the "D" or "R" position. Does the engine stall?

— Yes →

Solenoid valve is not completely closed → Replace the solenoid valve

Lock-up torque converter control valve is stuck → Overhaul the valve body

Lock-up torque converter is seized (heat seized) → Replace the torque converter assembly

Idle is incorrectly adjusted → Adjust the idle

— No →

Correct operation
(The lock-up torque converter did not operate)

Automatic Transmissions
MITSUBISHI KM170, KM171 & KM172 (Cont.)

**LOCK-UP TORQUE CONVERTER
DIAGNOSTIC TEST 2**

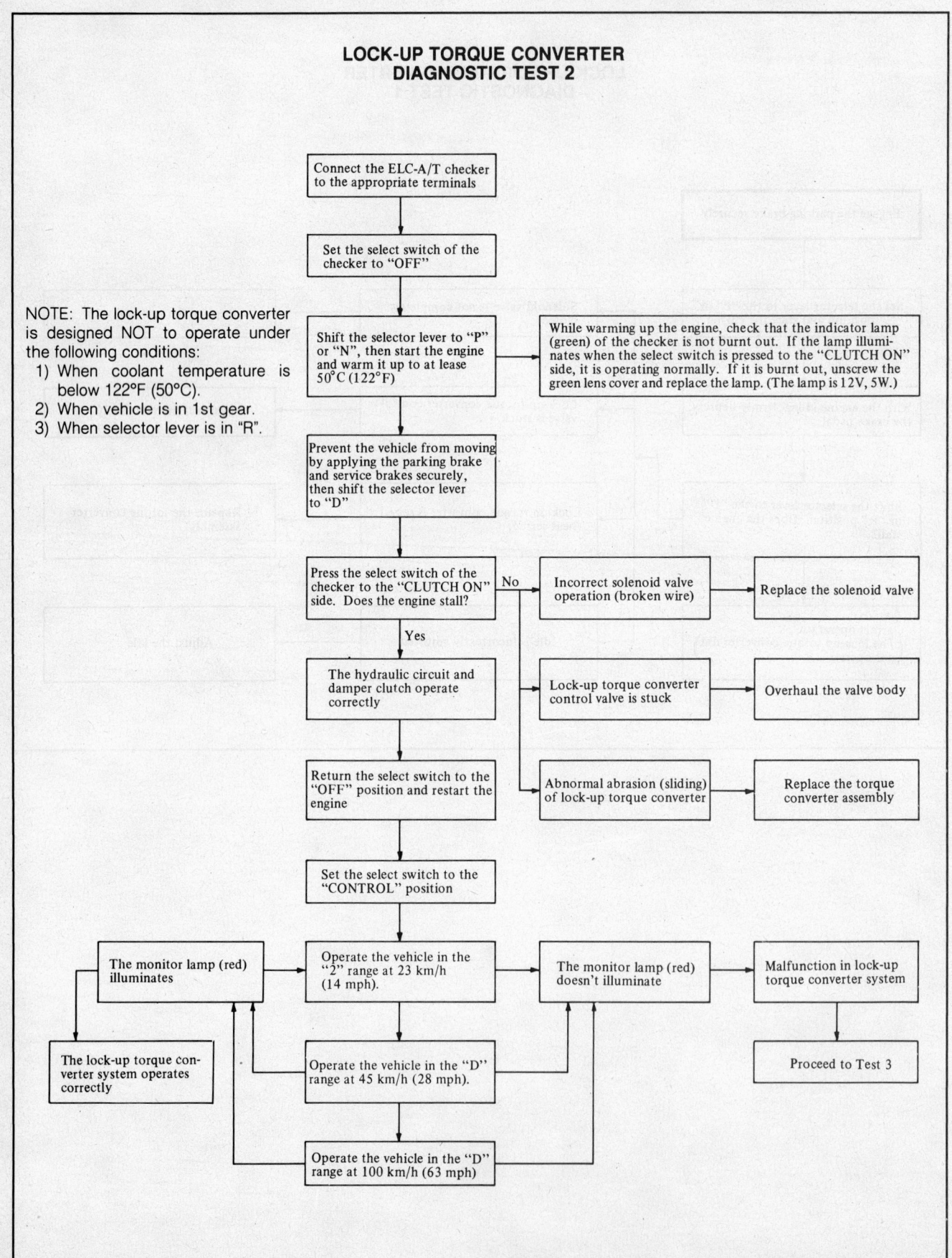

NOTE: The lock-up torque converter is designed NOT to operate under the following conditions:
1) When coolant temperature is below 122°F (50°C).
2) When vehicle is in 1st gear.
3) When selector lever is in "R".

Connect the ELC-A/T checker to the appropriate terminals

Set the select switch of the checker to "OFF"

Shift the selector lever to "P" or "N", then start the engine and warm it up to at lease 50°C (122°F)

While warming up the engine, check that the indicator lamp (green) of the checker is not burnt out. If the lamp illuminates when the select switch is pressed to the "CLUTCH ON" side, it is operating normally. If it is burnt out, unscrew the green lens cover and replace the lamp. (The lamp is 12V, 5W.)

Prevent the vehicle from moving by applying the parking brake and service brakes securely, then shift the selector lever to "D"

Press the select switch of the checker to the "CLUTCH ON" side. Does the engine stall? — No → Incorrect solenoid valve operation (broken wire) → Replace the solenoid valve

Yes

The hydraulic circuit and damper clutch operate correctly

Lock-up torque converter control valve is stuck → Overhaul the valve body

Return the select switch to the "OFF" position and restart the engine

Abnormal abrasion (sliding) of lock-up torque converter → Replace the torque converter assembly

Set the select switch to the "CONTROL" position

The monitor lamp (red) illuminates

Operate the vehicle in the "2" range at 23 km/h (14 mph).

The monitor lamp (red) doesn't illuminate

Malfunction in lock-up torque converter system

The lock-up torque converter system operates correctly

Operate the vehicle in the "D" range at 45 km/h (28 mph).

Proceed to Test 3

Operate the vehicle in the "D" range at 100 km/h (63 mph)

MITSUBISHI KM170, KM171 & KM172 (Cont.)

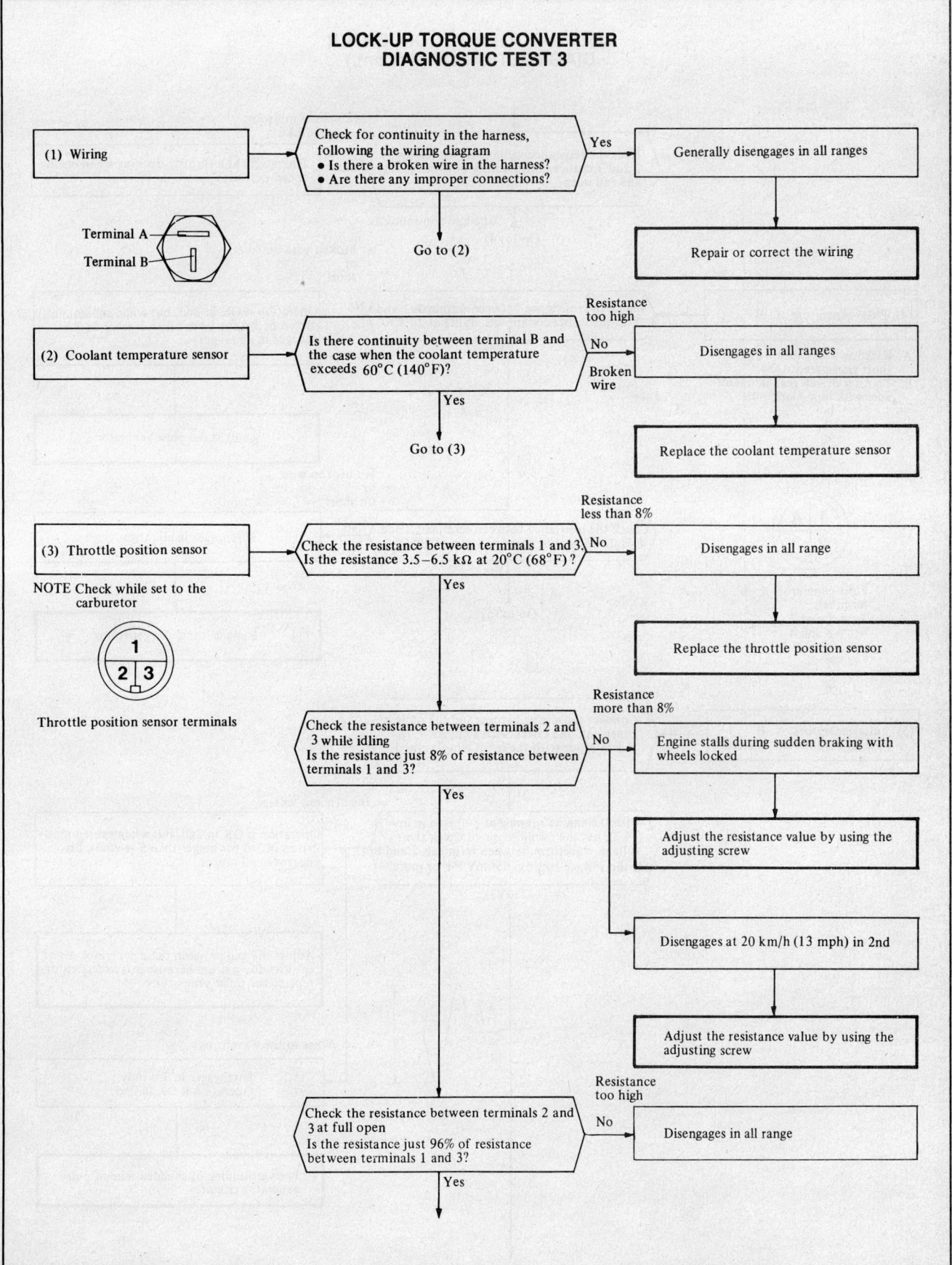

**LOCK-UP TORQUE CONVERTER
DIAGNOSTIC TEST 3**

(1) Wiring → Check for continuity in the harness, following the wiring diagram
● Is there a broken wire in the harness?
● Are there any improper connections?

— Yes → Generally disengages in all ranges → Repair or correct the wiring

Go to (2)

Terminal A
Terminal B

(2) Coolant temperature sensor → Is there continuity between terminal B and the case when the coolant temperature exceeds 60°C (140°F)?

Resistance too high
No
Broken wire
→ Disengages in all ranges → Replace the coolant temperature sensor

Yes

Go to (3)

(3) Throttle position sensor → Check the resistance between terminals 1 and 3. Is the resistance 3.5–6.5 kΩ at 20°C (68°F)?

NOTE Check while set to the carburetor

Throttle position sensor terminals

Resistance less than 8%
No
→ Disengages in all range → Replace the throttle position sensor

Yes

Check the resistance between terminals 2 and 3 while idling
Is the resistance just 8% of resistance between terminals 1 and 3?

Resistance more than 8%
No
→ Engine stalls during sudden braking with wheels locked → Adjust the resistance value by using the adjusting screw → Disengages at 20 km/h (13 mph) in 2nd → Adjust the resistance value by using the adjusting screw

Yes

Check the resistance between terminals 2 and 3 at full open
Is the resistance just 96% of resistance between terminals 1 and 3?

Resistance too high
No
→ Disengages in all range

Yes

Automatic Transmissions
MITSUBISHI KM170, KM171 & KM172 (Cont.)

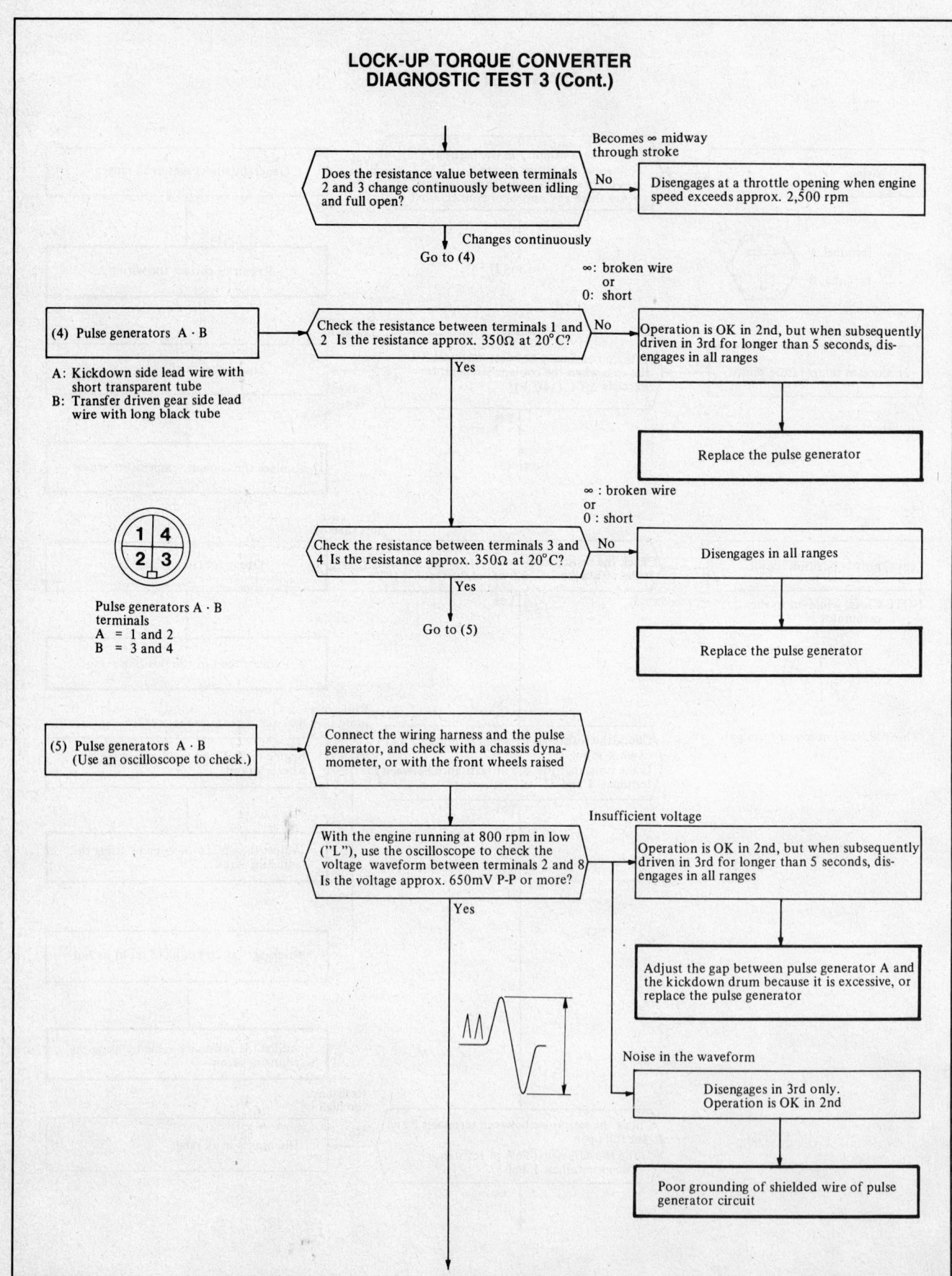

**LOCK-UP TORQUE CONVERTER
DIAGNOSTIC TEST 3 (Cont.)**

Does the resistance value between terminals 2 and 3 change continuously between idling and full open?

Becomes ∞ midway through stroke — No → Disengages at a throttle opening when engine speed exceeds approx. 2,500 rpm

Changes continuously
Go to (4)

(4) Pulse generators A · B

A: Kickdown side lead wire with short transparent tube
B: Transfer driven gear side lead wire with long black tube

∞: broken wire
or
0: short

Check the resistance between terminals 1 and 2 Is the resistance approx. 350Ω at 20°C?

No → Operation is OK in 2nd, but when subsequently driven in 3rd for longer than 5 seconds, disengages in all ranges → Replace the pulse generator

Yes

Pulse generators A · B terminals
A = 1 and 2
B = 3 and 4

∞ : broken wire
or
0 : short

Check the resistance between terminals 3 and 4 Is the resistance approx. 350Ω at 20°C?

No → Disengages in all ranges → Replace the pulse generator

Yes
Go to (5)

(5) Pulse generators A · B
(Use an oscilloscope to check.)

Connect the wiring harness and the pulse generator, and check with a chassis dynamometer, or with the front wheels raised

With the engine running at 800 rpm in low ("L"), use the oscilloscope to check the voltage waveform between terminals 2 and 8 Is the voltage approx. 650mV P-P or more?

Insufficient voltage → Operation is OK in 2nd, but when subsequently driven in 3rd for longer than 5 seconds, disengages in all ranges → Adjust the gap between pulse generator A and the kickdown drum because it is excessive, or replace the pulse generator

Yes

Noise in the waveform → Disengages in 3rd only. Operation is OK in 2nd → Poor grounding of shielded wire of pulse generator circuit

MITSUBISHI KM170, KM171 & KM172 (Cont.)

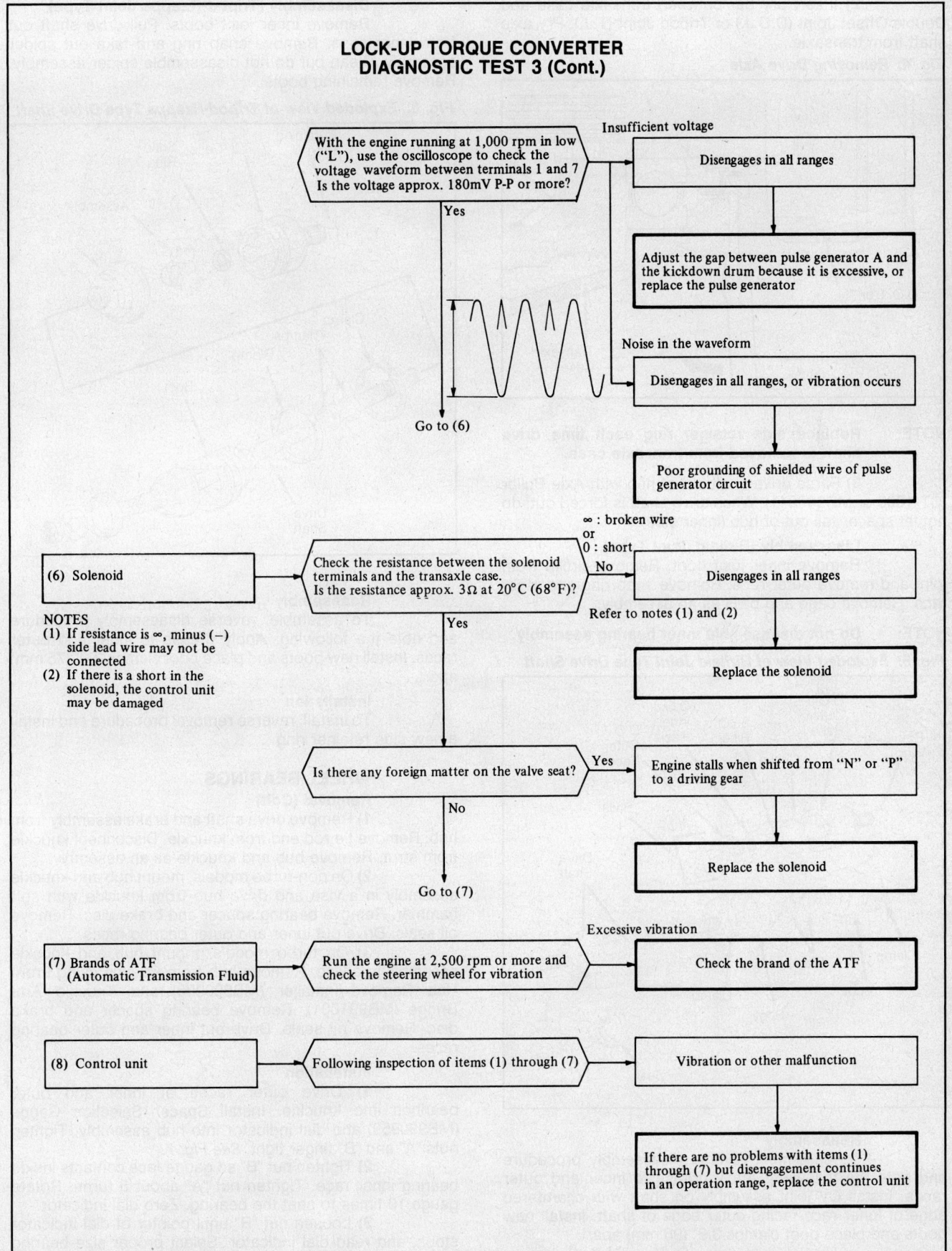

**LOCK-UP TORQUE CONVERTER
DIAGNOSTIC TEST 3 (Cont.)**

With the engine running at 1,000 rpm in low ("L"), use the oscilloscope to check the voltage waveform between terminals 1 and 7 Is the voltage approx. 180mV P-P or more?

Insufficient voltage → Disengages in all ranges → Adjust the gap between pulse generator A and the kickdown drum because it is excessive, or replace the pulse generator

Noise in the waveform → Disengages in all ranges, or vibration occurs → Poor grounding of shielded wire of pulse generator circuit

Yes → Go to (6)

(6) Solenoid → Check the resistance between the solenoid terminals and the transaxle case. Is the resistance approx. 3Ω at 20°C (68°F)?

∞ : broken wire or 0 : short No → Disengages in all ranges

Refer to notes (1) and (2) → Replace the solenoid

NOTES
(1) If resistance is ∞, minus (−) side lead wire may not be connected
(2) If there is a short in the solenoid, the control unit may be damaged

Yes → Is there any foreign matter on the valve seat?

Yes → Engine stalls when shifted from "N" or "P" to a driving gear → Replace the solenoid

No → Go to (7)

(7) Brands of ATF (Automatic Transmission Fluid) → Run the engine at 2,500 rpm or more and check the steering wheel for vibration

Excessive vibration → Check the brand of the ATF

(8) Control unit → Following inspection of items (1) through (7) → Vibration or other malfunction → If there are no problems with items (1) through (7) but disengagement continues in an operation range, replace the control unit

2) Insert pry bar between transaxle case and Double Offset Joint (D.O.J.) or Tripod Joint (T.J.). Pry axle shaft from transaxle.

Fig. 4: Removing Drive Axle

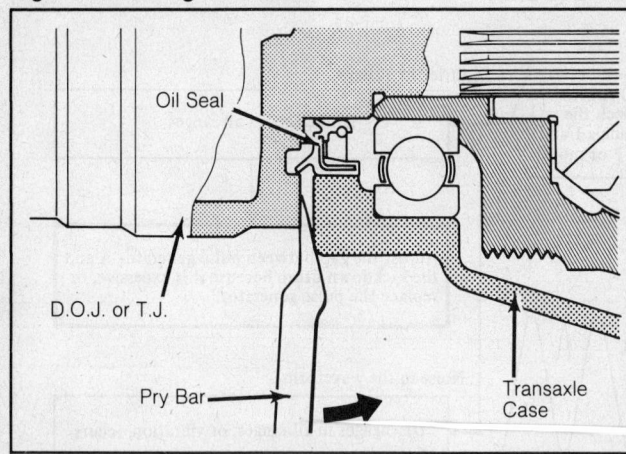

NOTE: **Replace side retainer ring each time drive shaft is removed from transaxle case.**

3) Force drive shaft out of hub with Axle Puller (CT-1003 or MB990241). When drive shaft is forced out, do not let spacer fall out of hub (inner side).

Disassembly (Birfield Joint Type)
Remove inner joint boot. Remove circlip from joint and remove outer race. Remove snap ring and inner race. Remove cage and balls as an assembly.

NOTE: **Do not disassemble inner bearing assembly.**

Fig. 5: Exploded View of Birfield Joint Type Drive Shaft

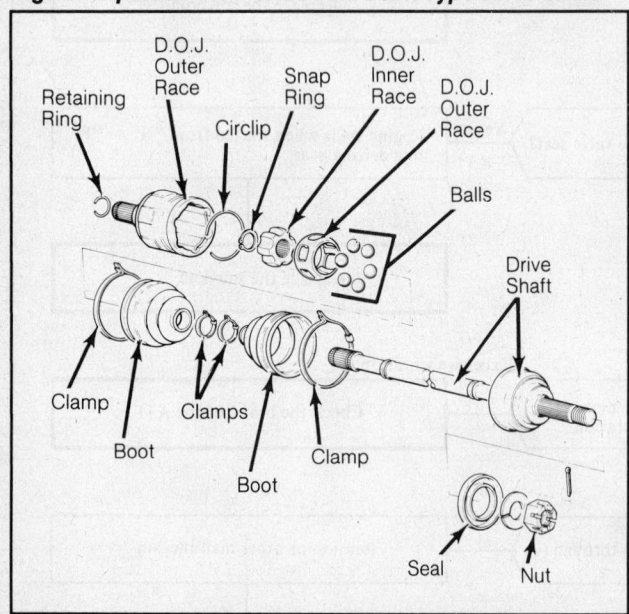

Reassembly
To assemble, reverse disassembly procedure and note the following: Apply grease to inner and outer races. Install CV joint assembly on shaft with chamfered edge of inner race facing outer edge of shaft. Install new boots and place boot clamps 3.5" (90 mm) apart.

Disassembly (Tripod-Rzeppa Joint Type)
Remove inner joint boots. Pull drive shaft out from inner case. Remove snap ring and take out spider assembly. Clean but do not disassemble spider assembly. Remove remaining boots.

Fig. 6: Exploded View of Tripod-Rzeppa Type Drive Shaft

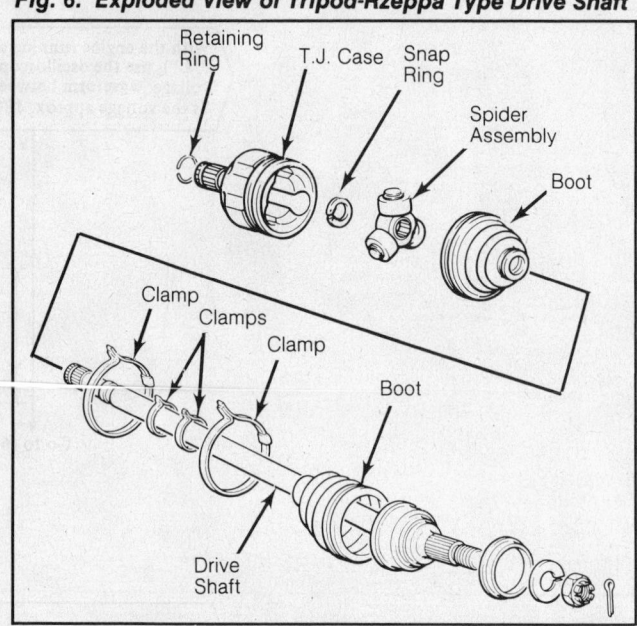

Reassembly
To assemble, reverse disassembly procedure and note the following: Apply grease to inner and outer races. Install new boots and place boot clamps 3.0" (75 mm) apart.

Installation
To install, reverse removal procedure and install a new side retainer ring.

WHEEL BEARINGS
Removal (Colt)
1) Remove drive shaft and brake assembly from hub. Remove tie rod end from knuckle. Disconnect knuckle from strut. Remove hub and knuckle as an assembly.

2) On non-turbo models, mount hub and knuckle assembly in a vise and drive hub from knuckle with soft hammer. Remove bearing spacer and brake disc. Remove oil seals. Drive out inner and outer bearing races.

3) On turbo models, mount hub and knuckle assembly in a vise. Remove hub from knuckle using Front Hub Remover/Installer (MB990998) and Knuckle Arm Bridge (MB991001). Remove bearing spacer and brake disc. Remove oil seals. Drive out inner and outer bearing races.

Installation
1) Drive outer races of inner and outer bearings into knuckle. Install Spacer Selection Gauge (MB990959) and dial indicator into hub assembly. Tighten nuts "A" and "B" finger tight. See Fig. 7.

2) Tighten nut "B" so gauge face contacts inside bearing inner race. Tighten nut "A" about 5 turns. Rotate gauge 10 times to seat the bearing. Zero dial indicator.

3) Loosen nut "B" until pointer of dial indicator stops, and read dial indicator. Select proper size bearing spacer according to the following table.

Fig. 7: Installing Gauge to Measure Bearing Spacer Selection on Colt

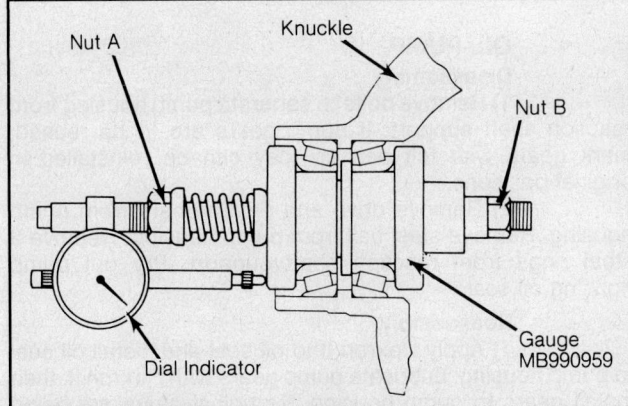

COLT WHEEL BEARING SPACER SELECTION

Dial Indicator Reading In. (mm)	Bearing Spacer Size In. (mm)	I.D. Color
.020-.024 (.54-.60)	.2212 (5.62)	Lt. Blue
.024-.026 (.60-.66)	.2236 (5.68)	Pink
.026-.028 (.66-.72)	.2260 (5.74)	Green
.028-.031 (.72-.78)	.2283 (5.80)	Red
.031-.033 (.78-.84)	.2307 (5.86)	White
.033-.035 (.84-.90)	.2330 (5.92)	None
.035-.038 (.90-.96)	.2354 (5.98)	Yellow
.038-.040 (.96-1.02)	.2378 (6.04)	Blue
.040-.042 (1.02-1.08)	.2402 (6.10)	Orange
.042-.045 (1.08-1.14)	.2425 (6.16)	Lt. Green
.045-.047 (1.14-1.20)	.2449 (6.22)	Brown
.047-.050 (1.20-1.26)	.2472 (6.28)	Gray
.050-.052 (1.26-1.32)	.2496 (6.34)	Navy Blue
.052-.054 (1.32-1.38)	.2520 (6.40)	Vermilion

4) Remove gauge, dial indicator and bearing inner races from knuckle. Apply grease to knuckle, oil seals and bearings. Mount brake disc to hub and tighten bolts evenly.

5) Install outer wheel bearing, then press in outer oil seal. Hold inner race of outer bearing with Bearing Holder (MB990776-A), then press hub into knuckle.

Removal (Colt Vista, Cordia & Tredia)

1) Remove brake caliper and suspend it with wire. Disconnect lower ball joint from knuckle. Remove strut bar and stabilizer bar from lower control arm. Disconnect tie rod end from knuckle. Remove drive shaft from hub.

2) Remove hub and knuckle as an assembly from strut. Remove hub from knuckle using Removers (MB990998 and MB991001). Mount knuckle in vise. Remove brake disc from hub.

3) Remove outer bearing race from hub using Bearing Removers (MB990330, MB990370 and MB990781). Remove oil seal from knuckle. Using a drift, drive outer race from knuckle.

Installation

1) Check that hub face has an identification mark at each side (4 marks total). Apply grease to outside surface of bearing outer race. Install bearing outer race into knuckle using a drift and sleeve.

2) Install disc to hub and tighten. Apply grease to bearings and inside surface of hub. Place outer bearing inner race into knuckle. Drive oil seal (hub side) into knuckle. Lubricate oil seal lip and hub contacting surface with grease.

3) Place inner bearing into knuckle. Tighten hub to knuckle. Rotate hub to seat bearing. Measure total preload. If total preload is zero, measure hub axial play.

HUB BEARING TOTAL PRELOAD

Application	INCH Lbs. (N.m)
Colt Vista, Cordia & Tredia	11.3 (1.3) Max.

HUB AXIAL PLAY

Application	In. (mm)
Colt Vista, Cordia & Tredia	.004 (.1) Max.

4) If total preload and hub axial play are incorrect, hub and/or knuckle are incorrectly installed. Remove, inspect and reinstall bearing, hub and knuckle assemblies.

5) Apply grease to bearing and inside of knuckle. Drive oil seal (drive shaft side) into knuckle until it contacts bearing outer race. Apply grease to oil seal lip. To complete installation, reverse removal procedure.

REMOVAL & INSTALLATION

See appropriate AUTOMATIC TRANSMISSION REMOVAL article in DOMESTIC GENERAL SERVICING section.

TORQUE CONVERTER

NOTE: Torque converter is a sealed unit and cannot be disassembled. Replace if defective.

TRANSAXLE DISASSEMBLY

1) Remove torque converter, speedometer pinion adapter, manual control lever and inhibitor switch. Attach dial indicator to measure input shaft end play. Record end play measurement.

2) Remove oil pan and filter. Disconnect throttle cable. Remove valve body, being careful that manual shift valve does not fall out of valve body.

NOTE: Low-reverse brake clutch "O" ring is attached to valve body with petroleum jelly. Be careful not to misposition seal when removing or installing valve body.

3) Remove throttle cable, accumulator and spring, being careful not to damage cable or retainer end.

4) Remove transfer shaft cover then attach dial indicator to measure transfer shaft end play. Record measurement. Rotate transaxle assembly so converter housing is up and remove converter housing.

5) Remove oil pump bolts and install pump Remover (MD998333) into pump removing holes (located in pump housing). Pump may tilt up (side "B") when removing. If so, tap on pump side "A" with a soft mallet. *See Fig. 8.*

Fig. 8: Removing Oil Pump from Transaxle Housing

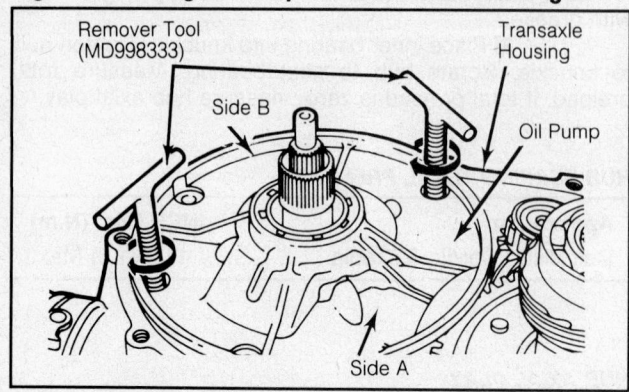

Pull pump straight up.

6) Remove differential assembly, then remove fiber thrust washer from front clutch assembly. Remove front clutch assembly and remove fiber thrust washer, 2 metal thrust races and 1 needle bearing. Remove rear clutch assembly, thrust washer and needle bearing. Remove clutch hub, 2 thrust washers and needle bearing. Remove kickdown drum and band.

7) Check height of planetary gear set. Long pinion should be same height as reverse sun gear. Remove center support bolts, then center support. *See Fig. 9.* Remove reverse sun gear and forward sun gear as an assembly. Remove planetary carrier assembly, thrust bearing and race.

Fig. 9: Center Support Bolt Location

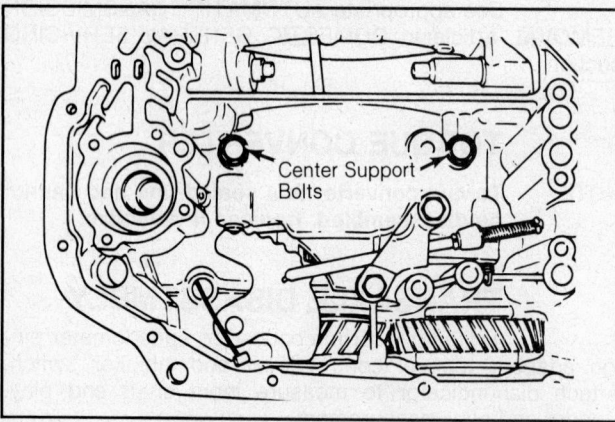

Bolt head has mark "8" on top.

8) Rotate transaxle assembly. Remove idler shaft lock plate, idler shaft and idler gear. Remove 2 bearing inner races and spacer from inside transaxle case.

NOTE: **For reassembly reference, note that machined groove in gear faces away from torque converter.**

9) Remove bearing cover and outer snap ring. Remove annulus gear bearing snap ring, then remove annulus gear, output flange, transfer drive gear and bearing as an assembly.

10) Remove transfer rear end snap ring. Use a brass drift to drive transfer shaft out toward engine mounting surface. Remove snap ring from transaxle case, then remove bearing inner and outer races.

COMPONENT DISASSEMBLY & REASSEMBLY

OIL PUMP
Disassembly

1) Remove bolts to separate pump housing from reaction shaft support. If pump gears are to be reused, mark gears with felt pen so they can be reinstalled in original positions.

2) Remove drive and driven gears from pump housing. Remove steel ball from pump housing. Remove 2 steel rings from reaction shaft support. Pry out pump housing oil seal.

Reassembly

1) Apply Dexron II to oil seal and install oil seal to pump housing. Lubricate pump gears with Dexron II, then install gears to pump housing. If original gears are being reinstalled, install them in original positions using marks made during disassembly.

2) Make the following measurements of pump gears to pump housing: driven gear-to-pump housing clearance, driven gear-to-crescent clearance, driven gear side clearance, drive gear-to-crescent clearance and drive gear side clearance. If clearances are incorrect, replace components as necessary.

OIL PUMP CLEARANCES

Application	In. (mm)
Driven Gear-to-Housing	.003-.006 (.08-.15)
Driven Gear-to-Crescent	.004-.009 (.11-.24)
Driven Gear Side Clearance	.001-.002 (.025-.05)
Drive Gear-to-Crescent	.009-.013 (.24-.34)
Drive Gear Side Clearance	.001-.002 (.025-.05)

3) Install steel ball in pump housing, then install 2 seal rings (coated with Dexron II) to reaction shaft support. Place reaction shaft support to pump housing, then tighten bolts finger tight.

4) Install Guide Pin (MD998336) and Pump Band (MD998335 or C-3759) to assembled pump, then tighten pump bolts to 90-102 INCH Lbs. (10-12 N.m). *See Fig. 10.*

5) After tightening bolts, make sure pump gear turns freely. If not, disassemble and recheck reassembly procedures and clearances. Install a new large "O" ring to outside circumference of pump and lubricate "O" ring with petroleum jelly.

Fig. 10: Assembling Oil Pump

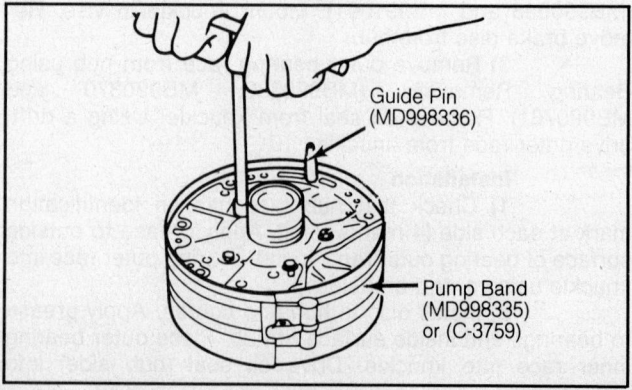

Tighten all bolts evenly.

Automatic Transmissions
MITSUBISHI KM170, KM171 & KM172 (Cont.)

FRONT CLUTCH
Disassembly

1) Remove snap ring, then remove 3 steel plates and 2 lined plates. If plates are to be reused, keep them in same order and direction (as removed) for reassembly. *See Fig. 11.*

2) Compress return spring, remove snap ring, spring retainer and return spring. Remove piston from front clutch. Remove "D" section rings from outside of piston and front clutch retainer.

Fig. 11: Front Clutch Components

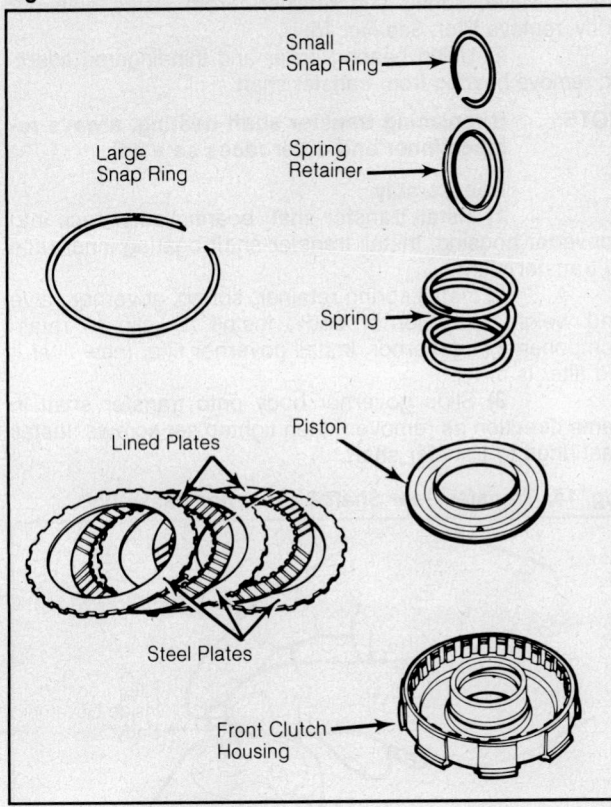

Small Snap Ring

Large Snap Ring

Spring Retainer

Spring

Lined Plates

Piston

Steel Plates

Front Clutch Housing

Reassembly

1) Install "D" section rings to piston and front clutch retainer (round side of ring facing out), then lubricate rings with Dexron II. Push piston into front clutch retainer by hand, being careful not to damage rings.

2) Compress spring and spring retainer to clutch retainer. Install small snap ring to hold spring to clutch retainer. Install 3 steel plates and 2 lined plates, starting with steel plate and alternating with a lined plate. If old plates are reinstalled, install them in same order and direction as removed.

NOTE: Soak new lined plates in Dexron II for at least 2 hours before installation.

3) Install large snap ring to clutch retainer and measure clearance between snap ring and steel plate. Clearance should be .016-.024" (.4-.6 mm). If clearance is incorrect, install a selective snap ring to give correct clearance. Snap rings are available in thicknesses from .063" (1.6 mm) to .118" (3.0 mm) in .008" (.2 mm) increments.

REAR CLUTCH
Disassembly

1) Remove large snap ring, reaction plate, 2 lined plates, clutch plate and pressure plate from rear clutch retainer. If plates are to be reused, keep them in same order and direction (as removed) for reassembly.

2) Remove seal ring, small snap ring and thrust race. Use a press to compress piston, then remove waved snap ring. Release pressure from press and remove waved snap ring, return spring and piston. Remove 2 "D" section rings from piston.

Reassembly

1) Install "D" section rings to piston with round side facing out. Lubricate rings with Dexron II and install piston in rear clutch retainer by hand. Be careful not to damage rings.

2) Install return spring with waved snap ring to clutch retainer. Use a press to compress return spring until waved snap ring seats in groove of clutch retainer. Install pressure plate, lined plate, clutch plate, lined plate and reaction plate. *See Fig. 12.*

Fig. 12: Rear Clutch Components

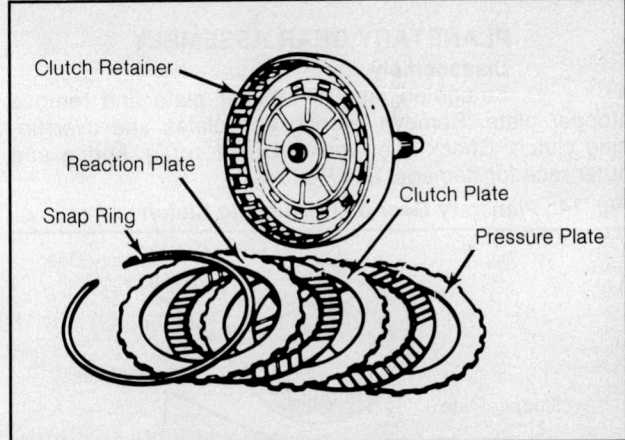

Clutch Retainer

Reaction Plate

Snap Ring

Clutch Plate

Pressure Plate

NOTE: Soak new lined plates in Dexron II for at least 2 hours before installation.

3) Install large snap ring to clutch retainer and measure clearance between reaction plate and snap ring. Clearance should be .012-.020" (.3-.5 mm). If clearance is incorrect, selective snap rings are available in thicknesses from .063" (1.6 mm) to .118" (3.0 mm) in .008" (.2 mm) increments. Install thrust race, small snap ring and new seal ring.

LOW-REVERSE BRAKE
Disassembly

1) Remove snap ring. Remove reaction plate, 4 lined plates, 3 steel plates and the pressure plates. If plates are to be reused, keep them in same order and direction (as removed) for reassembly.

2) Compress piston and remove piston snap ring, then remove return spring and waved spring. Remove piston, then remove "D" section rings from piston.

Reassembly

1) Install "D" section rings (round side out) to piston. Lubricate rings with Dexron II and install piston by hand, being careful not to damage rings. Install waved spring and return spring. Compress springs and install snap ring. Install pressure plate, then install plates starting with a lined plate and alternating with steel plates, ending with reaction plate. *See Fig. 13.*

2) Install large snap ring and measure clearance between reaction plate and snap ring. Clearance should be

.031-.040" (.8-1.0 mm). If clearance is incorrect, selective snap rings are available from .063" (1.6 mm) to .118" (3.0 mm) in .008" (.2 mm) increments.

Fig. 13: Low-Reverse Brake Components

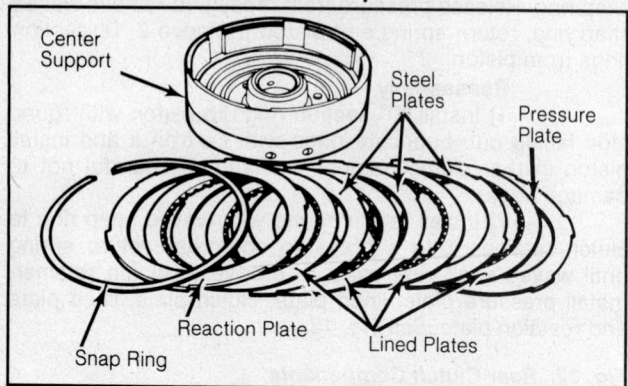

PLANETARY GEAR ASSEMBLY
Disassembly
Straighten tabs of stopper plate and remove stopper plate. Remove bearing end plates and overrunning clutch. Check overrunning clutch sprag, spring and outer race for damage. See Fig. 14.

Fig. 14: Planetary Gear & Overrunning Clutch

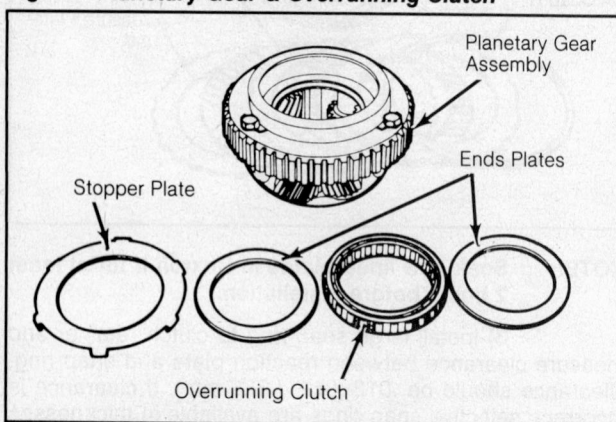

Reassembly
Install end plate to overrunning clutch. Install overrunning clutch to planetary gear assembly with arrow (stamped on outside of overrunning clutch) pointing toward planetary gears. Install end plate, then stopper plate. Bend tabs of stopper plate to secure stopper plate to planetary gear assembly.

ANNULUS GEAR, OUTPUT FLANGE & TRANSFER DRIVE GEAR
Disassembly
Remove snap ring from rear of output flange. Using a bearing puller, remove bearing, transfer drive gear and bearing. Remove snap ring and separate annulus gear from output flange.

NOTE: Annulus gear and output flange are a matched set. If damaged, replace both.

Reassembly
Install annulus gear to output flange and install snap ring. Using a bearing installer, install bearing, transfer

drive gear (grooved side up) and bearing. Select largest size snap ring that will fit in groove and install snap ring. Snap ring-to-bearing clearance should be 0-.002" (0-.06 mm). Snap rings are available from .074" (1.88 mm) to .081" (2.06 mm) in .002" (.06 mm) increments.

TRANSFER SHAFT & GOVERNOR
Disassembly
1) Remove seal rings from transfer shaft. Loosen governor set screws and slide governor off transfer shaft. Remove "E" clip from governor body, then remove weight, valve, spring and retainer. From inside governor body, remove filter. See Fig. 15.

2) Using bearing puller and thin-fingered adapter, remove bearing from transfer shaft.

NOTE: If replacing transfer shaft bearing, always replace inner and outer races as a set.

Reassembly
1) Install transfer shaft bearing outer race into converter housing. Install transfer shaft bearing inner race to transfer shaft.

2) Install spring retainer, spring, governor valve and weight to governor body. Install "E" clip to retain components in governor. Install governor filter (new filter if old filter is dirty).

3) Slide governor body onto transfer shaft in same direction as removed, then tighten set screws. Install seal rings to transfer shaft.

Fig. 15: Transfer Gear Shaft & Governor Assembly

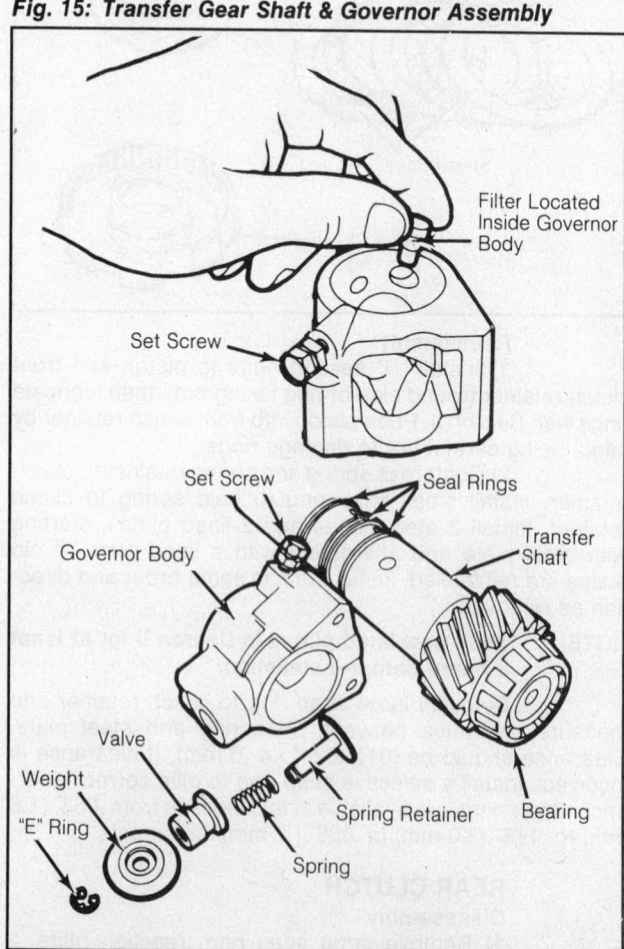

Note location of governor filter.

Automatic Transmissions

MITSUBISHI KM170, KM171 & KM172 (Cont.)

Fig. 16: Exploded View of Valve Body & Components

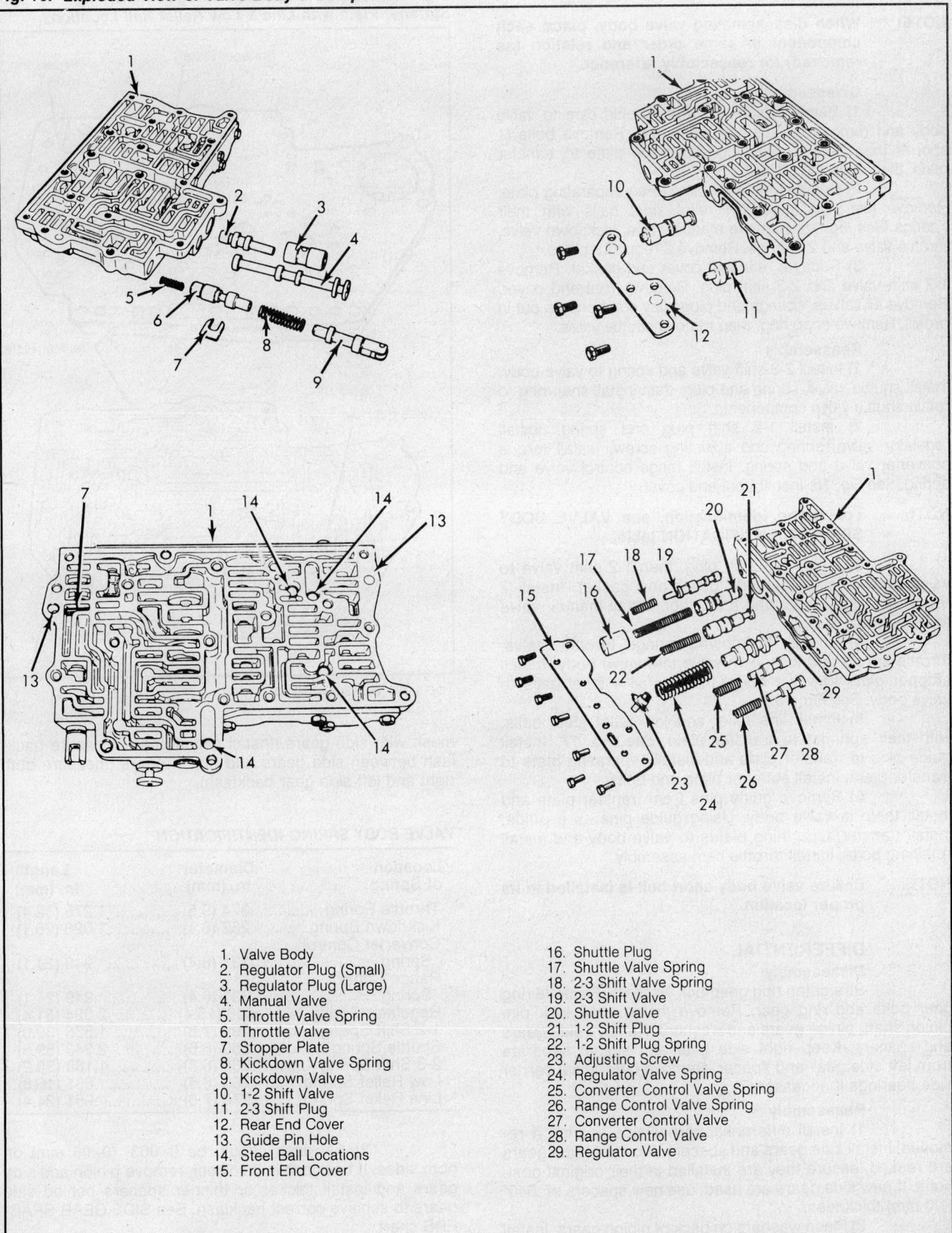

1. Valve Body
2. Regulator Plug (Small)
3. Regulator Plug (Large)
4. Manual Valve
5. Throttle Valve Spring
6. Throttle Valve
7. Stopper Plate
8. Kickdown Valve Spring
9. Kickdown Valve
10. 1-2 Shift Valve
11. 2-3 Shift Plug
12. Rear End Cover
13. Guide Pin Hole
14. Steel Ball Locations
15. Front End Cover
16. Shuttle Plug
17. Shuttle Valve Spring
18. 2-3 Shift Valve Spring
19. 2-3 Shift Valve
20. Shuttle Valve
21. 1-2 Shift Plug
22. 1-2 Shift Plug Spring
23. Adjusting Screw
24. Regulator Valve Spring
25. Converter Control Valve Spring
26. Range Control Valve Spring
27. Converter Control Valve
28. Range Control Valve
29. Regulator Valve

VALVE BODY

NOTE: **When disassembling valve body, place each component in same order and relation (as removed) for reassembly reference.**

Disassembly

1) Remove bolts securing throttle cam to valve body and remove throttle cam assembly. Remove bolts (1 shorter than others) attaching separating plate to transfer plate, then separate plates.

2) Remove stiffener plate, then separating plate. Remove line relief and low relief steel balls with their springs. See Fig. 16. Remove manual valve, kickdown valve, throttle valve and 2 springs. Remove 2 regulator plugs.

3) Remove rear end cover and gasket. Remove 1-2 shift valve and 2-3 shift plug. Remove front end cover. Remove all valves, springs and plugs (lay components out in order). Remove snap ring, then remove shuttle valve.

Reassembly

1) Install 2-3 shift valve and spring to valve body. Install shuttle valve, spring and plug, then install snap ring to retain shuttle valve components.

2) Install 1-2 shift plug and spring. Install regulator valve, spring and adjusting screw. Install torque converter valve and spring. Install range control valve and spring. See Fig. 16. Install front end cover.

NOTE: **For spring identification, see VALVE BODY SPRING IDENTIFICATION table.**

3) Install 2-3 shift plug, then 1-2 shift valve to valve body. Install rear end cover and gasket. Install 2 regulator plugs (small one first), then install manual valve to valve body.

4) Install kickdown spring, throttle valve, throttle spring and kickdown valve into valve body. Install stopper plate to valve body, then install 4 steel balls to valve body. See Fig. 16.

5) Install line relief and low relief steel balls, with their springs, to transfer plate. See Fig. 17. Install guide pins to transfer plate and install separating plate to transfer plate. Install stiffener plate and bolts.

6) Remove guide pins from transfer plate and install them in valve body. Using guide pins as a guide, install transfer/separating plates to valve body and install retaining bolts. Install throttle cam assembly.

NOTE: **Ensure valve body short bolt is installed in its proper location.**

DIFFERENTIAL

Disassembly

Straighten ring gear lock washers. Remove ring gear bolts and ring gear. Remove pinion shaft lock pin, pinion shaft, pinion gears and washers. Remove side gears and spacers. Keep right side gear and spacer separate from left side gear and spacer. Remove differential carrier side bearings if necessary.

Reassembly

1) Install differential carrier side bearing if removed. Install side gears and spacers. If original side gears are reused, ensure they are installed in their original positions. If new side gears are used, use new spacers of .040" (1.0 mm) thickness.

2) Place washers on back of pinion gears. Install both pinion gears at same time. Rotate pinion gears to

Fig. 17: Transfer Plate, Separating Plate & Stiffener Plate with Line & Low Relief Ball Locations

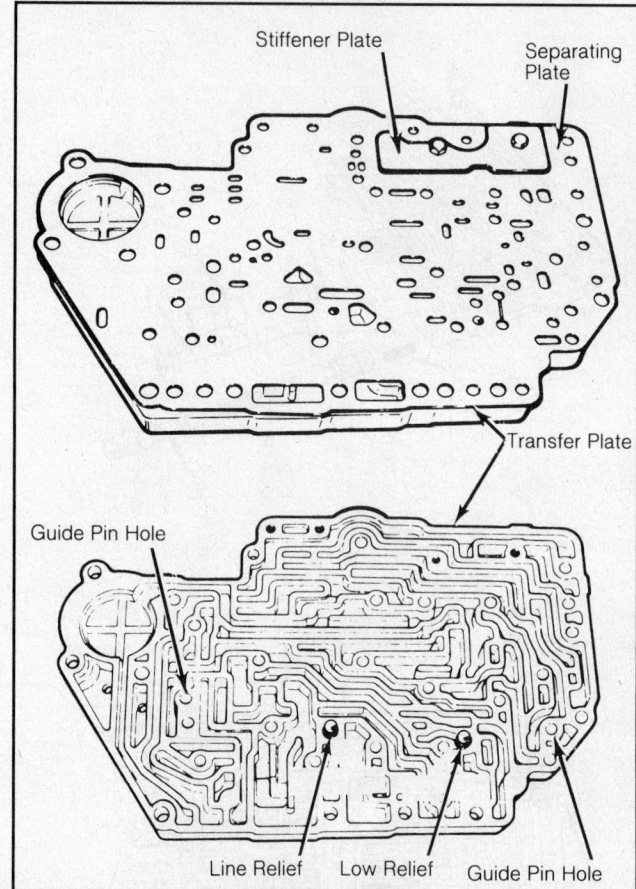

Top view of assembly is shown.

mesh with side gears. Install pinion shaft. Measure backlash between side gears and pinion gears (measure both right and left side gear backlash).

VALVE BODY SPRING IDENTIFICATION

Location of Spring	Diameter In. (mm)	Length In. (mm)
Throttle Spring	.374 (9.5)	1.276 (32.4)
Kickdown Spring	.252 (6.4)	1.028 (26.1)
Converter Control Spring	.331 (8.4)	.949 (24.1)
Range Control Spring	.331 (8.4)	.949 (24.1)
Regulator Spring	.606 (15.4)	2.024 (51.4)
1-2 Shift Spring	.299 (7.6)	1.535 (39.0)
Shuttle Spring	.260 (6.6)	2.343 (59.5)
2-3 Shift Spring	.268 (6.8)	1.189 (30.2)
Low Relief Spring	.260 (6.6)	.661 (16.8)
Line Relief Spring	.276 (7.0)	.961 (24.4)

3) Backlash should be 0-.003" (0-.08 mm) on both sides. If backlash is incorrect, remove pinion and side gears and install thicker or thinner spacers behind side gears to achieve correct backlash. See SIDE GEAR SPACERS chart.

SIDE GEAR SPACERS

Shim Part No.	Thickness In. (mm)
MA180862	.030-.033 (.75-.82)
MA180861	.033-.037 (.82-.92)
MA180860	.037-.040 (.92-1.0)
MA180875	.040-.043 (1.0-1.08)
MA180876	.043-.046 (1.08-1.16)

4) On KM 170 models, install ring gear and pinion shaft lock pin. Install ring gear bolts with new lock washers. Ensure 1 lock washer retains pinion shaft lock pin. Tighten ring gear bolts alternately and bend lock washers along a flat of ring gear bolts. Ensure lock washers are not cracked along bend. *See Fig. 18.*

5) On KM 171 models, install new pinion shaft lock pin. Ensure lock pin does not protrude more than .12" (3.0 mm) from differential case. Install ring gear and tighten bolts alternately.

Fig. 18: Installing Ring Gear Bolts on KM170 Models

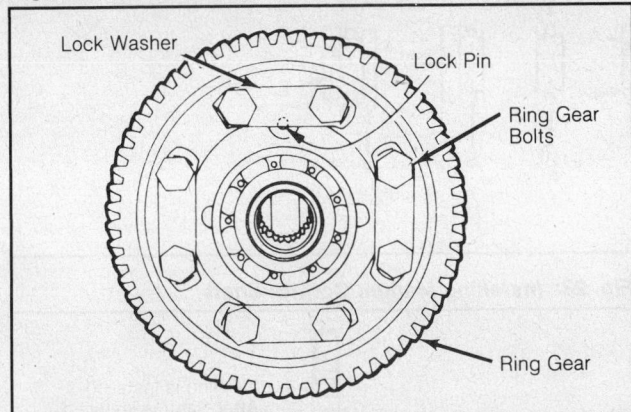

Tighten all bolts alternately.

TRANSAXLE REASSEMBLY

NOTE: Handle all parts carefully to avoid damaging bearing and mating surfaces. Lubricate all parts with Dexron II before reassembly. Gaskets and thrust washers may be held in place with petroleum jelly.

1) Place transaxle case on bench with oil pan mounting surface up. Install annulus gear and output flange assembly (with bearings and transfer drive gear attached) to inside of transaxle case. Install snap ring to bearing.

2) Install bearing outer races, inner races and spacer (in correct direction) to transfer idle gear. *See Fig. 19.* Install new "O" ring to idler shaft.

3) Install transfer idle gear assembly to transaxle case. Insert idler shaft from outside case, then screw in and tighten idler shaft to transaxle case.

4) Using a torque wrench and socket, measure output flange turning torque (preload). *See Fig. 20.* Preload should be 7 INCH Lbs. (0.8 N.m). If preload is incorrect, tighten or loosen transfer idler shaft until correct specification is obtained.

5) With preload adjusted correctly, install idler shaft lock plate and tighten bolt. Install new "O" ring to groove around output flange, then install bearing retainer.

Fig. 19: Installing Transfer Gear, Bearings & Spacer

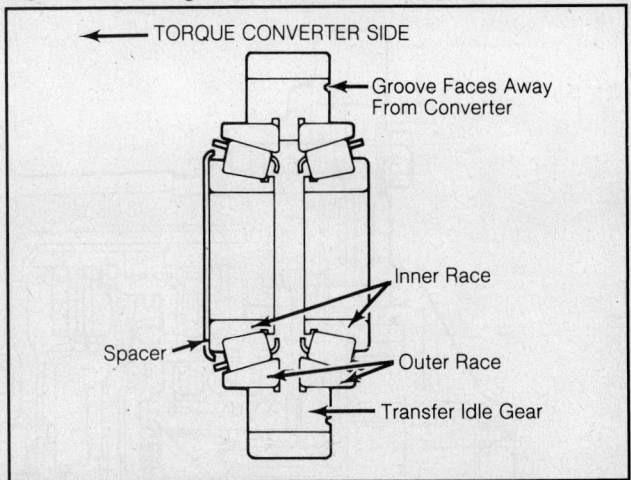

Fig. 20: Measuring Output Flange Preload

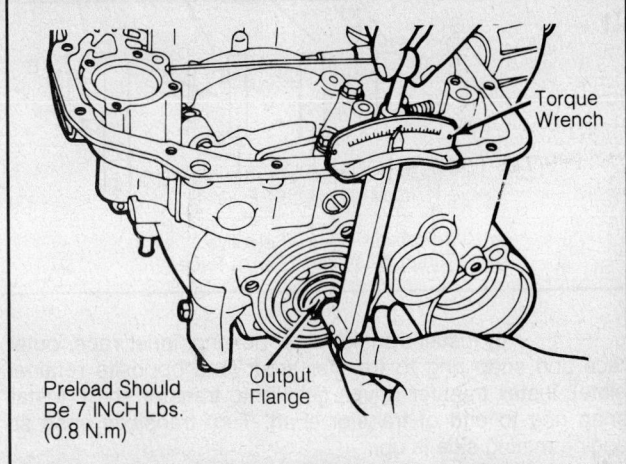

Rotate bearing several times to check preload.

Install transfer shaft, with governor, into case. Install Transfer Shaft Retainer Plate (MD998351) to converter housing mating surface (to retain transfer shaft). *See Fig. 21.*

Fig. 21: Transfer Shaft Retainer Plate

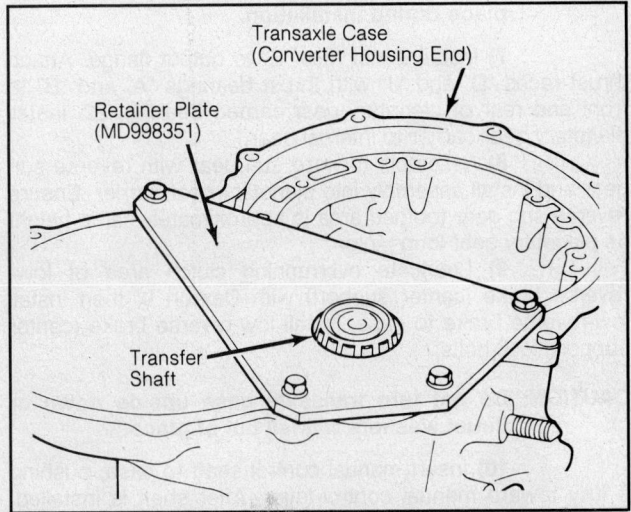

Fig. 22: *Cross-Sectional View Showing Locations of Thrust Bearings, Thrust Races & Thrust Washers*

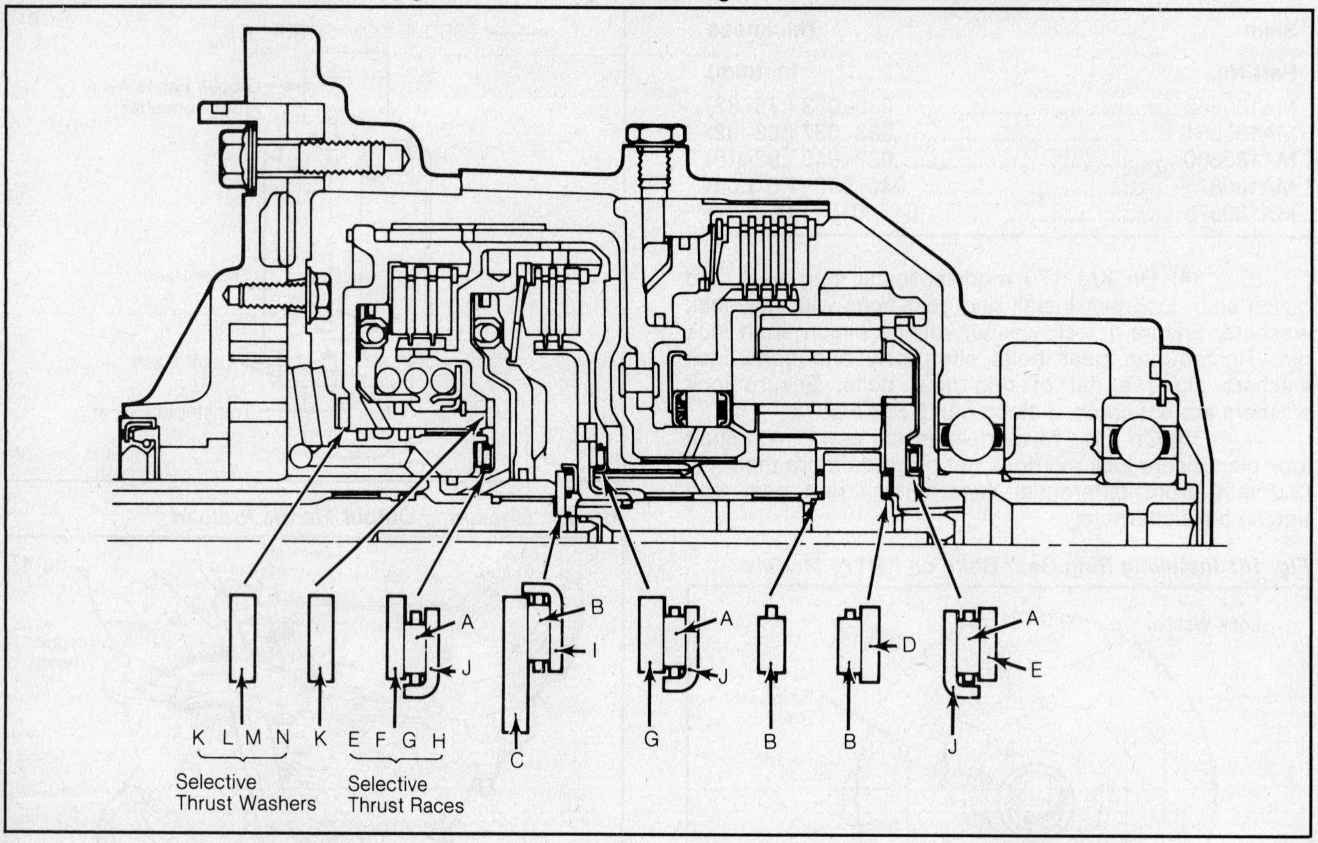

6) Install transfer shaft bearing, inner race, outer race and snap ring to transfer shaft (end opposite retainer plate). Install transfer driven gear onto transfer shaft. Install snap ring to end of transfer shaft. Turn transaxle case so engine mating side is up.

NOTE: See Fig. 22 for location of thrust bearings, thrust races and thrust washers. See THRUST BEARING, THRUST RACE & THRUST WASHER DIMENSIONS table for components available.

NOTE: Coat thrust races, thrust bearings and thrust washers with petroleum jelly to hold them in place during installation.

7) Install thrust race "E" to output flange. Attach thrust races "D" and "J" with thrust bearings "A" and "B" to front and rear of planetary gear carrier. *See Fig. 22.* Install planetary gear carrier to internal gear.

8) Assemble forward sun gear with reverse sun gear and install assembly into planetary gear carrier. Ensure reverse sun gear toothed area is approximately same height as planetary gear long pinion.

9) Lubricate overrunning clutch area of low-reverse brake (center support) with Dexron II, then install low-reverse brake to case. Install low-reverse brake (center support) lock bolts.

CAUTION: Do not turn transaxle case upside down or thrust washers will fall out of place.

10) Insert manual control shaft to case, pushing it fully toward manual control lever. After shaft is installed, install a new "O" ring to manual control shaft. *See Fig. 23.*

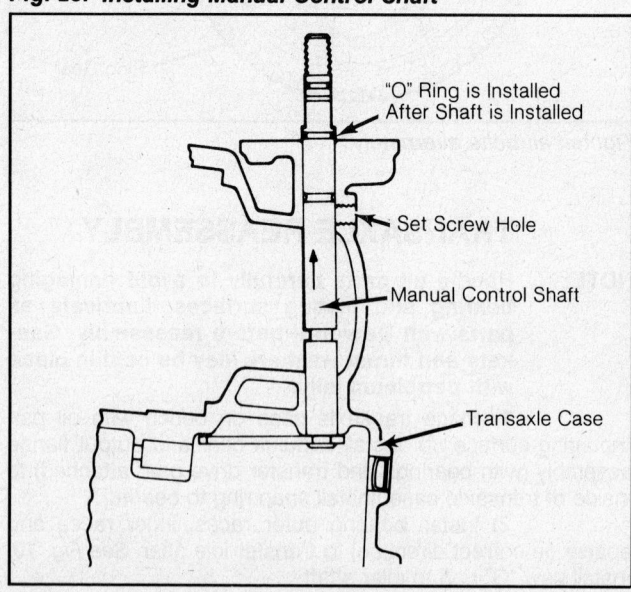

Fig. 23: *Installing Manual Control Shaft*

NOTE: If "O" ring is installed before shaft is pushed into case, "O" ring will be damaged by set screw hole.

11) Pull manual control shaft back into case until set screw groove is aligned with set screw hole and install set screw with gasket. Install detent ball and spring when shaft is pulled back to install set screw. *See Fig. 24.*

THRUST BEARING, THRUST RACE AND THRUST WASHER DIMENSIONS

Component I.D. Mark	Outside Diameter In. (mm)	Inside Diameter In. (mm)	Thickness In. (mm)
Thrust Bearing			
A	1.894 (48.1)	1.417 (36.0)	.....
B	1.437 (36.5)	.874 (22.2)	.....
Thrust Race			
C	1.378 (35.0)	.496 (12.6)	.094 (2.4)
D	1.457 (35.0)	.925 (23.5)	.031 (.8)
E	1.925 (48.9)	1.457 (37.0)	.031 (.8)
F	1.925 (48.9)	1.457 (37.0)	.047 (1.2)
G	1.925 (48.9)	1.457 (37.0)	.063 (1.6)
H	1.925 (48.9)	1.457 (37.0)	.080 (2.0)
I	1.496 (38.0)	.925 (23.5)	.....
J	1.482 (47.0)	1.354 (34.4)	.....
Thrust Washer			
K	2.756 (70.0)	2.193 (55.7)	.071 (1.8)
L	2.756 (70.0)	2.193 (55.7)	.087 (2.2)
M	2.756 (70.0)	2.193 (55.7)	.102 (2.6)
N	2.756 (70.0)	2.193 (55.7)	.118 (3.0)

Fig. 24: Installing Set Screw, Detent Ball & Spring to Manual Control Shaft

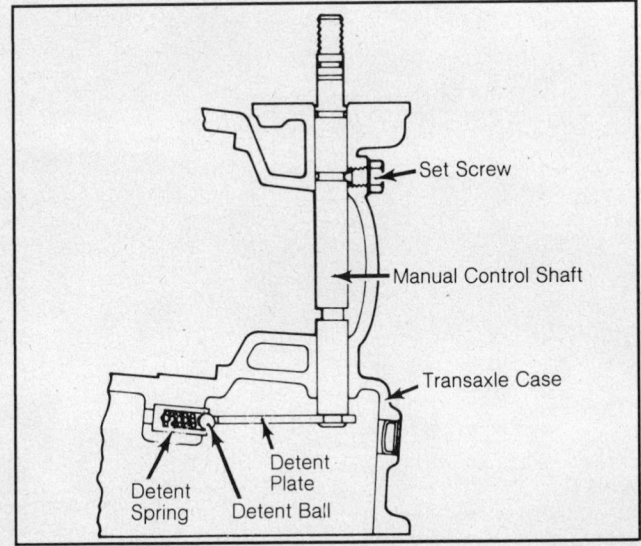

12) Install kickdown servo spring, piston and sleeve into case. Install large and small "D" section rings to piston and a new "O" ring to sleeve before installing piston. Using spring compressor, compress piston spring and install snap ring.

13) Install kickdown band. Attach band ends to end of anchor rod and servo piston adjusting screw. Install kickdown drum, meshing splines with reverse sun gear. Place kickdown band on kickdown drum and tighten kickdown servo adjusting screw to hold band in place.

14) Install thrust race "J" and a thrust bearing "A" to kickdown drum. See Fig. 22. Install thrust races "I" and "G" to both ends of clutch hub. Attach thrust bearing "B" to engine side of thrust race and install clutch hub to forward sun gear splines.

15) Install rear clutch assembly. Install thrust washer "K" to rear clutch retainer. Install thrust race "J" and a thrust bearing "A" to rear clutch retainer. Install front clutch assembly and differential assembly. Install a new oil pump gasket and install thrust washer to rear end of oil pump assembly.

16) If end play (measured during disassembly) is not .028-.056" (.7-1.4 mm), install selective thrust race (E,F,G or H) to obtain correct end play. See THRUST BEARING, THRUST RACE and THRUST WASHER DIMENSIONS chart for thrust race thicknesses.

NOTE: If thrust race was replaced with one of a different thickness, also replace thrust washer between oil pump and front clutch. Replacement thrust washer should be .040" (1.0 mm) thicker than thrust race.

17) Install new selected thrust washer, determined in preceding step, to front clutch. Install new "O" ring to oil pump groove and lubricate "O" ring with Dexron II. Install oil pump and tighten mounting bolts. Be careful thrust washer does not drop out of place. Recheck input shaft end play.

18) Ensure transfer shaft end play (measured during disassembly) is .001" (.025 mm). If end play is incorrect, install selective spacer. Spacers are available from .072" (1.84 mm) to .106" (2.68 mm) in .001" (.025 mm) increments. If installing selective spacer, remove bearing outer race from transaxle case and replace old spacer with new selective spacer. Reinstall bearing outer race.

19) Place spacer (removed during disassembly) on differential bearing outer race. Install new gasket to transaxle case and install converter housing. Check differential case end play. End play should be 0-.006" (0-.15 mm). Also recheck input shaft and transfer shaft end play. If end play measurements are incorrect, readjust.

20) Install transfer shaft cover and holder. Turn transaxle case so oil pan mounting surface is facing up. Install parking sprag rod to detent plate of manual control shaft. Install parking sprag rod and support. See Fig. 25.

Fig. 25: Installing Parking Sprag Rod & Support

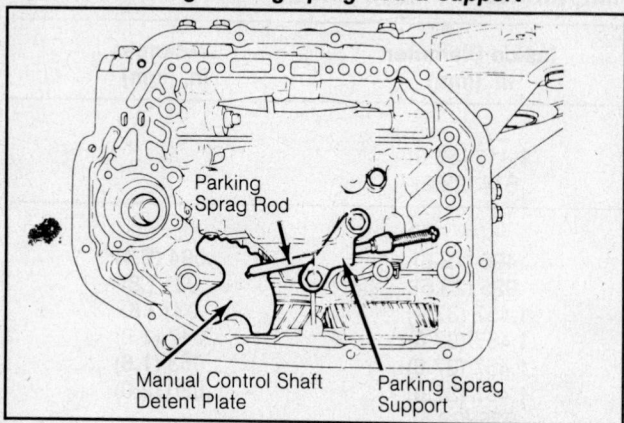

21) Install accumulator piston and spring. Install "O" ring at top center of valve body (brake oil pressure passage). Install valve body to transaxle case, fitting detent plate pin (for manual control shaft) in slot of manual valve. Install and tighten valve body bolts.

22) Insert throttle cable into transaxle case and connect throttle cable inner cable to throttle cam. Install oil filter, oil pan gasket and oil pan. Install drive shaft oil seals to transaxle.

23) Install inhibitor switch and manual lever, then adjust inhibitor switch. Lubricate torque converter surface (where converter slides into oil pump) with Dexron II fluid and carefully install converter, making sure converter meshes with oil pump drive gear.

24) After installing torque converter, measure distance from mating surface of converter housing to torque converter. If measurement is not more than .6" (15 mm), torque converter is not installed completely. Remove converter and check alignment of converter to oil pump.

TIGHTENING SPECIFICATIONS

Application	Ft. Lbs. (N.m)
Axle Shaft Nut	145-188 (196-255)
Center Support (Low-Reverse Brake)	15-19 (20-26)
Differential Carrier-to-Ring Gear	47-54 (64-73)
Drive Plate-to-Converter	26-30 (35-41)
Idler Shaft Lock Plate	15-19 (20-26)
Oil Pump Assembly	11-15 (15-20)
Rear Cover	14-17 (19-23)
Sprag Rod Support Bolts	15-19 (20-26)
Transaxle-to-Engine	
M8 Bolts	21-25 (29-34)
M10 Bolts	31-40 (42-54)
Transaxle-to-Mount Bracket	43-58 (58-78)

NISSAN/DATSUN PULSAR, SENTRA & STANZA

DESCRIPTION

The Sentra (gas), Stanza and Pulsar transaxles (Model RL3F01A) consist primarily of a 3-element hydraulic lock-up torque converter, 2 planetary gear sets and final gear. Desired function of the 2 planetary gear sets is obtained by 2 multiple-disc clutches, a multiple-disc brake, brake band and 1-way clutch.

All models use a hydraulic control system to operate friction elements and automatic shift controls and are equipped with a non-serviceable torque converter. The Sentra diesel transaxle (Model RN3F01A) is the same as the gas models except for a non-lockup torque converter.

The lock-up torque convertor is attached to the crankshaft through a flexible drive plate. This serves to directly couple the turbine runner and pump impeller through the lock-up piston which is controlled by the speed cut valve and lock-up control valve. Heat generated in the torque converter is dissipated by circulating the transaxle fluid through an oil-to-water type cooler in the radiator lower tank.

LUBRICATION & ADJUSTMENT

See appropriate AUTOMATIC TRANSMISSION SERVICING article in IMPORT GENERAL SERVICING section.

SERVICE (IN VEHICLE)

NOTE: The following units can be removed from transaxle without removing transaxle from vehicle: Oil Pan, Valve Body Assembly, Governor Shaft Assembly, Converter Housing Oil Seal and Governor Shaft Assembly. See procedures given in Transmission Disassembly and Transmission Reassembly.

DRIVE SHAFTS

NOTE: Replace the transaxle oil seal whenever either drive shaft is removed.

Removal

1) Raise and support vehicle. Remove wheel and tire. Remove brake caliper assembly and wire aside. Pry cotter pin out of hub. Loosen, but do not remove, wheel hub nut from drive shaft while preventing hub from turning.

2) Using tie rod end-to-steering Knuckle Remover (HT72520000), detach components. Remove lower ball joint from control arm and discard nuts. Drain gear oil from transaxle case. Remove and discard inner drive shaft circlip. Pull inner drive shaft from transaxle.

CAUTION: Do not attempt to remove outer drive shaft from transaxle by pulling apart from inner stub shaft or sliding joint will separate, damaging rubber boot. Replace circlip whenever driveshaft is removed.

3) Using oil seal Remover (ST33290001), remove oil seal(s) from transaxle. Insert a bar or equivalent tool into each side of differential case to prevent dropping of side gear.

4) Remove steering knuckle mount bolts. Remove hub and knuckle, with inner and outer drive shaft, as an assembly. Remove hub nut and pull hub off shaft.

Using Ball Joint Remover (HT72520000), separate lower ball joint from knuckle, if necessary.

Fig. 1: Exploded View of Sentra and Pulsar Front Axle Assembly

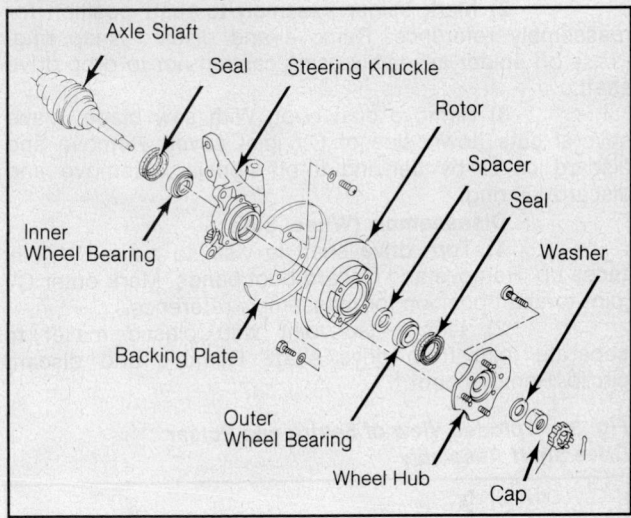

Use caution not to scratch or tear the new transaxle oil seal when replacing either left or right drive shafts.

Fig. 2: Exploded View of Stanza Front Axle Assembly

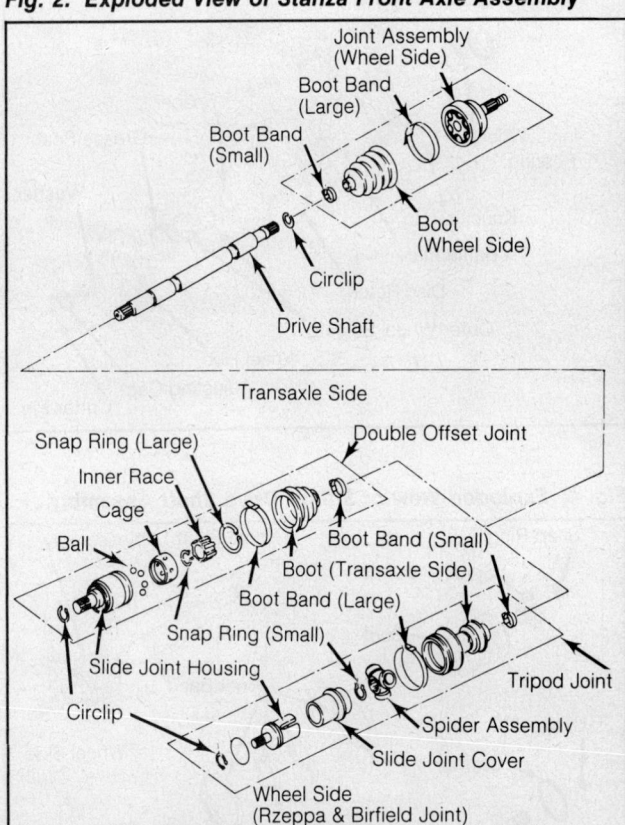

Replace circlips, grease seals, "O" rings, boot bands and snap rings whenever drive shafts are removed.

NOTE: Manufacturer does not recommend disassembly of CV joints. Replace joint assemblies as complete components, if defective.

Disassembly (Transaxle Side)

1) Place drive shaft in soft-jawed vise with inner CV joint facing up. Remove and discard boot bands from inner boot. Remove inner CV joint housing and stub axle from drive shaft.

2) Mark spider assembly-to-shaft position for reassembly reference. Remove and discard snap ring. Press off spider assembly using caution not to drop drive shaft.

3) Remove dust boot. With saw blade, make several cuts down side of CV joint cover. Remove and discard cover by bending it off housing. Remove and discard "O" ring.

Disassembly (Wheel Side)

1) Turn drive shaft in vise so outer CV joint faces up. Remove and discard boot bands. Mark outer CV joint-to-shaft position for reassembly reference.

2) Lightly tap joint with plastic mallet to separate joint from drive shaft. Remove and discard circlip. Remove boot.

Fig. 3: Exploded View of Sentra and Pulsar Drive Shaft Assembly

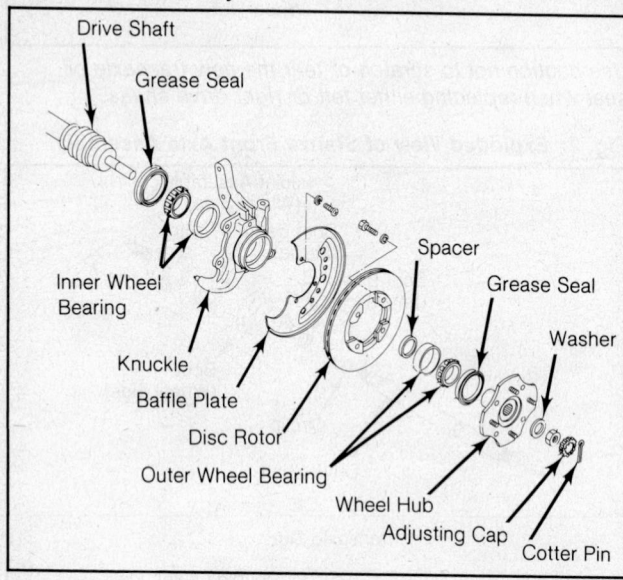

Fig. 4: Exploded View of Stanza Drive Shaft Assembly

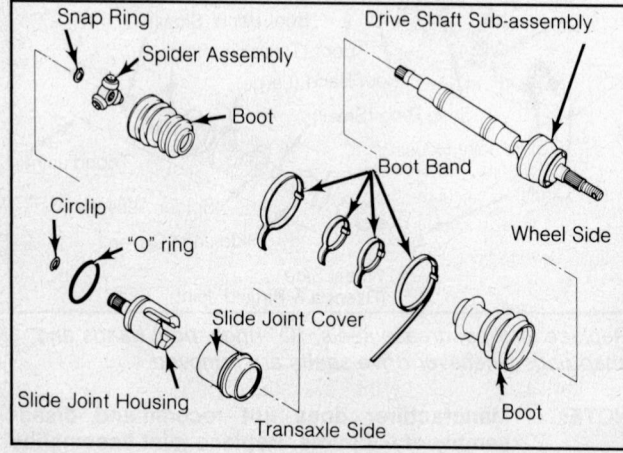

The circlip that was installed on shaft should not be reused again after drive shaft is removed.

Cleaning & Inspection

1) Clean parts in solvent and blow dry with compressed air. Replace drive shaft if cracked or twisted. Replace outer CV joint if damaged or deformed. Replace cracked, damaged or worn boots.

2) Check inner CV joint for worn or damaged needle bearings or washer. Check splines on drive shaft and spider assembly for wear. Check roller bearing surfaces of spider assembly for damage, scratches and wear. Replace defective components as required.

3) Inspect groove of sliding gear housing for cracks, wear or deformation. Replace as necessary. Check and replace any parts of double offset joint which show signs of burn, rust, wear or excessive play.

Reassembly (Wheel Side)

1) Mount drive shaft in soft-jawed vise with outer end facing up. Position dust boot and new small boot band on drive shaft. Do not tear boot on shaft splines.

2) Slide outer CV joint onto shaft, aligning marks made during disassembly. Seat joint by lightly tapping with plastic mallet. Retain joint with new snap ring.

3) Pack joint assemblies with proper type and amount of grease. For Sentra and Pulsar, use 3.53 oz. (100 gram) for Birfield joint and 3.88 oz. (110 gram) for Rzeppa joint. For Stanza, pack drive shaft with 10.23 oz. (290 gram) of grease. Install new large boot band.

4) Wrap band around boot 2 times and tighten using screwdriver and pliers. Using a punch, lock band in position. Cut off excess band, leaving amount equal to band width. Bend excess back over itself. Set dust boot on shaft so that it does not swell and deform when positioned at its proper length.

5) For Sentra and Pulsar, set boot length at 3.94" (100 mm) for Rzeppa joint and 3.54" (90 mm) for Birfield joint. For Stanza, set boot length at 4.74" (120.5 mm). Secure small band in position without deforming or buckling dust boot.

Reassembly (Transaxle Side)

1) Turn drive shaft in vise so inner end faces up. Coat new "O" ring with grease and install on CV joint housing. Install new slide joint cover on housing and bend outer edge at 2 points (180° apart). If necessary, use block of wood to prevent damage.

2) Ensure housing cover does not rattle. Apply sealant at outer edge of housing and cover. Position boot and new small band on drive shaft sub assembly. Slide spider assembly onto shaft, aligning marks made during disassembly.

NOTE:　If spider gears are not marked, position both wheel side and transaxle side spider gear assemblies so that their phases are nearly zero.

3) Press spider assembly into position with splined chamfer facing drive shaft. Retain in position with new snap ring (round surface facing spider assembly). Pack Sentra and Pulsar CV joint assembly with 6.35 oz. (180 gram) of grease. For Stanza, use 6.52 oz. (185 gram) of grease.

4) Install new large boot band and secure in same manner as for inner CV joint. Position dust boot on shaft so that it does not swell or deform when set to its proper length. For Sentra and Pulsar, set length to 3.31" (84 mm) and 4.45" (113 mm) for Stanza. Secure small band in position without deforming or buckling dust boot.

NISSAN/DATSUN PULSAR, SENTRA & STANZA (Cont.)

Installation

1) To install, reverse removal procedure. Place drive shaft in knuckle, aligning splines with hub splines. Place assembly in vise and draw shaft into hub by tightening hub nut. Check and adjust wheel bearing preload. See WHEEL BEARINGS in this article. Install new cotter pin in hub nut.

2) Apply automatic transaxle fluid to new differential oil seal surface and install using seal Installer Tool (ST33400001). Install new snap ring on drive shaft. Remove bar holding side gears (installed during removal) from differential case.

3) Install Guide Tool (KV38105500) along inner circumference of oil seal. Install drive shaft, ensuring splines are aligned. Remove guide tool. Push in drive shaft or tap on flange of inner CV joint cover. Press circlip on drive shaft into circlip groove of side gear.

4) After installation into differential case, try to pull flange out of inner CV joint housing by hand to ensure proper engagement of circlip. Use new cotter pins and lower ball joint nuts. Bleed brake system. Replace transaxle fluid.

WHEEL BEARINGS

NOTE: **For identification, steering knuckle spacers on Sentra and Pulsar are stamped with 2-digit numbers ranging from 05-to-22. Stanza spacers have a single digit letter ranging from A-to-R.**

Removal

1) Raise and support vehicle. Remove wheel and tire assembly. Remove brake caliper and wire aside. Remove knuckle/hub and drive shaft assembly. See DRIVE SHAFTS in this article.

2) Separate hub from knuckle using slide hammer and Adapter (KV40101000 and ST36230000). Remove hub-to-rotor bolts and press out hub. Remove and discard inner and outer grease seals. Note seal installed direction for reassembly reference.

3) Remove bearing spacer and set aside. Using a bearing puller, remove outer wheel bearing. Using a hammer and brass drift, drive out inner and outer bearing races.

NOTE: **Check grease seal for leakage during removal. Replace grease seal at every disassembly even if seal appears good.**

Cleaning & Inspection

Clean wheel bearings in solvent and blow dry with compressed air. Check bearings for noise, cracks, pitting or wear and replace as necessary. Check hub and knuckle for cracks by means of Magna-Flux or dyeing test. Replace component(s) if cracked.

NOTE: **When replacing wheel bearings, replace inner and outer bearings at the same time to prevent mixed use of bearings of different brands.**

Installation

1) Pack each bearing with multi-purpose grease. Install inner and outer bearing races into knuckle using a drift or installer tools and press. When grease seal, bearing or spacer is replaced, select spacer having the same mark as old one.

2) The old spacer may be reused if still serviceable. When knuckle is replaced, use a spacer determined by measuring distance between outer races. Record measurement. See Fig. 5.

3) From this measurement, subtract .0063" (.160 mm) for Sentra and Pulsar and .0209" (.530 mm) for Stanza. Final figure is size of required bearing spacer. Install proper size spacer. Coat seal lips with grease and install with seal facing in proper direction. Assemble hub to disc and tighten bolts.

NOTE: **Bearing spacers are available in size ranges of .2906-.2929" (7.381-7.440 mm) to .3307-.3331" (8.401-8.460 mm) thick, for Sentra and Pulsar. Stanza spacers range from .1539-.1551" (3.910-3.940 mm) to .1941-.1953" (4.930-4.960 mm) thick.**

Fig. 5: Measuring Bearing Spacer Requirement

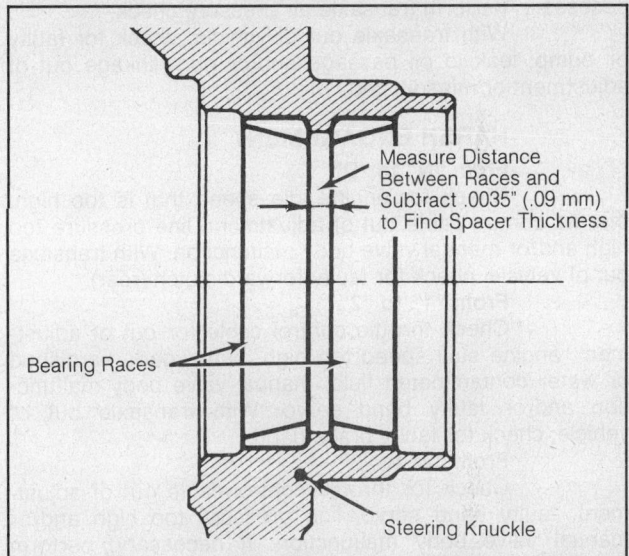

Measure gap between outer bearing races and calculate for proper thickness of spacer.

TROUBLE SHOOTING

NOTE: **The trouble shooting diagnosis steps are arranged in the order of probability.**

NO STARTER OPERATION IN "P" OR "N" RANGE

Check for faulty ignition switch or starter motor, control cable linkage out of adjustment or misadjusted, faulty inhibitor switch wiring and/or misadjusted inhibitor switch.

NO DRIVE IN "D" RANGE BUT RUNS IN "2", "1" AND "R" RANGE

Check for control cable linkage out of adjustment or misadjusted, line pressure too low and/or manual valve body malfunction. With transaxle out of vehicle, check for defective 1-way clutch.

Automatic Transmissions

NISSAN/DATSUN PULSAR, SENTRA & STANZA (Cont.)

NO DRIVE IN "R" RANGE
BUT RUNS IN "D", "2" AND "1" RANGE

If transaxle clutch slips and/or vehicle has very poor acceleration, check for low transaxle oil level, control cable linkage is out of adjustment or misadjusted and/or line pressure too low. Check for burnt, dark, varnished or water contaminated fluid and/or manual valve body malfunction. If necessary, perform transaxle air pressure check.

With transaxle out of vehicle, check for faulty forward clutch (rear), faulty high-reverse clutch (front), faulty low-reverse brake, oil passage leak and/or faulty high-reverse clutch (front) check ball.

NO DRIVE IN ANY RANGE

Check for low transaxle oil level, control cable linkage out of adjustment or misadjusted, line pressure too low, fluid that is burnt, dark, varnished or water contaminated and/or manual valve body malfunction. If necessary, perform transaxle air pressure check.

With transaxle out of vehicle, check for faulty oil pump, leak in oil passage and/or park linkage out of adjustment or misadjusted.

HARSH ENGAGEMENT
From "N" to "D"

Check for engine idle speed that is too high, throttle control cable out of adjustment, line pressure too high and/or manual valve body malfunction. With transaxle out of vehicle, check for faulty forward clutch (rear).

From "1" to "2"

Check throttle control cable for out of adjustment, engine stall speed too high, burnt, dark, varnished or water contaminated fluid, manual valve body malfunction and/or faulty band servo. With transaxle out of vehicle, check for faulty brake band.

From "2" to "3"

Check for throttle control cable out of adjustment, faulty band servo, line pressure too high and/or manual valve body malfunction. If necessary, perform transaxle air pressure check. With transaxle out of vehicle, check for faulty high-reverse clutch (front).

POOR ACCELERATION

Check for low fluid level, control cable linkage out of adjustment or misadjusted, fluid that is burnt, dark, varnished or water contaminated, line pressure too low, engine stall speed too low, manual valve body malfunction and/or faulty band servo.

With transaxle out of vehicle, check for faulty forward clutch (rear), faulty high-reverse clutch (front), faulty brake band, faulty low-reverse brake and/or defective oil pump.

TRANSAXLE OVERHEATS

Check for low fluid level or poor lubrication, line pressure too low, engine stall speed too low, burnt, dark, varnished or water contaminated fluid, manual valve body malfunction and/or faulty band servo. If necessary, perform transaxle air pressure check.

With transaxle out of vehicle, check for faulty high-reverse clutch (front), faulty brake band, faulty low-reverse brake, faulty torque converter 1-way clutch, faulty planetary gear set, defective oil pump and/or oil passage leak.

TRANSMISSION SLIPS ON "1-2" UPSHIFT

Check for low fluid level, manual control cable linkage out of adjustment, throttle control cable out of adjustment, line pressure too low, burnt, dark, varnished or water contaminated fluid, manual valve body malfunction and/or faulty band servo. If necessary, perform transaxle air pressure check. With transaxle out of vehicle, check for faulty brake band or leak in oil passage.

TRANSMISSION SLIPS ON "2-3" UPSHIFT

Check for low fluid level, manual control cable linkage out of adjustment, throttle control cable out of adjustment, line pressure too low, burnt, dark, varnished or water contaminated fluid, manual valve body malfunction and/or faulty band servo. If necessary, perform transaxle air pressure test. With transaxle out of vehicle, check for faulty high-reverse clutch (front), leak in oil passage and/or faulty high-reverse clutch (front) check ball.

TRANSMISSION SLIPS ON STARTS

Check for low fluid level, manual control cable linkage out of adjustment, line pressure to low, burnt, dark, varnished or water contaminated fluid, throttle control cable out of adjustment and/or manual valve body malfunction. If necessary, perform transaxle air pressure check. With transaxle out of vehicle, check for defective oil pump or oil passage leak.

NO DOWNSHIFT FROM "2" TO "1" OR "3" TO "1"

Check for throttle control cable out of adjustment, burnt, dark, varnished or water contaminated fluid, manual valve body malfunction, faulty governor and/or faulty band servo. If necessary, perform transaxle air pressure check. With transaxle out of vehicle, check for faulty brake band or faulty transaxle 1-way clutch.

NO "1-2" UPSHIFT

Check for manual control cable linkage out of adjustment, throttle control cable out of adjustment, faulty detent valve, burnt, dark, varnished or water contaminated fluid, manual valve body malfunction, faulty governor and/or faulty band servo. If necessary, perform transaxle air pressure check. With transaxle out of vehicle, check for faulty brake band and leak in oil passage.

NO "2-3" UPSHIFT

Check for manual control cable linkage out of adjustment, throttle control cable out of adjustment, faulty detent valve, burnt, dark, varnished or water contaminated fluid, manual valve body malfunction, faulty governor and/or faulty band servo. If necessary, perform transaxle air pressure check. With transaxle out of vehicle, check for faulty high-reverse clutch (front), faulty high-reverse clutch (front) check ball and/or leak in oil passage.

TORQUE CONVERTER DIAGNOSIS (ALL EXCEPT SENTRA DIESEL)
Converter Not Locked-Up

Check for a faulty governor or line pressure that is too low. With transaxle out of vehicle, check for defective input shaft "O" ring, defective torque converter,

NISSAN/DATSUN PULSAR, SENTRA & STANZA (Cont.)

faulty speed cut valve or lock-up control valve and/or defective oil pump.

Lock-Up Piston Slip

Check for line pressure that is too low. With transaxle out of vehicle, check for defective input shaft "O" ring, defective torque converter and/or oil pump.

Lock-Up Point Too High or Too Low

Check for a faulty governor. With transaxle removed from vehicle, check for faulty speed cut valve and/or lock-up control valve.

Engine Stops At "R", "D", "2"
And "1" Ranges

With transaxle out of vehicle, check for faulty torque converter and/or faulty lock-up control valve.

Transaxle Overheats

Check for line pressure that is too low. With transaxle removed from vehicle, check for defective input shaft "O" ring, defective torque converter or oil pump.

TESTING

NOTE: The transaxle is provided with four pressure test ports. All are useful for transaxle troubleshooting. Ports are; Line pressure, to high-reverse clutch (front). Line pressure, to forward clutch (rear). Governor pressure and Torque Converter lock-up pressure.

ROAD TEST

1) Before road testing, ensure fluid level, condition and control linkage adjustments have been checked and corrected as necessary. During test, transmission should upshift and downshift at approximately the same speeds as shown in *Shift Speeds* chart.

CAUTION: Do not shift transaxle into 1st gear from "D" range if car road speed is above 40 mph (65 km/h).

2) All shifts may vary slightly due to production tolerances or tire size. The important factor is the quality of the shifts. All shifts should be smooth and responsive with no slippage or engine speed runaway.

3) Slippage or engine runaway in any gear usually indicates clutch or band problems. The slipping clutch or band in a particular gear can usually be identified by noting transmission operation in other selector positions and comparing internal units which are applied in these positions. *See Clutch and Band Application chart.*

PULSAR & SENTRA SHIFT SPEEDS SPECIFICATIONS

Application	MPH
Minimum Throttle	
1-2 Upshift	7-13
2-3 Upshift	14-20
3-2 Downshift	12-17
2-1 Downshift	7-12
Full Throttle	
1-2 Upshift	30-35
2-3 Upshift	59-65
3-2 Downshift	58-62
2-1 Downshift	18-27
Lock-Up Shift Points	
Engaged	38-45
Disengaged	36-43

SENTRA DIESEL SHIFT SPEEDS SPECIFICATIONS

Application	MPH
Minimum Throttle	
1-2 Upshift	8-14
2-3 Upshift	13-19
3-2 Downshift	11-16
2-1 Downshift	7-13
Full Throttle	
1-2 Upshift	27-32
2-3 Upshift	54-60
3-2 Downshift	53-57
2-1 Downshift	17-27

CLUTCH AND BRAKE APPLICATION CHART (ELEMENTS IN USE)

Selector Lever Position	Clutch		Low-Reverse Brake	1-Way Clutch	Band Servo	
	High-Reverse (Front)	Forward (Rear)			Operation	Release
D – DRIVE						
Low		X	1	X		
Second		X			X	
Third 2	X	X			X	X
2 – Second Gear						
Low		X		X		
Second		X			X	
1 – First Gear						
Low		X	X	X		
Second		X			X	
R – Reverse	X		X			

NEUTRAL OR PARK – All clutches and brakes released and/or ineffective.

1 – Low & reverse brake applied to prevent free wheeling when coasting and to provide engine braking.

2 – Lock-up converter engaged on all models except Sentra Diesel.

STANZA SHIFT SPEEDS SPECIFICATIONS

Application	MPH
Minimum Throttle	
1-2 Upshift	8-14
2-3 Upshift	15-21
3-2 Downshift	13-18
2-1 Downshift	7-13
Full Throttle	
1-2 Upshift	32-37
2-3 Upshift	63-69
3-2 Downshift	62-66
2-1 Downshift	19-29
Lock-Up Shift Points	
Engaged	39-46
Disengaged	37-44

STALL SPEED TEST

Stall Test Precautions

A stall test should only be performed as a last resort due to the high temperature it generates and the excessive load it places on the engine and transaxle. DO NOT test more than two gear ranges without driving car to cool off drivetrain.

Before making a stall speed test, ensure that line pressure is correct. If line pressure is too low when performing a stall test, transmission can be damaged. During stall test, DO NOT hold throttle open for more than 5 seconds at a time.

Stall Test Procedure

1) Road test vehicle and warm transmission to normal operating temperature. Connect tachometer to engine. Position tachometer so that it can be read from driver's seat.

2) Set parking and service brakes. Start engine and place selector lever in "D". Depress accelerator pedal completely and note maximum RPM obtained. RPM should be approximately as shown in *Stall Speed* chart.

3) Place selector lever in "N" and allow engine to idle to cool off transmission. Then, place selector lever in "R" and repeat stall test. Stall RPM should be approximately as shown in *Stall Speed* chart.

NOTE: If stall test indicates proper stall RPM in "D" range, no further testing is necessary.

STALL SPEED SPECIFICATIONS

Application	Stall Speed (RPM)
Pulsar, Sentra	1800-2100
Sentra Diesel	1500-1800
Stanza	2000-2300

Stall Test Results

1) Satisfactory results in "D" range indicate forward clutch (rear), 1-way clutch of transaxle and sprag clutch of torque converter are functioning properly.

2) If the stall RPM in "D" range (1st gear) is above the specified vehicle RPM, the forward clutch (rear) is faulty. If the stall RPM in "R" range is above the specified vehicle RPM (for "D" range), the low and reverse brakes are faulty.

3) If the stall RPM in "D' range (1st gear) is below the specified vehicle RPM, the converter 1-way clutch is faulty or the engine is not performing properly.

4) If the converter 1-way clutch is frozen, vehicle will have poor high speed performance. If converter 1-way clutch is slipping, vehicle will be sluggish up to 30-40 MPH.

LINE PRESSURE TEST

NOTE: Measure line pressure at idling, at stall speed test and while road testing under different throttle conditions.

1) Road test vehicle to bring transaxle to normal operating temperature of 109-135° F (43-57° C). Connect pressure gauge to appropriate test port. Place gauge so that it is visible from driver's seat.

2) To test all forward range line pressures, connect gauge to rear line pressure port (2). *See Fig. 6.* Connect tachometer to engine. Start engine and if necessary, adjust idle speed.

Fig. 6: Transaxle Case Pressure Test Port Locations

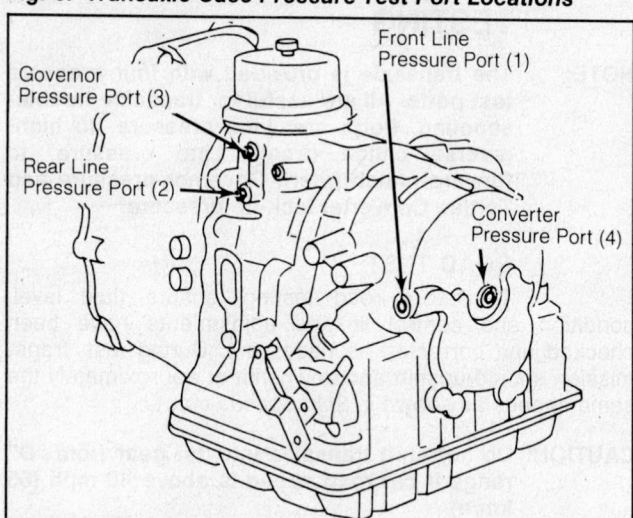

Connect the pressure gauge to the appropriate test port, with gauge in full view of the driver.

3) Depress brake pedal and place selector lever in "D". Note line pressure reading on gauge. Repeat procedure for each forward range. Pressure should be approximately as shown in *Line Pressure* chart.

4) Connect gauge to front line pressure port (1) to test reverse range line pressure. *See Fig. 6.* Repeat line pressure test with selector lever in "R". Pressure should be approximately as shown in *Line Pressure* chart.

LINE PRESSURE SPECIFICATIONS

Application	psi (kg/cm²)
Pulsar, Sentra (Gas/Diesel) & Stanza	
Idle	
In All Forward Ranges	36-50 (2.5-3.5)
In "R" Range	91-112 (6.4-7.9)
At Half Throttle	
In All Forward Ranges	73-94 (5.1-6.6)
At Full Throttle	
In All Forward Ranges	80-101 (5.6-7.1)
At Stall Speed Test	
In All Forward Ranges	80-101 (5.6-7.1)
In "R" Range	185-213 (13-15)

5) After testing at idle and during stall speed test, road test vehicle and note readings at different throttle positions. Pressure should be approximately as shown in *Line Pressure* chart.

LINE PRESSURE TEST RESULTS
Pressure Too High
If pressure is too high, check throttle cable adjustment. If cable is correctly adjusted and pressure is still high, regulator valve or throttle valve may be seized.
Pressure Too Low
If line pressure is too low, check for seizing of regulator valve or throttle valve in valve body. If valves are not seized, check pressure relief valve and oil pump assembly for damage. A defective oil pump assembly will usually make noise.

GOVERNOR PRESSURE TEST

NOTE: **Governor pressure is a "modified" line pressure and will be incorrect if line pressure is incorrect. Line pressure must be correct before checking governor pressure.**

Testing Procedures
Road test vehicle to warm transmission to normal operating temperature. Connect pressure gauge to governor pressure port (3) on transmission case. *See Fig. 6.* Position gauge so it is visible from driver's seat. Test drive vehicle in "D" and note pressure readings. Governor pressure increases directly with road speed and should always be less than line pressure.

TORQUE CONVERTER LOCK-UP TEST (EXCEPT SENTRA DIESEL)
1) Road test vehicle to warm transmission to normal operating temperature. Connect pressure gauge to torque converter pressure port (4) on transmission case. *See Fig. 6.*
2) Position gauge so it is visible from driver's seat. Test drive vehicle in "D" and note pressure readings. Pressure should be approximately as shown in *Torque Converter Lock-Up Pressure* chart.

TORQUE CONVERTER LOCK-UP PRESSURE SPECIFICATIONS

Application	psi (kg/cm²)
Pulsar, Sentra (Gas) & Stanza	
Lock-Up Engaged	Less than 7.0 (0.5)
Lock-Up Disengaged	Greater than 28.0 (2.0)

3) The torque converter lock-up pressure at idle should show a steady rise in pressure as vehicle speed increases under light load.
4) The pressure drop between shift points should not exceed 14 psi (1.0 kg/cm²). Excessive pressure drop may indicate an internal leak at a servo or clutch seal.

REMOVAL & INSTALLATION
See appropriate AUTOMATIC TRANSMISSION REMOVAL article in IMPORT GENERAL SERVICING section.

TORQUE CONVERTER
Torque converter is a sealed unit and cannot be disassembled for service. Replace if defective.

TRANSAXLE DISASSEMBLY
1) With transaxle removed from vehicle, clean outside case thoroughly and disassemble in a clean area. When cleaning and wiping parts, use nylon cloth or paper towels. Common shop rags will leave lint that can interfere with transaxle's operation.
2) Remove hex plug and drain fluid. Remove torque converter. Remove oil pump shaft and input shaft. Remove snap ring, governor cap with breather hose (if equipped) and "O" ring. Remove oil pan guard and oil pan and inspect its contents.

NOTE: **An inspection of any foreign matter in the oil pan can indicate the type of problems to look for while disassembling transaxle.**

3) Remove valve body bolts and valve body. Remove particle magnet and manual valve. Remove gear selector shaft inside and outside retaining nuts. Pull out retaining pin. Remove throttle lever, selector plate, selector shaft, selector range lever and parking rod assembly.
4) Disconnect and remove throttle cable from throttle lever. Remove parking actuator support from case. Loosen brake band piston stem lock nut. Back off piston stem. Apply compressed air to oil supply hole to remove accumulator piston. Place rag over piston to prevent it from jumping out of bore. *See Fig. 7.*

Fig. 7: Removing Accumulator Piston

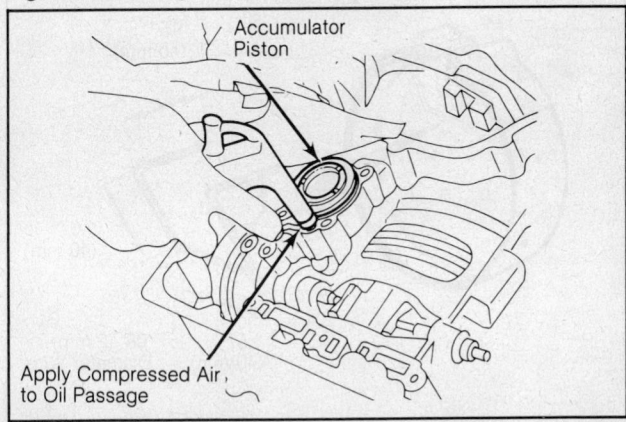

Place rag over piston to prevent it from jumping out of bore.

5) Remove converter housing mount bolts. Tap converter housing with plastic mallet to separate it from transaxle case. DO NOT drop final drive assembly. Remove final drive assembly and set aside. Pull out parking pawl shaft. Remove parking pawl and return spring.
6) With chisel and hammer, straighten tang on idler gear bolt lock washer. Remove idler gear bolt and lock washer. Turn transaxle case over. Remove front cover retaining bolts. Hold front cover and tap output shaft with plastic mallet to loosen. Remove output shaft and front cover as an assembly. DO NOT lose adjusting shim located on rear internal gear side of output shaft.

7) Remove front cover gasket. Tap out idler gear, idler gear shaft and bearings with drift and hammer. Remove planetary gear set seal bushing from case. Turn case so torque converter housing faces up. Remove governor shaft retaining bolt. Pull out governor shaft. Remove rear internal gear, bearing race and thrust washer.

8) Remove 1-way clutch snap ring. Lift out 1-way clutch assembly with rear carrier assembly. Remove bearing race and thrust washer. Remove low and reverse brake snap ring. Remove connecting shell, snap ring, thrust bearing and bearing race. Lift out planetary gear set (front carrier assembly and front internal gear), with thrust bearing and race, as an assembly.

9) Lift out forward clutch (rear) assembly and plastic thrust washer. Remove low-reverse brake retaining plate, driven plates and drive plates at the same time. Rotate and remove high-reverse clutch (front) assembly.

NOTE: **If high-reverse clutch (front) seal rings have expanded, front clutch assembly will be difficult to remove. DO NOT force out clutch assembly as seal damage may occur.**

10) To prevent brake linings from cracking or peeling, DO NOT stretch flexible band excessively. Before removing brake band, secure it with a clip placed into ends of band. Leave clip in position after removing brake band. Securing clip can be fabricated from .08" (2 mm) diameter wire stock. See Fig. 8.

Fig. 8: Brake Band Securing Clip Installation

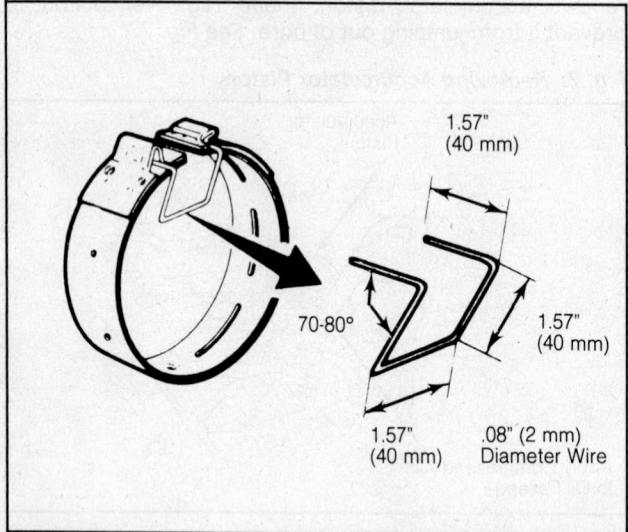

Use the specifications shown to fabricate a clip to secure the brake band.

11) Remove low-reverse brake retainer. Apply compressed air to oil passage to remove low-reverse brake piston. Place nylon cloth over piston to prevent it from jumping out. See Fig. 9. If compressed air is not available, use a screwdriver to carefully remove piston.

12) Remove oil pump assembly, nylon washer and thrust bearing by lifting straight out of case. Use care in lifting out oil pump; clearance is very close even though pump fits loosely. Remove inhibitor switch. Remove band servo piston and return spring. Remove transmission case as needed.

Fig. 9: Low-Reverse Brake Piston Removal

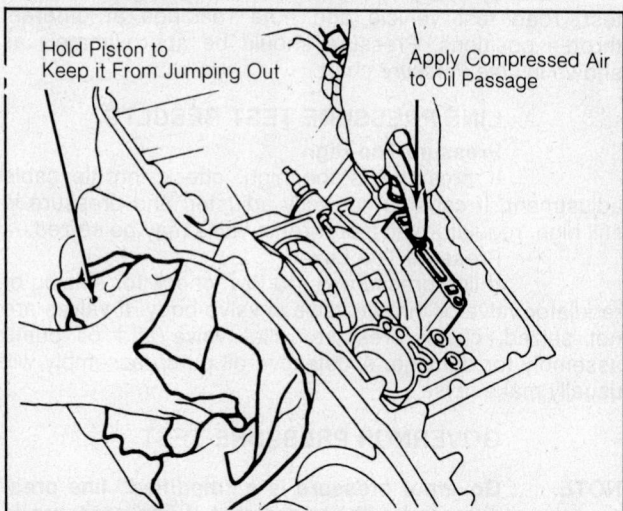

Apply compressed air to oil passage while holding a nylon cloth over piston.

COMPONENT DISASSEMBLY & REASSEMBLY

OIL PUMP ASSEMBLY
Disassembly

1) Remove bearing and thrust washer. Remove oil pump plate. Mark pump drive and driven gears for reassembly in same position. DO NOT punch marks.

2) Remove gear hub and gears from pump housing. Remove steel ball and pressure relief spring from its bore. See Fig. 10.

Fig. 10: Exploded View of Oil Pump Assembly

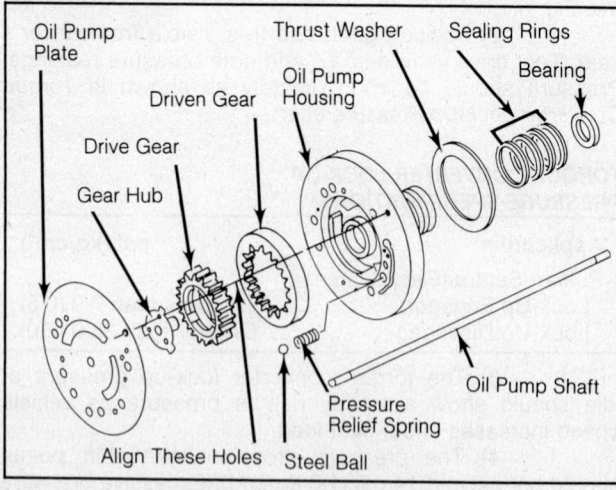

Mark gears for reassembly reference.

Cleaning & Inspection

1) Thoroughly clean all parts and dry with compressed air. Inspect parts for damage, wear, cracks, or scoring. Check oil pump shaft and ring groove areas of pump housing for wear.

2) If pump housing, cover plate, shaft, inner drive gear or outer driven gear requires replacement, complete oil pump assembly must be replaced as a matched set.

Reassembly

1) Install drive and driven gear into housing, aligning marks made at disassembly. Using a feeler gauge, measure clearance between pump driven gear and pump housing. *See Fig. 11.*

Fig. 11: Measuring Housing-to-Gear Face Clearance

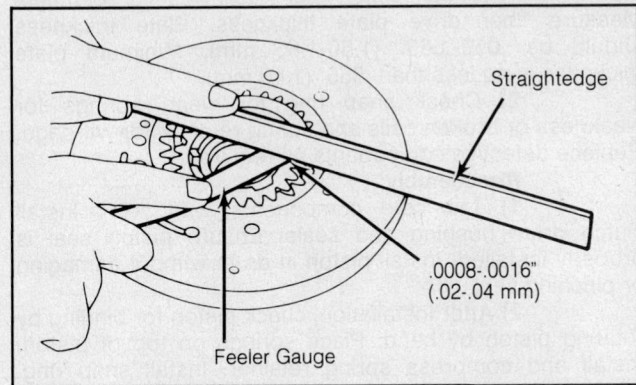

Use a straightedge and feeler gauge when measuring the gear-to-housing clearance.

2) Clearance should be .008-.012" (.20-.30 mm). If clearance exceeds .014" (.35 mm), replace oil pump assembly. Check clearance between driven gear and crescent. Clearance should be .008-.012" (.20-.30 mm). If clearance exceeds .014" (.35 mm), replace oil pump.

3) Using a straightedge and feeler gauge, check pump housing face-to-gear face clearance. Clearance should be .0008-.0016" (.020-.040 mm). If clearance exceeds .003" (.08 mm), replace oil pump assembly.

4) Measure clearance between seal rings and seal ring grooves. Clearance should be .004-.010" (.10-.25 mm). If clearance exceeds .010" (.25 mm), replace seal rings. Seal rings should be replaced during each overhaul procedure.

5) Lubricate all parts with ATF. Install gear hub, pressure relief spring and steel ball onto pump housing. Center oil pump plate on oil pump housing. Outer edge of plate must not extend beyond outer edge of housing. Install and tighten screws.

6) Install seal rings in proper locations. Rings with White markings are installed in grooves furthest away from pump housing. Rings with no markings are installed in grooves nearest pump housing.

HIGH-REVERSE CLUTCH (FRONT) ASSEMBLY

Disassembly

1) Using a screwdriver, remove large clutch retaining plate snap ring. Remove clutch plate assembly, noting number and arrangement of discs and plates.

2) Using a spring compressor (ST25420001), compress clutch springs and remove snap ring from spring retainer. Remove spring retainer and lift out springs.

3) Using a rubber-tipped air blower, apply compressed air to oil passage hole to remove clutch piston from drum. DO NOT damage piston during removal. *See Fig. 12.* Remove and discard seals. Remove drum bushing and set aside.

Fig. 12: Removing Front Clutch Piston

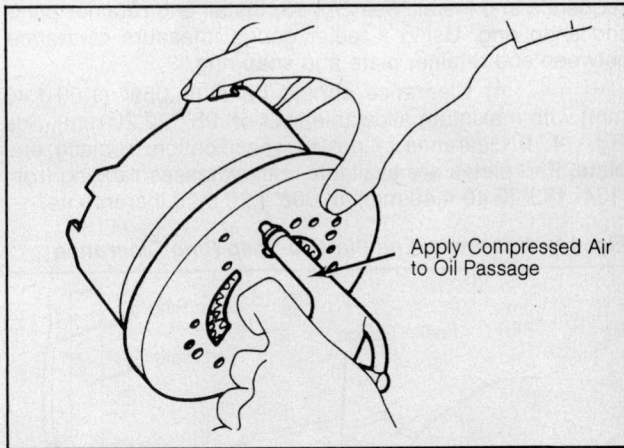

Apply compressed air to oil passage to remove the clutch piston from the drum.

Inspection

1) Check clutch discs for wear or damage. Measure plate thickness. Plate thickness should be .059-.065" (1.50-1.65 mm). Replace plate if any thickness measures less than .055" (1.40 mm).

2) Check snap ring for wear, springs for weakness or broken coils and spring retainer for warpage. Replace defective components as required.

Reassembly

1) Lubricate components with ATF. Install clutch drum bushing and seals. DO NOT stretch seals during installation. Ensure piston seal is installed in proper direction. *See Fig. 13.*

2) Install piston in drum without damaging or pinching seal. After installation, check for binding by rotating piston by hand. Place springs on top of piston. Install spring retainer. Compress spring retainer and install snap ring.

Fig. 13: Exploded View of Front Clutch Assembly

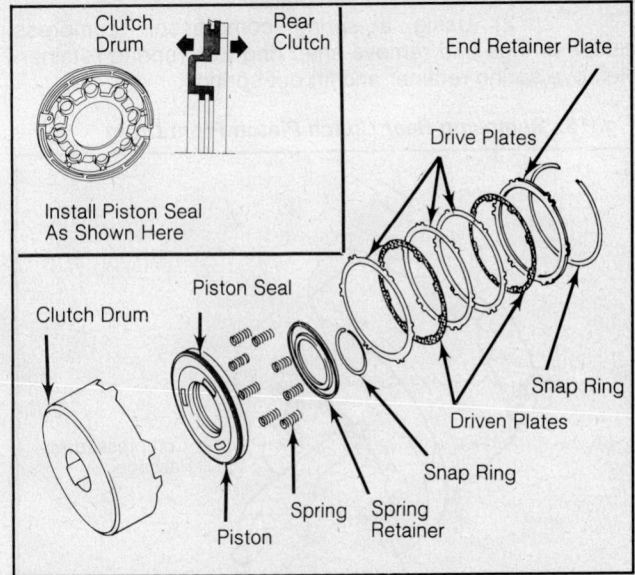

Note number and arrangement of drive plates and driven plates for reassembly reference.

Automatic Transmissions
NISSAN/DATSUN PULSAR, SENTRA & STANZA (Cont.)

3) Assemble clutch discs and plates in proper sequence and install. *See Fig. 13.* Install end retainer plate and snap ring. Using a feeler gauge, measure clearance between end retainer plate and snap ring.

4) Clearance should be .039-.055" (1.00-1.40 mm) with maximum allowable limit of .087" (2.20 mm). *See Fig. 14.* If clearance is not to specification, replace end plate. End plates are available in thicknesses ranging from .134-.173" (3.40-4.40 mm) in .008" (.20 mm) increments.

Fig. 14: Measuring End Plate-to-Snap Ring Clearance

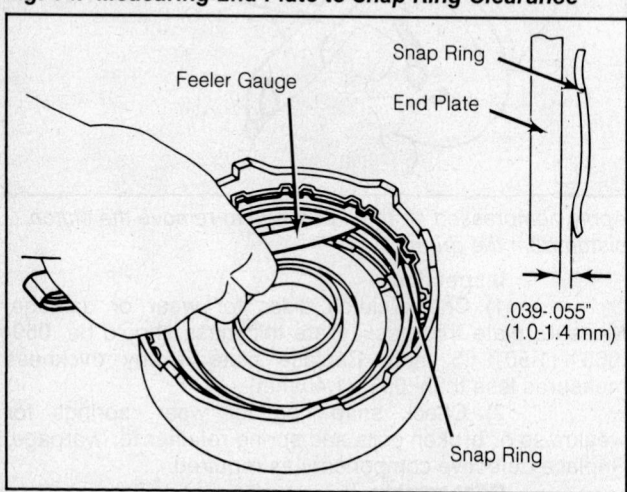

Replace the end plate if clearance is not to specification.

5) After complete assembly of front clutch, test clutch operation with compressed air. Engagement of piston should be heard when compressed air is applied to oil passage hole. *See Fig. 12.*

FORWARD CLUTCH (REAR) ASSEMBLY
Disassembly

1) Using a screwdriver, remove large clutch retaining snap ring. Remove clutch plates, noting number and arrangement of discs and plates.

2) Using a spring compressor, compress clutch springs and remove snap ring from spring retainer. Remove spring retainer and lift out springs.

Fig. 15: Removing Rear Clutch Piston From Drum

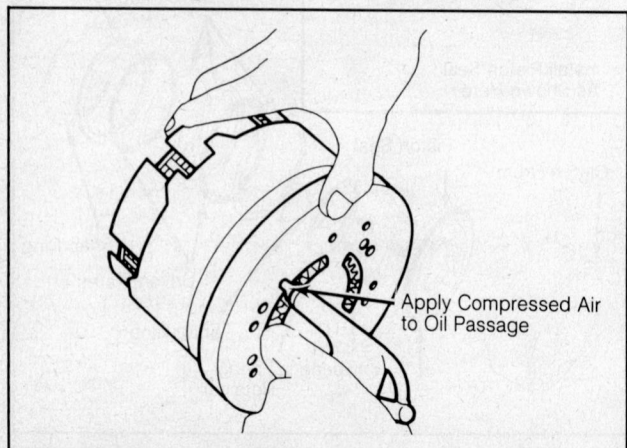

With rubber-tipped air blower, apply compressed air to oil passage to remove piston or to check piston operation.

3) Using a rubber-tipped air blower, apply compressed air to oil passage hole to remove clutch piston from drum. DO NOT damage piston during removal. *See Fig. 15.* Remove and discard seals. Remove drum bushing and set aside.

Inspection

1) Check clutch discs for wear or damage. Measure fiber drive plate thickness. Plate thickness should be .059-.065" (1.50-1.65 mm). Minimum plate thickness is no less than .055" (1.40 mm).

2) Check snap ring for wear, springs for weakness or broken coils and spring retainer for warpage. Replace defective components as required.

Reassembly

1) Lubricate components with ATF. Install clutch drum bushing and seals. Ensure piston seal is properly installed. Install piston in drum without damaging or pinching seal.

2) After installation, check piston for binding by rotating piston by hand. Place springs on top of piston. Install and compress spring retainer. Install snap ring. Install dished plate with beveled end facing piston.

3) Assemble clutch discs and plates in proper sequence and install. *See Fig. 16.* Install end plate and large snap ring. Using a feeler gauge, measure clearance between end plate and snap ring.

Fig. 16: Exploded View of Rear Clutch Assembly

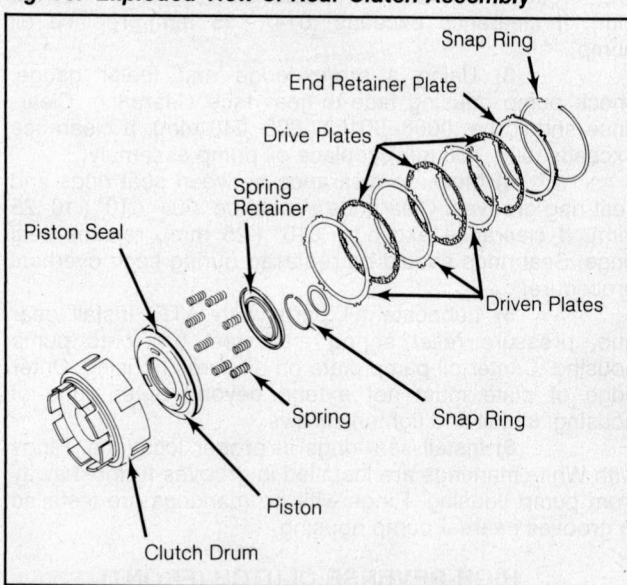

Note number and arrangement of discs and plates.

4) Clearance should be .031-.047" (.80-1.20 mm). Maximum allowable limit is .11" (2.8 mm). *See Fig. 17.* If clearance is not to specification, replace end plate. End plates are available in thicknesses ranging from .134-.173" (3.40-4.40 mm) in .008" (.20 mm) increments.

5) After complete assembly of rear clutch, test clutch operation with compressed air. Engagement of piston should be heard when compressed air is applied to oil passage hole. *See Fig. 15.*

NISSAN/DATSUN PULSAR, SENTRA & STANZA (Cont.)

Fig. 17: Measuring End Plate-to-Snap Ring Clearance

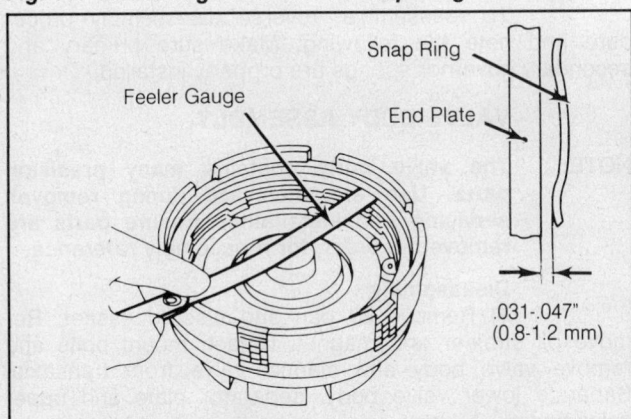

Replace the end retainer plate with one of the proper thickness if clearance is not to specification.

LOW-REVERSE BRAKE ASSEMBLY

Disassembly

1) Using a screwdriver, remove large retaining snap ring. Remove driven and drive plates. Note number and arrangement of steel discs and fiber plates.

2) Using a spring compressor, compress springs and remove snap ring from spring retainer. Remove spring retainer and lift out springs.

NOTE: Some models may use two plates instead of one rear end plate. Always install same configuration.

Inspection

1) Check discs for wear or damage. Measure fiber plate thickness. Plate thickness should be .075-.081" (1.90-2.05 mm). Replace plate if any thickness measures less than .071" (1.80 mm).

Fig. 18: Exploded View of Low-Reverse Brake Assembly

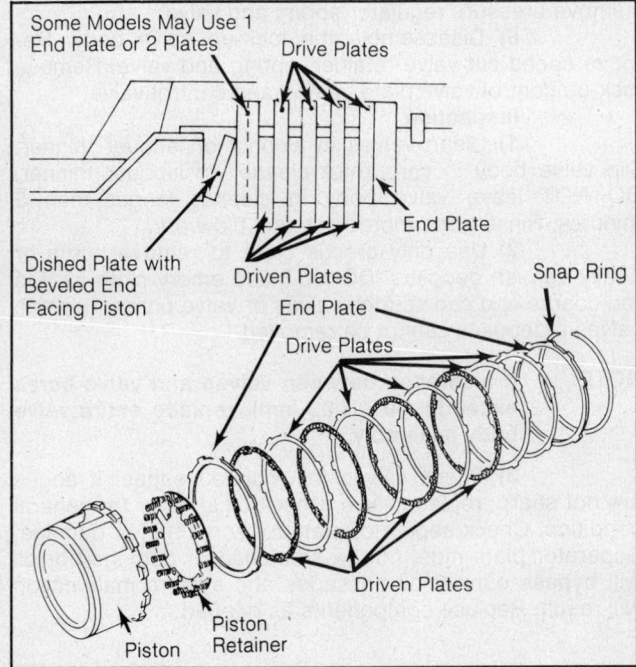

Note number and arrangement of discs and plates.

2) Check snap ring for wear, springs for weakness or broken coils and spring retainer for warpage. Replace defective components as required.

Reassembly

1) Lubricate components with ATF. Place springs in piston and install spring retainer. Compress spring retainer and install snap ring. Install dished plate with beveled end facing piston. Assemble clutch discs and plates in proper sequence and install. See Fig. 18.

2) Install end retainer plate and large snap ring. Using a feeler gauge, measure clearance between end plate and snap ring. Clearance should be .075-.087" (1.90-2.20 mm) with maximum allowable limit of .15" (3.8 mm).

3) If clearance is not to specification, replace end retainer plate. End plates are available in thicknesses ranging from .142-.173" (3.60-4.40 mm) in .008" (.20 mm) increments.

BRAKE BAND & BAND SERVO

Disassembly

Remove adjusting nut and washer from anchor pin. Remove anchor pin. Pull off band servo assembly. Remove snap ring and separate servo piston retainer from piston. Disassemble piston assembly and discard "O" rings. See Fig. 19.

Fig. 19: Exploded View of Brake Band and Band Servo Assembly

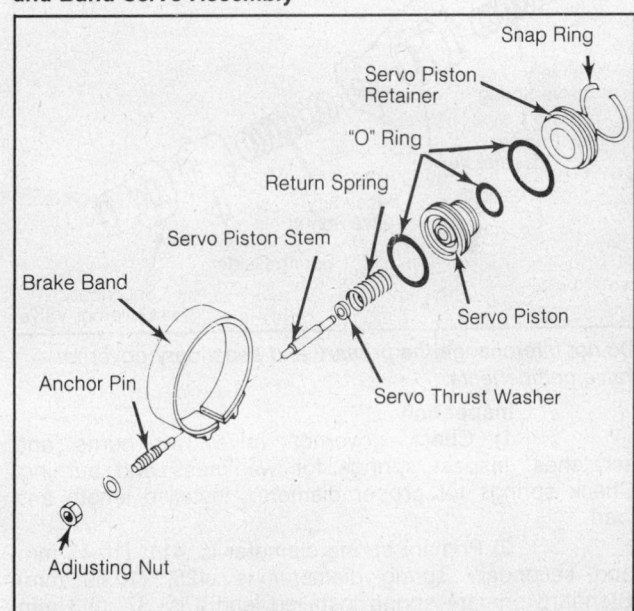

Replace "O" rings whenever band servo is disassembled.

Inspection

Check brake band friction material for wear. Replace band if cracked, chipped or burnt. Check band servo components and replace if worn or scored. Replace all "O" rings.

Reassembly

To reassemble, reverse disassembly procedure and note the following: Install new "O" rings and ensure snap ring is properly seated. Perform band adjustment during transaxle reassembly.

Automatic Transmissions

NISSAN/DATSUN PULSAR, SENTRA & STANZA (Cont.)

PLANETARY GEAR SET

Manufacturer does not recommend disassembly of planetary gear set. Measure clearance between planetary carrier and pinion washer. Normal clearance should be .008-.028" (.20-.70 mm). If clearance exceeds .032" (.80 mm) or gear set is worn or damaged, replace planetary gear set. Heat damage is revealed by Blue discoloration of gear sets.

GOVERNOR ASSEMBLY

Disassembly

1) Remove governor body-to-governor shaft bolts. Mount governor shaft in a soft-jawed vise and drive out gear retaining pin. Remove drive gear.

2) Disassemble governor valve body. Place components in order of disassembly. DO NOT interchange primary and secondary governor components. See Fig. 20.

Fig. 20: Exploded View of Governor Assembly

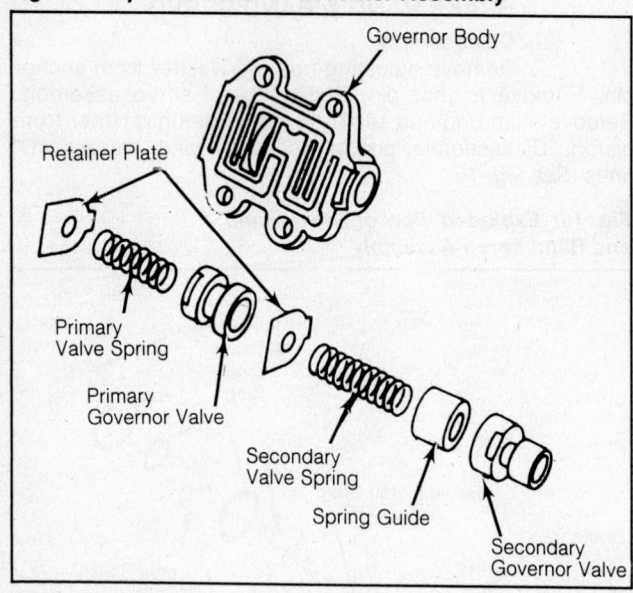

Do not interchange the primary and secondary governor valve components.

Inspection

1) Check governor valves for burns and scratches. Inspect springs for weakness and burning. Check springs for proper diameter, installed length and load.

2) Primary spring diameter is .411" (10.45 mm) and secondary spring diameter is .425" (10.80 mm). Standard primary spring installed length is .37" (9.3 mm) and load is .33 lb. (.15 kg).

3) Standard secondary spring installed length is 1.02" (26 mm) and load is 1.74 lb. (.79 kg). Replace defective components as required. See Governor Valve Spring chart.

GOVERNOR VALVE SPRING CHART

Governor Spring	Wire Dia. In. (mm)	Free Length In. (mm)
Primary Spring	.018 (.45)	1.25 (31.7)
Secondary Spring	.03 (.8)	1.50 (38.2)

Reassembly

To reassemble, reverse disassembly procedure and note the following: Make sure primary and secondary governor springs are properly installed.

VALVE BODY ASSEMBLY

NOTE: The valve body contains many precision parts. Use extreme care during removal, servicing and installation. Ensure parts are removed in order, for reassembly reference.

Disassembly

1) Remove oil pan and discard gasket. Remove oil strainer and magnet. Detach mount bolts and remove valve body and manual valve from transaxle. Separate lower valve body, separator plate and upper valve body.

NOTE: Check two reamer bolt locations for reassembly reference. During valve body separation, DO NOT lose the 6 steel balls from upper valve body.

2) Remove parallel pins from valve body by pushing out with a piece of wire. Remove valve body plugs. Extract 3-2 downshift valve and spring, 2-3 shift valve and spring, 1-2 shift valve, 1-2 control valve and spring from lower valve body. Place valves and springs in order of removal for reassembly reference.

3) Turn lower valve body over. Remove parallel pins by pushing out with wire. Remove valve body plugs. Remove fail-safe valve, detent valve, throttle valve, throttle modulator valve and spring guide.

4) Remove pressure modifier valve, 1st reducing valve, top reducing valve and check ball, 3-2 timing valve and all springs. Place components in order of removal for reassembly reference. See Fig. 21.

5) Using a small screwdriver, depress spring under back-up valve retaining plate. Remove retaining pin. Remove plug, retaining plate, spring and back-up valve. Remove pressure regulator spring and valve.

6) Disassemble the lock-up valve body. Remove speed cut valve retainer, spring and valve. Remove lock-up control valve plate, spring and control valve.

Inspection

1) Clean valves in alcohol or lacquer thinner. Dip valve body in carburetor cleaner or lacquer thinner. DO NOT leave valve body in cleaner longer than 5 minutes. Rinse parts thoroughly and blow dry.

2) Use only crocus cloth to remove burns or heavy varnish deposits. DO NOT use emery cloth as it is too coarse and can scratch valves or valve bores. Replace valves if deposits cannot be removed.

NOTE: If clearance between valves and valve bores exceeds .001" (.03 mm), replace entire valve body assembly.

3) Check valves for rounded edges. If edges are not sharp, replace valve. Check oil strainer for general condition. Check separator plate for scratches or damage. Separator plate must not be scratched or damaged or oil will bypass correct oil passages and system malfunction will result. Replace components as needed.

NISSAN/DATSUN PULSAR, SENTRA & STANZA (Cont.)

Fig. 21: Exploded View of Lower Control Valve Body Assembly

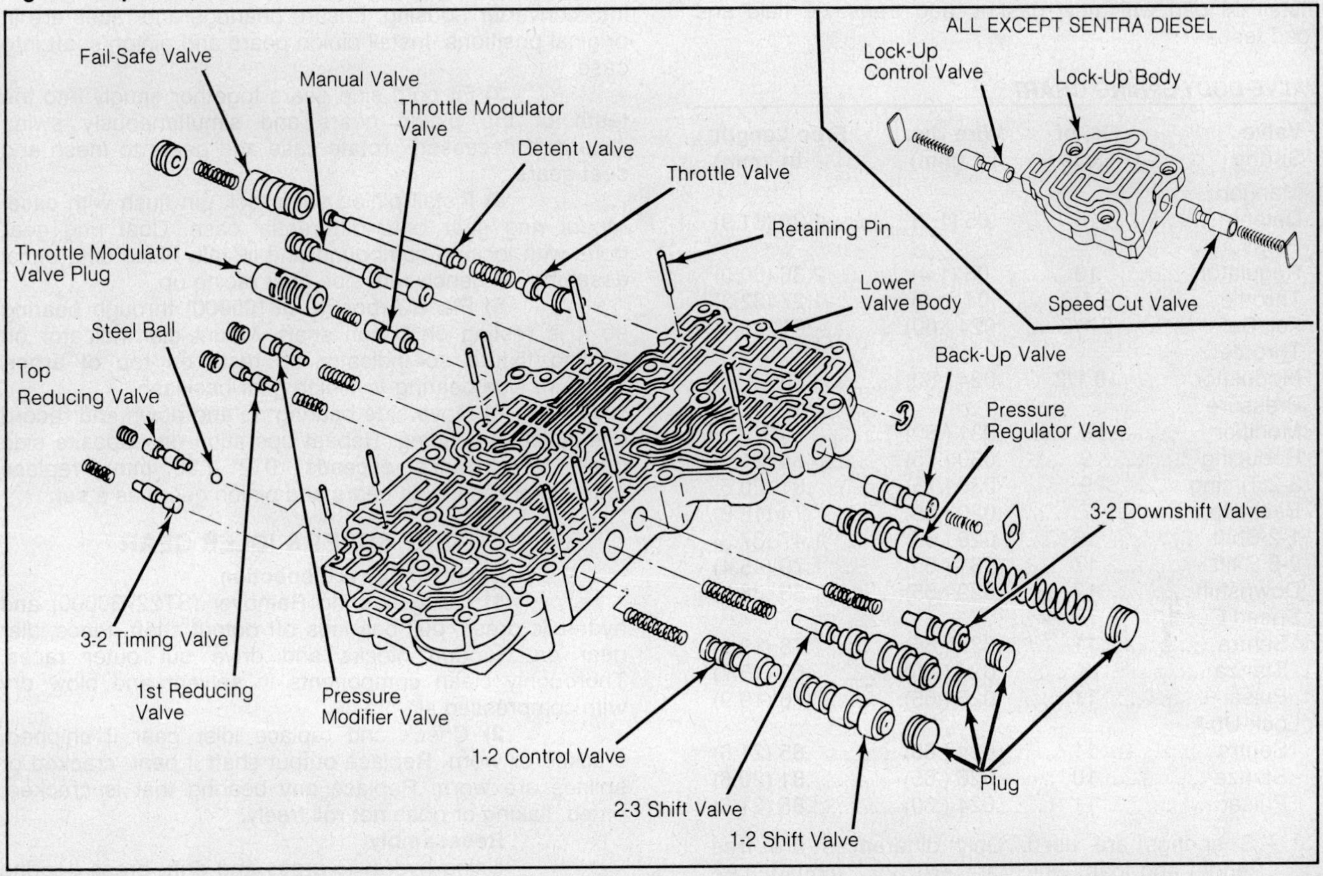

Fail-Safe Valve

Manual Valve

Throttle Modulator Valve

Detent Valve

Throttle Valve

Throttle Modulator Valve Plug

Steel Ball

Top Reducing Valve

3-2 Timing Valve

1st Reducing Valve

Pressure Modifier Valve

1-2 Control Valve

2-3 Shift Valve

1-2 Shift Valve

ALL EXCEPT SENTRA DIESEL

Lock-Up Control Valve

Lock-Up Body

Speed Cut Valve

Retaining Pin

Lower Valve Body

Back-Up Valve

Pressure Regulator Valve

3-2 Downshift Valve

Plug

Note position and configuration of all valve body parts and ensure components are reinstalled in proper locations.

4) Inspect upper and lower valve body oil passages for varnish deposits, scratches or other damage that would impair valve movement. Check for stripped threads. Repair any damaged thread holes. Replace bolts and screws as needed. Test valve springs for weakness. Replace defective components as required.

NOTE: If replacing pressure modifier valve spring, ensure new spring is the same type as the one which was removed.

Fig. 22: Upper Valve Body Check Ball Locations

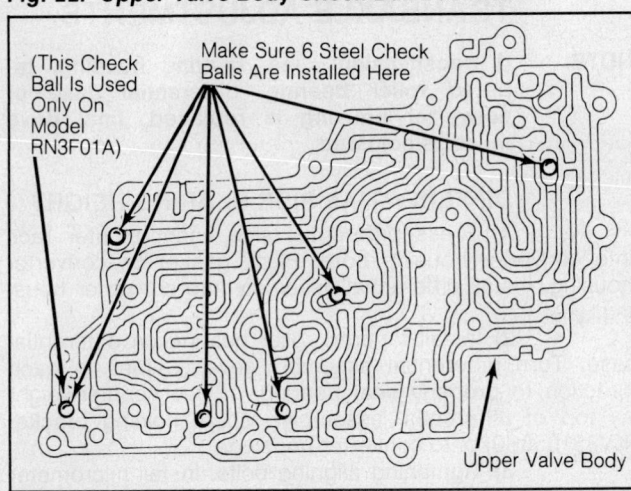

(This Check Ball Is Used Only On Model RN3F01A)

Make Sure 6 Steel Check Balls Are Installed Here

Upper Valve Body

Ensure check balls are properly positioned.

Reassembly

1) Install valves and springs in correct locations. Place 6 steel check balls in correct position in upper valve body. *See Fig. 22.* Assemble separator plate and valve bodies. Install reamer bolts first, then install and tighten remaining bolts. Install oil strainer and magnet.

2) Install manual valve after valve body is mounted on transaxle. On all models except Sentra diesel, shift point fine adjustment screw should be adjusted so that the distance from end of shaft to lock nut on valve body is .49-.51" (12.5-13.0 mm). *See Fig. 23.*

Fig. 23: Checking Shift Point Fine Adjusting Screw Position

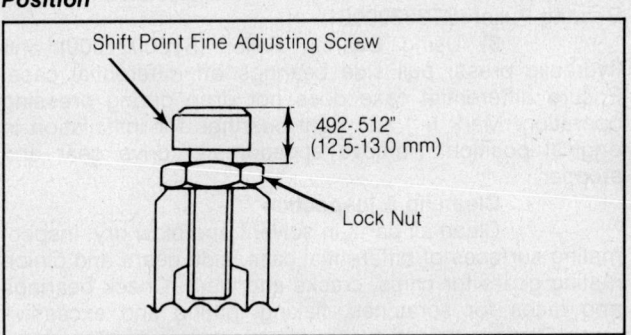

Shift Point Fine Adjusting Screw

.492-.512" (12.5-13.0 mm)

Lock Nut

Adjusting this screw can change the shift points about 3 mph (5 km/h), except in the kickdown mode.

3) Tightening the screw will cause the shift point to occur at a lower speed and vice versa. On Sentra diesel, tighten the shift point fine adjusting screw all the

NISSAN/DATSUN PULSAR, SENTRA & STANZA (Cont.)

way in and secure it with the lock nut. On all models, install oil pan with new gasket, add transaxle fluid and road test.

VALVE BODY SPRING CHART

Valve Spring	No. of Coils	Wire Dia. In. (mm)	Free Length In. (mm)
Manual Detent	16	.05 (1.2)	1.26 (31.9)
Pressure Regulator	10	.06 (1.4)	2.36 (60.0)
Throttle	9 1/2	.04 (1.0)	1.27 (32.3)
Fail-Safe Throttle	6 1/2	.024 (.60)	.91 (23.1)
Modulator Pressure	10 1/2	.024 (.60)	.89 (22.5)
Modifier [1]	9	.031 (.80)	[2]
Reducing	9	.030 (.75)	.84 (21.4)
3-2 Timing	9	.030 (.75)	.81 (20.6)
Back-Up	7	.020 (.50)	.74 (18.8)
1-2 Shift	16	.026 (.65)	1.47 (37.3)
2-3 Shift	17	.031 (.80)	1.79 (45.4)
Downshift	12	.022 (.55)	1.53 (38.9)
Speed Cut [3]			
Sentra	11	.026 (.65)	.78 (19.9)
Stanza	8	.024 (.60)	.62 (15.7)
Pulsar	11	.026 (.65)	.78 (19.9)
Lock-Up [3]			
Sentra	11	.024 (.60)	.85 (21.6)
Stanza	10	.026 (.65)	.81 (20.6)
Pulsar	11	.024 (.60)	.85 (21.6)

[1] – 3 springs are used. Only differences are free length and load, which are .97" (25.3 mm) @ 3.92 lb. (1.78 kg), .93" (23.6 mm) @ 3.37 lb. (1.53 kg) and .86" (21.8 mm) @ 2.82 lb. (1.28 kg).

[2] – The installed length for all 3 springs is .512" (13 mm).

[3] – Except Sentra diesel.

DIFFERENTIAL

Disassembly

1) Detach ring gear mount bolts. Separate ring gear from differential case. Using drift punch and hammer, drive out pinion shaft lock pin and remove pinion shaft.

2) Remove pinion gears and side gears from case. If bearings and races need replacement, remove races from converter housing and transmission case using Bearing Puller (ST33290001).

3) Using Bearing Puller (ST30031000) and hydraulic press, pull side bearings off differential case. Ensure differential case does not drop during pressing operation. Mark left and right bearings for installation in original position. Remove speedometer drive gear and stopper.

Cleaning & Inspection

Clean all parts in solvent and blow dry. Inspect mating surfaces of differential case, side gears and pinion mating gears for chips, cracks and wear. Check bearings and races for scratches, flaking, pitting and excessive wear. Replace defective components as required.

Reassembly

1) Install speedometer drive gear and stopper. Press side bearings onto differential case. Using Bearing Race Installers (ST30611000 and ST306621000), install bearing race into transaxle case.

2) Using race installers, install bearing race into converter housing. Ensure bearings and races are in original positions. Install pinion gears and pinion shaft into case.

3) Fit both side gears together snugly into the teeth of the pinion gears and simultaneously swing inward. If necessary, rotate case and gears to mesh and seat gears.

4) Install pinion shaft lock pin flush with case. Mount ring gear onto differential case. Coat ring gear bolts with locking compound and install. Place differential assembly on bench with side gear facing up.

5) Place Arbor (KV38105900) through bearing so it is resting on pinion shaft. Mount dial indicator on holding fixture so indicator tip rests on top of arbor. Measure side bearing-to-pinion gear backlash.

6) Move side bearing up and down and record dial indicator reading. Repeat operation on opposite side gear. If clearance exceeds .012" (.30 mm), replace differential case, side gears and pinion gears as a set.

OUTPUT SHAFT & IDLER GEAR

Disassembly & Inspection

1) Using bearing Remover (ST22730000) and hydraulic press, pull bearings off output shaft. Place idler gear on wooden blocks and drive out outer races. Thoroughly clean components in solvent and blow dry with compressed air.

2) Check and replace idler gear if chipped, cracked or worn. Replace output shaft if bent, cracked or splines are worn. Replace any bearing that is cracked, pitted, flaking or does not roll freely.

Reassembly

Using hydraulic press and drift, press bearing races into idler gear. Press bearings onto output shaft. Make sure bearings are properly seated and rotate without binding after installation.

TRANSMISSION CASE

Disassembly & Reassembly

Remove bearing housing from transmission case. Press bearing off housing. Press out oil seal. Remove and discard "O" ring. Coat new seal and "O" ring with gear oil and press into position. Press bearing into housing. Install housing in transmission case.

TRANSAXLE ADJUSTMENTS

NOTE: If transmission case, bearing housing, tapered roller bearing, differential case or converter housing is replaced, final drive must be adjusted.

DIFFERENTIAL SIDE BEARING HEIGHT

1) Press differential side bearing outer race into converter housing bore. Place gasket on converter housing. Install differential assembly into converter housing.

2) Install tapered roller bearing on differential case. Turn differential assembly several times in each direction to properly seat bearings. Place counterweight on top of differential assembly. Mount holding bracket (KV381058S0) onto converter housing.

3) Tightening aligning bolts. Install micrometer to bracket. Measure distance from upper gasket surface

NISSAN/DATSUN PULSAR, SENTRA & STANZA (Cont.)

of converter housing to upper surface of differential side bearing outer race. *See Fig. 24.* Record reading and subtract thickness of holding bracket to obtain actual measurement.

Fig. 24: Set-Up and Measuring Clearance Between Converter Housing and Differential Side Bearing

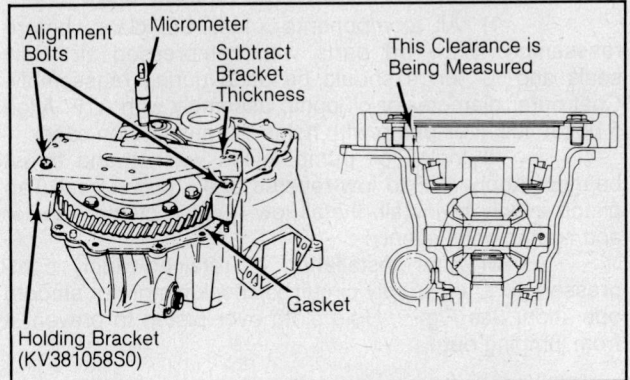

Subtract thickness of bracket to obtain actual distance.

4) Remove holding bracket and counterweight. With bearing housing installed in transmission case, rotate bearing several times in each direction to seat bearing.

5) Mount holding bracket on transmission case. Install micrometer to bracket and measure distance to bearing race. *See Fig. 25.* Record reading and subtract thickness of holding bracket to obtain actual measurement.

Fig. 25: Set-Up and Measuring Clearance to Bearing Race in Transmission Case

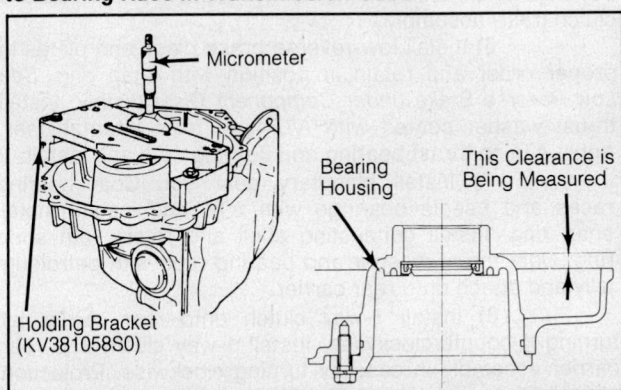

Subtract thickness of bracket to obtain actual distance.

6) Subtract measurement obtained in step 3) from reading obtained in step 5). Using this measurement, find proper shim (or shims) necessary to properly set differential side bearing height. See DIFFERENTIAL SIDE BEARING SHIM chart.

7) Remove bearing housing from transmission case. Remove bearing and "O" ring. Install selected shim(s) on bearing housing and install bearing. Coat "O" ring with petroleum jelly and install. Install bearing housing to transmission case.

8) Install differential in transmission case. Place gasket on converter housing. Attach converter housing to transmission case. Install and tighten all bolts. Seat differential assembly by rotating it at least 10 times in each direction.

9) Insert Preload Adapter (KV38105900) into differential assembly. Using an INCH lb. torque wrench,

measure rotational force of differential side bearings. If rotational force exceeds 52-65 INCH lbs. (5.7-7.2 N.m), disassemble transmission case and remove differential assembly.

NOTE: If rotational force reading varies 8.7 INCH lbs. (1.0 N.m) or binds during any revolution, repeat adjustment procedure.

10) Repeat adjustment procedures and recheck rotational force. Separate case and housing and remove differential assembly.

DIFFERENTIAL SIDE BEARING SHIM SPECIFICATIONS

Measured Distance In. (mm)	Required Shim In. (mm)
0-.0028 (0-.07)	.0150 (.38)
.0028-.0059 (.07-.15)	.0181 (.46)
.0059-.0091 (.15-.23)	.0213 (.54)
.0091-.0122 (.23-.31)	.0244 (.62)
.0122-.0154 (.31-.39)	.0276 (.70)
.0154-.0185 (.39-.47)	.0307 (.78)
.0185-.0217 (.47-.55)	.0339 (.86)
.0217-.0248 (.55-.63)	.0370 (.94)
.0248-.0280 (.63-.71)	.0402 (1.02)
.0280-.0311 (.71-.79)	.0433 (1.10)
.0311-.0343 (.79-.87)	.0465 (1.18)
.0343-.0374 (.87-.95)	.0496 (1.26)
.0374-.0406 (.95-1.03)	.0528 (1.34)
.0406-.0437 (1.03-1.11	.0559 (1.42)
.0437-.0469 (1.11-1.19)	.0591 (1.50)
.0469-.0500 (1.19-1.27)	.0622 (1.58)
.0500-.0531 (1.27-1.35)	.0654 (1.66)

OUTPUT SHAFT BEARING

1) If transmission case, output shaft, bearing or front cover is replaced, adjust output shaft. Apply ATF to bearing. Press bearing into transmission case bore. Place 2 or 3 shims on front cover. Press bearing into front cover bore. Install output shaft in converter housing.

2) Install gasket and front cover on converter housing. Tighten bolts. Rotate output shaft at least 10 times to seat bearings. Shaft should rotate smoothly without binding. Mount an adapter and INCH lb. torque wrench to output shaft.

NOTE: The output shaft bearing shims are available in sizes ranging from .0043" (.110 mm) to .0394" (1.00 mm) in increments of .0008" (.020 mm).

3) Measure rotational force of output shaft. If rotational force exceeds 3.1-4.2 INCH lbs. (.35-.47 N.m), remove front cover and output shaft. Remove or add shims as required to increase or decrease rotational force.

OUTPUT SHAFT END PLAY

1) After adjusting rotational force of output shaft bearing, measure output shaft end play. Install idler gear, with bearings, on idler shaft. Install idler gear and output shaft assembly in converter housing.

2) Clean front cover bolt threads and converter housing with solvent. Install front cover gasket and front cover on converter housing. Install and tighten bolts to 10-13 ft. lbs. (14-18 N.m).

3) Install idler gear bolt and lock washer. Tighten idler gear bolt to 20-27 ft. lbs. (26-36 N.m). Ensure lock washer is aligned with groove on converter housing.

4) After tightening bolt, turn output shaft at least 5 complete revolutions. Loosen idler gear bolt, then retighten to specification. Bend lock washer. Install rear internal gear.

5) Assemble governor shaft assembly, parking pawl, return spring and parking pawl shaft. Install governor shaft retaining bolt. Place 2 beads of solder .098" (2.50 mm) in diameter on internal gear. See Fig. 26.

6) If necessary, a soldering plate that is .098" (2.50 mm) thick and .2" (5 mm) in length may be used as maximum gear clearance is .091" (2.30 mm). If diameter or thickness is smaller than .098" (2.50 mm), also use shim(s). Solder is used in the same manner as using Plastigage.

Fig. 26: Installing Solder on Internal Gear

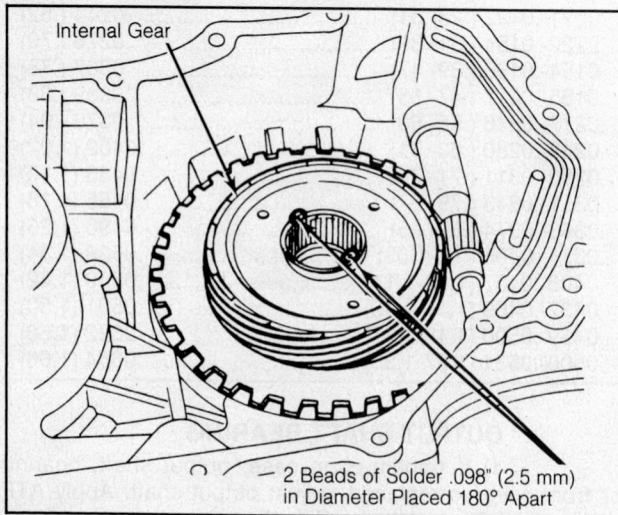

Pieces of Solder are used in same manner as Plastigage.

7) Install converter housing, with output shaft assembly installed, on transmission case. Install all converter housing-to-transmission case bolts and tighten.

8) Remove converter housing. Remove governor shaft retaining bolt. Remove parking pawl shaft, return spring, parking pawl and governor shaft assembly. Remove rear internal gear and disassemble output shaft.

NOTE: If soldering plate is used, subtract .002" (.05 mm) from thickness of plate to allow for elasticity of plate when compressed.

OUTPUT SHAFT SHIM SPECIFICATIONS

Measured Thickness [1] In. (mm)	Required Shim In. (mm)
.0217-.0335 (.55-.85)	.012 (.3)
.0295-.0413 (.75-1.05)	.020 (.5)
.0374-.0492 (.95-1.25)	.028 (.7)
.0453-.0571 (1.15-1.45)	.035 (.9)
.0531-.0650 (1.35-1.65)	.043 (1.1)
.0610-.0728 (1.55-1.85)	.051 (1.3)
.0689-.0807 (1.75-2.05)	.059 (1.5)
.0768-.0886 (1.95-2.25)	.067 (1.7)

[1] – Measured thickness of soldering plate after subtracting .002" (.50 mm).

9) Measure thickness of solder or soldering plate. Select proper shim from *Output Shaft Shim* chart to set output shaft end play at .0098-.0217" (.25-.55 mm). Place shim aside for use during reassembly.

TRANSAXLE REASSEMBLY

1) All components must be clean before reassembly. Blow off parts with compressed air. New seals and "O" rings should be used during reassembly. Coat outer diameter of oil pump assembly with ATF. Align 5 bolt holes in oil pump with holes in transmission case.

2) Install oil pump, nylon washer and thrust bearing. Apply ATF to low-reverse brake piston seal. Tap piston evenly to install. Install low-reverse piston retainer and tighten bolts evenly.

3) After installation of retainer, apply compressed air to oil supply circuit to check piston for smooth operation. See Fig. 9. Hold cloth over piston to prevent it from jumping out.

NOTE: After retainer installation, ensure piston seal is not turned over by the application of air. Piston is installed properly if it moves smoothly.

4) Install brake band. Remove securing clip after seating band. Coat brake band servo piston "O" ring with ATF. Install servo piston and return spring. Using a small "C" clamp, compress piston and spring. Install snap ring and remove clamp.

5) Coat oil pump housing seals with ATF and install high-reverse clutch (front) assembly. Coat thrust bearings and races with ATF and install. Install forward clutch (rear) assembly.

6) Install low-reverse brake discs and plates in proper order and retain in position with snap ring. See *Low-Reverse Brake under Component Disassembly.* Install thrust washer coated with ATF and front internal gear. Apply ATF to thrust bearing and bearing race and install.

7) Install planetary gear set. Coat bearing races and needle bearings with ATF and install. Install snap ring. Install connecting shell and retain with snap ring. Coat thrust washer and bearing race with petroleum jelly and attach onto rear carrier.

8) Install 1-way clutch onto rear carrier by turning it counterclockwise. Install 1-way clutch and rear carrier assembly in case by turning clockwise. Projection should face upward. See *Fig. 29.* Install large 1-way clutch snap ring so bent end does not interfere with parking pawl.

9) Coat bearing race and thrust washer with petroleum jelly and attach onto rear internal gear. Install rear internal gear. Assemble governor shaft assembly, parking pawl, return spring and parking pawl shaft. Install governor shaft retaining bolt.

10) Install seal bushing to prevent sun gear and output shaft from jamming. Perform output shaft end play adjustment. Check rotary frictional force of output shaft and idler gear bearings. Check differential side bearing height adjustment and rotary friction force. See *Adjustments.*

11) Install differential assembly on transmission case. Apply petroleum jelly to output shaft shim and attach onto output shaft. Place gasket on transmission

NISSAN/DATSUN PULSAR, SENTRA & STANZA (Cont.)

Fig. 27: Exploded View of Transaxle Assembly

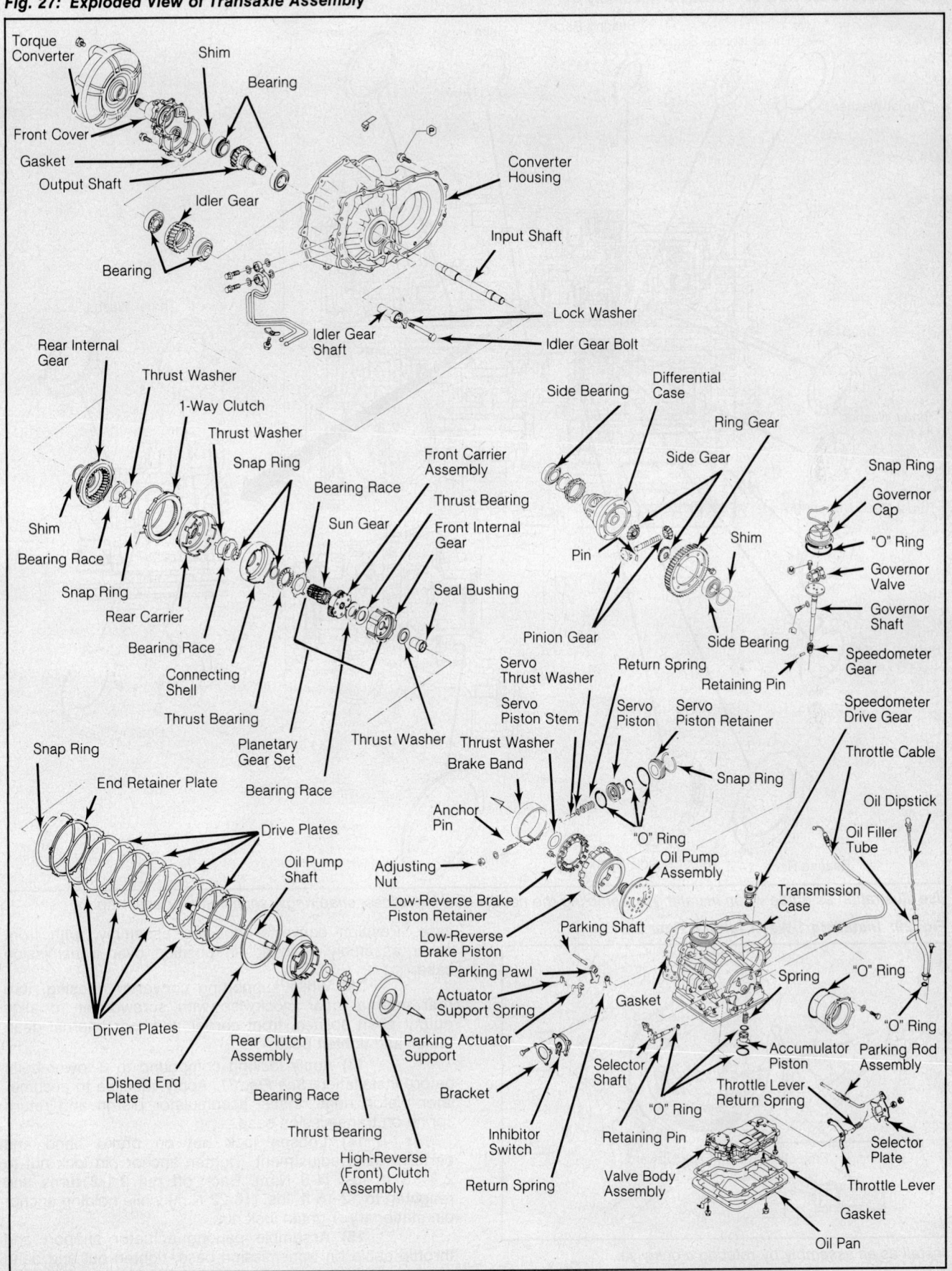

Fig. 28: Sectional View of Transaxle Assembly

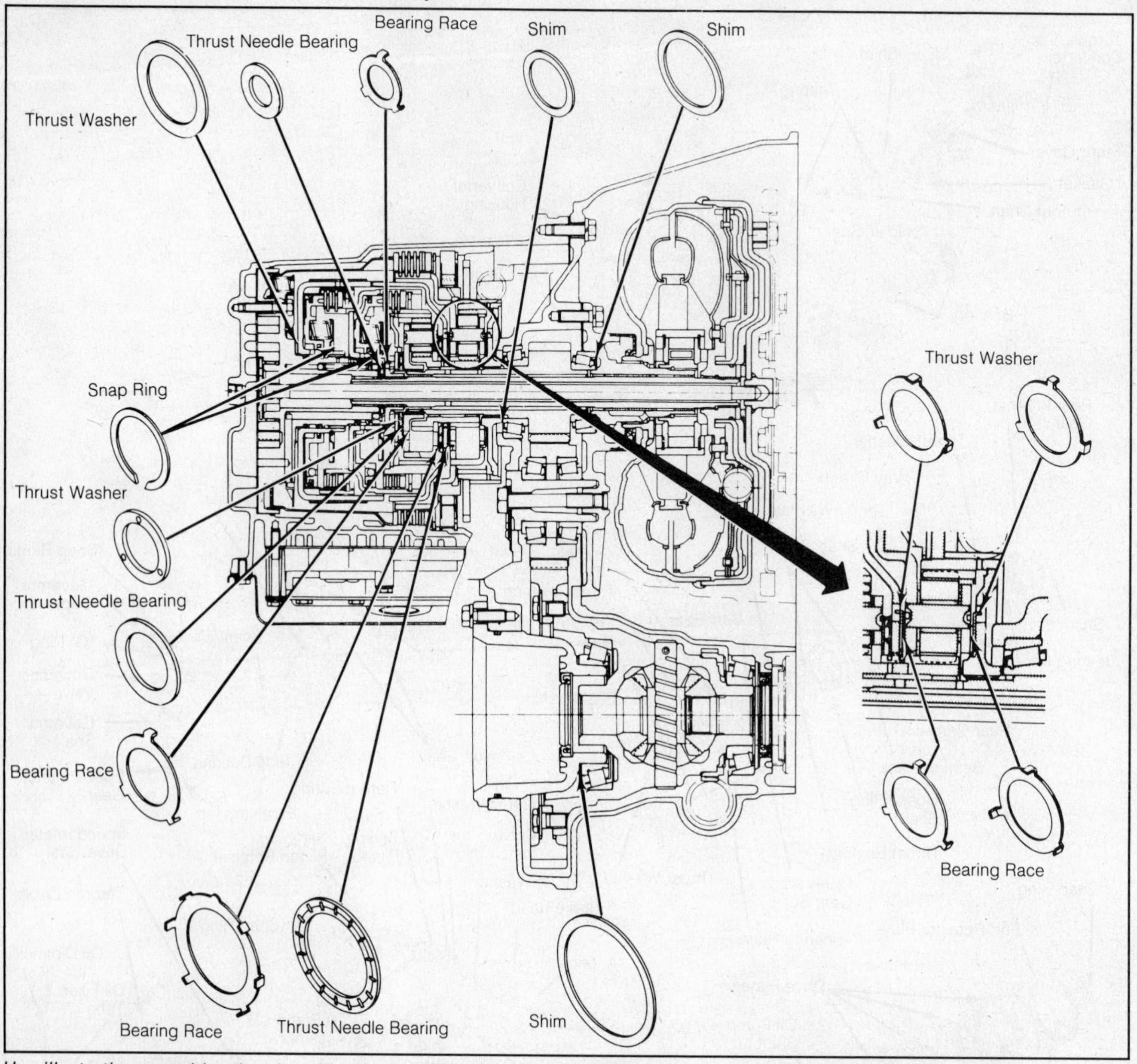

Thrust Washer

Thrust Needle Bearing

Bearing Race

Shim

Shim

Snap Ring

Thrust Washer

Thrust Needle Bearing

Bearing Race

Thrust Washer

Bearing Race

Bearing Race

Thrust Needle Bearing

Shim

Use illustration as guide when installing/assembling the needle bearing/races, snap rings, shims and/or seal ring.

Fig. 29: Installing 1-Way Clutch & Rear Carrier

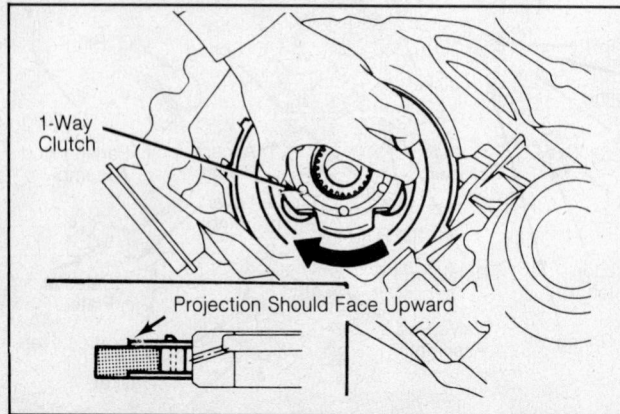

1-Way Clutch

Projection Should Face Upward

Install as an assembly by rotating clockwise.

case. Position converter housing assembly, with front cover assembly attached, in position over transmission case.

12) While supporting converter housing, turn rear internal gear clockwise with screwdriver to align output shaft splines, front carrier and rear internal gear. Install and tighten bolts.

13) Apply locking compound to 3 lower bolts before installation. *See Fig. 31.* Apply vaseline to accumulator piston rings. Install accumulator piston and return spring on transmission case.

14) Loosen lock nut on brake band and perform band adjustment. Tighten anchor pin lock nut to 2.9-4.3 ft. lbs. (4-6 N.m). Back off nut 2 1/2 turns and retighten to 12-16 ft. lbs. (16-22 N.m) while holding anchor pin stationary. Tighten lock nut.

15) Assemble parking actuator support and throttle cable on transmission case, tighten nut and bend

Automatic Transmissions

NISSAN/DATSUN PULSAR, SENTRA & STANZA (Cont.)

Fig. 30: *Hydraulic Circuits Diagram*

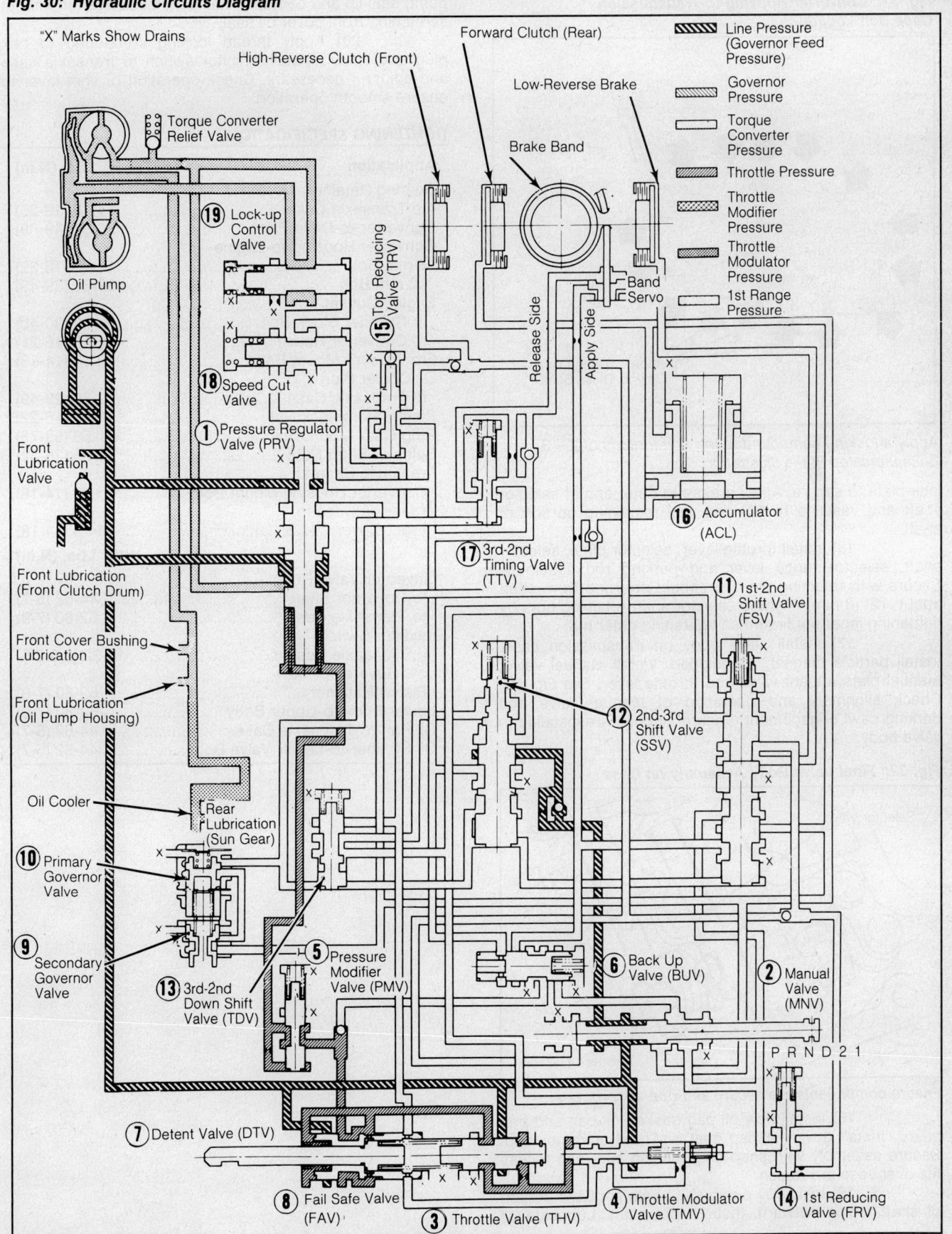

The illustration shown is with the transaxle in "N" (Neutral) range.

Automatic Transmissions

NISSAN/DATSUN PULSAR, SENTRA & STANZA (Cont.)

Fig. 31: *Converter Housing-to-Transmission Case Bolt Locations*

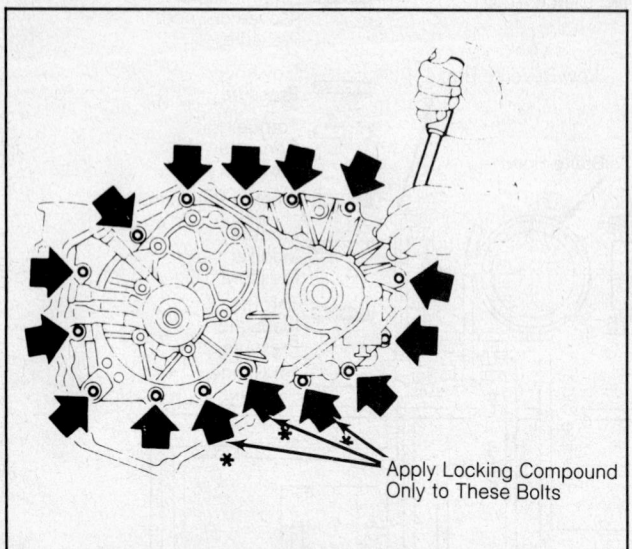

Apply a locking compound to the bolt threads of the 3 bolts indicated in the illustration.

lock-plate to secure. Apply grease to outer end of selector shaft and vaseline to "O" ring and remaining portion of shaft.

16) Install throttle lever, selector plate, selector shaft, selector range lever and parking rod assembly. Secure with retaining pin. Pin should protrude from shaft about .12" (3 mm). Tighten selector shaft retaining nuts by tightening inner nut first, then tightening outer nut.

17) Install valve body on transmission case. Install particle magnet, if equipped. Install manual valve, manual plate, detent valve and throttle lever. *See Fig. 32.* Check alignment and operation of manual valve and parking pawl engagement. Ensure all bolts are installed in valve body.

Fig. 32: *Final Valve Body Assembly on Case*

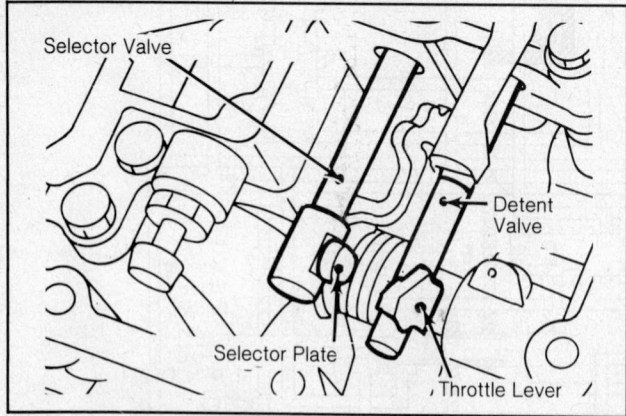

Ensure components are secure and operate properly.

18) Install new oil pan gasket, oil pan and pan guard. Install governor cap seal ring and governor cap. Secure assembly with snap ring, making sure cap recess fits over case protrusion.

19) Install oil pump shaft with concave portion of shaft facing outward. Install input shaft. Lubricate oil

pump seal lip and converter neck. Install converter without scratching front cover oil seal.

20) Apply thread locking compound to hex plug and install. Install inhibitor switch to transaxle case and adjust if necessary. Check operation of shift lever to ensure smooth operation.

TIGHTENING SPECIFICATIONS

Application	Ft. Lbs. (N.m)
Bearing Retainer	
to Transaxle Case	14-18 (19-25)
Converter-to-Drive Plate	36-51 (49-69)
Converter Housing-to-Engine	
8 mm Bolt	12-16 (16-22)
10 mm Bolt	29-36 (39-49)
Engine Gusset	
to Cylinder Block Bolt	22-30 (30-40)
to Converter Housing	12-15 (16-21)
Front Cover Mount Bolt	10-13 (14-18)
Oil Cooler Pipe	
to Transaxle Case	22-36 (29-49)
Piston Stem Lock Nut	12-16 (16-22)
Ring Gear Mount Bolt	51-58 (69-78)
Selector Shaft Nuts	19-23 (26-32)
Transaxle Case-to	
Converter Housing Mount Bolt	10-13 (14-18)
Transaxle Case to	
Front Cover	10-13 (14-18)
	INCH Lbs. (N.m)
Governor Valve Body	
to Governor Shaft	44-62 (5-7)
to Transaxle Case	62-80 (7-9)
Inhibitor Switch	
to Transaxle Case	18-22 (2.0-2.5)
Low-Reverse Brake	
Piston Retainer	62-80 (7-9)
Lower Body-to-Upper Body	62-80 (7-9)
Oil Pan-to-Transaxle Case	44-62 (5-7)
Oil Strainer-to-Lower Valve Body	44-62 (5-7)

Automatic Transmissions
PORSCHE 928S

DESCRIPTION

The A28.01 is a 4-speed automatic, consisting of a Ravigneaux planetary gear set, 2 brake bands, 2 multiple-disc clutches, 1 disc-type brake, primary and secondary hydraulic pumps, valve body, input and output shafts.

Torque converter is at front of transmission in 2-piece bell housing. Final drive section, containing ring and pinion, side gears and pinion gears, is behind transmission. Differentials are either conventional or limited slip type.

OPERATION

Drive flange is bolted to torque converter and connected to central shaft via clamping sleeve. Hydraulic torque converter mutiplies engine torque 2.12 times. Stall speed is 2200-2600 RPM.

Turbine wheel of torque converter drives large planetary sun gear through input shaft. Primary pump supplies transmission and torque converter with ATF under pressure.

The 1-way clutch locks in 1st and Reverse gear. Shifting is controlled by valve body assembly. Governor pressure changes with road speed and influences upshifts and downshifts in valve body.

Governor also drives secondary pump, which will provide emergency hydraulic pressure whenever vehicle is moving. This pressure makes it possible to tow start vehicle at speeds between 19-31 MPH. Secondary pump will also lubricate critical parts of transmission if vehicle is towed with rear wheels on ground.

CAUTION: If vehicle is towed with rear wheels on ground, maximum towing distance is 75 miles with maximum speed of 31 MPH. Secondary ATF pump will not provide lubrication beyond these limits and internal damage WILL occur.

LUBRICATION & ADJUSTMENT

Information not available from manufacturer.

TROUBLE SHOOTING

Information not available from manufacturer.

TESTING

NOTE: Specifications given are only information available from manufacturer.

ROAD TESTING

1) Before road testing, ensure that ATF level is correct and control linkage is adjusted. During road test, make sure upshifts and downshifts occur smoothly at correct speeds. See A28.01 SHIFT POINTS table.

2) Slipping (engine runaway) usually indicates clutch or band problems. Identify unit slipping by noting transmission operation in all selector positions and comparing clutch and band applications in those positions.

3) Confirm proper operation of good units through elimination process. Internal leakage or sticking valves could also cause most conditions. DO NOT remove transmission until all external testing has been completed.

HYDRAULIC PRESSURE TESTS

NOTE: Disconnect vacuum modulator and plug vacuum line for tests.

Modulation Pressure

Modulation pressure should be 63.09-64.54 psi (4.4-4.5 kg/cm^2) at road speed of 31 MPH. Disconnect and plug vacuum line to modulator. Specific adjustment procedure for modulation pressure is not available from manufacturer.

Operating Pressure

Operating pressure, which is not adjustable, should be 243.67-246.57 psi (17.1-17.3 kg/cm^2) with engine running at idle speed. Selector lever should be in "2", "3", or "D" positions. Vacuum modulator must be disconnected and vacuum line plugged.

Governor Pressure

1) Governor pressure, which is not adjustable, is checked with selector lever in "D" position and vehicle rolling with partial load. At 10 MPH, governor pressure reading should be .73-1.45 psi (.05-.10 kg/cm^2).

2) At 20 MPH, reading should be 13.78-15.23 psi (.97-1.07 kg/cm^2). At 55 MPH, reading should be 26.83-28.28 psi (1.89-1.99 kg/cm^2). At 80 MPH, reading should be 32.63-34.08 psi (2.29-2.40 kg/cm^2).

A28.01 SHIFT POINTS

Shift Conditions	MPH
928S	
Full Throttle	
1-2 Upshift	35-41
2-3 Upshift	70-81
3-4 Upshift	118-131
Partial Throttle	
1-2 Upshift	14-15
2-3 Upshift	16-21
3-4 Upshift	26-31
Kickdown	
1-2 Upshift	43-47
2-3 Upshift	79-82
3-4 Upshift	128-132
Full Throttle	
2-1 Downshift	18-15
3-2 Downshift	40-36
4-3 Downshift	95-84
Partial Throttle	
2-1 Downshift	11-10
3-2 Downshift	14-12
4-3 Downshift	21-17
Kickdown	
2-1 Downshift	28-24
3-2 Downshift	76-66
4-3 Downshift	126-114

REMOVAL & INSTALLATION

Information not available from manufacturer.

TRANSMISSION DISASSEMBLY

Porsche A28.01 4-speed is replaced only as unit item; all repairs are performed by manufacturer.

Automatic Transaxles

RENAULT FUEGO & SPORTWAGON

DESCRIPTION

The Fuego and 18i transaxle is a 3-speed unit consisting basically of torque converter, differential assembly and transmission assembly. Differential consists of ring and pinion gear set, worm gear to drive governor, and step-down gears to change direction of drive centerline.

Transmission assembly consists of a planetary gear train, 2 clutches, 2 brakes and main control systems for transaxle. Mechanical, electrical and hydraulic control systems are used.

LUBRICATION & ADJUSTMENT

See the appropriate article in AUTOMATIC TRANSMISSION SERVICING Section.

TROUBLE SHOOTING

ENGINE IDLES ROUGH OR STALLS

Idle speed incorrect. Check ignition timing and spark plug condition. Throttle cable out of adjustment. Leak in vacuum circuit.

VEHICLE CREEPS IN "N"

Shift lever out of adjustment. Defective or damaged E1 clutch.

EXCESSIVE CREEPING IN "A"

Idle speed incorrect. Throttle cable out of adjustment. Torque converter faulty or damaged.

SLIPS IN FORWARD & REVERSE

Incorrect fluid level. Pressure regulator damaged or out of adjustment. Torque converter faulty or damaged.

NO MOVEMENT

In 3rd, OK in Other Gears

E1 clutch faulty or defective. One-way clutch damaged or faulty.

In 3rd, "1" or "R"

Fluid level incorrect. Pressure regulator or shift control mechanism out of adjustment. Oil pump shaft or turbine shaft bent or damaged. Defective oil pump. Torque converter drive plate warped or otherwise damaged. Final drive assembly faulty. Torque converter damaged.

Fig. 1: Cross Sectional View of Renault Fuego & 18i Automatic Transaxle

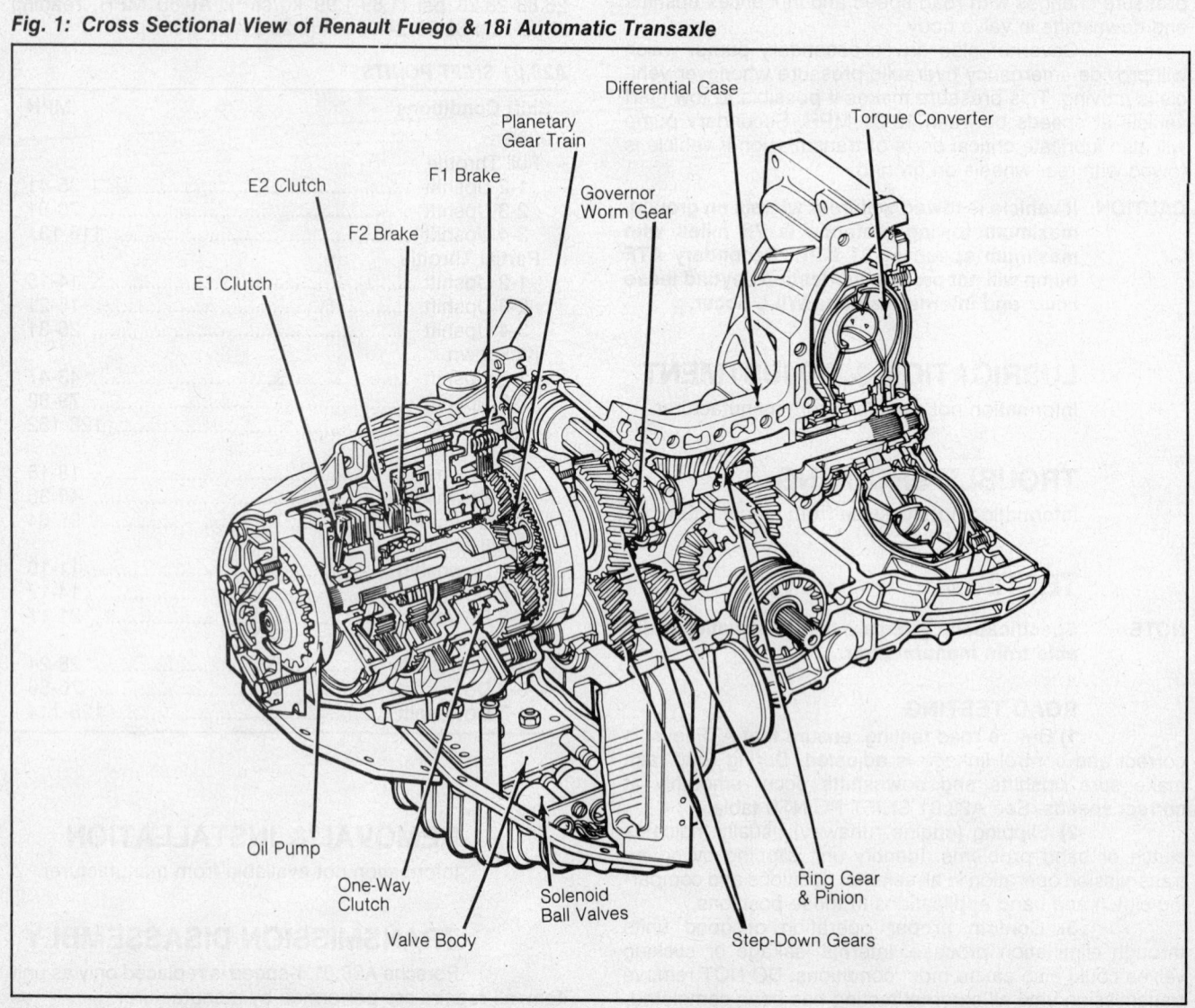

RENAULT FUEGO & SPORTWAGON (Cont.)

In 3rd or "1"
Defective E1 clutch.
In "R" or 3rd Gear
Faulty valve body. Defective E2 clutch.

SLIPPING ON SHIFTS

Incorrect fluid level. Fluid pressure regulator damaged or out of adjustment. Faulty valve body. Defective E1 or E2 clutch. Defective F1 or F2 brake.

ERRATIC STARTS

Idle speed incorrect. Throttle cable out of adjustment.

EXCESSIVE SHIFT SHOCK BETWEEN GEARS

Incorrect fluid level. Pressure regulator damaged or out of adjustment. Defective F1 brake. Leak in vacuum circuit. Faulty valve body.

SHIFT POINTS INCORRECT

Throttle cable, governor cable or kickdown switch out of adjustment. Governor cable faulty. Faulty wiring circuit. Loose ground connections. Governor computer faulty. Faulty valve body. Engine charging system.

NO REVERSE OR ENGINE BRAKING IN "1"

Faulty valve body. Defective F1 brake.

NO 1ST GEAR IN "A"

Faulty wiring circuit. Loose ground connections. Governor computer faulty. Solenoid ball valves damaged. One-way clutch faulty or damaged.

NO 2ND GEAR IN "A"

Faulty wiring circuit. Loose ground connections. Governor computer faulty. Solenoid ball valves damaged. Faulty valve body. Defective F2 brake.

NO 3RD GEAR IN "A"

Faulty wiring circuit. Loose ground connections. Governor computer faulty. Multi-function switch faulty. Solenoid ball valves damaged. Faulty valve body.

REMAINS IN 1ST GEAR IN "A"

Faulty wiring circuit. Loose ground connections. Governor computer faulty. Solenoid ball valves damaged. Faulty valve body.

REMAINS IN 3RD GEAR

Check for blown fuse, faulty wiring circuit, or loose ground connections. Governor computer faulty. Solenoid ball valves damaged. Faulty valve body.

SHIFTS FROM 1ST TO 3RD, SKIPS 2ND; SHIFT LEVER ABNORMAL

Shift lever out of adjustment. Selector control out of adjustment. Parking control mechanism and manual valve faulty.

IMPROPER OPERATION IN "P"

Shift lever out of adjustment. Shift control mechanism out of adjustment. Parking control mechanism and manual valve faulty.

STARTER NOT WORKING

Faulty wiring circuit. Loose ground connections. Shift lever out of adjustment. Multi-function switch faulty.

BACKUP LIGHTS NOT WORKING

Faulty wiring circuit. Loose ground connections. Multi-function switch faulty.

SLIPS WHEN STARTING OUT IN "A"

One-way clutch damaged or faulty.

TESTING

TESTING EQUIPMENT

1) No special equipment is needed for road testing. Hydraulic testing and transaxle diagnosis require the use of the following special test equipment: Test box (B. Vi. 797-01 or -02) and thermometer (B. Vi. 524-01). If test box (B. Vi. 797-01) is used, intermediate cable (B. Vi. 858) is required for hook-up to transaxle. In addition, hydraulic testing requires oil pressure switch (B. Vi. 466-04). The test box is equipped with indicator lights and gauges to diagnose various operating conditions of the Fuego and 18i transaxle.

2) The test box face consists of: 4 indicator lights, a digital display, potentiometer, circuit breaker, 4-scale dial (galvanometer), test selector switch and 3 fuses. A wiring harness is provided for electrical connection to the transaxle. This equipment must be used for proper diagnosis and testing. A description of the function of individual test box components follows.

Fig. 2: B. Vi. 797-01 (-02) Test Box

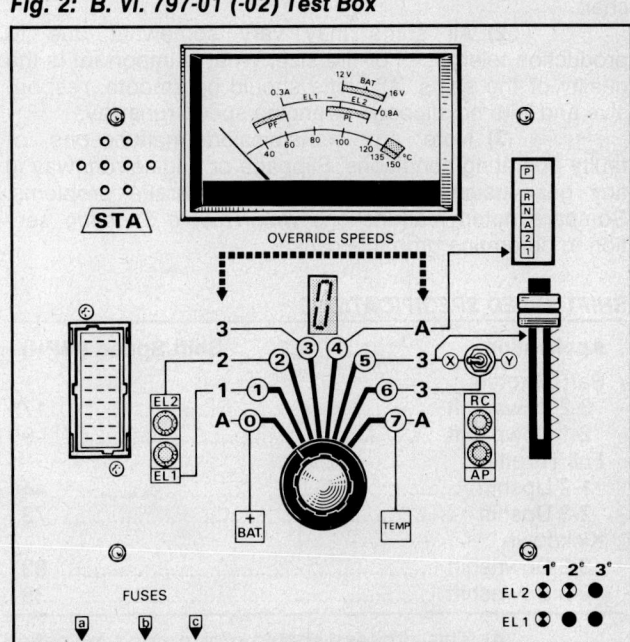

This test box must be used for complete testing and diagnosis of the Fuego/18i automatic transaxle.

Indicator Lights
EL1 light (Yellow) indicates status of solenoid ball valve 1 (lit when solenoid is energized). EL2 light (Yellow) indicates status of solenoid ball valve 2 (lit when

energized). The AP indicator light (Red) indicates whether emission control system is operating (this system not used in these tests). RC light (Green) indicates whether the kickdown switch is operating.

Digital Display
Indicates multifunction switch operation and computer condition.

Potentiometer and Circuit Breaker
Systems not used in these tests.

Galvanometer
The galvanometer has 4 scales: BAT scale for reading of battery voltage, EL1-EL2 scale to measure current passing through solenoid ball valves, and temperature scale to measure transmission oil temperature (Red zone indicates maximum operating temperature). The PF and PL scales are not used.

Test Selector Switch
This switch is used to selected desired test made. Position "0" gives battery voltage; "1" measures current and input in EL1; "2" measures current and input in EL2; "3" places vehicle in 3rd gear with shift lever in "A" position (solenoid ball valves not activated); "4", "5" and "6" are not used; "7" measures transmission fluid temperature (with thermometer in place).

Fuses
All fuses are 1 amp capacity. Fuse "a" protects test box, fuse "b" protects EL1 and fuse "c" protects EL2.

ROAD TEST

1) Before road testing, make sure that fluid level and condition and control linkage adjustments have been checked and corrected as needed. During test, transmission should upshift and downshift at approximately the speeds shown in *Shift Speed Specifications* chart.

2) All shifts may vary somewhat due to production tolerances or tire size. What is important is the quality of the shifts. All shifts should be smooth, responsive and with no slippage or engine speed runaway.

3) Note any transmission malfunctions or faulty operating conditions. Slippage or engine runaway in any gear usually indicates clutch or brake problems. Compare noted malfunctions with *Trouble Shooting* section to determine probable cause.

SHIFT SPEED SPECIFICATIONS

Application	Shift Speed (MPH)
Part Throttle	
3-2 Downshift	17
2-1 Downshift	9
Full Throttle	
1-2 Upshift	44
2-3 Upshift	73
Kickdown	
3-2 Downshift	63
2-1 Downshift	39

4) This process should give a good indication of which units are faulty and/or out of adjustment. It will also give a reasonable indication of which units are operating properly; however, it is extremely difficult to determine the exact cause of any particular malfunction. Practically any condition can be caused by leaking hydraulic circuits or sticking valves. Therefore, unless an obvious condition exists, do not disassemble transmission until hydraulic pressure tests have been made.

HYDRAULIC PRESSURE TESTS

Perform tests with transmission fluid at normal operating temperature of about 175°F (80°C). Attach thermometer to test box, remove dipstick from tube and insert thermometer. Hydraulic pressures are checked in 2 steps, "Initial Adjustment" and "Full Throttle Road Test".

Initial Adjustment

1) Connect pressure gauge at rear of transaxle, but DO NOT disconnect the vacuum capsule. *See Fig. 3.* Check fluid level and top off if needed. With parking brake engaged, wheels blocked and tachometer attached, place shift lever in "P" and check fluid pressure.

2) With engine running at 800 RPM, pressure should be 58 psi (4.2 kg/cm²). As engine speed is increased, pressure should increase rapidly to a maximum pressure of 189-203 psi (13.3-14.3 kg/cm²).

Fig. 3: Pressure Test Port Location

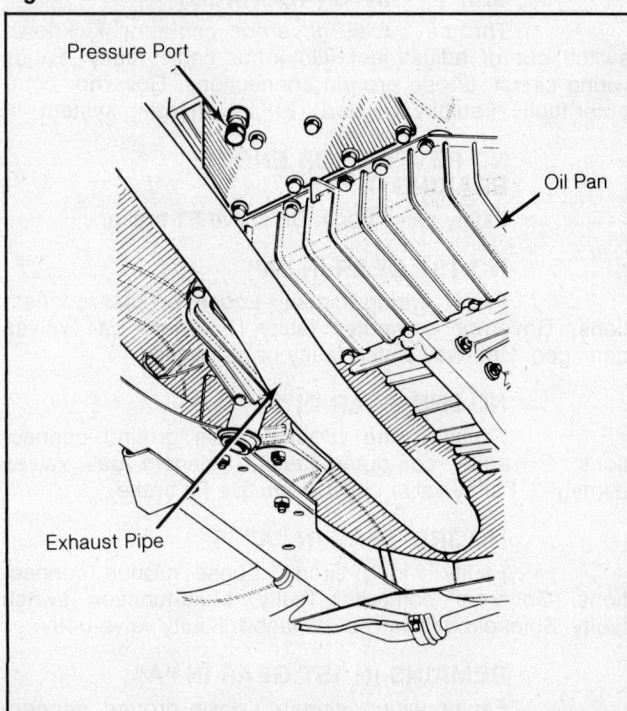

3) Move shift lever to "N", bring engine speed to 800 RPM, and read pressure at partial throttle. If pressure is not 36-39 psi (2.5-2.7 kg/cm²), adjust by turning the vacuum capsule one notch at a time. Changing capsule position by 1 notch will change pressure by about 1.5 psi (.11 kg/cm²). Pressure is increased as the vacuum capsule is screwed in.

Full Throttle Road Test

Reconnect vacuum capsule. Drive car to warm fluid. Place shift lever in "A". From standstill, press accelerator pedal to the floor. Read maximum fluid pressure obtained just before 1-2 upshift. If pressure is not about 58 psi (4.1 kg/cm²), check vacuum capsule and vacuum circuit. *See Service (In Vehicle)* in this article. Replace capsule if necessary and adjust full throttle pressure. If pressure will not adjust properly, check for faulty pressure regulator or transmission assembly.

Fig. 4: Vacuum Capsule Location

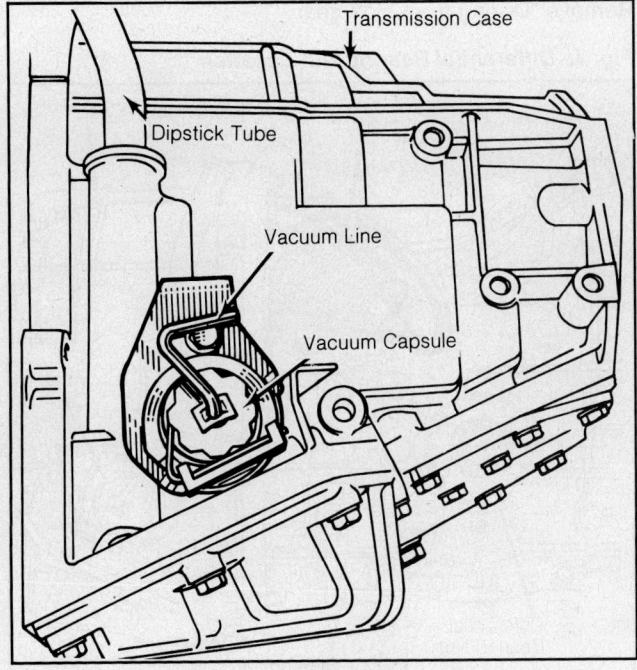

TRANSAXLE DIAGNOSIS

Static Testing (Vehicle at Rest)

1) Attach test box lead to diagnostic socket on transaxle (use adapter B. Vi. 858 with -01 test box). Remove dipstick and insert thermometer in dipstick tube as in *Hydraulic Testing*.

2) To check battery voltage, turn engine off and ignition switch on. Place shift lever in "A" position and turn selector switch on test box to "0". Digital display should read "1". Read battery voltage on BAT scale of galvanometer. If scale does not indicate 12-16 volts, transmission malfunction could result. If no voltage is indicated, check test box fuses.

Fig. 5: Location of Transaxle Test Connection for Test Box Diagnosis

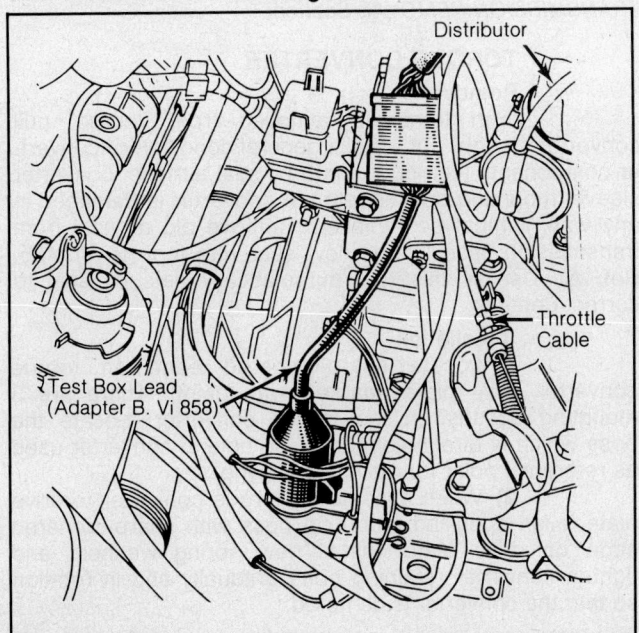

3) To check EL1 solenoid ball valve, move selector switch to "1". Digital display will read "3" and EL1 and EL2 indicator lights should light, indicating that solenoid ball valves are energized. Read current flow on EL1-EL2 scale of galvanometer. Current flow should be .3-.8 amps.

4) If current flow is correct, EL1 solenoid ball valve is in good electrical condition. Go to next step. If current is out of indicated range, check wiring and connecters. If wiring is good, solenoid ball valve is defective. If no current is indicated, check test box fuses.

5) EL2 solenoid ball valve is checked in the same manner as EL1, with the selector switch in the "2" position. If current is correct, go to next test.

6) Move selector switch to "3". Input current should still read .3-.8 amps. If current is incorrect, check test box leads and electrical controls. If input current is correct, transaxle malfunction is not in electrical system. Check hydraulic and mechanical systems.

Dynamic Testing (Vehicle in Motion)

1) With test equipment attached as before, position test box in vehicle so that it may be observed while vehicle is being driven. Start engine, place shift lever in "A" and begin driving with selector switch in "0". Digital display should show "1" and EL1 and EL2 lights should be on.

2) Continue driving. On 1-2 upshift, digital display should go to "2" and EL1 light should go out. Continue driving. On 2-3 upshift, digital display should go to "3" and both EL lights should be out.

3) Reduce speed to 40-45 MPH and move selector switch to "7". Press accelerator pedal to the floor to get 3-2 kickdown. RC light should come on. If it does not, check kickdown switch adjustment, ignition switch and the connecting wire.

SERVICE (IN VEHICLE)

AXLE SHAFTS & WHEEL BEARINGS

See Service (In Vehicle) in Renault Fuego & 18i 4 & 5-Speed manual transaxle article.

SOLENOID BALL VALVES

Removal

Solenoid ball valves are located on the valve body. To remove, drain transmission fluid, remove inspection plate, oil pan and gasket. Remove solenoid ball valve clips and disconnect wiring. Note color of wire attached to each valve. Remove support plate retaining bolts (2) and remove valves from valve body. *See Fig. 38.*

Installation

Reverse removal procedure to install. Do not reverse valve positions. Be sure to install correct wire to correct valve as noted during removal.

VACUUM CAPSULE

Inspection

1) With test equipment connected as in *Hydraulic Pressure Tests*, connect vacuum pump to vacuum hose on capsule. Apply a vacuum of about 15.7 in. Hg. If needle on test box does not move, check pressure at full and part throttle.

2) If the needle falls, there is a leak in the vacuum circuit and the capsule or its hose must be replaced. Make sure that the vacuum hose connection on the intake manifold is in good condition.

RENAULT FUEGO & SPORTWAGON (Cont.)

3) Check to make sure that the hose connection to the capsule is tight. An air leak in the capsule or pipe causes a whistling sound, irregular idling, excessive light throttle pressure, and slightly harsh gear shifts under light load.

Removal

Drain transmission fluid. Disconnect vacuum hose from capsule. Move retaining clip out of way and unscrew the capsule, counting the number of turns.

Installation

The vacuum capsule cannot be disassembled and must therefore be replaced as a unit if faulty. Screw in capsule the same number of turns as needed to remove it. Install retaining clip and connect vacuum hose. Refill transmission. Adjust pressure.

KICKDOWN SWITCH

Removal & Installation

Remove accelerator cable. Disconnect wire from kickdown switch. Unscrew 2 retaining bolts and remove switch. Reverse removal procedure to install.

Fig. 6: Accelerator Cable Housing

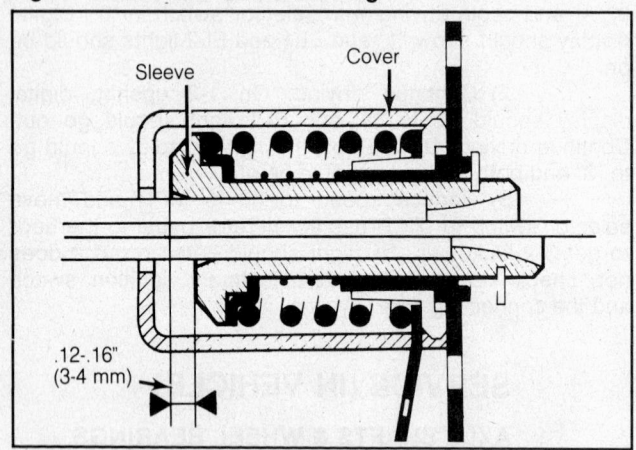

Adjust to allow .12-.16" (3-4 mm) free play in housing.

Adjustment

Adjustment is made with the accelerator cable. Make sure that the accelerator cable has enough play in it to allow .12-.16" (3-4 mm) movement in the sleeve when the accelerator pedal is depressed. Make sure that the cover is positioned correctly to prevent tarnishing of the contacts.

DIFFERENTIAL BEARING NUT & OIL SEAL

Removal

1) Raise and support vehicle. Disconnect battery. Drain transmission fluid. Disconnect vacuum capsule hose from intake manifold. Disconnect transaxle wiring connectors and remove support. Insert spacer tool (T. Av. 509-01) between lower shock mounting base and lower control arm pivot shaft on each side.

2) Remove drive shaft retaining roll pins with drift. Separate tie rod end ball joints and upper control arm ball joints from steering knuckle using puller. Tilt axle carriers away from transaxle to separate drive shafts from side gears.

3) Mark nut and housing for reassembly to same position. Remove lock nut. Remove nut with tool (B. Vi. 807). Count and record number of turns required to

remove nut. Remove lip seal and "O" ring from nut. Remove "O" ring from side gear.

Fig. 7: Differential Bearing Nut Location

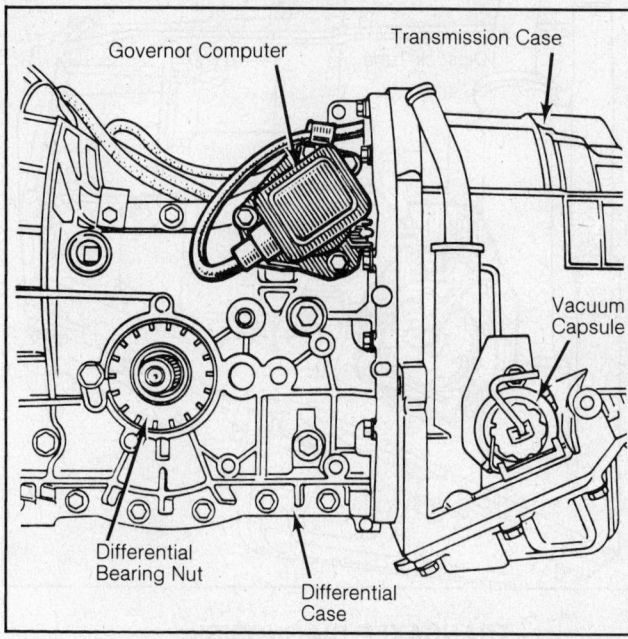

Installation

Install new lip seal and "O" ring on nut. Place tool (B. Vi. 813) around side gear to prevent damage to lip seal on installation. Install nut the same number of turns as was required to remove it. Align mark made during removal. Install nut lock. Remove tool from side gear and install new "O" ring. Reverse removal procedure to complete installation.

REMOVAL & INSTALLATION

TRANSAXLE

See the appropriate article in AUTOMATIC TRANSMISSION REMOVAL Section.

TORQUE CONVERTER

Removal

With transaxle removed from vehicle, pull converter straight out. Check general condition of converter components (i.e. input shaft, oil seal surface, converter sleeve, mounting bosses, etc.). If converter is damaged in any way, it must be replaced. Remove old oil seal from transmission case. Install new seal with tool (B. Vi. 465, Ref. A). Use of this tool automatically sets oil seal to correct depth.

Installation

1) Locate sharp-cornered edge on torque converter drive plate (marked with paint). There are 3 mounting bosses on the torque converter. Locate the boss which is directly opposite the hole in converter used as reference point for distributor timing.

2) When assembling torque converter to drive plate, align specified mounting boss with sharp-cornered edge on drive plate. Install new spring washers and tighten converter retaining bolts gradually and in rotation so that the converter is centered.

RENAULT FUEGO & SPORTWAGON (Cont.)

TRANSAXLE DISASSEMBLY

NOTE: It is very important that all components remain clean throughout operation. It is suggested that this work be carried out on a shock resistant bench (rubber or thick plastic).

1) Remove torque converter. Remove all wiring connections from transmission. Remove the governor computer and the multifunction switch, leaving the sealed plug connected.

Fig. 8: Valve Body Removal

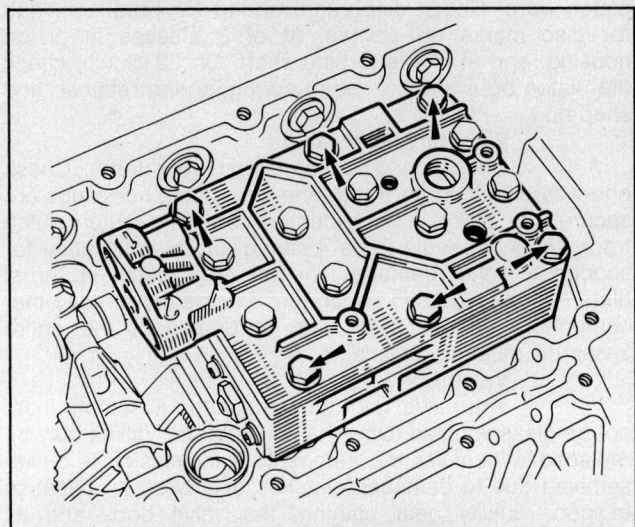

Remove only those bolts (6) indicated by arrows.

    2) Remove vacuum capsule, oil pan, bottom cover and gasket. Remove filter and seal. Retain suction tube seal for reassembly. Disconnect sealed plug socket and remove wiring. Remove valve body retaining bolts indicated in *Fig. 8*. Remove valve body.

    3) Remove the pump cover and shaft. If the oil pump driven gear is to be reused, mark upper face with felt pen or soft pencil so that it may be reinstalled in the same position. Remove drive gear. Remove 4 inner differential assembly bolts from transmission case. *See Fig. 9.*

Fig. 9: Inner Differential Assembly Bolts

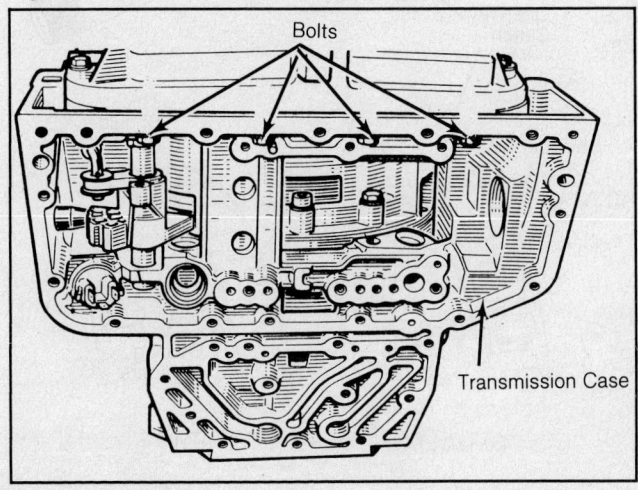

    4) Drive out shift shaft roll pin(s) with drift. Remove bolt "A" in *Fig. 10*. Remove shift arm from shaft. Pull out shaft and save toothed wheel. Remove control linkage.

Fig. 10: Removing Shift Shaft Assembly

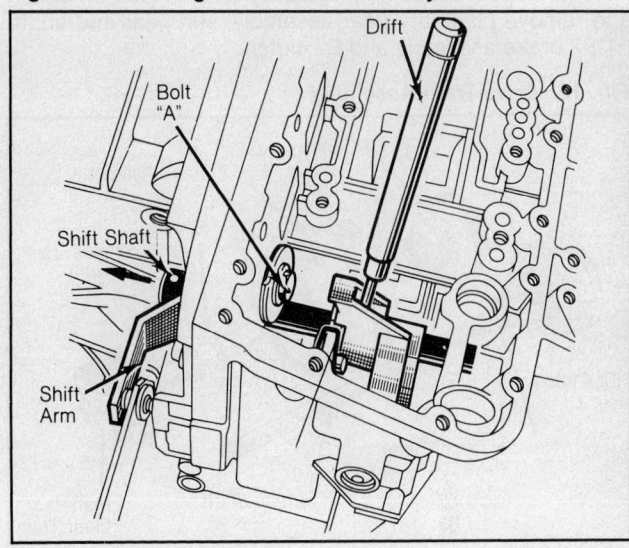

Drive out roll pins with drift.

NOTE: The socket containing the lock ball must not be removed unless it is to be replaced.

    5) Set transaxle on end (torque converter up), remove transmission-to-differential bolts and separate differential and transmission cases. Remove parking pawl assembly centering dowel from transmission case with a

Fig. 11: Brake Assembly Fixing Bolt Locations

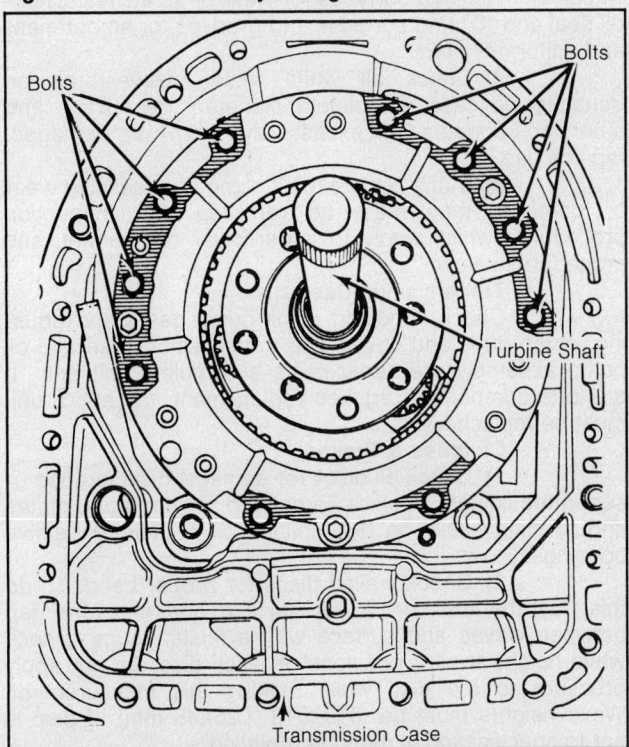

Remove bolts. Lift out drive train assembly by turbine shaft.

slide hammer. Remove pivot shaft, parking pawl and return spring.

6) Remove brake assembly fixing bolts. *See Fig. 11.* Grasp turbine shaft and lift out complete drive train assembly. Ensure that needle thrust bearing remains in case. Support assembly vertically on a 4" tube on bench and remove planetary gear assembly, sun gear and shaft, F1-F2 brake assembly and E2 clutch.

Fig. 12: Drive Train Assembly

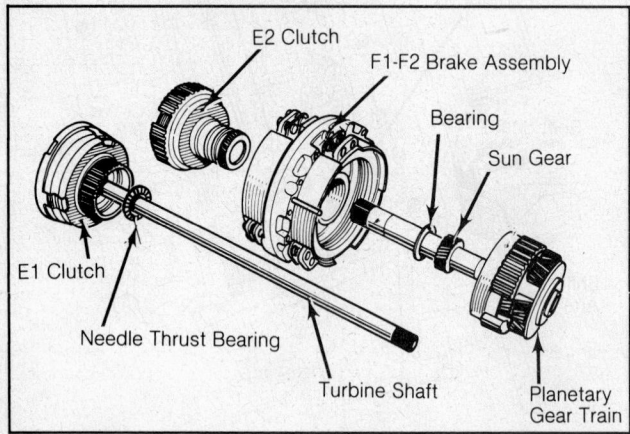

Separate components for disassembly.

COMPONENT DISASSEMBLY, REASSEMBLY & INSPECTION

INSPECTION

1) After disassembly and before reassembly, inspect condition of various components of transaxle. Check all machined surfaces for wear or scratches. Check oil seal and "O" ring surfaces and grooves for smoothness and uniformity of fit.

2) Check all white metal sleeves, as on transmission case, E2 clutch, planetary gear train, and other components. If excessively worn or damaged, replace part.

3) If any parts exhibit signs of excessive wear or damage, they must be replaced. For inspection procedures which apply to a particular component, see procedures below.

Transmission Case

Check condition of oil pump gears and housing, pump drive and cover. The transmission case and oil pump assembly are serviced as a complete unit only. If any one component requires replacement, the entire unit must be replaced.

Clutches & Brakes

1) Check all discs for damage, discoloration or separated linings. Replace as needed. All discs and plates should slide easily on hub splines or in their respective housings.

2) Check waved discs for proper bend. To do this, lay the disc on a flat surface and measure gap between waves and surface with a feeler gauge. Check wave height at all 3 positions on each disc. Do not apply pressure to the disc while making this measurement. Wave heights must be .010-.018" (.25-.45 mm). If disc is not to specification, it must be replaced.

3) Check all plates and thrust plates for signs of excessive wear, damage or overheating and replace as needed. Generally speaking, if one of the assemblies (E1, E2, F1, F2) has overheated, all intermediate discs and all with damaged linings must be replaced. All oil seals and "O" rings should be systematically replaced during any disassembly procedure.

4) E1 and E2 clutches utilize relief valve check balls which are crimped into place in the piston bodies (2 in E1 clutch, 1 in E2). Check that balls move freely in their sockets and do not stick to seat or crimped side. Total check ball travel should be about .04" (1 mm). If check ball operation is not satisfactory, the entire clutch piston assembly must be replaced.

5) On E1 clutch, check surface condition of piston bore. Check diaphragm spring for breakage, hub for disc marks on splines, fit of 2 sleeves in piston housing, and fit of the turbine shaft. On E2 clutch, check the piston bore and the return spring, spring retainer, and snap ring.

Planetary Gear Train

Check condition of planet gear teeth. Check one-way clutch. Ensure that one-way clutch hub plugs are securely in place. Check center bore and outer clutch track. Inspect needle thrust bearing and bearing plate for scoring or other damage. The one-way clutch or thrust plate may be replaced separately if damaged. If any other component of the gear train is damaged, the entire assembly must be replaced.

Valve Body

The valve body and regulator assembly must not be disassembled. Only the solenoid ball valves may be replaced. Whenever the automatic transmission is disassembled due to damaged clutches or brakes, or because of poor quality gear shifting, the valve body and its regulator must be replaced.

Fig. 13: Assembling Sun Gear Shaft & Planetary Gear Train

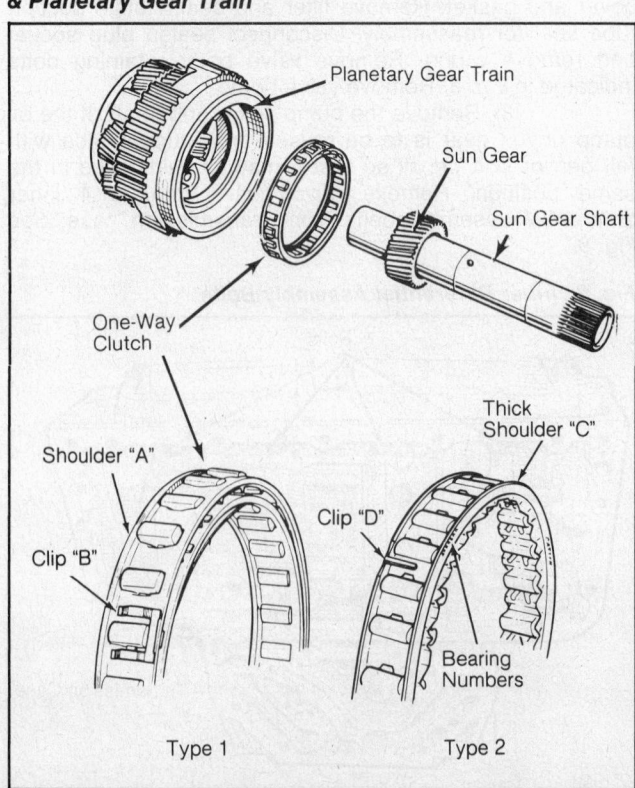

One-way clutch must be installed as shown.

Fig. 14: E1 Clutch and Turbine Shaft Assembly

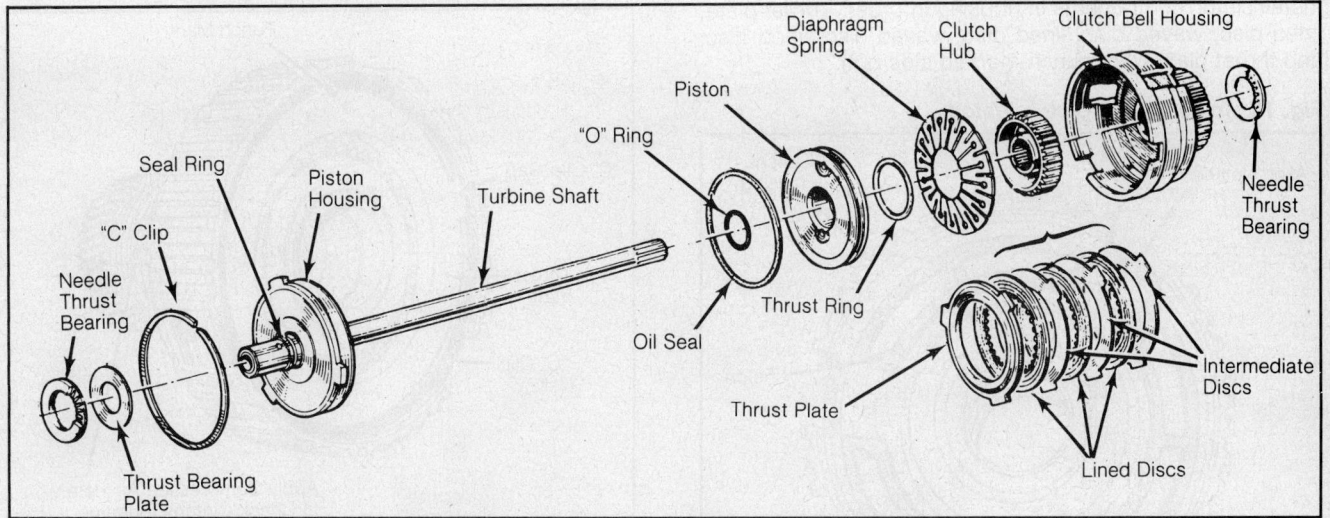

PLANETARY GEAR ASSEMBLY

Disassembly

Remove one-way clutch. Remove adjusting shim, needle bearing plate and needle thrust bearing. Remove remaining needle bearing plate. Leave inner needle thrust bearing in place.

Reassembly

Reverse disassembly procedure and note that there are 2 types of one-way clutch bearings. *See Fig. 13.* Be sure to install bearing correctly. Type 1 must be installed with shoulder "A" and clip "B" facing INWARD. Type 2 must be installed with thick shoulder "C", clip "D", and bearing numbers facing OUTWARD.

E1 CLUTCH

Disassembly

1) Remove seal ring from turbine shaft and remove needle thrust bearing plate. Push down on clutch housing and remove large "C" clip. Remove clutch bell housing. Apply compressed air at the piston housing input hole (in turbine shaft) to remove piston.

2) Remove diaphragm spring, thrust plate, clutch discs and clutch hub from housing. Piston housing and turbine shaft are a single unit and cannot be separated.

Reassembly

1) Install thrust ring on clutch piston. Lubricate piston seal and install on piston. Lubricate "O" ring seal and slide onto piston sleeve. Install piston in piston housing (flange away from housing).

2) Lubricate clutch lined discs with ATF fluid before clutch reassembly. Install clutch hub (recessed face out) in clutch housing. Then install intermediate disc, followed by lined disc and continue alternating intermediate and lined discs until all have been installed (3 intermediate, 3 lined). Install thrust plate (smooth side towards clutch pack) and diaphragm spring. Install complete assembly on turbine shaft.

3) Engage notches in clutch housing with tabs on piston housing and hold clutch in place with "C" clip. Make sure that gap in clip is positioned between 2 gaps in the clutch housing, and that clip is fully seated in its groove. Install needle thrust bearing plate and seal ring. Check clutch operation by applying compressed air at oil hole in turbine shaft.

Fig. 15: E1 Clutch "C" Clip Installation and Oil Hole Location

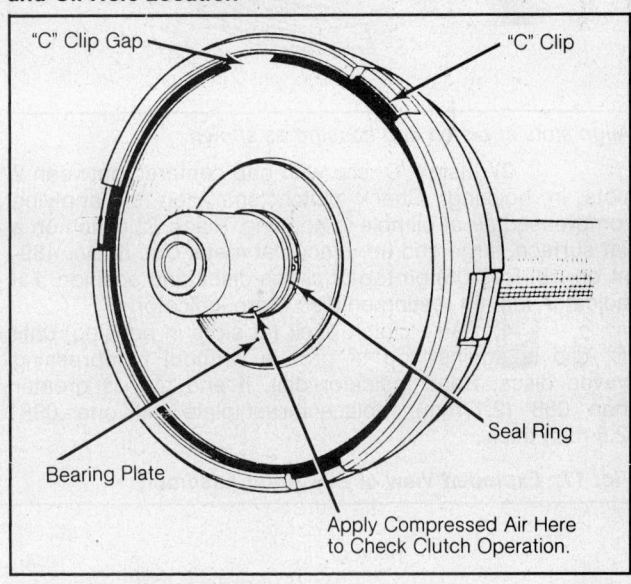

Install "C" clip with gap centered between housing notches.

E2 CLUTCH

Disassembly

Compress clutch return spring with press and tool (B. Vi. 489-14 or -19, Ref. 07) and remove snap ring. Lift out spring retainer and spring. Remove seal rings (3). Remove large "C" clip, thrust plate, clutch discs (3 lined, 2 waved) and flat disc from clutch housing. Remove piston by applying compressed air at oil hole in housing.

Reassembly

1) Install seal rings on clutch housing. Ensure that ring grooves are clean and square before installing rings. Lubricate piston seal and install on piston. Lubricate "O" ring seal and install on piston hub in clutch housing. Ensure that seals are firmly seated in their grooves.

2) Install piston in clutch housing so that slots in piston are aligned with slots in the housing. Install return spring and retainer. Compress spring and install

snap ring. Lubricate lined clutch discs with clean ATF. Install clutch components in housing in order: Thrust plate, lined disc, waved disc, lined disc, waved disc, lined disc, and thrust plate (with punch-marked side out).

Fig. 16: Installing E2 Clutch Piston

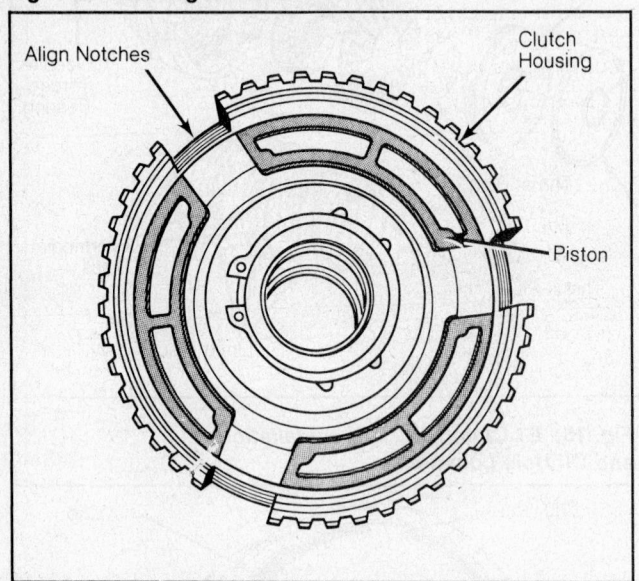

Align slots in piston and housing as shown.

3) Install "C" clip with gap centered between 2 slots in housing. Check clutch operation by applying compressed air at oil hole in housing. Place E2 clutch on a flat surface, large end up. Place flat metal disc (B. Vi. 489-14 or -19, Ref. 06) on top of clutch discs and position dial indicator with tip resting on disc. Zero indicator.

4) Raise clutch pack (at slots in housing) until "C" clip is against top of groove, without compressing waved discs. Read indicator dial. If end play is greater than .083" (2.1 mm), replace thrust plate with one .098" (2.5 mm) thick.

Fig. 18: Installing E2 Clutch "C" Clip

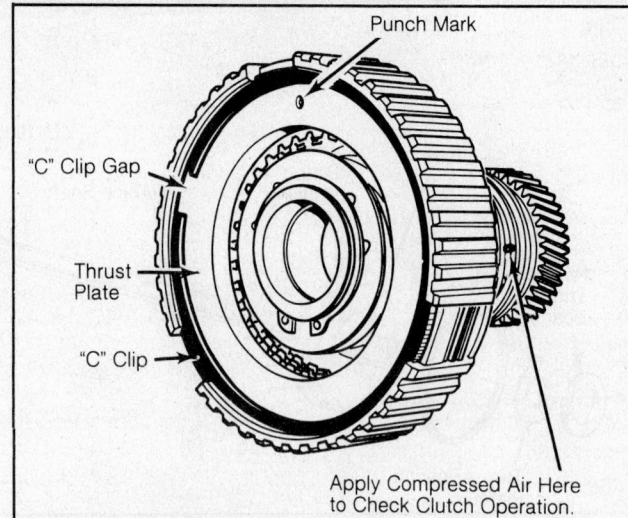

Install clip with gap located between notches in housing.

F1-F2 BRAKE ASSEMBLY

Disassembly

1) Remove 3 F1 brake bell housing retaining bolts. Remove housing and 6 piston return springs. Remove steel and lined discs, noting relative positions for reassembly reference. Note position of "O" ring between one-way clutch hub and F1 piston housing. Save "O" ring.

2) Remove 3 F2 brake bell housing retaining bolts. Remove housing and 6 piston return springs. Remove steel and lined discs, noting positions for reassembly reference. Note position of the "O" ring between one-way clutch hub and F1 piston housing. Save "O" ring. Apply compressed air at oil input holes to remove pistons. Remove piston seals (F1 and F2).

Reassembly

1) Check F2 brake operating play: Install F2 piston (without seal) in piston housing. Install flat disc

Fig. 17: Exploded View of E2 Clutch Assembly

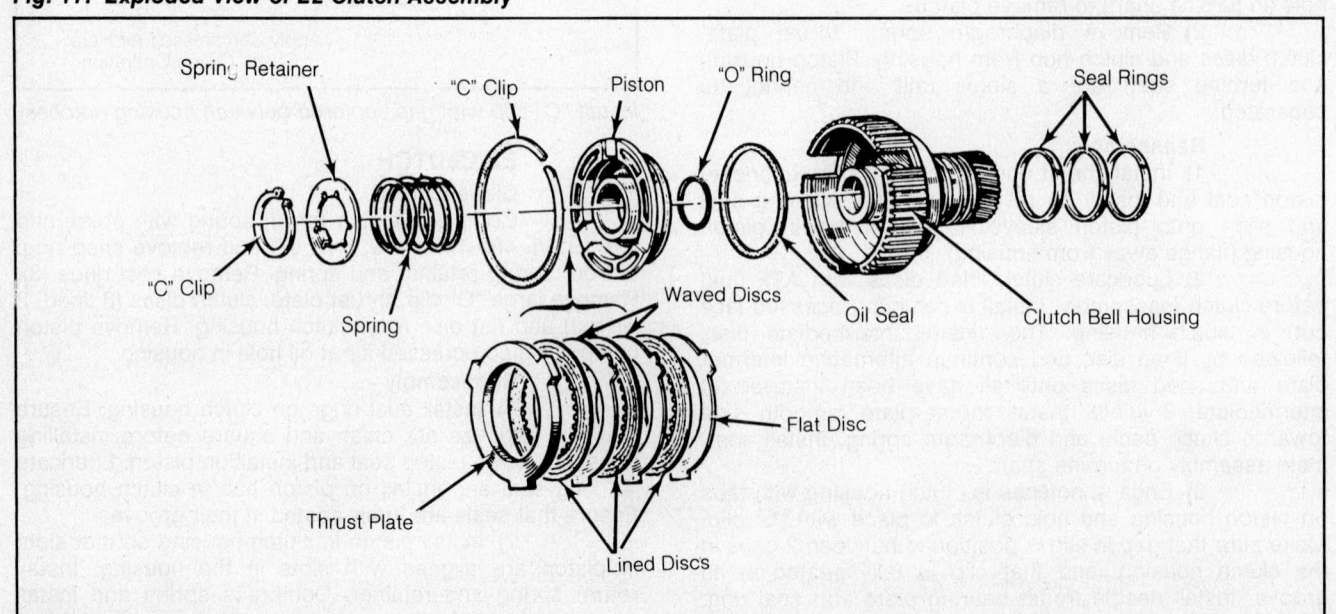

Fig. 19: *Complete F1-F2 Brake Assembly*

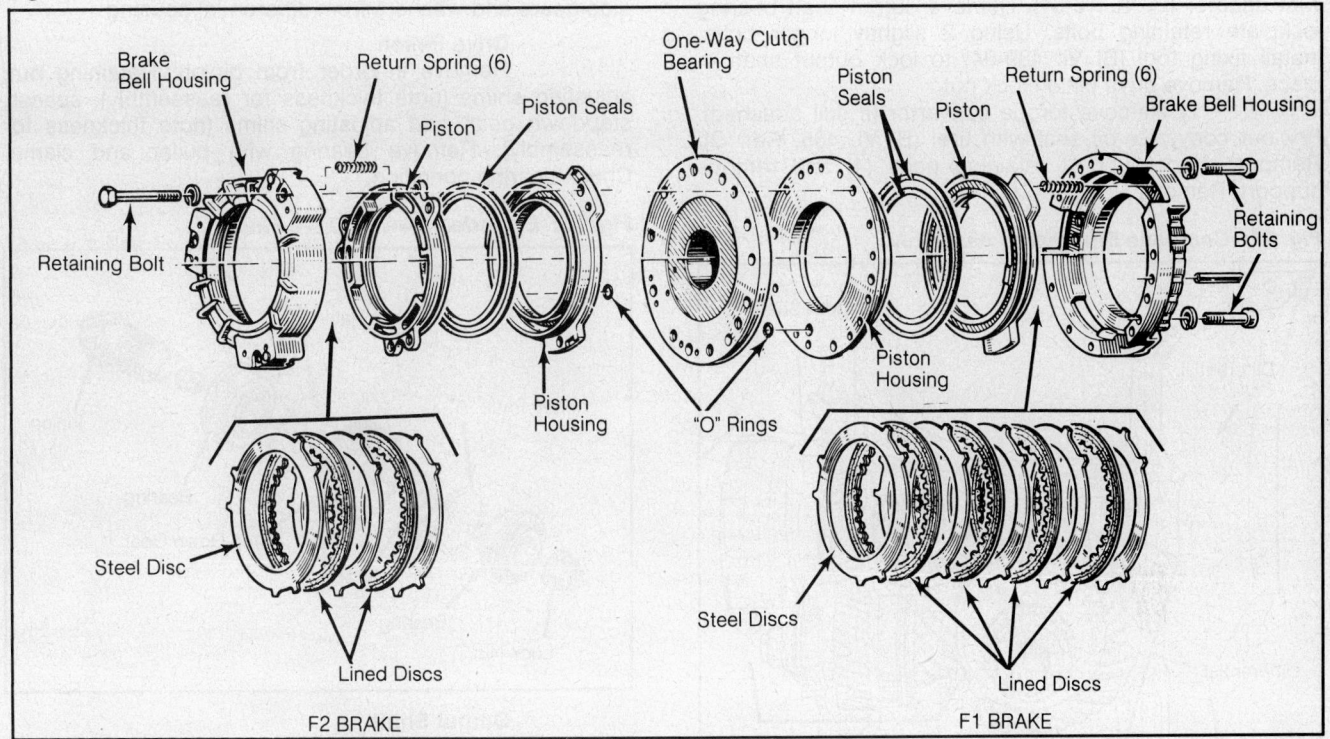

Fig. 20: *Installing F2 Brake Bell Housing*

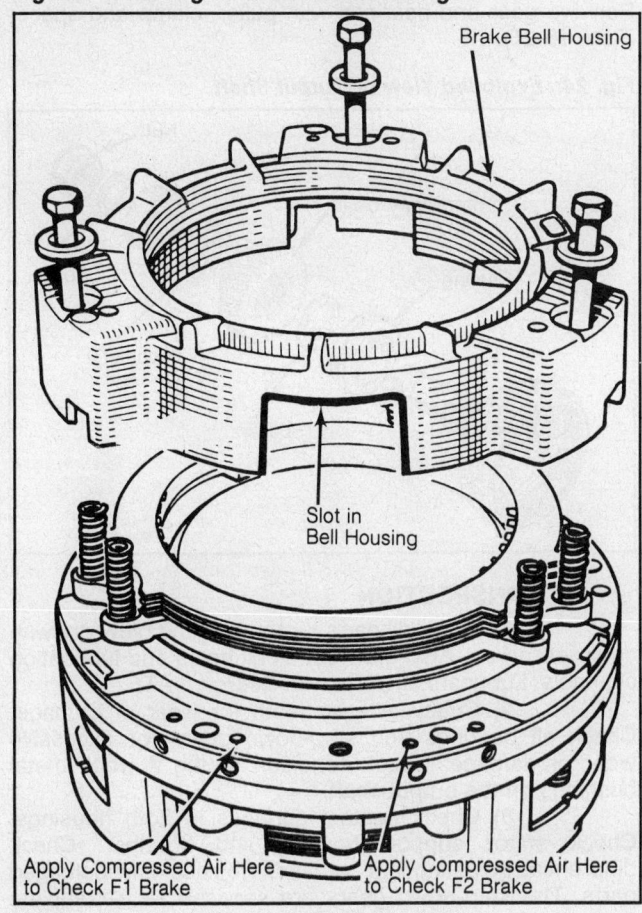

Note position of oil holes and slot in housing.

(.059", 1.5 mm thick), lined disc, waved disc (.079", 2 mm thick), lined disc and another flat disc in housing. Install brake bell housing and attach entire asembly to one-way clutch hub with bolts (3).

2) Position dial indicator with dial pin resting on a spline of the first lined disc. Zero indicator. Lift disc pack until it makes contact with bell housing. Read indicator dial. Take measurements at several points and average readings to obtain F2 operating play. If play is not .028-.067" (.70-1.70 mm), check piston and all discs for damage or distortion and replace as needed. Disassemble components.

3) Lubricate F1 and F2 piston seals and install in respective housings. Place "O" ring between one-way clutch hub and F1 piston housing. Install F1 piston in piston housing. Install flat and lined discs in the same order as removed (noted during disassembly). Install return springs and F1 brake bell housing. Secure bell housing with retaining bolts.

4) Turn assembly over so that it rests on the bell housing. Place "O" ring in position between one-way clutch hub and F2 housing. Insert F2 piston into housing. Install discs in same order as removed (noted in disassembly). Install return springs and F2 brake bell housing. Housing must be installed so that slot in side is positioned over oil holes in piston housing. Check F1 and F2 functions by applying compressed air at appropriate oil hole. *See Fig. 20.*

DIFFERENTIAL ASSEMBLY

DISASSEMBLY

NOTE: Do not disassemble differential unless specific repairs are required.

RENAULT FUEGO & SPORTWAGON (Cont.)

1) Place differential assembly on engine stand with adaptor (B. Vi. 16-01). Remove output shaft bearing lockplate retaining bolts. Using 2 slightly longer bolts, install fixing tool (B. Vi. 489-04) to lock output shaft in place. Remove drive pinion lock nut.

2) Remove torque converter (if still attached). Pry out converter oil seal with tool (B. Vi. 465, Ref. C). Remove stator support retaining bolts (4) and remove support. Remove side gear "O" rings.

Fig. 21: Complete Differential Assembly

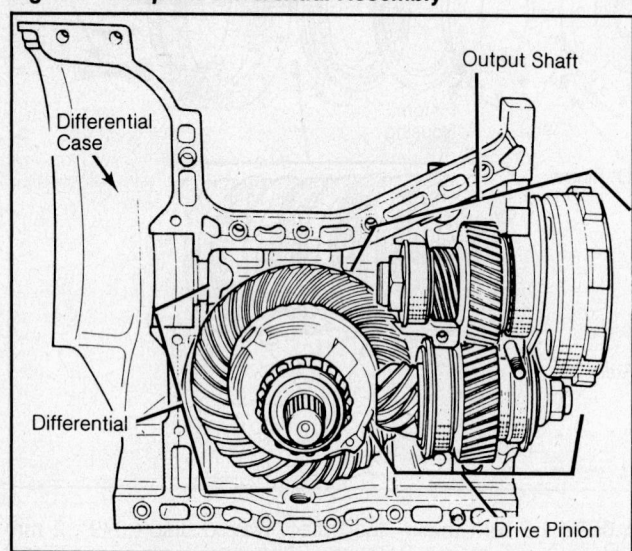

3) Remove bolts which secure the 2 differential half-housings together and separate half-housings (use a rubber mallet if needed). Remove output shaft, differential and drive pinion. Remove differential bearing adjusting nut lock washers, then remove adjusting nuts with tool (B. Vi. 807).

Differential

Remove 2 opposing ring gear-to-differential case retaining bolts. Support differential in soft-jawed vise and remove bearing from ring gear side with puller and clamp (T. Ar. 65 and B. Tr. 02). Turn differential over and remove bearing from opposite side. Remove remaining ring gear-to-case retaining bolts and discard all bolts.

Fig. 22: Exploded View of Differential

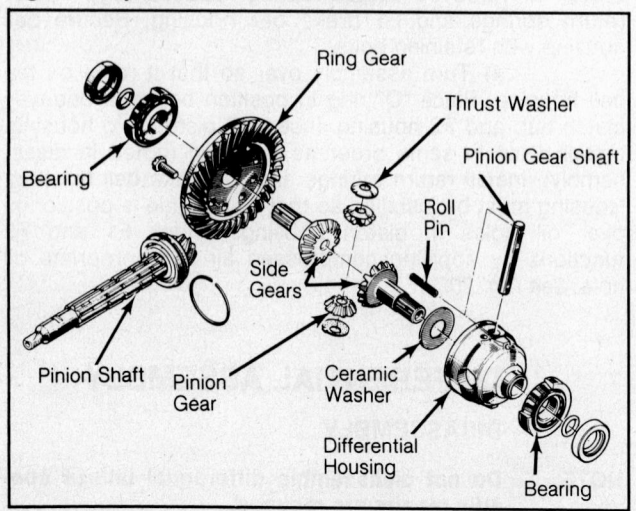

Drive out pinion gear shaft roll pin. Separate pinion gears, side gears and washers from differential housing.

Drive Pinion

Remove in order from pinion: Retaining nut, adjusting shims (note thickness for reassembly), spacer, stepdown gear, and adjusting shims (note thickness for reassembly). Remove bearing with puller and clamp. Check bearing condition.

Fig. 23: Exploded View of Drive Pinion

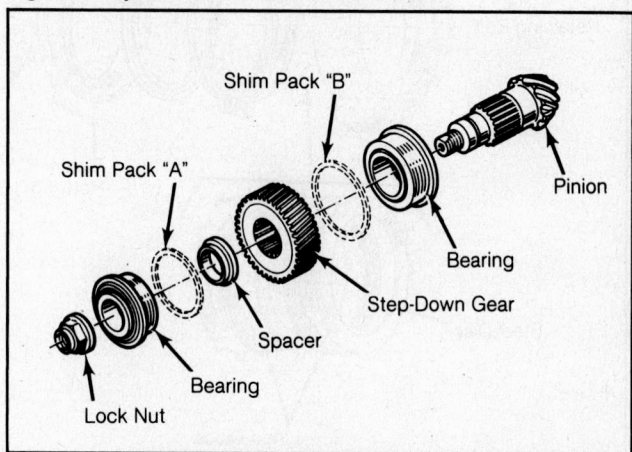

Output Shaft

Clamp fixing tool (B. Vi. 489-04) in vise and fit output shaft over it. Remove nut from end of shaft. Remove gear and bearings with puller, clamp and spacer (Rou. 15-01).

Fig. 24: Exploded View of Output Shaft

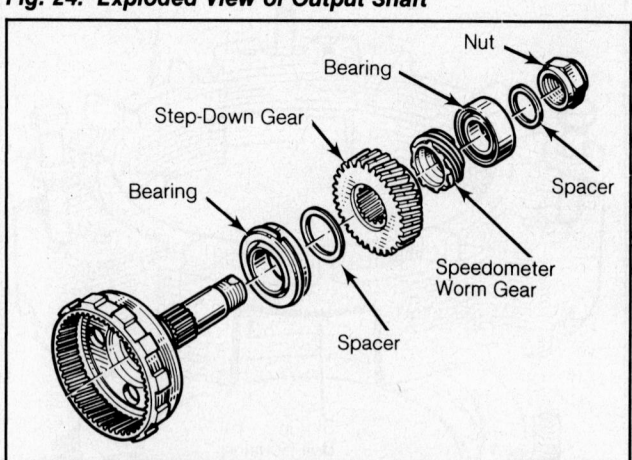

INSPECTION

1) Clean all parts thoroughly and blow dry with compressed air. Also blow out all oil holes and lubrication channels. Lubricate all parts with Dexron II ATF.

2) Check all gear teeth for wear or damage. Check all bearings and step-down gears for excessive wear or damage. Check condition of the 2 white metal bushings on the output shaft.

3) Check contact surfaces in both housings. Check stator support housing and breather. Check differential adjusting nut threads. Replace any damaged parts. The step-down gears are serviced as a complete set only. If either of the gears is damaged, both must be

RENAULT FUEGO & SPORTWAGON (Cont.)

replaced. Likewise, the ring gear and pinion are manufactured in matched pairs only and must always be replaced as a set.

REASSEMBLY

Output Shaft

Press bearing onto shaft, flange side first. Install parts in order: Spacer, step-down gear (flange towards speedometer worm gear), speedometer worm gear (large diameter bore end first), bearing, shim and lock nut. With fixing tool in vise, place output shaft on tool and tighten nut. Lock nut in place by crushing flange against flat side of shaft.

Drive Pinion

1) Press tapered bearing onto shaft. If old ring gear and pinion are being reused, install shim pack of equal width to that which was removed. If a new ring gear and pinion set is being installed, install a .043" (1.1 mm) shim pack.

2) Install step-down gear (flange side first) and spacer (large diameter face first). Install 2nd shim pack of same thickness as removed if old ring gear and pinion are being used, or .047" (1.2 mm) with new ring gear and pinion. Install bearing and lock nut. DO NOT tighten lock nut at this time.

Differential

1) Place ceramic washer into differential housing with oil groove toward side gear. Use a washer .077-.079" (1.96-2.0 mm) thick, unless side gear to pinion gear backlash is excessive. If so, use a washer .080-.081" (2.03-2.07 mm) thick. Dip side gear in ATF before installing.

2) Place pinion gears and thrust washers in housing (locking tabs on washers in holes in housing) and hold in position while pinion gear shaft is installed. Be sure that hole in shaft lines up with hole in housing. Drive roll pin into housing, through shaft, to a depth of about .25" (5 mm).

3) Dip other side gear in ATF and place in ring gear. Attach ring gear to differential housing with new self-locking bolts. Make sure that side gears mesh properly. Install bearings.

ADJUSTMENT

1) There are several numbers on the ring gear. For this application, the important ones are the 2-digit number followed by the 3-digit number, for example, 43 170. This indicates that the ring gear is part of the 43rd set manufactured on the 170th day of the year. This same combination must appear on the pinion shaft used.

2) A 3rd number may appear on the pinion shaft. This number indicates additional pinion depth (in hundredths of a millimeter) which must be set when the differential is assembled. For example, if the number is 20, pinion depth must be set at standard depth PLUS .20 mm (.008").

3) With governor side half-housing attached to engine stand, install differential bearing races and adjusting nuts on half-housing (make sure nuts are clean). Lubricate tapered faces of pinion depth adjusting tool (B. Vi. 489-12) and install in half-housing. Install drive pinion.

4) Install other half-housing and secure with bolts indicated in *Fig. 26*. Do not tighten bolts at this time. Hold drive pinion with tool (B. Vi. 489-04) and tighten lock nut. Now tighten half-housing bolts to specification.

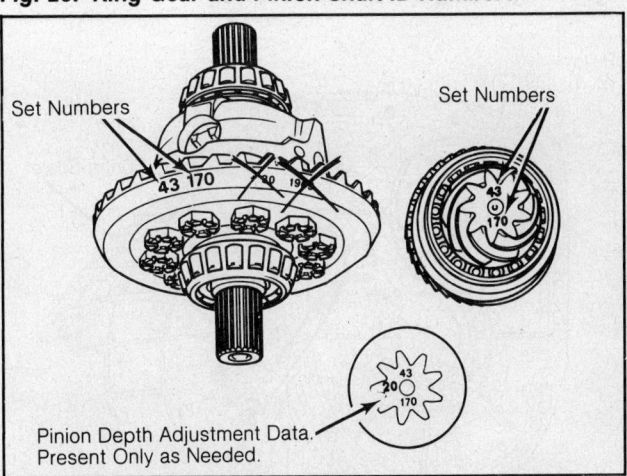

Fig. 25: Ring Gear and Pinion Shaft ID Numbers

Set numbers on ring gear and pinion must be identical.

5) Rotate drive pinion several times to seat bearings. If used bearings are used, pinion should turn freely with no play. If new bearings are used, preload must be checked. Attach pulley (B. Vi. 489-13) to pinion and check force (with spring scale) required to keep pinion turning. Preload should be 2.3-4.5 lbs. (1.0-2.0 kg).

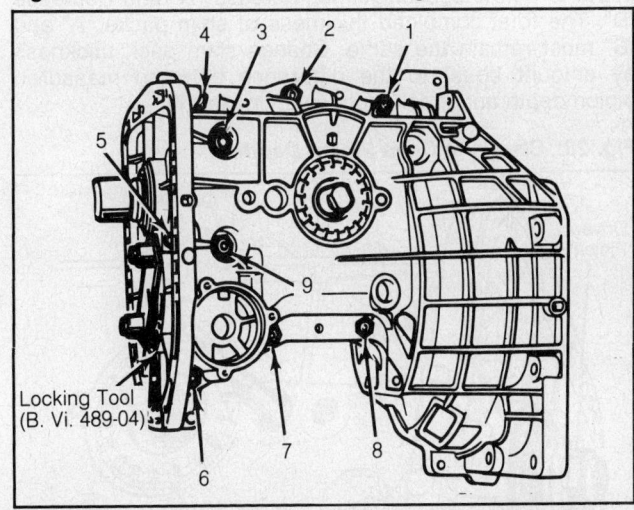

Fig. 26: Differential Case Half-Housing Bolts

Install 9 bolts shown during adjustment procedures.

6) Install differential bearing ring nuts with tool (B. Vi. 807). Tighten gradually and ensure that tool is centered correctly. Check drive pinion position with gauge rod. Gauge rod tool package (B. Vi. 489-15) contains 4 different rods sized from .270" (6.85 mm) to .281" (7.15 mm). Note which gauge rod fits freely into place between drive pinion and tool, with no play.

7) Pinion depth equals radius of pinion depth adjusting tool, 1.93" (49 mm), plus gauge rod diameter. Ideal pinion depth is 2.20" (56 mm). Remove drive pinion nut and upper half-housing.

8) If bearing preload is incorrect and pinion depth is correct, change thickness of shim pack "A" to obtain correct preload. See *Fig. 23*. If pinion depth is incorrect and preload is correct, change shim pack "A"

Fig. 27: Checking Drive Pinion Preload

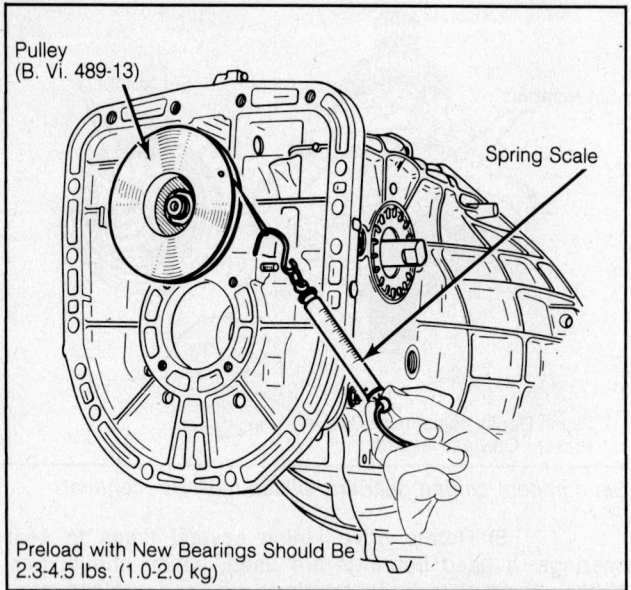

Pulley
(B. Vi. 489-13)

Spring Scale

Preload with New Bearings Should Be
2.3-4.5 lbs. (1.0-2.0 kg)

Preload must be checked when new bearings are installed.

and shim pack "B" by equal, but opposite, amounts: If pinion depth is too great, increase thickness of shim pack "B" and decrease thickness of shim pack "A"; if pinion depth is below specifications, increase "A" and decrease "B". The total combined thickness of shim packs "A" and "B" must remain the same. Change shim pack thickness by amount equal to the difference between measured pinion depth and ideal depth given in step **7**).

Fig. 28: Checking Drive Pinion Depth

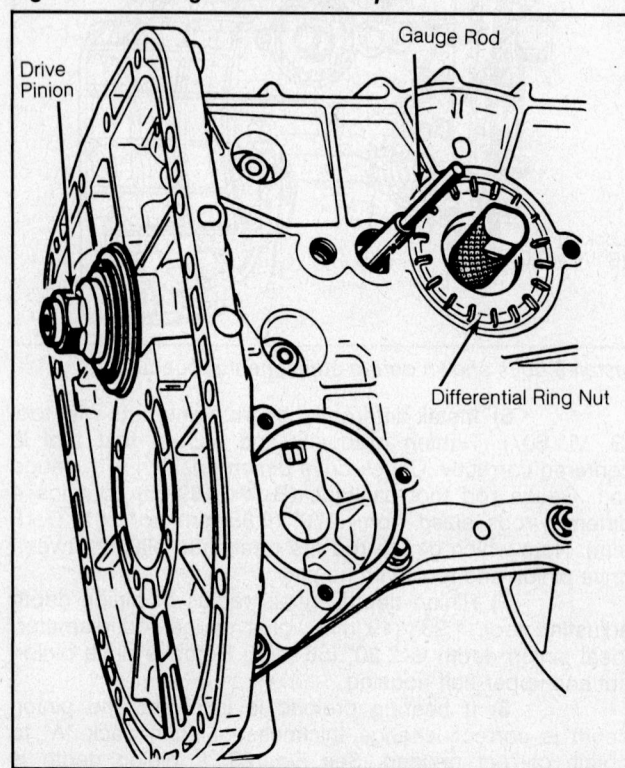

Drive
Pinion

Gauge Rod

Differential Ring Nut

Check depth by placing tool between drive pinion and tapered face of adjusting tool.

9) If pinion depth and bearing preload are both incorrect, adjust preload by changing thickness of shim pack "A" or "B", approximating the pinion depth adjustment as closely as possible. Check new bearing preload. When preload is correct, adjust pinion depth as in step **8**).

10) With half-housings separated, install differential without drive pinion or output shaft. Reassemble half-housings as before. Rotate ring gear several times to seat bearings. Tighten bearing ring nuts same number of turns as was required to remove them and line up match marks. Differential should turn freely with no play.

11) If new bearings are being used, preload must be checked. Run a hook and string through drive pinion hole and around the differential housing (several times) as close as possible to the ring gear. Attach a spring scale and measure the effort required to keep the differential housing turning.

12) Reading on scale should be 2.3-4.5 lbs. (1.0-2.0 kg). Adjust preload by tightening or loosening ring nuts as needed. When proper preload is obtained, mark new position of ring nuts.

Fig. 29: Checking Differential Bearing Preload

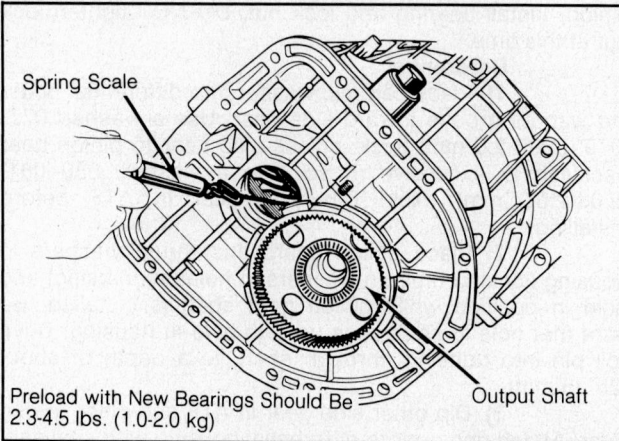

Spring Scale

Output Shaft

Preload with New Bearings Should Be
2.3-4.5 lbs. (1.0-2.0 kg)

Preload must be checked when new bearings are installed.

13) Separate half-housings. Install drive pinion and output shaft. Reassemble differential assembly, aligning ring nuts with match marks. Apply a thick bead of sealer to mating surface of one half-housing before assembly. Tighten bolts in order indicated in *Fig. 30*. Lock output shaft with tool (B. Vi. 489-04) and tighten drive pinion nut. Rotate output shaft a few times to seat bearings.

14) Install dial indicator support (B. Vi. 489-16) in housing as shown in *Fig. 31*. Screw extension onto dial indicator tip (use extension B. Vi. 489-16 if indicator has a 3 mm diameter tip and .60 mm pitch, extension B. Vi. 489-17 for 2.5 mm diameter tip and .45 mm pitch).

15) Fit assembly into support and tighten clamp bolt until dial is snug. Place tip of extension against tooth of ring gear and zero indicator dial. Measure backlash at several places on ring gear. Backlash should be .005-.010" (.12-.25 mm).

16) If backlash is incorrect, adjust by tightening one ring nut and loosening the other the same amount. When final adjustments have been made and backlash is within specifications, mark new position of ring nuts.

17) Remove nuts, counting number of turns. Replace seals and "O" rings. Apply sealer to ring nut

RENAULT FUEGO & SPORTWAGON (Cont.)

Fig. 30: *Differential Case Bolt Tightening Sequence*

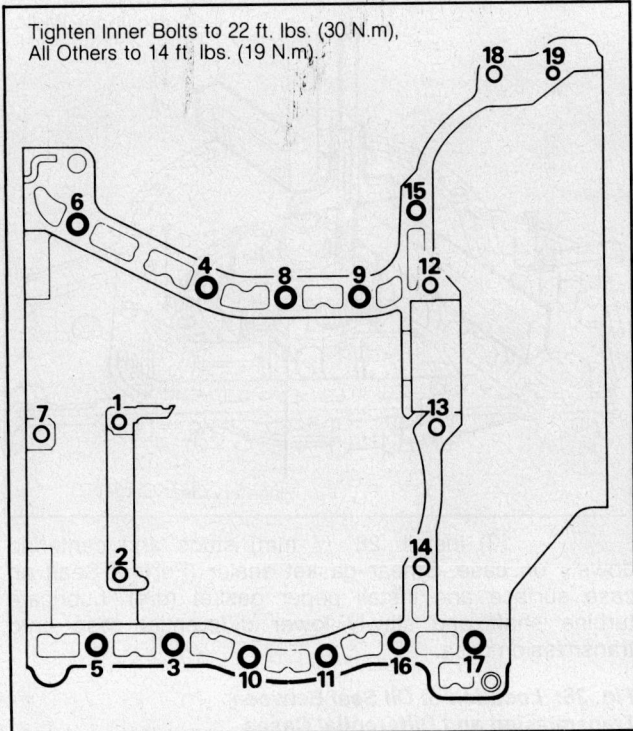

Tighten Inner Bolts to 22 ft. lbs. (30 N.m),
All Others to 14 ft. lbs. (19 N.m).

Fig. 31: *Checking Ring Gear Backlash*

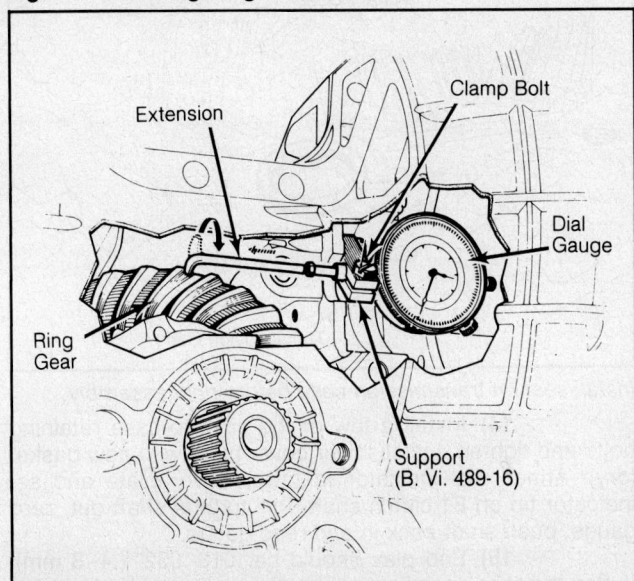

Check backlash at several points on gear.

threads and reinstall ring nuts same number of turns. Line up match marks. Install locks.

18) With adjustments correct and differential assembly assembled, check preload at output shaft. Starting force should be 3.3-7.7 lbs. (1.5-3.5 kg). Check condition of smooth part of stator support.

19) Lightly lubricate seal and tap gently into place with installer tool (B. Vi. 465, Ref. A). The tool will automatically position seal at the correct depth. Install torque converter and secure in place with retaining bracket.

Fig. 32: *Checking Differential Assembly Total Preload*

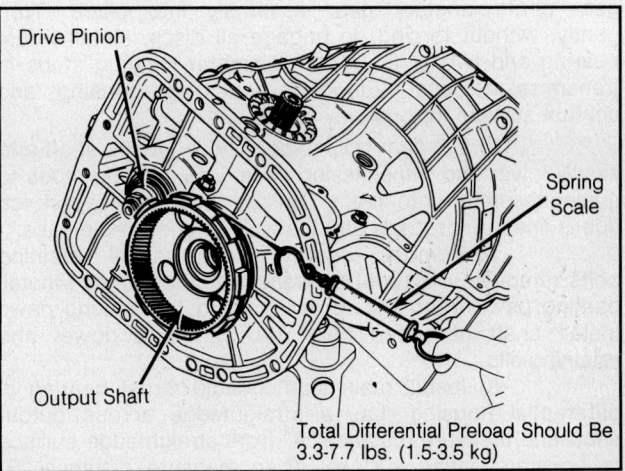

Total Differential Preload Should Be
3.3-7.7 lbs. (1.5-3.5 kg)

TRANSAXLE REASSEMBLY

1) Clean all transaxle components thoroughly. Blow out all oil holes and passages with compressed air. Lubricate all parts with clean ATF fluid before final assembly. Drain torque converter, pump out remaining fluid from center of turbine hub with a syringe and refill with clean fluid. Use Dexron II type transmission fluid only.

2) Support E1 clutch/turbine shaft assembly on a 4" diameter tube, clutch end down, during reassembly. Install needle thrust bearing on turbine shaft, bearing side up. Center clutch discs in E2 clutch and slide clutch assembly into position on turbine shaft.

3) Gently turn clutch assembly, do not force, until all discs are engaged with splines in E1 housing. When properly installed, there will be about .12" (4 mm) play between clutches.

4) Lubricate E2 seal rings and bearing contact surfaces on one-way clutch. Center discs in F2 brake and install complete brake assembly on E2 clutch. Turn brake assembly, without forcing, to engage all discs. Install thrust bearing on sun gear shaft/planetary gear assembly, bearing surface toward splined end of shaft.

Fig. 33: *Preparation for Gear Train Installation*

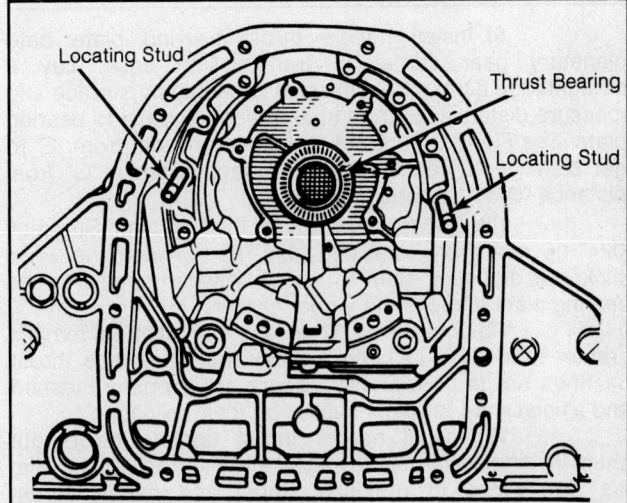

Install thrust bearing and locating studs as shown.

RENAULT FUEGO & SPORTWAGON (Cont.)

5) Center discs in F1 brake and lower sun gear shaft/planetary gear assembly into place. Turn gently, without forcing, to engage all discs. Install thrust bearing and two .275" (7 mm) diameter locating studs in transmission case. Lubricate seal ring housing and contact surface for one-way clutch hub.

6) Lift gear train assembly by turbine shaft and slowly lower into transmission case. Use locating studs to guide assembly into place. Ensure that one-way clutch hub is lined up properly and fits well up against the case.

7) Remove locating studs. Install retaining bolts removed in step **6)** of *Transaxle Disassembly*. Install parking pawl return spring on shaft. Install parking pawl. Install shaft (threaded hole up), centering dowel and retaining clip.

8) Install main shaft needle thrust bearing in differential housing. Lay a straightedge across output shaft and measure distance "A" from straightedge surface to housing mating surface. Then measure distance "B" from straightedge surface to needle bearing. Subtract "B" from "A" to get distance "C" and record. *See Fig. 34.*

Fig. 34: *Measuring Output Shaft Clearances*

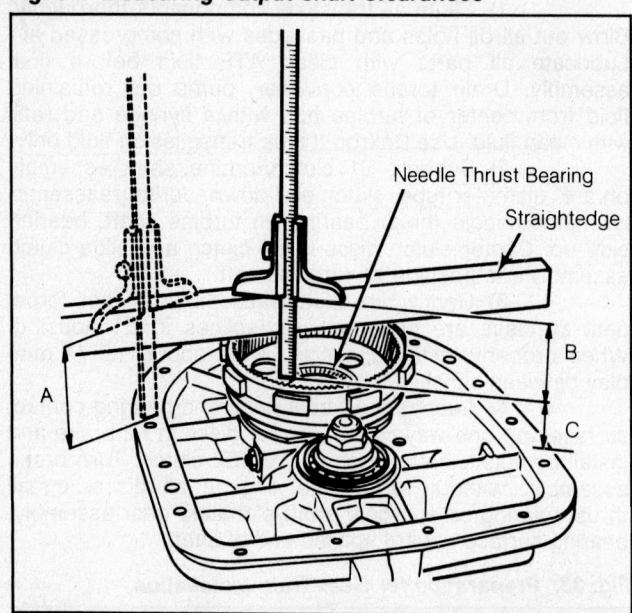

9) Install needle thrust bearing plate onto planetary gear carrier in transmission case. Lay a straightedge across transmission case mating surface and measure distance "E" from straightedge surface to bearing plate. *See Fig. 35.* Subtract straightedge width from "E" to get distance "D" and record. Subtract distance "C" from distance "D" to get total end play.

10) Desired end play is .024" (.6 mm). Subtract .024" (.6 mm) from total end play "D" to determine what thickness adjusting shim to install between needle thrust bearing plate and planetary gear carrier.

11) If end play "D" is less than .024" (.6 mm) or greater than .120" (3.1 mm), check that all needle thrust bearings are in position, sun gears are properly meshed and all discs are properly seated on their splines.

12) Install needle thrust bearing on output shaft in differential case. Install end-play adjusting shim (as determined in previous steps) and needle thrust bearing plate in transmission case. *See Fig. 36.*

Fig. 35: *Measuring Gear Train Clearances*

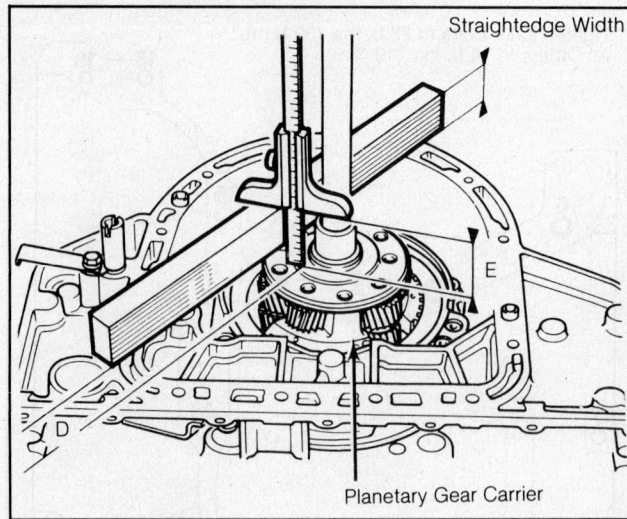

13) Install .28" (7 mm) studs and centering dowels on case. Smear gasket sealer (Perfect Seal) on case surface and install paper gasket (dry). Lubricate turbine shaft and slowly lower differential case onto transmission case.

Fig. 36: *Location of Oil Seal Between Transmission and Differential Cases*

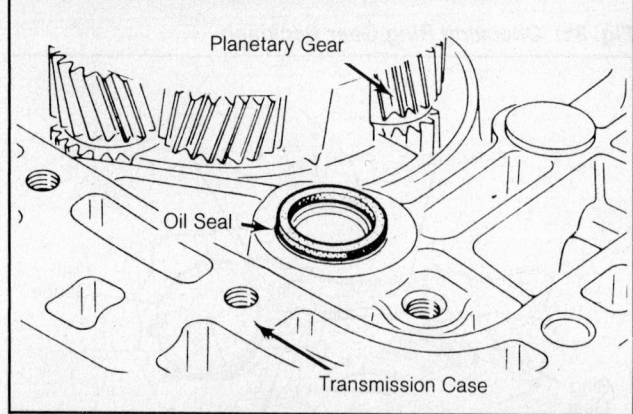

Install seal on transmission case before final assembly.

14) Install a few of the case-to-case retaining bolts and tighten. Install lower cover plate with new gasket (dry). Attach dial indicator to lower cover plate and set indicator tip on E1 clutch shaft. Pull turbine shaft out, zero gauge, push shaft back in and read gauge.

15) End play should be .016-.032" (.4-.8 mm). If play is not to specification, disassemble and replace end play adjusting shim as required. When correct play has been obtained, install remaining case-to-case bolts and tighten.

16) Reverse removal procedures to install shift control linkage and shift shaft. *See Transaxle Disassembly.* Check that valve body mounting surfaces and surfaces on case are clean and smooth. Make sure that centering dowels are in position on valve body and the 2 toothed wheels are properly meshed when in park.

17) Install valve body in housing, engaging the manual valve on shift lever. *See Fig. 38.* Tighten retaining screws in several steps. Install solenoid ball valves and

RENAULT FUEGO & SPORTWAGON (Cont.)

connect plug to sealed plug connector. Check that ball valves, valve body and plugs are all properly aligned. Install magnet at ball valve retaining clamp.

Fig. 37: Measuring Transaxle Total End Play

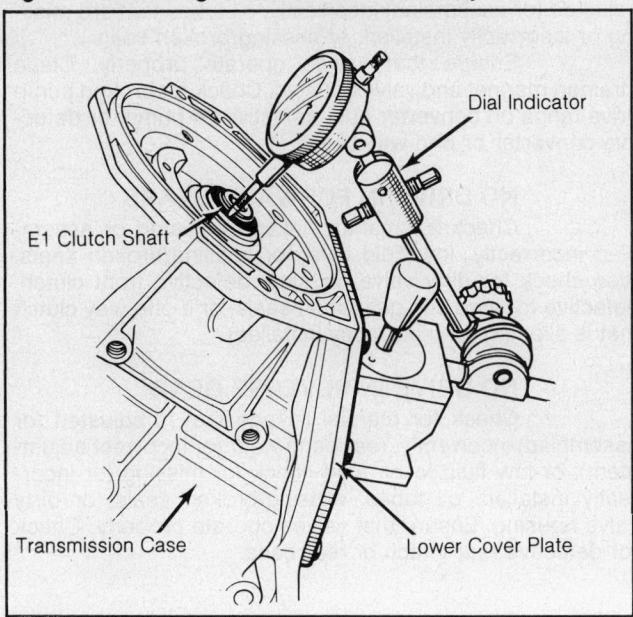

Total end play should be .016-.032" (.4-.8 mm)

18) Ensure pump housing cleanliness. Lubricate and install oil pump driven gear with marked side up (marked during disassembly). If a new gear is being used, install with chamfered edge in case first. Install drive gear and pump drive shaft.

19) Lubricate "O" ring on filter suction pipe and slip over end of pipe. Push pipe into its housing carefully. Install oil filter and tighten 2 bolts. Install oil pan and gasket. Check oil pump shaft rotation (first few turns may be stiff, this is normal). Check that pump shaft end play is .014-.031" (.35-.80 mm). Install pump shaft cover.

Fig. 38 Installing Valve Body

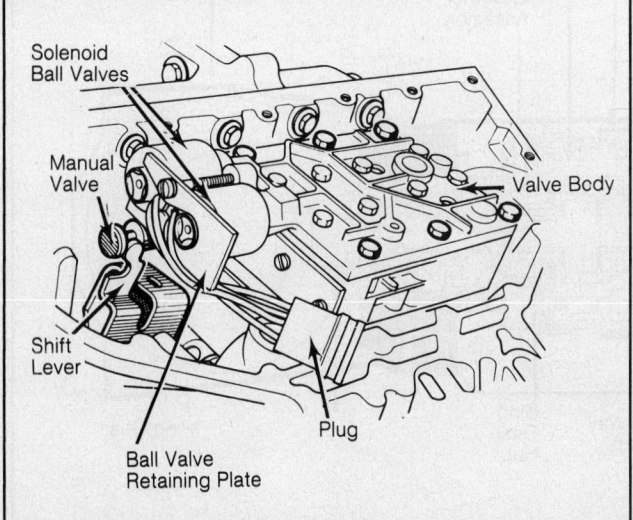

Make sure that shift lever and manual valve are properly engaged.

TIGHTENING SPECIFICATIONS

Application	Ft. Lbs. (N.m)
Torque Converter-to-Drive Plate	
Fuego	22 (30)
18i	24 (33)
Drive Plate-to-Crankshaft	52 (70)
Ring Gear-to-Differential Case	74 (101)
Drive Pinion Lock Nut	110 (150)
Half Housing-to-Half Housing	
Inner	22 (30)
Outer	14 (19)
	INCH Lbs. (N.m)
Transmission Housing-to-Differential Housing	180 (20)
Stator Support	180 (20)
Oil Pump Cover	96 (11)
Valve Body Bolts	60 (7)
Lower Cover Plate	72 (8)
Brake Retaining Bolts	96 (11)

Automatic Transmissions
SAAB – BORG-WARNER MODEL 37

900, 900 Turbo

IDENTIFICATION

All Saabs with A/T use the Borg-Warner model 37 transaxle. The transaxle identification number is stamped on a plate attached to torque converter housing near throttle cable.

DESCRIPTION

The transaxle assembly is a 3-speed unit mounted beneath engine. Transaxle assembly consists basically of a three-element torque converter, planetary gear set, two multi-disc clutches, a one-way clutch, two servos and brake bands, an oil pump, a hydraulic control system and a differential-type final drive assembly. Power is transmitted from turbine shaft of torque converter to input shaft of transmission via a sprocket/chain assembly.

LUBRICATION & ADJUSTMENTS

See appropriate AUTOMATIC TRANSMISSION SERVICING article in IMPORT GENERAL SERVICING section.

TROUBLE SHOOTING

NO DRIVE IN ANY LEVER POSITION

Check for low fluid level, manual linkage that is adjusted (or assembled) incorrectly, oil tubes that are missing or incorrectly installed, or missing/broken seals.

Ensure that valves operate properly. Clean strainer, magnet and valve housing. Check for broken pump drive tangs on converter hub, defective oil pump, or defective converter or one-way clutch.

NO DRIVE IN FORWARD GEARS

Check for manual linkage adjusted or assembled incorrectly, low fluid level, or missing/broken seals. Also check for dirty valve housing, defective front clutch, defective forward sun gear shaft seals, or a one-way clutch that is slipping (or incorrectly installed).

NO DRIVE IN REVERSE GEAR

Check for manual linkage that is adjusted (or assembled) incorrectly, rear band wear (or incorrect adjustment), or low fluid level. Also check for missing (or incorrectly installed) oil tubes, missing/broken seals, or dirty valve housing. Ensure that valves operate properly. Check for defective rear clutch or rear band.

Fig. 1: Cutaway View of Saab (Borg-Warner) Model 37 Automatic Transaxle Assembly

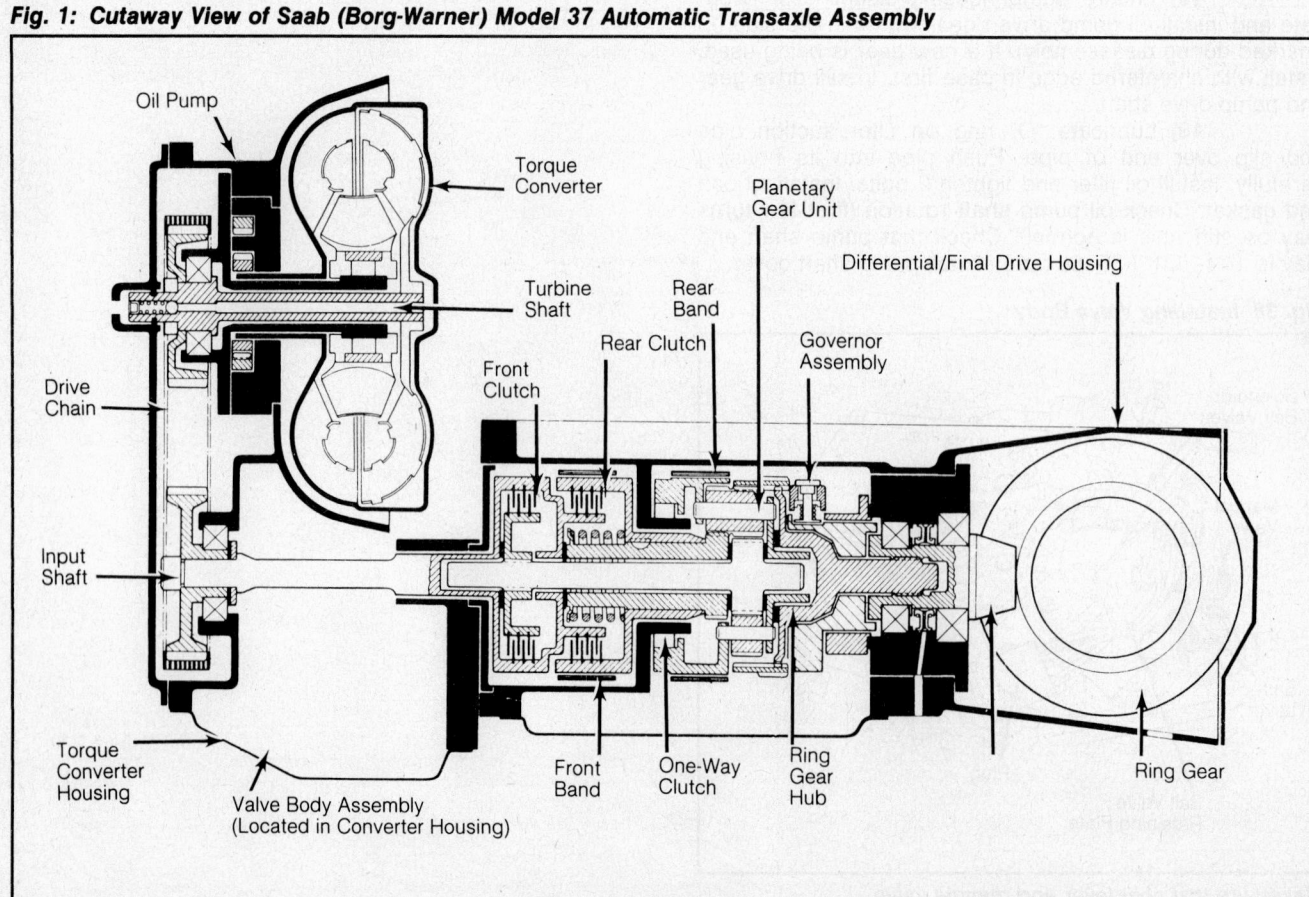

Automatic Transmissions
SAAB — BORG-WARNER MODEL 37 (Cont.)

Fig. 2: Saab (Borg-Warner) Model 37 Hydraulic Circuits Diagram

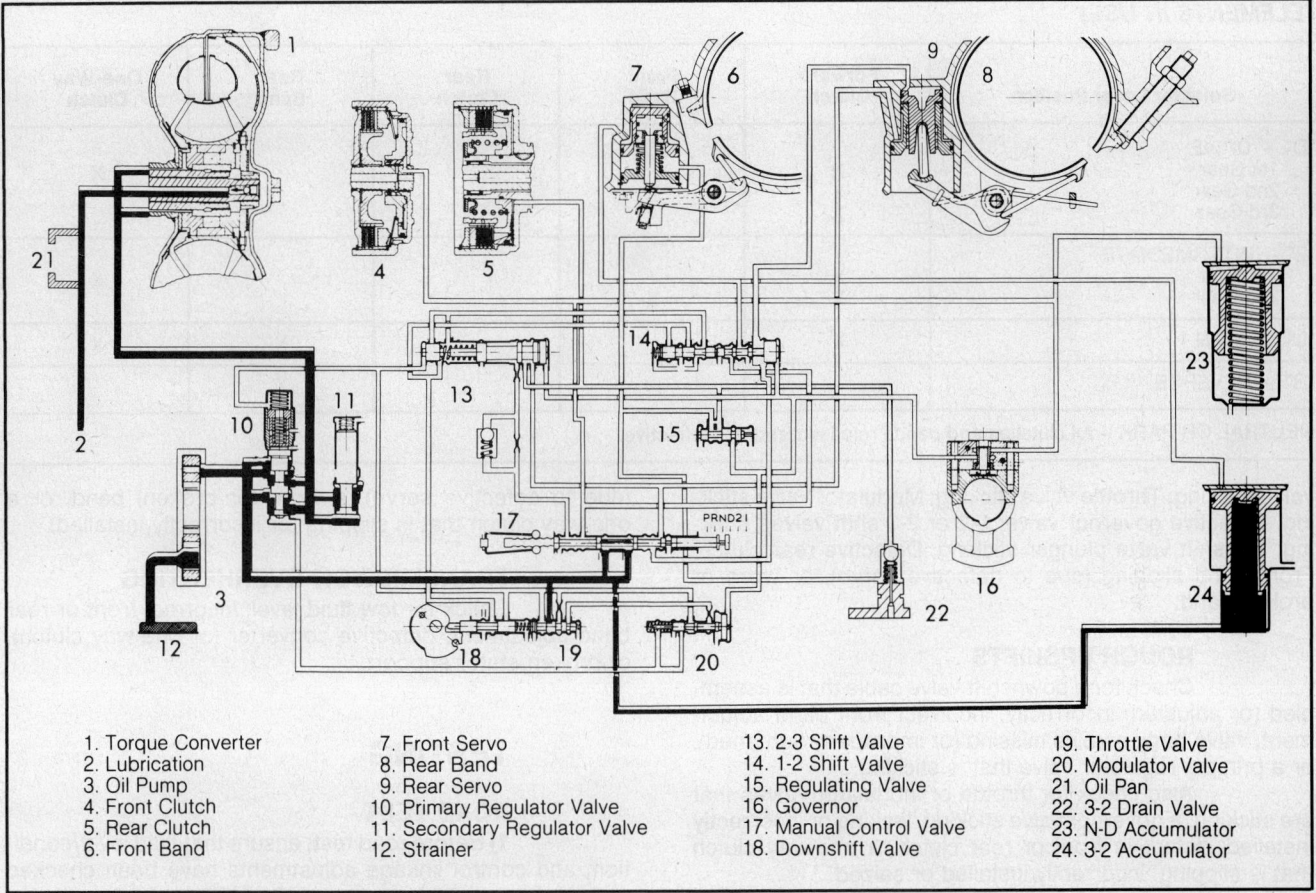

1. Torque Converter
2. Lubrication
3. Oil Pump
4. Front Clutch
5. Rear Clutch
6. Front Band
7. Front Servo
8. Rear Band
9. Rear Servo
10. Primary Regulator Valve
11. Secondary Regulator Valve
12. Strainer
13. 2-3 Shift Valve
14. 1-2 Shift Valve
15. Regulating Valve
16. Governor
17. Manual Control Valve
18. Downshift Valve
19. Throttle Valve
20. Modulator Valve
21. Oil Pan
22. 3-2 Drain Valve
23. N-D Accumulator
24. 3-2 Accumulator

HARSH ENGAGEMENT

Check for a downshift valve cable that is adjusted (or assembled) incorrectly, incorrect engine idle speed, missing (or improperly tightened) valve body screws, or a sticking primary regulator or throttle valve. Also check for a defective front or rear clutch.

DELAYED ENGAGEMENT

Check for low fluid level, manual linkage that is adjusted (or assembled) incorrectly, incorrect engine idle speed, missing (or incorrectly installed oil tubes, or a sticking primary regulator valve.

Also check for valve body screws that are missing or incorrectly tightened, broken or missing seals, defective front (or rear) clutch, broken pump drive tangs on converter, rear band slipping (due to defective servo), worn or broken band(s), turbine shaft check valve missing or binding, or a worn oil pump.

NO 1-2 OR 2-3 UPSHIFT

Check for the following problems: Manual linkage adjusted or assembled incorrectly; Incorrect front band adjustment (1-2 upshift only); Defective governor valve; 1-2 upshift valve sticking; Front band slipping (due to defective servo), worn/broken band; 2-3 shift valve or valve plunger sticking.

Also check for these problems: Turbine shaft check valve missing or binding (2-3 upshift only); Defective throttle valve; Defective modulator valve; Oil tubes missing

(or incorrectly installed); Seals missing/broken; Valve body screws missing (or improperly tightened); Defective regulator valve; Defective rear clutch (2-3 upshift only).

SHIFT POINTS INCORRECT
Upshifts

Check for a downshift valve cable assembled (or adjusted) incorrectly, missing/broken seals, valve body screws missing (or improperly tightened), or a primary regulator valve that is sticking.

Also check for throttle or modulator valve sticking, a governor valve sticking, leaking or incorrectly installed, 1-2 or 2-3 shift valves sticking, or 2-3 shift valve plunger sticking.

Downshifts

Check for downshift valve cable assembled (or adjusted) incorrectly, broken/missing seals, valve body screws missing (or improperly tightened), a sticking throttle valve, a sticking, leaking, (or incorrectly installed) governor valve, 1-2 or 2-3 shift valves sticking, or 2-3 shift valve plunger sticking.

SLIPPING ON UPSHIFTS

Check for the following problems: Incorrect fluid level; Downshift valve cable assembled (or adjusted) incorrectly; Manual linkage assembled (or adjusted) incorrectly; Incorrect front band adjustment; Oil tubes missing (or installed incorrectly); Broken/missing seals; Valve body screws missing (or improperly tightened); Primary regulator

Automatic Transmissions
SAAB – BORG-WARNER MODEL 37 (Cont.)

CLUTCH & BAND APPLICATION CHART
(ELEMENTS IN USE)

Selector Lever Position	Forward Clutch	Front Band	Rear Clutch	Rear Band	One-Way Clutch
"D" – DRIVE					
1st Gear	X				X
2nd Gear	X	X			
3rd Gear	X		X		
"2" – INTERMEDIATE					
1st Gear	X				X
2nd Gear	X	X			
"L1" – LOW 1	X			X	X
"R" – REVERSE			X	X	

NEUTRAL OR PARK – All clutches and bands released and/or ineffective.

---

valve sticking; Throttle valve sticking; Modulator valve sticking; Defective governor valve; 1-2 or 2-3 shift valves sticking; 2-3 shift valve plunger sticking; Defective rear clutch; Front band slipping (due to defective servo), or worn or broken band.

ROUGH UPSHIFTS

Check for a downshift valve cable that is assembled (or adjusted) incorrectly, incorrect front band adjustment, valve body screws missing (or improperly tightened), or a primary regulator valve that is sticking.

Also check for throttle or modulator valves that are sticking, a governor valve sticking, leaking or incorrectly installed, defective front or rear clutch, a one-way clutch that is slipping, incorrectly installed or seized.

NO 2-1 OR 3-2 DOWNSHIFT

Check for a downshfit valve cable that is assembled (or adjusted) incorrectly, a sticking, leaking, or incorrectly installed governor valve, or a sticking 1-2 shift valve. Also check for defective rear clutch, front (or rear) band slipping (due to defective servo), or worn/broken band.

SLIPPING ON DOWNSHIFTS

Check for incorrect front band adjustment, missing (or incorrectly installed) oil tubes, missing/broken seals, valve body screws that are missing (or improperly tightened), or a sticking primary regulator valve.

Also check for a sticking throttle valve, an orifice control valve that is sticking, a defective rear clutch, front clutch slipping (due to defective servo), a worn (or broken) band, or a one-way clutch slipping (or incorrectly installed).

ROUGH DOWNSHIFTS

Check for incorrect front band adjustment, broken/mising seals, valve body screws that are missing (or improperly tightened), a sticking primary regulator valve, or throttle valve.

Also check for an orifice control valve that is sticking, defective front (or rear) clutch, front band slipping (due to defective servo), a worn (or broken) band, or a one-way clutch that is slipping (or incorrectly installed).

TRANSMISSION OVERHEATING

Check for low fluid level, incorrect front or rear band adjustment, defective converter (or one-way clutch), or broken stator support.

TESTING

ROAD TEST

1) Before road test, ensure that fluid level/condition, and control linkage adjustments have been checked and corrected as necessary. During test, transmission should upshift and downshift at approximately same speed. See UPSHIFT & DOWNSHIFT SHIFT SPEEDS chart.

2) Shift speeds may vary slightly due to production tolerances or alternate tire size. All shifts should be smooth, responsive, and with no slippage or engine speed runaway.

3) Slippage or engine speed runaway in any gear usually indicates clutch or band problems. A slipping clutch or band in a particular gear can usually be identified by noting transmission operation in other selector positions and comparing internal units which are applied in these positions. See CLUTCH & BAND APPLICATION chart.

4) With vehicle at a standstill, accelerate both at minimum and full throttle and ensure that 1-2 and 2-3 shifts occur.

NOTE: **At minimum throttle opening, shifts may be difficult to detect. Confirmation that transmission is in 3rd gear may be obtained by shifting to "2" position when a 3-2 downshift should occur.**

5) With vehicle at 46-50 MPH in 3rd gear, depress accelerator to resistance point. Vehicle should accelerate without a downshift. With vehicle at 34-37 MPH in 3rd gear, depress accelerator beyond resistance point. Vehicle should downshift to 2nd gear, and then accelerate.

SAAB – BORG-WARNER MODEL 37 (Cont.)

UPSHIFT & DOWNSHIFT SHIFT SPEEDS

Application	Shift Points (MPH)	
	Minimum Throttle	Full Throttle
1-2 Upshift		
900	9-16	40-46
900 Turbo	9-17	40-48
2-3 Upshift		
900	12-19	67-75
900 Turbo	12-20	70-78
3-2 Downshift		
900		[1] 56-65
900 Turbo		[1] 62-72
2-1 Downshift		
900	1-11	27-36
900 Turbo	1-12	29-39

[1] – Kickdown.

6) With vehicle at 50 MPH, release accelerator and move selector lever to "2" position. Vehicle should downshift to 2nd gear and engine braking should be noticed.

7) Stop vehicle, put vehicle in Reverse. Check reverse operation by accelerating at full throttle and check for slipping and/or clutch break-away noise.

8) Stop vehicle on a hill facing downward. With vehicle in Park, release brakes and ensure parking pawl is operating. Repeat test with vehicle facing uphill.

STALL TEST
Precautions
When making test, do not hold throttle open any longer than 10 seconds. If engine speed exceeds limits, release accelerator immediately as clutch or band slippage is indicated. See STALL SPEED SPECIFICATIONS table.

Procedure
1) With engine at normal operating temperature, tachometer installed and parking and service brakes applied, perform transmission stall test in "D", "1" and "R" positions at full throttle, and note maximum RPM obtained. Engine speed should be within limits. See STALL SPEED SPECIFICATIONS table.

STALL SPEED SPECIFICATIONS

Application	Stall RPM
900	2150-2550
900 Turbo	2100-2600

2) If stall speed is about 300 RPM below specifications, engine is not operating at full power. If stall speed is about 800 RPM below specifications, torque converter assembly must be replaced.

3) A substantially higher stall speed than specifications indicates that converter is not receiving required oil supply, or that slippage is occurring in one of gearbox clutches.

SERVICE (IN VEHICLE)

WHEEL BEARINGS & DRIVE AXLE SHAFTS

NOTE: Downward movement of control arms is limited by rubber buffer inside each shock absorber. Therefore, it will be necessary either to remove shock absorber, or to support lower control arm at outer end, before raising vehicle.

Removal
1) Remove hub cap, loosen hub nut and wheel lugs. Raise and support vehicle. Remove wheels. Rotate brake disc to align recess along disc edge, with brake pads and caliper. Disconnect parking brake cable from each side. Remove caliper mounting bolts and hang caliper from coil spring using wire. DO NOT disconnect hydraulic line.

2) Remove hub and disc assembly using Extractor (89 96 084). Remove larger clamp on inner universal joint bellows. Remove steering arm and upper ball joint using Remover (89 95 409). Disconnect screws on lower control arm bracket. Separate inner CV joint from drive flange. Cover end of rubber bellows to prevent needle bearings from falling onto floor.

3) Pull axle assembly through wheel housing to remove. Thoroughly clean axle assembly. Place steering knuckle housing in a press and press out drive shaft. Remove snap ring from bearing housing. Press out and discard bearing.

Installation
1) Press bearing into steering knuckle housing, then install snap ring. Place axle shaft in press and press on knuckle housing and bearing. Install inner oil seal. Press wheel hub and brake disc onto axle splines and install washer. Install new lock nut, but do not tighten.

2) Install axle shaft through wheel housing. Install any needle bearings, which may have fallen out of inner CV joint, onto ends of "T" section. Attach inner CV joint to drive flange. Install upper ball joint to steering knuckle and reinstall lower control arm bracket. Install tie rod end on steering arm. Install brake caliper.

3) Reinstall front wheel and lower vehicle. Tighten hub lock nut, then secure in place by peening into locking groove. Pump brake pedal several times to seat brake pads.

CV JOINTS
NOTE: Axle shafts cannot be disassembled. If damaged or defective, replace as complete assembly.

VALVE BODY
NOTE: Valve body cannot be serviced in vehicle. Removal and disasssembly of the transaxle is necessary to service valve body assembly.

GOVERNOR ASSEMBLY
NOTE: Governor assembly cannot be serviced in vehicle. Removal and disasssembly of the transaxle is necessary to service governor assembly.

TRANSAXLE MOUNTS
Removal & Installation
1) Place transmission in Neutral. Unbolt exhaust pipe from manifold. Disconnect speedometer cable from transmission. Remove rear engine mounting bolt. Loosen front engine mounting bolt.

2) Attach hoist to 2 lifting rings, and raise engine and tranaxle assembly about 4". Remove bolts attaching front and rear mounts to frame, and remove mounts. To install, reverse removal procedure.

REMOVAL & INSTALLATION

TRANSAXLE
See appropriate AUTOMATIC TRANSMISSION REMOVAL article in IMPORT GENERAL SERVICING section.

TORQUE CONVERTER

NOTE: **Torque converter is a sealed unit and cannot be disassembled for service. If found defective, it must be replaced as a unit. Ventilation holes in torque converter housing must be kept free from dirt.**

TRANSAXLE DISASSEMBLY
1) Separate transaxle assembly from engine and mount on Transmission Stand (78 60 794). Attach Torque Converter Support (87 90 255). Drain fluid from transmission and final drive unit.

2) Remove all 5 covers from assembly. Remove sealing ring from turbine shaft. Hold drive chain sprockets stationary and remove sprocket attaching bolts. Remove drive chain and sprockets as an assembly. *See Fig. 3.*

Fig. 3: Removing Drive Chain and Sprockets

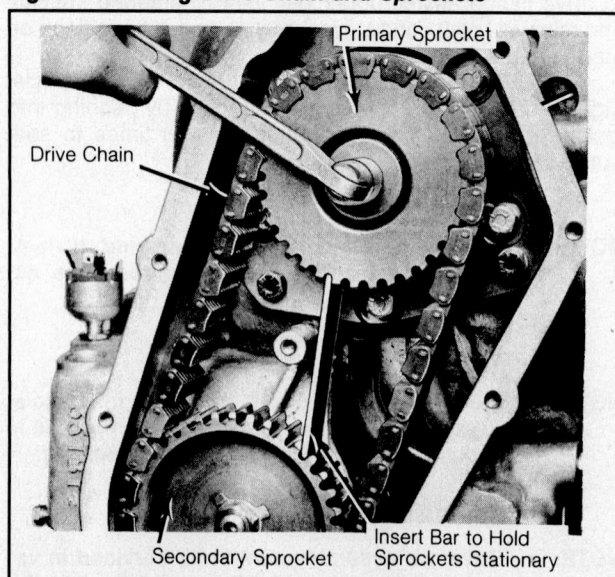

3) Turn transmission upside down. Remove oil screen and magnet. Remove oil tubes connecting front and rear sumps. Remove throttle valve cable. Remove oil pump

strainer. Remove all oil tubes except 2 from drain valve to servo piston.

4) Remove valve body retaining bolts and lift out valve body. Remove accumulator piston (under valve body). Remove torque converter housing-to-transaxle housing attaching bolts. While holding parking pawl away from gear with screwdriver, remove torque converter housing and gasket. If necessary, tap housing with plastic hammer to separate.

5) Pry out front band pivot shaft with screwdriver. Remove band lever and strut. Remove self adjusting screw. Unhook rear band lever tension spring. Remove pivot shaft toward front of case. Use a strong screwdriver to push out shaft.

6) Remove band lever and strut. Remove 3 bolts securing center support to transaxle housing. Attach sprocket and nut to input shaft. Tap sprocket to loosen cover and remove front clutch.

7) Remove rear clutch assembly and sun gear shaft. Save shaft bearing and thrust washers for reassembly. Remove front and rear bands, planetary gear assembly and center support. Remove front servo snap ring. Using compressed air, remove front servo piston. *See Fig. 6.* Remove rear servo piston in same manner. *See Fig. 7.*

8) Install Hub Remover (87 90 958), or long bolt, through middle of ring gear hub. Pull hub, governor and pinion output shaft, by slowly tightening bolt. Use parking pawl to hold hub during removal. Do not remove parking pawl unless it is to be replaced. If necessary, remove snap ring from pivot shaft, push out shaft and remove pawl and spring. *See Fig. 8.*

Fig. 4: Bottom View of Torque Converter Case

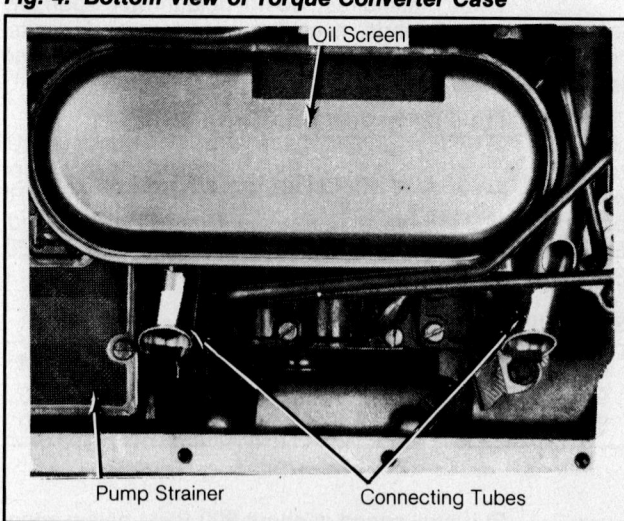

NOTE: **Before disassembling final drive unit, measure and record backlash and position of pinion for reassembly reference. See ADJUSTMENT procedures in TRANSAXLE REASSEMBLY. If ring and pinion gear assembly has been installed for less than 6000 miles, follow normal adjustment procedures on reassembly. If assembly has been installed for longer than 6000 miles, adjust to recorded measurements.**

9) Remove differential bearing housing retaining bolts (both sides). Using a puller and slide hammer, remove bearing housings and their axle shafts. Remove differential assembly from case.

Automatic Transmissions
SAAB – BORG-WARNER MODEL 37 (Cont.)

Fig. 5: Bottom View of Transaxle Case

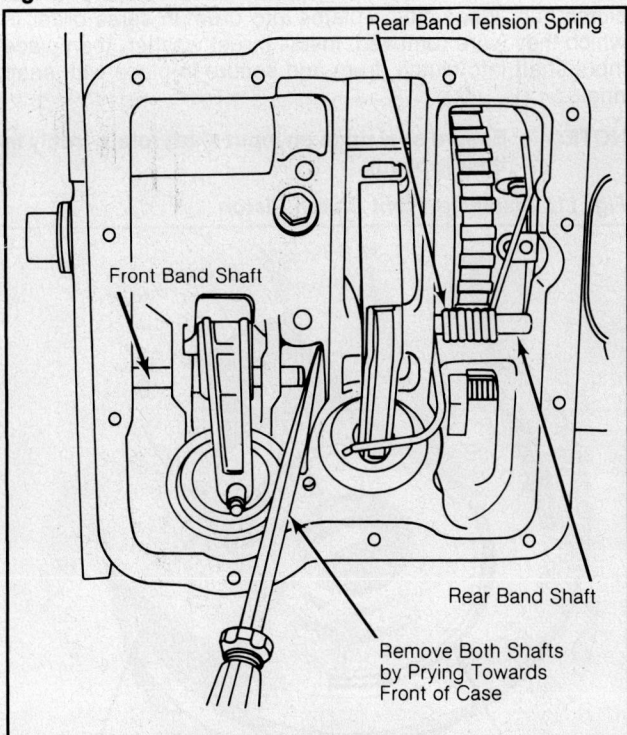

Fig. 6: Removing Front Servo Piston

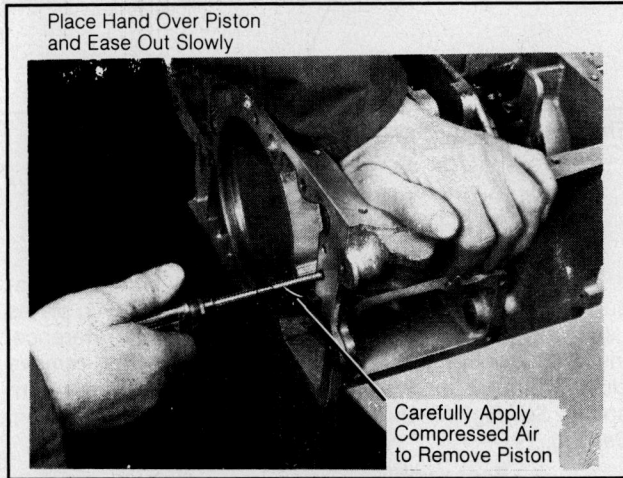

Place hand over piston to prevent possible damage.

10) Remove pinion bearing housing retaining bolts. Place transmission housing in press and press out pinion bearing housing and pinion seal housing (pressure applied at seal housing). *See Fig. 9.*

INPUT SHAFT END PLAY

NOTE: **To obtain correct input shaft end play, retaining nut depth must be set correctly.**

1) To accurately measure retaining nut depth, set depth gauge to 7.667" (195 mm) and install onto case. Measure distance between end of depth gauge and retaining nut using feeler gauge. Install shim of thickness equal to that of feeler gauge.

Fig. 7: Removing Rear Servo Piston

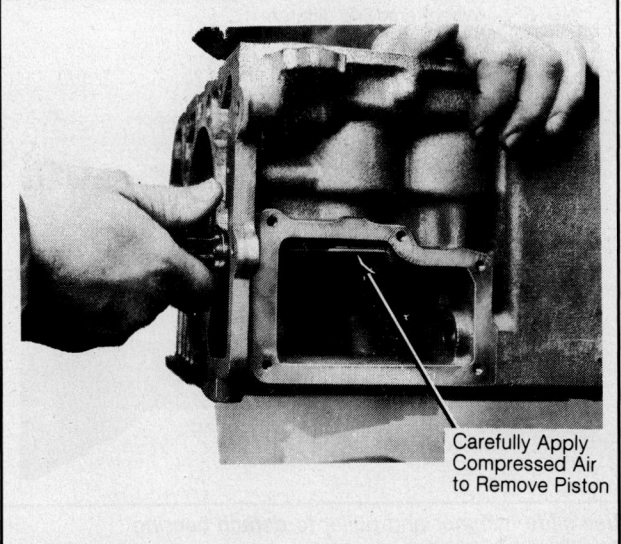

Place hand over piston and ease out gently.

Fig. 8: Removing Ring Gear Hub & Governor Assembly

Tighten bolt through center of assembly to press off components.

2) Using a micrometer, measure thickness of shim removed during disassembly. If original shim thickness equals required shim thickness, reinstall original shim. If not, install shim of proper thickness. Shims are available in thicknesses of .012" (.3 mm), .016" (.4 mm) and .02" (.05 mm). Install shim between retaining nut and reverse gear.

COMPONENT DISASSEMBLY & REASSEMBLY

FRONT CLUTCH ASSEMBLY
Disassembly
1) Slide clutch sealing plate from input shaft. Remove snap ring and lift input shaft and thrust washer from clutch drum. Lift out clutch hub and clutch plates from drum.

Fig. 9: *Removing Differential Bearing Housing*

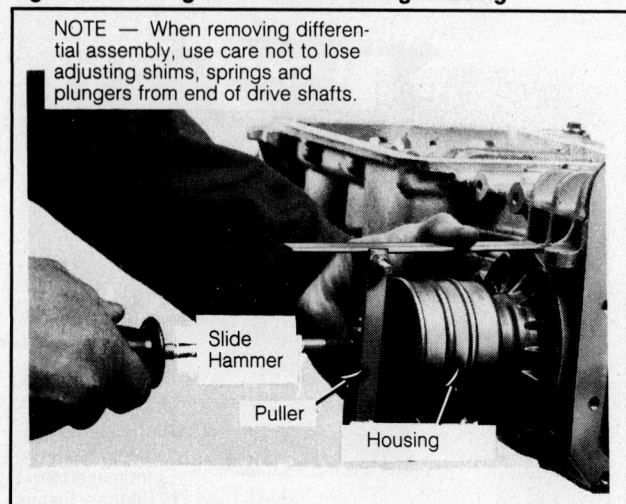

NOTE — When removing differential assembly, use care not to lose adjusting shims, springs and plungers from end of drive shafts.

Use slide hammer and puller to detach bearing housing/axle shaft assembly.

NOTE: **Record number of clutch plates used and order in which they are installed for reassembly reference.**

2) Remove pressure plate from clutch drum. Remove piston return spring snap ring and remove spring from clutch drum. Remove clutch piston from drum with aid of compressed air. *See Fig. 10.* Inspect all seals and clutch plates for wear or damage and replace if necessary.

Fig. 10: *Removing Front Clutch Piston*

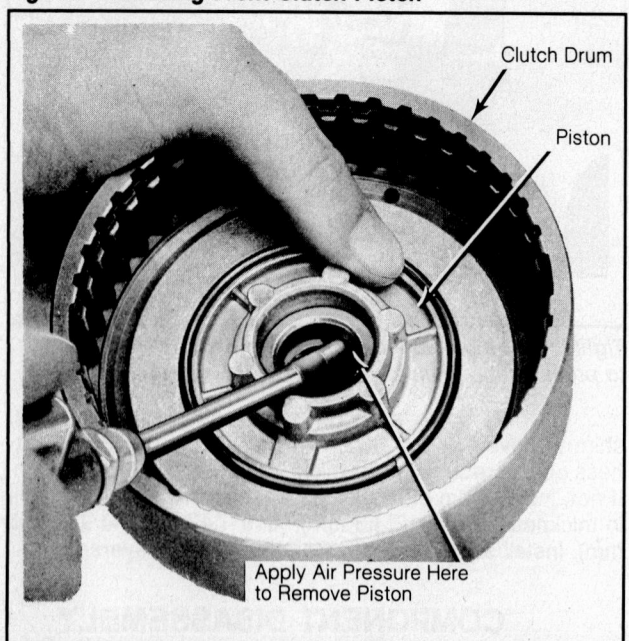

Hold piston as shown, while applying compressed air.

Reassembly
1) Prior to reassembly, lubricate all components with ATF. Install new "O" ring seal on clutch drum and in piston groove. Using seal protector, install piston into clutch drum until it is fully seated. Install clutch return spring into drum with convex side facing down, then install snap ring.

2) Install pressure plate with flat side up. Install clutch hub. Place clutch plates into drum in same order in which they were removed. Install thrust washer, then place input shaft into clutch drum and secure in place with snap ring.

NOTE: **Ensure seal rings on input shaft rotate freely in their grooves.**

Fig. 11: *Installing Front Clutch Piston*

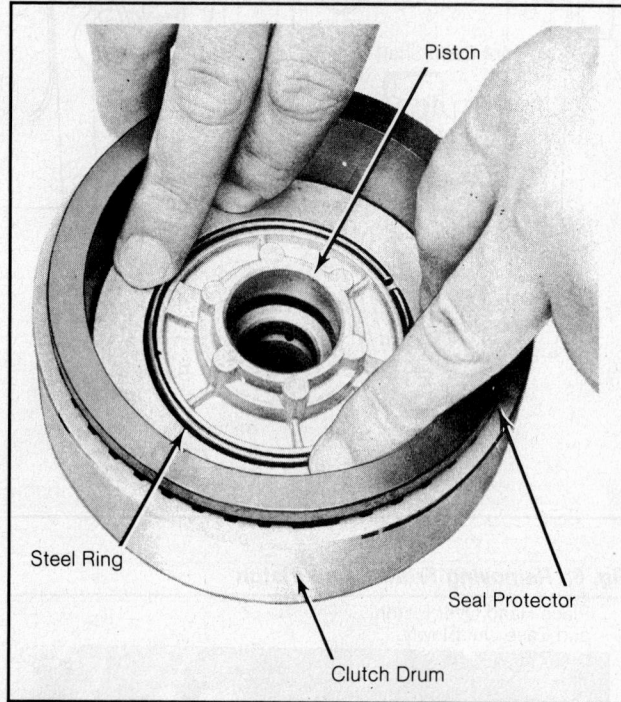

Ensure steel ring on piston is fully seated.

REAR CLUTCH ASSEMBLY
Disassembly
Remove clutch drum snap ring. Remove pressure plate and clutch plates, noting number of clutch plates used and order of installation for reassembly reference. Install Clutch Spring Compressor (87 90 018) and remove clutch return spring snap ring, spring seat and return spring. *See Fig. 13.* Use compressed air to remove piston. *See Fig. 14.*

Reassembly
NOTE: **Lubricate all parts with ATF before reassembly. Inner clutch plates must be soaked in ATF before final installation.**

1) Using Piston Installer (87 90 081) install piston (flat side down) until fully seated, then lubricate with petroleum jelly. Install return spring and spring seat. Compress return spring in a press, using Return Spring Installer (87 90 081) and install snap ring.

2) Assemble clutch plates, pressure plate and snap ring. Apply load to pressure plate, and measure clearance between pressure plate and snap ring. Clearance should be .025-.045" (.63-1.14 mm). If clearance is between .046-.064" (1.17-1.63 mm), install a thicker snap ring.

3) If clearance exceeds .064" (1.63 mm), install 2 thin snap rings. If clearance is below specification, replace

Fig. 12: Exploded View of Front Clutch Assembly and Input Shaft

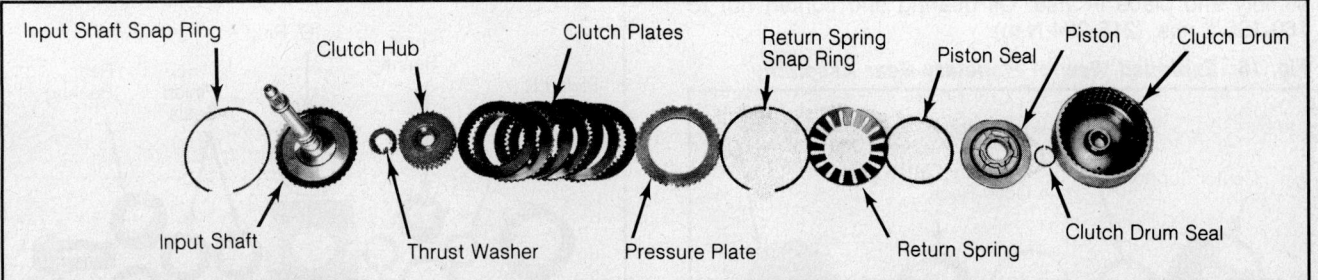

Fig. 13: Removing Rear Clutch Return Spring Snap Ring

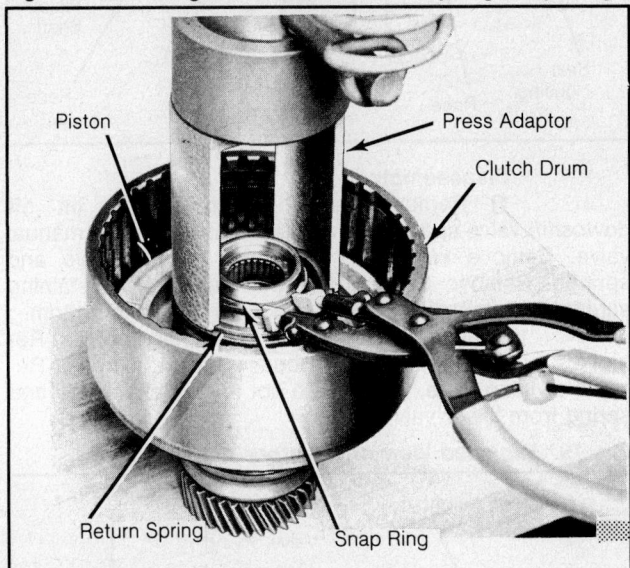

Fig. 14: Removing Rear Clutch Piston

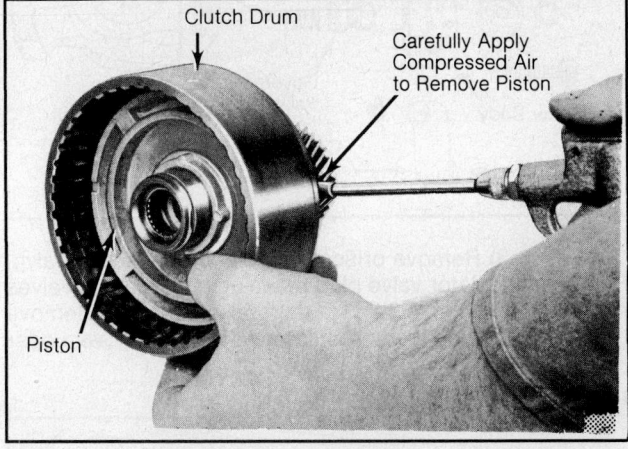

greatly concaved plates with slightly flatter plates (one at a time) until correct clearance is obtained. *See Fig. 15.*

PLANETARY GEAR ASSEMBLY
Disassembly
Remove center support from planetary gear assembly. Remove one-way clutch from outer race. Remove snap ring for one-way clutch outer race and remove race from planet carrier.

Fig. 15: Rear Clutch Plate Positions

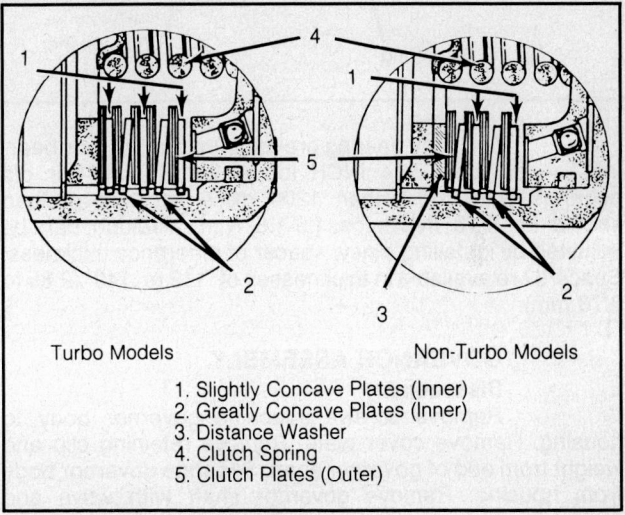

Turbo Models   Non-Turbo Models

1. Slightly Concave Plates (Inner)
2. Greatly Concave Plates (Inner)
3. Distance Washer
4. Clutch Spring
5. Clutch Plates (Outer)

Install plates in order shown.

Reassembly
Install one-way clutch outer race and secure in place with snap ring. Install one-way clutch, with flange on inner roller retainer facing outwards, into outer race. Install center support. After reassembly, one-way clutch should rotate in a clockwise direction only.

PINION BEARING HOUSING
Disassembly
1) Remove pinion bearing housing seal cover and "O" ring. Clamp Holding Fixture (87 90 636) and Extractor Ring (87 90 651) in a vise and fit housing in fixture. Install two 8 mm bolts in holes in holding fixture to act as stops for bearing housing. Remove pinion nut. Remove pinion from housing and press off rear pinion bearing.

2) Heat pinion bearing housing to about 212°F (100°C). Carefully pull out rear bearing race using Race Remover (87 90 966) and slide hammer. Remove pinion seals. Press off front bearing race with Race Remover (78 41 141).

NOTE: **Do not remove bearing races unless new bearings are to be installed.**

Reassembly
1) Clean ventilation channel of housing thoroughly before beginning reassembly. Press in new front bearing race (if needed). Install pinion seals using Seal Installer (87 90 900). Press in new rear bearing race (if removed). Press rear bearing on to pinion shaft.

2) Install pinion shaft in bearing housing. Install spacer and front bearing. Oil threads of pinion shaft and

install nut. Place complete assembly in tools as in disassembly and place in vise. Oil bearing and tighten nut to 160-195 ft. lbs. (215-264 N.m).

Fig. 16: Exploded View of Planetary Gear Assembly

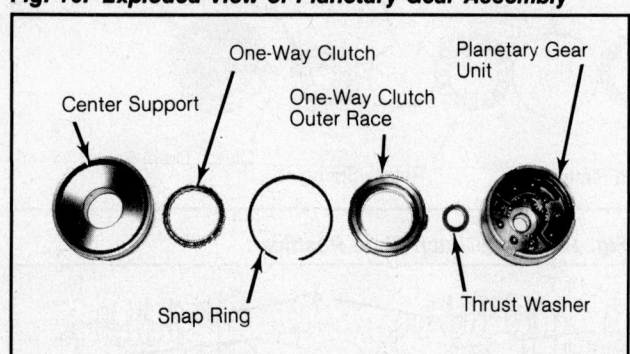

3) Check bearing preload. Preload for new bearings should be 19-24 INCH lbs. (2.2-2.7 N.m). For old bearings (with more than 1200 miles service), preload should be 8-13 INCH lbs. (.9-1.5 N.m). Preload can be adjusted by installing a new spacer of difference thickness. Spacers are available in thicknesses of .112 to .149" (2.85 to 3.78 mm).

GOVERNOR ASSEMBLY
Disassembly

Remove screws attaching governor body to housing. Remove cover plate. Remove retaining clip and weight from end of governor shaft. Separate governor body from housing. Remove governor shaft with valve and spring. Inspect all parts for wear or damage. Scratches on governor valve may be cleaned with fine emery cloth.

Reassembly

Before reassembly, lubricate all parts with ATF. To reassemble, reverse disassembly procedure. After reassembly, ensure governor valve moves freely.

VALVE BODY ASSEMBLY

NOTE: As valve trains are removed from each valve body bore, place individual parts in correct order and in relative position to valve body to simplify reassembly.

CAUTION: Valves and springs are not interchangeable; all parts must be installed in correct order in proper valve body bore. See Fig. 20.

Fig. 18: Exploded View of Pinion Bearing Assembly

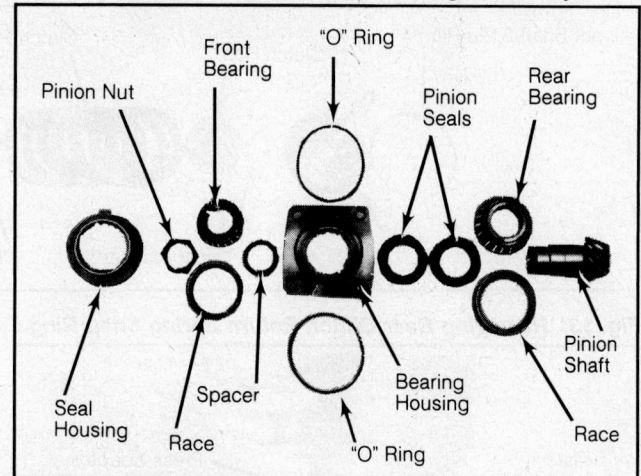

Disassembly

1) Remove retaining screws and lift off downshift valve carrier and cam assembly. Pull out manual valve. Remove kickdown valve and throttle valve and springs. Remove 6 upper-to-lower valve body retaining screws from top of assembly and 2 screws from bottom.

2) Separate upper and lower valve bodies. Remove 8 oil pipe plate-to-valve body retaining screws. Remove dividing plate, taking care not to lose check ball and spring from lower valve body.

Fig. 19: Exploded View of Governor Assembly

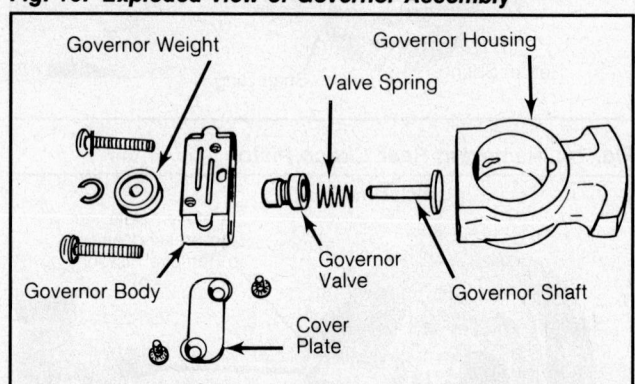

3) Remove orifice control valve stop and valve. Remove modulator valve plug retaining pin. Remove valves and springs. Remove 3 end plate retaining screws. Remove primary and secondary regulator valves. Remove upper

Fig. 17: Exploded View Showing Components of Rear Clutch Assembly

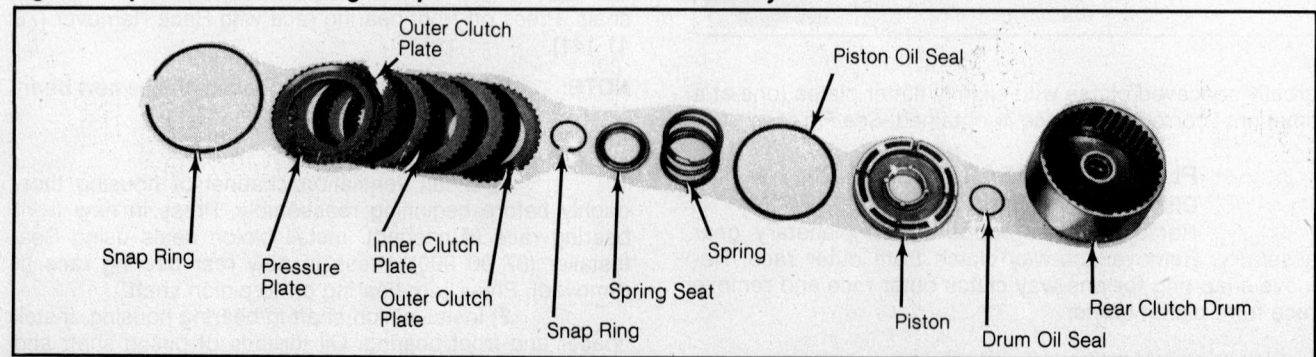

Automatic Transmissions
SAAB — BORG-WARNER MODEL 37 (Cont.)

Fig. 20: Exploded View of Upper and Lower Valve Body Assembly

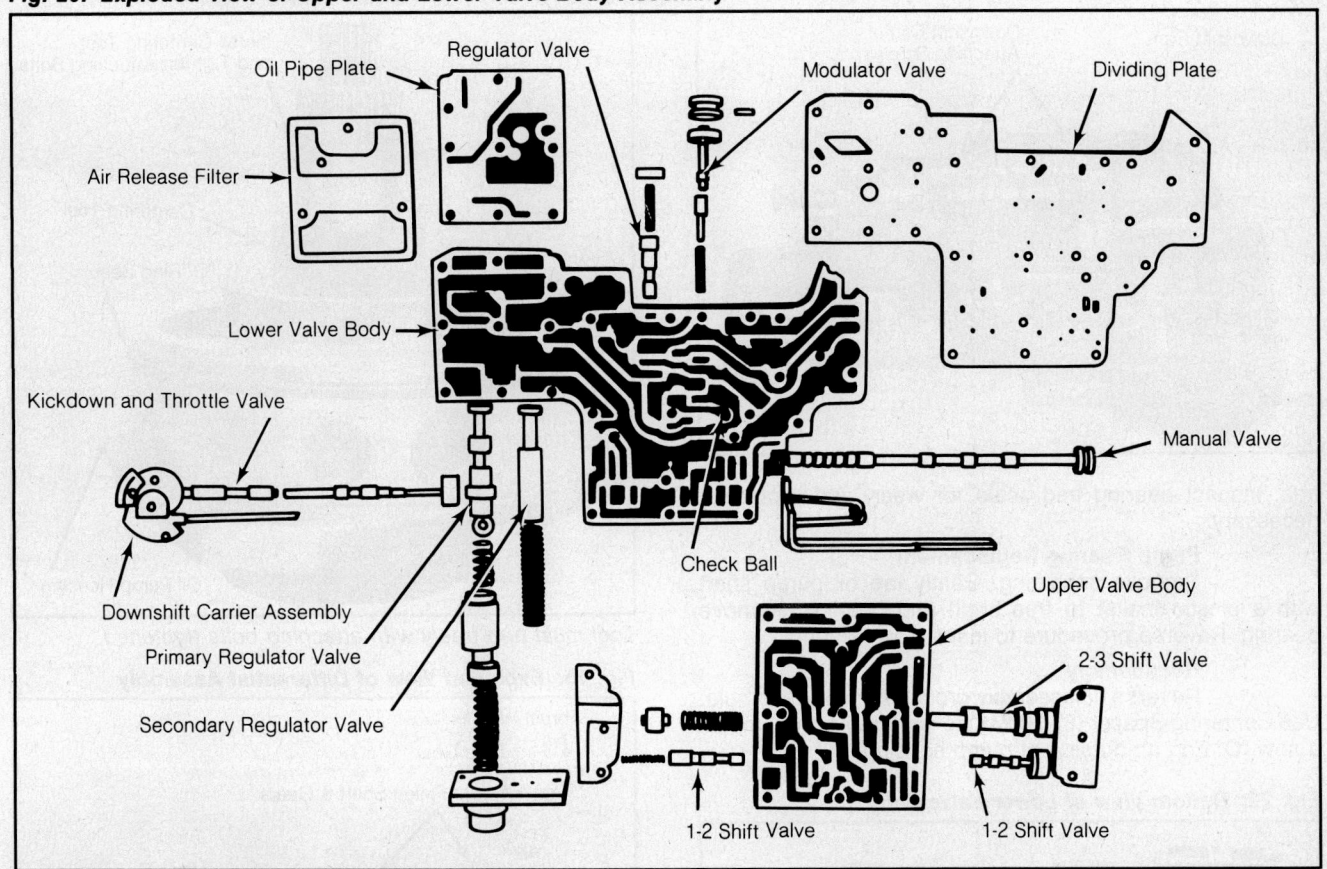

valve body cover screws. Remove cover. Remove 1-2 shift valve and 2-3 shift valve assemblies.

Reassembly

1) Reverse disassembly procedure and note following: Before reassembly, ensure that all components are thoroughly cleaned and are free of scratches. Small scratches on valves and valve body bores may be removed with fine emery cloth.

2) Dip all valves and plugs in ATF before installing. Rotate valves and plugs, when inserting into bores, to avoid shearing off soft body castings. Ensure all valves move freely and smoothly in their bores. Ensure check ball and spring are in correct position in lower valve body, before installing oil tube plate. *See Fig. 22.*

OIL PUMP
Disassembly

Remove 5 attaching screws and separate pump housings. Check back plate for scratches or other damage. Mark pump drive and driven gear for reassembly. DO NOT scribe mark on gears, use chalk or a soft pencil. Remove gears. Inspect gears for scratches or signs of other dam-

SAAB VALVE BODY SPRING IDENTIFICATION CHART

Valve Spring	Length In. (mm)	Diameter In. (mm)	Number Of Coils	Color
1-2 Shift Valve	1.094 (27.8)	.235 (5.97)	15.5	.....
2-3 Shift Valve	1.590 (40.4)	.352 (8.94)	24.5	.....
Primary Regulator Valve	2.850 (72.4)	.600 (15.24)	16.25	.....
Secondary Regulator Valve	2.593 (65.9)	.485 (12.24)	23.5	.....
Orifice Control Valve	1.005 (25.53)	.203 (5.16)	19	.....
Modulator Valve	1.069 (27.15)	.211 (5.36)	21	.....
Throttle Valve (Inner)	.807 (20.5)	.141 (3.58)	30	.....
Throttle Valve (Outer)	1.185 (30.1)	.236 (5.97)	20	.....

Automatic Transmissions
SAAB – BORG-WARNER MODEL 37 (Cont.)

Fig. 21: Top View of Lower Valve Body

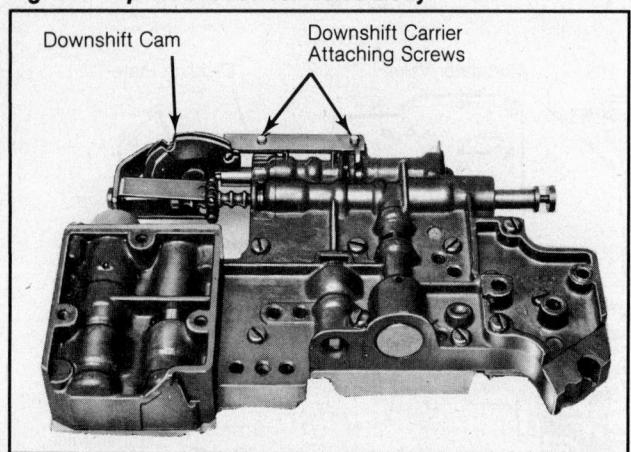

age. Inspect bearing and seals for wear, and replace if necessary.

Pump Bearing Replacement
Remove snap ring. Gently tap oil pump shaft with a plastic mallet to free shaft and bearing. Remove bearing. Reverse procedure to install new bearing.

Reassembly
Reverse disassembly procedure to reassemble. Use Centering Spacer (87 90 248) to center oil pump. Install a new "O" ring on outside of pump housing.

Fig. 22: Bottom View of Lower Valve Body

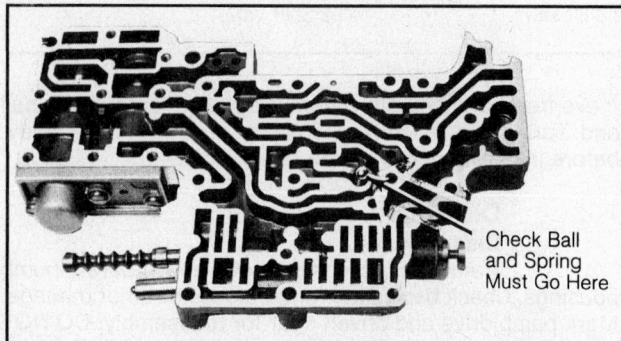

Fig. 23: Disassembled View of Oil Pump Assembly

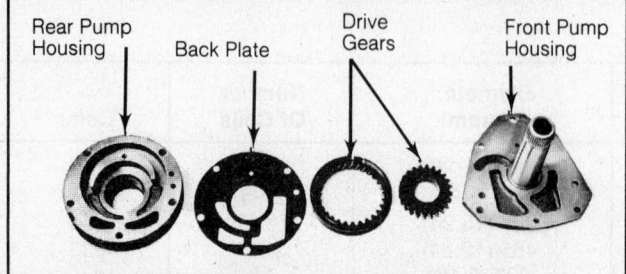

Use centering spacer when installing pump.

DIFFERENTIAL ASSEMBLY

Disassembly
1) Remove differential bearings only if they are to be replaced. Remove differential ring gear attaching bolts and separate ring gear from differential housing.

Fig. 24: Reassembling Oil Pump

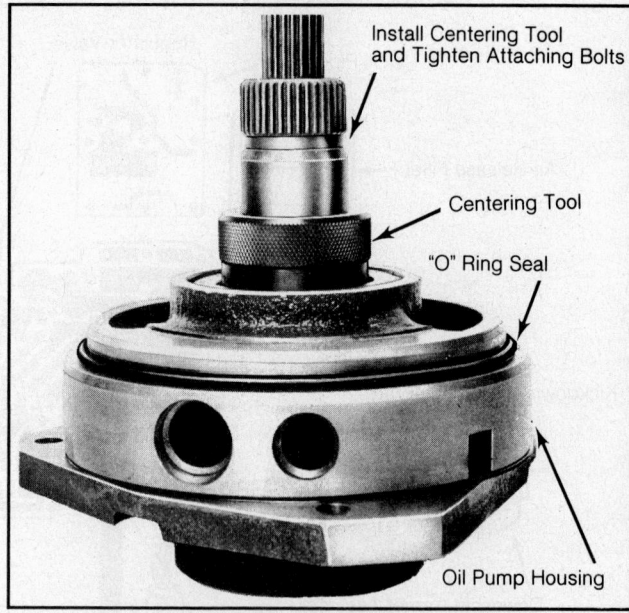

Tool must turn freely with attaching bolts tightened.

Fig. 25: Exploded View of Differential Assembly

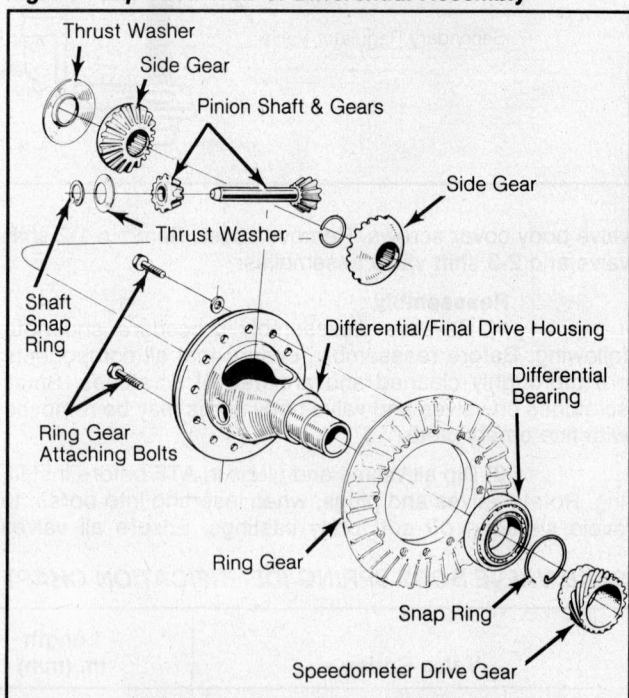

2) Remove snap ring, then push out differential pinion gear shaft. Remove pinion gears and side gears along with thrust washers from housing. If ring gear requires replacement, pinion shaft must also be replaced as they are serviced as a complete set.

NOTE: **Before left side bearing can be removed, speedometer drive gear must be pulled from housing.**

Reassembly
Install pinion gears and side gear along with thrust washers into differential housing, install pinion shaft

SAAB – BORG-WARNER MODEL 37 (Cont.)

and lock in place with snap ring. Mount ring gear on differential housing. Install attaching bolts using Loctite.

INNER DRIVE SHAFT ASSEMBLY
Disassembly
Remove drive shaft snap ring and press drive shaft from bearing housing. Using a screwdriver, remove oil seal from housing using care not to damage housing. On left side bearing housing, remove shaft and pull out speedometer drive assembly. On both sides, press out drive shaft bearing. If new differential bearings are to be installed, remove bearing outer race from housing using a drift.

NOTE: **A washer is located between right side race and bearing housing to improve bearing lubrication.**

Reassembly
Press new drive shaft bearing into bearing housing. If removed, press new differential bearing outer race into bearing housing. Ensure lubrication washer is installed before right side race. Using a drift, press bearing housing oil seal into housing until it protrudes approximately .08" (2 mm) above face of housing.

Fig. 26: Exploded View of Inner Drive Shaft Assembly

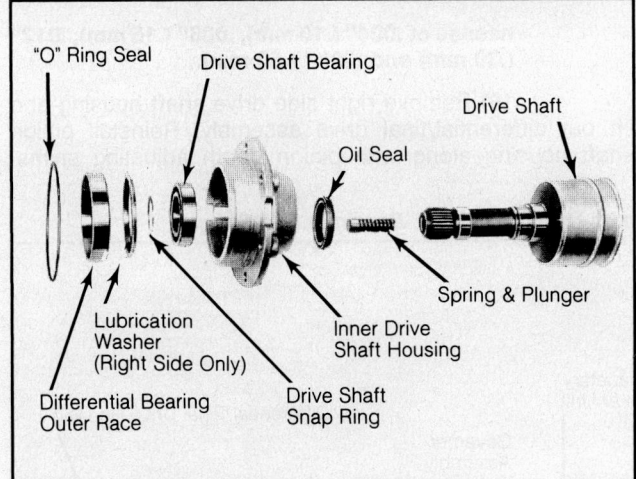

Right side assembly shown.

TRANSAXLE REASSEMBLY

NOTE: **Handle all parts carefully to avoid damaging bearing and mating surfaces. Lubricate all components with ATF. Use petrolatum to hold gaskets and thrust washers in place, where required. Replace all worn or damaged parts. See Fig. 29 for thrust washer and bearing locations.**

1) Blow out ventilation channels with compressed air. Install pinion bearing housing locating studs into case. Install pinion bearing shims. Lubricate bearing housing sealing rings.

2) Position complete pinion bearing housing assembly on locating stubs. Place case in press, and press in housing. Press bearing housing in as far as it can go. Remove locating studs and install retaining bolts. Check pinion clearance.

Fig. 27: Exploded View of Speedometer Drive Assembly

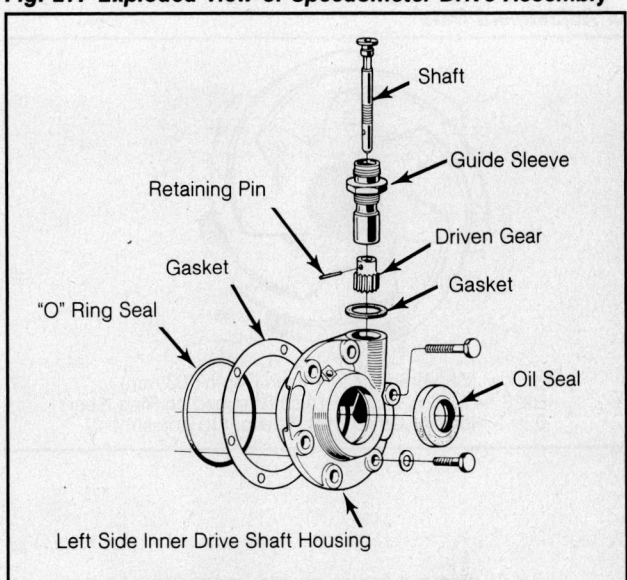

NOTE: **Pinion depth must be measured using Saab Measuring Instrument (83 90 155), which consists of a measuring jig (with attached dial indicator) and a gauge block for calibrating dial indicator. See Fig. 30.**

3) To calibrate indicator, place calibration stops of measuring tool against gauge block. Distance between stops and centerline of tool is 2.362" (60.00 mm), which is equal to distance from end face of pinion shaft to centerline of ring gear. Ensure that dial indicator pointer is zeroed when measuring tip touches gauge block.

4) Place measuring tool in transaxle case with measuring tip applied to flat end of pinion gear. Take a reading. When pinion gear is correctly positioned, dial indicator should show number of hundredths of a millimeter (+ or -) stamped into pinion, with a permitted tolerance of .002" (.05 mm). For example, if pinion is stamped +3, indicator should read +3 ± .05 mm.

5) If measured pinion depth reading is not within specifications (stamped on pinion), pinion shaft must be adjusted. To adjust, remove pinion shaft bearing housing. Add or remove shims between housing and transaxle case as follows: If reading is higher than specifications, reduce shim combination.

6) Reduce or increase shim combination according to difference between measured value and specified value. Pinion depth adjusting shims are available in thicknesses of .004" (.10 mm), .006" (.15 mm), .012" (.30 mm) and .020" (.50 mm).

7) Before reinstalling pinion housing and pinion depth adjusting shims, differential bearing preload must be adjusted. Place differential/final drive assembly into transaxle case, then install left side inner drive shaft housing (side with speedometer drive) without shims.

8) Install attaching bolts and tighten to 15-18 ft. lbs. (20-25 N.m). Oil differential bearing, and install right side drive shaft housing without shims. Tighten attaching bolts to 19 INCH lbs. (2.2 N.m) in 2 or 3 steps. Rotate differential assembly while tightening bolts.

Automatic Transmissions

SAAB – BORG-WARNER MODEL 37 (Cont.)

Fig. 28: View of Pinion Gear Showing Location of Adjustment Data

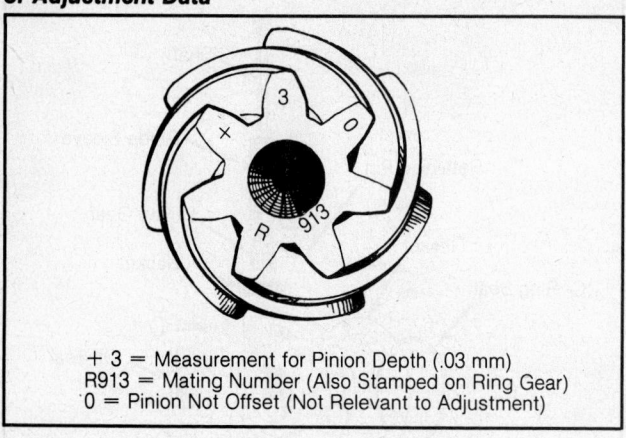

3
+
0
R
913
+ 3 = Measurement for Pinion Depth (.03 mm)
R913 = Mating Number (Also Stamped on Ring Gear)
0 = Pinion Not Offset (Not Relevant to Adjustment)

9) Using a feeler gauge, measure gap between right side drive shaft housing and transaxle case at 2 points opposite each other. Take average of 2 readings and select adjusting shims which will equal this value. Then add an additional .008" (.20 mm) in shim thickness to obtain correct bearing preload.

NOTE: **Up to 4 shims may be used to obtain correct preload. Adjusting shims are available in thicknesses of .004" (.10 mm), .006" (.15 mm), .012" (.30 mm) and .020" (.50 mm).**

Fig. 30: Using Special Tool to Measure Pinion Depth

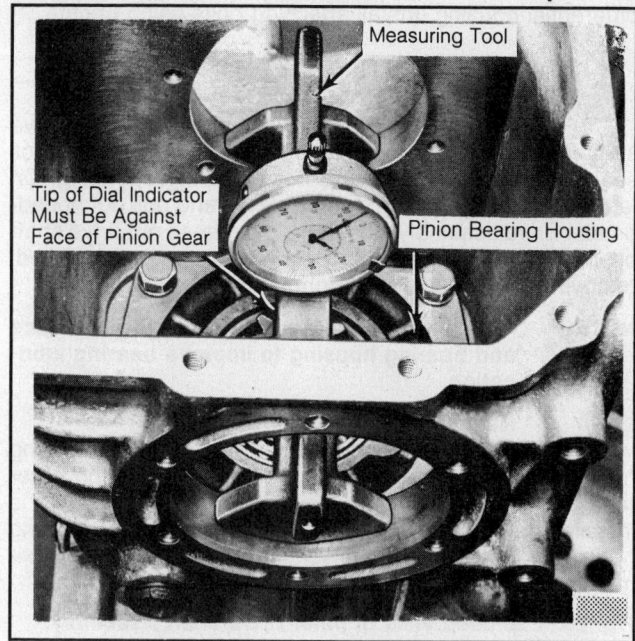

Measuring Tool
Tip of Dial Indicator Must Be Against Face of Pinion Gear
Pinion Bearing Housing

10) Remove right side drive shaft housing and lift out differential/final drive assembly. Reinstall pinion shaft housing along with pinion depth adjusting shims.

Fig. 29: Cutaway View of Transaxle Assembly Showing Location of Thrust Washers, Bearings and Shims

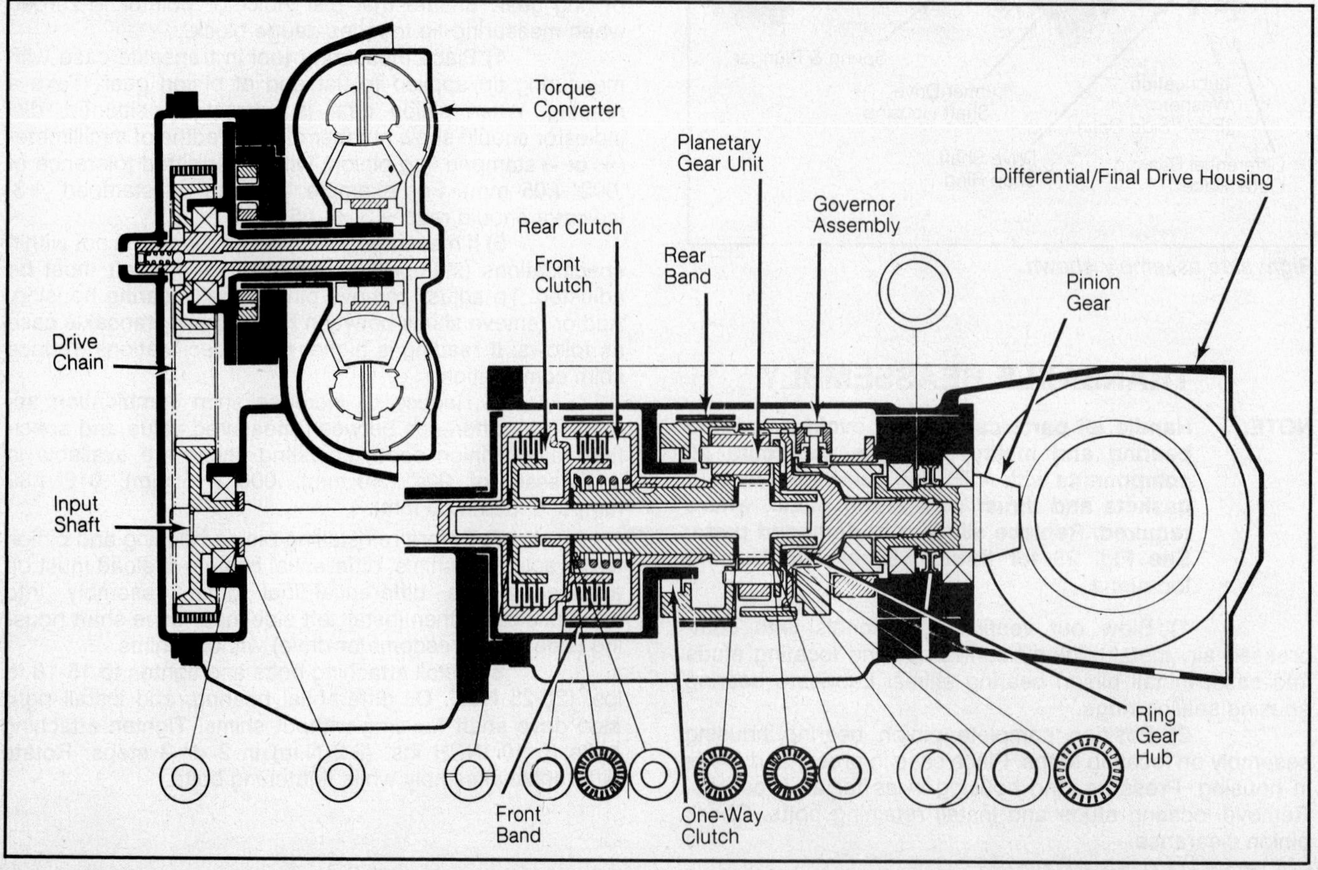

Torque Converter
Planetary Gear Unit
Differential/Final Drive Housing
Governor Assembly
Rear Clutch
Front Clutch
Rear Band
Pinion Gear
Drive Chain
Input Shaft
Ring Gear Hub
Front Band
One-Way Clutch

Fig. 31: Measuring Differential Bearing Preload

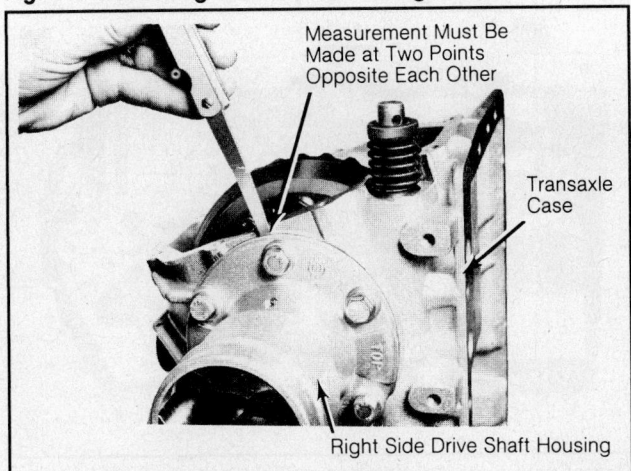

Recheck pinion depth adjustment. Reinstall differential/final drive assembly.

11) Reinstall right side drive shaft housing along with previously selected bearing preload adjusting shims and tighten attaching bolts. Grease sealing rings on output shaft. Place transmission housing in vise and support pinion with a drift.

12) Position output shaft on pinion, and carefully press on shaft. Be sure that shaft and pinion splines are properly aligned. Ensure that sealing rings on output shaft are located correctly in their grooves as they enter seal housing. Measure assembly depth in case with a large depth gauge. Total depth should be 7.561-7.578" (192.04-192.48 mm) including shims.

Fig. 32: Measuring Depth of Output Shaft/Ring Gear Assembly in Transmission Case

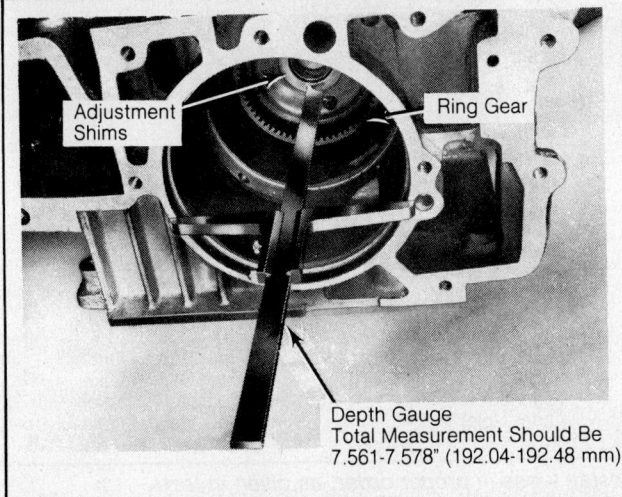

Total depth includes adjustment shims.

13) If parking pawl was removed during disassembly, reverse removal procedure to install. Grease front and rear servo piston "O" rings. Install pistons into servo cylinders in transaxle case.

14) Install rear brake band. Install thrust bearing, race and shims in planetary gear assembly. Install planetary gear and center support. Install front brake band.

NOTE: Soak brake bands (front and rear) in ATF prior to installation.

15) Install a thrust needle bearing on each side of sun gear on sun gear shaft. Carefully insert sun gear shaft into rear clutch assembly. Use care not to damage oil seal ring on shaft. Lubricate rear clutch sealing rings and install complete unit so that teeth mesh properly with planetary gear.

16) Install, in order, large bearing race, needle bearing and small washer in front clutch. Install front clutch assembly. Lubricate input shaft sealing rings and install shaft. Note position of lugs when properly installed. *See Fig. 33.*

Fig. 33: Installing Input Shaft

17) Place pin in rear servo piston. Place long band apply strut against rear band, then place rear band apply lever in position and insert shaft from side until it protrudes approximately .04" (10 mm).

18) Hold spring in place while sliding shaft into position so that it is engaged on shaft. Place short strut against front band. Place lever in position and press in lever shaft from side.

NOTE: When installing rear servo piston pivot shaft and spring, one end of spring must be in contact with lever at all times to prevent scratching servo cylinder.

19) Grease transmission housing-to-torque converter housing mating surface. Install gasket to transmission housing. Grease axial play thrust washer and shims, and install inside front bearing (in torque converter housing). Install shims first. Check that drain valve oil tubes are in position. Install torque converter.

20) Hold parking pawl out of way with a screwdriver. Place gear selector lever in transmission case. Guide front servo oil tube into position while installing torque converter housing-to-transmission case. Install converter housing-to-transmission case attaching bolts, and pull converter housing into position with bolts.

21) Check transaxle gear unit end play. Mount a dial indicator on torque converter housing, so that indicator tip is touching end of input shaft. Zero indicator. Pry forward on planetary gear assembly and read gear end play. End play should be .01-.03" (.25-.75 mm). If end play is not to housing-to-transmission case attaching bolts, and pull converter housing into position with bolts.

Automatic Transmissions
SAAB — BORG-WARNER MODEL 37 (Cont.)

22) Check transaxle gear unit end play. Mount a dial indicator on torque converter housing, so that indicator tip is touching end of input shaft. Zero indicator. Pry forward on planetary gear assembly and read gear end play. End play should be .01-.03" (.25-.75 mm). If end play is not to specifications, adjust by adding or removing shims between thrust washer and front bearing.

Fig. 34: Measuring Gear Unit End Play

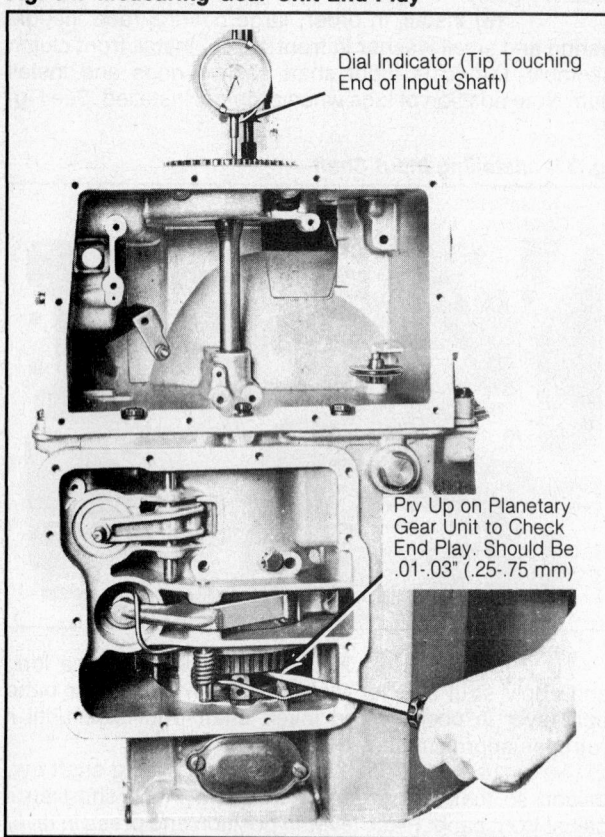

Dial Indicator (Tip Touching End of Input Shaft)

Pry Up on Planetary Gear Unit to Check End Play. Should Be .01-.03" (.25-.75 mm)

23) Install accumulator piston. Place valve body assembly into converter housing and ensure that manual gear selector is properly connected. Center valve body in position with 5 retaining bolts, tighten 2 and remove others. See Fig. 35. Attach cam disc cable to cam disc on valve body. Check that cable is positioned in pulley groove.

24) Install oil tubes in order. See Fig. 36. Tubes 16 and 17 should have been installed with drain valve. When installing tube 12, run it under tube 9 and install tube support (if equipped). Install oil strainer and magnet. Install connection pipes.

25) To adjust rear band, locate adjusting screw on outer left-hand side of transmission case. Loosen adjusting screw. Tighten screw to 10 ft. lbs. (14 N.m). Back adjusting screw off 1 turn, and tighten lock nut.

26) To adjust front band, loosen lock nut. Place Spacer (87 90 030), or 11/32" (8.9 mm) rod, between screw and piston pin. Tighten adjusting screw to 12 INCH lbs. (1.3 N.m). Remove spacer. Hold adjusting screw so it does not move, and tighten lock nut.

27) Install chain and sprockets. Place lock plate under retaining nuts and tighten nuts. Use a bar between sprockets to hold them in place while tightening bolts. Install turbine shaft seal. Install differential assembly and

Fig. 35: Positioning Valve Body in Case

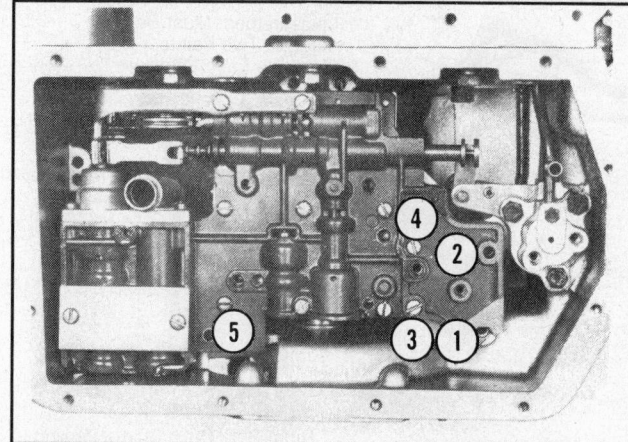

Center with bolts 1-5 as shown. Tighten bolts 3 and 4. Remove bolts 1, 2 and 5 for installation with oil pump strainer and air escape pipe.

Fig. 36: Correct Routing of Oil Tubes

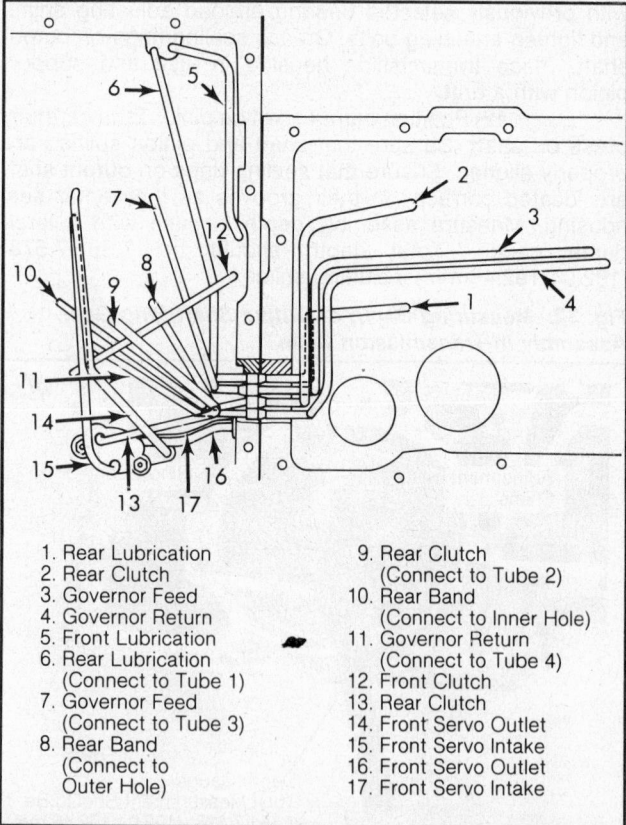

1. Rear Lubrication	9. Rear Clutch
2. Rear Clutch	(Connect to Tube 2)
3. Governor Feed	10. Rear Band
4. Governor Return	(Connect to Inner Hole)
5. Front Lubrication	11. Governor Return
6. Rear Lubrication	(Connect to Tube 4)
(Connect to Tube 1)	12. Front Clutch
7. Governor Feed	13. Rear Clutch
(Connect to Tube 3)	14. Front Servo Outlet
8. Rear Band	15. Front Servo Intake
(Connect to	16. Front Servo Outlet
Outer Hole)	17. Front Servo Intake

Install tubes in proper order, as given in text.

bearing housing. Install complete shim pack under right bearing seat.

28) To check ring gear backlash, mount dial indicator on transaxle case so that indicator tip is touching ring gear teeth. Measure backlash. Check backlash at 4 different points around ring gear. Measurements must not vary by more than .002" (.05 mm) from specifications.

NOTE: Backlash with a new ring and pinion set (or a used set with less than 6000 miles service) should be to specification which appears on ring gear. See Fig. 39. If a used gear set with more than 6000 miles service is being re-installed, backlash should be same as was recorded during transaxle disassembly.

29) Calculate difference between measured backlash and backlash reading desired. Move shims of correct thickness from right bearing housing to left side housing. DO NOT add or remove any shims. Combination of shims installed has been preselected and must not be changed.

Fig. 37: Adjusting Front Band

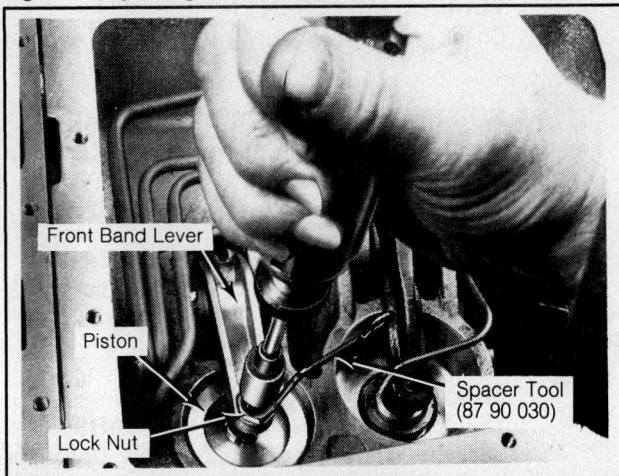

When tightening lock nut, do not allow adjusting screw to change position

Fig. 38: Measuring Ring Gear Backlash

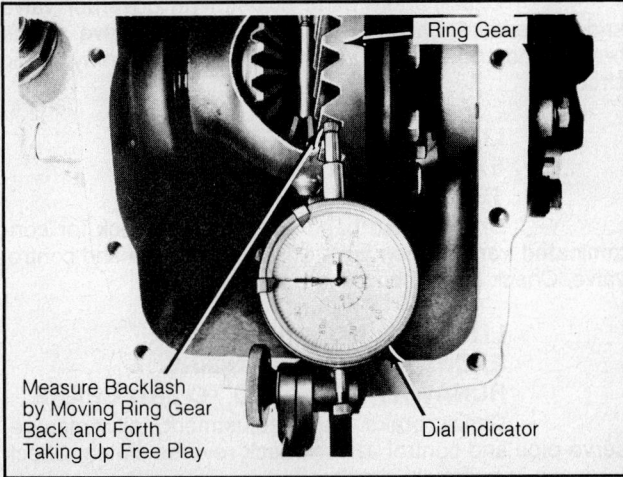

Take backlash measurements at 4 places around ring gear.

Fig. 39: View of Ring Gear Showing Adjustment Data

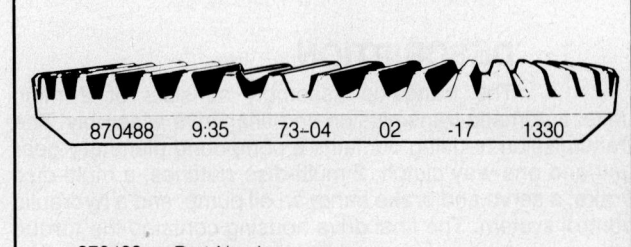

870488 = Part Number
9:35 = Ratio
73-04 = Date of Manufacture
02 = Material Code
-17 = Backlash of .17 mm (.007")
1330 = Mating Number (Also Stamped on Pinion Gear)

TIGHTENING SPECIFICATIONS

Application	Ft. Lbs. (N.m)
Adjusting Screw Lock Nut	
Front Band	15-20 (20-27)
Rear Band	29-39 (39-53)
A/T Case-To-Converter Housing	10-15 (14-20)
Center Support Bolts	10-18 (14-25)
Chain Cover-To-Converter	10-15 (14-20)
Converter-To-Flywheel Bolts	24-29 (33-39)
Differential Bearing Housing	16-18 (22-25)
Oil Pump Cover Bolts	17-21 (23-29)
Oil Pump-To-Converter Housing	13-18 (18-25)
Pinion Shaft Nut	160-195 (217-264)
Sprocket Wheel-To-	
Input Shaft	24-30 (33-40)
Turbine Shaft	19-24 (26-33)

	INCH Lbs. (N.m.)
Selector Rod Cover	71-106 (8-12)
Valve Body-To-A/T Case	53-106 (6-12)

Automatic Transmissions
SUBARU MODEL M41A

Subaru 1600 & 1800

DESCRIPTION

The transaxle assembly consists of 2 main units: automatic transmission and final drive assembly. The transmission housing contains a compound planetary gear unit and one-way clutch, 2 multi-disc clutches, a multi-disc brake, a servo and brake band, an oil pump, and a hydraulic control system. The final drive housing contains the torque converter, governor assembly, ring and pinion gears, and differential assembly.

The 4WD automatic transmission is similar to automatic transaxle in construction, the difference being the addition of a transfer case to rear of transmission housing. The rear transfer case consists of a hydraulic multi-disc clutch, transfer clucth valve and solenoid. These components are housed in the extension housing, along with a transfer gear. The transfer gear is connected to the final drive assembly through the transfer drive shaft.

Along with the adoption of a 4WD system, the final drive housing and transmission housing have been changed thoroughly. A new oil seal holder has been introduced in the reduction gear portion. The hydraulic clutch, planetary gear, control valve and other basic components are unchanged from those used in automatic transaxle.

LUBRICATION & ADJUSTMENTS

See appropriate AUTOMATIC TRANSMISSION SERVICING article in IMPORT GENERAL SERVICING section.

TROUBLE SHOOTING

NO DRIVE IN ANY RANGE
Check oil pressure, control valve and oil pump. Check for leaks in hydraulic circuit. Check parking linkage.

NO DRIVE IN FORWARD RANGES
Check oil pressure, control valve and forward clutch. Check for leaks in hydraulic circuit.

EXCESSIVE SLIP IN 4WD MODE VEHICLE O.K. IN FWD MODE
Check transfer valve. transfer pipe and rear shaft drive seal ring.

HARSH ENGAGEMENT
From "N" to "D"
Check oil pressure, control valve and forward clutch.

From 1st to 2nd Gear
Check brake band adjustment, oil pressure and control valve. Check brake band and band support.

From 2nd to 3rd Gear
Chack brake band adjustment, oil pressure and servo pipe. Check control valve, reverse clutch, brake band and band support.

POOR ACCELERATION & LOW TOP SPEED
Check stall speed, brake band adjustment and oil pressure. Check brake band and band support. Check low/reverse brake. Check torque converter one-way clutch.

VEHICLE BRAKED WHEN SHIFTED INTO "R"
Check brake band adjustment and forward clutch. Check brake band and band support. Check parking linkage.

VEHICLE MOVES IN "N"
Check control valve, forward clutch and reverse clutch.

NO SHIFT FROM 1ST TO 2ND GEAR
Check governor valve, servo pipe, control valve and nylon gear. Check brake band and band support. Check for leaks in hydraulic circuit.

NO SHIFT FROM 2ND TO 3RD GEAR
Check governor valve, brake band adjustment, servo pipe and control valve. Check reverse clutch. Check for leaks in hydraulic circuit.

SHIFT POINTS TOO HIGH FROM 1ST TO 2ND & 2ND TO 3RD GEARS
Check oil pressure and control valve. Check for leaks in hydraulic circuit.

SHIFTS FROM 1ST TO 3RD, SKIPPING 2ND
Check brake band adjustment, governor valve and oil pressure. Check servo pipe and control valve. Check brake band and band support. Check for leaks in hydraulic circuit.

LITTLE OR NO SHIFT SHOCK, EXCESSIVE SLIPPAGE FROM 1ST TO 2ND GEAR
Check brake band adjustment. Check for contaminated transmission fluid. Check servo pipe and control valve. Check brake band and band support.

LITTLE OR NO SHIFT SHOCK, EXCESSIVE SLIP & ENGINE RUNAWAY FROM 2ND TO 3RD GEARS
Check brake band adjustment, oil pressure, servo pipe and control valve. Check reverse clutch. Check for leaks in hydraulic circuit.

VEHICLE IS BRAKED WHEN SHIFTED FROM 1ST TO 2ND GEAR
Check control valve, low/reverse brake, reverse clutch and one-way clutch.

VEHICLE IS BRAKED WHEN SHIFTED FROM 2ND TO 3RD GEAR
Check brake band adjustment and control valve. Check brake band and band support.

SUBARU MODEL M41A (Cont.)

Fig. 1: Cross-Sectional View of Subaru Model M41A Automatic Transmission Assembly

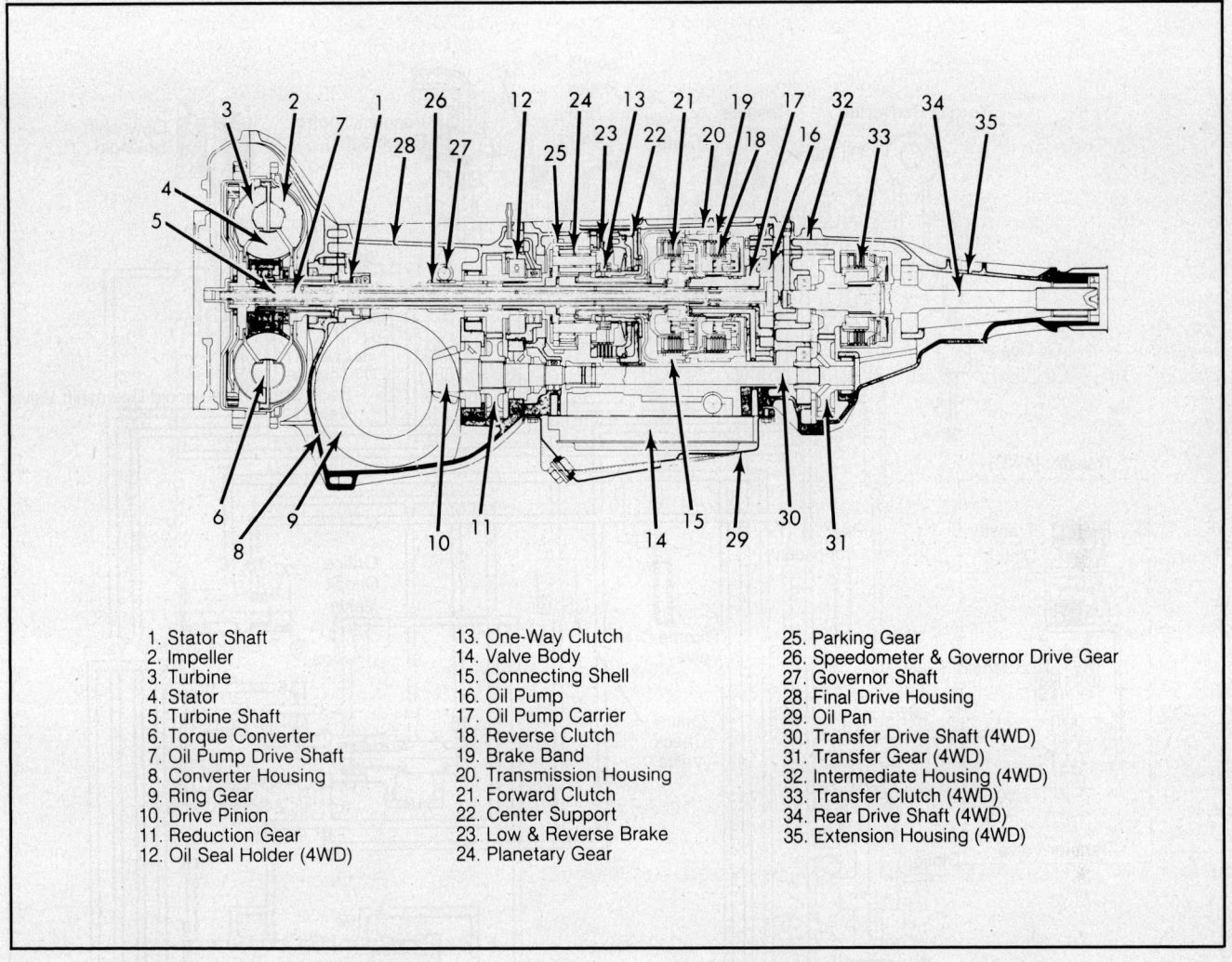

1. Stator Shaft	13. One-Way Clutch	25. Parking Gear
2. Impeller	14. Valve Body	26. Speedometer & Governor Drive Gear
3. Turbine	15. Connecting Shell	27. Governor Shaft
4. Stator	16. Oil Pump	28. Final Drive Housing
5. Turbine Shaft	17. Oil Pump Carrier	29. Oil Pan
6. Torque Converter	18. Reverse Clutch	30. Transfer Drive Shaft (4WD)
7. Oil Pump Drive Shaft	19. Brake Band	31. Transfer Gear (4WD)
8. Converter Housing	20. Transmission Housing	32. Intermediate Housing (4WD)
9. Ring Gear	21. Forward Clutch	33. Transfer Clutch (4WD)
10. Drive Pinion	22. Center Support	34. Rear Drive Shaft (4WD)
11. Reduction Gear	23. Low & Reverse Brake	35. Extension Housing (4WD)
12. Oil Seal Holder (4WD)	24. Planetary Gear	

NO 3RD TO 2ND DOWNSHIFT
Check governor valve, oil pressure, servo pipe and control valve. Check reverse clutch, brake band and band support. Check for leaks in hydraulic circuit.

NO 2ND TO 1ST OR 3RD TO 1ST DOWNSHIFT
Check governor valve, brake band adjustment and control valve. Check brake band and band support. Check one-way clutch.

SHIFTING SHOCK FELT ON DECELERATION
Check governor valve, oil pressure and control valve. Check for leaks in hydraulic circuit.

SHIFT POINTS TOO HIGH FROM 3RD TO 2ND OR 2ND TO 1ST GEARS
Check governor valve, oil pressure and control valve. Check for leaks in hydraulic circuit.

NO KICKDOWN AT NORMAL SPEEDS IN 3RD GEAR
Check governor valve, servo pipe and control valve. Check brake band and band support. Check for leaks in hydraulic circuit.

EXCESSIVE ENGINE RPM WHEN ACCELERATING IN 3RD GEAR ABOVE KICKDOWN SPEED
Check oil pressure, governor valve, control valve and reverse clutch. Check for leaks in hydraulic circuit.

ENGINE RUNAWAY OR TRANSMISSION SLIPPAGE ON 3RD TO 2ND GEAR KICKDOWN
Check brake band adjustment, oil pressure, servo pipe and control valve. Check reverse clutch, brake band and band support. Check for leaks in hydraulic circuit.

NO ENGINE BRAKING IN 1ST GEAR
Check oil pressure and control valve. Check low/reverse brake. Check for leaks in hydraulic circuit.

Automatic Transmissions
SUBARU MODEL M41A (Cont.)

Fig. 2: *Subaru Model M41A Automatic Transmission Hydraulic Circuits Diagram*

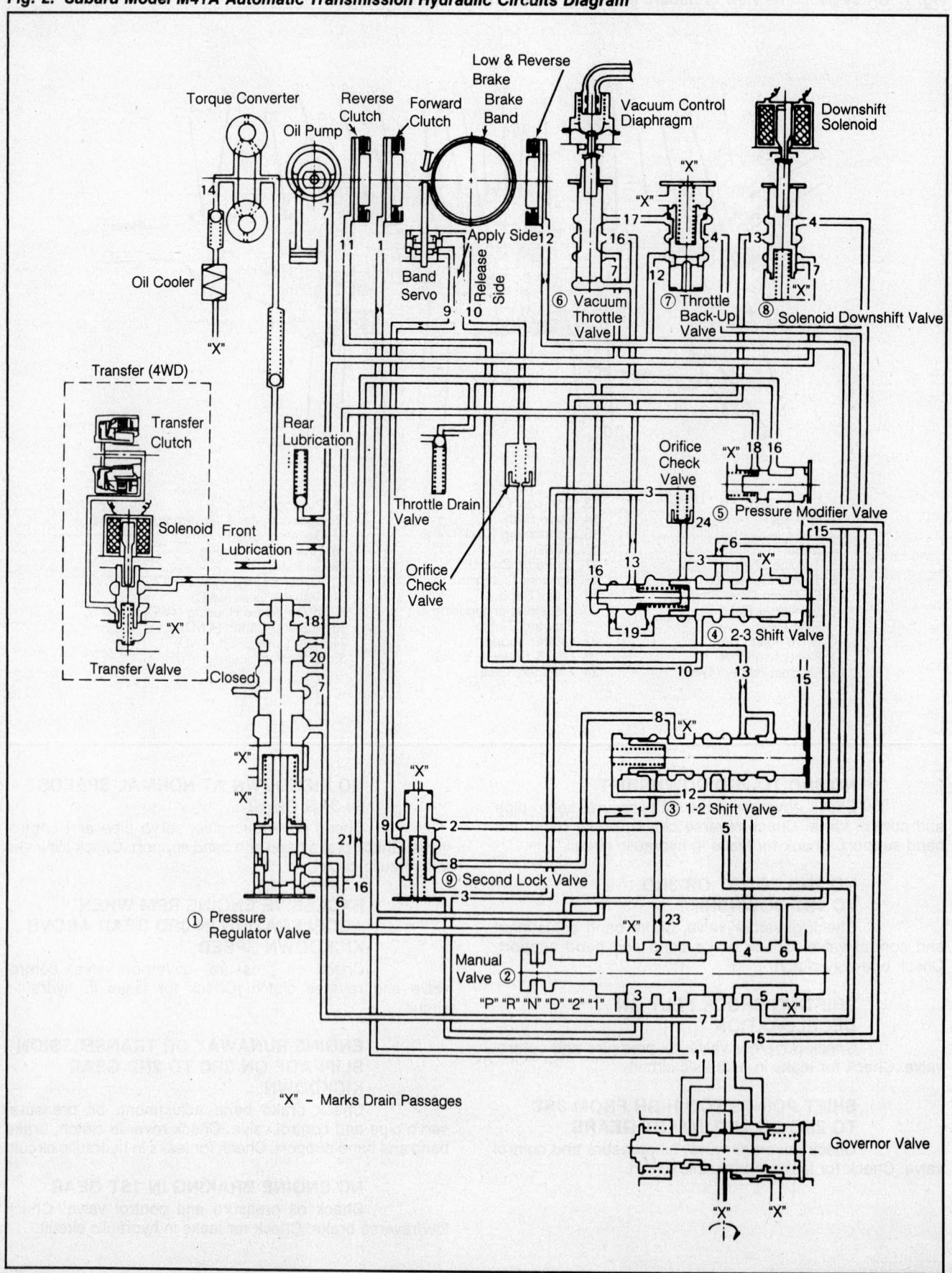

SUBARU MODEL M41A (Cont.)

TRANSMISSION OVERHEATS

Check oil pressure, stall speed and brake band adjustment. Check reverse clutch. Check brake band and band support. Check low/reverse brake, one-way clutch and forward clutch.

TRANSMISSION NOISY IN "N" OR "P"

Check oil pump.

TRANSMISSION NOISY IN "R" & ALL DRIVE RANGES

Check oil pump, one-way clutch and transfer gear.

TRANSMISSION NOISY IN 4WD MODE 3RD GEAR

Check planetary gear assembly.

TESTING

PRELIMINARY INSPECTION

1) Check engine idle speed and idling boost. Check stall speed. Check that linkage between accelerator pedal and carburetor are functioning properly. Check fully open and fully closed positions. Ensure that vacuum hose is not disconnected. Check for leaks at ATF cooler recirculation pipe.

2) Check that kickdown switch functions at normal pedal position. Check that electrical circuits of kickdown solenoid, transfer solenoid and inhibitor switch are functioning properly. Ensure that manual linkage adjustment is correct. Check for leaks out of transmission. Check that transmission and differential oil level are normal.

ROAD TEST
FWD Mode

1) All shifts may vary slightly due to production tolerances or tire size. The important factor is quality of shifts. All shifts should be smooth, responsive, and with no slippage or engine speed runaway. Slippage or engine runaway in any gear usually indicates clutch or band problems.

2) The slipping clutch or band in a particular gear can usually be identified by noting transmission operation in other selector positions and comparing internal units which are applied in these positions. See CLUTCH & BAND APPLICATION chart.

3) The process of elimination given can be used to detect any unit which slips and to confirm proper operation of good units, but actual cause of a malfunction cannot be easily decided.

4) Practically any condition can be caused by leaking hydraulic circuits or sticking valves. Unless an obvious condition exists, transmission should never be disassembled until hydraulic pressure tests have been made.

4WD Mode

With vehicle in 4WD mode, turn vehicle in a circle while lightly depressing accelerator pedal. Shift vehicle into FWD mode, a slight shifting shock should be felt. If an abnormality occurs in 4WD mode, check line pressure in transfer clutch circuit to determine cause of problem.

NON TURBO MODEL SHIFT SPEEDS CHART

Application	Shift Points MPH
Kickdown	
1-2 Upshift	29-34
2-3 Upshift	53-59
3-2 Downshift	48-55
2-1 Downshift	24-29
Half-Throttle	
1-2 Upshift	9-12
2-3 Upshift	18-23
3-2 or 3-1 Downshift	9-12
2-1 Downshift	9-12
Full Throttle	
2-1 Downshift [1]	21-27
Minimum Throttle	
2-1 Downshift [1]	21-27

[1] – Shifting selector from "D" to "1" range when vehicle is running at 31 MPH.

TURBO MODEL SHIFT SPEEDS CHART

Application	Shift Points MPH
Kickdown	
1-2 Upshift	35-40
2-3 Upshift	62-68
3-2 Downshift	57-63
2-1 Downshift	27-32
Half-Throttle	
1-2 Upshift	9-12
2-3 Upshift	40-45
3-2 or 3-1 Downshift	19-24
2-1 Downshift	9-12
Full Throttle	
2-1 Downshift [1]	.....
Minimum Throttle	
2-1 Downshift [1]	19-25

[1] – Shifting selector from "D" to "1" range when vehicle is running at 31 MPH.

STALL TEST
Testing Precautions

Do not hold throttle open any longer than 5 seconds to obtain steady gauge reading. After each stall test, move selector lever to "N" and allow engine to idle lower than 1200 RPM for at least a minute to cool down engine and transmission. If engine speed exceeds limits shown in STALL TEST SPEED table, release accelerator immediately as clutch or band slippage is indicated.

Testing Procedure

With engine at normal operating temperature, tachometer installed, and parking and service brakes applied, make transmission stall test in "D", "2", "1" and "R" ranges at full throttle and note maximum RPM obtained. Engine speed should be within limits shown in STALL TEST SPEED table.

Stall Test Results

1) If stall speed is below specifications, throttle was not fully opened, engine performance is unsatisfactory or one-way clutch is slipping. If stall speed is high, slippage of clutch, brake band or other components is indicated.

CLUTCH AND BAND APPLICATION CHART (ELEMENTS IN USE)

Selector Lever Position	Foward Clutch	Reverse Clutch	Low-Reverse Band	Brake Band	One-Way Clutch
P – PARK			X		
R – REVERSE		X	X		
D – DRIVE					
First Gear	X				X
Second Gear	X				
Third Gear	X	X			
2 – SECOND	X			X	
1 – LOW					
First	X		X		
Second	X			X	

N – NEUTRAL – All clutches and bands released and/or ineffective.

STALL TEST SPEED

Application	Stall RPM
Turbo Models	2700-2900
All Other Models	2300-2500

2) If stall speed is high in all drive ranges, check for low line pressure. If stall speed is high in "D" range only, one-way clutch is slipping. If stall speed is high in "2" range, brake band is slipping.

3) If stall speed is high in "R" range only, low/reverse brake or reverse clutch is slipping. Verify brake band slippage by road testing vehicle. If engine RPM is higher than specified, brake band is slipping.

4) Verify low/reverse brake or reverse clutch slippage by road testing vehicle. If engine can be used as a brake with selector lever in "1" range, reverse clutch is slipping. If engine cannot be used as a brake, low/reverse brake is slipping.

LINE PRESSURE TESTS
FWD Line Pressure

1) Connect a pressure gauge to line pressure checking plug on rear cover of transmission. See Fig. 3. Place gauge in position for viewing from driver's seat, route gauge hose through hole provided in floor-board (just left of steering column).

2) With engine at normal operating temperature and transmission fluid at correct level, perform line pressure test with transmission in Neutral and engine at idle (1500 RPM).

3) Perform line pressure test in "D", "2" and "R" ranges. Start vehicle from a standstill and slowly increase engine speed and note pressure in each range. Pressures should be approximately as shown in LINE PRESSURE table.

4WD Line Pressure

1) Connect a pressure gauge to line pressure checking plug located on transmission extension housing, behind oil pan. See Fig. 4. Place gauge in position for viewing from driver's seat.

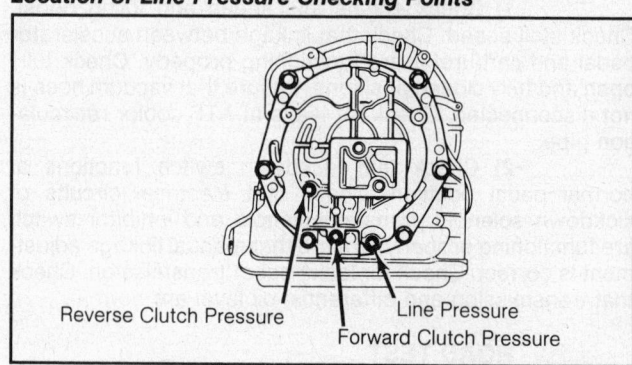

Fig. 3: Rear View of Transmission Housing Showing Location of Line Pressure Checking Points

Reverse Clutch Pressure   Line Pressure   Forward Clutch Pressure

2) With engine at normal operating temperature and transmission fluid at correct level, perform line pressure test with transmission in Neutral and engine at idle (1500 RPM).

3) Perform line pressure test in "D", "2" and "R" ranges (FWD mode). Start vehicle from a standstill and slowly increase engine speed and note pressure in each range. Pressures should be approximately as shown in LINE PRESSURE table.

FWD Line Pressure Test Results

1) If line pressure in Neutral is low; oil pump is worn or improperly adjusted, oil pressure circuit is leaking or pressure regulator valve is inoperative. If oil pressure in Neutral is high, check for leaking vacuum hose or leaking diaphragm, or for long diaphragm rod.

2) If engine is at full throttle and pressure fails to rise even though vacuum pressure drops, check if diaphragm rod was installed. If pressure rises but does not enter specified range, check for sticking throttle valve, pressure regulator valve or pressure regulator plug.

4WD Line Pressure Test Results

If pressure difference between FWD and 4WD modes is more than 4 psi (0.3 kg/cm^2), transfer pipe is disconnected or rear shaft seal ring is not installed. If pressure difference between FWD and 4WD modes is less than 4 psi (0.3 kg/cm^2), solenoid transfer valve is inoperative.

SUBARU LINE PRESSURE TABLE – psi (kg/cm²)

Range	Throttle Opening	Before Cut-Back Point (Under 9.5 MPH)	After Cut-Back Point (Over 22 MPH)
"D"	Full Throttle	121-142 (8.5-10.0) 188-202 (13.2-14.2) [1]	78-92 (5.5-6.4) 114-128 (8.0-9.0) [1]
	Minimum Throttle	43-57 (3.0-4.0) 43-47 (3.0-4.0) [1]	43-57 (3.0-4.0) 43-57 (3.0-4.0) [1]
"2"	Full Throttle	145-168 (10.2-11.8) 188-202 (13.2-14.2) [1]	84-98 (5.9-6.9) 114-128 (8.0-9.0) [1]
	Minimum Throttle	145-168 (10.2-11.8) 97-114 (6.8-8.0) [1]	84-98 (5.9-6.9) 97-114 (6.8-9.0) [1]
"R"	Full Throttle	199-228 (14-16) 284-313 (20.0-22.0) [1]	199-228 (14-16) 284-313 (20.0-22.0) [1]
	Minumum Throttle	67-81 (4.7-5.7) 81-95 (5.7-7.6) [1]	67-81 (4.7-5.7) 81-95 (5.7-7.6) [1]

[1] – Applies to 4WD Turbo Models.

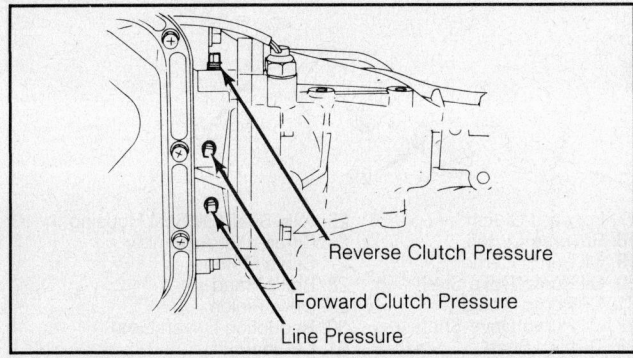

Fig. 4: Bottom View of Transmission Extension Housing Showing Location of Line Pressure Checking Points

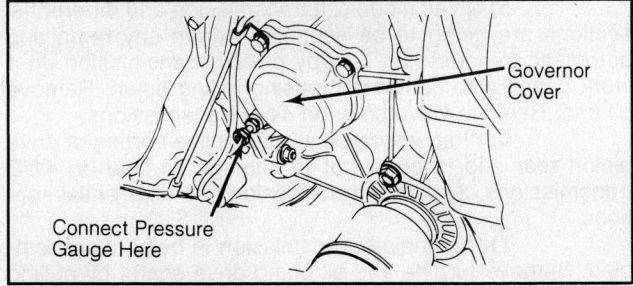

Fig. 5: View of Final Drive Housing Showing Location of Governor Pressure Checking Point

GOVERNOR PRESSURES

Vehicle Speed (MPH)	psi (kg/cm²)
9-12	
Turbo Models	0 (0)
Non-Turbo Models	0 (0)
25	
Turbo Models	24-27 (1.7-1.9)
Non-Turbo Models	21-24 (1.5-1.7)
50	
Turbo Models	63-65 (4.4-4.6)
Non-Turbo Models	60-63 (4.2-4.4)

Governor Pressure

1) Connect pressure gauge to governor pressure plug located on right side of final drive housing. *See Fig. 5.* Place gauge in driver's compartment as outlined in FWD line pressure test procedure.

2) With engine at normal operating temperature and transmission fluid level correct, check governor pressure at speeds shown in GOVERNOR PRESSURES chart with transmission in "2".

SERVICE (IN VEHICLE)

WHEEL BEARINGS

See SERVICE (IN VEHICLE) in SUBARU MANUAL TRANSAXLE article in MANUAL TRANSMISSION section.

DRIVE AXLE SHAFTS

See SERVICE (IN VEHICLE) in SUBARU MANUAL TRANSAXLE article in MANUAL TRANSMISSION section.

CONSTANT VELOCITY (CV) JOINTS

See SERVICE (IN VEHICLE) in SUBARU MANUAL TRANSAXLE article in MANUAL TRANSMISSION section.

TORQUE CONVERTER

Torque converter is a sealed unit and cannot be disassembled for service. Replace if found to be defective.

TRANSMISSION DISASSEMBLY

NOTE: Whenever working with transmission, it is important that normal standards of cleanliness be observed. Complete transmission assembly should be thoroughly steam cleaned before beginning any disassembly. Disassemble only those parts which require repair or replacement. Compressed air is preferred for drying components and oil passages, however, nylon cloth may be used. NEVER use fluffy rags or cloths to wipe parts dry.

Automatic Transmissions
SUBARU MODEL M41A (Cont.)

Fig. 6: Exploded View of Major Components of Subaru Automatic Transmission Assembly

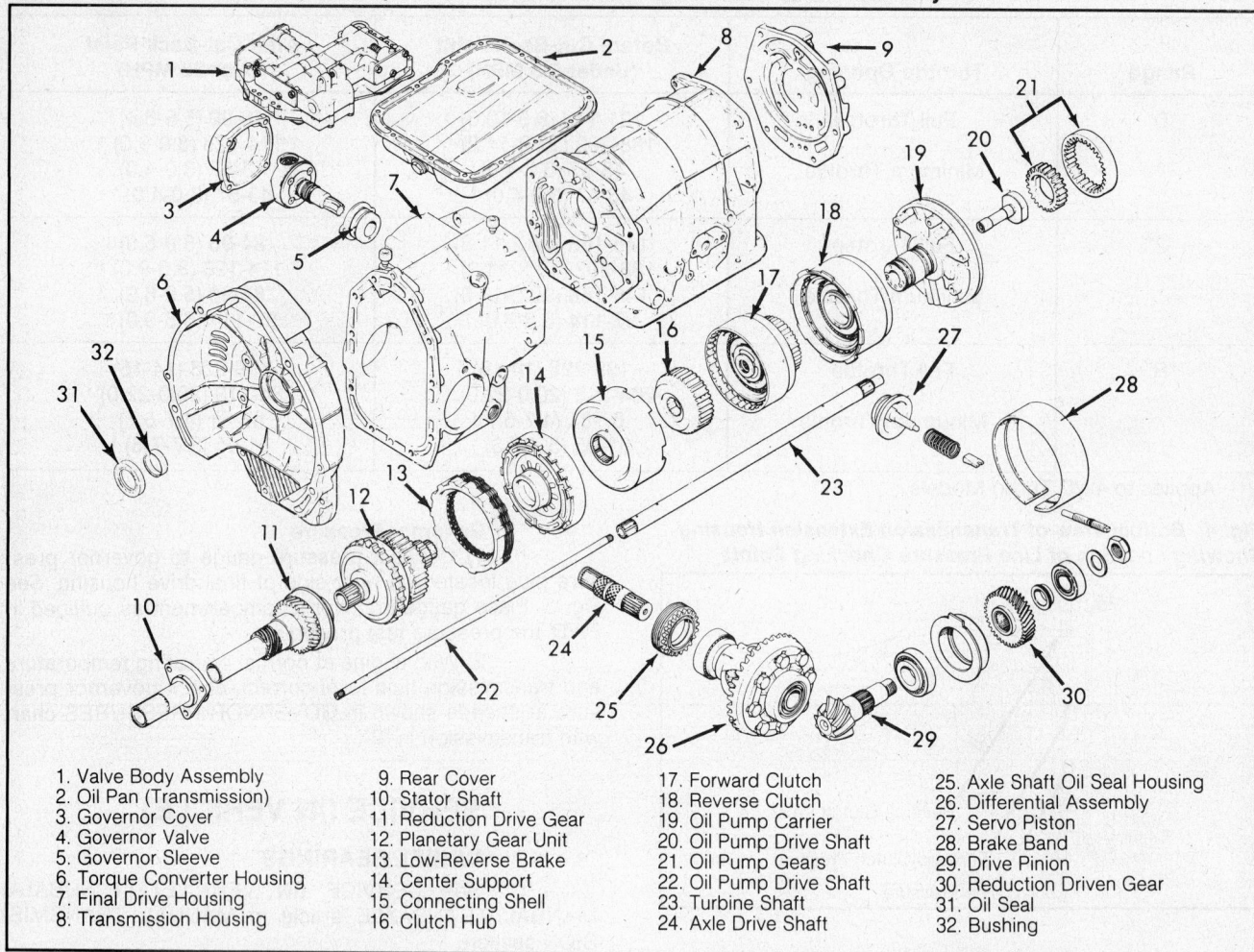

1. Valve Body Assembly	9. Rear Cover	17. Forward Clutch	25. Axle Shaft Oil Seal Housing
2. Oil Pan (Transmission)	10. Stator Shaft	18. Reverse Clutch	26. Differential Assembly
3. Governor Cover	11. Reduction Drive Gear	19. Oil Pump Carrier	27. Servo Piston
4. Governor Valve	12. Planetary Gear Unit	20. Oil Pump Drive Shaft	28. Brake Band
5. Governor Sleeve	13. Low-Reverse Brake	21. Oil Pump Gears	29. Drive Pinion
6. Torque Converter Housing	14. Center Support	22. Oil Pump Drive Shaft	30. Reduction Driven Gear
7. Final Drive Housing	15. Connecting Shell	23. Turbine Shaft	31. Oil Seal
8. Transmission Housing	16. Clutch Hub	24. Axle Drive Shaft	32. Bushing

1) On 4WD transmissions only, remove rear engine mount and place transmission on work bench with oil pan facing down. Remove solenoid from extension housing by turning it by hand. Disconnect temperature switch lead wire from clip and remove temperature switch from left side of extension housing.

2) On 4WD transmissions only, remove 8 (8 mm) bolts and remove extension housing. Drain automatic transmission fluid from extension housing, being careful not to drop rear drive gear thrust plate and transfer drive gear assembly. Remove washer from bearing bore on upper side of intermediate housing.

3) On 4WD transmissions only, remove rear shaft assembly from extension housing, being careful not to damage oil seal. Remove seal ring. Using Removal Plates (899864100 and 499717000), remove ball bearing, washer and transfer driven gear from shaft.

4) On 4WD transmissions only, remove drum and ball bearing. Disassemble transfer clutch assembly by removing snap ring and front pressure plate. Remove driven plates, drive plates and rear pressure plate.

NOTE: Automatic transmission and differential sections are not normally separated. If they must be separated, place transmission section on stand (399933610).

5) On all models, if transmission and differential sections are going to be separated, drain any remaining automatic transmission fluid by placing transmission on a work bench with converter housing facing down. Remove oil pan. Remove valve body on 4WD transmissions.

6) Wrap vinyl tape around spline portion of drive pinion rear end in order not to damage oil seal on 4WD transmissions. Separate transmission and differential sections.

7) If complete transmission is being disassembled: Remove turbine and oil pump drive shafts by pulling straight out with pliers (wrapped with vinyl tape), using care not to damage shafts. Disconnect oil cooler pipe from transmission housing.

8) Remove lead wire clips by removing nuts securing transmission housing to final drive housing. Remove downshift solenoid, transfer solenoid and temperature switch lead wire clips. Disconnect vacuum pipe and ground cable. Remove oil supply pipe from transmission after draining fluid. Do not lose "O" ring located at end of pipe.

9) Drain differential gear oil. Drain any remaining automatic transmission fluid by placing transmission on a work bench with converter housing facing down. Remove oil pan, downshift solenoid, vacuum diaphragm, diaphragm rod and "O" ring.

10) Remove servo apply and servo release tubes. Remove valve body. Remove transfer valve by separating bend portion of transfer tube clip from transfer pipe. Disconnect transfer tube and remove 2 bolts which secure transfer clutch body.

11) Remove oil pump assembly by tightening band adjustment screw until reverse clutch is lightly held. Remove bolts which secure transmission cover (intermediate housing on 4WD transmissions). Gently tap housing until oil pump assembly is removed. Do not lose thrust washer located on oil pump carrier.

NOTE: **Note positions of thrust washers, toothed thrust washers and needle bearings to be removed in following steps. DO NOT lose any of these parts.**

12) Move transfer drive shaft upward and remove transfer coupling from rear spline of drive pinion, then remove transfer drive shaft. Remove band servo piston and remove strut band. Remove brake band assembly, reverse clutch assembly and forward clutch assembly.

13) Remove connecting shell. Remove center support assembly by using 2 (6mm) bolts. Remove planetary input gears. Remove planetary gear assembly and low/reverse brake plates. Remove retaining plate. Remove planetary output gear.

14) If necessary, remove selector arm, manual plate and parking rod. Remove transmission housing by wrapping vinyl tape around splines of drive pinion to prevent damage to oil seal.

15) If necessary, remove nuts securing transmission housing to final drive housing. Separate transmission housing from final drive housing by gently tapping final drive housing. Remove parking pawl, parking pawl shaft and parking pawl support plate.

COMPONENT DISASSEMBLY & REASSEMBLY

REVERSE CLUTCH ASSEMBLY
Disassembly
1) Remove snap ring and lift out retaining plate, drive plates, driven plates and dished plate from clutch drum. Using a clutch spring compressor, compress clutch assembly return springs and remove retaining snap ring.

Fig. 7: Using Compressed Air to Remove Reverse Clutch Piston

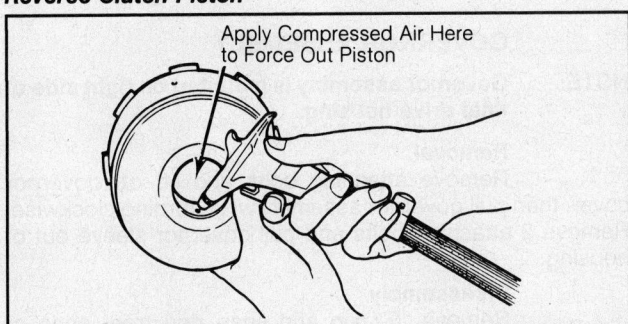

Apply Compressed Air Here to Force Out Piston

2) Remove return spring retainer and return springs. Apply compressed air to oil hole in clutch drum and remove clutch piston. *See Fig. 7.* Remove oil seal from clutch piston and drum.

Fig. 8: Exploded View of Reverse Clutch Assembly

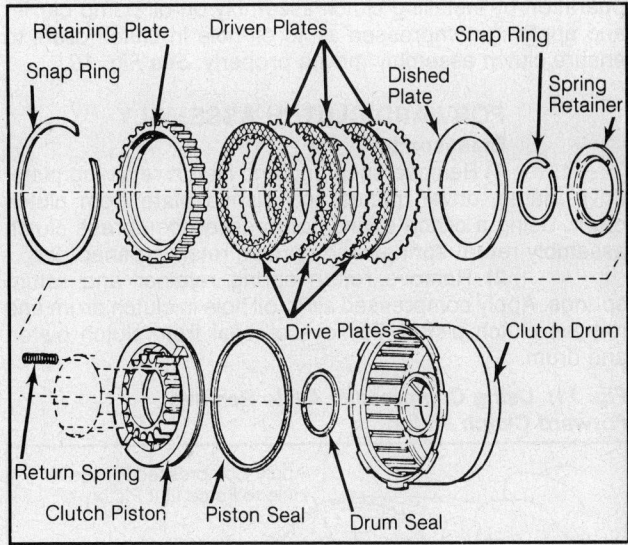

Retaining Plate — Driven Plates — Snap Ring
Snap Ring — Dished Plate — Spring Retainer
Drive Plates — Clutch Drum
Return Spring — Clutch Piston — Piston Seal — Drum Seal

Reassembly
1) To reassemble, reverse disassembly procedure. Coat all parts with automatic transmission fluid before installation. Install driven plates with missing tooth portion aligned with oil hole in clutch drum. Using a feeler gauge, check clearance between retaining plate and clutch assembly snap ring. Clearance should be .063-.071" (1.6-1.8 mm). *See Fig. 9.*

Fig. 9: Measuring Clearance Between Reverse Clutch Retaining Plate and Snap Ring

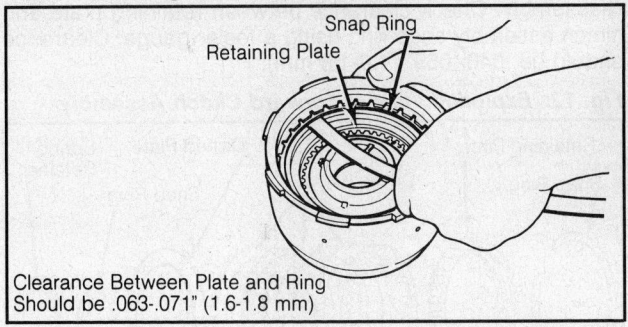

Snap Ring
Retaining Plate

Clearance Between Plate and Ring Should be .063-.071" (1.6-1.8 mm)

2) If clearance is not within specifications, correct by installing a retaining plate of different thickness. Reverse clutch retaining plates are available in thicknesses of 0.197" (5.0 mm) to 0.244" (6.2 mm) in .008" (0.2 mm) increments.

Fig. 10: Using Compressed Air to Check Operation of Reverse Clutch Assembly

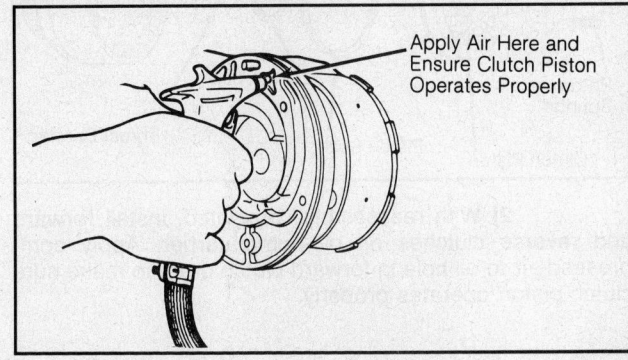

Apply Air Here and Ensure Clutch Piston Operates Properly

3) After clutch assembly is completed, check operation by installing clutch assembly on oil pump carrier and applying compressed air to oil hole in clutch drum to ensure clutch assembly moves properly. *See Fig. 10.*

FORWARD CLUTCH ASSEMBLY
Disassembly
1) Remove snap ring and lift out retaining plate, drive plates, driven plates and dished plate from clutch drum. Using a clutch spring compressor, compress clutch assembly return springs and remove retaining snap ring.

2) Remove return spring retainer and return springs. Apply compressed air to oil hole in clutch drum and remove clutch piston. Remove oil seal from clutch piston and drum.

Fig. 11: Using Compressed Air to Remove Forward Clutch Piston

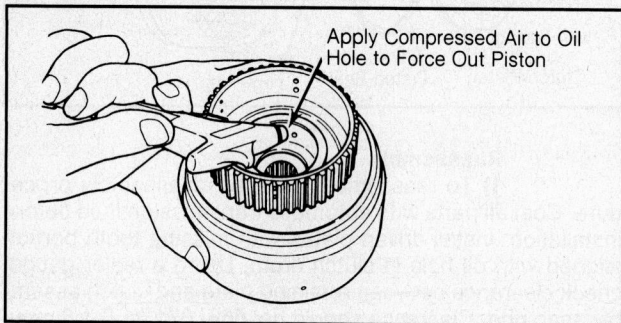

Apply Compressed Air to Oil Hole to Force Out Piston

Reassembly
1) To reassemble, reverse disassembly procedure. Coat all parts with automatic transmission fluid before reassembly. Check clearance between retaining plate and clutch assembly snap ring using a feeler gauge. Clearance should be .040-.059" (1.0-1.5 mm).

Fig. 12: Exploded View of Forward Clutch Assembly

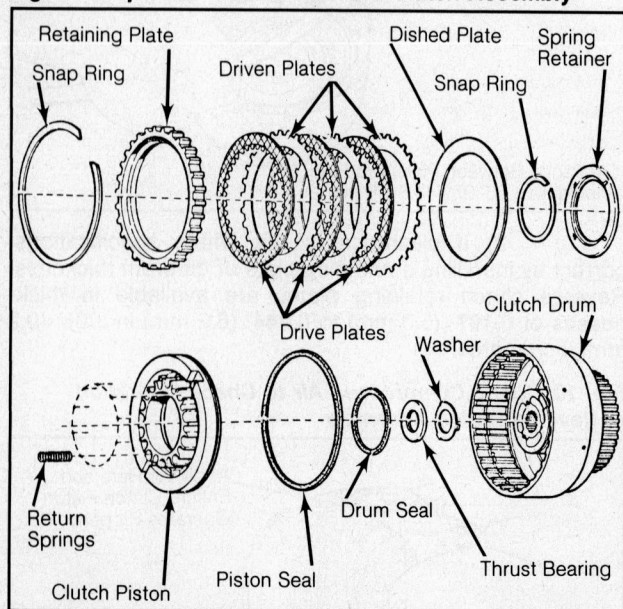

Retaining Plate
Snap Ring
Driven Plates
Dished Plate
Spring Retainer
Snap Ring
Clutch Drum
Washer
Drive Plates
Return Springs
Clutch Piston
Piston Seal
Drum Seal
Thrust Bearing

2) With reassembly completed, install forward and reverse clutches on oil pump carrier. Apply compressed air to oil hole in forward clutch drum to make sure clutch piston operates properly.

Fig. 13: Measuring Clearance Between Forward Clutch Retaining Plate and Snap Ring

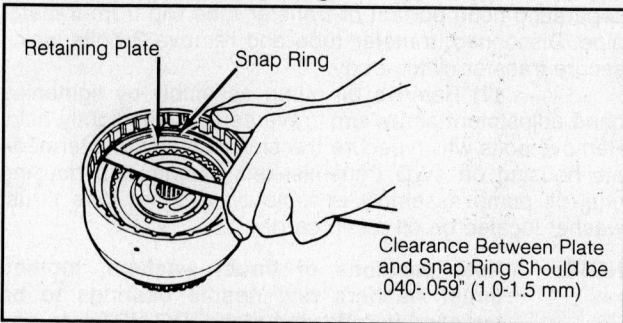

Retaining Plate
Snap Ring
Clearance Between Plate and Snap Ring Should be .040-.059" (1.0-1.5 mm)

Fig. 14: Using Compressed Air to Check Operation of Forward Clutch Assembly

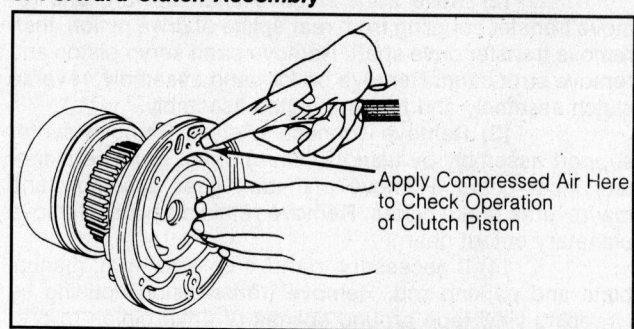

Apply Compressed Air Here to Check Operation of Clutch Piston

CENTER SUPPORT AND LOW-REVERSE BRAKE ASSEMBLY
NOTE: Low-reverse brake plates were removed at TRANSMISSION DISASSEMBLY and will be installed at TRANSMISSION REASSEMBLY.

Disassembly
Using a clutch spring compressor, compress low-reverse piston return spring and remove snap ring and lift out return spring and thrust ring. Apply compressed air to oil hole in center support and force low-reverse brake piston from center support. Remove oil seals from brake piston.

Reassembly
To reassemble, reverse disassembly procedure. Coat all parts with automatic transmission fluid before reassembly. When installing clutch piston to center support, use care not to damage piston oil seals.

GOVERNOR ASSEMBLY
NOTE: Governor assembly is mounted on right side of final drive housing.

Removal
Remove attaching bolts and lift off governor cover, then pull governor assembly while turning clockwise. Remove 2 attaching bolts and pull governor sleeve out of housing.

Disassembly
Remove "E" clip and snap ring from ends of valve body. Remove valve, springs and related components from valve body. Remove 2 governor shaft-to-valve body retaining bolts and separate valve body from shaft.

Fig. 15: Exploded View of Center Support and Low-Reverse Brake Assembly

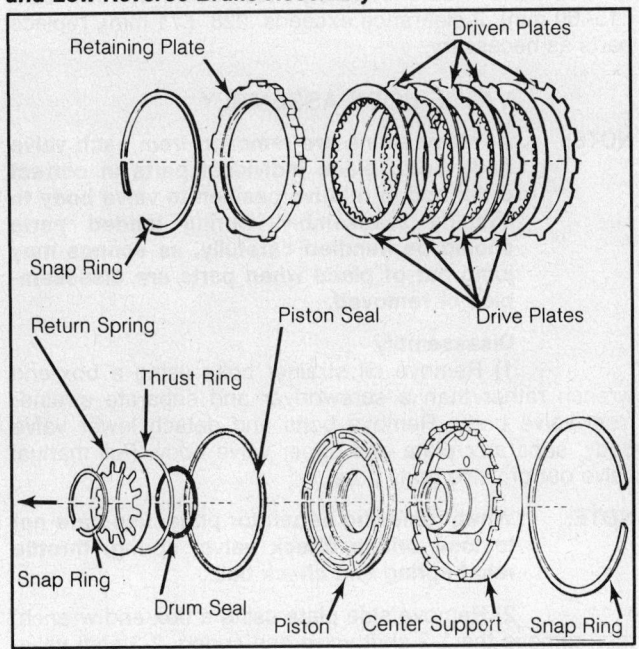

Fig. 16: Exploded View of Governor Assembly

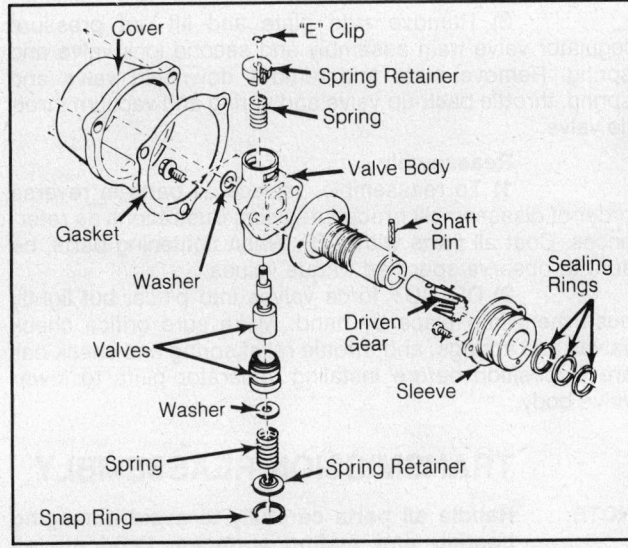

Reassembly

To reassemble, reverse disassembly procedure. Inspect all parts for wear or damage and replace as necessary. Ensure that parts move freely in governor bore when reassembly is completed. Inspect governor shaft oil seals and replace if worn or damaged.

Installation

To install, reverse removal procedure. Replace cover gasket and ensure that washer is installed. Use care to prevent damage to oil seals when installing governor assembly.

OIL PUMP

Disassembly

1) Remove bolts and disassemble oil pump carrier from transmission cover (intermediate housing on

4WD transmissions). Mark gears for reassembly in their original position and remove.

2) Inspect oil pump gears for wear or damage and replace as necessary. Inspect bushing and 2 needle roller bearings located in pump carrier and replace if necessary.

Fig. 17: Exploded View of Oil Pump and Transmission Cover Assembly

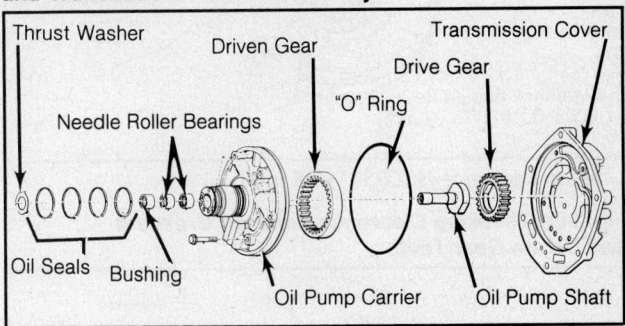

Oil Pump Bushing & Bearing Replacement

1) Remove bushing and needle roller bearings using Needle Bearing Remover (399903600). To install, use Needle Bearing Installer (399543600) to drive bearings into pump carrier. See Fig. 18.

2) When installing the center needle roller bearing, Adapter (398863600) must be used with installer to ensure center bearing is installed in correct position.

Fig. 18: Installation of Bushing and Bearings into Oil Pump Carrier

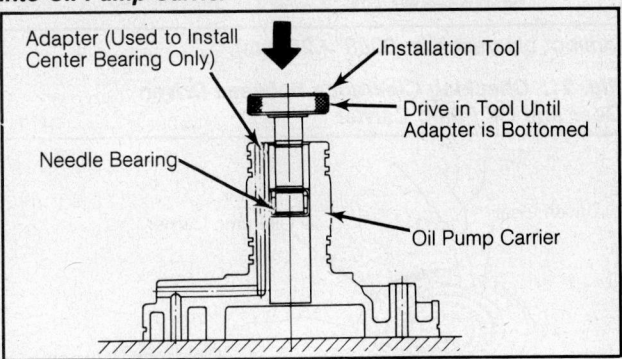

Reassembly

1) To reassemble, reverse disassembly procedure. Coat all parts with automatic transmission fluid before reassembly. Ensure that marks made at disassembly are aligned. With gears installed, check oil pump clearances.

2) Using a straightedge and feeler gauge, measure clearance between face of gears and transmission cover (intermediate housing). See Fig. 19. Clearance should be .0008-.0016" (.02-.04 mm).

3) Using a feeler gauge, check clearance between crescent and oil pump driven gear teeth. See Fig. 20. Clearance should be .0055-.0083" (.14-.21 mm).

4) Using a feeler gauge, check clearance between oil pump driven gear and oil pump carrier. See Fig. 21. Clearance should be .0020-.0079" (.05-.20 mm).

5) If clearance obtained in step 2) exceeds .0031" (.08 mm), replace pump gears. If clearance obtained in step 3) or 4) exceeds .0098" (.25 mm), replace pump gears. Pump gears must always be replaced as a matched set.

Fig. 19: Checking Clearance Between Face of Gears and Rear Cover of Transmission

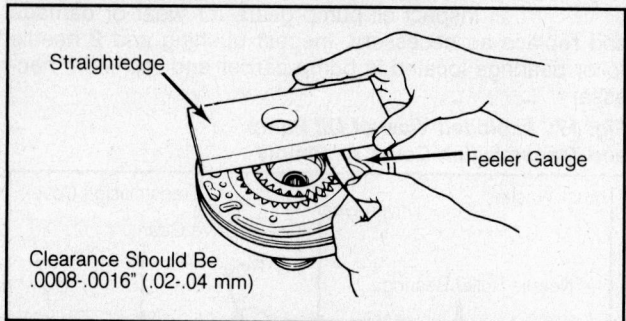

Limit of clearance is .0031" (.08 mm).

Fig. 20: Checking Clearance Between Crescent and Driven Gear Teeth

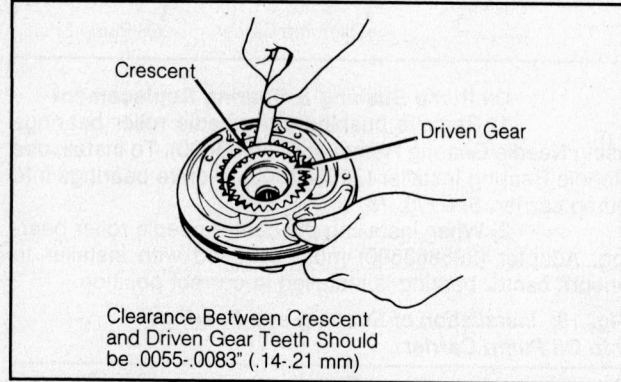

Limit of clearance is .0098" (.25 mm).

Fig. 21: Checking Clearance Between Driven Gear and Oil Pump Carrier

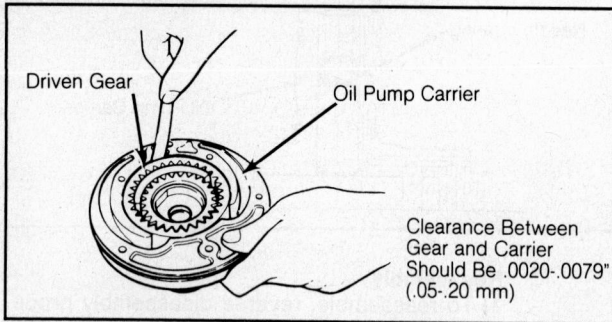

Limit of clearance is .0098" (.25 mm).

PLANETARY GEAR UNIT

Disassembly

Remove bolts securing one-way clutch outer race to planetary gear unit and separate one-way clutch from planetary gear unit. Push pinion pins out toward one-way clutch and remove short pinions, long pinions, thrust washers, needle roller bearings, spacers and thrust bearing. Separate one-way clutch from outer race.

Reassembly

1) To reassemble, reverse disassembly procedure. Use illustration as an assembly guide. *See Fig. 22.* Coat all parts with automatic transmission fluid. When installing one-way clutch on outer race, push "T" bar with finger to insert one-way clutch until a snap is felt, then secure retainer to outer race.

2) After reassembly, check planetary carrier-to-thrust washer clearance. Clearance should be .006-.024" (.15-.60 mm). If clearance exceeds .028" (.71 mm), replace parts as necessary.

VALVE BODY ASSEMBLY

NOTE: **As valve trains are removed from each valve body bore, place individual parts in correct order and in relative position to valve body to simplify reassembly. Spring loaded parts should be handled carefully, as springs may jump out of place when parts are disassembled or removed.**

Disassembly

1) Remove oil strainer bolts using a box-end wrench rather than a screwdriver and separate strainer from valve body. Remove bolts and detach lower valve body, separator plate and upper valve body. Pull manual valve out of valve body bore.

NOTE: **When removing separator plate, use care not to lose orifice check valve, spring, throttle relief spring and check ball.**

2) Remove side plate using a box-end wrench, then remove the 1-2 shift valve and spring, 2-3 shift valve and spring, 2-3 shift plug, pressure modifier valve and spring.

3) Remove side plate and lift out pressure regulator valve train assembly and second lock valve and spring. Remove plate and remove downshift valve and spring, throttle back-up valve and spring and vacuum throttle valve.

Reassembly

1) To reassemble, replace all parts in reverse order of disassembly procedure using illustrations as references. Coat all parts with ATF. When tightening parts, be sure to observe specified torque values.

2) DO NOT force valves into place, but lightly push them into place by hand. Make sure orifice check valves and springs, and throttle relief spring and check ball are in position before installing separator plate to lower valve body.

TRANSMISSION REASSEMBLY

NOTE: **Handle all parts carefully to avoid damaging bearing and mating surfaces. Lubricate all components with automatic transmission fluid prior to reassembly. Gaskets and thrust washers may be held in place by using petroleum jelly. Use all new gaskets and oil seals, and tighten bolts evenly. See Fig. 34 for thrust washer and thrust bearing locations.**

1) If only transmission section and differential section were separated: Place final drive housing with converter housing facing downward. Install Guide (499257100) on spline portion of drive pinion rear end and join differential section with transmission section. Install transfer drive shaft at this time also (4WD transmissions only).

2) Ensure that parking rod and parking actuator engages properly and sealing lip is not damaged. Install valve body, vacuum diaphragm assembly and downshift solenoid. Install servo apply and servo release tubes and install oil pan.

SUBARU MODEL M41A (Cont.)

Fig. 22: Exploded View of Planetary Gear Assembly

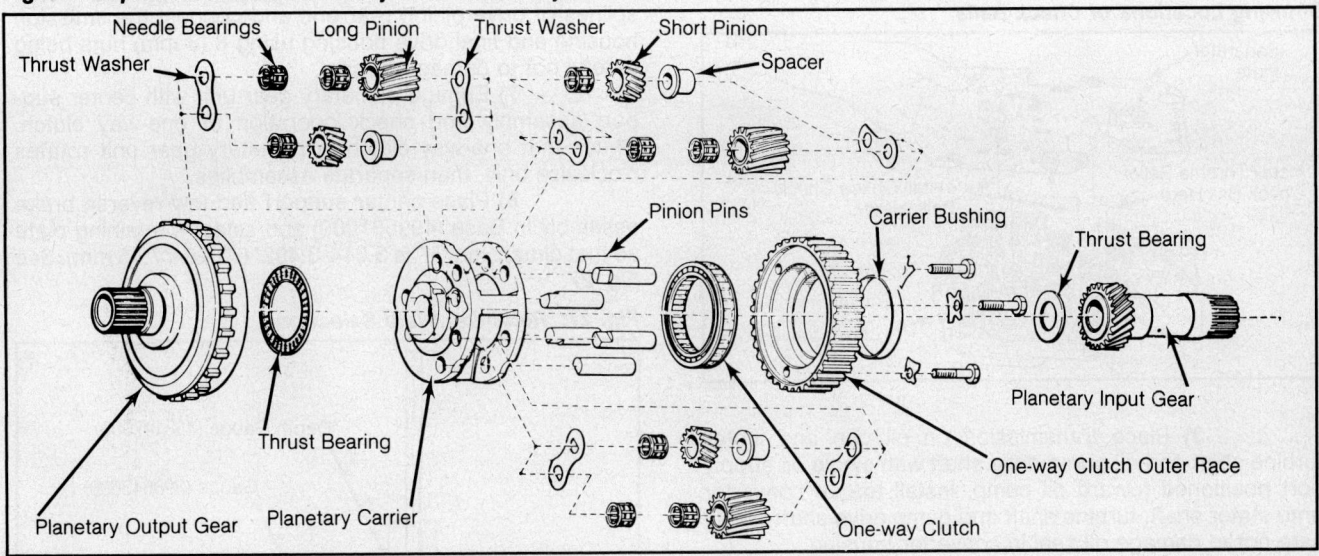

Fig. 23: Exploded View of Valve Body Assembly

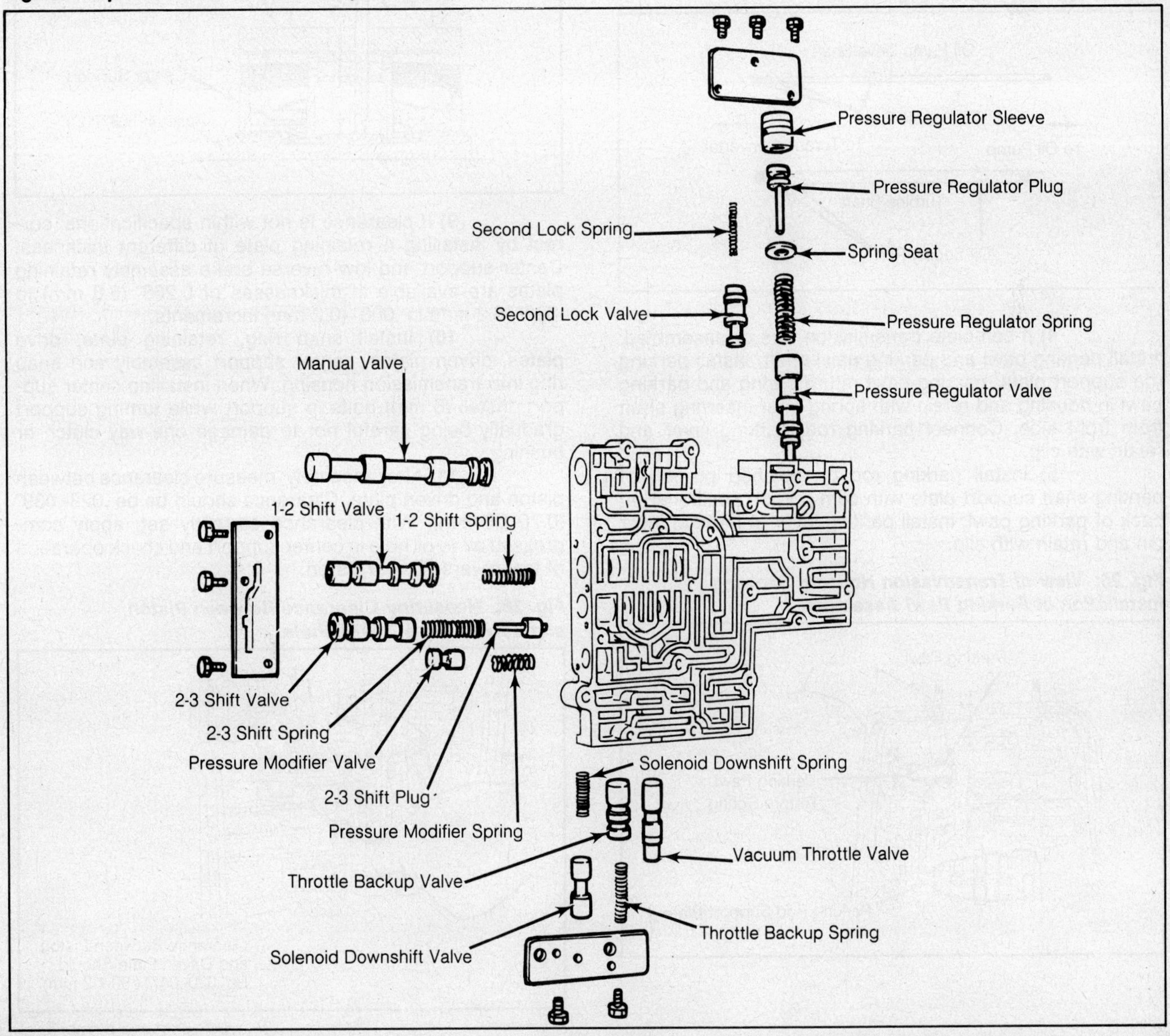

Automatic Transmissions

SUBARU MODEL M41A (Cont.)

Fig. 24: View of Lower Valve Body Showing Locations of Check Balls

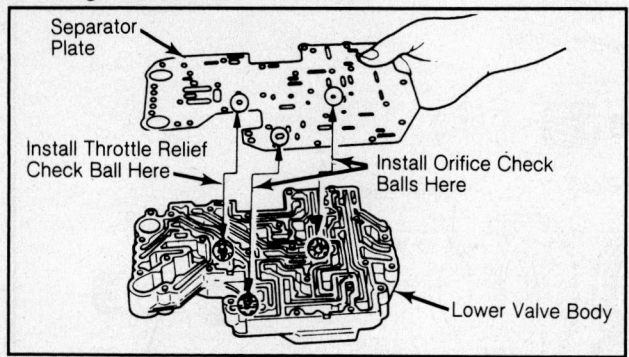

3) Place transmission on oil pan and install turbine shaft and oil pump drive shaft with single oil supply port positioned toward oil pump. Install torque converter onto stator shaft, turbine shaft and pump drive shaft taking care not to damage oil seal in converter housing.

Fig. 25: Oil Port Positioning

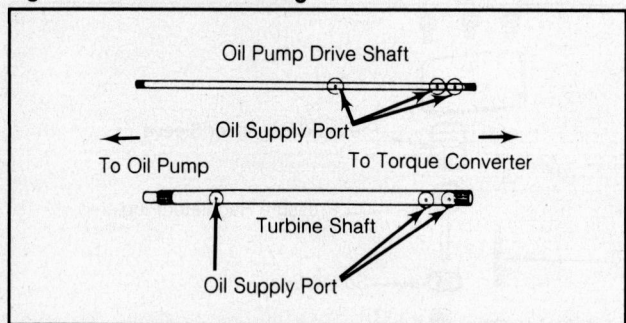

4) If complete transmission was disassembled: Install parking pawl and parking pawl shaft. Install parking rod support plate, parking pawl return spring and parking pawl in housing and retain with spring after inserting shaft from front side. Connect parking rod, parking lever and retain with clip.

5) Install parking rod on notched portion of parking shaft support plate with cam portion positioned at back of parking pawl. Install parking lever to parking lever pin and retain with clip.

Fig. 26: View of Transmission Housing Showing Installation of Parking Pawl Assembly

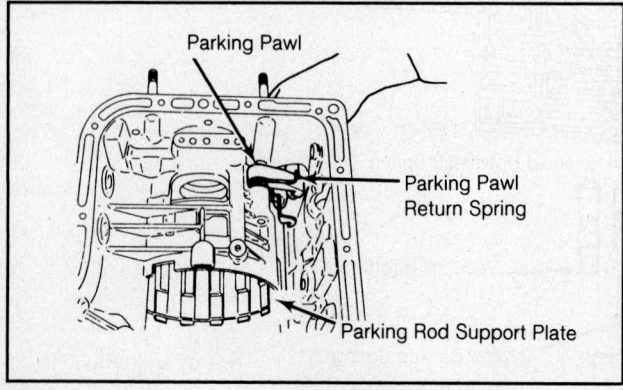

6) Install Drive Pinion Seal Guide (499257100) to splines of drive pinion rear end and connect transmission housing and final drive housing using 8 (8 mm) nuts being careful not to damage oil seal.

7) Engage planetary gear unit with center support assembly and check operation of one-way clutch. Check that one-way clutch in planetary gear unit rotates clockwise only, then separate assemblies.

8) Place center support and low-reverse brake assembly in Base (499687000) and select a retaining plate so that dimension "H" is 3.014-3.492" (77.25-77.45 mm). See Fig. 27.

Fig. 27: Retaining Plate Selection

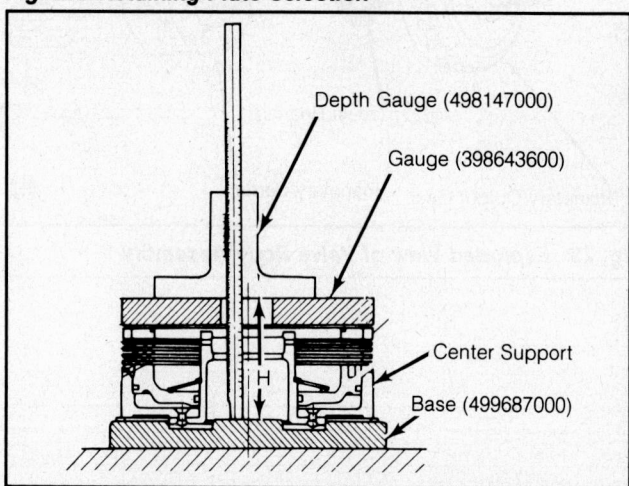

9) If clearance is not within specifications, correct by installing a retaining plate of different thickness. Center support and low-reverse brake assembly retaining plates are available in thicknesses of 0.268" (6.8 mm) to .323" (8.2 mm) in .008" (0.2 mm) increments.

10) Install snap ring, retaining plate, drive plates, driven plates, center support assembly and snap ring into transmission housing. When installing center support, install (6 mm) bolts in support while turning support gradually being careful not to damage one-way clutch or bushing.

11) After assembly, measure clearance between piston and driven plate. Clearance should be be .028-.039" (0.70-1.0 mm). With clearance correctly set, apply compressed air to oil hole in center support and check operation of low-reverse brake piston.

Fig. 28: Measuring Clearance Between Piston and Low-Reverse Driven Plate

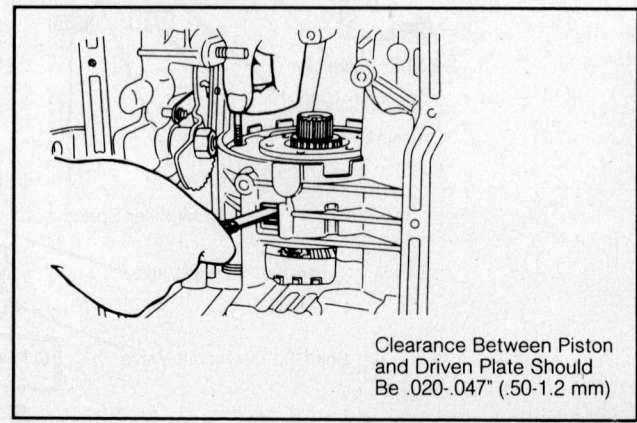

Clearance Between Piston and Driven Plate Should Be .020-.047" (.50-1.2 mm)

Fig. 29: Using Compressed Air to Check Operation of Low-Reverse Brake Piston

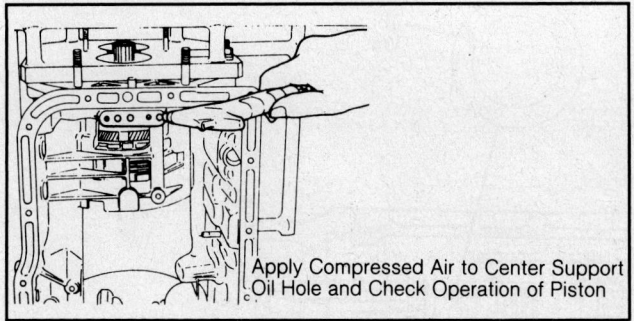

Apply Compressed Air to Center Support
Oil Hole and Check Operation of Piston

12) Install connecting shell and and clutch hub as an assembly to spline of reverse sun gear and forward sun gear. Install forward clutch assembly and reverse clutch assembly. Ensure that thickness of washer installed between forward clutch and clutch hub is .047" (1.2 mm).

13) Match projected portions of brake band with notches in transmission housing and install brake band. Using Depth Gauge Block (498147001) and Gauge (398643600), check transmission total end play with thrust bearing removed.

14) Place gauge block on rear face of transmission housing, then using depth gauge, measure distance "L" (from forward clutch to top of gauge block). *See Fig. 30.* Place gauge block on top of oil pump carrier (with thrust bearing installed).

Fig. 30: Measuring Distance "L" for Transmission End Play Adjustment

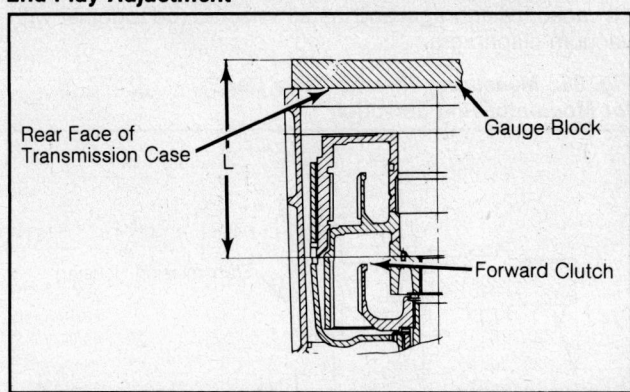

Rear Face of Transmission Case

Gauge Block

L

Forward Clutch

15) Measure distance "I" (from rear cover mounting surface to top of gauge block). *See Fig. 31.* Note both values just obtained for future reference. Add .016" (0.4 mm) to distance "L", then subtract allowable transmission end play of .010-.020" (.25-.50 mm).

16) Subtract distance "I" from value just obtained. Final value is thickness of washer to be installed. End play washers are available in thicknesses of .039" (1.0 mm) to .087" (2.2 mm) in increments of .008" (0.2 mm).

17) Using Depth Gauge Block (498147001) and Gauge (398643600), check reverse clutch end play. Place gauge on rear face of transmission housing and measure distance "M" (from rear face of reverse clutch drum to top of gauge block).

18) Place gauge block on oil pump face and measure distance "m" (from rear cover mounting surface to

Fig. 31: Measuring Distance "I" for Transmission End Play Adjustment

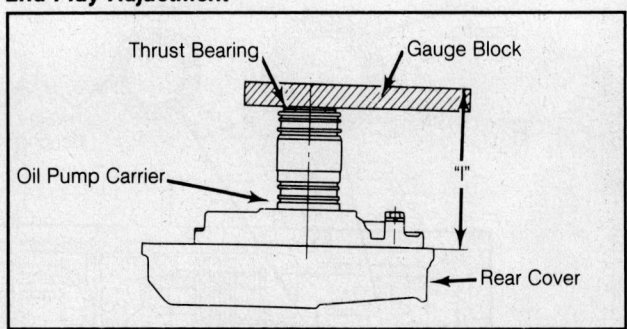

Thrust Bearing   Gauge Block

Oil Pump Carrier

"I"

Rear Cover

Fig. 32: Measuring Distance "M" for Reverse Clutch End Play Adjustment

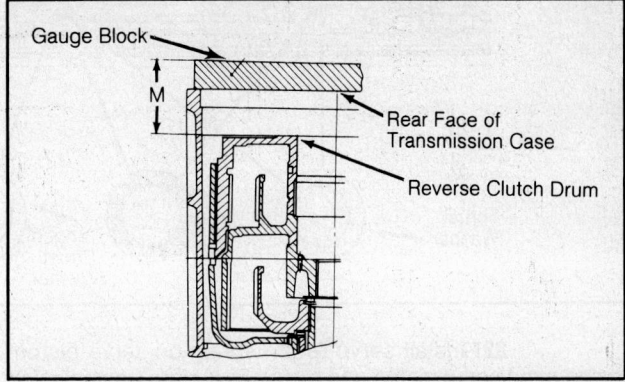

Gauge Block

M

Rear Face of Transmission Case

Reverse Clutch Drum

top of gauge block). Add .016" (0.4 mm) to distance "M", then subtract allowable end play of .020-.031" (0.5-0.8 mm). Subtract distance "m" from value just obtained.

19) Final value is thickness of reverse clutch drum thrust washer to be installed. Reverse clutch drum thrust washers are available in thicknesses of .039" (1.0 mm) to .087" (2.2 mm) in increments of .008" (0.2 mm).

Fig. 33: Measuring Distance "m" for Reverse Clutch End Play Adjustment

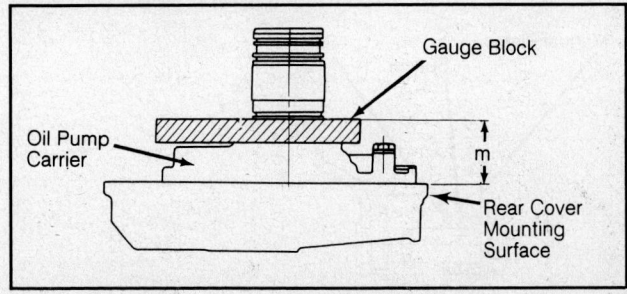

Gauge Block

Oil Pump Carrier

m

Rear Cover Mounting Surface

20) Install transfer drive shaft. Secure transfer coupling to transfer drive shaft with a new spring pin and engage shaft with drive pinion splines. Install thrust bearing on on forward clutch. Apply petroleum jelly to washers which have been selected and place them on oil pump carrier.

21) Before installing oil pump assembly ensure that mating surfaces of transmission cover (intermediate houing on 4WD transmissions) and transmission housing are free from oil. Install oil pump assembly being careful not to drop washers.

Fig. 34: *Cross-Sectional View of Transmission Housing Showing Thrust Washer and Thrust Bearing Locations*

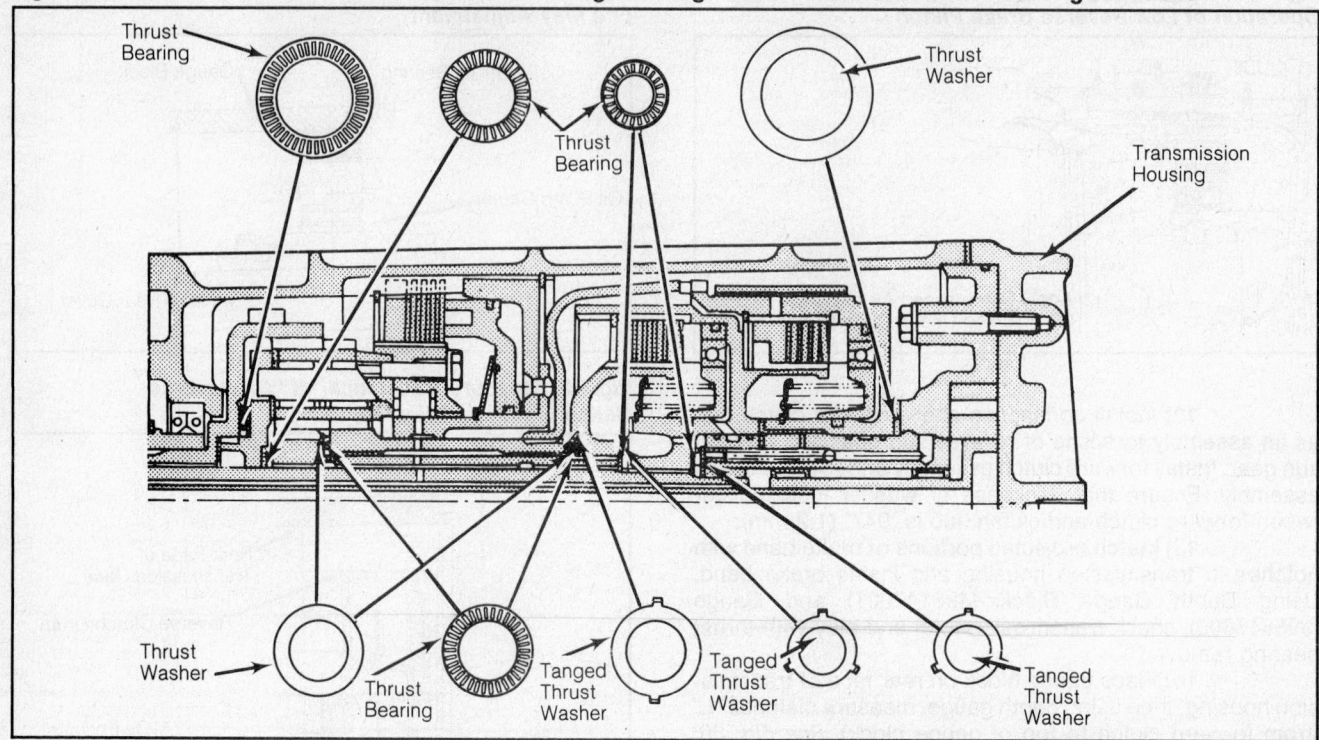

22) Install servo return spring on servo piston. Install band servo piston and piston cover into transmission housing by using piston rod as a guide. Ensure that "O" ring is not damaged. Secure piston with snap ring.

23) Install brake band apply strut and tighten band adjusting screw to 78 INCH lbs (9 N.m), then back screw off 2 complete turns and tighten lock nut to 20 ft. lbs. (27 N.m). Using shims, adjust clearance between manual plate and spacer to .012" (0.3 mm) and tighten nut to 25-33 ft. lbs. (33-44 N.m).

Fig. 35: *Cross-Section View Showing Manual Plate-to-Spacer Adjustment*

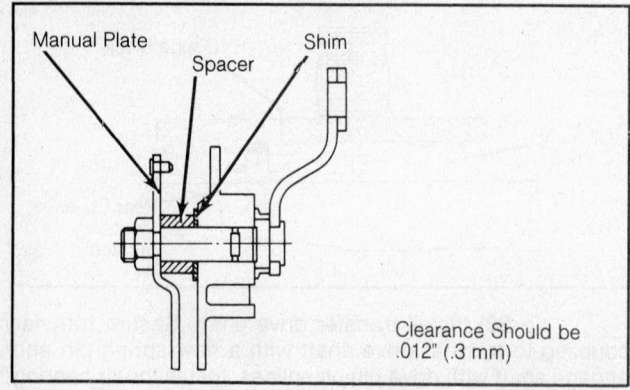

Clearance Should be .012" (.3 mm)

24) Install valve body into transmission housing, making sure that groove in manual valve engages pin in manual plate. Tighten valve body bolts to 52-70 INCH lbs (6-8 N.m). With valve body installed, fully compress vacuum throttle valve and measure distance from end of valve where modulator rod will seat to outside of transmission housing.

25) Resulting measurement will determine length of modulator rod to be installed. Select a rod from those listed in modulator rod selection table. Install "O" ring on vacuum diaphragm and install selected rod together with vacuum diaphragm.

Fig. 36: *Measuring Throttle Valve Depth for Modulator Rod Selection*

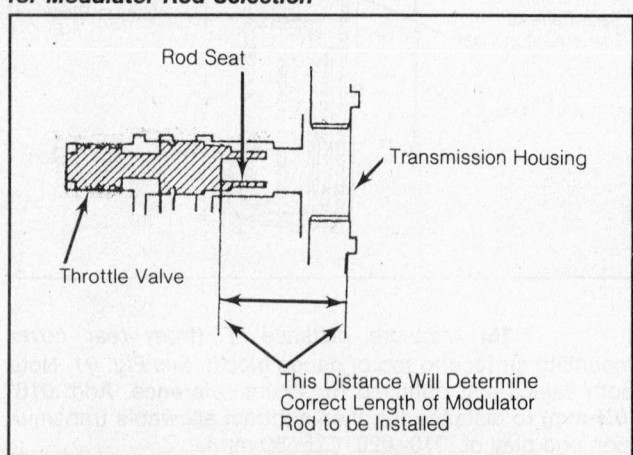

MODULATOR ROD SELECTION TABLE

Measurement In. (mm)	Rod to Use In. (mm)
1.201 (30.5) or Less	1.34 (34.0)
1.2067-1.2224 (30.65-31.05)	1.36 (34.5)
1.2264-1.2421 (31.15-31.55)	1.38 (35.0)
1.2461-1.2618 (31.65-32.05)	1.40 (35.5)
1.2618 (32.05) or More	1.42 (36.0)

SUBARU MODEL M41A (Cont.)

Fig. 37: Exploded View of Extension Housing Assembly

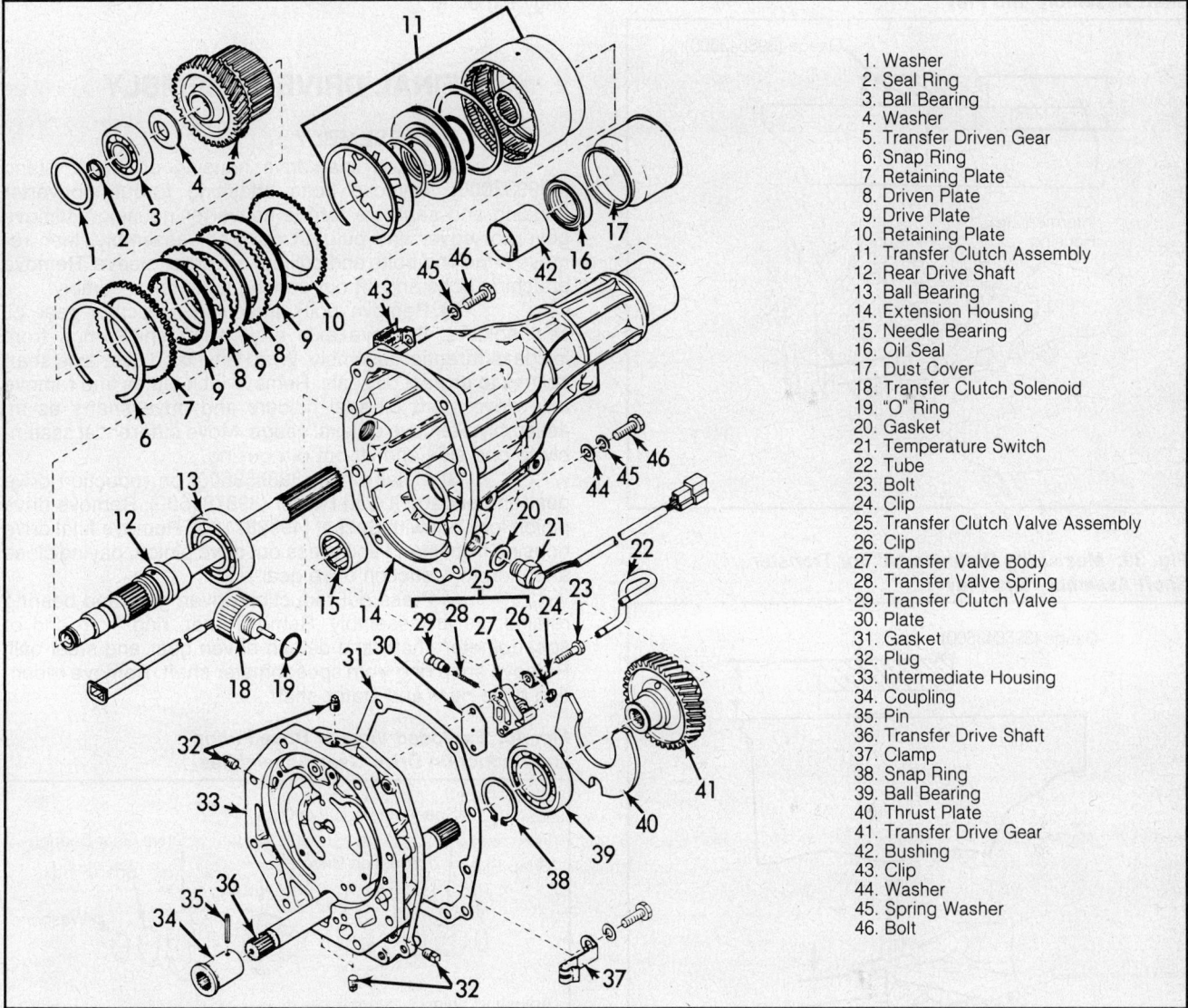

1. Washer
2. Seal Ring
3. Ball Bearing
4. Washer
5. Transfer Driven Gear
6. Snap Ring
7. Retaining Plate
8. Driven Plate
9. Drive Plate
10. Retaining Plate
11. Transfer Clutch Assembly
12. Rear Drive Shaft
13. Ball Bearing
14. Extension Housing
15. Needle Bearing
16. Oil Seal
17. Dust Cover
18. Transfer Clutch Solenoid
19. "O" Ring
20. Gasket
21. Temperature Switch
22. Tube
23. Bolt
24. Clip
25. Transfer Clutch Valve Assembly
26. Clip
27. Transfer Valve Body
28. Transfer Valve Spring
29. Transfer Clutch Valve
30. Plate
31. Gasket
32. Plug
33. Intermediate Housing
34. Coupling
35. Pin
36. Transfer Drive Shaft
37. Clamp
38. Snap Ring
39. Ball Bearing
40. Thrust Plate
41. Transfer Drive Gear
42. Bushing
43. Clip
44. Washer
45. Spring Washer
46. Bolt

Extension housing is used in 4WD vehicles only.

26) Install new servo apply and servo release tubes by lightly tapping them into position. Ensure that tube installed height does not exceed 1.61 (41 mm), as measured from transmission housing oil pan mating surface. Install oil pan. Place transmission on oil pan and install turbine shaft and oil pump drive shaft with single oil port toward oil pump.

27) On 4WD transmissions: Using Installers (899874100, 499277000 and 398177700), install bearing and transfer clutch (drum) assembly to rear shaft. Install rear pressure plate, plates and front pressure plate. Apply compressed air to oil hole located at end of rear shaft to ensure that piston moves freely.

28) On 4WD transmissions: Check clearance between retaining plate and clutch assembly snap ring using a feeler gauge. Clearance should be .016-.031" (0.4-0.8 mm) If clearance is not within specifications, correct by installing a retaining plate of different thickness.

29) On 4WD transmissions: Transfer clutch assembly retaining plates are available in thicknesses of .185" (4.7 mm) to .232" (5.9 mm) in .012" (0.3 mm) increments.

30) On 4WD transmissions: Install washer, bearing, transfer drive gear, washer, bearing and seal ring onto rear drive shaft. Install rear shaft assembly in extension housing, being careful not to damage bushing or seal at end of transfer drive shaft.

31) On 4WD transmissions: Place gauge block on rear face of intermediate case, then using depth gauge, measure distance "N" (intermediate case bearing bore to top of gauge block). See Fig. 38. Note value obtained for future reference.

32) On 4WD transmissions: Place gauge block on top of bearing, then using depth gauge, measure distance "n" (from extension housing to top of gauge block). See Fig. 39. Add .008" (0.2 mm) to distance "N", then subtract allowable end play of .012" (0.3 mm) from this value.

33) On 4WD transmissions: Subtract distance "n" from value just obtained. Resulting value is thickness of rear shaft thrust washers to be installed. Rear shaft thrust

Fig. 38: Measuring Distance "N" for Transfer Shaft Assembly End Play

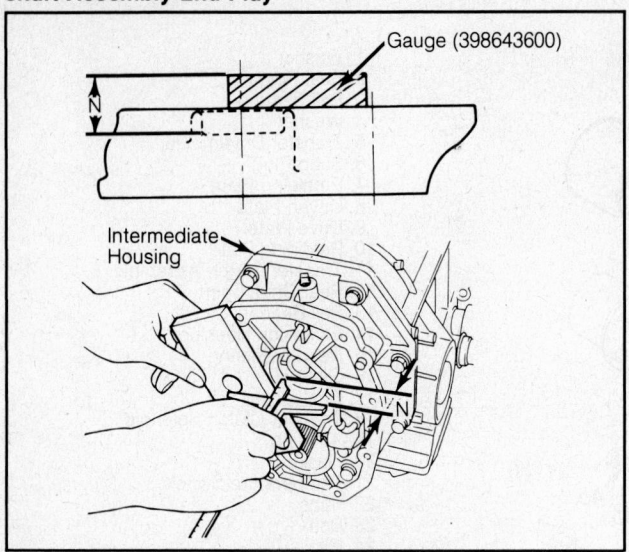

Fig. 39: Measuring Distance "n" for Transfer Shaft Assembly End Play

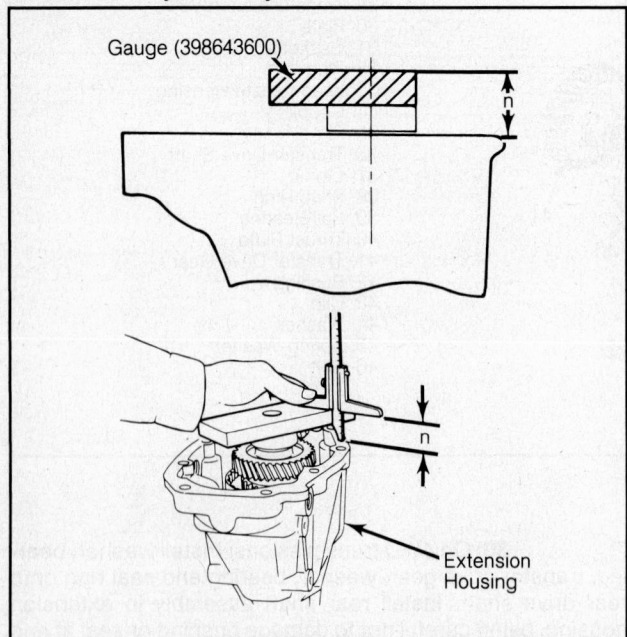

washers are available in thicknesses of .008" (0.2 mm) and .020" (0.5 mm). DO NOT install more than 3 thrust washers.

34) On 4WD transmissions: Install rear drive gear thrust plate and transfer drive gear in intermediate case. Ensure that thrust plate notch aligns with with mounting bolt. Install selected washer in intermediate housing. Install extension assembly and tighten bolts to 18 ft. lbs. (24 N.m).

NOTE: Be sure to install transfer solenoid wire harness clip and seal ring.

35) Install "O" ring to bore in extension housing. Install transfer solenoid and tighten (hand tight). Install temperature switch and gasket. Tighten to 13 ft. lbs. (18

N.m). Fasten wire harnesses with clips and install rear engine mount.

FINAL DRIVE ASSEMBLY

DISASSEMBLY
1) Place final drive housing on Work Stand (499937000). Remove bolts attaching torque converter housing and separate torque converter housing. Remove governor cover and pull out governor assembly, then remove attaching bolts and pull out governor sleeve. Remove attaching bolts and lift out parking actuator assembly.

2) Remove bolts attaching reduction gear oil seal holders. Remove axle drive shaft snap rings from inside differential assembly. Wrap vinyl tape over axle drive shaft splines to protect oil seals. Remove lock plates and remove axle drive shaft oil seal holders and drive shafts as an assembly. Remove oil level gauge. Move differential assembly to one side and lift out of housing.

3) Install Shaft (398653600) on reduction drive gear and engage it with Holder (398781600). Remove drive pinion lock nut with Socket (499987100). Remove final drive housing from stand and press out drive pinion, paying close attention to reduction drive gear end.

4) Press out reduction driven gear and bearing retainer as an assembly. Remove snap ring from end of speedometer shaft, and detach driven gear and steel ball. Remove snap ring from speedometer shaft. Remove reduction drive gear and stator shaft.

Fig. 40: Exploded View of Drive Pinion and Reduction Drive Gear Assemblies

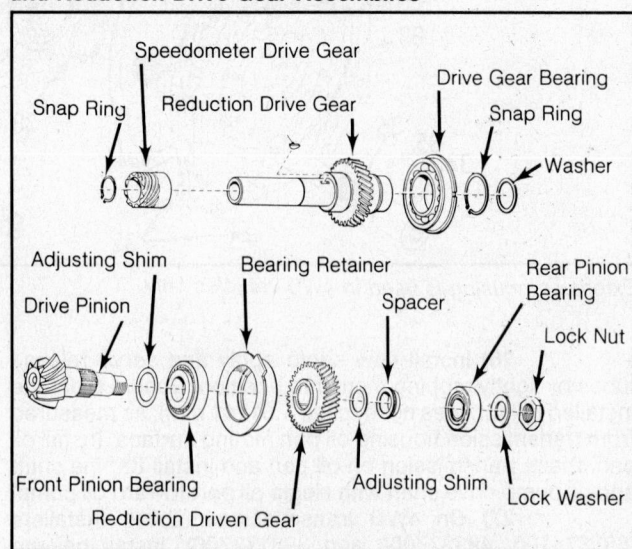

REASSEMBLY & ADJUSTMENT
1) Press thrust bearing retainer (with front bearing) and reduction driven gear into final drive housing. Be sure to align projection of retainer flange with groove of housing. Press retainer until retainer flage contacts housing.

2) Install transmission section front gasket and reduction drive gear on final drive housing. Install and snug down 3 bolts. Using Reduction Bearing Installer (499247200), press oil seal holder into bore of final drive housing being careful not to damage gasket.

Fig. 41: **Exploded View of Differential Assembly**

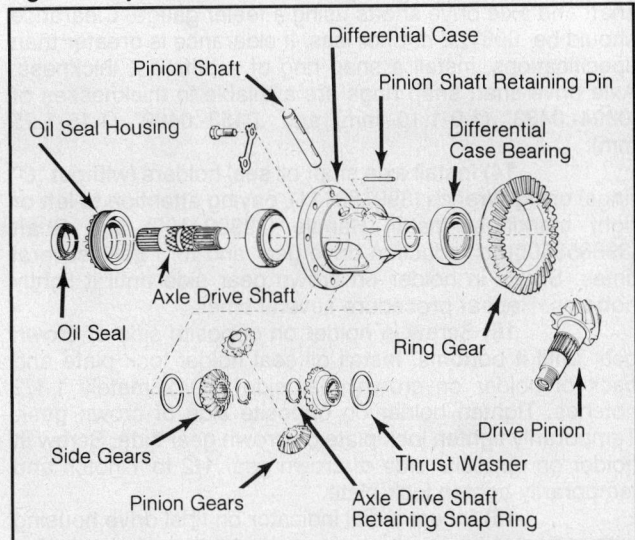

Fig. 42: **Installation of Drive Pinion Bearing Preload Measuring Tools**

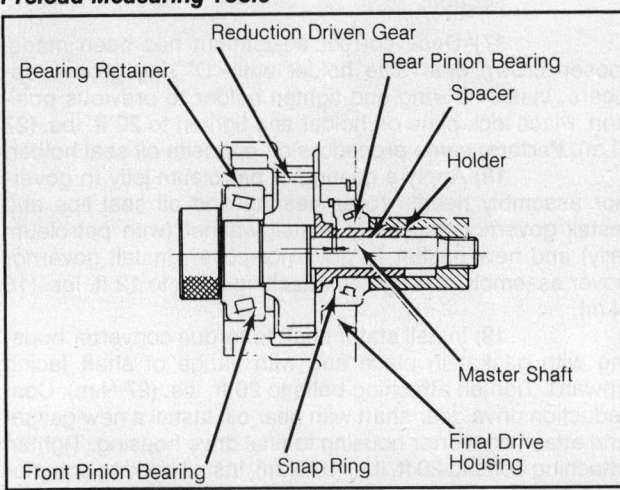

3) Attach final reduction housing to stand and tighten oil seal holder bolts to 18 ft. lbs. (24 N.m). Install speedometer driven gear. Ensure that runout at end of reduction drive gear shaft is within .003" (0.08 mm) by checking with Shaft (398653600) and Handle (899924100).

NOTE: Drive pinion bearing preload adjustment must now be performed. The following tools should be used to carry out adjustment: Spacer (399913604), Master Shaft (499917200), Holder (399913603), and Pulley (39853600). See Fig. 43 for installation of these special tools.

4) Install spacer, rear bearing, master shaft and holder in final drive housing. Using Socket (499987100) and an open end wrench (inside housing) to hold master shaft stationary, tighten holder to 84-108 INCH lbs. (9-11 N.m). DO NOT overtighten holder.

5) Attach pulley to hexagonal head of holder, then attach a spring pull gauge to pulley. Tighten holder until tension on pull gauge is 6.6-8.8 lbs. (3.0-4.0 kg), this will give the correct pinion bearing preload. With preload correctly set, starting torque of drive pinion will be 11-14 INCH lbs. (1.2-1.6 N.m).

Fig. 43: **Measuring Pinion Bearing Preload**

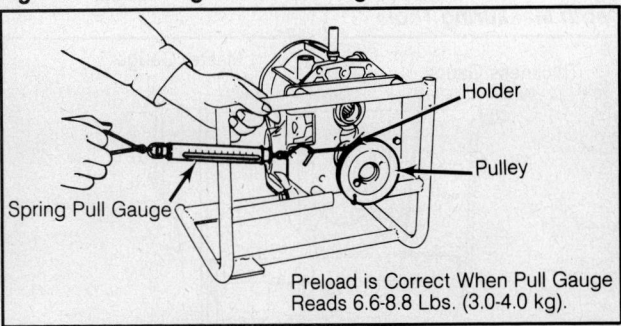

Preload is Correct When Pull Gauge Reads 6.6-8.8 Lbs. (3.0-4.0 kg).

6) Determine correct combination of shim and spacer needed to obtain correct bearing preload by leaving special tools installed and measuring end play between Spacer (399913604) and front bearing. *See Fig. 44.* Add .397" (10.08 mm) to end play reading.

Fig. 44: **Measuring End Play Between Spacer Tool and Front Pinion Bearing**

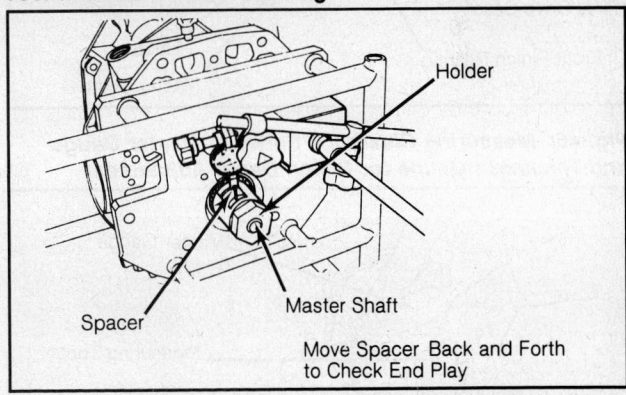

Move Spacer Back and Forth to Check End Play

7) Multiply the plus or minus number stamped on spacer by .001" (.025 mm) and add to reading obtained in step 6). The total sum is the thickness of shim and spacer needed to provide correct bearing preload.

8) Bearing preload adjusting shims are available in thicknesses of .024" (0.6 mm), .031" (0.8 mm) and .039" (1.0 mm). Spacers are available in thicknesses of .378" (9.60 mm) to .385" (9.78 mm) in increments of .001" (.025 mm). The selected shim and spacer should be installed after adjusting pinion depth.

NOTE: For drive pinion depth adjustment, pinion bearing preload measuring tools should be left installed. In addition, the following special pinion depth measuring tools should be installed as shown in Fig. 45: Thickness Gauge (398643600) and Master Gauge (399913601).

9) Install thickness gauge and master gauge into final drive housing. Measure and record clearance between thickness gauge and master gauge. To determine thickness of pinion depth adjusting shim(s) to be installed, proceed as follows:

Step 1: Multiply the plus or minus figure on master gauge (499917002) by .001" (.025 mm) and record the result.

Step 2: Multiply the plus or minus figure on thickness gauge (39863600) by .001" (.025 mm) and record the result.

Step 3: Measure clearance between master gauge and thickness gauge and record the result. *See Fig. 46.*

Fig. 45: Installation of Drive Pinion Depth Measuring Tools

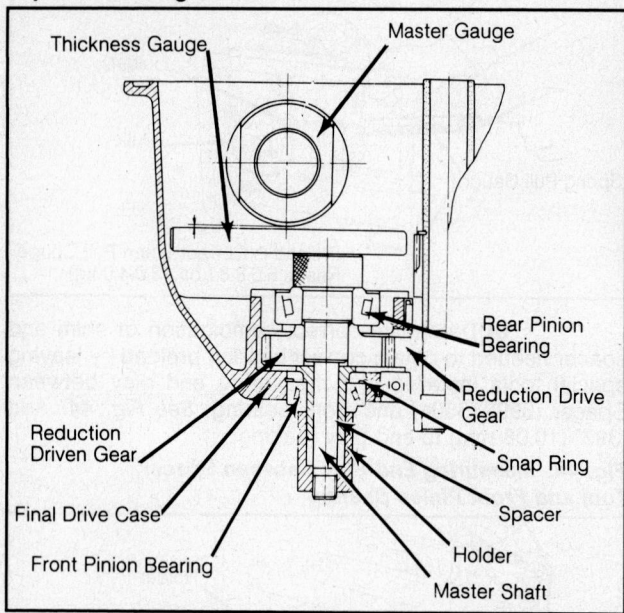

Fig. 46: Measuring Clearance Between Master Gauge and Thickness Gauge for Pinion Depth Adjustment

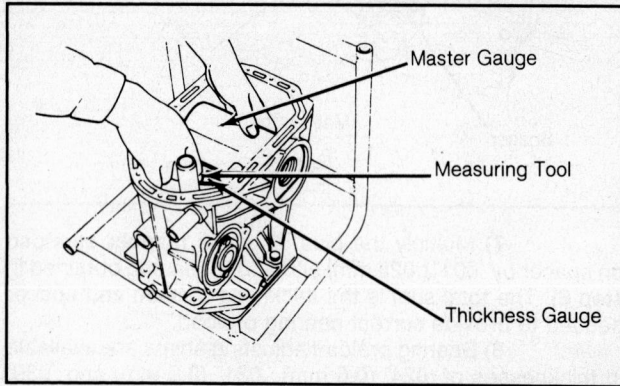

Step 4: Add totals of step 1, 2 and 3. The resulting sum is the shim thickness required for correct drive pinion depth.

10) Up to 3 adjusting shims may be installed to set pinion depth. Adjusting shims are available in thicknesses of .006" (.15 mm) to .020" (.50 mm) in increments of .001" (.025 mm). Remove and disassemble all measuring tools. Install selected pinion depth adjusting shim(s) onto drive pinion, then press on front bearing.

11) Install drive pinion into final drive housing. Install selected pinion bearing preload shim and spacer followed by rear bearing onto drive pinion. Install lock washer and nut. Tighten nut to 87 ft. lbs. (118 N.m). Install final drive housing on work stand and attach pulley and spring pull gauge to pinion lock nut.

12) Recheck pinion bearing preload and adjust as necessary. Stake lock nut at 2 places, if bearing preload is found to be okay. Install differential assembly without axle shaft in final drive housing, being careful not to damage oil seal holder bores. Install axle shafts and secure with snap rings.

13) Check clearance between differential pinion shaft and axle drive shafts using a feeler gauge. Clearance should be .008" (.2 mm) or less. If clearance is greater than specifications, install a snap ring of a different thickness. Axle drive shaft snap rings are available in thicknesses of .0394-.0433" (1.0-1.10 mm) and .0453-.0492" (1.15-1.25 mm).

14) Install axle shaft oil seal holders (without "O" rings) using Wrench (399780111), paying attention to left or right markings. Install Handle (899924100) and Shaft (398653600) to reduction drive gear and turn gear several times. Screw in holder on crown gear side until it lightly bottoms. Repeat procedure several times.

15) Screw in holder on opposite side of crown gear until it bottoms. Install oil seal holder lock plate and back of holder on crown gear side approximately 1 1/2 notches. Tighten holder on opposite side of crown gear. Temporarily tighten lock plate on crown gear side. Screw in holder on opposite side of crown gear 1/2 to 1 notch and temporarily tighten lock plate.

16) Mount a dial indicator on final drive housing with indicator tip touching ring gear teeth and check ring gear back lash. Ring gear backlash should be .004-.007" (.10-.18 mm). If backlash is not within specifications, recheck drive pinion depth adjustment and correct as necessary.

NOTE: As an additional check, a Gear Tooth Pattern test may be performed. See GEAR TOOTH CONTACT PATTERN in GENERAL SERVICING section.

17) Once correct adjustment has been made, loosen crown gear side holder until "O" ring groove appears. Install "O" ring and tighten holder to previous position. Place lock plate on holder and tighten to 20 ft. lbs. (27 N.m). Perform same procedure on opposite oil seal holder.

18) Apply a coating of petroleum jelly to governor assembly needle roller bearing and oil seal lips and install governor assembly. Install washer (with petroleum jelly) and new gasket to governor cover. Install governor cover assembly and tighten attaching bolts to 12 ft. lbs. (16 N.m).

19) Install stator shaft to torque converter housing with gasket in place and with flange of shaft facing upward. Tighten attaching bolts to 20 ft. lbs. (27 N.m). Coat reduction drive gear shaft with gear oil. Install a new gasket and attach converter housing to final drive housing. Tighten attaching bolts to 20 ft. lbs. (27 N.m). Install parking actuator assembly on final drive housing.

TIGHTENING SPECIFICATIONS

Application	Ft. Lbs. (N.m)
Band Adjust Screw Lock Nut	19-21 (26-28)
Converter Hsg.-to-Reduction Gear Housing	17-20 (23-27)
Drive Pinion Lock Nut	87 (118)
Manual Plate-to-Trans. Housing	25-33 (34-45)
Oil Pump Assembly	17-20 (23-27)
Stator Shaft Flange	17-20 (23-27)
Trans. Housing-to-Reduction Gear Housing	17-20 (23-27)
Transmission-to-Engine	34-40 (46-54)

TOYOTA A-40D, A-42DL, A-43D, A-43DE & A-44DL

A-40D 4-Speed
 Celica
A-42DL
 Corolla (RWD)
A-43D 4-Speed
 Pickup
A-43DE 4-Speed
 Cressida, Supra
A-44DL
 Van

DESCRIPTION

All transmissions have 4 forward speeds (4th is overdrive) and reverse. Gear shifts on Cressida and Supra models are controlled by an electronic control unit (ECU) and actuated by solenoids in the valve body. Shift points are determined by engine temperature, road speed, throttle position and selector position.

On all models, the torque converter is a 3-element type. All transmission models except A-40D and A-43D have torque converters with lock-up clutches. Planetary gears are actuated by 3 multi-disc brakes and 2 clutches. Except for Cressida and Supra models, engine load and speed determine gear changes by use of throttle valve position and output shaft speed. These automatic transmissions have no bands, eliminating the need for internal adjustments. The only external adjustments are throttle cable position, shift linkage adjustment and neutral start switch.

LUBRICATION & ADJUSTMENT

See appropriate AUTOMATIC TRANSMISSION SERVICING article in IMPORT GENERAL SERVICING section.

TROUBLE SHOOTING (CRESSIDA & SUPRA)

PRELIMINARY CHECKS

Trouble shooting of the electrcal control system should begin with a voltage check at the DG terminal while driving and when vehicle is stopped. Solenoid valves and speed sensor system have the capability to retain malfunctions in memory. Malfunctions will be retained in memory until ignition switch is turned off, even after malfunction is repaired.

Malfunctions of the throttle position sensor or stop light switch are not retained in memory. Charge battery before testing to prevent false diagnosis.

NOTE: **Use a circuit tester with an internal impedance of 10,000 ohms or more.**

DG TERMINAL VOLTAGE

1) With engine at normal operating temperature, connect voltmeter to DG terminal. Place pattern selection switch in "NORMAL" and shift selector in "D" with "OD" switch on. Road test vehicle and ensure voltage at DG terminal for each upshift is correct. See DG TERMINAL VOLTAGE table.

Fig. 1: Cressida Transmission Electrical Components

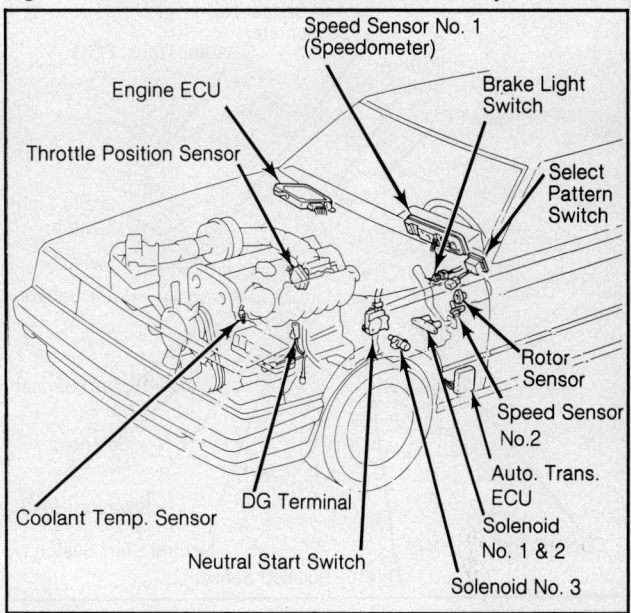

DG TERMINAL VOLTAGE

Gear Position	Voltage
1st	0
2nd	2
2nd Lock-Up	3
3rd	4
3rd Lock-Up	5
OD	6
OD & Lock-Up	7

2) If DG terminal voltage is constant at 4 volts, speed sensor is faulty. If DG terminal voltage is constant at 8 volts, solenoid is defective.

NOTE: **Voltage may rise between 0 and 8 volts before vehicle reaches 6 MPH in 1st gear. Voltage jump is normal and depends how far throttle is open.**

3) Stop vehicle, but DO NOT turn off engine or diagnostic codes in ECU memory will be erased. With engine running, recheck voltage at DG terminal. Zero volts indicates system is normal or defective brake system; 4 volts indicates faulty No. 2 speed sensor; 8 volts indicates faulty solenoid.

4) To check throttle position sensor system, turn off engine. While slowly depressing accelerator pedal, recheck voltage at DG terminal. Voltage should slowly rise to 8 volts.

5) To inspect brake signal, depress accelerator until DG terminal voltage is 8 volts. Depress brake pedal and check DG terminal voltage. With brake pedal released, there should be 8 volts. There should be 0 volts with brake pedal depressed.

MANUAL SHIFT TEST

To determine if transmissions problems are the result of electrical or mechanical/hydraulic malfunctions, unplug transmission ECU connector. Test drive

Fig. 2: Supra Transmission Electrical Components

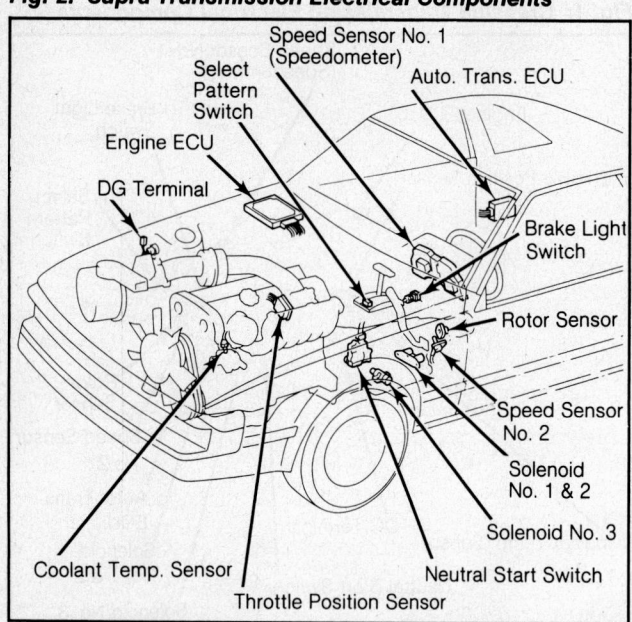

Fig. 3: Cressida Automatic Transmission ECU Wiring Diagram

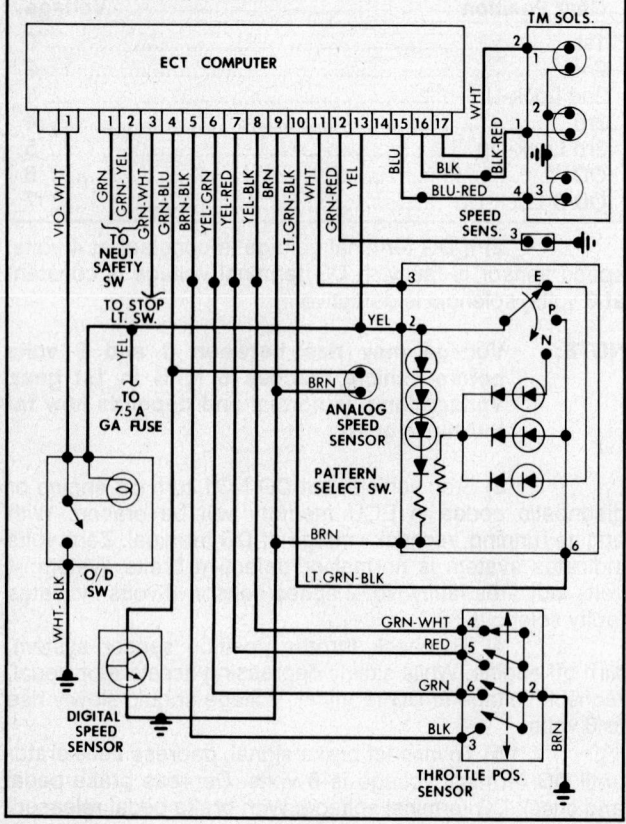

vehicle while manually shifting transmission through all forward gears. Also check if transmission performs correctly in "P", "N" and "R" range. If transmission will shift manually, problem is most likely in electrical system.

Fig. 4: Supra Automatic Transmission ECU Wiring Diagram

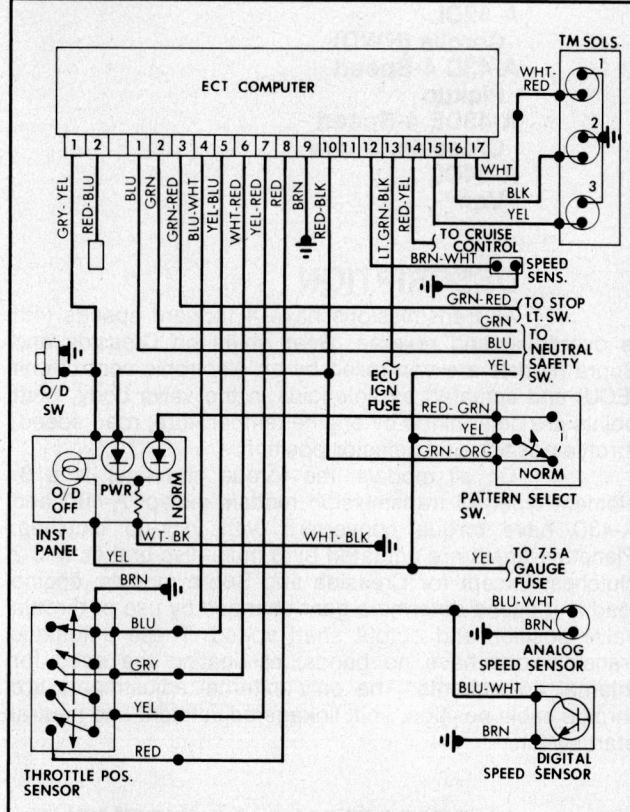

TROUBLE SHOOTING (ALL MODELS)

NO MOVEMENT IN ANY FORWARD GEAR OR REVERSE

Manual linkage out of adjustment. Faulty valve body or primary regulator. Park lock pawl faulty. Faulty torque converter. Converter drive plate damaged or broken. Oil pump intake screen blocked. ECU faulty (A-43DE transmission)

SHIFT LEVER POSITION INCORRECT

Manual linkage out of adjustment. Faulty manual valve and lever.

HARSH ENGAGEMENT INTO ANY DRIVE GEAR

Throttle cable out if adjustment. Faulty valve body, primary regulator or accumulator pistons.

DELAYED 1-2, 2-3, 3-OD UPSHIFTS, OR DOWNSHIFTS FROM OD-3 OR 3-2 THEN BACK TO OD OR 3

Faulty governor or valve body. ECU or solenoid valve faulty (A-43DE transmission).

TOYOTA A-40D, A-42DL, A-43D, A-43DE & A-44DL (Cont.)

SLIP ON ANY UPSHIFT OR SLIP OR SHUDDER ON TAKEOFF

Manual linkage or throttle cable out of adjustment. Valve body faulty. Solenoid valve faulty (A-43DE transmission).

HARSH DOWNSHIFT

Throttle cable out of adjustment or faulty. Accumulator pistons or valve body faulty.

NO DOWNSHIFT WHEN COASTING

Faulty governor or valve body. ECU or solenoid valve faulty (A-43DE transmission).

DOWNSHIFTS TOO SOON OR TOO LATE WHEN COASTING

Throttle cable out of adjustment or faulty. Faulty governor or valve body. ECU or solenoid valve faulty (A-43DE transmission).

NO OD-3, 3-2 OR 2-1 KICKDOWN

Throttle cable out of adjustment. Governor or valve body faulty. ECU or solenoid valve faulty (A-43DE transmission).

NO ENGINE BRAKING IN "2"

Faulty valve body. Faulty ECU or solenoid valve (A-43DE transmission).

VEHICLE DOES NOT HOLD IN "P"

Manual linkage out of adjustment. Parking lock pawl cam and spring faulty.

TESTING (CRESSIDA & SUPRA)

ECU CIRCUIT

Remove left kick panel (Cressida). Remove right pillar louver and arm rest (Supra). Turn ignition on. Measure voltage at each terminal of Auto. Trans. ECU connector. See *Fig. 5* and CRESSIDA & SUPRA ECU CONNECTOR VOLTAGE CHART.

COMPONENT TESTS

Transmission Solenoids

1) Unplug connector from Auto. Trans. ECU. Check resistance between S_1, S_2, S_ς and ground. Resistance should be 11-15 ohms. *See Fig. 5.*

2) Apply battery voltage to each solenoid to check operation. If there is foreign material in solenoid valve, there will be no fluid control even if solenoid operates.

3) Ensure No. 1 and No. 2 solenoids are applied in correct gear range. See CRESSIDA & SUPRA TRANSMISSION SOLENOID APPLICATION table.

Neutral Start Switch

Shift lever into "D" or "S". Unplug neutral start switch connector near starter motor. Check for continuity between L, S and ground. *See Fig. 5.*

Throttle Position Sensor

Unplug connector from throttle position sensor and remove rubber. Check for continuity between E_1 and other terminals. *See Fig. 6.* While slowly opening throttle valve, ensure continuity between E_1 and each respective terminal is as specified.

Fig. 5: Automatic Transmission ECU and Neutral Start Switch Connectors Terminal Identification

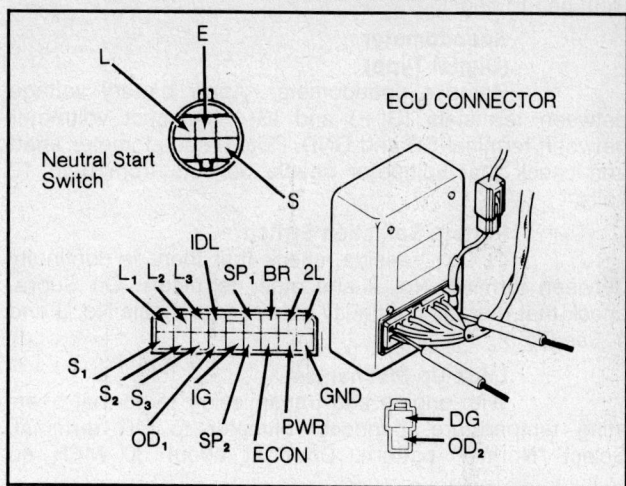

CRESSIDA & SUPRA TRANSMISSION SOLENOID APPLICATION TABLE

Gear Position	Solenoid No. 1	Solenoid No. 2
"D" Range		
OD	Off	Off
3rd	Off	On
2nd	On	On
1st	On	Off
"2" Range		
3rd	Off	On
2nd	On	On
1st	On	Off
"L" Range		
2nd	On	On
1st	On	Off

Fig. 6: Throttle Position Sensor Circuit Check

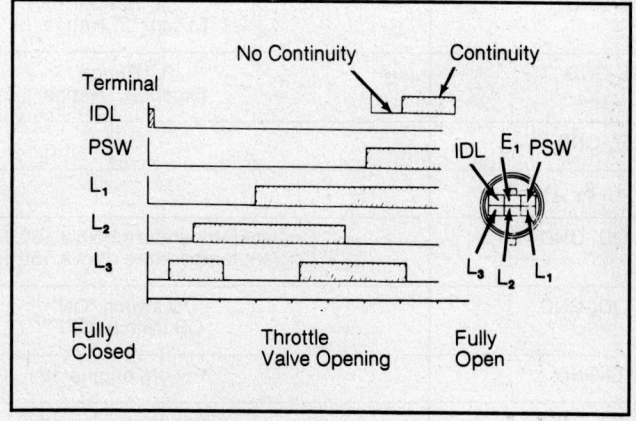

Speed Sensor

Jack up a rear wheel. Connect an ohmmeter between connector and ground. Spin wheel and check that ohmmeter needle deflects from 0 (zero) to infinity.

Automatic Transmissions

TOYOTA A-40D, A-42DL, A-43D, A-43DE & A-44DL (Cont.)

Speedometer
(Analog Type)

Remove speedometer from instrument panel. Connect ohmmeter between SP terminals. Rotate speedometer shaft and check that ohmmeter needle deflects from peg to peg.

Speedometer
(Digital Type)

Remove speedometer. Apply battery voltage between terminals IG(+) and IG(-). Connect voltmeter between terminal SP and GND. Rotate speedometer shaft and check that voltmeter needle deflects from 0 to 10 volts.

Pattern Selection Switch

1) On Cressida, check that there is continuity between terminal No. 2 and other terminals. On Supra, check that there is continuity between terminals No. 3 and 4. *See Fig. 7.*

Lock-Up Mechanism

With engine and transmission at normal operating temperature, connect voltmeter to DG terminal. Select "Normal" pattern. Drive at about 30 MPH so voltmeter reads between 5 and 3 volts (lock-up range). Depress accelerator pedal and note tachometer. If RPM jumps considerably, there is no lock-up.

NOTE: If torque converter lock-up clutch does not release when slowing to a stop, the cause may be a sticking lock-up relay valve in valve body.

Fig. 7: Pattern Select Switch Terminal Identification

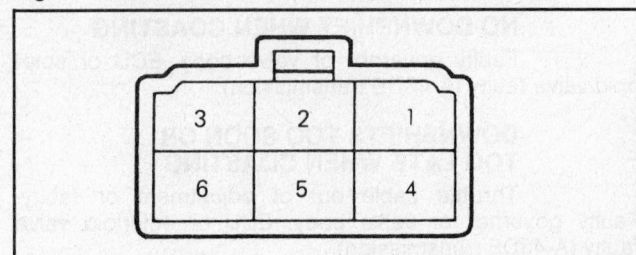

CRESSIDA AND SUPRA ECU CONNECTOR VOLTAGE CHART

Terminals	Conditions	Voltage (Denso Type)	Voltage (Aisin Type)
L₁-GND	Throttle valve fully closed Throttle valve fully open	5 0	12 0
L₂-GND	Throttle valve fully closed Throttle valve fully open	5 5	12 12
L₃-GND	Throttle valve fully closed Throttle valve fully open	5 5	12 12
IDL-GND	Throttle valve fully closed Throttle opening about 1.5°	0 4	0 4
SP₁-GND	Key on, engine off With engine running	12 or 0 6	12 or 0 6
BR-GND	Brake pedal depressed Brake pedal released	12 0	12 0
2-GND	"2" Range Except "2" Range	9-16 0-2	9-16 0-2
L-GND	"L" Range Except "L" Range	9-16 0-2	9-16 0-2
S₁-GND	.....	12	12
S₁, S₂-GND	.....	0	0
OD₁-GND	Coolant temperature below 150°F (70°C) Coolant temperature above 150°F (70°C)	0 5	0 12
OD₂-GND	OD switch "ON" OD switch "OFF"	12 0	12 0
IG-GND	Key on, engine off	12	12
SP₂-GND	Key on, engine off Engine running	5 or 0 4	12 or 0 10
PWR-GND	PWR pattern Except PWR pattern	12 1	12 1
ECON-GND (Cressida)	ECON pattern Except ECON pattern	12 1	12 1

TOYOTA A-40D, A-42DL, A-43D, A-43DE & A-44DL (Cont.)

TESTING
(ALL MODELS)

ROAD TEST
"D" Range Test
1) Engine must be at normal operating temperature. Shift into "D" range with "OD" switch on. Accelerate with throttle valve fully open and ensure all shifts occur at specified points. See SHIFT SPEED SPECIFCATIONS chart. Also check all downshift points.

NOTE: On all models except Cressida and Supra, there is no 3-OD upshift with a throttle opening of more than 86% or coolant temperature below 122°F (50°C). On Cressida and Supra models, there is no 3-OD upshift or lock-up with vehicle speed below 37 MPH or coolant temperature below 140°F (60°C).

2) While driving in "D" range, release foot from accelerator and shift into "2" and "L" ranges. Check engine braking effect in these ranges.

"D" Range Test Results
1) If there is no engine braking at "2" range, Brake No. 1 is defective. If no braking in "L" range, Brake No. 3 is defective.

NOTE: On Cressida and Supra models, perform test in "NORM", "ECON", and "PWR" ranges.

2) If there is no 1-2 upshift, 1-2 shift valve may be stuck. On Cressida and Supra models, check No. 2 solenoid. On all other models, check govenor valve. If there is no 2-3 upshift, check 2-3 shift valve. On Cressida and Supra models, check No. 1 solenoid.

3) On all models, check OD shift valve if there is no 3-OD upshift. If converter lock-up is defective, check lock-up relay valve in valve body. On Cressida and Supra models, also check No. 3 solenoid if lock-up is not correct.

"2" & "L" Range Test
1) Shift to "2" range and check for proper upshifts. Also, check engine braking effect with accelerator released.

2) Shift into "L" range. Ensure there is no upshift to "2" range. Check engine braking effect with accelerator released.

"P" & "R" Range Tests
Shift into "R" range. Check for slippage at full throttle. To check parking pawl, shift into "P" range while parked on a hill. Vehicle should not move.

HYDRAULIC PRESSURE TESTS
With transmission fluid at normal operating temperature, raise and support rear of vehicle so that rear wheels are free to turn. Connect pressure gauges to line pressure and governor pressure test ports on transmission. See Fig. 8.

NOTE: Pressures may also be tested on chassis dynamometer.

SHIFT SPEED SPECIFICATIONS

Shift Condition [1]	Shift Point (MPH)
Celica	
1-2 Upshift in "D"	35-45
2-3 Upshift In "D"	65-76
3-OD Upshift In "D"	[2]
3-2 Downshift In "D"	57-67
2-1 Downshift In "D"	26-34
Corolla (RWD)	
1-2 Upshift In "D"	29-39
2-3 Upshift In "D"	54-63
3-OD Upshift In "D"	[2]
3-2 Downshift In "D"	52-61
2-1 Downshift In "D"	23-30
Cressida [3] [4]	
1-2 Upshift In "D"	29-32
2-3 Upshift In "D"	59-63
3-OD Upshift in "D"	86-90
OD-3 Downshift In "D"	83-86
3-2 Downshift In "D"	56-59
2-1 Downshift In "D"	27-29
Pickup [5]	
22R Engine	
1-2 Upshift In "D"	35-45
2-3 Upshift In "D"	65-77
3-OD Upshift In "D"	[2]
3-2 Downshift in "D"	60-71
2-1 Downshift In "D"	24-34
22R-E Engine	
1-2 Upshift In "D"	37-47
2-3 Upshift In "D"	68-79
3-OD Upshift In "D"	[2]
3-2 Downshift in "D"	62-73
2-1 Downshift In "D"	25-35
Supra [3] [4]	
1-2 Upshift In "D"	29-32
2-3 Upshift In "D"	57-63
3-OD Upshift In "D"	84-89
OD-3 Downshift In "D"	81-86
2-1 Downshift in "D"	55-60
2-1 Downshift In "D"	26-29
Van [3] [6]	
1-2 Upshift In "D"	26-32
2-3 Upshift In "D"	52-59
3-OD Upshift In "D"	[2]
3-2 Downshift In "D"	50-58
2-1 Downshift in "D"	21-28

[1] – All upshift points given at full throttle.

[2] – No 3-OD upshifts occur at full throttle; 3-OD upshift occurs at closed throttle at 24-32 MPH.

[3] – With throttle valve fully open and "Normal" range pattern.

[4] – Lock-up "ON" point with closed throttle is 34-37 MPH; lock-up "OFF" with closed throttle is 31-34.

[5] – Lock-up "ON" point with closed throttle is 39-43 MPH; lock-up "OFF" with closed throttle is 35-40.

[6] – Lock-up "ON" point with closed throttle is 41-46 MPH; lock-up "OFF" with closed throttle is 39-43.

Fig. 8: Transmission Hydraulic Pressure Test Ports

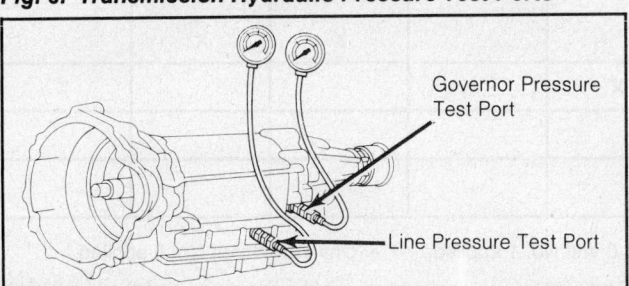

Governor Pressure Test Port

Line Pressure Test Port

Automatic Transmissions

TOYOTA A-40D, A-42DL, A-43D, A-43DE & A-44DL (Cont.)

Governor Pressure Test
(All Except Cressida & Supra)

1) Start engine and release parking brake. Slowly accelerate engine with transmission in "D" and check governor pressure at specified speed. See GOVERNOR PRESSURE SPECIFICATIONS table.

2) If governor pressures are incorrect, check for the following: incorrect line pressure, fluid leakage in governor pressure circuit, governor valve operation defective.

GOVERNOR PRESSURE SPECIFICATIONS

Vehicle Speed (MPH)	Output Shaft (RPM)	Pressure psi (kg/cm²)
All Except A-44DL		
17-21	1000	13-21 (.9-1.5)
34-37	1800	23-31 (1.6-2.2)
58-71	3500	58-75 (4.1-5.3)
A-44DL		
17	1000	20-26 (1.4-1.8)
32	1800	34-40 (2.4-2.8)
62	3500	73-84 (5.1-5.9)

Line Pressure Test
(All Models)

1) Fully apply parking brake and block all 4 wheels. Start engine and shift transmission into "D". Apply firm pressure to brake pedal and let engine idle. Line pressure should be as specified. See LINE PRESSURE SPECIFICATIONS table.

2) Increase engine to stall speed and recheck line pressure. See STALL TEST SPECIFICATIONS table. If specified line pressures are not obtained, check throttle cable adjustment and repeat test. Repeat line pressure tests with transmission in "R".

LINE PRESSURE SPECIFICATIONS

Application	In "D" psi (kg/cm²)	In "R" psi (kg/cm²)
At Idle Speed		
Celica	63-68 (4.4-4.8)	74-90 (5.2-6.3)
Corolla & Pickup (22R)	50-63 (3.5-4.4)	71-91 (5.0-6.4)
Cressida & Supra	53-58 (3.7-4.1)	73-81 (5.1-5.7)
Pickup (22R-E)	65-77 (4.6-5.4)	100-117 (7.0-8.2)
Van	64-73 (4.5-5.1)	97-108 (6.8-7.6)
At Stall Speed		
Celica	139-154 (9.8-10.8)	164-205 (11.5.-14.4)
Corolla & Pickup (22R)	137-156 (9.6-11.0)	95-242 (13.7-17.0)
Cressida & Supra	151-185 (10.6-13.0)	203-270 (14.3-19.0)
Pickup (22R-E) & Van	144-169 (10.1-11.9)	213-270 (15.0-19.0)

Line Pressure Test Results

1) If line pressure in all ranges is higher than specified, check for the following: defective regulator valve, defective throttle valve, or throttle cable out of adjustment.

2) If line pressure is low in all ranges, check for the following: defective oil pump, defective regulator

CLUTCH AND BRAKE APPLICATION CHART
(ELEMENTS IN USE – A-43DE ONLY)

Selector Lever Position	Overdrive Clutch	Front Clutch	Rear Clutch	Overdrive Brake	No.1 Brake	No.2 Brake	No.3 Brake
D – Drive							
First [1]	X	X					
Second [2]	X	X					
Third [3]	X	X	X [4]				
Overdrive		X	X [4]	X		X	
2 – Second [2]							
First [1]	X	X					
Second [2]	X	X			X	X	
Third [3]	X	X	X [4]			X	
L – LOW							
First [1]	X	X					
Second [2]	X	X			X	X	
R – REVERSE [3]	X		X				X
N – NEUTRAL	X						
P – PARK	X						

[1] – One-way clutch No. 0 and No. 2 applied.   [2] – One-way clutch No. 0 and No. 1 applied.   [3] – One-way clutch No. 0 applied.
[4] – Not applied in "POWER" mode.

TOYOTA A-40D, A-42DL, A-43D, A-43DE & A-44DL (Cont.)

valve, defective throttle valve, throttle cable out of adjustment, or defective OD clutch.

    3) If line pressure is low in "D" range only, check for the following: defective front clutch, fluid leak in "D" range circuit, or defective OD clutch.

    4) If line pressure is low in "R" range only, check for the following: defective rear clutch, defective No. 3 brake, fluid leak in "R" range circuit, or defective OD clutch.

STALL TEST

    1) With engine and transmission at normal operating temperature, connect a tachometer to engine. Apply parking brake and block front wheels.

NOTE: **DO NOT maintain stall RPM for more than 5 seconds.**

    2) Start engine, apply brake pedal and place transmission in "D". Accelerate engine to full throttle and check maximum speed obtained. Repeat test in "R".

STALL TEST SPECIFICATIONS

Application	Stall RPM
Celica	1750-2050
Corolla, Cressida	
& Supra	1950-2250
Pickup	
22R Engine	1700-2000
22R-E Engine	1750-2050
Van	2050-2350

Stall Test Results

    1) If stall speed is the same for both ranges but lower than specified , engine output may be insufficient, or stator one-way clutch may not be operating properly.

NOTE: **If stall RPM is more than 600 RPM lower than specifications, torque converter may be faulty.**

    2) If stall speed is higher than specified in "D" range, front clutch may be slipping, one-way No. 2 clutch may not be operating, line pressure may be low, or OD one-way clutch may not be operating.

    3) If stall speed in "R" is higher than specified, rear clutch and/or Brake No. 3 may be slipping, line pressure may be low, OD one-way clutch may not be operating.

    4) If stall speed in "R" and "D" is higher than specified, line pressure may be too low, fluid level may be wrong, or OD one-way clutch is not operating properly.

OVERDRIVE CIRCUIT

NOTE: **This section applies to all models except Cressida and Supra (A-43DE transmission).**

Overdrive Circuit Test

    1) Turn on ignition switch and overdrive switch. Unplug wire connector at thermo switch. Install jumper wire on connector. Repeatedly ground connector. A clicking sound from the overdrive solenoid and relay should be heard.

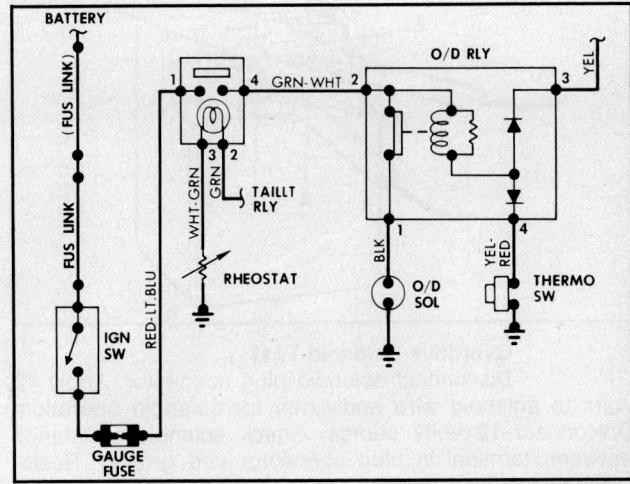

Fig. 9: Corolla & Van Overdrive Circuit Wiring Diagram

    2) Overdrive solenoid is located on left side of transmission. Thermo switch is located on thermostat housing on pickup and Celica models. On Corolla models, thermo switch is located on water pump inlet pipe. The thermo switch on Van models is located on the engine block behind the distributor.

    3) The OD relay is located on the steering column support on Celica models. The Van OD relay is under the center console next to the parking brake handle. Corolla OD relay is behind left side of instrument panel. OD relay is on brake pedal brake on pickup models.

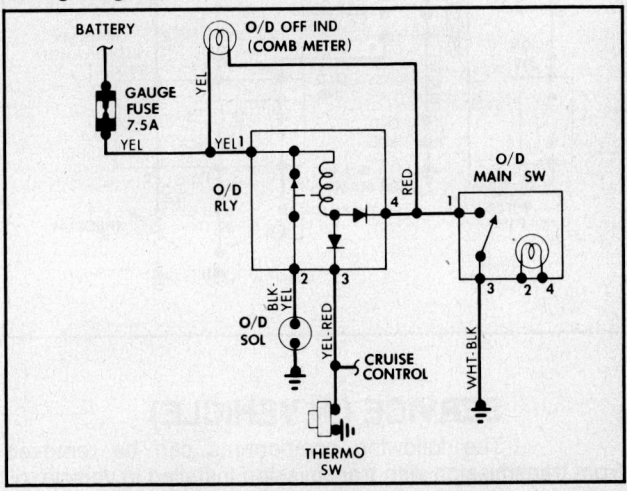

Fig. 10: Celica Overdrive Circuit Wiring Diagram

Overdrive Relay Test

    1) Using an ohmmeter, check that there is no continuity between terminals No. 1 and No. 2. *See Fig. 11.* Disconnect ohmmeter.

    2) Apply 12 volts across terminals No. 2 and No. 4. Ensure there is no continuity between terminals No. 1 and No. 2. Replace relay if defective.

Automatic Transmissions

TOYOTA A-40D, A-42DL, A-43D, A-43DE & A-44DL (Cont.)

Fig. 11: Overdrive Relay Test Points

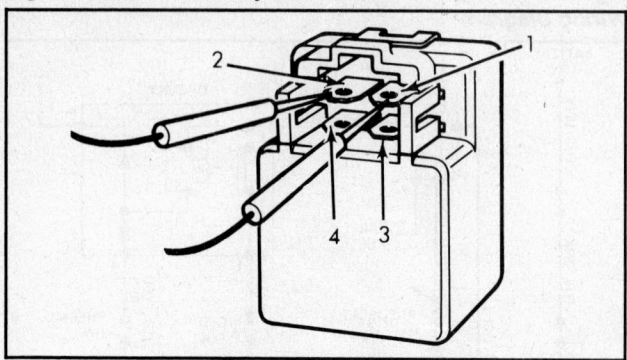

Overdrive Solenoid Test

Disconnect solenoid plug connector. Apply 12 volts to solenoid wire and listen for solenoid operation. Disconnect 12 volts source. Check solenoid resistance between terminal in plug connector and ground. Resistance should be 13 ohms.

Thermo Switch

Unplug thermo switch connector. Measure resistance between switch terminal and ground. There should be continuity below 109°F (43°C) and no continuity above 131°F (55°C).

Fig. 12: Pickup Overdrive Circuit Wiring Diagram

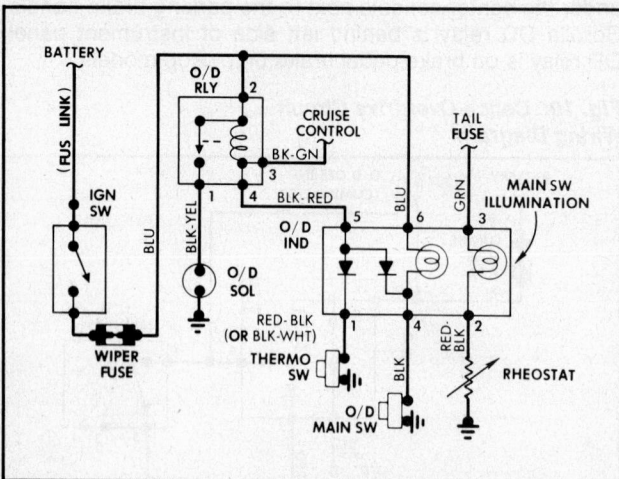

SERVICE (IN VEHICLE)

The following components can be removed from transmission with transmission installed in vehicle: oil pan, valve body assembly, throttle cable, parking pawl assembly, manual valve shaft oil seal, speedometer drive gear, rear oil seal, extension housing, speedometer driven gear, governor assembly, transmission solenoids, OD solenoid, speed sensor and rotor sensor. See TRANSMISSION DISASSEMBLY, COMPONENT DISASSEMBLY AND REASSEMBLY, AND TRANSMISSION REASSEMBLY in this article.

TRANSMISSION SOLENOIDS

**Removal & Installation
(A-43DE Transmission Only)**

Drain fluid. Remove oil pan, filler tube and gasket. Remove oil tubes. Unplug connectors from each

solenoid. Remove solenoid (and gaskets from No. 1 and 2 solenoids). DO NOT remove the 2 valve springs. To install solenoids, reverse removal procedure.

EXTENSION HOUSING & GOVERNOR/ROTOR SENSOR
Removal

1) Remove propeller shaft. Support transmission with a jack and raise slightly to remove weight from rear support. Disconnect speedometer cable. Remove speedometer driven gear. Remove speed sensor (A-43DE only).

2) Remove ground strap, exhaust hanger and rear support member. Remove extension housing. Remove rotor sensor (A-43DE only) or governor (all other models) from output shaft.

Installation

On A-43DE transmissions, install rotor sensor on output shaft, making sure key is installed in groove. To complete installation on all models, reverse removal procedure.

TORQUE CONVERTER

Converter Flushing

If transmission appears contaminated, thoroughly flush converter with transmission cleaner before reassembly. Clean outside of converter and case.

One-Way Clutch Test

1) With converter placed on work surface, insert One-Way Clutch Tester (09350-20013). Kit consists of 2 pieces: a turning tool and a stopper. Insert turning tool in inner race of one-way clutch, insert stopper to fit in notch of converter hub and other race of one-way clutch.

2) Clutch should lock when turned counterclockwise, but should turn freely when rotated clockwise. Torque required to turn clutch clockwise should be less than 22 INCH lbs. (2.5 N.m). If necessary, clean converter and retest clutch. Replace converter if clutch still fails test.

Converter Runout

Torque converter runout should be less than .012" (.30 mm). Drive plate runout should be less than .008" (.20 mm).

TRANSMISSION DISASSEMBLY

INPUT SHAFT END PLAY

Mount dial indicator on front of transmission case. Measure input shaft end play. End play should be .012-.035" (.30-.90 mm).

DISASSEMBLY

1) Remove torque converter. Remove solenoid retaining bolts and solenoid (except A-43DE). On A-43DE only, remove speedometer driven gear and speed sensor.

2) On all models, remove shift handle and neutral start switch. Remove front pump housing bolts. Pull oil pump assembly from transmission case using Puller (SST 09610-20012).

CAUTION: Do not damage the shaft bushing surface.

3) Grab oil pump by stator shaft and pull pump out of case. Do not lose bearing race behind pump.

TOYOTA A-40D, A-42DL, A-43D, A-43DE & A-44DL (Cont.)

Remove bellhousing retaining bolts (2 short, 4 long) and lift off bellhousing.

4) Remove speedometer driven gear housing (except A-43DE). On all models, remove extension housing and gasket. Remove speedometer drive gear and snap ring (except A-43DE).

5) On all except A-43DE, remove governor retaining bolt (if equipped). Pry up on governor retainer spring with a screwdriver and pull off governor assembly. Remove governor strainer if necessary.

6) On A-43DE only, remove rotor sensor and snap ring from output shaft.

7) On all models, remove oil pan retaining bolts. Remove pan by lifting case. DO NOT turn transmission over to remove pan as this will contaminate valve body with dirt. After removing oil pan, turn transmission over and remove oil tubes. Note installation position for reassembly reference.

8) On A-43DE only, unplug connector from No. 1, No. 2 and No. 3 solenoids. Remove grommet from transmission case. Pull solenoid wiring from case.

9) On all models, remove valve body attaching bolts. Valve body may have either 15 or 17 bolts. *See Fig. 13.* Carefully lift up valve body and disconnect throttle cable from throttle cam. Remove valve body from case. Hold throttle cable retainer with a 10 mm socket and pull cable from case.

Fig. 13: Removing Valve Body Bolts

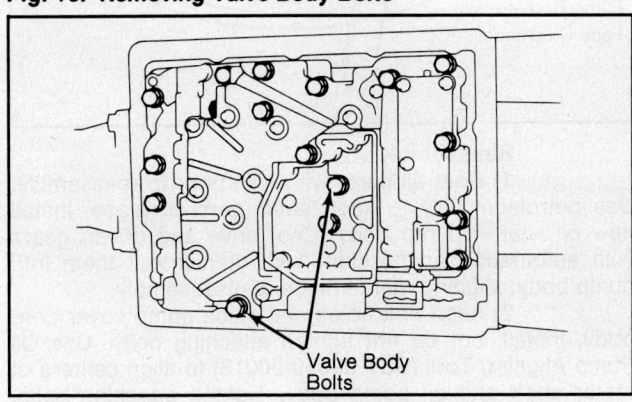

Valve Body Bolts

Van and Corolla is shown; other models are similar.

10) Remove accumulator pistons and springs from case by blowing compressed air through holes in case. *See Figs. 14 and 15.* Position a rag to catch piston when removing. Identify each accumulator piston and spring for reassembly reference.

11) Remove attaching bolts and parking lock pawl bracket. Remove lock rod after aligning lugs with manual valve lever. Remove parking pawl, pivot pin and spring. If necessary, pry manual shift lever shaft over to gain access to retaining pin. Drive out pin and remove shaft.

12) Stand transmission case upright with front of case facing up. Measure distance between top of case and clutch drum with Measuring Gauge (SST 09350-20013). Record reading for reassembly reference. *See Fig. 16.*

13) Lift out overdrive clutch assembly. Watch for bearings and races on both sides of assembly. Hold both sides of overdrive case and lift it from transmission case. Watch for bearings and races.

Fig. 14: Removing Accumulator Pistons and Springs (All Except A-40D)

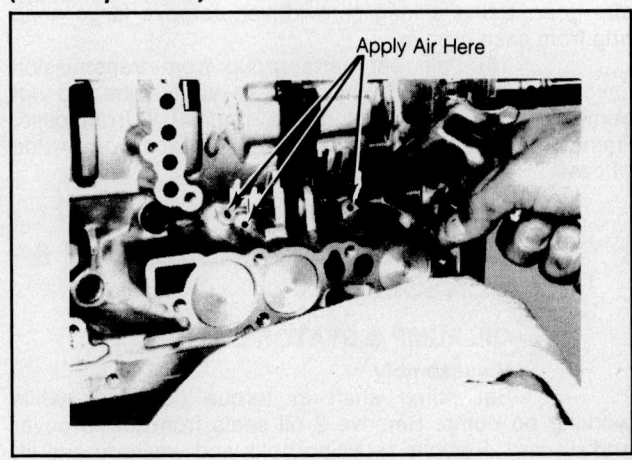

Apply Air Here

Fig. 15: Removing Accumulator Pistons and Springs (A-40D Transmission)

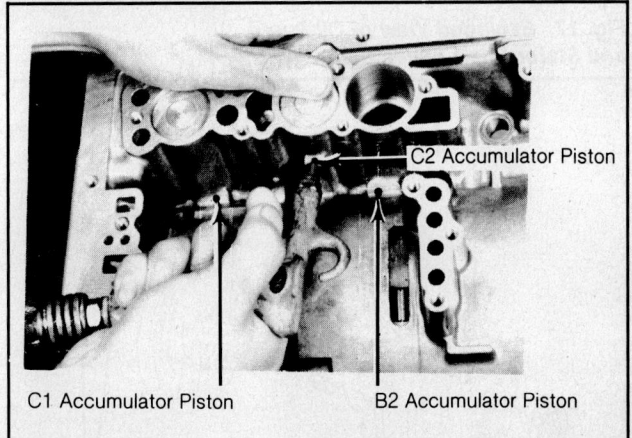

C2 Accumulator Piston

C1 Accumulator Piston

B2 Accumulator Piston

Apply compressed air at holes indicated.

Fig. 16: Measuring Case-to-Overdrive Clutch Drum Clearance

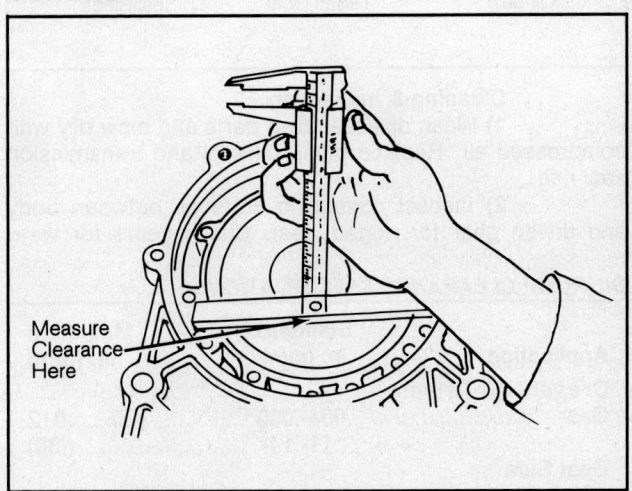

Measure Clearance Here

14) Grasp shaft and lift out front clutch assembly, bearings and races. Remove rear clutch from case. Remove 2 center support mounting bolts at valve body side of case.

Automatic Transmissions

TOYOTA A-40D, A-42DL, A-43D, A-43DE & A-44DL (Cont.)

15) Pull center support and sun gear shaft assembly from case. Watch for bearing race on end of sun gear. Using a long screwdriver, remove large snap ring from case groove.

16) Pull rear parts group from transmission case by intermediate shaft. If brake apply tube did not come out with rear parts group, remove it from case. Remove output shaft thrust bearing and race from inside of case.

COMPONENT DISASSEMBLY & REASSEMBLY

OIL PUMP & STATOR SHAFT

Disassembly

Set pump shaft in torque converter while working on pump. Remove 2 oil seals from pump cover and discard. Remove retaining bolts and washers and lift off pump cover. Remove large "O" ring from pump body. Mark drive and driven gears for reassembly reference and remove from pump body. Pry out front oil seal.

Fig. 17: Exploded View of Oil Pump and Stator Shaft Assembly

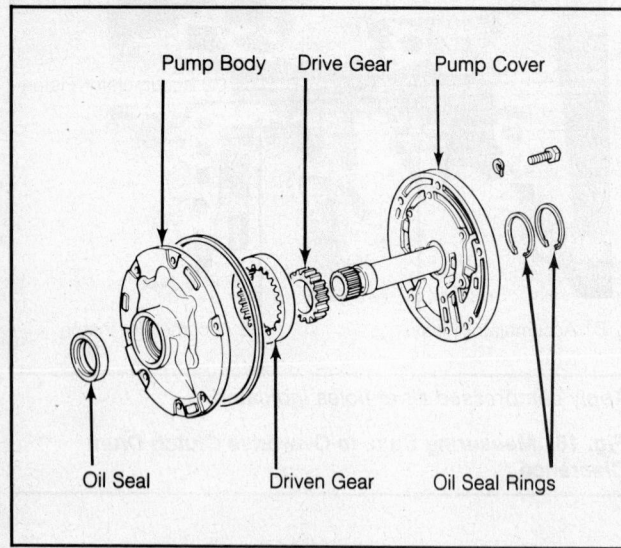

Pump Body   Drive Gear   Pump Cover

Oil Seal   Driven Gear   Oil Seal Rings

Cleaning & Inspection

1) Wash disassembled parts and blow dry with compressed air. Replace pump oil seal and transmission seal ring.

2) Inspect contacting surfaces between body and driven gear for ridged wear. Check gears for wear

OIL PUMP CLEARANCE SPECIFICATIONS

Application	Standard In. (mm)	Maximum In. (mm)
Cresent-to-Driven Gear	.004-.006 (.11-.14)	.012 (.30)
Gear Side Clearance	.0008-.002 (.02-.05)	.004 (.10)
Oil Pump-to-Body	.003-.006 (.07-.15)	.012 (.30)

and body crescent for damage. Check pump gear contacting surface on stator shaft for damage and wear.

3) With a feeler gauge, measure clearance between driven gear and oil pump body with gear pushed over to other side. If clearance exceeds maximum, replace pump.

4) Measure clearance between crescent and driven gear. Using a feeler gauge and straightedge, measure clearance between pump body face and top of gears. If clearance exceeds maximum, replace oil pump.

Fig. 18: Measuring Oil Pump Clearances

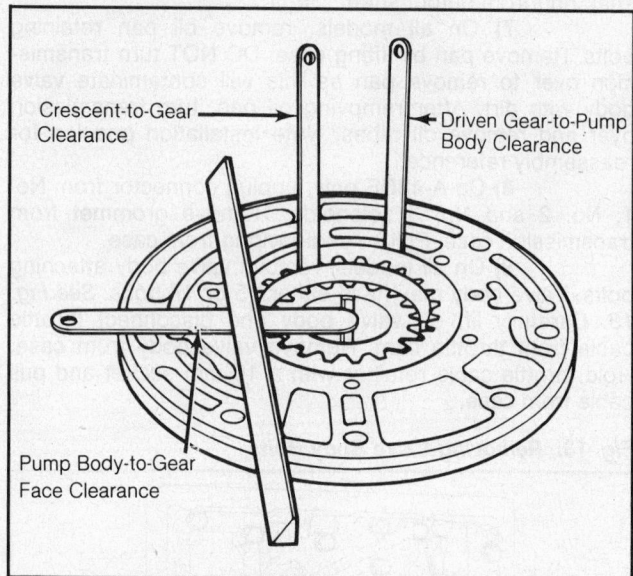

Crescent-to-Gear Clearance

Driven Gear-to-Pump Body Clearance

Pump Body-to-Gear Face Clearance

Reassembly

1) Coat all parts with ATF prior to reassembly. Use petroleum jelly to keep small parts in place. Install new oil seal in pump body. Coat drive and driven gears with automatic transmission fluid, then install them into pump body, aligning marks made at disassembly.

2) Align bolt holes and place pump cover onto body. Install, but do not tighten attaching bolts. Use Oil Pump Aligning Tool (SST 09350-20013) to align centers of stator shaft and oil pump body. Tighten attaching bolts. Install 2 new oil seal rings on pump cover.

CAUTION: Ensure oil seal ring ends are properly over-lapped.

3) With pump body and cover assembled, check drive gear with a screwdriver to ensure it rotates freely. Lubricate and install "O" ring on pump body.

OVERDRIVE CASE & BRAKE

NOTE: **New discs must be soaked in ATF at least 2 hours.**

Disassembly

1) Remove thrust bearing and race from overdrive case. Pry large snap ring from case. Lift out clutch flange, clutch discs, plates and cushion plate. Retain in correct order for reassembly.

2) Remove ring gear. Pry thrust washer from ring gear. Remove thrust bearings and races from case and note order and position for reassembly. Compress piston and remove snap ring, spring retainer and return springs.

3) Remove brake piston from case by applying compressed air. *See Fig. 19.* Remove and discard oil seal rings from case and "O" rings from piston.

Fig. 19: Using Compressed Air to Remove Piston from Overdrive Clutch Case

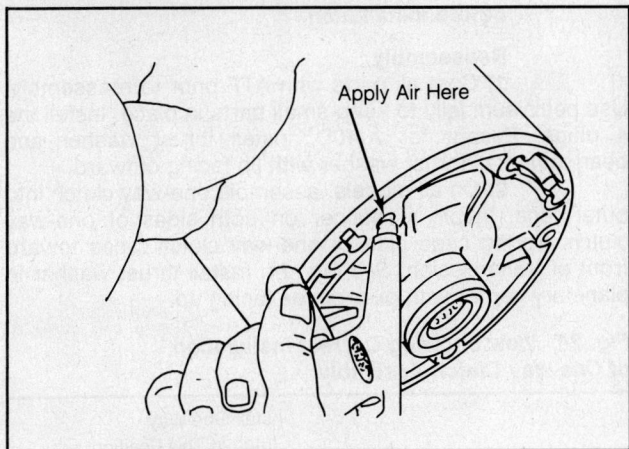

Cleaning & Inspection
1) Wash all parts (except discs) thoroughly in clean solvent. Air dry parts with compressed air.

2) Inspect all parts for wear or damage and replace as necessary. Inspect clutch plates, discs and flange for signs of burning. Check piston return springs for wear, damage and collapsed coils.

Fig. 20: Exploded View of Overdrive Case and Brake

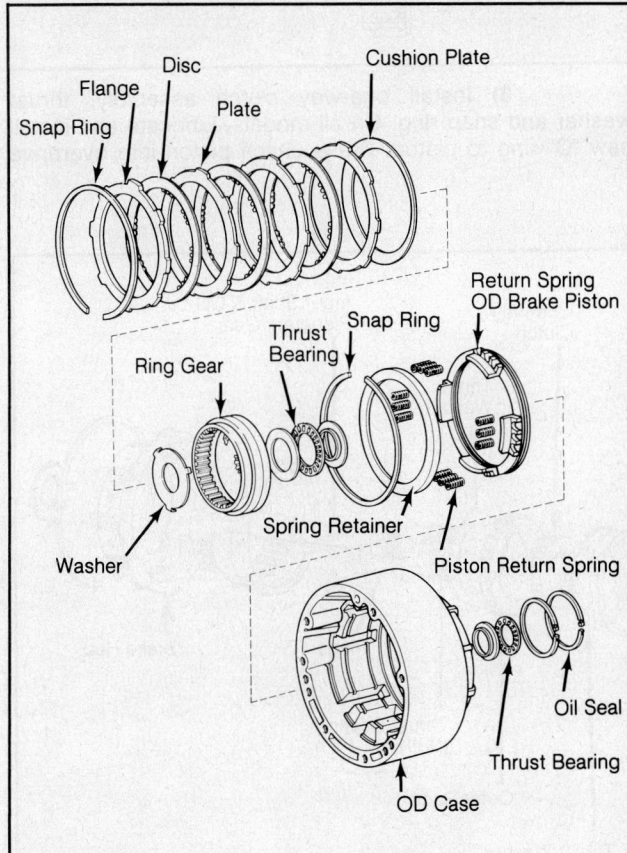

Reassembly
1) Coat all parts with ATF prior to reassembly. Use petroleum jelly to keep small parts in place. Lubricate and install oil seal rings on overdrive case ensure ring ends are properly overlapped. Install new "O" rings on brake piston. Carefully install piston (cup side up) into case. Save thrust washer for installation when transmission is reassembled.

2) Position return springs into pockets of clutch piston. Install spring retainer over springs. Compress return springs and install retaining snap ring, making sure snap ring gap is not aligned with a slot in housing.

3) Install bearing and races on ring gear in same positions as before disassembly. *See Fig. 21.* Install ring gear assembly into clutch case.

Fig. 21: View of Ring Gear Showing Correct Installation of Bearing and Races

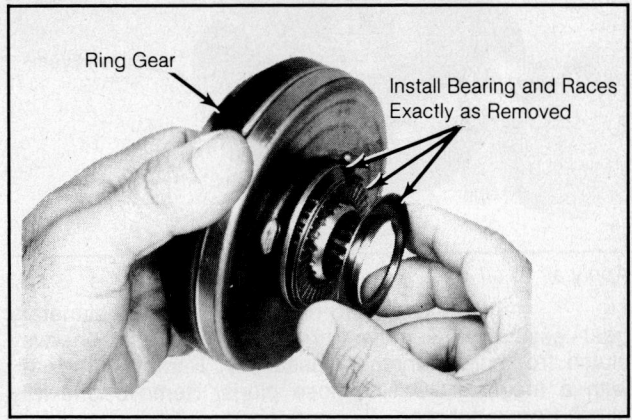

4) Install cushion plate into clutch case with beveled side down. Install clutch pack into case starting with an externally splined plate and alternating plates and discs. *See Fig. 20..* Install snap ring. Do not align snap ring end with slot in case.

5) Using a feeler gauge, measure clutch pack clearance between flange and snap ring. Thrust washer left over will be installed as transmission is assembled.

OVERDRIVE CASE CLUTCH PACK CLEARANCE SPECIFICATIONS

Application	Standard In. (mm)	Maximum In. (mm)
A-40D & A-43DE	.014-.063	.083
	(.35-1.60)	(2.1)
A-42DL	.034-.073	.....
	(.85-1.85)	.....
A-43D & A-44DL	.048-.91	.....
	(1.22-2.30)	.....

OVERDRIVE INPUT SHAFT & CLUTCH
Disassembly
1) Remove thrust bearings and races from clutch side by hand. Note position of races. *See Fig. 23.* Pry thrust washer from planetary gear side with a screwdriver. On A-40D, remove snap ring and hub from overdrive clutch assembly.

Automatic Transmissions

TOYOTA A-40D, A-42DL, A-43D, A-43DE & A-44DL (Cont.)

2) On all models, pull overdrive clutch assembly from input shaft. Remove thrust bearing and race (except A-40D). Remove snap ring and hub from overdrive clutch assembly. Remove thin snap ring, flange disc and plate.

3) Compress piston return springs and remove snap ring. Remove spring retainer and 18 springs. Assemble overdrive clutch on oil pump and blow out piston with compressed air. *See Fig. 22.* Remove overdrive clutch from oil pump. Remove clutch piston "O" rings.

Fig. 22: Removing Overdrive Direct Clutch

Apply air to oil hole.

4) Remove snap ring from overdrive planetary gear assembly. Remove thrust washers and one-way clutch from planetary gear assembly. Remove plugs (4) with a magnet. DO NOT lose plugs. Remove one-way clutch from outer race.

Cleaning & Inspection

Thoroughly clean all parts and inspect them for wear and damage. Check clutch plates for signs of

burning. Shake piston to make sure check ball is free. Apply low-pressure compressed air to check that valve does not leak. Replace parts as necessary.

NOTE: Do not let discs dry out. Soak new clutch plates and discs in ATF for at least 2 hours before installation.

Reassembly

1) Coat all parts with ATF prior to reassembly. Use petroleum jelly to keep small parts in place. Install the 4 plugs. Except for A-40D, install thrust washer and bearing. Install thrust washer with lip facing outward.

2) On all models, assemble one-way clutch into outer race. Install a retainer on both sides of one-way clutch. Spring cage side of one-way clutch faces toward front of transmission. *See Fig. 24.* Install thrust washer in planetary carrier with oil grooves facing up.

Fig. 24: View Showing Correct Installation of One-Way Clutch Assembly

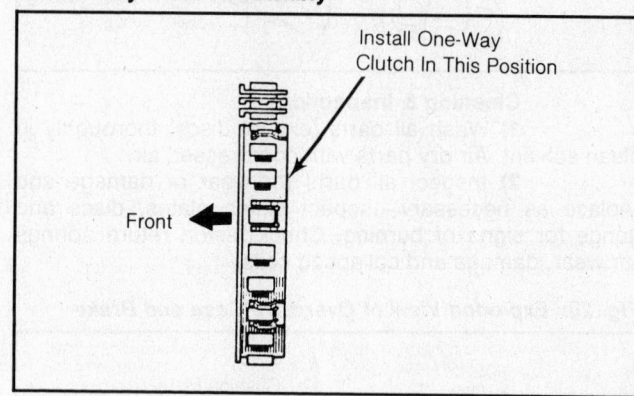

3) Install one-way clutch assembly, thrust washer and snap ring. On all models, lubricate and install new "O" ring to piston. Press clutch piston into overdrive

Fig. 23: Exploded View of Overdrive Input Shaft and Clutch

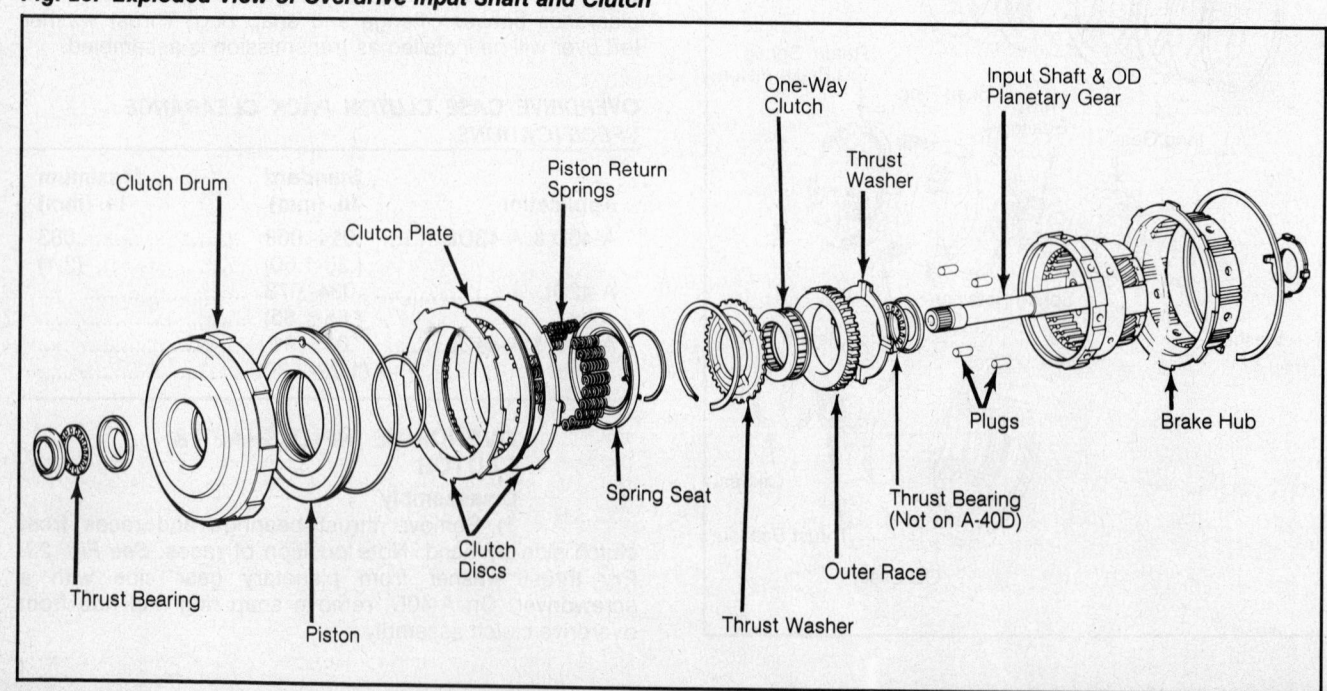

TOYOTA A-40D, A-42DL, A-43D, A-43DE & A-44DL (Cont.)

clutch drum with cup side up. Position return springs into pockets of piston. Install spring seat over springs.

4) Compress springs and seat and install retaining snap ring. Do not align snap ring gap with spring seat claw. Install clutch plates and discs into clutch drum in reverse order as removed. Do not install thin retaining snap ring on A-40D and A-43DE. Install thinner snap ring before measuring piston travel on other models.

5) To check piston travel, temporarily install overdrive clutch hub and outer snap ring. Install front clutch drum on oil pump body. Mount a dial indicator so indicator tip touches top of clutch piston. See Fig. 25.

Fig. 25: Checking Clutch C0 Piston Travel

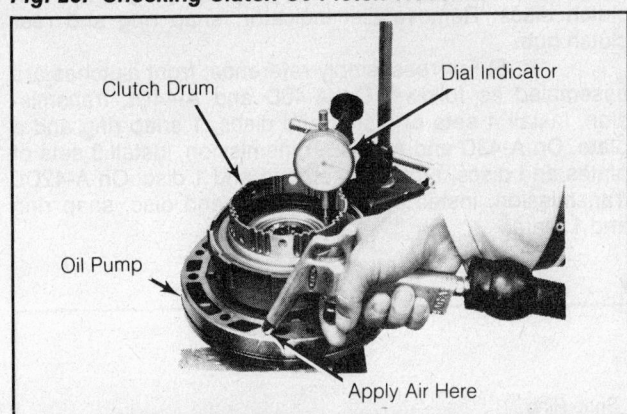

6) Apply pressure to oil hole in oil pump and read piston travel on dial indicator. Use 57-114 psi (4-8 kg/cm²) air pressure to apply piston. If stroke exceeds limit, clutch pack is probably worn. If stroke is less than specified, parts may be assembled incorrectly or there may be excess ATF on discs.

OVERDRIVE INPUT CLUTCH PACK CLEARANCE

Application	Standard In. (mm)	Maximum In. (mm)
A-40D &A-43DE	.0610-.0898 (1.55-2.28)	.0898 (2.28)
A-42DL, A-43D & A-44DL	.0579-.0898 (1.47-2.28)	

7) Remove dial indicator. On Celica, Cressida and Supra models, remove overdrive clutch outer snap ring and hub to install thinner snap ring. Check that snap ring ends are not aligned with cut-outs.

8) Install outer hub and outer snap ring. Check that snap ring ends are not aligned with cut-outs. Assemble overdrive clutch drum and overdrive planetary gear. Mesh hub with disc, twisting hub as necessary.

9) Check operation of one-way clutch. Hold clutch drum and turn input shaft. Input shaft should turn freely clockwise and lock counterclockwise.

CAUTION: Keep thrust washer, thrust bearings and races together.

FRONT CLUTCH
Disassembly
1) Remove thrust bearing and races from both sides of clutch. Note position of races. Use extension

housing as a work stand for remainder of disassembly. Remove snap ring and lift out front and rear clutches together. Remove thrust bearings and races.

2) Remove clutch plate on A-40D and A-42DL transmissions or disc on A-43D and A-43DE transmissions. Remove thin snap ring and noting number and placement, pull out remaining clutch plates and discs. Using a compressor tool, compress piston return spring and remove snap ring. Take out spring retainer and return springs (18).

3) Assemble clutch drum onto overdrive clutch case. Remove piston by applying compressed air to case oil hole. See Fig. 26. Remove "O" rings from clutch piston.

Fig. 26: Removing Front Clutch Piston Using Compressed Air

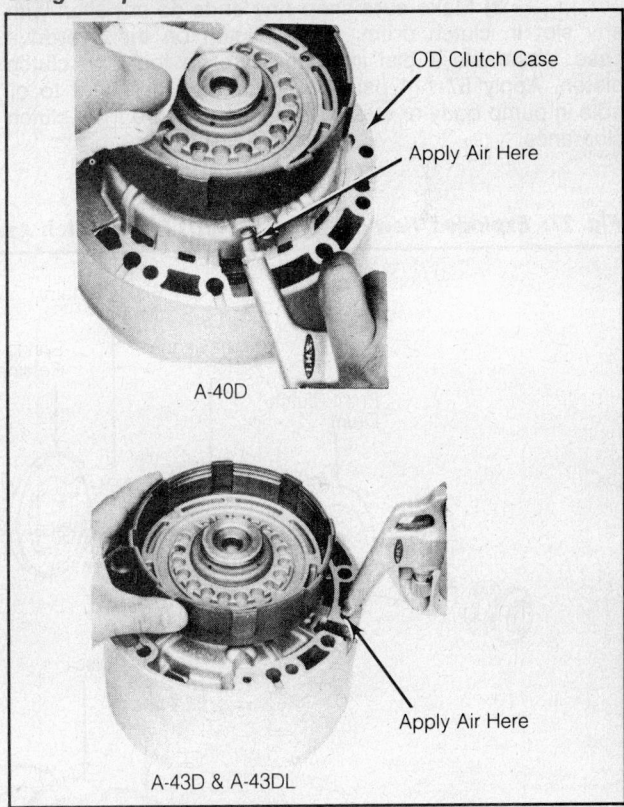

Cleaning & Inspection
1) Clean all parts and inspect for wear and damage. Check clutch plates and discs for signs of burning and replace as necessary.

NOTE: Soak new clutch plates in ATF for at least 2 hours before installation.

2) Check input shaft bearing and bushing contacting surfaces for damage, excessive wear and burning. Insert input shaft into torque converter and ensure it slides in smoothly without being loose.

3) Inspect toothed parts of clutch drum and clutch hubs for wear and damage. Inspect piston and clutch drum sliding surfaces for burning.

4) Check return springs for wear, damage or collapsed coils. Check for uniform spring length and replace spring if one is noticeably shorter than others. Replace any worn or damaged springs.

5) Inspect check ball in clutch piston for sticking by shaking piston. Apply compressed air from inner side of piston and inspect check ball for air leaks.

Reassembly

1) Lubricate and install new "O" ring onto clutch piston. Carefully install piston into clutch drum. Position piston return springs and seat on piston. Compress springs and install snap ring. Snap ring gap should not be aligned with spring retainer claw (if claw present).

2) Blow excess ATF off of clutch discs and plates with LOW pressure compressed air. Install ALL clutch discs and plates into drum without thin (inner) snap ring. Assembly always starts with a plate. Install rear clutch hub and outer snap ring.

3) Make sure snap ring ends do not align with any slot in clutch drum. Install clutch on the overdrive case. Assemble a dial indicator with tip touching clutch piston. Apply 57-114 psi (4-8 kg/cm²) air pressure to oil hole in pump body or overdrive case. Measure front clutch clearance.

FRONT CLUTCH PACK CLEARANCE SPECIFICATIONS

Application	In. (mm)
A-40D	.0646-.1047 (1.64-2.66)
A-42DL	.0465-.0921 (1.18-2.34)
A-43DE	
Cressida	.0724-.1126 (1.84-2.86)
Supra	.055-.063 (1.40-1.60)
A-43D	.0520-.1047 (1.32-2.34)
A-44DL	.0520-.0795 (1.32-2.02)

4) If clearance exceeds limit, clutch pack may be worn. If stroke is too short, component may be assembled improperly or there may be excess ATF on clutch discs. Remove dial indicator, snap ring and rear clutch hub.

5) For reassembly reference, front clutches are assembled as follows: On A-40D and A-44DL transmission, install 4 sets of plates and discs, 1 snap ring and a plate. On A-43D and A-43DE transmission, install 3 sets of plates and discs, a plate, snap ring and 1 disc. On A-42DL transmission, install 3 sets of plates and disc, snap ring and 1 plate.

Fig. 27: Exploded View of Pickup (A-43D) Front Clutch Assembly

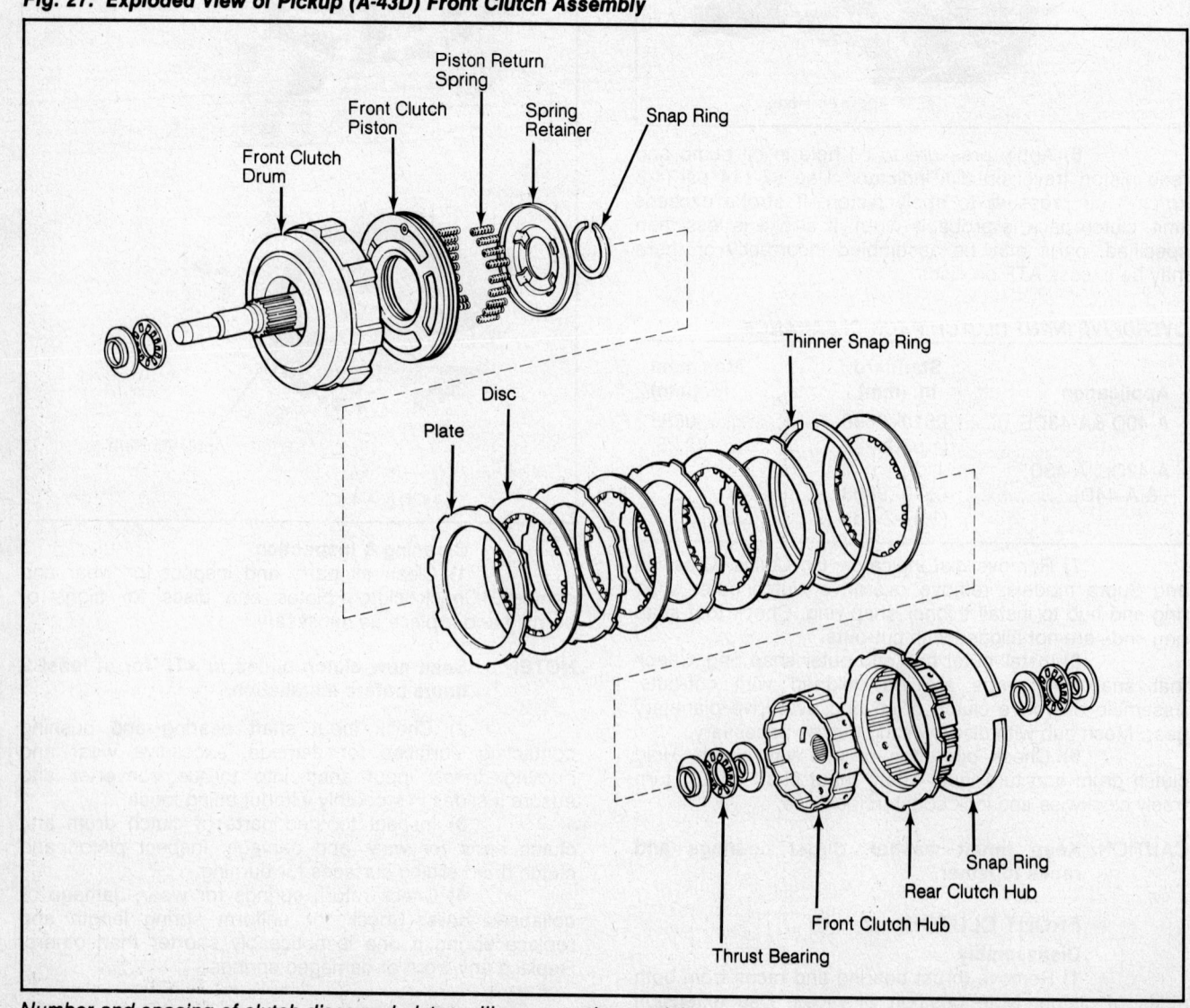

Number and spacing of clutch discs and plates will vary on other models

TOYOTA A-40D, A-42DL, A-43D, A-43DE & A-44DL (Cont.)

6) Coat inner thrust bearing and races with petroleum jelly to hold them in place and install. Make sure lip of race faces toward front of clutch body. Install front clutch hub, rear clutch hub and snap ring. Check that snap ring ends do not align with slot in clutch drum.

7) Set remaining thrust bearings and races aside for installation when transmission is reassembled.

REAR CLUTCH
Disassembly
1) Remove snap ring and lift clutch flange, clutch discs and clutch plates from rear clutch drum. Compress piston return spring with compressor tool and remove snap ring. Lift out piston, springs and spring retainer.

2) Assemble clutch drum on center support. Apply compressed air to oil hole(s) in center support and remove rear clutch piston (inner and outer pistons on A-40D) from clutch drum. *See Fig. 28.* Remove and discard "O" rings from piston(s).

Fig. 28: Using Compressed Air to Remove Rear Clutch Inner and Outer Pistons

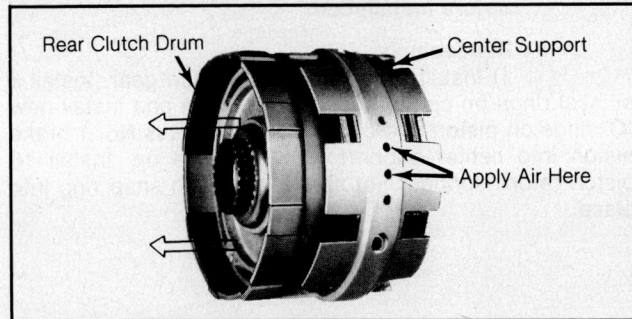

Rear Clutch Drum — Center Support — Apply Air Here

Cleaning & Inspection
1) Thoroughly clean all parts and inspect them for wear and damage. Inspect toothed parts and piston sliding surfaces of clutch drum for wear or damage.

2) Inspect clutch plates and discs for signs of burning. Check plate and disc splines (teeth) for wear and damage.

3) Inspect clutch pistons for wear and damage. Shake pistons and make sure check balls are free. Apply air pressure to check balls and check for leakage. Check piston return springs for even length.

NOTE: Do not let discs dry out. Soak new clutch plates and discs in ATF for at least 2 hours before installation.

Reassembly
1) Lubricate and install "O" rings on pistons. Insert pistons carefully into clutch drum, being carefull not to damage "O" rings.

2) Place piston return springs (18) and spring retainer on piston. Compress springs and install snap ring.

3) Install clutch plates, clutch discs and clutch flange into drum in correct sequence. *See Fig. 29.* Clutch packs on all models except Corolla are installed as shown in *Fig. 29.* Clutch pack on Corolla (A-42DL) are assembled as follows: plate, disc, plate, plate, disc and flange. Install clutch pack snap ring.

NOTE: Install clutch flange with flat end facing down.

4) Install rear clutch onto center support. Apply compressed air pressure of 57-114 psi (4-8 kg/cm²) to oil hole in center support and measure travel with a dial indicator.

Fig. 29: Exploded View of Rear Clutch Assembly

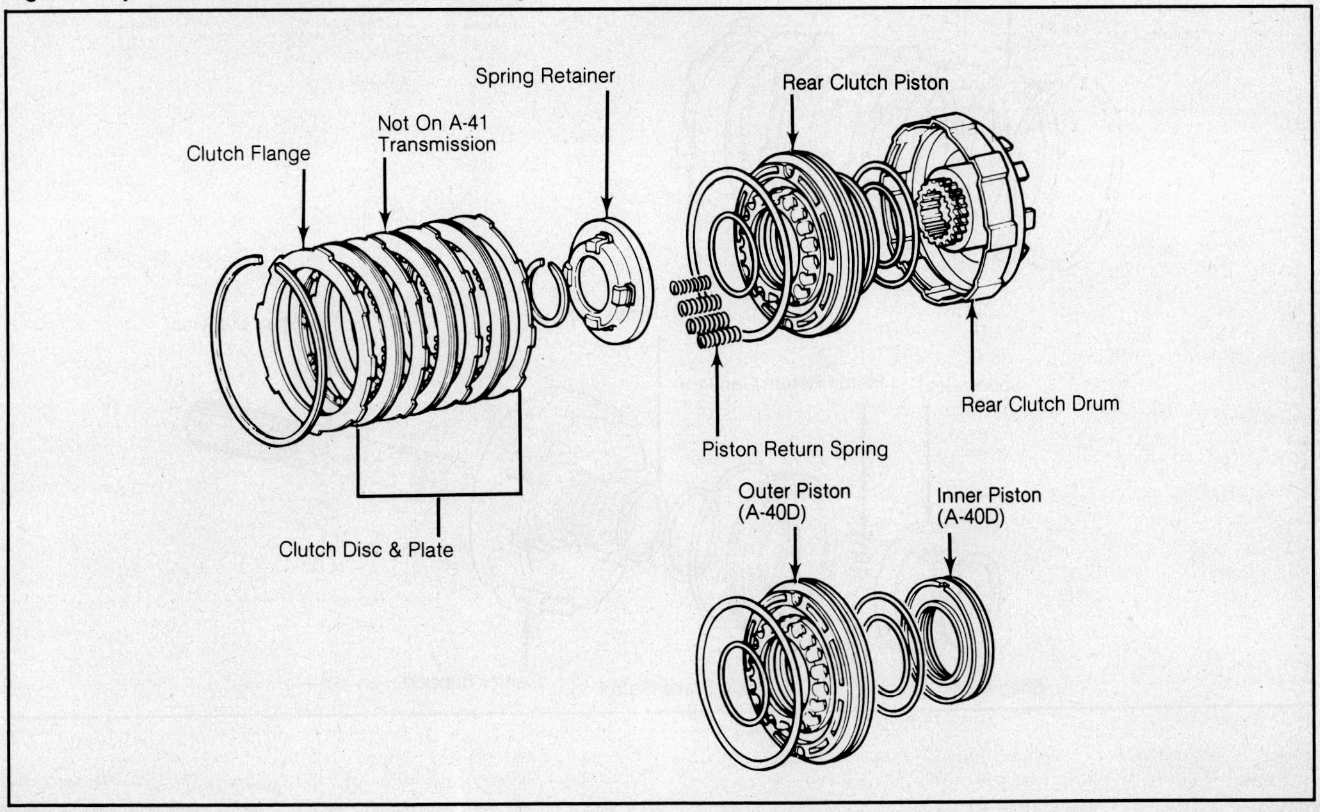

Spring Retainer — Rear Clutch Piston — Not On A-41 Transmission — Clutch Flange — Clutch Disc & Plate — Piston Return Spring — Rear Clutch Drum — Outer Piston (A-40D) — Inner Piston (A-40D)

REAR CLUTCH PISTON STROKE SPECIFICATIONS

Application	In. (mm)
A-40D	.0476-.0752 (1.21-1.91)
A-42DL	.0366-.0717 (.93-1.82)
A-43DE	
Cressida	.0512-.0358 (.91-1.30)
Supra	.0488-0835 (1.24-2.12)
A-43D & A-44DL	.0417-.0843 (1.06-2.14)

5) Excessive travel indicates worn clutch pack. If travel is below specifications, components may be misassembled or there may be excess ATF on clutch discs.

Fig. 30: Checking Rear Clutch Piston Travel

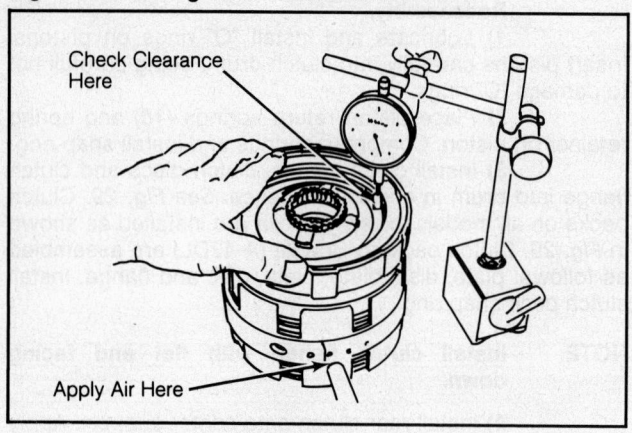

CENTER SUPPORT ASSEMBLY

Disassembly (A-40D)

1) Remove snap ring from end of planetary sun gear. Pull sun gear from center support.

2) Remove retaining snap ring, then lift flange, discs and plates for No. 1 brake from center support. Note order for reassembly reference. Compress piston return springs (16) and remove snap ring. Remove return springs and spring seat from center support.

3) Using compressed air, remove No. 1 brake piston from center support by blowing in oil holes in center support. Remove "O" rings from piston. Remove oil seal rings from center suppport. Remove oil seal rings from sun gear.

Cleaning & Inspection

Inspect all parts for wear or damage. Check plates and discs for signs of burning. Check free length of return springs. Replace any spring that is noticably shorter than others.

NOTE: **Do not let discs dry out. Soak new clutch plates and discs in ATF for at least 2 hours before installation.**

Reassembly

1) Install 2 oil seal rings on sun gear. Install 3 oil seal rings on center support. Lubricate and install new "O" rings on piston and center support. Press No. 1 brake piston into center support with cup side up. Install 16 piston return springs. Set spring seat with snap ring into place.

Fig. 31: Exploded View Of Center Support Assembly (A-40D Transmission)

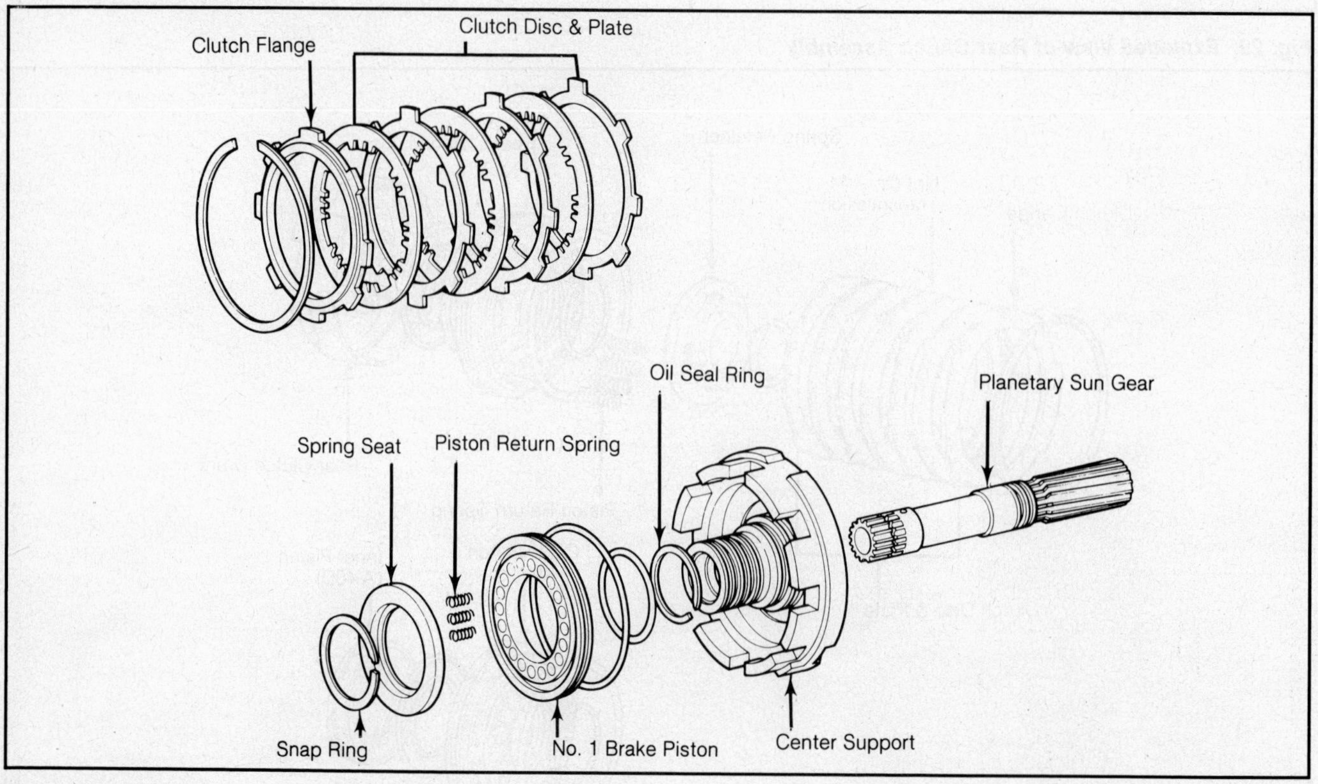

TOYOTA A-40D, A-42DL, A-43D, A-43DE & A-44DL (Cont.)

2) Compress springs. Install snap ring with screwdriver. Use low pressure compressed air to blow ATF from discs. Install No. 1 brake plates, discs and flange. Install in order noted during disassembly. *See Fig. 31.* Install flange with flat end down.

3) Install snap ring in center support. Check that snap ring ends are not aligned with a cut-out. Install dial indicator to measure piston stroke. Apply compressed

air to piston oil hole at 57-114 psi (4-8 kg/cm²) and measure stroke. Stroke should be .039-.047" (1.0-1.2 mm). Maximum stroke is .051" (1.3 mm).

4) Excessive travel indicates worn clutch pack. If travel is below specifications, components may be misassembled or there could be excess ATF on clutch discs. Assemble center support and sun gear shaft. Install snap ring on end of sun gear shaft.

Fig. 32: Exploded View of Center Support Assembly (A-42DL, A-43D, A-43DE & A-44DL Transmissions)

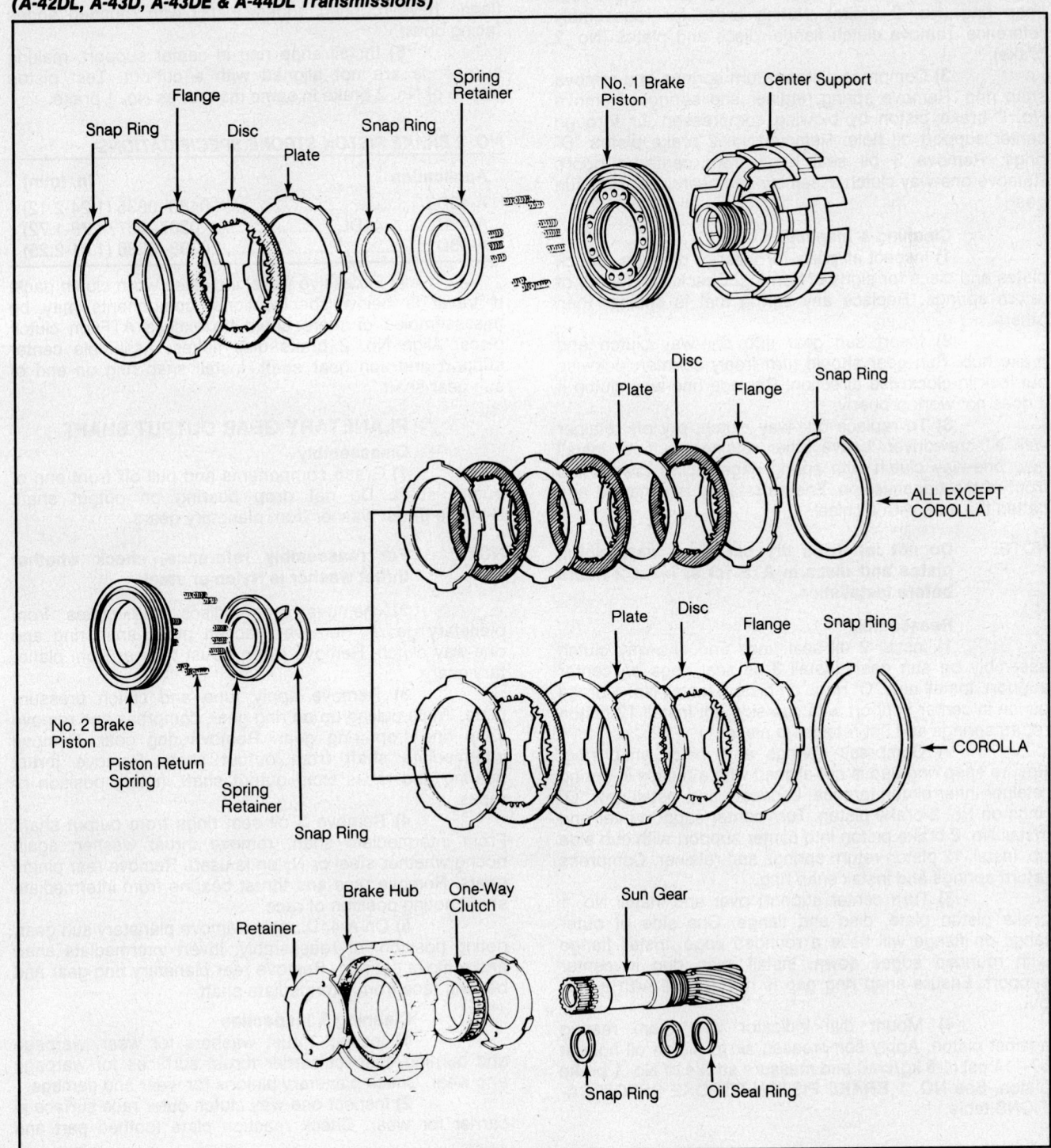

Automatic Transmissions

TOYOTA A-40D, A-42DL, A-43D, A-43DE & A-44DL (Cont.)

Disassembly
(All Other Transmissions)

1) Remove snap ring from end of sun gear shaft. Pull center support assembly from shaft. Remove snap ring from front of center support assembly. Remove clutch flange, disc and plate (No. 1 brake). Compress piston return springs and remove snap ring.

2) Remove spring retainer and 12 springs. Blow compressed air through center support oil hole to remove No. 1 brake piston. Remove No. 1 piston "O" rings. Turn center support assembly over and remove rear snap ring (No. 2 brake). Noting order for reassembly reference, remove clutch flange, discs and plates (No. 2 brake).

3) Compress piston return springs and remove snap ring. Remove spring retainer and springs. Remove No. 2 brake piston by blowing compressed air through center support oil hole. Remove No. 2 brake piston "O" rings. Remove 3 oil seal rings from center support. Remove one-way clutch assembly and seal rings from sun gear.

Cleaning & Inspection

1) Inspect all parts for wear or damage. Check plates and discs for signs of burning. Check free length of return springs. Replace any spring that is shorter than others.

2) Insert sun gear into one-way clutch and brake hub. Sun gear should turn freely counterclockwise but lock in clockwise direction. Replace one-way clutch if it does not work properly.

3) To replace one-way clutch, pry off retainer with a screwdriver. Leave other retainer on hub. Install new one-way clutch with spring cage facing toward the front of the transmission. Ensure retainer is centered and flatten the ears with a chisel.

NOTE: Do not let discs dry out. Soak new clutch plates and discs in ATF for at least 2 hours before installation.

Reassembly

1) Install 2 oil seal rings and one-way clutch assembly on sun gear. Install 3 oil seal rings on center support. Install new "O" rings on piston. Install No. 1 brake piston in center support with cup side up. Install 12 piston return springs and set retainer in place.

2) Compress springs and install snap ring. Ensure snap ring gap is not aligned with a recess in spring retainer inner circumference. Lubricate and install new "O" rings on No. 2 brake piston. Turn center support over and install No. 2 brake piston into center support with cup side up. Install 12 piston return springs and retainer. Compress return springs and install snap ring.

3) Turn center support over and install No. 1 brake piston plate, disc and flange. One side of outer tangs on flange will have a rounded edge. Install flange with rounded edges down. Install snap ring in center support. Ensure snap ring gap is not aligned with a cut-out.

4) Mount dial indicator with stem resting against piston. Apply compressed air to piston oil hole at 57-114 psi (4-8 kg/cm²) and measure stroke of No. 1 brake piston. See NO. 1 BRAKE PISTON STROKE SPECIFICATIONS table.

NO. 1 BRAKE PISTON STROKE SPECIFICATIONS

Application	In. (mm)
A-43DE	.037-.068 (.95-1.73)
All Others	.0228-.0512 (.58-1.30)

5) Excessive travel indicates worn clutch pack. If travel is below specifications, components may be misassembled or there could be excess ATF on clutch discs. Turn center support over and install No. 2 brake plates, disc and flange in order removed. If tangs on flange have rounded edges, install with rounded edges facing down.

6) Install snap ring in center support, making sure ends are not aligned with a cut-out. Test piston stroke of No. 2 brake in same manner as No. 1 brake.

NO. 2 BRAKE PISTON STROKE SPECIFICATIONS

Application	In. (mm)
A-43DE	.0488-.0835 (1.24-2.12)
A-42DL & A-44DL	.0307-.0677 (.78-1.72)
A-43D	.0398-.0886 (1.01-2.25)

7) Excessive travel indicates worn clutch pack. If travel is below specifications, components may be misassembled or there could be excess ATF on clutch discs. Align No. 2 brake disc flukes. Assemble center support and sun gear shaft. Install snap ring on end of sun gear shaft.

PLANETARY GEAR OUTPUT SHAFT
Disassembly

1) Grasp components and pull off front end of output shaft. Do not drop bearing on output shaft. Remove thrust washer from planetary gears.

NOTE: For reassembly reference, check whether thrust washer is Nylon or steel.

2) Remove brake discs and plates from planetary gears. Remove reaction plate, snap ring and one-way clutch. Remove nylon thrust washer from planetary gears.

3) Remove apply tube and clutch pressure plate. While pulling up on ring gear, compress and remove snap ring from ring gear. Remove ring gear. Remove intermediate shaft from output shaft. Remove thrust bearing and races from output shaft, noting position of races.

4) Remove 3 oil seal rings from output shaft. From intermediate shaft, remove thrust washer, again noting whether steel or Nylon is used. Remove rear pinion gears. Remove race and thrust bearing from intermediate shaft, noting position of race.

5) On A-44DL only, remove planetary sun gear, noting position for reassembly. Invert intermediate shaft and remove set ring. Remove rear planetary ring gear and bearing race from intermediate shaft.

Cleaning & Inspection

1) Inspect thrust washers for wear, warpage and burning. Inspect carrier thrust surfaces for warpage and wear. Check planetary pinions for wear and damage.

2) Inspect one-way clutch outer race surface in carrier for wear. Check reaction plate toothed part and

TOYOTA A-40D, A-42DL, A-43D, A-43DE & A-44DL (Cont.)

Fig. 33: Exploded View of Output Shaft and Planetary Gears

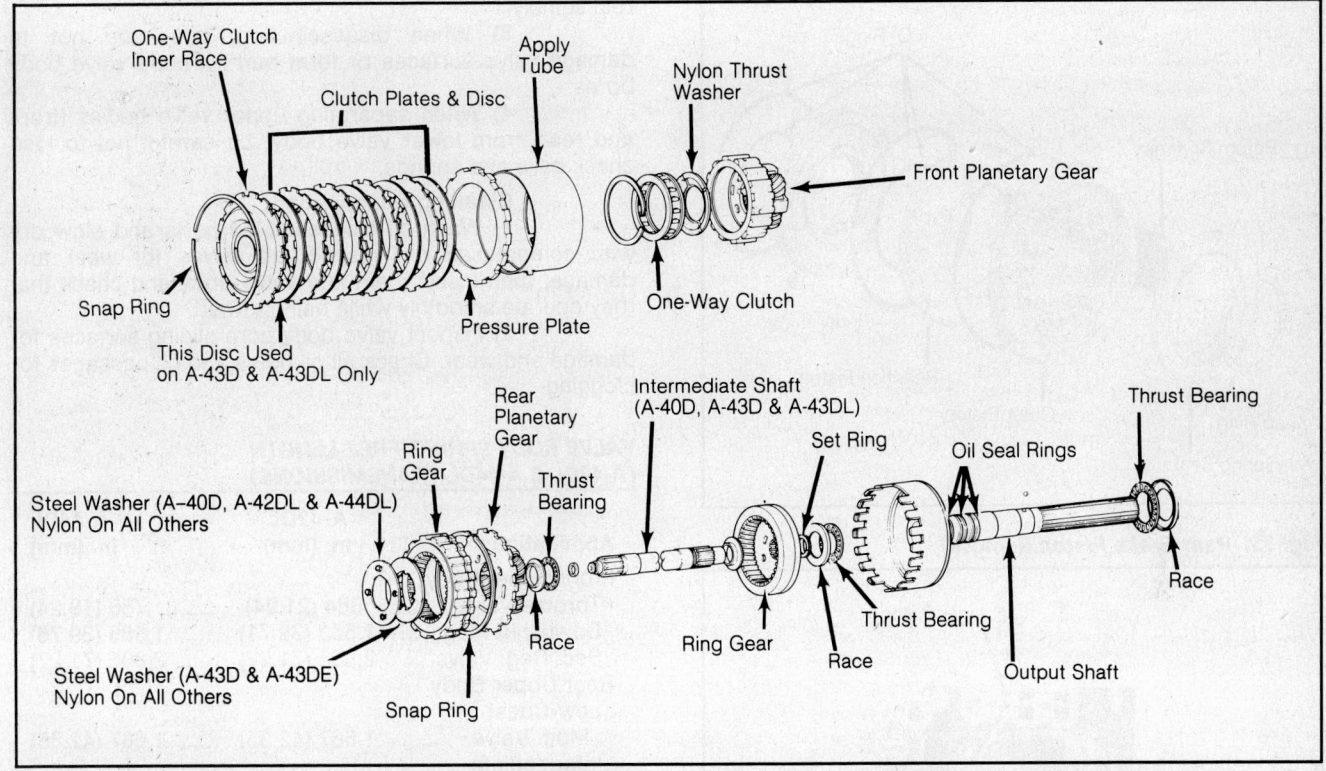

sliding surface for wear and damage. Check one-way clutch sliding surface or reaction plate for wear and damage.

NOTE: **Do not let discs dry out. Soak new clutch plates and discs in ATF for at least 2 hours before installation.**

Reassembly

1) Slip thrust bearing race and rear planetary ring gear onto shaft with exterior splines up. Install set ring on intermediate shaft. Turn over intermediate shaft and install thrust bearing and race.

2) Install pinion gear assembly thrust washer on rear planetary carrier (nylon washer on A-40D, A-42DL and A-44DL, steel on others). Install washer with lugs down, fitting into rear planetary carrier. Make sure lug shapes match opening on plate. Install 3 oil seal rings on output shaft.

3) Using extension housing as an assembly stand, install thrust bearing and race on output shaft. Hold race cup toward bearing. Install intermediate shaft assembly in output shaft. Install rear planetary carrier in output shaft. Slide into place and make sure lugs interlock.

4) On A-44DL only, install planetary sun gear. Install gear with non-splined portion of inner diameter facing up.

5) Install snap ring on front planetary ring gear. Align ends of snap ring with wide gap between teeth. Install ring gear on shaft and while pushing down on ring gear, squeeze ends of snap ring and install into groove. When snap ring is fully seated, gap is one lug wide.

6) Install nylon thrust washer in front planetary gear. Face lugs down and match them with slots in back of planetary gear. Install one-way clutch into outer race with spring cage toward front. Install snap ring.

7) Install one-way clutch into outer race, facing spring cage toward front. *See Fig. 24.* Temporarily install reaction plate on planetary gear and check clutch operation. On A-40D transmission, planetary gear should rotate freely clockwise and lock when turned counterclockwise. On all other transmissions, planet gear will rotate counterclockwise and lock in clockwise direction.

8) Remove reaction plate. Install thrust washer on front planetary gear (Nylon on A-43D and A-43DE, steel on all others). Match lugs with planetary carrier while installing. Hold washer in place with petroleum jelly for later assembly.

9) Install front planetary gear assembly on intermediate shaft. Make sure pinion gears mesh fully with ring gear. Install pressure plate with flat surface toward intermediate shaft.

10) Install No. 3 brake clutch pack discs and plates in same order as in removal. Assembly starts with a disc. Keep inner race, apply tube, thrust bearing and race together for installation when transmission is reassembled.

REAR BRAKE PISTON

Disassembly

1) Compress piston return springs and remove snap ring. Remove spring retainer and return springs. Position transmission with front opening facing down.

2) Place shop rags under rear brake piston. Using 2 air guns, blow SIMULTANEOUSLY through brake cylinder holes and remove inner piston, outer piston and brake reaction sleeve as a unit. *See Fig. 35.*

Fig. 34: Exploded View of Rear Brake Piston Assembly

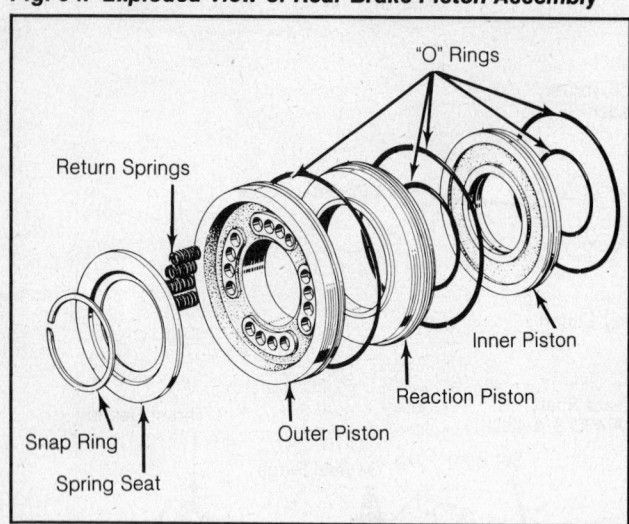

Fig. 35: Rear Brake Piston Removal

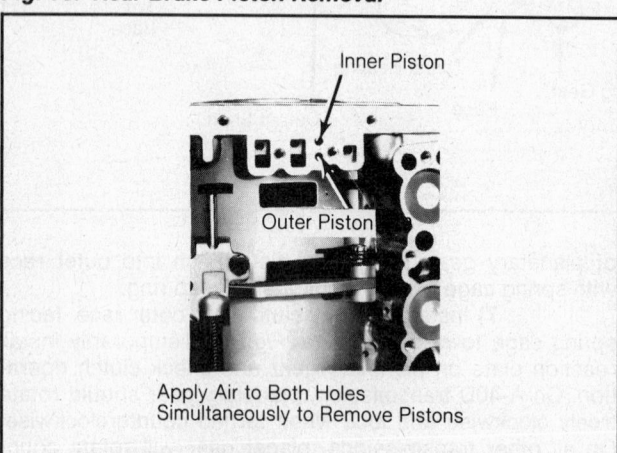

Apply Air to Both Holes
Simultaneously to Remove Pistons

Cleaning & Inspection

Wash all parts in clean solvent and blow dry with compressed air. Inspect piston and reaction sleeve for scoring, wear or other damage. Check return springs for uniform height and cracked or broken coils. Replace all "O" rings and any damaged parts.

Reassembly

1) Install new "O" rings to reaction sleeve and pistons. Thin "O" ring goes on outside of reaction sleeve. Install inner and outer pistons on reaction sleeve. Push inner piston into cupped side of reaction sleeve. Push outer piston onto other side of reaction sleeve.

2) After cleaning and inspecting case, install pistons and sleeve. Hold assembly with outer piston up and push assembly into its bore in case. Install return springs and spring retainer. Compress springs and install snap ring. Snap ring gap should be centered between 2 of the 3 lugs of the spring retainer.

VALVE BODY

Disassembly

1) Disassembly procedures for all valve bodies are similar. Use appropriate valve body figure as a guide and note the following:

2) As valve trains are removed from each valve body bore, place individual parts in correct order in relative position to valve body in order to simplify reassembly.

3) When disassembling, use care not to damage valve surfaces or form burrs around valve body bores.

4) When separating upper valve bodies (front and rear) from lower valve body, be careful not to lose check balls and springs.

Cleaning & Inspection

1) Wash all disassembled parts and blow dry with compressed air. Inspect all valves for wear and damage, then insert them into valve body and check that they operate smoothly while being turned.

2) Inspect valve body bore sliding surfaces for damage and wear. Check all oil holes and oil passages for clogging.

VALVE BODY SPRING FREE LENGTH (A-42DL & A-44DL TRANSMISSIONS)

Application	A-42DL In. (mm)	A-44DL In. (mm)
Front Upper Body		
Throttle Valve	.864 (21.24)	.756 (19.24)
Downshift Plug	1.563 (39.71)	1.565 (39.76)
Sec. Reg. Valve	2.806 (71.27)	2.806 (71.27)
Rear Upper Body		
Low-Coast		
Mod. Valve	1.667 (42.35)	1.667 (42.35)
Intermediate		
Mod. Valve	1.073 (27.26)	1.073 (27.26)
Reverse		
Sequence		
Valve	1.478 (37.55)	
Gov. Mod. Valve	1.420 (36.07)	
2-3 Shift Valve	1.382 (35.10)	1.32 (35.10)
Det. Reg. Valve	1.236 (31.39)	1.263 (32.08)
Rear Clutch		
Sequence		
Valve		1.478 (37.55)
Lower Body		
Reverse		
Sequence		
Valve	1.478 (37.55)	
1-2 Shift Valve	1.363 (34.62)	1.363 (34.62)
Pressure		
Relief Valve	1.265 (32.14)	1.265 (32.14)
Prim. Reg. Valve	2.887 (73.32)	.409 (61.20)
Damping Ball	.787 (20.00)	.787 (20.00)
3-4 Shift Valve	1.385 (35.18)	1.428 (36.28)
Oil Cooler		
By-Pass Valve	1.312 (33.32)	1.312 (33.32)
Lock-Up		
Relay Valve	.728 (18.50)	.728 (18.50)
Lock-Up		
Signal Valve	1.784 (45.31)	1.4894 (37.83)

3) Inspect all valve springs for wear, damage, excessive weakness and collapsed coils. Measure free length of all springs and replace if incorrect.

4) Inspect valve body cover plates and check balls for wear and damage. Check pressure relief valve for wear and damage. Inspect oil strainer for clogging and replace if necessary.

Automatic Transmissions

TOYOTA A-40D, A-42DL, A-43D, A-43DE & A-44DL (Cont.)

Fig. 36: Exploded View of A-40D and A-43D Transmission Valve Body

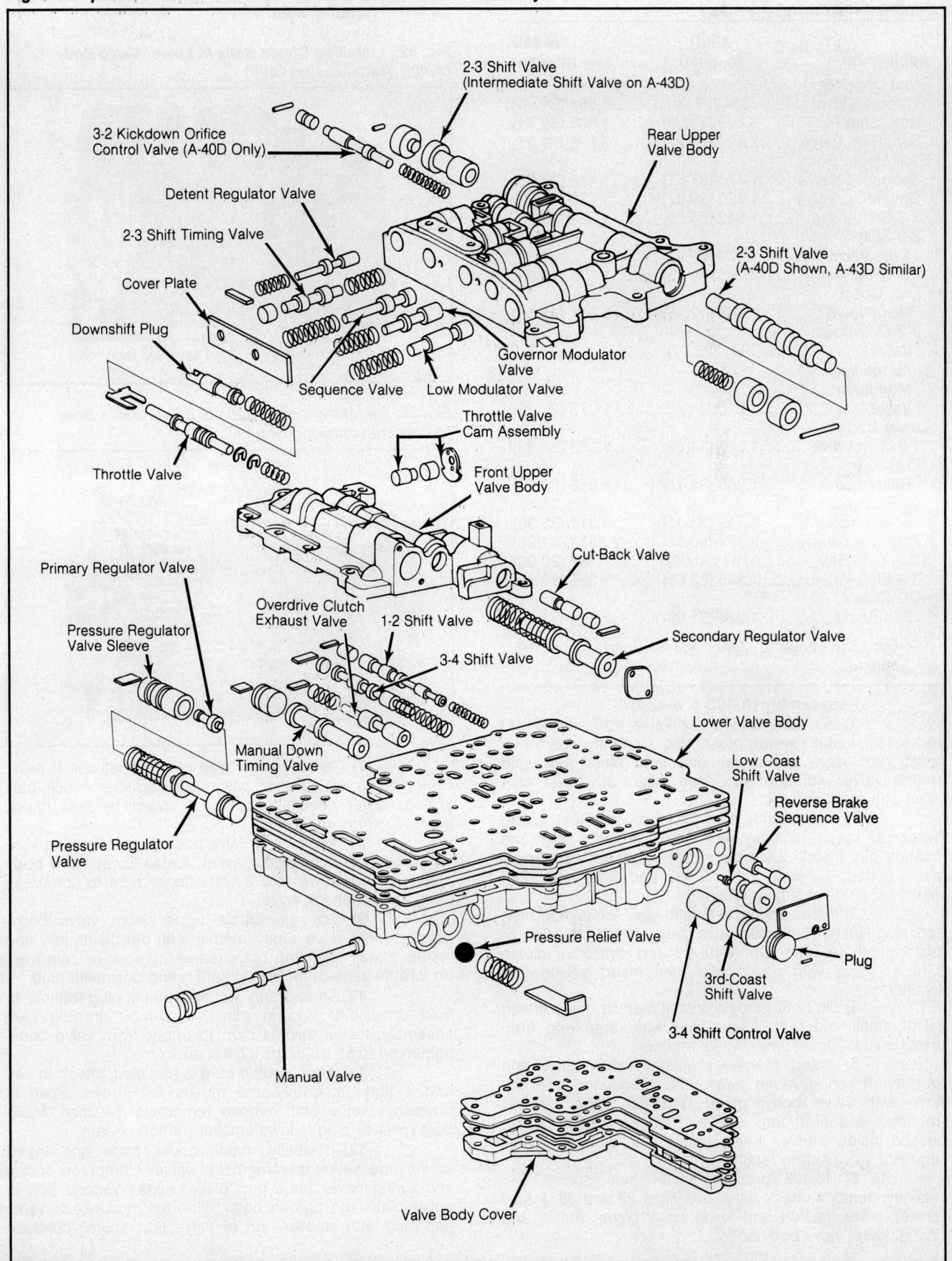

Valve Body Cover

VALVE BODY SPRING FREE LENGTH
(A-40D & A43D TRANSMISSIONS)

Application	A40D In. (mm)	A-43D In. (mm)
Front Upper Body		
Throttle Valve	.864 (21.94)	.864 (21.94)
Downshift Plug	1.693 (43.00)	1.563 (39.71)
Sec. Reg. Valve	2.806 (71.27)	2.806 (71.27)
Rear Upper Body		
Sequence Valve	1.478 (37.55)	1.478 (37.55)
Gov. Mod. Valve	1.420 (36.07)	1.420 (36.07)
2-3 Shift Valve	1.342 (34.09)	1.382 (35.10)
2-3 Shift		
Time Valve	1.174 (29.82)	....
Det. Reg. Valve	1.198 (30.43)	1.178 (29.93)
Low-Coast		
Mod. Valve	1.667 (42.35)	1.667 (42.35)
3-2 Kick-Down		
Valve	.991 (25.17)	....
Intermediate		
Modulator		
Valve		1.073 (27.26)
Lower Body		
1-2 Shift Valve	1.363 (34.62)	1.363 (34.62)
Pressure		
Relief Ball	1.265 (32.14)	1.265 (32.14)
Oil Cooler		
Check Valve	1.312 (33.32)	1.312 (33.32)
Prim. Reg. Valve	2.367 (60.13)	2.887 (73.32) [1]
Damping Ball	.787 (20.00)	.787 (20.00)
3-4 Shift Valve	1.325 (33.65)	1.325 (33.65)
OD Clutch		
Exh. Valve	1.224 (31.09)	....

[1] – For 22R engine; 2.409 (61.20 mm) on 22R-E engine.

Reassembly (A-40D & A-43D)

1) To assemble lower valve body on A-40D and A-43D, install reverse brake plug. Carefully insert low-coast shift valve with small end first. Insert 3-4 shift control valve with cup side first. Insert 3rd-coast shift valve with small end first.

2) Insert inside plug with thick face first. Using tweezers, insert locating pin. Insert outside plug and locating pin. Install cover plate. Set valve body on edge, insert spring, 1-2 shift valve (small part first) and plug. Install 1-2 shift valve plug retainer.

3) Install spring, 3-4 shift valve (small end first) and plug. Install 3-4 shift valve plug retainer (A-40D) or locating pin (A-43D). On A-40D, insert overdrive clutch exhaust valve with round end first. Insert spring and retainer.

4) On both models, install manual down timing valve, small end first. Insert plug with large end first. Install manual down timing valve retainer.

5) Insert primary regulator valve, large end first. Insert spring. Make sure primary regulator valve fits flush with valve body. Insert regulator valve plunger (rounded end first) into sleeve. Plunger should be recessed inside sleeve. Insert sleeve with plunger. Install regulator valve spring retainer.

6) Install pressure relief ball, spring and retainer. Install 4 check balls. See Figs. 37 and 38. Install gasket, plate, gasket and lower body cover. Install and tighten lower valve body bolts.

CAUTION: Lower valve body gaskets are NOT interchangeable.

Fig. 37: Installing Check Balls in Lower Valve Body (A-40D Transmission Only)

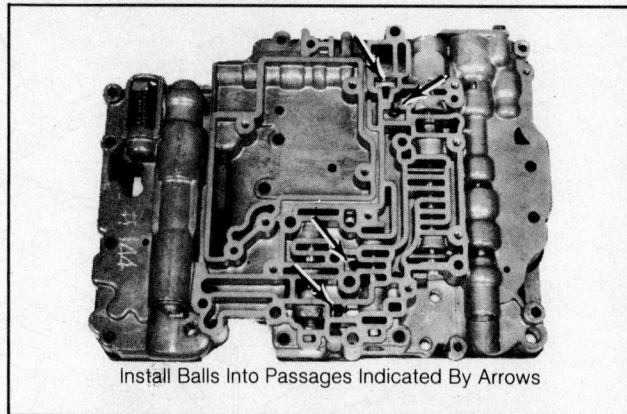

Install Balls Into Passages Indicated By Arrows

Fig. 38: Installing Check Balls in Lower Valve Body (A-43D Transmission Only)

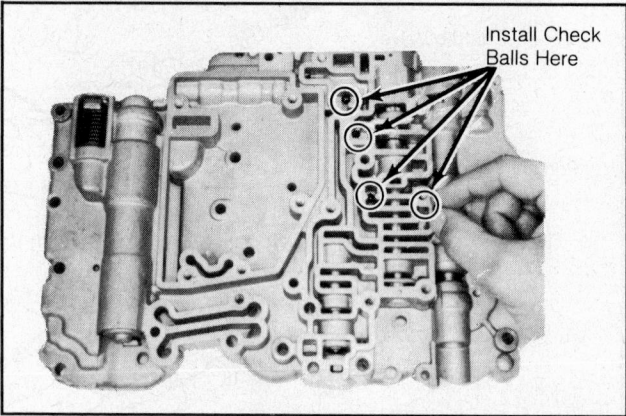

Install Check Balls Here

7) Note different size of 2 rubber check balls. Spring goes with larger ball. Install smaller check ball, spring, larger check ball and oil cooler by-pass check valve. See Figs. 39 and 40.

8) Install lower valve body gasket, making sure new gasket matches old gasket. Install lower valve body plate. Temporarily install 2 bolts finger tight to compress plate against check valve.

9) To reassemble upper front valve body, insert throttle valve. Coat retainer with petroleum jelly and install. Install adjusting rings (same number as removed) on throttle valve shaft. Insert spring and downshift plug.

10) Temporarily install cut-back plug retainer to hold downshift plug in place. Assemble throttle cam assembly. Install throttle cam to upper front valve body, tightening to 65 INCH lbs. (7.4 N.m).

11) After throttle cam is installed, check to see that it turns smoothly and moves full stroke. Push in downshift valve and remove temporary retainer. Make sure roller or plug follows smaller portion of cam.

12) Partially install cover plate and insert spring and secondary regulator valve. Compress spring and swing cover plate into place. Install second bolt in cover plate and tighten both bolts. Insert cut-back valve and plug with smaller end of valve first. Install cut-back

TOYOTA A-40D, A-42DL, A-43D, A-43DE & A-44DL (Cont.)

valve retainer. Install rubber check ball (except A-43DL). See Fig. 41.

Fig. 39: Installing Rubber Check Balls In Lower Valve Body (A-40D Transmission Only)

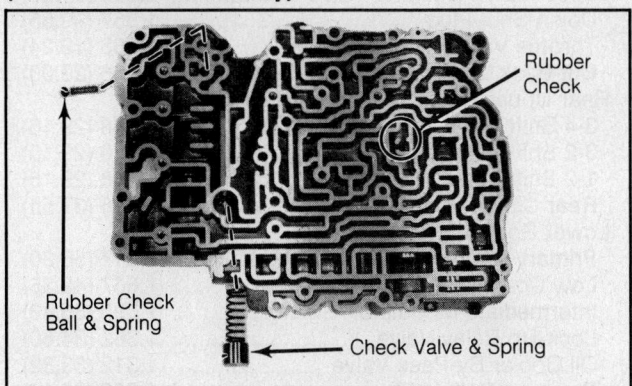

Fig. 40: Installing Rubber Check Balls In Lower Valve Body (A-43D Transmission Only)

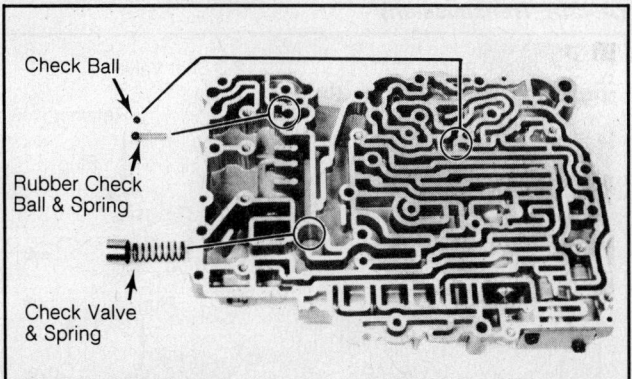

Fig. 41: Installing Check Ball to Front Upper Valve Body

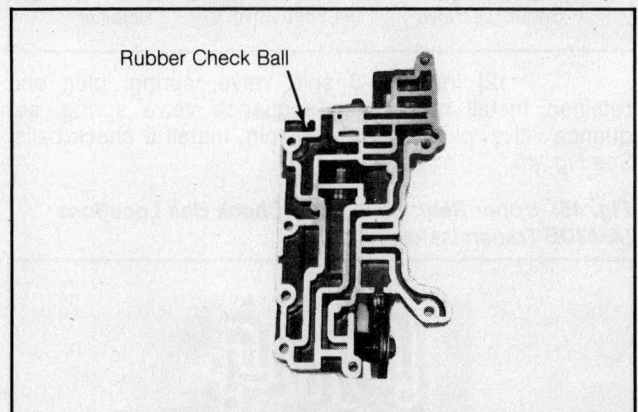

13) To reassemble upper rear body on A-40D and A-43D, install detent regulator valve with round end first. Compress spring and install retainer over spring. On A-40D only, install spring and 2-3 shift timing valve.

14) On A-43D only, install intermediate modulator valve (round end first), then install spring. On A-40D and A-43D, install valve body side cover with 1 bolt. Insert rear clutch sequence valve (round end first), then install spring.

15) Insert governor modulator valve (round end first). Insert spring. Insert low modulator valve (round end first), then install spring. Position cover and install second bolt. Tighten both cover bolts to 48 INCH lbs. (5.4 N.m).

16) On A-43D only, insert 2-3 shift valve (small end first) and insert plug. Compress plug and install intermediate shift valve retainer in valve body.

17) On A-40D only, insert 2-3 shift lower valve with smaller end first. Install plug into bore hole facing up. Insert pin into hole (coat pin with petroleum jelly). Insert 2-3 shift valve with large end first.

18) On A-40D and A-43D, insert spring and intermediate shift valve (round end up) in bore. Insert plug and retainer.

19) Install check balls. A-40D has 1 steel and 4 rubber balls; A-43D has 1 steel and 3 rubber balls. See Fig. 42.

Fig. 42: Check Ball Locations in Upper Rear Valve Body (A-40D and A-43D Transmissions)

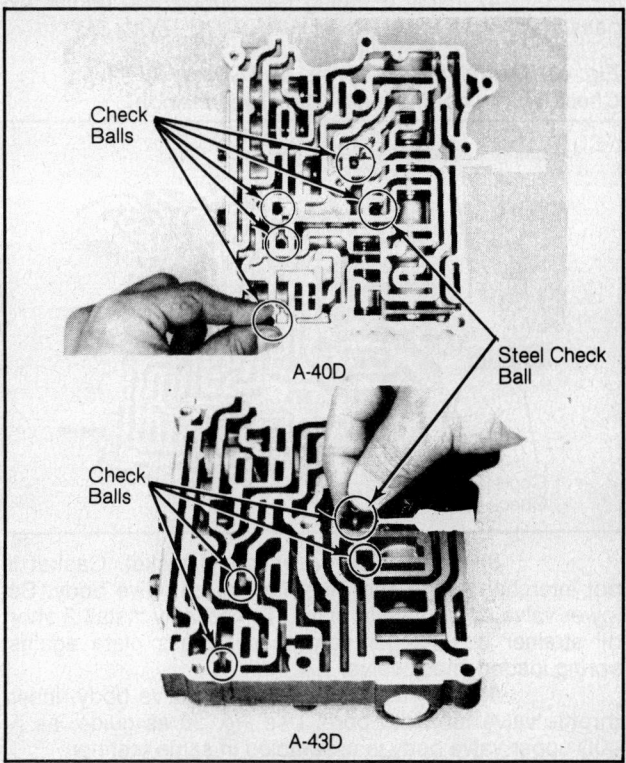

20) To reassemble valve body, make sure new gasket matches old and position on upper rear valve body. Align gasket at lower left corner. Place lower valve body with plate on top of upper rear valve body. Install and finger tighten 3 bolts in lower valve body to secure upper rear valve body.

21) Turn assembly over, check gasket alignment and finger tighten bolts in upper rear valve body. Remove temporary bolts from plate. Place lower and upper rear valve body assembly on upper front valve body. Install and finger tighten set bolts in lower valve body to secure upper front valve body.

22) Turn assembly over and finger tighten 5 bolts in upper front valve body. Recheck alignment of gaskets and tighten bolts in upper front and rear valve bodies. Turn assembly over and tighten bolts in lower valve body. Insert manual valve. Install detent spring and tighten bolts.

TOYOTA A-40D, A-42DL, A-43D, A-43DE & A-44DL (Cont.)

Reassembly (A-43DE)

1) Set valve body on edge. Drop in primary regulator valve (large end first) and spring. Ensure valve fits flush with valve body. Insert sleeve, plunger and regulator valve retainer.

2) Install lock-up relay valve, control valve, spring and retaining pin in valve body. Install No. 3 solenoid and temporarily tighten bolt. Install low-coast modulator valve and intermediate valve into bore. Install valve springs in bores. Short spring goes with low-coast modulator valve.

3) Install No. 1 and No. 2 solenoids with new gaskets. Install pressure relief ball, spring and retainer. Tighten bolt to 48 INCH lbs. (5.4 N.m). Install 2 valve body covers. Ensure retainers and locating pins are installed correctly.

NOTE: Use wave washer on smaller valve body cover.

4) Install damping ball, spring and cooler by-pass check valve. See Fig. 43.

Fig. 43: Damping Ball, Spring And Cooler By-Pass Check Valve Locations (A-43DE Transmission)

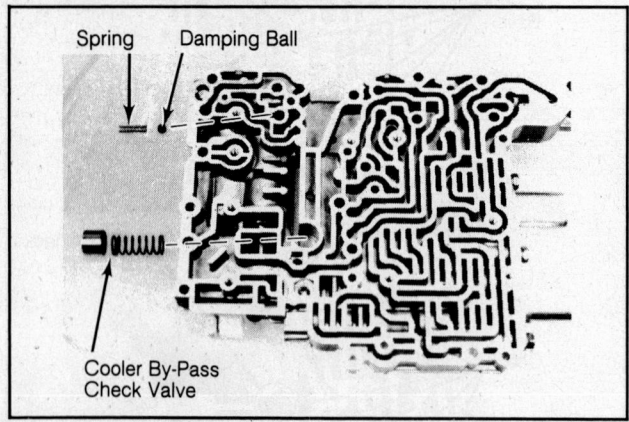

5) Install lower valve body gasket. Gasket is not interchangeable and must lay flat on valve body. Set lower valve body plate in place. Temporarily install 2 short oil strainer bolts finger tight to compress plate against spring loaded check valve.

6) To assemble upper front valve body, insert throttle valve fully into bore. Use Fig. 36 as guide, as A-40D upper valve body is assembled in same manner.

7) Coat throttle valve retainer clip with petroleum jelly and install in valve body. Install same number of adjusting rings on throttle valve as were removed during disassembly.

8) Slide throttle valve spring and down-shift plug into bore. Coat pin with petroleum jelly and install to hold the sleeve.

9) Assemble throttle cam and spring. Install throttle cam. Tighten bolt to 65 INCH lbs. (7.4 N.m). Install secondary regulator valve, spring and cover plate. Tighten bolts to 48 INCH lbs. (5.4 N.m).

10) Install spring, cut-back valve (smaller end first), plug and retainer. Install throttle valve retainer. Ensure sleeve is held by pin.

11) To assemble upper rear valve body, install 3-4 shift valve, spring, plug and retainer. Install 1-2 shift valve, spring and plate. Tighten bolts to 48 INCH lbs. (5.4 N.m).

VALVE BODY SPRING FREE LENGTH (A-43DE TRANSMISSION)

Application	In. (mm)
Front Upper Body	
Secondary Regulator Valve	2.806 (71.27)
Down-Shift Plug	1.557 (39.55)
Throttle Valve	.758 (19.24)
Cut-Back Valve	.906 (23.00)
Rear Upper Body	
3-4 Shift Valve	1.148 (29.15)
3-2 Shift Valve	1.148 (29.15)
1-2 Shift Valve	1.148 (29.15)
Rear Clutch Sequence Valve	1.478 (37.55)
Lower Body	
Primary Regulator Valve	2.217 (56.30)
Low Coast Modulator	1.667 (42.35)
Intermediate Modulator	1.395 (35.43)
Lock-Up Relay Valve	1.362 (34.60)
Oil Cooler By-Pass Valve	1.312 (33.32)
Pressure Relief Valve	1.265 (32.14)
Damping Check Ball	.787 (20.00)

Fig. 44: Exploded View of Upper Rear Valve Body (A-43DE Transmission)

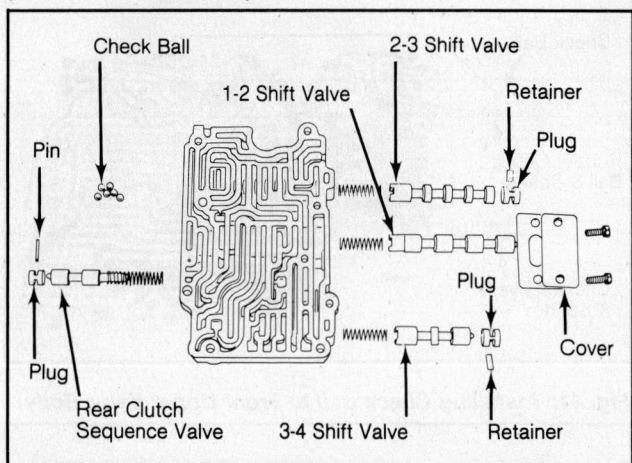

12) Install 2-3 shift valve, spring, plug and retainer. Install rear clutch sequence valve spring, sequence valve, plug and retainer pin. Install 6 check balls. See Fig. 45.

Fig. 45: Upper Rear Valve Body Check Ball Locations (A-43DE Transmission)

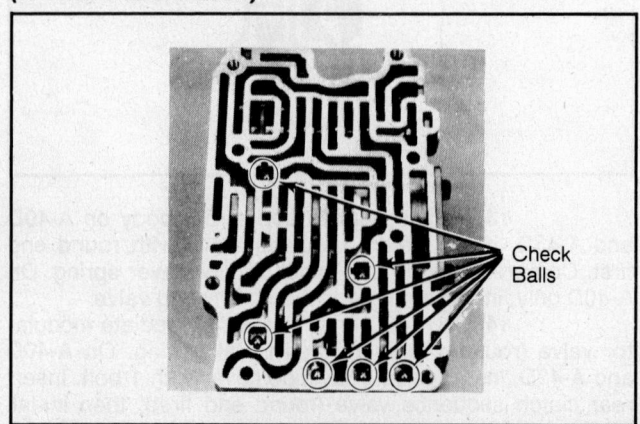

TOYOTA A-40D, A-42DL, A-43D, A-43DE & A-44DL (Cont.)

13) To reassemble valve body, make sure new gasket matches old and position on upper rear valve body. Align gasket at lower left corner. Place lower valve body with plate on top of upper rear valve body. Install and finger tighten 3 bolts in lower valve body to secure upper rear valve body.

14) Turn assembly over, check gasket alignment and finger tighten bolts in upper rear valve body. Remove temporary bolts from plate. Place lower and upper rear valve body assembly on upper front valve body. Install and finger tighten set bolts in lower valve body to secure upper front valve body.

15) Turn assembly over and finger tighten 5 bolts in upper front valve body. Recheck alignment of gaskets and tighten bolts in upper front and rear valve bodies. Turn assembly over and tighten bolts in lower valve body. Insert manual valve.

Reassembly (A-42DL & A-44DL)

1) To reassemble lower valve body, install brake sequence plug. Install low-coast shift valve with small end first. Insert 3-4 coast shift valve with cup side first. *See Fig. 48.*

2) Insert 3rd-coast valve with small end first. Install 2 plugs and 2 locating pins. Install cover plate.

3) Set valve body on edge. Insert spring, 1-2 shift upper valve, lower valve, plug and retainer. Insert

Fig. 47: *Installing Lock-Up Relay Valve in Valve Body*

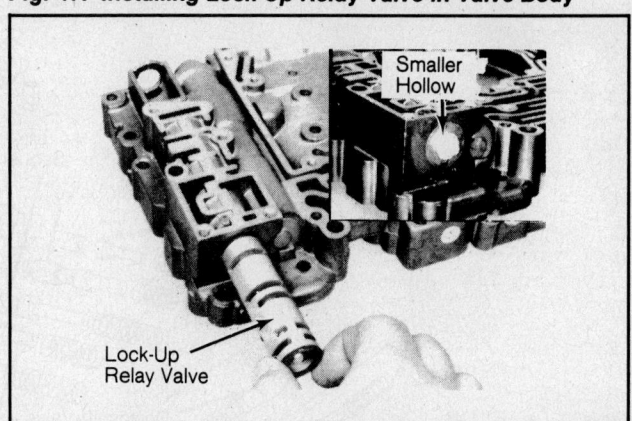

Smaller Hollow

Lock-Up Relay Valve

Illustration applies to A-42DL and A-44DL transmissions.

Fig. 46: *Exploded View of A-43DE Transmission Lower Valve Body Assembly*

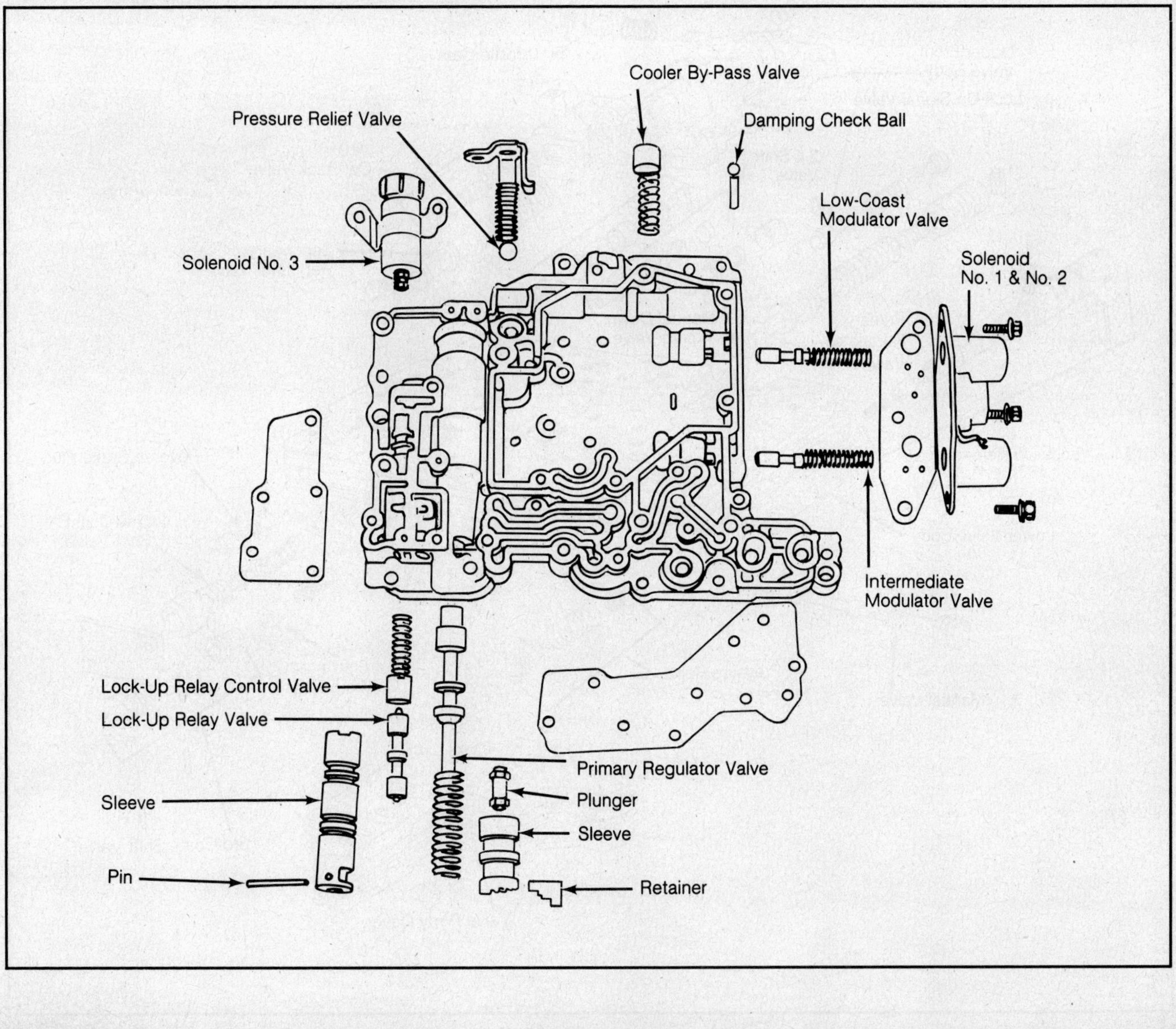

Pressure Relief Valve

Cooler By-Pass Valve

Damping Check Ball

Low-Coast Modulator Valve

Solenoid No. 3

Solenoid No. 1 & No. 2

Intermediate Modulator Valve

Lock-Up Relay Control Valve

Lock-Up Relay Valve

Sleeve

Pin

Primary Regulator Valve

Plunger

Sleeve

Retainer

Automatic Transmissions

TOYOTA A-40D, A-42DL, A-43D, A-43DE & A-44DL (Cont.)

Fig. 48: Exploded View of A-42DL And A-44DL Transmission Valve Body

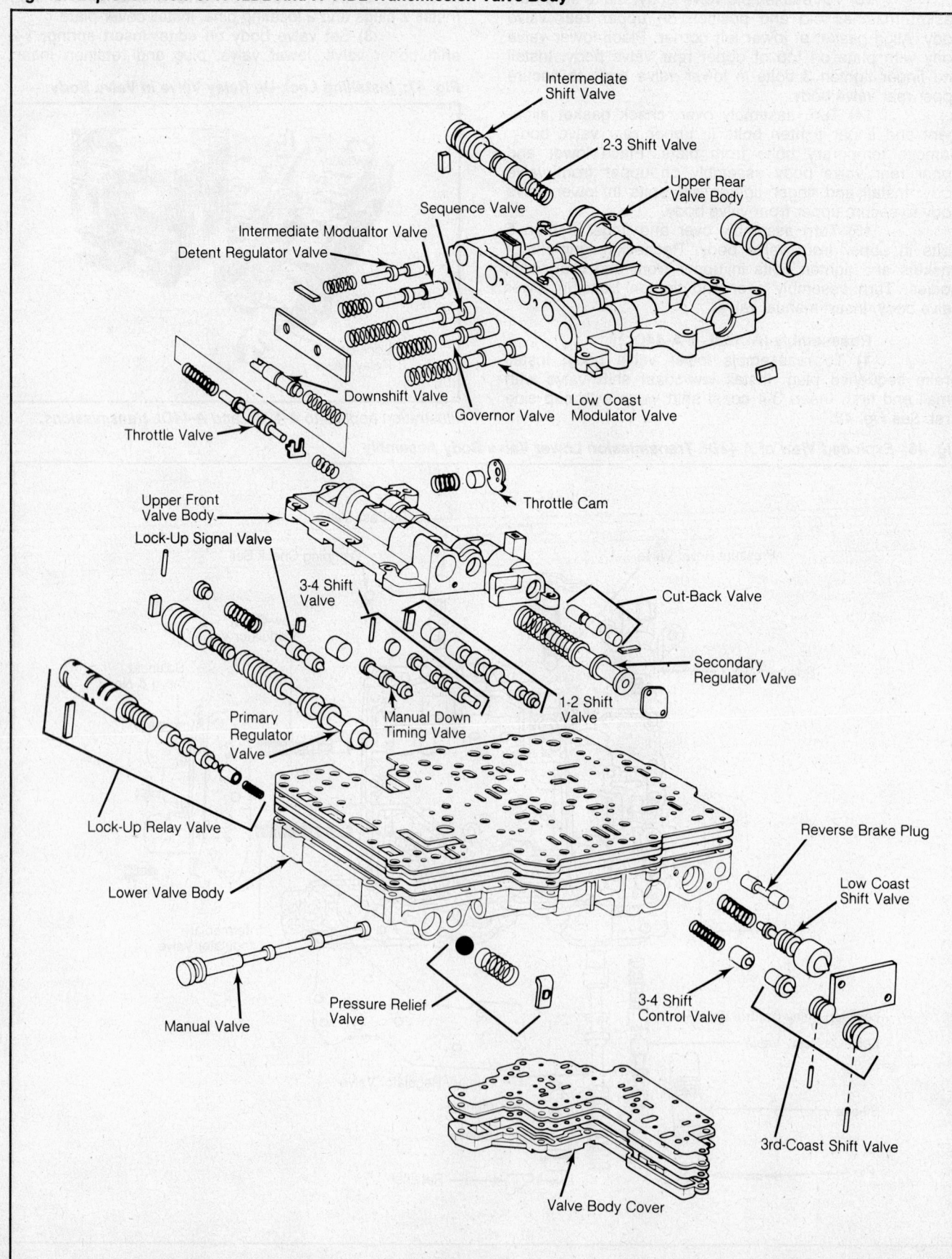

Intermediate Shift Valve

2-3 Shift Valve

Upper Rear Valve Body

Sequence Valve

Intermediate Modualtor Valve

Detent Regulator Valve

Downshift Valve

Low Coast Modulator Valve

Governor Valve

Throttle Valve

Throttle Cam

Upper Front Valve Body

Lock-Up Signal Valve

Cut-Back Valve

3-4 Shift Valve

Secondary Regulator Valve

1-2 Shift Valve

Primary Regulator Valve

Manual Down Timing Valve

Lock-Up Relay Valve

Reverse Brake Plug

Low Coast Shift Valve

Lower Valve Body

Manual Valve

Pressure Relief Valve

3-4 Shift Control Valve

3rd-Coast Shift Valve

Valve Body Cover

TOYOTA A-40D, A-42DL, A-43D, A-43DE & A-44DL (Cont.)

spring, 3-4 shift valve (small end first), plug and locating pin.

4) Install manual downtiming valve (small end first), plug and valve retainer. Insert lock-up signal valve (large end first), spring, plug and locating pin.

5) Insert primary regulator valve (large end first) and spring. Ensure valve fits flush with valve body. Insert regulator valve plunger (rounded end first) into sleeve. Install sleeve with plunger and regulator valve retainer.

6) Assemble spring, lock-up relay control valve, lock-up relay valve and plug into sleeve. Insert sleeve into bore with smaller hollow on sleeve top side facing upward. See Fig. 47. Install plug retainer.

7) Install plate with gasket. Install pressure relief ball, spring and retainer. Ensure all retainers and pins are installed correctly.

8) Install 4 check balls. See Fig. 49. Install lower body gasket, plate, gasket and cover. Gaskets are NOT interchangeable. Install lower body cover set bolts.

Fig. 49: Lower Valve Body Check Ball Locations (A-42DL And A-44DL Transmissions)

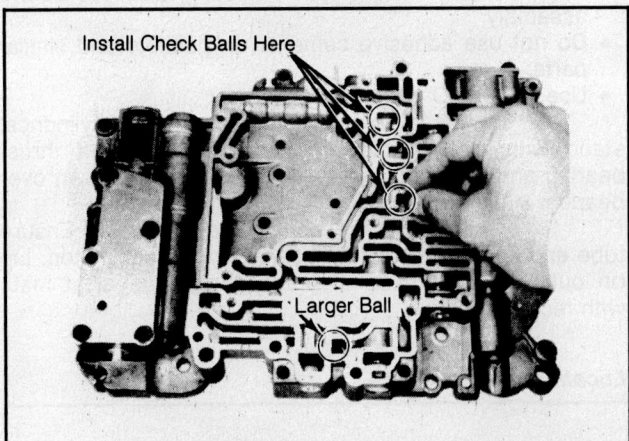

9) Note different size of 2 rubber check balls. The spring goes with larger ball for damping. Install check ball, damping check ball, spring, oil cooler by-pass valve and spring. See Fig. 50.

Fig. 50: Lower Valve Body Rubber Check Ball Locations (A-42DL And A-44DL Transmissions)

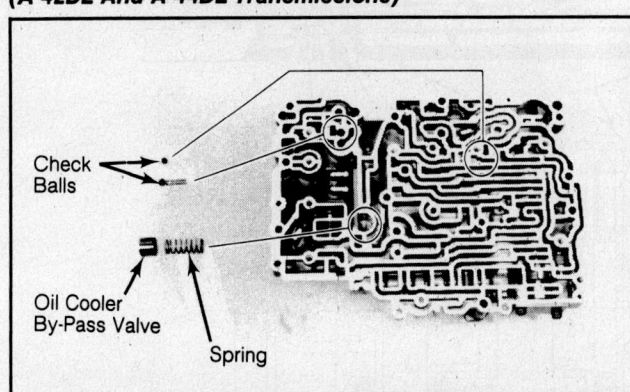

A-42DL is shown; A-44DL is similar.

10) Install lower valve body gasket. Ensure new gasket matches old one. Install lower valve body

plate. Temporarily install 2 short bolts finger tight to compress plate against spring loaded check valve.

11) To assemble upper front valve body, insert throttle valve fully into bore. Use Fig. 36 as a guide, as upper valve body is assembled in same manner.

12) Coat throttle valve retainer clip with petroleum jelly and install in valve body. Install same number of adjusting rings on throttle valve as were removed during disassembly.

13) Slide throttle valve spring and down-shift plug into bore. Coat pin with petroleum jelly and install to hold the sleeve.

14) Assemble throttle cam and spring. Install throttle cam. Tighten bolt to 65 INCH lbs. (7.4 N.m). Install secondary regulator valve, spring and cover plate. Tighten bolts to 48 INCH lbs. (5.4 N.m).

15) Install spring, cut-back valve (smaller end first), plug and retainer. Install throttle valve retainer. Ensure sleeve is held by pin. Install check ball. See Fig. 41.

16) To assemble upper rear valve body, insert detent regulator valve (round end first) into bore. Compress spring and install retainer so that it fully covers end of spring.

17) Insert intermediate modulator valve (round end first) and spring. Install valve body side cover with one bolt. Insert rear clutch sequence valve (round end first) and spring.

18) Insert governor modulator plug. Insert low modulator valve (round end first) and spring. Position cover and install bolt. Tighten to 48 INCH lbs. (5.4 N.m).

19) Insert 2-3 shift valve (smaller end first), plug and retainer. Insert intermediate shift valve (round end up), plug and retainer. Install 4 check balls. See Fig. 51.

Fig. 51: Upper Rear Valve Body Check Ball Locations (A-42DL And A-44DL Transmission)

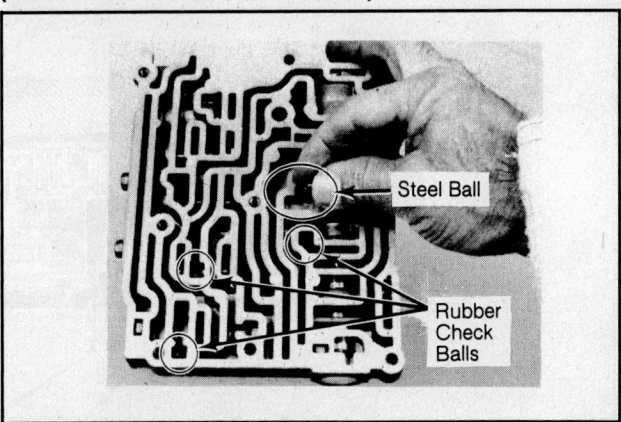

20) To reassemble valve body, make sure new gasket matches old and position on upper rear valve body. Align gasket at lower right corner. Place lower valve body with plate on top of upper rear valve body. Install and finger tighten 3 bolts in lower valve body to secure upper rear valve body.

21) Turn assembly over, check gasket alignment and finger tighten bolts in upper rear valve body. Remove temporary bolts from plate. Place lower and upper rear valve body assembly on upper front valve body. Install small cover.

Automatic Transmissions

TOYOTA A-40D, A-42DL, A-43D, A-43DE & A-44DL (Cont.)

22) Install and finger tighten set bolts in lower valve body to secure upper front valve body. Turn assembly over and finger tighten 5 bolts in upper front valve body.

23) Recheck alignment of gaskets and tighten bolts in upper front and rear valve bodies. Turn assembly over and tighten bolts in lower valve body. Insert manual valve. Install detent spring and tighten bolt to 48 INCH lbs. (5.4 N.m).

Fig. 52: Exploded View of Governor Assembly

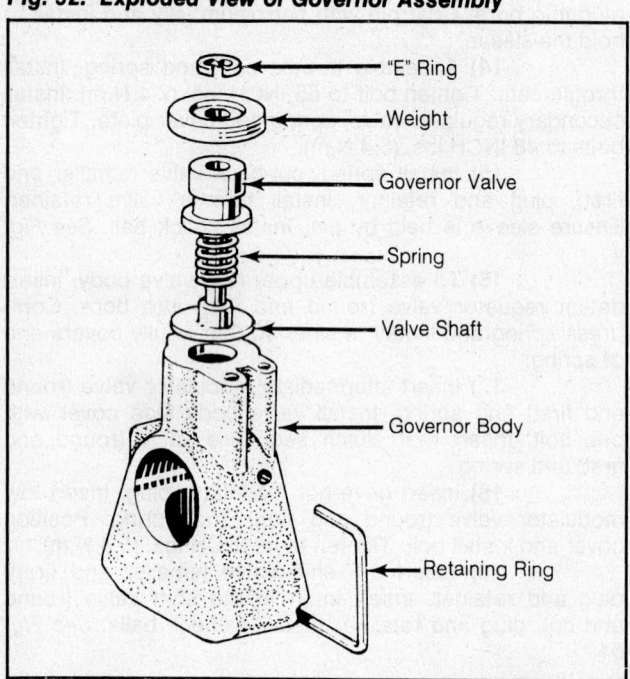

- "E" Ring
- Weight
- Governor Valve
- Spring
- Valve Shaft
- Governor Body
- Retaining Ring

GOVERNOR VALVE ASSEMBLY

Disassembly
Remove "E" ring and lift off governor weight. Remove governor valve shaft and spring from governor body.

Cleaning & Inspection
Inspect all parts for wear and damage. Insert valve shaft into body and make sure it slides smoothly. Check oil passage for clogging.

Reassembly
To reassemble governor valve assembly, reverse disassembly procedure.

TRANSMISSION REASSEMBLY

During transmission reassembly note the following:
- Dry all parts with compressed air. Never use waste or shop towels.
- Soak new clutch discs in automatic transmission fluid for at least 2 hours before installation.
- Apply ATF on all sliding and rotating surfaces before assembly.
- Do not use adhesive cements on gaskets and similar parts.
- Use all new "O" rings and gaskets.

1) Place transmission case on a cylindrical stand with front facing up. Install output shaft thrust bearing and race into case with race lip facing down over bearing.

2) Install brake apply tube into case. Ensure tube end lip are completely inserted into outer piston. Lip on outer circumference of brake apply tube must mate with recess in case.

Fig. 53: Toyota Automatic Transmission Thrust Bearing & Race Locations

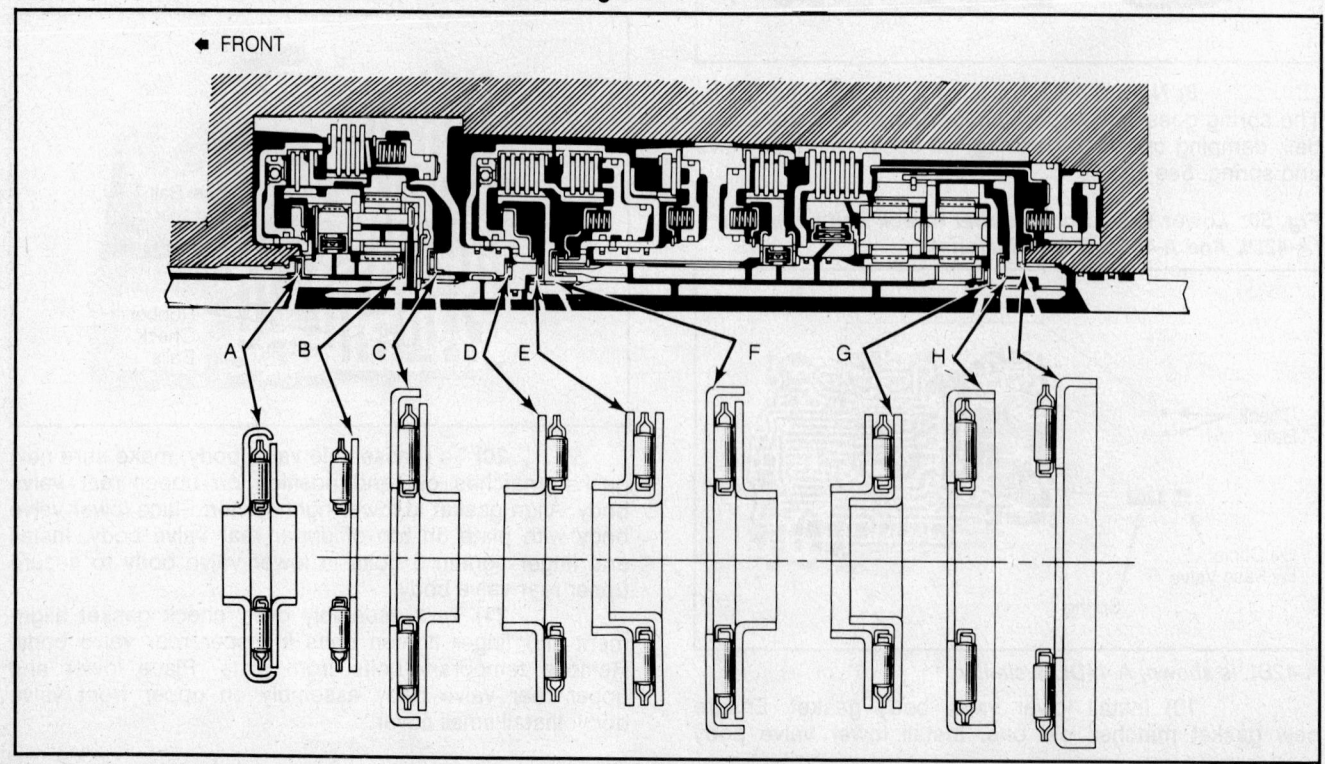

← FRONT

A   B   C   D   E   F   G   H   I

Automatic Transmissions

TOYOTA A-40D, A-42DL, A-43D, A-43DE & A-44DL (Cont.)

3) Align clutch plates on output shaft. Partially insert output shaft assembly into case. On models with slot in case, align notch in clutch plates with slot in case.

4) Check clutch pack clearance. Measure depth of ledge below snap ring groove. *See Fig. 54.* If clutch pack is not lower than ledge, components may be assembled incorrectly or excess ATF may be on discs.

CLUTCH PACK CLEARANCE SPECIFICATIONS

Application	In. (mm)
A-40D & A-43DE	.028-.098 (.72-2.50)
A-43D	.028-.087 (.72-2.20)
A-42DL & A-44DL	.054-.112 (1.36-2.85)

Fig. 54: *Measuring Rear Brake Clutch Pack Clearance*

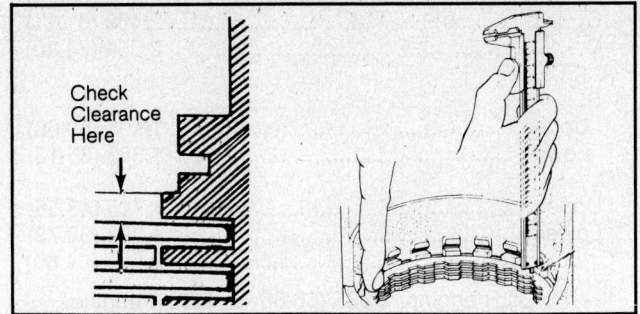

5) Position reaction plate notch tooth toward valve body side of case. Push plate into place. When correctly installed, snap ring groove is completely visible. Install snap ring. Work snap ring around case. Check that snap ring is seated and ends are between lugs. Push center support assembly into case.

6) Align oil hole and bolt hole of center support with those of body side. Align center support with holes in case and install support bolts with wave washers finger tight. Install rear clutch to case. Rotate clutch to mesh with center support.

7) When correctly installed, splined center of clutch will be flush with end of sun gear shaft. Install needle bearing race over splined end of rear clutch in case. Coat parts with petroleum jelly to hold in place. Place lip of race toward rear clutch.

8) Install thrust bearing and race on front clutch. Coat parts with petroleum jelly. Position lip of race outward. Align flukes of rear clutch discs and mesh with front clutch hub. Push front clutch assembly into case, being careful not to let thrust bearing fall out.

9) Place a straightedge across case top surface and measure clearance between clutch and straightedge. *See Fig. 16.* If value corresponds to distance recorded during disassembly, front clutch is installed correctly.

FRONT CLUTCH CLEARANCE SPECIFICATIONS

Application	In. (mm)
A-40D	1.34 (34.0)
All Others	.08 (2.0)

10) Install Guide Rods (SST09350-20013) finger tight in case bolt holes. Coat thrust bearing with petroleum jelly and install on front clutch. Coat thrust washer with petroleum jelly and install on overdrive case. Lip side should face overdrive case.

Fig. 55: *Testing Piston Operation*

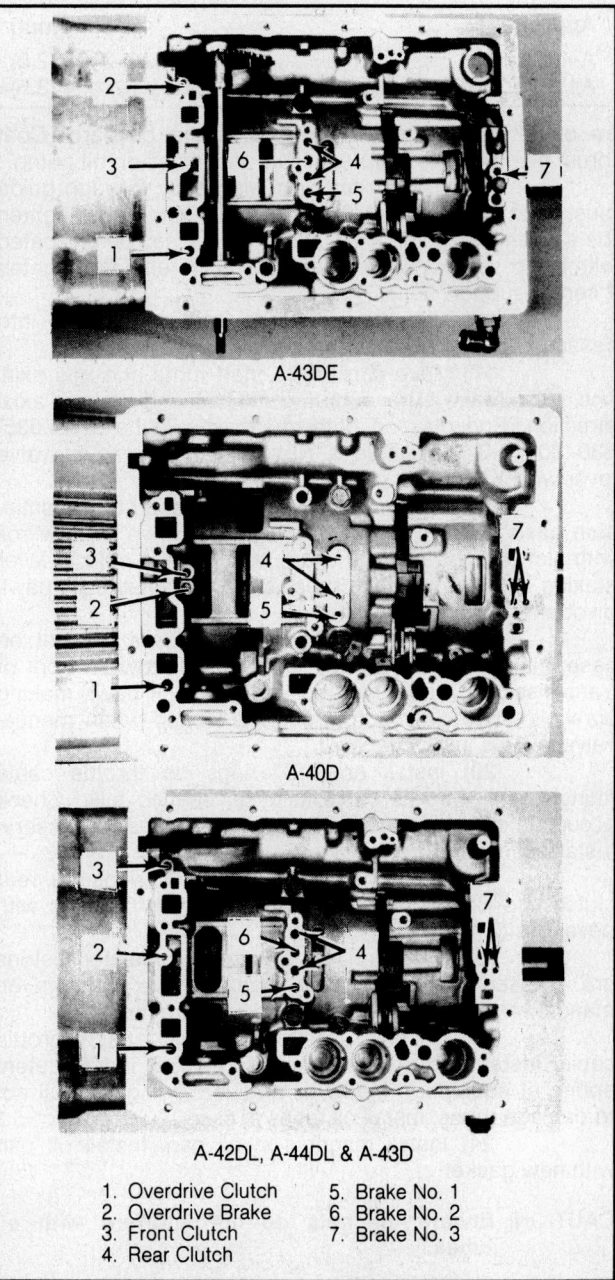

A-43DE

A-40D

A-42DL, A-44DL & A-43D

1. Overdrive Clutch	5. Brake No. 1
2. Overdrive Brake	6. Brake No. 2
3. Front Clutch	7. Brake No. 3
4. Rear Clutch	

Blow low pressure air into indicated passages.

11) Insert overdrive case gently through 2 guide pins. If guide pins are not used, ensure overdrive case and transmission case holes align. On all except A-40D, notch in bottom of outer circumference should face rear of transmission case.

12) Coat thrust washers with petroleum jelly. Install 1 washer to overdrive case and 1 washer to overdrive clutch. Washer lugs should be inserted to holes. Align flukes of discs in overdrive case.

13) Align flukes with slots of overdrive clutch and press overdrive clutch into case. Be careful that thrust washer does not fall out. Place a straightedge across case top surface and measure clearance between overdrive clutch and straightedge.

14) Install "O" ring on overdrive case. Install converter housing and tighten bolts. Install thrust washer

Automatic Transmissions

TOYOTA A-40D, A-42DL, A-43D, A-43DE & A-44DL (Cont.)

OVERDRIVE CLUTCH CLEARANCE SPECIFICATIONS

Application	In. (mm)
A-40D	.08 (2.0)
All Others	.14 (3.5)

on overdrive clutch with lip side facing outward. Coat thrust bearing with petroleum jelly and install on oil pump.

15) Install front oil pump gently through guide pins. Coat 5 set bolts with liquid sealer and finger tighten them. Remove guide pins and insert 2 set bolts coated with liquid sealer. Tighten set bolts in increments. Tighten 2 center support bolts.

16) Blow low-pressure compressed air into passages to test piston operation. See Fig. 55.

17) Make sure input shaft turns and has axial end play. Make sure output shaft has end play in axial direction. End play on both shafts should be .012-.035" (.30-.90 mm). Assemble a NEW collar to manual valve lever with a NEW roll pin.

18) Install manual valve lever shaft to transmission case through manual valve lever. Drive in new roll with slot at right angle to shaft. Match collar hole to lever staking hollow and stake collar to lever. Install park pawl, pivot pin and spring in case.

19) Install and tighten park pawl bracket on case, making sure collar on control rod is toward front of transmission. Check operation of park lock pawl, making sure planetary gear output shaft is locked when manual valve lever is in "P" range.

20) Install new "O" rings on throttle cable fitting. Install throttle cable in case, seating fully. Check accumulator spring free length. Replace as necessary. Install accumulator pistons and springs.

21) On A-40D only, install "O" rings on rear clutch and Brake No. 1 case holes. Install "O" rings with beveled side toward case.

22) On all models, ensure accumulator pistons are pressed into bore. Align manual valve with pin on manual valve lever. Place valve body on transmission.

23) Lift side of valve body and attach throttle cable. Install and tighten valve body bolts. Install detent spring (if equipped). Install oil strainer. Being carefull not to damage tubes, install oil tubes in case.

24) Install magnets in oil pan. Install oil pan with new gasket.

CAUTION: Ensure magnets do not interfere with oil tubes.

25) Install drain plug and gasket. If removed, install governor strainer. On all models except A-43DE, lift governor body retaining clip with screwdriver and slide governor body onto output shaft. Insert retaining clip end into hole on output shaft. Install lock screw and stake lock plate in place.

26) On A-43DE only, install sensor rotor and Woodruff key. Put large diameter snap ring at front. On all models, install lock ball, speedometer drive gear and snap rings.

27) Without using gasket sealer, install extension housing and new gasket. On A-43DE only, install speed sensor in extension housing.

28) On all models, install "O" rings, bushing and speedometer driven gear to shaft sleeve. Install speeometer driven gear assembly in extension housing. Insert shaft sleeve assembly into housing. Install lock plate with bolt and lock washer.

ACCUMULATOR SPRING FREE LENGTH

Application	In. (mm)
A-40D	
B_1	2.625 (66.86)
C_2	2.410 (61.21)
C_1	2.699 (68.56)
A-43D	
B_2	[1] 2.618 (66.50)
C_2	2.172 (55.18)
C_1	[2] 2.699 (68.56)
A-42DL	
B_2	2.618 (66.50)
C_2	2.409 (61.21)
C_1	2.551 (64.80)
A-44DL	
B_2	2.625 (66.68)
C_2	2.409 (61.21)
C_1	2.551 (64.80)
A-43DE	
B_2	
Upper	1.995 (50.68)
Lower	1.383 (35.13)
C_2	
Upper	1.715 (43.56)
Lower	1.289 (32.73)
C_1	2.551 (64.80)

[1] – For 22R engine; 2.625 (66.86) on 22R-E engine.
[2] – For 22R engine; 2.551 (64.80) on 22R-E engine.

29) Slide neutral start switch onto control shaft. Install grommet, facing groove toward switch body. Install washer and nut. Move switch so that slit in switch and neutral base line up. Tighten bolt and nut. Install shift handle. On all except A-43DE, install solenoid switch with 2 "O" rings.

TIGHTENING SPECIFICATIONS

Application	Ft. Lbs. (N.m)
Center Support-to-Case	19 (25)
Converter Housing-to-Case	
10 mm	25 (34)
14 mm	
A-42DL	42 (57)
All Others	25 (34)
17 mm	42 (57)
Converter-to-Drive Plate	13 (18)
Extension Housing-to-Case	25 (34)
Oil Pump-to-Case	15 (20)
Transmission-to-Engine	47 (64)

	INCH Lbs. (N.m)
Oil Pan-to-Case	
A-42DL	48 (5.4)
A-44DL	36 (4.0)
All Others	39 (4.4)
Lock Pawl Bracket-to-Case	
A-44DL	44 (5.0)
All Others	65 (7.4)
Strainer-to-Valve Body	48 (5.4)
Testing Plugs-to-Case	
A-44DL	44 (5.0)
All Others	65 (7.4)
Upper-to-Lower Valve Body	48 (5.4)
Valve Body-to-Case	84 (10)

TOYOTA MODEL A-55

Tercel

DESCRIPTION

The transaxle assembly is a 3-Speed unit consisting of an engine driven torque converter fitted to an oil pump which is coupled to the transaxle by a chain. The unit utilizes 2 clutches, 3 brakes, 2 planetary gear sets, a one-way clutch and a final drive assembly. Final drive assembly is directly below torque converter and connected to front of transmission. It consists of a housing, case, ring gear, pinion, side gears and pinion gears.

LUBRICATION & ADJUSTMENTS

See appropriate AUTOMATIC TRANSMISSION SERVICING article in IMPORT GENERAL SERVICING section.

SERVICE (IN VEHICLE)

AXLE DRIVE SHAFTS
Removal

1) From end of drive shaft, remove cotter pin and lock nut cap. Before removing brake caliper, loosen drive shaft lock nut while depressing brake pedal. Remove brake caliper from steering knuckle and suspend it with wire. Remove disc rotor.

2) Remove cotter pin and nut from tie rod end. Disconnect tie rod end from steering knuckle. For reference at reassembly, place marks on strut lower bracket and camber adjustment cam. Remove strut-to-knuckle bolts and disconnect knuckle from strut.

CAUTION: Avoid damaging boot; cover it with cloth.

3) Pull drive shaft from hub. Remove stiffener plate from transaxle assembly and engine (left side only). To remove drive shaft from vehicle, withdraw shaft from transaxle assembly.

Disassembly

1) Remove snap ring from inner joint. Check inner and outer joints for play and that inner joint slides smoothly in thrust direction. Disassemble boot clamps. Place reference marks on inner joint, tripod, and drive shaft.

CAUTION: Do not use a punch. Use a scribe.

NOTE: When marking tripod in relation to shaft, identify front of tripod, to make sure tripod goes on in same direction it came off, thereby allowing bearings to ride in original bores in joint.

2) Remove inner joint from drive shaft. Using a snap ring expander, remove tripod retaining snap ring. Tap uniformly along tripod to remove it from drive shaft.

CAUTION: Do not tap on the rollers.

3) Remove inner boot from shaft. Remove clamp and dynamic damper (left shaft only). Remove 2 outer boot clamps and outer boot from shaft. Check inside and outside of boots for damage.

CAUTION: Do not remove the outboard joint.

Fig. 1: Cross Sectional View of Toyota Tercel A-55 Automatic Transaxle

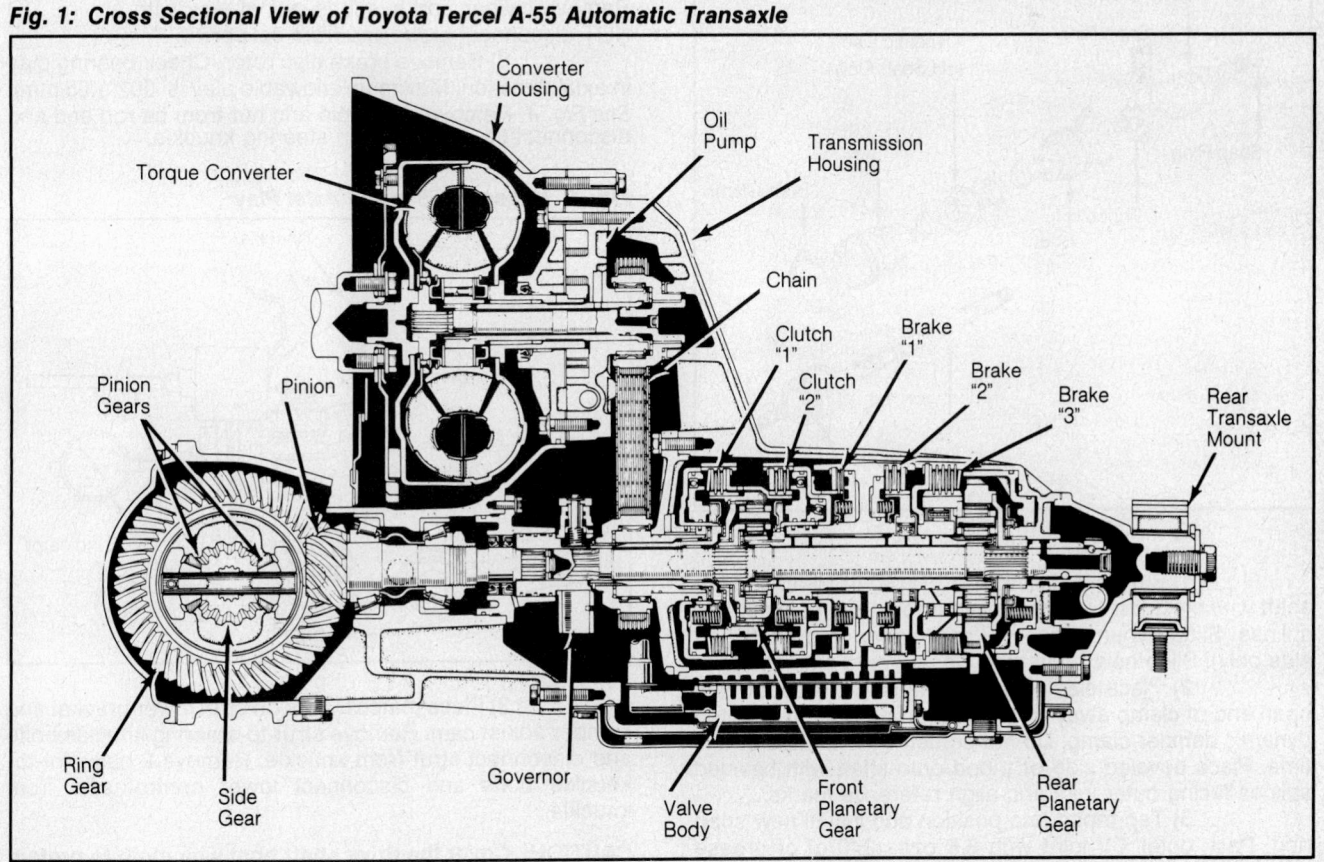

Automatic Transmissions
TOYOTA MODEL A-55 (Cont.)

Fig. 2: Exploded View of Drive Shaft & Knuckle Assy.

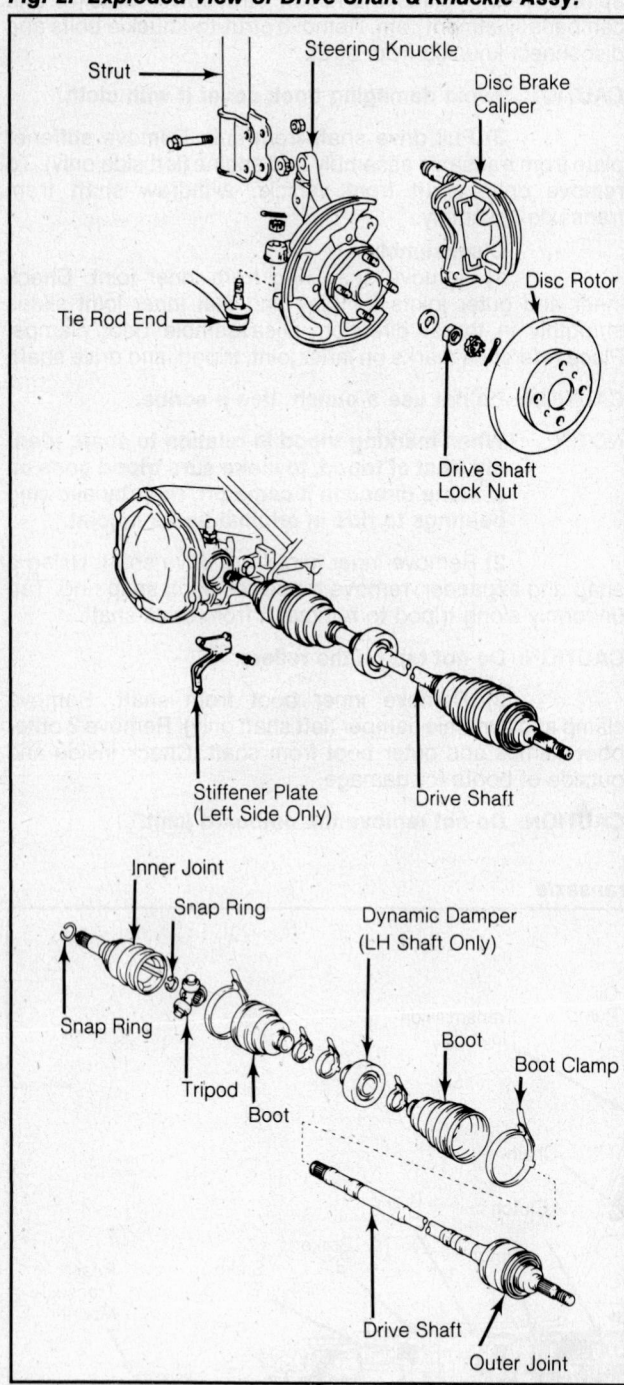

(supplied with boot kit). Install outer boot and tighten clamps.

4) Pack inner CV joint with 5 ozs. (140 g) of grease (supplied with boot kit). Align reference marks made at disassembly and install inner CV joint. Install inner CV joint boot and tighten clamps. Install new snap ring on axle shaft.

Installation

To install, reverse disassembly procedure. After installation of shafts, check front wheel alignment. Check boots for damage during installation. Measure the distance between drive shafts at transaxle. *See Fig. 3.* Distance should be less than 7.626" (193.7 mm).

Fig. 3: Checking Distance Between Drive Shafts

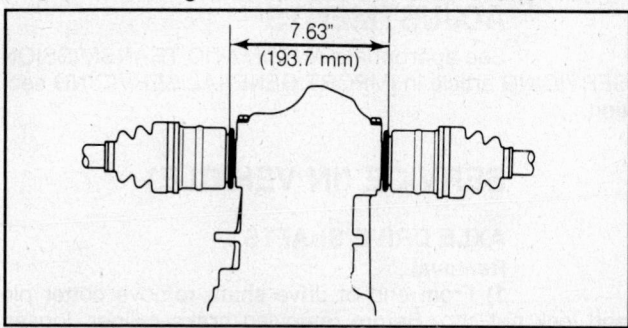

WHEEL BEARINGS
Removal

1) Raise and support vehicle. Remove wheel and tire assembly. Remove drive shaft cotter pin and nut cap. Press on brake pedal and loosen drive shaft nut. Remove caliper and suspend out of way with a wire. DO NOT disconnect brake line from caliper.

2) Remove brake disc rotor. Check bearing play in axial direction. Maximum allowable play is .002" (.05 mm). *See Fig. 4.* Remove cotter pin and nut from tie rod end and disconnect tie rod end from steering knuckle.

Fig. 4: Measuring Bearing Axial Play

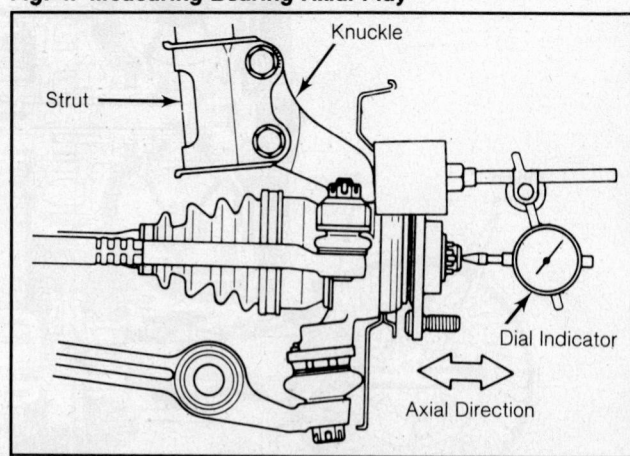

Reassembly

1) Before installing boots on shaft, wrap ends of shaft with electrical tape to protect boots from being cut by splines. Slide dynamic damper and clamp onto shaft (left side only). Slide new boots and clamps onto axle shaft.

2) Place clamping rings loosely over boot with open end of clamp away from direction of rotation. Tighten dynamic damper clamp. Do not tighten boot clamps at this time. Place beveled side of tripod onto shaft with beveled splines facing outer joint and align reference marks.

3) Tap tripod into position and install new snap ring. Pack outer CV joint with 8.5 ozs. (240 g) of grease

3) Place match marks on strut lower bracket and camber adjust cam. Remove strut-to-steering knuckle bolts and disconnect strut from knuckle. Remove 2 ball joint-to-knuckle bolts and disconnect lower control arm from knuckle.

CAUTION: Cover the drive shaft boot with cloth to protect it from damage.

TOYOTA MODEL A-55 (Cont.)

4) Pull hub and knuckle off of drive shaft. Place knuckle assembly in vise. From back side of knuckle remove dust deflector and inner oil seal. Using snap ring pliers, remove hole snap ring. Remove brake dust cover bolts. Press hub from bearing and knuckle.

NOTE: If hub has been removed, outer oil seal must be replaced.

5) Using a gear puller, remove bearing inner race (outer) from hub. Remove bearing inner race (inner) from bearing. Remove brake dust cover. Remove outer oil seal from knuckle. Install inner race (outer) in bearing. Using an arbor press, push bearing from knuckle.

Installation
To install, reverse removal procedure. Two types of bearings are used; KOYO and NSK. Be sure to use the correct one. Do not interchange inner and outer races when installing bearing and hub. Apply liquid sealer to dust cover and knuckle before assembly. When installing inner oil seal, be sure to tap it in 1/8" (3.2 mm) from the end surface. Check front wheel alignment.

TROUBLE SHOOTING

FLUID DISCOLORED OR SMELLS BURNT
Fluid contaminated. Torque converter faulty. Transmission faulty.

VEHICLE DOES NOT MOVE IN ANY FORWARD RANGE OR REVERSE
Manual linkage out of adjustment. Valve body or primary regulator faulty. Transmission faulty.

VEHICLE DOES NOT MOVE IN ANY RANGE
Park lock pawl faulty. Valve body or primary regulator faulty. Torque converter faulty. Converter drive plate broken. Oil pump intake screen blocked. Transmission faulty.

SHIFT LEVER POSITION INCORRECT
Manual linkage out of adjustment. Manual valve and lever faulty. Transmission faulty.

HARSH ENGAGEMENT INTO ANY DRIVE RANGE
Throttle linkage out of adjustment. Valve body or primary regulator faulty. Accumulator pistons faulty. Transmission faulty.

DELAYED 1-2 OR 2-3 UPSHIFT, OR DOWNSHIFTS FROM 3-2 THEN SHIFTS BACK TO 3
Throttle linkage out of adjustment. Governor faulty. Valve body faulty.

SLIPS ON 1-2 OR 2-3 UPSHIFT, OR SLIPS OR SHUDDERS ON TAKE-OFF
Manual linkage out of adjustment. Throttle linkage out of adjustment. Valve body faulty. Transmission faulty.

DRAG, BINDING OR TIE-UP ON 1-2 OR 2-3 UPSHIFTS
Manual linkage out of adjustment. Valve body faulty. Transmission faulty.

HARSH DOWNSHIFT
Throttle linkage out of adjustment. Accumulator pistons faulty. Valve body faulty. Transmission faulty.

NO DOWNSHIFT WHEN COASTING
Governor faulty. Valve body faulty.

DOWNSHIFT OCCURS TOO QUICK OR TOO LATE WHILE COASTING
Throttle linkage out of adjustment. Governor faulty. Valve body faulty. Transmission faulty.

NO 3-2 OR 2-1 KICKDOWN
Throttle linkage out of adjustment. Governor faulty. Valve body faulty.

NO ENGINE BRAKING IN "2" RANGE
Valve body faulty. Transmission faulty.

VEHICLE DOES NOT HOLD IN "P"
Manual linkage out of adjustment. Parking lock pawl cam and spring faulty.

TESTING

ROAD TEST
NOTE: Perform test with fluid at normal operating temperature.

"D" Range Test
1) Shift into "D" range and while driving with accelerator pedal held constant at a specified point (throttle valve opening 50% and 100%). At each throttle opening, check to see that 1-2 and 2-3 upshifts take place and that shift points conform with those in *Fig. 5.*

2) If there is no 1-2 upshift, governor valve may be defective or 1-2 shift valve may be stuck. If there is no 2-3 upshift, 2-3 shift valve may be stuck. If shift point is incorrect, throttle link may be out of adjustment, or throttle valve, 1-2 shift valve or 2-3 shift valve may be defective.

3) While performing step **1)** again, check for shock and slippage during 1-2 and 2-3 upshifts. If shock is severe, line pressure may be too high, accumulator may be defective or check ball may be defective. While in "D" range and in high gear, check for abnormal noise and vibration.

NOTE: Check for cause of abnormal noise and vibration must be made with extreme care as they could also be due to unbalance in differential, tires, torque converter, or bent power train components.

4) While in "D" and running in second or high gear, depress accelerator pedal fully to perform a kickdown and check to see that kick-down shift points, for 2-1, 3-1 and 3-2 kick-downs, conform to those in *Fig. 5.* Also check for abnormal shock and slip during kick-downs.

5) While running in high gear, move gear selector lever to "2" and "L" positions and check engine braking

Fig. 5: *Shift Speeds Diagram*

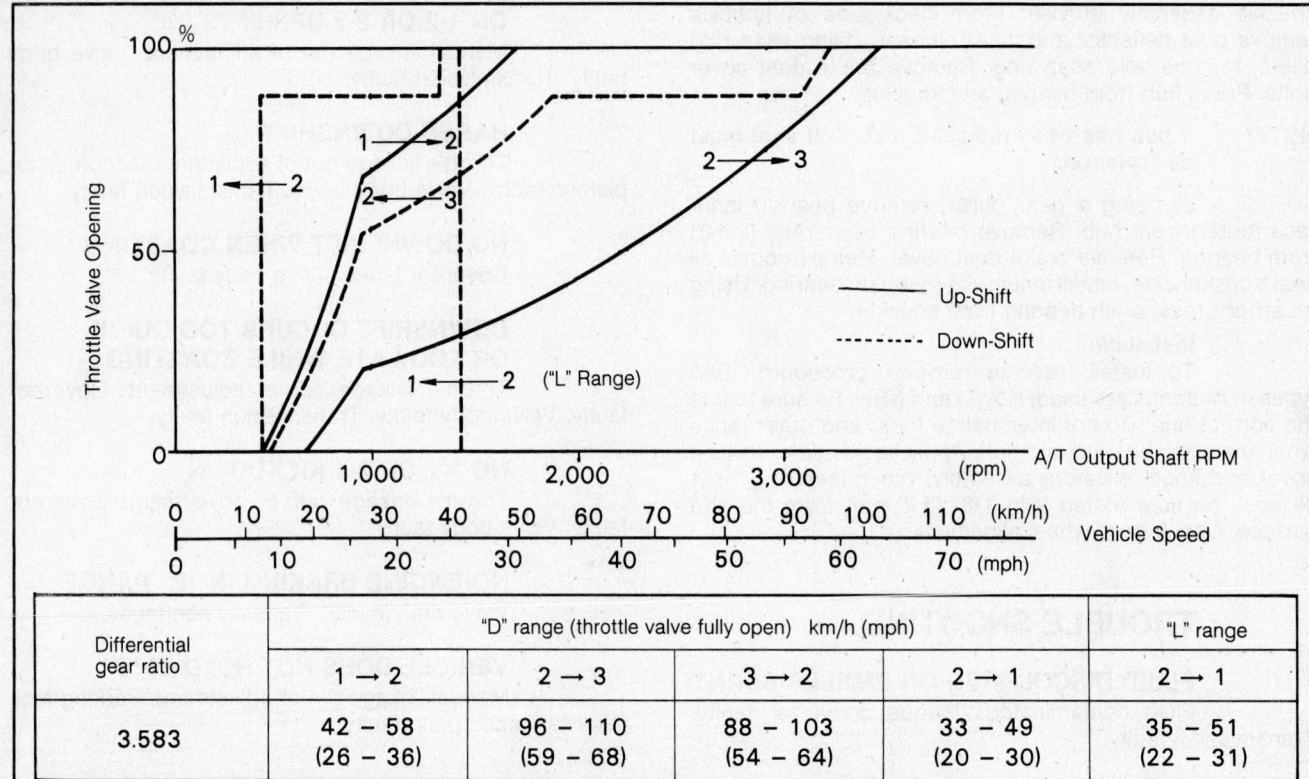

Differential gear ratio	"D" range (throttle valve fully open) km/h (mph)				"L" range
	1 → 2	2 → 3	3 → 2	2 → 1	2 → 1
3.583	42 – 58 (26 – 36)	96 – 110 (59 – 68)	88 – 103 (54 – 64)	33 – 49 (20 – 30)	35 – 51 (22 – 31)

effect at each of these ranges. If there is no engine braking effect in "2" range, brake No. 1 is defective. If there is no engine braking effect in "L" range, brake No. 3 is defective.

6) While running in high gear, release foot from accelerator pedal and move gear selector lever into "L" range. Check to see if 3-2 and 2-1 downshift points conform to those in *Fig. 5*.

"2" Range Test

1) Shift to "2" range and run with throttle valve opening at 50% and 100% respectively. Then check 1-2 upshift points at each throttle valve opening to see that they conform to those in *Fig. 5*. While running in "2" range and in second gear, release accelerator pedal and check engine braking effect.

2) While running in "2" range and in second, depress accelerator fully to perform a 2-1 kickdown and check to see if speeds conform to those in *Fig. 5*. Check for abnormal noise at acceleration and deceleration and for shock during upshift and downshift.

"L" Range Test

While running in "L" range, check to see that there is no upshift to second gear. While running in "L" range, release accelerator pedal and check engine braking effect. Check for abnormal noise at acceleration and deceleration.

"R" Range Test

Shift into "R" range and while running at full throttle, check for slipping.

"P" Range Test

Stop vehicle on a gradient (more than 5°) and after shifting into "P" range, release parking brake. Then check to see that parking lock pawl keeps the vehicle from moving.

STALL TEST

NOTE: **The object of this test is to check the overall performance of the transmission and engine by measuring the maximum engine speed at the "D" and "R" ranges.**

1) Chock front wheels. Mount an engine tachometer. Fully apply parking brake. Step down strongly on brake pedal with left foot. Start engine. Shift into "D" range. Step down fully on accelerator pedal with right foot. Quickly read highest engine RPM at this time.

NOTE: **Perform test with fluid at normal operating temperature.**

CAUTION: **Do not perform this test for longer than 5 seconds.**

2) If engine speed is the same for both ranges but lower than specified value, then engine output may be insufficient or stator one-way clutch may not be operating properly.

NOTE: **If more than 600 RPM below the specified value, the torque converter could be at fault.**

3) If stall speed in "D" range is higher than specified, then front clutch may be slipping, one-way clutch No. 2 may not be operating properly or line pressure may be too low.

4) If stall speed in "R" range is higher than specified, rear clutch may be slipping, brake No. 3 may be slipping or line pressure may be too low.

STALL SPEED SPECIFICATIONS

Application	Stall RPM
All Models	2100-2400

TIME LAG TEST

NOTE: If shift lever is shifted while engine is idling, there will be a certain time elapse or lag before shock can be felt. This is used for checking the condition of front clutch, rear clutch and brake No. 3.

1) Fully apply parking brake. Start engine. Ensure proper idle speed. Move gear selector lever from "N" to "D" range. Using a stop watch, measure the time it takes from shifting lever until shock is felt. Then measure time lag for "N" to "R". Compare findings with those in the TIME LAG SPECIFICATIONS table.

2) If "N" to "D" time lag is longer than specifications, line pressure may be too low or front clutch may be

TIME LAG SPECIFICATIONS

Application	Time Lag (Seconds)
"N" to "D"	Less Than 1.2
"N" to "R"	Less Than 1.5

Fig. 7: Hydraulic Pressure Test Port Hookup Points

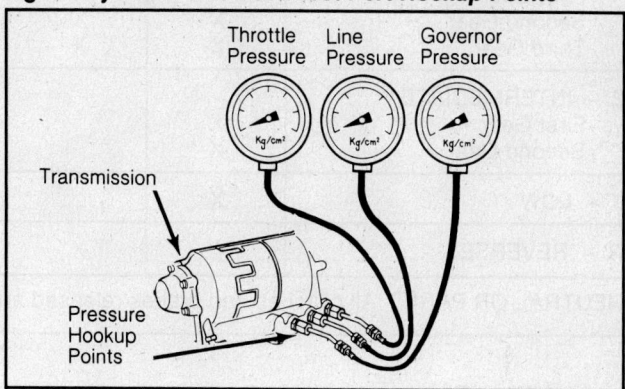

Fig. 6: Toyota Tercel Model A-55 Automatic Transmission Hydraulic Circuits Diagram

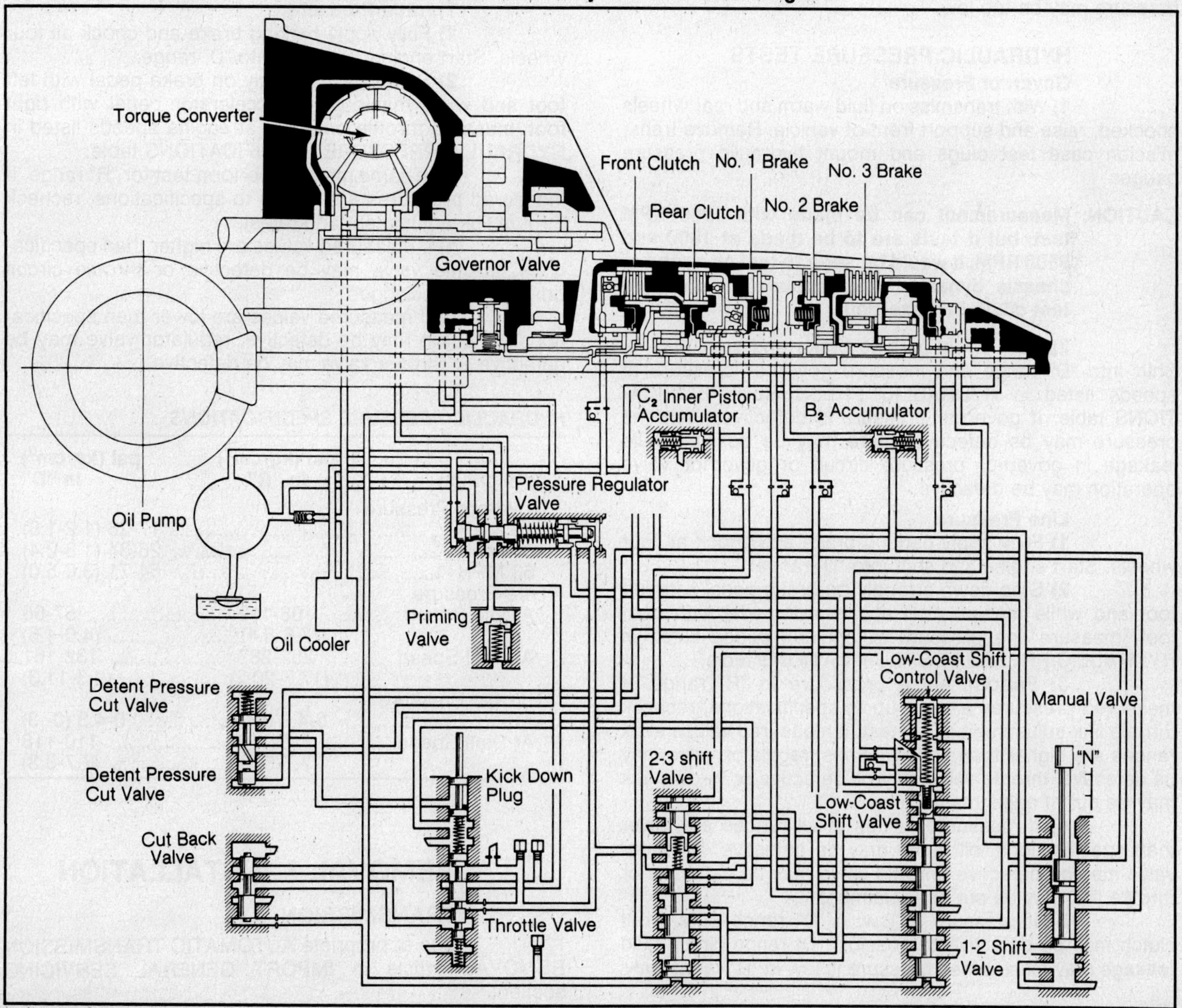

CLUTCH AND BRAKE APPLICATION CHART

Selector Lever Position	Clutch 1	Clutch 2		Brake 1	Brake 2	Brake 3	
		Inner Piston	Outer Piston			Inner Piston	Outer Piston
D – DRIVE							
First Gear	X				X		
Second Gear	X				X		
Third Gear	X	X			X		
2 – INTERMEDIATE							
First Gear	X				X		
Second Gear	X			X	X		
1 – LOW	X					X	
R – REVERSE		X	X			X	X

NEUTRAL OR PARK – All clutches and brakes released and/or ineffective.

worn. If "N" to "R" time lag is longer than specifications, rear clutch may be worn, brake No. 3 may be worn or line pressure may be too low.

HYDRAULIC PRESSURE TESTS
Governor Pressure
1) With transmission fluid warm and rear wheels chocked, raise and support front of vehicle. Remove transmission case test plugs and mount hydraulic pressure gauges.

CAUTION: **Measurement can be made with 1000 RPM test, but if tests are to be made at 1800 and 3500 RPM, it would be safer to test on a road or chassis dynamometer because an on-stand test could be hazardous.**

2) Fully apply parking brake and start engine. Shift into "D" range and measure governor pressure at speeds listed in HYDRAULIC PRESSURE SPECIFICATIONS table. If governor pressure is defective, then line pressure may be defective, there may be possible fluid leakage in governor pressure circuit or governor valve operation may be defective.

Line Pressure
1) Fully apply parking brake and chock all four wheels. Start engine and shift into "D" range.

2) Step down strongly on brake pedal with left foot and while manipulating accelerator pedal with right foot, measure line pressure at engine speeds listed in HYDRAULIC PRESSURE SPECIFICATIONS table.

3) Perform same procedure in "R" range. If measured pressures are not up to specifications, recheck throttle link adjustment and retest. If measured values at all ranges are higher than specifications, regulator valve may be defective, throttle valve may be defective or throttle link may be out of adjustment.

4) If measured values at all ranges are lower than specifications, oil pump may be defective, regulator valve may be defective, throttle valve may be defective or throttle link may be out of adjustment.

5) If pressure is low in "D" range only, front clutch may be defective or possible "D" range circuit fluid leakage may exist. When pressure is low in "R" range only,

rear clutch may be defective, brake No. 3 may be defective or possible "R" range circuit fluid leakage may exist.

Throttle Pressure
1) Fully apply parking brake and chock all four wheels. Start engine and shift into "D" range.

2) Step down strongly on brake pedal with left foot and while manipulating accelerator pedal with right foot, measure throttle pressure at engine speeds listed in HYDRAULIC PRESSURE SPECIFICATIONS table.

3) In same manner, perform test for "R" range. If measured pressures are not up to specifications, recheck throttle link adjustment and retest.

4) If measured values are higher than specifications, throttle valve may be defective or throttle circuit orifice may be clogged.

5) If measured values are lower than specifications, oil pump may be defective, regulator valve may be defective or throttle valve may be defective.

HYDRAULIC PRESSURE SPECIFICATIONS

Application	psi (kg/cm²) In "R"	psi (kg/cm²) In "D"
Governor Pressure		
19 MPH		17-26 (1.2-1.8)
31 MPH		26-34 (1.8-2.4)
63 MPH		54-71 (3.8-5.0)
Line Pressure		
At Idle Speed	108-119 (7.6-8.4)	57-65 (4.0-4.6)
At Stall Speed	252-287 (17.7-20.2)	132-161 (9.3-11.3)
Throttle Pressure		
At Idle Speed	0-4.3 (0-.3)	0-4.3 (0-.3)
At Stall Speed	110-118 (7.7-8.3)	110-118 (7.7-8.3)

REMOVAL & INSTALLATION
TRANSMISSION
See appropriate AUTOMATIC TRANSMISSION REMOVAL article in IMPORT GENERAL SERVICING section.

TOYOTA MODEL A-55 (Cont.)

TRANSMISSION DISASSEMBLY

1) Remove transmission from transaxle. Remove neutral start switch. Remove speedometer driven gear housing from extension housing. Remove extension housing and gasket. Remove speedometer drive gear. Remove output shaft sleeve.

NOTE: Be careful not to lose locking balls.

CAUTION: Do not turn transmission over as this will contaminate valve body with foreign materials in bottom of pan.

2) Remove pan and gasket. Examine particles in pan. Remove magnet and use it to collect any steel chips. Look carefully at chips and particles in pan and on magnet to anticipate what type of wear may be found in transmission.

Fig. 8: Removing Accumulator Pistons With Compressed Air

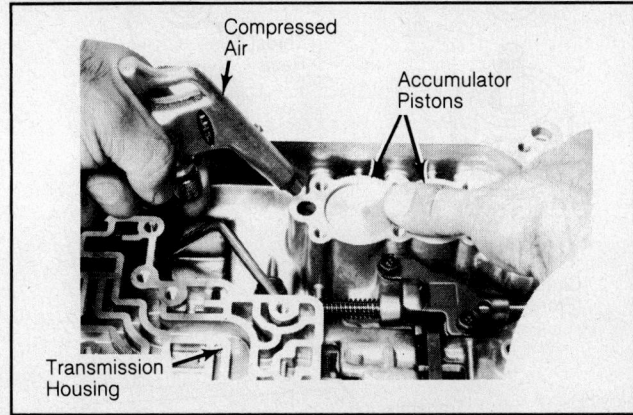

3) Steel (magnetic) means bearing, gear or clutch plate wear. Brass (nonmagnetic) means bushing wear. Turn transmission over and remove tubes by prying up both tube ends with a large screwdriver. Remove screen.

4) Remove valve body by removing 14 bolts, 6 steel balls and valve vibrating stopper. To remove accumulator pistons and springs, position a rag to catch each piston and using low pressure compressed air, 14 psi (1 kg/cm²), pop each piston into rag. See Fig. 8.

CAUTION: Keep face away to avoid injury. Do not use regular high pressure air.

5) Remove park lock rod, spring, pivot pin and parking lock pawl. Remove spacer by unstaking spacer and turning ring 90°. Using a hammer and punch, drive out slotted spring pin and remove manual valve lever shaft.

6) After removing bracket bolt, remove pump suction tube. To remove oil pump delivery tube and pressure tube, pry up both tube ends with a large screwdriver and remove tubes. Remove oil pump by loosening 3 pump body-to-pump body (inner) bolts and removing 7 pump body-to-case (outer) bolts, then pull pump from case.

7) Remove input shaft, driven sprocket and chain by removing snap ring and pulling both sprockets out uniformly. Place case, facing up, on a wooden block and remove front support. Measure clearance between case tip and front clutch tip for reference at reassembly. Clearance should be .024-.063" (.6-1.6 mm). See Fig. 12.

Fig. 9: Exploded View of Transmission Valve Body and Related Components

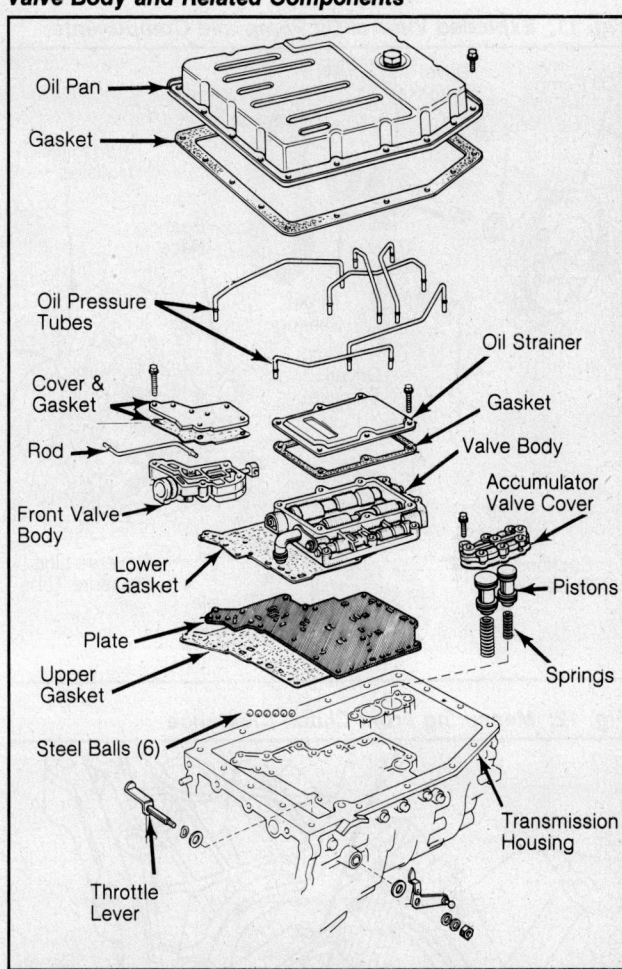

Fig. 10: Exploded View of Parking Lock Pawl and Manual Valve Shaft Components

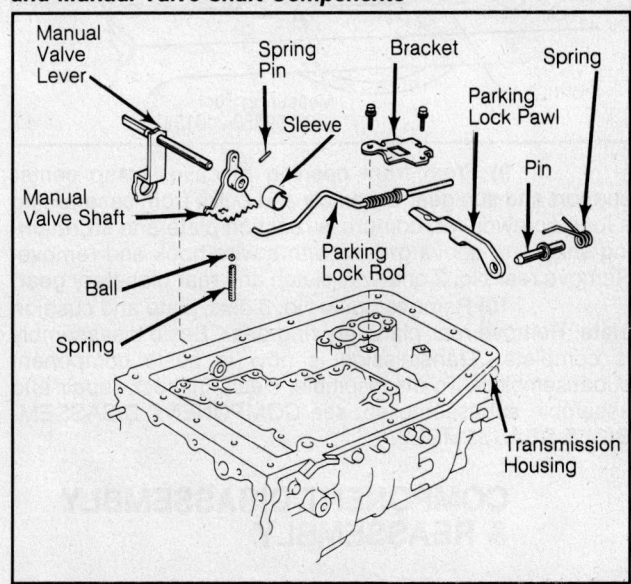

8) Remove front clutch and bearings by grasping shaft and pulling out front clutch assembly. Be careful of bearings and races on both sides of assembly. Remove

output shaft and front planetary gear. Grasp rear clutch hub and pull it from case. Remove two center support bolts.

Fig. 11: Exploded View of Oil Pump and Components

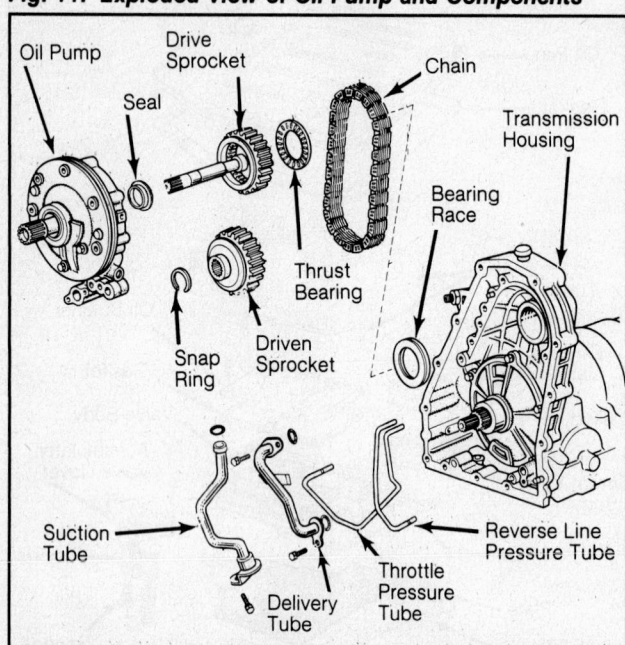

Fig. 12: Measuring Front Clutch Clearance

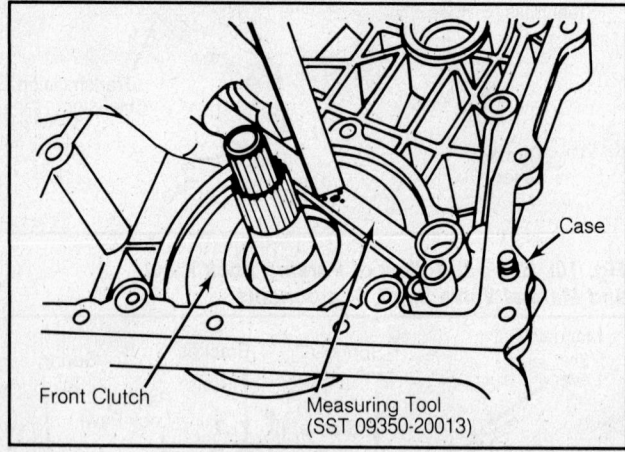

9) From front opening of case, grasp center support and sun gear assembly and pull it from case. Using a long screwdriver, compress reaction plate and lift retaining snap ring above groove with a wire hook and remove. Remove rear No. 2 one-way clutch and rear planetary gear.

10) Remove brake No. 3 disc, plate and cushion plate. Remove rear planetary ring gear. Basic disassembly is complete. Transmission is now in basic component subassemblies. To disassemble, clean, inspect, repair and assemble subassemblies, see COMPONENT DISASSEMBLY & REASSEMBLY.

COMPONENT DISASSEMBLY & REASSEMBLY

OIL PUMP AND REGULATOR VALVE
Disassembly
1) Remove large "O" ring from around pump, then remove 3 inside bolts attaching pump cover to pump

Fig. 13: Exploded View of Output Shaft & Components

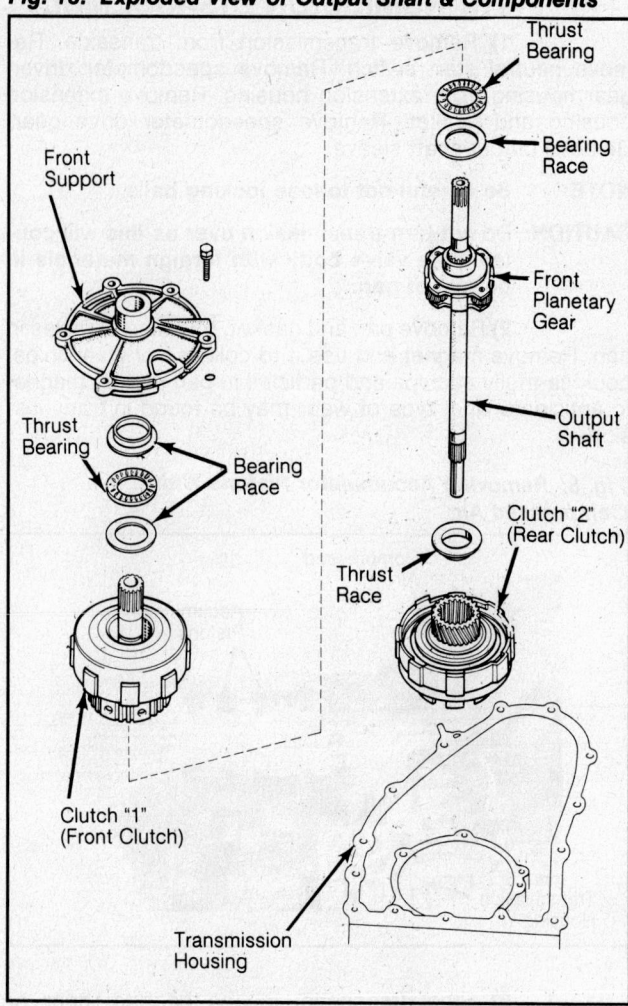

body. Remove snap ring and bearing race from rear of pump body.

2) Remove pump cover and plate from front of pump body, being careful not to let springs and check valves fly out. Remove check ball and spring, then remove priming valve and spring. Remove oil pump drive and driven gears. Remove snap ring, then remove regulator valve assembly. See Fig. 15.

NOTE: When adjusting shims are removed, keep shims together for reassembly.

Cleaning & Inspection
Check pump cover, plate, body and gears for wear or damage. Check bearing race, bushing and pump shaft for scoring, wear or damage. Check regulator valve body (in pump body) for wear or damage. Check regulator valve and spring for damage, scoring or wear. Check priming valve, check ball and springs for wear or damage. Measure spring lengths and replace if not to specifications.

NOTE: When adjusting shims are removed, keep shims together for reassembly.

TOYOTA MODEL A-55 (Cont.)

Fig. 14: Removing Center Support & Rear Clutch

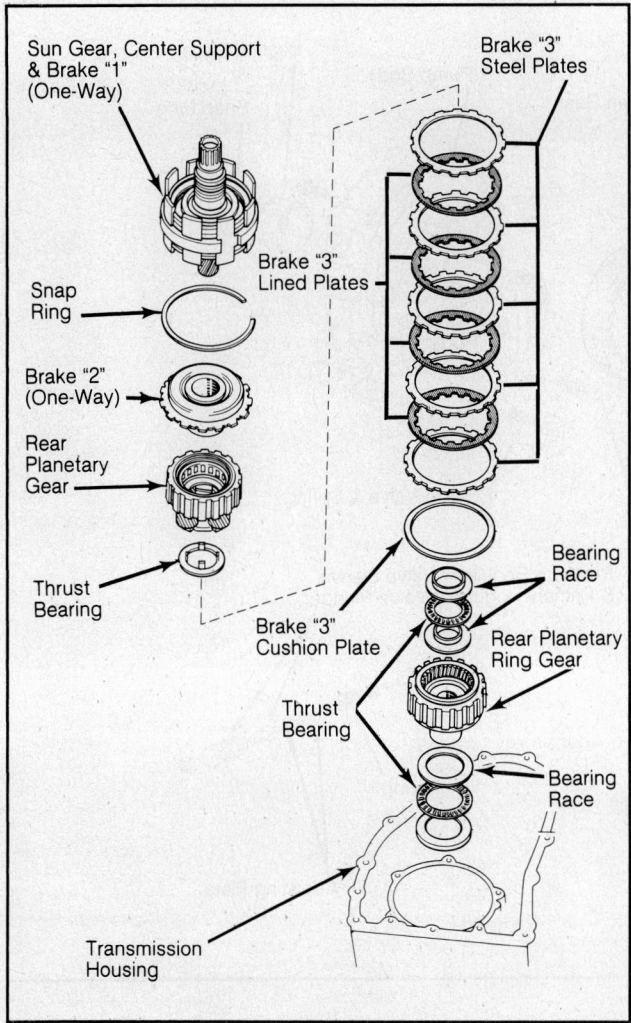

OIL PUMP SPRING FREE LENGTH

Application	In. (mm)
Regulator Spring	2.197 (55.8)
Check Ball Spring	1.032 (26.2)
Priming Valve	.756 (19.2)

Reassembly

1) Install oil pump driven and drive gears to pump body. Using a feeler gauge, measure clearance between a straightedge (layed across pump body) and pump gears. Clearance should be .0008-.002" (.02-.05 mm). Measure clearance between driven gear and pump body.

2) Clearance should be .0028-.0060" (.07-.15 mm). Next, measure clearance between driven gear tooth and crescent in pump body. Clearance should be .0043-.0055" (.11-.14 mm). *See Fig. 16.* If clearances are not to specifications, replace oil pump.

3) Install check ball valve spring and check ball to pump body. Install priming valve spring and priming valve to pump body. Lubricate large "O" ring with ATF fluid, then install onto pump cover. Assemble pump cover plate to pump cover and install pump cover to pump body.

NOTE: When installing pump cover, make sure check ball and priming valve seat into pump body correctly.

4) Temporarily install and tighten (by hand) inside bolts to retain pump cover in place. Check rotation of pump drive gear. Install pressure regulator valve, washer and spring to pump body. Assemble same number of adjusting shims as removed to plunger, then install plunger to spring in pump body. Install sleeve and snap ring.

INPUT SHAFT, GEARS & CHAIN
Disassembly

Check input shaft, drive and driven gears for wear or damage. Remove snap ring, roller bearing and thrust bearing from input shaft driven gear. Check components for wear, scoring or damage. Check input shaft drive gear rear thrust bearing and race for wear or damage. Inspect chain for wear or damage. Check input shaft oil seal rings for wear or damage.

Reassembly

Replace any components found worn or damaged. Replace oil seal rings if worn or damaged. Install thrust bearing and roller bearing into input shaft driven gear and install snap ring. Install thrust bearing and roller bearing to input shaft drive gear and install snap ring. Place thrust bearing and race to rear of input shaft.

FRONT SUPPORT
Disassembly

Check mating surfaces of front support for wear or damage. Check oil seal rings on support shaft and replace if worn or damaged. Check front support shaft bushing for wear or damage.

Reassembly

Install new oil seal rings if they were worn or damaged. Install new small "O" ring to front support.

NOTE: Oil seal ring ends are interlocking. Make sure rings fit together correctly.

CLUTCH "1" (FRONT CLUTCH)
Disassembly

1) Remove thrust bearing and race from front side of race. Note position of races. Remove large snap ring from front clutch drum. Remove front and rear clutch hub by lifting out together. Remove thrust bearings and races. Note position of races.

2) Remove clutch plate and disc. Remove thin snap ring. Remove remaining clutch plates and discs. Place compressor tool (SST09350-20013) on spring retainer and compress springs with a press. Using a screwdriver, remove snap ring. Remove spring retainer and all springs.

3) Slide front clutch onto front support. Apply compressed air to front support to remove piston. Remove front clutch from front support. *See Fig. 17.*

NOTE: Do NOT allow discs to dry out. Prepare new discs by soaking at least 2 hours in ATF.

Fig. 15: Exploded View of Oil Pump and Regulator Valve Assembly

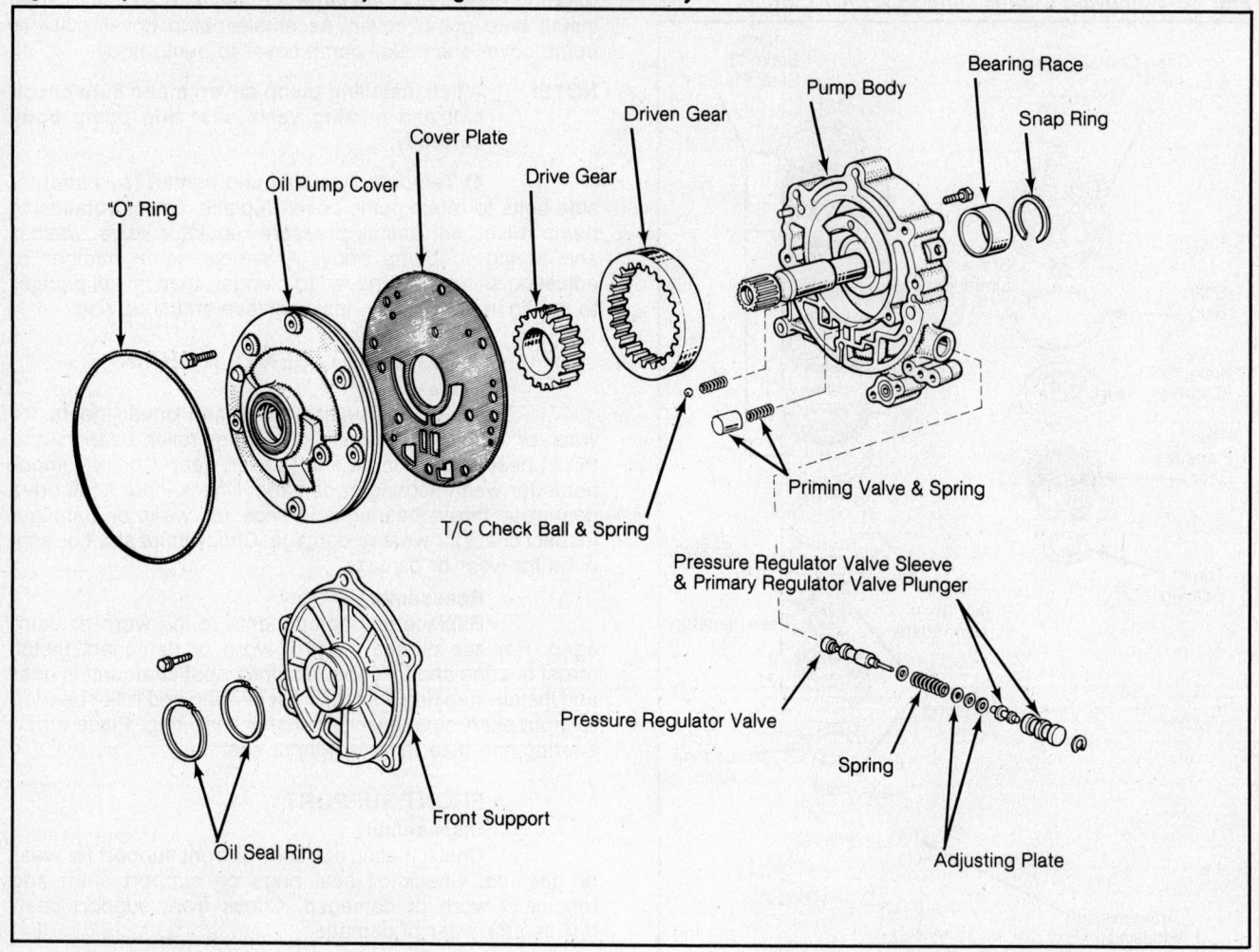

Cleaning & Inspection

Inspect front clutch piston. Check that check ball is free by shaking piston. Check that valve does not leak by applying low-pressure compressed air.

Reassembly

1) Install new "O" rings on piston. Install piston in front clutch drum. Press housing with cup side up (check ball down). Be careful not to damage "O" rings.

2) Install 20 piston return springs, spring retainer and snap ring into place. Compress return springs on spring retainer with Compressor (SST09350-20013) and arbor. Install snap ring with a screwdriver.

3) Using low-pressure compressed air, blow all excess ATF from discs. For measurement of clutch pack, install all plates and discs (temporarily without thinner snap ring). Install in following order: Cushion plate, plate, disc, plate, disc, plate, disc, plate.

4) Measure completely around circumference of front clutch. Standard clearance is .0118-.0587" (.30-1.49 mm). If not, use thicker snap ring. Remove snap ring, rear clutch hub and 1 plate and disc to allow installation of inner snap ring. Install inner race and needle bearing.

5) Press into place. Face lip of race toward front of clutch body. Install planetary ring gear, aligning disc lugs with hub teeth. Make sure hub meshes with all discs and is fully inserted. Install rear clutch drum and outer snap ring. Check that snap ring ends are not aligned with cut-outs.

OUTPUT SHAFT & FRONT PLANETARY GEAR
Disassembly

1) Remove thrust bearing and race from front side of planetary gear. Remove planetary gear snap ring. Pull planetary gear off output shaft. Check output shaft for wear or damage.

2) Check planetary gear for wear or damage. Check planetary gear thrust play. Thrust play should be .008-.020" (.2-.5 mm). Check planetary thrust bearing and race for wear or damage. Replace components as necessary.

Reassembly

To reassemble output shaft and front planetary gear, reverse disassembly procedure.

CLUTCH "2" (REAR CLUTCH)
Disassembly

1) Remove large snap ring, then remove steel plates and lined plates noting order of removal. Compress piston return spring seat and remove small snap ring.

2) Slowly remove pressure on spring seat, then remove spring seat with all return springs. Remove inner piston, then remove outer piston. See Fig. 18.

3) If pistons are difficult to remove, place clutch drum into center support. Using air pressure applied to

TOYOTA MODEL A-55 (Cont.)

Fig. 16: Measuring Oil Pump Gear Clearance

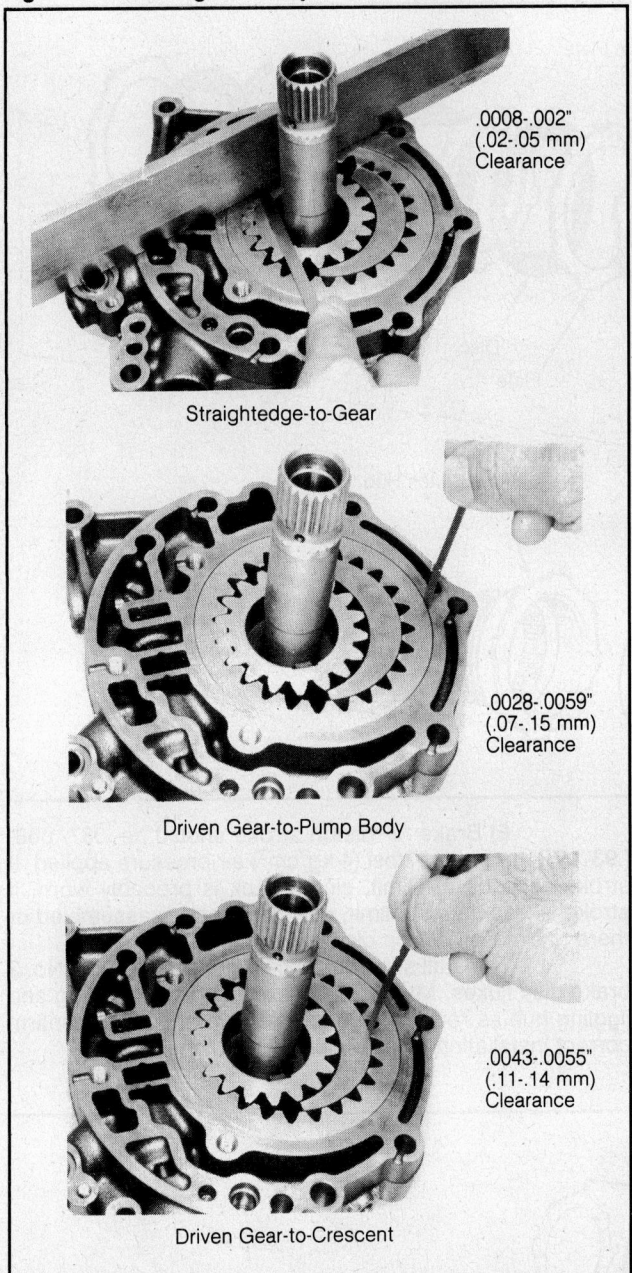

.0008-.002"
(.02-.05 mm)
Clearance

Straightedge-to-Gear

.0028-.0059"
(.07-.15 mm)
Clearance

Driven Gear-to-Pump Body

.0043-.0055"
(.11-.14 mm)
Clearance

Driven Gear-to-Crescent

inner piston port, blow out inner piston. Move air pressure to outer piston port and remove outer piston. *See Fig. 19.*

Cleaning & Inspection

1) Check clutch drum, sun gear, spring retainer and piston for wear or damage. Make sure seal ring contacting surface and snap ring groove areas are not damaged. Shake outer piston to make sure check ball has movement. Apply air to check ball orifice. No air should leak by.

2) Check inner piston in same manner as outer. Check return springs for a free length of 1.138" (28.9 mm), outside coil diameter of .315" (8.0 mm) and for 12 coils. Check steel plates and lined plates for burning, excessive wear or other damage.

Reassembly

1) Install new "O" rings to inner and outer pistons (lubricate "O" rings before installation). Lubricate pistons and install into clutch drum. Make sure spring seats in pistons are facing out of drum. With springs installed to pistons, install spring seat and compress to install snap ring. Make sure snap ring is seated properly before releasing spring compressor.

2) Install plates to clutch drum in this order: steel plate, lined plate, 2 steel plates, lined plate and cushion plate. Make sure round edge of cushion plate faces into drum. Install snap ring.

3) Install clutch "2" into center support and apply air pressure to center support. *See Fig. 20.* Measure piston stroke. Measurement should be .0386.0748" (.98-1.90 mm) with 56 psi (4 kg/cm^2) air pressure applied.

4) Apply air pressure to center support brake "2" pressure port to remove piston. Remove No. 2 piston "O" rings. Remove 3 oil seal rings from center support. Remove one-way clutch assembly and oil seal rings from sun gear.

CENTER SUPPORT AND COMPONENTS
Disassembly

1) Withdraw sun gear from center support. Remove front one-way clutch from center support. Remove large snap ring holding brake "1" plates, then remove steel plate, lined plate and cushion plate.

2) Compress spring retainer of brake "1". Remove small snap ring and slowly release compressor. Remove springs, then apply air pressure to remove piston. Remove No. 1 piston "O" rings.

3) Turn center support over and remove large snap ring, steel plates and lined plates for brake "2". Using a spring compressor, compress spring seat of brake "2" and remove small snap ring. Slowly release pressure and remove spring seat with springs.

Cleaning & Inspection

1) Check all components for wear or damage. Check center support oil seal rings and grooves for wear or damage. Check brake "1" and brake "2" springs for a free length of .635" (16.1 mm), coil outside diameter of .315" (8.0 mm) and for 6 coils.

2) Check front one-way clutch by inserting sun gear into clutch and checking for rotation. From sun gear tooth end, sun gear should rotate counterclockwise but lock up in clockwise rotation. Check oil seal rings on sun gear. Replace components as necessary.

Reassembly

1) Install new "O" rings and one-way clutch assembly on sun gear. Install new oil seal rings on center support. Install new "O" rings on brake pistons and lubricate with ATF fluid. Install brake "1" piston into center support by pressing in with cup side up, being careful not to damage "O" rings.

2) Rotate by hand to make sure it is seated correctly. Place springs on piston and position spring retainer with snap ring in place. Compress spring retainer and install small snap ring. Install new "O" rings on center support and piston.

3) Turn center support over and install brake "2" piston, springs and retainer in the same manner as brake "1". Turn center support over and install No. 1 brake "1" plates, disc and flange. Use low pressue compressed air to blow all excess ATF from discs. *See Fig. 20* for steel plate and lined plate installation sequence.

4) With large snap rings installed to brake plates, measure piston stroke of brake piston. Make sure

Automatic Transmissions
TOYOTA MODEL A-55 (Cont.)

Fig. 17: Exploded View of Clutch "1" (Front Clutch)

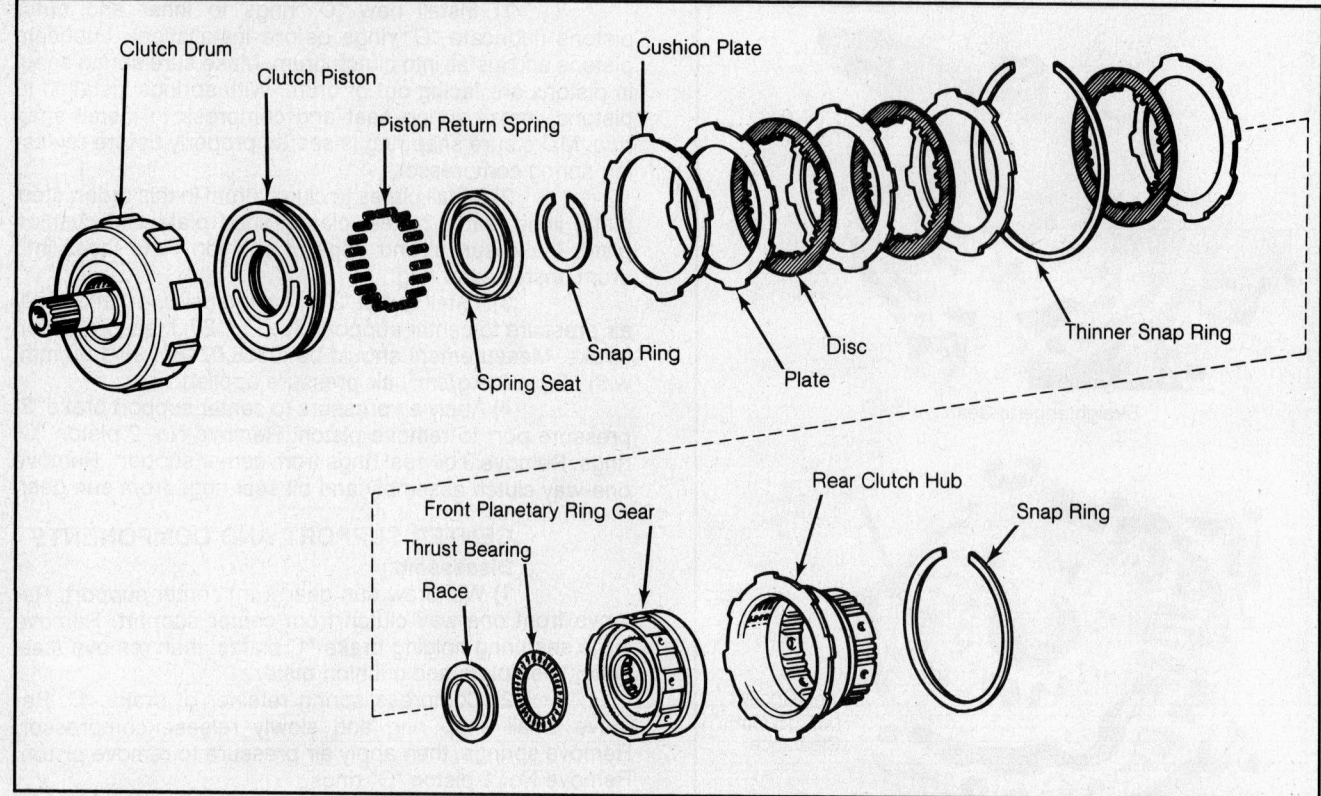

snap ring ends are not aligned with cut-outs. Brake "1" piston stroke should be .026-.051" (.65-1.3 mm) with 57 psi (4 kg/cm²) air pressure applied.

5) Turn center support over and install No. 2 brake piston plate, discs and flange in the same manner as No. 1. Using low pressure compressed air, blow all excess ATF from discs. Install snap ring to center support. Make sure snap ring is not aligned with cut-outs.

6) Brake "2" piston stroke should be .037-.068" (.93-1.72 mm) with 57 psi (4 kg/cm²) air pressure applied. If stroke exceeds the limit, clutch pack is probably worn. If stroke is less than the limit, parts may be misassembled or there is excess ATF on discs.

7) Install sun gear to center support. Align No. 2 brake disc flukes. Mesh brake hub with discs, twisting and jiggling hub as required. Check rotation of gear to confirm correct installation of front one-way clutch.

Fig. 18: Exploded View of Clutch "2" (Rear Clutch)

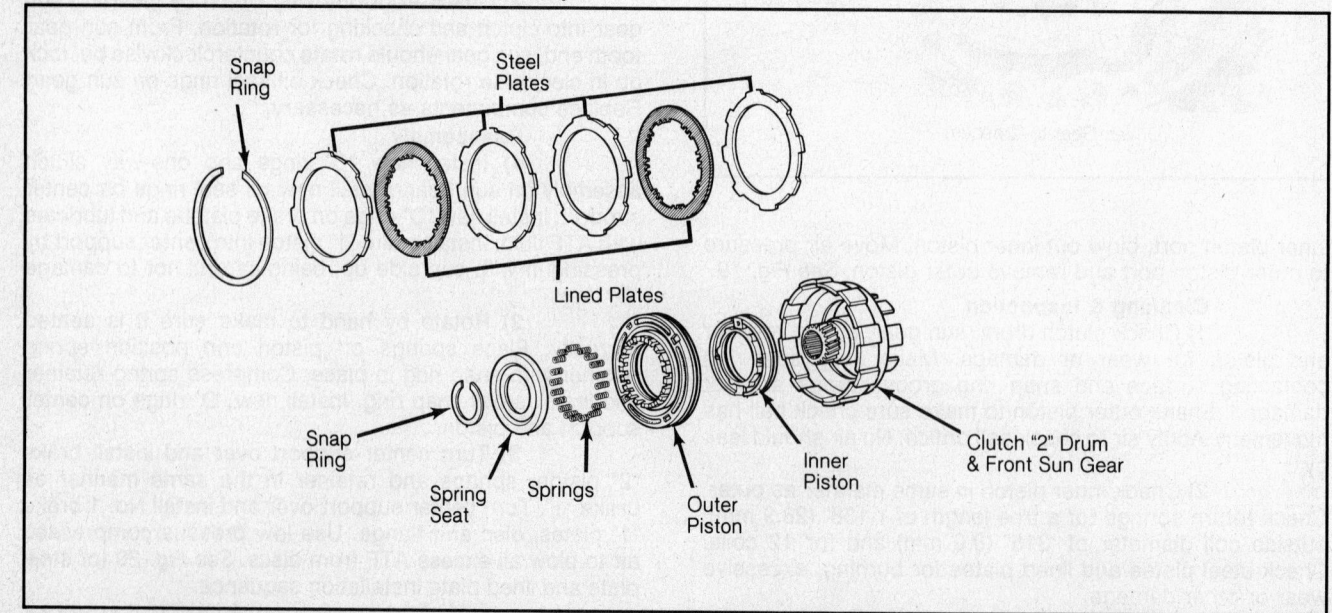

Fig. 19: *Removing Inner and Outer Pistons of Clutch "2" with Compressed Air*

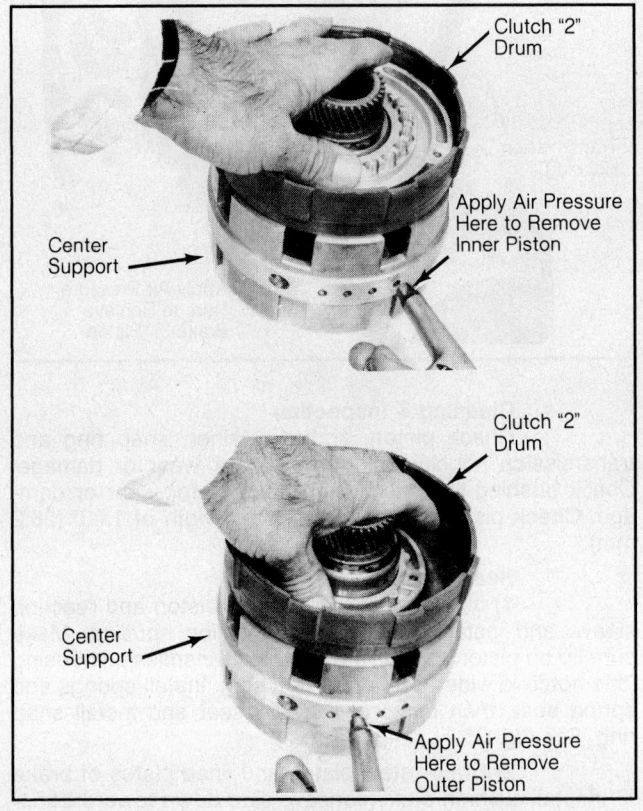

Fig. 21: *Checking Clutch "2" Piston Stroke*

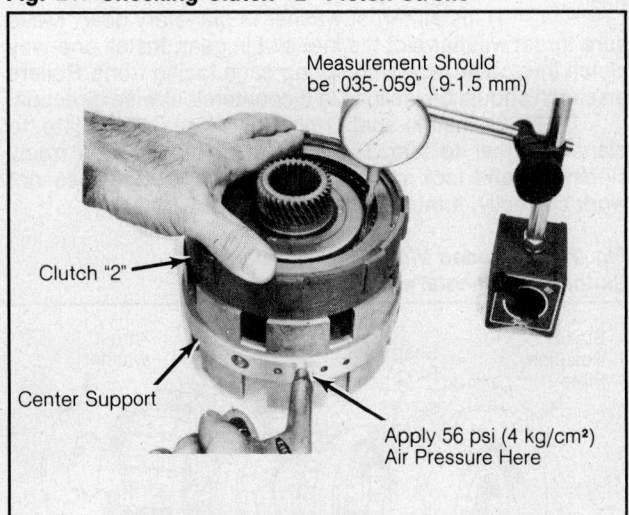

REAR ONE-WAY CLUTCH & PLANETARY GEAR

Disassembly

Remove thrust washer from rear of planetary gear. Remove brake reaction plate from front of planetary gear. Remove snap ring, one-way clutch and thrust washer from planetary gear. *See Fig. 22.*

Cleaning & Inspection

Check one-way clutch, brake reaction plate, and thrust washers for wear or damage. Check planetary gears for smooth rotation and any damage to gear teeth. Check all thrust bearings for damage or wear.

Fig. 20: *Exploded View of Center Support, Brake "1", Brake "2", Sun Gear and Front One-Way Clutch*

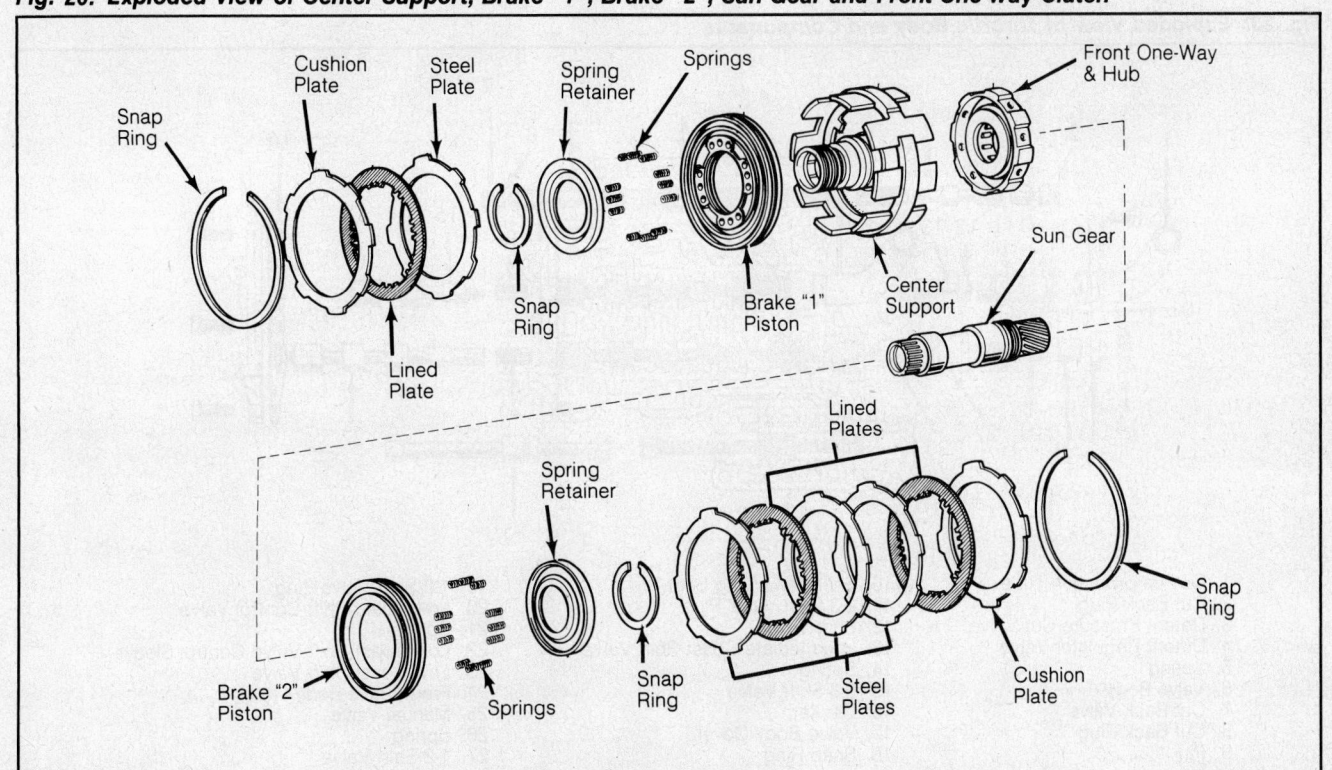

Reassembly

1) Install thrust washer in planetary gear. Make sure thrust washer slot fits into slot in gear. Install one-way clutch into outer race with spring cage facing front. Rollers on clutch should be inclined in a counterclockwise direction.

2) Install snap ring. Install reaction plate to planetary gear to test. Planetary gear must rotate freely clockwise and lock counterclockwise. If clutch does not work correctly, it must be replaced.

Fig. 22: Exploded View of Rear One-Way Clutch and Planetary Gear

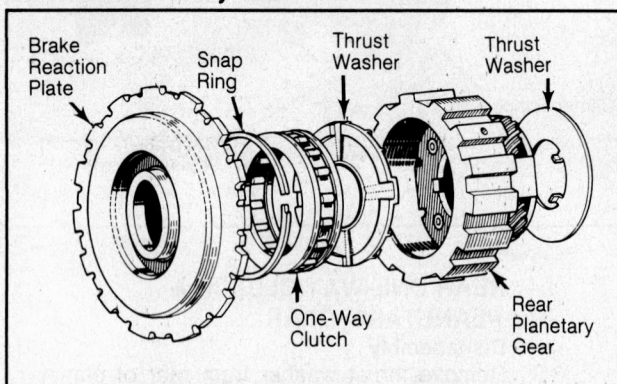

BRAKE "3" PISTON
Disassembly

Compress spring retainer. Remove small snap ring. Slowly release spring compressor and remove spring retainer and springs. Place shop towels on top of piston and ease piston out slowly while applying air pressure to brake "3" pressure port. *See Fig. 24.*

Fig. 24: Removing Brake "3" Piston with Air Pressure

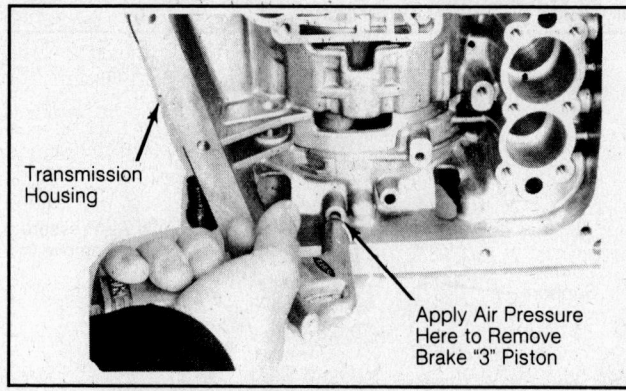

Cleaning & Inspection

Check piston, spring retainer, snap ring and transmission housing (piston area) for wear or damage. Check bushing in transmission housing for wear or damage. Check piston springs for a free length of 1.03" (26.2 mm).

Reassembly

1) Install a new "O" ring to piston and reaction sleeve and install piston to transmission housing. Make sure lip on piston mates with notch in transmission housing (this notch is wider than other notches). Install springs and spring seat, then compress spring seat and install snap ring. *See Fig. 25.*

2) Check steel plates and lined plates of brake "3". Install cushion plate (concave side down toward transmission housing). Install brake plates, starting with a steel plate and alternating with lined plates until all plates are installed.

Fig. 23: Exploded View of Throttle Body and Components

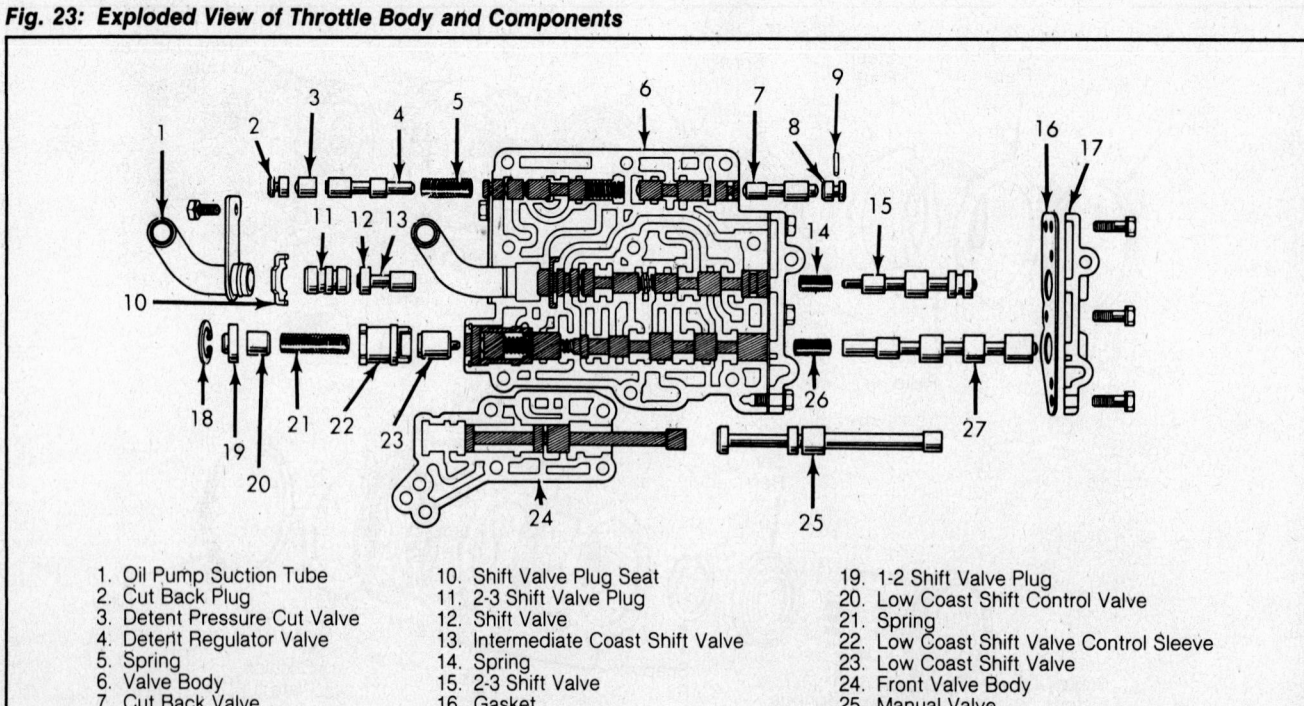

1. Oil Pump Suction Tube	10. Shift Valve Plug Seat	19. 1-2 Shift Valve Plug
2. Cut Back Plug	11. 2-3 Shift Valve Plug	20. Low Coast Shift Control Valve
3. Detent Pressure Cut Valve	12. Shift Valve	21. Spring
4. Detent Regulator Valve	13. Intermediate Coast Shift Valve	22. Low Coast Shift Valve Control Sleeve
5. Spring	14. Spring	23. Low Coast Shift Valve
6. Valve Body	15. 2-3 Shift Valve	24. Front Valve Body
7. Cut Back Valve	16. Gasket	25. Manual Valve
8. Cut Back Plug	17. Valve Body Cover	26. Spring
9. Pin	18. Snap Ring	27. 1-2 Shift Valve

Fig. 25: Exploded View of Brake "3"

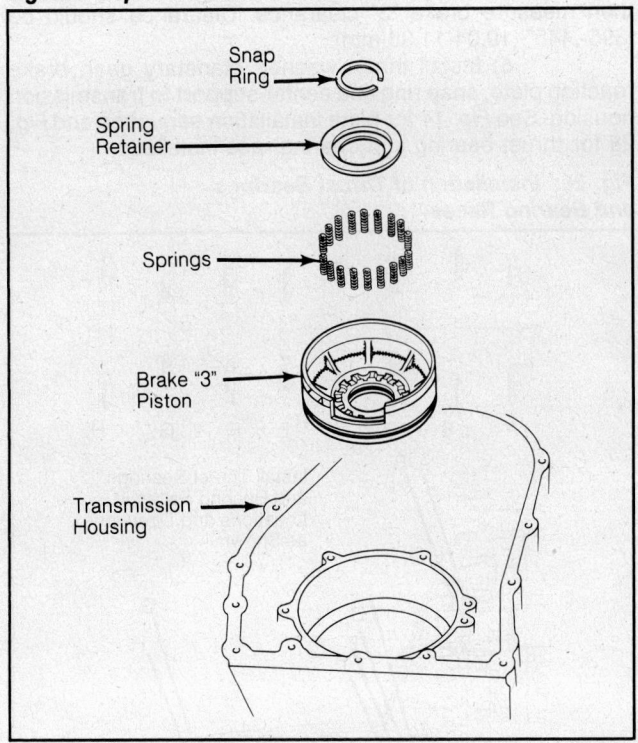

VALVE BODY SPRING FREE LENGTH

Application	In. (mm)
1-2 Shift Valve Spring	1.024 (26.0)
Low-Coast Valve Spring	1.437 (36.5)
2-3 Shift Valve Spring	.870 (22.1)
Detent Regulator Valve Spring	1.079 (27.4)
Throttle Valve Spring (Front)	1.193 (30.3)
Throttle Valve Spring (Rear)	1.083 (27.5)

Fig. 26: Exploded View of Throttle Valve

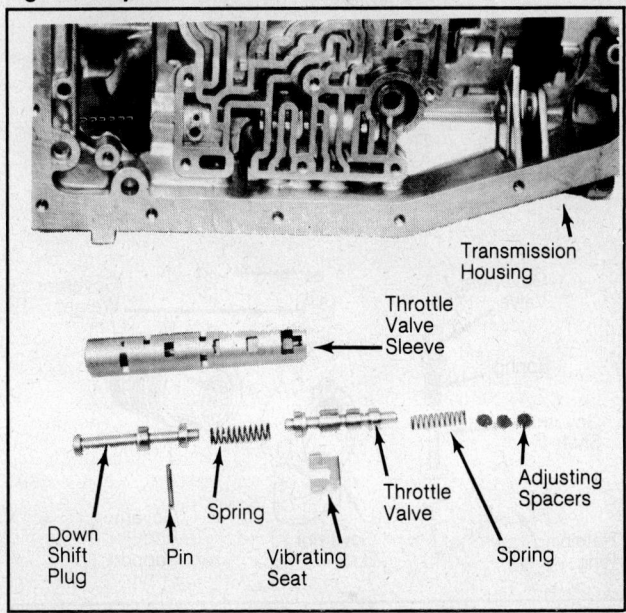

3) Measure brake "3" clearance. Clearance should be .395-.445" (10.04-11.30 mm). If clearance is not to specifications, recheck plates for excessive wear or a damaged cushion plate. Replace components as necessary.

VALVE BODY ASSEMBLY

NOTE: When disassembling valve body, lay removed components out in order for reassembly reference.

Disassembly

1) Remove valve body plate and gaskets. Remove manual valve from front valve body. Remove front valve body from valve body. Remove pin from cut back plug, then remove plug and cut back valve. Remove cover and gasket, then remove 2-3 shift valve seat, valve and spring.

2) Remove 1-2 shift valve and spring. Remove oil pump suction tube. Remove detent pressure cut valve plug then detent pressure cut valve. Remove detent regulator valve and spring.

3) Remove shift valve plug seat, 2-3 shift valve plug and intermediate coast shift valve. Remove snap ring, plug, low coast shift control valve and spring. Remove low coast shift control valve sleeve and valve. *See Fig. 23.*

4) Remove vibrating stopper for throttle valve. Remove downshift plug pin, then remove downshift plug. Remove throttle valve, spring and adjusting spacer(s). Remove throttle valve sleeve. Record number of adjusting spacers for reassembly reference. *See Fig. 26.*

Cleaning & Inspection

Check all components for wear, scoring or damage. Check springs for proper free length.

Reassembly

1) Install manual valve into front valve body. Insert low coast shift valve, low coast shift control valve

sleeve, low coast shift control valve, 1-2 shift valve plug, and snap ring to valve body. *See Fig. 23.* Insert intermediate coast shift valve with small end down to valve body.

2) Insert 2-3 shift valve plug into valve body and hold in place with shift valve plug seat (tangs on seat face into valve body). Place detent regulator valve spring, detent regulator valve, detent pressure cut valve and plug into valve body. Plug has a groove cut into it. Place edge of oil pump suction tube into this groove to hold components in place.

3) Attach suction tube to valve body with bolt. *See Fig. 23.* Insert 1-2 shift valve spring, 1-2 shift valve (small end down), 2-3 shift valve spring and 2-3 shift valve into valve body. Attach valve body cover, with gasket, to hold shift valves in position. Install cut back valve (small end down) and plug into valve body.

4) Insert pin into cut back valve plug. *See Fig. 23.* Install cut back valve retainer. Coat pin with petroleum jelly to keep it in place. Install same number of adjusting spacers into throttle valve sleeve as removed, then install sleeve into transmission housing. Insert spring, throttle valve, spring, down shift plug and pin into transmission housing.

5) Insert vibrating stopper into transmission housing. Apply petroleum jelly to hold it in place. *See Fig. 26.* Attach front valve body cover to valve body.

GOVERNOR VALVE

Disassembly

Remove snap ring and washer. Remove governor body support. Pry up retaining ring slightly with a screwdriver and pull out governor body with support. Compress spring by pushing up on the shaft and down on the weight. Remove "E" clip with screwdriver. Lift off governor weight. Remove governor valve by sliding it through bore. *See Fig. 27.*

Fig. 27: Exploded View of Governor Valve Assembly

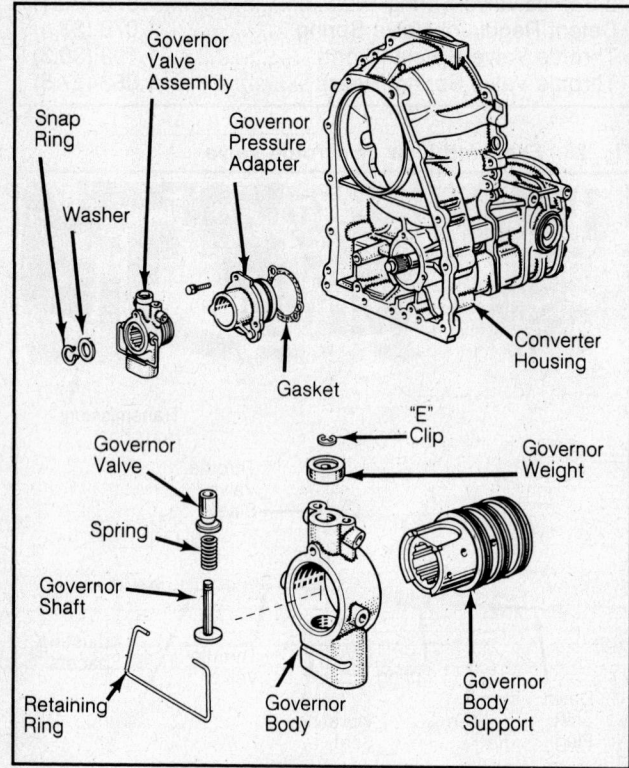

Cleaning & Inspection

Check all governor components for wear or damage. Check governor body support oil seal rings for wear or damage. Check governor spring for free length of .772" (19.6 mm). Clean oil strainer and check for wear or damage.

Reassembly

To reassemble governor, reverse disassembly procedure. Replace oil seal. Make sure retaining ring holes in governor body support are aligned with holes in governor body. When installing "O" ring and drive pinion, coat with multi-purpose grease.

TRANSMISSION REASSEMBLY

1) Install drive plate, with spacers, to crankshaft. Install front spacer, .127" (3.2 mm) thick, with beveled edge facing drive plate, then install drive plate. Install rear spacer, .056" (1.4 mm) thick, with cupped edge facing converter.

2) Install thrust bearing and races, then install rear planetary ring gear to transmission housing. Install cushion plate and steel and lined plates to transmission housing. Install thrust bearing by coating race with petroleum jelly and sticking to ring gear.

3) Align notch and tab of thrust washer and planetary gear, coat thrust washer with petroleum jelly and stick to planetary gear. Align disc flukes. Install rear planetary gear and thrust plate.

4) Make sure planetary ring gear is fully seated, then measure brake "3" clearance. Clearance should be .395-.445" (10.04-11.30 mm).

5) Install thrust washer, planetary gear, brake reaction plate, snap ring and center support to transmission housing. See *Fig. 14* for plate installation sequence and *Fig. 28* for thrust bearing and bearing race installation.

Fig. 28: Installation of Thrust Bearings and Bearing Races

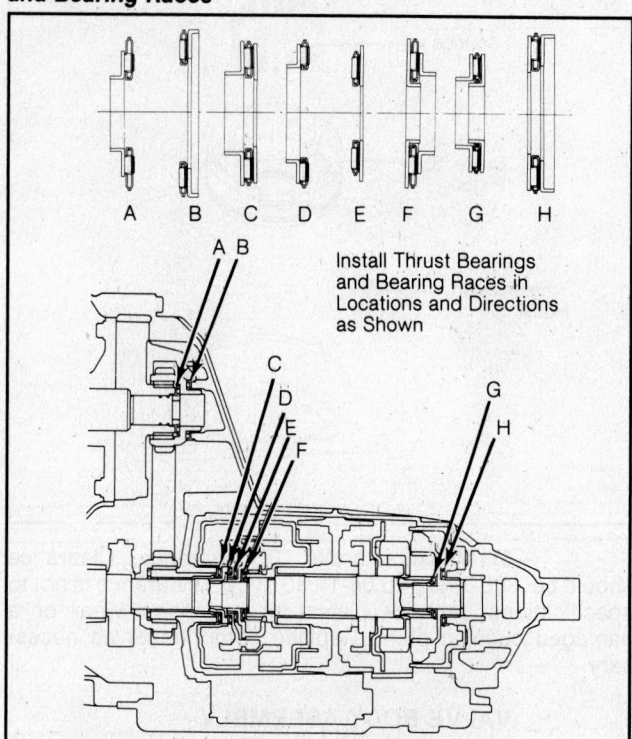

Install Thrust Bearings and Bearing Races in Locations and Directions as Shown

6) Install center support bolts, make sure oil holes in center support are aligned with oil holes in transmission housing and tighten center support bolts. After center support bolt installation, make sure planetary sun gear is easy to turn in a clockwise direction and hard to turn in a counterclockwise direction.

7) Install clutch "2", bearing race and output shaft to transmission housing. *See Fig. 13.* Install a thrust bearing and race over output shaft. Align the flukes of the rear clutch discs and mesh them with the front clutch hub. Install front clutch assembly into case (over output shaft).

8) After clutch "1" installation, lay a straightedge across clutch drum and transmission housing. Measure distance from straightedge to clutch drum. Distance should be the same as distance measured during disassembly. Standard distance is .024-.063" (.6-1.6 mm).

9) Install thrust bearing and race to clutch "1" shaft. Insert bearing race into front support. Install "O" ring to transmission housing. *See Fig. 29.* Coat thrust washer with petroleum jelly and set into front support with lip side to front support.

10) Install front support to transmission housing. Make sure there is no clearance between surfaces of support and case when pressing down. If there is clearance, front support is not correctly installed. Make sure there is thrust play on input shaft and tighten bolts diagonally a little at a time.

TOYOTA MODEL A-55 (Cont.)

Fig. 29: Installation of "O" Ring in Transmission Housing Oil Passage

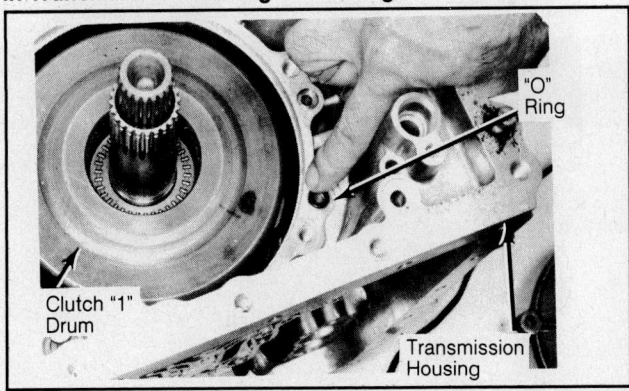

Fig. 31: Installation Locations of Valve Body Steel Balls

11) After front support installation, check clutch "1" shaft for ease of rotation and that end play is .0094-.0378" (.24-.96 mm). Check output shaft for ease of rotation and that end play is .012-.060" (.31-1.53 mm).

12) Place transmission so valve body side is down and install bearing race, thrust bearing, input shaft and drive sprocket to front of transmission housing. Install chain and driven sprocket, then secure driven sprocket with snap ring. Measure clearance between snap ring and driven sprocket. Clearance should be .0043-.027" (.11-.69 mm).

13) Install bearing race to input shaft, then install oil pump over input shaft. See Fig. 15. Install throttle pressure tube, then install reverse line pressure tube to front of transmission housing. Using new "O" rings, install oil pump delivery tube and oil pump suction to front of transmission housing. See Fig. 30.

14) Assemble new collar to manual valve lever. Install manual valve lever. While holding detent ball with plate, install manual valve shaft. Drive in slotted spring pin (always use new pin). After assembly, turn spacer 90° and stake.

15) Install park pawl, pivot pin and spring in case. Install park pawl bracket on case, making sure collar on control rod is toward front of transmission. Make sure planetary gear output shaft is locked when manual valve lever is in "P" range.

16) Turn transmission over so valve body side is up. Install accumulator springs and pistons, fully seating pistons by hand. Install accumulator gasket (straight side of gasket nearest housing), then install accumulator cover. See Fig. 10.

17) Install steel balls into valve body on transmission side. See Fig. 31. Make sure vibrating stopper is still in place and install upper valve body gasket. See Fig. 9 for gasket installation sequence. Also make sure cut back plug lock pin has not fallen out.

Fig. 30: Installation of Oil Tubes and Pipes to Front of Transmission Housing

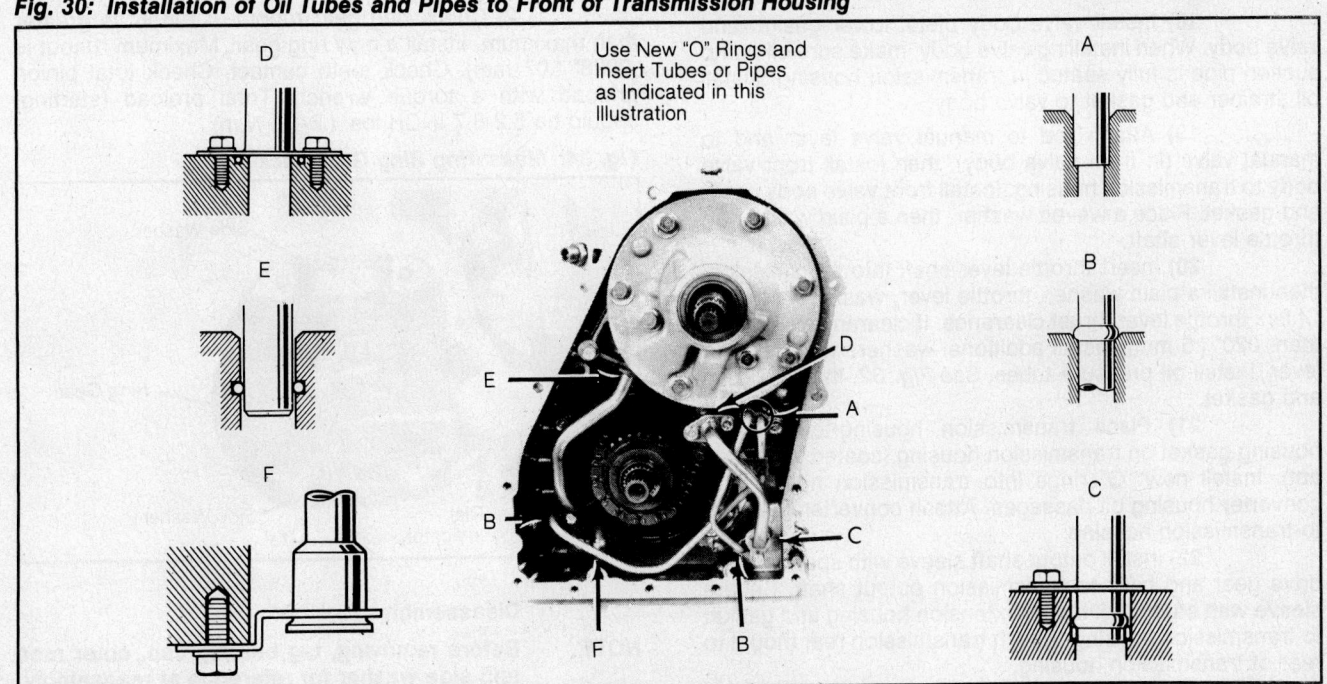

for gasket installation sequence. Also make sure cut back plug lock pin has not fallen out.

Fig. 32: Intallation of Oil Pressure Tubes

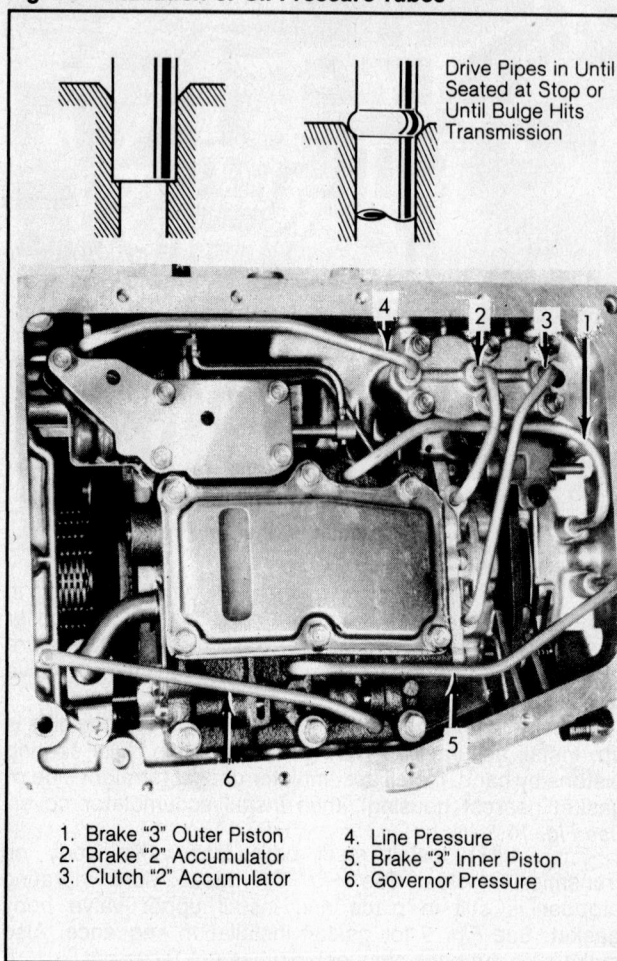

1. Brake "3" Outer Piston
2. Brake "2" Accumulator
3. Clutch "2" Accumulator
4. Line Pressure
5. Brake "3" Inner Piston
6. Governor Pressure

18) Install valve body plate, lower gasket and valve body. When installing valve body, make sure oil pump suction pipe is fully seated in transmission housing. Install oil strainer and gasket to valve body.

19) Attach rod to manual valve lever and to manual valve (in front valve body), then install front valve body to transmission housing. Install front valve body cover and gasket. Place a waved washer, then a plain washer on throttle lever shaft.

20) Insert throttle lever shaft into transmission, then install a plain washer, throttle lever, washers and nut. Check throttle lever thrust clearance. If clearance is greater than .020" (.5 mm), install additional washers to outside of lever. Install oil pressure tubes. See Fig. 32. Install oil pan and gasket.

21) Place transmission housing-to-converter housing gasket on transmission housing (coated with sealant). Install new "O" rings into transmission housing-to-converter housing oil passages. Attach converter housing-to-transmission housing.

22) Install output shaft sleeve with speedometer drive gear and balls to transmission output shaft. Secure sleeve with snap ring. Install extension housing and gasket to transmission housing. Attach transmission rear mount to rear of transmission housing.

Fig. 33: Aligning Neutral Start Switch

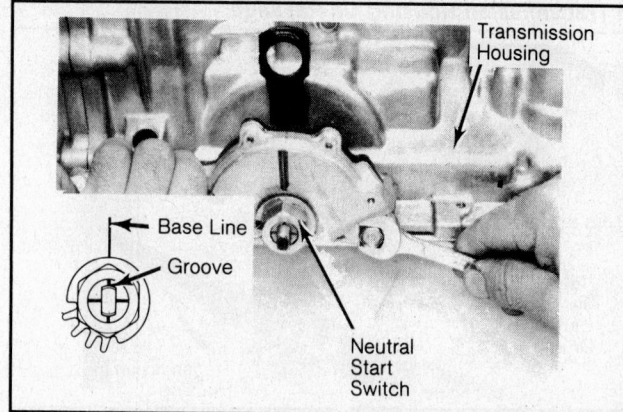

23) Install speedometer driven gear, neutral start switch, oil filler tube and control rod to transmission. When installing neutral start switch, align switch shaft groove to neutral base line. See Fig. 33. Install torque converter.

FINAL DRIVE

DIFFERENTIAL ASSEMBLY
Pre-Inspection

NOTE: If the differential is noisy, perform the following pre-inspection before disassembly to determine the cause of the noise.

1) Remove differential from transaxle. Install differential carrier on work stand with ring gear in horizontal position. Check ring gear backlash. See Fig. 34. If backlash in not within specification, adjust side bearing preload or repair as necessary. Backlash should be .0039-.0059" (.10-.15 mm).

2) Check ring gear runout. If runout is greater than maximum, install a new ring gear. Maximum runout is .0028" (.07 mm). Check teeth contact. Check total pinion preload with a torque wrench. Total preload (starting) should be 5.2-8.7 INCH lbs. (.6-1.0 N.m)

Fig. 34: Measuring Ring Gear Backlash

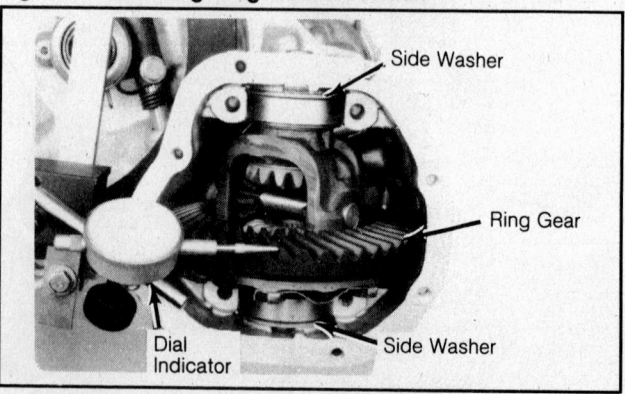

Disassembly

NOTE: Before removing, tag bearing cap, outer race and side washer for reference at reassembly.

1) Remove oil seals from differential carrier using a slide hammer. Remove side bearing caps. Remove side washer on ring gear teeth side using Side Washer Removal Tool (SST 09504-22010).

2) Remove differential case and bearing outer race. Remove side washer opposite ring gear. To remove governor body and governor pressure adaptor, use snap ring pliers to remove snap ring, then remove governor body. Wrap spline with tape and remove governor pressure adaptor.

3) Loosen staked part of drive pinion nut. Using drive pinion holding tool (SST 09564-16010 and SST 09556-16020) to loosen nut, turn drive pinion clockwise. Using a press, press drive pinion from housing.

Cleaning & Inspection

1) Inspect drive pinion bearings and outer races. If necessary, replace drive pinion bearing and outer race using a press to drive pinion from bearing.

NOTE: If drive pinion or ring gear is damaged, replace both as a set.

2) For drive pinion, select a plate washer of proper thickness, in accordance with teeth contact, inspected before disassembly. Install plate washer on drive pinion. Using a press, install new bearing on drive pinion.

3) Using a hammer and brass bar, remove pinion outer races by tapping on notched portions. Using a bearing race installer, install outer races.

4) Inspect case side bearings and outer races. If necessary, replace side bearings and outer races by removing side bearings with a gear puller. The hooked ends of the puller fit into the indentations in the case. Install new bearings using a press.

5) Inspect pinion and side gears. Check side gear backlash by holding one side gear toward case and measuring backlash of the other. Backlash should be .0016-.0094" (.04-.24 mm).

6) If it becomes necessary to replace ring gear, differential pinions and side gears, then lift lock plates and remove set bolts. Using a brass bar and hammer, tap on ring gear to separate it from differential case.

NOTE: If the ring gear is to be used again, before separating it, place marks on ring gear and case for reference at reassembly.

7) Using a pin punch and hammer, tap out pinion shaft retaining pin toward ring gear mating surface. Remove pinion shaft, pinion gears, side gears and thrust washers. Check gears, shaft, case and washers.

8) Install side gears, washers, pinion gears and shaft. Remeasure side gear backlash. If backlash is not within specifications, use proper thickness thrust washer to bring backlash within specifications. Thrust washers are available in thicknesses ranging from .0583-.0697" (1.48-1.77 mm) in increments of .0015" (.04 mm).

9) Using a hammer and punch, drive straight pin through case and hole in pinion shaft. Stake pin in place in differential case. Clean ring gear mating surface on case. Heat ring gear to 194-230°F (90-110°C) in an oil bath. Then quickly install ring gear on differential case.

CAUTION: Do not heat ring gear above 230°F (110°C).

10) Coat ring gear bolts with gear oil. Install lock plates and bolts. Tighten bolts uniformly, in steps and to specifications. Stake lock plate.

NOTE: Stake one claw flush with flat surface of nut. For claw contacting protruding portion of nut, stake (bend) only the half on the tightening side.

11) Inspect governor pressure adaptor oil seal. If necessary, replace oil seals using a press and a 29 mm socket wrench. Press in oil seal on transmission side then press in oil seal on differential side. Be sure oil seal is positioned correctly.

Fig. 35: Exploded View of Final Drive

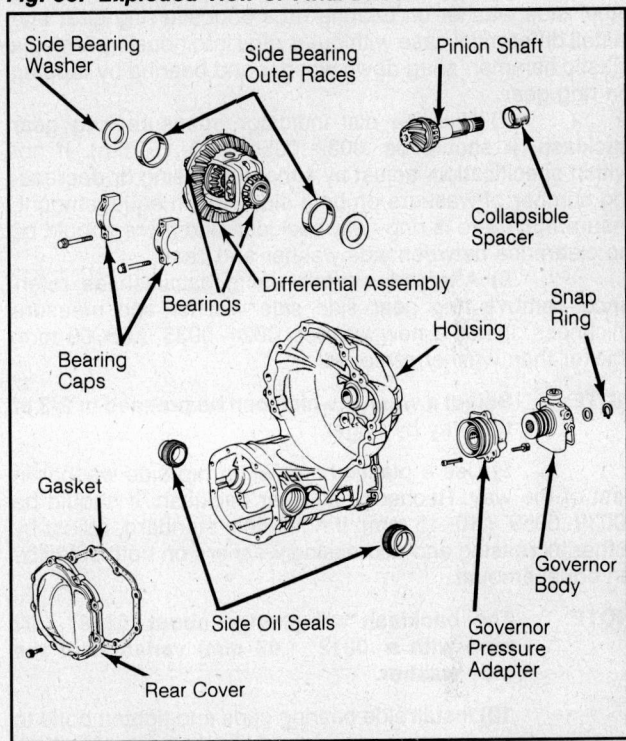

Reassembly

1) Install a new spacer on drive pinion. Install drive pinion into differential carrier. Using a press, temporarily press in bearing until threaded portion is protruding .12" (3 mm) without crushing spacer. Apply gear oil to the threaded portion of drive pinion.

2) Using Drive Pinion Holder (SST 09564-16010 and SST 09556-16020) install drive pinion nut. Apply gear oil to bearings. Snug down bearing by turning drive pinion several times. Using a torque wrench, check bearing preload. Preload should be 4.3-8.7 INCH lbs. (.5-1.0 mm) for new bearings and 2.6-4.3 INCH lbs. (.3-.5 mm) for used bearings.

3) If adjustment is needed, tighten drive pinion nut to 108 ft. lbs. (146 N.m). Measure preload. If preload is excessive, replace spacer and readjust. If preload is insufficient, increase torque in increments of 5-10 ft. lbs. (7-14 N.m) until proper preload is obtained, but do not exceed 268 ft. lbs. (363 N.m)

NOTE: If preload in not within specification after tightening nut to maximum, a new spacer must be used.

4) Install differential case, outer races and side washer on side nearest ring gear. Be sure ring gear has backlash. Snug down washer and bearing by tapping on ring gear with a plastic hammer. Push side bearing boss on

Automatic Transmissions

TOYOTA MODEL A-55 (Cont.)

teeth surface of ring gear and measure backlash. Backlash should be .0039" (.10 mm).

5) Select proper washer using backlash as reference. Side washers come in 23 different sizes ranging from .1028-.1295" (2.61-3.29 mm). After proper backlash side washer has been installed on side nearest ring gear, select a side washer for side farthest from ring gear, of a thickness which eliminates any clearance between outer race and housing.

6) Remove side washers and differential case. Install side washer into ring gear side of housing. Place other side washer on bearing race opposite ring gear and install differential case with outer race into housing. Using a plastic hammer, snug down washer and bearing by tapping on ring gear.

7) Using a dial indicator, measure ring gear backlash. It should be .0039-.0059" (.10-.15 mm). If not within specification, adjust by either increasing or decreasing number of washers on both sides by an equal amount. Insure that there is ring gear backlash and there should be no clearance between side washer and case.

8) After adjustment, using backlash as reference, remove ring gear side side washer and measure thickness. Install a new washer .0024-.0035" (.06-.09 mm) thicker than washer removed.

NOTE: Select a washer which can be pressed in 2/3 of the way by finger.

9) Use a plastic hammer to tap side washer in rest of the way. Recheck ring gear backlash. It should be .0039-.0059" (.10-.15 mm). If not within standard, adjust by either increasing and decreasing washers on both sides by an equal amount.

NOTE: The backlash will change about .0008" (.02 mm) with a .0012" (.03 mm) variation of the side washer.

10) Install side bearing caps and tighten bolts to specifications. To measure total preload, apply gear oil on bearings, turn drive pinion left and right several times and with a torque wrench measure total preload. Preload (starting) should be 2.6-4.3 INCH lbs. (.02-.03 N.m), in addition to drive pinion preload.

NOTE: If preload is not within standard, readjust ring gear side washer.

11) Measure ring gear backlash using a dial indicator. Measure at 3 places on outer edge of ring gear. Backlash should be .0039-.0059" (.10-.15 mm).

NOTE: If not within standard, adjust by either increasing or decreasing washers on both sides by an equal amount. The backlash will change about .0008" (.02 mm) with a .0012" (.03 mm) variation of the side washer.

12) To inspect teeth contact between ring gear and drive pinion, coat red lead on 3 or 4 teeth at 3 different positions of ring gear, rotate ring gear in both directions and inspect teeth pattern. If there is toe contact, replace pinion plate washer with a thinner one. If there is heel contact, replace pinion plate washer with a thicker one.

NOTE: If the plate washer thickness is altered .0039" (.10 mm), the center of the teeth contact will change about 1/8 of the total teeth surface.

13) If there is flank contact, increase backlash within standard specification. If there is face contact, decrease backlash within standard specification.

NOTE: Increase or decrease both side washers by an equal amount. The backlash will change about .0008" (.02 mm) with a .0012" (.03 mm) variation of the side washer.

14) Stake drive pinion nut using a chisel. Install differential carrier oil seal .331-.354" (8.4-9.0 mm) below surface using a hammer and seal installer. Install differential carrier cover and gasket and bolts.

15) After wrapping spline with tape, install governor pressure adaptor and governor body. Assemble with transmission.

TIGHTENING SPECIFICATIONS

Application	Ft. Lbs. (N.m)
Axle Shaft Nut	137 (186)
Ball Joint-to-Steering Knuckle	59 (80)
Center Support Bolts	19 (26)
Drive Plate	47 (64)
Engine Rear Mount-to-Body	67 (91)
Engine-to-Converter Housing	47 (64)
Lower Arm-to-Body	83 (113)
Lower Arm-to-Ball Joint	59 (80)
Pinion Nut	109-267 (148-362)
Ring Gear Bolts	71 (96)
Side Bearing Caps	36 (49)
Stabilizer Bracket	32 (43)
Stabilizer-to-Lower Arm	78 (106)
Strut-to-Steering Knuckle	105 (142)
Transmission-to-Converter Hsg.	14 (19)

TOYOTA A-130L & A-131L 3-SPEED

FWD Corolla

DESCRIPTION

The model A-130 and A-131L automatic transaxles have 3 forward speeds and reverse. Transaxle assembly consists of a 3-element torque converter, a gear driven oil pump, a valve body, a differential, and 2 planetary gear sets actuated by 3 multi-disc brakes and 2 clutches. Engine load and speed determine gear changes by use of throttle valve position and output shaft speed.

LUBRICATION & ADJUSTMENT

See appropriate AUTOMATIC TRANSMISSION SERVICNG article in IMPORT GENERAL SERVICING section.

TROUBLE SHOOTING

PRELIMINARY CHECKS

Trouble occuring with the automatic transaxle can be caused by either the engine or the transaxle. Isolate trouble to engine or transaxle before proceeding with trouble shooting. Trouble shooting should begin with simplest test procedure, working up in order of difficulty, and in the following sequence:
- Check oil level.
- Check throttle cable.
- Check shift linkage.
- Check Neutral safety switch.
- Check idle speed (cooling fan and A/C unit off).
- Check tire pressure.

CHECK ENGINE & TORQUE CONVERTER

Perform stall test and repair as necessary.

CHECK TRANSAXLE

Check each clutch, brake and gear for wear by performing time lag test. Confirm test results with road test. Repair as necessary.

CHECK LINE PRESSURE

Perform hydraulic test. Confirm shift point and extent of shock with road test. Repair as necessary.

ROAD TEST VEHICLE

Road test vehicle and confirm that trouble lies within transaxle. Perform on-vehicle service or overhaul transaxle.

TESTING

ROAD TEST
"D" Range Test

1) Allow ATF to reach a normal operating temperature of 122-176°F (50-80°C). Shift into "D" range, and while driving, hold throttle half open and then wide open.

2) Check that 1st to 2nd upshift takes place, then check that 2nd to 3rd upshift take place, and that upshift points conform to those indicated in diagram. *See Fig. 1.*

3) If there is no 1st to 2nd upshift, governor valve is defective or 1-2 shift valve is stuck. If there is no 2nd to 3rd upshift, 2-3 shift valve is stuck. If shift points are incorrect, throttle valve, 1-2 or 2-3 shift valves are stuck or defective.

4) Repeat procedure and check shock and slip from 1st to 2nd and from 2nd to 3rd. If shock is severe, line pressure is too high, accumulator is defective or check ball is defective.

5) While driving in "D" range, check for unusual noise and vibration. Abnormal noise and vibration may be due to an unbalanced propeller shaft, differential, tires, torque converter, or other drive train components.

6) With vehicle in "D" range, and while driving, hold throttle half open and then wide open. Check to see that 2nd to 1st, 3rd to 1st, and 3rd to 2nd kickdown speeds conform to those indicated in diagram. *See Fig. 1.* Also check for abnormal shock and slip at kickdown.

7) While driving in "D" range, shift to "2" and "L" range and check engine braking power. If there is no engine braking at "2" range, 2nd coast brake is defective. If there is no engine braking at "L" range, 1st and reverse is defective.

8) While driving in "D" range, remove foot from accelerator pedal and shift into "L" range. Check to see that 3rd to 2nd, and 2nd to 1st downshift points conform to those indicated indicated in diagram. *See Fig. 1.*

Lock-Up Mechanism

Connect a tachometer to engine and drive vehicle at around 40 MPH. Depress accelelator pedal and read tachometer. If there is a large jump in engine RPM, lock-up mechanism is not working.

"2" Range Test

1) Shift into "2" range and drive with throttle half open and then wide open. Check 1st to 2nd upshift points at each of the throttle valve openings to see that they conform with those indicated in diagram. *See Fig. 1.*

2) While driving in "2" range, release accelerator pedal and check for engine braking. Perform a kickdown in "2" range and check 2nd to 1st kickdown speed. Kickdown speed must conform with that indicated in diagram. Check for abnormal noise at acceleration and deceleration, and for shock at upshift and downshift.

"L" Range Test

While driving in "L" range, check to see that ther is no upshift to 2nd gear. Release accelerator pedal and check for engine braking. Also check for abnormal noise at acceleration and deceleration

"R" Range Test

Shift into "R" range and, while starting at full throttle, check for slipping.

"P" Range Test

Stop vehicle on a hill with more than a 9% grade and, after shifting into "P" range, release the parking brake. Check to see that parking lock pawl prevents the vehicle from moving.

HYDRAULIC PRESSURE TESTS
Governor Pressure Test

1) Allow ATF to reach a normal operating temperature of 122-176°F (50-80°C). Block rear wheels and apply parking brake. Jack up front of vehicle and support with safety stands.

2) Remove transmission test plugs and connect pressure gauges. Measurements can be made at 1000

Automatic Transmissions
TOYOTA A-130L & A-131L 3-SPEED (Cont.)

Fig. 1: *A-130L & A-131L TRANSAXLE DOWNSHIFT & UPSHIFT POINTS*

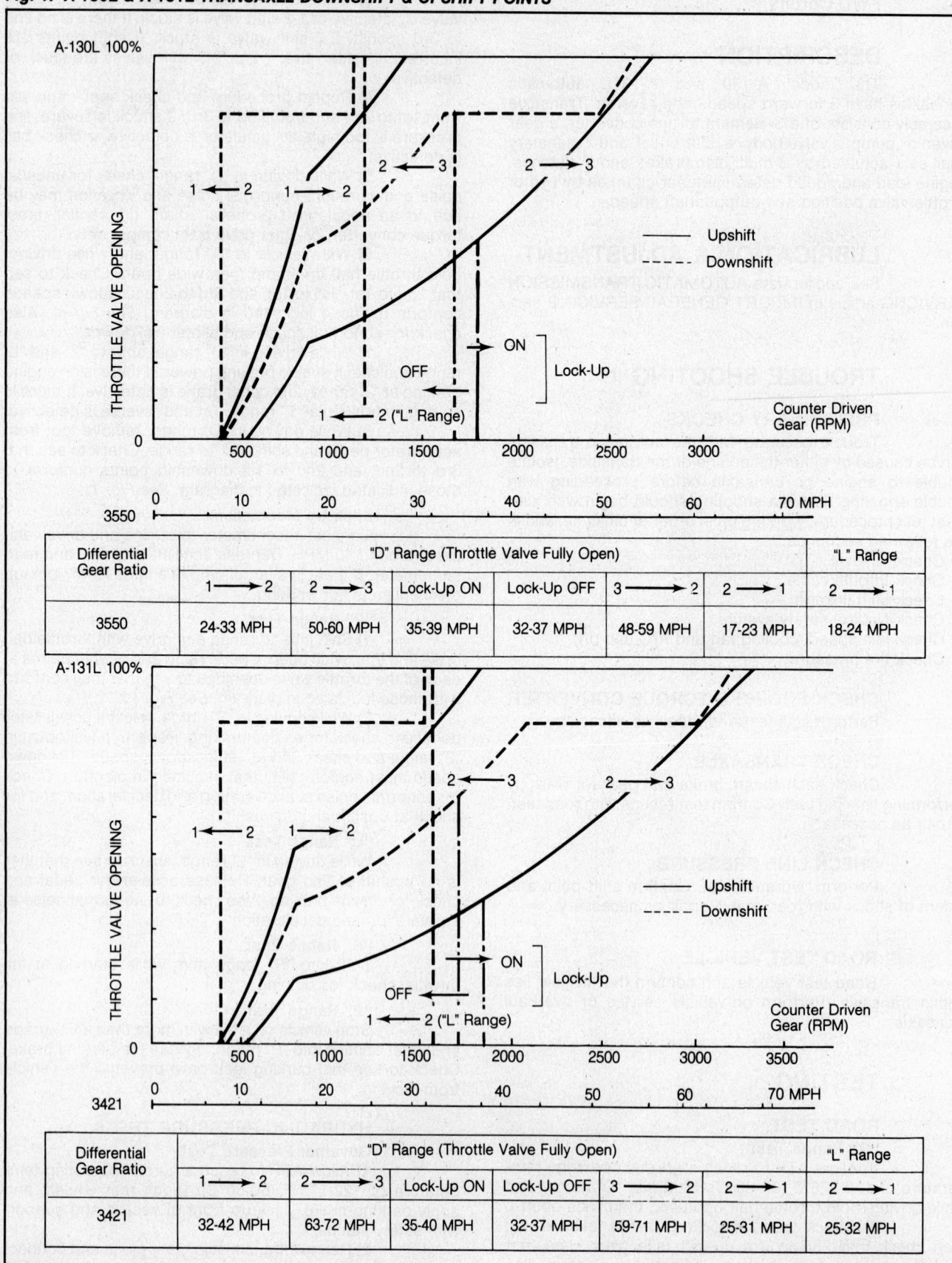

Differential Gear Ratio	"D" Range (Throttle Valve Fully Open)						"L" Range
	1 → 2	2 → 3	Lock-Up ON	Lock-Up OFF	3 → 2	2 → 1	2 → 1
3550	24-33 MPH	50-60 MPH	35-39 MPH	32-37 MPH	48-59 MPH	17-23 MPH	18-24 MPH

Differential Gear Ratio	"D" Range (Throttle Valve Fully Open)						"L" Range
	1 → 2	2 → 3	Lock-Up ON	Lock-Up OFF	3 → 2	2 → 1	2 → 1
3421	32-42 MPH	63-72 MPH	35-40 MPH	32-37 MPH	59-71 MPH	25-31 MPH	25-32 MPH

TOYOTA A-130L & A-131L 3-SPEED (Cont.)

RPM. If test are to be made at 1800 RPM or at 3500 RPM, perform these test on a road or a chassis dynamometer.

3) Ensure that parking brake is applied and start the engine. Shift into "D" range and measure governor pressure at specified speeds. If governor pressure is incorrect, line pressure may be incorrect, governor pressure circuit may be leaking or governor valve may be defective.

GOVERNOR PRESSURE SPECIFICATIONS

Application	psi (kg/cm^2)
At 1000 RPM [1]	
A-130L	14-26 (0.98-1.83)
A-131L	12-24 (0.84-1.69)
At 1800 RPM [2]	
A-130L	27-38 (1.90-2.67)
A-131L	24-36 (1.69-2.53)
AT 3500 RPM [3]	
A-130L	73-92 (5.13-6.47)
A-131L	61-81 (4.29-5.69)

[1] – Approximate vehicle speed is 20 MPH.
[2] – Approximate vehicle speed is 37 MPH.
[3] – Approximate vehicle speed is 71 MPH.

Line Pressure Test

1) Block all wheels and apply parking brake. Start engine and shift into "D" range. Step on brake pedal with left foot and with right foot control accelerator pedal. Measure line pressure at specified engine speeds. Repeat test in "R" range.

2) If pressure is lower than specified, check throttle cable adjustment and retest. If pressure in both ranges is higher than specified, throttle cable may be out of adjustment, throttle valve or regulator valve may be defective.

3) If pressure in both ranges is lower than specified, throttle cable may be out of adjustment, oil pump may be defective, throttle valve or regulator valve may be defective.

4) If pressure is low in "D" range only, "D" range circuit may be leaking or forward clutch may be defective. If pressure is low in "R" range only, "R" range circuit may be leaking, direct clutch may be defective, or 1st and reverse may be defective.

LINE PRESSURE SPECIFICATIONS IN "D" RANGE

Application	psi (kg/cm^2)
At Idle Speed	53-61 (3.73-4.29)
At Stall Speed	
A-130L	121-142 (8.51-9.98)
A-131L	131-152 (9.21-10.69)

LINE PRESSURE SPECIFICATIONS IN "R" RANGE

Application	psi (kg/cm^2)
At Idle Speed	77-102 (5.41-7.17)
At Stall Speed	
A-130L	188-222 (13.22-15.61)
A-131L	205-239 (14.41-16.80)

STALL TEST

NOTE: The object of this test is to check the overall performance of the transaxle and engine by measuring maximum engine speeds in the "D" and "R" ranges. Perform this test with ATF at a normal operating temperature of 122-176°F (50-80°C). DO NOT continously run this test longer than 5 seconds.

1) Block front and rear wheels and fully apply parking brake. Install tachometer. Step on brake pedal and start the engine. Shift into "D" range and fully depress accelerator pedal. Immediately read highest engine RPM.

2) Stall speed must be 1950-2250 RPM for gasoline engine equipped vehicles; between 1600-1900 RPM for diesel engine equipped vehicles. Repeat test in "R" range.

3) If stall speed is the same for both ranges but lower than specified, then engine output may be insufficient or stator one-way clutch is not operating properly. If stall speed is more than 600 RPM below the specified value, the torque converter could be at fault.

4) If stall speed in "D" range is higher than specified, line pressure may be too low, forward clutch may be slipping or No. 2 one-way clutch may not be operating properly.

5) If stall speed in "R" range is higher than specified, line pressure may be too low, direct clutch may be slipping or 1st and reverse brake may be slipping. If stall speed in "D" and "R" range is higher than specified, fluid level may be low or line pressure may be too low.

TIME LAG TEST

NOTE: If the shift lever is moved while the engine is idling, there will be a certain time lapse or lag before shock can be felt. This time lapse is used to check the condition of the forward clutch, direct clutch, and 1st and reverse brake. Allow a 1 minute interval between tests. Make 3 tests and take average value.

1) With ATF at a normal operating temperature of 122-176°F (50-80°C), apply parking and check idle speed. Using a stop watch, measure the time that it takes for shock to be felt when moving shift lever from "N" to "D" range. Time lag must be less than 1.2 seconds.

2) Repeat procedure from "N" to "R" range, time lag must be less than 1.5 seconds. If "N" to "D" time lag is longer than specified, line pressure may be too low or forward clutch may be worn. If "N" to "R" time lag is longer than specified, line pressure may be too low, direct clutch may be worn, or 1st and reverse brake may be worn.

ENGINE IDLE SPEED

Application	Range	RPM
Gasoline Engine		
With P/S	"N"	[1]800
Without P/S	"N"	[1]900
Diesel Engine	"N"	700

[1] – Subtract 50 RPM with transaxle in "D" range.

Automatic Transmissions
TOYOTA A-130L & A-131L 3-SPEED (Cont.)

CLUTCH AND BAND APPLICATION – A-130L & A-131L (ELEMENTS IN USE)

Selector Lever Position	Direct (Front) Clutch	Forward (Rear) Clutch	2nd Coast Brake Band	2nd Gear Brake Drum	1st & Reverse Gear Brake (Piston)	No. 1 One-Way Clutch	No. 2 One-Way Clutch
P – PARK							
R – REVERSE		X			X		
N – NEUTRAL							
D – DRIVE							
First	X						X
Second	X			X		X	
Third	X	X		X			
2 – SECOND							
First	X						X
Second	X		X	X		X	
1 – LOW							
First	X				X		X
Second ¹	X		X	X		X	

¹ – Downshift in "L" range, 2nd gear only; no upshift.

SERVICE (IN VEHICLE)

WHEEL BEARINGS
Removal

1) Remove cotter pin and lock nut cap. Depress brake pedal and loosen bearing lock nut. Remove brake caliper and disc brake rotor. Attach a dial indicator to steering knuckle arm and measure bearing end play. Bearing end play must be within 0.0020" (0.05 mm).

2) Remove cotter pin and nut from tie rod end. Using Puller (SST 09950-20014), disconnect tie rod from steering knuckle arm. Mark front suspension strut and camber adjustment cam for reassembly reference.

3) Remove bolts from steering knuckle and separate from strut. Remove bolts from lower control arm and disconnect arm from steering knuckle. Using Puller (SST 09950-20014), pull axle hub from drive shaft. Cover boot with cloth to prevent damage.

4) Using Ball Joint Remover (SST 09610-55012), remove ball joint from steering knuckle. Using a screwdriver, remove dust deflector. Using Puller (SST 09308-00010), remove oil seal from steering knuckle.

5) Remove 3 bolts securing disc brake dust cover to steering knuckle. Using Puller (SST 09950-20014), push out axle hub and disc brake dust cover out of steering knuckle. Remove inboard bearing inner race from bearing.

6) Using puller, remove outboard bearing inner race from axle hub. Using Puller (SST 09308-00010), remove oil seal from steering knuckle. Install outboard bearing inner race and press bearing out of hub.

Installation

1) Using Bearing/Oil Seal Installer (SST 09608-32010), press new bearing into steering knuckle. Rotate and insert side lip of new oil seal into installer. Press oil seal into steering knuckle.

2) Apply sealer to disc brake dust cover and steering knuckle. Install dust cover. Apply multipurpose grease between oil seal lip, oil seal, and bearing. Using Hub Installer (SST 09310-35010), press axle hub into steering knuckle.

3) Install snap ring in steering knuckle. Press new oil seal into steering knuckle, until metal part of seal is flush with bearing bore. Apply multipurpose grease to lip of oil seal.

4) Using Driver (SST 09218-46010), install a new dust deflector into into steering knuckle. Reverse removal procedure to complete installation. Check front wheel alignment.

DRIVE AXLE SHAFTS
Removal

1) Remove cotter pin and lock nut cap. Depress brake pedal and loosen bearing lock nut and drive axle shaft nuts. Remove bearing lock nut from axle hub.

2) Remove bolts from lower control arm and disconnect arm from steering knuckle. Remove brake caliper and disc brake rotor. Using Puller (SST 09950-20014), pull axle hub from drive shaft. Cover boot with cloth to prevent damage.

Installation

To install, reverse removal procedure. Depress brake pedal when tightening bearing lock nut.

CONSTANT VELOCITY JOINTS
Disassembly

1) Check CV joints for play. No noticeable play should be present in outboard joint. Inboard joint should move freely along axis of drive shaft, no noticeable radial play should exist. Remove boot clamps.

2) Mark inboard joint tulip for reassembly reference and remove from drive shaft. Using snap ring pliers,

remove snap ring. Mark tripod joint and shaft for reassembly. Using a hammer and punch, remove joint from shaft. Remove boots and inspect for damage.

Reassembly
1) Wrap vinyl tape around shaft splines. Install outboard boot and clamp. Remove tape. Install inboard boot and clamp. The inboard boot and clamp are larger than those of tripod joint.

2) Place beveled side of tripod axial spline toward outboard joint. Align marks, tap tripod joint onto shaft, and install snap ring. Place boot over outboard joint and pack with 5.8 oz. (165g) of grease supplied in kit.

3) Pack inboard joint tulip with 7.5 oz. (212g) of grease. Align marks, install tulip on drive shaft, and install boot on tulip. Install boot clamps. Ensure that boots are not stretched or collapsed.

GOVERNOR ASSEMBLY
Removal
Remove left drive shaft. Remove transaxle dust cover. Remove bracket bolts, governor cover and "O" ring. Remove governor body, washer, and thrust washer. Remove governor body adapter.

Installation
To install, reverse removal procedure.

THROTTLE CABLE
Removal
Disconnect throttle cable from throttle linkage. Disconnect transaxle control cable from manual shift lever and remove manual shift lever. Remove Neutral safety switch. Remove valve body. Remove throttle cable bolt and retaining plate. Pull throttle cable out of transaxle.

Installation
1) Install throttle cable in transaxle and push it all the way in. Install retaining bolt and plate. If throttle cable is new, bend cable about a 7.87" (200 mm) radius.

2) Pull inner cable lightly, until a slight resistance is felt, and hold in place. Stake stopper on inner cable, leaving a 0.031-0.059" (0.8-1.5 mm) gap between cable housing and stopper. See Fig. 2.

3) Connect throttle cable to throttle linkage. Adjust throttle cable. See appropriate AUTOMATIC TRANSMISSION SERVICNG article in IMPORT GENERAL SERVICING section.

4) Install Neutral safety switch and manual shift lever. Adjust Neutral safety switch. See appropriate AUTOMATIC TRANSMISSION SERVICNG article in IMPORT GENERAL SERVICING section. Connect transaxle control cable. Test drive vehicle.

Fig. 2: Throttle Cable Stopper Installation

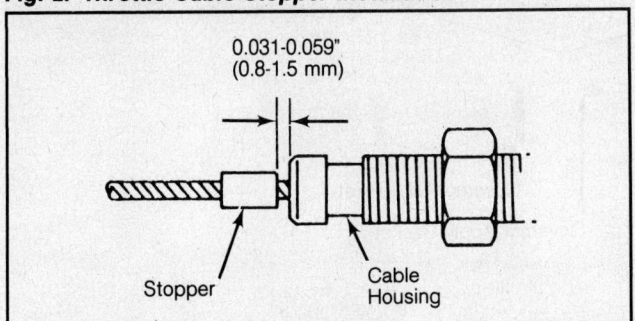

0.031-0.059"
(0.8-1.5 mm)

Stopper

Cable Housing

VALVE BODY
Removal
1) Clean exterior of transaxle to prevent contamination of valve body. Remove drain plug and drain ATF. Remove oil pan and gasket. Remove bolts and apply tube bracket. Remove 3 bolts and carefully remove oil strainer. Note position of oil tubes and, using a large screwdriver, remove oil tubes.

2) Remove manual detent spring. Remove manual valve. Remove 4 manual valve body bolts and note their length. Remove valve body. Remove 14 valve body bolts and note their length. Remove valve body. Remove governor pressure line strainer. Remove governor apply gasket.

Installation
1) Install governor apply gasket. Install governor pressure line strainer. Hold valve body cam down, and slip cable into slot. Install valve body in transaxle. Do not entangle kickdown switch wire.

2) Install 14 valve body bolts finger tight, then tighten. Align manual valve with pin on manual shift lever. Lower valve body into place. Install 4 valve body bolts finger tight, then tighten.

3) Install detent spring and tighten bolts. Check that manual valve lever is in contact with center of roller at tip of detent spring. Using a plastic hammer, tap oil tubes into place.

4) Install apply tube bracket. Install oil strainer. Install magnet in oil pan. Ensure that magnet does not interfere with oil tubes. Install oil pan and drain plug. Fill transaxle with Dexron II ATF and check fluid level. Do not overfill.

REMOVAL & INSTALLATION

TRANSAXLE
See appropriate AUTOMATIC TRANSMISSION REMOVAL article in IMPORT GENERAL SERVICING section.

TORQUE CONVERTER

NOTE: **The torque converter is a sealed unit and cannot be disassembled for service. Make the following tests to be certain that converter is defective. If transaxle is contaminated, the torque converter and transaxle cooler must be thoroughly cleaned and flushed.**

ONE-WAY CLUTCH TEST
1) Insert "T" Handle (SST 09350-32011) in inner race of torque converter one-way clutch. Insert Locking Tab (SST 09350-32011) so that it fits into notch of converter hub and into one-way clutch.

2) With converter positioned upright, one-way clutch should lock when turned counterclockwise. Clutch should rotate freely and smoothly when turned clockwise.

3) Less than 22 INCH lbs. (2.5 N.m) should be required to rotate clutch. If necessary, clean converter and retest. If clutch still fails test, replace torque converter.

Automatic Transmissions
TOYOTA A-130L & A-131L 3-SPEED (Cont.)

Fig. 3: Exploded View of A-130L & A-131L Automatic Transaxle

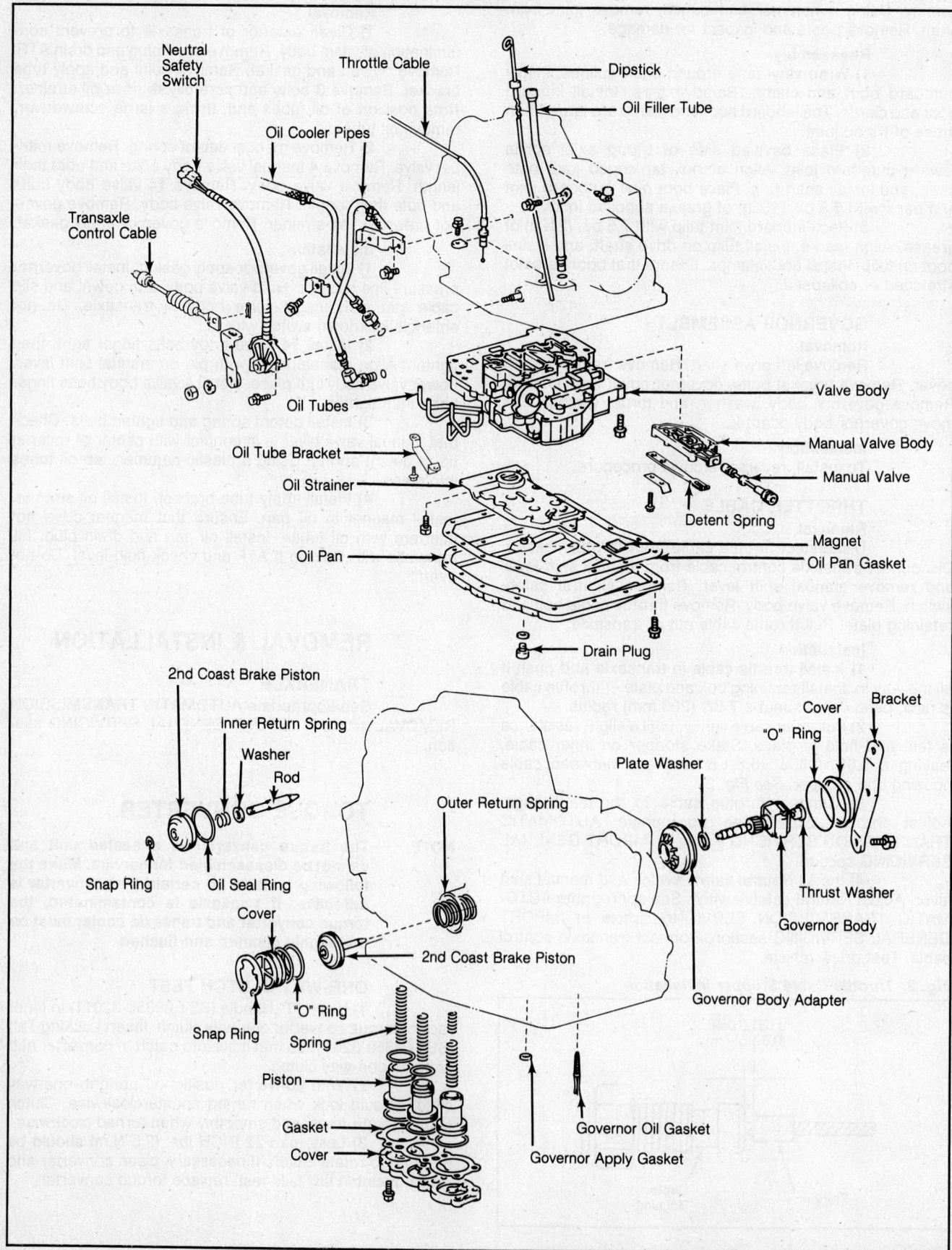

Fig. 4: Exploded View of A-130L & A-131L Automatic Transaxle

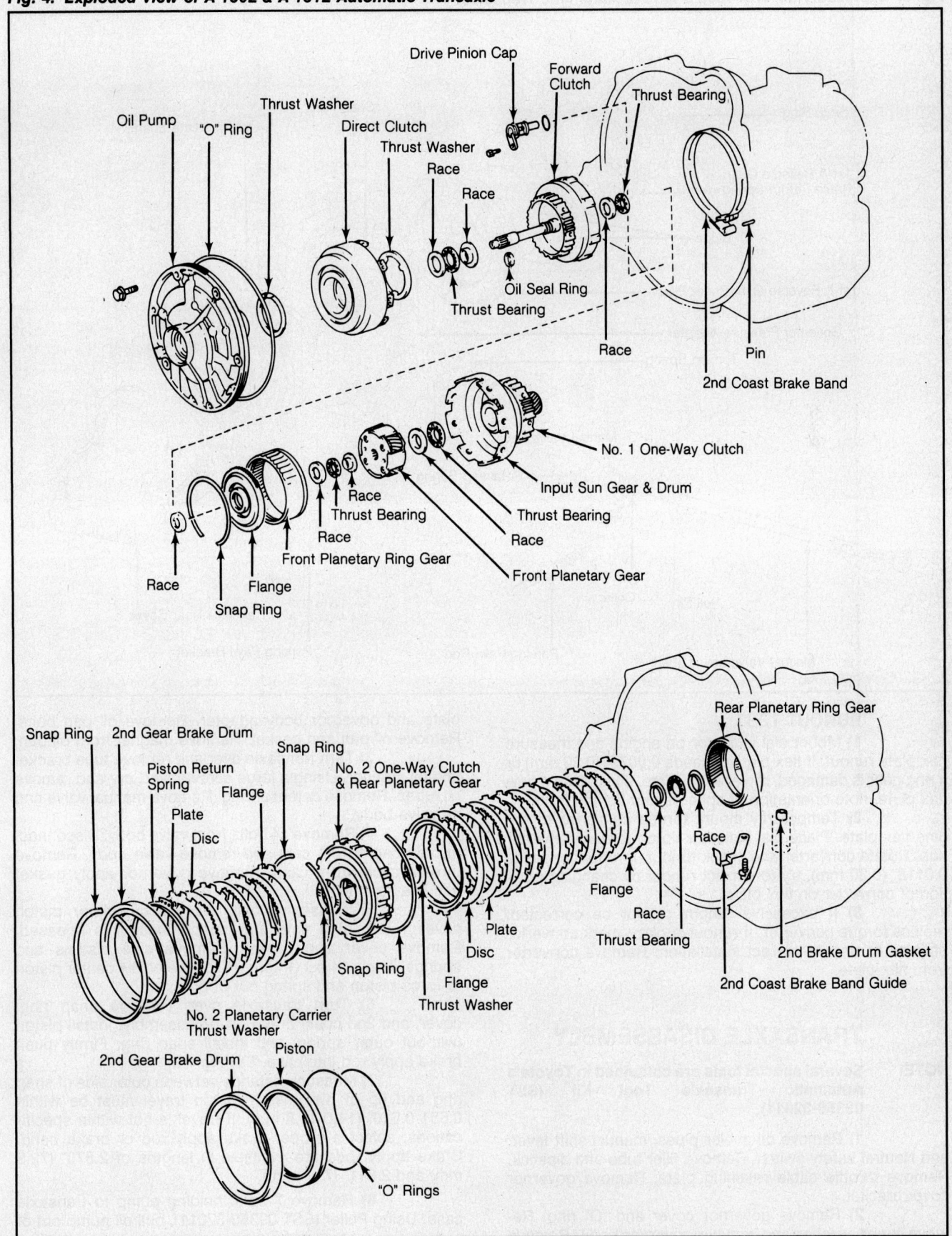

6-348

Automatic Transmissions
TOYOTA A-130L & A-131L 3-SPEED (Cont.)

Fig. 5: Exploded View of A-130L & A-131L Automatic Transaxle

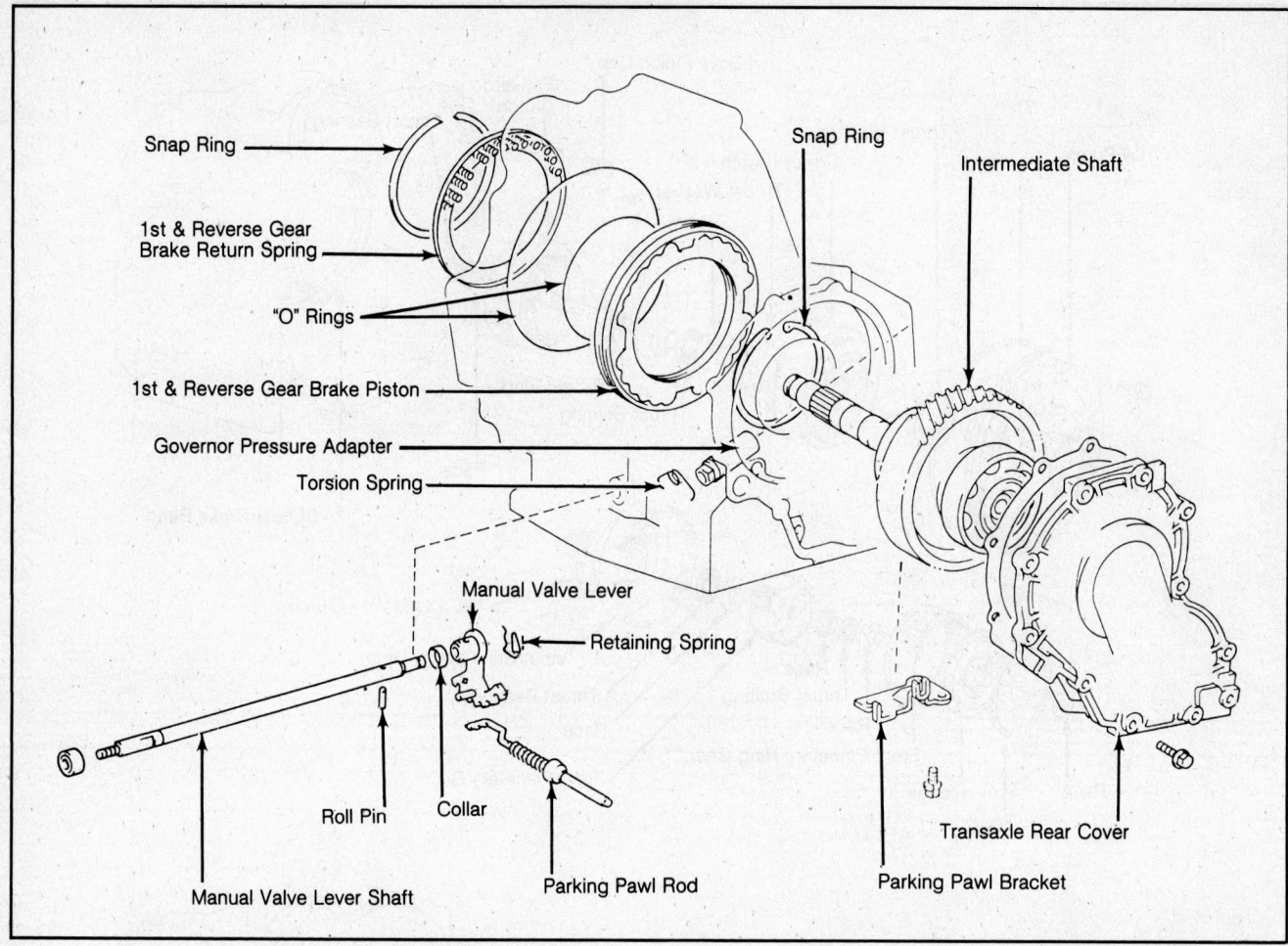

RUNOUT TEST

1) Mount dial indicator on engine and measure flex plate runout. If flex plate exceeds 0.0079" (0.20 mm) or if ring gear is damaged, replace flex plate. If installing a new flex plate, note orientation of spacers and tighten bolts.

2) Temporarily mount torque converter to engine flex plate. Place dial indicator tip on torque converter hub. Rotate converter and check runout. If runout exceeds 0.0118" (0.30 mm), try to correct runout by changing position of converter on flex plate.

3) If excessive runout cannot be corrected, replace torque converter. If runout is okay, mark converter position to ensure correct installation. Remove converter from flex plate.

TRANSAXLE DISASSEMBLY

NOTE: Several special tools are contained in Toyota's Automatic Transaxle Tool Kit (SST 09350-32011).

1) Remove oil cooler pipes, manual shift lever, and Neutral safety switch. Remove filler tube and dipstick. Remove throttle cable retaining plate. Remove governor cover bracket.

2) Remove governor cover and "O" ring. Remove thrust washer and remove governor body. Remove plate and governor body adapter. Remove oil pan bolts. Remove oil pan and gasket. Remove magnet from oil pan.

3) Turn transaxle over and remove tube bracket and oil strainer. Using a large screwdriver, pry and remove oil tubes. Remove detent spring. Remove manual valve and its valve body.

4) Remove 14 bolts from valve body. Disconnect throttle cable from cam and remove valve body. Remove throttle cable from case. Remove governor apply gasket and line strainer.

5) Loosen 5 bolts from accumulator piston cover 1 turn at a time until spring tension is released. Remove cover and gasket. Remove side pistons and springs. Apply 14 psi (1 kg/cm^2) to hole below center piston to force piston and spring out of bore.

6) Turn transaxle over. Remove snap ring, cover, and 2nd coast brake piston assembly. Install piston (without outer spring) and install snap ring. Firmly push brake apply rod into case. See Fig. 6.

7) Measure distance between outer side of snap ring and tip of piston rod. Piston travel must be within 0.551-0.610" (14.0-15.5 mm). If travel is not within specifications, select a proper brake apply rod or brake band. Brake apply rods are available in lengths of 2.870" (72.9 mm) and 2.811" (71.4 mm).

8) Remove 7 bolts holding pump to transaxle case. Using Puller (SST 09350-32011), pull oil pump out of

Automatic Transmissions
TOYOTA A-130L & A-131L 3-SPEED (Cont.)

6-349

Fig. 6: 2nd Coast Brake Piston Travel

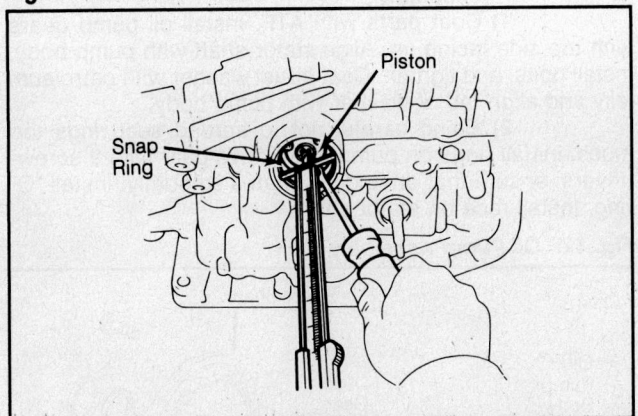

case. While holding input shaft, grasp pump stator shaft and pull oil pump and direct clutch out of case.

9) Remove direct clutch and thrust washer from rear of oil pump. Remove thrust, bearing, and race from forward (rear) clutch. Remove forward clutch. Remove bearing and race from rear of forward clutch.

10) Push 2nd coast brake band pin with a small screwdriver and remove it from oil pump mounting bolt hole. Remove 2nd coast brake band. Remove front planetary ring gear. Remove race and bearing from ring gear.

11) Remove planetary gear. Remove bearing and race from planetary gear. Remove sun gear, sun gear input drum, 2nd brake hub and No. 1 one-way clutch. Stand transaxle up and remove 2nd coast brake band guide.

12) Using a feeler gauge, measure the clearance between 2nd brake piston return spring assembly seat and top of plate. *See Fig. 7.* Clearance should be 0.0193-0.0626" (0.49-1.59 mm).

Fig. 7: Measuring 2nd Brake Piston Clearance

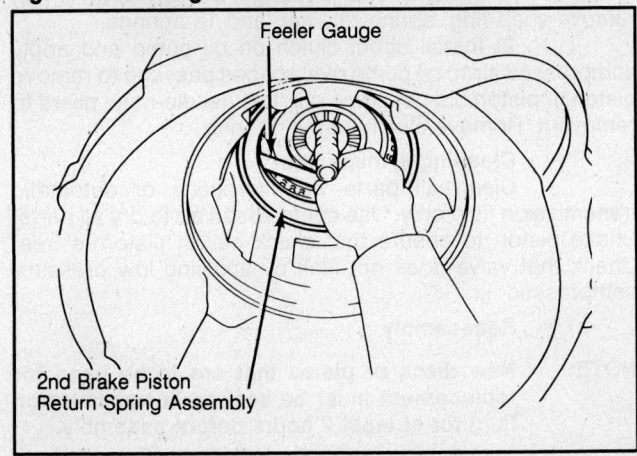

13) Remove snap ring holding 2nd brake drum to case. Remove 2nd brake drum, if piston is difficult to remove, lightly tap drum with a wooden block. Using a pin punch and hammer, tap out 2nd brake drum seal.

14) Remove 2nd brake piston return spring. Remove plate, disc, and flange assembly. Using compressed air, blow piston and oil seal out of 2nd brake drum. Remove snap ring holding No. 2 one-way clutch outer race to case.

15) Remove No. 2 one-way clutch and rear planetary gear. Remove thrust washers from both sides of

planetary carrier. Remove rear planetary ring gear and bearing. Remove bearing and race from ring gear.

16) Using a feeler gauge, measure clearance between 1st and reverse brake piston and flange. *See Fig. 8.* Clearance should be 0.0465-0.0953" (1.18-2.42 mm) on transaxle used with diesel engine. Clearance should be 0.0350-0.0831" (0.89-2.11 mm) on transaxle used with gasoline engine.

Fig. 8: Measuring 1st & Reverse Brake Clearance

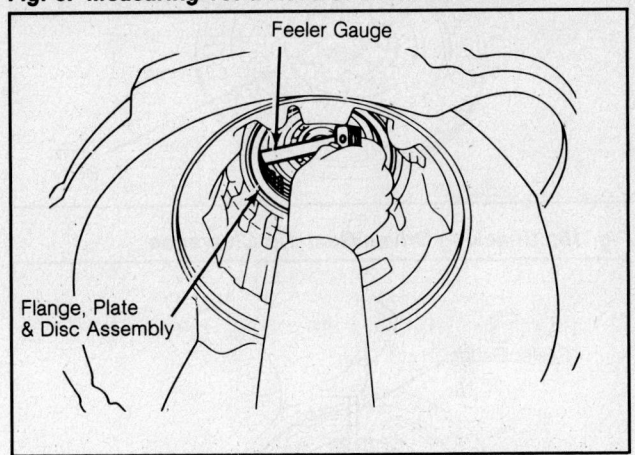

17) Remove snap ring holding flange to case. Remove flange, plate, and disc assembly. Turn transaxle case around. Remove 11 bolts holding rear cover to transaxle case. Tap rear cover with a plastic hammer and remove cover from case.

18) Remove intermediate shaft if it stayed in transaxle. Remove parking pawl bracket. Remove parking pawl rod. Remove parking pawl shaft. Remove spring and parking pawl.

COMPONENT DISASSEMBLY & REASSEMBLY

OIL PUMP
Disassembly
Remove race from stator shaft. Remove "O" ring from pump body. Remove 2 oil seal rings from back of stator shaft. Remove clutch drum thrust washer from stator shaft. Remove 11 bolts and stator shaft. Keep assembly in order.

Cleaning & Inspection
1) Note position (top side) of oil pump gears and remove if necessary. Clean all parts with kerosene or automatic transmission fluid only. Clean all fluid passages and holes, use compressed air to ensure that passages or holes are not clogged.

2) Push driven gear to one side of body. Using a feeler gauge, measure clearance between driven gear and pump body. *See Fig. 9.* Standard clearance is 0.0028-0.0059" (0.07-0.15 mm). Maximum allowable clearance is 0.012" (0.3 mm).

3) Using a feeler gauge, measure clearance between driven gear and cresent-shaped part of pump body. *See Fig. 10.* Standard clearance is 0.0043-0.0055" (0.11-0.14 mm). Maximum allowable clearance is 0.012" (0.3 mm).

6-350

Automatic Transmissions
TOYOTA A-130L & A-131L 3-SPEED (Cont.)

Fig. 9: Checking Driven Gear Clearance

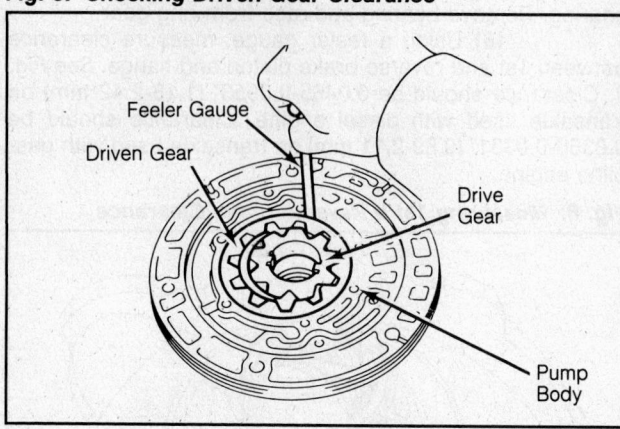

Fig. 10: Checking Driven Gear Tip Clearance

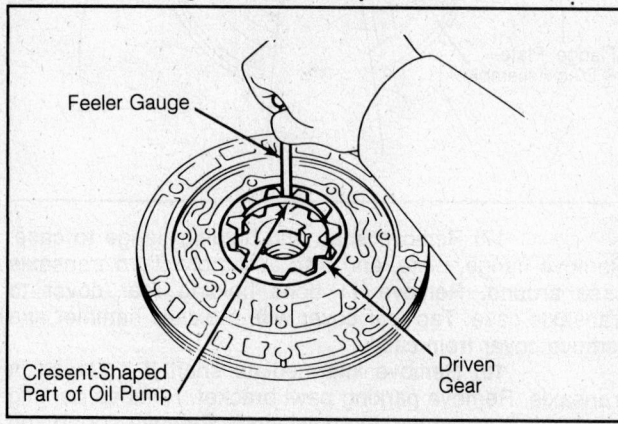

4) Using a feeler gauge and straightedge, measure oil pump gear side clearance. See Fig. 11. Standard clearance is 0.0008-0.0020" (0.02-0.05 mm). Maximum allowable clearance is 0.004" (0.1 mm).

5) Inspect front oil seal for wear, damage, or cracks. If necessary, replace oil seal as follows: Using a screwdriver, pry off oil seal. Using Driver (SST 09350-32011), install new oil seal. Seal should be flush with outer edge of pump body.

Fig. 11: Checking Oil Pump Gear Side Clearance

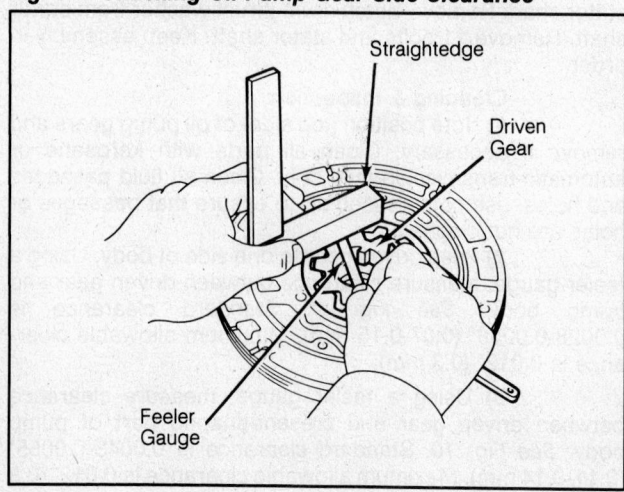

Reassembly

1) Coat parts with ATF. Install oil pump gears with top side facing up. Align stator shaft with pump body, install bolts, and tighten. Coat thrust washer with petroleum jelly and align tab of washer with pump body.

2) Being careful not to spread seal rings too much, install rings on pump. Turn drive gear with 2 screwdrivers, ensure that drive gear rotates smoothly. Install "O" ring. Install race on stator shaft.

Fig. 12: Oil Pump Assembly

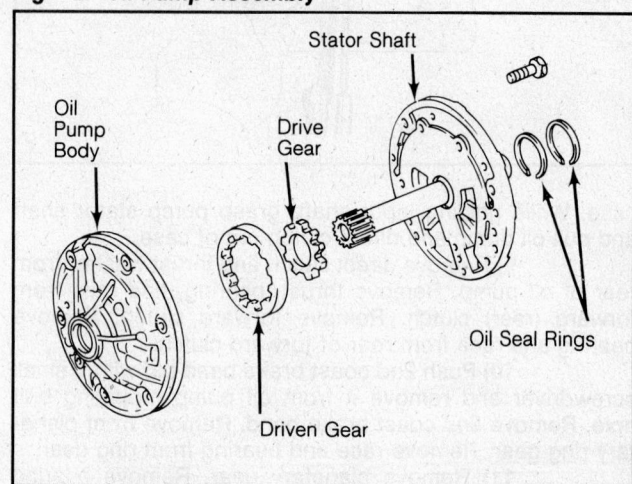

DIRECT CLUTCH
Disassembly

1) Using a feeler gauge, measure clearance between snap ring and flange. Clearance should be 0.0350-0.0575" (0.89-1.46 mm). Remove snap ring from clutch drum. Remove flange, disc, and plate assembly. Compress spring retainer and springs. Using a screwdriver, remove snap ring, spring retainer, and 18 springs.

2) Install direct clutch on oil pump and apply compressed air to oil pump oval shaped passage to remove piston. If piston did not come out, use needle-nose pliers to remove it. Remove clutch piston "O" ring.

Cleaning & Inspection

Clean all parts with kerosene or automatic transmission fluid only. Use compressed air to dry all parts. Shake piston to ensure that check ball in piston is free. Check that valve does not leak by applying low pressure compressed air.

Reassembly

NOTE: New discs or plates that are to be used for replacement must be soaked in transmission fluid for at least 2 hours before assembly.

1) Coat new "O" rings with ATF and install on piston. Press piston into drum with cupped side up. Do not damage "O" rings. Install 18 piston return springs, retainer, and snap ring. Ensure that snap ring gap is not aligned with spring retainer claw.

2) Install 1 plate, 1 disc, 2 plates, and 1 disc. See Fig. 13. Install flange with flat side facing downward. Install outer snap ring and check that snap ring gap is not aligned with a cut-out.

3) Using a feeler gauge, measure clearance between snap ring and flange. Clearance should be 0.0350-0.0575" (0.89-1.46 mm). Install direct clutch on oil

Automatic Transmissions
TOYOTA A-130L & A-131L 3-SPEED (Cont.)

6-351

pump and apply compressed air to oil pump oval shaped passage. Check to see that piston moves, if not, disassemble piston and inspect.

Fig. 13: Direct Clutch Assembly

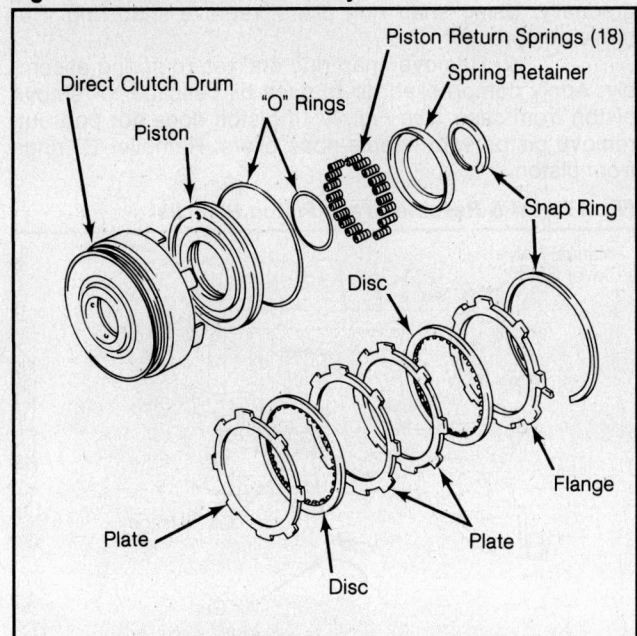

FORWARD (REAR) CLUTCH
Disassembly

1) Remove thrust bearings and races from both sides of clutch. Using a feeler gauge, measure clearance between snap ring and flange. Clearance should be 0.0163-0.0429" (0.414-1.090 mm).

2) Remove snap ring from clutch drum. Remove flange, disc, and plate assembly. Compress spring retainer and return springs. Remove snap ring with snap ring pliers. Remove spring retainer and 18 springs.

3) Apply compressed air to oil passage hole (nearest piston) on rear of forward clutch shaft. If piston does not come out, use needle-nose pliers to remove it. Remove oil seal rings.

Cleaning & Inspection

Clean all parts with kerosene or automatic transmission fluid only. Use compressed air to dry all parts. Shake piston to ensure that check ball in piston is free. Check that valve does not leak by applying low pressure compressed air.

Reassembly

NOTE: **New discs or plates that are to be used for replacement must be soaked in transmission fluid for at least 2 hours before assembly.**

1) Being careful not to spread oil seal rings too much, install rings on shaft. Coat new "O" rings with ATF and install on piston. Press piston into drum with cupped side up. Do not damage "O" rings. Install 18 piston return springs, retainer, and snap ring.

2) Ensure that snap ring gap is not aligned with spring retainer claw. Install 1 plate, 1 disc, 1 plate, 1 disc, 1 plate, and 1 disc. *See Fig. 14.* Install flange with flat side facing downward. Install outer snap ring and check that snap ring gap is not aligned with a cut-out.

3) Using a feeler gauge, measure clearance between snap ring and flange. Clearance should be 0.0163-0.0429" (0.414-1.090 mm). Apply compressed air to oil passage hole (nearest piston) on rear of forward clutch shaft. Check to see that piston moves, if not, disassemble piston and inspect.

Fig. 14: Forward (Rear) Clutch Assembly

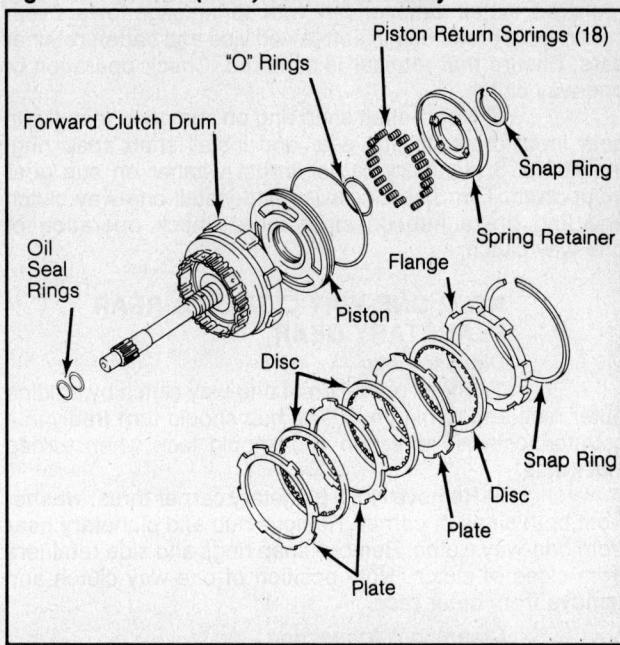

NO. 1 ONE-WAY CLUTCH & SUN GEAR
Disassembly

1) Check operation of one-way clutch by holding sun gear and turning hub. The hub should turn freely in a clockwise direction and should lock when turned counterclockwise.

2) Turn hub clockwise and remove one-way clutch from inner race. Remove No. 3 planetary carrier thrust washer from sun gear input drum. Remove shaft snap ring and remove sun gear input drum. Remove shaft snap ring. If necessary, pry off one-way clutch retainer and remove one-way clutch from hub.

Fig. 15: No. 1 One-Way Clutch & Sun Gear Assembly

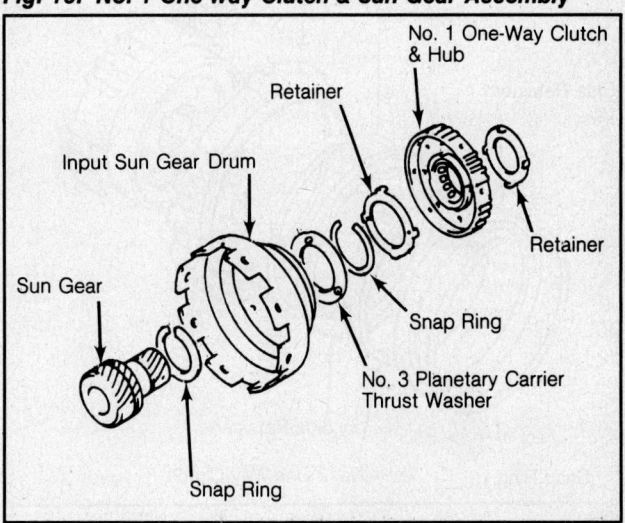

6-352

Automatic Transmissions
TOYOTA A-130L & A-131L 3-SPEED (Cont.)

Cleaning & Inspection
Clean all parts with kerosene or automatic transmission fluid only. Use compressed air to dry all parts. Check thrust bearings, races, and one-way clutch for wear or damage. Replace if necessary.

Reassembly
1) Coat parts with ATF. If one-way clutch was removed, install clutch on hub with spring cage toward rear cover. Hold brake hub in soft-jawed vise and flatten retainer ears. Ensure that retainer is centered. Check operation of one-way clutch.

2) Install shaft snap ring on sun gear. Install sun gear input drum on sun gear and install shaft snap ring. Install No. 3 planetary carrier thrust washer on sun gear input drum. Turn hub clockwise and install one-way clutch and 2nd brake hub on inner race. Check operation of one-way clutch.

NO. 2 ONE-WAY CLUTCH & REAR PLANETARY GEAR
Disassembly
1) Check operation of one-way clutch by holding outer race and turning hub. The hub should turn freely in a counterclockwise direction and should lock when turned clockwise.

2) Remove No. 2 planetary carrier thrust washer from both sides of carrier. Remove hub and planetary gear from one-way clutch. Remove snap rings and side retainers from sides of clutch. Note position of one-way clutch and remove from outer race.

Cleaning & Inspection
Clean all parts with kerosene or automatic transmission fluid only. Use compressed air to dry all parts. Check one-way clutch for wear or damage.

Reassembly
Coat all parts with ATF. Install one-way clutch into outer race with cage flange toward (front) oil pump. Reverse disassembly procedure to complete reassembly. Coat thrust washers with petroleum jelly. Check operation of one-way clutch.

Fig. 16: No. 2 One-Way Clutch & Rear Planetary Gear Assembly

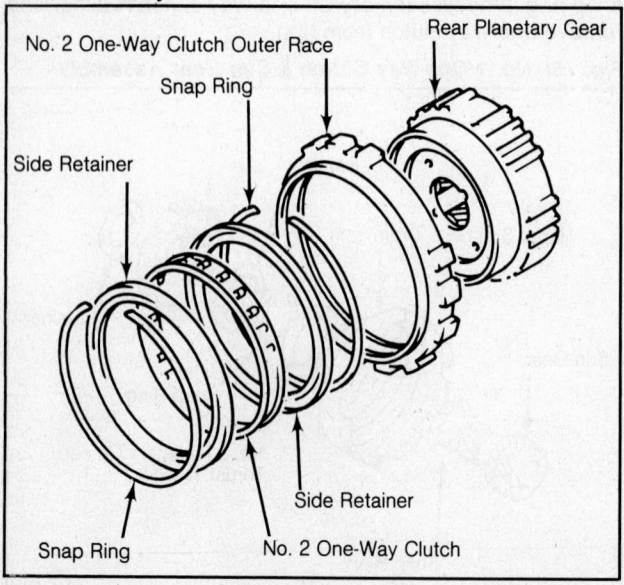

1ST & REVERSE BRAKE PISTON
Disassembly
1) Using 1st and Reverse Spring Compressor (SST 09350-32011), compress springs by tightening bolt gradually. Using snap ring pliers, remove snap ring. Remove compressor.

2) Remove snap ring and return spring assembly. Apply compressed air to case oil passage to remove piston from case. See Fig. 17. If piston does not pop out, remove piston with needle-nose pliers. Remove "O" rings from piston.

Fig. 17: 1st & Reverse Brake Piston Removal

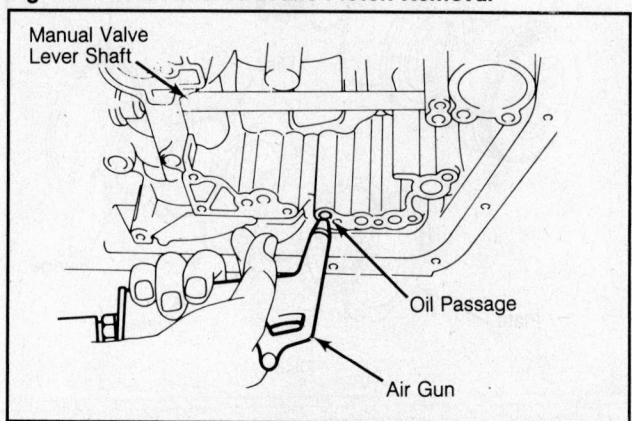

Cleaning & Inspection
Clean all parts with kerosene or automatic transmission fluid only. Use compressed air to dry all parts.

Reassembly
1) Coat new "O" rings with ATF and install on piston. Push piston into transaxle case with spring seats facing (up) forward. Install piston return spring assembly and snap ring in place.

2) Compress piston return springs to allow installation of snap ring. Avoid bending spring retainer or damaging case by overtightening compressor. Push snap ring into place with fingers.

3) Visually check snap ring to ensure that it is fully seated and centered by 3 lugs on spring retainer. Ensure that snap ring gap is not aligned with spring retainer claw. Remove compressor.

INTERMEDIATE SHAFT
Disassembly
Using Puller (SST 09950-00020), press intermediate shaft front and rear bearings out of shaft.

Reassembly
Reverse disassembly procedure to complete reassembly.

VALVE BODY
Disassembly
1) Remove 14 bolts. Remove lower valve body cover and gasket. Turn assembly over and remove 12 bolts from upper valve body and upper valve body cover. Remove upper valve body cover, strainer, and gasket.

2) Turn assembly over and remove 3 bolts from lower valve body. Hold valve body plate against lower valve body and carefully remove lower valve body. DO NOT allow check valve and ball to fall out. Note location of steel ball, retainers, and pins in valve body.

TOYOTA A-130L & A-131L 3-SPEED (Cont.)

3) Disassemble upper valve body as follows: Remove throttle valve retainer and check ball. Remove plug retainer with a magnet and remove plug. Remove lock-up relay valve, control valve, and spring. Remove sleeve retainer with a magnet, then remove sleeve. *See Fig. 18.*

4) Remove retainer with a magnet and remove cut-back valve. Remove retainer with a magnet and remove plug, throttle modulator valve, and spring. Remove retainer with a magnet and remove plug, spring, and accumulator control valve.

5) Remove pin with a magnet and remove plug, spring, and low coast modulator valve. Remove retainer with a magnet and remove spring and 2nd coast modulator valve. Loosen throttle cam bolt. Remove bolt, throttle cam, spring, and collar.

6) Remove pin with a magnet and remove downshift plug, sleeve, and spring. Remove throttle valve. Remove springs and adjustment rings from upper valve body. Note and record number of adjustment rings.

7) Disassemble lower valve body as follows: Remove lower valve body plate and gaskets. Remove cooler by-pass valve and spring. *See Fig. 19.* Remove damping check valve and spring. Note position of 3 lower valve body check balls. Remove check balls.

8) Remove retainer with a magnet and remove plug, sleeve, and plunger. Remove spring and primary regulator valve. Note and record number of adjustment rings. Remove retainer with a magnet and remove plug, secondary regulator valve, and spring.

9) Remove retainer with a magnet and remove plug, 1-2 shift valve, and spring. Remove retainer with a magnet and remove plug and low coast shift valve. Remove retainer with a magnet and remove plug and lock-up control valve.

10) Remove retainer with a magnet and remove plug, detent regulator valve, and spring. Remove retainer with a magnet and remove plug, 2-3 shift valve, and spring. Remove retainer with a magnet and remove plug and intermediate shift valve.

11) Remove retainer with a magnet and remove plug, lock-up signal valve, and spring. Remove retainer with a magnet and remove plug and 3-4 coast shift plug. Remove retainer with a magnet and remove plug and 3-4 shift plug.

Cleaning & Inspection

1) Clean all parts with kerosene or automatic transmission fluid only. Clean all fluid passages and holes, use compressed air to ensure that passages or holes are not clogged. After cleaning, arrange parts in proper order for inspection.

2) Inspect valve springs for damage, squareness, rust and collapsed coils. Measure spring free length and replace any spring whose length is less than specified. Keep valve body springs together with corresponding valve.

Fig. 18: Upper Valve Body Assembly

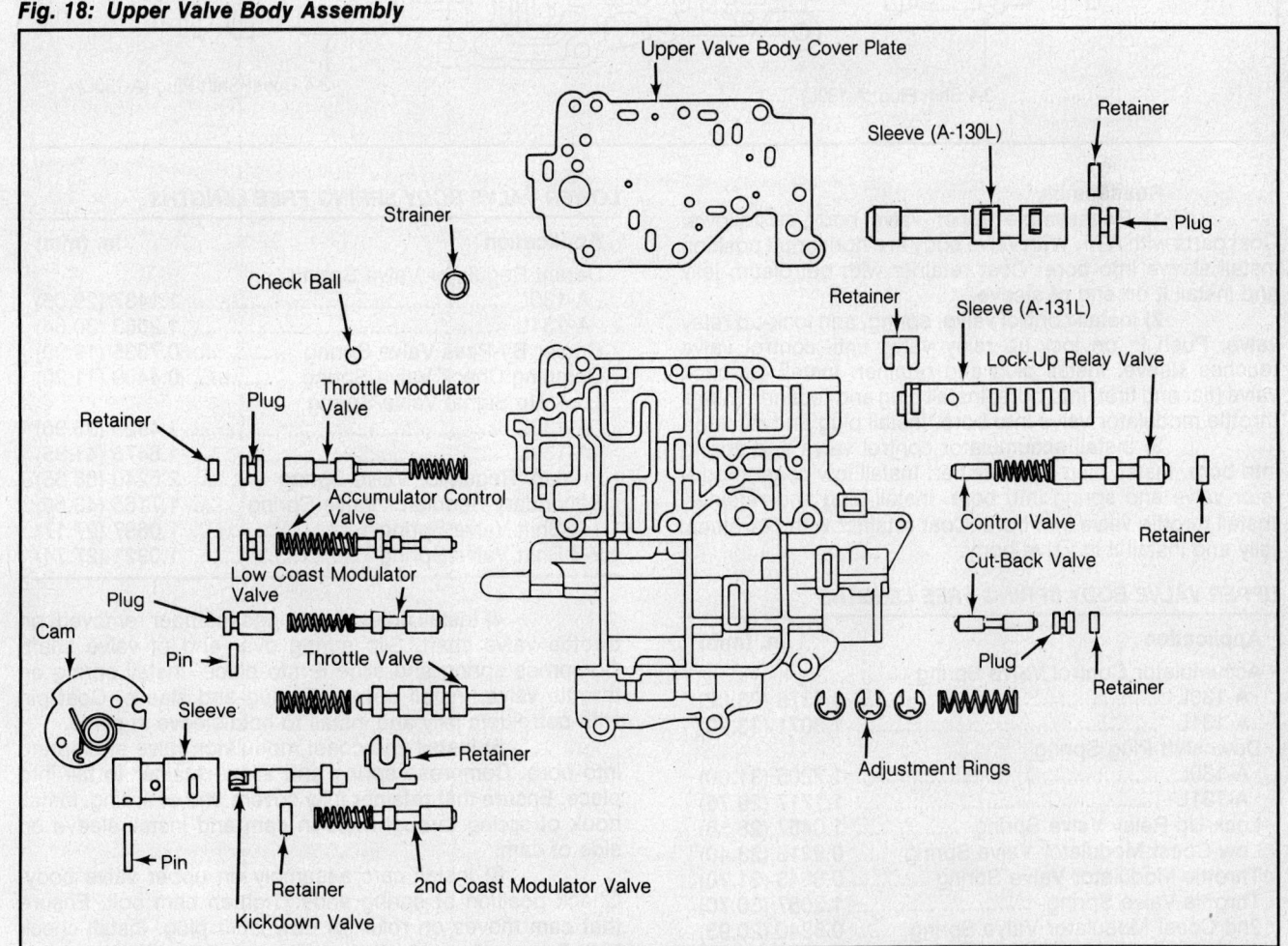

Automatic Transmissions
TOYOTA A-130L & A-131L 3-SPEED (Cont.)

Fig. 19: Lower Valve Body Assembly

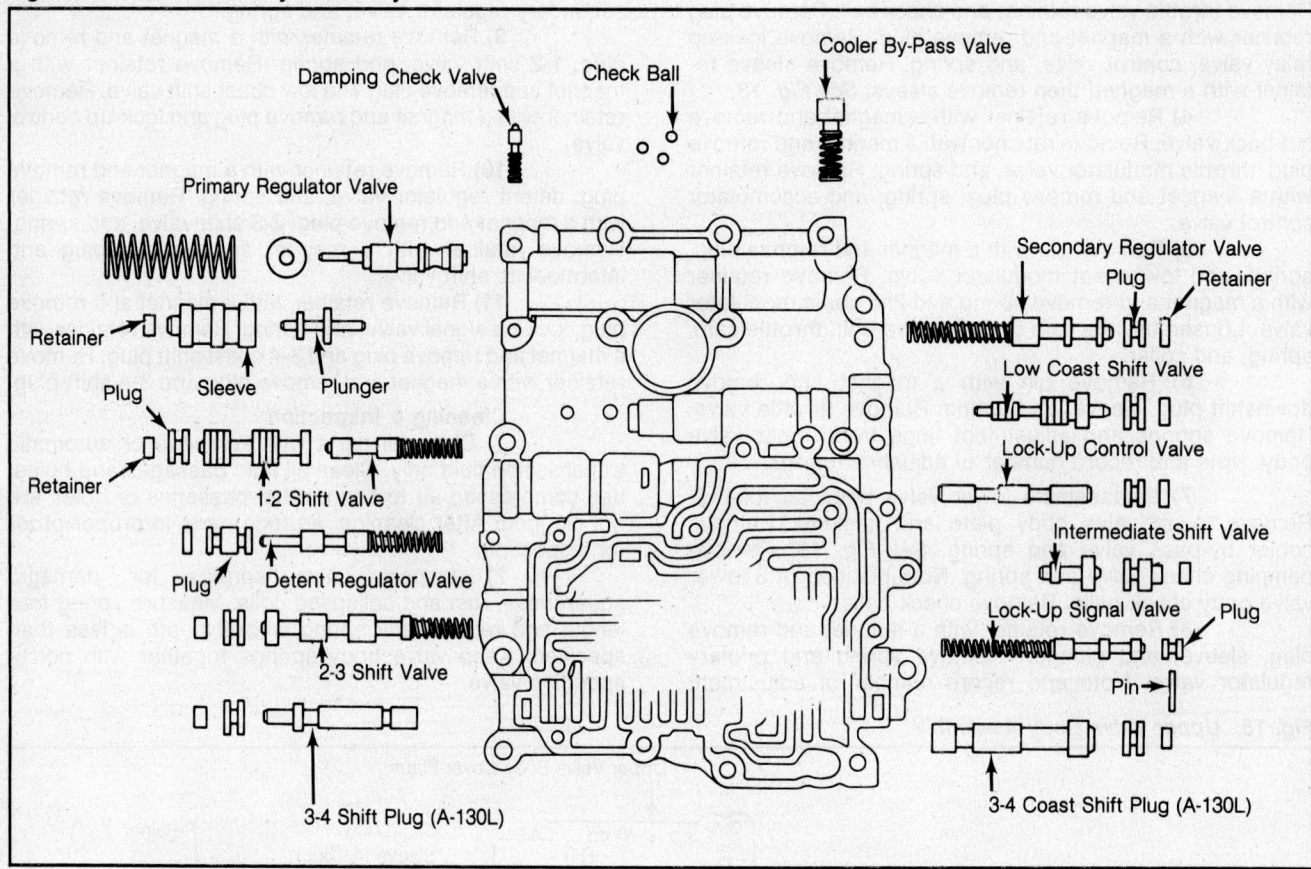

Reassembly

1) Reassemble upper valve body as follows: Coat parts with ATF. With valve body in a horizontal position install sleeve into bore. Coat retainer with petroleum jelly and install it on end of sleeve.

2) Install control valve, spring, and lock-up relay valve. Push in on lock-up relay valve until control valve touches sleeve. Install plug and retainer. Install cut-back valve (flat end first) into bore. Install plug and retainer. Install throttle modulator valve into bore. Install plug and retainer.

3) Install accumulator control valve and spring into bore. Install plug and retainer. Install low coast modulator valve and spring into bore. Install plug and retainer. Install throttle valve into bore. Coat retainer with petroluem jelly and install it in valve body.

UPPER VALVE BODY SPRING FREE LENGTHS

Application	In. (mm)
Accumulator Control Valve Spring	
A-130L	0.9378 (23.82)
A-131L	1.3071 (33.20)
Downshift Plug Spring	
A-130L	1.2205 (31.00)
A-131L	1.1717 (29.76)
Lock-Up Relay Valve Spring	1.0457 (26.56)
Low Coast Modulator Valve Spring	0.9213 (23.40)
Throttle Modulator Valve Spring	0.8543 (21.70)
Throttle Valve Spring	1.2087 (30.70)
2nd Coast Modulator Valve Spring	0.8240 (20.93)

LOWER VALVE BODY SPRING FREE LENGTHS

Application	In. (mm)
Detent Regulator Valve Spring	
A-130L	1.1437 (29.05)
A-131L	1.2063 (30.64)
Cooler By-Pass Valve Spring	0.7835 (19.90)
Damping Check Valve Spring	0.4409 (11.20)
Lock-Up Signal Valve Spring	
A-130L	1.4528 (36.90)
A-131L	1.6476 (41.85)
Primary Regulator Valve Spring	2.6240 (66.65)
Secondary Regulator Valve Spring	1.7165 (43.60)
1-2 Shift Valve Spring	1.0697 (27.17)
2-3 Shift Valve Spring	1.0921 (27.74)

4) Install adjustment rings (number removed) on throttle valve shaft. Slip spring over end of valve shaft. Compress spring and slide it into place. Install spring on throttle valve. Install downshift plug and sleeve. Coat pin with petroluem jelly and install to hold sleeve in place.

5) Install 2nd coast modulator valve and spring into bore. Compress spring and allow retainer to fall into place. Ensure that retainer fully covers end of spring. Install hook of spring through hole in cam and install sleeve on side of cam.

6) Install cam assembly on upper valve body. Check position of spring ends. Tighten cam bolt. Ensure that cam moves on roller of downshift plug. Install check ball. Ensure that pins and retainers are correctly installed and in place. *See Fig. 20.*

TOYOTA A-130L & A-131L 3-SPEED (Cont.)

Fig. 20: Upper Valve Body Check Ball, Pin & Retainer Locations

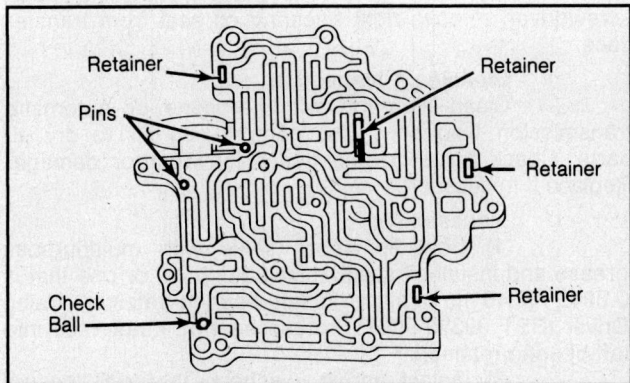

7) Reassemble lower valve body as follows: Coat parts with ATF. Place valve body in a horizontal position. Install adjustment rings (number removed) and spring seat on primary regulator valve. Place valve in bore. Stand valve body up and push valve in until it bottoms in bore. Install spring.

8) Insert plunger (short end first) into sleeve. Ensure that plunger is fully inserted in sleeve. Install sleeve and plunger in primary regulator valve bore. Install retainer.

9) Install spring and secondary regulator valve in bore. Install plug and retainer. Install spring and 1-2 shift valve in bore. Install plug and retainer. Install lock-up control valve in bore. Coat retainer with petroluem jelly and install plug and retainer.

10) Install spring and detent regulator valve (thin end first) into bore. Install plug and retainer. Install intermediate shift valve (small end first) into bore. Install plug and retainer. Install spring and 2-3 shift valve into bore. Install plug and retainer.

11) Install spring and lock-up signal valve in bore. Install plug and pin. Install 3-4 coast shift plug. Install plug and retainer. Install spring and cooler by-pass valve. Install spring and damping valve. Ensure that pin and retainers are correctly installed and in place. Install 3 check balls. *See Fig. 21.*

Fig. 21: Lower Valve Body Check Ball, Pin & Retainer Locations

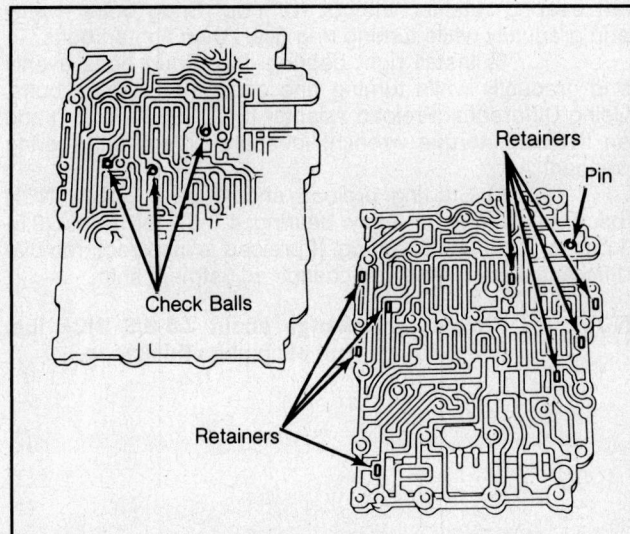

12) Place gasket having larger cooler by-pass valve hole against lower valve body. Place plate and second gasket on top of first gasket. Align bolt holes in valve body with gaskets and plate.

13) Tightly hold lower valve body, gaskets, and plate. Place lower valve body, gaskets, and plate on top of upper valve body. Align bolt holes in valve bodies, gaskets, and plate. Install and finger tighten 3 bolts in lower valve body. *See Fig. 22.*

14) Turn assembly over. Install and finger tighten 3 bolts in upper valve body. *See Fig. 23.* Install gasket, plate, and gasket on upper valve body. Install strainer on plate. Install upper valve body cover and finger tighten 9 bolts. *See Fig. 23.*

15) Turn assembly over. Install lower valve body gasket, cover, and finger tighten 14 bolts. *See Fig. 22.* Check alignment of gaskets and plates. Tighten lower valve body bolts. Turn assembly over and tighten upper valve body bolts.

Fig. 22: Lower Valve Body & Valve Body Cover Bolt Installation

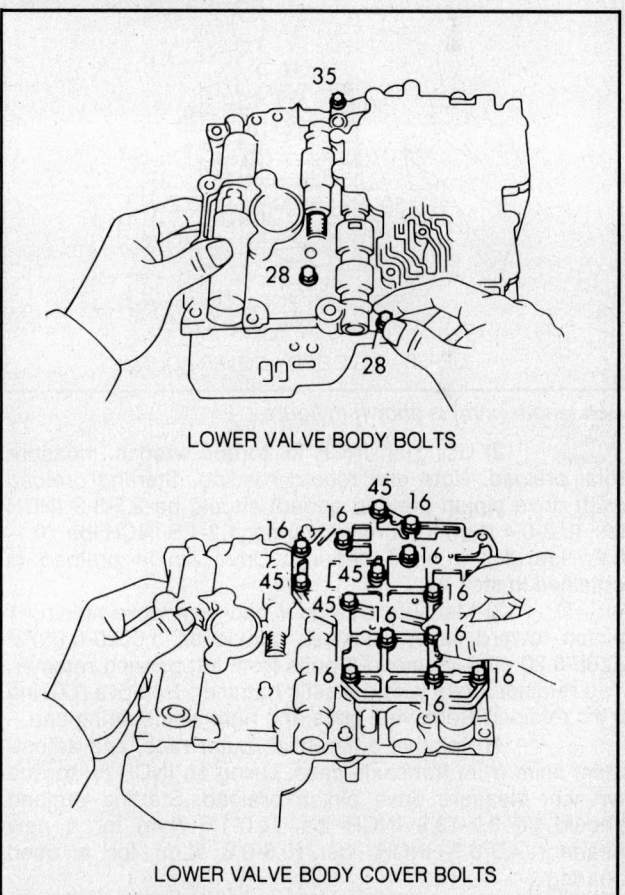

LOWER VALVE BODY BOLTS

LOWER VALVE BODY COVER BOLTS

Bolt length (mm) is shown in figure.

DIFFERENTIAL
Disassembly

1) Remove speedometer driven gear. Remove 11 transaxle rear cover bolts. Using a plastic hammer, tap rear cover loose, and remove. Remove intermediate shaft and carrier cover.

Automatic Transmissions

TOYOTA A-130L & A-131L 3-SPEED (Cont.)

Fig. 23: Upper Valve Body & Valve Body Cover Bolt Installation

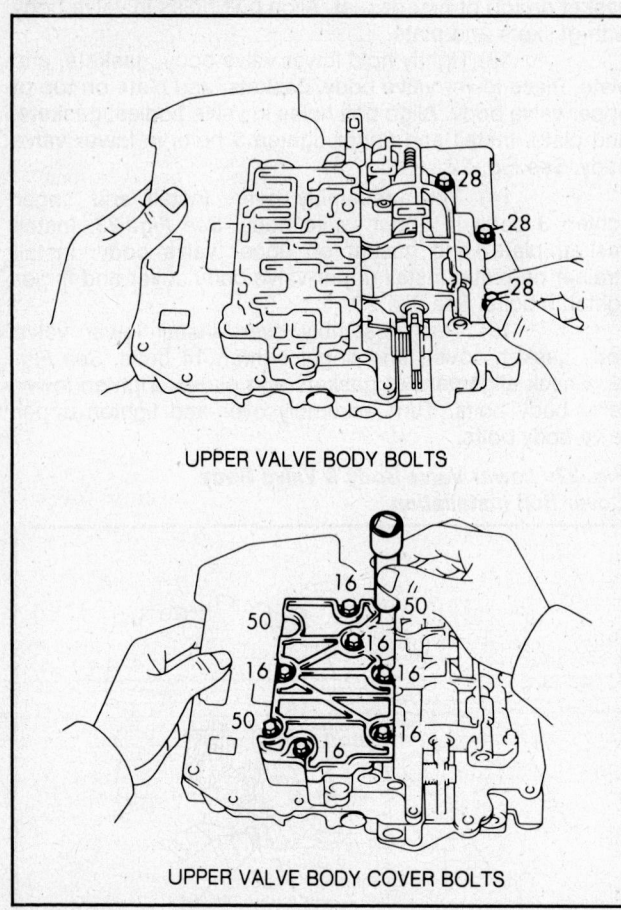

UPPER VALVE BODY BOLTS

UPPER VALVE BODY COVER BOLTS

Bolt length (mm) is shown in figure.

2) Using an INCH lb. torque wrench, measure total preload. Note and record reading. Starting preload (with drive pinion preload added) should be 2.5-3.9 INCH lbs. (0.3-0.4 N.m) for a new bearing; 1.2-1.9 INCH lbs. (0.1-0.2 N.m) for a used bearing. Drive pinion preload is obtained in step 4).

3) Measure side gear backlash while holding 1 pinion toward case. Backlash should be 0.0020-0.0079" (0.05-0.20 mm). Remove 6 bolts from left bearing retainer. Tap retainer loose with a plastic hammer. Remove "O" ring from retainer. Remove 2 bolts and right side bearing cap.

4) Remove differential, outer race, and adjustment shim from transaxle case. Using an INCH lb. torque wrench, measure drive pinion preload. Starting preload should be 8.7-13.9 INCH lbs. (1.0-1.6 N.m) for a new bearing; 4.3-6.9 INCH lbs. (0.5-0.8 N.m) for a used bearing.

5) Using Puller (SST 09502-10012), remove bearings from differential case. Remove speedometer drive gear. Mark ring gear and case for reassembly reference. Bend locking tabs on ring gear bolts. Remove 8 bolts and locking tabs. Using a brass hammer, tap ring gear and remove from case.

6) While holding 1 pinion against case, measure side gear backlash. If backlash is incorrect, disassemble case and change thrust washer on side gears. Drive out pinion shaft lock pin and remove pinion shaft. Remove pinions, side gears, and 4 thrust washers from each gear.

7) Remove oil seal from left bearing retainer. Press out of left bearing outer race and shim. Using a long screwdriver, remove right bearing oil seal from transfer case.

Cleaning & Inspection

Clean all parts with kerosene or automatic transmission fluid only. Use compressed air to dry all parts. Check bearings and gears for wear or damage. Replace if necessary.

Reassembly

1) Coat lip of oil seals with multipurpose grease and install oil seals. Install old shim, or one that is 0.0945" (2.40 mm) thick, in left bearing retainer. Using Driver (SST 09350-32011), press bearing outer race into left bearing retainer.

2) Select thrust washers that will ensure correct backlash. Install trust washers and side gears in case. If possible, install same size washers on both sides of gears. Install pinions and pinion shaft.

3) While holding 1 pinion against case, check side gear backlash. Backlash should be 0.0020-0.0079" (0.05-0.20 mm). If backlash is incorrect, disassemble case and change thrust washer on side gears.

NOTE: Side gear thrust washers are available in the following thickness variations: 0.0374" (0.95 mm), 0.0394" (1.00 mm), 0.0413" (1.05 mm), 0.0433" (1.10 mm), 0.0453" (1.15 mm), and 0.0472" (1.20 mm).

4) Using a hammer and punch, drive lock pin through case and into pinion shaft. Stake differential case to hold pin in place. Clean ring gear contact surface of case. Heat ring gear to 212°F (100°C) in an oil bath.

5) Clean contact surface of ring gear with cleaning solvent. Align ring gear with differential case, and quickly install ring gear on case. Install locking tabs and bolts. Tighten bolts evenly and a little at a time.

6) Using a hammer and punch, bend locking tabs. Stake 1st tab flush with flat surface of nut. Stake 2nd tab against corner of nut. Install speedometer drive gear. Using Bearing Installer (SST 09350-32011), press bearings onto differential case.

7) Install outer race and adjustment shim on right bearing. Install differential in transaxle case. Install left bearing retainer without "O" ring. Snug bolts evenly and gradually while turning ring gear, then tighten bolts.

8) Install right bearing cap. Snug bolts evenly and gradually while turning ring gear, then tighten bolts. Using Differential Preload Adapter (SST 09564-32011) and an INCH lb. torque wrench, measure differential bearing preload.

9) Starting preload should be 6.9-13.9 INCH lbs. (0.8-1.6 N.m) for a new bearing; 4.3-8.7 INCH lbs. (0.5-1.0 N.m) for a used bearing. If preload is incorrect, remove differential from case and change adjustment shim.

NOTE: Preload will change about 2.6-3.5 INCH lbs. (0.3-0.4 N.m) with each shim thickness.

Automatic Transmissions

TOYOTA A-130L & A-131L 3-SPEED (Cont.)

Fig. 24: Measuring Differential Bearing Preload

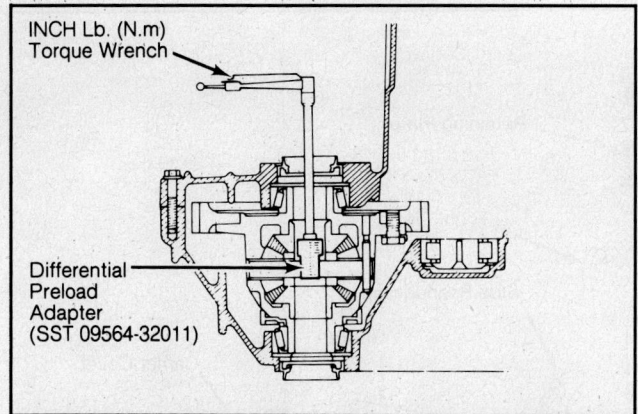

DIFFERENTIAL BEARING PRELOAD SHIM SELECTION

I.D. Mark	Thickness In. (mm)
A-130L	
01	0.0748 (1.90)
02	0.0768 (1.95)
03	0.0787 (2.00)
04	0.0807 (2.05)
05	0.0827 (2.10)
06	0.0846 (2.15)
07	0.0866 (2.20)
08	0.0886 (2.25)
09	0.0906 (2.30)
10	0.0925 (2.35)
11	0.0945 (2.40)
12	0.0965 (2.45)
13	0.0984 (2.50)
14	0.1004 (2.55)
15	0.1024 (2.60)
16	0.1043 (2.65)
17	0.1063 (2.70)
18	0.1083 (2.75)
19	0.1102 (2.80)
A-131L	
None	0.0630 (1.60)
None	0.0650 (1.65)
None	0.0669 (1.70)
None	0.0689 (1.75)
None	0.0709 (1.80)
None	0.0728 (1.85)
None	0.0748 (1.90)
None	0.0768 (1.95)
None	0.0787 (2.00)
None	0.0807 (2.05)
None	0.0827 (2.10)
None	0.0846 (2.15)
None	0.0866 (2.20)
None	0.0886 (2.25)
None	0.0906 (2.30)
None	0.0925 (2.35)
None	0.0945 (2.40)
None	0.0965 (2.45)
None	0.0984 (2.50)
None	0.1004 (2.55)
None	0.1024 (2.60)
None	0.1043 (2.65)

10) If preload is within specification, remove left bearing retainer, differential, and shim. Do not lose selected adjustment shim. Reinstall outer race and adjustment shim on right bearing. Install "O" ring on left bearing retainer.

11) Install differential and retainer on case. Clean threads of bolts and case with White gasoline. Coat bolt threads with sealer. Snug bolts evenly and gradually while turning ring gear. Install right bearing cap. Snug bolts evenly and gradually while turning ring gear. Tighten cap and left bearing retainer bolts.

12) With drive pinion installed in case, measure total preload. Starting preload (with drive pinion preload added) should be 2.5-3.9 INCH lbs. (0.3-0.4 N.m) for a new bearing; 1.2-1.9 INCH lbs. (0.1-0.2 N.m) for a used bearing.

NOTE: If drive pinion was diassembled, use bearing preload obtained during reassembly.

13) If total preload is not within specification, disassemble differential and readjust. If total preload is correct, stake counter driven gear lock nut. Install drive pinion cap.

14) Clean threads of bolts and case with White gasoline. Coat bolt threads with sealer. Install carrier cover over gasket. Install cover and tighten bolts.

15) Install intermediate shaft while turning counter driven gear. Do not damage bushing and oil seal. Install transaxle rear cover and tighten bolts. Install speedometer driven gear.

DIFFERENTIAL DRIVE PINION
Disassembly
1) Using an INCH lb. torque wrench, measure drive pinion preload. Starting preload should be 8.7-13.9 INCH lbs. (1.0-1.6 N.m) for a new bearing; 4.3-6.9 INCH lbs. (0.5-0.8 N.m) for a used bearing.

2) Remove drive pinion cap. Using a chisel, loosen staked part of counter driven gear lock nut. Install Holder (SST 09330-32011) on gear. Using Socket (SST 09330-00020), remove counter driven gear lock nut. Using Puller (SST 09350-32011), remove gear and bearing.

3) Using Puller (SST 09350-32011), remove bearing outer race. Remove oil slinger, bearing spacer, and governor body drive gear. If gear is too tight, remove it later. Remove snap ring using snap ring pliers.

4) Insert brass bar into hole and drive out drive pinion and bearing cage from bore. Press governor drive gear out of drive pinion shaft. Remove bearing cage from drive pinion. Remove "O" ring from bearing cage.

5) Using Bearing Remover (SST 09950-00020), press bearing out of counter driven gear. Using bearing remover, press bearing out of pinion shaft. Using Puller (SST 09350-32011) without bolt, drive bearing outer race from cage. Note position of lip on oil seals, and press seals out of cage.

Cleaning & Inspection
Clean all parts with kerosene or automatic transmission fluid only. Use compressed air to dry all parts. Check bearings and gears for wear or damage. Replace if necessary.

Automatic Transmissions

TOYOTA A-130L & A-131L 3-SPEED (Cont.)

Fig. 25: *Exploded View of A-130L & A131L Transaxle Differential & Drive Pinion Assemblies*

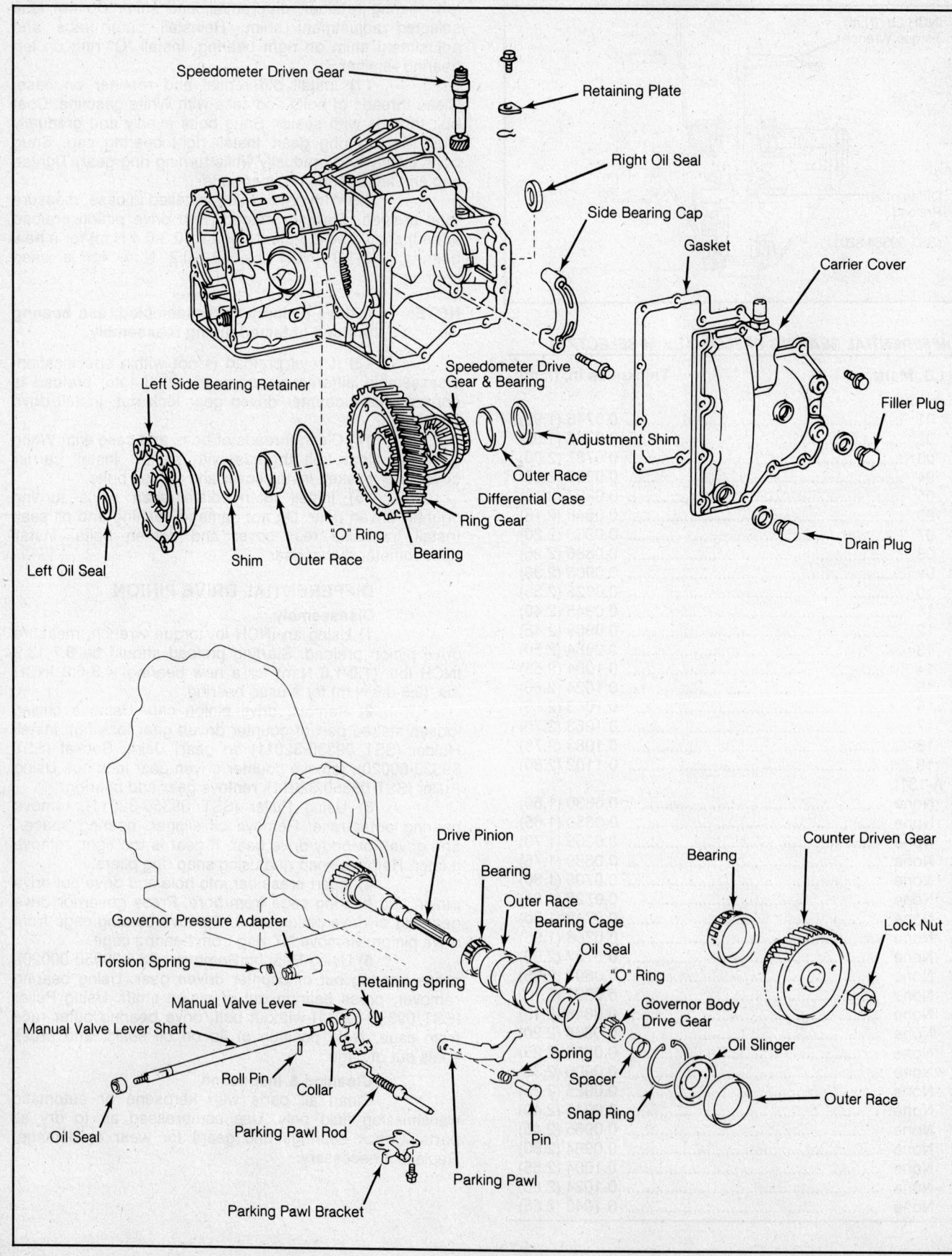

TOYOTA A-130L & A-131L 3-SPEED (Cont.)

Reassembly

1) Coat lip of cage oil seals with multipurpose grease. With lip of inner seal facing downward, press in oil seal until top of seal is at a depth of 0.43" (10 mm). With lip of outer seal facing upward, press in oil seal until it is flush with cage surface. Press outer bearing race into bearing cage.

2) Using Bearing Installer (SST 09350-32011), press bearing onto pinion shaft. Using bearing installer, press bearing onto counter driven gear. Install "O" ring on bearing cage. Install cage on drive pinion shaft. Do not damage oil seals with splines.

3) Press governor drive gear onto drive pinion shaft. Install shaft assembly into case. Tap bearing cage into case. Ensure that cage is past snap ring groove in bore, and that groove can be seen.

4) Install snap ring using snap ring pliers. Insert brass bar into hole and tap drive pinion shaft against snap ring. Ensure that snap ring is properly installed. Install oil slinger with lip facing outward. Drive outer race into case.

5) Install new bearing spacer, small end first. Insert a bar into hole and position against drive pinion shaft. Position other end of bar against a solid object. Drive counter driven gear onto shaft until lock nut can be installed. Do not tap on transaxle case.

6) Coat threads and lock nut with multipurpose grease. Install nut on shaft. Install Holder (SST 09330-32011) on gear. Using Socket (SST 09330-00020), tighten counter driven gear lock nut. Turn gear counterclockwise and then clockwise several times.

7) Using an INCH lb. torque wrench, measure drive pinion preload. Starting preload should be 8.7-13.9 INCH lbs. (1.0-1.6 N.m) for a new bearing; 4.3-6.9 INCH lbs. (0.5-0.8 N.m) for a used bearing. If preload is greater than specified, replace bearing spacer and repeat preload procedure.

8) If preload is less than specified, retighten lock nut 9 ft. lbs. (13 N.m) at a time until specified preload is obtained. If maximum torque of 213 ft. lbs. (289 N.m) is exceeded while retightening nut, replace bearing spacer and repeat procedure. DO NOT back off nut to reduce preload.

TRASAXLE REASSEMBLY

1) Place parking pawl and manual valve lever shaft in transaxle case. Hook spring end on pawl and case. Install pin in case, through spring and pawl. Install parking lock rod.

2) Install parking pawl bracket and tighten bolt. Check operation of pawl to ensure that counter driven gear is locked when manual valve lever is in the "P" range.

3) Install intermediate shaft. Install transaxle rear cover over gasket. Install cover and tighten bolts. Ensure that intermediate shaft turns smoothly. Check intermediate shaft end play. End play should be 0.0193-0.594" (0.049-1.51 mm).

4) Install 1st and reverse inner flange with flat side facing (oil pump) forward. Install 1 disc, 1 plate, 1 disc, 2 plates, 1 disc, 1 plate, 2 plates, 1 disc, 1 plate, and 1 disc. Install outer flange with flat side toward piston. Install snap ring.

5) Using a feeler gauge, measure clearance between 1st and reverse brake piston and flange. See Fig. 8. Clearance should be 0.0953-0.0465" (1.18-2.42 mm) on transaxle used with diesel engine. Clearance should be 0.0350-0.0831" (0.89-2.11 mm) on transaxle used with gasoline engine.

6) Apply compressed air to oil passage and check that piston moves. See Fig. 17. Coat No. 2 planetary carrier thrust washers with petroleum jelly and install them on carrier. Ensure that thrust washer lugs match openings in carrier.

7) Coat rear ring gear races and bearing with petroleum jelly and install them onto ring gear. Install planetary gear onto ring gear. Ensure that thrust bearing is installed in center of ring gear flange.

8) Align tabs of discs with 1st and reverse brake. Align splines of planetary carrier with tabs of discs and install rear planetary gear into 1st and reverse brake discs.

9) Place No. 2 one-way clutch in case. Install one-way clutch onto inner race while turning the planetary pinion counterclockwise with a screwdriver. Check operation on clutch by turning planetary carrier. The carrier should turn freely clockwise and should lock when turned counterclockwise. Install snap ring.

10) Install 2nd coast brake band guide and 2nd brake drum guide. Install band guide so that its tip touches case. Install 2nd brake flange with flat side toward 2nd brake piston. Install 1 disc, 1 plate, 1 disc, 1 plate, 1 disc, and 1 plate.

11) Install piston return spring assembly. Install each spring over protrusions in case. Align groove of 2nd brake drum with guide and install drum in case. Install snap ring so that end gap is installed in groove. Using 2 hammers, compress piston return springs with handles. Install snap ring into groove.

12) Using a feeler gauge, measure the clearance between 2nd brake piston return spring assembly seat and top of plate. See Fig. 7. Clearance should be 0.0193-0.0626" (0.49-1.59 mm). Apply compressed air to center oil passege (next to manual valve lever shaft) and ensure that piston moves.

13) Install 2nd brake drum seal in center oil passage until the distance between surface of case (passage) and top of seal is 1.140-1.144" (28.95-29.05 mm).

14) Align tabs of discs in 2nd brake. Align splines of 2nd brake hub and No. 1 one-way clutch with tabs of discs and install hub on 2nd brake discs. Install sun gear and sun gear input drum onto one-way clutch while turning sun gear clockwise.

NOTE: **Place sun gear in center of intermediate shaft to protect bushings from damage.**

15) Coat front ring gear races and bearing with petroleum jelly and install them onto ring gear. Coat race and bearing with petroluem jelly and install them onto carrier. Install front planetary gear onto ring gear. Install front planetary gear assembly onto sun gear.

16) If planetary gear and other parts are installed correctly in case, the bushing on the ring gear flange will be flush with shoulder of intermediate shaft. Coat race with petroluem jelly and install it onto tip of ring gear flange.

Automatic Transmissions

TOYOTA A-130L & A-131L 3-SPEED (Cont.)

17) Install 2nd coast brake band in case. Install pin through oil pump mounting bolt hole. Coat forward (rear) clutch races and bearing with petroleum jelly and install them onto both sides of clutch drum. Align tabs of discs in forward clutch.

18) Install clutch on sun gear. Hold sun gear input drum and rotate input shaft to mesh hub with clutch discs of forward clutch. Align center of input shaft and intermediate shaft, and while pushing on input shaft, rotate it to mesh hub and disc.

19) If tabs of discs are correctly meshed with hub, the protrusion around clutch drum will be flush with tip of input sun gear drum. Coat direct clutch drum thrust washer with petroleum jelly and install it with oil groove facing upward onto drum.

20) Align tabs of discs in direct clutch. Hold input shaft, and install clutch drum through and into 2nd coast brake band. Mesh hub with tabs of direct clutch while turning clutch drum. If tabs of discs are correctly meshed with hub, the end of bushing on direct clutch drum will be flush with thrust bearing on forward clutch.

21) Coat oil pump race with petroleum jelly and install it onto stator shaft. Insert oil pump (without "O" ring) through input shaft, and aling bolt holes with case. Hold input shaft and lightly press oil pump body to slide oil seal rings on stator shaft through direct clutch drum. Install and tighten bolts.

NOTE: Do not push strongly on oil pump or the seal rings will stick to direct clutch drum.

22) Ensure that input shaft rotates smoothly. Using a dial indicator, measure input shaft end play. End play should be 0.012-0.035" (0.3-0.9 mm). If end play is incorrect, remove oil pump and install a new oil pump race. Oil pump races are available in thicknesses of 0.031" (0.8 mm) and 0.055" (1.4 mm).

23) If input shaft end play is correct, remove oil pump. Install "O" ring around pump body. Insert oil pump through input shaft, and aling bolt holes with case. Hold input shaft and lightly press oil pump body to slide oil seal rings on stator shaft through direct clutch drum. Install and tighten bolts.

24) Ensure that input shaft rotates smoothly and recheck input shaft end play. Install 2nd coast brake piston (without outer spring) and install snap ring. Firmly push brake apply rod into case. See Fig. 6.

25) Measure distance between outer side of snap ring and tip of piston rod. Piston travel must be within 0.551-0.610" (14.0-15.5 mm). If travel is not within specifications, select a longer brake apply rod. Brake apply rods are available in lenghts of 2.870" (72.9 mm) and 2.811" (71.4 mm).

26) Re-measure piston travel. If travel is still more than specified, replace 2nd coast brake band with a new one. If travel is correct, remove installed parts from bore. Install outer spring, piston, and cover. Compress spring and install snap ring.

27) Apply compressed air to hole and check that piston rod moves. See Fig. 26. Install accumulator springs and pistons. Install cover, gasket, and bolts. Tighten bolts a little at a time.

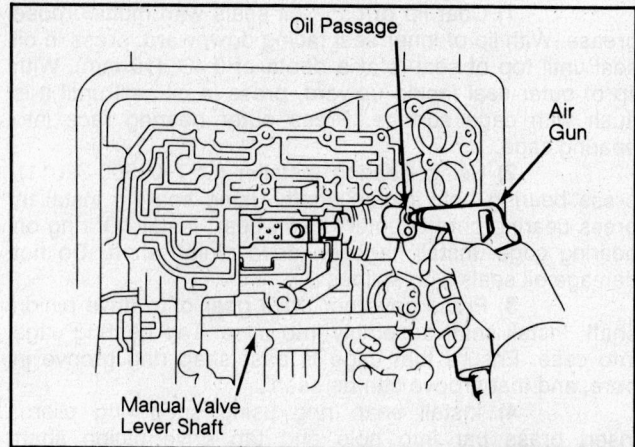

Fig. 26: Checking 2nd Coast Brake Band.

28) Install governor apply gasket and governor line strainer. Push throttle cable through case, being careful not to danage "O" ring. Ensure that cable is fully seated in case.

29) Place valve body in transaxle, and while holding cam down with your hand, slip cable end into slot in cam. Lower valve body into place. Install valve body bolts finger tight, and then tighten. See Fig. 27.

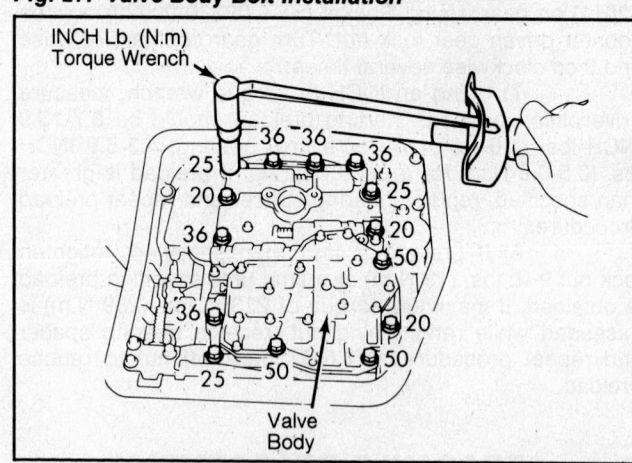

Fig. 27: Valve Body Bolt Installation

Bolt length (mm) is shown in figure.

30) Align manual valve with pin on manual shaft lever. Lower valve body into place. Install detent spring. Check that manual valve lever is touching center of detent spring roller. Install valve body bolts finger tight, and then tighten. See Fig. 28.

31) Using a plastic hammer, install oil tubes. Be careful not to bend or damage tubes. Install tube bracket. Install oil strainer. Install (2) 45 mm bolts on top of strainer, install a 50 mm bolt on strainer tab.

32) Install magnet in oil pan. Ensure that magnet does not interfere with oil tubes. Install oil pan, gasket, and tighten bolts. Install governor body adapter. Install governor body with plate washer.

TOYOTA A-130L & A-131L 3-SPEED (Cont.)

Fig. 28: Manual Valve Body Bolt Installation

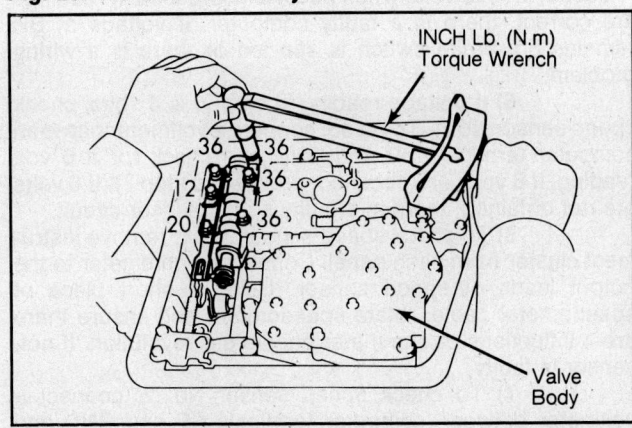

Bolt length (mm) is shown in figure.

33) Install thrust washer onto governor body. Install cover over "O" ring. Install cover bracket with 2 bolts. Install throttle cable retaining plate. Install filler tube and dipstick. Install seal (lip facing inward) and Neutral safety switch. Tighten nut and secure with lock washer. Install shift handle.

34) Connect an ohmmeter between Neutral switch terminals. Shift lever into "N" position. Adjust switch so that there is continuity between terminals. Tighten Neutral switch bolts. Install oil pipe bracket onto case. Connect pipes to union. Clamp pipes onto braket. Tighten union nuts.

TIGHTENING SPECIFICATIONS

Application	Ft. Lbs (N.m)
Carrier Cover Bolts	18 (25)
Counter Driven Gear Lock Nut	127 (172)
Flex Plate Bolts	61 (83)
Left Bearing Retainer Bolts	14 (19)
Oil Cooler Pipes	25 (34)
Oil Pump Bolts	16 (22)
Right Bearing Cap Bolts	36 (49)
Ring Gear Bolts	71 (96)
Torque Converter Bolts	13 (18)
Transaxle Rear Cover Bolts	18 (25)

Application	INCH Lbs. (N.m)
Governor Bracket Bolts	108 (12)
Manual Valve Body-to-Transaxle	84 (10)
Oil Pan Bolts	43 (5.0)
Oil Pump Stator Shaft Bolts	84 (10)
Oil Strainer Bolts-to-Valve Body	84 (10)
Oil Tube Bracket Bolts	84 (10)
Parking Pawl Bracket Bolt	65 (7.0)
Upper Valve Body Cam Bolt	65 (7.0)
Valve Body Bolts	48 (5.4)
Valve Body-to-Transaxle	84 (10)

Automatic Transmissions
TOYOTA MODEL A140E

Camry

TRANSAXLE IDENTIFICATION

Manufacturer uses Vehicle Indentification Number (VIN) for correct application of component parts and assemblies. This number is located at the top left of the instrument panel, and can be seen through the windshield from outside. Also, the VIN is stamped on the front cowl of the engine compartment and on the driver's door post. For ease when ordering parts, record VIN number.

DESCRIPTION

Transaxle combines a differential, 3-speed automatic transmission and overdrive assemblies into a single unit designed for use with front wheel drive vehicles.

The transmission shifting system is controlled by an electronic control module, located behind glove box. It is necessary to remove glove box and right-hand side radio speaker to gain access to the module.

The control module receives input signals from the water temperature sensing switch, which does not allow transaxle to shift into overdrive until coolant temperature has reached a minimum of 122°F (50°C), a throttle position switch, which is located at the throttle body of E.F.I. system, a shift pattern selection switch, which is located at the instrument panel, and is used for various driving conditions. Module recieves signals from 2 speed sensors, 1 is located at the transaxle (refered to as speed sensor No. 2) and the other at the speedometer (refered to as speed sensor No. 1). Also, the back-up lamp/neutral safety switch signals the module for starting and back-up lamp circuits.

The module controls and sends output signals to the stop lamps, back-up lamps. Module also controls shift control solenoids, located within transaxle.

LUBRICATION & ADJUSTMENTS

See appropriate AUTOMATIC TRANSMISSION SERVICING article in IMPORT GENERAL SERVICING section.

TROUBLE SHOOTING

NO SHIFT

1) Road test vehicle. If a slow acceleration from 0 to 37 MPH is not possible, transmission is faulty. If it is possible, check voltage at terminal DG while driving. If voltage rises from 0 to 7 volts in sequence, there is a stuck solenoid.

2) If not, stop vehicle and read voltage at terminal DG. If reading is 0 volts, check for 12 volts between terminals IG and GND (computer power source). If not, repair problem in computer power circuit.

3) If there is 12 volts, measure voltage between terminal IDL of throttle position sensor and GND. With throttle valve closed, reading should be 0 volts, and with throttle valve just off idle, reading should be 4 volts. If not, throttle position sensor is bad or improperly adjusted or there is a wiring problem.

4) If readings are okay, check brake signal. Connect voltmeter between computer terminal BR and GND terminals. Reading should be 0 volts with brake pedal released, and 12 volts when pedal is depressed. If readings are correct, there is a faulty computer. If voltage at BR remains on, brake switch is shorted or there is a wiring problem.

5) If voltage reading in step 2) is 4 volts, check speed sensor No. 1. To do so, connect a voltmeter between computer terminals SP and GND and check for a 6 volt reading. If 6 volts are obtained, proceed to step 7). If 6 volts are not obtained, there is a faulty speed sensor circuit.

6) To check speed sensor No. 1, remove instrument cluster from dash panel. Connect an ohmmeter to the output leads of speed sensor. Using a short piece of speedometer cable, rotate speedometer and ensure there are 4 influctions of ohmmeter needle per revolution. If not, sensor is faulty.

7) To check speed sensor No. 2, connect a voltmeter between computer terminals SP and GND and check for a 3 volt reading. If 3 volts are not obtained, speed sensor circuit is faulty.

8) If voltage reading in step 2) is 8 volts, check solenoid. To do so, disconnect computer connector and using an ohmmeter, check for 11 to 15 ohms of resistance between terminals S_1, S_2, S_3 and GND. If readings are correct, there is a faulty ECT computer. If not, there are faulty solenoids or problems in the wiring harness.

9) If any other readings, other than 0, 4 or 8 volts were obtained in step 2), check to see if voltage at terminal DG varies with changes in throttle opening. If not, check throttle position sensor. If its okay, there is a faulty ECT computer. If its bad, replacement is necessary.

10) If voltage does change, and/or after sensor replacement, check voltage between computer terminals L and GND. Shift transmission into "L" range. Voltage in "L" range should read 9 to 16 volts. Now shift transmission into "S" and "D" ranges. Voltage should be 0 to 2 volts.

11) If not, there is a faulty neutral safety switch or "L" terminal circuit is open. Check wiring. If readings in step 10) are okay, pull out ECT computer connector and road test. Ensure that when transmission is shifted into "D" range that OD is obtained. When transmission is shifted into "S" range that 3rd gear is obtained. And, when transmission is shifted to "L" range that it holds 1st gear only.

12) If transmission operates properly, there is a faulty computer. If not, there are problems within the transmission.

SHIFT POINTS TOO HIGH OR LOW

1) Bring engine coolant temperature and transmission fluid to normal operating temperatures. Connect a voltmeter to terminal DG and perform a road test. Confirm that terminal voltage rises in sequence while accelerating from 0 to 37 MPH.

2) Then, stop vehicle and read terminal DG voltage. Check if voltage rises while throttle valve is opening. If not and/or there is a constant 0 or 8 volt reading, go back to NO SHIFT.

3) If reading is 4 volts, check speed sensor No. 2. To do so, check if it is okay when circuit between computer terminals SP_2 and GND are short circuited. If so, there is a faulty speed sensor No. 2.

4) If reading in step 2) is correct, check pattern selection switch. To do so, connect a voltmeter between terminal "E" of switch and GND. When NORM or PWR button is actuated, reading should be 1 volt. When ECON button is actuated, a reading of 12 volts should be obtained.

TOYOTA MODEL A140E (Cont.)

5) Now, connect voltmeter between terminal "P" of switch and GND. When NORM or ECON button is actuated, reading should be 1 volt. When PWR button is actuated, reading should be 12 volts. If switch checks out okay, there is a fault with the ECT computer or transmission. If readings are incorrect, there is a fault within the selector switch. Replacement is necesary.

6) If selector switch checks out okay, check throttle position sensor. To do so, check voltage between terminals "L", "L$_1$", "L$_2$", IDL and GND. *See Fig. 3* for correct ranges.

7) If readings are correct, the ECT computer is at fault. If readings are incorrect, there is a fault in the throttle position sensor circuit.

NO UP-SHIFT TO OD

1) Perform a road test while shifting manually with computer connector pulled out. Check for up-shift in "D" range when shifting from "L" to "S" to "D". If there is no shift, there is a fault with transmission.

2) If shifting does occur, check OD cut-out signal. To do so, check for voltage between terminals ODC and GND. If equipped with Nippondenso, reading should be approximately 5 volts, when coolant temperature is above 70°C. If equipped with Aisin Seiko, reading should be 12 volts, when coolant temperature is above 70°C. (32°F.).

3) If voltage readings are correct in step **2)**, check "S" range signal. To do so, connect a voltmeter between computer terminals "S" and GND. Reading should be between 9 and 16 volts. If readings are correct, there is a fault with ECT computer. If readings are incorrect, check for a faulty "S" terminal at neutral safety switch or wiring harness.

4) If readings in step **2)** are incorrect, check OD cut-out signal. To do so, connect a voltmeter between computer terminals ODC and GND and check for normal voltage readings when cruise control computer connector is disconnected.

5) If readings do return to normal, there is a faulty cruise control computer. If readings still remain unchanged, there is a faulty engine control computer (short circuit in ECT wire harness or E.F.I. water temperature sensor is bad).

NO LOCK-UP
(AFTER WARM-UP)

1) Start engine and bring both engine and transmission fluid to normal operating temperature. Connect a voltmeter to terminal DG. Perform a road test and check for 7, 5 or 3 volts in lock-up range while driving.

2) If so, there is a fault with transmission such as a faulty lock-up mechanism or No. 3 solenoid is stuck. If readings are incorrect, stop vehicle and measure voltage at DG terminal.

3) If reading is 8 volts, there is a faulty No. 3 solenoid. If reading is 0 volts, check throttle position sensor and stop light switch. If switches are good, ECT computer is at fault. If switches are bad, replace faulty switch.

4) If reading is step **1)** is 4 volts, check and repair speed sensor. Then repeat procedure outlined in step **1)**.

TESTING

PRELIMINARY CHECK

Troubles occuring with the electronic controlled transaxle (ECT) can be caused either by the engine, ECT electrical control or the automatic transmission itself. It is necessary to isolate these 3 areas before proceeding with troubleshooting.
• Check transaxle oil level.
• Check throttle cable mark.
• Check shift linkage.
• Check neutral safety switch.
• Check idling speed.
• Check tire inflation pressure.

STALL TEST

CAUTION: Perform test at normal operating fluid temperature, 122-176°F. (50-80°C.). DO NOT continuously run this test longer than 5 seconds.

1) The object of this test is to check overall performance of the transmission and engine by measuring the maximum engine speeds at the "D" and "R" ranges.

2) Chock front and rear wheels. Hook up an engine tachometer. Fully apply parking and service brakes. Start engine. Shift transmission into "D" range. Step all the way down on the accelerator pedal.

3) Quickly read and record highest engine RPM at this time. Stall speed should be between 2150-2250 RPM. Perform same test in "R" range.

4) If engine speed is same for both ranges, but lower than specified RPM, engine output may be insufficient. Or, stator one-way clutch is not operating properly.

5) If reading is more than 600 RPM lower than specified, torque converter could be at fault. If stall speed in "D" range is higher than specified, forward clutch may be slipping, one-way clutch No. 2 is not operating properly, line pressure is too low, or overdrive clutch is slipping.

6) If stall speed in "R" range is higher than specified, direct clutch may be slipping, 1st and reverse brake could be slipping, line pressure is too low, or overdrive clutch is slipping.

TIME LAG TEST

CAUTION: Perform this test at normal operating fluid temperature 122°-176°F. (50-80°C.). Be sure to allow a 1 minute interval between tests. Make 3 measurements and take the average value.

1) If shift lever is shifted while engine is idling, there will be a certain time lapse or lag before shock can be felt. This test is used for checking condition of overdrive clutch, forward clutch, direct clutch and 1st and reverse brake.

2) Fully apply parking brake. Start engine and ensure idle speed is correct. Shift tranmission from "N" into "D" range. Using a stop watch, measure time it takes from shifting the lever until shock it felt.

3) Standard measured value is less than 1.2 seconds. In the same manner, measure time lag for "N" to "R". Standard measured value is less than 1.5 seconds.

4) If "N" to "D" time lag is longer than specified, line pressure is too low, forward clutch may be worn, overdrive clutch may be worn, or overdrive clutch is not operating.

5) If "N" to "R" time lag is longer than specified, direct clutch may be worn, 1st and reverse brake may be worn, line pressure is too low, or overdrive clutch may be worn.

HYDRAULIC TEST

CAUTION: Perform test at normal operating fluid temperature of 122-176°F. (50-80°C.).

1) Warm up transmission fluid and chock wheels. Jack up vehicle and support it on safety stands. Remove transmission case test plugs and mount hydraulic pressure gauges.

2) Fully apply parking brake. Start engine and shift into "D" range. Step down strongly on brake pedal with left foot while depressing accelerator pedal with right foot.

3) Measure line pressure at engine speeds specified in LINE PRESSURE TABLE. In the same manner, perform test in "R" range.

LINE PRESSURE TABLE

Selector Position	Pressure PSI (kg/cm²)
At Idle	
"D" Range	53-61 (3.7-4.3)
"R" Range	77-102 (5.4-7.2)
At WOT Stall	
"D" Range	131-152 (9.2-10.7)
"R" Range	205-239 (14.4-16.8)

NOTE: **If measured pressures are not up to specified values, check throttle cable adjustment and retest.**

4) If measured values in all ranges are higher than specified, regulator valve is defective, throttle valve is defective or throttle cable is out of adjustment.

5) If measured values in all ranges are lower than specified, oil pump is defective, regulator valve is defective, throttle valve is defective, throttle cable is out of adjustment, or overdrive clutch is defective.

6) If pressure is low in "D" range only, forward clutch is defective or "D" range circuit has a fluid leak.

7) If pressure is low in "R" range only, direct clutch is defective, 1st and reverse brake is defective, or "R" range circuit has a fluid leak.

ROAD TEST

CAUTION: Perform test at normal operating fluid temperature of 122-176°F. (50-80°C.).

"D" Range Test In
NORM, ECON & PWR Pattern Ranges
1) Shift into "D" range and hold accelerator pedal constant at half and at full throttle positions. Push in 1 of pattern selection buttons and check 1st to 2nd, 2nd to 3rd and 3rd to OD lock-up and up-shift points.

NOTE: **There is no overdrive up-shift when coolant temperature is below 122°F (50°C) and speed is under 12 MPH in ECON or 19 MPH in NORM or PWR selection modes. Also, there is no lock-up when vehicle speed is 6 MPH less than the set cruise control speed.**

- If there is no 1st to 2nd gear up-shift, 1st-2nd shift valve is stuck or No. 2 solenoid is stuck.
- If there is no 2nd to 3rd gear up-shift, 2-3 shift valve is stuck or No. 1 solenoid is stuck.
- If there is no 3rd to OD gear up-shift, (throttle valve opening at 50%), 3-OD shift valve is stuck.
- If all shift points are incorrect, throttle valve, 1-2 shift valve, 2-3 shift valve, 3-OD shift valve are defective.
- If all lock-up points are incorrect, lock-up relay valve is stuck or No. 3 solenoid is stuck.

2) In the same manner, check for shock and slip between 1st to 2nd gear, 2nd to 3rd gear and 3rd to OD gear up-shifts. If shock is harsh, line pressure is too high, accumulator is defective, or check ball is defective.

3) Run vehicle in "D" range lock-up or overdrive gear and check for abnormal noise and vibration.

NOTE: **To check for cause of abnormal noise and vibration must be made with extreme care as problem could be due to an unbalanced drive shaft, differential, tire, torque converter or torquing of power train.**

4) While running in "D" range, confirm proper kick-down vehicle speed limits for 2nd to 1st, 3rd to 1st, 3rd to 2nd, OD to 3rd and OD to 2nd gears. Also check for abnormal shock and slip at kick-down.

5) While running at about 50 MPH in "D" range OD gear or lock-up, shift to "S" and "L" ranges and check engine braking effect in all ranges. If there is no engine braking in "S" range in 3rd gear, brake is defective. If no braking effect is felt in 2nd gear, brake and coast brake are defective.

6) If there is no engine braking effect in "L" range in 2nd gear, brake and coast brake are defective. If no effect is felt in 1st gear, 1st and reverse brakes are defective.

7) While running in "D" range, release foot from accelerator and shift into "L" range. Check for proper down-shift points between OD to 3rd, 3rd to 2nd and 2nd to 1st gears.

8) To inspect lock-up mechanism, connect a voltmeter to the DG terminal of ECT. Set pattern selection switch in NORM mode. Accelerate vehicle to 50 MPH to where 7, 5 or 3 volts appear on voltmeter. This is lock-up range.

9) Depress accelerator pedal and read tachometer. If there is a big jump in engine RPM there is no lock-up.

"S" Range Test In
NORM, ECON & PWR Patterns
1) Shift into "S" range. Drive with accelerator pedal held constant at half or full throttle and push in 1 of the pattern selection buttons. Ensure that at each throttle position 1st to 2nd and 2nd to 3rd gear lock-up and up-shift take place and are operating properly.

NOTE: **There is no lock-up in PWR pattern mode.**

2) While running in "S" range, 3rd or 2nd gears, release accelerator pedal and check for engine braking effect. Also check for 3rd to 2nd down-shift and abnormal noise at acceleration and deceleration and for shock and up-shift and down-shift.

TOYOTA MODEL A140E (Cont.)

"L" Range Test

1) While operating vehicle above 50 MPH in "D" or "S" range, release accelerator pedal and shift into "L" range. Ensure that 2nd to 1st gear down-shift occurs at 31 MPH.

2) Operate vehicle in "L" range and ensure there is no up-shift to 2nd gear. Also check engine braking effect and abnormal noise at acceleration and deceleration.

"R" Range Test

Shift into "R" range. Accelerate vehicle from a stop at full throttle and check for slipping.

"P" Range Test

Stop vehicle on a slight grade. Shift transmission into "P". Release parking brake and check for proper parking pawl operation. Vehicle should not move.

SHIFT SPEED SPECIFICATIONS [1]

Application	MPH
"D" Range	
ECON or NORM	
1st to 2nd	33-37
2nd to 3rd	63-70
3rd to OD	94-100
3rd to OD [2]	23-20
OD to 3rd [2]	11-14
OD to 3rd	88-94
3rd to 2nd	60-65
2nd to 1st	28-31
PWR	
1st to 2nd	35-42
2nd to 3rd	68-79
3rd to OD	96-103
3rd to OD [2]	28-31
OD to 3rd [2]	11-14
OD to 3rd	90-96
3rd to 2nd	65-70
2nd to 1st	28-31
"S" Range	
ECON or NORM	
1st to 2nd	33-37
2nd to 3rd	63-70
3rd to 2nd	60-65
2nd to 1st	28-31
PWR	
1st to 2nd	35-42
2nd to 3rd	68-79
3rd to 2nd	62-67
2nd to 1st	28-31
"L" Range	
ECON, NORM or PWR	
2nd to 1st	30-34

[1] – At Wide Open Throttle.
[2] – At Fully Closed Throttle.

LOCK-UP SPEEDS [1]

Application	MPH
"D" Range	
NORM	
Lock-up ON in OD	40-44
Lock-up OFF in OD	39-42
ECON	
Lock-up ON in OD	35-39
Lock-up OFF in OD	34-37
PWR	
Lock-up ON in OD	43-47
Lock-up Off in OD	42-45
"S" Range	
NORM	
Lock-up ON in 3rd	52-55
Lock-up OFF in 3rd	47-52
ECON	
Lock-up ON in 3rd	32-35
Lock-up OFF in 3rd	30-33
PWR	[2]
"L" Range	[3]

[1] – Throttle at 50%.
[2] – There is no lock-up in PWR pattern.
[3] – There is no lock-up in "L" range.

NORMAL SOLENOID OPERATING PATTERN

Application	ON or OFF
Solenoid No. 1	
"D" Range	
1st	ON
2nd	ON
3rd	OFF
OD	OFF
"S" Range	
1st	ON
2nd	ON
3rd	OFF
"L" Range	
1st	ON
2nd	ON
Solenoid No. 2	
"D" Range	
1st	OFF
2nd	ON
3rd	ON
OD	OFF
"S" Range	
1st	OFF
2nd	ON
3rd	ON
"L" Range	
1st	OFF
2nd	ON

ELECTRONIC CONTROL CIRCUIT

Precautions When Checking
Voltage at Terminal DG

1) Diagnostic indications will be cancelled out if ignition switch is turned off.

2) All solenoid valves and speed sensor systems have the capability to retain malfunctions in memory and these will be retained in memory until ignition switch is turned off, even after problem has been repaired.

3) Malfunctions of throttle position sensor or stop lamp switch are not retained in memory. These should be checked by rotating throttle valve or by depressing brake pedal.

Fig. 1: Electronic Control Circuit

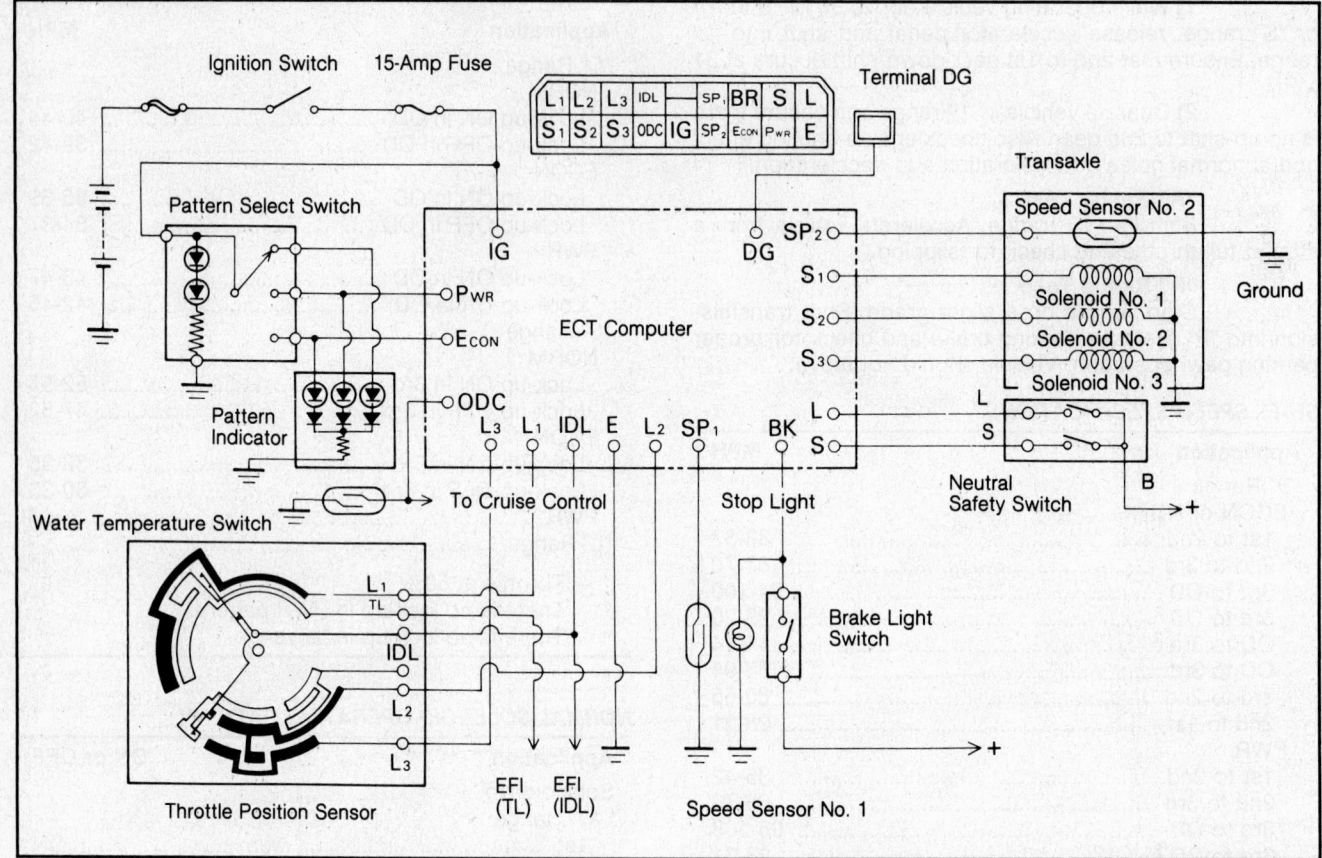

4) A low battery could result in a misdiagnosis. Always check battery voltage first.

5) Use a circuit tester with an internal impedance of 10,000 ohms or more.

Diagnosis

1) Troubles are diagnosed by voltage readings at terminal DG while driving vehicle and when vehicle is stopped.

2) If transmission indicates a NO SHIFT condition, and reading at terminal DG is a fixed 8 volts, check solenoids and ECT computer. If reading is 4 volts, check throttle position sensor. If reading is 0 volts, check throttle position sensor, ECT computer or brake signal. If reading is normal, check transmission, solenoids, neutral safety switch or pattern selection switch.

3) If transmission indicates an erratic shifting pattern, and reading at terminal DG is 8 volts, check solenoids and ECT computer. If reading is 4 volts, check speed sensors. If reading is 0 volts, check throttle position sensor, ECT computer or brake signal. If reading is normal, check transmission, throttle position sensor, ECT computer or pattern selection switch.

4) If transmission indicates no shift to overdrive (OD), check engine E.F.I. computer, cruise control computer and neutral safety switch.

5) If transmission fails to lock-up and voltage reading at terminal DG is 8 volts, check ECT computer. If reading is 4 volts, check speed sensor. If reading is 0 volts, check throttle position sensor, ECT computer and brake signal. If reading is normal, check transmission and ECT computer.

NOTE: With a 4 volt reading, even if speed sensor No. 2, located at transaxle, is malfunctioning, the ECT system is capable of functioning with speed sensor No. 1, located at speedometer. Be sure to inspect No. 2 sensor and recheck voltage at terminal DG.

NOTE: An 8 volt reading indicates a short or open circuit or continuity to solenoid. A separate check should be made for a sticking solenoid or presence of foreign material.

Testing

1) Warm up engine to normal operating temperature, 176°F. (80°C.). Ensure transmission fluid temperature is 122-140°F. (50-60°C.). Connect a voltmeter to terminal DG located in engine compartment.

2) Place pattern selection switch in NORM position and shift tranmission to "D". During road test, ensure that voltage is correct as indicated in DG TERMINAL VOLTAGE table. Check voltage for each up-shift position.

3) If voltage rises from 0 to 7 volts while shifting from 1st to OD lock-up, control system is okay. If there is a constant 4 volt reading, speed sensor No. 2 is faulty. If there is a constant 8 volt reading, solenoid is defective.

4) Stop vehicle. With engine at idle, check voltage at terminal DG. DO NOT turn ignition off as this will clear trouble memory. If voltage reading is 0, system is normal or there is a defective brake signal. If reading is 4 volts, there is a faulty speed sensor No. 2. If reading is 8 volts, there is a faulty solenoid.

TOYOTA MODEL A140E (Cont.)

DG TERMINAL VOLTAGE

Gear Position	Voltage
1st	0
2nd	2
2nd Lock-up	3
3rd	4
3rd Lock-up	5
OD	6
OD Lock-up	7

5) To inspect throttle position sensor system, turn off engine and while depressing accelerator pedal ensure voltage at terminal DG rises as pedal is depressed.

6) To check brake signal system, depress accelerator pedal to where 8 volts is indicated at terminal DG. Then, depress brake pedal and check voltage at terminal DG. When brake pedal is depressed, voltage reading should be 0. When released, reading should be 8 volts.

COMPUTER CONNECTOR VOLTAGE

Remove glove box and right-hand speaker to gain access to ECT computer. Turn ignition switch on and measure voltage as follows:

- Connect voltmeter between terminals L_1 and GND. With throttle valve fully closed, voltage should be 5 volts (Nippondenso) or 12 volts (Aisin Seiko). With throttle valve fully closed and then moved to fully open position, voltage should read 5 to 0 volts (Nippondenso) or 12 to 0 volts (Aisin Seiko). With throttle valve open, voltage should read 0 for both models.
- Connect voltmeter between terminals L_2 and GND. With throttle valve fully closed voltage should read 5 volts (Nippondenso) or 12 volts (Aisin Seiko). With throttle valve fully closed and then moved to fully open position, voltage should read 5 to 0 to 5 volts (Nippondenso) or 12 to 0 to 12 volts (Aisin Seiko). With throttle valve open, voltage should read 5 volts (Nippondenso) or 12 volts (Aisin Seiko).
- Connect voltmeter between terminals L_3 and GND. With throttle valve closed, voltage reading should be 5 volts (Nippondenso) or 12 volts (Aisin Seiko). With throttle valve fully closed and then moved to fully open position, voltage should read 5 to 0 to 5 to 0 to 5 volts (Nippondenso) or 12 to 0 to 12 to 0 to 12 volts (Aisin Seiko). With throttle valve open, voltage should read 5 volts (Nippondenso) or 12 volts (Aisin Seiko).
- Connect voltmeter between terminals IDL and GND. With throttle valve closed, voltage should read 0 volts for both units. With throttle valve opened above idle, voltage reading should be 4 volts for both units.
- Connect a voltmeter between terminals SP_1 and GND. With engine off, voltage should read 12 or 0 volts for both units. With engine running, voltage should read 6 volts for both units.
- Connect voltmeter between terminals BR and GND. When brake pedal is depressed, voltage reading should be 12 volts for both units. When brake pedal is released, voltage reading should be 0 volts for both units.
- Connect voltmeter between terminals S and GND. With transmission shifter positioned in "S", voltage reading should be 9 to 16 volts for both units. In any other range, reading should be 0 to 2 volts.
- Connect voltmeter between terminals L and GND. With transmission shifter positioned in "L" range, voltage should read 9 to 16 volts for both units. In any other range, reading should be 0 to 2 volts.

- Connect voltmeter between terminals S_1 and GND. Voltage reading for both units should be 12 volts.
- Connect voltmeter between terminals S_2, S_3 and GND. Voltage readings should be 0 volts for both units.
- Connect voltmeter between terminals ODC and GND. Voltage reading should be 12 volts for both units.
- Connect voltmeter between terminals IG and GND. When coolant temperature is below 158°F. (70°C.), voltage reading should be 0 for both units. When coolant temperature is above 158°F. (70°C.), reading should be 5 volts (Nippondenso) and 12 volts (Aisin Seiko).
- Connect voltmeter between terminals SP_2 and GND. With engine off, voltage reading should be 5 or 0 volts (Nippondenso) or 12 or 0 volts (Aisin Seiko). When engine is running, reading should be 4 volts (Nippondenso) or 10 volts (Aisin Seiko).
- Connect voltmeter between terminals PWR and GND. With PWR pattern button actuated, voltage should read 12 volts for both units. With any other pattern button actuated, reading should be 1 volt for both units.
- Connect voltmeter between terminals ECON and GND. With ECON pattern button actuated, voltage reading should be 12 volts for both units. With any other pattern button actuated, reading should be 1 volt for both units.

ELECTRIC COMPONENT TESTING

Solenoid

1) Disconnect wire harness from ECT computer. Using an ohmmeter, measure resistance between S_1, S_2, S_3 and GND. Standard resistance value is 11 to 15 ohms. See Fig. 1.

2) Apply battery voltage to solenoid. Solenoid should be heard operating at this time. If there is foreign material in solenoid valve, there will be no fluid control even with solenoid operation.

Neutral Safety Switch

Shift transmission into "D" or "S" range. Disconnect neutral safety switch connector. Using an ohmmeter, ensure continuity between L, S and ground. See Fig. 2.

Fig. 2: Neutral Safety Switch Connector

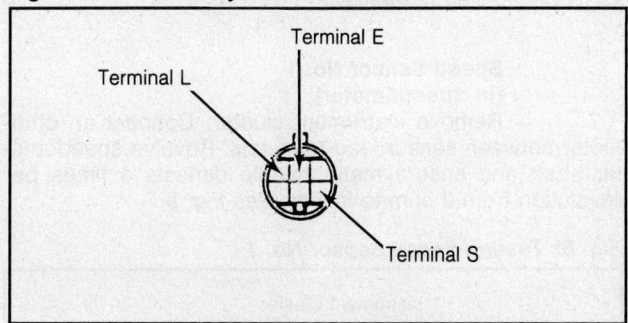

Throttle Position Sensor

Disconnect wire harness connector from throttle position sensor and remove rubber boot. Using an ohmmeter, ensure continuity between terminal E_1 and all other terminals. See Fig. 3.

NOTE: While slowly opening throttle valve, ensure continuity between E_1 and all other terminals.

Brake Signal

Ensure brake lights come on when brake pedal is depressed.

Fig. 3: Throttle Position Sensor Switch Connector

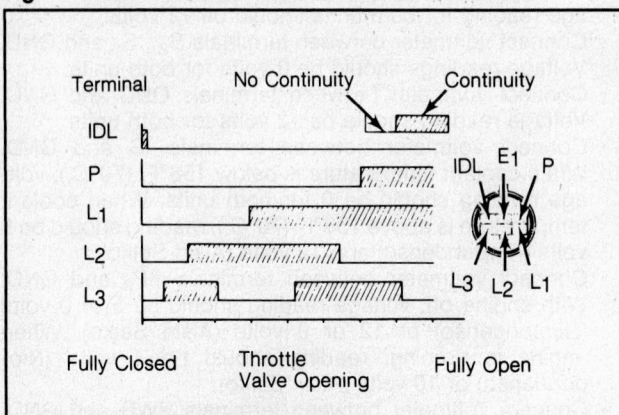

Speed Sensor No. 2
(At Transaxle)
Jack up a front wheel on 1 side. Connect an ohmmeter between sensor terminals. Spin wheel and ensure meter needle deflects from 0 ohms to infinity. *See Fig. 4.*

Fig. 4: Testing Speed Sensor No. 2

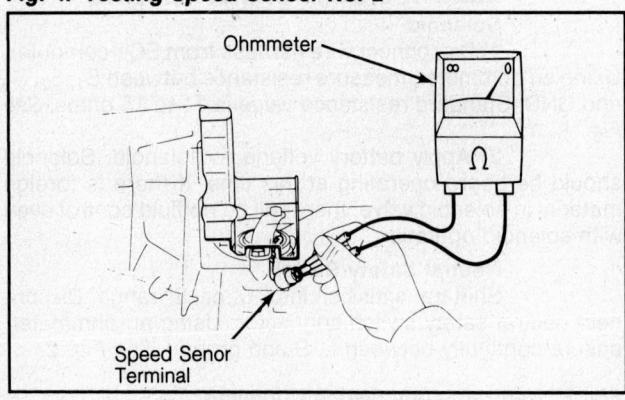

Sensor is located at transaxle.

Speed Sensor No. 1
(In Speedometer)
Remove instrument cluster. Connect an ohmmeter between sensor lead terminals. Revolve speedometer shaft and ensure meter needle deflects 4 times per revolution from 0 ohm to infinity. *See Fig. 5.*

Fig. 5: Testing Speed Sensor No. 1

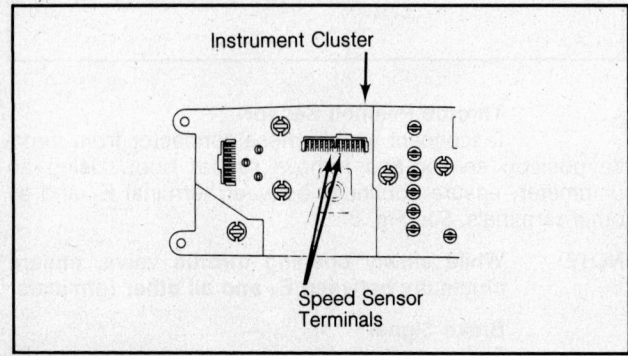

Sensor is located at speedometer.

Pattern Selection Switch
Using an ohmmeter, ensure continuity between 1 terminal and all other terminals. Note that there are diodes inside of switch. Continuity can only be checked with probes in proper polarity to diodes. *See Fig. 6*

Fig. 6: Testing Pattern Selection Switch

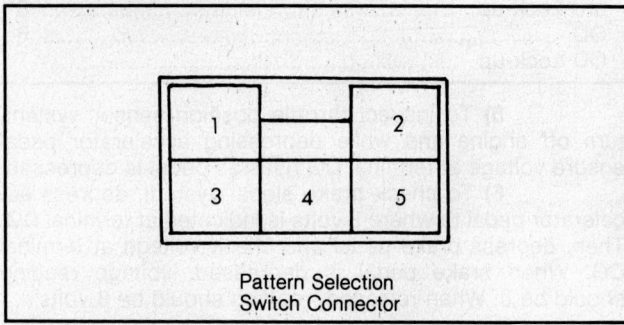

Switch is located in passenger compartment.

Lock-up Mechanism
Start engine and warm up engine coolant and transmission fluid to normal operating temperature. Connect a voltmeter to DG test terminal. Select NORM pattern. Drive vehicle at around 31 MPH to where 7, 5 or 3 volts appear on voltmeter. This is lock-up range. Depress accelerator pedal and read tachometer. If there is a big jump in engine RPM, there is no lock-up.

Manual Shifting
1) Remove glove box and right-hand speaker to gain acces to ECT computer. Disconnect wire harness connector. While driving vehicle, ensure there is respective gear change in each drive range.
- With lever in "D" range, ensure transmission shifts from 1st to 2nd to 3rd to OD.
- With lever in "S" range, ensure transmission shifts from 1st to 2nd to 3rd.
- With lever in "L" range, ensure transmission does not shift into any other gear.
- With lever in "R" range, ensure vehicle moves in reverse.
- With lever in "N" range, ensure vehicle does not move forward or backward.
- With lever in "P" range, ensure parking pawl locks.

2) If any range does not operated properly, check transmission.

SERVICE (IN VEHICLE)

SPEED SENSOR
Removal
Remove left-hand drive shaft. See AXLE SHAFTS in this article. Remove transmission dust cover. Remove 2 bolts securing bracket and remove bracket. Remove speed sensor and "O" ring.

Inspection
Connect an ohmmeter to speed sensor and ensure meter deflects when sensor is repeatedly brought close to a magnet and removed from it. *See Fig. 7.*

Installation
Reverse removal procedure. Replace "O" ring.

Fig. 7: Testing Speed Sensor

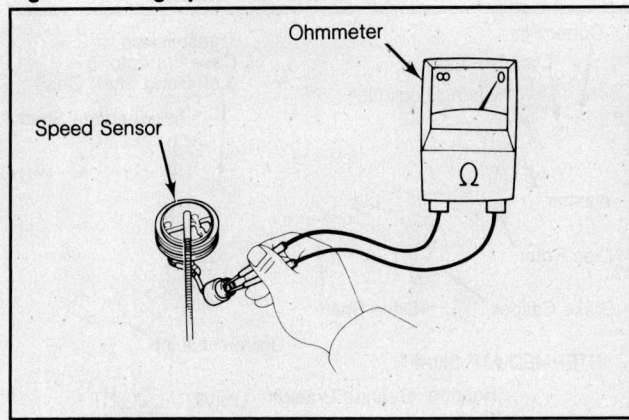

THROTTLE CABLE
Removal
1) Disconnect throttle cable housing from bracket at engine. Disconnect from throttle valve linkage. Remove clip and disconnect transmission control cable from manual shift lever.

2) Remove manual shift lever and neutral safety switch. Remove valve body. See VALVE BODY in this article. Remove bolt and retaining plate. Pull throttle cable out of transmission case.

Installation
1) To install, reverse removal procedure. New cables DO NOT have a cable stopper installed. To make adjustment possible, bend cable about 7.78" (200 mm) in radius, pull inner cable lightly until a slight resistance is felt, and hold it.

Fig. 8: Marking Replacement Throttle Cable

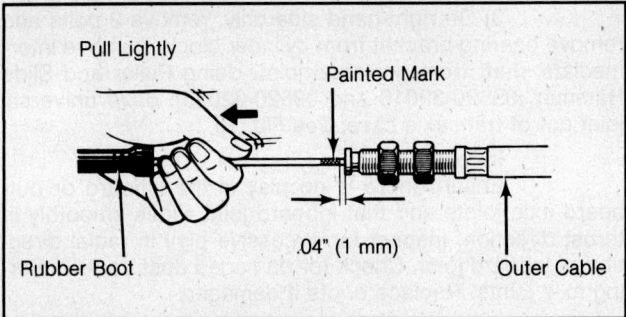

Fig. 9: Adjusting Neutral Safety Switch

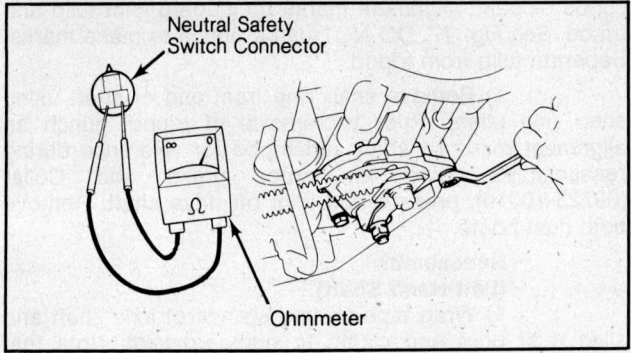

2) Pull rubber dust boot from end of cable sheathing. Paint a mark about .16" (4 mm) in width at .04" (1

mm) from end of cable sheathing. Connect cable and be sure to make necesary adjustments. *See Fig. 8.*

3) Install neutral saftey switch and manual shift lever. Adjust neutral safety switch. *See Fig. 9.* Connect transmission control cable and adjust transmission control cable. See appropriate article in AUTOMATIC TRANSMISSION SERVICING. Road test vehicle.

VALVE BODY ASSEMBLY
Removal
NOTE: Note bolt length and position during disassembly of valve body for ease in reassembly.

1) Clean exterior of transmission. Remove oil pan plug and drain transmission. Remove oil pan and gasket. Remove 2 bolts and apply tube bracket. Remove 3 bolts and oil filter.

2) Disconnect solenoid wiring lead connectors. Remove oil tubes. Remove manual detent spring. Remove manual valve and valve body. Remove 12 bolts, disconnect throttle cable from cam and remove valve body. Remove governor apply gasket.

Installation
1) While holding cam down, slip cable end into slot. DO NOT tangle kick-down switch wire. Install valve body and tighten bolts to specifications. Connect solenoid lead wires. *See Fig. 10.*

Fig. 10: Valve Body Bolt Length & Location

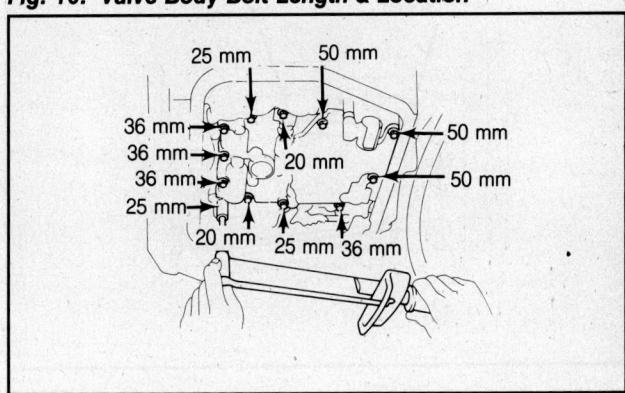

2) Align manual valve with pin on manual shift lever. Place lower valve body into position. Finger tighten 4 bolts first, then tighten to specifications. *See Fig. 11.*

Fig. 11: Manual Valve Body Bolt Length & Location

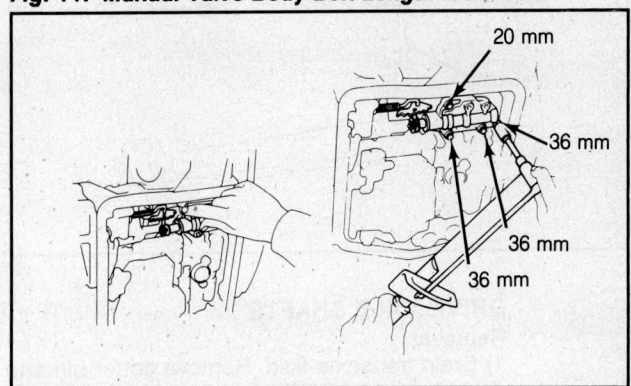

Fig. 12: Detent Spring Bolt Length & Location

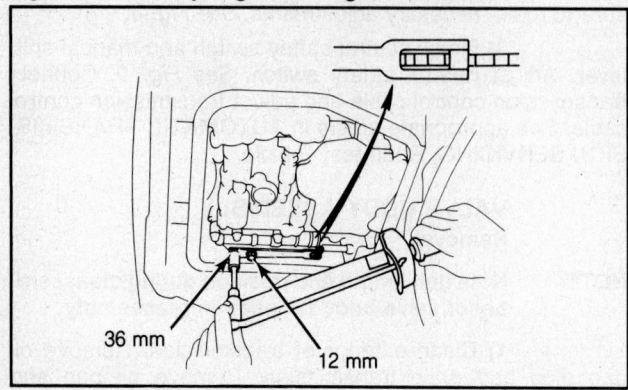

36 mm

12 mm

3) Install detent spring. See Fig. 12. Ensure manual valve lever is in contact with center of roller at tip of detent spring. Being careful not to bend or damage, tap oil tubes into proper positions. Install apply tube bracket. See Fig. 13.

4) Install oil strainer. See Fig. 14. Install magnet in oil pan making sure magnet does not interfere with oil tubes. Install oil pan and tighten bolts to specifications. Install drain plug with new washer gasket. Fill transmission with oil.

Fig. 13: Apply Tube Bracket Bolt Length & Location

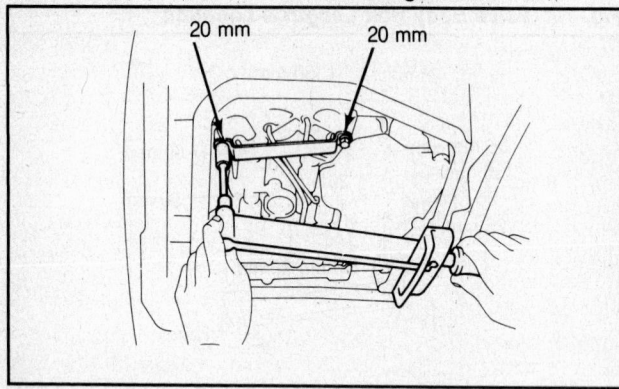

20 mm   20 mm

Fig. 14: Oil Strainer Bolt Length & Location

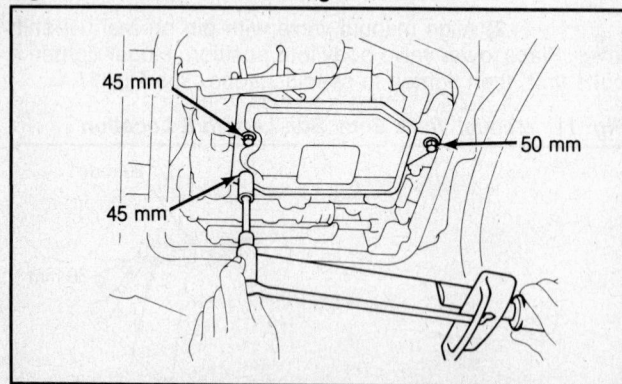

45 mm

50 mm

45 mm

DRIVE AXLE SHAFTS
Removal

1) Drain transaxle fluid. Remove cotter pin and lock nut cap. Loosen bearing lock nut while depressing brake pedal. Loosen nuts holding front drive axle shaft to intermediate shaft or differential side gear shaft.

Fig. 15: Exploded View of Drive Axle Shafts

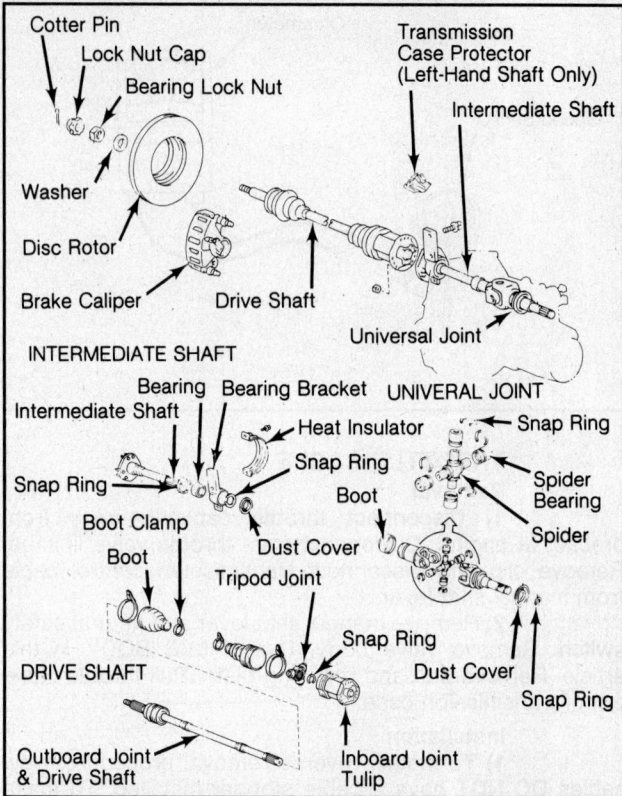

2) Remove brake caliper and suspend with wire. Remove disc rotor. On left-hand side, remove transaxle case protector. Wrap dust boot to prevent damage. Using Hub Puller (09950-20014), pull axle hub from drive shaft.

3) On right-hand side only, remove 2 bolts and remove bearing bracket from cylinder block. Remove intermediate shaft from universal joint. Using Puller and Slide Hammer (09520-32010 and 09520-32030), drive universal joint out of transaxle case. See Fig. 16.

Inspection

Ensure there is no play in the inboard or outboard axle joints and that inboard joint slides smoothly in thrust direction. Inspect for excessive play in radial direction of inboard joint. Check for damaged dust boots covering axle joints. Replace boots if damaged.

Disassembly

1) Remove boot clamps. Prior to disassembly, scribe or paint alignment marks on inboard joint tulip and tripod. See Fig. 17. DO NOT use a punch to make marks. Separate tulip from tripod.

2) Remove snap ring from end of shaft using snap ring pliers. Prior to removal of tripod, punch an alignment mark on shaft and tripod for reference during reassembly. Using an arbor press and Collar (09726-10010), press tripod joint off drive shaft. Remove both dust boots.

Reassembly
(Left-Hand Shaft)

1) Wrap tape around splines of axle shaft and slide dust boot and clamp to outboard joint. Note that outboard joint axle boot and clamp are larger. Slide clamp and dust boot onto axle shaft for inboard joint. DO NOT tighten boot clamps at this time.

TOYOTA MODEL A140E (Cont.)

Fig. 16: Removing Right-Hand Axle Universal Joint

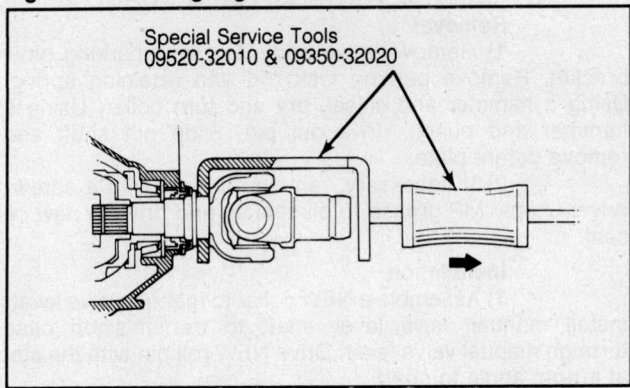

Fig. 17: Drive Axle Alignment Marks

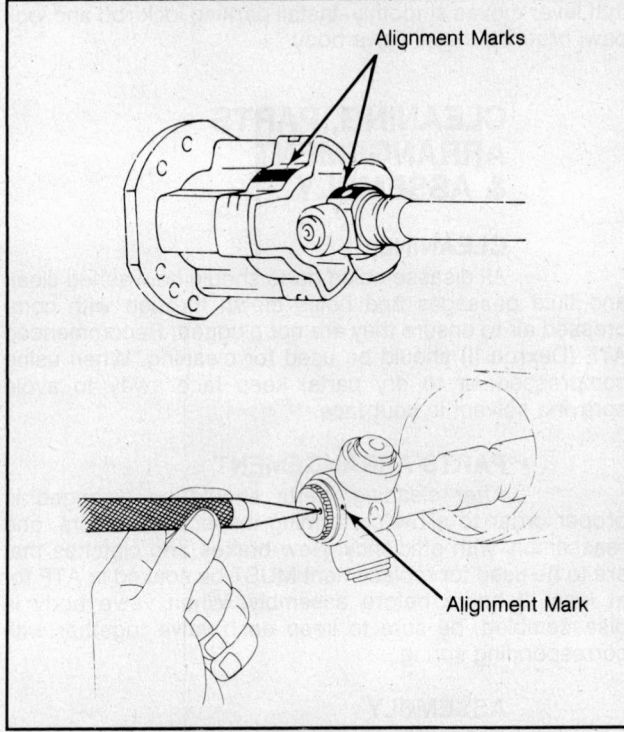

Both inner and outer joint is shown.

2) Align marks made during disassembly and install tripod joint with beveled side facing toward outboard joint. Using a brass drift and hammer, tap tripod onto drive shaft. Install a NEW snap ring.

3) Pack 0.4 lbs. (165 kg) of grease, supplied in boot kit, into outboard joint boot. Pack 0.5 lbs. (212 kg) of grease into inboard joint tulip. Align marks made during disassembly and install inboard joint tulip to drive shaft.

4) Install dust boot over joint tulip. Ensure boot sits in shaft groove. Install boot clamp and tighten. Ensure boot is not stretched or contracted when drive shaft is at standard length, 17.67-18.07" (449-459 mm).

Disassembly (Intermediate Shaft)

NOTE: **This procedure applies only to right-hand axle shaft**

1) Remove heat insulator from bearing bracket. Using a screwdriver, remove dust cover. Remove snap ring securing shaft to bearing bracket.

2) Using Press (09950-20014), push out intermediate shaft. Remove snap ring from bearing bracket and using an arbor press and Collar (09618-60010) press out bearing.

Reassembly (Intermediate Shaft)

1) Install bearing into bracket using an arbor press and Collar (09608-32030). Install NEW snap ring using a screwdriver. Using Collar (09608-32030) and an arbor press, press intermediate shaft into bearing bracket. Install NEW snap ring.

NOTE: **Be careful not to damage rubber seal of bearing.**

2) Position dust cover on Collar (09560-30011) and press in the intermediate shaft so there is a clearance of .04-.08" (1-2 mm) between dust cover and bearing bracket. Install heat shield.

Disassembly (Right-Hand Univeral Joint)

1) Using a screwdriver, remove snap ring from axle shaft. Remove dust boot. Using a screwdriver and hammer, remove dust cover. Prior to disassembly, scribe or paint alignment marks on shaft yoke and joint yoke.

2) Lightly tap in universal joint outer bearing races. Using 2 screwdrivers, remove 4 snap rings from grooves. Using Puller (09332-25010), push out bearing from universal joint. DO NOT damage bearings.

3) Clamp bearing outer race in a vise and tap off yoke with a hammer. Remove both bearings. Place removed bearings onto spider. Using Puller (09332-25010), push out bearing from yoke. Clamp bearing outer race in a vise and tap off yoke with a hammer. Remove both bearings.

Reassembly (Right-Hand Univeral Joint)

1) Apply a light coat of MP grease to spider and bearings. Align marks on shaft yoke and joint yoke made during disassembly. Fit NEW spider in yoke. Using Puller (09332-25010), install bearings on spider. Install both bearings.

2) Adjust both bearings so that snap ring grooves are at maximum and equal widths. Install snap rings, of equal width, which will allow 0-.0020" (0-.05 mm) of axial play. Snap rings are available in 3 different thicknesses and are color coded.

3) Using a hammer, tap yoke until there is no clearance between bearing outer race and snap ring. Ensure that spider movement is free and smooth. Check spider bearing axial play, which should be less than .0020" (.05 mm).

4) Install spider bearings using procedure outlined in steps **1)** through **3)**. Using a platic hammer, install dust cover. Install boot and then snap ring.

Installation

1) On right-hand side only, use Puller and Slide Hammer (09520-32010 and 09520-32030), to drive in universal joint to a point where shaft and differential pinion shaft touch.

2) On right-hand side only, install intermediate shaft to universal joint. Install bearing bracket onto cylinder block. Tighten bolts to specifications.

3) On both sides, position outboard joints in through axle hubs. DO NOT damage dust boots. Finger tighten nuts attaching drive shaft to intermediate shaft or differential side shaft. Then tighten to specifications.

4) On left-hand side only, install transaxle case protector. On both sides, install disc rotor and brake caliper to steering kunckle. Install bearing lock nut, lock nut cap and cotter pin. Tighten nuts while depressing brake pedal. Fill transaxle with fluid.

REMOVAL & INSTALLATION

TRANSAXLE

See appropriate AUTOMATIC TRANSMISSION REMOVAL article in IMPORT GENERAL SERVICING section.

TORQUE CONVERTER

CONVERTER CLEANING

If transmission is contaminated, torque converter and transmission cooler should be thoroughly flushed using a torque converter cleaner.

ONE-WAY CLUTCH CHECK

1) Insert a turning tool into inner race of one-way clutch. Install Stopper (09350-32010) so that it fits in notch of converter hub and other race of one-way clutch.

2) With converter placed in a normal operating position, clutch should lock up when turned counterclockwise. Converter should rotate freely and smoothly when turned clockwise.

3) There should be less than a 22 INCH lbs. (2.5 N.m) effort to rotate one-way clutch. If necessary, clean converter and retest clutch. Replace converter if clutch fails test.

CONVERTER SLEEVE RUNOUT CHECK

1) Temporarily mount torque converter to drive plate. Set up a dial indicator resting needle onto converter sleeve. Rotate converter. If runout exceeds .0118" (.30 mm), ensure converter is properly mounted to drive plate.

2) If converter is properly mounted and runout is still excessive, replace torque converter. Mark position of converter to ensure correct installation. Remove converter.

DRIVE PLATE RUNOUT CHECK

Set up a dial indicator. Measure drive plate runout. If runout exceeds .0079" (.20 mm), or if ring gear is damaged, replace drive plate. If installing a new drive plate, note position of spacers and tighten bolts.

OIL PUMP

Oil Seal Replacement

With torque converter removed, remove oil seal with Puller (09308-00010). To install, apply a light coat of MP grease to oil seal lip. Drive in oil seal using Seal Installer (09350-32010).

"O" Ring Replacement

Position transmission with oil pump facing upward. Remove bolts securing oil pump. Pull up oil pump just far enough to expose "O" ring. Using Remover (09350-32010), remove "O" ring. To install, replace "O" ring. Install and tighten oil pump mounting bolts.

MANUAL VALVE LEVER & SHAFT

Removal

1) Remove valve body. Remove parking pawl bracket. Remove parking lock rod and retaining spring. Using a hammer and chisel, pry and turn collar. Using a hammer and punch, drive out pin. Slide out shaft and remove detent plate.

2) If necessary, remove oil seal with a screwdriver. Apply MP grease to oil seal lip and drive in new oil seal.

Installation

1) Assemble a NEW collar to manual valve lever. Install manual valve lever shaft to transmission case through manual valve lever. Drive NEW roll pin with the slot at a right angle to shaft.

2) Match collar hole to lever calking hollow and press the collar to lever. Install retaining ring spring. Ensure that lever moves smoothly. Install parking lock rod and lock pawl bracket. Install valve body.

CLEANING, PARTS ARRANGEMENT & ASSEMBLY

CLEANING

All disassembled parts should be washed clean and fluid passages and holes blown through with compressed air to ensure they are not plugged. Recommended ATF (Dexron II) should be used for cleaning. When using compressed air to dry parts, keep face away to avoid spraying solvent in your face.

PARTS ARRANGEMENT

After cleaning, parts should be arranged in proper order to allow performing inspection, repairs, and reassembly with efficiency. New brakes and clutches that are to be used for replacement MUST be soaked in ATF for at least 2 hours before assembly. When valve body is disassembled, be sure to keep each valve together with corresponding spring.

ASSEMBLY

1) All oil seal rings, clutch discs, clutch plates, rotating parts, and sliding surfaces should be coated with ATF prior to reassembly. All gaskets and rubber "O" rings should be replaced. Make sure that ends of snap rings are not aligned with 1 of the cut-outs and are installed in the groove correctly.

2) If a worn bushing is to be replaced, replacement must be made with the subassembly containing that bushing. Check thrust bearings and races for wear or damage. Replace if necessary.

3) All gaskets and rubber "O" rings should be replaced. Make sure that ends of a snap ring are not aligned with cut-outs and are installed in groove correctly. Use petroleum jelly to hold parts in place.

TRANSMISSION DISASSEMBLY

1) Remove oil cooling tubes. Remove shift lever and neutral safety switch. Remove 2 bolts and remove solenoid. Remove oil filler tube. Remove throttle cable retaining plate and solenoid wire retaining bolt.

2) Remove 2 bolts and cover bracket. Remove speed sensor and "O" ring. Remove 15 bolts and oil pan by lifting transmission case. DO NOT turn transmission over as this will contaminate valve body with foreign material.

3) Place transmission on wooden blocks to prevent damage to pipe bracket. Examine particles found in oil pan. If particles are magnetic (steel), this indicates bearing, gear and clutch plate wear. If particles are non-magnetic (brass), this indicates bushing wear.

4) Turn transmission over and remove tube bracket, oil strainer and solenoid connectors. Using a screwdriver, remove 4 oil tubes. Remove manual detent spring. Remove manual valve and valve body.

5) Remove 12 bolts, disconnect throttle cable from cam and remove valve body. Remove throttle cable and solenoid wiring from case. Remove 2nd brake apply gasket.

6) To remove accumulator piston and springs, loosen 5 bolts 1 turn at a time until spring tension is released. Remove cover and gasket. Remove piston and spring for C_1 and C_2. Pop out piston B_2 into a rag, using low pressure compressed air, 15 psi (1 kg/cm^2). Force air into apply hole and remove piston and spring.

7) Turn transmission over and measure piston stroke of 2nd coast brake. To do so, remove snap ring and cover. Remove piston and outer spring. Install piston without outer spring. Install snap ring. Firmly push brake apply rod into case. Measure distance between outside of snap ring and tip of piston rod. Measurement should be .551-.610" (14-15.5 mm). There are 2 rods available to bring measurement into specifications.

8) Remove 7 bolts attaching oil pump to case. Pull oil pump free with Puller (09350-32010). Remove oil pump and direct clutch. To do so, hold input shaft, grasp stator shaft and pull oil pump and direct clutch together out of case.

NOTE: Push 2nd brake band into case, being careful not to catch it on direct clutch drum.

9) Remove direct clutch from oil pump. DO NOT lose race located behind oil pump. Remove clutch drum thrust washer. DO NOT lose bearing and race located on forward clutch.

10) Remove forward clutch. DO NOT lose bearing and race. Remove 2nd coast brake band. To do so, push pin with a small screwdriver and remove it from bolt hole of oil pump mounting. Remove brake band.

11) Remove front planetary ring gear. DO NOT lose race and bearing located on ring gear. Remove planetary gear. DO NOT lose race and bearing located on planetary gear.

12) Remove bearing from planetary sun gear. Remove sun gear, sun gear input drum, 2nd brake hub and No. 1 one-way clutch. Stand transmission case up and remove 2nd coast brake band guide.

13) Measure clearance of 2nd brake band. To do so, place a feeler gauge between the seat of return spring assembly and top of plate. Specified clearance is .0146-.0614" (.37-1.56 mm).

14) Remove snap ring holding 2nd brake drum to case. Remove 2nd brake drum. If piston is difficult to remove, lightly tap drum with a wooden block. Remove 2nd brake piston return spring.

15) Remove clutch plate, disc and flange. Hold piston straight and with air gun held slightly away from oil hole blow out piston with compressed air. Using a pin punch, drive out 2nd brake gasket.

16) Remove snap ring holding No. 2 one-way clutch outer race to case. Remove No. 2 one-way clutch and rear planetary gear. DO NOT lose planetary carrier thrust washers, located on both sides.

17) Remove rear planetary ring gear and bearing. DO NOT lose race and bearing located on ring gear. Measure clearance of 1st and reverse brake. To do so, place a feeler gauge between piston and flange end. Specified clearance is .0417-.0937" (1.06-2.38 mm).

18) Remove snap ring holding flange to case. Remove flanges, plates and discs. Turn transmission around. Remove 11 bolts attaching overdrive unit to transmission case.

19) To remove overdrive unit, tap on circumference of overdrive case with a plastic hammer. Remove overdrive planetary gear and counter gear if they remained in transmission. DO NOT DROP overdrive unit as it is heavy.

20) Remove case gasket. Remove governor apply gasket and overdrive brake apply gasket. Remove parking pawl bracket and lock rod. Remove lock pawl shaft. Remove spring and lock pawl.

COMPONENT DISASSEMBLY & REASSEMBLY

OIL PUMP

Disassembly

1) Remove race from stator shaft. Remove "O" ring from pump body. Remove 2 oil seals from back of stator shaft. Remove thrust washer of clutch drum from stator shaft.

2) Remove 11 bolts attaching oil pump body and stator shaft. Identify top and bottom and keep parts in order. See Fig. 18.

Fig. 18: Exploded View of Oil Pump

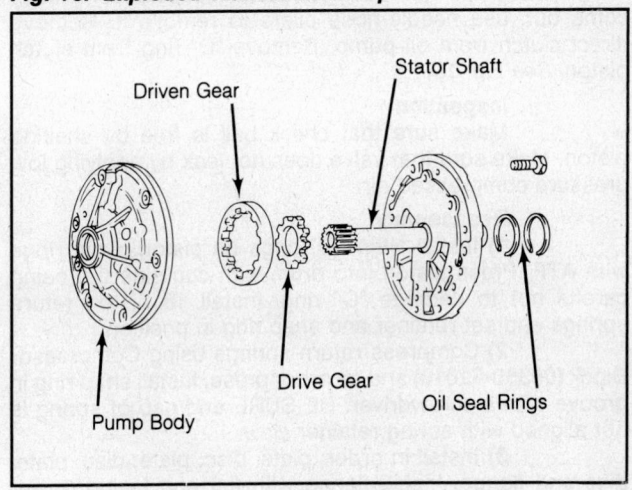

Inspection

1) Check body clearance of driven gear. To do so, push gear to one side of body. Using a feeler gauge, measure clearance. Standard specified body clearance is .0028-.0059" (.07-.15 mm). Maximum body clearance is .012" (.3 mm).

2) Check tip clearance of both gears. To do so, measure between gear teeth and cresent-shaped part of pump body. Standard specified clearance is .0043-.0055" (.11-.14 mm). Maximum clearance is .012 " (.3 mm).

3) Check side clearance of both gears. To do so, use a steel straightedge and a feeler gauge and measure side clearance of both gears. Standard specified clearance is .0008-.0020" (.02-.05 mm). Maximum clearance is .004" (.1 mm).

4) Inspect front oil seal for cracks, damage or wear. Replace oil seal if necesary. To do so, pry oil seal with screwdriver. Using Installer (09350-032010) and a hammer, install a NEW oil seal. Seal is properly installed when it is flush with the outer edge of pump body.

Reassembly

1) Install driven gear and drive gear. Ensure top of gears are facing upward. Install stator shaft onto pump body. Align bolt holes and install 11 bolts attaching stator shaft to oil pump body.

2) Coat thrust bearing with petroleum jelly. Align tab of washer with hollow of pump body and install thrust washer. Install 2 oil seal rings on oil pump. DO NOT spread ring lands too much.

3) Turn drive gear with screwdrivers to ensure a smooth rotation. DO NOT damage oil seal lip. Install race onto stator shaft.

DIRECT CLUTCH
Disassembly

1) Prior to disassembly, measure clearance of direct clutch. To do so, place a feeler gauge between snap ring and flange. Specified clearance is .0173-.0437" (.44-1.11 mm).

2) Remove snap ring from clutch drum. Remove flange, discs and plates. To compress piston return springs and remove snap ring, place Compressor Block (09350-32010) on spring retainer and compress springs with an arbor press.

3) Remove spring retainer and 18 springs. Slide direct clutch onto oil pump and remove piston by applying low pressure commpresed air. If piston does not completely come out, use needle-nose pliers to remove it. Remove direct clutch from oil pump. Remove "O" ring from clutch piston. See Fig. 19.

Inspection

Make sure that check ball is free by shaking piston. Make sure that valve does not leak by applying low pressure compressed air.

Reassembly

1) Install NEW "O" rings on piston. Coat rings with ATF. Press piston into drum with cup side up, being careful not to damage "O" ring. Install 18 piston return springs and set retainer and snap ring in position.

2) Compress return springs using Compressor Block (09350-32010) and an arbor press. Install snap ring in groove with a screwdriver. BE SURE end gap of spring is not aligned with spring retainer claw.

3) Install in order: plate, disc, plate, disc, plate, disc and flange. Install flange with flat end facing downward. Install outer snap ring. Ensure that end gap of snap ring is not aligned with any cut-outs.

4) Check clearance of direct clutch. To do so, place a feeler gauge between snap ring and flange. Specified clearance is .0173-.0437" (.44-1.11 mm). If incorrect, check order of assembly of plates and discs.

5) Check operation of direct clutch. To do so, install direct clutch onto oil pump. Apply compressed air

Fig. 19: Exploded View of Direct Clutch

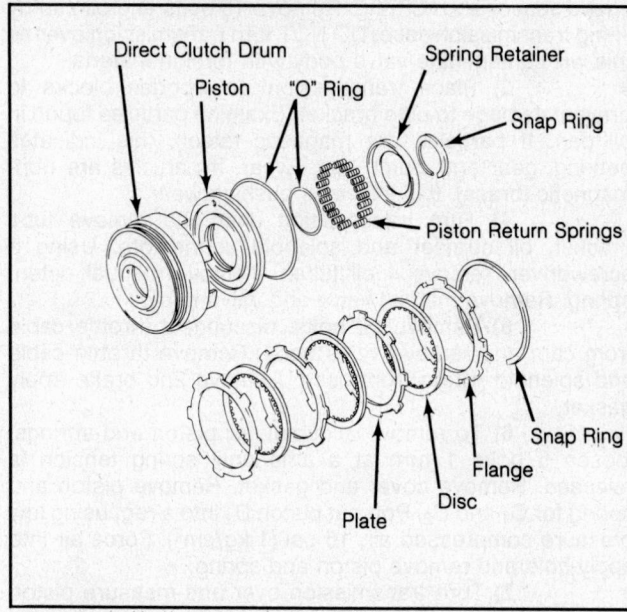

into passage with oil pump body and ensure movement of piston. If piston does not move, disassemble and inspect.

FORWARD CLUTCH
Disassembly

1) Remove thrust bearings and races from both sides of clutch. Measure clearance of forward clutch. To do so, place a feeler gauge between snap ring and flange. Specified clearance is .0163-.0573" (.414-1.456 mm).

2) Remove snap ring from clutch drum and remove flange, discs and plates. Place Compressor Block (09350-32010) on spring retainer and compress springs with an arbor press. Remove retainer and 18 springs.

3) Apply compressed air into oil passage to remove piston. If piston does not come out, use needle-nose pliers to remove it. See Fig. 20.

Fig. 20: Exploded View of Forward Clutch

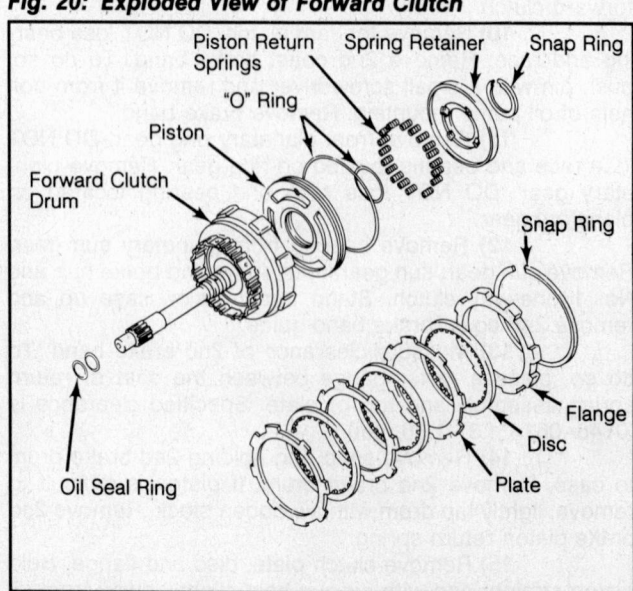

TOYOTA MODEL A140E (Cont.)

Inspection

Inspect clutch piston. Ensure that check ball is free by shaking piston. Ensure that valve does not leak by applying low pressure air. Replace oil seal rings. During installation, DO NOT spread ring ends too much.

Reassembly

1) Coat NEW "O" ring with ATF and install it onto piston. To install piston, press piston into drum with cup side up. Be careful not to damage "O" ring.

2) Set 18 piston return springs, retainer and snap ring into drum. Place compressor block onto top of retainer and compress using an arbor press. Install snap ring into groove with pliers. Be sure end gap of snap ring is not aligned with spring retainer claw.

3) Install in order: plate, disc, plate, disc, plate, disc and flange. Install flange with flat end facing downward. Install outer snap ring. Be sure not to align end gap of ring with any cut-outs.

4) Check clearance of forward clutch. To do so, place a feeler gauge between snap ring and flange. Specified clearance is .0163-.0573" (.414-1.456 mm).

5) To check operation of direct clutch, apply compressed air into oil passage of shaft. Ensure piston moves. If piston does not move, disassemble and inspect.

No. 1 ONE-WAY CLUTCH & SUN GEAR
Disassembly

1) Check operation of one-way clutch. Hold sun gear and turn hub. Hub should turn freely clockwise and should lock counterclockwise. While turning hub clockwise, remove one-way clutch from inner race.

2) Remove No. 3 planetary carrier thrust washer from sun gear input drum. Remove snap ring and remove sun gear input drum. Remove snap ring. See Fig. 21.

Fig. 21: Exploded View of No. 1 One-Way Clutch & Sun Gear

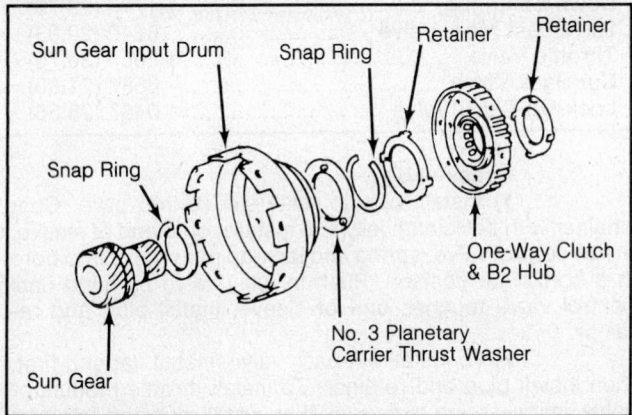

Inspection

If necessary, replace one-way clutch. To remove, pry off retainer with a screwdriver and remove clutch. To install, ensure spring cage is facing toward overdrive case. Hold brake hub in a vise and flatten ears with a chisel. Ensure retainer is centered. Check operation of one-way clutch.

Reassembly

1) Install shaft snap ring on sun gear. Install sun gear input drum on sun gear and install shaft snap ring.

Install No. 3 planetary carrier thrust washer on sun gear input drum.

2) While turning hub clockwise, slide one-way clutch onto inner race. Recheck operation of No. 1 one-way clutch.

No. 2 ONE-WAY CLUTCH & REAR PLANETARY GEAR
Disassembly

1) Prior to disassembly, check operation of one-way clutch. To do so, hold outer race and turn hub. Hub should turn freely counterclockwise and should lock clockwise. See Fig. 22.

2) Remove No. 2 planetary carrier thrust washer from both sides of carrier. Remove hub and plentary gear from one-way clutch to disassemble one-way clutch.

3) Remove both side snap rings and 2 side retainers. Remove one-way clutch from outer race.

Fig. 21: Exploded View of No. 1 One-Way Clutch & Sun Gear

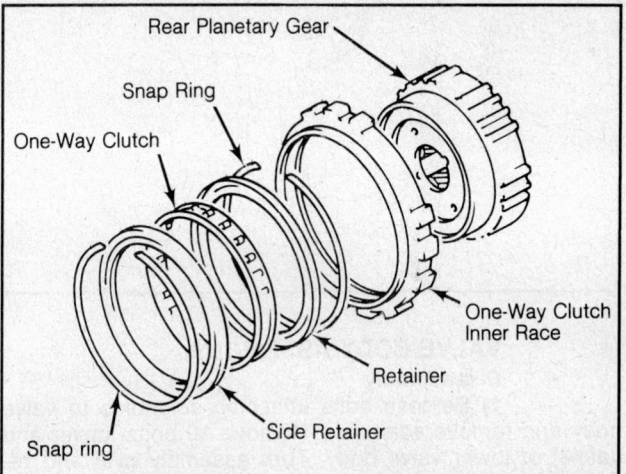

Reassembly

Install one-way clutch into outer race, facing flange of cage toward oil pump. Install 2 side retainers and 2 snap rings. Check operation of one-way clutch. Install No. 2 planetary carrier thrust washer onto both sides of carrier.

FIRST & REVERSE BRAKE PISTON
Disassembly

1) Using Compressor (09350-32010), gradually and evenly tighten tool bolt to compress springs. Using 2 screwdrivers, hook and remove snap ring. Remove piston return spring assembly and set snap ring in place.

2) Apply compressed air into oil passage of case to remove piston. Hold air gun away from hole and be sure piston does not tilt during removal. Remove "O" rings from piston.

Reassembly

1) Install NEW "O" rings onto piston. Coat rings with ATF. Install piston into bore of case facing spring seats upward. Place base of spring compressor under case. Install piston return springs and retainer and set snap ring into place.

2) Compress piston return springs slowly and evenly to allow installation of snap ring. DO NOT overtighten bolt as it will cause spring retainer to bend.

3) Push snap ring into place with fingers and visually check to ensure its fully seated and centered on the 3 lugs on spring retainer. Be sure end gap of ring is not

aligned with spring retainer claw. Remove compressor tool. *See Fig. 23.*

Fig. 23: Exploded View of First & Reverse Brake Piston

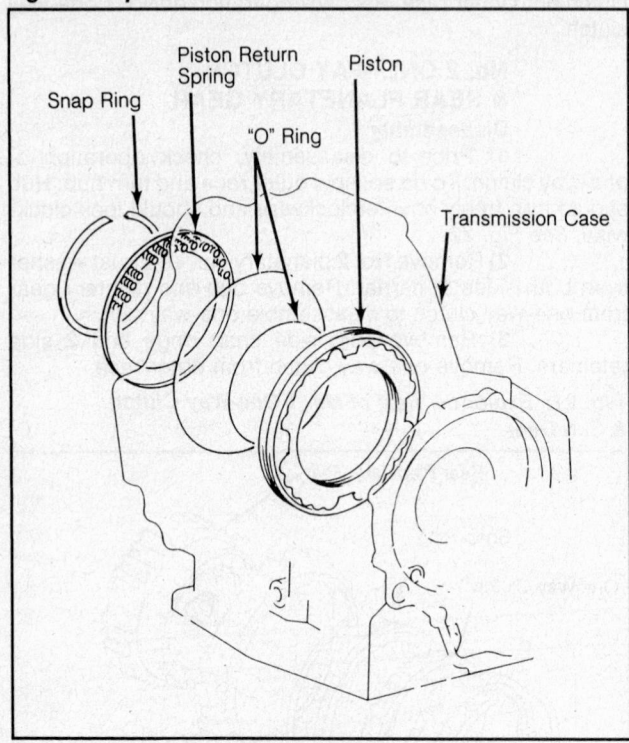

VALVE BODY ASSEMBLY
Disassembly

1) Remove bolts attaching solenoids to valve body and remove solenoids. Remove 10 bolts, cover and gasket of lower valve body. Turn assembly over and remove 12 bolts from upper valve body and upper valve body cover.

2) Remove upper valve body cover, strainer, gasket and plate. Turn assembly over and remove 3 bolts from lower valve body. Hold valve body plate to lower valve body and lift off lower valve body and plate as a unit. BE CAREFUL that check valve and balls do not fall out. DO NOT lose steel balls, retainers and pins in valve body.

Disassembly (Upper Valve Body)

1) Remove throttle valve retainer and 2 check balls. To remove lock-up relay valve, remove retainer for plug with a magnet and remove plug. Remove lock-up relay valve, control valve and spring.

2) Remove retainer for sleeve with a magnet and remove sleeve. To remove cut-back valve, remove retainer with a magnet and remove valve and spring. To remove throttle modulator valve, remove retainer with a magnet and remove plug, valve and spring.

3) To remove accumulator control valve, remove retainer with a magnet and remove plug, spring and control valve. To remove low coast modulator valve, remove pin with a magnet and remove plug, spring and valve. To remove 2nd coast modulator valve, remove retainer with a magnet and remove spring and valve.

4) To remove throttle cam, loosen bolt and remove cam, spring and collar. To remove down-shift plug and spring, remove pin with a magnet and remove plug with sleeve and spring. Remove throttle valve. Remove spring

and adjusting rings. Note number of adjusting rings installed. *See Fig. 24.*

Fig. 24: Exploded View of Upper Valve Body

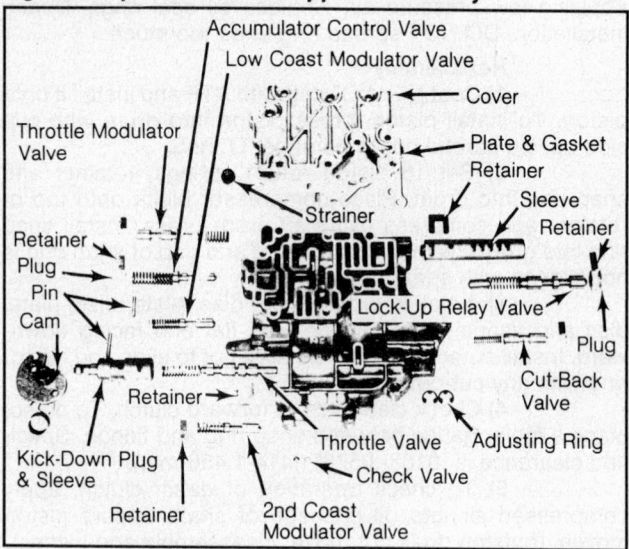

Inspection

Inspect valve springs for damage, squareness, rust and collapsed coils. Measure spring free height and replace if less than that shown in UPPER VALVE BODY VALVE SPRINGS table.

UPPER VALVE BODY VALVE SPRINGS

Application	Free Height In. (mm)
Throttle Mod. Valve	.8543 (21.70)
Accum. Control Valve	1.3071 (33.20)
Low Coast Mod. Valve	.9213 (23.40)
Down-Shift Plug	1.1717 (29.76)
2nd Coast Mod. Valve	.8240 (20.93)
Throttle Valve	1.2087 (30.70)
Cut-Back Valve	.8587 (21.80)
Lock-Up Relay Valve	1.0457 (26.56)

Reassembly

1) Install lock-up relay sleeve into bore. Coat retainer with petroleum jelly and install it onto end of sleeve. Install control valve, spring and lock-up relay valve into bore in a horizontal position. Push in relay valve by hand until control valve touches end of sleeve. Install plug and retainer.

2) To install cut-back valve, install flat end first, then install plug and retainer. To install throttle modulator valve, install spring and valve, then install plug and retainer.

3) To install accumulator control valve, install valve and spring, then install plug and retainer. To install low coast modulator valve, install valve and spring, then install plug and pin.

4) To install 2nd coast modulator valve, install valve and spring, then compress spring and allow retainer to fall into place. Ensure retainer fully covers end of spring. To install throttle valve and retainer, install throttle valve, coat retainer with petroleum jelly and install it into place in valve body.

5) To install adjusting rings and spring on throttle valve shaft, install same number of rings as were

TOYOTA MODEL A140E (Cont.)

removed during assembly. Slip spring over end of valve shaft. Compress and slide into place.

6) Install spring into throttle valve. Install down-shift plug with sleeve. Coat pin with petroleum jelly and install to hold sleeve in place. To assemble throttle cam, install spring with hood through hole in cam. Insert sleeve through 1 side of cam.

7) Install cam assembly on upper valve body. Check position of spring ends. Tighten bolt to specification. Ensure cam moves on roller of down-shift plug. Install 2 check balls making sure that pins and retainer are installed correctly.

Disassembly (Lower Valve Body)

1) Remove lower valve body plate and gaskets. Remove cooler by-pass valve and spring. Remove damping valve and spring. Remove 4 check balls and strainer.

2) To remove primary regulator valve, hold valve body face down, and press in on valve sleeve. Retainer will drop out. Remove sleeve and plunger. Remove spring and valve. Note number of adjusting rings.

3) To remove secondary regulator valve, remove retainer and plug. Then, remove valve and spring. To remove lock-up signal valve, compress spring with a screwdriver and remove retainer with a magnet. Remove valve and spring.

4) To remove 2nd-3rd shift valve, remove retainer and plug. Then, remove spring and valve. To remove 1st-2nd shift valve, remove retainer and plug, then, remove valve and spring.

5) To remove 3rd-4th shift valve, remove retainer with a magnet, remove plug, then remove 3rd-4th shift valve. *See Fig. 25.*

LOWER VALVE BODY VALVE SPRINGS

Application	Free Height In. (mm)
Primary Reg. Valve	2.6240 (66.65)
1st-2nd Shift Valve	1.1524 (29.27)
2nd-3rd Shift Valve	1.1524 (29-27)
3rd-4th Shift Valve	1.1524 (29.27)
Lock-Up Signal Valve	1.1811 (30.00)
Secondary Reg. Valve	1.7165 (43.60)
Damping Valve	.4409 (11.20)
Cooler By-Pass Valve	.7835 (19.90)

2) Stand valve body upward and push valve into bore until its tip touches bore. Install valve spring. Insert plunger with short end first. Ensure it is fully inserted. Plunger should be recesssed inside sleeve. Install sleeve with plunger. Ensure regulator valve fits with bore. Install retainer.

3) To install secondary regulator valve, install spring and valve, then install plug and retainer. To install lock-up signal valve, install valve and spring, then compress spring with a screwdriver and install retainer.

4) To install 2nd-3rd shift valve, install valve and spring, then install plug and retainer. To install 1st-2nd shift valve, install valve and spring, then install plug and retainer. To install 3rd-4th shift valve, install valve flat and spring, then install plug and retainer.

5) Check retainers and locating pin. Ensure retainers and pin are installed correctly. Install spring and cooler by-pass valve. Install spring and damping valve. Install check balls as shown in *Fig. 26.* Install strainer onto lower valve body.

Fig. 25: Exploded View of Lower Valve Body

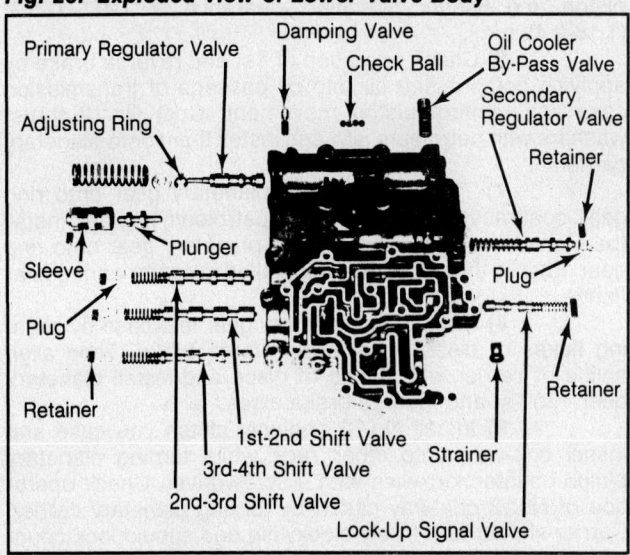

Inspection
Inspect valve spring for damage, squareness, rust and distorted coils. Measure spring free length and replace if less than that shown in LOWER VALVE BODY VALVE SPRINGS.

Reassembly
1) To install primary regulator valve, install adjusting rings and spring seat. Install same number of rings as were removed. Place valve into bore in horizontal position.

Fig. 26: Location of Check Balls in Lower Valve Body

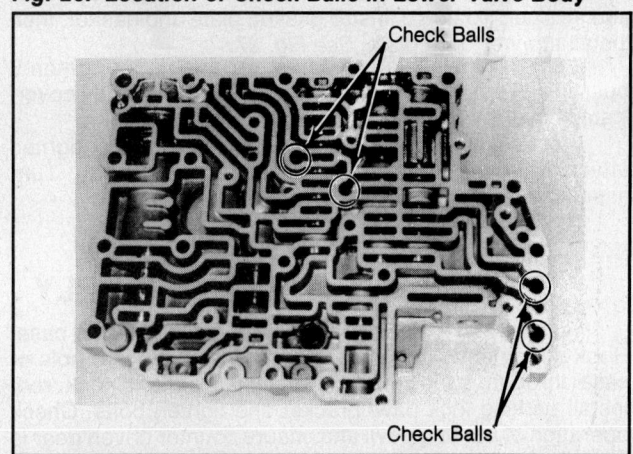

Reassembly (Valve Body Assembly)

NOTE: Install lower valve body on upper valve body together with plate.

1) Position gasket with larger cooler by-pass valve hole to lower valve body. Place gasket and plate onto lower valve body. Align each bolt hole in valve with gasket and plate.

2) Position new gasket on upper valve body. Align gasket with each bolt hole. Place lower valve body with plate on top of upper valve body. Hold lower valve body and plate securely so they DO NOT separate. Align each bolt hole in valve bodies with gasket and plate.

Fig. 27: Noted Length & Location of Valve Body Bolts

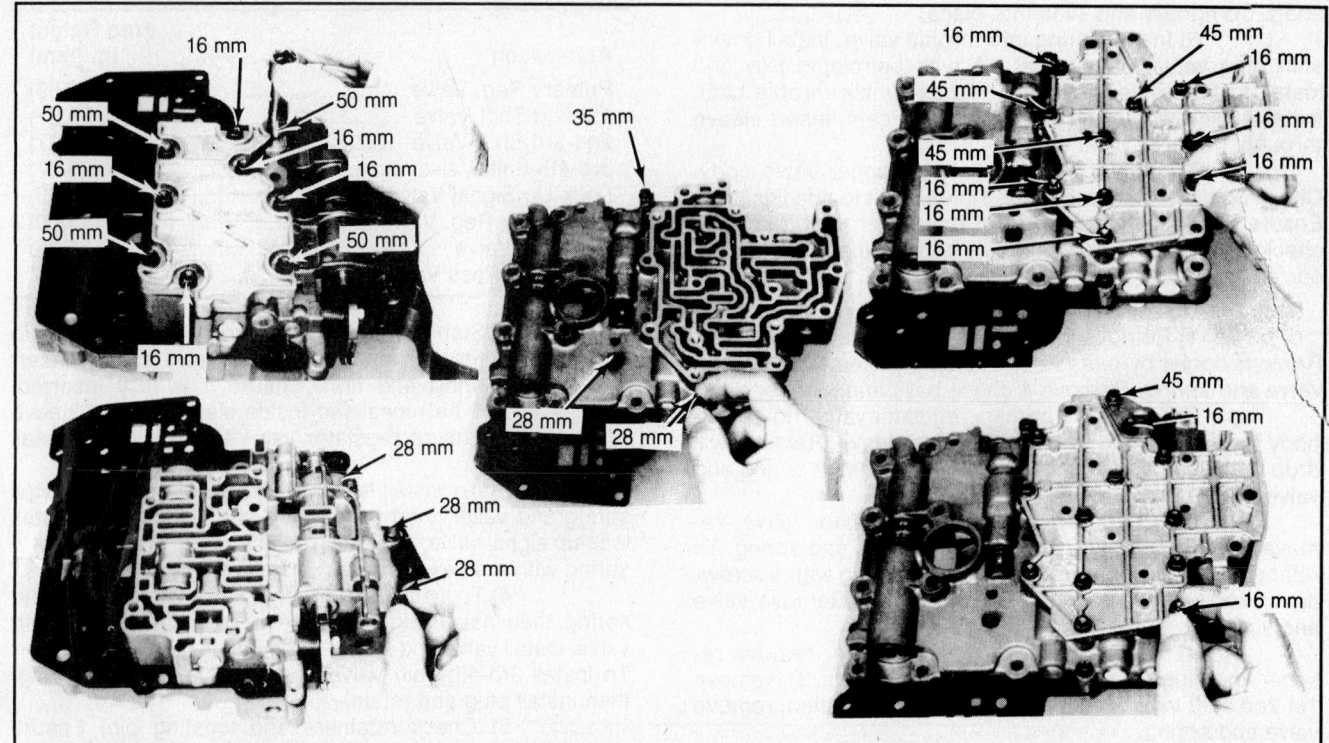

3) Note length and location of bolts. Install and finger tighten 3 bolts in lower valve body to secure upper valve body. Turn valve body over. Install and finger tighten 3 bolts in upper valve body. Install upper valve body cover and strainer. To do so, install gasket, plate and gasket, then install strainer onto plate. *See Fig. 27.*

4) Install valve body cover and finger tighten 9 bolts in valve body cover. To install lower valve body cover, install cover over gasket and finger tighten 10 bolts.

5) Install Nos. 1 and 2 solenoids and tighten attaching bolts. Tighten bolts in upper valve body. Turn assembly over and tighten bolts in lower valve body.

TRANSMISSION REASSEMBLY

1) To install parking pawl, place pawl onto case. Hook spring ends to case and pawl. Install pin into hole of case through spring and pawl. Install parking lock rod. Install parking lock pawl bracket and tighten bolts. Check operation of parking pawl and ensure counter driven gear is locked when manual lever is in "P" range.

2) To install gaskets on transmission case, coat gaskets with petroleum jelly to hold them in place. Install both overdrive brake and governor apply gaskets over appropriate case openings.

3) Align each bolt hole in gasket and case and install overdrive unit over gasket. Tighten fastening bolts. Check intermediate shaft end play. To do so, ensure shaft has thrust play in axial (in and out) direction. Standard specified thrust play is .0193-.0594" (.49-1.51 mm). Ensure shaft turns smoothly.

4) Install 1st and reverse brake in case by installing inner flange facing flat end toward oil pump side. Install in order: flange, disc, plate, disc, plate, disc, plate, disc, plate, disc, plate, disc and flange. Install outer flange flat side facing toward piston side.

5) Install snap ring being sure ring end gap is installed into groove. At this time, check clearance of 1st and reverse brake. To do so, place a feeler gauge between piston and flange. Specified clearance is .0465-.0953" (1.18-2.42 mm).

6) Check operation of 1st and reverse brake by applying compressed air into oil passage of transmission case and confirm piston movement. Coat No. 2 thrust washers with petroleum jelly and install them onto planetary carrier.

7) To assemble rear planetary gear onto ring gear, coat races and bearing with petroleum jelly and install them onto ring gear. Then, install planetary gear onto ring gear. Ensure thrust bearing is installed in center of ring gear flange.

8) Install rear planetary gear into case by aligning flukes of discs in 1st and reverse brake. Then align spline of carrier with flukes of discs and install planetary gear into 1st and reverse brake discs.

9) Install No. 2 one-way clutch into case and install one-way onto inner race while turning planetary pinion counterclockwise with a screwdriver. Check operation of No. 2 one-way clutch by turning planetary carrier. Carrier should turn freely clockwise and should lock counterclockwise.

10) Install snap ring and ensure end gap is installed into groove. Install 2nd coast brake band guide and 2nd brake drum guide. Install band guide so that its tip touches case.

11) Install 2nd brake into case by installing flange facing flat end toward 2nd brake piston. Install in order: flange, disc, plate, disc, plate, disc, plate. Install piston return spring assembly with each spring end installed onto protrusion of case.

TOYOTA MODEL A140E (Cont.)

12) Install 2nd brake drum into case. Align grooves of drum with guide and place it into case. Place snap ring into case so that end gap is installed into groove. While compressing piston return springs over drum with 2 bars, install snap ring into groove.

13) Using a feeler guage, check clearance of 2nd brake between plate and seat of return spring assembly. Specified clearance is .0146-.0614" (.37-1.56 mm). Apply compressed air into oil passage of case and ensure piston moves freely.

14) Install 2nd brake drum seal by driving seal until distance between surface of case and top of seal is 1.14" (29 mm). Install No. 1 one-way clutch and 2nd brake hub by aligning flukes of discs in 2nd brake. Then, align spline of hub with flukes of discs and install hub into 2nd brake discs.

15) Install sun gear and sun gear input drum by turning sun gear clockwise and installing it into one-way clutch. Be sure to place sun gear in center of intermediate shaft to protect bushings from damage.

16) To install front planetary gear onto ring gear, coat races and bearing with petroleum jelly and install them onto ring gear. Then coat race and bearing with petroleum jelly and install them onto carrier. Install planetary gear onto ring gear.

17) Install front planetary gear assembly onto sun gear. If planetary gear and other parts are installed correctly into case, end of bushing with ring gear flange will be flush with intermediate shaft. Coat race with petroleum jelly and install it onto tip of ring gear flange.

18) Install 2nd coast brake band by placing band into case and installing pin through oil pump mounting bolt hole. Install forward clutch into case by coating races and bearing with petroleum jelly and installing them onto both sides of clutch drum.

19) Then align flukes of disc in forward clutch and while holding sun gear input drum and rotating the input shaft to mesh hub with clutch discs of forward clutch. Align center of input shaft and intermediate shaft, and while pushing on the input shaft, rotate it to mesh hub and disc.

20) Install direct clutch. To do so, coat clutch drum thrust washer with petroleum jelly and install it with oil groove upward onto drum. Align flukes of discs in direct clutch. Hold input shaft and put direct clutch drum through into 2nd coast brake band. Mesh hub with flukes of direct clutch while turning clutch drum. If flukes of discs are meshed with hub correctly, end of bushing with direct clutch drum is flush with thrust bearing on forward clutch.

21) Install oil pump. To do so, coat race with petroleum jelly and install it onto stator shaft. After installing oil pump, measure input shaft thrust play. If thrust play is excessive, select and insert 1 of 2 different size shims.

22) Place oil pump through input shaft and align bolt holes of pump body at transmission case. Hold input shaft and lightly press oil pump body to slide oil seal rings on stator shaft though direct clutch drum. DO NOT push on oil pump hard or oil seal ring will stick to direct clutch drum. Install and tighten oil pump mounting bolts.

23) Measure thrust play of input shaft. To do so, measure thrust play in an axial direction. Specifed thrust play is .012-.035" (.3-.9 mm). There are 2 different thickness, .031" (.8 mm) or .055" (1.4 mm), of races for end of stator shaft.

24) Check input shaft rotation and ensure it turns smoothly. Measure 2nd coast brake piston stroke. To do so, install brake piston without outer spring into bore.

Install snap ring. Push end of piston rod firmly. At this time, measure distance between tip of piston rod and outside of snap ring. Specified piston stroke is .551-.610" (14.0-15.5 mm).

25) If stroke is more than specified, replace piston rod with a longer one. Piston rods are available in 2 different sizes, 2.870" (72.9 mm) or 2.811" (71.4 mm). After installation of new rod, remeasure stroke. If it is more than specified value, replace brake band.

26) Install 2nd coast brake piston. To do so, remove installed parts from bore. Install outer spring with piston. Place cover into bore and using snap ring pliers, install snap ring while pressing in on cover.

27) Check operation of 2nd coast brake by applying compressed air into hole of case and ensure that piston rod moves. Install accumulator pistons and springs. To do so, install springs and pistons into bore. Place cover with gasket and tighten five-20 mm bolts gradually and in sequence.

28) Install governor apply gasket. Install throttle cable and solenoid wiring. To do so, push them through case, being careful not to damage "O" ring. Ensure everything is fully seated.

CAUTION: DO NOT roll case over cable and break cable fitting.

29) Place valve body on transmission and while holding cam down with your hand, slip cable end into slot. Lower valve body into position. DO NOT entangle throttle cable.

30) Ensure proper length and location and finger tighten all bolts. Then tighten them to specifications. Connect solenoid wire connectors. *See Fig. 28.*

Fig. 28: Valve Body Mounting Bolt Length & Location

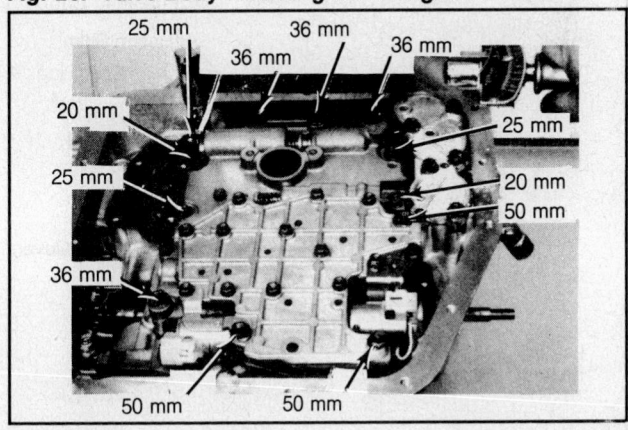

31) Place manual valve and body on transmission and align manual lever with pin of manual shaft lever. Lower valve body into position. Ensure proper length and location and finger tighten bolts. Then tighten bolts with torque wrench to specifications.

32) Install detent spring. To do so, ensure proper length and location of each bolt and finger tighten. Then tighten to specifications and check for proper operation of manual valve lever. Ensure lever is touching center of detent spring tip roller.

33) Install oil tubes using a plastic hammer. DO NOT bend or damage tubes. Install tube bracket. Note length and proper location of bolts. Tighten bolts to specifications. Install oil strainer. Note length and proper location of bolts. Tighten bolts to specifications.

34) Install magnet on oil pan. Be sure magnet DOES NOT interfere with oil tubes. Install oil pan with gasket. Tighten pan bolts to specifications. Install speed sensor with "O" ring and install cover bracket with 2 bolts.

35) Install throttle and solenoid wiring retainers. Install filler tube and gauge. Install solenoid. To do so, coat "O" rings with ATF and push tip of solenoid into hole. Tighten pipes to union, clamping pipes onto bracket and tighten union nuts.

DIFFERENTIAL & DRIVE PINION
SERVICE (IN VEHICLE)

Left-Hand Output Shaft Seal
Replacement
1) Remove dust cover and fender apron seal. Drain out 1 qt. (1 L) of ATF. Remove axle shaft. Remove speed sensor. Remove side gear shaft using Puller (09520-32010). Remove side bearing retainer.

Fig. 29: Exploded View of Differential Unit

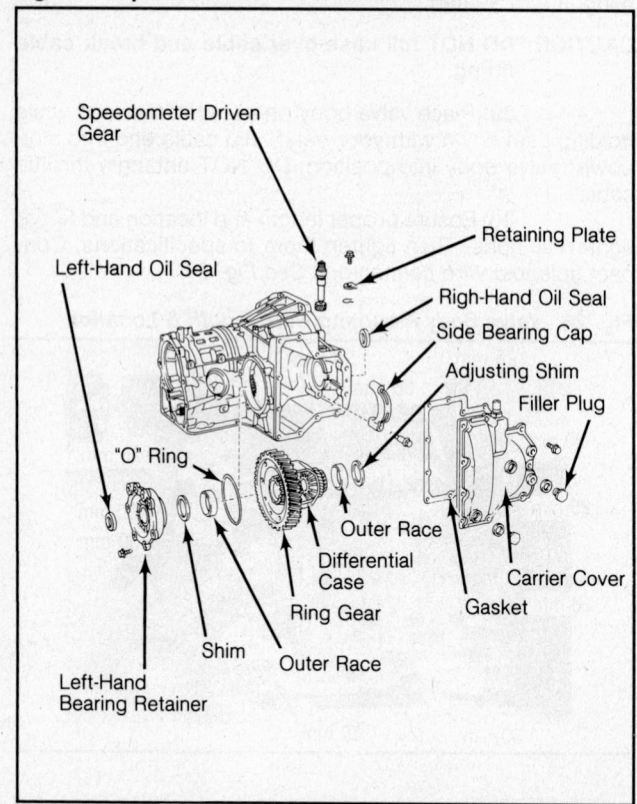

2) Press out seal from retainer. Using Seal Installer (09350-32010) and an arbor press, press in NEW oil seal. Seal should be recessed .106" (2.7 mm) when properly installed.

3) Coat lip of seal with MP grease. Coat threads with sealer (3 Bond 1324) and install side bearing retainer. Tighten retainer bolts to specifications. Using Slide Hammer (0950-32010), install side gear shaft until it contacts pinion shaft.

4) Install drive shaft and speed sensor. Fill differential with ATF. Install fender apron seal and dust seal.

Right-Hand Output Shaft Seal
Replacement
1) Remove fender apron seal. Drain out 1 qt. (1 L) of ATF from differential. Remove drive shaft. Remove intermediate shaft. Remove universal joint using Slide Hammer and Adapter (09520-32010 and 09520-32030).

2) Remove oil seal using Inside Puller/Slide Hammer (09308-0010). Using Seal Installer (09350-32010), drive seal into case until its surface is flush with surface of case. Coat lip of seal with MP grease.

3) Install universal joint using Slide Hammer and Adapter (09520-32010 and 09520-32030). Install intermediate shaft and drive shaft. Fill differential with ATF. Install fender apron seal.

DISASSEMBLY
1) Remove neutral safety switch, speedometer driven gear, speed sensor, oil pan, valve body. Remove 11 bolts and tap overdrive case with a plastic hammer to remove it. If intermediate shaft did not come out with overdrive case, remove it from transmission case.

2) Remove overdrive clutch apply gasket and brake gasket. Remove parking pawl lock bracket and rod. Remove parking lock pawl. Remove manual shaft and lever. Remove carrier cover.

3) Using a torque wrench, measure total preload at starting point. Record measured value. Measure side gear backlash while holding 1 pinion against carrier casing. Standard specified backlash is .002-.0079" (.05-.20 mm).

4) Remove 6 bolts and tap left-hand bearing retainer with a plastic hammer to remove it. Remove "O" ring from retainer. Remove 2 bolts and right-hand bearing retainer. Remove differential carrier, outer race and adjusting shim from case.

Drive Pinion Shaft
1) Using a torque meter, measure preload of drive pinion. Specified preload at starting point with a used bearing is between 4.3-6.9 INCH lbs. (1-1.5 N.m). Remove transmission case cap.

2) To remove counter driven gear, use a chisel to loosen staked part of nut. Install Holder (09330-0020) and remove nut. Using Puller (09350-32010), remove counter driven gear.

3) Remove outer race from case using Puller (09350-32010). Remove oil slinger, spacer and rotor sensor. Remove drive pinion snap ring using snap ring pliers. Insert a brass bar into case hole to tap out drive pinion.

4) Tap drive pinion and remove bearing cage from bore. Remove bearing cage from drive pinion. Remove "O" ring from bearing cage.

INSPECTION & REPLACEMENT
OF DIFFERENTIAL COMPONENTS
Carrier Bearings
Using Bearing Puller (09502-10012), remove bearings from both sides of carrier. Remove speedometer drive gear from right-hand side. Using Installer (09350-32010) and an arbor press, press side bearings onto differential carrier.

Carrier Bearing Races
1) To replace left-hand bearing race, remove oil seal. Using Remover/Installer (09350-32010) and an arbor press, remove outer race and shim.

2) To replace, place shim onto retainer. Using Remover/Installer (09350-32010), press outer race into retainer. Use either same shim which was removed or one that is .0945" (2.40 mm).

3) Replace oil seal. Ensure seal is driven .106" (2.7 mm) below outer surface of retainer. Replace right-hand output shaft oil seal. Install seal so it is flush with case.

Ring Gear

1) Loosen staked part of lock plate. Place alignment marks on ring gear and carrier. Remove 8 bolts and locking plates. Using a copper hammer, tap on ring gear to remove it from carrier.

2) Measure side gear backlash while holding 1 pinion toward carrier case. Specified standard backlash is .002-.0079" (.05-.20 mm). If backlash if out of specification, install correct thrust washer to side gears. *See Fig. 30.*

Fig. 30: Measuring Side Gear Backlash

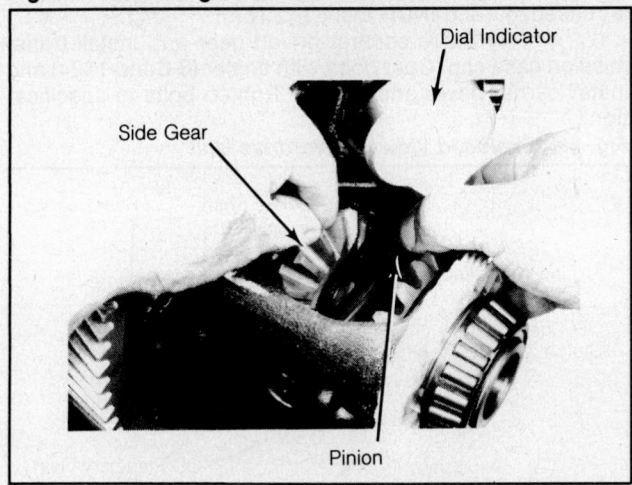

3) To remove pinion and side gears from differential carrier, drive out pinion shaft lock pin. Remove pinion shaft from carrier. Remove 2 pinion and 2 side gears with 4 thrust washers from each gear.

4) To assemble, install correct thrust washers and side gears. Refer to SIDE GEAR THRUST WASHER THICKNESS table. Try to select washers of the same size for both sides.

SIDE GEAR THRUST WASHER THICKNESS

Part. No.	Thickness In. (mm)
42361-22140	.0374 (.95)
42361-22020	.0394 (1.00)
42361-22150	.0413 (1.05)
42361-22030	.0433 (1.10)
42361-22160	.0453 (1.15)
42361-22040	.0472 (1.20)

5) Install thrust washers and side gears in carrier. Measure side gear backlash of side gear while holding one pinion gear against carrier case. Standard specified backlash is .002-.0079" (.05-.20 mm). If backlash is not within specification, install a thrust washer of different thickness.

6) Using a hammer and punch, drive lock pin through carrier case and hole in pinion shaft. Stake differential carrier case to retain lock pin.

Counter Driven Gear Bearing

Using a bearing puller and arbor press, press bearing off gear. Use Installer (09350-32010) and a press to install bearing.

Drive Pinion Shaft
Bearing & Outer Race

Using a bearing puller and arbor press, press bearing from gear. Use Installer (09350-32010) and a press to install bearing. Place bearing cage in Stand (09350-32010) and using a driver handle and hammer drive out bearing race from cage. Use Bearing Race Installer (09350-32010) and a press to install race.

Cage Oil Seals

1) Using Remover/Installer (09350-32010) and a press, press out 2 oil seals together. To install, position oil seal with lip facing downward. Place a mark on tool marking 11 mm depth. *See Fig. 31.* Using an arbor press and Remover/Installer (09350-32010), press in seal to a depth of 11 mm below surface of flat end of cage.

Fig. 31: Marking Seal Installer

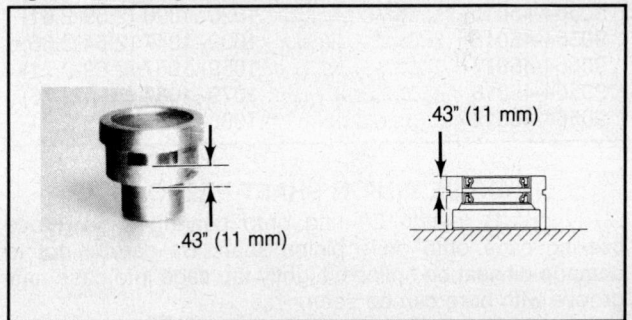

Place a mark on tool to signify depth.

2) Position second seal, lip facing upward, into cage and press in seal until it is flush with case. Coat lip of both seals with MP grease.

ADJUSTMENTS

DIFFERENTIAL SIDE BEARING PRELOAD ADJUSTMENT

1) Place outer race and adjusting shim onto right-hand side bearing. Place differential carrier with shim into case. Install left-hand bearing retainer into case without "O" ring.

2) DO NOT coat threads with sealer yet. Temporarily tighten retainer bolts evenly and gradually while turning ring gear. Install right-hand side bearing cap. Tighten bolts to specifications. Tighten left-hand bearing retainer bolts to specifications.

3) To adjust ring gear preload, use a torque meter and measure preload. Note and record torque required to turn ring gear at its starting point. Specified preload for a NEW bearing is 8.7-13.9 INCH lbs. (1-1.5 N.m). For a used bearing its 4.3-6.9 INCH lbs. (.5-.8 N.m).

4) If preload is not within specifications, remove ring gear from case and select a shim from RIGHT-HAND ADJUSTING SHIM table.

NOTE: Preload will change by about 2.6-3.5 INCH lbs. (.3-.4 N.m) with each increase or decrease of shim thickness.

5) If preload is adjusted properly, remove bearing retainer, ring gear, right-hand side bearing and shim. DO NOT lose shim.

RIGHT-HAND ADJUSTING SHIM

Part. No.	Thickness In. (mm)
90564-45001	.0744-.0752 (1.89-1.91)
90564-45002	.0764-.0772 (1.94-1.96)
90564-45003	.0783-.0791 (1.99-2.01)
90564-45004	.0803-.0811 (2.04-2.06)
90564-45005	.0823-.0831 (2.09-2.11)
90564-45006	.0843-.0850 (2.14-2.16)
90564-45007	.0862-.0870 (2.19-2.21)
90564-45008	.0882-.0890 (2.24-2.26)
90564-45009	.0902-.0909 (2.29-2.31)
90564-45010	.0921-.0929 (2.34-2.36)
90564-45011	.0941-.0949 (2.39-2.41)
90564-45012	.0961-.0969 (2.44-2.46)
90564-45013	.0980-.0988 (2.49-2.51)
90564-45014	.1000-.1008 (2.54-2.56)
90564-45015	.1020-.1028 (2.59-2.61)
90564-45016	.1039-.1047 (2.64-2.66)
90564-45017	.1059-.1067 (2.69-2.71)
90564-45018	.1079-.1087 (2.74-2.76)
90564-45019	.1098-.1106 (2.79-2.81)

DRIVE PINION SHAFT PRELOAD

1) Install "O" ring onto bearing cage. Place bearing cage onto drive pinion shaft. Be careful not to damage oil seal on splines. Lightly tap cage into case until groove with bore can be seen.

2) Drive in bearing cage until surface of bearing cage passes through groove in bore. Install snap ring and lightly tap bearing cage to fit snap ring into groove. Install rotor sensor.

3) Install oil slinger with lip facing outward. Install outer race using Installer (09350-32010) and a hammer. Install NEW spacer with small end first. Install counter driven gear onto shaft.

4) To do so, place a bar at the drive pinion side and position other end of bar against a vise. Drive gear onto shaft until nut can be installed on thread of shaft. DO NOT cause a shock to transmission case.

5) Adjust drive pinion preload. To do so, coat threads and surface of nut with MP grease. Use Socket and Holder (09350-32010 and 09330-00020) to hold gear and tighten nut. Tighten nut specifications.

6) Rotate gear counterclockwise and clockwise several times. Using a torque meter, measure preload of drive pinion at its starting point. Specified preload with a NEW bearing is is 8.7-13.9 INCH lbs. (1-1.5 N.m). If old bearing was reused, it should be 4.3-6.9 INCH lbs. (.5-.8 N.m).

7) If preload is greater than specified, replace bearing spacer. If preload is less than specified, retighten shaft nut 108 INCH lbs. (12 N.m) at a time until specified preload is reached.

8) If maximum torque is exceeded while retightening shaft nut, replace bearing spacer and repeat preload procedure. DO NOT back off nut to reduce preload. Maximum shaft nut torque is 213 ft. lbs. (288 N.m).

REASSEMBLY

1) Place outer race and selected adjusting shim onto right-hand side carrier bearing. Place differential carrier into case. Ensure shim is properly installed.

2) Install "O" ring onto left-hand bearing retainer. Install retainer by tapping it while keeping carrier centered with retainer. Clean threads of bolts and case with White gas. Coat threads of bolts with sealer (3 Bond 1324).

3) Finger tighten bolts evenly and gradually while turning ring gear. Install right-hand side bearing cap and tighten bolts evenly and slowly while turning ring gear. Tighten bolts to specifications.

4) Tighten left-hand carrier bearing retainer bolts to specifications. Using a torque meter, measure total preload. Specified drive pinion preload at starting point with a NEW bearing is 2.2-4.1 INCH lbs. (.2-.5 N.m). If old bearing is reused, 1.1-2.0 INCH lbs. (.1-.2 N.m).

5) Stake counter driven gear nut. Install transmission case cap. Coat bolts with sealer (3 Bond 1324) and install carrier cover and gasket. Tighten bolts to specifications.

Fig. 32: Exploded View of Overdrive Unit

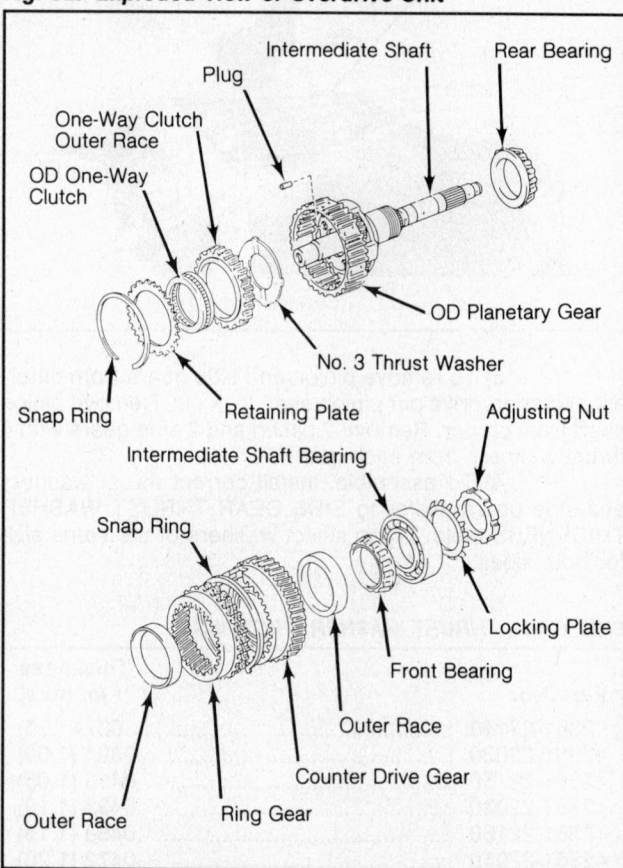

OVERDRIVE UNIT COMPONENT OVERHAUL

OVERDRIVE BRAKE
Disassembly

1) Pull up overdrive planetary gear and counter gear from transmission case. Measure clearance of overdrive brake. Place feeler gauge between piston and cushion plate. Specified clearance is .0201-.0661" (.51-1.68 mm).

2) Remove overdrive brake drum by using a TORX socket to loosen 4 screws 1 turn at a time until spring tension is released. Remove overdrive brake drum with piston.

3) Remove piston return spring assembly, cushion plate and plates, discs and flange. Apply compressed air to oil hole to remove piston. Hold air gun slightly away from oil hole and do not let piston tilt. Remove "O" ring from piston.

4) Remove snap ring and overdrive clutch from case. Remove bearing and race from clutch drum and case.

Reassembly

1) Install "O" rings onto piston. Coat "O" ring with ATF and install piston into drum. Be careful not to damage "O" ring. Install snap ring. Be sure ring snaps into groove.

2) Install flange facing flat end upward. Install in order: flange, disc, plate, disc, plate, disc, plate, cushion plate. Install cushion plate facing rounded end downward.

3) Install piston return spring assembly. Install OD brake drum. Using a TORX socket, tighten 4 screws evenly and gradually until return springs are snug. Make sure that screw heads are lower than surface of case.

4) Check clearance of OD brake. Place a feeler gauge between cushion plate and piston. Specified clearance is .0201-.0661" (.51-1.68 mm). Apply compressed air into oil passage with drum and listen for piston movement. If piston does not move, disassemble and inspect.

OVERDRIVE CLUTCH
Disassembly

1) Remove snap ring and hub from OD clutch drum. Remove 1 disc and thinner snap ring. Measure clearance of overdrive clutch. To do so, install disc hub and snap ring without thinner snap ring.

2) Measure clearance between piston and end of plate. Specified clearance is .0283-.0661" (.72-1.68 mm). Remove snap ring, hub and plates and discs.

3) Use a spring compressor block and arbor press to compress piston return spring and remove snap ring. Remove snap ring with a screwdriver. Remove spring retainer and 18 springs.

4) Install OD clutch drum on case. Apply compressed air to pressure apply passage of case. Remove OD clutch drum from case. If piston does not come out completely, use needle-nose pliers to remove it. Remove "O" ring from piston.

Inspection

Inspect check ball of piston for free movement by shaking piston. Check that valve does not leak by applying low pressure compressed air.

Reassembly

1) Coat NEW "O" ring with ATF and install on piston. Press piston into drum with cup side up. DO NOT damage "O" ring. Install 18 springs and set retainer and snap ring in place.

2) Set spring compressor block on spring retainer and using an arbor press, compress springs. Install snap ring by hand. Be sure end gap of ring is not aligned with spring retainer claw.

3) Install in order: plate, disc, plate, disc and flange without installing thinner snap ring. Using low pressure compressed air, blow excessive ATF from discs. DO NOT use high pressure air as damage to discs could result.

4) Install hub and snap ring. Check clearance of OD clutch. To do so, place a feeler gauge between piston

and end of plate. Specified clearance is .0283-.0661" (.72-1.68 mm).

5) If specified clearance is exceeded, clutch pack is probably worn. If clearance is less than specified, parts may be incorrectly assembled or an excess amount of ATF may be on discs.

6) Remove OD clutch outer snap ring, hub and disc to allow installation of thinner snap ring. Compress and install snap ring into groove by hand. Be sure that ends of snap ring are not aligned with cut-outs.

7) Install disc, hub and outer snap ring. Be sure that ends of snap ring are not aligned with cut-outs. Install OD clutch into case. Apply compressed air into case passage and confirm that piston moves. If piston does not move, disassemble and inspect. Remove OD clutch from case.

OVERDRIVE ONE-WAY CLUTCH
Disassembly

1) Install OD clutch into one-way clutch while turning OD gear clockwise. Hold OD clutch and turn intermediate shaft. Shaft should turn freely clockwise and should lock counterclockwise.

2) Remove snap ring and retaining plate. Remove one-way clutch and outer race together. Remove No. 3 OD planetary thrust washer. Note position of one-way clutch and remove from outer race. Remove 4 plugs with magnet.

Reassembly

1) Install 4 plugs into hole of pinion shaft. Install one-way clutch into outer race. Be sure that flange of cage faces toward oil pump. Install a retainer on both sides of one-way clutch.

2) Install No. 3 OD planetary thrust washer facing groove toward OD case. Install OD one-way clutch into hub. Be sure it is installed in correct direction. Install retaining plate and snap ring.

3) Install overdrive clutch into one-way clutch. Hold OD clutch and turn intermediate shaft. Shaft should turn freely clockwise and should lock counterclockwise. Remove OD clutch from one-way clutch.

OVERDRIVE CASE
Disassembly

1) To disassemble accumulator piston of OD clutch, remove snap ring, retaining plate and spring. Assemble OD clutch onto case and apply compressed air to oil passage to remove piston. Remove OD clutch.

2) Push 1 end of ring into groove and unhook both ends of ring by hand. Spread ring apart and remove it.

Reassembly

Spread ring apart and install ring into groove. Push 1 one end of ring into groove and hook both ends by hand. Install piston spring, retainer plate and snap ring.

COUNTER DRIVE GEAR & BEARING
Disassembly

1) Pry off locking washer with screwdriver. Hold shaft in soft-jawed vise and loosen adjusting nut. Remove nut and washer. Remove intermediate shaft bearing by using a bearing puller and an arbor press.

2) Using a press, remove counter drive gear and front bearing together. Remove rear bearing using a bearing puller and arbor press. To remove OD planetary ring

Automatic Transmissions

TOYOTA MODEL A140E (Cont.)

gear from counter drive gear, pull up ring gear, compress snap ring with needle-nose pliers and remove it from groove.

3) Remove ring gear from counter drive gear. Using a brass bar and hammer, drive outer races from counter drive gear. Remove snap ring from counter drive gear.

Reassembly

1) Install snap ring into counter drive gear. Using a bearing race installer and arbor press, install 2 outer races into counter drive gear. Press in outer races until they touch snap ring.

2) While pushing down on ring gear, squeeze snap ring end with needle-nose pliers and install OD planetary ring gear into counter drive gear. When snap ring is fully seated, end is free.

3) Using a plate and arbor press, install rear bearing into shaft. Press in bearing until side surface of inner race touches shaft. Install counter drive gear onto shaft and mesh ring gear with planetary pinions. Place front bearing onto shaft. Hold ring gear to prevent it from falling.

4) Press in bearing until axial play between bearings is .020" (.5 mm). Using Bearing Collar (09350-32010) and arbor press, install intermediate shaft bearing. Press bearing until it just touches with front bearing of counter drive gear.

5) Place locking washer and adjusting nut onto intermediate shaft. Adjust preload of counter drive gear. To do so, place Gauge (09350-32010) onto adjusting nut and hold shaft in a soft-jawed vise.

6) Rotate counter drive gear right and left several times before measuring preload. Then, tighten adjusting nut to the point where the following gear starting load occurs. Specified preload is 2.0-3.4 INCH lbs. (920-1520 G). Bend locking washer tab until it is even with adjusting nut groove.

COMPONENT INSTALLATION

OVERDRIVE CLUTCH

Install thrust bearing and races on case and OD clutch. Make sure that races are installed in correct direction. Coat bearing and races with petroleum jelly to hold them in place. Install OD clutch onto case.

OVERDRIVE BRAKE

1) Install "O" rings onto piston. Coat "O" ring with ATF and install piston into drum. Be careful not to damage "O" ring. Install snap ring. Be sure ring snaps into groove.

2) Install flange facing flat end upward. Install in order: flange, disc, plate, disc, plate, disc, plate, cushion plate. Install cushion plate facing rounded end downward.

3) Install piston return spring assembly. Install OD brake drum. Using a TORX socket, tighten 4 screws evenly and gradually until return springs are snug. Make sure that screw heads are lower than surface of case.

4) Check clearance of OD brake. Place a feeler gauge between cushion plate and piston. Specified clearance is .0201-.0661" (.51-1.68 mm). Apply compressed air into oil passage with drum and listen for piston movement. If piston does not move, disassemble and inspect.

OVERDRIVE GEAR ASSEMBLY

1) Install OD gear assembly onto case and align center of shaft and bearing. Lock OD clutch drum with screwdriver and turn counter drive gear clockwise.

2) When meshing flukes of discs with hub, also mesh one-way clutch with inner race. If OD gear assembly is properly installed to OD case, clearance between them will be about .138" (3.5 mm).

TIGHTENING SPECIFICATIONS

Application	Ft. Lbs. (N.m)
Converter-to-Drive Plate Bolts	13 (18)
Converter Dust Cover Attaching Bolts	18 (24)
Drive Plate Mounting Bolts	61 (83)
Oil Pan Drain Plug	22 (30)
Oil Pump Mounting Bolts	16 (22)
Oil Cooler Tube Union Nuts	25 (34)
Overdrive Unit-to-Transmission Case Mounting Bolts	18 (24)
Stiffener Plate Mounting Bolts	27 (37)
Transmission Housing Mounting Bolts	
12 mm Bolts	47 (64)
10 mm Bolts	25 (34)
Differential	
Carrier Bearing Cap Bolts	
Left-Hand	14 (19)
Right-Hand	53 (72)
Carrier Cover Bolts	18 (24)
Counter Driven Gear Mounting Nut	127 (172)
Maximum Torque (Preload Adj.)	213 (289)
Ring Gear Mounting Bolts	71 (96)
Side Bearing Retainer	14 (19)

	INCH Lbs. (N.m)
Cam Assembly Mounting Bolt	65 (7.2)
Detent Spring Mounting Bolts	89 (10)
Lower-to-Upper Valve Body Attaching Bolts	44-52 (4.9-5.8)
Manual Valve & Body Attaching Bolts	89 (10)
Oil Pan Attaching Bolts	43 (4.8)
Oil Strainer Attaching Bolts	89 (10)
Parking Pawl Mounting Bolt	165 (7.2)
Speed Sensor Bracket Bolt	108 (12)
Stator Shaft-to-Oil Pump Attaching Bolts	89 (10)
Tube Bracket Attaching Bolts	89 (10)
Upper-to-Lower Valve Body Attaching Bolts	44-52 (4.9-5.8)
Valve Body Mounting Bolts	89 (10)

VOLKSWAGEN TYPE 010 3-SPEED

Jetta, Rabbit, Scirocco

TRANSAXLE IDENTIFICATION

Transmission type may be identified by a group of numbers cast into top of case, behind the center case rib, near the ATF dipstick. One of the numbers is "010". This denotes the VW "two planetary" type transmission.

Transmission used in diesel engined Jetta and Rabbit models (and some gas models) includes an "E-Mode" option. Models equipped with this transmission can be identified by an "E" position between "N" and "D" on the shift console.

Transmission model may be identified by a group of figures stamped into the top of the converter housing near the governor. Figures consist of a model code ("TK" and "TN" with gas engine, "TH" for non "E-Mode" with diesel engine or "TM" for "E-Mode" with diesel engine) and a build date code.

The differential is identified by either a stamping (4 semi-circles at 90° to each other within a circle) or a cast "E" mark on the differential housing.

NOTE: All references to "Rabbit" include Convertible.

DESCRIPTION

Transaxle assembly consists of 2 main units: Automatic transmission and final drive assembly. The transmission housing contains 2 planetary gear sets, 2 multiple-disc clutches, 1 brake band and servo, 1 multiple-disc brake, a 1-way clutch and a hydraulic control system. The final drive housing contains torque converter, governor for transmission, three-gear type ring and pinion assembly and differential unit.

Transmissions with "E-Mode" operation are designed to improve fuel economy. The transmission valve body has redesigned ATF passages and some additional valves. The forward clutch is also redesigned. With selector lever in "E" position, transmission is disengaged from differential whenever accelerator pedal is released. In any other selector lever position, transmission operates the same as the conventional model.

CAUTION: Never tow a vehicle with this automatic transmission with the front wheels on the ground. Bearings can be damaged by lack of lubrication. If vehicle must be towed, place selector in "N" and lift front wheels. Do not tow vehicle backwards.

LUBRICATION & ADJUSTMENT

See appropriate AUTOMATIC TRANSMISSION SERVICING article in IMPORT GENERAL SERVICING section.

Fig. 1: Cross-Sectional View of Volkswagen Type 010 3-Speed Automatic Transmission Assembly

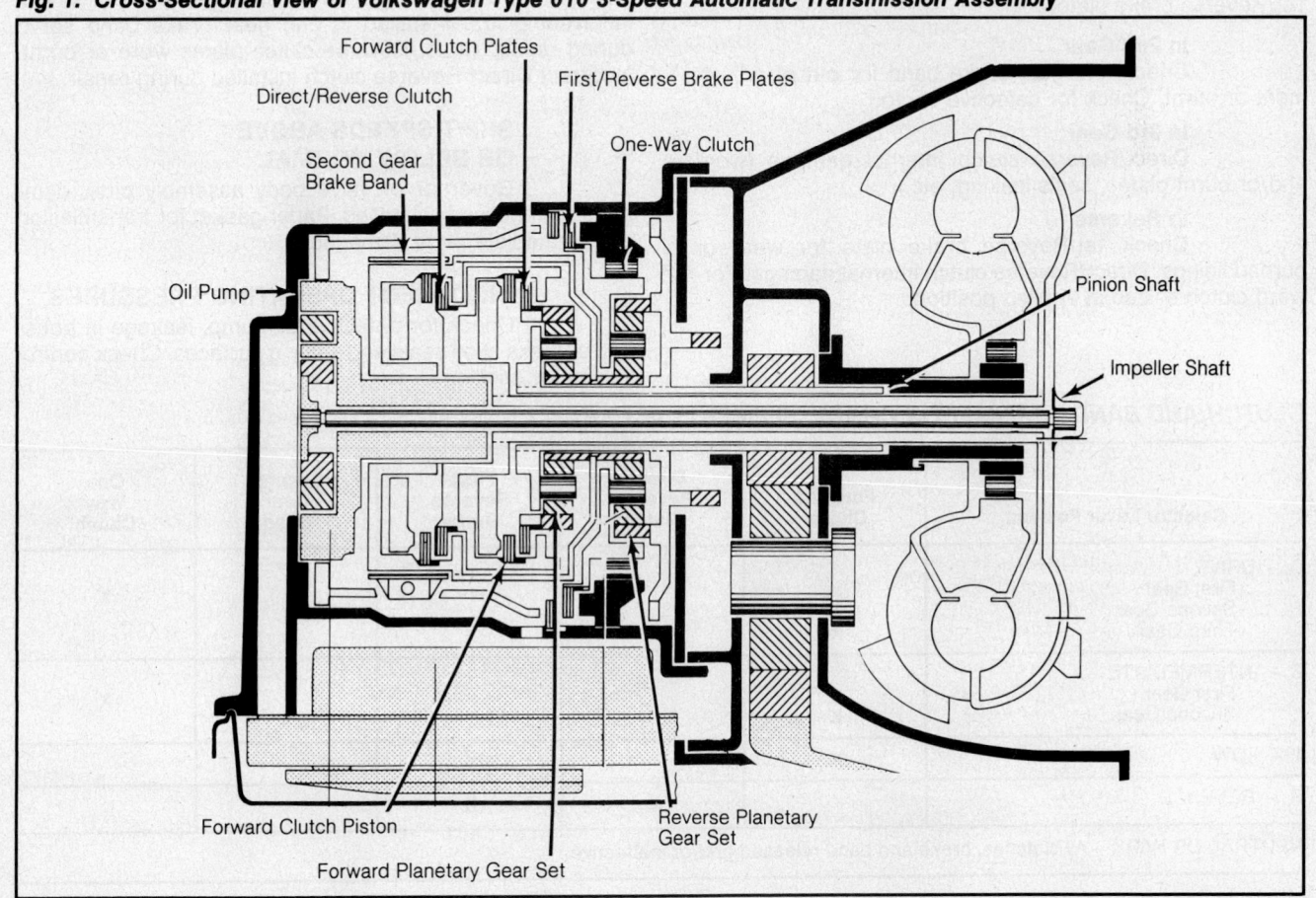

Automatic Transmissions
VOLKSWAGEN TYPE 010 3-SPEED

SERVICE (IN VEHICLE)

DRIVE AXLE SHAFTS
& WHEEL BEARINGS

See SERVICE (IN VEHICLE) in Volkswagen Jetta, Pickup, Rabbit & Scirocco 4 & 5-Speed Manual Transaxle article.

TROUBLE SHOOTING

NOTE: The trouble shooting diagnosis steps are arranged in the order of probability.

NO MOVEMENT
In Any Gear

Low ATF fluid level. Manual lever cable disconnected from manual valve. Drive plate broken or not bolted to torque converter. Main pressure valve sticking. Oil pump or pump drive faulty/no pressure. Broken gear or shaft, possibly in final drive.

In Forward Gears

Forward clutch internal damage (worn or burned plates, spring broken, seals leaking, etc.).

In 1st Gear (In "D" Or "2")

Check 1st gear 1-way clutch for slipping or forward clutch internal damage.

In 1st Gear (In "1")

Check transmission for worn and/or burnt 1st/Reverse brake plates.

In 2nd Gear

Check 2nd gear brake band for out of adjustment or burnt. Check for defective servo.

In 3rd Gear

Direct/Reverse clutch internal damage (worn and/or burnt plates, seals leaking, etc.).

In Reverse

Check 1st/Reverse brake plate for wear or burned linings. Direct/Reverse clutch internal damage. Forward clutch seized in applied position.

IRREGULAR MOVEMENT
In All Forward Gears

Check for low ATF fluid level and/or oil pump pick-up strainer partially clogged.

NO UPSHIFT
Into 2nd Gear

Governor drive defective. Governor dirty or improperly assembled during repair. Accumulator cover plate loose. Valve body assembly dirty. 1st/2nd gear shift valve sticking.

Into 3rd Gear

Governor dirty. Valve body assembly dirty. 2nd/3rd gear shift valve sticking. Sealing balls missing from transfer plate.

NO DOWNSHIFTS
Into 2nd And/Or 1st Gear

Governor or valve body dirty. Check 1st/2nd and/or 2nd/3rd gear shift valves for sticking, in valve body.

DELAYED ENGAGEMENT ON UPSHIFTS
1st-2nd

Fluid level too low. Valve body assembly dirty. 2nd gear brake band out of adjustment, worn or burnt. Incorrect piston installed in 2nd gear brake band servo during repair.

2nd-3rd

Fluid level too low. Valve body assembly dirty. 2nd gear brake band out of adjustment, worn or burnt. Incorrect piston installed in 2nd gear brake band servo during repair. Direct/Reverse clutch plates worn or burnt. Incorrect Direct/Reverse clutch installed during repair.

SHIFT SPEEDS ABOVE
OR BELOW NORMAL

Governor or valve body assembly dirty, damaged or improperly installed. Paper gasket for transmission or intermediate plate damaged.

INCORRECT OPERATING PRESSURES

Check for defective oil pump, leakage in housing, oil leaks at oil seals and sealing surfaces. Check control valves for sticking.

CLUTCH AND BAND APPLICATION CHART (ELEMENTS IN USE)

Selector Lever Position	Forward Clutch	Direct-Reverse Clutch	First-Reverse Brake	Second Gear Band	One Way Clutch
D – DRIVE					
First Gear	X				X
Second Gear	X			X	
Third Gear	X	X			
2 – INTERMEDIATE					
First Gear	X				X
Second Gear	X			X	
1 – LOW	X		X		
R – REVERSE		X	X		

NEUTRAL OR PARK – All clutches, brake and band released and/or ineffective.

IMPROPER "E-MODE" OPERATION
Transmission Does Not Disengage
From Engine At Closed Throttle
With Shift Lever In "E"

Accelerator cable or shift lever cable incorrectly adjusted. Main pressure is to high. Declutching valve in valve body sticking.

TESTING

ROAD TEST

1) Before road testing, be certain that fluid level, condition and control linkage adjustments have been checked and corrected as necessary. During test, transmission should upshift and downshift at approximately the speeds shown in chart. See SHIFT SPEED SPECIFICATIONS.

2) All shifts may vary somewhat due to production tolerances or tire size. The important factor is the quality of the shifts. All shifts should be smooth, responsive and with no slippage or engine speed runaway.

3) Slippage or engine runaway in any gear usually indicates clutch, band or brake problems. The slipping unit in a particular gear can usually be identified by noting transmission operation in other selector positions and comparing which internal units are applied in those positions. See CLUTCH & BAND APPLICATION Chart.

4) This process of elimination can be used to detect any unit which slips and to confirm proper operation of good units. However, the actual cause of the malfunction usually cannot be easily decided.

5) Practically any condition can be caused by leaking hydraulic circuits or sticking valves. Therefore, unless an obvious condition exists, do not disassemble transmission until hydraulic pressure tests have been made.

NOTE: If shift points are incorrect or transmission does not kick down, check accelerator cable adjustments.

HYDRAULIC PRESSURE TEST

NOTE: To properly check hydraulic pressure, tests should be made on a dynamometer. If necessary, full throttle test may be made while driving vehicle on highway.

CAUTION: The engine idle speed must be adjusted to specification when performing pressure tests or readings will be inaccurate.

1) Connect 0-150 psi (0-10 kg/cm²) pressure gauge to main pressure test point on case (adjacent to servo cover). See Fig. 2. Run engine until transmission is at normal operating temperature. Place selector lever in "D". Run engine to over 31 MPH, release throttle and read pressure on gauge (with engine idling).

2) With transmission in "D", run engine at full throttle (with vehicle speed above 31 MPH). Note pressure. With vehicle at rest, place selector lever in "R" position. Note reading on pressure gauge with engine idling.

3) Pressures in each part of test should be as shown in chart. See MAIN PRESSURES chart. If pressures obtained do not match those shown in chart, refer to INCORRECT OPERATING PRESSURES in TROUBLE SHOOTING section. Remove pressure gauge and install pressure tap plug.

SHIFT SPEED SPECIFICATIONS

Application	Shift Points (MPH)[1]	
	Full Throttle	Kickdown
Transmission I.D. Codes "TF", "TK" & "TN"		
1st-2nd Upshift	21-33	37-39
2nd-3rd Upshift	50-61	64-66
3rd-2nd Downshift	36-48	61-63
2nd-1st Downshift	15-18	26-29
Transmission I.D. Code "TH"		
1st-2nd Upshift	23-27	34-37
2nd-3rd Upshift	49-61	58-60
3rd-2nd Downshift	32-45	53-55
2nd-1st Downshift	17-21	28-30
Transmission I.D. Code "TM"		
1st-2nd Upshift	21-24	35-37
2nd-3rd Upshift	50-61	61-62
3rd-2nd Downshift	33-45	56-58
2nd-1st Downshift	16-19	30-33

[1] – When checking the shift points, the speedometer readings may vary within permissible manufacturing tolerances.

MAIN PRESSURES

Application	psi (kg/cm²)
"D" @ Idle [1]	42-44 (2.9-3.0)
"D" @ Full Throttle [2]	85-86 (5.85-5.95)
"R" @ Idle [1]	131-145 (9.0-10.0)

[1] – Test should be performed on a dynamometer whenever possible. Perform idle test with vehicle stationary.

[2] – Full throttle test up to more than 31 MPH.

Fig. 2: View of Transmission Case Showing Pressure Test Connection

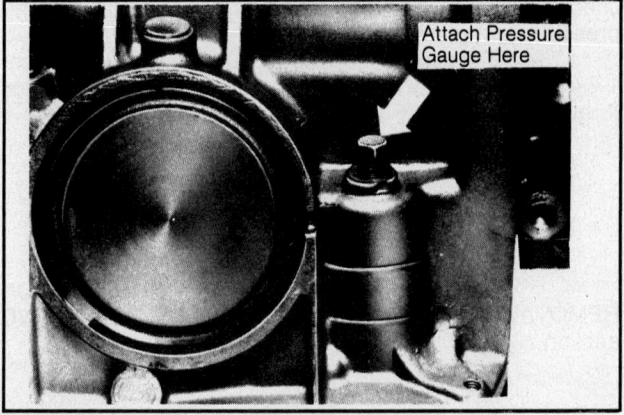

Attach Pressure Gauge Here

Only if defect cannot be found during other checks should a pressure check be carried out.

STALL SPEED TEST

Testing Precautions

Check stall speed only if vehicle shows poor performance or acceleration (despite a properly tuned engine). When making test, do not hold throttle open any longer than the time it takes to read tachometer or torque convertor will overheat. Maximum stall speed test time is 20 seconds (5 seconds with "E-Mode"). If test must be repeated, wait at least 20 seconds.

If engine speed exceeds limits shown, release accelerator immediately as clutch or band slippage is indicated. See STALL SPEED SPECIFICATIONS.

Testing Procedure

1) With engine at normal operating temperature, connect a tachometer to engine. Start engine and set parking and service brakes. Place selector lever in "D".

2) Depress accelerator briefly to full throttle and note maximum RPM obtained. Repeat test with selector lever in "1" position. Engine speed should be within limits shown in table.

NOTE: **Normal stall speed will drop about 125 RPM per 3200 feet altitude (4000 feet with "E-Mode"). Also, stall speed will drop slightly at high ambient temperature.**

STALL SPEED SPECIFICATIONS

Application	Stall RPM
Transmission Code Letters	
TF [1]	2300-2600
TH [2]	2500-2800
TM [3]	2555-2805
Engine Size	
1.5L	2250-2500
1.6L	2100-2350
1.7L	2200-2500

[1] – Torque convertor code letter "M".
[2] – Torque convertor code letter "X".
[3] – With "E-Mode".

Test Results

1) If stall speed is too high in "D", but OK in "1", 1-way clutch is defective. If stall speed is too high in both ranges, forward clutch is faulty.

2) If stall speed is about 200 RPM below normal, check engine operation (ignition timing, fuel injection, compression, pump timing).

3) If stall speed is about 400 RPM too low, stator 1-way clutch in torque converter is defective. Replace torque converter.

REMOVAL & INSTALLATION

TRANSAXLE ASSEMBLY

See appropriate AUTOMATIC TRANSMISSION REMOVAL article in IMPORT GENERAL SERVICING section.

TORQUE CONVERTER

NOTE: **The torque convertor only requires removal when seal or bushing replacement is needed or to clean unit when transmission failure has contaminated the ATF.**

CAUTION: **Do not rock or tilt convertor during removal or installation. Damage to seal, stator 1-way clutch or other components in convertor hub can occur.**

Removal

Remove transaxle assembly. Remove wire or securing bar that was installed across mouth of bellhousing during transaxle removal. Hold torque convertor with both hands while pulling it (with a twisting motion) off its support tube on final drive housing.

Cleaning & Inspection

1) Torque converter is a sealed unit and cannot be disassembled for service. Replace the unit if leaky or noisy, loose welds are evident or if stall speed test shows unit to be faulty.

2) When charred material from a burned clutch disc or other pollutants have entered the ATF, residual pollutants must be removed from torque convertor. Attach a piece of plastic hose (with 5/16" I.D.) to a plastic squeeze bottle.

3) Ensure both hose connection and cap are an airtight fit on bottle. If necessary, cut free end of hose at an angle to allow it to lay nearly flat against lowest part of convertor interior.

4) Lay convertor on work surface with one side elevated (low side toward hose and bottle). Place bottle lower than convertor. Squeeze bottle and insert hose in convertor. Release bottle and, as soon as ATF begins to flow, loosen cap to allow air to escape. Siphon out remaining ATF.

5) If torque convertor requires replacement, inspect convertor for identification code mark (stamped on boss on outside diameter of unit). Ensure the same code is stamped on replacement unit. See TORQUE CONVERTOR CODE LETTER & APPLICATION table.

NOTE: **A leaking oil seal is ofter caused by a worn bushing in convertor hub. Check bushing for excessive wear or out-of-round whenever seal is replaced.**

Oil Seal Replacement

1) Check converter hub seal seat for scoring, pitting or excessive wear. If seal seat on hub is rough, worn or damaged, replace converter. Do not attempt to smooth seal contact area of convertor with emery cloth.

NOTE: **Ensure oil seal seat edge is chamfered. If not, round front edge with emery cloth to prevent seal damage during convertor installation.**

2) Remove any sharp edges and burrs with fine emery cloth. Do not damage surface where oil seal makes contact. If removal is necessary, note installed position, pry off oil seal and discard. Clean seal seat.

3) Dip new oil seal in clean ATF and drive into position using Oil Seal Installer (US4450). Do not allow gas or solvent to contact silicone-type seal or seal must be replaced.

NOTE: **Torque convertor replacement bushings are manufactured to size and require no reaming or honing.**

VOLKSWAGEN TYPE 010 3-SPEED (Cont.)

TORQUE CONVERTOR CODE LETTER & APPLICATION

Application	Code Letter
1.5L Engine (Gas)	U
1.6L Engine (Gas)	M
1.6L Engine (Diesel)	X
1.7L Engine (Gas)	K

Bushing Replacement

1) Check bushing I.D. for excessive wear and out-of-round using an inside micrometer. Bushing wear limit is 1.348" (34.25 mm) Maximum allowable out-of-round is .001" (.03 mm).

2) To replace bushing, assemble Bushing Pullers (VW201 and US691) and Adapter (US4452). Withdraw bushing from converter hub. *See Fig. 3.* Press new bushing into place using Bushing Drivers (VW412, VW420 and VW474) and Support (VW401).

Fig. 3: Removing Torque Converter Bushing

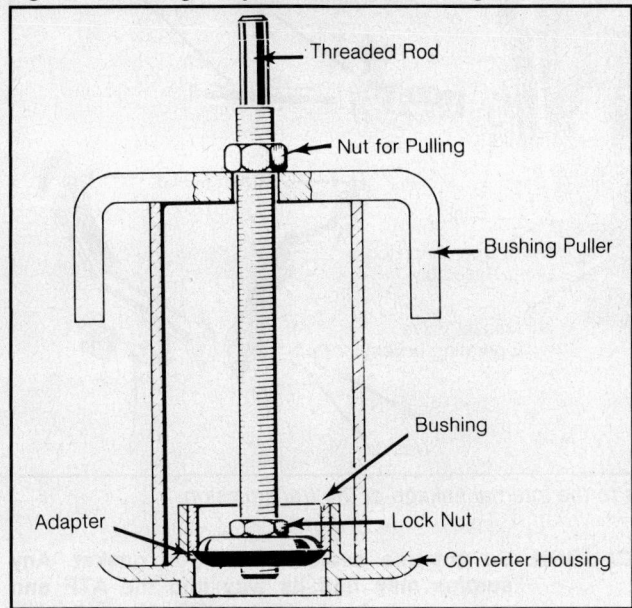

- Threaded Rod
- Nut for Pulling
- Bushing Puller
- Bushing
- Adapter
- Lock Nut
- Converter Housing

Ensure the converter housing is not damaged during bushing removal and installation.

Installation

1) Install torque convertor in reverse of removal procedure. Ensure pump shaft is completely seated in pump (inside transmission) by checking splined ends for proper length.

2) Correct pump shaft length is 13 15/16" (354 mm), measured from tip-to-tip. Install convertor by turning slowly clockwise and counterclockwise so turbine and pump shaft splines will engage.

TRANSMISSION INTERNAL LINKAGE (PARKING LOCK, KICKDOWN & MANUAL VALVE LINKAGE)

NOTE: The kickdown valve operating lever and parking lock operating rod have been modified. With modified operating rod, parking lock engagement lever is secured with only 1 circlip. The kickdown valve operating lever has been flattened slightly at contact surface. The new-type kickdown valve operating lever can be used on earlier transmissions. Do not install earlier-type operating lever in transmissions with new kickdown valve.

Removal & Disassembly

1) With ATF drained, oil pan detached and gasket discarded, remove valve body assembly from the transmission. Note linkage component locations for reassembly reference.

2) Remove "E" clip from parking lock operating lever pin. Detach parking lock pawl spring from under pawl. Detach "E" clip from operating rod guide pin. Pull operating rod assembly out of parking lever and detach from manual valve operating lever.

3) Slide parking lever off pin. From inside transmission case; detach small kickdown lever nut, with washer, from kickdown operating lever shaft. Remove kickdown valve operating lever.

4) Detach large manual lever retainer nut, with flat and lock washers, from cable lever. Slide manual lever off of cable lever. If necessary, pull cable lever from transmission case. Detach shaft and operating levers as needed. Discard "O" rings. *See Fig. 4.*

Inspection

1) Check parking lever roller and roller spring for excessive wear, damage and ease of movement. Inspect parking lock pawl, kickdown lever detent notches and manual lever detent notches for excessive wear or damage.

2) Check pin for parking lock pawl for location in case and straightness. If any linkage components are excessively worn or damaged, replace components as an assembly.

Reassembly & Installation

1) To complete installation, reverse removal procedures. To prevent ATF leaks when installing pin for parking lock pawl, ensure end of pin is flush with transmission case edge.

2) Install spring under parking lock pawl so that it will retract the pawl from engagement with notches in the periphery of the annular gear flange. Check the operation of the parking lock mechanism before installing valve body.

3) If cable lever was removed, install new "O" rings, lubricate with ATF and slide into transmission case. When installing operating lever for kickdown valve, ensure angled end of lever points toward center of transmission.

VALVE BODY ASSEMBLY

NOTE: The valve body assembly may be removed with transaxle in the vehicle.

Removal

1) Raise and support vehicle. Drain ATF. Detach oil pan mounting screws, remove oil pan and discard gasket. Detach mounting screws holding pump pick-up's ATF strainer to valve body assembly, then remove strainer.

2) Detach 10 (of 11) mounting bolts holding valve body assembly. Keep 1 bolt (near accumulator piston spring) installed so valve body does not fall.

3) While supporting valve body, remove remaining bolt. Remove valve body assembly. On transmissions through model No. 20 040, remove pump-to-valve body ATF strainer and discard. Do not replace this strainer.

4) If accumulator piston and spring require inspection, remove 3 galvanized screws from accumulator cover plate. Remove cover plate, spring and piston. If

Fig. 4: Bottom View of Transmission Case Showing Parking Lock, Kickdown & Manual Valve Linkage

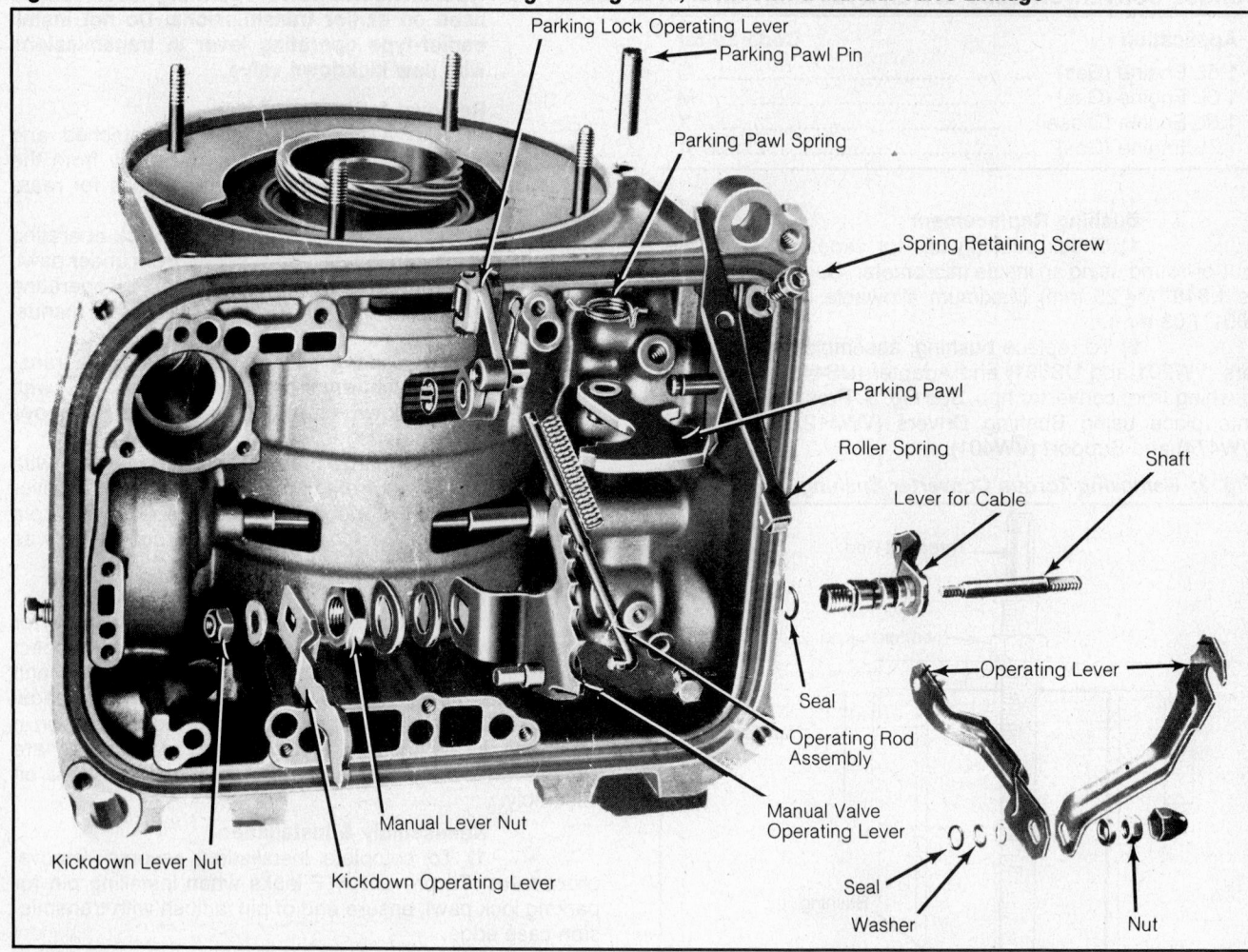

The oil pan and valve body assembly must be removed for access to the internal linkage of the transmission.

necessary, use circlip expanding pliers inserted into spring recess of piston to withdraw piston from transmission case. Inspect accumulator piston and note if sealing ring is separate or permanent type.

NOTE: On accumulator piston with separate sealing ring, install ring with lip toward pressure side of piston. Both separate and bonded sealing ring type pistons are interchangeable.

Installation
1) If accumulator piston was removed, lubricate sealing ring with ATF and install piston, spring and cover. Tighten mounting screws. If new valve body is being installed, ensure correct code letter of old valve body matches new valve body.

NOTE: The code letter is the only reliable indication that the valve body is suitable for the vehicle.

2) Position new valve body assembly on transmission with manual valve and kickdown valve correctly engaged with their operating levers. Attach valve body assembly to transmission case with 1 mounting bolt (near accumulator).

3) Install remaining bolts. Working in a diagonal patten, gradually tighten all mounting bolts. Install ATF strainer and tighten mounting bolts.

CAUTION: Do not use sealer on oil pan gasket. Any surplus may find its way into the ATF and cause control valve(s) to stick. Never tighten oil pan mounting bolts to more than 15 ft. lbs. (20 N.m) in an attempt to cure a leaking gasket. Overtightening will deform the pan and make it impossible to obtain a good seal. Always install a new gasket to correct leaks.

4) Install ATF oil pan (with new gasket) and tighten mounting bolts gradually, in a diagonal pattern. Refill transmission with new ATF, warm engine to operating temperature and recheck ATF level.

GOVERNOR

NOTE: Governor is located beneath a round, pressed steel cover on top of final drive housing, just right of transmission case. The cover is held in place with a spring wire clip. Governor may be removed with transaxle in vehicle.

1) Thoroughly clean governor housing and governor cover so that dirt cannot accidentally enter transaxle as cover is removed. Pry off spring wire clip that holds governor to transmission housing.

2) Remove cover and discard gasket. Withdraw governor by pulling with a twisting motion to allow drive gear to disengage from helical gear on transmission's annulus gear flange.

3) Inspect thrust plate and drive end of governor shaft for wear and/or scoring. Replace worn or damaged parts.

NOTE: Because replacing the entire governor could possibly change governor pressure, new governor shafts are available separately to replace those that are worn or damaged.

CAUTION: On transmission with I.D. code "TF", "TK" or "TN" and valve body code "FL", a new governor, with code letter "A", must be used. On transmission with I.D. code "TH" or "TM" and valve body code "GK", use new governor with code letter "B". The new governor may only be used with new type valve body. Previous type governor may also be used with new valve body.

Installation

Ensure governor assembly installed is the correct replacement part. To install governor assembly (with new gasket), reverse removal procedure. Turn governor, as it is installed, to engage drive gear.

TRANSMISSION HOUSING STUDS
Removal & Installation

If a transmission housing stud is broken or has damaged threads, replace stud with one of the same type. Transmission-to-final drive unit mounting studs (900 028 01) should project out of case no more than 1.732" (44 mm).

When replacing transmission mounting stud (Short Stud 014 517 01 and Long Stud 014 692 01), ensure stud projects the proper amount. Short stud should project .551" (14 mm) and long stud should project 1.339" (34 mm) from case.

TRANSAXLE DISASSEMBLY

NOTE: Final drive disassembly and reassembly procedures are covered at end of this article.

TRANSMISSION ASSEMBLY
Disassembly

1) With final drive housing/transmission assembly removed from vehicle, clean outside case thoroughly and disassemble in a clean area. When cleaning and wiping parts, use nylon cloth or paper towels. Common shop rags will leave lint that can interfere with transaxle's operation. Mount assembly on Repair Fixture (VW351 and VW309). Drain ATF from transmission.

CAUTION: When removing/installing torque converter, do not rock or tilt converter. This could damage the converter oil seal, stator 1-way clutch or other components in torque converter hub.

NOTE: Remove governor before separating transmission from final drive unit.

2) Withdraw torque converter from final drive housing using a twisting motion. Set converter aside and cover hub opening. Remove governor cover and gasket.

Pull governor from final drive housing. Use a clockwise twisting motion to disengage governor drive gear from gear on transmission annulus gear.

3) Turn transmission/final drive assembly so gear oil cannot leak. Remove 4 nuts from 1 3/4" (44 mm) transmission-to-final drive studs. Separate transmission case from final drive housing. Drain gear oil from final drive if unit is to be repaired.

4) Withdraw 13.937" (354 mm) long pump shaft and 10.44" (265.1 mm) long turbine shaft from transmission (check turbine shaft rings for wear and proper seating).

NOTE: Once transmission and final drive assemblies are separated, keep out dirt by covering open end of transmission when final drive is being worked on or both ends of final drive as transmission is being repaired.

5) Detach screws retaining separation plate in transmission case. Remove plate and discard gasket. Withdraw annulus gear assembly (governor drive gear/Reverse planetary ring gear) from case. *See Fig. 6.*

6) Withdraw needle bearing and thrust washer from top of reverse (front) planetary gear set (some models may have thrust washer in place of needle bearing).

7) Using screwdriver, pry out large circlip retaining 1-way clutch assembly in case. Fabricate 2 hooks from 3/16" welding rod. Using hooks, lift 1-way clutch, internally and externally splined 1st/Reverse gear brake discs (3 fiber and 3 steel) and the reverse planetary gear set from case. *See Fig. 5.*

Fig. 5: Removing 1-Way Clutch from Case

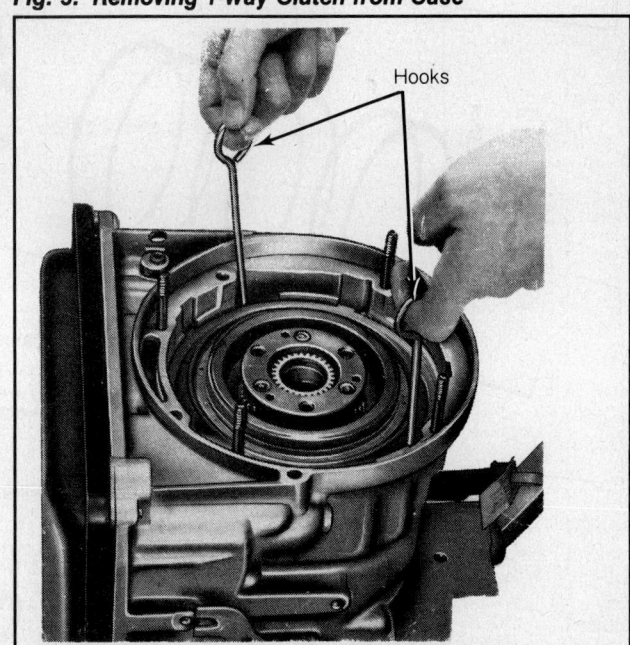

Use 2 fabricated hooks to lift assembly out of case.

8) Remove thrust washer(s). Withdraw apply shell (with internally splined washer), forward (rear) planetary gear set (with sun gear), needle bearing (some models may have thrust washer in place of needle bearing) and forward clutch as an assembly.

NOTE: When removing forward clutch assembly, ensure thrust washers and/or thrust needle bearing (radial-roller type) which oil pump rides against are not lost or damaged.

Fig. 6: *Exploded View of Automatic Transmission Assembly*

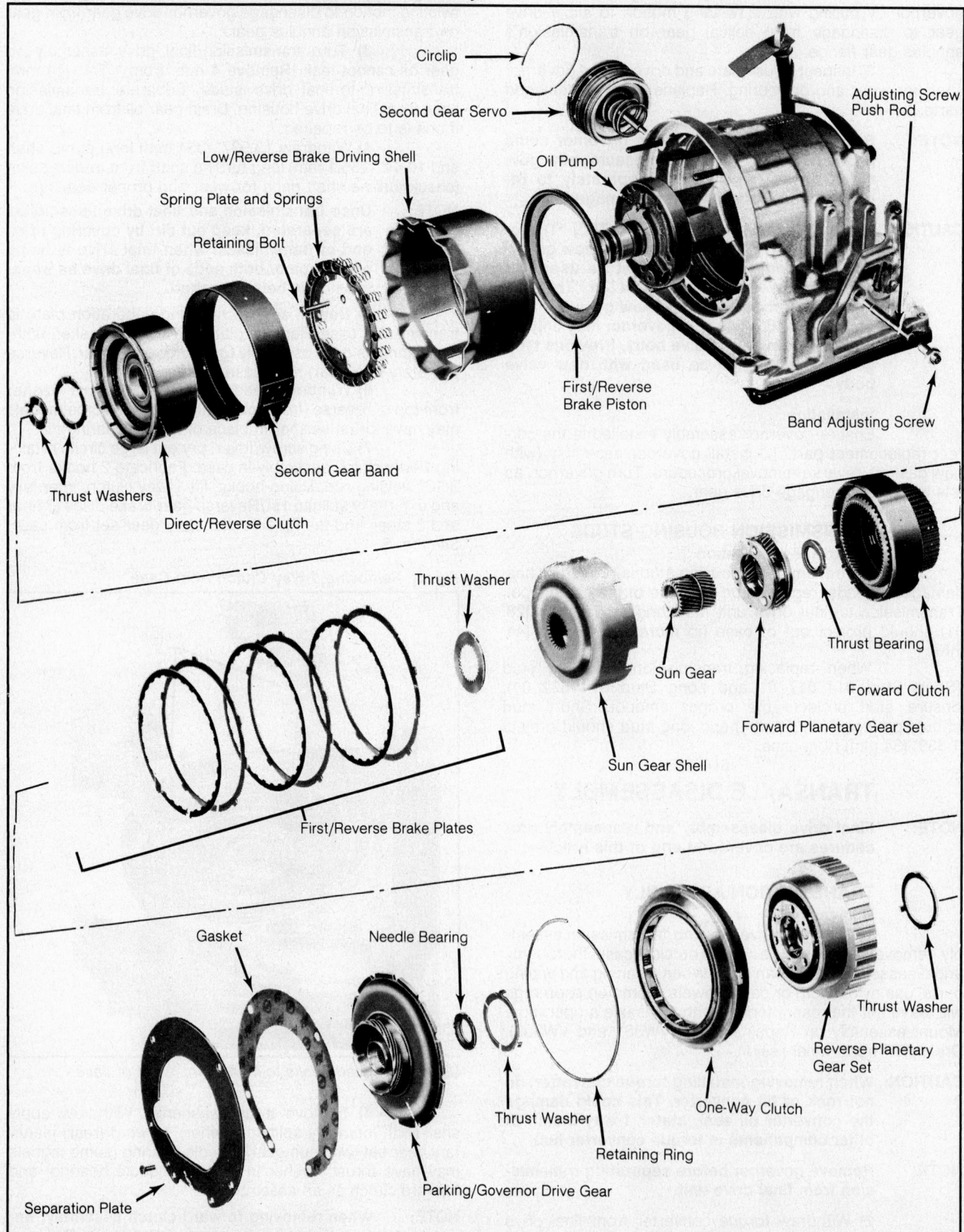

Circlip

Second Gear Servo

Adjusting Screw
Push Rod

Low/Reverse Brake Driving Shell

Oil Pump

Spring Plate and Springs

Retaining Bolt

First/Reverse
Brake Piston

Band Adjusting Screw

Thrust Washers

Second Gear Band

Direct/Reverse Clutch

Thrust Washer

Thrust Bearing

Sun Gear

Forward Clutch

Forward Planetary Gear Set

First/Reverse Brake Plates

Sun Gear Shell

Gasket

Needle Bearing

Thrust Washer

Reverse Planetary
Gear Set

Thrust Washer

One-Way Clutch

Retaining Ring

Separation Plate

Parking/Governor Drive Gear

9) Remove forward clutch-to-Direct/Reverse clutch thrust washer and radial-roller thrust bearing (some models may have thrust washer in place of bearing). Push 2nd gear brake band servo piston assembly down into transmission case. Remove retaining circlip. Withdraw servo assembly (cover, piston and spring) from case.

10) If servo assembly sticks, tap cover with rubber mallet until piston pops out under spring pressure. On opposite side of case, loosen lock nut for 2nd gear brake band adjusting screw. Detach screw (with lock nut) and withdraw push rod. Remove Direct/Reverse clutch from case. From inside case, withdraw 2nd gear brake band. Remove 5 bolts from 1st/Reverse gear brake spring plate.

11) Withdraw plate and springs. Pull 1st/Reverse apply shell, brake piston and ATF oil pump assembly from case. Position transmission case on bench with oil pan facing upward. Remove pan mount bolts. Withdraw pan and gasket. Remove oil strainer screws from valve body.

NOTE: An inspection of any foreign matter in the oil pan can indicate the type of problems to look for while disassembling transaxle.

12) Remove 11 hex-head mount bolts from valve body. Lift valve body from case. Use care not to lose manual valve. Withdraw accumulator spring and piston from case. If necessary for parts replacement, disassemble parking lock, kickdown and manual valve linkage. *See Fig. 4.*

COMPONENT DISASSEMBLY & REASSEMBLY

OIL PUMP ASSEMBLY

NOTE: There are 2 ATF pumps available, 1 with a thrust washer and 1 with a radial-roller thrust bearing. The pump installed determines the type of forward clutch drum and turbine shaft used.

Disassembly

1) To remove metal sealing rings, first unhooking small ring ends with needle nose pliers. Carefully remove small ring from front of pump housing. Unhook large ring end and remove ring from housing.

2) Remove thrust washer or radial-roller thrust bearing from front of pump housing. Hold cover plate tight against housing (plate is under spring tension). Remove 2 cover plate mounting screws (4 mm) and cover plate.

3) Remove the 7/16" (11 mm) check ball and spring. Withdraw pump drive plate. Mark pump gears for reassembly reference and remove gears. *See Fig. 7.*

Inspection
Wash all parts in solvent and air dry. Blow out oil passages with compressed air. Check parts for wear, scoring, chipped teeth or any other damage. Replace parts as necessary.

Reassembly

1) Coat pump gears with ATF. Install gears into pump housing, aligning marks made at disassembly. Position drive plate on top of inner gear. Ensure extended hub of drive plate is inserted into shaft opening of housing. Set check ball, with spring, in housing.

2) Place cover plate over rear of assembly. Compress spring and check ball, taking care not to displace them. Install and tighten cover-to-housing screws. Install thrust washer so that claws on washer face away from piston ring grooves and are engaged on lug on pump housing. *See Fig. 7.*

3) Install large and small sealing rings with ends locked together. To check for proper oil pump operation, insert pump shaft into oil pump and rotate gears. Pump assembly must rotate freely, with no sticking or binding.

CAUTION: If pump's internal parts are jammed or binding, owing to incorrect assembly or installation, severe damage can result when engine is started.

Fig. 7: Exploded View of Oil Pump Assembly

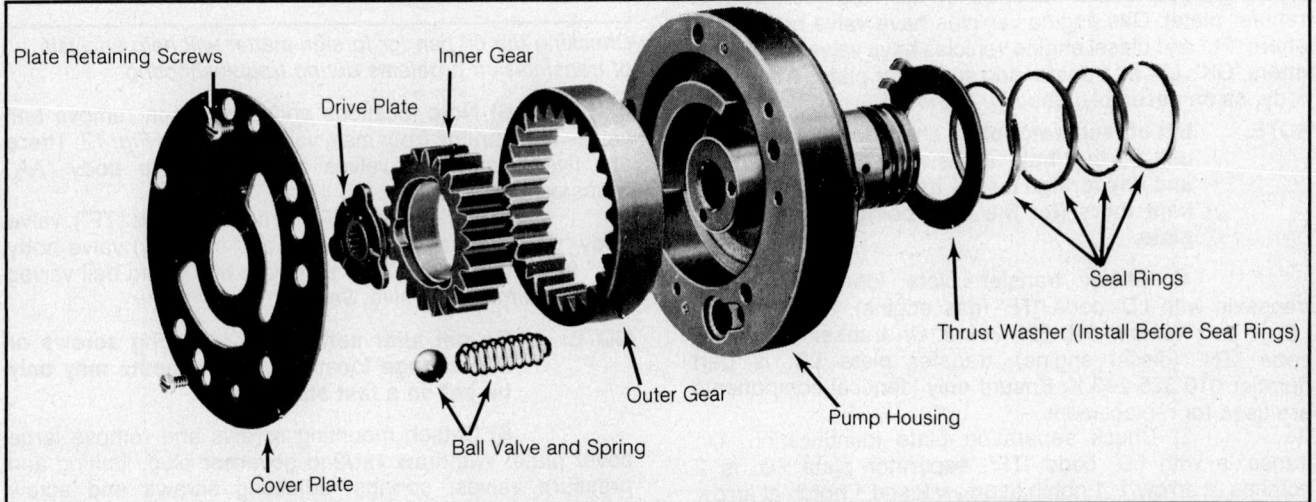

The thrust washer must be installed on pump housing before the clutch piston sealing rings are installed.

VALVE BODY ASSEMBLY
Disassembly Precautions

As a rule, valve body disassembly is necessary only for cleaning. Disassemble valve body if ATF is very dirty or contaminated by large solid particles. Otherwise, immerse complete valve body assembly in cleaning fluid and blow dry with compressed air. Do not hold air jet so close that it moves the valves violently or spring damage can occur.

Valve body components, especially the springs, are very similar in appearance. If removed, ensure all components are separated and marked for identification, for reassembly reference.

Spring washers are no longer used in the following locations:
- Detent spring-to-transmission housing.
- Oil pump-to-transmission housing.
- End (cover) plate-to-valve body assembly.
- Support plate-to-transfer plate.
- Transfer plate-to-valve body assembly.
- Oil strainer-to-transfer plate.
- Oil pan-to-transmission housing.
- Support tube-to-final drive.
- Speedometer drive-to-final drive.
- Oil filler pipe-to-transmission.

When disassembling late model transmission, check previously listed bolts and nuts for a spring washer. If equipped, reinstall bolts and nuts with new spring washers.

Disassembly

1) With ATF drained and oil pan and gasket detached, remove valve body assembly from transmission. Remove oil strainer-to-valve body mount screws. Remove strainer cover, strainer and gasket. See Fig. 8.

2) Note position of galvanized valve body (accumulator piston cover) mounting screws for reassembly reference. Remove 3 galvanized screws, then remove 19 transfer plate-to-main valve body mounting screws.

NOTE: When removing and disassembling valve body components, ensure valve body I.D. tag remains on valve body assembly during repairs.

3) Inspect valve body for proper identification by checking code letters stamped on I.D. tag (screwed to transfer plate). Gas engine vehicles have valve body code letters "FL" and diesel engine vehicles have valve body code letters "GK". Lift off transfer and separator plates from main body, as an assembly. See Fig. 9 and 10.

NOTE: Lift off separator plate and transfer plate as a unit so that ball valves remain in valve body and any foreign matter in transfer plate will be kept there (for the time being) by separator plate.

4) Check transfer plate identification. On transaxle with I.D. code "TF" (gas engine), transfer plate I.D. is part number 010 325 283 J. On transaxle with I.D. code "TH" (diesel engine), transfer plate I.D. is part number 010 325 283 K. Ensure only identical components are used for replacement.

5) Check separation plate identification. On transaxle with I.D. code "TF", separator plate I.D. is 2 notches at arrow 1, 1 notch at arrow 2 and 1 notch at arrow 3. See Fig. 11. On transaxle with I.D. code "TH", separator plate I.D. is 3 notches at arrow 1, 2 notches at arrow 2 and 1 notch at arrow 3. Ensure only identical components are used for replacement.

Fig. 8: Exploded View of Oil Pan, Oil Strainer Components, Valve Body Assembly & Transmission Case

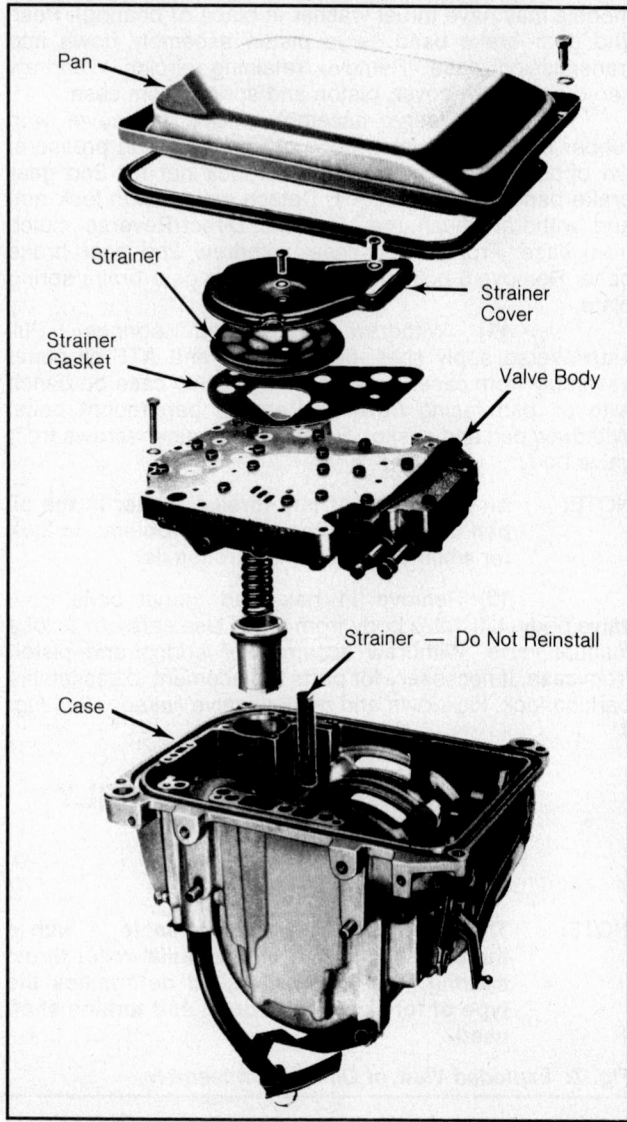

Pan

Strainer

Strainer Cover

Strainer Gasket

Valve Body

Strainer — Do Not Reinstall

Case

Checking the oil pan for foreign matter will help analysis of transmission problems during troubleshooting.

6) Note locations and sizes, then remove ball valves and springs from main valve body. See Fig. 12. There are five 6 mm ball valves in (early) valve body "AA" (transaxle code "EQ").

7) In valve body "FL" (transaxle code "TF"), valve body "GK" (transaxle code "TH") and in (early) valve body "BL" (transaxle code "TB"), there are five 6 mm ball valves and one 3 mm ball valve. See Fig. 12.

NOTE: Do not alter settings of adjusting screws or interchange locations. Adjustments may only be set on a test stand.

8) Detach mounting screws and remove large cover plate. Withdraw 1st/2nd governor plug, limiting and pressure valves, springs, adjusting screws and screw sleeves. Do not turn adjusting screws, they are factory set and can only be reset on a test stand.

9) Remove remaining cover plates one at a time and withdraw all valves, plugs, springs, spring seats and

VOLKSWAGEN TYPE 010 3-SPEED (Cont.)

Fig. 9: *Exploded View Of Transfer Plate, Separation Plate & Valve Body Assembly (Gas Engine)*

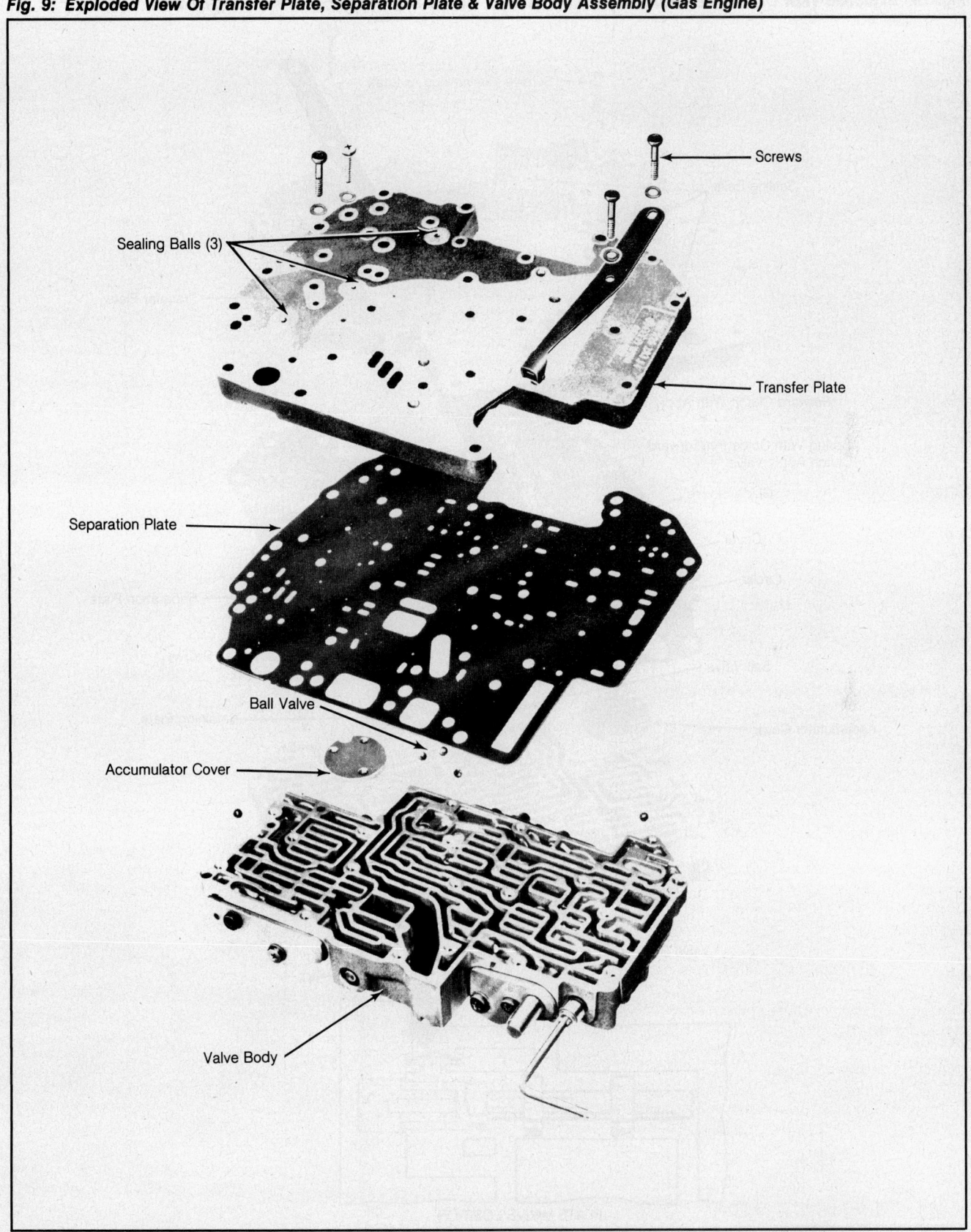

Transaxle (I.D. code "TF") components shown are transfer plate (010 325 283 J), separation plate (see step 5) and valve body (I.D. code "FL").

Automatic Transmissions
VOLKSWAGEN TYPE 010 3-SPEED (Cont.)

Fig. 10: *Exploded View Of Transfer Plate, Separation Plate & Valve Body Assembly (Diesel Engine With "E-Mode")*

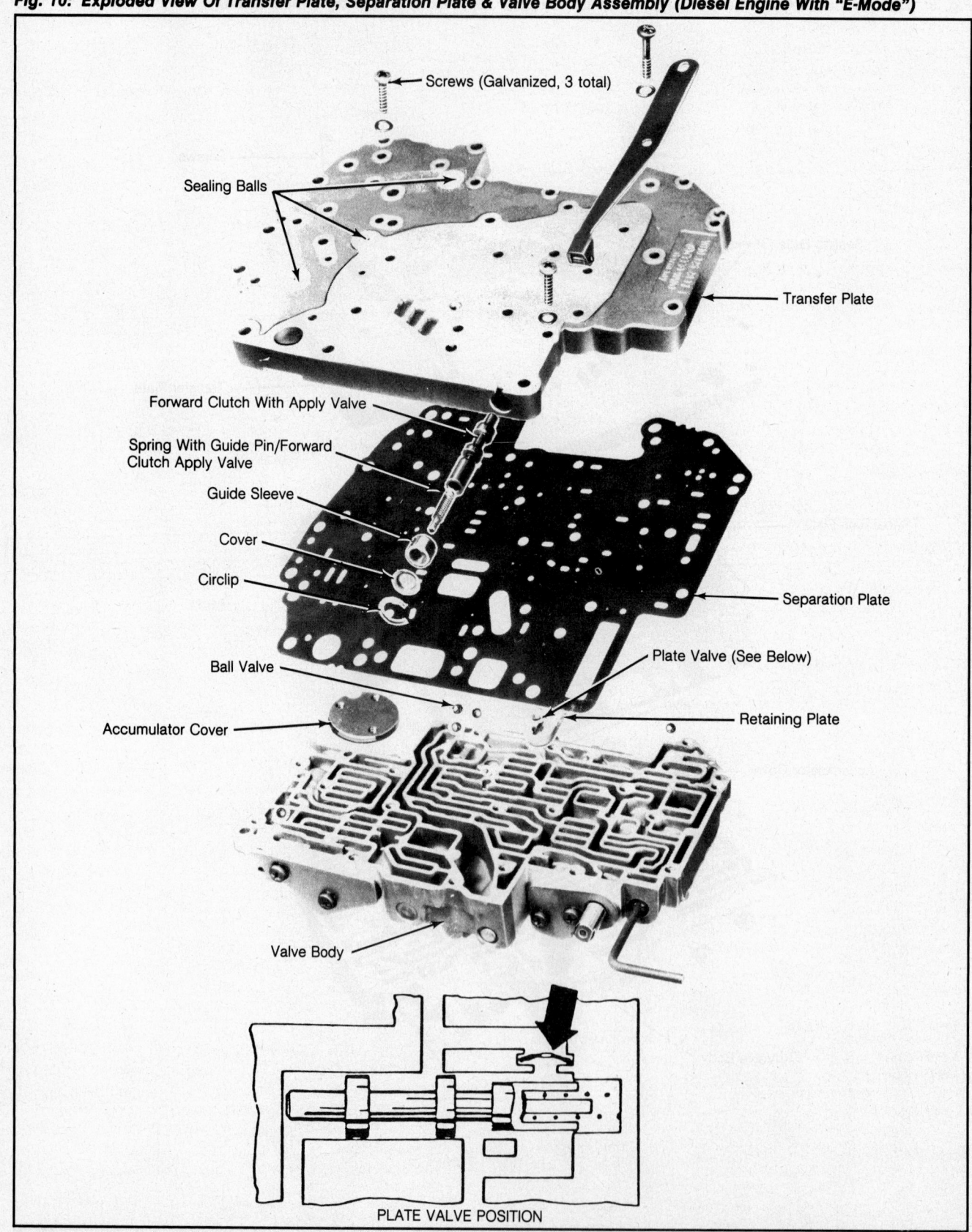

Transaxle (I.D. code "TH") componets shown are transfer plate (010 325 283 K), separation plate (see step 5) and valve body (I.D. code "GK").

Fig. 11: Separation Plate Identification

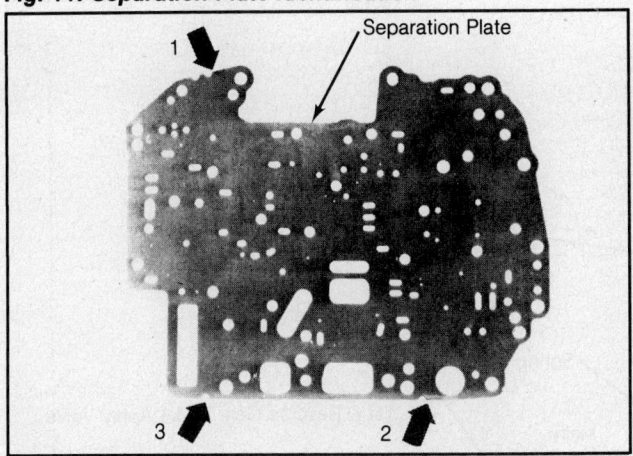

Check for the proper separation plate identification by inspecting the number of notches at arrow locations.

Fig. 12: Location of Check Balls in Valve Body

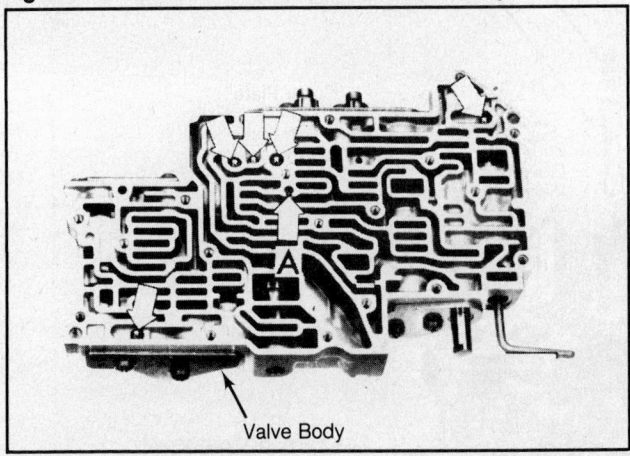

Valve Body

The diameter of check ball "A" is .12" (3 mm). All other check balls are .24" (6 mm).

adjusting screws (with sleeves). Tag all components, or arrange in relationship to valve body, to ensure correct reassembly.

Inspection

1) Disassemble valve body and place components in Compartmental Storage Tray (2008). If necessary, use a brass rod to press out sticking or tight-fitting valves. Wash all parts in solvent and air dry only. Check all parts for burrs and scores.

CAUTION: **Do not wash components in water or use fluffy rags for drying as rust and lint will cause valves to stick in bores.**

2) Replace assembly if excessive wear, rust or damage is found. When valves are clean and lubricated with fluid, they should fall of their own weight in respective bore. If not, inspect valves and body for valve or bore damage. Used valves must be returned to their original locations. Do not install a used valve in place of some other valve that is physically identical.

NOTE: **Several valve body springs have the same dimensions but are not interchangeable due to different tolerances. Ensure all springs are the**

correct type for the application and are installed in their proper positions.

CAUTION: **If springs are not kept separate and marked for identification, each spring must be measured with a micrometer (prior to reassembly) in order to find its correct position.**

3) Check all springs for damage and collapsed coils. Take care not to disturb settings of adjusting screws; pressures affected by these screws can only be measured and adjusted accurately on a test stand.

4) If transmission was disassembled due to failure to shift into 3rd gear, trouble may be caused by a missing sealing ball in transfer plate. If any ball is missing, use following procedure to install replacement balls.

5) To install new sealing ball, stick .118" (3 mm) diameter ball to end of 8 mm punch with small amount of grease. Drive the ball flush into the transfer plate hole. See Fig. 13.

Fig. 13: View of Valve Body Showing Location of Transfer Plate Sealing Balls

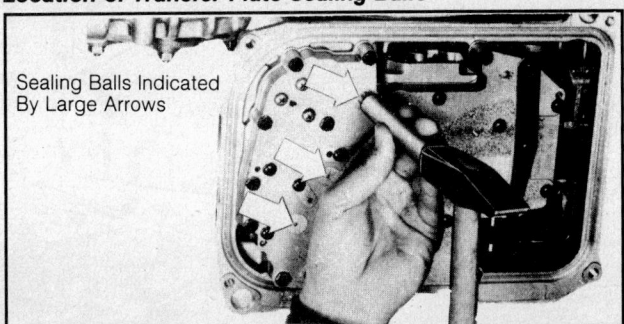

Sealing Balls Indicated By Large Arrows

Drive new sealing balls into place with 8 mm punch.

Reassembly

1) Lubricate all parts with ATF. Install valve components into proper valve body bores in reverse order of removal. If used valves are installed, ensure valves are returned to their original locations. Make sure all valves slide freely in bores.

CAUTION: **Do not overtighten cover plate mounting screws or valve body may distort and cause valve(s) to stick.**

2) Ensure check balls are installed in proper body passages. Install transfer plate-to-main body screws and tighten from center outward. Install valve body onto transmission case so that manual valve and kickdown valve are correctly engaged with their operating levers. Tighten valve body mounting bolts to 35 INCH lbs. (4 N.m), in a diagonal pattern.

3) Install new oil strainer assembly. Install oil pan, with new gasket, and tighten mount bolts to 14 ft. lbs. (19 N.m) maximum. Install final drive housing if removed. Refill transmission with ATF, install transaxle assembly and road test vehicle for proper operation.

GOVERNOR

NOTE: **Disassemble governor only if it contains debris from burnt clutch plates or brake band linings. Otherwise, just clean in solvent and blow dry with compressed air.**

CAUTION: **Ensure a new, matching governor is installed whenever a new valve body is installed, even if old governor is still serviceable.**

Automatic Transmissions
VOLKSWAGEN TYPE 010 3-SPEED (Cont.)

Fig. 14: Exploded View of Main Valve Body Assembly

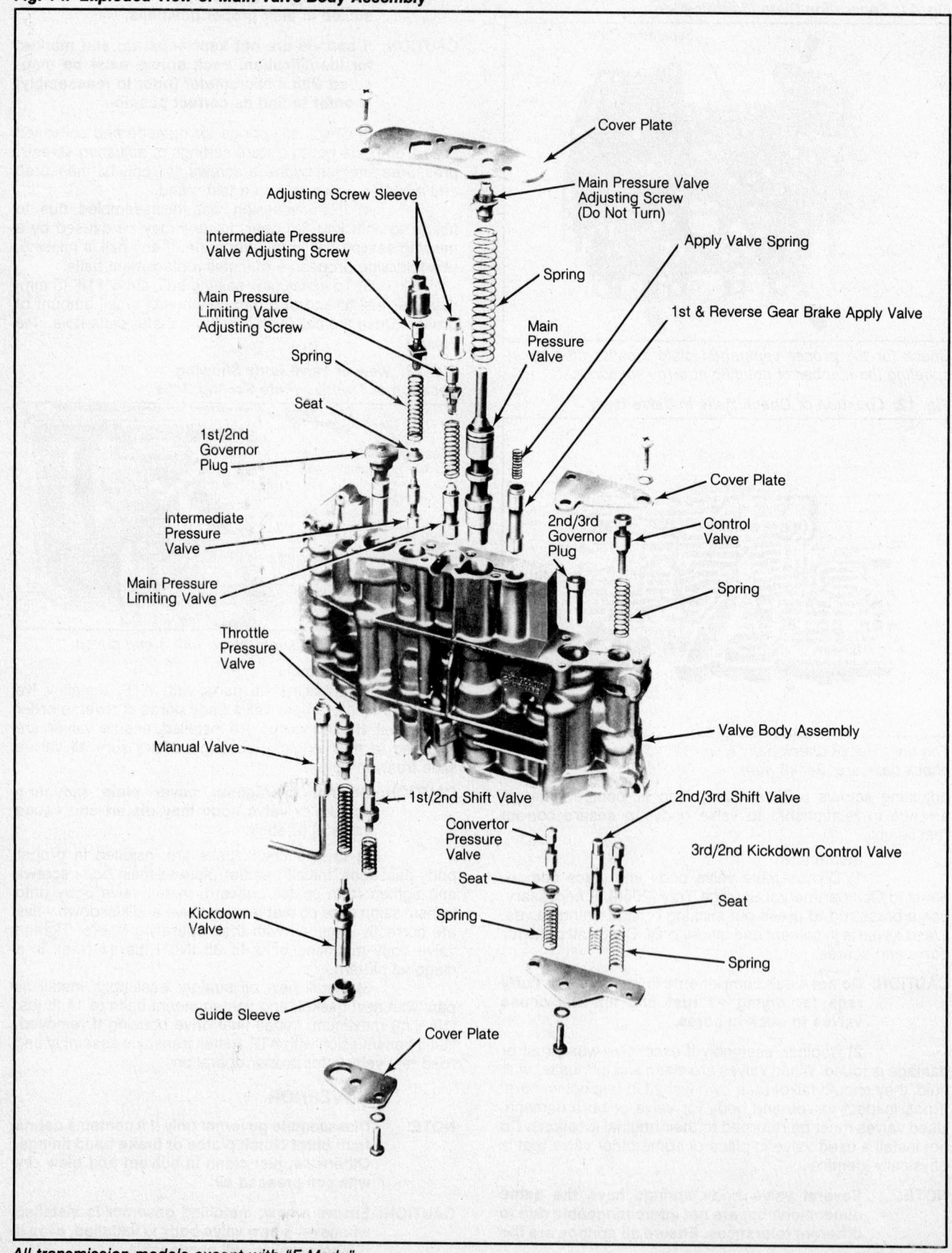

Cover Plate

Main Pressure Valve Adjusting Screw (Do Not Turn)

Adjusting Screw Sleeve

Apply Valve Spring

Intermediate Pressure Valve Adjusting Screw

Spring

1st & Reverse Gear Brake Apply Valve

Main Pressure Limiting Valve Adjusting Screw

Main Pressure Valve

Spring

Seat

1st/2nd Governor Plug

Cover Plate

2nd/3rd Governor Plug

Control Valve

Intermediate Pressure Valve

Spring

Main Pressure Limiting Valve

Throttle Pressure Valve

Valve Body Assembly

Manual Valve

2nd/3rd Shift Valve

1st/2nd Shift Valve

Convertor Pressure Valve

3rd/2nd Kickdown Control Valve

Seat

Seat

Kickdown Valve

Spring

Spring

Guide Sleeve

Spring

Cover Plate

All transmission models except with "E-Mode".

Fig. 15: *Exploded View of Main Valve Body Assembly*

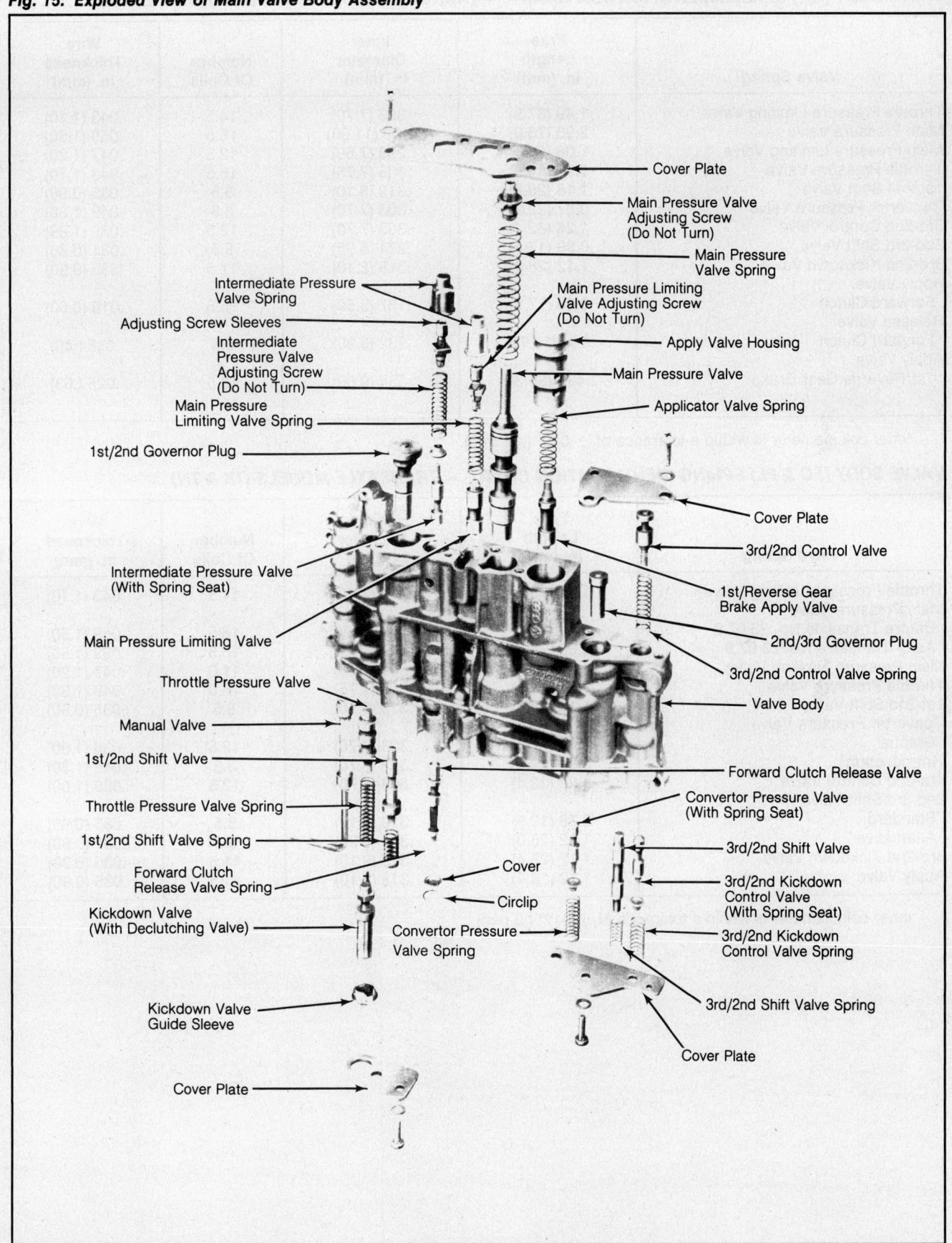

Cover Plate

Main Pressure Valve Adjusting Screw (Do Not Turn)

Main Pressure Valve Spring

Intermediate Pressure Valve Spring

Adjusting Screw Sleeves

Main Pressure Limiting Valve Adjusting Screw (Do Not Turn)

Apply Valve Housing

Intermediate Pressure Valve Adjusting Screw (Do Not Turn)

Main Pressure Valve

Main Pressure Limiting Valve Spring

Applicator Valve Spring

1st/2nd Governor Plug

Cover Plate

3rd/2nd Control Valve

Intermediate Pressure Valve (With Spring Seat)

1st/Reverse Gear Brake Apply Valve

2nd/3rd Governor Plug

Main Pressure Limiting Valve

3rd/2nd Control Valve Spring

Throttle Pressure Valve

Valve Body

Manual Valve

1st/2nd Shift Valve

Forward Clutch Release Valve

Throttle Pressure Valve Spring

Convertor Pressure Valve (With Spring Seat)

1st/2nd Shift Valve Spring

3rd/2nd Shift Valve

Forward Clutch Release Valve Spring

Cover

3rd/2nd Kickdown Control Valve (With Spring Seat)

Circlip

Kickdown Valve (With Declutching Valve)

Convertor Pressure Valve Spring

3rd/2nd Kickdown Control Valve Spring

Kickdown Valve Guide Sleeve

3rd/2nd Shift Valve Spring

Cover Plate

Cover Plate

All transmission models with "E-Mode".

Automatic Transmissions
VOLKSWAGEN TYPE 010 3-SPEED (Cont.)

VALVE BODY (GK) SPRING IDENTIFICATION CHART – TRANSAXLE MODELS (TH & TM) WITH E-MODE

Valve Spring	Free Length In. (mm)	Inner Diameter In. (mm) [1]	Number Of Coils	Wire Thickness In. (mm)
Throttle Pressure Limiting Valve	1.49 (37.9)	.303 (7.70)	14.5	.043 (1.10)
Main Pressure Valve	2.95 (75.0)	.468 (11.90)	16.5	.059 (1.50)
Main Pressure Limiting Valve	1.08 (27.5)	.299 (7.60)	12.5	.047 (1.20)
Throttle Pressure Valve	1.73 (44.0)	.305 (7.75)	16.5	.043 (1.10)
1st-2nd Shift Valve	1.13 (28.8)	.319 (8.10)	8.5	.035 (0.90)
Converter Pressure Valve	0.87 (22.2)	.303 (7.70)	8.5	.049 (1.30)
3rd-2nd Control Valve	1.28 (32.4)	.303 (7.70)	12.5	.039 (1.00)
2nd-3rd Shift Valve	0.69 (17.4)	.274 (6.95)	8.5	.031 (0.80)
3rd-2nd Kickdown Valve	1.12 (28.4)	.319 (8.10)	11.5	.035 (0.90)
Apply Valve Forward Clutch	0.68 (17.2)	.137 (3.50)	15.5	.019 (0.50)
Release Valve Forward Clutch	.578 (14.70)	.232 (5.90)	6.5	.015 (.40)
Apply Valve 1st/Reverse Gear Brake	1.429 (36.30)	.354 (9.00)	10.5	.025 (.63)

[1] – Inner coil diameter is within a tolerance of ±.012" (.30 mm).

VALVE BODY (FG & FL) SPRING IDENTIFICATION CHART – TRANSAXLE MODELS (TK & TN)

Valve Spring	Free Length In. (mm)	Inner Diameter In. (mm) [1]	Number Of Coils	Wire Thickness In. (mm)
Throttle Pressure Limiting Valve	1.39 (35.3)	.302 (7.70)	14.5	.043 (1.10)
Main Pressure Valve				
Before Transaxle No. 23 07 9	2.82 (71.6)	.468 (11.90)	16.5	.059 (1.50)
As of Transaxle No. 23 07 9	3.03 (77.0)	.468 (11.90)	16.5	.059 (1.50)
Main Pressure Limiting Valve	1.28 (32.4)	.302 (7.70)	11.0	.047 (1.20)
Throttle Pressure Valve	1.71 (43.4)	.305 (7.75)	16.0	.049 (1.30)
1st-2nd Shift Valve	1.13 (28.8)	.319 (8.10)	8.5	.035 (0.90)
Converter Pressure Valve				
Gradual	1.28 (32.4)	.303 (7.70)	12.5	.039 (1.00)
Introduction	0.87 (22.2)	.303 (7.70)	8.5	.049 (1.30)
3rd-2nd Control Valve	1.28 (32.4)	.303 (7.70)	12.5	.039 (1.00)
2nd-3rd Shift Valve				
Standard	0.78 (19.9)	.319 (8.10)	6.5	.035 (0.90)
Alternative	1.02 (26.0)	.323 (8.20)	9.5	.031 (0.80)
3rd-2nd Kickdown Valve	1.12 (28.4)	.319 (8.10)	11.5	.035 (0.90)
Apply Valve	1.12 (28.4)	.319 (8.10)	11.5	.035 (0.90)

[1] – Inner coil diameter is within a tolerance of ±.012" (.3 mm).

Fig. 16: Exploded View of Governor Assembly

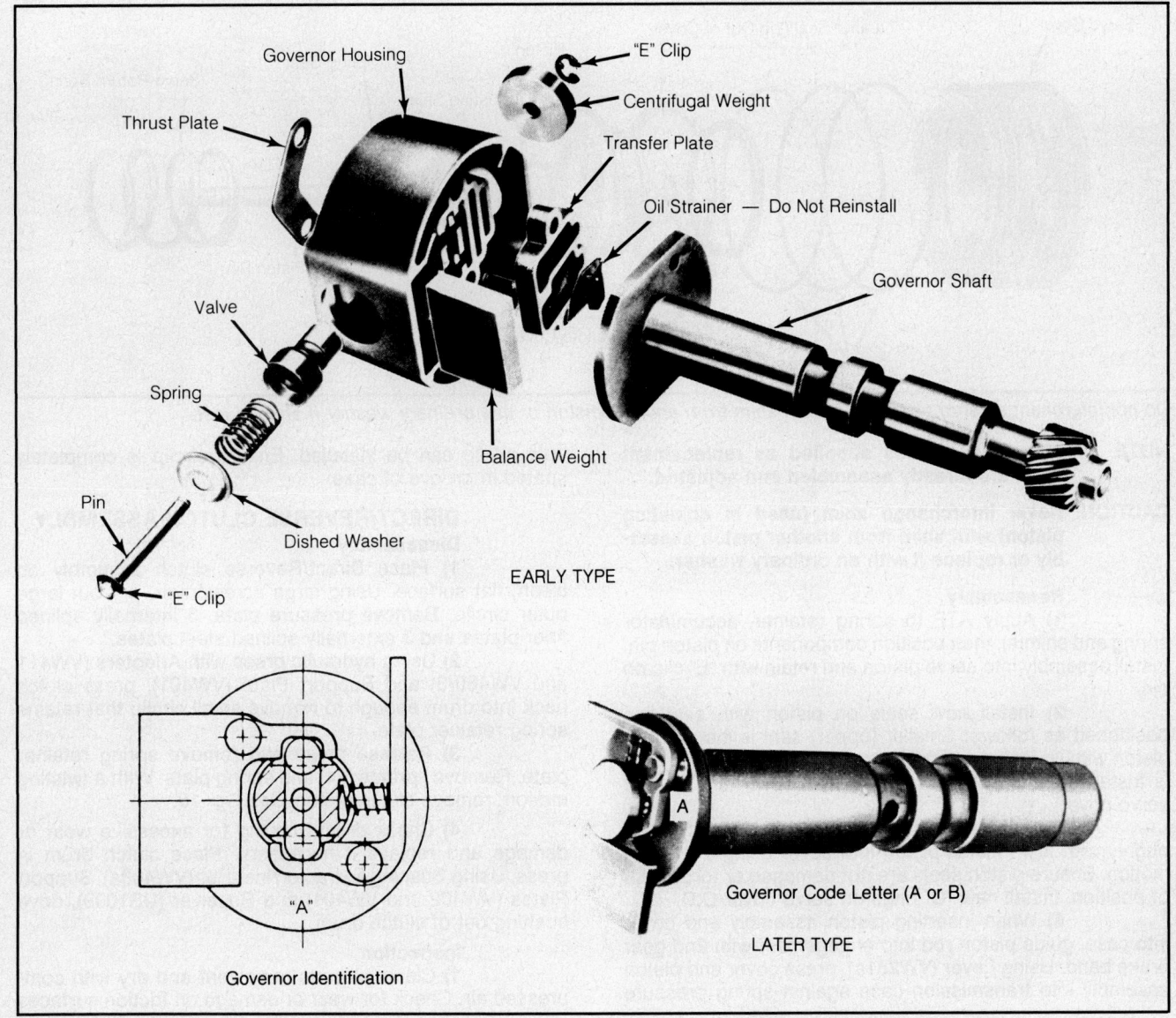

EARLY TYPE

Governor Identification

"A"

Governor Code Letter (A or B)

LATER TYPE

If present during disassembly, do not reinstall the oil strainer in governor assembly.

Disassembly
1) Detach 2 mounting screws (5 x 40 mm) and remove thrust plate and housing. Take out transfer plate, balance weight and oil strainer (if equipped).
2) If necessary, detach 1 "E" clip and withdraw centrifugal weight, valve, spring and dished washer from pin. *See Fig. 16.*

Inspection
Wash governor components in solvent and blow dry with compressed air. Inspect governor shaft for wear and thrust plate for scoring. Replace components as necessary.
NOTE: **Do not interchange balance weight in governor, unit is balanced by the manufacturer.**

Reassembly
To complete reassembly, reverse disassembly procedure and note the following: Lubricate all parts with ATF during assembly. Ensure angle in thrust plate is in center of housing so cover will bear against it. If strainer was present during disassembly, do not reinstall.

2nd GEAR BRAKE BAND SERVO PISTON ASSEMBLY
NOTE: **The 2nd gear brake band servo piston can be removed from vehicle with transmission installed.**

Disassembly
1) Apply inward pressure to servo piston using Lever (VW281a). Remove retaining circlip. Using a rubber mallet, tap piston cover until spring forces piston and cover out of case. Pull servo piston assembly out of cover.
2) Remove and discard "O" ring seals from cover O.D. Remove retaining clip. Separate piston pin, accumulator spring, spring seat and adjusting shim(s) from servo piston. *See Fig. 17.*

Inspection
Clean all parts and check for wear, scoring or other damage. Standard piston O.D. is 3.228" (82 mm). If piston is worn or damaged, replace piston, pin, spring retainer, accumulator spring and shim(s) as an assembly only.

Fig. 17: Exploded View of 2nd Gear Brake Band Servo Piston Assembly

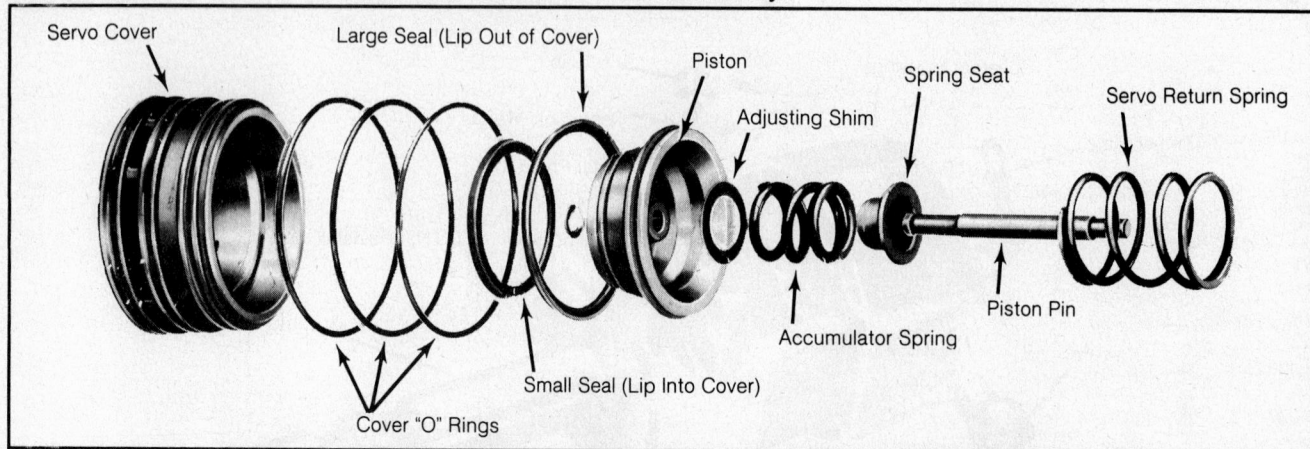

Do not interchange servo piston shim with shim from another piston or use ordinary washer if shim is lost.

NOTE: **Piston assemblies supplied as replacement parts are already assembled and adjusted.**

CAUTION: **Never interchange shim (used in adjusting piston) with shim from another piston assembly or replace it with an ordinary washer.**

Reassembly

1) Apply ATF to spring retainer, accumulator spring and shim(s), then position components on piston pin. Install assembly into servo piston and retain with "E" clip on pin.

2) Install new seals on piston with seal lips positioned as follows: Smaller (upper) seal is installed on piston with lip facing upward (into servo cover). Larger seal is installed on piston with lip pointed downward (out of servo cover).

3) Lubricate piston and cover assembly thoroughly with ATF. Install piston into cover using a twisting motion. Ensure piston seals are not damaged or forced out of position. Install new "O" rings on servo cover O.D.

4) When inserting piston assembly and cover into case, guide piston rod into engagement with 2nd gear brake band. Using Lever (VW281a), press cover and piston assembly into transmission case against spring pressure until circlip can be installed. Ensure circlip is completely seated in groove of case.

DIRECT/REVERSE CLUTCH ASSEMBLY
Disassembly

1) Place Direct/Reverse clutch assembly on clean, flat surface. Using large screwdriver, pry out large outer circlip. Remove pressure plate, 3 internally splined fiber plates and 3 externally splined steel plates.

2) Using hydraulic press with Adapters (VW411 and VW460/3) and Support Plate (VW401), press clutch pack into drum enough to remove small circlip that retains spring retainer plate.

3) Release press and remove spring retainer plate. Remove springs (24) and spring plate. With a twisting motion, remove clutch piston. *See Fig. 18.*

4) Check drum bushing for excessive wear or damage and replace if necessary. Place clutch drum in press. Using Bushing Extractor/Installer (VW408a), Support Plates (VW402 and VW401) and Receiver (US1099), drive bushing out of clutch drum.

Inspection

1) Clean all parts in solvent and dry with compressed air. Check for wear or damage on friction surfaces

Fig. 18: Exploded View of Direct/Reverse Clutch Assembly

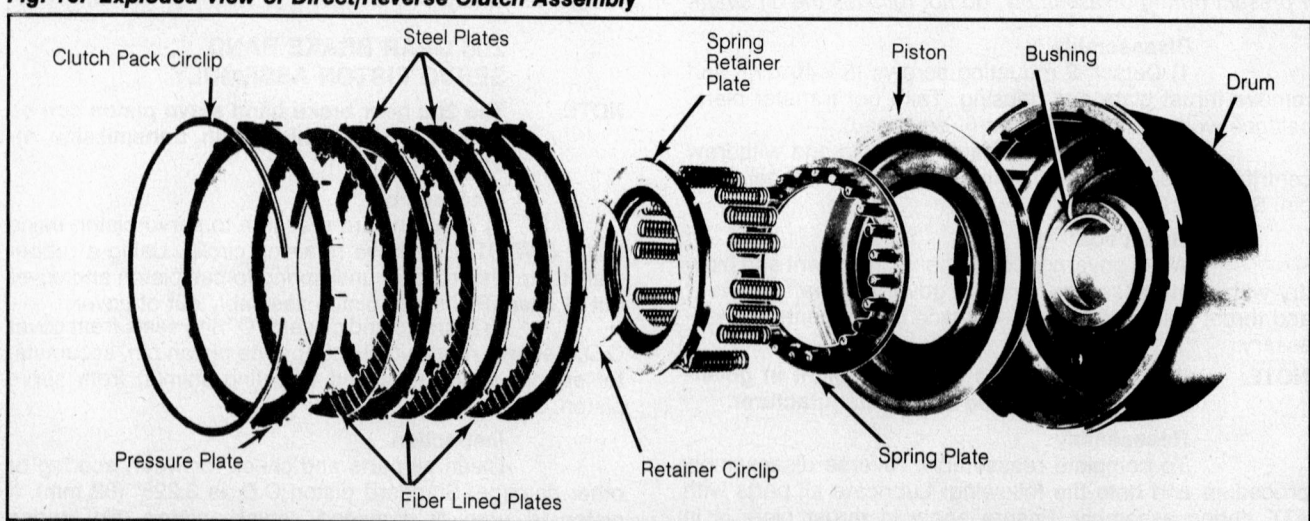

When installing new fiber-lined clutch plates, ensure surface pattern of plates is identical to those removed.

of piston and drum. Check for wear or damage of grooves that externally splined plates ride in.

NOTE: **The Direct/Reverse piston seals are vulcanized to the piston. Replace entire piston if there is leakage past seals or if seals are obviously worn or damaged.**

2) Replace piston and/or drum as necessary. Ensure drum has proper inside dimension of 1.063" (27 mm), measured from top of circlip groove to piston contact surface of drum.

3) Inspect steel plates for wear and burn marks. Replace if excessively worn or blued from overheating. Check fiber-lined plates for wear, cracking or chipping. Replace any damaged plates.

NOTE: **When installing new fiber-lined clutch plates, ensure surface pattern of plates is identical to those removed. Do not install plates with a different pattern of markings.**

4) Inspect ball valve in clutch drum for freedom of operation and proper sealing. Ensure clutch drum drilled passage for ball valve is clear. Check piston return springs for distortion, broken or collapsed coils. Replace any damaged parts.

Reassembly
1) If drum bushing is removed, install new bushing using hydraulic press with Bushing Driver (VW433), bushing extractor/installer and support plates. Install new clutch drum hub bushing flush with hub surface.

2) Using old bushing (between press tool and new bushing), press new bushing into hub until it is .067" (1.70 mm) below hub lip. Remove old bushing from hub bore with pliers.

3) Completely lubricate piston assembly with ATF. Insert a 1 1/2-2" (38-51 mm) wide, thin (but flexible) plastic sheet around inside diameter of drum to protect piston seals during installation. Lubricate seals with ATF, then install piston assembly into drum with a twisting motion. Remove plastic sheet.

4) Position spring plate on top of piston and springs on spring plate. Place retainer on top of springs. Compress drum assembly in press and install small circlip. Lubricate all clutch plates with ATF. Ensure new fiber-lined plates are marked with a pattern of vertical and horizontal lines and are identical to plates removed.

NOTE: **Soak new fiber-lined plates in ATF for 15 minutes prior to installation.**

5) Install 1 steel plate (external splines), then 1 lined plate (internal splines) into drum. Continue alternating steel and lined plates until all clutch plates are installed. Install pressure plate and thinnest available Clutch Pack Retaining Circlip (010 323 157 A).

6) Using feeler gauges (in various combinations), measure clearance between clutch pack retaining circlip and pressure plate. The clearance should be within .081-.098" (2.05-2.50 mm). See Fig. 19.

7) If clearance is incorrect, remove clutch pack circlip. Replace it with circlip of correct thickness to bring clearance within specifications. Recheck clearance after installing replacement circlip.

NOTE: **Circlips are available in thicknesses of .059" (1.50 mm), .067" (1.70 mm), .079" (2.00 mm), .091" (2.30 mm) and .098" (2.50 mm).**

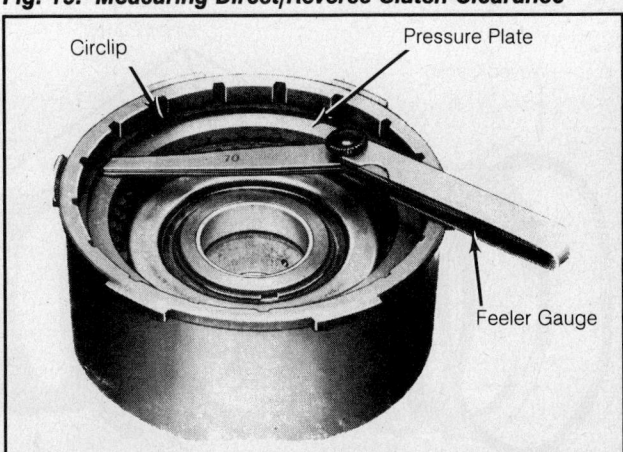

Fig. 19: Measuring Direct/Reverse Clutch Clearance

The circlip-to-pressure plate clearance should be within .081-.098" (2.05-2.50 mm).

8) To check operation of assembled Direct/Reverse clutch, lubricate sealing rings with ATF and temporarily install ATF pump in Direct/Reverse clutch assembly.

9) Blow compressed air into oil port and check that clutch piston audibly compresses clutch plates. When air pressure is released, ensure clutch plates release and piston returns to original position.

FORWARD CLUTCH ASSEMBLY
Disassembly
1) Using a screwdriver, pry out waved clutch plate circlip from clutch drum (flat circlip with "E-Mode"). Remove pressure plate, 3 fiber-lined clutch plates and 2 steel clutch plates, foreward planetary ring gear and thrust plate.

CAUTION: **Clutch piston sealing rings are vulcanized onto piston. Do not damage sealing rings during removal. If seal lips are obviously worn or damaged or leakage past rings is found, replace entire piston as an assembly.**

2) On all models (except with "E-Mode"), remove flat circlip and diaphragm spring. See Fig. 20. On models with "E-Mode", remove spring washer and spring. Use press to compress spring plate and remove small circlip.

3) Slowly release pressure on spring plate. Remove plate. Remove spring retaining ring, spring assembly and spring support ring. On all models, remove clutch piston from clutch drum by pulling with a twisting motion or expelling with compressed air. See Fig. 21.

Inspection
1) Clean all parts in solvent and dry with compressed air. Check for wear or damage on friction surfaces of piston and drum. Check for wear or damage of grooves that externally splined plates ride in. Replace piston and/or drum as necessary.

2) Ensure drum I.D. is 1.031" (26.20 mm), measured from top of circlip groove to piston contact surface of drum. Inspect for proper ball valve movement by shaking clutch drum. Rattle of ball valve should be heard. If not, clean drilling. Replace faulty drum as needed, ball valve is not replaceable separately.

Fig. 20: Exploded View of Forward Clutch Assembly

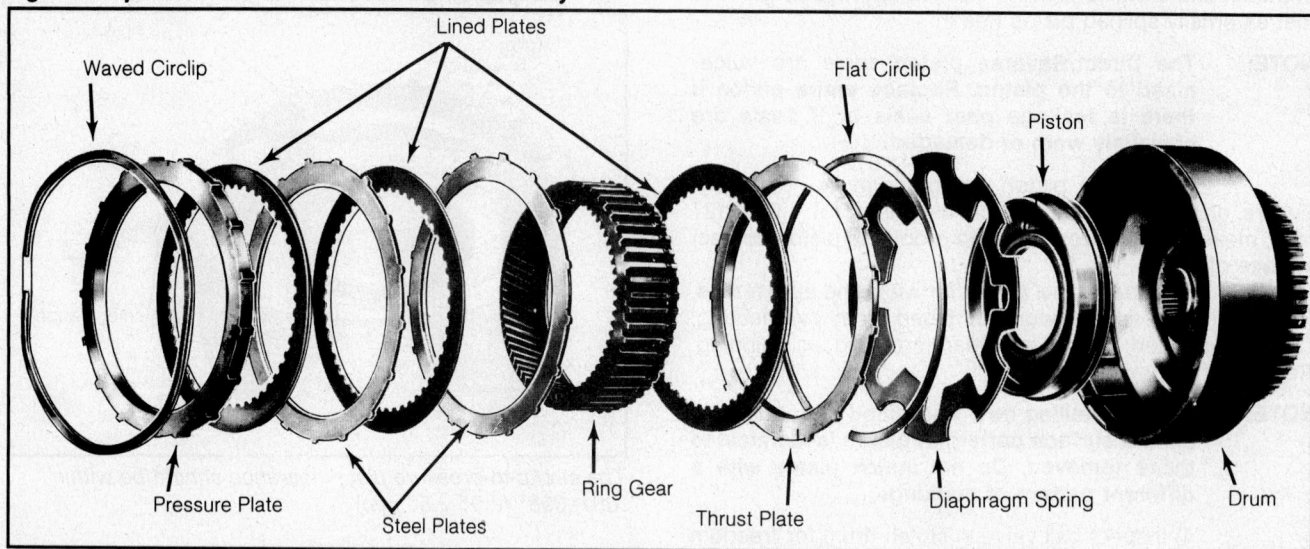

All models except with "E-Mode" transmission.

3) Inspect steel plates for wear and burn marks. Replace if excessively worn or blued from overheating. Check fiber-lined plates for wear, cracking or chipping. Replace any damaged plates.

NOTE: When installing new fiber-lined clutch plates, ensure surface pattern of plates is identical to those removed. Do not install plates with a different pattern of markings.

4) Check planetary ring gear inner and outer splines for wear, scoring or other damage. Replace as needed. Check diaphragm spring for settling by placing in drum. Spring should reach at least to the lower edge of circlip groove. Replace faulty spring as necessary.

CAUTION: Clutch drum with drillings must not be used in transmission with ATF pump that has radial-roller thrust bearing. Clutch drum without drillings must not be used in transmission with (early) ATF pump that has only a thrust washer.

NOTE: Soak new fiber-lined plates in ATF for 15 minutes prior to installation.

Reassembly

1) Coat clutch piston and sealing rings with ATF. Install piston assembly into drum using a twisting motion. On all models except with "E-Mode", position diaphragm spring in drum with convex side towards bottom of drum. Install flat 2.03 mm Retaining Circlip (010 323 157).

NOTE: With circlip installed, diaphragm spring should be under some tension and circlip should not be easily snapped into groove. If inserting circlip does not put spring under tension, replace spring.

2) On models with "E-Mode", install spring support ring, spring retaining ring and spring assembly and spring plate. Retaining ring and springs must be installed with small diameter end of springs up (towards spring plate).

3) Compress spring plate and install small circlip. Install spring and spring washer. Ensure that spring and washer are installed with convex side down (into drum).

Fig. 21: Exploded View of Forward Clutch Assembly

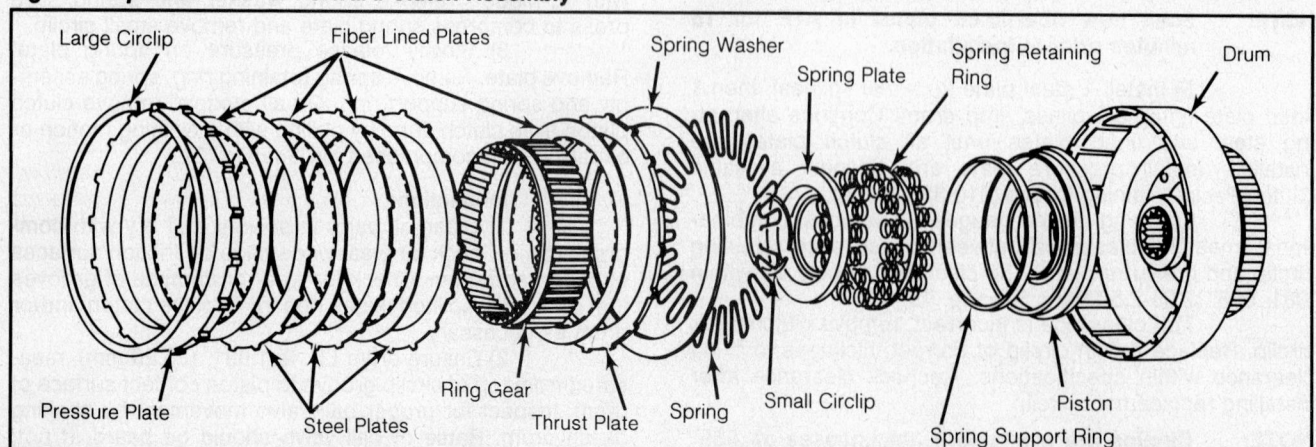

All models with "E-Mode" transmission.

FORWARD CLUTCH PLATE CHART

Application	Steel Plates	Lined Plates
With "E-Mode"	3	4
All Others	2	3

4) On all models, lubricate components with ATF. Install thrust plate and 1 fiber-lined plate in clutch drum. If 1 side of thrust plate is chamfered, install chamfered side toward diaphragm spring.

5) Install planetary ring (annulus) gear into assembly, engaging short splines (beneath retaining ridge) into inner splines of fiber-lined plate. After soaking in ATF, install remaining clutch plates, starting with 1 steel plate and alternating fiber-lined and steel plates until all plates are installed. Install pressure plate and Circlip (010 323 159 B).

6) Position dial indicator on assembly with indicator pointer resting on pressure plate. Zero indicator. Pull up and down on planetary ring gear and note movement on dial. Record end play. End play must be between .020-.035" (.50-.90 mm). See Fig. 22.

Fig. 22: Measuring Forward Clutch End Play

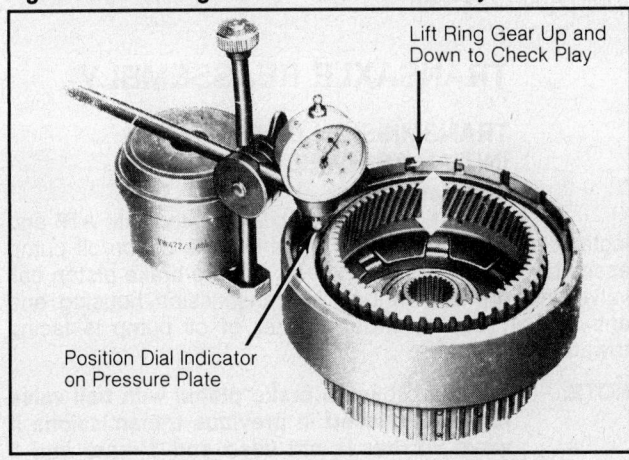

Lift Ring Gear Up and Down to Check Play

Position Dial Indicator on Pressure Plate

Check end play with feeler gauge, between circlip and pressure plate, if dial indicator is not available.

7) If end play is incorrect, replace pressure plate (large circlip on models with "E-Mode") with selective circlip of required thickness to bring play to proper specifications.

8) Pressure plates are available in thicknesses of .236" (6.00 mm), .252" (6.40 mm), .268" (6.80), .283" (7.20 mm) and .299" (7.60 mm). On "E-Mode" models, circlips are available in thicknesses of .059" (1.50 mm), .067" (1.70 mm), .079" (2.00 mm), .091" (2.30 mm), .098" (2.50 mm), .114" (2.90 mm), .126" (3.20 mm) and .138" (3.50 mm).

9) Assemble Direct/Reverse clutch with thrust washers and forward clutch onto oil pump. Blow compressed air into oil port and check that clutch piston audibly compresses clutch plates. When air pressure is released, ensure clutch plates release and piston returns to original position.

1st GEAR 1-WAY CLUTCH
Disassembly
1) With large circlip that retains 1-way clutch in transmission case removed, pull 1-way clutch assembly from case. Remove rollers and springs. On steel cage, detach upper and lower circlips. Using plastic hammer,

drive cage out of outer race (from flat side of outer race toward angled side). See Fig. 23.

Fig. 23: Exploded View of 1-Way Clutch Assembly (With Steel Roller & Spring Cage)

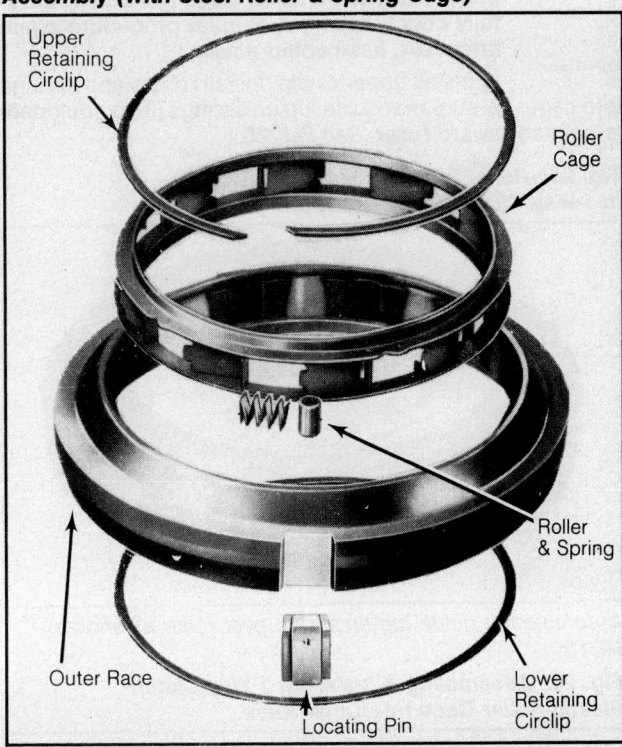

Upper Retaining Circlip

Roller Cage

Roller & Spring

Outer Race

Locating Pin

Lower Retaining Circlip

Before reassembly, ensure roller cage is marked with "B" and outer race has groove machined in angled outer face.

Fig. 24: Steel Roller Cage Installation In 1st Gear 1-Way Clutch Outer Race

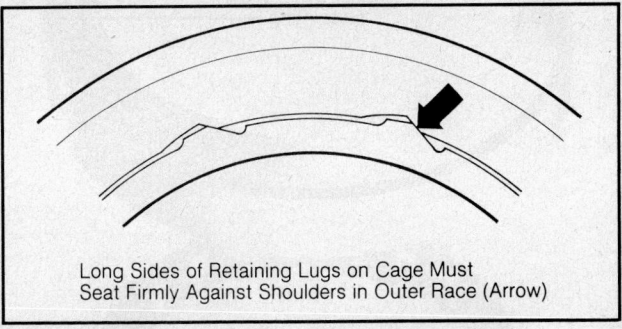

Long Sides of Retaining Lugs on Cage Must Seat Firmly Against Shoulders in Outer Race (Arrow)

Ensure the roller cage is positioned properly in the outer race and rests against the lower circlip.

2) On plastic cage, push roller cage out of outer race (from angled side of outer race toward flat side). On all models, Inspect all parts for wear, scoring or other damage and replace as needed.

Reassembly
1) On steel roller and spring cage, install lower circlip in groove of outer race. If necessary, heat outer race to 300-390° F (150-200° C) and set roller cage on ice. Place roller cage into outer race with 2 pair of pliers. See Fig. 24.

2) If necessary, turn roller cage slightly, immediately after installing, to locate it properly against the outer race.

Automatic Transmissions
VOLKSWAGEN TYPE 010 3-SPEED (Cont.)

NOTE: During installation, heat from outer race will transfer quickly to roller cage, causing cage to stick inside race. If cage is incorrectly positioned against lower circlip, do not attempt to press into position after cage has stuck. Carefully knock cage out. Repeat procedure again after race has cooled down.

3) Install upper circlip. Install rollers and springs into cage. Be sure that guide lug on springs (if so equipped) is pointed toward roller. *See Fig. 25.*

Fig. 25: Roller & Spring Installation in 1-Way Clutch Assembly (Steel Cage)

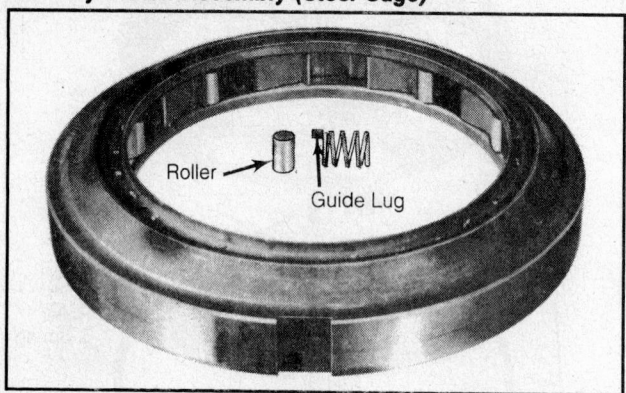

Assemble the guide lug on spring over roller as shown.

Fig. 26: Assembling & Installing 1-Way Clutch Plastic Roller Cage Into Outer Race

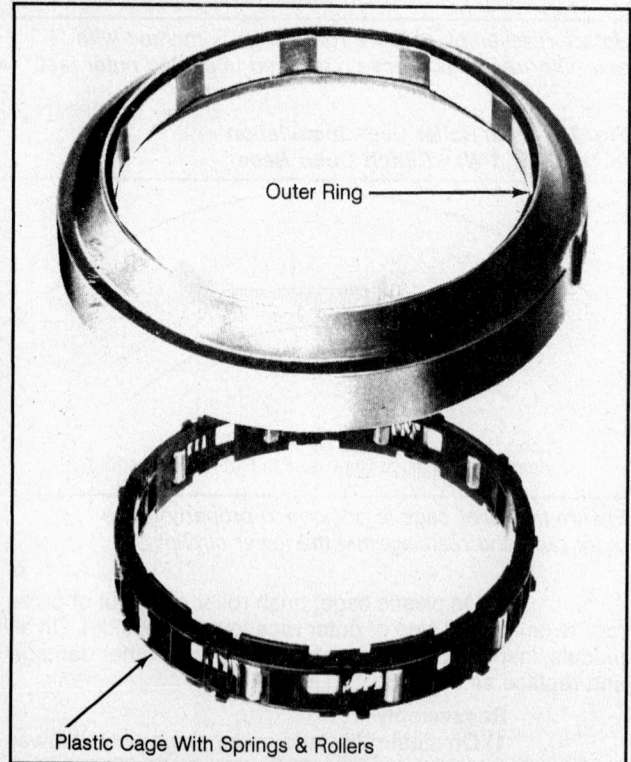

Assemble plastic cage segments to form a ring. Install (with springs and rollers) into outer race from flat side.

NOTE: Springs with and without tabs can be used together and are interchangeable. New plastic cage can be service installed in earlier transmissions. Do not use circlips with plastic cage.

4) On plastic roller and spring cage, assemble 10 segments of plastic cage to form a ring. Install all springs and rollers. Ensure each spring guide tab (lug) faces toward its roller.

5) Insert roller cage from flat side of outer race (small ledge toward tapered side and large ledge toward flat side). *See Fig. 26.* With outer race/roller cage assembled and laying on flat side, turn cage clockwise to secure. It should not be possible to turn assembly counterclockwise.

ANNULUS GEAR (2-PART) GOVERNOR DRIVE GEAR/PLANETARY RING GEAR
Disassembly & Reassembly
The annulus gear engages the planet gears of the reverse planetary gearset. The 2-part gear should be disassembled only if necessary to replace 1 of the components. To disassemble, detach circlip, then remove governor drive gear/hub from flanged annulus gear. Inspect for damage or excessive wear and replace components as necessary. If new circlip is needed, replace with proper Circlip (090 323 369).

TRANSAXLE REASSEMBLY

TRANSMISSION COMPONENT INITIAL ASSEMBLY
Reassembly
1) Coat 1st/Reverse brake piston with ATF and install on oil pump housing. Insert brake piston/oil pump assembly into transmission case. Ensure brake piston ball valve lines up with drilling in transmission housing and anti-rotation lug for thrust washer of oil pump is facing toward top of case.

NOTE: New 1st/Reverse brake piston with ball valve may be installed in previous transmissions if wave washer is not used and 3 inner and 3 outer splined plates are installed.

2) Before installing 1st/Reverse gear apply shell, measure overall length to ensure proper component is installed. Shell length is 3.957" (100.50 mm). Install apply shell into case so that tab of shell engages upper groove in transmission case. *See Fig. 27.*

Fig. 27: Installing 1st/Reverse Gear Apply Shell

When installed, shell tab must engage with case groove.

VOLKSWAGEN TYPE 010 3-SPEED (Cont.)

3) Position 1st/Reverse brake piston return springs on spring plate. Ensure springs have a wire thickness of .039" (1 mm). If necessary, use petroleum jelly to adhere springs to plate. Insert assembly into case with springs downward and bolt holes in spring plate matching those in ATF pump.

4) Install spring plate mount bolts and gradually tighten, in a diagonal pattern, to 61 INCH lbs. (7 N.m). After installation, temporarily insert pump driveshaft into oil pump. Turn assembly by hand to ensure parts are not jammed and there is no binding.

5) Position 2nd gear brake band in transmission case. With new "O" rings installed on servo piston cover and coated with ATF, install 2nd gear servo piston in case. Ensure piston pin engages band end inside case. Using Lever (VW281a), push cover/piston assembly against spring pressure. Install circlip.

6) Turn transmission case horizontal (servo piston cover pointed down). On opposite side of case, install 2nd gear brake band adjusting screw push rod. Be sure rod engages band end inside case. Install adjusting screw just enough to hold band in place.

7) Lubricate Direct/Reverse clutch with ATF and insert unit into transmission case, sliding it onto neck of ATF pump and into 2nd gear brake band. Use care not to damage pump seal rings. Tighten 2nd gear brake band adjusting screw to 7.5 ft. lbs. (10 N.m) in order to prevent brake band from shifting its position. Turn transmission case upward.

8) Coat forward clutch-to-Direct/Reverse clutch thrust washers with petroleum jelly and position on rear end of forward clutch. Install forward clutch into Direct/Reverse clutch. Make sure that splines on forward clutch drum fully engage splines on Direct/Reverse clutch lined plates.

9) Ensure inner thrust washer, thrust bearing and outer thrust washer are between oil pump piston end and forward clutch. Install forward planetary gearset-to-forward clutch thrust bearing into forward clutch. Install forward planetary gearset into ring gear in forward clutch.

10) Install sun gear (short end first) into gear set. Install apply shell and thrust washer over sun gear. Position thrust washer on underside of reverse planetary gear set. Install gear set into case and onto sun gear.

11) Check for proper identification mark of "B1" on 1st gear inner splined plates. Install 3 fiber-lined and 3 steel plates in case alternately, starting with steel plate. If any new fiber-lined plates are used, soak plates in transmission fluid for 15 minutes prior to installation.

12) Install 1st gear 1-way clutch assembly into transmission case. Using Clutch Holder (VW458), push clutch downward while rotating reverse planetary gear set clockwise to fully engage parts. Do not attempt to rotated clutch assembly counterclockwise. With all parts engaged, install 1-way clutch-to-case retaining circlip. See Fig. 28.

CAUTION: With correctly installed components, circlip groove should be uncovered. Do not force in circlip on an incorrectly assembled transmission.

13) Position needle bearing and thrust washer on rear side of governor drive gear/ring gear assembly. Install unit into transmission case, fully engaging reverse planetary gear set. Install separation plate gasket, with plate, over case studs. Install and tighten plate mount screws. Check transmission end play (whether or not new parts were installed).

Fig. 28: Installing 1st Gear 1-Way Clutch Circlip

Parts Are Installed Properly if Groove For One-Way Clutch Circlip is Exposed

With 1-way clutch installed, it should not be possible to rotate reverse planetary gear set counterclockwise.

NOTE: When adjusting 2nd gear brake band, transmission must be horizontal in order to keep band from slipping or jamming. If band slips, transmission must be partially disassembled to correct problem.

14) Adjust 2nd gear brake band as follows: Tighten band adjusting screw to 89 INCH lbs. (10 N.m). Loosen and retighten adjusting screw to 44 INCH lbs. (5 N.m). From this position, back off screw exactly 2 1/2 turns and tighten lock nut to 14 ft. lbs. (19 N.m).

15) If case linkage was disassembled, reinstall in case using Fig. 4 as an assembly guide. Install new seal on accumulator piston (lip pointing toward case). Install piston and spring into case.

16) Install valve body assembly, making sure manual valve engages manual lever and kickdown valve engages kickdown lever. Install valve body-to-case bolts and tighten from center outward. Install oil pan with new gasket.

FINAL DRIVE

DISASSEMBLY, ADJUSTMENT & REASSEMBLY
Disassembly

1) Place final drive assembly in Holding Stand (VW353). Drain ATF, then remove oil pan and discard gasket. Rotate differential assembly in case until differential pinion gear opening appears. Use 2 screwdrivers to remove 2 clips retaining axle drive flanges in differential. See Fig. 29.

2) Pull axle drive flanges out of final drive housing together with side gear shafts. Turn drive flanges slightly during removal to prevent side gear thrust washers from catching in circlip grooves of side gear shafts.

3) Remove retaining bolt and withdraw speedometer driven gear assembly straight out of case. If bearings are to be reused, scribe a match mark on differential side bearing adjusting ring and case for reassembly reference.

4) Remove lock clip from adjusting ring. Using Spanner Wrench (VW182), screw ring out of case. See Fig. 31. On opposite side of case, remove nuts and withdraw the

Automatic Transmissions
VOLKSWAGEN TYPE 010 3-SPEED (Cont.)

Fig. 29: *Location of Drive Flange Retaining Clips*

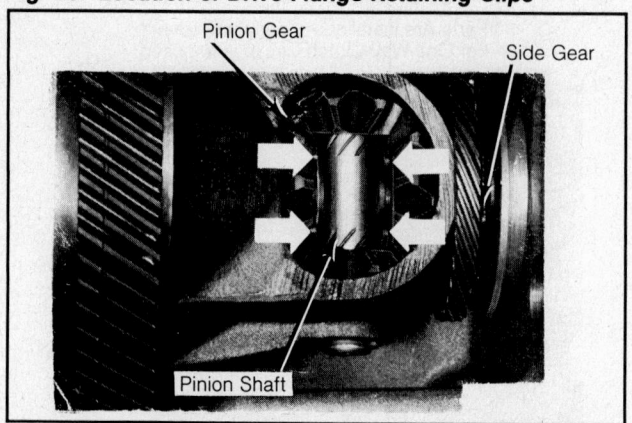

Use 2 screwdrivers to press clips (ends are indicated by White arrows) off of shaft.

other differential side bearing retainer (cover). Grasp differential and ring gear assembly and remove from final drive case. *See Fig. 30.*

   5) Inside converter housing area of final drive case, mark relationship of intermediate gear shaft and case

Fig. 31: *Removing Differential Side Bearing Adjusting Ring*

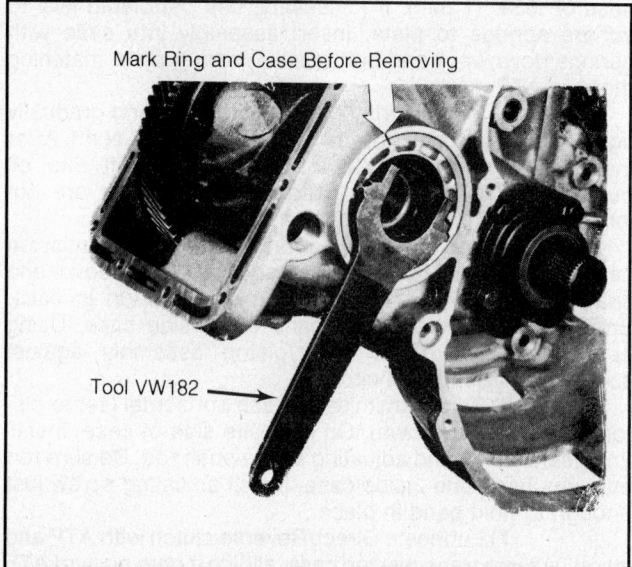

After index marking case and adjusting ring, screw ring out of case with spanner wrench.

Fig. 30: *Exploded View of Differential & Related Parts in Final Drive Case*

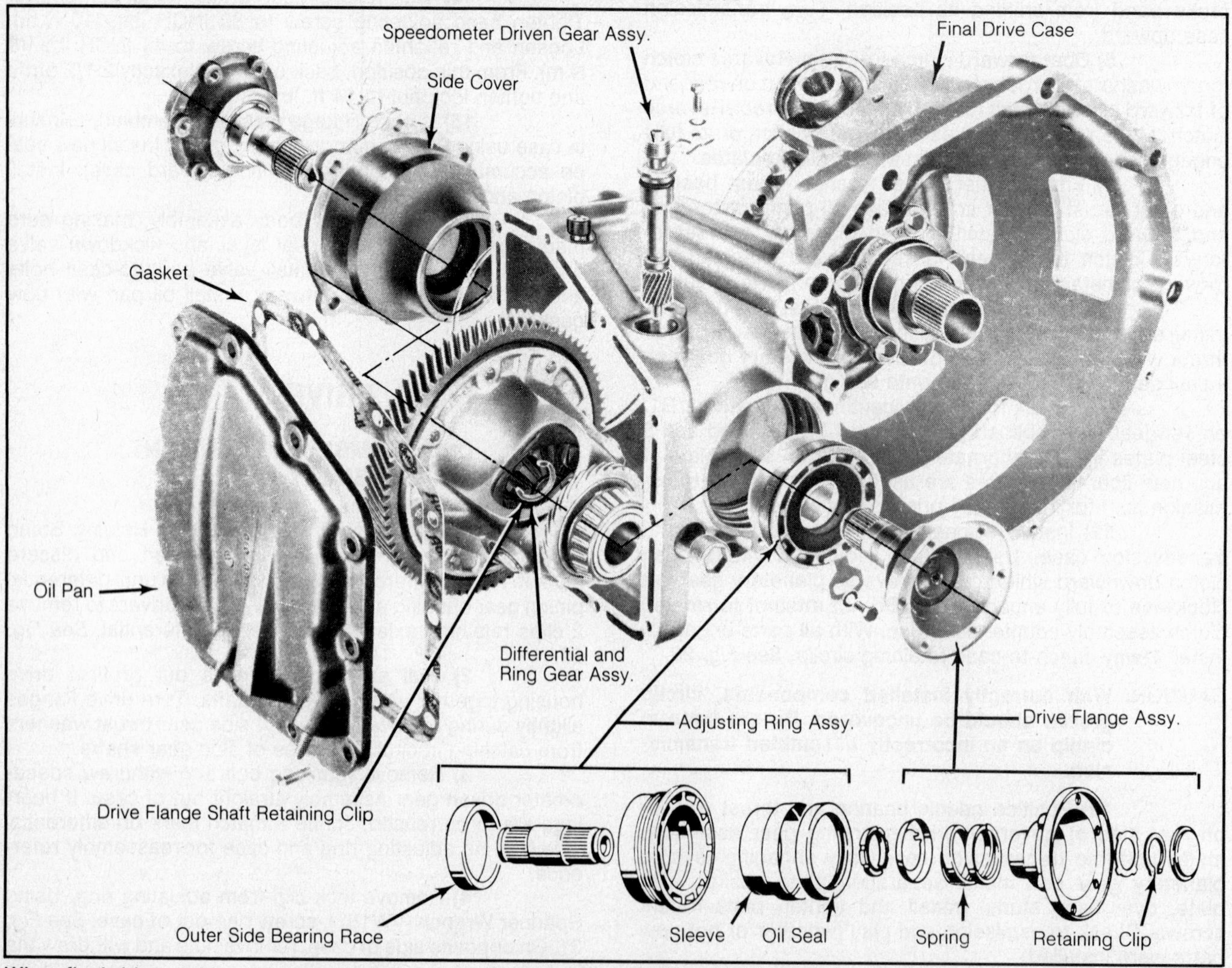

When final drive and/or transmission are repaired, ensure the end play of the final drive/transmission is checked.

with scribe. Remove lock clip from intermediate gear shaft. Using special tool, screw shaft out of case. *See Fig. 32.*

Fig. 32: Removing Intermediate Gear Shaft

Mark Shaft and Case Before Removing Shaft

Use tool to remove the intermediate gear shaft from the final drive housing.

6) From inside case, remove intermediate gear, bearings and thrust washer. *See Fig. 33.* Remove bolts retaining 1-way clutch support to converter housing area of case. Withdraw support and drive pinion shaft assembly from case.

7) To disassemble differential assembly, remove 2 differential pinion shaft retaining snap rings. Remove drive shaft from case with drift. Move differential pinion gears around to case openings. Remove pinion gears and thrust washers. Remove differential side gears and thrust washers.

8) Remove ring gear-to-differential case mount bolts. Using hydraulic press, Adapters (VW411 and VW295a) with Support Plates (VW401 and VW402), separate ring gear from case. If required, withdraw differential side bearings and speedometer drive gear from case with press and Adapter (US1078).

9) Withdraw bearing races from adjusting ring and side cover. If replacement of pinion bearings or pinion shaft is required, proceed as follows: Place pinion assembly in press. With press plates positioned under bearings, drive bearings from pinion shaft.

10) Place stator support in press. Drive out pinion bearing race along with preload shim and pinion oil

Fig. 33: Exploded View of Intermediate Gear & Pinion Gear Assemblies in Final Drive Case

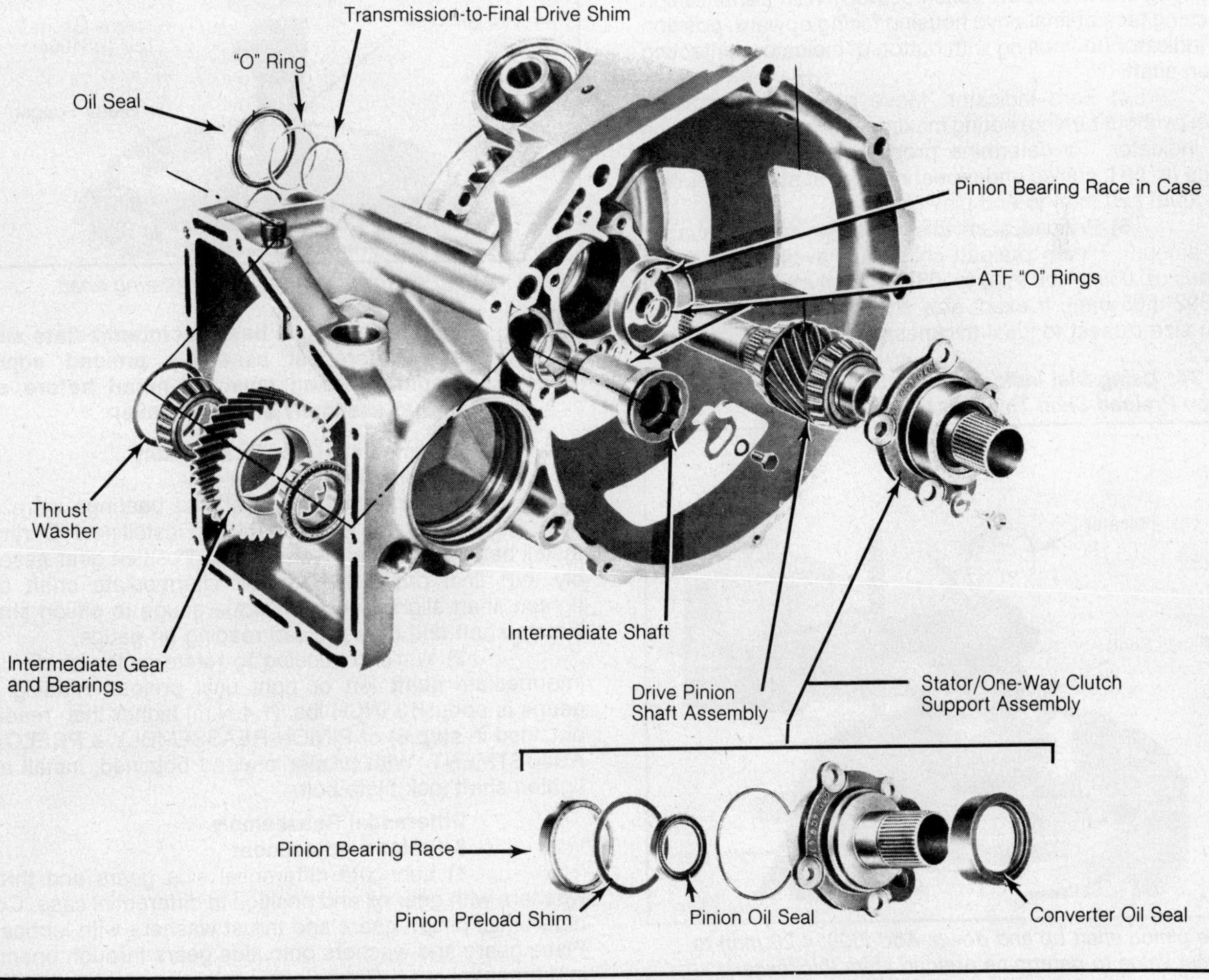

Transmission-to-Final Drive Shim

"O" Ring

Oil Seal

Pinion Bearing Race in Case

ATF "O" Rings

Thrust Washer

Intermediate Shaft

Intermediate Gear and Bearings

Drive Pinion Shaft Assembly

Stator/One-Way Clutch Support Assembly

Pinion Bearing Race

Pinion Preload Shim

Pinion Oil Seal

Converter Oil Seal

During disassembly, note installed positions of differential components for reassembly reference.

seal. Using hammer and drift, drive remaining pinion bearing race out of final drive case. Inspect ATF drillings in 1-way clutch/stator support assembly.

11) Check ball valve in support for proper action by installing a piece of tight fitting hose into ball valve hole. Apply suction. Ball valve must seal to prevent ATF from draining out of torque convertor when engine is not running. If ball does not seal, replace 1-way clutch support.

Pinion Reassembly
& Preload Adjustment

1) If pinion gear and/or pinion bearings were replaced, lubricate bearings with gear oil. If preload check must be done, do not lubricate bearings until after check has been completed.

2) Press bearings onto pinion shaft. Using drift, install pinion bearing race into final drive housing. Temporarily install remaining pinion bearing race (without adjusting shim) into stator support.

NOTE: When measuring end play of pinion shaft, do not lubricate bearings or turn drive pinion. If pinion is lubricated, turned when seating against outer race or when installing in final drive housing, measurement will be inaccurate.

3) Install pinion assembly into final drive case, tightening stator support bolts securely. With transmission attaching face of final drive housing facing upward, position dial indicator on housing with button of indicator contacting pinion shaft.

4) Zero indicator. Move pinion shaft up and down (without turning) noting maximum end play reading on dial indicator. To determine proper pinion preload shim usage (to be installed under bearing race in stator support), add .008" (.20 mm) to end play reading.

5) Preload shim thickness should be equal to this amount. Pinion preload shims are available in thicknesses of .039" (1.00 mm) to .087" (2.20 mm) in increments of .002" (.05 mm). If exact size shim is not available, use shim size closest to ideal thickness.

Fig. 34: Using Dial Indicator to Determine
Pinion Preload Shim Thickness

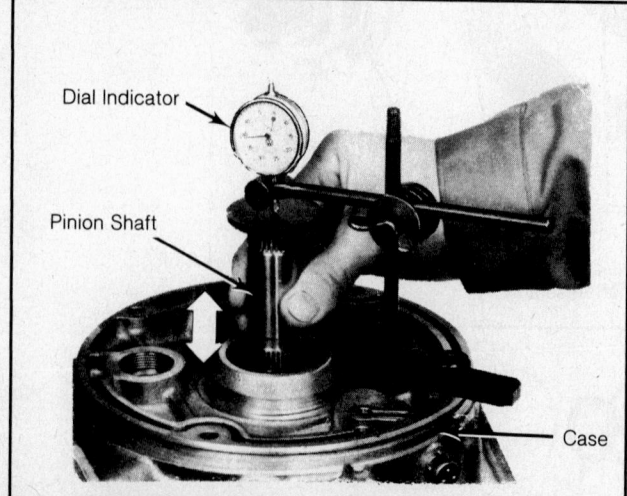

Move pinion shaft up and down. Add .008" (.20 mm) to highest value to determine preload shim thickness.

NOTE: When installing used shim, measure shim in several places to ensure thickness accuracy. Do not use burred or damaged shims.

6) Remove pinion assembly from final drive case. Press bearing race out of stator support. Install pinion oil seal into support. Install preload shim determined in steps 2) and 3). Position bearing race in support and press into place.

7) Install converter oil seal on front side of support. Install sealing "O" ring on rear side. Install new transmission fluid passage "O" rings in final drive case, at stator support attaching face. Thoroughly coat pinion bearings with gear oil.

8) Position pinion assembly in final drive case. Install stator support and tighten mount bolts. Install Torque Gauge (VW249) and rapidly turn pinion shaft 15-20 times to settle bearings. Turn shaft with torque gauge and record turning torque reading for future reference.

Fig. 35: Checking Pinion Bearing Preload

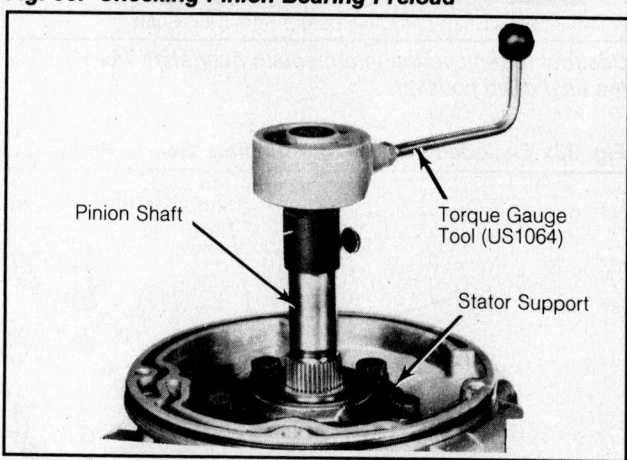

Check reading on torque gauge while rotating shaft.

NOTE: Torque reading is basis for intermediate shaft and differential assembly preload adjustments. Reading must be noted before any further assembly steps are taken.

Intermediate Gear Reassembly
& Preload Adjustment

1) If intermediate gear and bearings were replaced, coat bearings with gear oil and install new "O" rings. Install bearings in intermediate gear. Position gear assembly into final drive case. Insert intermediate shaft and tighten shaft slightly. Attach torque gauge to pinion shaft. Rotate shaft and note preload reading on gauge.

2) While continuing to rotate pinion shaft, turn intermediate shaft left or right until preload reading on gauge is about 13 INCH lbs. (1.4 N.m) higher than reading obtained in step 6) of PINION REASSEMBLY & PRELOAD ADJUSTMENT. With proper preload obtained, install and tighten shaft lock plate bolt.

Differential Reassembly
& Preload Adjustment

1) Lubricate differential side gears and thrust washers with gear oil and position in differential case. Coat differential pinion gears and thrust washers with lubricant. Place gears and washers onto side gears through opening in differential case. Rotate gears into alignment with differential pinion shaft bores in case.

NOTE: **Pinion gears must be exactly opposite one another in order to install pinion shaft.**

2) Install differential pinion shaft into differential case and through pinion gears. Install pinion shaft retaining clips. If removed, press differential side bearings and speedometer drive gear onto differential case.

3) If ring gear is being replaced, install guide pins into differential case bolt hole. Heat ring gear in hot oil to about 212° F (100° C). Using pins to guide ring gear into place, install gear on case. Install and tighten mount bolts.

Fig. 36: Exploded View of Differential & Ring Gear Assembly

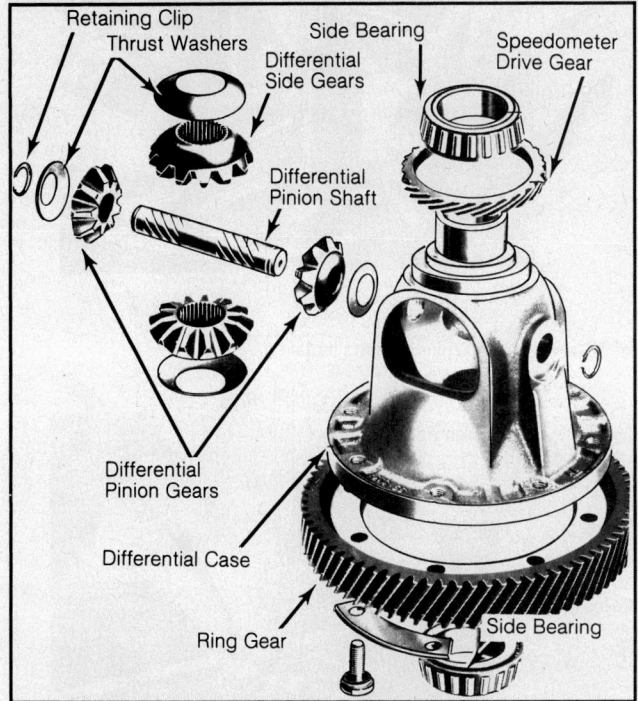

- Retaining Clip
- Thrust Washers
- Side Bearing
- Differential Side Gears
- Speedometer Drive Gear
- Differential Pinion Shaft
- Differential Pinion Gears
- Differential Case
- Ring Gear
- Side Bearing

4) If differential case, pinion gears, side gears, thrust washers or axle drive flange shafts are replaced, drive flange shaft retaining rings must be selected. Two sizes of retaining rings are available. To determine which rings to use, go to step **5)**. If parts listed are being reused, go to step **6)**.

5) To select drive flange shaft retaining rings, install each flange shaft into differential case and bottom against differential pinion shaft. While holding side gear against differential case, attempt to install the thicker of the 2 available circlips. If ring jams at sides and cannot be installed, thinner retaining ring must be used when drive flanges are installed.

NOTE: **If differential must be adjusted, ensure old oil seals are removed. Do not install new oil seals until turning torque reading is recorded.**

6) Install side bearing races and new oil seals in adjusting ring and side cover (if removed). Install new sealing "O" rings on ring and cover. Thoroughly coat ring gear and side bearings with final drive lubricant.

7) Position differential assembly in final drive case and engage with intermediate gear. Install side cover to engage with side bearing, then install and tighten cover retaining nuts. Screw side bearing adjusting ring into case and over side bearing so differential is firmly supported.

8) With torque gauge attached to pinion shaft, rotate shaft and note torque reading. While continuing to rotate pinion shaft rapidly, gradually rotate side bearing adjuster left or right until preload reading is about 6 INCH lbs. (.7 N.m) greater than last reading obtained in INTER-MEDIATE GEAR REASSEMBLY & PRELOAD ADJUSTMENT.

9) With proper preload obtained, install and tighten adjusting ring lock. If disassembled, install drive flanges onto flange shafts. Secure with spring rings and lock clips. Install end caps into flange shafts. Install shafts into final drive case, securing with retaining clips selected in step 5). Install oil pan with new gasket and fill final drive with proper amount of gear oil.

NOTE: **Final drive oil capacity is .8 qts. (.75L) of SAE 90W hypoid gear oil.**

TRANSAXLE REASSEMBLY

FINAL COMPONENT ASSEMBLY
End Play Checking & Adjustment
1) Measure end (axial) play between final drive and transmission: Place a straightedge on transmission attaching face of final drive housing. Using a depth gauge, measure distance from top surface of straightedge to surface of pinion bearing inner race. This is measurement "A".

2) Measure distance from top surface of straightedge to face of final drive housing. This is measurement "B". Subtract "B" from "A" to obtain "C". Record for future reference.

3) Place a new gasket on transmission separation plate. Position straightedge on transmission case and measure distance from top surface of straightedge to gasket surface. This is measurement "D".

4) Measure distance from top surface of straightedge down to inner shoulder of governor drive gear. This is measurement "E". Subtract "E" from "D" to obtain "F" and record.

5) Subtract "F" from "C". This amount is end play (without shims) between final drive and transmission. Determine shim pack thickness required. See END PLAY SHIM CHART. Shims are available in thicknesses of .016" (.40 mm) and .047" (1.20 mm). Combine shims as required to obtain correct total thickness.

6) Install selected shim(s) into final drive case, on top of pinion bearing inner race. Next, install sealing "O" ring and final drive-to-transmission oil seal into pinion cavity of final drive housing. Install turbine shaft and ATF pump shaft fully into transmission.

7) Position new "O" ring seal on final drive case. Mate final drive and transmission cases. Install final drive-to-transmission case nuts and tighten. Place new "O" ring seals on governor, governor cover and speedometer driven gear assembly.

8) Install components in transmission case. Install torque converter to complete assembly. Install transaxle assembly into vehicle, fill with ATF and road test for proper operation.

NOTE: **When filling dry transaxle with ATF, capacity is 6.4 qts. (6.1L). Refill capacity of transaxle is 3.2 qts. (3.0L). Use only DEXRON or DEXRON II type transmission fluid.**

Fig. 37: Measuring Transmission-to-Final Drive End Play

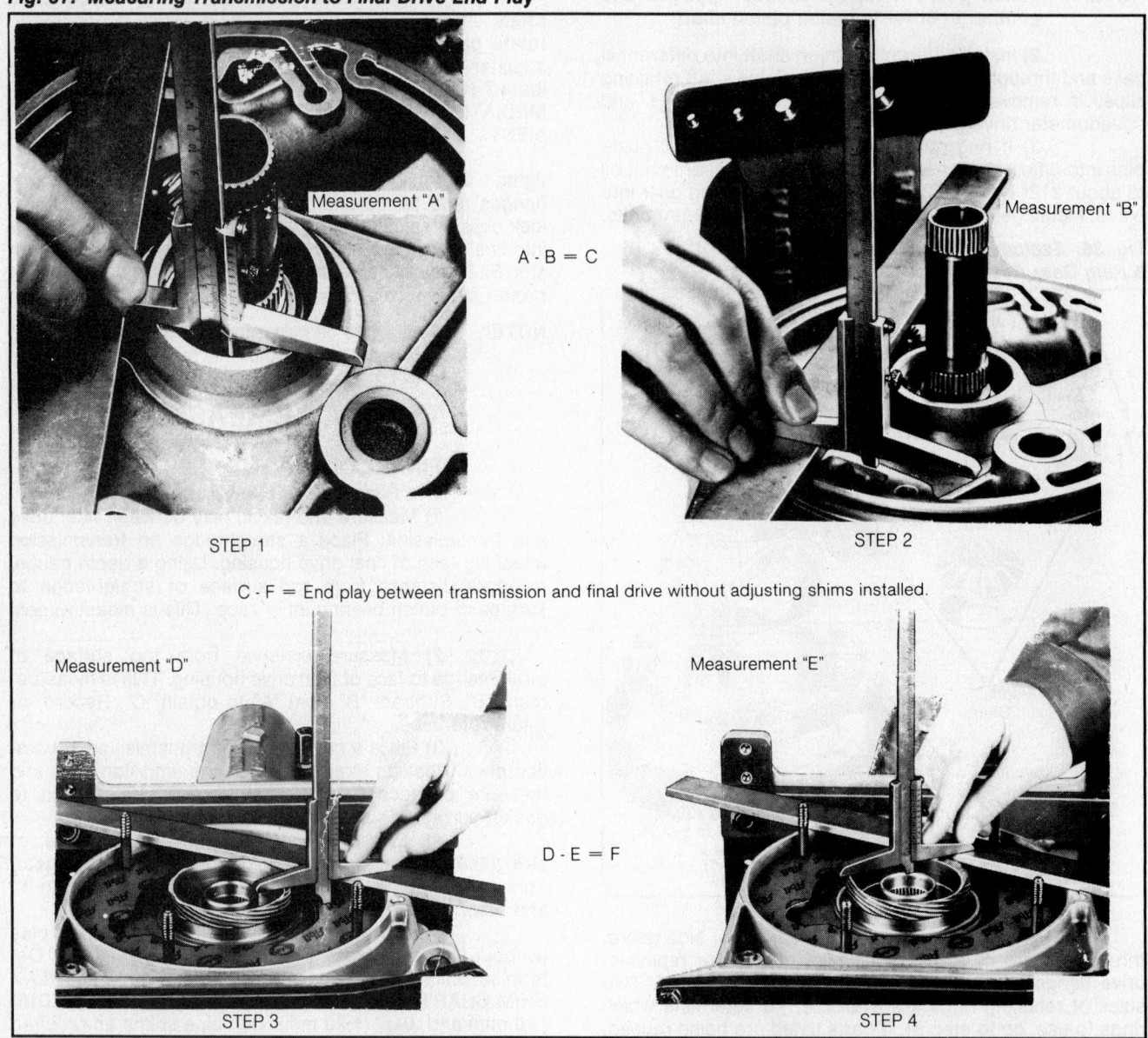

Measurement "A"

A - B = C

Measurement "B"

STEP 1

STEP 2

C - F = End play between transmission and final drive without adjusting shims installed.

Measurement "D"

Measurement "E"

D - E = F

STEP 3

STEP 4

END PLAY SHIM CHART

If End Play Is In (mm)	Install Shim Pack In. (mm)
.009-.033 (0.23-0.84)	None
.034-.049 (0.85-1.24)	.016 (0.40)
.050-.065 (1.25-1.64)	.032 (0.80)
.066-.080 (1.65-2.04)	.048 (1.20)
.081-.096 (2.05-2.44)	.064 (1.60)
.097-.112 (2.45-2.84)	.080 (2.00)
.113-.128 (2.85-3.24)	.096 (2.40)
.129-.143 (3.25-3.64)	.112 (2.80)
.144-.153 (3.65-3.88)	.128 (3.20)

TIGHTENING SPECIFICATIONS

Application	Ft. Lbs. (N.m)
Drive Shaft	
CV Joint-to-Drive Flange	33 (45)
Final Drive Housing (Differential)	
1-Way Clutch Support Mounting Bolt	18 (25)
Housing Cover-to-Housing Mounting Bolt	22 (30)
Intermediate Gear Shaft	
Lock Plate-to-Housing	11 (15)
Ring Gear Mounting Bolt	51 (70)
Side Bearing Cover Mounting Nut	22 (30)
Transmission	
2nd Gear Brake Band	
Adjusting Screw Lock Nut	15 (20)
Converter-to-Drive Plate	22 (30)
Converter Cover Plate-to-Bell Housing	11 (15)
Kickdown Valve-to-Shaft Nut	11 (15)
Manual Valve-to-Shaft Nut	15 (20)
Oil Pan-to-Transmission Case	15 (20)
Operating Lever	
to-Shaft (New Type)	15 (20)
to-Shaft (For Kickdown Valve)	11 (15)
Protection Plate-to-Transaxle	
Mounting Bolt (8 mm)	15 (20)
Mounting Bolt (10 mm)	18 (25)
Selector Segment Spring-to-Trans. Case	15 (20)
Side Cover-to-Final Drive Housing	22 (30)
Starter-to-Bell Housing	22 (30)
Transaxle-to-Engine Mount Bolt	41 (56)
Transmission Case-to-Final Drive Housing	22 (30)

Application	INCH lbs. (N.m)
Final Drive Housing (Differential)	
Adjusting Ring Lock Plate-to-Housing	89 (10)
Transmission	
ATF Pump-to-Transmission Case	62 (7)
Accumulator Cover	
to-Transmission Case	27 (3)
Main Pressure Tap Plug	89 (10)
Operating Lever Shaft Lock Bolt	35 (4)
Separating Plate-to-Transmission Case	62 (7)
Strainer-to-Valve Body	27 (3)
Valve Body	
to-Separator & Transfer Plates	35 (4)
to-Transmission Case	35 (4)

Automatic Transmissions

VOLKSWAGEN VANAGON

TRANSAXLE IDENTIFICATION

Transmission portion of transaxle assembly may be identified by a group of numbers stamped into top of transmission case. One of the numbers is "090". This denotes the Volkswagen "2-planetary" type transmission. Final drive portion of transaxle assembly is identified by a group of figures stamped into final drive housing near governor assembly. These figures consist of a 2 letter model code and a build date code.

DESCRIPTION

Transaxle assembly consists of two main units: Automatic transmission and final drive assembly. The transmission housing contains two planetary gear sets, two multi-disc clutches, one brake band and servo, one multiple-disc brake, a one-way clutch, and a hydraulic control system. The final drive housing contains the torque converter, governor assembly for transmission, ring and pinion gear, and the differential assembly.

LUBRICATION & ADJUSTMENT

See the appropriate AUTOMATIC TRANSMIS-SION SERVICING article in IMPORT GENERAL SERVICING section.

SERVICE (IN VEHICLE)

For Axle Drive Shaft, Constant Velocity (CV) Joint, and Rear Wheel Bearing Housing removal and installation see the appropriate article in MANUAL TRANSMISSIONS section.

TROUBLE SHOOTING

NO MOVEMENT

In Any Gear

Low fluid level. Manual lever not connected to manual valve. Torque converter disconnected from drive plate. Main pressure valve sticking. Oil pump drive plate and/or shaft defective.

In Forward Gears

Forward clutch internal damage (worn plates, broken diaphragm spring, seals leaking, etc.). Forward planetary gear set damaged.

In First Gear in "D" or "2"

One-way clutch not holding. Forward clutch internal damage.

In First Gear in "1"

1st/Reverse brake plates worn or burnt.

In Second Gear

2nd gear brake band out of adjustment, or burnt, or servo defective.

In Reverse

1st/Reverse brake plates damaged, worn or burnt. Direct/Reverse clutch internal damage. Forward clutch seized in applied position.

NO UPSHIFTS

Into Second Gear

Governor drive defective. Governor dirty or improperly assembled. Accumulator cover plate loose. Valve body dirty. 1-2 shift valve sticking. 2nd gear brake band burnt or worn.

Into Third Gear

Governor or valve body dirty. 2-3 shift valve sticking. Oil pump bolts loose.

Fig. 1: Volkswagen Vanagon Automatic Transaxle Assembly

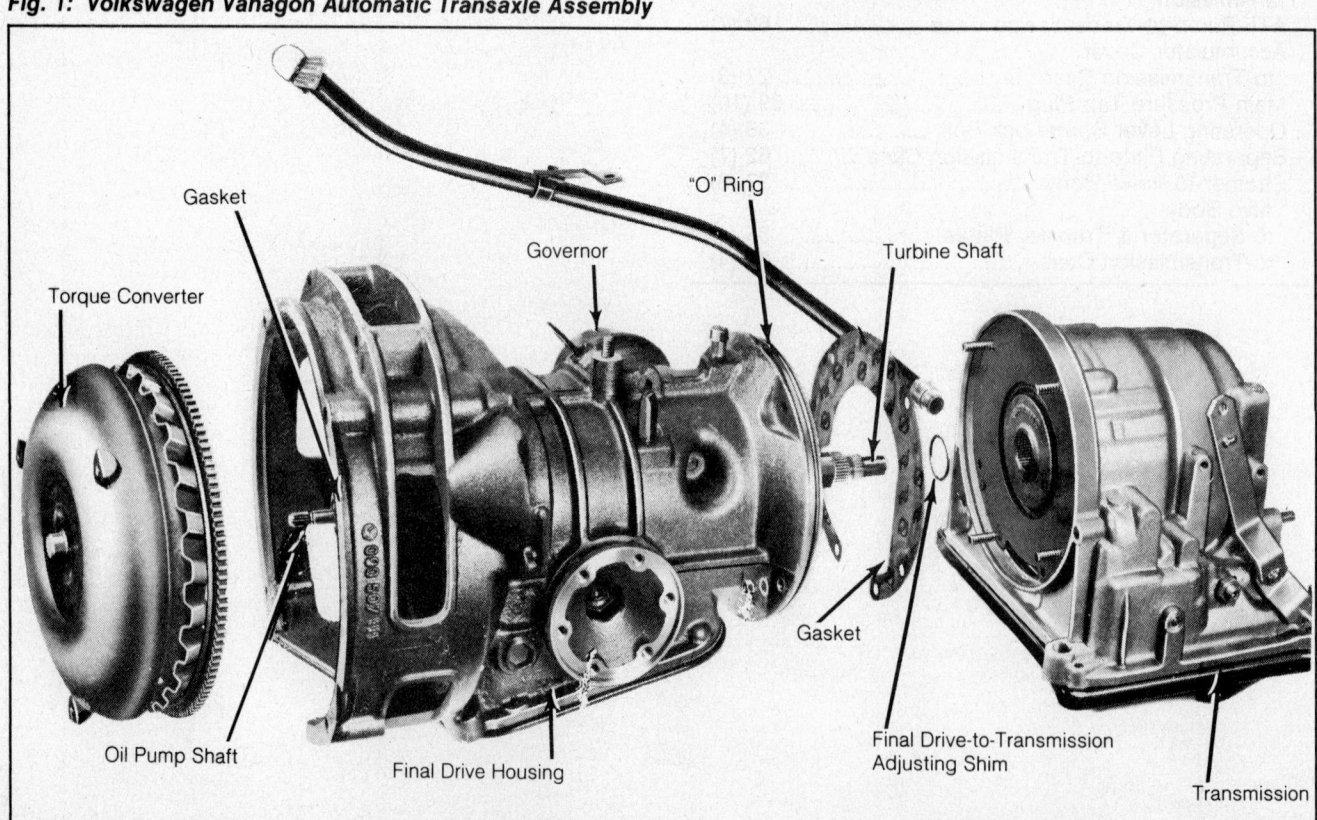

Torque Converter — Gasket — Governor — "O" Ring — Turbine Shaft — Oil Pump Shaft — Final Drive Housing — Gasket — Final Drive-to-Transmission Adjusting Shim — Transmission

VOLKSWAGEN VANAGON (Cont.)

NO DOWNSHIFTS
Into Second Gear
Governor dirty. 2-3 shift valve sticking.
Into First Gear
Governor dirty. 1-2 shift valve sticking.

DELAYED ENGAGEMENT ON UPSHIFTS
1-2 Upshift
Low fluid level. Dirty valve body. 2nd gear brake band worn, burnt or out of adjustment. 2nd gear servo defective.
2-3 Upshift
Low fluid level. Dirty valve body. 2nd gear brake band worn, burnt or out of adjustment. 2nd gear servo defective. Direct/Reverse clutch plates worn or burnt. Wrong Direct/Reverse clutch installed.

ERRATIC DRIVE
Low fluid level. Bushing in one-way clutch support and turbine shaft worn. Oil filter dirty.

INCORRECT SHIFT SPEEDS
Governor dirty. Valve body dirty. Planetary gears or separation plate gasket damaged.

TESTING

ROAD TEST
1) Before road testing, be certain that fluid level and condition, and control linkage adjustments have been checked and corrected as necessary. During the test, transmission should upshift and downshift at approximately the speeds shown in *Shift Speeds* chart. All shifts may vary somewhat due to production tolerances or tire size. The important factor is the quality of the shifts. All shifts should be smooth, responsive, and with no slippage or engine speed runaway.
2) Slippage or engine runaway in any gear usually indicates clutch, band or brake problems. The slipping unit in a particular gear can usually be identified by noting transmission operation in other selector positions and comparing which internal units are applied in those positions. *See Clutch and Band Application Chart.*

3) This process of elimination can be used to detect any unit which slips, and to confirm proper operation of good units. However, the actual cause of the malfunction usually cannot be easily determined. Most conditions can be caused by leaking hydraulic circuits or sticking valves. Therefore, unless an obvious condition exists, do not disassemble transmission until a hydraulic pressure test has been made.

SHIFT SPEED SPECIFICATIONS

Application	Shift Points (MPH)	
	Full Throttle	Kickdown
1-2 Upshift	16-22	30-32
2-3 Upshift	37-47	55-56
3-2 Downshift	27-37	52-53
2-1 Downshift	11-12	27-29

HYDRAULIC PRESSURE TEST
1) Connect a pressure gauge to main pressure test point on case (adjacent to servo cover). Bring

Fig. 2: View of Transmission Case Showing Main Pressure Test Point

Arrow Indicates Pressure Connection

CLUTCH AND BAND APPLICATION CHART
(ELEMENTS IN USE)

Selector Lever Position	Forward Clutch	Direct-Reverse Clutch	First-Reverse Brake	Second Gear Band	One-Way Clutch
D – DRIVE					
First Gear	X				X
Second Gear	X			X	
Third Gear	X	X			
2 – INTERMEDIATE					
First Gear	X				X
Second Gear	X			X	
1 – LOW (First)	X		X		
R – REVERSE		X	X		

NEUTRAL OR PARK – All clutches, brakes, and bands released and/or ineffective.

transmission to normal operating temperature and place selector lever in "D". Accelerate to about 30 MPH, release throttle completely and read pressure on gauge.

NOTE: **This test, as well as full throttle test performed next, should be carried out on a dynamometer when possible.**

2) Next, run engine at full throttle with vehicle speed about 30 MPH, and again note pressure reading in "D".

3) Finally, with vehicle at a standstill, place selector lever in "R" position, and note reading on pressure gauge.

4) Pressures obtained in each phase of test should be approximately as shown in *Main Pressure* chart. If not, disassemble and clean valve body and check especially for sticking valves.

MAIN PRESSURE SPECIFICATIONS

Application	psi (kg/cm²)
"D" at Idle [1]	41-43 (2.9-3.0)
"D" at Full Throttle	83-85 (5.9-6.0)
"R" at Idle [2]	129-138 (9.1-9.7)

[1] – Engine speed at about 30 MPH, throttle released.
[2] – With vehicle stationary.

STALL TEST

Testing Precautions

When making test, do not hold throttle open any longer than the time it takes to read tachometer. Maximum stall speed test time is 5 seconds. If repetition is necessary, wait at least 20 seconds between tests. If engine speed exceeds limits shown in *Stall Speeds* table, release accelerator immediately as clutch or band slippage is indicated.

Testing Procedure

With engine at normal operating temperature, connect a tachometer. Start engine and set parking and service brakes. Place selector lever in "D". Depress accelerator briefly to full throttle and note maximum RPM obtained. Engine speed should be within limits shown in *Stall Speeds* table.

NOTE: **Normal stall speed will drop approximately 125 RPM per 3200 feet altitude. Also, stall speed will drop slightly at high ambient temperatures.**

STALL SPEED SPECIFICATIONS

Application	Stall RPM
All Models	1950-2250

Stall Test Results

1) If stall speed is higher than specified, forward clutch or 1st gear one-way clutch is slipping. If stall speed in "D" is too high, repeat stall test in "1". If RPM is within specifications, one-way clutch for 1st gear is defective. If stall speed RPM is still too high, forward clutch is defective.

2) If stall speed is approximately 200 RPM below specifications, engine performance may be unsatisfactory. If stall speed is approximately 400 RPM below

specifications, torque converter stator one-way clutch is defective and complete converter should be replaced.

REMOVAL & INSTALLATION

See appropriate AUTOMATIC TRANSMISSION REMOVAL article in IMPORT GENERAL SERVICING section.

TORQUE CONVERTER

NOTE: **The torque converter is a sealed unit and cannot be disassembled for service. However, the bushing in converter hub may be replaced as follows:**

BUSHING REPLACEMENT

1) Check bushing wear using an inside micrometer. Wear limit of bushing is 1.348" (34.25 mm), and maximum allowable out-of-round is .001" (.03 mm).

2) To replace bushing, use a bushing puller to withdraw bushing from converter hub. Press new bushing into place until it is fully seated in hub. Ensure that inside diameter of new bushing is 1.340-1.341" (34.03-34.05 mm).

TRANSMISSION DISASSEMBLY

NOTE: **To separate transaxle units, withdraw torque converter from final drive housing and remove oil pump shaft from center of turbine shaft. Disconnect oil filler pipe. Remove attaching nuts from transmission studs that attach final drive to transmission, then separate final drive unit from transmission case. Withdraw turbine shaft from final drive assembly pinion shaft. For final drive disassembly and reassembly, see Final Drive information at rear of this article.**

Fig. 3: Removing First Gear One-Way Clutch Assembly Retaining Snap Ring

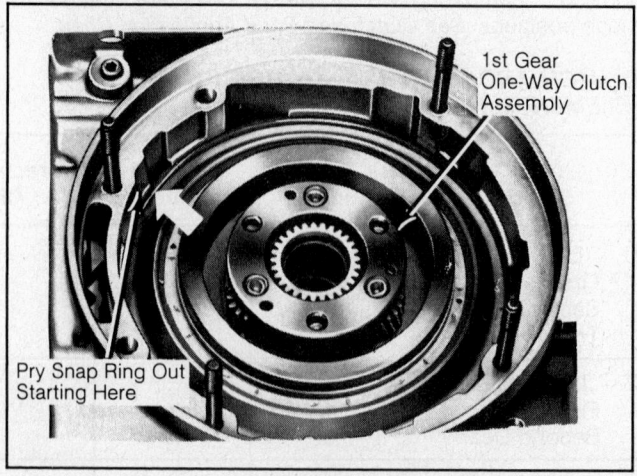

1st Gear One-Way Clutch Assembly

Pry Snap Ring Out Starting Here

1) Mount transmission assembly in a work stand. Remove separation plate attaching screws and lift plate and gasket from transmission case. Remove forward annulus gear and 2 thrust washers behind it from case.

VOLKSWAGEN VANAGON (Cont.)

2) Using a screwdriver, carefully pry large snap ring retaining 1st gear one-way clutch assembly from case. Lift out one-way clutch, 1st/Reverse gear brake plates, and reverse planetary gear set as a unit.

3) Remove thrust washers, then lift the following components from case as an assembly: Sun gear, driving shell, forward planetary gear set, and forward clutch assembly.

Fig. 4: *Removing Brake Band Servo Assembly*

Tap cover until cover and piston pop out under spring pressure.

4) Remove 2nd gear brake band servo cover snap ring. Then using a rubber mallet, tap cover until cover and piston assembly pop out under spring tension.

5) Loosen 2nd gear brake band adjusting screw lock nut and remove lock nut and screw, then withdraw push rod for adjusting screw.

6) Lift out remaining planetary gear set components that are housed in 1st/Reverse gear brake shell. Remove bolt from 1st/Reverse brake spring plate, withdraw spring plate and springs, then pull driving shell, brake piston, and oil pump from case.

7) Invert transmission so that oil pan is facing up. Remove attaching bolts and lift off pan and gasket. Remove screws from oil strainer and separate strainer from valve body.

8) Remove the valve body attaching bolts and lift valve body assembly from case using care not to drop manual valve. Remove attaching screws from accumulator cover plate, then remove cover, spring and accumulator piston. If necessary for parts replacement, disassemble kickdown and selector linkage using *Fig. 5* as a disassembly guide.

COMPONENT DISASSEMBLY & REASSEMBLY

OIL PUMP ASSEMBLY

CAUTION: Oil pump cover is under spring tension.

Disassembly

1) Remove pump cover attaching screws and separate cover from housing. Remove check ball and

Fig. 5: *Bottom View of Transmission Case Showing Kickdown and Selector Linkage*

"E" Clip
Parking Pawl Pin
Parking Lock Operating Lever
Roller Spring
Spring Retaining Bolt
Parking Pawl
Kickdown Lever
Parking Pawl Spring
Support Ring
"O" Ring
Lever Shaft
Manual Lever
"O" Ring
Operating Lever Rod & Spring
Manual Lever Nut
Kickdown Operating Lever
Manual Operating Lever
Kickdown Lever Nut

NOTE: From Transmission Number 22050, Operating Lever is Stamped Steel with Pressed in Bushings and Rollers. Operating Rod and Spring Cannot be Disassembled, Rod and Spring are Attached to Operating Lever with an "E" Clip.

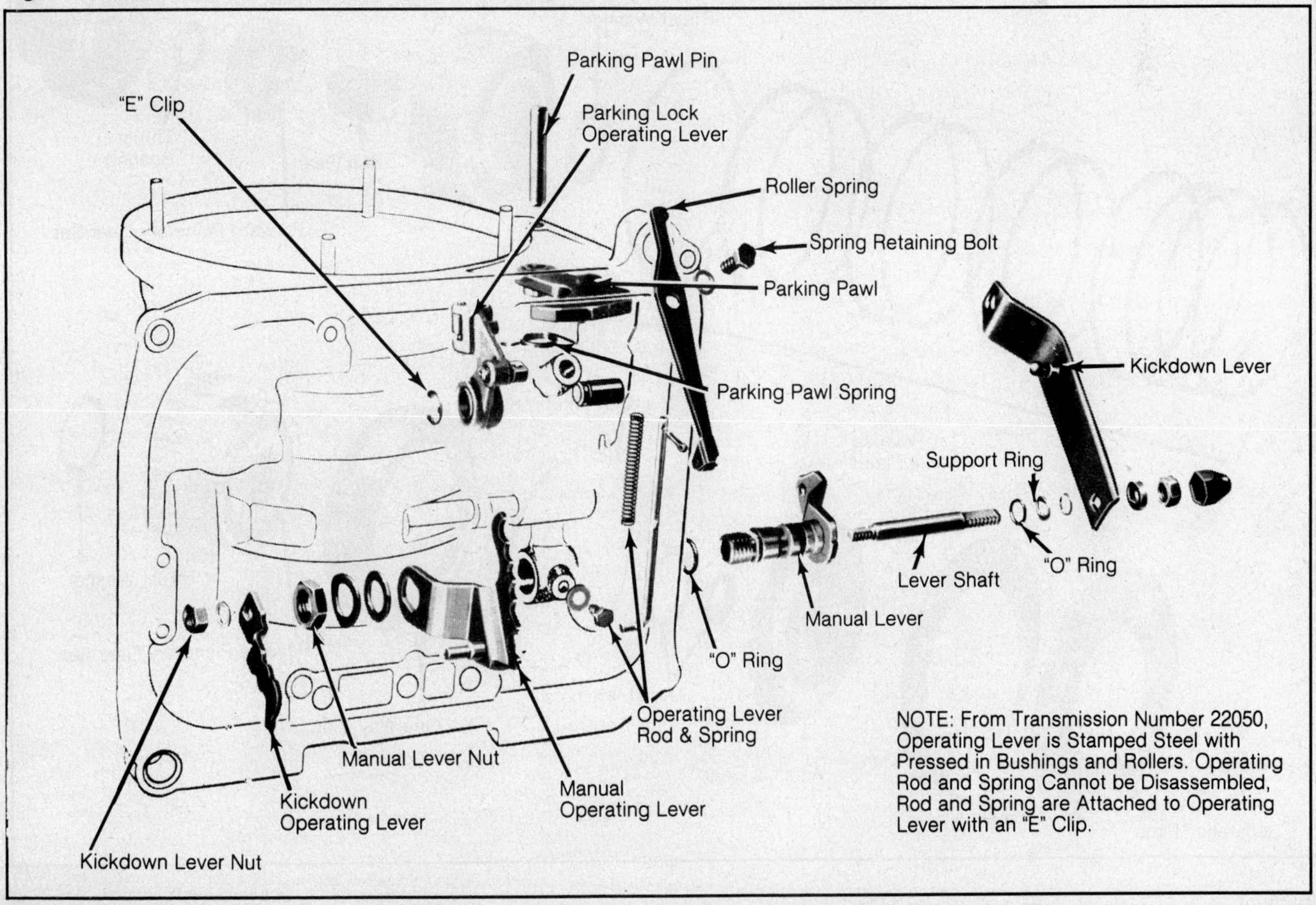

Automatic Transmissions

VOLKSWAGEN VANAGON (Cont.)

Fig. 6: Exploded View Showing Major Components of Transmission Assembly

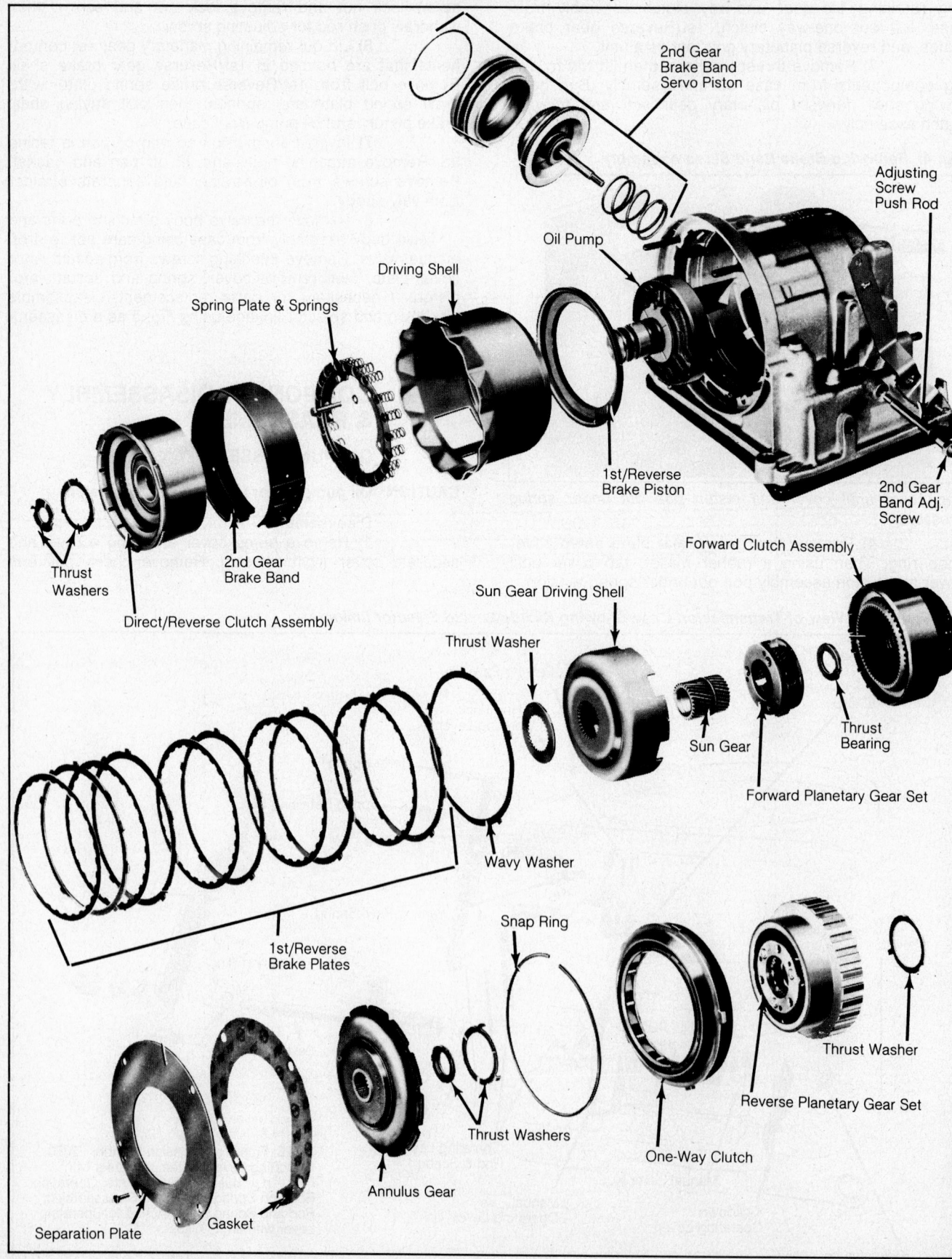

2nd Gear Brake Band Servo Piston

Adjusting Screw Push Rod

Oil Pump

Driving Shell

Spring Plate & Springs

1st/Reverse Brake Piston

2nd Gear Band Adj. Screw

Thrust Washers

2nd Gear Brake Band

Direct/Reverse Clutch Assembly

Forward Clutch Assembly

Sun Gear Driving Shell

Thrust Washer

Sun Gear

Thrust Bearing

Forward Planetary Gear Set

1st/Reverse Brake Plates

Wavy Washer

Snap Ring

Thrust Washer

Reverse Planetary Gear Set

One-Way Clutch

Thrust Washers

Annulus Gear

Separation Plate

Gasket

VOLKSWAGEN VANAGON (Cont.)

Fig. 7: Exploded View of Oil Pump Assembly

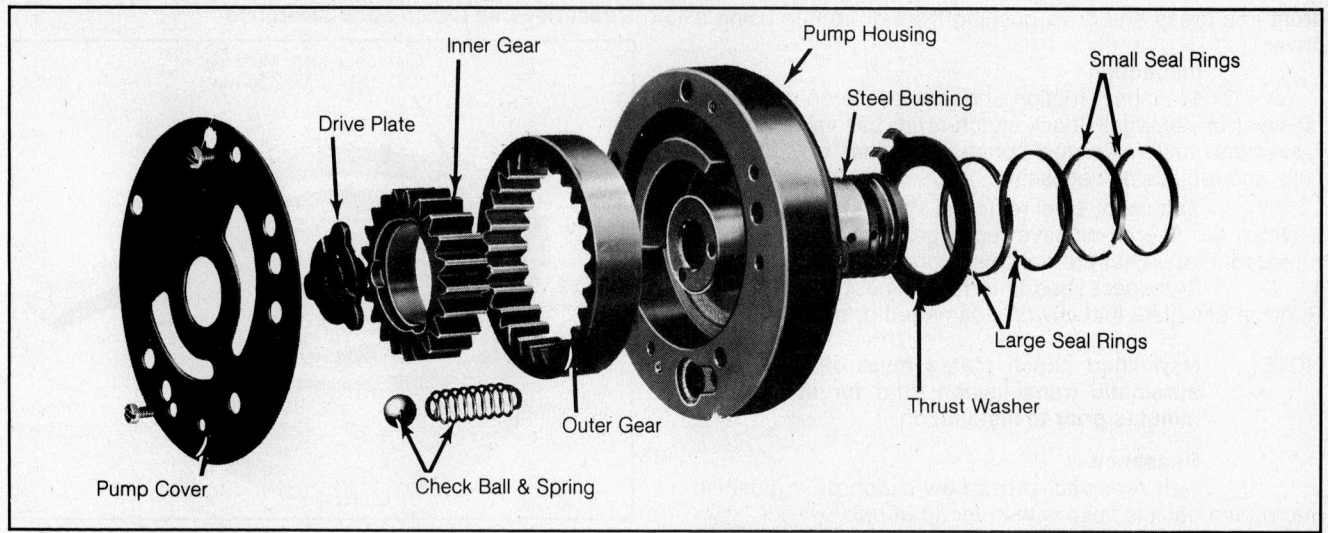

spring, then lift out inner and outer pump gears along with drive plate.

2) Using needle-nose pliers, unhook oil seal ring ends and carefully remove seal rings from pump housing. Remove thrust washer from pump housing.

Inspection

Wash all parts in kerosene and blow out oil passages with compressed air. Inspect all parts for wear, scoring, chipped teeth, and any other damage. Replace parts as necessary.

NOTE: If either of the pump gears, the pump housing or cover are damaged, then entire oil pump assembly must be replaced. The drive plate, oil seal rings, and thrust washers can be replaced individually.

Reassembly

1) Install thrust washer on pump housing. Carefully install first the large oil seal rings and then the small seal rings onto pump housing, ensuring that ring ends hook correctly.

2) Lubricate all parts with automatic transmission fluid. Install inner and outer pump gears into housing,

then install drive plate with extended hub inserted into pump housing shaft opening. Install check ball and spring into housing. Align cover with housing, then install and tighten attaching screws.

NOTE: After pump has been reassembled, insert pump shaft into pump and ensure that gears rotate freely and smoothly. Gear rotation should also be checked after oil pump is installed into transmission case.

DIRECT/REVERSE CLUTCH

Disassembly

1) Using a screwdriver, pry clutch pack retaining snap ring from clutch drum. Withdraw clutch pressure plate, lined clutch plates and steel clutch plates from drum.

2) Place clutch drum in a press, apply downward pressure to piston spring retainer and remove snap ring. Release press and remove spring retainer. Using a twisting motion, remove piston with return springs from drum. Remove piston seals and springs from piston.

Fig. 8: Exploded View of Direct/Reverse Clutch Assembly

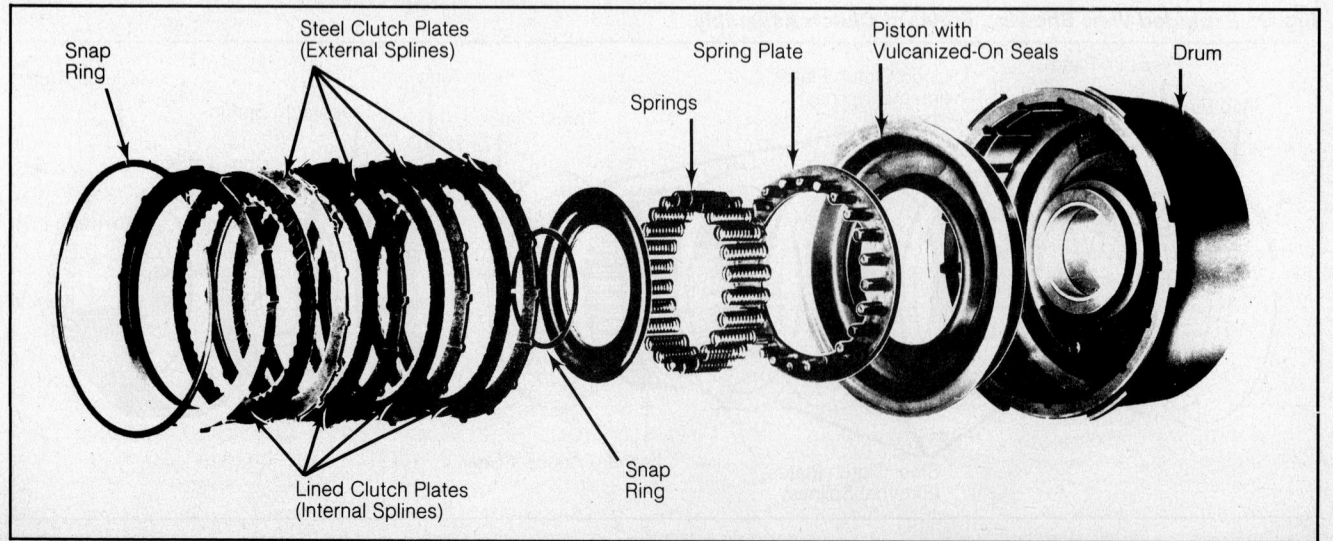

3) If necessary for replacement, place clutch drum in a press and drive bushing from drum hub using a driver.

Inspection

1) Inspect friction surfaces of piston and drum for wear or damage. Check clutch drum ball valve for free movement. Inspect piston springs for wear or collapsed coils and replace as necessary.

2) Inspect steel (external splines) clutch plates. If plates are scored or have radial grooves, they must be replaced. Plates that are only discolored can be reused.

3) Inspect lined (internal splines) clutch plates. Replace any plate that is worn, damaged or burnt.

NOTE: **New lined clutch plates must be soaked in automatic transmission fluid for at least 15 minutes prior to installation.**

Reassembly

1) If removed, press new clutch drum bushing into drum until it is flush with outer lip of hub.

2) Lubricate piston seals with automatic transmission fluid, then install them into clutch drum with lips facing into drum. Using a stiff plastic sheet to protect seals, install piston into drum using a twisting motion. Remove plastic sheet from drum.

3) Position piston return spring plate and springs on piston. Place spring retainer on springs, compress retainer and install snap ring. Install clutch plates into drum starting with a steel (external splines) plate and alternating lined and steel plates until all clutch plates are installed.

4) Install pressure plate and clutch pack retaining snap ring. Using a feeler gauge, measure clearance between pressure plate and retaining snap ring. Clearance should be .081-.098" (2.05-2.50 mm); if not, remove clutch pack snap ring and replace with a snap ring of sufficient thickness to bring clearance within specifications.

NOTE: **Direct/Reverse clutch pack snap rings are available in various thicknesses from .059" (1.5 mm) to .098" (2.5 mm).**

5) Install correct thickness snap ring. Recheck clutch pack clearance to ensure correct snap ring has been installed.

Fig. 9: Exploded View Showing Forward Clutch Assembly

Fig. 10: Using a Feeler Gauge to Measure Direct/Reverse Clutch Pack Clearance

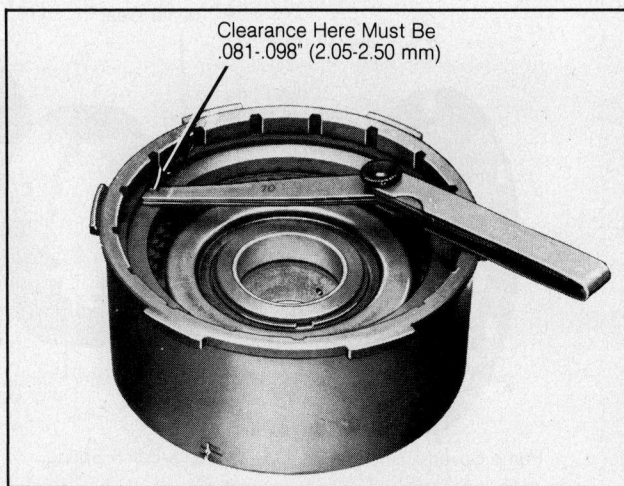

Insert feeler gauge between snap ring and pressure plate.

DIRECT/REVERSE CLUTCH PLATE CHART

Application	Steel Plates	Lined Plates
All Models	4	4

FORWARD CLUTCH

Disassembly

1) Using a screwdriver, pry clutch pack retaining snap ring from clutch drum. Then withdraw pressure plate, forward annulus gear, lined and steel clutch plates, and thrust plate.

2) Carefully pry out diaphragm spring snap ring. Remove diaphragm spring. Lift out piston.

NOTE: **It may be necessary to force piston from clutch drum using compressed air.**

Inspection

1) Inspect clutch drum for scoring, wear, or other damage. Check clutch drum ball valve for free movement and ensure that drilling is clear.

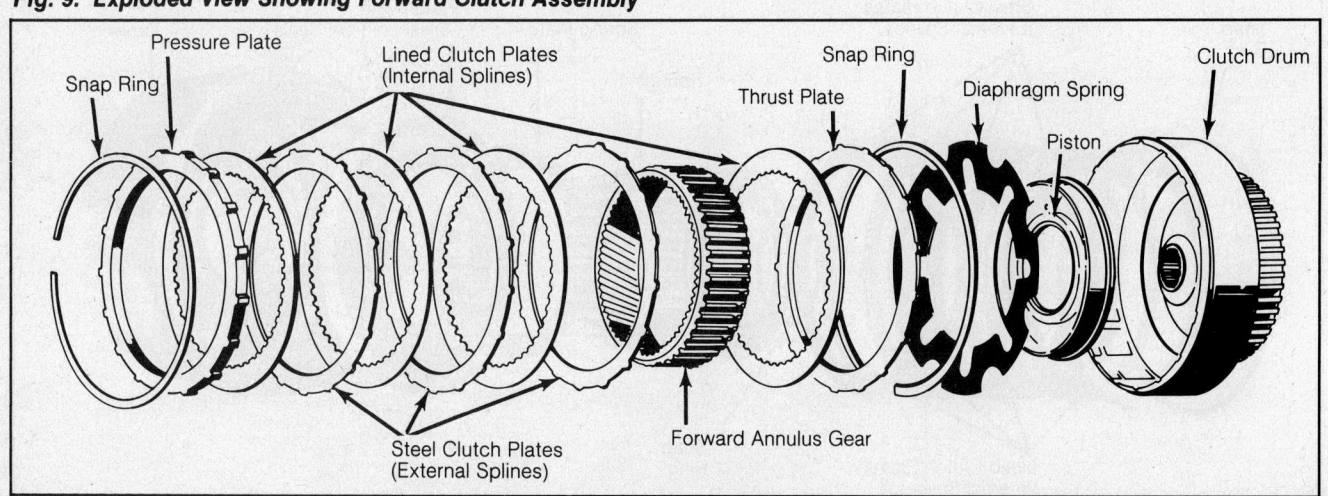

VOLKSWAGEN VANAGON (Cont.)

2) Inspect diaphragm spring and piston for damage. Also, place diaphragm spring onto piston and ensure that top of spring reaches to at least the lower edge of snap ring groove; if not, replace spring.

NOTE: The forward clutch piston sealing lips are vulcanized to the piston. Replace the piston if there is damage to the sealing lips or if there is leakage past the sealing lips.

3) Use Direct/Reverse clutch inspection procedures to inspect the lined and steel clutch plates.

NOTE: If new lined (internal splines) clutch plates are to be installed, they must be soaked in automatic transmission fluid for at least 15 minutes prior to installation.

Reassembly

1) Lubricate piston sealing lips with automatic transmission fluid, then install piston into drum using a twisting motion. Install diaphragm spring, with convex side toward piston, into clutch drum. Install retaining snap ring.

NOTE: With snap ring installed, diaphragm spring should be lightly tensioned; if not, replace spring.

2) Install thrust plate into drum. If one side of thrust plate is chamfered, install chamfered side toward diaphragm spring.

3) Install one lined (internal splines) clutch plate into drum, then install annulus gear so that short splines beneath its retaining ridge are engaged in the lined clutch plate. Install remaining clutch plates starting with a steel (external splines) plate and alternating lined and steel clutch plates until all plates have been installed.

FORWARD CLUTCH PLATE CHART

Application	Steel Plates	Lined Plates
All Models	3	4

4) Install pressure plate and retaining snap ring into clutch drum. Next, position a dial indicator on clutch assembly so that indicator tip contacts pressure plate, then zero dial face.

Fig. 11: Using a Dial Indicator to Measure Forward Clutch End Play

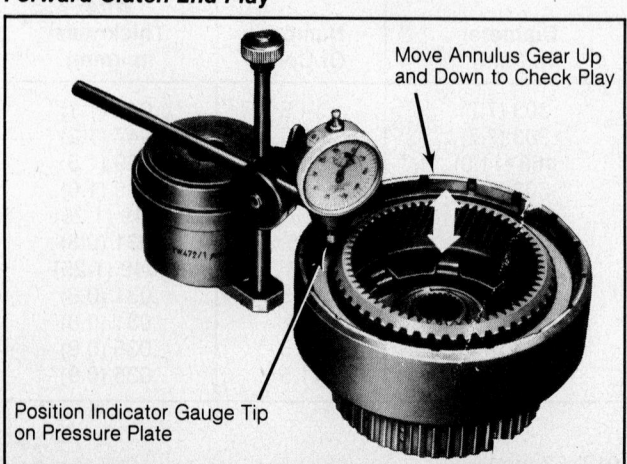

Move Annulus Gear Up and Down to Check Play

Position Indicator Gauge Tip on Pressure Plate

5) Measure forward clutch end play by moving annulus gear up and down so that dial indicator will show play between pressure plate and snap ring.

6) Forward clutch end play should be .020-.035" (.50-.90 mm). If not, replace pressure plate with one of sufficient thickness to bring end play within specifications. After correct pressure plate is installed, recheck end play.

NOTE: Forward clutch pressure plates are available in thicknesses of .236" (6.0 mm) to .299" (7.6 mm) in increments of .016" (.4 mm).

FIRST GEAR ONE-WAY CLUTCH
Disassembly

Remove one-way clutch rollers and springs. Remove snap rings. Using a plastic mallet, carefully drive roller cage out of outer race.

Fig. 12: Modified One-Way Clutch and Retaining Ring

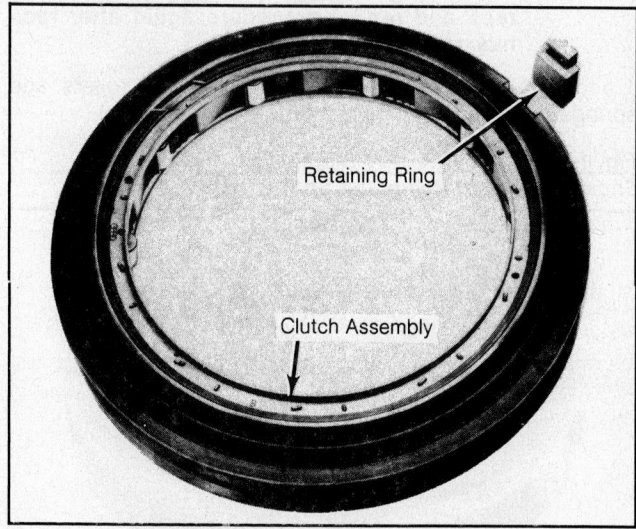

Retaining Ring

Clutch Assembly

Fig. 13: Exploded View of First Gear One-Way Clutch Assembly

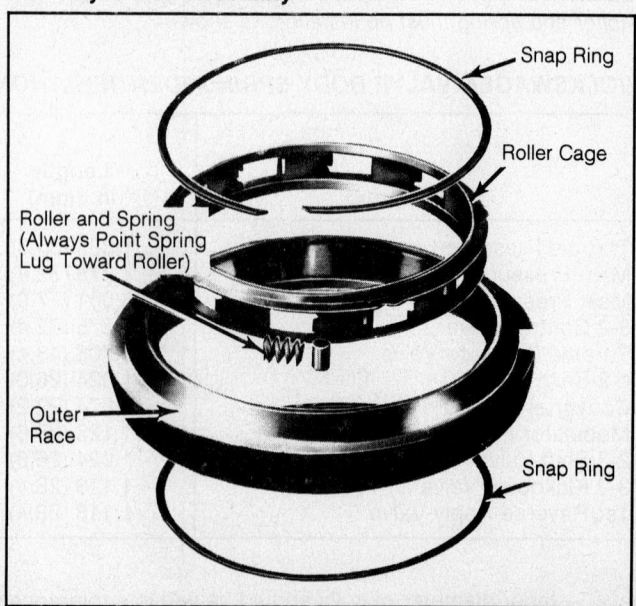

Snap Ring

Roller Cage

Roller and Spring (Always Point Spring Lug Toward Roller)

Outer Race

Snap Ring

VOLKSWAGEN VANAGON (Cont.)

Inspection
Inspect all parts for wear scoring, or other damage and replace as necessary.

NOTE: One-way clutch has been modified and now has a retaining key to hold ring from turning in transmission housing. Previously, 5 protruding lugs served this purpose. New type clutch cannot be installed in transmission with old type clutch.

Reassembly
1) Install lower snap ring in groove of outer race. If necessary, heat outer race to 300°F (150°C), then place roller cage into race using 2 pair of pliers.

NOTE: The heat from outer race will transfer quickly to roller cage, causing cage to stick inside race. If cage is not correctly positioned against lower snap ring inside race, DO NOT attempt to press it into position after cage has stuck. Carefully knock cage out of outer race and repeat procedure again after race has cooled down.

2) Install upper snap ring. Install rollers and springs into cage as shown in *Fig. 14*.

Fig. 14: View of One-Way Clutch Assembly Showing Correct Roller and Spring Installation

Roller and spring must be installed as shown.

REVERSE ANNULUS GEAR

NOTE: Reverse annulus gear should be disassembled only if parts replacement is necessary.

Fig. 15: Disassembled View of Reverse Annulus Gear

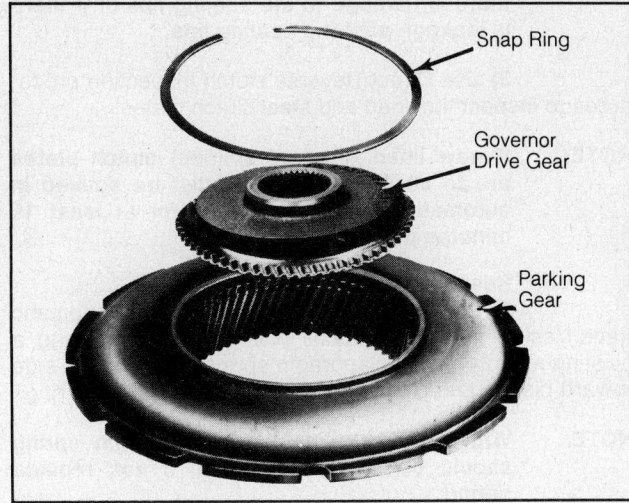

Disassembly & Reassembly
Remove snap ring and lift governor drive gear out of parking gear. Inspect parking lock notches on parking gear and replace worn part. To reassemble, reverse disassembly procedure.

VALVE BODY ASSEMBLY

NOTE: As valve body components are removed from each valve bore, place individual parts in correct order in relative position to valve body to simplify reassembly.

Disassembly
1) Remove transfer plate-to-valve body attaching screws. Lift transfer plate and separator plate from main valve body. Remove .24" (6 mm) check balls (5) and .12" (3 mm) check ball (1) from valve body. *See Fig. 17.*

VOLKSWAGEN VALVE BODY SPRING IDENTIFICATION CHART

Valve Spring	Length In. (mm)	Diameter In. (mm) [1]	Number Of Coils	Wire Thickness In. (mm)
Throttle Pressure Limiting Valve	1.389 (35.3)	.303 (7.7)	14.5	.043 (1.1)
Main Pressure Limiting Valve	1.275 (32.4)	.303 (7.7)	11	.047 (1.2)
Main Pressure Valve	3.031 (77.0)	.468 (11.9)	16.5	.059 (1.5)
3-2 Control Valve	1.275 (32.4)	.303 (7.7)	12.5	.039 (1.0)
Throttle Pressure Valve	1.708 (43.4)	.305 (7.75)	16	.049 (1.25)
1-2 Shift Valve	1.024 (26.0)	.323 (8.2)	9.5	.031 (0.8)
Converter Pressure Valve	0.874 (22.2)	.303 (7.7)	8.5	.049 (1.25)
Modulator Pressure Valve	1.126 (28.6)	.305 (7.75)	11.5	.031 (0.8)
2-3 Shift Valve	1.024 (26.0)	.323 (8.2)	9.5	.031 (0.8)
3-2 Kickdown Valve	1.118 (28.4)	.318 (8.1)	11.5	.035 (0.9)
1st/Reverse Apply Valve	1.118 (28.4)	.318 (8.1)	11.5	.035 (0.9)

[1] – Inner diameter of coils should be within a tolerance of ± .012" (.3 mm).

VOLKSWAGEN VANAGON (Cont.)

*Fig. 16: Exploded View Showing Removal
of Strainers and Valve Body Assembly*

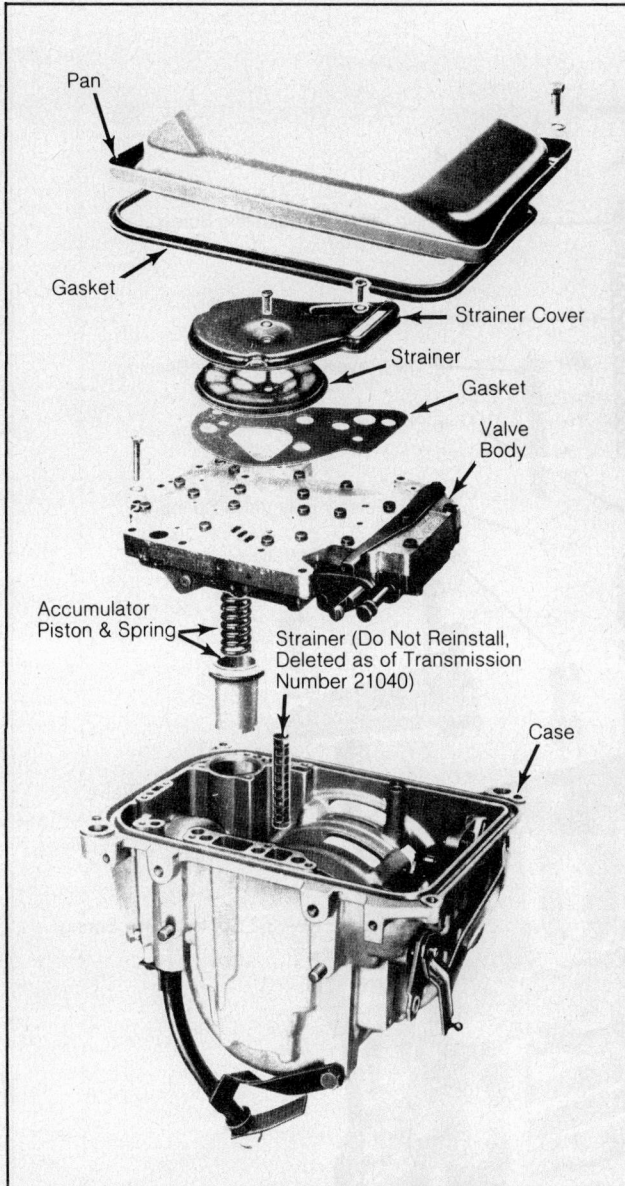

**CAUTION: DO NOT alter setting of adjusting screws
when removing from valve body.**

2) Remove rear end cover plate and withdraw
valves, springs and adjusting screws. Remove remaining
end plates, one at a time, and withdraw all valves, plugs,
springs and adjusting screws. Tag all parts for reassembly
reference.

Inspection
1) Wash all parts in clean kerosene and dry
them with compressed air only (do not use fluffy rags,
etc.). Check all parts for burrs and scores; replace
assembly if damage is found.

2) When valves are clean and lubricated with
fluid, they should fall freely of their own weight in
respective bore; if not, check for valve or bore damage.

3) Check all valve body springs for damage or
collapsed coils.

**CAUTION: Several valve body springs have similar
dimensions; however, they must not be
interchanged as they have different tolerances. See Valve Body Spring Identification
table.**

4) Take care not to disturb settings of adjusting screws; pressures affected by these screws can only
be measured and adjusted accurately on a test stand.

*Fig. 17: View of Main Valve Body
Showing Check Ball Locations*

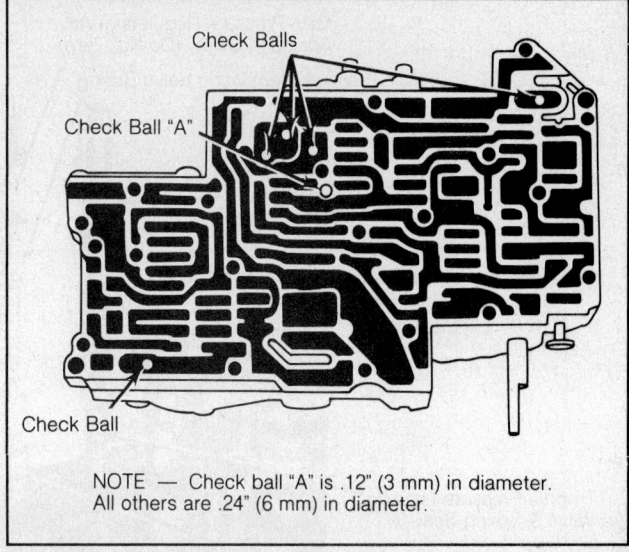

NOTE — Check ball "A" is .12" (3 mm) in diameter.
All others are .24" (6 mm) in diameter.

Fig. 18: View of Valve Body Installed

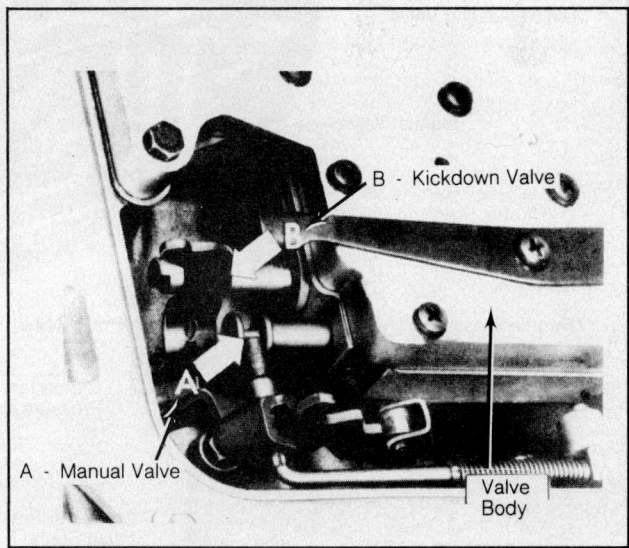

*Arrows show relation of operating levers to manual control
valves.*

Reassembly
1) Lubricate all parts with automatic transmission fluid and install into proper valve body bores, in
reverse order of disassembly. When tightening end plate
attaching screws, be careful not to overtighten them as
this could easily strip the threads or distort the valve body
enough to cause a valve to stick.

Fig. 19: *Exploded View Showing Main Body Assembly Valve Trains*

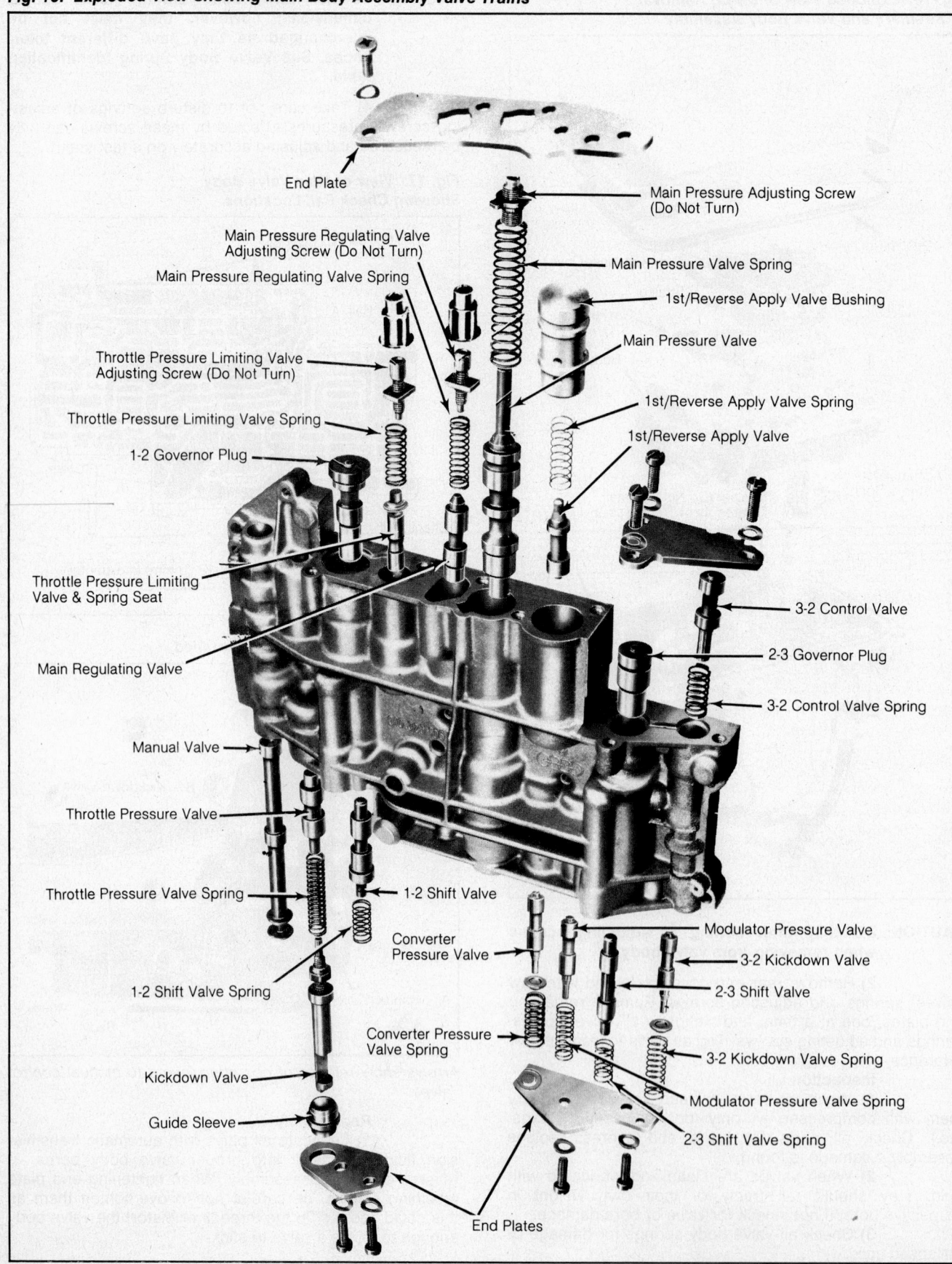

End Plate

Main Pressure Adjusting Screw (Do Not Turn)

Main Pressure Regulating Valve Adjusting Screw (Do Not Turn)

Main Pressure Regulating Valve Spring

Main Pressure Valve Spring

1st/Reverse Apply Valve Bushing

Main Pressure Valve

Throttle Pressure Limiting Valve Adjusting Screw (Do Not Turn)

1st/Reverse Apply Valve Spring

1st/Reverse Apply Valve

Throttle Pressure Limiting Valve Spring

1-2 Governor Plug

Throttle Pressure Limiting Valve & Spring Seat

3-2 Control Valve

2-3 Governor Plug

Main Regulating Valve

3-2 Control Valve Spring

Manual Valve

Throttle Pressure Valve

Throttle Pressure Valve Spring

1-2 Shift Valve

Modulator Pressure Valve

Converter Pressure Valve

3-2 Kickdown Valve

2-3 Shift Valve

1-2 Shift Valve Spring

Converter Pressure Valve Spring

3-2 Kickdown Valve Spring

Kickdown Valve

Modulator Pressure Valve Spring

Guide Sleeve

2-3 Shift Valve Spring

End Plates

VOLKSWAGEN VANAGON (Cont.)

Fig. 20: Exploded View Showing Components of Governor Assembly

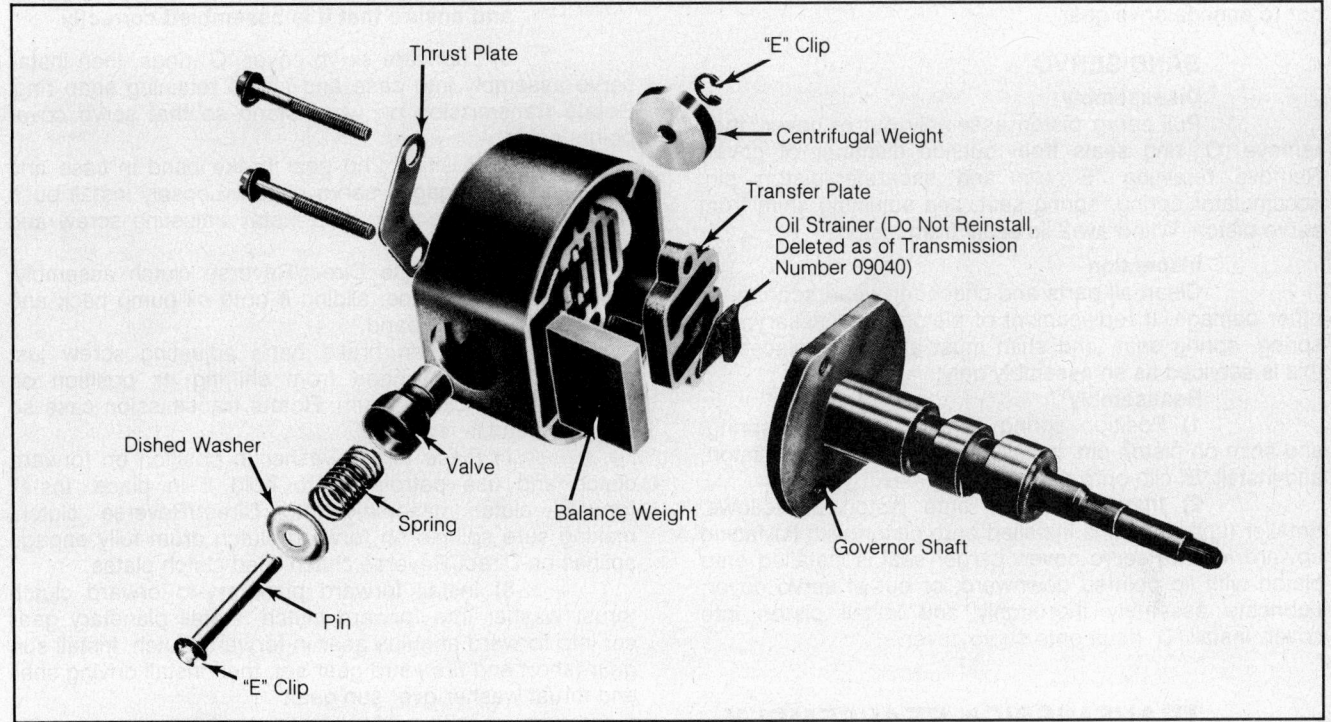

2) Ensure all check balls are installed in proper valve body passages. Install transfer plate-to-main valve body screws and tighten from center outward, taking care not to overtighten.

NOTE: Two collar-type screws are used for attaching roller assembly to body, 3 galvanized screws are for accumulator cover plate, and the remaining 19 screws are used for transfer plate-to-main body attachment.

GOVERNOR ASSEMBLY

NOTE: The governor is mounted in the final drive housing.

Removal

Remove attaching bolts and washers and remove governor cover and "O" ring from final drive housing. Withdraw governor from housing using a clockwise twisting motion that will allow governor drive gear to disengage drive pinion gear.

Disassembly

Remove 2 attaching screws and withdraw thrust plate and governor housing. Remove transfer plate, balance weight, and if equipped, oil strainer. Remove "E" clips and withdraw centrifugal weight, valve, spring, and dished washer from pin.

Reassembly

Reverse disassembly procedure to assemble. Do not reinstall oil strainer in governor. Make sure angle in thrust plate is in center of housing so cover will bear against it.

Installation

Reverse removal procedure and note the following: Prior to installation, check governor oil seal and needle bearing in final drive case for damage and wear,

Fig. 21: Disassembled View of Servo Assembly

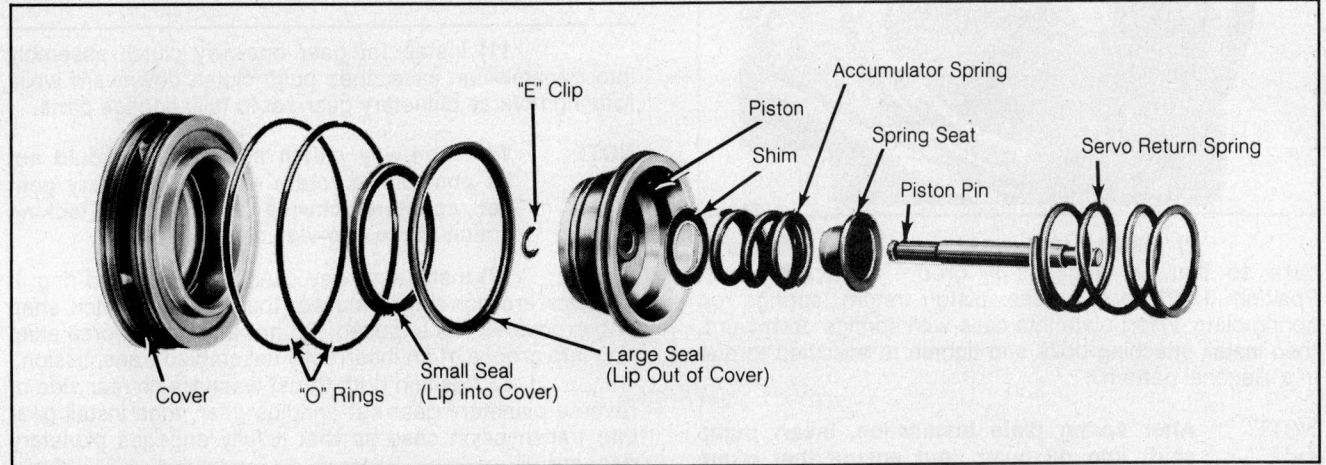

and replace if necessary. After installation, rotate governor to engage drive gear.

BAND SERVO
Disassembly
Pull servo piston assembly out of cover, then remove "O" ring seals from outside diameter of cover. Remove retaining "E" clip and separate piston pin, accumulator spring, spring seat, and adjusting shim from servo piston. Withdraw 2 lip seals from piston.

Inspection
Clean all parts and check for wear, scoring, or other damage. If replacement of piston is necessary, pin, spring, spring seat, and shim must also be replaced as this is serviced as an assembly only.

Reassembly
1) Position spring seat, accumulator spring, and shim on piston pin, install assembly into servo piston, and install "E" clip onto piston.

2) Install lip seals onto piston as follows: Smaller (upper) seal is installed onto piston with lip facing upward, or into servo cover. Larger seal is installed onto piston with lip pointed downward, or out of servo cover. Lubricate assembly thoroughly and install piston into cover. Install "O" rings onto servo cover.

TRANSMISSION REASSEMBLY
1) Lubricate 1st/Reverse gear brake piston with automatic transmission fluid. Install brake piston on oil pump. Install oil pump and piston assembly into transmission case, and position pump so that lug is toward top of case.

Fig. 22: Internal View of Transmission Case Showing Brake Shell Installation

Lug Must Engage Groove at Top of Case

2) Install 1st/Reverse gear brake shell into case so that lug engages in groove at top of case. Position 1st/Reverse brake piston return springs on spring plate, insert plate into case with springs downward, then install attaching bolts and tighten to specified torque in a diagonal pattern.

NOTE: After spring plate installation, insert pump shaft into oil pump and ensure that pump

gears rotate freely; if not, remove oil pump and ensure that it is assembled correctly.

3) Lubricate servo cover "O" rings, then install servo assembly into case and install retaining snap ring. Rotate transmission on work stand so that servo cover points down.

4) Position 2nd gear brake band in case and ensure that it engages servo piston. Loosely install push rod for adjusting screw, then install adjusting screw and lock nut.

5) Lubricate Direct/Reverse clutch assembly, then install it into case, sliding it onto oil pump neck and into 2nd gear brake band.

6) Tighten brake band adjusting screw just enough to prevent band from shifting its position on Direct/Reverse clutch drum. Rotate transmission case so that open end is facing up.

7) Place thrust washer in position on forward clutch and use petrolatum to hold it in place. Install forward clutch assembly into Direct/Reverse clutch, making sure splines on forward clutch drum fully engage splines on Direct/Reverse clutch lined clutch plates.

8) Install forward planetary-to-forward clutch thrust washer into forward clutch. Install planetary gear set into forward annulus gear in forward clutch. Install sun gear (short end first) into gear set, then install driving shell and thrust washer over sun gear.

NOTE: Ensure lugs of driving shell engage tabs of Direct/Reverse clutch drum.

9) Install thrust washer on underside of reverse planetary gear set and use petrolatum to hold in place. Install gear set into case and onto sun gear.

NOTE: Lined brake plates must be soaked in automatic transmission fluid for at least 15 minutes prior to installation

10) Install 1st/Reverse brake waved washer into case. Install 1st/Reverse brake plates into case starting with a steel (external splines) plate and alternating lined (internal splines) plates and steel plates until all brake plates are installed.

FIRST/REVERSE BRAKE PLATE CHART

Application	Steel Plates	Lined Plates
All Models	5	5

11) Install 1st gear one-way clutch assembly into transmission case, then push clutch downward while rotating reverse planetary gear set to fully engage parts.

NOTE: With one-way clutch installed, it should not be possible to rotate reverse planetary gear set counterclockwise due to the locking action of the one-way clutch.

12) Install one-way clutch-to-case snap ring. If all parts are correctly installed, the one-way clutch snap ring groove will be exposed. Do not attempt to force snap ring into groove of an incorrectly assembled transmission.

13 Position both thrust washers on rear side of reverse planetary gear set annulus gear, then install gear into transmission case so that it fully engages planetary gear set.

VOLKSWAGEN VANAGON (Cont.)

Fig. 23: Checking for Correct Parts Installation

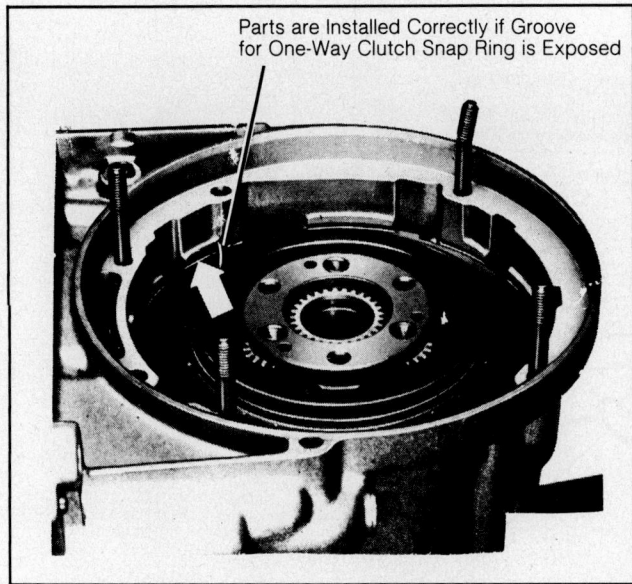

Parts are Installed Correctly if Groove for One-Way Clutch Snap Ring is Exposed

14) Install separation plate gasket over case studs, place separation plate on top of gasket, then install and tighten attaching screws.

NOTE: At this time 2nd gear brake band must be adjusted. To adjust band, the transmission case must be horizontal to prevent band from jamming. Adjust band as follows:

15) Loosen lock nut and tighten brake band adjusting screw to 87 INCH lbs. (10 N.m). Loosen screw. Retighten again to 43 INCH lbs. (5.0 N.m). Back off adjusting screw 2 1/2 turns and tighten adjusting screw lock nut.

16) If case linkage was disassembled, reassemble in case using *Fig. 5* as an assembly guide.

17) Install a new seal on accumulator piston (lip pointing toward case), and install piston and spring into case. Install valve body assembly into case, making sure manual valve engages manual lever, and that kickdown valve engages kickdown lever. Install valve body-to-case attaching bolts and tighten from center outward.

NOTE: Do not use sealer on oil pan gasket, as any surplus sealer may find its way into transmission fluid and cause control valves to stick.

18) Position a new oil pan gasket on transmission case. Install oil pan and tighten attaching bolts.

FINAL DRIVE

DISASSEMBLY

NOTE: Measure pinion shaft turning torque BEFORE disassembly. See Pinion Depth and Bearing Preload adjustment for checking procedure.

1) Remove retaining bolts from center of axle drive flange shafts and pull drive flanges from final drive housing. Mark position of each side bearing adjusting ring on ring and housing, then measure screw-in depth of each ring in housing using a micrometer. Record measurements for reassembly reference.

2) Remove final drive pan bolts and pan, then remove side bearing adjusting ring lock plates. While supporting differential, unscrew side bearing adjusting rings, move differential to right side of case, tilt upward, and remove from final drive housing.

3) If necessary for replacement, use a hook type puller and remove oil seal from each side bearing adjusting ring.

4) If differential side bearings are to be replaced, use a drift and drive bearing outer race from each adjusting ring.

5) Loosen ring gear attaching bolts, tap on bolts with a soft hammer to break loose ring gear, then remove ring gear from differential case.

6) If side bearings require replacement, pull from case using a puller. Using a screwdriver, pry differential housing cover from housing. Drive out pinion gear shaft, then withdraw differential pinion gears and thrust washers, side gears and thrust washers, and nuts for drive flange shaft retaining bolts.

7) Remove pinion shaft cover from final drive housing. Withdraw pinion shaft from final drive housing.

8) If necessary for replacement, use a press and press pinion oil seals out of pinion cover. If pinion shaft bearings are to be replaced, press bearing outer race from pinion cover.

9) Use a hook type puller and remove pinion oil seal from final drive housing. Remove other pinion shaft bearing outer race from final drive housing using a puller (US 1039 and US 1037) as shown in *Fig. 24*.

Fig. 24: Removing Pinion Bearing Outer Race from Final Drive Housing

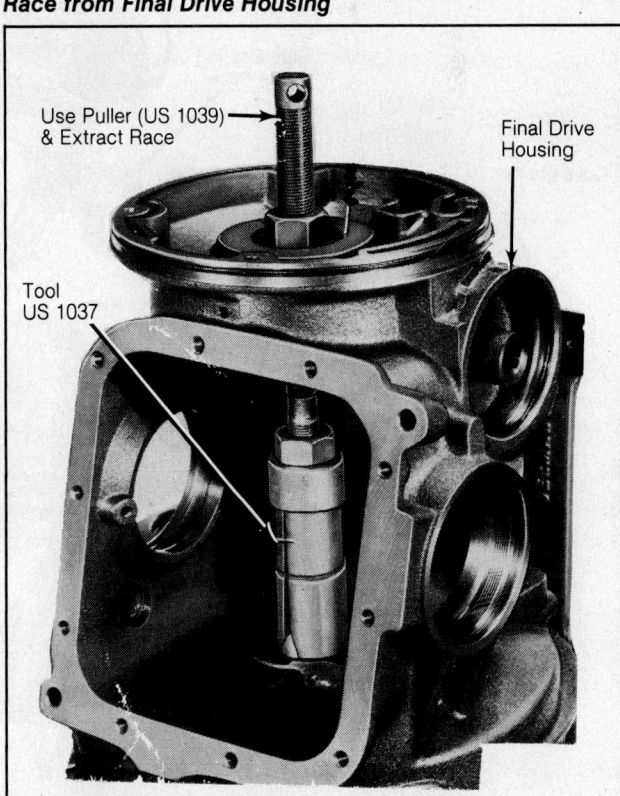

Use Puller (US 1039) & Extract Race

Final Drive Housing

Tool US 1037

Automatic Transmissions
VOLKSWAGEN VANAGON (Cont.)

Fig. 25: Exploded View Showing Main Components of Final Drive Assembly

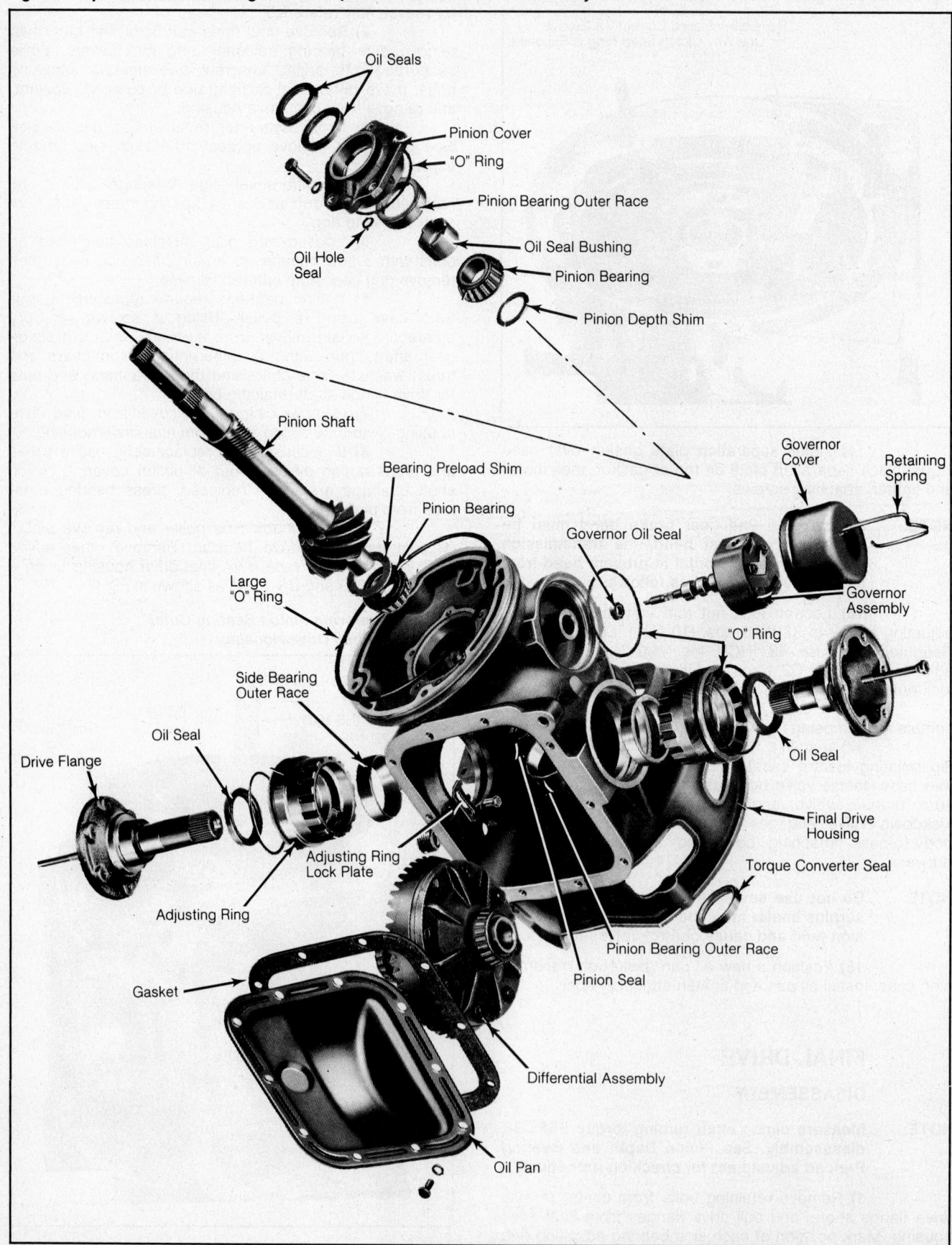

VOLKSWAGEN VANAGON (Cont.)

10) If necessary for replacement, use a press (with press plates to support bearing) and press bearings, shims and oil seal bushing from pinion shaft.

11) Use pullers to extract torque converter oil seal and governor oil seal from final drive housing.

REASSEMBLY & ADJUSTMENTS
Differential Assembly

1) Inspect all thrust surfaces on differential housing, cover, ring gear, pinion gear shaft and thrust washers. Replace all worn parts. Inspect gear teeth for burrs, or excessive wear and replace as necessary.

NOTE: **If ring gear requires replacement, pinion shaft must also be replaced as they are a matched set.**

2) Position differential side gears, large thrust washers, dished washers, drive flange retaining bolt nuts and pinion gears in differential housing. Align pinion gear holes with pinion shaft holes in housing, then drive pinion gear shaft through gears.

NOTE: **If differential pinion gear shaft does not fit tightly, replace it with a new shaft.**

3) Heat ring gear in hot oil to approximately 212°F (100°C). Place differential cover on housing. Install ring gear on housing, then install attaching bolts through cover and into ring gear. Tighten attaching bolts to specified torque.

4) If differential side bearings were removed, heat them in hot oil to approximately 212°F (100°C) and press them onto differential housing and cover. Press side bearing outer races into position in side bearing adjusting rings.

Pinion Depth and Bearing Preload

1) If original parts are reinstalled, use the same thickness pinion depth and bearing preload adjusting shims as were removed. If a new ring and pinion gear set is installed, new adjusting shims must be selected.

2) Press new pinion shaft bearing outer races into final drive housing and pinion cover until they are fully seated. Install new pinion oil seal into final drive case. Install new oil seal into final drive side of pinion cover with open side of seal towards final drive housing, then install a new oil seal into transmission side of pinion cover with open side towards transmission.

3) Heat pinion shaft bearings to 212°F (100°C) in hot oil. Install both bearings (without shims) onto pinion shaft until they are seated.

4) Install pinion shaft into final drive housing. Install pinion cover on housing, then install attaching bolts and tighten to 18 ft. lbs. (24 N.m).

NOTE: **For correct pinion depth and bearing preload adjustment, measuring tools called out in the following procedures must be used.**

5) Attach a dial indicator onto final drive housing using holder (VW 387) as shown in *Fig. 27*. Then, place measuring plate (VW 385/17) on end of pinion. Zero dial indicator without preload.

6) Move pinion shaft up and down (without turning) and note dial indicator reading. To this reading add .004" (.10 mm) for bearing preload and .004" (.10 mm) for settling of bearings. The resulting sum is the total thickness of adjusting shims necessary for correct pinion depth and bearing preload adjustment. Record sum for future reference.

7) Remove pinion shaft. Press bearing from gear end of shaft. Select shims of correct thickness as

Fig. 26: Exploded View of Differential Assembly

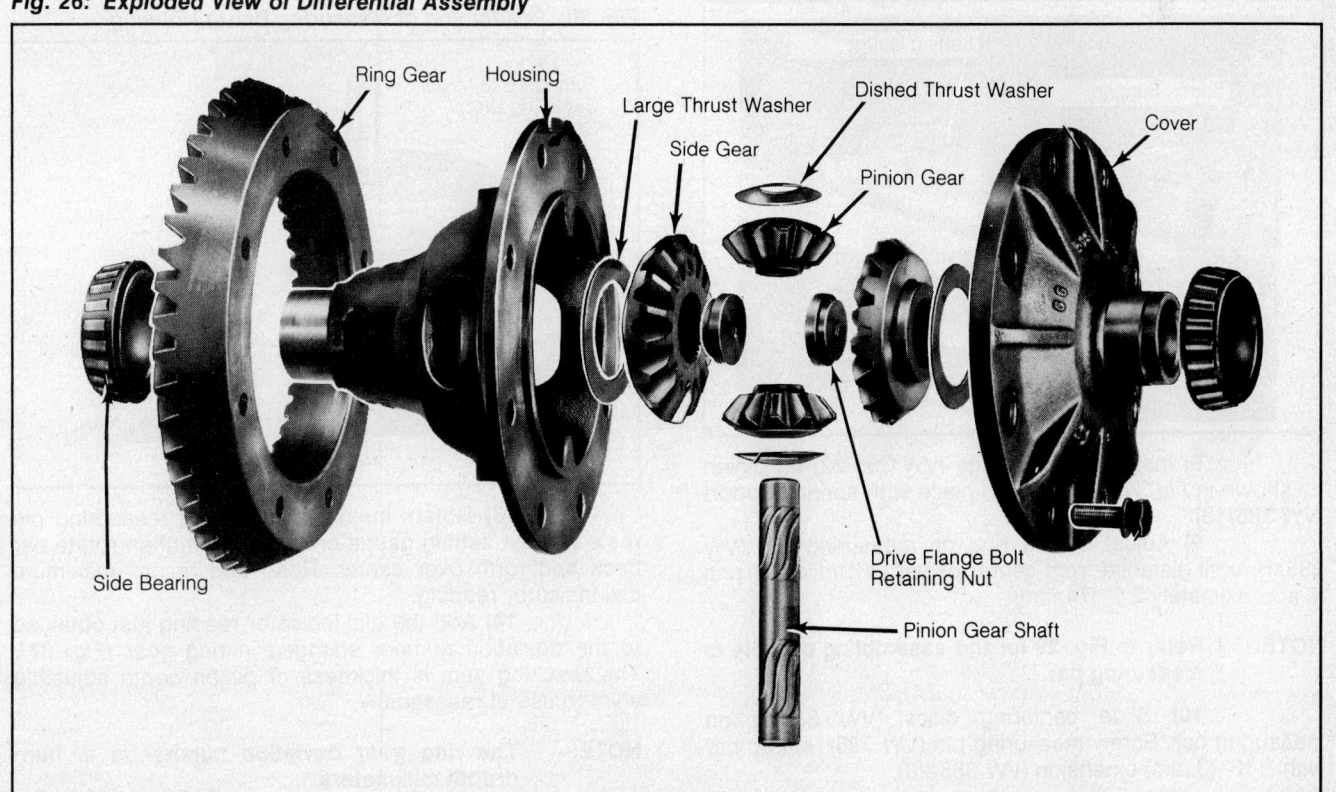

Ring Gear · Housing · Large Thrust Washer · Dished Thrust Washer · Cover · Side Gear · Pinion Gear · Side Bearing · Drive Flange Bolt Retaining Nut · Pinion Gear Shaft

Automatic Transmissions

VOLKSWAGEN VANAGON (Cont.)

Fig. 27: *Measuring Pinion Shaft Play to Determine Total Pinion Adjusting Shim Thickness*

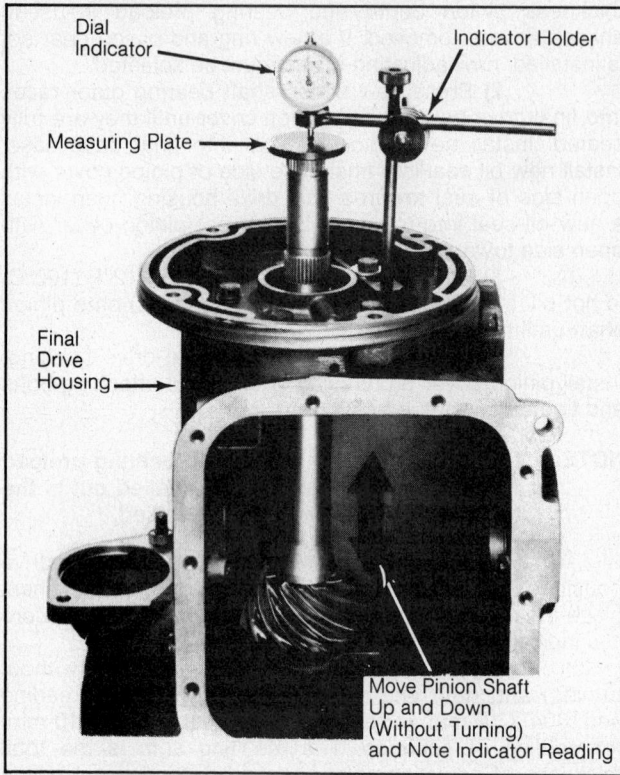

determined in step **6)**, and install them on gear end of shaft. Reinstall bearing onto shaft, then install shaft into final drive housing.

Fig. 28: *Installation of Setting Gauge on Pinion Shaft*

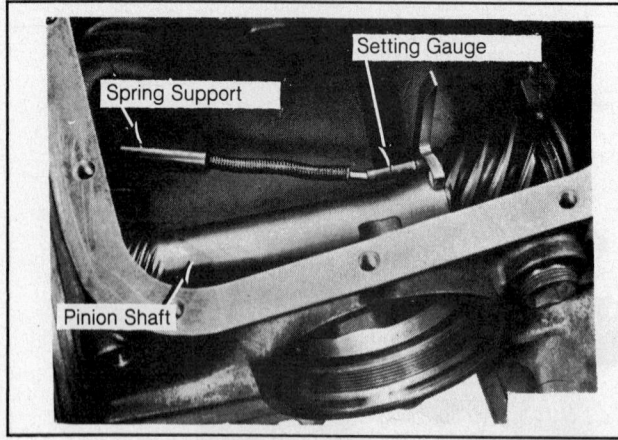

8) Install setting gauge (VW 385/22) on pinion as shown in *Fig. 28*, and hold in place with spring support (VW 385/19).

9) Adjust setting ring on measuring bar (VW 385/1), until distance from center of bar to outside of ring is approximately 2.9" (74 mm).

NOTE: Refer to *Fig. 29* for the assembling of tools to measuring bar.

10) Slide centering discs (VW 385/2) on measuring bar. Screw measuring pin (VW 385/14) into bar with .118" (3 mm) extension (VW 385/20).

Fig. 29: *Assembling Special Measuring Tools for Pinion Depth Shim Selection*

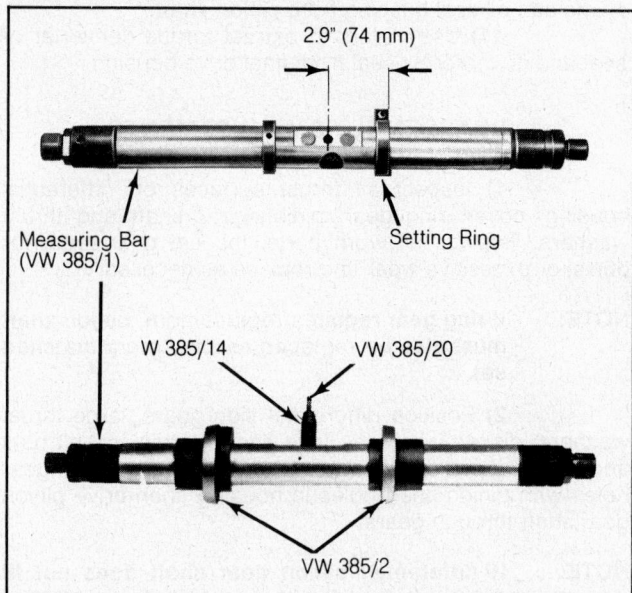

11) Screw left side differential side bearing adjusting ring into final drive housing until it is flush with housing. Place measuring bar assembly in final drive housing as shown in *Fig. 30*. Install right side bearing adjusting ring into final drive housing.

12) Turn knob on end of measuring bar to move centering discs outward until bar can just barely be turned by hand. Attach a dial indicator to measuring bar. Place setting block (VW 385/21) on measuring bar as shown in *Fig. 30*, then zero dial indicator without preload. Remove setting block.

Fig. 30: *Positioning of Measuring Bar in Housing*

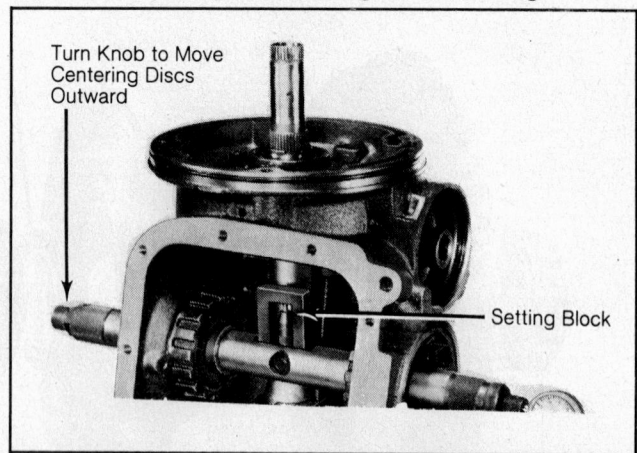

13) Rotate measuring bar until measuring pin rests against setting gauge on pinion face, then rotate bar back and forth over center. Read and record maximum dial indicator reading.

14) Add the dial indicator reading just obtained to the deviation number stamped in ring gear (*Fig. 31*). The resulting sum is thickness of pinion depth adjusting shim to use at reassembly.

NOTE: The ring gear deviation number is in hundredth millimeters.

Fig. 31: Location of Deviation Number on Ring Gear

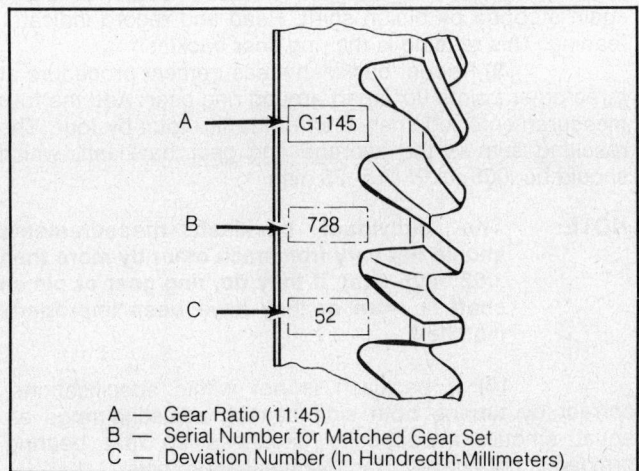

A — Gear Ratio (11:45)
B — Serial Number for Matched Gear Set
C — Deviation Number (In Hundredth-Millimeters)

15) Next, subtract the thickness of pinion depth shim just selected from the total pinion adjusting shim thickness obtained in step **6)**. The remainder is thickness of pinion bearing preload shim to use at reassembly.

NOTE: Pinion depth and bearing preload shims are available in thicknesses from .043" (1.1 mm) to .075" (1.9 mm) in increments of .001" (.025 mm). Also, shim thickness should be measured at several points on shim prior to installation to ensure correct thickness shims are being installed.

16) Remove measuring tools and pinion shaft from final drive housing. Press bearings from pinion shaft. Install the selected pinion bearing preload shim onto gear end of pinion shaft, then press bearing back onto shaft. Place the selected pinion depth shim on opposite end of shaft, then press remaining bearing onto shaft along with pinion oil seal bushing.

17) Install pinion shaft into final drive housing and lubricate bearings with hypoid gear oil. Reinstall measuring bar into housing and zero dial indicator with .04" (1.0 mm) preload.

18) Recheck pinion depth and bearing preload adjustment. If correct shims have been installed, dial indicator reading should be equal to the ring gear deviation number with a tolerance of ± .0016" (.04 mm). Remove measuring bar and side bearing adjusting rings.

19) Finally, attach a torque wrench to pinion shaft and check pinion shaft turning torque. Turning torque should be at least 12.4 INCH lbs. (1.4 N.m).

NOTE: Turning torque value given is for new bearings only. If used bearings are installed, turning torque should be measured piror to final drive disassembly. When assembled correctly, turning torque with used bearings should be approximately 1.7-3.5 INCH lbs. (.2-.4 N.m) greater than it was prior to disassembly.

Side Bearing Preload & Ring Gear Backlash
1) With pinion shaft correctly adjusted, install differential assembly into final drive housing. Coat "O" rings and threads of side bearing adjusting rings with

Fig. 32: Adjusting Ring Settings for Side Bearing Preload Adjustment

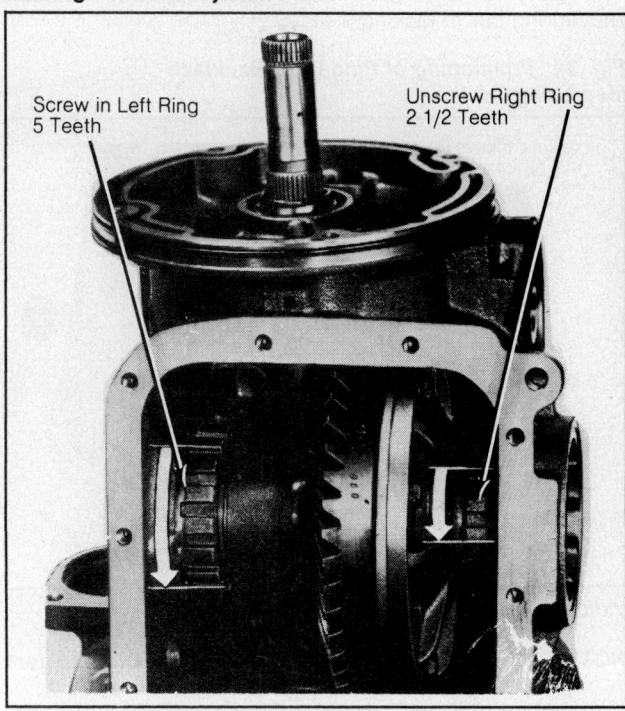

multi-purpose grease and coat side bearings with hypoid gear oil.

2) Install both adjusting rings into final drive housing until they are flush with housing. Next, adjust right side (ring gear end) adjusting ring in until ring gear meshes with pinion shaft gear with no backlash, then screw left ring in and preload slightly so that side bearings have no play.

3) From this position, unscrew right adjusting ring 2 1/2 teeth, then screw in left adjusting ring 5 teeth. This should correctly set side bearing preload and ring gear backlash.

4) To check ring gear backlash, rotate pinion shaft several times in both directions to settle bearings. Install locking sleeve (VW 521/4) with slotted sleeve (VW 521/7) in differential and secure with nut. See Fig. 33.

Fig. 33: Installation of Backlash Measuring Bar on Locking Sleeve

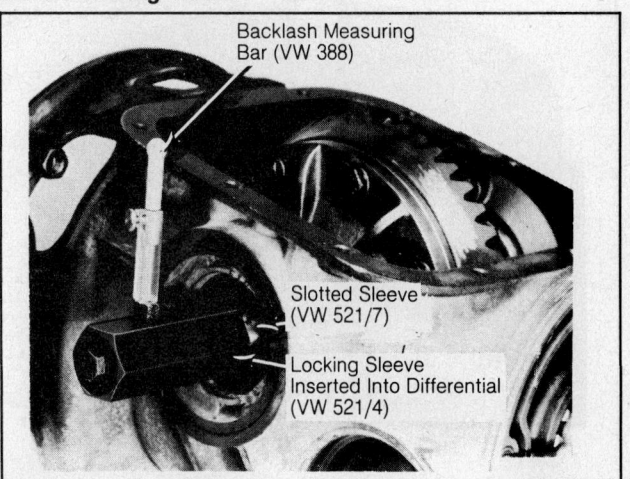

5) Adjust length of backlash measuring bar (VW 388) to 3.15" (80 mm). Attach correctly adjusted measuring bar to locking sleeve.

Fig. 34: Positioning of Ring Gear Backlash Measuring Tools

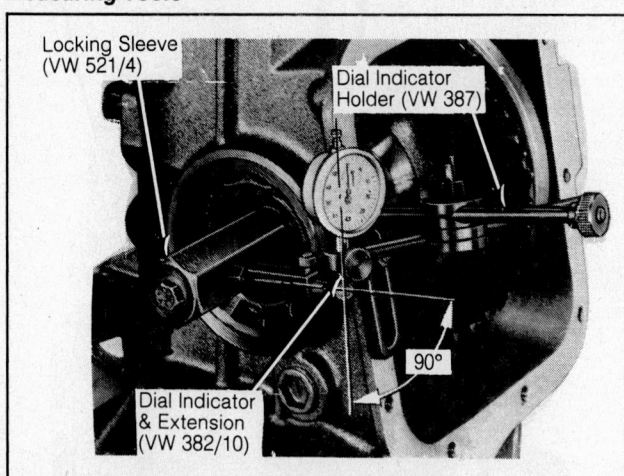

Locking Sleeve (VW 521/4)
Dial Indicator Holder (VW 387)
90°
Dial Indicator & Extension (VW 382/10)

Indicator must be at right angle to measuring bar.

NOTE: Refer to Fig. 34 for positioning of ring gear backlash measuring tools.

6) Install dial indicator with .24" (6 mm) flat end extension (VW 382/10) in indicator holder (VW 387). Bolt holder to final drive housing so that indicator is located at a right angle to backlash measuring bar.

7) Turn ring gear (via pinion shaft) until measuring bar contacts dial indicator gauge pin, then turn ring gear further until indicator shows .04" (1 mm) preload. Attach locking clamp (VW 386) to pinion shaft as shown in *Fig. 35*, then tighten clamp screw to lock pinion shaft.

8) Turn ring gear away from dial indicator until it is stopped by the locked pinion shaft, then zero dial

Fig. 35: Attaching Locking Clamp to Pinion Shaft

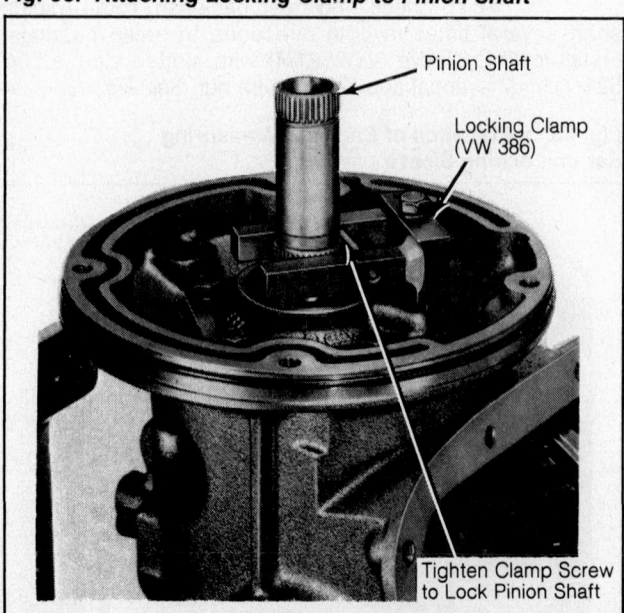

Pinion Shaft
Locking Clamp (VW 386)
Tighten Clamp Screw to Lock Pinion Shaft

indicator. Next, turn ring gear towards indicator until it is again stopped by pinion shaft. Read and record indicator reading. This reading is the ring gear backlash.

9) Repeat backlash measurement procedure at three other points 90° apart around ring gear. Add the four measurements together, then divide the total by four. The resulting sum is the average ring gear backlash, which should be .006-.010" (.15-.25 mm).

NOTE: The individual backlash measurements should not vary from each other by more than .002" (.05 mm); if they do, ring gear or pinion shaft is worn or they have been improperly installed.

10) If backlash is not within specifications, correct by turning both side bearing adjusting rings an equal amount in opposite directions so that bearing preload is not altered. Remove measuring tools.

11) With backlash correct, check pinion shaft turning torque. Total pinion shaft turning torque, with differential installed, should be 14.2 INCH lbs. (1.6 N.m).

12) Install side bearing adjusting ring lock plates and tighten bolts to specified torque. Install new oil seals in adjusting rings. Install final drive oil pan using a new gasket.

13) Install a new torque converter oil seal into final drive housing. Install a new governor oil seal into housing with lip pointing toward governor, then install governor assembly.

FINAL TRANSAXLE ASSEMBLY

1) To measure play between final drive and transmission, place a straightedge on transmission attaching face of final drive housing, and using a depth gauge, measure distance from top surface of straightedge down to edge of pinion shaft oil seal bushing.

2) Next, measure distance from top surface of straightedge to face of final drive housing. Subtract this second measurement from first measurement obtained in step 1) and note for future reference.

3) Place a new gasket on transmission separation plate, position straightedge on transmission case, and measure distance from top surface of straightedge down to gasket surface. Next, measure distance from top of straightedge down to shim surface on shoulder of annulus gear flange. Subtract this measurement from first measurement obtained in this step and record for future reference.

4) Subtract the last measurement obtained in step 3) from last measurement obtained in step 2). Remainder is end play (without shims) between final drive and transmission. Select proper end play shim(s) to use by finding applicable end play reading in first column of *End Play Shim Chart*, and obtaining shim thickness noted in second column.

NOTE: Transmission-to-final drive end play adjusting shims are available in thicknesses of .016" (.4 mm) and .047" (1.2 mm). Combine shim thicknesses to obtain total thickness required.

5) Install selected shim(s) into final drive case, on top of pinion shaft oil seal bushing. Next, lubricate and

VOLKSWAGEN VANAGON (Cont.)

Fig. 36: Using a Depth Gauge to Determine Transmission-to-Final Drive End Play Shim

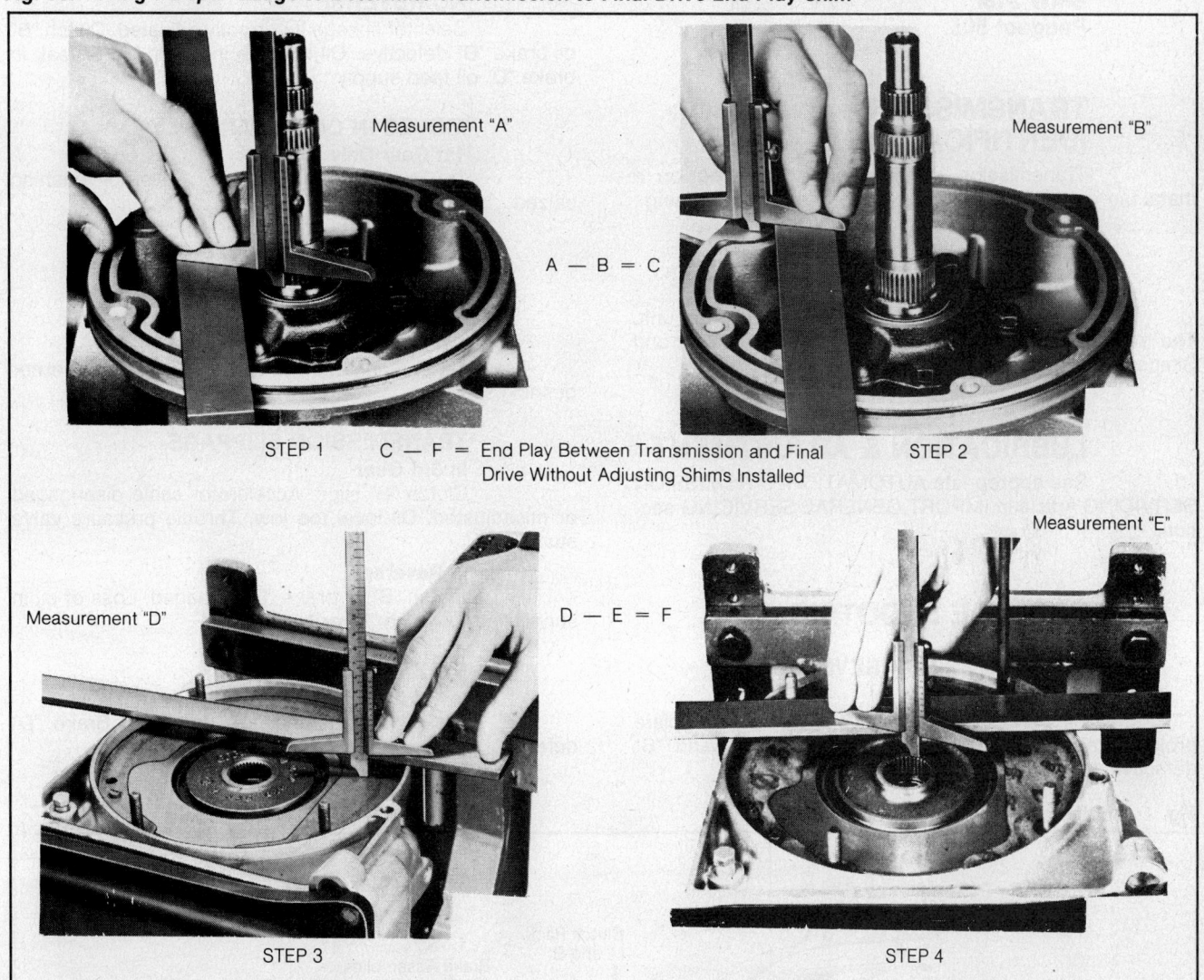

Measurement "A"

A — B = C

STEP 1

Measurement "B"

C — F = End Play Between Transmission and Final
Drive Without Adjusting Shims Installed

STEP 2

Measurement "D"

D — E = F

STEP 3

Measurement "E"

STEP 4

END PLAY SHIM SELECTION CHART

If End Play Is In. (mm)	Install This Shim In. (mm)
.009-.033 (.23-.84)	None
.034-.049 (.85-1.24)	.016 (.4)
.050-.065 (1.25-1.64)	.032 (.8)
.066-.080 (1.65-2.04)	.048 (1.2)
.081-.096 (2.05-2.44)	.064 (1.6)
.097-.112 (2.45-2.84)	.080 (2.0)
.113-.128 (2.85-3.24)	.096 (2.4)
.129-.143 (3.25-3.64)	.112 (2.8)
.144-.153 (3.65-3.88)	.128 (3.2)

install sealing "O" ring into groove on transmission end of final drive housing.

6) Install turbine shaft into final drive pinion shaft, then install oil pump shaft into turbine shaft. Position a new final drive-to-transmission gasket onto transmission case studs, then mate final drive to transmission. Install final drive-to-transmission case nuts and tighten to specified torque.

7) Set torque converter carefully on one-way support, then move converter back and forth and insert into splines ensuring that it does not jam.

TIGHTENING SPECIFICATIONS

Application	Ft. Lbs. (N.m)
Transmission	
Kickdown Lever Nut	11 (15)
Manual Valve Lever Nut	14 (19)
Oil Pan-to-Case	14 (19)
Transmission-to-Final Drive	22 (30)
Final Drive	
Converter-to-Drive Plate	18 (24)
Drive Flange Bolt	18 (24)
Final Drive-to-Engine	22 (30)
Oil Pan-to-Case	7 (10)
Pinion Cover-to-Case	18 (24)
Ring Gear Bolts	51 (70)

	INCH Lbs. (N.m)
Transmission	
Brake Spring Plate Bolts	60 (7)
Oil Pump Cover-to-Housing	60 (7)
Strainer-to-Valve Body	24 (3)
Valve Body-to-Case	36 (4)
Final Drive	
Adjusting Ring Lock Plate	84 (10)

Automatic Transmissions
ZF 3HP 22

BMW 318i
Peugeot 505

TRANSMISSION IDENTIFICATION

Transmission identification is stamped on a metal tag fastened to the lower left of the center housing.

DESCRIPTION

Transmission is a fully automatic 3-speed unit. The transmission is equipped with a torque converter and Simpson planetary gear set.

LUBRICATION & ADJUSTMENT

See appropriate AUTOMATIC TRANSMISSION SERVICING article in IMPORT GENERAL SERVICING section.

TROUBLE SHOOTING

NO FORWARD OR REVERSE MOVEMENT

Oil level too low. Defective oil pump. Drive plate broken. Parking lock pawl stuck. Clutches "A" and "B" defective. Input or output shaft broken.

NO REVERSE

Selector linkage incorrectly adjusted. Clutch "B" or brake "D" defective. Oil leakage in clutch "B" or leak in brake "D" oil feed supply.

MOVES IN ONE GEAR ONLY
1st Gear Only
1st-2nd shift valve stuck. Governor bushing seized.

2nd Gear Only
1st-2nd and 2nd-3rd shift valve stuck.

1st & 2nd Gears Only
2nd-3rd shift valve stuck.

3rd Gear Only
1st-2nd and 2nd-3rd shift valve stuck. Governor bushing seized.

TRANSMISSION SLIPPAGE
In 3rd Gear
Clutch "B" slips. Accelerator cable disengaged or misadjusted. Oil level too low. Throttle pressure valve stuck.

In Reverse
Clutch "B" or brake "D" damaged. Loss of oil in supply line to clutch "B" or brake "D".

NO BRAKING EFFECT
In 1st Gear In "2" & "1"
Brake valve/damper "D" defective. Brake "D" defective.

Fig. 1: Sectional View of ZF 3HP 22 Transmission

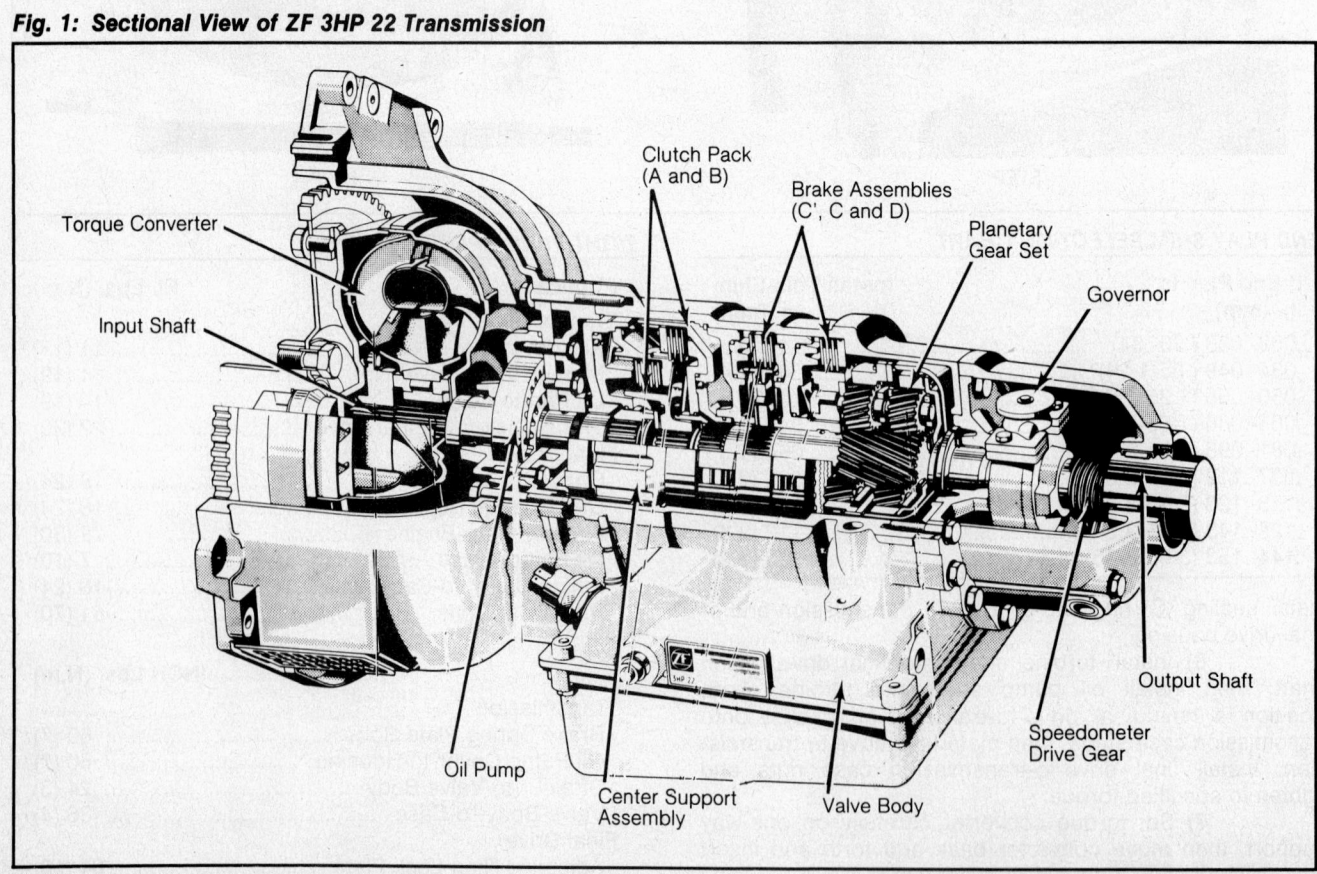

ZF 3HP 22 (Cont.)

In 2nd Gear In "2" & "1"
Brake C' defective.

SHIFT POINTS INCORRECT
Too High
Throttle cable adjustment incorrect. Governor bushing jammed, or seal rings leaking. Valve body faulty.

Too Low
Throttle cable adjustment incorrect. Governor bushing jammed. Valve body faulty.

NO KICKDOWN
In "1-2" & "2-3"
Throttle pressure too low. Accelerator cable not adjusted properly. Throttle pressure valve seized. Balls in valve body worn.

NO UPSHIFT
To 2nd Gear
Governor seized. 1-2 shift valve seized.

To 3rd Gear
Governor seized. Throttle pressure too high. Throttle pressure valve stuck. Clutch "B" damaged.

TRANSMISSION NOISES
In All Positions When Cold
Suction noise at oil pump due to loose valve body bolts. Defective valve body.

Noise in 1st Gear On Acceleration and Deceleration
Worn planetary gears.

Light Grinding Noise Which Is Speed Sensitive
Needle bearing in transmission extension housing defective.

TESTING

ROAD TEST
1) Before testing, make sure fluid level is correct and all linkage adjustments are correct. Transmission should shift at approximate speeds shown in BMW & PEUGEOT SHIFT SPEEDS charts. Speeds may vary due to tire size and axle ratio. The important factor is that all shifts should be smooth, with no slipping or engine racing.

2) Slipping or engine racing during shifts usually indicates clutch or brake slipping problems. Unless an

BMW SHIFT SPEEDS

Shift Conditions	MPH
318i	
Full Throttle	
1-2 Upshift	27-32
2-3 Upshift	61-67
Kickdown	
1-2 Upshift	38-45
2-3 Upshift	69-75
3-2 Downshift	47-54
2-1 Downshift	35-41
Manual Downshift (Max.)	
3-2	70-77
2-1	38-45

PEUGEOT SHIFT SPEEDS

Shift Conditions	MPH
505	
Full Throttle	
Gasoline Models	
1-2 Upshift	25
2-3 Upshift	58
3-2 Downshift	46
2-1 Downshift	15
Diesel Models	
1-2 Upshift	22
2-3 Upshift	43
3-2 Downshift	35
2-1 Downshift	19
Kickdown	
Gasoline Models	
1-2 Upshift	39
2-3 Upshift	65
3-2 Downshift	63
2-1 Downshift	32
Diesel Models	
1-2 Upshift	29
2-3 Upshfit	50
3-2 Downshift	48
2-1 Downshift	28
Minimum Throttle	
Gasoline Models	
1-2 Upshift	9
2-3 Upshift	20
3-2 Downshift	14
2-1 Downshift	4
Diesel Models	
1-2 Upshift	12
2-3 Upshift	20
3-2 Downshift	17
2-1 Downshift	6
604 Turbo Diesel	
Full Throttle	
1-2 Upshift	25
2-3 Upshift	50
3-2 Downshift	40
2-1 Downshift	24
Kickdown	
1-2 Upshift	33
2-3 Upshift	55
3-2 Downshift	53
2-1 Downshift	30
Minimum Throttle	
1-2 Upshift	14
2-3 Upshift	23
3-2 Downshift	20
2-1 Downshift	10

obvious condition exists, transmission should never be disassembled until hydraulic pressure tests have been performed.

STALL TEST
1) With engine and transmission at normal operating temperature, connect a tachometer to engine. Apply service and parking brakes and place selector lever in "D".

CAUTION: DO NOT maintain stall speed more than 10 seconds.

Automatic Transmissions
ZF 3HP 22 (Cont.)

2) Accelerate engine to full throttle and note engine speed. Repeat test with selector lever in position "R".

Stall Test Results

If stall speeds are below specifications, check engine output for being below specifications. If stall speeds are above specifications, refer to CLUTCH AND BAND APPLICATION chart for clutches or brakes that could be slipping.

STALL SPEED SPECIFICATIONS

Application	Stall RPM
BMW	
318i	1970-2070
Peugeot	
504	2150-2200
505 & 604	2050-2150

HYDRAULIC PRESSURE

NOTE: The following procedure applies to BMW models only. Information not available from Peugeot.

1) On BMW 318i models only, use Special Adaptor (88 88 6 240 029) when connecting pressure gauge hose to main pressure port. *See Fig. 2.* Disconnect transmission kickdown cable from throttle linkage and set engine idle speed to 1200-1500 RPM.

2) With rear wheels off the ground and transmission in "R", check main pressure. Pressure obtained should be within limits specified in BMW HYDRAULIC PRESSURE charts. To check kickdown pressures, pull on kickdown cable.

3) Place transmission in Neutral and run engine at idle to cool transmission. With transmission in any position except "R", repeat check. Pressure obtained should be within limits specified in BMW HYDRAULIC PRESSURE charts.

Fig. 2: Checking BMW Hydraulic Pressure

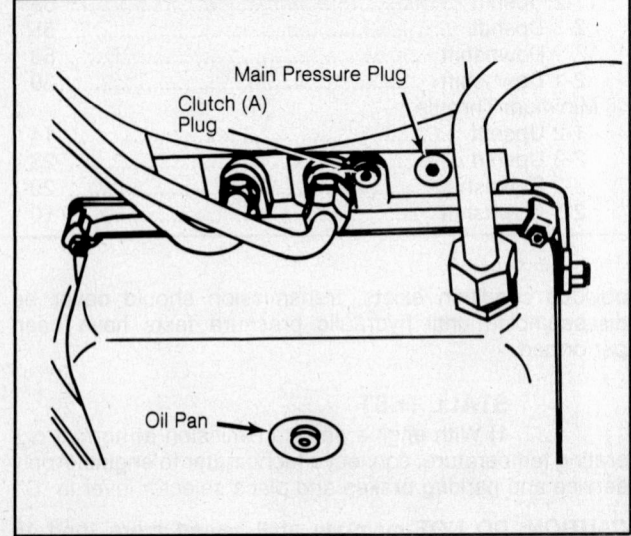

Main Pressure Plug

Clutch (A) Plug

Oil Pan →

Allow transmission to cool between checks.

BMW HYDRAULIC PRESSURES

Application	psi (kg/cm²)
318i	
In "R"	
Idle	178-206 (12.5-14.5)
Kickdown	234-260 (17.1-19.0)
All Other Positions	
Idle	78-91 (5.4-6.4)
Kickdown	102-113 (7.4-8.3)

REMOVAL & INSTALLATION

See the appropriate AUTOMATIC TRANSMISSION REMOVAL article in IMPORT GENERAL SERVICING section.

TRANSMISSION DISASSEMBLY

1) Place transmission in a holding fixture. Remove torque converter. Remove oil pan and gasket. Remove Torx bolts retaining valve body and remove valve body.

2) Remove retaining circlips from 4 oil supply bores in transmission case and withdraw compression springs. Using a puller that will thread into sleeves, remove sealing sleeves from oil bores. Screw tool into sleeve and pull out sharply.

3) Lock transmission output shaft by engaging parking gear. Hold output flange stationary. Remove retaining nut and flange. Remove extension housing. Using a puller, pull off speedometer drive gear. Remove washer and snap ring.

4) Loosen governor assembly retaining nut. Unscrew governor stud about 3 turns and pull governor off shaft. Remove torque converter housing with oil pump, seal, intermediate plate, thrust washer, needle bearing and angled disc. Remove and separate components. Remove input shaft and clutch "A".

5) Remove clutch "A" carrier plate, plastic thrust washer and metal thrust washer. Remove clutch "B" snap ring. Using 2 hooks, remove clutch "B". *See Fig. 3.* Catch washer and seal as they are pulled out with clutch "B".

6) Remove large snap ring and pull out center support and output shaft as an assembly. *See Fig. 4.* Remove thrust washer, needle bearing and angled disc from output shaft.

7) Remove center support assembly from output shaft. Remove planetary gears with sun gear shaft. Note position of needle bearing and thrust washer on end of sun gear shaft and remove. *See Fig. 5.*

COMPONENT DISASSEMBLY & REASSEMBLY

CONVERTER HOUSING & OIL PUMP ASSEMBLY
Disassembly

Remove torque converter. Remove converter housing with intermediate plate. Remove intermediate plate from converter housing by loosening 2 bolts. DO NOT remove bolts. *See Fig. 6.* Separate primary pump from

ZF 3HP 22 (Cont.)

CLUTCH AND BAND APPLICATION CHART (ELEMENTS IN USE)

Selector Lever Position	Clutch A	Clutch B	Brake C'	Brake C	Brake D	Front Overrunning Clutch	Rear Overrunning Clutch
"1" – FIRST GEAR	X				X [1]		X
"2" – SECOND GEAR	X		X	X		X	
"3" – THIRD GEAR	X	X		X			
REVERSE		X			X		

PARK OR NEUTRAL – All bands and clutches released and/or ineffective.

[1] – Applied in "1" and "2" selector positions only.

Fig. 3: Removing Clutch "B"

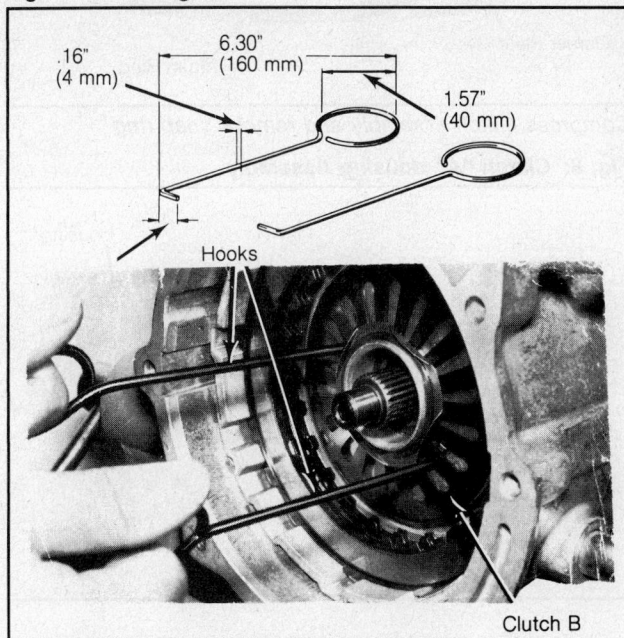

Fabricate hooks using dimensions shown.

Fig. 4: Removing Center Support & Output Shaft Assembly

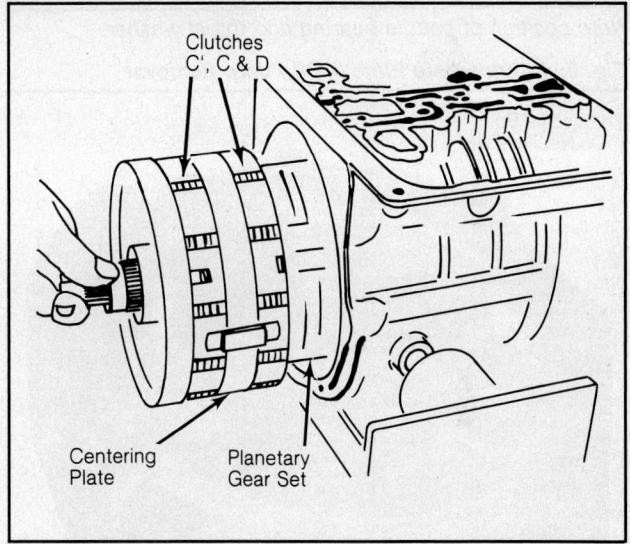

Note position of thrust washer on output shaft.

converter housing by tapping lightly. Remove bolts and pump.

Inspection
1) Clean all parts and check for signs of scoring or other wear. Check clearance between pump driven gear and pump housing; clearance must be .003-.006" (.07-.16 mm).

2) Check pump housing-to-gear face clearance; clearance must be .0012-.0019" (.03-.05 mm) on BMW models and .0008-.0015" (.02-.04 mm) on Peugeot models. On Peugeot models, check the clearance between gear and crescent; the clearance must be .010-.015" (.250-.386 mm).

3) On all models, if any component is defective, complete pump assembly must be replaced. If any measurement is not within specifications, replace oil pump assembly.

Reassembly
Reassemble in reverse of disassembly, noting the following: Install drive and driven gears with punch marks up, if equipped. Replace all gaskets and seals. Install angled disc on input shaft, with collar facing needle bearing. Hold thrust washer on converter housing with grease.

CLUTCH "A"
Disassembly
1) Using a press, compress clutch assembly and remove large snap ring. See Fig. 7. Remove spacer plates, clutch plates, discs and diaphragm spring. Remove carrier plate. Note number and arrangement of plates and discs.

2) Remove snap ring from input shaft and separate input shaft from input hub. Remove piston from hub by applying compressed air to oil hole. Remove diaphragm spring and seals.

Reassembly
1) Coat all discs and plates with ATF. Insert input shaft into hub and retain with snap ring. Place diaphragm spring in hub with curved surface facing down. Replace all seals.

Automatic Transmissions
ZF 3HP 22 (Cont.)

Fig. 5: Removing Planetary Gears & Sun Gear Shaft

Note position of needle bearing and thrust washer.

Fig. 6: Intermediate Plate & Oil Pump Removal

Loosen bolts and tap pump lightly.

2) Alternate plates and discs until the number and position of plates and discs are installed as they were removed. *See Fig. 8.* Peugeot 604 models use 5 clutch plates. Install spacer plates and carrier plate. Compress clutch assembly and install large snap ring.

CLUTCH "B"
Disassembly
1) Remove washer and "O" ring from center of clutch "B" housing. Remove large snap ring. Remove end plate, clutch plates and discs, noting number and arrangement of plates and discs for reassembly reference.
2) Compress diaphragm spring and remove snapring. Remove piston from housing by applying compressed air to oil feed hole. Remove and discard seals and "O" rings.
Reassembly
1) Coat discs and plates with ATF. Replace all seals and "O" rings. Position piston in housing and install diaphragm spring. Compress spring and install snap ring.

Fig. 7: Clutch "A" Snap Ring Removal

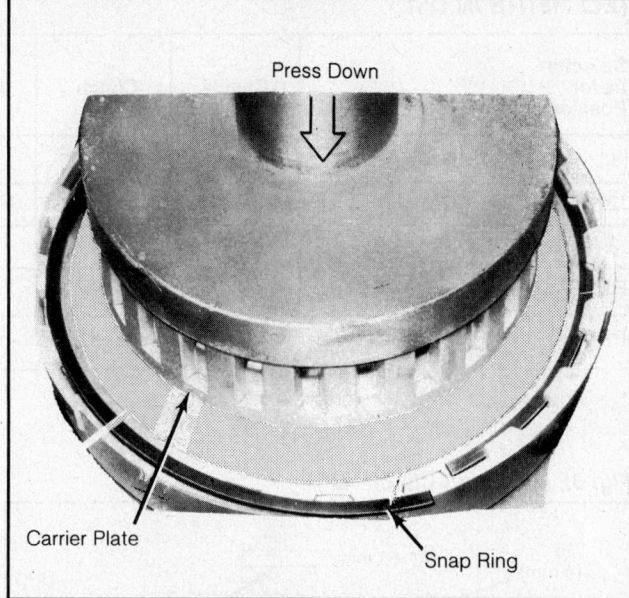

Compress clutch assembly and remove snap ring.

Fig. 8: Clutch "A" Housing Assembly

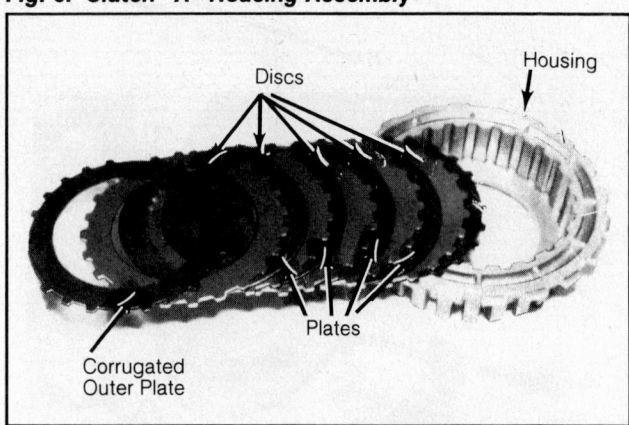

2) Alternate plates and discs until the number and position of plates and discs are installed as they were removed. *See Fig. 9.* Install end plate and large snap ring. Replace "O" ring and washer in center of housing.

CENTER SUPPORT ASSEMBLY
Disassembly
1) Insert assembly into a pipe with an inside diameter of 1.142" (29 mm) and clamp assembly in a vise. Remove centering plate. Remove outer disc (2 on some models), plates and one-way clutch for brake C'. *See Fig. 10.*

2) Remove brake C' snap ring (if equipped). Remove end plate, discs and plates, noting number and arrangement for reassembly reference.

3) Lift center support assembly off output shaft. Remove brake "D" snap ring. Remove end plate, discs and plates, noting number and arrangement for reassembly reference.

4) Place center support assembly on work bench. Compress diaphragm spring and remove split retaining ring. Turn assembly over and remove large snap

Fig. 9: Clutch "B" Housing Assembly

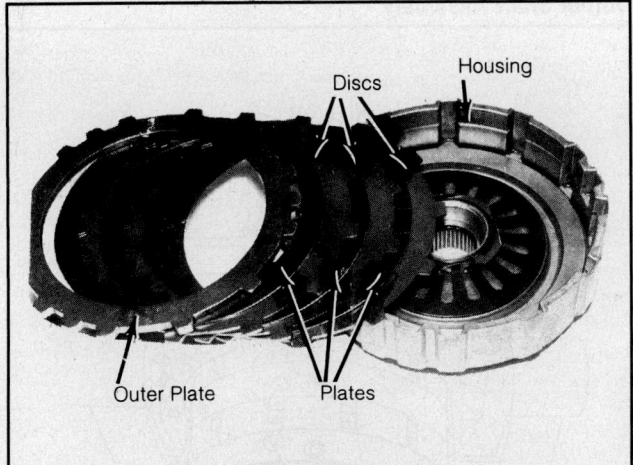

Note number and arrangement of plates and discs.

Fig. 10: Brake C' One-Way Clutch & Plates

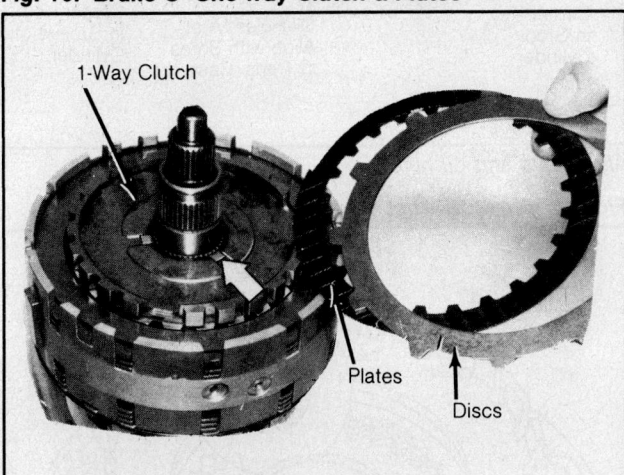

Note number and position of plates and discs.

Fig. 11: Center Support Housing

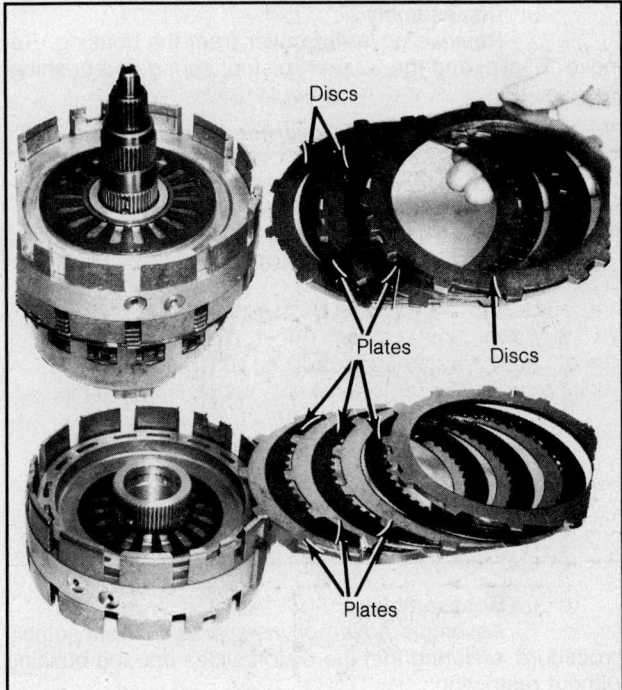

Note disc and plate sequence for brakes C and D.

PLATE & DISC USAGE CHART

Application	No. of Plates
Clutch "A" 318i & Peugeot 505	
Spacer Plates	2
Discs	5
Plates	4
Clutch "B"	
BMW 318i & Peugeot 505	
End Plate	1
Discs	3
Plates	3
Brake C'	
BMW 318i & Peugeot 505	
Disc	1
Plate	1
Brake "C"	
Brake "D"	
BMW 318i & Peugeot 505	
End Plate	1
Discs	3
Plates	3

ring. Remove diaphragm springs. Place brake C' on bench and compress diaphragm. Remove split retaining ring.

5) Apply compressed air to respective oil input hole to remove brake pistons. Remove and discard piston "O" rings and seals. Replace with new "O" rings and seals.

Reassembly

1) To reassemble center support assembly, reverse disassembly procedure and note the following: Coat all discs and plates with ATF. Make sure all plates and discs are installed in proper sequence and number as when removed. See PLATE & DISC charts.

2) If discs or plates are replaced, soak new parts in warm ATF (160°F/70°C) for 20 minutes before installing.

PLANETARY GEAR SET
Disassembly

1) Place output shaft in a support with output shaft facing down. Remove one-way clutch and front planetary gear set. Remove sun gear shaft. Remove large snap ring and lift off ring gear. Lift off rear planetary gear set.

2) Remove intermediate shaft from output shaft housing. Remove roller bearing and washer from output shaft housing and intermediate shaft. Remove large snap ring holding input ring gear to intermediate shaft. Remove washers and bearing. Remove other large snap ring.

Reassembly

To reassemble planetary gear set, reverse disassembly procedure and note the following: Make sure a large snap ring is on both sides of input ring gear when assembled to intermediate shaft. When installing mainshaft to output shaft, place washer onto output shaft first, then the roller bearing. Make sure all snap rings are properly installed and fully seated.

GOVERNOR ASSEMBLY
Disassembly
Remove governor cover from the housing. Remove "E" clip, and the washer, piston, spring and bushing. *See Fig. 12.*

Fig. 12: Exploded View of Governor Assembly

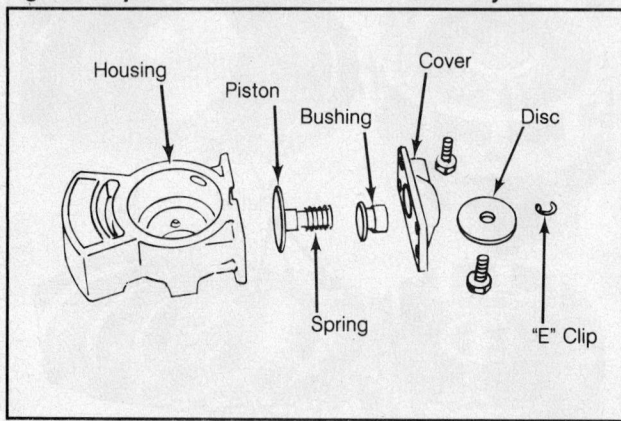

Reassembly
Assemble governor in reverse of disassembly procedure, ensuring that the piston slides into the bushing without restriction.

VALVE BODY ASSEMBLY
NOTE: Valve body disassembly is not recommended. If a valve body malfunction is determined, replace valve body.

TRANSMISSION REASSEMBLY
1) Install angled disc, needle bearing and thrust washer on output shaft. Install needle bearing and thrust washer on sun gear shaft and install planetary gear set onto output shaft. Assemble center support assembly to output shaft assembly.

2) Guide center support and output shaft assembly into transmission case, aligning keys in the center of cylinder groove. The 4 oil bores in the center support assembly must be aligned with bores in case. *See Fig. 13.* Retain in position with large snap ring.

3) Install clutch "B" and press in seal with washer. Retain clutch "B" in position with snap ring. Lubricate plastic thrust washer and metal thrust washer with grease. Install plastic thrust washer on carrier plate, aligning tabs with openings in carrier plate. *See Fig. 14.* Install metal thrust washer.

4) Install carrier plate in clutch "A" by turning back and forth slightly. Install clutch "A" into transmission case. Install angled disc on input shaft, with collar facing needle bearing. Install thrust washer and gasket on converter housing. Slide converter housing onto input shaft and secure.

5) Check input shaft end play. End play should be .012-.059" (.3-1.5 mm). *See Fig. 15.* Press piston rings together to slide governor assembly onto output shaft. Remove stud to help find the depression in the output shaft. Secure the governor by aligning the stud with the depression. Lock governor by counterpunching the stud.

Fig. 13: Installing Center Support & Output Shaft Assembly

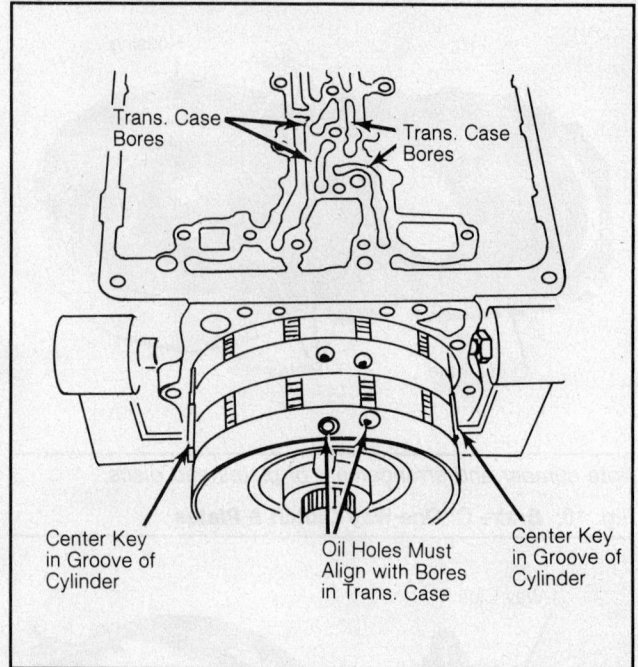

Align keys and oil holes.

Fig. 14: Plastic Thrust Washer Installation

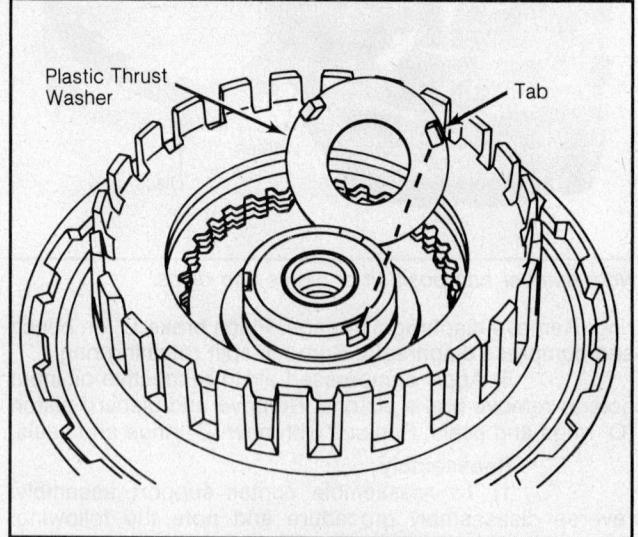

Align tabs on washer with carrier plate openings.

6) Install washer and snapring on output shaft. Install speedometer drive gear. Install extension housing. Install seal and transmission output flange, securing with lock plate and nut.

7) Using a punch, drive in the 4 sealing sleeves, up to the stop. Install and secure springs. Both of the short springs are installed on the selector lever side. *See Fig. 16.*

8) Install valve body so that the clamp on the selector sliding valve can be engaged in the opening arm of the pawl, by tightening the transmission cable slightly. *See Fig. 17.*

9) Align valve body with pin in the throttle pressure piston. Clearance must be .45" (11.5 mm). *See Fig.*

18. Tighten valve body screws. Install oil pan gasket and magnetic disc, next to oil filter screen. Install oil pan with short arm of retaining bracket pressing down on oil pan.

Fig. 15: Checking Input Shaft End Play

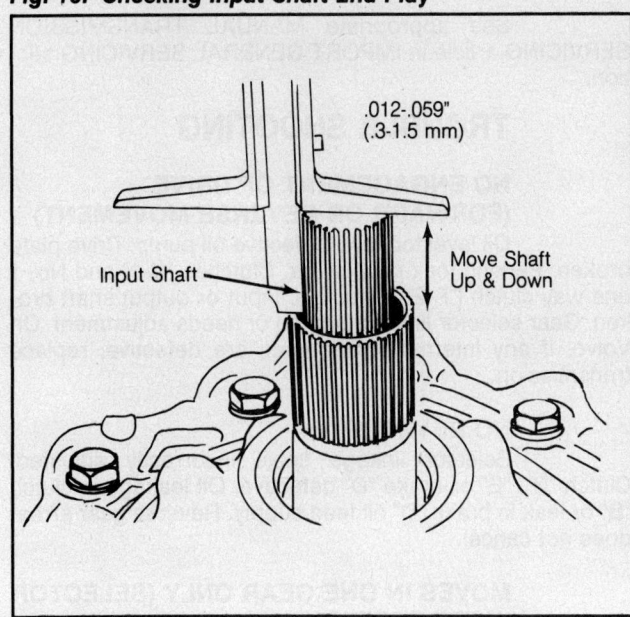

Fig. 16: Aligning Sliding Valve & Control Arm

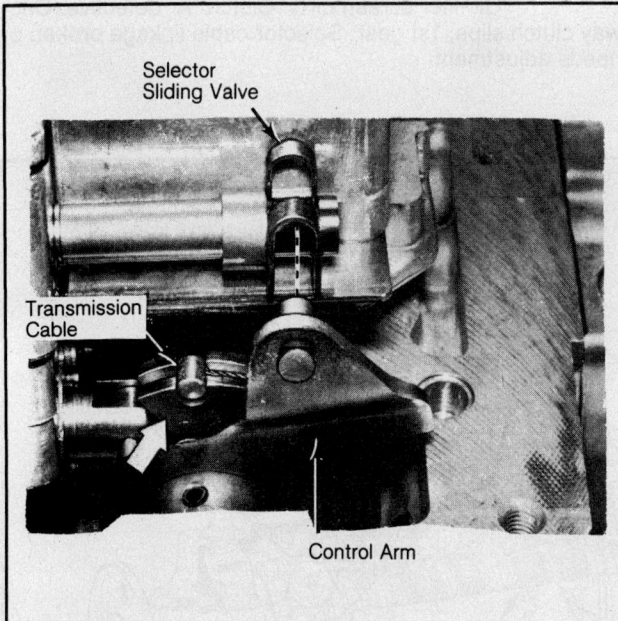

Align valve body by tightening transmission cable.

Fig. 17: Installing Springs in Valve Body

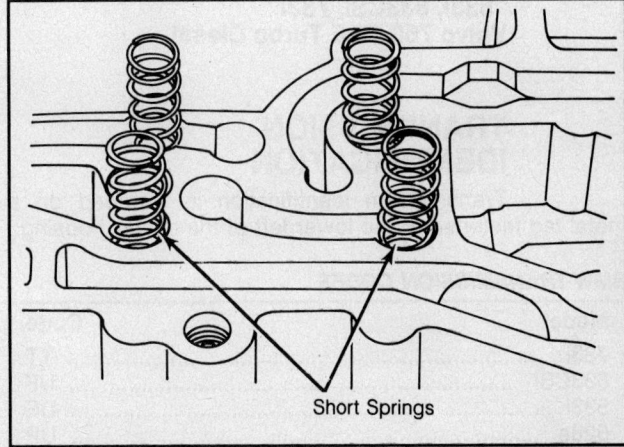

Install short springs on selector lever side.

Fig. 18: Aligning Valve Body

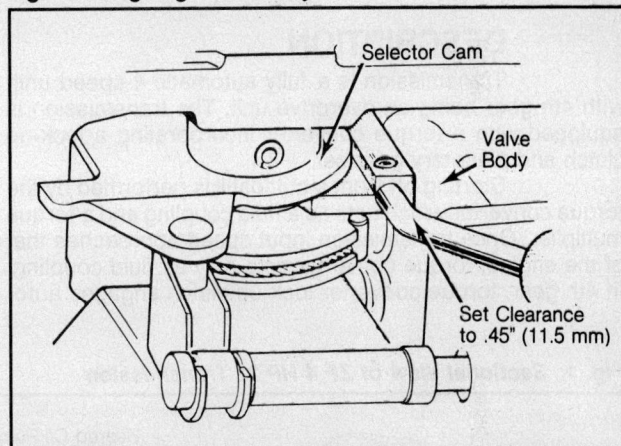

Align valve body with pin in throttle pressure piston.

TIGHTENING SPECIFICATIONS

Application	Ft. Lbs. (N.m)
BMW	
Transmission-to-Engine	
8 mm Bolts	18-20 (24-27)
Converter-to-Drive Plate	[2] 35-38 (48-51)
Bellhousing-to-Transmission Case	17-19 (23-26)
Extension Housing	17-19 (23-26)
Flange Nut	74-85 (100-115)
Peugeot	
Transmission-to-Engine	37 (50)
Converter-to-Drive Plate	22 (30)
Bellhousing-to-Transmission Case	18 (25)
Extension Housing	18 (25)
Propeller Shaft Tube	37 (50)

	INCH Lbs. (N.m)
BMW	
Governor Studs	26-31 (3-3.5)
Oil Pump	84-96 (9.5-11)

Automatic Transmissions
ZF 4HP 22

BMW 325e, 528e,
533i, 633CSi, 733i
Volvo 760 GLE Turbo Diesel

TRANSMISSION IDENTIFICATION

Transmission identification is stamped on a metal tag fastened to the lower left of the center housing.

BMW TRANSMISSION CODES

Model	Code
733i	TT
633CSi	UF
533i	UE
528e	UP
325e	TY

DESCRIPTION

Transmission is a fully automatic 4-speed unit, with 4th gear being an overdrive unit. The transmission is equipped with a torque converter incorporating a lock-up clutch and planetary gear set.

Starting off from a standstill is performed by the torque converter which acts as a fluid coupling and a torque multiplier. Once transmission input speed approaches that of the engine, torque converter acts only as fluid coupling. In 4th gear, torque converter lock-up clutch engages auto- matically, depending on road speed, so that there is a direct mechanical link between engine and transmission.

LUBRICATION & ADJUSTMENT

See appropriate MANUAL TRANSMISSION SERVICING article in IMPORT GENERAL SERVICING section.

TROUBLE SHOOTING

NO ENGAGEMENT OF DRIVE (FORWARD OR REVERSE MOVEMENT)

Oil level too low. Defective oil pump. Drive plate broken. Parking lock pawl stuck. Clutches "C-1" and No. 1 one-way clutch ("F-2") defective. Input or output shaft broken. Gear selector linkage broken or needs adjustment. On Volvo, if any internal components are defective, replace transmission.

NO REVERSE

Selector linkage cable incorrectly adjusted. Clutch "B", "E" or brake "D" defective. Oil leakage in clutch "B" or leak in brake "D" oil feed supply. Reverse gear arrest does not cancel.

MOVES IN ONE GEAR ONLY (SELECTOR IN "D" POSITION)
No Power Flow

Oil filter screen dirty. Clutch "A" defective. One-way clutch slips, 1st gear. Selector cable linkage broken or needs adjustment.

Fig. 1: Sectional View of ZF 4 HP 22 Transmission

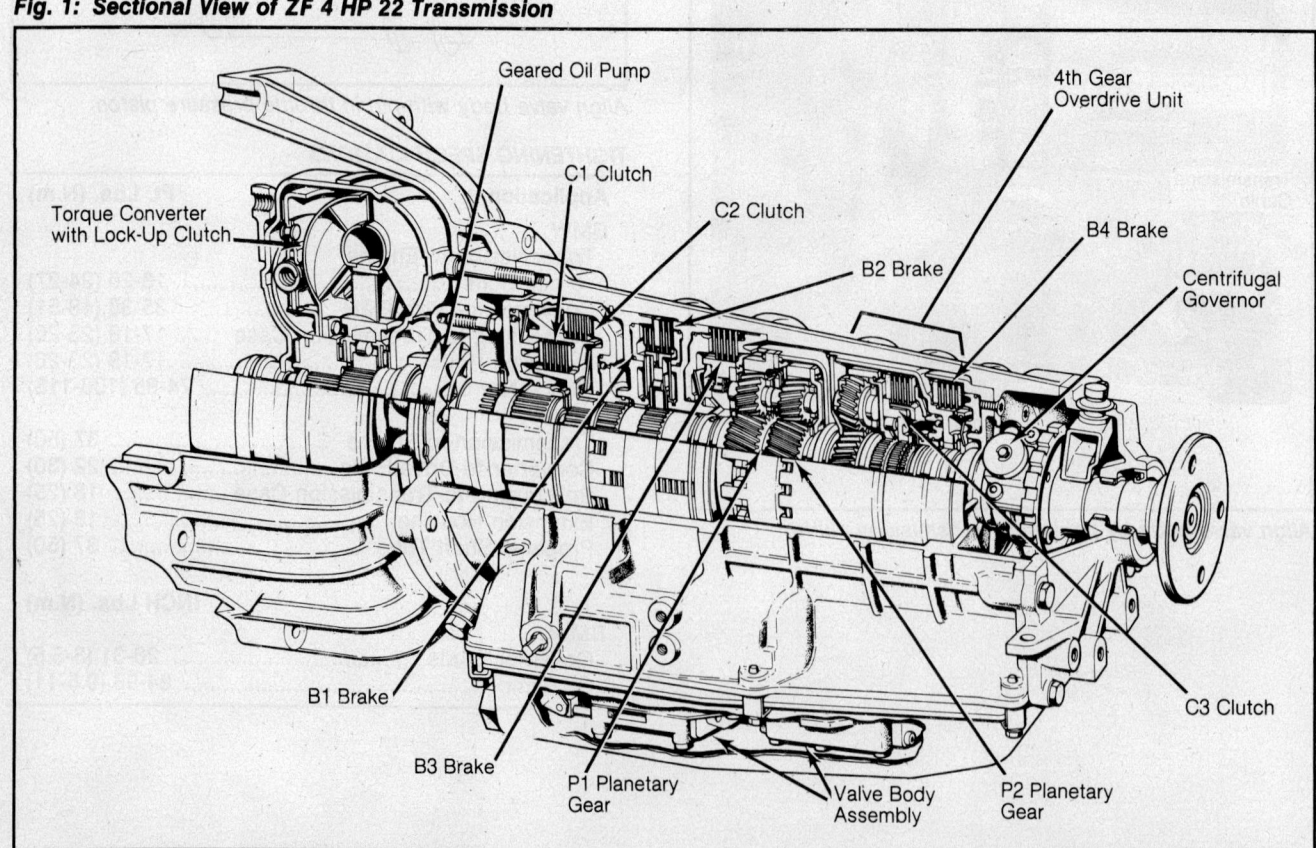

1st Gear Only
1st/2nd shift valve stuck. Governor bushing seized. Brake "C" defective.

2nd Gear Only
1st/2nd and 2nd/3rd shift valve stuck.

1st and 2nd Gears Only
2nd/3rd shift valve stuck.

3rd Gear Only
1st/2nd, 2nd/3rd or 3rd/4th shift valve stuck. Governor bushing seized.

4th Gear Only
Brake "F" defective

TRANSMISSION SLIPPAGE

In "D" Position
Clutch "A" slips. Oil level too low. Throttle pressure valve stuck.

In Reverse
Clutch "B" or brake "D" damaged. Loss of oil in supply line to clutch "B" or brake "D".

NO BRAKING EFFECT

In 3rd Gear Position
Clutch "E" damaged.

In 2nd Gear Position
Brake C' defective.

SHIFT POINTS INCORRECT

Too High
Throttle cable adjustment incorrect. Governor bushing jammed, or seal rings leaking. Valve body faulty.

Too Low
Throttle cable adjustment incorrect. Governor bushing jammed. Valve body faulty.

NO KICKDOWN

In "1-2" and "2-3"
Accelerator cable not adjusted properly. Throttle pressure valve seized. Balls in valve body worn.

NO UPSHIFT

To 2nd Gear
Governor seized. 1-2 shift valve seized.

To 3rd Gear
Governor seized. Throttle pressure too high. Throttle pressure valve stuck. Clutch "B" damaged.

To 4th Gear
Kickdown valve 4-3 seized.

TRANSMISSION NOISES

In All Positions When Cold
Suction noise at oil pump due to loose valve body bolts. Defective valve body. Low fluid level.

Noise in 1st Gear On Acceleration and Deceleration
Worn planetary gears.

Light Grinding Noise Which Is Speed Sensitive
Needle bearing in transmission extension housing defective.

Loud, Screeching Noise In All Positions
Oil level to low. Valve body leaks.

Loud Noise When Converter Closes
Torsion damper defective. Defective torque converter.

TESTING

ROAD TEST
1) Before testing, make sure fluid level is correct and all linkage adjustments are correct. Transmission should shift at approximate speeds shown in SHIFT SPEED charts. Speeds may vary due to model, tire size and axle ratio. The important factor is that all shifts should be smooth, with no slipping or engine racing.

2) Slipping or engine racing during shifts usually indicates clutch or brake slipping problems. Unless an obvious condition exists, transmission should never be disassembled until hydraulic pressure tests have been performed.

STALL TEST
1) With engine and transmission at normal operating temperature, connect a tachometer to engine. Apply service and parking brakes and place selector lever in "D".

CAUTION: DO NOT maintain stall speed more than 10 seconds.

BMW SHIFT SPEEDS

Shift Conditions	RPM
325e & 528e	
Full Throttle	
1-2 Upshift	3370-3950
2-3 Upshift	4000-4320
3-4 Upshift	3740-3980
Kickdown	
1-2 Upshift	4410-4910
2-3 Upshift	4510-4810
4-3 Downshift	Immediately
3-2 Downshift	3030-3250
2-1 Downshift	2550-2790
Manual Downshift (Max.)	
4-3	Immediately
3-2	2890-3230
2-1	2020-2500
533i, 633CSi & 733i	
Full Throttle	
1-2 Upshift	4140-4790
2-3 Upshift	4960-5340
3-4 Upshift	4580-4880
Kickdown	
1-2 Upshift	5430-5970
2-3 Upshift	5570-5930
4-3 Downshift	Immediately
3-2 Downshift	3690-3940
2-1 Downshift	2920-3290
Manual Downshift	
4-3	Immediately
3-2	3620-4030
2-1	2570-3040

2) Accelerate engine to full throttle and note engine speed. Repeat test with selector lever in position "R".

Stall Test Results

If stall speeds are below specifications, check engine output for being below specifications. Check stall speeds for proper specifications, refer to STALL SPEED SPECIFICATIONS.

VOLVO SHIFT SPEEDS

Shift Conditions	MPH
760 GLE Turbo Diesel	
Full Throttle (Kickdown Engaged)	
1-2 Upshift	29
2-3 Upshift	52
3-4 Upshift	61
4-3 Downshift	21
3-2 Downshift	49
2-1 Downshift	24

STALL SPEED SPECIFICATIONS

Application	Stall RPM
BMW	
325e & 528e	1900-2050
533i, 633CSi & 733i	1970-2120
Volvo	
760 GLE Turbo Diesel	1800-2000

HYDRAULIC PRESSURE

NOTE: The following procedure applies to BMW models only. Information not available from Volvo.

1) Connect Pressure Gauge Hose (24 0 021) to Pressure Tester (13 3 061). Remove pertinent pressure plugs for pump pressure, clutch "A" and converter pressure.

2) To test pump pressure, install Adapter (24 0 070) with seal on transmission. Connect Elbow Pipe (24 0 023) in conjunction with Hose (24 0 021).

3) To test converter pressure, install Adapter (24 0 030) on transmission. Connect Elbow Pipe (24 0 023) in conjunction with Hose (24 0 021).

BMW HYDRAULIC PRESSURES

Application	psi (kg/cm²)
325e & 528e	
In "R"	
Idle	156-185 (11-13)
Kickdown	229-260 (16.3-19.0)
In "D" Position	
Idle	85-107 (6-7.5)
Kickdown	141-156 (9.9-10.9)
533i, 633CSi & 733i	
In "R"	
Idle	215-245 (15.5-17.1)
Kickdown	246-276 (17.3-19.4)
All Other Positions	
Idle	85-107 (6-7.5)
Kickdown	132-146 (7.9-10.2)

Fig. 2: Hydraulic Pressure Connections

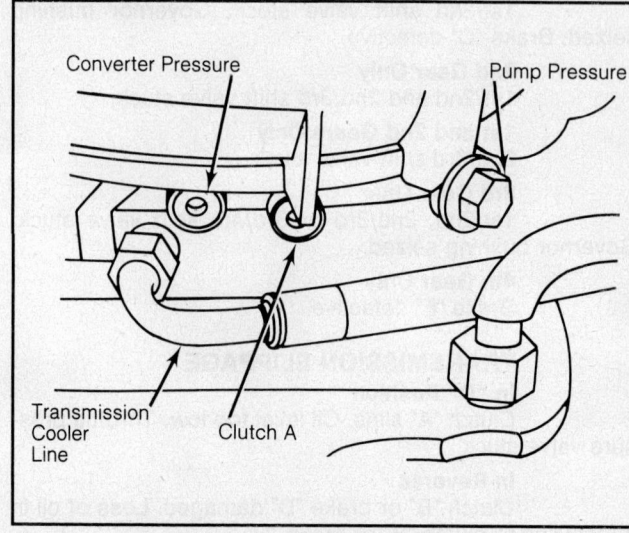

Be sure to check fluid level before testing.

4) Connect main pressure port. See Fig. 2. Disconnect transmission kickdown cable from throttle linkage and set engine idle speed to 1200-1500 RPM.

5) With rear wheels off the ground and transmission in "R", check main pressure. Pressure obtained should be within limits specified in HYDRAULIC PRSSURE charts. To check kickdown pressures, pull on kickdown cable.

6) Place transmission in Neutral and run engine at idle to cool transmission. With transmission in any position except "R", repeat check. Pressure obtained should be within limits specified in HYDRAULIC PRESSURE charts.

REMOVAL & INSTALLATION

See appropriate MANUAL TRANSMISSION REMOVAL article in IMPORT GENERAL SERVICING section.

SERVICE (IN VEHICLE)

The following units may be removed from transmission without removing transmission from vehicle: Oil Pan and Gasket, Shift Valve Body, Speedometer Driven Gear Assembly, Secondary Pump Assembly, Extension Housing, Pressure Receiving Piston, Modulating Pressure Housing, Speedometer Drive Gear, Secondary Pump Eccentric, Governor Assembly, Parking Pawl and Parking Linkage. See procedures given in TRANSMISSION DISASSEMBLY and TRANSMISSION REASSEMBLY.

TORQUE CONVERTER

NOTE: Torque converter is a sealed unit and cannot be disassembled for service. If hub or torque converter is scored, or if metallic particles are found in transmission fluid, replace converter assembly.

Fig. 3: ZF 4HP 22 Power Flow Diagram and Clutch Component Applications.

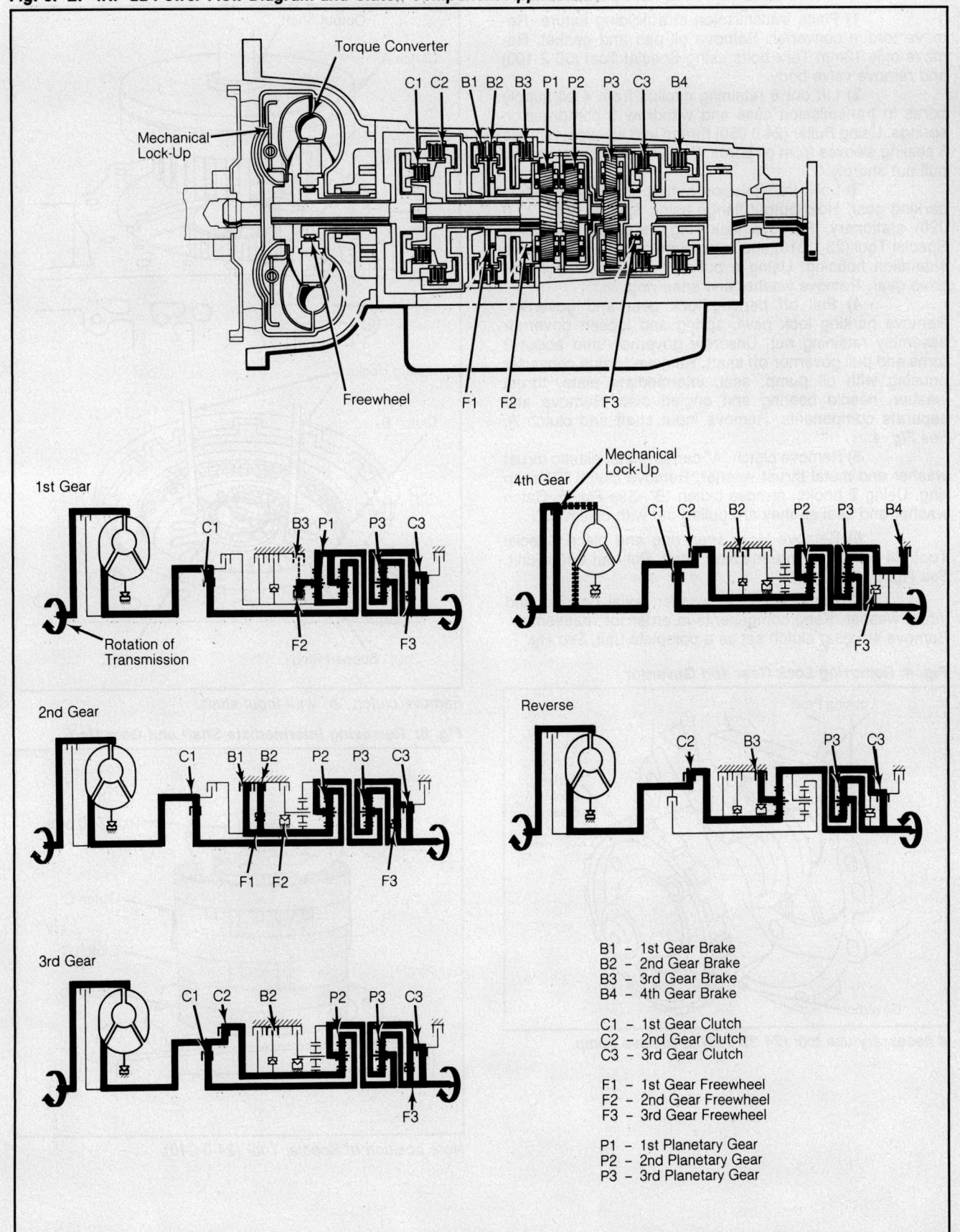

B1 – 1st Gear Brake
B2 – 2nd Gear Brake
B3 – 3rd Gear Brake
B4 – 4th Gear Brake

C1 – 1st Gear Clutch
C2 – 2nd Gear Clutch
C3 – 3rd Gear Clutch

F1 – 1st Gear Freewheel
F2 – 2nd Gear Freewheel
F3 – 3rd Gear Freewheel

P1 – 1st Planetary Gear
P2 – 2nd Planetary Gear
P3 – 3rd Planetary Gear

TRANSMISSION DISASSEMBLY

1) Place transmission in a holding fixture. Remove torque converter. Remove oil pan and gasket. Remove only 12mm Torx bolts using Special Tool (00 2 100) and remove valve body.

2) Lift out 8 retaining circlips from 4 oil supply bores in transmission case and withdraw 8 compression springs. Using Puller (24 0 050) thread into sleeves, remove 8 sealing sleeves from oil bores. Screw tool into sleeve and pull out sharply.

3) Lock transmission output shaft by engaging parking gear. Hold output flange using Special Tool (23 0 020) stationary. Remove lock ring, retaining nut using Special Tool (23 1 210) and remove output flange. Remove extension housing. Using a puller, pull off speedometer drive gear. Remove washer and snap ring.

4) Pull off parking lock gear and governor. Remove parking lock pawl, spring and loosen governor assembly retaining nut. Unscrew governor stud about 3 turns and pull governor off shaft. Remove torque converter housing with oil pump, seal, intermediate plate, thrust washer, needle bearing and angled disc. Remove and separate components. Remove input shaft and clutch A. *See Fig. 4.*

5) Remove clutch "A" carrier plate, plastic thrust washer and metal thrust washer. Remove clutch "B" snap ring. Using 2 hooks, remove clutch "B". *See Fig. 5.* Catch washer and seal as they are pulled out with clutch "B".

6) Remove large snap ring and place Special Tool (24 0 040) on intermediate shaft. Pull out entire unit. *See Fig. 6.*

7) Remove angled washer, axial bearing and thrust washer. Keep components in order for reassembly. Remove 4th gear clutch set as a complete unit. *See Fig. 7.*

Fig. 4: Removing Lock Gear and Governor

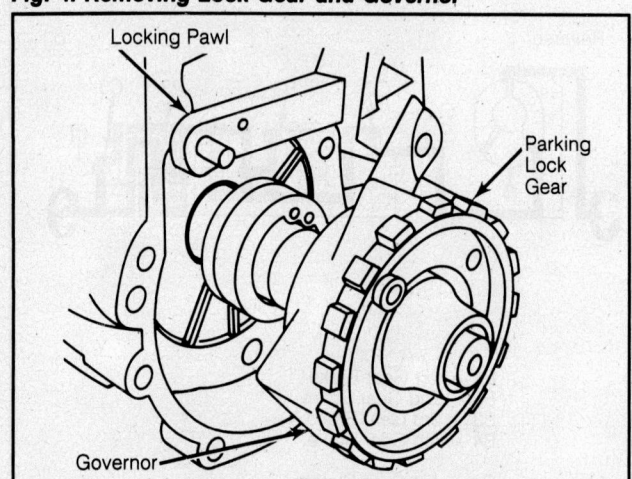

If necessary use tool (24 32 002) to remove pump.

Fig. 5: Removing Clutches "A" and "B".

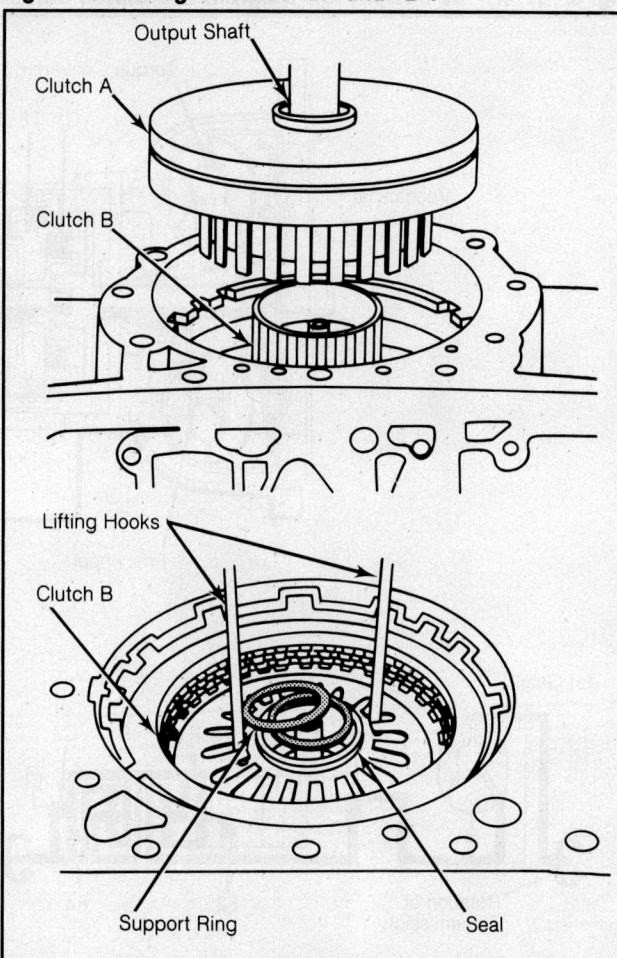

Remove clutch "A" with input shaft.

Fig. 6: Removing Intermediate Shaft and Gear Unit

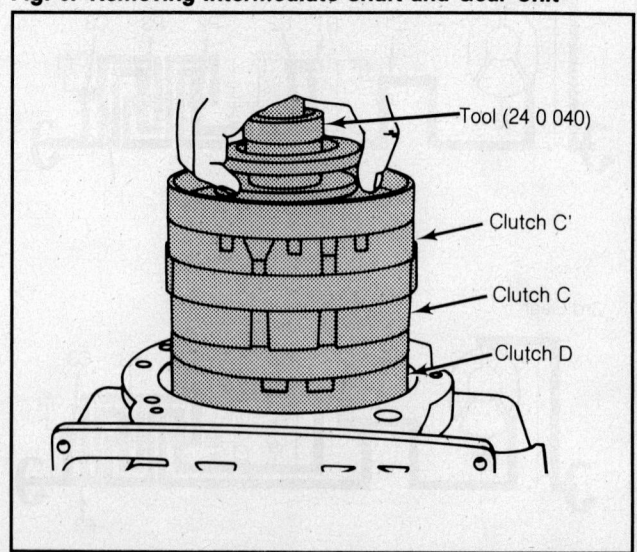

Note position of Special Tool (24 0 040).

Fig. 7: Removing Angled Washer, Axial Bearing and Thrust Washer

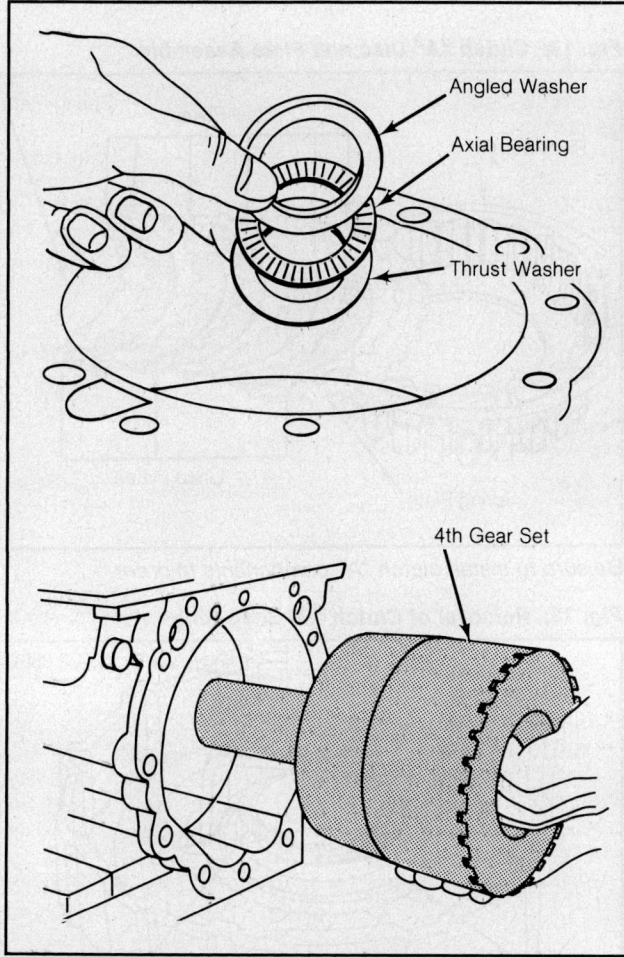

Note position of components for reassembly.

COMPONENT DISASSEMBLY & REASSEMBLY

PRIMARY PUMP ASSEMBLY
Disassembly
Remove torque converter. Remove converter housing with intermediate plate. Remove intermediate plate from converter housing by loosening 2 bolts. DO NOT remove bolts. Separate primary pump from converter housing by tapping lightly. Remove bolts and pump.

Inspection
1) Clean all parts and check for signs of scoring or other wear. Check clearance between pump driven gear and pump housing; clearance must be .003-.006" (.07-.16 mm).

2) Check pump housing-to-gear radial play while rotating gear 360°; clearance must be .0008-.0016" (.02-.04 mm).

3) Check running of primary pump with Measuring Tool (24 3 140).

4) Check axial play of both gears to face surface with a precision depth micrometer; axial play must be .008-.016" (.02-.04 mm). *See Fig. 8.*

5) If any component is defective, complete pump assembly must be replaced. If any measurement is not within specifications, replace oil pump assembly.

Fig. 8: Checking Primary Pump

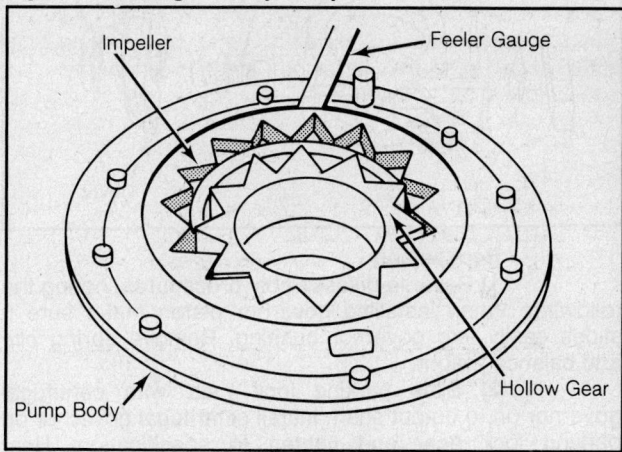

Measure while rotating pump 360°.

Reassembly
Reassemble in reverse of disassembly, noting the following: Install pump drive and gears with punch marks up, if equipped. Replace all gaskets and seals. Install angled disc on input shaft, with collar facing needle bearing. Hold thrust washer on converter housing with grease.

Fig. 9: Centrifugal Governor Assembly

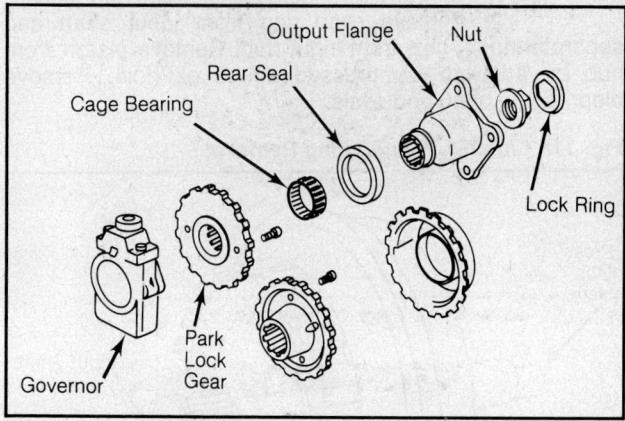

CENTRIFUGAL GOVERNOR
Disassembly
1) Remove transmission extension. Pull off parking lock gear with centrifugal governor. If equipped with bearing race, pull off parking lock gear with a Kukko puller. *See Fig. 9.*

2) Detach parking lock gear on centrifugal governor. Take off cover on case and lift out retainer and remove washer. Remove governor piston, spring and governor bushing. Remove spring clip and balance weight.

3) Clean all parts and check for signs of scoring or other wear. If any components show wear, replace complete governor assembly. *See Fig. 10.*

Automatic Transmissions

ZF 4HP 22 (Cont.)

Fig. 10: Exploded View of Centrifugal Governor

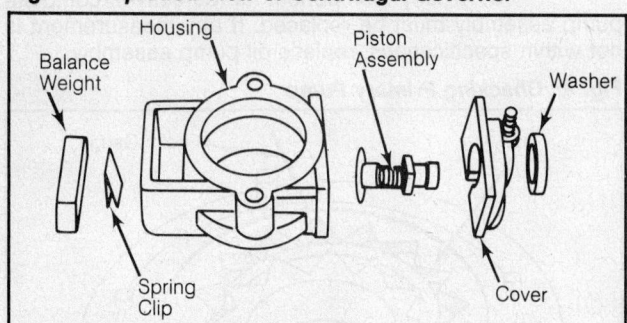

Reassembly

1) Reverse disassembly procedures, noting the following: When installing governor piston make sure it slides easily into governor bushing. Remove spring clip and balance weight.

2) Slide parking lock gear with centifugal governor on to output shaft. Install centrifugal governor on parking lock gear and tighten to specification. Heat bearing race to about 175° F (80°C). and slide on to output shaft.

CLUTCH "A"

Disassembly

1) With transmission disassembled, press out input shaft. Using press, compress clutch assembly and remove large snap ring. See Fig. 11. Remove spacer plates, clutch plates, discs, diaphragm spring and carrier plate. Note number and arrangement of plates and discs.

2) Remove snap ring from input shaft and separate input shaft from input hub. Remove piston from hub by applying compressed air to oil hole. Remove diaphragm spring and seals.

Fig. 11: Clutch "A" Snap Ring Removal

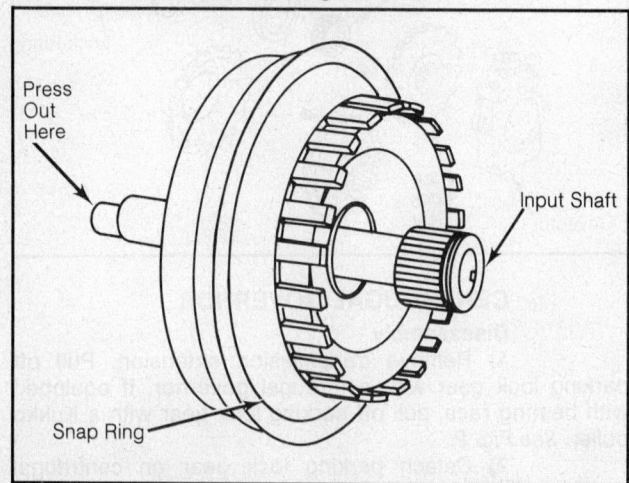

Compress clutch assembly and remove snap ring.

Reassembly

1) Reverse disassembly procedures, noting the following: Coat all discs and plates with ATF. Insert input shaft into hub and retain with snap ring. Place diaphragm spring in hub with curved surface facing down. Replace all seals.

2) Alternate plates and discs until the number and position of plates and discs are installed as they were

removed. See Fig. 12. Install spacer plates and carrier plate. Compress clutch assembly and install large snap ring.

Fig. 12: Clutch "A" Disc and Plate Assembly

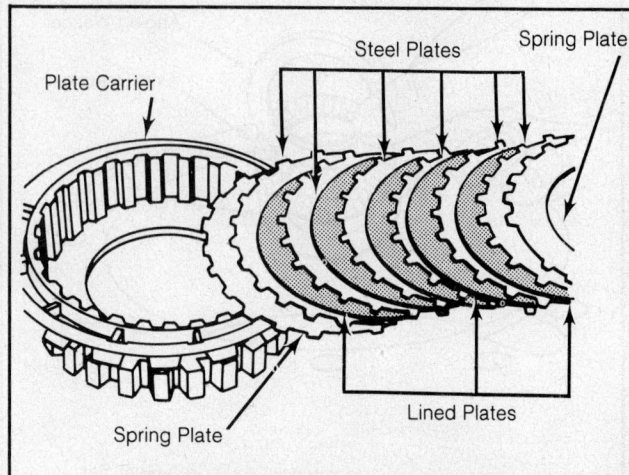

Be sure to install clutch "A" components in order.

Fig. 13: Removal of Clutch "B" Snap Ring

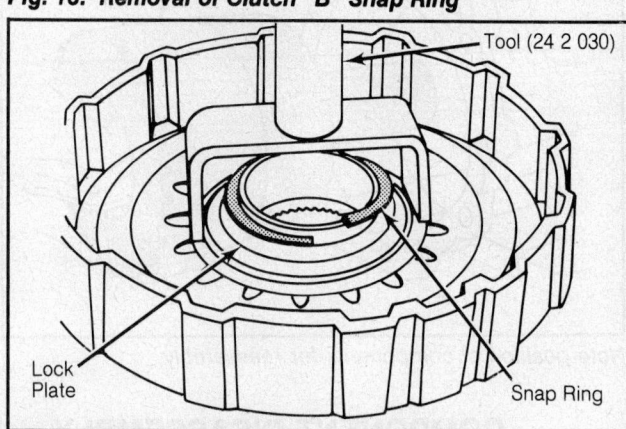

CLUTCH "B"

Disassembly

1) Remove snap ring from center of clutch "B" housing. Remove steel and lined plates, noting number and arrangement of plates and discs for reassembly reference. Bend open lock plate and press down on diaphragm spring with Special Tool (24 2 030) and remove snap ring. See Fig. 13.

2) Remove piston from housing by applying compressed air to oil feed hole. Remove and discard seals and "O" rings.

Reassembly

1) Reverse disassembly procedures, noting the following: Coat discs and plates with ATF. Replace all seals, "O" rings and lock plate. Position piston in housing and install diaphragm spring. Compress spring and install snap ring.

2) Alternate plates and discs until the number and position of plates and discs are installed as they were removed. See Fig. 14. Install end plate and large snap ring. Replace "O" ring and washer in center of housing.

ZF 4HP 22 (Cont.)

Fig. 14: Exploded View of Clutch B Assembly

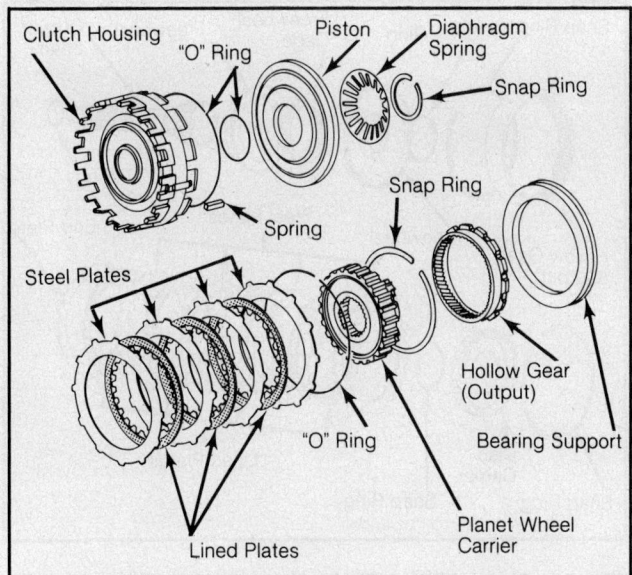

Note number and arrangement of plates and discs.

CLUTCH C' & "C"
Disassembly

1) Insert assembly into a pipe with an inside diameter of 1.142" (29 mm) and clamp assembly in a vise. Remove centering plate. Remove outer disc (2 on some models), plates and 1-way clutch for brake C'. *See Fig. 15.*

Fig. 15: Brake C' One-Way Clutch and Plates

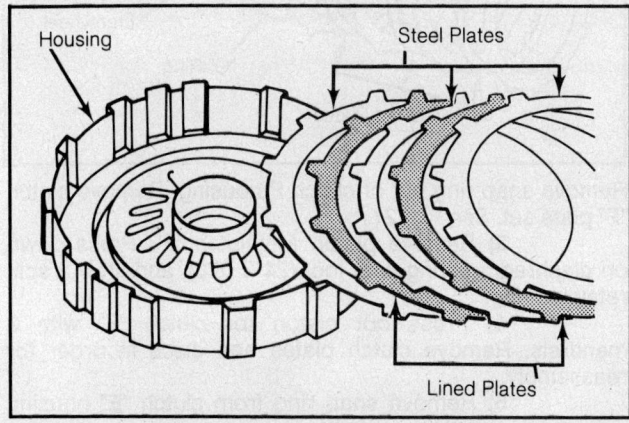

Note number and position of plates and discs.

2) Remove brake C' snap ring (if equipped). Remove end plate, discs and plates, noting number and arrangement for reassembly reference.

3) Lift center support assembly off output shaft. Remove brake "D" snap ring. Remove end plate, discs and plates, noting number and arrangement for reassembly reference.

4) Place center support assembly on work bench. Using tool (24 2 030) compress diaphragm spring and remove split retaining ring. Turn assembly over and remove large snap ring. Remove diaphragm springs and place brake C' on bench and compress diaphragm. Remove split retaining ring.

5) Apply compressed air to respective oil input hole to remove brake pistons. Remove and discard piston "O" rings and seals. Replace with new "O" rings and seals.

Fig. 16: Exploded View of Clutch Plate "C" & "D"

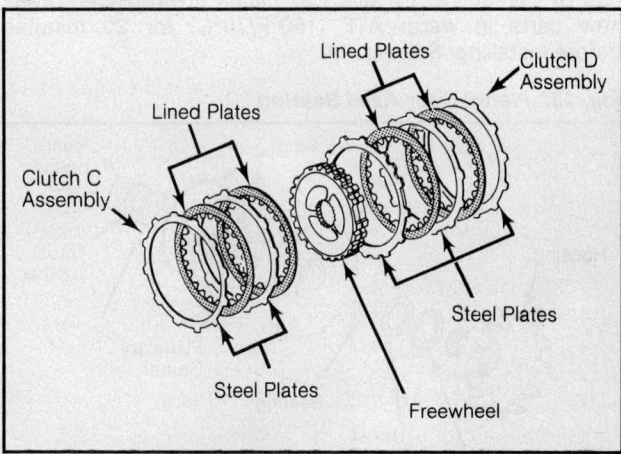

Note disc and plate sequence for brakes "C" & "D".

Reassembly

1) Reverse disassembly procedures, noting the following: Coat all discs and plates with ATF. Make sure all plates and discs are installed in proper sequence and number as when removed. See PLATE and DISC charts.

2) If discs or plates are replaced, soak new parts in warm ATF (160°F/70°C) for 20 minutes before installing.

Fig. 17: Exploded View of Clutch "D" Assembly

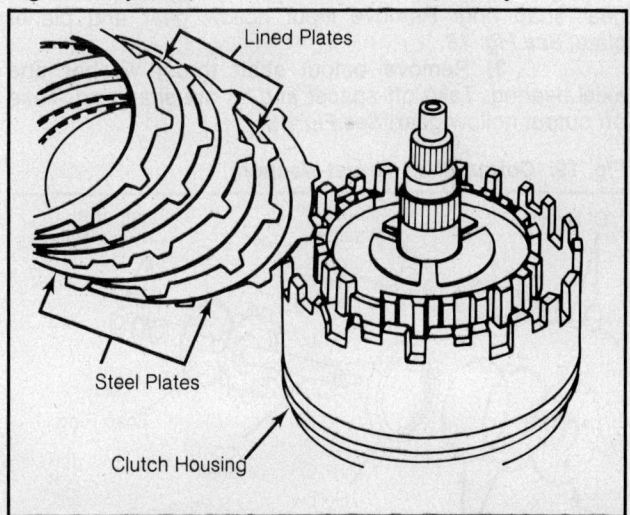

Note sequence of plates and disc for brake "D".

CLUTCH "D"
Disassembly

1) With clutches C' and "C" removed. Lift clutch member with "D" off of planet gear set. Remove snap ring and outer disc and lined plates. *See Fig. 17.*

2) Press down on diaphragm spring with Special Tool (24 2 030) and lift out snap ring. Press out clutch "D" piston with compressed air applied through oil bore. Discard "O" rings and seals.

Reassembly

1) Reverse disassembly procedures, noting the following: Insert diaphragm spring with curved surface facing up. Replace "O" rings and seals, lubricate "O" rings with a light coat of ATF.

2) Place planet plate with one-way clutch on hub of cylinder "D". If discs or plates are replaced, soak new parts in warm ATF (160°F/70°C) for 20 minutes before installing. *See Fig. 17.*

Fig. 18: Planet Gear Axial Bearing

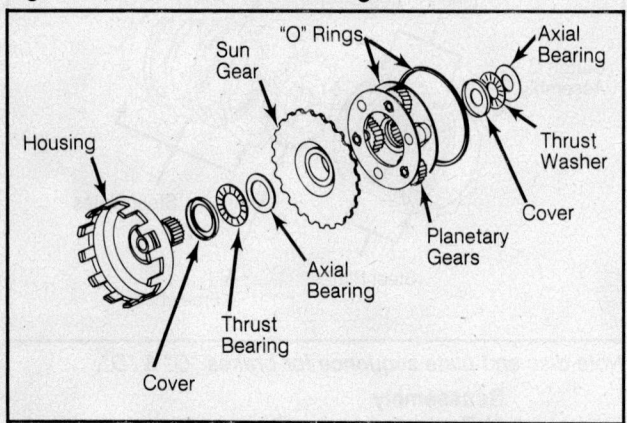

FRONT PLANETARY GEAR SET

Disassembly

1) Disassemble 1st planet gear assembly. Remove support ring for 2nd planet gear and remove 2nd planet gear assembly.

2) Pull out sun gear shaft. Remove axial bearing and input shaft thrust washer. Lift out input hollow gear snap ring. Remove input hollow gear and planet plate. *See Fig. 18.*

3) Remove output shaft thrust washer and axial bearing. Take off spacer and lift out snap ring. Take off output hollow gear. *See Fig. 19.*

Fig. 19: Output Shaft Thrust Washers

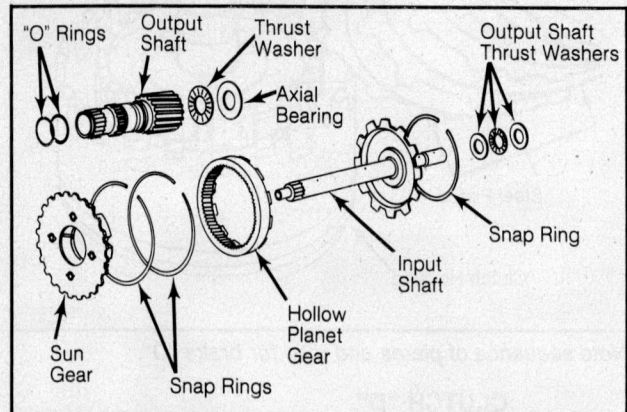

Reassembly

Reverse disassembly procedures, noting the following: Replace any worn or scored parts. Mount support ring with fins facing down.

CLUTCHES "E" & "F"

Disassembly

1) Remove sun, planet and planet carrier. Remove angled washer, axial bearing and thrust washer. Lift clutch housing "F" off of clutch housing "E".

2) Lift off housing "E" on output shell. Take off thrust washer, axial bearing and steel/copper angled washer, keep components in order for reassembly.

Fig. 20: Clutch "E" Assembly

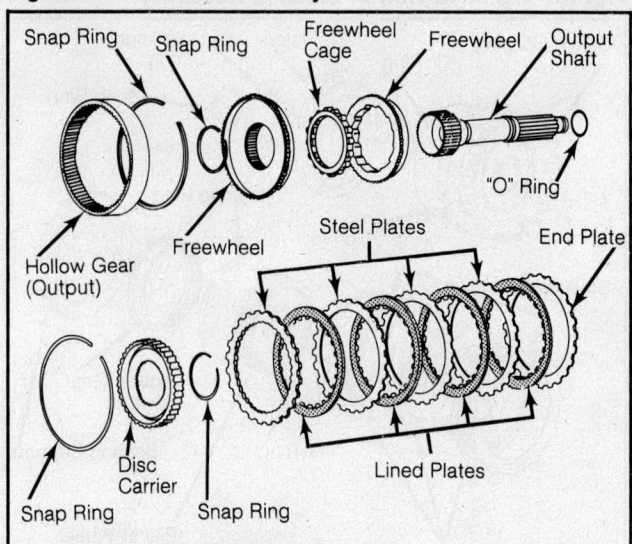

Fig. 21: Clutch "F" Assembly

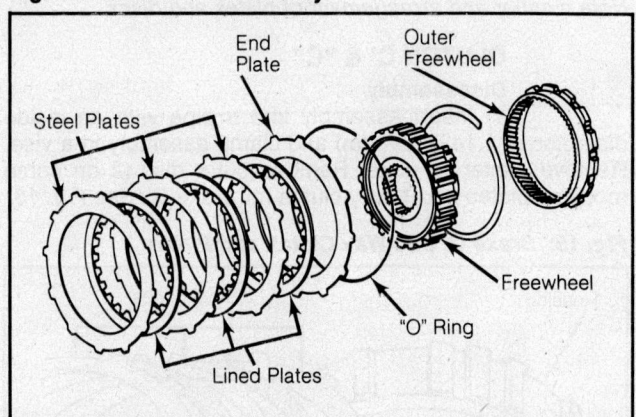

Remove snap ring out of clutch F housing. Remove clutch "F" plate set. *See Fig. 21.*

3) Remove piston for clutch "F". Press down on diaphragm spring with tool (24 2 020), and lift out split retaining ring.

4) Press out piston for clutch "F" with 2 mandrels. Remove clutch plates and discs in order for reassembly.

5) Remove snap ring from clutch "E" housing and remove clutch plate set. Keep components in order for reassembly. *See Fig. 20.*

6) Remove piston for clutch "E". Press down on disphragm spring with tool (24 2 020) and remove retaining ring.

7) Lift off cover and press clutch "E" piston with compressed air applied through oil bore. Discard "O" rings and seal.

Reassembly

1) Reverse disassembly procedures, noting the following: Replace all "O" rings and seals. Lubricate all components with ATF for ease of reassembly.

2) Insert diaphragm spring with curved surface facing up in clutch housing "E" and "F". Make sure all clutch plates and discs are installed in proper order.

3) Connect cylinders "E" and "F" by turning housing. Collar on output shaft must protrude by distance A = approx. .394" (10 mm).

Fig. 22: One-Way Clutch

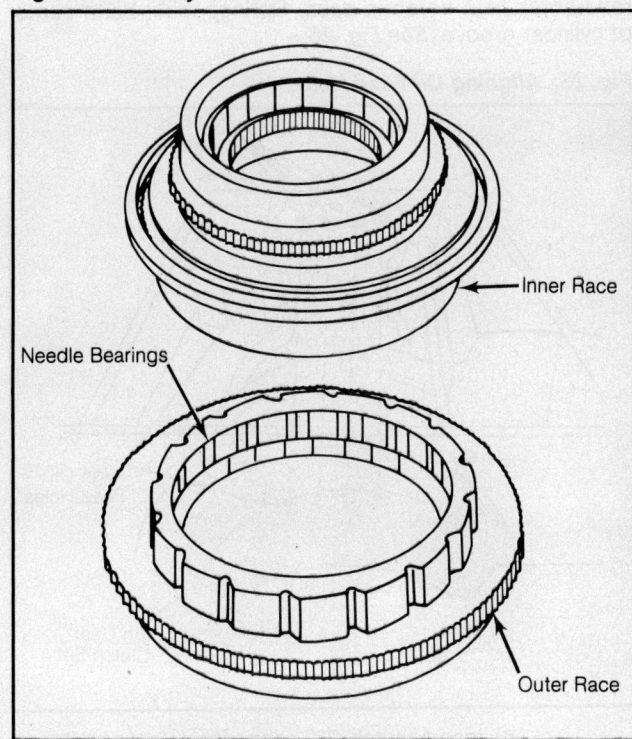

Be careful not to lose needle bearings.

ONE-WAY CLUCTCH
Disassembly & Reassembly

1) Lift out snap ring. Press output shaft from clutch unit. Lift off plate carrier. Carefully press one-way clutch cage out of outer race. Be careful, needle bearings can jump out of cage. *See Fig. 22.*

2) Place one-way clutch cage on outer race and align. Press in one-way clutch cage against stop and then turn until metal edge engages in holding groove of outer race.

3) Use plate carrier to turn one-way clutch outer race clockwise and mount race on inner race. Clearance between one-way clutch inner race and outer race should be at least .004" (.1 mm). *See Fig. 23.*

Fig. 23: Checking Clearance of One-Way Clutch

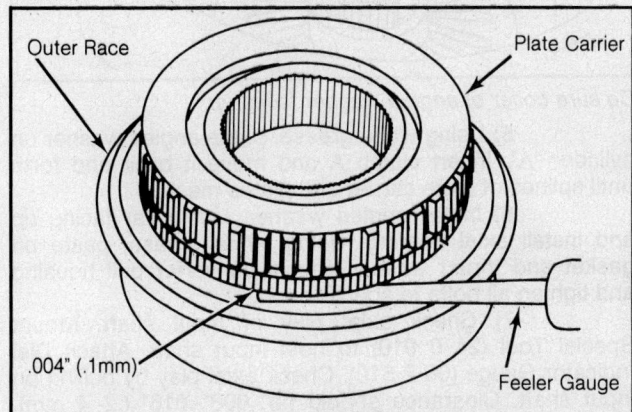

Check clearance between inner and outer race

PLATE & DISC USAGE CHART

Application	No. of Plates
All BMW Models	
Clutch A	
Spacer Plates	2
Discs	6
Plates	5
Clutch B	
End Plate	1
Discs	4
Plates	4
Clutch C	
Discs	2
Plates	2
End Plate	1
Brake C'	
Discs	2
Plates	2
End Plate	1
Brake D	
End Plate	1
Discs	4
Plates	4
Brake E	
Discs	4
Plates	4
End Plate	1
Brake F	
Discs	4
Plates	4
End Plates	1

Fig. 24: Exploded Veiw of Rear Plantery Gear Assembly

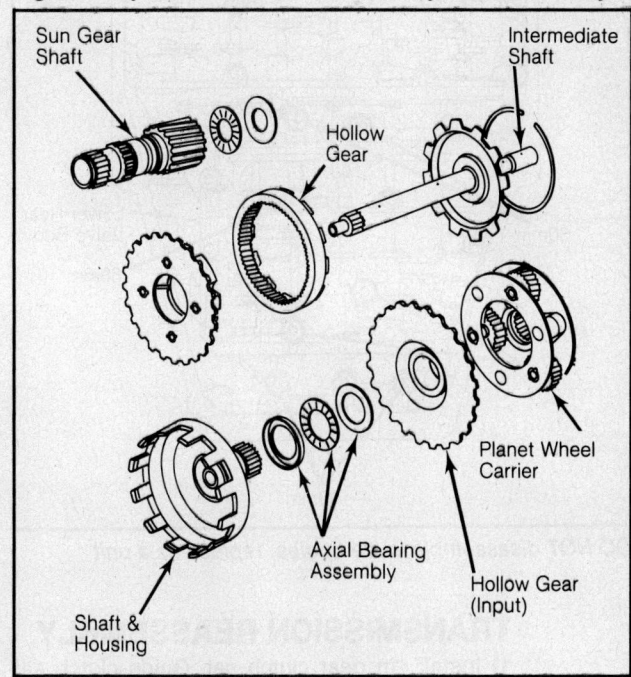

REAR PLANETARY GEAR
Disassembly

1) Place output shaft in a support with output shaft facing down. Remove one-way clutch and front planetary gear set. Remove sun gear shaft. Remove large snap ring and lift off ring gear. Lift off rear planetary gear set.

2) Remove intermediate shaft from output shaft housing. Remove roller bearing and washer from output shaft housing and intermediate shaft. Remove large snap ring holding input ring gear to intermediate shaft. Remove washers and bearing. Remove other large snap ring.

Reassembly

To reassemble planetary gear set, reverse disassembly procedure, noting the following: Make sure large snap rings are on both sides of input ring gear when assembled to intermediate shaft. When installing mainshaft to output shaft, place washer onto output shaft first, then the roller bearing. Make sure all snap rings are properly installed and fully seated.

VALVE BODY ASSEMBLIES

NOTE: **Valve body disassembly is not recommended. If a valve body malfunction is determined, replace valve body. See Fig. 25.**

Fig. 25: Valve Body Assemblies

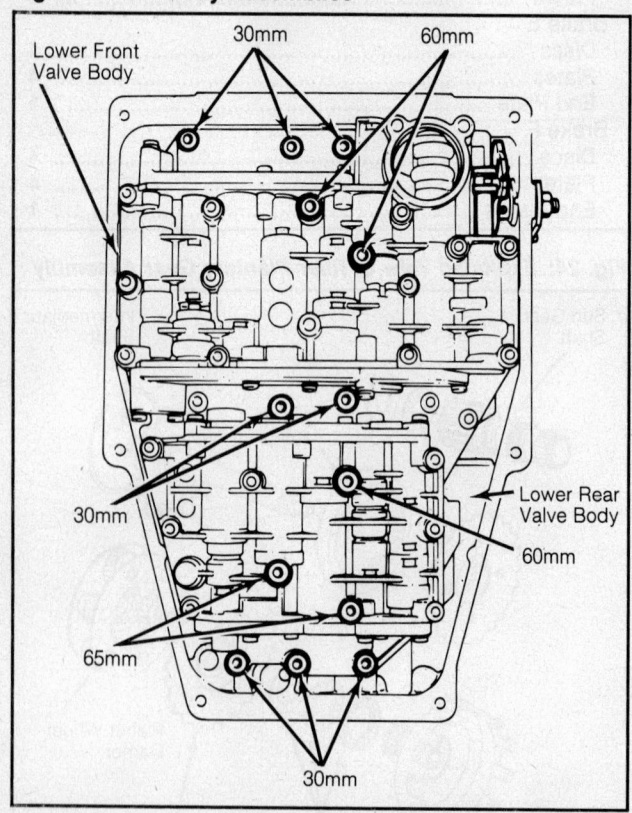

DO NOT disassemble valve bodies, replace as a unit

TRANSMISSION REASSEMBLY

1) Install 4th gear clutch set. Guide clutch set into transmission case so that 4 oil feed bores are aligned with bores in case. Bolt down clutch set with Special Tools (00 2 100 & 00 2 050). Tighten to specifications.

2) Set transmission upright. Insert thrust washer, axial bearing and angled washer with collar facing up.

3) Place entire gear set into case. Align 4 oil feed bores with bores in case. Springs must be in center of cylinder groove. *See Fig. 26.*

Fig. 26: Aligning Oil Feed Holes

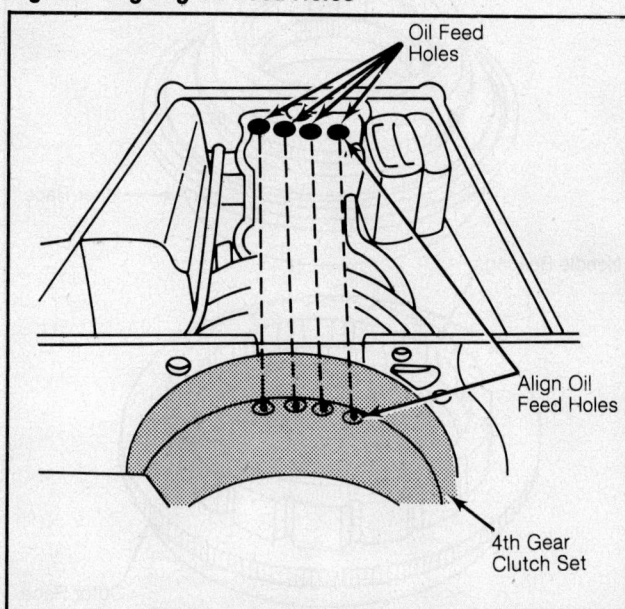

4) Insert clutch "B" snap ring into case. Insert and push clutch "B" against stop. Install seal, support and snap ring. Insert plate carrier and thrust washer and axial bearing. *See Fig. 27.*

Fig. 27: Installing Thrust Washer and Bearing

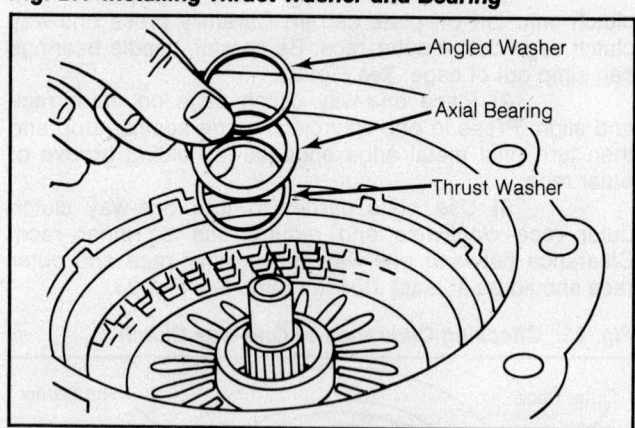

Be sure collar of angled washer faces up.

5) Using white grease, paste angled washer on cylinder "A". Insert clutch A and move it back and forth until splines of plate carrier and plates mesh.

6) Install angled washer with collar facing up and install axial bearing. Using white grease, paste on gasket and thrust washer. Install converter bell housing and tighten all bolts to specification.

7) Check axial play of input shaft. Mount Special Tool (24 0 010) to hold input shaft. Attach Dial Indicator Gauge (00 2 510). Check axial play by pulling on input shaft. Clearance should be .008"-.016" (.2-.4 mm). *See Fig. 28.*

ZF 4HP 22 (Cont.)

Fig. 28: Checking Axial Play of Input Shaft

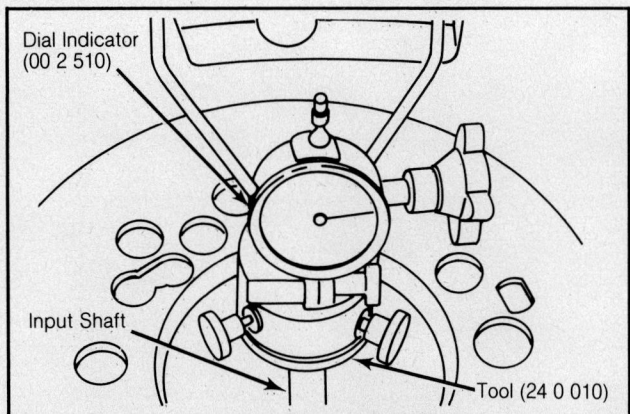

Check axial play by pulling on input shaft.

8) If play deviates, take off converter bell housing again and replace thrust washer with a thicker or thinner one. Recheck axial play. Tighten down converter bell housing to specification. Remove Special Tool (24 1 010).

9) Install parking lock pawl. Attach return spring in bore of pawl. Lubricate "O" ring with ATF. Push on parking lock gear and governor.

10) Using white grease, place gasket on transmission extension housing. Install housing to transmission and tighten to specification.

11) Install output flange. Install collar nut and using Special Tool (23 0 020) hold output flange. Using Special Tool (23 1 210), tighten collar nut. Install lock plate and lock in groove.

12) Install 8 sealing sleeves into valve body. Being careful not to damage sealing sleeves, press in sealing sleeves against stop. Install 8 springs and 8 circlips. Use longer springs to face cylinder "F". *See Fig. 29.*

Fig. 29: Sleeve & Spring Locations

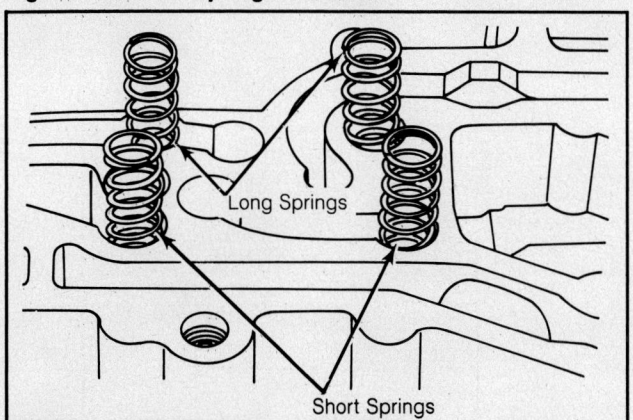

DO NOT damage sealing sleeves

13) Mount valve body so that selector valve can be connected in operating finger of pawl. This requires pulling throttle cable slighty, so that accelerator cam does not clamp on throttle pressure valve.

14) Tighten valve body bolts only finger tight. Align valve body with Special Tool (24 3 050). Distance between valve body case and throttle pressure piston must be .453" (11.5 mm).

15) Using Special Tools (00 2 100 & 00 2 050) tighten bolts to specification. Install "O" ring between valve body and oil filter screen. Install and bolt down oil filter screen.

16) Place magnets in oil pan and install gasket. Install oil sump and tighten bolts with brackets attached. Make sure both brackets with straight short legs are mounted on straight side of oil sump.

TIGHTENING SPECIFICATIONS

Application	Ft. Lbs. (N.m)
BMW	
Transmission-to-Engine	
12 mm Bolts	56-64 (78-88)
10 mm Bolts	[1] 35-38 (48-51)
8 mm Bolts	18-20 (24-27)
Converter-to-Drive Plate	17-19 (23-26)
Bellhousing-to-Transmission Case	33 (46)
Extension Housing	17-19 (23-26)
Flange Nut	74-85 (100-115)

	INCH Lbs. (N.m)
BMW	
Governor Studs	26-31 (3-3.5)
Oil Pump	84-96 (9.5-11)

[1] – BMW 528e models = 34-37 (46-50).

SECTION 7

IMPORT MANUAL TRANSMISSIONS

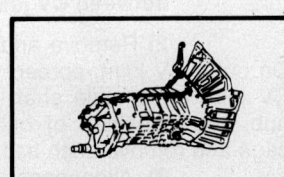

NOTE: ALSO SEE GENERAL INDEX.

AUDI 4000 & VOLKSWAGEN QUANTUM 5-SPEED

DESCRIPTION

This transaxle is a 5-speed unit, fully synchronized in all forward gears. The mainshaft and pinion shaft are supported by roller bearings housed in the gear carrier. The final drive housing contains the clutch housing, clutch release mechanism as well as a ring and pinion gear differential.

The differential drive pinion shaft also serves as the countershaft for the transmission. Fifth gear is housed in the rear cover and all others are contained in the gear carrier.

LUBRICATION & ADJUSTMENT

See the appropriate article in MANUAL TRANSMISSION SERVICING Section.

SERVICE (IN VEHICLE)

AXLE DRIVE SHAFTS

NOTE: **Vehicle weight must be resting on wheels to remove axle shaft nut.**

Removal

1) Loosen axle shaft nut. Raise and support vehicle. Remove axle nut and wheel. Disconnect and remove exhaust pipe from exhaust manifold and transaxle bracket on right side of engine. Remove Allen bolts connecting inner constant velocity (CV) joint to differential case drive flange.

2) Mark position of both ball joint flanges on control arms. Remove ball joint from control arm and pull pivot mounting outward while removing drive shaft. Press drive shaft out of hub and guide past transaxle.

NOTE: **Axle drive shafts should be disassembled ONLY to replace defective boots. If boots are replaced, check all components for damage or wear and replace as a complete assembly if necessary.**

Disassembly

1) On inner CV joint, remove circlip from axle shaft and drive protective cap from CV joint. Place axle shaft in holder (VW402) and press CV joint from shaft with adapter (VW408a), supporting hub to prevent damage.

Pivot hub and cage assembly out of inner joint, then push out and remove balls. Align ball hub grooves with cage and remove hub.

Fig. 2: Removing Inner CV Joint Ball Hub

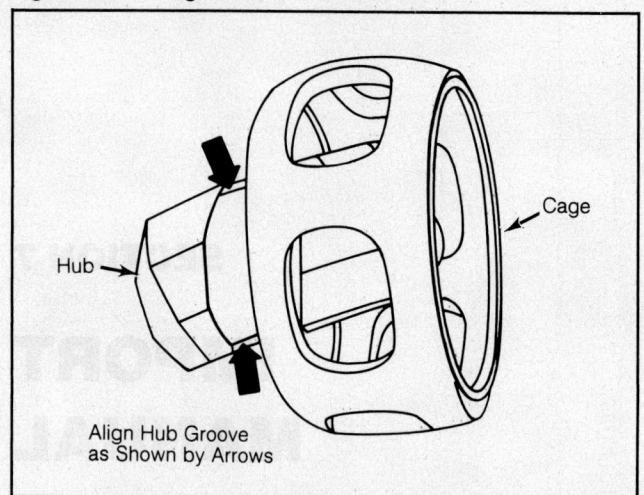

NOTE: **Inner CV joint and ball hub are matched sets. DO NOT interchange with outer joint. Also, balls of CV joints cannot be interchanged between CV joints.**

2) Remove and discard inner clamp and boot. On outer CV joint, spread circlip inside ball hub and drive CV joint off of axle shaft with brass drift by tapping on hub. Mark position of ball hub and outer joint, then tilt cage and remove each ball.

3) Align cage perpendicular to joint. Align 2 large openings in cage with raised portions of joint and remove cage and hub. Position 1 retainer of hub in large opening of cage and remove hub by tilting outward. Remove and discard outer boot and clamp.

Reassembly

1) To reassemble CV joints, reverse disassembly procedure and note the following: Lubricate joints with 3 ozs. of molybdenum disulphide grease. Chamfer of ball hub splines must face larger diameter of joint. When rotating ball and cage into joint, ensure that wide ball groove and narrow hub groove are on same side of joint. See Fig. 4.

Fig. 1: Exploded View of Audi/Volkswagen 5-Speed Transaxle

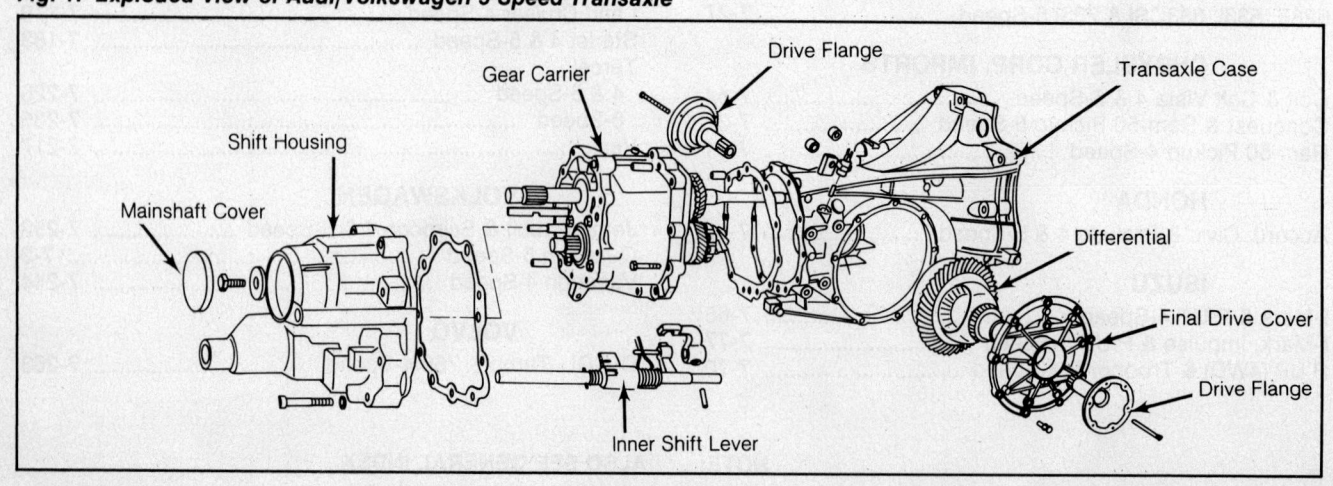

AUDI 4000 & VOLKSWAGEN QUANTUM 5-SPEED (Cont.)

Fig. 3: Exploded View of Axle Drive Shaft

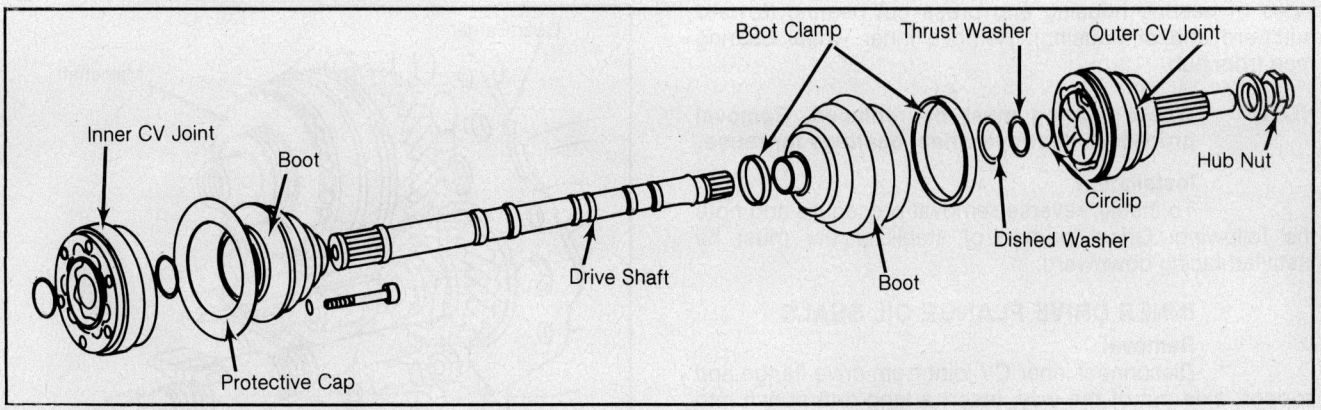

Fig. 4: Installing Ball Hub and Cage in Inner CV Joint

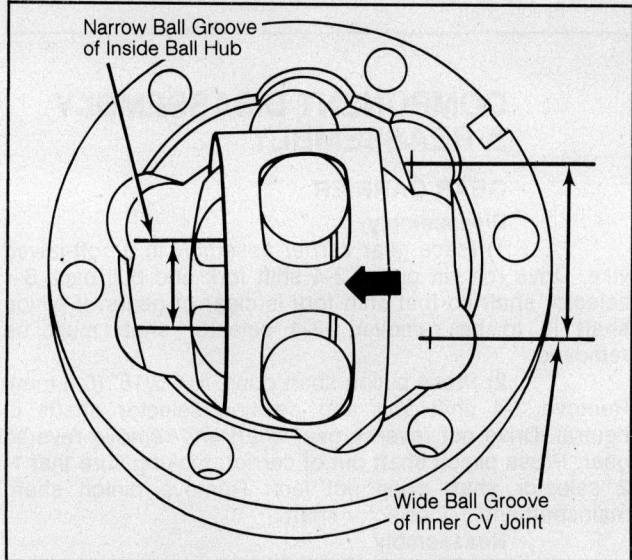

2) Outer CV joint alignment marks must align after reassembly. Inside ball hub chamfer faces axle shaft on both joints. Concave side of dished washer faces CV joint on both joints and convex side of thrust washer faces CV joint on outer joint. Always use new circlips to retain CV joints on shafts. Open end of boot clamps should face opposite direction of normal rotation of shaft. See Fig. 5.

Fig. 5: Cutaway View of Outer CV Joint Showing Installation of Dished and Thrust Washers

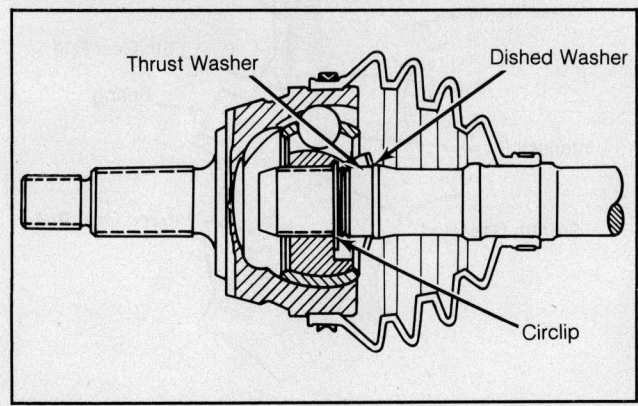

Installation

To install, reverse removal procedure and note the following: After installing axle shafts, align ball joint flanges with marks made at disassembly and tighten nuts. Check camber setting and adjust as necessary.

FRONT WHEEL BEARINGS

Removal

1) With vehicle supported and axle drive shafts removed, remove stabilizer bar clamps. Remove caliper mounting bolts and hang caliper from frame with wire. DO NOT disconnect hydraulic line or allow caliper to hang by hydraulic line. Remove brake disc and ball joint bolt. Press off tie rod and remove ball joint from hub.

Fig. 6: Exploded View of Front Suspension Strut Assembly

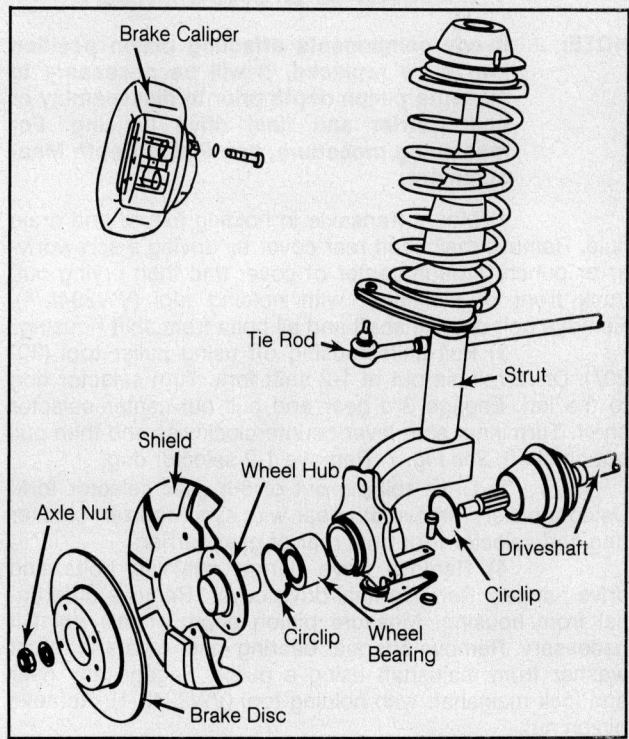

2) Support suspension strut with jack and remove upper strut retaining nuts from inside engine compartment. Remove strut assembly from vehicle and place in holding fixture. Press out wheel hub with hub

AUDI 4000 & VOLKSWAGEN QUANTUM 5-SPEED (Cont.)

removal tool (VW295 & 295a). Remove circlips from both sides of bearing housing and press out bearing (toward outboard end of housing). Remove inner wheel bearing race from hub.

NOTE: **Wheel bearing must be replaced. Removal procedure destroys wheel bearings for reuse.**

Installation
To install, reverse removal procedure and note the following: Offset portion of stabilizer bar must be installed facing downward.

INNER DRIVE FLANGE OIL SEALS
Removal
Disconnect inner CV joint from drive flange and support axle out of the way. Insert a long drift punch into one drive flange hole to prevent rotation, then remove drive flange bolt. Place drip pan under transaxle and pull out drive flange. Pry out oil seal.
Installation
Lightly lubricate seal lips and fully seat seal with driver (30-212). Install drive flange and tighten drive flange retaining bolt. Install drive axle and tighten bolts. Check and add lubricant to transaxle if necessary.

TRANSAXLE REMOVAL & INSTALLATION
See the appropriate article in MANUAL TRANS-MISSION REMOVAL Section.

TRANSAXLE DISASSEMBLY

NOTE: **If any components affecting pinion position are to be replaced, it will be necessary to measure pinion depth prior to disassembly of gear carrier and final drive housing. For measuring procedure, see Pinion Depth Measurement.**

1) Mount transaxle in holding fixture and drain fluid. Remove mainshaft rear cover by driving a screwdriver or punch through center of cover and then prying out. Lock front of mainshaft with holding tool (VW294b/1). Remove bolt on mainshaft and all bolts from shift housing.

2) Pull shift housing off using puller tool (30-207). Drive roll pin out of 1-2 shift fork. Turn selector dog to the left. Engage 3rd gear and pull out center selector shaft. Turn inner shift lever counterclockwise and then pull out on shaft. *See Fig. 7.* Remove 1-2 selector dog.

3) Drive roll pin out of 5th gear selector fork. Using a puller, remove 5th gear with synchronizer, blocker ring and selector fork from rear of gear carrier.

4) Remove drive flange retaining bolts and drive flanges. Remove final drive cover. Remove differential from housing. Measure pinion depth at this point if necessary. Remove 5th gear bearing inner race and thrust washer from mainshaft using a puller. Engage any gear and lock mainshaft with holding tool (VW294b/1). Remove pinion nut.

5) Remove 5th gear from pinion shaft. Shift gear train into neutral. Remove gear carrier-to-final drive housing bolts and dowel pins. Pull complete gear carrier assembly off of final drive housing.

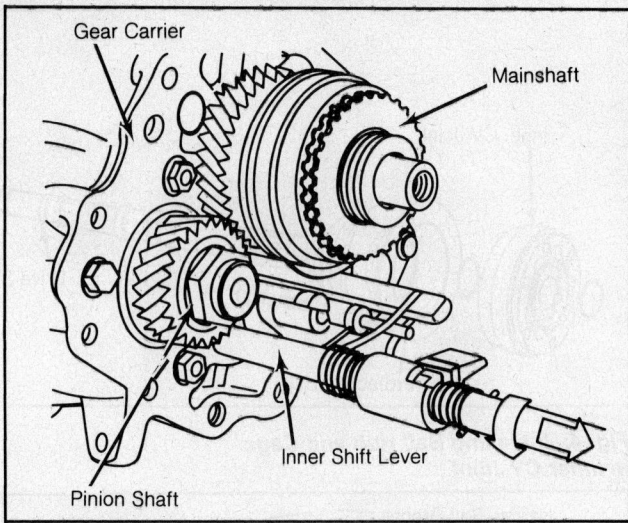

Fig. 7: *Inner Shift Lever Removal*

COMPONENT DISASSEMBLY & REASSEMBLY

GEAR CARRIER
Disassembly
1) Place gear carrier assembly in a soft-jawed vise. Drive roll pin out of 3-4 shift fork and pull back 3-4 selector shaft so that shift fork is clear of gears. If pinion shaft is to be removed, 3-4 selector shaft must be removed.

2) Press pinion shaft down 1/4-5/16" (6-8 mm). Remove 3-4 shift fork and position selector shafts in neutral. Drive out reverse gear shaft and remove reverse gear. Press pinion shaft out of carrier, making sure that 1-2 selector shaft does not jam. Remove pinion shaft, mainshaft and 1-2 selector shaft.

Reassembly
1) Check to make sure that all interlock plungers and detents are in proper position. *See Fig. 8.* Position 1-2 shift fork with selector shaft onto pinion shaft. Mesh pinion shaft gear teeth with mainshaft gear teeth. Install assembled gear shafts into gear carrier.

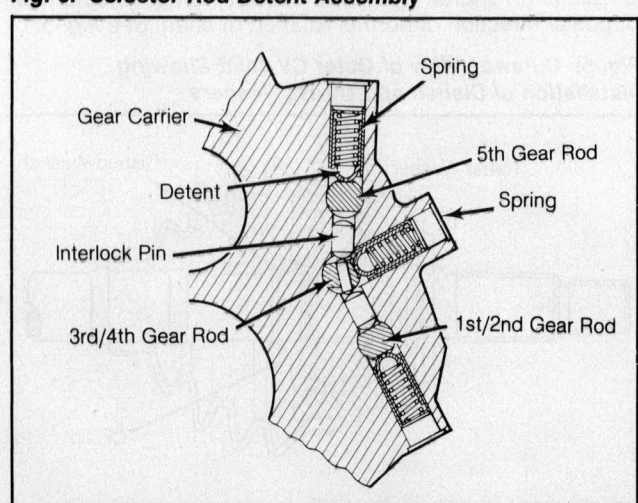

Fig. 8: *Selector Rod Detent Assembly*

AUDI 4000 & VOLKSWAGEN QUANTUM 5-SPEED (Cont.)

Fig. 9: Exploded View of Mainshaft Assembly

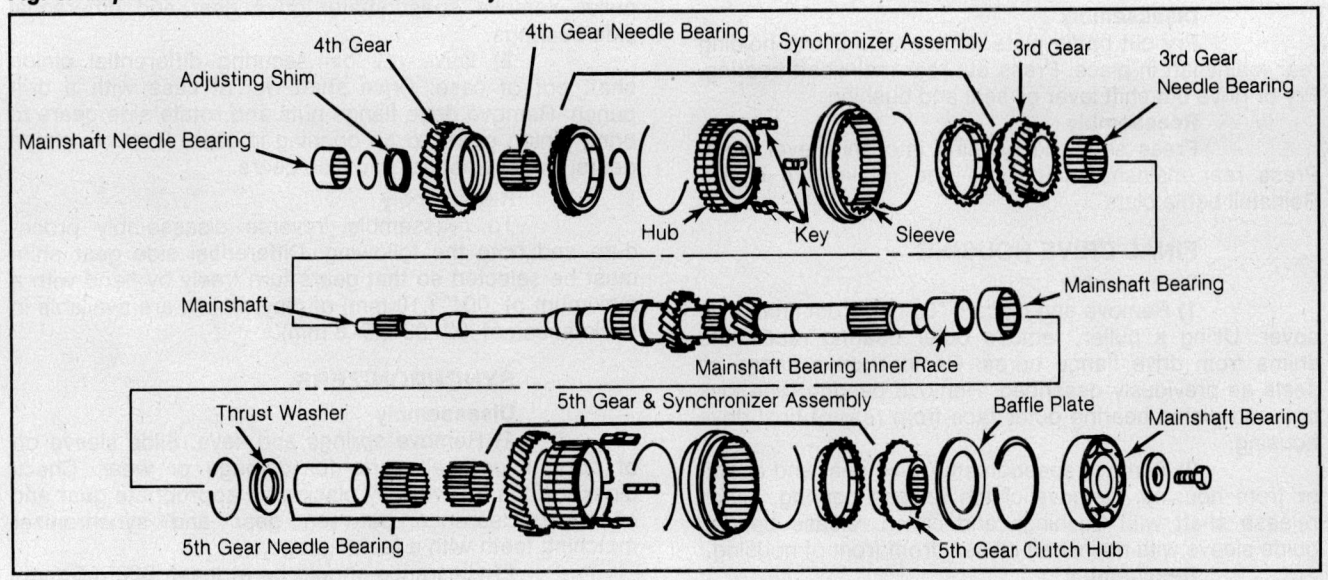

2) Install reverse gear and shaft. Position selector shafts in neutral. Install 3-4 selector shaft with small interlock pin and secure with roll pin at 3-4 shift fork.

3) Press inner bearing race onto pinion shaft. Install mainshaft thrust washer. Heat 5th gear inner bearing race to 250°F (121°C) and install onto mainshaft. Heat 5th gear to 250°F (121°C) and install onto mainshaft.

4) Install 5th gear and synchronizer assembly with blocker ring onto mainshaft. Heat synchronizer clutch hub to 250°F (121°C) and install on to mainshaft.

MAINSHAFT

Disassembly

1) Remove circlip from end of mainshaft. Remove shim, 4th gear, needle bearing and blocker ring. Remove and discard circlip holding 3-4 synchronizer onto shaft. Press 3-4 synchronizer hub and sleeve off of shaft.

2) Remove 3rd gear and needle bearing. Press mainshaft bearing inner race off rear of mainshaft. Remove circlip retaining mainshaft bearing outer race to gear carrier. Press outer race out of carrier. Drive mainshaft needle bearing out of final drive housing.

Reassembly

Check all bearings for damage or excessive wear. To reassemble, reverse disassembly procedure and

note the following: End play measured between 4th gear and shim should be .004-.016" (.10-.40 mm). If end play is not within specifications, adjust by changing shim thickness. Shims are available in the following sizes: .137" (3.47 mm), .141" (3.57 mm) and .145" (3.67 mm).

PINION SHAFT

Disassembly

Engage 2nd gear. Press pinion rear bearing inner race and 1st gear off of shaft. Press 1-2 synchronizer hub with sleeve and 2nd gear off of pinion shaft. Press 3rd gear off shaft and then remove circlip retaining 4th gear. Press 4th gear off of shaft and then remove pinion front bearing inner race.

Reassembly

1) Ensure that pinion shaft is free of all traces of grease and oil. Reinstall front bearing onto pinion shaft. Heat 4th gear to 250°F (121°C) and install onto pinion shaft until fully seated.

2) Press 3rd gear onto shaft and retain with a selective fit snap ring. Snap rings are available in thicknesses of .060-.063" (1.5-1.6 mm). Install 2nd gear, blocker ring and 1-2 synchronizer onto shaft. Groove on edge of synchronizer hub faces 1st gear. Press 1st gear bearing inner race and 1st gear onto shaft. Press pinion rear bearing inner race onto pinion shaft.

Fig. 10: Exploded View of Pinion Shaft Assembly

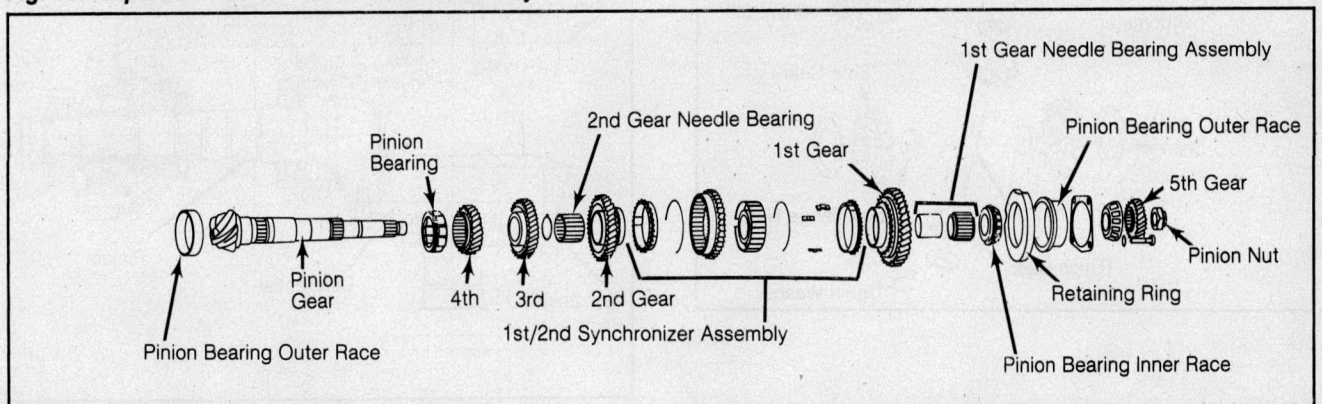

Manual Transmissions

AUDI 4000 & VOLKSWAGEN QUANTUM 5-SPEED (Cont.)

SHIFT HOUSING

Disassembly

Pry out baffle plate and remove circlip holding rear mainshaft in place. Press out rear mainshaft bearing. Pry or drive out shift lever oil seal and bushing.

Reassembly

Press seal and bushing into shift lever bore. Press rear mainshaft into bore and retain with circlip. Reinstall baffle plate.

FINAL DRIVE HOUSING

Disassembly

1) Remove and discard "O" ring from final drive cover. Using a puller, remove outer bearing races and shims from drive flange bores. Remove drive flange oil seals as previously described. Remove bearing race lock bolt and pinion bearing outer race from rear of final drive housing.

2) Remove speedometer drive gear and adapter from housing. Remove clutch release bearing, clutch release shaft with bushings and clutch release bearing guide sleeve with mainshaft oil seal from front of housing.

Reassembly

1) Inspect all bearings for damage or excessive wear. Replace seals as necessary. Reinstall new mainshaft oil seal after filling lips of seal with multi-purpose grease. Reinstall clutch release bearing guide sleeve, but do not lubricate.

2) Coat moving parts of clutch release shaft with molybdenum disulphide grease and reinstall along with release bearing. Replace mainshaft needle bearing and pinion bearing outer race into rear of housing. Secure pinion bearing outer race with lock bolt.

DIFFERENTIAL

Disassembly

1) Place differential, with ring gear facing down, in a soft-jawed vise. Remove ring gear bolts and

drive ring gear off of differential with a drift punch. Using a puller, remove speedometer drive gear and differential side bearings.

2) Drive roll pin securing differential pinion shaft out of case. Drive shaft out of case with a drift punch. Remove drive flange nuts and rotate side gears to bring pinion gears to an opening in case. Remove pinion gears, thrust washers and side gears.

Reassembly

To reassemble, reverse disassembly procedure and note the following: Differential side gear shim must be selected so that gears turn freely by hand with a maximum of .004" (.10 mm) of play. Shims are available in thicknesses of .02-.03" (.5-.8 mm).

SYNCHRONIZERS

Disassembly

1) Remove springs and keys. Slide sleeve off of hub. Inspect all parts for damage or wear. Check blocker rings for wear by placing on appropriate gear and checking clearance between gear and synchronizer matching teeth with a feeler gauge.

2) Clearance should be at least .020" (.5 mm). If clearance is not within specifications, replace blocker ring.

Reassembly

Slide sleeve over hub and insert keys. Install springs with open ends 120° offset. On 1-2 synchronizer, groove on edge of hub faces 1st gear. On 3-4 synchronizer, groove on edge of hub faces 4th gear.

TRANSAXLE REASSEMBLY & ADJUSTMENTS

SIDE BEARING PRELOAD MEASUREMENT

1) Remove drive flange oil seals, differential bearing outer races and preload shims. Reinstall side bearing outer races without shims. With pinion gear and gear carrier removed, install differential and ring gear (without speedometer drive gear) into final drive housing. Install final drive cover and tighten bolts in a diagonal sequence.

Fig. 11: Exploded View of Differential Assembly

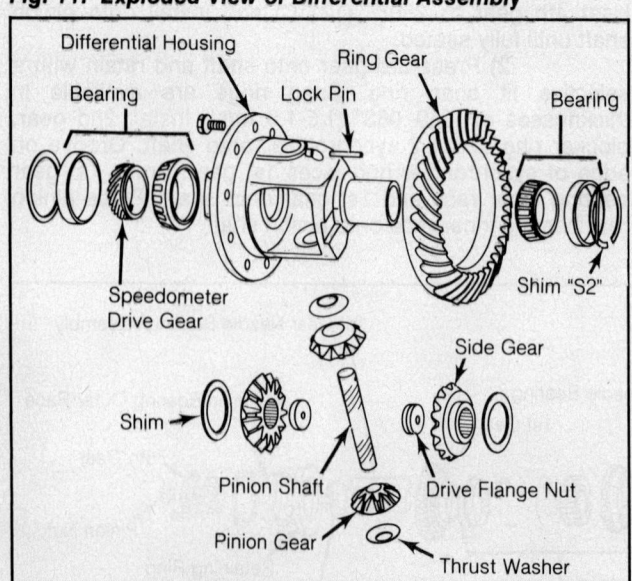

- Differential Housing
- Bearing
- Ring Gear
- Lock Pin
- Bearing
- Speedometer Drive Gear
- Shim "S2"
- Shim
- Side Gear
- Pinion Shaft
- Drive Flange Nut
- Pinion Gear
- Thrust Washer

Fig. 12: Final Drive Adjustment Locations

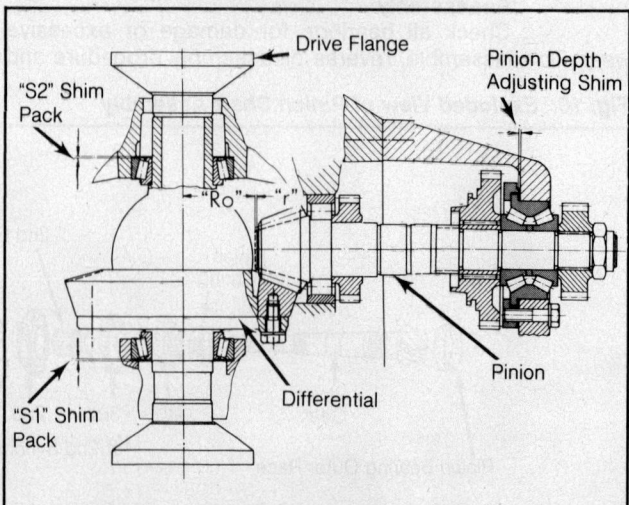

- Drive Flange
- Pinion Depth Adjusting Shim
- "S2" Shim Pack
- "Ro" "r"
- Pinion
- "S1" Shim Pack
- Differential

AUDI 4000 & VOLKSWAGEN QUANTUM 5-SPEED (Cont.)

2) Place an end plate (VW385/17) on cover end of differential. Assemble a dial indicator to read differential end play. Move differential up and down. Note dial indicator reading.

3) Add dial indicator reading to a preload constant of .0197" (.50 mm) on 5-cylinder models and .0157" (.40 mm) on 4-cylinder models to obtain total differential side bearing shim thickness. Temporarily install entire shim pack behind side bearing outer race on "S2" side of differential. *See Fig. 12.*

4) Check rotational torque of differential using an INCH lb. torque wrench together with adapters (VW521/8 & VW521/4). Torque should be at least 23 INCH lbs. (2.5 N.m) for new bearings and 2.7 INCH lbs. (.30 N.m) for used bearings. Remove final drive cover and differential.

PINION DEPTH MEASUREMENT

NOTE: Production (factory) gearsets are not marked with a pinion depth deviation specification. If any parts affecting pinion depth (final drive housing, rear pinion bearings, gear carrier and/or 1st gear needle bearing are to be replaced), pinion depth must be measured prior to disassembly of transaxle and gear carrier.

1) Assemble measuring bar. Slide setting ring about 2" (50 mm) from center of bar. Set master gauge (VW385/30) to "Ro" or 2.22" (56.40 mm) for 5-cylinder models and 1.99" (50.70 mm) for 4-cylinder models and place on measuring bar. Preload dial indicator travel by .079" (2 mm) and then zero dial face. Move setting ring back to stop. *See Fig. 13.*

2) Place end plate on end of pinion gear and install measuring bar in housing. Install final drive cover together with bearing outer race and tighten bolts. Adjust center ring outward until measuring bar can just be turned by hand.

Fig. 13: *Measuring Bar Assembly & Adjustment*

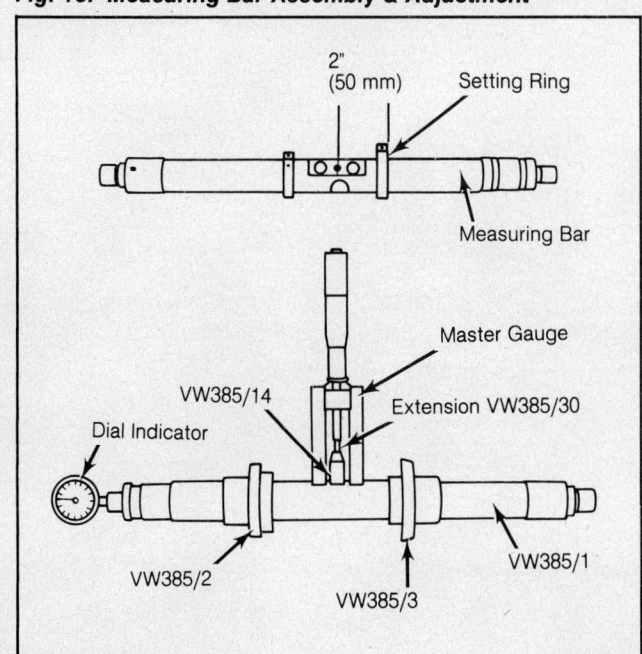

2"
(50 mm)
Setting Ring

Measuring Bar

Master Gauge

VW385/14

Extension VW385/30

Dial Indicator

VW385/2

VW385/3

VW385/1

CAUTION: Dial indicator extension must contact pinion measuring plate and remain in contact with plate until measurement is completed. Otherwise dial indicator extension may push measuring plate off of pinion face when measuring bar is turned. Do not strike final drive cover when installing, as this may upset dial indicator reading.

3) Turn measuring bar back and forth slightly until maximum dial indicator reading is reached. This reading, when taken prior to gear carrier removal, is "r" or deviation from nominal pinion depth. Pinion depth deviation, when added to nominal pinion depth ("Ro") included in gauge travel in step **1)**, results in actual pinion depth ("R").

4) When this reading is taken during reassembly, pinion depth shim(s) should not be in place. Deviation from nominal pinion depth ("r"), whether marked on side of new service gear or measured at disassembly, should be subtracted from dial indicator reading to provide shim thickness necessary for reassembly. Remove final drive cover and measuring bar.

PINION DEPTH ADJUSTMENT

NOTE: This procedure may be carried out by installing mainshaft together with shift forks and selector shafts at the same time as pinion shaft as described in Gear Carrier Reassembly. However, if it becomes necessary to remove pinion shaft to add or subtract shim thickness, the extra components involved will complicate the procedure.

1) Press pinion rear bearing outer race into gear carrier together with correct pinion depth shim selected previously. Install race retaining ring and bolts. Install preassembled pinion shaft into gear carrier. Press pinion rear bearing inner race onto rear of pinion shaft.

2) Place gear carrier assembly in soft-jawed vise. Install spacer (VW472/2) in place of pinion shaft 5th gear. Install and tighten pinion nut to specifications. Install gear carrier onto final drive housing and secure with 4 bolts. Recheck pinion depth measurement and correct as necessary.

RING GEAR BACKLASH ADJUSTMENT

1) With entire side bearing shim pack installed behind outer bearing race of "S2" side of differential, install differential and side cover into housing. Install fully assembled gear carrier with correct pinion depth shim onto final drive housing. Lock pinion shaft with holding tool (VW381/11). Attach dial indicator to differential. *See Fig. 14.*

2) Turn ring gear to stop and zero dial indicator. Turn ring gear back and note backlash. Loosen locking bolts and rotate ring gear 90°. Retighten locking bolts and repeat procedure 3 more times at equally spaced points around the ring gear. Add all 4 dial indicator readings together and divide total by 4 to obtain average backlash.

3) Subtract average backlash from total side bearing shim pack thickness determined during *Side Bearing Preload Measurement* and add .006" (.15 mm) to the result to obtain "S2" shim pack thickness. Subtract

AUDI 4000 & VOLKSWAGEN QUANTUM 5-SPEED (Cont.)

Fig. 14: Backlash Measurement

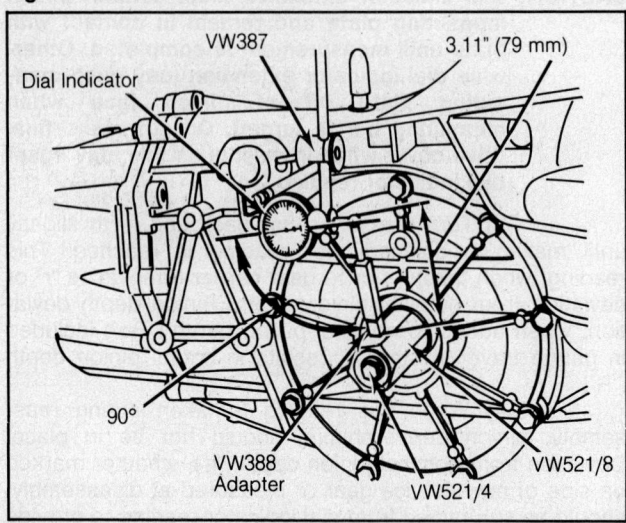

"S2" shim pack thickness from total thickness to obtain "S1" thickness. Install shims in appropriate location. *See Fig. 12.* Recheck backlash and correct as necessary.

TRANSAXLE REASSEMBLY

1) Lightly coat sealing face on final drive housing with sealing compound. Install new gasket and dowel pins. Attach gear carrier housing to final drive housing and install bolts. Engage any gear and lock mainshaft with holding tool (VW294b/1). Install and tighten pinion nut to specifications.

2) Install selector dog for 1st/2nd gear and shift transaxle into 3rd gear (pull out selector shaft). Install inner shift lever selector, placing ends of spring on 3-4 gear shaft and supporting selector dog against selector shaft. Position all selector shafts in neutral.

3) Align selector dog for 1st/2nd gear selector shaft and drive in roll pin. Install new gasket between gear carrier and shift housings. Press on shift housing and install bolts. Install new mainshaft cover.

TIGHTENING SPECIFICATIONS

Application	Ft. Lbs. (N.m)
Axle Shaft Hub Nut	167 (226)
Inner CV Joint Bolts	25 (34)
Drive Flange Retaining Bolt	18 (24)
Transaxle-to-Engine Bolts	40 (54)
Shift Housing-to-Gear Carrier Bolts	18 (24)
Gear Carrier-to-Final Drive Housing Bolts	18 (24)
Final Drive Cover Bolts	18 (24)
Mainshaft Bearing Retainer Bolt	33 (45)
Pinion Nut	72 (98)
Pinion Bearing Outer Race Retainer	18 (24)
Reverse Lever Bolt	25 (34)
Ring Gear Bolts	51 (69)

AUDI 5000 & PORSCHE 944 5-SPEED

DESCRIPTION

The 5-speed transaxle (code 915/63) combines both transmission and differential into a single assembly consisting of 3 subassemblies: Front cover, gear housing and transmission/clutch housing.

In all gears, power flows from input shaft to pinion shaft through respective gear pairs. Torque is transferred to pinion gear, ring gear and drive axles. Reverse gear power flows from input shaft through reverse idler gear, sliding gear and then to pinion shaft.

LUBRICATION & ADJUSTMENT

See appropriate MANUAL TRANSMISSION SERVICING article in IMPORT GENERAL SERVICING section.

SERVICE (IN VEHICLE)

DRIVE AXLE SHAFTS

NOTE: Axle drive shafts should only be disassembled to replace defective rubber boots. If boots are being replaced, inspect all parts for damage or wear and replace as a complete assembly if necessary.

Removal (5000)

Loosen axle shaft nut. Raise and support vehicle. Remove wheels and any shields or guards that may interfere with axle shaft removal. Remove bolts connecting inner constant velocity (CV) joint to transaxle drive flange. Press driveshaft out of hub and guide past transaxle. Remove locking compound from shaft splines.

Removal (944)

Raise and support vehicle. Remove bolts attaching inner CV joint to transaxle drive flange. Remove bolts attaching outer CV joint to wheel shaft. Remove axle drive shaft from vehicle.

Disassembly (All Models)

1) On inner CV joint, remove circlip and drive protective cap off of CV joint. Press drive shaft out of inner CV joint. To remove outer CV joints on 944 models, repeat procedure used for inner CV joints.

2) To remove outer CV joints on 5000 models, cut clamps off of boot and discard. Slide boot away from joint and remove circlip from inside of joint. Drive CV joint off of shaft with a soft-faced hammer or copper drift by striking inner hub.

3) On all models, tilt cage and hub out of CV joint to remove balls and disassemble joint. See Fig. 2, 3 and 4. Inspect parts for abnormal wear or damage. Parts cannot be interchanged between joints. DO NOT mix parts. If any part of joint is damaged, replacement of entire CV joint is necessary.

Reassembly (All Models)

Reverse disassembly procedure and note the following: Pack each side of CV joints with 1.6 oz. of molybdenum disulfide grease.

Installation (All Models)

Reverse removal procedure and note the following: On 5000 models, apply a narrow bead of locking compound to outer end of splines on shaft that extends from outer CV joint. On all models, splines on shaft and in

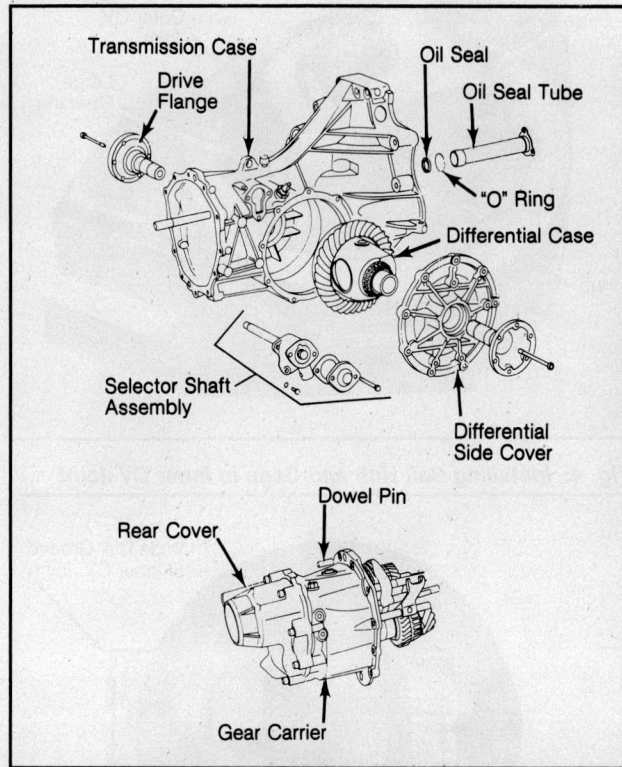

Fig. 1: Exploded View of Audi-Porsche 5-Speed Transaxle Assembly

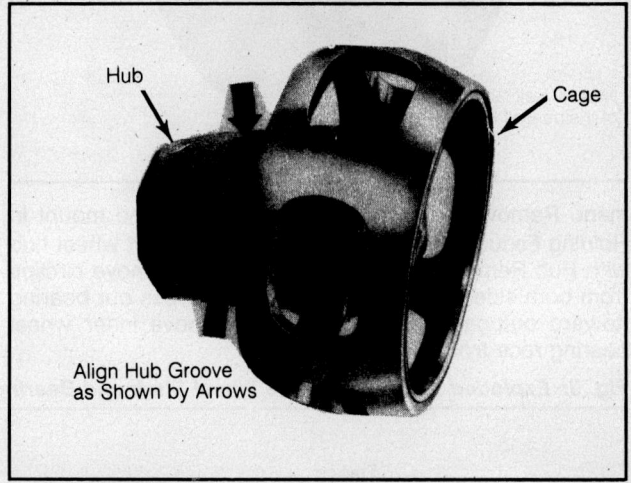

Fig. 2: Removing Inner CV Joint Ball Hub

hub must be free of oil, grease and old locking compound prior to installation of shaft.

FRONT WHEEL BEARINGS (5000 ONLY)
Removal

1) With vehicle supported and drive axle shafts removed, remove stabilizer bar clamps. Remove caliper mounting bolts and hang caliper from frame with wire, DO NOT disconnect hydraulic line. Remove brake disc and ball joint bolt. Press off tie rod and remove ball joint from knuckle.

2) Support suspension strut with jack and remove 3 strut retaining nuts from inside engine compart-

Manual Transmissions

AUDI 5000 & PORSCHE 944 5-SPEED (Cont.)

Fig. 3: Removing Outer CV Joint Ball Hub

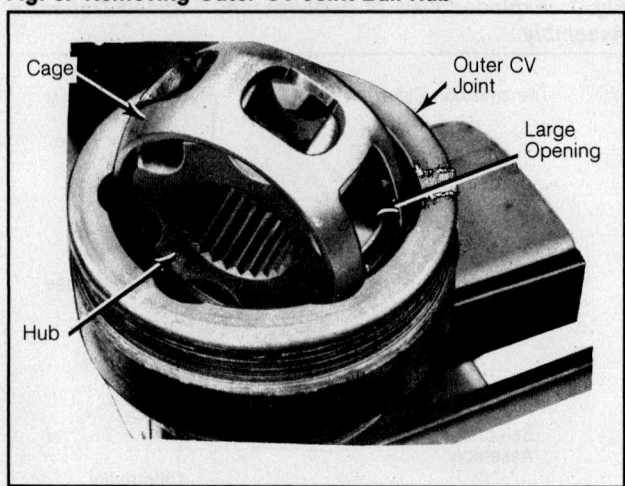

Fig. 4: Installing Ball Hub and Cage in Inner CV Joint

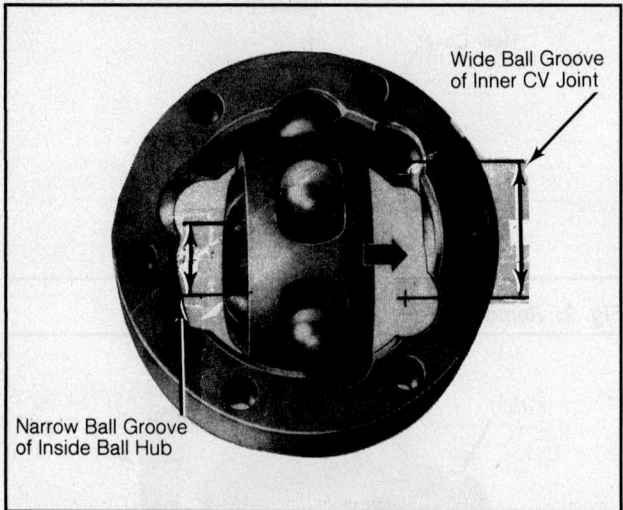

ment. Remove strut assembly from vehicle and mount in Holding Fixture (VW401 and VW402). Press out wheel hub with Hub Remover (VW295 and VW295a). Remove circlips from both sides of bearing housing and press out bearing (toward outboard end of housing). Remove inner wheel bearing race from hub. *See Fig. 5.*

NOTE: Wheel bearing must be replaced. Removal procedure destroys wheel bearing for reuse.

Installation
To install, reverse removal procedure.

REAR WHEEL BEARINGS (944 ONLY)
Removal
Remove brake drum and wheel. Disconnect drive shaft from axle flange. Press shaft from housing with double arm puller. Pry seal out of housing, remove circlip and drive grooved ball bearing and roller bearing out with soft drift.

Installation
Press grooved ball bearing in inner end of housing and replace circlip. Put spacer in housing and drive roller bearing in place (flanged side facing out). Install seal in inboard side of housing. Place outer spacer on shaft and press in along with inner bearing race, using castellated nut and driver. *See Fig. 6.*

DRIVE FLANGE OIL SEALS
NOTE: On some models, removal of certain guards may be necessary to provide access to oil seals.

Removal
1) Disconnect inner CV joint from drive flange and support drive axle out of the way. Insert a long drift punch in 1 drive flange hole to prevent drive flange movement, then remove drive flange retaining bolt.

2) Place a drip pan under transmission housing and pull out drive flange. Pry out oil seal.

Installation
1) Lightly lubricate seal lips and fully seat seal with a seal installer. Install drive flange and tighten drive flange retaining bolt.

2) Install axle drive shafts and tighten bolts. Check and add lubricant to transaxle if necessary.

Fig. 5: Exploded View of 944 Axle Wheel Shaft and Bearing Assembly

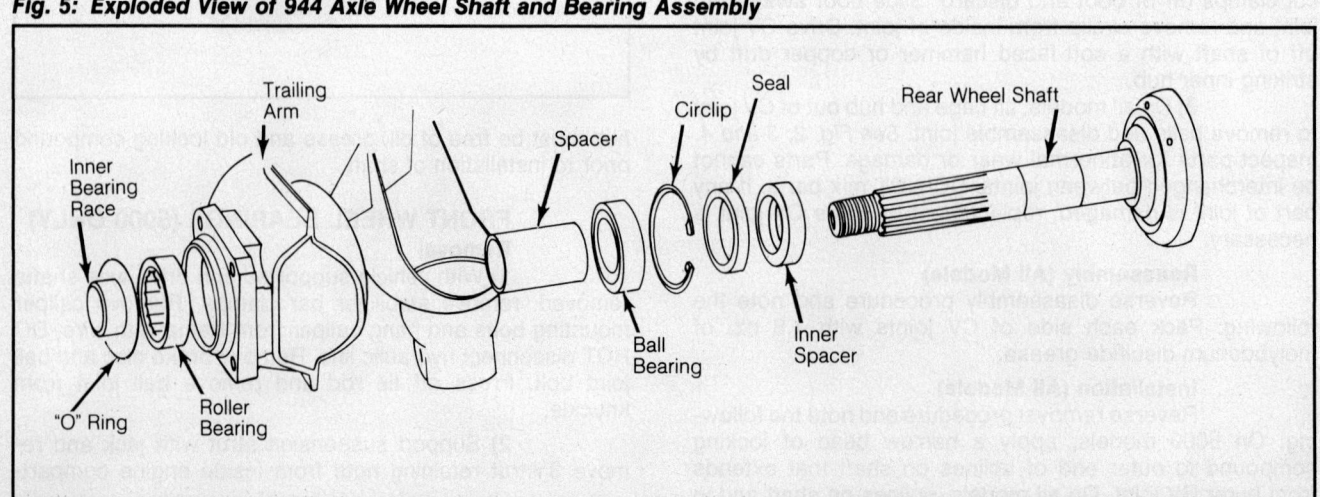

AUDI 5000 & PORSCHE 944 5-SPEED (Cont.)

Fig. 6: Exploded View of 5000 Front Suspension Strut Assembly

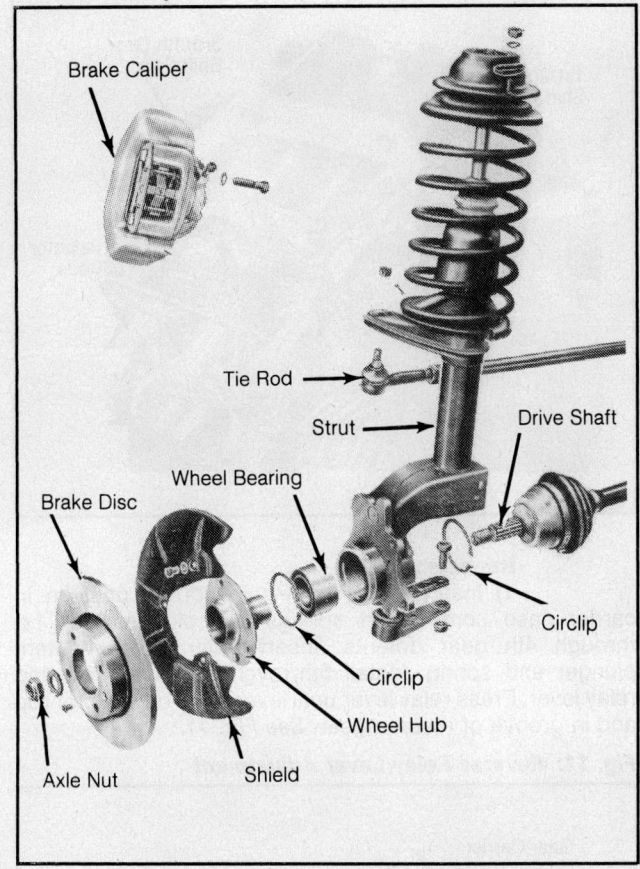

Fig. 8: Removing Rear Cover from Gear Carrier

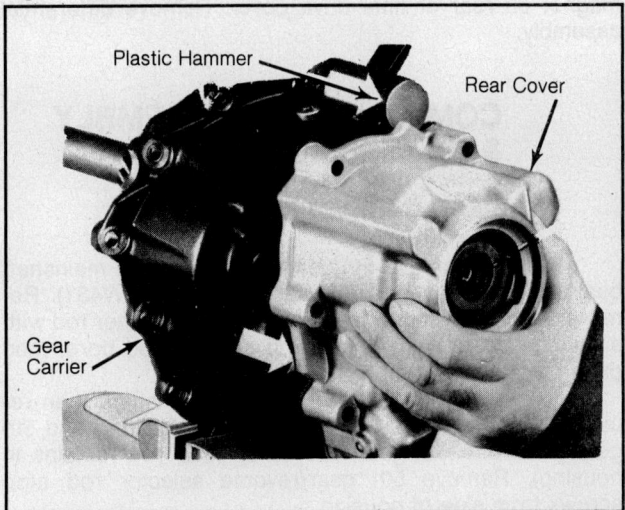

REMOVAL & INSTALLATION

TRANSAXLE

See appropriate MANUAL TRANSMISSION REMOVAL article in IMPORT GENERAL SERVICING section.

TRANSAXLE DISASSEMBLY

1) Mount transaxle in Holding Fixture (VW 540) and drain oil. Remove selector shaft. On 944 models, loosen bolts securing mainshaft oil seal tube. Place Seal Protector (9113) over mainshaft splines. Pry tube loose with an offset screwdriver. Remove tube and remove seal from tube.

2) On all models, remove transaxle case-to-gear carrier bolts, drive out dowel pins and separate gear carrier from transaxle case. On all models, remove input shaft front oil seal. On 944 models, remove input shaft front needle bearing from transmission case using a puller.

3) Mount gear carrier in soft-jawed vise with rear cover facing up. Remove cap from end of rear cover by driving a screwdriver into center of cap and prying up. Remove bolt from end of mainshaft.

4) Reposition gear carrier in vise, clamping lower portion of gear carrier. Remove cover attaching bolts and drive cover from gear carrier with plastic hammer. Remove mainshaft inner bearing race.

5) Remove drive flange retaining bolt and drive flange. Remove final drive cover attaching bolts and pry

Fig. 7: Exploded View of Typical Axle Drive Shaft

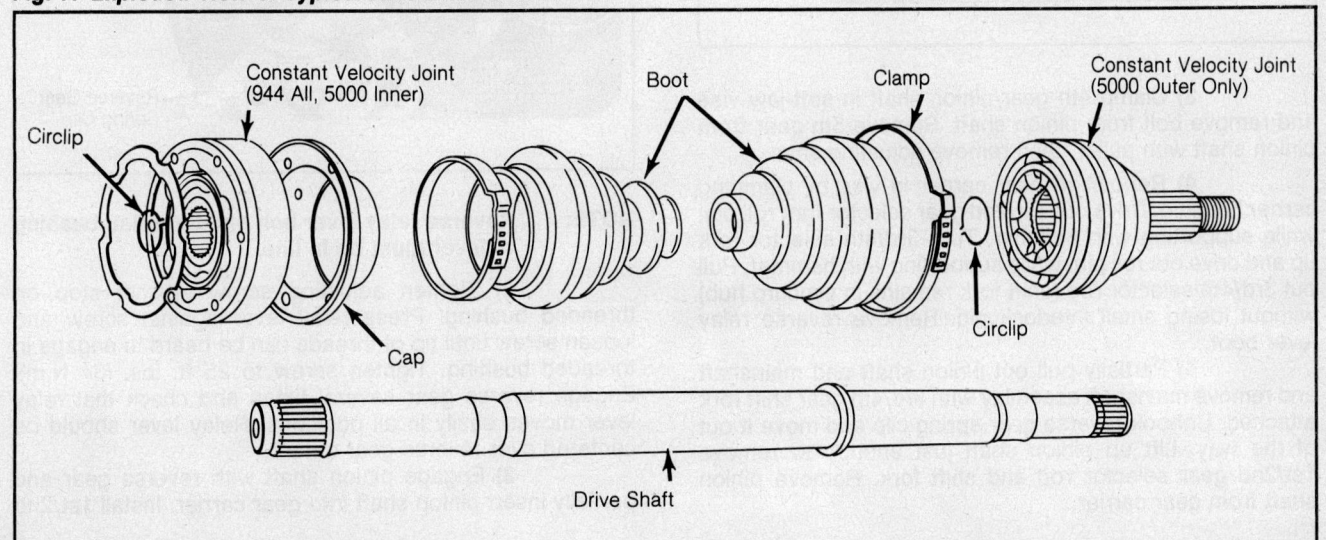

AUDI 5000 & PORSCHE 944 5-SPEED (Cont.)

cover from housing using 2 screwdrivers. DO NOT lose magnet on rear of final drive cover. Remove differential assembly.

COMPONENT DISASSEMBLY & REASSEMBLY

GEAR CARRIER ASSEMBLY
Disassembly

1) Remove 5th gear clutch hub and mainshaft bearing with Puller and Adapter (US1078 & VW431). Remove 5th gear synchronizer ring. Support selector rod with a hammer to prevent damage to selector rod bore, then drive out 5th gear shift fork roll pin.

2) Remove snap ring from mainshaft, then remove 5th gear with synchro hub, needle bearing and 5th gear shift fork (5th gear/reverse selector rod remains in housing). Remove 5th gear/reverse selector rod stop screws from side of housing.

Fig. 9: Removing Snap Ring Retaining 5th Gear Components to Mainshaft

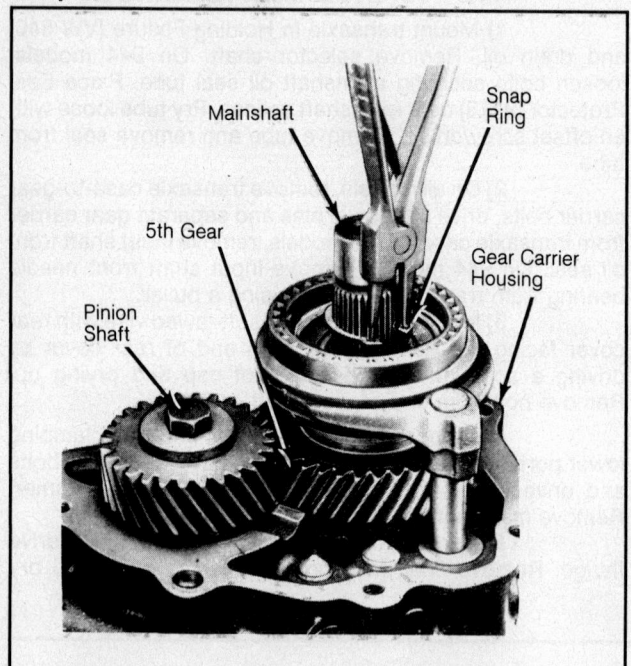

3) Clamp 4th gear/pinion shaft in soft-jaw vise and remove bolt from pinion shaft. Remove 5th gear from pinion shaft with puller, then remove adjusting shim.

4) Reposition gear carrier in vise by clamping carrier housing. Drive out 1st/2nd gear selector fork roll pin, while supporting with hammer. Turn 3rd/4th selector fork up and drive out roll pin, while supporting with hammer. Pull out 3rd/4th selector rod (shift fork remains in synchro hub) without losing small interlock pin. Remove reverse relay lever boot.

5) Partially pull out pinion shaft and mainshaft and remove mainshaft assembly with 3rd/4th gear shift fork attached. Unhook reverse gear spring clip and move it out of the way. Lift up pinion shaft just enough to remove 1st/2nd gear selector rod and shift fork. Remove pinion shaft from gear carrier.

Fig. 10: Removing Shift Fork Roll Pins

Reassembly

1) Insert interlock pins in correct position in carrier case bore. Insert springs and plungers for 1st through 4th gear detents. Insert reverse gear detent plunger and spring. Install 5th/reverse selector rod and relay lever. Press relay lever until lever rests on selector rod and in groove of reverse gear. See Fig. 11.

Fig. 11: Reverse Relay Lever Adjustment

NOTE: Reverse relay lever bolt and threaded bushing of lever must be in line.

2) Tighten adjusting screw against stop on threaded bushing. Press relay lever against screw and loosen screw until tip of threads can be heard to engage in threaded bushing. Tighten screw to 25 ft. lbs. (34 N.m). Engage reverse gear several times and check that relay lever moves easily in all positions. Relay lever should be centered over reverse gear detent.

3) Engage pinion shaft with reverse gear and partially insert pinion shaft into gear carrier. Install 1st/2nd

AUDI 5000 & PORSCHE 944 5-SPEED (Cont.)

gear shift fork and selector rod, then press pinion shaft into housing. Push 3rd/4th gear shift fork onto 5th/reverse gear selector rod.

4) Press off mainshaft inner bearing race, then partially install mainshaft into housing. Insert 3rd/4th gear shift fork into clutch sleeve and press mainshaft into housing until fully seated. Move selector rods into neutral position and check for proper position of interlock pins.

5) Install 3rd/4th gear shift rod and insert small interlock pin (coated with grease). Secure 3rd/4th and 1st/2nd gear shift forks and selector rods with roll pins. Install selector rod stop screws into carrier housing using new gaskets.

6) Position gear carrier assembly in a soft-jawed vise, with jaws clamped on 4th gear of pinion shaft. Using a depth gauge, measure dimension "A" as shown in *Fig. 12* to determine correct 5th gear adjusting shim to install. Select correct 5th gear adjusting shim using the following table:

NOTE: See Fig. 12 for Dimension "A" measurement.

PINION SHAFT 5TH GEAR ADJUSTING SHIM CHART

If "A" Is In. (mm)	Use this Shim In. (mm)
.331-.339 (8.4-8.6)	.043 (1.1)
.343-.350 (8.7-8.9)	.055 (1.4)
.354-.362 (9.0-9.2)	.067 (1.7)
.366-.374 (9.3-9.5)	.079 (2.0)
.378-.386 (9.6-9.8)	.091 (2.3)

Fig. 12: 5th Gear Pinion Shaft Adjusting Shim Selection

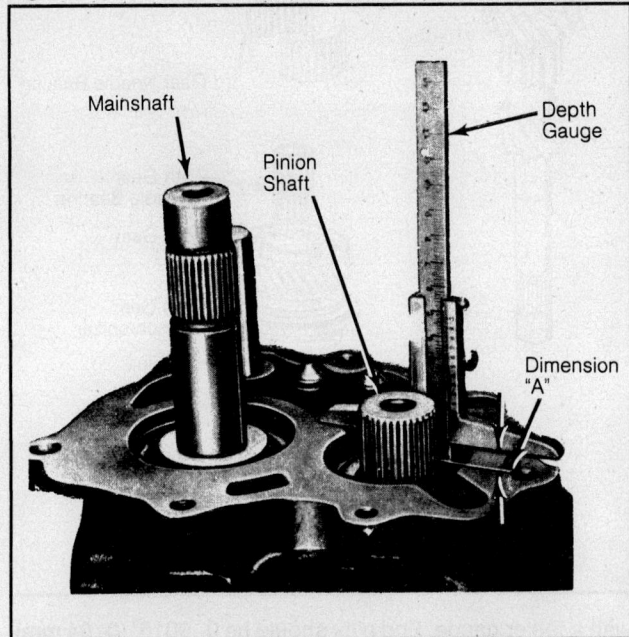

Measure Depth at "A" and Convert to Shim Size Using Chart

7) Install selected 5th gear adjusting shim, then heat 5th gear to 250°F (120°C) and slide onto pinion shaft until seated. Install washer and bolt on end of pinion shaft and tighten bolt. Collar of washer must face pinion head.

8) Clamp mainshaft in soft-jawed vise so that mainshaft and pinion shaft are vertical. Heat mainshaft

bearing inner race to 250°F (120°C) and slide it onto mainshaft until seated.

9) Install 5th gear with synchronizer hub, needle bearing and shift rod onto mainshaft. Install shift fork roll pin into fork and selector rod. Select a snap ring that will provide a maximum mainshaft end play of .002" (.05 mm), then install snap ring into mainshaft groove.

NOTE: **Mainshaft snap rings are available in following thicknesses: .050" (1.35 mm), .055" (1.40 mm) and .060" (1.45 mm).**

10) Install 5th gear synchronizer ring. Heat 5th gear clutch hub to 250°F (120°C) and install it on mainshaft until fully seated. Drive on mainshaft bearing inner race, then install guide sleeve and new gasket on gear carrier housing. Install rear cover on carrier housing.

11) Heat other half of mainshaft bearing inner race and drive onto mainshaft. Install washer and bolt on end of mainshaft and tighten bolt. Install and tighten rear cover mounting bolts. Install new rear cover cap.

MAINSHAFT ASSEMBLY
Disassembly
Remove snap ring from end of shaft. Remove 4th gear thrust washer, 4th gear, 4th gear needle bearings, synchronizer ring and snap ring. Using a press, press off 3rd gear, synchronizer ring, 3rd/4th gear synchro assembly and 3rd gear needle bearing.

Reassembly
1) Inspect all components for wear or damage and replace as necessary. Install 3rd gear needle bearing onto mainshaft. Place synchro assembly, 3rd gear synchro ring and 3rd gear in correct relationship atop each other.

NOTE: **Turn synchronizer ring so grooves are in line with hollow keys. Also, groove on synchronizer hub or wide collar must face 4th gear.**

2) Press mainshaft into 3rd gear and synchronizer assembly. To determine correct snap ring to install, use a feeler gauge to measure 3rd/4th gear synchronizer hub end play as shown in *Fig. 13*. Install a snap ring that will allow an end play of 0-.002" (0-0.5 mm).

NOTE: **Snap rings for 3rd/4th synchronizer hub end play adjustments are available in the following thicknesses: .059" (1.59 mm), .061" (1.56 mm) and .064" (1.62 mm).**

3) Install synchronizer ring on 4th gear side of synchronizer hub, then install 4th gear needle bearing, 4th gear, thrust washer and snap ring. Measure clearance between thrust washer and snap ring. Clearance should be .008-.013" (.20-.35 mm). If not, correct by installing a different thickness snap ring.

NOTE: **Snap rings for 4th gear end play adjustment are available in the following thicknesses: .065" (1.65 mm), .067" (1.70 mm) and .069" (1.75 mm).**

PINION SHAFT
Disassembly
1) Mount pinion shaft assembly into a holding fixture. Using a press, remove small inner bearing and 1st gear by pressing from shaft.

AUDI 5000 & PORSCHE 944 5-SPEED (Cont.)

Fig. 13: Checking 3rd/4th Gear Synchronizer Hub End Play

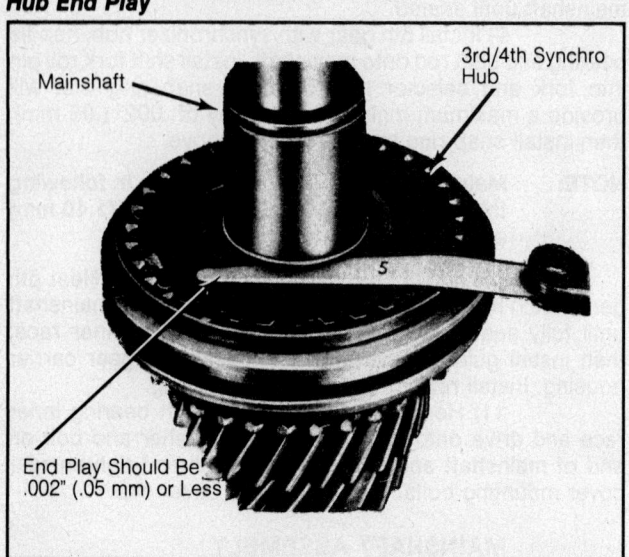

Mainshaft

3rd/4th Synchro Hub

End Play Should Be .002" (.05 mm) or Less

Fig. 14: Exploded View of Mainshaft Assembly

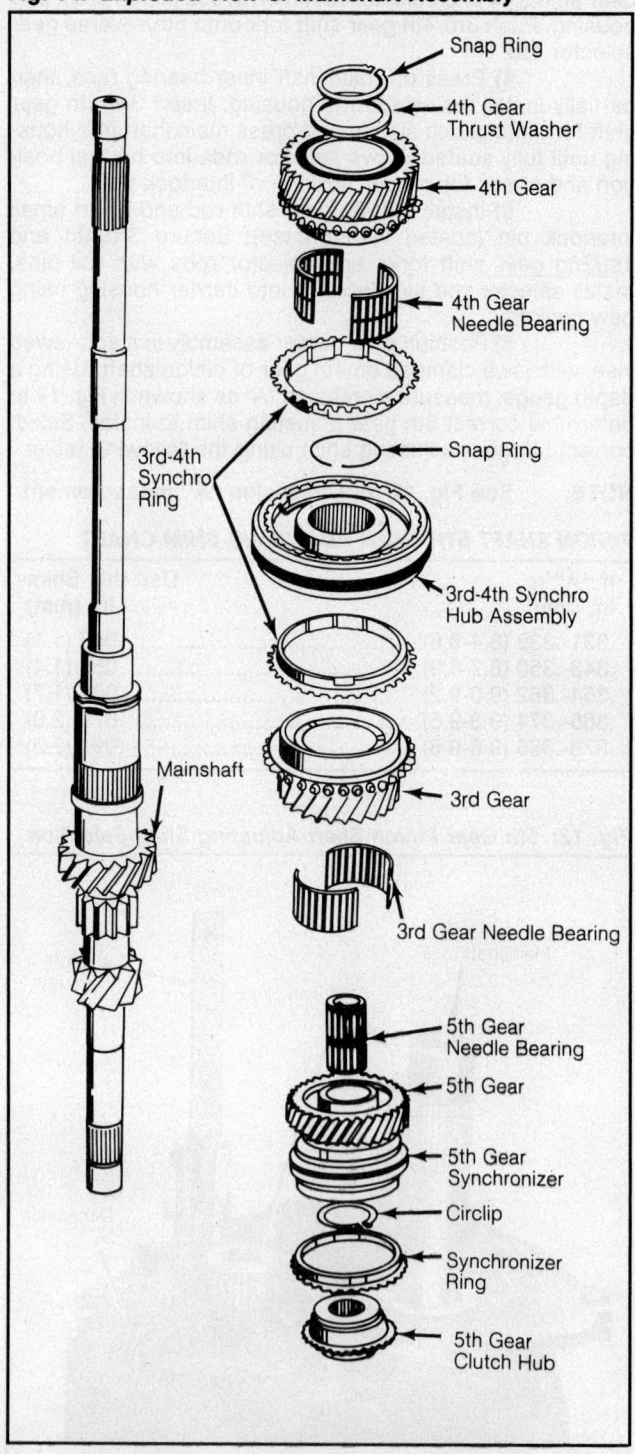

Snap Ring

4th Gear Thrust Washer

4th Gear

4th Gear Needle Bearing

Snap Ring

3rd-4th Synchro Ring

3rd-4th Synchro Hub Assembly

Mainshaft

3rd Gear

3rd Gear Needle Bearing

5th Gear Needle Bearing

5th Gear

5th Gear Synchronizer

Circlip

Synchronizer Ring

5th Gear Clutch Hub

2) Remove 1st gear needle bearing and synchro ring. Remove snap ring, then press off 1st/2nd gear synchro hub assembly, 2nd gear synchro ring and 2nd gear.

3) Remove 2nd gear needle bearing, snap ring, then press off 3rd gear. Remove circlip, then remove 4th gear snap ring and press off 4th gear and large bearing from shaft.

Reassembly

1) Ensure all gears and shaft are oil-free and replace any damaged or defective parts. Press large bearing onto pinion shaft. Heat 4th gear to 250°F (120°C), slide gear onto pinion shaft (shoulder facing 3rd gear) and press until fully seated.

NOTE: After approximately 3 minutes, press 4th gear onto shaft again to ensure correct adjustment of end play. After 4th gear has cooled, continue reassembly procedure.

2) Measure 4th gear end play with a feeler gauge and adjust end play to not more than .0008" (.02 mm) with correct snap ring. Snap rings are available in sizes ranging from .088" (2.24 mm) to .094" (2.40 mm) in .0008" (.02 mm) increments.

3) Install a .094" (2.4 mm) snap ring into second snap ring groove of pinion shaft. Heat 3rd gear to 250°F (120°C) and slide gear onto shaft with shoulder toward 2nd gear.

4) Press gear onto shaft until seated against snap ring, then install retaining snap ring. Using a feeler gauge, measure 3rd gear end play as shown in *Fig. 16*. End play should be 0-.002" (0-.05 mm). If not, install a different retaining snap ring.

NOTE: Snap rings for 3rd gear end play adjustment are available in the following thicknesses: .065" (1.65 mm), .067" (1.70 mm) and .069" (1.75 mm).

5) Oil 2nd gear needle bearing and install on shaft. Place 2nd gear, 2nd gear synchro ring and synchro hub assembly atop one another. Press all components onto pinion shaft. Measure synchronizer hub assembly end play

with a feeler gauge. End play should be 0-.0016" (0-.04 mm). Adjust end play with a snap ring.

NOTE: Snap rings for 1st/2nd synchronizer hub adjustment are available in the following thicknesses: .059" (1.50 mm), .061" (1.55 mm) and .063" (1.60 mm).

6) Install remaining synchronizer ring onto hub. Oil and install 1st gear needle bearing, then slide 1st gear onto pinion shaft. Press pinion shaft small bearing onto shaft until fully seated.

AUDI 5000 & PORSCHE 944 5-SPEED (Cont.)

Fig. 15: Exploded View of Pinion Shaft Assembly

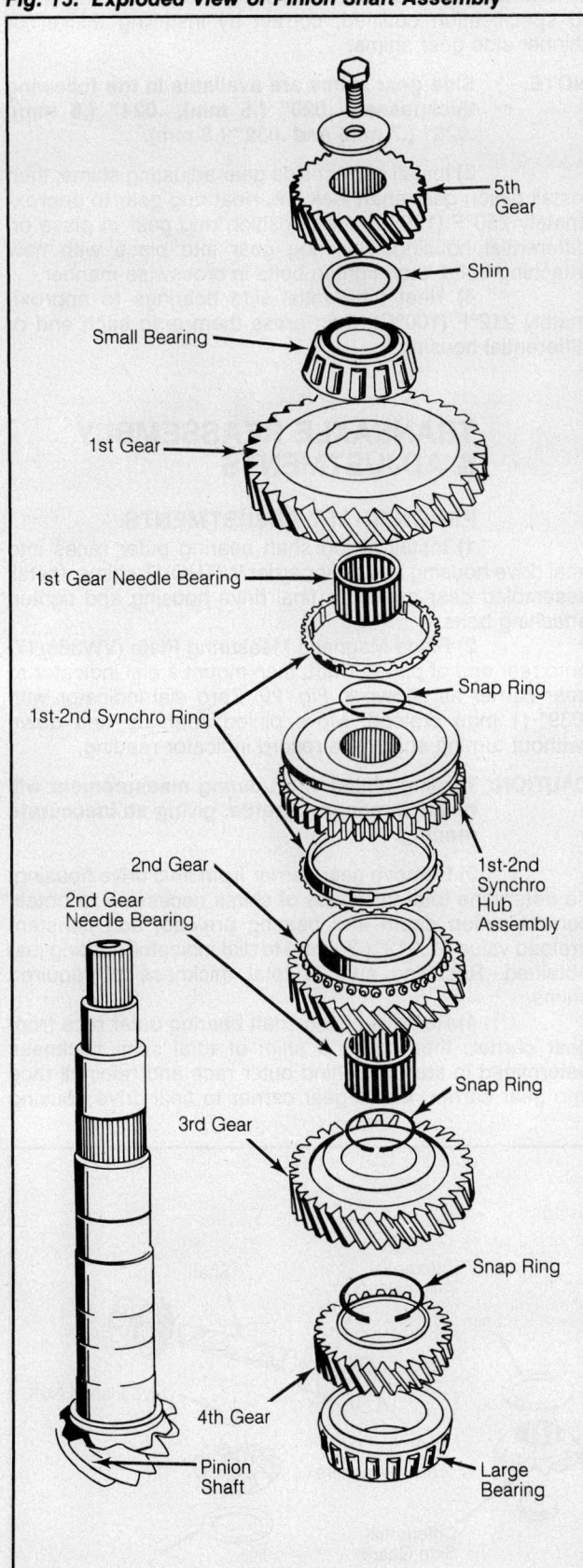

- 5th Gear
- Shim
- Small Bearing
- 1st Gear
- 1st Gear Needle Bearing
- 1st-2nd Synchro Ring
- Snap Ring
- 1st-2nd Synchro Hub Assembly
- 2nd Gear
- 2nd Gear Needle Bearing
- Snap Ring
- 3rd Gear
- Snap Ring
- 4th Gear
- Pinion Shaft
- Large Bearing

Fig. 16: Checking 3rd Gear End Play

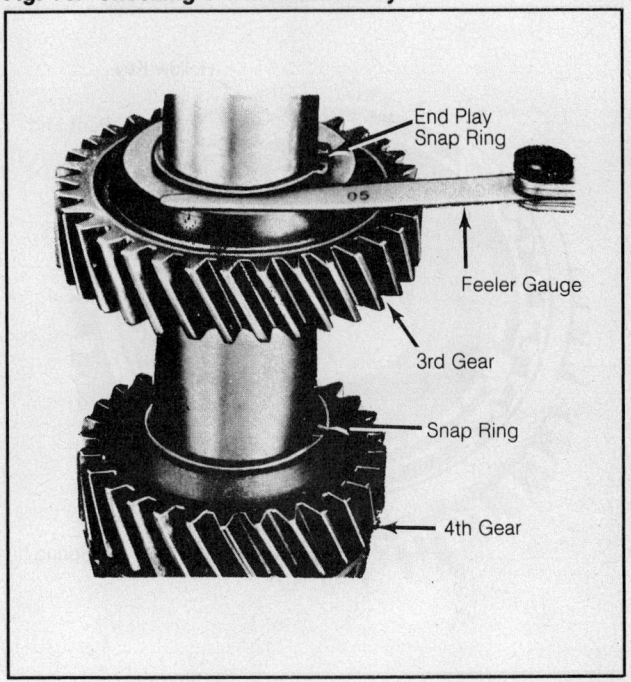

- End Play Snap Ring
- Feeler Gauge
- 3rd Gear
- Snap Ring
- 4th Gear

Disassembly

Remove snap ring and separate synchronizer hub from sleeve. DO NOT lose or damage synchronizer keys and springs.

Inspection

Check all parts for wear or damage. Using a feeler gauge, check synchronizer rings for wear as shown in *Fig. 17*. Clearance "A" should be .039-.075" (1.0-1.9 mm) for 5th gear synchro or .039-.067" (1.0-1.7 mm) for all others.

Fig. 17: Checking Synchronizer Rings for Wear

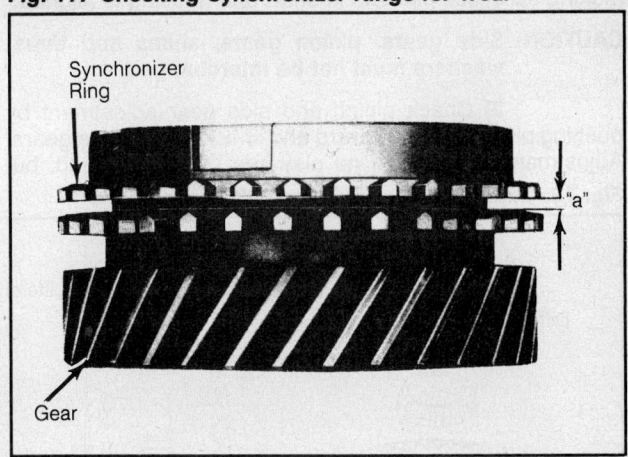

- Synchronizer Ring
- "a"
- Gear

Reassembly

Reverse disassembly procedure and use *Fig. 18* as an assembly guide. Install springs with ends 120° offset. Bent end of spring must engage hollow synchro key.

DIFFERENTIAL
Disassembly

1) Place differential assembly in soft-jawed vise. Remove ring gear bolts and ring gear. Using a puller, remove differential side bearings.

AUDI 5000 & PORSCHE 944 5-SPEED (Cont.)

Fig. 18: Assembled View of Synchronizer Assembly

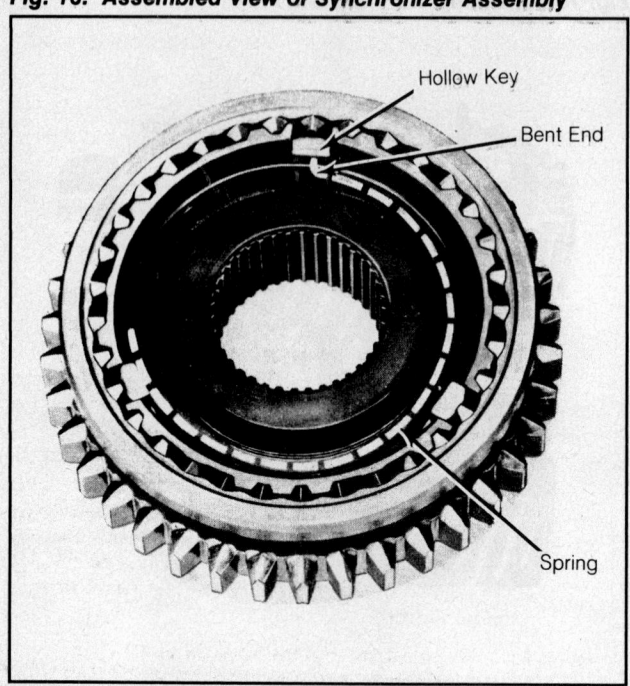

Hollow Key

Bent End

Spring

2) Drive out pinion shaft lock pin with a punch. Then drive out pinion shaft with a punch. Rotate differential gear set and remove pinion gears, side gears, shims, thrust washers and drive flange nuts through opening in differential housing.

Reassembly

1) Lubricate pinion gears and side gears with transmission oil. Position side gears with shims in housing. Stick thrust washers to pinion gears with grease, then position pinion gears in housing. Install pinion gear shaft, making sure lock pin hole in shaft and housing is aligned.

CAUTION: Side gears, pinion gears, shims and thrust washers must not be interchanged.

2) Check pinion and side gear adjustment by pushing pinion gears outward and check play of side gears. Adjustment is correct if no play can be felt by hand, but

Fig. 19: Exploded View of Differential Assembly

differential gears can be turned easily without binding. If not to specification outlined, correct by installing thicker or thinner side gear shims.

NOTE: Side gear shims are available in the following thicknesses: .020" (.5 mm), .024" (.6 mm), .028" (.7 mm) and .032" (.8 mm).

3) Install correct side gear adjusting shims, then install pinion gear shaft lock pin. Heat ring gear to approximately 250°F (120°C), then position ring gear in place on differential housing. Pull ring gear into place with new attaching bolts, then tighten bolts in crosswise manner.

4) Heat differential side bearings to approximately 212°F (100°C), then press them onto each end of differential housing.

TRANSAXLE REASSEMBLY & ADJUSTMENTS

PINION SHAFT ADJUSTMENTS

1) Install pinion shaft bearing outer races into final drive housing and gear carrier WITHOUT shims. Install assembled gear carrier to final drive housing and tighten attaching bolts.

2) Place Magnetic Measuring Plate (VW385/17) onto rear end of pinion shaft, then mount a dial indicator to gear carrier as shown in *Fig. 20.* Zero dial indicator with .039" (1 mm) preload. Move pinion shaft up and down (without turning shaft) and record indicator reading.

CAUTION: Turning pinion shaft during measurement will cause bearings to settle, giving an inaccurate reading.

3) Remove gear carrier from final drive housing. To determine total thickness of shims necessary to obtain correct pinion depth and bearing preload, add constant preload value of .012" (.30 mm) to dial indicator reading just obtained. Resulting sum is total thickness of required shims.

4) Remove pinion shaft bearing outer race from gear carrier, then install a shim of total shim thickness determined in step **3)** behind outer race and reinstall race into gear carrier. Install gear carrier to final drive housing

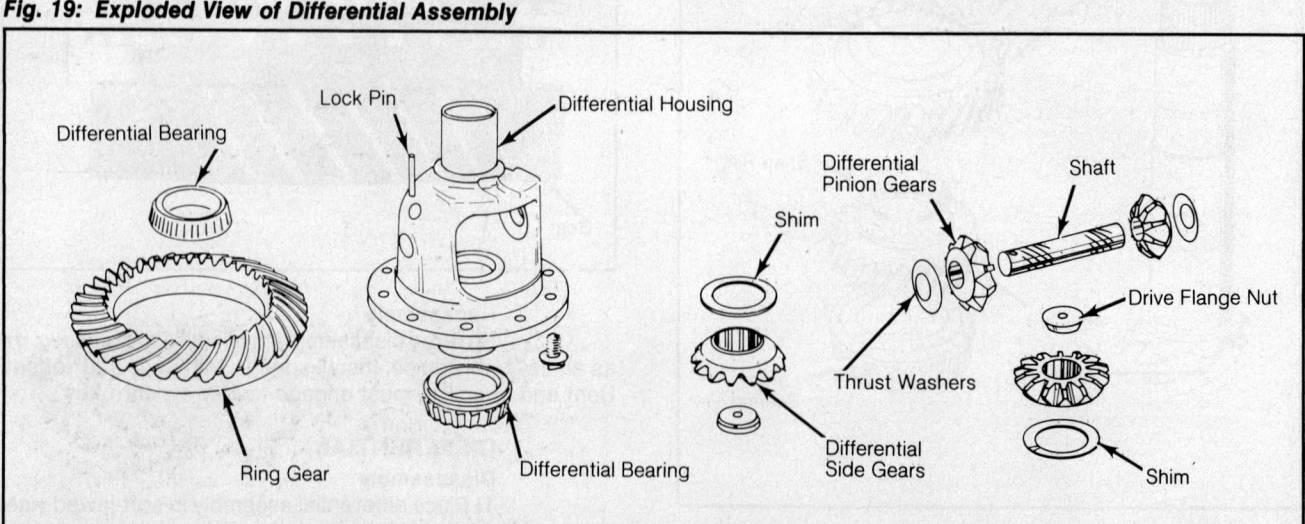

Differential Bearing

Lock Pin

Differential Housing

Differential Pinion Gears

Shaft

Shim

Drive Flange Nut

Thrust Washers

Ring Gear

Differential Bearing

Differential Side Gears

Shim

AUDI 5000 & PORSCHE 944 5-SPEED (Cont.)

and tighten attaching bolts. Turn pinion shaft several times in each direction to settle bearings.

Fig. 20: *Measuring Pinion Shaft End Play to Determine Total Pinion Adjusting Shim Thickness*

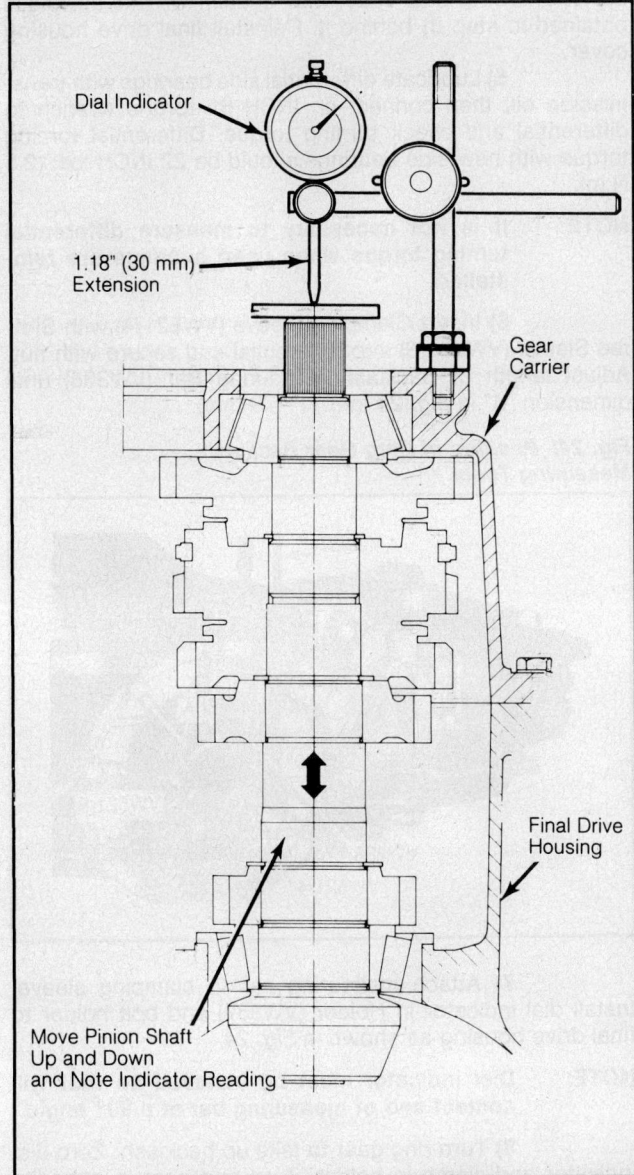

Fig. 21: *Assembling Measuring Tools for Pinion Depth Shim Selection*

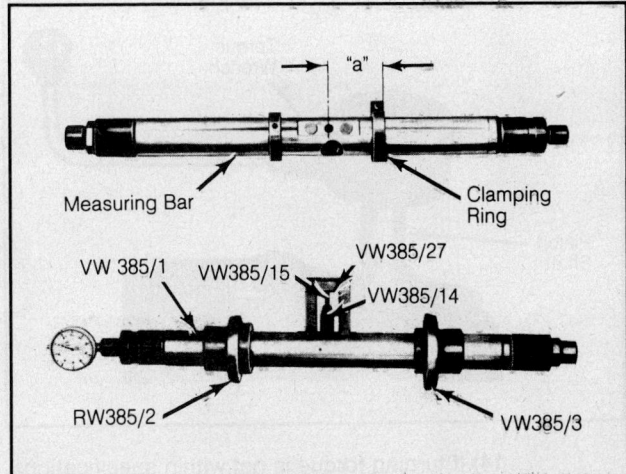

5) Adjust clamping ring on Measuring Bar (VW385/1) so dimension "a" in *Fig. 21* is 2" (50 mm). Next, assemble the following measuring tools onto measuring bar as shown in *Fig. 21*: Dial Indicator, Centering Discs (VW385/2 and 3), Measuring Pin (VW385/14), Measuring Pin Extension (VW385/15), and Setting Gauge (VW385/27). With all tools assembled to bar, zero dial indicator with .039" (1 mm) preload and remove Setting Gauge (VW385/27).

NOTE: Move clamping ring back to stop.

6) Place Magnetic Measuring Plate (VW385/17) on end of pinion shaft. Install assembled measuring bar into final drive housing with Centering Disc (VW385/2) facing final drive cover. Install final drive cover and secure with 4 bolts.

7) Turn knob on end of measuring bar to move clamping ring and the other Centering Disc (VW385/3) outward, until bar can just barely be turned by hand.

8) Rotate measuring bar until measuring pin extension rests squarely against magnetic plate on pinion shaft. Then rotate bar back and forth over center. Read and record maximum dial indicator reading.

9) To determine correct pinion depth adjusting shim(s) to install behind bearing outer race in gear carrier, add the deviation number stamped on ring gear to the dial indicator reading obtained in step **8)**.

NOTE: Deviation number stamped on ring gear is in hundredth millimeters. A marking of 25 would be .25 mm.

10) To determine thickness of shim to install under pinion bearing outer race in final drive housing, subtract thickness of pinion depth shim determined in step **9)** from total pinion shim thickness obtained in step **3)**.

NOTE: Shims for outer race installed in gear carrier are available in thicknesses of .008" (.20 mm) to .045" (1.15 mm) in various increments. Shims for outer bearing race in final drive housing are available in thicknesses of .009" (.24 mm) to .056" (1.41 mm) in various increments.

11) Remove measuring bar assembly from final drive housing. Separate gear carrier from final drive housing. Remove pinion shaft bearing outer race from gear carrier and final drive housing, then install selected shims with outer race back into carrier and housing.

12) Install gear carrier to final drive and tighten attaching bolts. To check adjustment, reinstall measuring bar assembly and recheck measurements. If correct shims have been installed, dial indicator reading (counterclockwise) should be the ring gear deviation number with a tolerance of ±.0016" (.04 mm).

13) To check pinion bearing preload, lubricate pinion bearings with transmission oil, then check pinion shaft turning torque with a torque wrench. Pinion shaft turning torque with NEW bearings installed should be 17-34 INCH lbs. (2-3.8 N.m). Turning torque with USED bearings installed should be 2.5-5.0 INCH lbs. (0.3-0.6 N.m). *See Fig. 22.*

Manual Transmissions

AUDI 5000 & PORSCHE 944 5-SPEED (Cont.)

Fig. 22: Checking Pinion Shaft Turning Torque

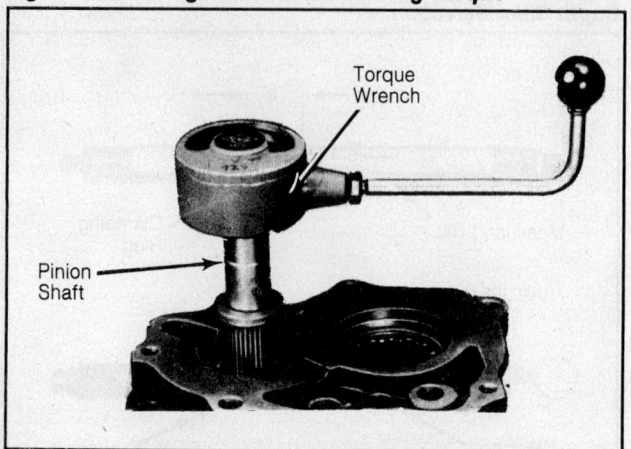

14) If turning torque is not within specifications, sufficient shim thickness for bearing preload and bearing settling has not been allowed.

RING GEAR ADJUSTMENTS

1) Remove gear carrier from final drive housing. Remove differential oil seals and side bearing outer races from final drive housing and take out shims. Reinstall side bearing outer races WITHOUT shims. Install differential assembly into final drive housing. Install final drive cover and tighten attaching bolts in a diagonal pattern to 18 ft. lbs. (24 N.m).

NOTE: **Differential assembly is installed with ring gear side facing final drive cover.**

Fig. 23: Measuring Differential Bearing Preload

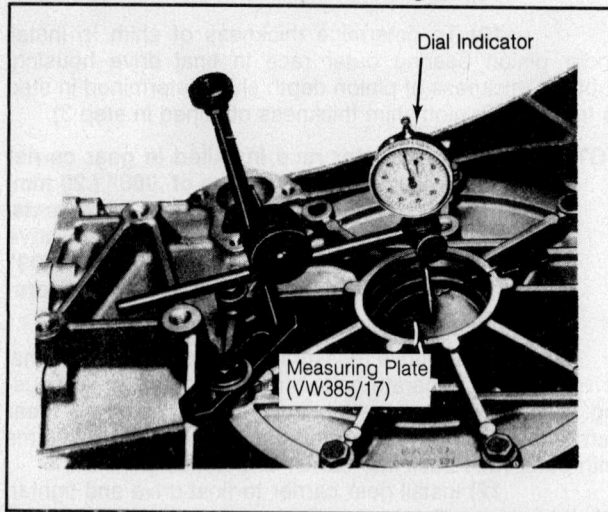

2) Position Magnetic Measuring Plate (VW385/17) and dial indicator as shown in *Fig. 23*, then zero dial indicator with .039" (1 mm) preload. Move differential assembly up and down and note dial indicator reading.

CAUTION: DO NOT rotate differential while taking measurement as bearings will settle and make measurement inaccurate.

3) To the dial indicator reading obtained in step 2), add the constant preload value of .020" (.50 mm).

Resulting sum is thickness of shims necessary for correct differential bearing preload.

4) Remove measuring tools and final drive housing cover. Remove differential side bearing outer race from cover, then reinstall race with a shim of the thickness obtained in step 3) behind it. Reinstall final drive housing cover.

5) Lubricate differential side bearings with transmission oil, then connect an INCH lb. torque wrench to differential and check turning torque. Differential turning torque with new side bearings should be 22 INCH lbs. (2.5 N.m).

NOTE: **It is not necessary to measure differential turning torque when used bearings are reinstalled.**

6) Insert Clamping Sleeve (VW521/4) with Slotted Sleeve (VW521/8) into differential and secure with nut. Adjust length of Backlash Measuring Bar (VW388) until dimension "A" in *Fig. 24* in 3.11" (79 mm).

Fig. 24: Position of Ring Gear Backlash Measuring Tools

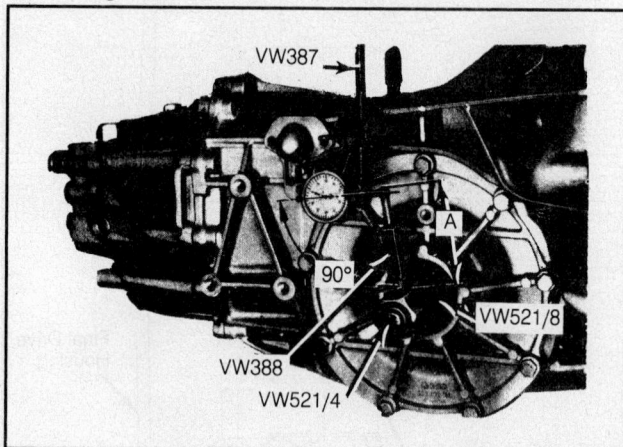

7) Attach measuring bar to clamping sleeve. Install dial indicator in Holder (VW387) and bolt holder to final drive housing as shown in *Fig. 24*.

NOTE: **Dial indicator must be installed so foot will contact end of measuring bar at a 90° angle.**

8) Turn ring gear to take up backlash. Zero dial indicator and clamp in holder. Turn ring gear in opposite direction until it is stopped and note indicator reading. This reading is ring gear backlash.

9) Check ring gear at 4 locations (90° apart) around circumference of ring gear. Add the 4 measurements together, then divide by 4 to find the average ring gear backlash. Ring gear backlash should be .004-.008" (.10-.20 mm).

NOTE: **Difference between the 4 ring gear backlash measurements must not exceed .002" (.06 mm). If measurements differ more than this, ring gear is incorrectly installed or final drive housing is damaged.**

10) To determine thickness of shim to install behind differential bearing outer race in final drive housing cover (opposite ring gear side), subtract the average ring gear backlash from the total shim thickness obtained in

AUDI 5000 & PORSCHE 944 5-SPEED (Cont.)

step **3)**. To this value add the constant preload value of .006" (.15 mm). Resulting sum is the thickness of ring gear adjusting shim to install in final drive housing cover.

NOTE: **Ring gear adjusting shims for final drive housing cover are available in thicknesses from .006" (.15 mm) to .047" (1.2 mm) in various increments.**

11) To determine thickness of ring gear adjusting shim to install behind differential side bearing outer race in final drive housing (ring gear side), subtract thickness of shim determined in step **10)** from the total ring gear adjusting shim thickness determined in step **3)**.

FINAL ASSEMBLY

1) On 944 models, install input shaft front needle bearing and input shaft seal. On all models, lightly coat joints of gear carrier and final drive housings with sealing compound. Mate units together and tighten bolts. Coat selector shaft with sealing compound and install into case. Tighten bolts.

2) Place differential assembly into final drive housing. Install differential cover magnet at the bottom. Install both drive axle flanges and tighten bolts.

3) On 5000 models, install speedometer driven gear and adapter. Install input shaft seal. Install clutch release shaft, spring and bearing assembly into clutch housing. Lubricate release shaft with multi-purpose grease. Install shifter adapter (9155/1) and check operation of transmission in all gears.

TIGHTENING SPECIFICATIONS

Application	Ft. Lbs. (N.m)
Axle Shaft Nut	
944 (Rear 1st Step)	275 (373)
944 (Rear 2nd Step)	326 (442)
5000 (Front)	202 (274)
CV Joint Bolts	30 (41)
Gear Carrier-to-Final Drive Housing	18 (24)
Drive Flange Bolts	18 (24)
Final Drive Cover	18 (24)
Mainshaft End Bolt	36 (49)
5th Gear End Bolt	36 (49)
Reverse Relay Lever Bolt	25 (34)
Ring Gear Bolts	72 (98)
Upper Strut Retaining Nuts (5000)	18 (24)
Transaxle-to-Engine (5000)	40 (54)
Central Tube-to-Transaxle (944)	
10 mm Bolts	30 (41)
12 mm Bolts	61 (83)
Central Tube-to-Clutch Housing (944)	30 (41)

Manual Transmission
BMW GETRAG 240 5-SPEED

318i

DESCRIPTION
The Getreg Model 240 5-speed transmission is fully synchronized, and uses constant mesh, helical-cut forward gears, and non-synchronized, helical-cut reverse gears. Shifting is accomplished through 3 shift rails and forks. Transmission case is of 2-piece design.

LUBRICATION & ADJUSTMENT
See appropriate MANUAL TRANSMISSION SERVICING article in IMPORT GENERAL SERVICING section.

TROUBLE SHOOTING
See MANUAL TRANSMISSION TROUBLE SHOOTING article in IMPORT GENERAL SERVICING section.

SERVICE (IN VEHICLE)

OUTPUT FLANGE & SELECTOR SHAFT SEALS
Removal
1) Disconnect propeller shaft from output flange and center support mount. Remove output flange lock plate. Install Special Tool (23 1 200) and hold output flange with Special Tool (23 0 020). Remove collar nut with Special

Socket (23 1 210). Pull off output flange using Special Tool (33 1 150). Using a screwdriver, pry out output flange radial oil seal.

2) To remove shift selector shaft oil seal, remove shift selector shaft locking sleeve. Drive shift selector shaft retainer pin upwards and remove shift selector shaft. Using an ice pick, pry out shift selector shaft oil seal.

Installation
To install, reverse removal procedure. Lubricate lips of radial seals with grease. Install shift selector shaft oil seal using Special Tool (23 1 240). Install output flange radial oil seal using Special Tool (23 1 260).

REMOVAL & INSTALLATION

TRANSMISSION
See appropriate MANUAL TRANSMISSION REMOVAL article in IMPORT GENERAL SERVICING section.

TRANSMISSION DISASSEMBLY

TRANSMISSION CASE
1) Remove crossmember and exhaust support bracket (if necessary). Secure transmission in holding device and drain oil. Remove guide sleeve. Unscrew back up light switch.

2) Remove reverse lock-out detent cap, spring and lock pin. Remove input shaft snap ring and washer. Remove reverse gear selector arm retainer bolt.

Fig. 1: Exploded View of Getreg 240 5-Speed Transmission

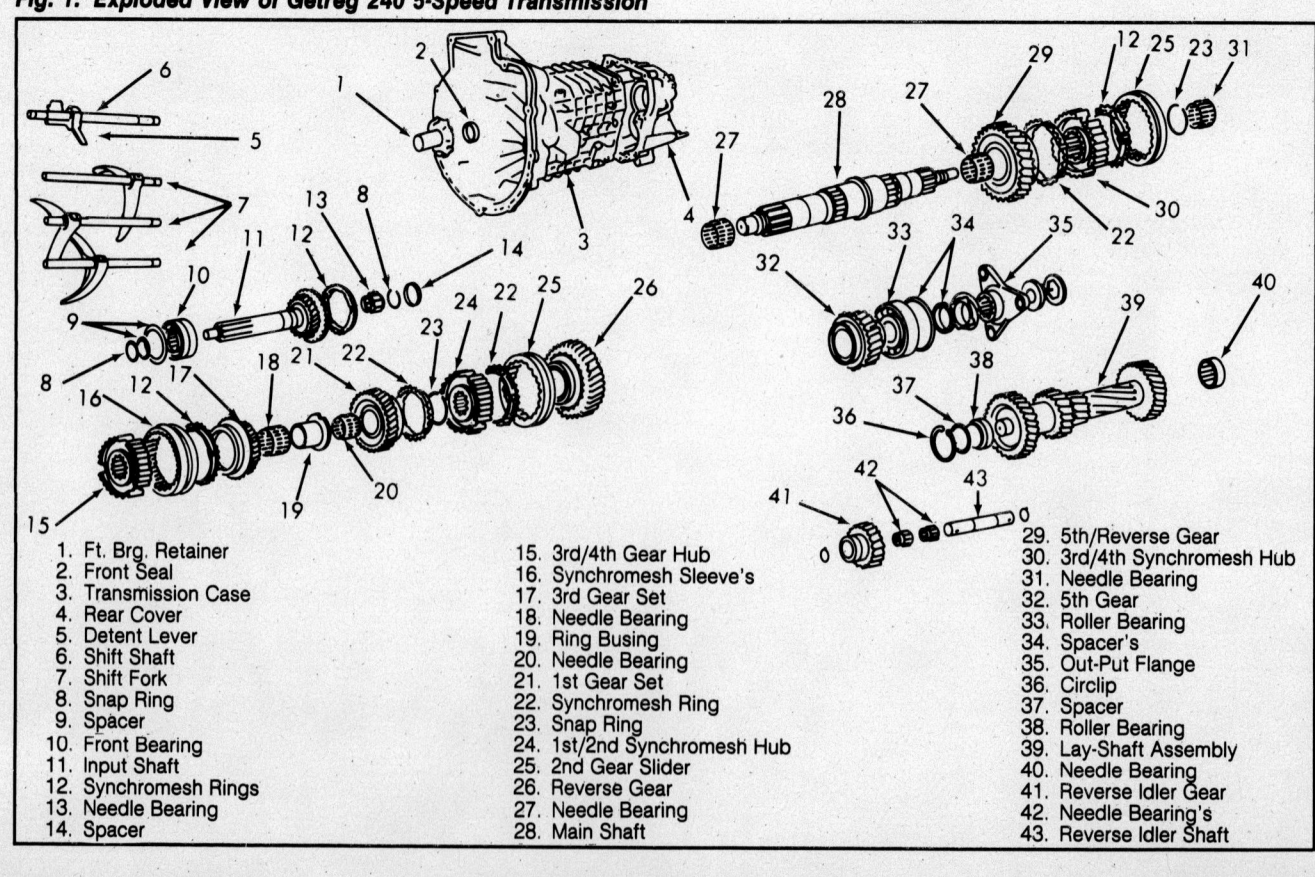

1. Ft. Brg. Retainer	15. 3rd/4th Gear Hub	29. 5th/Reverse Gear
2. Front Seal	16. Synchromesh Sleeve's	30. 3rd/4th Synchromesh Hub
3. Transmission Case	17. 3rd Gear Set	31. Needle Bearing
4. Rear Cover	18. Needle Bearing	32. 5th Gear
5. Detent Lever	19. Ring Busing	33. Roller Bearing
6. Shift Shaft	20. Needle Bearing	34. Spacer's
7. Shift Fork	21. 1st Gear Set	35. Out-Put Flange
8. Snap Ring	22. Synchromesh Ring	36. Circlip
9. Spacer	23. Snap Ring	37. Spacer
10. Front Bearing	24. 1st/2nd Synchromesh Hub	38. Roller Bearing
11. Input Shaft	25. 2nd Gear Slider	39. Lay-Shaft Assembly
12. Synchromesh Rings	26. Reverse Gear	40. Needle Bearing
13. Needle Bearing	27. Needle Bearing	41. Reverse Idler Gear
14. Spacer	28. Main Shaft	42. Needle Bearing's
		43. Reverse Idler Shaft

BMW GETRAG 240 5-SPEED

3) Drive forward the transmission rear housing locating pins. Remove transmission rear housing bolts. Pull off front transmission housing section.

Reassembly

1) To reassemble, reverse disassembly procedure. Install reverse gear roller bearing on layshaft so that small diameter end of bearing faces up.

2) Coat transmission front section in area of reverse gear shaft with Loctite (573). Surface must be thoroughly clean and dried of oil.

NOTE: When installing reverse lock-out detent pin make sure that pin seats into the selector shaft groove.

TRANSMISSION GEAR ASSEMBLIES

1) Remove transmission case front section. Remove output flange lock plate and collar nut using Special Tools (23 1 200, 23 0 020 and 23 1 210). Remove output flange using Special Tool (33 1 150).

2) Remove counter shaft gear bolt, holder and counter shaft retainer bolt. Remove countershaft with reverse gear and needle bearing. Remove operating lever retainer pin.

3) Pull out reverse gear selector rail. Engage 4th gear and drive in shift detent lever retainer pin.

NOTE: Only drive in shift detent lever retainer pin far enough so that selector shaft can be pulled back and out.

4) Pull out shift selector shaft, be careful not to loose rollers on shaft. Remove shift rail retainer plate. Carefully remove the shift rods 3 detent plugs and springs.

5) Drive out 3rd/4th shift fork retainer pin. Pull 3rd/4th shift rod forward. Engage 2nd/Reverse by pushing 1st/2nd and 5th/Reverse selector rods forward.

6) Using Special Tool (23 1 050), press out input shaft, output shaft and layshaft from rear case section. Be careful not to clamp selector rods and layshaft while pressing out components.

NOTE: To avoid damage on sealing surface, use a piece of wood, aluminum or similar material between claws and sealing surface.

CLEANING & INSPECTION

COUNTERSHAFT

Check shaft and gears for wear or damage. Lightly polish any scoring from shaft surfaces.

REVERSE IDLER GEAR & SHAFT

Inspect components for wear or damage and replace if necessary.

SYNCHROMESH ASSEMBLIES

Check all parts for wear or damage. Blocking rings must be replaced if tapered clutch surface is pitted or excessively worn. Place each synchromesh ring into position on its respective gear. Using a feeler gauge, measure clearance between ring and gear. If clearance is less than .040" (1 mm), replace synchromesh ring.

COMPONENT DISASSEMBLY & REASSEMBLY

MAINSHAFT
Disassembly

1) Remove input shaft, synchromesh blocking ring and needle bearing off mainshaft. Remove 5th gear, brass synchromesh ring and needle bearing. Remove circlip and spacer from inside of 5th gear operating sleeve.

2) Using Special Press Plate Tool (23 1 490), press off 3rd gear with guide, operating sleeve and needle bearing. Using Special Press Plate Tool (23 1 490), press off 2nd gear. Remove 2nd gear nickle-plated synchromesh ring and needle bearing.

3) Remove 1st gear circlip. Using Special Press Plate Tool (23 1 490), press off 1st gear, operating sleeve and needle bearing. Remove reverse gear circlip and press off reverse gear, guide, operating sleeve and needle bearing.

Reassembly

NOTE: Allways replace circlips during reassembly.

1) Install output shaft next to collar. Install needle bearing, reverse gear, brass synchromesh ring with coat of Molybdenum grease. Press on guide sleeve to fit tight with Special Tool (23 1 290). Make sure tabs on synchromesh ring are aligned with openings in guide sleeve while installing.

2) Move operating sleeve in direction of reverse gear. Adjust guide sleeve with circlip to take up all play. Adjust play between circlip and guide sleeve to .0035" (.09 mm). Install needle bearing, 1st gear and nickle-plated synchromesh ring.

NOTE: Circlips are available in different thickness .067-.079" (1.7-2.0 mm).

3) Install 2nd gear needle bearing and nickle-plated synchromesh ring. Collar for bearing sleeve on output shaft must protrude slightly, if necessary check circlip for proper fit.

4) Heat bearing sleeve to approximately 175°F (80°C) and install on output shaft. Install needle bearing, 3rd gear and nickle-plated synchromesh ring. Install guide and operating sleeve on spline with groove facing 4th gear. To complete reassembly, reverse disassembly procedure.

SYNCHROMESH ASSEMBLIES
Disassembly

Remove blocking ring, and push hub from sleeve. Separate inserts and insert springs from hub.

Inspection

Check all parts for wear or damage. Blocking rings must be replaced if tapered clutch surface is pitted or excessively worn. Place each synchromesh ring into position on its respective gear. Using a feeler gauge, measure clearance between ring and gear. If clearance is less than .040" (1 mm), replace synchromesh ring.

Reassembly

Evenly stagger hooks of insert springs in notches in hub. Install inserts and push sleeve over hub. Install blocking ring on hub and install synchromesh on mating gear.

Manual Transmission
BMW GETRAG 240 5-SPEED (Cont.)

COUNTERSHAFT
Disassembly
Pull bearing off front of countershaft, and press off 4th gear. Remove snap ring and press off 3rd gear. Remove rear snap rings, making note of shims. Pull outer bearing off rear of countershaft, and press off 5th gear. Pull off inner bearing.

Inspection
Check shaft and gears for wear or damage. Lightly polish any scoring from shaft surfaces.

Reassembly
To assemble, reverse disassembly procedure. Heat gears to 250-300°F (120-150°C) when installing gears on shaft.

REVERSE IDLER GEAR & SHAFT
Disassembly
Remove end plate. Unscrew hex bolt while holding shaft at front. Remove bolt and washers. Install a bolt in tapped bore and push out assembly towards rear. Separate needle bearing and gear from shaft.

Inspection
Inspect components for wear or damage and replace if necessary.

Reassembly
Reverse disassembly procedure using Loctite (or equivalent) on holding bolt.

TRANSMISSION REASSEMBLY

GEAR & SHAFT CONTROL ASSEMBLIES
1) Install mainshaft and countershaft assemblies in intermediate transmission case. Install appropriate shim, heat bearing race to about 175°F (80°C) and push onto mainshaft. Press needle bearing and reverse gear onto mainshaft. Slide 5th gear synchromesh assembly onto mainshaft.

2) Push 5th/Reverse shift rod up to spring in transmission case from input shaft end. Insert locking balls and press down, pushing rod on through to lock.

3) Insert 5th/Reverse shift fork in sliding sleeve. Install sleeve on mainshaft with pins facing out. Guide 5th/Reverse shift fork onto rod and drive in a .24 x .94" (6 x 24 mm) pin.

4) Drive sleeve against stop on mainshaft spline. Heat bearing race to about 175°F (80°C) and push on mainshaft to sleeve. Install synchromesh blocking ring, needle bearing and 5th gear onto mainshaft.

5) Install inner roller bearing and 5th countergear on countershaft. Using appropriate driver, drive bearing race onto countershaft.

6) Measure distance between spacer and bearing race and take up countershaft end play with appropriate shims. Install locking snap ring with .20 x 1" (5 x 26 mm) pin on countershaft.

7) Install washer with bevelled side out on mainshaft. Heat speedometer gear and push onto mainshaft. Install 1st/2nd and 3rd/4th shift forks. Push in 3rd/4th shift rod through shift fork to spring.

8) Insert locating ball and locking ball and press down. Push 3rd/4th shift rod on through to lock making sure that opening on shift rod faces 5th/Reverse shift rod. Drive in retainer pin.

9) Push in 1st/2nd shift rod through fork to spring in transmission case. Install driving dog. Install locating ball and locking ball and press down. Push 1st/2nd shift rod on through to lock and drive in retainer pin.

10) Push in upper selector rod with opening facing out. Install selector arm with long side facing 3rd/4th shift rod.

11) Install lower selector rod with opening facing up. Install operating lever with sharp edge facing up and push in rod.

12) Install bolt in top of transmission case with Loctite (or equivalent) making sure that center engages bore of operating lever. Test operating lever for ease of movement. Push clamp onto lower selector rod with bevelled side facing shift fork.

13) Install bolt in side of transmission case with Loctite (240) making sure that center engages groove in lower selector rod. Hold 4 rollers on selector rod with grease.

TIGHTENING SPECIFICATIONS

Application	Ft. Lbs. (N.m)
Crossmember	16-17 (22-23)
Propeller Shaft Flange Nut	72 (98)
Rear Seal Flange Bolts	7 (9.5)
Rubber Mount	32-35 (43-47)
Transmission Cover Plate Bolts	
Front & Rear	18 (24)
Trans. Rear Cover-to-Trans. Case	16-17 (22-23)
Transmission-to-Engine (or Clutch Hsg.)	
8 mm Bolts	18-19 (24-26)
10 mm Bolts	35-37 (47-50)
12 mm Bolts	54-60 (72-80)

BMW ZF S5-16 5-SPEED

318i

DESCRIPTION

The ZF Model S5-16 5-speed transmission is fully synchronized, and uses constant mesh, helical gears in forward speeds, and non-synchronized, helical reverse gears. Shifting is accomplished through 3 shift rails and forks. Transmission case is of 2-section design.

LUBRICATION & ADJUSTMENT

See appropriate MANUAL TRANSMISSION SERVICING article in IMPORT GENERAL SERVICING section.

TROUBLE SHOOTING

OIL ON CLUTCH BELL HOUSING

Check the following: "O" ring for guide flange, Radial oil seals for input shaft and crankshaft rear main bearing, end cover gasket.

OIL ON OUTPUT FLANGE

Check the following: Radial seals for output shaft and selector shaft.

OIL ON VENT

Oil level too high. Wrong type of oil grade (excessive foaming).

JUMPS OUT OF GEAR

Sliding sleeve worn, guide rail defective, springs broken. Sliding sleevers for 1st/2nd and 3rd/4th gear mixed up. Shift console loose. Selector forks worn. Output flange loose.

HARD SHIFTS

Check clutch release, pedal travel, clutch disc for wear, clutch disc seized on transmission input shaft, clutch pilot bearing seized, air in clutch hydraulic system, bushings for selector rod damaged, excessive play in shift lever mount, selector forks worn and sliding sleeve worn.

TRANSMISSION GRABS WHEN SHIFTING

Clutch release insufficient. Synchromesh rings or sliding sleeve worn. Improper shifting into reverse gear (3 second shift break).

TRANSMISSION LOUD

Oil level too low. Transmission shaft bearings defective. Gears are damaged. Needle bearing of input or output shaft defective. Pilot bearing for transmission input shaft defective.

SERVICE (IN VEHICLE)

OUTPUT SHAFT, FLANGE & OIL SEAL
Removal

1) Remove propeller shaft at front and center. Remove output shaft lockplate and nut. Install Special Tool (23 1 200) and hold output flange with Special Tool (23 0 020).

2) Unscrew collar nut with Special Tool (23 1 210). Remove output flange with Special Tool (33 1 150). Pry out oil seal.

Installation

To install, reverse removal procedure. Lubricate oil seal with transmission oil. Install oil seal with Special Tool (23 2 160).

REAR TRANSMISSION MOUNT
Removal & Installation

1) Remove exhaust assembly. Support rear of transmission. Remove bolts for rear crossmember and upper retaining nut for transmission mount.

2) To install, reverse removal procedure.

REMOVAL & INSTALLATION

TRANSMISSION

See appropriate MANUAL TRANSMISSION REMOVAL article in IMPORT GENERAL SERVICING section.

TRANSMISSION DISASSEMBLY

1) Remove transmission from vehicle. Install Special Tool (23 0 090) on Special Tool (00 1 490). Mount transmission on work stand. Drain oil.

2) Remove guide sleeve. Lift out circlip. Unscrew back-up light switch. Drive back locating pins. Remove all rear housing bolts.

3) Pull off front case section using Special Tool (23 1 460 and 33 1 301). Drive out end cap. Drive out grooved ball bearing in direction of clutch housing.

4) Remove output flange with Special Tool (33 1 150). Remove all end caps. Carefully remove end springs (under tension).

5) Pull out 3 stop pins with circlip pliers as far as possible (stem locks have to be taken off before stop pins can be pulled out completely). Drive pins (4 and 5) out of selector fork for 3rd/4th gear (counterhold).

6) Push back leaf spring for reverse gear far enough with Special Tool (23 2 170) until selector arm is accesible. It should be possible to move selector shaft back and forth easily. Swing selector arm out of groove in selector rod.

7) Pull out 3rd/4th gear selector rod. Remove lock in socket of bolt. Unscrew bolt. Remove reverse gear, reverse gear shaft, needle bearing and thrust washer.

8) Remove operating lever bolt. Engage reverse gear by moving sliding sleeve forward before pressing out gear set. Press input shaft, outshaft and layshaft out of case rear section with Special Tool (23 1 050). Remove reverse gear. Remove gear train.

Manual Transmission
BMW ZF S5-16 5-SPEED (Cont.)

Fig. 1: Exploded View Of ZF S5-16 5-Speed Transmission

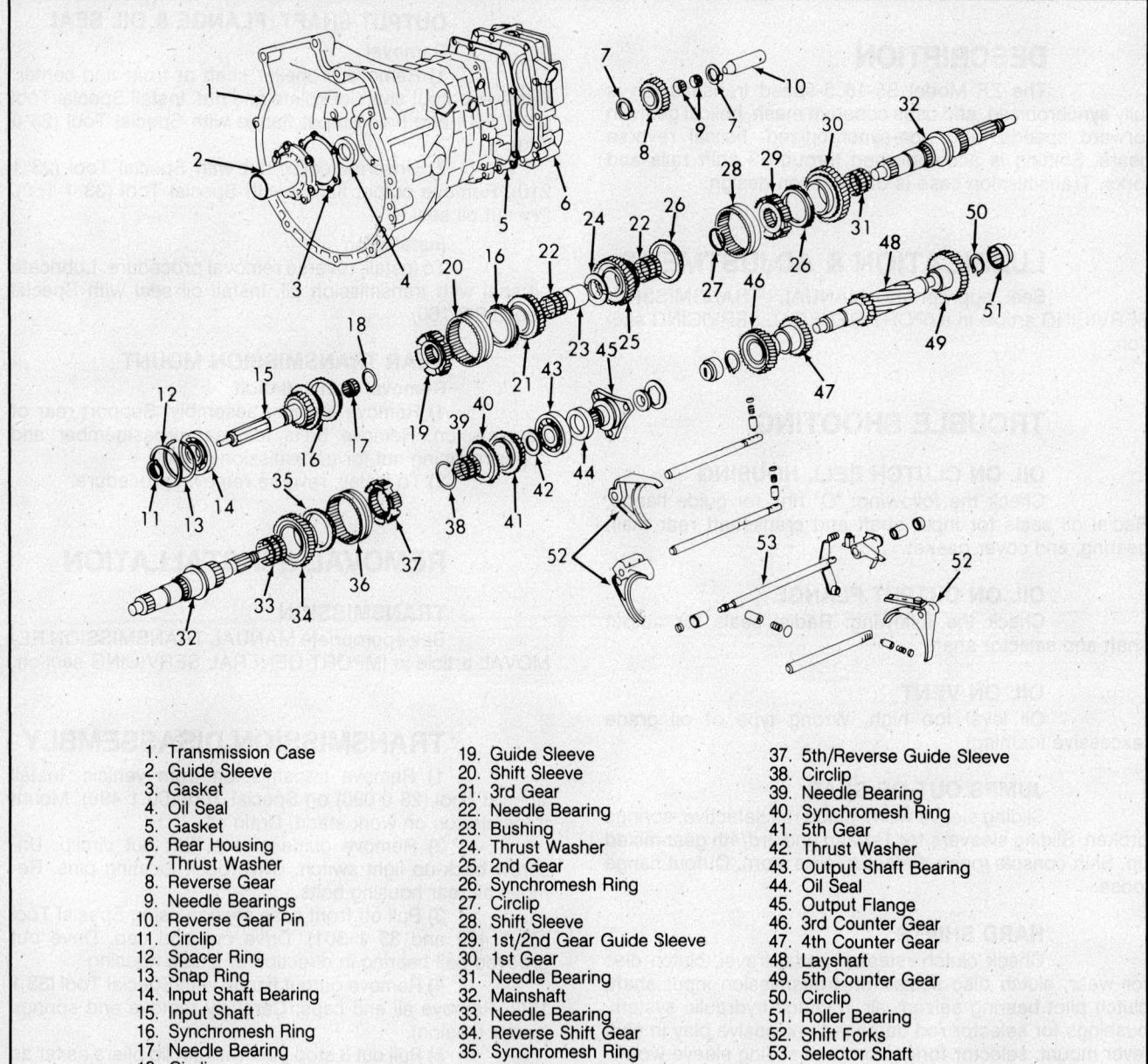

1. Transmission Case	19. Guide Sleeve	37. 5th/Reverse Guide Sleeve
2. Guide Sleeve	20. Shift Sleeve	38. Circlip
3. Gasket	21. 3rd Gear	39. Needle Bearing
4. Oil Seal	22. Needle Bearing	40. Synchromesh Ring
5. Gasket	23. Bushing	41. 5th Gear
6. Rear Housing	24. Thrust Washer	42. Thrust Washer
7. Thrust Washer	25. 2nd Gear	43. Output Shaft Bearing
8. Reverse Gear	26. Synchromesh Ring	44. Oil Seal
9. Needle Bearings	27. Circlip	45. Output Flange
10. Reverse Gear Pin	28. Shift Sleeve	46. 3rd Counter Gear
11. Circlip	29. 1st/2nd Gear Guide Sleeve	47. 4th Counter Gear
12. Spacer Ring	30. 1st Gear	48. Layshaft
13. Snap Ring	31. Needle Bearing	49. 5th Counter Gear
14. Input Shaft Bearing	32. Mainshaft	50. Circlip
15. Input Shaft	33. Needle Bearing	51. Roller Bearing
16. Synchromesh Ring	34. Reverse Shift Gear	52. Shift Forks
17. Needle Bearing	35. Synchromesh Ring	53. Selector Shaft
18. Circlip	36. Shift Sleeve	

NOTE: Use a soft material (wood, aluminum or a similar material) between claws and sealing surface to avoid damage on sealing surface.

CLEANING & INSPECTION

Inspection
Check all parts for wear or damage. Blocking rings must be replaced if tapered clutch surface is pitted or excessively worn. Place each synchromesh ring into position on its respective gear. Using a feeler gauge, measure clearance between ring and gear. If clearance is less than .040" (1 mm), replace synchromesh ring.

COMPONENT DISASSEMBLY & REASSEMBLY

INPUT AND OUTPUT SHAFT ASSEMBLY
Disassembly
1) Pull off input shaft, synchromesh ring (made of brass) and needle bearing. Lift out circlip. Press 3rd gear with guide and sliding sleeve off of input shaft with Special Tool (23 1 490). Remove needle bearing.

2) Remove circlip for reverse gear. Press guide sleeve with sliding sleeve and reverse gear off of output shaft. Remove needle bearing. Press guide sleeve with sliding sleeve and reverse gear off of output shaft. Remove needle bearing.

BMW ZF S5-16 5-SPEED (Cont.)

NOTE: Always replace circlips when reassembling gear units.

Reassembly

1) Install output shaft next to collar. Install needle bearing, reverse gear and brass synchromesh ring with 6 grease held balls. Install guide and sliding sleeve with narrow collar facing reverse gear.

2) Press on guide sleeve to fit tight with Special Tool (23 1 290). Make sure that short tabs of synchromesh ring are aligned with groove in pressure pieces when pressing on guide sleeve.

3) Move sliding sleeve in reverse gear direction. Adjust guide sleeve with circlip to take up all play. Circlips are available in different thicknesses. Install circlip.

4) Install brass synchromesh ring with sort tabs of synchromesh ring in groove of pressure pieces. Install needle bearing and 5th gear. Heat thrust washer to approximately 175°F (80°C) and install on output shaft.

5) Install 1st gear needle bearing and sintered steel synchromesh ring. Install guide sleeve and sliding sleeve with narrow collar facing 1st gear. Press guide sleeve to fit tight with Special Tool (23 1 290).

NOTE: When pressing on make sure that short tabs of synchromesh ring are aligned with groove in thrust pieces.

6) Move sliding sleeve in 1st gear direction. Adjust guide sleeve to be without play. Circlips are available in different thicknesses. Install sintered steel synchromesh ring with short tabs of synchromesh ring in groove of pressure pieces. Install needle bearing and 2nd gear.

7) Check output shaft. Output shaft collar for thrust washer must protrude slightly. If necessary, check circlip for correct fit. Heat thrust washer to approximately 175°F (80°C) and install on output shaft.

8) Heat bearing sleeve to 175°F (80°C) and install on output shaft. Install 3rd gear, needle bearing and brass synchromesh ring. Install guide sleeve and sliding sleeve with long collar facing 3rd gear.

9) Press on guide sleeve to fit tight with Special Tool (23 1 290). Adjust axial play of input shaft with output shaft and case front section installed. Input shaft must rest on synchromesh ring. Measure distance from guide sleeve sealing surface to input shaft.

10) Measure distance from guide sleeve sealing surface to circlip bearing surface. Measure distance from bearing outer race to circlip. Axial play required is .043-.051" (1.1-1.3 mm). Circlips are available in different thicknesses for making corrections. Install grooved ball bearing and circlip.

NOTE: If a spacer is found between the circlip and case when removing the bearing, it must be installed again for measuring distance.

11) Measure distance from bearing outer race to circlip. Heat grooved ball bearing inner race and case front section in area of bearing to 175°F (80°C). Push grooved ball bearing on to input shaft as far as possible.

12) Press grooved ball bearing on to input shaft and into case front section with Special Tools (23 1 007, 23 1 000 and 23 1 006). Insert Special Tools (23 1 006) that flat side faces input shaft.

13) Drive on grooved ball bearing further simultaneously with light hammer knocks. Install circlip and reverse gear switch.

SYNCHROMESH RINGS
Disassembly

With output shaft disassembled, measure clearance in area of stops between synchromesh ring and clutch (.040" 1 mm). If not to specifications, replace synchromesh ring. To disassemble, press sliding sleeve off of guide sleeve. Remove spring, pressure piece and ball.

Reassembly

1) Flat teeth of sliding sleeve must be aligned wiht pressure pieces. Install all springs, pressure pieces and balls. Shouldered end of pressure pieces faces collar.

2) Press in balls one after the other into sliding sleeve. For 1st/2nd, check installed position of sliding sleeve (wide web of sliding sleeve faces thick collar). For 5th/Reverse gear, check installed position of sliding sleeve (wide web of sliding sleeve faces narrow collar).

TRANSMISSION REASSEMBLY

1) Install mainshaft and countershaft assemblies, in intermediate transmission case. Install appropriate shim, heat bearing race to about 175°F (80°C) and push onto mainshaft. Press needle bearing and reverse gear onto mainshaft. Slide 5th gear synchronizer assembly onto mainshaft.

2) Push 5th/Reverse shift rod up to spring in transmission case from input shaft end. Insert locking balls and press down, pushing rod on through to lock.

3) Insert 5th/Reverse shift fork in sliding sleeve. Install sleeve on mainshaft with pins facing out. Guide 5th/Reverse shift fork onto rod and drive in retainer pin (roll pin).

4) Drive sleeve against stop on mainshaft spline. Heat bearing race to about 175°F (80°C) and push mainshaft onto sleeve. Install synchromesh blocking ring, needle bearing and 5th gear onto mainshaft.

5) Install inner roller bearing and 5th countergear on countershaft. Using appropriate driver, drive bearing race onto countershaft. Measure distance between spacer and bearing race and take up countershaft end play with appropriate shims.

6) Install locking circlip with retainer pin (roll pin) on countershaft. Install washer with bevelled side out on mainshaft. Carefully heat speedometer gear and push onto mainshaft.

7) Install 1st/2nd and 3rd/4th shift forks. Push in 3rd/4th shift rod through shift fork to spring. Insert locating ball and locking ball. Press down and push 3rd/4th shift rod through to lock. Make sure that opening on shift rod faces 5th/Reverse shift rod. Drive in retainer pin (roll pin).

8) Push in 1st/2nd shift rod through fork and up to spring in transmission case. Install driving dog, locating ball and locking ball. Press and hold down. Push 1st/2nd shift rod on through to lock and drive in retainer pin (roll pin).

9) Push in upper selector rod with opening facing out. Install selector arm with long side facing 3rd/4th shift rod.

10) Install lower selector rod with opening facing up. Install operating lever with sharp edge facing up and push in rod. Install bolt in top of transmission case with Loctite (573) making sure that center engages bore of operating lever.

Manual Transmission
BMW ZF S5-16 5-SPEED (Cont.)

11) Test operating lever for ease of movement. Push clamp onto lower selector rod with bevelled side facing shift fork. Using Loctite (573), install bolt in side of transmission. Make sure that center engages groove in lower selector rod.

12) Install output flange. Install collar nut using Loctite (573). Hold output flange using Special Tool (23 0 020) and tighten nut using Special Tool (23 1 210). Install lockplate.

13) Reassemble transmission front and rear cases.

TIGHTENING SPECIFICATIONS

Application	Ft. Lbs. (N.m)
Crossmember	16-17 (22-23)
Propeller Shaft Flange Nut	72 (98)
Rear Seal Flange Bolts	7 (9.5)
Rubber Mount	32-35 (43-47)
Transmission Cover Plate Bolts	
Front & Rear	18 (24)
Transmission-to-Engine (or Clutch Hsg.)	
8 mm Bolts	18-19 (24-26)
10 mm Bolts	35-37 (47-50)
12 mm Bolts	54-60 (72-80)

Manual Transmission
BMW 528e, 533i, 633CSi & 733i 5-SPEED

DESCRIPTION

The Getrag Model 260 5-speed transmission is fully synchronized, and uses constant mesh, helical gears in forward speeds, and non-synchronized, helical reverse gears. Shifting is accomplished through 3 shift rails and forks. Transmission case is of 3-section design.

LUBRICATION & ADJUSTMENT

See appropriate MANUAL TRANSMISSION SERVICING article in IMPORT GENERAL SERVICING section.

TROUBLE SHOOTING

See MANUAL TRANSMISSION TROUBLE SHOOTING article in IMPORT GENERAL SERVICING section.

SERVICE (IN VEHICLE)

OUTPUT FLANGE & SECTOR SHAFT OIL SEAL
Removal

1) Remove complete exhaust system. Install Special Strap Tool (26 1 011) on the Guibo coupling. This strap is used for removal and installation of propeller shaft to prevent stress in the Guibo coupling.

Fig. 1: Exploded View of Getrag 260 5-Speed Transmission

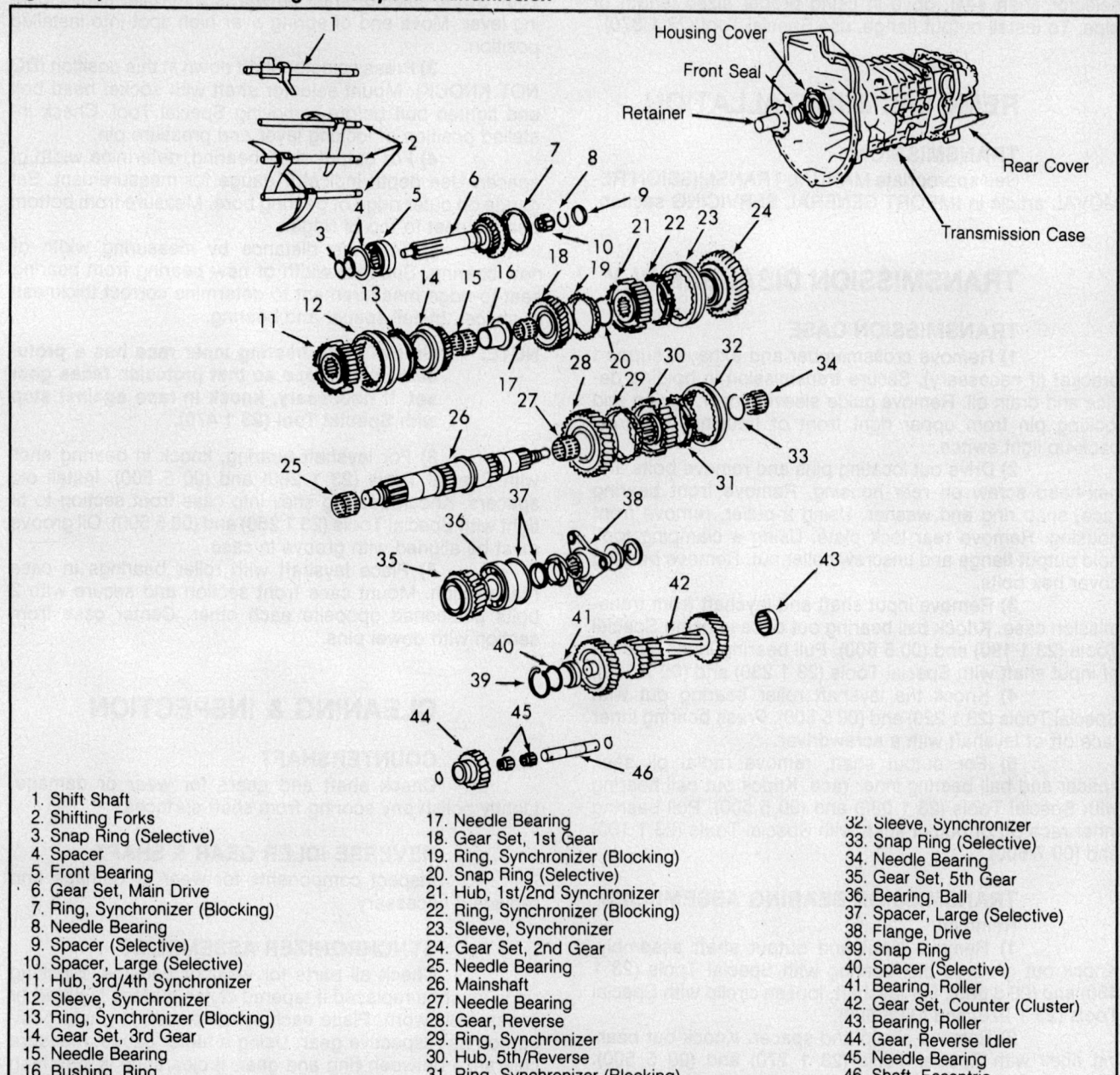

1. Shift Shaft
2. Shifting Forks
3. Snap Ring (Selective)
4. Spacer
5. Front Bearing
6. Gear Set, Main Drive
7. Ring, Synchronizer (Blocking)
8. Needle Bearing
9. Spacer (Selective)
10. Spacer, Large (Selective)
11. Hub, 3rd/4th Synchronizer
12. Sleeve, Synchronizer
13. Ring, Synchronizer (Blocking)
14. Gear Set, 3rd Gear
15. Needle Bearing
16. Bushing, Ring
17. Needle Bearing
18. Gear Set, 1st Gear
19. Ring, Synchronizer (Blocking)
20. Snap Ring (Selective)
21. Hub, 1st/2nd Synchronizer
22. Ring, Synchronizer (Blocking)
23. Sleeve, Synchronizer
24. Gear Set, 2nd Gear
25. Needle Bearing
26. Mainshaft
27. Needle Bearing
28. Gear, Reverse
29. Ring, Synchronizer
30. Hub, 5th/Reverse
31. Ring, Synchronizer (Blocking)
32. Sleeve, Synchronizer
33. Snap Ring (Selective)
34. Needle Bearing
35. Gear Set, 5th Gear
36. Bearing, Ball
37. Spacer, Large (Selective)
38. Flange, Drive
39. Snap Ring
40. Spacer (Selective)
41. Bearing, Roller
42. Gear Set, Counter (Cluster)
43. Bearing, Roller
44. Gear, Reverse Idler
45. Needle Bearing
46. Shaft, Eccentric

7-28

Manual Transmission
BMW 528e, 533i, 633CSi & 733i 5-SPEED (Cont.)

2) Tighten Special Strap Tool (26 1 011) until bolts can be pulled out by hand. Remove strap. Remove lower heat shield attached to rear transmission mount bracket. Remove center bearing bracket. Pull propeller shaft down and out of the way.

3) Support rear of transmission and remove transmission mount bracket. Install Special Tool (23 1 200). Counterhold output flange with Special Tool (23 1 150). Unscrew collared nut with Special Tool (23 1 210). Remove output flange. Remove radial oil seal with Special Tool (00 5 000).

4) With output flange removed, engage 1st gear. Lift out selector shaft lock sleeve and drive out retaining pin (upward). Using an ice pick, pry out radial oil seal.

Installation
To install, reverse removal procedure. Fill output flange and selector shaft seals with grease. To install selector shaft seal, drive in using proper sized length of pipe. To install output flange, use Special Tool (23 1 370).

REMOVAL & INSTALLATION

TRANSMISSION
See appropriate MANUAL TRANSMISSION REMOVAL article in IMPORT GENERAL SERVICING section.

TRANSMISSION DISASSEMBLY

TRANSMISSION CASE
1) Remove crossmember and exhaust support bracket (if necessary). Secure transmission in holding device and drain oil. Remove guide sleeve, cover, spring and locking pin from upper right front of housing. Unscrew back-up light switch.

2) Drive out locating pins and remove bolts and hex-head screw on rear housing. Remove front bearing race, snap ring and washer. Using a puller, remove front housing. Remove rear lock plate. Using a clamping tool, hold output flange and unscrew collar nut. Remove bearing cover hex bolts.

3) Remove input shaft and layshaft from transmission case. Knock ball bearing out of case using Special Tools (23 1 190) and (00 5 500). Pull bearing inner race off of input shaft with Special Tools (23 1 230) and (00 7 500).

4) Knock the layshaft roller bearing out with Special Tools (23 1 220) and (00 5 500). Press bearing inner race off of layshaft with a screwdriver.

5) For output shaft, remove radial oil seal, spacer and ball bearing inner race. Knock out ball bearing with Special Tools (23 1 080) and (00 5 500). Pull bearing inner race off of output shaft with Special Tools (23 1 100) and (00 7 500).

TRANSMISSION BEARING ASSEMBLIES
Removal
1) Remove input and output shaft assembly. Knock out grooved ball bearing with Special Tools (23 1 480) and (00 5 500). For layshaft, loosen circlip with Special Tools (23 1 270) and (00 5 500).

2) Remove circlip and spacer. Knock out bearing shell with Special Tools (23 1 270) and (00 5 500). Remove selector shaft detent bolt and spring.

3) Install Special Tool (23 1 250) to remove the selector shaft. Remove socket head bolt. Remove selector shaft from above.

4) Remove output shaft bearing holder. Locking lever should remain on holder. Remove radial seal. Knock out grooved ball bearing with Special Tools (23 1 120) and (00 5 500).

5) To remove layshaft bearing, install Special Tool (23 1 280) with thickerend inserted in the bearing shell. Install Special Tool (33 4 020) and screw in Special Tool (23 1 300). Pull out bearing shell.

Installation
1) For layshaft, knock in bearing shell with Special Tools (23 1 260) and (00 5 500). Determine axial play by using a dial gauge and holder. Install dial gauge so that tip is on tooth of layshaft.

2) Insert selector shaft with Special Tool (23 1 250). Swing selector shaft outwards with roller above locking lever. Move end of spring over high spot into installed position.

3) Press selector shaft down in this position (DO NOT KNOCK). Mount selector shaft with socket head bolt and tighten bolt before removing Special Tool. Check installed position of locking lever and pressure pin.

4) For output shaft bearing, determine width of spacer. Use depth indicator gauge for measurement. Set gauge on outer ridge of bearing bore. Measure from bottom bearing seat to top of ridge.

5) Measure distance by measuring width of new bearing. Subtract width of new bearing from bearing seat-to-ridge measurement to determine correct thickness of spacer. Install spacer and bearing.

NOTE: Grooved ball bearing inner race has a protusion. Install race so that protusion faces gear set. If necessary, knock in race against stop with Special Tool (23 1 470).

6) For layshaft bearing, knock in bearing shell with Special Tools (23 1 260) and (00 5 500). Install old spacers. Knock bearing shell into case front section to fit tight with Special Tools (23 1 260) and (00 5 500). Oil groove must be aligned with groove in case.

7) Place layshaft with roller bearings in case rear section. Mount case front section and secure with 2 bolts positioned opposite each other. Center case front section with dowel pins.

CLEANING & INSPECTION

COUNTERSHAFT
Check shaft and gears for wear or damage. Lightly polish any scoring from shaft surfaces.

REVERSE IDLER GEAR & SHAFT
Inspect components for wear or damage and replace if necessary.

SYNCHRONIZER ASSEMBLIES
Check all parts for wear or damage. Blocking rings must be replaced if tapered clutch surface is pitted or excessively worn. Place each synchromesh ring into position on its respective gear. Using a feeler gauge, measure clearance between ring and gear. If clearance is less than .040" (1 mm), replace synchromesh ring.

BMW 528e, 533i, 633CSi & 733i 5-SPEED (Cont.)

COMPONENT DISASSEMBLY & REASSEMBLY

MAINSHAFT

Disassembly

1) With gear assembly removed from transmission, pull off input shaft, synchromesh ring and needle bearing. Pull off thrust washer, 5th gear, synchromesh ring and needle bearing. Remove circlip and spacer.

2) Press off 3rd gear with guide sleeve and operating sleeve, using Special Tool (23 1 490). Remove needle bearing. Press off bearing bushing and 2nd gear with Special Tool (23 1 490).

3) Remove needle bearing and synchromesh ring (nickle plated). Remove circlip before pressing off the 1st gear. Press off 1st gear, guide sleeve and operating sleeve with Special Tool (23 1 490).

4) Remove needle bearing. Remove reverse gear circlip and press off reverse gear. Press guide sleeve, operating sleeve and reverse gear off of ouput shaft. Remove needle bearing.

Reassembly

1) Mount needle bearing, reverse gear and brass synchromesh ring. Slide guide sleeve and operating sleeve on spline of output shaft. Press on guide sleeve to fit tight with Special Tool (23 1 290).

NOTE: **When pressing on make sure tabs on synchromesh ring are aligned with openings in guide sleeve.**

2) Switch operating sleeve in direction of reverse gear. Adjust guide sleeve to be without play using circlip. Install circlip.

3) Mount needle bearing, 1st gear and nickel plated synchromesh ring. Slide guide sleeve and operating sleeve on spline of output shaft. Press on guide sleeve to fit tight with Special Tool (23 1 290). When pressing on make sure tabs on synchromesh ring are aligned with openings in guide sleeve.

4) Switch operating sleeve in direction of 1st gear. Adjust guide sleeve to be without play. Install circlip. Mount needle bearing, nickel plated synchromesh ring and 2nd gear. The collar for the bearing bushing on ouput shaft must project a little. Check circlip for proper seating.

5) Heat bearing bushing to about 175°F (80°C) and install on output shaft. Mount needle bearing, 3rd gear and brass synchromesh ring. Place guide sleeve and operating sleeve on spline with long collar facing 3rd gear.

6) Press guide sleeve to fit tight with Special Tool (23 1 290). When pressing on, make sure tabs on synchromesh ring are aligned with openings in guide sleeve. Install spacer and circlip.

SYNCHRONIZER ASSEMBLIES

Disassembly

Remove blocking ring, and push hub from sleeve. Separate inserts and insert springs from hub.

Inspection

Check all parts for wear or damage. Blocking rings must be replaced if tapered clutch surface is pitted or excessively worn. Place each synchromesh ring into position on its respective gear. Using a feeler gauge, measure clearance between ring and gear. If clearance is less than .040" (1 mm), replace synchromesh ring.

Reassembly

Evenly stagger hooks of insert springs in notches in hub. Install inserts and push sleeve over hub. Install blocking ring on hub and install synchromesh on mating gear.

COUNTERSHAFT

Disassembly

Pull bearing off front of countershaft, and press off 4th gear. Remove snap ring and press off 3rd gear. Remove rear snap rings, making note of shim positions. Pull outer bearing off rear of countershaft, and press off 5th gear. Pull off inner bearing.

Inspection

Check shaft and gears for wear or damage. Lightly polish any scoring from shaft surfaces.

Reassembly

To assemble, reverse disassembly procedure. Heat gears to 250-300°F (120-150°C) when installing gears on shaft.

REVERSE IDLER GEAR & SHAFT

Disassembly

Remove end plate. Unscrew hex bolt while holding shaft at front. Remove bolt and washers. Install a bolt in tapped bore and push assembly out towards rear. Separate needle bearing and gear from shaft.

Inspection

Inspect components for wear or damage and replace if necessary.

Reassembly

Reverse disassembly procedure using Loctite (or equivalent) on holding bolt.

TRANSMISSION REASSEMBLY

GEAR & SELECTOR SHAFT ASSEMBLIES

1) Install mainshaft and countershaft assemblies in intermediate transmission case. Install appropriate shim. Heat bearing race to about 175°F (80°C) and push onto mainshaft. Press needle bearing and reverse gear onto mainshaft. Slide 5th gear synchromesh assembly onto mainshaft.

2) Push 5th/Reverse shift rod up to spring in transmission case from input shaft end. Insert locking balls and press down, pushing rod on through to lock.

3) Insert 5th/Reverse shift fork in sliding sleeve. Install sleeve on mainshaft with pins facing out. Guide 5th/Reverse shift fork onto selector rod and drive in retainer pin (roll pin).

4) Drive sleeve against stop on mainshaft spline. Heat bearing race to about 175°F (80°C) and push mainshaft on to sleeve. Install synchromesh blocking ring, needle bearing and 5th gear onto mainshaft.

5) Install inner roller bearing and 5th countergear on countershaft. Using appropriate driver, drive bearing race onto countershaft. Measure distance between spacer and bearing race and take up countershaft end play with appropriate shims. Install washer with bevelled side out on mainshaft. Heat speedometer gear and push onto mainshaft.

Manual Transmission

BMW 528e, 533i, 633CSi & 733i 5-SPEED (Cont.)

6) Install 1st/2nd and 3rd/4th shift forks. Push in 3rd/4th shift rod through shift fork to spring. Insert locating ball and locking ball and press down. Push 3rd/4th shift rod on through to lock making sure that opening on shift rod faces 5th/Reverse shift rod. Drive in retainer pin (roll pin).

7) Push in 1st/2nd shift rod through fork to spring in transmission case. Install driving dog. Install locating ball and locking ball and press down. Push 1st/2nd shift rod on through to lock and drive in retainer pin (roll pin).

8) Push in upper selector rod with opening facing out. Install selector arm with long side facing 3rd/4th shift rod.

9) Install lower selector rod with opening facing up. Install operating lever with sharp edge facing up and push in selector rod.

10) Install bolt in top of transmission case with Loctite (or equivalent) making sure that center engages bore of operating lever. Test operating lever for ease of movement. Push clamp onto lower selector rod with bevelled side facing shift fork.

11) Install bolt in side of transmission case with Loctite (or equivalent) making sure that center engages groove in lower selector rod. Hold 4 rollers on selector rod with grease.

TRANSMISSION CASE

Thoroughly clean all sealing surfaces, coat with Loctite or equivalent and reverse disassembly procedure.

TIGHTENING SPECIFICATIONS

Application	Ft. Lbs. (N.m)
Crossmember	16-17 (22-23)
Propeller Shaft Flange Nut	72 (98)
Rear Seal Flange Bolts	7 (9.5)
Rubber Mount	32-35 (43-47)
Transmission Cover Plate Bolts	
Front & Rear	18 (24)
Transmission-to-Engine (or Clutch Hsg.)	
8 mm Bolts	18-19 (24-26)
10 mm Bolts	35-37 (47-50)
12 mm Bolts	54-60 (72-80)

CHRYSLER CORP. IMPORTS & MITSUBISHI KM 130/144 4-SPEED

Chrysler Corp. & Mitsubishi Pickups

IDENTIFICATION

Transmission may be identified by a serial number stamped on clutch housing.

DESCRIPTION

The KM 130 (2WD) and KM 144 (4WD) 4-speed transmissions are fully synchronized, constant mesh-type units. All forward gears, and countergear, are located in the transmission case. Reverse and idler gears are located in extension housing (2WD).

Access to transmission gears is obtained with bottom pan removed. Shift lever is mounted to extension housing or transfer case and is connected to shift control rod which connects to shift rails located at rear of transmission case.

LUBRICATION & ADJUSTMENT

See appropriate MANUAL TRANSMISSION SERVICING article in IMPORT GENERAL SERVICING section.

TROUBLE SHOOTING

DIFFICULTY MESHING GEARS

Malfunction of gearshift lever or control shaft. Synchro rings or gear conical surfaces worn or excessive play. Synchro shift keys worn or damaged.

JUMPS OUT OF GEAR

Shifting forks worn or detent springs broken. Mainshaft or mainshaft support bearings worn or damaged. Clearance between synchro hub and sleeve excessive. Gears or gear bushings worn. Countergear worn.

NOISE IN TRANSMISSION

Lubrication oil incorrect or insufficient. Gears or bearings worn. Mainshaft spline worn or damaged.

SERVICE (IN VEHICLE)

Manufacturer does not provide in vehicle service procedures.

REMOVAL & INSTALLATION

TRANSMISSION

See appropriate MANUAL TRANSMISSION REMOVAL article in IMPORT GENERAL SERVICING section. On 4WD models, transfer case may be removed with or without transmission assembly.

TRANSMISSION DISASSEMBLY

NOTE: Transmission case and extension housing are made of aluminum and care should be exercised when handling machined surfaces.

1) To remove transfer case assembly, complete the following: Remove back-up light switch from lower right adapter. Take out steel ball. Remove plug from right side of transfer case. Take out select spring and select plunger. Remove 6 bolts securing transmission and transfer case control lever assembly.

2) Remove control lever and gasket. Remove plug from top of adapter and take out neutral return plunger and spring. Remove bolts securing transfer case adapter to transmission. Tilt change shifter toward left, remove control finger from shift lug groove and remove transfer case.

3) To disassemble transfer case, see appropriate TRANSFER CASE article in IMPORT TRANSFER CASE section. On all models, clean exterior of transmission case before proceeding with disassembly.

4) In clutch housing, use a 3/16" (4.76 mm) punch to drive out spring pin in clutch shaft. Remove clutch shaft from clutch housing. Remove release fork, felt packing and return springs. See Fig. 1.

Fig. 1: Removing Spring Pin From Clutch Cross Shaft

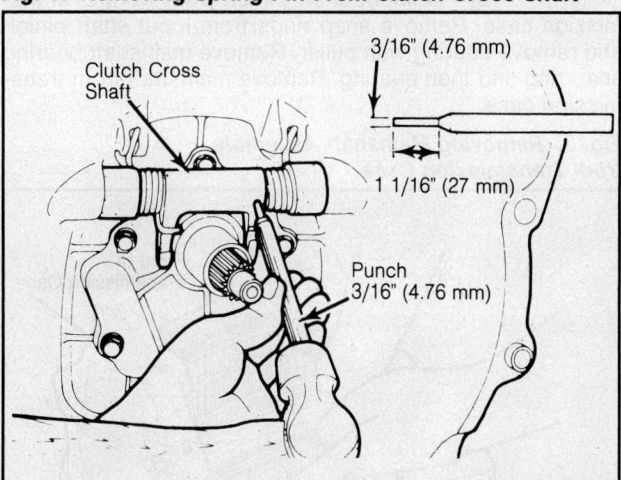

5) Remove speedometer driven gear assembly from extension housing. Remove control lever assembly. Remove extension housing attaching bolts. Rotate control lever to left, remove control finger from shift lug groove and remove extension housing.

6) Remove bottom pan from transmission case. Remove detent plugs, springs and balls. Position 1st-2nd shift rail in Neutral position. Remove Reverse shaft rail and fork assembly together with Reverse idler gear.

7) Using a 3/16" (4.76 mm) punch, drive out 1st-2nd and 3rd-4th shift fork spring pins. Pull each shift rail and selector out toward rear of case. Remove shift fork. Keep shift rail and selector together as an assembly. Ensure interlock plungers are not lost when removing shafts.

8) Remove snap ring from rear of countergear. Remove counter reverse gear and spacer. Remove mainshaft lock nut and Reverse gear from mainshaft. Remove 5 retaining screws and then rear bearing retainer. Remove front bearing retainer.

7-32

Manual Transmissions
CHRYSLER CORP. IMPORTS & MITSUBISHI KM 130/144 4-SPEED (Cont.)

Fig. 2: Removing Countergear Rear Bearing from Transmission Case

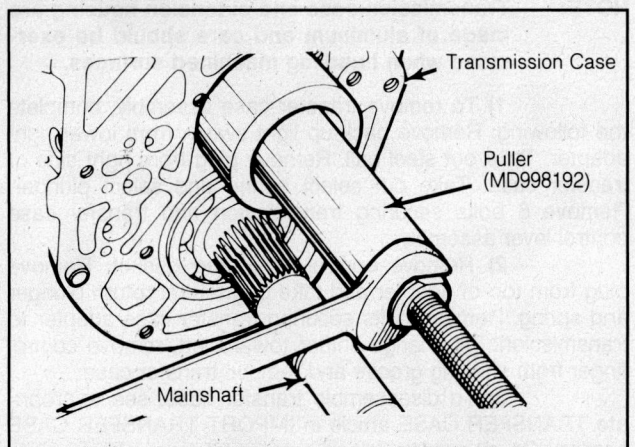

9) Press countergear rearward and remove snap ring. Use bearing puller to remove countergear rear bearing. Remove snap ring from front of countergear bearing, then remove bearing with bearing puller. Remove countergear from transmission case.

10) Pull input shaft pinion from front of transmission case. Remove snap rings from input shaft pinion and remove bearing with puller. Remove mainshaft bearing snap ring and then bearing. Remove mainshaft from transmission case.

Fig. 3: Removing Mainshaft Assembly from Transmission Case

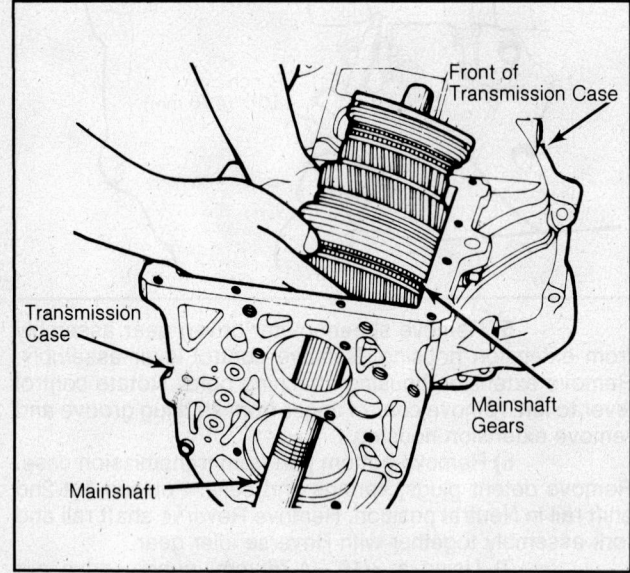

CLEANING & INSPECTION

1) All parts should be thoroughly washed in cleaning solvent and air dried. Remove old gaskets with stiff brush or scraper. Rinse bearings in clean solvent and air dry. DO NOT spin bearings dry.

2) Lubricate with light grade oil and wrap in clean paper until ready to install. Examine all gear teeth and splines for chips, wear, breaks or nicks. Check transmission case and extension housing for cracks and damage.

3) Check bearings and synchronizers for wear, damage and proper fit. Lubricate all moving parts before installation. Use new gaskets, seals and snap rings.

COMPONENT DISASSEMBLY & REASSEMBLY

MAINSHAFT
Disassembly

1) Pull 1st gear, 1st-2nd synchro and 2nd gear toward rear of mainshaft. Remove snap ring from forward end of mainshaft, then remove 3rd-4th synchro and 3rd gear.

2) Using a 3/16" (4.76 mm) punch, remove gear shifter locking pin. Remove control shaft assembly. Press gear shifter forward and pull lock pin off, being careful not to bend control shaft.

Cleaning & Inspection

1) Check mainshaft for worn or damaged gear area, bearing surfaces and splines. Check spacers and bearings for wear or damage. Check all bearings for smooth rolling action. Replace parts as necessary.

2) Check all gears for damaged, worn or chipped teeth. Check gear inside diameter for wear or damage. Check all synchro assemblies for worn or damaged teeth, conical surface, internal surface and rings.

3) Check synchro ring-to-gear clearance on all synchro rings. See Fig. 4. If the clearance is not .032" (.8 mm) replace synchro ring. With hub and sleeve assembled, ensure sleeve slides smoothly and that it is not excessively loose. If either part is defective, replace both synchro sleeve and hub as an assembly.

Fig. 4: Checking Synchro Ring-to-Gear Clearance

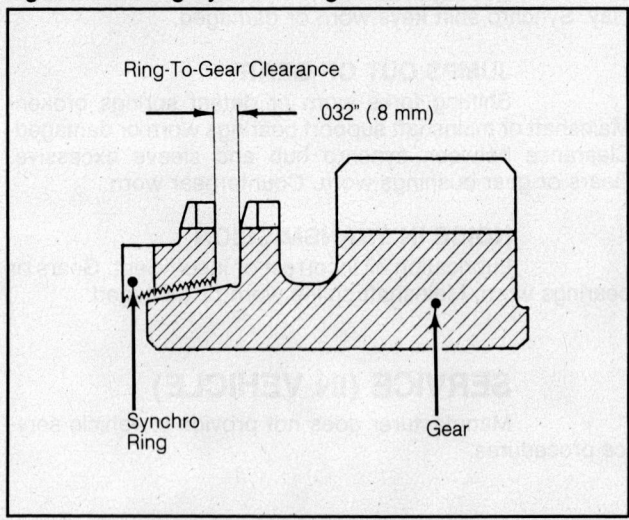

4) Check synchro pieces for wear and damage, especially the projecting part. Check synchro springs for deterioration and breakage. Check countergear for wear or chipped teeth.

5) Check Reverse idler gear and shaft for wear or damage. Check shift forks, rail and selector for wear or damage. Check clearance between shift fork and fork groove on synchro sleeve and gear.

6) Clearance should be .006-.014" (.15-.35 mm) for Overdrive and reverse, .004-.012" (.1-.3 mm) for all

Manual Transmissions
CHRYSLER CORP. IMPORTS & MITSUBISHI KM 130/144 4-SPEED (Cont.)

7-33

others. Check detent ball slots for wear. Check clearance between selector and lever. Clearance should be .004-.012" (.1-.3 mm).

Fig. 5: Using a Feeler Gauge to Check 3rd Gear End Play

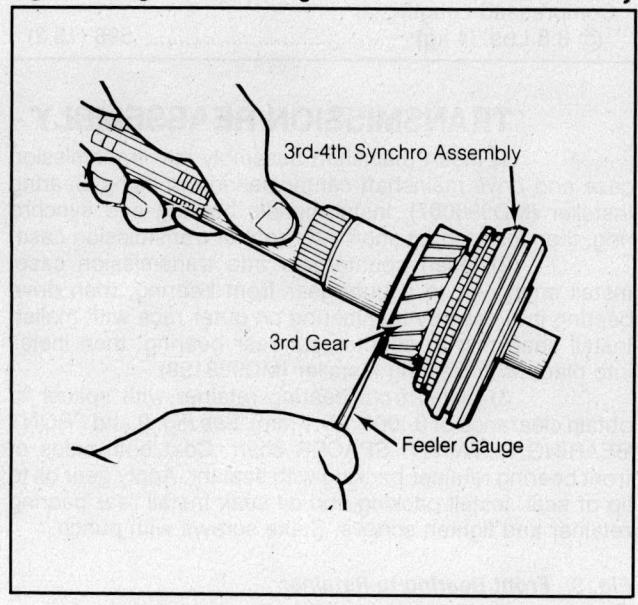

7) Check detent balls and springs for damage or breakage. Check shift rails, control lever and forks for wear, damage or breakage. If any parts do not meet above specifications, they must be replaced.

Reassembly
1) Assemble both synchro assemblies. Ensure components are positioned correctly. *See Fig. 6.* Install needle bearing, 3rd gear, synchro ring and 3rd-4th synchro assembly onto front of mainshaft.

NOTE: Ensure synchro rings and assemblies are re-installed in original position.

2) Select snap ring of proper size so 3rd-4th synchro hub end play is 0-.003" (0-.08 mm). See 3RD-4TH SYNCHRONIZER HUB END PLAY chart.

3RD-4TH SYNCHRONIZER HUB END PLAY CHART

Application (Color)	Thickness In. (mm)
No Color	.085 (2.16)
Yellow	.087 (2.21)
Green	.090 (2.29)
White	.093 (2.36)

3) Check 3rd gear end play using a feeler gauge. Specified end play is .002-.008" (.04-.20 mm). *See Fig. 5.* If end play is not to specifications, check conical part of 3rd gear and conical part of 3rd-4th synchro assembly for wear. Replace components as necessary.

4) Install needle bearing, 2nd gear, synchro assembly, bearing sleeve, needle bearing, 1st gear and bearing spacer onto rear of mainshaft. Press bearing spacer forward and check end play of 2nd and 1st gears. End play should be .002-.008" (.04-.20 mm). *See Fig. 7.*

INPUT SHAFT
Disassembly, Cleaning & Inspection
1) Check front end outside and inside diameter of needle bearing area for damage or wear. Check synchro conical surface for wear or damage. Check gear and splines for damage or wear.

2) Rotate input shaft ball bearing and check for noise or roughness. Replace bearing, if necessary, using Bearing Puller (MD998056). Check conical surface of gear for wear or damage.

Reassembly
To install input shaft ball bearing, use Bearing Installer (MD998029). Then install selective fit snap ring to obtain clearance between snap ring and bearing of 0-.002" (0-.05 mm). See INPUT SHAFT SNAP RING chart.

Fig. 6: Correct Position and Assembly of Synchronizer Assembly Components

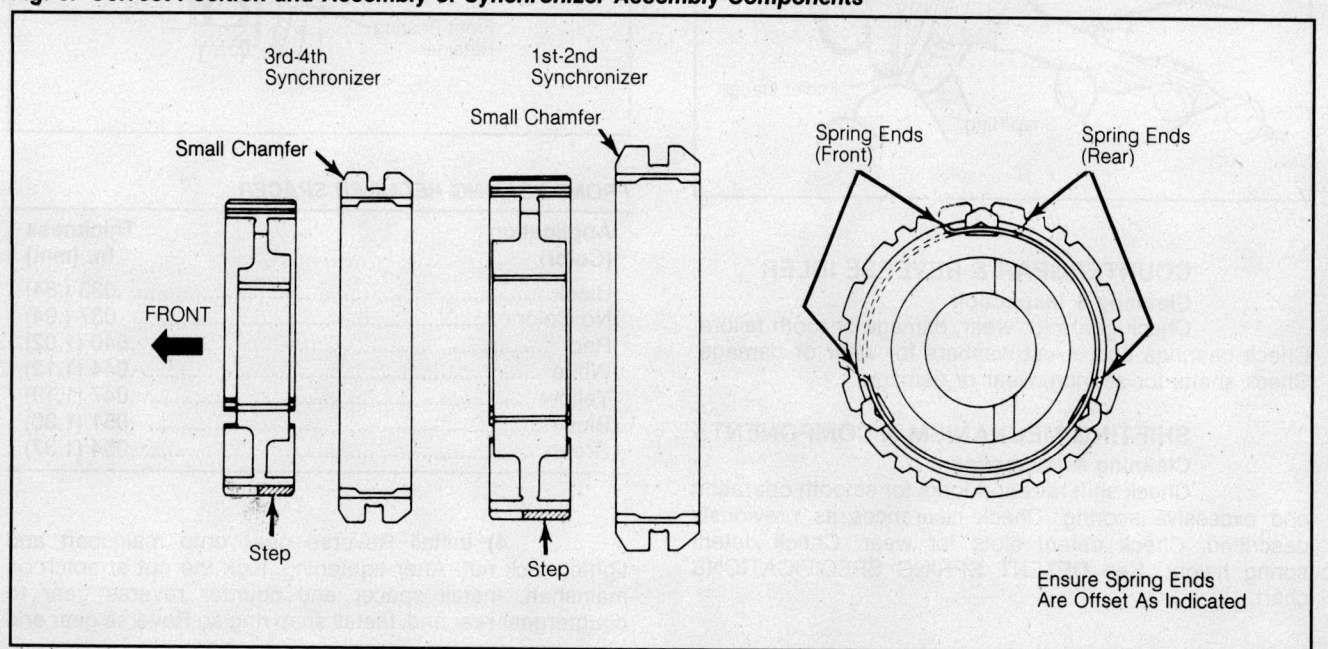

7-34

Manual Transmissions
CHRYSLER CORP. IMPORTS & MITSUBISHI KM 130/144 4-SPEED (Cont.)

Fig. 7: Checking 1st-2nd Gear End Play

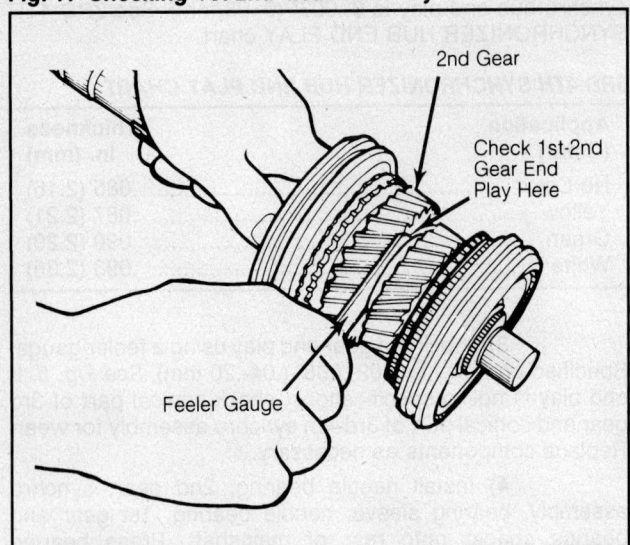

2nd Gear

Check 1st-2nd Gear End Play Here

Feeler Gauge

INPUT SHAFT SNAP RING

Application (Color)	Thickness In. (mm)
No Color	.091 (2.30)
Red	.092 (2.35)
White	.094 (2.40)
Blue	.096 (2.45)
Green	.098 (2.50)

Fig. 8: Checking Input Shaft Bearing End Play

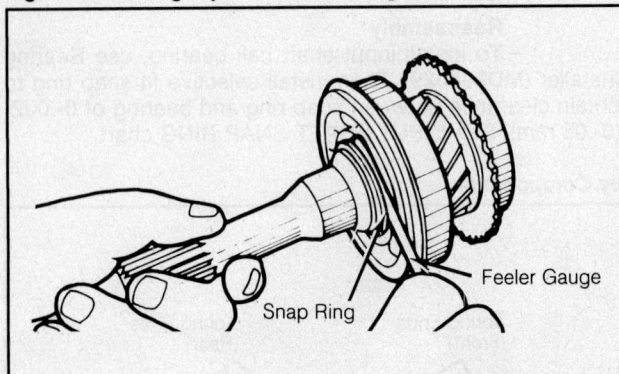

Snap Ring

Feeler Gauge

COUNTERGEAR & REVERSE IDLER
Cleaning & Inspection
Check gears for wear, damage or tooth failure. Check bearings and thrust washers for wear or damage. Check shafts for scoring, wear or damage.

SHIFTING MECHANISM & COMPONENTS
Cleaning & Inspection
Check shift rails and forks for smooth operation and excessive scoring. Check clearances as previously described. Check detent slots for wear. Check detent spring height. See DETENT SPRING SPECIFICATIONS chart.

DETENT SPRING SPECIFICATIONS

Application	In. (mm)
Free Length	.744 (18.9)
Compressed Length @ 8.8 Lbs. (4 kg)	.598 (15.2)

TRANSMISSION REASSEMBLY

1) Insert mainshaft assembly into transmission case and drive mainshaft center bearing in using Bearing Installer (MD998067). Install needle bearing and synchro ring, then insert input shaft into front of transmission case.

2) Insert countergear into transmission case. Install snap ring to countergear front bearing, then drive bearing into case by hammering on outer race with mallet. Install snap ring to countergear rear bearing, then install into place with Bearing Installer (MD998199).

3) Install front bearing retainer with spacer to obtain clearance of 0-.004" (0-.1 mm). See Fig. 9 and FRONT BEARING RETAINER SPACER chart. Coat both sides of front bearing retainer packing with sealant. Apply gear oil to lip of seal. Install packing and oil seal. Install rear bearing retainer and tighten screws. Stake screws with punch.

Fig. 9: Front Bearing-to-Retainer Clearance Measurement

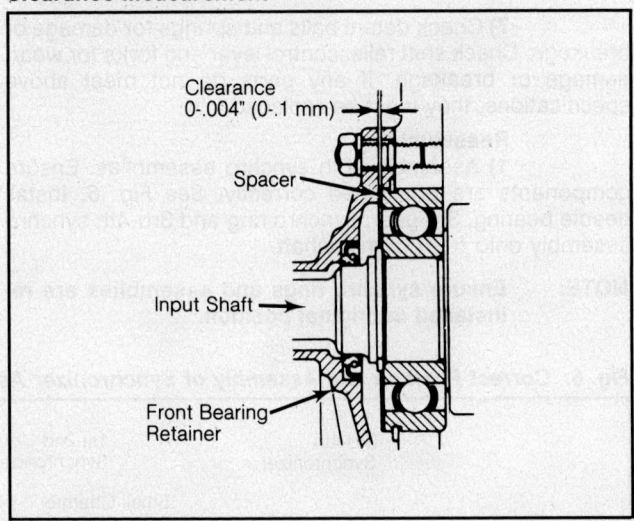

Clearance 0-.004" (0-.1 mm)

Spacer

Input Shaft

Front Bearing Retainer

FRONT BEARING RETAINER SPACER

Application (Color)	Thickness In. (mm)
Black	.033 (.84)
No Color	.037 (.94)
Red	.040 (1.02)
White	.044 (1.12)
Yellow	.047 (1.19)
Blue	.051 (1.30)
Green	.054 (1.37)

4) Install Reverse gear onto mainshaft and tighten lock nut. After tightening, lock the nut at notch on mainshaft. Install spacer and counter reverse gear to countergear rear end. Install snap ring so Reverse gear end

CHRYSLER CORP. IMPORTS & MITSUBISHI KM 130/144 4-SPEED (Cont.)

Fig. 10: Exploded View of Chrysler Corp. KM130 4-Speed Transmission

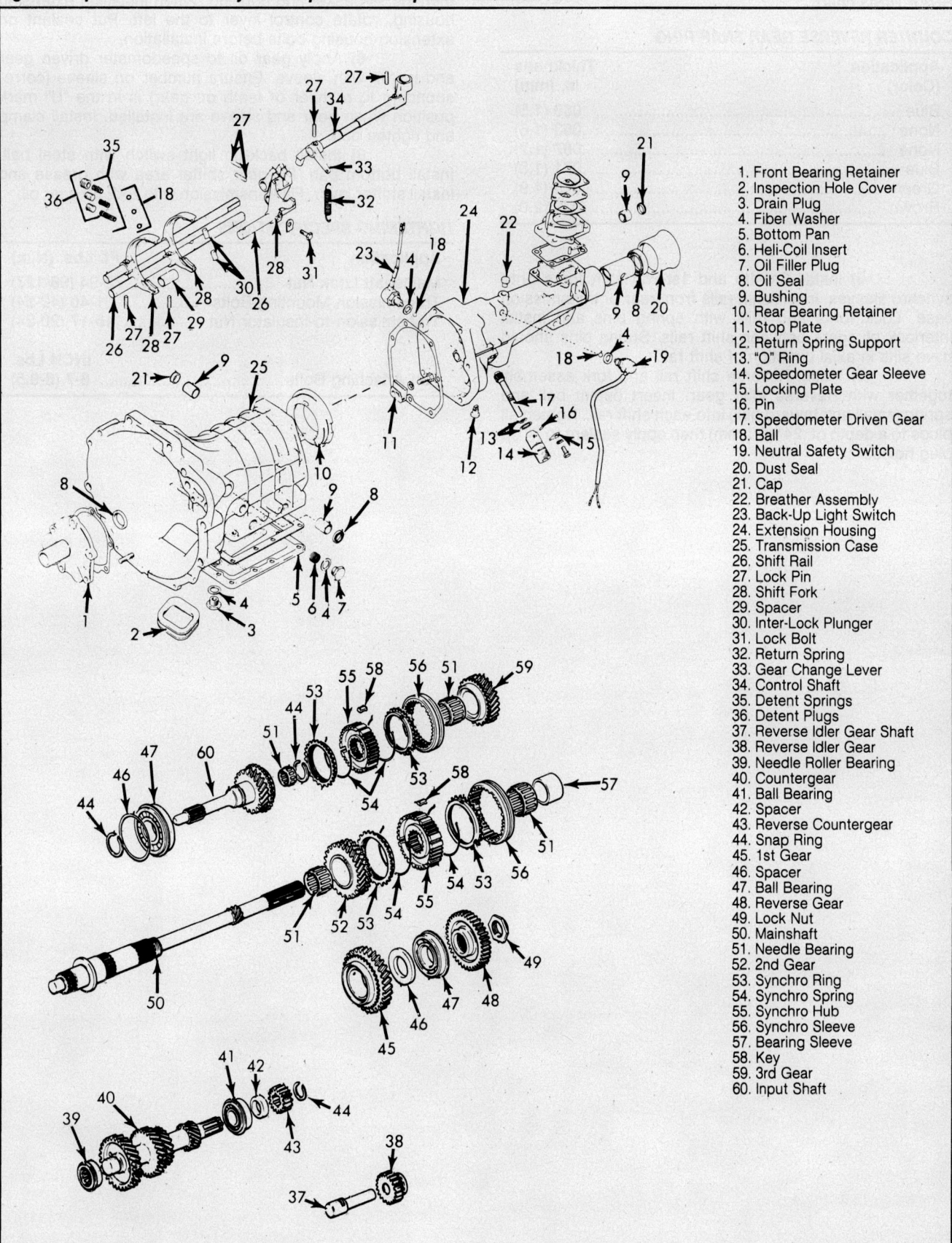

1. Front Bearing Retainer
2. Inspection Hole Cover
3. Drain Plug
4. Fiber Washer
5. Bottom Pan
6. Heli-Coil Insert
7. Oil Filler Plug
8. Oil Seal
9. Bushing
10. Rear Bearing Retainer
11. Stop Plate
12. Return Spring Support
13. "O" Ring
14. Speedometer Gear Sleeve
15. Locking Plate
16. Pin
17. Speedometer Driven Gear
18. Ball
19. Neutral Safety Switch
20. Dust Seal
21. Cap
22. Breather Assembly
23. Back-Up Light Switch
24. Extension Housing
25. Transmission Case
26. Shift Rail
27. Lock Pin
28. Shift Fork
29. Spacer
30. Inter-Lock Plunger
31. Lock Bolt
32. Return Spring
33. Gear Change Lever
34. Control Shaft
35. Detent Springs
36. Detent Plugs
37. Reverse Idler Gear Shaft
38. Reverse Idler Gear
39. Needle Roller Bearing
40. Countergear
41. Ball Bearing
42. Spacer
43. Reverse Countergear
44. Snap Ring
45. 1st Gear
46. Spacer
47. Ball Bearing
48. Reverse Gear
49. Lock Nut
50. Mainshaft
51. Needle Bearing
52. 2nd Gear
53. Synchro Ring
54. Synchro Spring
55. Synchro Hub
56. Synchro Sleeve
57. Bearing Sleeve
58. Key
59. 3rd Gear
60. Input Shaft

Manual Transmissions
CHRYSLER CORP. IMPORTS & MITSUBISHI KM 130/144
4-SPEED (Cont.)

play is 0-.003" (0-.07 mm). See COUNTER REVERSE GEAR SNAP RING chart.

COUNTER REVERSE GEAR SNAP RING

Application (Color)	Thickness In. (mm)
Blue	.059 (1.5)
None	.063 (1.6)
None	.067 (1.7)
Blue	.071 (1.8)
Green	.075 (1.9)
Brown	.079 (2.0)

5) Install 3rd-4th and 1st-2nd shift forks onto synchro sleeves. Insert shift rails from rear of transmission case. Lock forks and rails with spring pins and install interlock plungers between shift rails. Spring pins should have slits in axial direction of shift rail.

6) Install Reverse shift rail and fork assembly together with Reverse idler gear. Insert detent ball and spring (small end toward ball) into each shift rail. Tighten all plugs to a depth of .24" (6.1 mm) then apply sealant to fill up plug holes.

7) Apply sealant to extension housing gasket, then install gasket and housing. When installing extension housing, rotate control lever to the left. Put sealant on extension housing bolts before installation.

8) Apply gear oil to speedometer driven gear and install with sleeve. Ensure number on sleeve (corresponding to number of teeth on gear) is in the "U" mark position when gear and sleeve are installed. Install clamp and tighten bolt.

9) Install back-up light switch with steel ball. Install bottom pan. Fill gear shifter area with grease and install shifter lever. Fill transmission with SAE 80 gear oil.

TIGHTENING SPECIFICATIONS

Application	Ft. Lbs. (N.m)
Mainshaft Lock Nut	72-94 (98-127)
Transmission Mounting Bolts	31-40 (42-54)
Transmission-to-Insulator Nut	15-17 (20-24)

	INCH Lbs.
Pan Attaching Bolts	6-7 (8-9.5)

CHRYSLER CORP. IMPORTS & MITSUBISHI KM 132/145
5-SPEED

Chrysler Corp. Conquest, Ram-50 Pickup
Mitsubishi Montero, Pickup & Starion

IDENTIFICATION

Transmission may be identified by a serial number stamped on clutch housing.

DESCRIPTION

The models KM 132 (2WD) and KM 145 (4WD) transmissions are 5-speed fully synchronized type with constant mesh in all forward gears. Forward gears are helical type. Reverse gear is a non-synchronized spur type. First through 3rd gears are located in transmission case, 4th gear is direct, 5th and reverse gears are located in the extension housing (2WD). Shift lever assembly is located on the top of extension housing or transfer case.

LUBRICATION & ADJUSTMENT

See appropriate MANUAL TRANSMISSION SERVICING article in IMPORT GENERAL SERVICING section.

TROUBLE SHOOTING

DIFFICULTY MESHING GEARS

Malfunction of gearshift lever or control shaft. Synchro rings or gear coned surfaces worn or excessive play. Synchro shift keys worn or damaged.

JUMPS OUT OF GEAR

Shifting forks worn or detent springs broken. Mainshaft or mainshaft support bearings worn or damaged. Clearance between synchro hub and sleeve excessive. Gears or gear bushings worn. Countergear worn.

NOISE IN TRANSMISSION

Lubricating oil incorrect or insufficient. Gears or bearings worn. Mainshaft spline worn or damaged.

REMOVAL & INSTALLATION

TRANSMISSION

See appropriate MANUAL TRANSMISSION REMOVAL article in IMPORT GENERAL SERVICING section. On 4WD models, transfer case may be removed with or without transmission assembly.

TRANSMISSION DISASSEMBLY

1) To remove transfer case assembly on 4WD models, complete the following: Remove back-up light switch and steel ball from lower right adapter. Remove plug from right side of transfer case. Remove select spring and select plunger. Remove 6 bolts securing transmission and transfer case control lever assembly.

2) Remove control lever and gasket. Remove plugs from top of adapter and remove detent spring and ball, and neutral return springs and plungers. Use a pin punch and remove change shifter lock pin.

3) Remove transfer case-to-adapter nuts and bolts, and remove transfer case. To disassemble transfer case, see appropriate TRANSFER CASE article in IMPORT TRANSFER CASE section.

4) On all models, remove return clip, then clutch release bearing and carrier. Using a 3/16" (4.76 mm) punch, drive roll pin from clutch release shaft. See Fig. 1. Remove shaft, felt, return spring(s) and clutch release arm. Remove bottom pan from transmission case.

Fig. 1: Removing Roll Pin From Clutch Release Shaft

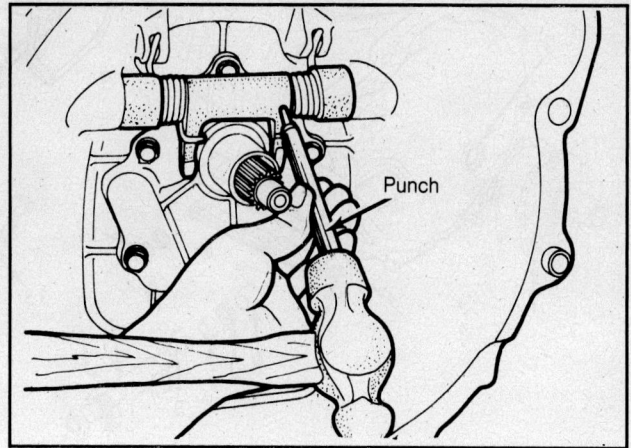

Punch

5) On Starion and Conquest models, remove control lever assembly. Remove resistance spring and ball from extension housing. Remove both neutral return plunger plugs, springs and plungers. See Fig. 11. Remove back-up light switch and steel ball.

6) Remove speedometer sleeve clamp and remove speedometer sleeve assembly. Remove extension housing mounting bolts. Push change shifter down to the left to move control finger from selector grooves.

7) On all other models, remove extension housing bolts. Loosen neutral return plunger plug "B". Rotate change shifter to the left. See Fig. 2.

Fig. 2: Separating Extension Housing From Transmission

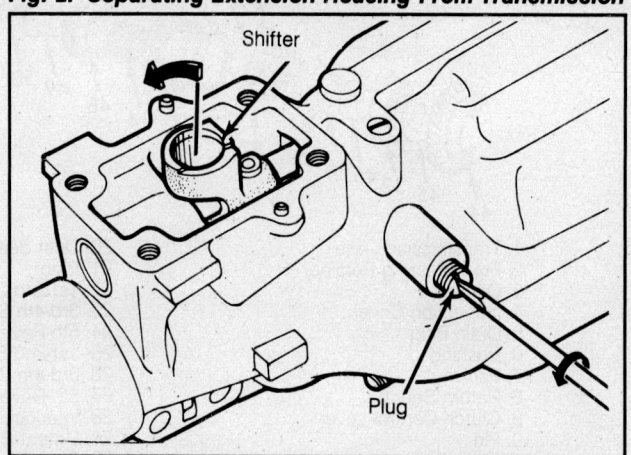

Shifter

Plug

8) On all models, slide extension housing from transmission case and mainshaft. On Pickup and Montero models, remove snap ring and ball bearing from rear end of mainshaft. Remove 3 detent spring plugs, springs and balls.

7-38

Manual Transmissions
CHRYSLER CORP. IMPORTS & MITSUBISHI KM 132/145
5-SPEED (Cont.)

Fig. 3: Exploded View of Chrysler Corp. KM132 5-Speed Transmission Assembly

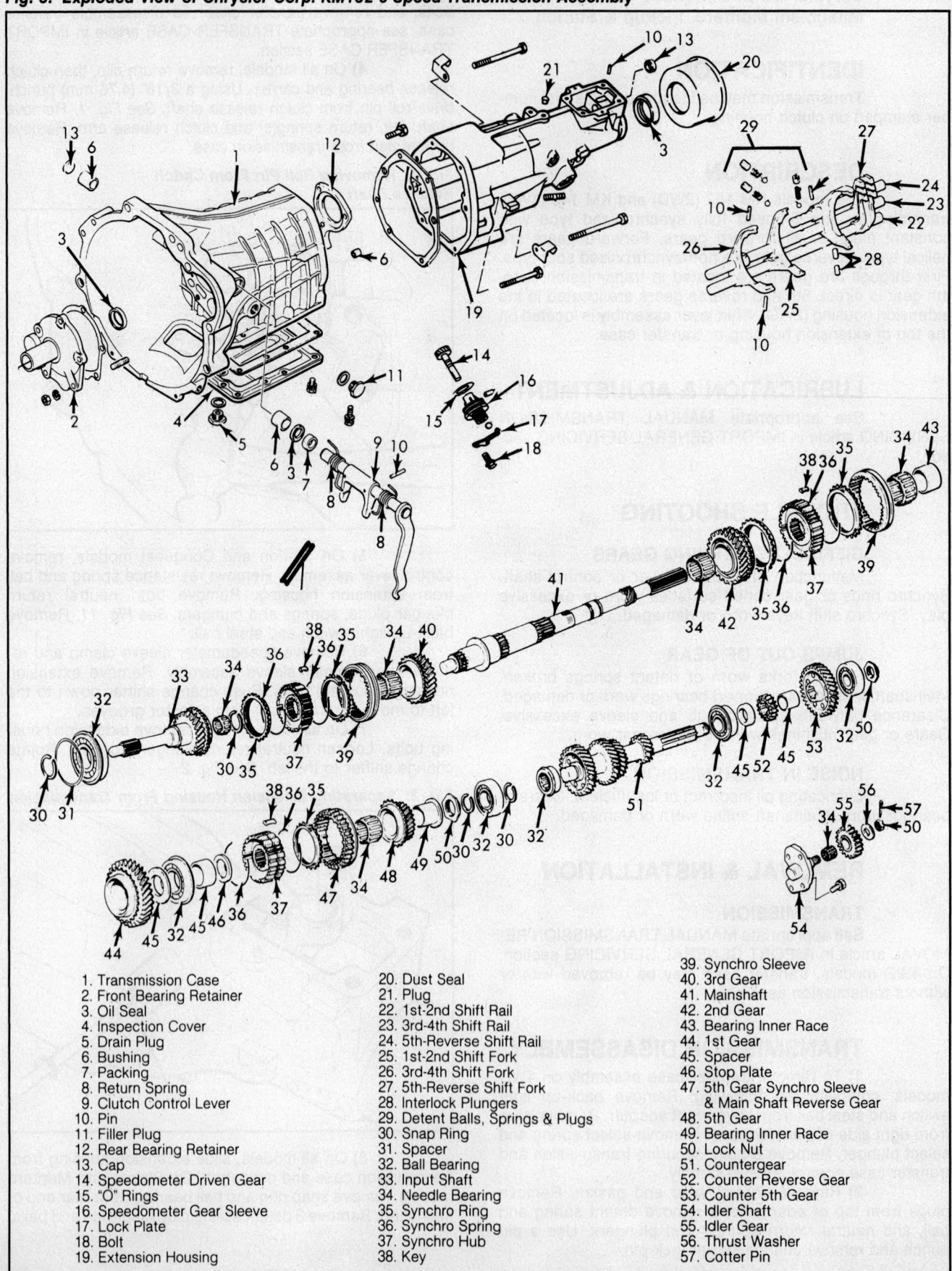

1. Transmission Case	20. Dust Seal	39. Synchro Sleeve
2. Front Bearing Retainer	21. Plug	40. 3rd Gear
3. Oil Seal	22. 1st-2nd Shift Rail	41. Mainshaft
4. Inspection Cover	23. 3rd-4th Shift Rail	42. 2nd Gear
5. Drain Plug	24. 5th-Reverse Shift Rail	43. Bearing Inner Race
6. Bushing	25. 1st-2nd Shift Fork	44. 1st Gear
7. Packing	26. 3rd-4th Shift Fork	45. Spacer
8. Return Spring	27. 5th-Reverse Shift Fork	46. Stop Plate
9. Clutch Control Lever	28. Interlock Plungers	47. 5th Gear Synchro Sleeve
10. Pin	29. Detent Balls, Springs & Plugs	& Main Shaft Reverse Gear
11. Filler Plug	30. Snap Ring	48. 5th Gear
12. Rear Bearing Retainer	31. Spacer	49. Bearing Inner Race
13. Cap	32. Ball Bearing	50. Lock Nut
14. Speedometer Driven Gear	33. Input Shaft	51. Countergear
15. "O" Rings	34. Needle Bearing	52. Counter Reverse Gear
16. Speedometer Gear Sleeve	35. Synchro Ring	53. Counter 5th Gear
17. Lock Plate	36. Synchro Spring	54. Idler Shaft
18. Bolt	37. Synchro Hub	55. Idler Gear
19. Extension Housing	38. Key	56. Thrust Washer
		57. Cotter Pin

Manual Transmissions

7-39

CHRYSLER CORP. IMPORTS & MITSUBISHI KM 132/145
5-SPEED (Cont.)

9) On all models, using a 3/16" (4.76 mm) punch, drive 3rd-4th and 1st-2nd roll pins from shift forks. Remove 5th-reverse roll pin. On Pickup and Montero models, remove shift rails and forks. *See Fig. 4.*

Fig. 4: Driving Out 5th-Reverse Roll Pin

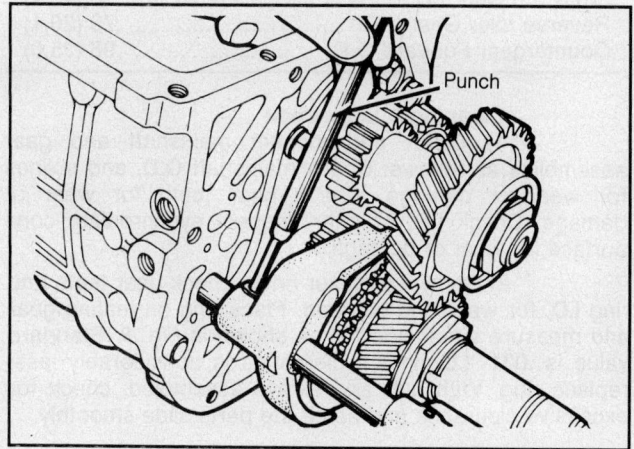

10) On all models, place transmission with front side down. Remove mainshaft rear bearing and snap rings. Bend back mainshaft and countershaft lock washer tabs. Loosen mainshaft and countershaft nuts. (Nuts can be loosened by double-engaging 2nd and reverse gears to lock mainshaft and countergear).

11) Remove detent plugs, springs and balls. Using a puller, remove countergear 5th gear and ball bearing. *See Fig. 5.* Remove gear, bearing and 1-2 shift rail at same time. Remove spacers and reverse gear from countergear.

Fig. 5: Pulling 5th Gear & Bearing From Countergear

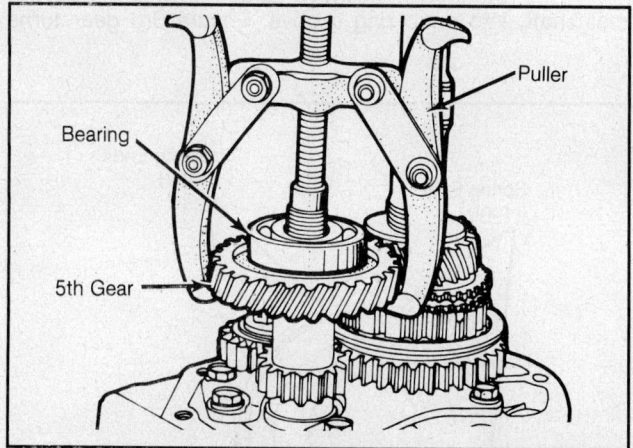

12) Remove 3-4 shift rail toward rear of case. Remove 5th-reverse shift rail and shift fork. Remove spacer, steel ball, 5th gear, needle bearing and bearing spacer from mainshaft. Remove bearing sleeve, 5th gear synchronizer assembly, stopper plate and spacer from mainshaft.

13) On Pickup and Montero models, remove synchronizer hub and 5th gear bearing sleeve using Bearing Puller (MD998056) and Adapter (MB998056-10). Remove synchronizer key, stop plate and distance spacer

from mainshaft. Remove roll pin from reverse idler gear shaft.

14) On all models, remove reverse idler gear shaft locking nut. Remove thrust washer, reverse idler gear and needle bearing. Remove reverse idler gear shaft retaining bolts. Working from inside case, use a punch to drive reverse idler shaft from case. *See Fig. 6.*

Fig. 6: Driving Reverse Idler Shaft From Transmission Case

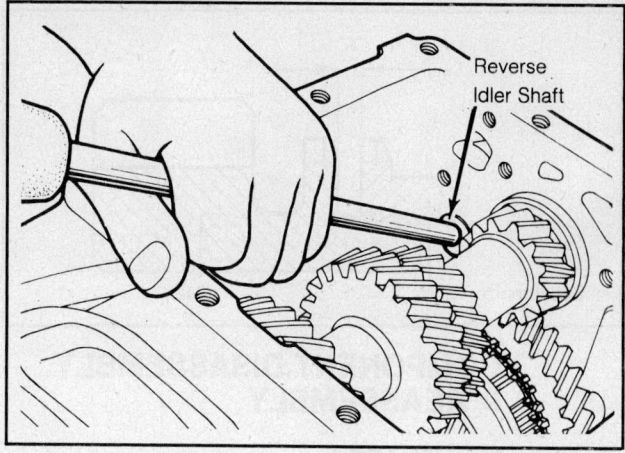

15) Remove rear bearing retainer from case. Remove front bearing retainer from case. On Pickup and Montero models, remove main drive gear and main drive gear bearing snap rings. Remove main drive gear bearing using Bearing Puller (MB998056).

16) On all models, remove mainshaft center bearing snap ring. Remove mainshaft center bearing using Bearing Puller (MB998020) and Adapter (MB998028). Remove countergear front and rear bearing outer races from case.

17) Pull countergear up in case and remove main drive gear with bearing toward front of case. Remove countergear from transmission case. Remove shift forks from mainshaft. Remove mainshaft from transmission case.

18) Remove mainshaft bearing snap ring and pull bearing from case and shaft, then remove mainshaft assembly from case. *See Fig. 7.*

Fig. 7: Pulling Mainshaft Bearing From Transmission Case

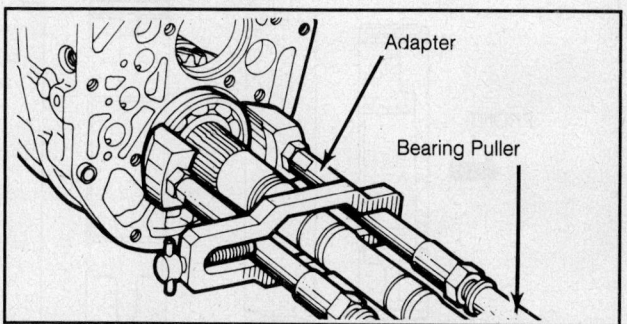

CLEANING & INSPECTION

1) All parts should be thoroughly washed in cleaning solvent and air dried. Remove old gaskets with stiff brush or scraper. Rinse bearings in clean solvent and air dry. DO NOT spin bearings dry.

7-40

Manual Transmissions
CHRYSLER CORP. IMPORTS & MITSUBISHI KM 132/145 5-SPEED (Cont.)

2) Lubricate with light grade oil and wrap in clean paper until ready to install. Examine all gear teeth and splines for chips, wear, breaks or nicks. Check transmission case and extension housing for cracks and damage.

3) Check bearings and synchronizers for wear, damage and proper fit. Lubricate all moving parts before installation. Use new gaskets, seals and snap rings.

Fig. 8: Measuring Synchronizer Ring-to-Gear Clearance

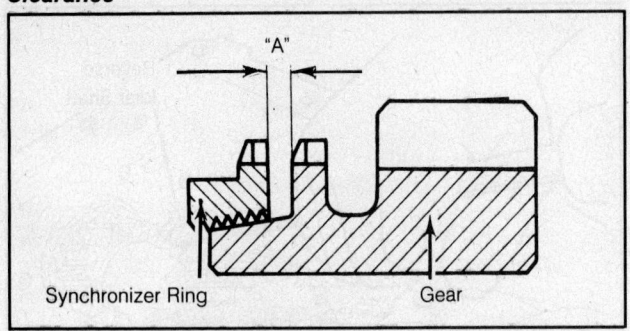

Synchronizer Ring   Gear

COMPONENT DISASSEMBLY & REASSEMBLY

MAINSHAFT
Disassembly
1) On Pickup models, support 2nd gear on press plate. Press bearing inner race, gear bearing sleeve, 1st gear, 1st-2nd synchronizer and 2nd gear from rear of mainshaft. Remove snap ring from front end of mainshaft. Remove 3rd-4th synchronizer, 3rd gear and needle bearing.

2) Remove 1st gear and inner race of double row bearing using bearing puller. Remove 1st-2nd synchronizer and 2nd gear off rear of mainshaft. Remove snap ring from forward end of mainshaft. Slide 3rd-4th synchronizer and 3rd gear from mainshaft.

TRANSMISSION GEAR STANDARD DIMENSIONS

Application	Specification In. (mm)
1st & 2nd Gear I.D.	1.89 (48.0)
3rd & 5th Gear I.D.	1.58 (40.1)
Reverse Idler Gear I. D.	.79 (20.1)
Countergear Forward O.D.	.98 (25.0)

Cleaning & Inspection
1) Clean and inspect mainshaft and gear assemblies as follows: Check mainshaft O.D. and splines for wear or damage. Check gear teeth for wear or damage. Check I.D. of gear. Inspect synchronizer cone surface for wear or damage.

2) On synchronizer rings, check gear teeth and ring I.D. for wear and damage. Place ring on mating gear and measure dimension "A" as shown in *Fig. 8*. Standard value is .031" (.8 mm). If clearance is considerably less, replace ring. With hub and sleeve assembled, check for excessive clearance and see if the parts slide smoothly.

NOTE: **If sleeve or hub need replacing, always replace them as an assembly. Check shift fork groove in sleeve for wear.**

Reassembly
1) Assemble 1st-2nd and 3rd-4th synchronizers. *See Fig. 9.* Place needle bearing, 3rd gear, synchronizer ring and 3rd-4th synchronizer assembly on front of mainshaft.

2) Synchronizer sleeve has a tooth missing in 3 or 6 positions. Assemble hub to sleeve so that center tooth between 2 missing teeth will touch synchronizer key. Install 1st-2nd synchronizer hub and sleeve. Ensure synchronizer hub and sleeve are reinstalled in original directions.

3) Install thickest snap ring on front of mainshaft, into snap ring groove. Ensure 3rd gear turns

Fig. 9: Synchronizer Assembly and Spring Location

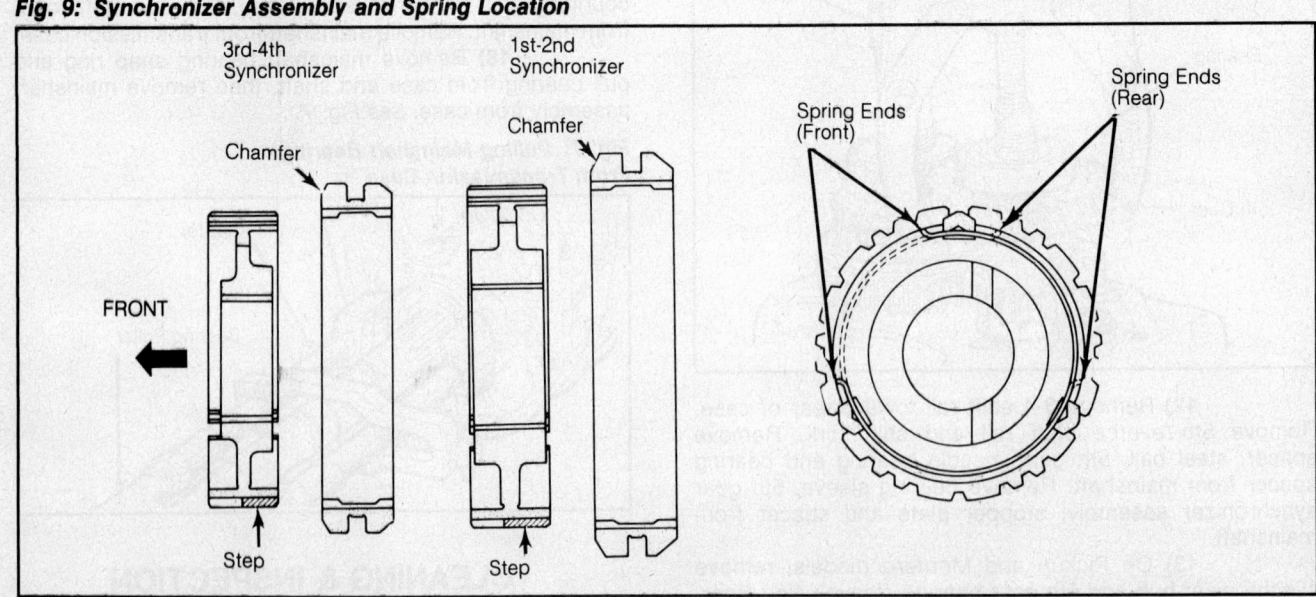

Manual Transmissions
CHRYSLER CORP. IMPORTS & MITSUBISHI KM 132/145
5-SPEED (Cont.)

7-41

smoothly. Install 1st-2nd synchronizer hub and sleeve. Ensure synchronizer hub and sleeve are reinstalled in original directions.

Fig. 10: Measuring Synchronizer Hub End Play

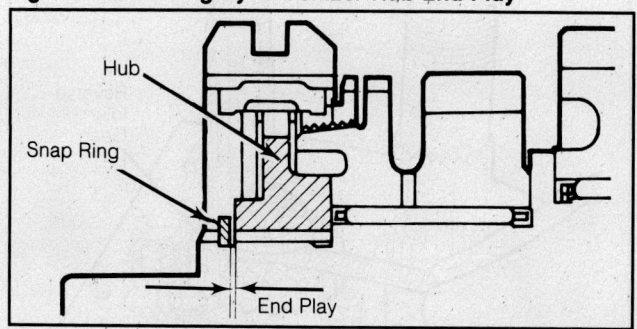

4) Place needle bearing, 2nd gear, synchronizer assembly, synchronizer ring, bearing sleeve, needle bearing, 1st gear and bearing spacer on mainshaft from rear. Pressing forward with bearing spacer, measure 1st and 2nd gear end play. End play should be the same as shown in table.

SYNCHRONIZER SNAP RING END PLAY

Application	Clearance In. (mm)
1st & 2nd Gear End Play	.002-.008 (.05-.2)
3rd Gear End Play	.002-.008 (.05-.2)
3rd & 4th Synchronizer Hub End Play	0-.003 (0-.08)

NOTE: Synchronizer snap rings are available in different sizes, from .085" (2.15 mm) to .093" (2.36 mm).

INPUT SHAFT/PINION GEAR
Disassembly

Remove main drive gear and bearing snap rings. Remove bearing from main drive gear using Bearing Puller (MB998020).

Inspection

Check O.D. of forward end and I.D. of rear end of input shaft. Inspect tapered synchronizer surface, gear teeth and clutch disc splines for wear or damage.

INPUT SHAFT STANDARD DIMENSIONS

Application	Specification In. (mm)
O.D. of Forward End	.59 (14.9)
I.D. of Rear End	1.02 (25.9)

Reassembly

Press ball bearing onto input shaft using Bearing Installer (MD998029). Install thickest main drive gear snap ring that will fit in snap ring groove.

REVERSE IDLER SHAFT
Inspection

Check shaft O.D. for wear or damage. O.D. should be .63" (16.0 mm).

SHIFTING MECHANISMS
Inspection

Check shift fork ends for wear or damage. Check each shift rail for warpage and detent ball slot for wear. Check forward end of control finger and shift lug groove for wear. Replace any worn or damaged parts.

SHIFT MECHANISM STANDARD DIMENSIONS

Application	Specification In. (mm)
Shift Fork, Sleeve Groove	.197 (5.00)
Shift Fork-to-Sleeve	.004-.012 (.1-.3)
Shift Fork-to-Sleeve (5th Gear)	.006-.014 (.15-.36)
Warpage of Shift Rail	.0016 (.04) Max.
Control Finger-to-Shift Lug	.004-.012 (.1-.3)
Detent Spring Length	.744 (18.90)

EXTENSION HOUSING
Disassembly

1) Remove locking plate and speedometer driven gear. Remove 3 screw plugs, springs, neutral return plungers ("A" and "B") and detent balls from housing. *See Fig. 11.*

2) Press gear shifter all the way forward in housing. Using a 3/16" (4.76 mm) punch, drive roll pin from shifter. Separate shifter and control shaft by pulling shaft out front of housing.

Inspection

Inspect forward end of neutral return plunger and detent ball slot for wear. Check neutral return springs and detent spring for collapsing or beakage. Length of neutral return springs is 1.64" (41.6 mm) and detent spring is 1.09" (27.7 mm).

Fig. 11: Removing Neutral Return Plungers From Extension Housing

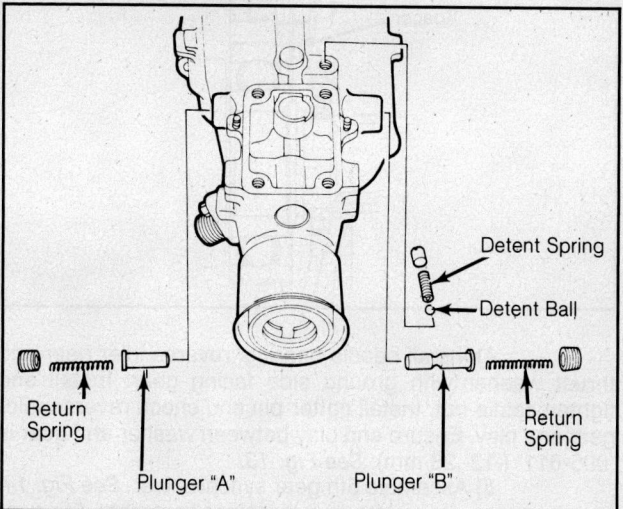

Reassembly

See TRANSMISSION REASSEMBLY in this article for extension housing reassembly.

Manual Transmissions
CHRYSLER CORP. IMPORTS & MITSUBISHI KM 132/145 5-SPEED (Cont.)

TRANSMISSION REASSEMBLY

NOTE: Replace all gaskets, seals and roll pins with new ones. Oil all rolling or sliding parts and grease seal lips before reassembly.

1) Place mainshaft assembly into transmission case. Install needle bearing on front end of mainshaft. Install synchronizer, then slide input shaft/pinion gear assembly into transmission case with needle bearing engaging end of mainshaft. Install 1st-2nd and 3rd-4th shift forks in synchronizer sleeve grooves.

2) Position countergear into case. Install respective snap rings on front needle bearing and rear ball bearing. Drive needle bearing and ball bearing into case. Install front bearing retainer with a bearing spacer which will give a clearance of 0-.004" (0-.1 mm) at dimension "C" See Fig. 12. Apply sealer to both sides of gasket.

FRONT BEARING RETAINER SPACER SIZES

Identification Color	Thickness In. (mm)
Black	.033 (.84)
No Color	.037 (.94)
Red	.040 (1.0)
White	.044 (1.1)
Yellow	.047 (1.2)
Blue	.051 (1.3)
Green	.054 (1.4)

3) Install rear bearing retainer. Place reverse idler shaft into position and install bolts to act as guides. Using a large drift, drive reverse idler shaft into case.

Fig. 12: Retainer-to-Bearing Clearance Measurement

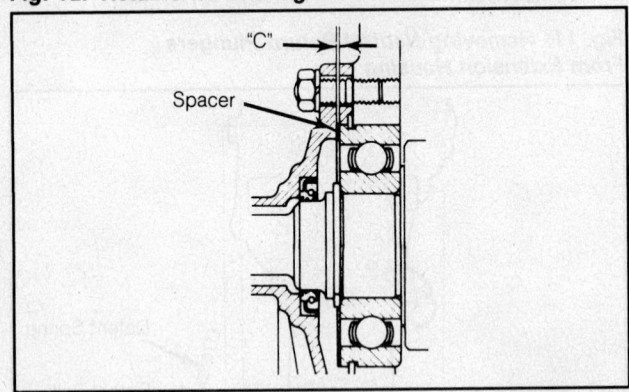

4) Install needle bearing, reverse idler gear and thrust washer with ground side facing gear. Install and tighten castle nut. Install cotter pin and check reverse idler gear end play. Ensure end play between washer and gear is .005-011" (.12-.28 mm). See Fig. 13.

5) Assemble 5th gear synchronizer. See Fig. 14. Install spacer, stop plate, synchronizer assembly, 5th gear bearing sleeve, needle bearing, synchronizer ring and 5th gear onto mainshaft from the rear end. Install and tighten lock nut, staking it at a notch in mainshaft.

6) End play measured between 5th gear and lock nut should be .004-.010" (.10-.25 mm). Install spacer, counter reverse gear, spacer, 5th countergear and ball

Fig. 13: Using a Feeler Gauge to Check Reverse Idler Gear End Play

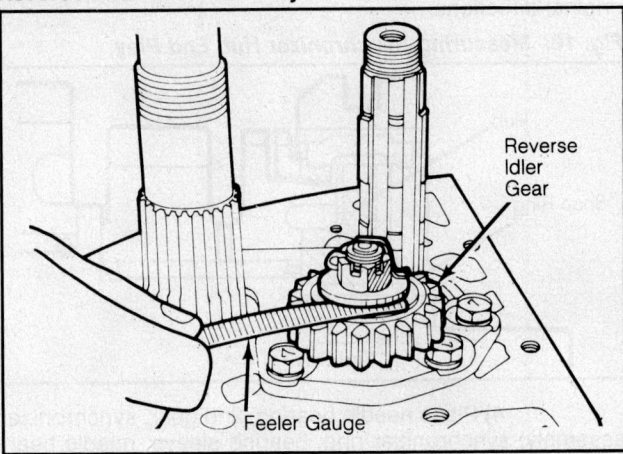

bearing onto countershaft gear from rear end. Tighten lock nut and stake into notch at rear end of countergear.

7) Insert 1st-2nd and 3rd-4th shift forks in their respective synchronizer sleeves. Slide shift rails into position and install shift fork roll pin. Install interlock plunger between shift rails.

Fig. 14: 5th Gear Synchronizer Assembly

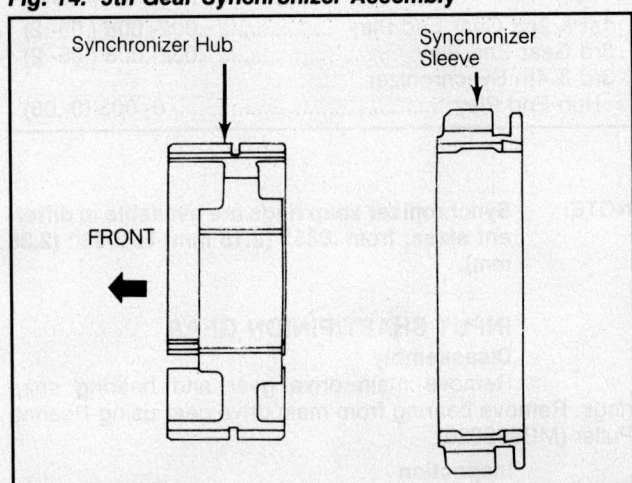

8) Install all 3 detent balls and springs with small end of spring facing ball. Screw detent plugs approximately .24" (6.1 mm) into case and apply sealer to head of plugs. See Fig. 15.

9) Install snap ring in forward groove of mainshaft. Install bearing retaining snap ring. Install speedometer gear snap ring and speedometer gear. Apply sealer to both sides of extension housing gasket and position on housing.

10) While holding shifter fully to the left, slide housing onto mainshaft. Ensure forward end of control finger is snugly fitted in slot of shift lug. Apply sealer to threads of attaching bolts and tighten bolts.

11) Install neutral return plungers "A" and "B", springs and plugs. Then install detent ball, spring and plug. Screw all plugs flush with housing and apply sealer to head of plugs. See Fig. 16.

12) Using sealer, install speedometer drive lock plate. Place steel ball in position and screw back-up light switch into housing. Install bottom pan and gasket.

Manual Transmissions
CHRYSLER CORP. IMPORTS & MITSUBISHI KM 132/145
5-SPEED (Cont.)

7-43

Fig. 15: Installing Detent Balls, Springs & Plugs

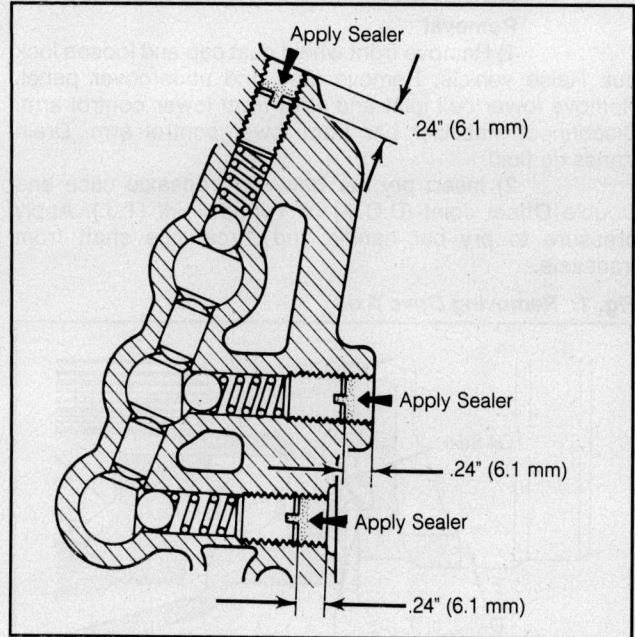

Fig. 16: Installing Neutral Return Plungers

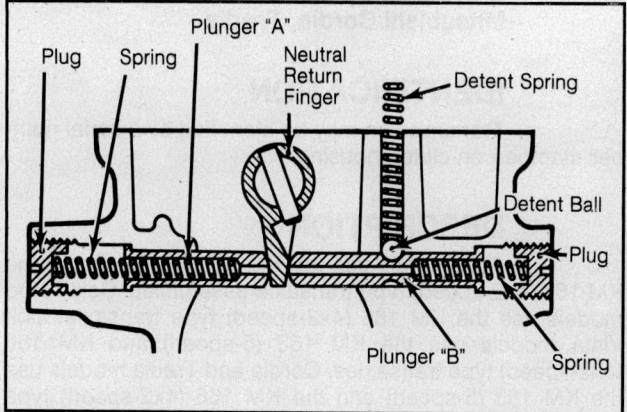

13) Install stopper bracket assembly to extension housing cover. Ensure reverse resistance plate moves smoothly on bracket. Install extension housing cover on extension housing.

TIGHTENING SPECIFICATIONS

Application	Ft. Lbs. (N.m)
Transmission Case-to-Engine Bolts	22-30 (30-41)
Countergear Lock Nut	50-72 (68-98)
Idler Shaft Lock Nut	15-43 (20-58)
Mainshaft Lock Nut	72-94 (98-128)

Manual Transmissions
CHRYSLER CORP. IMPORTS & MITSUBISHI 160 SERIES; 4x2, 4 & 5-SPEED TRANSAXLES

Chrysler Corp. Colt, Colt Vista
Mitsubishi Cordia, Tredia

IDENTIFICATION

Transmission may be identified by a serial number stamped on clutch housing.

DESCRIPTION

Colt models use the KM 160 (4-speed) and the KM 165 (4x2-speed) type transaxle assemblies. Colt Turbo models use the KM 166 (4x2-speed) type transaxle. Colt Vista models use the KM 163 (5-speed) and KM 166 (4x2-speed) type transaxles. Cordia and Tredia models use the KM 163 (5-speed) and the KM 166 (4x2-speed) type transaxles.

All transaxles are fully synchronized and incorporate an input shaft, intermediate shaft and output shaft. The major difference is that the KM 165 and KM 166 have a high and low gear on the input shaft which allows 2 speed ranges that can be selected. The differential assembly consists of a differential drive gear in mesh with output shaft gear, side gears and pinion gears.

LUBRICATION & ADJUSTMENT

See appropriate MANUAL TRANSMISSION SERVICING article in IMPORT GENERAL SERVICING section.

TROUBLE SHOOTING

DIFFICULTY MESHING GEARS

Malfunction of gearshift lever or control shaft. Synchro rings or gear conical surfaces worn or excessive play. Synchro shift keys worn or damaged.

JUMPS OUT OF GEAR

Shifting forks worn or detent springs broken. Mainshaft or mainshaft support bearings worn or damaged. Clearance between synchro hub and sleeve excessive. Gears or gear bushings worn. Countergear worn.

NOISE IN TRANSMISSION

Lubrication oil incorrect or insufficient. Gears or bearings worn. Mainshaft spline worn or damaged.

WILL NOT SHIFT TO 5TH

Malfunctioning actuator. Broken 5th position sensor. Malfunctioning vacuum control. Short circuit in vacuum control.

DELAYED 4-5 SHIFT

Worn 5th position sensor.

SERVICE (IN VEHICLE)

AXLE SHAFTS
Removal & Installation

To remove drive axle shafts, see WHEEL BEARING REMOVAL and INSTALLATION procedure in this article.

CONSTANT VELOCITY (CV) JOINTS
Removal

1) Remove front wheel dust cap and loosen lock nut. Raise vehicle. Remove tires and undercover panel. Remove lower ball joint and strut from lower control arm. Disconnect stabilizer bar from lower control arm. Drain transaxle fluid.

2) Insert pry bar between transaxle case and Double Offset Joint (D.O.J.) or Tripod Joint (T.J.). Apply pressure to pry bar handle and force axle shaft from transaxle.

Fig. 1: Removing Drive Axle

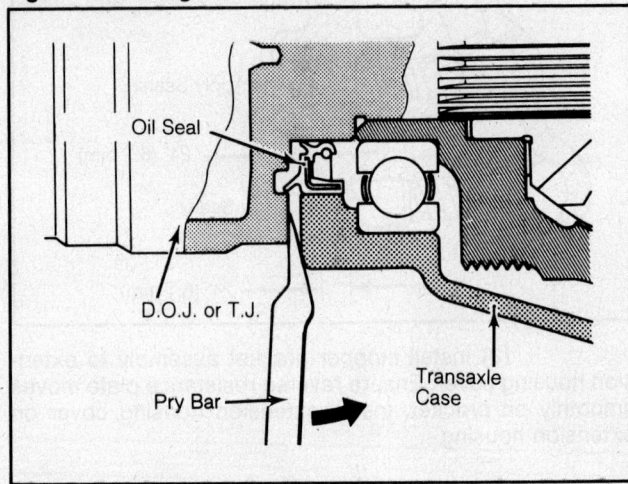

Installing pry bar too far will damage oil seal.

NOTE: Replace side retainer ring each time drive shaft is removed from transaxle case.

3) Force drive shaft out of hub with Axle Puller (CT-1003). When drive shaft is forced out, do not let spacer fall out of hub (inner side).

Disassembly
(Birfield-Double Offset Joint Type)

Remove inner joint boot. Remove circlip from joint and remove outer race. Remove snap ring and inner race. Remove cage and balls as an assembly.

NOTE: Do not disassemble inner bearing assembly as they are mated parts and should not be disturbed.

Reassembly

CAUTION: Drive shaft joint requires special grease. DO NOT use grease other than specified Multipurpose Grease (SAE J310a NLGI Grade 2 EP). Use of grease other than specified may cause premature CV joint failure.

To assemble, reverse disassembly procedure and note the following: Apply grease to inner and outer races. Install CV joint assembly on shaft with chamfered edge of inner race facing outer edge of shaft. Install new boots and place boot clamps 3.5" (90 mm) apart.

Disassembly (Tripod-Rzeppa Joint Type)

Remove inner joint boots. Pull drive shaft out from inner case. Remove snap ring and take out spider assembly. Clean, but do not disassemble spider assembly. Remove remaining boots.

CHRYSLER CORP. IMPORTS & MITSUBISHI 160 SERIES; 4x2, 4 & 5-SPEED TRANSAXLES (Cont.)

Fig. 2: Exploded View of Drive Shaft (Birfield-Double Offset Joint Type)

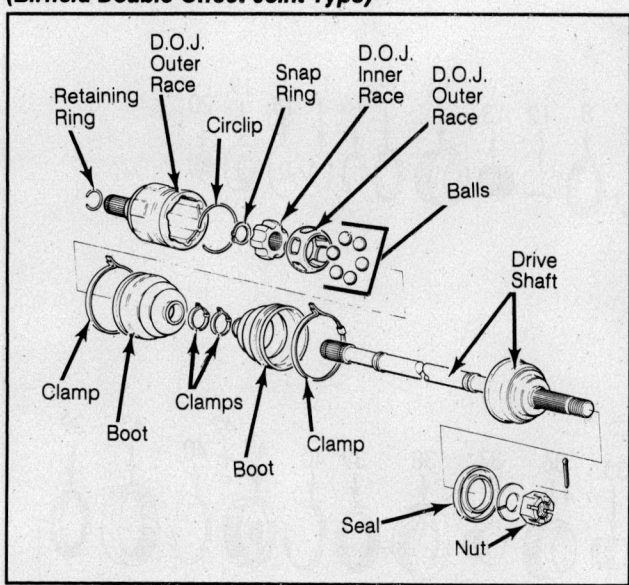

Fig. 3: Exploded View of Drive Shaft (Tripod-Rzeppa Joint Type)

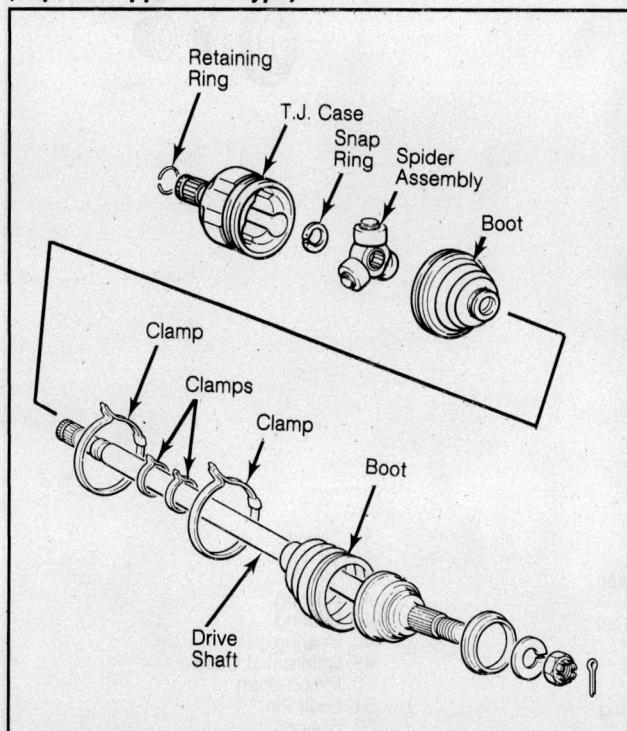

Reassembly

To assemble, reverse disassembly procedure and note the following: Apply grease to inner and outer races. Install new boots and place boot clamps 3.0" (75 mm) apart.

Installation

To install, reverse removal procedure and install a new side retainer ring.

WHEEL BEARINGS

Removal

1) Remove drive shaft and brake assembly from hub. Remove tie rod end from knuckle. Disconnect knuckle from strut. Remove hub and knuckle as an assembly.

2) Mount hub and knuckle assembly in a vise and drive hub from knuckle with soft hammer. Remove bearing spacer and brake disc. Using a hammer and drift, drive out inner and outer bearing races.

Installation

1) Drive outer races of inner and outer bearings into knuckle. Install Spacer Selection Gauge (MB990959) and dial indicator into hub assembly. Tighten nuts "A" and "B" finger tight.

2) Tighten nut "B" so gauge face contacts inside bearing inner race. Tighten nut "A" about 5 turns. Rotate gauge 10 times to seat bearing. Zero dial indicator.

3) Loosen nut "B" until pointer of dial indicator stops, and read dial indicator. Select proper size bearing spacer according to WHEEL BEARING SPACER SELECTION table.

WHEEL BEARING SPACER SELECTION

Dial Indicator Reading In. (mm)	Bearing Spacer Size In. (mm)	I.D. Color
.020-.023 (.52-.58)	.2236 (5.68)	Pink
.023-.025 (.58-.64)	.2260 (5.74)	Green
.025-.028 (.64-.70)	.2283 (5.80)	Red
.028-.030 (.70-.76)	.2307 (5.86)	White
.030-.032 (.76-.82)	.2330 (5.92)	None
.032-.035 (.82-.88)	.2354 (5.98)	Yellow
.035-.037 (.88-.94)	.2378 (6.04)	Blue
.037-.039 (.94-1.00)	.2402 (6.10)	Orange
.039-.042 (1.00-1.06)	.2425 (6.16)	Lt. Green
.042-.044 (1.06-1.12)	.2449 (6.22)	Brown
.044-.046 (1.12-1.18)	.2472 (6.28)	Gray
.046-.049 (1.26-1.32)	.2496 (6.34)	Navy Blue
.049-.051 (1.24-1.30)	.2520 (6.40)	Vermilion
.051-.054 (1.30-1.36)	.2543 (6.46)	Purple

4) Remove spacer selection gauge, dial indicator and bearing inner races from the knuckle. Apply grease to knuckle, oil seals and bearings. Mount brake disc to hub and tighten bolts evenly.

5) Install outer wheel bearing, then press in outer oil seal. Hold inner race of outer bearing with Bearing Holder (MB990776-A), then press hub into knuckle.

TRANSAXLE MOUNTS

Removal & Installation

1) Support engine and transaxle assembly. On 5-speed models, remove select control valve bolts. Remove transaxle mounting bracket bolts and bracket.

2) Remove cap from inside of right inner fender shield. Remove transaxle insulator bracket mounting bolts. Remove transaxle insulator bracket. To install, reverse removal procedure.

REMOVAL & INSTALLATION

TRANSAXLE

See appropriate MANUAL TRANSMISSION REMOVAL article in IMPORT GENERAL SERVICING section.

Manual Transmissions

CHRYSLER CORP. IMPORTS & MITSUBISHI 160 SERIES; 4x2, 4 & 5-SPEED TRANSAXLES (Cont.)

Fig. 4: Exploded View of Transaxle Gear Components

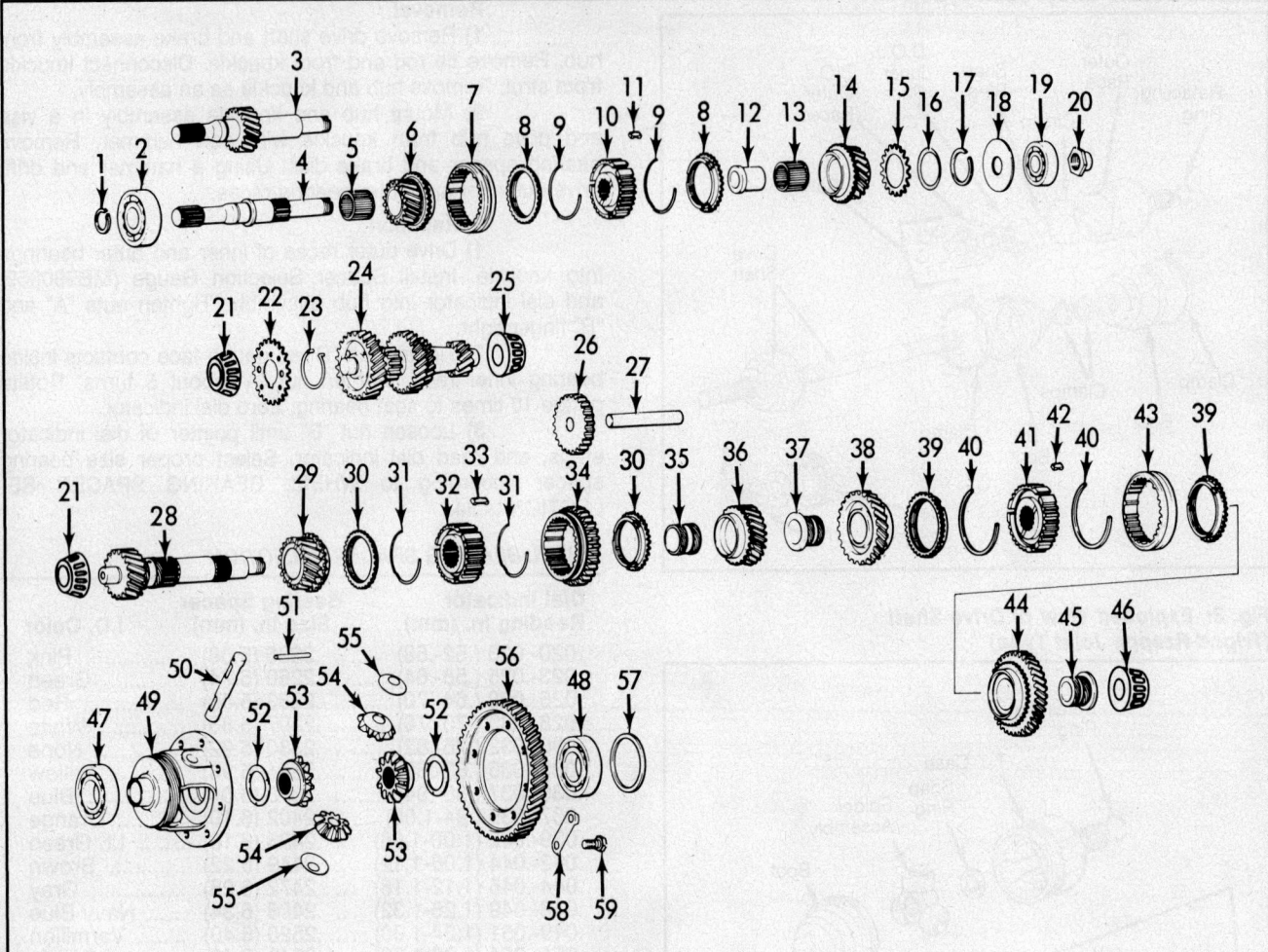

1. Snap Ring	22. Sub-Gear
2. Bearing	23. Spring
3. Input Shaft [1]	24. Intermediate Gear
4. Input Shaft [2]	25. Bearing
5. Bearing [2]	26. Reverse Idler Gear
6. Input Low Gear [2]	27. Idler Gear Shaft
7. Sleeve [2]	28. Output Shaft
8. Synchronizer Ring [2]	29. 4th Gear
9. Synchronizer Spring [2]	30. Synchronizer Ring
10. Synchronizer Hub [2]	31. Spring
11. Synchronizer Key [2]	32. Synchronizer Hub
12. Sleeve [2]	33. Synchronizer Key
13. Bearing [2]	34. Synchronizer Sleeve
14. Input High Gear [2]	35. Sleeve
15. Sub-Gear	36. 3rd Gear
16. Spacer	37. Sleeve
17. Snap Ring	38. 2nd Gear
18. Spacer	39. Synchronizer Ring
19. Bearing	40. Spring
20. Lock Nut	41. Synchronizer Hub
21. Bearing	42. Synchronizer Key

43. Sleeve
44. 1st Gear
45. Sleeve
46. Bearing
47. Bearing
48. Bearing
49. Differential Case
50. Pinion Shaft
51. Lock Pin
52. Spacer
53. Differential Side Gear
54. Differential Pinion
55. Washer
56. Differential Drive Gear
57. Spacer
58. Lock Washer
59. Bolt
[1] – KM 160 Only
[2] – KM 165 Only

CHRYSLER CORP. IMPORTS & MITSUBISHI 160 SERIES; 4x2, 4 & 5-SPEED TRANSAXLES (Cont.)

TRANSAXLE DISASSEMBLY

NOTE: On KM 163 transaxle, 5th gear shift rail and fork are part of 3rd-4th rail and fork assemblies.

1) Remove clutch cable and transaxle mounting brackets. Remove back-up light switch and steel ball from case. Remove speedometer gear assembly. Remove transaxle case and gasket. On KM 165 and 166 transaxles, remove adapter and gasket.

2) Remove differential end play adjustment spacer. Remove 3 detent plugs, springs and balls. Remove distance collar and reverse idler shaft. Remove reverse shift lever assembly and reverse shift rail. Remove 3rd-4th gear shift rail spacer collar.

3) Remove 1st-2nd and 3rd-4th shift forks. Remove 1st-2nd shift rail from case. Shift fork and rail cannot be removed from case as a unit. Remove 3rd-4th shift rail from case. Remove 2 interlock plungers from clutch housing.

4) Shift 3rd-4th synchronizer sleeve to 4th gear position and remove output shaft assembly. Remove differential assembly. On KM 165 and 166 models, remove input shaft detent plug, spring and ball. On all models, remove input shaft bearing retainer.

5) On KM 165 and 166 models, remove input shaft assembly, shift rail and fork with intermediate shaft. On all models, remove shift shaft spring retainer.

Fig. 5: Removing Input Shaft & Intermediate Shaft From Case

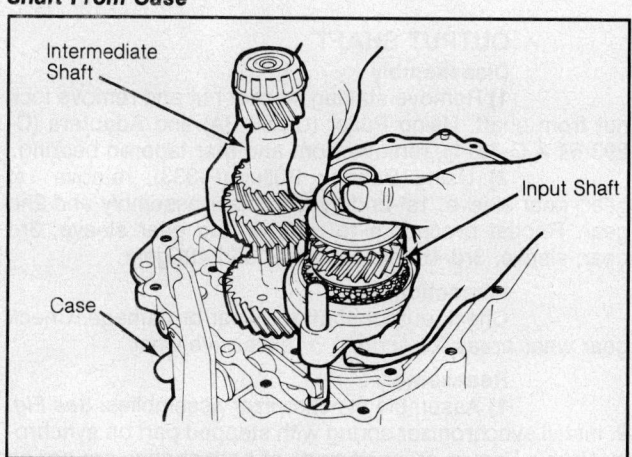

6) Remove shift shaft roll pin with pliers, then remove shift shaft through case hole. When removing shift shaft, place finger over control finger hole to prevent detent ball from falling out. Remove control finger, 2 springs, spacer collar, detent spring and ball.

7) Remove selector finger lock pin, selector shaft and selector finger (KM 165 and 166). Place identification mark on bearing outer race and remove bearing. Outer race must be installed in original position. Remove speedometer driven gear assembly.

CLEANING & INSPECTION

1) All parts should be thoroughly washed in cleaning solvent and air dried. Remove old gaskets with stiff brush or scraper. Rinse bearings in clean solvent and let air dry. DO NOT spin bearings dry.

2) Lubricate with light grade oil and wrap in clean paper until ready to install. Examine all gear teeth and splines for chips, wear, breaks or nicks. Check transmission case and extension housing for cracks and damage.

3) Check bearings and synchronizers for wear, damage and proper fit. Lubricate all moving parts before installation. Use new gaskets, seals and snap rings.

COMPONENT DISASSEMBLY & REASSEMBLY

INPUT SHAFT
Disassembly (KM 160)

Remove snap ring from front bearing. Using Puller (C-293-PA) and Adapter (C-293-53), press off front bearing. Remove staking from lock nut on rear of shaft and remove lock nut. Support spacer under rear bearing with press plates and press shaft from bearing.

Inspection

Check splines for damage and wear. Check oil seal area for damage or wear.

Reassembly

1) Using Bearing Installer (MD998323), press front bearing onto input shaft. Carefully install new snap ring. Snap rings are available in 3 sizes; use thickest snap ring that will fit in groove.

FRONT BEARING SNAP RING THICKNESS

I. D. Color	Thickness In. (mm)	Part Number
None	.0870-.0894 (2.21-2.27)	MD706497
Blue	.0898-.0921 (2.29-2.34)	MD706498
Brown	.0925-.0949 (2.35-2.41)	MD706499

2) Install sub-gear onto input shaft high gear and apply oil to entire surface. Install cone spring. Ensure cone spring is installed in proper direction. See Fig. 6. Install new snap ring, ensuring inner side of cone spring is not in groove.

Fig. 6: Installing Sub-Gear & Cone Spring

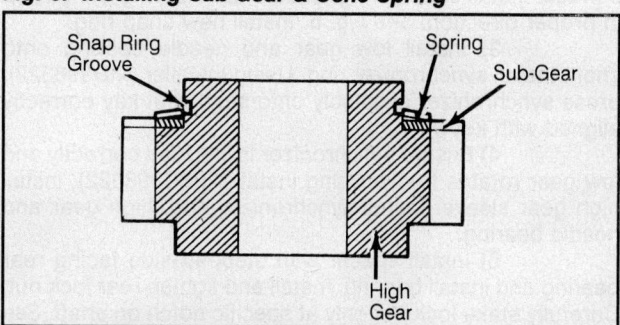

Ensure cone spring is installed correctly.

3) Install spacer on rear of shaft with stepped side facing rear of bearing. Using Installer (MD998322), press rear bearing onto shaft. Install and tighten lock nut. Carefully stake lock nut only at specific notch on shaft. See Fig. 7.

CHRYSLER CORP. IMPORTS & MITSUBISHI 160 SERIES; 4x2, 4 & 5-SPEED TRANSAXLES (Cont.)

Fig. 7: Staking Input Shaft Lock Nut

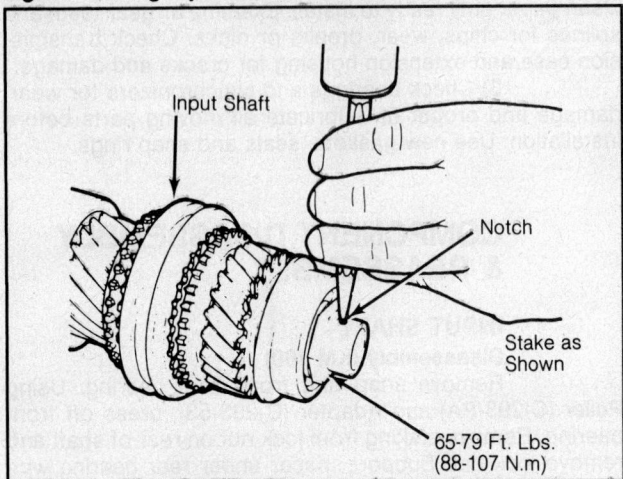

Carefully stake lock nut. If shaft is distorted, it will interfere with breather and result in breakage.

Disassembly (KM 163, 165 & 166)

NOTE: **Be careful not to set press plates under low gear clutch gear, otherwise input low gear and clutch gear will be disengaged.**

Remove front bearing snap ring. Using Puller (C-293-PA) and Adapter (C-293-53), remove bearing. Remove staking at rear lock nut and remove lock nut. Support low gear with press plates and press input shaft from input high gear, gear sleeve, synchronizer assembly, input low gear and rear bearing.

Inspection

Check splines for wear or damage. Check oil seal fitting area for damage or wear. Check gear bearing surface for wear or scoring.

Reassembly

1) Using Bearing Installer (MD998323), install front bearing onto input shaft. Install snap ring. Snap rings are available in 3 sizes, use thickest snap ring that will fit. See FRONT BEARING SNAP RING THICKNESS table.

2) Install synchronizer assembly onto input shaft. Install sub-gear onto high gear and apply oil to entire surface. Install cone spring. Ensure cone spring is installed in proper direction. *See Fig. 6.* Install new snap ring.

3) Install low gear and needle bearing onto shaft. Install synchronizer ring. Using Installer (MD998322), press synchronizer assembly onto shaft with key correctly aligned with keyway.

4) Ensure synchronizer is installed correctly and low gear rotates freely. Using Installer (MD998322), install high gear sleeve. Install synchronizer ring, high gear and needle bearing.

5) Install spacer with stepped side facing rear bearing and install bearing. Install and tighten rear lock nut. Carefully stake lock nut only at specific notch on shaft. *See Fig. 7.*

INTERMEDIATE SHAFT

Disassembly

Using Puller (C-293-PA) and Adapters (C-293-54 and C-4571), remove tapered front roller bearing. Discard bearing. Remove sub-gear and spring. Remove rear bearing using same puller as used on front.

Inspection

Inspect gears for wear or damage. Replace any defective parts as required.

Reassembly

Install sub-gear spring on intermediate shaft gear. Install sub-gear onto shaft while positioning longer leg of spring through .16" (4 mm) hole opposite keyway. Using Installer (MD998322), install new front tapered bearing first, then install new rear bearing. Replace outer bearing races.

Fig. 8: Installing Sub-Gear

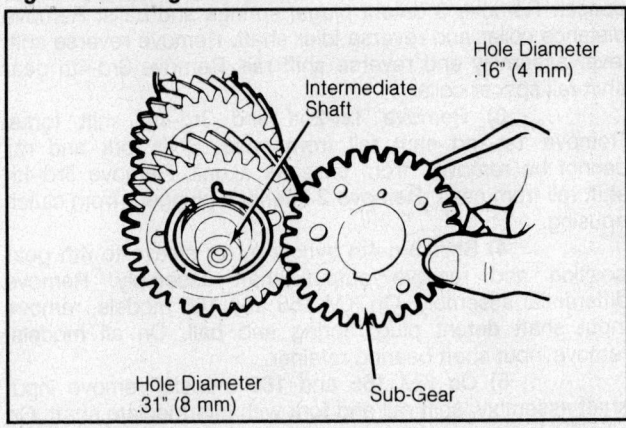

Install longer leg of sub-gear spring through .16" (4 mm) hole in sub-gear.

OUTPUT SHAFT

Disassembly

1) Remove staking on rear nut and remove lock nut from shaft. Using Puller (C-293-PA) and Adapters (C-293-54 & C-4571), remove front and rear tapered bearing.

2) Using Bearing Puller (P-333), remove 1st gear, gear sleeve, 1st-2nd synchronizer assembly and 2nd gear. Repeat procedure to remove 2nd gear sleeve, 3rd gear, sleeve, 3rd-4th synchronizer and 4th gear.

Inspection

Check output shaft for wear or damage. Check gear wear areas for scoring or excessive wear.

Reassembly

1) Assemble synchronizer assemblies. *See Fig. 9.* Install synchronizer spring with stepped part on synchronizer key. Ensure stepped parts of both springs are not on same key.

2) Install 4th gear onto output shaft and apply oil to thrust surfaces and gear. Install synchronizer ring. Using Installer (MD998323), press 3rd-4th synchronizer assembly onto shaft. Check 4th gear for smooth rotation on output shaft.

NOTE: **Apply transmission lubricant to all parts before reassembly.**

3) Install synchronizer ring onto output shaft. Using Installer (MB998323), press on 3rd gear sleeve. Install 3rd gear. Using installer, install 2nd gear sleeve. Check operation of 3rd gear.

4) Install 2nd gear. Install 1st-2nd synchronizer ring. Using same installer, install 1st-2nd synchronizer assembly. Check that 2nd gear rotates freely on shaft. Install synchronizer ring.

Manual Transmissions
7-49

CHRYSLER CORP. IMPORTS & MITSUBISHI 160 SERIES; 4x2, 4 & 5-SPEED TRANSAXLES (Cont.)

Fig. 9: Identifying Synchronizer Hub & Sleeve

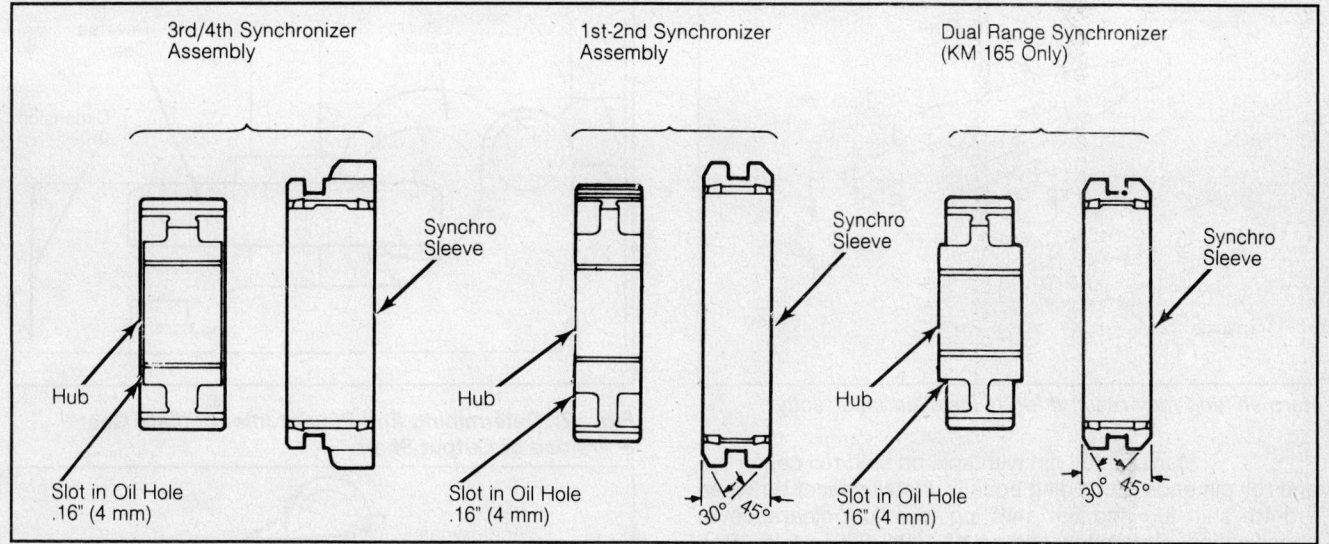

Ensure hub is assembled to sleeve with .16" (4 mm) diameter slot in oil groove toward clutch (engine side).

5) Install 1st-2nd synchronizer ring. Assemble 1st gear to gear sleeve and press 1st gear onto output shaft. Using Installer (MD998322), press front and rear bearings onto shaft.

6) Check clearance between synchronizer ring and gear. Clearance should be .032" (.8 mm). Replace ring, if clearance is less than specifications or if internal screw of ring is damaged.

DIFFERENTIAL ASSEMBLY
Disassembly
1) Remove 8 differential drive gear bolts and remove drive gear. Using Puller (C-293-PA), Adapter (C-293-53) and Extension (SP-3183), remove ball bearings. Using pin punch, drive pinion shaft lock pin outward from recessed end of pin.

2) Remove pinion shaft, differential pinion and washer. Remove differential side gears and spacers. Keep spacers and gears separate and identified to ensure assembly in proper location.

Inspection
Check splines for damage or wear. Check gears for chipped or worn teeth.

Reassembly
1) If reusing parts, position spacers in original location on back of differential side gears. Install gears in differential case. If using new parts, install spacers of medium thickness, on new side gears and install in case.

DIFFERENTIAL GEAR SPACER THICKNESS

Part Number	Thickness In. (mm)
MA180876	.030-.032 (.75-.82)
MA180861	.033-.036 (.83-.92)
MA180860	.037-.039 (.93-1.0)
MA180875	.040-.043 (1.01-1.09)
MA180876	.043-.046 (1.09-1.16)

2) Place washers behind pinion gears and mesh both pinions with side gears while rotating pinions to slip them in place. Install pinion shaft. Measure backlash between pinion and side gears.

3) Backlash should be 0-.003" (0-.076 mm). Install spacers on both sides to arrive at proper backlash which must be equal for both sides. With proper backlash obtained, install pinion shaft lock pin.

NOTE: Always use new lock washers when reassembling ring gear (10 mm bolts only).

4) Press bearings on both ends of differential carrier, applying load to inner race only. Install ring gear to case. Apply lock sealant to only 12 mm bolt threads. Tighten bolts in criss-cross pattern to specifications and secure with lock washer tabs.

TRANSAXLE REASSEMBLY

NOTE: On KM 163 transaxle, 5th gear shift rail and fork are part of 3rd-4th rail and fork assemblies.

1) Rotate sub-gear in direction of arrrow to align .31" (8 mm) hole in intermediate gear with hole in sub-gear. Insert .31" (8 mm) diameter, 1.38" (35 mm) long dummy pin through intermediate gear and into sub-gear.

2) Assemble select shift fork and rail assembly to the synchronizer sleeve of input shaft. Install intermediate shaft, shift rail and shift fork as an assembly. Install front bearing retainer and tighten 3 retaining bolts to 11-15 ft. lbs. (15-21 N.m).

3) Install select shaft detent ball, spring and plug. Install plug until flush with housing. Apply sealer to head of plug. Install differential assembly to clutch housing. Install output shaft assembly. Ensure gears are properly meshed and remove dummy pin from sub-gear and intermediate gear.

4) Install 5th gear shift lug on pin on clutch housing (5-speed only). Insert 2 interlock plungers into holes in clutch housing. Install 1st-2nd and 3rd-4th (3rd-4th-5th on 5-speed) shift rail assembly, 1 at a time. Both shift rails cannot be installed at same time. *See Fig. 10.*

CHRYSLER CORP. IMPORTS & MITSUBISHI 160 SERIES; 4x2, 4 & 5-SPEED TRANSAXLES (Cont.)

Fig. 10: Installing 5th Gear Shift Lug on KM 163 Transaxle

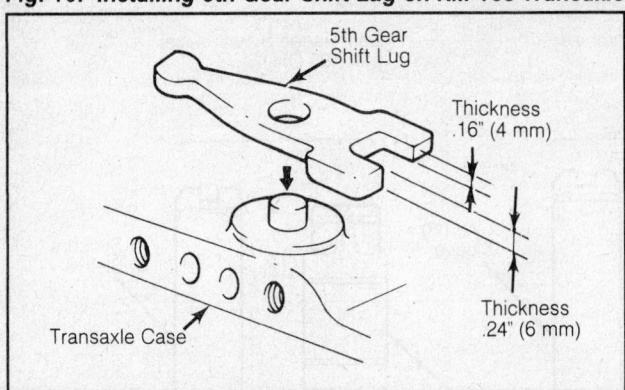

Hard shifting may result if lug is installed incorrectly.

5) Install roll pin with split on shift rail centerline and roll pin ends protruding equally. Install spacer between 3rd-4th shift lug and 5th shift lug to adjust clearance to specification. Clearance should be .004-.020" (.1-.5 mm). See 5TH GEAR SELECT SPACER THICKNESS chart.

5TH GEAR SELECT SPACER THICKNESS

Thickness Inches (mm)	Mark
.024 (.6)	G
.035 (.9)	F
.047 (1.2)	E
.059 (1.5)	D
.071 (1.8)	C
.083 (2.1)	B
.094 (2.4)	A
.106 (2.7)	None

6) Install reverse shift rail into clutch housing. Install detent balls, springs and plugs. Ensure smaller end of spring is toward ball and spring with White marking (shorter length) is for reverse shift rail. Install reverse shift lever assembly and tighten 2 retaining bolts to 11-15 ft. lbs. (15-21 N.m).

7) Install reverse idler gear with chamfered side upward. Install idler gear shaft through gear into housing. Install spacer collar. Place reverse shift rail in neutral position. Measure dimension "A". *See Fig. 11.* If dimension "A" is not 1.675-1751" (42.08-44.48 mm), replace reverse shift lever assembly.

8) Adjust output shaft, intermediate shaft and differential case end play or preload as follows: Remove output shaft and intermediate shaft bearing outer races from transaxle case.

9) Place 2 pieces of Plastigage, .4" (10 mm) long, in-line on outer race of transmission case. *See Fig. 12.* Insert outer races in case and press firmly to hold Plastigage in position.

10) Place 2 pieces of Plastigage .79" (20 mm) long on ball bearing outer race. *See Fig. 13.* Install transaxle case with gasket and tighten 13 bolts to 26-30 ft. lbs. (35-41 N.m).

Fig. 11: Measuring Reverse Idler Gear Height

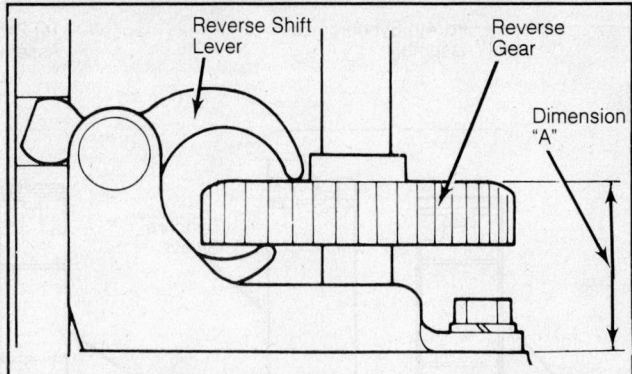

Fig. 12: Determining End Play of Intermediate Gear & Preload of Output Shaft

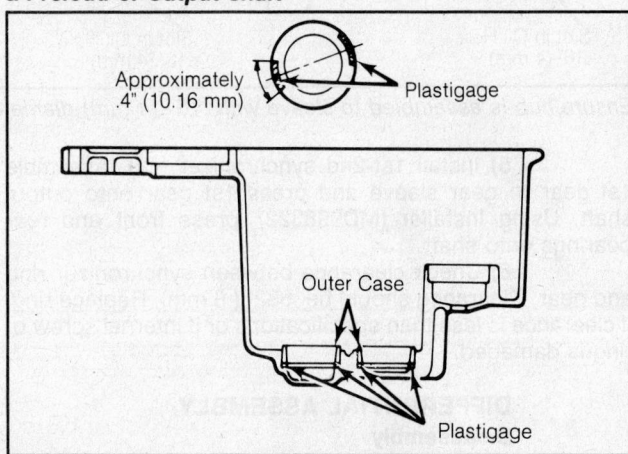

Place Plastigage on shoulder of outer race hole in transmission case.

Fig. 13: Measuring Differential End Play

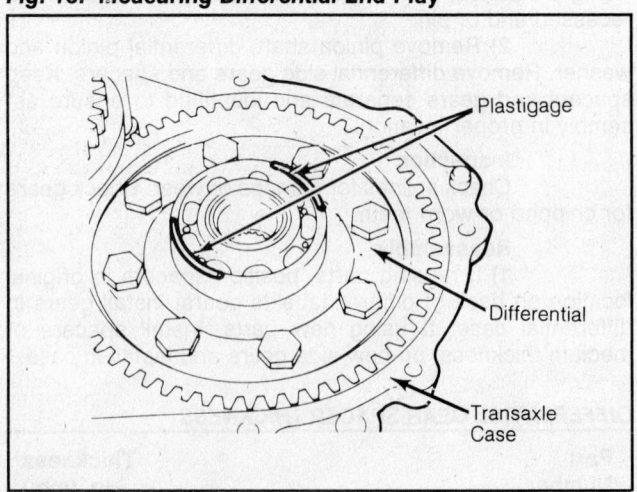

11) Remove bolts and transaxle case. Measure thickness of Plastigage. Select spacer of proper thickness to obtain correct end play. End play should be 0-.006" (0-.15 mm). See DIFFERENTIAL CASE END PLAY SPACER table.

12) Remove both taper bearing outer races from transaxle case. Measure Plastigage and determine proper spacer to obtain proper intermediate gear end play and output shaft preload. End play should be 0-.002" (0-.05 mm).

Manual Transmissions

7-51

CHRYSLER CORP. IMPORTS & MITSUBISHI 160 SERIES; 4x2, 4 & 5-SPEED TRANSAXLES (Cont.)

DIFFERENTIAL CASE END PLAY SPACER

Part No.	Identification Mark	Thickness In. (mm)
MD706574	E	.0516 (1.31)
MD706573	None	.0551 (1.40)
MD706572	C	.0587 (1.49)
MD706571	B	.0622 (1.58)
MD706570	A	.0657 (1.67)
MD706575	F	.0693 (1.76)

Preload should be .006-.008" (.15-.20 mm). Spacers range in thickness from .0724-.1055" (1.84-2.68 mm) in .0012" (.03 mm) increments.

13) Install intermediate gear end play spacers and taper roller bearing outer races into transaxle case. Install differential case end play spacer on differential ball bearing. Apply drying sealer to clutch housing side of transaxle case gasket and non-drying sealer to adapter side of gasket.

14) Install adapter. Apply drying sealer to adapter side of gasket and non-drying sealer to case side. Install transaxle case assembly on clutch housing and tighten 13 bolts to 26-30 ft. lbs. (35-41 N.m). Ensure control shaft shifts smoothly using Control Shaft Seal Installer (MB998324).

15) Install speedometer gear assembly into clutch housing and tighten flange bolt. On KM 163 models, connect select actuator rod to select shift rail and insert pin. Install snap ring on pin. Tighten actuator mounting bolts to specification.

16) On all models, place transaxle in neutral. Install select switch, by aligning mating marks. *See Fig. 14.* Tighten select switch mounting bolts. Install steel ball and back-up light switch. On KM 165 and 166 models, install transaxle mounting and clutch cable brackets.

Fig. 14: Aligning Select Switch Mating Marks

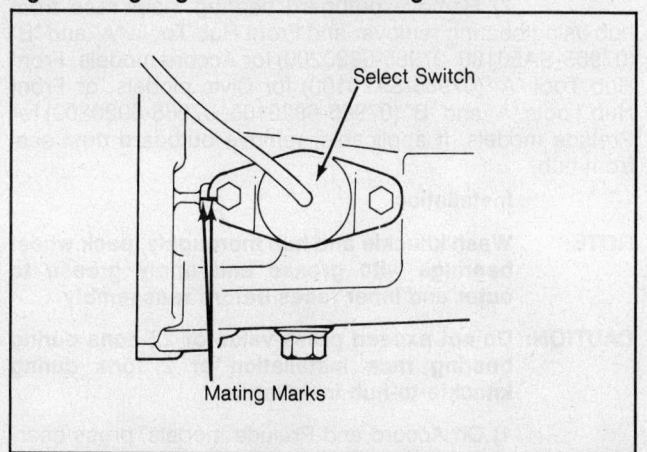

TRANSAXLE SPECIFICATIONS

Application	In. (mm)
Differential Case End Play	0-.006 (0-.15)
Intermediate Gear End Play	0-.002 (0-.05)
Output Shaft Preload	.006-.008 (.15-.20)
Pinion Gear-to-Side Gear Backlash	0-.003 (0-.08)
Reverse Idler Gear Height	1.44-1.54 (36.7-39.0)
Synchronizer Ring-to-Gear	.032 (.8)

TIGHTENING SPECIFICATIONS

Application	Ft. Lbs. (N.m)
Rear Cover	14-16 (19-22)
Engine-to-Transaxle	
Bolt with Washer	22-25 (30-34)
All Others	32-39 (43-53)
Clutch Housing-to-Transaxle	26-30 (35-41)
Input Shaft Lock Nut	65-79 (88-107)
Output Shaft Lock Nut	65-79 (88-107)
Ring Gear Bolts	
10 mm	47-54 (64-73)
12 mm	94-101 (128-137)

Manual Transmissions
HONDA 4 & 5-SPEED

Accord, Civic & Prelude

TRANSAXLE IDENTIFICATION

Transaxle identification number is stamped into top of transaxle case flange near transaxle-to-engine union.

MANUAL TRANSAXLE TYPES

Application	Type
Accord 5-Speed	
(Calif. & Hi. Alt.)	GS
(Federal)	GY
Civic	
4-Speed	GV
5-Speed	GW
Prelude 5-Speed	GM

DESCRIPTION

Transmission and final drive are mounted in a common 2-piece case. Accord and Prelude models use a 5-speed unit exclusively, while Civic models offer both a 4 and 5-speed.

The transmission is fully synchronized in all forward gears. All forward gears are helically cut and are in constant mesh. Reverse gears are spur cut and are engaged by a sliding reverse idler gear.

On 5-speed transaxles, 5th gear is mounted on mainshaft on rear side of transaxle case (inside end cover). Power transfer to the final drive assembly is by direct mesh of differential ring gear to a gear on transmission countershaft.

LUBRICATION & ADJUSTMENT

See appropriate MANUAL TRANSMISSION SERVICING article in IMPORT GENERAL SERVICING section.

TROUBLE SHOOTING

HARSH SHIFTS OR NOISY LOW GEAR OPERATION

Idle speed too high. Clutch not fully releasing.

SLIPS OUT OF GEAR

Synchronizer teeth worn. Interlock mechanism damaged. Weak interlock spring. Shift linkage out of adjustment.

TRANSMISSION NOISY

Worn or damaged gear teeth or bearings. Improperly adjusted clutch. Oil soaked or damaged clutch.

REVERSE GEAR ENGAGEMENT DURING FORWARD GEAR CHANGE

Check for a weak or damaged reverse interlock mechanism.

SERVICE (IN VEHICLE)

WHEEL BEARINGS
Removal

1) With vehicle on ground, remove cotter pin and loosen hub spindle nut. Raise and support front of vehicle. Remove wheel and spindle nut. Remove caliper mount bolts and support caliper out of way with wire.

2) Do not disconnect hydraulic line. Remove two 6 mm disc mount screws. Install two 8 x 1.25 x 12 bolts in disc. Turn each bolt 2 turns at a time to force disc from hub evenly. Remove lower ball joint cotter pin and castellated nut.

3) Using Ball Joint Puller (07941-6920001), separate lower ball joint from knuckle. Remove tie rod end from knuckle in similar manner. On Accord and Civic models, remove knuckle-to-shock absorber pinch bolt. Tap knuckle with hammer until knuckle is free from shock.

NOTE: Replace wheel bearings whenever hub is removed from vehicle.

4) On Prelude models, remove upper ball joint dust shield from knuckle. Remove upper ball joint cotter pin and castellated nut. Detach upper ball joint from knuckle, using ball joint puller if necessary. On all models, pull drive shaft off knuckle and remove knuckle/hub assembly from vehicle using hydraulic press.

5) If necessary, remove splash guard from knuckle/hub assembly. On Accord and Prelude models, detach snap ring and remove outboard bearing. Turn knuckle over and remove inboard dust seal, inboard bearing and inner race. On Civic models, remove circlip.

6) Press bearing outer race out of knuckle using Front Hub Tools "C" and "D" (07965-6920300, 07965-6920400) and Driver (07749-0010000) for Accord and Prelude models or Hub Tool "A" (07965-6340301) and Driver (07947-634000) for Civic models.

7) Remove outboard bearing inner race from hub using bearing remover and Front Hub Tools "A" and "B" (07965-SA50100, 07965-6920200) for Accord models, Front Hub Tool "A" (07965-SA70100) for Civic models, or Front Hub Tools "A" and "B" (07965-6920100, 07965-6920200) for Prelude models. If applicable, remove outboard dust seal from hub.

Installation

NOTE: Wash knuckle and hub thoroughly, pack wheel bearings with grease and apply grease to outer and inner races before reassembly

CAUTION: Do not exceed press value of 2.5 tons during bearing race installation or 2 tons during knuckle-to-hub installation.

1) On Accord and Prelude models, press bearing outer race into knuckle using Hub Tools "A", "B" and "F" (07965-6340301, 07965-6920200, 07965-SA00600) and Driver (07749-0010000).

2) Install outboard ball bearing and inner race in knuckle. Install snap ring. Pack grease in groove and around sealing lip of outboard dust seal. Drive outboard dust seal into knuckle until flush with knuckle surface using Hub Tool "F" and driver. Install splash guard.

3) Turn knuckle upside-down and install inboard ball bearing and race. Press knuckle into hub using Hub Tools "A", "B" and "E" ("E", 07965-6920500) Dis/assembly

HONDA 4 & 5-SPEED (Cont.)

Fig. 1: Accord Front Hub Assembly

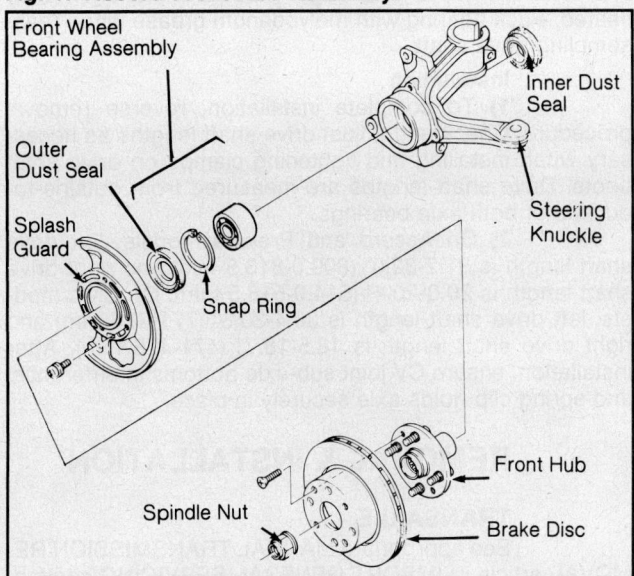

Fig. 2: Civic Front Hub Assembly

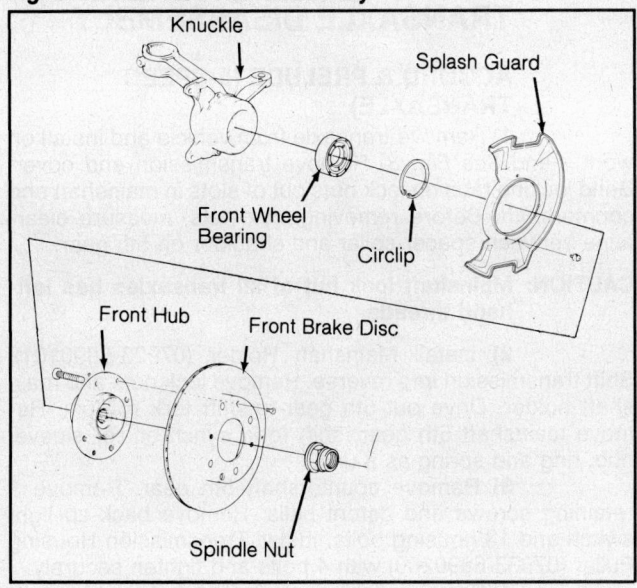

Fig. 3: Prelude Front Hub Assembly

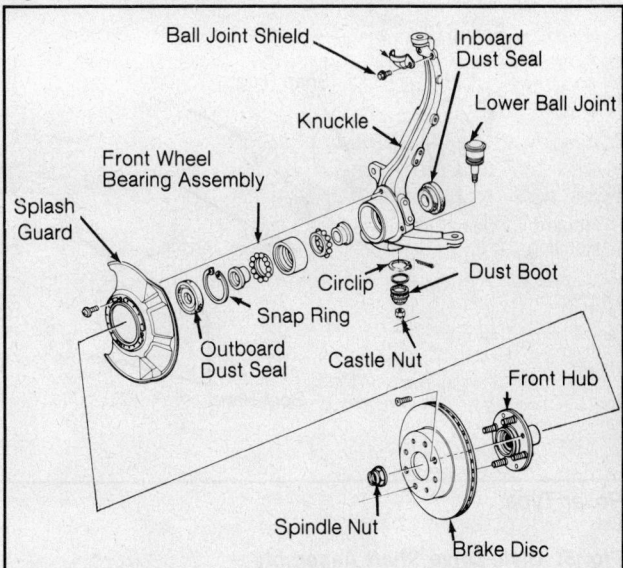

Tool "B" (07965-6920200) and driver. Pack grease in groove and around sealing lip of inboard dust seal. Drive inboard dust seal into knuckle using Hub Tools "C" and "F" ("C", 07965-6920300) and driver for Accord models or Hub Tools "B" and "F" and driver for Prelude models.

4) On Civic models, push bearing assembly into knuckle with hydraulic press and Bearing Driver Tools (07749-0010000, 07946-SB20000, 07746-0010600). Install circlip and splash guard. Push front hub into knuckle with hydraulic press and hub tools.

DRIVE AXLE SHAFTS
Removal
1) With vehicle on ground, remove cotter pin and loosen hub spindle nut. Raise and support front of vehicle, then remove wheel and spindle nut. Drain transaxle.

2) On Accord models, remove ball joint bolt. Disconnect tie rods from steering knuckles. Remove stabi-

lizer bar bolts. Using plastic hammer, tap lower control arm free of knuckle. Pull the hub outward, all the way off drive shaft.

3) On Civic models, remove ball joint cotter pin and castellated nut. Separate ball joint from front hub using ball joint puller. Pull front hub outward, all the way off drive shaft.

4) On Prelude models, remove damper fork bolt and damper pinch bolt. Remove damper fork. Separate lower control arm ball joint from lower control arm. Pull hub outward, completely off drive shaft.

NOTE: **DO NOT pull on the inboard CV joint as it may come apart.**

5) On all models, pry inner CV joint out approximately .50" (12.7 mm) to force spring clip past groove in splines of differential side gear. Do not damage oil seal when prying axle. Pull drive shaft out of transmission case.

CAUTION: Outer CV joint on all models cannot be serviced. If joint is found to be worn or damaged, complete axle shaft assembly must be replaced. Always replace inboard housing spring clip when axle shafts are removed.

Disassembly
1) On Accord, Civic and Prelude roller type models, remove dust boot retaining band from inner CV joint, then slide boot back away from joint. Remove and discard inner CV joint spring clip. Separate joint housing from drive shaft. *See Fig. 4.*

2) Wipe grease from joint, remove snap ring and separate shaft from spider assembly. Slide spider and rollers off shaft. On all models, remove inner retaining band from dust boot and slide boot off shaft. Remove outer retaining band from outer CV joint and clean grease from joint. Check operation of joint.

3) On Civic ball type models, remove retaining band from damper weight and slide weight off shaft. Remove dust boot retaining band from inner CV joint. Slide boot back away from joint. Remove and discard inner CV joint spring clip. Separate joint housing from drive shaft. *See Fig. 5.*

Manual Transmissions
HONDA 4 & 5-SPEED (Cont.)

Fig. 4: Accord, Civic & Prelude Drive Shaft Assembly

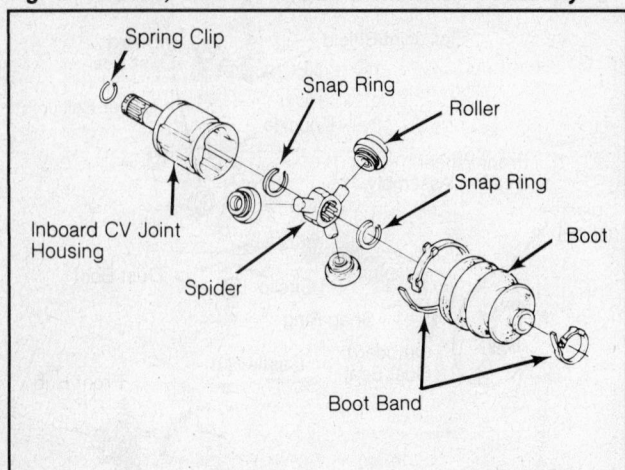

Roller Type

Fig. 5: Civic Drive Shaft Assembly

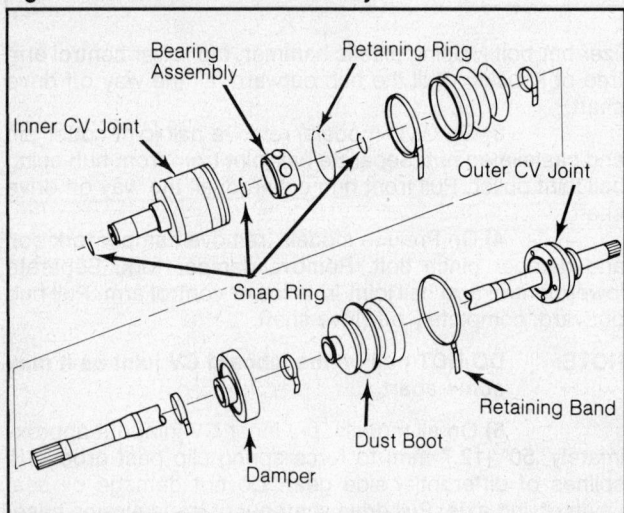

Ball Type

4) Wipe grease from joint, remove snap ring and separate shaft from ball bearing assembly. Slide ball bearing assembly off shaft. To inspect inboard CV joint bearing, place ball bearing assembly on work bench. Disassemble by gently prying each ball out of cage using dull screwdriver.

NOTE: Individual parts for CV joints are not available. The inboard joint is available as a complete assembly only.

5) Inspect ball bearing race for wear and scoring. Check splines for wear or damage. Inspect balls for wear and pitting. Check bearing cage for wear. Replace assembly if any component is excessively worn or damaged.

Reassembly

1) On roller type models, reassemble drive shaft assembly by reversing disassembly procedure. Thoroughly pack both inner and outer CV joints with grease. Install new boots as needed. Install new bands on all boots.

2) On Civic ball type models, assemble ball bearing assembly by installing bearing race with chamfered

end toward small end of cage. Press balls in until firmly seated. Pack bearing with molybdenum grease when reassembling drive shaft.

Installation

1) To complete installation, reverse removal procedure. Check and adjust drive shaft lengths as necessary when installing and tightening clamps on drive shaft boots. Drive shaft lengths are measured from outside-to-outside of both axle bearings.

2) On Accord and Prelude models, left drive shaft length is 31.2-32.0" (809.0-813.5 mm) and right drive shaft length is 20.0-20.4" (514.0-518.5 mm). On Civic models, left drive shaft length is 30.4-30.6" (771-776 mm) and right drive shaft length is 18.5-18.7" (471-476 mm). After installation, ensure CV joint sub-axle bottoms in differential and spring clip holds axle securely in place.

REMOVAL & INSTALLATION

TRANSAXLE

See appropriate MANUAL TRANSMISSION REMOVAL article in IMPORT GENERAL SERVICING section.

TRANSAXLE DISASSEMBLY

ACCORD & PRELUDE (5-SPEED TRANSAXLE)

1) Remove transaxle from vehicle and install on work stand See Fig. 8. Remove transmission end cover. Bend locking tabs on lock nuts out of slots in mainshaft and countershaft. Before removing lock nuts, measure clearance between spacer collar and shoulder on 5th gear.

CAUTION: Mainshaft lock nut of all transaxles has left-hand threads.

2) Install Mainshaft Holder (07923-6890101). Shift transmission into reverse. Remove lock nuts and main shaft holder. Drive out 5th gear-to-shift fork roll pin. Remove mainshaft 5th gear, shift fork, synchronizer sleeve, hub, ring and spring as a unit.

3) Remove countershaft 5th gear. Remove 3 retaining screws and detent balls. Remove back-up light switch and 13 housing bolts. Install Transmission Housing Puller (07933-6890200) with 4 bolts and tighten securely.

4) Screw puller bolt against end of countershaft until transmission housing breaks loose. Lift off housing. Before further disassembly, measure clearance between 5th/reverse shift shaft pin and reverse shift fork. Standard (new) clearance is .002-.014" (.05-.35 mm). Service limit is .02" (.5 mm).

5) If clearance is out of limit, measure width of slot in reverse shift fork. Standard (new) slot width is .278-.285" (7.05-7.25 mm). Check reverse idler gear-to-shift fork clearance. Standard (new) gear-to-fork clearance is .008-.040" (.20-1.00 mm). Service limit is .07" (1.7 mm).

6) Pull out reverse idler shaft and remove gear. If gear-to-fork clearance is beyond limit, measure gap between ends of shift fork fingers. Standard (new) clearance is .46-.48" (11.8-12.1 mm). Shift transaxle into neutral. Detach three 8 mm mount bolts and remove mainshaft bearing retainer plate.

7) Pull out shift guide shaft and reverse idler shaft. Remove gear. Pull 3rd/4th and 1st/2nd shift shafts up, to shift into 4th and 2nd. Remove the 5th/reverse shift shaft by pulling it up while lifting the reverse shift fork.

HONDA 4 & 5-SPEED (Cont.)

8) Push shift rod in. Tilt interlock and shift guide to the side, then lift them out. Remove countershaft and mainshaft as an assembly, with 1st/2nd and 3rd/4th shift shafts. Using Driver (07749-0010000) and Adapter (07947-6340500), remove differential assembly.

9) Remove snap ring in transaxle housing. Pry out differential oil seal from housing. Replace shift rod oil seal. On clutch housing, remove mainshaft bearing retaining plates. Remove countershaft bearing with Bearing Remover (07936-6340000) and Attachment (07936-6890101).

10) Remove mainshaft bearing and seal from clutch. Replace both bearings and oil seal whenever removed. Drive in countershaft bearing. Install retainer plate, tighten screws with impact driver and stake screw heads. On transaxle housing, expand snap ring and remove mainshaft and countershaft bearings. If necessary, remove snap rings and clean grooves in housing.

CIVIC (4 & 5-SPEED TRANSAXLE)

1) Disassembly of Civic 4 and 5 speed transaxles is similar. *See Fig. 9 and Fig. 10.* If necessary to remove speedometer gear holder from 4 or 5-speed transmission, remove retaining bolt and clip. Lift out gear holder and remove speedometer driven gear from gear holder.

2) Check speedometer gear and bushing wear. If excessively worn, replace gear holder assembly including "O" ring. Ensure proper speedometer driven gear is identified by type of transmission and tire size. See CIVIC SPEEDOMETER DRIVEN GEAR IDENTIFICATION TABLE. Align slot in gear holder with lock plate. Set holder in clutch housing and tighten lock plate.

CIVIC SPEEDOMETER DRIVEN GEAR IDENTIFICATION TABLE

Application	Gear Teeth
4-Speed	
1300 Hatchback	
w/P165/70 SR 13 Tires	21T
5-Speed	
1300 Coupe	
w/P16/70 R 13 Tires	21T
1500 Coupe	
w/175/70 SR 13 Tires	20T
1500 Hatchback DX	
w/R175/70 R 13 Tires	20T
1500 Hatchback S	
w/175/SR 13 Tires	20T
1500 Sedan	
w/P175/70 R 13 Tires	20T
1500 Wagon	
w/R175/70 SR 13 Tires	20T

3) For 4-speed transmission end cover snap ring inspection, remove bolts from end cover and remove end cover. Remove ball bearing from mainshaft. Inspect bearing for wear. Clean sealant residue from transmission housing. Replace bearing and at two different points measure distance from top of bearing's outer race to mounting flange for end cover.

4) To measure end cover snap ring, remove spring washer and snap ring from end cover. With a straightedge and at two different points on end cover, measure depth on snap ring installation hole *See Fig. 6.*

Subtract thickness of straightedge from reading. Select correct thickness snap ring as follows:
- Subtract bearing height from depth of end cover.
- Subtract spring washer free height .033" (.850 mm) from demension determined in above step.

5) For 5-speed transmission 5th gear housing snap ring inspection, remove six 5th gear housing mounting bolts. Remove spring pin from 5th gear shift fork. Remove outside parts from mainshaft. *See Fig. 7.*

Fig. 6: Measuring End Cover Snap Ring

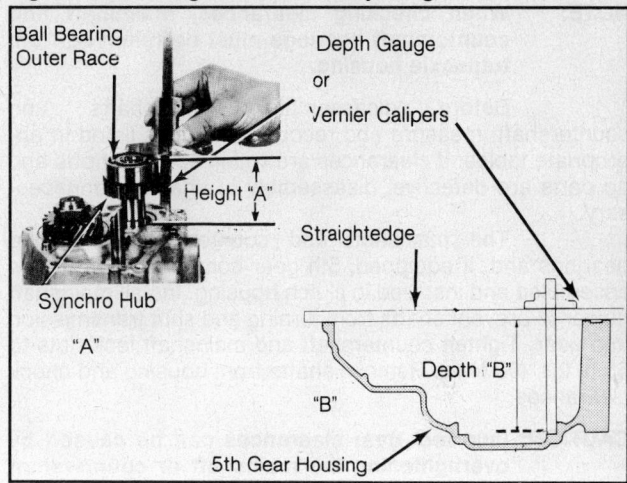

Fig. 7: 5th Gear Assembly

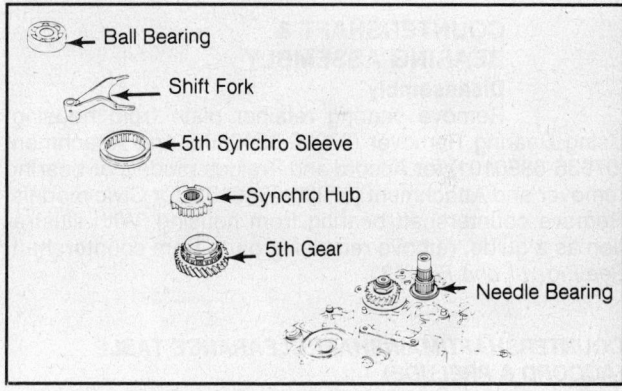

6) Inspect parts for wear. Reinstall synchro hub and ball bearing onto mainshaft. Use cleaning and measuring procedures from steps **3)** and **4)**.

7) For 5-speed housing disassembly, drive out spring securing 5th gear shift fork to shaft. Remove ball bearing. Remove shift fork and synchro-hub as a unit. Remove synchro-ring, spring and mainshaft 5th gear. Remove needle bearing and thrust washer.

8) On 4 and 5-speed transmissions, remove detent ball retaining bolts, springs and balls. Detach 11 housing mount bolts. Loosen transmission housing from gasket by tapping bosses around its edge with soft faced hammer.

9) Pull out reverse idler gear shaft and remove gear. Remove dowel pin. Remove nut and spring washer on reverse shift fork then remove reverse shift fork. On 5-speed models, remove detent ball and spring from reverse shift fork.

10) On both models, bend down tabs on the 3 locking plates and remove bolt. Remove reverse shift shaft and reverse shift guide. Remove 1st/2nd gear shift shaft. Remove 3rd/4th gear shift shaft and shift fork. Shift synchro into 2nd and remove 1st/2nd gear shift fork. Remove countershaft and mainshaft as an assembly.

COMPONENT DISASSEMBLY & REASSEMBLY

NOTE: When checking clearances, mainshaft and countershaft bearings must be removed from transaxle housing.

Before disassembling mainshafts and countershaft, measure and record clearances listed in appropriate tables. If clearances are within specifications and no parts are defective, disassembly of shafts is unnecessary.

The mainshaft and countershaft, (including bearings and, if equipped, 5th gear components) must be assembled and installed in clutch housing. Install mainshaft holder to prevent shafts from turning and shift transmission into gear. Tighten countershaft and mainshaft lock nuts to 65 ft. lbs. (90 N.m). Remove shafts from housing and check clearances.

CAUTION: Incorrect gear clearances can be caused by overtightening the mainshaft or countershaft lock nuts. Ensure torque wrench used is correctly calibrated.

COUNTERSHAFT & BEARING ASSEMBLY

Disassembly

Remove bearing retainer plate from housing. Using Bearing Remover (07936-6340000) and Attachment (07936-6890101) for Accord and Prelude models or bearing remover and Attachment (07936-6340101) for Civic models. Remove countershaft bearing from housing. With illustration as a guide, remove remaining parts from countershaft. *See Fig. 11 and Fig. 12.*

COUNTERSHAFT/MAINSHAFT CLEARANCE TABLE (ACCORD & PRELUDE)

Application 5 Speed	Specification In. (mm)
1st Gear Shoulder-to-Thrust Washer	
Standard	.001-.003 (.03-.08)
2nd-to-3rd Gear Shoulder	
Standard	.0012-.0040 (.030-.100)
Limit	.007 (.18)
Gear-to-Synchro Ring	
Standard	.033-.043 (.85-1.10)
Limit	.016 (.40)
All Shift Fork-to-Synchro Sleeve	
Standard	.014-.026 (.35-.65)
Limit	.039 (1.0)
Synchro Sleeve	
Groove Width	.266-.270 (6.75-6.85)
3rd/4th Shift Shaft-to-Shift Guide	
Standard	.008-.020 (.20-.50)
Limit	.03 (.8)

COUNTERSHAFT/MAINSHAFT CLEARANCE TABLE (CIVIC)

Application 4 & 5 Speed	Specification In. (mm)
1st Gear-to-Thrust Washer	
Standard	.001-.003 (.03-.08)
Limit	.007 (.18)
2nd Gear-to-Spacer Plate	
Standard	.002-.005 (.05-.12)
Limit	.007 (.18)
3rd Gear Shoulder-to-Spacer Plate	
Standard	.002-.005 (.05-.12)
Limit	.007 (.18)
4th Gear Shoulder-to-Spacer Collar	
Standard	.002-.005 (.05-.12)
Limit	.007 (.18)
5th Gear Shoulder-to-Thrust Washer	
Standard	.002-.015 (.05-.38)
Limit	.016 (.40)
All Shaft Forks-to-Synchro Rings	
Standard	.02-.03 (.5-.7)
Limit	.04 (1.0)
Shift Fork Finger Thickness	
Standard	.25-.26 (6.4-6.5)
Limit	.24 (6.0)

MAINSHAFT DIAMETER TABLE

Application In. (mm)	Dimension
Accord & Prelude Models	
5-Speed	
"A"	
Standard	1.0238-1.0243 (26.004-26.017)
Limit	1.022 (25.95)
"B"	
Standard	1.2592-1.2598 (31.984-32.000)
Limit	1.257 (31.93)
"C"	
Standard	.9835-.9840 (24.980-24.993)
Limit	.980 (24.93)
Civic Models	
4-Speed	
"A"	
Standard	1.102-1.103 (27.997-28.010)
Limit	1.100 (27.940)
"B"	
Standard	.08656-.08661 (21.987-22.000)
Limit	.863 (21.930)
5-Speed	
"A"	
Standard	1.102-1.103 (27.997-28.010)
Limit	.981 (24.93)
"B"	
Standard	.8653-.8661 (21.987-22.000)
Limit	.863 (21.93)

NOTE: On Accord and Prelude countershaft, 3rd, 4th and 5th gear needle bearings are identical but 1st and 2nd gear needle bearings are not. On Civic countershaft, all needle bearings are identical.

Fig. 8: Exploded View of Accord and Prelude 5-Speed Manual Transaxle Assembly

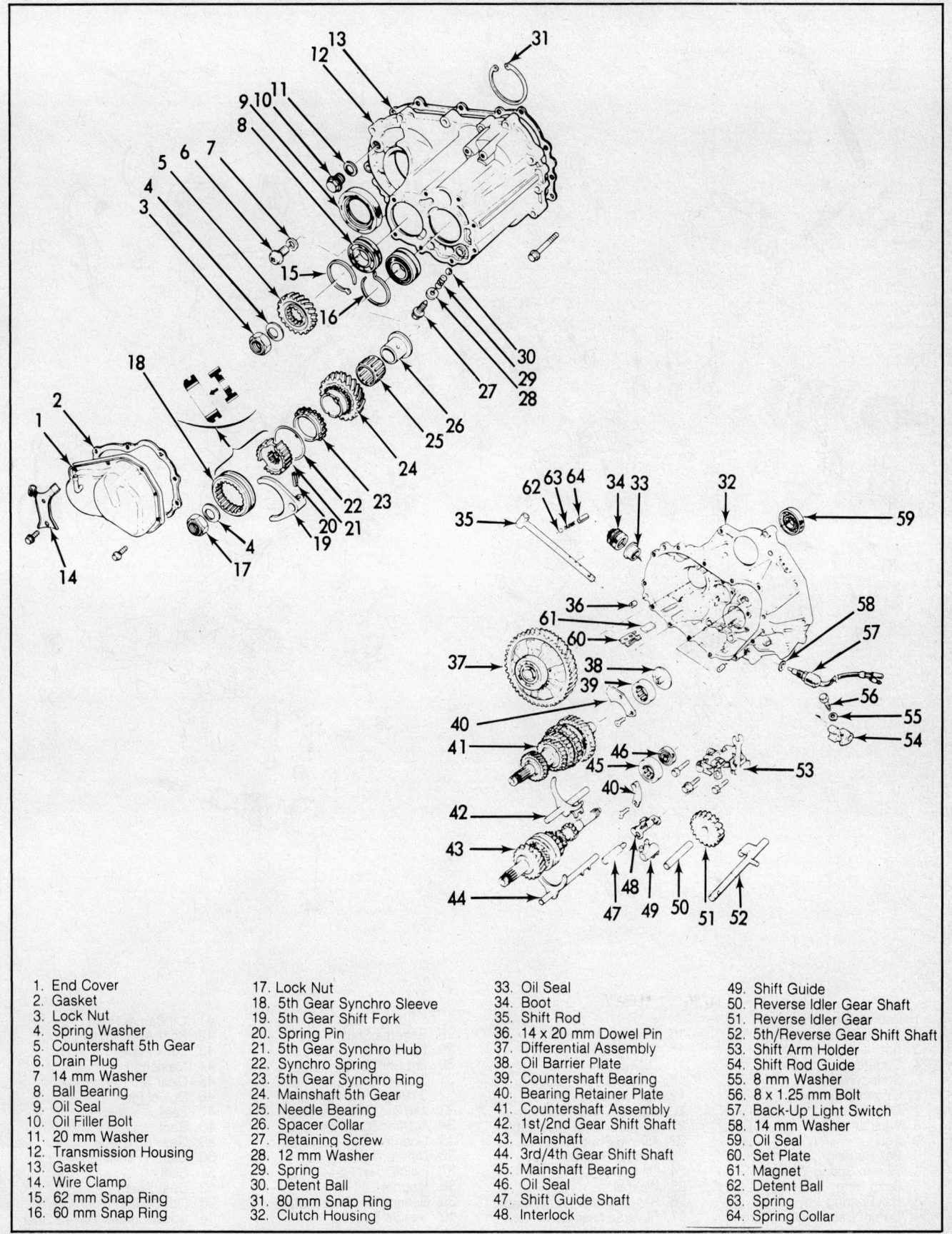

1. End Cover	17. Lock Nut	33. Oil Seal	49. Shift Guide
2. Gasket	18. 5th Gear Synchro Sleeve	34. Boot	50. Reverse Idler Gear Shaft
3. Lock Nut	19. 5th Gear Shift Fork	35. Shift Rod	51. Reverse Idler Gear
4. Spring Washer	20. Spring Pin	36. 14 x 20 mm Dowel Pin	52. 5th/Reverse Gear Shift Shaft
5. Countershaft 5th Gear	21. 5th Gear Synchro Hub	37. Differential Assembly	53. Shift Arm Holder
6. Drain Plug	22. Synchro Spring	38. Oil Barrier Plate	54. Shift Rod Guide
7. 14 mm Washer	23. 5th Gear Synchro Ring	39. Countershaft Bearing	55. 8 mm Washer
8. Ball Bearing	24. Mainshaft 5th Gear	40. Bearing Retainer Plate	56. 8 x 1.25 mm Bolt
9. Oil Seal	25. Needle Bearing	41. Countershaft Assembly	57. Back-Up Light Switch
10. Oil Filler Bolt	26. Spacer Collar	42. 1st/2nd Gear Shift Shaft	58. 14 mm Washer
11. 20 mm Washer	27. Retaining Screw	43. Mainshaft	59. Oil Seal
12. Transmission Housing	28. 12 mm Washer	44. 3rd/4th Gear Shift Shaft	60. Set Plate
13. Gasket	29. Spring	45. Mainshaft Bearing	61. Magnet
14. Wire Clamp	30. Detent Ball	46. Oil Seal	62. Detent Ball
15. 62 mm Snap Ring	31. 80 mm Snap Ring	47. Shift Guide Shaft	63. Spring
16. 60 mm Snap Ring	32. Clutch Housing	48. Interlock	64. Spring Collar

Manual Transmissions
HONDA 4 & 5-SPEED (Cont.)

Fig. 9: Exploded View of Civic 4-Speed Manual Transaxle Assembly

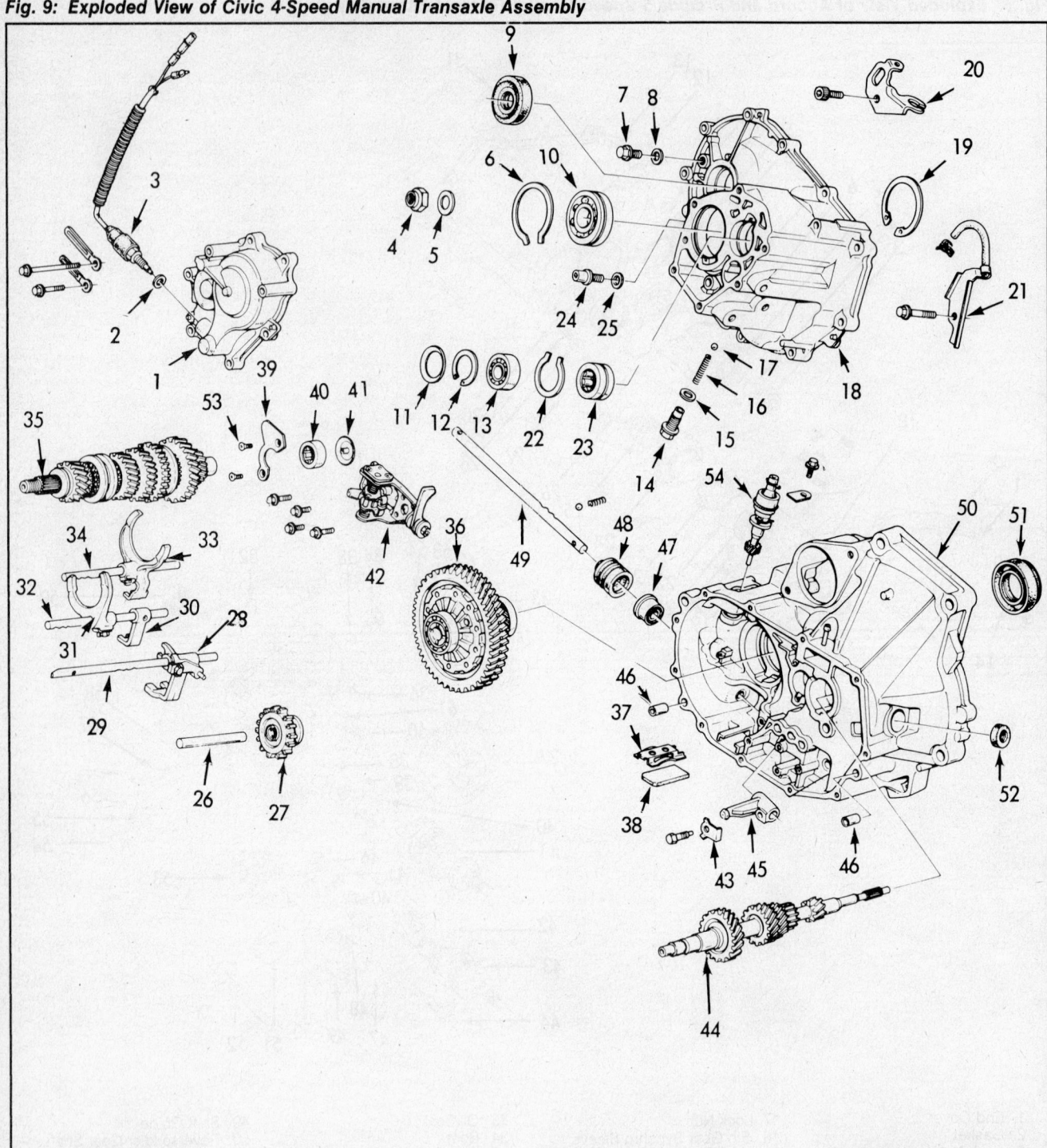

1. End Cover	15. Washer	28. Reverse Shift Guide	41. Oil Barrier Plate
2. 14 mm Washer	16. Detent Spring	29. Reverse Shift Shaft	42. Shift Arm Holder
3. Back-Up Lamp Switch	17. Detent Ball	30. 3rd Shift Shaft Guide	43. Lock Plate
4. Countershaft Locknut	18. Transmission Housing	31. 3rd/4th Gear Shift Fork	44. Mainshaft
5. Spring Washer	19. 72 mm Snap Ring	32. 3rd/4th Gear Fork Shaft	45. Gear Shift Arm
6. 65 mm Snap Ring	20. Clutch Cable Bracket	33. 1st/2nd Gear Shift Fork	46. Dowel Pin
7. Oil Filler Bolt	21. Breather Tube Assembly	34. 1st/2nd Gear Fork Shaft	47. Seal
8. Washer	22. 45 mm Snap Ring	35. Countershaft Assembly	48. Boot
9. Seal	23. Needle Bearing	36. Differential	49. Gear Shift Rod
10. Ball Bearing	24. Oil Drain Plug	37. Hold-Down Plate	50. Clutch Housing
11. 52 mm Spring Washer	25. Washer	38. Magnet	51. Seal
12. Snap Ring	26. Reverse Idler Gear Shaft	39. Bearing Retainer Plate	52. Dust Seal
13. Ball Bearing	27. Reverse Idler Gear	40. Needle Bearing	53. Flat Screw
14. Detent Ball Retainer Screw			54. Speedometer Driven Gear

Fig. 10: Exploded View of Civic 5-Speed Manual Transaxle Assembly

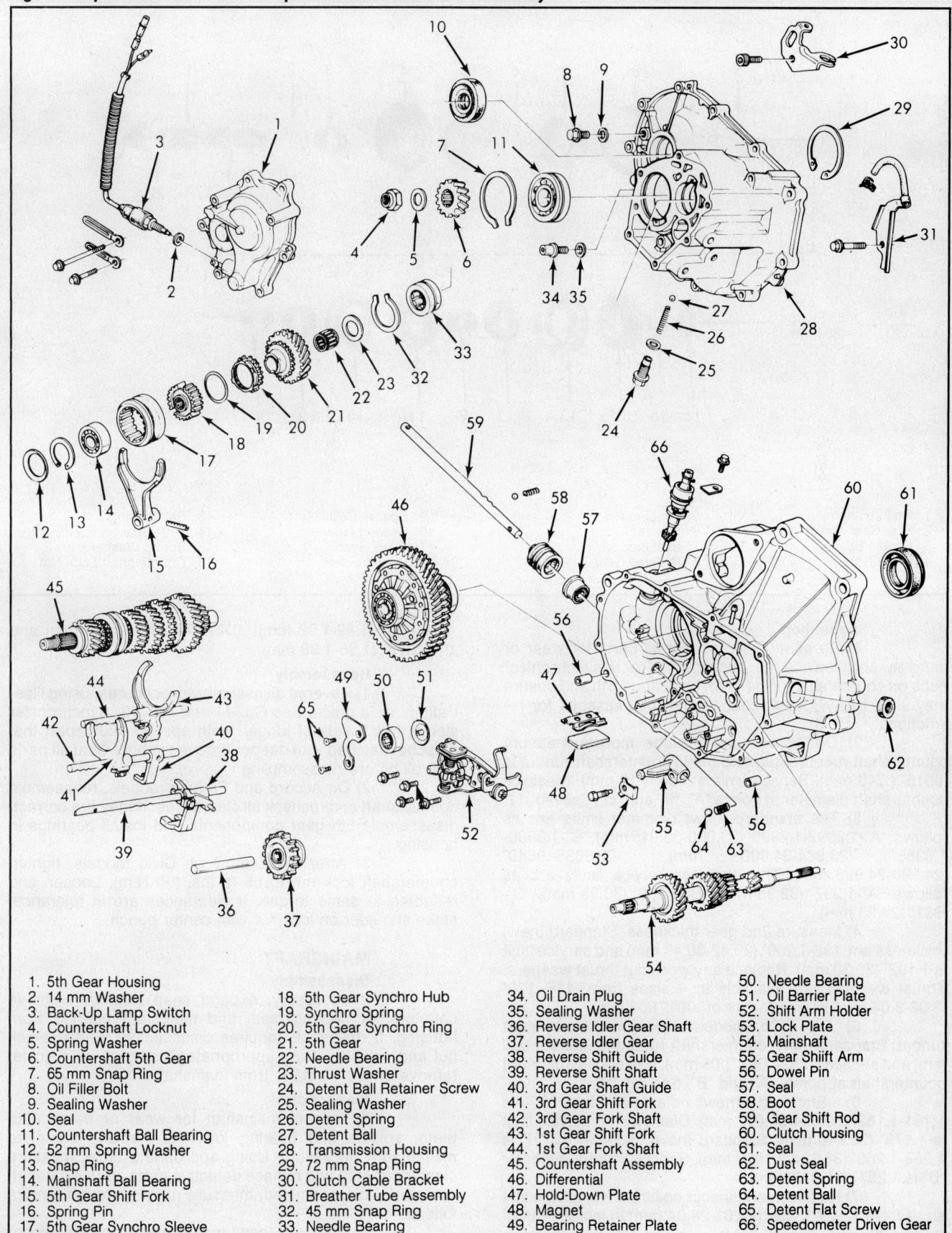

1. 5th Gear Housing	18. 5th Gear Synchro Hub	34. Oil Drain Plug	50. Needle Bearing
2. 14 mm Washer	19. Synchro Spring	35. Sealing Washer	51. Oil Barrier Plate
3. Back-Up Lamp Switch	20. 5th Gear Synchro Ring	36. Reverse Idler Gear Shaft	52. Shift Arm Holder
4. Countershaft Locknut	21. 5th Gear	37. Reverse Idler Gear	53. Lock Plate
5. Spring Washer	22. Needle Bearing	38. Reverse Shift Guide	54. Mainshaft
6. Countershaft 5th Gear	23. Thrust Washer	39. Reverse Shift Shaft	55. Gear Shift Arm
7. 65 mm Snap Ring	24. Detent Ball Retainer Screw	40. 3rd Gear Shaft Guide	56. Dowel Pin
8. Oil Filler Bolt	25. Sealing Washer	41. 3rd Gear Shift Fork	57. Seal
9. Sealing Washer	26. Detent Spring	42. 3rd Gear Fork Shaft	58. Boot
10. Seal	27. Detent Ball	43. 1st Gear Shift Fork	59. Gear Shift Rod
11. Countershaft Ball Bearing	28. Transmission Housing	44. 1st Gear Fork Shaft	60. Clutch Housing
12. 52 mm Spring Washer	29. 72 mm Snap Ring	45. Countershaft Assembly	61. Seal
13. Snap Ring	30. Clutch Cable Bracket	46. Differential	62. Dust Seal
14. Mainshaft Ball Bearing	31. Breather Tube Assembly	47. Hold-Down Plate	63. Detent Spring
15. 5th Gear Shift Fork	32. 45 mm Snap Ring	48. Magnet	64. Detent Ball
16. Spring Pin	33. Needle Bearing	49. Bearing Retainer Plate	65. Detent Flat Screw
17. 5th Gear Synchro Sleeve			66. Speedometer Driven Gear

Manual Transmissions
HONDA 4 & 5-SPEED (Cont.)

Fig. 11: Exploded View of Accord and Prelude Countershaft Assembly

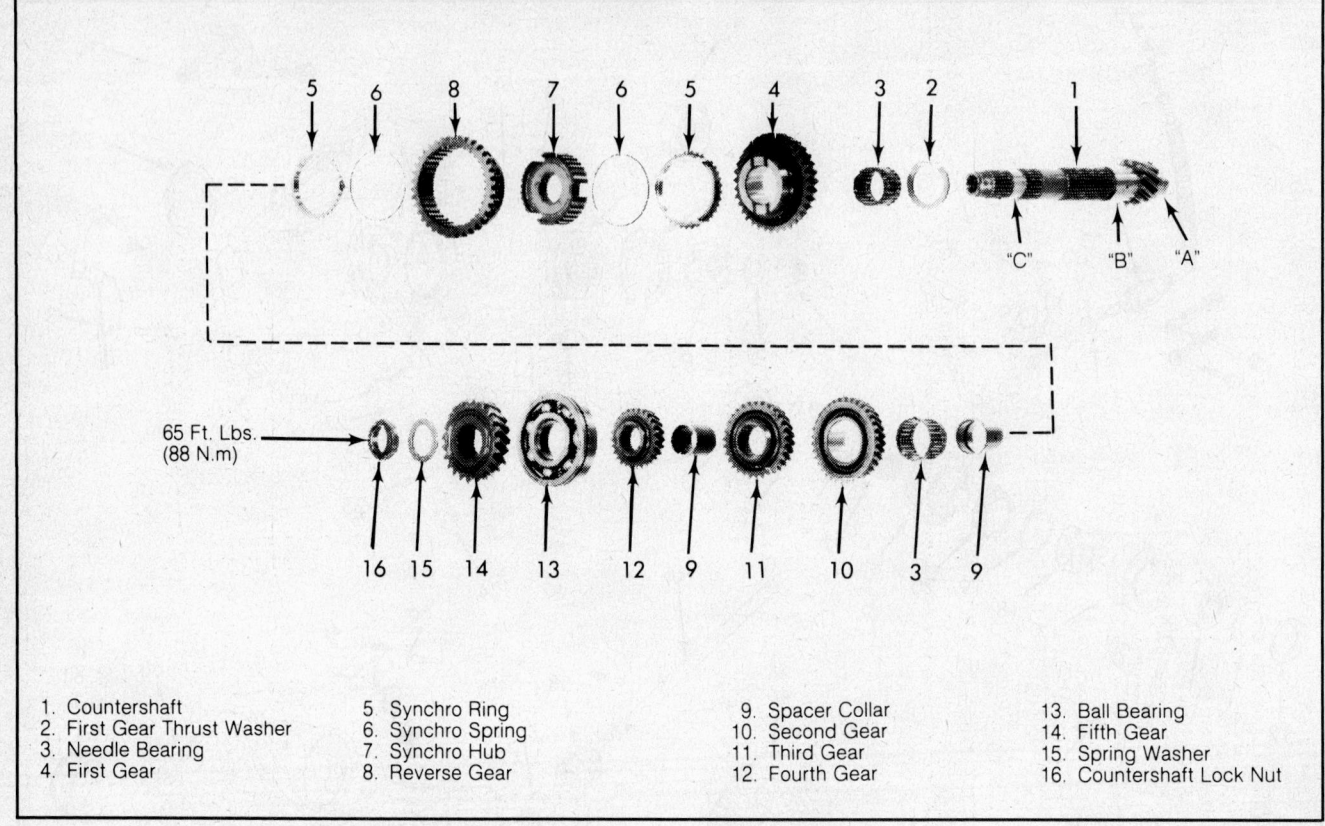

65 Ft. Lbs.
(88 N.m)

1. Countershaft
2. First Gear Thrust Washer
3. Needle Bearing
4. First Gear
5. Synchro Ring
6. Synchro Spring
7. Synchro Hub
8. Reverse Gear
9. Spacer Collar
10. Second Gear
11. Third Gear
12. Fourth Gear
13. Ball Bearing
14. Fifth Gear
15. Spring Washer
16. Countershaft Lock Nut

Inspection

1) On all models, inspect all parts for wear or damage and replace as necessary. Place synchronizer hubs on countershaft, slide them back and forth and ensure they slide freely. Check countershaft oil passages for restrictions.

2) On Accord and Prelude models measure countershaft runout. Standard (new) countershaft runout is .0016" (.040 mm). Service limit is .004" (.10 mm). Measure countershaft diameter at points "A", "B" and "C". *See Fig. 11.*

3) The standard (new) diameter limits are as follows: "A"-1.2992-1.2998" (33.000-33.015 mm), "B"-1.3380-1.3386" (33.984-34.000 mm), "C"-.9835-.9840" (24.980-24.993 mm). The diameter service limits are as follows: "A"-1.297" (32.95 mm), "B"-1.336" (33.93 mm), "C"-.981" (24.93 mm).

4) Measure 2nd gear thickness. Standard (new) thickness is 1.198-1.200" (30.42-30.47 mm) and service limit is 1.192" (30.30 mm). Replace any worn out thrust washers. Thrust washers are available in 4 sizes from .116-.120" (3.02-3.04 mm) in increments of .001" (.03 mm).

5) On Civic models measure countershaft runout. Standard (new) countershaft runout is .0008" (.020 mm) and service limit is .002" (.05 mm). Measure diameter of countershaft at points "A" and "B". *See Fig. 12.*

6) Standard (new) diameter for "A" is 1.181-1.182" (30.004-30.017 mm). Diameter "A" service limit is 1.179" (29.940 mm). Standard (new) diameter for "B" is 1.259-1.260" (31.984-32.000 mm). Service limit for diameter "B" is 1.257" (31.930 mm).

7) Replacement spacer collars are available in 4 sizes from 1.103-1.104" (28.01-28.04 mm) in increments of .001" (.03 mm). Thrust washers are available in 3 sizes; .074-.076" (1.89-1.92 mm), .076-.077" (1.92-1.95 mm) and .077-.078" (1.95-1.98 mm).

Reassembly

1) Reverse disassembly procedures, using illustrations as a guide. *See Fig. 11 and Fig. 12.* Synchronizer sleeve has 3 sets of longer teeth spaced 120° apart that must be matched with deeper grooves in hub. Coat all parts with oil before reassembling.

2) On Accord and Prelude models, reassemble countershaft and recheck all clearances. If they are correct, disassemble 5th gear components and install bearings in housing.

3) After reassembly on Civic models, tighten countershaft lock nut to 65 ft. lbs. (90 N.m). Loosen and retighten to same torque. If clearances are in tolerance, stake shoulder on lock nut with center punch.

MAINSHAFT
Disassembly

If necessary, expand snap ring and remove countershaft bearing, seal and mainshaft bearing from housing. If mainshaft requires disassembly, remove lock nut and washer. Using appropriate illustration as a guide, remove remaining parts from mainshaft.

Inspection

1) Inspect mainshaft for wear or damage to teeth, splines and bearing journals. Replace complete mainshaft if necessary. Using appropriate table, measure clearance listed and replace defective parts. With mainshaft completely disassembled, measure runout through 2 revolutions.

2) Standard (new) mainshaft runout for Accord and Prelude models is .0016" (.040 mm). Service limit is

HONDA 4 & 5-SPEED (Cont.)

Fig. 12: Exploded View of Civic Countershaft Assembly

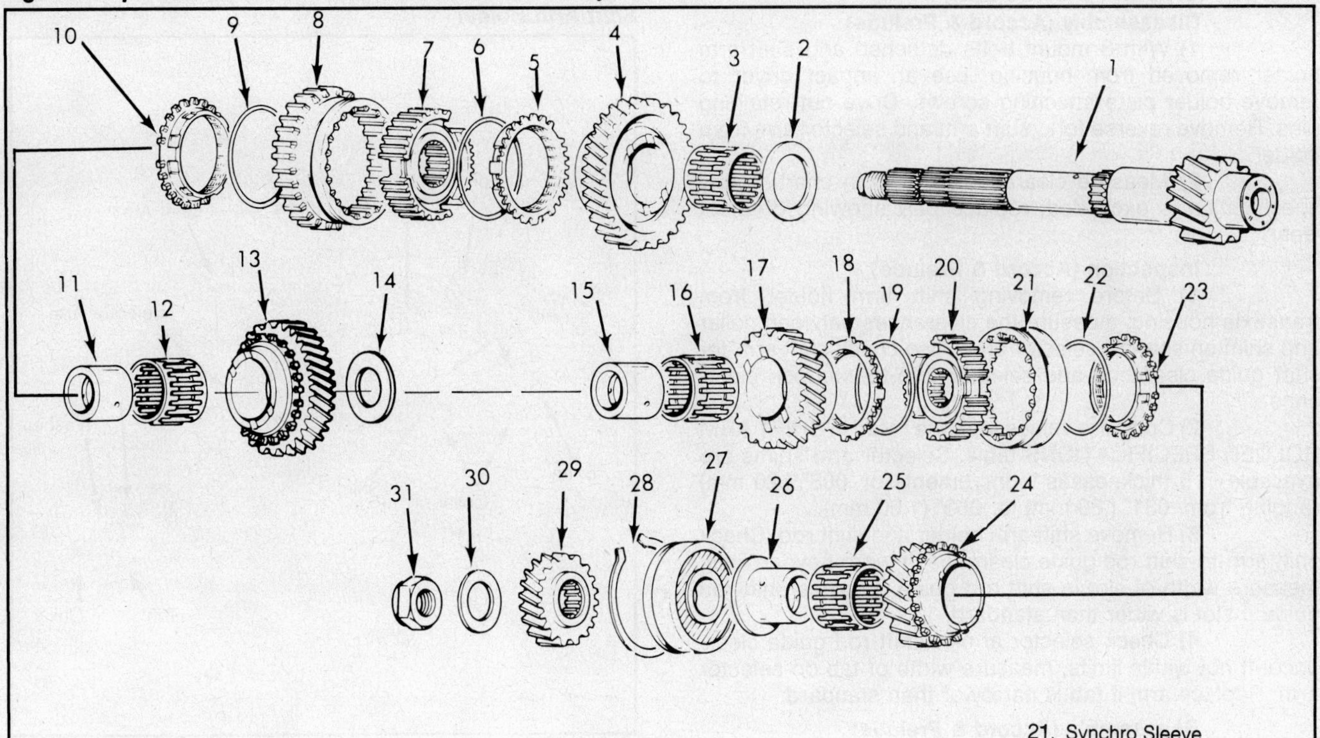

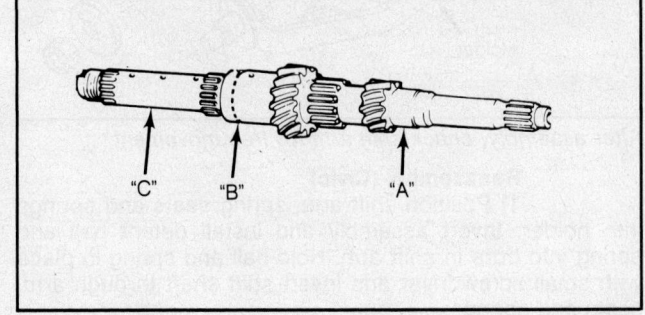

1. Countershaft	11. 28 mm Spacer
2. 32 mm Thrust Washer	12. Needle Bearing
3. Needle Bearing	13. 2nd Gear
4. 1st Gear	14. 26 mm Thrust Washer
5. Synchro Ring	15. 28 mm Spacer
6. Synchro Spring	16. Needle Bearing
7. Synchro Hub	17. 3rd Gear
8. Synchro Sleeve	18. Synchro Ring
9. Synchro Spring	19. Synchro Spring
10. Synchro Ring	20. Synchro Hub

21. Synchro Sleeve
22. Synchro Spring
23. Synchro Ring
24. 4th Gear
25. Needle Bearing
26. Flanged Spacer
27. Ball Bearing
28. 65mm Snap Ring
29. 5th Gear
30. Spring Washer
31. Locknut

.004" (.10 mm). Standard (new) mainshaft runout for Civic models is .0008" (.020 mm). Service limit is .002" (.05 mm). If specification is exceeded or oil passages are plugged, replace shaft.

 3) On Accord and Prelude models, measure mainshaft diameter at points "A", "B" and "C". *See Fig. 13.* On Civic models, measure mainshaft diameter at points "A" and "B" on 5-speed and point "A" on 4-speed. *See Fig. 14.* Check clearances against MAINSHAFT DIAMETER TABLE. Replace mainshaft if splines are damaged or shaft is worn beyond limits.

Fig. 13: Measuring Accord & Prelude Mainshaft Diameter

 4) On Accord and Prelude models, measure 3rd and 4th gear thicknesses. Standard 3rd and 4th gear

Fig. 14: Measuring Civic Mainshaft Diameter

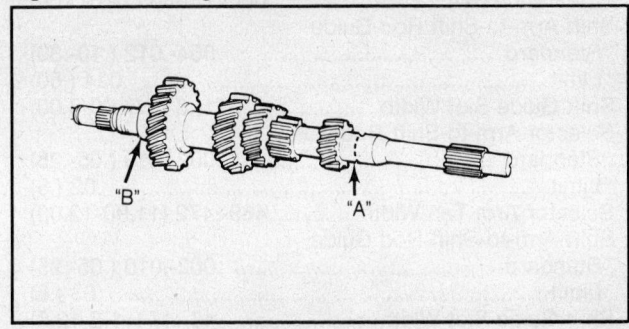

thickness is 1.158-1.160" (29.42-29.47 mm). Replace if thickness is less than 1.15" (29.30 mm). Measure 5th gear thickness. Standard 5th gear thickness is 1.060-1.062" (26.92-26.97 mm). Replace 5th gear if thickness is less than 1.055" (26.80 mm).

 Reassembly
 1) Reverse disassembly procedure and note the following: Coat all parts with oil before reassembly. Ensure correct thickness spacer collars and thrust washers are installed (if used).
 2) On all mainshafts, clearances must be rechecked after assembly. Make sure lock nut is tightened to specification.

SHIFT ARM HOLDER
Disassembly (Accord & Prelude)
1) With 3 mount bolts detached and shift arm holder removed from housing, use an impact driver to remove holder plate attaching screws. Drive out retaining pins. Remove reverse fork, shift arm and selector arm from holder.

2) Measure clearances shown in chart. If any specification is exceeded, replace part showing greatest wear.

Inspection (Accord & Prelude)
1) Before removing shift arm holder from transaxle housing, measure the clearances between collar and shim on shaft of selector arm. Also check shift arm-to-shift guide clearance and selector arm-to-interlock clearance.

2) Compare values to those listed in SHIFT ARM HOLDER SPECIFICATIONS table. Selector arm shims are available in 5 thicknesses in increments of .008" (.20 mm) ranging from .031" (.80 mm) to .063" (1.60 mm).

3) Remove shift arm holder and shift rod. Check shift arm-to-shift rod guide clearance. If worn beyond limit, measure width of slot in shift rod guide. Replace shift rod guide if slot is wider than standard.

4) Check selector arm-to-shift rod guide clearance. If not within limits, measure width of tab on selector arm. Replace arm if tab is narrower than standard.

Reassembly (Accord & Prelude)
To reassemble, reverse disassembly procedure and note the following: If collar-to-shim clearances are not correct, select new shim for reassembly.

SHIFT ARM HOLDER SPECIFICATIONS (ACCORD & PRELUDE)

Application In. (mm)	Specification
Collar-to-Shim	
Clearance (All)	.0004-.0080 (.010-.200)
Shift Arm-to-Shift Rod Guide	
Standard	.004-.012 (.10-.30)
Limit	.024 (.60)
Shift Guide Slot Width	.311-.315 (7.90-8.00)
Selector Arm-to-Shift Rod Guide	
Standard	.002-.010 (.05-.25)
Limit	.02 (.5)
Selector Arm Tab Width	.469-.472 (11.90-12.00)
Shift Arm-to-Shift Rod Guide	
Standard	.002-.010 (.05-.25)
Limit	.03 (.8)
Shift Guide Slot Width	.46-.47 (11.8-12.0)
Selector Arm-to-Interlock	
Standard	.002-.010 (.05-.35)
Limit	.03 (.7)
Selector Arm Finger	
End Gap	.396-.400 (10.05-10.15)

Disassembly (Civic)
1) With 4 mount bolts detached and shift arm holder removed from housing, use an impact driver to remove retainer plate attaching screws and remove retainer plate.

2) Pull out shift arm shaft and interlock shaft. Remove detent ball and spring. Remove shift arm, shift springs and shift retainers.

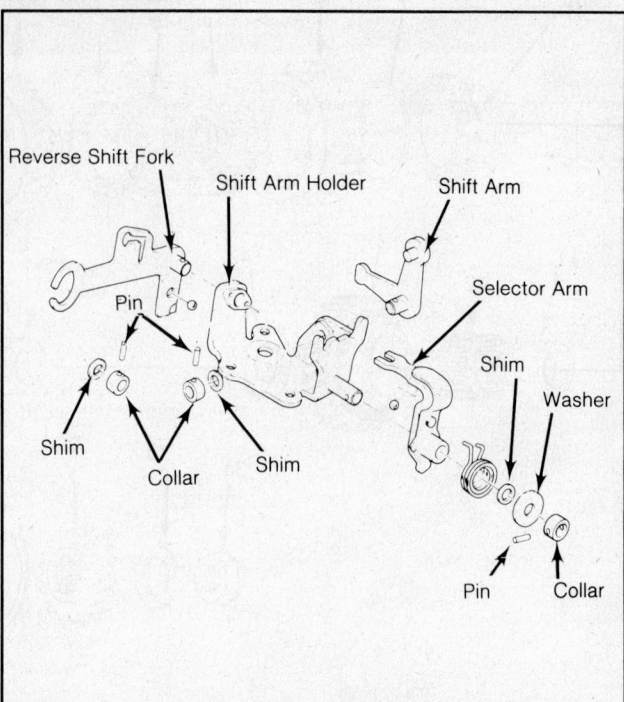

Fig. 15: *Exploded View of Accord & Prelude Shift Arm Holder*

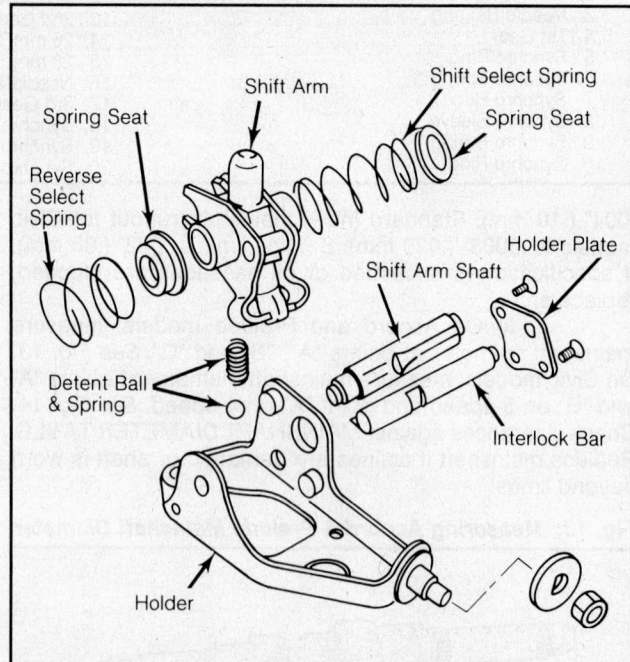

Fig. 16: *Exploded View of Civic Shift Arm Holder*

After assembly, check shift arm for free movement.

Reassembly (Civic)
1) Position shift arm, spring seats and springs into holder. Invert assembly and install detent ball and spring into bore in shift arm. Hold ball and spring in place with small screwdriver and insert shift shaft through arm, seats and springs.

2) Install interlock shaft. Install retainer plate and tighten attaching screws with impact driver. Stake screws in place with a center punch. After reassembly, check gear shift arm for free movement.

HONDA 4 & 5-SPEED (Cont.)

DIFFERENTIAL

CAUTION: Ring gear bolts have LEFT HAND threads.

Disassembly

Using a bearing puller, pull bearings from differential housing. Detach mount bolts and lift ring gear from differential. Using a pin punch, remove pinion gear shaft retaining spring pin. Remove pinion shaft, pinion gears, side gears and thrust washers from housing.

Inspection

Wash parts in solvent and dry with compressed air. Inspect ring gear teeth for chipping, wear and smooth rotation. Inspect pinion shaft for scoring or burrs. Check bearings for wear and smooth rotation. Replace any worn or damaged parts.

Reassembly

1) Coat all parts with Molykote before reassembly. Set pinion gears in place exactly opposite each other, in mesh with side gears. Install a thrust washer behind each one. Washers must be of equal thickness.

2) Rotate gears until shaft holes in pinion gears line up with shaft holes in carrier. Insert pinion shaft and align spring pin holes in one end with matching holes in carrier. Drive in spring pin.

3) After reassembly, place differential assembly on blocks and install drive axle shaft. Using a dial indicator, check pinion gear-to-side gear backlash. Measure at edge of teeth. Backlash should be .002-.006" (.05-.15 mm) for all models.

4) If backlash exceeds limit, disassemble differential and select new thrust washers of different thickness. Thrust washers must be of equal thickness. Thrust washers are available from .028" (.70 mm) to .039" (1.00 mm) in increments of .004" (.10 mm).

5) Check backlash again. If still out of tolerance, replace both pinion gears and recheck backlash. If still out of tolerance, replace side gears and recheck backlash. If still out of tolerance, replace carrier assembly.

6) After final backlash check and with all tolerances correct, install ring gear. Ensure chamfer on inside

Fig. 17: Exploded View of Differential Assembly

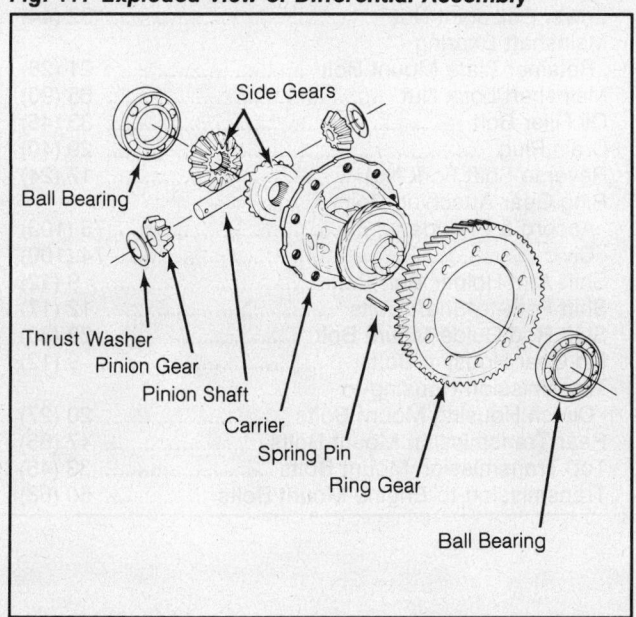

diameter of ring gear is toward carrier. Complete installation by reversing removal procedure.

TRANSAXLE REASSEMBLY & ADJUSTMENT

DIFFERENTIAL BEARING PRELOAD

1) Install differential bearing retaining snap ring into position in clutch housing, but do not install oil seals at this time. Install differential assembly into place in clutch housing using driver and Attachment "E" (07947-6340500) to ensure it is seated.

2) Install all transmission gear assemblies in clutch housing. See TRANSAXLE REASSEMBLY. Shift transmission into 3rd gear to position shift shaft guide for reassembly. Install new gasket, dowel pins and transmission housing onto clutch housing. Install all attaching bolts and tighten, in sequence, to specification. *See Fig. 18.*

Fig. 18: Tightening Transaxle Housing Bolts

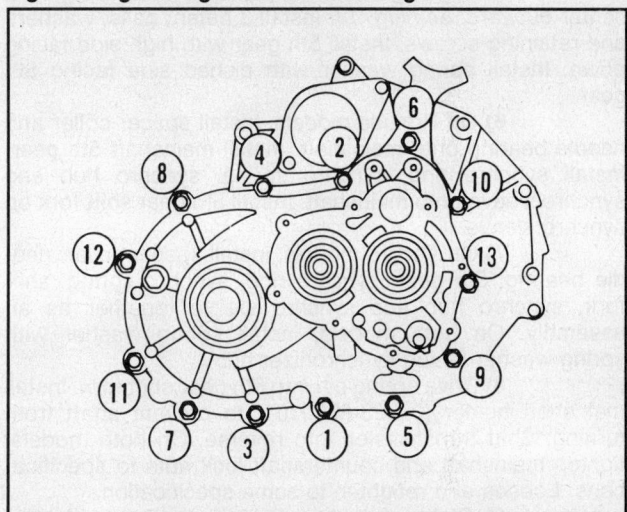

NOTE: If transaxle housing, differential carrier or differential bearings were replaced, the differential side clearance must be measured.

3) Ensure snap ring is installed in transmission housing. Use hammer and driver to bottom differential assembly in housing. Using a feeler gauge, measure clearance between snap ring and outer race of bearing in transmission housing.

4) Clearance should not exceed .006" (.15 mm). If thickness is not within specification, select a new snap ring of appropriate thickness. Install differential seals using driver and attachment (07947-6110500).

NOTE: Snap rings for Accord and Prelude models are available in thicknesses from .098" (2.50 mm) to .114" (2.90 mm) in increments of .004" (.10 mm). Civic model snap rings are available in thicknesses from .096" (2.45 mm) to .116" (2.95 mm) in .004" (.10 mm) increments.

TRANSAXLE REASSEMBLY
Accord & Prelude Models

1) Install differential assembly into clutch housing. Install mainshaft, countershaft, 1st/2nd gear shift shaft and 3rd/4th gear shift shaft together as an assembly.

Manual Transmissions

HONDA 4 & 5-SPEED (Cont.)

Ensure forks are in 4th and 2nd gear positions to make installation easier.

2) On Accord models, lift mainshaft and install interlock and shift guide together. On Prelude models, lift mainshaft and install interlock into selector arm. On both models, place shift rod in neutral. Hook interlock into selector arm, 1st/2nd gearshift shaft and 3rd/4th gearshift shaft. Hook shift guide into shift arm.

3) Install 5th/reverse shift shaft and hook its pin into reverse shift fork slot. Install shift guide so that it bottoms in clutch housing hole. Ensure guide shaft does not protrude more than .5" (12 mm) above interlock plate.

4) On Prelude models, install mainshaft bearing retainer plate. On both models, install reverse idler gear, shaft and back-up light switch with new washer. Place new gasket on clutch housing and install dowel pins. Shift transaxle into 3rd gear to position shift guide shaft for reassembly.

5) Install transmission housing, being sure to line up shafts. Shift guide shaft must seat in blind hole in transaxle housing. Tighten bolts in sequence starting from center outward. *See Fig. 18.* Install 3 detent balls, washers and retaining screws. Install 5th gear with high side facing down. Install spring washer with dished side facing 5th gear.

6) On Prelude models, install spacer collar and needle bearing onto mainshaft. Install mainshaft 5th gear. Install synchro ring, synchro spring, synchro hub and synchro sleeve onto mainshaft. Install 5th gear shift fork on synchro sleeve.

7) On Accord models, install spacer collar, needle bearing, 5th gear, synchro ring, synchro spring, shift fork, synchro hub and synchro sleeve together as an assembly. On both models, install spring washer with spring washer facing synchronizer hub.

8) Drive spring pin into 5th gear shift fork. Install mainshaft holder (07923-6890101) to prevent shaft from turning. Shift transmission into reverse. On both models, tighten mainshaft and countershaft lock nuts to specifications. Loosen and retighten to same specification.

9) Stake shoulders on lock nuts into slots in mainshaft and countershaft. Install end cover on transmission housing with new gasket and tighten mount bolts in sequence. Install proper sized snap ring into transmission housing. Install differential oil seals. Ensure part number side faces away from snap ring and bearing.

Civic Models

1) Install shift rod, selector arm, new lock plate and bolt. Bend lock tab on lock plate over against bolt head. Ensure snap ring is install in clutch housing. Install differential assembly into clutch housing.

2) Align shift arm with selector arm and install shift arm holder assembly onto clutch housing. Ensure mount bolts are installed in correct locations and tightened to specifications. Mesh mainshaft gears with countershaft gears, then install both assemblies into clutch housing.

3) Lift countershaft 1st/2nd synchronizer sleeve to shift transmission into 2nd gear. Install 1st/2nd gear shift fork on synchronizer sleeve. Rotate into place so that lugs on back of fork fit over shift arm. Insert 3rd/4th shift fork shaft into 3rd/4th shift guide and install spring pin.

4) Install 3rd/4th shift fork shaft into 3rd/4th shift fork. Install shift fork and hook shift guide to shift arm. Install 1st/2nd shift shaft. Hook reverse (5th/reverse on 5-speed) shift guide to shift arm and install shift shaft.

5) On 5-speed models, install spring and detent ball in hole in clutch housing. Ensure reverse shift fork is aligned with detent ball. On all models, install reverse shift fork with special washer and nut. Install reverse idler gear and shaft. Install lock plates and bolts on shift shafts and bend tabs.

6) Install transaxle housing and gasket while expanding countershaft bearing snap ring. Tighten housing bolts in sequence from center of housing to outer edge. *See Fig. 18.* Install 3 detent balls, washers, springs and retaining screws.

7) On 5-speed models, install mainshaft 5th gear, needle bearing and thrust washer. Install synchronizer ring and spring. Install synchronizer hub. Install sleeve and shift fork together as an assembly. Install synchronizer sleeve with chamfered surface facing end cover and synchronizer hub with high side facing 5th gear.

8) Drive spring pin into 5th gear shift fork. Install new gasket and dowel pins. On all models, expand snap ring with pliers and install housing cover bearing part way into cover. Ensure part number facing end cover. Release snap ring pliers and push bearing down until ring snaps into place around bearing. Install housing cover and tighten cover bolts.

9) Install mainshaft holder. Install mainshaft lock nut and tighten to specification. Loosen and retighten to same specification. Stake shoulder on lock nut into slot in mainshaft. Install oil barrier with plate tang aligned with housing groove.

10) Install end cover. Install snap ring and differential seals. Ensure seal part number faces away from bearing. Complete component assembly and installation in reverse of removal and disassembly procedures.

TIGHTENING SPECIFICATIONS

Application	Ft. Lbs. (N.m)
Back-Up Lamp Switch	18 (25)
Countershaft Lock Nut	65-80 (90-110)
Cover-to-Transaxle	9 (12)
Damper Fork Bolt	47 (65)
Damper Locking Bolt	32 (44)
Detent Ball Retainer Screw	16 (22)
End Cover Mount Bolt	9 (12)
Hub Spindle Nut	134 (185)
Lower Ball Joint Nut	32 (44)
Mainshaft Bearing	
Retainer Plate Mount Bolt	21 (28)
Mainshaft Lock Nut	65 (90)
Oil Filler Bolt	33 (45)
Drain Plug	29 (40)
Reverse Shift Fork Nut	17 (24)
Ring Gear Attaching Bolts	
Accord & Prelude	75 (103)
Civic	74 (100)
Shift Arm Holder Bolt	9 (12)
Shift Fork-to-Shaft Bolts	12 (17)
Shift Rod Guide Mount Bolt	22 (30)
5th Gear Housing Bolts	9 (12)
Transmission Housing-to	
Clutch Housing Mount Bolts	20 (27)
Rear Transmission Mount Bolts	47 (65)
Top Transmission Mount Bolts	33 (45)
Transmission-to-Engine Mount Bolts	50 (68)

ISUZU 4-SPEED

Isuzu I-Mark, P'UP

DESCRIPTION

Transmission is a floor shifted, fully synchronized 4-speed unit with block ring type synchronizers and a sliding mesh type reverse. The unit consists of a case with integral clutch housing, center support, rear extension, and gears. A shifter cover, located on top of rear extension housing, contains the transmission control mechanism. The case, center support and rear extension case are aluminum alloy to reduce weight.

LUBRICATION & ADJUSTMENT

See the appropriate article in MANUAL TRANSMISSION SERVICING Section.

TROUBLE SHOOTING

HARD SHIFTING

Improperly adjusted clutch. Weakened insert spring. Face of blocker ring, in contact with insert, worn. Cones on blocker ring and gear worn or not in proper contact.

SLIPS OUT OF GEAR

Bearings worn or defective. Excessive play between gears and collars. Play in clutch hub and sliding sleeve. Shift arm worn. Lock ball spring weak or broken.

TRANSMISSION NOISY

Low or incorrect lubricant. Gears or bearings worn or damaged. Worn collars. Worn clutch hub or mainshaft splines. Incorrectly meshed gears.

REMOVAL & INSTALLATION

See the appropriate article in MANUAL TRANSMISSION REMOVAL Section.

Fig. 1: Removing Throw-Out Bearing & Clutch Fork

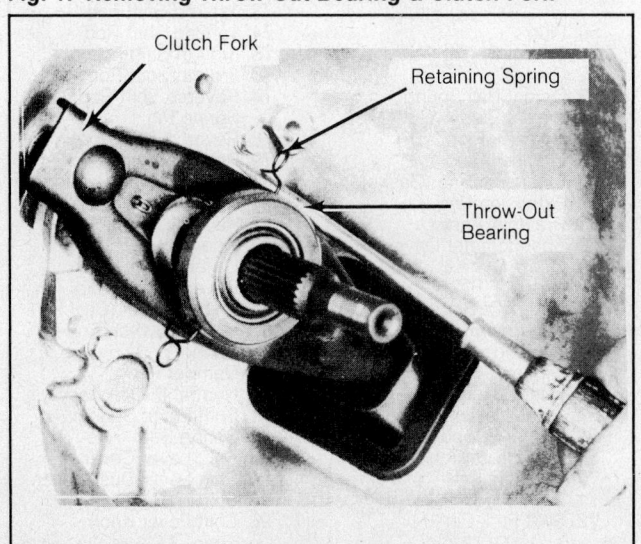

TRANSMISSION DISASSEMBLY

1) Disconnect retaining springs from throw-out bearing and remove bearing, dust cover and clutch fork. Remove 4 front bearing retainer bolts and remove retainer, gasket and spring washer.

2) Remove speedometer gear attaching bolt and take out speedometer driven gear assembly. Unscrew shifter cover bolts and remove cover and gasket.

3) Remove back-up light switch and CRS switch (if equipped). Remove rear extension attaching bolts, then remove extension and gasket.

4) Remove thrust washers and reverse idler gear from reverse idler gear shaft, then remove snap rings, speedometer drive gear and key from mainshaft.

5) Drive out roll pin from reverse shifter fork and remove shifter fork and reverse gear. Remove snap ring from outer edge of input shaft bearing. Slide off center support assembly from transmission case. Drive out roll pins from 3rd-4th and 1st-2nd shift forks.

Fig. 2: Removing Reverse Gear

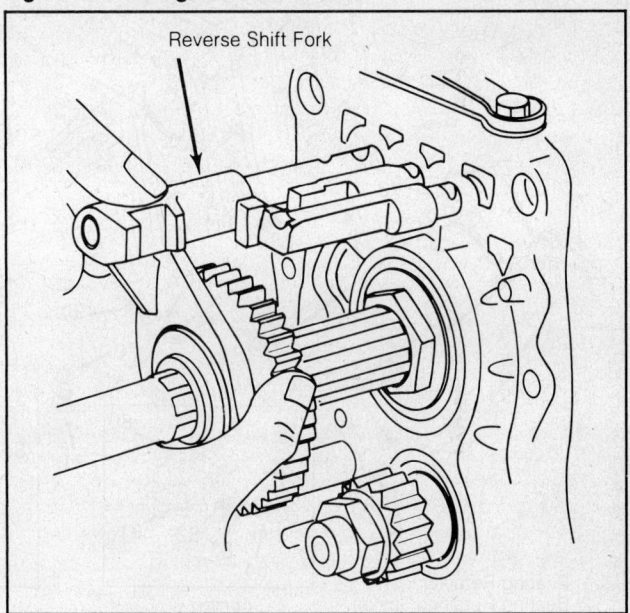

NOTE: Be careful not to damage shift forks when removing roll pins.

6) Remove detent spring plate, springs and balls from center support. Slide out 1st-2nd and 3rd-4th shift rods and remove shift forks. Remove reverse shift rod through front of case as it is fitted with detent interlock pins located between shifter rods in center support.

7) Move both synchros rearward to lock mainshaft. It may be necessary to tap synchros with hammer handle to engage them both. Straighten tab on lock washer and remove lock nut and washer from mainshaft.

8) Remove locking nut, washer, countergear reverse gear and collar from rear of countergear. Remove countergear bearing snap ring by expanding snap ring and tapping on front face of center support. Remove mainshaft rear bearing snap ring and remove center support.

Manual Transmissions

ISUZU 4-SPEED (Cont.)

Fig. 3: Exploded View of Isuzu 4-Speed Transmission Assembly

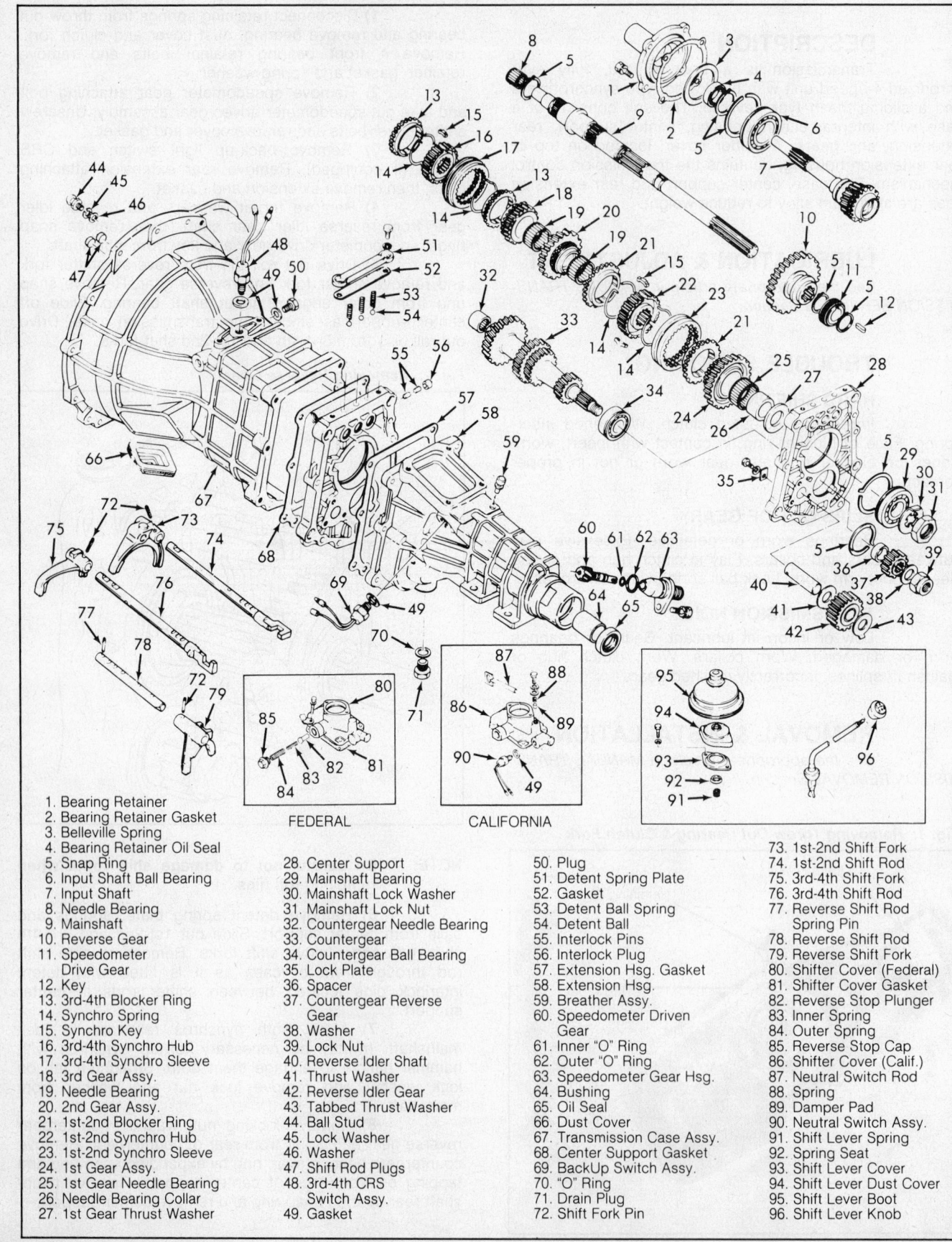

FEDERAL   CALIFORNIA

1. Bearing Retainer
2. Bearing Retainer Gasket
3. Belleville Spring
4. Bearing Retainer Oil Seal
5. Snap Ring
6. Input Shaft Ball Bearing
7. Input Shaft
8. Needle Bearing
9. Mainshaft
10. Reverse Gear
11. Speedometer Drive Gear
12. Key
13. 3rd-4th Blocker Ring
14. Synchro Spring
15. Synchro Key
16. 3rd-4th Synchro Hub
17. 3rd-4th Synchro Sleeve
18. 3rd Gear Assy.
19. Needle Bearing
20. 2nd Gear Assy.
21. 1st-2nd Blocker Ring
22. 1st-2nd Synchro Hub
23. 1st-2nd Synchro Sleeve
24. 1st Gear Assy.
25. 1st Gear Needle Bearing
26. Needle Bearing Collar
27. 1st Gear Thrust Washer

28. Center Support
29. Mainshaft Bearing
30. Mainshaft Lock Washer
31. Mainshaft Lock Nut
32. Countergear Needle Bearing
33. Countergear
34. Countergear Ball Bearing
35. Lock Plate
36. Spacer
37. Countergear Reverse Gear
38. Washer
39. Lock Nut
40. Reverse Idler Shaft
41. Thrust Washer
42. Reverse Idler Gear
43. Tabbed Thrust Washer
44. Ball Stud
45. Lock Washer
46. Washer
47. Shift Rod Plugs
48. 3rd-4th CRS Switch Assy.
49. Gasket

50. Plug
51. Detent Spring Plate
52. Gasket
53. Detent Ball Spring
54. Detent Ball
55. Interlock Pins
56. Interlock Plug
57. Extension Hsg. Gasket
58. Extension Hsg.
59. Breather Assy.
60. Speedometer Driven Gear
61. Inner "O" Ring
62. Outer "O" Ring
63. Speedometer Gear Hsg.
64. Bushing
65. Oil Seal
66. Dust Cover
67. Transmission Case Assy.
68. Center Support Gasket
69. BackUp Switch Assy.
70. "O" Ring
71. Drain Plug
72. Shift Fork Pin

73. 1st-2nd Shift Fork
74. 1st-2nd Shift Rod
75. 3rd-4th Shift Fork
76. 3rd-4th Shift Rod
77. Reverse Shift Rod Spring Pin
78. Reverse Shift Rod
79. Reverse Shift Fork
80. Shifter Cover (Federal)
81. Shifter Cover Gasket
82. Reverse Stop Plunger
83. Inner Spring
84. Outer Spring
85. Reverse Stop Cap
86. Shifter Cover (Calif.)
87. Neutral Switch Rod
88. Spring
89. Damper Pad
90. Neutral Switch Assy.
91. Shift Lever Spring
92. Spring Seat
93. Shift Lever Cover
94. Shift Lever Dust Cover
95. Shift Lever Boot
96. Shift Lever Knob

ISUZU 4-SPEED (Cont.)

Fig. 4: Removing Center Support from Transmission Case

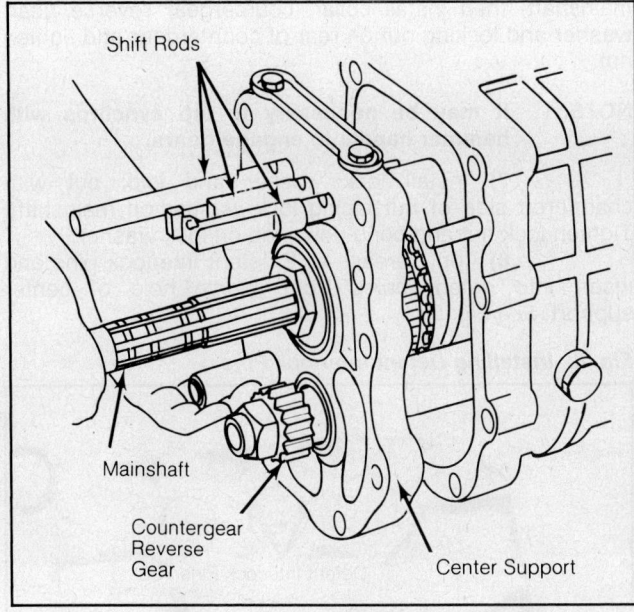

COMPONENT DISASSEMBLY & REASSEMBLY

MAINSHAFT

Disassembly

1) Separate input shaft, needle bearing and blocker ring from mainshaft. Using adapter plate tool (J-22912) and an arbor press, remove rear bearing from mainshaft. Remove thrust washer, 1st gear, needle bearing, collar and blocker ring.

2) Remove 1st-2nd synchro assembly. Remove 2nd gear, blocker ring and needle bearing. Remove snap ring, 3rd-4th synchro assembly and blocker ring. Remove 3rd gear and needle bearings. Remove snap ring from input shaft and press bearing off shaft. Using adapter plate tool (J-22912) and an arbor press, remove countergear bearing from countergear.

Fig. 5: Mainshaft Components

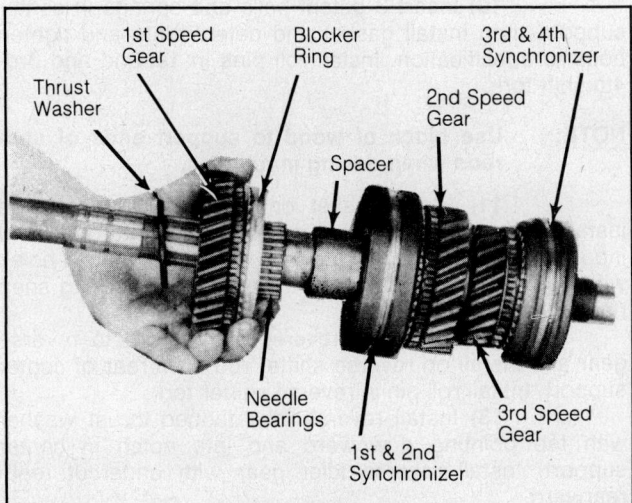

Inspection

1) Check mainshaft for wear, scoring or excessive runout. Maximum mainshaft runout is .002" (.05 mm). Check all gear teeth and splines for wear and/or damage. Check all bearings for smooth operation.

2) Check synchronizer assemblies for wear by holding blocker ring against cone section of gear and measuring clearance. If clearance exceeds .032" (.8 mm), replace blocker ring. Measure inside diameter of 1st, 2nd and 3rd gears. Measurements should be 1.773-1.776" (45.0-45.1 mm) for 1st gear; 1.615-1.619" (41.0-41.1 mm) for 2nd and 3rd gear.

3) Measure inside diameter of 1st gear and outside diameter of collar. If clearance exceeds .0197" (.5 mm), replace gear. Measure outside diameter of reverse idler gear shaft and inside diameter of gear bushing. Shaft diameter should be .866" (22 mm). If clearance between shaft and bushing exceeds .006" (.15 mm), replace bushing. Measure clearance between synchronizer hub splines and mainshaft splines in normal direction of rotation.

4) If clearance exceeds .008" (.2 mm), replace synchro-clutch hub. Check grooves in shift arms and blocks for wear and/or distortion. If thickness of shift arm pad is less than .256" (6.5 mm) for 3rd-4th shift arm and .276" (7.0 mm) for all other shift arms, replace as required.

Fig. 6: Measuring Blocker Ring Clearance

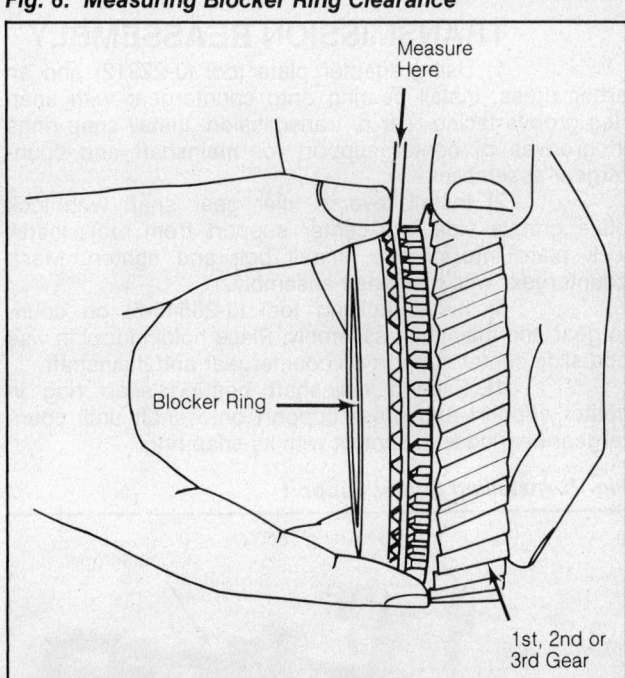

5) Check shift rod detent springs for weakening and/or damage. Measure spring free length. If less than 1.083" (27.5 mm) for all forward gears, or 1.051" (26.7 mm) for reverse gear, replace springs as required.

Reassembly

1) Hold front of mainshaft upward. Install 3rd gear with tapered side facing front of mainshaft and install needle bearing. Install blocker ring with teeth upward. Install synchro hub with heavy boss toward face of sleeve with small chamfer on outer edge.

2) Place keys into key grooves and position synchro springs into hole inside face of hub. Make sure

Manual Transmissions

ISUZU 4-SPEED (Cont.)

hub and sleeve slide smoothly. Install 3rd-4th synchro assembly on mainshaft with face of sleeve with small chamfer on outer edge facing rearward. Install snap ring.

3) Hold rear of mainshaft upward. Install 2nd gear and needle bearing with taper surface of gear facing rearward on mainshaft. Install blocker ring with teeth downward. Install 1st-2nd synchro assembly with small chamfer on sleeve facing front of mainshaft. Install synchro hub with chamfer on inner edge toward face of sleeve with large chamfer on outer edge.

4) Place keys into key grooves and position synchro springs into hole in either side face of hub. Make sure hub and sleeve slide smoothly. Install blocker ring with teeth rearward. Install collar, needle bearing and 1st gear with tapered side of gear facing front of mainshaft.

5) Install 1st gear thrust washer with grooved side facing 1st gear on mainshaft. Place rear bearing on mainshaft with snap ring groove facing front of mainshaft. Press bearing onto shaft using adapter plate tool (J-22912) and an arbor press. Place input shaft bearing on input shaft with snap ring groove facing front of input shaft.

6) Press bearing onto shaft using adapter plate tool (J-22912) and an arbor press. Install snap ring on input shaft bearing and install needle bearing, blocker ring and input shaft assembly to front of mainshaft.

TRANSMISSION REASSEMBLY

1) Using adapter plate tool (J-22912) and an arbor press, install bearing onto countergear with snap ring groove facing rear of transmission. Install snap rings in grooves of center support for mainshaft and countergear assemblies.

2) Install reverse idler gear shaft with lock plate groove side into center support from rear. Install lock plate into groove, install bolt and tighten. Mesh countergear with mainshaft assembly.

3) Install holding tool (J-26545-5) on countergear and mainshaft assembly. Place holding tool in vise and slide center support on countergear and mainshaft.

4) Expand mainshaft bearing snap ring in center support and press support onto shaft until countergear bearing is in contact with its snap ring.

Fig. 7: Installing Center Support

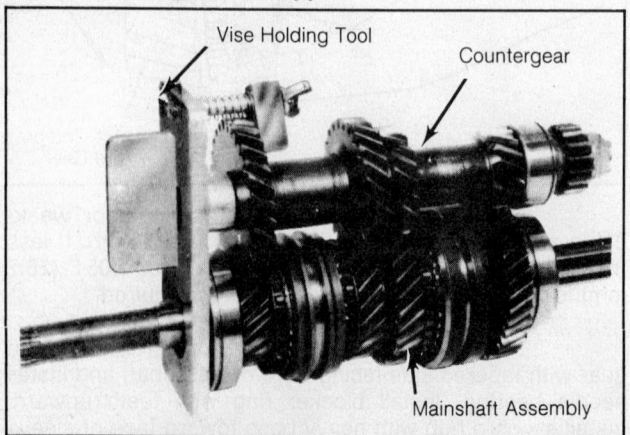

5) Expand countergear bearing snap ring and press center support further until the mainshaft and countergear snap rings snap into their grooves.

6) Remove holding tool from countergear and mainshaft assembly. Slide both synchros rearward to lock mainshaft, then install collar, countergear reverse gear, washer and locking nut on rear of countergear and tighten nut.

NOTE: It may be necessary to tap synchros with hammer handle to engage gears.

7) Install lock washer and lock nut with chamfered side of nut facing lock washer on mainshaft. Tighten lock nut and bend down tab on lock washer.

8) Apply grease to 2 detent interlock pins and insert into detent holes from middle hole of center support. See Fig. 8.

Fig. 8: Installing Detent Interlock Pins

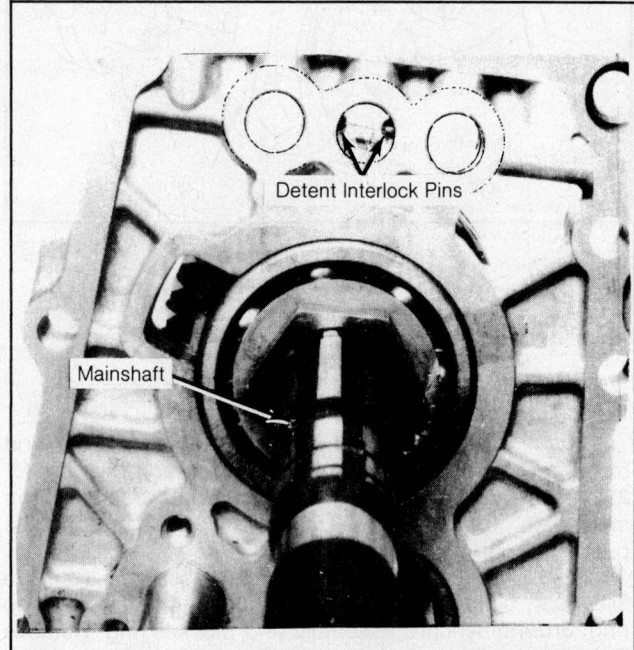

9) Place shift forks into position on synchronizer grooves then install 1st-2nd and 3rd-4th shifter rods through holes in center support and shift forks from front side of center support.

10) Insert 3 detent balls and springs in center support, then install gasket and detent plate and tighten bolts to specification. Install roll pins in 1st-2nd and 3rd-4th shift fork.

NOTE: Use block of wood to support ends of shift rods when driving in roll pins.

11) Place gasket on transmission case and install center support with mainshaft, countergear and input shaft assembly, making sure to align dowel pin holes with dowel pins correctly. Install input shaft bearing snap ring.

12) Assemble reverse shifter fork to reverse gear and install on reverse shifter rod from rear of center support. Install roll pin in reverse shifter fork.

13) Install reverse idler tabbed thrust washer with tab pointing downward and into notch in center support. Install reverse idler gear with undercut teeth rearward.

Fig. 9: Installing Reverse Idler Gear

Thrust Washer
Tab

14) Install speedometer drive gear snap ring and Woodruff key on mainshaft, then install speedometer drive gear on shaft, aligning gear with key. Install snap ring.

15) Coat outer reverse idler thrust washer with grease and install in extension housing with tab pointing downward into notch in housing. Check gear backlash. It should not exceed .016" (.4 mm) for all gears. If not, replace gears as required.

16) Place gasket on center support and install extension housing. Make sure to align dowel pin correctly. Install and tighten bolts. Install back-up light and CRS (Federal models) switches.

17) Install gasket and gear shift cover on extension housing and tighten bolts to specification, then install speedometer driven gear to rear extension and tighten bolt.

18) Install spring washer on shaft, with dished face toward input shaft gear bearing. Install input shaft bearing retainer gasket and retainer. Tighten bolts.

NOTE: The 2 shorter bolts are used on countergear front bearing side of bearing retainer.

19) Install dust cover, clutch fork and throw-out bearing with retaining springs. Install drain plug and refill transmission with correct fluid.

TIGHTENING SPECIFICATIONS

Application	Ft. Lbs. (N.m)
Countergear Lock Nut	108 (146)
Mainshaft Lock Nut	94 (127)
Detent Plate Bolts	14 (19)
Extension Housing-to-Center Support Bolts	27 (37)
Shift Cover Bolts	14 (19)
Input Shaft Bearing Retainer	14 (19)

Manual Transmissions

ISUZU 4-SPEED WITH INTEGRAL TRANSFER CASE

Isuzu P'UP (4WD), Trooper II

DESCRIPTION

Transmission is a floor shifted, fully synchronized 4-speed unit with block ring type synchronizers and a sliding mesh type reverse. This unit consists of a transmission case with integral clutch housing, center support, transfer case with transfer side case and gears. A shifter cover, located on top of transfer case, contains the transmission control mechanism. Another shifter cover located on the transfer side case contains the range and four wheel drive shifting mechanism.

LUBRICATION & ADJUSTMENT

See the appropriate article in MANUAL TRANSMISSION SERVICING Section.

REMOVAL & INSTALLATION

See the appropriate article in MANUAL TRANSMISSION REMOVAL Section.

TROUBLE SHOOTING

HARD SHIFTING

Improperly adjusted clutch. Weakened insert spring. Face of blocker ring, in contact with insert, worn. Cones on blocker ring and gear worn or not in proper contact.

SLIPS OUT OF GEAR

Bearings worn or defective. Excessive play between gears and collars. Play in clutch hub and sliding sleeve. Shift arm worn. Lock ball spring weak or broken.

TRANSMISSION NOISY

Low or incorrect lubricant. Gears or bearings worn or damaged. Worn gears or collars. Worn clutch hub or mainshaft splines. Incorrectly meshed gears.

TRANSMISSION DISASSEMBLY

1) Remove retainer springs, throw-out bearing, clutch fork and boot. Remove 4 bolts holding bearing retainer-to-transmission case. Remove bearing retainer, gasket and spring washer. Remove speedometer gear mount bolt, bushing and driven gear assembly.

2) Remove back-up light and coasting richer switch (Federal models) switches. Remove snap ring from input shaft bearing. Remove 8 bolts holding transfer case, center support and transmission case together. Separate transmission case and gasket from center support and transfer case.

3) Remove 4 bolts attaching transfer countershaft lock plate. Remove lock plate and shim. Remove center support assembly from transfer case. Drive spring pins out from 3rd-4th and 1st-2nd shift forks. Remove spring pin from reverse shifter fork.

4) Remove detent spring plate from center support, then remove detent springs and balls. Remove 1st-2nd and 3rd-4th shift rods from center support. Remove shift forks. Remove reverse shifter rod forward to avoid losing the detent interlock pins.

CAUTION: Remove shifter rods carefully so as not to lose detent interlock pins located between shifter rods in center support.

5) Move both synchronizers rearward to prevent mainshaft from turning. Synchronizers may need to be tapped with hammer handle to engage. Place support tool (J-26545), with mainshaft countergear assembled, into a vise. Remove mainshaft lock nut with spacer.

6) Remove transfer clutch hub, transfer input gear, needle bearing, collar, reverse clutch hub, reverse sleeve, reverse gear, needle bearing, collar and thrust washer from rear of mainshaft.

7) Remove countergear lock nut, washer and collar from rear of countergear. Remove countergear snap ring by inserting snap ring pliers into hole in center support. Tap on front of center support while expanding snap ring.

8) Remove center support while expanding mainshaft rear bearing snap ring. If necessary, remove countergear front bearing using bearing removers (J-26544 and J-8092).

COMPONENT DISASSEMBLY & REASSEMBLY

MAINSHAFT

Disassembly

1) Separate input shaft gear, needle bearing and blocker ring from mainshaft assembly. Using bearing removal tool (J-22912) and an arbor press, remove rear bearing from mainshaft.

2) Remove thrust washer, 1st gear, needle bearing, collar and blocker ring. Remove 1st-2nd gear synchronizer assembly. Remove 2nd gear, blocker ring and needle bearing.

3) Remove snap ring, 3rd-4th synchronizer assembly and blocker ring. Remove 3rd gear and needle bearings.

4) Remove snap ring from input shaft gear. Remove bearing using an arbor press and bearing removal tool. Remove countershaft reverse gear and countergear bearing using bearing removal tool (J-22912) and an arbor press.

Inspection

1) Check mainshaft outer face, needle bearing fitting faces and splined portion of shaft for wear, scoring or warpage. Maximum permissable runout of mainshaft is .002" (.05 mm). Check all gear teeth for wear or damage. Inspect all bearings for smooth operation.

2) Check synchronizer assemblies for wear by holding blocker ring against cone section of gear and measure clearance. If clearance is less than .032" (.80 mm), replace blocker ring. Measure clearance between synchronizer clutch hub splines and mainshaft splines in normal direction of rotation.

3) If clearance exceeds .008" (.20 mm), replace synchronizer clutch hub. Check grooves in shift arms and blocks for wear and/or damage. If thickness of shift arm pads is less than .256" (6.50 mm) for 3rd-4th shift arm, .276" (7 mm) for 1st-2nd, .256" (6.50 mm) for reverse shift arm and .236" (6 mm) for transfer range and 4WD shift arms, replace shift arms.

4) Inspect shift rods for bending or wear and replace as needed. Check shift rod detent springs for weakening and/or distortion. Measure spring free length.

ISUZU 4-SPEED WITH INTEGRAL TRANSFER CASE (Cont.)

Fig. 1: Exploded View Showing 4-Speed Transmission Case & Transfer Case with Shifting Mechanism

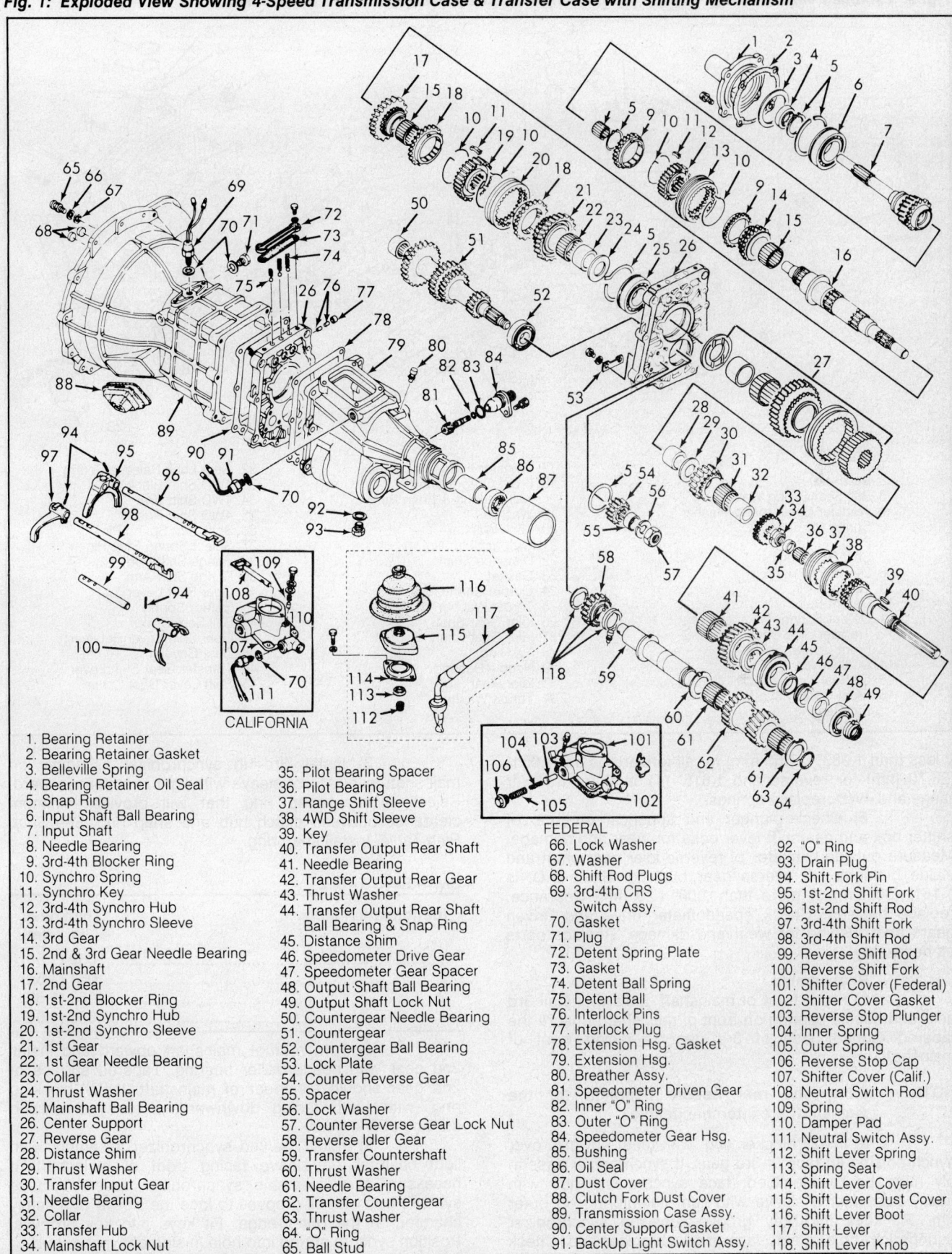

1. Bearing Retainer
2. Bearing Retainer Gasket
3. Belleville Spring
4. Bearing Retainer Oil Seal
5. Snap Ring
6. Input Shaft Ball Bearing
7. Input Shaft
8. Needle Bearing
9. 3rd-4th Blocker Ring
10. Synchro Spring
11. Synchro Key
12. 3rd-4th Synchro Hub
13. 3rd-4th Synchro Sleeve
14. 3rd Gear
15. 2nd & 3rd Gear Needle Bearing
16. Mainshaft
17. 2nd Gear
18. 1st-2nd Blocker Ring
19. 1st-2nd Synchro Hub
20. 1st-2nd Synchro Sleeve
21. 1st Gear
22. 1st Gear Needle Bearing
23. Collar
24. Thrust Washer
25. Mainshaft Ball Bearing
26. Center Support
27. Reverse Gear
28. Distance Shim
29. Thrust Washer
30. Transfer Input Gear
31. Needle Bearing
32. Collar
33. Transfer Hub
34. Mainshaft Lock Nut

35. Pilot Bearing Spacer
36. Pilot Bearing
37. Range Shift Sleeve
38. 4WD Shift Sleeve
39. Key
40. Transfer Output Rear Shaft
41. Needle Bearing
42. Transfer Output Rear Gear
43. Thrust Washer
44. Transfer Output Rear Shaft Ball Bearing & Snap Ring
45. Distance Shim
46. Speedometer Drive Gear
47. Speedometer Gear Spacer
48. Output Shaft Ball Bearing
49. Output Shaft Lock Nut
50. Countergear Needle Bearing
51. Countergear
52. Countergear Ball Bearing
53. Lock Plate
54. Counter Reverse Gear
55. Spacer
56. Lock Washer
57. Counter Reverse Gear Lock Nut
58. Reverse Idler Gear
59. Transfer Countershaft
60. Thrust Washer
61. Needle Bearing
62. Transfer Countergear
63. Thrust Washer
64. "O" Ring
65. Ball Stud

66. Lock Washer
67. Washer
68. Shift Rod Plugs
69. 3rd-4th CRS Switch Assy.
70. Gasket
71. Plug
72. Detent Spring Plate
73. Gasket
74. Detent Ball Spring
75. Detent Ball
76. Interlock Pins
77. Interlock Plug
78. Extension Hsg. Gasket
79. Extension Hsg.
80. Breather Assy.
81. Speedometer Driven Gear
82. Inner "O" Ring
83. Outer "O" Ring
84. Speedometer Gear Hsg.
85. Bushing
86. Oil Seal
87. Dust Cover
88. Clutch Fork Dust Cover
89. Transmission Case Assy.
90. Center Support Gasket
91. BackUp Light Switch Assy.

92. "O" Ring
93. Drain Plug
94. Shift Fork Pin
95. 1st-2nd Shift Fork
96. 1st-2nd Shift Rod
97. 3rd-4th Shift Fork
98. 3rd-4th Shift Rod
99. Reverse Shift Rod
100. Reverse Shift Fork
101. Shifter Cover (Federal)
102. Shifter Cover Gasket
103. Reverse Stop Plunger
104. Inner Spring
105. Outer Spring
106. Reverse Stop Cap
107. Shifter Cover (Calif.)
108. Neutral Switch Rod
109. Spring
110. Damper Pad
111. Neutral Switch Assy.
112. Shift Lever Spring
113. Spring Seat
114. Shift Lever Cover
115. Shift Lever Dust Cover
116. Shift Lever Boot
117. Shift Lever
118. Shift Lever Knob

ISUZU 4-SPEED WITH INTEGRAL TRANSFER CASE (Cont.)

Fig. 2: Exploded View Showing 4-Speed Transmission Side Case Gears and Shift Mechanism

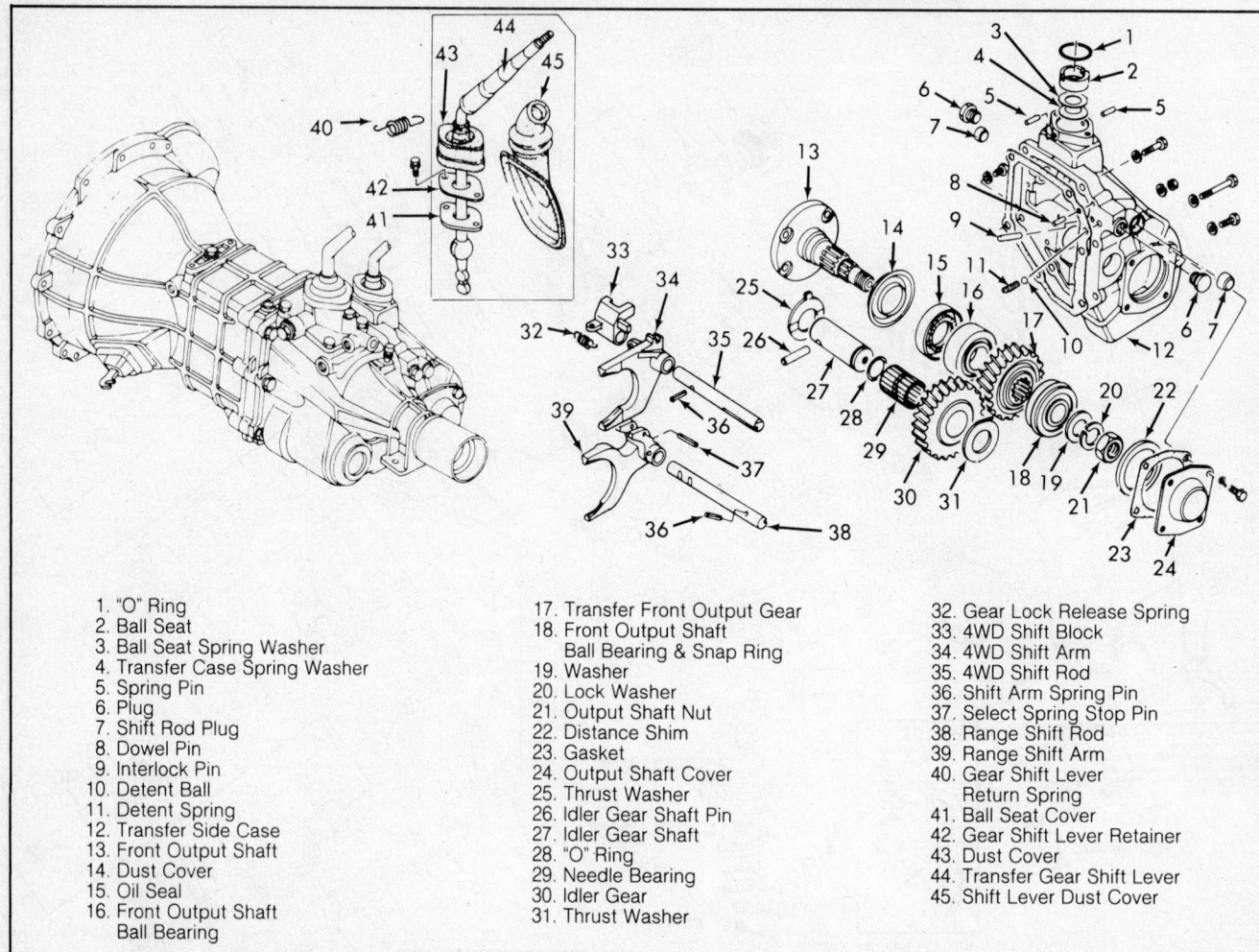

1. "O" Ring	17. Transfer Front Output Gear	32. Gear Lock Release Spring
2. Ball Seat	18. Front Output Shaft	33. 4WD Shift Block
3. Ball Seat Spring Washer	Ball Bearing & Snap Ring	34. 4WD Shift Arm
4. Transfer Case Spring Washer	19. Washer	35. 4WD Shift Rod
5. Spring Pin	20. Lock Washer	36. Shift Arm Spring Pin
6. Plug	21. Output Shaft Nut	37. Select Spring Stop Pin
7. Shift Rod Plug	22. Distance Shim	38. Range Shift Rod
8. Dowel Pin	23. Gasket	39. Range Shift Arm
9. Interlock Pin	24. Output Shaft Cover	40. Gear Shift Lever
10. Detent Ball	25. Thrust Washer	Return Spring
11. Detent Spring	26. Idler Gear Shaft Pin	41. Ball Seat Cover
12. Transfer Side Case	27. Idler Gear Shaft	42. Gear Shift Lever Retainer
13. Front Output Shaft	28. "O" Ring	43. Dust Cover
14. Dust Cover	29. Needle Bearing	44. Transfer Gear Shift Lever
15. Oil Seal	30. Idler Gear	45. Shift Lever Dust Cover
16. Front Output Shaft	31. Thrust Washer	
Ball Bearing		

If less than 1.083" (27.50 mm) for all forward gears, 1.051" (26.70 mm) for reverse and 1.615" (41 mm) for transfer range and 4WD, replace springs.

    5) Check plunger and spherical portions of shifter box and gearshift lever boss for wear and damage. Measure outside diameter of reverse idler gear shaft and inside diameter of reverse gear bushing. Shaft O.D. is 1.181" (30 mm). If more than .008" (.20 mm) clearance, replace bushing. Check speedometer drive and driven gears and bushing for wear and damage. Replace parts as necessary.

Reassembly

    1) Place front of mainshaft upward. Install 3rd gear and needle bearing on front of mainshaft. Ensure the tapered (coned) side of 3rd gear is facing front of mainshaft.

NOTE: **Front and rear needle bearings for the mainshaft are interchangeable.**

    2) Install blocker ring, with teeth upward, over synchronizing surface of 3rd gear. If synchronizer assembly must be reassembled, face synchronizer hub with heavy boss facing sleeve with light chamfering on outer rim. Fit keys into key groove. Position synchronizer springs into hole in side face of synchronizer hub. Check that hub and sleeve slide smoothly.

    3) Install 3rd-4th synchronizer assembly on mainshaft with face of sleeve with light chamfer rearward. Select thickest snap ring that will provide minimum clearance between clutch hub and snap ring. *See Snap Ring Table.* Install snap ring.

SNAP RING TABLE

Identification Mark	Thickness In. (mm)
1	.059 (1.50)
2	.061 (1.55)
3	.063 (1.60)
4	.065 (1.65)

    4) Turn rear of mainshaft upward and install 2nd gear with needle roller bearing. Tapered surface of 2nd gear should face rear of mainshaft. Install blocking ring, with teeth facing downward, over synchronizing surface of 2nd gear.

    5) Install 1st-2nd synchronizer assembly, with light chamfer on sleeve facing front of mainshaft. If necessary to reassemble synchronizer assembly, face synchro hub with oil grooves to face the sleeve with heavy chamfer on the outer edge. Fit keys into key grooves. Position synchro spring into hole in side of synchro hub.

ISUZU 4-SPEED WITH INTEGRAL TRANSFER CASE (Cont.)

6) Install blocker ring with teeth facing rearward. Install collar, needle bearing and 1st gear on mainshaft. Tapered side of gear should face front of mainshaft. Install 1st gear thrust washer on mainshaft with grooved side facing 1st gear.

7) Install rear bearing onto mainshaft using bearing removal tool (J-22912) and an arbor press. Ensure snap ring groove in bearing is facing front of mainshaft.

8) If removed, install ball bearing onto input shaft, using bearing removal tool (J-22912) and an arbor press. Ensure snap ring groove on bearing is facing front of transmission. Install snap ring on input shaft. Install needle bearing, blocker ring and input shaft assembly onto front of mainshaft.

TRANSFER CASE
Disassembly
1) Remove thrust washer, reverse idler gear and thrust washer with ball (pin). Remove range shift sleeve and pilot needle bearing from rear of output shaft.

2) Lightly tap transfer countershaft assembly out through shaft hole in transfer case. Expand rear output shaft front bearing snap ring and remove output shaft assembly.

3) Remove "O" ring, thrust washer, countergear, needle bearings and thrust washer from transfer countershaft. Remove rear output shaft nut. Press rear bearing off output shaft using press. Remove spacer, speedometer drive gear and key distance piece from output shaft.

4) Press output shaft front bearing, with thrust washer and rear output gear, from output shaft. Remove output gear needle bearing and 4WD shift sleeve from output shaft.

Inspection
1) Check the outer face and needle bearing fitting faces of rear output shaft for wear or scoring. Check splines for damage. Light scoring or damage can be corrected with an oil stone, otherwise replace shaft.

2) Inspect bearings for smoothness of rotation, abnormal noises, play in direction of thrust and cracking, wear or corrosion on needle rollers. Check gears for step wear or roughness. Replace components that are worn or damaged beyond correction.

Reassembly
1) Install new oil seal into transfer case using seal installer (J-29769). If removed, install output shaft front bearing snap ring to transfer case. Install 4WD shift sleeve, with heavy chamfered side toward output gear, on rear of output shaft.

2) Install needle bearing, output gear and thrust washer on output shaft. Ensure oil grooved side of thrust washer faces output gear. Press output shaft front bearing onto output shaft. Ensure snap ring groove on bearing is turned rearward.

3) Install shim (with oil grooved side toward front bearing), speedometer drive gear key, drive gear and spacer to output shaft. Press output shaft rear bearing, with sealed face toward the rear, onto output shaft. Install output shaft nut and tighten. Stake nut to groove in shaft.

4) Apply grease to needle bearings and both faces of thrust washers. Install thrust washer on countershaft (with oil groove facing countergear) by aligning finger on washer with cutaway portion of shaft. Install needle bearing, countergear, needle bearing, thrust washer and new "O" ring onto transfer countershaft.

5) Install output shaft assembly into transfer case by expanding front bearing snap ring into transfer case groove far enough so front bearing can be inserted. Allow snap ring to engage bearing groove.

6) Install transfer countershaft assembly into transfer case. Ensure cutaway portion at front end of countershaft is positioned correctly. The finger on thrust washer, on rear of shaft, should be aligned with groove in transfer case. See Fig. 3 and Fig. 4.

Fig. 3: Alignment of Transfer Countershaft in Transfer Case

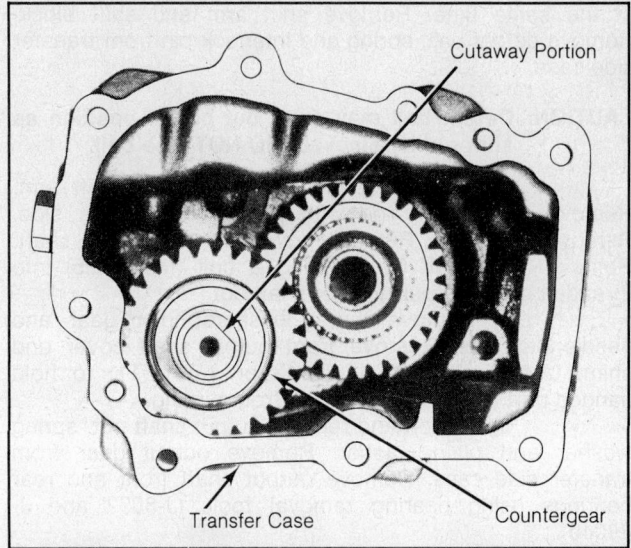

Ensure that the cutaway portion at front end of the countershaft is positioned as shown.

Fig. 4: Alignment of Thrust Washer on Transfer Countershaft in Transfer Case

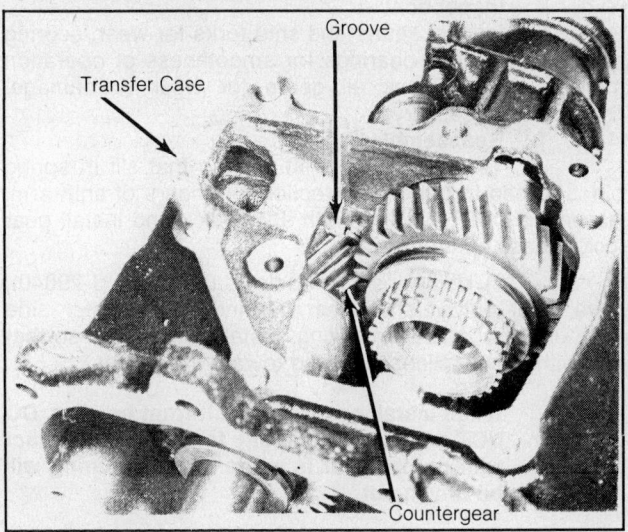

Ensure that finger on thrust washer fitted to rear of shaft is aligned with groove in case.

7) Grease output shaft pilot bearing. Install bearing and range shift sleeve on output shaft. Ensure end of sleeve with heavy chamfering is toward front of transfer case.

ISUZU 4-SPEED WITH INTEGRAL TRANSFER CASE (Cont.)

8) Install thrust washer with ball (pin), reverse idler gear (with shift arm) and thrust washer (with oil groove side toward reverse idler gear).

TRANSFER SIDE CASE
Disassembly

1) Remove range shift rod detent spring and ball. Remove 4WD indicator light switch (if equipped). Remove screw plug from each shift rod. Remove spring pin from 4WD shift arm.

2) Hold range shift rod in high range position. Drive out 4WD shift rod from rear side. Plug will come out at the same time. Remove shift arm and shift block. Remove detent ball, spring and interlock pin from transfer side case.

CAUTION: Detent ball may snap out out of position as shift rod is removed. DO NOT lose ball.

3) Remove spring pin from range shift arm. Remove range shift rod with plug through front side. Remove shift arm. Remove dowel pin from idler shaft. Remove idler shaft by inserting a bolt (M8 x 1.25) into threaded hole and pulling idler shaft out.

4) Remove thrust washers, idler gear and needle bearings. Remove front output shaft cover and shim. Use pin wrench (J-29042 or J-8614-11) to hold flanged part of front output shaft from turning.

5) Loosen and remove output shaft nut, spring washer and plain washer. Remove output gear from transfer side case. Remove output shaft front and rear bearings using bearing removal tools (J-8092 and J-29040).

NOTE: **Remove front bearing with oil seal.**

6) Remove gear lock release spring from 4WD shift arm, then disconnect shift arm and shift block. Remove spring pin from range shift arm.

Inspection

Inspect shafts and shift forks for wear, scoring or damage. Check bearings for smoothness of operation and for wear. Check all gears for wear or damage. Replace as necessary.

Reassembly

1) Install range shift arm so that slit in spring pin is turned in opposite direction as fingers of shift arm. Assemble 4WD shift arm with shift block and install gear lock release spring. See Fig. 5.

2) Using installer tools (J-8092 and J-29040), drive front output shaft rear bearing into transfer side case until it contacts snap ring. Install output gear so that end with uncut splines is turned toward front side.

NOTE: **When installing output shaft front bearing, DO NOT drive bearing in any farther once contact with output gear is made or rear bearing will be driven out.**

3) Using installer tools, drive output shaft front bearing into transfer side case until it contacts output gear. After installing front bearing, check rear bearing snap ring for proper contact with case. Install output shaft oil seal using seal installer (J-29037).

4) Install output shaft, plain washer, spring washer and output shaft nut. Use pin wrench to hold shaft from turning and tighten output shaft nut. Install shim in

transfer side case. Install output shaft cover and tighten bolts.

Fig. 5: Assembling 4WD Shift Arm with Shift Block

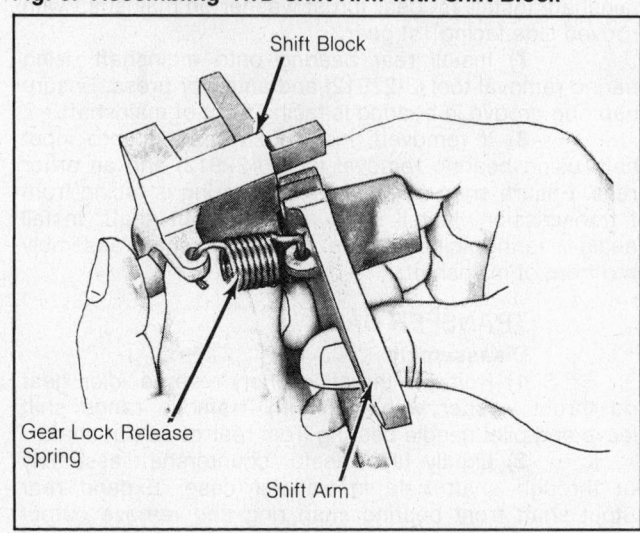

5) Apply grease to both sides of idler gear thrust washer and install with oil grooved face toward gear. Ensure tab on washer aligns with notch in case. Grease idler gear needle bearing and install bearings on gear. Ensure heavier bossed end is turned toward front.

6) Apply grease to new "O" ring on idler shaft. Install idler shaft, with dowel pin groove turned downward, into case until groove lines up with dowel pin fitting hole. Install dowel pin into transfer side case. Dowel should protrude .355-.433" (9-11 mm).

7) Install range shift arm and shift rod, then install spring pin to hold parts in place. Install interlock pin, 4WD shift rod detent spring and detent ball into case. Hold range shift rod in high range and install 4WD shift arm and shift block (with shift rod) into transfer side case.

8) Insert spring pin to secure parts. Install shift rod plugs and screw plugs. Install range shift rod detent ball and spring into position. Install 4WD indicator light switch. See Fig. 6.

TRANSMISSION REASSEMBLY

1) If removed, install countershaft reverse gear and countergear ball bearing with snap ring groove facing rear of transmission. Use adapter (J-22912) and press to install bearing. If removed, install snap rings in grooves in inner circumference of countergear and mainshaft bores of center support.

2) If removed, install countergear front bearing using bearing installer tools (J-26544 and J-8092). Mesh gears of mainshaft and countergear together and install on a holding fixture (J-26545). Install holding fixture in a vise, then install center support.

3) While installing center support, expand mainshaft snap ring and press center support onto mainshaft and countergear until countergear bearing hits its snap ring. Expand countergear snap ring and press center support further until both snap rings fit into grooves.

4) Move both synchronizers rearward to prevent mainshaft from turning. If necessary, tap synchronizers with hammer handle to engage them. Install

ISUZU 4-SPEED WITH INTEGRAL TRANSFER CASE (Cont.)

washers and lock nut on rear of countergear. Tighten nut to 80 ft. lbs. (110 N.m.).

Fig. 6: Installation of 4WD Shift Rod, Fork, Range Shift Rod, Range Shift Fork and Detent Spring

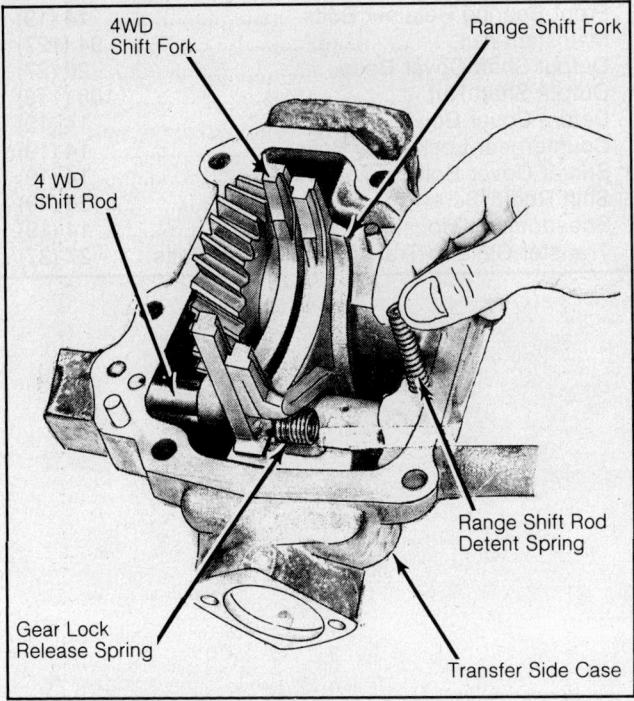

5) Install reverse gear thrust washer on mainshaft with grooved side facing reverse gear. Install collar, needle bearing and reverse gear on mainshaft. The clutch teeth side of reverse gear should be facing rear of mainshaft.

6) Assemble sleeve with reverse clutch hub. Ensure stepped face of hub is on chamfered side of sleeve. Install reverse clutch hub and sleeve. Ensure chamfered face of sleeve is turned to front side of mainshaft.

7) Install collar, needle bearing and input gear onto mainshaft. Ensure input gear is installed with clutching teeth rearward. Install transfer clutch hub on mainshaft with chamfering on outer edge facing rear of mainshaft. Install lock nut on mainshaft and tighten. Caulk lock nut to prevent loosening. Install spacer to mainshaft.

8) Remove holding fixture from mainshaft and countergear and remove assembly from vise. Apply grease to 2 interlock pins. Insert pins into detent holes from middle hole of center support. Install 1st and 2nd shifter forks and 3rd and 4th shifter forks into their grooves in synchronizer assembly.

NOTE: **The 3rd-4th shifter rod can be identified by 2 detent grooves on side of rod.**

9) Install 3rd-4th shifter rod from rear of center support through middle hole. Then install into 1st-2nd and 3rd-4th shifter forks. Align spring pin hole in shifter fork with hole in shifter rod.

10) Install 1st-2nd shifter rod from rear of center support, through 1st-2nd shifter fork. Align hole in rod to hole in shifter fork. The reverse detent spring is identified as the shorter of the 3 springs. Install reverse shifter fork into its groove in reverse sliding sleeve.

11) Install reverse shifter rod from the front of center support through the reverse shifter fork. Align hole in rod with hole in shifter fork. Install 3 spring pins in 1st-2nd, 3rd-4th and reverse shifter forks.

NOTE: **When installing spring pins, ensure shifter rod is supported, by round bar against end of shifter rod, to prevent damage.**

12) Install detent balls, detent spring, gasket and retainer on top of center support. Tighten cover bolts to 14 ft. lbs. (19 N.m). Place transfer case upright on wooden blocks. Apply thin coat of grease to end of reverse shift rod, mainshaft and transfer countershaft. Install center support assembly and new gasket into transfer case.

13) Ensure the following parts are installed together in the following order: reverse shift rod-to-reverse shift rod hole fitting, mainshaft-to-output shaft fitting, transfer countershaft-to-countershaft hole fitting, countershaft reverse gear-to-reverse idler gear engaged, input gear-to-transfer countergear engaged, range shift sleeve-to-clutch hub is engaged and dowel pins fit into dowel pin holes. *See Fig. 7.*

Fig. 7: Installation of Center Support to Transfer Case

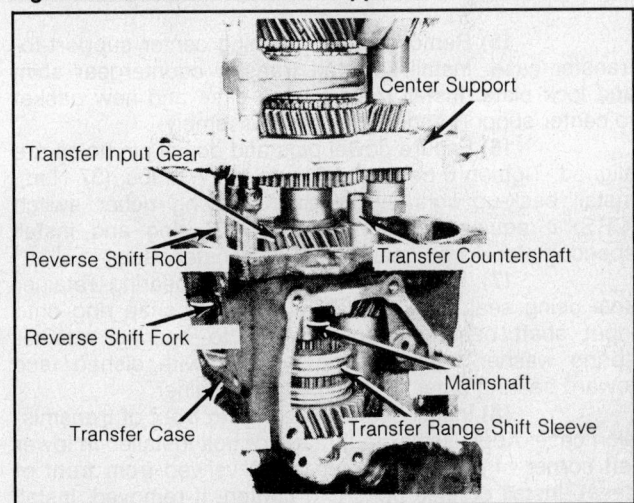

When installing center support, ensure components are installed in the proper sequence.

14) Tighten 4 bolts attaching center support-to-transfer case evenly. Measure how much transfer countershaft protrudes from center support. Select distance shim so thrust clearance will be .004-.014" (.10-.35 mm). *See Fig. 8.*

TRANSFER COUNTERGEAR DISTANCE SHIMS

Countergear Measurement	Shim Thickness	Color Code
.106-.114"	.118"	Red
(2.70-2.90 mm)	(3.00 mm)	
.114-.122"	.126"	Orange
(2.90-3.10 mm)	(3.20 mm)	
.122-.130"	.134"	No Color
(3.10-3.30 mm)	(3.40 mm)	
.130-.138"	.142"	Green
(3.30-3.50 mm)	(3.60 mm)	
.138-.142"	.150"	Blue
(3.50-3.60 mm)	(3.80 mm)	

ISUZU 4-SPEED WITH INTEGRAL TRANSFER CASE (Cont.)

Fig. 8: Measuring Transfer Countershaft for Distance Shim Selection

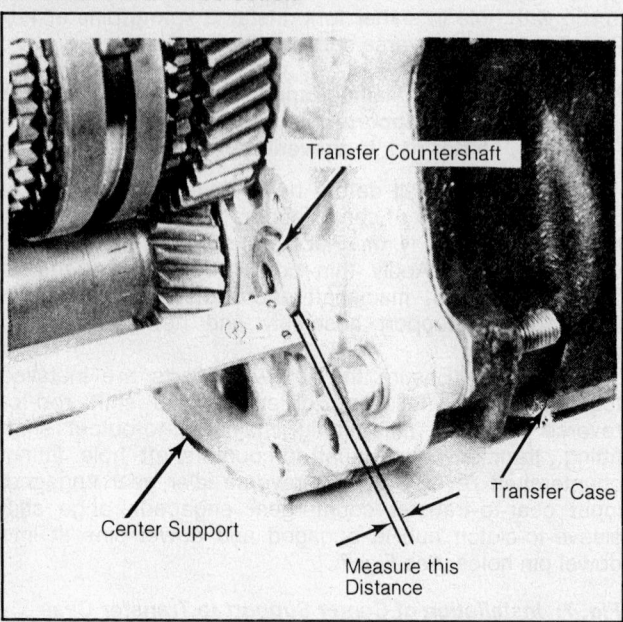

Transfer Countershaft

Transfer Case

Center Support

Measure this Distance

TIGHTENING SPECIFICATIONS

Application	Ft. Lbs. (N.m)
Clutch Ball Stud-to-Case	30 (41)
Countergear Nut	80 (110)
Front Bearing Retainer Bolts	14 (19)
Mainshaft Nut	94 (127)
Output Shaft Cover Bolts	20 (27)
Output Shaft Nut	108 (146)
Detent Cover Bolts	14 (19)
Countergear Lock Plate Bolts	14 (19)
Shifter Cover Bolts	14 (19)
Shift Rod & Screw Plugs	36 (49)
Speedometer Housing Retainer Bolt	14 (19)
Transfer Case-to-Transmission Case Bolts	27 (37)

15) Remove bolts attaching center support-to-transfer case. Install selected transfer countergear shim and lock plate. Install transmission case and new gasket to center support and tranfer case assembly.

16) Ensure dowel pins and dowel pin holes are aligned. Tighten 6 bolts and 8 nuts to 27 ft. lbs. (37 N.m). Install back-up light switch and coasting richer switch (CRS) if equipped. Lubricate new "O" ring and install speedometer driven gear to rear of transfer case.

17) If removed, install front bearing retainer seal using seal installer (J-26540). Install snap ring onto input shaft bearing. Apply grease to bearing retainer spring washer. Install spring washer, with dished face toward bearing outer race, in bearing retainer.

18) Install bearing retainer to front of transmission case. Apply sealer to threads of bolt installed in lower left corner of transmission case (as veiwed from front of case). Install other 3 bolts and tighten. If removed, install ball stud to transmission case.

19) Install dust boot, clutch fork and throw-out bearing. Install retaining springs. Apply molybdenum grease to input shaft splines and shift fork support. Apply regular grease to shift block. Ensure hook on clutch fork is installed on support correctly. Install drain plug on transfer case.

20) If removed, install transfer side case studs to transmission. Position transmission, with transfer side case fitting face down, in vehicle. Slide forward guiding clutch gear into pilot bearing. Install transmission-to-engine mount bolts. Install shifter cover with new gasket and tighten mount bolts.

21) Install transfer side case-to-transfer case by aligning grooves in shift arms and sleeve. Install components with shift arms and shift sleeves held in the 4H position. Complete transmission installation by reversing removal procedure. After installation, fill transmission with 2.37 qts. (2.5L) of gear oil.

Manual Transmissions

ISUZU 5-SPEED

Isuzu I-Mark, Impulse, P'UP

DESCRIPTION

Five speed fully synchronized unit with blocker ring synchronizers and a constant mesh reverse gear. First through fourth gears are housed within the case. Reverse and fifth gears are contained in the extension housing. The input/output shaft and the countershaft are supported by 3 ball bearings. The bearings are located in the front wall of the case, the center support and the extension housing. All gear teeth are helical cut.

LUBRICATION & ADJUSTMENT

See the appropriate article in MANUAL TRANS-MISSION SERVICING Section.

TROUBLE SHOOTING

HARD SHIFTING

Improperly adjusted clutch. Synchronizers worn or broken. Shift shafts or forks worn.

SLIPS OUT OF GEAR

Shift shafts and/or bearings worn. Drive gear retainer broken or loose. Excessive play in synchronizers.

TRANSMISSION NOISY

Low or incorrect lubricant. Gears or bearings worn or damaged. Worn clutch hub or mainshaft splines. Incorrectly meshed gears.

REMOVAL & INSTALLATION

See the appropriate article in MANUAL TRANS-MISSION REMOVAL Section.

TRANSMISSION DISASSEMBLY

1) Remove plug and drain transmission. Remove release bearing and fork assembly. Remove input shaft bearing retainer and Belleville spring. See Fig. 3.

2) Remove speedometer driven gear, retainer and back-up light switch. Remove shift lever quadrant and coasting fuel cut switch. Remove extension housing from transmission case.

Fig. 1: Cutaway View of Isuzu 5-Speed Transmission

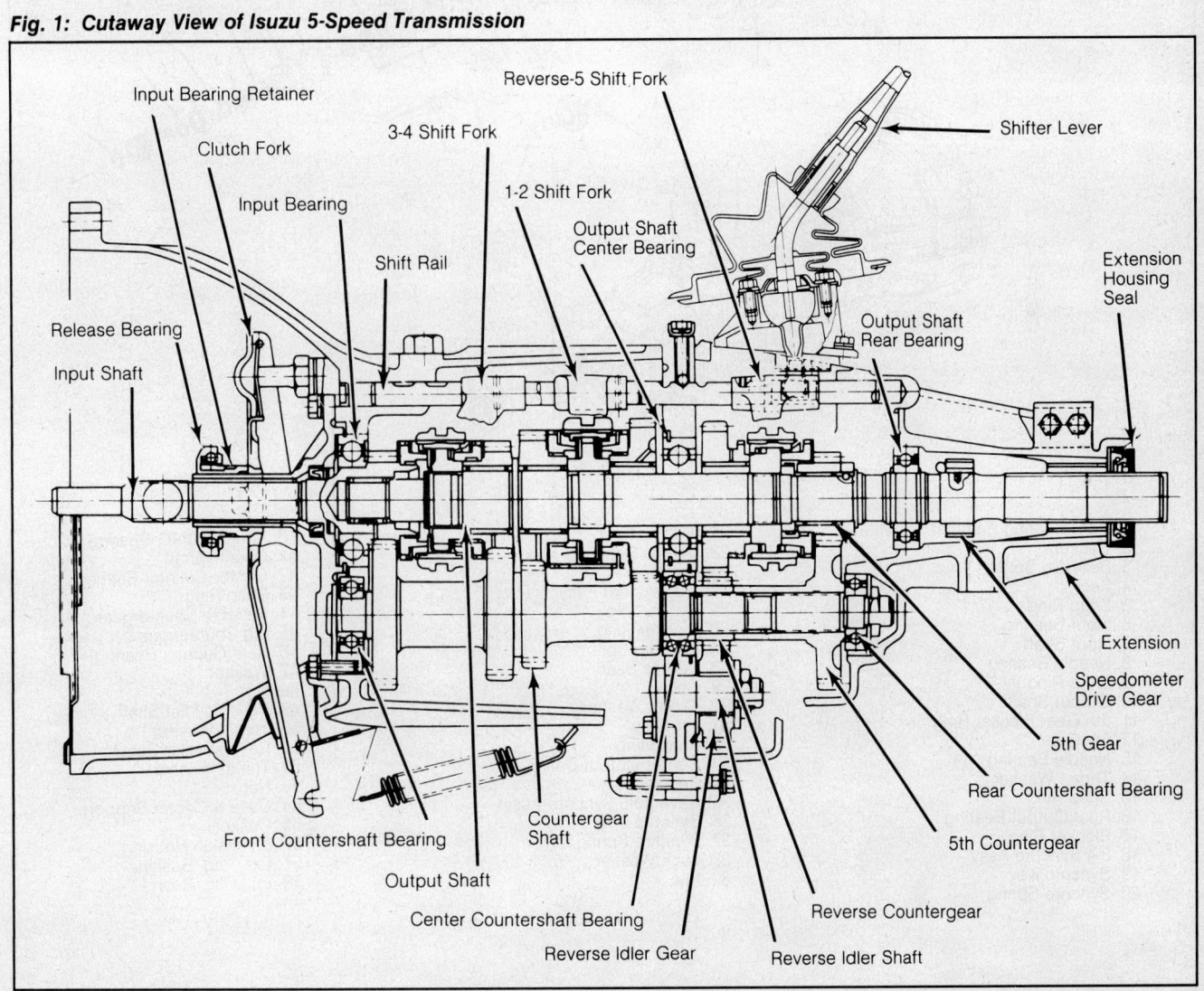

Manual Transmissions

ISUZU 5-SPEED (Cont.)

Fig. 2: *Exploded View of Isuzu 5-Speed Transmission*

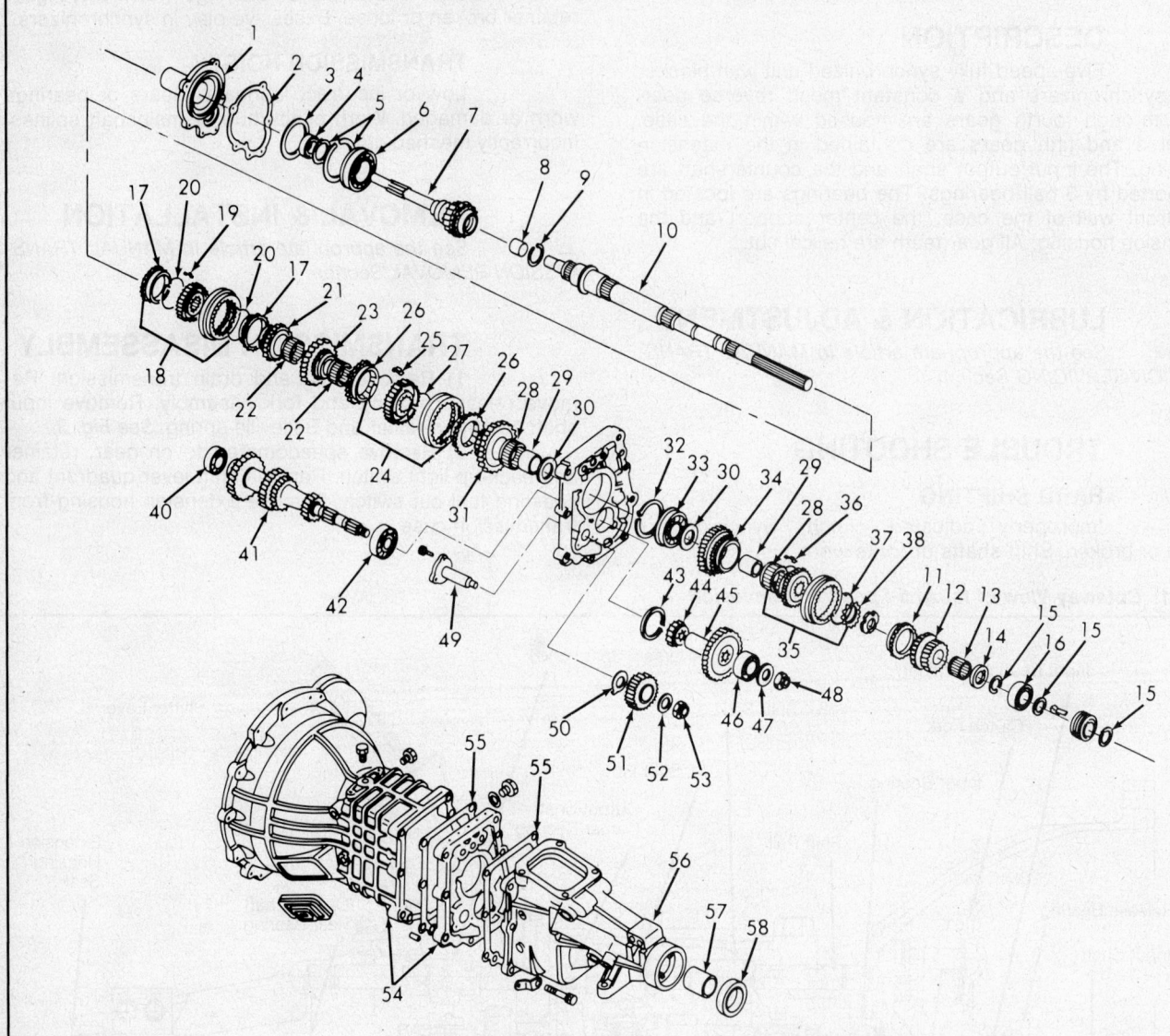

1. Input Bearing Retainer	21. 3rd Gear	40. Front Counter Bearing
2. Gasket	22. Needle Bearing	41. Countershaft
3. Belleville Spring	23. 2nd Gear	42. Center Counter Bearing
4. Seal	24. 1-2 Synchro Assy.	43. Snap Ring
5. Snap Ring	25. Synchro Key	44. Reverse Countergear
6. Input Bearing	26. Blocker Ring	45. 5th Countergear
7. Input Shaft	27. Synchro Spring	46. Rear Counter Bearing
8. Needle Bearing	28. Needle Bearing	47. Washer
9. Snap Ring	29. Collar	48. Nut
10. Output Shaft	30. Thrust Washer	49. Reverse Idler Shaft
11. 5th Gear Blocker Ring	31. 1st Gear	50. Thrust Washer
12. 5th Gear	32. Snap Ring	51. Reverse Idler Gear
13. Needle Bearing	33. Center Output Bearing	52. Thrust Washer
14. Thrust Washer	34. Reverse Gear	53. Nut
15. Snap Ring	35. Reverse-5 Synchro Assy.	54. Case & Center Support
16. Rear Output Bearing	36. Synchro Key	55. Gasket
17. Blocker Ring	37. Synchro Spring	56. Extension Housing
18. 3-4 Synchro Assy.	38. Lock Washer	57. Ext. Hsg. Bushing
19. Synchro Key	39. Nut	58. Ext. Hsg. Seal
20. Synchro Spring		

ISUZU 5-SPEED (Cont.)

3) Remove speedometer drive gear, snap rings, spacer and bearing. Remove snap ring from main shaft, thrust washer and lock ball. Remove outer snap ring from input shaft bearing. Remove center support from case with all gears attached.

4) Using a punch, drive pins out of shift forks, making sure to support ends of shift shafts. Remove detent spring plate, springs and detent balls. Remove shift shafts from center support. Remove shift forks from synchronizer sleeves. Remove interlock pins. See Fig. 4.

Fig. 3: Input Bearing Retainer Assembly

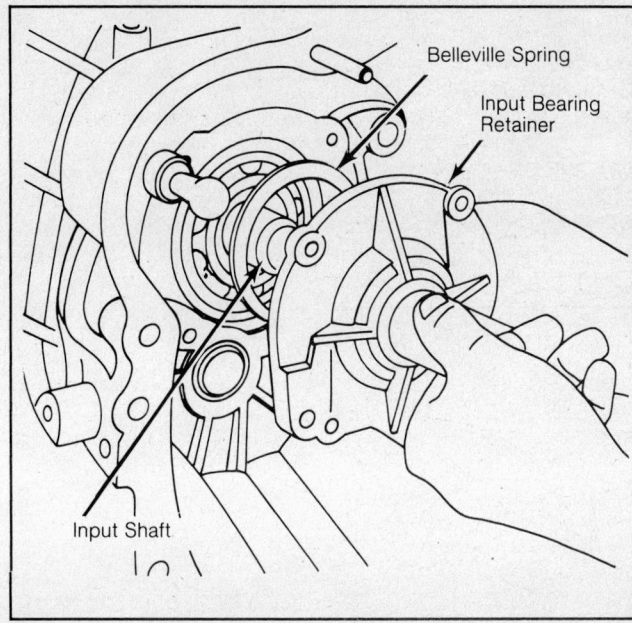

Dished side of spring faces rearward.

5) Engage 1st and 3rd gears to prevent rotation of countershaft. Install holding fixture (J-29768) onto front of gear assembly. Remove nut from rear of countershaft. Using a puller, remove rear countershaft bearing and 5th gear.

Fig. 4: Exploded View of Shift Shaft Assembly

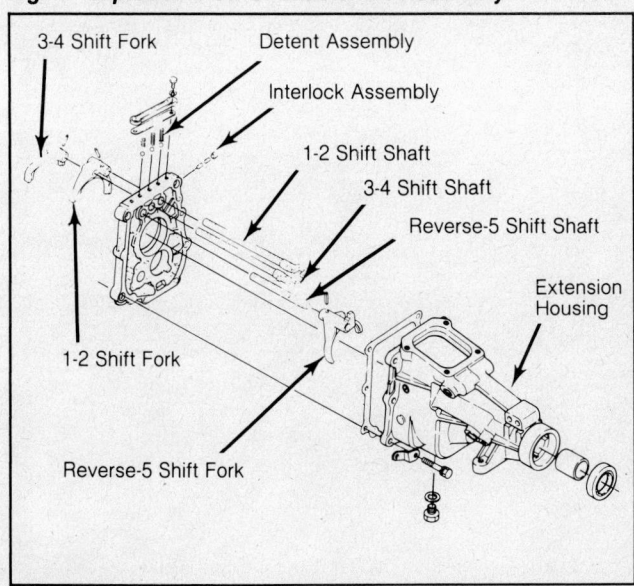

6) Remove 5th gear, needle bearings and blocker ring from output shaft. Remove thrust washers, reverse idler gear and retaining nut from reverse idler shaft.

7) Bend locking retainer back and remove mainshaft nut. Remove retainer and reverse-5th synchronizer assembly. Remove reverse gear, collar, needle bearings and thrust washer from rear of output shaft. Remove reverse gear from countershaft. Remove holding fixture.

8) Return synchronizers to neutral position. Expand countergear center bearing snap ring. Gently tap on front of center support to remove countershaft. Expand output shaft center bearing snap ring. Remove output shaft from center support. Remove input shaft, needle bearings and 4th gear blocker ring from output shaft.

COMPONENT DISASSEMBLY & REASSEMBLY

OUTPUT SHAFT

Disassembly

1) Using a press, remove output shaft center bearing. Remove thrust washer, 1st gear, needle bearings and spacer. Remove 1-2 synchronizer, 2nd gear and needle bearings.

2) Remove snap ring from front of output shaft. Remove 3-4 synchronizer and 3rd gear blocker ring. Remove 3rd gear and needle bearings.

Inspection

Check all parts for excessive wear or damage. Check bearings and synchronizers for rough operation. Replace damaged parts as necessary.

Reassembly

1) Install 3rd gear onto front of output shaft. Synchronizer cone faces forward. Install 3rd needle bearings. Install 3-4 synchronizer with chamfered end forward. Retain synchronizer with selective fit snap ring. Snap ring size should be selected to minimize end play.

2) Install 2nd gear and needle bearings on rear of shaft. Coned end of 2nd gear faces rearward. Install 1-2 synchronizer on rear of shaft with chamfered end facing rearward.

3) Install spacer, needle bearings and 1st gear on rear of shaft. Coned end of 1st gear faces forward. Install 1st gear thrust washer with slots facing gear. Press center bearing onto shaft. Groove on bearing faces front of transmission.

INPUT SHAFT

Disassembly

Remove snap ring from front of shaft. Press bearing off of shaft.

Reassembly

Press bearing onto shaft, so bearing groove faces toward front of transmission. Install snap ring.

COUNTERSHAFT

Disassembly & Reassembly

Countershaft bearings are removed and installed using a bearing separator and press. Groove on center bearing faces rearward.

Manual Transmissions

ISUZU 5-SPEED (Cont.)

OIL SEALS

Removal & Installation

Remove seals by prying with a screwdriver or small chisel. Coat outside of new extension housing seal with sealer (Permatex No. 2 or equivalent). Install seals with seal driver (Ext. Hsg. J-26508; Input J-26540).

TRANSMISSION REASSEMBLY

1) If removed, install center support snap rings and reverse idler shaft. Install input shaft onto front of output shaft. Engage countershaft with input and output shaft gears. Install gear assembly into holding fixture (J-29768).

2) Install center support onto gear assembly. Expand center support snap rings. Position center support and seat snap rings into bearing grooves. Engage 1st and 3rd gears to prevent countershaft rotation.

3) Install reverse countergear. Install reverse thrust washer with oil groove facing rearward. Install reverse gear with needle bearing and collar assembly onto rear of output shaft. Install reverse-5th synchronizer. Recessed side of synchronizer hub faces rearward.

4) Install locking retainer and nut onto rear of output shaft. Chamfered side of nut faces forward. Tighten to 94 ft. lbs. (127 N.m), then bend down retainer to lock nut in place.

5) Install reverse idler gear and thrust washers onto idler shaft. Flange on side thrust washer is fitted to stopper on center support. Install new self-locking nut on idler shaft.

6) Install 5th gear with blocker ring and needle bearing onto output shaft. Install 5th countergear, bearing and new self-locking nut onto countershaft. Remove assembly from holding fixture. Shift synchronizers to neutral position.

7) Grease interlock pins and install in center support. Install shift forks onto synchronizer sleeves. Insert shift shafts through center support and shift forks. Install detent balls and springs in center support, then install gasket and detent plate.

8) Support shift shafts and replace shift fork retaining pins. Place a new gasket on rear of transmission case. Install center support and gear assembly into case. Do not apply load to mainshaft rear end.

9) Install outer snap ring on input shaft bearing. Install lock ball, thrust washer and snap ring onto rear of output shaft. Check clearance between 5th gear and thrust washer with a feeler gauge. Clearance should be .004-.012" (.10-.30 mm). Adjust clearance as necessary with selective thickness thrust washers. Do not bend or distort thrust washer snap ring.

10) Install speedometer drive gear front snap ring, ball bearing and spacer. Align lug in speedometer drive gear with groove and install on shaft, then install rear snap ring.

11) Install gasket on rear of center support. Install extension housing. Install gasket and shift lever quadrant on extension housing. Install speedometer driven gear and back-up light switch.

12) Install belleville washer with dished side to drive gear bearing. Install gasket and input bearing retainer into front of transmission. Seal lower 3 retainer bolts with sealer (Permatex No. 2 or equivalent). Install release bearing and fork assembly.

TIGHTENING SPECIFICATIONS

Application	Ft. Lbs. (N.m)
Input Shaft Bearing Retainer Bolts	14 (19)
Shift Box Bolts	14 (19)
Reverse Idler Shaft Bolts	14 (19)
Extension Housing Bolts	27 (37)
Countergear Nut	80 (108)
Reverse Idler Gear-to-Shaft	80 (108)
Output Shaft Nut	94 (127)

MAZDA FRONT WHEEL DRIVE 4 & 5-SPEED

626 & GLC

DESCRIPTION

Transaxle combines a 4 or 5-speed transmission, a differential and a clutch housing into an integral drivetrain. This unit is designed for a transverse engine, front wheel drive vehicle. All gear assemblies are supported by tapered roller bearings with preload being adjusted by shims. Helical cut gears are used throughout, so adjustment of gear tooth contact is not necessary.

LUBRICATION & ADJUSTMENT

See the appropriate article in MANUAL TRANS-MISSION SERVICING Section.

SERVICE (IN VEHICLE)

AXLE DRIVE SHAFTS

Removal

1) Raise and support vehicle. Drain transaxle fluid. Remove wheels and axle hub cap. Loosen drive shaft lock nut. Remove lower ball joint nut and swing lower control arm away from steering knuckle.

2) Separate the drive shaft from the transaxle by pulling out firmly but slowly on steering knuckle. Pull drive shaft out of steering knuckle and lower away from vehicle.

Disassembly

1) Remove boot retaining band from inner CV joint. Remove circlip from outer ring of inner CV joint. Separate outer ring from spider and drive shaft.

2) Remove snap ring retaining spider to drive shaft. Slide spider off of shaft and pry balls out of cage with a screwdriver. Turn spider slightly and remove from inner cage.

Reassembly

1) Reverse disassembly procedure and note the following: Outer CV joint cannot be serviced. Do not remove ring located on inner end of drive shaft splines unless replacement is necessary.

2) Use tape on splines when installing boots to prevent damage. Vibration dampener on right side drive shaft should be 14.45" (367 mm) from outer end of outer CV joint.

Fig. 1: Exploded View of Mazda Transaxle Assembly

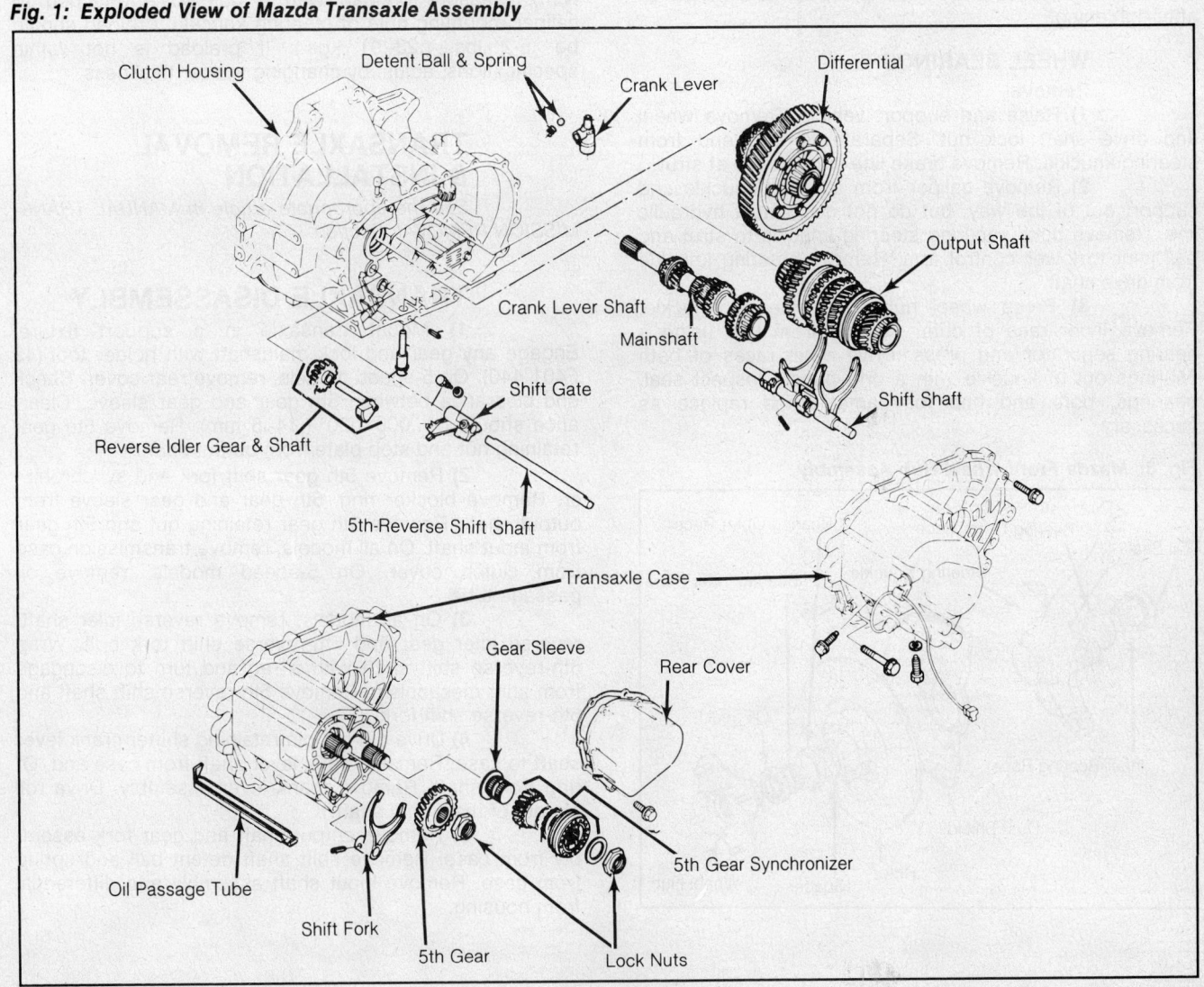

Manual Transmissions

MAZDA FRONT WHEEL DRIVE 4 & 5-SPEED (Cont.)

Fig. 2: Exploded View of Axle Drive Shaft

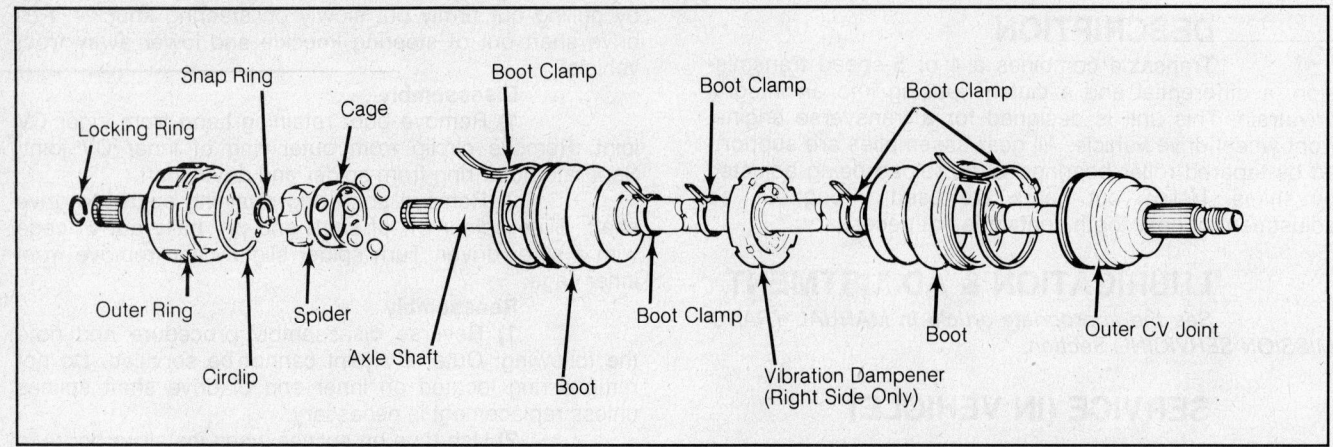

Installation

1) Reverse removal procedure and note the following: Check the seals at both ends of the drive shaft and replace prior to installation if necessary.

2) Lubricate the transaxle seal lip with ATF and the wheel hub seal lip with grease before installing drive shaft. Stake the drive shaft nut in place with a blunt punch after tightening.

WHEEL BEARINGS
Removal

1) Raise and support vehicle. Remove wheel and drive shaft lock nut. Separate tie rod end from steering knuckle. Remove brake line support clip at strut.

2) Remove caliper from steering knuckle and support out of the way, but do not disconnect hydraulic line. Remove bolts securing steering knuckle to strut and ball joint to lower control arm. Remove steering knuckle from drive shaft.

3) Press wheel hub from steering knuckle. Remove inner race of outer bearing from hub using a bearing separator and press. Drive outer races of both bearings out of knuckle with a drift punch. Inspect seal, bearings, bore and hub for damage and replace as necessary.

Fig. 3: Mazda Front Wheel Hub Assembly

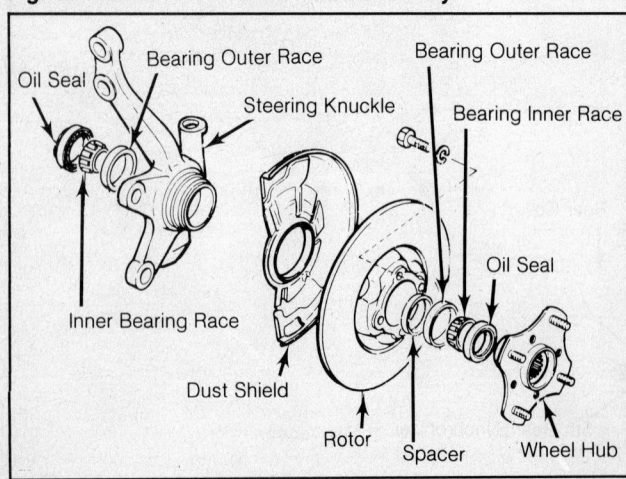

Installation

1) Reverse removal procedure and note the following: Bearing preload must be checked using the spacer selector tool (49 B001 727). Use the original spacer for measurement.

2) Tighten spacer selector to 145 ft. lbs. (197 N.m). Measure preload with a pull scale attached to caliper mounting hole of steering knuckle. Preload should be .5-2 lbs. (.23-.91 kgs). If preload is not within specifications, adjust by changing spacer thickness.

TRANSAXLE REMOVAL & INSTALLATION

See the appropriate article in MANUAL TRANSMISSION REMOVAL Section.

TRANSAXLE DISASSEMBLY

1) Mount transaxle in a support fixture. Engage any gear and lock mainshaft with holder tool (49 F401 440). On 5-speed models, remove rear cover. Check end clearance between 5th gear and gear sleeve. Clearance should be .006-.020" (.14-.5 mm). Remove 5th gear retaining nut and stop plate from output shaft.

2) Remove 5th gear shift fork and synchronizer. Remove blocker ring, 5th gear and gear sleeve from output shaft. Remove 5th gear retaining nut and 5th gear from input shaft. On all models, remove transmission case from clutch cover. On 5-speed models, remove oil passage tube.

3) On all models, remove reverse idler shaft, reverse idler gear and 5th-reverse shift fork bolt. Wrap 5th-reverse shift shaft with a rag and turn to disengage from shift mechanism. Remove 5th-reverse shift shaft and 5th-reverse shift fork.

4) Drive out roll pin retaining shifter crank lever shaft to case. Remove crank lever shaft from case and "O" ring from shaft. Remove crank lever assembly. Drive roll pin out of main shift shaft.

5) Remove output shaft and gear fork assembly from case. Remove shift shaft detent ball and spring from case. Remove input shaft assembly and differential from housing.

MAZDA FRONT WHEEL DRIVE 4 & 5-SPEED (Cont.)

Fig. 4: Exploded View of Transaxle Case and Related Components

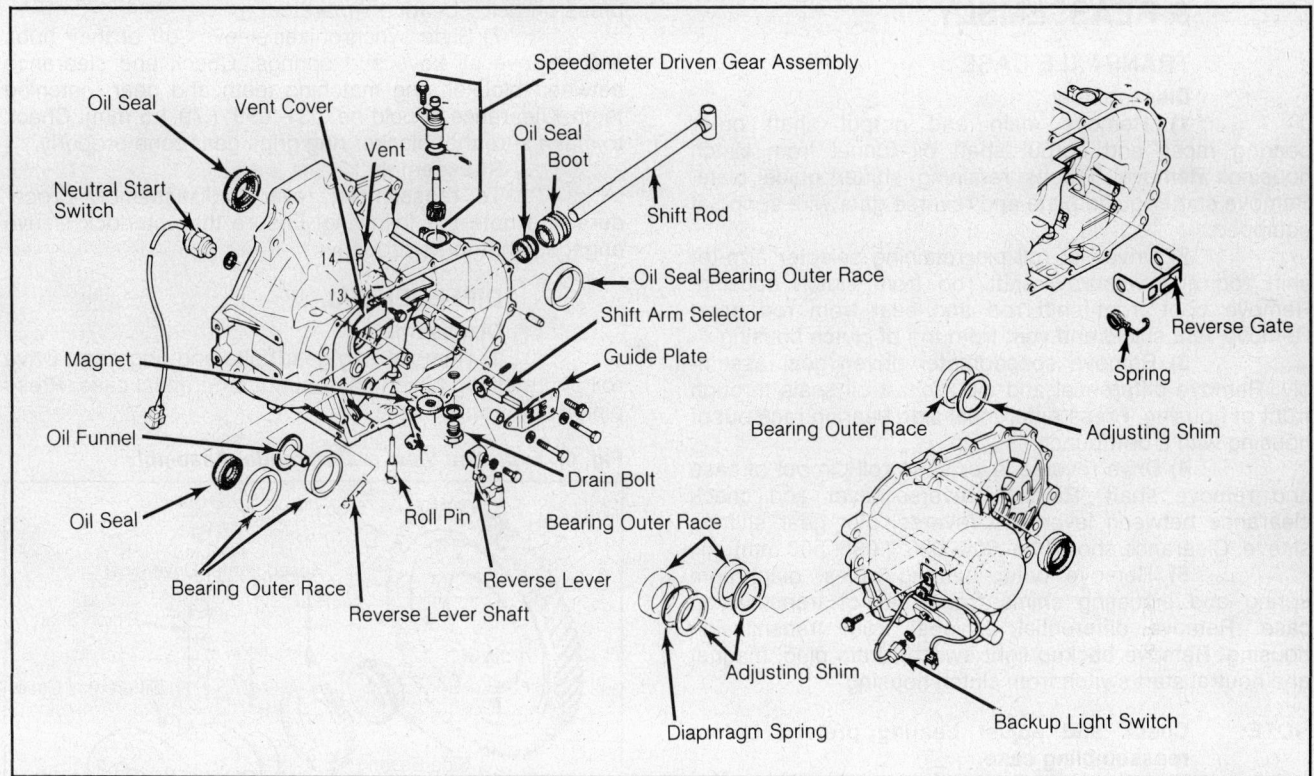

Fig. 5: Exploded View of Transaxle Gear Shafts

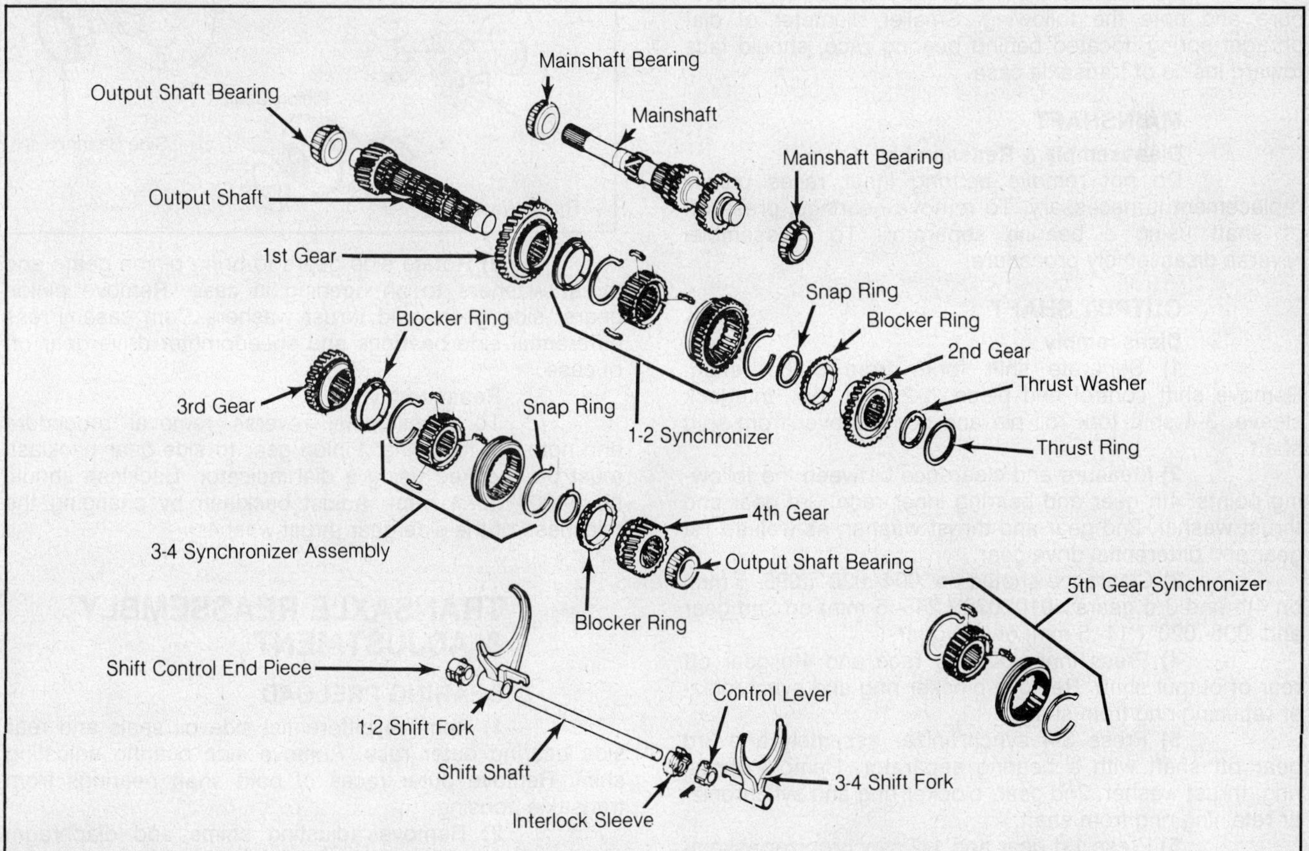

MAZDA FRONT WHEEL DRIVE 4 & 5-SPEED (Cont.)

COMPONENT DISASSEMBLY & REASSEMBLY

TRANSAXLE CASE

Disassembly

1) Remove main and output shaft outer bearing races and output shaft oil funnel from clutch housing. Remove 3 bolts retaining shifter guide plate. Remove shifter guide plate and reverse gate with spring, if equipped.

2) Drive out roll pin retaining selector arm-to-shift rod and withdraw shift rod from clutch housing. Remove boot from shift rod and seal from rod bore. Remove vent shield and vent from top of clutch housing.

3) Remove speedometer driven gear assembly. Remove differential and input shaft oil seals through front of housing. Press differential side bearing race out of housing with a drift punch.

4) Drive reverse lever shaft roll pin out of case and remove shaft. Remove reverse lever and check clearance between lever and reverse idler gear shifting sleeve. Clearance should be .004-.020" (.095-.500 mm).

5) Remove outer bearing races, diaphragm spring and adjusting shims from rear of transmission case. Remove differential oil seal from transmission housing. Remove backup light switch, drain plug, magnet and neutral start switch from clutch housing.

NOTE: **Check and adjust bearing preload before reassembling case.**

Reassembly

To reassemble, reverse disassembly procedure and note the following: Smaller diameter of diaphragm spring, located behind bearing race, should face toward inside of transaxle case.

MAINSHAFT

Disassembly & Reassembly

Do not remove bearing inner races unless replacement is necessary. To remove bearings, press off of shaft using a bearing separator. To reassemble, reverse disassembly procedure.

OUTPUT SHAFT

Disassembly

1) Separate shift forks from output shaft. Remove shift control end piece, 1-2 shift fork, interlock sleeve, 3-4 shift fork roll pin and control lever from shift shaft.

2) Measure end clearance between the following points: 4th gear and bearing inner race, 3rd gear and thrust washer, 2nd gear and thrust washer, as well as 1st gear and differential drive gear.

3) Clearance should be .004-.020" (.095-.5 mm) on 4th and 3rd gears, .010-.020 (.245-.5 mm) on 2nd gear and .006-.020" (.14-.5 mm) on 1st gear.

4) Press inner bearing race and 4th gear off rear of output shaft. Remove blocker ring and synchronizer retaining ring from shaft.

5) Press 3-4 synchronizer assembly and 3rd gear off shaft with a bearing separator. Remove thrust ring, thrust washer, 2nd gear, blocker ring and synchronizer retaining ring from shaft.

6) Press 1st gear and 1-2 synchronizer assembly off of shaft. Do not remove front bearing inner race

unless replacement is necessary. To remove bearing, press off using bearing separator.

7) Slide synchronizer sleeves off of their hubs and remove all keys and springs. Check end clearance between blocker ring matching teeth and gear matching teeth. Clearance should be .031-.059" (.79-1.5 mm). Check to make sure that blocker ring grips gear cone properly.

Reassembly

To reassemble, reverse disassembly procedure and note the following: Ensure that interlock sleeve engages shift forks properly.

DIFFERENTIAL

Disassembly

1) Remove ring gear bolts and ring gear. Drive roll pin retaining pinion shaft out of differential case. Press pinion shaft out of case.

Fig. 6: Exploded View of Differential Assembly

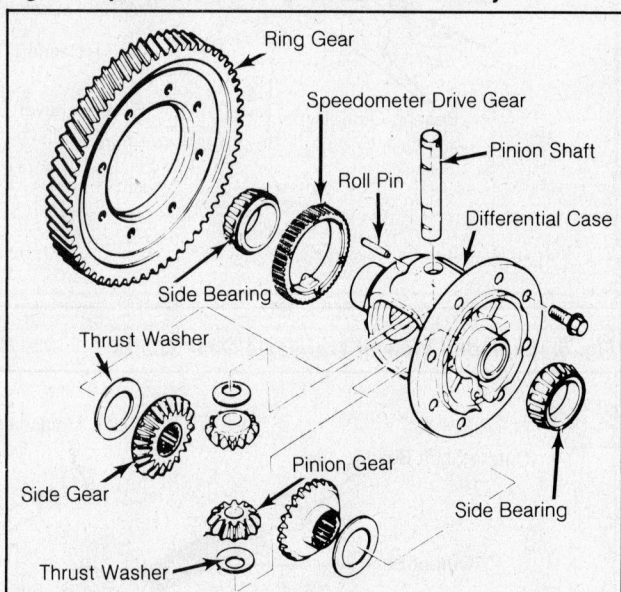

2) Rotate side gears to bring pinion gears and thrust washers to an opening in case. Remove pinion gears, side gears and thrust washers from case. Press differential side bearings and speedometer drive gear off of case.

Reassembly

To reassemble, reverse removal procedure and note the following: Pinion gear to side gear backlash must be checked using a dial indicator. Backlash should be 0-.004" (0-.1 mm). Adjust backlash by changing the thickness of the side gear thrust washer.

TRANSAXLE REASSEMBLY & ADJUSTMENT

BEARING PRELOAD

1) Remove differential side oil seals and rear side bearing outer race. Remove side bearing adjusting shim. Remove outer races of both shaft bearings from transaxle housing.

2) Remove adjusting shims and diaphragm spring. Reinstall shaft bearing races without shims or

MAZDA FRONT WHEEL DRIVE 4 & 5-SPEED (Cont.)

Fig. 7: Bearing Preload Adjustment Procedure

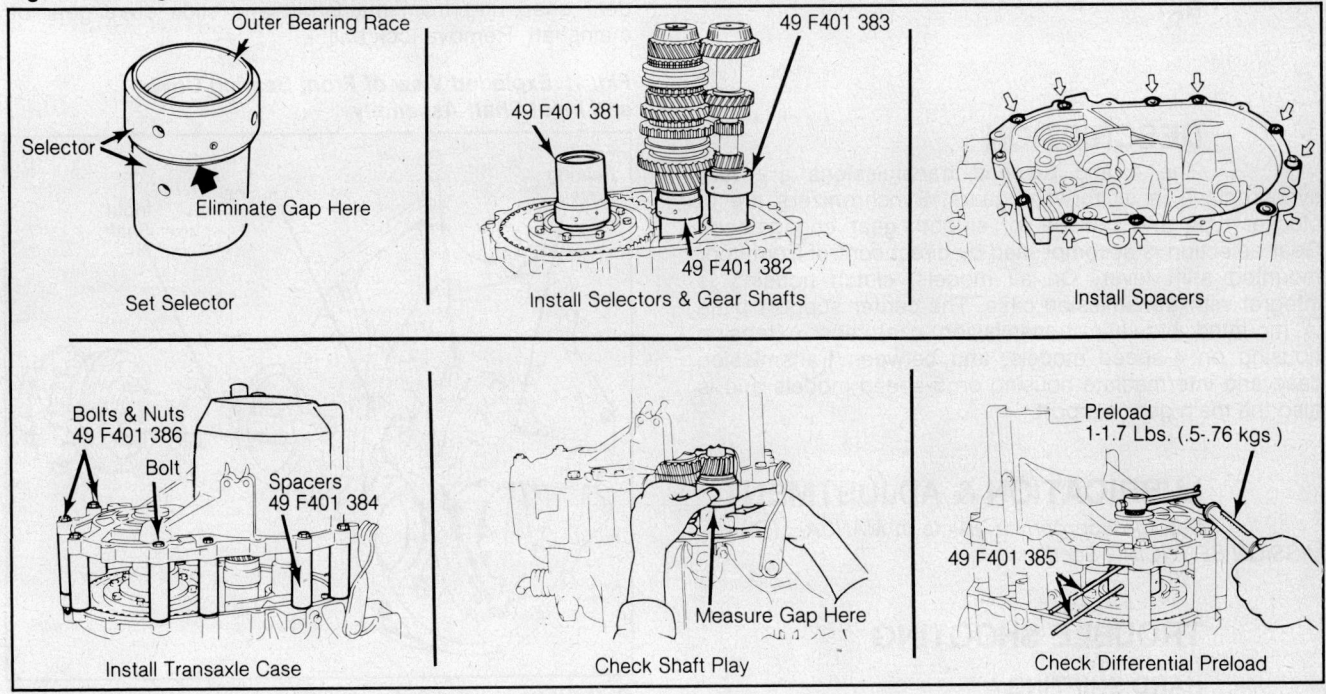

spring. Remove outer races of both shaft gears from clutch housing.

    3) Insert rear differential race and front shaft races into shim selector tools (49 401 383 for mainshaft, 49 F401 382 for output shaft and 49 F401 381 for differential).

    4) Adjust all 3 selector tools to minimum height. Place clutch housing on bench or support fixture with clutch housing flange facing down. Install differential in case.

    5) Place selector tools for mainshaft and output shaft into proper bearing bore and install both gear shafts. Install differential selector tool on top of differential. Install transaxle case and secure with 10 spacers and bolts (49 F401 384 & 386). Tighten bolts.

    6) Using turning bars (49 F401 385), rotate collars of tools until fully expanded. Turn collars of the 2 gear shaft tools to bring them back to collapsed position.

    7) Expand collars as far as possible by hand and measure gap around entire circumference of tools. Subtract thickness of diaphragm spring .04" (1 mm) from tool reading on mainshaft.

    8) Select a shim equal to or the next size larger than result of step **4)** for each shaft. Shims are available in sizes from .008" (.2 mm) to .022" (.55 mm) in increments of .002" (.05 mm).

    9) Install preload adapter shaft and attachment arm (49 FT01 515 & 49 01080 510A) into the differential. Attach a pull scale to hole in end of arm.

    10) Adjust tool collars until 1-1.7 lbs. (.5-.76 kgs) are required to turn differential. Measure gap around entire circumference of tool.

    11) Round gap measurement off to next larger shim size. No more than 3 shims should be used to make up required thickness. Shims are available in the sizes from .004" (.10 mm) to .036" (.90 mm) in increments of .004" (.10 mm).

TRANSAXLE REASSEMBLY

    1) Reverse disassembly procedure and note the following: Install selected shim packs behind the appropriate bearing races. Recessed side of 5th gear synchronizer faces 5th gear.

    2) Recheck differential preload with transaxle assembled. Using input shaft holder and pull scale, check mainshaft preload.

    3) Force required to rotate mainshaft should be .88-1.54 lbs. (.40-.70 kgs). Check operation of shift mechanism to ensure proper engagement of all gears.

TIGHTENING SPECIFICATIONS

Application	Ft. Lbs. (N.m)
Transaxle Mounting Bolts	
Top 4 Bolts	47-69 (64-94)
Bottom 2 Bolts	65-86 (88-117)
All Others	27-40 (37-54)
Starter Bolts	27-40 (37-54)
Crossmember-to-Frame	45-63 (61-85)
Transaxle Mount Bolts	24-34 (33-46)
Ring Gear Bolts	51-61 (70-85)
Transaxle Case-to-Clutch Housing	13-19 (18-26)
Gear Shaft Lock Nuts	
(5-Speed Only)	94-152 (127-206)
	INCH Lbs. (N.m)
Rear Cover Bolts	
(5-Speed Only)	72-96 (8-11)

Manual Transmissions

MAZDA REAR WHEEL DRIVE 4 & 5-SPEED

**B2000 & B2200 Pickup
RX7**

DESCRIPTION

The 4 and 5-speed transmissions are fully synchronized in all forward gears. Synchronizers are of blocker type and provide for smooth gear engagement. Gear selection is accomplished by direct control from floor mounted shift lever. On all models, clutch housing is integral with transmission case. The center support plate is mounted between transmission case and extension housing on 4-speed models, and between transmission case and intermediate housing on 5-speed models and is also the main gear support.

LUBRICATION & ADJUSTMENT

See the appropriate article in MANUAL TRANS-MISSION SERVICING Section.

TROUBLE SHOOTING

HARD SHIFTING

Improperly adjusted clutch. Weakened synchronizer insert spring. Face of synchronizer ring, in contact with insert, worn. Cones on synchronizer ring and gear worn or not in proper contact.

SLIPS OUT OF GEAR

Bearings worn or defective. Excessive play between gears and collars. Play in clutch hub and sliding sleeve. Shift arm worn. Lock ball spring weak or broken.

TRANSMISSION NOISY

Low or incorrect lubricant. Gears or bearings worn or damaged. Worn gears or collars. Worn clutch hub or mainshaft splines. Incorrectly meshed gears.

REMOVAL & INSTALLATION

See the appropriate article in MANUAL TRANS-MISSION REMOVAL Section.

TRANSMISSION DISASSEMBLY

1) Clean exterior of transmission assembly. On GLC models, remove clutch cross-shaft bolt, cross-shaft, release lever, spring and throw-out bearing. On all other models, remove dust cover, throw-out bearing and clutch release fork. Remove front cover bolts (or nuts) and remove front cover, shim, gasket and oil seal.

2) Remove gearshift lever retainer and gasket from extension housing. Remove extension housing bolts and slide extension housing off mainshaft with control lever positioned to the left as far as possible. Remove control lever end attaching bolt and remove control lever end and control rod from housing.

3) Remove speedometer driven gear assembly, back-up light switch and overdrive switch from extension housing. Remove top switch from transmission

case. On 4-speed models, remove speedometer drive gear snap ring from mainshaft and slide drive gear off mainshaft. Remove lock ball.

Fig. 1: Exploded View of Front Bearing Cover and Input Shaft Assembly

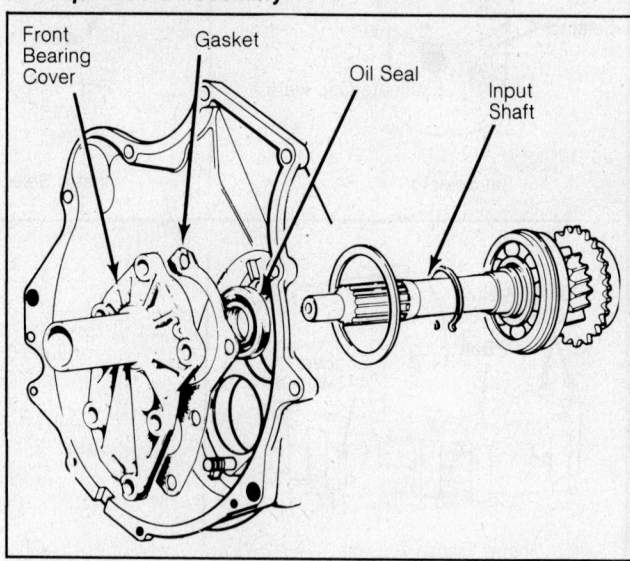

GLC (Wagon) model shown; other models similiar.

4) On all models, remove snap ring from input shaft and countershaft. Separate transmission case from bearing plate/intermediate housing using push tool (49 0305 430) or by tapping input shaft with plastic faced hammer. Remove input shaft bearing from transmission case. Using bearing puller tool (49 0710 520), remove countershaft front bearing from countershaft.

5) On 5-speed models, remove speedometer drive gear snap ring from mainshaft and slide drive gear off mainshaft. Remove lock ball and drive gear positioning snap ring. On 4-speed models, remove 3 spring cap bolts and remove springs and shift locking balls.

6) On 5-speed models, remove shift rod end attaching bolts and remove shift rod ends. Separate bearing plate from intermediate housing by lightly tapping housing with plastic faced hammer.

7) On 4-speed models, remove reverse shift rod, shift fork assembly and reverse gear from bearing plate. Remove shift fork set screws. Remove shift rods and forks by pushing shift rods rearward through shift forks and bearing plate. Remove reverse shift rod locking ball, spring and interlock pins from bearing plate.

8) On 5-speed models, remove 3 spring cap bolts and remove springs and shift locking balls. Remove 3 shift rod snap rings. Remove shift fork attaching bolts, shift fork rods and shift forks. Remove lock ball, spring and interlock pins.

NOTE: On 5-speed, be careful not to lose lock ball when removing 5th-Reverse shift rod.

9) On 4-speed models, straighten lock washer tab and secure mainshaft with holding tool (49 0259 440) and loosen lock nut using wrench. Remove reverse gear and key from mainshaft. Remove countershaft snap ring and counter reverse gear.

10) Remove bearing cover and reverse idler gear shaft from bearing plate. Using plastic faced

MAZDA REAR WHEEL DRIVE 4 & 5-SPEED (Cont.)

Fig. 2: Exploded View of Mazda 4 and 5-Speed Transmission Gears and Shafts

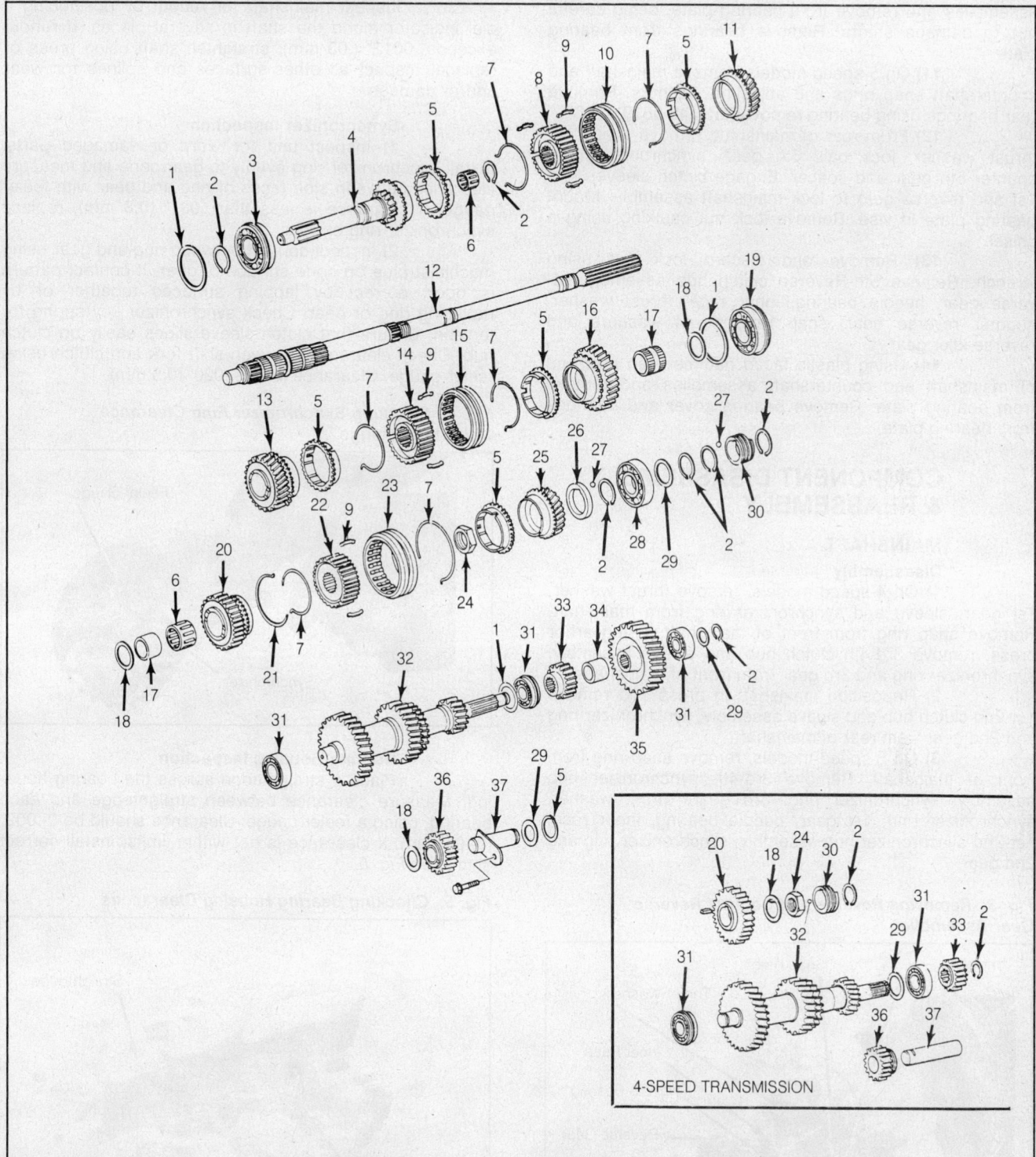

4-SPEED TRANSMISSION

1. Adjusting Shim	11. 3rd Gear	21. Retaining Ring	31. Bearing
2. Snap Ring	12. Mainshaft	22. 5th & Reverse Clutch Hub	32. Countershaft
3. Bearing	13. 2nd Gear	23. Hub Sleeve	33. Counter Reverse Gear
4. Input Shaft	14. 1st & 2nd Clutch Hub	24. Lock Nut	34. Spacer
5. Synchro Ring	15. Hub Sleeve	25. 5th Gear	35. Counter 5th Gear
6. Bearing	16. 1st Gear	26. Thrust Washer	36. Reverse Idler Gear
7. Synchro Key Spring	17. Gear Sleeve	27. Locking Ball	37. Idler Gear Shaft
8. 3rd & 4th Clutch Hub	18. Thrust Washer	28. Bearing	
9. Synchro Key	19. Bearing	29. Adjusting Washer	
10. Hub Sleeve	20. Reverse Gear	30. Speedometer Drive Gear	

Manual Transmissions

MAZDA REAR WHEEL DRIVE 4 & 5-SPEED (Cont.)

hammer, tap rear end of mainshaft and countershaft assemblies and remove from bearing plate, being careful not to damage shafts. Remove bearings from bearing plate.

11) On 5-speed models, remove mainshaft and countershaft snap rings and adjusting washers. Remove rear bearings using bearing removal tool (49 0839 425C).

12) From rear of mainshaft, remove snap ring, thrust washer, lock ball, 5th gear, synchronizer ring, counter 5th gear and spacer. Engage clutch sleeves into 1st and reverse gear to lock mainshaft assembly. Mount bearing plate in vise. Remove lock nut caulking using a chisel.

13) Remove and discard lock nut using wrench. Remove 5th-Reverse clutch hub assembly, reverse gear, needle bearing, inner race, thrust washer, counter reverse gear, snap ring, thrust washers and reverse idler gear.

14) Using plastic faced hammer, tap rear end of mainshaft and countershaft assemblies and remove from bearing plate. Remove bearing cover and bearings from bearing plate.

COMPONENT DISASSEMBLY & REASSEMBLY

MAINSHAFT

Disassembly

1) On 4-speed models, remove thrust washer, 1st gear, sleeve and synchronizer ring from mainshaft. Remove snap ring from front of mainshaft. Using arbor press, remove 3rd-4th clutch hub and sleeve assembly, synchronizer ring and 3rd gear from front of mainshaft.

2) Reposition mainshaft in press and remove 1st-2nd clutch hub and sleeve assembly, synchronizer ring and 2nd gear from rear of mainshaft.

3) On 5-speed models, remove snap ring from front of mainshaft. Remove 3rd-4th synchronizer hub assembly, synchronizer ring, 3rd gear, thrust washer, synchronizer ring, 1st gear, needle bearing, inner race, 1st-2nd synchronizer hub assembly, synchronizer ring and 2nd gear.

Fig. 3: Removing Reverse and Counter Reverse Gear Assemblies

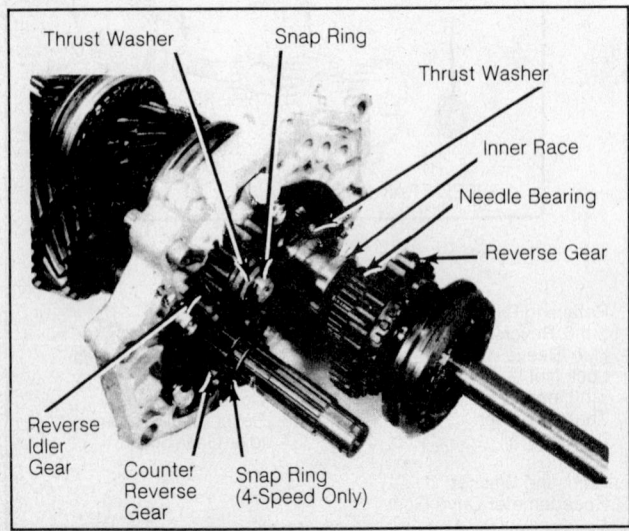

Mainshaft Inspection

Inspect mainshaft for runout by positioning a dial indicator along the shaft in several places. If runout exceeds .0012" (.03 mm), straighten shaft using press or replace. Inspect all other surfaces and splines for wear and/or damage.

Synchronizer Inspection

1) Inspect unit for worn or damaged parts. Install synchronizer ring evenly to gear cone and measure clearance between side faces of ring and gear with feeler gauge. If clearance is less than .031" (0.8 mm), replace synchronizer ring or gear.

2) Inspect contact between ring and gear using machinist blue on cone surface of gear. If contact pattern is poor, correct by lapping surfaces together or by replacing ring or gear. Check synchronizer key spring for tension. Ensure that clutch sleeve slides easily on clutch hub. Check clearance between shift fork and clutch using feeler gauge. Clearance limit is .020" (0.5 mm).

Fig. 4: Checking Synchronizer Ring Clearance with Feeler Gauge

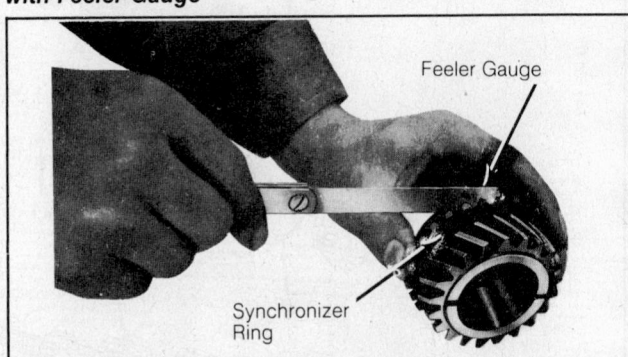

Bearing Housing Inspection

Place a straightedge across the bearing housing. Measure clearance between straightedge and each bearing, using a feeler gauge. Clearance should be 0-.002" (0-.05 mm). If clearance is not within limits, install correct shim. See Fig. 5.

Fig. 5: Checking Bearing Housing Clearances

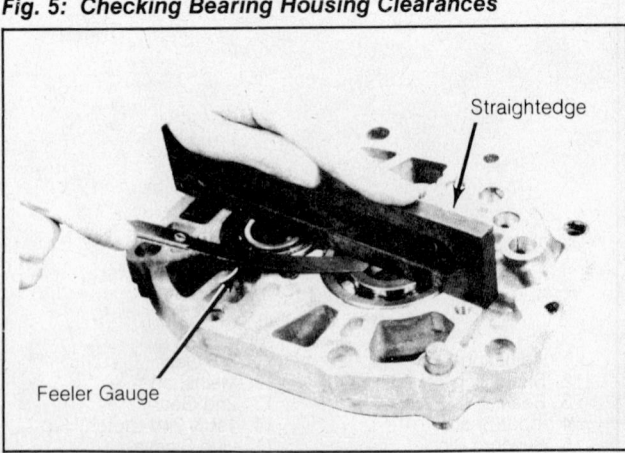

Reassembly

1) On 4-speed models, from rear of mainshaft, install 2nd gear, synchronizer ring, 1st-2nd clutch hub and sleeve assembly using arbor press.

MAZDA REAR WHEEL DRIVE 4 & 5-SPEED (Cont.)

2) Reposition mainshaft in press and install 3rd gear, synchronizer ring, 3rd-4th clutch hub and sleeve assembly. Install snap ring on front of mainshaft and install synchronizer ring, sleeve, 1st gear and thrust washer.

3) On 5-speed models, install 2nd gear, synchronizer ring, 1st-2nd clutch hub assembly, inner race, needle bearing, 1st gear, synchronizer ring, thrust washer, 3rd gear, synchronizer ring and 3rd-4th clutch hub assembly. Install snap on front of mainshaft. On all models, install input shaft with needle bearing onto mainshaft.

Fig. 6: Synchronizer Position on Mainshaft

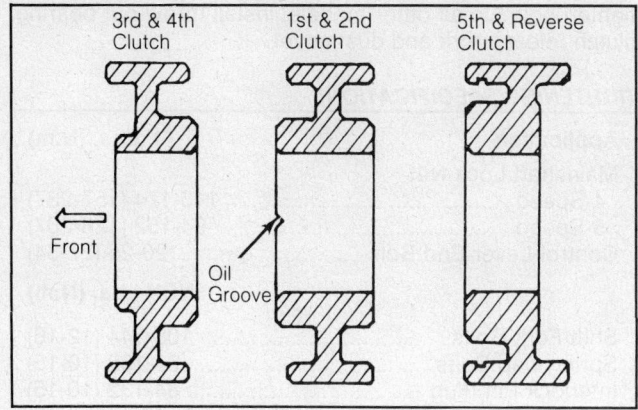

TRANSMISSION REASSEMBLY

1) Install countershaft and mainshaft rear bearings into bearing plate and check clearance between bearing plate bore and bearing height. If clearance exceeds .004" (0.1 mm), replace adjusting shim. Using arbor press, install countershaft and mainshaft assembly into bearing plate.

2) Install bearing cover and reverse idler gear shaft. On 4-speed models, install reverse gear with key onto mainshaft and chamfer on teeth of gear facing rearward. Secure mainshaft with holding tool (49 0259 440) and install and tighten lock nut using wrench.

3) Bend over lock washer tab. Install countershaft reverse gear and snap ring. On 5-speed models, install thrust washer, reverse idler gear, thrust washer and snap ring on reverse idler shaft. Check clearance between thrust washer and snap ring using feeler gauge.

4) If clearance exceeds .004-.012" (0.1-0.3 mm), replace thrust washer. Thrust washers are available in .106" (2.6 mm), .110" (2.8 mm) and .118" (3.0 mm) sizes. On all models, install counter reverse gear and spacer (5-speed only) on countershaft.

5) On 5-speed models, install thrust washer, reverse gear, needle bearing and sleeve on rear end of mainshaft. Install 5th-Reverse clutch hub and sleeve and new lock nut on mainshaft. Engage clutch sleeves into 1st and reverse gear to lock mainshaft assembly. Tighten mainshaft lock nut using wrench and caulk lock nut.

6) Install synchronizer ring, 5th gear, counter 5th gear, thrust washer, lock ball and snap ring to rear end of mainshaft.

7) Check clearance between 5th gear thrust washer and snap ring using feeler gauge. If clearance exceeds .004-.012" (0.1-0.3 mm), replace thrust washer.

Fig. 7: Assembled View of Reverse Shift Fork and Shift Rod Assemblies

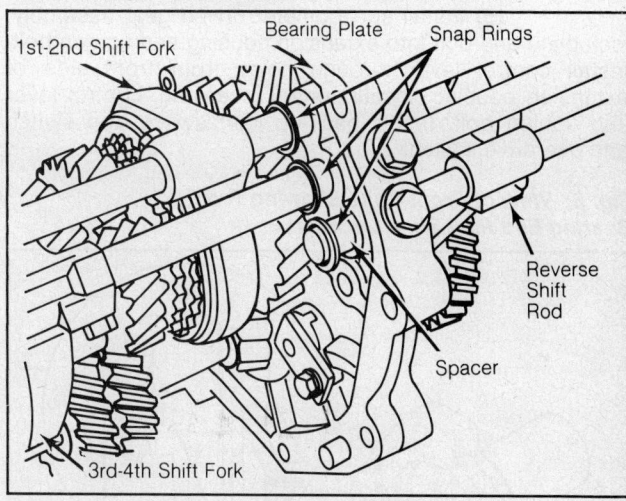

Thrust washers are available in .252" (6.4 mm), .256" (6.5 mm), .260" (6.6 mm), and .264" (6.7 mm) sizes. Install mainshaft rear bearing using wrench tool (49 1243 465A).

8) Install bearing, adjusting washer and snap ring. Check clearance between mainshaft adjusting washer and snap ring using feeler gauge. If clearance exceeds .004" (0.1 mm), replace adjusting washer. Adjusting washers are available in .075" (1.9 mm), .079" (2.0 mm), .083" (2.1 mm) and .087" (2.2 mm) sizes.

9) Install countershaft rear bearing using bearing installer tool (49 0500 330). Install countershaft thrust washer and snap ring. Check clearance between thrust washer and snap ring using feeler gauge. If clearance exceeds .004" (0.1 mm), replace thrust washer. Thrust washers are available in .079" (2.0), .083" (2.1 mm), .087" (2.2 mm), .091" (2.3 mm) and .094" (2.4 mm) sizes.

10) On all models, install reverse shift spring and locking ball into bearing plate. Push ball down using screwdriver and install reverse shift rod, shift fork and reverse idler gear (4-speed only) at same time. Install washer and snap ring (5-speed only).

11) Install 1st-2nd and 3rd-4th shift forks onto clutch sleeves. Using guide tools (49 0862 350 & 49 0187 451A), install each shift fork rod and interlock pin. Align bolt holes in both shift forks and rods. Install and tighten lock bolts. Install snap rings onto shift rods (5-speed only).

NOTE: **On 4-speed, make sure that spacer is installed in position on reverse shift fork rod.**

12) Install shift locking balls and springs into respective bores in bearing plate. Install and tighten spring cap bolts. On 4-speed models, apply thin coat of sealer on contact surfaces of bearing plate and transmission case and assemble.

13) On 5-speed models, apply thin coat of sealer on contact surfaces of bearing plate and intermediate housing and assemble. Install shift rod ends to shift rods and install and tighten bolts. On all models, install speedometer drive gear, lock ball and snap ring on mainshaft.

14) On 5-speed models, apply thin coat of sealer on contact surfaces of bearing plate and transmission case, and assemble. On all models, install input shaft bearing, using bearing installer tool (49 0500 330), and

Manual Transmissions

MAZDA REAR WHEEL DRIVE 4 & 5-SPEED (Cont.)

install snap ring. Install countershaft front bearing, using bearing installer tool (49 0180 321A).

15) Install speedometer driven gear assembly, lock plate and bolt into extension housing and tighten bolt. Install control lever through holes from front side of extension housing. Install control lever end, control lever and tighten bolt. Install back-up light switch, top switch and overdrive switch.

Fig. 8: View of Front Case Showing Front Bearing End Play Shim Location

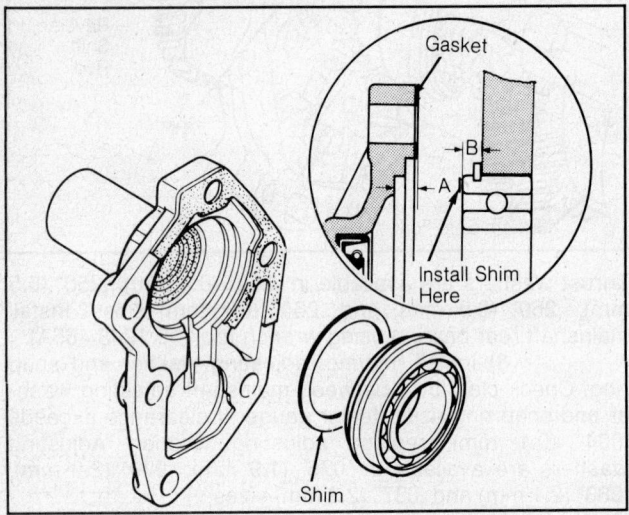

16) Apply thin coat of sealer on contact surfaces of bearing plate/intermediate housing and extension housing and assemble with control lever positioned to the left as far as possible. Install and tighten bolts, making sure control rod operates properly. Install gearshift lever retainer and gasket to extension housing.

17) Lubricate lip of oil seal inside front cover and install front cover to transmission case. Check clearance between bearing outer race and front cover using feeler gauge. If clearance exceeds .004" (0.1 mm), replace adjusting shim. Adjusting shims are available in .006" (1.5 mm) and .012" (.30 mm) sizes.

18) On GLC models, install throw-out bearing, spring, release lever, cross-shaft and cross-shaft bolt and tighten bolt. On all other models, install throw-out bearing, clutch release fork and dust cover.

TIGHTENING SPECIFICATIONS

Application	Ft. Lbs. (N.m)
Mainshaft Lock Nut	
4-Speed	116-174 (157-237)
5-Speed	94-152 (128-207)
Control Lever End Bolt	20-25 (27-34)
	INCH Lbs. (N.m)
Shift Fork Bolts	108-144 (12-16)
Spring Cap Bolts	84-132 (10-15)
Interlock Pin Plug	84-132 (10-15)
Shift Rod End Bolts	72-108 (8-12)

Fig. 9: Exploded View of 4-Speed Transmission Shift Control Linkage

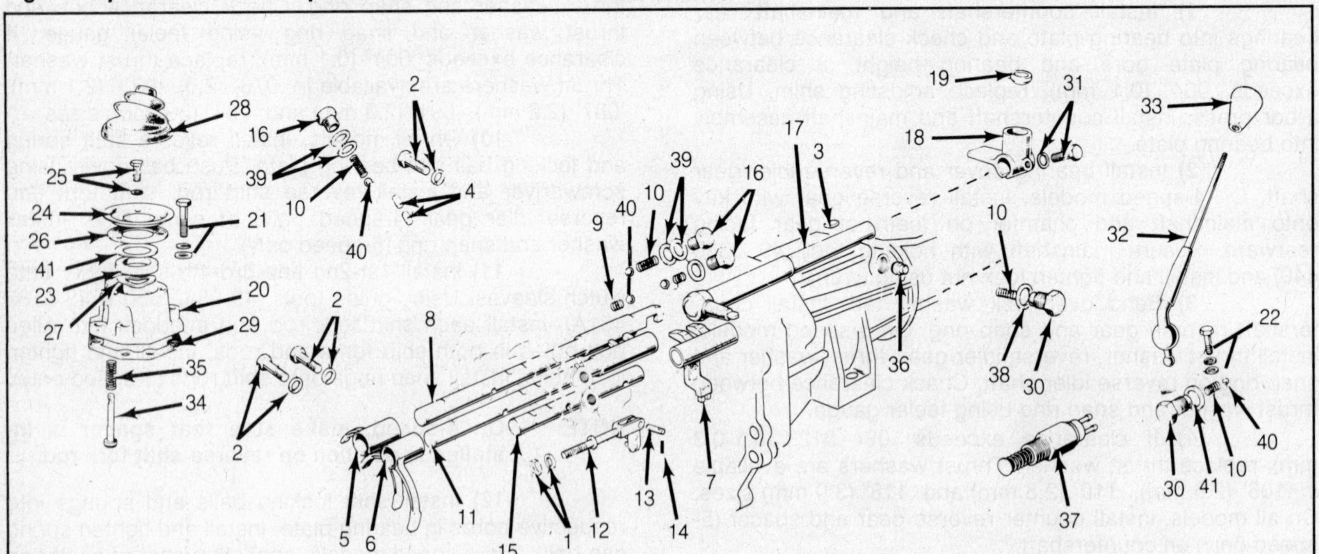

1. Nut & Lock Washer	12. Shift Lever	22. Bolt & Washer	32. Shift Lever
2. Bolt & Spring Washer	13. Pin	23. Bushing	33. Knob
3. Key	14. Pin	24. Cover Plate	34. Select Lock Spindle
4. Interlock Pin	15. Reverse Shift Rod	25. Bolt & Spring Washer	35. Spring
5. 1st-2nd Shift Fork	16. Plug	26. Gasket	36. Detent
6. 3rd-4th Shift Fork	17. Control Lever	27. Wave Washer	37. Back-Up Light Switch
7. Reverse Shift Fork	18. Control Rod End	28. Dust Boot	38. Washer
8. Shift Rod	19. Spring Seat	29. Gasket	39. Washer
9. Spring	20. Shifter Housing	30. Spring Cap	40. Detent Ball
10. Spring	21. Retaining Bolt & Washer	31. Lock Bolt	41. Shim
11. Shift Rod			

5-speed shift control linkage similar.

NISSAN/DATSUN PULSAR, SENTRA & STANZA
4 & 5-SPEED TRANSAXLE

DESCRIPTION

The Nissan manual transaxle assembly contains the clutch, transmission and final drive (differential). Transmission is a 4-speed (Sentra model RN4F30A) or 5-speed (Pulsar and Sentra model RS5F30A, Stanza model RS5F31A) unit, fully synchronized in all forward gears. All forward gears are helically cut and in constant mesh.

Final drive is directly coupled to transmission and housed in transmission case. Transmission and final drive are lubricated from a common oil supply. Constant velocity (CV) joints are used on both ends of drive axle shafts.

LUBRICATION & ADJUSTMENT

See appropriate MANUAL TRANSMISSION SERVICING article in IMPORT GENERAL SERVICING section.

REMOVAL & INSTALLATION

See appropriate MANUAL TRANSMISSION REMOVAL article in IMPORT GENERAL SERVICING section.

SERVICE (IN VEHICLE)

WHEEL BEARINGS
Removal
1) Loosen, but do not remove, wheel hub nut from drive shaft. Raise and support vehicle. Remove wheel and tire. Remove brake caliper and hang aside with wire. Pry cotter pin out of hub.

2) Detach tie-rod end from steering knuckle using Ball Joint Remover (HT72520000). Remove lower ball joint and discard nuts. Drain gear oil, remove drive shaft from transaxle and discard drive shaft circlip.

NOTE: **Always replace axle shaft oil seals in transaxle whenever drive shafts are removed. DO NOT pull on drive shaft assembly during removal or inner CV joint may come apart.**

3) Insert Side Gear Holder (KV38105500) and/or bar into each side of differential to prevent side gears from falling into differential case. If necessary, detach lower ball joint from knuckle using ball joint remover. Remove knuckle mount bolts.

4) Remove hub, knuckle and drive shaft assembly as a unit. Remove hub nut and washer. Withdraw axle shaft from hub. Separate wheel hub from knuckle using Slide Hammer and Adapter (KV40101000 and ST36230000). Remove hub-to-rotor mount bolts. Remove outboard grease seal from hub and discard.

NOTE: **Always replace inner and outer grease seals whenever seals are removed from knuckle or hub.**

5) Using puller, remove outboard wheel bearing from hub. Remove spacer and outboard wheel bearing race from knuckle using a puller. Remove inboard grease seal from knuckle and discard. Remove outer race of

Fig. 1: Exploded View of Pulsar & Sentra Hub/Steering Knuckle Assembly

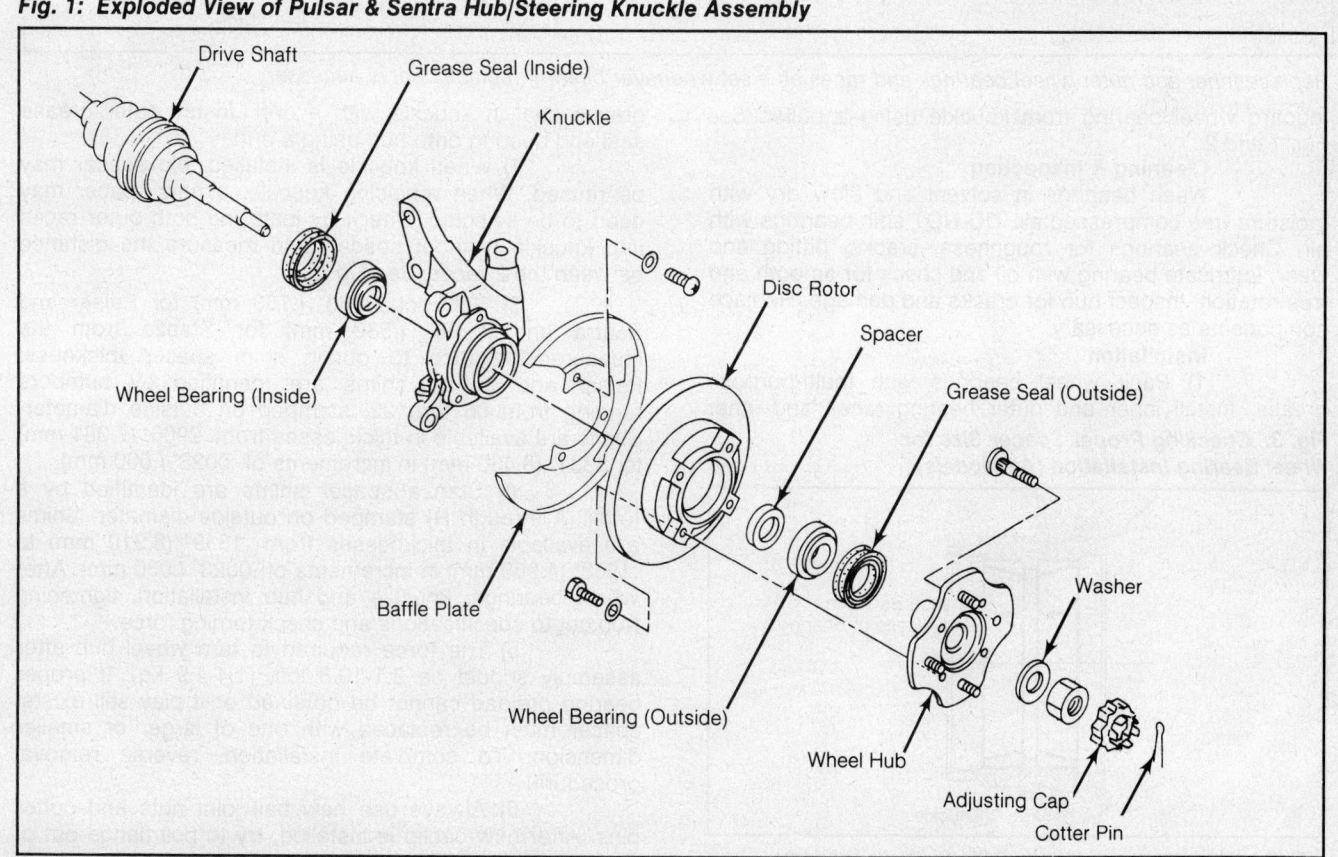

Replace inner and outer wheel bearings and races as a set whenever bearing replacement is necessary.

Manual Transmissions

NISSAN/DATSUN PULSAR, SENTRA & STANZA
4 & 5-SPEED TRANSAXLE (Cont.)

Fig. 2: Exploded View of Stanza Hub/Steering Knuckle Assembly

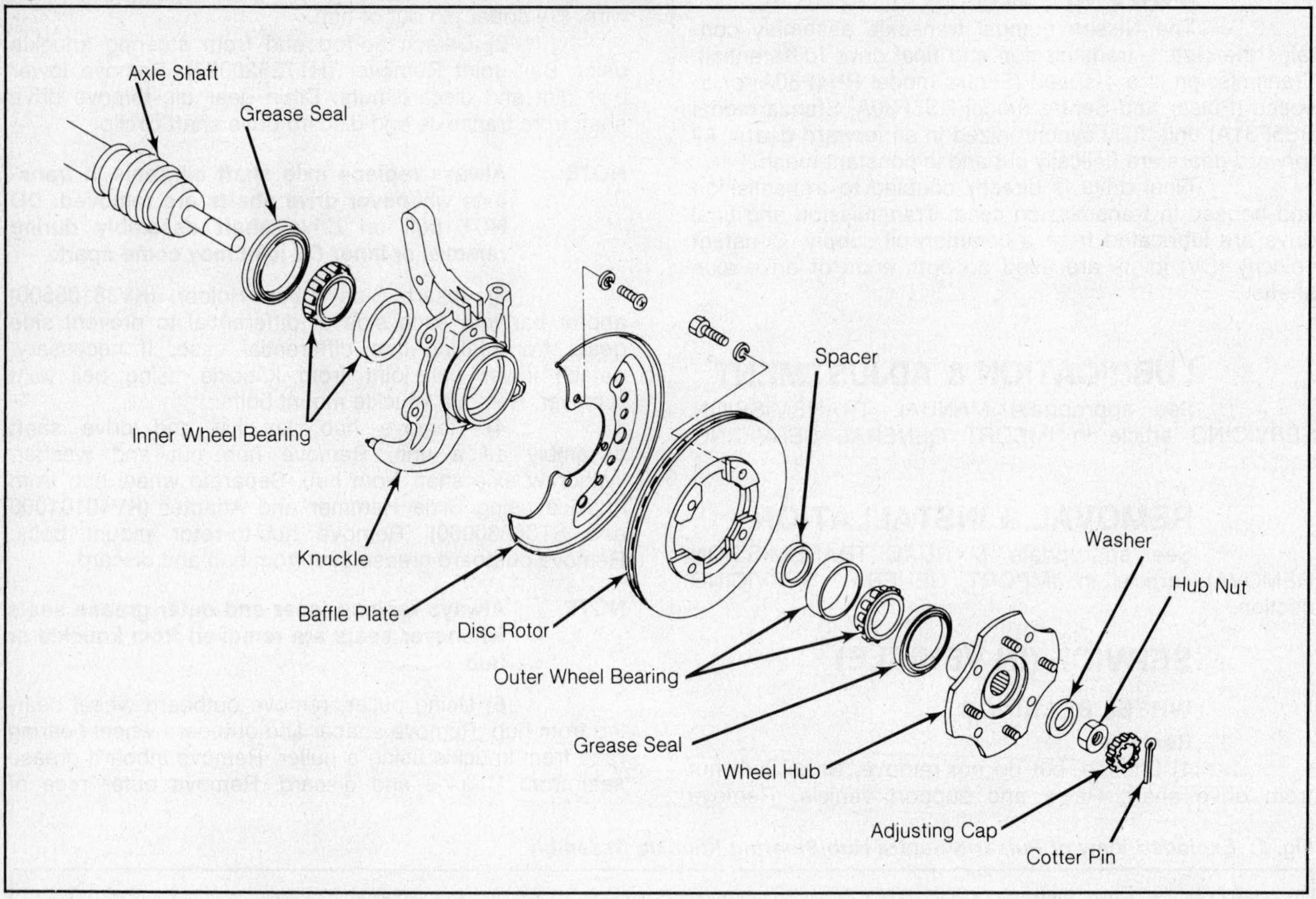

Axle Shaft
Grease Seal
Spacer
Washer
Hub Nut
Inner Wheel Bearing
Knuckle
Baffle Plate
Disc Rotor
Outer Wheel Bearing
Grease Seal
Wheel Hub
Adjusting Cap
Cotter Pin

Replace inner and outer wheel bearings and races as a set whenever bearing replacement is necessary.

inboard wheel bearing from knuckle using a puller. *See Fig. 1 and 2.*

Cleaning & Inspection

Wash bearings in solvent and blow dry with moisture free compressed air. DO NOT spin bearings with air. Check bearings for roughness, cracks, pitting and wear. Lubricate bearing with oil and check for smooth and free rotation. Inspect hub for cracks and damage. Replace components as necessary.

Installation

1) Pack wheel bearings with multi-purpose grease. Install inner and outer bearing races and inner

Fig. 3: Checking Proper Spacer Size for Wheel Bearing Installation (All Models)

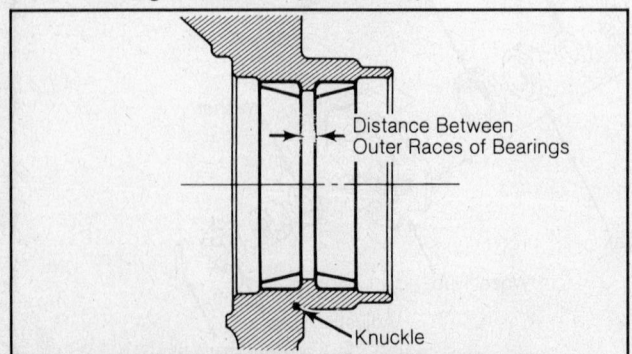

Distance Between Outer Races of Bearings

Knuckle

Install both outer races into knuckle (without spacer) and measure the distance between the 2 races.

grease seal in knuckle with a drift. Install outer grease seal and bearing onto hub using a drift.

2) When knuckle is installed, old spacer may be reused. When replacing knuckle, a new spacer may need to be selected. Check by installing both outer races into knuckle (without spacer) and measure the distance between the 2 races. *See Fig. 3.*

3) Subtract .0063" (.160 mm) for Pulsar and Sentra and .0209" (.530 mm) for Stanza from the measured distance to obtain shim spacer thickness. Pulsar and Sentra shims are identified by numbers ranging from 05 thru 22, stamped on outside diameter. Shims are available in thicknesses from .2906" (7.381 mm) to .3331" (8.460 mm) in increments of .0023" (.060 mm).

4) Stanza spacer shims are identified by a letter (A through R) stamped on outside diameter. Shims are available in thicknesses from .1539" (3.910 mm) to .1953" (4.960 mm) in increments of .0023" (.060 mm). After wheel bearings, knuckle and hub installation, tightening hub nut to specifications and check turning force.

5) The force required to turn wheel hub after assembly should be 3.1-10.8 lbs. (1.4-4.9 kg). If proper bearing preload cannot be obtained or if play still exists, spacer must be replaced with one of larger or smaller dimension. To complete installation, reverse removal procedure.

6) Always use new ball joint nuts and cotter pins. After new circlip is installed, try to pull flange out of

NISSAN/DATSUN PULSAR, SENTRA & STANZA
4 & 5-SPEED TRANSAXLE (Cont.)

Fig. 4: Exploded View of Pulsar & Sentra Axle Shaft Components

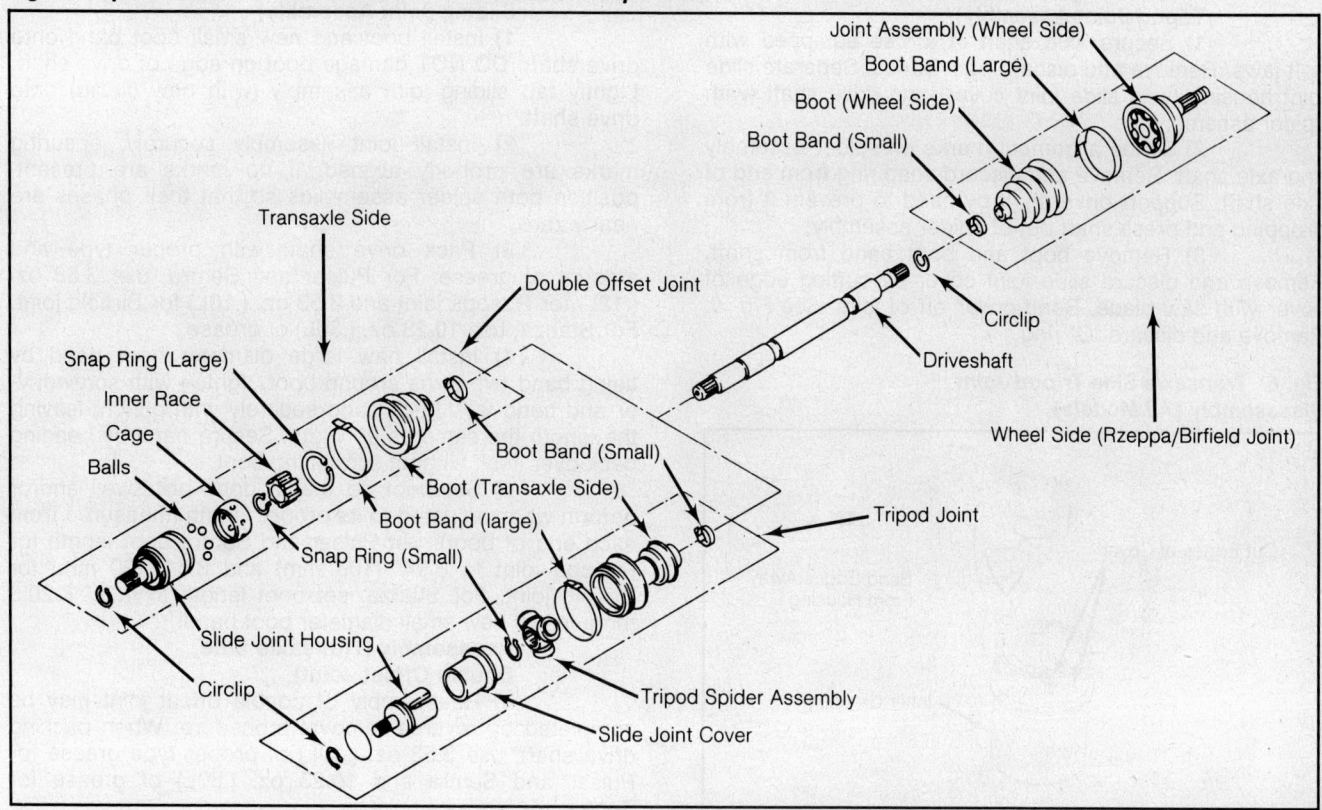

The outer sliding joint (Rzeppa or Birfield type) and inner CV joint (Tripod or Double Offset) are not serviceable, if worn or damaged, replace either joint as an assembly.

Fig. 5: Exploded View of Stanza Axle Shaft Components

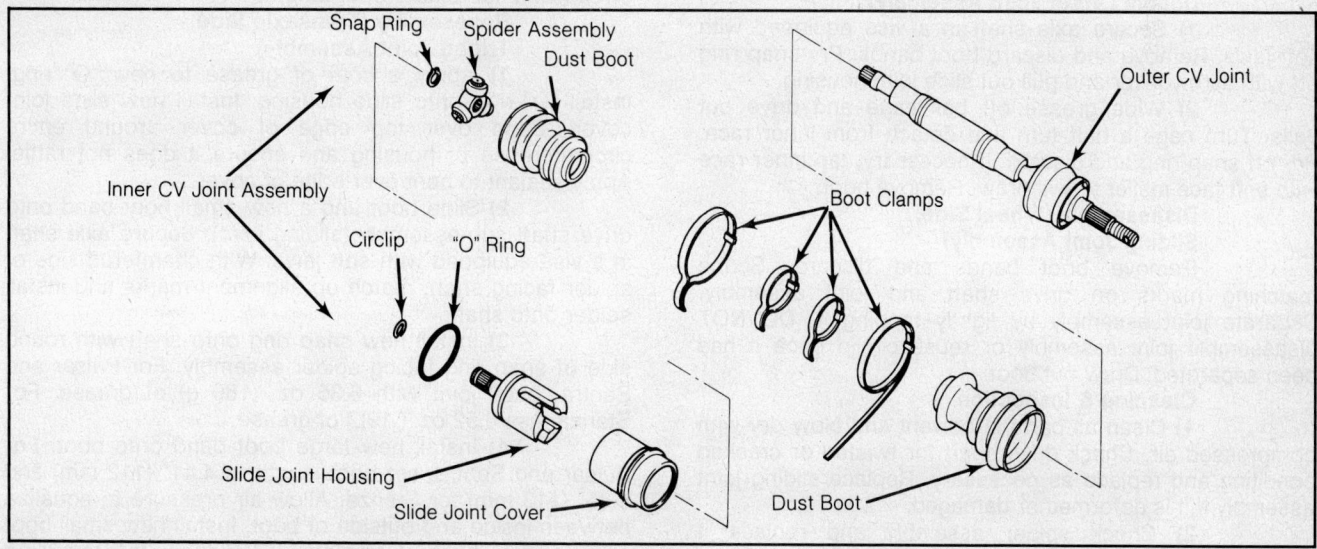

Outer sliding joint and inner CV joint (Tripod) are not serviceable, if worn or damaged, replace either joint as an assembly.

slide joint by hand to ensure circlip is properly meshed with side gear and will not come out.

AXLE SHAFTS
Removal & Installation
To remove drive axle shafts, see WHEEL BEARING REMOVAL and INSTALLATION procedure.

CONSTANT VELOCITY (CV) JOINTS

NOTE: Inner Tripod or Double Offset joint and outer Sliding joint assemblies are non-serviceable and should not be disassembled except as designated. Remove axle shaft from vehicle for inspection and replacement.

Manual Transmissions

NISSAN/DATSUN PULSAR, SENTRA & STANZA 4 & 5-SPEED TRANSAXLE (Cont.)

Disassembly (Transaxle Side, Tripod Joint Assembly)

1) Secure axle shaft in a vise equipped with soft jaws. Remove and discard boot bands. Separate slide joint housing (with slide joint cover) and drive shaft (with spider assembly).

2) Scribe alignment marks on spider assembly and axle shaft. Remove and discard snap ring from end of axle shaft. Support drive shaft by hand to prevent it from dropping and press shaft out of spider assembly.

3) Remove boot and boot band from shaft. Remove and discard slide joint cover by cutting edge of cover with saw blade. Bend cover off of joint. *See Fig. 6.* Remove and discard "O" ring.

Fig. 6: Transaxle Side Tripod Joint Disassembly (All Models)

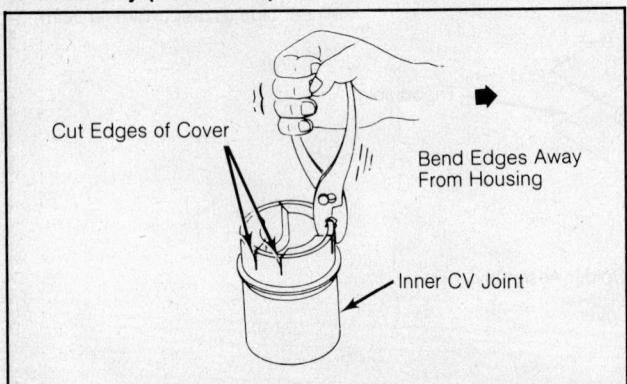

Remove and discard slide joint cover by cutting edge of cover with saw blade and bending cover off joint.

Disassembly (Transaxle Side, Double Offset Joint Assembly)

1) Secure axle shaft in a vise equipped with soft jaws. Remove and discard boot bands. Pry snap ring off with screwdriver and pull out slide joint housing.

2) Wipe grease off ball cage and drive out balls. Turn cage a half turn and detach from inner race. Pry off snap ring and discard. If necessary, tap inner race with soft face mallet to withdraw. Remove boot.

Disassembly (Wheel Side, Sliding Joint Assembly)

Remove boot bands and discard. Scribe matching marks on drive shaft and joint assembly. Separate joint assembly by lightly tapping it. DO NOT disassemble joint assembly or reuse circlip once it has been separated. Draw out boot.

Cleaning & Inspection

1) Clean all parts in solvent and blow dry with compressed air. Check drive shaft for twisted or cracked condition and replace as necessary. Replace sliding joint assembly if it is deformed or damaged.

2) Check spider assembly and replace if needle bearings and washer are damaged. Inspect serrated portions for deformation and replace as necessary. Check slide joint housing and roller surfaces for scratches, excessive wear or damage.

3) Inspect double offset joint assembly for signs of burn, rust, wear or excessive play. Check groove of sliding joint housing for cracks, wear or deformation. Check boots for fatigue, cracks and wear. Replace components as necessary.

Reassembly (Wheel Side, Sliding Joint Assembly)

1) Install boot and new small boot band onto drive shaft. DO NOT damage boot on edge of drive shaft. Lightly tap sliding joint assembly (with new circlip) onto drive shaft.

2) Install joint assembly securely, ensuring marks are properly aligned. If no marks are present, position both spider assemblies so that their phases are nearly zero.

3) Pack drive shaft with proper type and amount of grease. For Pulsar and Sentra, use 3.88 oz. (.12L) for Rzeppa joint and 3.53 oz. (.10L) for Birfield joint. For Stanza, use 10.23 oz. (.30L) of grease.

4) Install new large diameter boot band by tieing band two turns around boot, tighten with screwdriver and bend 90°. Lock band securely with punch, leaving the length the same as its width. Secure band by bending back over itself without scratching boot.

5) Set boot so that it does not swell and/or deform when adjusted to its proper length (measured from each end of boot). Set Pulsar and Sentra boot length for Rzeppa joint to 3.94" (100 mm) and 3.54" (90 mm) for Birfield joint. For Stanza, set boot length to 4.74" (120.5 mm). Install new small diameter boot band.

Reassembly (Transaxle Side, Double Offset Joint)

1) Reassembly of double offset joint may be completed by reverse removal procedure. When packing drive shaft, use 3.53 oz. (.10L) of proper type grease for Pulsar and Sentra and 10.23 oz. (.30L) of grease for Sentra.

2) Install boot and boot bands. Set boot length for Pulsar and Sentra to 3.31" (84 mm) and 4.74" (120.5 mm) for Stanza. Ensure boot does not deform and/or swell when set to its proper length.

Reassembly (Transaxle Side, Tripod Joint Assembly)

1) Apply a coat of grease to new "O" ring. Install "O" ring onto slide housing. Install new slide joint cover. Bend over top edge of cover around entire circumference of housing and ensure it does not rattle. Apply sealant to bent over edge of cover.

2) Slide boot and a new small boot band onto drive shaft sub-assembly (sliding joint). Secure axle shaft in a vise equipped with soft jaws. With chamfered side of spider facing shaft, match up alignment marks and install spider onto shaft.

3) Install new snap ring onto shaft with round side of snap ring facing spider assembly. For Pulsar and Sentra, pack joint with 6.35 oz. (180 g) of grease. For Stanza, use 6.52 oz. (.19L) of grease.

4) Install new large boot band onto boot. For Pulsar and Sentra, set boot length to 4.41" (112 mm) and 4.45" (113 mm) for Stanza. Allow air pressure to equalize between inside and outside of boot. Install new small boot clamp onto boot. Complete installation by reversing removal procedure.

TRANSAXLE DISASSEMBLY & REASSEMBLY

TRANSAXLE CASE

Disassembly

1) Wipe dirt and grease off of transaxle. Drain oil from transaxle case. Remove transmission case mount

NISSAN/DATSUN PULSAR, SENTRA & STANZA
4 & 5-SPEED TRANSAXLE (Cont.)

bolts. Note location of long mount bolt for reassembly reference. Using a plastic hammer, tap transmission case to dislodge it from the clutch housing.

2) Remove transmission case from clutch housing by lifting (and slightly tilting on 5-speed models, to prevent 5th shift fork from interfering with case) away from clutch housing. Remove back-up light switch and oil gutter from transmission case.

3) Remove input shaft rear bearing. Remove case cover and mainshaft bearing adjusting shim and spacer. Remove mainshaft rear bearing outer race and differential side bearing outer race.

4) Clean transmission case and inspect for cracks or cavities. Check all gasket surfaces for nicks, projections or excess sealant. Replace any seals suspected of leakage.

Reassembly

1) Press differential side bearing and mainshaft rear bearing outer races into transmission case. Install input shaft needle bearing. Apply sealer to input shaft access welch plug and install plug into case. Install oil gutter.

2) Apply sealer to back-up light switch and install in transmission case. If transmission case is replaced, adjust differential side bearing and mainshaft rotary frictional force by selecting proper shims.

3) Before installing new transmission case, determine appropriate thickness of differential side bearing adjusting shim with both main and input shafts removed from case. See ADJUSTMENTS – DIFFERENTIAL in this article.

4) After properly adjusting the bearings, clean mating surface of transmission case and clutch housing and apply sealant to clutch housing. When applying sealant, apply an even, continuous coat to prevent leakage.

5) Assemble transmission case onto clutch housing noting that 1 of the 12 attaching bolts is longer than the others. Install case cover with convex side facing out.

6) Measure gear rotary frictional force and ensure that gear moves smoothly and without binding. *See Adjustments in this article.* Make sure that gears shift smoothly. Apply sealant to drain plug and install in transmission case.

CLUTCH HOUSING
Disassembly

1) Clean dirt and grease off outside of transaxle. Drain oil. Remove transmission case. Remove reverse idler spacer and shift fork shaft. Remove 5th, 3rd and 4th shift forks, without dropping shifter caps. Remove control bracket with 1st and 2nd shift fork.

2) On 5-speed transaxles, be careful not to lose detent ball, spring or shift caps. On Sentra and Pulsar models, remove the 3 screws securing bearing retainer to clutch housing.

3) One of the screws is a torx-head screw and requires the use of an offset Torx-bit screwdriver for removal. Do not remove reverse idler shaft from clutch

Fig. 7: Exploded View of Pulsar, Sentra and Stanza Transaxle Case Assembly

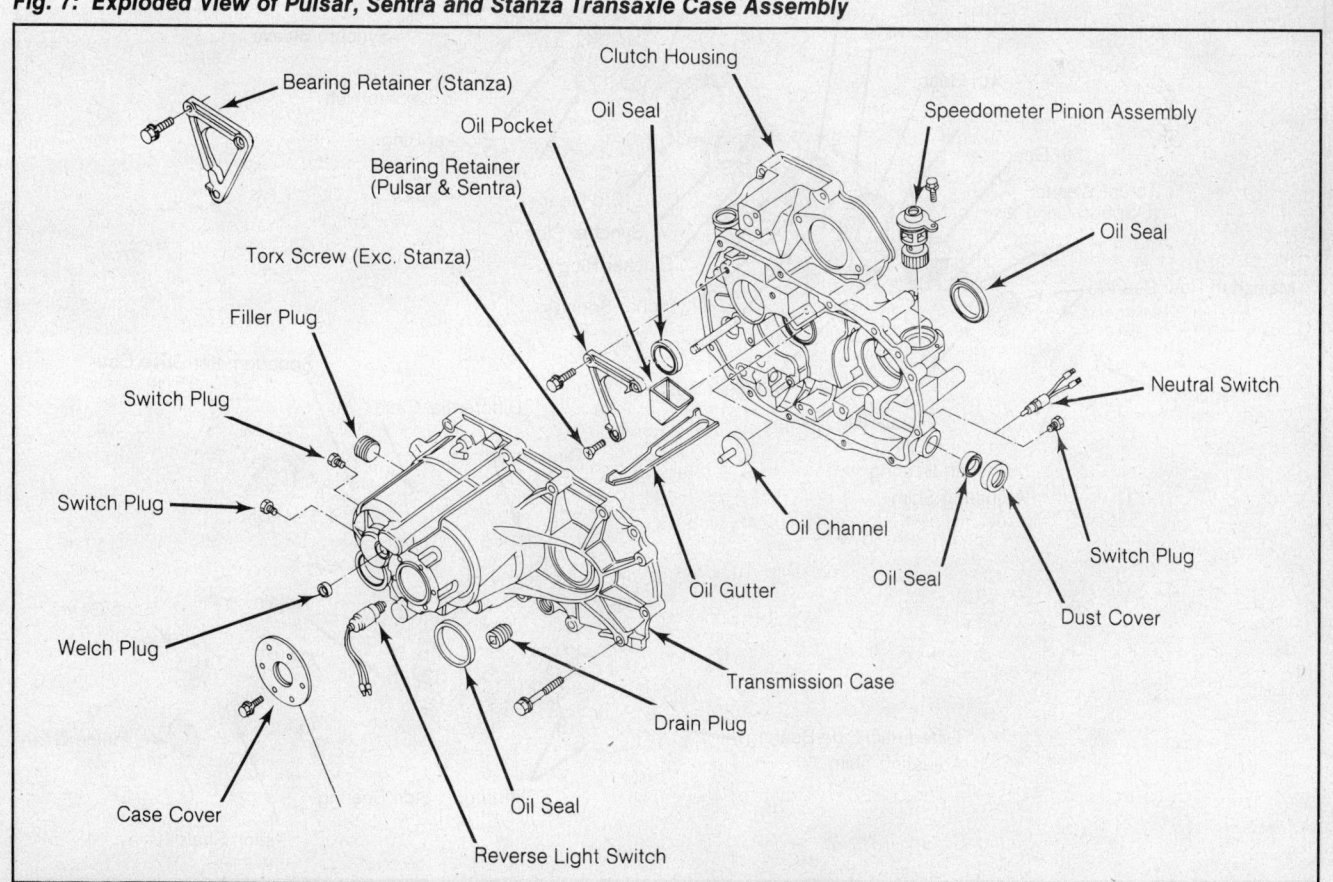

The transaxle case assemblies are the same for all models except for the Stanza bearing retainer.

Manual Transmissions

NISSAN/DATSUN PULSAR, SENTRA & STANZA 4 & 5-SPEED TRANSAXLE (Cont.)

Fig. 8: Exploded View of 4 and 5-Speed Transaxle Gears

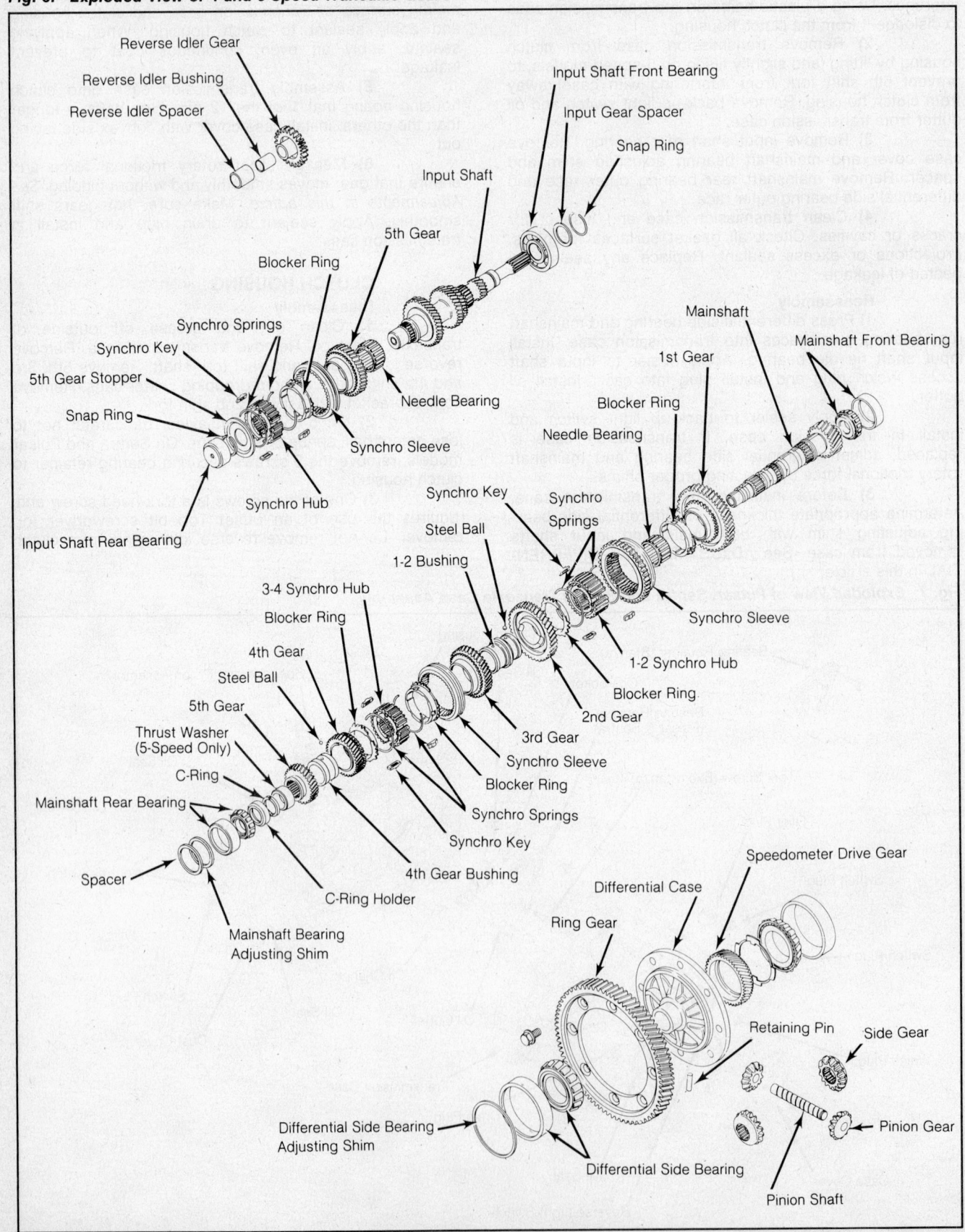

The 5-speed Transaxle is shown; the 4-speed does not use 5th gear or related components.

NISSAN/DATSUN PULSAR, SENTRA & STANZA
4 & 5-SPEED TRANSAXLE (Cont.)

Fig. 9: Exploded View of Shift Mechanism (All Models)

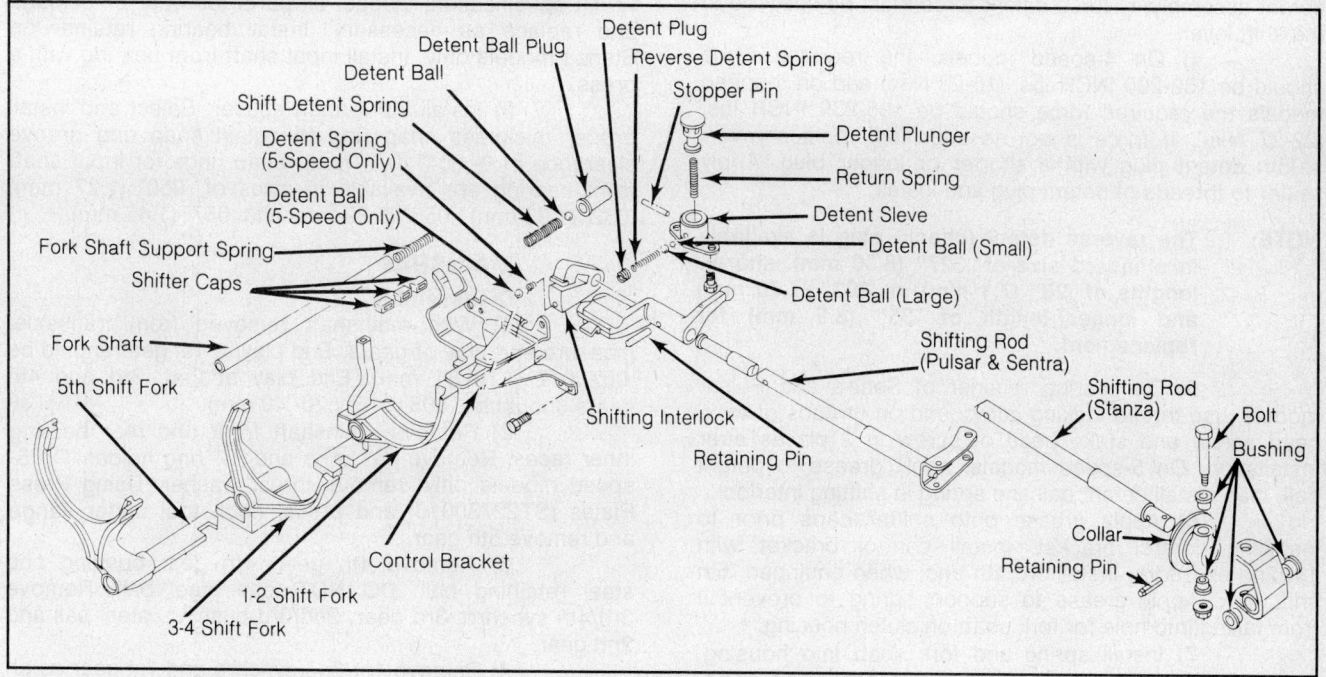

The Pulsar, Sentra and Stanza have the same shift mechanism except for the Stanza shifting rod yoke, which is somewhat different from the others.

housing. Turn clutch housing so that bottom side faces down.

4) Lightly tap on engine side of input shaft with plastic hammer to dislodge shaft from housing. Remove mainshaft and input shaft as an assembly. When removing gearshafts, pull straight away from housing to avoid breaking plastic oil channel on clutch housing side.

5) Ensure that differential does not fall out when gearshafts are removed and that input shaft oil seal is not damaged by input shaft splines. Remove the reverse idler gear and differential assembly.

6) On Stanza models, remove mainshaft and differential assembly. When removing mainshaft, pull straight out from housing to avoid damaging plastic oil channel on clutch housing side.

7) Remove input shaft bearing retainer mount bolts. Turn clutch housing so that bottom side faces down. Lightly tap on engine side of input shaft with a plastic hammer to dislodge shaft from housing.

8) Remove input shaft together with bearing retainer and reverse idler gear. Make sure that input shaft oil seal is not damaged by input shaft splines. Do not remove reverse idler shaft from housing.

9) On all models, remove oil pocket, shift detent ball, detent springs and detent ball plug. Drive roll pin out of shifting rod. Remove shifting rod, shifting lever and shifting interlock. Tape edges of shifting rod to prevent seal from being damaged when rod is removed.

10) Remove reverse and 5th detent plug, detent balls and detent spring. Remove 5th and reverse detent assembly. Remove clutch control shaft, release bearing and clutch lever.

11) Remove mainshaft bearing outer race and differential side bearing outer race. Remove oil channel. Clean clutch housing and check for cracks or cavities. Check mating surfaces of clutch housing for nicks,

projections or excess sealer. Replace any seals suspected of leakage.

Reassembly

1) Install a new oil channel making sure that channel oil groove faces housing oil pocket. Install mainshaft bearing outer race and differential side bearing outer race.

2) Install clutch control shaft, clutch release bearing and clutch lever. Install oil pocket and make sure that oil flows from oil pocket to oil channel. See Fig. 10.

Fig. 10: Checking Lubrication Passage

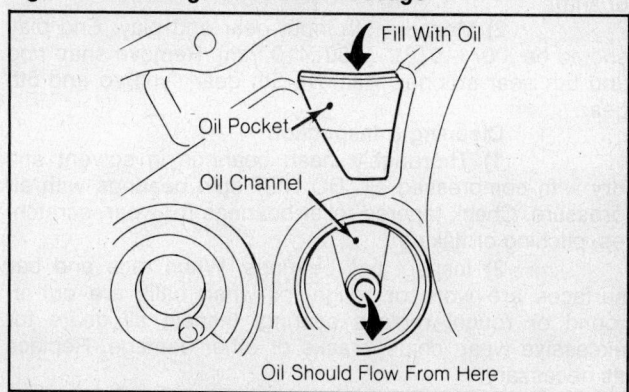

When the oil pocket is installed, ensure oil flows from the pocket to the oil channel.

NOTE: **When installing reverse/5th check assembly, install smaller check ball first, then install larger check ball, spring and reverse/5th check plug.**

3) Reverse remainder of disassembly procedure to complete reassembly, and note the following:

Manual Transmissions

NISSAN/DATSUN PULSAR, SENTRA & STANZA
4 & 5-SPEED TRANSAXLE (Cont.)

When replacing any part that affects the reverse (and 5th) detent assembly, reverse detent force must be checked at the shift lever.

4) On 4-speed models, the required force should be 139-200 INCH lbs. (16-23 N.m) and on 5-speed models the required force should be 195-239 INCH lbs. (22-27 N.m). If force is not as specified, replace reverse/5th detent plug with a shorter or longer plug. Apply sealer to threads of detent plug and install.

NOTE: The reverse detent (check) plug is available in standard size of .327" (8.30 mm), shorter lengths of .28" (7.1 mm) or .303" (7.70 mm) and longer length of .35" (8.9 mm) for replacement.

5) On bearing retainer of Sentra and Pulsar models, use thread locking compound on threads of torx-head screw and stake head of screw in 2 places after installation. On 5-speed models, apply grease to detent ball, then install detent ball and spring in shifting interlock.

6) Apply grease onto shifter caps prior to installing control bracket. Install control bracket with 1st/2nd shift fork. Install 3rd/4th and, when equipped, 5th shift fork. Apply grease to support spring to prevent it from falling into hole for fork shaft on clutch housing.

7) Install spring and fork shaft into housing. Install reverse idler spacer. Install transmission case. Measure gear rotary frictional force and ensure that gears move smoothly and without binding. See ADJUSTMENTS in this article. Apply sealer to drain plug and install into case.

COMPONENT DISASSEMBLY & REASSEMBLY

INPUT SHAFT
Disassembly
1) With input shaft removed from transaxle, remove and discard snap ring. Remove spacer from front of input shaft. Using bearing puller, draw front bearing off of shaft.

2) Measure 5th input gear end play. End play should be .0071-.0161" (.180-.410 mm). Remove snap ring and 5th gear stopper. Remove 5th gear synchro and 5th gear.

Cleaning & Inspection
1) Thoroughly clean bearings in solvent and dry with compressed air. DO NOT spin bearings with air pressure. Check tapered roller bearings for wear, scratches, pitching or flaking.

2) Inspect ball bearings. When race and ball surfaces are worn or rough, or when balls are out-of-round or rough, replace bearing. Inspect all gears for excessive wear, chips, cracks or other damage. Replace as necessary.

3) Check shaft for bending, cracks or worn splines. Inspect needle bearings and replace if worn or damaged. Check synchro rings for deformation, cracks or excessive damage. Replace components as necessary.

Reassembly
1) Install 5th gear and 5th gear synchronizer onto shaft. Install 5th gear stopper onto shaft. Select and install proper thickness snap ring to obtain snap ring groove clearance of 0-.004" (0-.10 mm). Shims for input shaft 5th gear at available in sizes of .0787" (2 mm) to .0906" (2.3 mm) in increments of .002" (.05 mm).

2) Recheck 5th gear end play. If end play is not within specification, inspect all parts for wear or damage and replace as necessary. Install bearing retainer on Stanza models only. Install input shaft front bearing with a press.

3) Install input shaft spacer. Select and install proper thickness snap ring to obtain snap ring groove clearance of 0-.004" (0-.1 mm). Snap rings for input shaft front bearing are available in sizes of .050" (1.27 mm), .052" (1.33 mm), .055" (1.39 mm) and .057" (1.45 mm).

MAINSHAFT
Disassembly
1) With mainshaft removed from transaxle, measure end play of gears. End play at 1st gear should be .007-.012" (.18-.31 mm). End play at 2nd, 3rd and 4th gears should be .008-.016" (.20-.40 mm).

2) Remove mainshaft front and rear bearing inner races. Remove "C" rings and "C" ring holder. On 5-speed models only, remove thrust washer. Using Press Plates (ST22730010) and press, hook tool under flange and remove 5th gear.

3) Remove 4th gear, 4th gear bushing and steel retaining ball. DO NOT lose steel ball. Remove 3rd/4th synchro, 3rd gear, 2nd/3rd bushing, steel ball and 2nd gear.

4) Remove 1st/2nd synchro and 1st gear as an assembly. Remove 1st gear needle bearing. Inspect all parts for wear or damage and replace as necessary.

Reassembly
1) Apply gear oil to 1st gear needle bearing. Install needle bearing, 1st gear and 1st gear synchro ring onto shaft. Install 1st/2nd synchro onto shaft with shallow side of hub and shift fork groove facing toward 1st gear.

2) Install 2nd gear synchro ring. Apply gear oil to 2nd/3rd bushing outer surface. Coat steel retaining ball with grease. Install steel retaining ball, 2nd gear, 2nd/3rd bushing (line up groove in bushing with steel ball), 3rd gear and 3rd/4th synchronizer assembly.

3) Apply grease to steel retaining ball and install ball into shaft. Apply gear oil to outside of 4th gear bushing. Install bushing, making sure to line up groove in bushing with steel ball. Install 4th gear onto shaft. For 5-speed models, install 5th gear and thrust washer.

4) Select and install proper thickness "C" ring to obtain shaft groove clearance of 0-.004" (0-.10 mm). Install mainshaft front and rear bearing inner races. Recheck end play measurement of all gears. If end play is not to specification, inspect all parts for wear or damage and replace as necessary.

SYNCHRONIZERS
Disassembly
Remove springs and keys from synchro assembly. Note component positions and locations for reassembly reference. Slide coupling sleeve off of synchro hub.

Cleaning & Inspection
1) Wash all parts in solvent and blow dry with compressed air. Check synchro ring for deformation, cracking or excessive wear. Check clearance by placing synchro ring in position on gauge cone.

2) While holding ring against gear as far as it will go, measure gap between synchro ring and outer gear. Standard synchro ring-to-gear clearance is .039-

NISSAN/DATSUN PULSAR, SENTRA & STANZA
4 & 5-SPEED TRANSAXLE (Cont.)

.053" (1.00-1.35 mm). Service limit is .028" (.70 mm) or less.

3) Inspect synchro key for wear at shoulders of key. Check synchro hub and sleeve for smooth movement. Inspect remaining parts for damage or wear. Replace components as necessary.

Reassembly

1) To reassemble, reverse disassembly procedure. Fit shifting keys in the three grooves in synchro hub. Insert protrusion of spread spring into groove so that key is securely attached to inner side of coupling sleeve.

2) Install other spread spring on opposite side of synchro hub. Be careful not to hook front and rear ends of spread spring to the same synchro key. Ensure that open portion of springs are offset.

DIFFERENTIAL

Disassembly

1) With differential removed from transaxle, detach ring gear mount bolts. Remove ring gear from differential. Using a punch, drive out pinion shaft retaining lock pin. Remove pinion shaft from differential.

2) Remove differential pinion gears and side gears. Remove differential side bearing carrier assembly. Using hydraulic press and press plates (ST30031000), pull bearings from carrier.

3) DO NOT interchange left and right side bearings. Using bearing remover (ST33290001), pull bearing races from clutch housing and transmission case. Remove speedometer drive gear and stop ring from differential.

Inspection

Wash all parts in solvent and blow dry with compressed air. Inspect mating surfaces of differential case, side gears and pinion gears. Check all parts for excessive wear or damage. Replace components as necessary.

Reassembly

1) Install speedometer drive gear and stop ring. Press new differential side bearings onto carrier. Using hammer and Bearing Race Installers (ST30611000 and ST30621000), drive new races into case and housing.

2) Install differential pinion gears and pinion shaft into differential. Install pinion shaft retaining pin flush with differential case. Install side gears directly opposite each other against pinion gears.

3) Simultaneously rotate side gears into their proper position in differential case. Measure side gear-to-pinion gear clearance. Using shaft adapter (KV38105900), insert shaft into side gear and mount dial indicator.

4) With shaft positioned against back of side gear and dial indicator tip on end of shaft, move side gear up and down and note measurement. Perform measurement on both side gears. Clearance should be no more than .012" (.30 mm).

5) If clearance exceeds specification, replace side bearing adjusting shim with one of proper size. Adjusting shims are available in sizes of .0173" (.440 mm), .0189" (.480 mm) and .0220" (.560 mm) thru .0346" (.880 mm) in increments of .0016" (.040 mm).

6) If components are excessively worn, replace pinion gears, side gears and case as a set. Apply thread locking compound to ring gear bolts and install ring gear.

ADJUSTMENTS

MAINSHAFT

1) If the mainshaft, mainshaft front and/or rear bearings, clutch housing or transmission case were replaced, mainshaft bearing rotary frictional force should be checked and, if necessary, adjusted.

2) To properly adjust rotary force, apply gear oil to mainshaft rear bearing outer race. Install outer race and spacer. Using a depth gauge, measure distance from case surface to spacer. *See Fig. 11.*

Fig. 11: Mainshaft Preload Adjustment

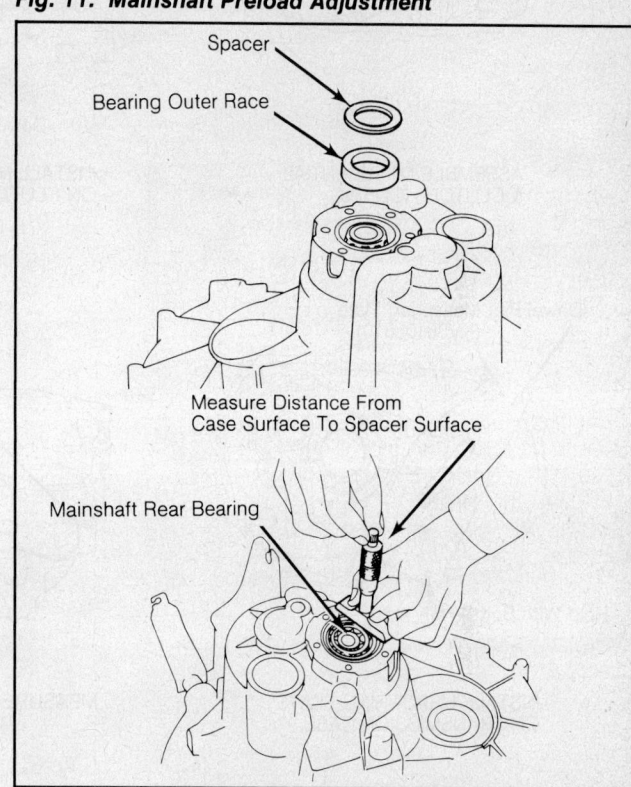

Mainshaft shim must be checked and replaced (if needed) to achieve proper side bearing rotary frictional force.

3) Select the proper thickness of shim so that total thickness of shim is closest to measured distance plus .008" (.20 mm). Install proper shim between bearing outer race and spacer.

4) Mainshaft shims are available in sizes from .004" (.10 mm) to .0394" (1 mm) in increments of .002" (.05 mm). After shim selection and replacement, install case cover and tighten bolts to specifications.

DIFFERENTIAL

1) Ensure that differential side bearing rotary frictional force is within specifications. Shift into 4th gear and turn input shaft at least 10 times to seat bearings. Insert Wrench Adapter (KV38105900) into differential through axle shaft hole.

2) Connect a torque wrench to wrench adapter. Measure the force required to rotate differential assembly. Required force should be 65-95 INCH lbs. (7.5-11 N.m). Fluctuations in required force should be no more 9 INCH lbs. (1 N.m). If specifications are not met, change

Manual Transmissions

NISSAN/DATSUN PULSAR, SENTRA & STANZA
4 & 5-SPEED TRANSAXLE (Cont.)

Fig. 12: Differential Side Bearing Preload Adjustment

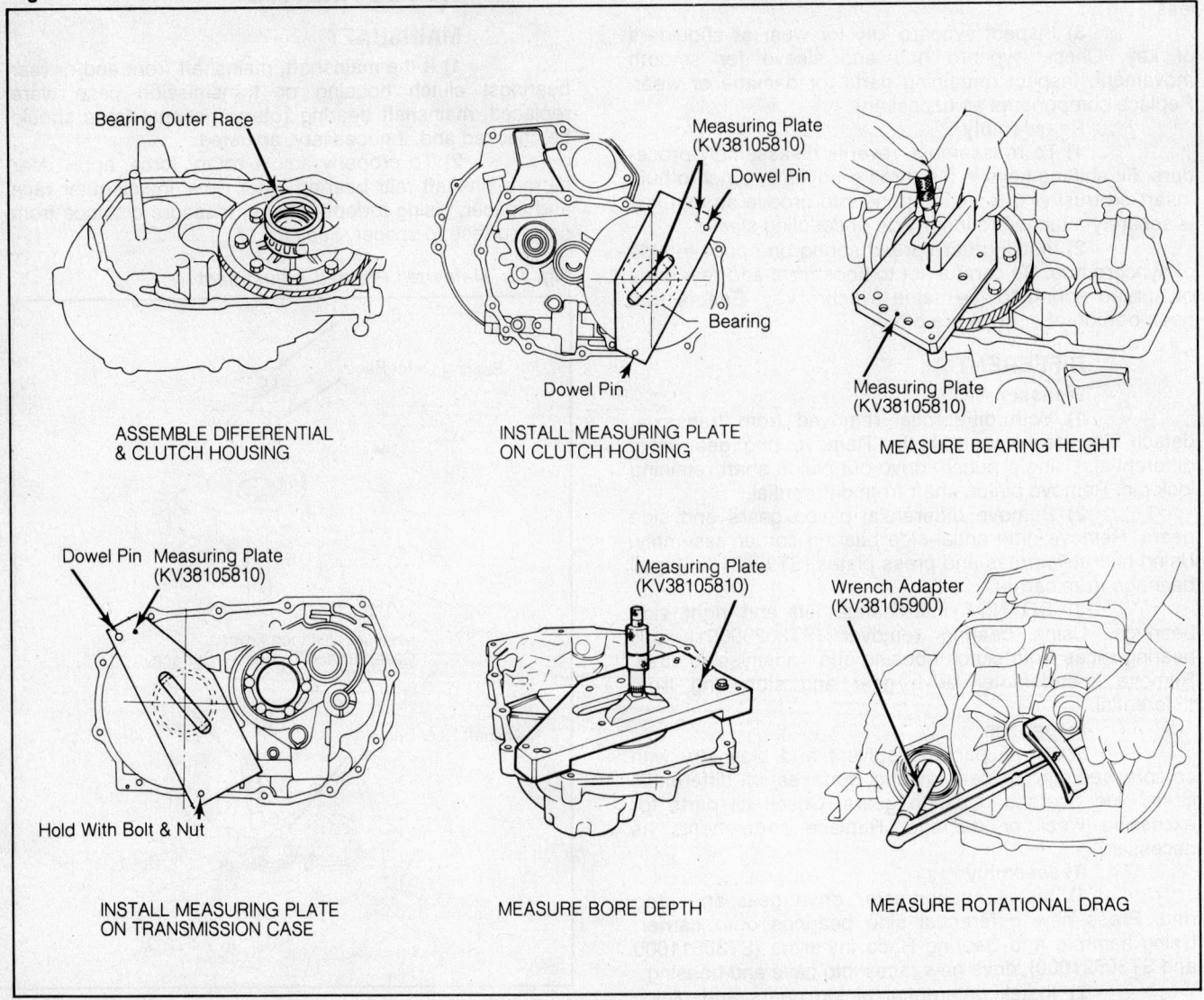

ASSEMBLE DIFFERENTIAL & CLUTCH HOUSING

INSTALL MEASURING PLATE ON CLUTCH HOUSING

MEASURE BEARING HEIGHT

INSTALL MEASURING PLATE ON TRANSMISSION CASE

MEASURE BORE DEPTH

MEASURE ROTATIONAL DRAG

If any abnormalities are noted during preload adjustment or rotary frictional force is incorrect, the transmission case/clutch housing must be disassembled, proper shim installed and reassembled.

differential side bearing shim thickness to obtain desired result.

3) If the differential, side bearings, clutch housing or transmission case have been replaced, housing must be measured for new differential side bearing shim. Clean mating surfaces of clutch housing and transmission case with solvent.

4) Install differential assembly and side bearing outer race into clutch housing. Hold bearing in place and turn differential several turns to seat bearings. Attach Measuring Plate (KV38105810) to clutch housing and side bearing race. *See Fig. 12.*

5) Using a depth gauge, measure distance from upper surface of side bearing outer race to surface of measuring plate. Subtract .9449" (24 mm) from measured distance to obtain bearing height.

6) Attach measuring plate to surface of transmission case. Measure the distance from bottom of side bearing outer race bore to surface of measuring

plate. Subtract thickness of measuring plate, which is .9449" (24 mm), from measured distance to obtain bore depth.

7) To obtain shim thickness, subtract bearing height from bore depth and add .012" (.30 mm) to the result. Select a shim whose thickness is nearest the value determined by the above equation.

8) Shims are available in thicknesses from .0173" (.440 mm) to .0346" (.880 mm) in increments of .0016" (.040 mm). Install shim behind outer race of side bearing in transmission case.

9) With differential in position, assemble transmission case to clutch housing. Insert Wrench Adapter (KV38105900) into differential through axle shaft hole. Connect a torque wrench to wrench adapter. Rotate differential at least 10 times to seat bearings.

10) Measure the force required to rotate differential assembly. With input shaft and mainshaft removed, required force should be 43-65 INCH lbs. (5.0-

NISSAN/DATSUN PULSAR, SENTRA & STANZA
4 & 5-SPEED TRANSAXLE (Cont.)

7.5 N.m). Fluctuations in required force should be no more than 9 INCH lbs. (1 N.m).

11) If specifications are not met, change differential side bearing shim thickness to obtain desired result. After obtaining correct preload, separate transmission case from clutch housing and install remainder of transaxle components.

TIGHTENING SPECIFICATIONS

Application	Ft. Lbs. (N.m)
Back-Up Light Switch	14-22 (19-30)
Bearing Retainer-to Clutch Housing	12-15 (16-20)
Brake Rotor-to-Hub	
Pulsar & Sentra	18-25 (24-34)
Stanza	28-38 (38-51)
Clutch Housing-to Transmission Case	12-15 (16-20)
Drain Plug	18-25 (24-34)
Filler Plug	18-25 (24-34)
Neutral Switch	14-22 (19-29)
Ring Gear Mount Bolts	54-65 (73-88)
Switch Plug	11-14 (15-19)
Transaxle-to-Engine Mount Bolt	12-15 (16-20)
Wheel Hub Nut	
Pulsar & Sentra	87-145 (118-196)
Stanza	145-203 (196-275)
5th/Reverse Detent Plug	14-18 (19-24)

	INCH Lbs. (N.m)
Brake Baffle Plate Mount Bolt	
Pulsar & Sentra	28-38 (3.2-4.3)
Stanza	71-97 (8-11)
Control Bracket-to Clutch Housing Mount Bolt	55-73 (6.2-8.2)
Shift Rod Yoke Mount Bolt (Stanza)	55-73 (6.2-8.2)
Speedometer Gear Assembly Mount Bolt	32-44 (4-5)
Transmission Case Cover Mount Bolt	55-73 (6.2-8.2)
5th/Reverse Detent Assembly	55-73 (6.2-8.2)

Manual Transmissions

NISSAN/DATSUN MAXIMA, PICKUP, 200SX & 300ZX 5-SPEED

DESCRIPTION

The FS5W71B and C transmissions are fully synchronized with constant mesh gears. All forward gears are helical type. The 5th overdrive (O.D.) gear rides freely on mainshaft. The countershaft 5th gear is fitted to countershaft by splines. The 5th gear synchronizer system is also on rear of mainshaft.

Placing control lever in 5th gear position will bring reverse and 5th gear coupling sleeve on mainshaft into mesh with countershaft gear. The main components of transmission are: Transmission case, adapter plate and rear extension housing.

LUBRICATION & ADJUSTMENT

See appropriate MANUAL TRANSMISSION SERVICING article in IMPORT GENERAL SERVICING section.

REMOVAL & INSTALLATION

See appropriate MANUAL TRANSMISSION REMOVAL article in IMPORT GENERAL SERVICING section.

TRANSMISSION DISASSEMBLY

1) Clean transmission case before disassembly. Drain gear oil. If equipped, remove O.D. gear switch. Remove "E" clip and stopper guide pin. Remove shifter return spring plug, spring and plunger from extension housing.

2) Remove rear extension housing by turning shifter control fully to the left while lightly tapping housing. Use standard puller to help remove housing, if necessary. Remove lock pin and striking rod.

3) Remove Reverse check sleeve. Remove dust cover, release bearing and withdrawal lever. Remove back-up light switch, speedometer driven gear and front cover with gasket.

4) Detach countershaft front bearing shim. Remove input shaft bearing snap ring. Separate transmission case from adapter plate, using a soft hammer.

COMPONENT DISASSEMBLY & REASSEMBLY

GEAR ASSEMBLY

Disassembly

1) Install gear and fork assembly onto adapter setting plate (ST23810001) and install assembly in vise. Remove 3 check ball plugs and check springs. Drive out retaining pins from fork rods with pin punch. *See Fig. 1.*

2) Drive out fork rods from adapter plate, by tapping lightly on front of rods. Remove 4 interlock balls and 3 check balls. Before disassembling mainshaft, measure gear backlash.

3) *Refer to Gear End Play Chart for measurement limits.* Record gear end play measurements for reassembly reference.

4) With 2nd and Reverse gears engaged, remove countershaft front bearing, using a puller. Remove countergear snap ring. Remove counterdrive gear and input shaft assembly.

Fig. 1: Exploded View of Shift Control Components

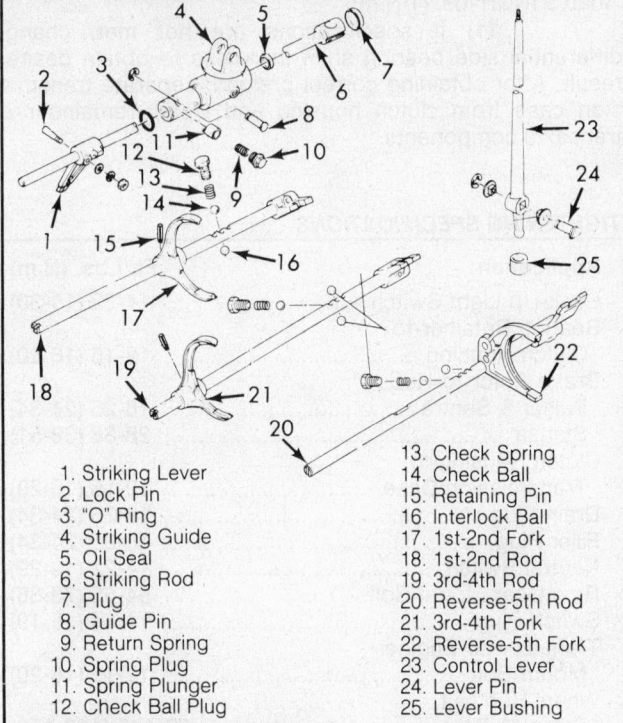

1. Striking Lever	13. Check Spring
2. Lock Pin	14. Check Ball
3. "O" Ring	15. Retaining Pin
4. Striking Guide	16. Interlock Ball
5. Oil Seal	17. 1st-2nd Fork
6. Striking Rod	18. 1st-2nd Rod
7. Plug	19. 3rd-4th Rod
8. Guide Pin	20. Reverse-5th Rod
9. Return Spring	21. 3rd-4th Fork
10. Spring Plug	22. Reverse-5th Fork
11. Spring Plunger	23. Control Lever
12. Check Ball Plug	24. Lever Pin
	25. Lever Bushing

Model C is similar.

GEAR END PLAY MEASUREMENTS

Application	In. (mm)
1st Gear	.011-.013 (.27-.34)
2nd Gear	.005-.008 (.12-.19)
3rd Gear	.005-.015 (.13-.37)
5th Gear (O.D.)	.012-.014 (.31-.35)
Reverse Gear	.002-.020 (.05-.50)

NOTE: When drawing out main drive gear assembly, do not drop pilot needle bearing and synchro ring.

5) Remove snap ring and thrust washer from mainshaft. Remove 3rd and 4th synchronizer assembly. Remove 3rd gear. Engage 2nd and Reverse gears. Release staking on countershaft and mainshaft nuts. Remove and discard countershaft nut.

6) Using puller, remove countershaft 5th gear and bearing. Remove counter reverse idler gear and spacer. Remove countershaft by tapping lightly at the rear end. Remove reverse idler gear snap ring and reverse idler gear.

7) Remove snap rings, steel ball, speedometer gear and bearing from rear of mainshaft. Remove snap ring on mainshaft bearing. Remove mainshaft end bearing with puller (KV32101330).

8) Remove mainshaft nut, thrust washer, steel roller, needle bearing, O.D. gear and baulk ring. Remove mainshaft reverse gear, overdrive synchronizer, insert retainer and overdrive gear bushing.

9) Remove components by tapping rear end of mainshaft gear assembly and countershaft. While tapping, hold front of mainshaft assembly to prevent dropping

NISSAN/DATSUN MAXIMA, PICKUP, 200SX & 300ZX
5-SPEED (Cont.)

counter gear. Remove thrust washer, steel ball, 1st gear and needle bearing. Do not lose steel ball retaining thrust washer.

10) Hold mainshaft so as not to drop it. Using bearing puller (ST30031000), press out 1st gear mainshaft bushing together with 2nd gear, 1st synchronizer and 2nd synchronizer. Disassemble synchronizers. *See Fig. 2 and 3.*

NOTE: **Countershaft and mainshaft nuts should be discarded and replaced with new nuts.**

Fig. 2: Exploded View of 1st & 2nd and 3rd & 4th Gear Synchronizer

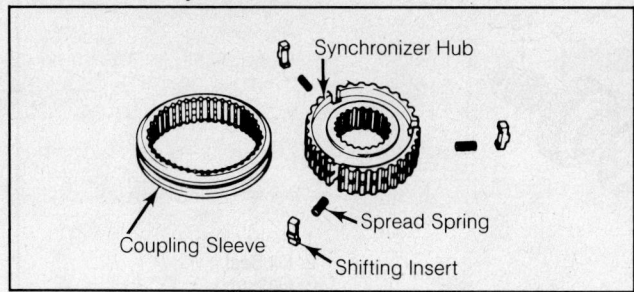

- Synchronizer Hub
- Coupling Sleeve
- Spread Spring
- Shifting Insert

All synchronizers (except 5th O.D. synchronizer) are the same as illustrated above.

Fig. 3: Exploded View of 5th (O.D.) Gear Synchronizer & Reverse Main Gear

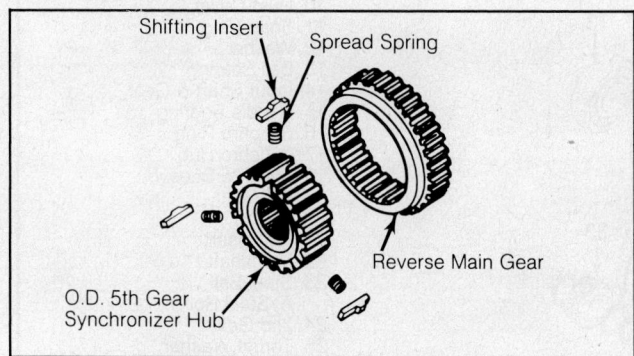

- Shifting Insert
- Spread Spring
- Reverse Main Gear
- O.D. 5th Gear Synchronizer Hub

Inspection

1) Wash all parts in a cleaning solvent and check for wear, damage or other faulty conditions. Inspect bearing race and ball surfaces for rough or worn condition. Check balls for rough or out of round. Replace as necessary.

2) Check transmission case and extension housing for cracks, damage or other faulty conditions. If rear extension housing bushing is worn or cracked, replace extension housing and bushing as an assembly.

3) Check synchro assemblies (baulk rings) for wear. Place synchro ring on gear cone as far as it will go. Measure gap between gear and synchro ring. Standard clearance for 1st-4th gears is .047-.063" (1.20-1.60 mm) and .039-.055" (1.00-1.40 mm) for 5th O.D. gear.

4) If clearance is less than .031" (.80 mm) on 1st-4th gears or .020" (.50 mm) on 5th gear, replace synchro ring. Check oil seal for spring out of position and cracked or deformed sealing lip. Check oil seal lip contact with shaft. If necessary, replace oil seal and shaft as an assembly.

Reassembly

1) Place new dowel pins (2) and mainshaft bearing on adapter plate and tap into position. Install oil gutter on adapter plate, bending it on front side and expanding it on rear side.

2) Install Reverse idle shaft and bearing retainer. Tighten two screws and stake at two points. Install rear countershaft bearing with soft face hammer. Assembly coupling sleeve and hub. Position spread springs and shifting inserts in three slots in synchronizer hub.

3) Place coupling sleeve (Reverse main gear) on synchronizer hub. Install 2nd gear needle bearing, 2nd gear, 2nd gear synchro ring, 1st and 2nd gear synchro assembly, 1st gear synchro ring, 1st gear bushing, needle bearing, 1st gear, steel ball and thrust washer on mainshaft. *See Fig. 5.*

4) Place adapter plate on transmission press stand (KV31100401). *See Fig. 6.* Press mainshaft assembly onto adapter plate. Ensure bearing is placed squarely against shaft when pressed into place.

5) Install new Woodruff keys in grooves in countershaft and tap lightly until seated. Place adapter plate assembly and mainshaft assembly so that countershaft rear bearing rests on transmission press stand. Install countershaft into adapter plate.

6) Install 3rd gear needle bearing, mainshaft 3rd gear, synchro ring and 3rd and 4th gear synchro assembly on front of mainshaft. Ensure 3rd and 4th gear synchronizers are facing in the proper direction. Install thrust washer and secure with a snap ring of the proper thickness to minimize clearance of groove in mainshaft.

NOTE: **Snap rings are available in the following thicknesses: .055" (1.40 mm), .059" (1.50 mm) and .063" (1.60 mm).**

7) Using transmission adapter plate (ST23860000) and press stand (KV31100401), press input shaft bearing onto input shaft, making sure that snap ring groove on shaft clears bearing. Place input bearing spacer on input shaft bearing and secure bearing with a snap ring that will eliminate end play. *See Main Drive Bearing Snap Ring Chart.*

MAIN DRIVE BEARING SNAP RINGS

No.	Thickness In. (mm)
1	.0681 (1.730)
2	.0709 (1.800)
3	.0736 (1.870)
4	.0764 (1.940)
5	.0791 (2.010)
6	.0819 (2.080)

8) On Maxima Diesel vehicles only, install washer on countershaft. Install torsional damper-to-counter drive gear. Insert coil spring end in .2" (5 mm) hole in sub gear. Insert other spring end into .2" (5 mm) hole in counter drive gear. Rotate sub gear 2 teeth counterclockwise and engage with input shaft gear.

9) On all models, mesh and install countershaft gear and input shaft, onto transmission shaft assemblies. *See Fig. 8.* Press countershaft front bearing onto countershaft.

Manual Transmissions

NISSAN/DATSUN MAXIMA, PICKUP, 200SX & 300ZX 5-SPEED (Cont.)

Fig. 4: Exploded View of FS5W71B 5-Speed Transmission Assembly

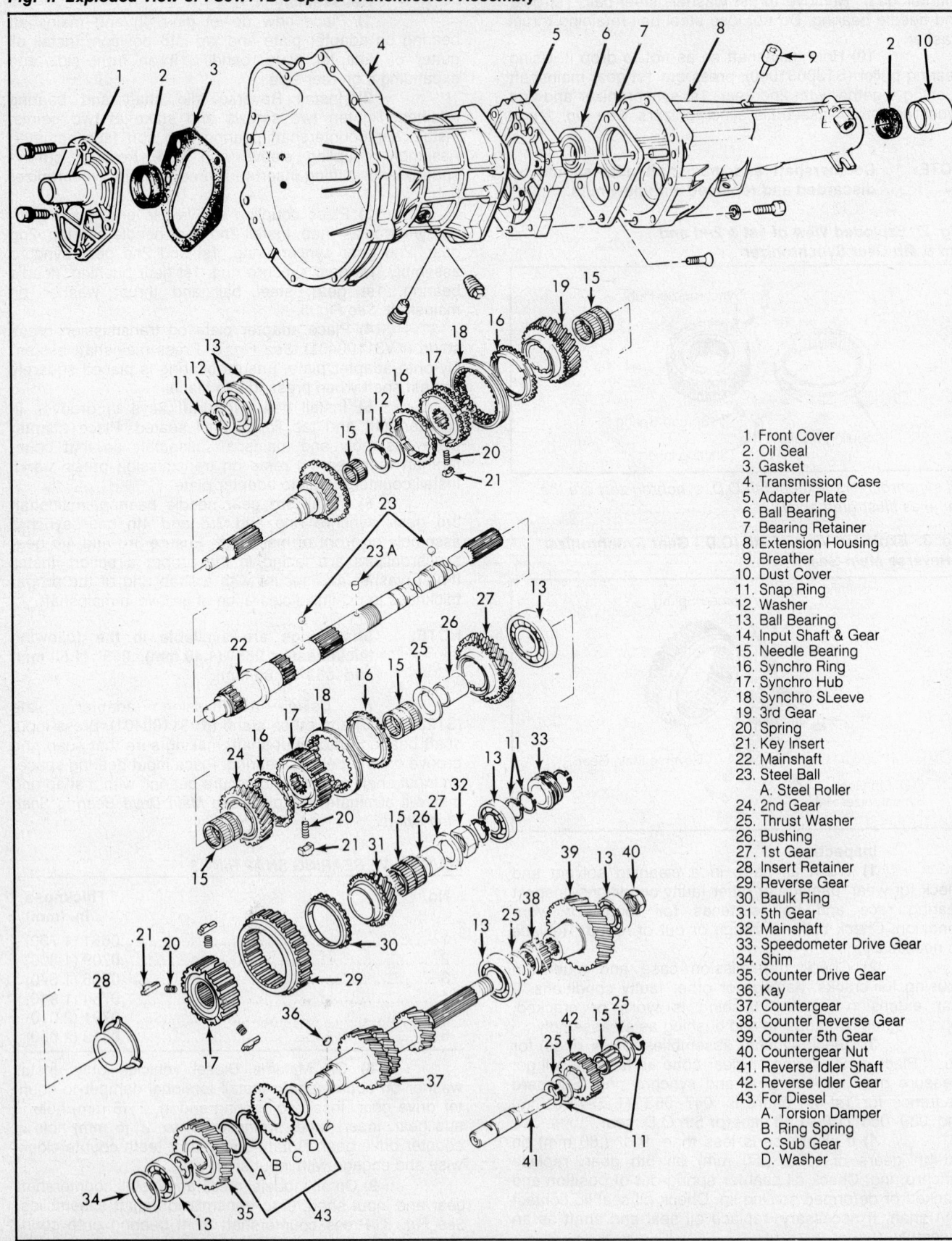

1. Front Cover
2. Oil Seal
3. Gasket
4. Transmission Case
5. Adapter Plate
6. Ball Bearing
7. Bearing Retainer
8. Extension Housing
9. Breather
10. Dust Cover
11. Snap Ring
12. Washer
13. Ball Bearing
14. Input Shaft & Gear
15. Needle Bearing
16. Synchro Ring
17. Synchro Hub
18. Synchro SLeeve
19. 3rd Gear
20. Spring
21. Key Insert
22. Mainshaft
23. Steel Ball
   A. Steel Roller
24. 2nd Gear
25. Thrust Washer
26. Bushing
27. 1st Gear
28. Insert Retainer
29. Reverse Gear
30. Baulk Ring
31. 5th Gear
32. Mainshaft
33. Speedometer Drive Gear
34. Shim
35. Counter Drive Gear
36. Kay
37. Countergear
38. Counter Reverse Gear
39. Counter 5th Gear
40. Countergear Nut
41. Reverse Idler Shaft
42. Reverse Idler Gear
43. For Diesel
   A. Torsion Damper
   B. Ring Spring
   C. Sub Gear
   D. Washer

FS5W71C 5-speed is similar.

NISSAN/DATSUN MAXIMA, PICKUP, 200SX & 300ZX 5-SPEED (Cont.)

Fig. 5: Component Installation (on Mainshaft)

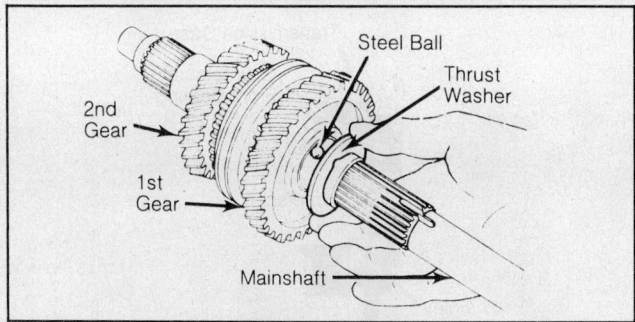

Apply grease to the steel ball and thrust washer before installing on the mainshaft.

Fig. 6: Installing Mainshaft Assembly

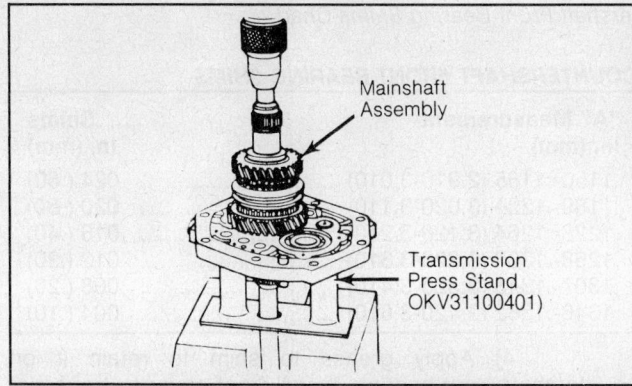

When installing assembly, ensure that the bearing is placed squarely against the shaft.

10) Place adapter plate in a vise. Position synchronizer ring, band brake, thrust block and anchor block on overdrive clutch gear. Install circlip. *See Fig. 8.* After front side is assembled, install counter reverse gear spacer, snap ring, spacer, needle bearing, reverse idler gear, spacer and snap ring.

NOTE: When assembling O.D.-reverse synchronizer hub, ensure components are installed in the proper direction.

Fig. 7: Exploded View of Overdrive (5th) Gear Assembly

Fig. 8: Installing Countershaft Front Bearing

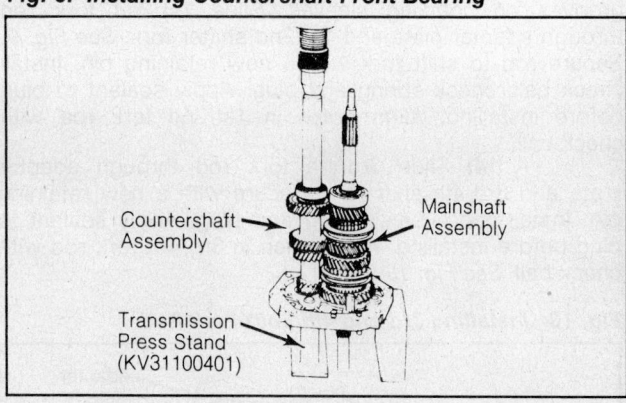

11) Install 5th O.D. gear and reverse synchronizer assembly, 5th gear, steel ball and thrust washer on the rear of mainshaft. Using mainshaft bearing drift (ST22350000), install new O.D. gear bushing as needed. Lubricate needle bearing with gear oil. Install counter reverse gear, counter 5th gear, bearing and new countershaft nut.

12) Tighten mainshaft and countershaft nuts and stake to shafts. Check each gears end play and adjust if necessery. *Refer to Gear End Play Chart for measurement limits*. Fit snap rings, steel ball and speedometer drive gear.

Fig. 9: Installing 1st and 2nd Shift Fork Rod

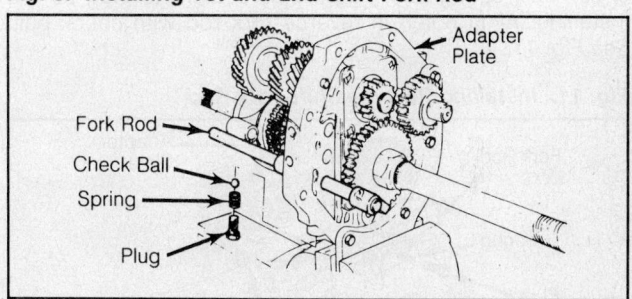

NOTE: Long end of shift fork, for 1st and 2nd gear, is placed on the countergear side.

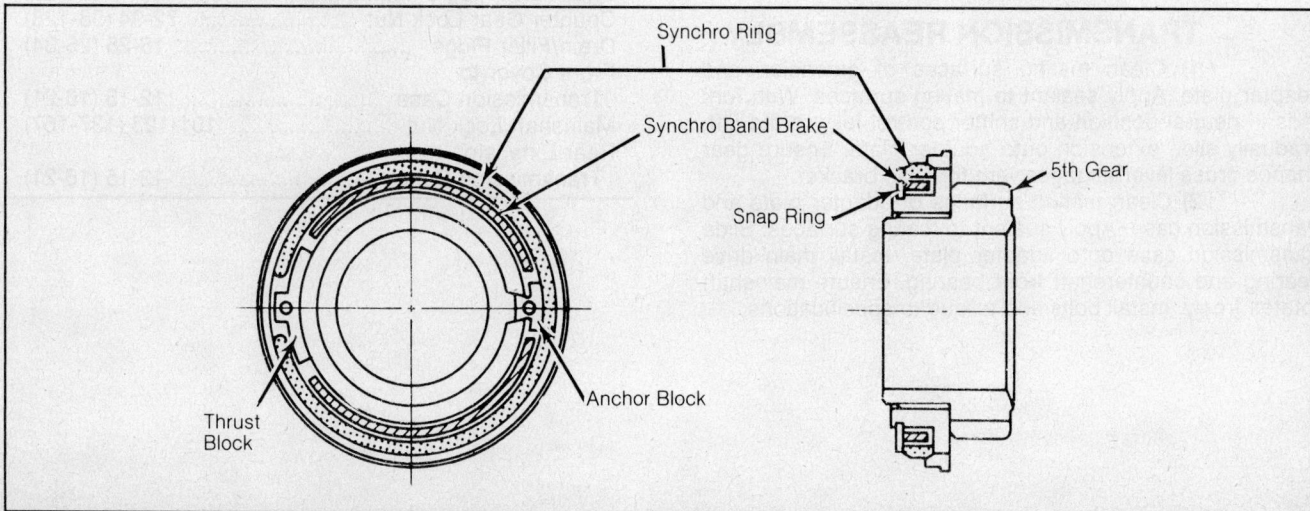

NISSAN/DATSUN MAXIMA, PICKUP, 200SX & 300ZX
5-SPEED (Cont.)

13) Install 1st/2nd and 3rd/4th shift forks into grooves on coupling sleeves. Slide 1st/2nd fork rod through adapter plate and 1st/2nd shifter fork. *See Fig. 9.* Secure rod to shift fork with a new retaining pin. Install check ball, check spring and plug. Apply sealant to plug before installing. Align notch in 1st/2nd fork rod with check ball.

14) Slide 3rd/4th fork rod through adapter plate and 3rd/4th shift fork. Secure with a new retaining pin. Install check ball, spring and plug. Apply sealant to plug before installing. Align notch in 3rd/4th fork rod with check ball. *See Fig. 10.*

Fig. 10: Installing 3rd and 4th Shift Fork Rod

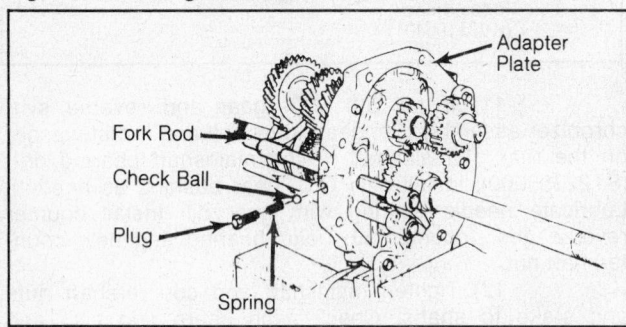

15) Place reverse shift fork in reverse idler gear. Slide reverse fork rod through reverse shift fork and adapter plate and secure with a new retaining pin. Install check ball, spring and plug. Apply sealant to plug before installing. Align notch in reverse fork rod with check ball. *See Fig. 11.*

Fig. 11: Installing Reverse Shift Fork Rod

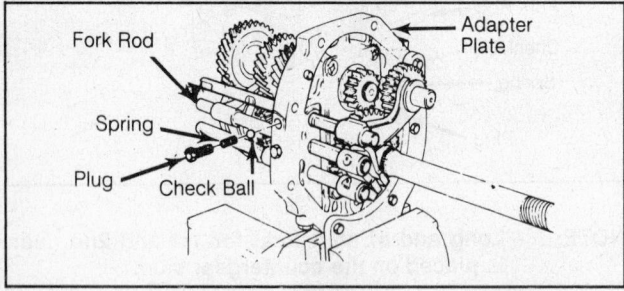

TRANSMISSION REASSEMBLY

1) Clean mating surfaces of extension and adapter plate. Apply sealant to mating surfaces. With fork rods in neutral position and shifter control fully to the left, gradually slide extension onto adapter plate. Ensure gear change cross lever engages with fork rod bracket.

2) Clean mating surfaces of adapter plate and transmission case. Apply sealant to mating surfaces. Slide transmission case onto adapter plate. Install main drive bearing and countershaft front bearing. Ensure mainshaft rotates freely. Install bolts and torque to specifications.

Fig. 12: Countershaft Front Bearing Shim

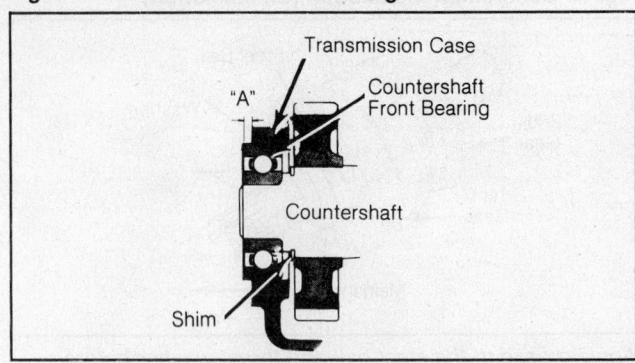

3) Measure depth "A" from front end of transmission case-to-countershaft front bearing. *See Fig. 12.* Select a countershaft front bearing shim from *Countershaft Front Bearing Shims Chart.*

COUNTERSHAFT FRONT BEARING SHIMS

"A" Measurement In. (mm)	Shims In. (mm)
.1150-.1185 (2.910-3.010)	.024 (.60)
.1189-.1224 (3.020-3.110)	.020 (.50)
.1228-.1264 (3.120-3.210)	.016 (.40)
.1268-.1303 (3.220-3.310)	.012 (.30)
.1307-.1343 (3.320-3.410)	.008 (.20)
.1346-.1382 (3.420-3.510)	.004 (.10)

4) Apply grease to shim to retain it on countershaft front bearing. Install front cover to transmission case. Apply grease to reverse select return plunger and install in rear extension.

5) Install speedometer pinion assembly on rear extension. Apply grease to release bearing. Temporarily install control lever and shift control lever. Shift transmission through all gears to ensure correct operation.

TIGHTENING SPECIFICATIONS

Application	Ft. Lbs. (N.m)
Backup Lamp Switch	14-22 (20-29)
Ball Pin	14-25 (20-34)
Bearing Retainer-to-Adapter	12-17 (16-25)
Check Ball Plug	14-18 (20-25)
Counter Gear Lock Nut	72-94 (98-128)
Drain/Filler Plugs	18-25 (25-34)
Front Cover-to Transmission Case	12-15 (16-21)
Mainshaft Lock Nut	101-123 (137-167)
Rear Extension-to Transmission Case	12-15 (16-21)

Manual Transmissions

NISSAN/DATSUN 300ZX 5-SPEED

IDENTIFICATION

FS5R90A (BW-T5) 5-speed transmission is used on turbocharged models. Serial number is stamped on top of bellhousing portion of transmission case. Shifter is top mounted on extension housing. Remaining components are transmission case and case cover. All forward gears are fully synchronized.

LUBRICATION & ADJUSTMENT

See appropriate MANUAL TRANSMISSION SERVICING article in IMPORT GENERAL SERVICING section.

REMOVAL & INSTALLATION

See appropriate MANUAL TRANSMISSION REMOVAL article in IMPORT GENERAL SERVICING section.

Fig. 1: Exploded View of Major Components of FS5R90A (BW-T5) Transmission

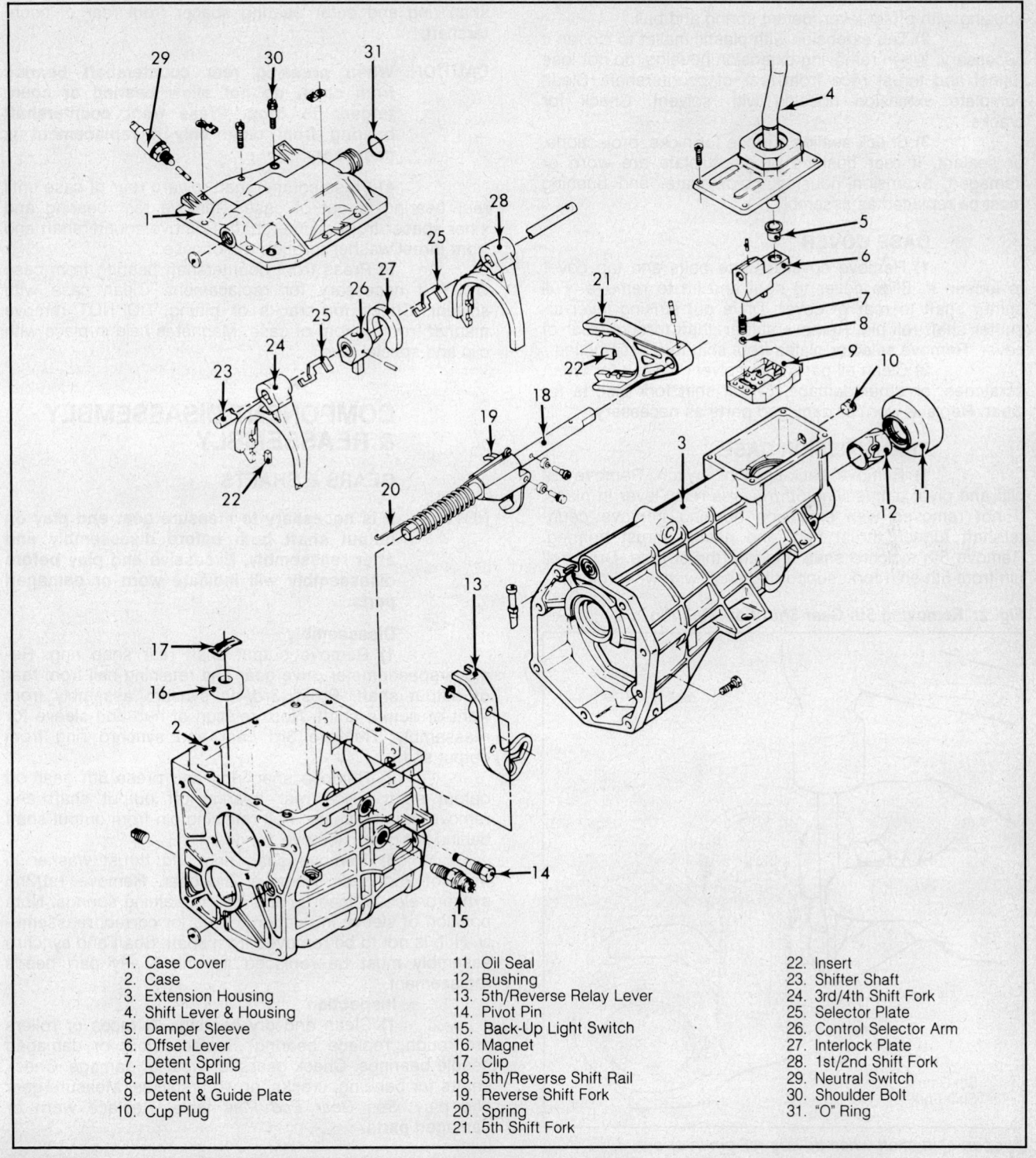

1. Case Cover	11. Oil Seal	22. Insert
2. Case	12. Bushing	23. Shifter Shaft
3. Extension Housing	13. 5th/Reverse Relay Lever	24. 3rd/4th Shift Fork
4. Shift Lever & Housing	14. Pivot Pin	25. Selector Plate
5. Damper Sleeve	15. Back-Up Light Switch	26. Control Selector Arm
6. Offset Lever	16. Magnet	27. Interlock Plate
7. Detent Spring	17. Clip	28. 1st/2nd Shift Fork
8. Detent Ball	18. 5th/Reverse Shift Rail	29. Neutral Switch
9. Detent & Guide Plate	19. Reverse Shift Fork	30. Shoulder Bolt
10. Cup Plug	20. Spring	31. "O" Ring
	21. 5th Shift Fork	

Manual Transmissions

NISSAN/DATSUN 300ZX 5-SPEED (Cont.)

TRANSMISSION DISASSEMBLY

NOTE: Before beginning disassembly of transmission, clean all external parts thoroughly to remove dirt and grease.

REAR EXTENSION

1) Drain oil. Select neutral position with shift lever. Remove shift lever assembly and damper sleeve. Drive roll pin from offset lever. Unbolt rear extension housing from transmission case. Remove rear extension housing with offset lever, detent spring and ball.

2) Tap extension with plastic mallet to loosen if necessary. When removing extension housing, do not lose funnel and thrust race from rear of countershaft. Clean complete extension housing with solvent. Check for cracks.

3) Check sealing surface for nicks, projections, or sealant. If rear bushing or guide plate are worn or damaged, extension housing, guide plate, and bushing must be replaced as assembly.

CASE COVER

1) Remove cover-to-case bolts and tap cover to loosen it. Slide cover to right and lift to remove. Pull shifter shaft to rear of cover. Drive out striking lever-to-shifter shaft roll pin. Remove shifter shaft through rear of cover. Remove selector plates from shift fork assemblies.

2) Clean all parts with solvent. Check for wear, scratches, or other damage. Check shift fork inserts for wear. Replace worn or damaged parts as necessary.

TRANSMISSION CASE

1) Remove back-up light switch. Remove "E" clip and pivot pin, leaving 5th/reverse relay lever in place. If not removed with extension housing, remove countershaft funnel, thrust ring, and needle thrust bearing. Remove 5th synchro snap ring and thrust race. Drive roll pin from 5th shift fork, supporting shaft with wood block.

Fig. 2: Removing 5th Gear Shift Fork Roll Pin

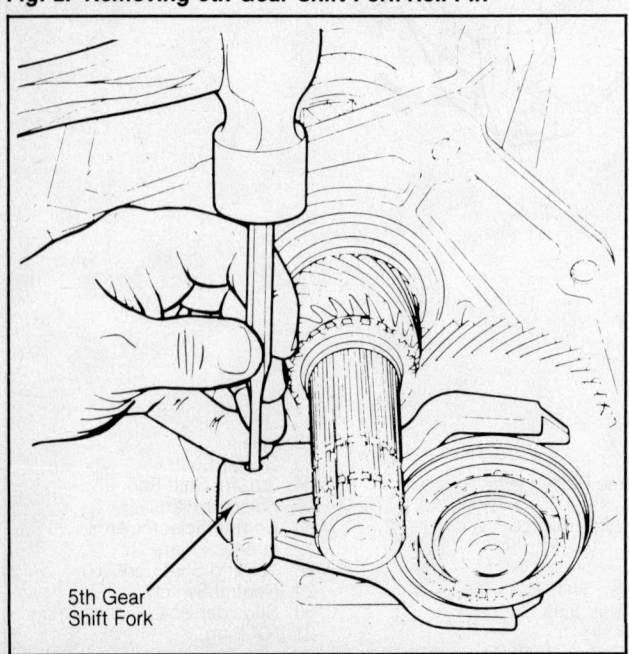

5th Gear
Shift Fork

Support shift shaft when driving roll pin in or out.

2) Remove 5th shift fork, synchro, and counter gear. Mark synchro hub-to-sleeve position for reassembly procedure. Unbolt and remove input shaft bearing retainer. Rotate input shaft and main drive gear assembly until flat on main drive gear faces countershaft. Remove input shaft assembly through front of case.

3) Remove rear output shaft bearing outer race. Remove output shaft assembly through top of case. Remove 5th shift rail. Remove reverse fork with spring. Remove 5th/reverse relay lever. Drive roll pin from reverse idler shaft. Remove reverse idler shaft and gear. Remove snap ring and outer bearing spacer from rear of countershaft.

CAUTION: When pressing rear countershaft bearing from case, do not allow bearing or countergear to drop. Press front countershaft bearing from case only if replacement is necessary.

4) Press countershaft toward rear of case until rear bearing is out of case. Remove rear bearing and inner spacer from countershaft. Remove countershaft and front thrust washer through top of case.

5) Press front countershaft bearing from case ONLY if necessary for replacement. Clean case with solvent. Check for cracks or pitting. DO NOT remove magnet from bottom of case. Magnet is held in place with clip and special glue.

COMPONENT DISASSEMBLY & REASSEMBLY

GEARS & SHAFTS

NOTE: It is necessary to measure gear end play on output shaft both before disassembly and after reassembly. Excessive end play before disassembly will indicate worn or damaged parts.

Disassembly

1) Remove output shaft rear snap ring. Remove speedometer drive gear and retaining ball from rear of output shaft. Press 3rd/4th synchro assembly from front of output shaft. Note relation of hub and sleeve for reassembly. Remove 3rd gear and synchro ring from output shaft.

2) Remove snap ring and press 5th gear off output shaft. Slide rear bearing off output shaft and remove thrust washer. Pull retaining pin from output shaft behind 1st gear. Remove 1st gear.

3) Remove snap ring and thrust washer in front of 2nd gear. Remove 2nd gear. Remove 1st/2nd synchro sleeve, inserts, and insert retaining springs. Note position of sleeve in relation to hub for correct reassembly. Hub is not to be removed from shaft. Shaft and synchro assembly must be replaced as unit if any part needs replacement.

Inspection

1) Clean and dry bearings. If races or rollers are rough, replace bearing. Replace worn or damaged needle bearings. Check gears for wear or damage. Check shafts for bending, cracks, or worn splines. Measure gear end play. *See Gear End Play* table. Replace worn or damaged parts.

NISSAN/DATSUN 300ZX 5-SPEED (Cont.)

Fig. 3: *Exploded View of Gears and Shafts*

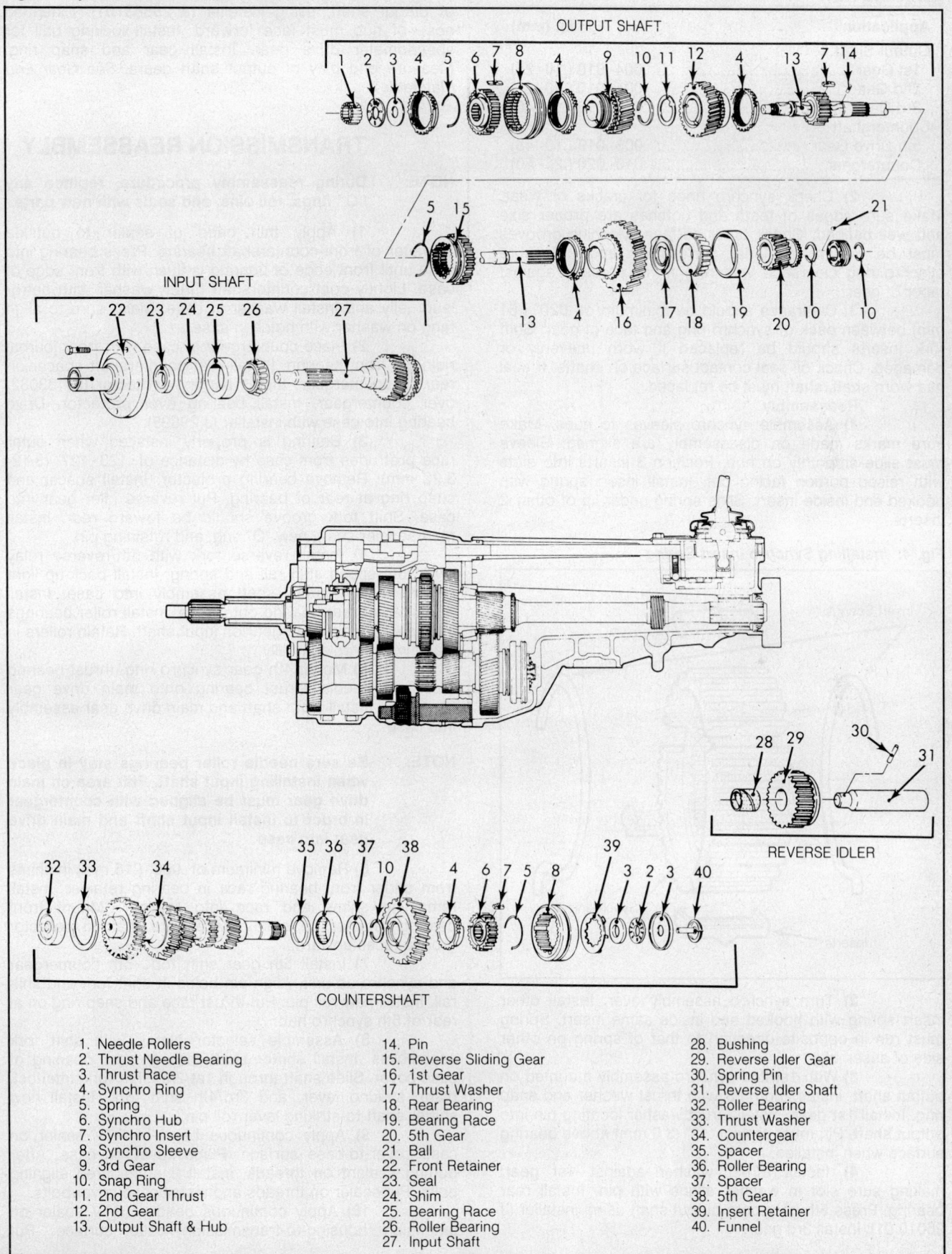

1. Needle Rollers	14. Pin	28. Bushing
2. Thrust Needle Bearing	15. Reverse Sliding Gear	29. Reverse Idler Gear
3. Thrust Race	16. 1st Gear	30. Spring Pin
4. Synchro Ring	17. Thrust Washer	31. Reverse Idler Shaft
5. Spring	18. Rear Bearing	32. Roller Bearing
6. Synchro Hub	19. Bearing Race	33. Thrust Washer
7. Synchro Insert	20. 5th Gear	34. Countergear
8. Synchro Sleeve	21. Ball	35. Spacer
9. 3rd Gear	22. Front Retainer	36. Roller Bearing
10. Snap Ring	23. Seal	37. Spacer
11. 2nd Gear Thrust	24. Shim	38. 5th Gear
12. 2nd Gear	25. Bearing Race	39. Insert Retainer
13. Output Shaft & Hub	26. Roller Bearing	40. Funnel
	27. Input Shaft	

Manual Transmissions

NISSAN/DATSUN 300ZX 5-SPEED (Cont.)

GEAR END PLAY

Application	In. (mm)
Output Shaft	
1st Gear	.004-.010 (.10-.25)
2nd Gear	.004-.010 (.10-.25)
3rd Gear	.006-.016 (.15-.40)
Countershaft	
5th Drive Gear	.003-.019 (.10-.48)
Countergear	.010-.020 (.25-.50)

2) Check synchro rings for cracks or wear. Make sure edges of teeth and notches are proper size and well defined. Check taper surface. Machine grooves must be evident on inner surface of taper. Measure synchro ring clearance with ring firmly pressed against taper of gear.

3) Clearance should be minimum of .020" (.51 mm) between back of synchro ring and face of gear. Shift fork inserts should be replaced if worn unevenly or damaged. Check oil seal contact surface on shafts. If seal has worn shaft, shaft must be replaced.

Reassembly

1) Assemble synchro sleeves to hubs. Make sure marks made on disassembly are aligned. Sleeve must slide smoothly on hub. Position 3 inserts into slots with raised portion facing out. Install insert spring with hooked end inside insert. Slide spring under lip of other 2 inserts.

Fig. 4: Installing Synchro Insert Spring

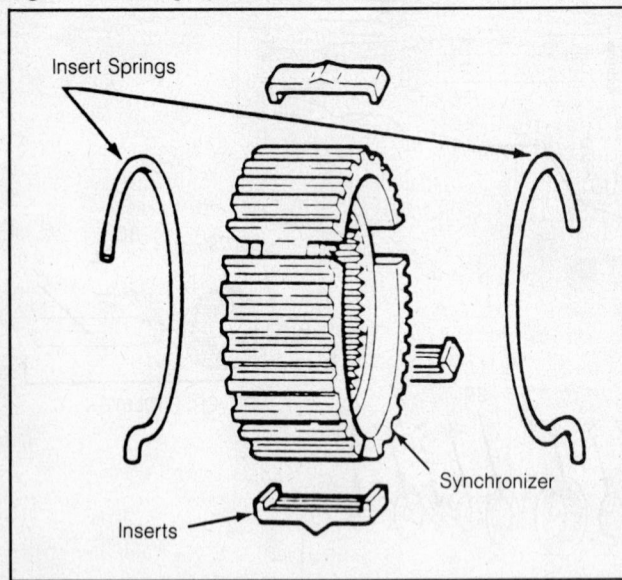

2) Turn synchro assembly over. Install other insert spring with hooked end inside same insert. Spring must run in opposite direction to that of spring on other side of assembly.

3) With 1st/2nd synchro assembly mounted on output shaft, install 2nd gear with thrust washer and snap ring. Install 1st gear. Install thrust washer locating pin into output shaft. Pin must project .12" (3.0 mm) above bearing surface when installed.

4) Install thrust washer against 1st gear, making sure slot in washer aligns with pin. Install rear bearing. Press 5th gear onto output shaft using installer (J 26010 01). Install 3rd gear.

5) Press 3rd/4th synchro assembly onto front of output shaft, using installer (J 25863 01). Extended nose of hub must face forward. Install locking ball for speedometer drive gear. Install gear and snap ring. Measure end play of output shaft gears. See *Gear End Play* table.

TRANSMISSION REASSEMBLY

NOTE: **During reassembly procedure, replace any "O" rings, roll pins, and seals with new parts.**

1) Apply thin bead of sealer to outside diameter of front countershaft bearing. Press bearing into case until front edge of bearing is flush with front edge of case. Lightly coat countershaft thrust washer with petroleum jelly and install washer in case. Make sure to align tang on washer with notch in case.

2) Place countergear in case with front journal riding in front bearing. Install rear countershaft spacer on rear of countergear. Install bearing protector (9J 33032) over countergear. Install bearing over protector. Drive bearing into case with installer (J 29895).

3) Bearing is properly installed when outer race protrudes from case by distance of .123-.127" (3.12-3.22 mm). Remove bearing protector. Install spacer and snap ring at rear of bearing. Put reverse idler gear into case. Shift fork groove should be toward rear. Install reverse idler shaft, new "O" ring, and retaining pin.

4) Install reverse fork with 5th/reverse relay lever, 5th speed shift rail and spring. Install back-up light switch. Install output shaft assembly into case. Install output shaft rear bearing outer race. Install roller bearings into rear of main drive gear on input shaft. Retain rollers in place with petroleum jelly.

5) Mount 4th gear synchro ring, thrust bearing race and needle thrust bearing onto main drive gear assembly. Install input shaft and main drive gear assembly into case.

NOTE: **Be sure needle roller bearings stay in place when installing input shaft. Flat area on main drive gear must be aligned with countergear in order to install input shaft and main drive gear into case.**

6) Remove minimum of .006" (.15 mm) in shims from under front bearing race in bearing retainer. Install remaining shims and race into retainer. Mount front bearing retainer on case. Make sure that oil collector groove faces upward.

7) Install 5th gear shift fork, 5th countergear and synchro as unit. Align pin holes in shift fork and shift rail. Install new roll pin. Put thrust race and snap ring on at rear of 5th synchro hub.

8) Assemble selector plates with shift fork assemblies. Install shifter shaft through rear opening of case cover. Slide shaft through 1st/2nd shift fork, interlock plate, striking lever, and 3rd/4th shift fork. Install new shifter shaft-to-striking lever roll pin.

9) Apply continuous bead of RTV sealer on case cover-to-case surface. Place cover on case. After putting sealant on threads, install 2 shouldered aligning bolts. Put sealer on threads and install case cover bolts.

10) Apply continuous bead of RTV sealer on extension housing-to-transmission case surface. Put

NISSAN/DATSUN 300ZX 5-SPEED (Cont.)

needle thrust bearing, race and funnel on rear of countershaft. Retain in place with coating of petroleum jelly. Place detent ball, spring and offset lever in place on guide plate. *See Fig. 5.*

Fig. 5: Offset Lever, Ball & Spring Location

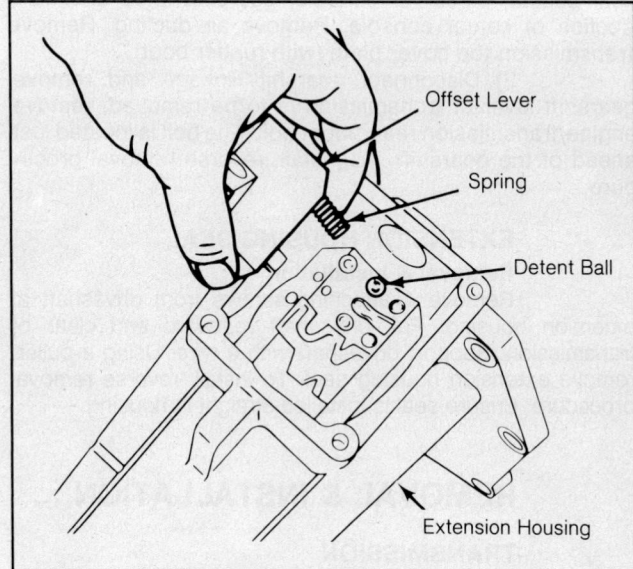

Offset Lever

Spring

Detent Ball

Extension Housing

11) Install extension housing onto transmission case. Align hole in offset lever with hole in shifter shaft. Drive in roll pin. Install and tighten extension housing-to-transmission case bolts. Apply continuous bead of RTV sealer to control lever housing opening on extension housing.

12) Put damper sleeve into offset lever. Install shift lever and tighten shifter housing-to-extension housing bolts. Operate shift lever through entire shift pattern. Make sure gear changes occur smoothly. Install drain plug with sealant on threads.

13) Remove extension housing oil seal. Lightly coat oil seal surface with transmission oil. Drive seal into housing with installer (J 28894). Push input shaft to rear. Mount dial indicator so tip touches front end of input shaft. Zero indicator dial.

14) Push output shaft forward. Record dial indicator reading as "A". Remove indicator. Remove bearing retainer. Remove bearing race from retainer. Select proper thickness of shim to give preload "B" of .0051-.0098" (.129-.248 mm) on bearing race.

15) To determine preload shim thickness; add value "A", which is dial indicator reading from step **14**), to value "B", which is desired preload amount. If dial indicator reading "A" is .10 mm (end play clearance) and preload desired "B" is .20 mm, shim thickness needed would be .30 mm.

16) Install selected shims and bearing race into front bearing retainer. Install new oil seal into bearing retainer, using driver (J 23096). Apply continuous bead of RTV sealant to bearing retainer sealing surface. Install bearing retainer with oil collector groove up.

TIGHTENING SPECIFICATIONS

Application	Ft. Lbs. (N.m)
Clutch Housing-to-Case	30-51 (41-69)
Extension-to-Case	20-46 (27-62)

	INCH Lbs. (N.m)
Cover-to-Case	72-132 (8-14)
Bearing Retainer-to-Case	132-240 (15-27)
Back-Up Light Switch	144-204 (17-24)
Reverse Pivot Pin	180-300 (21-33)
Shift Lever Housing	132-240 (15-27)

Manual Transmissions
PEUGEOT 5-SPEED

DESCRIPTION

The 5-speed transmission has a split aluminum case. Gear assembly can be accessed after one half of case is removed. All forward gears are helical-type, and are synchronized for smooth gear engagement. Shift linkage is floor mounted with external linkage. Reverse and 5th gears are located in extension housing.

LUBRICATION & ADJUSTMENT

See appropriate MANUAL TRANSMISSION SERVICING article in IMPORT GENERAL SERVICING section.

TROUBLE SHOOTING

HARD SHIFTING

Improperly adjusted clutch. Excessive input shaft end play. Face of syncro hub in contact with cone, worn. Syncro cones worn, damaged, distorted or not in proper contact.

SLIPS OUT OF GEAR

Bearings worn or defective. Excessive play between gears and syncro cage. Play in syncro hub. Shift arm worn. Lock ball spring weak or broken. Lock ball missing.

TRANSMISSION NOISY

Low or incorrect lubricant. Gears or bearing worn or damaged. Worn syncro gears and/or cage. Excessive input shaft end play. Worn syncro hub or splines. Incorrectly meshed gears.

SERVICE (IN VEHICLE)

GEAR SHIFT LEVER
Removal & Installation

1) Remove emergency brake handle cover, rear section of center console, gearshift knob and front section of center console. Remove air ducting. Remove transmission top cover plate (with rubber boot).

2) Disconnect gearshift linkage and remove gearshift lever. If transmission is to be removed, remove engine/transmission rear mount bolt. The bolt is located just ahead of the gearshift. To install, reverse removal procedure.

EXTENSION HOUSING SEAL
Removal & Installation

Remove 4 attaching screws from driveshaft at extention housing. Pull driveshaft rearward and clear of transmission. Support driveshaft with a wire. Using a puller, remove extension housing seal. To install, reverse removal procedure. Ensure seal is installed straight in housing.

REMOVAL & INSTALLATION

TRANSMISSION

See appropriate MANUAL TRANSMISSION REMOVAL article in IMPORT GENERAL SERVICING section.

TRANSMISSION DISASSEMBLY

1) Place transmission on holding fixture with right side facing away from fixture. From extension housing,

Fig. 1: Sectional View of Peugeot 5-Speed Transmission

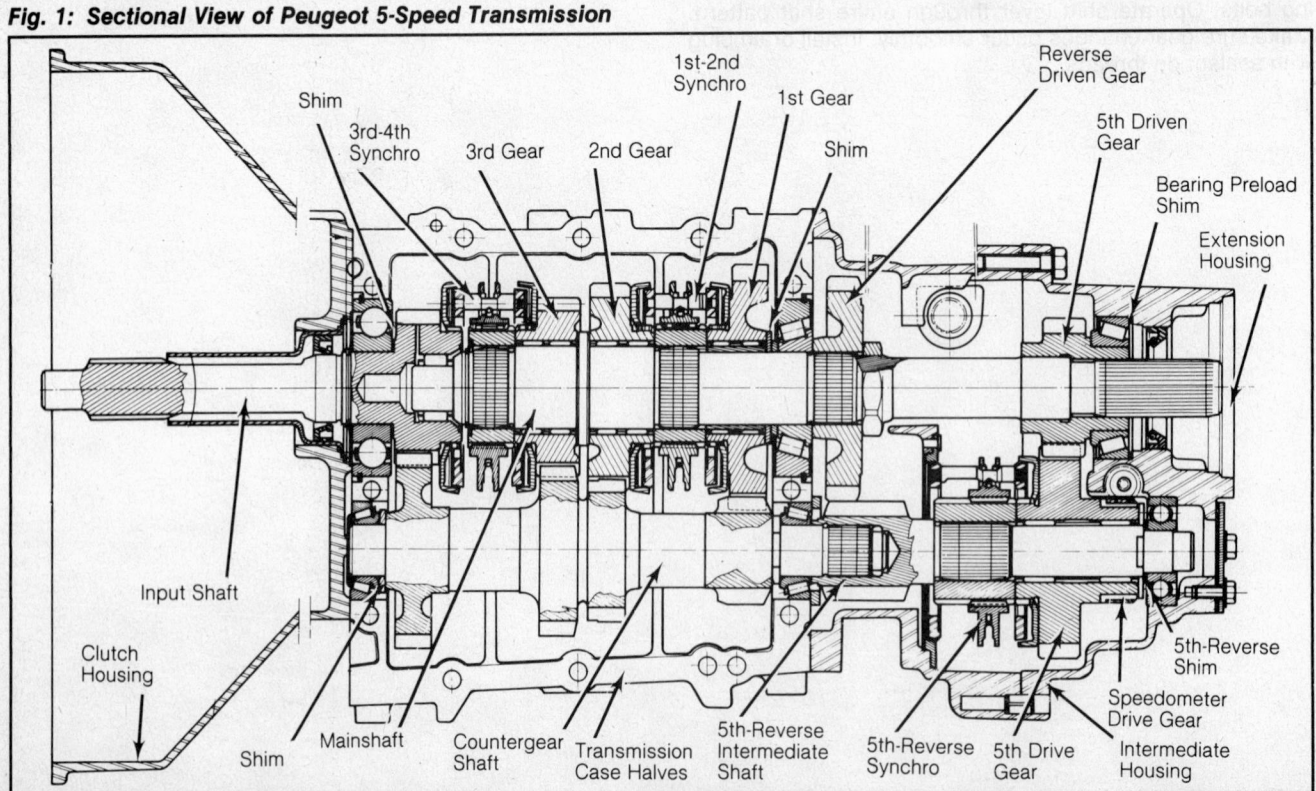

PEUGEOT 5-SPEED (Cont.)

Fig. 2: Exploded View of Peugeot 5-Speed Transmission

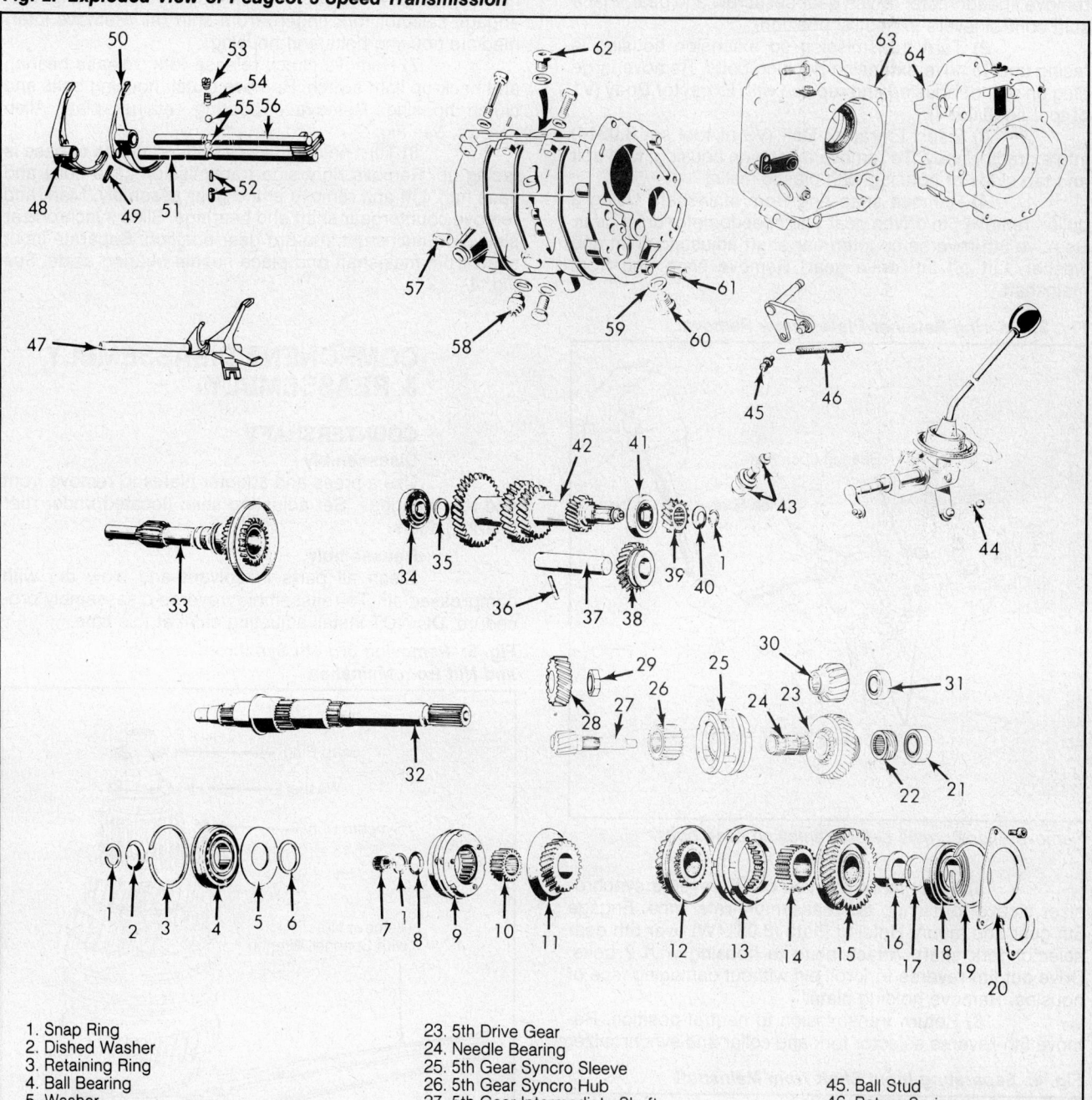

1. Snap Ring	23. 5th Drive Gear	
2. Dished Washer	24. Needle Bearing	
3. Retaining Ring	25. 5th Gear Syncro Sleeve	
4. Ball Bearing	26. 5th Gear Syncro Hub	45. Ball Stud
5. Washer	27. 5th Gear Intermediate Shaft	46. Return Spring
6. Thrust Washer Shim	28. Reverse Gear	47. 5th/Reverse Shift Rail
7. Needle Bearing	29. Nut	48. 3rd/4th Shift Fork
8. Washer	30. 5th Driven Gear	49. Roll Pin
9. 3rd/4th Syncro Ring	31. Bearing	50. 1st/2nd Shift Fork
10. 3rd/4th Syncro Hub	32. Mainshaft	51. 3rd/4th Shift Rail
11. 3rd Gear	33. Input Shaft	52. Interlock Plunger & Pin
12. 2nd Gear	34. Bearing	53. Detent Plug
13. 1st/2nd Syncro Sleeve	35. Thrust Washer Shim	54. Interlock Spring
14. 1st/2nd Syncro Hub	36. Roll Pin	55. Interlock Ball
15. 1st Gear	37. Idler Shaft	56. 1st/2nd Shift Rail
16. 1st Gear Pinion	38. Reverse Idler Gear	57. Dowel Pin
Spacer Bushing	39. Reverse Drive Gear	58. Back-Up Light Switch
17. Shim	40. Dished Washer	59. Copper/Asbestos Gasket
18. Shaft-To-Release Bearing	41. Bearing	60. Drain Plug
19. Snap Ring	42. Countergear Shaft	61. Dowel Pin
20. Bearing Retainer Plate	43. Reverse Gear Interlock	62. Fill Plug
21. Bearing	Plunger Assembly	63. Intermediate Housing
22. Speedometer Drive Gear	44. Ball Stud	64. Extention Housing

Manual Transmissions
PEUGEOT 5-SPEED (Cont.)

remove speedometer driven gear set screw and gear. Place shift control levers in neutral position.

2) Turn transmission so extension housing is facing up. Remove extension housing bolts. Remove large plug on rear of housing and replace with Extractor Body (V1 of tool set 8.0314).

3) Insert Extractor Bolt (V2 of tool set 8.0314) into extractor body. To remove extension housing, turn bolt and tap sides of housing with plastic mallet.

4) Remove snap ring from mainshaft. Using a puller, remove 5th driven gear and speedometer drive gear. Remove 5th-reverse countergear shaft adjusting shim and washer. Lift off 5th drive gear. Remove snap ring from mainshaft.

Fig. 3: Bearing Retainer Plate Screw Removal

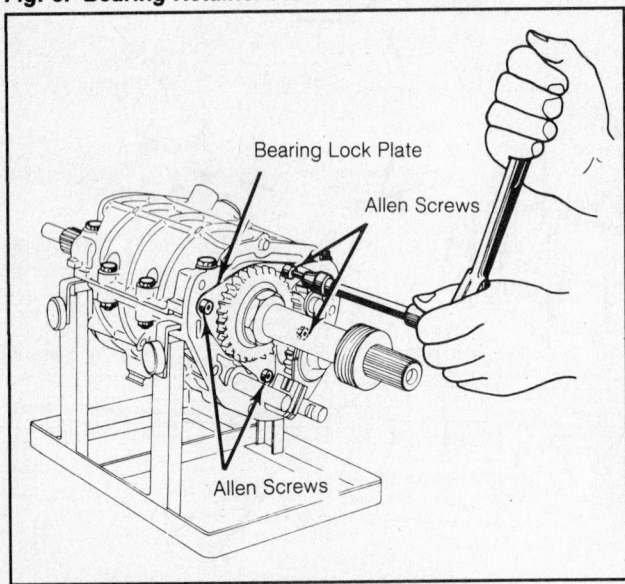

Bearing Lock Plate
Allen Screws
Allen Screws

Remove Allen screws before removing case bolts.

5) Index mark position of 5th-reverse synchronizer sleeve to its hub for reassembly reference. Engage 5th gear and mount Holding Plate (8.0314W) over 5th gear selector fork shaft. Attach plate to housing with 2 bolts. Drive out 5th-reverse fork roll pin without damaging face of housing. Remove holding plate.

6) Return transmission to neutral position. Remove 5th-reverse selector fork and collar and synchronizer

Fig. 4: Separating Input Shaft from Mainshaft

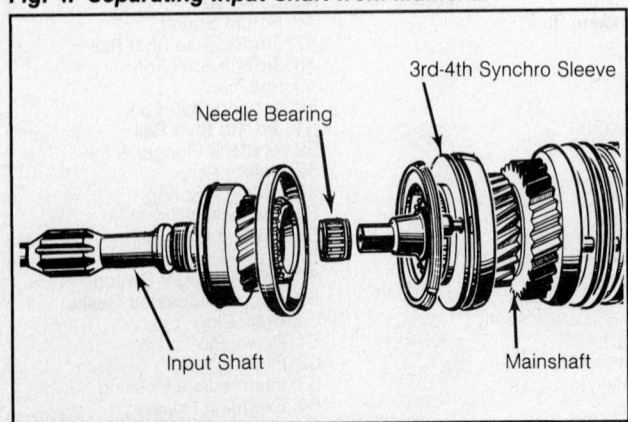

Needle Bearing
3rd-4th Synchro Sleeve
Input Shaft
Mainshaft

Remove needle bearing and place aside.

hub. Lift 5th-reverse intermediate shaft from housing. Disengage selector fork fingers from shift rail. Remove intermediate housing bolts and housing.

7) Remove clutch release fork, release bearing and back-up light switch. Remove clutch housing bolts and clutch housing. Remove 4 bearing retainer plate Allen screws. See Fig. 3.

8) Turn holding fixture until right side of case is facing up. Remove right side transmission case bolts and case half. Lift and remove entire gear assembly. Mark and remove countergear shaft end bearings. Slide synchronizer sleeve on mainshaft into 3rd gear position. Separate input shaft from mainshaft and place needle bearing aside. See Fig. 4.

COMPONENT DISASSEMBLY & REASSEMBLY

COUNTERSHAFT
Disassembly
Use a press and adapter plates to remove front and rear bearings. Set adjusting shim (located under rear bearing) aside.

Reassembly
Clean all parts in solvent and blow dry with compressed air. To reassemble, reverse disassembly procedure. DO NOT install adjusting shim at this time.

Fig. 5: Removing 3rd-4th Synchronizer Hub and Nut from Mainshaft

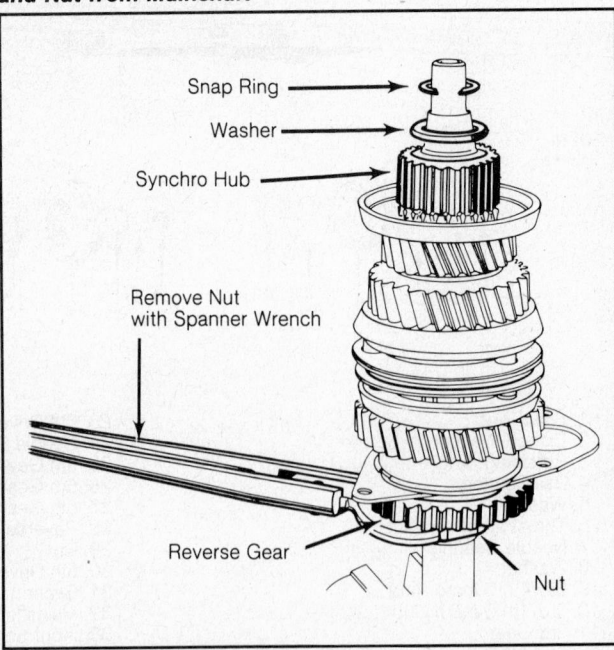

Snap Ring
Washer
Synchro Hub
Remove Nut with Spanner Wrench
Reverse Gear
Nut

Hold mainshaft reverse gear and remove lock nut.

MAINSHAFT
Disassembly
1) Mark position of 3rd-4th speed synchronizer sleeve to its hub for reassembly reference. Remove synchronizer sleeve. Place mainshaft in vise, rear end down. Remove snap ring and washer from 3rd-4th synchronizer hub. While holding mainshaft reverse gear, use Spanner Wrench (8.0310P) to loosen mainshaft rear lock nut.

2) Using a press with adapter plates placed beneath outer edge of 3rd gear, press off synchronizer hub and 3rd gear. Position mainshaft upside down with input shaft end facing down.

3) Place Safety Plate (8.0310K) between press and mainshaft. Press on mainshaft until bearing is released. Remove safety plate and press.

4) Remove following components from mainshaft and arrange in order of removal (facing correct direction): lock nut, reverse gear, retainer plate, bearing, adjusting shim, 1st gear, bushing, needle bearings, 1st-2nd synchronizer (without separating hub from sleeve), needle bearings and 2nd gear.

Cleaning & Inspection
Inspect all parts for wear or damage and replace necessary components.

Reassembly
Clean all parts in solvent and blow dry with compressed air. To reassemble, reverse disassembly procedure and align marks scribed during disassembly. If mainshaft, gears or synchronizers are replaced, install a new .13" (3.3 mm) adjusting shim. If none of above parts are replaced, install original shim.

Fig. 6: Mainshaft Rear Components

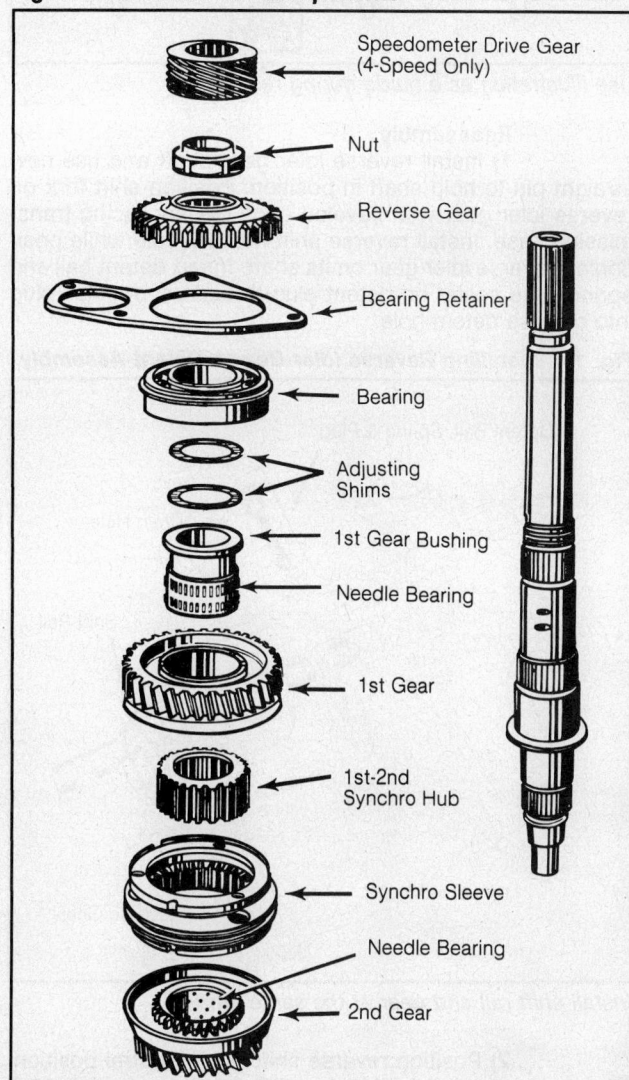

Speedometer Drive Gear (4-Speed Only)

Nut

Reverse Gear

Bearing Retainer

Bearing

Adjusting Shims

1st Gear Bushing

Needle Bearing

1st Gear

1st-2nd Synchro Hub

Synchro Sleeve

Needle Bearing

2nd Gear

Note position and direction of components.

INPUT SHAFT
NOTE: Shafts which have oil slingers are identified by grooves in front of bearing.

Disassembly
If necessary to replace bearing, remove snap ring and press off old bearing. When bearing is removed, pay particular attention to thickness of shims for reassembly reference. Also note position of oil slinger, if equipped.

Cleaning & Inspection
Inspect all parts for wear or damage. Check bearing by rotating by hand and check for noise or roughness.

Reassembly
To reassemble, reverse disassembly procedure. If input shaft, 3rd-4th synchronizer or 3rd-4th shift shaft have been replaced, install a .20" (.50 mm) adjusting shim (.14"/.50 mm on shafts with oil slinger). If none of above parts are replaced, install original shim.

INTERMEDIATE SHAFT
Disassembly
If necessary to replace bearing or speedometer drive gear, use a universal bearing puller and adapter. Pull off bearing and speedometer drive gear.

Cleaning & Inspection
Inspect all parts for wear or damage. Check bearing by rotating by hand and check for noise or roughness. Inspect all components of intermediate housing and mating surfaces of housing for wear, damage and warpage.

Reassembly
To reassemble, reverse disassembly procedure. Ensure undercut side of speedometer drive gear faces away from bearing.

SHIFTING MECHANISMS
Disassembly
1) Place 1st-2nd shift rail in 2nd gear position and remove pin in 1st-2nd gear shift fork. With pin removed,

Fig. 7: Removing Pins from Shift Forks

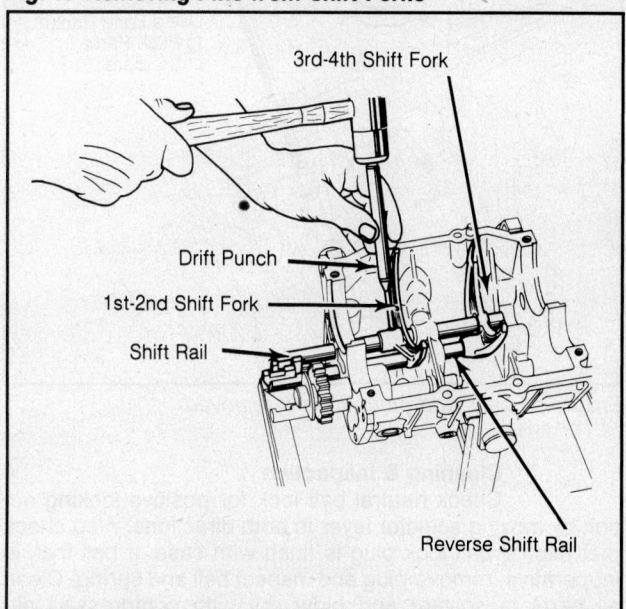

3rd-4th Shift Fork

Drift Punch

1st-2nd Shift Fork

Shift Rail

Reverse Shift Rail

Use a drift punch to drive out roll pins.

Fig. 8: Removing Detent Plug

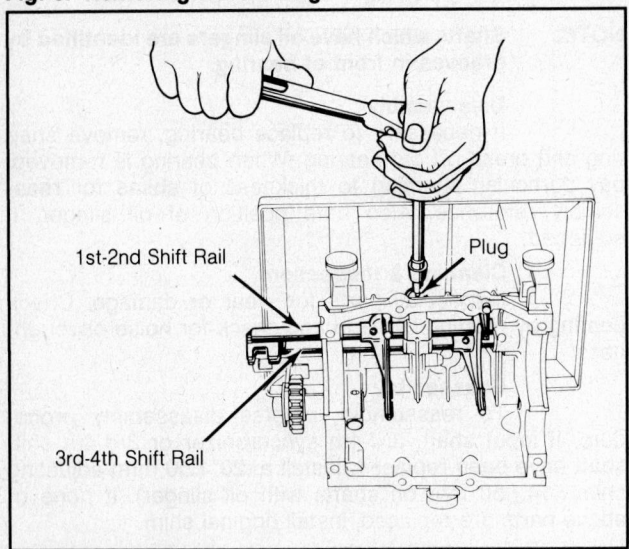

Catch detent ball and spring if they pop out.

move shift rail back to neutral position. Shift 3rd-4th shift rail into 4th gear position and remove pin in shift fork. Return shift rail to neutral position.

2) Turn transmission case so it is on its side and remove detent plug. *See Fig. 8.* Remove shift rail for 1st-2nd gear and 3rd-4th gears. As shift rails are removed, catch detent ball and spring. Remove and set aside lock-out needle for 3rd-4th shift rail.

3) Remove 5th-reverse detent plug, spring and ball from side of case. Remove reverse shift fork with idler gear. Using a punch, drive out reverse idler shaft pin. Remove shaft by pushing it toward outside of case. Using a long punch, push interlock balls and plunger out of case.

Fig. 9: Removing Interlock Balls and Plunger

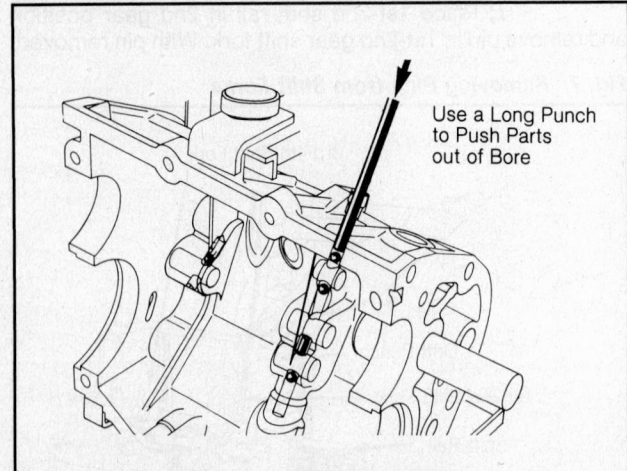

Ensure all balls and plungers are removed.

Cleaning & Inspection
Check neutral ball lock for positive locking action by moving selector lever in both directions. Also check that neutral ball lock plug is flush with case. If ball lock is inoperative, remove plug and inspect ball and spring. Clean all parts in solvent and blow dry with compressed air.

Inspect all parts for wear or damage and replace necessary components.

Fig. 10: Detent and Interlock Positions

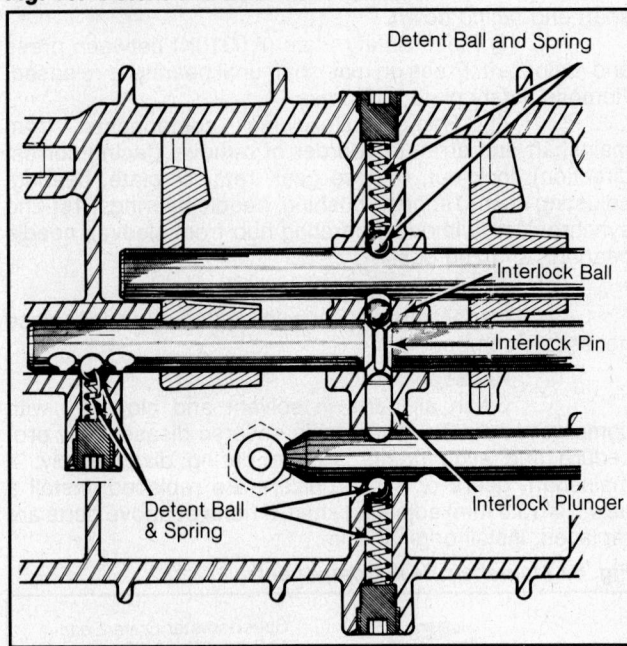

Use illustration as a guide during reassembly.

Reassembly
1) Install reverse idler gear shaft and use new straight pin to hold shaft in position. Position shift fork on reverse idler gear with beveled edge of gear facing transmission case. Install reverse shift rail into hole while positioning reverse idler gear on its shaft. Insert detent ball and spring. Use sealer on detent plug threads and install plug into reverse detent hole.

Fig. 11: Installing Reverse Idler Gear & Detent Assembly

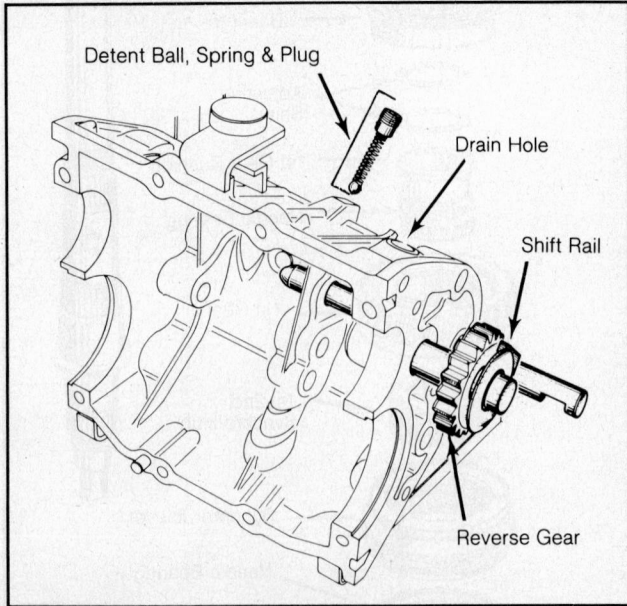

Install shift rail and gear at the same time.

2) Position reverse shift rail in neutral position. Flip case over to other side. Install 3rd-4th-reverse interlock

plunger in case and seat it against reverse shift rail. Grease and install interlock pin into 3rd-4th shift rail.

Fig. 12: Interlock Plunger Position in Case Half

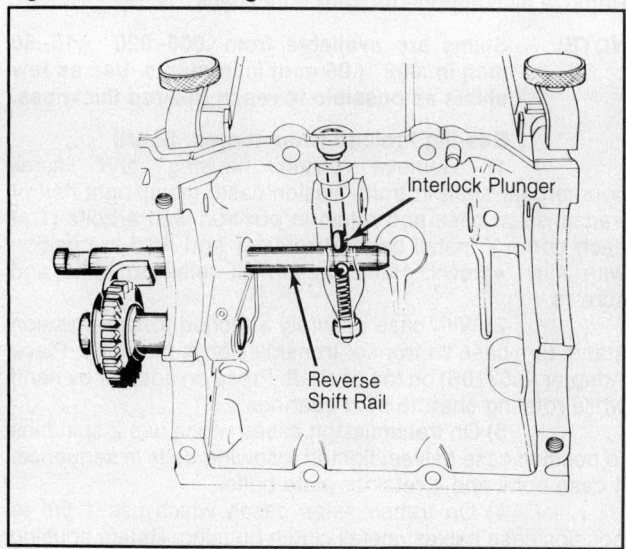

Plunger should seat against reverse shift rail.

3) Turn case and install 1st-2nd shift fork (larger of 2) and 3rd-4th shift fork in transmission case. Insert 3rd-4th shift rail into case, through both shift forks, until shaft is flush with edge of detent hole.

4) Insert 1 detent spring and ball into detent hole. Use drift punch to compress spring and ball assembly. Slide shift rail forward until punch can be released and ball will not jump out of hole.

Fig. 13: Installing 3rd-4th Shift Rail and Fork

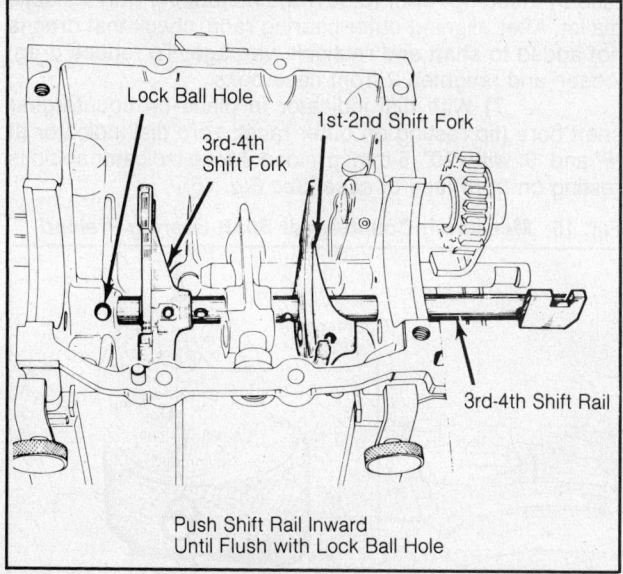

Compress detent ball and spring to install shift rail.

5) Shift 3rd-4th shift rail into neutral position. Insert detent ball into hole and push it against 3rd-4th shift rail. Engage 1st-2nd shift rail and insert detent ball and spring into hole. Coat threads of detent plug with sealant and install. Place 1st-2nd shift rail in neutral position. Lock shift forks onto shift rails with new pins.

Fig. 14: Completed Shifting Mechanism Installation

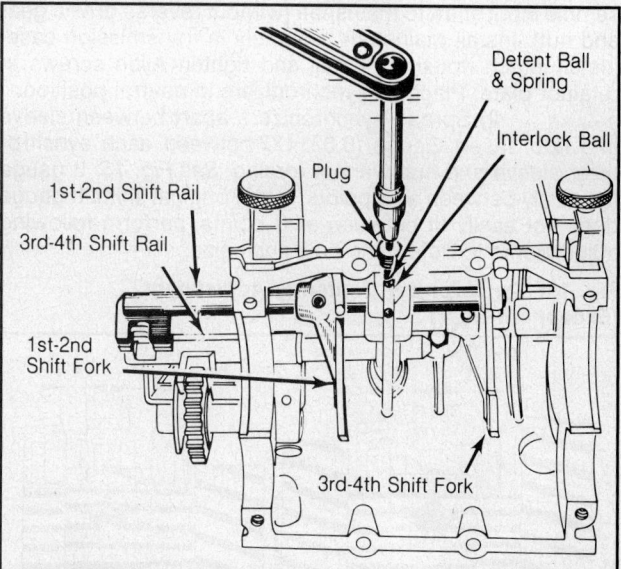

Note position of shift rails, forks and lock-out components.

CLUTCH HOUSING
Disassembly
If equipped with oil seal, carefully pry out seal without damaging case. Remove release bearing guide snap ring and press out guide. Transmissions which use an oil slinger on input shaft do not use an oil seal.

Cleaning & Inspection
Mount a dial indicator and measure runout of front and rear mating surfaces of housing. If runout exceeds .004" (.10 mm), replace clutch housing. Inspect all mating surfaces for wear or damage.

Reassembly
Lightly coat bearing face of release bearing guide with grease. Press in guide with slot (if equipped) facing housing openings and install snap ring. On models with oil seal, DO NOT install seal at this time.

INTERMEDIATE HOUSING
Disassembly
Using a punch, drive out each roll pin. Compress shift rail spring and remove 4 bushings. Remove shift rail. Separate components and set aside. Remove and discard "O" ring from hole.

Reassembly
Lubricate bushings. Install new "O" ring in hole. Insert shift rail into case while positioning shift fork, spring and bushings on rail. Install roll pins so that pin splits face opposite directions (1 split should face to right; other to left).

TRANSMISSION REASSEMBLY & ADJUSTMENTS

ADJUSTMENTS
Centering 1st, 2nd, 3rd & 5th Gear Synchronizers

NOTE: This adjustment is made by changing size of shim located under mainshaft bearing.

Manual Transmissions
PEUGEOT 5-SPEED (Cont.)

1) Install needle bearing inside input shaft. Assemble input shaft to mainshaft (without reverse driven gear and nut). Install mainshaft assembly in transmission case. Install clutch housing. Install and tighten Allen screws in retainer plate. Place all synchronizers in neutral position.

2) Spread synchronizers apart between sleeve and hub. Insert Gauge (8.0314X) between each synchronizer sleeve and hub without forcing. *See Fig. 15.* If gauge fits easily between all 3 points, retain original shim. If gauge does not easily fit between all 3 points, perform following adjustments to determine new shim size.

Fig. 15: Synchronizer Centering Adjustment (Except 4th Gear)

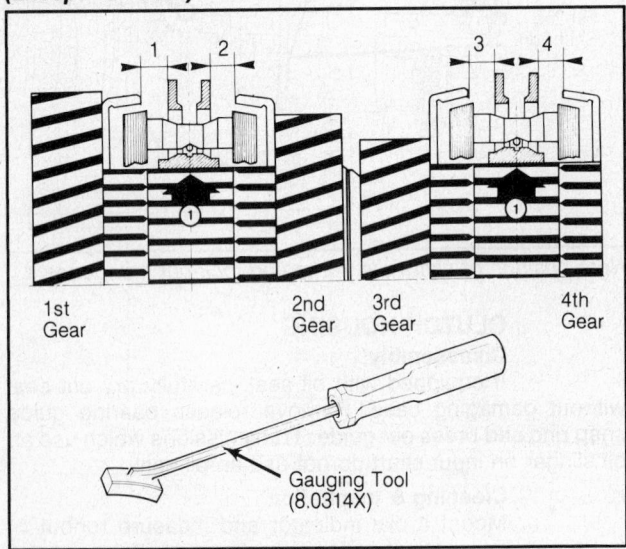

Do not force gauge between synchronizers.

3) If gauge does not easily fit between points 1 and/or 3 of *Fig. 15*, insert gauge and feeler gauge at point 2. Insert feeler gauge of various thicknesses to determine amount of change. Reduce shim thickness by this amount.

4) If gauge does not easily fit at point 2 of *Fig. 15*, measure clearance at points 1 and 3. Increase shim thickness by smaller of readings.

NOTE: Shims are available in sizes .094-.134" (2.4-3.4 mm) for transmissions without shouldered 1st gear spacer. Shims for shouldered applications are .0098", .0118", .0138", .0157" and .0236" (.25, .30, .35, .40 and .60 mm).

Centering 4th Gear Synchronizer

NOTE: This adjustment is made by changing size of shims located under input shaft bearing.

1) Spread 4th gear synchronizer apart and insert gauge without forcing. If gauge slides in freely, measure excess clearance. If clearance is .039" (1 mm) or less, retain original shims. If clearance exceeds .039" (1 mm), increase shims to equal thickness of original shim plus measured excess.

2) If gauge does not fit, remove mainshaft, input shaft and clutch housing. Separate input shaft from mainshaft and remove shims. Reinstall components and measure and record clearance at 4th gear synchronizer. On transmissions equipped with an oil slinger, leave slinger on shaft at all times.

3) Remove components, disassemble input shaft and install shims of thickness equal to measured clearance. Reinstall all components and recheck clearance. Remove all components after final check.

NOTE: Shims are available from .006-.020" (.15-.50 mm) in .002" (.05 mm) increments. Use as few shims as possible to reach desired thickness.

Bearing Preload (Countergear Shaft)

1) Remove clutch housing and install countergear shaft in transmission case. Install right half of transmission case and retain in position with 4 bolts (1 at each corner). Install bearing retainer and hold in position with Allen screws. Hand tighten all retaining bolts and screws.

2) With case securely attached to transmission stand, turn case so front of transmission is facing up. Place Adapter (8.0310S) on top of shaft. Press on adapter by hand while rotating shaft to seat bearings.

3) On transmission cases which use 2 split pins to position case halves, tighten following bolts in sequence: 4 case bolts and 4 retainer plate bolts.

4) On transmission cases which use 1 pin to position case halves, install clutch housing. Retain housing to case by using 4 bolts, 2 on each half of case. Tighten clutch housing bolts, case bolts and retainer plate bolts. Remove clutch housing. Check offset between case halves with Gauge Block (8.0310FZ) and dial indicator. If offset exceeds .0008" (.02 mm), remove all components and repeat procedure.

5) On all models, center hole in gauge block on countergear shaft. Install dial indicator so indicator tip rests against bearing outer race surface. Rotate indicator through 1 complete revolution. Warpage between case halves must not exceed .0008" (.02 mm).

6) If specification is exceeded, align bearing race by inserting Arbor (8.0310S) and tapping with a plastic mallet. After aligning outer bearing race, check that drag is not added to shaft and recheck warpage. To reduce drag, loosen and retighten 2 front case bolts.

7) With dial indicator in place on countergear shaft bore (tip resting on outer race), zero dial indicator at "5" and "0" with .20" (5 mm) preload. Move indicator so tip is resting on front face of case. *See Fig. 16.*

Fig. 16: Measuring Countergear Shaft Bearing Preload

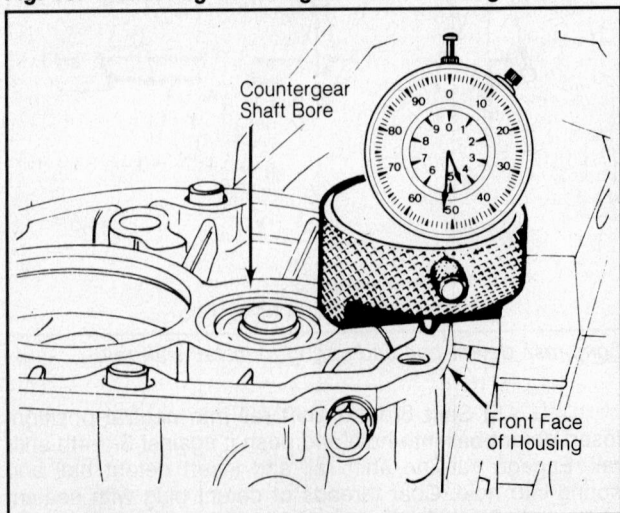

Zero dial indicator with .20" (5 mm) preload.

8) Note dial indicator reading. Add .004" (.10 mm) to reading. Subtract bearing preload of .20" (5 mm) to calculate thickness of shim to be installed between bearing and countergear shaft. Round result to nearest .002" (.05 mm). Remove countergear shaft. Remove front bearing and insert shim of determined thickness with inside chamfer facing gear. Reinstall bearing.

NOTE: **Shims are available from .089-.134" (2.25-3.40 mm) in .002" (.05 mm) increments.**

REASSEMBLY

1) Install retaining plate with machined surface toward bearing. Install reverse driven gear on mainshaft with teeth chamfer facing rearward. Install new nut and stake in position.

2) Install needle bearing inside input shaft and assemble input shaft and mainshaft. Place 3rd-4th synchronizer in neutral position. Install outer races onto outer bearings of countergear shaft. Mesh countergear shaft with mainshaft and input shaft.

3) With teeth of shaft assemblies meshed and while holding assembly together in this manner, install assembly into transmission case. See Fig. 17. Ensure shift forks engage with synchronizer sleeves. Apply a thin coat of sealer to faces of case halves.

Fig. 17: Installing Shafts into Transmission Case

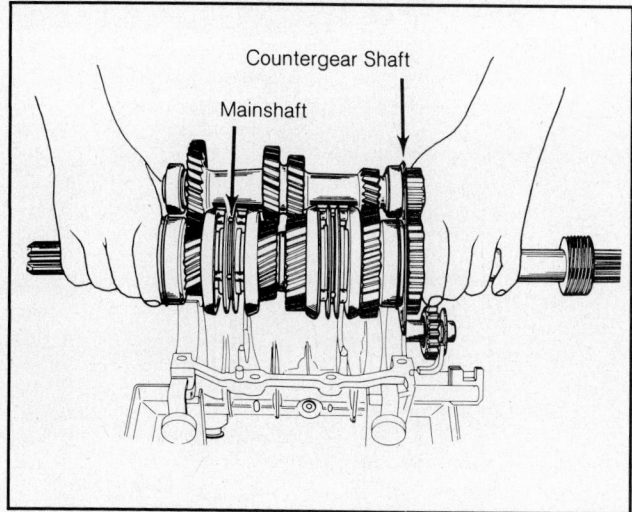

Ensure shift forks engage synchronizer sleeves.

4) With countergear and mainshaft installed, assemble 2 halves of transmission case together. Ensure positioning dowels are in place. Install new prelubricated input shaft oil seal. Using a seal protector, install clutch housing with small amount of sealant on rear face of clutch housing.

5) Tighten case half bolts. Rotate input shaft to seat bearings. Tighten retainer plate bolts. Loosen 4 bearing bolts and tap case half while turning input shaft. Tighten 4 bearing bolts.

6) On transmissions which use 1 dowel pin for positioning, rotate case so clutch housing faces down. Using a dial indicator, measure to determine if case halves are aligned with one another. If case half alignment varies more than .0008" (.02 mm), loosen case half bolts and try to align case halves. Retighten bolts.

Fig. 18: Measuring Case Half Alignment

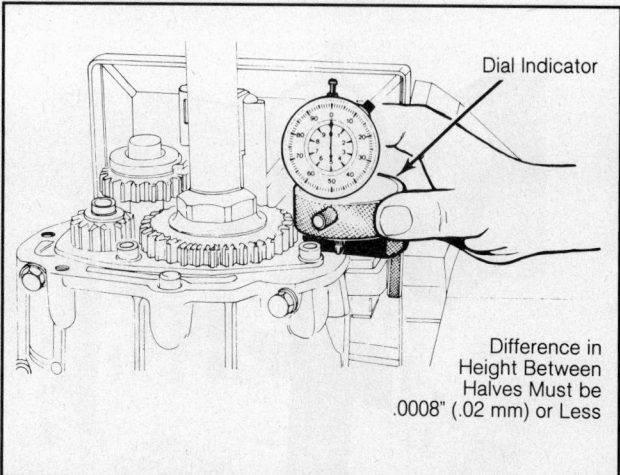

Measure alignment on cases which are positioned with only 1 dowel pin.

7) Apply a thin coat of sealant on gasket surfaces of case and intermediate housing. Install intermediate housing dowels. Install housing while engaging selector fingers in fork shaft gates. Tighten bolts and nuts.

8) Install 5th-reverse intermediate shaft and synchronizer. Position synchronizer so mark made during disassembly is visible (if new, so circular groove on face points toward reverse).

9) Place 5th-reverse selector shaft in 5th gear. At same time, install 5th-reverse synchronizer sleeve and fork, aligning reference marks made during disassembly. Install Retainer (8.0314W) on case housing and install new roll pin in 5th-reverse shift fork. Remove retainer and place assembly in neutral.

10) Install 5th drive gear, needle bearing and spacer. Ensure lugs on spacer are properly aligned. Install extension housing without bearing. Mount dial indicator and holder on extension housing with indicator tip resting on countergear shaft shoulder (not on spacer). Zero dial indicator with .236" (6 mm) preload.

11) Remove extension housing and press bearings into housing. Place Gauge Block (8.0314G) under countergear shaft bearing. Mount dial indicator on extension housing with indicator tip resting on gauge block and note reading.

12) Subtract preload amount of .236" (6 mm). From difference, subtract .002" (.05 mm). Round off reading to nearest .002" (.05 mm) and install this size shim on 5th-reverse shaft. Remove dial indicator and gauge block.

13) Install snap ring in mainshaft groove. Lubricate machined surface of mainshaft and press 5th driven gear and speedometer drive onto mainshaft using Bushing (8.0310Y) and Installers (8.0310P and 8.0314).

14) Install new snap ring to retain 5th driven gear and speedometer drive gear. Using Bearing Driver (8.0314Y), install lubricated extension housing seal until driver contacts housing surface.

15) Install 2 locating dowel pins in extension housing and coat housing mating surfaces with sealant. Install extension housing while engaging selector finger with selector fork shaft gate. Tap housing just above 5th-reverse intermediate shaft with a mallet and tighten bolts.

Manual Transmissions

PEUGEOT 5-SPEED (Cont.)

Fig. 19: Countergear Shaft Shim Measurement

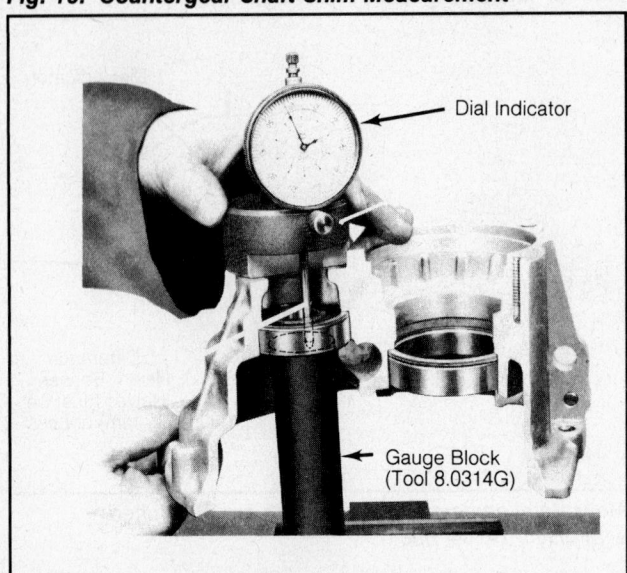

Dial Indicator

Gauge Block
(Tool 8.0314G)

Place indicator tip on gauge block.

16) Install plug and new "O" ring in extension housing. Install speedometer driven gear with 2 new "O" rings. Retain speedometer driven gear with set screw.

17) Pack dust boot in clutch housing with grease. Apply grease to release bearing guide. Install clutch fork with retaining spring behind dust boot. Place push rod inside rubber protector on outside of clutch housing and install release bearing. Install back-up light switch.

TIGHTENING SPECIFICATIONS

Application	Ft. Lbs. (N.m)
Case Half	
4 Bearing Bolts	11 (15)
Clutch Housing-To-Trans. Case	20 (27)
Extension Housing-To-Trans. Case	11 (15)
Intermediate Hsg.-To-Trans.	
Nuts	13 (18)
Bolts	11 (15)
Mainshaft Lock Nut	40 (54)
Propeller Shaft Hsg.-To-Extension Hsg.	44 (60)

	INCH Lbs. (N.m)
Case Half Bolts	7.25 (9.8)
Retainer Plate	7.25 (9.8)

PORSCHE 911 CARRERA 5-SPEED TRANSAXLE

DESCRIPTION

The 5-speed transaxle (code 915/68 or 915/70) combines both transmission and differential into a single assembly consisting of 3 subassemblies: Front cover, gear housing and transmission/clutch housing.

In all gears, power flows from input shaft to pinion shaft through respective gear pairs. Torque is transferred to pinion gear, ring gear and drive axles. Reverse gear power flows from input shaft through reverse idler gear, sliding gear and then to pinion shaft.

The 915 transaxle is also equipped with a oil pump. The oil pump is driven by the input shaft. Oil drawn from the transmission oil sump through a pickup tube and forces it through passages in the pump cover and pressure lines.

LUBRICATION & ADJUSTMENT

See appropriate MANUAL TRANSMISSION SERVICING article in IMPORT GENERAL SERVICING section.

SERVICE (IN VEHICLE)

FLANGED SHAFT SEAL
Removal

Remove socket head screws at inner end of shaft, then disconnect and support axle drive shaft. Remove inner flange bolt while holding flange from turning by inserting punch in drive flange bolt hole. Remove flange and pull out seal with Seal Removal Tool (VW 681).

Installation

Fill cavity between sealing and dust lips with multi-purpose grease and drive seal in place with Seal Installer Tool (VW 195). Replace flange and drive shaft and tighten to specifications.

REAR WHEEL BEARINGS
Removal

With brake calipers off and drive shaft disconnected at axle flange, press shaft from housing, remove circlip and drive grooved ball bearing and roller bearing out with soft drift.

Installation

Press grooved ball bearing in inner end of housing and replace circlip. Put spacer in housing and drive roller bearing in place (flanged side facing out). Install seal in inboard side of housing. Put outer spacer in shaft and press in along with bearing inner race using castellated nut and driver.

DRIVE AXLE SHAFTS
Removal & Installation

Raise vehicle on hoist. Remove bolts from constant velocity joint-to-mating flange and remove drive axle from vehicle. To install, reverse removal procedure and tighten to specifications.

CONSTANT VELOCITY JOINTS

NOTE: Axle shafts must be removed from vehicle before servicing.

Fig. 1: Exploded View of 911 5-Speed Transaxle

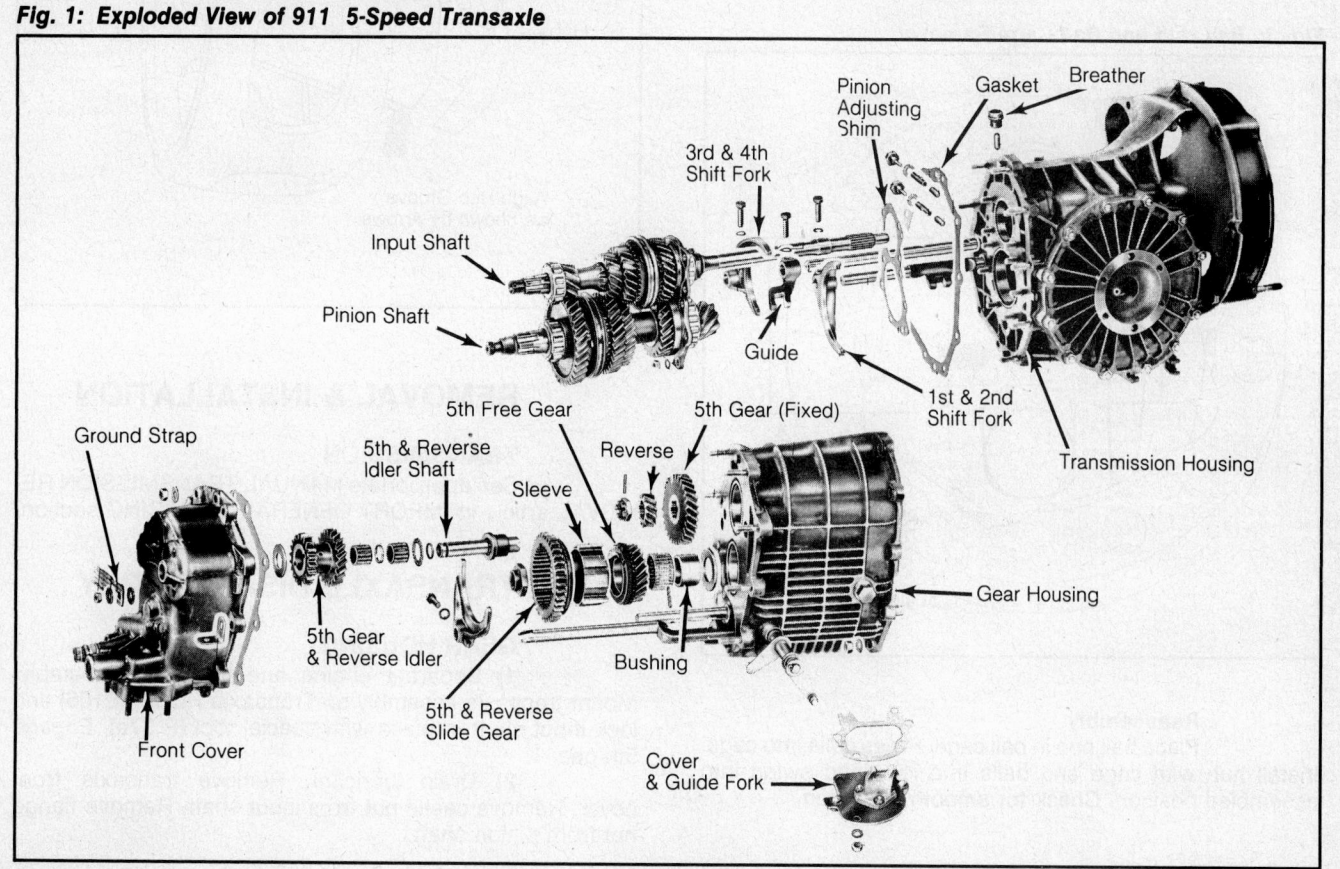

Manual Transmissions

PORSCHE 911 CARRERA 5-SPEED TRANSAXLE (Cont.)

Fig. 2: Exploded View of Rear Axle Shaft Assembly

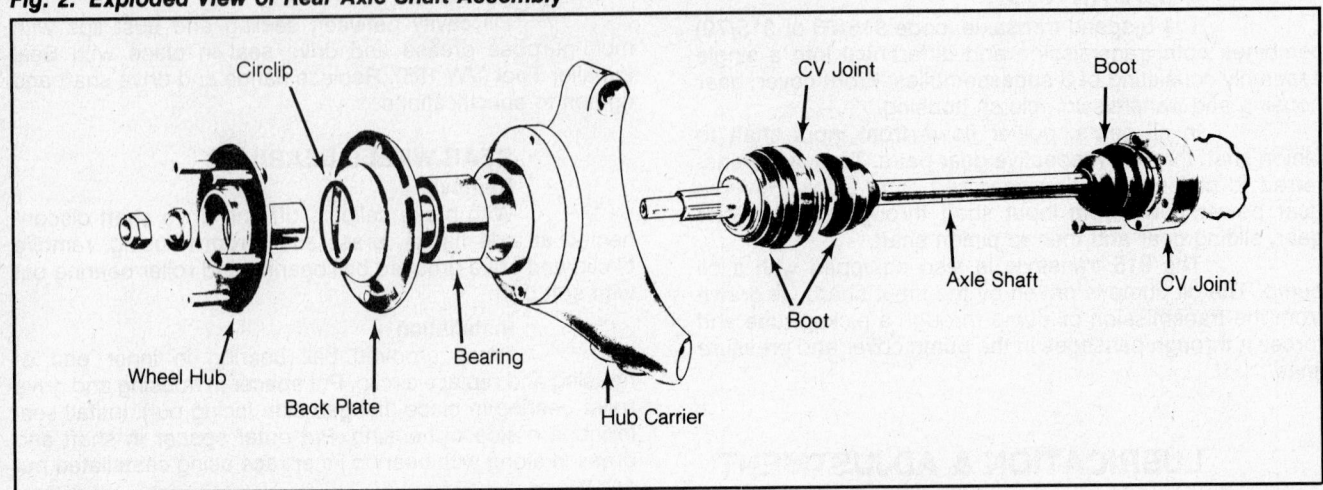

Removal

Clamp axle shaft in a vise with soft jaws. Remove boot clamp and push boot to center of axle. Remove circlip from axle shaft, press joint from axle shaft using CV Joint Removal Tools (VW 401 and VW 408).

Disassembly

Swing ball and ball cage from joint and press out in direction of arrow. *See Fig. 3.* Tilt ball hub out of ball cage via ball groove. *See Fig. 4.* Clean all parts in a cleaning solvent and blow dry. Inspect for wear and damage.

NOTE: **Ball hub and joint are paired. DO NOT mix parts. The 6 balls are also mated together and cannot be mixed with others.**

Fig. 3: Ball Hub and Ball Cage Removal

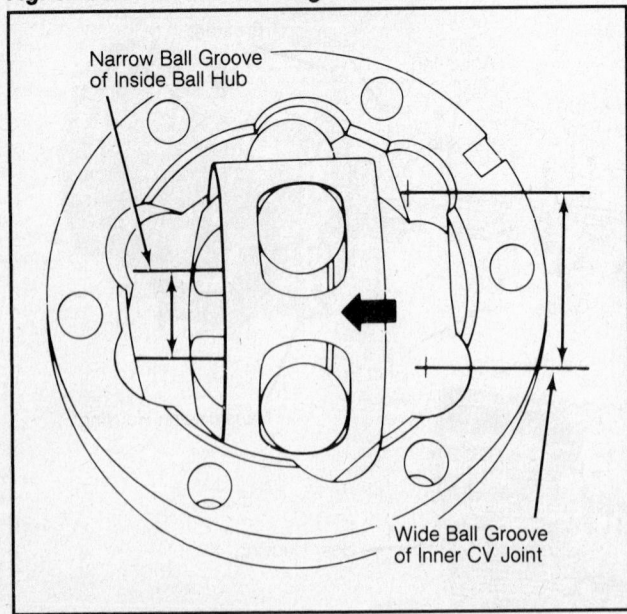

Reassembly

Place ball hub in ball cage. Press balls into cage. Install hub with cage and balls into joint and swing into assembled position. Check for smooth operation.

Installation

To install, reverse removal procedure. Install a new gasket on flange cover. Pack joint with molybdenum grease.

Fig. 4: Removal of Ball Hub from Cage

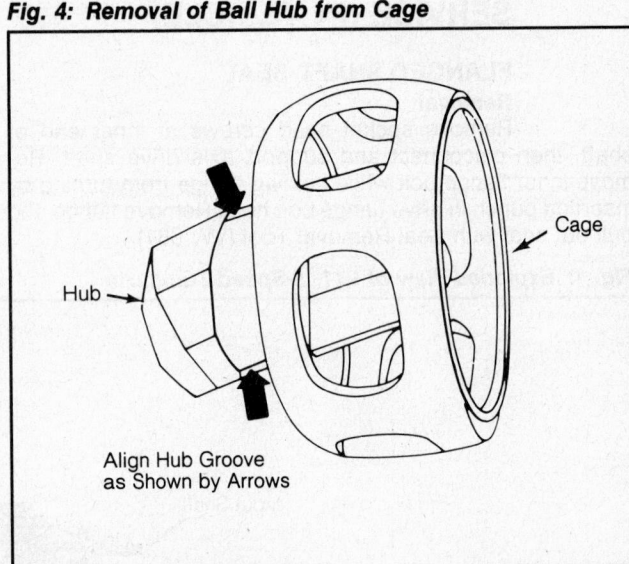

REMOVAL & INSTALLATION

TRANSMISSION

See appropriate MANUAL TRANSMISSION REMOVAL article in IMPORT GENERAL SERVICING section.

TRANSAXLE DISASSEMBLY

GEAR HOUSING

1) Separate engine and transaxle assembly. Mount transaxle assembly on Transaxle Holder (9106) and lock input shaft in place with special tool (P 37a). Engage 5th gear.

2) Drain lubricant. Remove transaxle front cover. Remove castle nut from input shaft. Remove flange nut from pinion shaft.

Fig. 5: Exploded View of Gear Housing

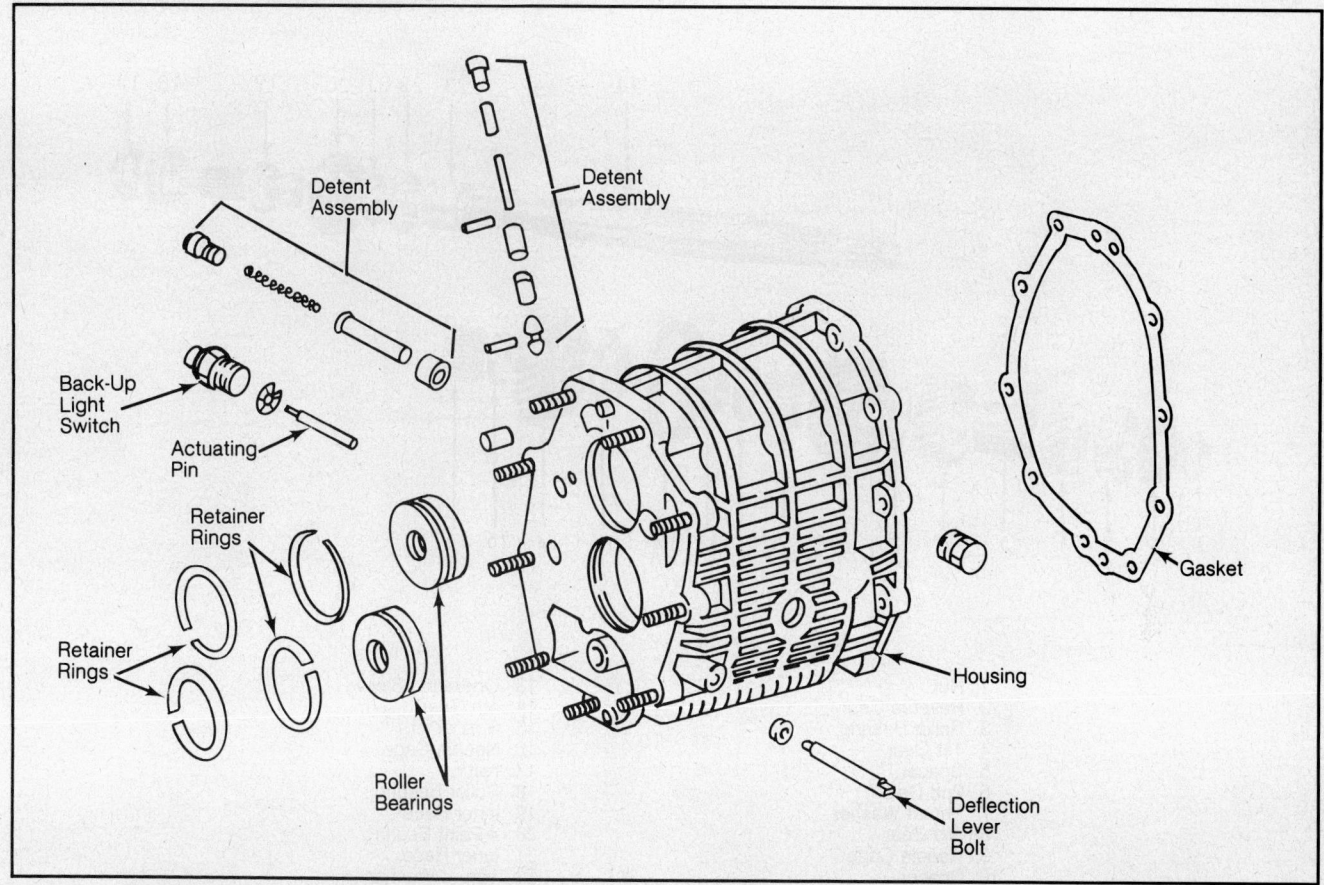

3) Identify needle bearing of 5th speed free gear to aid in reassembly. When assembling transmission, needle bearings, gears and other matched parts must be replaced in original positions. Remove guide fork cover and gasket.

4) Remove gear housing nuts (12). Remove housing and selector fork rod (5th and reverse) and fork rod and shaft. It may be necessary to tap gently with mallet to remove assembly from studs.

NOTE: **Shift fork rod for 5th and reverse must be in NEUTRAL position. If not, housing will jam.**

5) Remove reverse gear lock plug on left lower side of transaxle. Remove 3rd/4th gear detent plug. Take out spring and detent. Remove bolt from 1st/2nd gear selector fork. Spread clamp with screwdriver. Remove input and pinion shaft retaining plates.

6) Remove input and pinion shaft assemblies from case. Shift fork rod for 3rd and 4th gear and shift fork for 1st and 2nd gear should come out with assembly. Remove selector shaft detent.

7) Remove 1st/2nd shift detent plug and take out spring and detent. Pull out 1st/2nd shift fork rod.

NOTE: **Be sure to make note of the number and thickness of shims between transaxle housing and retaining plates for reassembly.**

8) To disassemble gear housing, drive shift detents securing roll pins out of respective seats. Drive out half-round dowel pin.

NOTE: **Be sure to take out pins and half-round dowel in order given. Detent assemblies are under spring tension.**

9) If bearing outer races are to be removed, Special Tool (US 8050) must be used. Gear housing must be heated to about 250°F (120°C) to drive out races.

INPUT SHAFT
1) Place Support Plate (P 355a) in a vise and insert input shaft assembly. Remove flange nut with Special Tool (P 252a). Press roller bearing off shaft using Thrust Plates (VW 401 and 402) and Thrust Disc (VW 412).

2) Remove remaining parts in order shown in *Fig. 6*. Keep respective gear and needle bearing assemblies together for assembly in original locations.

3) Press roller bearing off input shaft with Thrust Tube (VW 415a) and Press Punch (VW 407).

PINION SHAFT
Carefully press roller bearing off pinion shaft using Thrust Plate (VW 401), Disc (VW 412) and Tube (P 255a). Remove pinion shaft components. Keep needle bearings and gear pairs together; these parts MUST be installed in original position. Remove speedometer drive gear.

SYNCHRONIZERS
Remove clip from gear. Disassemble as shown in *Figs. 7 and 8*. Check all parts for wear or damage and replace as necessary.

Manual Transmissions

PORSCHE 911 CARRERA 5-SPEED TRANSAXLE (Cont.)

Fig. 6: Exploded View of Input Shaft Assembly

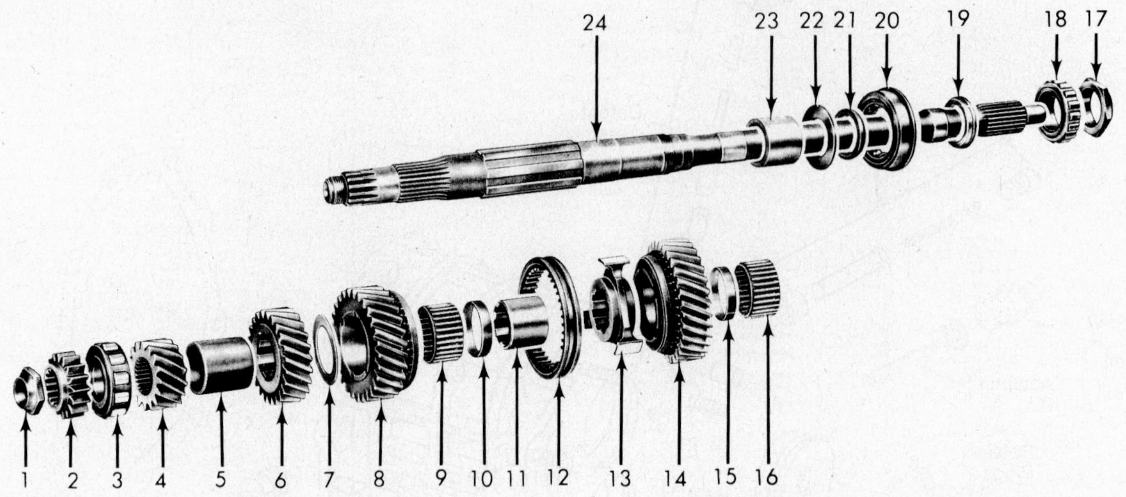

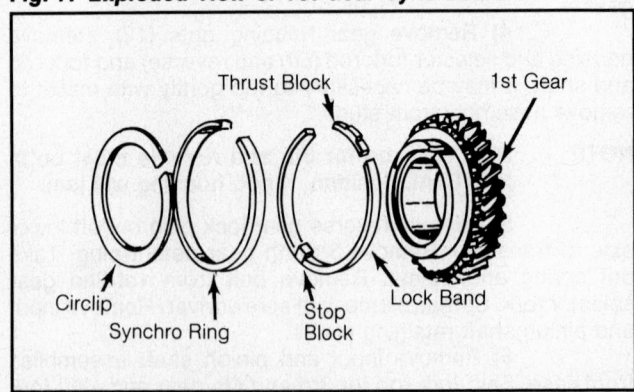

1. Nut	13. Operating Sleeve
2. Reverse Gear	14. 4th Gear
3. Roller Bearing	15. Spacer
4. 1st Gear	16. Needle Cage
5. Spacer	17. Nut
6. 2nd Gear	18. Roller Bearing
7. Thrust Washer	19. Inner Race
8. 3rd Gear	20. 4-Point Bearing
9. Needle Cage	21. Inner Race
10. Spacer	22. Thrust Washer
11. 3rd Gear Bushing	23. 4th Gear Bushing
12. Gearshift Sleeve	24. Drive Shaft

FRONT COVER

Remove parts as shown in *Fig. 9.* If speedometer gear shaft bushing is to be removed, heat front cover to about 250°F (120°C). Pull out bushing. If necessary, bushing may be carefully drilled out. Clean cover and check for cracks or damage. Replace parts as necessary.

FINAL DRIVE (DIFFERENTIAL)

1) Remove expansion bolt from center of flange. Withdraw flange shaft. Drive seals and outer bearing races out of final drive housing and side cover with drift.

2) Drive roll pin from differential pinion shaft, then drive pinion shaft out and remove anchor piece. Remove tapered roller bearing with puller and Thrust Piece (P 263). Puller arms must fit through openings in magnetic carrier disc to remove bearing from side opposite ring gear.

3) Do not interchange spacer washers and shims. Right and left side must be kept separate and installed in original positions. Remove lock plates from ring gear retaining bolts. Remove bolts and ring gear.

FINAL DRIVE HOUSING

1) Remove adjusting lever spring and circlip. Pull adjusting lever off shaft and disengage auxiliary spring while pressing clutch release lever toward front transmission cover. Drive release lever shaft and bushings from housing.

Fig. 7: Exploded View of 1st Gear Synchronizer

Thrust Block

1st Gear

Circlip

Synchro Ring

Stop Block

Lock Band

2) Remove snap ring from input shaft bearing race. Bearing must first be driven slightly away from snap ring with soft punch.

3) Heat differential housing to about 250°F (120°C), and drive out both bearing races using Thrust Blocks (US 8050 and P 254d).

INPUT SHAFT SEAL

Remove both countersunk Phillips head bolts on guide tube. Pull out drive shaft seal guide tube with hook and bar without bending tube lip. Remove seal from tube with Remover (P 381).

PORSCHE 911 CARRERA 5-SPEED TRANSAXLE (Cont.)

Fig. 8: Exploded View of Pinion Shaft Assembly

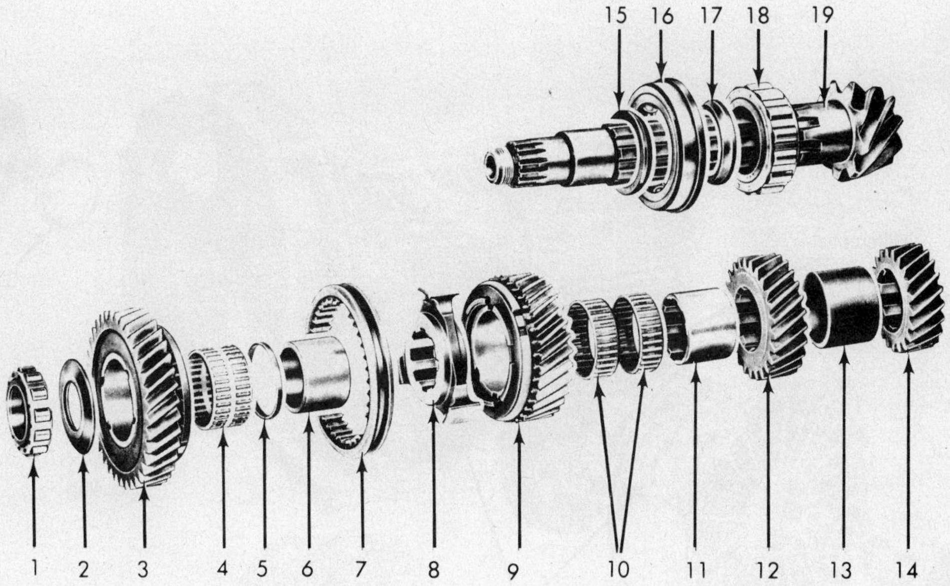

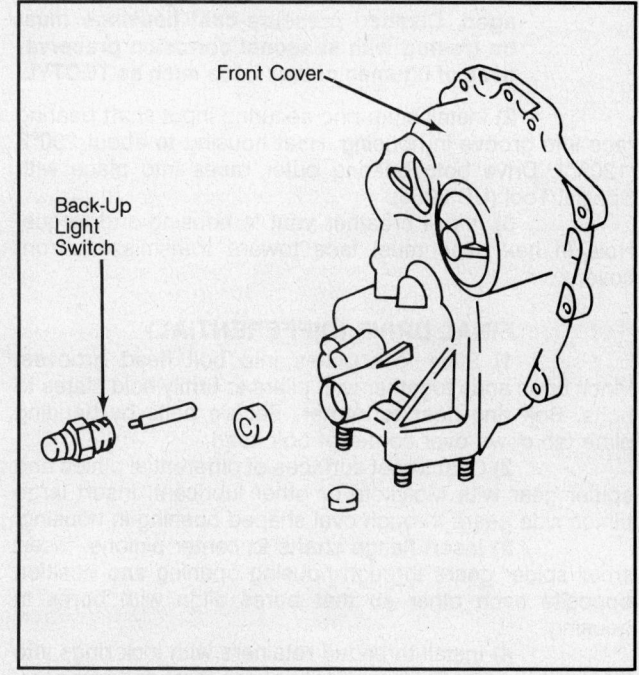

1. Roller Bearing
2. Thrust Washer
3. 1st Gear
4. Needle Cage
5. Spacer
6. 1st Gear Sleeve
7. Operating Sleeve
8. Guide Sleeve
9. 2nd Gear
10. Needle Cage
11. 2nd Gear Sleeve
12. 3rd Gear
13. Spacer
14. 4th Gear
15. Bearing Inner Race
16. 4-Point Bearing
17. Bearing Inner Race
18. Roller Bearing
19. Drive Pinion

TRANSAXLE REASSEMBLY & ADJUSTMENT

INPUT SHAFT SEAL

Drive in seal to stop with piece of pipe. Install rubber seal. Lubricate rubber seal and sealing lip. Insert tube with rubber seal. Install guide sleeve for release bearing and coat with White grease.

CLUTCH RELEASE LEVER AND SHAFT

1) Install bushings with Driver (P 375). *See Fig. 12.* Lubricate and install operating shaft, release fork and roll pin.

2) Install release lever on shaft along with spring and adjusting screw. Secure in place with pin. Snap auxiliary spring past dead point to stop pin in order to pretension against lever.

NOTE: Do not install adjusting lever until after transaxle assembly has been installed in vehicle.

FINAL DRIVE HOUSING

1) Ensure all parts are clean and dry. If pinion shaft or ring gear was damaged or broken, check center web bearing bores for cracks or damage. Replace housing if necessary.

Fig. 9: Exploded View of Front Cover Assembly

Front Cover

Back-Up Light Switch

Manual Transmissions

PORSCHE 911 CARRERA 5-SPEED TRANSAXLE (Cont.)

Fig. 10: Exploded View of Final Drive and Housing

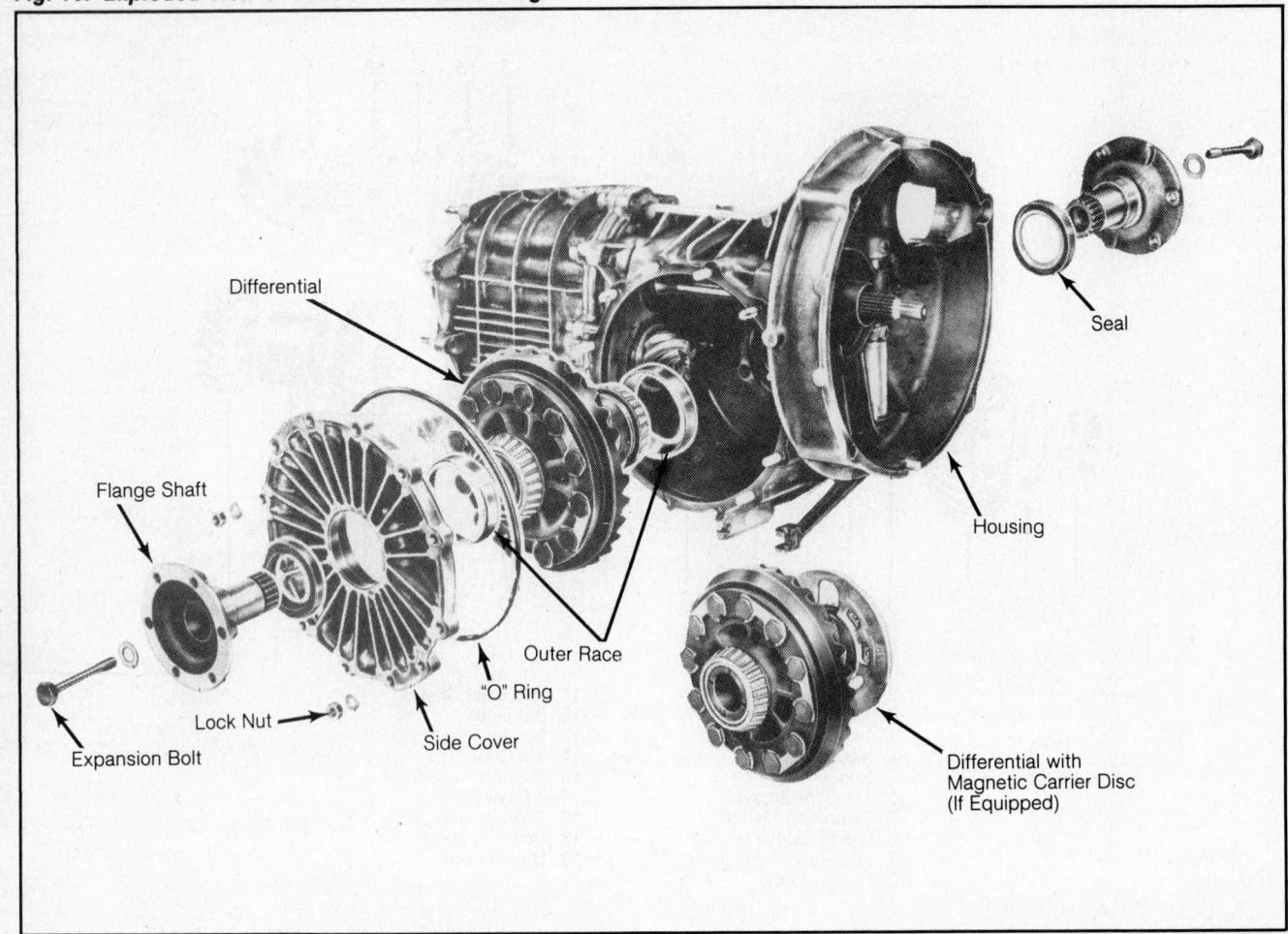

NOTE: Do not clean pressure-cast housings in corrosive liquids as magnesium alloy will be damaged. Cleaned pressure-cast housings must be treated with seasonal corrosion preservatives of bitumen or wax base such as TECTYL.

2) Install snap ring securing input shaft bearing race into groove in housing. Heat housing to about 250°F (120°C). Drive both bearing outer races into place with Special Tool (US 8050).

3) Install breather vent in housing and torque. Hole in hex head must face toward transmission front cover.

FINAL DRIVE (DIFFERENTIAL)

1) Slide lock plates into bolt head grooves. Pinch open ends together with pliers to firmly hold plates to bolts. Bolt ring gear to carrier. Secure bolts by bending plate tab down over corner of bolt head.

2) Coat thrust surfaces of differential pinion and spider gear with Molykote or other lubricant. Insert large pinion side gears through oval shaped opening in housing.

3) Insert flange shafts to center pinions. Insert small spider gears through housing opening and position opposite each other so that bores align with bores in housing.

4) Install threaded retainers with lock rings into large side gears. Slide anchor between threaded retainers.

CAUTION: Differential pinion shaft must be positioned so pinion shaft hole aligns with hole in anchor.

5) Hold anchor in place and drive in pinion shaft. Install bearing shims and spacer washers in CORRECT ORIGINAL locations on differential housing. Install anchor pin.

6) Install tapered roller bearing using Thrust Plate (P 264). When replacing magnetic carrier disc, tapered roller preload does not have to be checked if same shims are reused.

NOTE: If only differential has been replaced, proceed to RING GEAR & PINION ADJUSTMENT. If transmission gears have been removed and disassembled, proceed to correct assembly steps for remainder of transmission, then proceed to adjustment.

SYNCHRONIZERS

1) Place synchro ring on clutch carrier; rough ring surfaces face shift sleeve. Insert thrust block, stop block and lock band(s).

NOTE: First gear synchro ring has only 1 lock band. Also, 1st gear synchro ring is identified by a groove on both sides.

2) Single lock band must be inserted with recess facing outward to accommodate small stop block. Stop

PORSCHE 911 CARRERA 5-SPEED TRANSAXLE (Cont.)

Fig. 11: Exploded View of Ring Gear and Carrier Assembly

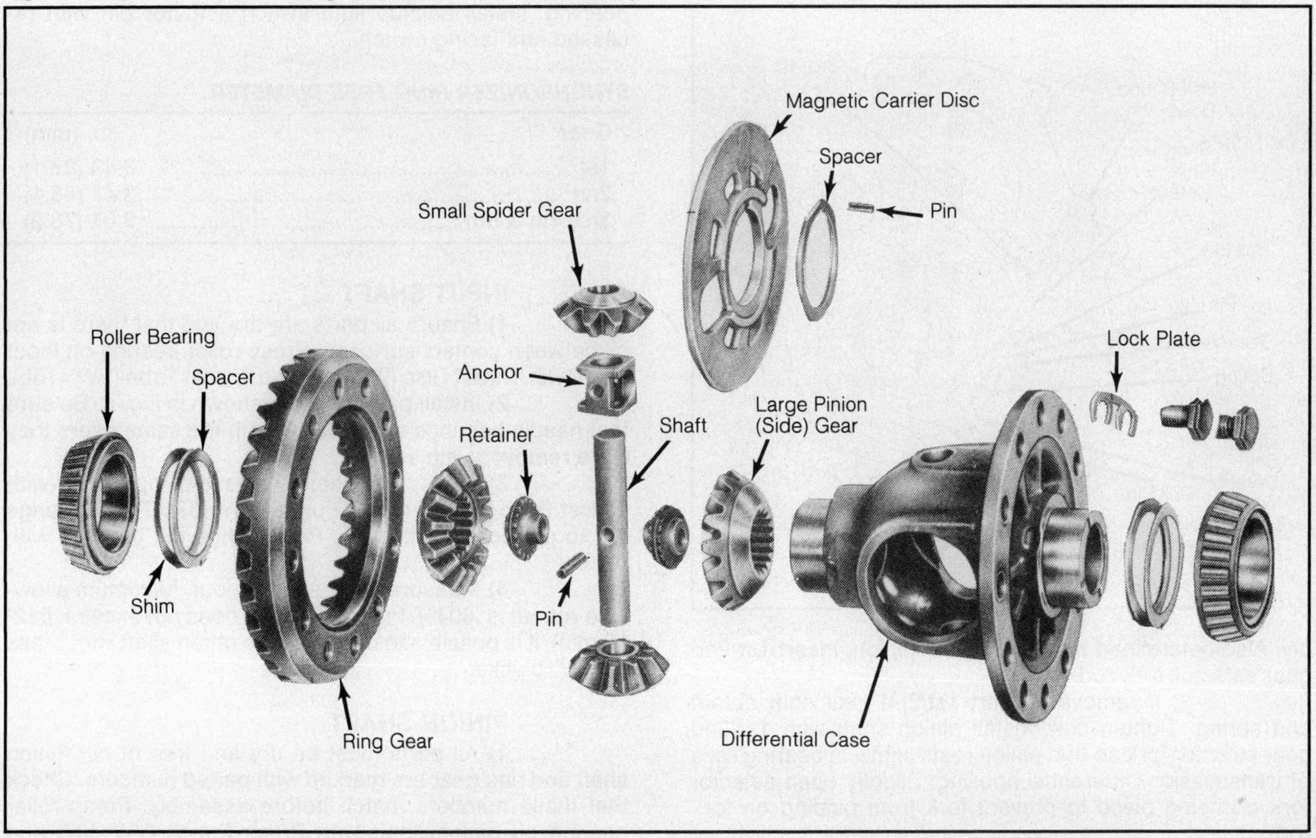

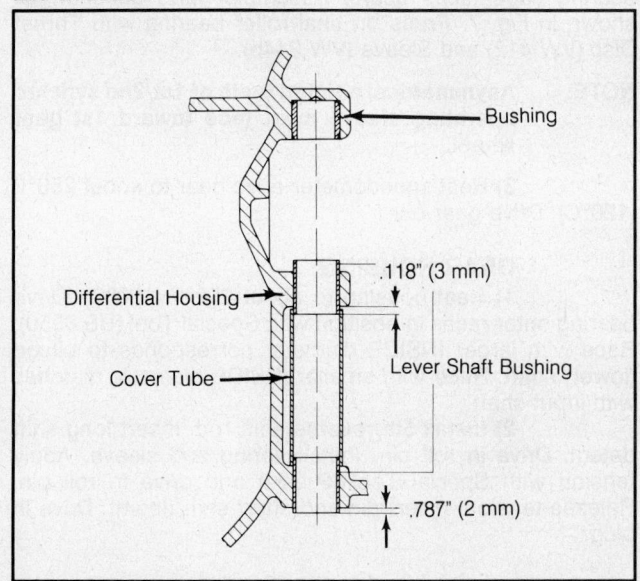

Fig. 12: Clutch Lever Shaft Bushing Installation and Location

Fig. 13: Second Gear Synchronizer

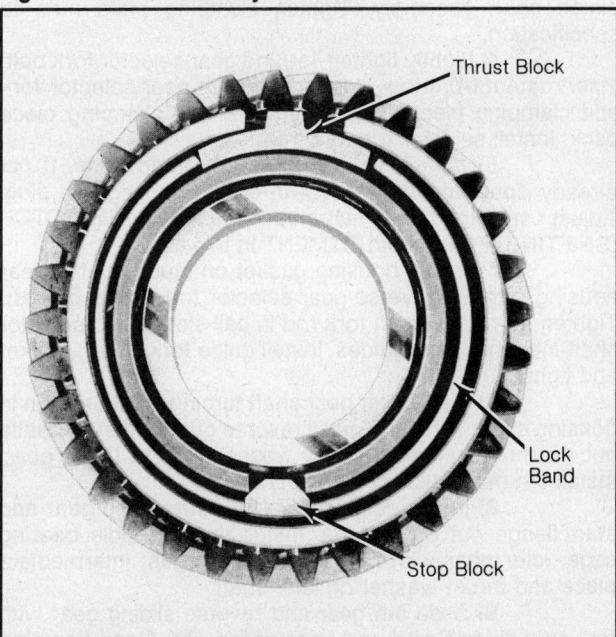

block is directly opposite longer thrust block on 2nd gear synchro. Small stop block for 1st gear synchro is slightly offset and is bevelled on one side only. Install circlip after lock band, stop and thrust blocks are installed.

3) Maximum clearance between selector fork and shifting sleeve of 1st through 5th gear is .02" (.5 mm).

Free diameter of synchronizer rings should be as shown in SYNCHRONIZER RING FREE DIAMETER table.

INPUT & PINION ASSEMBLY-TO-HOUSING

1) Install same number and thickness of shims on transmission housing studs as noted during disassem-

PORSCHE 911 CARRERA 5-SPEED TRANSAXLE (Cont.)

Fig. 14: Cross-Sectional View Showing Detent Positions

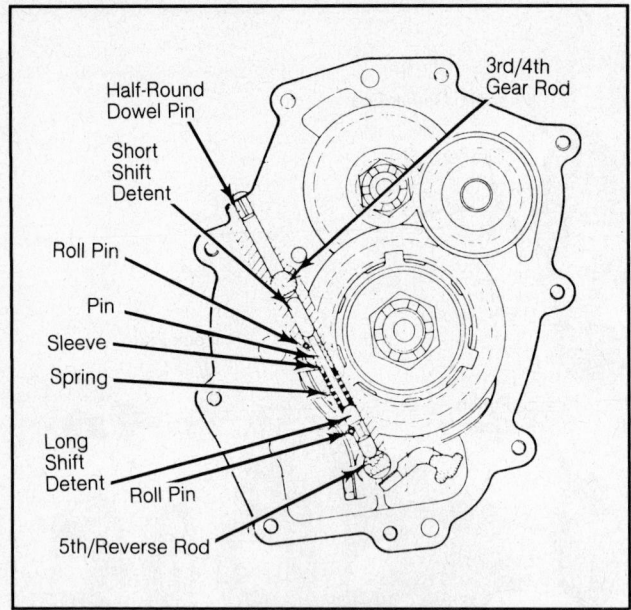

bly. Also determined by adjusting the pinion. Insert 1st/2nd gear selector fork rod.

2) If removed. insert 1st/2nd gear shift detent and spring. Tighten bolt. Install pinion shaft with 1st/2nd gear selector fork so that pinion rests lightly in bearing race of transmission/differential housing. Slightly open selector fork clamping piece to prevent fork from binding on fork rod.

3) Insert input shaft and press into place with pinion shaft assembly. Tighten clamping plate nuts to specification.

4) Lightly tighten 1st/2nd gear selector fork bolt. Insert detent from top. Unscrew 3rd/4th gear selector fork and clamping piece bolts. Push fork and clamping piece back. Install selector fork and rod.

5) Lightly tighten fork and clamp bolts. If not already done, insert detent with spring and tighten plug. Adjust selector forks at this time. See SELECTOR (SHIFTING) FORK ADJUSTMENT in this article.

6) Install housing gasket on studs. Install gear housing with 5th/reverse gear selector fork rod and shaft. Tighten correctly. Push fork rod in ball sleeve and selector shaft into shift pawl guides. Install guide fork cover, gasket and tighten.

7) Install idler gear shaft turning shaft until pin in housing stops rotation. Install reverse gear and start castle nut on threads. Install thrust washer for 5th (free) gear. Install 5th (free) gear needle bearing.

8) Install guide sleeve for 5th/reverse gear and start flange nut on threads. Install thrust needle bearing cage, idler gear with needle bearing cages, intermediate piece and thrust washer on idler shaft.

9) Slide 5th gear and reverse sliding gear with fork onto guide sleeve and selector fork rod. Open clamping piece on fork slightly for easier assembly. Lightly tighten selector fork bolt.

10) Apply light coat of oil to "O" ring and install. Use tool (P 37a) to block input shaft and engage 5th gear. Tighten input and pinion shaft nuts to specification.

11) Adjust 5th/reverse gear selector fork. See SELECTOR (SHIFTING) FORK ADJUSTMENT in this arti-

cle. Secure castle nut with roll pin. Secure flange nut by peening. Install backup light switch actuator pin with recessed end facing switch.

SYNCHRONIZER RING FREE DIAMETER

Gear	In. (mm)
1st	3.43 (87.1)
2nd	3.47 (88.1)
3rd, 4th & 5th	3.07 (78.0)

INPUT SHAFT

1) Ensure all parts are dry and that there is not oil between contact surfaces. Press roller bearing on input shaft with Thrust Disc (VW 412) and Thrust Tube (VW 416b).

2) Install parts in order shown in *Fig. 6.* Be sure that needle bearings are installed with the same gears they were removed with.

3) Press roller bearing on end of input shaft with Thrust Plate (VW 401) and Punch (VW 407). Torque flange nut to correct specification. Peen flange nut in place with punch.

4) Measure input shaft runout. Maximum allowable runout is .004" (.1 mm). If runout does not exceed .012" (.3 mm), it is possible to carefully straighten shaft with press and "V" blocks.

PINION SHAFT

1) All parts must be dry and free of oil. Pinion shaft and ring gear are marked with paired numbers. Check that these numbers match before assembly. Press roller bearing on pinion shaft with Press Punch (VW 407) and Tube (VW 415a).

2) Bearing must be installed so ring of 2-part bearing cage faces gears. Assemble parts on shaft as shown in *Fig. 7.* Press on final roller bearing with Thrust Disc (VW 412) and Sleeve (VW 244b).

NOTE: **Asymmetrical pointed teeth of 1st/2nd synchro operating sleeve must face toward 1st gear wheel.**

3) Heat speedometer drive gear to about 250°F (120°C). Drive gear on.

GEAR HOUSING

1) Heat housing to about 250°F (120°C). Drive bearing outer races in position with Special Tool (US 8050). Race with larger INSIDE diameter corresponds to pinion (lower) shaft. Race with smaller INSIDE diameter matches with input shaft.

2) Install 5th/reverse shift rod. Insert long shift detent. Drive in roll pin. Install spring and sleeve. Apply tension with Special Tool (P 366) and drive in roll pin. Release tension. Insert pin and short shift detent. Drive in plug.

ADJUSTMENTS

GEARHSIFT ADJUSTMENT

1) Loosen selector rod clamp. Turn selector rod for transmission's inner selecor lever left in neutral to stop.

2) Move selector lever in neutral position so that the lower part of the selector lever is vertical and on right stop (3rd and 4th gear). Tighten selector rod clamp slightly.

PORSCHE 911 CARRERA 5-SPEED TRANSAXLE (Cont.)

3) Check shift travel is just as much in 1st through 4th gears and if reverse is easy to engage. Correct adjustments if necessary.

CAUTION: Unit must be assembled correctly. Front cover should not be installed at this time. Parts should be clean and dry.

Fig. 15: Ring and Pinion Identification

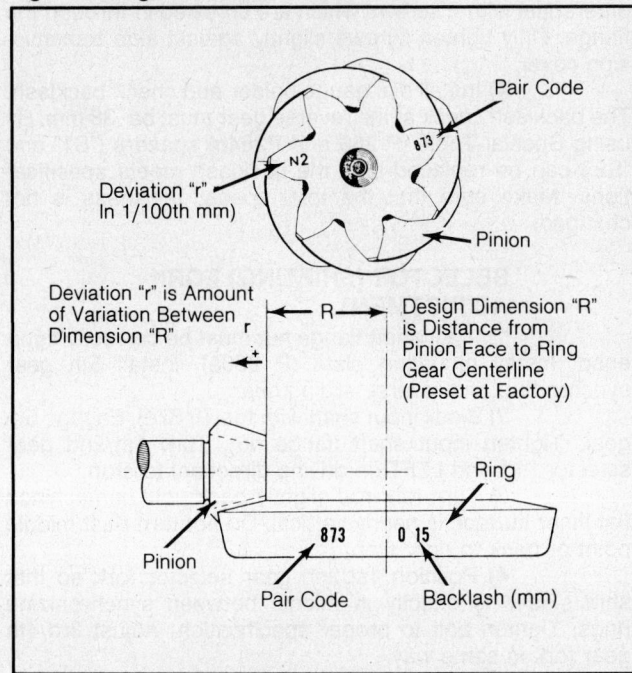

DRIVE PINION

1) Distance "E" is calculated by adding together design distance "R" and deviation "r" as indicated on face of drive pinion. Install preassembled drive pinion and drive shaft without shims and tighten to specifications.

2) Install 4th gear with operating and guide sleeve, and shift into 4th gear. Slide a 1.92 X .16 X 5.92" (48 X 4 X 148 mm) piece of pipe onto drive pinion.

3) Install thrust washer and cylindrical roller bearing. Mount gear housing and secure with 2 nuts. Install reverse gears. Place appropriate pin or reverse gear shaft in bore of transmission case and slide in reverse gear.

4) Tighten drive pinion nut to specifications. Make sure that the taper roller bearing outer races fit tight in transmission case and side cover. Set adjusting ring of Universal Gauge (VW 385/1) to distance "A" (2.32" 58 mm).

5) Slide Centering Discs (9109) on gauge. Screw in Gauge Plunger (VW 385/14) with 1.2" (30 mm) Dial Gauge Extension (VW 385/56). Install taper roller bearing from differential, or spare taper roller bearing on centering discs.

6) Install Master Gauge (VW 385/55), and set dial gauge (3 mm) range at zero with .040" (1 mm) preload (small indicator faces 1, large 0). Remove master gauge after setting dial gauge.

7) Place Gauge Plate (VW 385/17) on head of drive pinion. Place gauge mandrel in transmission case. The dial gauge extention is near the gauge plate. Install side transmission cover without seal and tighten the 4 nuts crosswise.

NOTE: DO NOT use a hammer to set up the side transmission cover (this could cause the

gauge plate, held by a magnet, to fall down). **Position the cover by tightening the nuts evenly.**

8) Pull second centering disc so far out with the spindle that the guage mandrel can just barely be turned by hand. Turn gauge mandrel carefully until the dial gauge extention is vertical to the face of the drive pinion head. At this moment the dial gauge needle will be at its point of inflection, so that it can be read.

9) Check the following when reading the dial gauge: Design distance "R"= 3.29" (82.29 mm) has been set with Master Gauge (VW 385/55). If the dial gauge reading differs from the design distance in clockwise direction, the distance is smaller than the design distance, so that the amount from "0" has to be substracted from the design distance.

10) The small dial gauge indicator needle is between 1 and 2, the large needle points to 0.10 mm. For an example, see the following:
- Design distance: 3.29" (82.29 mm).
  Less dial gauge reading: -.004" (.10 mm).
  Drive pinion face distance:=3.28" (82.19 mm).
- Distance "E": 3.30" (82.41 mm).
  Drive pinion face distance: -3.28" (82.19 mm).
- Thickness of shims: .008" (.22 mm).

The drive pinion must therefore be moved .008" (.20 mm) away from the center of the ring gear. This is accomplished be inserting a .008" (.20 mm) thick shim.

11) Recheck distance "E" after installing the shims. A deviation of .013" (.33 mm) is permissable. It is not necessary to check the surface appearance.

NOTE: If the correct size shims have been chosen, the dial gauge will show deviation "r" (.004" .12 mm or .007" .18 mm) with a tolerance of .001" (.03 mm).

12) The small dial gauge needle with .040" (1 mm), the large needle points to deviation "r" with a tolerance of .001" (.03 mm).

NOTE: In order to check backlash correctly, spacer (S1) should be .004" (.1 mm) thinner than 1/2 the sum of spacers (S1) and (S2). Spacer (S2) should be .004" (.1 mm) thicker than 1/2 the total thickness of (S1) and (S2).

RING GEAR BACKLASH ADJUSTMENT
Determining Total Thickness of Spacers For Ring Gear Adjustment

1) Install gear cluster with shims determined during pinion shaft adjustment. Be sure to tighten pinion shaft flange nut if not already done.

2) Make sure that the taper roller bearing outer races fit tight in the transmission case or side cover. Place a .14" (3.5 mm) thick spacer on the ring gear end of the differential housing in question and a .12" (3.0 mm) thick spacer underneath the taper roller bearing or magnetic support disc on the opposite end.

3) Insert differential with taper roller bearing into transmission case and install side transmission cover without rubber seal. Press side transmission cover against the taper roller bearing by slightly tightening 2 nuts located opposite each other.

NOTE: Reference data for pressing taper roller bearing is .06" (.15 mm).

Manual Transmissions

PORSCHE 911 CARRERA 5-SPEED TRANSAXLE (Cont.)

4) If the reference data of .06" (.15 mm) is not given, replace spacer. See the following example:
- Distance measure with feeler gauge: = .016" (.40 mm) Less axial pressure reference data: = .006" (.15 mm)
- The .14" (3.5 mm) thick spacer "S1" installed is .01" (.25 mm) too thick. Install a .13" (3.25 mm). Tighten side transmission cover.

NOTE: **All nuts must be installed and tightened to specifications to assure correct results.**

5) Slide disc from Special Tool (P 357) onto flange and install flange. Tighten stretch bolt with washer. Using a torque gauge, check rotational torque of assembled differential. The following data is required:
- SKF bearings = 22-31 INCH lbs. (2.5-3.5 N.m)
- FAG bearings = 35-57.5 INCH lbs. (4-6.5 N.m)

6) The drive pinion may not engage when checking the rotational torque and the seal on the side transmission cover must be removed to avoid any additional friction. The specified torque must be given to assure correct axial pressure on the taper roller bearings. If necessary, replace the spacer again until the torque meets specifications.

7) Remove differential, pull off both taper roller bearings and check thickness of spacers with a micrometer at 4 positions around the circumference. The thickness of both spacers together is the total thickness of spacers for ring gear adjustments.

8) Spacer "S1" is chosen 008" (.2 mm) thinner than spacer "S2" as a starting point for later adjustments of the backlash (ring gear to drive pinion). *See Fig. 16.*

Fig. 16: Backlash Adjustment Formula

$$\frac{6.25 \text{ mm}}{2} = \begin{array}{r} 3.125 \\ - \quad 0.10 \\ \hline 3.025 \end{array}$$

Thickness of spacer   "S2"

$$\frac{6.25 \text{ mm}}{2} = \begin{array}{r} 3.125 \\ + \quad 0.10 \\ \hline 3.225 \end{array}$$

NOTE: **Spacers with thicknesses from 2.4 to 3.7 mm are available in steps of .10 mm.**

9) A .25 mm thick shim allows spacers in steps of .05 mm. Round off the calculated spacer thicknesses so that the total thickness of spacers "S1" and "S2" is not changed. See the following example:
- Calculated spacer thickness. "S1" + "S2" = 3.025 + 3.225 = 6.25 mm.
- Rounded off spacer thickness. "S1" + "S2" = 3.0 + 3.25 = 6.25 mm.

10) Check thickness of spacers with a micrometer at 4 locations around circumference. Maximum deviation is .02 mm. Remove any burrs along edges of spacers before checking thickness.

Ring Gear Backlash Adjustment

1) Assemble change gear with those shims determined for the drive pinion settng. Make sure that the drive pinion nut is tightened to specifications before adjusting the backlash.

2) Install differential with taper roller bearings and calculated spacers ("S1" and "S2") and position side transmission cover. Tighten side transmission cover hex nuts to specifications.

NOTE: **When tightening the nuts keep checking for a certain amount of backlash. Never allow the drive pinion to jam.**

3) Slide disc from Special Tool (P 357) onto a stub axle and secure flange on ring gear end. Block differential with 2 screws which are screwed in through the flange. Only tighten screws slightly against side transmission cover.

4) Install dial gauge holder and check backlash. The backlash check at the reverse gear must be .38 mm. By using Special Tools (P 263 and P264b) spacers ("S1" and "S2") can be replaced until the backlash meets specifications. Make sure that the total spacer thickness is not changed.

SELECTOR (SHIFTING) FORK ADJUSTMENT

1) Input shaft flange nut must be correctly tightened. Install mounting plate (P 260a). Install 5th gear synchro hub and reverse sliding gear.

2) Block input shaft with tool (P 37a). Engage 5th gear. Tighten input shaft flange nut. Turn 1st/2nd gear selector fork rod LEFT (in driving direction) to stop.

3) Turn fork rod slightly back until unmachined flat inner surface is nearly vertical. Do not turn past middle point or back to right stop.

4) Position 1st/2nd gear selector fork so that shift sleeve is exactly in middle between synchronizing rings. Tighten bolt to proper specification. Adjust 3rd/4th gear fork in same way.

5) Position 3rd/4th gear shift guide even with selector fork. Be sure there is .08-.12" (2-3 mm) clearance between 3rd/4th shift guide and 1st/2nd shift guide. They must not touch. Check ease of shifting and readjust as necessary.

6) Adjust 5th/reverse gear fork as follows: Push idler gear on shaft against 5th (fixed) gear. Adjust idler gear and sliding gear to obtain a clearance of .040" (1 mm) in NEUTRAL position.

7) Press idler gear gently in direction of travel. There should be no play between shift fork and sliding gear groove.

FRONT COVER

Heat cover to about 250°F (120°C) and drive gear shift bushing in place. Drive shift rod seal on with mandrel (P 369). Install new gasket and tighten front cover nuts to specification.

TIGHTENING SPECIFICATIONS

Application	Ft. Lbs. (N.m)
Guide Fork Cover Nuts	18 (24)
Input Shaft Flange Nut	120 (163)
Input Shaft Castle Nut	95 (129)
Pinion Shaft Flange Nut	180 (244)
Ring Gear Bolts	
Standard Differential	84 (115)
Positive Traction Differentials	
Grade 11.9 Bolts	105 (142)
Grade 12.9 Bolts	112 (152)
Retaining Plate & Trans.	
Support Attachment	15 (20)
Starter Nut	35 (47)

PORSCHE 928S 5-SPEED TRANSAXLE

DESCRIPTION

The Porsche 928S is equipped with a manual transmission (type G28/08) which has 5 speeds. Engine and transaxle are connected by a rigid central tube which also houses the propeller shaft and supports the gear shift lever. Bell housings on each end of this tube attach to the engine and transaxle.

The propeller shaft is splined to the clutch disc at the front and is connected to the transmission mainshaft at the rear by a coupling. Access to this coupling is through an inspection hole in the rear bellhousing.

A hypoid ring and pinion differential assembly drives joint rear axle drive shafts. The whole assembly is mounted to the unitized body by 2 front engine mounts and 2 rear transmission mounts.

NOTE: **The term "Transaxle" in this article refers to the rear axle transmission/differential assembly. The central tube and bellhousings may be referred to as the "transaxle tube". Axle drive shafts include the flexible couplings. Rear wheel axle shaft indicates the driven axle shaft mounted in the trailing arms of the rear wheel suspension.**

LUBRICATION & ADJUSTMENT

See appropriate MANUAL TRANSMISSION SERVICING article in IMPORT GENERAL SERVICING section.

SERVICE (IN VEHICLE)

FLANGED SHAFT SEAL
Removal

Remove socket head screws at inner end of shaft, then disconnect and support axle drive shaft. Remove inner flange bolt while holding flange from turning by inserting punch in drive flange bolt hole. Remove flange and pull out seal with Seal Removal Tool (VW 681).

Installation

Fill cavity between sealing and dust lips with multi-purpose grease and drive seal in place with Seal Installer Tool (VW 195). Replace flange and drive shaft and tighten to specifications.

REAR WHEEL BEARINGS
Removal

With brake calipers off and drive shaft disconnected at axle flange, press shaft from housing, remove circlip and drive grooved ball bearing and roller bearing out with soft drift.

Installation

Press grooved ball bearing in inner end of housing and replace circlip. Put spacer in housing and drive roller bearing in place (flanged side facing out). Install seal in inboard side of housing. Put outer spacer in shaft and press in along with bearing inner race using castellated nut and driver.

Fig. 1: Cross-Section of Porsche 928S Manual Transaxle Assembly

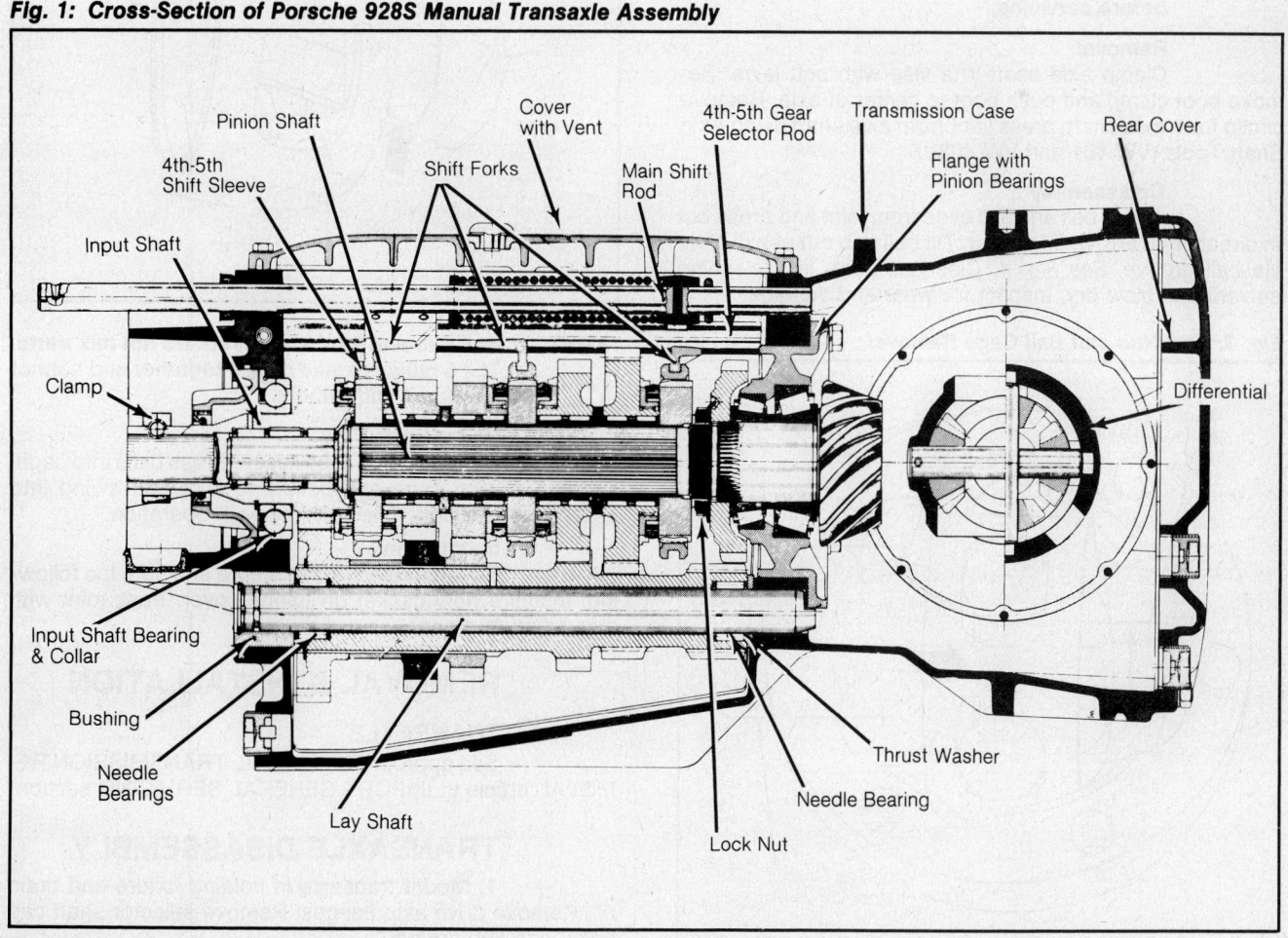

Manual Transmissions

PORSCHE 928S 5-SPEED TRANSAXLE (Cont.)

Fig. 2: Exploded View of Rear Axle Shaft Assembly

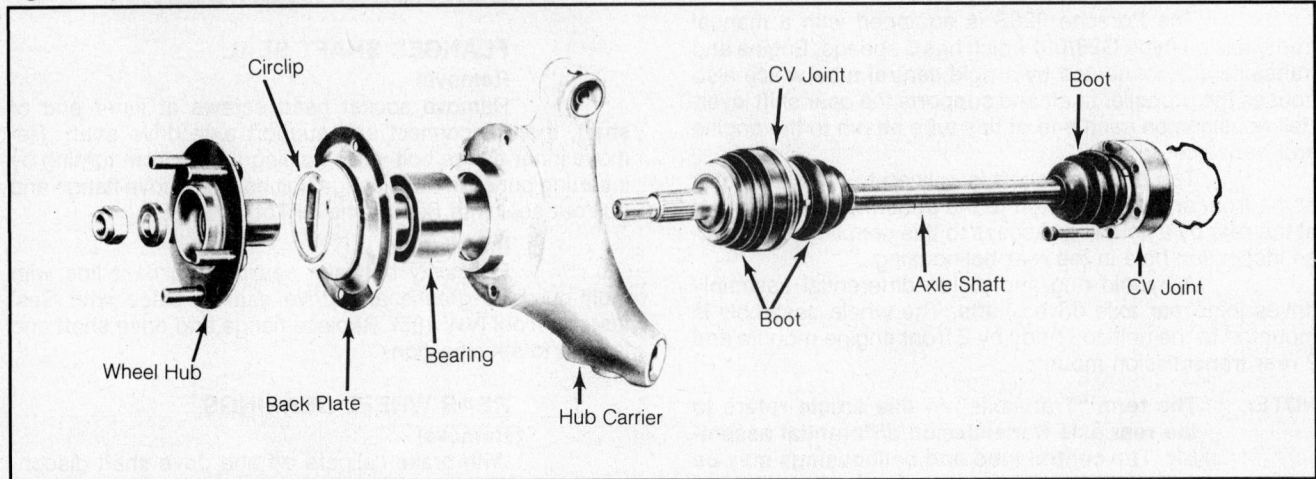

AXLE DRIVE SHAFTS

Removal & Installation

Raise vehicle on hoist. Remove bolts from constant velocity joint-to-mating flange and remove drive axle from vehicle. To install, reverse removal procedure and tighten to specifications.

CONSTANT VELOCITY JOINTS

NOTE: Axle shafts must be removed from vehicle before servicing.

Removal

Clamp axle shaft in a vise with soft jaws. Remove boot clamp and push boot to center of axle. Remove circlip from axle shaft, press joint from axle shaft using Axle Shaft Tools (VW 401 and VW 408).

Disassembly

Swing ball and ball cage from joint and press out in direction of arrow. See Fig. 3. Tilt ball hub out of ball cage via ball groove. See Fig. 4. Clean all parts in a cleaning solvent and blow dry. Inspect for wear and damage.

Fig. 3: Ball Hub and Ball Cage Removal

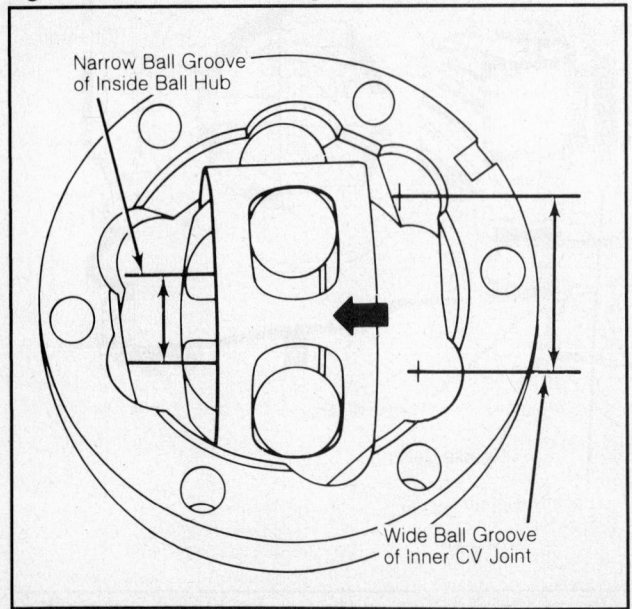

Fig. 4: Removal of Ball Hub from Cage

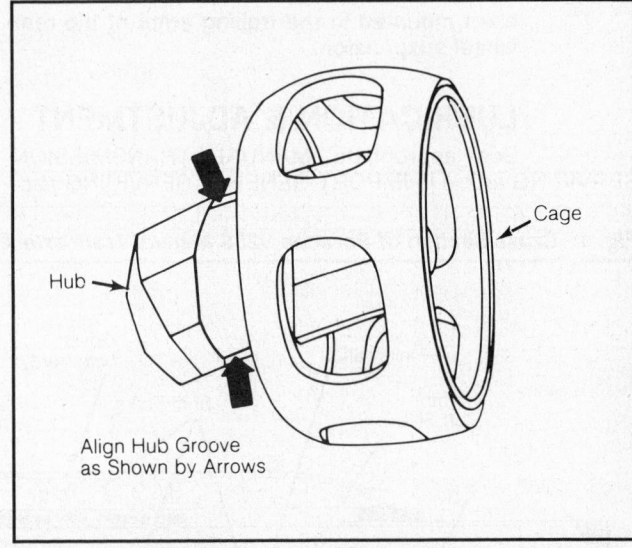

NOTE: Ball hub and joint are paired. Do not mix parts. The 6 balls are also mated together and cannot be mixed with others.

Reassembly

Place ball hub in ball cage. Press balls into cage. Install hub with cage and balls into joint and swing into assembled position. Check for smooth operation.

Installation

Reverse removal procedure and note the following: Install a new gasket on flange cover. Pack joint with molybdenum grease.

REMOVAL & INSTALLATION

TRANSAXLE

See appropriate MANUAL TRANSMISSION REMOVAL article in IMPORT GENERAL SERVICING section.

TRANSAXLE DISASSEMBLY

1) Mount transaxle in holding fixture and drain oil. Remove drive axle flanges. Remove selector shaft cap bolts, cap and spring.

2) Remove shift finger and shift fork pins. Slide selector shaft in as far as possible. Remove end plate mounting bolts and separate gear case from transaxle housing. Remove differential cover bolts and differential assembly.

COMPONENT DISASSEMBLY & REASSEMBLY

TRANSMISSION CASE
Disassembly

1) Mount transmission in a holding fixture and remove end cover and top cover. Remove main shift rod toward the rear.

Fig. 5: Top View Showing Shift Rods and Forks

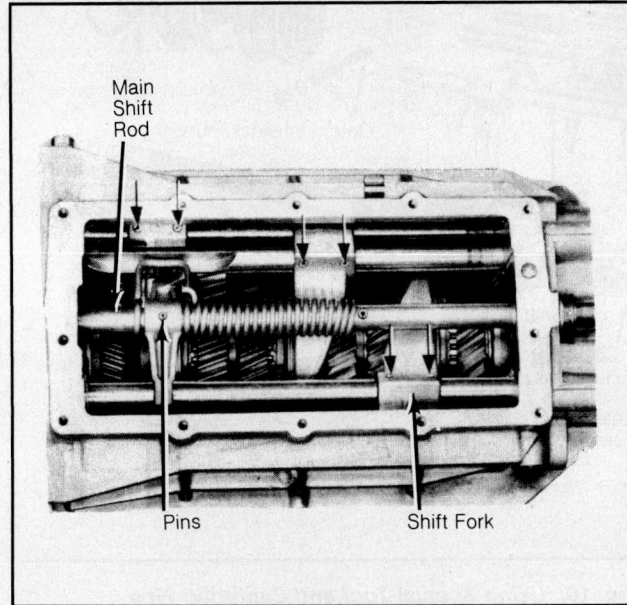

2) Remove remaining shift rods and forks toward rear of case insuring that reverse gear and 1st-2nd gears remain in neutral.

3) Remove the input shaft using Special Tools (9140 and 9148) and pulling shaft from the case.

4) Remove pinion shaft assembly using Removal Tools (9148 and P263) to press out assembly. Drive out reverse idler gear shaft, then remove reverse idler gear assembly.

NOTE: Transmission and differential case (transaxle) repairs include replacement of seals and bearing races. Case temperature should be at least 300°F (150°C) when installing bearing races. Press load should be maintained for about 2 minutes until case and bearing race have reached the same temperature.

Reassembly

1) Place input shaft in case. Using mandrel, drive input shaft into ball bearing up to the stop. Work alternately over outer race to insure shaft is to the stop.

2) Attach Installer Tool (9144) to pinion bearing cover. Fabricate 2 centering pins and install as shown in *Fig. 10.* Using centering pins as guides, install pinion shaft

Fig. 6: View Showing Input Shaft Removal

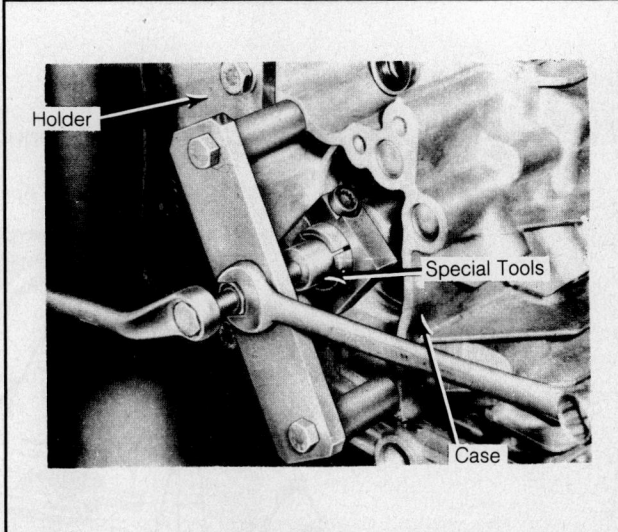

Fig. 7: View Showing Pinion Shaft Removal

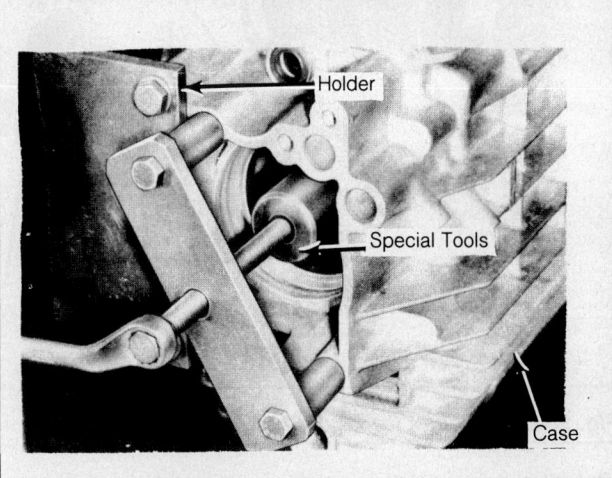

into case. Check that clearance between input shaft and 4th-5th speed hub on pinion shaft is .008-.012" (.2-.3 mm).

3) Install shift rods with shift forks and shift interlock components. Install main shift rod with shift finger. Install relaxed lock out spring so that one end rests on "U" spring and the other end of roll pin faces up.

4) Using Special Tool (9155), turn main shift rod until shift finger pin can be installed. In this position, the lock out spring will be under tension and depression for set screw in main shift rod faces left.

INPUT SHAFT
Disassembly

Place shaft assembly in press. Using Arbor (VW 457), press off ball bearing. Remove synchronizer ring, shift band and thrust block. Remove 2 needle bearings and spacer from inside shaft.

NOTE: All parts must be clean and free of grease before reassembly.

Reassembly

Install both needle bearings into shaft bore with spacer between bearings. Install shift band and thrust

Manual Transmissions

PORSCHE 928S 5-SPEED TRANSAXLE (Cont.)

Fig. 8: Exploded View of Transmission Assembly

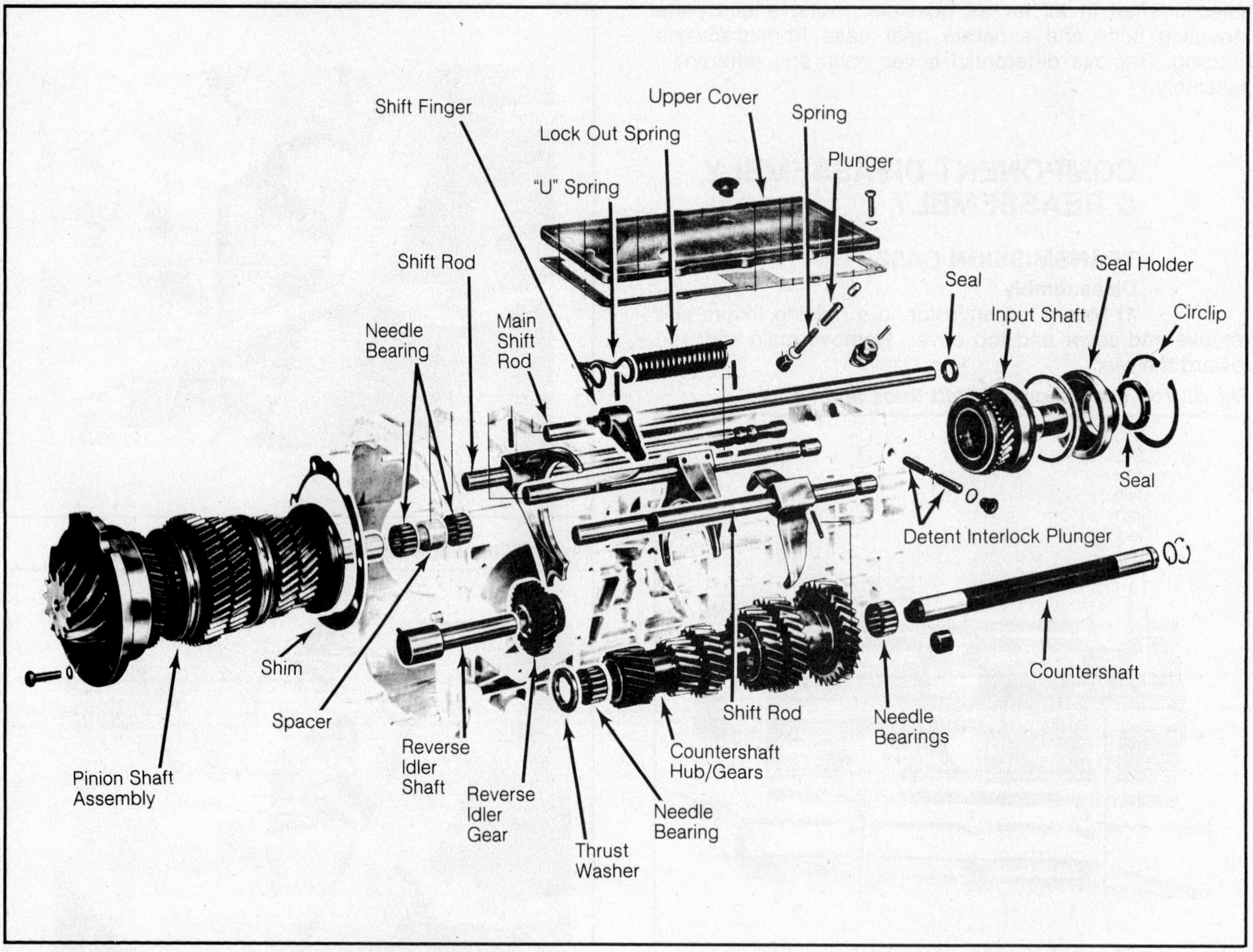

Shift Finger
Upper Cover
Spring
Lock Out Spring
Plunger
"U" Spring
Shift Rod
Main Shift Rod
Needle Bearing
Seal
Seal Holder
Input Shaft
Circlip
Seal
Detent Interlock Plunger
Shim
Spacer
Countershaft
Pinion Shaft Assembly
Reverse Idler Shaft
Reverse Idler Gear
Thrust Washer
Needle Bearing
Countershaft Hub/Gears
Shift Rod
Needle Bearings

Fig. 9: Drive Points for Input Shaft Installation

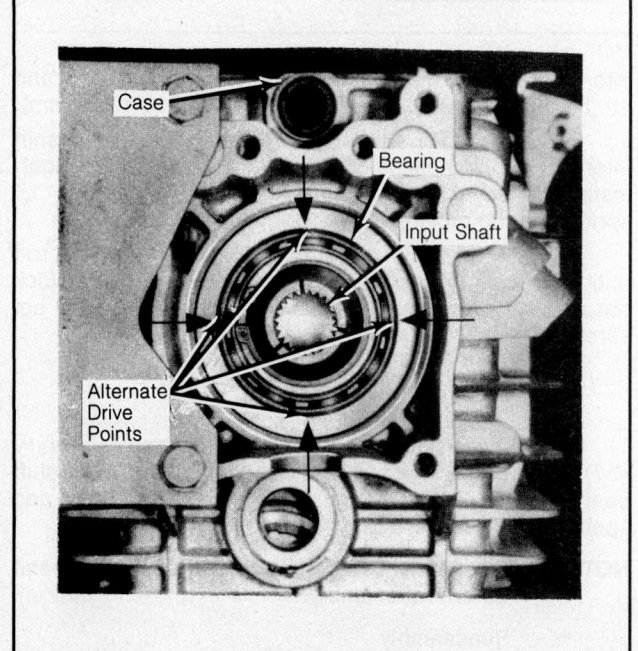

Case
Bearing
Input Shaft
Alternate Drive Points

Fig. 10: Using Special Tool and Centering Pins for Pinion Shaft Installation

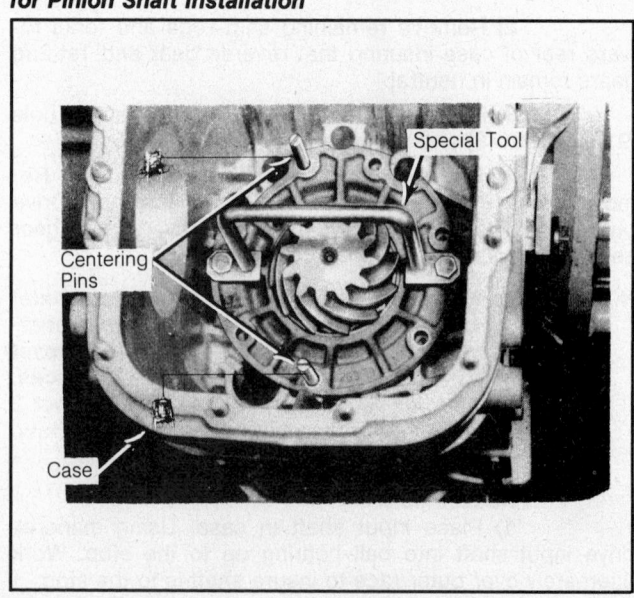

Special Tool
Centering Pins
Case

PORSCHE 928S 5-SPEED TRANSAXLE (Cont.)

Fig. 11: *Measuring Clearance Between Input Shaft and 4th-5th Speed Hub*

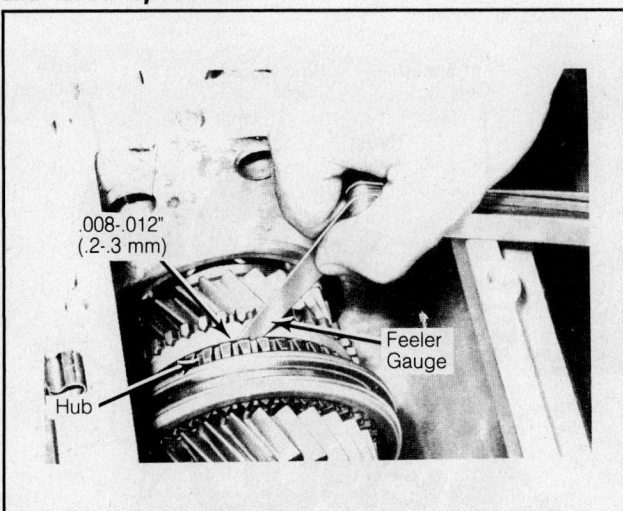

Fig. 12: *Sectional View of Shift Rods and Interlock Components*

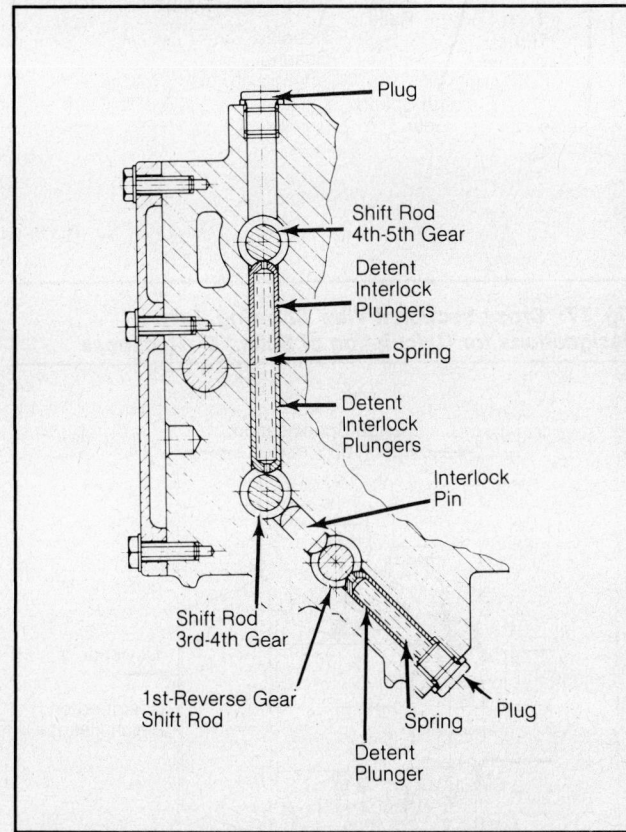

Fig. 13: *View Showing Main Shift Rod Alignment*

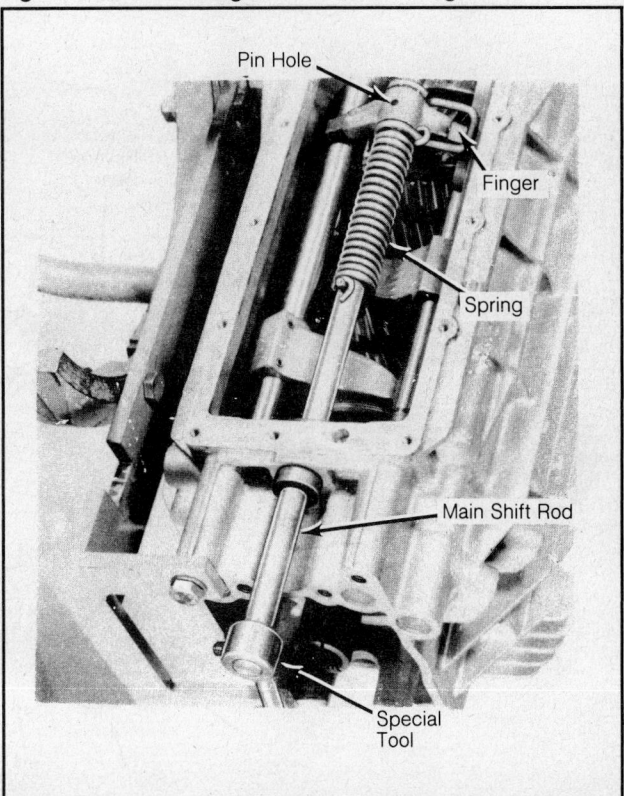

Fig. 14: *Exploded View of Input Shaft Assembly*

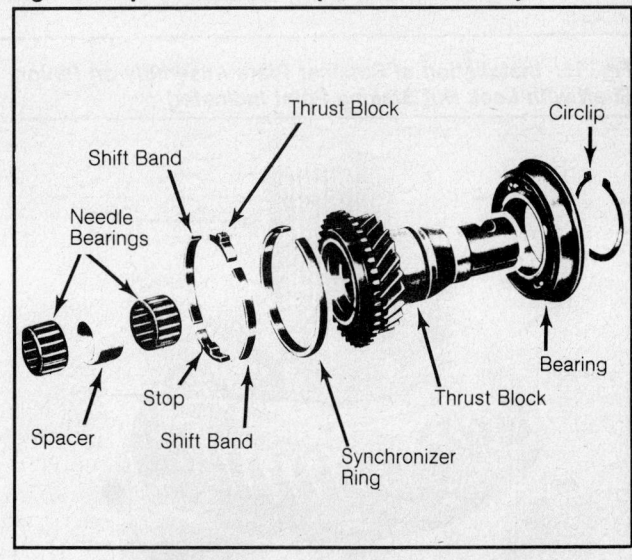

block. Install synchronizer ring. Heat ball bearing (100°C) and press bearing onto shaft until tight. Hold pressure for 2 minutes until bearing cools. Install circlip.

PINION SHAFT
Disassembly
1) Mount pinion shaft assembly in a holding fixture and remove circlip and shim. Place shaft assembly in press and press off shift sleeve and hub.

2) Remove needle bearing and inner race and mark for reassembly. Remove 4th gear, thrust washer, needle bearing and inner race and mark for reassembly.

3) Remove 3rd gear, shift sleeve and hub. Remove needle bearing and inner race and mark for reassembly. Remove 2nd gear, thrust washer, needle bearing and inner race and mark for reassembly.

4) Remove 1st gear, shift sleeve and hub, shim and lock nut, then remove reverse gear. Press off tapered roller bearing with bearing retaining plate as a unit. Using Arbor (US 1103), press off tapered roller bearing.

Manual Transmissions

PORSCHE 928S 5-SPEED TRANSAXLE (Cont.)

Fig. 15: *Exploded View of Pinion Shaft Assembly*

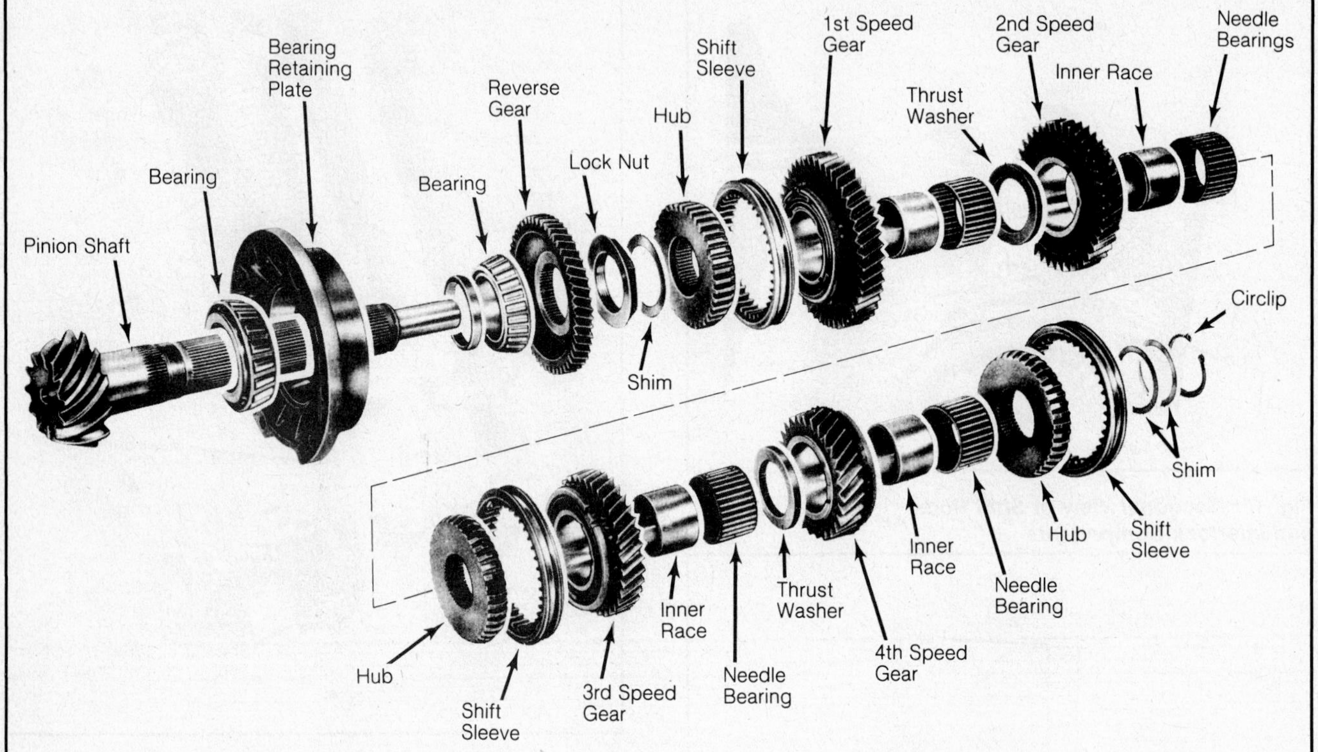

Pinion Shaft — Bearing — Bearing Retaining Plate — Bearing — Reverse Gear — Lock Nut — Shim — Hub — Shift Sleeve — 1st Speed Gear — Thrust Washer — 2nd Speed Gear — Inner Race — Needle Bearings — Circlip — Shim — Shift Sleeve — Hub — Needle Bearing — Inner Race — 4th Speed Gear — Thrust Washer — Needle Bearing — Inner Race — 3rd Speed Gear — Shift Sleeve — Hub

Fig. 16: *Installation of Retainer Plate Assembly on Pinion Shaft with Lock Nut Staking Point Indicated*

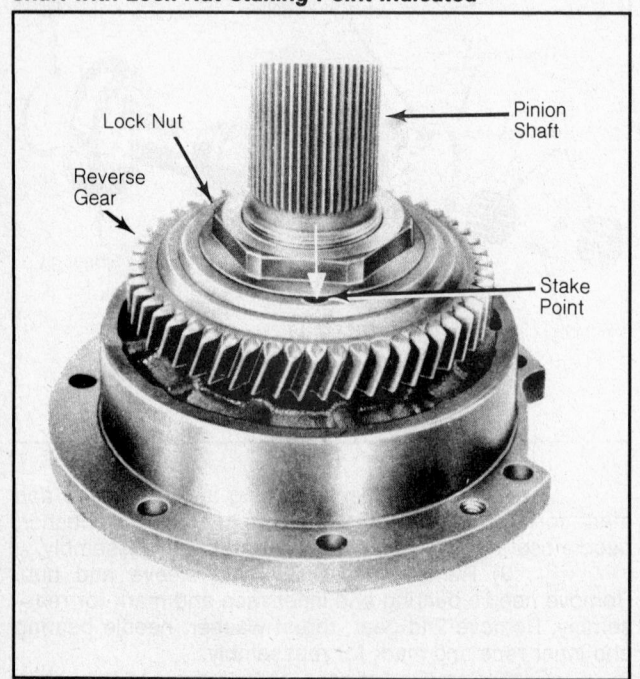

Lock Nut — Pinion Shaft — Reverse Gear — Stake Point

Fig. 17: *Cross-Sectional View Showing Point Designations for Calculation of Shim "X" Thickness*

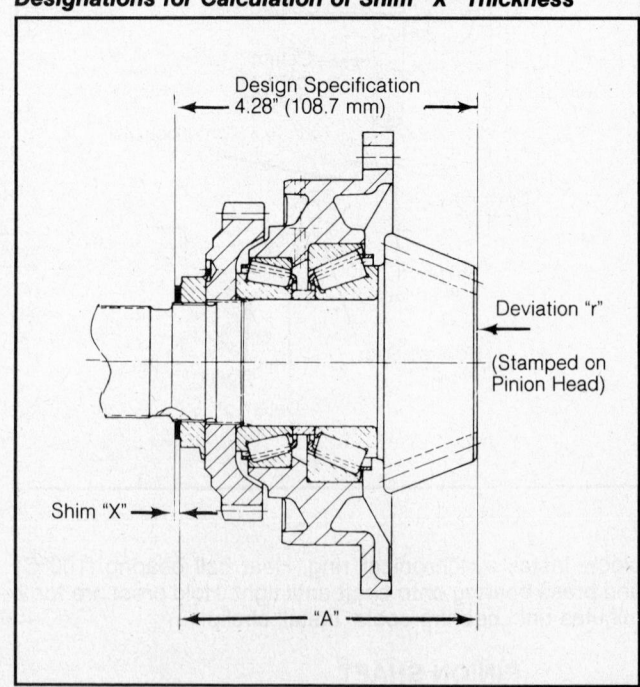

Design Specification 4.28" (108.7 mm)

Deviation "r"

(Stamped on Pinion Head)

Shim "X"

"A"

PORSCHE 928S 5-SPEED TRANSAXLE (Cont.)

NOTE: It is imperative that all parts are free of grease and fingerprints during assembly unless otherwise specified. Large taper bearings and inner races must be heated to 212°F (100°C) prior to installation. Hold until temperature has balanced itself.

Reassembly
1) Press tapered roller bearing onto shaft. Press bearing retaining plate complete with tapered roller bearing and shim onto shaft. Install reverse gear with cavity facing lock nut. Install lock nut, then tighten to specifications and stake in place. *See Fig. 16.*

2) To determine thickness of shim "X" in *Fig. 17*, measure and record distance from end of pinion shaft head to lock nut (dimension "A" in *Fig. 17*) with a caliper. Shim thickness is equal to dimension "A" plus deviation "r" (stamped on pinion head) subtracted from design specification of 4.28" (108.7 mm).

3) Install selected shim, hub and sleeve making sure flat surface on side flank faces 1st gear. Install 1st gear and check synchronization. Install needle bearings and inner races marked for 2nd, 3rd and 4th gears.

4) Check synchronization. Install needle bearing and inner race, hub and sleeve, shim and circlip. Install a shim between hub and circlip to eliminate all end play. *See Fig. 19.*

SYNCHRONIZER ASSEMBLIES

NOTE: Synchronizers MUST be replaced in pairs only.

Disassembly
Transmission is equipped with modified synchronization for all forward speeds. Each synchronizer is different, therefore no parts are interchangeable between synchronizers. Mark synchronizers before disassembly to facilitate reassembly. Axial movement is eliminated by using a shift band with beveled flanks. *See Fig. 18.*

Inspection
Clean and dry all parts. Check for chipped teeth or any other irregularity. Using a micrometer, check all synchronizer rings at the thickest point. Measurement should read 3.38-3.40" (85.76-86.24 mm).

Fig. 19: Selecting Gear Set End Shim

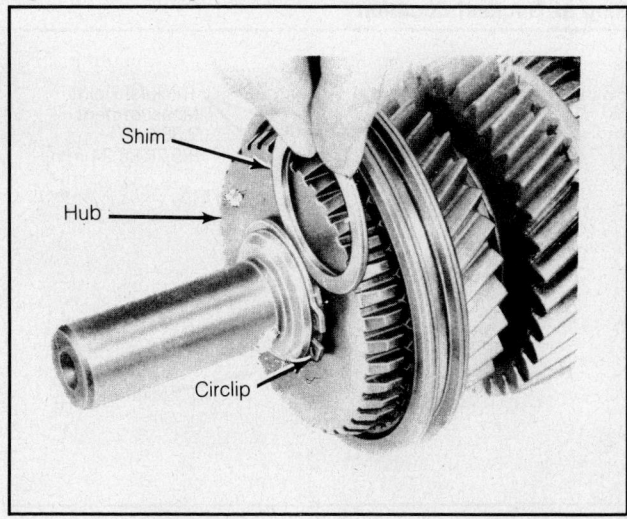

Reassembly
To reassemble, reverse disassembly procedure, insuring that correct parts for particular synchronizer are used.

NOTE: When reassembling 1st gear, short side of shift band must be to right of thrust block. When reassembling 2nd gear, bevelled side of stop must face to right as seen from top view.

COUNTERSHAFT
Disassembly
Remove circlip and needle bearing. Place countershaft assembly in a press. Using Support Rail (VW 457) and Arbor (VW 407), press off countershaft drive gear and spacer. Remove countershaft 4th speed and 3rd speed gears. Remove end needle bearing.

Inspection
Clean and dry all parts. Check for chips, burrs or any irregularities.

NOTE: When replacement of a gear is required, replace in pairs only.

Fig. 18: Sectional View of Synchronizer Rings

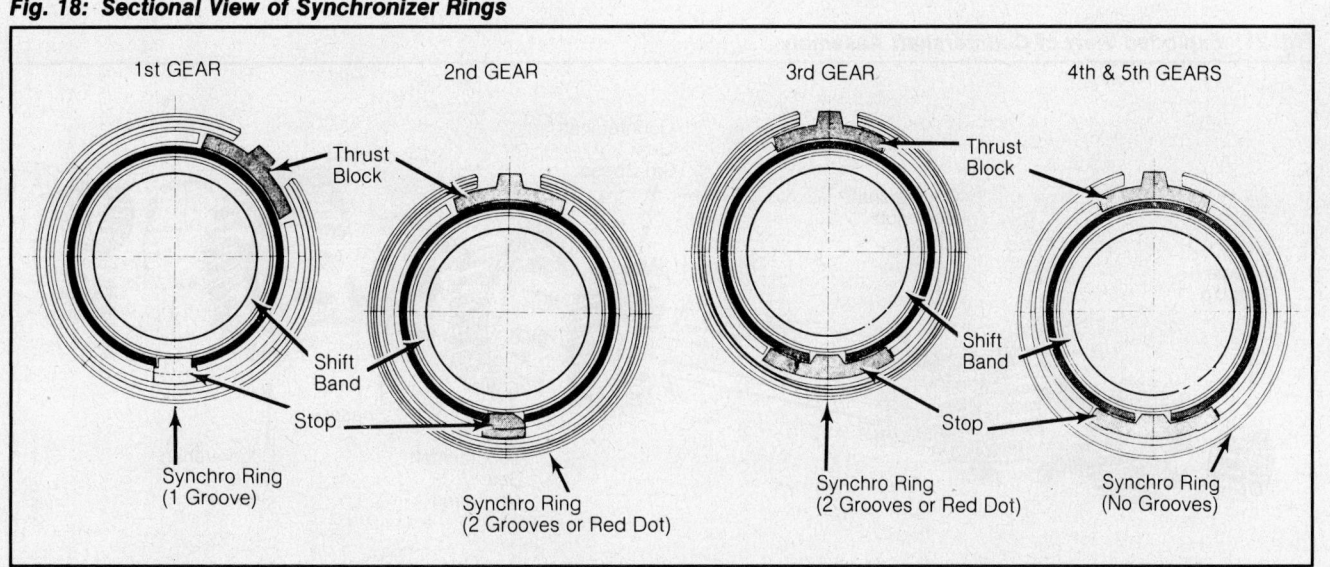

Manual Transmissions

PORSCHE 928S 5-SPEED TRANSAXLE (Cont.)

Fig. 20: *Correct Position for Measuring Synchronizer Ring at Thickest Location*

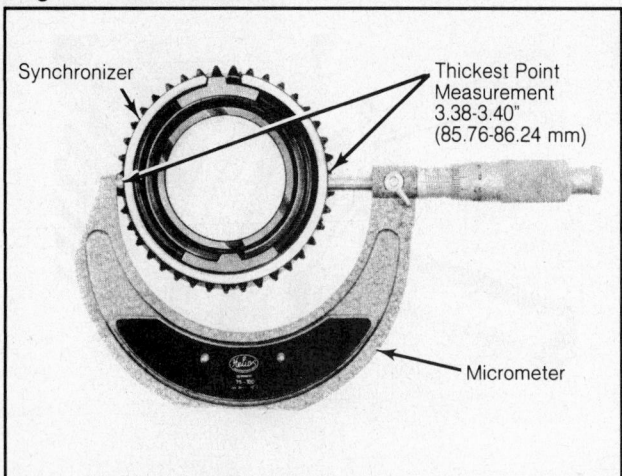

Synchronizer

Thickest Point Measurement 3.38-3.40" (85.76-86.24 mm)

Micrometer

Reassembly

To reassemble, heat gears to 212°F (100°C) and reverse disassembly procedure making note of the following: Place 3rd gear onto shaft so small shoulder faces stop. Place 4th gear onto shaft so large shoulder faces 3rd gear. Place countershaft gear onto shaft so large shoulder faces spacer. *See Fig. 21.*

DIFFERENTIAL

Disassembly

1) Place differential assembly in vise fitted with jaw protectors. Remove ring gear bolts and drive ring gear off housing. Remove bearings (if required) using a double arm puller.

2) Remove pinion shaft lock pin, then remove pinion shaft, pinion gears, side gear drive flange nuts and side gears. Note location and thickness of any shims removed from side gears.

Reassembly

1) Heat ring gear to about 212°F (100°C) and place on differential using centering pins to align bolt holes. Install new retaining bolts and tighten to specifications in an alternating sequence. Slide lock plate into bolt head groove, bend ends together, then bend lock plate ends down over side of bolt head.

2) Place correct shims under large gears and insert in case. Hold small gear thrust washers in place with grease and install small gears. Align gear and washer holes with bore and insert shaft. Position correctly and lock in position with lock pin.

3) If bearings were removed, heat inner bearing race to 212°F (100°C) and press on case.

Fig. 22: *Exploded View of Differential Assembly*

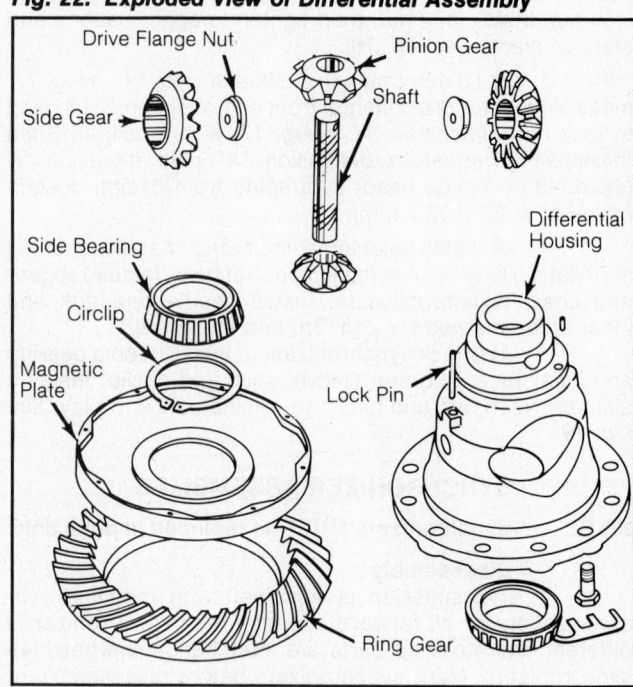

Drive Flange Nut

Pinion Gear

Side Gear

Shaft

Side Bearing

Differential Housing

Circlip

Magnetic Plate

Lock Pin

Ring Gear

Fig. 21: *Exploded View of Countershaft Assembly*

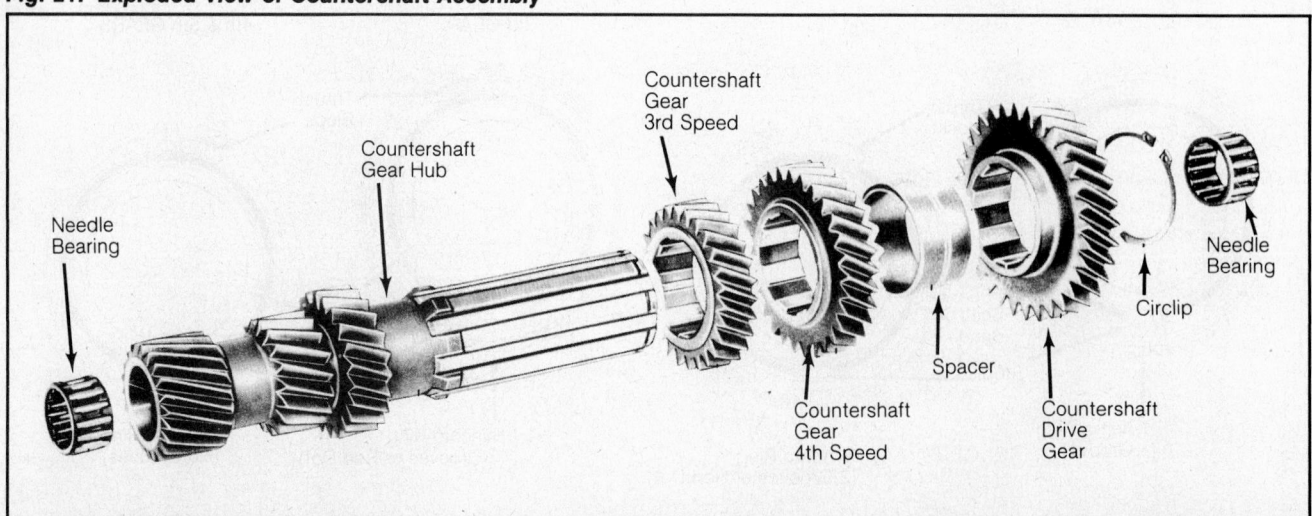

Needle Bearing

Countershaft Gear Hub

Countershaft Gear 3rd Speed

Needle Bearing

Circlip

Spacer

Countershaft Gear 4th Speed

Countershaft Drive Gear

PORSCHE 928S 5-SPEED TRANSAXLE (Cont.)

TRANSAXLE REASSEMBLY & ADJUSTMENT

NOTE: Differential assembly must be adjusted ONLY when repairs to assembly require replacement parts. Adjust ring gear if transmission case, side cover, pinion bearing and retaining plate, pinion and ring gear set, differential housing or differential bearings are replaced. Adjust pinion gear if transmission case, pinion bearing and retaining plate or pinion and ring gear set are replaced.

PINION GEAR ADJUSTMENT

1) Pinion depth adjustment is calculated by adding design specification "R", which equals 2.78" (70.7 mm), to deviation "r" stamped on pinion gear face. *See Fig. 23.* Pinion depth is adjusted by shims "S3". *See Fig. 27.*

Fig. 23: Location of Stamped Codes and Specifications of Pinion and Ring Gears

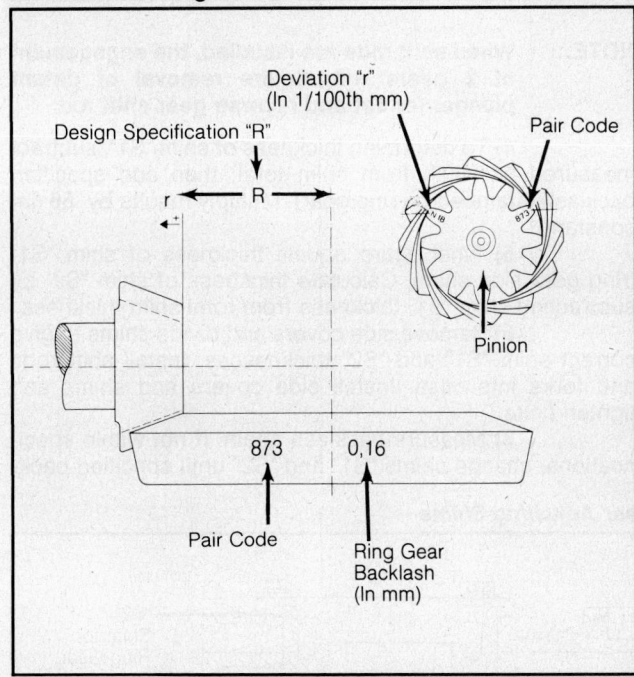

2) Install input shaft. Install pinion without shim(s) and tighten bearing retaining plate bolts. Install 1 side cover without "O" ring and secure with 2 bolts. Set adjusting ring of Universal Master Gauge (VW 385/1) at 2.36" (60 mm) from gauge center point. *See Fig. 24.*

3) Install Centering Discs (VW 385/4) onto master gauge and attach Gauge Plunger (VW 385/14) with dial indicator extension. *See Fig. 25.* Install opposite side cover without "O" ring and secure with 2 bolts.

4) Install master gauge and set dial indicator at zero with .004" (1 mm) preload. Install gauge plate on pinion head. Carefully turn universal gauge until dial gauge extension is perpendicular to face of pinion head. At this time dial gauge needle will reach reversal point (highest point). Read and record dial gauge. *See Fig. 26.*

5) Remove master gauge and pinion shaft. Install calculated shim rounded off to nearest .002" (.05 mm)

Fig. 24: Universal Master Measuring Gauge

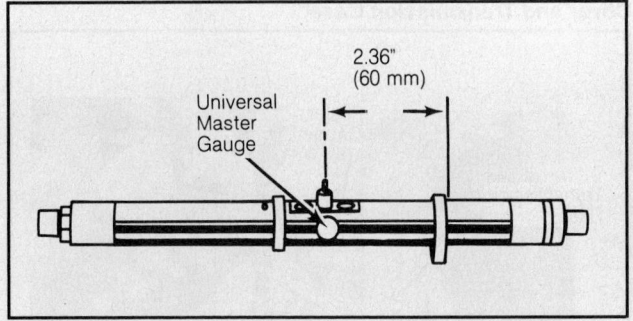

Fig. 25: Universal Master Measuring Gauge with Dial Indicator Attached

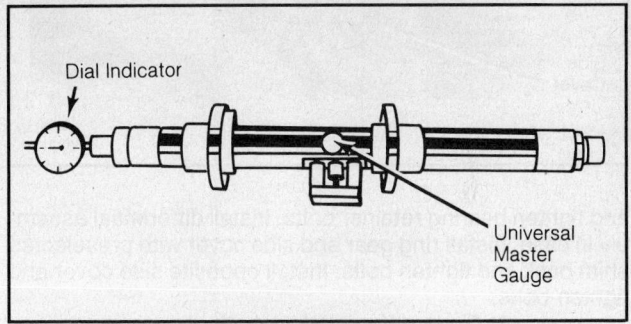

Fig. 26: Measuring Pinion Depth with Master Gauge

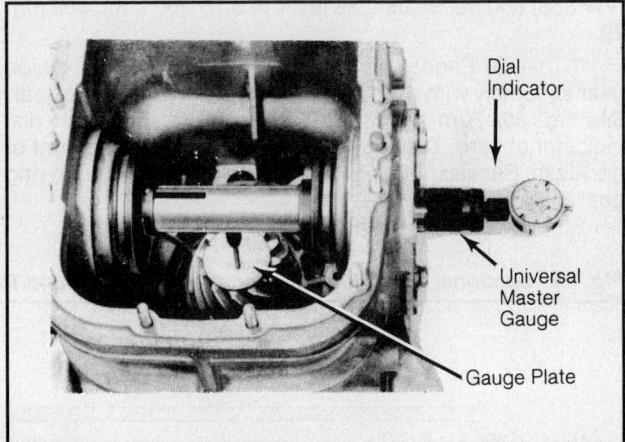

and pinion shaft. Recheck pinion depth adjustment. Adjustment should be 2.78" (70.7 mm) with variation of ±.001" (.03 mm).

RING GEAR ADJUSTMENT

1) Remove pinion gear and preselected shim(s). Install differential assembly in case. Install ring gear end side cover without shims and tighten bolts. Carefully install opposite side cover.

2) Using a feeler gauge, measure clearance between transmission case and side cover. Total required shim thickness is equal to measured clearance, minus (-) .012" (.3 mm) for bearing preload.

RING GEAR BACKLASH ADJUSTMENT

1) Install countershaft assembly into transmission case. Install pinion shaft with preselected shim ("S3")

Manual Transmissions

PORSCHE 928S 5-SPEED TRANSAXLE (Cont.)

Fig. 27: *Measuring Shim Thickness Between Side Cover and Transmission Case*

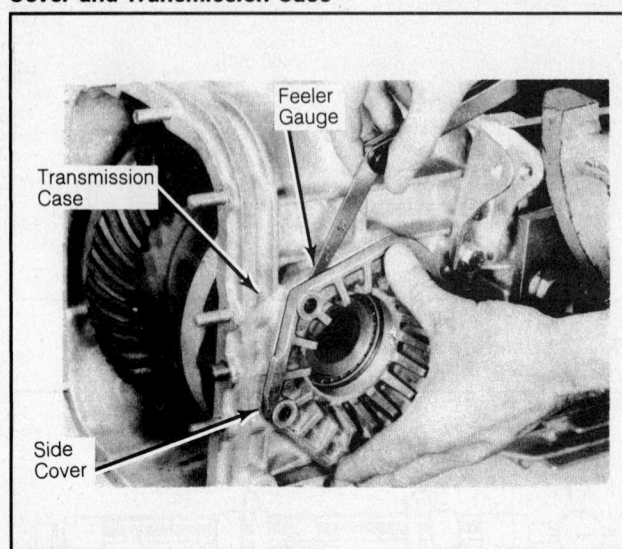

Fig. 29: *Gauge Installation for Measuring Backlash*

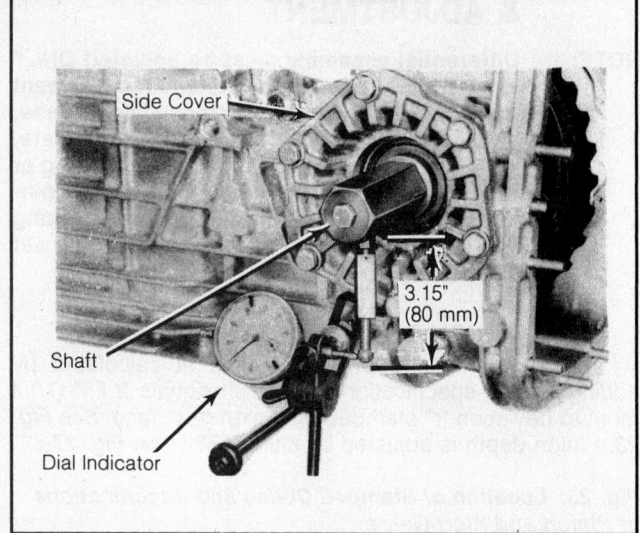

and tighten bearing retainer bolts. Install differential assembly in case. Install ring gear end side cover with preselected shim pack and tighten bolts. Install opposite side cover and tighten bolts.

      2) Turn differential in both directions several times to seat bearings. Mount Dial Indicator with Support (VW 388) and set adjustable lever at 3.15" (80 mm). *See Fig. 29.*

      3) Engage 5th and reverse gears. Hold pinion gear assembly with a locally fabricated tool on reverse gear. *See Fig. 30.* Turn ring gear to stop by hand and set dial indicator at zero. Turn ring gear back and record amount of backlash. Backlash should be equal to that stamped on ring gear.

NOTE: **When shift rods are installed, the engagement of 2 gears will require removal of detent plunger for 1st and reverse gear shift rod.**

      4) To determine thickness of shim "S1", subtract measured backlash from shim total, then add specified backlash (stamped on ring gear). Multiply results by .66 (lift constant).

      5) Final figure equals thickness of shim "S1" (ring gear side shim). Calculate thickness of shim "S2" by subtracting shim "S1" thickness from total shim thickness.

      6) Remove side covers and divide shims to give correct shim "S1" and "S2" thicknesses. Install shift rods and forks into case. Install side covers and shims and tighten bolts.

      7) Measure backlash again. If not within specifications, change shims "S1" and "S2" until specified back-

Fig. 28: *Sectional View Showing Location of Pinion and Ring Gear Adjusting Shims*

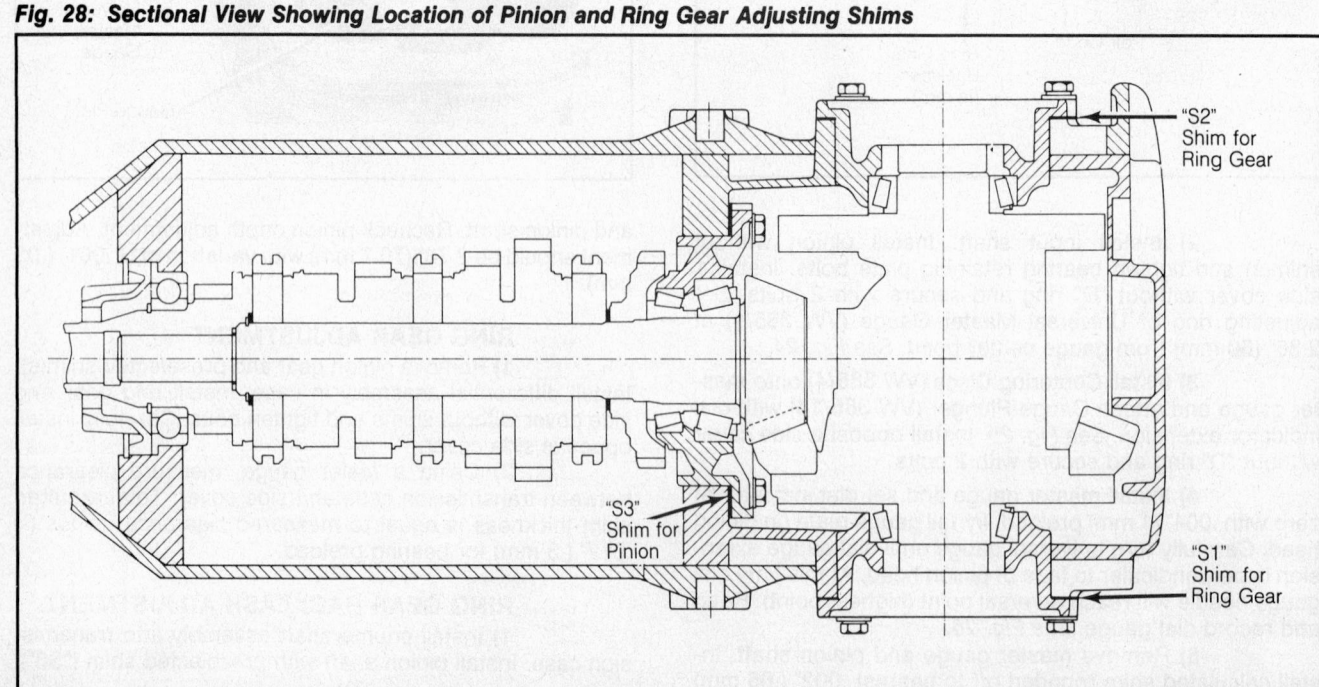

PORSCHE 928S 5-SPEED TRANSAXLE (Cont.)

lash is obtained. Check backlash 4 times by turning ring gear 90° each time. The 4 measurements must not deviate from each other by more than .002" (.05 mm).

Fig. 30: Installation of Fabricated Tool on Reverse Gear to Hold Pinion Gear Assembly in Position

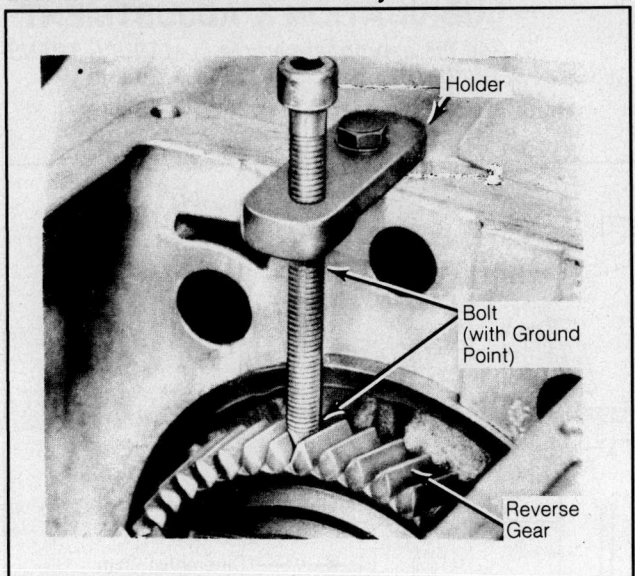

TIGHTENING SPECIFICATIONS

Application	Ft. Lbs. (N.m)
Central Tube-to-Transaxle	40 (54)
Pinion Retaining Nut	202 (280)
Pinion Retaining Plate-to-Case	25 (34)
Ring Gear Retaining Bolts	120 (163)
Side Cover Bolts	17 (23)
Rear Cover Bolts	17 (23)
Drive Shaft-to-Input Shaft Coupling	35 (47)
Axle Shaft Flange Bolts	30 (41)

Manual Transmissions
RENAULT FUEGO & SPORTWAGON
4 & 5-SPEED TRANSAXLE

DESCRIPTION

Transaxle consists of a removable clutch housing, a split gear case and a rear cover. The rear cover houses the shift mechanism as well as 5th gear on 5-speed models. All forward gears are in constant mesh and are fully synchronized. Final drive is located in front of transmission section of transaxle.

The only difference between the 2 transaxles is the addition of 5th gear on 5-speed units.

NOTE: The following procedures are for the 5-speed transaxle. For 4-speed transaxles, disregard any references to 5th gear components.

LUBRICATION & ADJUSTMENT

See the appropriate article in MANUAL TRANS-MISSION SERVICING Section.

Fig. 1: Cutaway View of Renault Manual Transaxle

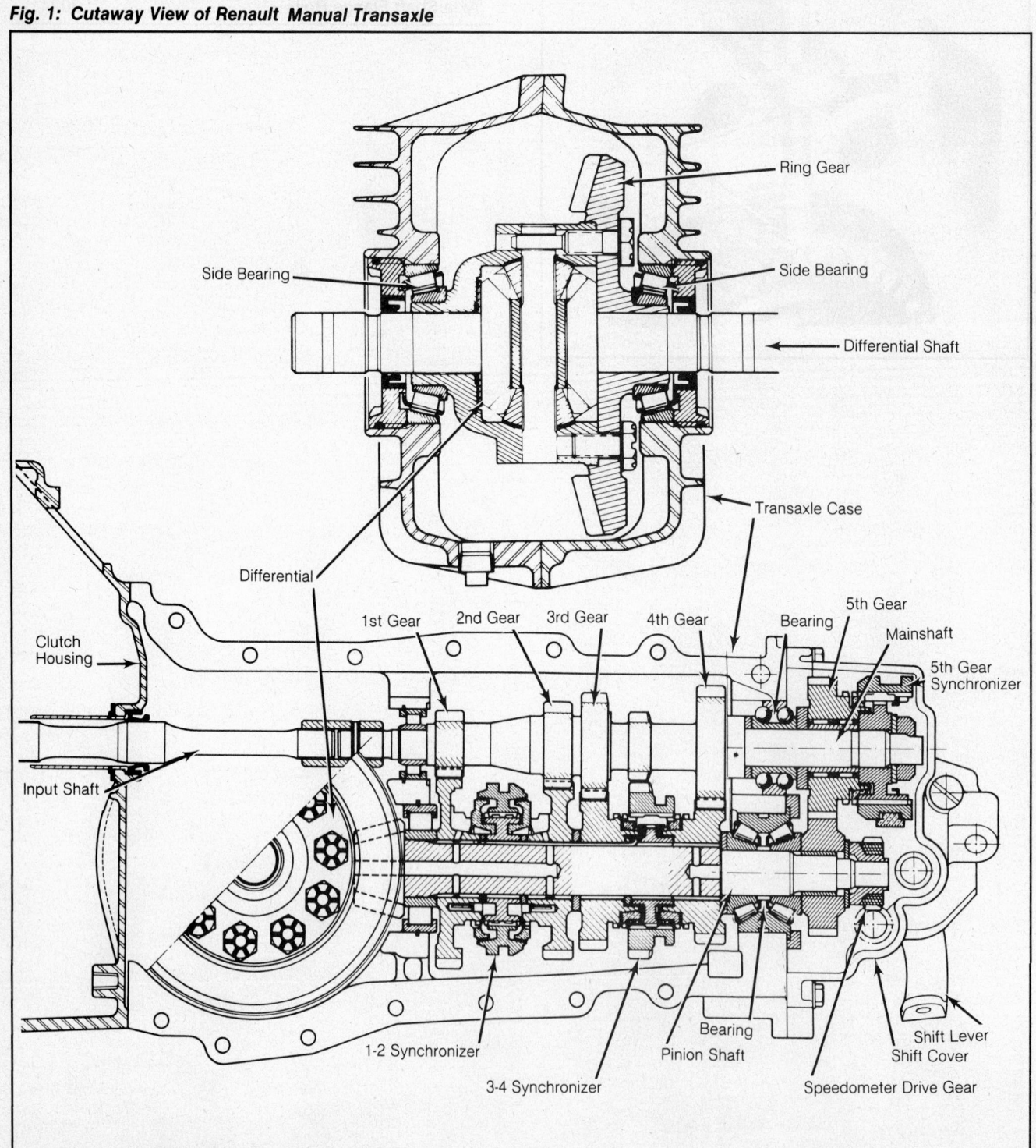

5-speed model shown here. 4-speed is similar.

RENAULT FUEGO & SPORTWAGON
4 & 5-SPEED TRANSAXLE (Cont.)

SERVICE (IN VEHICLE)

AXLE DRIVE SHAFTS

Removal

1) Raise and support vehicle. Compress control arm assembly and insert spacer (T. Av. 509-01) between lower control arm pivot shaft and bottom of shock absorber. Hold hub stationary and remove hub nut. Loosen upper ball joint nut and tie rod end nut, but do not remove.

2) Press on ball joint and tie rod end studs to loosen from steering knuckle. Remove brake caliper, but do not disconnect hydraulic line. Remove ball joint and tie rod end nuts.

3) Tilt steering knuckle outward to allow removal of drive shaft. Separate drive shaft from hub. Drive roll pin out of inner CV joint and separate drive shaft from transaxle.

Disassembly

1) Remove boot retaining collar from outer CV joint. Remove as much grease as possible from joint. Remove bell shaped stub axle from drive shaft by lifting arms of retaining starplate one at a time. Do not twist arms off of starplate. Separate stub axle from drive shaft and remove boot if necessary.

Fig. 2: Separating Retaining Starplate from Outer End of Drive Shaft

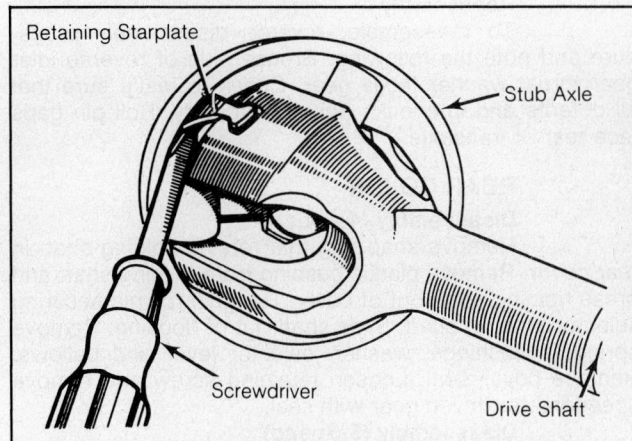

Be careful not to break off arms when removing plate.

2) Protect sealing surface of inner CV joint with tape or a plastic cap. Cut retaining collar and boot off of inner CV joint and remove as much grease as possible.

Fig. 3: Cutaway View of Inner CV Joint

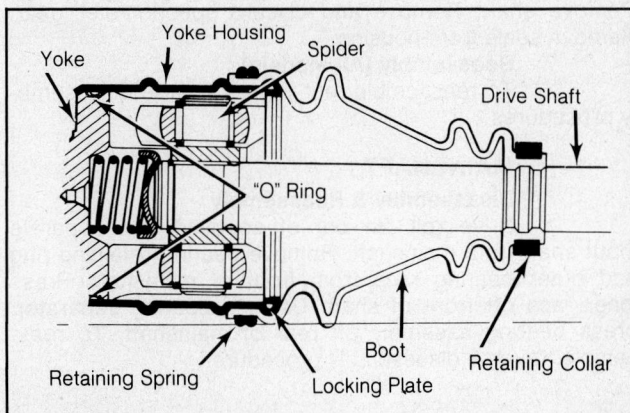

3) Bend 3 locking plate tabs out of the way and remove yoke. Do not remove rollers from their journals. If necessary, use tape to secure rollers. Using a press, remove drive shaft from inner CV joint spider.

NOTE: Never use thinner for cleaning of any component parts.

Reassembly

1) Install seal expander (T. Av. 537-02) over outer end of drive shaft. Place drive shaft in soft-jawed vise. Using motor oil, lubricate entire surface of tool and inside of boot. Slide boot onto end of tool and smooth out first fold of boot.

Fig. 4: Cutaway View of Outer CV Joint

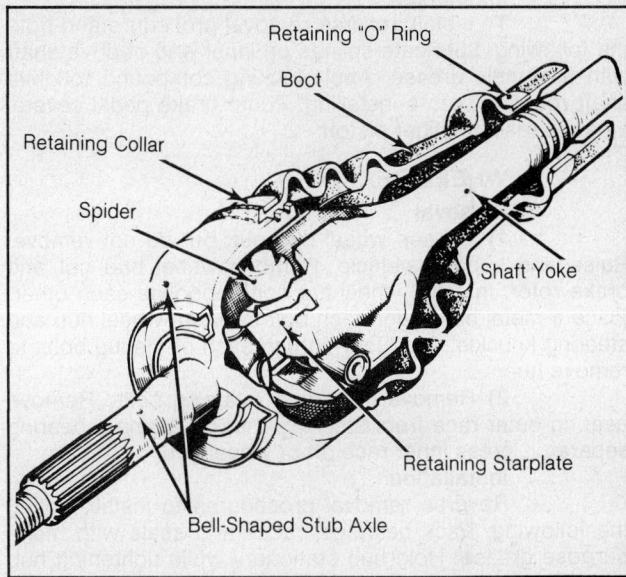

2) Move boot as close as possible toward drive shaft, then let it slide back on tool. Repeat 4 to 5 times to stretch boot, adding oil as necessary. When boot becomes easier to slide back and forth, slide it all the way into position on drive shaft. Remove tool.

3) Install spring and thrust ball joint into spider. Position roller cages in center of joint. Align retaining starplate so that each arm is between 2 roller cages. Reinstall drive shaft into bell-shaped stub axle. Fill boot and spider with about 5.25 ozs. (150 grams) of grease and secure boot with retaining rings.

4) On inner CV joint, if yoke and any other parts are replaced, proceed as follows: Lubricate drive shaft and slide on boot with retaining collar. Slide metal yoke housing onto drive shaft. Install spider onto drive shaft splines and stake in place at 3 equally spaced points around shaft.

5) Install new "O" ring onto yoke perforation. Install yoke into metal housing by tapping in until fully seated and hold with a press. Crimp end of housing that faces transaxle onto housing. Proceed to step 8).

6) If only boot or spider was replaced, proceed as follows: Lubricate drive shaft and slide on boot with retaining collar. Install spider onto drive shaft and stake in place at 3 equally spaced points around shaft. Remove tape from roller cages and engage spider with yoke.

7) Fabricate a shim from .098" (2.5 mm) flat stock measuring 1.575" (40 mm) long, .236" (6 mm) at

Manual Transmissions

RENAULT FUEGO & SPORTWAGON
4 & 5-SPEED TRANSAXLE (Cont.)

each end and having a 1.772" (45 mm) radius across one of the long sides. Insert this shim under each of the locking tabs on yoke while tapping tabs back into place using a drift punch.

8) To complete assembly of inner CV joint, fill yoke and boot with about 5.25 ozs. (150 grams) of grease. Position lips of boot in grooves of drive shaft and yoke housing. Place retaining collar on drive shaft end of boot. Insert a smooth round-ended rod under yoke end of boot to allow air to escape.

9) Extend or compress joint until distance from back of yoke housing (not splined coupling) to drive shaft end of boot is 6.34-6.42" (161-163 mm). Remove rod from boot. Place retaining spring around yoke end of boot being careful not to stretch spring.

Installation
To install, reverse removal procedure and note the following: Lubricate splines on inner end of drive shaft with assembly grease. Apply locking compound to drive shaft roll pins before installing. Pump brake pedal several times to reseat caliper piston.

WHEEL BEARINGS
Removal
1) Loosen wheel hub nut, but do not remove. Raise and support vehicle. Remove wheel hub nut and brake rotor. Install 2 wheel lug bolts opposite each other. Place a metal bar under each bolt between wheel hub and steering knuckle. Gradually tighten each of the lug bolts to remove hub.

2) Remove 6 bearing retaining bolts. Remove bearing outer race from steering knuckle. Using a bearing separator, press inner race off of wheel hub.

Installation
Reverse removal procedures to install, noting the following: Pack bearings, races and seals with multi-purpose grease. Hold hub stationary while tightening hub nut.

TRANSAXLE REMOVAL & INSTALLATION
See the appropriate article in MANUAL TRANS-MISSION REMOVAL Section.

TRANSAXLE DISASSEMBLY
1) Drain transaxle, remove backup light switch and mount transaxle in a support fixture. Remove bell housing attaching bolts. Remove 5th gear detent screw, spring, and ball.

2) Shift transaxle into neutral and remove rear cover while turning selector lever to disengage. Engage 5th and 2nd gear. Remove 5th gear synchronizer nut and washer. Remove speedometer drive gear nut. Return shift forks to neutral.

3) Engage 3rd gear and drive roll pin out of 5th gear shift fork. Mark 5th gear synchronizer hub and sleeve for reassembly reference. Remove 5th gear synchronizer assembly and shift fork.

4) Remove 5th gear from mainshaft with needle bearing and ring. Remove speedometer drive gear, nut and washer. Remove 5th gear and bearing thrust washer from pinion shaft.

5) Remove differential nut lock stops. Remove differential nuts. Remove housing-half bolts and separate halves. Remove differential assembly. Secure outer race of pinion bearing to inner race and remove pinion shaft. Remove mainshaft.

COMPONENT DISASSEMBLY & REASSEMBLY

TRANSAXLE CASE
Disassembly
1) Return all shift forks to neutral and remove 5th gear shift shaft. Drive roll pin out of 3-4 shift fork, then remove fork and shaft. Remove detent ball, spring and interlock disc.

2) Remove reverse gear selector and shaft. Drive roll pin out of 1-2 shift fork, then remove fork and shaft. Remove detent ball and spring.

3) Remove circlip retaining reverse idler gear to shaft. Remove reverse idler gear, shaft, thrust washer, guide, detent ball and spring. Drive side bearing outer races out of case and remove adjusting nut seals.

NOTE: DO NOT reassemble case until the various adjustments of gear position and preload have been made.

Reassembly
To reassemble, reverse disassembly procedure and note the following: Bronze side of reverse idler gear thrust washer faces gear. Check to make sure that all detents and interlocks operate properly. Roll pin gaps face rear of transaxle.

REAR COVER
Disassembly (4-Speed)
Remove snap ring that retains holding shaft in rear cover. Remove plastic bushing from holding shaft and press holding shaft out of cover. Remove roll pin securing selector lever to shaft. Slide shaft out of housing. Remove spring, 2 bushings, washer, selector lever and bellows. Remove cover seal. Loosen retaining screw and remove speedometer driven gear with seal.
Disassembly (5-Speed)
1) Remove roll pins securing selector lever to shaft. Slide out selector lever shaft. Remove bushings, spring, selector lever and bellows. Remove cover seal.

2) Remove snap ring and plastic bushing from holding shaft. Press holding shaft out of rear cover. Pry open catches holding speedometer drive gear onto shaft. Remove shaft. Remove and discard speedometer gear. Remove seals from housing.
Reassembly (All Models)
To reassemble rear cover, reverse disassembly procedures.

MAINSHAFT
Disassembly & Reassembly
Drive roll pin out of coupling and separate input shaft from mainshaft. Remove bearing retaining ring and outer bearing race from front of mainshaft. Press inner race off front of shaft. Using a bearing separator, press bearing assembly off rear of mainshaft. To reassemble, reverse disassembly procedure.

RENAULT FUEGO & SPORTWAGON 4 & 5-SPEED TRANSAXLE (Cont.)

Fig. 5: Exploded View of Mainshaft Assembly

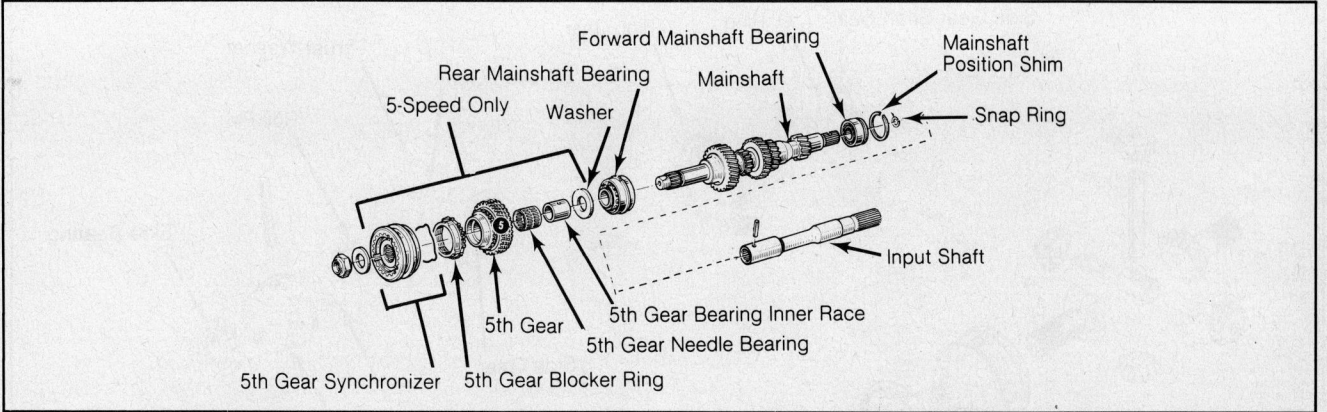

PINION SHAFT

Disassembly

1) Support shaft in a vise by clamping onto 1st gear. Remove double taper bearing, 4th gear, 4th gear blocker ring and 3-4 synchronizer sleeve with keys and springs (scribe a reference mark on hub and sleeve for reassembly).

NOTE: Observe position of synchro springs and hub offset during disassembly. Differences in pinion shaft design require that the synchronizer be assembled and installed exactly as it was removed. Also, location of 3-4 synchro snap ring and lock washer can be on either side of 3-4 synchro hub depending on snap ring groove location. Snap ring and lock washer must be installed in same position that they were removed from. The only exception is when pinion shaft is replaced with one of different design. If this is the case, reverse orientation of 3-4 synchro hub, springs, keys, lock washer and snap ring. Do not reverse orientation of 3-4 synchro sleeve.

2) Remove snap ring and lock washer (if installed). Using a bearing separator, press 3-4 synchronizer hub off of shaft. Remove snap ring and lock washer (if installed). Remove 3rd gear and 3rd gear blocker ring.

3) Remove 2nd gear lock washers, snap ring, 2nd gear, 2nd gear blocker ring, 1-2 synchronizer sleeve (scribe a reference mark on hub and sleeve for reassembly) with keys and springs, and 1-2 synchronizer hub lock washer.

4) Using a bearing separator, press 1-2 synchronizer hub off of shaft. Remove 1st gear blocker ring, lock washer, snap ring and 1st gear. Remove front bearing from pinion shaft.

Reassembly

To reassemble, reverse disassembly procedure and note the following: Snap rings and speedometer drive gear cannot be reused. Orientation of components related to the 3-4 synchro depends on snap ring groove location. After tightening the speedometer drive gear to specifications, stake the gear to the shaft.

Fig. 6: Exploded View of Pinion Shaft Assembly

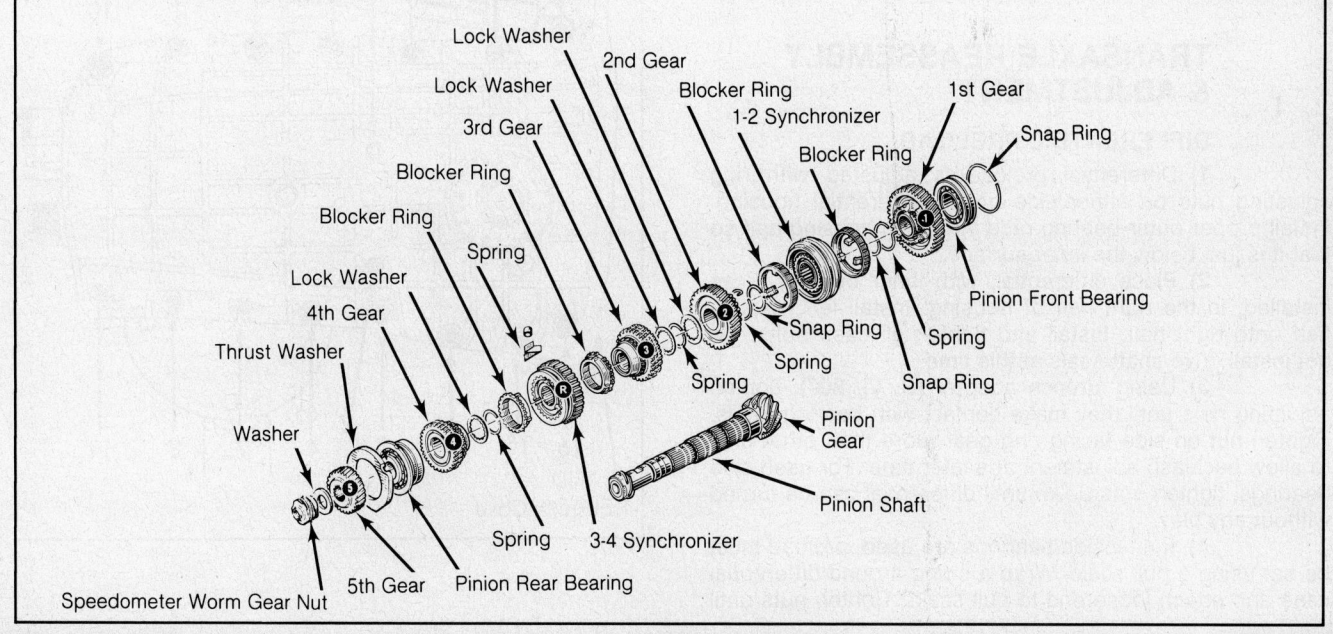

Manual Transmissions
RENAULT FUEGO & SPORTWAGON 4 & 5-SPEED TRANSAXLE (Cont.)

Fig. 7: Exploded View of Differential Assembly

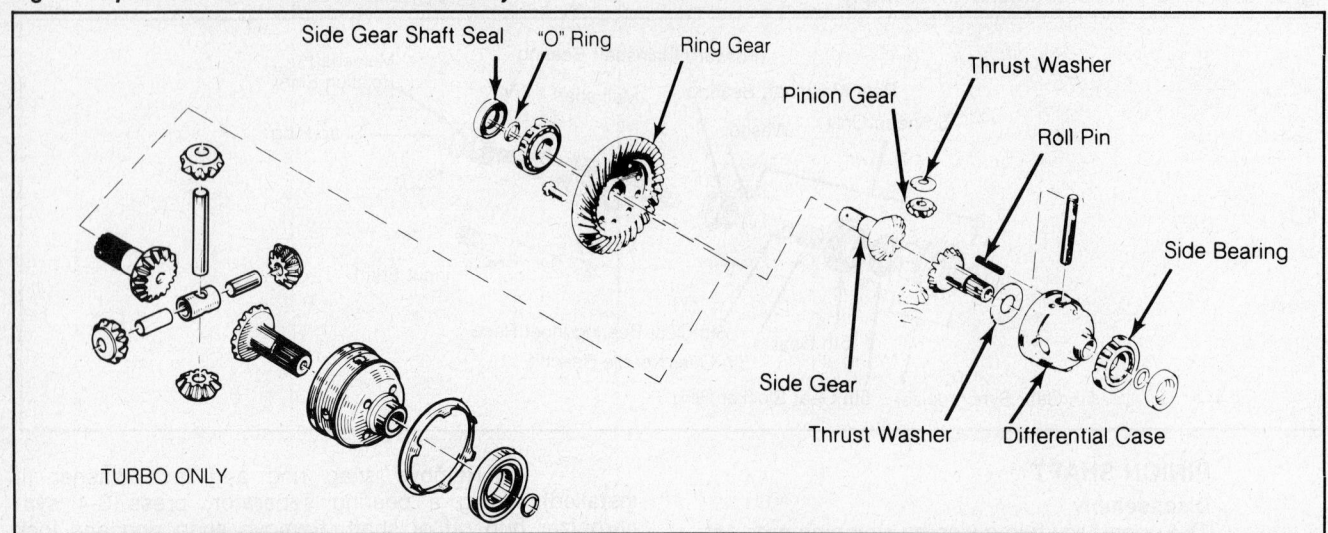

DIFFERENTIAL

Disassembly & Reassembly (Turbo Only)

Remove and discard 4 ring gear bolts. Attach a 3-jaw puller to side bearings and remove side bearings from housing. Remove and discard remainder of ring gear bolts. Remove pressed-on collar to gain access to pinion shafts. Separate ring gear from differential housing. Slide pinion shafts out of housing and remove pinion gears. To reassemble, reverse disassembly procedure.

Disassembly (All Exc. Turbo)

Remove and discard all ring gear bolts except for 2 directly opposite each other. Remove side bearings with puller. Remove and discard remainder of ring gear bolts. Drive roll pin out of pinion shaft. Remove pinion shaft, pinion gears and side gears.

Reassembly (All Exc. Turbo)

To reassemble, reverse disassembly procedure and note the following: Lubrication groove on side gear thrust washer must face gear. Use oversize thrust washer if excessive end play exists. Locking pin of pinion thrust washers should engage hole in case.

TRANSAXLE REASSEMBLY & ADJUSTMENT

DIFFERENTIAL PRELOAD

1) Differential preload is adjusted with ring adjusting nuts on either side of the differential housing. Install proper outer bearing race into each housing half so that it is just below the inner surface.

2) Place differential, with inner bearing races installed, in the right half of housing. Install left housing half onto right half. Install and tighten all case bolts. Do not install drive shaft seals at this time.

3) Using wrench adapter (B. Vi. 807), tighten adjusting nuts until they make contact with bearing races. Tighten nut on side facing ring gear more than other side to allow backlash adjustment at a later time. For used side bearings, tighten nuts down until differential can be turned without any play.

4) If new side bearings are used, preload must be set using a pull scale. Wrap a string around differential case and attach loose end to pull scale. Tighten nuts until a force of 2-7 lbs. (1-3 kgs) is required to rotate differential. Mark position of both differential adjusting nuts on case. Remove nuts from case, separate case halves and remove differential.

TRANSAXLE REASSEMBLY

1) To reassemble, reverse disassembly procedure and note the following: Align differential adjusting nuts with reference marks made during preload adjustment procedure.

2) Before installing clutch housing, ring gear backlash must be checked and adjusted if necessary. Mount dial indicator on front of transaxle housing so that plunger squarely contacts a ring gear tooth. Lock pinion shaft in place and check backlash by rotating differential.

Fig. 8: Case Bolt Tightening Sequence

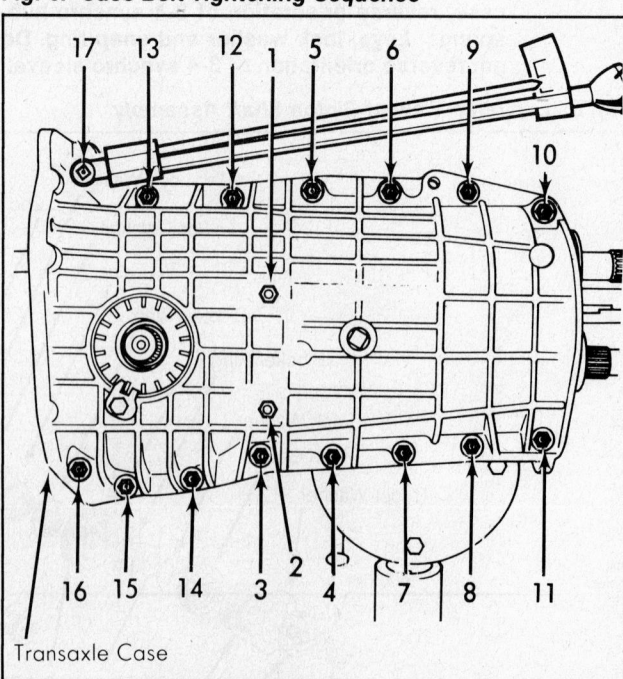

RENAULT FUEGO & SPORTWAGON
4 & 5-SPEED TRANSAXLE (Cont.)

3) Adjust backlash, if necessary, by turning 1 adjusting nut in and the other adjusting nut out an equal number of turns (to maintain preload setting) to move differential in required direction. Backlash should be .005-.010" (.12-.25 mm).

4) Recheck backlash at 4 equally spaced points around ring gear. Variation between points should be minimal. If variation exceeds specification range, disassemble case and check for proper installation of bearings.

TIGHTENING SPECIFICATIONS

Application	Ft. Lbs. (N.m)
Clutch Housing-to-Transaxle	
8 mm Bolts	18 (24)
10 mm Bolts	26 (35)
Speedometer Worm Gear Nut	74-89 (100-121)
Input Shaft Nut (5-Speed Only)	74-89 (100-121)
Ring Gear Bolts	92 (125)
Wheel Hub Nut	185 (251)
	INCH Lbs. (N.m)
Case Half Bolts	
7 mm Bolts	180-228 (20-26)
8 mm Bolts	240-288 (27-33)
Rear Cover Bolts	120 (14)
Reverse Relay Lever Bolt	228 (26)
Differential Adjusting Nut Lock Bolt	216 (24)
Wheel Bearing Retaining Bolts	132 (15)

Manual Transmissions
SAAB 900 5-SPEED TRANSAXLE

IDENTIFICATION

All Saabs with M/T use a 5-speed transaxle. Identification number is stamped on top of clutch slave cylinder. The 1st character of the I.D. number (G) designates manual transaxle, and the 3rd character of the I.D. number (5) designates the number of forward gears.

DESCRIPTION

The transaxle assembly is a 2-piece unit, containing both transmission and final drive assemblies. Transaxle assembly is located underneath engine, and portion of transmission case serves as engine oil sump. Transmission and final drive are assembled in rear section of transaxle, and primary gear unit is housed in front section.

All forward gears are in constant mesh, while reverse gear is engaged by a sliding gear. A chain-driven primary gear unit transmits engine power through the clutch, to the transmission. Final drive assembly consists of differential assembly, pinion shaft, and drive axle shaft housings.

NOTE: **Ensure that any gears being replaced match up to old gears. Noise and durability problems will result if incorrect gears are used.**

LUBRICATION & ADJUSTMENT

See appropriate MANUAL TRANSMISSION SERVICING article in IMPORT GENERAL SERVICING section.

TROUBLE SHOOTING

JUMPS OUT OF GEAR

Shift linkage damaged or out of adjustment. Engine mounts loose or broken. Clutch shaft or roller bearings worn. Pilot bushing worn. Gear teeth worn or damaged. Shift lever binding.

HARD SHIFTING

Clutch worn. Incorrect fluid level or type. Shift rail binding or bent. Clutch disc warped or deformed. Shift linkage binding.

NOISY IN FORWARD GEARS

Incorrect fluid level or type. Clutch housing bolts loose. Worn bearing or gears. Speedometer gear/teeth worn or damaged.

LOCKED IN GEAR

Damaged or incorrectly positioned shift linkage. Shift fork loose on shift rail. Broken gear teeth on clutch shaft.

SERVICE (IN VEHICLE)

DRIVE AXLE SHAFTS & WHEEL BEARINGS

NOTE: **Downward movement of control arms is limited by rubber buffer inside each shock absorber.**

Therefore, it will be necessary either to remove shock absorber, or to support lower control arm at the outer end, before raising the vehicle.

Removal

1) Remove hub cap, loosen hub nut and wheel lugs. Raise and support vehicle. Remove wheels. Rotate brake disc to align recess along disc edge, with brake pads and caliper. Disconnect parking brake cable from each side. Remove caliper mounting bolts and hang caliper from coil spring using wire. DO NOT disconnect hydraulic line.

Fig. 1: Sectional View of Steering Knuckle

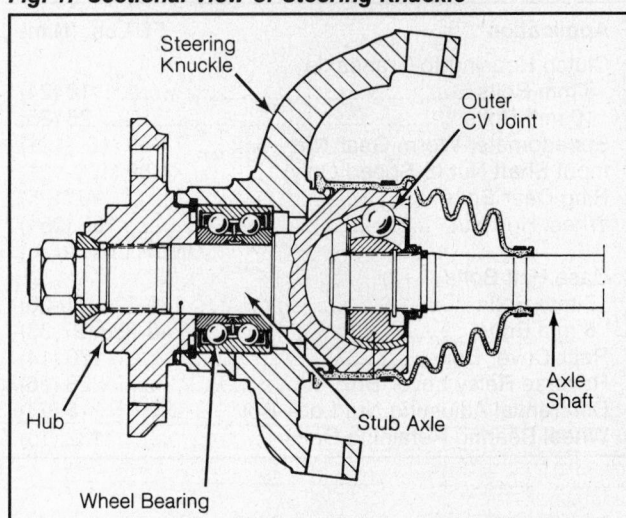

2) Remove hub and disc assembly using Extractor (89 96 084). Remove larger clamp on inner universal joint bellows. Remove steering arm and upper ball joint using Remover (89 95 409). Disconnect screws on lower control arm bracket. Separate inner CV joint from drive flange. Cover end of rubber bellows to prevent needle bearings from falling onto floor.

3) Pull axle assembly through wheel housing to remove. Thoroughly clean axle assembly. Place steering knuckle housing in a press and press out drive shaft. Remove snap ring from bearing housing. Press out and discard bearing.

NOTE: **Axle shafts cannot be disassembled. If damaged or defective, replace as complete assembly.**

Installation

1) Press bearing into steering knuckle housing, then install snap ring. Place axle shaft in press and press on knuckle housing and bearing. Install inner oil seal. Press wheel hub and brake disc onto axle splines and install washer. Install new lock nut, but do not tighten.

2) Install axle shaft through wheel housing. Install any needle bearings, which may have fallen out of inner CV joint, onto ends of "T" section. Attach inner CV joint to drive flange. Install upper ball joint to steering knuckle and reinstall lower control arm bracket. Install tie rod end on steering arm. Install brake caliper.

3) Reinstall front wheel and lower vehicle. Tighten hub lock nut, then secure in place by peening into locking groove. Pump brake pedal several times to seat brake pads.

SAAB 900 5-SPEED TRANSAXLE (Cont.)

TRANSAXLE MOUNTS
Removal & Installation

1) Place transmission in Neutral. Unbolt exhaust pipe from manifold. Disconnect speedometer cable from transmission. Remove rear engine mounting bolt. Loosen front engine mounting bolt.

2) Attach hoist to 2 lifting rings, and raise engine and transaxle assembly about 4". Remove bolts attaching front and rear mounts to frame, and remove mounts. To install, reverse removal procedure.

REMOVAL & INSTALLATION

TRANSAXLE

See appropriate MANUAL TRANSMISSION REMOVAL article in IMPORT GENERAL SERVICING section.

TRANSAXLE DISASSEMBLY

NOTE: Prior to disassembly of transmission gears, measure and record ring-to-pinion gear back-lash and pinion depth. See PINION DEPTH ADJUSTMENT.

1) Place transaxle assembly on a work stand and drain fluid. Remove primary gear housing front and side covers. Remove oil filler plug cover and final drive cover. Measure and record ring-to-pinion gear backlash and pinion depth. Remove axle shaft housing attaching bolts and remove housings using a puller.

NOTE: When removing axle housings, do not lose spring and plunger located in end of inner shaft. Also, note number and thickness of adjusting shims installed with housings.

2) Tilt differential assembly to one side and remove assembly from case. Remove reverse gear operating lever retaining bolt and lever. Engage reverse gear and 5th gear to lock transmission. Unstake output shaft tab washer (lower primary gear), then remove unit. Remove chain tensioner.

3) Remove snap ring (located behind upper primary gear). Using slide hammer and Puller (87 90 891), remove primary gears and chains simultaneously. Free countershaft gear from output shaft countergear by loos-

Fig. 2: Exploded View of Transaxle Assembly

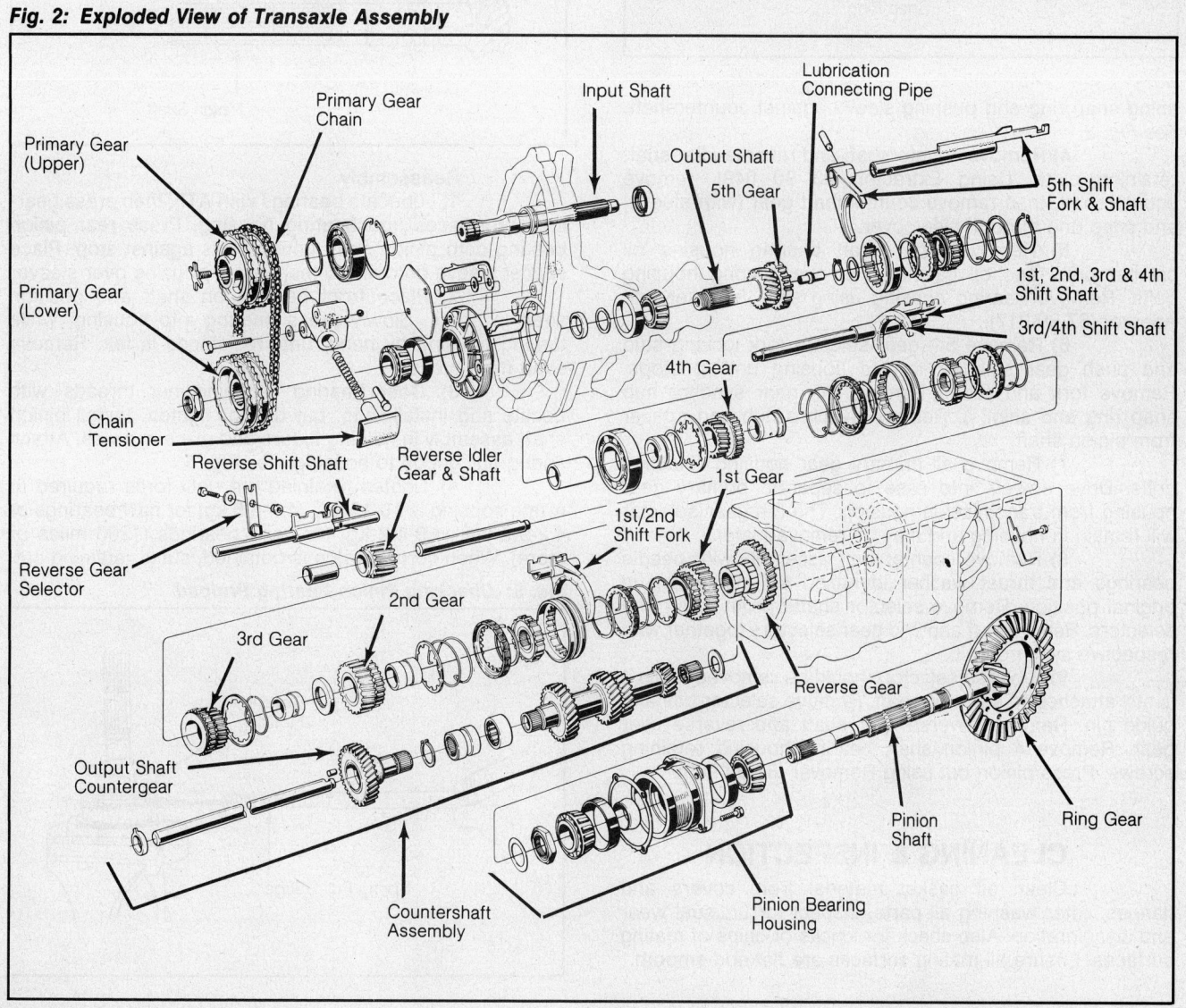

Fig. 3: Disconnecting Mainshaft Countergear

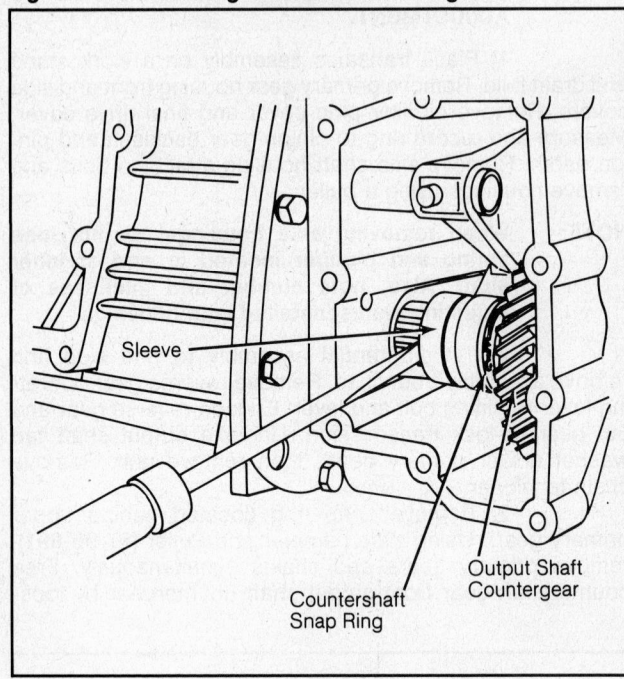

ening snap ring and pushing sleeve against countershaft. *See Fig. 3.*

4) Remove countershaft and reverse idler shaft retaining plate. Using Extractor (83 90 049), remove countershaft, then remove countershaft gear (with sleeve) and snap ring through side cover.

5) Remove input shaft bearing housing oil catcher bolts and oil catcher. Remove bearing housing bolts. Remove bearing housing using slide hammer and Adapter (87 90 917).

6) Remove 5th gear selector fork locking stud and push gear selector toward housing until it stops. Remove fork and slider. Remove 5th gear synchro hub snap ring and shim(s). Remove synchro hub and spacer from pinion shaft.

7) Remove all primary gear housing retaining bolts. Drive dowels into case to separate primary gear housing from transmission housing. The 5th gear selector will remain in housing and may be removed later.

8) Remove countershaft assembly with needle bearings and thrust washer identified for installation in original position. Remove selector shafts (from front) and selectors. Remove 1st and 2nd gear selectors together with respective synchro unit.

9) Reverse selector should be removed while it is still attached to selector shaft. Remove selector ball and guide pin. Remove reverse idler shaft and reverse idler gear. Remove 4 pinion shaft bearing housing retaining screws. Press pinion out using Remover (87 90 909).

CLEANING & INSPECTION

Clean all gasket material from covers and flanges. After washing all parts, inspect for unusual wear and discoloration. Also check for knicks or chips of mating surfaces. Ensure all mating surfaces are flat and smooth.

COMPONENT DISASSEMBLY & REASSEMBLY

PINION SHAFT
Disassembly

Place pinion shaft in a holding fixture, then remove pinion bearing retaining nut from shaft. Place shaft in a press and press pinion shaft and rear pinion bearing from bearing housing. Press rear bearing from shaft, then using a driver, remove pinion bearing outer races from bearing housing, then remove spacer sleeve from housing.

Fig. 4: Exploded View of Pinion Shaft Assembly

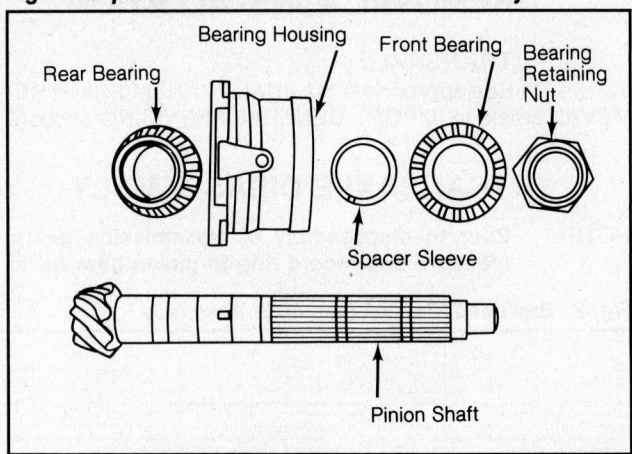

Reassembly

1) Lubricate bearings with ATF, then press bearing outer races into bearing housing. Press rear pinion bearing onto pinion shaft until it butts against stop. Place spacer sleeve onto shaft, then install housing over sleeve.

2) Place front bearing on shaft and position shaft in press. Slowly press bearing into housing, while turning housing by hand, until resistance is felt. Remove shaft from press.

3) Coat bearing retaining nut threads with Loctite and install nuts, but do not tighten. Install pinion shaft assembly in holding fixture and place in a vise. Attach spring pull gauge to housing. *See Fig. 5.*

4) Tighten retaining nut until force required to rotate housing is 10-15 lbs. (4.5-6.8 kg) for new bearings or 4.2-9.2 lbs. (1.9-4.2 kg) for used bearings (1200 miles or more). When correct value is obtained, stake retaining nut.

Fig. 5: Checking Pinion Bearing Preload

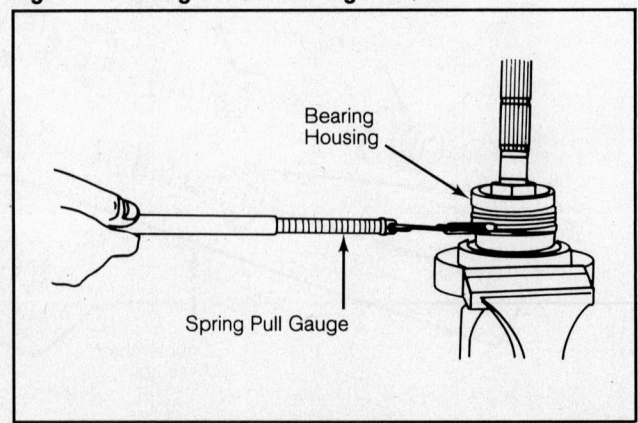

SAAB 900 5-SPEED TRANSAXLE (Cont.)

NOTE: With retaining nut correctly tightened, pinion bearing preload is set to correct specification.

PRIMARY GEAR HOUSING
Disassembly

Remove 4 Allen head screws from input shaft bearing retainer and remove retainer. Drive out bearing using Drift (83 90 106) and Sleeve (83 90 148). Remove needle bearing from primary gear case using a drift. Pry out input shaft oil seal. Remove upper primary gear snap ring. Using Sleeve (87 90 842), press bearing out of upper primary gear.

NOTE: DO NOT remove lever control ball valve. Check that ball moves freely and securely sets on seat. Ball acts at low speeds while going down hills to prevent oil from running from gear case into primary gear housing.

Reassembly

Inspect all parts for wear or damage; replace as necessary. Press in new input shaft oil seal and needle bearing (mark facing outward in housing). Press input shaft bearing into housing. Install bearing retainer. Apply Loctite to Allen head screw threads. Install and tighten screws.

OUTPUT SHAFT BEARING HOUSING
Disassembly

Remove oil catcher from bearing housing. Press output shaft from bearing housing using Support (83 90 098), being careful not to damage lubrication connection pipe. Retain front bearing, spacer and shims. Using Support (87 90 636) and Ring (87 90 933), press rear bearing off output shaft. Using a drift, knock bearing outer races from bearing housing.

Reassembly

1) Press rear bearing onto output shaft. Press outer races into bearing housing. Install output shaft, shims, spacer and bearing into bearing housing (shims must be installed between rear bearing and spacer).

2) Lubricate bearings and press together using Support (83 90 098) and Drift (78 41 075). While pressing using 3 tons (2722 kg) pressure, rotate bearing housing against upper and lower bearings 40 times in each direction to seat ball bearings.

3) Install dial indicator. *See Fig. 6.* Maintain installation pressure and check axial play of bearing housing. Adjust axial play to 0 by inserting correct shim.

4) After installing correct shim, recheck axial play. If axial play cannot be removed with shims, replace spacer. Bearings should have no resistance to movement or play. Install oil catcher in bearing housing.

NOTE: Shims are available in .004" (.10 mm), .006" (.15 mm), .010" (.25 mm) and .020" (.50 mm) thicknesses. Spacers are available in .3181" (8.08 mm), .3185" (8.09 mm), .3189" (8.10 mm) and .3192" (8.11 mm) lengths.

SYNCHRONIZER ASSEMBLIES
Disassembly

Synchronizer rings are removed by removing snap ring which attaches ring to gear. Fifth gear synchronizer ring is removed by removing snap ring in front of guide ring. DO NOT remove synchronizer ring snap ring.

Reassembly

1) Install guide ring for retaining ring, then, on 3rd and 4th gears only, lock guide rings in place on gears with snap rings.

2) Install retaining spring on gear with long wire end nearest guide ring, then position other end on gear so there are 11 teeth between spring ends (5 teeth on 5th gear). Retaining spring for 1st gear is shorter and softer.

NOTE: Guide rings for 3rd and 4th gears are assembled during production and are peened into position. DO NOT peen replacement guide rings.

3) Install synchronizer ring onto gear so ends of spring fit into spaces between teeth. Install snap ring.

Fig. 6: Checking Axial Play of Output Shaft Bearing Housing

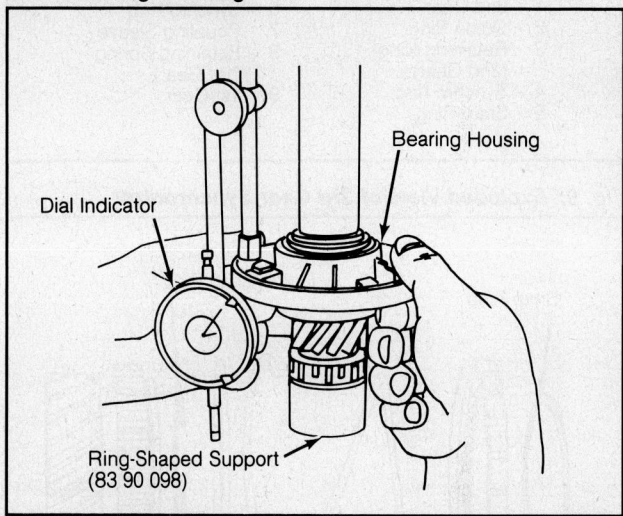

NOTE: Synchronizer ring for 2nd gear has molybdenum-coated synchronizing surface for identification.

Fig. 7: Separating Synchronizer Ring from 1st-4th Gears

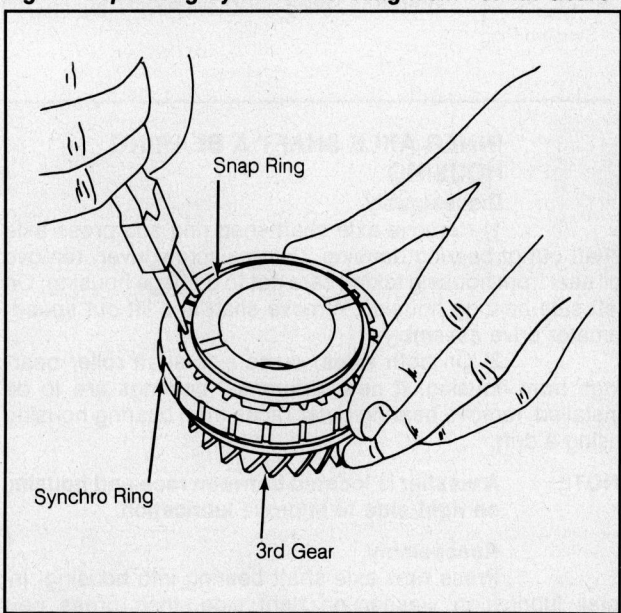

Manual Transmissions
SAAB 900 5-SPEED TRANSAXLE (Cont.)

Fig. 8: Exploded View of 1st/2nd Gear Synchronizer

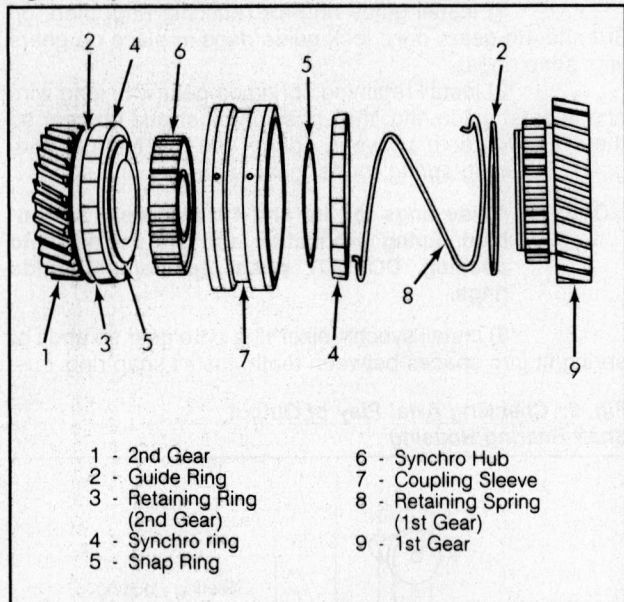

1 - 2nd Gear	6 - Synchro Hub
2 - Guide Ring	7 - Coupling Sleeve
3 - Retaining Ring (2nd Gear)	8 - Retaining Spring (1st Gear)
4 - Synchro ring	9 - 1st Gear
5 - Snap Ring	

Fig. 9: Exploded View of 3rd Gear Synchronizer

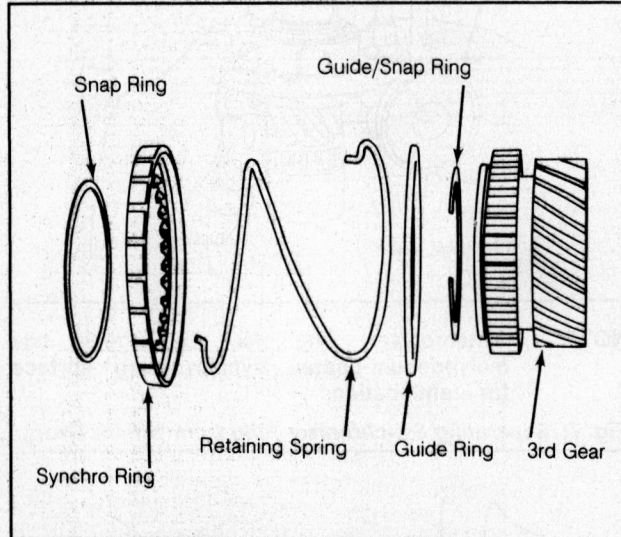

Fig. 10: Installing Synchronizer Retaining Spring

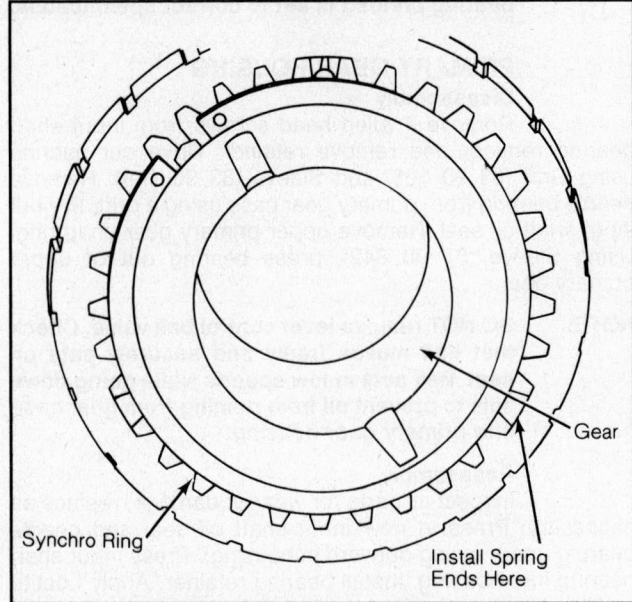

Fig. 11: Removing Axle Shaft Snap Ring From Housing

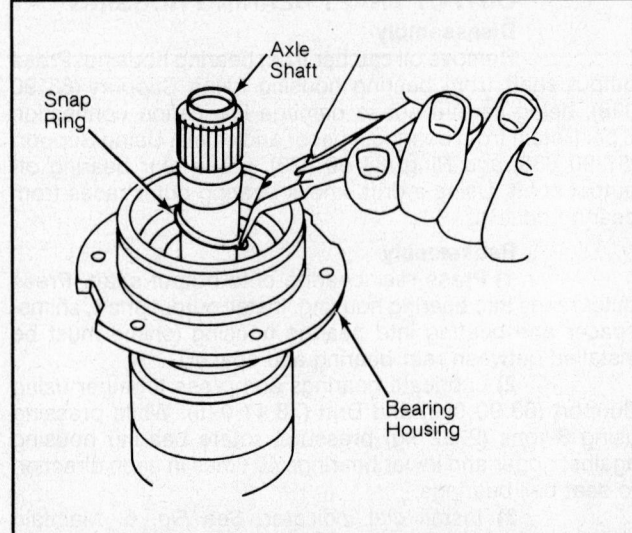

INNER AXLE SHAFT & BEARING HOUSING

Disassembly

1) Remove axle shaft snap ring and press axle shaft out of bearing housing. Using a screwdriver, remove oil seal from housing taking care not to damage housing. On left side bearing housing, remove shaft and lift out speedometer drive assembly.

2) On both sides, press axle shaft roller bearings from housing. If new differential bearings are to be installed, remove bearing outer races from bearing housing using a drift.

NOTE: A washer is located between race and housing on right side to improve lubrication.

Reassembly

Press new axle shaft bearing into housing. Install lubrication washer on right side, then press new differential bearing outer races into bearing housing. Using a drift, press bearing housing oil seal into housing until it protrudes .08" (2 mm) above face of housing.

NOTE: Axle shafts will be installed during Transaxle Reassembly.

DIFFERENTIAL ASSEMBLY

Disassembly

1) If differential bearings require replacement, remove speedometer drive gear from left side and use puller to remove bearings from differential housing.

2) Remove ring gear bolts and separate ring gear from differential. Remove snap ring, then press out pinion shaft. Remove pinion gears and side gears, thrust washers and gear springs from housing.

Reassembly

Install pinion gears and side gears, thrust washers and springs into housing. Install pinion shaft and secure with snap ring. Install ring gear on differential housing, apply Loctite to threads, and install attaching bolts. If

SAAB 900 5-SPEED TRANSAXLE (Cont.)

removed, press new bearings onto housing, then install speedometer drive gear.

Fig. 12: Exploded View of Left Side Inner Axle Shaft and Differential Bearing Housing

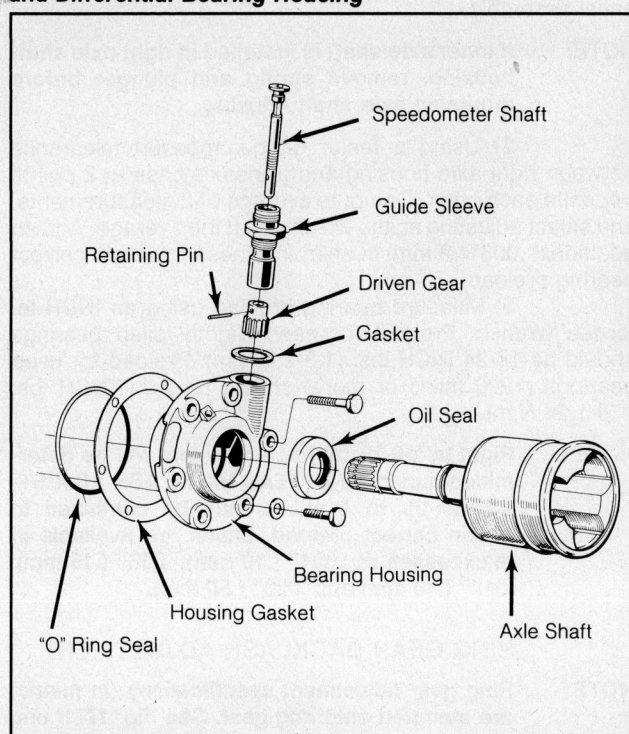

Fig. 13: Exploded View of Differential Assembly

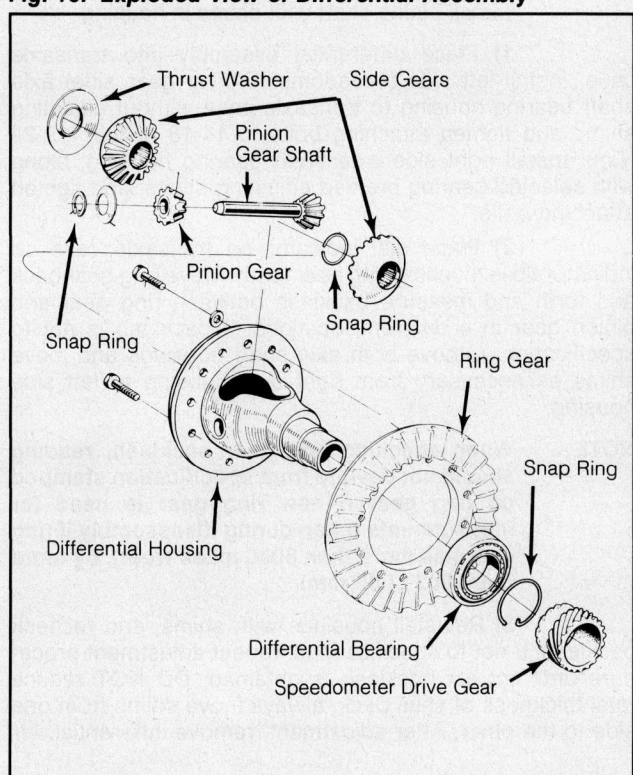

TRANSAXLE REASSEMBLY & ADJUSTMENT

PINION DEPTH ADJUSTMENT

NOTE: Pinion bearing preload must be correctly adjusted before adjusting pinion depth. See PINION SHAFT REASSEMBLY. Pinion Depth Adjustment specifications (in metric) are stamped into end face of pinion shaft gear. See Fig. 14.

1) Pinion depth must be measured using Saab Measuring Instrument (83 90 155), which consists of a measuring jig, attached dial indicator, and a gauge block for calibrating dial indicator.

2) To calibrate indicator, place calibration stops of measuring tool against gauge block. Distance between stops and centerline of tool should be 2.362" (60 mm), which is equal to distance from end face of pinion shaft gear to centerline of ring gear.

3) Ensure that dial indicator pointer is at zero when measuring tip touches gauge block.

Fig. 14: Pinion Shaft Gear Depth Adjustment Specifications

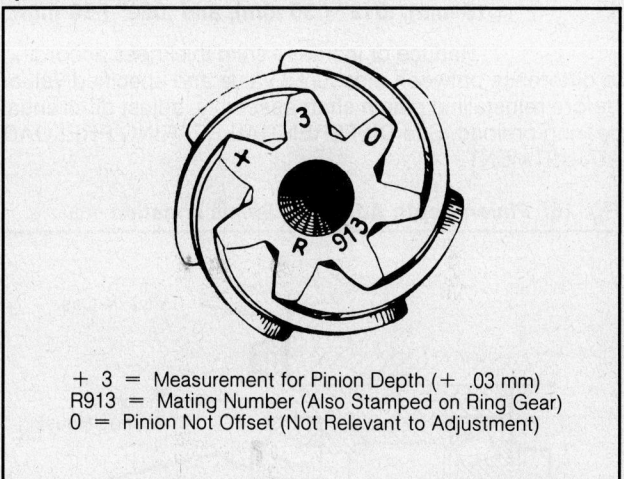

+ 3 = Measurement for Pinion Depth (+ .03 mm)
R913 = Mating Number (Also Stamped on Ring Gear)
0 = Pinion Not Offset (Not Relevant to Adjustment)

4) Install pinion shaft into transaxle case and tighten bolts. Position measuring tool in transaxle case with measuring tip applied to flat end of pinion gear. See Fig. 15. Record reading.

5) When pinion gear is correctly positioned, dial indicator should read (in hundredths of millimeters; plus or minus) same number as that stamped into pinion (with a permitted tolerance of .002" (.05 mm)). For example, if pinion is stamped -7, indicator should read a negative (-) .07 mm with a tolerance of ± .05 mm.

NOTE: On dial indicator, clockwise movement of needle is positive.

NOTE: If ring and pinion gear set have been in use for over 6000 miles, reassemble pinion shaft to specifications recorded during disassembly.

6) If measured pinion depth is not within specification stamped on pinion gear, pinion shaft must be adjusted. Remove pinion shaft from case and add thicker shim if reading is higher than specifications, reduce shim thickness if reading is lower than specification.

Manual Transmissions
SAAB 900 5-SPEED TRANSAXLE (Cont.)

Fig. 15: Measuring Transaxle Case

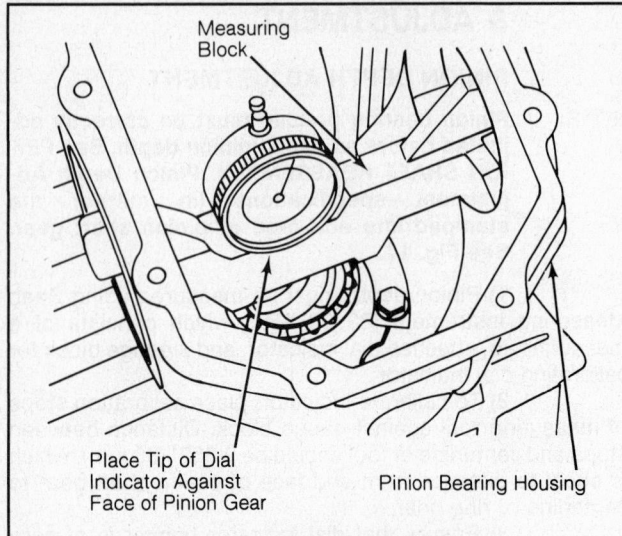

NOTE: Pinion depth adjusting shims are available in following thicknesses: .004" (.10 mm), .006" (.15 mm), .012" (.30 mm), and .020" (.50 mm).

7) Reduce or increase shim thickness according to difference between measured value and specified value. Before reinstalling pinion shaft assembly, adjust differential bearing preload. See DIFFERENTIAL BEARING PRELOAD ADJUSTMENT.

Fig. 16: Pinion Depth Adjusting Shims Location

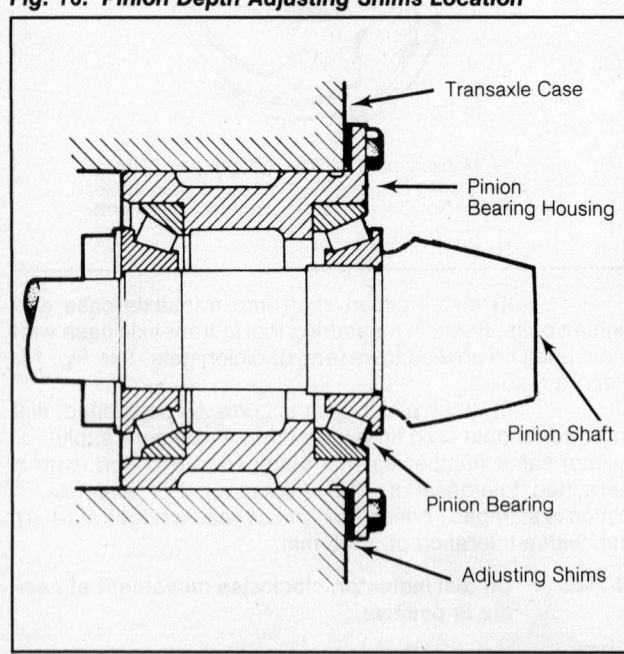

DIFFERENTIAL BEARING PRELOAD ADJUSTMENT

NOTE: Differential bearing preload must be adjusted prior to installation of pinion shaft.

1) Position differential assembly in transaxle case, then install left side (side with speedometer drive gear) axle shaft bearing housing without shims and tighten bolts to 14-18 ft. lbs. (19-24 N.m). Oil differential bearings, install right side axle shaft bearing housing and tighten attaching bolts to 19 ft. lbs. (26 N.m) while rotating differential assembly.

NOTE: If inner axle shaft is installed in right axle shaft housing, remove spring and plunger before mounting axle shaft housing.

2) Using a feeler gauge, measure clearance between right axle housing and transaxle case at 2 points opposite each other. Compute average of 2 measurements, and select adjusting shims which equal the average. Add an additional .008" (.2 mm) in shim thickness to obtain correct bearing preload.

3) Measure bearing preload using an INCH lb. torque wrench. Preload for new, slightly oiled bearings should be 16-24 INCH lbs. (1.8-2.7 N.m). Preload for used bearings (1200 miles or more) should be 7-11 INCH lbs. (.79-1.24 N.m).

NOTE: Right-to-left distribution of shims will be determined during RING GEAR BACKLASH ADJUSTMENT. Up to 4 shims may be combined to obtain correct preload. Shims are available in thicknesses of: .004" (.10 mm), .006" (.15 mm), .012" (.30 mm) and .020" (.50 mm).

RING GEAR BACKLASH ADJUSTMENT

NOTE: Ring gear adjustment specifications (in metric) are stamped onto ring gear. See Fig. 17. If ring and pinion gear set have been in use for over 6000 miles, reassemble differential according to specifications recorded during disassembly. Install pinion shaft with shims in housing.

1) Place differential assembly into transaxle case. Install left side (speedometer drive gear side) axle shaft bearing housing to transaxle case without adjusting shims and tighten attaching bolts to 14-18 ft. lbs. (19-24 N.m). Install right side axle shaft bearing housing, along with selected bearing preload adjusting shims, and tighten attaching bolts.

2) Place dial indicator on transaxle case so indicator tip is touching ring gear teeth. Move ring gear back and forth and measure backlash between ring gear and pinion gear in 4 different locations. If backlash is not to specification, remove both axle shaft housings and move shims as necessary from right side housing to left side housing.

NOTE: When checking ring gear backlash, reading should not deviate from specification stamped on ring gear if new ring gear is used (or measurments taken during disassembly if ring gear has more than 6000 miles wear), by more than .002" (.05 mm).

3) Reinstall housings with shims, and recheck backlash. If not to specifications, repeat adjustment procedure until correct backlash is obtained. DO NOT reduce total thickness of shim pack, always move shims from one side to the other. After adjustment, remove differential.

TRANSAXLE REASSEMBLY

1) Install 2 Locating Studs (87 90 438) into pinion shaft bearing housing mounting holes. Install preselected

SAAB 900 5-SPEED TRANSAXLE (Cont.)

Fig. 17: Ring Gear Backlash Adjustment Specifications

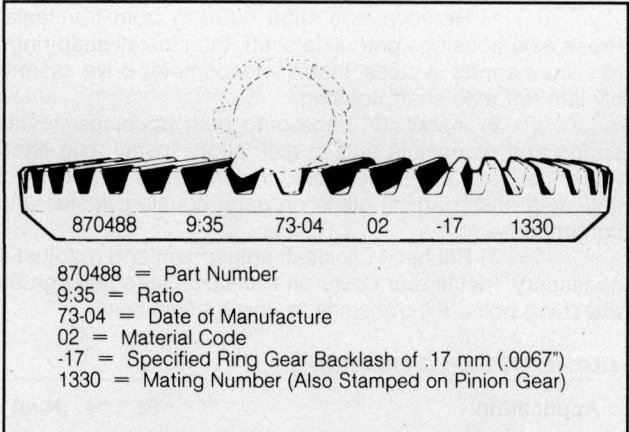

| 870488 | 9:35 | 73-04 | 02 | -17 | 1330 |

870488 = Part Number
9:35 = Ratio
73-04 = Date of Manufacture
02 = Material Code
-17 = Specified Ring Gear Backlash of .17 mm (.0067")
1330 = Mating Number (Also Stamped on Pinion Gear)

Fig. 18: Measuring Ring Gear Backlash

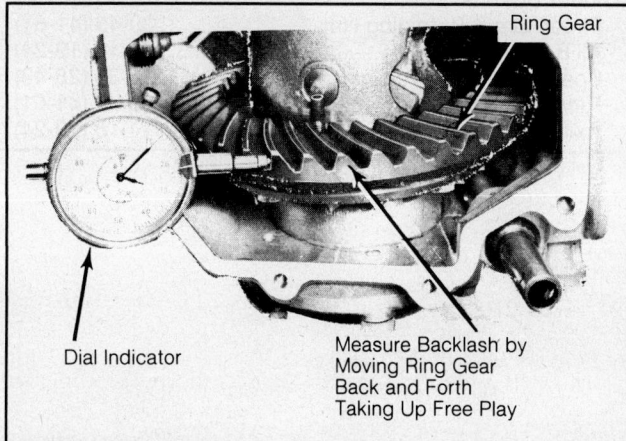

Ring Gear

Dial Indicator

Measure Backlash by Moving Ring Gear Back and Forth Taking Up Free Play

Fig. 19: Measuring Retaining Nut Depth

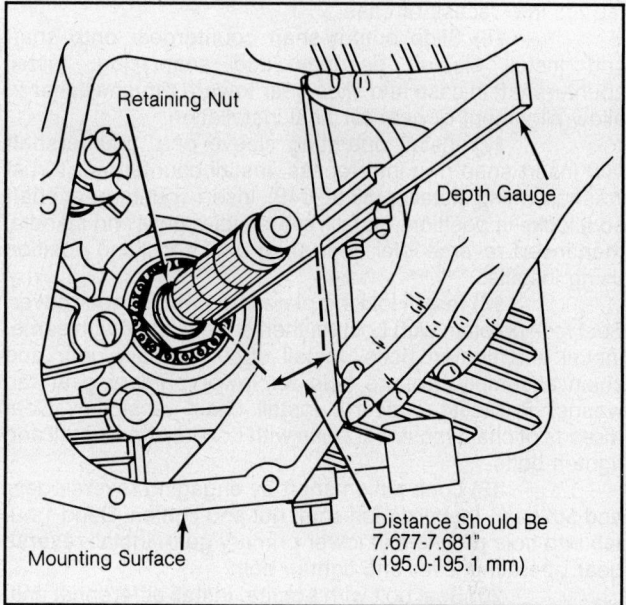

Retaining Nut

Depth Gauge

Mounting Surface

Distance Should Be 7.677-7.681" (195.0-195.1 mm)

pinion depth adjusting shims on bearing housing. Position pinion shaft in transaxle case, using locating studs as guides.

2) Gently tap pinion shaft using plastic mallet until fully seated in case, then remove locating studs. Apply Loctite to bearing housing mounting bolt threads. Install and tighten bolts.

3) Before installing reverse gear, measure distance from pinion bearing retaining nut to primary gear housing mounting surface on transaxle case. Distance should be 7.677-7.681" (195.0-195.1 mm).

4) To accurately measure distance, set depth gauge to proper distance and install onto case. *See Fig. 19.* Measure distance between end of depth gauge and retaining nut using feeler gauge. Install shim of thickness equal to that of feeler gauge.

5) Using a micrometer, measure thickness of shim removed during disassembly. If original shim thickness equals required shim thickness, reinstall original shim. If not, install shim of proper thickness. Shims are available in thicknesses of .012" (.3 mm), .016" (.4 mm) and .02" (.05 mm). Install shim between retaining nut and reverse gear.

6) Install reverse gear on pinion shaft. Fit 1st gear on bearing sleeve of reverse gear. Install 1st/2nd synchronizer hub onto pinion shaft. Insert 1st/2nd gear shift fork into 1st/2nd coupling sleeve and install onto synchronizer hub.

7) Install 2nd gear sleeve using Installer (83 90 148). Install 2nd gear onto sleeve. Install 3rd gear spacer and sleeve on pinion shaft, then install 3rd gear on sleeve.

8) Install 3rd/4th synchronizer hub onto pinion shaft. Install 3rd/4th gear shift fork into 3rd/4th gear coupling sleeve, then install on synchronizer hub. Install 4th gear bushing onto pinion shaft, then install 4th gear onto bushing. Install selector shaft with double lock out guide pin.

9) Place transmission gears in Neutral, then install gear shift rail for 1st/2nd and 3rd/4th gearshift forks. Install reverse operating lever onto reverse selector shaft. Apply Loctite to shaft stop bolt. Install and tighten stop bolt. Install 5th gear selector onto reverse selector shaft.

10) Install countershaft gear needle bearing into countershaft gear and install countershaft gear into housing. Install countershaft gear shaft, while aligning countershaft, just enough to hold gears in position. Thrust washer will be installed later.

11) Install 5th gear spacer, 5th gear synchronizer hub and snap ring onto pinion shaft. Measure distance between coupling sleeve and hub using feeler gauge so there is no play between parts on pinion shaft. Shims are available in .012" (.3 mm) and .016" (.4 mm) thicknesses.

12) Remove snap ring, hub and spacer. Apply sealing compound to gasket surfaces of primary gear housing. Install gasket and housing to transmission housing.

13) Install spacer and 5th gear synchronizer hub on output shaft. Install shims selected to provide zero play between parts on shaft, then install snap ring. Install 5th gear operating sleeve and selector fork.

14) Install 3 Output Shaft Guide Pins (87 90 438) into lower primary gear bearing housing mounting bolt holes. Insert output shaft with bearing housing, oil catcher and oil connecting pipe installed on Adapter (87 90 917). Install lower primary gear socket between adapter and bearing housing.

15) Insert bearing housing and output shaft assembly using slide hammer, so bearing housing is seated and output shaft meets operating sleeve. Install output

Manual Transmissions
SAAB 900 5-SPEED TRANSAXLE (Cont.)

shaft countershaft thrust washer, coated with grease, so tab fits into recess of case.

16) Slide output shaft countergear onto shaft and install sleeve, bearings and snap ring. Install countershaft in case and slide gear toward thrust washer to allow alignment of gear for final installation.

17) Install operating sleeve onto countershaft and insert snap ring into recess. Install countergear thrust washer. Using Installer (83 90 049), insert countergear shaft so it locks in position. Install reverse idler gear and spindle, then insert reverse idler gear shaft until it locks in position using installer.

18) Install locking plate into primary gear cover. Seal locking plate with Loctite, then coat threads with same. Install and tighten bolts. Install upper primary gear and chain assembly. Ensure hole for lower primary gear tab washer is facing outward. Install chain tensioner. Coat threads of chain tensioner bolts with Loctite, then install and tighten bolts.

19) Lock pinion shaft by engaging reverse gear and 5th gear. Install pinion shaft nut and tighten. Bend 1 nut tab into hole provided in lower primary gear. Install reverse gear operating lever and tighten bolt.

20) Seal bolt with Loctite. Install differential unit. Install selector ball and gearbox top cover gasket and cover. Install primary gear housing gasket and cover.

FINAL ASSEMBLY

1) Remove axle shaft housing from transaxle. Press axle housings onto axle shaft, then install snap rings to secure shafts in place. Install speedometer drive assembly into left axle shaft housing.

2) Install "O" rings onto both housings. Install spring and plunger in end of axle shaft. Install axle shaft housings onto transaxle case, making sure that correct adjusting shims are in place on each housing. Install and tighten bolts.

3) Recheck backlash adjustment and readjust if necessary. Install rear cover on transaxle case and tighten attaching bolts. Fill transaxle to correct fluid level.

TIGHTENING SPECIFICATIONS

Application	Ft. Lbs. (N.m)
Hub-To-Rotor Bolts	22-36 (30-49)
Front Hub Nut	251-266 (340-361)
Input Shaft Nut	67-81 (91-110)
Pinion Shaft Retaining Nut	30-45 (41-61)
All 8 mm Bolts	14-18 (19-24)
Speedometer Drive Shaft	21-36 (28-49)
Ring Gear Attaching Bolts	30-45 (41-61)
Axle Shaft Housing Bolts	14-18 (19-24)

SUBARU 4 & 5-SPEED

DL, GL & STD

DESCRIPTION

Transmission has 4 or 5 speeds with synchromesh in all forward gears. Both transmission and differential are mounted in the same 2-piece aluminum housing. A hypoid-type gear is used for the final drive. Gear shift linkage is incorporated in transmission cover.

Transmission and differential are lubricated from a common oil supply. Front axle drive shafts employ constant velocity joints at transaxle drive flange and axle shaft.

Four-wheel drive models have rear drive shaft which rotates with drive pinion at gear ratio of 1 to 1. Rear drive shaft is equipped with a claw clutch for 4-wheel drive shifting. Claw clutch has conventional type synchromesh system to ensure no damage to gears when shifting to 4-wheel drive while vehicle is in motion.

LUBRICATION & ADJUSTMENT

See the appropriate article in MANUAL TRANS-MISSION SERVICING Section.

TROUBLE SHOOTING

TRANSMISSION NOISE

Lubricant insufficient. Worn or chipped gears or bearings. If gear tooth surface is excessively worn, a growling sound should be apparent at high speed. When teeth are chipped, periodic knocking is audible at both high and low speeds.

DIFFERENTIAL NOISE

Lubricant insufficient. Tapered roller bearings out of adjustment. Ring and/or pinion gear out of adjustment, ring gear loose. Worn differential side gears, washers or pinion.

Fig. 1: Exploded View of Front Axle Assembly

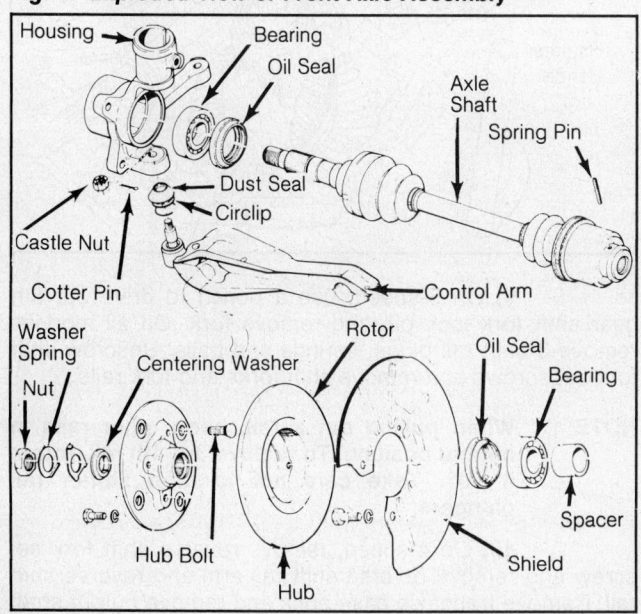

NOTE: Noise from exhaust system, tires, wheel bearings etc. is easily mistaken for differential noise. Eliminate these noises prior to disassembling differential.

HARD SHIFTING

Clutch not properly adjusted or hanging up when released. Worn, damaged or burred sleeve on gear spline or chamfered parts. Scratched bushings. Defective contact or worn synchro ring and gear cone.

SLIPS OUT OF GEAR

Loose engine mounts. Worn shifter fork or broken shifter fork rail spring. Damaged ball bearing. Excessive clearance between synchro hub and sleeve splines. Worn gears or bushings.

SERVICE (IN VEHICLE)

WHEEL BEARINGS

Removal

1) Raise and support vehicle. Remove wheels. Disconnect parking brake linkage from caliper. Remove caliper mounting bolts and hang caliper from frame with wire. Do NOT remove hydraulic connection.

2) Remove bolts connecting shock absorber strut to housing. Remove parking brake hangar from tie rod, then remove cable bracket from housing. Straighten staked portion of axle nut and remove nut.

3) Remove tie rod ball joint and lower control arm ball joint from housing. Using a puller, remove hub and rotor assembly from axle shaft. Remove shield from housing and use a puller to remove housing from axle shaft.

Disassembly

Using brass drift and hammer, knock inner bearing from support housing. Pull out spacer and knock out outer bearing. Seals come out with bearings.

Reassembly

Use press drift and adapter to reassemble. Set bearing into adapter and press into outer side of housing until race is totally seated. Place .5 oz. bearing grease inside support housing, then insert spacer. Repeat above procedure to install outer bearing. Lubricate lips of oil seals lightly and press into position.

Installation

To install, reverse removal procedure and tighten all bolts.

AXLE DRIVE SHAFTS

Removal

1) Disconnect negative battery cable. Apply parking brake. Remove front wheel cap and cotter pin, and loosen castle nut and wheel nuts. Raise and support vehicle and remove front tires and wheels. Release parking brake. Remove parking brake cable bracket from transverse link.

2) Drive out spring pin of double offset joint. Remove disc brake assembly, disconnect tie-rod, transverse link and dampner strut. Remove axle shaft from differential spindle along with housing. Remove housing from axle shaft by using puller (921121000).

Manual Transmissions

SUBARU 4 & 5-SPEED (Cont.)

Installation

To install, reverse removal procedure. Use a new retaining pin to secure inner axle shaft to drive axle. Tighten all bolts.

CONSTANT VELOCITY (CV) JOINTS

Disassembly

1) Straighten bent claw of larger end of boot on double offset joint side. Loosen band by means of screwdriver or pliers taking care not to damage boot. Remove boot band on the small end of double offset joint boot in the same manner.

2) Remove the larger end of boot on double offset joint side. Pry and remove round circlip located at the neck of outer race on double offset joint side with a screwdriver. Take out the outer race on double offset joint side from the shaft assembly.

3) Wipe off the grease and take out the balls. Move the cage to the boot side. Remove snap ring with snap ring pliers. Take out the inner race of the double offset joint.

4) Take out the cage of the double offset joint from the shaft and remove the boot from double offset joint with care not to damage it. Pull out the boot on the constant velocity joint side.

Fig. 2: Removing Outer Race and Ball Bearings

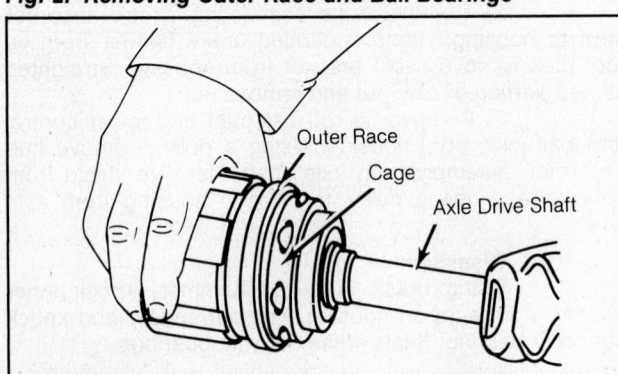

Inspection

Examine CV joint for corrosion, damage or wear. Ensure axle drive shaft does not have excessive deflection, twist or wear. Replace components as necessary.

Reassembly

To reassemble, reverse disassembly procedure. Grease constant velocity joint and double offset joint with Molylex No. 2 grease.

TRANSAXLE REMOVAL & INSTALLATION

See the appropriate article in MANUAL TRANSMISSION REMOVAL Section.

TRANSAXLE DISASSEMBLY

All Except Dual Range Models

1) Mount transaxle in work stand. Disconnect release bearing holder return springs. On 4WD single range models, remove transfer case cover and gasket.

Drive out shift fork retaining pin. Remove transfer shift rail, then remove shift fork, ball and spring.

2) Remove extension housing retaining bolts, extension housing and gasket. Lock transaxle in gear and install gear holder (498787000). Remove staking from pinion shaft lock nut and then remove lock nut. Shift gear to 1st position. Remove lock washer and transfer drive gear from pinion shaft.

3) Remove transfer case mounting bolts. Using a plastic hammer, tap transfer case off and remove gasket and shim. When removing shifter fork rail, be careful ball does not pop out of transmission case.

4) On all models, remove clutch release fork and release bearing holder. Remove transmission rear case, main case rear gasket, main shaft rear plate and back-up light clip. Remove drive pinion attaching bolts.

5) Clean spline portion of the axle drive shafts on right and left sides and wrap with vinyl tape. Separate transmission main case into right and left halves. Remove clutch cable bracket, back-up light cord clip, radio ground and oxygen sensor harness clip.

6) Remove drive pinion as shown in Fig. 3. Remove transmission main shaft. Remove differential. On 5-speed models, remove spring pin and 5th shifter fork. Do not mix right and left roller bearing outer races.

7) On all models, remove plugs, gaskets, springs and balls from case. Unscrew shifter fork set screws, and remove 3rd-4th and 1st-2nd shifter forks as well as shifter rails. Remove shifter set screw, reverse shifter rail arm and reverse shifter rail.

8) Remove oil seal holder lock plates, axle shaft oil seal holders and "O" rings. Remove snap ring and speedometer driven gear. Remove knock pins, reverse idler gear shaft, reverse idler gear and shifter lever.

Fig. 3: Prying Pinion Shaft Out of Case

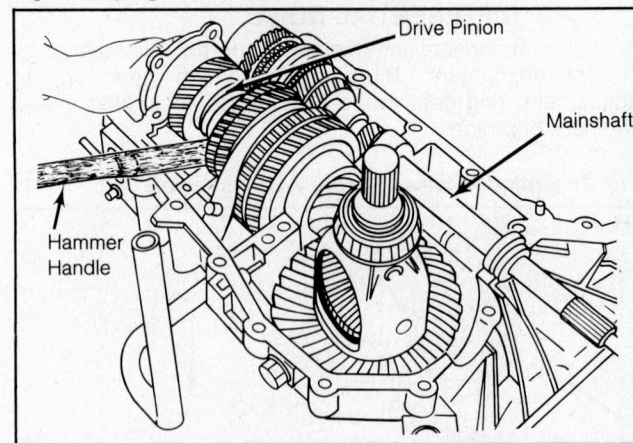

9) On 5-speed, use a punch to drive out 5th gear shift fork lock pin and remove fork. On all models, remove 3 shift rail plugs, springs and balls. Unscrew shift fork set screws and remove shift forks and fork rails.

NOTE: When pulling out a rail, keep other rails in neutral position. To remove 3rd-4th rail, rotate it 90°. Take care not to drop shifter rail plungers.

10) On 4-speed, remove reverse shift fork set screw and remove reverse shift rail arm and reverse shift rail. Remove transaxle case bolts and remove output shaft

SUBARU 4 & 5-SPEED (Cont.)

oil seal holder lock plates. Using remover (399780111), remove drive axle shaft oil seal holder and "O" ring.

11) Remove speedometer driven gear snap ring and gear. Lightly tap speedometer shaft out of case. Oil seal should come out with shaft. Remove reverse idler gear shaft retaining pins. Remove reverse idler gear shaft, idler gear and shift lever.

12) On 5-speed, remove reverse idler gear shaft retaining pins. Remove reverse idler gear shaft, idler gear and shift lever. Remove reverse shift rail outer snap ring, then remove shift rail arm and shift rail. Remove reverse shift ball, spring and plunger.

13) Remove output shaft oil seal holder. Using remover (399780111), remove drive axle shaft oil seal holder and "O" ring. Remove speedometer driven gear snap ring and gear. Lightly tap speedometer shaft out of case. Oil seal should come out with shaft.

NOTE: When removing reverse shift rail arm, ensure ball does not pop out of case.

Fig. 4: Removing Mainshaft and Differential Assembly from Transaxle Case

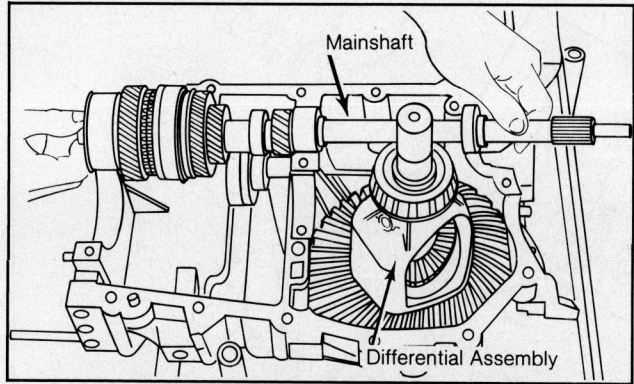

Mainshaft

Differential Assembly

Dual Range 4WD Models

1) Set transmission in stand. Remove clutch release fork and release bearing holder complete. Remove transfer case cover. Punch out the spring pin connecting high-low shifter rod to rod arm. Remove clip on transfer shifter rail with screwdriver after shifting transfer shifter rail into "4WD LO" position.

2) Pull out transfer shifter rail after shifting into "4WD HI" position. When pulling out, fix both high-low shifter arm and transfer shifter fork into "4WD HI" position in order not to interlock plunger. Be careful that ball does not fly out and drop into transfer case. Remove pin and clip on interlock rail with pliers.

3) Pull out interlock rail by turning 90°. Be careful that pin and clip on interlock rail do not fly out. Remove transfer shifter fork from transfer case, turning it in order not to interfere with high-low shifter rail. Be carefull not to loose ball and spring. Remove extension assembly.

4) Loosen front nut of rod adjusting screw connecting high-low shifter rod with ball joint assembly, and loosen rear nut (nut is left-hand threaded). Disconnect high-low shifter rod from rod arm by turning rod adjust arm screw clockwise. Disconnect rod ball joint assembly from high-low shifter center pivot by removing nut.

5) Punch out spring pin connecting high-low shifter rail to rod arm and remove rod arm. Punch out

spring pin connecting high-low shifter rail to high-low shifter arm and remove high-low shifter rail and arm. Be careful not to lose ball and plunger. Lock transmission main shaft with stopper (498787000). Release staking and remove lock nut.

6) Shift gear to 1st position to prevent shaft from turning. Remove transfer case attaching bolts. Pull out transfer case by about .040" (10 mm). Separate transfer case from main case by tapping with plastic hammer. Remove ball bearing attaching bolts at the drive pinion gear.

7) Remove input shaft holder attaching bolts. Wrap spline portions of axle shafts with vinyl tape. Separate transmission main case into left and right halves. Remove clutch cable bracket, oxygen sensor harness clip, radio ground, back-up light clips, clutch cable clamp, and stopper plate.

8) Punch out spring pin and remove high-low shift lever center pivot. Turn 90° and remove high-low shift fork. Pull countergear shaft forward until it hits on transmission main case and remove clip with screwdriver. Slide countergear washer to the rear and remove knock pin from countergear shaft.

9) Remove countergear shaft from main case being careful not to drop countergear and washers. Remove countergear from main case. Remove drive pinion as shown in *Fig. 3*. Remove transmission main shaft. Remove differential. *See Fig. 4.* Do not mix right and left roller bearing outer races.

10) Remove plugs, gaskets, springs and balls from case. Unscrew shifter fork set screws, and remove 3rd-4th and 1st-2nd shifter forks as well as shifter rails. Remove shifter set screw, reverse shifter rail arm and reverse shifter rail.

11) Remove oil seal holder lock plates, axle shaft oil seal holders and "O" rings. Remove snap ring and speedometer driven gear. Remove knock pins, reverse idler gear shaft, reverse idler gear and shifter lever.

12) Remove 3 shift rail plugs, springs and balls. Unscrew shift fork set screws and remove shift forks and fork rails. When pulling out a rail, keep other rails in neutral position. To remove 3rd-4th rail, rotate it 90°. Take care not to drop shifter rail plungers.

13) Remove reverse shift fork set screw and remove reverse shift rail arm and reverse shift rail. Remove transaxle case bolts and remove output shaft oil seal holder lock plates. Using remover (399780111), remove drive axle shaft oil seal holder and "O" ring.

14) Remove speedometer driven gear snap ring and gear. Lightly tap speedometer shaft out of case. Oil seal should come out with shaft. Remove reverse idler gear shaft retaining pins. Remove reverse idler gear shaft, idler gear and shift lever.

NOTE: When removing reverse shift rail arm, ensure ball does not pop out of case.

COMPONENT DISASSEMBLY & REASSEMBLY

MAINSHAFT
Disassembly
1) On 4WD dual range models, separate mainshaft assembly from input shaft, and remove high-low

Manual Transmissions
SUBARU 4 & 5-SPEED (Cont.)

Fig. 5: Exploded View of Transaxle Assembly Components

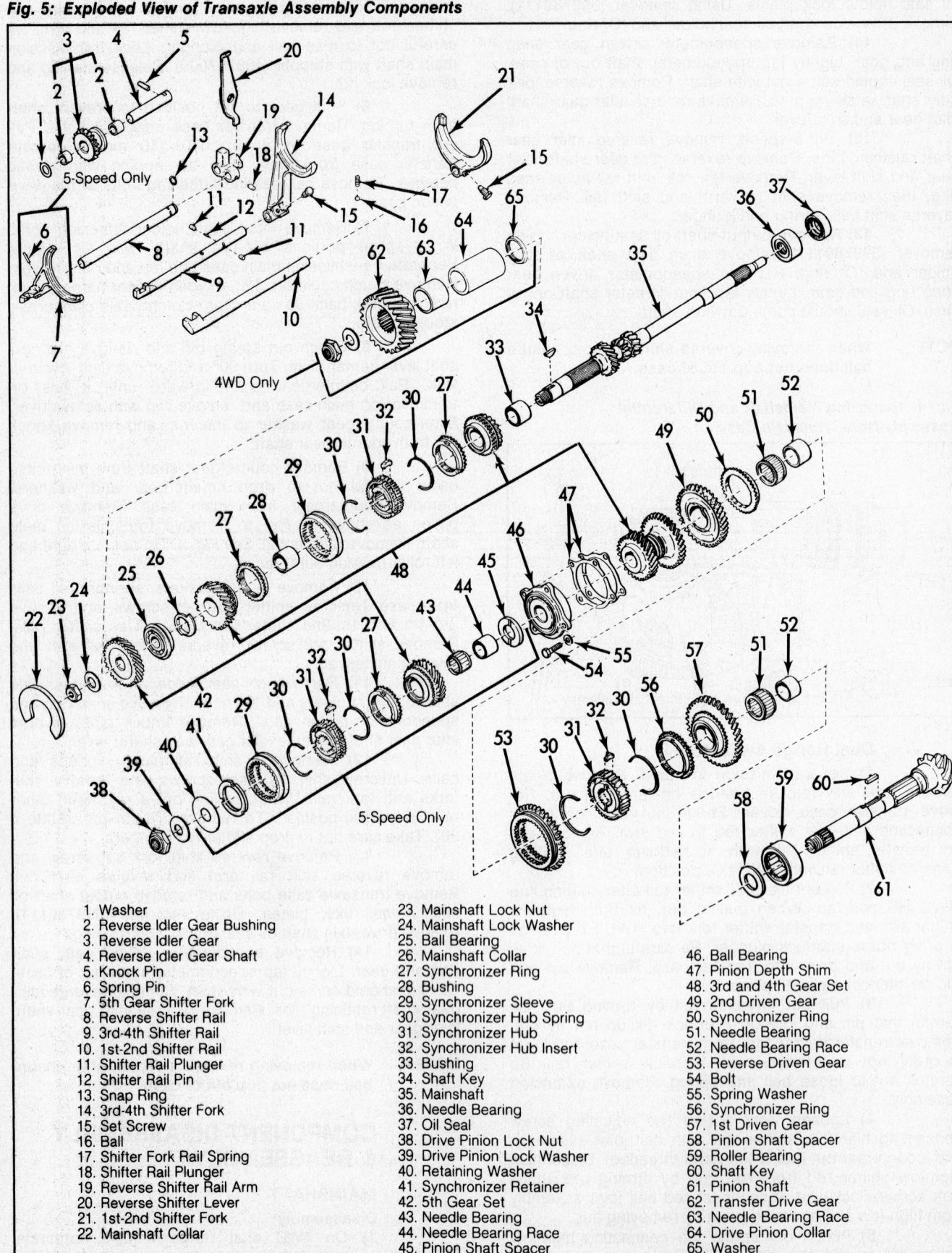

1. Washer
2. Reverse Idler Gear Bushing
3. Reverse Idler Gear
4. Reverse Idler Gear Shaft
5. Knock Pin
6. Spring Pin
7. 5th Gear Shifter Fork
8. Reverse Shifter Rail
9. 3rd-4th Shifter Rail
10. 1st-2nd Shifter Rail
11. Shifter Rail Plunger
12. Shifter Rail Pin
13. Snap Ring
14. 3rd-4th Shifter Fork
15. Set Screw
16. Ball
17. Shifter Fork Rail Spring
18. Shifter Rail Plunger
19. Reverse Shifter Rail Arm
20. Reverse Shifter Lever
21. 1st-2nd Shifter Fork
22. Mainshaft Collar
23. Mainshaft Lock Nut
24. Mainshaft Lock Washer
25. Ball Bearing
26. Mainshaft Collar
27. Synchronizer Ring
28. Bushing
29. Synchronizer Sleeve
30. Synchronizer Hub Spring
31. Synchronizer Hub
32. Synchronizer Hub Insert
33. Bushing
34. Shaft Key
35. Mainshaft
36. Needle Bearing
37. Oil Seal
38. Drive Pinion Lock Nut
39. Drive Pinion Lock Washer
40. Retaining Washer
41. Synchronizer Retainer
42. 5th Gear Set
43. Needle Bearing
44. Needle Bearing Race
45. Pinion Shaft Spacer
46. Ball Bearing
47. Pinion Depth Shim
48. 3rd and 4th Gear Set
49. 2nd Driven Gear
50. Synchronizer Ring
51. Needle Bearing
52. Needle Bearing Race
53. Reverse Driven Gear
54. Bolt
55. Spring Washer
56. Synchronizer Ring
57. 1st Driven Gear
58. Pinion Shaft Spacer
59. Roller Bearing
60. Shaft Key
61. Pinion Shaft
62. Transfer Drive Gear
63. Needle Bearing Race
64. Drive Pinion Collar
65. Washer

SUBARU 4 & 5-SPEED (Cont.)

synchronizer ring. Be careful not to drop needle bearing in input shaft. Remove snap ring with expander (899474100).

2) Remove the following parts by hand: High-low synchronizer hub with inserts, springs and sleeve, high-low synchronizer ring, input low gear, input low gear collar, needle bearing, input low gear spacer, ball and needle bearing.

3) On 5-speed models, remove lock nut staking, then remove lock nut. Using a press, remove 5th gear from shaft. Remove shaft key. On 4-speed models, remove snap ring from end of mainshaft.

NOTE: Snap ring should not be reused.

4) On all models, use press to remove ball bearing, 4th drive gear thrust plate, 4th drive gear, synchronizer hub, 4th drive gear bushing and 3rd drive gear.

NOTE: Do not remove 3rd drive gear bushing unless it is defective. If replacement is necessary, cut a groove in bushing, then press from mainshaft.

Fig. 6: Pressing Gears Off of Mainshaft

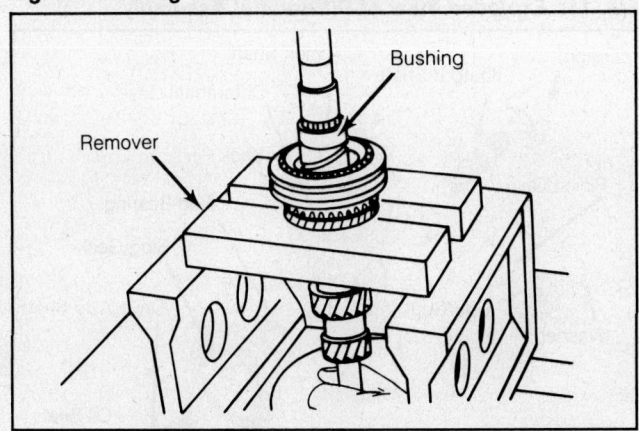

Cleaning & Inspection
Clean all parts and inspect carefully. Replace any parts which are worn or damaged. Lubricate all bearings with gear oil and spin to check for smooth and quiet operation. Replace synchro ring if ring gap is reduced to below limit .020" (.50 mm) when ring is pressed against cone. Standard clearance is .06" (1.5 mm).

Reassembly
1) If removed, install new 3rd gear bushing using press and installer (899580100) and retainer (899714110). Assemble synchro assemblies ensuring that hub spring ends are 120° apart. Note also that the shorter inserts are installed in 3rd-4th synchro and longer inserts in the 1st-2nd synchro.

2) Install 3rd drive gear and synchro assembly on mainshaft ensuring that narrower tooth width of synchro spline is on 3rd gear side. Press synchro assembly on mainshaft, if necessary.

3) Press 4th drive gear bushing onto mainshaft. Install 4th drive gear and thrust plate. Press bearing onto shaft. On 4-speed models, install 1 of 12 available snap rings on shaft to obtain 0-.002" (0-.05 mm) end play. On 5-speed models, install shaft key and press 5th drive gear onto shaft. Install lock nut, tighten and restake.

Fig. 7: Exploded View of Synchro Hub Assembly

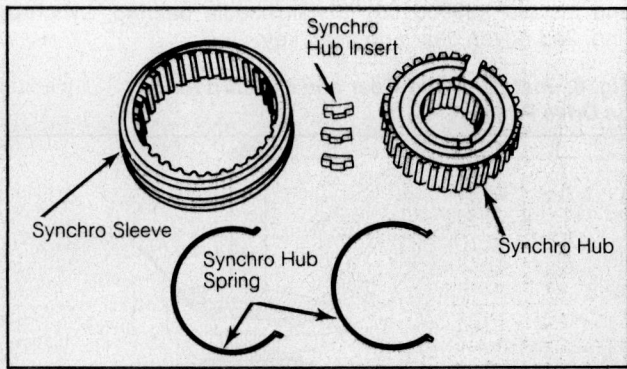

4) On 4WD single range models, install washer, drive pinion collar, transfer needle bearing race and transfer drive gear to drive pinion with press and installer (899580100). Tighten lock washer and nut. Do not stake at this time.

5) On 4WD dual range models, install 3 high-low synchronizer inserts, sleeve and 2 springs on synchronizer hub. Install springs so that relative positions of cut ends are 120° apart.

6) Install needle bearing, ball, input low gear spacer, needle bearing, input low gear collar, input low gear, high-low synchronizer ring and hub assembly previously assembled.

PINION SHAFT
Disassembly
1) Remove pinion shaft lock nut if still installed. On 5-speed models, remove lock washer, insert stopper plate, insert guide, synchro hub, 5th driven gear and needle bearing. Press 5th needle bearing race, 5th driven gear thrust plate and bearing from shaft.

2) On all models, use a press to remove 3rd-4th driven gear, rear bearing and any components between bearing and end of shaft. Remove 2nd driven gear and needle bearing.

3) Using a press, remove 1st driven gear, synchro/reverse driven gear assembly and needle bearing race. Remove shaft key and needle bearing. Use a press to remove pinion spacer and needle bearing race. Remove roller bearing.

Cleaning & Inspection
Clean all parts and inspect carefully. Replace any parts which are worn or damaged. Lubricate all bearings with engine oil and spin to check for smooth and quiet operation. Replace synchro ring if ring gap is reduced to below limit of .020" (.50 mm) when ring is pressed against cone. Standard clearance is .06" (1.5 mm).

Reassembly
1) Install roller bearing on drive pinion and install drive pinion thrust plate with a press and drive pinion installers (899278600, 899874100 and 899580100).

2) Install three 1st-2nd synchro inserts, reverse driven gear and 2 synchro springs on 1st-2nd synchro hub. Ensure synchro spring cut ends are 120° apart. Also check that toothed side of reverse driven gear and lower boss of synchro hub point in same direction.

3) Install needle bearing race with press and installers (899874100 and 899580100). Install needle bearing, 1st driven gear and synchro/reverse driven gear

assembly. Install 1st-2nd needle bearing race with press and installer (89958100). Install needle bearing, synchro ring, 2nd driven gear and shaft key.

Fig. 8: Installing 2nd Gear and Synchro Ring on Drive Pinion

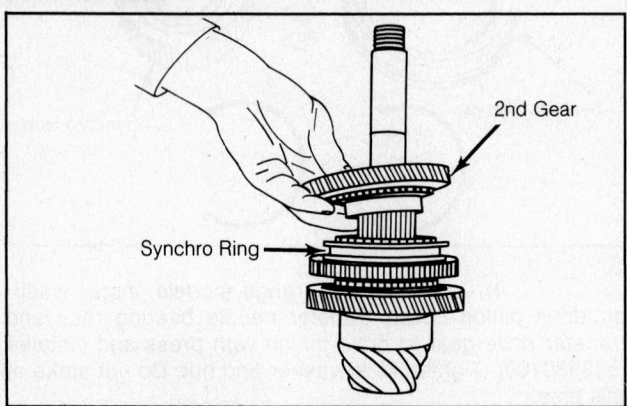

4) Install 3rd-4th driven gear using a press and installer (899580100). Install rear bearing using press and installer tool (899874100).

NOTE: **If bearing slides onto shaft without being pressed on, no problem is indicated.**

Fig. 9: Installing 3rd-4th Driven Gear on Drive Pinion

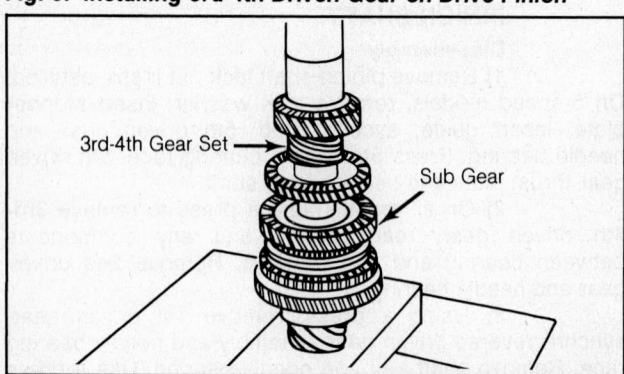

5) On 4-speed, install lock washer and tighten lock nut. On 5-speed, install thrust plate, then press needle bearing race onto shaft. Install needle bearing, 5th driven gear, synchro hub, insert guide, insert stopper plate, lock washer and lock nut. On 4WD, install washer, pinion shaft collar, rear shaft drive gear, lock washer and lock nut.

NOTE: **On all models except 4WD, stake pinion shaft lock nut at this time.**

DIFFERENTIAL ASSEMBLY

Disassembly

1) Remove snap rings securing drive axle shafts to differential assembly and remove shafts. Right and left shafts are not interchangeable; mark for reassembly reference. Bend back ring gear bolt locking tabs. Remove ring gear bolts and lift off ring gear.

2) Using a drift, remove pinion shaft retaining pin and pull out pinion shaft. Remove side gears, pinion gears and thrust washers. Remove side bearings with a puller.

Cleaning & Inspection

Wash and carefully inspect all parts. Replace all worn or damaged parts.

Fig. 10: Removing or Installing Pinion Shaft in Differential Case

Fig. 11: Exploded View of Differential Assembly

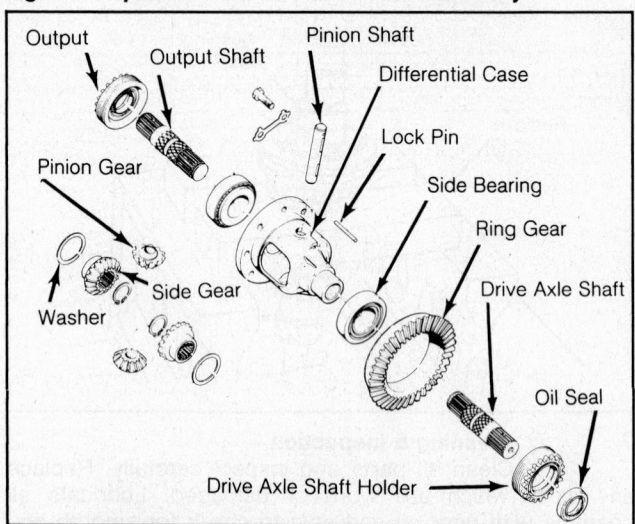

Reassembly

1) Install differential side gears, pinions and washers in differential case. Insert pinion shaft. Measure side gear and pinion backlash. Backlash should be .005-.007" (.13-.18 mm). If backlash is not correct, make adjustments by selecting a different thickness of washer.

2) Align pinion shaft with holes in case and drive lock pin from ring gear side until pin falls about .039" (1 mm) below surface. Lock pin in position by peening hole. Press side bearings onto case. Install ring gear. Install and tighten ring gear bolts, then bend locking tabs to hold bolts.

3) Install drive axle shafts and secure with snap rings. Measure clearance between pinion shaft and tip of drive axle shaft. Adjust clearance to less than .008" (.2 mm) by using thicker snap ring.

NOTE: **Snap rings are available in 2 thicknesses: .039-.043" (1.0-1.1 mm) and .045-.049" (1.15-1.25 mm).**

SUBARU 4 & 5-SPEED (Cont.)

Fig. 12: Pressing Differential Bearings onto Case

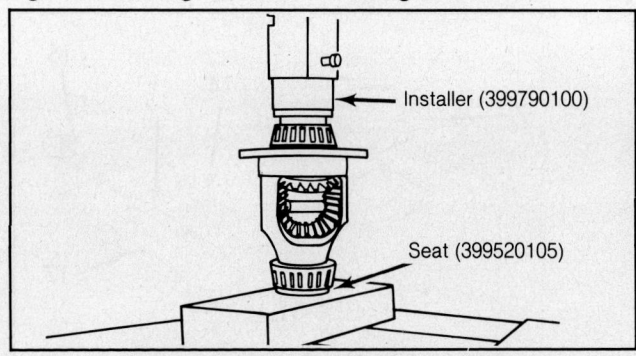

TRANSFER CASE (4WD MODELS ONLY)

Disassembly
Remove "O" ring from shifter arm and remove arm. Remove filler plug and gasket from transfer case. Remove reverse accent spring and ball. Remove back-up light switch and gasket. Remove plug, gasket, reverse accent shaft and spring. Using a hammer and aluminum rod, drive needle bearing out of case.

Cleaning & Inspection
Wash and carefully inspect all parts. Replace all worn or damaged parts.

Reassembly
1) Place needle bearing in bore of case with marked side toward front of case and press in until marked side is flush with case. Install snap ring to transfer case with fingers. Insert reverse return spring and reverse accent shaft, fit an aluminum adjusting gasket on plug and tighten plug.

2) Place an aluminum gasket on back-up light switch and install switch. Install ball and shifter fork rail spring in case, place aluminum washer on filler plug and tighten plug. Slide shifter arm into case and install "O" ring on arm.

EXTENSION HOUSING (4WD MODELS ONLY)

Disassembly
1) Remove snap ring from extension housing, then drive rear drive shaft from housing using a hammer and aluminum rod. Remove oil seal from rear of housing. Shift synchro into drive position. Install holder (899884100) on shaft and mount assembly in a vise.

2) Unstake lock nut and remove lock nut and lock washer. Mount shaft assembly on retainer (899714110) and press out shaft. Remove bearing, spacer collar, rear driven gear, bushing, synchro hub and spacer.

Cleaning & Inspection
Wash and carefully inspect all parts. Replace all worn or damaged parts. Pay particular attention to extension housing rear bushing. If it is excessively worn or scratched, replace it.

Reassembly
1) Assemble synchronizer sleeve on the synchronizer hub. Be sure to use sleeve without reverse taper. Press rear bearing onto shaft. Install new oil seal in rear of extension housing. Using a plastic hammer, tap rear drive shaft into extension housing. Install snap ring in groove in extension housing. Install rear drive spacer, synchro hub and sleeve assembly to rear drive shaft.

2) Using a press, install driven gear bushing to rear drive shaft. Fit transfer driven gear and 4th drive gear thrust plate to rear drive shaft. Press fit front bearing on shaft. Shift synchro sleeve into drive position, install holder on driven gear, install lock washer and tighten lock nut. Stake nut.

Fig. 13: Removing Snap Ring from Extension Housing

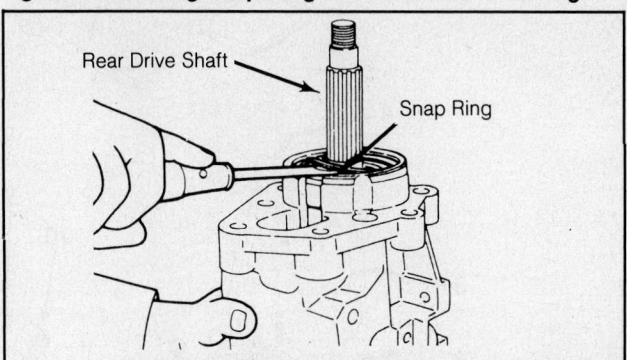

TRANSAXLE REASSEMBLY & ADJUSTMENT

PINION SHAFT DEPTH ADJUSTMENT

NOTE: This adjustment must be performed using Subaru Pinion Gauge (899914100).

1) Install pinion shaft assembly in transaxle case half (right half) with no shims between rear bearing and case. Install and tighten 2 pinion shaft retaining bolts to 22 ft. lbs. (30 N.m).

2) Place pinion gauge on its edge on a level surface, then loosen 2 setting bolts on gauge plate. Adjust gauge plate so scale indicates 0.5 when edges of plate and scale are even. Tighten bolts. Place calibrated gauge into case as shown in *Fig. 14*.

NOTE: Ensure dowel pins of gauge are installed in dowel holes of transaxle case.

3) Slide gauge scale along plate until it comes in contact with drive pinion, then read and record value shown on scale. The thickness of shim(s) required to obtain correct drive pinion depth is determined by adding or subtracting value stamped on end of pinion to or from gauge scale value.

Fig. 14: Measuring Pinion Shaft Depth Using Special Gauge

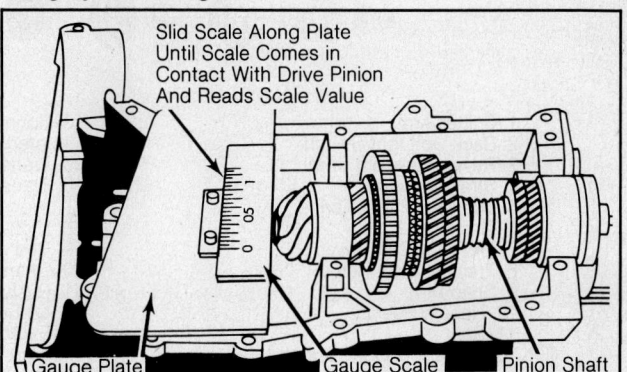

Manual Transmissions

SUBARU 4 & 5-SPEED (Cont.)

Fig. 15: *Exploded View of 4WD Transfer Case, Extension Housing and Related Components*

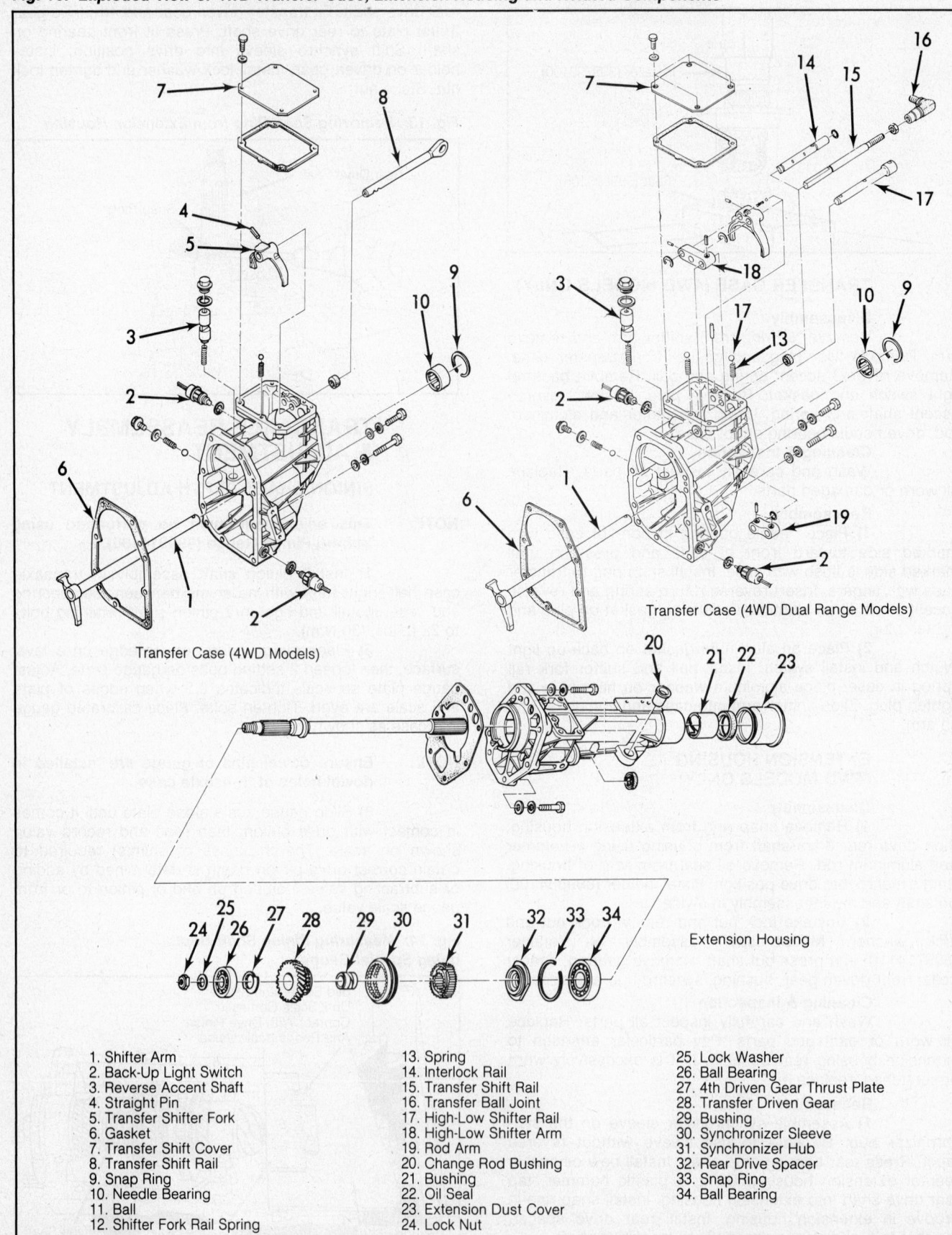

Transfer Case (4WD Models)

Transfer Case (4WD Dual Range Models)

Extension Housing

1. Shifter Arm	13. Spring	25. Lock Washer
2. Back-Up Light Switch	14. Interlock Rail	26. Ball Bearing
3. Reverse Accent Shaft	15. Transfer Shift Rail	27. 4th Driven Gear Thrust Plate
4. Straight Pin	16. Transfer Ball Joint	28. Transfer Driven Gear
5. Transfer Shifter Fork	17. High-Low Shifter Rail	29. Bushing
6. Gasket	18. High-Low Shifter Arm	30. Synchronizer Sleeve
7. Transfer Shift Cover	19. Rod Arm	31. Synchronizer Hub
8. Transfer Shift Rail	20. Change Rod Bushing	32. Rear Drive Spacer
9. Snap Ring	21. Bushing	33. Snap Ring
10. Needle Bearing	22. Oil Seal	34. Ball Bearing
11. Ball	23. Extension Dust Cover	
12. Shifter Fork Rail Spring	24. Lock Nut	

SUBARU 4 & 5-SPEED (Cont.)

4) Add if value stamped on pinion is prefixed by a "+"; subtract if value is prefixed by a "-". Select from 1 to 3 adjusting shims which will equal value just obtained. Remove gauge and pinion shaft from case.

NOTE: **If no value is stamped on pinion, value is zero. Adjusting shim(s) will be installed during Transaxle Reassembly.**

TRANSAXLE REASSEMBLY
All Except 4WD Dual Range Models

1) Press new oil seals into axle drive shaft holders. Place speedometer shaft side of transmission case in a work stand, then screw axle shaft holder (without "O" ring) into case until threads are embedded completely in case.

2) Install speedometer shaft outer snap ring and washer on shaft, then install assembly in case. Install speedometer driven gear on shaft and retain with outer snap ring. Press in new speedometer shaft oil seal.

NOTE: **Install speedometer driven gear snap ring from driven gear side to avoid damaging oil seal.**

3) On 5-speed, insert reverse shift arm spring and ball into reverse shift rail arm. Install reverse shift rail into case, then fit shift rail arm onto shift rail and install snap ring. Install shift fork rail spring, ball and gasket into case and tighten shift rail spring plug.

4) Install reverse idler gear and shaft. Select shift lever that will provide .06-.12" (1.5-3.0 mm) clearance between reverse idler gear and case wall when shifting reverse shift rail. Remove reverse idler gear and shaft. Install and tighten correct shift lever. Shift lever to neutral position and reinstall reverse idler gear and shaft.

5) Select washer that will provide a clearance of less than .02" (.5 mm) between washer and case wall. Remove reverse idler gear and shaft. Install washer and reinstall reverse idler assembly. Install retaining pins. Install 5th shift fork onto reverse shift rail and secure with spring pin.

6) On all other models, install reverse shift lever into case. Install reverse idler gear and shaft into case and retain with pin. Install reverse shift rail arm to end of reverse shift lever, then install reverse shift rail and tighten set screw. Install reverse shift fork rail spring, ball and gasket into case. Tighten spring plug.

7) Move reverse shift rail to reverse position and measure clearance between reverse idler gear and case. Install shift rail arm which will provide .06-.12" (1.5-

RAIL CLEARANCE VALUES

Application	In. (mm)
1600 cc Models	
"A"	.012-.063 (0.3-1.6)
"B"	.012-.063 (0.3-1.6)
1800 cc Models	
"A"	.012-.063 (0.3-1.6)
"B"	.071-.122 (1.8-3.1)

3.0 mm) clearance between gear and case. Install shift rail arm and secure with retaining pin.

8) On all models, wrap vinyl tape around splines of drive axle shafts to protect seals, then install differential in case. Install mainshaft in case, ensuring that dowel pin on case is fitted into hole in needle bearing outer race. Install shift rail pin in 3rd-4th shift rail, then install rail and 3rd-4th shift fork. Tighten set screw.

9) Install previously selected pinion depth adjusting shim(s) on pinion shaft rear bearing. If more than 1 shim is used, do not place slit ends of shims on same side. Install pinion shaft in case, ensuring that dowel pin on case is fitted into hole in rear bearing outer race.

10) Place shift rail plunger into hole in case. Install 1st-2nd shift rail and shift fork, then tighten set screw. Install shift rail balls, springs and plugs. Force mainshaft and pinion shaft toward front of case until there is no clearance between shafts and case.

Fig. 17: Transaxle Case Tightening Sequence

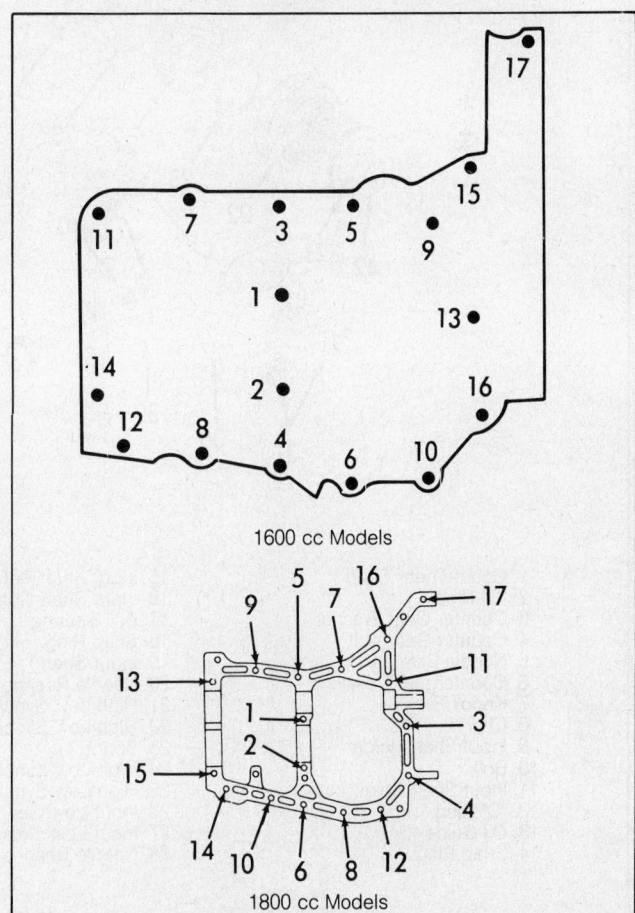

1600 cc Models

1800 cc Models

Fig. 16: Clearances Between Rails

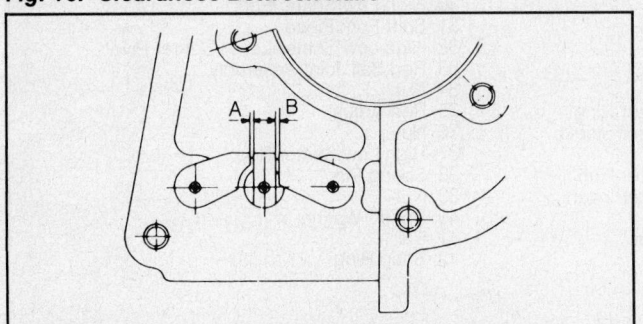

Manual Transmissions

SUBARU 4 & 5-SPEED (Cont.)

Fig. 18: Auxiliary Transmission and High-Low Shift Linkage (4WD Dual Range Models)

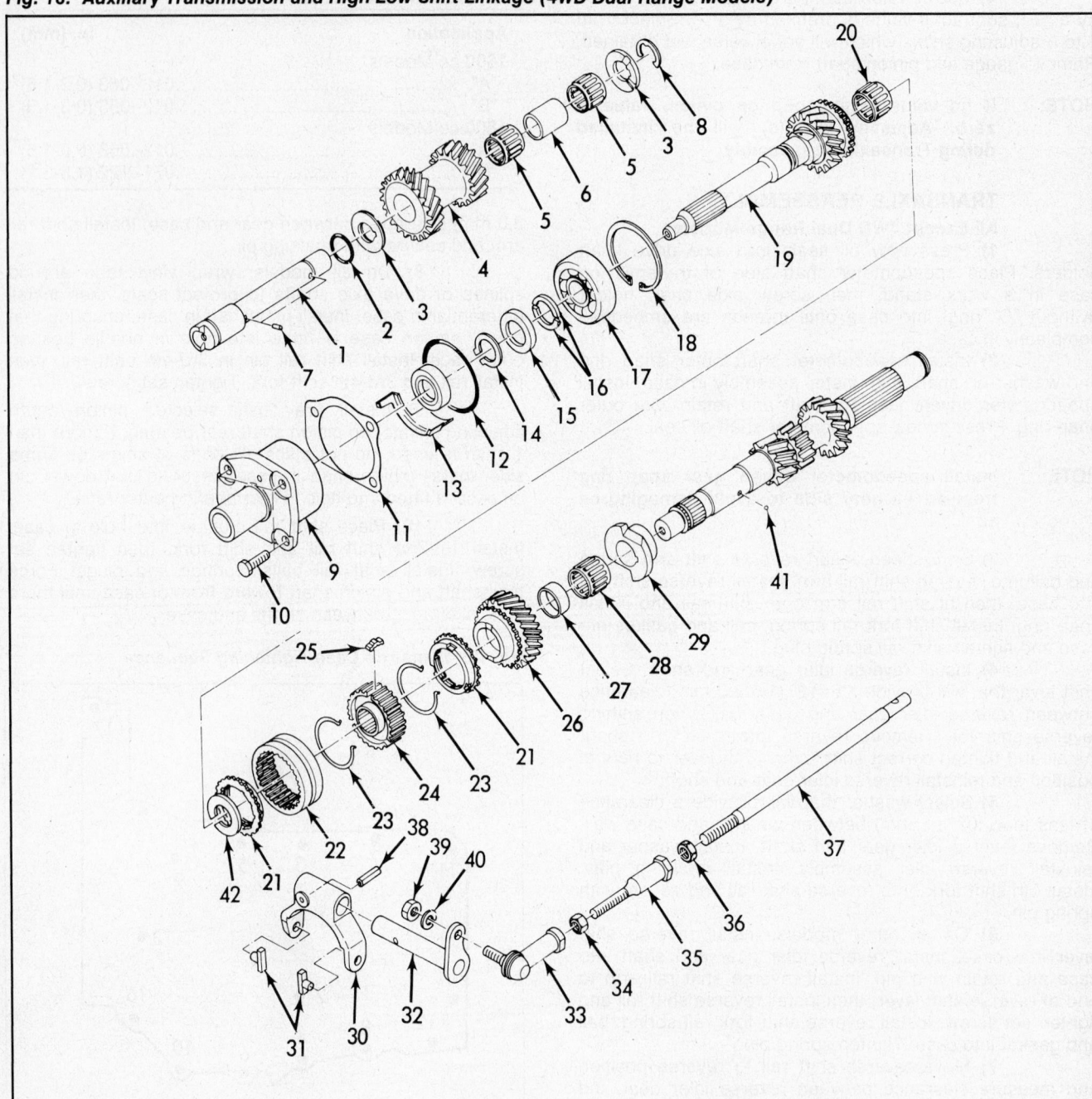

1. Countergear Shaft	15. Input Shaft Retainer	29. Input Low Gear Spacer
2. "O" Ring	16. Input Shaft Cotter	30. High-Low Shifter Fork
3. Counter Gear Washer	17. Ball Bearing	31. Shift Fork Piece
4. Counter Gear	18. Snap Ring	32. High-Low Shifter Lever Center Pivot
5. Needle Bearing	19. Input Shaft	33. Rod Ball Joint Assembly
6. Countergear Collar	20. Needle Bearing	34. Nut
7. Knock Pin	21. High-Low Synchronizer Ring	35. Rod Adjust
8. Clip	22. High-Low Synchronizer Sleeve	36. Nut
9. Input Shaft Holder	23. Spring	37. High-Low Shifter Rod
10. Bolt	24. High-Low Synchronizer Hub	38. Spring Pin
11. Input Shaft Shim	25. High-Low Synchronizer Insert	39. Nut
12. "O" Ring	26. Input Low Gear	40. Spring Washer
13. Oil Guide	27. Input Low Gear Collar	41. Ball
14. Snap Ring	28. Needle Bearing	42. Snap Ring

SUBARU 4 & 5-SPEED (Cont.)

11) Check that synchro sleeves (with rails in neutral) are centered between respective gears. Check that clearance between 5th driven gear and synchro sleeve is .41" (10.5 mm). If not, select correct shift forks (5 available) to provide this alignment.

12) Check clearance between edges of each shift rail. *See Fig. 16.* If clearance is not as listed in table, replace rail, fork and set screw. Install mainshaft oil seal. Clean mating surfaces of transaxle case halves, then apply sealant to all mating surfaces.

13) Align case halves while slightly shifting case so pinion depth shim(s) is not caught between case halves, then install and tighten attaching bolts. *See Fig. 17.* Install clutch cable bracket, back-up light cord clip, radio ground cord and oxygen sensor harness clip. Install and tighten pinion shaft retaining bolts.

Dual Range 4WD Models

1) Press new oil seals into axle drive shaft holders. Place speedometer shaft side of transmission case in a work stand, then screw axle shaft holder (without "O" ring) into case until threads are embedded completely in case.

2) Install speedometer shaft outer snap ring and washer on shaft, then install assembly in case. Install speedometer driven gear on shaft and retain with outer snap ring. Press in new speedometer shaft oil seal.

NOTE: Install speedometer driven gear snap ring from driven gear side to avoid damaging oil seal.

3) Install reverse shift lever into case. Install reverse idler gear and shaft into case and retain with pin. Install reverse shift rail arm to end of reverse shift lever, then install reverse shift rail and tighten set screw.

4) Install reverse shift fork rail spring, ball and gasket into case. Tighten spring plug. Move reverse shift rail to reverse position and measure clearance between reverse idler gear and case. Install shift rail arm which will provide .06-.12" (1.5-3.0 mm) clearance between gear and case.

5) Install shift rail arm and secure with retaining pin. Wrap vinyl tape around splines of drive axle shafts to protect seals, then install differential in case. Install "O" ring and knock pin at front side onto countergear shaft.

6) Install the following parts onto the countergear shaft when installing it into main case: 2 countergear washers, 2 needle bearings, countergear collar, knock pin and clip. Make sure the cut-out end surface of the countergear shaft does not protrude above the end surfaces of the case. *See Fig. 19.*

Fig. 19: Countergear Shaft Positioning

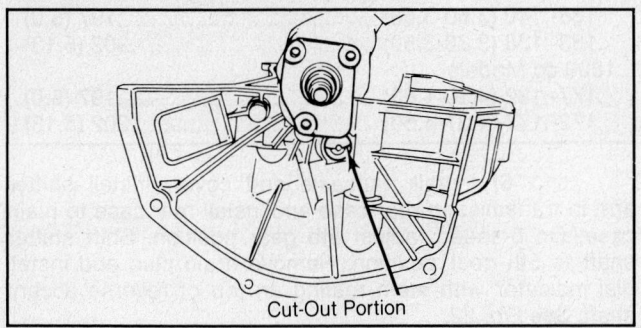

Cut-Out Portion

7) Put mainshaft assembly, needle bearing, high-low synchronizing ring and input shaft together. Shim input shaft with shim number determined by calculating measurement "D" shown in *Fig. 20.*

SHIM DETERMINATION ("D" Distance)

Shim Used	In. (mm)
No Shim	More than 1.984 (50.39)
No. 1	1.983-1.964 (50.38-49.89)
No. 2	Less than 1.96 (49.88)

Fig. 20: Adjustment of Input Shaft

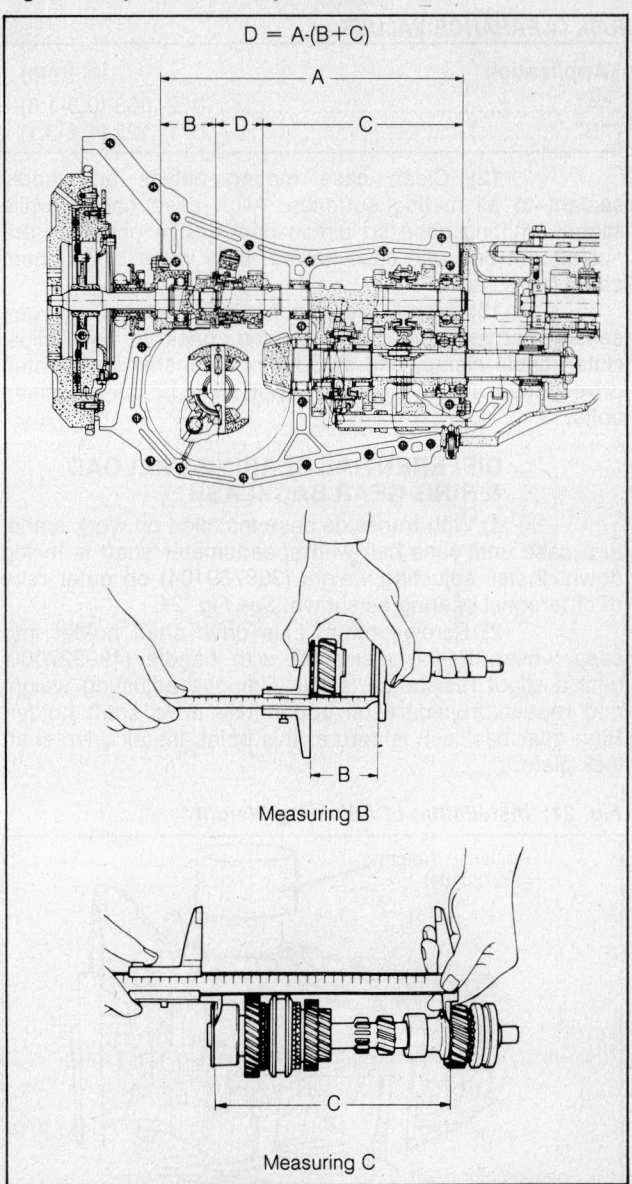

Measuring B

Measuring C

8) Install transmission mainshaft into case. Install high-low shifter fork with 2 high-low shifter pieces into high-low shifter sleeve. Install high-low shift lever into high-low shift fork through the case and install the pin.

9) Install the 3rd-4th shifter fork and rail with plunger and tighten set screw. Install previously selected shims and drive pinion assembly into case. Make sure the knock pin is fit to roller bearing outer race. Fit plunger to

SUBARU 4 & 5-SPEED (Cont.)

case and install 1st-2nd shifter fork and rail. Tighten set screw.

10) Fit 3rd-4th and 1st-2nd shifter fork rail springs, balls, and gaskets into the case. Tighten the shifter rail spring plugs. Force mainshaft and pinion shaft toward front of case until there is no clearance between shafts and case.

11) Check that synchro sleeves (with rails in neutral) are centered between respective gears. Check clearance between edges of each shift rail. If clearance is not as shown in table, replace rail, fork and set screw. *See Fig. 17.*

RAIL CLEARANCE VALUES

Application	In. (mm)
"A"	.012-.063 (0.3-1.6)
"B"	.071-.122 (1.8-3.1)

12) Clean case mating halves and apply sealant to all mating surfaces. Align case halves while slightly shifting case so pinion depth shim or shims are not caught between case halves, then install and tighten attaching bolts.

13) Install the clutch cable bracket, oxygen sensor harness clip, radio ground, back-up light clips, clutch cable clamp, and stopper plate. Install and tighten drive pinion bolts. Tighten 3 input shaft holder attaching bolts.

DIFFERENTIAL BEARING PRELOAD & RING GEAR BACKLASH

1) With transaxle case installed on work stand, turn case until case half with speedometer shaft is facing down. Install adjusting weight (399780104) on outer race of differential bearing as shown. *See Fig. 21.*

2) Screw bottom axle drive shaft holder into case while rotating mainshaft with handle (499927000) until a slight resistance is felt. Remove adjusting weight and repeat procedure on upper axle drive shaft holder. Ring gear backlash is zero at this point. Install drive shaft lock plate.

Fig. 21: Installation of Adjusting Weight

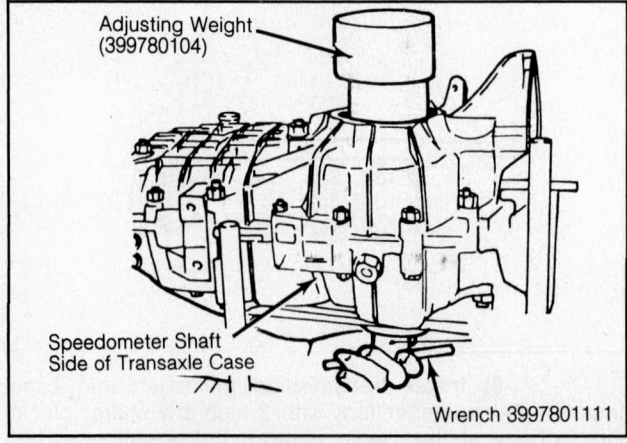

Adjusting Weight (399780104)

Speedometer Shaft Side of Transaxle Case

Wrench 3997801111

3) Loosen bottom drive shaft holder 1 1/2 notches, then screw in upper holder by the same amount to obtain ring gear backlash. Turn upper holder in an additional 1/2 to 1 notch to obtain differential bearing preload.

4) Tighten holder lock plates, then mark position of both holders for later readjustment. Turn mainshaft many times while tapping around axle shaft bearing holder lightly with a plastic hammer.

5) Install a dial indicator to transaxle case with tip of indicator inserted through transaxle drain hole and touching ring gear teeth. Measure ring gear backlash by rotating drive shafts back and forth taking up free play. If backlash does not match specification in table, repeat adjustment procedure.

RING GEAR BACKLASH

Application	In. (mm)
1600 cc Models	.004-.007 (.10-.18)
1800 cc Models	.005-.007 (.13-.18)

FINAL ASSEMBLY
All Except 4WD Dual Range

1) With differential bearing preload and ring gear backlash correctly adjusted, remove both axle drive shaft holders. Install "O" ring seal on each holder. Reinstall holders into transaxle case, making sure alignment marks on holders and case are aligned.

2) Remove tape from around axle drive shaft splines. On 4WD models, remove pinion shaft lock nut, washer and rear shaft drive gear. Select a mainshaft collar which will provide 0-.012" (0-.30 mm) clearance between mainshaft bearing and transfer case.

3) Install gasket and transfer case (with selected mainshaft collar) on transaxle and install, but do not tighten, transfer case-to-transaxle mounting nuts. Install rear shaft drive gear, washer and lock nut. Tighten lock nut and stake in 4 places. Tighten transfer case-to-transaxle mounting nuts.

4) Install new "O" ring in shift arm groove. Install gasket and extension housing on transfer case and tighten bolts. Install rear drive shift fork. Install shift rail spring and ball in transfer case, then install rear drive shift rail. Install roll pin to secure fork to rail. Install gasket and transfer case cover.

5) On all models, use depth gauge to measure the amount of ball bearing protrusion from transmission main case surface and select mainshaft collar according to table. Before measuring, lightly tap the end of the mainshaft with a plastic hammer.

MAINSHAFT COLLAR SELECTION

Bearing Protrusion In. (mm)	Collar Thickness In. (mm)
1600 cc Models	
.138-.140 (3.50-3.63)	.197 (5.0)
.133-.138 (3.38-3.50)	.202 (5.13)
1800 cc Models	
.177-.182 (4.50-4.63)	.197 (5.0)
.172-.177 (4.37-4.50)	.202 (5.13)

6) Install transaxle end cover. Install shifter arm in transmisson rear case and install rear case to main case. On 5-speed, adjust 5th gear position. Shift shifter shaft to 5th gear position. Remove drain plug and install dial indicator with stem resting on top of reverse accent shaft. *See Fig. 22.*

SUBARU 4 & 5-SPEED (Cont.)

Fig. 22: Measuring Contact Clearance for 5th Gear Positioning

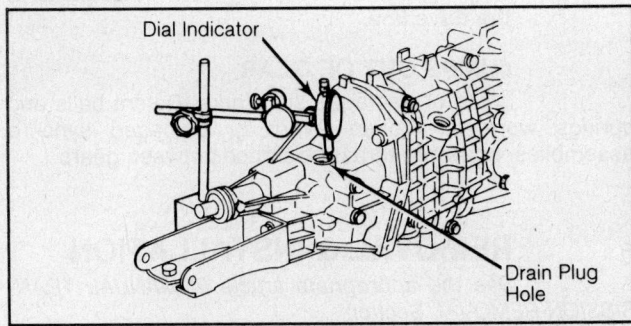

7) Measure clearance when shifter shaft is turned to revese side lightly. Select a reverse accent shaft so that contact clearance is within .002-.015" (.05-.40 mm). On all models, adjust gear selector as follows: Insert a rod through hole in shift arm and shift into 3rd gear.

8) Arm should move easily toward 1st-2nd gear side, but harder toward reverse side because of return spring action. Next, make adjustment to effort required to move lever to either position. Adjustment is performed by removing plug on cover and changing thickness of aluminum gasket.

9) On all except 4WD models, make adjustment so the heavy stroke (reverse side) is a little more than light side. On 4WD models, adjust strokes to take equal effort. On all models, install release bearing guide on case together with 2 release spring brackets.

10) Install clutch release fork and release bearing holder. Secure with release bearing holder spring. Install clutch release fork seal ring and spring. Fill internal groove of release bearing holder with grease.

4WD Dual Range

1) Remove lock plate, lock washer and transfer drive gear from drive pinion. Measure bearing protrusion and select proper bearing plate. Fit transfer case assembly with gasket and plate on main case and tighten bolts.

2) Transfer drive gear should be installed when clearance between main case and transfer case becomes approximately .394" (10 mm). Install lock washer and lock nut on drive pinion. When tightening, the gear should be shifted to the 1st position.

3) High-low shifter lever should be shifted to "HI" or "LO" position. After tightening nut, stake it. Install "O" ring in the side of high-low shifter rail bushing. Apply grease to plunger and fit into high-low shifter arm. Fit shifter fork rail spring and ball in transfer case, and install high-low shifter rail with high-low shifter arm.

4) Punch in straight pin into high-low shifter rail. Install extension assembly with transfer rear gasket and tighten. Before tightening, ensure that shifter arm center pivot can be shifted to any selected direction. Apply gear oil on shifter arm center pivot, and make sure oil seal fits.

5) Transfer drive and transfer driven gears should engage each other. Fit plunger, shifter fork rail spring and ball into transfer shifter fork, and install it to synchronizer sleeve. Apply gear oil to interlock rail, fit "O" ring to rail and insert rail into transfer case.

6) Punch in clip onto interlock rail groove, and insert knock pin into interlock rail hole. Install transfer ball joint assembly to transfer shifter rail. Adjust to 6.7-7.2" (171-185 mm) and tighten nut. Fit shifter fork rail spring and ball in transfer case, and install transfer shifter rail center pivot with transfer case in "4WD HI" so interlock mechanisim does not operate.

7) Fit clip onto transfer shifter rail groove. Fit nut, rod adjusting screw, nut and ball joint assembly to high-low shifter rod. Shorten linkage length by turning turnbuckle clockwise.

8) Insert rod arm into rear portion of high-low shifter rod, and punch in straight pin. Connect rod ball joint assembly with high-low shifter lever center pivot and tighten nut to the specified torque. Confirm operation by moving rod back and forth.

9) Shift transfer shifter rail into "4WD LO" position and fix high-low shifter rail by inserting stopper pin into its hole. Shift high-low shifter lever into LO position and lengthen linkage by turning turnbuckle counterclockwise while holding high-low shifter rod. Align holes of rod arm and high-low shifter rod, and punch in straight pin.

10) While holding rod ball joint assembly, turn rod adjusting screw counterclockwise and then turn back 90° clockwise at the point where ball joint movement becomes tight. Tighten rear nut, and then tighten front nut while holding rod ball joint assembly. Pull out stopper pin and confirm shift operation.

11) Install transfer case cover with gasket and tighten bolts. Insert a bar through shifter arm hole and shift gear to 3rd gear position. Shifter arm should turn lightly toward the 1st-2nd gear side and heavily toward the reverse side.

12) Remove plug on the transfer case and change the thickness of the aluminum gasket to adjust the heavy stroke (reverse side) to be the same as the light stroke. Install clutch release fork and release bearing holder by installing retainer spring into fork.

13) While pushing fork to pivot and twisting it to fit both sides, fit retainer spring onto constricted portion of pivot. Install holder and fasten with 2 clips. Install release fork seal ring.

TIGHTENING SPECIFICATIONS

Application	Ft. Lbs. (N.m)
Ball Joint Nut	25 (34)
Tie Rod Nut	22 (30)
Axle Shaft Nut	145 (197)
Drive Pinion-to-Case	22 (30)
Ring Gear-to-Differential	42-50 (57-68)
Transaxle Case Bolts	
8 mm Bolts	18 (24)
10 mm Bolts	29 (39)
Axle Shaft Holder Lock Plate	18 (24)
Drive Pinion Lock Nut	58 (79)
Transaxle Cover Bolts	16 (22)

Manual Transmissions

TOYOTA 4-SPEED — MODEL H42

Land Cruiser

DESCRIPTION

The Toyota model H42 transmission is a 4-speed unit, synchronized in all forward gears due to the use of blocker type synchronizer assemblies. All forward transmission gears are helical cut and in constant mesh. Reverse gears are spur cut type and are engaged by a sliding reverse idler gear.

NOTE: For Transfer Case service and repair procedures see appropriate article in OVERDRIVES & TRANSFER CASE Section.

LUBRICATION & ADJUSTMENT

See the appropriate article in MANUAL TRANSMISSION SERVICING Section.

TROUBLE SHOOTING

HARD SHIFTING

Clutch not releasing. Check for proper adjustment, deformed clutch disc, seized or damaged pilot bearing. Incorrect or insufficient lubricant. Gearshift lever retainer binding or improperly lubricated. Shift forks worn or damaged. Shift shafts bent.

NOISY OPERATION

Improper or insufficient lubricant. Worn or damaged bushings, bearings and/or gears. Worn splines.

NOTE: When checking transmission for noise, ensure that it is not coming from other parts of the drive line.

JUMPS OUT OF GEAR

Worn or damaged shift forks. Detent balls and springs worn or broken. Worn or damaged synchro assemblies. Improper thrust clearance between gears.

REMOVAL & INSTALLATION

See the appropriate article in MANUAL TRANSISSION REMOVAL Section.

TRANSMISSION DISASSEMBLY

1) Remove transmission rear bearing retainer and spacer. Remove transmission shift cover assembly and side cover. Remove front bearing retainer from transmission case.

2) Remove countershaft front bearing retaining snap rings (inner and outer), then remove bearing from transmission case using a puller. Using the same procedure, remove countershaft rear bearing and thrust washer.

3) Drive input shaft assembly and bearing from case. Remove output shaft bearing snap ring, then pull bearing from transmission case with a puller.

4) Hold 1st gear tightly against the other gears to prevent gear from sliding off, then lift output shaft assembly from transmission case. See Fig. 2. Remove countershaft from case.

5) Drive reverse idler gear shaft out rear of case using care not to lose Woodruff key. Lift reverse idler

Fig. 1: Disassembled View of Land Cruiser 4-Speed Transmission Assembly

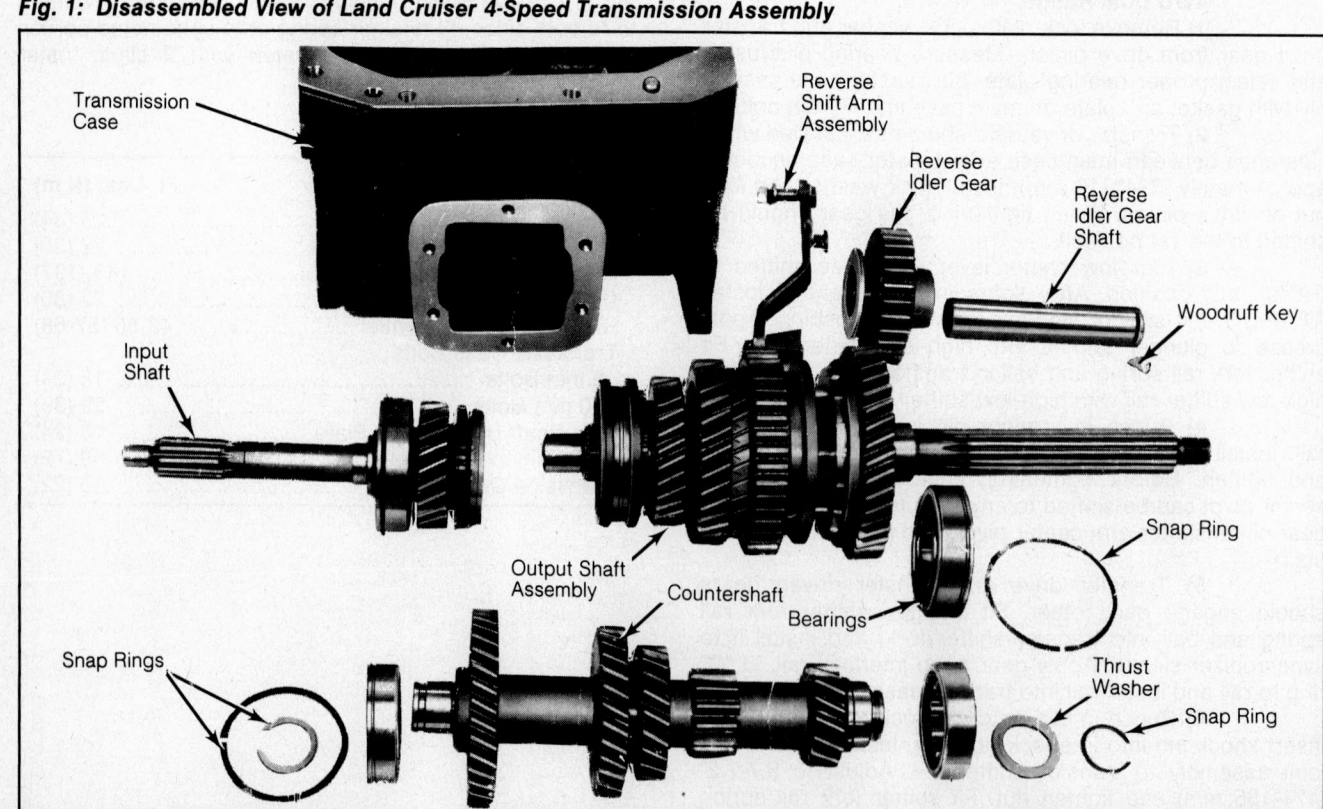

TOYOTA 4-SPEED — MODEL H42 (Cont.)

gear from bottom of transmission case. Remove reverse shift arm assembly from case.

Fig. 2: Lifting Output Shaft Assembly from Transmission Case

COMPONENT DISASSEMBLY & REASSEMBLY

OUTPUT SHAFT ASSEMBLY
Disassembly

1) From rear of output shaft, remove 1st gear thrust washer, then slide off 1st gear and needle bearing using care not to lose pin. Slide 1st-2nd synchronizer assembly from output shaft.

2) Remove snap ring from front of output shaft, then slide off 3rd-4th synchronizer hub. Pull 3rd gear and bushing off shaft using care not to lose ball. Finally, slide 2nd gear and needle bearing off output shaft.

3) To disassemble synchronizer assembly, slide synchronizer hub sleeve from hub, then remove key springs and keys.

Inspection

1) Check output shaft surfaces for wear and damage. Inspect output shaft bushing for excessive wear and damage. Also, check bushing-to-3rd gear oil clearance (clearance between outer diameter of bushing and inner diameter of gear). Clearance should be .003-.005" (.07-.12 mm).

2) Inspect gears for wear or damage to teeth, thrust faces, inside diameter and coned surfaces. Inspect output shaft ball bearing and needle bearings for wear and damage.

3) Assemble synchronizer ring on 3rd gear and check ring-to-gear clearance as shown in Fig. 3. Clearance should be .031" (.8 mm). Repeat measurement for 4th gear ring.

4) Assemble 1st and 2nd gears to synchronizer assembly. Measure thickness of synchronizer ring protruding from gears as shown in Fig. 5. Thickness for

Fig. 3: Measuring 3rd and 4th Gear to Synchronizer Ring Clearance

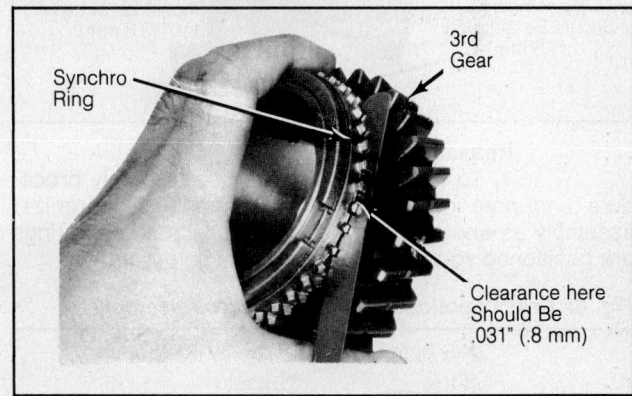

Fig. 4: Exploded View Showing Output Shaft and Components

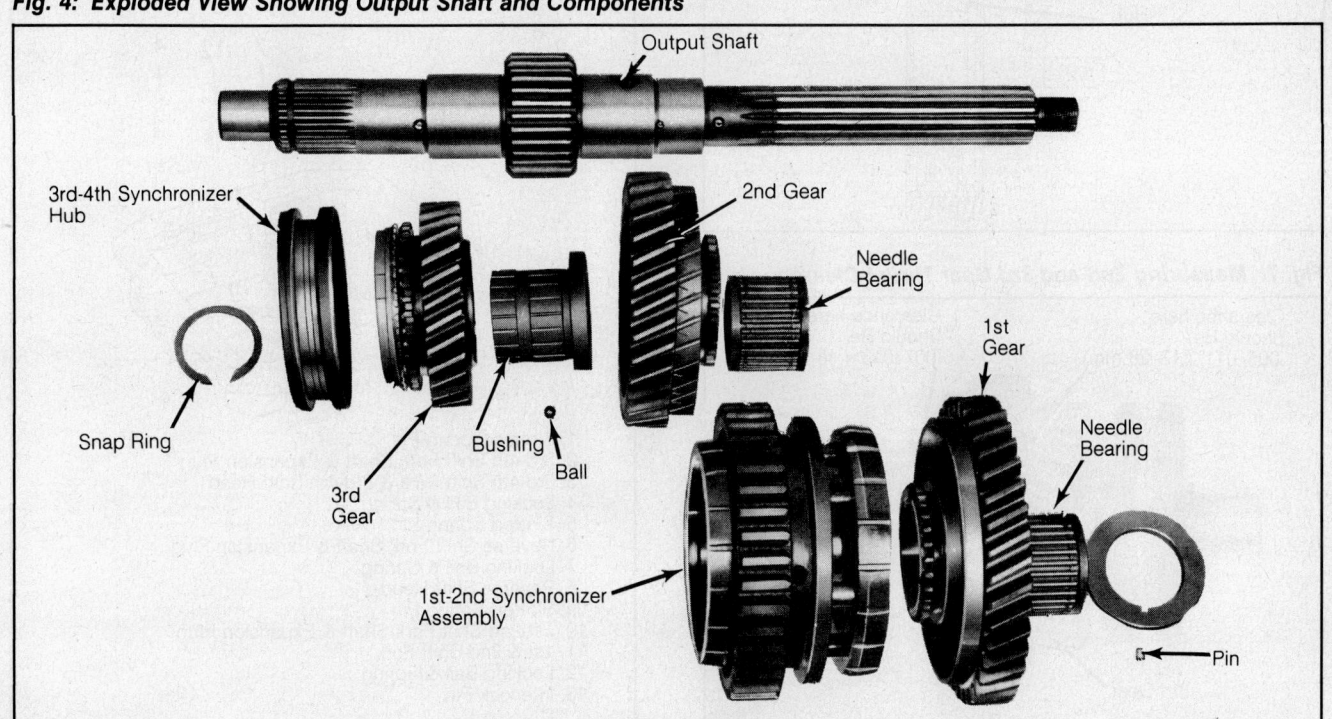

TOYOTA 4-SPEED — MODEL H42 (Cont.)

1st gear ring should be at least .110" (2.8 mm) and for 2nd gear ring at least .071" (1.8 mm).

5) Inspect splines of synchronizer hub and hub sleeve for damage and wear. Inspect the center humped part of keys for damage and wear. Inspect key springs for weakening and damage.

6) Finally, insert shift forks into their respective synchronizer hub sleeve and measure clearance between shift fork and sleeve. Clearance should be less than .032" (.8 mm).

Fig. 5: Checking 1st and 2nd Gear Synchronizer Ring Wear

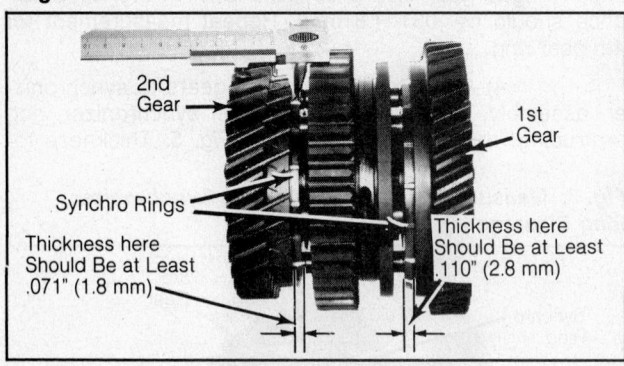

Reassembly

1) To reassemble, reverse disassembly procedure and note the following: Reassemble synchronizer assembly as shown in *Fig. 6* and ensure that key springs are positioned so that end gaps will not be in line.

Fig. 6: Cross-Sectional View of Synchro Assembly

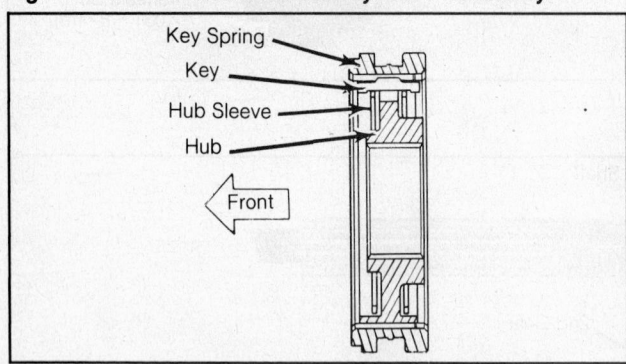

Fig. 7: Measuring 2nd and 3rd Gear Thrust Clearance

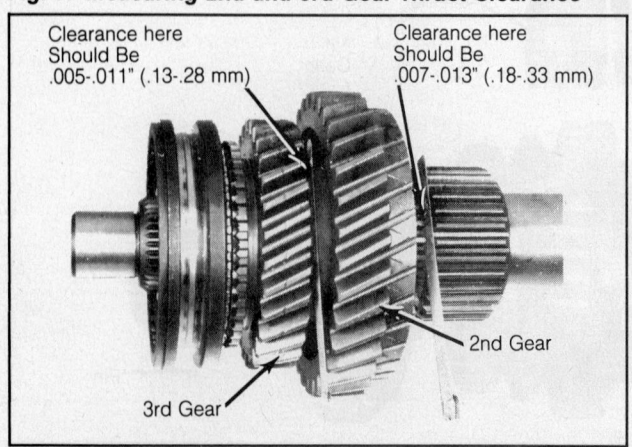

2) To install bushing on output shaft, place ball in hole of output shaft, then slide bushing onto shaft, aligning groove of bushing with ball.

3) Install thickest possible snap ring on front of output shaft that will provide a gear thrust clearance of .007-.013" (.18-.33 mm) for 2nd gear and .005-.011" (.13-.28 mm) for 3rd gear. *See Fig. 7.*

SHIFT COVER ASSEMBLY

Disassembly

1) Remove attaching bolts and lift off shift lever retainer and gasket. Move shift forks and shafts into neutral position. Invert shift cover assembly and drive out spring pin retaining 3rd-4th shift fork-to-shift fork shaft.

2) Drive out shift fork shaft together with expansion plug using a brass drift. Cover service hole with hand to prevent locking ball from flying out. Remove 3rd-4th shift fork and interlock pin. Remove locking ball and spring with magnet.

Fig. 8: Exploded View of Shift Cover Assembly

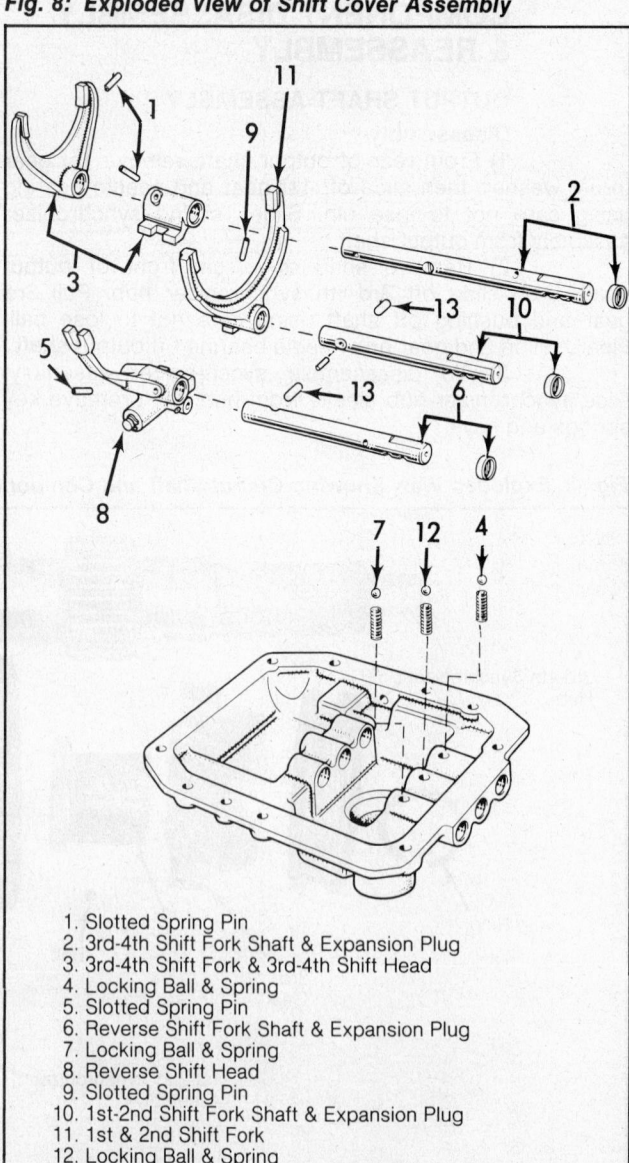

1. Slotted Spring Pin
2. 3rd-4th Shift Fork Shaft & Expansion Plug
3. 3rd-4th Shift Fork & 3rd-4th Shift Head
4. Locking Ball & Spring
5. Slotted Spring Pin
6. Reverse Shift Fork Shaft & Expansion Plug
7. Locking Ball & Spring
8. Reverse Shift Head
9. Slotted Spring Pin
10. 1st-2nd Shift Fork Shaft & Expansion Plug
11. 1st & 2nd Shift Fork
12. Locking Ball & Spring
13. Interlock Pin

TOYOTA 4-SPEED — MODEL H42 (Cont.)

3) Drive out spring pin retaining reverse shift head. Drive out shift fork shaft together with expansion plug. Cover service hole with hand. Remove 2nd locking ball and spring with magnet.

4) Drive out slotted spring pin to remove 1st-2nd shift fork. Drive out fork shaft together with expansion plug. Cover service hole with hand. Remove interlock pin from shaft using magnet. Remove 3rd locking ball and spring with magnet. Remove lock pins from case.

5) If necessary to disassemble reverse shift head, remove cotter pin and remove spring and lock ball from bore in shift head. Next, remove "C" washer and pull out reverse shift return plunger and spring.

Fig. 9: Disassembled View of Reverse Shift Head

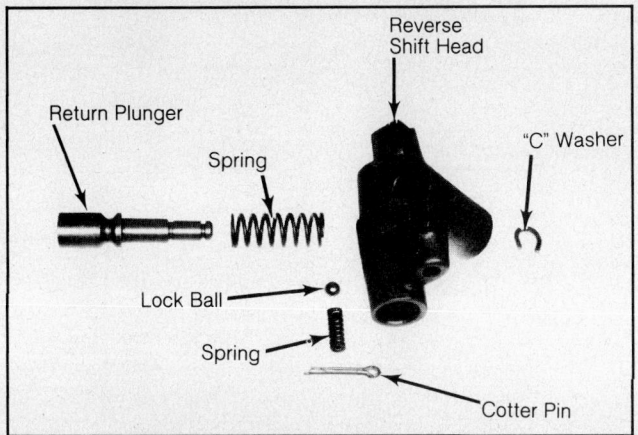

Inspection

Inspect shift fork shafts and heads for bending and wear or damage at sliding surfaces. Check shift cover bores for wear or damage. Inspect detent balls and springs for wear or damage.

Reassembly

Reverse disassembly procedure ensuring that shift forks and heads are correctly positioned before installing shift forks. Coat expansion plugs with a sealer and install in shift cover. Plugs must not be driven in more than .10" (2.5 mm) below cover surface.

INPUT SHAFT

Inspection

Inspect input shaft gear teeth, splines, coned surfaces, and bearing for damage and wear. Check inner surface of input shaft for damage and wear. Also, inspect needle bearings for wear and replace bearings as a set if necessary.

Input Shaft Bearing Replacement

Remove snap ring and press off old bearing. Press new bearing in position and select a snap ring of proper thickness to provide the minimum amount of axial play. Snap rings are available in 2 thicknesses: .130-.135" (3.31-3.42 mm) and .126-.130" (3.20-3.31 mm). Install snap ring, ensuring that it is fully seated in groove.

COUNTERSHAFT ASSEMBLY

Inspection

Inspect countergear teeth for wear and damage. Inspect front and rear bearings for wear and damage and replace if necessary. If rear bearing requires replacement, press bearing inner race from countershaft. Install new inner race on countershaft using a press.

NOTE: Make sure to position new inner race so that its flanged side will be towards front of countershaft.

REVERSE IDLER GEAR & SHAFT

Inspection

Inspect reverse idler gear, bushing and shaft for wear and damage. Also, check oil clearance between gear and shaft. Clearance should be .0063" (.16 mm). If bushing requires replacement, proceed as follows:

Reverse Idler Gear Bushing Replacement

Using press with a 24 mm socket, press bushings from gear. Using the same tools, press new bushings into the gear. Press bushings into gear until each bushing is .039" (1 mm) from gear end face.

Fig. 10: Replacing Reverse Idler Gear Bushing

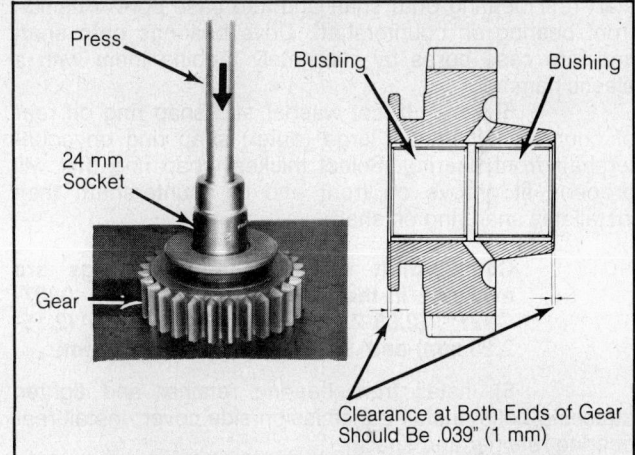

REVERSE SHIFT ARM

Inspection

Inspect shift arm shoe for damage or wear. Shoe thickness should be at least .32" (8.1 mm). Inspect shift arm at shoe mounting end and pivot mounting end for wear or damage. Check for maximum clearance of .028" (.7 mm) between shoe and reverse idler gear slot.

Fig. 11: Disassembled View of Reverse Shift Arm

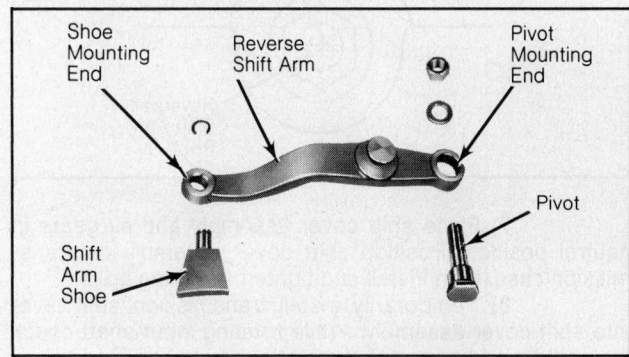

TRANSMISSION REASSEMBLY

1) Position reverse idler gear in transmission case. Install Woodruff key in reverse idler gear shaft, then install shaft into case and through gear. Install reverse shift arm assembly.

TOYOTA 4-SPEED — MODEL H42 (Cont.)

NOTE: **Ensure punch mark on end of reverse shift arm pivot is positioned straight up before locking pivot nut.**

2) Lay countershaft in bottom of transmission case. Install output shaft assembly into transmission case. Drive output shaft rear bearing onto shaft and into case bore until it is fully seated.

3) Install the 17 needle bearings into input shaft bore and use grease to hold them in place. Assemble synchronizer ring to synchronizer hub on input shaft. Using a plastic hammer, drive input shaft into transmission case.

NOTE: **Use care not to damage synchronizer ring when installing input shaft.**

4) Align countershaft with bores in case, then start rear bearing onto shaft and into case bore. Position front bearing on countershaft. Drive bearings onto shaft and into case bores by alternately tapping them with a plastic hammer.

5) Install thrust washer and snap ring on rear of countershaft. Install large (outer) snap ring on countershaft front bearing. Select thickest snap ring that will properly fit groove on front end of countershaft, then install this snap ring on shaft.

NOTE: **Countershaft selective fit snap rings are available in the following thicknesses: .0807-.0827" (2.05-2.10 mm), .0846-.0866" (2.15-2.20 mm) and .0886-.0906" (2.25-2.30 mm).**

6) Install front bearing retainer and tighten attaching bolts. Install transmission side cover. Install rear bearing retainer and spacer.

Fig. 12: Reverse Shift Arm Pivot Adjustment

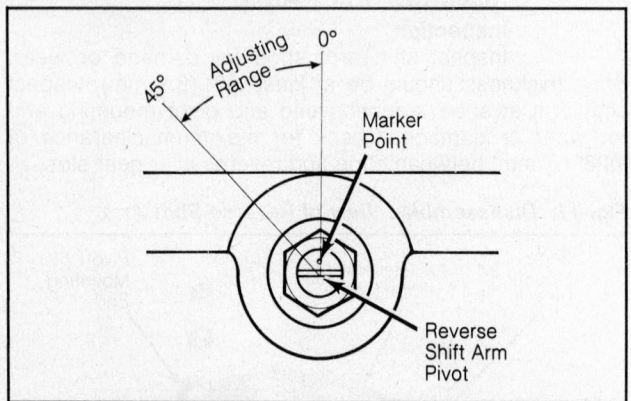

7) Place shift cover assembly and all gears in neutral position. Position shift cover assembly on transmission case, then install and tighten attaching bolts.

8) Temporarily install transmission shift lever into shift cover assembly. While rotating input shaft check the shifting and output shaft rotational relationship.

9) If abnormal noise develops while turning input shaft, correct by adjusting reverse shift arm pivot within range of 0° to 45° of marker point (punch mark). *See Fig. 12.*

TIGHTENING SPECIFICATIONS

Application	Ft. Lbs. (N.m)
Shift Cover-to-Case	22-33 (30-45)
Front Bearing Retainer-to-Case	7-12 (10-16)
Transfer Case-to-Transmission	36-58 (49-79)
Clutch Housing-to-Transmission	36-58 (49-79)
Output Shaft Rear Nut	80-101 (109-138)

TOYOTA 4 & 5-SPEED — MODELS G40 & G52

Pickup
G40 2WD
G52 4WD

DESCRIPTION

These transmissions are fully synchronized units available in 4 or 5-speed versions. All forward gears are helical cut and in constant mesh. Reverse gear is spur cut. Reverse and 5th gears are in constant mesh and are mounted on rear side of intermediate plate.

Fig. 1: Toyota G40 Transmission

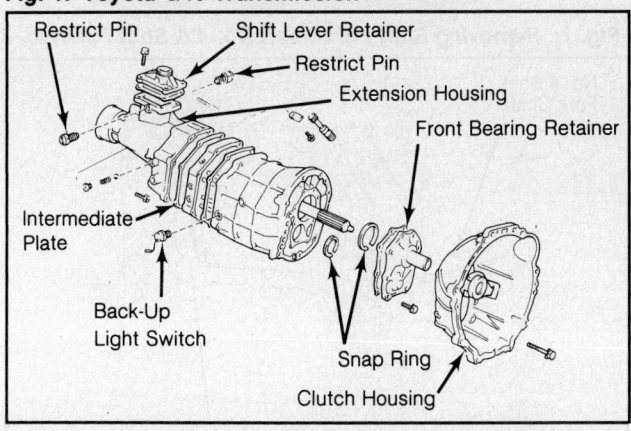

The floor shifter actuates a single control rod in extension housing/transfer adapter operating 3 shift rails mounted in intermediate plate and main case. The G40 transmission is used in 2WD vehicles and the G52 is used in 4WD vehicles.

Fig. 2: Toyota G52 Transmission

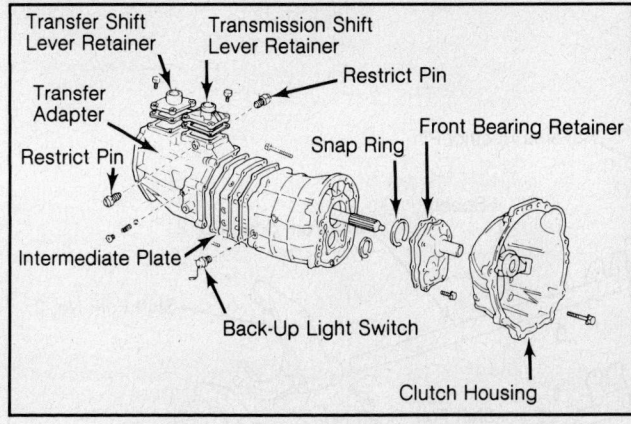

LUBRICATION & ADJUSTMENT

See appropriate MANUAL TRANSMISSION SERVICING article in IMPORT GENERAL SERVICING section.

REMOVAL & INSTALLATION

See appropriate MANUAL TRANSMISSION REMOVAL article in IMPORT GENERAL SERVICING section.

TRANSMISSION DISASSEMBLY

EXTENSION HOUSING/TRANSFER ADAPTER

1) Remove clutch release fork and bearing. Remove back-up light switch, speedometer driven gear (2WD), shift lever retainer and restrict pins. Remove clutch housing from transmission case.

2) Using a Torx head socket, remove screw plug from extension housing (2WD) or transfer adapter (4WD). See Fig. 3.

Fig. 3: Removing Screw Plug, Spring & Ball

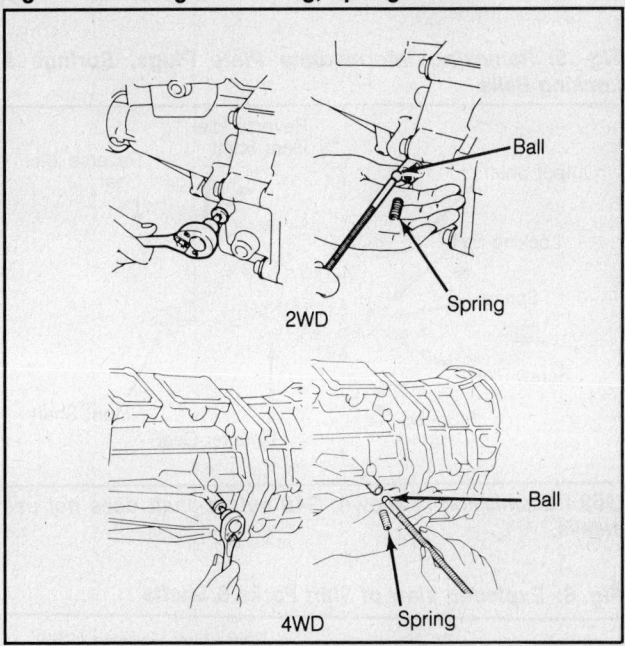

3) On 2WD models, remove the 8 extension housing bolts. Working throught shift lever opening, remove shift lever housing set bolt and lock washer. Using a plastic hammer, tap extension housing and remove shift lever housing and the shift and select lever.

NOTE: Leave the gasket attached to the intermediate plate.

4) On 4WD models, remove Allen head plug from rear face of transfer adapter. Remove shift lever housing set bolt and lock washer.

5) Remove shift lever shaft and housing. Remove the 8 transfer adapter bolts. Using a plastic hammer, remove transfer adapter.

NOTE: Leave the gasket attached to the intermediate plate.

INTERMEDIATE PLATE
Shift Fork Shafts
1) On 2WD and 4WD models, remove front bearing retainer and 2 bearing snap rings from front of transmission case. Using a plastic hammer, carefully separate transmission case from intermediate plate.

2) Install bolts, flat washers and nuts through lower 2 holes of intermediate plate. Mount intermediate plate in vise. See Fig. 4.

Manual Transmissions

TOYOTA 4 & 5-SPEED – MODELS G40 & G52 (Cont.)

Fig. 4: Mounting Intermediate Plate in Vise

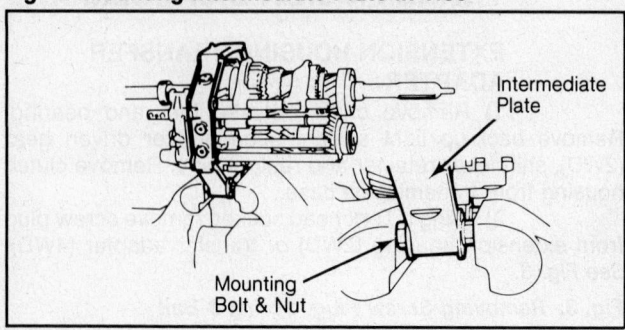

3) Using a Torx head socket, remove the screw plugs, locking balls and springs from intermediate plate. Four-speed units have 3 plugs; 5-speed units have 4 plugs. *See Fig. 5.*

4) Using a hammer and pin punch, drive out the 5 shift fork-to-shift rail pins. Remove the shift rail "E" rings. There are 4 "E" rings on the 4-speed model and 2 "E" rings on the 5-speed model.

5) On 5-speed units only, pull out shift fork shaft No. 4 from intermediate plate catching interlock balls (2) and pin. If they don't fall out, remove with a magnetic finger. Remove shift fork shaft No. 4 and shift fork No. 3. *See Fig. 7.*

Fig. 5: Removing Intermediate Plate Plugs, Springs & Locking Balls

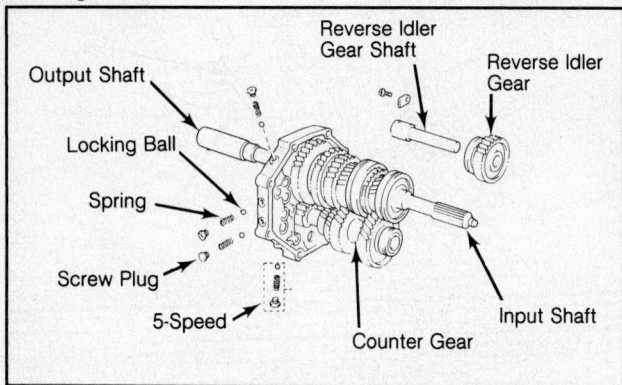

G52 transmission is shown; G40 output shaft does not use sleeve.

Fig. 7: Removing Shift Fork Shaft No. 4 & Shift Fork No. 3

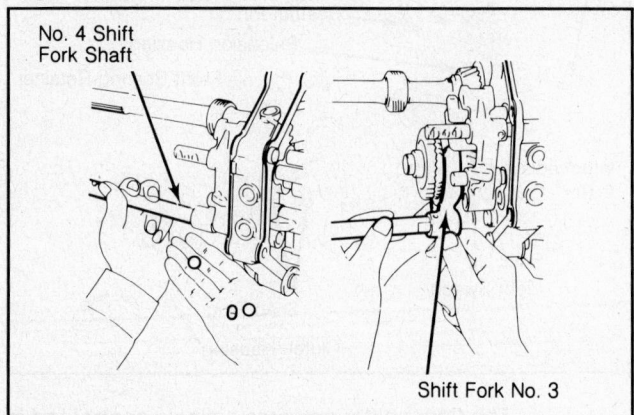

Illustration applies to 5-speed transmission only.

Fig. 6: Exploded View of Shift Forks & Shafts

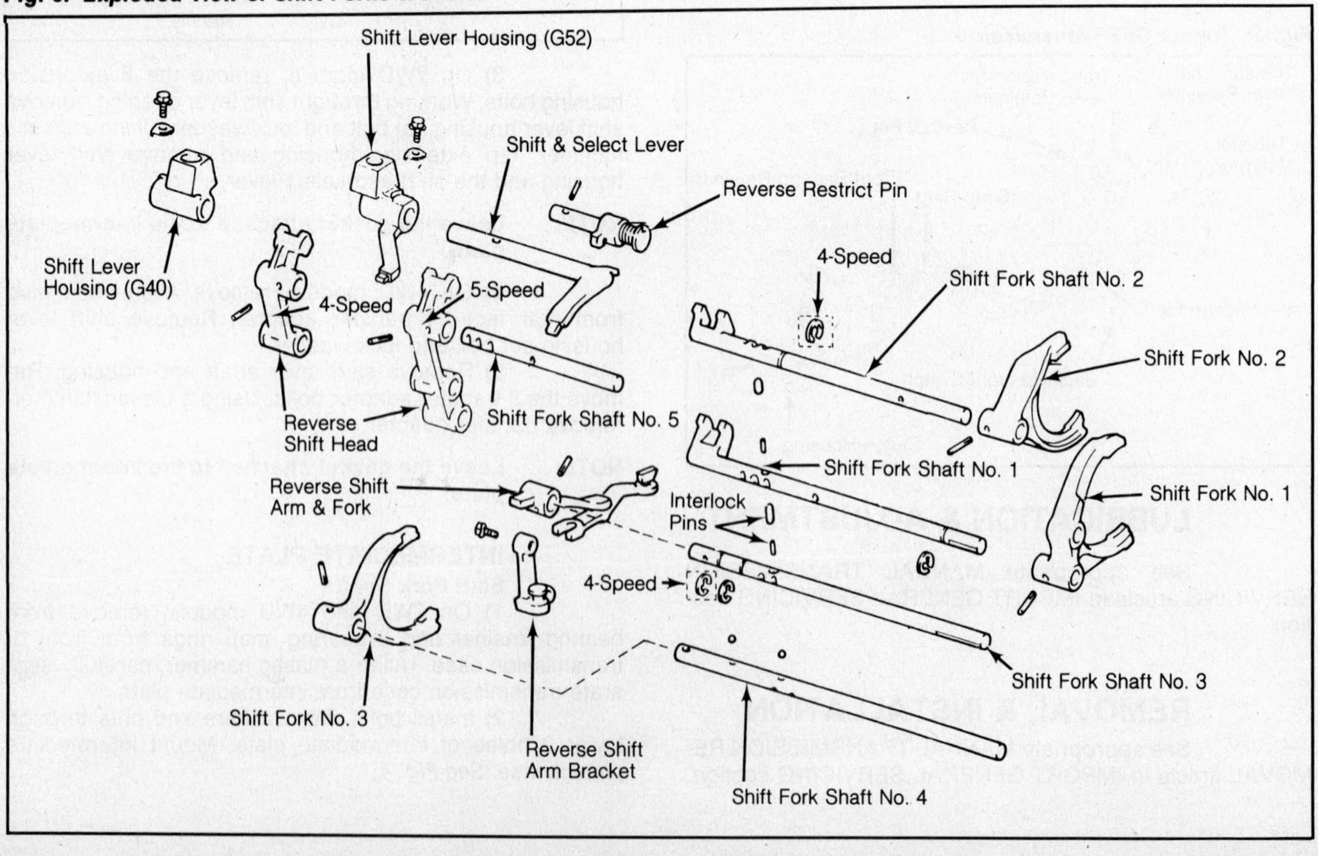

TOYOTA 4 & 5-SPEED — MODELS G40 & G52 (Cont.)

COUNTERSHAFT 5TH GEAR END PLAY SPECIFICATIONS

Application	In. (mm)
Standard	.0039-.0118 (.10-.30)
Maximum	.0118 (.30)

Fig. 8: Measuring Point For Countershaft 5th Gear End Play

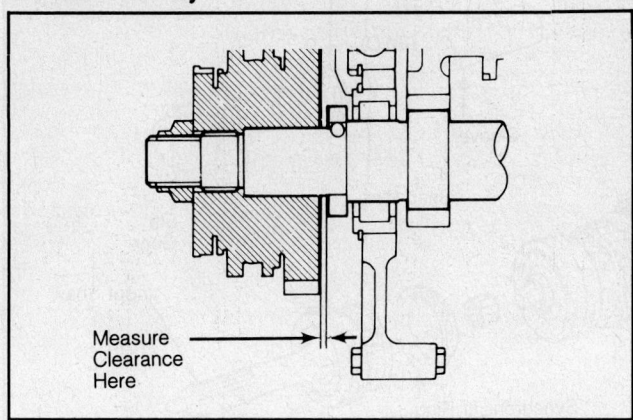

Measure Clearance Here

6) On 4 and 5-speed models, pull out shift fork shaft No. 5 from the intermediate plate, and remove it with the reverse shift head. Pull out shift fork shaft No. 3 from the intermediate plate catching interlock pins (2) as they fall out. If they do not come out, remove with magnetic finger.

7) Remove shift fork shaft No. 1 and its interlock pin from the intermediate plate. Pull out shift fork shaft No. 2 and remove shift fork No. 2 and No. 1.

Input, Output & Countershafts

1) Remove the reverse idler gear shaft stopper. Remove the reverse idler gear and shaft. Remove the reverse shift arm from reverse shift arm bracket.

2) On 5-speed models only, measure the countershaft 5th gear end play. See Fig. 8.

3) On 5-speed models only, loosen the staked part of the lock nut on the gear spline piece No. 5. See Fig. 11. Remove the lock nut. Using gear puller, remove gear spline piece No. 5, synchronizer ring, needle roller bearing and counter 5th gear. Remove spacer and ball.

4) On 4-speed models only, loosen the staked part of lock nut on gear spline piece No. 5. Remove nut and oil separator. See Fig. 11.

5) On 4 and 5-speed models, remove the 2 bolts and the reverse shift arm bracket. Using Torx head socket, remove the 4 rear bearing retainer bolts. Remove the rear bearing snap ring.

6) Remove the output shaft, countershaft and input shaft as a unit from the intermediate plate by pulling on the countergear and tapping on the intermediate plate with a plastic hammer. Remove the input shaft and needle roller bearings (14) from the output shaft.

7) Remove countershaft rear bearing from intermediate plate. On 2WD models only, remove both snap rings, speedometer drive gear and steel ball. On 4WD models only, remove the sleeve from the output shaft using a gear puller.

COMPONENT DISASSEMBLY & REASSEMBLY

OUTPUT SHAFT
Disassembly
1) Measure the end play of each gear on output shaft.

OUTPUT SHAFT END PLAY SPECIFICATIONS

Application	In. (mm)
1st, 2nd & 3rd Gear	
Standard	.0039-.0098 (.10-.25)
Maximum	.0098 (.25)

Fig. 9: Measuring Output Shaft Gear End Play

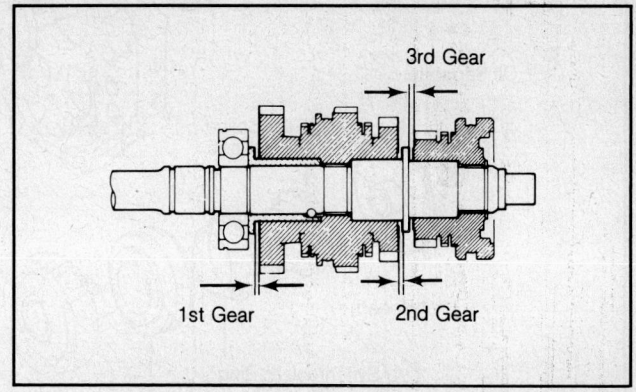

3rd Gear

1st Gear   2nd Gear

2) On 5-speed models only, remove the snap ring and press the 5th gear, rear bearing, 1st gear and inner race from the output shaft. Remove the needle roller bearing.

3) On 5-speed models only, remove the snap ring and press off the rear bearing, 1st gear and inner race. Remove the needle roller bearing.

4) On all models, remove the synchronizer ring. Remove the locking ball using a magnetic finger. Press hub sleeve No. 1, synchronizer ring and 2nd gear off of output shaft. See Fig. 10. Remove the needle roller bearing.

Fig. 10: Removing Locking Ball, Hub Sleeve No. 1 And 2nd Gear

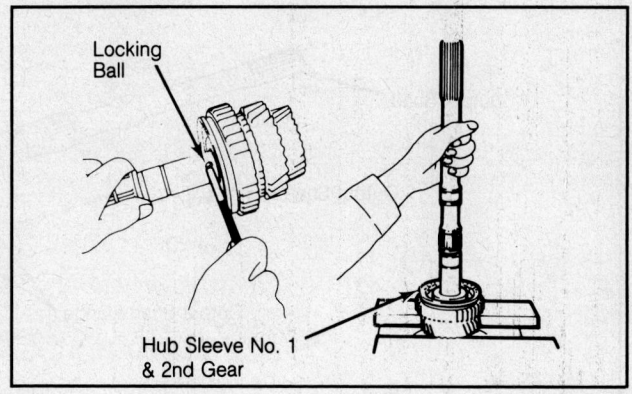

Locking Ball

Hub Sleeve No. 1 & 2nd Gear

5) Remove the snap ring and press hub sleeve No. 2, synchronizer ring and 3rd gear off of output shaft. Remove the needle roller bearing.

Manual Transmissions
TOYOTA 4 & 5-SPEED – MODELS G40 & G52 (Cont.)

Fig. 11: *Exploded View of Toyota G40 & G52 Transmission Gears*

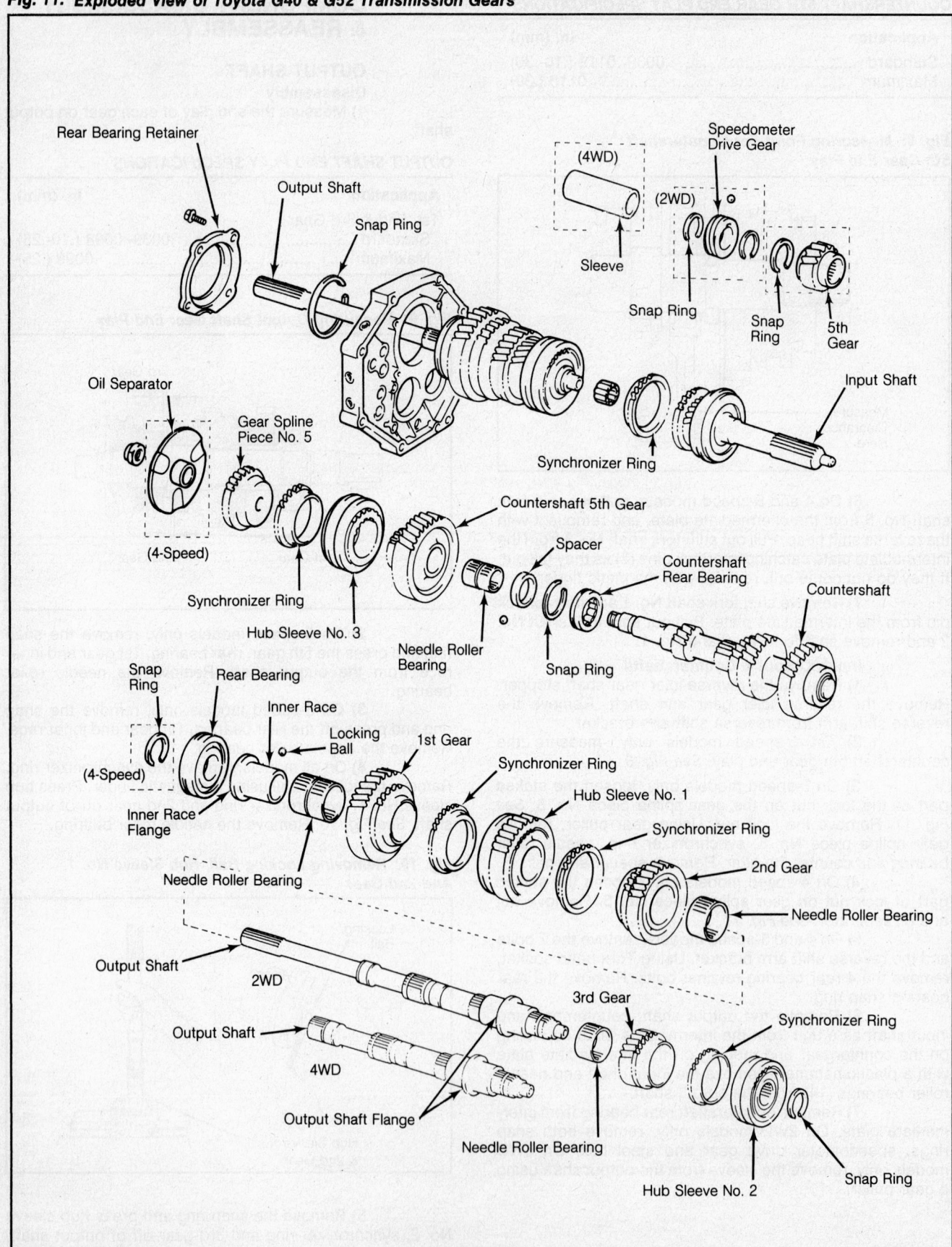

TOYOTA 4 & 5-SPEED – MODELS G40 & G52 (Cont.)

Cleaning & Inspection

1) Clean all parts in solvent. Inspect output shaft and inner race for wear or damage. Using Vernier calipers, measure output shaft flange thickness and inner race flange thickness.

2) Using a micrometer, measure outer diameter of output shaft journal surface and outer diameter of inner race. Mount output shaft between 2 "V" blocks and measure shaft runout at center of shaft.

OUTPUT SHAFT SPECIFICATIONS

Application	In. (mm)
Output Shaft Flange	
Minimum Thickness	.1890 (4.80)
Inner Race Flange	
Minimum Thickness	.1571 (3.99)
Inner Race Outer Diameter	
Minimum Thickness	1.5348 (38.985)
Output Shaft Journal (Outer Diameter)	
Minimum Thickness	
2nd Gear	1.495 (37.984)
3rd Gear	1.3773 (34.984)
Maximum Runout	.002 (.05)

3) Using a dial indicator, measure oil clearance between 1st gear and inner race with needle roller bearing installed. Measure oil clearance between output shaft and 2nd gear between shaft and 3rd gear. Measure oil clearance between countershaft and 5th gear.

GEAR-TO-SHAFT OIL CLEARANCE SPECIFICATIONS

Application	Standard In. (mm)	Maximum In. (mm)
1st Gear-to- Inner Race	.00035-.00126 (.009.-032)	.0126 (.032)
2nd Gear-to- Shaft	.00035-.00130 (.009-.033)	.00130 (.033)
3rd Gear-to- Shaft	.00035-.00130 (.009-.033)	.00130 (.033)
5th Gear-to- Countershaft	.00035-.00126 (.009-.032)	.00126 (.032)

4) Check all synchronizer rings for wear or damage. Turn the ring and push in to check the braking action. Measure clearance between synchronizer ring back and gear spline end. *See Fig. 12.*

SYNCHRONIZER RING CLEARANCE SPECIFICATIONS

Application	In. (mm)
Standard	.039-.079 (1.0-2.0)
Maximum	.031 (.8)

5) Measure clearance between shift forks and hubs. Maximum clearance is .039" (1.0 mm).

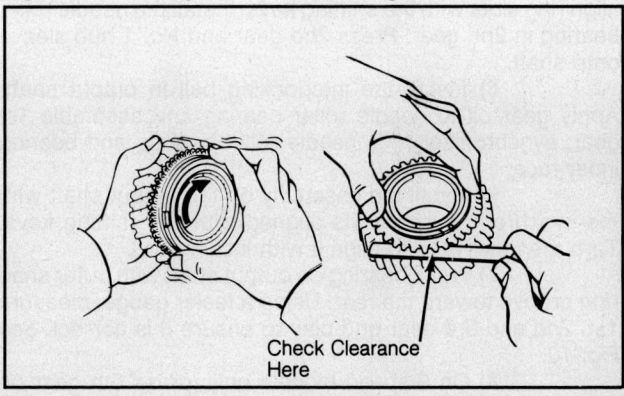

Fig. 12: Checking Synchronizer Rings

Check Clearance Here

Reassembly

1) Install clutch hub and shifting keys in hub sleeve. *See Fig. 13.* Install the shifting key springs under shifting keys.

CAUTION: Install key springs so that their end gaps are not aligned.

2) Apply gear oil to shaft and needle roller bearing. Place synchronizer ring on gear and align ring slots

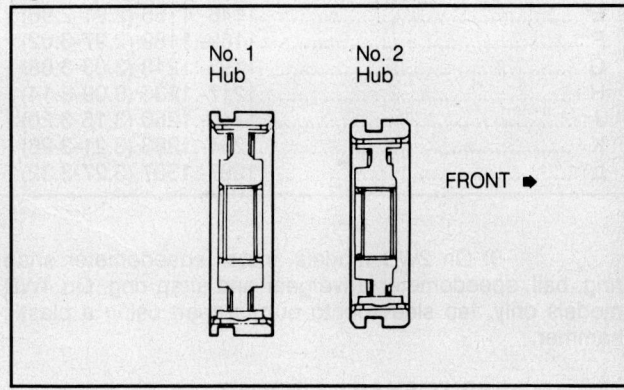

Fig. 13: Sectional View of Clutch Hubs

No. 1 Hub   No. 2 Hub

FRONT ➡

with the shifting keys. Install the needle roller bearing in 3rd gear.

3) Press 3rd gear and No. 2 hub sleeve on output shaft. Select a snap ring that will allow minimum axial end play and install it on shaft. See NO. 2 HUB SLEEVE SNAP RING SIZES table. Using feeler gauge, measure 3rd gear end play to ensure it is correct.

NO. 2 HUB SLEEVE SNAP RING SIZES

Mark	Thickness In. (mm)
C-1	.0689-.0709 (1.75-1.80)
D	.0709-.0728 (1.80-1.85)
D-1	.0728-.0748 (1.85-1.90)
E	.0748-.0768 (1.90-1.95)
E-1	.0768-.0787 (1.95-2.00)
F	.0787-.0807 (2.00-2.05)
F-1	.0807-.0827 (2.05-2.10)

4) Install synchronizer ring on 2nd gear and align ring slots with the shifting keys. Install the needle roller bearing in 2nd gear. Press 2nd gear and No. 1 hub sleeve onto shaft.

5) Install the interlocking ball in output shaft. Apply gear oil to needle roller bearing and assemble 1st gear, synchronizer ring, needle roller bearing and bearing inner race.

6) Install the assembly on the output shaft with the synchronizer ring slots aligned with the shifting keys. Turn the inner race to align it with locking ball.

7) Press bearing on output shaft with outer snap ring groove toward the rear. Using a feeler gauge, measure 1st, 2nd and 3rd gear end play to ensure it is correct. *See Fig. 10.*

8) On 5-speed models only, press 5th gear on end of output shaft. On 4 and 5-speed models, install a snap ring that will allow minimum axial end play. See OUTPUT SHAFT SNAP RING SELECTION table.

OUTPUT SHAFT SNAP RING SELECTION

Mark	Thickness In. (mm)
A	.1051-.1071 (2.67-2.72)
B	.1075-.1094 (2.73-2.78)
C	.1098-.1118 (2.79-2.84)
D	.1122-.1142 (2.85-2.90)
E	.1146-.1165 (2.91-2.96)
F	.1169-.1189 (2.97-3.02)
G	.1193-.1213 (3.03-3.08)
H	.1217-.1236 (3.09-3.14)
J	.1240-.1260 (3.15-3.20)
K	.1264-.1283 (3.21-3.26)
L	.1287-.1307 (3.27-3.32)

9) On 2WD models, install speedometer snap ring, ball, speedometer drive gear and snap ring. On 4WD models only, tap sleeve onto output shaft using a plastic hammer.

INPUT SHAFT & FRONT BEARING RETAINER

1) Inspect input shaft and bearing for wear or damage. If necessary, press new bearing on input shaft. Select a snap ring that will allow minimum axial end play and install it on shaft. See COUNTERSHAFT & INPUT SHAFT SNAP RING SELECTION table.

2) Inspect front input shaft bearing retainer for damage. Replace oil seal. Install oil seal .441-.480" (11.2-12.2 mm) below transmission case surface.

COUNTERSHAFT & INPUT SHAFT SNAP RING SELECTION

Mark	Thickness In. (mm)
0	.0807-.0827 (2.05-2.10)
1	.0827-.0846 (2.10-2.15)
2	.0846-.0866 (2.15-2.20)
3	.0866-.0886 (2.20-2.25)
4	.0886-.0906 (2.25-2.30)
5	.0906-.0925 (2.30-2.35)

COUNTERSHAFT

1) Inspect countershaft gear teeth for wear or damage. Check front bearing for wear or damage. Replace worn parts if necessary.

2) Bearing may be pressed off of shaft after removing snap ring. When pressing new front bearing on countershaft, select a snap ring that will allow minimum axial end play. See COUNTERSHAFT & INPUT SHAFT SNAP RING SELECTION table.

EXTENSION HOUSING/TRANSFER ADAPTER
Speedometer Gear Oil Seal

On 2WD models only, replace speedometer driven gear oil seal. Press in new seal to a depth of .79" (20 mm) below threaded end of sleeve.

Reverse Restrict Pin

1) On 2WD and 4WD models, check reverse restrict pin for wear or damage. To replace restrict pin, remove screw plug using a Torx head socket. Drive out the slotted spring pin with a punch and hammer.

2) Pull off the lever housing and slide out the shaft. To install, reverse removal procedure.

Extension Housing Oil Seal & Bushing (2WD Models Only)

1) If extension housing bushing is worn, remove oil seal with slide hammer. Heat extension housing end to 176-212°F (80-100°C) in an oil bath.

2) Using Extension Housing Bushing Replacer (09307-30010), press old bushing out of housing. Install new bushing with same tool. Press new bushing in so that rear edge of bushing is flush with rear shoulder of bushing bore.

TRANSMISSION REASSEMBLY

INTERMEDIATE PLATE
Input, Output & Countershafts

1) Place intermediate plate in vise. Apply grease to the 14 needle roller bearings and install them in the input shaft. Install output shaft in intermediate plate by pulling on output shaft and tapping on the plate.

2) Install input shaft on output shaft with synchronizer ring slots aligned with shifting keys. Install countershaft on intermediate plate.

3) Install countershaft rear bearing using hammer and Installer Tool (09316-60010). Install output shaft rear bearing snap ring. Ensure snap ring is flush with intermediate plate surface. Install rear bearing retainer.

4) Install reverse shift arm bracket. Install ball and spacer. On 4-speed models only, install oil separator.

5) On 5-speed models only, install the shifting keys and hub sleeve No. 3 onto the countershaft 5th gear. *See Fig. 14.* Install shifting key springs under the shifting keys.

CAUTION: Install shifting keys springs so their end gaps are not aligned.

6) On 5-speed models only, install countershaft 5th gear, hub sleeve No. 3 and bearings onto countershaft. Install synchronizer ring on gear spline piece No. 5.

7) Using Installer Tool (09316-60010), drive in gear spline piece No. 5 with synchronizer ring slots aligned with shifting keys.

TOYOTA 4 & 5-SPEED – MODELS G40 & G52 (Cont.)

Fig. 14: Sectional View of 5th Countershaft Gear & No. 3 Hub Sleeve

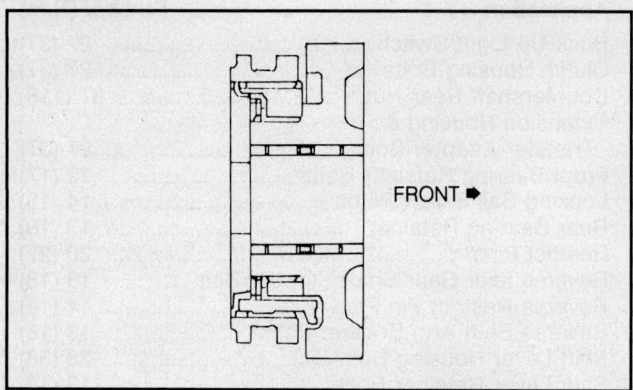

FRONT ➡

NOTE: When installing spline piece No. 5, support front of countershaft with a 5 lb. hammer.

8) On all models, install and tighten lock nut on rear of countershaft. Stake nut after installation. On 5-speed models only, measure countershaft 5th gear end play to ensure it is correct. *See Fig. 8.*

9) Connect reverse shift arm to reverse shift arm bracket. Install reverse idler gear on countershaft. Align reverse shift arm shoe to reverse idler gear groove. Insert reverse idler gear shaft in intermediate plate. Install reverse idler gear shaft stopper and tighten bolt.

Shift Fork Shafts

1) Place shift forks No. 1 and No. 2 into groove of hub sleeves No. 1 and No. 2. Install fork shaft No. 2 through the intermediate plate and into shift forks No. 1 and No. 2.

2) Apply grease to the interlock pins. Using a magnetic finger and screwdriver, install No. 1 shift fork shaft interlock pin in intermediate plate. *See Fig. 15.*

Fig. 15: Installing No. 1 Shift Fork Shaft & Interlock Pin in Intermediate Plate

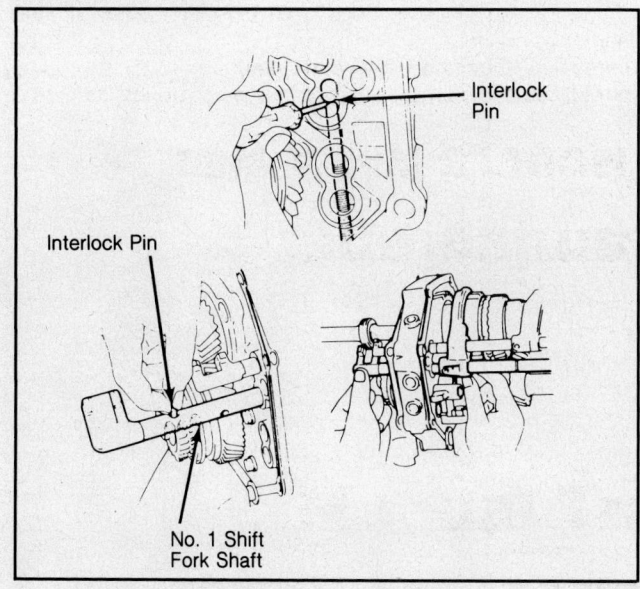

Interlock Pin

Interlock Pin

No. 1 Shift Fork Shaft

3) Place interlock pin in hole in No. 1 shift fork shaft. Install No. 1 shift fork shaft through intermediate plate and into shift fork No. 1.

4) Install No. 3 shift fork shaft interlock pin in intermediate plate. Install interlock pin in No. 3 shift fork shaft hole. Install No. 3 shift fork shaft through intermediate plate and into reverse shift arm. *See Fig. 16.*

Fig. 16: Installing No. 3 Shift Fork Shaft & Interlock Pin in Intermediate Plate

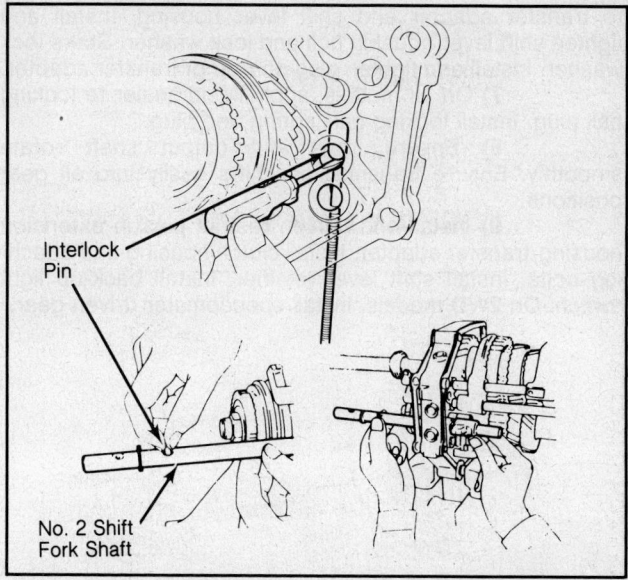

Interlock Pin

No. 2 Shift Fork Shaft

5) Install reverse shift head onto fork shaft No. 5. Insert fork shaft No. 5 through intermediate plate while sliding reverse shift head into shift fork shaft No. 3.

6) On 5-speed models only, using a magnetic finger and screwdriver, install locking ball into reverse shift head hole. Shift hub sleeve No. 3 to 5th gear position.

7) Place shift fork No. 3 onto No. 3 hub sleeve. Slide shift fork shaft No. 4 through No. 3 shift fork and into reverse shift head. Install shift fork shaft No. 4 locking ball in intermediate plate. Slide shift fork shaft No. 4 through intermediate plate.

8) Check shaft operation. Slide shift fork shaft No. 1 to 1st gear position. No other fork shaft should move.

9) Using a pin punch and hammer, drive roll pins into each shift fork, reverse shift arm and reverse shift head. Install fork shaft "E" rings (4 on 4-speed models, 2 on 5-speed models).

10) Install remaining locking balls and springs in intermediate plate. Apply liquid sealer to plugs and install.

NOTE: Short spring is installed in bottom hole of intermediate plate on 5-speed models.

EXTENSION HOUSING/TRANSFER ADAPTER

1) Dismount intermediate plate from vise and remove nuts, bolts and washers. Using a new gasket, install transmission case to intermediate plate. Install 2 front bearing snap rings.

2) Install front bearing retainer with new gasket. Apply liquid sealer to retainer bolts. Install and tighten bolts.

3) On 2WD models only, install a new gasket on the intermediate plate. Insert the shift and select lever into the extension housing. Connect the shift and select lever to the fork shaft.

4) Align fork shaft No. 5 to the extension housing installation hole. Install and tighten the extension hous-

7-182

Manual Transmissions
TOYOTA 4 & 5-SPEED – MODELS G40 & G52 (Cont.)

ing bolts. Install and tighten shift lever housing bolt and new lock washer.

5) On 4WD models only, install new gasket on intermediate plate. Install transfer adapter with 8 attaching bolts.

6) Insert shift lever housing to the transfer adapter and connect the fork shafts. Insert shift lever shaft to transfer adapter and shift lever housing. Install and tighten shift lever housing bolt and lock washer. Stake lock washer. Install and tighten plug on rear of transfer adapter.

7) On all models, apply liquid sealer to locking ball plug. Install locking ball, spring and plug.

8) Ensure input and output shaft rotate smoothly. Ensure transmission shifts easily into all gear positions.

9) Install and tighten restrict pins in extension housing/transfer adapter. Install clutch housing and attaching bolts. Install shift lever retainer. Install back-up light switch. On 2WD models, install speedometer driven gear.

TIGHTENING SPECIFICATIONS

Application	Ft. Lbs. (N.m)
Back-Up Light Switch	27 (37)
Clutch Housing Bolts	27 (37)
Countershaft Rear Nut [1]	87 (118)
Extension Housing & Transfer Adapter Bolts	27 (37)
Front Bearing Retainer Bolts	12 (17)
Locking Ball Screw Plugs	14 (19)
Rear Bearing Retainer	13 (18)
Restrict Pins	20 (27)
Reverse Idler Gear Shaft Stopper Bolt	13 (18)
Reverse Restrict Pin Plug	14 (19)
Reverse Shift Arm Bracket Bolts	13 (18)
Shift Lever Housing Bolt	28 (38)
Shift Lever Retainer Bolts	13 (18)

[1] – Stake nut after installation.

TOYOTA 4 & 5-SPEED – MODELS K40 & K50

Starlet

DESCRIPTION

The K40 is a 4-speed transmission and the K50 is a 5-speed transmission. Both models are fully synchronized in all forward gears. Synchronizers are of the blocker type. Gear selection is accomplished by direct control through floor mounted shift lever. Clutch housing is integral with transmission case.

LUBRICATION & ADJUSTMENT

See the appropriate article in MANUAL TRANSMISSION SERVICING Section.

TROUBLE SHOOTING

HARD SHIFTING

Improperly adjusted clutch. Worn face of synchronizer ring in contact with insert. Cones on synchronizer ring and gear not in proper contact.

TRANSMISSION SLIPS OUT OF GEAR

Bearings worn or defective. Excessive play between gears and collars. Play in clutch hub and sliding sleeve. Shift fork worn. Lock ball spring weak or broken.

TRANSMISSION NOISY

Low or incorrect lubricant. Gears or bearings worn or damaged. Worn clutch hub or mainshaft splines. Incorrectly meshed gears.

REMOVAL & INSTALLATION

See the appropriate article in MANUAL TRANSMISSION REMOVAL Section.

TRANSMISSION DISASSEMBLY

1) Clean exterior of transmission. Remove back-up light switch. Remove clutch release bearing,

Fig. 2: Measuring Countergear End Play

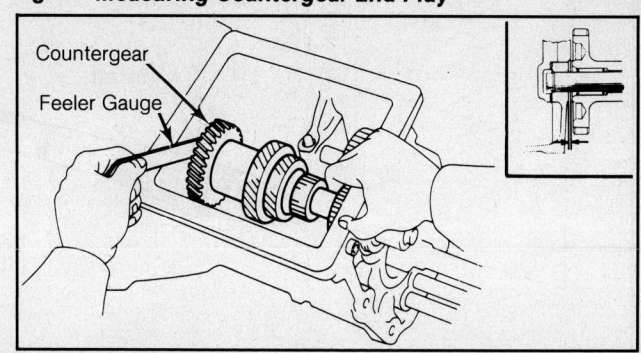

Fig. 1: Shift Lever Assemblies For K40 & K50 Transmissions

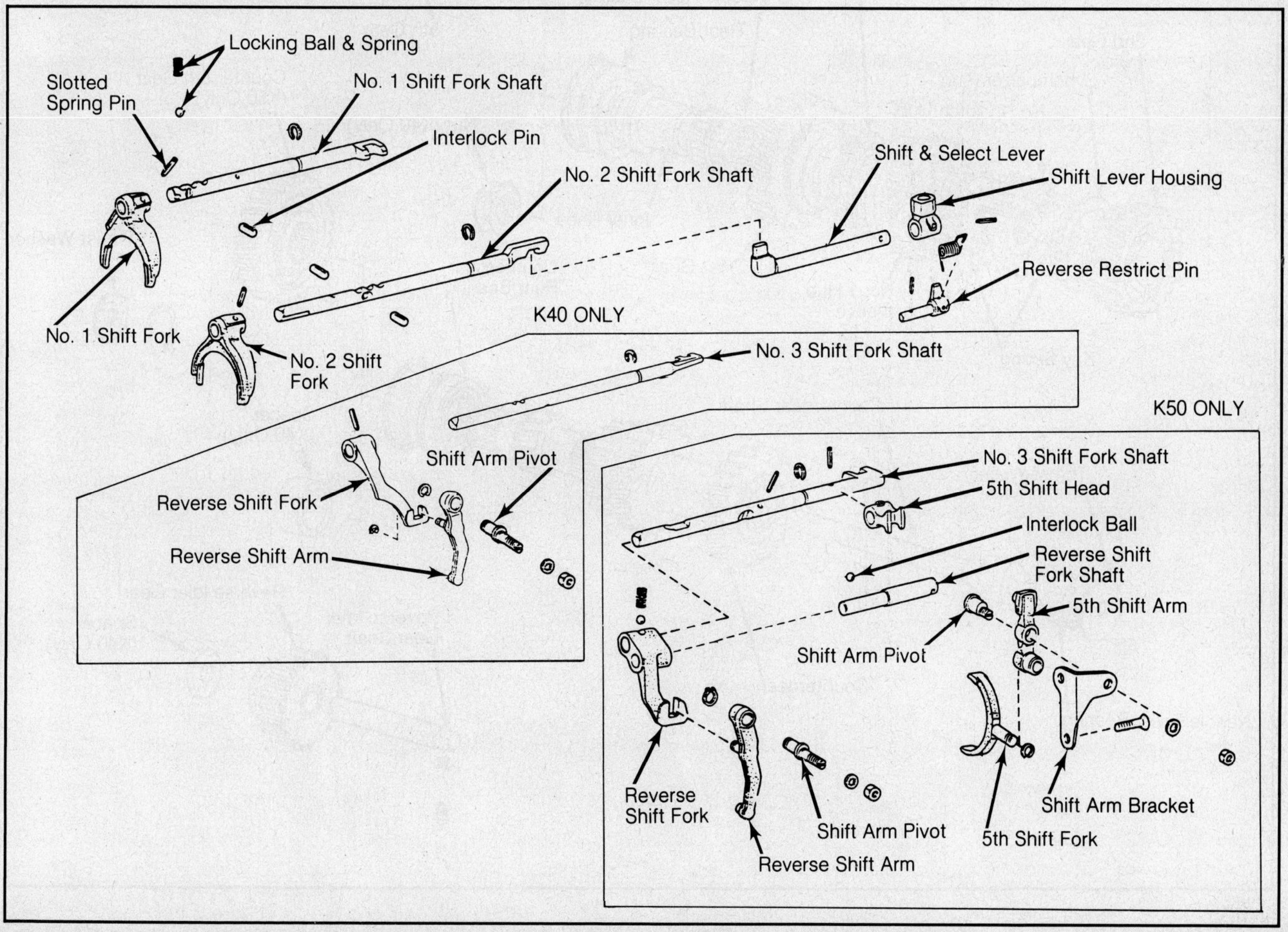

Manual Transmissions

TOYOTA 4 & 5-SPEED — MODELS K40 & K50 (Cont.)

Fig. 3: Exploded View of Transmission Gears and Shafts

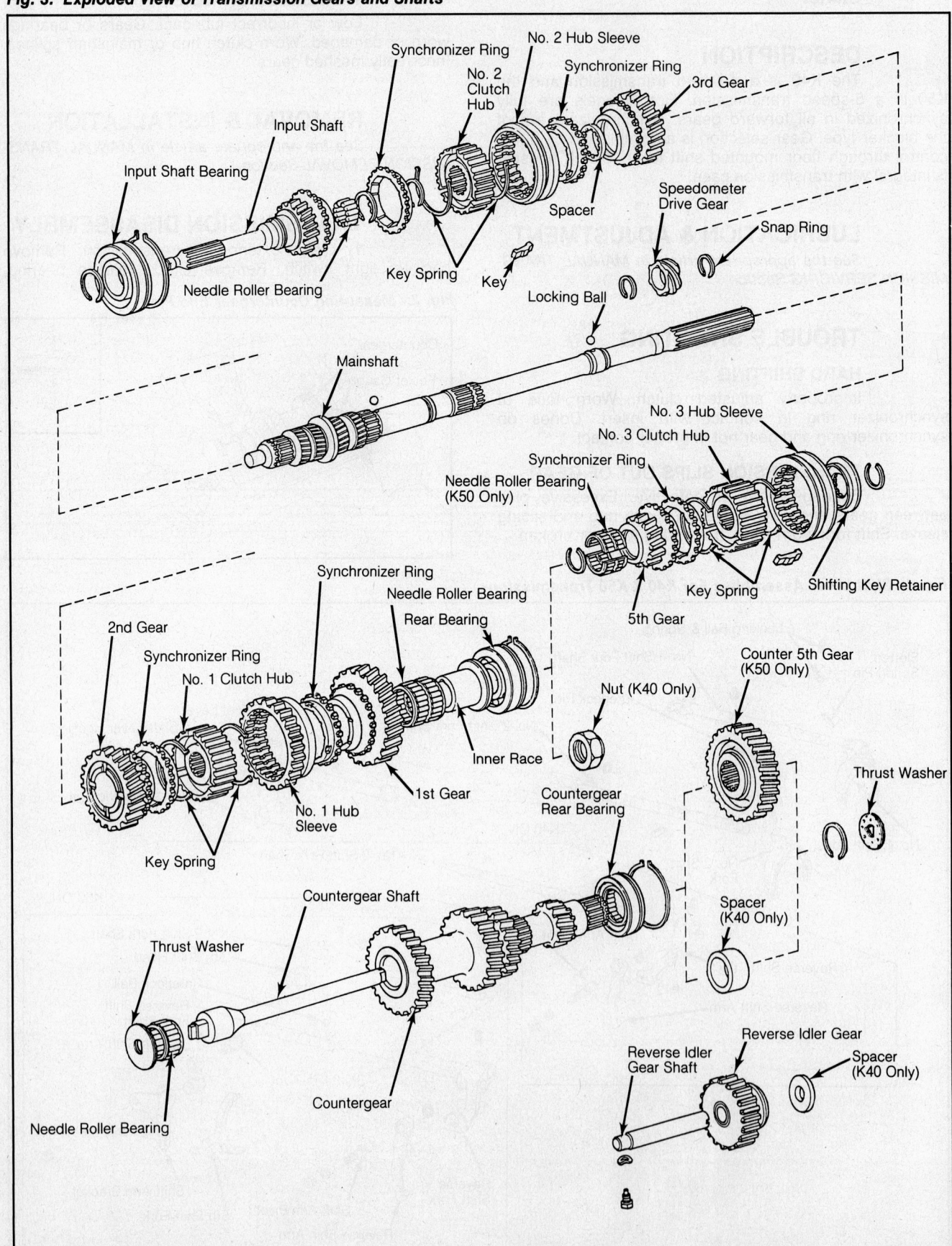

TOYOTA 4 & 5-SPEED – MODELS K40 & K50 (Cont.)

release fork, boot and spring. Remove speedometer driven gear, transmission oil pan and shift lever retainer.

2) Measure the countergear end play between the countergear and transmission case. *See Fig. 2.* Clearance should be .003-.016" (.08-.40 mm).

3) Remove shift lever retainer. Disconnect the select from the fork shaft and remove the extension housing. Remove the countergear thrust rear washer. Remove snap ring, speedometer drive gear, and other snap ring.

4) On K50 models only, measure end play between the 5th gear and transmission case. Clearance should be .0079-.0118" (.20-.30 mm). Remove No. 3 shift fork and arm assembly. *See Fig. 1.* Remove snap ring, key, No. 3 hub sleeve, synchronizer ring, 5th gear, and needle roller bearing.

5) On both models, remove the snap ring and lift off the spacer (K40) or 5th countergear (K50). Remove the retainer bolt and lift out the reverse idler gear, shaft, and spacer.

6) Remove countergear bearing snap ring and pry out bearing outer race. Remove countergear, shaft, thrust washer, and needle roller bearing. Remove case cover. On K40 models, remove 3 locking ball and 3 springs. There are 4 springs and balls on K50 models.

7) On both models, using a pin punch, drive out roll pins from shift forks. Set the No. 1 shift fork shaft to 2nd speed position when removing pin. On K50 models, set No. 3 shift fork shaft to reverse position to remove pin.

8) On K40 models, remove the reverse shift fork and No. 3 shaft. On K50 models, remove the No. 3 shaft, interlock ball, and reverse shift fork and shaft. Set to 2nd speed position to remove.

9) On both models, remove the No. 2 shift fork and shaft. Lift out pin from shaft. Set the No. 1 shift fork to the 2nd gear position and and remove it. Remove the plug from the case and remove the 2 interlock pins.

10) Remove input shaft and front bearing retainer, synchronizer ring, and bearing. Remove snap ring and push out mainshaft and bearing from case. Remove assembly out front of case. Remove reverse shift arm.

COMPONENT DISASSEMBLY

MAINSHAFT

1) Measure thrust clearances of gears on mainshaft for reassembly reference. *See Fig. 4.* On K40 models, loosen the staked part of mainshaft nut with chisel and hammer. Remove nut. On K50 models, remove snap ring.

Fig. 4: Measuring Thrust Gear Clearance

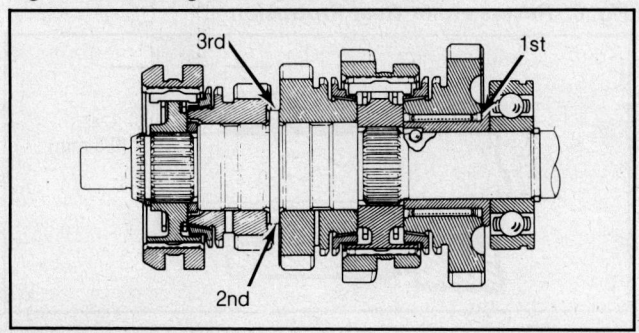

2) On both models, shift No. 1 hub sleeve onto 2nd gear. Press 1st gear and rear bearing off shaft. Remove synchronizer ring, bearing, and locking ball. Press 2nd gear and synchronizer ring off shaft. Remove the snap ring, 3rd gear, sleeve, and synchronizer ring from shaft.

3) Expand snap ring and press input shaft from retainer. If necessary, disassemble the reverse shift arm and pivot, 5th arm, No. 3 shift fork, and (K50 only) 5th shift head and No. 3 fork shaft.

INSPECTION & REPAIR

MAINSHAFT

1) Inspect shaft for wear or damage. Mainshaft maximum runout limit is .0024" (.06 mm). Mainshaft flange minimum thickness is .138" (3.50 mm). Minimum diameter of mainshaft bushing surface is 1.25" (31.8 mm).

2) The minimum thickness of the mainshaft inner race flange is .132" (3.35 mm). Minimum diameter of the race outer diameter is 1.25" (31.85 mm). Replace any worn parts.

GEARS

Measure oil clearance between 1st gear and inner race (needle bearings installed), between 2nd gear and mainshaft, between 3rd gear and mainshaft, and between reverse gear and mainshaft. Measure oil clearance between 5th gear and mainshaft (needle bearing installed). *See Gear Oil Clearance Specifications* table.

GEAR OIL CLEARANCE SPECFICATIONS

Application	Standard In. (mm)	Maximum In. (mm)
1st Gear	.0004-.0024 (.01-.06)	.0059 (.15)
2nd Gear	.0024-.0039 (.06-.10)	.0079 (.20)
3rd Gear	.0024-.0039 (.06-.10)	.0079 (.20)
5th Gear	.0004-.0020 (.01-.05)	.0059 (.15)
Reverse Gear	.0019-.0033 (.048-.084)	.0118 (.30)

SYNCHRONIZER RINGS

NOTE: **Check synchronizer braking action by placing synchronizer ring against cone and turning while pressing. Synchronizer should stick to cone.**

Measure clearance between the synchronizer ring back and gear spline end. Standard clearance is .039-.079" (1.0-2.0 mm). Maximum is .031" (.80 mm).

INPUT SHAFT

Remove snap ring and press bearing off of shaft if necessary. Select a snap ring that will allow minimum axial play. Two sizes of snap ring are available.

SHIFT FORKS

Clearance limit between shift fork and hub sleeve is .031" (.80 mm). Check sliding action of shift levers in case.

Manual Transmissions

TOYOTA 4 & 5-SPEED — MODELS K40 & K50 (Cont.)

SEALS & EXTENSION HOUSING BUSHING

1) Remove speedometer driven gear oil seal if necessary. Install new seal so that edge of seal is .79" (20 mm) from threaded end of sleeve. Front bearing retainer oil seal may be replaced by prying out with a screwdriver. Press in new seal using 27mm socket.

2) If necessary, remove extension housing oil seal with slide hammer. Heat the extension housing to 212°F (100°C) in oil bath. Press bushing out of housing. Install new bushing with oil hole facing UPWARD. Install new oil seal with driver (09325-12010).

COMPONENT REASSEMBLY

MAINSHAFT

1) Coat mainshaft with multi-purpose grease. Assemble clutch hubs and sleeves. Do not install them backwards. See Fig. 5. Install the key springs under the keys. Key spring ends must overlap.

Fig. 5: Identifying Synchronizer Assemblies

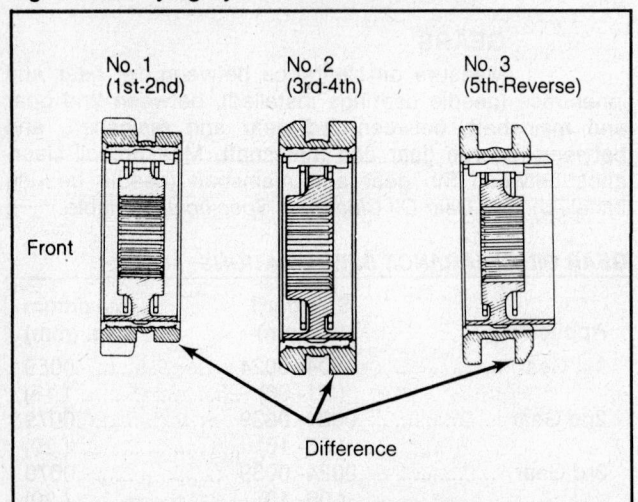

2) Install 3rd gear, synchronizer ring, and spacer on mainshaft. Align the ring slots with the shifting keys and press on No. 2 hub sleeve. Measure 3rd gear end play. If not within specifications, remove hub sleeve and replace spacer. See Mainshaft End Play Specifications table.

3) Install a snap ring that will allow minimum axial end play and install it on the mainshaft. Snap rings are available in sizes from .0807" (2.05 mm) to .0965" (2.45 mm).

4) Assembly 2nd gear, synchronizer ring, and No. 1 hub sleeve. Align the ring slots with the shifting keys. Press the assembly on the mainshaft.

5) Install the locking ball on the shaft. Apply gear oil to the needle bearings. Assemble the 1st gear, synchronizer ring, bearing, and bearing inner race. Install assembly on mainshaft. Align slots and shifting keys. Turn inner race to align it with the locking ball.

6) Install the rear bearing on mainshaft with snap ring groove toward the rear. Install locking ball in mainshaft. Apply gear oil to needle bearing. Assemble 1st gear, synchronizer ring, bearing, and inner race. Install on mainshaft with slots aligned with shifting keys. Turn inner race to align it with locking ball.

7) On K40 models, install mainshaft nut and tighten to specification. Stake the nut with a pin punch and hammer.

8) On K50 models, install the snap ring. Select a snap ring which will allow minimum axial end play. Snap rings are available in thicknesses from .0807" (2.05 mm) to .1004" (2.55 mm).

9) Measure the 1st and 2nd gear end play clearances. See Mainshaft End Play Specifications table. If not within specifications, inspect all parts for wear and replace as necessary.

MAINSHAFT END PLAY SPECIFICATIONS

Application	Standard In. (mm)	Maximum In. (mm)
1st Gear	.0071-.0110	.012
	(.18-.28)	(.30)
2nd Gear	.0039-.0098	.012
	(.10-.25)	(.30)
3rd Gear	.0020-.0079	.012
	(.05-.20)	(.30)

TRANSMISSION REASSEMBLY

1) If removed, install reverse shift arm. Insert mainshaft from front of transmission case. Stand case upright and pull mainshaft up. Install bearing and secure with a snap ring.

2) Apply gear oil to input shaft needle bearing and install it in input shaft. Apply liquid sealer to new gasket. Install input shaft in transmission with synchronizer ring slots aligned with shifting keys. Apply liquid sealer to attaching bolts and install.

3) If removed, install the No. 1 shift fork and No. 1 shaft. Install the No. 2 shift fork and No. 2 shaft. On K40 models only, connect the fork to the reverse shift arm. Install it and No. 3 shaft.

4) On K50 models only, connect the fork to the reverse shift arm. Install it with the reverse shaft. Apply multipurpose grease to the interlock ball. Align fork hole with shaft groove. Push ball in with a screwdriver until it falls into shaft groove. Install the No. 3 shaft.

5) On both models, align the interlock holes of the shafts. Coat pins with multipurpose grease and install the 3 interlock pins through hole in side of case. After installation of the 3 pins, insert a piece of wire and check to see if it goes in about 1.38" (35 mm). Set shafts in neutral position. Apply liquid sealer to plug and install.

6) Align the shift fork and shaft holes. Install the 3 roll pins until they are flush with the forks. Install 3 locking balls and springs on K40 models and 4 balls and springs on K50 models. Install top case cover and bolts.

Fig. 6: Reverse Idler Gear Protrusion

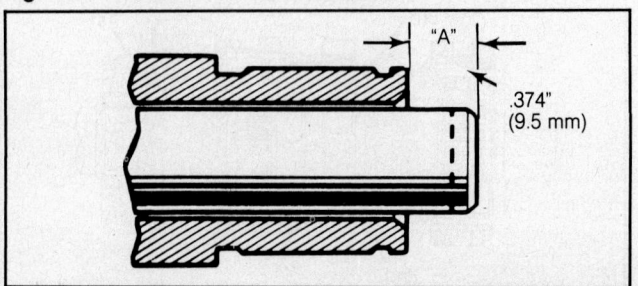

TOYOTA 4 & 5-SPEED — MODELS K40 & K50 (Cont.)

7) Assemble countergear, front thrust washer, and needle roller bearing. Install assembly. Oil groove side of thrust washer faces toward gear. Push on countergear and confirm shaft protrudes .374" (9.50 mm) from gear. *See Fig. 6.*

8) Expand snap ring and drive in countergear bearing outer race. Install rear needle bearing.

9) On K40 models, install the reverse idler gear, shaft, and spacer with bolt. On K50 models, install reverse idler gear, shaft, and bolt. On both models, turn pivot and adjust idler gear-to-countergear clearance to .039-.079" (1.0-2.0 mm). *See Fig. 7.*

Fig. 7: Measuring Reverse Idler Gear Clearance

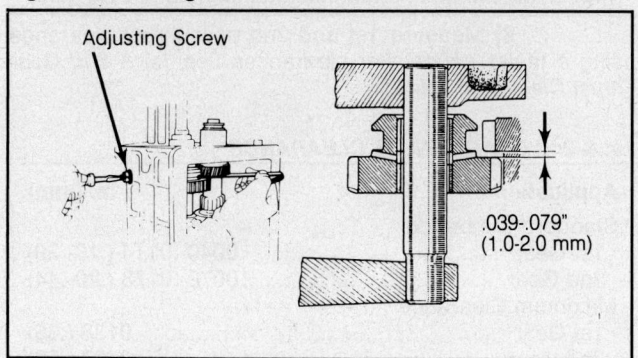

10) On K50 models, install the 5th countergear (spacer on K40 models). The inside, stepped hub of the 5th countergear faces forward. On both models, install snap ring. Select a snap ring that will allow the minimum axial end play.

11) On K50 models, apply gear oil to the No. 3 hub sleeve roller bearings. Install the bearing on the shaft. Install the 5th gear, synchronizer ring, and No. 3 hub sleeve. Align the ring slots with the shifting keys.

12) Install a snap ring that will give an axial end play of .0079-.0118" (.20-.30 mm). Snap rings are available in thicknesses from .0807" (2.05 mm) to .1102" (2.80 mm).

13) Install the No. 3 shift fork and arm assembly. Install and tighten bolts. Engage 5th gear and 5th countergears. Adjust pivot bolt so there is .039-.079" (1.0-2.0 mm) clearance between gears.

14) On both models, install speedometer drive gear and snap rings. Install countergear rear thrust washer with oil groove toward the gear. Install extension housing with a new gasket.

NOTE: **Take care not to damage oil seal in extension housing.**

15) Measure countergear end play. If not within .0031-.0157" (.08-.40 mm), remove extension housing and adjust by changing rear thrust washer. Install oil pan and shift lever retainer with new gaskets.

TIGHTENING SPECIFICATIONS

Application	Ft. Lbs (N.m)
Extension Housing Bolts	22-32 (30-44)
Front Bearing Retainer Bolts	11-15 (15-20)
Interlock Pin Plug	8-11 (11-15)
Mainshaft Nut	33-72 (45-98)
No. Shift Fork Screws	10-12 (14-16)
Reverse Idler Gear Shift Arm Bolt	10-13 (14-18)
Transmission-to-Engine Bolts	37-50 (50-68)

	INCH Lbs. (N.m)
Case Cover Bolts	52-78 (6-9)
Oil Pan Bolts	48-60 (5-7)

Manual Transmissions

TOYOTA S41 4-SPEED & S50 5-SPEED

Corolla FWD – 4-Speed
Camry & Corolla FWD – 5-Speed

DESCRIPTION

The Toyota Camry utilizes a five speed fully synchronized manual transaxle. Fifth gear is overdrive with a .732:1 ratio. The fluid type used is Dexron II automatic transmission fluid.

LUBRICATION & ADJUSTMENT

See appropriate article in MANUAL TRANSMISSION SERVICING Section.

TRANSAXLE REMOVAL & INSTALLATION

See the appropriate article in MANUAL TRANSMISSION REMOVAL Section.

TRANSAXLE DISASSEMBLY

1) Remove release fork, bearing, back-up light switch and speedometer driven gear. Remove release bearing retainer. Remove transmission case cover. Remove bolt with lock washer. Measure 5th gear thrust clearance using a dial indicator. Standard clearance is .0079-.0157" (.20-.40 mm). Maximum clearance is .0177" (.45 mm).

2) To remove output shaft lock nut, engage gear double meshing, remove lock nut and then disengage gear double meshing. Lock nut has left hand threads. Remove hub sleeve and shift fork No. 3 by removing snap ring and shifting key retainer. Using 3 case cover set bolts, tighten bolts a little at a time and remove hub sleeve and shift fork No. 3.

3) Remove 5th gear, synchronizer ring, needle roller bearings and spacer. Remove 5th gear using a gear puller. Remove lock ball assembly by loosening lock nut. Remove selecting bell crank. Remove shift and select lever assembly. Remove rear bearing retainer. Remove 2 bearing snap rings using snap ring pliers. Remove reverse idler gear shaft lock bolt.

4) Remove differential side bearing retainer and shim. Remove transmission case by removing 17 retaining bolts and tap case with a plastic hammer. To remove reverse shift arm bracket, shift fork shaft into reverse and remove 2 bolts. Remove reverse idler gear and shaft by pulling out on shaft.

5) Remove shift fork shaft No. 1, shift head No. 1, shift fork No. 1 and No. 2 by driving out slotted spring pin from fork shaft No. 1, driving out slotted spring pin from shift head and fork shaft No. 1, and pulling out fork shaft No. 1 with shift head and shift forks. Remove reverse shift fork and interlock pin.

6) Remove fork shaft No. 2 by removing straight screw plug from side of case. Using a pin punch and hammer, drive out slotted spring pin. Pull out shaft. Remove input and output shaft together from transaxle case. Remove differential assembly. Remove Magnet. Measure 3rd and 4th gear thrust clearance using a feeler gauge. For clearances See 3rd & 4th Gear Thrust Clearance Table.

7) Remove snap ring from input shaft. Remove radial ball bearing, 4th gear, needle roller bearings, synchronizer ring and spacer from input shaft. Remove snap ring from hub sleeve No. 2 assembly and press hub sleeve No. 2 assembly, 3rd gear, synchronizer ring and needle roller bearing from shaft.

3rd & 4th GEAR THRUST CLEARANCE

Application	In. (mm)
Standard Clearance	
3rd Gear	.0039-.0098 (.10-.25)
4th Gear	.0079-.0177 (.20-.45)
Maximum Clearance	
3rd Gear	.0118 (.30)
4th Gear	.0197 (.50)

8) Measure 1st and 2nd gear thrust clearance using a feeler gauge. For clearances See 1st & 2nd Gear Thrust Clearance Table.

1st & 2nd GEAR THRUST CLEARANCE

Application	In. (mm)
Standard Clearance	
1st Gear	.0040-.0114 (.10-.29)
2nd Gear	.0079-.0173 (.20-.44)
Maximum Clearance	
1st Gear	.0138 (.35)
2nd Gear	.0197 (.50)

9) Remove radial ball bearing, 4th driven gear and output gear spacer from output shaft. Remove 3rd driven gear, 2nd gear, needle roller bearing, spacer and synchronizer ring. Remove snap ring and then hub sleeve No. 1 assembly, 1st gear, synchronizer ring and needle roller bearing and spacer.

10) To disassemble shift and select lever assembly, remove lever lock pin and nut. Remove control shift lever. Remove dust boot. Remove control shaft cover. Remove 2 "E" rings. Remove select spring seat No. 2 and spring.

11) Remove shift inner lever No. 2. Using a pin punch and hammer, drive out slotted spring pin. Remove shift fork lock plate, shift inner lever No. 1, select spring seat No. 1 and spring.

DIFFERENTIAL DISASSEMBLY

1) With the following parts removed: neutral start switch, speedometer driven gear, speed sensor, oil pan, valve body, overdrive unit, governor apply gasket and overdrive brake gasket, parking lock bracket and rod, parking lock pawl, manual shaft and lever, remove carrier cover.

2) Measure total preload using a torque wrench and note the value. Preload (at starting) with drive pinion preload added, should be 2.2-4.1 INCH Lbs. (.25-.46 N.m) for a new bearing and for a used bearing, 1.1-2.0 INCH Lbs. (.12-.23 N.m).

3) Measure backlash of side gears. Standard backlash is .0020-.0079" (.05-.20 mm). Remove left bearing retainer. Remove right side bearing cap. Remove differential case, outer race and adjusting shim. Measure drive pinion preload using a torque wrench. Preload should be 8.7-13.9 INCH Lbs. (.99-1.58 N.m) for a new bearing and for a used bearing, 4.3-6.9 INCH Lbs. (.49-.78 N.m).

TOYOTA S41 4-SPEED & S50 5-SPEED (Cont.)

Fig. 1: Exploded View of External Parts

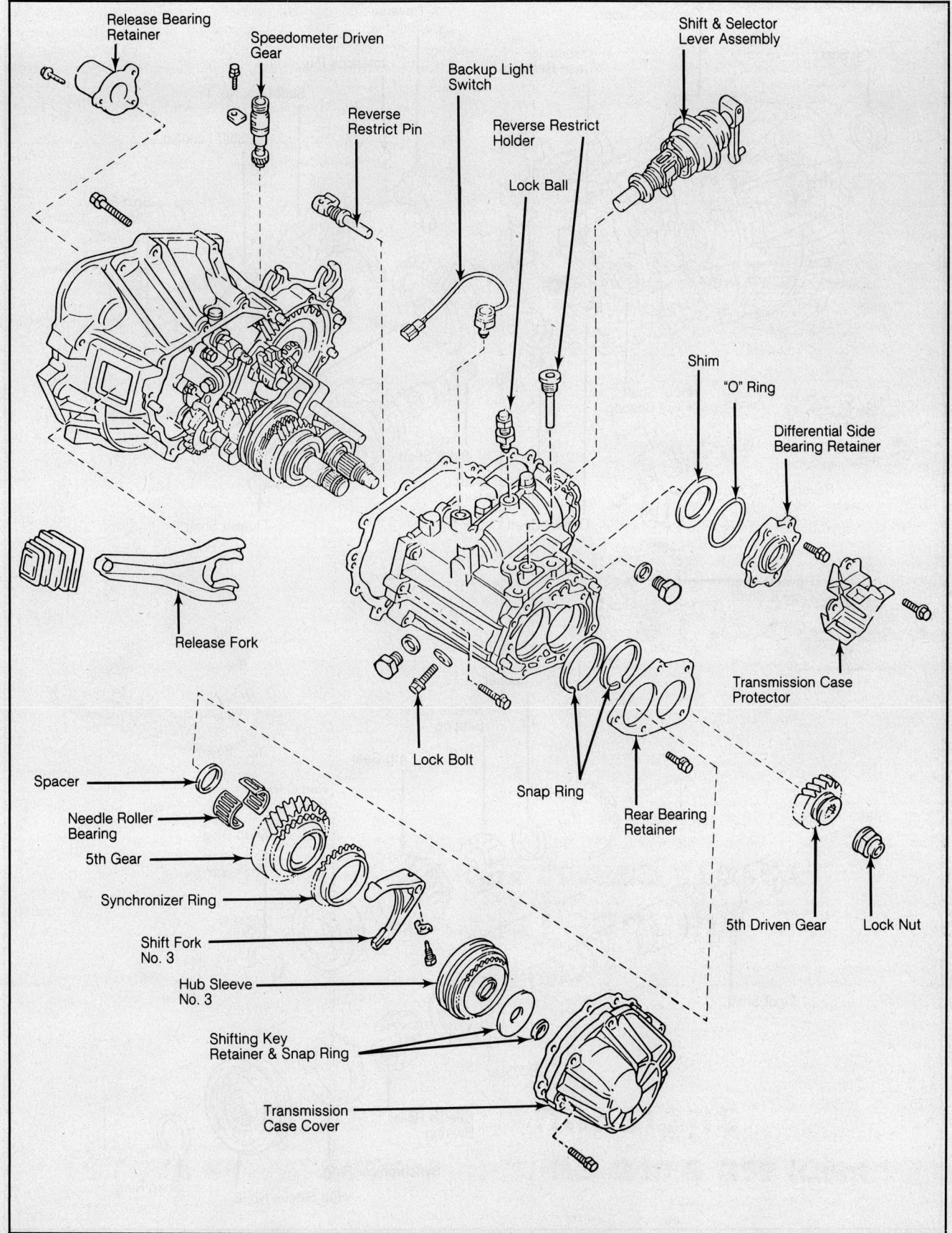

Manual Transmissions

TOYOTA S41 4-SPEED & S50 5-SPEED (Cont.)

Fig. 2: Exploded View of Internal Parts

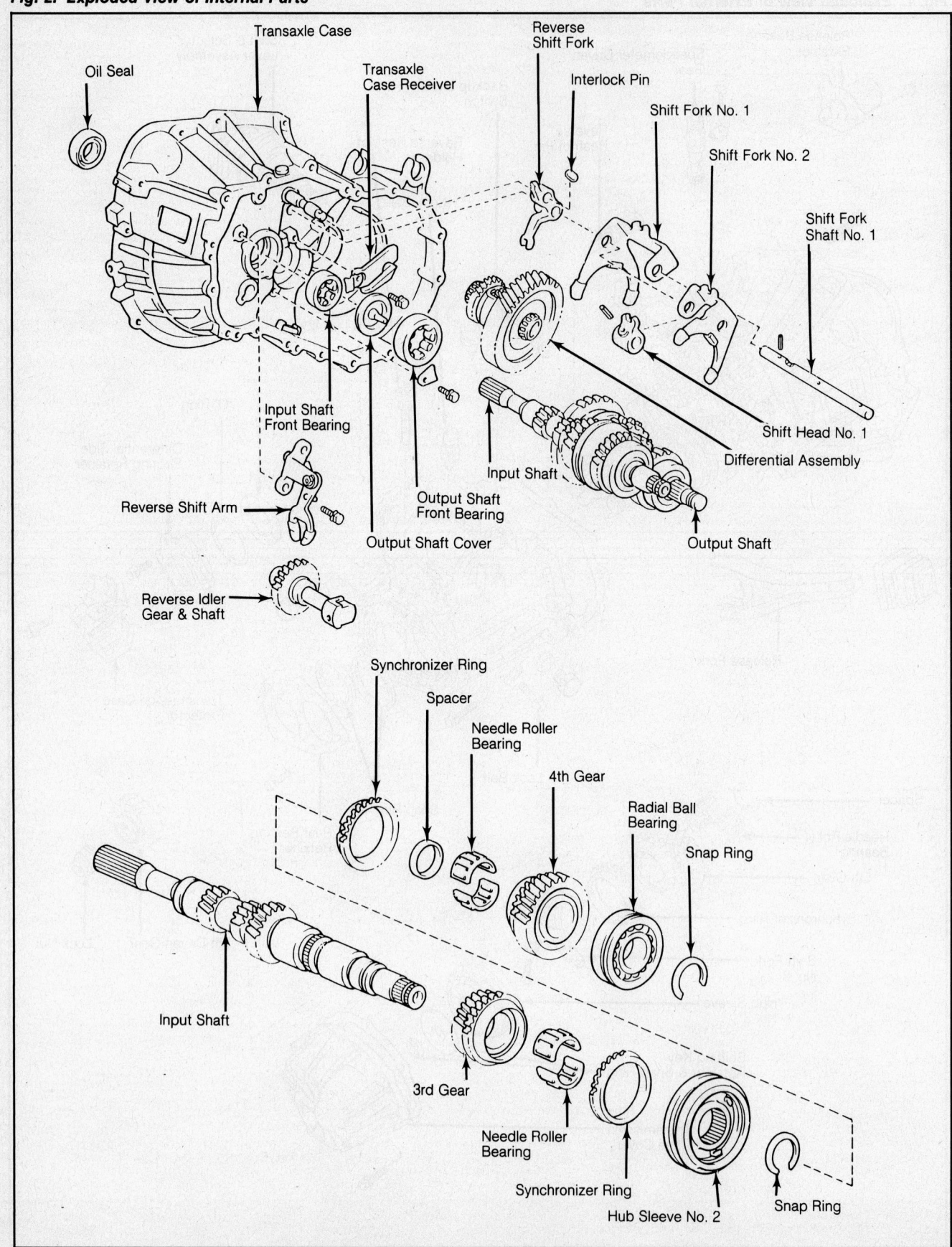

TOYOTA S41 4-SPEED & S50 5-SPEED (Cont.)

Fig. 3: Exploded View of Output Shaft

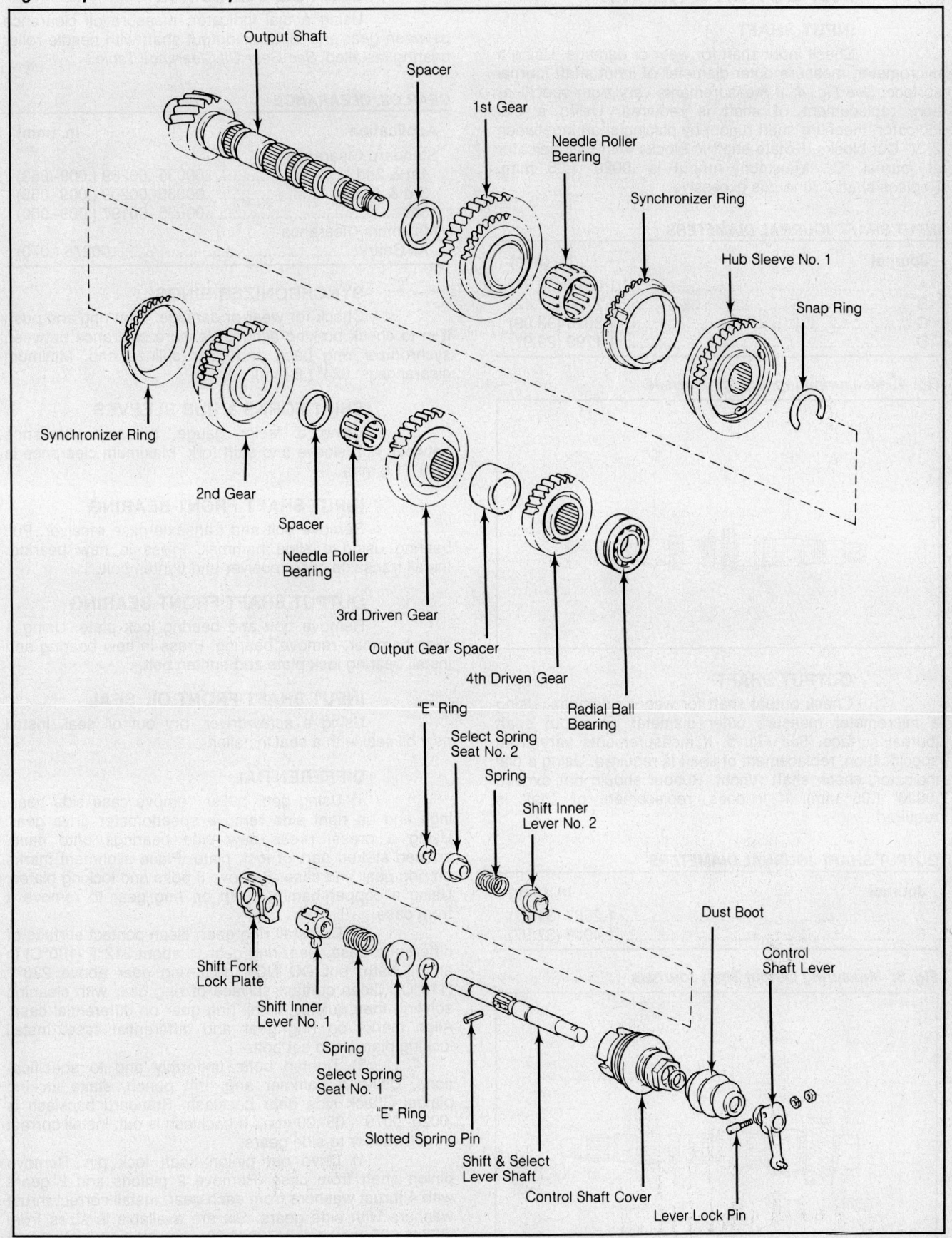

Output Shaft

Spacer

1st Gear

Needle Roller Bearing

Synchronizer Ring

Hub Sleeve No. 1

Snap Ring

Synchronizer Ring

2nd Gear

Spacer

Needle Roller Bearing

3rd Driven Gear

Output Gear Spacer

4th Driven Gear

Radial Ball Bearing

"E" Ring

Select Spring Seat No. 2

Spring

Shift Inner Lever No. 2

Dust Boot

Control Shaft Lever

Shift Fork Lock Plate

Shift Inner Lever No. 1

Spring

Select Spring Seat No. 1

"E" Ring

Slotted Spring Pin

Shift & Select Lever Shaft

Control Shaft Cover

Lever Lock Pin

TOYOTA S41 4-SPEED & S50 5-SPEED (Cont.)

INSPECTION & REPAIR

INPUT SHAFT

Check input shaft for wear or damage. Using a micrometer, measure outer diameter of input shaft journal surface. *See Fig. 4.* If measurements vary from specification, replacement of shaft is required. Using a dial indicator, measure shaft runout by placing shaft inbetween 2 "V" Cut blocks. Rotate shaft in blocks with dial indicator at journal "C". Maximum runout is .0020" (.05 mm). Replace shaft if runout is excessive.

INPUT SHAFT JOURNAL DIAMETERS

Journal	In. (mm)
A	1.0618 (26.97)
B	1.2764 (32.42)
C	1.3028 (33.09)
D	1.1799 (29.97)

Fig. 4: Measuring Input Shaft Journals

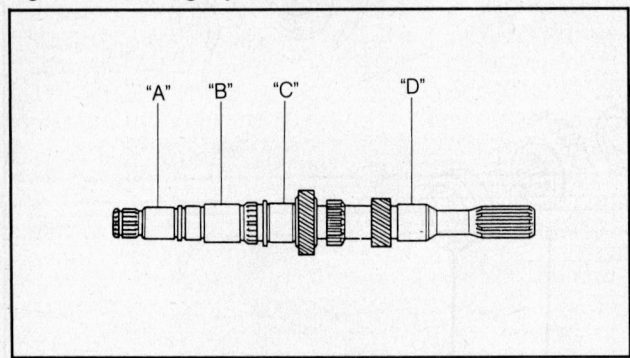

OUTPUT SHAFT

Check output shaft for wear or damage. Using a micrometer measure outer diameter of output shaft journal surface. *See Fig. 5.* If measurements vary from specification, replacement of shaft is required. Using a dial indicator, check shaft runout. Runout should not exceed .0020" (.05 mm). If it does, replacement of shaft is required.

OUTPUT SHAFT JOURNAL DIAMETERS

Journal	In. (mm)
A	1.2587 (31.97)
B	1.4949 (37.97)

Fig. 5: Measuring Output Shaft Journals

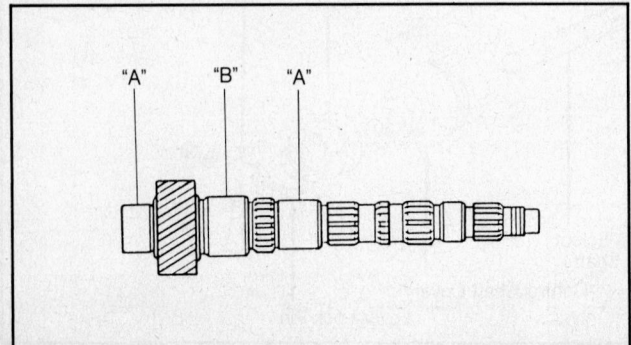

GEAR OIL CLEARANCE

Using a dial indicator, measure oil clearance between gear and input or output shaft with needle roller bearing installed. *See Gear Oil Clearance Table.*

GEAR OIL CLEARANCE

Application	In. (mm)
Standard Clearance	
1st & 2nd	.00035-.00209 (.009-.053)
3rd & 4th	.00035-.00209 (.009-.053)
5th	.00035-.00197 (.009-.050)
Maximum Clearance	
All Gears	.00276 (.070)

SYNCHRONIZER RINGS

Check for wear or damage. Turn ring and push it in to check braking action. Measure clearance between sychronizer ring back and gear splined end. Minimum clearance is .024" (.6 mm).

SHIFT FORKS & HUB SLEEVES

Using a feeler gauge, measure clearance between hub sleeve and shift fork. Maximum clearance is .039" (1.0 mm).

INPUT SHAFT FRONT BEARING

Remove bolt and transaxle case receiver. Pull bearing using a slide hammer. Press in new bearing. Install transaxle case receiver and tighten bolt.

OUTPUT SHAFT FRONT BEARING

Remove bolt and bearing lock plate. Using a slide hammer, remove bearing. Press in new bearing and install bearing lock plate and tighten bolt.

INPUT SHAFT FRONT OIL SEAL

Using a screwdriver, pry out oil seal. Install new oil seal with a seal installer.

DIFFERENTIAL

1) Using gear puller, remove case side bearings and on right side remove speedometer drive gear. Using a press, press new side bearings onto case. Loosen staked part of lock plate. Place alignment marks on ring gear and case. Remove 8 bolts and locking plates. Using a copper hammer, tap on ring gear to remove it from case.

2) To install ring gear, clean contact surface of differential case. Heat ring gear to about 212°F (100°C) in an oil bath, but DO NOT heat ring gear above 230°F (110°C). Clean contact surface of ring gear with cleaning solvent, then quickly install ring gear on differential case. Align marks on ring gear and differential case. Install locking plates and set bolts.

3) Tighten bolts uniformly and to specifications. Using a hammer and drift punch, stake locking plates. Check side gear backlash. Standard backlash is .0020-.0079" (.05-.20 mm). If backlash is out, install correct thrust washer to side gears.

4) Drive out pinion shaft lock pin. Remove pinion shaft from case. Remove 2 pinions and 2 gears with 4 thrust washers from each gear. Install correct thrust washers with side gears. Six are available in sizes from .0374" (.95 mm) to .0472" (1.20 mm). With correct thrust

TOYOTA S41 4-SPEED & S50 5-SPEED (Cont.)

washer in place install lock pin using a hammer and punch, and drive lock pin through case and hole in pinion shaft. Stake case.

COMPONENT DISASSEMBLY & REASSEMBLY

1) Measure drive pinion preload using a torque wrench. Preload for a new bearing is 8.7-13.9 INCH Lbs. (.99-1.58 N.m) and for a used bearing 4.3-6.9 INCH Lbs. (.49-.78 N.m). Remove transmission case cap. Remove counter driven gear and outer race from case.

2) Remove oil slinger, spacer and rotor sensor. Remove drive pinion. Remove bearing cage from drive pinion. Remove "O" ring from bearing cage. Replace bearing of counter driven gear. Replace bearing and outer race of drive pinion shaft. Replace oil seal of cage. Press oil seal to a depth of .43" (11 mm).

3) To adjust differential side bearing preload, place outer race and adjusting shim onto right side bearing. Place differential case into case. Install left bearing retainer. Install right side bearing cap. Tighten left bearing retainer. Adjust ring gear preload with a torque wrench.

4) Preload (at starting) for a new bearing is 8.7-13.9 INCH Lbs. (.99-1.58 N.m) and for a used bearing 4.3-6.9 INCH Lbs. (.49-.78 N.m). If preload is not within specifications, remove ring gear from case and reselect another right adjusting shim. Twenty shims are available in sizes from .0744-.0752" (1.89-1.91 mm) to .1098-.1106" (2.79-2.81 mm).

NOTE: **The preload will change about 2.6-3.5 INCH lbs. (.015-.020 kg/cm²) with each shim thickness.**

5) If preload is adjusted within specification, remove bearing retainer, ring gear, right side bearing and shim. Be sure not to lose adjusting shim.

TRANSAXLE REASSEMBLY

1) Install clutch hub No. 2 and shifting keys into hub sleeve. Install shifting key springs under shifting keys. Install key springs positioned so their end gaps are not in line. Install 3rd gear, needle roller bearings, synchronizer ring and hub sleeve No. 2 assembly to input shaft.

2) Install snap ring. Select one that will allow minimum axial play and install it on shaft. Six are offered in thicknesses ranging from .0768-.0886" (1.95-2.25 mm). Measure 3rd gear thrust clearance with a feeler gauge. Standard clearance is .0040-.0098" (.10-.25 mm) and maximum clearance is .0118" (.30 mm).

3) Install synchronizer ring, spacer, needle roller bearing, 4th gear and radial ball bearing. Install snap ring. Select a snap ring that will allow minimum axial play and install it on shaft. Five are offered in thicknesses ranging from .0846-.0945" (2.15-2.40 mm). Measure 4th gear thrust clearance using a feeler gauge. Standard clearance is .0079-.0177" (.20-.45 mm) and maximim clearance is .0197" (.50 mm).

4) Insert clutch hub No. 1 into hub sleeve along with shifting keys and install shifting key springs under shifting keys. Install key springs positioned so their end gaps are not in line. Install spacer, 1st gear, needle roller bearing, synchronizer ring and hub sleeve No. 1 to output shaft.

5) Install snap ring that will allow minimum axial play. Six are offered in thicknesses ranging from .0984-.1102" (2.50-2.80 mm). Measure 1st gear thrust clearance with a feeler gauge. Standard clearance is .0039-.0114" (.10-.29 mm) and maximum clearance is .0138" (.35 mm).

6) Install spacer, synchronizer ring, 2nd gear, needle roller bearing and 3rd driven gear. Measure 2nd gear thrust clearance with a feeler gauge. Standard clearance is .0079-.0173" (.20-.44 mm) and maximum clearance is .0197" (.50 mm). Install output gear spacer, 4th driven gear and radial ball bearing.

7) Install magnet. Adjust differential side bearing preload by installing differential to transaxle case. Tighten case bolts to specifications. Install thinnest shim into transmission case. Install bearing retainer without an "O" ring. Install and tighten retainer bolts. Using a torque wrench, measure preload. Preload (starting) should be 8.7-13.9 INCH Lbs. (.99-1.58 N.m).

8) If preload is not within specifications, remove bearing retainer and reselect another adjusting shim. The preload will change about 2.7-3.5 INCH Lbs. (.31-.40 N.m). If preload is adjusted within specifications, remove bearing retainer, shim and transmission case with gasket. Do not lose shim.

9) Install input and output shafts together. Install fork shaft No 2. Install reverse shift fork and interlock pin. Install reverse shift arm. Install reverse idler gear and shaft. Install shift fork No. 1, No. 2, shift head No. 1 and fork shaft No. 1.

10) Install transmission case with a new gasket. Install shim and side bearing retainer with "O" ring. Install and tighten reverse idler gear shaft lock bolt. Install input and output shaft bearing snap rings, then install rear bearing retainer. Assemble shift and select lever assembly. Install shift and select lever assembly.

11) Install and adjust lock ball assembly. Fully loosen lock nut and screw in lock ball. Turn lock ball to where play at shift outer lever tip is .004-.020" (.1-.5 mm). Hold lock ball and tighten lock nut. Check shift outer lever tip play. Lever tip play should be same. Install 5th driven gear.

12) Install spacer, needle roller bearings, 5th gear and synchronizer ring. Insert clutch hub No. 3 into hub sleeve by installing clutch and shifting keys to hub sleeve and installing shifting key springs under shifting keys. Install key springs, positioned so their end gaps are not in line.

13) Install hub sleeve No. 3 assembly with shift fork No. 3. Align synchronizer ring slots with shifting keys. Measure 5th gear thrust clearance using a dial indicator. Standard clearance is .0079-.0157" (.20-.40 mm) and maximum clearance is .0177" (.45 mm).

14) Install shifting key retainer and snap ring. Select a snap ring that will allow minimum axial play and install it on shaft. Snap rings come in 15 sizes ranging from .0630-.0650" (1.60-1.65 mm) to .0906-.0925" (2.30-2.35 mm). Install output shaft lock nut and tighten to specifications, then stake nut.

15) Install bolt with lock washer and tighten bolt to specifications. Install transmission case cover and tighten bolts to specifications. Install release bearing retainer and tighten to specifications. Install release fork and bearing. Install back-up light switch and speedometer driven gear.

Manual Transmissions

TOYOTA S41 4-SPEED & S50 5-SPEED (Cont.)

Fig. 6: *Exploded View of Differential Assembly*

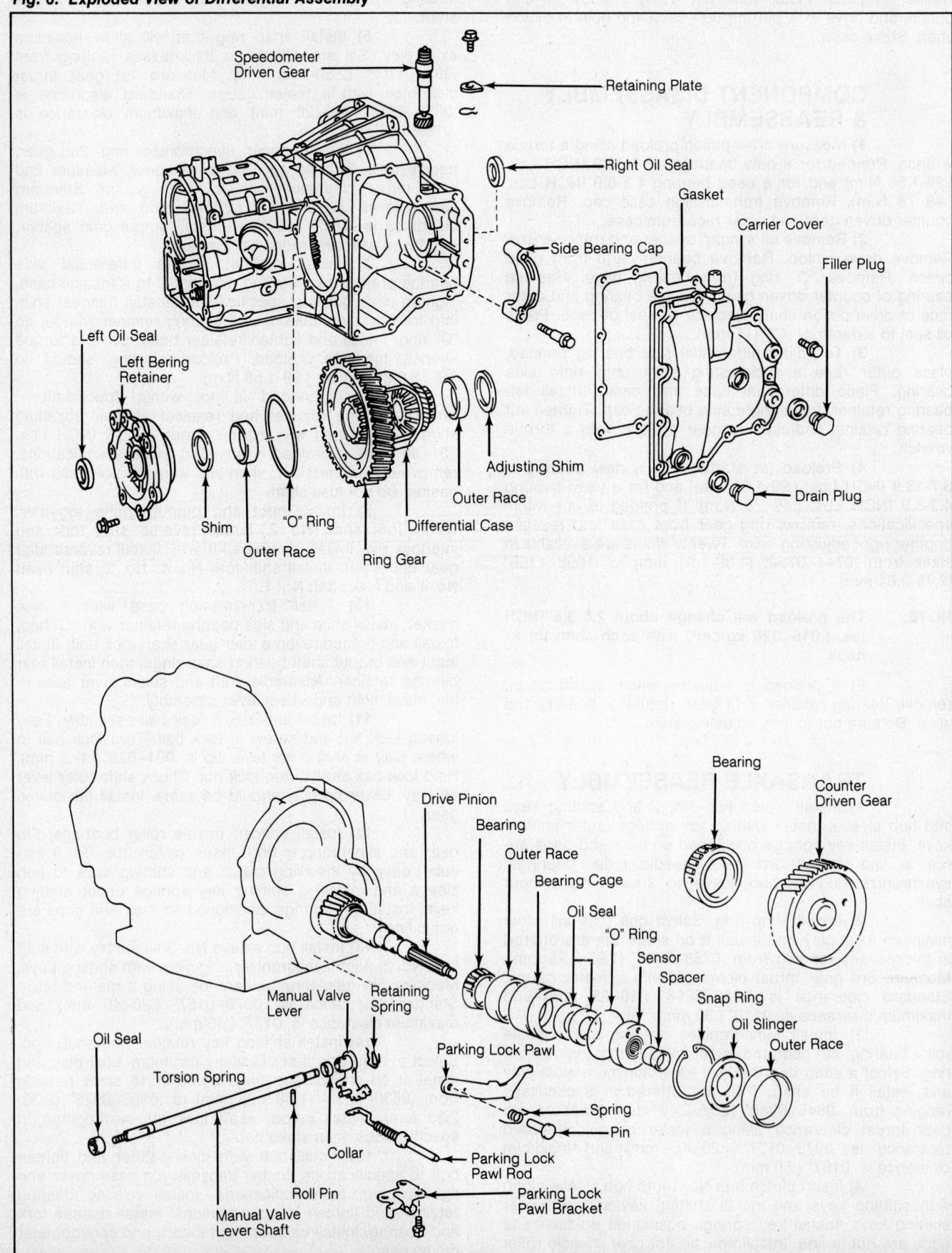

Speedometer Driven Gear

Retaining Plate

Right Oil Seal

Gasket

Carrier Cover

Side Bearing Cap

Filler Plug

Left Oil Seal

Left Bering Retainer

Drain Plug

Shim

Adjusting Shim

"O" Ring

Outer Race

Outer Race

Differential Case

Ring Gear

Bearing

Counter Driven Gear

Drive Pinion

Bearing

Outer Race

Bearing Cage

Oil Seal

"O" Ring

Sensor

Spacer

Snap Ring

Oil Slinger

Outer Race

Manual Valve Lever

Retaining Spring

Parking Lock Pawl

Oil Seal

Torsion Spring

Collar

Spring

Pin

Parking Lock Pawl Rod

Roll Pin

Manual Valve Lever Shaft

Parking Lock Pawl Bracket

TOYOTA S41 4-SPEED & S50 5-SPEED (Cont.)

DIFFERENTIAL REASSEMBLY

1) Install "O" ring onto bearing cage. Place bearing cage onto drive pinion shaft. Install drive pinion shaft into case. Install snap ring into case. Install rotor sensor. Install oil slinger. Install outer race. Install new spacer. Install counter driven gear onto shaft, but do not cause a shock to transmission case.

2) Adjust drive pinion preload. Preload (at starting) with a new bearing is 8.7-13.9 INCH lbs. (.05-.08 kg/cm²) and with a used bearing 4.3-6.9 INCH lbs. (.03-.04 kg/cm²). Place outer race and selected adjusting shim onto right side bearing. Place differential case into case. Install left bearing retainer.

3) Install right side bearing cap. Tighten left bearing retainer. Measure total preload. Total preload (at starting) with drive pinion preload added is 2.2-4.1 INCH lbs. (.013-.024 kg/cm²) for a new bearing and 1.1-2.0 INCH lbs. (.006-.012 kg/cm²) for a used bearing. If preload is incorrect, disassemble and readjust.

4) Stake counter driven gear nut. Install transmission case cap. Install carrier cover. Install the following parts: manual shaft and lever, parking lock pawl, parking lock rod and bracket, governor apply gasket and overdrive brake gasket, overdrive unit, valve body, speed sensor, oil pan, speedometer driven gear and neutral safety switch, to complete reassembly.

TIGHTENING SPECIFICATIONS

Application	Ft. Lbs. (N.m)
Back-Up Light Switch	33 (45)
Case Cover	13 (18)
Case Protector	13 (18)
Case & Lock Plate	18 (24)
Control Shaft Cover	27 (37)
Drain Plug	29 (39)
Filler Plug	29 (390)
Lock Ball Assembly	27 (37)
Output Shaft Bearing Lock Plate	13 (18)
Rear Bearing Retainer	13 (18)
Reverse Idler Shaft Lock Bolt	18 (24)
Reverse Restrict Pin Holder	9 (12)
Reverse Shift Arm Bracket	13 (18)
Reverse Shift Arm Pivot	13 (18)
Shift Fork No. 3	9 (12)
Side Bearing Retainer	13 (18)
Steering Screw Plug	9 (12)
Transmission-to-Transaxle	22 (30)
5th Driven Gear Lock Nut	90 (122)

Application	INCH Lbs. (N.m)
Control Shift Lever	56 (6)
Clutch Release Brg. Ret.	65 (7)
Input Shaft Oil Receiver	65 (7)
Speedo Driven Gr. Lock Plate	48 (5)

Manual Transmissions

TOYOTA 4 & 5-SPEED – MODELS W42 & W52

Pickup (Exc. 4WD & Diesel)

DESCRIPTION

The transmission is 4-speed (W42) or 5-speed (W52) fully synchronized unit. All forward gears are helical cut and in constant mesh. Reverse gear is spur cut. Reverse and 5th gears are in constant mesh and are mounted on rear side of intermediate plate (inside extension housing). Floor shifter actuates a single control rod in extension housing operating 3 shift rails mounted in intermediate plate and main case.

Fig. 1: Exterior View of W42 & W52 Transmission

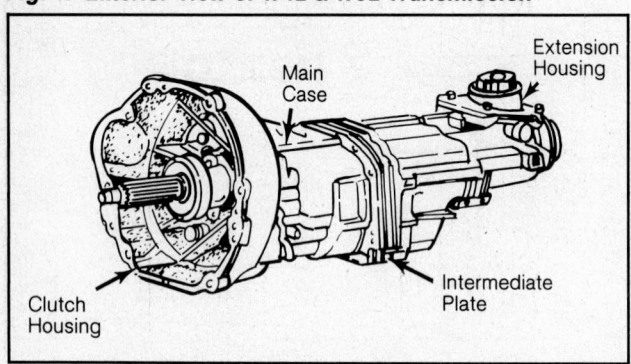

LUBRICATION & ADJUSTMENT

See the appropriate article in MANUAL TRANS-MISSION SERVICING Section.

TROUBLE SHOOTING

HARD SHIFTING

Clutch not disengaging properly. Bushings in cross shaft worn or damaged. Synchronizer rings making faulty contact with gear cone. Synchronizer worn or pitted.

SLIPS OUT OF GEAR

Improper meshing of gears due to shift rails being out of adjustment. Shift forks worn or ball locks broken. Excessive play in synchronizer hub No. 2, output shaft or drive gear worn. Reverse idler gear or bushing worn. Countergear, bushing or shaft worn.

TRANSMISSION NOISY

Gears or bearings worn or damaged. Insufficient or incorrect lubricant. Mainshaft splines worn or damaged. Reverse idler gear bushing worn.

REMOVAL & INSTALLATION

See the appropriate article in MANUAL TRANS-MISSION REMOVAL Section.

TRANSMISSION DISASSEMBLY

1) Drain transmission. Remove clutch release bearing and arm. From inside of clutch housing remove bolts which hold clutch housing to transmission case.

2) Remove speedometer driven gear and control shift lever retainer cover. From below shift lever cover, remove reverse restrict pins and springs on side of extension housing. Remove back-up light switch (if equipped).

3) Remove bolts from extension housing, turn shift lever counterclockwise (as viewed from rear), tap housing with a plastic hammer and pull housing from case. *See Fig. 2.*

Fig. 2: Removing Shift Lever from Shift Fork Shaft

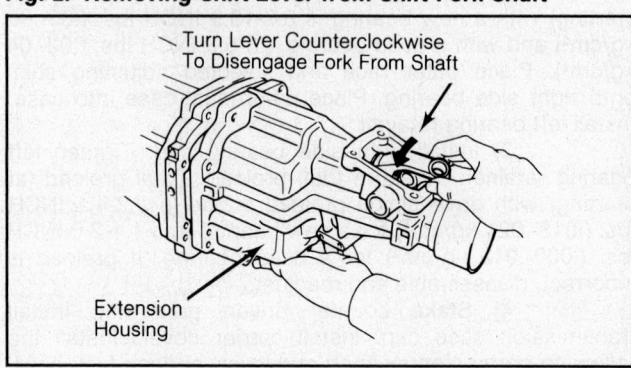

4) Remove front bearing retainer, countershaft cover, and spacer. Use snap ring pliers to remove snap ring from input shaft bearing and countershaft front bearing.

5) Use soft-faced hammer to the separate intermediate plate from transmission case. Place plate in soft-jawed vise. From side of plate, remove 3 straight screw plugs, spring and locking balls.

NOTE: Input shaft, countergear and all associated parts will be retained on intermediate plate.

6) Use pin punch to drive out roll pins which hold shift forks to shift fork shafts. Remove No. 1 shift fork and shaft from intermediate plate. Remove No. 2 shaft. Remove No. 1 and No. 2 interlock pins.

7) On W42 models, remove snap ring from No. 3 shift fork shaft. Remove No. 2 and 3 shift forks. Remove No. 3 shaft. On W52 models, remove shift fork No. 2, No. 3, and shaft No. 3.

8) On both models, remove snap ring, speedometer drive gear, locking ball, and spacer. Use bearing puller (SST 09950-20014) to remove mainshaft rear bearing. Remove snap ring which was in front of rear bearing.

9) Remove snap ring from countershaft. Using a bearing puller, remove countergear rear bearing.

10) On W42 models, remove spacer. On W52 models, countershaft 5th gear. On both models, remove countershaft reverse gear and center bearing side race.

11) On W52 models, measure 5th gear end play. Standard clearance is .0039-.0098" (.10-.25 mm). Maximum clearance is .0118" (.30 mm).

12) On both models, remove snap ring from mainshaft. On W42 models, remove spacer. On W52 models, remove 5th gear assembly.

CAUTION: Do not lose ball which locks 5th gear inner race.

13) On both models, remove hub sleeve No. 3 assembly. Measure reverse idler gear end play. Standard clearance is .0059-.0098" (.15-.25 mm) and maximum clearance is .0118" (.30 mm).

TOYOTA 4 & 5-SPEED — MODELS W42 & W52 (Cont.)

Fig. 3: Removing 5th Gear from Mainshaft

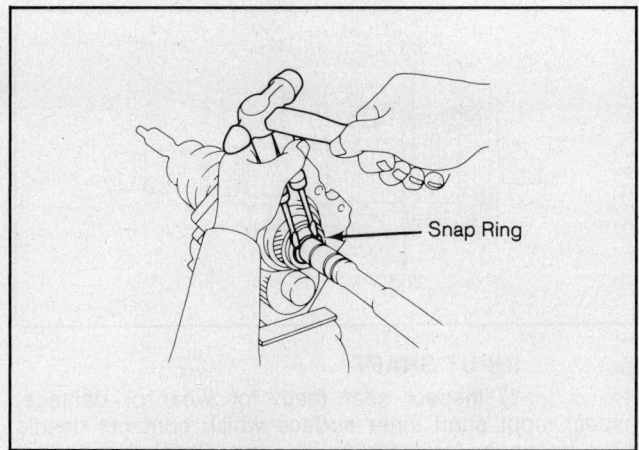

Snap Ring

Illustration applies to W52 models only.

14) Remove reverse idler gear, shaft, and spacer. Remove center bearing retainer and spacer. Lift off mainshaft and countershaft as a unit from intermediate plate. Separate input and mainshaft.

COMPONENT DISASSEMBLY & REASSEMBLY

MAINSHAFT

Disassembly

1) Measure end play of 1st, 2nd, and 3rd gear for reassembly reference. Shift hub sleeve No. 1 onto 2nd gear. Press the center bearing, 1st gear, needle roller bearing, inner race, and synchronizer ring off of shaft. Remove locking ball from mainshaft.

2) Press No. 1 hub sleeve, 2nd gear, and synchronizer ring off of mainshaft. Remove snap ring and press hub sleeve No. 2 assembly and 3rd gear off of mainshaft.

Inspection

1) Use "V" block or shaft holding fixture to measure mainshaft runout. Runout should not exceed .0024" (.06 mm).

2) Measure mainshaft, 1st gear inner race, and 5th gear inner race flange minimum thicknesses. Replace any worn parts. *See Fig. 4.*

Fig. 4: Measuring Mainshaft & Inner Race Flanges

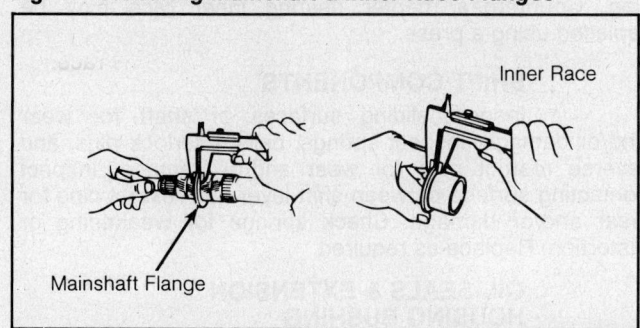

Inner Race

Mainshaft Flange

3) Measure mainshaft journal diameter and outer diameter of both inner races. *See Mainshaft Specifications* table.

MAINSHAFT SPECIFICATIONS

Application	In. (mm)
Mainshaft	
Flange Minimum Thickness	.189 (4.80)
Journal Minimum Diameter	1.606 (40.80)
1st Gear Inner Race	
Flange Minimum Thickness	.179 (4.55)
Minimum O.D.	1.687 (42.85)
5th Gear Inner Race	
Flange Minimum Thickness	.152 (3.85)
Minimum O.D.	1.372 (34.85)

4) Inspect all gear toothed surfaces, thrust faces, inside diameter surfaces and coned parts for wear and/or damage. Inspect mainshaft rear bearing and needle roller bearing surfaces for wear and damage.

5) Measure oil clearance between 1st gear and inner race and 5th gear and inner race. Needle roller bearings must be installed during inspection. Measure oil clearance between 2nd gear and mainshaft and between 3rd gear and mainshaft. *See Gear Oil Clearance Specifications* table.

GEAR OIL CLEARANCE SPECIFICATIONS

Application	Standard In. (mm)	Maximum In. (mm)
1st Gear	.0004-.0021 (.009-.053)	.006 (.15)
2nd & 3rd Gear	.0024-.0041 (.06-.103)	.008 (.20)
5th Gear	.0004-.0020 (.009-.051)	.006 (.15)

6) Check braking effect of synchronizer rings by installing ring into respective gear and trying to rotate ring while pressing inward. If ring does not rotate, braking effect is correct.

7) If ring does rotate, check clearance between synchronizer ring and gear spline end. *See Fig. 5.* If clearance is incorrect, replace synchronizer ring. *See Synchronizer Ring Oil Clearance Specifications* table.

Fig. 5: Checking Synchronizer Ring-to-Gear Clearance

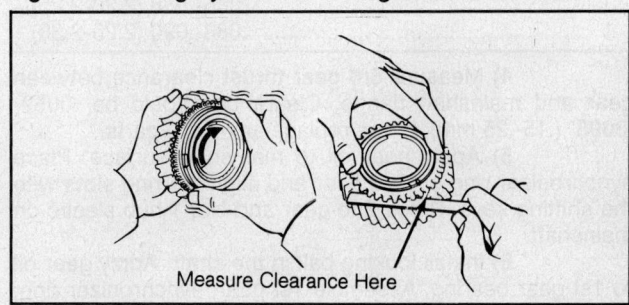

Measure Clearance Here

SYNCHRONIZER RING OIL CLEARANCE SPECIFICATIONS

Application	Standard In. (mm)	Minimum In. (mm)
1st, 2nd & 5th	.028-.067 (.70-1.70)	.020 (.50)
3rd & 4th	.039-.079 (1.0-2.0)	.031 (.80)

Manual Transmissions

TOYOTA 4 & 5-SPEED – MODELS W42 & W52 (Cont.)

8) Inspect splines on both synchronizer hubs and sleeves for wear or damage. Inspect keys for rounded corners and for wear or damage. Also check key springs. Inspect contact surfaces between hub sleeves and shift forks. Clearance should be no more than .039" (1.0 mm) as measured between fork and groove, with fork held into groove.

Reassembly

1) Install clutch hub No. 1 and No. 2 and shifting keys into their respective hub sleeves. Install key springs under the shifting keys so that their ends overlap.

Fig. 6: Sectional View of No. 1 & No. 2 Synchronizers

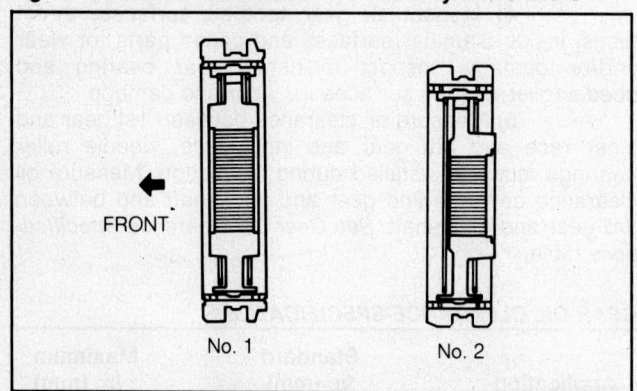

No. 1   No. 2

2) Apply gear oil to shaft. Place the synchronizer ring the 3rd gear and align the ring slots with the shifting keys. Press 3rd gear and hub sleeve No. 2 on mainshaft.

3) Install a snap ring that will allow minimum axial play. Snap rings are available in various sizes. *See Snap Ring Size Specifications* table.

SNAP RING SIZE SPECIFICATIONS

Snap Ring Mark	Thickness In. (mm)
No Mark	.078-.080 (2.00-2.05)
0	.080-.082 (2.05-2.10)
1	.082-.084 (2.10-2.15)
2	.084-.086 (2.15-2.20)
3	.086-.088 (2.20-2.25)
4	.088-.090 (2.25-2.30)

4) Measure 3rd gear thrust clearance between gear and mainshaft flange. Clearance should be .0059-.0098" (.15-.25 mm). If not, replace any worn parts.

5) Apply gear oil to mainshaft surface. Place synchronizer ring on 2nd gear and align the ring slots with the shifting keys. Press 2nd gear and No. 1 hub sleeve on mainshaft.

6) Install locking ball in the shaft. Apply gear oil to 1st gear bearing. Assemble 1st gear, synchronizer ring, needle roller bearing, and bearing inner race. Install on mainshaft with ring slots aligned with the shifting keys. Turn inner race to align it with the locking ball.

7) Press mainshaft center bearing on shaft with outer race snap ring groove toward the rear. Hold 1st gear inner race to prevent it from falling.

8) Measure 1st and 2nd gear end play on mainshaft. Standard clearance is .0059-.0098" (.15-.25 mm). Wear limit is .0118" (.30 mm). If not within limits, replace any worn parts. *See Fig. 7.*

Fig. 7: Checking Gear End Play Clearances

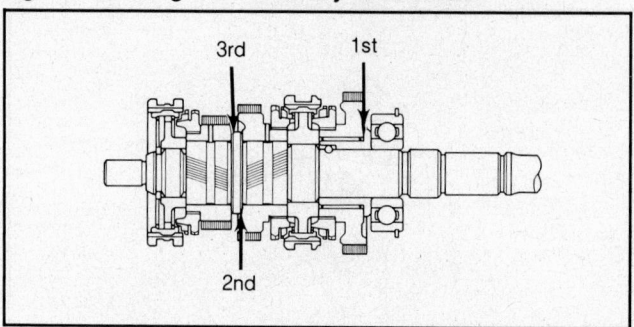

3rd   1st

2nd

INPUT SHAFT

1) Inspect gear teeth for wear or damage. Inspect input shaft inner surface which contacts needle roller bearings, for wear or damage. Check input shaft bearing for wear by rotating bearing and listening for noise.

2) If necessary to replace input shaft bearing, remove snap ring and press off of shaft. When installing new bearing, select snap ring which will allow minimum axial play. Snap rings are available in various sizes. *See Input Shaft Snap Ring Size* table.

INPUT SHAFT SNAP RING SIZE

Snap Ring Mark	Thickness In. (mm)
0	.080-.082 (2.05-2.10)
1	.082-.084 (2.10-2.15)
2	.084-.086 (2.15-2.20)
3	.086-.088 (2.20-2.25)
4	.088-.090 (2.25-2.30)
5	.090-.092 (2.30-2.35)

COUNTERGEAR

1) Inspect teeth of countergear for wear or damage. Inspect front bearing and rear bearing for wear or damage. Inspect roller bearing and inner race for wear or damage.

2) If necessary to replace countergear front bearing, remove snap ring and use bearing puller or press. Note direction of bearing for assembly reference. If necessary, side of inner race may be ground off slightly and race may be removed with a hammer and chisel.

3) Press new bearing on shaft. Install snap ring. Countergear center bearing inner race may be replaced using a press.

SHIFT COMPONENTS

Inspect sliding surfaces of shaft for wear and/or damage. Inspect springs, balls, interlock pins, and reverse restrict pins for wear and/or damage. Inspect contacting surface between shift lever and restrict pins for wear and/or damage. Check springs for weakening or distortion. Replace as required.

OIL SEALS & EXTENSION HOUSING BUSHING

1) Inspect the front bearing retainer and speedometer driven gear oil seals. Replace if necessary. The speedometer driven gear oil seal must be installed so that edge of seal is .79" (20.0 mm) from threaded end of sleeve.

TOYOTA 4 & 5-SPEED – MODELS W42 & W52 (Cont.)

Fig. 8: Exploded View of W42 & W52 Transmission Gear Assemblies

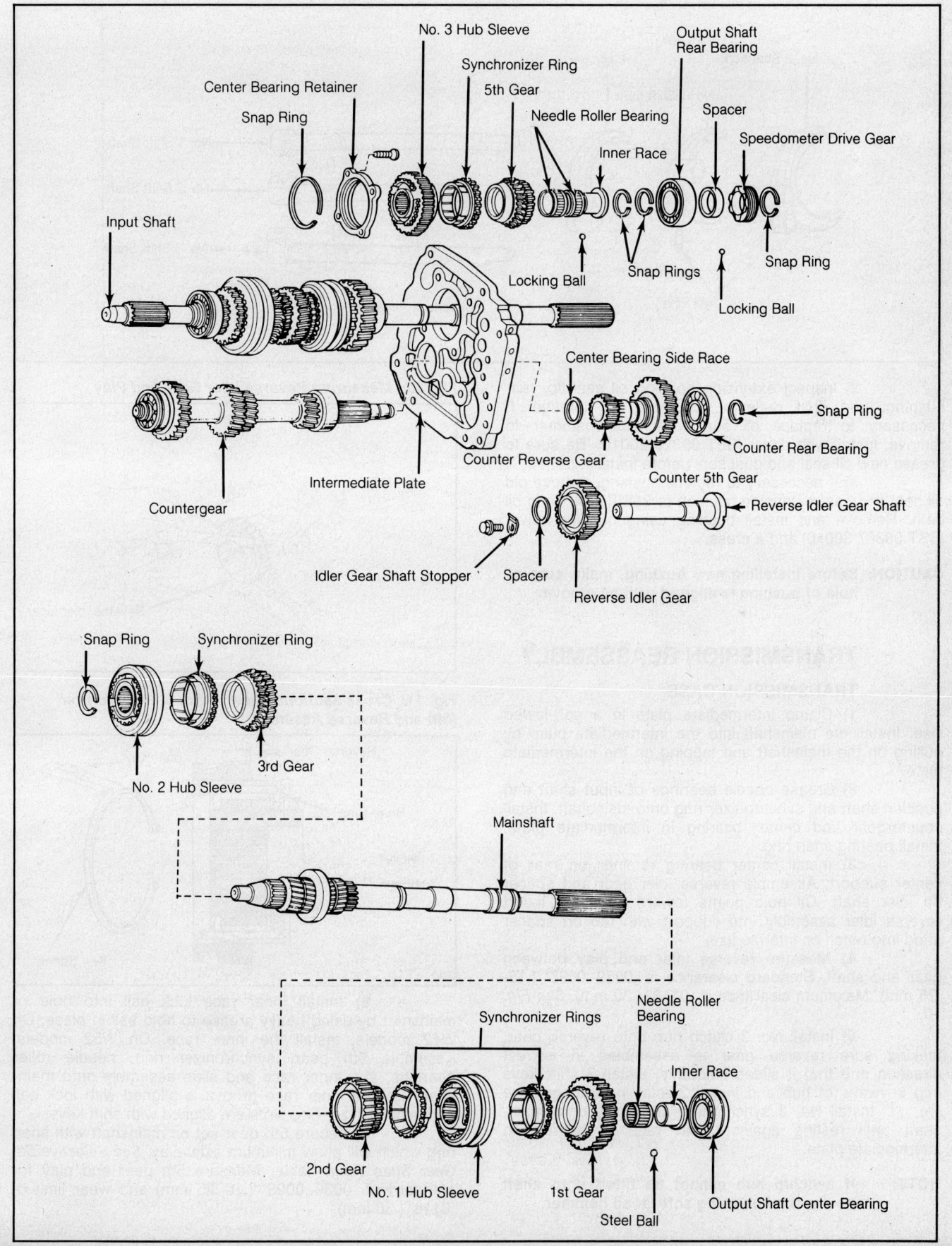

Manual Transmissions

TOYOTA 4 & 5-SPEED — MODELS W42 & W52 (Cont.)

Fig. 9: *Exploded View of Shift Fork Assemblies*

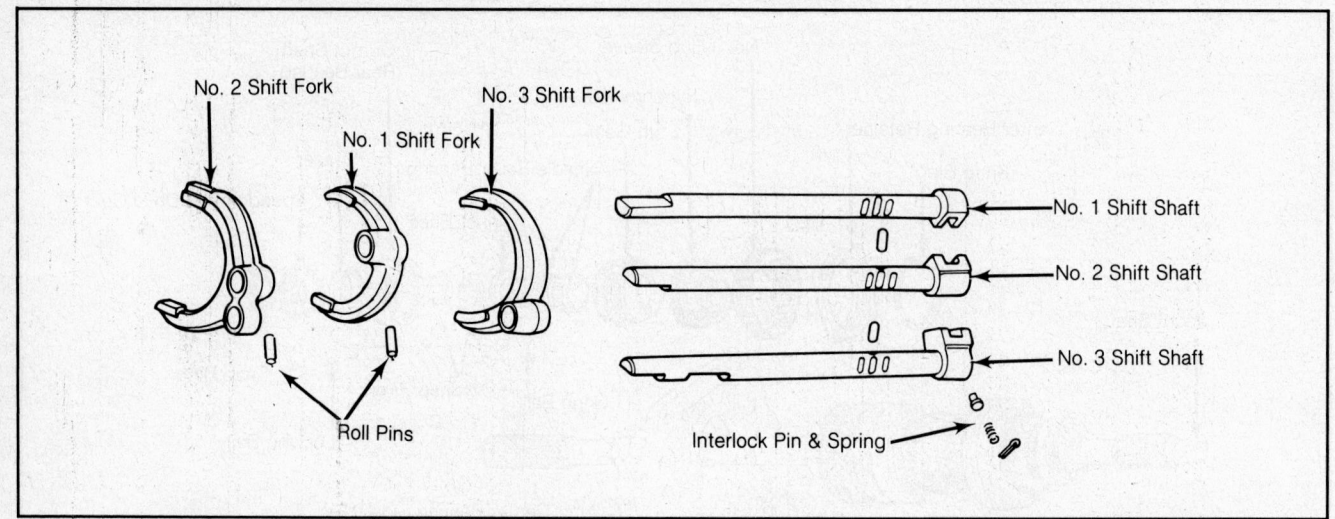

2) Inspect extension housing oil seal lip, rear bushing, and dust deflector for wear or damage. If necessary to replace oil seal, use slide hammer to remove. Install with driver (SST 09325 20010). Be sure to grease new oil seal and dust seal before installing.

3) If necessary to replace bushing, remove old oil seal and heat extension housing to 212°F (100°C) in oil bath. Remove and install bushing using bushing driver (SST 09307 30010) and a press.

CAUTION: Before installing new bushing, make sure oil hole of bushing is aligned with oil groove.

TRANSMISSION REASSEMBLY

TRANSMISSION CASE

1) Clamp intermediate plate in a soft-jawed vise. Install the mainshaft into the intermediate plate by pulling on the mainshaft and tapping on the intermediate plate.

2) Grease needle bearings of input shaft and position shaft and synchronizer ring onto mainshaft. Install countergear and center bearing in intermediate plate. Install bearing snap ring.

3) Install center bearing retainer on rear of center support. Assemble reverse idler gear and spacer on idler shaft. Oil hole points toward the rear. Insert reverse idler assembly into support with tab on spacer fitted into notch on intermediate.

4) Measure reverse idler end play between gear and shaft. Standard clearance is .0059-.0098" (.15-.25 mm). Maximum clearance is .0118" (.30 mm). *See Fig. 10.*

5) Install No. 3 clutch hub onto reverse gear, making sure reverse gear is assembled in correct direction and that it slides smoothly. Install 3 shift keys into keyways of hub and install 2 retaining springs. *See Fig. 11.* Install No. 3 synchronizer assembly onto mainshaft until resting against inner race of bearing in intermediate plate.

NOTE: If synchro hub cannot be fitted onto shaft easily, tap hub using soft-faced hammer.

Fig. 10: *Measuring Reverse Idler Gear End Play*

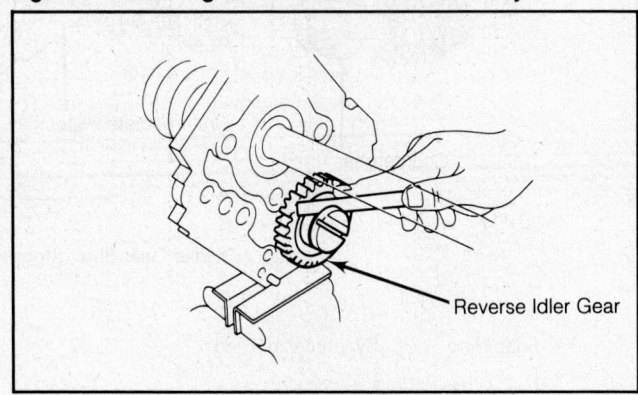

Fig. 11: *Cross-Sectional View of No. 3 Synchronizer (5th and Reverse Assembly)*

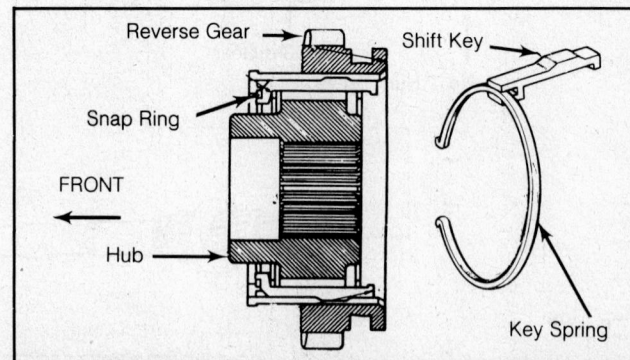

6) Install inner race lock ball into hole of mainshaft by using heavy grease to hold ball in place. On W42 models, install the inner race. On W52 models, Assemble 5th gear, synchronizer ring, needle roller bearings, and inner race and slide assembly onto mainshaft. Ensure inner race groove is aligned with lock ball and synchronizer ring slots are aligned with shift keys.

7) Secure 5th gear set on mainshaft with snap ring which will allow minimum axial play. *See Selective 5th Gear Snap Rings* table. Measure 5th gear end play for standard of .0039-.0098" (.10-.25 mm) and wear limit of .0118" (.30 mm).

TOYOTA 4 & 5-SPEED — MODELS W42 & W52 (Cont.)

SELECTIVE 5TH GEAR SNAP RINGS

Snap Ring Mark	Thickness In. (mm)
1	.074-.076 (1.89-1.94)
2	.077-.079 (1.95-2.00)
3	.079-.081 (2.01-2.06)
4	.081-.083 (2.07-2.12)
5	.084-.086 (2.13-2.18)
6	.086-.088 (2.19-2.24)
7	.089-.091 (2.25-2.30)
8	.091-.093 (2.31-2.36)
9	.093-.095 (2.37-2.42)
10	.096-.098 (2.43-2.48)
11	.098-.100 (2.49-2.54)
12	.100-.102 (2.55-2.60)
13	.103-.105 (2.61-2.66)

8) On both models, install countershaft reverse gear until it rests against inner bearing. On W42 models, install spacer. On W52 models, install 5th countergear.

9) On both models, install countershaft rear bearing. Select snap ring that will allow minimum axial end play and install on countershaft. *See Selective Countergear Bearing Snap Rings* table.

SELECTIVE COUNTERGEAR BEARING SNAP RINGS

Snap Ring Thickness	Thickness In. (mm)
1	.079-.081 (2.00-2.05)
2	.071-.073 (1.80-1.85)
3	.063-.065 (1.60-1.65)
4	.055-.057 (1.40-1.45)

10) Install mainshaft rear snap ring and bearing. Install spacer, locking ball, and speedometer drive gear. Use heavy grease to prevent ball from falling out of hole in mainshaft.

11) Install No. 3 shift fork and shaft in intermediate plate. Install No. 2 shift fork in No. 2 hub sleeve. Insert No. 3 fork shaft into No. 2 shift fork. On W42 models, install the snap ring. On both models, install the greased interlock pins into bores of intermediate plate and shift forks.

12) Install No. 2 fork shaft through the intermediate plate and No. 2 shift fork. Install greased interlock pin. Install all lock balls and springs into bores of plate. Coat plugs with sealer, and install and tighten.

13) Install new roll pins into shift forks and shafts to secure assemblies. With new gasket in place, slide transmission case onto intermediate plate. Install snap ring for input shaft bearing and countershaft front bearing.

CLUTCH & EXTENSION HOUSING

1) With gasket in place, install extension housing over output shaft. With extension housing approximately .8-1.1" (20-30 mm) from intermediate plate, hold shift lever housing to the counterclockwise position.

2) Rotate shift lever housing clockwise to engage shift fork shafts. If necessary, tap lightly on rear housing to bring it flush against center support. Install bolts and tighten to specification.

3) Install the restrict pins in the extension housing. The short restrict spring is installed on the left side as viewed from the rear. Long spring is installed on the right side. Secure springs with plugs. Install oil baffle and shift lever retainer.

4) Select countershaft front spacer by pressing firmly in on countergear and measuring depth of front bearing. *See Countergear Spacer Sizes* table.

5) Select the appropriate spacer and install spacer front bearing retainer. Make sure oil return hole is aligned before tightening bearing retainer bolts.

COUNTERGEAR SPACER SIZES

Clearance In. (mm)	Mark	Thickness In. (mm)
.113-.118 (2.87-2.99)	•	.077-.081 (1.95-2.05)
.118-.122 (3.00-3.10)	••	.083-.087 (2.10-2.20)
.122-.125 (3.10-3.20)	•••	.087-.093 (2.25-2.35)
.126-.130 (3.20-3.30)	••••	.095-.098 (2.40-2.50)

6) Install clutch housing and tighten retaining bolts. Install shift lever retainer on extension housing. Install speedometer driven gear in extension housing and retain with lock plate. Install back-up light switch, drain plug, and fill plug on case.

TIGHTENING SPECIFICATIONS

Application	Ft. Lbs. (N.m)
Clutch Housing-to-Case Bolts	37-50 (50-68)
Clutch Housing-to-Engine Bolts	37-50 (50-68)
Extension Housing Bolts	29-40 (39-54)
Lock Ball Plugs	14-22 (19-30)
Restrict Pin Plugs	27-33 (37-45)
Reverse Pivot Lock Nut	11-15 (15-20)
Reverse Shift Arm Bracket	11-15 (15-20)
Shift Lever Housing Bolts	11-15 (15-20)

	INCH Lbs. (N.m.)
Front Bearing Retainer Bolts	84-120 (9-14)
Output Shaft Bearing Retainer	96-132 (11-15)

Manual Transmissions
TOYOTA COROLLA RWD 5-SPEED

RWD Corolla

IDENTIFICATION

The T50 5-speed transmission can be identified from other Toyota transmissions by its ribbed and split (2-piece) aluminum transmission case.

Fig. 1: Exterior View of Transmission Case

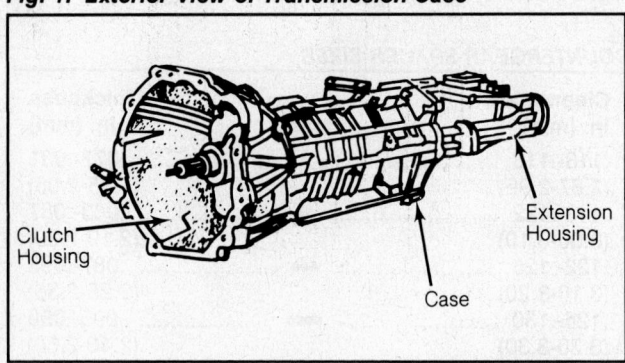

DESCRIPTION

Transmission is a 5-speed, fully synchronized unit, in which all gears are helical cut and in constant mesh. Gear engagement is accomplished through use of 3 blocker-type synchronizer assemblies. Floor shift lever operates a single control rod in extension housing, which in turn is connected to shifting rails in rear of transmission case. To access internal parts, it is necessary to separate transmission case halves.

LUBRICATION & ADJUSTMENT

See appropriate MANUAL TRANSMISSION SERVICING article in IMPORT GENERAL SERVICING section.

TROUBLE SHOOTING

See MANUAL TRANSMISSION TROUBLE SHOOTING article in IMPORT GENERAL SERVICING section.

SERVICE (IN VEHICLE)

GEAR SHIFT LEVER
Removal & Installation

Pull up rubber shift lever boot. Remove 4 bolts holding shift lever to transmission. Pull shift lever out of transmission. To install, reverse removal procedure.

EXTENSION HOUSING SEAL
Removal & Installation

Remove center driveshaft support bearing and heat insulating shield. Remove drive shaft. Use a puller to remove seal. To install, reverse removal procedure. Ensure seal is installed straight and even in bore. Apply multipurpose grease to oil seal.

REMOVAL & INSTALLATION

TRANSMISSION

See appropriate MANUAL TRANSMISSION RE-MOVAL article in IMPORT GENERAL SERVICING section.

TRANSMISSION DISASSEMBLY

CLUTCH HOUSING

Release spring clips and remove clutch release fork and bearing. Loosen bolts evenly and remove clutch housing. Ensure oil seal lip is not damaged. Do not drop cone washers between transmission and housing.

EXTENSION HOUSING

Remove speedometer driven gear retainer bolt. Remove shaft sleeve and driven gear. Remove back-up light switch. Remove 6 housing bolts. When removing extension housing, ensure that output spline does not damage rear oil seal. Remove reverse restricting pin by removing plug with hexagon wrench. Drive out slotted spring pin with punch and remove reverse restricting pin.

TRANSMISSION CASE

1) Remove plate holding shift fork rail locking balls and springs. Remove balls and springs with magnet. Remove bolts holding case halves together and separate case halves by tapping on protrusion of right case half with plastic hammer. Be sure to retain locking balls between cases and countergear bearing.

Fig. 2: Using a Hammer to Separate Case Halves

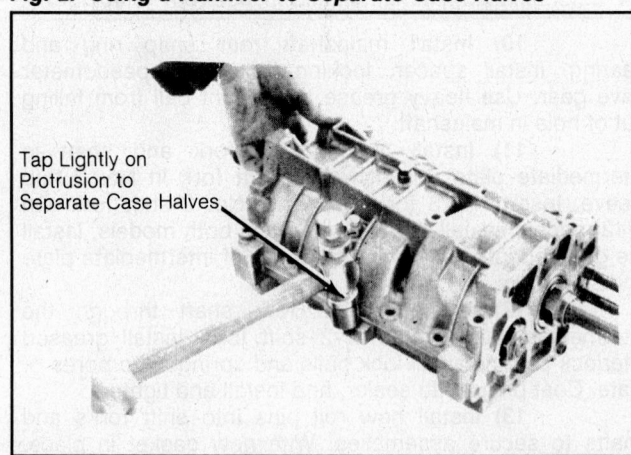

2) With left half of case removed, lift mainshaft from right half of case, then lift out countergear assembly. Using pin punch, drive out pins holding shift forks to rails. Note that pin holding No. 1 fork is driven out through hole in case. Drive out pin in No. 2 and No. 3 shift forks. Place all shift rails in neutral position and pull individually from rear of case.

CLEANING & INSPECTION

Clean all mating surfaces, and check for warpage. Check all components for abnormal wear, and discoloration from overheating. Verify that components are not cracked or chipped.

TOYOTA COROLLA RWD 5-SPEED (Cont.)

Fig. 3: Exploded View of T50 Transmission

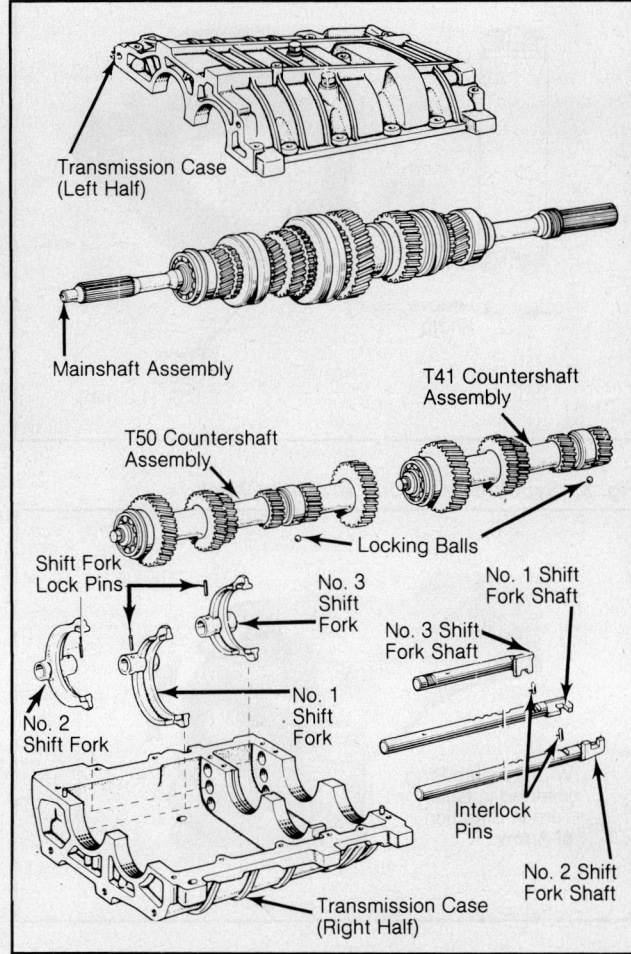

THRUST CLEARANCE

Application [1]	Standard In. (mm)	[2] Wear Limit In. (mm)
1st Gear	.006-.011 (.15-.28)	.020 (.5)
2nd Gear	.006-.010 (.15-.25)	.020 (.5)
3rd Gear	.006-.012 (.15-.30)	.024 (.6)
Reverse	.008-.013 (.20-.32)	.024 (.6)
Reverse Idler	.002-.020 (.05-.50)	.039 (1.0)
5th Gear	.004-.040 (.10-.93)	.024 (.6)

[1] – See text for measurement procedure.
[2] – Represents maximum wear limit.

2) Remove snap ring for rear bearing. Remove rear bearing using Puller (SST 09950-20014). Remove spacer, 5th gear, synchronizer ring, needle roller bearings, spacer and steel ball. Remove snap ring, then remove No. 3 clutch hub and sleeve. Remove reverse gear, needle bearing and bushing by pressing down on output shaft while supporting reverse gear with vise jaws.

3) Remove center bearing, bushing, needle bearing, 1st gear, and synchronizer ring. Remove and retain locking ball, then press output shaft from 1st gear assembly using same procedure as for reverse gear. Remove snap ring from front of shaft, then press No. 2 clutch hub and sleeve with 3rd gear and synchronizer ring from shaft.

NOTE: When pressing gear assemblies from mainshaft, support shaft with hand to prevent dropping shaft when it clears hub splines. Retain all locking balls.

Inspection

1) Inspect output shaft for wear, damage or distortion. Minimum thickness of flange between 2nd and 3rd gear is .157" (4.0 mm). Minimum diameter of 2nd and 3rd gear journals is 1.488" (37.8 mm). Check shaft deflection at speedometer drive gear journal while rotating shaft. Maximum deflection is .002" (.06 mm).

2) Check each gear, bushing and bearing surface for wear or damage. Check inside gear limits. See BEARING SURFACE INSIDE DIAMETER WEAR LIMIT table. Note that oil clearance for 1st gear is .0004-.0024" (.01-.06 mm); 2nd and 3rd gear is .0024-.004" (.06-.10 mm); 5th gear is .0004-.002" (.01-.05 mm).

3) Disassemble clutch hubs using care not to mix parts and inspect for wear or damage. Check clearance limit of .039" (1.0 mm) between shift fork and sleeve grooves. Groove maximum width is .335" (8.5 mm).

BEARING SURFACE INSIDE DIAMETER WEAR LIMIT

Application	Specification In. (mm)
1st	1.66 (42.15)
2nd	1.50 (38.15)
3rd	1.50 (38.15)
5th	1.42 (36.15)
Reverse	1.66 (42.15)

COMPONENT DISASSEMBLY & REASSEMBLY

MAINSHAFT

Disassembly

1) Measure thrust clearances of each gear, and record measurements for reassembly reference. *See Fig. 4.* Remove snap rings holding speedometer drive gear in position and remove drive gear.

Fig. 4: Thrust Clearance Measurement Points

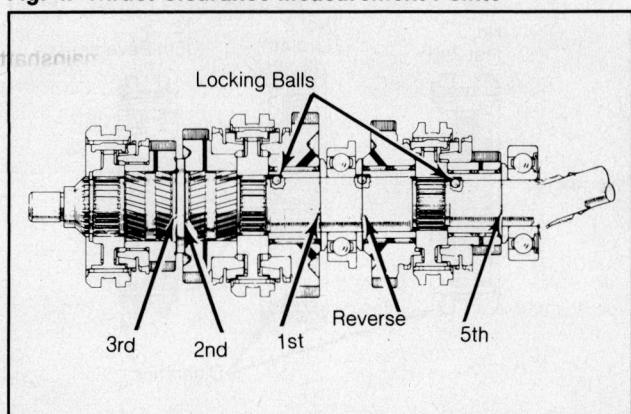

4) Check synchronizer rings for wear or damage and braking effect. Ring should stick to gear cone when turned and pressed against cone. Standard clearance between synchronizer ring and gear is .039-.079" (1.0-2.0 mm). Minimum clearance is .031" (.8 mm). Replace ring and/or gear as required. Inspect shift keys and springs for wear or damage and replace if necessary.

Fig. 5: Disassembled View of Mainshaft Assembly

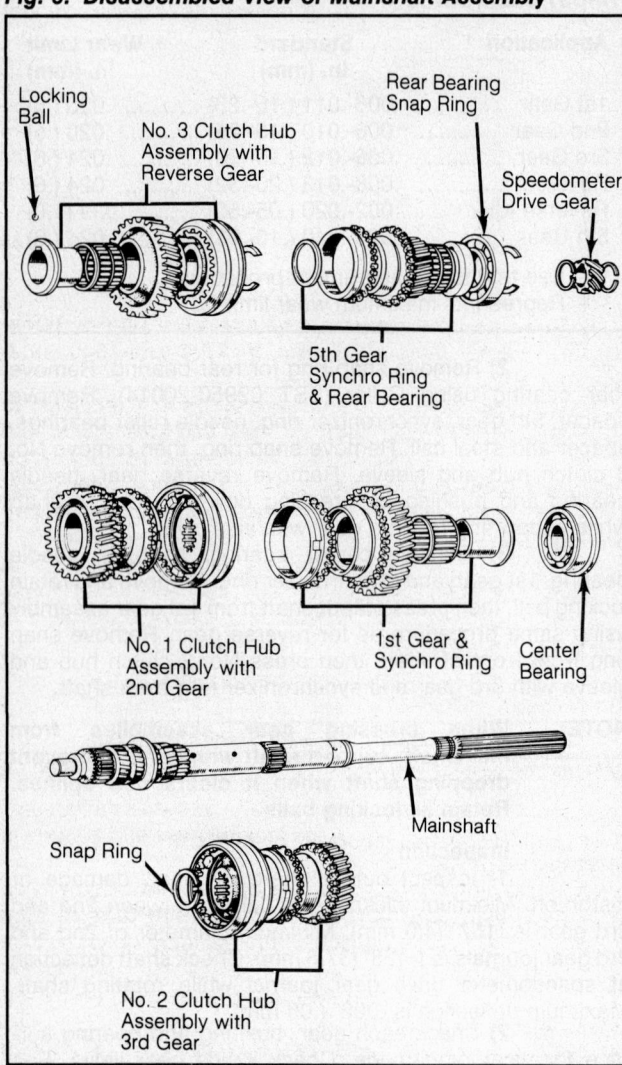

- Locking Ball
- No. 3 Clutch Hub Assembly with Reverse Gear
- Rear Bearing Snap Ring
- Speedometer Drive Gear
- 5th Gear Synchro Ring & Rear Bearing
- No. 1 Clutch Hub Assembly with 2nd Gear
- 1st Gear & Synchro Ring
- Center Bearing
- Mainshaft
- Snap Ring
- No. 2 Clutch Hub Assembly with 3rd Gear

Fig. 6: Mainshaft Inspection Points

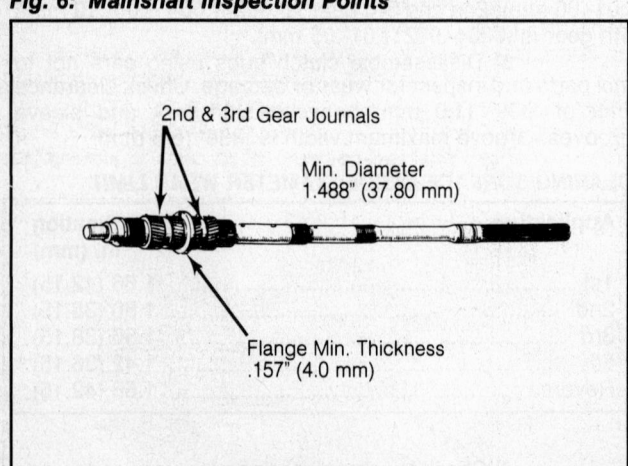

- 2nd & 3rd Gear Journals
- Min. Diameter 1.488" (37.80 mm)
- Flange Min. Thickness .157" (4.0 mm)

Reassembly

1) Assemble synchronizer assemblies individually, ensuring that key spring ends are staggered. Note location and identification of each synchronizer assembly.

Fig. 7: Checking Shift Fork Groove Clearance

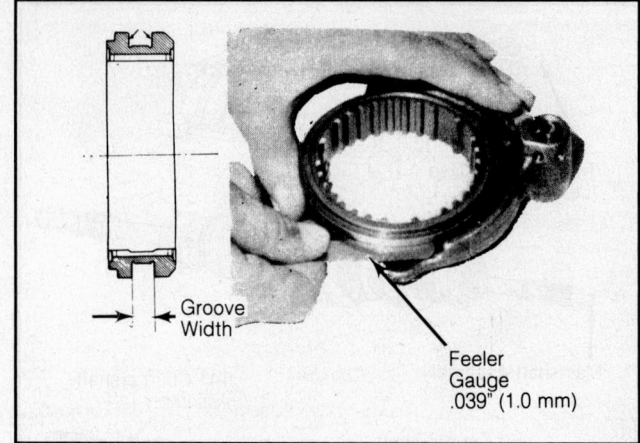

- Groove Width
- Feeler Gauge .039" (1.0 mm)

Fig. 8: Synchronizer Ring Braking Check

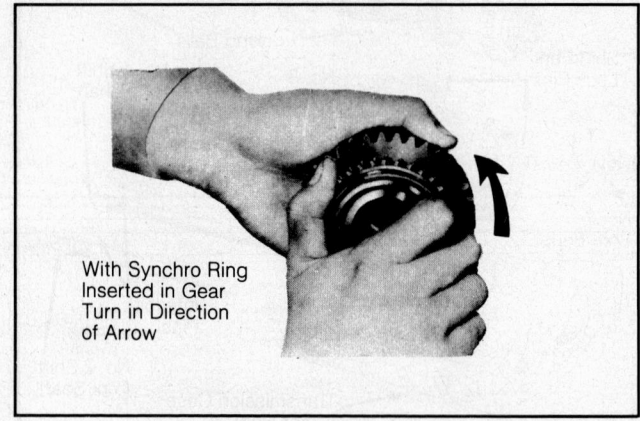

With Synchro Ring Inserted in Gear Turn in Direction of Arrow

2) From rear of mainshaft, slide 2nd gear on shaft. With synchro No. 2 assembled, including synchro rings, slide assembly on shaft from rear. Slide on 1st gear, with coned surface facing front of shaft. Install bearing sleeve lock ball in mainshaft. Slide 1st gear roller bearing and sleeve on from rear of shaft and install them inside 1st gear.

3) Slide center support radial ball bearing directly behind 1st gear. Install bearing sleeve lock ball in shaft and install bearing and sleeve. Install reverse gear and

Fig. 9: View Showing Synchronizer Identification

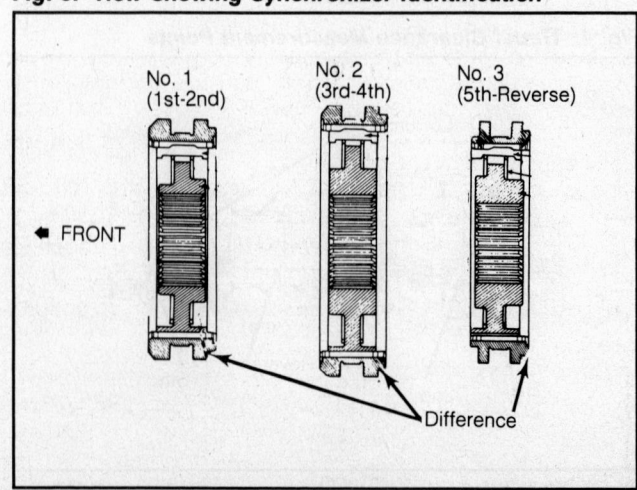

- No. 1 (1st-2nd)
- No. 2 (3rd-4th)
- No. 3 (5th-Reverse)
- FRONT
- Difference

TOYOTA COROLLA RWD 5-SPEED (Cont.)

reverse synchro hub (No. 3). Install 5th gear, bushing, bearing, sleeve lock ball and rear bearing.

INPUT SHAFT, BEARING & RETAINER
Inspection

1) Check input shaft spline by placing input shaft into clutch disc and checking that shaft slides smoothly. Ensure there is no excessive play.

2) Check input shaft bearing by pressing on front of bearing and rotating input shaft. If there is abnormal resistance or noise, it will be necessary to replace bearing. To replace bearing, use snap ring pliers and remove front snap ring. Use press and Adapter (SST 09506-10010) to press off old bearing. Use Adapter (SST 09316-60010) to press on new bearing. Choose a selective snap ring which will engage securely in groove and eliminate play between bearing and shaft.

INPUT SHAFT SNAP RING SPECIFICATIONS

Application	In. (mm)
T50	.100-.102 (2.55-2.60)
	.098-.100 (2.50-2.55)
	.097-.098 (2.45-2.50)
	.095-.097 (2.40-2.45)
	.093-.096 (2.35-2.40)

3) Check front bearing retainer and oil seal for wear or damage. If seal shows evidence of leakage, it must be replaced. Also check mating surfaces of transmission case and clutch housing.

COUNTERGEAR, REVERSE IDLER GEAR & SHAFT
Inspection

1) Check countergear faces and bearings for wear or damage. To replace front bearing, remove bearing lock plate and take off snap ring. Use Puller (SST 09950-20014) to remove old bearing and press new bearing in position by supporting inner race and pressing on countershaft.

2) Remove snap ring. Support 5th gear on steel plate to remove 5th gear and rear bearing. Press out countershaft. Remove reverse gear and center bearing. Install center bearing with larger diameter of roller cage to front, and install reverse gear.

Fig. 10: Measuring Reverse Idler Gear Thrust Clearance

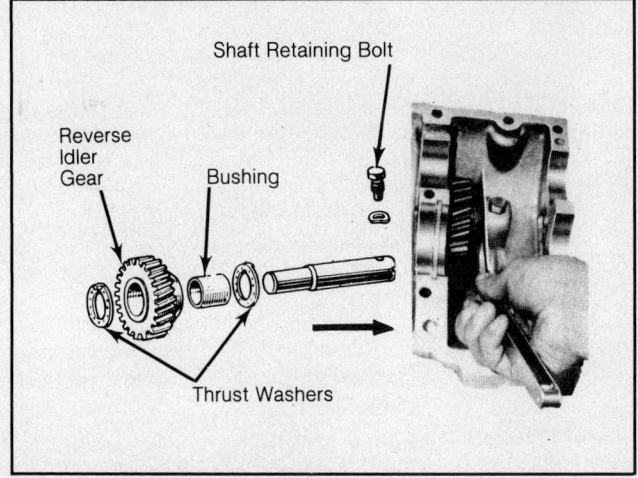

COUNTERGEAR SHAFT SNAP RING SPECIFICATIONS

Application	In. (mm)
T50	.063-.065 (1.60-1.65)
	.071-.073 (1.80-1.85)
	.079-.081 (2.00-2.05)

3) Using support for rear bearing, hold up reverse gear and press in bearing and 5th gear at same time. Install snap ring which will provide minimum end clearance.

4) Measure reverse idler thrust clearance between case and gear. Standard clearance is .002-.020" (.05-.50 mm) with a maximum limit of .039" (1.0 mm). Remove shaft and gear with thrust washers. Bushing bore wear limit is .634" (16.1 mm) and shaft diameter wear limit is .626" (15.9 mm). If installing new bushing, ensure that oil holes in bushing and gear line up.

SHIFT FORK RAILS & SELECTOR SHAFT
Inspection

Check sliding action of shift fork rails and selector shaft. Rails and shaft should move freely without binding or excessive play. Check springs, balls and interlock pins for wear and damage

EXTENSION HOUSING
Inspection

1) Inspect speedometer gear and oil seal for wear or damage. Replace inner seal and outer "O" ring as necessary. Inspect rear oil seal and bushing for wear or damage. If seal replacement is required, use Puller (SST 09308-00010) to remove old oil seal and Installer (SST 09325-12010) to drive in new seal.

2) To replace rear bushing, heat extension housing to 176-212°F (80-100°C) and drive out old bushing with Bushing Driver (SST 09307-12010). Ensure that oil hole is positioned at top of housing and use same driver to install new bushing to proper depth of .59" (15.0 mm) below end of extension housing. Install new seal and apply multipurpose grease to seal lips.

TRANSMISSION REASSEMBLY

SHIFT RAILS & FORKS

Apply multipurpose grease to interlock pins and insert them in case. Insert, and slide center (No. 2) shift rail and fork to neutral position. Insert No. 1 rail and fork, then

Fig. 11: Cutaway View of Case Showing Locking Pins and Fork Rail Installation

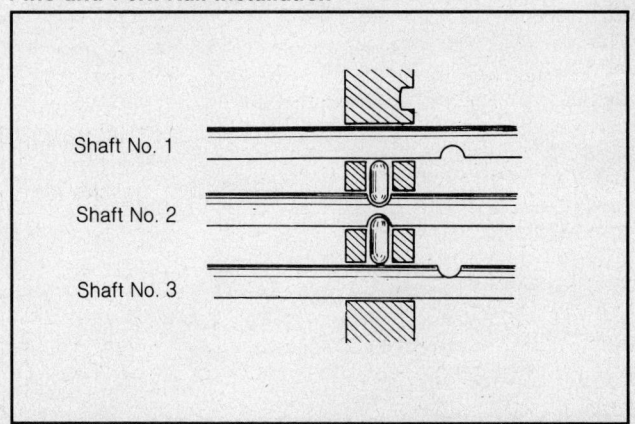

Manual Transmissions
TOYOTA COROLLA RWD 5-SPEED (Cont.)

No. 3 rail and fork (short rail) to neutral position. Install all 3 shift fork pins, then pull center rail out to 3rd speed position. No. 1 and No. 2 rail should not move.

TRANSMISSION CASE

1) Apply multipurpose grease to input shaft needle bearings and assemble input shaft to output shaft. Line up synchronizer grooves and shift forks to neutral position. Ensure that shifting keys are lined up with key slots in synchronizer rings. Install mainshaft assembly in right half of transmission case.

2) Install countergear assembly in case and insert locking ball in case groove. Clean case joining surfaces and bearing recesses. Apply liquid sealer to case joining faces and bolt threads. Install left half of case to right half and tighten bolts gradually in sequence. See Fig. 12.

3) Check front end of input shaft to see that there is about .012" (.3 mm) play radially. Check to see that shift rods move smoothly to all gear selections.

Fig. 12: Transmission Case Bolt Tightening Sequence

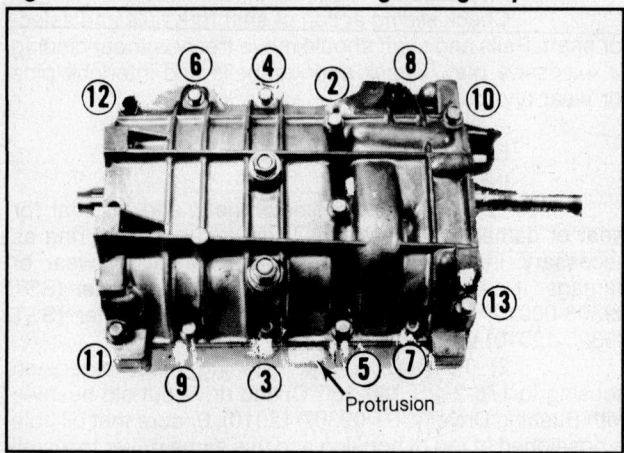

EXTENSION HOUSING & CLUTCH HOUSING

1) Apply liquid sealer to both sides of gasket. Place gasket on rear of transmission housing and carefully install extension housing. Shift selector shaft should engage in No. 2 fork rail. Install and tighten extension housing bolts.

2) Install restricting pins (White on left and Black on right) and tighten. Install shift lever retainer on extension housing. Install speedometer drive gear. Install shift rail detent balls, springs and retainer plate. Install back-up light switch.

3) Apply multipurpose grease to oil seal lip in clutch housing and to washers. Install cone washers in recesses with dished side to rear of transmission. See Fig. 13. Apply liquid sealer to joining surfaces and install clutch housing on transmission.

NOTE: **When installing transmission on clutch housing, ensure that pilot shaft splines do not damage lip of oil seal.**

4) Tighten housing bolts in 3 or 4 steps, in a criss-cross pattern. Apply multipurpose grease to sliding surfaces and install clutch release fork and bearing.

Fig. 13: Installing Cone & Flat Washer

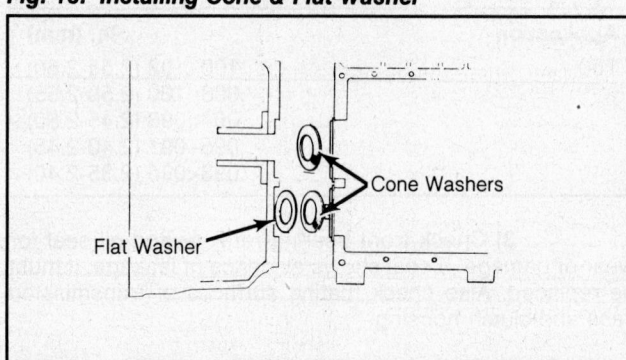

TIGHTENING SPECIFICATIONS

Application	Ft. Lbs. (N.m)
Reverse Idler Shaft Retaining Bolt	10-13 (14-18)
Case Half Bolts	14-15 (19-20)
Extension Housing-to-Case Bolts	22-33 (30-45)
Clutch Housing-to-Case Bolts	22-33 (30-45)
Clutch Housing-to-Engine	37-50 (50-70)
Restricting Pins	27-32 (37-45)

TOYOTA C-51 5-SPEED TRANSAXLE

FWD Corolla

DESCRIPTION

The model C51 transaxle is a fully synchronized 5-speed unit. All forward gears are helical cut and in constant mesh. Reverse gears are spur cut and are engaged by a sliding reverse idler gear. Transaxle assembly consists of a 3-piece aluminum case, a differential, and input and output shaft (gear) assemblies. Transaxle and differential are lubricated from a common sump.

LUBRICATION & ADJUSTMENT

See appropriate MANUAL TRANSMISSION SERVICING article in IMPORT GENERAL SERVICING section.

TROUBLE SHOOTING

EXCESSIVE NOISE

Transaxle or differential faulty. Wrong oil grade. Low oil level.

OIL LEAKAGE

Oil level too high. Oil seal, "O" ring, or gaskets worn or damaged.

HARD TO SHIFT
OR WILL NOT SHIFT

Control cable faulty. Transaxle faulty.

JUMPS OUT OF GEAR

Transaxle faulty.

SERVICE (IN VEHICLE)

WHEEL BEARINGS
Removal

1) Remove cotter pin and lock nut cap. Depress brake pedal and loosen bearing lock nut. Remove brake caliper and disc brake rotor. Attach a dial indicator to steering knuckle arm and measure bearing end play. Bearing end play must be within 0.0020" (0.05 mm).

2) Remove cotter pin and nut from tie rod end. Using Puller (SST 09950-20014), disconnect tie rod from steering knuckle arm. Mark front suspension strut and camber adjustment cam for reassembly reference.

3) Remove bolts from steering knuckle and separate from strut. Remove bolts from lower control arm and disconnect arm from steering knuckle. Using Puller (SST 09950-20014), pull axle hub from drive shaft. Cover boot with cloth to prevent damage.

4) Using Ball Joint Remover (SST 09610-55012), remove ball joint from steering knuckle. Using a screwdriver, remove dust deflector. Using Puller (SST 09308-00010), remove oil seal from steering knuckle.

5) Remove 3 bolts securing disc brake dust cover to steering knuckle. Using Puller (SST 09950-20014), push out axle hub and disc brake dust cover out of steering knuckle. Remove inboard bearing inner race from bearing.

6) Using puller, remove outboard bearing inner race from axle hub. Using Puller (SST 09308-00010), remove oil seal from steering knuckle. Install outboard bearing inner race and press bearing out of hub.

Installation

1) Using Bearing/Oil Seal Installer (SST 09608-32010), press new bearing into steering knuckle. Rotate and insert side lip of new oil seal into installer. Press oil seal into steering knuckle.

2) Apply sealer to disc brake dust cover and steering knuckle. Install dust cover. Apply multipurpose grease between oil seal lip, oil seal, and bearing. Using Hub Installer (SST 09310-35010), press axle hub into steering knuckle.

3) Install snap ring in steering knuckle. Press new oil seal into steering knuckle, until metal part of seal is flush with bearing bore. Apply multipurpose grease to lip of oil seal.

4) Using Driver (SST 09218-46010), install a new dust deflector into into steering knuckle. Reverse removal procedure to complete installation. Check front wheel alignment.

DRIVE AXLE SHAFTS
Removal

1) Remove cotter pin and lock nut cap. Depress brake pedal and loosen bearing lock nut and drive axle shaft nuts. Remove bearing lock nut from axle hub.

2) Remove bolts from lower control arm and disconnect arm from steering knuckle. Remove brake caliper and disc brake rotor. Using Puller (SST 09950-20014), pull axle hub from drive shaft. Cover boot with cloth to prevent damage.

Installation

To install, reverse removal procedure. Depress brake pedal when tightening bearing lock nut.

CONSTANT VELOCITY JOINTS
Disassembly

1) Check CV joints for play. No noticeable play should be present in outboard joint. Inboard joint should move freely along axis of drive shaft, no noticeable radial play should exist. Remove boot clamps.

2) Mark inboard joint tulip for reassembly reference and remove from drive shaft. Using snap ring pliers, remove snap ring. Mark tripod joint and shaft for reassembly. Using a hammer and punch, remove joint from shaft. Remove boots and inspect for damage.

Reassembly

1) Wrap vinyl tape around shaft splines. Install outboard boot and clamp. Remove tape. Install inboard boot and clamp. The inboard boot and clamp are larger than those of tripod joint.

2) Place beveled side of tripod axial spline toward outboard joint. Align marks, tap tripod joint onto shaft, and install snap ring. Place boot over outboard joint and pack with 5.8 oz. (165 g) of grease supplied in kit.

3) Pack inboard joint tulip with 7.5 oz. (212 g) of grease. Align marks, install tulip on drive shaft, and install boot on tulip. Install boot clamps. Ensure that boots are not stretched or collapsed.

TRANSAXLE MOUNTS

Information not available from manufacturer.

Manual Transmissions
TOYOTA C-51 5-SPEED TRANSAXLE (Cont.)

Fig. 1: Exploded View of Front Transaxle Case

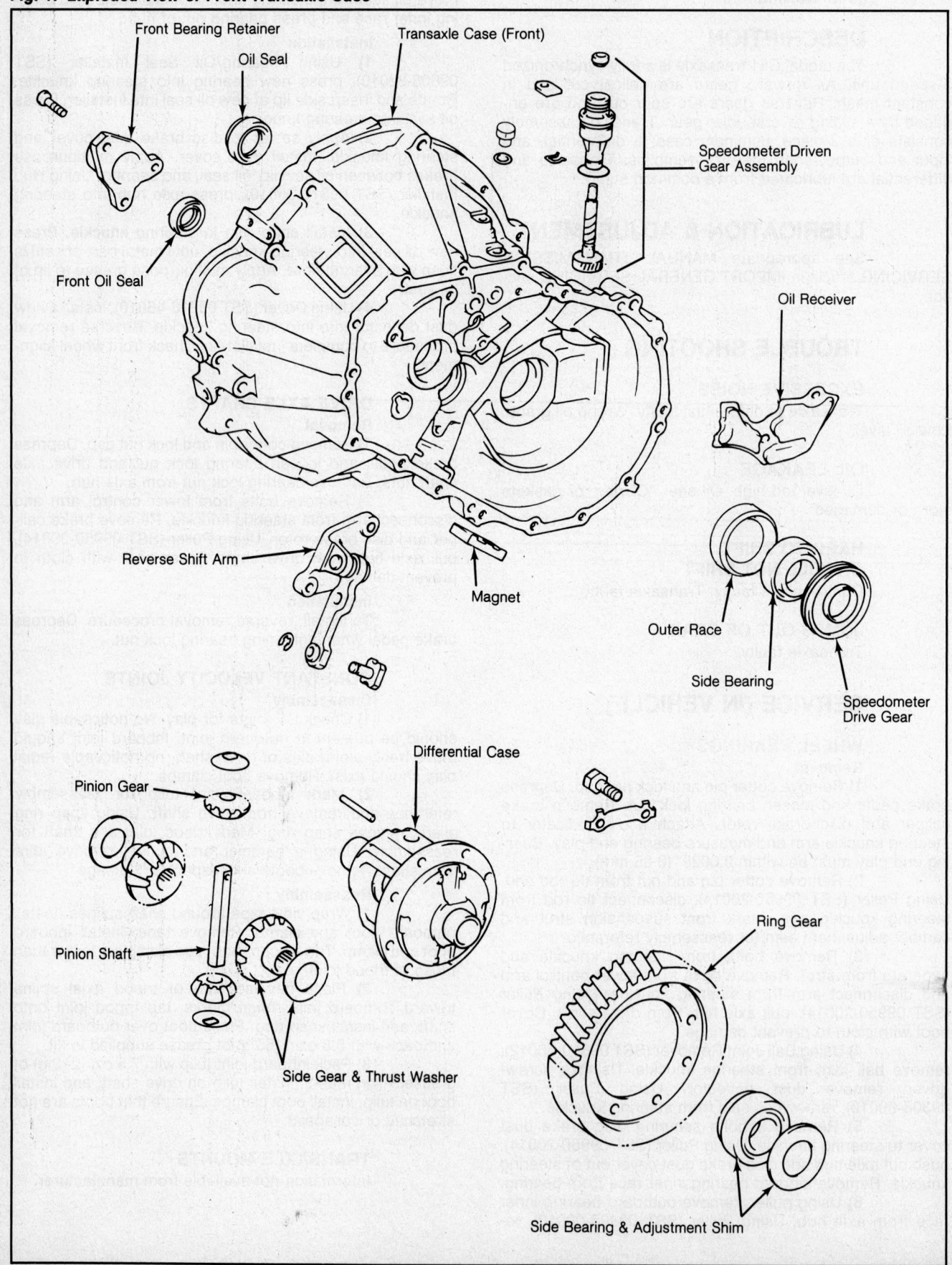

Front Bearing Retainer

Oil Seal

Transaxle Case (Front)

Speedometer Driven Gear Assembly

Front Oil Seal

Oil Receiver

Reverse Shift Arm

Magnet

Outer Race

Side Bearing

Speedometer Drive Gear

Pinion Gear

Differential Case

Ring Gear

Pinion Shaft

Side Gear & Thrust Washer

Side Bearing & Adjustment Shim

TOYOTA C-51 5-SPEED TRANSAXLE (Cont.)

Fig. 2: Exploded View of Input & Output Shaft Assemblies

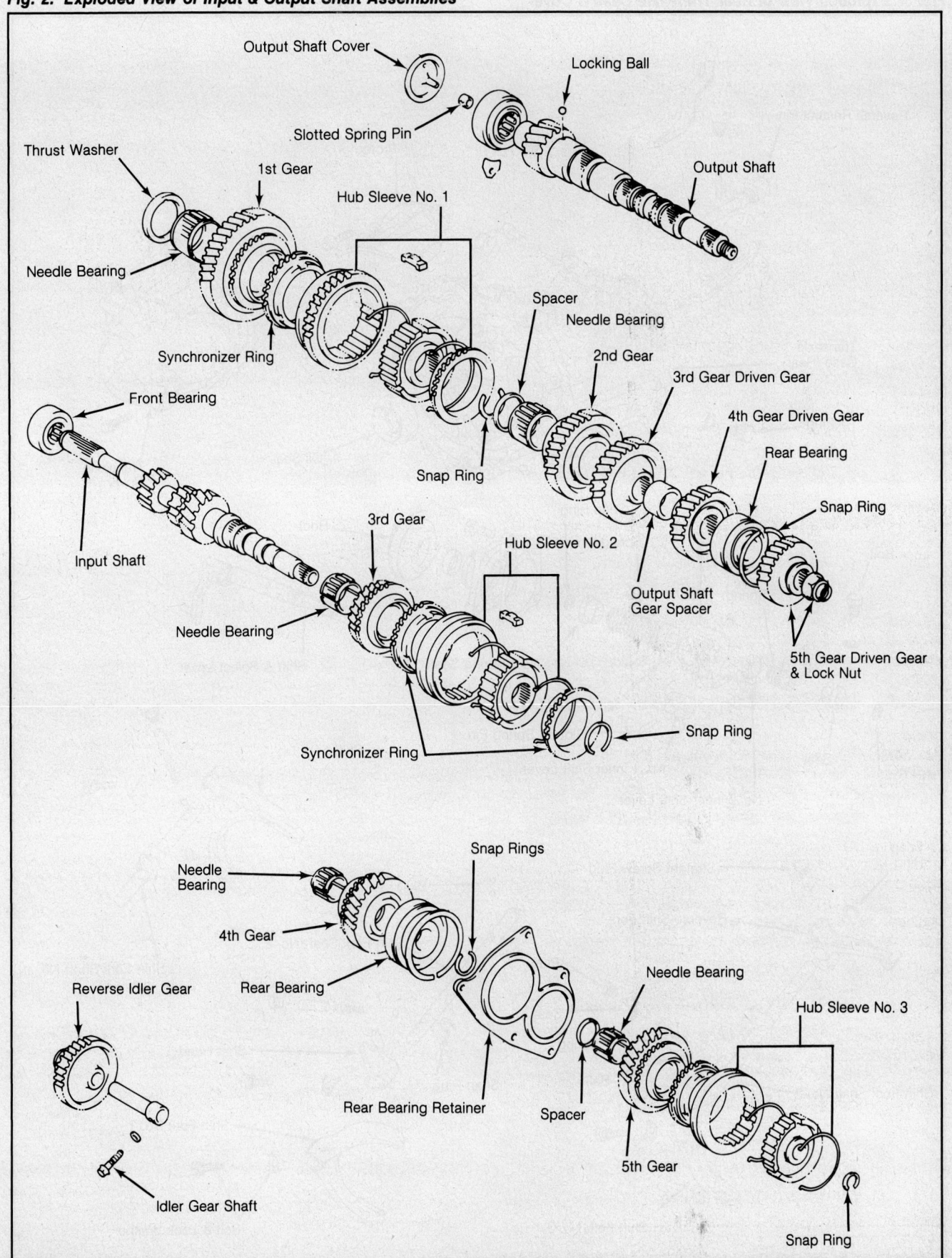

Manual Transmissions
TOYOTA C-51 5-SPEED TRANSAXLE (Cont.)

Fig. 3: Exploded View of Rear Transaxle Case & Cover

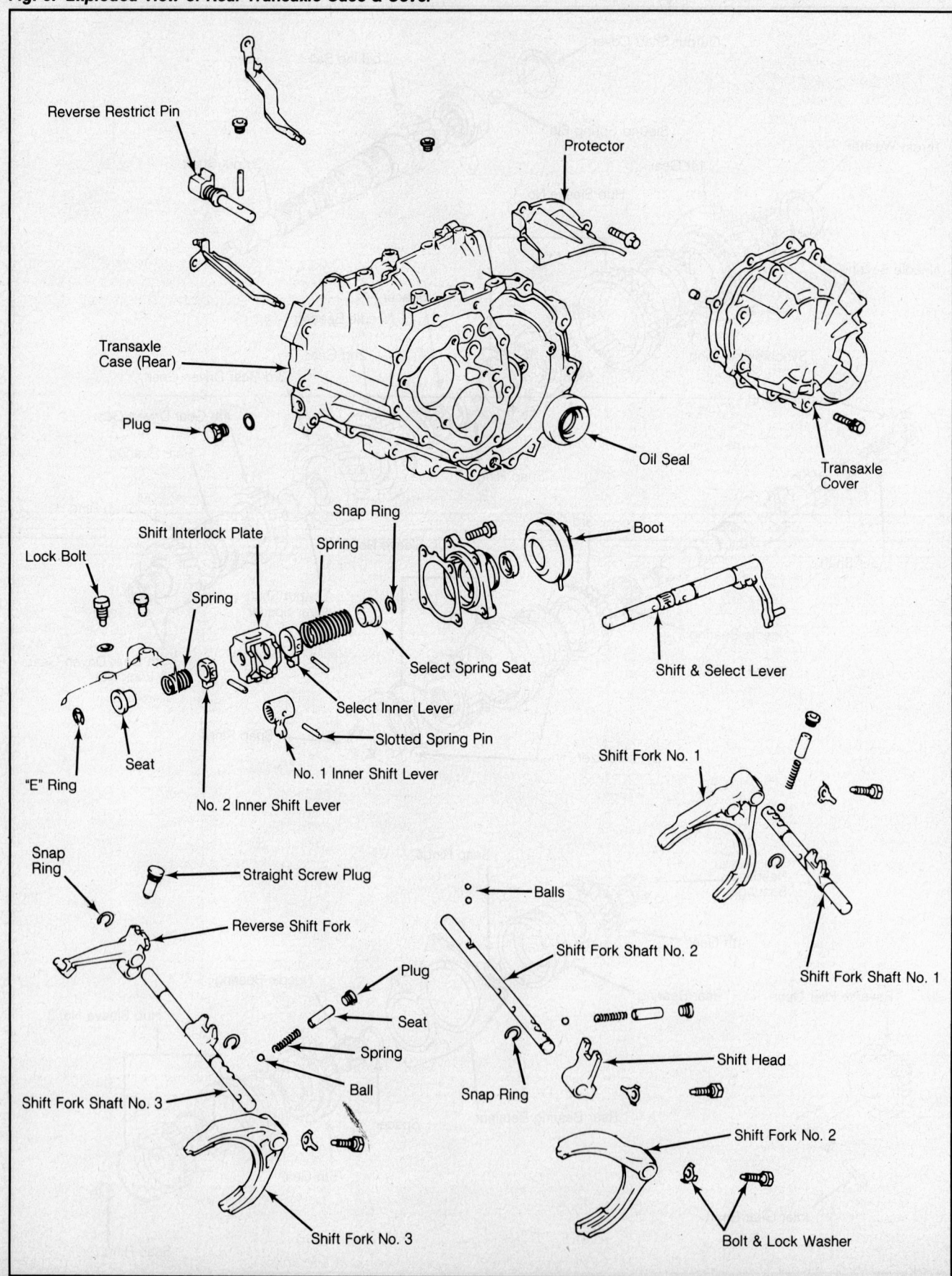

TOYOTA C-51 5-SPEED TRANSAXLE (Cont.)

REMOVAL & INSTALLATION

TRANSAXLE
See appropriate MANUAL TRANSMISSION REMOVAL article in IMPORT GENERAL SERVICING section.

TRANSAXLE DISASSEMBLY

1) Remove release fork, bearing, and speedometer driven gear. Using Socket (SST 09817-16010), remove back-up light switch. Remove front bearing retainer. Remove transaxle case cover.

2) Using a dial indicator, measure 5th gear thrust clearance. Clearance should be between 0.0039-0.0224" (0.10-0.57 mm). Maximum allowable clearance is 0.0256" (0.65 mm).

3) Remove selecting bellcrank. Remove lock bolt. Remove shift and select lever assembly. Engage gear double meshing and remove lock bolt. Disengage gear double meshing.

4) Remove bolt with lock washer from shift fork No. 3. Using 2 screwdrivers and a hammer, tap out snap ring. Using Puller (SST 09950-20014), remove hub sleeve No. 3 assembly and shift fork No. 3.

5) Remove 5th gear, synchronizer ring, needle roller bearing, and spacer. Using Puller (SST 09950-20014), remove 5th gear driven gear. Remove rear bearing retainer. Using snap ring pliers, remove 2 bearing snap rings.

6) Remove reverse idler gear shaft lock bolt. Using 2 screwdrivers and hammer, tap out and remove snap ring from No. 2 shift fork shaft. Using Socket (SST 09313-30021), remove 4 transaxle plugs. Using a magnetic pick-up tool, remove 4 springs and balls.

7) Remove tranxaxle case cover bolts (16) and tap case apart with a plastic hammer. Remove 2 bolts and pull out reverse shaft arm bracket. Pull out reverse idler gear and shaft.

8) Using 2 screwdrivers and a hammer, tap out 3 snap rings. Pry out lock washers and remove 3 set bolts. Remove fork shaft No. 2 and shift head. Using a magnetic pick-up tool, remove 2 balls. Remove fork shaft No. 3 and reverse shift fork.

9) Pull out shift fork shaft No. 1. Remove shift forks No. 1 and No. 2. Remove input and output shafts as an assembly. Remove differential assembly. Remove magnet and oil receiver.

CLEANING & INSPECTION

GEAR OIL CLEARANCE
With needle bearing installed and using a dial indicator, measure oil clearance between gear and input (output) shaft. *See Fig. 4.* Oil cleranace should be between 0.0006-0.0023" (0.15-0.058 mm). Maximum allowable clearance is 0.0028" (0.070 mm).

INPUT SHAFT
Check input shaft for wear or damage. Using a micrometer, measure outer diameter of input shaft journals. *See Fig. 5.* Using a dial indicator and "V" blocks, check input shaft for runout. Maximum allowable runout is 0.0020" (0.05 mm).

INPUT SHAFT MINIMUM JOURNAL DIAMETERS

Journal	Diameter In. (mm)
"A"	0.9791 (24.87)
"B"	1.0421 (26.47)
"C"	1.2193 (30.97)
"D"	0.9831 (24.97)

Fig. 4: Checking Gear Oil Clearance

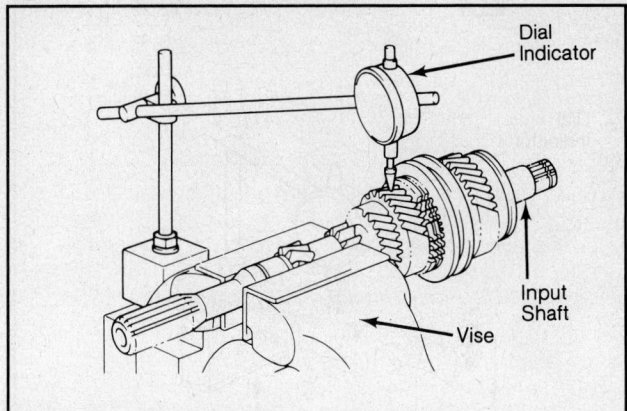

Fig. 5: Measuring Input Shaft Runout & Journal Diameters

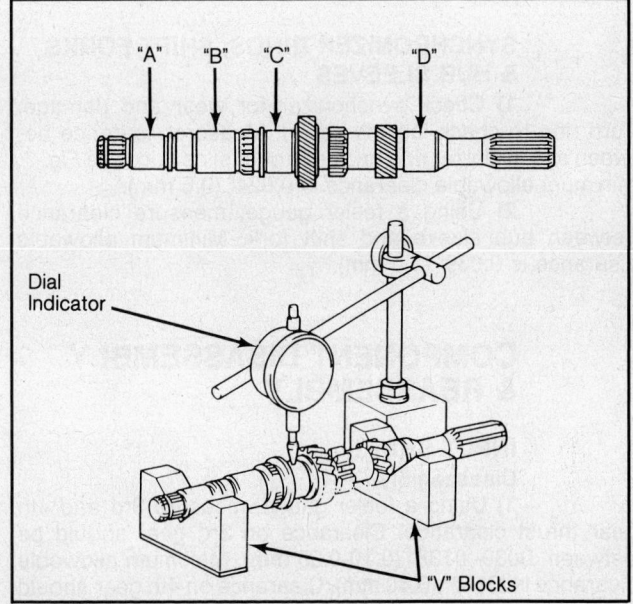

OUTPUT SHAFT
Check output shaft for wear or damage. Using a micrometer, measure outer diameter of output shaft journals. *See Fig. 6.* Using a dial indicator and "V" blocks, check input shaft for runout. Maximum allowable runout is 0.0020" (0.05 mm).

OUTPUT SHAFT MINIMUM JOURNAL DIAMETERS

Journal	Diameter In. (mm)
"A"	1.2980 (32.97)
"B"	1.4949 (37.97)
"C"	1.2587 (31.97)

Manual Transmissions

TOYOTA C-51 5-SPEED TRANSAXLE (Cont.)

Fig. 6: Measuring Output Shaft Runout & Journal Diameters

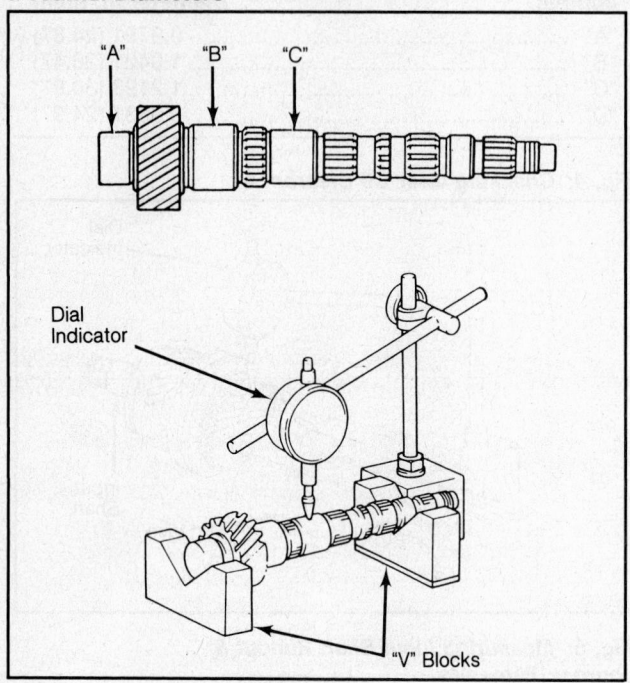

Fig. 7: Checking Synchronizer Rings, Shift Forks & Hub Sleeve Clearance

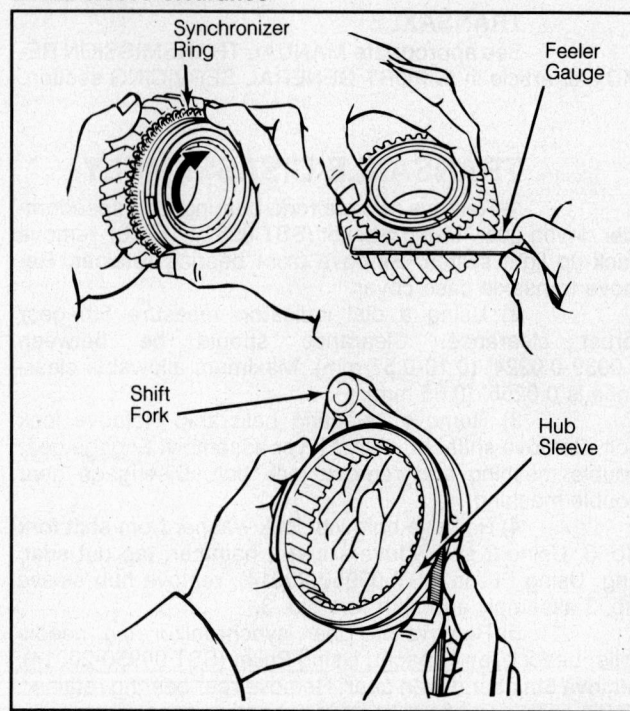

SYNCHRONIZER RINGS, SHIFT FORKS & HUB SLEEVES

1) Check synchonizer for wear and damage. Turn ring to check locking action. Measure clearance between synchronizer ring back and gear sline end. *See Fig. 7.* Minimum allowable clearance is 0.024" (0.6 mm).

2) Using a feeler gauge, measure clearance between hub sleeve and shift fork. Minimum allowable clearance is 0.039" (1.0 mm).

COMPONENT DISASSEMBLY & REASSEMBLY

INPUT SHAFT

Disassembly

1) Using a feeler gauge, measure 3rd and 4th gear thrust clearance. Clearance on 3rd gear should be between .0039-.0138" (0.10-0.35 mm). Maximum allowable clearance is .0157" (0.40 mm). Clearance on 4th gear should be between .0039-.0217" (0.10-0.55 mm). Maximum allowable clearance is .0236" (0.60 mm).

2) Using 2 screwdrivers and a hammer, tap out and remove snap ring from input shaft. Press ball bearing and 4th gear out of input shaft. Remove needle bearing and synchronizer ring.

3) Using snap ring pliers, remove hub sleeve No. 2 snap ring. Press hub sleeve No. 2, 3rd gear, synchronizer ring, and needle bearing out of input shaft.

Reassembly

1) Install clutch hub and shifting keys onto hub sleeve No. 2. Install shifting key springs under shifting keys. Ensure that key spring end gaps are not in line.

2) Apply multipurpose grease to needle bearing. Place synchronizer ring on 3rd gear and align ring slots with

shifting keys. Press 3rd gear and hub sleeve No. 2 onto input shaft.

3) Select 3rd gear snap ring that will allow minimum axial play on shaft. Install snap ring. Using a feeler gauge, measure 3rd gear thrust clearance. Maximum allowable clearance is 0.0039" (0.10 mm).

THIRD GEAR SNAP RING SELECTION

I.D. Mark	Thickness In. (mm)
0	0.0906 (2.30)
1	0.0929 (2.36)
2	0.0953 (2.42)
3	0.0976 (2.48)
4	0.1000 (2.54)
5	0.1024 (2.60)

Fig. 8: Measuring Third Gear Thrust Clearance

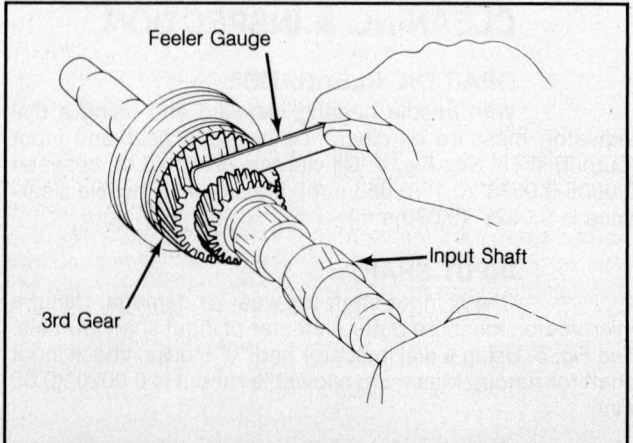

Manual Transmissions

TOYOTA C-51 5-SPEED TRANSAXLE (Cont.)

FOURTH GEAR SNAP RING SELECTION

I.D. Mark	Thickness In. (mm)
"A"	0.0902 (2.29)
"B"	0.0925 (2.35)
"C"	0.0949 (2.41)
"D"	0.0972 (2.47)
"E"	0.0996 (2.53)
"F"	0.1020 (2.59)

Fig. 9: Measuring Fourth Gear Thrust Clearance

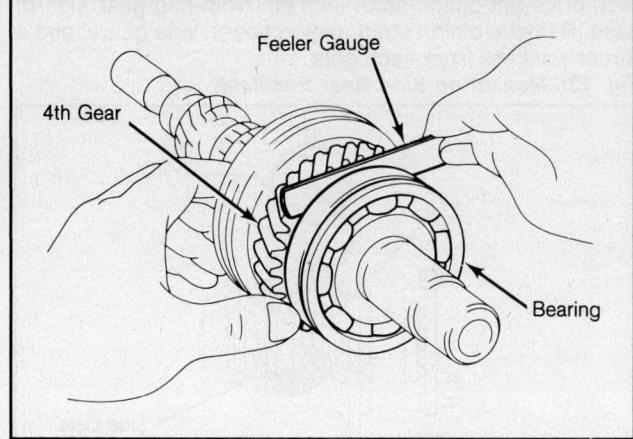

4) Apply multipurpose grease to needle bearing. Place synchronizer ring on 4th gear and align ring slots with shifting keys. Install assembly on input shaft. Press ball bearing onto input shaft.

5) Select 4th gear snap ring that will allow minimum axial play on shaft. Install snap ring. Using a feeler gauge, measure 4th gear thrust clearance. Maximum allowable clearance is 0.0039" (0.10 mm).

INPUT SHAFT FRONT OIL SEAL

Using a screwdriver, pry oil seal out of case. Using Seal Installer (SST 09608-12010), drive in oil seal.

INPUT & OUTPUT SHAFT FRONT BEARING

Remove bolt and oil receiver (lock plate). Using Puller (SST 09308-00010), remove front bearing. Press in bearing using Driver (SST 09310-35010). Install oil receiver, lock plate, and tighten bolt.

OUTPUT SHAFT

Disassembly

1) Using a feeler gauge, measure 1st and 2nd gear thrust clearance. Clearance on 1st gear should be .0039-.0157" (0.10-0.40 mm). Maximum allowable clearance is .0177" (0.45 mm).

2) Clearance on 2nd gear should be .0039-.0177" (0.10-0.45 mm). Maximum allowable clearance is .0197" (0.50 mm). *See Fig. 11.*

3) Press ball bearing and 4th gear driven gear out of output shaft. Remove spacer. Shift hub sleeve No. 1 into 1st gear. Press 3rd gear driven gear and 2nd gear out of output shaft. Remove needle bearing, spacer, and synchronizer ring.

4) Using 2 screwdrivers and a hammer, tap out and remove hub sleeve No. 1 snap ring. Press hub sleeve

No. 1, 1st gear, and synchronizer ring out of output shaft. Remove needle bearing, thrust washer, and lock ball.

Reassembly

1) If input shaft was replaced, drive slotted spring pin in end of output shaft to a depth of 0.236" (6 mm). Install clutch hub and shifting keys on hub sleeve.

2) Install shifting key springs under shifting keys. Ensure that key spring end gaps are not in line. Install locking ball in output shaft. Install thrust washer on shaft and fit thrust washer groove securely over locking ball.

3) Apply multipurpose grease to needle bearing. Place synchronizer ring on 1st gear and align ring slots with shifting keys. Press 1st gear and hub sleeve No. 1 onto output shaft.

4) Select 1st gear snap ring that will allow minimum axial play on shaft. Install snap ring. Using a feeler gauge, measure 1st gear thrust clearance. Maximum allowable clearance is 0.0039" (0.10 mm).

FIRST GEAR SNAP RING SELECTION

I.D. Mark	Thickness In. (mm)
"A"	0.0984 (2.50)
"B"	0.1008 (2.56)
"C"	0.1031 (2.62)
"D"	0.1055 (2.68)
"E"	0.1079 (2.74)
"F"	0.1102 (2.80)

Fig. 10: Measuring First Gear Thrust Clearance

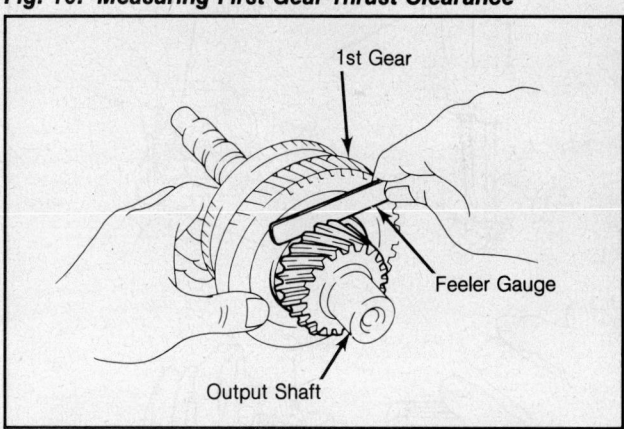

Fig. 11: Measuring Second Gear Thrust Clearance

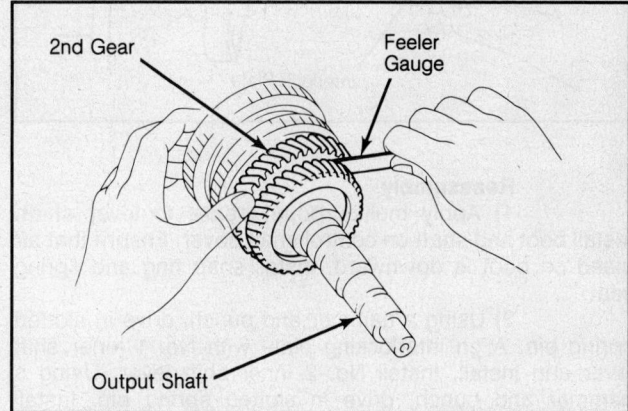

5) Install spacer. Apply multipurpose grease to needle bearing. Place synchronizer ring on 2nd gear and align ring slots with shifting keys. Install 2nd gear on shaft. Press 3rd gear driven gear onto output shaft.

6) Using a feeler gauge, measure 2nd gear thrust clearance. Clearance should be between 0.0039-0.0177" (0.10-0.45 mm). Maximum allowable clearance is 0.0197" (0.50 mm). Install spacer. Using Bearing Installer (SST 09608-12010), press 4th gear driven gear and bearing onto output shaft.

SHIFT & SELECT LEVER ASSEMBLY
Disassembly

1) Remove "E" clip and compression spring. Using a pin punch and a hammer, drive out slotted spring from No. 1 and No. 2 inner shift levers. Remove No. 2 inner lever. Remove No. 1 inner shift lever and shift interlock plate.

2) Using a pin punch and a hammer, drive out the slotted spring pin from select inner lever. Remove select lever, compression spring and spring seat. Using 2 screwdrivers and a hammer, tap out and remove snap ring from lever shaft. Remove lever shaft and boot.

Fig. 12: Disassembly of Shift & Select Lever Assembly

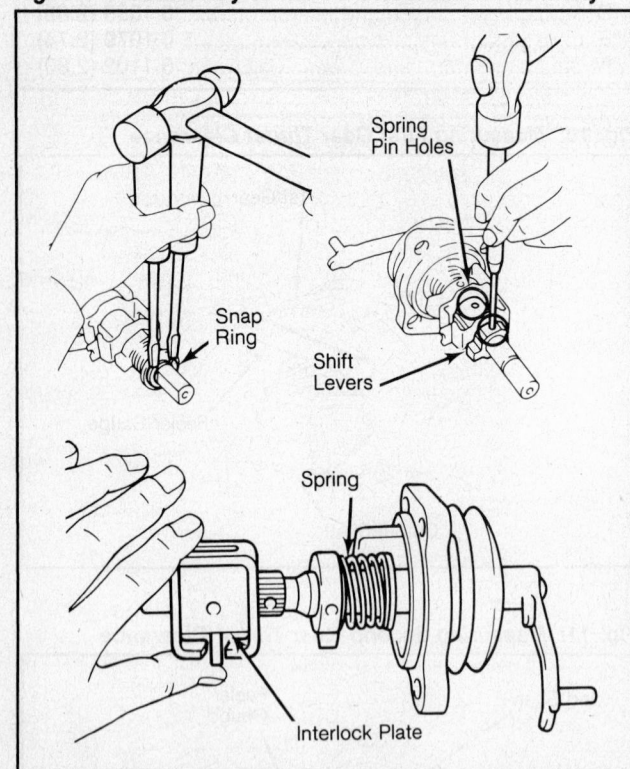

Reassembly

1) Apply multipurpose grease to lever shaft. Install boot and shaft on control shaft cover. Ensure that air bleed on boot is downward. Install snap ring and spring seat.

2) Using a hammer and punch, drive in slotted spring pin. Align interlocking plate with No. 1 inner shift lever and install. Install No. 2 inner shift lever. Using a hammer and punch, drive in slotted spring pin. Install compression spring, seat, and "E" clip.

DIFFERENTIAL
Disassembly

1) Using Puller (SST 09502-10012), remove bearings from differential case. Remove speedometer drive gear. Mark ring gear and case for reassembly reference. Bend locking tabs on ring gear bolts. Remove 8 bolts and locking tabs. Using a copper hammer, tap ring gear and remove from case.

2) While holding 1 pinion against case, measure side gear backlash. *See Fig. 13.* Backlash should be between 0.0020-0.0079" (0.05-0.20 mm). If backlash is incorrect, drive out pinion shaft lock pin from ring gear side of case. Remove pinion shaft, pinion gears, side gears, and 4 thrust washers from each gear.

Fig. 13: Measuring Side Gear Backlash

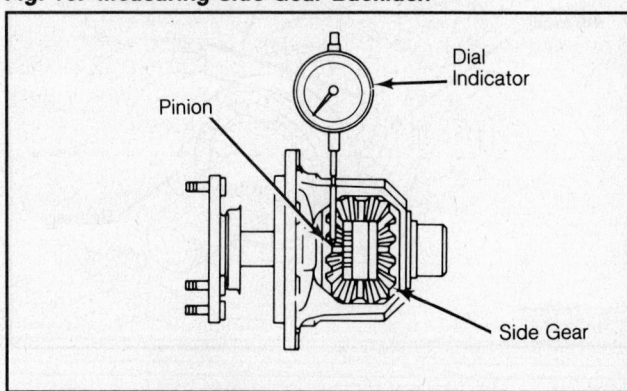

Reassembly

1) If backlash is incorrect, select thrust washers that will ensure correct backlash. If backlash is correct, use thrust washers removed during disassembly. Install thrust washers, side gears, pinion gears, and pinion shaft in case.

2) While holding 1 pinion gear against case, check side gear backlash. Backlash should be between 0.0020-0.0079" (0.05-0.20 mm). If backlash is incorrect, disassemble case once more and install thrust washer of a different thickness. Try to install washers of equal size.

NOTE: Side gear thrust washers are available in the following thickness variations: 0.0374" (0.95 mm), 0.0394" (1.00 mm), 0.0413" (1.05 mm), 0.0433" (1.10 mm), 0.0453" (1.15 mm), and 0.0472" (1.20 mm).

Fig. 14: Installing Side Gear & Thrust Washer

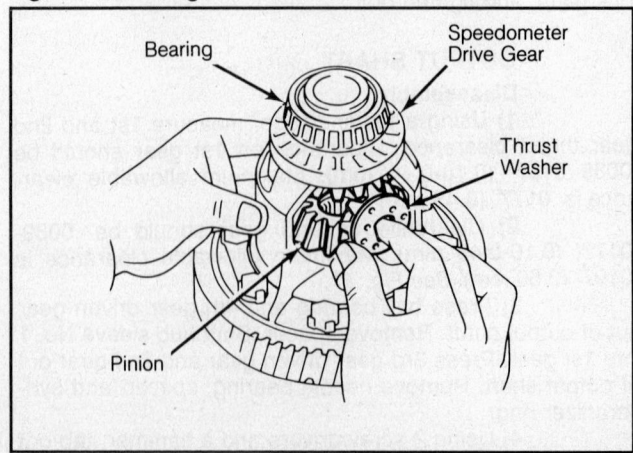

TOYOTA C-51 5-SPEED TRANSAXLE (Cont.)

3) Using a hammer and punch, drive lock pin through case and into pinion shaft. Stake differential case to hold pin in place. Clean ring gear contact surface of case. Heat ring gear to 212°F (100°C) in an oil bath.

4) Clean contact surface of ring gear with cleaning solvent. Align ring gear with differential case, and quickly install ring gear on case. Install locking tabs and bolts. Tighten bolts evenly and a little at a time. Tighten ring gear bolts.

5) Using a hammer and punch, bend locking tabs. Stake 1st tab flush with flat surface of nut. Stake 2nd tab against corner of nut. Install speedometer drive gear. Using Bearing Installer (SST 09350-32011), press bearings onto case.

CONTROL SHAFT COVER OIL SEAL

Using a screwdriver, pry oil seal out of cover. Using Seal Installer (SST 09608-12011), drive in oil seal.

SIDE BEARING OUTER RACE

Using Puller (SST 09612-65013), pull out bearing outer race and shim. Place shim into case. Using Bearing Installer (SST 09608-20011), drive in outer race.

SIDE BEARING OIL SEALS

Using a screwdriver, drive oil seal out of case. Using Seal Installer (SST 09350-32011), drive in oil seal until it is flush with case. Coat lip of seal with multipurpose grease.

SPEEDOMETER DRIVEN GEAR OIL SEAL

Using Puller (SST 09921-00010), pull out oil seal. Using Seal Installer (SST 09201-60011), drive oil seal 0.79" (20 mm) into bore.

TRANSAXLE REASSEMBLY

1) Install magnet on transaxle case. Install oil receiver and 2 bolts. Install thinnest shim into transaxle case. Using Bearing Installer (SST 09608-20011), drive in side bearing outer race. Install differential on transaxle case.

2) Install transaxle case and tighten bolts. Using Differential Preload Adapter (SST 09564-32011) and an INCH lb. torque wrench, measure differential side bearing preload.

3) Starting preload should be between 6.9-13.9 INCH lbs. (0.8-1.6 N.m) for a new bearing; 4.3-8.7 INCH lbs. (0.5-1.0 N.m) for a used bearing. If preload is incorrect, remove transaxle case, side bearing outer race, and change adjustment shim.

NOTE: Preload will change about 2.6-3.5 INCH lbs. (0.3-0.4 N.m) with each shim thickness.

4) If preload is within specification, remove outer race, shim and transaxle case. Do not lose selected adjustment shim. Install input and output shafts as an assembly.

5) Install shift forks No. 1 and No. 2 into hub sleeves No. 1 and No. 2. Install shift fork No.1 in shift fork hole. Insert interlocking balls into reverse shift fork hole.

6) Install fork shaft No. 3 and reverse shift fork. Install shift fork shaft No. 2 and shift head. Install 3 lock

DIFFERENTIAL BEARING PRELOAD SHIM SELECTION

I.D. Mark	Thickness In. (mm)
"Q"	0.0827 (2.10)
"R"	0.0846 (2.15)
"S"	0.0866 (2.20)
"T"	0.0886 (2.25)
"U"	0.0906 (2.30)
"A"	0.0925 (2.35)
"B"	0.0945 (2.40)
"C"	0.0965 (2.45)
"D"	0.0984 (2.50)
"E"	0.1004 (2.55)
"F"	0.1024 (2.60)
"G"	0.1043 (2.65)
"H"	0.1063 (2.70)
"J"	0.1083 (2.75)
"K"	0.1102 (2.80)
"L"	0.1122 (2.85)
"M"	0.1142 (2.90)
"N"	0.1161 (2.95)
"P"	0.1181 (3.00)

Fig. 15: Measuring Differential Bearing Preload

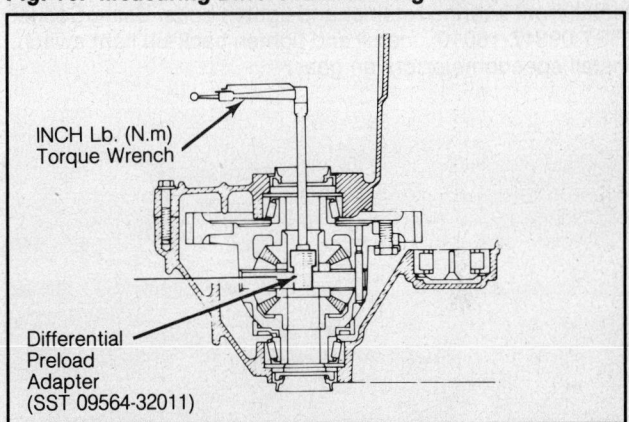

washers and shift fork bolts. Tighten bolts. Using pliers, bend lock washers against bolts.

7) Install 3 snap rings. Assemble reverse fork pivot and reverse shift arm. Install assembly in transaxle case. Intall bolts and tighten. Install reverse idler gear and shaft.

8) Apply sealant to transaxle case, install cover and tighten bolts. Insert balls, springs, and seats into holes. Apply sealant to plugs. Using Socket (SST 09313-30021), tighten 4 transaxle plugs.

9) Install and tighten reverse idler gear shaft lock bolt. Install 2 bearing snap rings. Install snap ring on fork shaft No. 2. Install rear bearing retainer and tighten bolts.

10) Using Installer (SST 09309-12020), press 5th gear driven gear onto shaft. Install spacer. Apply grease to needle bearing. Install 5th gear, needle bearing and synchronizer ring.

11) Install clutch hub and shifting keys on hub sleeve No. 3. Ensure that key spring end gaps are not in line. Align synchronizer ring slots with shifting keys. Using Installer (SST 09612-22011), drive in hub sleeve No. 3 with shift fork onto shaft.

Manual Transmissions

TOYOTA C-51 5-SPEED TRANSAXLE (Cont.)

12) Using a dial indicator, measure 5th gear thrust clearance. Maximum allowable clearance is 0.0039" (0.10 mm). Select 5th gear snap ring that will allow minimum axial play on shaft and install snap ring.

FIFTH GEAR SNAP RING SELECTION

I.D. Mark	Thickness In. (mm)
"A"	0.0886 (2.25)
"B"	0.0909 (2.31)
"C"	0.0933 (2.37)
"D"	0.0957 (2.43)
"E"	0.0980 (2.49)
"F"	0.1004 (2.55)
"G"	0.1028 (2.61)

13) Engage gear double meshing. Install lock nut and tighten. Disengage gear double meshing. Stake lock nut. Install shift fork lock washer and bolt. Tighten bolt and bend lock washer against bolt.

14) Install gasket on shift and select lever assembly control shaft cover. Install assembly on transfer case and tighten bolts. Install bellcrank on case. Install and tighten lock bolt.

15) Install transaxle cover and tighten bolts. Install front bearing retainer and tighten bolts. Using Socket (SST 09817-16010), install and tighten back-up light switch. Install speedometer driven gear.

TIGHTENING SPECIFICATIONS

Application	Ft. Lbs. (N.m)
Axle Bearing Lock Nut	137 (186)
Back-Up Light Switch	30 (41)
Ball Joint Nut	82 (111)
Brake Caliper Bolts	65 (88)
Differential Ring Gear	71 (96)
Drain & Fill Plugs	29 (39)
Drive Axle Shaft Nuts	27 (36)
Lower Control Arm Bolts	47 (64)
Rear Bearing Retainer	14 (19)
Reverse Idler Shaft Lock Bolt	17 (23)
Reverse Shift Arm Bracket	13 (18)
Shift Fork Screw Plugs	18 (24)
Shift & Select Lever Assembly	14 (19)
Steering Knuckle Bolts	105 (142)
Tie Rod End-to-Steering Knuckle	36 (49)
Transaxle Case	22 (30)
Transaxle Case Cover	13 (18)
Transaxle Screw Plugs	29 (39)
5th Gear Driven Gear Lock Nut	87 (118)

	INCH Lbs. (N.m)
Front Bearing Retainer	96 (11)
Oil Receiver	96 (11)
Output Shaft Bearing Lock Plate	96 (11)
Shift Fork & Lock Bolts	108 (12)
Speedometer Driven Gear Lock Plate	96 (11)

TOYOTA G53 5-SPEED

Van Wagon

DESCRIPTION

The G53 is a 5-speed transmission. It is fully synchronized in all forward gears. Synchronizers are of the blocker type. Gear selection is accomplished by direct control through floor mounted shift lever.

LUBRICATION & ADJUSTMENT

See appropriate MANUAL TRANSMISSION SERVICING article in IMPORT GENERAL SERVICING section.

TROUBLE SHOOTING

1) If transmission is hard to shift or will not shift, the splines on input shaft may be dirty or burred, or the transmission may be faulty. Disassemble, inspect or repair as necessary.

2) If transmission jumps out of gear, transmission could be faulty. Disassemble and inspect transmission.

REMOVAL & INSTALLATION

TRANSMISSION
Removal

1) Disconnect battery negative cable. Raise vehicle and drain transmission. Place reference marks on drive shaft flanges. Disconnect drive shaft flange from flange on differential. Pull yoke from transmission.

2) Disconnect select cable from select outer lever and remove clip and select cable. Disconnect shaft cable from shift outer lever. Remove clip and shift cable. Remove clutch slave cylinder. Remove starter.

3) Disconnect speedometer cable and bond cable. Disconnect back-up light switch connector. Remove exhaust pipe clamp and bracket. Remove stiffener plate. Raise transmission enough to remove weight from rear support.

4) Disconnect rear mounting and bracket. Remove bracket from body. Remove transmission mounting bolts and remove transmission assembly.

Installation
To install, reverse removal procedure.

TRANSMISSION DISASSEMBLY

1) Remove release fork and bearing. Remove back-up light switch and speedometer driven gear. Remove clutch housing from transmission. Remove shift lever housing assembly. Remove 8 extension housing bolts. Using a plastic hammer, tap extension housing and remove shift lever housing and shift and select lever.

NOTE: **Leave gasket attached to intermediate plate.**

2) Remove front bearing retainer and 2 bearing snap rings. Using a plastic hammer, carefully tap off transmission case. Remove transmission case from intermediate plate. Mount intermediate plate in vise, but DO NOT score mounting surfaces.

3) Using a Torx socket wrench, remove 4 plugs. Using a magnetic finger, remove 4 springs and balls. Using a pin punch and hammer, drive out 5 pins. Remove 3 "E" clips. Pull out shift fork shaft No. 3 from intermediate plate.

CAUTION: The locking balls and interlock pin may fall from holes so be sure to catch them by hand. If they do not come out, remove them with a magnet.

4) Remove shift fork and shaft No. 3. Remove locking ball and reverse shift head. Pull out shift fork shaft No. 4 from intermediate plate

CAUTION: The interlock pins may fall from hole so be sure to catch them by hand. If they do not come out, remove them with a magnet.

5) Remove shift fork shaft No. 4. Remove shift fork shaft No. 2 from intermediate plate. Be carefull to avoid having pin fall from hole so be sure to catch it by hand. If it does not come out, remove it with a magnet.

6) Remove shift fork shaft No. 2 and shift fork No. 2. Pull out shift fork shaft No. 1 and remove shift fork No. 2, No. 1 and 1st and 2nd shift head. Remove reverse idler gear shaft stopper. Remove reverse idler gear and shaft.

7) Remove reverse shift arm from reverse shift arm bracket. Using a feeler gauge, measure counter 5th gear trust clearance. Standard clearance is .0039-.0118" (.10-.30 mm). Maximum clearance is .0118" (.30 mm).

8) Slide synchronizers to engage 2nd and 3rd gears. Using a hammer and chisel, loosen staked part of nut. Remove lock nut. Disengage synchronizers. Using a gear puller, remove gear spline piece No. 5 synchronizer ring, needle roller bearing and counter 5th gear.

9) Remove spacer and ball using a magnet. Remove 2 bolts and reverse shift arm bracket. Using torx socket wrench, remove 4 bolts and rear bearing retainer. Remove bearing snap ring. Remove output shaft, counter gear and input shaft as a unit from intermediate plate by pulling on counter gear and tapping on intermediate plate with a plastic hammer.

10) Remove input shaft with 14 needle roller bearings from output shaft. Remove counter rear bearing from intermediate plate. Remove speedometer drive gear by removing snap ring. Remove speedometer drive gear and ball. Using magnet, remove steel ball. Using snap ring pliers remove snap ring.

11) Measure thrust clearance of each gear. Standard clearance is .0039-.0098" (.10-.25 mm) and maximum clearance is .0098" (.25 mm). Using 2 screwdrivers and a hammer, tap out 5th gear retaining snap ring. Using a press, remove 5th gear, rear bearing, 1st gear and inner race. Remove needle roller bearing.

12) Remove synchronizer ring. Using a magnet, remove locking ball. Using a press, remove hub sleeve No. 1, synchronizer ring and 2nd gear. Remove needle roller bearing. Using snap ring pliers, remove snap ring. Using a press, remove hub sleeve No. 2, synchronizer ring and 3rd gear. Remove needle roller bearing.

13) Remove lever lock pin and nut. Remove select outer lever and lever shaft from shift lever housing. Remove lever lock pin and pull out shift outer lever and boot. Using a pin punch and hammer, drive out slotted spring pin.

14) Remove shift and select lever and shaft. Remove rear and compression spring. Remove tight plug.

Manual Transmissions
TOYOTA G53 5-SPEED (Cont.)

Fig. 1: Exploded View of Case & Shifter Fork Assemblies

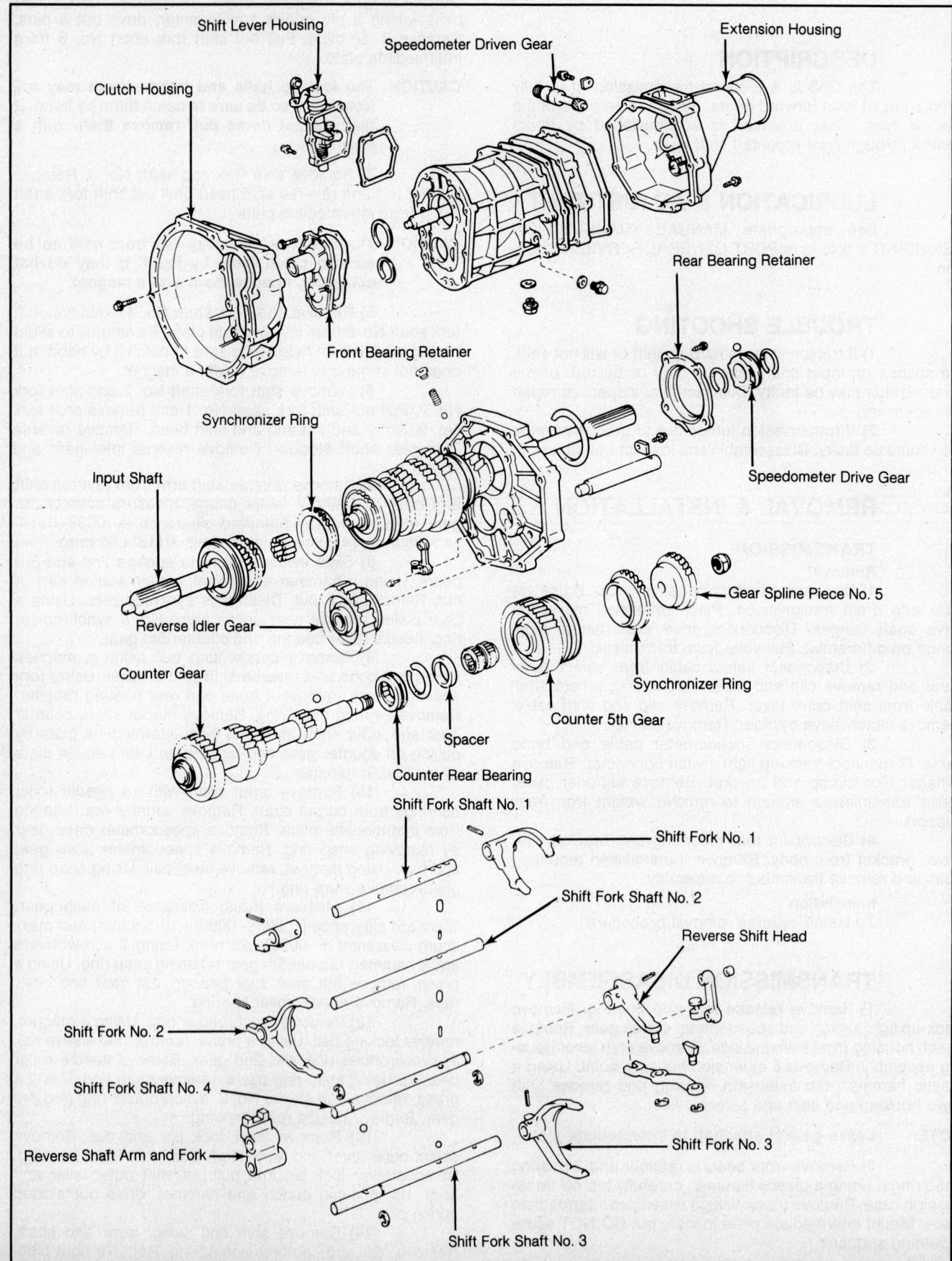

Shift Lever Housing

Speedometer Driven Gear

Extension Housing

Clutch Housing

Rear Bearing Retainer

Front Bearing Retainer

Speedometer Drive Gear

Synchronizer Ring

Input Shaft

Gear Spline Piece No. 5

Reverse Idler Gear

Synchronizer Ring

Counter Gear

Counter 5th Gear

Spacer

Counter Rear Bearing

Shift Fork Shaft No. 1

Shift Fork No. 1

Shift Fork Shaft No. 2

Reverse Shift Head

Shift Fork No. 2

Shift Fork Shaft No. 4

Reverse Shaft Arm and Fork

Shift Fork No. 3

Shift Fork Shaft No. 3

Fig. 2: Exploded View of Gear Assemblies

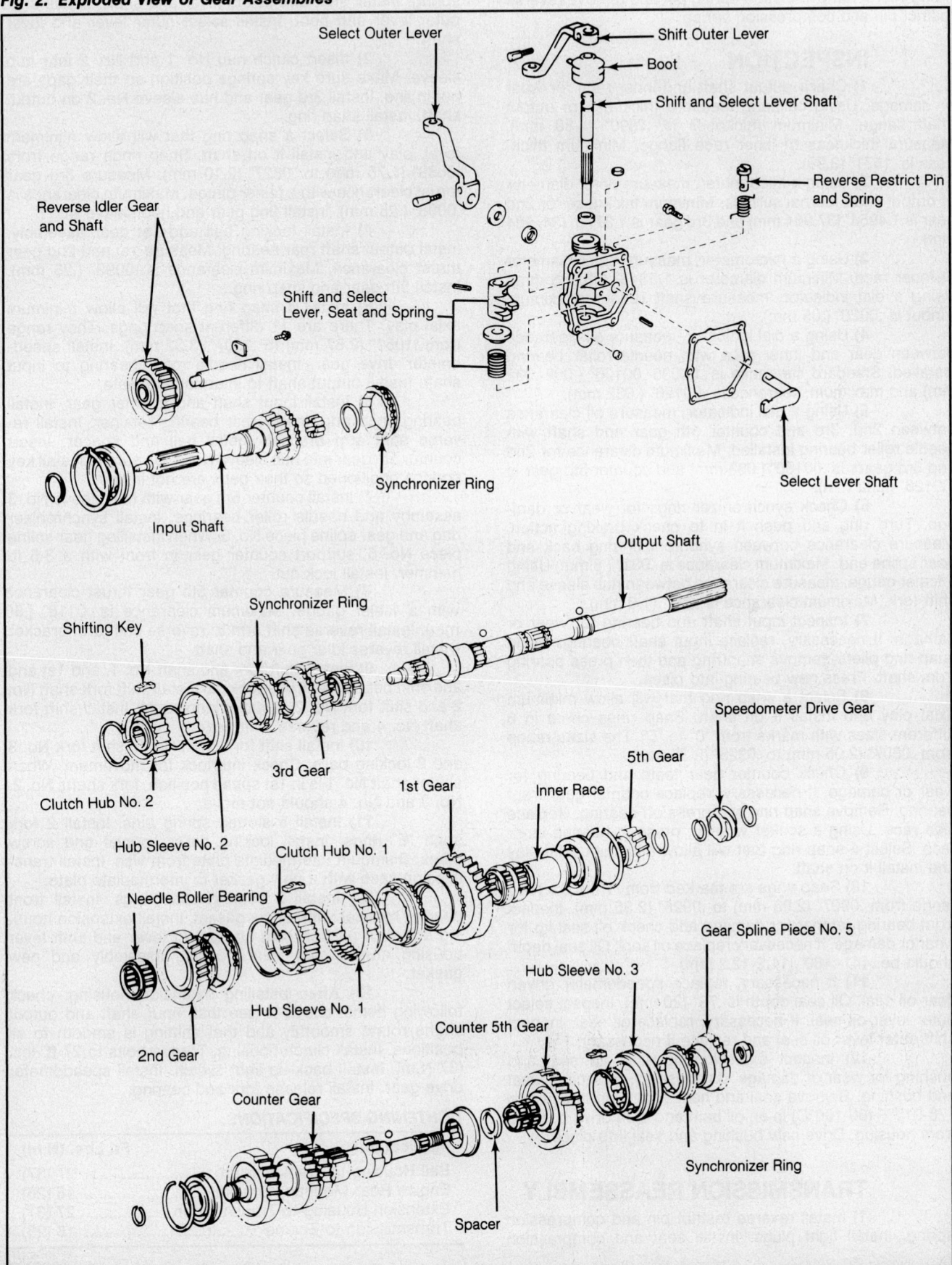

Select Outer Lever

Shift Outer Lever

Boot

Shift and Select Lever Shaft

Reverse Restrict Pin and Spring

Reverse Idler Gear and Shaft

Shift and Select Lever, Seat and Spring

Select Lever Shaft

Synchronizer Ring

Input Shaft

Output Shaft

Synchronizer Ring

Shifting Key

Speedometer Drive Gear

3rd Gear

Clutch Hub No. 2

1st Gear

Inner Race

5th Gear

Hub Sleeve No. 2

Clutch Hub No. 1

Gear Spline Piece No. 5

Needle Roller Bearing

Hub Sleeve No. 3

Hub Sleeve No. 1

Counter 5th Gear

2nd Gear

Counter Gear

Synchronizer Ring

Spacer

Manual Transmissions

TOYOTA G53 5-SPEED (Cont.)

Using pliers, remove slotted spring pin and remove reverse restrict pin and compression spring.

INSPECTION

1) Check output shaft and inner race for wear or damage. Using calipers, measure thickness of output shaft flange. Minimum thickness is .1890" (4.80 mm). Measure thickness of inner race flange. Minimum thickness is .1571" (3.99).

2) Using a micormeter, measure outer diameter of output shaft journal surface. Minimum thickness for 2nd gear is 1.4954" (37.984 mm) and 3rd gear is 1.3773" (34. 984 mm).

3) Using a micrometer, measure outer diameter of inner race. Minimum diameter is 1.5348" (38.985 mm). Using a dial indicator, measure shaft runout. Maximum runout is .0020" (.05 mm).

4) Using a dial indicator, measure oil clearance between gear and inner race with needle roller bearing installed. Standard clearance is .00035-.00126" (.009-.032 mm) and maximum clearance is .00126" (.032 mm).

5) Using a dial indicator, measure oil clearance between 2nd, 3rd and counter 5th gear and shaft with needle roller bearing installed. Maximum clearance for 2nd and 3rd gears is .00130" (.033 mm) and counter 5th gear is .00126" (.032 mm).

6) Check synchronizer rings for wear or damage. Turn ring and push it in to check braking action. Measure clearance between synchronizer ring back and gear spline end. Maximum clearance is .031" (.8 mm) Using a feeler gauge, measure clearance between hub sleeve and shift fork. Maximum clearance is .039" (1.0 mm).

7) Inspect input shaft and bearing for wear or damage. If necessary, replace input shaft bearing. Using snap ring pliers, remove snap ring and then press bearing from shaft. Press new bearing into place.

8) Select a snap ring that will allow minimum axial play and install it on shaft. Snap rings come in 6 different sizes with marks from "0" to "5". The sizes range from .0807" (2.05 mm) to .0925" (2.35 mm).

9) Check counter gear teeth and bearing for wear or damage. If necessary, replace counter gear front bearing. Remove snap ring and press off bearing. Replace side race. Using a socket wrench, press in bearing inner race. Select a snap ring that will allow minimum axial play and install it on shaft.

10) Snap rings are marked from "1" to "6". They range from .0807" (2.05 mm) to .0925" (2.35 mm). Inspect front bearing retaner for damage and check oil seal lip for wear or damage. If necessary replace oil seal. Oil seal depth should be .441-.480" (11.2-12.2 mm).

11) If necessary, replace speedometer driven gear oil seal. Oil seal depth is .79" (20 mm). Inspect select outer lever oil seal. If necessary, replace oil seal. Inspect shift outer lever oil seal and replace if necessary.

12) Inspect extension housing, oil seal and bushing for wear or damage. If necessary, replace oil seal and bushing. Remove seal and heat extension housing to 176-212°F (80-100°C) in an oil bath and then drive bushing from housing. Drive new bushing and seal into place.

TRANSMISSION REASSEMBLY

1) Install reverse restrict pin and compression spring. Install tight plugs. Install seat and compression spring. Install shift and select lever and shaft. Install shift outer lever and boot. Install select outer lever and lever shaft.

2) Insert clutch hub No. 1 and No. 2 into hub sleeve. Make sure key springs position so their gaps are not in line. Install 3rd gear and hub sleeve No. 2 on output shaft. Install snap ring.

3) Select a snap ring that will allow minimum axial, play and install it on shaft. Snap rings range from .0689" (1.75 mm) to .0827" (2.10 mm). Measure 3rd gear thrust clearance with a feeler gauge. Maximum clearance is .0098" (.25 mm). Install 2nd gear and hub sleeve No. 1.

4) Install locking ball and 1st gear assembly. Instal output shaft rear bearing. Measure 1st and 2nd gear thrust clearance. Maximim clearance is .0098" (.25 mm). Install 5th gear and snap ring.

5) Install a snap ring that will allow minimum axial play. There are 11 different snap rings. They range from .1051" (2.67 mm) to .1307" (3.32 mm). Install speedometer drive gear. Install needle roller bearing to input shaft. Install output shaft to intermediate plate.

6) Install input shaft and counter gear. Install bearing snap ring. Install rear bearing retainer. Install reverse shift arm bracket. Install ball and spacer. Insert counter 5th gear into hub sleeve No. 3. Be sure to install key springs positioned so their gaps are not in line.

7) Install counter 5th gear with hub sleeve No. 3 assemby and needle roller bearings. Install synchronizer ring and gear spline piece No. 5. When installing gear spline piece No. 5, support counter gear in front with a 3-5 lb hammer. Install lock nut.

8) Measure counter 5th gear thrust clearance with a feeler gauge. Maximum clearance is .0118" (.30 mm). Install reverse shift arm to reverse shift arm bracket. Install reverse idler gear and shaft.

9) Install shift fork and shaft No. 1, and 1st and 2nd shift head. Install interlock pin Install shift fork shaft No. 2 and shift fork No. 2. Install interlock pin. Install shift fork shaft No. 4 and reverse shift head.

10) Install shift fork shaft No. 3, shift fork No. 3 and 2 locking balls. Check interlock for movement. When shifter shaft No. 1 is in 1st speed position, fork shafts No. 2, No. 3 and No. 4 should not move.

11) Install 5 slotted spring pins. Install 2 fork shaft "E" rings. Install locking balls, springs and screw plugs. Dismount intermediate plate from vise. Install transmission case with a new gasket to intermediate plate.

12) Install 2 bearing snap rings. Install front bearing retainer with a new gasket. Install extension housing and new gasket, shift and select lever and shift lever housing. Install shift lever housing assembly and new gasket.

13) After installing extension housing, check following items: check to see that input shaft and output shafts rotate smoothly and that shifting is smooth to all positions. Install clutch housing. Torque bolts to 27 ft. lbs. (37 N.m). Install back-up light switch. Install speedometer drive gear. Install release fork and bearing.

TIGHTENING SPECIFICATIONS

Application	Ft. Lbs. (N.m)
Bell Housing-to-Transmission	27 (37)
Engine Rear Mounting Bracket	18 (25)
Extension Housing-to-Transmission	27 (37)
Transmission-to-Engine	18 (25)

TOYOTA 5-SPEED — MODEL W58

Celica, Cressida, Supra

TRANSMISSION IDENTIFICATION

The W58 transmission uses a 4-piece transmission case assembly. Main components are clutch housing, transmission case, intermediate plate and extension housing.

DESCRIPTION

Transmission is a 5-speed, fully synchronized unit. All forward gears are helical cut and in constant mesh. Reverse gear is spur cut. Reverse and 5th gears are in constant mesh and are mounted on rear side of intermediate plate (inside extension housing). Floor shifter actuates a single control rod in extension housing operating 3 shift rails mounted in intermediate plate and main case.

LUBRICATION & ADJUSTMENT

See the appropriate article in MANUAL TRANS-MISSION SERVICING Section.

TROUBLE SHOOTING

HARD SHIFTING

Clutch not disengaging properly. Bushings in cross shaft worn or damaged. Synchro rings making faulty contact with gear cone. Synchro worn or pitted.

SLIPS OUT OF GEAR

Improper meshing of gears due to shift rails being out of adjustment. Shift forks worn or ball locks broken. Excessive play in synchro hub No. 2. Output shaft of drive gear worn. Reverse idler gear or its bushing is worn. Countergear or its bushing or shaft is worn.

NOISE IN TRANSMISSION

Gears or bearings worn or damaged. Insufficient or incorrect lubricant. Input shaft splines worn or damaged. Reverse idler gear bushing worn.

REMOVAL & INSTALLATION

See the appropriate article in MANUAL TRANS-MISSION REMOVAL Section.

TRANSMISSION DISASSEMBLY

CLUTCH HOUSING

Removal
Release spring clips and remove clutch release fork and bearing. Loosen bolts evenly and remove clutch housing from transmission.

EXTENSION HOUSING

Removal
Remove speedometer driven gear retainer bolt and take out shaft sleeve and driven gear. Remove 9 housing bolts and take care, when removing extension housing, that output spline does not damage rear oil seal.

Fig. 1: Removing Extension Housing

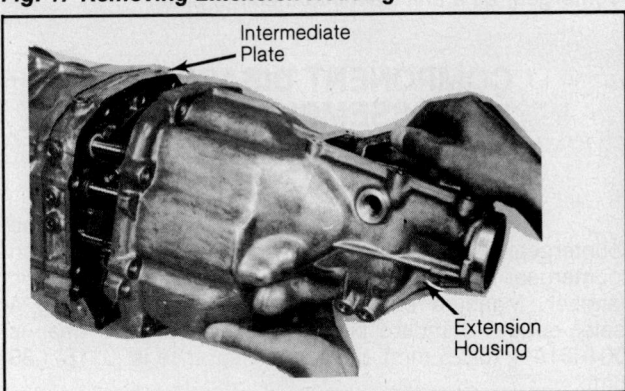

TRANSMISSION CASE

Removal
1) Remove back-up light switch wire clamp and back-up light switch. Remove 7 bolts and front bearing retainer. Using snap ring pliers, remove 2 snap rings. Separate intermediate plate from transmission case by carefully tapping transmission case with a plastic hammer. Pull transmission case from intermediate plate. Leave gasket attached to intermediate plate.

2) Mount intermediate plate in vise. Use 2 long clutch housing bolts, plate washers and nuts. Install in 2 bottom holes on intermediate plate to prevent damage on plate. Install plate washers in reverse of normal. Increase or decrease plate washers so that bolt tip and front tip surface of nut are aligned and mounted evenly in vise.

3) Remove 4 straight screw plugs with tool (SST 09313-30021). Remove 3 springs and balls. Remove shift forks and shafts by prying out lock washers of shift fork No. 1 and No. 2. Remove 2 set bolts. Using 2 drivers and hammer, tap out 2 snap rings of No. 1 and No. 2 fork shafts. Remove reverse idler gear shaft stopper.

4) Remove shift fork and shaft No. 1. Using magnet, remove interlock pin No. 1 and No. 2. Remove shift fork and shaft No. 2. Using magnet, remove interlock pin No. 3. Remove reverse idler gear and shaft. Using a pin punch and hammer, drive out No. 3 fork shaft pin. Pull out shaft fork No. 4. Remove shift fork No. 3 and reverse shift arm with pin.

5) Remove speedometer drive gear by prying both ends of clip. Measure counter 5th gear thrust clearance using feeler gauge. Standard clearance is .004-.016" (.10-.41 mm). Maximum clearance is .018" (.46 mm). Remove snap ring. Using puller (SST 09213-36010) remove counter rear bearing, spacer, 5th gear and needle bearing. Remove spacer.

NOTE: Be careful not to catch the output shaft rear bearing roller on the counter 5th gear.

6) Using 2 drivers and a hammer, tap out snap ring. Use sleeve remover (SST 09950-20014) to remove hub sleeve No. 3 assembly. Be sure to latch claw of tool onto clutch hub. Be careful not to latch it on shifting key retainer. Tap out snap ring from output shaft. Remove output shaft rear bearing and 5th gear with puller (SST 09312-20010). Remove snap ring and remove reverse gear using puller (SST 09950-20014).

Manual Transmissions

TOYOTA 5-SPEED — MODEL W58 (Cont.)

7) Remove center bearing retainer using a torx-type socket. Unscrew torx screw and remove retainer. Remove bearing snap ring. Remove output shaft and countergear as a unit from intermediate plate.

COMPONENT DISASSEMBLY & REASSEMBLY

INPUT & OUTPUT SHAFTS

Disassembly

1) Remove output shaft, input shaft and countergear as a unit from intermediate plate by pulling on countergear and tapping on intermediate plate with plastic hammer. Measure each gear thrust clearance using a feeler gauge. Standard clearance between each gear is .004-.010" (.10-.25 mm). Maximum clearance is .0118" (.30 mm).

2) Remove input shaft from output shaft. Shift hub sleeve No. 1 onto 2nd gear. Remove center bearing with press. Pull off 1st gear, needle roller bearing, inner race and synchronizer ring.

3) Remove locking ball. Remove hub sleeve No. 1 assembly, 2nd gear and needle roller bearing, using a press. Remove parts as an assembly. Remove snap ring with snap ring pliers. Remove hub sleeve No. 2, synchronizer ring and 3rd gear with a press.

Inspection

1) Inspect output shaft and inner race for wear or damage. Using caliper, measure output shaft flange thickness. Minimum thickness is .221" (5.60 mm). Using calipers, measure inner race flange thickness. Minimum thickness is .185" (4.70 mm).

2) Measure 2nd gear with micrometer; minimum is 1.69" (42.85 mm). Measure 3rd gear; minimum is 1.49" (37.80 mm). Using micrometer, measure outer diameter of inner race. Minimum diameter is 1.69" (42.85 mm). Use dial indicator to check runout. Measurement should be .0024" (.06 mm).

3) Inspect output shaft rear bearing. Check bearing and outer race for wear or damage. If necessary, replace bearing and outer race. Inspect output shaft center bearing, gears and needle roller bearings for wear or damage.

Fig. 2: Exploded View of W58 5-Speed Transmission

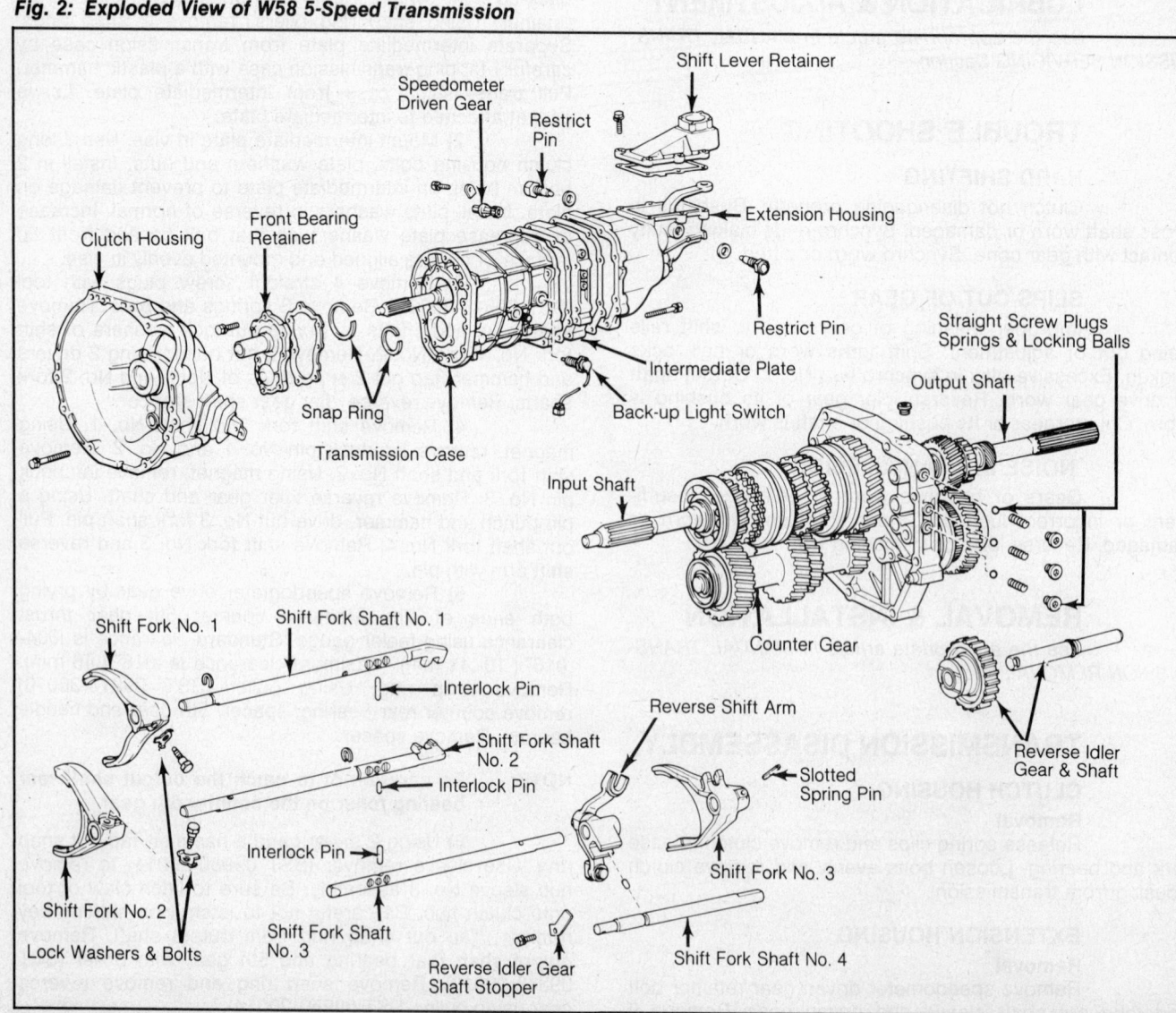

TOYOTA 5-SPEED — MODEL W58 (Cont.)

Fig. 3: *Exploded View of W58 5-Speed Transmission*

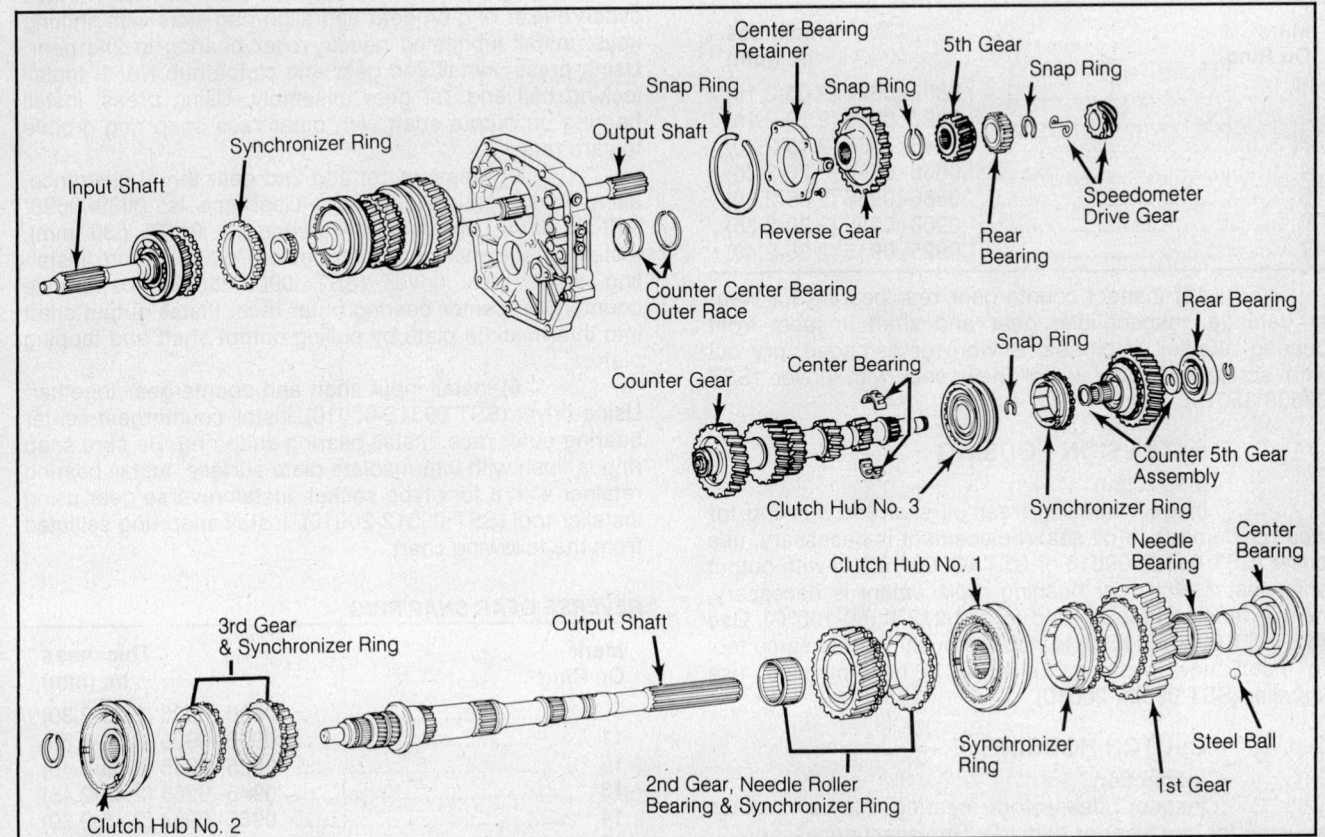

4) Check oil clearance of 1st gear with a dial indicator. Measure oil clearance between gear and inner race with needle roller bearing installed. Standard clearance is .0004-.0024" (.009-.060 mm). Maximum clearance is .0059" (.15 mm).

5) Check oil clearance of 2nd gear and counter 5th gear with a dial indicator. Measure oil clearance between gear and output shaft with needle roller bearing installed. Standard clearance for 2nd gear is .0004-.0024" (.009-.060 mm). Standard clearance for 5th gear is .0004-.0024" (.009-.062 mm). Maximum clearance is .0059" (.15 mm).

6) Check oil clearance of 3rd gear using dial indicator. Measure oil clearance between gear and output shaft. Standard clearance is .0024-.0040" (.060-.103 mm). Maximum clearance is .0079" (.20 mm).

7) Inspect synchronizer rings for wear or damage. Turn ring and push it in to check braking action. Measure clearance between synchro ring back and gear spline end. Standard clearance is .028-.067" (.7-1.7 mm). Minimum clearance is .020" (.5 mm).

8) Inspect clutch hubs, sleeve keys and key springs for wear or damage. Measure clearance of shift forks and hub sleeves, with a feeler gauge, between hub sleeve and shift fork. Maximum clearance is .039" (1.0 mm).

9) Inspect clearance of reverse shift arm shoe and reverse idler gear using feeler gauge. Measure clearance between reverse shift arm shoe and gear groove. Maximum clearance is .035" (.9 mm). Inspect shift forks and shafts for wear or damage.

10) Inspect input shaft and bearing for wear or damage. If replacement is necessary, remove snap ring. Using a press, remove bearing. Install new bearing with tool (SST 09506-35010) on press. Use following snap ring chart to select a snap ring that will allow minimum axial play and install it on shaft.

INPUT SHAFT SNAP RING SIZE CHART

Mark On Ring	Thickness In. (mm)
1	.0807-.0827 (2.05-2.10)
2	.0827-.0846 (2.10-2.15)
3	.0846-.0866 (2.15-2.20)
4	.0866-.0886 (2.20-2.25)
5	.0886-.0906 (2.25-2.30)
11	.0906-.0925 (2.30-2.35)
12	.0925-.0945 (2.35-2.40)

11) Inspect countergear and bearing for wear or damage. If replacement of countergear front bearing is necessary, remove snap ring and press out bearing with tool (SST 09555-55010). Check side of race for wear or damage. If replacement of side race is necessary, use puller (SST 09950-20014).

12) If side race cannot be removed with puller, grind part of side race and cut it off with a chisel. Using a socket, press in bearing, side race and inner race. Select a snap ring from following chart that will allow minimum axial play and install it on shaft.

Manual Transmissions

TOYOTA 5-SPEED – MODEL W58 (Cont.)

COUNTERGEAR SNAP RING SIZES

Mark On Ring	Thickness In. (mm)
1	.0807-.0827 (2.05-2.10)
2	.0827-.0846 (2.10-2.15)
3	.0846-.0866 (2.15-2.20)
4	.0866-.0886 (2.20-2.25)
5	.0886-.0906 (2.25-2.30)
6	.0906-.0925 (2.30-2.35)
7	.0925-.0945 (2.35-2.40)

13) Inspect countergear rear bearing for wear or damage. Inspect idler gear and shaft. Inspect front bearing retainer. If oil seal is worn or damaged, pry out with screwdriver and install new seal with driver (SST 09608-35013).

EXTENSION HOUSING

Inspection

Inspect housing, rear oil seal and bushing for wear or damage. If oil seal replacement is necessary, use puller (SST 09308-00010 or SST 09308-10010) with output shaft installed. If rear bushing replacement is necessary, heat extension housing end to 176-212°F (80-100°C). Use tool (SST 09307-30010) to remove bushing. Use same tool to install new bushing. To drive in new oil seal, use installer (SST 09325-20010).

CLUTCH HOUSING

Inspection

Inspect release fork, bearing, clips and clutch housing for any wear or damage. Replace if necessary.

TRANSMISSION REASSEMBLY

TRANSMISSION CASE

1) Install No. 1 and No. 2 clutch hub and shifting keys to hub sleeve. Install shifting key springs under shifting keys. Install key springs so that their end gaps are not in line with each other.

2) Install 3rd gear and clutch hub No. 2 on output shaft. Apply oil to shaft. Place synchro ring on gear and align ring slots with shifting keys. Using press, install 3rd gear and clutch hub No. 2. Select a snap ring that will allow minimum axial play from following chart and install it on shaft.

OUTPUT SHAFT SNAP RING

Mark On Ring	Thickness In. (mm)
D	.0709-.0728 (1.80-1.85)
11	.0732-.0752 (1.86-1.91)
12	.0756-.0776 (1.92-1.97)
13	.0780-.0799 (1.98-2.03)
14	.0803-.0823 (2.04-2.09)
15	.0827-.0846 (2.04-2.15)

3) Measure 3rd gear thrust clearance using feeler gauge. Standard clearance is .0039-.0098" (.10-.25 mm). Maximum clearance is .0118" (.30 mm). Install clutch hub No. 1 into hub sleeve and install shifting keys. Place key springs under shifting keys. Be sure end gaps do not line up on key springs.

4) Install 2nd gear and clutch hub No. 1. Place synchronizer ring on gear and align ring slots with shifting keys. Install lubricated needle roller bearing in 2nd gear. Using press, install 2nd gear and clutch hub No. 1. Install locking ball and 1st gear assembly. Using press, install bearing on output shaft with outer race snap ring groove toward rear.

5) Measure 1st and 2nd gear thrust clearance, using feeler gauge. Standard clearance is .0039-.0098" (.10-.25 mm). Maximum clearance is .0118" (.30 mm). Install output shaft into intermediate plate. Before installing shaft, use driver (SST 0908-35013) to remove countergear center bearing outer race. Install output shaft into intermediate plate by pulling output shaft and tapping plate.

6) Install input shaft and countergear together. Using driver (SST 09316-60010), install countergear center bearing outer race. Install bearing snap ring. Be sure snap ring is flush with intermediate plate surface. Install bearing retainer with a torx-type socket. Install reverse gear using installer tool (SST 09312-20010). Install snap ring selected from the following chart.

REVERSE GEAR SNAP RING

Mark On Ring	Thickness In. (mm)
5	.0886-.0906 (2.25-2.30)
11	.0906-.0925 (2.30-2.35)
12	.0925-.0945 (2.35-2.40)
13	.0945-.0965 (2.40-2.45)
14	.0965-.0984 (2.45-2.50)
15	.0984-.1004 (2.50-2.55)
16	.1004-.1024 (2.55-2.60)
17	.1028-.1047 (2.61-2.66)
18	.1051-.1071 (2.67-2.72)
19	.1075-.1094 (2.73-2.78)
20	.1098-.1118 (2.79-2.84)
21	.1122-.1142 (2.85-2.90)
22	.1146-.1165 (2.91-2.96)
23	.1169-.1189 (2.97-3.02)

7) Install 5th gear and output shaft rear bearing using installer (SST 09312-20010). Select snap ring from following chart that will allow minimum axial play and install it on shaft.

OUTPUT SHAFT REAR BEARING SNAP RING

Mark On Ring	Thickness In. (mm)
8	.0909-.0929 (2.31-2.36)
9	.0933-.0953 (2.37-2.42)
10	.0957-.0976 (2.43-2.48)
11	.0980-.1000 (2.49-2.54)
12	.1004-.1024 (2.55-2.60)
13	.1028-.1047 (2.61-2.66)
14	.1055-.1075 (2.68-2.73)
15	.1079-.1098 (2.74-2.79)

8) Install clutch hub No. 3 and shifting key to the hub sleeve. Install shifting key springs under shifting keys. Install key springs so that their end gaps are not in line. Install shifting key retainer using (SST 09238-47012).

9) Install clutch hub No. 3 using driver (SST 09316-60010) while supporting countershaft in front with a 3-5 lb. hammer or equivalent. Select a snap ring from

TOYOTA 5-SPEED — MODEL W58 (Cont.)

following chart that will allow minimum axial play and install it on shaft.

CLUTCH HUB NO. 3 SNAP RING

Mark On Ring	Thickness In. (mm)
2	.0811-.0831 (2.06-2.11)
3	.0835-.0854 (2.12-2.17)
4	.0858-.0878 (2.18-2.23)
5	.0882-.0902 (2.24-2.29)

10) Install bearing spacer. Apply counter 5th gear, synchronizer ring and lubricated needle roller bearings. Install 5th gear assembly with synchronizer ring slots aligned with shifting keys.

11) Using a hammer and socket wrench, drive in spacer and bearing. Support countershaft in front with 3-5 lb. hammer or equivalent. Select a snap ring from following chart that will allow minimum axial play and install it on shaft.

5th GEAR ASSEMBLY SNAP RING

Mark On Ring	Thickness In. (mm)
1	.0748-.0768 (1.90-1.95)
2	.0772-.0791 (1.96-2.01)
3	.0795-.0815 (2.02-2.07)
4	.0819-.0839 (2.08-2.13)
5	.0843-.0862 (2.14-2.19)
6	.0866-.0886 (2.20-2.25)
7	.0890-.0909 (2.26-2.31)

12) Put a clip on output shaft and install speedometer drive gear slot to clip. Slide drive gear with clip into hole. Install reverse idler gear and shaft. Insert lubricated pin into reverse shift fork No. 3 and reverse shift arm. Align shift fork No. 3 to hub sleeve No. 3 groove, put reverse shift arm into pivot of bearing retainer and install shift fork shaft No. 3 to intermediate plate.

13) Install shift fork shaft No. 4 by pushing the pin, which was inserted into reverse shift arm hole, into groove of shift fork shaft No. 3. Install shift fork shaft No. 4 to intermediate plate. Install shift fork shaft No. 4 by aligning pin hole in fork with hole in shaft. Using a pin punch, drive in slotted spring pin until it is flush with fork. Install lubricated interlock pin No. 3 into intermediate plate hole.

14) Install lubricated interlock pin No. 2 to shaft hole. Install shift fork No. 2 into groove of hub sleeve No. 2. Install fork shaft No. 2 to shift fork shaft No. 2 through intermediate plate. Install No. 2 fork shaft snap ring.

15) Install lubricated interlock pin No. 1 into intermediate plate. Install shift fork No. 1 into groove of hub sleeve No. 2. Install fork shaft No. 1 to shift fork shaft No. 1 through intermediate plate. Install No. 1 fork shaft snap ring.

16) Install shift fork set bolts with lock washers. Install 3 springs and 3 locking balls. Install 4 straight screw plugs using socket wrench. Install reverse idler gear shaft stopper and tighten bolt.

17) Remove intermediate plate from vise. Remove the nuts, bolts, plate washers and gaskets. Install transmission case to intermediate plate. Use soft hammer and tap case to install plate.

18) Install 2 bearing snap rings. Install bearing retainer with new gasket. Install and tighten bolts. Install shift lever retainer together with new gasket and tighten bolt. Install back-up light switch wire clamp. Install speedometer driven gear, lock plate and bolt.

EXTENSION HOUSING

1) Put new gasket in position on intermediate plate before installing extension housing. Push shift lever housing forward and, with it turned clockwise, push in extension housing so it is positioned 1.57-1.97" (40-50 mm) from intermidiate plate. Slighty revolve extension housing clockwise and connect select lever to shift fork shaft.

2) With shift lever housing fully turned clockwise, push in extension housing. Install restrict pins (black pin at reverse gear/5th gear side, silver on opposite side) together with a gasket and tighten pins.

CLUTCH HOUSING

Install clutch housing and tighten bolts. Install release fork and bearing. Bearing is held in place by 2 clips.

TIGHTENING SPECIFICATIONS

Application	Ft. Lbs. (N.m)
Clutch Housing Bolts	27 (37)
Extension Housing Bolts	22-32 (30-44)
Front Bearing Retainer	15-21 (20-29)
Idler Gear Shaft Stopper	14-22 (19-30)
Restrict Pins	27-32 (37-44)
Shift Lever Retainer	11-15 (15-20)
Starter Bolts	37-57 (50-78)
Straight Screw Plugs	14-22 (19-30)
Transmission-to-Engine Bolts	37-57 (50-78)

	INCH Lbs. (N.m)
Release Cylinder Bolts	96-132 (11-15)
Shift Fork Set Bolt	96-120 (11-14)
Speedometer Driven Gear Bolt	96-132 (11-15)

Manual Transmissions

TOYOTA TERCEL 4 & 5-SPEED

DESCRIPTION

Transaxle assembly consists of transmission case, transfer case adapter and extension housing with common oil supply. Transmission is fully synchronized in all forward gears.

LUBRICATION & ADJUSTMENT

See the appropriate article in MANUAL TRANS-MISSION SERVICING Section.

SERVICE (IN VEHICLE)

AXLE DRIVE SHAFTS

FRONT

Removal

1) Raise and support vehicle. Remove tire and wheel. Remove cotter pin and lock nut cap. Depress brake pedal and loosen bearing lock nut. Remove brake caliper and suspend caliper from frame. Remove brake disc.

2) Remove cotter pin and nut from tie rod end. Using adapter (SST09610-20012), disconnect tie rod end from the steering knuckle.

3) Mark shock absorber lower bracket and camber adjust cam for reassembly reference. Remove bolts and nuts and disconnect the steering knuckle and shock absorber.

4) Pull off axle hub from drive shaft. Cover boot with cloth to prevent damage. Remove stiffener plate from left side of transaxle assembly and engine.

5) Using support tool (SST09648-16010) and hammer, tap out front drive shaft. After puling out shaft, insert retainer (SST09563-16010)

Fig. 1: Exploded View of Axle Drive Shaft Assembly

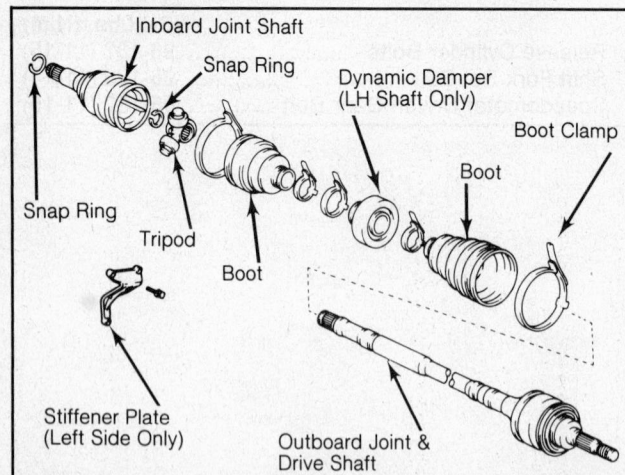

Disassembly

1) Remove snap ring from inboard joint. Check that there is no play in outer joint. Check that inner joint slides smoothly in thrust direction and that there is no remarkable play in radial direction of inner joint.

2) Disassemble boot clamps. Draw alignment marks on inner joint shaft and drive shaft with chalk. Remove inner joint from drive shaft.

3) Using snap ring expander, remove tripod joint snap ring. Using a punch, place alignment marks on

shaft and tripod. Evenly tap tripod joint from drive shaft. DO NOT tap on roller.

4) Remove boot from inner joint. Remove clamp and dynamic damper from left shaft. Remove 2 boot clamps from boot of outer joint. Remove boot from outer joint. DO NOT remove outer joint. Check inside and outside of boot for damage.

Reassembly

1) Wrap vinyl tape around spline of shaft. Slide new boots and clamp onto outer joint. DO NOT tighten clamps at this time. Install dynamic damper and clamp on left shaft. Install boot and clamp for inner joint to drive shaft.

2) Assemble boot clamps onto drive shaft. Place beveled side of tripod onto shaft with beveled splines facing outer joint and align reference marks.

3) Before tapping tripod into final position, align centers of inner and outer joints. See Fig. 2. Using a brass bar and hammer, tap tripod onto drive shaft. Using a snap ring expander, install new snap ring.

4) Pack outer joint with 8 ozs. (240 g) of grease (supplied with boot kit). Install outer boot and tighten clamps.

Fig. 2: Cutaway View Showing Alignment of Inner and Outer CV Joint Centers

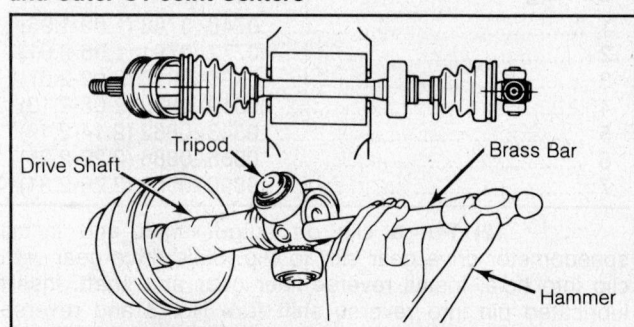

5) Pack inner CV joint with 5 ozs. (140 g) of grease (supplied with boot kit). Align reference marks made at disassembly and install inner joint shaft to drive shaft. Install inner joint boot and tighten clamps.

6) Assemble boot clamps to both boots, ensure that boot is on shaft groove. Bend new clamp on inner joint side around hollow part of cover.

7) Bend band and lock it. Ensure that boot is not stretched or contracted when drive shaft is at standard length. Right axle shaft is 28.50" (724 mm) long. Left shaft is 24.61" (625 mm) long. Install new snap ring to inner joint shaft.

Installation

1) Coat MP grease on drive shaft oil seal lip. Using support (SST09648-16010) and hammer, install drive shaft. Using care not to damage boot and oil seal lip, install hub to drive shaft. Install disc.

2) Lower stablizer bar and assemble steering knuckle to shock absorber lower bracket. Insert bolts from front side and align reference marks on camber adjust cam. Tighten bolts to 105 ft. lbs. (143 N.m).

3) Install brake caliper to steering knuckle. Connect tie rod end to steering knuckle. Tighten castle nut and secure with cotter pin.

4) Depress brake pedal, install and tighten bearing lock nut to 137 ft. lbs. (186 N.m). Install lock nut

TOYOTA TERCEL 4 & 5-SPEED (Cont.)

cap and, using pliers, install cotter pin. Install stiffener plate to engine and transaxle assembly.

5) Check entire circumference of boots for damage. Check that length between left and right shaft is less than 7.626" (193.7 mm). Check front wheel alignment.

REAR
Removal
Raise and support vehicle. Remove wheel and brake drum. Remove 4 backing plate mounting nuts. Using (SST09520-00031), pull out rear axle. Be careful not to damage oil seal.

Disassembly
1) Inspect rear axle shaft and flange for wear, damage or runout. If rear axle shaft or flange are damaged or worn, or if runout is greater than maximum, replace rear axle shaft.

REAR AXLE SHAFT & FLANGE RUNOUT

Application	In. (mm)
Maximum Flange Runout	.008 (0.2 mm)
Maximum Shaft Runout	.079 (2.0 mm)

2) Inspect rear axle bearing for wear or damage. If necessary to replace, use a grinder to grind inner retainer. Using a hammer and chisel, cut off retainer and remove it from shaft. Using bearing remover (SST09527-20011), press bearing off shaft.

3) Inspect oil seal for wear or damage. If necessary to replace, use seal remover (SST09308-00010) to remove seal.

Reassembly
1) Using bearing installer (SST09515-20010), press bearing outer retainer and new bearing on shaft. Heat bearing inner retainer to about 302°F (150°C) in an oil bath.

2) Using retainer installer (SST09515-20010), press retainer on shaft while retainer is still hot. Ensure that there is no oil or grease on rear axle shaft or retainer. Face non-beveled side of inner retainer toward bearing.

3) Apply MP grease to axle housing oil seal. Using seal installer (SST09517-12010), drive in oil seal to a depth of .22" (5.6 mm).

Installation
Install bearing retainer (with notches pointing down) and gasket on axle shaft. Install rear axle in housing and tighten 4 new self-locking nuts to 44-53 ft. lbs. (60-72 N.m). Use care not to damage oil seal or oil deflector inside axle housing. Install brake drum and wheel.

WHEEL BEARINGS
FRONT
Removal
1) Raise and support vehicle. Remove tire and wheel. Remove cotter pin and bearing lock nut cap. Apply brakes and loosen bearing lock nut. Remove brake caliper and suspend from frame with wire.

2) Remove cotter pin and nut from tie rod end. Disconnect and remove tie rod end with remover (SST09610-20012). Place alignment marks on shock absorber lower bracket and camber adjust cam. Remove bolt and nut and separate steering knuckle and shock absorber.

3) Remove 2 bolts holding ball joint to steering knuckle. Pull off axle hub from drive shaft. Cover drive shaft boot with cloth. Using driver, remove dust deflector.

4) Using seal remover (SST09308-00010), pull oil seal out of steering knuckle. Using snap ring pliers, remove hole snap ring. Remove brake dust cover set bolts. Using hub remover (SST09950-20014), push axle hub off steering knuckle.

5) Remove outer oil seal and bearing inner race (inner) from bearing. Using (SST09950-20014), pull off bearing inner race (outer) from axle hub. Remove disc brake dust cover.

6) Using seal remover (SST09308-00010), pull oil seal out of steering knuckle. Install inner race (outer side) of bearing to be removed. Using bearing remover (SST09228-22020 and 09950-20014), press out bearing.

Installation
1) Using a press and bearing installer (SST09309-35010), press new bearing into steering knuckle. Note that there are 2 types of bearings available, KOYO and NSK.

2) Install bearing inner race (outer side) before installing new oil seal. Using seal installer (SST09515-35010), drive new oil seal into steering knuckle.

3) Apply liquid sealer to disc brake dust cover and steering knuckle. Install dust cover. Install inner races into inner bearing. Using installer (SST09228-22020 and 09310-35010), press in inner race until it is tightly against shoulder of hub.

NOTE: DO NOT interchange inner and outer race when installing.

4) Using snap ring pliers, install hole snap ring into steering knuckle. Using seal installer (SST09309-35010), drive new oil seal into steering knuckle. Tap in .126-.134" (3.2-3.3 mm) from end surface.

Fig. 3: Installing Inner Oil Seal

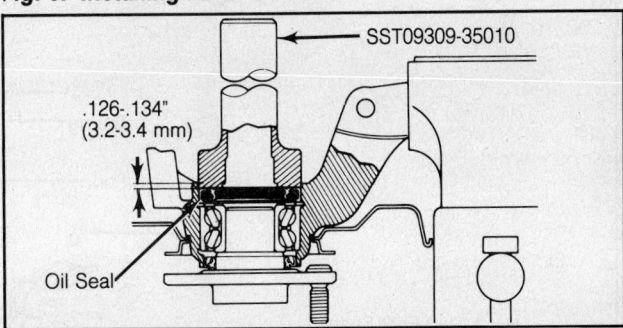

5) Using driver (SST09316-60010), drive new dust deflector into steering knuckle. Install steering knuckle with axle hub to lower arm and tighten to 59 ft. lbs. (80 N.m).

6) Using care not to damage drive shaft boot and oil seal lip, install axle hub to drive shaft. Install lower stabilizer bar and assemble steering knuckle to shock absorber lower bracket.

7) Insert bolts from front side and align marks of camber adjust cam. Tighten bolts to 105 ft. lbs. (143 N.m). Install disc to hub. Install brake caliper to steering knuckle and tighten bolts.

8) Connect tie rod end to steering knuckle and tighten castle nut. Install cotter pin. Depress brake pedal. Install and tighten bearing lock nut to 137 ft. lbs. (186 N.m). Install adjusting nut cap and cotter pin. Check front wheel alignment.

Manual Transmissions

TOYOTA TERCEL 4 & 5-SPEED (Cont.)

Fig. 4: *Exploded View of Transaxle Components*

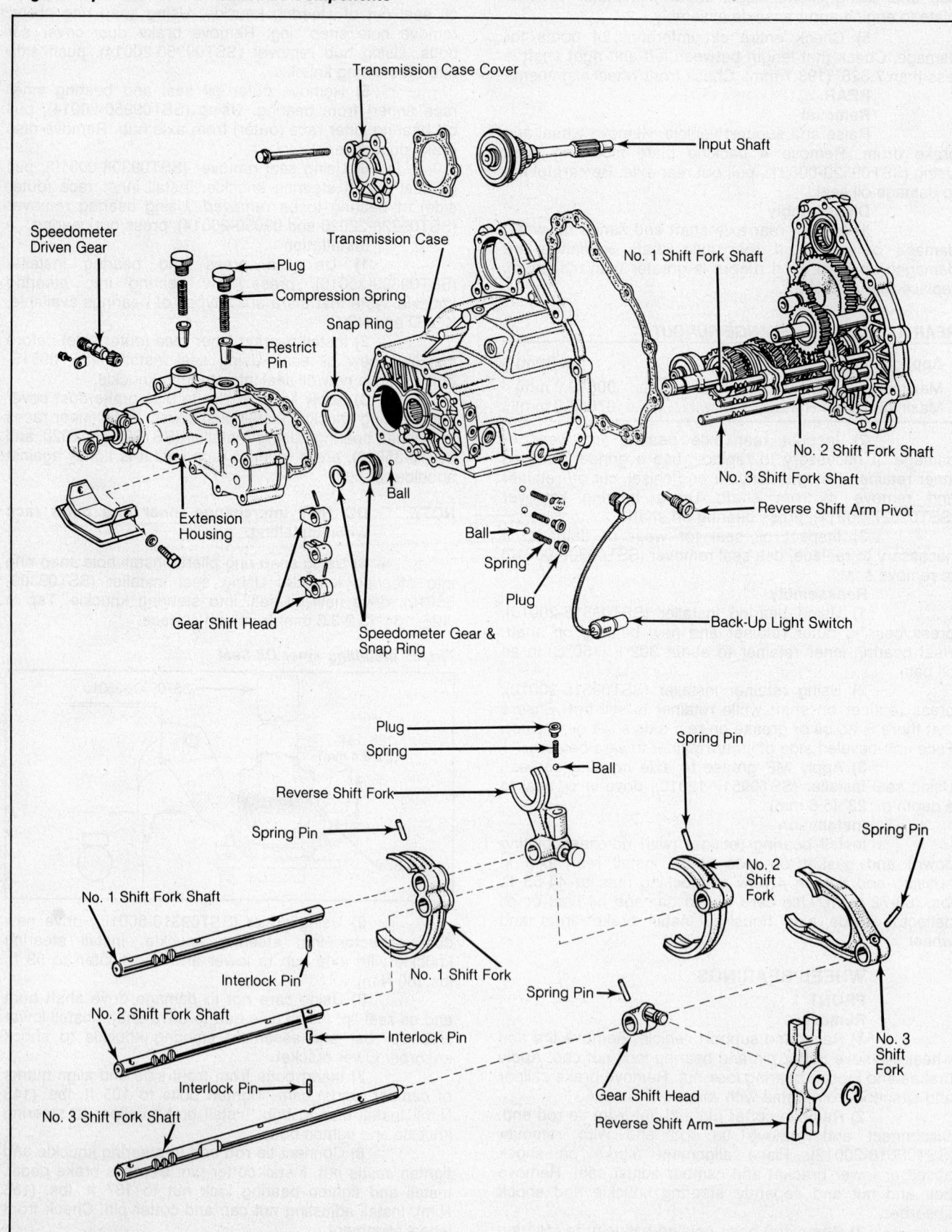

TOYOTA TERCEL 4 & 5-SPEED (Cont.)

Fig. 5: *Exploded View of Transaxle Gears*

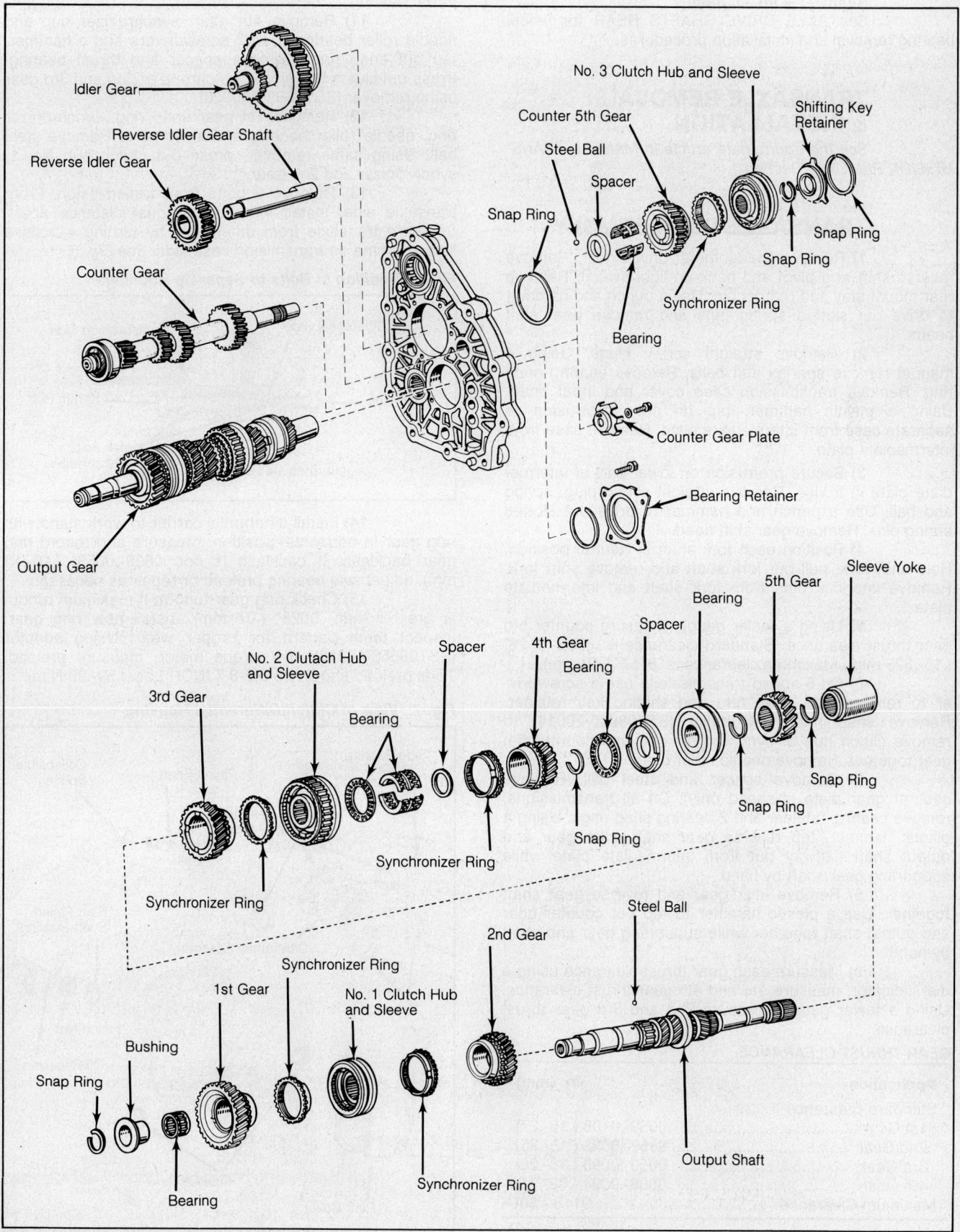

TOYOTA TERCEL 4 & 5-SPEED (Cont.)

REAR
Removal & Installation
See AXLE DRIVE SHAFTS REAR for wheel bearing removal and installation procedures.

TRANSAXLE REMOVAL & INSTALLATION
See the appropriate article in MANUAL TRANSMISSION REMOVAL Section.

TRANSAXLE DISASSEMBLY

1) Remove speedometer driven gear. Remove reverse shift arm pivot and back-up light switch. Remove rear mount stay and restrict pin. Use a punch and hammer to drive out slotted spring pins and remove gear shift heads.

2) Remove straight screw plugs. Using a magnet remove springs and balls. Remove bearing snap ring. Remove transmission case cover and input shaft. Using a plastic hammer, tap on case protrusion to separate case from intermediate plate. Remove case from intermediate plate.

3) Secure protrusion on lower part of intermediate plate in a vise. Remove straight screw plug, spring and ball. Use a punch and hammer to drive out slotted spring pins. Remove gear shift head.

4) Position each fork shaft in Neutral position. Hold shift fork, pull out fork shaft and remove shift fork. Remove interlock pins from fork shaft and intermediate plate.

5) Using a feeler gauge, measure counter 5th gear thrust clearance. Standard clearance is .0059-.0128" (.15-.325 mm). Maximum clearance is .0157" (.40 mm).

6) On 5-speed transmissions use a screwdriver to remove hole snap ring and shifting key retainer. Remove snap ring. Use puller (SST09950-20014) to remove clutch hub 3, synchronizer ring and counter 5th gear together. Remove needle roller bearing.

7) Remove spacer and steel ball. Remove counter gear plate (4-speed only). On all transmissions, remove bearing retainer and 2 bearing snap rings. Using a plastic hammer, tap reverse gear shaft, idler gear and output shaft halfway out from intermediate plate while supporting gear shaft by hand.

8) Remove idler gear and reverse gear shaft together. Use a plastic hammer to tap out counter gear and output shaft together while supporting gear and shaft by hand.

9) Measure each gear thrust clearance using a dial indicator, measure 1st and 4th gear thrust clearance. Using a feeler gauge, measure 2nd and 3rd gear thrust clearance.

GEAR THRUST CLEARANCE

Application	In. (mm)
Standard Clearance	
1st Gear	.0059-.0108 (.15-.27)
2nd Gear	.0059-.0098 (.15-.25)
3rd Gear	.0059-.0098 (.15-.25)
4th Gear	.0008-.0094 (.02-.24)
Maximum Clearance	.0118 (.30)

10) Using remover (SST09950-00020), press out sleeve yoke, remove snap ring and press out 5th gear, remove snap ring and press out bearing, spacer and thrust bearing.

11) Remove 4th gear, synchronizer ring and needle roller bearing. Use 2 screwdrivers and a hammer, tap out snap ring. Remove spacer and thrust bearing. Press out clutch hub No. 2, synchronizer ring and 3rd gear using remover (SST09950-00020).

12) Remove 1st gear snap ring, synchronizer ring, needle roller bearing and inner race. Remove steel ball. Using same remover, press out clutch hub No. 1, synchronizer ring and 2nd gear.

13) Remove 9 bolts from transmission. From transaxle side, install 4 bolts an equal distance apart. Separate transaxle from differential by turning 4 bolts a little at a time on transmision case side. *See Fig. 6.*

Fig. 6: Position of Bolts to Separate Housings

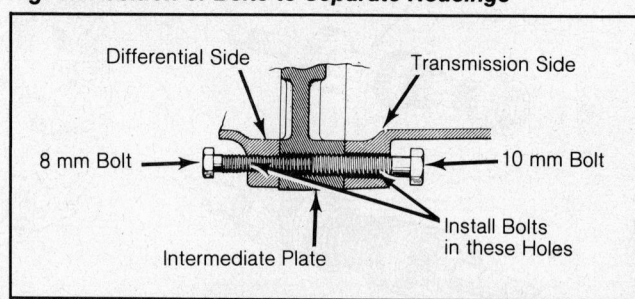

14) Install differential carrier to work stand with ring gear in horizontal position. Measure and record ring gear backlash. If backlash is not .0039-.0059" (.10-.15 mm), adjust side bearing preload or repair as necessary.

15) Check ring gear runout. If maximum runout is greater than .0028" (.07 mm), install new ring gear. Inspect teeth pattern for proper wear. Using adaptor (SST09556-16010) and torque meter, measure preload. Total preload should be 5.2-8.7 INCH Lbs. (.59-.98 N.m).

Fig. 7: View of Clutch/Differential Housing

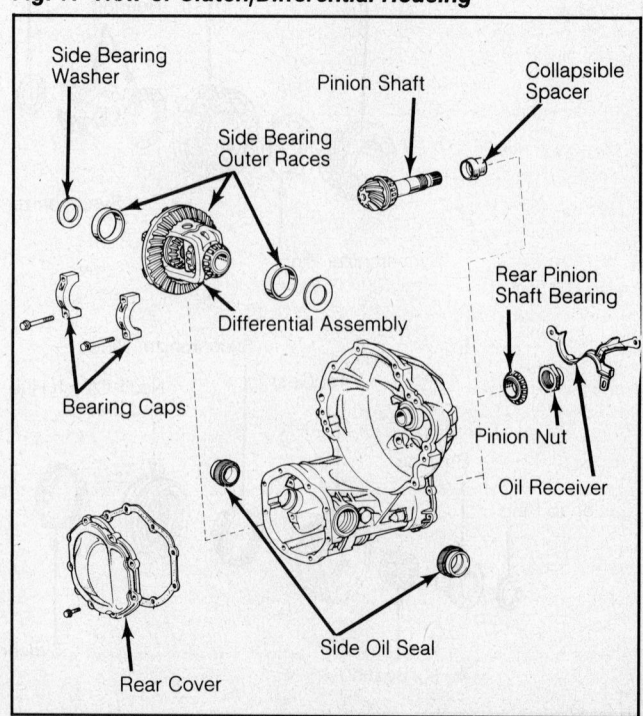

TOYOTA TERCEL 4 & 5-SPEED (Cont.)

16) Using remover (SST09308-00010), remove oil seals from differential carrier. Remove side bearing caps. Tag bearing cap, outer race and side washer to show reassembly location.

17) Using remover (SST09504-22010), remove side washer on ring gear teeth side. Remove differential case and bearing outer race. Remove side washer and oil reservoir.

18) Loosen staked part of drive pinion nut. Using remover (SST09556-16010), loosen nut and turn drive pinion clockwise. Using press, remove drive pinion.

COMPONENT INSPECTION & REPAIR

DIFFERENTIAL DRIVE PINION BEARINGS & OUTER RACES

1) If bearings or races ar worn or damaged, use remover (SST09950-00020) to press out rear bearing from drive pinion. Install plate washer with one of same thickness as was assembled.

2) Using installer (SST09608-2011) and press, install bearing. Using a hammer and brass bar, remove outer race by tapping on notched portion. Using installer (SST09608-30011 for front and SST09608-30021 for rear) and hammer, install new outer race.

DIFFERENTIAL SIDE BEARINGS & OUTER RACES

Using remover (SST09502-10012), remove side bearing from differential case. Using installer (SST09608-20011) and press, install new bearing.

DIFFERENTIAL PINION & SIDE GEARS

1) Measure side gear backlash while holding another side gear toward the case. Standard backlash is .0016-.0094" (.04-.24 mm). If necessary, replace ring gear, differential pinions and side gears.

2) Lift lock plates and remove set bolts. Using a brass bar and hammer, tap on ring gear to separate it from differential case. If ring gear is to be reused, place alignment marks before separating it. If ring gear or drive pinion are damaged, replace them as a set.

3) Using a pin punch and hammer, tap out straight pin toward ring gear installation surface. Remove pinion shaft, pinion gears, side gears and thrust washers. Check gears, shaft, case and washers. Install side gears, washers, pinion gears and shaft.

4) Measure side gear backlash while holding another side gear toward the case. Standard backlash is .0016-.0094" (.04-.24 mm). If backlash is not within specifications, use different thickness thrust washers. Washers are available in sizes from .0583-.0598" (1.48-1.52 mm) to .0681-.0697" (1.73-1.77 mm) in .0020" (.05 mm) increments.

5) Using a hammer and punch, drive straight pin through case and hole in pinion shaft. Stake pin and differential case. Clean contact surface of differential case. Heat ring gear to 194-230°F (90-110°C) in an oil bath. Quickly install ring gear on differential case.

6) Coat ring gear set bolts with gear oil. Install lock plates and set bolts. Tighten bolts, a little at a time, to 67-75 ft. lbs. (91-102 N.m). Stake lock plate.

INPUT SHAFT & REAR BEARING

1) Check for wear or damage. If bearing is worn or damaged, replace it. Using snap ring pliers, remove snap ring. Using remover (SST09950-00020), press out bearing.

2) Using press and remover (SST09515-20010), press in bearing. Ensure that outer race groove is facing toward rear. Select a snap ring that allows minimum axial play and install it on the shaft. Snap rings are available in .0827-.0846" (2.10-2.15 mm) and .0886-.0906" (2.25-2.30 mm) sizes.

IDLER GEAR BEARING

1) Check for wear or damage. If bearing is worn or damaged, replace it. Using snap ring pliers, remove snap ring. Using remover (SST09950-00020), press out bearing.

2) Using a press and remover (ST09506-30011), press in bearing. Ensure that outer race groove is facing toward front. Select a snap ring that allows minimum axial play and install it on the shaft. Snap rings are available in .0945-.0965" (2.40-2.45 mm) and .1004-.1024" (2.55-2.60 mm) sizes.

1ST GEAR

Using a dial indicator, measure oil clearance between gear and inner race with needle roller bearing installed. Standard clearance is .0004-.0024" (.009-.060 mm).

2ND & 3RD GEAR

Using a dial indicator, measure oil clearance between gear and output shaft. Standard clearance is .0024-.0039" (.06-.10 mm). Maximum clearance is .0043" (.11 mm).

SYNCHRONIZER RINGS

Check for wear or damage. Turn ring and push it in to check braking action. Using a feeler gauge, measure clearance between synchronizer ring back and gear spline end. Minimum clearance is .024" (.60 mm).

SHIFT FORKS & HUB SLEEVES

Using a feeler gauge, measure clearance between hub sleeve and shift fork. Maximum clearance is .039" (1.0 mm).

COUNTER GEAR & REAR BEARING

1) Check gear teeth and bearing for wear or damage. If bearing is worn or damaged, replace it. Remove snap ring. Using a press and remover (SST09950-00020), press out bearing.

2) Using a press and remover (SST09515-20010), press in bearing. Ensure that outer race groove is facing toward the rear. Select a snap ring that will allow minimum axial play and install it on the shaft. Snap rings are available in 2 thicknesses, .0709-.0728" (1.80-1.85 mm) and .0768-.0787 (1.95-2.0 mm).

SELECT LEVER OIL SEAL

Check oil seal for wear or damage. If oil seal is worn or damaged, use a screwdriver to pry it out. Using installer (SST09304-30012), drive in new oil seal.

Manual Transmissions

TOYOTA TERCEL 4 & 5-SPEED (Cont.)

INPUT SHAFT FRONT BEARING & OIL SEAL

1) Check for wear or damage. If bearing is worn or damaged, replace it. Using a screwdriver and hammer, drive out oil seal. Remove lock plate.

2) Using remove/installer (SST09608-30021), drive out old bearing and drive in new bearing. Ensure that outer race groove is facing upward. Install lock plate. Using remover/installer, drive in oil seal.

COUNTER GEAR CENTER BEARING

Check for wear or damage. Replace as necessary. Using remover/installer (SST097100-30020) and press, press out old bearing and press in new bearing.

IDLER GEAR REAR BEARING

Check for wear or damage and replace as necessary. Remove oil receiver. Using remover (SST09612-10091), remove bearing. Using installer (SST09304-47010) and hammer, drive in bearing. Install oil receiver.

OUTPUT SHAFT REAR BEARING

Check for wear or damage and replace as necessary. Remove oil receiver. Using remover/installer (SST09304-47010) and hammer, drive out old bearing and drive in new bearing. Install oil receiver.

COUNTER GEAR FRONT BEARING

Check for wear or damage and replace as necessary. Using removers (SST09310-36021 and SST09612-10091), remove the bearing (5-speed only). Using installer (SST09304-47010) and hammer, drive in bearing until it is level with end surface of transaxle case.

EXTENSION HOUSING OIL SEAL & BUSHING

1) Check for wear or damage and replace as necessary. Check sliding action of lever. Using a plastic hammer, lightly tap in lever lock pin.

2) Remove oil seal. Using seal installer (SST09304-12012), drive in new oil seal. Install lever lock pin, aligning its notch with groove of shift lever shaft.

SPEEDOMETER GEAR OIL SEAL

Check for wear or damage and replace as necessary. Using remover (SST09921-00010), remove oil seal. Using installer (SST09201-60011), install new oil seal.

TRANSAXLE REASSEMBLY & ADJUSTMENT

1) Install new spacer to differential drive pinion. Install drive pinion to differential carrier. Using installer (SST09612-22010) and press, temporarily press in bearing until threaded portion is protruding .12" (3 mm) from carrier.

2) Apply gear oil onto threaded portion of drive pinion. Using tools (SST09564-16010 and 09556-16010), tighten nut to 108 ft. lbs. (147 N.m). Apply gear oil onto bearings.

3) Using adaptor (SST09556-16010), snug down bearing by turning drive pinion several times. Using adaptor and torque meter, measure differential drive pinion preload. Preload for new bearing is 4.3-8.7 INCH Lbs. (.49-.99 N.m).

4) If preload is not correct, tighten nut to 108 ft. lbs. (147 N.m). Remeasure preload. If excessive, replace spacer. If insufficient, increase tightening 5-10° at a time and remeasure each time.

5) If preload is insufficient even after specified torque range is exceeded, loosen nut and tighten to 268 ft. lbs. (364 N.m). If preload is still not correct, replace spacer.

6) Set transaxle case with back side of ring gear facing down. Install differential case. Install only side washer on ring gear back side. Ensure that ring gear has backlash. Snug down washer and bearings by tapping on ring gear with a plastic hammer.

7) Push side bearing boss on teeth surface of ring gear and measure backlash. If backlash is not .0039" (.10 mm), select a ring gear back side washer using backlash as a reference.

DIFFERENTIAL RING GEAR BACK SIDE WASHER SELECTION

I.D. No.	Thickness In. (mm)
1	.1028-.1035 (2.61-2.63)
2	.1039-.1047 (2.64-2.66)
3	.1051-.1059 (2.67-2.69)
4	.1063-.1071 (2.70-2.72)
5	.1075-.1083 (2.73-2.75)
6	.1087-.1094 (2.76-2.78)
7	.1098-.1106 (2.79-2.81)
8	.1110-.1118 (2.82-2.84)
9	.1122-.1130 (2.85-2.87)
10	.1134-.1142 (2.88-2.90)
11	.1146-.1154 (2.91-2.93)
12	.1157-.1165 (2.94-2.96)
13	.1169-.1177 (2.97-2.99)
14	.1181-.1189 (3.00-3.02)
15	.1193-.1201 (3.03-3.05)
16	.1205-.1213 (3.06-3.08)
17	.1217-.1224 (3.09-3.11)
18	.1228-.1236 (3.12-3.14)
19	.1240-.1248 (3.15-3.17)
20	.1252-.1260 (3.18-3.20)
21	.1264-.1272 (3.21-3.23)
22	.1276-.1283 (3.24-3.26)
23	.1287-.1295 (3.27-3.29)

8) Select a ring gear teeth side washer of a thickness which eliminates any clearance between outer race and case. Remove side washers and differential case. Install side washer into lower part of case.

9) Place other side washer onto differential case. Install differential case with outer race into transaxle case. Using a plastic hammer, snug down washer and bearing by tapping ring gear.

10) Using dial indicator, measure ring gear backlash. If backlash is not .0039-.0059" (.10-.15 mm), adjust by either increasing or decreasing number of washers on both sides by an equal amount. There should be no clearance between side washer and case and there should be ring gear backlash.

11) After adjustment, using backlash as reference, remove ring gear teeth side washer and measure thickness. Install a new washer .0024-.0035" (.06-.09 mm) thicker than washer removed. Select a washer that can be pressed in 2/3 of the way by finger.

12) Using a plastic hammer, tap in side washer. Recheck ring gear backlash. If still not correct,

TOYOTA TERCEL 4 & 5-SPEED (Cont.)

adjust by either increasing and decreasing the washers on both sides by an equal amount. Install side bearing caps and tighten bolts to 33-39 ft. lbs. (45-53 N.m).

Fig. 8: Measuring Ring Gear Backlash

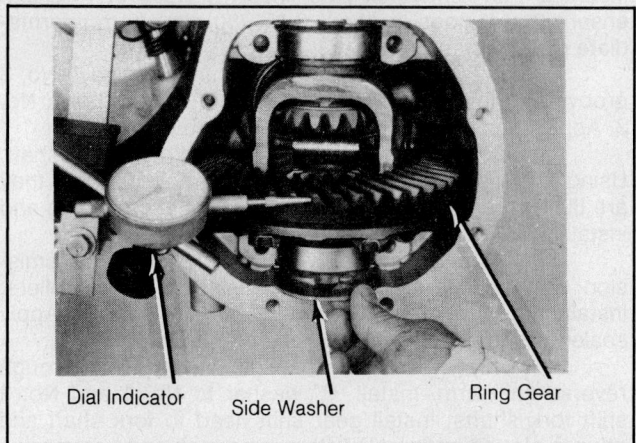

Dial Indicator   Side Washer   Ring Gear

13) Apply gear oil on the bearings. Using adaptor (SST09556-16010), turn drive pinion left and right several times. Using adaptor and torque meter, measure total preload. Preload should be 2.6-4.3 INCH Lbs. (.29-.49 N.m) in addition to drive pinion preload. If not, readjust ring gear teeth side washer.

14) Using dial indicator, measure ring gear backlash at 3 places on outer circumference of ring gear. Backlash should be .0039-.0059" (.10-.15 mm). If not, adjust by either increasing or decreasing washers on both sides by equal amount.

15) Using a chisel, stake drive pinion lock nut. Using installer (SST09223-46011) and hammer, install new differential carrier oil seal. Ensure that distance "A" is .331-.354" (8.4-9.0 mm). See Fig. 9.

Fig. 9: Installing Differential Carrier Oil Seal

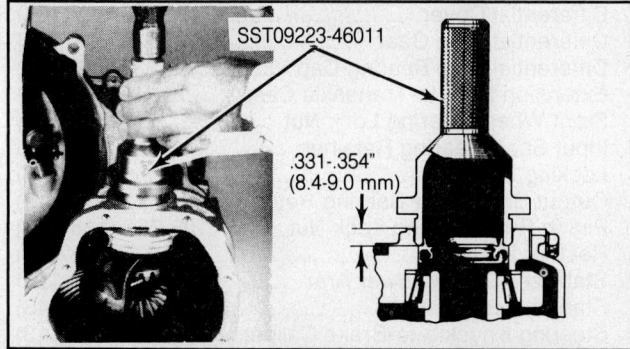

SST09223-46011

.331-.354"
(8.4-9.0 mm)

16) Install differential carrier cover and gasket. Tighten set bolts to 96-132 INCH Lbs. (11-15 N.m). Install oil reservoir.

17) Install clutch hub and shifting keys to hub sleeve. Install shifting key springs under shifting keys. Ensure that key springs are positioned so that end gaps are not in line.

18) Apply gear oil to output shaft. Place synchronizer ring on 2nd gear and align ring slots with shifting keys. Using installer (SST09515-30010) and a press, install 2nd gear and clutch hub No. 1.

19) Install locking ball in shaft. Apply gear oil to needle roller bearing. Assemble 1st gear, synchronizer ring, needle roller bearing and inner race.

20) Place synchronizer ring on 1st gear and align ring slots with shifting keys. Fit inner race groove securely over locking ball. Select a snap ring that allows minimum axial play and install on output shaft.

OUTPUT SHAFT SNAP RING SELECTION

I.D. Mark	Thickness In. (mm)
1	.0846-.0866 (2.15-2.20)
2	.0866-.0886 (2.20-2.25)
3	.0886-.0906 (2.25-2.30)
4	.0906-.0925 (2.30-2.35)
5	.0925-.0945 (2.35-2.40)
6	.0945-.0965 (2.40-2.45)
7	.0965-.0984 (2.45-2.50)
8	.0984-.1004 (2.50-2.55)
9	.1004-.1024 (2.55-2.60)

21) Using a dial indicator, measure 1st gear thrust clearance. Using a feeler gauge, measure 2nd gear thrust clearance.

1ST & 2ND GEAR THRUST CLEARANCE

Application	In. (mm)
Standard Clearance	
1st Gear	.0059-.0108 (.15-.27)
2nd Gear	.0059-.0098 (.15-.25)
Maximum Clearance	.0118 (.30)

22) Install shifting keys and key springs to No. 2 clutch hub. Install clutch hub to hub sleeve. Apply gear oil to output shaft. Place synchronizer on 3rd gear and align ring slots with shifting keys.

23) Using installer (SST09515-30010) and a press, install 3rd gear and clutch hub No. 2. Assemble widest thrust bearing to No. 2 clutch hub.

24) Apply gear oil and install 4th gear needle roller bearing and synchronizer. Line up shifting keys with key slots in synchronizer ring. Install spacer and tap in snap ring.

25) Stick thrust bearing onto spacer with MP grease. Using installer (SST09612-22010) and press, install spacer. Using installer and press, install output shaft front bearing. Ensure that outer race groove is facing toward front. Select snap ring that allows minimum axial play and install it on output shaft.

OUTPUT SHAFT SNAP RING SELECTION

I.D. Mark	Thickness In. (mm)
2	.0827-.0846 (2.10-2.15)
3	.0846-.0866 (2.15-2.20)
4	.0866-.0886 (2.20-2.25)
5	.0886-.0906 (2.25-2.30)
6	.0906-.0925 (2.30-2.35)
7	.0925-.0945 (2.35-2.40)
8	.0945-.0965 (2.40-2.45)
9	.0965-.0984 (2.45-2.50)
10	.0984-.1004 (2.50-2.55)

26) Using a feeler gauge, measure 3rd gear thrust clearance. Using a dial indicator, measure 4th gear thrust clearance.

Manual Transmissions

TOYOTA TERCEL 4 & 5-SPEED (Cont.)

3RD & 4TH GEAR THRUST CLEARANCE

Application	In. (mm)
Standard Clearance	
3rd Gear	.0059-.0098 (.15-.25)
4th Gear	.0008-.0094 (.02-.24)
Maximum Clearance	.0118 (.30)

27) Using an installer (SST09612-22010) and press, install 5th gear. Select and install a snap ring that allows minimum axial play and install it on output shaft. Using a press, install sleeve yoke.

5TH GEAR SNAP RING SELECTION

I.D. Mark	In. (mm)
2	.0827-.0846 (2.10-2.15)
3	.0846-.0866 (2.15-2.20)
4	.0866-.0886 (2.20-2.25)
5	.0886-.0906 (2.25-2.30)
6	.0906-.0925 (2.30-2.35)

28) Mount intermediate plate in vise by securing lower portrusion. Using a plastic hammer, tap in output shaft and counter gear together about halfway. Align idler with notched portion of reverse idler gear shaft.

29) Using plastic hammer, tap in idler gear shaft bearing about halfway. Ensure that idler gear and output shaft spacer are not contacting each other. Using a plastic hammer, tap each gear shaft until bearing is in as far as possible.

30) Using snap ring pliers, install 2 snap rings. Install bearing retainer and tighten bolts to 108 INCH Lbs. (12 N.m). On 4-speed transmissions, install counter gear plate and tighten bolt to 108 INCH Lbs. (12 N.m). On 5-speed transmissions, install steel ball in shaft. Align spacer groove with steel ball and install spacer.

31) Install clutch hub No. 3 and shifting keys to hub sleeve. Install shifting key springs under shifting keys with key end gaps not in line. Apply gear oil to 5th gear needle roller bearing.

32) Install counter 5th gear, needle roller bearing and synchronizer ring on shaft. Using installer (SST09612-222010) and press, install clutch hub. Line up shifting keys with key slots in synchronizer ring.

33) Select a snap ring that allows minimum axial play and install it on shaft. Snap rings are available in sizes from .0709-.0728" (1.80-1.85 mm) to .0827-.0846" (2.10-2.15 mm) with .0020" (.05 mm) increments. Using a feeler gauge, measure 5th counter gear thrust clearance.

5TH COUNTER GEAR THRUST CLEARANCE

Application	In. (mm)
Standard Clearance	.0059-.0128 (.15-.32)
Maximum Clearance	.0157 (.40)

34) Install shifting key retainer and hole snap ring. On all transmissions, insert shift fork shaft No. 1 through shift fork No. 1 and reverse shift fork. Align reverse shift fork into reverse gear groove, align shift fork No. 1 with hub sleeve No. 1 groove and install shift fork shaft No. 1 through intermediate plate.

35) Align shift fork No. 2 into hub sleeve No. 2 groove. Install shift fork shaft No. 2 to intermediate plate through shift forks No. 1 and No. 2. Insert shift fork shaft No. 3 to gear shift head and install so pin hole of shift fork shaft No. 3 aligns with interlock pin hole.

36) Insert piece of wire into interlock pin hole and confirm that it goes in about 4.72" (120 mm) from intermediate plate circumference. Coat interlock pins with MP grease and push them in with a piece of wire. After inserting the 3 interlock pins, insert a piece of wire and ensure that it goes in about 3.15" (80 mm) from intermediate plate circumference.

37) Align shift fork No. 3 into hub sleeve No. 3 groove and insert shift fork shaft No. 3 into shift fork No. 3. Apply sealer to straight screw plug and install it.

38) Align pin hole in fork with hole in shaft. Using a pin punch, drive in slotted spring pins until they are flush with fork. Apply sealer to straight screw plug and install it with spring and ball.

39) Apply sealer to gasket and install transmission case to intermediate plate. Using snap ring pliers, install snap ring. Install 3 locking balls and springs. Apply sealer to straight screw plugs and install them.

40) Insert reverse shift arm pivot through reverse shift arm. Install "C" washer to No. 1 and No. 2 shift fork shafts. Install gear shift head to fork shaft and drive in slotted spring pin with a pin punch and hammer.

41) Install speedometer drive gear, steel ball and snap ring. Align end of shift lever shaft and gear shift head No. 2 and install extension housing. Tighten bolts to 19 ft. lbs. (26 N.m).

42) Install locking ball and spring. Install transmission case cover and tighten bolts. Install shift lever retainer and tighten bolt.

43) Install restrict pins to extension housing. Note that Green pin is located on 1st and 2nd gear and Yellow pin is located on 5th and reverse gear. Install speedometer driven gear, extension housing mount stay and back-up light switch. Install transmission case cover.

TIGHTENING SPECIFICATIONS

Application	Ft. Lbs. (N.m)
Counter Gear Plate (4-Speed)	9 (12)
Differential Cover	8-11 (11-15)
Differential Ring Gear	67-75 (91-102)
Differential Side Bearing Cap	33-39 (45-53)
Extension Hsg.-to-Transaxle Case	19 (26)
Front Wheel Bearing Lock Nut	137 (186)
Input Shaft Bearing Retainer	15-21 (20-28)
Locking Ball Plug	16 (22)
Output Shaft Rear Bearing Retainer	9 (12)
Pinion Rear Bearing Lock Nut	109-267 (148-362)
Restrict Pin Plug	27-32 (37-43)
Stabilizer Bar-to-Lower Arm	66-90 (89-122)
Stabilizer Bracket	32 (43)
Steering Knuckle-to-Brake Caliper	57-83 (77-113)
Steering Knuckle-to-Lower Arm	59 (80)
Steering Knuckle-to-Shock Absorber	105 (142)
Steering Knuckle-to-Tie Rod End	29-43 (39-58)
Transaxle-to-Transmission	18 (24)
Transaxle-to-Engine	37-57 (50-77)

TOYOTA TERCEL 6-SPEED

DESCRIPTION

Transaxle assembly consists of transmission case, transfer case adapter and extension housing with common oil supply. Tramsmission is fully synchronized in all forward gears.

LUBRICATION & ADJUSTMENT

See the appropriate article in MANUAL TRANS-MISSION SERVICING Section.

SERVICE (IN VEHICLE)

AXLE DRIVE SHAFTS
FRONT
Removal

1) Raise and support vehicle. Remove tire and wheel. Remove cotter pin and lock nut cap. Depress brake pedal and loosen bearing lock nut. Remove brake caliper and suspend caliper from frame. Remove brake disc.

2) Remove cotter pin and nut from tie rod end. Using adapter (SST09610-20012), disconnect tie rod end from the steering knuckle.

3) Mark shock absorber lower bracket and camber adjust cam for reassembly reference. Remove bolts and nuts and disconnect the steering knuckle and shock absorber.

4) Pull off axle hub from drive shaft. Cover boot with cloth to prevent damage. Remove stiffener plate from left side of transaxle assembly and engine. 5) Using support tool (SST09648-16010) and hammer, tap out front drive shaft. After puling out shaft, insert retainer (SST09563-16010)

Fig. 1: Exploded View of Axle Drive Shaft Assembly

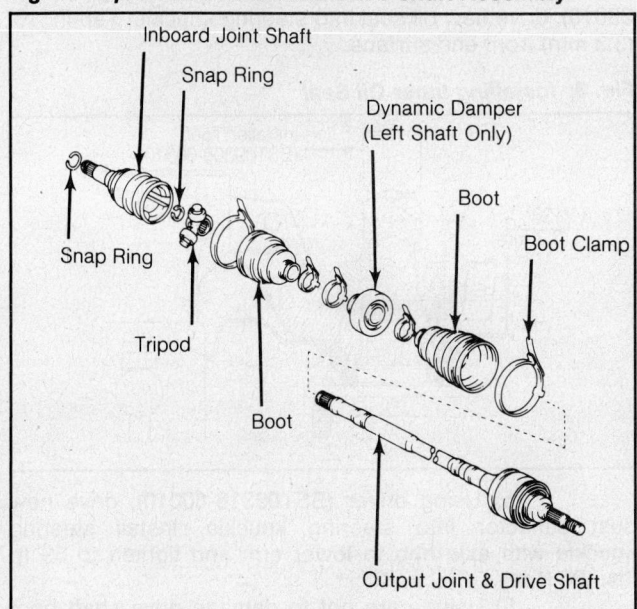

Disassembly

1) Remove snap ring from inboard joint. Check that there is no play in outer joint. Check that inner joint slides smoothly in thrust direction and that there is no remarkable play in radial direction of inner joint.

2) Disassemble boot clamps. Draw alignment marks on inner joint shaft and drive shaft with chalk. Remove inner joint from drive shaft.

3) Using snap ring expander, remove tripod joint snap ring. Using a punch, place alignment marks on shaft and tripod. Evenly tap tripod joint from drive shaft. Do not tap on roller.

4) Remove boot from inner joint. Remove clamp and dynamic damper from left shaft. Remove 2 boot clamps from boot of outer joint. Remove boot from outer joint. Do not remove outer joint. Check inside and outside of boot for damage.

Reassembly

1) Wrap vinyl tape around spline of shaft. Slide new boots and clamp onto outer joint. Do not tighten clamps at this time. Install dynamic damper and clamp on left shaft. Install boot and clamp for inner joint to drive shaft.

2) Assemble boot clamps onto drive shaft. Place beveled side of tripod onto shaft with beveled splines facing outer joint and align reference marks.

3) Before tapping tripod into final position, align centers of inner and outer joints. *See Fig. 2.* Using a brass bar and hammer, tap tripod onto drive shaft. Using a snap ring expander, install new snap ring.

4) Pack outer joint with 8 ozs. (240 g) of grease (supplied with boot kit). Install outer boot and tighten clamps.

Fig. 2: Cutaway View Showing Alignment of Inner and Outer CV Joint Centers

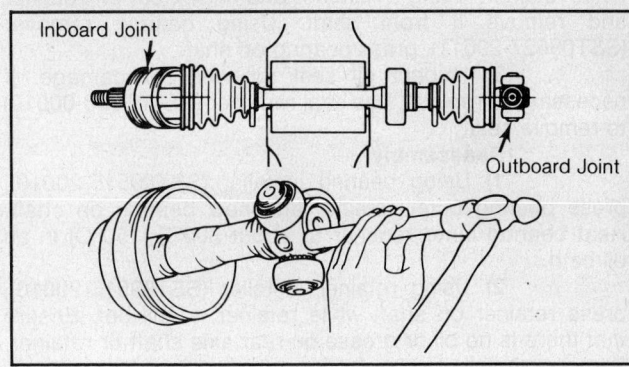

5) Pack inner CV joint with 5 ozs. (140 g) of grease (supplied with boot kit). Align reference marks made at disassembly and install inner joint shaft to drive shaft. Install inner joint boot and tighten clamps.

6) Assemble boot clamps to both boots, ensure that boot is on shaft groove. Bend new clamp on inner joint side around hollow part of cover.

7) Bend band and lock it. Ensure that boot is not stretched or contracted when drive shaft is at standard length. Right axle shaft is 28.50" (724 mm) long. Left shaft is 24.61" (625 mm) long. Install new snap ring to inner joint shaft.

Installation

1) Coat MP grease on drive shaft oil seal lip. Using support (SST09648-16010) and hammer, install drive shaft. Using care not to damage boot and oil seal lip, install hub to drive shaft. Install disc.

2) Lower stablizer bar and assemble steering knuckle to shock absorber lower bracket. Insert bolts from front side and align reference marks on camber adjust cam. Tighten bolts to 105 ft. lbs. (143 N.m).

Manual Transmissions

TOYOTA TERCEL 6-SPEED (Cont.)

3) Install brake caliper to steering knuckle. Connect tie rod end to steering knuckle. Tighten castle nut and secure with cotter pin.

4) Depress brake pedal, install and tighten bearing lock nut to 137 ft. lbs. (186 N.m). Install lock nut cap and, using pliers, install cotter pin. Install stiffener plate to engine and transaxle assembly.

5) Check entire circumference of boots for damage. Check that length between left and right shaft is less than 7.626" (193.7 mm). Check front wheel alignment.

REAR
Removal

Raise and support vehicle. Remove wheel and brake drum. Remove 4 backing plate mounting nuts. Using (SST09520-00031), pull out rear axle. Be careful not to damage oil seal.

Disassembly

1) Inspect rear axle shaft and flange for wear, damage or runout. If rear axle shaft or flange are damaged or worn, or if runout is greater than maximum, replace rear axle shaft.

REAR AXLE SHAFT & FLANGE RUNOUT

Application	In. (mm)
Maximum Flange Runout	.008 (0.2 mm)
Maximum Shaft Runout	.079 (2.0 mm)

2) Inspect rear axle bearing for wear or damage. If necessary to replace, use a grinder to grind inner retainer. Using a hammer and chisel, cut off retainer and remove it from shaft. Using bearing remover (SST09527-20011), press bearing off shaft.

3) Inspect oil seal for wear or damage. If necessary to replace, use seal remover (SST09308-00010) to remove seal.

Reassembly

1) Using bearing installer (SST09515-20010), press bearing outer retainer and new bearing on shaft. Heat bearing inner retainer to about 302°F (150°C) in an oil bath.

2) Using retainer installer (SST09515-20010), press retainer on shaft while retainer is still hot. Ensure that there is no oil or grease on rear axle shaft or retainer. Face non-beveled side of inner retainer toward bearing.

3) Apply MP grease to axle housing oil seal. Using seal installer (SST09517-12010), drive in oil seal to a depth of .22" (5.6 mm).

Installation

Install bearing retainer (with notches pointing down) and gasket on axle shaft. Install rear axle in housing and tighten 4 new self-locking nuts to 44-53 ft. lbs. (60-72 N.m). Use care not to damage oil seal or oil deflector inside axle housing. Install brake drum and wheel.

WHEEL BEARINGS
FRONT
Removal

1) Raise and support vehicle. Remove tire and wheel. Remove cotter pin and bearing lock nut cap. Apply brakes and loosen bearing lock nut. Remove brake caliper and suspend from frame with wire.

2) Remove cotter pin and nut from tie rod end. Disconnect and remove tie rod end with remover (SST09610-20012). Place alignment marks on shock absorber lower bracket and camber adjust cam. Remove bolt and nut and separate steering knuckle and shock absorber.

3) Remove 2 bolts holding ball joint to steering knuckle. Pull off axle hub from drive shaft. Cover drive shaft boot with cloth. Using driver, remove dust deflector.

4) Using seal remover (SST09308-00010), pull oil seal out of steering knuckle. Using snap ring pliers, remove hole snap ring. Remove brake dust cover set bolts. Using hub remover (SST09950-20014), push axle hub off steering knuckle.

5) Remove outer oil seal and bearing inner race (inner) from bearing. Using (SST09950-20014), pull off bearing inner race (outer) from axle hub. Remove disc brake dust cover.

6) Using seal remover (SST09308-00010), pull oil seal out of steering knuckle. Install inner race (outer side) of bearing to be removed. Using bearing remover (SST09228-22020 and 09950-20014), press out bearing.

Installation

1) Using a press and bearing installer (SST09309-35010), press new bearing into steering knuckle. Note that there are 2 types of bearings available, KOYO and NSK.

2) Install bearing inner race (outer side) before installing new oil seal. Using seal installer (SST09515-35010), drive new oil seal into sterering knuckle.

3) Apply liquid sealer to disc brake dust cover and steering knuckle. Install dust cover. Install inner races into inner bearing. Using installer (SST09228-22020 and 09310-35010), press in inner race until it is tightly against shoulder of hub.

NOTE: Do not interchange inner and outer race when installing.

4) Using snap ring pliers, install hole snap ring into steering knuckle. Using seal installer (SST09309-35010), drive new oil seal into steering knuckle. Tap in .13" (3.3 mm) from end surface.

Fig. 3: Installing Inner Oil Seal

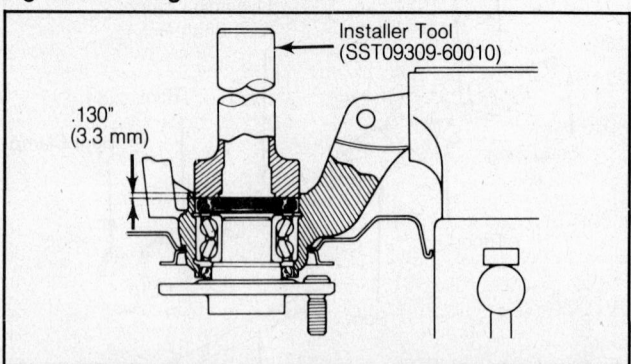

5) Using driver (SST09316-60010), drive new dust deflector into steering knuckle. Install steering knuckle with axle hub to lower arm and tighten to 59 ft. lbs. (80 N.m).

6) Using care not to damage drive shaft boot and oil seal lip, install axle hub to drive shaft. Lower stabilizer bar and assemble steering knuckle to shock absorber lower bracket.

7) Insert bolts from front side and align marks of camber adjust cam. Tighten bolts to 105 ft. lbs. (143 N.m). Install disc to hub. Install brake caliper to steering knuckle and tighten bolts.

TOYOTA TERCEL 6-SPEED (Cont.)

8) Connect tie rod end to steering knuckle and tighten castle nut. Install cotter pin. Depress brake pedal. Install and tighten bearing lock nut to 137 ft. lbs. (186 N.m). Install adjusting nut cap and cotter pin. Check front wheel alignment.

REAR
Removal & Installation
See AXLE DRIVE SHAFTS REAR for wheel bearing removal and installation procedures.

TRANSAXLE REMOVAL & INSTALLATION
See the appropriate article in MANUAL TRANS-MISSION REMOVAL Section.

TRANSAXLE DISASSEMBLY

1) Remove speedometer driven gear, reverse shift arm pivot, back-up light and 4WD switches, rear mount stay and restrict pin. Remove transmission case cover. Using magnetic probe, remove spring and ball.

2) Using remover (SST09313-30021), remove straight screw plug. Using pin punch and hammer, drive out pin. Remove 6 bolts and shift lever housing, set bolt and lock plate.

3) Remove extension housing. Using plug remover (SST09313-30021), remove straight screw plug. Using magnetic probe, remove spring and ball. Remove shift fork shaft with hub, hub sleeve and shift fork.

4) Temporarily install input shaft. Cover input shaft tip with shop cloth and secure with pliers. Remove oil pump drive shaft. Note that drive shaft has left hand threads.

5) Remove gear shift No. 4 head set bolt and lock plate. Using snap ring plier, remove snap ring. Remove No. 4 shift fork with shift fork shaft. Use care that shifting key does not fly out. Using magnetic probe, remove interlock pin.

6) Remove transfer case adaptor from transmission case. Turn select lever and remove tip from shift head groove. Remove transfer adaptor with select lever and extra low gear from transmission case.

7) Remove output shaft and oil pump gear from extension housing. Remove speedometer drive gear. Using a pin punch and hammer, drive out slotted spring pins and remove gear shift heads. Remove "C" washer from No. 1 and 2 shift fork shafts.

8) Using hexagon wrench, remove straight screw plugs. Using magnetic probe, remove springs and balls. Using snap ring pliers, remove bearing snap ring. Remove transmission case cover and input shaft.

9) Using a plastic hammer, tap on case protrusion to separate case from intermediate plate. Remove case from intermediate plate. Mount intermediate plate in vise by securing protrusion on lower part of plate.

10) Remove straight screw plug, spring and ball. Using a pin punch, drive out 4 slotted spring pins. Remove gear shift head. Set each fork shaft to neutral positon.

11) Holding shift fork, pull out fork shaft and remove fork. Remove interlock pins from fork shaft and intermediate plate. Using feeler gauge, measure counter 5th gear thrust clearance.

COUNTER 5TH GEAR THRUST CLEARANCE

Application	In. (mm)
Standard	.0059-.0128 (.15-.32)
Maximum	.0157 (.40)

12) Using screwdriver, remove hole snap ring. Remove shifting key retainer. Using snap ring pliers, remove snap ring. Using hub remover (SST09950-20014), remove clutch hub No. 3, synchro ring and counter 5th gear together. Remove needle roller bearing.

13) Remove spacer, steel ball and bearing retainer. Using snap ring pliers, remove 2 snap rings. Using plastic hammer, tap reverse gear shaft, idler gear and output shaft halfway out from intermediate plate. Support gear shaft by hand.

14) Remove idler gear and reverse gear shaft together. Using plastic hammer, tap out counter gear and output shaft together. Support gear and shaft by hand. Using dial indicator, measure 1st and 4th gear thrust clearance.

GEAR THRUST CLEARANCE

Application	In. (mm)
Standard Clearance	
1st Gear	.0059-.0108 (.15-.27)
2nd & 3rd Gear	.0059-.0098 (.15-.25)
4th Gear	.0008-.0094 (.02-.24)
Maximum Clearance	.0118 (.30)

15) Using remover (SST09950-00020), press out sleeve yoke. Using snap ring pliers, remove snap ring. Using remover (SST09950-00020), press out 5th gear.

16) Using snap ring pliers, remove output shaft front bearing snap ring. Using remover (SST09950-00020), press out output shaft front bearing, spacer and thrust bearing.

17) Remove 4th gear, synchronizer ring and needle roller bearing. Use care not to drop needle roller bearing when removing gear. Using 2 screwdrivers and a hammer, tap out snap ring, spacer and thrust bearing.

18) Using remover (SST09950-00020), press out clutch hub No. 2, synchronizer ring and 3rd gear. Using snap ring pliers, remove 1st gear snap ring. Remove 1st gear, synchronizer, needle roller bearing and inner race.

19) Remove steel ball. Using remover (SST09950-00020), press out clutch hub No. 1, synchronizer and 2nd gear.

20) Remove differential from transaxle. Install differential carrier to work stand with ring gear in horizontal position. Measure and record ring gear backlash. If backlash is not .0039-.0059" (.10-.15 mm), adjust side bearing preload or repair as necessary.

21) Check ring gear runout. If maximum runout is greater than .0028" (.07 mm), install new ring gear. Inspect teeth pattern for proper wear. Using adaptor (SST09556-16010) and torque meter, measure preload. Total preload should be 5.2-8.7 INCH Lbs. (.59-.98 N.m)

22) Using remover (SST09308-00010), remove oil seals from differential carrier. Remove side bearing caps. Tag bearing cap, outer race and side washer to show reassembly location.

23) Using remover (SST09504-22010), remove side washer on ring gear teeth side. Remove differential

Manual Transmissions

TOYOTA TERCEL 6-SPEED (Cont.)

Fig. 4: Exploded View of Toyota 6-Speed Transaxle

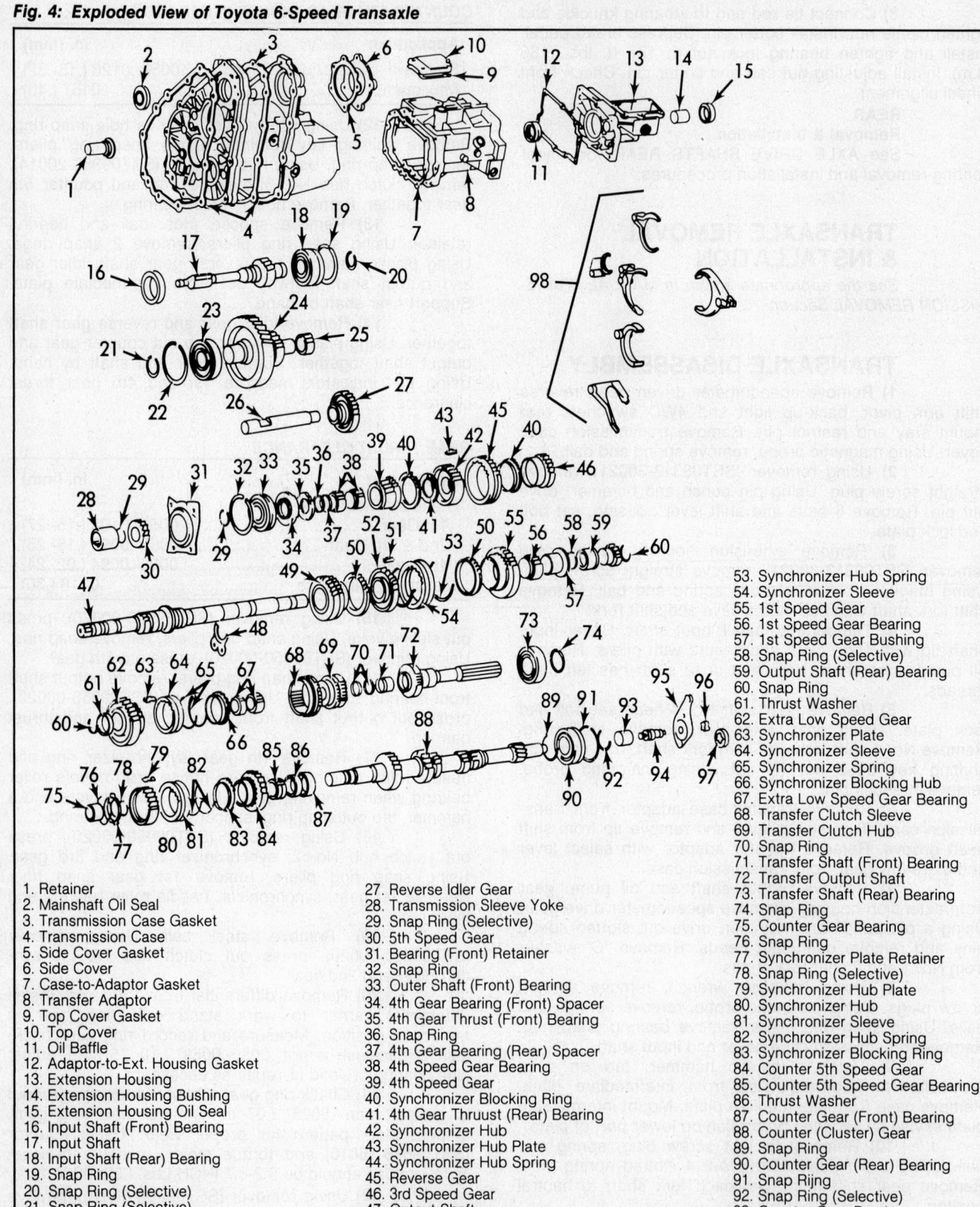

53. Synchronizer Hub Spring
54. Synchronizer Sleeve
55. 1st Speed Gear
56. 1st Speed Gear Bearing
57. 1st Speed Gear Bushing
58. Snap Ring (Selective)
59. Output Shaft (Rear) Bearing
60. Snap Ring
61. Thrust Washer
62. Extra Low Speed Gear
63. Synchronizer Plate
64. Synchronizer Sleeve
65. Synchronizer Spring
66. Synchronizer Blocking Hub
67. Extra Low Speed Gear Bearing
68. Transfer Clutch Sleeve
69. Transfer Clutch Hub
70. Snap Ring
71. Transfer Shaft (Front) Bearing
72. Transfer Output Shaft
73. Transfer Shaft (Rear) Bearing
74. Snap Ring
75. Counter Gear Bearing
76. Snap Ring
77. Synchronizer Plate Retainer
78. Snap Ring (Selective)
79. Synchronizer Hub Plate
80. Synchronizer Hub
81. Synchronizer Sleeve
82. Synchronizer Hub Spring
83. Synchronizer Blocking Ring
84. Counter 5th Speed Gear
85. Counter 5th Speed Gear Bearing
86. Thrust Washer
87. Counter Gear (Front) Bearing
88. Counter (Cluster) Gear
89. Snap Ring
90. Counter Gear (Rear) Bearing
91. Snap Rijng
92. Snap Ring (Selective)
93. Counter Gear Bearing
94. Oil Pump Drive Shaft
95. Oil Pump Cover
96. Oil Pump Drive Cover
97. Oil Pump Driven Rotor
98. Shifting Fork

1. Retainer
2. Mainshaft Oil Seal
3. Transmission Case Gasket
4. Transmission Case
5. Side Cover Gasket
6. Side Cover
7. Case-to-Adaptor Gasket
8. Transfer Adaptor
9. Top Cover Gasket
10. Top Cover
11. Oil Baffle
12. Adaptor-to-Ext. Housing Gasket
13. Extension Housing
14. Extension Housing Bushing
15. Extension Housing Oil Seal
16. Input Shaft (Front) Bearing
17. Input Shaft
18. Input Shaft (Rear) Bearing
19. Snap Ring
20. Snap Ring (Selective)
21. Snap Ring (Selective)
22. Idler Gear Snap Ring
23. Idler Gear (Front) Bearing
24. Idler Gear
25. Idler Gear (Rear) Bearing
26. Reverse Idler Shaft

27. Reverse Idler Gear
28. Transmission Sleeve Yoke
29. Snap Ring (Selective)
30. 5th Speed Gear
31. Bearing (Front) Retainer
32. Snap Ring
33. Outer Shaft (Front) Bearing
34. 4th Gear Bearing (Front) Spacer
35. 4th Gear Thrust (Front) Bearing
36. Snap Ring
37. 4th Gear Bearing (Rear) Spacer
38. 4th Speed Gear Bearing
39. 4th Speed Gear
40. Synchronizer Blocking Ring
41. 4th Gear Thruust (Rear) Bearing
42. Synchronizer Hub
43. Synchronizer Hub Plate
44. Synchronizer Hub Spring
45. Reverse Gear
46. 3rd Speed Gear
47. Output Shaft
48. Bearing (Rear) Retainer
49. 2nd Speed Gear
50. Synchronizer Blocking Ring
51. Synchronizer Hub Plate
52. Synchronizer Hub

TOYOTA TERCEL 6-SPEED (Cont.)

Fig. 5: Exploded View of Toyota Differential

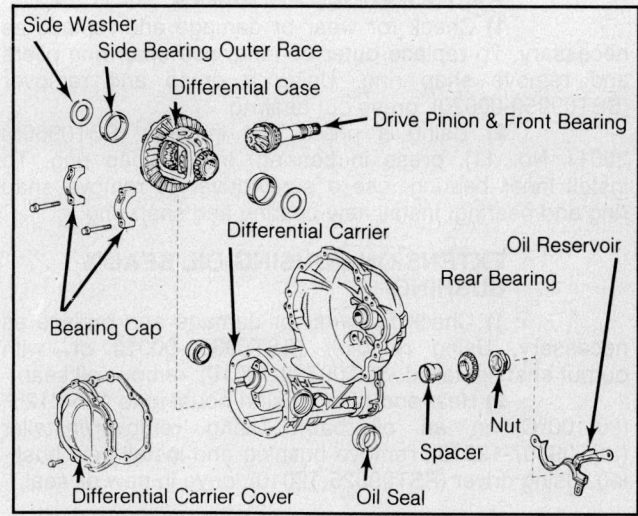

case and bearing outer race. Remove side washer and oil reservoir.

24) Loosen staked part of drive pinion nut. Using remover (SST09556-16010), loosen nut and turn drive pinion clockwise. Using press, remove drive pinion.

COMPONENT INSPECTION & REPAIR

DIFFERENTIAL DRIVE PINION BEARINGS & OUTER RACES

1) If bearings or races ar worn or damaged, use remover (SST09950-00020) to press out rear bearing from drive pinion. Install plate washer with one of same thickness as was assembled.

2) Using installer (SST09608-2011) and press, install bearing. Using a hammer and brass bar, remove outer race by tapping on notched portion. Using installer (SST09608-30011 for front and SST09608-30021 for rear) and hammer, install new outer race.

DIFFERENTIAL SIDE BEARINGS & OUTER RACES

Using remover (SST09502-10012), remove side bearing from differential case. Using installer (SST09608-20011) and press, install new bearing.

DIFFERENTIAL PINION & SIDE GEARS

1) Measure side gear backlash while holding another side gear toward the case. Standard backlash is .0016-.0094" (.04-.24 mm). If necessary, replace ring gear, differential pinions and side gears.

2) Lift lock plates and remove set bolts. Using a brass bar and hammer, tap on ring gear to separate it from differential case. If ring gear is to be reused, place alignment marks before separating it. If ring gear or drive pinion are damaged, replace them as a set.

3) Using a pin punch and hammer, tap out straight pin toward ring gear installation surface. Remove pinion shaft, pinion gears, side gears and thrust washers. Check gears, shaft, case and washers. Install side gears, washers, pinion gears and shaft.

4) Measure side gear backlash while holding another side gear toward the case. Standard backlash is

.0016-.0094" (.04-.24 mm). If backlash is not within specifications, use different thickness thrust washers. Washers are available in sizes from .0583-.0598" (1.48-1.52 mm) to .0681-.0697" (1.73-1.77 mm) in .0020" (.05 mm) increments.

5) Using a hammer and punch, drive straight pin through case and hole in pinion shaft. Stake pin and differential case. Clean contact surface of differential case. Heat ring gear to 194-230°F (90-110°C) in an oil bath. Quickly install ring gear on differential case.

6) Coat ring gear set bolts with gear oil. Install lock plates and set bolts. Tighten bolts, a little at a time, to 67-75 ft. lbs. (91-102 N.m). Stake lock plate.

INPUT SHAFT & REAR BEARING

1) Check for wear or damage. If bearing is worn or damaged, replace it. Using snap ring pliers, remove snap ring. Using remover (SST09950-00020), press out bearing.

2) Using press and remover (SST09515-20010), press in bearing. Ensure that outer race groove is facing toward rear. Select a snap ring that allows minimum axial play and install it on the shaft. Snap rings are available in .0827-.0846" (2.10-2.15 mm) and .0886-.0906" (2.25-2.30 mm) sizes.

IDLER GEAR BEARING

1) Check for wear or damage. If bearing is worn or damaged, replace it. Using snap ring pliers, remove snap ring. Using remover (SST09950-00020), press out bearing.

2) Using a press and remover (ST09506-30011), press in bearing. Ensure that outer race groove is facing toward front. Select a snap ring that allows minimum axial play and install it on the shaft. Snap rings are available in .0945-.0965" (2.40-2.45 mm) and .1004-.1024" (2.55-2.60 mm) sizes.

1ST GEAR

Using a dial indicator, measure oil clearance between gear and inner race with needle roller bearing installed. Standard clearance is .0004-.0024" (.009-.060 mm).

2ND & 3RD GEAR

Using a dial indicator, measure oil clearance between gear and output shaft. Standard clearance is .0024-.0039" (.06-.10 mm). Maximum clearance is .0043" (.11 mm).

SYNCHRONIZER RINGS

Check for wear or damage. Turn ring and push it in to check braking action. Using a feeler gauge, measure clearance between synchronizer ring back and gear spline end. Minimum clearance is .024" (.60 mm).

SHIFT FORKS & HUB SLEEVES

Using a feeler gauge, measure clearance between hub sleeve and shift fork. Maximum clearance is .039" (1.0 mm).

COUNTER GEAR & REAR BEARING

1) Check gear teeth and bearing for wear or damage. If bearing is worn or damaged, replace it. Using 2 drivers and a hammer, tap out snap ring. Using a press and remover (SST09950-00020), press out bearing.

2) Install front snap ring. Using a press and remover (SST09608-20011 No. 11), press in bearing. Select a snap ring that will allow minimum axial play and install it on the shaft.

COUNTER GEAR REAR BEARING SNAP RING SELECTION

I.D. Mark	Thickness In. (mm)
A	1.925-1.975 (.0758-.0778)
B	1.975-2.025 (.0778-.0797)
C	2.025-2.075 (.0797-.0817)
D	2.075-2.125 (.0817-.0837)
E	2.125-2.175 (.0837-.0856)
F	2.175-2.225 (.0856-.0876)

OIL PUMP DRIVE SHAFT

Check that left hand threads are not damaged. Check that pump drive shaft slides smoothly in axial direction.

SELECT LEVER OIL SEAL

Check oil seal for wear or damage. If oil seal is worn or damaged, use a screwdriver to pry it out. Using installer (SST09304-30012), drive in new oil seal.

INPUT SHAFT FRONT BEARING & OIL SEAL

1) Check for wear or damage. If bearing is worn or damaged, replace it. Using a screwdriver and hammer, drive out oil seal. Remove lock plate.

2) Using remove/installer (SST09608-30021), drive out old bearing and drive in new bearing. Ensure that outer race groove is facing upward. Install lock plate. Using remover/installer, drive in oil seal.

COUNTER GEAR CENTER BEARING

Check for wear or damage. Replace as necessary. Using remover/installer (SST097100-30020) and press, press out old bearing and press in new bearing.

IDLER GEAR REAR BEARING

Check for wear or damage and replace as necessary. Remove oil receiver. Using remover (SST09612-10091), remove bearing. Using installer (SST09304-47010) and hammer, drive in bearing. Install oil receiver.

OUTPUT SHAFT REAR BEARING

Check for wear or damage and replace as necessary. Remove oil receiver. Using remover/installer (SST09304-47010) and hammer, drive out old bearing and drive in new bearing. Install oil receiver.

COUNTER GEAR FRONT BEARING

Check for wear or damage and replace as necessary. Using removers (SST09310-36021 and 09612-10091), remove the bearing. Using installer (SST09304-47010) and hammer, drive in bearing until it is level with end surface of transaxle case.

COUNTER SHAFT BEARING

Check for wear or damage and replace as necessary. Using socket and press, press out old bearing. Using installer (SST09304-12012) and press, press in bearing.

OUTPUT SHAFT BEARINGS

1) Check for wear or damage and replace as necessary. To replace outer bearing, use snap ring pliers and remove snap ring. Using a press and remover (SST09950-00020), press out bearing.

2) Using a press and installer (SST09608-20011 No. 11), press in bearing. Install snap ring. To install inner bearing, use a screwdriver to remove snap ring and bearing. Install new bearing and snap ring.

EXTENSION HOUSING OIL SEAL & BUSHING

1) Check for wear or damage and replace as necessary. Using remover (SST09308-00010 or, with output shaft installed, SST09308-10010), remove oil seal.

2) Heat end of extension housing to 176-212°F (80-100°C) in an oil bath. Using remover/installer (SST09307-12010), remove bushing and install new bushing. Using driver (SST09325-12010), drive in new oil seal.

SPEEDOMETER GEAR OIL SEAL

Check for wear or damage and replace as necessary. Using remover (SST09921-00019), remove oil seal. Using installer (SST09201-60011), install new oil seal.

TRANSAXLE REASSEMBLY & ADJUSTMENT

1) Install new spacer to differential drive pinion. Install drive pinion to differential carrier. Using installer (SST09612-22010) and press, temporarily press in bearing until threaded portion is protruding .12" (3 mm) from carrier.

2) Apply gear oil onto threaded portion of drive pinion. Using tools (SST09564-16010 and 09556-16010), tighten nut to 108 ft. lbs. (147 N.m). Apply gear oil onto bearings.

3) Using adaptor (SST09556-16010), snug down bearing by turning drive pinion several times. Using adaptor and torque meter, measure differential drive pinion preload. Preload for new bearing is 4.3-8.7 INCH Lbs. (.49-.99 N.m).

4) If preload is not correct, tighten nut to 108 ft. lbs. (147 N.m). Remeasure preload. If excessive, replace spacer. If insufficient, increase tightening 5-10° at a time and remeasure each time.

5) If preload is insufficient even after specified torque range is exceeded, loosen nut and tighten to 268 ft. lbs. (364 N.m). If preload is still not correct, replace spacer.

6) Set transaxle case with back side of ring gear facing down. Install differential case. Install only side washer on ring gear back side. Ensure that ring gear has backlash. Snug down washer and bearings by tapping on ring gear with a plastic hammer.

7) Push side bearing boss on teeth surface of ring gear and measure backlash. If backlash is not .0039" (.10 mm), select a ring gear back side washer using backlash as a reference.

8) Select a ring gear teeth side washer of a thickness which eliminates any clearance between outer race and case. Remove side washers and differential case. Install side washer into lower part of case.

TOYOTA TERCEL 6-SPEED (Cont.)

DIFFERENTIAL RING GEAR BACK SIDE WASHER SELECTION

I.D. No.	Thickness In. (mm)
1	.1028-.1035 (2.61-2.63)
2	.1039-.1047 (2.64-2.66)
3	.1051-.1059 (2.67-2.69)
4	.1063-.1071 (2.70-2.72)
5	.1075-.1083 (2.73-2.75)
6	.1087-.1094 (2.76-2.78)
7	.1098-.1106 (2.79-2.81)
8	.1110-.1118 (2.82-2.84)
9	.1122-.1130 (2.85-2.87)
10	.1134-.1142 (2.88-2.90)
11	.1146-.1154 (2.91-2.93)
12	.1157-.1165 (2.94-2.96)
13	.1169-.1177 (2.97-2.99)
14	.1181-.1189 (3.00-3.02)
15	.1193-.1201 (3.03-3.05)
16	.1205-.1213 (3.06-3.08)
17	.1217-.1224 (3.09-3.11)
18	.1228-.1236 (3.12-3.14)
19	.1240-.1248 (3.15-3.17)
20	.1252-.1260 (3.18-3.20)
21	.1264-.1272 (3.21-3.23)
22	.1276-.1283 (3.24-3.26)
23	.1287-.1295 (3.27-3.29)

9) Place other side washer onto differential case. Install differential case with outer race into transaxle case. Using a plastic hammer, snug down washer and bearing by tapping ring gear.

10) Using dial indicator, measure ring gear backlash. If backlash is not .0039-.0059" (.10-.15 mm), adjust by either increasing or decreasing number of washers on both sides by an equal amount. There should be no clearance between side washer and case and there should be ring gear backlash.

11) After adjustment, using backlash as reference, remove ring gear teeth side washer and measure thickness. Install a new washer .0024-.0035" (.06-.09 mm) thicker than washer removed. Select a washer that can be pressed in 2/3 of the way by finger.

12) Using a plastic hammer, tap in side washer. Recheck ring gear backlash. If still not correct, adjust by either increasing and decreasing the washers on both sides by an equal amount. Install side bearing caps and tighten bolts to 33-39 ft. lbs. (45-53 N.m).

13) Apply gear oil on the bearings. Using adaptor (SST09556-16010), turn drive pinion left and right several times. Using adaptor and torque meter, measure total preload. Preload should be 2.6-4.3 INCH Lbs. (.29-.49 N.m) in addition to drive pinion preload. If not, readjust ring gear teeth side washer.

14) Using dial indicator, measure ring gear backlash at 3 places on outer circumference of ring gear. Backlash should be .0039-.0059" (.10-.15 mm). If not, adjust by either increasing or decreasing washers on both sides by equal amount.

15) Using a chisel, stake drive pinion lock nut. Using installer (SST09223-46011) and hammer, install new differential carrier oil seal. Ensure that distance "A" is .331-.354" (8.4-9.0 mm). See Fig. 6.

16) Install differential carrier cover and gasket. Tighten set bolts to 96-132 INCH Lbs. (11-15 N.m). Install oil reservoir.

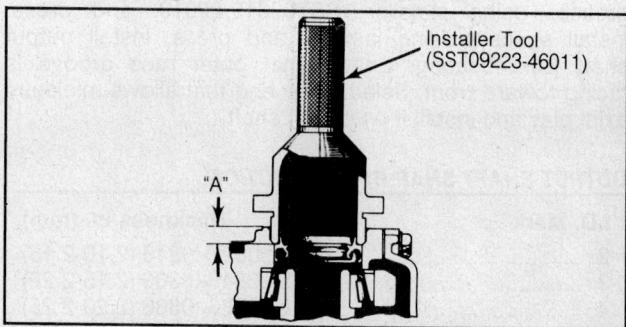

Fig. 6: *Installing Differential Carrier Oil Seal*

Installer Tool (SST09223-46011)

"A"

17) Install clutch hub and shifting keys to hub sleeve. Install shifting key springs under shifting keys. Ensure that key springs are positioned so that end gaps are not in line.

18) Apply gear oil to output shaft. Place synchronizer ring on 2nd gear and align ring slots with shifting keys. Using installer (SST09515-30010) and a press, install 2nd gear and clutch hub No. 1.

19) Install locking ball in shaft. Apply gear oil to needle roller bearing. Assemble 1st gear, synchronizer ring, needle roller bearing and inner race.

20) Place synchronizer ring on 1st gear and align ring slots with shifting keys. Fit inner race groove securely over locking ball. Select a snap ring that allows minimum axial play and install on output shaft.

OUTPUT SHAFT SNAP RING SELECTION

I.D. Mark	Thickness In. (mm)
1	.0846-.0866 (2.15-2.20)
2	.0866-.0886 (2.20-2.25)
3	.0886-.0906 (2.25-2.30)
4	.0906-.0925 (2.30-2.35)
5	.0925-.0945 (2.35-2.40)
6	.0945-.0965 (2.40-2.45)
7	.0965-.0984 (2.45-2.50)
8	.0984-.1004 (2.50-2.55)
9	.1004-.1024 (2.55-2.60)

21) Using a dial indicator, measure 1st gear thrust clearance. Using a feeler gauge, measure 2nd gear thrust clearance.

1ST & 2ND GEAR THRUST CLEARANCE

Application	In. (mm)
Standard Clearance	
1st Gear	.0059-.0108 (.15-.27)
2nd Gear	.0059-.0098 (.15-.25)
Maximum Clearance	.0118 (.30)

22) Install shifting keys and key springs to No. 2 clutch hub. Install clutch hub to hub sleeve. Apply oil to output shaft. Place synchronizer on 3rd gear and align ring slots with shifting keys.

23) Using installer (SST09515-30010) and a press, install 3rd gear and clutch hub No. 2. Assemble widest thrust bearing to No. 2 clutch hub.

24) Apply gear oil and install 4th gear needle roller bearing and synchronizer. Line up shifting keys with key slots in synchronizer ring. Install spacer and tap in snap ring.

Manual Transmissions

TOYOTA TERCEL 6-SPEED (Cont.)

25) Stick thrust bearing onto spacer with MP grease. Using installer (SST09612-22010) and press, install spacer. Using installer and press, install output shaft front bearing. Ensure that outer race groove is facing toward front. Select snap ring that allows minimum axial play and install it on output shaft.

OUTPUT SHAFT SNAP RING SELECTION

I.D. Mark	Thickness In. (mm)
2	.0827-.0846 (2.10-2.15)
3	.0846-.0866 (2.15-2.20)
4	.0866-.0886 (2.20-2.25)
5	.0886-.0906 (2.25-2.30)
6	.0906-.0925 (2.30-2.35)
7	.0925-.0945 (2.35-2.40)
8	.0945-.0965 (2.40-2.45)
9	.0965-.0984 (2.45-2.50)
10	.0984-.1004 (2.50-2.55)

26) Using a feeler gauge, measure 3rd gear thrust clearance. Using a dial indicator, measure 4th gear thrust clearance.

3RD & 4TH GEAR THRUST CLEARANCE

Application	In. (mm)
Standard Clearance	
3rd Gear	.0059-.0098 (.15-.25)
4th Gear	.0008-.0094 (.02-.24)
Maximum Clearance	.0118 (.30)

27) Using an installer (SST09612-22010) and press, install 5th gear. Select and install a snap ring that allows minimum axial play and install it on output shaft. Using a press, install sleeve yoke.

5TH GEAR SNAP RING SELECTION

I.D. Mark	In. (mm)
2	.0827-.0846 (2.10-2.15)
3	.0846-.0866 (2.15-2.20)
4	.0866-.0886 (2.20-2.25)
5	.0886-.0906 (2.25-2.30)
6	.0906-.0925 (2.30-2.35)

28) Mount intermediate plate in vise by securing lower portrusion. Using a plastic hammer, tap in output shaft and counter gear together about halfway. Align idler with notched portion of reverse idler gear shaft.

29) Using plastic hammer, tap in idler gear shaft bearing about halfway. Ensure that idler gear and output shaft spacer are not contacting each other. Using a plastic hammer, tap each gear shaft until bearing is in as far as possible.

30) Using snap ring pliers, install 2 snap rings. Install bearing retainer and tighten bolts to 108 INCH Lbs. (12 N.m). Install steel ball in shaft. Align spacer groove with steel ball and install spacer.

31) Install clutch hub No. 3 and shifting keys to hub sleeve. Install shifting key springs under shifting keys with key end gaps not in line. Apply gear oil to 5th gear needle roller bearing.

32) Install counter 5th gear, needle roller bearing and synchronizer ring on shaft. Using installer (SST09612-222010) and press, install clutch hub. Line up shifting keys with key slots in synchronizer ring.

33) Select a snap ring that allows minimum axial play and install it on shaft. Snap rings are available in sizes from .0709-.0728" (1.80-1.85 mm) to .0827-.0846" (2.10-2.15 mm) with .0020" (.05 mm) increments. Using a feeler gauge, measure 5th counter gear thrust clearance.

5TH COUNTER GEAR THRUST CLEARANCE

Application	In. (mm)
Standard Clearance	.0059-.0128 (.15-.32)
Maximum Clearance	.0157 (.40)

34) Install shifting key retainer and hole snap ring. Insert shift fork shaft No. 1 through shift fork No. 1 and reverse shift fork. Align reverse shift fork into reverse gear groove, align shift fork No. 1 with hub sleeve No. 1 groove and install shift fork shaft No. 1 through intermediate plate.

35) Align shift fork No. 2 into hub sleeve No. 2 groove. Install shift fork shaft No. 2 to intermediate plate through shift forks No. 1 and No. 2. Insert shift fork shaft No. 3 to gear shift head and install so pin hole of shift fork shaft No. 3 aligns with interlock pin hole.

36) Insert piece of wire into interlock pin hole and confirm that it goes in about 4.72" (120 mm) from intermediate plate circumference. Coat MP grease to interlock pins and push them in with a piece of wire. After inserting the 3 interlock pins, insert a piece of wire and ensure that it goes in about 3.15" (80 mm) from intermediate plate circumference.

37) Align shift fork No. 3 into hub sleeve No. 3 groove and insert shift fork shaft No. 3 into shift fork No. 3. Apply sealer to straight screw plug and install it.

38) Align pin hole in fork with hole in shaft. Using a pin punch, drive in slotted spring piins until they are flush with fork. Apply sealer to straight screw plug and install it with spring and ball.

39) Apply sealer to gasket and install transmission case to intermediate plate. Using snap ring pliers, install snap ring. Install 3 locking balls and springs. Apply sealer to straight screw plugs and install them.

40) Insert reverse shift arm pivot through reverse shift arm. Install "C" washer to No. 1 and No. 2 shift fork shafts. Install gear shift head to fork shaft and drive in slotted spring pin with a pin punch and hammer.

41) Install speedometer drive gear, steel ball and snap ring. Install extra low gear and shifting keys to hub sleeve. Install shifting key springs, with end gaps not positioned in line, under shifting keys.

42) Install select lever to transfer adaptor. Install extra low gear and shift fork No. 4 to transfer adaptor. Install bearing to output shaft. Install transfer adaptor to extra low gear and select lever as a unit. Turn select lever and insert tip into shaft head groove. Tighten bolt to 19 ft. lbs. (26 N.m).

43) Install interlock pin. Insert gear shift head No. 4 into shift fork shaft and install fork shaft. Install gear shift head No. 4 set bolt and tighten to 108 INCH Lbs. (12 N.m). Stake one lock plate claw flush with flat surface of nut. For claw contacting protruding portion of nut, stake only half on tightening side.

44) Temporarily install input shaft. Cover tip of input shaft with shop cloth, secure it with pliers and install oil pump drive shaft. Note left hand threads on oil pump drive shaft.

45) Install synchronizer ring No. 3 and transfer clutch hub. Install snap ring to output shaft. Install shift

TOYOTA TERCEL 6-SPEED (Cont.)

fork into 4WD shift inner lever. Install locking ball and spring. Using installer (SST09313-300021), install straight screw plug.

46) Insert lever housing into select lever and install extension housing to transfer adaptor. Tighten bolts to 19 ft. lbs. (26 N.m). Install lock plate and set belt to lever housing. Tighten bolts to 25 ft. lbs. (34 N.m). Stake one lock plate claw flush with flat surface of nut. For claw contacting protruding portion of nut, stake only half on tightening side.

47) Align end of shift lever shaft and gear shift head No. 2 and install extension housing. Tighten bolts to 19 ft. lbs. (26 N.m).

48) Align pin hole in fork with hole in shaft. Using a pin punch, drive in slotted spring pin until it is flush with fork. Using installer (SST09313-30021), install straight screw plug.

49) Install locking ball and spring. Install transmission case cover and tighten bolts. Install shift lever retainer and tighten bolt.

50) Install restrict pins to extension housing. Note that Green pin is located on 1st and 2nd gear and Yellow pin is located on 5th and reverse gear. Install speedometer driven gear, extension housing mount stay, back-up light and 4WD switches. Install transmission case cover.

TIGHTENING SPECIFICATIONS

Application	Ft. Lbs. (N.m)
Brake Caliper-to-Steering Knuckle	57-83 (78-113)
Shift Lever Retainer Bolt	14 (19)
Tie Rod End-to-Steering Knuckle Nut	29-43 (39-58)
Transmission Case Cover Bolts	14 (19)

Manual Transmissions

VOLKSWAGEN VANAGON 4-SPEED

TRANSMISSION IDENTIFICATION

The Volkswagen Vanagon uses a Type 091 manual transmission. First 3 digits of transmission part number cast in right side of transmission case indicate transmission model. Transmission code letters (DK) and date of manufacture are stamped on bottom of transmission case.

DESCRIPTION

The transaxle assembly is a 2-piece unit containing both the transmission and final drive. The transmission and final drive are asembled in one section and clutch is housed in second section.

The transaxle is mounted at rear of vehicle and engine is mounted to rear of transaxle. The transmission is a 4-speed manual type. Gears are in constant mesh in all forward gears. The final drive, mounted between transmission and engine, uses a hypoid ring gear and pinion.

The rear axle unit is a double joint type, using constant velocity (CV) joints on both ends of axle drive shafts. Outer wheel bearings are mounted in a housing connected to control arm.

LUBRICATION & ADJUSTMENT

See the appropriate article in MANUAL TRANSMISSION SERVICING Section.

SERVICE (IN VEHICLE)

AXLE DRIVE SHAFTS
Removal & Installation

Remove socket head screws at each CV joint. Tilt shaft down and remove. To install, place shaft in position. Install and tighten socket head screws.

CONSTANT VELOCITY JOINTS
Disassembly

1) Carefully drive protective cap off joint with small punch and pull cap back so that boot is turned inside out on driveshaft. Remove circlip from groove in

Fig. 1: Removing Ball Hub from Ball Cage

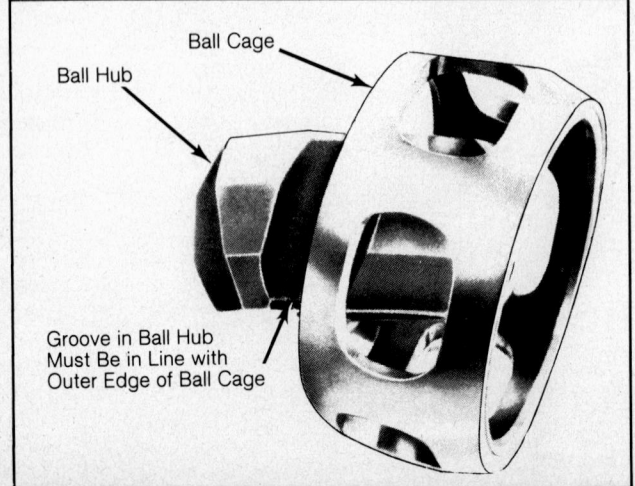

Ball Cage

Ball Hub

Groove in Ball Hub Must Be in Line with Outer Edge of Ball Cage

shaft and slide outer ring towards end of shaft. Press shaft out of center ball hub. Remove cover and boot from shaft.

2) Push ball hub and cage from outer ring. Lift the 6 steel cage balls out of cage, taking care not to damage balls or cage. Rotate center ball hub to position in cage shown in *Fig. 1*. Hub groove must be in line with outer edge of ball cage. Tip hub out of ball cage.

NOTE: All CV joint components are machined for close tolerance fit with other components; do not intermix components of one CV joint with components of another.

Reassembly

Clean all components and check for wear or damage. Replace as necessary. Coat all CV joint components with molybdenum grease. Reverse disassembly procedure to assemble CV joint and install on axle. Make sure chamfered end of spline in center ball hub is on same side as large diameter side of outer ring. Check joint for smooth operation throughout entire range of travel.

Fig. 2: Exploded View of Constant Velocity Joints

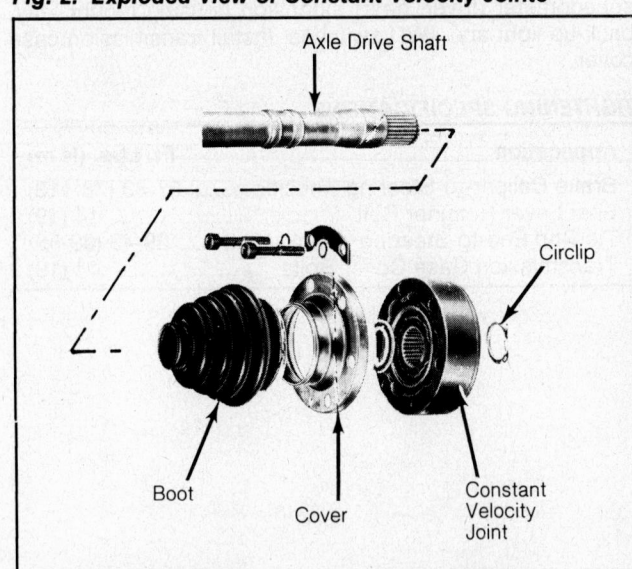

Axle Drive Shaft

Circlip

Boot

Cover

Constant Velocity Joint

REAR WHEEL BEARING HOUSING

Removal

1) With vehicle on ground, remove cotter pin and loosen large nut at center of brake drum. Raise vehicle and position on safety stands. Disconnect axle drive shaft at wheel bearing flange. Wire axle up out of way. Remove brake drum and wheel hub.

2) Remove brake backing plate bolts, and position brake backing plate out of way without disconnecting brake line or parking brake cable. Mark position of bearing housing, spring plate and control arm. Remove 4 bearing housing bolts and remove housing.

Disassembly

1) Place bearing housing in a vise and clamp against spring plate flange. Remove brake components if not previously removed. Using a puller, press axle shaft out of housing. Pry out oil seals, and remove circlip.

2) Remove inner roller bearing race and spacer sleeve. Using a punch that contacts only bearing outer race, drive ball bearing out of housing. Remove roller bearing outer race if necessary.

VOLKSWAGEN VANAGON 4-SPEED (Cont.)

Fig. 3: Exploded View of Rear Wheel Bearing Housing and Related Parts

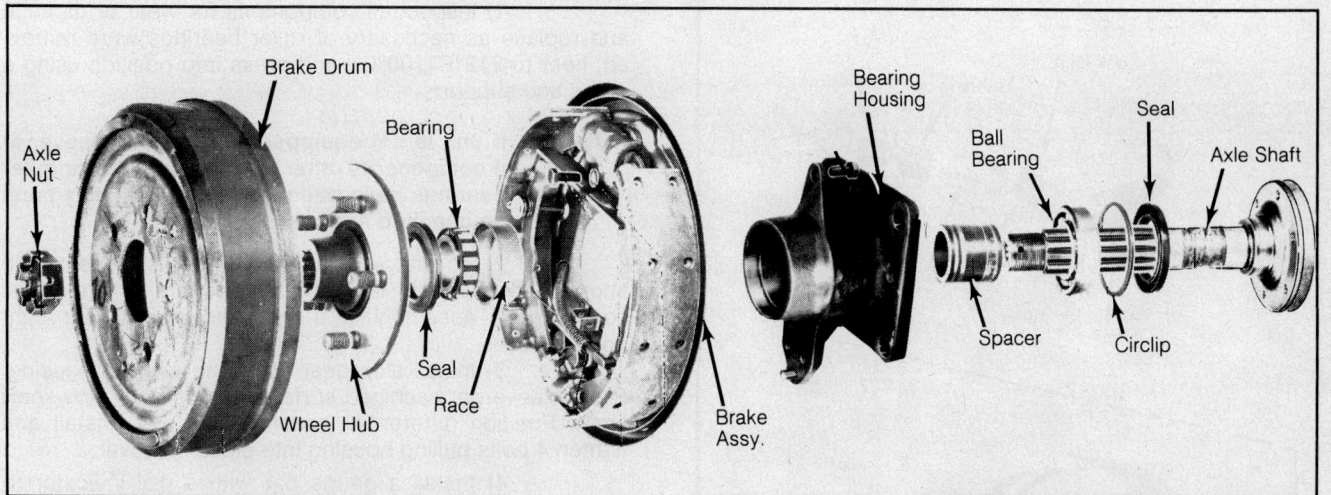

Reassembly

1) To reassemble, reverse disassembly procedure noting that if replacing spacer sleeve on one axle, the one on the opposite axle must also be replaced due to difference in diameter from original equipment.

2) Fill housing with multi-purpose grease prior to inserting spacer sleeve, then drive wheel shaft in with soft punch or pull on with two arm puller. Apply sealer to sealing edge around bearing housing and brake backing plate if installing at this time.

Installation

Install bearing housing on spring plate and control arm, carefully aligning index marks made during removal. To complete installation, reverse removal procedure. Tighten axle nut to specification with vehicle on ground and install a new cotter pin.

TRANSAXLE REMOVAL & INSTALLATION

See the appropriate article in MANUAL TRANS-MISSION REMOVAL Section.

TRANSAXLE DISASSEMBLY

1) Before attempting to remove clutch housing, loosen left differential adjusting ring to relieve tension in housing. Mark position of ring before loosening for ease of assembly. Remove (10) housing nuts from studs.

2) Separate housing from transmission case. Remove circlip from input shaft. Pull reverse drive gear forward and unscrew input shaft from stud in end of mainshaft. Pry out drive flange center caps.

3) Remove circlips and wavy spacers from center of flanges. Use 2 levers to pry drive flanges off of output shafts.

4) Remove screws from adjusting ring lock plates and remove lock plates. Measure depth of adjusting ring or mark position in case. Remove adjusting rings.

5) Making sure ring gear teeth stay in mesh with pinion gear, rotate differential toward rear of transmission case and pull out through rear of case.

6) Remove attaching nuts and lift shift housing from gear carrier. Remove pinion bearing retaining ring

from bearing race on differential end of case. Remove selector link, shaft and bracket from face of gear carrier.

7) Remove (9) nuts from gear carrier mounting studs on transmission case. Apply leverage to end of pinion gear and press gear train and carrier out of case.

8) Loosen nut on reverse lever support clamp sleeve. Turn shaft far enough to remove reverse slider and shift fork. Slide shift forks off shift rods. Remove circlip from end of mainshaft.

9) Press out mainshaft and drive pinion at the same time by applying pressure to end of mainshaft. Care must be taken not to damage any gear train components.

COMPONENT DISASSEMBLY & REASSEMBLY

CLUTCH HOUSING

Disassembly

1) Pry retaining springs off spring clips and remove clutch release bearing. Remove release bearing guide sleeve. Remove circlip from end of clutch shaft. Pry off lever and remove return spring and spring collar.

2) Remove clutch shaft lock bolt. Slide shaft outward, pressing out bushing and rubber seals. Remove bushing, seals and flat washer from shaft. Pull shaft inward and out of housing to remove. Pry oil seal out of input shaft hole in housing.

Reassembly

Coat outside of new seal with a sealing compound. Position in hole with lip toward transmission side of housing and drive squarely into place. To complete clutch housing reassembly, reverse disassembly procedure.

DIFFERENTIAL

Disassembly

1) Remove ring gear bolts and drive ring gear off differential housing with a punch. Remove differential cover with a slide hammer. Remove side gears and thrust washers from housing and cover.

2) If necessary, remove roller bearing using a press and supports. Drive out pinion shaft lock pin. Drive pinion shaft out of differential housing. Remove pinion gears, spacer and thrust washer.

Manual Transmissions

VOLKSWAGEN VANAGON 4-SPEED (Cont.)

Fig. 4: Exploded View of Clutch Housing

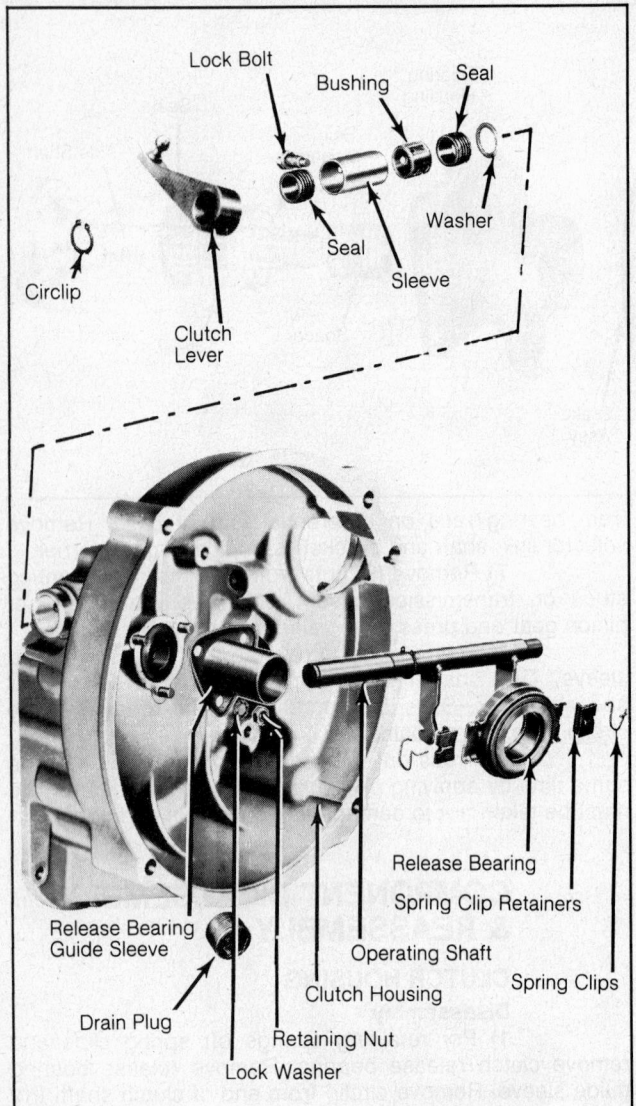

Reassembly

1) Inspect all components for wear or damage and replace as necessary. If roller bearings were removed, heat to 212°F (100°C), and press into position using a press and supports.

NOTE: **If unit is not equipped with spacer sleeve, or if components other than pinion shaft or roller bearings have been replaced, axial play must be checked and adjusted.**

2) To check axial play, install side gear with short shaft and both large thrust washers in differential cover. Place assembly in a vise and clamp gear tight against cover.

3) Install side gear with long shaft in housing. Place sleeve on machined surface of side gear with short shaft. Position differential housing on cover. Install and tighten 4 bolts pulling housing into place on cover.

4) Install a gauge bar with a dial indicator to end of drive gear shaft in housing. Dial indicator plunger must contact differential housing neck. Press down on side gear shaft and zero dial indicator with .080" (2 mm) preload.

Fig. 6: Measuring Differential Gear Axial Play

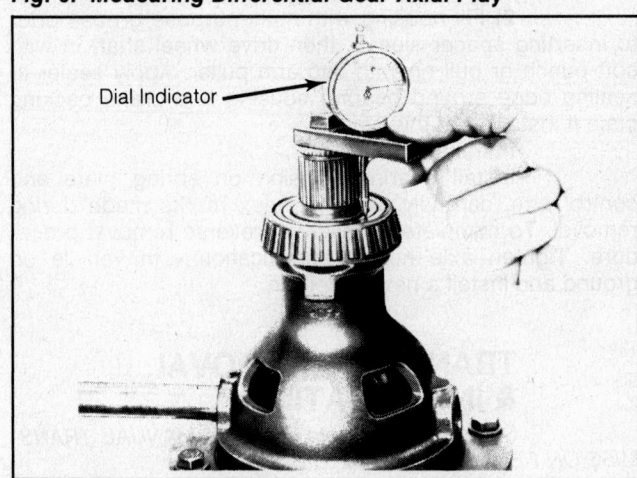

Fig. 5: Exploded View of Differential Assembly

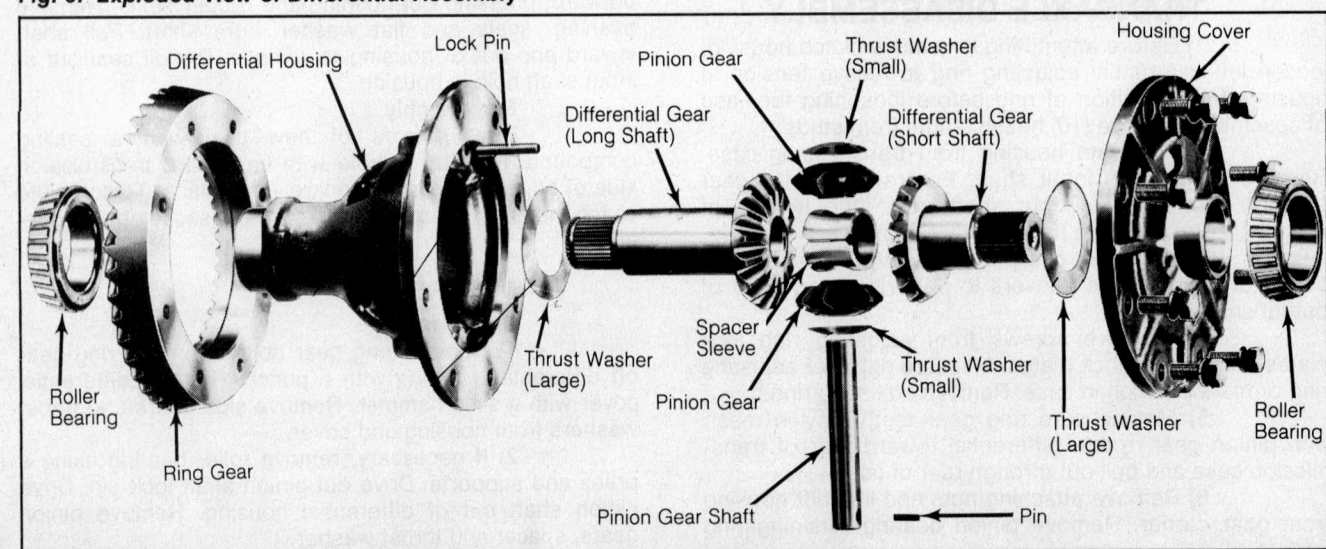

VOLKSWAGEN VANAGON 4-SPEED (Cont.)

5) Move side gear up and down to determine axial play. Play should be .001-.004" (.03-.11 mm). If not to specifications, install a spacer of correct size to obtain specified play.

6) Recheck play after installing correct spacer. Spacers are available in the following lengths: 1.253" (31.84 mm), 1.257" (31.93 mm), 1.261" (32.02 mm), 1.264" (32.11 mm), and 1.268" (32.20 mm).

MAINSHAFT
Disassembly
1) With mainshaft removed from gear carrier, remove 4th gear, needle bearing and synchro ring. Remove circlip and slide off clutch gear assembly. Remove remaining circlip and slide off 3rd gear.

Fig. 7: Exploded View of Mainshaft Assembly

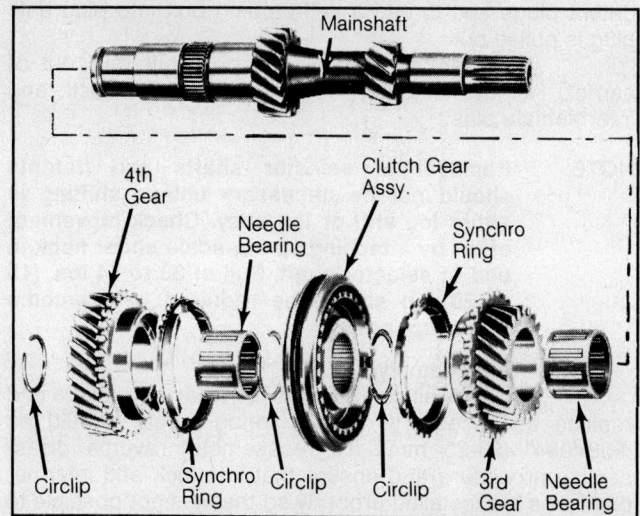

2) Open split in needle bearing cage just enough to slide over mainshaft splines and remove bearing. If necessary, remove spring rings from clutch gear assembly. Then separate synchronizer hub from sleeve.

Reassembly
1) Inspect all parts for wear or damage and replace as necessary. Press synchro ring onto gear by hand and check clearance as shown in illustration.

2) Specified clearance is .040-.075" (1.0-1.9 mm). If clearance is less than .023" (.6 mm), replace synchro ring or gear. If clutch gear assembly was disassembled, reassemble synchronizer hub to sleeve by meshing the teeth in various positions until a free sliding fit is obtained.

3) Spring ring diameter for 3rd-4th gear clutch hub is 2.91" (74 mm) while larger ring for 1st-2nd clutch

Fig. 8: Measuring Synchro Ring-to-Gear Clearance

gear should be 3.07" (78 mm). Open ends of springs on opposite sides of assembly must be installed 120° apart with angled ends over the keys.

NOTE: **Synchronizer rings must be installed in exactly the same relationships that existed before removal. The 1st gear ring can be identified by having no notches in blank area on outer edge. Synchronizers for 2nd, 3rd and 4th gears each have 3 notches (depressions) in blank area on outer edge. Replacement synchronizers for 2nd, 3rd and 4th gears have teeth completely around the outer edge with no blanked off areas.**

4) To complete reassembly of mainshaft, reverse disassembly procedure, noting the following procedures: Install clutch gear assembly so that side with .040" (1 mm) deep groove is toward 4th gear, and the side of the clutch gear hub having the wide chamfer on teeth goes toward 3rd gear.

DRIVE PINION SHAFT
Disassembly
1) Hold 4th gear down tight against spring on shaft. This will collapse spring and ease removal of circlip on end of shaft. With circlip removed, press shaft out of inner bearing race while supporting 4th gear.

2) Remove spring and next circlip. Remove 3rd gear, 2nd gear, needle bearing, synchro rings, circlip, 1st/2nd synchro assembly, 1st gear and needle bearing.

Fig. 9: Exploded View of Pinion Shaft Assembly

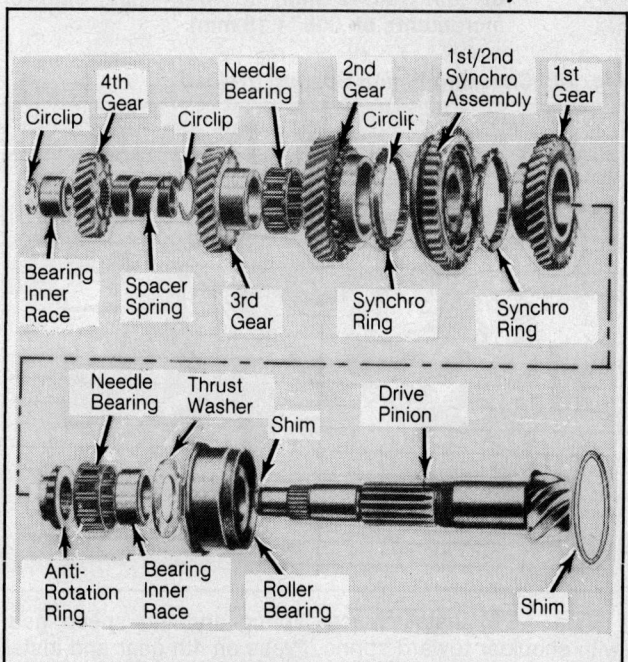

3) Note that inner needle bearing race is threaded and notched on end away from pinion. Place pinion in appliance (VW293) to hold notched race, and place splined socket over pinion shaft. Turn shaft counterclockwise to remove inner race/nut.

4) If necessary, disassemble synchro assembly hub. Press off tapered roller bearing with outer race. If required, use separating tool and press off inner race.

Manual Transmissions

VOLKSWAGEN VANAGON 4-SPEED (Cont.)

Reassembly

1) Inspect all parts for wear or damage and replace as necessary. Press 1st and 2nd gear synchro rings onto gears and check clearance of 3rd and 4th gear.

2) Specified clearance for new parts is .043-.071" (1.1-1.8 mm), with a minimum clearance of .023" (.6 mm) for used parts. If 1st/2nd synchro assembly was disassembled, reassemble in the same manner as for 3rd/4th synchro assembly.

3) Heat tapered roller bearing to about 212°F (100°C) and press into position. Allow to cool to room temperature.

4) Heat inner race to about 140°F (60°C) and press on shaft by hand as far as possible. Place pinion in same appliance used for disassembly and tighten inner race to 144 ft. lbs. (195 N.m).

5) Check pinion bearing preload by installing shaft in transmission case and tightening retaining ring. Check for turning torque of 5-18 INCH lbs. (.6-.2 N.m) for new bearing and 3-6 INCH lbs. (.3-.7 N.m) for used bearing.

6) Install needle bearing, 1st gear, 1st/2nd synchro assembly with synchro rings, and install circlip. Synchro ring grooves must align with keys when pressing on. Assemble needle bearing, 2nd gear and 3rd gear on shaft, then fit circlip properly in groove.

7) Check axial play between circlip and 3rd gear. Correct play is .004-.010" (.10-.25 mm), with the lower limit preferred. Install proper circlip to obtain specified clearance.

NOTE: 3rd gear circlips are available in thicknesses of .057" (1.45 mm) to .087" (2.2 mm) in increments of .006" (.15 mm).

Fig. 10: Checking Pinion Bearing Preload

8) Install spacer spring and 4th speed gear with shoulder toward spring. Press on 4th gear and install circlip.

TRANSMISSION CASE
Disassembly

Remove reverse gear shaft circlip from inside gear case. Remove reverse drive gear, shaft and needle bearing as a unit with a plastic hammer. Remove lock rings from mainshaft needle bearing and drive bearing out.

Reassembly

Insert shaft, bearing and reverse drive gear as a unit. Drive mainshaft needle bearing in case with lettered side of bearing towards the driver. Install lock rings.

GEAR CARRIER
Disassembly

1) Remove selector link shaft and selector link. Remove 2 bolts and then remove link bracket. Remove drive pinion bearing lock bolt.

2) Using a mandrel, press out mainshaft bearing and pinion shaft bearing. Loosen clamp sleeve and remove with reverse lever support and union nut from carrier.

3) Remove (4) relay shaft bracket bolts, brackets and relay shaft. Detent plugs and shift rails should only be removed if necessary. To remove, drill out detent plugs and thread a self-tapping bolt into plug until plug is pulled out.

4) Remove circlips and pull shift rails out of carrier. Remove detent springs, balls and interlock, and intermediate pins.

NOTE: Removal of selector shafts and detents should not be necessary unless shifting is either too stiff or too easy. Check movement effort by attaching spring scale under hook in end of selector shaft. Pull of 33 to 44 lbs. (15 to 20 kg) should be required to overcome detent springs.

Reassembly

Check all components for wear or damage and replace as necessary. Detent spring length should be .906-.984" (23-25 mm). To reassemble, reverse disassembly procedure and ensure that interlock and intermediate pins are installed properly so that it is not possible to engage 2 gears at the same time.

Fig. 11: Vanagon Shift Housing Assembly

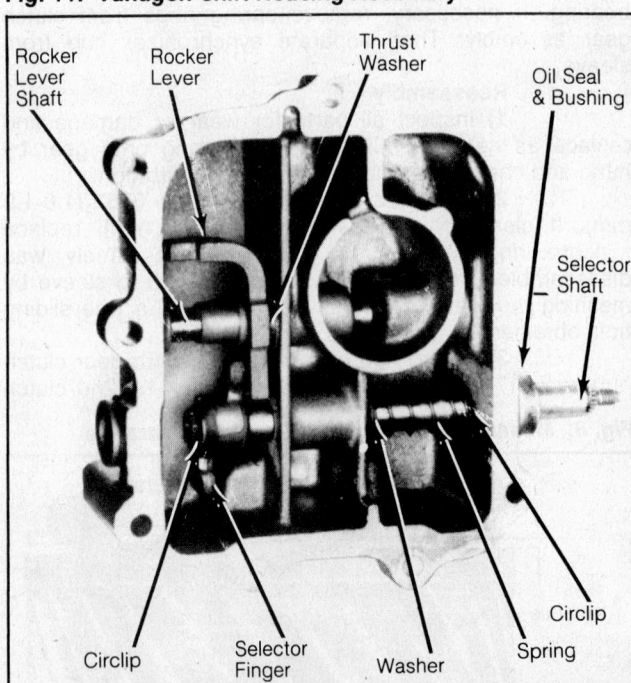

Fig. 12: *Exploded View of Gear Carrier Assembly*

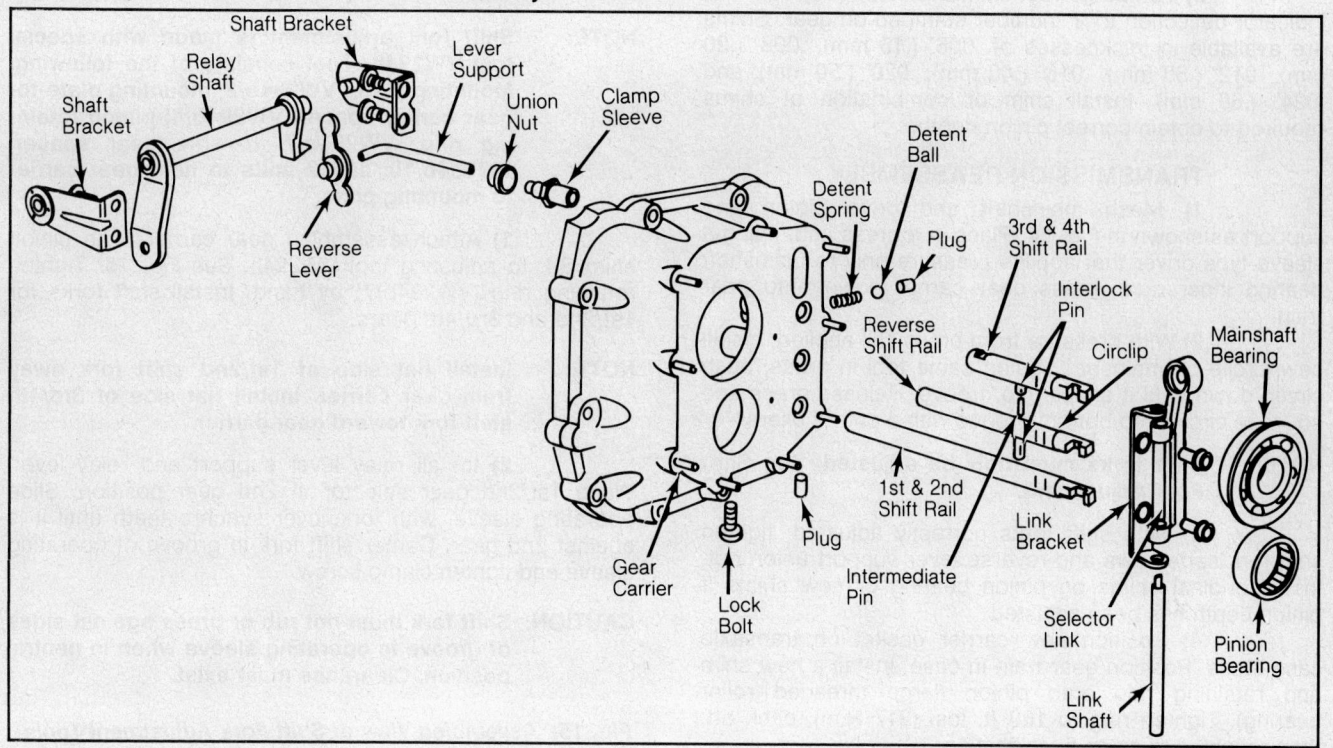

SHIFT HOUSING

Disassembly

1) Drill and tap plugs for rocker lever shaft. Remove rocker lever shaft, rocker lever and thrust washer. Remove backup light switch plug and seal. Remove selector shaft oil seal and bushing.

2) Remove circlips from selector shaft. Push selector shaft out of shift housing. As selector shaft slides out, remove selector finger, washer and spring.

Reassembly

To reassemble shift housing, reverse disassembly procedures and install new seals.

TRANSAXLE REASSEMBLY & ADJUSTMENT

PINION DEPTH

NOTE: **Pinion bearing preload must be correctly adjusted before adjusting pinion depth; see Drive Pinion Shaft Reassembly**

1) Pinion depth is checked using Universal Measuring Bar (VW385/1). Screw in right adjusting ring until ring outer surface is flush with transaxle case. Install magnetic measuring plate (VW385/17) on end of pinion gear.

2) Set dimension "A" *(see Fig. 13)* to 2.95" (75 mm) by sliding setting ring to correct distance from center of measuring bar. Slide 2 centering discs (VW385/4) onto measuring bar until they contact setting rings.

3) Attach measuring pin (VW385/14) with extension (VW385/16) to gauge pin hole in center of measuring bar. Attach a dial indicator to end of bar.

4) Position measuring bar in transaxle case. Install left adjusting ring in case until outer edge is flush with case. Loosen second setting ring and slide out with centering ring until measuring bar can just barely be turned by hand. Tighten screw in setting ring.

Fig. 13: *Installation of Pinion Depth Checking Tools*

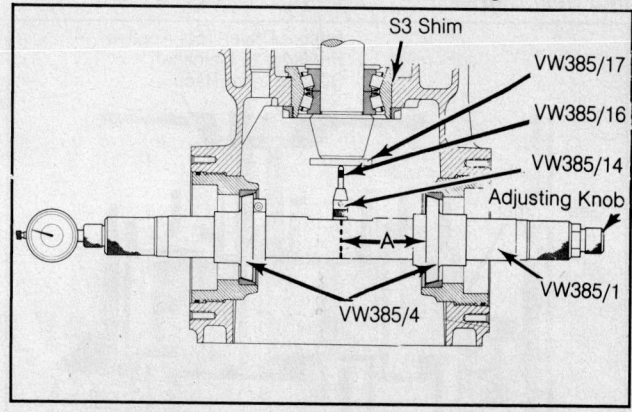

5) Using setting block (VW385/1), zero dial indicator. Turn measuring bar by hand until measuring pin extension is against measuring plate on pinion gear. Turn bar back and forth over center. Record maximum reading on dial indicator. Read deviation number stamped on ring gear.

NOTE: **Although production gears are no longer marked with deviation "r" in .01 mm readings, replacement gear sets will have this number. Shims (S3) must be installed between pinion bearing shoulder and gear case to correct axial placement of pinion gear for proper meshing with ring gear teeth.**

VOLKSWAGEN VANAGON 4-SPEED (Cont.)

6) To find correct shim thickness (S3), add dial indicator deflection to "r" number stamped on gear. Shims are available in thicknesses of .006" (.15 mm), .008" (.20 mm), .012" (.30 mm), .016" (.40 mm), .020" (.50 mm), and .024" (.60 mm). Install shim or combination of shims required to obtain correct pinion depth.

TRANSMISSION REASSEMBLY

1) Mesh mainshaft and drive pinion and support as shown in *Fig. 14*. Place in a press and, using a sleeve type driver that applies pressure only to mainshaft bearing inner race, press gear carrier down onto gear train.

2) With pressure from press still applied, install new circlip on mainshaft. Using same tool in press, push circlip down until it snaps into groove. Release press and squeeze circlip into bottom groove with a pair of pliers.

NOTE: Shift forks must now be adjusted. See Shift Fork Adjustment.

3) With shift forks correctly adjusted, tighten shift fork set screws and reverse lever support union nut. Install original shims on pinion bearing or new shims if pinion depth has been adjusted.

4) Position new carrier gasket on transaxle case studs. Position gear train in case. Install a new shim and retaining ring onto pinion (large threaded roller bearing). Tighten ring to 160 ft. lbs. (217 N.m), back off, then retighten to same specification.

5) Install and tighten gear carrier nuts in a diagonal pattern. Install selector link, bracket and link shaft. Tighten bolts. Install shift housing using new gasket. Make sure rocker lever and selector finger engages selector shafts correctly. Tighten shift housing bolts.

Fig. 14: *Pressing Mainshaft and Pinion Shaft into Gear Carrier*

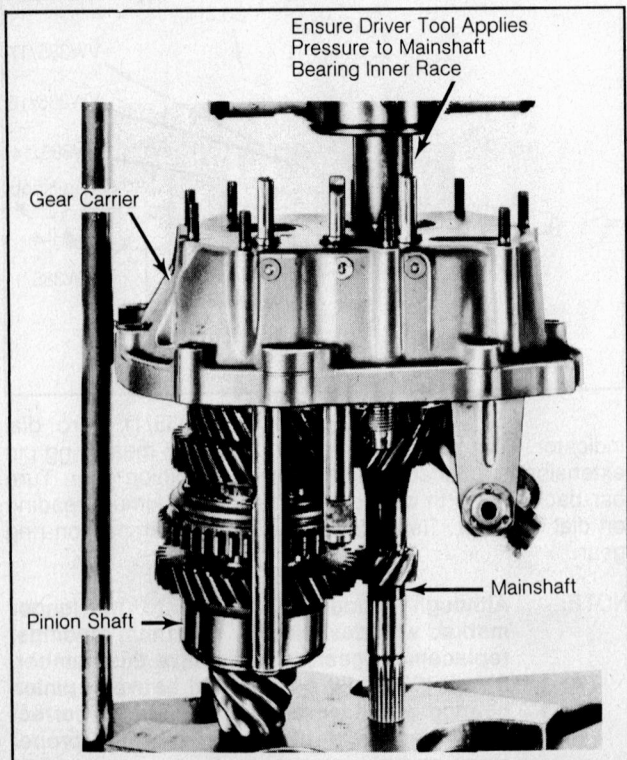

SHIFT FORK ADJUSTMENT

NOTE: Shift fork adjustment is made with special tool VW294b. Tool consists of the following: Mounting plate, VW294b/2; mounting plate-to-gear carrier spacer, VW294b/4; pinion retaining ring, VW294b/7; reverse gear spacer, VW294b/10; and 2 bolts to hold gear carrier to mounting plate.

1) Attach assembled gear carrier, with pinion shim S3, to adjusting tool VW294b. *See Fig. 15.* Tighten retaining ring (VW294b/7) by hand. Install shift forks for 1st/2nd and 3rd/4th gears.

NOTE: Install flat side of 1st/2nd shift fork away from gear carrier. Install flat side of 3rd/4th shift fork toward gear carrier.

2) Install relay lever support and relay lever. Place 1st/2nd gear selector in 2nd gear position. Slide operating sleeve, with fork, over synchro teeth until it is against 2nd gear. Center shift fork in groove of operating sleeve and tighten clamp screw.

CAUTION: Shift fork must not rub or press against sides of groove in operating sleeve when in neutral position. Clearance must exist.

Fig. 15: *Assembled View of Shift Fork Adjustment Tools*

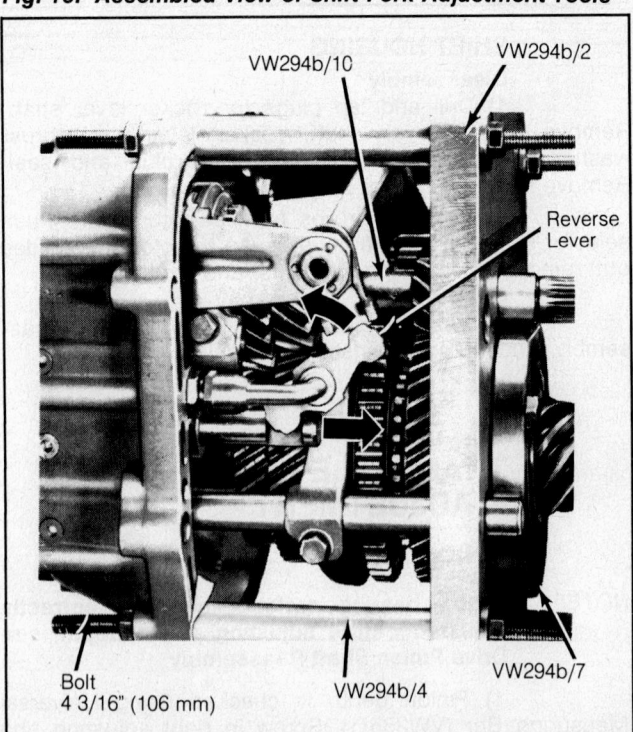

3) Select 1st and 2nd gear position several times while turning mainshaft. Check clearance of shift fork in operating sleeve in each position. If necessary, reposition shift fork until there is same amount of clearance on selector shaft in both end positions, then tighten clamp screw.

4) Place 3rd/4th gear selector shaft in 3rd gear position and adjust 3rd/4th gear shift fork in same manner as 1st/2nd.

VOLKSWAGEN VANAGON 4-SPEED (Cont.)

CAUTION: For correct adjustment of 3rd/4th gears, mainshaft bearing must be pressed fully into gear carrier housing.

5) Place reverse gear selector shaft into reverse gear position. Adjust reverse gear so that sliding gear is fully in mesh with teeth on operating sleeve for 1st/2nd gear. Tighten union nut on relay lever support.

6) Shift out of reverse gear and press sliding gear lightly toward gear carrier. Clearance between reverse gear and 2nd gear on mainshaft must be a minimum of .020" (.5 mm).

7) Engage 2nd gear and check clearance between operating sleeve and reverse sliding gear. Adjust if necessary. Check interlock mechanism. When gear is engaged, it must not be possible to engage any other gear.

SIDE BEARING PRELOAD & RING GEAR BACKLASH

1) Remove oil seals from side bearing adjusting rings. Install adjusting ring on ring gear side of case and screw in until ring is approximately .004-.008" (.1-.2 mm) below measuring surface of case.

2) Install differential in case, with ring gear on left side. Install opposite adjusting ring and tighten until differential is supported without preload.

3) Turn transaxle so that differential is at top and install spacer bridge (VW381/8) on dowel pins to prevent case spreading. Install a torque wrench on ring gear side of differential.

4) Spin differential 15-20 turns in each direction while lubricating the side bearings with hypoid oil. While turning, screw in adjusting ring on side opposite ring gear until preload measured on torque wrench is 26-30 INCH lbs. (3.0-3.4 N.m) for new bearings and 3-6 INCH lbs. (.3-.7 N.m) for used bearings.

5) Measure and record depth to which adjusting rings are screwed in. Mark position of adjusting rings in case. Remove adjusting rings and differential. Rings must be installed on the same side from which they are removed.

6) Install transmission gear train. *See Transmission Reassembly.* Install differential and adjusting rings. Turn adjusting rings until marks made during side bearing preload are aligned. Install a measuring bracket (VW381/7) on ring gear bolts.

7) Mount a spacer bar and dial indicator across ring gear end of case. Turn mainshaft until dial indicator stem contacts measuring bracket on ring gear. Continue turning mainshaft until dial indicator shows .060" (1.5 mm) preload. Lock pinion shaft with a clamping bar bolted on gear carrier.

8) Turn ring gear by hand away from dial indicator until it is stopped by locked pinion. Now zero dial indicator. Again turn ring gear by hand toward dial indicator until it is stopped by locked pinion. The reading on dial indicator is ring gear backlash.

9) Backlash should be .006-.010" (.15-.25 mm). If backlash not to specifications, screw one adjusting ring inward and the other ring outward by exactly the same amount until backlash is within specification.

10) Recheck backlash measuring procedure at three other points on ring gear, 90° apart. All measurements must be within specification and not vary more than .002" (.06 mm).

11) Install new oil seals and "O" rings in adjusting rings if not previously done. Coat outer surface of adjusting rings with an anti-rust preventative sealer. Install new adjusting ring lock plates and tighten screws evenly.

NOTE: Do not tighten left hand adjusting ring until the clutch housing has been fitted and the nuts tightened.

FINAL ASSEMBLY

Install clutch housing and tighten nuts to specification. Install thrust rings, axle drive shaft flanges and new circlips. It may be necessary to lift differential pinion gear shaft slightly to gain clearance for installation of circlips. Install new plastic caps in center of axle drive shaft flanges.

TRANSAXLE SPECIFICATIONS

Application	Measurement
Synchro Ring-to-Gear Clearance	.040-.067" (1.0-1.7 mm)
Ring and Pinion Backlash	.006-.010" (.15-.25 mm)
Pinion Bearing Preload	
New Bearings	5-18 INCH Lbs. (.6-2.0 N.m)
Used Bearings	3-6 INCH Lbs. (.3-.7 N.m)
Side Bearing Preload	
New Bearings	26-30 INCH Lbs. (3.0-3.4 N.m)
Used Bearings	3-6 INCH Lbs. (.3-.7 N.m)

TIGHTENING SPECIFICATIONS

Application	Ft. Lbs. (N.m)
Pinion Shaft Retainer Ring	160 (217)
Ring Gear Bolts	36 (49)
Gear Carrier	14 (19)
Clutch Housing	14 (19)
Reverse Shift Shaft Bracket	18 (24)
Clamp Sleeve	32 (43)
Union Nut	21 (28)
Shift Housing	14 (19)
Drive Shaft Flange Bolts	32 (43)
Wheel Hub-to-Axle Shaft Nut	253 (343)
Transaxle-to-Engine	22 (30)

Manual Transmissions

VOLKSWAGEN JETTA, RABBIT & SCIROCCO 4 & 5-SPEED TRANSAXLE

DESCRIPTION

Transaxles are 4 or 5-speed, fully synchronized units, mounted transversely at the front of vehicle. Transmission gears are all helical cut and are in constant mesh with mating gears on countershaft.

Forward gear engagement is accomplished through blocker ring type synchronizer assemblies. Reverse gears are spur type and are not in constant mesh, and are engaged by a sliding type reverse idler gear.

Final drive portion of transaxle consists of a drive pinion shaft (which also carries some of the transmission gears), and a differential and ring gear assembly.

The 4-speed transmission and final drive components are carried in a common 2-piece case. The 5-speed is almost identical to the 4-speed except the 5th gear assembly is located on the end of the pinion and mainshaft in a separate housing.

Transaxle codes (020 for 4-speed, 020F for 5-speed) are stamped on lower side of transaxle case, adjacent to left axle drive flange.

LUBRICATION & ADJUSTMENT

See the appropriate article in MANUAL TRANSMISSION SERVICING Section.

SERVICE (IN VEHICLE)

AXLE DRIVE SHAFTS

NOTE: **Vehicle weight must be resting on wheels to remove axle shaft nut.**

Removal

Remove axle shaft nut. Raise and support vehicle; remove tire and wheel. Remove Allen bolts connecting inner constant velocity (CV) joint to differential case drive flange. Press drive shaft and guide shaft out of hub, past transaxle assembly.

NOTE: **Axle drive shafts should be disassembled ONLY to replace defective rubber boots. If boots are replaced, check all components for wear or damage and replace as complete assembly.**

Disassembly

1) On inner CV joint, remove circlip from axle shaft and drive protective cap from CV joint. Place axle shaft in holder (VW402) and press CV joint from shaft with adapter (VW408a), supporting hub to prevent damage.

2) Pivot hub and cage assembly out of inner joint, then push out and remove balls. Align ball hub grooves with cage and remove hub.

NOTE: **Inner CV joint and ball hub are matched sets. DO NOT interchange with outer joint. Also, balls of CV joints cannot be interchanged between CV joints.**

Fig. 2: Removing Inner CV Joint Ball Hub

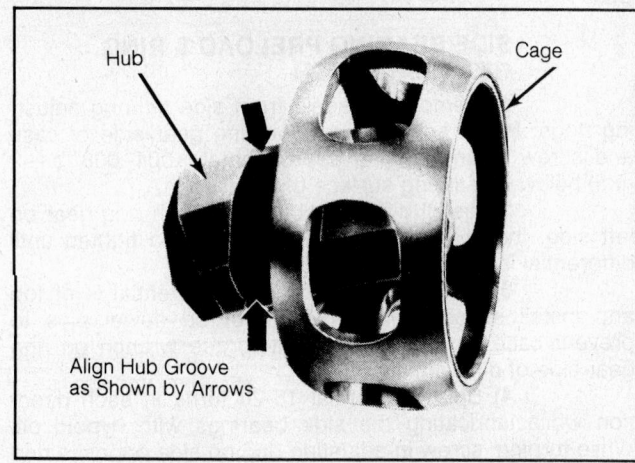

3) Remove and discard inner boot clamp and boot. On outer CV joint, spread circlip inside ball hub and drive CV joint off axle shaft with brass drift; tap on hub.

4) Mark position of ball hub and outer joint, then tilt cage and remove each ball. Align cage perpendicular to joint, align 2 large openings of cage with raised portions of joint and remove cage and hub.

5) Position 1 retainer of hub in large opening and remove hub by tilting outward. Remove and discard outer boot and clamp.

Reassembly

1) To reassemble CV joints, reverse disassembly procedure and note the following: Lubricate joints with 3 ozs. (90 g) of molybdenum disulphide grease. After

Fig. 1: Exploded View of Axle Drive Shafts

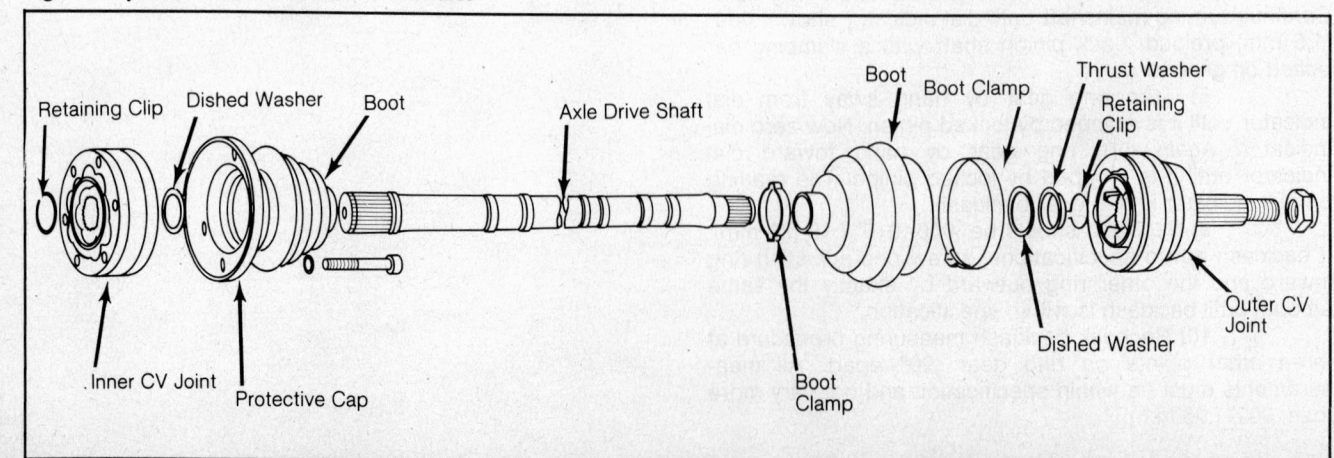

VOLKSWAGEN JETTA, RABBIT & SCIROCCO
4 & 5-SPEED TRANSAXLE (Cont.)

inserting balls into inner CV joint hub and cage, insert hub and cage into joint perpendicularly.

2) Chamfer of ball hub splines must face larger diameter of joint. Then rotate ball and cage into position and ensure CV joint wide ball groove and narrow hub groove are on same side of joint. *See Fig. 3.* Joint is correctly assembled if hub can move over shaft splines by hand.

Fig. 3: Installing Ball Hub and Cage in Inner CV Joint

3) Outer CV joint alignment marks must match after reassembly. Replace dust boots and clamps. Install CV joints onto drive axle shaft with inside ball hub chamfer facing shaft. Outer CV joint must be assembled with dished washer concave side facing thrust washer and convex side of thrust washer facing CV joint. *See Fig. 4.*

Installation
To install, reverse removal procedures.

Fig. 4: Cutaway View of Outer CV Joint Showing Installation of Dished and Thrust Washers

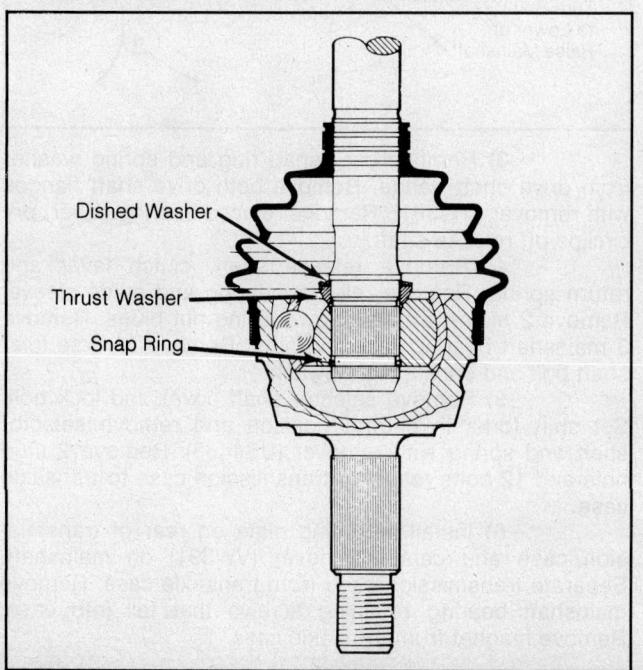

NOTE: The CV joint assembly shown in Fig. 4 is a new production assembly which may be installed on Jetta, Rabbit Convertible and Scirocco models. Former production assembly has snap ring installed closer to thrust washer. DO NOT interchange components between assemblies

FRONT WHEEL BEARINGS
Removal
1) With vehicle supported and drive axle shafts removed, remove caliper mounting bolts. Hang caliper from frame with wire; DO NOT disconnect hydraulic line. Remove brake disc.

2) Remove lower steering knuckle housing-to-ball joint retaining bolt. Remove ball joint castellated nut and cotter pin, then separate ball joint from steering knuckle.

3) Separate tie rod end from steering knuckle. Mark position of camber adjustment bolt (upper bolt securing steering knuckle to strut assembly). Remove bolts securing steering knuckle to strut assembly and remove steering knuckle.

NOTE: Camber adjustment must be checked after wheel bearing replacement. DO NOT lose camber adjustment bolt or eccentric washer.

4) Mount steering knuckle in holding fixture and press out wheel hub. Remove dust shield. Remove circlips from both sides of bearing housing and press out bearing (toward outboard end of housing) with tools shown in *Fig. 5.* Remove inner wheel bearing race from hub.

NOTE: Wheel bearing must be replaced. Removal procedure destroys wheel bearing for re-installation.

Fig. 5: Identification of Tools to Be Used to Replace Front Wheel Bearing

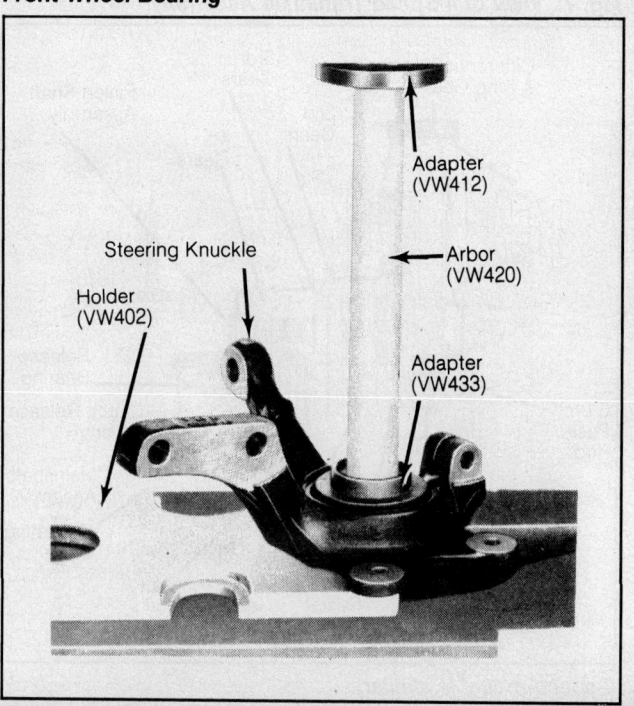

7-254

Manual Transmissions
VOLKSWAGEN JETTA, RABBIT & SCIROCCO
4 & 5-SPEED TRANSAXLE (Cont.)

Installation
To install, reverse removal procedure and note the following: Ensure circlips are fully seated. Always replace ball joint cotter pin.

AXLE DRIVE FLANGE OIL SEALS
Removal
Disconnect axle shaft from drive flange and position out of the way. Remove cap from drive flange, then withdraw retaining snap ring and dished washer. Fasten a puller (VW391) to drive flange and pull flange from transmission. Using a seal puller (VW681), pry oil seal from housing.

Fig. 6: Using Puller to Remove Axle Drive Flange

Remove Flange with Puller after Removing Snap Ring

Installation
Drive new seal into housing with driver (US4450). Install drive flange using puller used during removal (reverse puller for installation). Place dished washer on shaft with convex side away from flange, then drive circlip in place with driver (VW30-23). Replace dust cap and install drive shaft.

Fig. 7: View of 4-Speed Transaxle Assembly

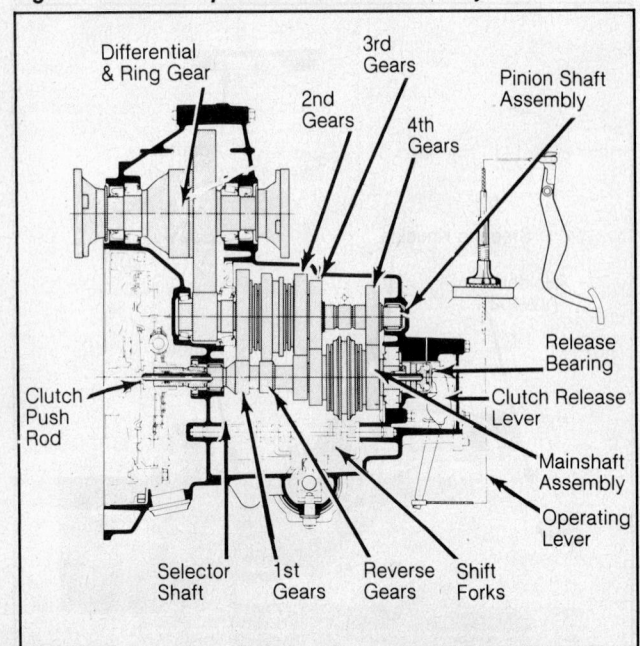

5-speed model is similar.

NOTE: Pack open side of seals with multi-purpose lubricant prior to installation. Check gear lube level and add as required.

TRANSAXLE REMOVAL & INSTALLATION
See the appropriate article in MANUAL TRANSMISSION REMOVAL Section.

TRANSAXLE DISASSEMBLY
NOTE: Before disassembly, measure and record pinion depth and ring gear backlash.

4-SPEED
1) Mount transaxle in holding fixture and drain fluid. Remove clutch release push rod from center of mainshaft and withdraw from bell housing end.

2) Install support bar (30-211) across mouth of bell housing and install support block (VW 295a) between support bar and mainshaft. Tighten bolt of bar to take up clearance between bar and mainshaft. See Fig. 8.

Fig. 8: Installation of Mainshaft Support Fixture

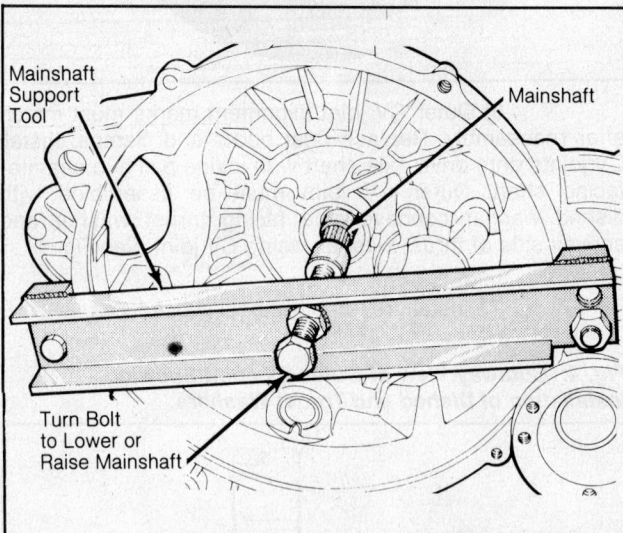

Mainshaft Support Tool / Mainshaft / Turn Bolt to Lower or Raise Mainshaft

3) Remove cap, snap ring and spring washer from drive shaft flange. Remove both drive shaft flanges with remover (VW391). Remove release bearing cover, pry circlips off release shaft.

4) Remove release shaft, clutch lever and return spring. Remove release bearing and guide sleeve. Remove 2 mainshaft bearing retaining nut plugs. Remove 3 mainshaft bearing retaining nuts. Remove reverse idler shaft bolt and backup light switch.

5) Remove selector shaft cover and lock bolt. Set shift forks in neutral position and remove selector shaft and spring with remover (US4463). Remove 2 stud nuts and 12 bolts retaining transmission case to transaxle case.

6) Install mounting plate on rear of transmission case and center remover (VW391) on mainshaft. Separate transmission case from transaxle case. Remove mainshaft bearing retaining screws that fell into case. Remove magnet from transaxle case.

VOLKSWAGEN JETTA, RABBIT & SCIROCCO
4 & 5-SPEED TRANSAXLE (Cont.)

7) Remove mainshaft bearing shim. Remove 2 "E" clips from shift fork and pull shift fork shaft from housing. Swing shift forks to one side and remove reverse gear and shaft. Remove 4th gear snap ring from pinion shaft. Remove mainshaft assembly and 4th gear on pinion shaft as an assembly.

8) Remove snap ring, 3rd gear, 2nd gear, 2nd gear needle bearing and race and 2nd gear synchronizer ring. Using a puller, simultaneously remove 1st gear, 1st gear synchronizer ring, 1st-2nd gear synchronizer, 1st gear needle bearing and thrust washer. Remove pinion bearing cover bolts, remove cover and pull pinion shaft out of bore. Lift out differential unit.

NOTE: **All gears must be removed from pinion shaft before shaft and differential can be removed from case.**

5-SPEED

1) Mount transaxle in holding fixture and drain fluid. Remove clutch release push rod from center of mainshaft and withdraw from bell housing end. Install support bar (30-211) across mouth of bell housing and install support block (VW295a) between support bar and mainshaft. Tighten bolt of bar to take up clearance between bar and mainshaft. *See Fig. 8.*

Fig. 9: Exploded View of 4-Speed Transmission Case

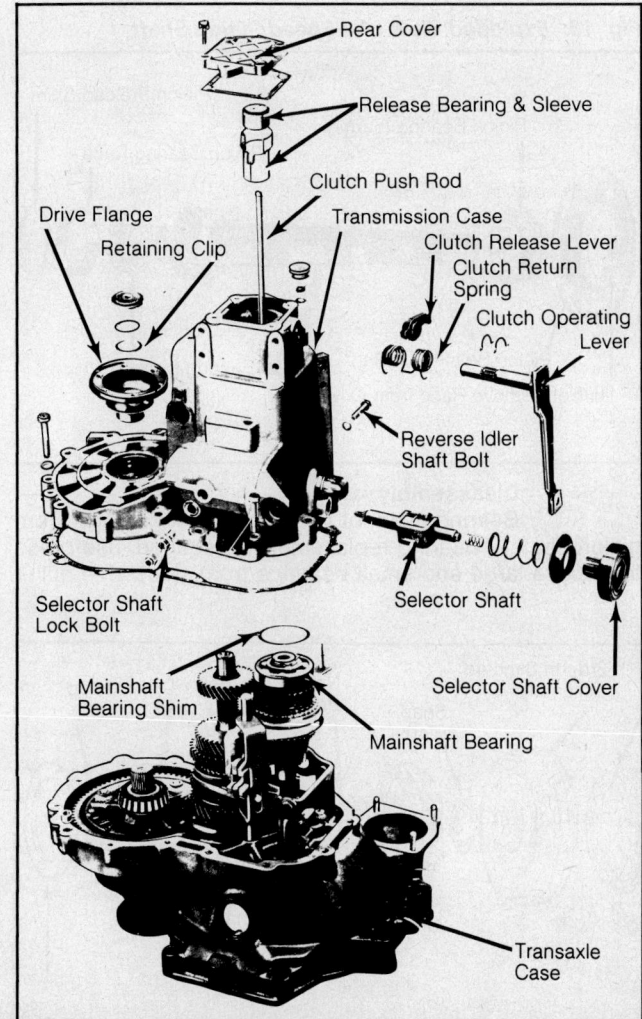

2) Remove rear housing bolts and rear housing. Remove backup light switch, 5th gear lock out and selector shaft detent. Remove selector shaft cover. Set gears in neutral position and remove selector shaft and spring. Remove cap, snap ring and spring washer from drive shaft flange. Remove both drive shaft flanges with remover (VW391).

Fig. 10: View of 4-Speed Pinion Shaft Assembly

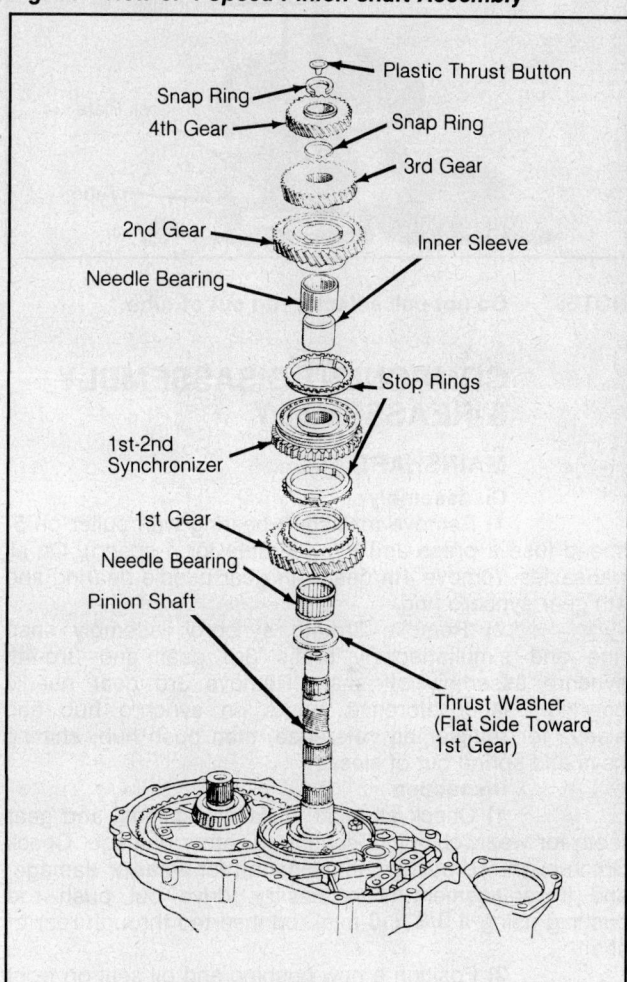

3) Lock transmission in 5th and reverse gears and remove 5th gear synchronizer hub retaining bolt. Pry locking plate loose until tube can be turned and screw tube out of shift fork in a counterclockwise rotation with remover (3059).

4) Remove tube with remover (3038). Remove 5th gear synchronizer, 5th gear and shift fork from transmission case. Remove circlip and thrust washer from 5th gear and pull 5th gear off pinion shaft with a puller.

5) Remove recess bolts from mainshaft retainer plate. Remove transmission housing-to-transaxle housing bolts. Using remover (3042), remove transmission housing. Remove shift fork rod and forks. Remove 4th gear snap ring from pinion shaft. Remove mainshaft assembly and 4th gear on pinion shaft as an assembly.

6) Remove circlip from 3rd gear and remove 3rd gear, 2nd gear synchronizer, bearing and reverse gear. Use puller and remove 1st gear synchronizer and 1st gear. Remove pinion bearing retainer plate and pinion shaft. Remove differential assembly from case.

Manual Transmissions
VOLKSWAGEN JETTA, RABBIT & SCIROCCO
4 & 5-SPEED TRANSAXLE (Cont.)

Fig. 11: Removing 5th Gear Synchronizer Assembly

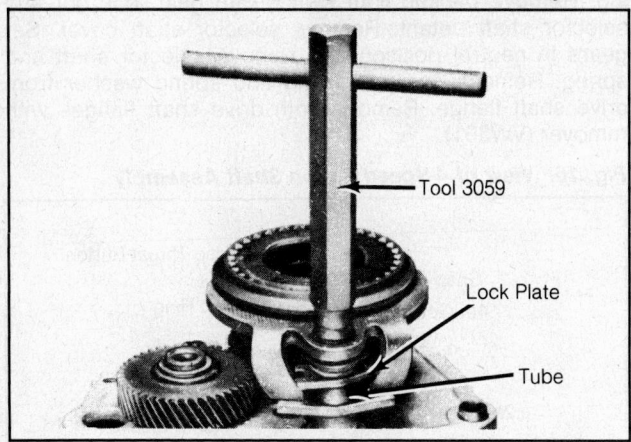

- Tool 3059
- Lock Plate
- Tube

NOTE: Do not pull selector rod out of tube.

COMPONENT DISASSEMBLY & REASSEMBLY

MAINSHAFT

Disassembly

1) Remove mainshaft bearing with puller on 5-speed (use a press and VW402 plate for 4-speed). On all transaxles, remove 4th gear, 4th gear needle bearing and 4th gear synchro ring.

2) Remove 3rd-4th synchro assembly snap ring and simultaneously press 3rd gear and 3rd-4th synchro assembly off shaft. Remove 3rd gear needle bearing. Place reference marks on synchro hub and sleeve for reassembly reference, then push hub, shifting keys and spring out of sleeve.

Inspection

1) Check all shaft surfaces, splines, and gear teeth for wear, chipping, scoring, or other damage. Check clutch push rod bushing in mainshaft for wear or damage, and if replacement is necessary, drive out push rod bushing using a 3/8" (10 mm) rod inserted through rear of shaft.

2) Position a new bushing and oil seal on front of mainshaft, and press into shaft until flush. Assemble synchro rings on gears and check ring-to-gear clearance. Clearance for new parts should be .044-.069" (1.12-1.75 mm) for 3rd gear, .051-.075" (1.3-1.9 mm) for 4th gear. Wear limit for used parts is .020" (.5 mm).

NOTE: Replacement of any gear necessitates replacement of meshing gear, as gears are available as matched pairs only.

Reassembly

1) Position shifting keys in slots of synchronizer hub, then install hub into synchronizer sleeve, after aligning reference marks. Install key springs into assembly, making sure springs are positioned 120° offset of one another and that angled ends of springs engage hollowed-out portions of shifting keys. On 5th gear, install synchro key retainer plate.

2) Install 3rd gear needle bearing on shaft. Assemble 3rd gear, 3rd gear synchro ring and synchro assembly, ensuring notches in synchro ring engage 3 keys in synchro assembly and that splines in synchro hub face 3rd gear. Press mainshaft into assembled synchro assembly, 3rd gear and synchro ring. Install snap ring, 4th gear synchro ring, needle bearing and 4th gear. On 5-speed transmission, press bearing on mainshaft with press.

PINION SHAFT

NOTE: Gears and synchronizer assembly were removed during Transmission Disassembly, and will be installed during Transmission Reassembly. Synchronizer overhaul and bearing replacement are covered below.

Fig. 13: Exploded View of 4-Speed Pinion Shaft

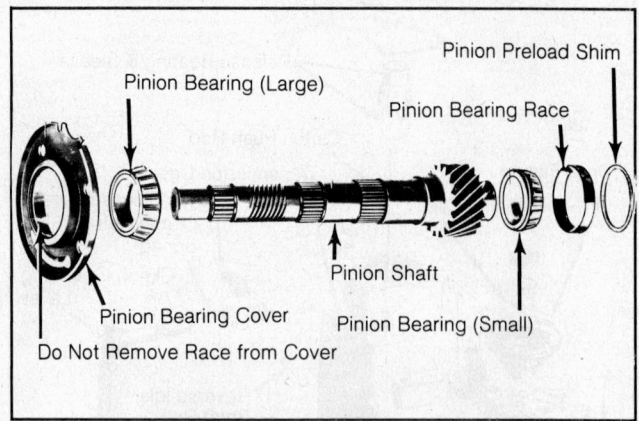

- Pinion Bearing (Large)
- Pinion Preload Shim
- Pinion Bearing Race
- Pinion Shaft
- Pinion Bearing Cover
- Pinion Bearing (Small)
- Do Not Remove Race from Cover

Disassembly

Bearings cannot be reused after removal from pinion shaft. If bearing replacement is required, use press to remove large and small bearings from shaft. Use puller

Fig. 12: Exploded View of 4-Speed Mainshaft Assembly

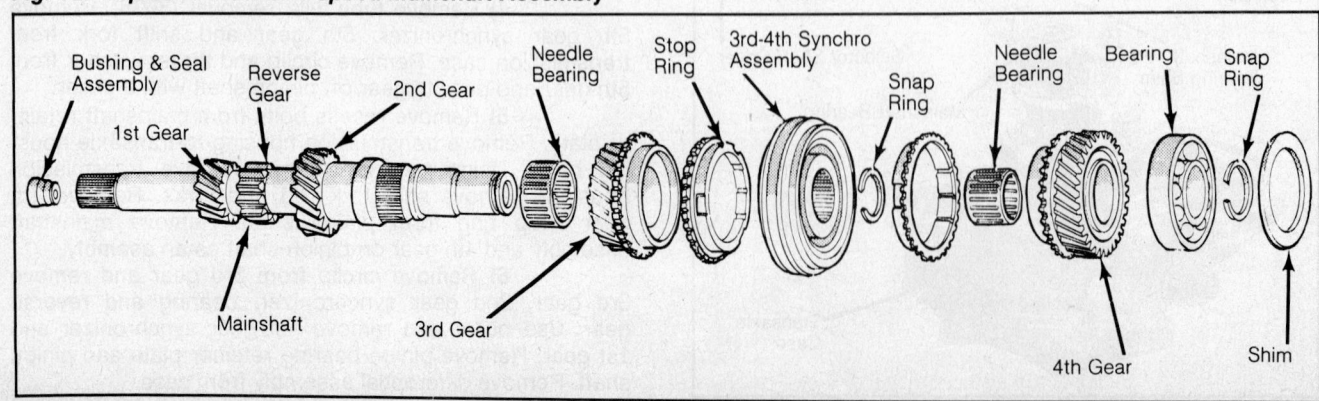

- Bushing & Seal Assembly
- 1st Gear
- Reverse Gear
- 2nd Gear
- Needle Bearing
- Stop Ring
- 3rd-4th Synchro Assembly
- Snap Ring
- Needle Bearing
- Bearing
- Snap Ring
- Mainshaft
- 3rd Gear
- 4th Gear
- Shim

VOLKSWAGEN JETTA, RABBIT & SCIROCCO
4 & 5-SPEED TRANSAXLE

to remove small bearing outer race from case. For reassembly reference, scribe reference marks on synchro hub and operating sleeve. Then, push hub, shifting keys and springs out of sleeve.

Inspection

Check all shaft surfaces, splines and gear teeth for wear, chipping, scoring or other damage. Assemble synchro rings on gears and check ring-to-gear clearance. Clearance for new parts should be .043-.067" (1.1-1.7 mm). Wear limit for used parts is .020" (.5 mm).

NOTE: Replacement of any gear necessitates replacement of meshing gear, as gears are available as matched pairs only.

Reassembly

If bearings were removed from pinion shaft, heat new bearings to approximately 212°F (100°C) and install on pinion shaft with press. Install shifting keys into synchronizer hub, then install hub into synchronizer sleeve, making sure reference marks are aligned. Install shifting key springs into assembly with springs offset 120° from each other. Angled ends of springs must engage hollowed out portions of shifting keys.

NOTE: DO NOT install pinion bearing race into case half at this time; adjustment of pinion is required and will be covered in Transmission Reassembly.

REVERSE IDLER GEAR & SHAFT

The stop sleeve is no longer installed on idler gear shaft. Gear end movement is limited by the stop on drive pinion shaft bearing retainer. To install, loosely install idler gear support bolt in idler gear shaft. Align shaft as shown in *Fig. 21*. Bolt in shaft should be an equal distance from each bolt hole in flange of case.

Fig. 14: Reverse Idler Gear Stop on Pinion Cover Plate

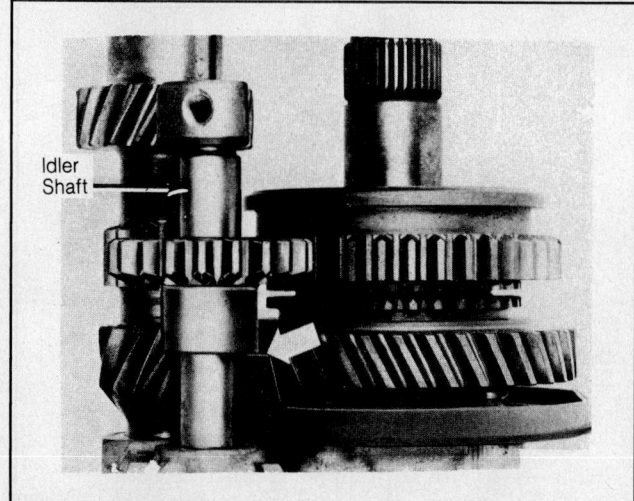

Idler Shaft

DIFFERENTIAL
Disassembly

1) Ring gear is attached to differential housing by rivets on 5-speed. Drill out rivet heads with a 15/32" (12 mm) drill bit, then knock out rivets with a drift. Remove ring gear bolt lock plate and remove bolts on 4-speed. Place assembly in a press and press off differential ring gear.

NOTE: Ring gear is reinstalled with special bolts, washers and nuts. Serrations on shank of bolts lock bolt in housing.

2) Remove snap rings from differential pinion shaft, and drive shaft out of housing. Remove snap rings securing side gears to axle drive flange shafts, and remove shafts from housing. Remove pinions and side gears. Rotate thrust cage and remove from housing.

Fig. 15: Cutaway View of Differential Showing Flange Shaft Snap Ring Installation

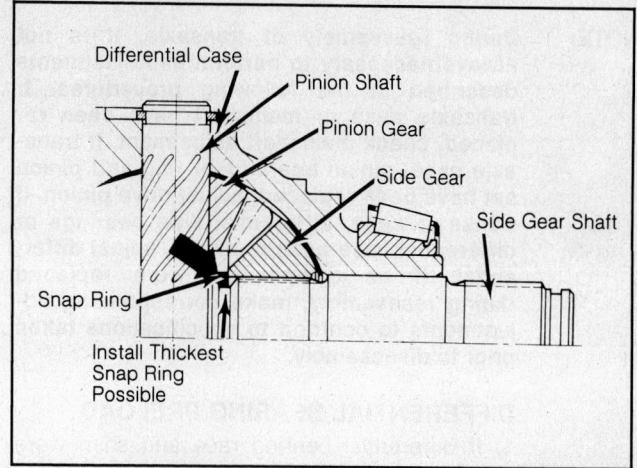

Differential Case
Pinion Shaft
Pinion Gear
Side Gear
Side Gear Shaft
Snap Ring
Install Thickest Snap Ring Possible

Reassembly

1) Insert thrust cage into differential housing. Insert pinion gears into housing and drive in pinion shaft. Install pinion shaft snap rings. Rotate thrust cage to align side gear shaft holes with side gear shaft holes of housing.

NOTE: If bearings were removed from case, heat bearings to approximately 212°F (100°C) and use a press to drive bearings into place.

2) Insert and position side gears so they mesh with pinion gears and are 180° apart. Rotate side gears into position inside housing. Install axle drive flange shafts, and push each shaft firmly against differential pinion shaft and install thickest snap ring possible. See Fig. 15.

Fig. 16: Exploded View of Differential Assembly

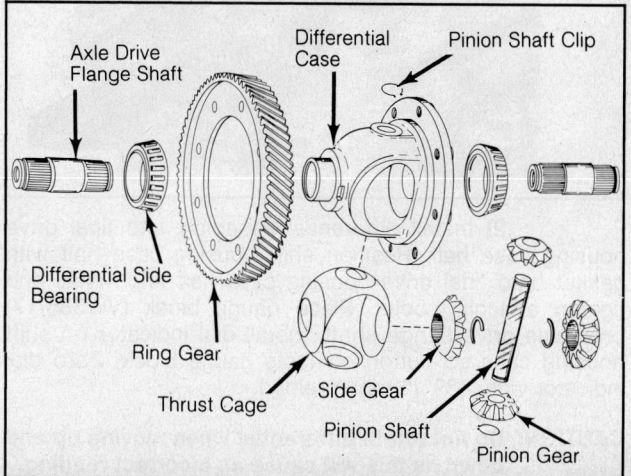

Axle Drive Flange Shaft
Differential Case
Pinion Shaft Clip
Differential Side Bearing
Ring Gear
Thrust Cage
Side Gear
Pinion Shaft
Pinion Gear

Manual Transmissions
VOLKSWAGEN JETTA, RABBIT & SCIROCCO
4 & 5-SPEED TRANSAXLE (Cont.)

NOTE: There are two available snap rings. One is .079" (2.0 mm) thick, and the other is .091" (2.3 mm). If thicker snap ring jams sideways, install thinner snap ring.

3) Heat ring gear to about 212°F (100°C). Drive bolts into differential housing and place heated ring gear onto housing. Install washers and nuts onto ring gear bolts and tighten to 50 ft. lbs. (68 N.m).

TRANSAXLE REASSEMBLY & ADJUSTMENT

NOTE: During reassembly of transaxle, it is not always necessary to perform all adjustments described in the following procedures. If transaxle case or mainshaft have been replaced, check mainshaft adjustment. If transaxle case, pinion bearings or ring and pinion set have been replaced, adjust drive pinion. If transaxle case, differential side bearings or differential have been replaced, adjust differential. If no components were replaced during reassembly, make corresponding adjustments to conform to specifications taken prior to disassembly.

DIFFERENTIAL BEARING PRELOAD

1) If differential bearing race and shim were removed from final drive housing case half, position a .039" (1 mm) shim in bearing race bore and press in bearing race. Remove bearing race and shim from shift housing case half (if not already removed), and reinstall bearing race into housing **without shims.**

Fig. 17: Using a Dial Indicator to Measure Differential Side Play in Case

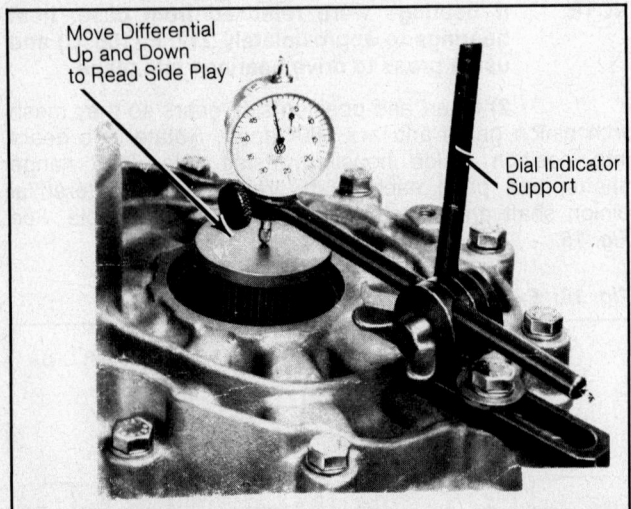

2) Install differential assembly into final drive housing case half. Position shift housing case half with gasket onto final drive housing case half and install and tighten attaching bolts. Place gauge block (VW385/17) onto axle drive flange shaft. Install dial indicator on shift housing case so button contacts gauge block. Zero dial indicator with .039" (1 mm) preload.

CAUTION: Do not rotate differential when moving up and down as this will cause an incorrect reading.

3) Move differential assembly up and down and note reading on dial indicator. Add constant preload figure of .016" (.4 mm) to dial indicator reading to obtain thickness of shim to install under shift housing case half differential bearing race.

4) Separate housings and remove differential. Press out shift housing case half differential bearing race, install shim just determined in bearing race bore, then reinstall bearing race with a press.

NOTE: Adjusting shims are available in various thicknesses from .006" (.15 mm) to .039" (1 mm). Install a combination of shims as required to make up shim pack. Thickest shim should be inserted first, with thinnest against bearing race.

5) Lubricate bearings with hypoid oil and reinstall in transaxle case. Install adapter and INCH lb. torque wrench to drive axle flange shaft and check rotating torque.

6) Rotating torque should be 11-31 INCH lbs. (1.2-3.5 N.m) for new bearings and 3 INCH lbs. (.34 N.m) for used bearings. If not within specifications, recheck bearing condition and verify proper shim thickness.

PINION BEARING PRELOAD

1) If not already removed, use a puller to withdraw pinion bearing race from final drive housing case half. Temporarily install a .025" (.65 mm) shim into bearing race bore of case half, then reinstall race using a press.

Fig. 18: Method Used to Measure Pinion Shaft End Play

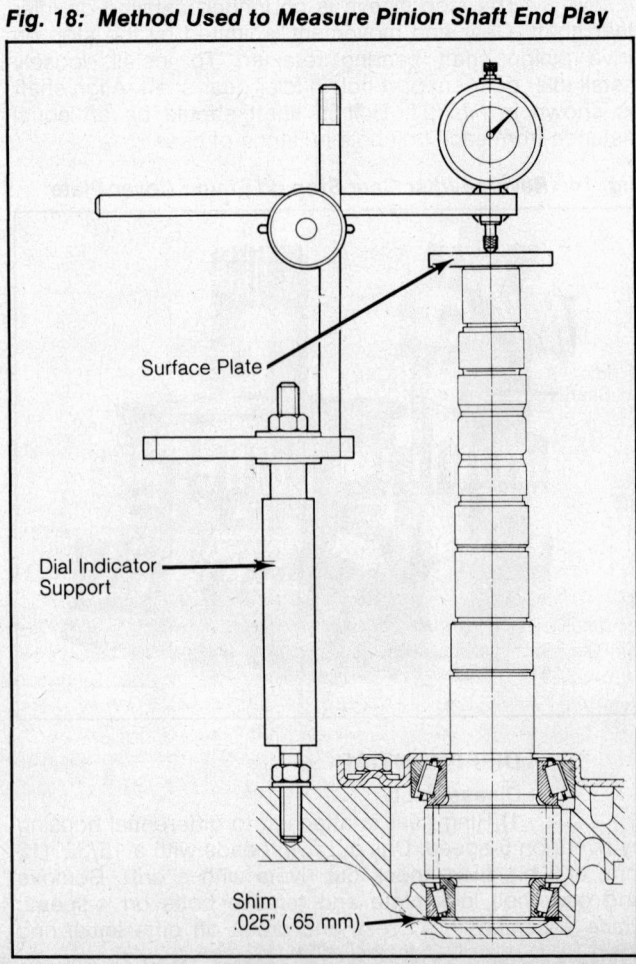

VOLKSWAGEN JETTA, RABBIT & SCIROCCO
4 & 5-SPEED TRANSAXLE (Cont.)

Install pinion shaft into bearing race, then install pinion bearing cover, tightening cover-to-case half bolts securely.

CAUTION: Do not rotate pinion when moving up and down as this will cause an incorrect reading.

2) Install surface plate on top of pinion shaft. Install dial indicator and support on case half so button of indicator contacts surface plate. *See Fig. 18.* Preload dial indicator with .039" (1 mm) and zero dial face. Move pinion up and down and note maximum dial indicator reading.

3) To dial indicator reading, add thickness of shim temporarily installed under bearing race (.025" — .65 mm), plus a constant preload figure of .008" (.2 mm). Total of 3 figures equals thickness of shims to install under pinion bearing race in case half. Remove pinion and bearing race, replace .025" (.65 mm) shim with shim pack just determined, then reinstall bearing race.

NOTE: Adjusting shims are available in thicknesses ranging from .026" (.65 mm) to .055" (1.4 mm) in increments of .002" (.5 mm). Install a combination of shims as required to make up shim pack.

DIFFERENTIAL & PINION INSTALLATION

1) Place final drive housing on work bench and lubricate differential bearings with gear oil. Install differential assembly into transaxle case. Lubricate pinion bearings with gear oil and install pinion shaft. Install pinion bearing cover and tighten bearing retainer plate and transmission case-to-transaxle case attaching bolts.

2) Install adapter (VW548) onto pinion shaft, and measure rotating torque with an INCH lb. torque wrench. Rotating torque should be 5-13 INCH lbs. (.56-1.5 N.m) for new bearings and at least 3 INCH lbs. (.34 N.m) for used bearings.

PINION SHAFT REASSEMBLY

1) With pinion shaft mounted in case, install thrust washer (recess facing downward) and 1st gear needle bearing over end of pinion shaft and down against cover. Install 1st gear onto pinion shaft and follow with 1st gear synchro ring (110° tooth angle and 3 teeth missing around circumference).

2) Position 1st-2nd synchro assembly (shift fork slot facing upward) onto shaft. While ensuring correct engagement of synchro assembly, press synchro onto shaft.

NOTE: Special 1st gear synchro ring (110° tooth angle) is not available as replacement part. If defective, replace with standard synchro ring used for 2nd, 3rd or 4th gear.

3) Install 2nd synchro ring into 1st-2nd synchronizer. Position 2nd gear needle bearing inner race over pinion shaft and press into place against synchro hub. Install 2nd gear needle bearing and 2nd gear, then follow with 3rd gear. Install selective snap ring that will provide clearance of 0-.008" (0-.2 mm) between snap ring and 3rd gear.

NOTE: Always use a new snap ring when reassembling. Final installation of 4th gear and snap ring will be performed after mainshaft installation.

MAINSHAFT INSTALLATION & ADJUSTMENT
4-Speed

1) Install mainshaft into final drive housing case half so gears of mainshaft mesh with gears of pinion gears.

NOTE: Select a new mainshaft adjusting shim as described in the following procedure only if mainshaft or either half of transaxle case has been replaced. If no adjustment is required, install original shim in bore of shift housing case half and proceed to step 8).

2) Install a support bar (30-211) onto clutch housing side of final drive housing case half so adjusting bolt contacts front of mainshaft. Lift mainshaft up with adjusting bolt until a clearance of .039" (1 mm) exists between 2nd gear of pinion shaft and 3rd gear of mainshaft.

3) Lock adjusting bolt, ensure clearance has not changed, and install dummy bearing measuring sleeve (VW549) onto mainshaft.

Fig. 19: *Measuring 4-Speed Mainshaft Installed Height*

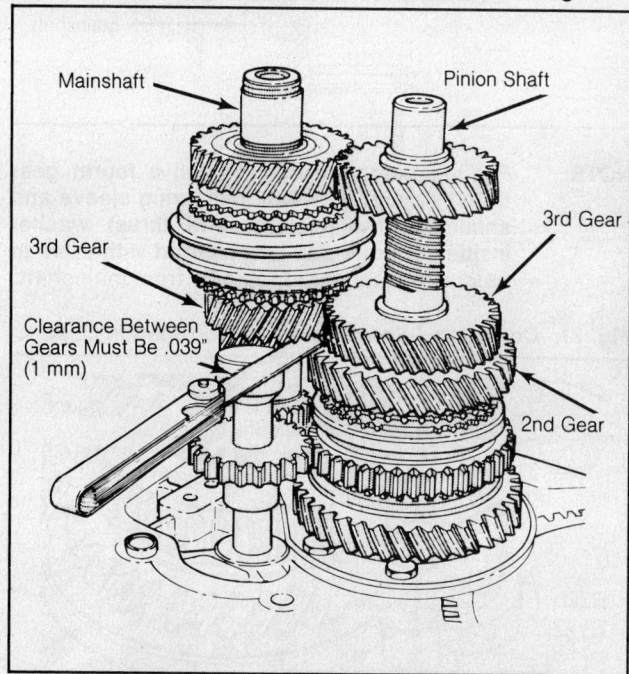

4) Install a new gasket onto final drive case half. Install shift housing case (without mainshaft ball bearing or clamping bolts installed) onto assembly. Install and tighten 5 bolts to 14 ft. lbs. (19 N.m) to secure case halves.

5) Install dial indicator assembly onto outside of shift housing case half. Position button of indicator against measuring sleeve tool. Zero dial indicator with .12" (.3 mm) preload.

6) Grasp measuring sleeve and move up and down; read resulting play indicated on dial indicator. Select a shim (to be installed under bearing in shift housing case half) from table.

Manual Transmissions

VOLKSWAGEN JETTA, RABBIT & SCIROCCO 4 & 5-SPEED TRANSAXLE (Cont.)

Fig. 20: Measuring 4-Speed Mainshaft End Play

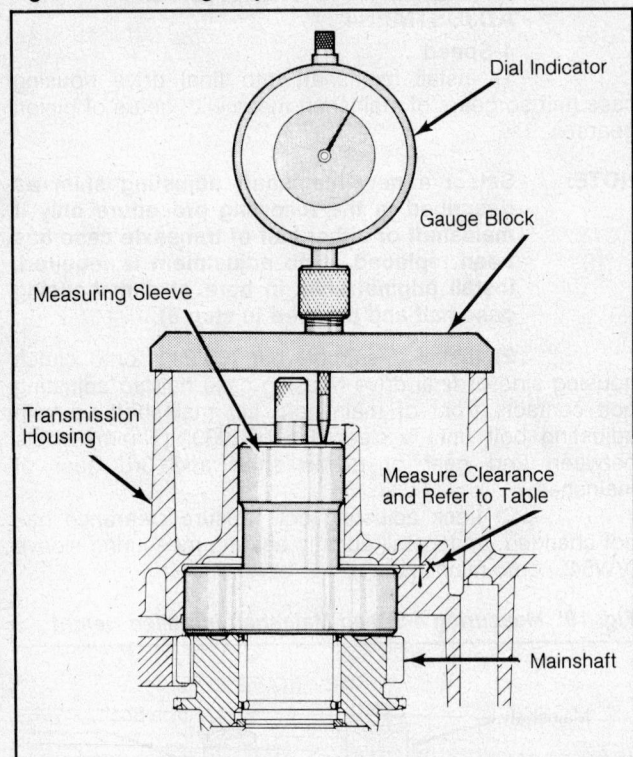

NOTE: For measurement only, install a fourth gear thrust washer between measuring sleeve and shoulder of mainshaft. The thrust washer inside diameter can be enlarged with a file to ease installation and removal from mainshaft.

Fig. 21: Centering 4-Speed Reverse Idler Shaft in Case

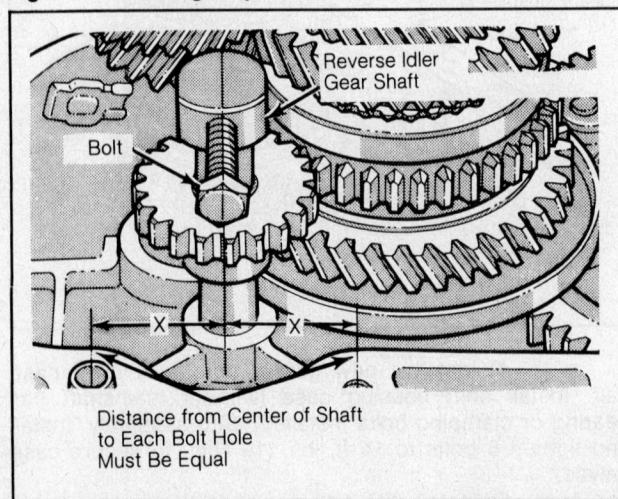

7) Remove dial indicator and separate case halves. Remove measuring sleeve and thrust washer. Install proper shim(s) just selected, into mainshaft ball bearing bore in shift housing case half.

NOTE: Closed side of bearing cage MUST be installed toward shim(s) and housing, and press tool must contact bearing outer race only.

MAINSHAFT BEARING SHIM SELECTION (4-SPEED ONLY)

End Play In. (mm)	Shim Thickness In. (mm)
0-.018 (0-.46)	None
.019-.029 (.47-.75)	.012 (.30)
.030-.041 (.76-1.04)	.024 (.60)
.042-.057 (1.05-1.45)	¹ .036 (.90)

¹ — Use .012" (.30 mm) and .024" (.60 mm) shims.

8) Install mainshaft bearing on top of shims and press into bore. Install clamping bolts and tighten to 11 ft. lbs. (15 N.m). Install plastic caps on nuts outside housing.

5-Speed
1) Install mainshaft without shims into case. Hold mainshaft in place with special tool 30-211 and adapter VW295a. Install 4th gear on pinion shaft and install circlip. Press mainshaft bearing with old shim into case. Install clamping plate and insert lower spring for selector rod into gear carrier housing.

2) Insert 1st-2nd gear shift fork into operating sleeve. Lift selector rod slightly and swing shift fork around pinion shaft, guiding 3rd-4th shift fork into synchronizer sleeve and reverse shift fork into relay lever. Push selector rod in and align shift forks.

Fig. 22: Installing 5-Speed Shift Forks

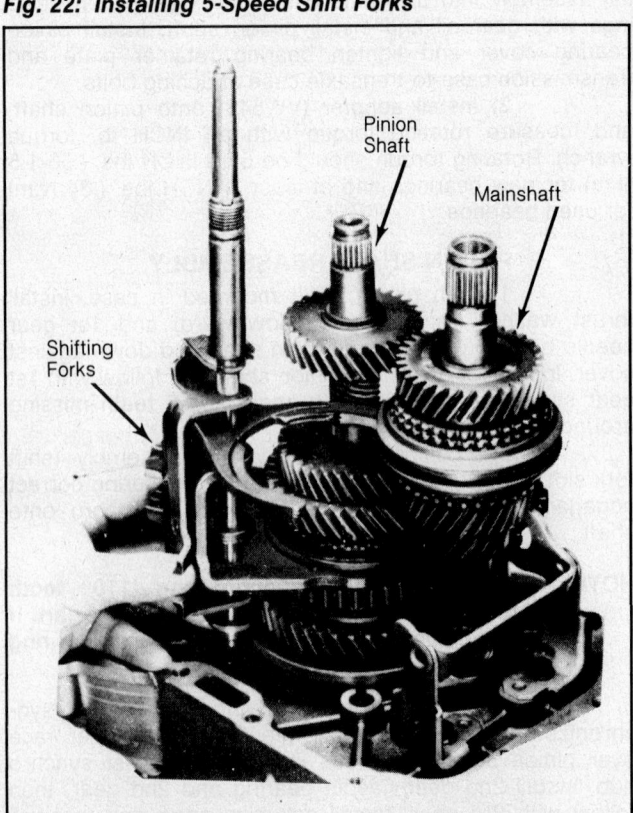

REVERSE IDLER INSTALLATION

Temporarily install reverse idler shaft retaining bolt into idler shaft, then position shaft into case bore. Center reverse idler bolt so center of shaft is equal from each bolt hole of case. Remove bolt without disturbing shaft alignment.

VOLKSWAGEN JETTA, RABBIT & SCIROCCO
4 & 5-SPEED TRANSAXLE (Cont.)

SHIFT FORKS & SHIFT HOUSING INSTALLATION

4-Speed

1) Install reverse shift fork and support onto case, and engage fork with reverse idler gear. Install 1st-2nd and 3rd-4th shift forks into sleeves of synchronizer assemblies, and reverse operating fork into engagement with all 3 shift forks.

2) With all parts in correct position, press fork shaft into housing and install 2 "E" clips to secure forks. Install 4th gear onto pinion shaft and secure with snap ring.

3) Make sure reverse idler shaft is still correctly positioned and that all gears are in neutral position. Install shift housing case half onto unit, making sure mainshaft is aligned with ball bearing, and pinion shaft is aligned with its needle bearing. Dowel holes should align one half of case with other.

Fig. 23: Shift Fork Retaining Clip Locations

Secure Forks to Shaft with "E" Clips

Fig. 24: Installing 4-Speed Mainshaft Bearing Snap Ring

Install Snap Ring Through Shift Housing to Secure Mainshaft

4) Support mainshaft firmly with support bar (30-211). Drive ball bearing onto mainshaft using a bearing driver (30-23), applying force to inner bearing race only. Install reverse idler shaft bolt and tighten to 14 ft. lbs. (19 N.m).

5) Install case bolts and tighten in a diagonal pattern to 18 ft. lbs. (24 N.m). Working through clutch release area of shift housing, install mainshaft-to-ball bearing snap ring. See Fig. 24.

Fig. 25: Cutaway View of Case Showing Selector Shaft and Shaft Adjusting Components

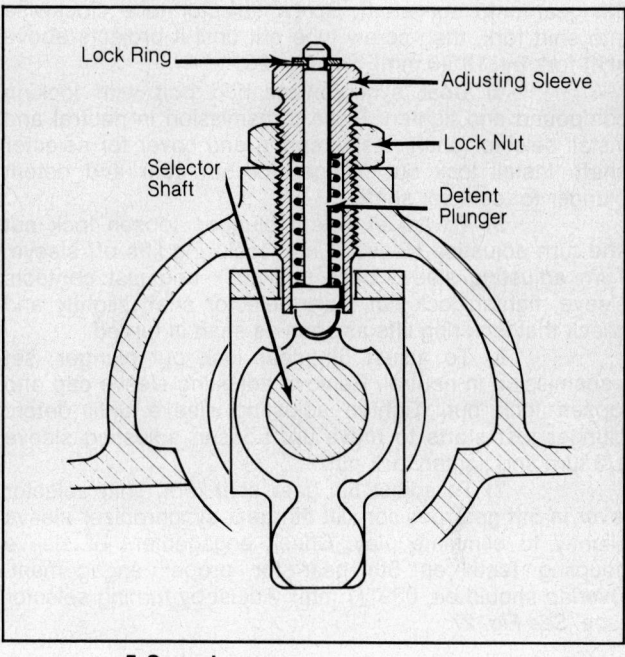

Lock Ring
Adjusting Sleeve
Lock Nut
Selector Shaft
Detent Plunger

5-Speed

1) Install special tool VW295a on mainshaft, install transmission case onto gear carrier. Install reverse gear shaft lock bolt and tighten. Install transmission case-to-gear case bolts and tighten.

2) Install backup light switch. Tighten mainshaft bearing clamping plate bolts. Install drive shaft flange, install spring washer and circlip, press circlip into place and check for proper setting.

CAUTION: Do not pull selector rod out of tube because shift forks in transmission will fall apart and transmission will have to be disassembled again.

Fig. 26: View Showing Synchronizer with 5th Gear Installation and Tube Adjustment

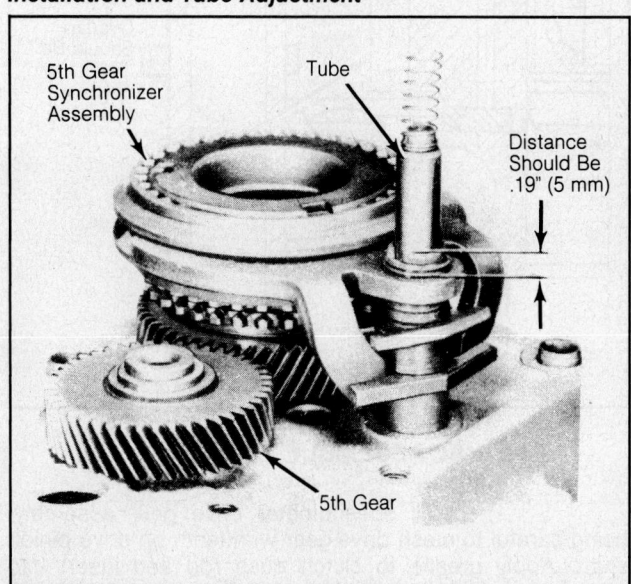

5th Gear Synchronizer Assembly
Tube
Distance Should Be .19" (5 mm)
5th Gear

Manual Transmissions
VOLKSWAGEN JETTA, RABBIT & SCIROCCO 4 & 5-SPEED TRANSAXLE (Cont.)

3) Heat 5th gear to 212°F (100°C) and install. Install thrust washer and circlip. Install synchronizer with 5th gear onto mainshaft. Screw selector tube clockwise into shift fork, then screw tube out until it projects above shift fork by .19" (5 mm). *See Fig. 26.*

4) Coat synchronizer hub bolt with locking compound and tighten. Place transmission in neutral and install selector shaft. Install spring and cover for selector shaft. Install lock out plunger for 5th gear and detent plunger for selector shaft.

5) To adjust detent plunger, loosen lock nut and turn adjusting sleeve in until lock ring lifts off sleeve. Turn adjusting sleeve back until lock ring just contacts sleeve, tighten lock nut. Turn selector shaft slightly and check that lock ring lifts as soon as shaft is turned.

6) To adjust 5th gear lock out plunger, set transmission in neutral. Remove adjusting sleeve cap and loosen lock nut. Tighten adjusting sleeve until detent plunger just starts to move up. Loosen adjusting sleeve 1/3 turn and tighten lock nut.

7) To adjust 5th gear shift fork, shift selector lever in 5th gear position, lift 5th gear synchronizer sleeve slightly to eliminate play. Check engagement of sleeve coupling teeth on 5th gear for proper engagement. Overlap should be .039" (1 mm). Adjust by turning selector tube. *See Fig. 27.*

Fig. 27: Adjusting 5th Gear Shift Fork Position

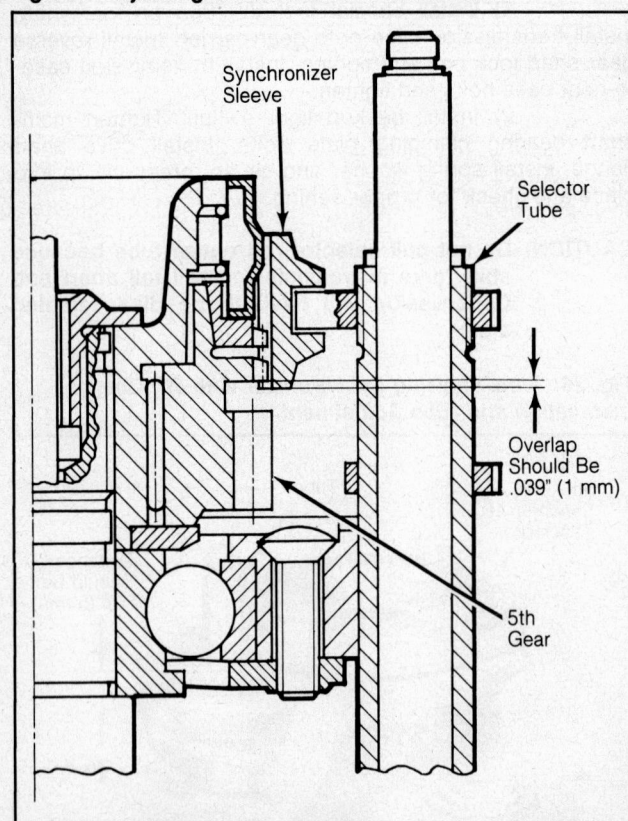

FINAL ASSEMBLY
4-Speed
1) Install speedometer drive gear assembly, being careful to mesh drive gear with teeth on drive pinion shaft. Apply grease to clutch push rod and insert into mainshaft. Install release bearing and sleeve into rear end of shift housing.

Fig. 28: Installing Clutch Release Lever Clips

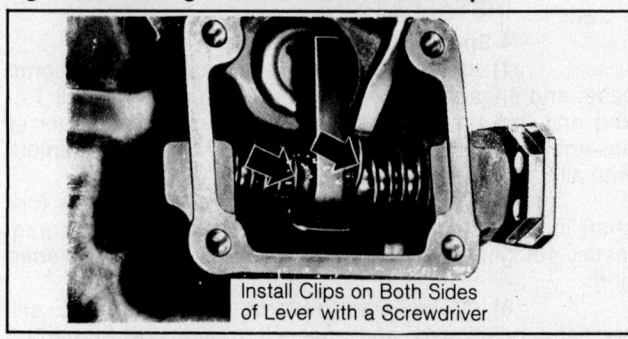

Install Clips on Both Sides of Lever with a Screwdriver

2) Position clutch release lever and return spring in rear of shift housing, then install clutch operating lever through release lever and spring.

NOTE: **Bent ends of spring must contact housing, and center part of spring hooks over release lever. Install 2 snap rings to secure assembly.**

3) Apply grease to selector shaft and install into shift housing, engaging shift forks. Install 2 springs, spring seat and cover into case. Install selector shaft locking bolt into case and tighten. To adjust interlock plunger, loosen lock nut and turn adjusting sleeve in until lock ring lifts off sleeve.

4) Back off adjusting sleeve until lock ring just touches sleeve and tighten lock nut. Turn selector shaft slightly and check that lock ring lifts as soon as shaft is turned.

NOTE: **Transmission must be in neutral with linkage disconnected when adjusting selector shaft.**

5) Install rear cover with a new gasket onto shift housing. If removed, install a new seal into selector shaft bore (shift lever end).

6) Install new drive flange oil seals into housing, position drive flange onto shafts and retain with washers and snap rings. Install new plastic caps into flanges. If removed, install backup light switch, drain and fill plugs into case.

5-Speed
Install new gasket and install transmission case cover with release bearing. Lubricate clutch push rod at ends and at bearing. Select all gears in sequence and check that they engage easily without jamming.

TIGHTENING SPECIFICATIONS

Application	Ft. Lbs. (N.m)
Axle Shaft Nut	173 (235)
Case Half Bolts	18 (24)
Drive Shaft-to-Flange	32 (43)
Fifth Gear Synchro Assembly	50 (68)
Mainshaft Bearing Retaining Nuts	14 (19)
Pinion Bearing Cover	29 (39)
Release Bearing Cover Bolts	11 (15)
Reverse Fork Support Bolts	11 (15)
Reverse Idler Bolt	14 (19)
Reverse Shaft Bolt	22 (30)
Ring Gear Nuts	50 (68)
Selector Shaft Cover	32 (43)
Selector Shaft Lock Nut	14 (19)
Transaxle-to-Engine Bolts	40 (54)

VOLVO 4-SPEED – MODEL M46

DL, GL, Turbo, 760

DESCRIPTION

Transmission is a 4-speed fully synchronized unit with all gears in constant mesh except reverse gear. Gears on the mainshaft are carried by bronze or needle bearings. Input shaft and mainshaft rotate on ball bearings. Countershaft rotates on roller bearings. In Neutral position, the mainshaft gears rotate freely. An overdrive unit is bolted to the rear of the transmission and can only be engaged in 4th gear. Engagement of gears is accomplished by means of a synchronizer sleeve working together with a synchronizer ring. The synchronizer sleeve moves sideways on synchronizer hub splines.

LUBRICATION & ADJUSTMENT

See the appropriate article in MANUAL TRANS-MISSION SERVICING Section.

TROUBLE SHOOTING

HARD SHIFTING

Clutch may not release fully due to deformed clutch disc or being out of adjustment. Pilot bearing seized, damaged or dry. Selector plate damaged. Shift forks bent.

SLIPS OUT OF GEAR

Selector plate damaged or worn. Detent balls and springs worn or broken. Shift forks bent or worn. Transmission and clutch housing misaligned.

NOISY OPERATION

Insufficient or wrong type lubricant. Worn or damaged bushings and/or gears. Worn splines.

NOTE: When checking transmission for noise, ensure that it is not coming from other parts of the drive line.

SERVICE (IN VEHICLE)

TRANSMISSION REAR OIL SEAL
Removal
Raise rear of vehicle and support with floor stands. Disconnect propeller shaft at overdrive unit. Remove drive flange nut. Using a puller (2261), pull flange from mainshaft. Usng a screwdriver, pry out oil seal.
Installation
Using tool (2412), install new oil seal with seal lip facing rear cover. Press drive flange on mainshaft using tool (1845) and tighten nut to specification. Reverse removal procedure for remaining components and check transmission oil level.

REMOVAL & INSTALLATION

See the appropriate article in MANUAL TRANS-MISSION REMOVAL Section.

TRANSMISSION DISASSEMBLY

1) Fit transmission in work stand and drain lubricant. Disconnect wires at overdrive solenoid, remove back-up light switch and overdrive switch. Remove transmission top cover and lift out detent spring and ball. Remove selector plate assembly, return spring, gasket, glide washers and shifter lock pin.

Fig. 1: Selector Plate Assembly

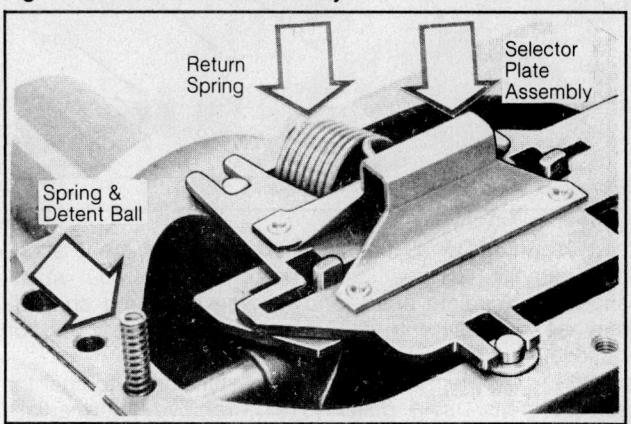

2) Remove overdrive retaining nuts from intermediate flange and remove overdrive. Remove gearshift carrier assembly. Remove sleeve over gearshift rod joint and knock out rear pin. Turn rod, knock out front pin and remove rod. Unbolt intermediate housing from transmission and remove with gasket and shims.

Fig. 2: Removing Gearshift Carrier Assembly

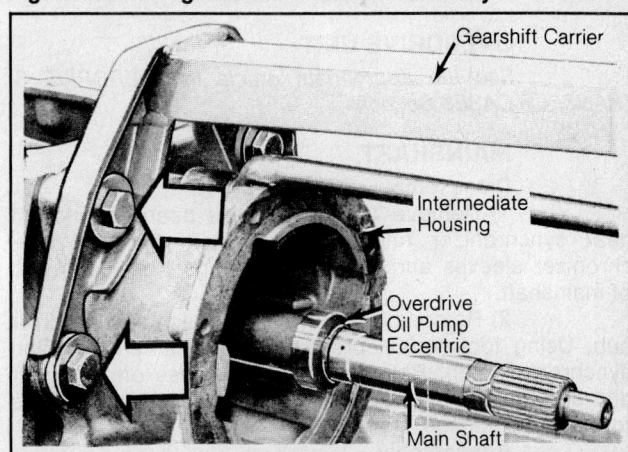

3) Remove selector rail, shifter and shift forks. Remove lock ring and pull off overdrive oil pump eccentric. Catch and retain drive key. Remove lock ring and spacer ring for main shaft bearing.
4) Place adapter (2985) between input shaft and front synchronizer ring. Using puller and adapters (5058, 5147 and 5148) as required, pull off mainshaft bearing and remove thrust washer.
5) Remove clutch fork, bell housing, gasket and shims. On cast iron models, remove intermediate shaft rear bearing race by tapping shaft back until race is free, then tap forward until front race can be removed. On aluminum housing models, tap shaft back only enough to install puller (5177), and remove races.

Manual Transmissions

VOLVO 4-SPEED – MODEL M46 (Cont.)

Fig. 3: Removing Mainshaft Bearing

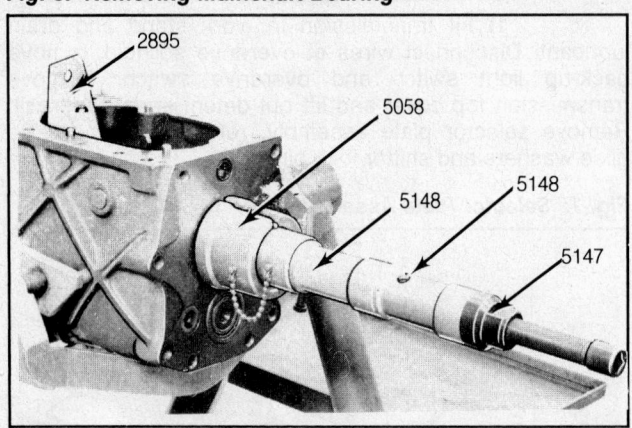

6) On all transmissions, pull out input shaft, then remove 4th gear synchronizer ring. Lift out mainshaft, intermediate shaft, and reverse gear and shaft. It may be necessary to tap reverse gear shaft back for removal.

7) Remove reverse gear shift fork and seal for selector rail. Using puller (5131), remove intermediate shaft bearings. Remove rubber ring from gearshift rod joint and gearshift rod bushings. Remove bell housing seal.

COMPONENT DISASSEMBLY & REASSEMBLY

OVERDRIVE UNIT

See the appropriate article in OVERDRIVE & TRANSFER CASES Section.

MAINSHAFT
Disassembly

1) Remove 1st gear, needle bearings and 1st gear synchronizer ring from mainshaft. Remove synchronizer sleeves and synchronizer rings from each end of mainshaft.

2) Remove circlips retaining each synchronizer hub. Using tool (2853), press off 2nd gear and 1st/2nd synchronizer hub. Reverse shaft and press off 3rd gear and 3rd/4th synchronizer hub. Clean and inspect all parts for wear or damage, replace as necessary.

Reassembly

1) Connect 1st/2nd and 3rd/4th synchronizer hubs. Position hub in sleeve so that hub slots align chamfered teeth in sleeve. Insert dogs (3) and lock them with springs. With curved lock ring, align springs to let free ends press against synchronizer ring.

2) Install bell housing seal using drift (2867) and handle (1801). Position rubber ring in gearshift rod joint, use grease to retain ring on right side. Install gearshift rod bushings. Use drift (5065) to install selector rail seal.

3) Assemble synchronizer sleeve assemblies, making sure insert springs are correctly installed. Using tool (2852), install 3rd gear and synchronizer ring, then 3rd/4th synchronizer hubs on mainshaft. Install lock ring.

4) Using same tool, install 2nd gear and synchronizer ring and 1st/2nd synchronizer hub on

mainshaft, then install lock ring. Install 1st gear and synchronizer ring.

Fig. 4: View of Synchronizer Hub

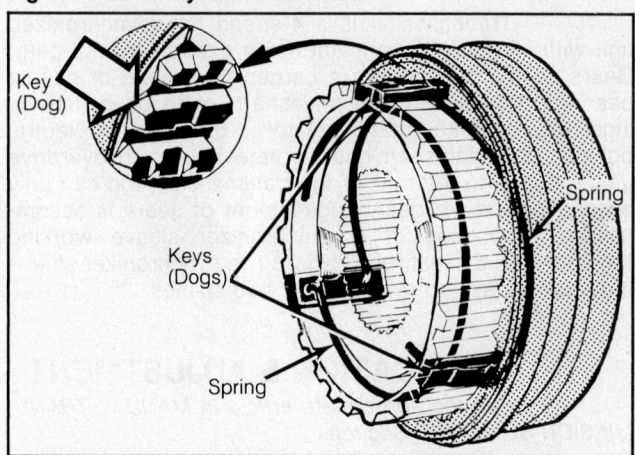

TRANSMISSION REASSEMBLY

1) Use drift (2986) to install intermediate shaft bearings. Use correct type bearings. Use drift (2412) to press input shaft bearing on input shaft. Install lock ring. DO NOT install spacer ring on bearing at this time.

NOTE: Intermediate shaft small end bearing is different for diesel applications.

2) Determine intermediate shaft preload. Place intermediate shaft in housing and use drift (5180) to install bearing races. Install clutch housing with gasket and tighten bolts. Turn transmission vertically so clutch housing is down. Use drift (5180) to tap rear race in position so that clearance is eliminated and shaft turns in a slightly sluggish manner.

Fig. 5: Adjusting Clearance Between Reverse Gear and Shift Fork

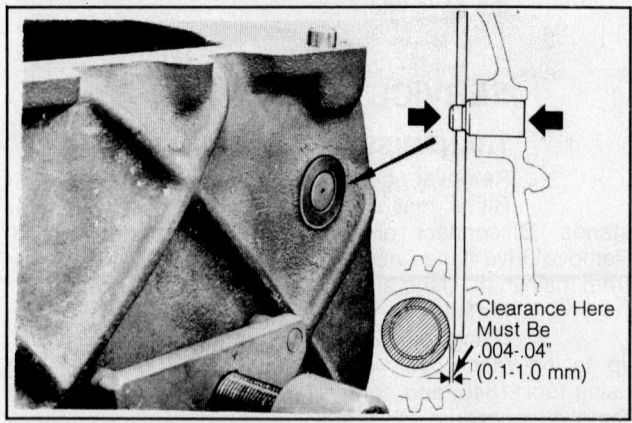

Clearance Here Must Be .004-.04" (0.1-1.0 mm)

3) Using a depth gauge, measure distance to outer race from rear surface of housing. Add measured distance to gasket thickness of .010" (.25 mm) plus preload of .001-.003" (.03-.08 mm). Total measurement is shim size required, select shim within this range and set aside for reassembly. Shims are available in the following thicknesses: .002" (.05 mm), .004" (.10 mm), .006" (.15 mm), .014" (.35 mm), .020" (.50 mm), .027" (.70 mm) and .039" (1.0 mm).

VOLVO 4-SPEED – MODEL M46 (Cont.)

Fig. 6: Exploded View of M46 4-Speed Transmission Assembly

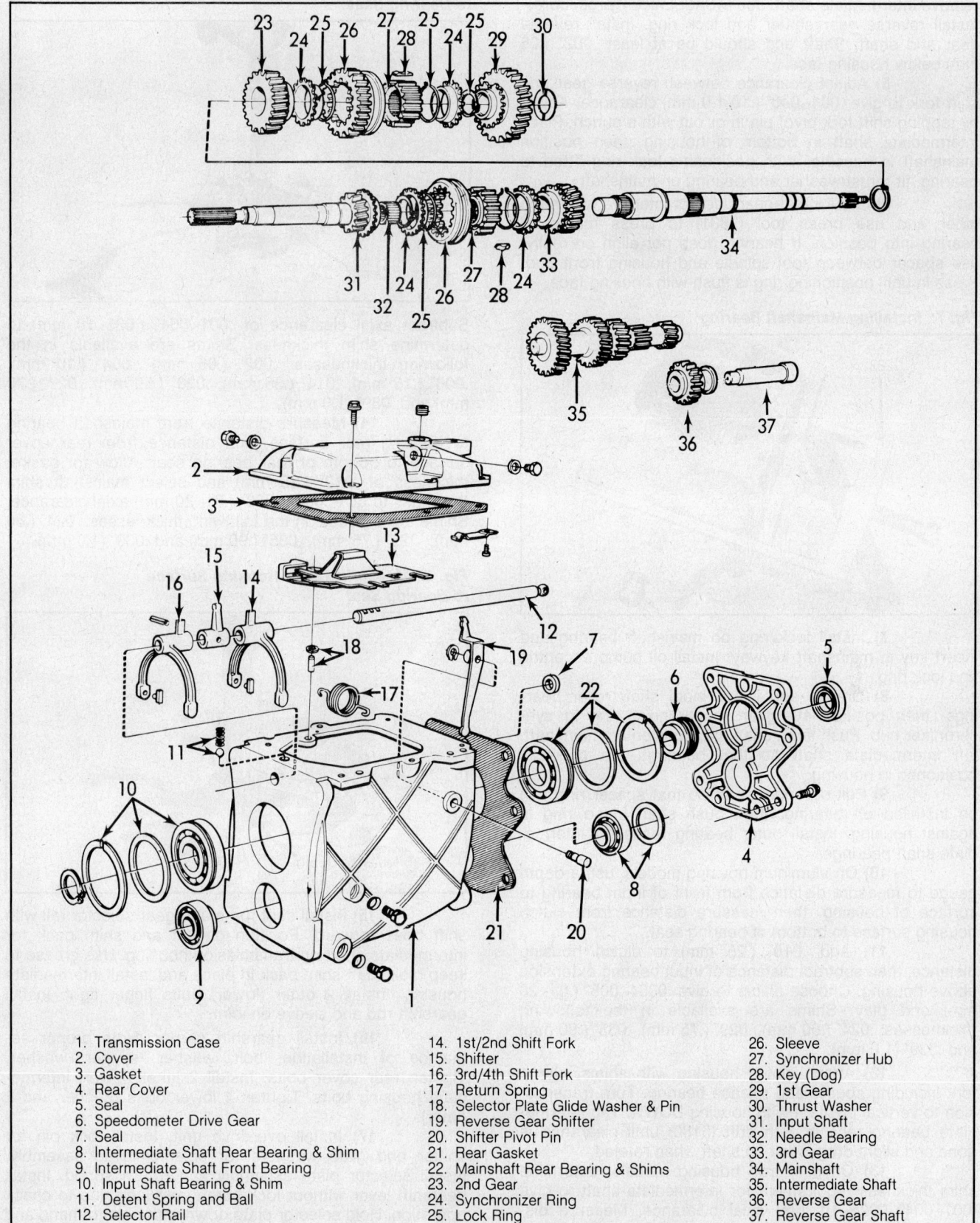

1. Transmission Case
2. Cover
3. Gasket
4. Rear Cover
5. Seal
6. Speedometer Drive Gear
7. Seal
8. Intermediate Shaft Rear Bearing & Shim
9. Intermediate Shaft Front Bearing
10. Input Shaft Bearing & Shim
11. Detent Spring and Ball
12. Selector Rail
13. Selector Plate Assembly
14. 1st/2nd Shift Fork
15. Shifter
16. 3rd/4th Shift Fork
17. Return Spring
18. Selector Plate Glide Washer & Pin
19. Reverse Gear Shifter
20. Shifter Pivot Pin
21. Rear Gasket
22. Mainshaft Rear Bearing & Shims
23. 2nd Gear
24. Synchronizer Ring
25. Lock Ring
26. Sleeve
27. Synchronizer Hub
28. Key (Dog)
29. 1st Gear
30. Thrust Washer
31. Input Shaft
32. Needle Bearing
33. 3rd Gear
34. Mainshaft
35. Intermediate Shaft
36. Reverse Gear
37. Reverse Gear Shaft

Manual Transmissions

VOLVO 4-SPEED – MODEL M46 (Cont.)

4) Remove clutch housing and gasket, then remove intermediate shaft. *See DISASSEMBLY procedures.* Install reverse gear shifter and lock ring. Install reverse gear and shaft. Shaft end should be at least .002" (.05 mm) below housing face.

5) Adjust clearance between reverse gear and shift fork to give .004-.040" (.10-1.0 mm) clearance. Adjust by tapping shift fork pivot pin in or out with a punch. Place intermediate shaft in bottom of housing, then position mainshaft in housing. With positioning lock ring fitted to bearing, fit thrust washer and bearing on mainshaft.

6) Ensure that gears do not interfere with each other and use press tool (2831) to press mainshaft bearing into position. If bearing does not align correctly, use spacer between tool spindle and housing front end. Press in until positioning ring is flush with housing face.

Fig. 7: Installing Mainshaft Bearing

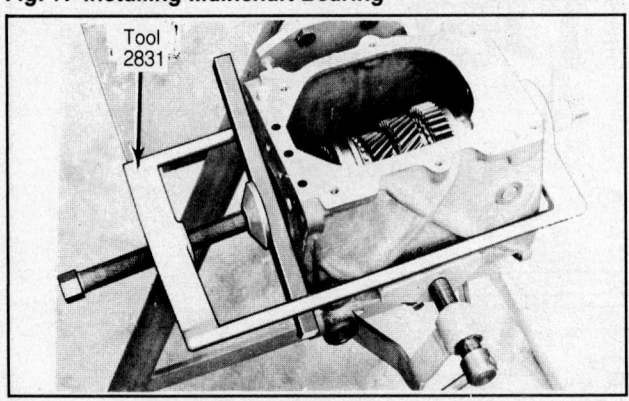

7) Install lock ring on mainshaft bearing and insert key in mainshaft keyway. Install oil pump eccentric and lock ring.

8) Grease and install input shaft roller bearings, then position 4th gear synchronizer ring in synchronizer hub. Push input shaft into position on mainshaft. Lift intermediate shaft so that bearings are correctly positioned in housing.

9) Pull out input shaft so that spacer ring can be installed on bearing, then push shaft in so ring is against housing. Install outer bearing races for intermediate shaft bearings.

10) On aluminum housing models, use a depth gauge to measure distance from front of input bearing to surface of housing, then measure distance from clutch housing surface to bottom of bearing seat.

11) Add .010" (.25 mm) to clutch housing distance, then subtract distance of input bearing extension above housing. Choose shims to give .0004-.008" (.01-.20 mm) end play. Shims are available in the following thicknesses: .024" (.60 mm), .029" (.75 mm), .035" (.90 mm) and .039" (1.0 mm).

12) Attach clutch housing with shims, clutch fork including spacer and release bearing. Turn transmission to vertical position with housing DOWN. Tap intermediate bearing race in with drift (5180) until clearance is gone and slight drag is felt on shaft when rotated.

13) On cast iron housing models, determine shim thickness requirement for intermediate shaft to give .001-.004" (.025-.10 mm) axial clearance. Measure distance from rear housing surface to intermediate shaft outer race and add gasket thickness of .010" (.25 mm).

Fig. 8: Measuring Clutch Housing Surface to Bearing Seat

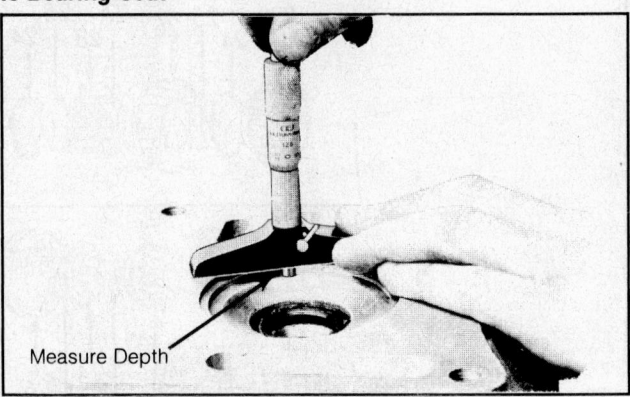

Measure Depth

Subtract axial clearance of .001-.004" (.025-.10 mm) to determine shim thickness. Shims are available in the following thicknesses: .002" (.05 mm), .004" (.10 mm), .006" (.15 mm), .014" (.35 mm), .020" (.50 mm), .027" (.70 mm) and .039" (1.0 mm).

14) Measure distance from mainshaft bearing to housing rear surface, and distance from rear cover surface to bottom of rear bearing seat. Allow for gasket thickness of .010" (.25 mm) and select mainshaft shim thickness to give .0004-.008" (.01-.20 mm) axial clearance. Shims are available in the following thicknesses: .024" (.60 mm), .029" (.75 mm), .035" (.90 mm) and .039" (1.0 mm).

Fig. 9: Measuring Rear Housing Surface to Bearing Seat

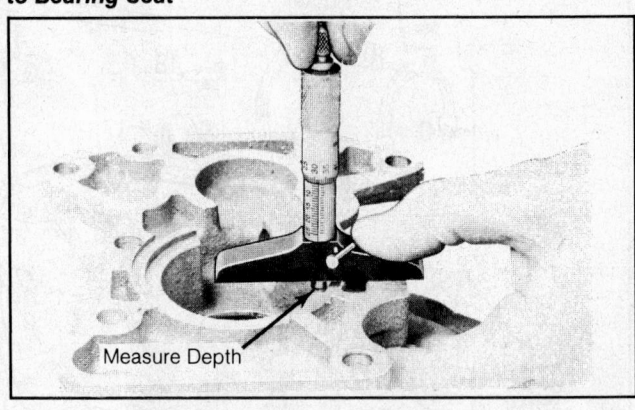

Measure Depth

15) Install shift forks and gear selector rail with shift boss forward. Position gasket and shim pack for intermediate shaft on transmission housing. Use grease to keep mainshaft shim pack in place and install intermediate housing. Install 2 outer (lower) bolts finger tight. Install gearshift rod and sleeve on joint.

16) Install gearshift carrier. Note proper sequence of installation, bolt, washer, spacer, washer. Tighten rear cover bolts. Install 2 inner (lower) intermediate housing bolts. Tighten 4 lower bolts (2 inner and 2 outer).

17) Install overdrive unit. Install lock pin for shifter and glide washers for selector plate assembly. Install selector plate assembly and return spring. Install gearshift lever without lock screw and lock ring to check operation. Hold selector plate down with palm of hand and check gearshift operation. Correct as necessary, then remove gearshift lever.

VOLVO 4-SPEED – MODEL M46 (Cont.)

Fig. 10: Installing Shift Forks and Shifter

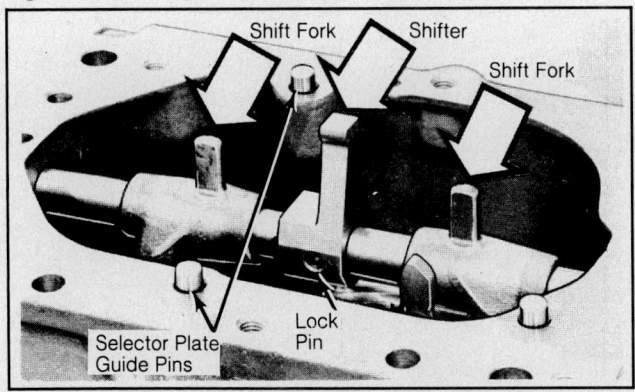

18) Install detent ball and spring, then install top cover with new gasket. Install overdrive switch, back-up light switch and wires at overdrive solenoid. Lower transmission rear and fill with transmission fluid. Install fill plug.

Fig. 11: Checking Gearshift Operation

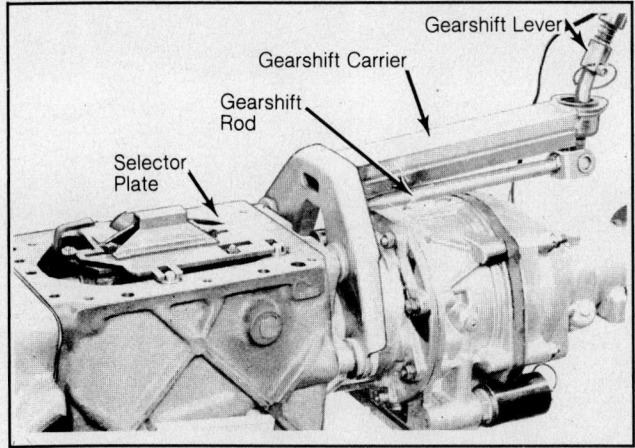

TIGHTENING SPECIFICATIONS

Application	Ft. Lbs. (N.m)
Clutch Housing-to-Transmission	25-35 (34-48)
Rear Cover Attaching Bolts	25-35 (34-48)
Drive Flange Nut	65-80 (88-109)
Intermediate Housing	25-35 (34-48)
Shift Cover Bolts	11-18 (15-24)

SECTION 8

IMPORT OVERDRIVES & TRANSFER CASES

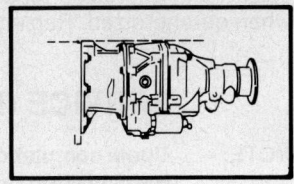

NOTE: **ALSO SEE GENERAL INDEX.**

Overdrives

LAYCOCK "J" TYPE

**Volvo DL, GL, 760 GLE,
GT, Coupe & Diesel**

DESCRIPTION & OPERATION

Overdrive is a hydraulically operated unit, mounted to rear of transmission and splined directly to transmission mainshaft. Unit consists of a single planetary assembly, a sliding clutch actuated by hydraulic pressure, and an overrunning clutch. A single planetary gear train is used, consisting of a central sun gear in mesh with three planetary pinion gears, which in turn mesh with an internally toothed annulus (ring) gear. The pinion carrier is connected to transmission mainshaft through the sun gear and an overrunning clutch. The annulus gear and overdrive mainshaft are an integral one-piece assembly. Hydraulic system pressure is developed by a plunger type pump driven by a cam keyed to transmission mainshaft. Pump draws oil from sump, through oil pan filter, and delivers it through a non-return valve and pressure filter to the clutch apply pistons, solenoid valve, and relief valve assembly.

TROUBLE SHOOTING

OVERDRIVE DOES NOT ENGAGE

Low lubricant level. Solenoid is not energizing. Solenoid is energizing but not operating. Insufficient hydraulic pressure. Damaged pump or internal damage to overdrive unit.

OVERDRIVE DOES NOT RELEASE

CAUTION: Do not place vehicle in reverse or extensive damage may occur.

Electrical control circuit faulty. Solenoid valve sticking. Relief valve sticking causing high residual pressure. Control orifice blocked. Clutch sliding member sticking. Internal damage to overdrive unit.

SLIPS WHEN ENGAGED

Low lubricant level. Solenoid valve sticking. Control orifice blocked. Worn or glazed clutch linings. Defective filter, non-return valve, or relief valve causing low operating pressure.

SLOW DISENGAGEMENT AND/OR FREEWHEELS ON OVERRUN

Relief valve sticking. Control valve sticking or blocked. Control orifice blocked. Internal damage to overdrive unit.

TESTING

HYDRAULIC PRESSURE TEST

1) Lift and support vehicle so rear wheels are free to turn. Remove plug adjacent to solenoid and install pressure gauge with necessary adapter(s). With overdrive disengaged, start engine, shift into high gear and operate at 25 MPH. Hydraulic pressure should read 21 psi (1.5 kg/cm²).

2) Engage overdrive and pressure should be approximately that shown in *Hydraulic Pressure Specifica-*

tions table. Disengage overdrive and pressure should return to normal in 3 seconds or less.

HYDRAULIC PRESSURE SPECIFICATIONS

Application	psi (kg/cm²)
4-Cylinder	380-440 (27-31)
6-Cylinder	455-510 (32-36)

Fig. 1: Gauge Hook-Up for Hydraulic Pressure Test

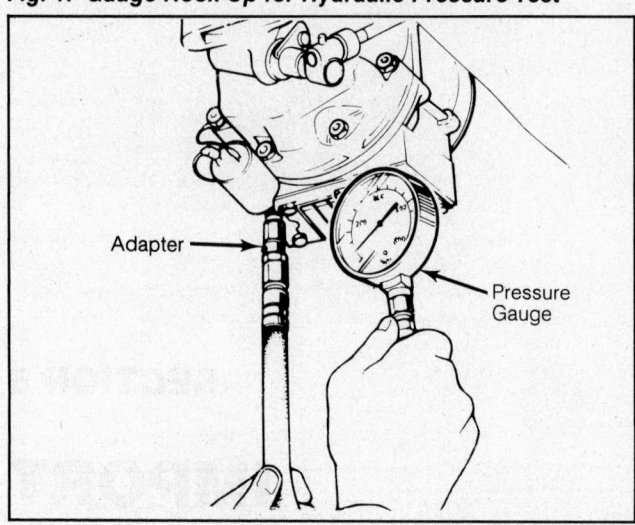

SOLENOID VALVE

Remove solenoid from overdrive unit. Test solenoid with 12 volt battery and an ammeter. When energized, solenoid draw should be approximately 2 amps. Check that valve plunger moves fully forward when solenoid is energized, and returns under spring pressure when de-energized. Replace unit if defective.

SERVICE (IN VEHICLE)

NOTE: **Upon completion of all in-vehicle service, fill transmission and overdrive unit and check operation. Recheck fluid level. DO NOT use any type of anti-friction additives.**

SOLENOID VALVE

Removal

Raise vehicle on a hoist and disconnect wires from solenoid valve. Remove valve from overdrive unit using a 25 mm open end wrench.

CAUTION: Do not attempt to remove valve using pliers or similar tools as valve is easily damaged.

Installation

Install new "O" ring seal on valve end of solenoid. Install solenoid into overdrive unit and tighten with a 25 mm open end wrench. Connect wires to solenoid valve.

SUMP FILTER & PRESSURE FILTER

Removal

Remove sump cover attaching bolts and sump cover. Remove gasket and pull sump filter out. Remove

LAYCOCK "J" TYPE (Cont.)

pressure filter base plug (largest plug under sump cover). Aluminum gasket and pressure filter will come out with plug.

Cleaning & Inspection

Clean pressure filter and sump filter in solvent or kerosene. Use reduced compressed air pressure to dry filters, or place on a lint-free cloth to air dry. If either filter is damaged or plugged so it cannot be cleaned, replace filter.

Installation

Install new aluminum washer on plug, then install pressure filter and plug into overdrive unit. Install sump filter, gasket and sump cover.

RELIEF VALVE ASSEMBLY

Removal

Remove sump cover, filter and gasket. Remove relief valve piston plug (bore farthest from pressure filter bore). Remove dashpot piston assembly, relief valve and spring assembly. Remove relief valve body and valve sleeve by using pliers with narrow jaws and pulling from case with firm pressure. Use tool 5183 to remove cylinder and washer. *See Fig. 3.*

Fig. 2: Disassembled View of Relief Valve Assembly

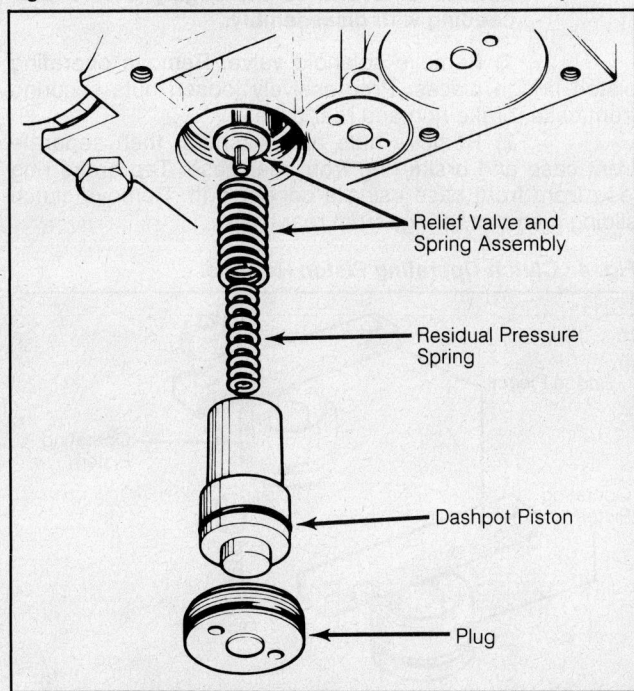

- Relief Valve and Spring Assembly
- Residual Pressure Spring
- Dashpot Piston
- Plug

Cleaning & Inspection

Wash all parts in solvent and blow dry with filtered compressed air. Inspect piston, sleeve, and valve body for scratches, nicks, burrs, cracks, corrosion and excessive wear. Make sure piston moves freely in sleeve. Check for broken, worn or distorted springs. Discard old "O" rings.

NOTE: Do not clean orifice with wire.

Installation

1) Clean control orifice, located in relief valve bore in case, with compressed air. Install new "O" rings, lightly oil all components with transmission oil. Install relief body in bore and use relief valve outer sleeve to seat

body, making sure end of body with "O" ring is nearest to outside of case.

Fig. 3: Relief Valve Removal

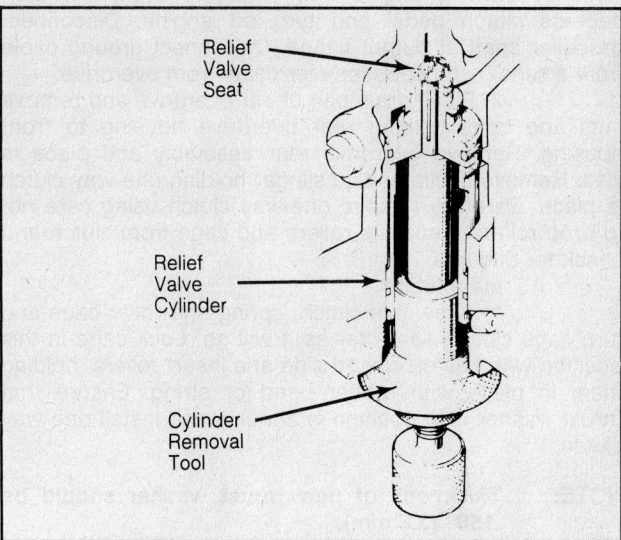

- Relief Valve Seat
- Relief Valve Cylinder
- Cylinder Removal Tool

2) Position relief valve and spring assembly into dashpot cup while ensuring that both ends of residual pressure spring are correctly positioned. Position components in relief valve outer sleeve while engaging relief valve piston in housing. Install base plug and tighten until flush with casing. Install sump filter, gasket, and sump cover.

PUMP NON-RETURN VALVE

Removal

Remove sump cover, filter and gasket. Remove pump plug (center bore), then remove valve seat spring and check ball, making sure not to lose spring and ball when plug is removed. Remove non-return valve seat using a magnet or wire loop.

Cleaning & Inspection

Clean all parts in solvent and blow dry with filtered compressed air. Check valve seat and ball for pitting, corrosion, wear, nicks, burrs, and scratches. Inspect spring for distortion, loss of tension, or breakage. Discard "O" ring.

Installation

Install new "O" ring on pump plug, place spring in plug, position check ball on top of spring and valve seat on check ball. Carefully thread assembly into case and tighten until flush with casing. Install sump filter, gasket, and sump cover.

REAR OIL SEAL

Removal

Raise vehicle on hoist. Mark rear universal joint and pinion yoke for reassembly reference and remove propeller shaft. Remove drive flange nut, washer, and drive flange. Use a tool to remove rear oil seal.

Installation

Lubricate new seal with transmission oil and install in rear case, making sure seal is fully seated. Install drive flange, washer and a new self-locking nut. Install propeller shaft, aligning marks made during removal. Check and correct lubricant level in transmission and overdrive, then lower vehicle.

LAYCOCK "J" TYPE (Cont.)

ONE-WAY CLUTCH REPLACEMENT
Removal
1) With vehicle raised on hoist, unload overdrive by starting engine and engaging overdrive, then depress clutch pedal and turn off engine. Disconnect propeller shaft at output flange. Disconnect ground cable from solenoid and speedometer cable from overdrive.

2) Place drain pan under overdrive and remove nuts and bolts holding rear overdrive housing to front housing. Remove overdrive rear assembly and place in vise. Remove circlip and oil slinger holding one-way clutch in place. Carefully remove one-way clutch using care not to drop rollers. Separate rollers and cage from clutch and check for damage.

Installation
1) Assemble clutch, spring and roller cage and turn cage clockwise as far as it will go. Lock cage in this position with key on closed side and insert rollers, holding them in place with rubber band or string. Ensure that thrust washer is in position in annulus and install one-way clutch.

NOTE: **Thickness of new thrust washer should be .150" (3.8 mm).**

2) Install oil slinger and circlip. Ensure that gasket in front of brake has not been damaged. Fit new gasket to mounting face and install overdrive rear assembly. Connect ground cable, speedometer cable and drive shaft.

OVERDRIVE REMOVAL & INSTALLATION

REMOVAL
NOTE: **Before removing transmission and overdrive unit from vehicle, operate vehicle, engage overdrive, then disengage overdrive with clutch pedal depressed. This procedure will relieve torque loading on overrunning clutch and pinion carrier, thereby easing removal.**

1) Remove transmission with overdrive unit attached. *See appropriate article in MANUAL TRANSMISSION Section for transmission removal.*

2) Remove 8 nuts securing overdrive main case to adapter. Separate overdrive from transmission while leaving adaptor plate in position on transmission.

3) Slide overdrive over mainshaft and off transmission. If difficulty is encountered in separating the overdrive from transmission, proceed as follows: Remove plug adjacent to solenoid, then screw in and tighten adapter to allow oil to be pumped into unit using lubrication gun. This will pressurize unit and release spline loading on mainshaft and allow easy removal.

4) De-energize solenoid when overdrive has separated from adapter 3/4" (19.05 mm).

INSTALLATION
1) Clean gasket surfaces of overdrive case and transmission adapter. Apply a light coat of sealer to case-to-adapter gasket and position on overdrive front case, taking care not to tear gasket on studs.

2) Using a long screwdriver, rotate overrunning clutch splines (innermost set of splines) in a counterclockwise direction until splines are in line with splines in planet carrier. Ensure that pump cam and sun gear snap ring are correctly positioned on mainshaft.

3) Rotate transmission mainshaft so peak of pump cam is at bottom. Position transmission in low gear. Install overdrive to transmission while rotating output shaft of overdrive in a clockwise direction and applying slight pressure until splines are engaged.

4) Pump strap assembly should ride smoothly onto cam and overdrive should butt up to adapter plate without undue force. If overdrive unit will not come within 5/8" (15.88 mm) of adapter, then planet carrier and overrunning clutch splines are not properly aligned and overdrive must be removed and splines aligned.

5) Install and tighten 8 nuts attaching overdrive to adapter. Install transmission and overdrive into vehicle and fill with lubricant.

OVERDRIVE DISASSEMBLY

NOTE: **Extreme cleanliness must be observed at all times in working on overdrive unit. Clean outside of overdrive thoroughly before proceeding with disassembly.**

1) Remove solenoid valve. Remove operating piston bridge pieces. Progressively loosen nuts securing front case, brake ring and rear case.

2) Remove nuts and washers, then separate front case and brake ring from rear case. Tap brake ring lose from front case using a copper drift. Remove clutch sliding member springs from rear case.

Fig. 4: Clutch Operating Piston Removal

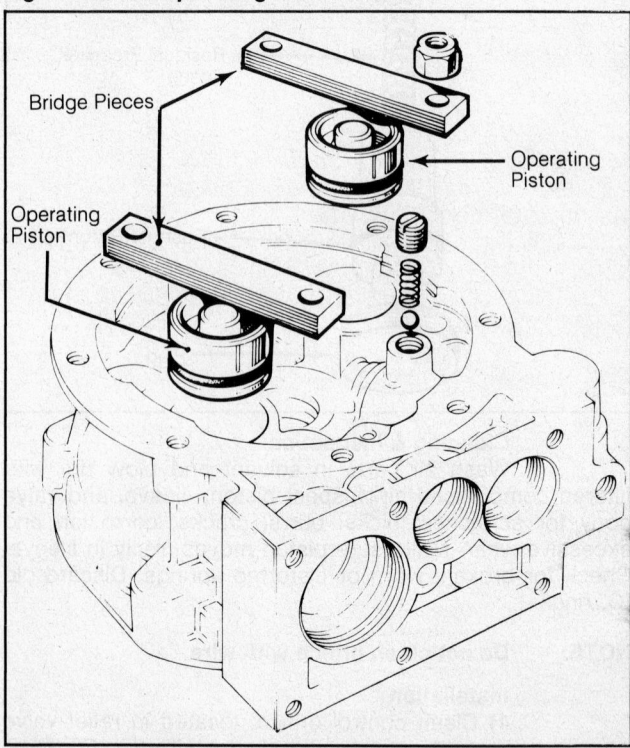

3) Using a pair of pliers, carefully remove operating pistons from front case and identify them with

LAYCOCK "J" TYPE (Cont.)

their respective bores. Remove sump cover, gasket and sump filter. Remove pressure filter base plug (largest plug under sump cover), aluminum gasket and pressure filter.

4) Remove relief valve piston plug (bore farthest from pressure filter bore), dashpot piston assembly, relief valve residual pressure spring, and relief valve and spring assembly. Remove relief valve body and valve sleeve by using pliers with narrow jaws and pulling from case with firm pressure.

5) Remove pump non-return valve plug (center bore), then remove valve seat spring and check ball. Remove non-return valve seat using a magnet or wire loop with hooked end. Remove pump body and pump plunger.

Fig. 5: Exploded View of Front Case Valves and Filters

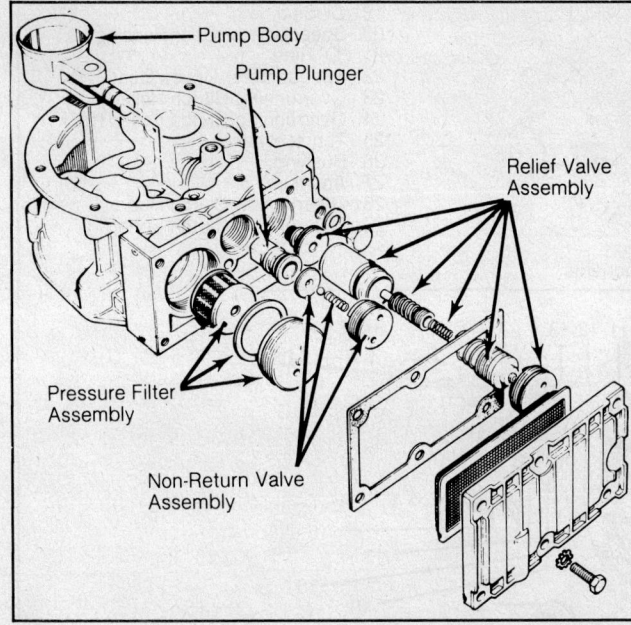

6) Remove sliding clutch, sun gear and thrust bearing cover assembly from annulus in rear case. Remove planet carrier assembly taking care not to damage oil catcher attached to underside of carrier assembly. Remove sun gear snap ring and sliding clutch snap ring, then push sun gear out of sliding clutch hub.

7) Insert a remover tool into sliding clutch hub, support thrust bearing cover, and tap on end of tool to drive clutch hub from thrust bearing. Remove thrust bearing snap ring, then press bearing from cover using an arbor press.

8) Remove snap ring and oil thrower. Insert a tool over the overrunning clutch, reach through tool with finger and pull overrunning clutch into tool, and remove tool and overrunning clutch as an assembly. Remove mainshaft thrust washer from recess in annulus.

9) Separate overrunning clutch from removal tool and disassemble. Remove speedometer driven gear attaching bolt, housing and driven gear from rear housing. Remove drive flange attaching nut and washer. Remove drive flange using a tool.

10) Drive annulus from rear case using a soft mallet and striking on end of tail shaft. Remove front bearing, speedometer drive gear and spacer from annulus. Remove oil seal from rear case and drive out rear bearing.

CLEANING & INSPECTION

CLEANING

NOTE: **Do not clean sliding clutch or solenoid valve in solvent. Wipe off with a clean lint-free cloth.**

Thoroughly wash all parts in clean solvent. After cleaning, dry all parts with dry filtered compressed air. Blow out all passages to remove any foreign material or cleaning solvent. To clean valve portion of solenoid valve, immerse valve portion (up to threads) in clean solvent, allow to soak until clean, then air dry on a clean shop cloth.

INSPECTION
Front Case
Cracks in case or in valve or piston bores. Nicks, scratches, grooves or warpage on mating surfaces or in valve or piston bores. Worn or stripped threads on plugs, studs, or in valve bores. Blocked oil passages or control orifice.

Rear Case
Cracks in case or in mainshaft bearing snap ring groove. Nick, scratches, or warpage on mating surfaces. Worn, stripped, or galled threads in stud holes. Worn or loose rear bushing.

Pump, Valves & Pistons
Scratches, nicks, burrs, excessive wear, pitting, or corrosion of any pump or valve component. Weak, broken or distorted relief valve springs. Torn, distorted or plugged sump filter or pressure filter. Cracked or warped sump cover. Nicks, scratches or wear on operating pistons. Wear, grooves, burrs and cracks in piston bores.

Brake Ring
Worn, grooved, distorted, or burned clutch surfaces. Cracks in brake ring or at stud holes.

Sliding Clutch, Thrust Bearing & Cover
Worn, burned, loose or peeling friction material. Cracks in clutch hub or friction surface. Worn, rough, galled bearings and races in thrust bearing. Weak, broken or distorted clutch return springs.

Annulus, Planet Carrier & Sun Gear
Loose or worn bushing in annulus gear bore. Chipped, worn or broken teeth in annulus gear. Worn, broken or chipped splines on sun gear and mainshaft. Bent or distorted mainshaft. Plugged lubrication holes. Worn, burned, or rough clutch surface on annulus gear. Cracks in mainshaft or sun gear. Loose or worn pins in planet carrier. Cracked, worn or chipped teeth on planet carrier gears. Rough, galled or worn bearings.

Overrunning Clutch
Cracked or worn hub and rollers. Broken or distorted spring, or cracked, bent, or broken cage. Worn thrust washer. Worn clutch race in annulus gear bore. Cracked clutch hub. Worn splines.

OVERDRIVE REASSEMBLY

NOTE: **Use new gaskets, "O" rings, lock washers and seals when reassembling. Maximum cleanliness must be maintained during all reassembly procedures.**

1) Position speedometer drive gear into rear case with plain boss facing front bearing. Press front

Overdrives

LAYCOCK "J" TYPE (Cont.)

Fig. 6: Disassembled View of Overdrive Components

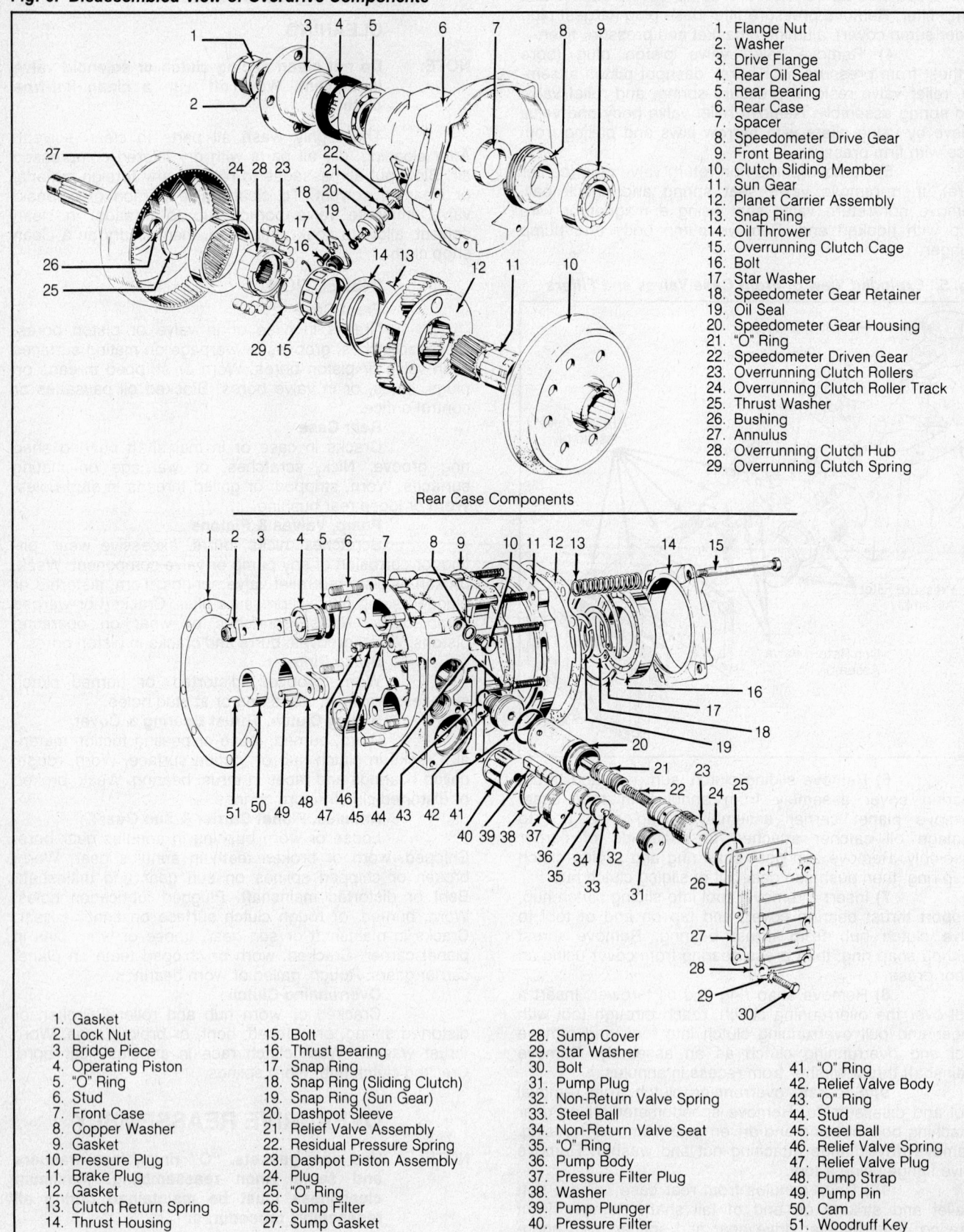

Rear Case Components

1. Flange Nut
2. Washer
3. Drive Flange
4. Rear Oil Seal
5. Rear Bearing
6. Rear Case
7. Spacer
8. Speedometer Drive Gear
9. Front Bearing
10. Clutch Sliding Member
11. Sun Gear
12. Planet Carrier Assembly
13. Snap Ring
14. Oil Thrower
15. Overrunning Clutch Cage
16. Bolt
17. Star Washer
18. Speedometer Gear Retainer
19. Oil Seal
20. Speedometer Gear Housing
21. "O" Ring
22. Speedometer Driven Gear
23. Overrunning Clutch Rollers
24. Overrunning Clutch Roller Track
25. Thrust Washer
26. Bushing
27. Annulus
28. Overrunning Clutch Hub
29. Overrunning Clutch Spring

Front Case Components

1. Gasket
2. Lock Nut
3. Bridge Piece
4. Operating Piston
5. "O" Ring
6. Stud
7. Front Case
8. Copper Washer
9. Gasket
10. Pressure Plug
11. Brake Plug
12. Gasket
13. Clutch Return Spring
14. Thrust Housing
15. Bolt
16. Thrust Bearing
17. Snap Ring
18. Snap Ring (Sliding Clutch)
19. Snap Ring (Sun Gear)
20. Dashpot Sleeve
21. Relief Valve Assembly
22. Residual Pressure Spring
23. Dashpot Piston Assembly
24. Plug
25. "O" Ring
26. Sump Filter
27. Sump Gasket
28. Sump Cover
29. Star Washer
30. Bolt
31. Pump Plug
32. Non-Return Valve Spring
33. Steel Ball
34. Non-Return Valve Seat
35. "O" Ring
36. Pump Body
37. Pressure Filter Plug
38. Washer
39. Pump Plunger
40. Pressure Filter
41. "O" Ring
42. Relief Valve Body
43. "O" Ring
44. Stud
45. Steel Ball
46. Relief Valve Spring
47. Relief Valve Plug
48. Pump Strap
49. Pump Pin
50. Cam
51. Woodruff Key

LAYCOCK "J" TYPE (Cont.)

bearing into rear case until seated against shoulder in case. Press front bearing along with rear casing and speedometer driving gear onto annulus until front bearing seats on shoulder of annulus. Install spacer onto annulus mainshaft. Press rear bearing into rear case and onto annulus mainshaft. Install new oil seal and press on drive flange. Install washer, new self-locking nut, and tighten to specifications.

Fig. 7: Speedometer Drive Gear and Front Bearing Positions in Rear Case

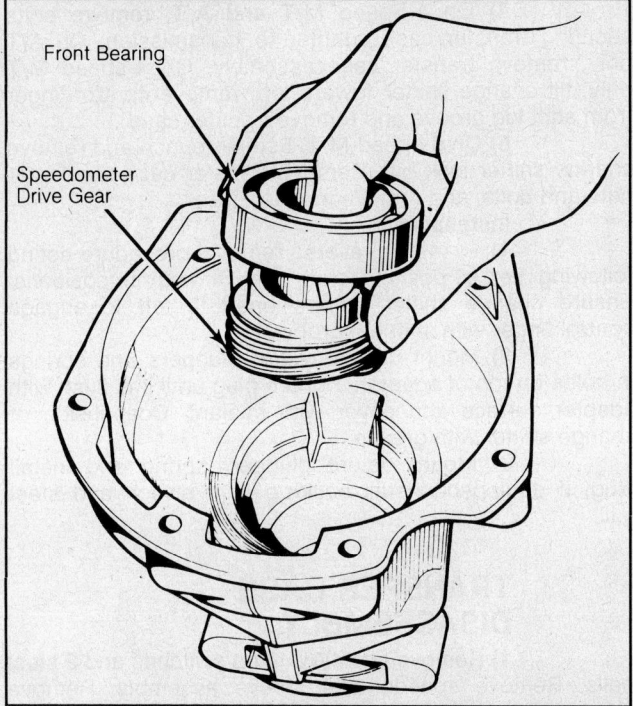

Fig. 8: Exploded View of Main Components of Laycock "J" Type Overdrive Unit

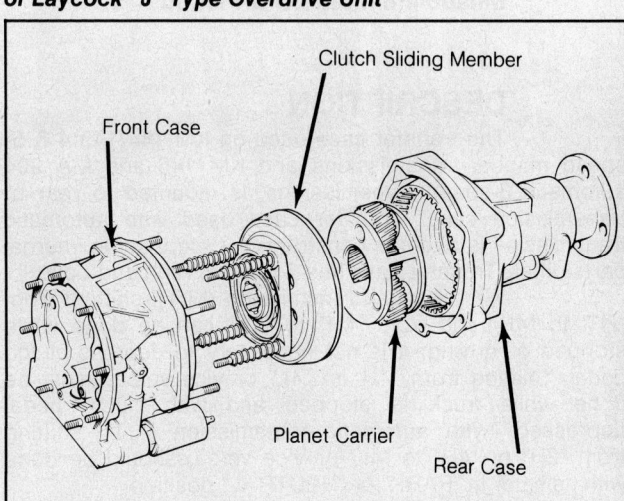

2) Position clutch hub and spring into cage of overrunning clutch. Position spring so cage is spring loaded in a counterclockwise direction (when viewed from front). Position assembly into assembling tool (L178 or equivalent), with open end of cage up. Rotate cage in a clockwise direction until all rollers are installed. Install thrust washer into annulus. Transfer overrunning clutch from assembly tool into its race in annulus. Install oil thrower and snap ring.

NOTE: Check that overrunning clutch rotates in counterclockwise direction only.

3) Press thrust bearing into housing and install snap ring. Install thrust bearing housing onto hub of clutch sliding member and install snap ring securing bearing to hub. Install sun gear into hub and install snap ring on sun gear extension.

4) Lubricate operating pistons with transmission oil, install new "O" rings, then install pistons (counterbored end out) in their respective bores. Install solenoid valve with new "O" ring, making sure not to overtighten. Install new aluminum washer on pressure filter plug, then install pressure filter and plug into front case. Install pump body and pump plunger. Install new "O" ring on pump plug, place spring in plug, position check ball on top of spring and valve seat on check ball. Carefully thread assembly into case and tighten.

5) Install relief body in bore and use relief valve outer sleeve to seat body, making sure that end of body with "O" ring is nearest to outside of case. Position relief valve and spring assembly into dashpot cup while ensuring that both ends of residual pressure spring is correctly positioned. Position components in relief valve outer sleeve while engaging relief valve piston in housing. Install base plug and tighten. Install sump filter, gasket and sump cover.

6) Mount rear case assembly upright in a soft-jawed vise, then install planet carrier assembly. Install sliding clutch assembly including return springs onto cone of annulus. Engage sun gear with planet carrier gears. Apply light coat of sealer to new gaskets and install on both sides of brake ring. Install brake ring to rear case and align stud holes.

NOTE: Gears can be meshed in any position.

7) Position front case over thrust housing pins while aligning with studs in brake ring. Install and tighten nuts evenly, securing front and rear case assemblies, while making sure copper washers are installed to 2 top studs. Install 2 bridge pieces and install new self-locking nuts.

NOTE: Clutch return spring pressure should be felt as cases draw together.

TIGHTENING SPECIFICATIONS

Application	Ft. Lbs. (N.m)
Sump Cover	6 (8)
Pressure Filter Cover	16 (22)
Relief Valve Plug	16 (22)
Operation Piston Bridge	5-12 (7-16)
Front-to-Rear Cover	5-12 (7-16)
Drive Flange Nut	120-130 (163-176)

Transfer Cases

CHRYSLER CORP. IMPORTS & MITSUBISHI

Chrysler Corp. Ram-50 Pickup
Mitsubishi Montero & Pickup

DESCRIPTION

The transfer case used on KM 144/145 4 & 5-speed manual transmissions and KM 146 and MA 904 automatic 3-speed transmissions, is mounted to rear of transmission case. Transfer case used with automatic transmission is of same construction except some internal parts differ. Transfer case has 2 ranges, High and Low.

With manual transmission (M/T), shifting from "2H" to "4H" and from "4H" to "2H" can be done while stopped or driving; it is not necessary to depress clutch pedal. Shifting from "4H" to "4L" or vice versa, must be done while truck is stopped and with clutch pedal depressed. With automatic transmission (A/T), shifting from "2H" or "4H" to "4L" or vice versa, should be done with selector in "PARK" or "NEUTRAL" position.

LUBRICATION

Check lubricant level every 30,000 miles.

FLUID TYPE

Transfer case uses MOPAR Hypoid gear oil (specification API GL-4) or equivalent.

CAPACITY

Fill transfer case to slightly below oil filler plug hole.

REMOVAL & INSTALLATION

TRANSFER CASE ASSEMBLY

Removal

1) Remove transmission/transfer case assembly from vehicle. *See appropriate article in MANUAL*

TRANSMISSION REMOVAL Section. Remove back-up light switch from lower right adapter. Take out steel ball.

2) Remove plug from right side of transfer case. Take out select spring and select plunger. Remove 6 bolts securing transmission and transfer case control lever assembly. Remove control lever and gasket.

3) On 4-speed M/T, remove plug from top of adapter and take out neutral return plunger and spring. On 5-speed M/T, remove plugs from top of adapter and remove detent spring and ball, and neutral return springs and plungers.

4) On 4-Speed M/T and A/T, remove bolts securing transfer case adapter to transmission. On A/T only, remove transfer case assembly. On 4-speed M/T only, tilt change shifter toward left, remove control finger from shift lug groove and remove transfer case.

5) On 5-speed M/T, use pin punch and remove change shifter lock pin. Remove transfer case-to-adapter nuts and bolts, and remove transfer case.

Installation

1) To install, reverse removal procedure noting following items: position shift rails in neutral positions. Ensure change shifter is positioned to left to engage control finger with shift lug groove.

2) Mount neutral return plungers and springs in holes on top of adapter. Tighten plug until it is flush with adapter surface and cover with sealant. Coat inside of change shifter with grease.

3) Mount detent plunger, spring and install plug, if equipped. Install back-up light switch and steel ball.

TRANSFER CASE DISASSEMBLY

1) Remove two 4WD lamp switches and 2 steel balls. Remove speedometer sleeve assembly. Remove rear cover, gasket and wave spring. Remove cover and gasket and remove wave spring and spacer. Drive out spring pin from H-L shift fork with a 3/16" punch.

Fig. 1: Exploded View of Transfer Case Assembly

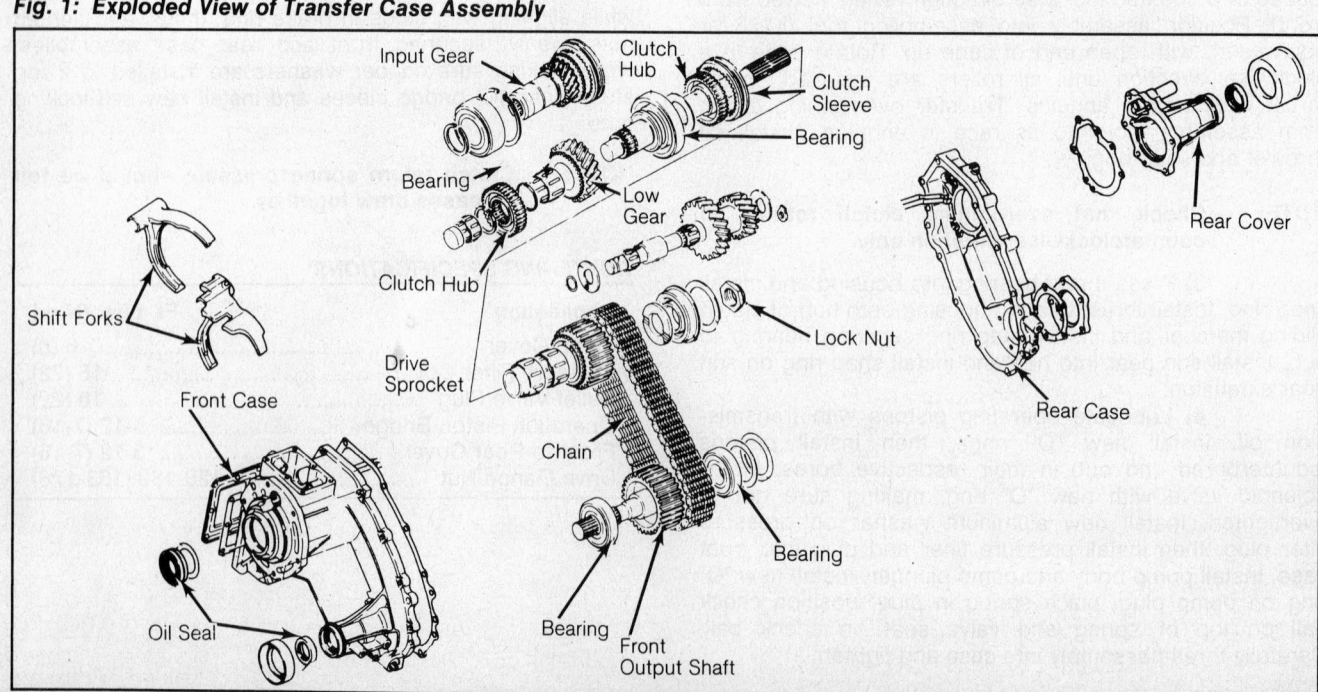

CHRYSLER CORP. IMPORTS & MITSUBISHI (Cont.)

Fig. 2: Driving Out High-Low Shift Fork Spring Pin

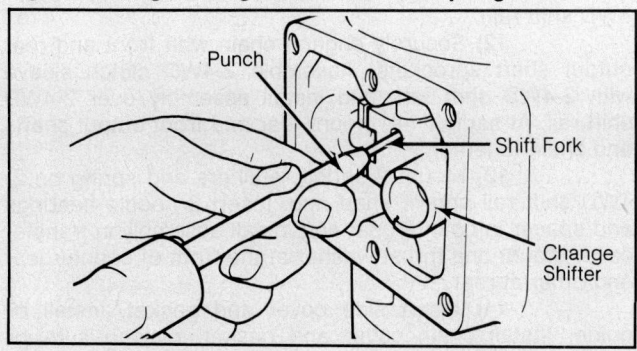

2) Remove 2 seal plugs and take out 2 poppet springs and 2 balls. Pull out H-L shift rail backward. Take out interlock plunger. Remove snap ring from rear bearing on output shaft. Remove chain cover, oil guide and side cover. Remove countershaft locking plate and pull out countershaft.

Fig. 3: Removing Countershaft

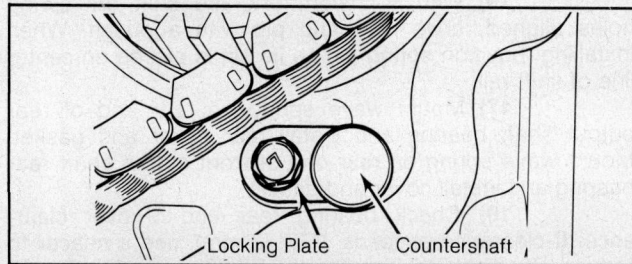

Remove locking plate and pull out countershaft.

3) Take out countergear, 2 thrust washers, 2 needle bearings and spacer through side cover opening. Remove snap ring from 2-4WD shift rail and remove spring retainers and spring from shift rail. Remove front output shaft, rear output shaft and chain together as an assembly from transfer case.

4) Remove 2-4WD shift rail. Remove H-L shift fork and clutch sleeve. Remove needle bearing and snap ring from input gear and remove input gear assembly. Remove snap ring from front of rear output shaft. Remove H-L clutch hub, low speed gear thrust washer and needle bearing.

5) Remove detent from lock nut of rear output shaft. Remove lock nut. Pull out ball bearing from rear end with bearing puller. Remove sprocket spacer and steel balls. Remove drive sprocket, 2 needle bearings, sprocket sleeve and steel ball.

6) Remove 2-4WD clutch sleeve, hub and stop plate and remove ball bearing using puller or press. Remove snap ring from input gear. Support bearing with press base, and push on front end of input gear to remove bearing. Remove 2 bearings from front output shaft with a puller.

7) When replacing control shaft oil seal or input gear oil seal (press fit in front of transfer case), drive out lock pin from transmission control change shifter and separate transfer case from adapter.

TRANSFER CASE REASSEMBLY

NOTE: **While reassembling transfer case, replace all gaskets, oil seals, etc. with new parts. Coat gaskets and threads with sealant. Apply transmission oil to sliding and rotating parts before assembling. Do not reuse spring pins.**

1) Press fit control shaft oil seal, input gear oil seal and front output shaft oil seal in transfer case. When press fitting seals, push down on circumference uniformly. Pack grease between lips.

2) Assemble adapter and transfer case with a new gasket. Tighten bolts and nuts. Be sure to install change shifter over control shaft before tightening nuts and bolts. Make sure to remove burrs from change shifter.

3) Press fit bearing into input gear, pushing down on inner race. After fitting, check to see that bearing rotates smoothly. Fit snap ring over front end of input gear. Snap rings are available in 5 thickness; select thickest one that will fit in groove. *See Input Shaft Snap Ring Table No. 1.*

4) Press fit 2 ball bearings over front output shaft, pushing down on inner race. After fitting, check to see if they rotate smoothly. Install ball bearing over rear output shaft from the rear. Press fit into place by pushing down on inner race. Check for smooth rotation.

5) Mount stop plate and install 2-4WD clutch hub and sleeve. Make sure to install in correct direction. *See Fig. 5.* Mount steel ball (for sprocket sleeve positioning) on rear output shaft and mount sprocket sleeve.

6) Mount 2 needle bearings on outer circumference of sprocket sleeve and mount drive sprocket. Mount steel balls and sprocket spacer, and press fit ball bearing on inner race. Check for smooth rotation.

Fig. 4: Cross Sectional View of Rear Output Shaft

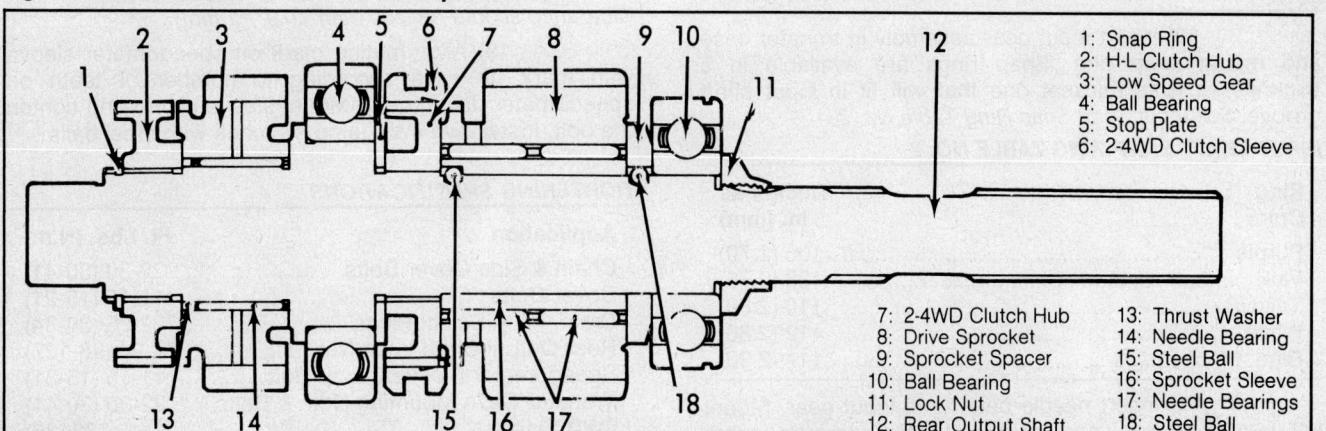

1: Snap Ring
2: H-L Clutch Hub
3: Low Speed Gear
4: Ball Bearing
5: Stop Plate
6: 2-4WD Clutch Sleeve
7: 2-4WD Clutch Hub
8: Drive Sprocket
9: Sprocket Spacer
10: Ball Bearing
11: Lock Nut
12: Rear Output Shaft
13: Thrust Washer
14: Needle Bearing
15: Steel Ball
16: Sprocket Sleeve
17: Needle Bearings
18: Steel Ball

CHRYSLER CORP. IMPORTS & MITSUBISHI (Cont.)

INPUT SHAFT SNAP RING TABLE NO. 1

Ring Color	Thickness In. (mm)
None	.091 (2.30)
Red	.093 (2.35)
White	.094 (2.40)
Blue	.096 (2.45)
Green	.098 (2.50)

7) Tighten mainshaft lock nut and drive in detent section with a punch. After lock nut is tightened, check that drive sprocket rotates smoothly. Mount needle bearing, thrust washer and low speed gear on rear output shaft from the front end.

8) Mount needle bearing, thrust washer, and low speed gear on rear output shaft from the front end. Mount H-L clutch hub, making sure to install in correct direction. See Fig. 5.

Fig. 5: Installation Direction of 2-4WD Clutch Hub & Sleeve and H-L Clutch Hub

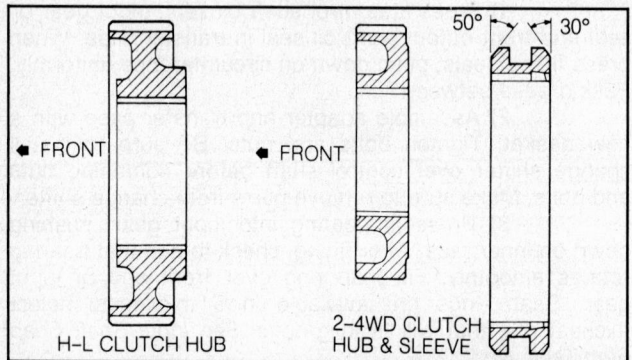

9) Mount H-L clutch hub snap ring on front end of the rear output shaft. Snap rings are available in 5 thicknesses. Use thickest one that will fit in output shaft groove. See Output Shaft Snap Ring Table.

OUTPUT SHAFT SNAP RING TABLE

Ring Color	Thickness In. (mm)
None	.084 (2.14)
Yellow	.087 (2.21)
White	.090 (2.28)
Blue	.093 (2.35)
Red	.095 (2.42)

10) Insert input gear assembly in transfer case and mount snap ring. Snap rings are available in 5 thicknesses. Use thickest one that will fit in input shaft groove. See Input Shaft Snap Ring Table No. 2.

INPUT SHAFT SNAP RING TABLE NO. 2

Ring Color	Thickness In. (mm)
Purple	.106 (2.70)
Pink	.108 (2.75)
Yellow	.110 (2.80)
White	.112 (2.80)
Blue	.114 (2.90)

11) Insert needle bearing in input gear. Mount H-L clutch sleeve and shift fork, mounting in same direction as clutch sleeve for 2-4WD. See Fig. 5. Install 2-4WD shift rail.

12) Securely engage chain with front and rear output shaft sprockets. Assemble 2-4WD clutch sleeve with 2-4WD shift fork and install assembly over 2-4WD shift rail. At same time, mount rear and front output shafts and chain together.

13) Mount 2 spring retainers and spring on 2-4WD shift rail and fit snap ring. Insert 2 needle bearings and spacer in countergear and install assembly in transfer case. Mount one thrust washer at the front of countergear and other at rear.

14) Insert side cover and gasket. Install oil guide. Install chain cover and gasket, making sure oil guide end fits in chain cover opening. Fit snap ring in groove of rear output shaft rear bearing. Insert interlock plunger.

15) Insert H-L shift rail and pass through H-L shift fork. Unless 2-4WD shift fork is shifted to 4WD side, H-L shift rail cannot be inserted. Mount 2 poppet balls and 2 springs and mount the seal plug. When mounting poppet spring, face smaller end toward the ball.

16) With H-L shift fork and shift rail spring holes aligned, drive in spring pin with a punch. When installing, position spring pin so its slit is placed on center line of shift rail.

17) Mount wave spring on rear end of rear output shaft bearing and install rear cover and gasket. Mount wave spring on rear end of front output shaft rear bearing and install cover and gasket.

18) Check bearing rear end-to-cover clearance. If clearance exceeds .079" (2 mm), use a spacer to reduce clearance to less than .079" (2 mm). See Fig. 6. Insert speedometer sleeve assembly in rear cover.

Fig. 6: Bearing-to-Cover Clearance

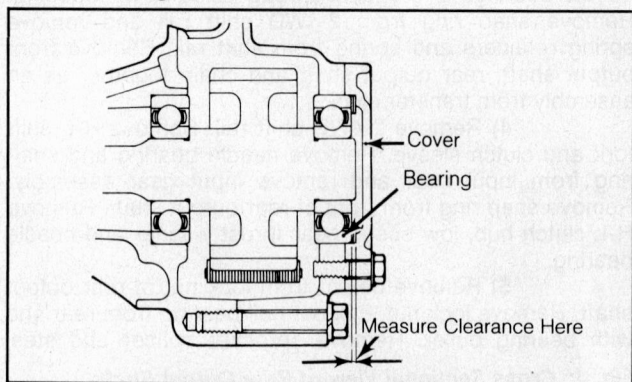

Clearance should be less than .079" (2 mm).

19) Align mating mark on speedometer sleeve with mark on case according to number of teeth on speedometer driven gear. Mount sleeve clamp and tighten the bolt. Install two 4WD lamp switches with steel balls.

TIGHTENING SPECIFICATIONS

Application	Ft. Lbs. (N.m)
Chain & Side Cover Bolts	22-30 (30-41)
Cover Bolts	11-15 (15-21)
Drain, Fill & Select Plugs	22-25 (30-34)
Rear Output Shaft Lock Nut	73-94 (98-127)
Speedometer Sleeve Clamp Bolt	11-15 (15-31)
Transfer Case Mounting Nuts & Bolts	22-30 (30-41)
4WD Switch	22 (30)

Transfer Cases

NISSAN/NISSAN 4WD PICKUP

DESCRIPTION

The transfer case used on Datsun/Nissan 4WD Pickup is bolted to frame and transmission. The case is connected to rear and front axles by propeller shafts. Transfer case has 2 ranges, High and Low. Transfer case can be shifted into 4WD High range at any speed, providing locking hubs are in the lock position. Vehicle must be stopped before shifting transfer case into 4WD Low range. Transfer case is provided with an indicator switch and light. Indicator light will come on when transfer lever is in any position except 2WD High range (light is on in 4WD High, Neutral or 4WD Low).

LUBRICATION

SERVICE INTERVAL

Check fluid level every 15,000 miles or 12 months (whichever comes first). When towing trailer, change fluid every 30,000 miles or 24 months (whichever comes first).

FLUID TYPE

Use SAE 90 gear oil (API-GL-4).

CAPACITY

3.0 pts (1.4L).

REMOVAL & INSTALLATION

TRANSFER CASE ASSEMBLY

Removal

1) Disconnect negative battery cable. From inside vehicle, disconnect transfer case shift lever boot from floor pan. Raise and support vehicle. Remove transfer case protector pan.

2) Remove transfer case-to-transmission propeller shafts, front axle and rear axle. Disconnect wire connector from 4WD indicator switch. Disconnect speedometer cable and remove exhaust pipe. Support transfer case with a transmission jack.

3) Loosen transfer case insulator bolts. Make sure transfer case shift lever boot is free of floor pan and lower transfer case (with transfer case-to-transmission propeller shaft) out of vehicle. Remove insulators from transfer case.

Installation

Install transfer case in the reverse order of removal. Make sure transfer case is filled with the proper amount and type of lubricant after installation.

TRANSFER CASE DISASSEMBLY

1) Make sure transfer case is clean of dirt and grease. Drain gear oil. Place control lever in 4WD Low

---

Fig. 1: Exploded View of Datsun/Nissan 4WD Pickup Transfer Case and Shifting Assembly

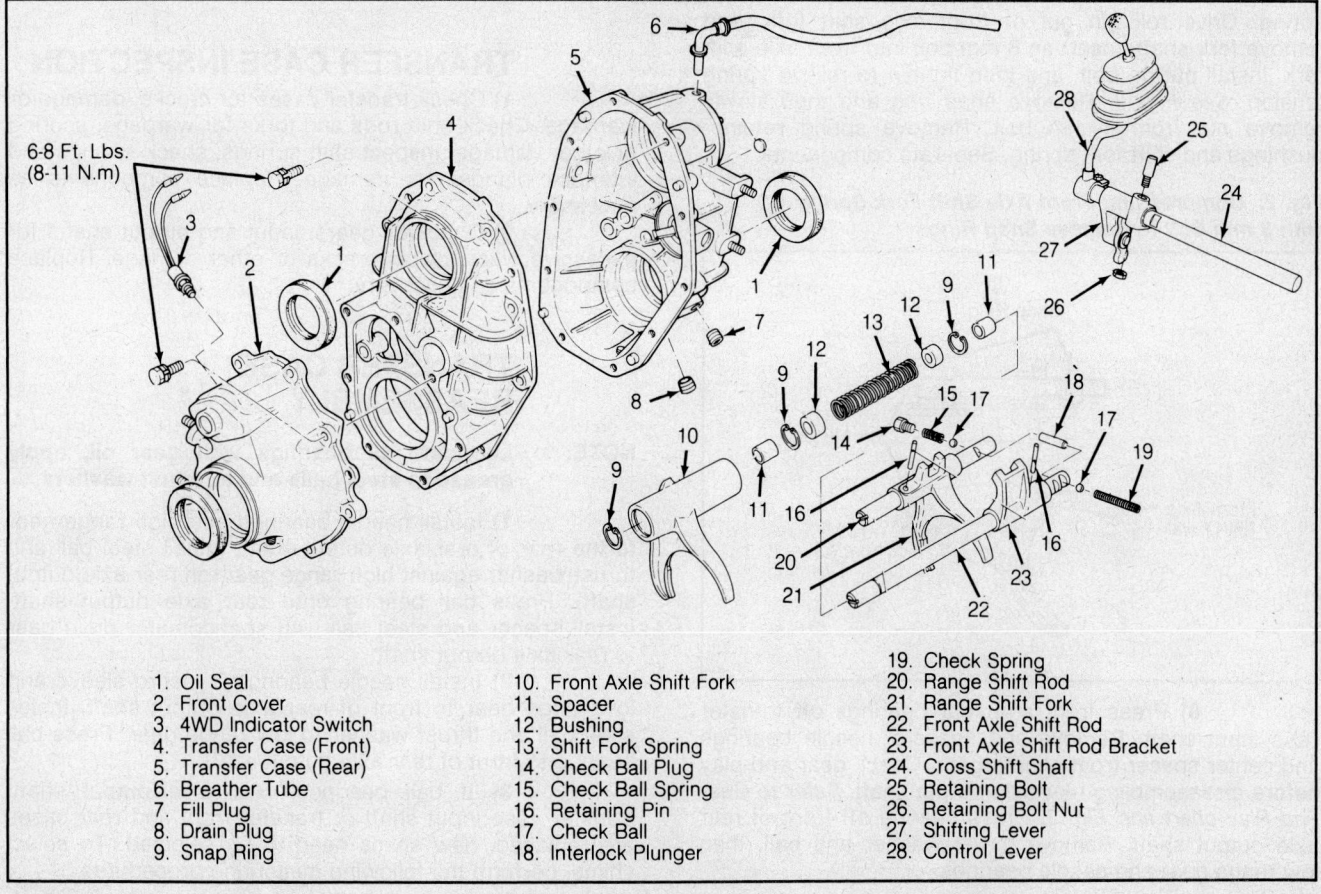

1. Oil Seal	19. Check Spring
2. Front Cover	20. Range Shift Rod
3. 4WD Indicator Switch	21. Range Shift Fork
4. Transfer Case (Front)	22. Front Axle Shift Rod
5. Transfer Case (Rear)	23. Front Axle Shift Rod Bracket
6. Breather Tube	24. Cross Shift Shaft
7. Fill Plug	25. Retaining Bolt
8. Drain Plug	26. Retaining Bolt Nut
9. Snap Ring	27. Shifting Lever
10. Front Axle Shift Fork	28. Control Lever
11. Spacer	
12. Bushing	
13. Shift Fork Spring	
14. Check Ball Plug	
15. Check Ball Spring	
16. Retaining Pin	
17. Check Ball	
18. Interlock Plunger	

6-8 Ft. Lbs. (8-11 N.m)

NISSAN/NISSAN 4WD PICKUP (Cont.)

range or 2WD High range to aid in removing companion flange lock nuts.

2) Place companion flange holding tool (ST31530000) on companion flange, then remove companion flanges and nuts. Remove 4WD indicator switch. Remove transfer case front cover (tapping cover with a mallet will aid in removal.)

3) Remove front axle output shaft and needle bearing. Remove snap ring retaining front axle shift fork, then remove shift fork assembly with spacer and synchro sleeve. *Refer to Fig. 1.*

4) Remove synchro hub snap ring, then remove synchro hub. Remove front transfer case bolts then front case (tapping with mallet to aid removal).

NOTE: Do not pry the case halves apart with screwdriver.

5) Remove retaining bolt nut then drive retaining bolt out with a punch. Remove cross shift shaft. Remove control lever retaining nut then remove control lever. Remove shifting lever with differential lever. Remove check ball plug, check spring and check ball.

6) Drive retaining pin out of range shift fork. Tap rear axle output shaft assembly with mallet and remove it with range shift fork and countergear assembly. Then remove transfer case input shaft assembly from transfer case.

NOTE: When removing countergear assembly, be careful not to drop needle bearings.

7) Remove transfer case front shim. Remove range fork rods, interlock plunger, steel ball and check spring. Drive roll pin out of front axle shift fork, and remove fork shaft. Insert an 8 mm bolt into front axle shift fork, install nut on bolt, and then tighten to relieve spring tension. *See Fig. 2.* Remove snap ring and then slowly remove nut from 8 mm bolt. Remove spring retainer bushings and shift fork spring. Separate components.

Fig. 2: Compressing Front Axle Shift Fork Spring with 8 mm Bolt to Remove Snap Rings

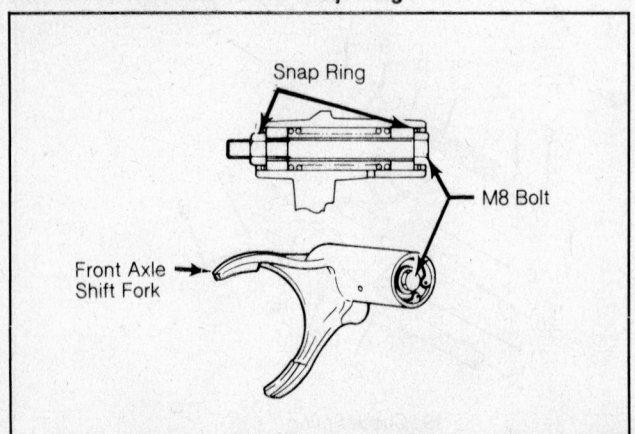

8) Press front and rear bearings off transfer case input shaft. Remove end spacers, needle bearings and center spacer from countergear. Check gear end play before disassembling rear axle output shaft. *Refer to Gear End Play chart and Fig. 3.* Press bearing off front of rear axle output shaft. Remove thrust washer and ball, then low range gear and needle bearings.

GEAR END PLAY

Application	In. (mm)
High Range Gear	.004-.008 (.1-.2)
Low Range Gear	.004-.008 (.1-.2)
Synchro Hub	0-.008 (0-.2)

Fig. 3: Checking Gear End Play of Rear Axle Output Shaft

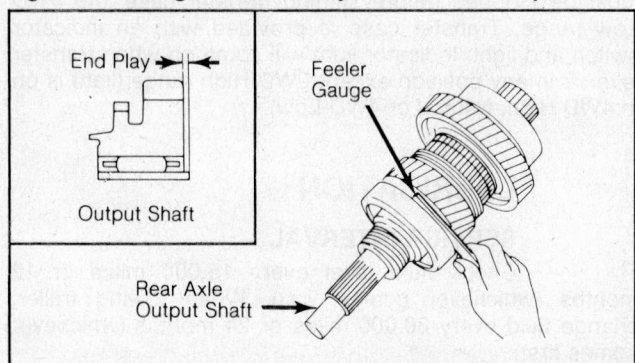

9) Press speedometer drive gear off rear of rear axle output shaft. Remove spacer and ball. Press bearing off rear axle output shaft. Remove thrust washer and steel ball, then remove high range gear, needle bearings and synchro sleeve.

10) If transfer case, bearings or oil seals are damaged in transfer case assembly, remove damaged components as follows. On front cover, pry oil seal out, remove snap ring then press bearing out. On transfer front and rear cases, pry out damaged oil seals.

TRANSFER CASE INSPECTION

1) Check transfer cases for cracks, damage or warpage. Check shift rods and forks for warpage, scoring or other damage. Inspect shift springs, check springs and interlock plunger for damage. Replace components as necessary.

2) Check all gears, input and output shafts for excessive wear, chips, cracks or other damage. Replace components as necessary.

TRANSFER CASE REASSEMBLY

NOTE: Lubricate all bearings with gear oil, apply grease to steel balls and to thrust washers.

1) Install needle bearings and high range gear to the rear of rear axle output shaft. Install steel ball and thrust washer against high range gear (on rear axle output shaft). Press ball bearing onto rear axle output shaft. Install spacer and steel ball with speedometer drive gear to rear axle output shaft.

2) Install needle bearings, synchro sleeve and low range gear to front of rear axle output shaft. Install steel ball and thrust washer to low range gear. Press ball bearing to front of rear axle output shaft.

3) If ball bearings, rear axle output shaft, transfer case input shaft or transfer front and rear cases are replaced, new shims need to be selected. To select shims, perform the following measuring procedures.

NISSAN/NISSAN 4WD PICKUP (Cont.)

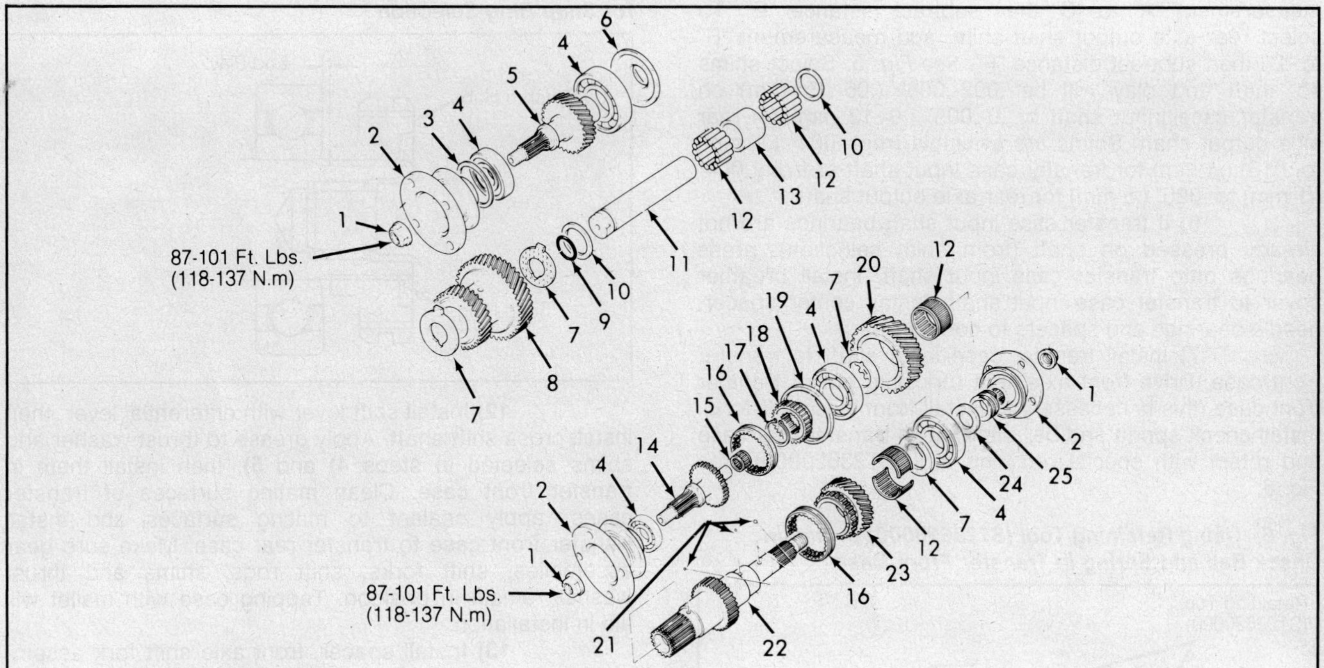

Fig. 4: Exploded View of Datsun/Nissan 4WD Pickup Transfer Case Gear Assembly

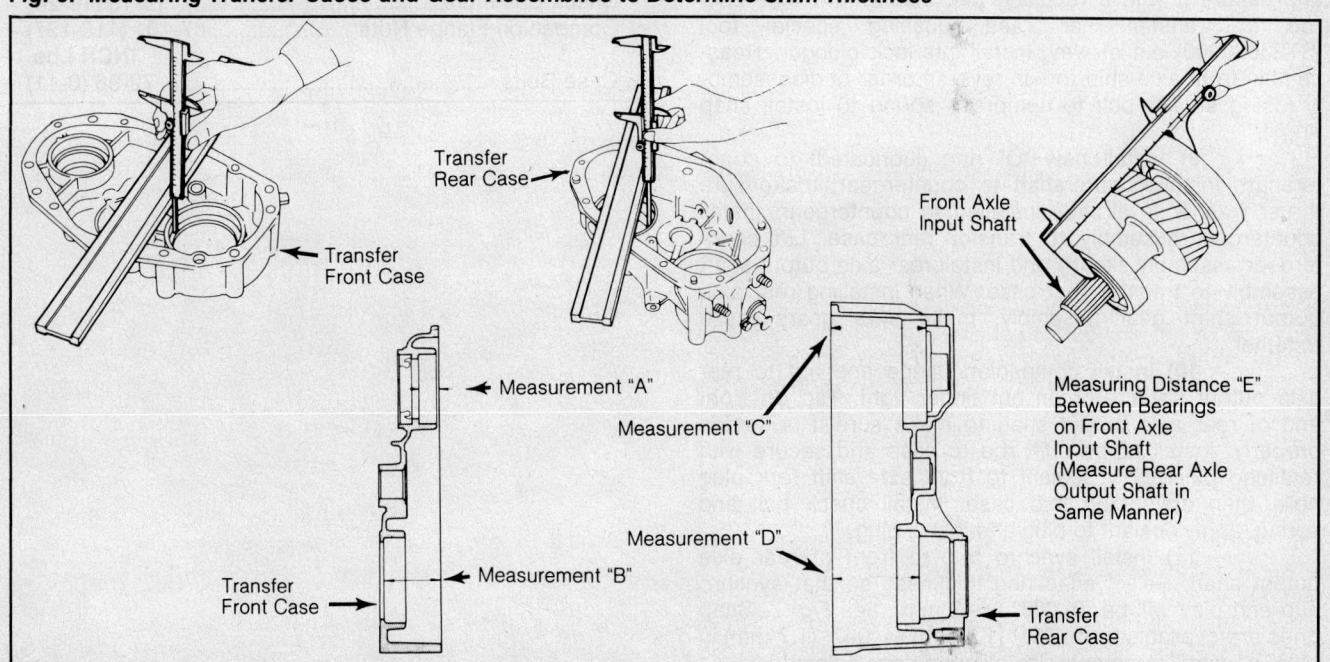

87-101 Ft. Lbs.
(118-137 N.m)

87-101 Ft. Lbs.
(118-137 N.m)

1. Companion Flange Nut
2. Companion Flange
3. Shim
4. Ball Bearing
5. Transfer Case Input Shaft
6. Breather Cover
7. Thrust Washer
8. Countergear
9. "O" Ring
10. Spacer
11. Countershaft
12. Needle Bearings
13. Spacer
14. Front Axle Output Shaft
15. Pilot Bearing
16. Synchro Sleeve
17. Snap Ring
18. Synchro Hub
19. Shim
20. Low Range Gear
21. Steel Ball
22. Rear Axle Output Shaft
23. High Range Gear
24. Spacer
25. Speedometer Drive Gear

4) Measure bearing seating depths on both transfer cases ("A", "B", "C" and "D"). *Refer to Fig. 5.* When measuring bearing seating depth "C", be sure breather cover is installed. With new ball bearings installed on transfer case input shaft, measure distance ("E") between outer edge of bearings. Then measure distance ("F") between outer edge of bearings on rear axle output shaft.

Fig. 5: Measuring Transfer Cases and Gear Assemblies to Determine Shim Thickness

Transfer
Rear Case

Transfer
Front Case

Front Axle
Input Shaft

Measurement "A"

Measurement "C"

Measuring Distance "E"
Between Bearings
on Front Axle
Input Shaft
(Measure Rear Axle
Output Shaft in
Same Manner)

Measurement "D"

Measurement "B"

Transfer
Front Case

Transfer
Rear Case

NISSAN/NISSAN 4WD PICKUP (Cont.)

5) To select transfer case input shaft shim, add measurement "A" to "C" then subtract distance "E". To select rear axle output shaft shim, add measurement "B" to "D" then subtract distance "F". *See Fig. 5.* Select shims so shaft end play will be .002-.006" (.06-.15 mm) on transfer case input shaft or .0-.005" (.0-.13 mm) on rear axle output shaft. Shims are available from .004" (.1 mm) to .016" (.4 mm) for transfer case input shaft or from .004" (.1 mm) to .020" (.5 mm) for rear axle output shaft.

6) If transfer case input shaft bearings are not already pressed on shaft (from shim selection), press bearings onto transfer case input shaft. Install breather cover to transfer case input shaft. Install center spacer, needle bearings and spacers to countergear.

7) Install transfer case input shaft to transfer front case. Drive front axle shift fork plug out of transfer front case (this is necessary to install front axle shift fork). Install check spring and ball into hole in transfer rear case and retain with special retaining tool (ST23620000). *See Fig. 6.*

Fig. 6: Using Retaining Tool (ST23620000) to Retain Check Ball and Spring in Transfer Front Case

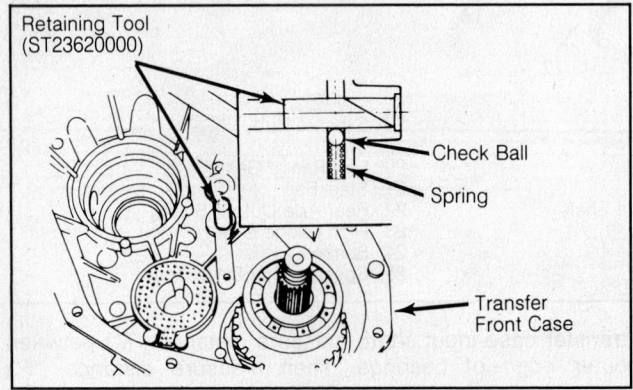

8) Install range shift fork to its synchro sleeve. Attach front axle shift rod bracket to front axle shift rod and secure it with a retaining pin. Install front axle shift rod to transfer rear case, pushing special tool (ST23620000) out of way. Install interlock plunger. Reassemble front axle shift fork in reverse order of disassembly (using an M8 bolt to compress spring to install snap rings).

9) Install new "O" ring (lubricated) to countershaft. Install countershaft to countergear, make sure thrust washer is already installed to countergear. Install countergear assembly to transfer rear case. Lift countergear assembly slightly and install rear axle output shaft assembly to transfer rear case. When installing rear axle output shaft gear assembly, make sure gears mesh together.

10) Install companion flange and nut to rear axle output shaft. Tighten nut finger tight. Tap on front end of rear axle output shaft to make sure it is seated properly. Install range shift rod to case and secure with retaining pin. Apply sealant to front axle shift fork plug hole, then drive plug into case. Install check ball and spring, apply sealant to plug and install plug.

11) Install synchro hub to front of rear axle output shaft. Select snap ring thickness so that synchro hub end play will be .0-.008" (.0-.2 mm). *See Fig. 7.* Snap rings are available from .051" (1.3 mm) to .067" (1.7 mm) in .004" (.1 mm) increments. Install snap rings selected.

Fig. 7: Measuring Synchro Hub to Bearing Clearance for Snap Ring Selection

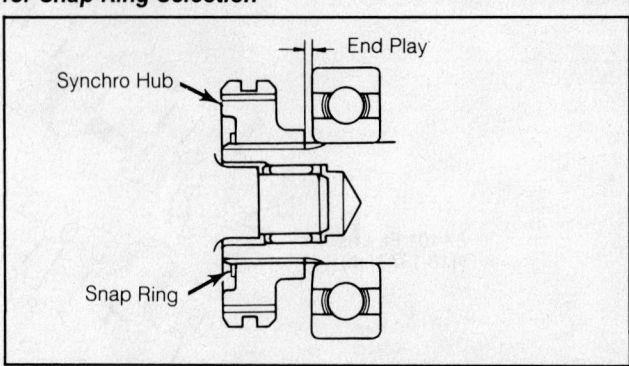

12) Install shift lever with differential lever, then install cross shift shaft. Apply grease to thrust washer and shims selected in steps **4)** and **5)**, then install them in transfer front case. Clean mating surfaces of transfer cases, apply sealant to mating surfaces and install transfer front case to transfer rear case. Make sure gear assemblies, shift forks, shift rods, shims and thrust washer remain in position. Tapping case with mallet will aid in installation.

13) Install spacer, front axle shift fork assembly and spacer, then secure with snap ring. Install greased pilot bearing to rear axle output shaft, then install front axle output shaft to rear axle output shaft. Clean mating surfaces of transfer case and front cover, apply sealant to mating surfaces and install front cover. Install other 2 companion flanges.

14) Remove previously installed companion flange nut (it was tightened finger tight), then install all new companion flange nuts and tighten. Install 4WD indicator switch.

TIGHTENING SPECIFICATIONS

Application	Ft. Lbs. (N.m)
Check Ball Plug	14-18 (19-24)
Companion Flange Nuts	87-101 (118-137)
	INCH Lbs.
Case Bolts	72-96 (8-11)

TOYOTA LAND CRUISER

DESCRIPTION

The transfer case used on Toyota Land Cruiser models equipped with a 4-speed transmission is mounted on back of transmission. Transfer case provides a direct drive high speed and an underdrive low speed to rear axle and to front axle when 4WD is selected. High and low speeds as well as 4WD are selected through an auxiliary shifter.

LUBRICATION

SERVICE INTERVAL

Check fluid level every 12 months or 15,000 miles. Replace fluid every 12 months or 15,000 miles on vehicles used for pulling trailers or operated off-road.

FLUID TYPE

Use SAE-90 gear oil (API service GL-4).

CAPACITY

Fill up to just below level of filler plug hole.

REMOVAL & INSTALLATION

TRANSFER CASE ASSEMBLY

Removal

Remove PTO (if equipped) from transfer case and hang from frame with wire. Remove transmission and transfer case assembly from vehicle. *See appropriate article in MANUAL TRANSMISSION REMOVAL Section.*

Installation

Reverse removal procedure and refill gear cases with lubricant.

TRANSFER CASE DISASSEMBLY

1) Remove speedometer driven gear, bolt and retainer. Remove transfer shift lever assembly. Check rear output shaft bearing preload. Preload should be 15-25 INCH lbs. (1.7-2.8 N.m) for new bearings and 6-10 INCH lbs. (.68-1.1 N.m) for used bearings. Remove detent balls and springs. Remove transmission output shaft cover and gasket.

Fig. 1: Exploded View of Toyota Land Cruiser Transfer Case

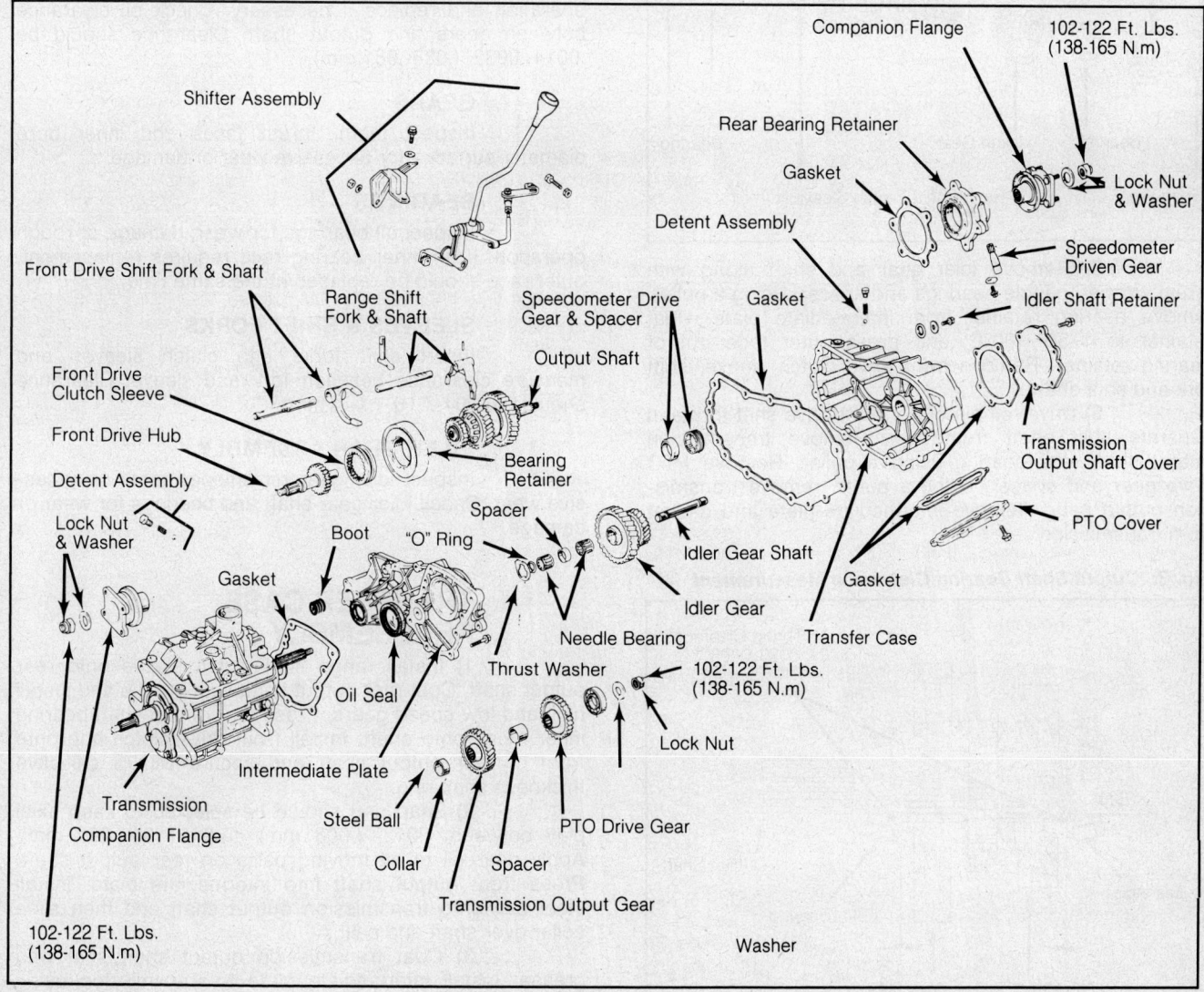

Transfer Cases

TOYOTA LAND CRUISER (Cont.)

2) Shift transfer case into 4WD Low range. Remove transmission output shaft nut and transfer case companion flange nuts. Remove both companion flanges. Remove rear output shaft bearing retainer and gasket. Remove idler gear shaft lock plate. Remove PTO cover on models not equipped with PTO.

3) Measure idler gear thrust clearance through PTO opening. Clearance should be .0108-.0246" (.274-.625 mm). If clearance exceeds specifications, idler gear thrust washer will need to be replaced at reassembly. Remove transfer case-to-intermediate plate attaching bolts.

4) Separate transfer case from intermediate plate. Remove speedometer drive gear and spacer from rear output shaft. Remove rear output shaft together with range shift fork and shift shaft. Drive roll pin out of range shift fork and separate fork from shaft.

Fig. 2: Exploded View of Transfer Case Rear Output Shaft

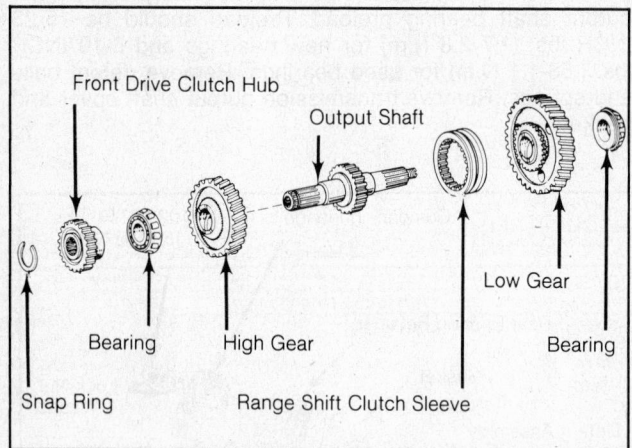

5) Remove idler gear and shaft along with thrust washer, needle bearings and spacer. Using a puller, remove bearing retainer from intermediate plate. Heat retainer to 175°F (80°C) and press outer race out of bearing retainer. Remove front drive clutch sleeve, shift fork and shift shaft.

6) Drive roll pin out of front drive shift fork and separate shift shaft from fork. Remove transmission output shaft rear bearing using a puller. Remove PTO drive gear and spacer. Using a puller, remove transmission output gear. Remove intermediate plate and gasket from transmission.

Fig. 3: Output Shaft Bearing Clearance Measurement

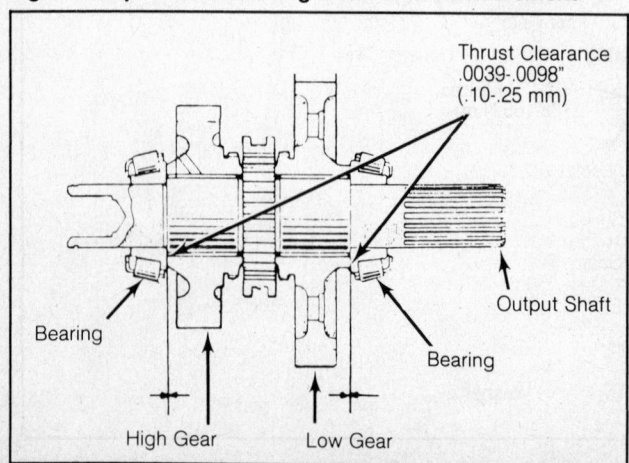

7) Remove spacer and steel ball from transmission output shaft. Using a press, remove transfer case front output shaft from intermediate plate. Measure clearance between output shaft bearings and high and low gears on rear output shaft. Clearance should be .0039-.0098" (.10-.25 mm).

8) Remove snap ring from front of rear output shaft. Using a press, remove low gear and bearing from rear output shaft. Press high gear and bearing off front of rear output shaft. Remove clutch sleeve from rear output shaft.

CLEANING & INSPECTION

TRANSFER CASE & INTERMEDIATE PLATE

Inspect case, intermediate plate, PTO cover (if applicable) and bearing retainer for cracks or damage. Inspect oil seals and front output shaft bearing for wear.

OUTPUT SHAFT

Inspect front and rear output shafts for damage or wear. Check output shaft pilot bearing for rough operation and replace if necessary. Check oil clearance between gears and output shaft. Clearance should be .0014-.0032" (.035-.081 mm).

GEARS

Inspect teeth, thrust faces and inner bore diameter surfaces for excessive wear or damage.

BEARINGS

Inspect all bearings for wear, damage or rough operation. If an inner bearing race requires replacement, outer race should be replaced at the same time.

SLEEVES & SHIFT FORKS

Insert shift forks into clutch sleeves and measure clearance between fork and sleeve. Clearance should be .004-.016" (.1-.4 mm).

IDLER GEAR ASSEMBLY

Inspect idler gear for chipped teeth or excessive wear. Check idler gear shaft and bearings for wear or damage.

TRANSFER CASE REASSEMBLY

1) Install range shift clutch sleeve onto rear output shaft. Coat rear output shaft with grease and install high and low speed gears. Press rear output shaft bearing inner races onto shaft. Install front drive clutch hub onto front of rear output shaft and secure with a selective thickness snap ring.

2) Snap ring should be selected to keep axial play between .0012" (.003 mm) and .0118" (.299 mm). Apply gear oil to all moving parts on rear output shaft. Press front output shaft into intermediate plate. Install steel ball onto transmission output shaft and then slide collar over shaft and ball.

3) Coat transmission output shaft seal with grease. Install intermediate plate to transmission using sealer on all attaching bolts. Press transmission output

TOYOTA LAND CRUISER (Cont.)

gear onto shaft. Install spacer and PTO drive gear onto transmission output shaft. Press transmission output shaft rear bearing onto shaft and secure with a washer and lock nut. Install lock nut finger tight only.

4) Install front drive shift shaft into shift fork and secure with a roll pin. Place front drive shift sleeve into fork and install assembly into intermediate plate. Press rear output shaft front bearing outer race into bearing retainer. Tap bearing retainer into intermediate plate.

5) Install range shift fork onto shift shaft and secure with roll pin. Place range shift fork onto shift sleeve. Install rear output shaft and shift fork assembly into intermediate plate. Coat the idler gear thrust washer with grease and stick to intermediate plate, making sure that tab on thrust washer engages slot on plate.

6) Install front "O" ring onto idler gear shaft. Place idler gear on intermediate plate and install idler gear shaft so that 2" (50 mm) of shaft extends beyond gear. Install spacer and speedometer drive gear onto rear output shaft.

7) If idler gear thrust clearance was not to specifications at disassembly, select a thrust washer that will correct clearance. Clearance should be .0108-.0246" (.275-.625 mm). Coat idler gear thrust washer with grease and place on transfer case, making sure that tab on thrust washer engages slot in case.

8) Install transfer case onto intermediate plate, taking care to engage range selector lever tip with groove in range shift shaft. Install transfer case attaching bolts using liquid sealer.

9) Rotate idler gear shaft so that locking groove aligns with bolt hole. Install idler shaft rear "O" ring and tap shaft into place. Secure shaft with locking plate and bolt. Check operation of range shift lever to ensure smooth operation and proper engagement.

10) Recheck idler gear thrust clearance. Install rear bearing retainer, making sure that rib on case and retainer line up. Shift transfer case to 4WD Low range. Install front and rear companion flanges and secure with washers and lock nuts. Hold output shaft stationary and tighten companion flange nuts and transmission output shaft nut.

11) Disengage front drive and check rear output shaft bearing preload. Rotating torque should be 13-24 INCH lbs. (1.47-2.71 N.m) for new bearings and 6-10 INCH lbs. (.678-1.13 N.m) for used bearings.

12) If preload is not within specifications, preload shims must be changed. The preload shims are located between the rear bearing retainer and the rear output shaft bearing outer race.

13) Install PTO cover (if applicable) and transmission output shaft cover using liquid sealer on all bolts. Install shifter assembly and check for smooth operation and proper engagement of all gear ranges.

TIGHTENING SPECIFICATIONS

Application	Ft. Lbs. (N.m)
Intermediate Plate Bolts	37-57 (50-77)
Transfer Case-to-Intermediate Plate Bolts	
10 mm Bolts	26-32 (35-43)
12 mm Bolts	37-57 (50-77)
Rear Bearing Retainer	22-33 (30-45)
Companion Flange Nuts	102-122 (138-165)
Transmission Output Shaft Nut	102-122 (138-165)

Transfer Cases

TOYOTA 4-WD PICKUP

DESCRIPTION

The transfer case used on Toyota 4WD Pickup is mounted to rear of transmission by an adapter housing. Transfer case has 2 ranges, High and Low. Transfer case can be shifted into 4WD in either range (High or Low) and can be shifted into 4WD High range at any time, providing the locking hubs are in the "Lock" position. Transfer case is provided with an indicator switch to tell what position transfer selector lever is in.

LUBRICATION

SERVICE INTERVAL

Check fluid level every 12,000 miles or 15 months (whichever comes first). Drain and refill transfer case every 30,000 miles or 24 months.

FLUID TYPE

Use SAE 80W-90 gear oil (API-GL-4, GL-5).

CAPACITY

3.4 pts. (1.6 liters).

REMOVAL & INSTALLATION

TRANSFER CASE ASSEMBLY

NOTE: **Transmission and transfer case are removed together as an assembly.**

Removal

1) Disconnect battery negative cable. Remove starter upper mounting bolt. Using Special Wrench (SST09305-20012), remove transmission shift lever. Remove transfer shift lever. Raise and support vehicle.

2) Drain transfer case. Mark propeller shaft "U" joint positions on transfer case and differential flanges for reassembly reference. Remove propeller shaft. Remove clutch release cylinder and hose from transmission, but do not disconnect hydraulic line from cylinder. Disconnect all electrical connectors from transmission and transfer case. Remove starter and speedometer cable.

3) Remove engine rear mounting bolts. Support transmission case with a jack and remove crossmember. Lower jack until transmission and transfer case are low enough to be removed. Support engine with safety stand

Fig. 1: Exploded View of Toyota 4WD Pickup Transfer Case Assembly

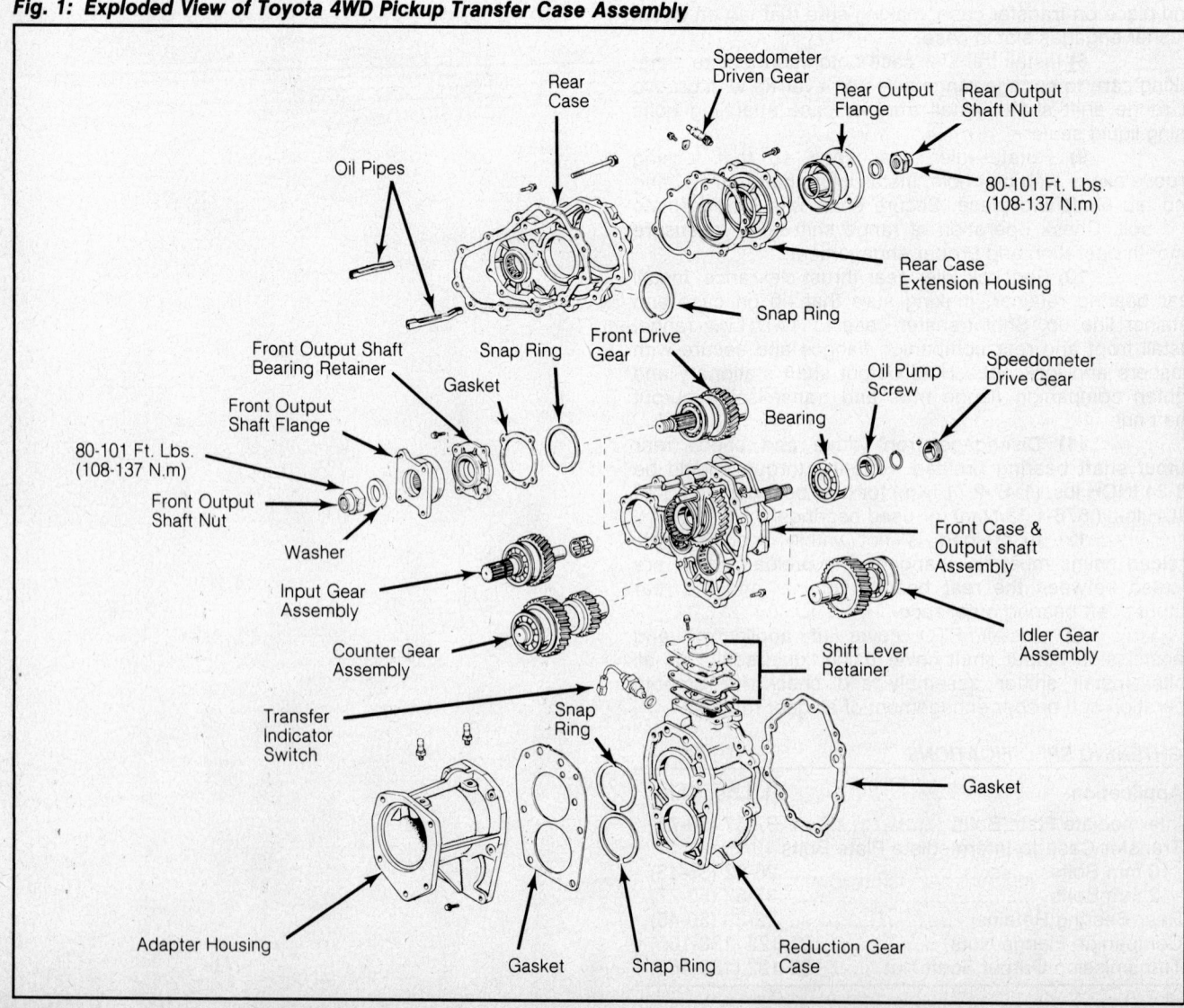

TOYOTA 4-WD PICKUP (Cont.)

Fig. 2: Exploded View of Toyota 4WD Pickup Transfer Case Gears

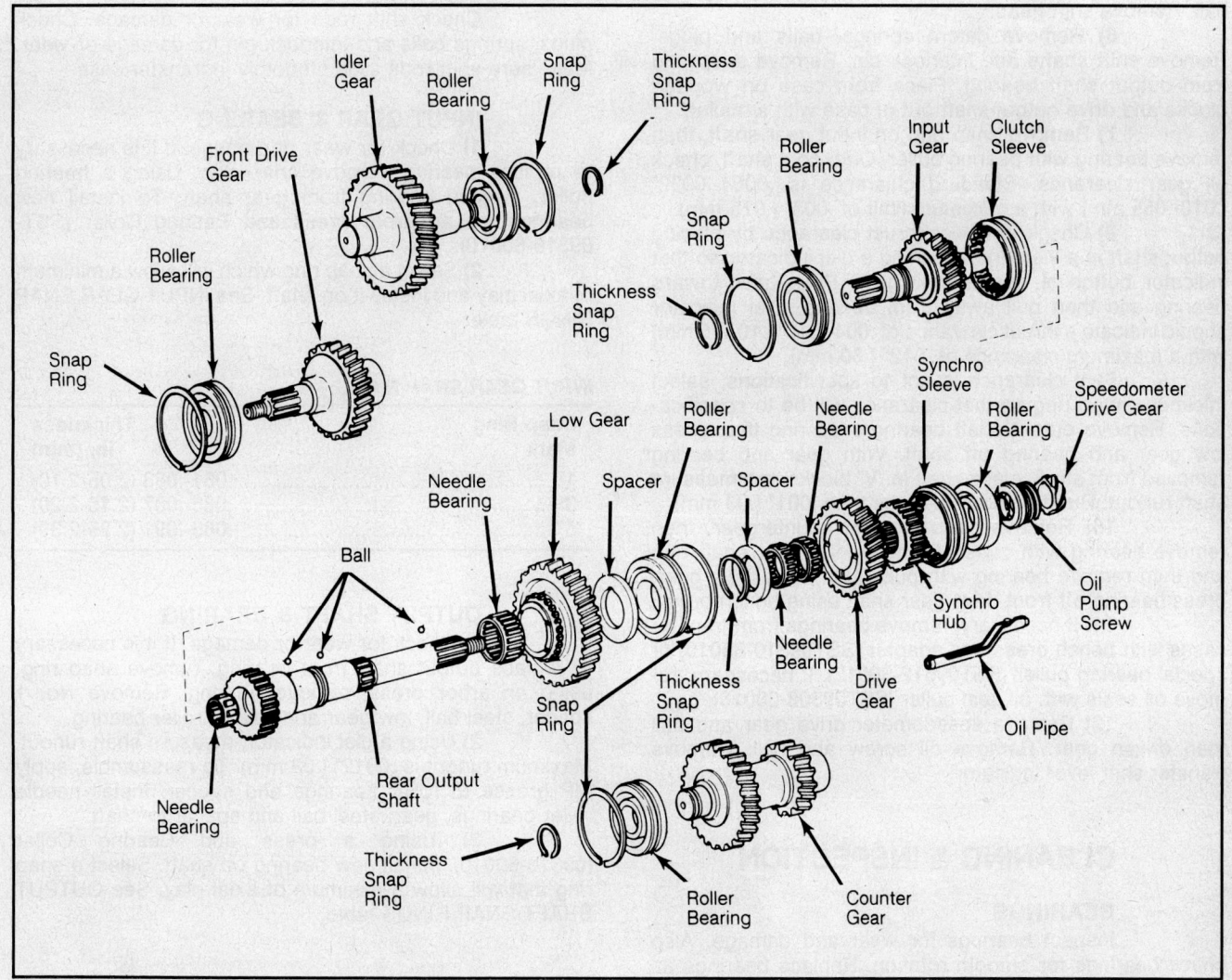

and wooden block under oil pan. Remove bolts attaching transmission to engine and remove transmission and transfer case as an assembly.

4) Separate transfer case from transmission by removing bolts attaching adapter housing to transmission. Do not pry on transmission or adapter housing when separating.

Installation

Install transmission and transfer case in the reverse order of removal. Make sure marks on propeller shaft are aligned correctly and all electrical connectors are connected. Fill transfer case with correct type and amount of gear oil.

TRANSFER CASE DISASSEMBLY

Disassembly

1) Remove shifter assembly, speedometer driven gear and transfer indicator switch. Remove front output shaft nut. Remove flange and front drive gear

bearing retainer. Remove adapter housing bolts and adapter housing. Remove reduction gear case together with input gear and countergear by tapping with a mallet.

2) Remove snap rings from input gear bearing and from countergear bearing. Then remove input gear and countergear by tapping with a mallet.

3) Remove output shaft nut, flange and bearing retainer housing. Remove speedometer drive gear, steel ball, oil pump screw and bearing. Remove case with idler gear by tapping with a mallet. Remove snap ring from idler gear bearing and remove idler gear by tapping with a mallet.

4) Hold front drive gear upright so clutch hub and ball will not fall out. Remove snap ring from front drive gear bearing. Tap front drive gear out of front case.

NOTE: When removing front drive gear, hold front case upright or clutch hub and ball will fall out.

5) Move the shift forks to 2WD High range. Drive out spring pins from both shift forks and shift head. Remove shift forks with synchronizer sleeves. Remove synchronizer

hub, transfer drive gear, needle bearings, spacer and steel ball. Remove shift head.

6) Remove detent springs, balls and plugs. Remove shift shafts and interlock pin. Remove snap ring from output shaft bearing. Place front case on wooden blocks and drive output shaft out of case with a mallet.

7) Remove snap ring on input gear shaft, then remove bearing with bearing puller. On output shaft, check oil gear clearance. Standard clearance is .0004-.0022" (.010-.055 mm) with a maximum limit of .003" (.075 mm).

8) Check low gear thrust clearance by placing output shaft in a vise and attaching a dial indicator so that indicator button is against low gear. Push gear toward bearing and then pull away from bearing. Dial indicator should indicate a thrust clearance of .004-.010" (.10-.25 mm) with a maximum clearance of .012" (.30 mm).

9) If clearance is not to specifications, select thickness snap ring so that clearance will be to specifications. Remove output shaft bearing snap ring then press low gear and bearing off shaft. With gear and bearing removed from shaft, place shaft in "V" blocks and measure shaft runout. Runout should be less than .001" (.03 mm).

10) Remove snap ring on countergear, then remove bearing with puller. Remove idler gear snap ring and then remove bearing with puller. On front drive gear, press bearing off front drive gear shaft using bench press.

11) If necessary, remove bearings from transfer cases with bench press and adapter (SST09310-35010) or special bearing puller (SST09612-30012). If necessary, remove oil seals with oil seal puller (SST09308-00010).

12) Remove speedometer drive gear and ball then driven gear. Remove oil screw and ball. Remove transfer shift lever indicator.

CLEANING & INSPECTION

BEARINGS

Inspect bearings for wear and damage. Also check bearings for smooth rotation. Replace bearings as necessary.

GEARS

1) Check oil clearance and thrust clearance of transfer low gear. To do so, use a dial indicator, measure clearance between gear and shaft with needle roller bearing installed. Standard clearance is .0004-.0022" (.010-.055 mm). Maximum clearance is .003" (.075 mm).

2) Check oil and thrust clearance of transfer drive gear. To do so, use a dial indicator, measure oil clearance between gear and shaft with needle roller bearing installed. Standard clearance is .0004-.002" (.009-.051 mm). Maximum clearance is .0028" (.071 mm).

3) Using a dial indicator, measure thrust clearance with clutch hub and spacer installed. Standard clearance is .0035-.0106" (.09-.27 mm). Maximum clearance is .0126" (.32 mm).

SYNCHRO HUBS, SLEEVES & SHIFT FORKS

Check synchro hub and sleeve for smooth sliding operation. Check synchro hub on shaft splines for smooth operation. Using a feeler gauge, check clearance of shift forks to synchro sleeves. Clearance should be a maximum of .040" (1.0 mm).

SHIFT RODS

Check shift rods for wear or damage. Check plugs, springs balls and interlock pin for damage or wear. Make sure shift rods slide smoothly in transfer case.

INPUT GEAR & BEARING

1) Check for wear or damage. If it is necessary to replace bearing, remove snap ring. Using a bearing puller, remove bearing from gear shaft. To install new bearing, use an arbor press and Bearing Collar (SST-09316-60010).

2) Select a snap ring which will allow a minimum of axial play and install it on shaft. See INPUT GEAR SNAP RINGS table.

INPUT GEAR SNAP RINGS

Snap Ring Mark	Thickness In. (mm)
1	.081-.083 (2.05-2.10)
3	.085-.087 (2.15-2.20)
5	.089-.091 (2.25-2.30)

OUTPUT SHAFT & BEARING

1) Check for wear or damage. If it is necessary to replace output shaft front bearing, remove snap ring. using an arbor press, remove bearing. Remove No. 1 spacer, steel ball, low gear and needle roller bearing.

2) Using a dial indicator, measure shaft runout. Maximum runout is .0012" (.03 mm). To reassemble, apply MP grease to roller bearings and spacer. Install needle roller bearings, gear, steel ball and spacer to shaft.

3) Using a press and Bearing Collar (09316-60010), install new bearing on shaft. Select a snap ring that will allow a minimum of axial play. See OUTPUT SHAFT SNAP RINGS table.

OUTPUT SHAFT SNAP RINGS

Snap Ring Mark	Thickness In. (mm)
0	.094-.096 (2.40-2.45)
1	.096-.098 (2.45-2.50)
2	.098-.100 (2.50-2.55)
3	.100-.102 (2.55-2.60)
4	.102-.104 (2.60-2.65)
5	.104-.106 (2.65-2.70)

COUNTER GEAR & REAR BEARING

1) Check for wear or damage. If necessary to replace counter gear rear bearing, remove snap ring. Using a bearing puller, remove bearing. Use a press and Bearing Installer (09310-35010) to install new bearing.

2) Select a snap ring which will allow a minimum of axial play. See COUNTER GEAR SNAP RINGS table.

IDLER GEAR & BEARINGS

1) If it is necessary to replace idler gear front bearing, use a press and Bearing Installer/Remover (09310-35010). Use press and bearing installer/remover to install new bearing.

COUNTER GEAR SNAP RINGS

Snap Ring Mark	Thickness In. (mm)
1	.083-.085 (2.10-2.15)
3	.087-.089 (2.20-2.25)

2) If it is necessary to replace idler gear rear bearing, remove snap ring. Using an arbor press, remove bearing. Using a press and Bearing Collar (09316-60010), install new bearing.

3) Select a snap ring that will allow a minimum of axial play. Maximum play is .006" (.15 mm). See IDLER GEAR SNAP RINGS table.

IDLER GEAR SNAP RINGS

Snap Ring Mark	Thickness In. (mm)
A	.059-.061 (1.50-1.55)
B	.063-.065 (1.60-1.65)

FRONT DRIVE GEAR & BEARINGS

1) If necesary to replace front bearing, use a press to remove bearing. To install a new bearing, use a press and Bearing Remover (09316-60010).

2) If it is necessary to replace front drive rear bearing, use a press and Bearing Remover (09612-30012). Use a press and Bearing Installer (09310-35010) to install a new bearing.

SPEEDOMETER GEAR & OIL SEAL

1) Check speedometer gear for scoring, damage and smooth operation. Check "O" ring for damage.

2) If it is necessary to replace oil seal, use a press and Seal Remover (09921-00010). To install a new seal, use a press and Seal Installer (09201-60011). Press seal in to a depth of .79" (20 mm).

EXTENSION HOUSING & OIL SEAL

1) Check for damage to housing. Check oil seal lip for wear or damage. If it is necessary to replace oil seals, use an inside puller and slide hammer to remove seals.

2) To install new bottom seal, use Seal Installer (09310-35010) and a hammer to drive in new seal. Be sure to position new seal for oil pump screw, position flat surface upward.

3) To install new top seal, use Seal Installer (09325-20010) and a hammer to drive in new seal. Ensure groove direction. DO NOT interchange this seal with front drive gear oil seal.

NOTE: Extension housing seal has an arrow mark pointing counterclockwise to distinguish it from front drive gear oil seal.

FRONT DRIVE GEAR OIL SEAL

1) If it is necessary to replace front drive oil seal, place case on wooden blocks. Use a hammer and Seal Remover (09325-20010) to drive seal from case.

2) To install a new oil seal, use a press and Seal Installer (09325-20010). Press seal into case to a depth of .28" (7 mm). Use a hammer and Dust Cover Installer (09325-20010) to drive in new dust cover

TRANSFER CASE REASSEMBLY

NOTE: Apply gear lubricant to all gears, bearings, shafts and seals during assembly.

1) Install rear output shaft into front case then install snap ring to roller bearing. Install bearing retainer to front case and tighten bolts.

2) Place case on wooden blocks. Using a plastic hammer, install input gear and counter gear. Install roller bearing on input shaft. Install No. 2 shift fork on input shaft.

3) Place a new gasket on front of case. Install reduction gear case together with input gear and counter gear. Install and tighten bolts. Using a plastic hammer, install front drive gear. Install snap ring.

Fig. 3: Installation Bolts Needed when Installing Reduction Gear Case to Front Case

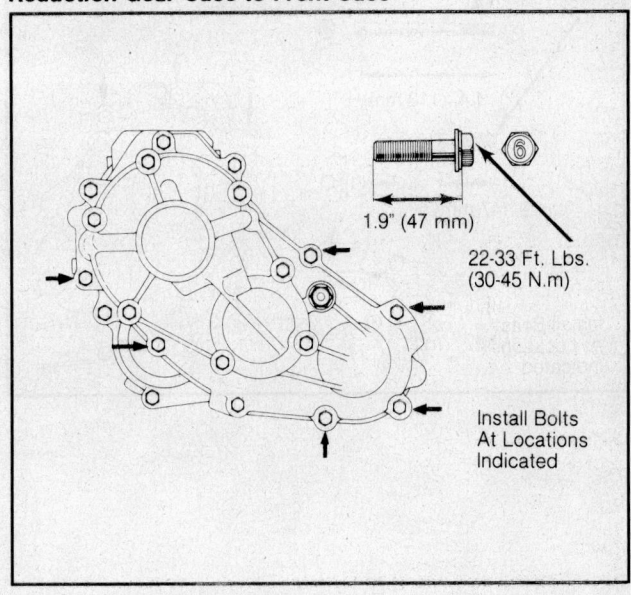

1.9" (47 mm)

22-33 Ft. Lbs. (30-45 N.m)

Install Bolts At Locations Indicated

4) Place a new gasket on front case. Apply MP grease to oil seal lip. Install bearing retainer. Install and tighten bolts. Insert high-low shift fork shaft to No. 2 shift fork.

5) Align slotted spring hole in fork with hole in shaft. Drive in spring pin. Place a new gasket to rear case. Apply MP grease to oil seal lips. Install extension housing. Install and tighten case bolts.

6) Install transfer case cover. Install and tighten bolts. Install companion flange, install washer and nut. Tighten nut to specifications and then stake nut. Install transfer indicator switch with washer. Install speedomter driven gear. Secure gear with lock plate and bolt.

Transfer Cases
TOYOTA 4-WD PICKUP (Cont.)

Fig. 4: *Installation Bolts Needed when Installing Extension Housing to Rear Case*

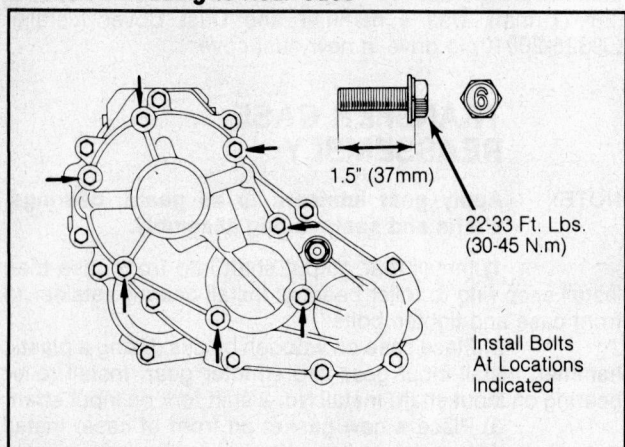

Fig. 5: *Installation Bolts Needed when Installing Rear Case to Front Case*

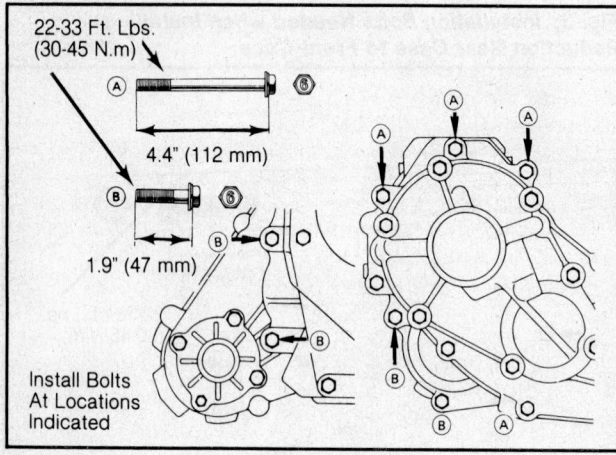

Fig. 6: *Installation Bolts Needed when Installing Adapter Housing to Reduction Gear Case*

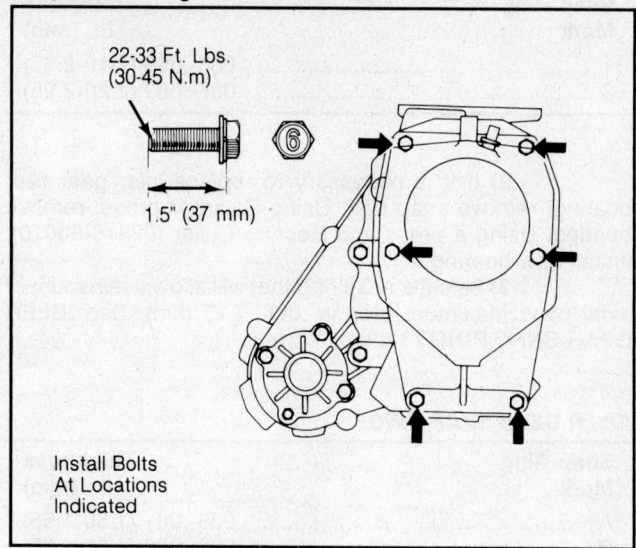

TIGHTENING SPECIFICATIONS

Application	Ft. Lbs. (N.m)
Adapter Housing Bolts	22-33 (30-45)
Bearing Retainer Bolts	
Front Output Shaft	12-16 (16-22)
Rear Output Shaft	7-12 (9-16)
Crossmember-to-Frame	54-76 (73-103)
Crossmember-to-Transfer Case	7-12 (9-16)
Front Output Shaft Nut	80-101 (108-137)
Propeller Shaft-to-Flange	29-43 (39-58)
Rear Case-to-Front Case	22-33 (30-45)
Rear Case-to-Extension Hsg.	22-33 (30-45)
Rear-Output Shaft Nut	80-101 (108-137)
Reduction Gear Housing Bolts	22-33 (30-45)
Shift Lever Retainer	7-12 (9-16)
Speedometer Driven Gear Retainer	7-12 (9-16)
Transfer Indicator Switch	22-36 (30-40)
Transmission-to-Engine Bolts	36-58 (49-79)

NOTE: The Latest Changes and Corrections represent a collection of the last minute 1985 information which arrived too late to be included into the regular data pages. In addition, we have included information on prior year models which we have received since last year's edition.

This information is numbered to assist you in relating them to the regular data pages. To correctly use them, simply write the corresponding number within the small box and the year of the edition on the appropriate page(s) of the text.

AUTOMATIC TRANSMISSIONS

HONDA

1 *1983 HONDA ACCORD WITH AUTOMATIC TRANSAXLE: TRANSAXLE SLIP OR SHIFT IN AND OUT OF GEAR* – Some 1983 Accord models with automatic transaxles may slip or shift in or out of gear. This situation may be due to the torque converter continually locking and unlocking. This condition is refered to as "hunting" and may be repaired as follows.

1) Check the throttle cable and bracket and adjust them if necessary. Road test the vehicle at 55 MPH on a level road and watch the tachometer for signs of torque converter hunting. Do not use the cruise control.

2) If the torque converter hunts, shorten the throttle control cable 1 turn clockwise. Continue shortening the throttle cable until the torque converter stays locked at 55 MPH.

3) The cable may be shortened up to 3 turns clockwise. Exceeding this adjustment may cause harsh shifting on partial-throttle upshift and closed-throttle downshift.

4) Road test the vehicle at 55 MPH using the cruise control. If the converter hunts with the cruise control engaged, but functions properly with the cruise control disengaged, adjust the cruise control cable at the actuator to its minimum specification.

ISUZU

2 *1978-84 ISUZU I-MARK AND P'UP WITH AISIN-WARNER OR BORG-WARNER AUTOMATIC TRANSMISSION: VALVE BODY MODIFICATION* – The valve body exploded view for the Aisin-Warner 55 and Borg-Warner 55 transmissions is incorrect as shown in all previous editions of Mitchell's TRANSMISSION SERVICE & REPAIR manual. The Governor Modulator Valve and spring (No. 8 in the illustration) was deleted from Borg-Warner 55 model transmissions in the 1978 model year. In addition, the Cutback Valve (No. 3 in illustration) spring was deleted at the same time. Check balls in the lower valve body and in the rear upper valve body were also deleted. The correct valve body and check ball illustrations appear in the 1985 edition.

JAGUAR

3 *1975-84 JAGUAR XJ6 WITH AUTOMATIC TRANSMISSION: NO REVERSE LIGHTS OR STARTER* – Some Jaguar XJ6 models with automatic transmissions may suffer from non-operation of the reverse lights or starter. This condition may be caused by an improperly mounted or misadjusted transmission starter/reverse light switch (DAC 2726). To correct the condition, use the following procedure:

1) Remove the starter/reverse light switch from the transmission. Enlarge the mounting hole with a 7/32" drill or small round file. This will allow for movement and adjustment of the transmission switch.

2) Remount switch and adjust for satisfactory operation. Tighten mounting bolt to secure switch in stationary position.

1975-84 Jaguar Reverse/Starter Switch

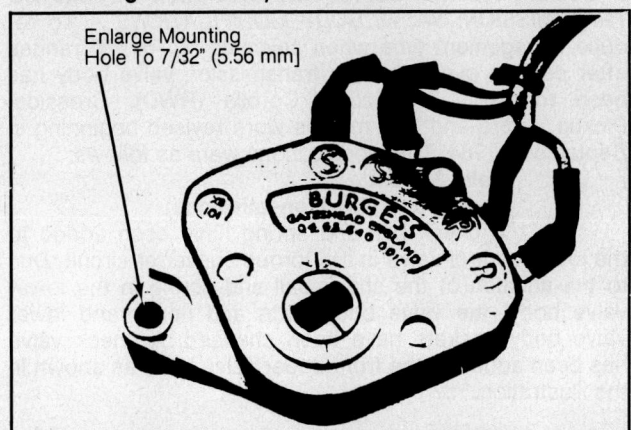

Enlarge Mounting Hole To 7/32" (5.56 mm]

SAAB

4 *1979-84 SAAB 900 WITH AUTOMATIC TRANSAXLE: PROTECTION PLATE* – A new protection plate is now available for all Saab 900 model vehicles equipped with automatic transmissions. This new protective plate provides additional protection and replaces the existing longitudinal skid bars. It is installed in the existing mounting system.

Saab 900 Automatic Transaxle Protection Plate

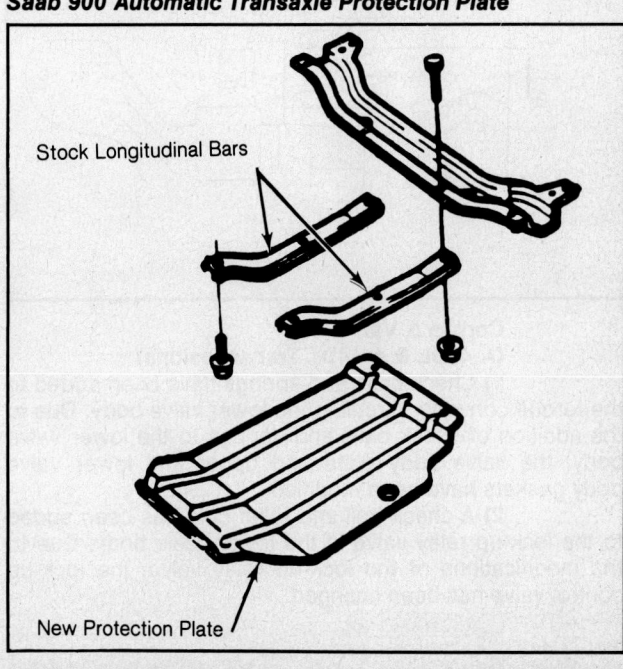

Stock Longitudinal Bars

New Protection Plate

Latest Changes & Corrections

FOR 1984 & EARLIER IMPORT MODELS (Cont.)

TOYOTA

5▷ *1984 CELICA, CRESSIDA, PICKUP AND SUPRA WITH AUTOMATIC TRANSMISSIONS: AUTOMATIC TRANS-MISSION FLUID USAGE* – For worldwide standardization, Dexron II automatic transmission fluid will be used instead of Type F for 1984 Celica, Cressida, Pickup and Supra models. If in doubt about fluid usage, a "D II" will be stamped on transmission oil pan drain plug. Also, Dexron II usage is also indicated on the oil level gauge of all affected vehicles. DO NOT mix Type F and Dexron II. If mixed, shift quality will be affected.

6▷ *1984-85 TOYOTA CELICA, COROLLA (RWD), CRESSIDA, PICKUP, SUPRA AND VAN WITH AUTOMATIC TRANSMISSION: VALVE BODY MODIFICATIONS* – To re-duce engagement time when selecting "D" or "R" ranges after parking overnight, the transmission valve body has been modified. All Celica, Corolla (RWD), Cressida, Pickup, Supra and Van models were revised beginning in September, 1984. The modifications were as follows:

Celic & Pickup
(A-40D & A-43D Transmissions)

A check ball and spring have been added to the lower control valve in the torque converter circuit. Due to the addition of the check ball and spring in the lower valve body, the valve body plate and upper and lower valve body gaskets have been changed. A check valve has been added to the front upper valve body as shown in the illustration.

Front Upper Valve Body Modification On Celica & Pickup Automatic Transmissions

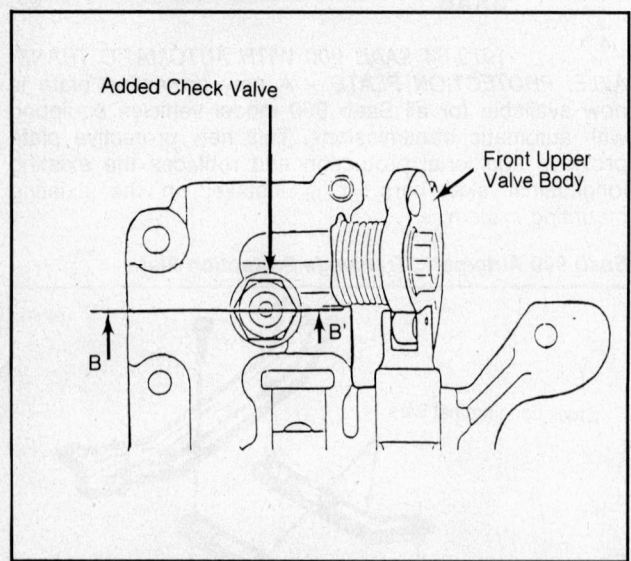

Corolla & Van
(A-42DL & A-44DL Transmissions)

1) Check balls and springs have been added to the torque converter circuit in the lower valve body. Due to the addition of check balls and springs to the lower valve body, the valve body plate and upper and lower valve body gaskets have been modified.

2) A check ball and relief hole has been added to the lock-up relay valve in the lower valve body. Due to the modifications of the lock-up relay valve, the lock-up control valve has been changed.

Lower Valve Body Modifcations For Corolla (RWD) & Van Automatic Transmissions

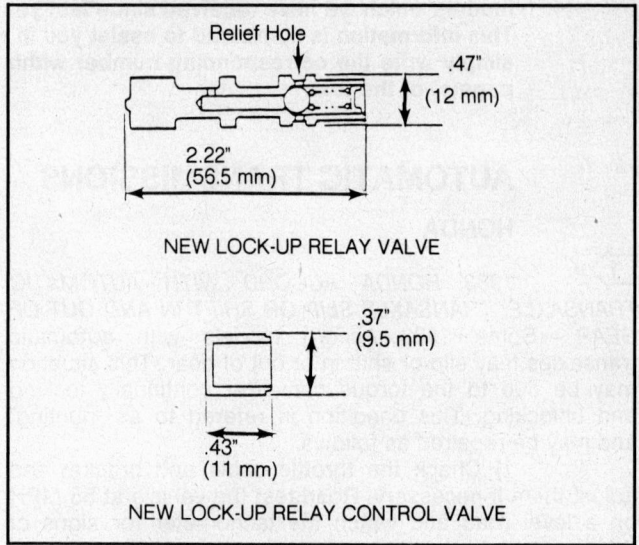

Cressida & Supra
(A-43DE Transmission)

1) Check balls and springs have been added to the torque converter circuit in the lower valve body. Due to the addition of check balls and springs to the lower valve body, the valve body plate and upper and lower valve body gaskets have been modified.

2) A check ball and relief hole has been added to the lock-up relay valve in the lower valve body. With the addition of the check ball and relief hole in the lock-up relay valve, the lock-up relay control valve has been discontinued.

3) The lock-up relay valve sleeve has been modified as shown in the illustration. The lock-up control valve spring free length has also been changed to 1.28" (32.6mm).

Lower Valve Body Modifcations For Cressida & Supra Automatic Transmissions

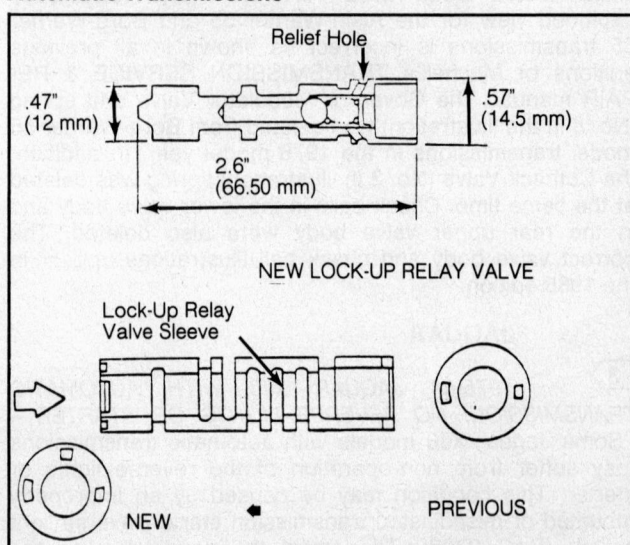

Latest Changes & Corrections

FOR 1984 & EARLIER IMPORT MODELS (Cont.)

7 *1984 TOYOTA COROLLA, CRESSIDA, SUPRA AND VANS WITH AUTOMATIC TRANSMISSIONS: TORQUE CONVERTER LOCK-UP CLUTCH DOES NOT RELEASE* – Some Toyota vehicles produced after August, 1984 may have torque converter lock-up clutches which do not release when slowing to a stop in any gear range. The models and transmissions affected are listed in the table.

TOYOTA TRANSMISSION APPLICATIONS

Model	Transmission
Corolla (RWD)	A-42DL
Cressida & Supra	A-43DE
Van	A-44DL

A possible cause of this condition may be foreign material between the lock-up relay valve and relay valve sleeve. This may be the result of an abrasive contact between the plastic check ball No. 3 (35428-30020), and the metal compression spring (90504-04005).

Diagnosis

1) Check automatic transmission fluid for correct level. Disconnect the ECT ECU computer. Start engine with selector lever in "P" range.

2) With the brake pedal depressed, shift the transmission from "P" to "D" range. If lock-up clutch does not release, repairs to the valve body may be necessary. Reconnect the ECT ECU computer.

Repair

1) Drain transmission fluid into container. Examine for particles in the fluid. Remove transmission oil pan. Check for particles in the oil pan. Clean pan and magnet if necessary.

2) Remove entire valve body. Remove the small lower valve body cover plate to gain access to the lock-up relay valve and sleeve assembly retaining pin. Inspect for any foreign material and clean this area as necessary.

3) Remove lock-up relay valve and sleeve. Check the relay valve and sleeve for sticking, scratches and spring particles.

4) If scratches or sticking are evident, clean and polish the valve and sleeve surfaces. If the valve or sleeve surfaces cannot be cleaned and polished for smooth operation, replace the valve and sleeve as an assembly.

No. 3 Check Ball Location on Toyota Transmission Valve Body

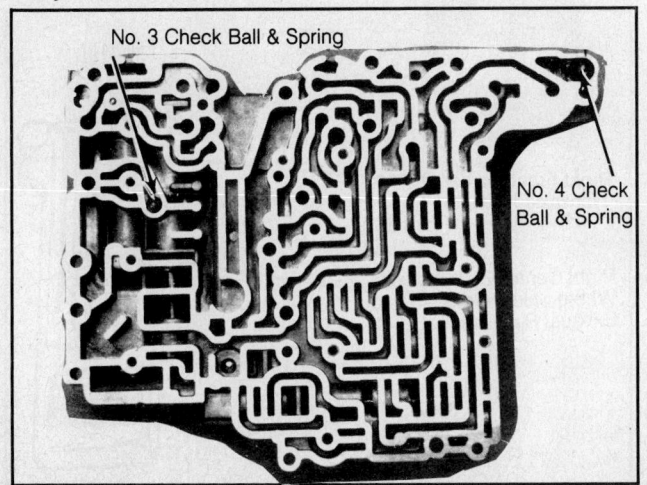

No. 3 Check Ball & Spring

No. 4 Check Ball & Spring

5) Remove upper front valve body and upper rear valve body along with the valve body plate and gaskets. Watch for check balls, retainer and pins in all valve bodies.

6) Remove the No. 3 check ball and spring from the lower valve body. The vehicle will operate without the No. 3 check ball and spring. Check and remove any spring particles in this area.

7) Reassemble the valve body the repaired or new lock-up relay valve and sleeve. Use new gaskets. Check remaining valves in the valve body for free movement and correct travel.

8) Reinstall valve body in transmission. Reinstall oil pan and plug. Fill transmission with Dexron II fluid.

VOLKSWAGEN

8 *1983-84 VANAGON WITH 1.9L ENGINE AND AUTOMATIC TRANSAXLE: HARD SHIFTING* – Some 1983-84 Vanagon models may exhibit hard shifting when warm. A new design selector shaft (091 311 534 B) is now available to correct this condition. To repair transaxle, proceed as follows:

1) Remove shifting linkage. Remove selector shaft cover, sealing ring, spring and retainer as shown in illustration.

2) Remove selector shaft and replace it with new design. Reassemble the transaxle.

1983-84 Vanagon Selector Shaft

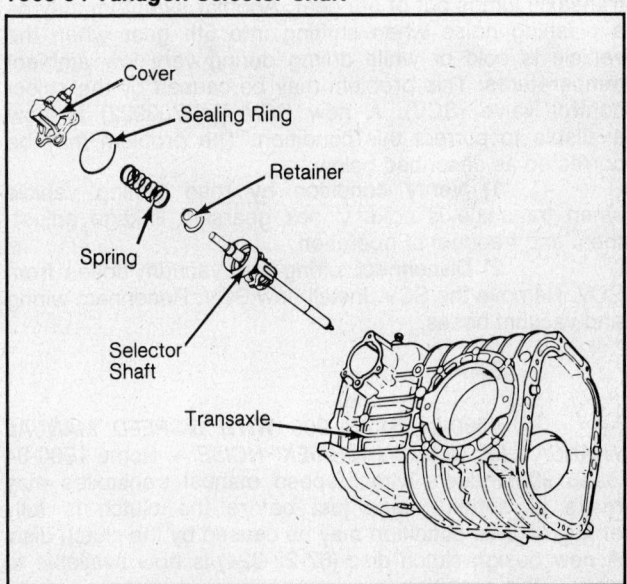

Cover

Sealing Ring

Retainer

Spring

Selector Shaft

Transaxle

VOLVO

9 *1975-84 VOLVO 240 AND 260 WITH AISIN-WARNER AUTOMATIC TRANSMISSION: NO OR DELAYED GEAR SHIFT WHEN COLD* – Some 1975-84 Volvo 240 and 260 models with Aisin-Warner automatic transmissions may have no or delayed gear shift from a cold start. This condition may be caused by air bubbles entering the oil pump. A new design upper front valve body (130084-1) and ball valve (1340085-8) are now available to correct this condition. Repair valve body as follows:

1) Drian transmission oil. Remove oil pan and remove valve body assembly. Separate upper front portion of valve body.

2) Remove components from oil upper front valve body and place in new design upper front valve body. Install ball valve. Using gasket key (274029-8), reassemble valve body. Reinstall valve body assembly and oil pan. Fill transmission and check for proper operation.

10 *1978-84 VOLVOS WITH AISIN-WARNER OR BORG-WARNER AUTOMATIC TRANSMISSION: VALVE BODY MODIFICATION* – The valve body exploded view for the Aisin-Warner 55 and Borg-Warner 55 transmissions is incorrect as shown in all previous editions of Mitchell's TRANSMISSION SERVICE & REPAIR manual. The Governor Modulator Valve and spring (No. 8 in the illustration) was deleted from Borg-Warner 55 model transmissions in the 1978 model year. In addition, the Cutback Valve (No. 3 in illustration) spring was deleted at the same time. Check balls in the lower valve body and in the rear upper valve body were also deleted. The correct valve body and check ball illustrations appear in the 1985 edition.

MANUAL TRANSMISSIONS

CHRYSLER CORP. IMPORTS

1 *1984 COLT VISTA: JUMPS OUT OF 5TH GEAR* – Some 1984 Colt Vista models equipped with a 5-speed manual transaxle may exhibit a condition where the transaxle jumps out of 5th gear. Another symptom may be a clashing noise when shifting into 5th gear when the vehicle is cold or while drivng during very low ambient temperatures. This problem may be caused by the select control valve (SCV). A new SCV (MD703922) is now available to correct this condition. The problem may be corrected as described below.

1) Verify condition by road testing vehicle when transaxle is cold. Check gearshift linkage adjustment and freedom of operation.

2) Disconnect wiring and vacuum hoses from SCV. Remove the SCV. Install new SCV. Reconnect wiring and vacuum hoses.

SAAB

2 *1980-84 SAAB 900 WITH 5-SPEED MANUAL TRANSAXLES: CLUTCH "SHRIEK" NOISE* – Some 1980-84 Saab 900 models with 5-speed manual transaxles may make a "shriek" noise just before the clutch is fully engaged. This condition may be caused by the clutch disc. A new design clutch disc (87-22-324) is now available to correct this condition.

3 *1984 SAAB 900 AND 1985 900 TURBO MODELS WITH 5-SPEED MANUAL TRANSAXLE: NEW CLUTCH SLAVE CYLINDER* – Some 1984 Saab 900 and all 1985 900 Turbo models with 5-speed manual transaxle were built with a new design clutch slave cylinder. Different release tool are required for servicing the new design.

If any service procedure requires the removal of the clutch slave cylinder, it must be identified for correct tool usage. The different designs may be identified by measuring the outside diameter of the release bearing. The early design bearing (87-21-995) is 2.75" (70 mm) and the new design bearing (87-04-728) is 2.50" (63mm).

DO NOT use Release Tool (83-93-175) to service the new design slave cylinder. If removal is required, depress clutch pedal and insert Spacer Ring Tool (83-90-023).

TOYOTA

4 *1983 TOYOTA TERCEL: CLUTCH PEDAL "SNAPPING" NOISE* – Some 1983 Toyota Tercel models with a self-adjusting clutch may exhibit a "snapping" noise when the clutch pedal is depressed. This condition may be caused by lack of lubrication between the groove and gear teeth as shown. Apply multipurpose grease to the groove and gear teeth as shown.

1983 Toyota Tercel Self-Adjusting Clutch Pedal Lubrication Points

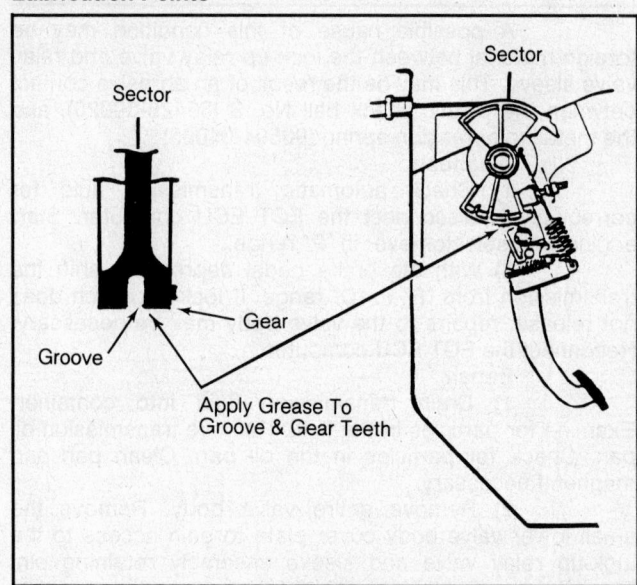

5 *1983 TOYOTA TERCEL 4WD WAGON WITH MANUAL TRANSAXLE: TRANSAXLE VIBRATION NOISE* – Due to the existence of rough edges on the transaxle housing, there is a potential for the transaxle cover in the chassis gravel shield to contact the transaxle housing.

This may cause a vibration noise to occur at various RPM's. The noise may be eliminated by grinding away the portion of the transaxle cover making contact with the transaxle in the locations shown.

1983 Toyota Tercel Transaxle Cover

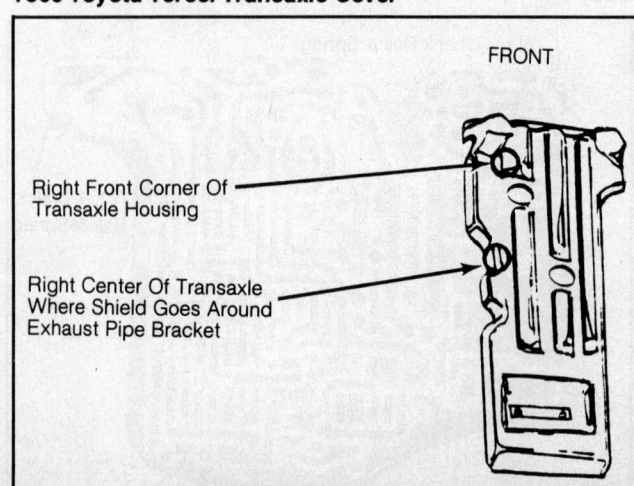

Latest Changes & Corrections

FOR 1984 & EARLIER IMPORT MODELS (Cont.)

The areas shown may be modified with a grinder or a round file. Do not attempt to fix the problem by grinding the rough areas on the transaxle or by adding washers to the front attachment bolts.

6▷ *1983-84 TOYOTA CELICA, CRESSIDA AND SUPRA WITH MANUAL TRANSMISSION: GRINDING NOISE WHEN SHIFTING INTO REVERSE* – Some 1983-84 Celica, Cressida and Supra models equipped with W58 transmission may exhibit gear grinding noises when shifting into Reverse. To correct this problem, a "Pre-Balk" system has been added to the shift fork and select shafts as shown in the illustration.

1983-84 Toyota Celica, Cressida & Supra Manual Transmission Modifications

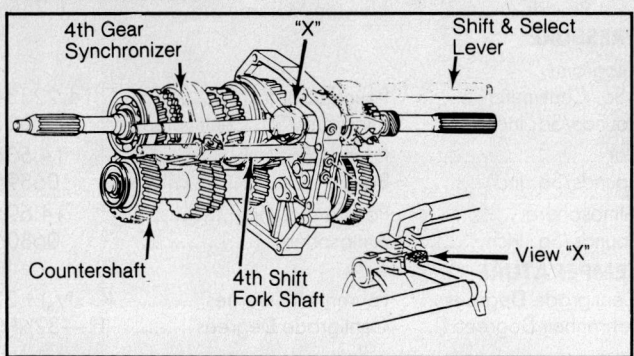

When shifting into Reverse, the 3rd and 4th shift fork shaft is pushed forward by a protrusion on the shift and select lever at the same time. This causes the 4th gear synchronizer mechanism to provide a brake effect on the input shaft. This prevents the input shaft and countershaft from rotating. Therefore, gear grinding noise is reduced when shifting into Reverse gear.

VOLKSWAGEN

7▷ *1984 VOLKSWAGEN JETTA, RABBIT, PICKUP AND SCIROCCO: MODIFIED DIFFERENTIAL PINION SHAFT RETAINERS* – As of transaxle number 15 10 2, 1984 Jetta, Rabbit, Pickup and Scirocco models with manual

1984 Volkswagen Jetta, Rabbit, Pickup and Scirocco Pinion Shaft Removal

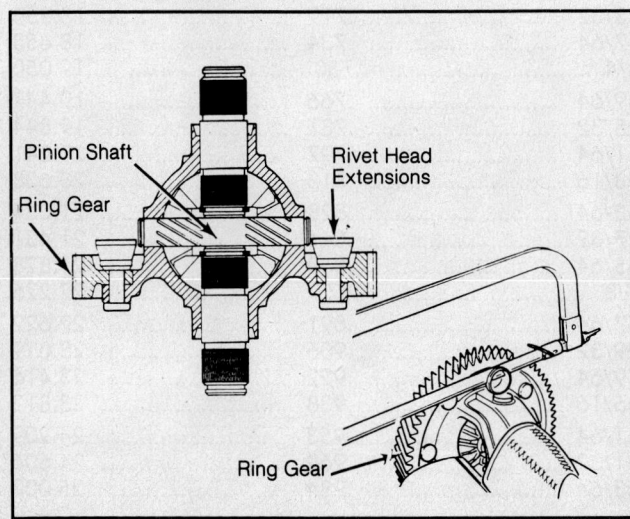

transaxles will have the pinion shaft held in place by 2 ring gear rivet head extensions. When repair procedures require the removal of this pinion shaft design, the rivet head extensions will have to hacksawed off. Replacement pinion shaft (020-409-177A) and 2 circlips (N 042 363-1) are now available to service this pinion shaft design.

8▷ *1984 VOLKSWAGEN QUANTUM WITH 5-SPEED MANUAL TRANSMISSION: NEW MAINSHAFT AND 4TH GEAR CIRCLIP* – Volkswagen Quantums with 5-speed manual transmissions (models 013 and 093) have a modified mainshaft as of transmission No. 16 06 3.

The 4th gear is no longer retained on the mainshaft by a thrust washer and circlip. The groove in the mainshaft has been moved and enlarged to accomodate a new circlip. A thrust washer is not used and end play is no longer adjusted. Service installation of the new version mainshaft in an earlier gearbox requires use of new version circlip (901 028 01).

Modified Mainshaft & 4th Gear Circlip For Volkswagen Quantum

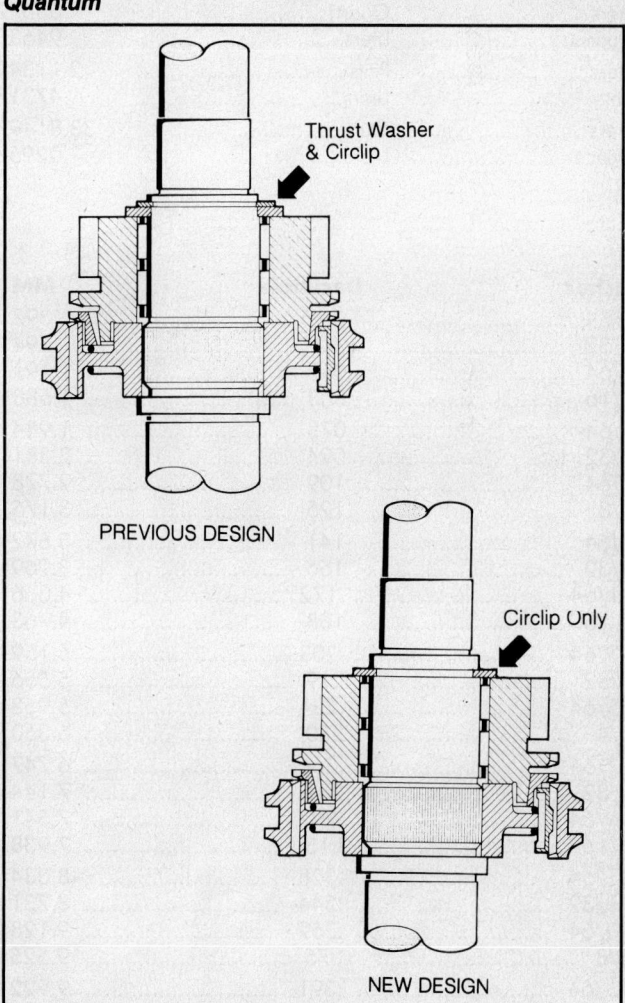

English-Metric Conversion Chart

CONVERSION FACTORS

Unit	To	Unit	Multiply By
LENGTH			
Millimeters		Inches	.03937
Inches		Millimeters	25.4
Meters		Feet	3.28084
Feet		Meters	.3048
Kilometers		Miles	.62137
Miles		Kilometers	1.60935
AREA			
Square Centimeters		Square Inches	.155
Square Inches		Square Centimeters	6.45159
VOLUME			
Cubic Centimeters		Cubic Inches	.06103
Cubic Inches		Cubic Centimeters	16.38703
Liters		Cubic Inches	61.025
Cubic Inches		Liters	.01639
Liters		Quarts	1.05672
Quarts		Liters	.94633
Liters		Pints	2.11344
Pints		Liters	.47317
Liters		Ounces	33.81497
Ounces		Liters	.02957

Unit	To	Unit	Multiply By
WEIGHT			
Grams		Ounces	.03527
Ounces		Grams	28.34953
Kilograms		Pounds	2.20462
Pounds		Kilograms	.45359
WORK			
Centimeter Kilograms		Inch Pounds	.8676
Inch Pounds		Centimeter Kilograms	1.15262
Meter Kilograms		Foot Pounds	7.23301
Foot Pounds		Newton Meters	1.3558
PRESSURE			
Kilograms/ Sq. Centimeter		Pounds/Sq. Inch	14.22334
Pounds/Sq. Inch		Kilograms/Sq. Centimeter	.07031
Bar		Pounds/Sq. Inch	14.504
Pounds/Sq. Inch		Bar	.06895
Atmosphere		Pounds/Sq. Inch	14.696
Pounds/Sq. Inch		Atmosphere	.06805
TEMPERATURE			
Centigrade Degrees		Fahrenheit Degrees	$(C° \times 9/5) + 32$
Fahrenheit Degrees		Centigrade Degrees	$(F° - 32) \times 5/9$

Inches	Decimals	MM
1/64	.016	.397
1/32	.031	.794
3/64	.047	1.191
1/16	.063	1.588
5/64	.078	1.984
3/32	.094	2.381
7/64	.109	2.778
1/8	.125	3.175
9/64	.141	3.572
5/32	.156	3.969
11/64	.172	4.366
3/16	.188	4.763
13/64	.203	5.159
7/32	.219	5.556
15/64	.234	5.953
1/4	.250	6.350
17/64	.266	6.747
9/32	.281	7.144
19/64	.297	7.541
5/16	3.13	7.938
21/64	.328	8.334
11/32	.344	8.731
23/64	.359	9.128
3/8	.375	9.525
25/64	.391	9.922
13/32	.406	10.319
27/64	.422	10.716
7/16	.438	11.113
29/64	.453	11.509
15/32	.469	11.906
31/64	.484	12.303
1/2	.500	12.700

Inches	Decimals	MM
33/64	.516	13.097
17/32	.531	13.494
35/64	.547	13.891
9/16	.563	14.288
37/64	.578	14.684
19/32	.594	15.081
39/64	.609	15.478
5/8	.625	15.875
41/64	.641	16.272
21/32	.656	16.669
43/64	.672	17.066
11/16	.687	17.463
45/64	.703	17.859
23/32	.719	18.256
47/64	.734	18.653
3/4	.750	19.050
49/64	.766	19.447
25/32	.781	19.844
51/64	.797	20.241
13/16	.813	20.638
53/64	.828	21.034
27/32	.844	21.431
55/64	.859	21.828
7/8	.875	22.225
57/64	.891	22.622
29/32	.906	23.019
59/64	.922	23.416
15/16	.938	23.813
61/64	.953	24.209
31/32	.969	24.606
63/64	.984	25.003

METRIC CONVERSIONS

Metric conversions are making life more difficult for the mechanic. In addition to doubling the number of tools required, metric-dimensioned nuts and bolts are used alongside English components in many new vehicles. The mechanic has to decide which tool to use, slowing down the job. The tool problem can be solved by trial and error, but some metric conversions aren't so simple.

Converting temperature, lengths or volumes requires a calculator and conversion charts, or else a very nimble mind. Conversion charts are only part of the answer though, becuase they don't help you "think" metric, or "vizualize" what you are converting. The following examples are intended to help you "see" metric sizes:

LENGTH

Meters are the standard unit of length in the metric system. The smaller units are 10ths (decimeter), 100ths (centimeter), and 1000ths (millimeter) of a meter. These common examples might help you to visualize the metric units:

* A meter is slightly longer than a yard (about 40 inches).
* An aspirin tablet is about one centimeter across (.4 inches).
* A millimeter is about the thickness of a dime.

VOLUME

Cubic meters and centimeters are used to measure volume, just as we normally think of cubic feet and inches. Liquid volume measurements include the liter and milliliter, like the English quarts or ounces.

* One teaspoon is about 5 cubic centimeters.
* A liter is about one quart.
* A liter is about 61 cubic inches.

WEIGHT

The metric weight system is based on the gram, with the most common unit being the kilogram (1000 grams). Our comparable units are ounces and pounds:

* A kilogram is about 2.2 pounds.
* An ounce is about 28 grams.

TORQUE

Torque is somewhat complicated. The term describes the amount of effort exerted to turn something. A chosen unit of weight or force is applied to a lever of standard length. The resulting leverage is called torque. In our standard system, we use the weight of one pound applied to a lever a foot long—resulting in the unit called a foot-pound. A smaller unit is the inch-pound (the lever is one inch long). Metric units include the meter kilogram (lever one meter long with a kilogram of weight applied) and the Newton-meter(lever one meter long with force of one Newton applied). Some conversions are:

* A meter kilogram is about 7.2 foot pounds.
* A Newton-meter is about 1.4 foot pounds.
* A centimeter kilogram (cmkg) is equal to .9 inch pounds.

PRESSURE

Pressure is another complicated measurement. Pressure is described as a force or weight applied to a given area. Our common unit is pounds per square inch. Metric units can be expressed in several ways. One is the kilogram per square centimeter (kg/cm²). Another unit of pressure is the Pascal (force of one Newton on an area of one square meter), which equals about 4 ounces on a square yard. Since this is a very small amount of pressure, we usually see the kiloPascal, or kPa (1000 Pascals). Another common automotive term for pressure is the bar (used by German manufacturers), which equals 10 Pascals. Thoroughly confused? Try the examples below:

* Atmospheric pressure at sea level is about 14.7 psi.
* Atmospheric pressure at sea level is about 1 bar.
* Atmospheric pressure at sea level is about 1 kg/cm².
* One pound per square inch is about 7 kPa.

**WE ENCOURAGE
PROFESSIONALISM**

**THROUGH TECHNICIAN
CERTIFICATION**

Mitchell Information Services also offers audio visual presentations for mechanic training and microfiche products. For details on ordering, please contact:

MITCHELL INFORMATION SERVICES, INC.
P.O. Box 26260
San Diego, CA 92126

Notes

Notes

Notes

Notes

Notes

Notes

Notes

Notes